PERIODIC TABLE OF THE ELEMENTS

KEY: ATOMIC NUMBER 30 — ATOMIC WEIGHT 65.37 — BOILING POINT, °C 906 — MELTING POINT, °C 419.5 — SYMBOL Zn

Notes:
1. Values for gaseous elements are for liquids at the boiling point.
2. Outlined symbols are for elements synthetically prepared.
3. Proposed, but not yet officially accepted.

Reprinted by permission of the Dyna-Slide Company, Chicago, Illinois.

PERIOD	GROUP IA	IIA	IIIB	IVB	VB	VIB	VIIB	VIII	VIII	VIII	IB	IIB	IIIA	IVA	VA	VIA	VIIA	INERT GASES
1	1 H 1.00797 −252.7 −259.2 See Note 1 Hydrogen																	2 He 4.0026 −268.9 −269.7 Helium
2	3 Li 6.939 1330 108.5 Lithium	4 Be 9.0122 2770 1277 Beryllium											5 B 10.811 — (2030) Boron	6 C 12.0111 4830 3727? Carbon	7 N 14.0067 −195.8 −210 Nitrogen	8 O 15.9994 −183 −218.8 Oxygen	9 F 18.9984 −188.2 −219.6 Fluorine	10 Ne 20.183 −246 −248.6 Neon
3	11 Na 22.9898 892 97.8 Sodium	12 Mg 24.312 1107 650 Magnesium											13 Al 26.9815 2450 660 Aluminum	14 Si 28.086 2680 1410 Silicon	15 P 30.9738 280w 44.2w Phosphorus	16 S 32.064 444.6 119.0 Sulfur	17 Cl 35.453 −34.7 −101.0 Chlorine	18 Ar 39.948 −185.8 −189.4 Argon
4	19 K 39.102 760 63.7 Potassium	20 Ca 40.08 1440 838 Calcium	21 Sc 44.956 2730 1539 Scandium	22 Ti 47.90 3260 1668 Titanium	23 V 50.942 3450 1900 Vanadium	24 Cr 51.996 2665 1875 Chromium	25 Mn 54.938 2150 1245 Manganese	26 Fe 55.847 3000 1536 Iron	27 Co 58.933 2900 1495 Cobalt	28 Ni 58.71 2730 1453 Nickel	29 Cu 63.54 2595 1083 Copper	30 Zn 65.37 906 419.5 Zinc	31 Ga 69.72 2237 29.8 Gallium	32 Ge 72.59 2830 937.4 Germanium	33 As 74.922 613° 817 Arsenic	34 Se 78.96 685 217 Selenium	35 Br 79.909 58 −7.2 Bromine	36 Kr 83.80 −152 −157.3 Krypton
5	37 Rb 85.47 688 38.9 Rubidium	38 Sr 87.62 1380 768 Strontium	39 Y 88.905 2927 1509 Yttrium	40 Zr 91.22 3580 1852 Zirconium	41 Nb 92.906 3300 2415 Niobium	42 Mo 95.94 5560 2610 Molybdenum	43 Tc (99) 2200 See Note 2 Technetium	44 Ru 101.07 4900 2500 Ruthenium	45 Rh 102.905 4500 1966 Rhodium	46 Pd 106.4 3980 1552 Palladium	47 Ag 107.870 2210 960.8 Silver	48 Cd 112.40 765 320.9 Cadmium	49 In 114.82 2000 156.2 Indium	50 Sn 118.69 2270 231.9 Tin	51 Sb 121.75 1380 630.5 Antimony	52 Te 127.60 989.8 449.5 Tellurium	53 I 126.904 183 113.7 Iodine	54 Xe 131.30 −108.0 −111.9 Xenon
6	55 Cs 132.905 690 28.7 Cesium	56 Ba 137.34 1640 714 Barium	57 La★ 138.91 3470 920 Lanthanum	72 Hf 178.49 5400 2222 Hafnium	73 Ta 180.948 5425 2996 Tantalum	74 W 183.85 5930 3410 Wolfram	75 Re 186.2 5900 3180 Rhenium	76 Os 190.2 5500 2700 Osmium	77 Ir 192.2 5300 2454 Iridium	78 Pt 195.09 4530 1769 Platinum	79 Au 196.967 2970 1063 Gold	80 Hg 200.59 357 −38.4 Mercury	81 Tl 204.37 1457 303 Thallium	82 Pb 207.19 1725 327.4 Lead	83 Bi 208.980 1560 271.3 Bismuth	84 Po (210) — 254 Polonium	85 At (210) — (302) Astatine	86 Rn (222) (−61.8) (−71) Radon
7	87 Fr (223) (27) Francium	88 Ra (226) — 700 Radium	89 Ac★★ (227) — 1050 Actinium															

★ 6	58 Ce 140.12 3468 795 Cerium	59 Pr 140.907 3127 935 Praseodymium	60 Nd 144.24 3027 1024 Neodymium	61 Pm (147) — (1027) Promethium	62 Sm 150.35 1900 1072 Samarium	63 Eu 151.96 1439 826 Europium	64 Gd 157.25 3000 1312 Gadolinium	65 Tb 158.924 2800 1356 Terbium	66 Dy 162.50 2600 1407 Dysprosium	67 Ho 164.930 2600 1461 Holmium	68 Er 167.26 2900 1497 Erbium	69 Tm 168.934 1727 1545 Thulium	70 Yb 173.04 1427 824 Ytterbium	71 Lu 174.97 3327 1652 Lutetium
★★ 7	90 Th 232.038 3850 1750 Thorium	91 Pa (231) — (1230) Protactinium	92 U 238.04 3818 1132 Uranium	93 Np (237) — 637 Neptunium	94 Pu (242) 3235 640 Plutonium	95 Am (243) — — Americium	96 Cm (247) — — Curium	97 Bk (247) — — Berkelium	98 Cf (251) — — Californium	99 Es (254) — — Einsteinium	100 Fm (253) — — Fermium	101 Md (256) — — Mendelevium	102 No (254) — — Nobelium	103 (Lw) (257) — — See Note 3 (Lawrencium)

9/6 R5'68

Chemical Engineers' Handbook

McGraw-Hill Chemical Engineering Series

THE SERIES

ANDERSEN AND WENZEL—*Introduction to Chemical Engineering*
ARIES AND NEWTON—*Chemical Engineering Cost Estimation*
BADGER AND BANCHERO—*Introduction to Chemical Engineering*
BENNETT AND MYERS—*Momentum, Heat, and Mass Transfer*
COMINGS—*High Pressure Technology*
COUGHANOWR AND KOPPEL—*Process Systems Analysis and Control*
DODGE—*Chemical Engineering Thermodynamics*
GRISWOLD—*Fuels, Combustion, and Furnaces*
GROGGINS—*Unit Processes in Organic Synthesis*
HARRIOTT—*Process Control*
HENLEY AND BIEBER—*Chemical Engineering Calculations*
HUNTINGTON—*Natural Gas and Natural Gasoline*
JOHNSTONE AND THRING—*Pilot Plants, Models, and Scale-up Methods in Chemical Engineering*
KATZ, CORNELL, KOBAYASHI, POETTMANN, VARY, ELENBAAS, AND WEINAUG—*Handbook of Natural Gas Engineering*
KIRKBRIDE—*Chemical Engineering Fundamentals*
KNUDSEN AND KATZ—*Fluid Dynamics and Heat Transfer*
KOHL AND RIESENFELD—*Gas Purification*
LAPIDUS—*Digital Computation for Chemical Engineers*
LEVA—*Fluidization*
LEWIS, RADASCH, AND LEWIS—*Industrial Stoichiometry*
MANTELL—*Adsorption*
MANTELL—*Electrochemical Engineering*
MCADAMS—*Heat Transmission*
MCCABE AND SMITH, J. C.—*Unit Operations of Chemical Engineering*
MICKLEY, SHERWOOD, AND REED—*Applied Mathematics in Chemical Engineering*
NELSON—*Petroleum Refinery Engineering*
PERRY (EDITOR)—*Chemical Business Handbook*
PERRY (EDITOR)—*Chemical Engineers' Handbook*
PETERS—*Elementary Chemical Engineering*
PETERS—*Plant Design and Economics for Chemical Engineers*
REID AND SHERWOOD—*The Properties of Gases and Liquids*
ROBINSON AND GILLILAND—*Elements of Fractional Distillation*
SCHECHTER—*The Variational Method in Engineering*
SCHMIDT AND MARLIES—*Principles of High-polymer Theory and Practice*
SCHWEYER—*Process Engineering Economics*
SHERWOOD AND PIGFORD—*Absorption and Extraction*
SHREVE—*Chemical Process Industries*
SMITH, B. D.—*Design of Equilibrium Stage Processes*
SMITH, J. M.—*Chemical Engineering Kinetics*
SMITH, J. M., AND VAN NESS—*Introduction to Chemical Engineering Thermodynamics*
TREYBAL—*Liquid Extraction*
TREYBAL—*Mass-transfer Operations*
VILBRANDT AND DRYDEN—*Chemical Engineering Plant Design*
VOLK—*Applied Statistics for Engineers*
WALAS—*Reaction Kinetics for Chemical Engineers*
WALKER, LEWIS, MCADAMS, AND GILLILAND—*Principles of Chemical Engineering*
WILLIAMS AND JOHNSON—*Stoichiometry for Chemical Engineers*
WILSON AND RIES—*Principles of Chemical Engineering Thermodynamics*

McGRAW-HILL HANDBOOKS

ABBOTT AND STETKA · National Electrical Code Handbook, 10th ed.
ALJIAN · Purchasing Handbook
AMERICAN INSTITUTE OF PHYSICS · American Institute of Physics Handbook
AMERICAN SOCIETY OF MECHANICAL ENGINEERS · ASME Handbooks:
Engineering Tables — Metals Engineering—Processes
Metals Engineering—Design — Metals Properties
AMERICAN SOCIETY OF TOOL AND MANUFACTURING ENGINEERS · Die Design Handbook
AMERICAN SOCIETY OF TOOL AND MANUFACTURING ENGINEERS · Handbook of Fixture Design
AMERICAN SOCIETY OF TOOL AND MANUFACTURING ENGINEERS · Tool Engineers Handbook, 2d ed.
BEEMAN · Industrial Power Systems Handbook
BERRY, BOLLAY, AND BEERS · Handbook of Meteorology
BLATZ · Radiation Hygiene Handbook
BRADY · Materials Handbook, 8th ed.
BURINGTON · Handbook of Mathematical Tables and Formulas, 3d ed.
BURINGTON AND MAY · Handbook of Probability and Statistics with Tables
CARROLL · Industrial Instrument Servicing Handbook
COCKRELL · Industrial Electronics Handbook
CONDON AND ODISHAW · Handbook of Physics
CONSIDINE · Process Instruments and Controls Handbook
CROCKER · Piping Handbook, 4th ed.
CROFT AND CARR · American Electricians' Handbook, 8th ed.
DAVIS · Handbook of Applied Hydraulics, 2d ed.
DUDLEY · Gear Handbook
ETHERINGTON · Nuclear Engineering Handbook
FACTORY MUTUAL ENGINEERING DIVISION · Handbook of Industrial Loss Prevention
FINK · Television Engineering Handbook
FLÜGGE · Handbook of Engineering Materials
FRICK · Petroleum Production Handbook, 2 vols.
GUTHRIE · Petroleum Products Handbook
HARRIS · Handbook of Noise Control
HARRIS AND CREDE · Shock and Vibration Handbook, 3 vols.
HENNEY · Radio Engineering Handbook, 5th ed.
HUNTER · Handbook of Semiconductor Electronics, 2d ed.
HUSKEY AND KORN · Computer Handbook
JASIK · Antenna Engineering Handbook
JURAN · Quality Control Handbook, 2d ed.
KALLEN · Handbook of Instrumentation and Controls
KETCHUM · Structural Engineers' Handbook, 3d ed.
KING · Handbook of Hydraulics, 4th ed.
KNOWLTON · Standard Handbook for Electrical Engineers, 9th ed.
KOELLE · Handbook of Astronautical Engineering
KORN AND KORN · Mathematical Handbook for Scientists and Engineers
KURTZ · The Lineman's Handbook, 3d ed.
LA LONDE AND JANES · Concrete Engineering Handbook
LANDEE, DAVIS, AND ALBRECHT · Electronic Designers' Handbook
LANGE · Handbook of Chemistry, 10th ed.
LAUGHNER AND HARGAN · Handbook of Fastening and Joining of Metal Parts
LE GRAND · The New American Machinist's Handbook
LIDDELL · Handbook of Nonferrous Metallurgy, 2d ed.
MAGILL, HOLDEN, AND ACKLEY · Air Pollution Handbook
MANAS · National Plumbing Code Handbook
MANTELL · Engineering Materials Handbook
MARKS AND BAUMEISTER · Mechanical Engineers' Handbook, 6th ed.
MARKUS · Handbook of Electronic Control Circuits
MARKUS AND ZELUFF · Handbook of Industrial Electronic Circuits
MARKUS AND ZELUFF · Handbook of Industrial Electronic Control Circuits
MAYNARD · Industrial Engineering Handbook
MERRITT · Building Construction Handbook
MOODY · Petroleum Exploration Handbook
MORROW · Maintenance Engineering Handbook
PERRY · Chemical Business Handbook
PERRY · Chemical Engineers' Handbook, 3d ed.
SHAND · Glass Engineering Handbook, 2d ed.
STANIAR · Plant Engineering Handbook, 2d ed.
STREETER · Handbook of Fluid Dynamics
STUBBS · Handbook of Heavy Construction
TERMAN · Radio Engineers' Handbook
TRUXAL · Control Engineers' Handbook
URQUHART · Civil Engineering Handbook, 4th ed.
WALKER · NAB Engineering Handbook, 5th ed.
WOODS · Highway Engineering Handbook
YODER, HENEMAN, TURNBULL, AND STONE · Handbook of Personnel Management and Labor Relations

Chemical Engineers' Handbook

JOHN H. PERRY

Editor of First, Second, and Third Editions

FOURTH EDITION

Prepared by a Staff of Specialists under the Editorial Direction of

ROBERT H. PERRY

PROFESSOR OF CHEMICAL ENGINEERING
UNIVERSITY OF ROCHESTER

CECIL H. CHILTON

EDITOR-IN-CHIEF, *Chemical Engineering*

SIDNEY D. KIRKPATRICK

FORMER EDITORIAL DIRECTOR,
Chemical Engineering AND *Chemical Week*

McGRAW-HILL BOOK COMPANY

New York San Francisco Toronto London Sydney

CHEMICAL ENGINEERS' HANDBOOK

Library of Congress Catalog Card Number: 61-13168

6 7 8 9 - MP - 9 8 7

LIST OF CONTRIBUTORS

Joseph B. Aidala, M.E.E., Professor, Department of Electrical Technology, Queensborough Community College, Bayside, N.Y. (Electrical Engineering)

George E. Alves, M.S., Chemical Engineer, Engineering Research Laboratory, E. I. du Pont de Nemours & Co., Inc., Wilmington, Del. (Fluid and Particle Mechanics)

Charles M. Ambler, B.S.Ch.E., Director of Chemical Engineering, The Sharples Corp., Philadelphia, Pa. (Centrifuges)

William F. Ames, M.S., Associate Professor, Department of Mechanical Engineering, University of Delaware, Newark, Del. (Mathematics)

***Robert Ammon, B.S.,** Chief Metallurgist, American Zinc, Lead and Smelting Co., St. Louis, Mo. (Concentration of Ores by Sink-and-float Methods)

***Anthony Anable, B.S.,** Engineer, The Dorr Co., Inc., New York, N.Y. (Classification and Sedimentation)

***Evald Anderson, B.S.,** Late Technical Director, Western Precipitation Corp., Los Angeles, Calif. (Separation of Dusts and Mists)

***Robert S. Aries, Sc.D., Ch.E.,** Consulting Engineer and Economist; Adjunct Professor of Chemical Engineering, Polytechnic Institute, Brooklyn, N.Y. (Plant Location)

***H. R. Arnold, M.S.,** Chemist, E. I. du Pont de Nemours & Co., Inc., Wilmington, Del. (Physical and Chemical Data)

***Walter L. Badger, M.S.,** Late Consulting Engineer and formerly Professor of Chemical Engineering, University of Michigan, Ann Arbor, Mich. (Evaporation)

Eno Bagnoli, M.S., Senior Research Engineer, E. I. du Pont de Nemours & Co., Inc., Wilmington, Del. (Section Editor: Humidification and Drying; Psychrometry, Drying of Solids)

***Lawrence H. Bailey, M.S.,** Chief Engineer, F. J. Stokes Machine Co., Philadelphia, Pa. (Compacting)

***E. M. Baker, B.S.,** Late Professor of Chemical Engineering, University of Michigan, Ann Arbor, Mich. (Gas Absorption)

H. Carl Bauman, B.S., Manager, Cost Engineering Department, Engineering and Construction Division, American Cyanamid Co., Wayne, N.J. (Cost and Profitability Estimation)

***Theodore Baumeister, B.S., M.E.,** Professor of Mechanical Engineering, Columbia University. (Power and Power Machinery)

***Hugh W. Bellas, B.S.,** Engineer, E. I. du Pont de Nemours & Co., Inc., Wilmington, Del. (Filtration)

***A. F. Benning, B.S.,** Engineer, E. I. du Pont de Nemours & Co., Inc., Wilmington, Del. (Materials of Construction)

***Olaf P. Bergelin, Sc.D.,** Associate Professor of Chemical Engineering, University of Delaware, Newark, Del. (Miscellaneous Over-all Coefficients of Heat Transfer)

***C. E. Berry, B.S.,** Chemical Engineer, E. I. du Pont de Nemours & Co., Inc., Wilmington, Del. (Miscellaneous Methods of Mechanical Separation and Concentration, Size Reduction and Size Enlargement)

* Contributions by these authors were made for previous editions and have been revised or rewritten by others for this edition. The stated professional position in these cases is that held by the author at the time of his contribution.

Louis Bertrand, M.Sc., Consultant on Chemical Engineering, E. I. du Pont de Nemours & Co., Inc., Wilmington, Del. (Control of Distillation Columns)

***A. D. Blake, M.E.,** Editor, *Combustion*, Combustion Engineering Co., Inc., New York, N.Y. (Power Generation)

***Harding Bliss, Ph.D.,** Professor of Chemical Engineering, Yale University, New Haven, Conn. (Engineering Thermodynamic Properties)

F. William Bloecher, Jr., M.S.M., Assistant Manager, Mining Chemicals Department, Cyanamid International, Wayne, N.J. (Froth Flotation)

Donald F. Boucher, Ph.D., Chemical Engineer, Engineering Research Laboratory, E. I. du Pont de Nemours & Co., Inc., Wilmington, Del. (Section Editor: Fluid and Particle Mechanics)

Ludwig Braun, Jr., D.E.E., Assistant Professor of Electrical Engineering, Polytechnic Institute of Brooklyn, Brooklyn, N.Y. (Section Editor: Electrical Engineering)

***P. W. Bridgman, Ph.D., D.Sc.,** Hollis Professor of Mathematics and Natural Philosophy, Harvard University, Cambridge, Mass. (Dimensional Analysis)

Glenn F. Brockett, B.S., Vice President-Sales, Fisher Governor Co., Marshalltown, Iowa. (Final Control Elements)

William J. Bronkala, B.Met.E., Chief Metallurgist, Stearns Magnetic Products, Milwaukee, Wis. (Dense Media and Magnetic Separation)

Coleman B. Brosilow, B.S., M.Ch.E., Senior Research Fellow, Microwave Research Institute, Polytechnic Institute of Brooklyn, Brooklyn, N.Y. (Electrochemical Cells and Electrophysics)

Frederick M. Brunn, B.S., Mechanical Engineer, Foster-Wheeler Corp., New York, N.Y. (Heat Transport)

***W. M. D. Bryant, B.S.,** Chemist, E. I. du Pont de Nemours & Co., Inc., Wilmington, Del. (Physical and Chemical Principles)

H. Leslie Bullock, B.M.E., Consulting Engineer, New York, N.Y. (Paste Mixing and Processing)

***C. P. Cabell, B.S.,** Chemical Engineer, General Electric Co., Schnectady, N.Y. (Screening)

***W. S. Calcott, Ch.E., LL.D.,** Late Assistant Director (Development) Chemical Division, Organic Chemicals Department, E. I. du Pont de Nemours & Co., Inc., Wilmington, Del. (Sweating)

***James S. Carey, Sc.D.,** Chemical Engineer, E. B. Badger & Sons Co., Syracuse, N.Y. (Humidification, Dehumidification, and Spray Ponds)

***Willis H. Carrier, M.E., D.E.,** Late Chairman of the Board, Carrier Corp., Syracuse, N.Y. (Humidification, Dehumidification, and Spray Ponds)

Edwin E. Cockrell, B.S., Application Engineer, Machinery Division, Director, Customer Service Laboratory, W. S. Tyler Co., Cleveland, Ohio. (Screening)

***Allan P. Colburn, Ph.D.,** Late Assistant to the President and Professor of Chemical Engineering, University of Delaware, Newark, Del. (Miscellaneous Coefficients of Heat Transfer, General Theory of Diffusional Operations, Plate Efficiencies for Distillation Columns, Packed Distillation Towers, Gas Absorption)

***C. N. Collard, M.S.,** Chemical Engineer, E. B. Badger & Sons Co., Boston, Mass. (Plate Calculations for Multicomponent Mixtures)

Paul E. Cook, Director of Technical Publications, Denver Equipment Co., Denver, Colo. (Sampling Soldis)

Douglas M. Considine, B.S.Chem.Eng., Director, Marketing Planning, Hughes Aircraft Co., Culver City, Calif. (Section Editor: Process Control; Process Measurements)

Carl S. Cragoe, A.B., Assistant Chief, Heat and Power Division, National Bureau of Standards, Washington, D.C. (Conversion Tables)

***P. W. Crane, Ch.E., M.S.,** Assistant Director of Sales, Polychemicals Department, E. I. du Pont de Nemours & Co., Inc., Wilmington, Del. (Extrusion)

***C. W. Cuno, Ph.D.,** Late Chemical Engineer and Consultant, The Lehon Co., St. Louis, Mo. (Economic Factors in Chemical Plant Location)

***Harry A. Curtis, Ph.D.,** Director, Tennessee Valley Authority, Knoxville, Tenn. (Solid Fuels)

Donald A. Dahlstrom, Ph.D., Vice President and Director of Research and Development, The Eimco Corp., Salt Lake City, Utah. (Gravity Sedimentation Operations)

Lawrence A. Dale, B.S.Ch.E., Research Engineer, The Eimco Corp., Salt Lake City, Utah. (Gravity Sedimentation Operations)

Steven Danatos, M.E., M.S., Associate Editor, *Chemical Engineering,* McGraw-Hill Publishing Co., New York, N.Y. (Process Measurements)

***Dale S. Davis, M.S.,** Professor of Chemical Engineering, Virginia Polytechnic Institute, Blacksburg, Va. (Mathematics: Alignment Charts)

Charles E. Day, Jr., B.E.E., Senior Serviee Engineer, Engineering Department, E. I. du Pont de Nemours & Co., Inc., Wilmington, Del. (Fuels)

***James G. DeFlon, B.S.,** Technical Advisor of Sales Department, Fluor Corp. Ltd., Los Angeles, Calif. (Cooling Towers)

Fred D. DeVaney, E.M., M.S., Director of Metallurgy and Research, Picklands, Mather and Co., Duluth, Minn. (Jigging and Tabling)

***Barnett F. Dodge, B.Sc.,** Professor and Chairman, Department of Chemical Engineering, Yale University, New Haven, Conn. (High-pressure Technique, Refrigeration: Low Temperature Processes)

***K. H. Donaldson, B.S.,** Professor and Head, Department of Mining Engineering, Case Institute of Applied Science, Cleveland, Ohio. (Screening, Jigging, Tabling, Elutriation)

***Thomas B. Dorris, Ph.D.,** Chief Chemical Engineer, Sprout, Waldron & Co., Muncie, Pa. (Cutting)

***Thomas B. Drew, M.S.,** Professor of Chemical Engineering, Columbia University, New York, N.Y. (Flow of Fluids)

***Raymond W. Dull,** Late Consulting Engineer, Chicago, Ill. (Mathematics)

***H. H. Dunkle,** Engineer, Goetze Division, Johns-Manville Sales Corp., New York, N.Y. (Gaskets, Chemical Resistance of Gasket Materials)

***Hans C. Duus, Ph.D.,** Chemical Engineer, E. I. du Pont de Nemours & Co., Inc., Wilmington, Del. (Refrigeration, Thermodynamic Tables)

William P. Dyrenforth, M.E., Vice President and Technical Director, Carpco Research and Engineering, Inc., Jacksonville, Fla. (Electrostatic Separations)

***Joseph C. Elgin, Ph.D.,** Professor of Engineering, Princeton University, Princeton, N.J. (Solvent Extraction)

R. E. Emmert, Ph.D., Research Supervisor, Engineering Research Laboratory, E. I. du Pont de Nemours & Co., Inc., Wilmington, Del. (Gas Absorption and Solvent Extraction)

Robert C. Emmett, Jr., B.S.Ch.E., Research Engineer, The Eimco Corp., Salt Lake City, Utah. (Gravity Sedimentation Operations)

***C. H. Evans, B.S.,** Chemical Engineer, E. I. du Pont de Nemours & Co., Inc., Wilmington, Del. (Furnaces and Kilns)

***E. C. Fetter, B.S.,** Managing Editor, *Chemical Engineering,* McGraw-Hill Publishing Co., New York, N.Y. (Chemical Resistance of Gasket Materials)

***Charles M. Fields, A.B.,** Technical Products Engineer, Shellmar Products Corp. (Extrusion)

Donald Finn, Ph.D., Graduate Fellow, University of Oklahoma. Norman, Okla. (Thermodynamics)

***A. E. Flowers, M.E. in E.E., M.M.E., Ph.D.,** Late Engineer-in-charge of Development, The DeLaval Separator Co., Poughkeepsie, N.Y. (Centrifuges)

***J. H. Foote,** Assistant Research Director, Pulverizing Machinery Co., Summit, N.J. (Machining)

***Samuel J. Friedman, M.S.,** Chemical Engineer, E. I. du Pont de Nemours & Co., Inc., Wilmington, Del. (Drying)

Frank H. Fuller, M.S., Consulting Engineer, E. I. du Pont de Nemours, & Co., Inc., Wilmington, Del. (Air Conditioning)

***I. H. Fullmer, B.S.,** Assistant Chief, Gage Section, National Bureau of Standards, Washington, D.C. (Wire and Sheet Metal Gages)

W. R. Gambill, B.S., Ch.E., Research Engineer, Oak Ridge National Laboratory, Union Carbide Nuclear Corp., Oak Ridge, Tenn. (Prediction and Correlation of Physical Properties)

***J. F. C. Gartshore, B.Sc., Ph.D.,** Chemical Engineer, British Dyestuff Corp., London, England. (Sublimation)

Raymond P. Genereaux, Ch.E., Chemical Engineer, E. I. du Pont de Nemours & Co., Inc., Wilmington, Del. (Section Editor: Transport and Storage of Fluids)

J. A. Gerster, Ph.D., Professor of Chemical Engineering, University of Delaware, Newark, Del. (Section Editor: Distillation)

Richard C. Gillette, B.S.Elec.Eng., M.A., Account Executive, Wilson, Haight and Welsh, Inc., Hartford, Conn. (Telemetry, Automatic Controllers)

***J. L. Gillson, Sc.D.,** Geologist, E. I. du Pont de Nemours & Co., Inc., Wilmington, Del. (Electrostatic Methods of Concentration)

Charles H. Gilmour, M.S., Senior Engineering Consultant, Union Carbide Chemical Co., So. Charleston, W. Va. (Section Editor: Heat Transmission)

***S. L. Godshalk, Ch.E.,** Chemist, E. I. du Pont de Nemours & Co., Inc., Wilmington, Del. (Spray Painting)

***G. D. Graves, Ph.D.,** Chemist, E. I. du Pont de Nemours & Co., Inc., Wilmington, Del. (Organic Chemistry)

Donald W. Green, Ph.D., Research Engineer, Continental Oil Co., Ponca City, Okla. (Reaction Kinetics, Reactor Design)

THE SERIES

ANDERSEN AND WENZEL—*Introduction to Chemical Engineering*
ARIES AND NEWTON—*Chemical Engineering Cost Estimation*
BADGER AND BANCHERO—*Introduction to Chemical Engineering*
BENNETT AND MYERS—*Momentum, Heat, and Mass Transfer*
COMINGS—*High Pressure Technology*
COUGHANOWR AND KOPPEL—*Process Systems Analysis and Control*
DODGE—*Chemical Engineering Thermodynamics*
GRISWOLD—*Fuels, Combustion, and Furnaces*
GROGGINS—*Unit Processes in Organic Synthesis*
HARRIOTT—*Process Control*
HENLEY AND BIEBER—*Chemical Engineering Calculations*
HUNTINGTON—*Natural Gas and Natural Gasoline*
JOHNSTONE AND THRING—*Pilot Plants, Models, and Scale-up Methods in Chemical Engineering*
KATZ, CORNELL, KOBAYASHI, POETTMANN, VARY, ELENBAAS, AND WEINAUG—*Handbook of Natural Gas Engineering*
KIRKBRIDE—*Chemical Engineering Fundamentals*
KNUDSEN AND KATZ—*Fluid Dynamics and Heat Transfer*
KOHL AND RIESENFELD—*Gas Purification*
LAPIDUS—*Digital Computation for Chemical Engineers*
LEVA—*Fluidization*
LEWIS, RADASCH, AND LEWIS—*Industrial Stoichiometry*
MANTELL—*Adsorption*
MANTELL—*Electrochemical Engineering*
MCADAMS—*Heat Transmission*
MCCABE AND SMITH, J. C.—*Unit Operations of Chemical Engineering*
MICKLEY, SHERWOOD, AND REED—*Applied Mathematics in Chemical Engineering*
NELSON—*Petroleum Refinery Engineering*
PERRY (EDITOR)—*Chemical Business Handbook*
PERRY (EDITOR)—*Chemical Engineers' Handbook*
PETERS—*Elementary Chemical Engineering*
PETERS—*Plant Design and Economics for Chemical Engineers*
REID AND SHERWOOD—*The Properties of Gases and Liquids*
ROBINSON AND GILLILAND—*Elements of Fractional Distillation*
SCHECHTER—*The Variational Method in Engineering*
SCHMIDT AND MARLIES—*Principles of High-polymer Theory and Practice*
SCHWEYER—*Process Engineering Economics*
SHERWOOD AND PIGFORD—*Absorption and Extraction*
SHREVE—*Chemical Process Industries*
SMITH, B. D.—*Design of Equilibrium Stage Processes*
SMITH, J. M.—*Chemical Engineering Kinetics*
SMITH, J. M., AND VAN NESS—*Introduction to Chemical Engineering Thermodynamics*
TREYBAL—*Liquid Extraction*
TREYBAL—*Mass-transfer Operations*
VILBRANDT AND DRYDEN—*Chemical Engineering Plant Design*
VOLK—*Applied Statistics for Engineers*
WALAS—*Reaction Kinetics for Chemical Engineers*
WALKER, LEWIS, MCADAMS, AND GILLILAND—*Principles of Chemical Engineering*
WILLIAMS AND JOHNSON—*Stoichiometry for Chemical Engineers*
WILSON AND RIES—*Principles of Chemical Engineering Thermodynamics*

***C. R. Groves, Ch.E.**, Engineer, E. I. du Pont de Nemours & Co., Inc., Wilmington, Del. (Safety and Fire Protection)

C. Fred Gurnham, D.Eng.Sci., Professor of Civil and Chemical Engineering, Illinois Institute of Technology, Chicago, Ill. (Expression)

George A. Hall, Jr., B.S., Advanced Systems Development, Westinghouse Electric Corp., Pittsburgh, Pa. (Fundamentals of Automatic Control)

***Selden H. Hall, M.E.**, Consulting Engineer and Registered Patent Agent, Poughkeepsie, N.Y. (Centrifuges)

***Charles R. Harte, Jr., Ph.D.**, Chemical Engineer, Standard Oil Co., (Indiana) Whiting, Inc. (Gas Absorption)

W. F. Heneghan, B.S., Commercial Development Manager, Sonneborn Chemical and Refining Corp., New York, N.Y. (Manufacturing Cost Estimation)

***Carl V. Herrmann, B.S., M.A.**, E. I. du Pont de Nemours & Co., Inc., Wilmington, Del. (Properties of Commercial Acids and Salts in Aqueous Solution)

K. C. D. Hickman, Ph.D., Consultant and Technical Director, Aquastills, Inc., Rochester, N.Y. (Molecular Distillation)

Nevin K. Hiester, Ph.D., Chairman, Chemical and High-Temperature Technology Dept., Stanford Research Institute, Palo Alto, Calif. (Adsorption and Ion Exchange)

***W. G. Hillen, M.E.**, Director, Sales Training, Carrier Corp., Syracuse, N.Y. (Humidification, Dehumidification and Spray Ponds)

Arthur E. Hoerl, M.A., Group Supervisor, Engineering Dept., E. I. du Pont de Nemours & Co., Inc., Wilmington, Del. (Section Editor: Mathematics)

Emil G. Holmberg, B.S.(Met.E.), Application Engineer (in charge of Process Industries), Development and Research Division, International Nickel Co., New York, N.Y. (Physical and Corrosion Properties of Metals and Alloys)

Arthur D. Holt, Chief, Vibratory and Heat-processing Equipment Research, The Jeffrey Manufacturing Co., Columbus, Ohio. (Indirect Heat Transmission of Solids)

Leland R. Honnaker, B.S.(Ch.E.), Senior Consultant, Engineering Services Division, Engineering Dept., E. I. du Pont de Nemours & Co., Inc., Wilmington, Del. (Corrosion and Its Various Forms)

Hoyt C. Hottel, S.M., Professor of Fuel Engineering and Director, Fuels Research Laboratory, Massachusetts Institute of Technology, Cambridge, Mass. (Radiant Heat Transmission)

***H. G. Houghton, D.Sc.**, Professor of Meteorology and Head of Department, Massachusetts Institute of Technology, Cambridge, Mass. (Spray Nozzles)

Wilfred H. Howe, B.S.Elec.Eng., M.B.A., Chief Engineer, The Foxboro Co., Foxboro, Mass. (Indicators and Recorders)

***Wilbur G. Hudson, M.E.**, Consulting Engineer, Chicago, Ill. (Materials Handling Equipment)

***Wilbert J. Huff, Ph.D., D.Sc.**, Chairman, Department of Chemical Engineering, University of Maryland, College Station, Md. (Gaseous Fuels)

Robert J. Hunn, M.S., Senior Service Engineer, Engineering Dept., E. I. du Pont de Nemours & Co., Inc., Wilmington, Del. (Machine Computation)

***Reed W. Hyde**, Metallurgical Engineer and President, Sintering Machinery Corp. (Feeders and Feeding Mechanisms)

***Donald F. Irvin, B.S.**, Engineer, Oliver-United Filters, Inc., New York, N.Y. (Filtration)

John Johnson, B.S. in M.E., Engineering Manager of Instrument Products Division, Engineering Department, E. I. du Pont de Nemours & Co., Inc., Wilmington, Del. (Economics of Chemical Process Instrumentation; Organizing and Training for Instrument Responsibility)

Victor J. Johnson, B.S., Chief, Cryogenic Technical Service, National Bureau of Standards, Boulder, Colo. (Cryogenic Processes)

J. B. Jones, M.S.Chem.Eng., Consultant on Mass Transfer, Engineering Department, E. I. du Pont de Nemours & Co., Inc., Wilmington, Del. (Control of Distillation Columns)

***Lewis V. Judson, Ph.D.**, Chief of Length Section, National Bureau of Standards, Washington, D.C. (Conversion Tables, Specific Gravity, Weights and Measures, and Wire and Sheet Metal Gages)

Karl Kammermeyer, Sc.D., Professor and Head, Department of Chemical Engineering, University of Iowa, Iowa City, Iowa. (Section Editor: Other Diffusional Operations)

***S. B. Kanowitz, B.S.**, Late Chemical Engineer, Raymond Pulverizer Division, Combustion Engineering Co., Inc., New York, N.Y. (Crushing, Grinding and Pulverizing)

Carl F. Kayan, M.E., Professor of Mechanical Engineering, Columbia University, New York, N.Y. (Section Editor: Refrigeration)

***M. S. Kharasch, Ph.D.**, Professor of Chemistry, University of Chicago, Chicago, Ill. (Physical and Chemical Data)

Gerhard Klein, M.S., Associate Research Engineer, Sea Water Conversion Laboratory, Institute of Engineering Research, University of California, Berkeley, Calif. (Sorbent Properties, Adsorption and Ion Exchange)

***R. V. Kleinschmidt, A.B., A.M., S.B., Sc.D.**, Professor of the Practice of Mechanical Engineering, Harvard Graduate School of Engineering, Cambridge, Mass. (Theory of Dispersion of Liquid Droplets)

Riki Kobayashi, Ph.D., Associate Professor of Chemical Engineering, Rice University, Houston, Tex. (Thermodynamics)

***R. W. Lahey, B.S.**, American Cyanamid Company, Wayne, N.J. (Packaging Equipment)

***James A. Lane, Ph.D.**, Chemical Engineer, Head Design Department, Technical Division, Oak Ridge National Laboratory, Oak Ridge, Tenn. (Dialysis)

***Norbert A. Lange, Ph.D.**, Western University; Handbook Publishers, Inc., Sandusky, Ohio. (Physical Properties of Inorganic and Organic Compounds)

***C. D. Lapple, Chem. E.**, Chemical Engineer, E. I. du Pont de Nemours & Co., Inc., Wilmington, Del. (Dust and Mist Collection)

***James A. Lee, B.S., M.A.**, Southwestern Editor, *Chemical Engineering*, McGraw-Hill Publishing Co., Inc., Houston, Tex. (Materials of Construction)

Thomas W. Leland, Ph.D., Associate Professor of Chemical Engineering, Rice University, Houston, Tex. (Thermodynamics)

***E. T. Lessig, Ph.D.**, Physical Chemist, B. F. Goodrich Rubber Co., Akron, Ohio. (Physical and Chemical Data)

Peter E. Liley, Ph.D., D.I.C., A.R.C.S., Thermophysical Properties Research Center, School of Mechanical Engineering, Purdue University, Lafayette, Ind. (Section Editor: Physical and Chemical Data)

Robert L. Lucas, B.S., Chemical Engineer, E. I. du Pont de Nemours & Co., Inc., Wilmington, Del. (Gas-Solids Separations)

***F. L. Lucker, M.E.,** Special Representative to Chemical Industry, Ingersoll-Rand Co., New York, N.Y. (Movement of Liquids and Gases, Compression of Gas)

***Gordon MacLean, Ch.E.,** Technical Director, Allied Foods Co., New York, N.Y. (Mixing of Material)

Coleman J. Major, Ph.D., Professor of Chemical Engineering, University of Iowa, Iowa City, Iowa. (Leaching, Sublimation, Freeze Drying)

***Charles L. Mantell, Ph.D.,** Consulting Chemical Engineer, New York, N.Y. (Adsorption, Electrochemistry)

***W. R. Marshall, Jr., Ph.D.,** Associate Professor, Chemical Engineering Depart., University of Wisconsin, Madison, Wis. (Drying)

***H. L. Maxwell, Ph.D.,** Metallurgist, Engineering Department, E. I. du Pont de Nemours & Co., Inc., Wilmington, Del. (Materials of Construction)

***William H. McAdams, Sc.D.,** Professor of Chemical Engineering, Massachusetts Institute of Technology, Cambridge, Mass. (Heat Transmission by Conduction and Convection)

***Warren L. McCabe, Ph.D.,** Director of Research, The Flintkote Co., Whippany, N.J. (Crystallization)

Paul Y. McCormick, B.S., Chemical Engineer, E. I. du Pont de Nemours & Co., Inc., Wilmington, Del. (Section Editor: Gas-Solid Systems)

John J. McKetta, Ph.D., Graduate Professor and Chairman, Department of Chemical Engineering, University of Texas, Austin, Tex. (Dimensional Analysis)

Alfred H. McKinney, B.S., Consultant, Engineering Services Division, Engineering Department, E. I. du Pont de Nemours & Co., Inc., Wilmington, Del. (Dryer Instrumentation)

***F. T. McNamara, Ph.D., E.E.,** Associate Professor of Electrical Engineering, Yale University, New Haven, Conn. (Electricity and Electrical Engineering)

Robert F. McNamara, M.S., Chemical Engineer, Ford, Bacon and Davis, Inc., New York, N.Y. (Slurry Transportation)

***E. J. Meyers, E.E.,** Assistant Manager, Safety and Fire Protection Division, E. I. du Pont de Nemours & Co., Inc., Wilmington, Del. (Safety and Fire Protection)

A. W. Michalson, E.M., Sales Manager, Illinois Water Treatment Co., Rockford, Ill. (Ion-exchange Equipment)

***Fred A. Miller,** Materials Handling Consultant, E. I. du Pont de Nemours & Co., Inc., Wilmington, Del. (Industrial Trucks, Tractors and Trailers)

***G. H. Miller,** Industrial Relations Division, Service Department, E. I. du Pont de Nemours & Co., Inc., Wilmington, Del. (Safety and Fire Protection)

Shelby A. Miller, Ph.D., Professor and Head, Chemical Engineering Department, University of Rochester, Rochester, N.Y. (Filtration and Liquid-Gas Systems)

***H. L. Miner,** Manager, Safety and Fire Protection Division, E. I. du Pont de Nemours & Co., Inc., Wilmington, Del. (Safety and Fire Protection)

G. P. Monet, M.S., Research Associate, E. I. du Pont de Nemours & Co., Inc., Wilmington, Del. (Electrodyalysis)

Elmer S. Monroe, M.M.E., Consultant, Engineering Department, E. I. du Pont de Nemours & Co., Inc., Wilmington, Del. (Combustion Equipment Design)

***G. L. Montgomery, M.E.,** Late Associate, *Food Industries,* McGraw-Hill Publishing Co., Inc., New York, N.Y. (Movement and Storage of Materials)

***L. H. Morrison, B.S. in M.E.,** Late Associate Editor, *Power,* McGraw-Hill Publishing Co., Inc., New York, N.Y. (Refrigeration)

A. C. Mueller, Ph.D., Senior Consultant, Engineering Department, E. I. du Pont de Nemours & Co., Inc., Wilmington, Del. (Heat Storage)

***W. A. Myers, B.S.E., M.S.E.,** Assistant Manager, Research and Development Department, Atlantic Refining Co., Philadelphia, Pa. (Liquid Fuels)

Julian Nardi, B.S., M.E., Late Chief Mechanical Engineer, Ford, Bacon and Davis, Inc., New York, N.Y. (Slurry Transportation)

***Harlan W. Nelson, Ph.D.,** Supervisor, Fuels Research, Battelle Memorial Institute, Columbus, Ohio. (Solid Fuels)

Robert B. Norden, B.S.(Ch.E.), Senior Associate Editor, *Chemical Engineering,* McGraw-Hill Publishing Co., Inc., New York, N.Y. (Section Editor: Materials of Construction)

Robert W. Norris, M. S., Consulting Engineer, E. I. du Pont de Nemours & Co., Inc., Wilmington, Del. (Evaporative Cooling)

James Y. Oldshue, Ph.D., Director of Research, Mixing Equipment Co., Rochester, N.Y. (Circulation Mixers, Leaching Equipment)

***Theodore R. Olive, M.S.,** Associate Editor, *Chemical Engineering,* McGraw-Hill Publishing Co., Inc., New York, N.Y. (Measurement and Control of Process Variables)

Philip P. O'Neill, M.S., Mechanical Equipment Consultant, E. I. du Pont de Nemours & Co., Inc., Beaumont, Tex. (Pumping of Liquids and Gases)

James O. Osburn, Ph.D., Professor of Chemical Engineering, University of Iowa, Iowa City, Iowa. (Crystallization)

***E. L. Peffer, B.S., A.M.,** Late Chief of Capacity and Density Section, National Bureau of Standards, Washington, D.C. (Specific Gravity)

Rowan P. Perkins, B.S.M.E., Senior Engineer, Engineering Department, E. I. du Pont de Nemours & Co., Inc., Wilmington, Del. (Combustion)

***John H. Perry, Ph.D.,** Development Department, E. I. du Pont de Nemours & Co., Inc., Wilmington, Del. (Mathematics, Physical and Chemical Data, Physical and Chemical Principles)

Robert H. Perry, Ph.D., Professor, Department of Chemical Engineering, University of Rochester, Rochester, N.Y. (Mathematical Tables, Mathematics, Physical and Chemical Data, Thermodynamics, Reaction Kinetics and Reactor Design)

Fritz W. Peterson, B.S.Eng., Manager of Projects, The M. W. Kellogg Co., New York, N.Y. (Mechanical, Plant and Project Engineering)

Robert L. Pigford, Ph.D., Colburn Professor of Chemical Engineering, University of Delaware, Newark, Del. (Section Editor: Gas Absorption and Solvent Extraction)

***Richard W. Porter, B.S.,** Editorial Director, *The Paper Industry and Paper World,* Chicago, Ill. (Process Control)

John E. Powers, Ph.D., Professor of Chemical Engineering, University of Oklahoma, Norman, Okla. (Thermal Diffusion)

***E. J. Prindle, M.E., LL.D.**, Late Patent Lawyer, Senior Member, Prindle, Bean and Mann. (Patents and Patent Law)

***George A. Prochazka, Jr., E.M.**, Manager Consultant; formerly Chemical Economist, E. I. du Pont de Nemours & Co., Inc., Wilmington, Del. (Accounting and Cost Finding)

***R. B. Purdy, M.E.**, Formerly, Associate Editor of *Power*, McGraw-Hill Publishing Co., Inc., New York, N.Y. (Power Generation)

***W. E. Rahm**, Technical Field Service, E. I. du Pont de Nemours & Co., Inc., Wilmington, Del. (Molding of Plastics)

***A. F. Randolph, B.S., Ch.E.**, Assistant to Director of Sales, Polychemicals Department, E. I. du Pont de Nemours & Co., Inc., Wilmington, Del. (Molding of Plastics)

***Francis W. Reichelderfer, A.B., Sc.D.**, Chief, United States Weather Bureau, Washington, D.C. (Weather)

***E. E. Reid, Ph.D.**, Chemical Consultant, Baltimore, Md. (Physical and Chemical Data)

Neal Richter, Ph.D., Assistant Professor of Chemical Engineering, California Institute of Technology, Pasadena, Calif. (Fundamentals of Automatic Control)

J. W. Riggle, M.S., Research Engineer, E. I. du Pont de Nemours & Co., Inc., Wilmington, Del. (Dialysis)

J. Tom Roberts, Ph.D., Senior Chemical Engineer, Oak Ridge National Laboratory, Union Carbide Nuclear Corp., Oak Ridge, Tenn. (Ion-exchange Equipment)

Sanford M. Roberts, Ph.D., Bonner and Moore Associates, Inc., Houston, Tex. (Computer Process Control)

David B. Rossheim, C.E., Chief Mechanical Engineer, The M. W. Kellogg Co., New York, N.Y. (Section Editor: Mechanical, Plant and Project Engineering)

***Frederick D. Rossini, Ph.D.**, Professor and Head, Department of Chemistry, Carnegie Institute of Technology, Pittsburgh, Pa. (Mathematical Tables and Weights and Measures, Physical and Chemical Data, Physical and Chemical Principles)

***Percy H. Royster, A.B., A.M.**, Technical Advisor, Metallurgical Division, U.S. Bureau of Mines, Washington, D.C. (Furnaces and Kilns)

Frank L. Rubin, B.A., B.Ch.E., Product Engineer, Heat Transfer Equipment, Downingtown Iron Works, Inc., Downingtown, Pa. (Section Editor: Heat-transfer Equipment)

***T. R. Running, Ph.D.**, Late Professor Emeritus of Mathematics, University of Michigan, Ann Arbor, Mich. (Mathematics, Graphical Calculus)

Lenard O. Rutz, Ph.D., Assistant Professor of Chemical Engineering, University of Iowa, Iowa City, Iowa. (Gaseous Diffusion)

***W. P. Ryan, S.M.**, Late Professor of Chemical Engineering, Massachusetts Institute of Technology, Cambridge, Mass. (Industrial Stoichiometry)

Carl W. Sanders, B.S.Chem.Eng., Consulting Engineer, Engineering Services Division, Engineering Department, E. I. du Pont de Nemours & Co., Inc., Wilmington, Del. (Heat-exchange Instrumentation)

Edward G. Scheibel, Ph.D., Chief Engineer, Otto H. York Co., Inc., West Orange, N.J. (Liquid-Gas Systems)

***Gilbert E. Seil, M.S., Ph.D.**, Late Technical Consultant, Day & Zimmermann, Inc., Philadelphia, Pa. (Size Enlargement by Fusion)

***W. M. Sheldon, B.S.**, Director of Research, Pulverizing Machinery Co., Summit, N.J. (Machining)

***Thomas K. Sherwood, Ph.D.**, Professor of Chemical Engineering, Massachusetts Institute of Technology, Cambridge, Mass. (Drying)

I. H Silberberg, Ph.D., Department of Chemical Engineering, University of Texas, Austin, Tex. (Dimensional Analysis)

C. M. Sliepcevich, Ph.D., Associate Dean of Engineering, University of Oklahoma, Norman, Okla. (Thermodynamics)

***C. K. Sloan, A.B., M.S., Ph.D.**, Research Chemist, E. I. du Pont de Nemours & Co., Inc., Wilmington, Del. (Emulsification, Flocculation)

Julian C. Smith, B.Chem., Ch.E., Professor of Chemical Engineering, Cornell University, Ithaca, N.Y. (Section Editor: Liquid-Solid Systems; Agitated Pan Dryers, Centrifuges, Leaching Equipment)

***Paul Sollenberger**, Principal Astronomer, U.S. Naval Observatory, Washington, D.C. (Time)

F. C. Standiford, M.S., W. L. Badger Associates, Inc., Ann Arbor, Mich. (Evaporation)

***William Staniar, M.E.**, Consulting Engineer, Wilmington, Del. (Mechanical Power Transmission)

***W. O. Stauffer, M.S.**, Manager, Research Section of Technical Division, Remington Arms Co., Bridgeport, Conn. (Physical and Chemical Data)

Arthur L. Stern, B.Chem., Partner, Arthur L. Stern Co., South Orange, N.J. (Size Reduction)

***Jesse W. Stillman, Ph.D.**, E. I. du Pont de Nemours & Co., Inc., Wilmington, Del. (Indicators, Sampling)

Thomas M. Stout, Ph.D., Manager, Process Analysis Department, TRW Computer Co. Division, Thompson Ramo Woolridge, Inc., Canoga Park, Calif. (Computer Process Control)

David Stuhlbarg, Ch.E., Project Manager, Processes Research, Inc., Cincinnati, Ohio. (Tank Coils and Jacketed Vessels)

***Daniel R. Stull, Ph.D.**, The Dow Chemical Co., Midland, Mich. (Physical and Chemical Data)

Morgan C. Sze, Sc.D., Executive Staff Engineer, The Lummus Co., New York, N.Y. (Gas-Gas Systems)

***Hugh S. Taylor, Sc.D.**, Research Professor of Chemistry, Princeton University, Princeton, N.J. (Catalysis)

***J. E. Teagarden, Ph.D.**, E. I. du Pont de Nemours & Co., Inc., Wilmington, Del. (Molding of Plastics)

Aaron J. Teller, Ph.D., Dean, College of Engineering, Cooper Union for the Advancement of Science and Art, New York, N.Y. (Section Editor: Liquid-Gas Systems)

Joseph C. Thompson, B.S., District Manager, General American Transportation Corp., New York, N.Y. (Storage and Bulk Transport of Fluids)

***P. V. Tilden, B.S. in M.E.**, Safety and Fire Protection Division, E. I. du Pont de Nemours & Co., Inc., Wilmington, Del. (Safety and Fire Protection)

Yeram S. Touloukian, Ph.D., Thermophysical Properties Research Center, School of Mechanical Engineering, Purdue University, Lafayette, Ind. (Physical and Chemical Data)

Robert E. Treybal, Ph.D., Professor of Chemical Engineering, New York University, New York, N.Y. (Liquid-Liquid Systems)

***W. Trinks**, Professor Emeritus, Carnegie Institute of Technology, Pittsburgh, Pa. (Furnaces and Kilns)

***Louis B. Tuckerman, Ph.D.**, Assistant Chief, Mechanics Division, National Bureau of Standards, Washington, D.C. (Gravity)

D. Barton Turkington, M.S.M.E., Professor and Chairman, School of Mechanical Engineering, University of Oklahoma, Norman, Okla. (Section Editor: Heat Generation, Transport and Storage)

***Kenneth S. Valentine, A.B., Ch.E.**, New York Manager, The Patterson Foundry & Machine Co., East Liverpool, Ohio. (Mixing of Material)

***D. J. Van Marie, Ch.E.**, Chemical Engineer, Buflovak Equipment Division, Blaw-Knox Co., Buffalo, N.Y. (Flaking)

***J. V. Vaughen, Ph.D.**, Chemist, E. I. du Pont de Nemours & Co., Inc., Wilmington, Del. (Physical and Chemical Data)

Theodore Vermeulen, Ph.D., Professor of Chemical Engineering, University of California; Chemical Engineer, Lawrence Radiation Laboratory, Berkeley, Calif. (Adsorption and Ion Exchange)

***H. C. Vernon, M.S.**, Engineering Department, E. I. du Pont de Nemours & Co., Inc., Wilmington, Del. (Mathematics, Physical and Chemical Data, Sublimation)

Christian M. Vogrin, C.E., Engineering Department, Socony-Mobil Oil Co., Inc., New York, N.Y. (Mechanical, Plant and Project Engineering)

Edward R. Vrablik, B.S.Ch.E., M.B.A., Project Engineer, The Eimco Corp., Salt Lake City, Utah. (Gravity Sedimentation Operations)

***Donald D. Wagman, B.S., M.A.**, National Bureau of Standards, Washington, D.C. (Physical and Chemical Data)

***R. G. Warner, Ph.D., E.E.**, Vice President, United Illuminating Co., New Haven, Conn. (Electricity and Electrical Engineering)

James B. Weaver, M.S., Director, Development Appraisal Department, Atlas Chemical Industries, Inc., Wilmington, Del. (Section Editor: Cost and Profitability Estimation)

William D. Webb, Development Engineer, E. I. du Pont de Nemours & Co., Inc., Wilmington, Del. (Pipe and Fittings)

Eric Weger, Dr. Eng., Associate Professor, Washington University, St. Louis, Mo. (Radiation Bibliography)

Sherman S. Weidenbaum, Ph.D., Director, Israel Silicate Institute, c/o Corning Glass Works, Corning, N.Y. (Section Editor: Gas-Gas, Liquid-Liquid, and Solid-Solid Systems; Solid-Solid Mixing)

***H. M. Weir, B.Ch.E., Ph.D.**, Consulting Engineer, Philadelphia, Pa. (Liquid Fuels)

David F. Wells, B.S., Chemical Engineer, E. I. du Pont de Nemours & Co., Inc., Wilmington, Del. (Fluidized-bed Systems)

***F. L. Whitney, Jr., B.S.**, Engineer, E. I. du Pont de Nemours & Co., Inc., Wilmington, Del. (Materials of Construction)

***John C. Whitwell, Ch.E.**, Professor of Chemical Engineering, Princeton University, Princeton, N.J. (Physical and Chemical Data)

***Richard Wiebe, Ph.D.**, U.S. Bureau of Agricultural and Industrial Chemistry, Washington, D.C. (Physical and Chemical Data)

Glenn O. Wilson, Registered Professional Engineer, Director, Technical Coordination, Dorr-Oliver, Inc., Stamford, Conn. (Classification)

***H. S. Winnicki, B.S.**, Head of Chemistry Section, Research Division, Westvaco Chlorine Products Corp., South Charleston, W.Va. (Measurement and Control of Process Variables)

***F. W. Woodfield, Jr., M.S.**, Chemical Engineer, General Electric Co., Schenectady, N.Y. (Distillation)

Lincoln T. Work, Ph.D., Consulting Engineer, New York, N.Y. (Section Editor: Size Reduction and Size Enlargement)

***Hood Worthington, M.S.**, Chemical Engineer, E. I. du Pont de Nemours & Co., Inc., Wilmington, Del. (High-pressure Technique)

***Raymond Wynkoop, Ph.D.**, Chemical Engineer, Standard Oil Co. (Indiana), Whiting, Ind. (Solvent Extraction)

***J. I. Yellott, B.S., M.M.E.**, Director of Research, Locomotive Development Committee, Bituminous Coal Research, Inc., Pittsburgh, Pa. (Explosive Disintegration)

***Henry L. Young, B.S.**, Sales Department, Aridye Corp., Division, Interchemical Corp., New York, N.Y. (Measurement and Control of Process Variables)

***Stanley B. Zdonik, S.M.**, Chemical Engineer, E. B. Badger & Sons Co., Boston, Mass. (Azeotropic and Extractive Distillation)

***F. C. Zeisberg**, Late Technical Investigator, E. I. du Pont de Nemours & Co., Inc., Wilmington, Del. (Reports and Report Writing)

Robert G. Zilly, M.S., Editor and Engineer, *Building Construction*, Chicago, Ill. (Section Editor: Solids Transport and Storage)

PREFACE TO THE FOURTH EDITION

As chemical engineering has changed over the years, so have its tools—both academic and industrial. Increase in emphasis on the physical sciences and mathematics has been truly dramatic. For the chemical engineer, this change has entailed greater recognition and more rigorous use of the underlying engineering sciences of thermodynamics, of reaction kinetics, of solid and fluid mechanics, and of mass and energy transfer.

The unit operations—long unique and useful tools of chemical engineering—are thus being integrated into the broader framework of these sciences. Empirical and experimental studies have given way to more sophisticated techniques, using statistical analysis and other tools of the mathematician. Computers are being more generally used for engineering design and process simulation, control and operation. Finally, the tools of economic evaluation have become sharper and better appreciated and hence are more widely employed as guides to profitable production.

Taking note of all these developments, the editors of this Fourth Edition of the late John H. Perry's *Chemical Engineers' Handbook* have squarely faced up to the critical need for evaluation and reorganization, as well as updating and adding to the content of the earlier editions. Basically, in our considered opinion, the unit-operation concept still remains the most practical approach to the application of chemical engineering principles. But we are also convinced that the unit operations must be integrated into more general categories of closely related characteristics and phenomena, if they are to serve effectively as bases for new and ever broadening applications. Likewise, by grouping and comparing cognate data on equipment design and performance, we can help to unify our technology and thereby increase the reference value of this handbook, both to the practicing chemical engineer and to the student who seeks a comprehensive supplement to his standard textbooks.

The extent to which we have succeeded in this effort may be judged from the following paragraphs, which give brief and interpretative summaries of what the various section editors believe has been accomplished:

Summary of Content and New Material in This Fourth Edition

Section 1. Mathematical Tables

New sets of discount and present-worth factors reflect the chemical engineer's increasing responsibility for economic decisions. Tables of statistical factors supplement the descriptive material on techniques as developed in Section 2.

Section 2. Mathematics

This section has been completely rewritten and enlarged to include more advanced mathematical principles and tools which are finding more frequent use in chemical engineering, e.g., an up-to-date summary of electronic computer techniques.

Section 3. Physical and Chemical Data

Utility of these data has been enhanced by replacing older tabulations with useful diagrams and by providing more extensive reference lists for information on thermal conductivity, viscosity, etc. A valuable new subsection deals with the prediction and extrapolation of physical-property data.

Section 4. Reaction Kinetics, Reactor Design, and Thermodynamics

Thermodynamic principles are developed from the generalized mass, energy and entropy balances, with particular emphasis on the application of the second law to the concept of availability of energy, i.e., the maximum-work principle. Recent developments are presented for evaluating deviations from ideal behavior of the properties of both pure substances and mixtures.

A new subsection, concerned with reaction kinetics and reactor design, has been added. This also covers the planning and programming of kinetic experiments. Generalized differential equations are presented and simplified to permit the practicing chemical engineer to review the theoretical basis, plan and interpret experimental results, and then complete the reactor design.

Section 5. Fluid and Particle Mechanics

New and recently advanced developments in two-phase and non-Newtonian flow, fluidized beds, high-vacuum and unsteady-state fluid dynamics are presented. Chemical engineers will also find useful formulas and charts for solving such practical problems as orifice design, economic pipe diameters, and pressure drop across tube banks.

Section 6. Transport and Storage of Fluids

This section has been designed to facilitate the selection and application of equipment for handling fluids,—viz., pumps, compressors, blowers, ejectors, valves, piping, gas holders, etc. New material covers axial-flow compressors and shaft seals, as well as up-to-date data on welding fittings and plastic piping.

Section 7. Solids Transport and Storage

Included are the types of conveying, packaging, and storage equipment most often used in the chemical process industries, with prime emphasis on process application rather than mechanical design. Greater attention is also given to pneumatic and fluidized conveying and to bin design.

Section 8. Size Reduction and Size Enlargement

In addition to comprehensive data on the principles and practices of crushing and grinding, including latest developments in vibratory mills and jet pulverizers, this section deals with the opposite but related functions of agglomerization, granulation, and compacting.

Section 9. Heat Generation, Transport, and Storage

Here, completely rewritten and coordinated with recent developments, is pertinent material previously found in three sections of earlier editions—viz., Fuels, Furnaces, and Power Generation and Transmission.

Section 10. Heat Transmission

Treated here are theory and application of heat-transfer principles in exact and approximate solution of heat-transfer problems in conduction, convection, and radiation. Also included are new predictive charts and tables directly applicable to chemical engineering design. Many sample problems and their solutions are presented.

Section 11. Heat-transfer Equipment

Basically, this section is a new contribution to handbook literature. Here, for the first time, theory and "hardware" have been adequately coordinated. Construction details, cost and performance data for all types of commercial heat exchangers are presented. The classic treatment of evaporators, as prepared for the original edition, has been completely rewritten and updated.

Section 12. Refrigeration

The increasing impact of low-temperature processes lends emphasis to the chemical engineer's present-day interest in cryogenic principles and applications. Accordingly, a new subsection on cryogenics has been added to supplement conventional material on refrigeration processes. New data are presented on the properties of materials at low temperatures.

Section 13. Distillation

This section covers theory and basic principles of distillation processes (for equipment, see Section 18). It represents a new level of sophistication, with greater emphasis on the application of thermodynamic principles in order to reduce the need for relying solely on experimental data and empirical correlations. Completely new material deals with the use of computers in the design of multicomponent distillation columns, with worked-out examples, and with the dynamics of distillation processes.

Section 14. Gas Absorption and Solvent Extraction

Here we are concerned with theory and principles of gas absorption and liquid-liquid extraction in order to establish sound procedures for design calculations. Included is a wealth of equilibrium and mass-transfer data. (Equipment performance is covered in Sections 18–21.) Again, emphasis is on the application of thermodynamic principles as a way to reduce dependence on experimentation and empiricism.

Section 15. Humidification and Drying

Once again, theory and underlying principles, rather than mechanical design and performance, are presented for the unit operations involved in the mass transfer of water vapor to and from air, viz., evaporative cooling, air conditioning, and the drying of solids. New data presented here will help in the prediction of heat- and mass-transfer coefficients.

Section 16. Adsorption and Ion Exchange

A new unified approach to theory and principles in this rapidly advancing field should lead to sounder design calculations and equipment applications. For the first time, adsorption and ion exchange are treated not only from the thermodynamic (equilibrium) viewpoint but also from the kinetic (rate-process) approach.

Section 17. Other Diffusional Operations

Such unit operations as leaching, crystallization, sublimation, freeze drying, molecular distillation, gaseous and thermal diffusion, dialysis, and electrodialysis—now currently so important in such processes as the desalting of seawater—are viewed from basic theory and principles leading to better design procedures.

Section 18. Liquid-Gas Systems

This is a unified, coordinated treatment of mass-transfer kinetics and fluid dynamics of liquid-gas systems. New subject matter is included on the interrelationship of construction and performance of equipment utilized for contacting and/or separating vapor and liquid streams. In all instances, power consumption, cost data, and economical optimization are presented and compared.

Section 19. Liquid-Solid Systems

Design considerations, performance and cost data are presente for the wide range of processing e q uipment involved in liquid-solid systems,—viz., filters and centrifuges, thickeners and clarifiers, paste mixers and agitators, and leaching, ion-exchange, and slurry-transportation systems. A completely revised and enlarged subsection on centrifuges includes equations and data for scaling-up laboratory and pilot-plant results. The subsection on ion-exchange equipment covers design and performance not only of batch exchangers but also of both static and moving-bed continuous units.

Section 20. Gas-Solid Systems

Contacting equipment commonly employed in heat and mass transfer between solid and gas streams is uniquely presented, quite independently of the specific unit operations involved. Detailed descriptions of mechanical designs, with typical applications and procedures for equipment selection, are supplemented with commercial specifications and up-to-date cost data.

Section 21. Gas-Gas, Liquid-Liquid, and Solid-Solid Systems

This new section covers under one approach all equipment for contacting and separation of these phases. New devices developed during the past ten years are described objectively and evaluated for chemical engineering applications. Entirely new material is included for sampling, screening, froth flotation, and electrostatic separation of minerals based on recent advances in materials science and engineering.

Section 22. Process Control

Coverage of this important, fast-moving field has been substantially expanded. Comprehensive but concise summaries include the fundamentals of process measurement and automatic control, modern telemetering, electronic computer and other controls of major unit operations and processes. A new subsection deals with the organization and economic philosophy underlying the establishment of instrument departments in chemical process industries.

Section 23. Materials of Construction

In addition to augmented and updated data on corrosion resistance of metallic and nonmetallic materials of construction, new information is provided on problems involving high and low temperatures and pressure and vacuum applications. The properties and performance of the newer plastics and metals are adequately presented—all directed toward one objective, economic selection.

Section 24. Mechanical, Plant, and Project Engineering

This fourth edition, for the first time, draws heavily on these closely allied disciplines for industry standards, principles and practices. Code requirements for pressure vessels and process plant piping are interpreted to help the chemical engineer in his joint responsibilities with the mechanical engineer and equipment fabricator in providing safe as well as economical design and construction. Plant engineering, as considered here, encompasses a wide range of mechanical and electrical equipment and auxiliary services not ordinarily in the province of the chemical engineer, yet important to over-all process-plant operations.

Section 25. Electrical Engineering

The goals of this section are to present the principles of electrical engineering of prime importance to chemical engineers and to outline in terms of these basic ideas the operating characteristics and areas of application of electrical equipment. Subsections on electrochemistry and electrical instruments round out this presentation.

Section 26. Cost and Profitability Estimation

This is a fitting climax to a modern engineering handbook. It covers the fundamentals of economic analysis and provides definite guide lines for estimation of fixed-capital and manufacturing costs and over-all profitability. Rigorous in treatment, it should prove extremely helpful to the engineer searching for economically optimum solutions to many of his problems. Valuable additions include a glossary of cost estimating terms, charts of unit costs of various types of plant facilities, and forms and procedures for calculating that most important of criteria, return on investment.

As the list of section editors and contributors on the preceding pages attests, this Fourth Edition adds the names of almost a hundred engineers, chemists, and other specialists to the already long roll of those who have contributed to the content of the *Chemical Engineers' Handbook* since its original publication in 1934. This herculean effort would not have been possible without their willingness to share valuable knowledge and experience in many diversified fields of activity. As editors who have reason to know and appreciate the cost of their contributions in time and effort, we join with others in the profession in acknowledging our indebtedness to them and to the companies, universities, and other organizations they serve.

ROBERT H. PERRY
CECIL H. CHILTON
SIDNEY D. KIRKPATRICK

CONTENTS

For the detailed contents of any section, consult the title page of that section. See also the alphabetical index in the back of this handbook.

Chemical Engineers' Handbook

SECTION 1

MATHEMATICAL TABLES

BY

Robert H. Perry, Ph.D., Professor, Department of Chemical Engineering, University of Rochester; Member, American Society for Enginering Education, American Association for the Advancement of Science.

CONTENTS

MATHEMATICAL TABLES

Table 1-1. Five-place Common Logarithms of Numbers

100—170

No.	L	0	1	2	3	4	5	6	7	8	9
100	00	000	043	087	130	173	217	260	303	346	389
101		432	475	518	561	604	647	689	732	775	817
102		860	903	945	988	*030	*072	*115	*157	*199	*242
103	01	284	326	368	410	452	494	536	578	620	662
104		703	745	787	828	870	912	953	995	*036	*078
105	02	119	160	202	243	284	325	366	408	449	490
106		531	572	612	653	694	735	776	816	857	898
107		938	979	*019	*060	*100	*141	*181	*222	*262	*302
108	03	342	383	423	463	503	543	583	623	663	703
109		743	782	822	862	902	941	981	*021	*060	*100
110	04	139	179	218	258	297	336	376	415	454	493
111		532	571	610	650	689	727	766	805	844	883
112		922	961	999	*038	*077	*115	*154	*192	*231	*269
113	05	308	346	385	423	461	500	538	576	614	652
114		690	729	767	805	843	881	918	956	994	*032
115	06	070	108	145	183	221	258	296	333	371	408
116		446	483	521	558	595	633	670	707	744	781
117		819	856	893	930	967	*004	*041	*078	*115	*151
118	07	188	225	262	298	335	372	408	445	482	518
119		555	591	628	664	700	737	773	809	846	882
120		918	954	990	*027	*063	*099	*135	*171	*207	*243
121	08	279	314	350	386	422	458	493	529	565	600
122		636	672	707	743	778	814	849	884	920	955
123		991	*026	*061	*096	*132	*167	*202	*237	*272	*307
124	09	342	377	412	447	482	517	552	587	621	656
125		691	726	760	795	830	864	899	934	968	*003
126	10	037	072	106	140	175	209	243	278	312	346
127		380	415	449	483	517	551	585	619	653	687
128		721	755	789	823	857	890	924	958	992	*025
129	11	059	093	126	160	193	227	261	294	327	361
130		394	428	461	494	528	561	594	628	661	694
131		727	760	793	826	860	893	926	959	992	*024
132	12	057	090	123	156	189	222	254	287	320	353
133		385	418	450	483	516	548	581	613	646	678
134		710	743	775	808	840	872	905	937	969	*001
135	13	033	066	098	130	162	194	226	258	290	322
136		354	386	418	450	481	513	545	577	609	640
137		672	704	735	767	799	830	862	893	925	956
138		988	*019	*051	*082	*114	*145	*176	*208	*239	*270
139	14	301	333	364	395	426	457	489	520	551	582
140		613	644	675	706	737	768	799	829	860	891
141		922	953	983	*014	*045	*076	*106	*137	*168	*198
142	15	229	259	290	320	351	381	412	442	473	503
143		534	564	594	625	655	685	715	746	776	806
144		836	866	897	927	957	987	*017	*047	*077	*107
145	16	137	167	197	227	256	286	316	346	376	406
146		435	465	495	524	554	584	613	643	673	702
147		732	761	791	820	850	879	909	938	967	997
148	17	026	056	085	114	143	173	202	231	260	289
149		319	348	377	406	435	464	493	522	551	580
150	17	609	638	667	696	725	754	782	811	840	869
151		898	926	955	984	*013	*041	*070	*099	*127	*156
152	18	184	213	241	270	299	327	355	384	412	441
153		469	498	526	554	583	611	639	667	696	724
154		752	780	808	837	865	893	921	949	977	*005
155	19	033	061	089	117	145	173	201	229	257	285
156		312	340	368	396	424	451	479	507	535	562
157		590	618	645	673	700	728	756	783	811	838
158		866	893	921	948	976	*003	*030	*058	*085	*112
159	20	140	167	194	222	249	276	303	330	358	385
160		412	439	466	493	520	548	575	602	629	656
161		683	710	737	763	790	817	844	871	898	925
162		952	978	*005	*032	*059	*085	*112	*139	*165	*192
163	21	219	245	272	299	325	352	378	405	431	458
164		484	511	537	564	590	617	643	669	696	722
165		748	775	801	827	854	880	906	932	958	985
166	22	011	037	063	089	115	141	168	194	220	246
167		272	298	324	350	376	401	427	453	479	505
168		531	557	583	608	634	660	686	712	737	763
169		789	814	840	866	891	917	943	968	994	*019
170	23	045	070	096	121	147	172	198	223	249	274
No.	L	0	1	2	3	4	5	6	7	8	9

Proportional parts

	44	43	42	41	40	39	38	37	36	35	34	33	32	31	30	29	28	27	26
1	4.4	4.3	4.2	4.1	4.0	3.9	3.8	3.7	3.6	3.5	3.4	3.3	3.2	3.1	3.0	2.9	2.8	2.7	2.6
2	8.8	8.6	8.4	8.2	8.0	7.8	7.6	7.4	7.2	7.0	6.8	6.6	6.4	6.2	6.0	5.8	5.6	5.4	5.2
3	13.2	12.9	12.6	12.3	12.0	11.7	11.4	11.1	10.8	10.5	10.2	9.9	9.6	9.3	9.0	8.7	8.4	8.1	7.8
4	17.6	17.2	16.8	16.4	16.0	15.6	15.2	14.8	14.4	14.0	13.6	13.2	12.8	12.4	12.0	11.6	11.2	10.8	10.4
5	22.0	21.5	21.0	20.5	20.0	19.5	19.0	18.5	18.0	17.5	17.0	16.5	16.0	15.5	15.0	14.5	14.0	13.5	13.0
6	26.4	25.8	25.2	24.6	24.0	23.4	22.8	22.2	21.6	21.0	20.4	19.8	19.2	18.6	18.0	17.4	16.8	16.2	15.6
7	30.8	30.1	29.4	28.7	28.0	27.3	26.6	25.9	25.2	24.5	23.8	23.1	22.4	21.7	21.0	20.3	19.6	18.9	18.2
8	35.2	34.4	33.6	32.8	32.0	31.2	30.4	29.6	28.8	28.0	27.2	26.4	25.6	24.8	24.0	23.2	22.4	21.6	20.8
9	39.6	38.7	37.8	36.9	36.0	35.1	34.2	33.3	32.4	31.5	30.6	29.7	28.8	27.9	27.0	26.1	25.2	24.3	23.4

Proportional parts

* Indicates change in the first two decimal places.

Table 1-1. Five-place Common Logarithms of Numbers—(*Continued*)

170—240

No.	L	0	1	2	3	4	5	6	7	8	9
170	23	045	070	096	121	147	172	198	223	249	274
171		300	325	350	376	401	426	452	477	502	528
172		553	578	603	629	654	679	704	729	754	776
173		805	830	855	880	905	930	955	980	*005	*030
174	24	055	080	105	130	155	180	204	229	254	279
175		304	329	353	378	403	428	452	477	502	527
176		551	576	601	625	650	674	699	724	748	773
177		797	822	846	871	895	920	944	969	993	*018
178	25	042	066	091	115	139	164	188	212	237	261
179		285	310	334	358	382	406	431	455	479	503
180		527	551	575	600	624	648	672	696	720	744
181		768	792	816	840	864	888	912	935	959	983
182	26	007	031	055	079	102	126	150	174	198	221
183		245	269	293	316	340	364	387	411	435	458
184		482	505	529	553	576	600	623	647	670	694
185		717	741	764	788	811	834	858	881	905	928
186		951	975	998	*021	*045	*068	*091	*114	*138	*161
187	27	184	207	231	254	277	300	323	346	370	393
188		416	439	462	485	508	531	554	577	600	623
189		646	669	692	715	738	761	784	807	830	853
190		875	898	921	944	967	990	*012	*035	*058	*081
191	28	103	126	149	172	194	217	240	262	285	308
192		330	353	375	398	421	443	466	488	511	533
193		556	578	601	623	646	668	691	713	735	758
194		780	803	825	847	870	892	914	937	959	981
195	29	003	026	048	070	092	115	137	159	181	203
196		226	248	270	292	314	336	358	380	403	425
197		447	469	491	513	535	557	579	601	623	645
198		667	688	710	732	754	776	798	820	842	863
199		885	907	929	951	973	994	*016	*038	*060	*081
200	30	103	125	146	168	190	211	233	255	276	298
201		320	341	363	384	406	428	449	471	492	514
202		535	557	578	600	621	643	664	685	707	728
203		750	771	792	814	835	856	878	899	920	942
204		963	984	*006	*027	*048	*069	*091	*112	*133	*154
205	31	175	197	218	239	260	281	302	323	345	366
206		387	408	429	450	471	492	513	534	555	576
207		597	618	639	660	681	702	723	744	765	785
208		806	827	848	869	890	911	931	952	973	994
209	32	015	035	056	077	098	118	139	160	181	201
210		222	243	263	284	305	325	346	366	387	408
211		428	449	469	490	511	531	552	572	593	613
212		634	654	675	695	715	736	756	777	797	818
213		838	858	879	899	919	940	960	980	*001	*021
214	33	041	062	082	102	122	143	163	183	203	224
215		244	264	284	304	325	345	365	385	405	425
216		445	465	486	506	526	546	566	586	606	626
217		646	666	686	706	726	746	766	786	806	826
218		846	866	885	905	925	945	965	985	*005	*025
219	34	044	064	084	104	124	143	163	183	203	223
220		242	262	282	301	321	341	361	380	400	420
221		439	459	479	498	518	537	557	577	596	616
222		635	655	674	694	713	733	753	772	792	811
223		830	850	869	889	908	928	947	967	986	*005
224	35	025	044	064	083	102	122	141	160	180	199
225		218	238	257	276	295	315	334	353	372	392
226		411	430	449	468	488	507	526	545	564	583
227		603	622	641	660	679	698	717	736	755	774
228		793	813	832	851	870	889	908	927	946	965
229		984	*003	*021	*040	*059	*078	*097	*116	*135	*154
230	36	173	192	211	229	248	267	286	305	324	342
231		361	380	399	418	436	455	474	493	511	530
232		549	568	586	605	624	642	661	680	698	717
233		736	754	773	791	810	829	847	866	884	903
234		922	940	959	977	996	*014	*033	*051	*070	*088
235	37	107	125	144	162	181	199	218	236	254	273
236		291	310	328	346	365	383	401	420	438	457
237		475	493	511	530	548	566	585	603	621	639
238		658	676	694	712	731	749	767	785	803	822
239		840	858	876	894	912	931	949	967	985	*003
240	38	021	039	057	075	093	112	130	148	166	184
No.	L	0	1	2	3	4	5	6	7	8	9

Proportional parts

	25	24	23	22	21	20	19	18
1	2.5	2.4	2.3	2.2	2.1	2.0	1.9	1.8
2	5.0	4.8	4.6	4.4	4.2	4.0	3.8	3.6
3	7.5	7.2	6.9	6.6	6.3	6.0	5.7	5.4
4	10.0	9.6	9.2	8.8	8.4	8.0	7.6	7.2
5	12.5	12.0	11.5	11.0	10.5	10.0	9.5	9.0
6	15.0	14.4	13.8	13.2	12.6	12.0	11.4	10.8
7	17.5	16.8	16.1	15.4	14.7	14.0	13.3	12.6
8	20.0	19.2	18.4	17.6	16.8	16.0	15.2	14.4
9	22.5	21.6	20.7	19.8	18.9	18.0	17.1	16.2

* Indicates change in the first two decimal places.

Table 1-1. Five-place Common Logarithms of Numbers—(*Continued*)

240—310

No.	L	0	1	2	3	4	5	6	7	8	9
240	38	021	039	057	075	093	112	130	148	166	184
241		202	220	238	256	274	292	310	328	346	364
242		382	399	417	435	453	471	489	507	525	543
243		561	579	596	614	632	650	668	686	703	721
244		739	757	775	792	810	828	846	863	881	899
245		917	934	952	970	987	*005	*023	*041	*058	*076
246	39	094	111	129	146	164	182	199	217	235	252
247		270	287	305	322	340	358	375	393	410	428
248		445	463	480	498	515	533	550	568	585	602
249		620	637	655	672	690	707	724	742	759	777
250	39	794	811	829	846	863	881	898	915	933	950
251		967	985	*002	*019	*037	*054	*071	*088	*106	*123
252	40	140	157	175	192	209	226	243	261	278	295
253		312	329	346	364	381	398	415	432	449	466
254		483	500	518	535	552	569	586	603	620	637
255		654	671	688	705	722	739	756	773	790	807
256		824	841	858	875	892	909	926	943	960	976
257		993	*010	*027	*044	*061	*078	*095	*111	*128	*145
258	41	162	179	196	212	229	246	263	280	296	313
259		330	347	364	380	397	414	430	447	464	481
260		497	514	531	547	564	581	597	614	631	647
261		664	681	697	714	731	747	764	780	797	814
262		830	847	863	880	896	913	929	946	963	979
263		996	*012	*029	*045	*062	*078	*095	*111	*127	*144
264	42	160	177	193	210	226	243	259	275	292	308
265		325	341	357	374	390	406	423	439	456	472
266		488	504	521	537	553	570	586	602	619	635
267		651	667	684	700	716	732	749	765	781	797
268		813	830	846	862	878	894	911	927	943	959
269		975	991	*008	*024	*040	*056	*072	*088	*104	*120
270	43	136	152	169	185	201	217	233	249	265	281
271		297	313	329	345	361	377	393	409	425	441
272		457	473	489	505	521	537	553	569	584	600
273		616	632	648	664	680	696	712	727	743	759
274		775	791	807	823	838	854	870	886	902	917
275		933	949	965	981	996	*012	*028	*044	*059	*075
276	44	091	107	122	138	154	170	185	201	217	232
277		248	264	279	295	311	326	342	358	373	389
278		404	420	436	451	467	483	498	514	529	545
279		560	576	592	607	623	638	654	669	685	700
280		716	731	747	762	778	793	809	824	840	855
281		871	886	902	917	932	948	963	979	994	*010
282	45	025	040	056	071	086	102	117	133	148	163
283		179	194	209	225	240	255	271	286	301	317
284		332	347	362	378	393	408	423	439	454	469
285		484	500	515	530	545	561	576	591	606	621
286		637	652	667	682	697	712	728	743	758	773
287		788	803	818	834	849	864	879	894	909	924
288		939	954	969	984	*000	*015	*030	*045	*060	*075
289	46	090	105	120	135	150	165	180	195	210	225
290		240	255	270	285	300	315	330	345	359	374
291		389	404	419	434	449	464	479	494	509	523
292		538	553	568	583	598	613	627	642	657	672
293		687	702	716	731	746	761	776	790	805	820
294		835	850	864	879	894	909	923	938	953	967
295		982	997	*012	*026	*041	*056	*070	*085	*100	*115
296	47	129	144	159	173	188	202	217	232	246	261
297		276	290	305	319	334	349	363	378	392	407
298		422	436	451	465	480	494	509	524	538	553
299		567	582	596	611	625	640	654	669	683	698
300	47	712	727	741	756	770	784	799	813	828	842
301		857	871	886	900	914	929	943	958	972	986
302	48	001	015	029	044	058	073	087	101	116	130
303		144	159	173	187	202	216	230	245	259	273
304		287	302	316	330	344	359	373	387	402	416
305		430	444	458	473	487	501	515	530	544	558
306		572	586	601	615	629	643	657	671	686	700
307		714	728	742	756	770	785	799	813	827	841
308		855	869	883	897	911	926	940	954	968	982
309		996	*010	*024	*038	*052	*066	*080	*094	*108	*122
310	49	136	150	164	178	192	206	220	234	248	262
No.	L	0	1	2	3	4	5	6	7	8	9

Proportional parts

	18	17	16	15	14
1	1.8	1.7	1.6	1.5	1.4
2	3.6	3.4	3.2	3.0	2.8
3	5.4	5.1	4.8	4.5	4.2
4	7.2	6.8	6.4	6.0	5.6
5	9.0	8.5	8.0	7.5	7.0
6	10.8	10.2	9.6	9.0	8.4
7	12.6	11.9	11.2	10.5	9.8
8	14.4	13.6	12.8	12.0	11.2
9	16.2	15.3	14.4	13.5	12.6

* Indicates change in the first two decimal places.

Table 1-1. Five-place Common Logarithms of Numbers—(*Continued*)

310—380

No.	L	0	1	2	3	4	5	6	7	8	9
310	49	136	150	164	178	192	206	220	234	248	262
311		276	290	304	318	332	346	360	374	388	402
312		415	429	443	457	471	485	499	513	527	541
313		554	568	582	596	610	624	638	651	665	679
314		693	707	721	734	748	762	776	790	803	817
315		831	845	859	872	886	900	914	927	941	955
316		969	982	996	*010	*024	*037	*051	*065	*079	*092
317	50	106	120	133	147	161	174	188	202	215	229
318		243	256	270	284	297	311	325	338	352	365
319		379	393	406	420	433	447	461	474	488	501
320		515	529	542	556	569	583	596	610	623	637
321		651	664	678	691	705	718	732	745	759	772
322		786	799	813	826	840	853	866	880	893	907
323		920	934	947	961	974	987	*001	*014	*028	*041
324	51	055	068	081	095	108	121	135	148	162	175
325		188	202	215	228	242	255	268	282	295	308
326		322	335	348	362	375	388	402	415	428	441
327		455	468	481	495	508	521	534	548	561	574
328		587	601	614	627	640	654	667	680	693	706
329		720	733	746	759	772	786	799	812	825	838
330		851	865	878	891	904	917	930	943	957	970
331		983	996	*009	*022	*035	*048	*061	*075	*088	*101
332	52	114	127	140	153	166	179	192	205	218	231
333		244	257	271	284	297	310	323	336	349	362
334		375	388	401	414	427	440	453	466	479	492
335		504	517	530	543	556	569	582	595	608	621
336		634	647	660	673	686	699	711	724	737	750
337		763	776	789	802	815	827	840	853	866	879
338		892	905	917	930	943	956	969	982	994	*007
339	53	020	033	046	058	071	084	097	110	122	135
340		148	161	173	186	199	212	224	237	250	263
341		275	288	301	314	326	339	352	365	377	390
342		403	415	428	441	453	466	479	491	504	517
343		529	542	555	567	580	593	605	618	631	643
344		656	668	681	694	706	719	732	744	757	769
345		782	795	807	820	832	845	857	870	883	895
346		908	920	933	945	958	970	983	995	*008	*020
347	54	033	045	058	070	083	095	108	120	133	145
348		158	170	183	195	208	220	233	245	258	270
349		283	295	307	320	332	345	357	370	382	394
350	54	407	419	432	444	456	469	481	494	506	518
351		531	543	555	568	580	593	605	617	630	642
352		654	667	679	691	704	716	728	741	753	765
353		777	790	802	814	827	839	851	864	876	888
354		900	913	925	937	949	962	974	986	998	*011
355	55	023	035	047	060	072	084	096	108	121	133
356		145	157	169	182	194	206	218	230	242	255
357		267	279	291	303	315	328	340	352	364	376
358		388	400	413	425	437	449	461	473	485	497
359		509	522	534	546	558	570	582	594	606	618
360		630	642	654	666	678	691	703	715	727	739
361		751	763	775	787	799	811	823	835	847	859
362		871	883	895	907	919	931	943	955	967	979
363		991	*003	*015	*027	*038	*050	*062	*074	*086	*098
364	56	110	122	134	146	158	170	182	194	205	217
365		229	241	253	265	277	289	301	313	324	336
366		348	360	372	384	396	407	419	431	443	455
367		467	478	490	502	514	526	538	549	561	573
368		585	597	608	620	632	644	656	667	679	691
369		703	714	726	738	750	761	773	785	797	808
370		820	832	844	855	867	879	891	902	914	926
371		937	949	961	972	984	996	*008	*019	*031	*043
372	57	054	066	078	089	101	113	124	136	148	159
373		171	183	194	206	217	229	241	252	264	276
374		287	299	310	322	334	345	357	368	380	392
375		403	415	426	438	449	461	473	484	496	507
376		519	530	542	553	565	577	588	600	611	623
377		634	646	657	669	680	692	703	715	726	738
378		749	761	772	784	795	807	818	830	841	852
379		864	875	887	898	910	921	933	944	956	967
380		978	990	*001	*013	*024	*035	*047	*058	*070	*081
No.	L	0	1	2	3	4	5	6	7	8	9

Proportional parts

	14
1	1.4
2	2.8
3	4.2
4	5.6
5	7.0
6	8.4
7	9.8
8	11.2
9	12.6

	13
1	1.3
2	2.6
3	3.9
4	5.2
5	6.5
6	7.8
7	9.1
8	10.4
9	11.7

	12
1	1.2
2	2.4
3	3.6
4	4.8
5	6.0
6	7.2
7	8.4
8	9.6
9	10.8

* Indicates change in the first two decimal places.

Table 1-1. Five-place Common Logarithms of Numbers—*(Continued)*

380—450

No.	L	0	1	2	3	4	5	6	7	8	9
380	57	978	990	*001	*013	*024	*035	*047	*058	*070	*081
381	58	093	104	115	127	138	149	161	172	184	195
382		206	218	229	240	252	263	275	286	297	309
383		320	331	343	354	365	377	388	399	411	422
384		433	444	456	467	478	490	501	512	524	535
385		546	557	569	580	591	602	614	625	636	647
386		659	670	681	692	704	715	726	737	749	760
387		771	782	794	805	816	827	838	850	861	872
388		883	894	906	917	928	939	950	961	973	984
389		995	*006	*017	*028	*040	*051	*062	*073	*084	*095
390	59	106	118	129	140	151	162	173	184	195	207
391		218	229	240	251	262	273	284	295	306	318
392		329	340	351	362	373	384	395	406	417	428
393		439	450	461	472	483	494	506	517	528	539
394		550	561	572	583	594	605	616	627	638	649
395		660	671	682	693	704	715	726	737	748	759
396		770	780	791	802	813	824	835	846	857	868
397		879	890	901	912	923	934	945	956	966	977
398		988	999	*010	*021	*032	*043	*054	*065	*076	*086
399	60	097	108	119	130	141	152	163	173	184	195
400	60	206	217	228	239	249	260	271	282	293	304
401		314	325	336	347	358	369	379	390	401	412
402		423	433	444	455	466	477	487	498	509	520
403		531	541	552	563	574	584	595	606	617	627
404		638	649	660	670	681	692	703	713	724	735
405		746	756	767	778	788	799	810	821	831	842
406		853	863	874	885	895	906	917	927	938	949
407		959	970	981	991	*002	*013	*023	*034	*045	*055
408	61	066	077	087	098	109	119	130	140	151	162
409		172	183	194	204	215	225	236	247	257	268
410		278	289	300	310	321	331	342	352	363	374
411		384	395	405	416	426	437	448	458	469	479
412		490	500	511	521	532	542	553	563	574	584
413		595	606	616	627	637	648	658	669	679	690
414		700	711	721	731	742	752	763	773	784	794
415		805	815	826	836	847	857	868	878	888	899
416		909	920	930	941	951	962	972	982	993	*003
417	62	014	024	034	045	055	066	076	086	097	107
418		118	128	138	149	159	170	180	190	201	211
419		221	232	242	252	263	273	284	294	304	315
420		325	335	346	356	366	377	387	397	408	418
421		428	439	449	459	469	480	490	500	511	521
422		531	542	552	562	572	583	593	603	614	624
423		634	644	655	665	675	685	696	706	716	726
424		737	747	757	767	778	788	798	808	818	829
425		839	849	859	870	880	890	900	910	921	931
426		941	951	961	972	982	992	*002	*012	*022	*033
427	63	043	053	063	073	083	094	104	114	124	134
428		144	155	165	175	185	195	205	215	225	236
429		246	256	266	276	286	296	306	317	327	337
430		347	357	367	377	387	397	407	417	428	438
431		448	458	468	478	488	498	508	518	528	538
432		548	558	568	579	589	599	609	619	629	639
433		649	659	669	679	689	699	709	719	729	739
434		749	759	769	779	789	799	809	819	829	839
435		849	859	869	879	889	899	909	919	929	939
436		949	959	969	979	988	998	*008	*018	*028	*038
437	64	048	058	068	078	088	098	108	118	128	137
438		147	157	167	177	187	197	207	217	227	237
439		246	256	266	276	286	296	306	316	326	335
440		345	355	365	375	385	395	404	414	424	434
441		444	454	464	473	483	493	503	513	523	532
442		542	552	562	572	582	591	601	611	621	631
443		640	650	660	670	680	689	699	709	719	729
444		738	748	758	768	777	787	797	807	816	826
445		836	846	856	865	875	885	895	904	914	924
446		933	943	953	963	972	982	992	*002	*011	*021
447	65	031	040	050	060	070	079	089	099	108	118
448		128	137	147	157	167	176	186	196	205	215
449		225	234	244	254	263	273	283	292	302	312
450		321	331	341	350	360	369	379	389	398	408
No.	L	0	1	2	3	4	5	6	7	8	9

Proportional parts

	11
1	1.1
2	2.2
3	3.3
4	4.4
5	5.5
6	6.6
7	7.7
8	8.8
9	9.9

	10
1	1.0
2	2.0
3	3.0
4	4.0
5	5.0
6	6.0
7	7.0
8	8.0
9	9.0

	9
1	0.9
2	1.8
3	2.7
4	3.6
5	4.5
6	5.4
7	6.3
8	7.2
9	8.1

Proportional parts

* Indicates change in the first two decimal places.

Table 1-1. Five-place Common Logarithms of Numbers—(*Continued*)

450—520

No.	L	0	1	2	3	4	5	6	7	8	9
450	65	321	331	341	350	360	369	379	389	398	408
451		418	427	437	447	456	466	475	485	495	504
452		514	523	533	543	552	562	571	581	591	600
453		610	619	629	639	648	658	667	677	686	696
454		706	715	725	734	744	753	763	773	782	792
455		801	811	820	830	839	849	858	868	877	887
456		896	906	916	925	935	944	954	963	973	982
457		992	*001	*011	*020	*030	*039	*049	*058	*068	*077
458	66	087	096	106	115	124	134	143	153	162	172
459		181	191	200	210	219	229	238	247	257	266
460		276	285	295	304	314	323	332	342	351	361
461		370	380	389	398	408	417	427	436	445	455
462		464	474	483	492	502	511	521	530	539	549
463		558	567	577	586	596	605	614	624	633	642
464		652	661	671	680	689	699	708	717	727	736
465		745	755	764	773	783	792	801	811	820	829
466		839	848	857	867	876	885	894	904	913	922
467		932	941	950	960	969	978	987	997	*006	*015
468	67	025	034	043	052	062	071	080	090	099	108
469		117	127	136	145	154	164	173	182	191	201
470		210	219	228	238	247	256	265	274	284	293
471		302	311	321	330	339	348	357	367	376	385
472		394	403	413	422	431	440	449	459	468	477
473		486	495	504	514	523	532	541	550	560	569
474		578	587	596	605	614	624	633	642	651	660
475		669	679	688	697	706	715	724	733	742	752
476		761	770	779	788	797	806	815	825	834	843
477		852	861	870	879	888	897	906	916	925	934
478		943	952	961	970	979	988	997	*006	*015	*024
479	68	034	043	052	061	070	079	088	097	106	115
480		124	133	142	151	160	169	178	187	196	205
481		215	224	233	242	251	260	269	278	287	296
482		305	314	323	332	341	350	359	368	377	386
483		395	404	413	422	431	440	449	458	467	476
484		485	494	502	511	520	529	538	547	556	565
485		574	583	592	601	610	619	628	637	646	655
486		664	673	682	690	699	708	717	726	735	744
487		753	762	771	780	789	797	806	815	824	833
488		842	851	860	869	878	886	895	904	913	922
489		931	940	949	958	966	975	984	993	*002	*011
490	69	020	028	037	046	055	064	073	082	090	099
491		108	117	126	135	144	152	161	170	179	188
492		197	205	214	223	232	241	249	258	267	276
493		285	294	302	311	320	329	338	346	355	364
494		373	381	390	399	408	417	425	434	443	452
495		461	469	478	487	496	504	513	522	531	539
496		548	557	566	574	583	592	601	609	618	627
497		636	644	653	662	671	679	688	697	705	714
498		723	732	740	749	758	767	775	784	793	801
499		810	819	827	836	845	854	862	871	880	888
500	69	897	906	914	923	932	940	949	958	966	975
501		984	992	*001	*010	*018	*027	*036	*044	*053	*062
502	70	070	079	088	096	105	114	122	131	140	148
503		157	165	174	183	191	200	209	217	226	234
504		243	252	260	269	278	286	295	303	312	321
505		329	338	346	355	364	372	381	389	398	406
506		415	424	432	441	449	458	467	475	484	492
507		501	509	518	526	535	544	552	561	569	578
508		586	595	603	612	621	629	638	646	655	663
509		672	680	689	697	706	714	723	731	740	749
510		757	766	774	783	791	800	808	817	825	834
511		842	851	859	868	876	885	893	902	910	919
512		927	935	944	952	961	969	978	986	995	*003
513	71	012	020	029	037	046	054	063	071	079	088
514		096	105	113	122	130	139	147	155	164	172
515		181	189	198	206	214	223	231	240	248	257
516		265	273	282	290	299	307	315	324	332	341
517		349	357	366	374	383	391	399	408	416	425
518		433	441	450	458	467	475	483	492	500	508
519		517	525	533	542	550	559	567	575	584	592
520		600	609	617	625	634	642	650	659	667	675
No.	L	0	1	2	3	4	5	6	7	8	9

Proportional parts

	10	9	8
1	1.0	0.9	0.8
2	2.0	1.8	1.6
3	3.0	2.7	2.4
4	4.0	3.6	3.2
5	5.0	4.5	4.0
6	6.0	5.4	4.8
7	7.0	6.3	5.6
8	8.0	7.2	6.4
9	9.0	8.1	7.2

* Indicates change in the first two decimal places.

Table 1-1. Five-place Common Logarithms of Numbers—(*Continued*)

520—590

No.	L	0	1	2	3	4	5	6	7	8	9
520	71	600	609	617	625	634	642	650	659	667	675
521		684	692	700	709	717	725	734	742	750	759
522		767	775	784	792	800	809	817	825	834	842
523		850	858	867	875	883	892	900	908	917	925
524		933	941	950	958	966	975	983	991	999	*008
525	72	016	024	032	041	049	057	066	074	082	090
526		099	107	115	123	132	140	148	156	165	173
527		181	189	198	206	214	222	230	239	247	255
528		263	272	280	288	296	305	313	321	329	337
529		346	354	362	370	378	387	395	403	411	419
530		428	436	444	452	460	469	477	485	493	501
531		509	518	526	534	542	550	559	567	575	583
532		591	599	607	616	624	632	640	648	656	665
533		673	681	689	697	705	713	722	730	738	746
534		754	762	770	779	787	795	803	811	819	827
535		835	844	852	860	868	876	884	892	900	908
536		916	925	933	941	949	957	965	973	981	989
537		997	*006	*014	*022	*030	*038	*046	*054	*062	*070
538	73	078	086	094	102	111	119	127	135	143	151
539		159	167	175	183	191	199	207	215	223	231
540		239	247	255	264	272	280	288	296	304	312
541		320	328	336	344	352	360	368	376	384	392
542		400	408	416	424	432	440	448	456	464	472
543		480	488	496	504	512	520	528	536	544	552
544		560	568	576	584	592	600	608	616	624	632
545		640	648	656	664	672	679	687	695	703	711
546		719	727	735	743	751	759	767	775	783	791
547		799	807	815	823	830	838	846	854	862	870
548		878	886	894	902	910	918	926	934	941	949
549		957	965	973	981	989	997	*005	*013	*020	*028
550	74	036	044	052	060	068	076	084	092	099	107
551		115	123	131	139	147	155	162	170	178	186
552		194	202	210	218	225	233	241	249	257	265
553		273	280	288	296	304	312	320	327	335	343
554		351	359	367	374	382	390	398	406	414	421
555		429	437	445	453	461	468	476	484	492	500
556		507	515	523	531	539	547	554	562	570	578
557		586	593	601	609	617	624	632	640	648	656
558		663	671	679	687	695	702	710	718	726	733
559		741	749	757	764	772	780	788	796	803	811
560		819	827	834	842	850	858	865	873	881	889
561		896	904	912	920	927	935	943	950	958	966
562		974	981	989	997	*005	*012	*020	*028	*035	*043
563	75	051	059	066	074	082	089	097	105	113	120
564		128	136	143	151	159	166	174	182	189	197
565		205	213	220	228	236	243	251	259	266	274
566		282	289	297	305	312	320	328	335	343	351
567		358	366	374	381	389	397	404	412	420	427
568		435	442	450	458	465	473	481	488	496	504
569		511	519	526	534	542	549	557	565	572	580
570		587	595	603	610	618	626	633	641	648	656
571		664	671	679	686	694	702	709	717	724	732
572		740	747	755	762	770	778	785	793	800	808
573		815	823	831	838	846	853	861	868	876	884
574		891	899	906	914	921	929	937	944	952	959
575		967	974	982	989	997	*005	*012	*020	*027	*035
576	76	042	050	057	065	072	080	087	095	103	110
577		118	125	133	140	148	155	163	170	178	185
578		193	200	208	215	223	230	238	245	253	260
579		268	275	283	290	298	305	313	320	328	335
580		343	350	358	365	373	380	388	395	403	410
581		418	425	433	440	448	455	462	470	477	485
582		492	500	507	515	522	530	537	545	552	559
583		567	574	582	589	597	604	612	619	626	634
584		641	649	656	664	671	678	686	693	701	708
585		716	723	730	738	745	753	760	768	775	782
586		790	797	805	812	819	827	834	842	849	856
587		864	871	879	886	893	901	908	916	923	930
588		938	945	953	960	967	975	982	989	997	*004
589	77	012	019	026	034	041	048	056	063	070	078
590		085	093	100	107	115	122	129	137	144	151
No.	L	0	1	2	3	4	5	6	7	8	9

Proportional parts

	9
1	0.9
2	1.8
3	2.7
4	3.6
5	4.5
6	5.4
7	6.3
8	7.2
9	8.1

	8
1	0.8
2	1.6
3	2.4
4	3.2
5	4.0
6	4.8
7	5.6
8	6.4
9	7.2

	7
1	0.7
2	1.4
3	2.1
4	2.8
5	3.5
6	4.2
7	4.9
8	5.6
9	6.3

Proportional parts

* Indicates change in the first two decimal places.

Table 1-1. Five-place Common Logarithms of Numbers—(*Continued*)

590—660

No.	L	0	1	2	3	4	5	6	7	8	9	Proportional parts
590	77	085	093	100	107	115	122	129	137	144	151	
591		159	166	173	181	188	195	203	210	218	225	
592		232	240	247	254	262	269	276	283	291	298	
593		305	313	320	327	335	342	349	357	364	371	
594		379	386	393	401	408	415	422	430	437	444	
595		452	459	466	474	481	488	495	503	510	517	
596		525	532	539	546	554	561	568	576	583	590	
597		597	605	612	619	627	634	641	648	656	663	
598		670	677	685	692	699	706	714	721	728	735	
599		743	750	757	764	772	779	786	793	801	808	
600	77	815	822	830	837	844	851	859	866	873	880	
601		887	895	902	909	916	924	931	938	945	952	
602		960	967	974	981	989	996	*003	*010	*017	*025	
603	78	032	039	046	053	061	068	075	082	089	097	
604		104	111	118	125	132	140	147	154	161	168	
605		176	183	190	197	204	211	219	226	233	240	
606		247	254	262	269	276	283	290	297	305	312	
607		319	326	333	340	347	355	362	369	376	383	
608		390	398	405	412	419	426	433	440	447	455	
609		462	469	476	483	490	497	505	512	519	526	
610		533	540	547	554	561	569	576	583	590	597	
611		604	611	618	625	633	640	647	654	661	668	
612		675	682	689	696	704	711	718	725	732	739	
613		746	753	760	767	774	781	789	796	803	810	
614		817	824	831	838	845	852	859	866	873	880	
615		888	895	902	909	916	923	930	937	944	951	
616		958	965	972	979	986	993	*000	*007	*014	*021	
617	79	029	036	043	050	057	064	071	078	085	092	
618		099	106	113	120	127	134	141	148	155	162	
619		169	176	183	190	197	204	211	218	225	232	
620		239	246	253	260	267	274	281	288	295	302	
621		309	316	323	330	337	344	351	358	365	372	
622		379	386	393	400	407	414	421	428	435	442	
623		449	456	463	470	477	484	491	498	505	512	
624		518	525	532	539	546	553	560	567	574	581	
625		588	595	602	609	616	623	630	637	644	651	
626		657	664	671	678	685	692	699	706	713	720	
627		727	734	741	748	754	761	768	775	782	789	
628		796	803	810	817	824	831	837	844	851	858	
629		865	872	879	886	893	900	906	913	920	927	
630		934	941	948	955	962	969	975	982	989	996	
631	80	003	010	017	024	030	037	044	051	058	065	
632		072	079	085	092	099	106	113	120	127	134	
633		140	147	154	161	168	175	182	188	195	202	
634		209	216	223	229	236	243	250	257	264	271	
635		277	284	291	298	305	312	318	325	332	339	
636		346	353	359	366	373	380	387	393	400	407	
637		414	421	428	434	441	448	455	462	468	475	
638		482	489	496	502	509	516	523	530	536	543	
639		550	557	564	570	577	584	591	598	604	611	
640		618	625	632	638	645	652	659	665	672	679	
641		686	693	699	706	713	720	726	733	740	747	
642		754	760	767	774	781	787	794	801	808	814	
643		821	828	835	841	848	855	862	868	875	882	
644		889	895	902	909	916	922	929	936	943	949	
645		956	963	969	976	983	990	996	*003	*010	*017	
646	81	023	030	037	043	050	057	064	070	077	084	
647		090	097	104	111	117	124	131	137	144	151	
648		158	164	171	178	184	191	198	204	211	218	
649		224	231	238	245	251	258	265	271	278	285	
650	81	291	298	305	311	318	325	331	338	345	351	
651		358	365	371	378	385	391	398	405	411	418	
652		425	431	438	445	451	458	465	471	478	485	
653		491	498	505	511	518	525	531	538	544	551	
654		558	564	571	578	584	591	598	604	611	618	
655		624	631	637	644	651	657	664	671	677	684	
656		690	697	704	710	717	723	730	737	743	750	
657		757	763	770	776	783	790	796	803	809	816	
658		823	829	836	842	849	856	862	869	875	882	
659		889	895	902	908	915	921	928	935	941	948	
660		954	961	968	974	981	987	994	*000	*007	*014	
No.	L	0	1	2	3	4	5	6	7	8	9	Proportional parts

Proportional parts:

	8
1	0.8
2	1.6
3	2.4
4	3.2
5	4.0
6	4.8
7	5.6
8	6.4
9	7.2

	7
1	0.7
2	1.4
3	2.1
4	2.8
5	3.5
6	4.2
7	4.9
8	5.6
9	6.3

	6
1	0.6
2	1.2
3	1.8
4	2.4
5	3.0
6	3.6
7	4.2
8	4.8
9	5.4

* Indicates change in the first two decimal places.

Table 1-1. Five-place Common Logarithms of Numbers—(*Continued*)

660—730

No.	L	0	1	2	3	4	5	6	7	8	9	Proportional parts
660	81	954	961	968	974	981	987	994	*000	*007	*014	
661	82	020	027	033	040	046	053	060	066	073	079	
662		086	092	099	105	112	119	125	132	138	145	
663		151	158	164	171	178	184	191	197	204	210	
664		217	223	230	236	243	250	256	263	269	276	
665		282	289	295	302	308	315	321	328	334	341	
666		347	354	360	367	374	380	387	393	400	406	
667		413	419	426	432	439	445	452	458	465	471	
668		478	484	491	497	504	510	517	523	530	536	
669		543	549	556	562	569	575	582	588	595	601	
670		607	614	620	627	633	640	646	653	659	666	
671		672	679	685	692	698	705	711	718	724	730	
672		737	743	750	756	763	769	776	782	789	795	
673		802	808	814	821	827	834	840	847	853	860	
674		866	872	879	885	892	898	905	911	918	924	
675		930	937	943	950	956	963	969	975	982	988	
676		995	*001	*008	*014	*020	*027	*033	*040	*046	*052	
677	83	059	065	072	078	085	091	097	104	110	117	
678		123	129	136	142	149	155	161	168	174	181	
679		187	193	200	206	213	219	225	232	238	245	7
680		251	257	264	270	276	283	289	296	302	308	1 0.7
681		315	321	327	334	340	347	353	359	366	372	2 1.4
682		378	385	391	398	404	410	417	423	429	436	3 2.1
683		442	448	455	461	468	474	480	487	493	499	4 2.8
684		506	512	518	525	531	537	544	550	556	563	5 3.5
685		569	575	582	588	594	601	607	613	620	626	6 4.2
686		632	639	645	651	658	664	670	677	683	689	7 4.9
687		696	702	708	715	721	727	734	740	746	753	8 5.6
688		759	765	771	778	784	790	797	803	809	816	9 6.3
689		822	828	835	841	847	853	860	866	872	879	
690		885	891	898	904	910	916	923	929	935	942	
691		948	954	960	967	973	979	986	992	998	*004	
692	84	011	017	023	029	036	042	048	055	061	067	
693		073	080	086	092	098	105	111	117	123	130	
694		136	142	148	155	161	167	173	180	186	192	
695		198	205	211	217	223	230	236	242	248	255	
696		261	267	273	280	286	292	298	305	311	317	
697		323	330	336	342	348	354	361	367	373	379	
698		386	392	398	404	410	417	423	429	435	442	
699		448	454	460	466	473	479	485	491	497	504	
700	84	510	516	522	528	535	541	547	553	559	566	
701		572	578	584	590	597	603	609	615	621	628	
702		634	640	646	652	658	665	671	677	683	689	
703		696	702	708	714	720	726	733	739	745	751	
704		757	763	770	776	782	788	794	800	807	813	
705		819	825	831	837	844	850	856	862	868	874	6
706		880	887	893	899	905	911	917	924	930	936	1 0.6
707		942	948	954	960	967	973	979	985	991	997	2 1.2
708	85	003	009	016	022	028	034	040	046	052	059	3 1.8
709		065	071	077	083	089	095	101	107	114	120	4 2.4
710		126	132	138	144	150	156	163	169	175	181	5 3.0
711		187	193	199	205	211	217	224	230	236	242	6 3.6
712		248	254	260	266	272	278	285	291	297	303	7 4.2
713		309	315	321	327	333	339	345	352	358	364	8 4.8
714		370	376	382	388	394	400	406	412	418	425	9 5.4
715		431	437	443	449	455	461	467	473	479	485	
716		491	497	503	510	516	522	528	534	540	546	
717		552	558	564	570	576	582	588	594	600	606	
718		612	618	625	631	637	643	649	655	661	667	
719		673	679	685	691	697	703	709	715	721	727	
720		733	739	745	751	757	763	769	775	781	788	
721		794	800	806	812	818	824	830	836	842	848	
722		854	860	866	872	878	884	890	896	902	908	
723		914	920	926	932	938	944	950	956	962	968	
724		974	980	986	992	998	*004	*010	*016	*022	*028	
725	86	034	040	046	052	058	064	070	076	082	088	
726		094	100	106	112	118	124	130	136	141	147	
727		153	159	165	171	177	183	189	195	201	207	
728		213	219	225	231	237	243	249	255	261	267	
729		273	279	285	291	297	303	308	314	320	326	
730		332	338	344	350	356	362	368	374	380	386	
No.	L	0	1	2	3	4	5	6	7	8	9	Proportional parts

* Indicates change in the first two decimal places.

Table 1-1. Five-place Common Logarithms of Numbers—(*Continued*)

730—800

No.	L	0	1	2	3	4	5	6	7	8	9
730	86	332	338	344	350	356	362	368	374	380	386
731		392	398	404	410	416	421	427	433	439	445
732		451	457	463	469	475	481	487	493	499	504
733		510	516	522	528	534	540	546	552	558	564
734		570	576	581	587	593	599	605	611	617	623
735		629	635	641	646	652	658	664	670	676	682
736		688	694	700	705	711	717	723	729	735	741
737		747	753	759	764	770	776	782	788	794	800
738		806	812	817	823	829	835	841	847	853	859
739		864	870	876	882	888	894	900	906	911	917
740		923	929	935	941	947	953	958	964	970	976
741		982	988	994	999	*005	*011	*017	*023	*029	*035
742	87	040	046	052	058	064	070	075	081	087	093
743		099	105	111	116	122	128	134	140	146	151
744		157	163	169	175	181	186	192	198	204	210
745		216	221	227	233	239	245	251	256	262	268
746		274	280	286	291	297	303	309	315	320	326
747		332	338	344	350	355	361	367	373	379	384
748		390	396	402	408	413	419	425	431	437	442
749		448	454	460	466	471	477	483	489	495	500
750	87	506	512	518	523	529	535	541	547	552	558
751		564	570	576	581	587	593	599	604	610	616
752		622	628	633	639	645	651	656	662	668	674
753		680	685	691	697	703	708	714	720	726	731
754		737	743	749	754	760	766	772	777	783	789
755		795	800	806	812	818	823	829	835	841	846
756		852	858	864	869	875	881	887	892	898	904
757		910	915	921	927	933	938	944	950	955	961
758		967	973	978	984	990	996	*001	*007	*013	*018
759	88	024	030	036	041	047	053	059	064	070	076
760		081	087	093	099	104	110	116	121	127	133
761		138	144	150	156	161	167	173	178	184	190
762		196	201	207	213	218	224	230	235	241	247
763		252	258	264	270	275	281	287	292	298	304
764		309	315	321	326	332	338	343	349	355	360
765		366	372	378	383	389	395	400	406	412	417
766		423	429	434	440	446	451	457	463	468	474
767		480	485	491	497	502	508	514	519	525	530
768		536	542	547	553	559	564	570	576	581	587
769		593	598	604	610	615	621	627	632	638	643
770		649	655	660	666	672	677	683	689	694	700
771		705	711	717	722	728	734	739	745	750	756
772		762	767	773	779	784	790	795	801	807	812
773		818	824	829	835	840	846	852	857	863	868
774		874	880	885	891	897	902	908	913	919	925
775		930	936	941	947	953	958	964	969	975	981
776		986	992	997	*003	*009	*014	*020	*025	*031	*037
777	89	042	048	053	059	064	070	076	081	087	092
778		098	104	109	115	120	126	131	137	143	148
779		154	159	165	170	176	182	187	193	198	204
780		209	215	221	226	232	237	243	248	254	260
781		265	271	276	282	287	293	298	304	310	315
782		321	326	332	337	343	348	354	360	365	371
783		376	382	387	393	398	404	409	415	421	426
784		432	437	443	448	454	459	465	470	476	481
785		487	493	498	504	509	515	520	526	531	537
786		542	548	553	559	564	570	575	581	586	592
787		597	603	609	614	620	625	631	636	642	647
788		653	658	664	669	675	680	686	691	697	702
789		708	713	719	724	730	735	741	746	752	757
790		763	768	774	779	785	790	796	801	807	812
791		818	823	829	834	840	845	851	856	862	867
792		873	878	883	889	894	900	905	911	916	922
793		927	933	938	944	949	955	960	966	971	977
794		982	988	993	998	*004	*009	*015	*020	*026	*031
795	90	037	042	048	053	059	064	069	075	080	086
796		091	097	102	108	113	119	124	129	135	140
797		146	151	157	162	168	173	179	184	189	195
798		200	206	211	217	222	227	233	238	244	249
799		255	260	266	271	276	282	287	293	298	304
800		309	314	320	325	331	336	342	347	352	358
No.	L	0	1	2	3	4	5	6	7	8	9

Proportional parts

	6
1	0.6
2	1.2
3	1.8
4	2.4
5	3.0
6	3.6
7	4.2
8	4.8
9	5.4

	5
1	0.5
2	1.0
3	1.5
4	2.0
5	2.5
6	3.0
7	3.5
8	4.0
9	4.5

* Indicates change in the first two decimal places.

Table 1-1. Five-place Common Logarithms of Numbers—(*Continued*)

800—870

No.	L	0	1	2	3	4	5	6	7	8	9
800	90	309	314	320	325	331	336	342	347	352	358
801		363	369	374	380	385	390	396	401	407	412
802		417	423	428	434	439	445	450	455	461	466
803		472	477	482	488	493	499	504	509	515	520
804		526	531	536	542	547	553	558	563	569	574
805		580	585	590	596	601	607	612	617	623	628
806		634	639	644	650	655	660	666	671	677	682
807		687	693	698	704	709	714	720	725	730	736
808		741	747	752	757	763	768	773	779	784	789
809		795	800	806	811	816	822	827	832	838	843
810		849	854	859	865	870	875	881	886	891	897
811		902	907	913	918	924	929	934	940	945	950
812		956	961	966	972	977	982	988	993	998	*004
813	91	009	014	020	025	030	036	041	046	052	057
814		062	068	073	078	084	089	094	100	105	110
815		116	121	126	132	137	142	148	153	158	164
816		169	174	180	185	190	196	201	206	212	217
817		222	228	233	238	243	249	254	259	265	270
818		275	281	286	291	297	302	307	312	318	323
819		328	334	339	344	350	355	360	365	371	376
820		381	387	392	397	403	408	413	418	424	429
821		434	440	445	450	455	461	466	471	477	482
822		487	492	498	503	508	514	519	524	529	535
823		540	545	551	556	561	566	572	577	582	587
824		593	598	603	609	614	619	624	630	635	640
825		645	651	656	661	666	672	677	682	687	693
826		698	703	709	714	719	724	730	735	740	745
827		751	756	761	766	772	777	782	787	793	798
828		803	808	814	819	824	829	834	840	845	850
829		855	861	866	871	876	882	887	892	897	903
830		908	913	918	924	929	934	939	944	950	955
831		960	965	971	976	981	986	991	997	*002	*007
832	92	012	018	023	028	033	038	044	049	054	059
833		065	070	075	080	085	091	096	101	106	111
834		117	122	127	132	137	143	148	153	158	163
835		169	174	179	184	189	195	200	205	210	215
836		221	226	231	236	241	247	252	257	262	267
837		273	278	283	288	293	298	304	309	314	319
838		324	330	335	340	345	350	355	361	366	371
839		376	381	387	392	397	402	407	412	418	423
840		428	433	438	443	449	454	459	464	469	474
841		480	485	490	495	500	505	511	516	521	526
842		531	536	542	547	552	557	562	567	572	578
843		583	588	593	598	603	609	614	619	624	629
844		634	639	645	650	655	660	665	670	675	681
845		686	691	696	701	706	711	717	722	727	732
846		737	742	747	752	758	763	768	773	778	783
847		788	793	799	804	809	814	819	824	829	834
848		840	845	850	855	860	865	870	875	881	886
849		891	896	901	906	911	916	921	927	932	937
850	92	942	947	952	957	962	967	973	978	983	988
851		993	998	*003	*008	*013	*018	*024	*029	*034	*039
852	93	044	049	054	059	064	069	075	080	085	090
853		095	100	105	110	115	120	125	131	136	141
854		146	151	156	161	166	171	176	181	186	192
855		197	202	207	212	217	222	227	232	237	242
856		247	252	258	263	268	273	278	283	288	293
857		298	303	308	313	318	323	328	334	339	344
858		349	354	359	364	369	374	379	384	389	394
859		399	404	409	414	420	425	430	435	440	445
860		450	455	460	465	470	475	480	485	490	495
861		500	505	510	515	520	526	531	536	541	546
862		551	556	561	566	571	576	581	586	591	596
863		601	606	611	616	621	626	631	636	641	646
864		651	656	661	666	671	677	682	687	692	697
865		702	707	712	717	722	727	732	737	742	747
866		752	757	762	767	772	777	782	787	792	797
867		802	807	812	817	822	827	832	837	842	847
868		852	857	862	867	872	877	882	887	892	897
869		902	907	912	917	922	927	932	937	942	947
870		952	957	962	967	972	977	982	987	992	997
No.	L	0	1	2	3	4	5	6	7	8	9

Proportional parts

	6
1	0.6
2	1.2
3	1.8
4	2.4
5	3.0
6	3.6
7	4.2
8	4.8
9	5.4

	5
1	0.5
2	1.0
3	1.5
4	2.0
5	2.5
6	3.0
7	3.5
8	4.0
9	4.5

* Indicates change in the first two decimal places.

Table 1-1. Five-place Common Logarithms of Numbers—(*Continued*)

870—940

No.	L	0	1	2	3	4	5	6	7	8	9	Proportional parts
870	93	952	957	962	967	972	977	982	987	992	997	
871	94	002	007	012	017	022	027	032	037	042	047	
872		052	057	062	067	072	077	082	087	091	096	
873		101	106	111	116	121	126	131	136	141	146	
874		151	156	161	166	171	176	181	186	191	196	
875		201	206	211	216	221	226	231	236	240	245	
876		250	255	260	265	270	275	280	285	290	295	
877		300	305	310	315	320	325	330	335	340	345	
878		349	354	359	364	369	374	379	384	389	394	
879		399	404	409	414	419	424	429	433	438	443	
880		448	453	458	463	468	473	478	483	488	493	
881		498	503	507	512	517	522	527	532	537	542	
882		547	552	557	562	567	571	576	581	586	591	
883		596	601	606	611	616	621	626	630	635	640	
884		645	650	655	660	665	670	675	680	685	689	
885		694	699	704	709	714	719	724	729	734	738	
886		743	748	753	758	763	768	773	778	783	787	
887		792	797	802	807	812	817	822	827	832	836	
888		841	846	851	856	861	866	871	876	880	885	
889		890	895	900	905	910	915	919	924	929	934	
890		939	944	949	954	959	963	968	973	978	983	
891		988	993	998	*002	*007	*012	*017	*022	*027	*032	
892	95	036	041	046	051	056	061	066	071	075	080	
893		085	090	095	100	105	109	114	119	124	129	
894		134	139	143	148	153	158	163	168	173	177	
895		182	187	192	197	202	207	211	216	221	226	
896		231	236	240	245	250	255	260	265	270	274	
897		279	284	289	294	299	303	308	313	318	323	
898		328	332	337	342	347	352	357	361	366	371	
899		376	381	386	390	395	400	405	410	415	419	
900	95	424	429	434	439	444	448	453	458	463	468	
901		472	477	482	487	492	497	501	506	511	516	
902		521	525	530	535	540	545	550	554	559	564	
903		569	574	578	583	588	593	598	602	607	612	
904		617	622	626	631	636	641	646	650	655	660	
905		665	670	674	679	684	689	694	698	703	708	
906		713	718	722	727	732	737	742	746	751	756	
907		761	766	770	775	780	785	789	794	799	804	
908		809	813	818	823	828	832	837	842	847	852	
909		856	861	866	871	875	880	885	890	895	899	
910		904	909	914	918	923	928	933	938	942	947	
911		952	957	961	966	971	976	980	985	990	995	
912		999	*004	*009	*014	*019	*023	*028	*033	*038	*042	
913	96	047	052	057	061	066	071	076	080	085	090	
914		095	099	104	109	114	118	123	128	133	137	
915		142	147	152	156	161	166	171	175	180	185	
916		190	194	199	204	209	213	218	223	227	232	
917		237	242	246	251	256	261	265	270	275	280	
918		284	289	294	298	303	308	313	317	322	327	
919		332	336	341	346	350	355	360	365	369	374	
920		379	384	388	393	398	402	407	412	417	421	
921		426	431	435	440	445	450	454	459	464	468	
922		473	478	483	487	492	497	501	506	511	515	
923		520	525	530	534	539	544	548	553	558	563	
924		567	572	577	581	586	591	595	600	605	609	
925		614	619	624	628	633	638	642	647	652	656	
926		661	666	670	675	680	685	689	694	699	703	
927		708	713	717	722	727	731	736	741	745	750	
928		755	759	764	769	774	778	783	788	792	797	
929		802	806	811	816	820	825	830	834	839	844	
930		848	853	858	862	867	872	876	881	886	890	
931		895	900	904	909	914	918	923	928	932	937	
932		942	946	951	956	960	965	970	974	979	984	
933		988	993	997	*002	*007	*011	*016	*021	*025	*030	
934	97	035	039	044	049	053	058	063	067	072	077	
935		081	086	090	095	100	104	109	114	118	123	
936		128	132	137	142	146	151	155	160	165	169	
937		174	179	183	188	192	197	202	206	211	216	
938		220	225	230	234	239	243	248	253	257	262	
939		267	271	276	280	285	290	294	299	304	308	
940		313	317	322	327	331	336	341	345	350	354	
No.	L	0	1	2	3	4	5	6	7	8	9	Proportional parts

Proportional parts:

	5
1	0.5
2	1.0
3	1.5
4	2.0
5	2.5
6	3.0
7	3.5
8	4.0
9	4.5

	4
1	0.4
2	0.8
3	1.2
4	1.6
5	2.0
6	2.4
7	2.8
8	3.2
9	3.6

* Indicates change in the first two decimal places.

Table 1-1. Five-place Common Logarithms of Numbers—(*Concluded*)

940—1000

No.	L	0	1	2	3	4	5	6	7	8	9
940	97	313	317	322	327	331	336	341	345	350	354
941		359	364	368	373	377	382	387	391	396	400
942		405	410	414	419	424	428	433	437	442	447
943		451	456	460	465	470	474	479	483	488	493
944		497	502	506	511	516	520	525	529	534	539
945		543	548	552	557	562	566	571	575	580	585
946		589	594	598	603	607	612	617	621	626	630
947		635	640	644	649	653	658	663	667	672	676
948		681	685	690	695	699	704	708	713	717	722
949		727	731	736	740	745	750	754	759	763	768
950		772	777	782	786	791	795	800	804	809	813
951		818	823	827	832	836	841	845	850	855	859
952		864	868	873	877	882	887	891	896	900	905
953		909	914	918	923	928	932	937	941	946	950
954		955	959	964	968	973	978	982	987	991	996
955	98	000	005	009	014	019	023	028	032	037	041
956		046	050	055	059	064	069	073	078	082	087
957		091	096	100	105	109	114	118	123	127	132
958		137	141	146	150	155	159	164	168	173	177
959		182	186	191	195	200	205	209	214	218	223
960		227	232	236	241	245	250	254	259	263	268
961		272	277	281	286	290	295	299	304	308	313
962		318	322	327	331	336	340	345	349	354	358
963		363	367	372	376	381	385	390	394	399	403
964		408	412	417	421	426	430	435	439	444	448
965		453	457	462	466	471	475	480	484	489	493
966		498	502	507	511	516	520	525	529	534	538
967		543	547	552	556	561	565	570	574	579	583
968		588	592	597	601	605	610	614	619	623	628
969		632	637	641	646	650	655	659	664	668	673
970		677	682	686	691	695	700	704	709	713	717
971		722	726	731	735	740	744	749	753	758	762
972		767	771	776	780	785	789	793	798	802	807
973		811	816	820	825	829	834	838	843	847	851
974		856	860	865	869	874	878	883	887	892	896
975		900	905	909	914	918	923	927	932	936	941
976		945	949	954	958	963	967	972	976	981	985
977		989	994	998	*003	*007	*012	*016	*021	*025	*029
978	99	034	038	043	047	052	056	061	065	069	074
979		078	083	087	092	096	100	105	109	114	118
980		123	127	131	136	140	145	149	154	158	162
981		167	171	176	180	185	189	193	198	202	207
982		211	216	220	224	229	233	238	242	247	251
983		255	260	264	269	273	277	282	286	291	295
984		300	304	308	313	317	322	326	330	335	339
985		344	348	352	357	361	366	370	374	379	383
986		388	392	397	401	405	410	414	419	423	427
987		432	436	441	445	449	454	458	463	467	471
988		476	480	484	489	493	498	502	506	511	515
989		520	524	528	533	537	542	546	550	555	559
990		564	568	572	577	581	585	590	594	599	603
991		607	612	616	621	625	629	634	638	642	647
992		651	656	660	664	669	673	677	682	686	691
993		695	699	704	708	712	717	721	726	730	734
994		739	743	747	752	756	760	765	769	774	778
995		782	787	791	795	800	804	808	813	817	822
996		826	830	835	839	843	848	852	856	861	865
997		870	874	878	883	887	891	896	900	904	909
998		913	917	922	926	930	935	939	944	948	952
999		957	961	965	970	974	978	983	987	991	996
1000	00	000	004	009	013	017	022	026	030	035	039
No.	L	0	1	2	3	4	5	6	7	8	9

Proportional parts

	5
1	0.5
2	1.0
3	1.5
4	2.0
5	2.5
6	3.0
7	3.5
8	4.0
9	4.5

	4
1	0.4
2	0.8
3	1.2
4	1.6
5	2.0
6	2.4
7	2.8
8	3.2
9	3.6

Proportional parts

* Indicates change in the first two decimal places.

Table 1-2. Natural Trigonometric Functions and Their Logarithms

Degrees	Radians	Sines	Log sines	Cosines	Log cosines	Tangents	Log tangents	Cotangents	Log cotangents	Radians	Degrees
		Nat.		Nat.		Nat.		Nat.			
0° 00′	0.0000	0.0000	.....	1.0000	0.0000	0.0000	.....	....	.....	1.5708	90° 00′
10	.0029	.0029	7.4637	1.0000	.0000	.0029	7.4637	343.77	2.5363	1.5679	50
20	.0058	.0058	7.7648	1.0000	10.0000	.0058	7.7648	171.89	2.2352	1.5650	40
30	.0087	.0087	7.9408	1.0000	10.0000	.0087	7.9409	114.59	2.0591	1.5621	30
40	.0116	.0116	8.0658	0.9999	10.0000	.0116	8.0658	85.940	1.9342	1.5592	20
50	.0145	.0145	8.1627	.9999	10.0000	.0146	8.1627	68.750	1.8373	1.5563	10
1° 00′	.0175	.0175	8.2419	.9999	9.9999	.0175	8.2419	57.290	1.7581	1.5533	89° 00′
10	.0204	.0204	8.3088	.9998	9.9999	.0204	8.3089	49.104	1.6911	1.5504	50
20	.0233	.0233	8.3668	.9997	9.9999	.0233	8.3669	42.964	1.6331	1.5475	40
30	.0262	.0262	8.4179	.9997	9.9999	.0262	8.4181	38.188	1.5819	1.5446	30
40	.0291	.0291	8.4637	.9996	9.9998	.0291	8.4639	34.368	1.5362	1.5417	20
50	.0320	.0320	8.5050	.9995	9.9998	.0320	8.5053	31.242	1.4947	1.5388	10
2° 00′	.0349	.0349	8.5428	.9994	9.9997	.0349	8.5431	28.636	1.4569	1.5359	88° 00′
10	.0378	.0378	8.5776	.9993	9.9997	.0378	8.5779	26.432	1.4221	1.5330	50
20	.0407	.0407	8.6097	.9992	9.9996	.0408	8.6101	24.542	1.3899	1.5301	40
30	.0436	.0436	8.6397	.9991	9.9996	.0437	8.6401	22.904	1.3599	1.5272	30
40	.0465	.0465	8.6677	.9989	9.9995	.0466	8.6682	21.470	1.3318	1.5243	20
50	.0495	.0494	8.6940	.9988	9.9995	.0495	8.6945	20.206	1.3055	1.5213	10
3° 00′	.0524	.0523	8.7188	.9986	9.9994	.0524	8.7194	19.081	1.2806	1.5184	87° 00′
10	.0553	.0552	8.7423	.9985	9.9993	.0553	8.7429	18.075	1.2571	1.5155	50
20	.0582	.0581	8.7645	.9983	9.9993	.0582	8.7653	17.169	1.2348	1.5126	40
30	.0611	.0611	8.7857	.9981	9.9992	.0612	8.7865	16.350	1.2135	1.5097	30
40	.0640	.0640	8.8059	.9980	9.9991	.0641	8.8067	15.605	1.1933	1.5068	20
50	.0669	.0669	8.8251	.9978	9.9990	.0670	8.8261	14.924	1.1739	1.5039	10
4° 00′	.0698	.0698	8.8436	.9976	9.9989	.0699	8.8446	14.301	1.1554	1.5010	86° 00′
10	.0727	.0727	8.8613	.9974	9.9989	.0729	8.8624	13.727	1.1376	1.4981	50
20	.0756	.0756	8.8783	.9971	9.9988	.0758	8.8795	13.197	1.1205	1.4952	40
30	.0785	.0785	8.8946	.9969	9.9987	.0787	8.8960	12.706	1.1040	1.4923	30
40	.0814	.0814	8.9104	.9967	9.9986	.0816	8.9119	12.251	1.0882	1.4893	20
50	.0844	.0843	8.9256	.9964	9.9985	.0846	8.9272	11.826	1.0728	1.4864	10
5° 00′	.0873	.0872	8.9403	.9962	9.9983	.0875	8.9420	11.430	1.0581	1.4835	85° 00′
10	.0902	.0901	8.9545	.9959	9.9982	.0904	8.9563	11.059	1.0437	1.4806	50
20	.0931	.0930	8.9683	.9957	9.9981	.0934	8.9701	10.712	1.0299	1.4777	40
30	.0960	.0959	8.9816	.9954	9.9980	.0963	8.9836	10.385	1.0164	1.4748	30
40	.0989	.0987	8.9945	.9951	9.9979	.0992	8.9966	10.078	1.0034	1.4719	20
50	.1018	.1016	9.0070	.9948	9.9978	.1022	9.0093	9.7882	0.9907	1.4690	10
6° 00′	.1047	.1045	9.0192	.9945	9.9976	.1051	9.0216	9.5144	.9784	1.4661	84° 00′
10	.1076	.1074	9.0311	.9942	9.9975	.1081	9.0336	9.2553	.9664	1.4632	50
20	.1105	.1103	9.0426	.9939	9.9973	.1110	9.0453	9.0098	.9547	1.4603	40
30	.1134	.1132	9.0539	.9936	9.9972	.1139	9.0567	8.7769	.9433	1.4573	30
40	.1164	.1161	9.0648	.9932	9.9971	.1169	9.0678	8.5556	.9323	1.4544	20
50	.1193	.1190	9.0755	.9929	9.9969	.1198	9.0786	8.3450	.9214	1.4515	10
7° 00′	.1222	.1219	9.0859	.9926	9.9968	.1228	9.0891	8.1443	.9109	1.4486	83° 00′
10	.1251	.1248	9.0961	.9922	9.9966	.1257	9.0995	7.9530	.9005	1.4457	50
20	.1280	.1276	9.1060	.9918	9.9964	.1287	9.1096	7.7704	.8904	1.4428	40
30	.1309	.1305	9.1157	.9914	9.9963	.1317	9.1194	7.5958	.8806	1.4399	30
40	.1338	.1334	9.1252	.9911	9.9961	.1346	9.1291	7.4287	.8709	1.4370	20
50	.1367	.1363	9.1345	.9907	9.9959	.1376	9.1385	7.2687	.8615	1.4341	10
8° 00′	.1396	.1392	9.1436	.9903	9.9958	.1405	9.1478	7.1154	.8522	1.4312	82° 00′
10	.1425	.1421	9.1525	.9899	9.9956	.1435	9.1569	6.9682	.8431	1.4283	50
20	.1454	.1449	9.1612	.9894	9.9954	.1465	9.1658	6.8269	.8342	1.4254	40
30	.1484	.1478	9.1697	.9890	9.9952	.1495	9.1745	6.6912	.8255	1.4224	30
40	.1513	.1507	9.1781	.9886	9.9950	.1524	9.1831	6.5606	.8169	1.4195	20
50	.1542	.1536	9.1863	.9881	9.9948	.1554	9.1915	6.4348	.8085	1.4166	10
9° 00′	.1571	.1564	9.1943	.9877	9.9946	.1584	9.1997	6.3138	.8003	1.4137	81° 00′
10	.1600	.1593	9.2022	.9872	9.9944	.1614	9.2078	6.1970	.7922	1.4108	50
20	.1629	.1622	9.2100	.9868	9.9942	.1644	9.2158	6.0844	.7842	1.4079	40
30	.1658	.1651	9.2176	.9863	9.9940	.1673	9.2236	5.9758	.7764	1.4050	30
40	.1687	.1679	9.2251	.9858	9.9938	.1703	9.2313	5.8708	.7687	1.4021	20
50	.1716	.1708	9.2324	.9853	9.9936	.1733	9.2389	5.7694	.7611	1.3992	10
10° 00′	.1745	.1737	9.2397	.9848	9.9934	.1763	9.2463	5.6713	.7537	1.3963	80° 00′
10	.1774	.1765	9.2468	.9843	9.9931	.1793	9.2536	5.5764	.7464	1.3934	50
20	.1804	.1794	9.2538	.9838	9.9929	.1823	9.2609	5.4845	.7391	1.3904	40
30	.1833	.1822	9.2606	.9833	9.9927	.1853	9.2680	5.3955	.7320	1.3875	30
40	.1862	.1851	9.2674	.9827	9.9924	.1884	9.2750	5.3093	.7250	1.3846	20
50	.1891	.1880	9.2741	.9822	9.9922	.1914	9.2819	5.2257	.7181	1.3817	10
11° 00′	.1920	.1908	9.2806	.9816	9.9920	.1944	9.2887	5.1446	.7114	1.3788	79° 00′
10	.1949	.1937	9.2871	.9811	9.9917	.1974	9.2954	5.0658	.7047	1.3759	50
20	.1978	.1965	9.2934	.9805	9.9915	.2004	9.3020	4.9894	.6981	1.3730	40
30	.2007	.1994	9.2997	.9799	9.9912	.2035	9.3085	4.9152	.6915	1.3701	30
40	.2036	.2022	9.3058	.9793	9.9909	.2065	9.3149	4.8430	.6851	1.3672	20
50	.2065	.2051	9.3119	.9788	9.9907	.2095	9.3212	4.7729	.6788	1.3643	10
12° 00′	.2094	.2079	9.3179	.9782	9.9904	.2126	9.3275	4.7046	.6725	1.3614	78° 00′
		Nat.		Nat.		Nat.		Nat.			
Degrees	Radians	Cosines	Log cosines	Sines	Log sines	Cotangents	Log cotangents	Tangents	Log tangents	Radians	Degrees

Table 1-2. Natural Trigonometric Functions and Their Logarithms—(*Continued*)

Degrees	Radians	Sines	Log sines	Cosines	Log cosines	Tangents	Log tangents	Cotangents	Log cotangents	Radians	Degrees
		Nat.		Nat.		Nat.		Nat.			
12° 00′	0.2094	0.2079	9.3179	0.9782	9.9904	0.2126	9.3275	4.7046	0.6725	1.3614	78° 00′
10	.2123	.2108	9.3238	.9775	9.9901	.2156	9.3337	4.6383	.6664	1.3584	50
20	.2153	.2136	9.3296	.9769	9.9899	.2186	9.3397	4.5736	.6603	1.3555	40
30	.2182	.2164	9.3353	.9763	9.9896	.2217	9.3458	4.5107	.6542	1.3526	30
40	.2211	.2193	9.3410	.9757	9.9893	.2248	9.3517	4.4494	.6483	1.3497	20
50	.2240	.2221	9.3466	.9750	9.9890	.2278	9.3576	4.3897	.6424	1.3468	10
13° 00′	.2269	.2250	9.3521	.9744	9.9887	.2309	9.3634	4.3315	.6366	1.3439	77° 00′
10	.2298	.2278	9.3575	.9737	9.9884	.2339	9.3691	4.2747	.6309	1.3410	50
20	.2327	.2306	9.3629	.9730	9.9881	.2370	9.3748	4.2193	.6252	1.3381	40
30	.2356	.2335	9.3682	.9724	9.9878	.2401	9.3804	4.1653	.6197	1.3352	30
40	.2385	.2363	9.3734	.9717	9.9875	.2432	9.3859	4.1126	.6141	1.3323	20
50	.2414	.2391	9.3786	.9710	9.9872	.2462	9.3914	4.0611	.6086	1.3294	10
14° 00′	.2443	.2419	9.3837	.9703	9.9869	.2493	9.3968	4.0108	.6032	1.3265	76° 00′
10	.2473	.2447	9.3887	.9696	9.9866	.2524	9.4021	3.9617	.5979	1.3235	50
20	.2502	.2476	9.3937	.9689	9.9863	.2555	9.4074	3.9136	.5926	1.3206	40
30	.2531	.2504	9.3986	.9682	9.9859	.2586	9.4127	3.8667	.5873	1.3177	30
40	.2560	.2532	9.4035	.9674	9.9856	.2617	9.4178	3.8208	.5822	1.3148	20
50	.2589	.2560	9.4083	.9667	9.9853	.2648	9.4230	3.7760	.5770	1.3119	10
15° 00′	.2618	.2588	9.4130	.9659	9.9849	.2680	9.4281	3.7321	.5720	1.3090	75° 00′
10 ′	.2647	.2616	9.4177	.9652	9.9846	.2711	9.4331	3.6891	.5669	1.3061	50
20	.2676	.2644	9.4223	.9644	9.9843	.2742	9.4381	3.6471	.5619	1.3032	40
30	.2705	.2672	9.4269	.9636	9.9839	.2773	9.4430	3.6059	.5570	1.3003	30
40	.2734	.2700	9.4314	.9629	9.9836	.2805	9.4479	3.5656	.5521	1.2974	20
50	.2763	.2728	9.4359	.9621	9.9832	.2836	9.4527	3.5261	.5473	1.2945	10
16° 00′	.2793	.2756	9.4403	.9613	9.9828	.2868	9.4575	3.4874	.5425	1.2915	74° 00′
10	.2822	.2784	9.4447	.9605	9.9825	.2899	9.4622	3.4495	.5378	1.2886	50
20	.2851	.2812	9.4491	.9596	9.9821	.2931	9.4669	3.4124	.5331	1.2857	40
30	.2880	.2840	9.4533	.9588	9.9817	.2962	9.4716	3.3759	.5284	1.2828	30
40	.2909	.2868	9.4576	.9580	9.9814	.2994	9.4762	3.3402	.5238	1.2799	20
50	.2938	.2896	9.4618	.9572	9.9810	.3026	9.4808	3.3052	.5192	1.2770	10
17° 00′	.2967	.2924	9.4659	.9563	9.9806	.3057	9.4853	3.2709	.5147	1.2741	73° 00′
10	.2996	.2952	9.4701	.9555	9.9802	.3089	9.4898	3.2371	.5102	1.2712	50
20	.3025	.2979	9.4741	.9546	9.9798	.3121	9.4943	3.2041	.5057	1.2683	40
30	.3054	.3007	9.4781	.9537	9.9794	.3153	9.4987	3.1716	.5013	1.2654	30
40	.3083	.3035	9.4821	.9528	9.9790	.3185	9.5031	3.1397	.4969	1.2625	20
50	.3113	.3063	9.4861	.9520	9.9786	.3217	9.5075	3.1084	.4925	1.2595	10
18° 00′	.3142	.3090	9.4900	.9511	9.9782	.3249	9.5118	3.0777	.4882	1.2566	72° 00′
10	.3171	.3118	9.4939	.9502	9.9778	.3281	9.5161	3.0475	.4839	1.2537	50
20	.3200	.3145	9.4977	.9492	9.9774	.3314	9.5203	3.0178	.4797	1.2508	40
30	.3229	.3173	9.5015	.9483	9.9770	.3346	9.5245	2.9887	.4755	1.2479	30
40	.3258	.3201	9.5052	.9474	9.9765	.3378	9.5287	2.9600	.4713	1.2450	20
50	.3287	.3228	9.5090	.9465	9.9761	.3411	9.5329	2.9319	.4672	1.2421	10
19° 00′	.3316	.3256	9.5126	.9455	9.9757	.3443	9.5370	2.9042	.4630	1.2392	71° 00′
10	.3345	.3283	9.5163	.9446	9.9752	.3476	9.5411	2.8770	.4589	1.2363	50
20	.3374	.3311	9.5199	.9436	9.9748	.3509	9.5451	2.8502	.4549	1.2334	40
30	.3403	.3338	9.5235	.9426	9.9744	.3541	9.5492	2.8239	.4509	1.2305	30
40	.3432	.3366	9.5271	.9417	9.9739	.3574	9.5532	2.7980	.4469	1.2275	20
50	.3462	.3393	9.5306	.9407	9.9734	.3607	9.5571	2.7725	.4429	1.2246	10
20° 00′	.3491	.3420	9.5341	.9397	9.9730	.3640	9.5611	2.7475	.4389	1.2217	70° 00′
10	.3520	.3448	9.5375	.9387	9.9725	.3673	9.5650	2.7228	.4350	1.2188	50
20	.3549	.3475	9.5409	.9377	9.9721	.3706	9.5689	2.6985	.4311	1.2159	40
30	.3578	.3502	9.5443	.9367	9.9716	.3739	9.5727	2.6746	.4273	1.2130	30
40	.3607	.3529	9.5477	.9357	9.9711	.3772	9.5766	2.6511	.4234	1.2101	20
50	.3636	.3557	9.5510	.9346	9.9706	.3805	9.5804	2.6279	.4196	1.2072	10
21° 00′	.3665	.3584	9.5543	.9336	9.9702	.3839	9.5842	2.6051	.4158	1.2043	69° 00′
10	.3694	.3611	9.5576	.9325	9.9697	.3872	9.5879	2.5826	.4121	1.2014	50
20	.3723	.3638	9.5609	.9315	9.9692	.3906	9.5917	2.5605	.4083	1.1985	40
30	.3752	.3665	9.5641	.9304	9.9687	.3939	9.5954	2.5387	.4046	1.1956	30
40	.3782	.3692	9.5673	.9294	9.9682	.3973	9.5991	2.5172	.4009	1.1926	20
50	.3811	.3719	9.5704	.9283	9.9677	.4007	9.6028	2.4960	.3972	1.1897	10
22° 00′	.3840	.3746	9.5736	.9272	9.9672	.4040	9.6064	2.4751	.3936	1.1868	68° 00′
10	.3869	.3773	9.5767	.9261	9.9667	.4074	9.6100	2.4545	.3900	1.1839	50
20	.3898	.3800	9.5798	.9250	9.9661	.4108	9.6136	2.4342	.3864	1.1810	40
30	.3927	.3827	9.5828	.9239	9.9656	.4142	9.6172	2.4142	.3828	1.1781	30
40	.3956	.3854	9.5859	.9228	9.9651	.4176	9.6208	2.3945	.3792	1.1752	20
50	.3985	.3881	9.5889	.9216	9.9646	.4211	9.6243	2.3750	.3757	1.1723	10
23° 00′	.4014	.3907	9.5919	.9205	9.9640	.4245	9.6279	2.3559	.3722	1.1694	67° 00′
10	.4043	.3934	9.5948	.9194	9.9635	.4279	9.6314	2.3369	.3687	1.1665	50
20	.4072	.3961	9.5978	.9182	9.9629	.4314	9.6348	2.3183	.3652	1.1636	40
30	.4102	.3988	9.6007	.9171	9.9624	.4348	9.6383	2.2998	.3617	1.1606	30
40	.4131	.4014	9.6036	.9159	9.9619	.4383	9.6418	2.2817	.3583	1.1577	20
50	.4160	.4041	9.6065	.9147	9.9613	.4418	9.6452	2.2637	.3548	1.1548	10
24° 00′	.4189	.4067	9.6093	.9136	9.9607	.4452	9.6486	2.2460	.3514	1.1519	66° 00′
		Nat.		Nat.		Nat.		Nat.			
Degrees	Radians	Cosines	Log cosines	Sines	Log sines	Cotangents	Log cotangents	Tangents	Log tangents	Radians	Degrees

Table 1-2. Natural Trigonometric Functions and Their Logarithms—(*Continued*)

Degrees	Radians	Sines	Log sines	Cosines	Log cosines	Tangents	Log tangents	Cotangents	Log cotangents	Radians	Degrees
		Nat.		Nat.		Nat.		Nat.			
24° 00′	0.4189	0.4067	9.6093	0.9136	9.9607	0.4452	9.6486	2.2460	0.3514	1.1519	66° 00′
10	.4218	.4094	9.6121	.9124	9.9602	.4487	9.6520	2.2286	.3480	1.1490	50
20	.4247	.4120	9.6149	.9112	9.9596	.4522	9.6554	2.2113	.3447	1.1461	40
30	.4276	.4147	9.6177	.9100	9.9590	.4557	9.6587	2.1943	.3413	1.1432	30
40	.4305	.4173	9.6205	.9088	9.9584	.4592	9.6620	2.1775	.3380	1.1403	20
50	.4334	.4200	9.6232	.9075	9.9579	.4628	9.6654	2.1609	.3346	1.1374	10
25° 00′	.4363	.4226	9.6260	.9063	9.9573	.4663	9.6687	2.1445	.3313	1.1345	65° 00′
10	.4392	.4253	9.6287	.9051	9.9567	.4699	9.6720	2.1283	.3280	1.1316	50
20	.4422	.4279	9.6313	.9038	9.9561	.4734	9.6752	2.1123	.3248	1.1286	40
30	.4451	.4305	9.6340	.9026	9.9555	.4770	9.6785	2.0965	.3215	1.1257	30
40	.4480	.4331	9.6366	.9013	9.9549	.4806	9.6817	2.0809	.3183	1.1228	20
50	.4509	.4358	9.6392	.9001	9.9543	.4841	9.6850	2.0655	.3150	1.1199	10
26° 00′	.4538	.4384	9.6418	.8988	9.9537	.4877	9.6882	2.0503	.3118	1.1170	64° 00′
10	.4567	.4410	9.6444	.8975	9.9530	.4913	9.6914	2.0353	.3086	1.1141	50
20	.4596	.4436	9.6470	.8962	9.9524	.4950	9.6946	2.0204	.3054	1.1112	40
30	.4625	.4462	9.6495	.8949	9.9518	.4986	9.6977	2.0057	.3023	1.1083	30
40	.4654	.4488	9.6521	.8936	9.9512	.5022	9.7009	1.9912	.2991	1.1054	20
50	.4683	.4514	9.6546	.8923	9.9505	.5059	9.7040	1.9768	.2960	1.1025	10
27° 00′	.4712	.4540	9.6571	.8910	9.9499	.5095	9.7072	1.9626	.2928	1.0996	63° 00′
10	.4741	.4566	9.6595	.8897	9.9492	.5132	9.7103	1.9486	.2897	1.0966	50
20	.4771	.4592	9.6620	.8884	9.9486	.5169	9.7134	1.9347	.2866	1.0937	40
30	.4800	.4618	9.6644	.8870	9.9479	.5206	9.7165	1.9210	.2835	1.0908	30
40	.4829	.4643	9.6668	.8857	9.9473	.5243	9.7196	1.9074	.2805	1.0879	20
50	.4858	.4669	9.6692	.8843	9.9466	.5280	9.7226	1.8940	.2774	1.0850	10
28° 00′	.4887	.4695	9.6716	.8830	9.9459	.5317	9.7257	1.8807	.2743	1.0821	62° 00′
10	.4916	.4720	9.6740	.8816	9.9453	.5355	9.7287	1.8676	.2713	1.0792	50
20	.4945	.4746	9.6763	.8802	9.9446	.5392	9.7318	1.8546	.2683	1.0763	40
30	.4974	.4772	9.6787	.8788	9.9439	.5430	9.7348	1.8418	.2652	1.0734	30
40	.5003	.4797	9.6810	.8774	9.9432	.5467	9.7378	1.8291	.2622	1.0705	20
50	.5032	.4823	9.6833	.8760	9.9425	.5505	9.7408	1.8165	.2592	1.0676	10
29° 00′	.5061	.4848	9.6856	.8746	9.9418	.5543	9.7438	1.8041	.2563	1.0647	61° 00′
10	.5091	.4874	9.6878	.8732	9.9411	.5581	9.7467	1.7917	.2533	1.0617	50
20	.5120	.4899	9.6901	.8718	9.9404	.5619	9.7497	1.7796	.2503	1.0588	40
30	.5149	.4924	9.6923	.8704	9.9397	.5658	9.7526	1.7675	.2474	1.0559	30
40	.5178	.4950	9.6946	.8689	9.9390	.5696	9.7556	1.7556	.2444	1.0530	20
50	.5207	.4975	9.6968	.8675	9.9383	.5735	9.7585	1.7438	.2415	1.0501	10
30° 00′	.5236	.5000	9.6990	.8660	9.9375	.5774	9.7614	1.7321	.2386	1.0472	60° 00′
10	.5265	.5025	9.7012	.8646	9.9368	.5812	9.7644	1.7205	.2357	1.0443	50
20	.5294	.5050	9.7033	.8631	9.9361	.5851	9.7673	1.7090	.2328	1.0414	40
30	.5323	.5075	9.7055	.8616	9.9353	.5891	9.7702	1.6977	.2299	1.0385	30
40	.5352	.5100	9.7076	.8602	9.9346	.5930	9.7730	1.6864	.2270	1.0356	20
50	.5381	.5125	9.7097	.8587	9.9338	.5969	9.7759	1.6753	.2241	1.0327	10
31° 00′	.5411	.5150	9.7118	.8572	9.9331	.6009	9.7788	1.6643	.2212	1.0297	59° 00′
10	.5440	.5175	9.7139	.8557	9.9323	.6048	9.7816	1.6534	.2184	1.0268	50
20	.5469	.5200	9.7160	.8542	9.9315	.6088	9.7845	1.6426	.2155	1.0239	40
30	.5498	.5225	9.7181	.8526	9.9308	.6128	9.7873	1.6319	.2127	1.0210	30
40	.5527	.5250	9.7201	.8511	9.9300	.6168	9.7902	1.6213	.2099	1.0181	20
50	.5556	.5275	9.7222	.8496	9.9292	.6208	9.7930	1.6107	.2070	1.0152	10
32° 00′	.5585	.5299	9.7242	.8481	9.9284	.6249	9.7958	1.6003	.2042	1.0123	58° 00′
10	.5614	.5324	9.7262	.8465	9.9276	.6289	9.7986	1.5900	.2014	1.0094	50
20	.5643	.5348	9.7282	.8450	9.9268	.6330	9.8014	1.5798	.1986	1.0065	40
30	.5672	.5373	9.7302	.8434	9.9260	.6371	9.8042	1.5697	.1958	1.0036	30
40	.5701	.5398	9.7322	.8418	9.9252	.6412	9.8070	1.5597	.1930	1.0007	20
50	.5730	.5422	9.7342	.8403	9.9244	.6453	9.8098	1.5497	.1903	0.9977	10
33° 00′	.5760	.5446	9.7361	.8387	9.9236	.6494	9.8125	1.5399	.1875	.9948	57° 00′
10	.5789	.5471	9.7381	.8371	9.9228	.6536	9.8153	1.5301	.1847	.9919	50
20	.5818	.5495	9.7400	.8355	9.9219	.6577	9.8180	1.5204	.1820	.9890	40
30	.5847	.5519	9.7419	.8339	9.9211	.6619	9.8208	1.5108	.1792	.9861	30
40	.5876	.5544	9.7438	.8323	9.9203	.6661	9.8235	1.5013	.1765	.9832	20
50	.5905	.5568	9.7457	.8307	9.9194	.6703	9.8263	1.4919	.1737	.9803	10
34° 00′	.5934	.5592	9.7476	.8290	9.9186	.6745	9.8290	1.4826	.1710	.9774	56° 00′
10	.5963	.5616	9.7494	.8274	9.9177	.6788	9.8317	1.4733	.1683	.9745	50
20	.5992	.5640	9.7513	.8258	9.9169	.6830	9.8344	1.4641	.1656	.9716	40
30	.6021	.5664	9.7531	.8241	9.9160	.6873	9.8371	1.4550	.1629	.9687	30
40	.6050	.5688	9.7550	.8225	9.9151	.6916	9.8398	1.4460	.1602	.9657	20
50	.6080	.5712	9.7568	.8208	9.9143	.6959	9.8425	1.4370	.1575	.9628	10
35° 00′	.6109	.5736	9.7586	.8192	9.9134	.7002	9.8452	1.4282	.1548	.9599	55° 00′
10	.6138	.5760	9.7604	.8175	9.9125	.7046	9.8479	1.4193	.1521	.9570	50
20	.6167	.5783	9.7622	.8158	9.9116	.7089	9.8506	1.4106	.1494	.9541	40
30	.6196	.5807	9.7640	.8141	9.9107	.7133	9.8533	1.4020	.1467	.9512	30
40	.6225	.5831	9.7657	.8124	9.9098	.7177	9.8559	1.3934	.1441	.9483	20
50	.6254	.5854	9.7675	.8107	9.9089	.7221	9.8586	1.3848	.1414	.9454	10
36° 00′	.6283	.5878	9.7692	.8090	9.9080	.7265	9.8613	1.3764	.1387	.9425	54° 00′
		Nat.		Nat.		Nat.		Nat.			
Degrees	Radians	Cosines	Log cosines	Sines	Log sines	Cotangents	Log cotangents	Tangents	Log tangents	Radians	Degrees

Table 1-2. Natural Trigonometric Functions and Their Logarithms—*(Concluded)*

Degrees	Radians	Sines	Log sines	Cosines	Log cosines	Tangents	Log tangents	Cotangents	Log cotangents	Radians	Degrees
		Nat.		Nat.		Nat.		Nat.			
36° 00′	0.6283	0.5878	9.7692	0.8090	9.9080	0.7265	9.8613	1.3764	0.1387	0.9425	54° 00′
10	.6312	.5901	9.7710	.8073	9.9070	.7310	9.8639	1.3680	.1361	.9396	50
20	.6341	.5925	9.7727	.8056	9.9061	.7355	9.8666	1.3597	.1334	.9367	40
30	.6370	.5948	9.7744	.8039	9.9052	.7400	9.8692	1.3514	.1308	.9338	30
40	.6400	.5972	9.7761	.8021	9.9042	.7445	9.8719	1.3432	.1282	.9308	20
50	.6429	.5995	9.7778	.8004	9.9033	.7490	9.8745	1.3351	.1255	.9279	10
37° 00′	.6458	.6018	9.7795	.7986	9.9024	.7536	9.8771	1.3270	.1229	.9250	53° 00′
10	.6487	.6041	9.7811	.7969	9.9014	.7581	9.8797	1.3190	.1203	.9221	50
20	.6516	.6065	9.7828	.7951	9.9004	.7627	9.8824	1.3111	.1176	.9192	40
30	.6545	.6088	9.7845	.7934	9.8995	.7673	9.8850	1.3032	.1150	.9163	30
40	.6574	.6111	9.7861	.7916	9.8985	.7720	9.8876	1.2954	.1124	.9134	20
50	.6603	.6134	9.7877	.7898	9.8975	.7766	9.8902	1.2876	.1098	.9105	10
38° 00′	.6632	.6157	9.7893	.7880	9.8965	.7813	9.8928	1.2799	.1072	.9076	52° 00′
10	.6661	.6180	9.7910	.7862	9.8955	.7860	9.8954	1.2723	.1046	.9047	50
20	.6690	.6202	9.7926	.7844	9.8946	.7907	9.8980	1.2647	.1020	.9018	40
30	.6720	.6225	9.7942	.7826	9.8935	.7954	9.9006	1.2572	.0994	.8988	30
40	.6749	.6248	9.7957	.7808	9.8925	.8002	9.9032	1.2497	.0968	.8959	20
50	.6778	.6271	9.7973	.7790	9.8915	.8050	9.9058	1.2423	.0942	.8930	10
39° 00′	.6807	.6293	9.7989	.7772	9.8905	.8098	9.9084	1.2349	.0916	.8901	51° 00′
10	.6836	.6316	9.8004	.7753	9.8895	.8146	9.9110	1.2276	.0891	.8872	50
20	.6865	.6338	9.8020	.7735	9.8884	.8195	9.9135	1.2203	.0865	.8843	40
30	.6894	.6361	9.8035	.7716	9.8874	.8243	9.9161	1.2131	.0839	.8814	30
40	.6923	.6383	9.8050	.7698	9.8864	.8292	9.9187	1.2059	.0813	.8785	20
50	.6952	.6406	9.8066	.7679	9.8853	.8342	9.9213	1.1988	.0788	.8756	10
40° 00′	.6981	.6428	9.8081	.7660	9.8843	.8391	9.9238	1.1918	.0762	.8727	50° 00′
10	.7010	.6450	9.8096	.7642	9.8832	.8441	9.9264	1.1847	.0736	.8698	50
20	.7039	.6472	9.8111	.7623	9.8821	.8491	9.9289	1.1778	.0711	.8668	40
30	.7069	.6495	9.8125	.7604	9.8811	.8541	9.9315	1.1709	.0685	.8639	30
40	.7098	.6517	9.8140	.7585	9.8800	.8591	9.9341	1.1640	.0659	.8610	20
50	.7127	.6539	9.8155	.7566	9.8789	.8642	9.9366	1.1572	.0634	.8581	10
41° 00′	.7156	.6561	9.8169	.7547	9.8778	.8693	9.9392	1.1504	.0608	.8552	49° 00′
10	.7185	.6583	9.8184	.7528	9.8767	.8744	9.9417	1.1436	.0583	.8523	50
20	.7214	.6604	9.8198	.7509	9.8756	.8796	9.9443	1.1369	.0557	.8494	40
30	.7243	.6626	9.8213	.7490	9.8745	.8847	9.9468	1.1303	.0532	.8465	30
40	.7272	.6648	9.8227	.7470	9.8733	.8899	9.9494	1.1237	.0507	.8436	20
50	.7301	.6670	9.8241	.7451	9.8722	.8952	9.9519	1.1171	.0481	.8407	10
42° 00′	.7330	.6691	9.8255	.7431	9.8711	.9004	9.9544	1.1106	.0456	.8378	48° 00′
10	.7359	.6713	9.8269	.7412	9.8699	.9057	9.9570	1.1041	.0430	.8348	50
20	.7389	.6734	9.8283	.7392	9.8688	.9110	9.9595	1.0977	.0405	.8319	40
30	.7418	.6756	9.8297	.7373	9.8676	.9163	9.9621	1.0913	.0380	.8290	30
40	.7447	.6777	9.8311	.7353	9.8665	.9217	9.9646	1.0850	.0354	.8261	20
50	.7476	.6799	9.8324	.7333	9.8653	.9271	9.9671	1.0786	.0329	.8232	10
43° 00′	.7505	.6820	9.8338	.7314	9.8641	.9325	9.9697	1.0724	.0303	.8203	47° 00′
10	.7534	.6841	9.8351	.7294	9.8630	.9380	9.9722	1.0661	.0278	.8174	50
20	.7563	.6862	9.8365	.7274	9.8618	.9435	9.9747	1.0599	.0253	.8145	40
30	.7592	.6884	9.8378	.7254	9.8606	.9490	9.9773	1.0538	.0228	.8116	30
40	.7621	.6905	9.8391	.7234	9.8594	.9545	9.9798	1.0477	.0202	.8087	20
50	.7650	.6926	9.8405	.7214	9.8582	.9601	9.9823	1.0416	.0177	.8058	10
44° 00′	.7679	.6947	9.8418	.7193	9.8569	.9657	9.9848	1.0355	.0152	.8029	46° 00′
10	.7709	.6968	9.8431	.7173	9.8557	.9713	9.9874	1.0295	.0126	.7999	50
20	.7738	.6988	9.8444	.7153	9.8545	.9770	9.9899	1.0236	.0101	.7970	40
30	.7767	.7009	9.8457	.7133	9.8532	.9827	9.9924	1.0176	.0076	.7941	30
40	.7796	.7030	9.8469	.7112	9.8520	.9884	9.9950	1.0117	.0051	.7912	20
50	.7825	.7051	9.8482	.7092	9.8507	.9942	9.9975	1.0058	.0025	.7883	10
45° 00′	.7854	.7071	9.8495	.7071	9.8495	1.0000	0.0000	1.0000	0.0000	.7854	45° 00′
		Nat.		Nat.		Nat.		Nat.			
Degrees	Radians	Cosines	Log cosines	Sines	Log sines	Cotangents	Log cotangents	Tangents	Log tangents	Radians	Degrees

Table 1-3a. Circular Segments

Angle in degrees

Central angle, degrees	Height/R	Chord/R	Height/Chord	Area/R^2	Central angle, degrees	Height/R	Chord/R	Height/Chord	Area/R^2	Central angle, degrees	Height/R	Chord/R	Height/Chord	Area/R^2
1	0.000038	0.017453	0.002177	0.0000005	61	0.138371	1.01508	0.136315	0.0950155	121	0.507576	1.74071	0.291591	0.6273404
2	.000151	.034905	.004326	.0000035	62	.142833	1.03008	.138662	.0995782	122	.515190	1.74924	.294522	.6406267
3	.000343	.052354	.006552	.0000119	63	.147360	1.04500	.141014	.1042754	123	.522841	1.75763	.297469	.6540421
4	.000609	.069799	.008725	.0000283	64	.151952	1.05984	.143373	.1091083	124	.530528	1.76590	.300429	.6675852
5	.000952	.087239	.010913	.0000554	65	.156609	1.07460	.145737	.1140780	125	.538251	1.77402	.303411	.6812546
6	.001371	.104672	.013098	.0000956	66	.161329	1.08928	.148106	.1191858	126	.546010	1.78201	.306401	.6950488
7	.001865	.122097	.015275	.0001519	67	.166114	1.10387	.150483	.1244328	127	.553802	1.78987	.309409	.7089613
8	.002436	.139513	.017461	.0002266	68	.170962	1.11839	.152864	.1298199	128	.561629	1.79759	.312434	.7230052
9	.003083	.156918	.019647	.0003226	69	.175874	1.13281	.155255	.1353483	129	.569489	1.80517	.315477	.7371642
10	.003805	.174311	.021829	.0004423	70	.180848	1.14715	.157650	.1410188	130	.577382	1.81262	.318534	.7514417
11	.004604	.191692	.024018	.0005886	71	.185885	1.16140	.160053	.1468325	131	.585307	1.81992	.321611	.7658357
12	.005479	.209057	.026207	.0007639	72	.190983	1.17557	.162460	.1527902	132	.593263	1.82709	.324704	.7803448
13	.006428	.226406	.028391	.0009708	73	.196143	1.18965	.164875	.1588927	133	.601251	1.83412	.327814	.7949670
14	.007454	.243739	.030582	.0012121	74	.201365	1.20363	.167298	.1651409	134	.609269	1.84101	.330943	.8097006
15	.008555	.261052	.032771	.0014901	75	.206647	1.21752	.169728	.1715355	135	.617317	1.84776	.334089	.8245437
16	.009732	.278346	.034963	.0018076	76	.211989	1.23132	.172164	.1780773	136	.625393	1.85436	.337255	.8394945
17	.010984	.295619	.037156	.0021671	77	.217392	1.24503	.174608	.1847666	137	.633499	1.86084	.340437	.8545511
18	.012312	.312867	.039352	.0025711	78	.222854	1.25864	.177059	.1916045	138	.641632	1.86716	.343641	.8697117
19	.013714	.330095	.041547	.0030222	79	.228375	1.27216	.179518	.1985914	139	.649793	1.87334	.346863	.8849742
20	.015192	.347296	.043744	.0035229	80	.233956	1.28558	.181985	.2057277	140	.657980	1.87939	.350103	.9003667
21	.016745	.364471	.045943	.0040756	81	.239594	1.29890	.184459	.2130141	141	.666193	1.88528	.353366	.9157968
22	.018373	.381618	.048145	.0046829	82	.245290	1.31212	.186942	.2204508	142	.674432	1.89104	.356646	.9313529
23	.020075	.398736	.050347	.0053473	83	.251044	1.32524	.189433	.2280384	143	.682695	1.89665	.359948	.9470027
24	.021852	.415823	.052551	.0060712	84	.256855	1.33826	.191932	.2357772	144	.690983	1.90211	.363272	.9627442
25	.023704	.432879	.054759	.0068570	85	.262723	1.35118	.194440	.2436676	145	.699294	1.90743	.366616	.9785754
26	.025630	.449902	.056968	.0077072	86	.268646	1.36400	.196955	.2517094	146	.707628	1.91261	.369980	.9944937
27	.027630	.466891	.059178	.0086242	87	.274626	1.37671	.199481	.2599034	147	.715985	1.91764	.373368	1.0104973
28	.029704	.483844	.061392	.0096103	88	.280660	1.38932	.202012	.2682494	148	.724363	1.92252	.376778	1.0265840
29	.031852	.500760	.063607	.0106679	89	.286750	1.40182	.204556	.2767476	149	.732762	1.92726	.380209	1.0427512
30	.034074	.517638	.065826	.0117993	90	.292893	1.41421	.207107	.2853982	150	.741181	1.93185	.383664	1.0589969
31	.036370	.534477	.068048	.0130069	91	.299091	1.42650	.209668	.2942010	151	.749620	1.93630	.387140	1.0753188
32	.038738	.551275	.070270	.0142930	92	.305342	1.43868	.212238	.3031559	152	.758078	1.94059	.390643	1.0917144
33	.041180	.568031	.072496	.0156598	93	.311645	1.45075	.214816	.3122632	153	.766555	1.94474	.394168	1.1081816
34	.043695	.584743	.074725	.0171095	94	.318002	1.46271	.217406	.3215226	154	.775049	1.94874	.397718	1.1247180
35	.046283	.601412	.076957	.0186444	95	.324410	1.47456	.220005	.3309339	155	.783560	1.95259	.401293	1.1413210
36	.048944	.618034	.079193	.0202666	96	.330869	1.48629	.222614	.3404970	156	.792088	1.95630	.404891	1.1579885
37	.051676	.634609	.081430	.0219784	97	.337380	1.49791	.225234	.3502115	157	.800632	1.95985	.408517	1.1747179
38	.054481	.651136	.083671	.0237818	98	.343941	1.50942	.227863	.3600772	158	.809191	1.96325	.412169	1.1915068
39	.057359	.667614	.085917	.0256790	99	.350552	1.52081	.230503	.3700937	159	.817765	1.96651	.415845	1.2083528
40	.060307	.684040	.088163	.0276720	100	.357212	1.53209	.233153	.3802606	160	.826352	1.96962	.419549	1.2252533
41	.063328	.700415	.090415	.0297629	101	.363922	1.54325	.235815	.3905775	161	.834952	1.97257	.423281	1.2422059
42	.066420	.716736	.092670	.0319538	102	.370680	1.55429	.238488	.4010440	162	.843566	1.97537	.427042	1.2592082
43	.069582	.733002	.094927	.0342465	103	.377485	1.56522	.241171	.4116594	163	.852191	1.97803	.430828	1.2762575
44	.072816	.749213	.097190	.0366432	104	.384339	1.57602	.243867	.4224232	164	.860827	1.98054	.434643	1.2933512
45	.076121	.765367	.099457	.0391456	105	.391239	1.58671	.246572	.4333348	165	.869474	1.98289	.438488	1.3104871
46	.079495	.781462	.101730	.0417558	106	.398185	1.59727	.249299	.4443935	166	.878131	1.98509	.442363	1.3276623
47	.082940	.797498	.104000	.0444755	107	.405177	1.60771	.252021	.4555999	167	.886797	1.98714	.446268	1.3448744
48	.086455	.813473	.106278	.0473066	108	.412215	1.61803	.254764	.4669494	168	.895472	1.98904	.450203	1.3621207
49	.090039	.829386	.108561	.0502508	109	.419297	1.62823	.257517	.4784450	169	.904154	1.99079	.454169	1.3793987
50	.093692	.845237	.110847	.0533100	110	.426424	1.63830	.260284	.4900846	170	.912844	1.99238	.458165	1.3967057
51	.097415	.861022	.113139	.0564859	111	.433594	1.64825	.263063	.5018674	171	.921541	1.99383	.462196	1.4140393
52	.101206	.876742	.115434	.0597801	112	.440807	1.65808	.265854	.5137923	172	.930244	1.99513	.466257	1.4313966
53	.105067	.892396	.117736	.0631944	113	.448063	1.66777	.268660	.5258585	173	.938952	1.99627	.470358	1.4487751
54	.108994	.907981	.120040	.0667303	114	.455361	1.67734	.271478	.5380648	174	.947664	1.99726	.474482	1.4661721
55	.112989	.923497	.122349	.0703895	115	.462700	1.68678	.274310	.5504103	175	.956381	1.99810	.478645	1.4835852
56	.117052	.938943	.124664	.0741733	116	.470081	1.69610	.277154	.5628938	176	.965101	1.99878	.482845	1.5010115
57	.121182	.954318	.126983	.0780835	117	.477501	1.70528	.280013	.5755142	177	.973823	1.99931	.487080	1.5184484
58	.125380	.969619	.129308	.0821214	118	.484962	1.71433	.282887	.5882703	178	.982548	1.99970	.491348	1.5358933
59	.129644	.984847	.131639	.0862884	119	.492462	1.72326	.285773	.6011611	179	0.991274	1.99992	.495657	1.5533435
60	.133975	1.000000	.133975	.0905860	120	.500000	1.73205	.288684	.6141847	180	1.00000	2.00000	.500000	1.5707963

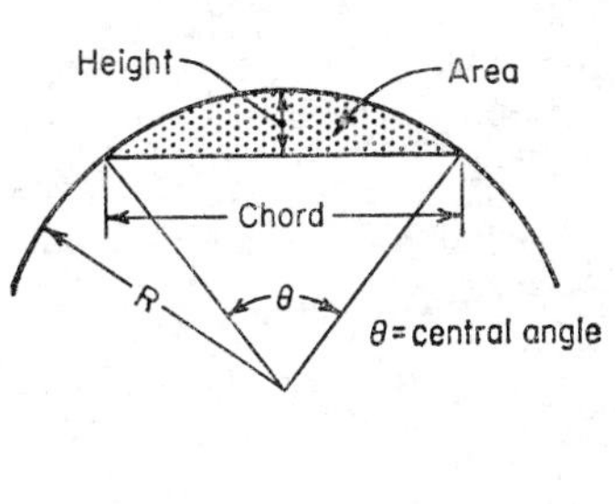

Table 1-3b. Circles: Areas of Segments

Height = h; Diameter = D; Area = A

h/D	A	h/D	A	h/D	A	h/D	A	h/D	A	h/D	A	h/D	A	h/D	A	h/D	A	h/D	A
		0.050	0.01468	0.100	0.04087	0.150	0.07387	0.200	0.11182	0.250	0.15355	0.300	0.19817	0.350	0.24498	0.400	0.29337	0.450	0.34278
0.001	0.00004	.051	.01512	.101	.04148	.151	.07459	.201	.11262	.251	.15441	.301	.19908	.351	.24593	.401	.29435	.451	.34378
.002	.00012	.052	.01556	.102	.04208	.152	.07531	.202	.11343	.252	.15528	.302	.20000	.352	.24689	.402	.29533	.452	.34477
.003	.00022	.053	.01601	.103	.04269	.153	.07603	.203	.11423	.253	.15615	.303	.20092	.353	.24784	.403	.29631	.453	.34577
.004	.00034	.054	.01646	.104	.04330	.154	.07675	.204	.11504	.254	.15702	.304	.20184	.354	.24880	.404	.29729	.454	.34676
.005	.00047	.055	.01691	.105	.04391	.155	.07747	.205	.11584	.255	.15789	.305	.20276	.355	.24976	.405	.29827	.455	.34776
.006	.00062	.056	.01737	.106	.04452	.156	.07819	.206	.11665	.256	.15876	.306	.20368	.356	.25071	.406	.29926	.456	.34876
.007	.00078	.057	.01783	.107	.04514	.157	.07892	.207	.11746	.257	.15964	.307	.20460	.357	.25167	.407	.30024	.457	.34975
.008	.00095	.058	.01830	.108	.04576	.158	.07965	.208	.11827	.258	.16051	.308	.20553	.358	.25263	.408	.30122	.458	.35075
.009	.00113	.059	.01877	.109	.04638	.159	.08038	.209	.11908	.259	.16139	.309	.20645	.359	.25359	.409	.30220	.459	.35175
.010	.00133	.060	.01924	.110	.04701	.160	.08111	.210	.11990	.260	.16226	.310	.20738	.360	.25455	.410	.30319	.460	.35274
.011	.00153	.061	.01972	.111	.04763	.161	.08185	.211	.12071	.261	.16314	.311	.20830	.361	.25551	.411	.30417	.461	.35374
.012	.00175	.062	.02020	.112	.04826	.162	.08258	.212	.12153	.262	.16402	.312	.20923	.362	.25647	.412	.30516	.462	.35474
.013	.00197	.063	.02068	.113	.04889	.163	.08332	.213	.12235	.263	.16490	.313	.21015	.363	.25743	.413	.30614	.463	.33573
.014	.00220	.064	.02117	.114	.04953	.164	.08406	.214	.12317	.264	.16578	.314	.21108	.364	.25839	.414	.30712	.464	.35673
.015	.00244	.065	.02166	.115	.05016	.165	.08480	.215	.12399	.265	.16666	.315	.21201	.365	.25936	.415	.30811	.465	.35773
.016	.00268	.066	.02215	.116	.05080	.166	.08554	.216	.12481	.266	.16755	.316	.21294	.366	.26032	.416	.30910	.466	.35873
.017	.00294	.067	.02265	.117	.05145	.167	.08629	.217	.12563	.267	.16843	.317	.21387	.367	.26128	.417	.31008	.467	.35972
.018	.00320	.068	.02315	.118	.05209	.168	.08704	.218	.12646	.268	.16932	.318	.21480	.368	.26225	.418	.31107	.468	.36072
.019	.00347	.069	.02366	.119	.05274	.169	.08779	.219	.12729	.269	.17020	.319	.21573	.369	.26321	.419	.31205	.469	.36172
.020	.00375	.070	.02417	.120	.05338	.170	.08854	.220	.12811	.270	.17109	.320	.21667	.370	.26418	.420	.31304	.470	.36272
.021	.00403	.071	.02468	.121	.05404	.171	.08929	.221	.12894	.271	.17198	.321	.21760	.371	.26514	.421	.31403	.471	.36372
.022	.00432	.072	.02520	.122	.05469	.172	.09004	.222	.12977	.272	.17287	.322	.21853	.372	.26611	.422	.31502	.472	.36471
.023	.00462	.073	.02571	.123	.05535	.173	.09080	.223	.13060	.273	.17376	.323	.21947	.373	.26708	.423	.31600	.473	.36571
.024	.00492	.074	.02624	.124	.05600	.174	.09155	.224	.13144	.274	.17465	.324	.22040	.374	.26805	.424	.31699	.474	.36671
.025	.00523	.075	.02676	.125	.05666	.175	.09231	.225	.13227	.275	.17554	.325	.22134	.375	.26901	.425	.31798	.475	.36771
.026	.00555	.076	.02729	.126	.05733	.176	.09307	.226	.13311	.276	.17644	.326	.22228	.376	.26998	.426	.31897	.476	.36871
.027	.00587	.077	.02782	.127	.05799	.177	.09384	.227	.13395	.277	.17733	.327	.22322	.377	.27095	.427	.31996	.477	.36971
.028	.00619	.078	.02836	.128	.05866	.178	.09460	.228	.13478	.278	.17823	.328	.22415	.378	.27192	.428	.32095	.478	.37071
.029	.00653	.079	.02889	.129	.05933	.179	.09537	.229	.13562	.279	.17912	.329	.22509	.379	.27289	.429	.32194	.479	.37171
.030	.00687	.080	.02943	.130	.06000	.180	.09613	.230	.13646	.280	.18002	.330	.22603	.380	.27386	.430	.32293	.480	.37270
.031	.00721	.081	.02998	.131	.06067	.181	.09690	.231	.13731	.281	.18092	.331	.22697	.381	.27483	.431	.32392	.481	.37370
.032	.00756	.082	.03053	.132	.06135	.182	.09767	.232	.13815	.282	.18182	.332	.22792	.382	.27580	.432	.32491	.482	.37470
.033	.00791	.083	.03108	.133	.06203	.183	.09845	.233	.13900	.283	.18272	.333	.22886	.383	.27678	.433	.32590	.483	.37570
.034	.00827	.084	.03163	.134	.06271	.184	.09922	.234	.13984	.284	.18362	.334	.22980	.384	.27775	.434	.32689	.484	.37670
.035	.00864	.085	.03219	.135	.06339	.185	.10000	.235	.14069	.285	.18452	.335	.23074	.385	.27872	.435	.32788	.485	.37770
.036	.00901	.086	.03275	.136	.06407	.186	.10077	.236	.14154	.286	.18542	.336	.23169	.386	.27969	.436	.32887	.486	.37870
.037	.00938	.087	.03331	.137	.06476	.187	.10155	.237	.14239	.287	.18633	.337	.23263	.387	.28067	.437	.32987	.487	.37970
.038	.00976	.088	.03387	.138	.06545	.188	.10233	.238	.14324	.288	.18723	.338	.23358	.338	.28164	.438	.33086	.488	.38070
.039	.01015	.089	.03444	.139	.06614	.189	.10312	.239	.14409	.289	.18814	.339	.23453	.389	.28262	.439	.33185	.489	.38170
.040	.01054	.090	.03501	.140	.06683	.190	.10390	.240	.14494	.290	.18905	.340	.23547	.390	.28359	.440	.33284	.490	.38270
.041	.01093	.091	.03559	.141	.06753	.191	.10469	.241	.14580	.291	.18996	.341	.23642	.391	.28457	.441	.33384	.491	.38370
.042	.01133	.092	.03616	.142	.06822	.192	.10547	.242	.14666	.292	.19086	.342	.23737	.392	.28554	.442	.33483	.492	.38470
.043	.01173	.093	.03674	.143	.06892	.193	.10626	.243	.14751	.293	.19177	.343	.23832	.393	.28652	.443	.33582	.493	.38570
.044	.01214	.094	.03732	.144	.06963	.194	.10705	.244	.14837	.294	.19268	.344	.23927	.394	.28750	.444	.33682	.494	.38670
.045	.01255	.095	.03791	.145	.07033	.195	.10784	.245	.14923	.295	.19360	.345	.24022	.395	.28848	.445	.33781	.495	.38770
.046	.01297	.096	.03850	.146	.07103	.196	.10864	.246	.15009	.296	.19451	.346	.24117	.396	.28945	.446	.33880	.496	.38870
.047	.01339	.097	.03909	.147	.07174	.197	.10943	.247	.15095	.297	.19542	.347	.24212	.397	.29043	.447	.33980	.497	.38970
.048	.01382	.098	.03968	.148	.07245	.198	.11023	.248	.15182	.298	.19634	.348	.24307	.398	.29141	.448	.34079	.498	.39070
.049	.01425	.099	.04028	.149	.07316	.199	.11102	.249	.15268	.299	.19725	.349	.24403	.399	.29239	.449	.34179	.499	.39170
																		.500	.39270

Rules for Using Table: (1) Divide height of segment by the diameter; multiply the area in the table corresponding to the quotient, height/diameter, by the diameter squared. When segment exceeds a semicircle, its area is: Area of circle minus the area of a segment whose height is the circle diameter minus the height of the given segment. (2) To find the diameter when given the chord and the segment height: the diameter = [(½ chord)²/height] + height.

Table 1-4. Spheres: Segments*

h = segment height; D = sphere diameter

h/D	Segment vol./D^3	Segment vol./Sphere vol.	h/D	Segment vol./D^3	Segment vol./Sphere vol.	h/D	Segment vol./D^3	Segment vol./Sphere vol.	h/D	Segment vol./D^3	Segment vol./Sphere vol.
0.01	0.000156	0.000298	0.16	0.035923	0.068608	0.31	0.119756	0.228718	0.41	0.191877	0.366458
.02	.000619	.001184	.17	.040251	.076874	.32	.126534	.241664	.42	.199503	.381024
.03	.001385	.002646	.18	.044787	.085536	.33	.133426	.254826	.43	.207180	.395686
.04	.002446	.004672	.19	.049522	.094582	.34	.140425	.268192	.44	.214901	.410432
.05	.003796	.007250	.20	.054454	.104000	.35	.147524	.281750	.45	.222660	.425250
.06	.005429	.010368	.21	.059573	.113778	.36	.154717	.295488	.46	.230450	.440128
.07	.007338	.014014	.22	.064875	.123904	.37	.161998	.309394	.47	.238265	.455054
.08	.009517	.018176	.23	.070353	.134366	.38	.169361	.323456	.48	.246099	.470016
.09	.011960	.022842	.24	.076001	.145152	.39	.176799	.337662	.49	.253946	.485002
.10	.014661	.028000	.25	.081812	.156250	.40	.184306	.352000	.50	.261799	.500000
.11	.017613	.033638	.26	.087780	.167648						
.12	.020809	.039744	.27	.093900	.179334						
.13	.024246	.046306	.28	.100160	.191296						
.14	.027914	.053312	.29	.106560	.203522						
.15	.031809	.060750	.30	.113097	.216000						

* Given the segment height h and the sphere diameter D, first form the ratio h/D, and find from the table the value of (segment volume/D^3); then multiply this latter value by D^3, that is: (segment volume/D^3) × D^3 = segment volume.

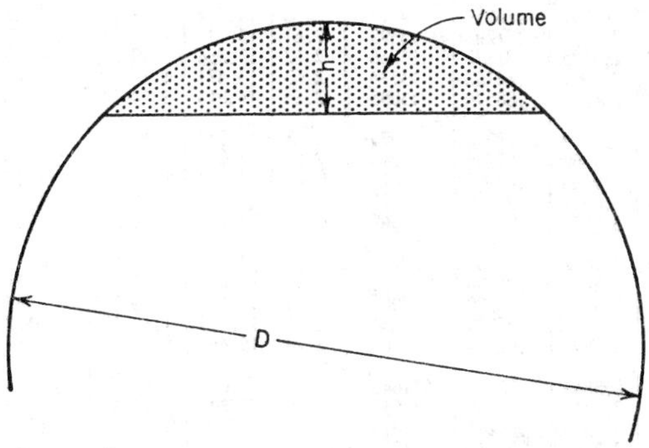

Table 1-5. Values of e^x and e^{-x}

x	e^x Value	e^x $\log_{10}$	e^{-x} (value)	x	e^x Value	e^x $\log_{10}$	e^{-x} (value)	x	e^x Value	e^x $\log_{10}$	e^{-x} (value)	x	e^x value	e^x $\log_{10}$	e^{-x} (value)
0.00	1.0000	0.00000	1.00000	0.30	1.3499	0.13029	0.74082	0.60	1.8221	0.26058	0.54881	0.90	2.4596	0.39087	0.40657
0.01	1.0101	.00434	0.99005	0.31	1.3634	.13463	.73345	0.61	1.8404	.26492	.54335	0.91	2.4843	.39521	.40252
0.02	1.0202	.00869	.98020	0.32	1.3771	.13897	.72615	0.62	1.8589	.26926	.53794	0.92	2.5093	.39955	.39852
0.03	1.0305	.01303	.97045	0.33	1.3910	.14332	.71892	0.63	1.8776	.27361	.53259	0.93	2.5345	.40389	.39455
0.04	1.0408	.01737	.96079	0.34	1.4049	.14766	.71177	0.64	1.8965	.27795	.52729	0.94	2.5600	.40824	.39063
0.05	1.0513	.02171	.95123	0.35	1.4191	.15200	.70469	0.65	1.9155	.28229	.52205	0.95	2.5857	.41258	.38674
0.06	1.0618	.02606	.94176	0.36	1.4333	.15635	.69768	0.66	1.9348	.28664	.51685	0.96	2.6117	.41692	.38289
0.07	1.0725	.03040	.93239	0.37	1.4477	.16069	.69073	0.67	1.9542	.29098	.51171	0.97	2.6379	.42127	.37908
0.08	1.0833	.03474	.92312	0.38	1.4623	.16503	.68386	0.68	1.9739	.29532	.50662	0.98	2.6645	.42561	.37531
0.09	1.0942	.03909	.91393	0.39	1.4770	.16937	.67706	0.69	1.9937	.29966	.50158	0.99	2.6912	.42995	.37158
0.10	1.1052	.04343	.90484	0.40	1.4918	.17372	.67032	0.70	2.0138	.30401	.49659	1.00	2.7183	.43429	.36788
0.11	1.1163	.04777	.89583	0.41	1.5068	.17806	.66365	0.71	2.0340	.30835	.49164	1.01	2.7456	.43864	.36422
0.12	1.1275	.05212	.88692	0.42	1.5220	.18240	.65705	0.72	2.0544	.31269	.48675	1.02	2.7732	.44298	.36060
0.13	1.1388	.05646	.87809	0.43	1.5373	.18675	.65051	0.73	2.0751	.31703	.48191	1.03	2.8011	.44732	.35701
0.14	1.1503	.06080	.86936	0.44	1.5527	.19109	.64404	0.74	2.0959	.32138	.47711	1.04	2.8292	.45167	.35345
0.15	1.1618	.06514	.86071	0.45	1.5683	.19543	.63763	0.75	2.1170	.32572	.47237	1.05	2.8577	.45601	.34994
0.16	1.1735	.06949	.85214	0.46	1.5841	.19978	.63128	0.76	2.1383	.33006	.46767	1.06	2.8864	.46035	.34646
0.17	1.1853	.07383	.84366	0.47	1.6000	.20412	.62500	0.77	2.1598	.33441	.46301	1.07	2.9154	.46470	.34301
0.18	1.1972	.07817	.83527	0.48	1.6161	.20846	.61878	0.78	2.1815	.33875	.45841	1.08	2.9447	.46904	.33960
0.19	1.2092	.08252	.82696	0.49	1.6323	.21280	.61263	0.79	2.2034	.34309	.45384	1.09	2.9743	.47338	.33622
0.20	1.2214	.08686	.81873	0.50	1.6487	.21715	.60653	0.80	2.2255	.34744	.44933	1.10	3.0042	.47772	.33287
0.21	1.2337	.09120	.81058	0.51	1.6653	.22149	.60050	0.81	2.2479	.35178	.44486	1.11	3.0344	.48207	.32956
0.22	1.2461	.09554	.80252	0.52	1.6820	.22583	.59452	0.82	2.2705	.35612	.44043	1.12	3.0649	.48641	.32628
0.23	1.2586	.09989	.79453	0.53	1.6989	.23018	.58860	0.83	2.2933	.36046	.43605	1.13	3.0957	.49075	.32303
0.24	1.2712	.10423	.78663	0.54	1.7160	.23452	.58275	0.84	2.3164	.36481	.43171	1.14	3.1268	.49510	.31982
0.25	1.2840	.10857	.77880	0.55	1.7333	.23886	.57695	0.85	2.3396	.36915	.42741	1.15	3.1582	.49944	.31664
0.26	1.2969	.11292	.77105	0.56	1.7507	.24320	.57121	0.86	2.3632	.37349	.42316	1.16	3.1899	.50378	.31349
0.27	1.3100	.11726	.76338	0.57	1.7683	.24755	.56553	0.87	2.3869	.37784	.41895	1.17	3.2220	.50812	.31037
0.28	1.3231	.12160	.75578	0.58	1.7860	.25189	.55990	0.88	2.4109	.38218	.41478	1.18	3.2544	.51247	.30728
0.29	1.3364	.12595	.74826	0.59	1.8040	.25623	.55433	0.89	2.4351	.38652	.41066	1.19	3.2871	.51681	.30422
0.30	1.3499	.13029	.74082	0.60	1.8221	.26058	.54881	0.90	2.4596	.39087	.40657	1.20	3.3201	.52115	.30119

Table 1-5. Values of e^x and e^{-x}—(*Concluded*)

x	e^x Value	e^x $\log_{10}$	e^{-x} (value)
1.20	3.3201	0.52115	0.30119
1.21	3.3535	.52550	.29820
1.22	3.3872	.52984	.29523
1.23	3.4212	.53418	.29229
1.24	3.4556	.53853	.28938
1.25	3.4903	.54287	.28650
1.26	3.5254	.54721	.28365
1.27	3.5609	.55155	.28083
1.28	3.5966	.55590	.27804
1.29	3.6328	.56024	.27527
1.30	3.6693	.56458	.27253
1.31	3.7062	.56893	.26982
1.32	3.7434	.57327	.26714
1.33	3.7810	.57761	.26448
1.34	3.8190	.58195	.26185
1.35	3.8574	.58630	.25924
1.36	3.8962	.59064	.25666
1.37	3.9354	.59498	.25411
1.38	3.9749	.59933	.25158
1.39	4.0149	.60367	.24908
1.40	4.0552	.60801	.24660
1.41	4.0960	.61236	.24414
1.42	4.1371	.61670	.24171
1.43	4.1787	.62104	.23931
1.44	2.2207	.62538	.23693
1.45	4.2631	.62973	.23457
1.46	4.3060	.63407	.23224
1.47	4.3492	.63841	.22993
1.48	4.3929	.64276	.22764
1.49	4.4371	.64710	.22537
1.50	4.4817	.65144	.22313
1.51	4.5267	.65578	.22091
1.52	4.5722	.66013	.21871
1.53	4.6182	.66447	.21654
1.54	4.6646	.66881	.21438
1.55	4.7115	.67316	.21225
1.56	4.7588	.67750	.21014
1.57	4.8066	.68184	.20805
1.58	4.8550	.68619	.20598
1.59	4.9037	.69053	.20393
1.60	4.9530	.69487	.20190
1.61	5.0028	.69921	.19989
1.62	5.0531	.70356	.19790
1.63	5.1039	.70790	.19593
1.64	5.1552	.71224	.19398
1.65	5.2070	.71659	.19205
1.66	5.2593	.72093	.19014
1.67	5.3122	.72527	.18825
1.68	5.3656	.72961	.18637
1.69	5.4195	.73396	.18452
1.70	5.4739	.73830	.18268
1.71	5.5290	.74264	.18087
1.72	5.5845	.74699	.17907
1.73	5.6407	.75133	.17728
1.74	5.6973	.75567	.17552
1.75	5.7546	.76002	.17377
1.76	5.8124	.76436	.17204
1.77	5.8709	.76870	.17033
1.78	5.9299	.77304	.16864
1.79	5.9895	.77739	.16696
1.80	6.0496	.78173	.16530

x	e^x Value	e^x $\log_{10}$	e^{-x} (value)
1.80	6.0496	0.78173	0.16530
1.81	6.1104	.78607	.16365
1.82	6.1719	.79042	.16203
1.83	6.2339	.79476	.16041
1.84	6.2965	.79910	.15882
1.85	6.3598	.80344	.15724
1.86	6.4237	.80779	.15567
1.87	6.4883	.81213	.15421
1.88	6.5535	.81647	.15259
1.89	6.6194	.82082	.15107
1.90	6.6859	.82516	.14957
1.91	6.7531	.82950	.14808
1.92	6.8210	.83385	.14661
1.93	6.8895	.83819	.14515
1.94	6.9588	.84253	.14370
1.95	7.0287	.84687	.14227
1.96	7.0993	.85122	.14086
1.97	7.1707	.85556	.13946
1.98	7.2427	.85990	.13807
1.99	7.3155	.86425	.13670
2.00	7.3891	.86859	.13534
2.01	7.4633	.87293	.13399
2.02	7.5385	.87727	.13266
2.03	7.6141	.88162	.13134
2.04	7.6906	.88596	.13003
2.05	7.7679	.89030	.12873
2.06	7.8460	.89465	.12745
2.07	7.9248	.89899	.12619
2.08	8.0045	.90333	.12493
2.09	8.0849	.90768	.12369
2.10	8.1662	.91202	.12246
2.11	8.2482	.91636	.12124
2.12	8.3311	.92070	.12003
2.13	8.4149	.92505	.11884
2.14	8.4994	.92939	.11765
2.15	8.5849	.93373	.11648
2.16	8.6711	.93808	.11533
2.17	8.7583	.94242	.11418
2.18	8.8463	.94676	.11304
2.19	8.9352	.95110	.11192
2.20	9.0250	.95545	.11080
2.21	9.1157	.95979	.10970
2.22	9.2073	.96413	.10861
2.23	9.2999	.96848	.10753
2.24	9.3933	.97282	.10646
2.25	9.4877	.97716	.10540
2.26	9.5831	.98151	.10435
2.27	9.6794	.98585	.10331
2.28	9.7767	.99019	.10228
2.29	9.8749	.99453	.10127
2.30	9.9742	.99888	.10026
2.31	10.074	1.00322	.09926
2.32	10.176	1.00756	.09827
2.33	10.278	1.01191	.09730
2.34	10.381	1.01625	.09633
2.35	10.486	1.02059	.09537
2.36	10.591	1.02493	.09442
2.37	10.697	1.02928	.09348
2.38	10.805	1.03362	.09255
2.39	10.913	1.03796	.09163
2.40	11.023	1.04231	.09072

x	e^x Value	e^x $\log_{10}$	e^{-x} (value)
2.40	11.023	1.04231	0.09072
2.41	11.134	1.04665	.08982
2.42	11.246	1.05099	.08892
2.33	11.359	1.05534	.08804
2.44	11.473	1.05968	.08716
2.45	11.588	1.06402	.08629
2.46	11.705	1.06836	.08543
2.47	11.822	1.07271	.08458
2.48	11.941	1.07705	.08374
2.49	12.061	1.08139	.08291
2.50	12.182	1.08574	.08208
2.51	12.305	1.09008	.08127
2.52	12.429	1.09442	.08046
2.53	12.554	1.09877	.07966
2.54	12.680	1.10311	.07887
2.55	12.807	1.10745	.07808
2.56	12.936	1.11179	.07730
2.57	13.066	1.11614	.07654
2.58	13.197	1.12048	.07577
2.59	13.330	1.12482	.07502
2.60	13.464	1.12917	.07427
2.61	13.599	1.13351	.07353
2.62	13.736	1.13785	.07280
2.63	13.874	1.14219	.07208
2.64	14.013	1.14654	.07136
2.65	14.154	1.15088	.07065
2.66	14.296	1.15522	.06995
2.67	14.440	1.15957	.06925
2.68	14.585	1.16391	.06856
2.69	14.732	1.16825	.06788
2.70	14.880	1.17260	.06721
2.71	15.029	1.17694	.06654
2.72	15.180	1.18128	.06587
2.73	15.333	1.18562	.06522
2.74	15.487	1.18997	.06457
2.75	15.643	1.19431	.06393
2.76	15.800	1.19865	.06329
2.77	15.959	1.20300	.06266
2.78	16.119	1.20734	.06204
2.79	16.281	1.21168	.06142
2.80	16.445	1.21602	.06081
2.81	16.610	1.22037	.06020
2.82	16.777	1.22471	.05961
2.83	16.945	1.22905	.05901
2.84	17.116	1.23340	.05843
2.85	17.288	1.23774	.05784
2.86	17.462	1.24208	.05727
2.87	17.637	1.24643	.05670
2.88	17.814	1.25077	.05613
2.89	17.993	1.25511	.05558
2.90	18.174	1.25945	.05502
2.91	18.357	1.26380	.05448
2.92	18.541	1.26814	.05393
2.93	18.728	1.27248	.05340
2.94	18.916	1.27683	.05287
2.95	19.106	1.28117	.05234
2.96	19.298	1.28551	.05182
2.97	19.492	1.28985	.05130
2.98	19.688	1.29420	.05079
2.99	19.886	1.29854	.05029
3.00	20.086	1.30288	.04979

x	e^x Value	e^x $\log_{10}$	e^{-x} (value)
3.00	20.086	1.30288	0.04979
3.05	21.115	1.32460	.04736
3.10	22.198	1.34631	.04505
3.15	23.336	1.36803	.04285
3.20	24.553	1.38974	.04076
3.25	25.790	1.41146	.03877
3.30	27.113	1.43317	.03688
3.35	28.503	1.45489	.03508
3.40	29.964	1.47660	.03337
3.45	31.500	1.49832	.03175
3.50	33.115	1.52003	.03020
3.55	34.813	1.54175	.02872
3.60	36.598	1.56346	.02732
3.65	38.475	1.58517	.02599
3.70	40.447	1.60689	.02472
3.75	42.521	1.62860	.02352
3.80	44.701	1.65032	.02237
3.85	46.993	1.67203	.02128
3.90	49.402	1.69375	.02024
3.95	51.935	1.71546	.01925
4.00	54.598	1.73718	.01832
4.10	60.340	1.78061	.01657
4.20	66.686	1.82404	.01500
4.30	73.700	1.86747	.01357
4.40	81.451	1.91090	.01227
4.50	90.017	1.95433	.01111
4.60	99.484	1.99775	.01005
4.70	109.95	2.04118	.00910
4.80	121.51	2.08461	.00823
4.90	134.29	2.12804	.00745
5.00	148.41	2.17147	.00674
5.10	164.02	2.21490	.00610
5.20	181.27	2.25833	.00552
5.30	200.34	2.30176	.00499
5.40	221.41	2.34519	.00452
5.50	244.69	2.38862	.00409
5.60	270.43	2.43205	.00370
5.70	298.87	2.47548	.00335
5.80	330.30	2.51891	.00303
5.90	365.04	2.56234	.00274
6.00	403.43	2.60577	.00248
6.25	518.01	2.71434	.00193
6.50	665.14	2.82291	.00150
6.75	854.06	2.93149	.00117
7.00	1096.6	3.04006	.00091
7.50	1808.0	3.25721	.00055
8.00	2981.0	3.47436	.00034
8.50	4914.8	3.69150	.00020
9.00	8103.1	3.90865	.00012
9.50	13360.	4.12580	.00007
10.00	22026.	4.34924	.00005

CONVERSION TABLES

Table 1-6. Alphabetical Listing of Common Conversions

To convert from	To	Multiply by
Acres	Square feet	43,560
Acres	Square meters	4074
Acres	Square miles	0.001563
Acres	Square yards	4840
Ampere-hours (absolute)	Coulombs (absolute)	3600
Angstrom units	Inches	3.937×10^{-9}
Angstrom units	Centimeters	1×10^{-8}
Angstrom units	Microns	1×10^{-4}
Atmospheres	Millimeters of mercury at 32°F.	760
Atmospheres	Dynes per square centimeter	1.0133×10^{6}
Atmospheres	Feet of water at 39.1°F.	33.90
Atmospheres	Grams per square centimeter	1033.3
Atmospheres	Inches of mercury at 32°F.	29.921
Atmospheres	Pounds per square foot	2116.3
Atmospheres	Pounds per square inch	14.696
Bags (cement)	Pounds (cement)	94
Barrels (cement)	Pounds (cement)	376
Barrels (oil)	Gallons	42
Barrels (cement)	Bags	4
Barrels (U.S. liquid)	Cubic meters	0.11924
Barrels (U.S. liquid)	Gallons	31.5
Barrels per day	Gallons per minute	0.02917
Bars	Atmospheres	0.9869
Bars	Pounds per square inch	14.504
Board feet	Cubic feet	1/12
Boiler horsepower	Btu per hour	33,480
Boiler horsepower	Kilowatts	9.803
B.t.u.	Calories (gram)	252
B.t.u.	Centigrade heat units (c.h.u.)	1.80
B.t.u.	Foot-pounds	777.9
B.t.u.	Horsepower-hours	3.929×10^{-4}
B.t.u.	Joules	1054.6
B.t.u.	Liter-atmospheres	10.41
B.t.u.	Pounds carbon to CO_2	6.88×10^{-5}
B.t.u.	Pounds water evaporated from and at 212°F.	0.001036
B.t.u.	Cubic foot–atmospheres	3676
B.t.u.	Kilowatt-hours	2.930×10^{-4}
B.t.u. per minute	Horsepower	0.02357
B.t.u. per pound per degree Fahrenheit	Calories per gram per degree centigrade	1
B.t.u. per square foot per minute	Kilowatts per square foot	0.1758
B.t.u. per square foot per second for a temperature gradient of 1°F. per inch	Calories, gram (15°C.), per square centimeter per second for a temperature gradient of 1°C. per centimeter	1.2405
B.t.u. (60°F.) per degree Fahrenheit	Calories per degree centigrade	453.6
Bushels (U.S. dry)	Cubic feet	1.2444
Calories, gram	B.t.u.	3.968×10^{-3}
Calories, gram	Foot-pounds	3.087
Calories, gram	Joules	4.185
Calories, gram	Liter-atmospheres	4.130×10^{-2}
Calories, gram	Horsepower-hours	1.5591×10^{-6}
Calories, kilogram	Kilowatt-hours	0.0011626
Calories, kilogram per second	Kilowatts	4.185
Candle power (spherical)	Lumens	12.556
Carats (metric)	Grams	0.2
Centimeters	Angstrom units	1×10^{8}
Centimeters	Feet	0.03281
Centimeters	Inches	0.3937
Centimeters	Microns	10,000
Centimeters of mercury at 0°C.	Atmospheres	0.013158
Centimeters of mercury at 0°C.	Feet of water at 39.1°F.	0.4460
Centimeters of mercury at 0°C.	Pounds per square foot	27.845
Centimeters of mercury at 0°C.	Pounds per square inch	0.19337
Centimeters per second	Feet per minute	1.9685
Circular mils	Square centimeters	5.067×10^{-6}
Circular mils	Square inches	7.854×10^{-7}
Circular mils	Square mils	0.7854
Cords	Cubic feet	128
Cubic centimeters	Cubic feet	3.532×10^{-5}
Cubic centimeters	Gallons	2.6417×10^{-4}
Cubic centimeters	Ounces (U.S. fluid)	0.03381
Cubic centimeters	Quarts (U.S. fluid)	0.0010567
Cubic feet	Bushels (U.S.)	0.8036
Cubic feet	Cubic centimeters	28,317
Cubic feet	Cubic meters	0.028317
Cubic feet	Cubic yards	0.03704
Cubic feet	Gallons	7.481
Cubic feet	Liters	28.316
Cubic foot–atmospheres	Foot-pounds	2116.3
Cubic foot–atmospheres	Liter-atmospheres	28.316
Cubic feet of water (60°F.)	Pounds	62.37
Cubic feet per minute	Cubic centimeters per second	472.0
Cubic feet per minute	Gallons per second	0.1247
Cubic feet per second	Gallons per minute	448.8
Curies	Disintegrations per minute	2.2×10^{12}
Curies	Coulombs per minute	1.1×10^{12}
Degrees	Radians	0.017453
Drams (apothecaries' or troy)	Grams	3.888
Drams (avoirdupois)	Grams	1.7719
Fathoms	Feet	6
Feet	Centimeters	30.48
Feet per minute	Centimeters per second	0.5080
Feet per minute	Miles per hour	0.011364
Foot-poundals	B.t.u.	3.995×10^{-5}

Table 1-6. Alphabetical Listing of Common Conversions—(*Concluded*)

To convert from	To	Multiply by
Foot-poundals	Joules	0.04214
Foot-poundals	Liter-atmospheres	4.159×10^{-4}
Foot-pounds	B.t.u.	0.0012856
Foot-pounds	Calories, gram	0.3239
Foot-pounds	Foot-poundals	32.174
Foot-pounds	Horsepower-hours	5.051×10^{-7}
Foot-pounds	Kilowatt-hours	3.766×10^{-7}
Foot-pounds	Liter-atmospheres	0.013381
Foot-pounds per second	Horsepower	0.0018182
Foot-pounds per second	Kilowatts	0.0013558
Furlongs	Miles	0.125
Gallons	Barrels (U.S. liquid)	0.03175
Gallons	Cubic centimeters	3785
Gallons	Cubic feet	0.13368
Gallons	Gallons (Imperial)	0.8327
Gallons	Liters	3.785
Gallons	Ounces (U.S. fluid)	128
Gallons per minute	Cubic feet per hour	8.021
Gallons per minute	Cubic feet per second	0.002228
Grains	Grams	0.06480
Grains per gallon	Parts per million	17.118
Grams	Drams (avoirdupois)	0.5644
Grams	Drams (troy)	0.2572
Grams	Pounds (avoirdupois)	0.0022046
Grams	Pounds (troy)	0.002679
Grams per cubic centimeter	Pounds per cubic foot	62.43
Grams per cubic centimeter	Pounds per gallon	8.345
Grams per liter	Grains per gallon	58.42
Grams per liter	Pounds per cubic foot	0.0624
Grams per square centimeter	Pounds per square foot	2.0482
Grams per square centimeter	Pounds per square inch	0.014223
Horsepower (British)	B.t.u. per minute	42.42
Horsepower (British)	B.t.u. per hour	2545
Horsepower (British)	Foot-pounds per minute	33,000
Horsepower (British)	Foot-pounds per second	550
Horsepower (British)	Kilowatts (g = 980.665)	0.74570
Horsepower (British)	Horsepower (metric)	1.0139
Horsepower (British)	Pounds carbon to CO_2 per hour	0.175
Horsepower (British)	Pounds water evaporated per hour at 212°F.	2.64
Joules (absolute)	B.t.u. (mean)	9.480×10^{-4}
Joules (absolute)	Calories, gram (mean)	0.2389
Joules (absolute)	Cubic foot-atmospheres	0.3485
Joules (absolute)	Foot-pounds	0.7376
Joules (absolute)	Kilowatt-hours	2.7778×10^{-7}
Joules (absolute)	Liter-atmospheres	0.009869
Kilograms per square centimeter	Pounds per square inch	14.223
Kilowatt-hours	B.t.u.	3414
Kilowatt-hours	Foot-pounds	2.6552×10^{6}
Kilowatts	Horsepower	1.3410
Knots (nautical miles per hour)	Miles per hour	1.1516
Lamberts	Candles per square inch	2.054
Liter-atmospheres	Cubic foot-atmospheres	0.03532
Liter-atmospheres	Foot-pounds	74.74
Liters	Cubic feet	0.03532
Liters	Gallons	0.26418
Lumens	Watts	0.001496
Microns	Angstrom units	1×10^{4}
Microns	Centimeters	1×10^{-4}
Miles (nautical)	Feet	6080
Miles (nautical)	Miles (U.S. statute)	1.1516
Miles	Feet	5280
Miles per hour	Centimeters per second	44.70
Miles per hour	Feet per second	1.4667
Milliliters	Cubic centimeters	1.000027
Mils	Centimeters	0.00254
Mils	Inches	0.001
Ounces (avoirdupois)	Ounces (troy)	0.9115
Ounces (troy)	Ounces (apothecaries')	1.0000
Poundals	Dynes	13,825
Pounds (avoirdupois)	Grams	453.59
Pounds (avoirdupois)	Pounds (troy)	1.2153
Pounds water evaporated from and at 212°F.	Horsepower-hours	0.379
Pound-centigrade units (p.c.u.)	B.t.u.	1.80
Pounds per square foot	Kilograms per square meter	4.882
Pounds per square inch	Kilograms per square centimeter	0.07031
Pounds per cubic foot	Grams per cubic centimeter	0.016018
Pounds per square foot	Atmospheres	4.725×10^{-4}
Pounds per square inch	Atmospheres	0.06805
Radians	Degrees	57.30
Revolutions per minute	Radians per second	0.10472
Slugs	Gee pounds (pounds of mass)	1
Slugs	Kilograms	14.594
Slugs	Pounds	32.17
Square centimeters	Square feet	0.0010764
Square feet	Square centimeters	929.0
Square inches	Square centimeters	6.452
Tons (metric)	Tons (short)	1.1023
Tons (long)	Pounds	2240
Tons (short)	Pounds	2000
Tons per square inch	Kilograms per square millimeter	1.5479
Tons (metric)	Pounds	2204.6
Tons (refrigeration)	B.t.u. per hour	12,000
Tons (British shipping)	Cubic feet	42.00
Tons (U.S. shipping)	Cubic feet	40.00

Table 1-7. Special Tables of Conversion Factors

To convert from	To	Multiply by
	h = heat-transfer coefficient	
p.c.u./(hr.)(ft.²)(°C.)	B.t.u./(hr.)(ft.²)(°F.)	1
kg.-cal./(hr.)(m.²)(°C.)	B.t.u./(hr.)(ft.²)(°F.)	0.2048
g.-cal./(sec.)(cm.²)(°C.)	B.t.u./(hr.)(ft.²)(°F.)	7380
watts/(cm.²)(°C.)	B.t.u./(hr.)(ft.²)(°F.)	1760
watts/(in.²)(°F.)	B.t.u./(hr.)(ft.²)(°F.)	490
B.t.u./(hr.)(ft.²)(°F.)	p.c.u./(hr.)(ft.²)(°C.)	1
B.t.u./(hr.)(ft.²)(°F.)	kg.-cal./(hr.)(m.²)(°C.)	4.88
B.t.u./(hr.)(ft.²)(°F.)	g.-cal./(sec.)(cm.²)(°C.)	0.0001355
B.t.u./(hr.)(ft.²)(°F.)	watts/(cm.²)(°C.)	0.000568
B.t.u./(hr.)(ft.²)(°F.)	watts/(in.²)(°F.)	0.00204
B.t.u./(hr.)(ft.²)(°F.)	hp./(ft.²)(°F.)	0.000394
	μ = viscosity	
centipoises	g./(sec.)(cm.) or poise	0.01
centipoises	lb./(sec.)(ft.)	0.000672
centipoises	lb./(hr.)(ft.)	2.42
centipoises	kg./(hr.)(m.)	3.60
centimeters per second	square feet per second	929
	k = thermal conductivity	
g.-cal./(sec.)(cm.²)(°C./cm.)	B.t.u./(hr.)(ft.²)(°F./in.)	2903.0
watts/(cm.²)(°C./cm.)	B.t.u./(hr.)(ft.²)(°F./in.)	694.0
g.-cal./(hr.)(cm.²)(°C./cm.)	B.t.u./(hr.)(ft.²)(°F./in.)	0.8064

Table 1-8. Values of the Gas-law Constant

Temp. scale	Press. units	Vol. units	Wt. units	Energy units	*R*
Kelvin.....	....	....	g.-moles	calories	1.9872
	....	....	g.-moles	joules (abs.)	8.3144
	....	....	g.-moles	joules (int.)	8.3130
	atm.	cm.³	g.-moles	atm.-cm.³	82.057
	atm.	liters	g.-moles	atm.-liters	0.08205
	mm. Hg	liters	g.-moles	mm. Hg-liters	62.361
	bar	liters	g.-moles	bar-liters	0.08314
	kg./cm.²	liters	g.-moles	kg./(cm.²)(liters)	0.08478
	atm.	ft.³	lb.-moles	atm.-ft.³	1.314
	mm. Hg	ft.³	lb.-moles	mm. Hg-ft.³	998.9
	....	....	lb.-moles	c.h.u. or p.c.u.	1.9872
Rankine....	....	....	lb.-moles	B.t.u.	1.9872
	....	....	lb.-moles	hp.-hr.	0.0007805
	....	....	lb.-moles	kw.-hr.	0.0005819
	atm.	ft.³	lb.-moles	atm.-ft.³	0.7302
	in. Hg	ft.³	lb.-moles	in. Hg-ft.³	21.85
	mm. Hg	ft.³	lb.-moles	mm. Hg-ft.³	555.0
	lb./in.² abs.	ft.³	lb.-moles	(lb.)(ft.³)/in.²	10.73
	lb./ft.² abs.	ft.³	lb.-moles	ft.-lb.	1545.0

Table 1-9. Specific Gravity, Degrees Baumé, Degrees A.P.I., Degrees Twaddell, Pounds per Gallon, Pounds per Cubic Foot*

$$°Bé. = 145 - \frac{145}{sp.\ gr.}\ (heavier\ than\ H_2O);\ °Bé. = \frac{140}{sp.\ gr.} - 130\ (lighter\ than\ H_2O);\ °Tw. = \frac{sp.\ gr.\ 60°/60°F. - 1}{0.005}$$

Sp. gr. 60°/60°	°Bé.	°A.P.I.	Lb. per gal. at 60°F. wt. in air	Lb. per cu. ft. at 60°F. wt. in air	Sp. gr. 60°/60°	°Bé.	°A.P.I.	Lb. per gal. at 60°F. wt. in air	Lb. per cu. ft. at 60°F. wt. in air	Sp. gr. 60°/60°	°Bé.	°A.P.I.	Lb. per gal. at 60°F. wt. in air	Lb. per cu. ft. at 60°F. wt. in air	Sp. gr. 60°/60°	°Bé.	°A.P.I.	Lb. per gal. at 60°F. wt. in air	Lb. per cu. ft. at 60°F. wt. in air
0.600	103.33	104.33	4.9929	37.350	.700	70.00	70.64	5.8268	43.587	0.800	45.00	45.38	6.6606	49.825	.900	25.56	25.72	7.4944	56.062
.605	101.40	102.38	5.0346	37.662	.705	68.58	69.21	5.8685	43.899	.805	43.91	44.28	6.7023	50.137	.905	24.70	24.85	7.5361	56.374
.610	99.51	100.47	5.0763	37.973	.710	67.18	67.80	5.9101	44.211	.810	42.84	43.19	6.7440	50.448	.910	23.85	23.99	7.5777	56.685
.615	97.64	98.58	5.1180	38.285	.715	65.80	66.40	5.9518	44.523	.815	41.78	42.12	6.7857	50.760	.915	23.01	23.14	7.6194	56.997
.620	95.81	96.73	5.1597	38.597	.720	64.44	65.03	5.9935	44.834	.820	40.73	41.06	6.8274	51.072	.920	22.17	22.30	7.6612	57.310
.625	94.00	94.90	5.2014	39.910	.725	63.10	63.67	6.0352	45.146	.825	39.70	40.02	6.8691	51.384	.925	21.35	21.47	7.7029	57.622
.630	92.22	93.10	5.2431	39.222	.730	61.78	62.34	6.0769	45.458	.830	38.67	38.98	6.9108	51.696	.930	20.54	20.65	7.7446	57.934
.635	90.47	91.33	5.2848	39.534	.735	60.48	61.02	6.1186	45.770	.835	37.66	37.96	6.9525	52.008	.935	19.73	19.84	7.7863	58.246
.640	88.75	89.59	5.3265	39.845	.740	59.19	59.72	6.1603	46.082	.840	36.67	36.95	6.9941	52.320	.940	18.94	19.03	7.8280	58.557
.645	87.05	87.88	5.3682	40.157	.745	57.92	58.43	6.2020	46.394	.845	35.68	35.96	7.0358	52.632	.945	18.15	18.24	7.8697	58.869
.650	85.38	86.19	5.4098	40.468	.750	56.67	57.17	6.2437	46.706	.850	34.71	34.97	7.0775	52.943	.950	17.37	17.45	7.9114	59.181
.655	83.74	84.53	5.4515	40.780	.755	55.43	55.92	6.2854	47.018	.855	33.74	34.00	7.1192	53.255	.955	16.60	16.67	7.9531	59.493
.660	82.12	82.89	5.4932	41.092	.760	54.21	54.68	6.3271	47.330	.860	32.79	33.03	7.1609	53.567	.960	15.83	15.90	7.9947	59.805
.665	80.53	81.28	5.5349	41.404	.765	53.01	53.47	6.3688	47.642	.865	31.85	32.08	7.2026	53.879	.965	15.08	15.13	8.0364	60.117
.670	78.96	79.69	5.5766	41.716	.770	51.82	52.27	6.4104	47.953	.870	30.92	31.14	7.2443	54.191	.970	14.33	14.38	8.0780	60.428
.675	77.41	78.13	5.6183	42.028	.775	50.65	51.08	6.4521	47.265	.875	30.00	30.21	7.2860	54.503	.975	13.59	13.63	8.1197	60.740
.680	75.88	76.59	5.6600	42.340	.780	49.49	49.91	6.4938	48.577	.880	29.09	29.30	7.3277	54.815	.980	12.86	12.89	8.1615	61.052
.685	74.38	75.07	5.7017	42.652	.785	48.34	48.75	6.5355	48.889	.885	28.19	28.39	7.3694	55.127	.985	12.13	12.15	8.2032	61.364
.690	72.90	73.57	5.7434	42.963	.790	47.22	47.61	6.5772	49.201	.890	27.30	27.49	7.4111	55.438	.990	11.41	11.43	8.2449	61.676
.695	71.44	72.10	5.7851	43.275	.795	46.10	46.49	6.6189	49.513	.895	26.42	26.60	7.4528	55.750	.995	10.70	10.71	8.2866	61.988
															1.000	10.00	10.00	8.3283	62.300

Sp. gr. 60°/60°	°Bé.	°Tw.	Lb. per gal. at 60°F. wt. in air	Lb. per cu. ft. at 60°F. wt. in air	Sp. gr. 60°/60°	°Bé.	°Tw.	Lb. per gal. at 60°F. wt. in air	Lb. per cu. ft. at 60°F. wt. in air	Sp. gr. 60°/60°	°Bé.	°Tw.	Lb. per gal. at 60°F. wt. in air	Lb. per cu. ft. at 60°F. wt. in air	Sp. gr. 60°/60°	°Bé.	°Tw.	Lb. per gal. at 60°F. wt. in air	Lb. per cu. ft. at 60°F. wt. in air
1.005	0.72	1	8.3700	62.612	1.255	29.46	51	10.4546	78.206	1.505	48.65	101	12.5392	93.800	1.755	62.38	151	14.6238	109.394
1.010	1.44	2	8.4117	62.924	1.260	29.92	52	10.4963	78.518	1.510	48.97	102	12.5809	94.112	1.760	62.61	152	14.6655	109.705
1.015	2.14	3	8.4534	63.236	1.265	30.38	53	10.5380	78.830	1.515	49.29	103	12.6226	94.424	1.765	62.85	153	14.7072	110.017
1.020	2.84	4	8.4950	63.547	1.270	30.83	54	10.5797	79.141	1.520	49.61	104	12.6643	94.735	1.770	63.08	154	14.7489	110.329
1.025	3.54	5	8.5367	63.859	1.275	31.27	55	10.6214	79.453	1.525	49.92	105	12.7060	95.047	1.775	63.31	155	14.7906	110.641
1.030	4.22	6	8.5784	64.171	1.280	31.72	56	10.6630	79.765	1.530	50.23	106	12.7477	95.359	1.780	63.54	156	14.8323	110.953
1.035	4.90	7	8.6201	64.483	1.285	32.16	57	10.7047	80.077	1.535	50.54	107	12.7894	95.671	1.785	63.77	157	14.8740	111.265
1.040	5.58	8	8.6618	64.795	1.290	32.60	58	10.7464	80.389	1.540	50.84	108	12.8310	95.983	1.790	63.99	158	14.9157	111.577
1.045	6.24	9	8.7035	65.107	1.295	33.03	59	10.7881	80.701	1.545	51.15	109	12.8727	96.295	1.795	64.22	159	14.9574	111.889
1.050	6.91	10	8.7452	65.419	1.300	33.46	60	10.8298	81.013	1.550	51.45	110	12.9144	96.606	1.800	64.44	160	14.9990	112.200
1.055	7.56	11	8.7869	65.731	1.305	33.89	61	10.8715	81.325	1.555	51.75	111	12.9561	96.918	1.805	64.67	161	15.0407	112.512
1.060	8.21	12	8.8286	66.042	1.310	34.31	62	10.9132	81.636	1.560	52.05	112	12.9978	97.230	1.810	64.89	162	15.0824	112.824
1.065	8.85	13	8.8703	66.354	1.315	34.73	63	10.9549	81.948	1.565	52.35	113	13.0395	97.542	1.815	65.11	163	15.1241	113.136
1.070	9.49	14	8.9120	66.666	1.320	35.15	64	10.9966	82.260	1.570	52.64	114	13.0812	97.854	1.820	65.33	164	15.1658	113.448
1.075	10.12	15	8.9537	66.978	1.325	35.57	65	11.0383	82.572	1.575	52.94	115	13.1229	98.166	1.825	65.55	165	15.2075	113.760
1.080	10.74	16	8.9954	67.290	1.330	35.98	66	11.0800	82.884	1.580	53.23	116	13.1646	98.478	1.830	65.77	166	15.2492	114.072
1.085	11.36	17	9.0371	67.602	1.335	36.39	67	11.1217	83.196	1.585	53.52	117	13.2063	98.790	1.835	65.98	167	15.2909	114.384
1.090	11.97	18	9.0787	67.914	1.340	36.79	68	11.1634	83.508	1.590	53.81	118	13.2480	99.102	1.840	66.20	168	15.3326	114.696
1.095	12.58	19	9.1204	68.226	1.345	37.19	69	11.2051	83.820	1.595	54.09	119	13.2897	99.414	1.845	66.41	169	15.3743	115.007
1.100	13.18	20	9.1621	68.537	1.350	37.59	70	11.2467	84.131	1.600	54.38	120	13.3313	99.725	1.850	66.62	170	15.4160	115.318
1.105	13.78	21	9.2038	68.849	1.355	37.99	71	11.2884	84.443	1.605	54.66	121	13.3730	100.037	1.855	66.83	171	15.4577	115.630
1.110	14.37	22	9.2455	69.161	1.360	38.38	72	11.3301	84.755	1.610	54.94	122	13.4147	100.349	1.860	67.04	172	15.4993	115.943
1.115	14.96	23	9.2872	69.473	1.365	38.77	73	11.3718	85.067	1.615	55.22	123	13.4564	100.661	1.865	67.25	173	15.5410	116.255
1.120	15.54	24	9.3289	69.785	1.370	39.16	74	11.4135	85.379	1.620	55.49	124	13.4981	100.973	1.870	67.46	174	15.5827	116.567
1.125	16.11	25	9.3706	70.097	1.375	39.55	75	11.4552	85.691	1.625	55.77	125	13.5398	101.285	1.875	67.67	175	15.6244	116.879
1.130	16.68	26	9.4123	70.409	1.380	39.93	76	11.4969	86.003	1.630	56.04	126	13.5815	101.597	1.880	67.87	176	15.6661	117.191
1.135	17.25	27	9.4540	70.721	1.385	40.31	77	11.5386	86.315	1.635	56.32	127	13.6232	101.909	1.885	68.08	177	15.7078	117.503
1.140	17.81	28	9.4957	71.032	1.390	40.68	78	11.5803	86.626	1.640	56.59	128	13.6649	102.220	1.890	68.28	178	15.7495	117.814
1.145	18.36	29	9.5374	71.344	1.395	41.06	79	11.6220	86.938	1.645	56.85	129	13.7066	102.532	1.895	68.48	179	15.7912	118.126
1.150	18.91	30	9.5790	71.656	1.400	41.43	80	11.6637	87.250	1.650	57.12	130	13.7483	102.844	1.900	68.68	180	15.8329	118.438
1.155	19.46	31	9.6207	71.968	1.405	41.80	81	11.7054	87.562	1.655	57.39	131	13.7900	103.156	1.905	68.88	181	15.8746	118.740
1.160	20.00	32	9.6624	72.280	1.410	42.16	82	11.7471	87.874	1.660	57.65	132	13.8317	103.468	1.910	69.08	182	15.9163	119.062
1.165	20.54	33	9.7041	72.592	1.415	42.53	83	11.7888	88.186	1.665	57.91	133	13.8734	103.780	1.915	69.28	183	15.9580	119.374
1.170	21.07	34	9.7458	72.904	1.420	42.89	84	11.8304	88.498	1.670	58.17	134	13.9150	104.092	1.920	69.48	184	15.9996	119.686
1.175	21.60	35	9.7875	73.216	1.425	43.25	85	11.8721	88.810	1.675	58.43	135	13.9567	104.404	1.925	69.68	185	16.0413	119.998
1.180	22.12	36	9.8292	73.528	1.430	43.60	86	11.9138	89.121	1.680	58.69	136	13.9984	104.715	1.930	69.87	186	16.0830	120.309
1.185	22.64	37	9.8709	73.840	1.435	43.95	87	11.9555	89.433	1.685	58.95	137	14.0401	105.027	1.935	70.06	187	16.1247	120.621
1.190	23.15	38	9.9126	74.151	1.440	44.31	88	11.9972	89.745	1.690	59.20	138	14.0818	105.339	1.940	70.26	188	16.1664	120.933
1.195	23.66	39	9.9543	74.463	1.445	44.65	89	12.0389	90.057	1.695	59.45	139	14.1235	105.651	1.945	70.45	189	16.2081	121.245
1.200	24.17	40	9.9960	74.775	1.450	45.00	90	12.0806	90.369	1.700	59.71	140	14.1652	105.963	1.950	70.64	190	16.2498	121.557
1.205	24.67	41	10.0377	75.087	1.455	45.34	91	12.1223	90.681	1.705	59.96	141	14.2069	106.275	1.955	70.83	191	16.2915	121.869
1.210	25.17	42	10.0793	75.399	1.460	45.68	92	12.1640	90.993	1.710	60.20	142	14.2486	106.587	1.960	71.02	192	16.3332	122.181
1.215	25.66	43	10.1210	75.711	1.465	46.02	93	12.2057	91.305	1.715	60.45	143	14.2903	106.899	1.965	71.21	193	13.3749	122.493
1.220	26.15	44	10.1627	76.022	1.470	46.36	94	12.2473	91.616	1.720	60.70	144	14.3320	107.210	1.970	71.40	194	16.4166	122.804
1.225	26.63	45	10.2044	76.334	1.475	46.69	95	12.2890	91.928	1.725	60.94	145	14.3737	107.522	1.975	71.58	195	16.4583	123.116
1.230	27.11	46	10.2461	76.646	1.480	47.03	96	12.3307	92.240	1.730	61.18	146	14.4153	107.834	1.980	71.77	196	16.5000	123.428
1.235	27.59	47	10.2878	76.958	1.485	47.36	97	12.3724	92.552	1.735	61.34	147	14.4570	108.146	1.985	71.95	197	16.5417	123.740
1.240	28.06	48	10.3295	77.270	1.490	47.68	98	12.4141	92.864	1.740	61.67	148	14.4987	108.458	1.990	72.14	198	16.5833	124.052
1.245	28.53	49	10.3712	77.582	1.495	48.01	99	12.4558	93.176	1.745	61.91	149	14.5404	108.770	1.995	72.32	199	16.6250	124.364
1.250	29.00	50	10.4129	77.894	1.500	48.33	100	12.4975	93.488	1.750	62.14	150	14.5821	109.082	2.000	72.50	200	16.6667	124.676

* Prepared by Lewis V. Judson, Ph.D., Chief of Length Section of National Bureau of Standards with the advice and assistance of E. L. Peffer, B.S., A.M., late Chief of Capacity and Density Section, National Bureau of Standards.

Table 1-10. Wire and Sheet Metal Gages*

Values in approximate decimals of an inch

As a number of gages are in use for various shapes and metals, it is **advisable to state the thickness in thousandths when specifying gage number.**

Gage number	**American** (A.W.G.) or **Brown & Sharpe** (B. & S.) (for nonferrous wire and sheet)†	**U.S. Steel Wire** (Stl. W.G.) or **Washburn & Moen** or **Roebling** or **Am. Steel & Wire Co.** [A. (steel) W.G.] (for steel wire)	**Birmingham** (B.W.G.) (for steel wire) or **Stubs Iron Wire** (for iron or brass wire)‡	**U.S. Standard** (for sheet and plate metal, wrought iron)	**Standard Birmingham** (B.G.) (for sheet and hoop metal)	**Imperial Standard Wire Gage** (S.W.G.) (British legal standard)	Gage number
0000000	......	0.4900	......	0.500	0.6666	0.500	**0000000**
000000	......	.4615	......	.469	.6250	.464	**000000**
00000	......	.4305	......	.438	.5883	.432	**00000**
0000	0.460	.3938	0.454	.406	.5416	.400	**0000**
000	.410	.3625	.425	.375	.5000	.372	**000**
00	.365	.3310	.380	.344	.4452	.348	**00**
0	.325	.3065	.340	.312	.3964	.324	**0**
1	.289	.2830	.300	.281	.3532	.300	**1**
2	.258	.2625	.284	.266	.3147	.276	**2**
3	.229	.2437	.259	.250	.2804	.252	**3**
4	.204	.2253	.238	.234	.2500	.232	**4**
5	.182	.2070	.220	.219	.2225	.212	**5**
6	.162	.1920	.203	.203	.1981	.192	**6**
7	.144	.1770	.180	.188	.1764	.176	**7**
8	.128	.1620	.165	.172	.1570	.160	**8**
9	.114	.1483	.148	.156	.1398	.144	**9**
10	.102	.1350	.134	.141	.1250	.128	**10**
11	.091	.1205	.120	.125	.1113	.116	**11**
12	.081	.1055	.109	.109	.0991	.104	**12**
13	.072	.0915	.095	.094	.0882	.092	**13**
14	.064	.0800	.083	.078	.0785	.080	**14**
15	.057	.0720	.072	.070	.0699	.072	**15**
16	.051	.0625	.065	.062	.0625	.064	**16**
17	.045	.0540	.058	.056	.0556	.056	**17**
18	.040	.0475	.049	.050	.0495	.048	**18**
19	.036	.0410	.042	.0438	.0440	.040	**19**
20	.032	.0348	.035	.0375	.0392	.036	**20**
21	.0285	.0317	.032	.0344	.0349	.032	**21**
22	.0253	.0286	.028	.0312	.0313	.028	**22**
23	.0226	.0258	.025	.0281	.0278	.024	**23**
24	.0201	.0230	.022	.0250	.0248	.022	**24**
25	.0179	.0204	.020	.0219	.0220	.020	**25**
26	0.0159	0.0181	0.018	0.0188	0.0196	0.018	**26**
27	.0142	.0173	.016	.0172	.0175	.0164	**27**
28	.0126	.0162	.014	.0156	.0156	.0148	**28**
29	.0113	.0150	.013	.0141	.0139	.0136	**29**
30	.0100	.0140	.012	.0125	.0123	.0124	**30**
31	.0089	.0132	.010	.0109	.0110	.0116	**31**
32	.0080	.0128	.009	.0102	.0098	.0108	**32**
33	.0071	.0118	.008	.0094	.0087	.0100	**33**
34	.0063	.0104	.007	.0086	.0077	.0092	**34**
35	.0056	.0095	.005	.0078	.0069	.0084	**35**
36	.0050	.0090	.004	.0070	.0061	.0076	**36**
37	.0045	.0085	.....	.0066	.0054	.0068	**37**
38	.0040	.0080	.....	.0062	.0048	.0060	**38**
39	.0035	.0075	.....	.....	.0043	.0052	**39**
40	.0031	.0070	.....	.....	.0039	.0048	**40**
41	......	.0066	.....	.....	.0034	.0044	**41**
42	......	.0062	.....	.....	.0031	.0040	**42**
43	......	.0060	.....	.....	.0027	.0036	**43**
44	......	.0058	.....	.....	.0024	.0032	**44**
45	......	.0055	.....	.....	.0022	.0028	**45**
46	......	.0052	.....	.....	.0019	.0024	**46**
47	......	.0050	.....	.....	.0017	.0020	**47**
48	......	.0048	.....	.....	.0015	.0016	**48**
49	......	.0046	.....	.....	.0014	.0012	**49**
50	......	.0044	.....	.....	.0012	.0010	**50**

Metric wire gage is ten times the diameter in millimeters.

* Courtesy of Dr. Lewis V. Judson with I. H. Fullmer, National Bureau of Standards.

† Sometimes used for iron wire.

‡ Sometimes used for copper plate and for steel plate 12 gage and heavier and for steel tubes.

Table 1-11. Temperature Conversion

General formula: °F. = (°C. × 9/5) + 32; °C. = (°F. − 32) × 5/9

C.		F.	C.		F.	C.		F.	C.		F.	C.		F.	C.		F.	C.		F.	C.		F.	C.		F.
−273.1	**−459.4**		−17.8	**0**	32	10.0	**50**	122.0	38	**100**	212	260	**500**	932	538	**1000**	1832	816	**1500**	2732	1093	**2000**	3632	1371	**2500**	4532
−268	**−450**		−17.2	**1**	33.8	10.6	**51**	123.8	43	**109**	230	266	**510**	950	543	**1010**	1850	821	**1510**	2750	1099	**2010**	3650	1377	**2510**	4550
−262	**−440**		−16.7	**2**	35.6	11.1	**52**	125.6	49	**120**	248	271	**520**	968	549	**1020**	1868	827	**1520**	2768	1104	**2020**	3668	1382	**2520**	4568
−257	**−430**		−16.1	**3**	37.4	11.7	**53**	127.4	54	**130**	266	277	**530**	986	554	**1030**	1886	832	**1530**	2786	1110	**2030**	3686	1388	**2530**	4586
−251	**−420**		−15.6	**4**	39.2	12.2	**54**	129.2	60	**140**	284	282	**540**	1004	560	**1040**	1904	838	**1540**	2804	1116	**2040**	3704	1393	**2540**	4604
−246	**−410**		−15.0	**5**	41.0	12.8	**55**	131.0	66	**150**	302	288	**550**	1022	566	**1050**	1922	843	**1550**	2822	1121	**2050**	3722	1399	**2550**	4622
−240	**−400**		−14.4	**6**	42.8	13.3	**56**	132.8	71	**160**	320	293	**560**	1040	571	**1060**	1940	849	**1560**	2840	1127	**2060**	3740	1404	**2560**	4640
−234	**−390**		−13.9	**7**	44.6	13.9	**57**	134.6	77	**170**	338	299	**570**	1058	577	**1070**	1958	854	**1570**	2858	1132	**2070**	3758	1410	**2570**	4658
−229	**−380**		−13.3	**8**	46.4	14.4	**58**	136.4	82	**180**	356	304	**580**	1076	582	**1080**	1976	860	**1580**	2876	1138	**2080**	3776	1416	**2580**	4676
−223	**−370**		−12.8	**9**	48.2	15.0	**59**	138.2	88	**190**	374	310	**590**	1094	588	**1090**	1994	866	**1590**	2894	1143	**2090**	3794	1421	**2590**	4694
−218	**−360**		−12.2	**10**	50.0	15.6	**60**	140.0	93	**200**	392	316	**600**	1112	593	**1100**	2012	871	**1600**	2912	1149	**2100**	3812	1427	**2600**	4712
−212	**−350**		−11.7	**11**	51.8	16.1	**61**	141.8	99	**210**	410	321	**610**	1130	599	**1110**	2030	877	**1610**	2930	1154	**2110**	3830	1432	**2610**	4730
−207	**−340**		−11.1	**12**	53.6	16.7	**62**	143.6	100	**212**	413	327	**620**	1148	604	**1120**	2048	882	**1620**	2948	1160	**2120**	3848	1438	**2620**	4748
−201	**−330**		−10.6	**13**	55.4	17.2	**63**	145.4	104	**220**	428	332	**630**	1166	610	**1130**	2066	888	**1630**	2966	1166	**2130**	3866	1443	**2630**	4766
−196	**−320**		−10.0	**14**	57.2	17.8	**64**	147.2	110	**230**	446	338	**640**	1184	616	**1140**	2084	893	**1640**	2984	1171	**2140**	3884	1449	**2640**	4784
−190	**−310**		−9.44	**15**	59.0	18.3	**65**	149.0	116	**240**	464	343	**650**	1202	621	**1150**	2102	899	**1650**	3002	1177	**2150**	3902	1454	**2650**	4802
−184	**−300**		−8.89	**16**	60.8	18.9	**66**	150.8	121	**250**	482	349	**660**	1220	627	**1160**	2120	904	**1660**	3020	1182	**2160**	3920	1460	**2660**	4820
−179	**−290**		−8.33	**17**	62.6	19.4	**67**	152.6	127	**260**	500	354	**670**	1238	632	**1170**	2138	910	**1670**	3038	1188	**2170**	3938	1466	**2670**	4838
−173	**−280**		−7.78	**18**	64.4	20.0	**68**	154.4	132	**270**	518	360	**680**	1256	638	**1180**	2156	916	**1680**	3056	1193	**2180**	3956	1471	**2680**	4856
−169	**−273**	−459.4	−7.22	**19**	66.2	20.6	**69**	156.2	138	**280**	536	366	**690**	1274	643	**1190**	2174	921	**1690**	3074	1199	**2190**	3974	1477	**2690**	4874
−168	**−270**	−454	−6.67	**20**	68.0	21.1	**70**	158.0	143	**290**	554	371	**700**	1292	649	**1200**	2192	927	**1700**	3092	1204	**2200**	3992	1482	**2700**	4892
−162	**−260**	−436	−6.11	**21**	69.8	21.7	**71**	159.8	149	**300**	572	377	**710**	1310	654	**1210**	2210	932	**1710**	3110	1210	**2210**	4010	1488	**2710**	4910
−157	**−250**	−418	−5.56	**22**	71.6	22.2	**72**	161.6	154	**310**	590	382	**720**	1328	660	**1220**	2228	938	**1720**	3128	1216	**2220**	4028	1493	**2720**	4928
−151	**−240**	−400	−5.00	**23**	73.4	22.8	**73**	163.4	160	**320**	608	388	**730**	1346	666	**1230**	2246	943	**1730**	3146	1221	**2230**	4046	1499	**2730**	4946
−146	**−230**	−382	−4.44	**24**	75.2	23.3	**74**	165.2	166	**330**	626	393	**740**	1364	671	**1240**	2264	949	**1740**	3164	1227	**2240**	4064	1504	**2740**	4964
−140	**−220**	−364	−3.89	**25**	77.0	23.9	**75**	167.0	171	**340**	644	399	**750**	1382	677	**1250**	2282	954	**1750**	3182	1232	**2250**	4082	1510	**2750**	4982
−134	**−210**	−346	−3.33	**26**	78.8	24.4	**76**	168.8	177	**350**	662	404	**760**	1400	682	**1260**	2300	960	**1760**	3200	1238	**2260**	4100	1516	**2760**	5000
−129	**−200**	−328	−2.78	**27**	80.6	25.0	**77**	170.6	182	**360**	680	410	**770**	1418	688	**1270**	2318	966	**1770**	3218	1243	**2270**	4118	1521	**2770**	5018
−123	**−190**	−310	−2.22	**28**	82.4	25.6	**78**	172.4	188	**370**	698	416	**780**	1436	693	**1280**	2336	971	**1780**	3236	1249	**2280**	4136	1527	**2780**	5036
−118	**−180**	−292	−1.67	**29**	84.2	26.1	**79**	174.2	193	**380**	716	421	**790**	1454	699	**1290**	2354	977	**1790**	3254	1254	**2290**	4154	1532	**2790**	5054
−112	**−170**	−274	−1.11	**30**	86.0	26.7	**80**	176.0	199	**390**	734	427	**800**	1472	704	**1300**	2372	982	**1800**	3272	1260	**2300**	4172	1538	**2800**	5072
−107	**−160**	−256	−0.56	**31**	87.8	27.2	**81**	177.8	204	**400**	752	432	**810**	1490	710	**1310**	2390	988	**1810**	3290	1266	**2310**	4190	1543	**2810**	5090
−101	**−150**	−238	0	**32**	89.6	27.8	**82**	179.6	210	**410**	770	438	**820**	1508	716	**1320**	2408	993	**1820**	3308	1271	**2320**	4208	1549	**2820**	5108
−95.6	**−140**	−220	0.56	**33**	91.4	28.3	**83**	181.4	216	**420**	788	443	**830**	1526	721	**1330**	2426	999	**1830**	3326	1277	**2330**	4226	1554	**2830**	5126
−90.0	**−130**	−202	1.11	**34**	93.2	28.9	**84**	183.2	221	**430**	806	449	**840**	1544	727	**1340**	2444	1004	**1840**	3344	1282	**2340**	4244	1560	**2840**	5144
−84.4	**−120**	−184	1.67	**35**	95.0	29.4	**85**	185.0	227	**440**	824	454	**850**	1562	732	**1350**	2462	1010	**1850**	3362	1288	**2350**	4262	1566	**2850**	5162
−78.9	**−110**	−166	2.22	**36**	96.8	30.0	**86**	186.8	232	**450**	842	460	**860**	1580	738	**1360**	2480	1016	**1860**	3380	1293	**2360**	4280	1571	**2860**	5180
−73.3	**−100**	−148	2.78	**37**	98.6	30.6	**87**	188.6	238	**460**	860	466	**870**	1598	743	**1370**	2498	1021	**1870**	3398	1299	**2370**	4298	1577	**2870**	5198
−67.8	**−90**	−130	3.33	**38**	100.4	31.1	**88**	190.4	243	**470**	878	471	**880**	1616	749	**1380**	2516	1027	**1880**	3416	1304	**2380**	4316	1582	**2880**	5216
−62.2	**−80**	−112	3.89	**39**	102.2	31.7	**89**	192.2	249	**480**	896	477	**890**	1634	754	**1390**	2534	1032	**1890**	3434	1310	**2390**	4334	1588	**2890**	5234
−56.7	**−70**	−94	4.44	**40**	104.0	32.2	**90**	194.0	254	**490**	914	482	**900**	1652	760	**1400**	2552	1038	**1900**	3452	1316	**2400**	4352	1593	**2900**	5252
−51.1	**−60**	−76	5.00	**41**	105.8	32.8	**91**	195.8				488	**910**	1670	766	**1410**	2570	1043	**1910**	3470	1321	**2410**	4370	1599	**2910**	5270
−45.6	**−50**	−58	5.56	**42**	107.6	33.3	**92**	197.6				493	**920**	1688	771	**1420**	2588	1049	**1920**	3488	1327	**2420**	4388	1604	**2920**	5288
−40.0	**−40**	−40	6.11	**43**	109.4	33.9	**93**	199.4				499	**930**	1706	777	**1430**	2606	1054	**1930**	3506	1332	**2430**	4406	1610	**2930**	5306
−34.4	**−30**	−22	6.67	**44**	111.2	34.4	**94**	201.2				504	**940**	1724	782	**1440**	2624	1060	**1940**	3524	1338	**2440**	4424	1616	**2940**	5324
−28.9	**−20**	−4	7.22	**45**	113.0	35.0	**95**	203.0				510	**950**	1742	788	**1450**	2642	1066	**1950**	3542	1343	**2450**	4442	1621	**2950**	5342
−23.3	**−10**	14	7.78	**46**	114.8	35.6	**96**	204.8				516	**960**	1760	793	**1460**	2660	1071	**1960**	3560	1349	**2460**	4460	1627	**2960**	5360
−17.8	**0**	32	8.33	**47**	116.6	36.1	**97**	206.6				521	**970**	1778	799	**1470**	2678	1077	**1970**	3578	1354	**2470**	4478	1632	**2970**	5378
			8.89	**48**	118.4	36.7	**98**	208.4				527	**980**	1796	804	**1480**	2696	1082	**1980**	3596	1360	**2480**	4496	1638	**2980**	5396
			9.44	**49**	120.2	37.2	**99**	210.2				532	**990**	1814	810	**1490**	2714	1088	**1990**	3614	1366	**2490**	4514	1643	**2990**	5414
						37.8	**100**	212.0										1093	**2000**	3632				1649	**3000**	5432

Note.—The numbers in bold-face type refer to the temperature (in either centigrade or Fahrenheit degrees) which it is desired to convert into the other scale. If converting from Fahrenheit degrees to centigrade degrees the equivalent temperature is in the left column, while if converting from degrees centigrade to degrees Fahrenheit, the equivalent temperature is in the column on the right. This table, made by Albert Sauveur, is published by permission of Mrs. Albert Sauveur.

Interpolation Factors

C.		F.	C.		F.
0.56	**1**	1.8	3.33	**6**	10.8
1.11	**2**	3.6	3.89	**7**	12.6
1.67	**3**	5.4	4.44	**8**	14.4
2.22	**4**	7.2	5.00	**9**	16.2
2.78	**5**	9.0	5.56	**10**	18.0

Table 1-12a. Weights and Measures of Various Systems*

United States Customary System

Linear Measure

12 inches (in.) or (″)	= 1 foot (ft.) or (′)
3 feet	= 1 yard (yd.)
16.5 feet, 5.5 yards	= 1 rod (rd.)
5280 feet, 320 rods	= 1 mile (mi.)
1 mil	= 0.001 inch

Nautical:

6080.2 feet	= 1 nautical mile
6 feet	= 1 fathom
120 fathoms	= 1 cable length
1 knot	= 1 nautical mile per hour
60 knots	= 1° (measured at equator)

Square Measure

144 sq. inches (sq. in.) or (in.^{2}) or (□″)	= 1 sq. foot (ft.^{2}) or (□′)
9 sq. feet (ft.^{2}) (□′)	= 1 sq. yard (yd.^{2})
30.25 sq. yards	= 1 sq. rod, pole, or perch
160 sq. rods = {10 sq. chains, 43,560 sq. ft.}	= 1 acre
640 acres = 1 sq. mile	= 1 section
1 circular inch (area of circle of 1 inch diameter)	= 0.7854 sq. inch
1 sq. inch	= 1.2732 circular inch
1 circular mil	= area of circle of 0.001 inch diameter
1,000,000 circular mils	= 1 circular inch

Circular Measure

60 seconds (″) (sec.)	= 1 minute (min.) or (′)
60 minutes (′)	= 1 degree (°)
90 degrees (°)	= 1 quadrant
360 degrees (°)	= 1 circumference
57.29578 degrees	= 1 radian (rad.) = 57° 17′ 44.81″

Volume Measure

Solid:

1728 cubic in. (cu. in.) (in.^{3})	= 1 cubic foot (cu. ft.) (ft.^{3})
27 cu. ft.	= 1 cubic yard (cu. yd.)

Dry Measure:

2 pints	= 1 quart
8 quarts	= 1 peck
4 pecks	= 1 bushel
1 United States Winchester bushel	= 2150.42 cubic inches

Liquid:

4 gills	= 1 pint (pt.)
2 pints	= 1 quart (qt.)
4 quarts	= 1 gallon (gal.)
7.4805 gallons	= 1 cubic foot

Apothecaries' Liquid:

60 minims (min. or ♏)	= 1 fluid dram or drachm
8 drams (ʒ)	= 1 fluid ounce
16 ounces (oz. ℥)	= 1 pint

Water Measure:

1 miner's inch = amount of water flowing through an orifice of 1 sq. in. cross section under a head varying from 4 to 6.5 in. (as fixed by state law). Units now most generally used are: 1 cu. ft. per sec. (1 ft.^{3}/sec.) or 1 gal. per sec. (1 gal./sec.).

Avoirdupois Weight

16 drams	= 437.5 grains	= 1 ounce (oz.)
16 ounces	= 7000 grains	= 1 pound (lb.)
100 pounds	= 1 hundredweight (cwt.)	
2000 pounds	= 1 short ton; 2240 pounds	= 1 long ton

Troy Weight

24 grains	= 1 pennyweight (dwt.)
20 pennyweights	= 1 ounce (oz.)
12 ounces	= 1 pound (lb.)

Apothecaries' Weight

20 grains (gr.)	= 1 scruple (℈)
3 scruples	= 1 dram (ʒ)
8 drams	= 1 ounce (℥)
12 ounces	= 1 pound (lb.)

Board Measure (B.M.)

1 board foot = product of 1 foot length, 1 foot breadth, and 1 inch thickness.

Metric System

Linear Measure

1 micromicron (μμ)	= 0.000001 micron
1 Ångström unit (Å.)	= 0.0001 micron
1 millimicron (mμ)	= 0.001 micron (μ)
1 micron (μ)	= 0.001 millimeter (mm.)
10 millimeters (mm.)	= 1 centimeter (cm.)
10 centimeters (cm.)	= 1 decimeter (dm.)
10 decimeters (dm.), 100 centimeters (cm.)	= 1 meter (m.) = 39.37 inches
1 dekameter (dkm.)	= 10 meters (m.)
1 hectometer (hm.)	= 100 meters (m.)
1 kilometer (km.)	= 1,000 meters (m.)
1 myriameter	= 10,000 meters (m.)
1 megameter	= 1,000,000 meters (m.)

Square Measure

1 sq. millimeter (mm.^{2})	= 0.01 sq. centimeter (sq. cm.)
1 sq. centimeter (cm.^{2})	= 0.01 sq. decimeter (sq. dm.)
1 sq. decimeter (dm.^{2})	= 0.01 sq. meter (sq. m.)
1 sq. meter (centiare) or (m.^{2})	= 0.01 sq. dekameter (sq. dkm.)
1 sq. dekameter (are)	= 0.01 sq. hectometer (sq. hm.)
1 hectare (ha.)	= 10,000 sq. meters
1 sq. kilometer (km.^{2})	= 100 sq. hectometers

Volume Measure

1 cubic millimeter	= 10^{-6} liter	= 0.001 cu. cm.
1 cubic centimeter	= 10^{-3} liter	= 0.001 cu. dm.
1 cubic decimeter	= 1 liter†	= 0.001 cu. m.
1 decistere	= 0.1 cubic meter	
1 stere	= 1 cubic meter	
1 dekastere	= 10 cubic meters	
1 microliter(μl. or λ)	= 10^{-6} liter	= 0.000001 liter
1 milliliter(ml.)	= 10^{-3} liter	= 0.001 liter
1 centiliter(cl.)	= 10^{-2} liter	= 0.01 liter
1 deciliter(dl.)	= 10^{-1} liter	= 0.1 liter
1 dekaliter(dkl.)	= 10 liters	
1 hectoliter(hl.)	= 10^2 liters	= 100 liters

Mass Measure

1 microgram(μg. or γ)	= 10^{-6} gram	
1 milligram(mg.)	= 10^{-3} gram	
1 centigram(cg.)	= 10^{-2} gram	
1 decigram(dg.)	= 10^{-1} gram	= 0.1 gram
15.432 grains(gr.)	= 1 gram	
1 dekagram(dkg.)	= 10 grams	
1 hectogram(hg.)	= 10^2 grams	= 100 grams
1 kilogram (kg.)	= 10^3 grams	= 1,000 grams
1 metric ton	= 10^6 grams	= 1,000,000 grams
1 metric carat	= 200 milligrams	

* By Dr. Lewis V. Judson, National Bureau of Standards.

† Accurately: 1 liter = 1.000028 cubic decimeters.

Table 1-12b. Weights and Measures of Different Countries

1. Metric system (compulsory in all civilized countries except the British Commonwealth of Nations and the United States; optional in these two countries. Old non-metric units still in use in some countries. Compulsory use of the metric system in Japan effective Dec. 31, 1958):

1 meter (m.) = 443.284 Paris lignes = 3.280833 United States feet = 3.18620 Prussian feet
1 kilometer (km.) = 10 hectometers (hm.) = 0.6214 United States mile = 0.1328 Prussian mile = 0.9374 Russian verst = 0.5390 nautical mile
1 hectare (ha.) = 100 ares (a.) = 10,000 sq. m. = 0.01 sq. km. = 2.471 United States acres
1 liter (l.) = 0.001 cu. m. = 1000 ml. = 0.2642 United States gallons
1 hectoliter (hl.) = 0.1 cu. m. = 100 l. = 26.42 United States gallons
1 kilogram (kg.) = 1000 g. = weight of water at +4°C. = 2 German and Swiss pounds (zollpfund) = 2.2046 pounds avoirdupois = 1.7857 Austrian pounds = 2.3525 Swedish pounds = 2.4419 Russian pounds
1 gram (g.) = 15.432 grains (English and United States)
1 quintal = 100 kg. = 220.46 lb. avoirdupois = 1 cwt. 3 qrs. 0.84 lb.
1 metric ton = 1000 kg. = 0.9842 English ton and 0.9842 United States long ton = 1.1023 United States short tons (at 2000 lb.)

2. Great Britain and Ireland:

1 inch = 25.39998 mm.
1 foot = 0.3047997 m.
1 yard = 3 feet = 0.9143992 m.
1 fathom = 2 yards = 1.829 m.
1 rod (pole, perch) = 5½ yards = 5.0292 m.
1 chain = 22 yards 80 chains = 1 mile
1 statute mile = 8 furlongs = 320 poles = 1760 yards = 5280 feet = 1.6093 kilometers (km.)
1 nautical mile = 6080 feet = 1853.2 m.
1 acre = 160 square rods = 0.40468 ha. = 43,560 square feet = 4046.8 square meters
1 square mile = 640 acres = 258.998 ha.
1 gallon = 4 quarts = 8 pints = 277.42 cubic inches = 4.536 liters = 10 lb. water = 70,000 grains water = 4.535924 kg. water = 1.20094 United States gallons
1 cubic foot = 1728 cubic inches = 28.3162 l.
1 cubic inch = 16.3865 ml.
1 quarter = 8 bushels = 32 pecks = 64 gallons = 2.909 hl.
1 bushel = 8 gallons = 1.03205 United States bushels
1 fluid ounce = 1/20 pint = 28.412 ml.
1 pound avoirdupois (lb.) = 16 ounces (oz.) = 7000 grains = 0.4535924 kg.
1 ounce avoirdupois = 437½ grains = 28.35 g.
1 hundredweight (cwt.) = 4 quarters (qr.) = 8 stones = 112 lb. = 50.8024 kg.
1 ton = 20 cwt. = 2240 lb. = 1016.047 kg.

Apothecaries' Weight:

1 ounce apothecaries' = 8 drams = 24 scruples = 480 grains = 31.1035 g.
1 ounce troy (for gold and precious stones) = 20 pennyweight (dwt.) = 480 grains = 31.1035 g.
1 pennyweight (dwt.) = 1.5552 g.
1 grain (common to avoirdupois, apothecaries', and troy weight) = 0.06479892 g.

3. Russia: Metric measure and weight compulsory. The following units of the old system are sometimes still employed:

1 foute (foot) = 1 English or United States foot
1 sashen = 7 feet = 3 arshin = 12 tchetvert = 48 vershok = 2.1336 m.
1 verst = 500 sashen = 1066.80 m.
1 dessatine = 2400 square sashens = 10.925 sq. m.
1 vedro = 10 krushky (stoof) = 12.299 l. = 3.249 United States gallons
1 tchetvert = 2 osmini = 4 payok = 8 tchetverik = 209.9 l.
1 funt (pound) = 32 loth = 96 solotnik = 9216 doli = 0.9028 United States lb. = 409.512 g.
1 berkovetz = 10 poods = 400 lb. = 163.80 kg.
1 pood = 40 pounds = 36.113 United States lb. = 16.3805 kg.

4. Sweden: Metric measure and weight compulsory. The following units of the old system are sometimes still employed.

1 fot (foot) = 10 turn (inches) = 100 lines = 0.97408 United States foot = 0.2969 m.
1 famn (fathom) = 3 alnar (ells) = 6 feet = 5.8445 United States feet = 1.7814 m.
1 mil (mile) = 6000 fathoms = 6.6415 United States statute miles = 10.6884 km.
1 kanna = 0.69135 United States gallon = 2.617 l.
1 skålpund = 100 ort = 1000 korn = 0.9371 United States lb. = 425.076 g.
1 centner = 100 skålpund
1 skippund = 20 liespund = 400 skålpund

5. Switzerland: Metric measure and weight compulsory. The following units of the old system are sometimes still employed:

1 fuss = 0.3000 m. = 0.9842 United States foot
1 juchart = 36 are = 0.88957 United States acre
1 maass = 1.5 l.
1 saum = 100 maass = 150 l.

6. Central and South America (Bolivia, Chile, Costa Rica, Cuba, Dominican Republic, Ecuador, Guatemala, Honduras, Nicaragua, Peru, Venezuela): 1 quintal = 46.0093 kg.

Country	Quintal	Kilograms
Argentina	1	45.94
Brazil	1	58.752
Colombia	1	50.00
Mexico	1	46.0246
Paraguay	1	45.94
San Salvador	1	45.94
Uruguay	1	45.94

Square Feet, Square Meter:

1 square meter (sq. m.) = 10.764 square feet (United States, English, and Russian) = 10.008 square feet (Austrian) = 10.152 square feet (Prussian) = 11.344 square feet (Swedish)
1 square foot (United States, English, and Russian) = 0.09290 square meter

Cubic Feet, Cubic Meter:

1 cubic meter (cu. m.) = 35.314 cubic feet (English, United States, and Russian)
1 cubic meter (cu. m.) = 31.661 cubic feet (Austrian)
1 cubic meter (cu. m.) = 32.346 cubic feet (Prussian)
1 cubic meter (cu. m.) = 38.209 cubic feet (Swedish)
1 cubic foot (United States, English, and Russian) = 0.028315 cubic meter
1 kilogram per running meter = 0.6720 United States and English pound per linear foot = 0.6277 zollpfund per Prussian foot
1 United States and English pound per 1 United States and English foot = 1.4882 kg. per running meter
1 kilogram per square centimeter (for steam pressure) = 14.223 United States and English pounds per square inch = 13.681 zollpfund per Prussian square inch = 13.878 zollpfund per Austrian square inch

Table 1-12c. Horsepower (Per Second)

Kg.-cm.	Austria,* foot-pounds	Prussia, foot-pounds	England,† foot-pounds	Sweden, foot-pounds	Russia, foot-pounds
75	474.53	477.93	542.47	594.27	600.87
76.04	481.11	484.56	550	602.51	609.20

* Zollpfund. † Also United States.

75 kilogram-meters taken as unit,
550 English foot-pounds taken as unit
= 1 horsepower per second; or
33,000 foot-pounds per minute.

Table 1-13. Fundamental Physical Constants*

1 sec. = 1.00273791 sidereal second	sec. = mean solar second
g_0 = 980.665 cm./sec.^{2}	Definition: g_0 = standard gravity
1 liter = 1000.028 ± 0.004 cu. cm.	
1 atm. = 1,013,250 dynes/sq. cm.	Definition: atm. = standard atmosphere
1 mm. Hg (pressure) = (1/760) atm.	mm. Hg (pressure) = standard millimeter mercury
= 1333.2237 dynes/sq. cm.	
1 int. ohm = 1.000495 ± 0.000015 abs. ohm†	int. = international; abs. = absolute
1 int. amp. = 0.999835 ± 0.000025 abs. amp.†	amp. = ampere
1 int. coul. = 0.999835 ± 0.000025 abs. coul.†	coul. = coulomb
1 int. volt = 1.000330 ± 0.000029 abs. volt†	
1 int. watt = 1.000165 ± 0.000052 abs. watt†	
1 int. joule = 1.000165 ± 0.000052 abs. joule†	
1 cal. = 4.1840 abs. joule	Definition: cal. = thermochemical calorie
= 4.1833 int. joule	
= 41.2929 ± 0.0020 cu. cm. atm.	
= 0.0412917 ± 0.0000020 liter atm.	
$T_{0°C.}$ = 273.160 ± 0.010°K.	Absolute temperature of the ice point, 0°C.
$(PV)_{0°C.}^{P=0} = (RT)_{0°C.}$ = 2271.16 ± 0.04 abs. joule/mole	*PV* product for ideal gas at 0°C.
= 22,414.6 ± 0.4 cu. cm. atm./mole	
= 22.4140 ± 0.0004 liter atm./mole	
R = 8.31439 ± 0.00034 abs. joule/deg. mole	R = gas constant per mole
= 1.98719 ± 0.00013 cal./deg. mole	
= 82.0567 ± 0.0034 cu. cm. atm./deg. mole	
= 0.0820544 ± 0.0000034 liter atm./deg. mole	
ln 10 = 2.302585	ln = natural logarithm (base e)
R ln 10 = 19.14460 ± 0.00078 abs. joule/deg. mole	
= 4.57567 ± 0.00030 cal./deg. mole	
N = (6.02283 ± 0.0022) × 10^{23}/mole	N = Avogadro number
$k = (R/N)$ = (1.38048 ± 0.00050) × 10^{-16} erg/deg.	k = Boltzmann constant
h = (6.6242 ± 0.0044) × 10^{-27} erg sec.	h = Planck constant
c = (2.99776 ± 0.00008) × 10^{10} cm./sec.	c = velocity of light
$(h^2/8\pi^2 k)$ = (4.0258 ± 0.0037) × 10^{-39} g. sq. cm. deg.	Constant in rotational partition function of gases
$(h/8\pi^2 c)$ = (2.7986 ± 0.0018) × 10^{-39} g. cm.	Constant relating wave number and moment of inertia
$Z = Nhc$ = 11.9600 ± 0.0036 abs. joule cm./mole	Z = constant relating wave number and energy per mole
= 2.85851 ± 0.0009 cal. cm./mole	
$(Z/R) = (hc/k) = c_2$ = 1.43847 ± 0.00045 cm. deg.	c_2 = second radiation constant
$\mathfrak{F}$ = 96,501.2 ± 10.0 int. coul./g.-equiv. or int. joule/int. volt g.-equiv.	$\mathfrak{F}$ = Faraday constant
= 96,485.3 ± 10.0 abs. coul./g.-equiv. or abs. joule/abs. volt g.-equiv.	
= 23,068.1 ± 2.4 cal./int. volt g.-equiv.	
= 23,060.5 ± 2.4 cal./abs. volt g.-equiv.	
e = (1.60199 ± 0.00060) × 10^{-19} abs. coul.	e = electronic charge
= (1.60199 ± 0.00060) × 10^{-20} abs. e.m.u.	
= (4.80239 ± 0.00180) × 10^{-10} abs. e.s.u.	
1 int. electron-volt/molecule = 96,501.2 ± 10 int. joule/mole	
= 23,068.1 ± 2.4 cal./mole	
1 abs. electron-volt/molecule = 96,485.3 ± 10. abs. joule/mole	
= 23,060.5 ± 2.4 cal./mole	
1 int. electron-volt = (1.60252 ± 0.00060) × 10^{-12} erg	
1 abs. electron-volt = (1.60199 ± 0.00060) × 10^{-12} erg	
hc = (1.23916 ± 0.00032) × 10^{-4} int. electron-volt cm.	Constant relating wave number and energy per molecule
= (1.23957 ± 0.00032) × 10^{-4} abs. electron-volt cm.	
k = (8.61442 ± 0.00100) × 10^{-5} int. electron-volt/deg.	k = Boltzmann constant
= (8.61727 ± 0.00100) × 10^{-5} abs. electron-volt/deg.	
1 I.T. cal. = (1/860) = 0.00116279 int. watt-hr.	Definition of I.T. cal.: I.T. = International steam tables
= 4.18605 int. joule	
= 4.18674 abs. joule	
= 1.000654 cal.	cal. = thermochemical calorie
1 I.T. cal./g. = 1.8 B.t.u./lb.	Definition of B.t.u.: B.t.u. = I.T. British Thermal Unit
1 B.t.u. = 251.996 I.T. cal.	
= 0.293018 int. watt-hr.	
= 1054.866 int. joule	
= 1055.040 abs. joule	
= 252.161 cal.	cal. = thermochemical calorie
1 horsepower = 550 ft.-lb. (wt.)/sec.	Definition of horsepower (mechanical): lb. (wt.) = weight of 1 lb. at standard gravity
= 745.578 int. watt	
= 745.70 abs. watt	Definition of in.: in. = U.S. inch
1 in. = (1/0.3937) = 2.54000508 cm.	ft. = U.S. foot (1 ft. = 12 in.)
1 ft. = 30.4800610 cm.	Definition; lb. = avoirdupois pound
1 lb. = 453.5924277 g.	Definition; gal. = U.S. gallon
1 gal. = 231 cu. in.	
= 0.133680555 cu. ft.	
= 3785.43449 cu. cm.	
= 3.785329 liter	

* From the tables of Selected Values of Properties of Hydrocarbons of the American Petroleum Institute Research Project 44 and the tables of Selected Values of Chemical Thermodynamic Properties of the National Bureau of Standards, as of Dec. 31, 1947.

† The electrical units used in these tables are those in terms of which certification of standard cells, standard resistances, etc., is made by the National Bureau of Standards. Since January 1, 1948, all such certifications are in terms of absolute volts and absolute resistances.

Table 1-14. Compound Interest Factors

For examples demonstrating use see end of table

n	Single payment: Compound-amount factor	Single payment: Present-worth factor	Uniform annual series: Sinking-fund factor	Uniform annual series: Capital-recovery factor	Uniform annual series: Compound-amount factor	Uniform annual series: Present-worth factor	n
	Given P, to find S $(1+i)^n$	Given S, to find P $\frac{1}{(1+i)^n}$	Given S, to find R $\frac{i}{(1+i)^n-1}$	Given P, to find R $\frac{i(1+i)^n}{(1+i)^n-1}$	Given R, to find S $\frac{(1+i)^n-1}{i}$	Given R, to find P $\frac{(1+i)^n-1}{i(1+i)^n}$	
	3% Compound Interest Factors						
1	1.030	0.9709	1.00000	1.03000	1.000	0.971	1
2	1.061	.9426	0.49261	0.52261	2.030	1.913	2
3	1.093	.9151	.32353	.35353	3.091	2.829	3
4	1.126	.8885	.23903	.26903	4.184	3.717	4
5	1.159	.8626	.18835	.21835	5.309	4.580	5
6	1.194	.8375	.15460	.18460	6.468	5.417	6
7	1.230	.8131	.13051	.16051	7.662	6.230	7
8	1.267	.7894	.11246	.14246	8.892	7.020	8
9	1.305	.7664	.09843	.12843	10.159	7.786	9
10	1.344	.7441	.08723	.11723	11.464	8.530	10
11	1.384	.7224	.07808	.10808	12.808	9.253	11
12	1.426	.7014	.07046	.10046	14.192	9.954	12
13	1.469	.6810	.06403	.09403	15.618	10.635	13
14	1.513	.6611	.05853	.08853	17.086	11.296	14
15	1.558	.6419	.05377	.08377	18.599	11.938	15
16	1.605	.6232	.04961	.07961	20.157	12.561	16
17	1.653	.6050	.04595	.07595	21.762	13.166	17
18	1.702	.5874	.04271	.07271	23.414	13.754	18
19	1.754	.5703	.03981	.06931	25.117	14.324	19
20	1.806	.5537	.03722	.06722	26.870	14.877	20
21	1.860	.5375	.03487	.06487	28.676	15.415	21
22	1.916	.5219	.03275	.06275	30.537	15.937	22
23	1.974	.5067	.03081	.06081	32.453	16.444	23
24	2.033	.4919	.02905	.05905	34.426	16.936	24
25	2.094	.4776	.02743	.05743	36.459	17.413	25
26	2.157	.4637	.02594	.05594	38.553	17.877	26
27	2.221	.4502	.02456	.05456	40.710	18.327	27
28	2.288	.4371	.02329	.05329	42.961	18.764	28
29	2.357	.4243	.02211	.05211	45.219	19.188	29
30	2.427	.4120	.02102	.05102	47.575	19.600	30
31	2.500	.4000	.02000	.05000	50.003	20.000	31
32	2.575	.3883	.01905	.04905	52.503	20.389	32
33	2.652	.3770	.01816	.04816	55.078	20.766	33
34	2.732	.3660	.01732	.04732	57.730	21.132	34
35	2.814	.3554	.01654	.04654	60.462	21.487	35
40	3.262	.3066	.01326	.04326	75.401	23.115	40
45	3.782	.2644	.01079	.04079	92.720	24.519	45
50	4.384	.2281	.00887	.03887	112.797	25.730	50
55	5.082	.1968	.00735	.03735	136.072	26.774	55
60	5.892	.1697	.00613	.03613	163.053	27.676	60
65	6.830	.1464	.00515	.03515	194.333	28.453	65
70	7.918	.1263	.00434	.03434	230.594	29.123	70
75	9.179	.1089	.00367	.03367	272.631	29.702	75
80	10.641	.0940	.00311	.03311	321.363	30.201	80
85	12.336	.0811	.00265	.03265	377.857	30.631	85
90	14.300	.0699	.00226	.03226	443.349	31.002	90
95	16.578	.0603	.00193	.03193	519.272	31.323	95
100	19.219	.0520	.00165	.03165	607.288	31.599	100

Table 1-14. Compound Interest Factors—(*Continued*)

n	Single payment		Uniform annual series				n
	Compound-amount factor	Present-worth factor	Sinking-fund factor	Capital-recovery factor	Compound-amount factor	Present-worth factor	
	Given P, to find S $(1+i)^n$	Given S, to find P $\frac{1}{(1+i)^n}$	Given S, to find R $\frac{i}{(1+i)^n - 1}$	Given P, to find R $\frac{i(1+i)^n}{(1+i)^n - 1}$	Given R, to find S $\frac{(1+i)^n - 1}{i}$	Given R, to find P $\frac{(1+i)^n - 1}{i(1+i)^n}$	
			4% Compound Interest Factors				
1	1.040	0.9615	1.00000	1.04000	1.000	0.962	1
2	1.082	.9246	0.49020	0.53020	2.040	1.886	2
3	1.125	.8890	.32035	.36035	3.122	2.775	3
4	1.170	.8548	.23549	.27549	4.246	3.630	4
5	1.217	.8219	.18463	.22463	5.416	4.452	5
6	1.265	.7903	.15076	.19076	6.633	5.242	6
7	1.316	.7599	.12661	.16661	7.898	6.002	7
8	1.369	.7307	.10853	.14853	9.214	6.733	8
9	1.423	.7026	.09449	.13449	10.583	7.435	9
10	1.480	.6756	.08329	.12329	12.006	8.111	10
11	1.539	.6496	.07415	.11415	13.486	8.760	11
12	1.601	.6246	.06655	.10655	15.026	9.385	12
13	1.665	.6006	.06014	.10014	16.627	9.986	13
14	1.732	.5775	.05467	.09467	18.292	10.563	14
15	1.801	.5553	.04994	.08994	20.024	11.118	15
16	1.873	.5339	.04582	.08582	21.825	11.652	16
17	1.948	.5134	.04220	.08220	23.698	12.166	17
18	2.026	.4936	.03899	.07899	25.645	12.659	18
19	2.107	.4746	.03614	.07614	27.671	13.134	19
20	2.191	.4564	.03358	.07358	29.778	13.590	20
21	2.279	.4388	.03128	.07128	31.969	14.029	21
22	2.370	.4220	.02920	.06920	34.248	14.451	22
23	2.465	.4057	.02731	.06731	36.618	14.857	23
24	2.563	.3901	.02559	.06559	39.083	15.247	24
25	2 666	.3751	.02401	.06401	41.646	15.622	25
26	2.772	.3607	.02257	.06257	44.312	15.983	26
27	2.883	.3468	.02124	.06124	47.084	16.330	27
28	2.999	.3335	.02001	.06001	49.968	16.663	28
29	3.119	.3207	.01888	.05888	52.966	16.984	29
30	3.243	.3083	.01783	.05783	56.085	17.292	30
31	3.373	.2965	.01686	.05686	59.328	17.588	31
32	3.508	.2851	.01595	.05595	62.701	17.874	32
33	3.648	.2741	.01510	.05510	66.210	18.148	33
34	3.794	.2636	.01431	.05431	69.858	18.411	34
35	3.946	.2534	.01358	.05358	73.652	18.665	35
40	4.801	.2083	.01052	.05052	95.026	19.793	40
45	5.841	.1712	.00826	.04826	121.029	20.720	45
50	7.107	.1407	.00655	.04655	152.667	21.482	50
55	8.646	.1157	.00523	.04523	191.159	22.109	55
60	10.520	.0951	.00420	.04420	237.991	22.623	60
65	12.799	.0781	.00339	.04339	294.968	23.047	65
70	15.572	.0642	.00275	.04275	364.290	23.395	70
75	18.945	.0528	.00223	.04223	448.631	23.680	75
80	23.050	.0434	.00181	.04181	551.245	23.915	80
85	28.044	.0357	.00148	.04148	676.090	24.109	85
90	34.119	.0293	.00121	.04121	827.983	24.267	90
95	41.511	.0241	.00099	.04099	1,012.785	24.398	95
100	50.505	.0198	.00081	.04081	1,237.624	24.505	100

Table 1-14. Compound Interest Factors—(*Continued*)

n	Single payment: Compound-amount factor. Given P, to find S $(1+i)^n$	Single payment: Present-worth factor. Given S, to find P $\frac{1}{(1+i)^n}$	Uniform annual series: Sinking-fund factor. Given S, to find R $\frac{i}{(1+i)^n-1}$	Uniform annual series: Capital-recovery factor. Given P, to find R $\frac{i(1+i)^n}{(1+i)^n-1}$	Uniform annual series: Compound-amount factor. Given R, to find S $\frac{(1+i)^n-1}{i}$	Uniform annual series: Present-worth factor. Given R, to find P $\frac{(1+i)^n-1}{i(1+i)^n}$	n
			5% Compound Interest Factors				
1	1.050	0.9524	1.00000	1.05000	1.000	0.952	1
2	1.103	.9070	0.48780	0.53780	2.050	1.859	2
3	1.158	.8638	.31721	.36721	3.153	2.723	3
4	1.216	.8227	.23201	.28201	4.310	3.546	4
5	1.276	.7835	.18097	.23097	5.526	4.329	5
6	1.340	.7462	.14702	.19702	6.802	5.076	6
7	1.407	.7107	.12282	.17282	8.142	5.786	7
8	1.477	.6768	.10472	.15472	9.549	6.463	8
9	1.551	.6446	.09069	.14069	11.027	7.108	9
10	1.629	.6139	.07940	.12950	12.578	7.722	10
11	1.710	.5847	.07039	.12039	14.207	8.306	11
12	1.796	.5568	.06283	.11283	15.917	8.863	12
13	1.886	.5303	.05646	.10646	17.713	9.394	13
14	1.980	.5051	.05102	.10102	19.599	9.899	14
15	2.079	.4810	.04634	.09634	21.579	10.380	15
16	2.183	.4581	.04227	.09227	23.657	10.838	16
17	2.292	.4363	.03870	.08870	25.840	11.274	17
18	2.407	.4155	.03555	.08555	28.132	11.690	18
19	2.527	.3957	.03275	.08275	30.539	12.085	19
20	2.653	.3769	.03024	.08024	33.066	12.462	20
21	2.786	.3589	.02800	.07800	35.719	12.821	21
22	2.925	.3418	.02597	.07597	38.505	13.163	22
23	3.072	.3256	.02414	.07414	41.430	13.489	23
24	3.225	.3101	.02247	.07247	44.502	13.799	24
25	3.386	.2953	.02095	.07095	47.727	14.094	25
26	3.556	.2812	.01956	.06956	51.113	14.375	26
27	3.733	.2678	.01829	.06829	54.669	14.643	27
28	3.920	.2551	.01712	.06712	58.403	14.898	28
29	4.116	.2429	.01605	.06605	62.323	15.141	29
30	4.322	.2314	.01505	.06505	66.489	15.372	30
31	4.538	.2204	.01413	.06413	70.761	15.593	31
32	4.765	.2099	.01328	.06328	75.299	15.803	32
33	5.003	.1999	.01249	.06249	80.064	16.003	33
34	5.253	.1904	.01176	.06176	85.067	16.193	34
35	5.516	.1813	.01107	.06107	90.320	16.374	35
40	7.040	.1420	.00828	.05828	120.800	17.159	40
45	8.985	1113	.00626	.05626	159.700	17.774	45
50	11.467	.0872	.00478	.05478	209.348	18.256	50
55	14.636	.0683	.00367	.05367	272.713	18.633	55
60	18.679	.0535	.00283	.05283	353.584	18.929	60
65	23.840	.0419	.00219	.05219	456.798	19.161	65
70	30.426	.0329	.00170	.05170	588.529	19.343	70
75	38.833	.0258	.00132	.05132	756.654	19.485	75
80	49.561	.0202	.00103	.05103	971.229	19.596	80
85	63.254	.0158	.00080	.05080	1,245.087	19.684	85
90	80.730	.0124	.00063	.05063	1,594.607	19.752	90
95	103.035	.0097	.00049	.05049	2,040.694	19.806	95
100	131.501	.0076	.00038	.05038	2,610.025	19.848	100

Table 1-14. Compound Interest Factors—*(Continued)*

n	Single payment: Compound-amount factor, Given P, to find S, $(1+i)^n$	Single payment: Present-worth factor, Given S, to find P, $\frac{1}{(1+i)^n}$	Uniform annual series: Sinking-fund factor, Given S, to find R, $\frac{i}{(1+i)^n-1}$	Uniform annual series: Capital-recovery factor, Given P, to find R, $\frac{i(1+i)^n}{(1+i)^n-1}$	Uniform annual series: Compound-amount factor, Given R, to find S, $\frac{(1+i)^n-1}{i}$	Uniform annual series: Present-worth factor, Given R, to find P, $\frac{(1+i)^n-1}{i(1+i)^n}$	n
			6% Compound Interest Factors				
1	1.060	0.9434	1.00000	1.06000	1.000	0.943	1
2	1.124	.8900	0.48544	0.54544	2.060	1.833	2
3	1.191	.8396	.31411	.37411	3.184	2.673	3
4	1.262	.7921	.22859	.28859	4.375	3.465	4
5	1.338	.7473	.17740	.23740	5.637	4.212	5
6	1.419	.7050	.14336	.20336	6.975	4.917	6
7	1.504	.6651	.11914	.17914	8.394	5.582	7
8	1.594	.6274	.10104	.16104	9.897	6.210	8
9	1.689	.5919	.08702	.14702	11.491	6.802	9
10	1.791	.5584	.07587	.13587	13.181	7.360	10
11	1.898	.5268	.06679	.12679	14.972	7.887	11
12	2.012	.4970	.05928	.11928	16.870	8.384	12
13	2.133	.4688	.05296	.11296	18.882	8.853	13
14	2.261	.4423	.04758	.10758	21.015	9.295	14
15	2.397	.4173	.04296	.10296	23.276	9.712	15
16	2.540	.3936	.03895	.09895	25.673	10.106	16
17	2.693	.3714	.03544	.09544	28.213	10.477	17
18	2.854	.3503	.03236	.09236	30.906	10.828	18
19	3.026	.3305	.02962	.08962	33.760	11.158	19
20	3.207	.3118	.02718	.08718	36.786	11.470	20
21	3.400	.2942	.02500	.08500	39.993	11.764	21
22	3.604	.2775	.02305	.08305	43.392	12.042	22
23	3.820	.2618	.02128	.08128	46.996	12.303	23
24	4.049	.2470	.01968	.07968	50.816	12.550	24
25	4.292	.2330	.01823	.07823	54.865	12.783	25
26	4.549	.2198	.01690	.07690	59.156	13.003	26
27	4.822	.2074	.01570	.07570	63.706	13.211	27
28	5.112	.1956	.01459	.07459	68.528	13.406	28
29	5.418	.1846	.01358	.07358	73.640	13.591	29
30	5.743	.1741	.01265	.07265	79.058	13.765	30
31	6.088	.1643	.01179	.07179	84.802	13.929	31
32	6.453	.1550	.01100	.07100	90.890	14.084	32
33	6.841	.1462	.01027	.07027	97.343	14.230	33
34	7.251	.1379	.00960	.06960	104.184	14.368	34
35	7.686	.1301	.00897	.06897	111.435	14.498	35
40	10.286	.0972	.00646	.06646	154.762	15.046	40
45	13.765	.0727	.00470	.06470	212.744	15.456	45
50	18.420	.0543	.00344	.06344	290.336	15.762	50
55	24.650	.0406	.00254	.06254	394.172	15.991	55
60	32.988	.0303	.00188	.06188	533.128	16.161	60
65	44.145	.0227	.00139	.06139	719.083	16.289	65
70	59.076	.0169	.00103	.06103	967.932	16.385	70
75	79.057	.0126	.00077	.06077	1,300.949	16.456	75
80	105.796	.0095	.00057	.06057	1,746.600	16.509	80
85	141.579	.0071	.00043	.06043	2,342.982	16.549	85
90	189.465	.0053	.00032	.06032	3,141.075	16.579	90
95	253.546	.0039	.00024	.06024	4,209.104	16.601	95
100	339.302	.0029	.00018	.06018	5,638.368	16.618	100

Table 1-14. Compound Interest Factors—(*Continued*)

n	Single payment		Uniform annual series				n
	Compound-amount factor	Present-worth factor	Sinking-fund factor	Capital-recovery factor	Compound-amount factor	Present-worth factor	
	Given P, to find S $(1+i)^n$	Given S, to find P $\frac{1}{(1+i)^n}$	Given S, to find R $\frac{i}{(1+i)^n-1}$	Given P, to find R $\frac{i(1+i)^n}{(1+i)^n-1}$	Given R, to find S $\frac{(1+i)^n-1}{i}$	Given R, to find P $\frac{(1+i)^n-1}{i(1+i)^n}$	
			8% Compound Interest Factors				
1	1.080	0.9259	1.00000	1.08000	1.000	0.926	1
2	1.166	.8573	0.48077	0.56077	2.080	1.783	2
3	1.260	.7938	.30803	.38803	3.246	2.577	3
4	1.360	.7350	.22192	.30192	4.506	3.312	4
5	1.469	.6806	.17046	.25046	5.867	3.993	5
6	1.587	.6302	.13632	.21632	7.336	4.623	6
7	1.714	.5835	.11207	.19207	8.923	5.206	7
8	1.851	.5403	.09401	.17401	10.637	5.747	8
9	1.999	.5002	.08008	.16008	12.488	6.247	9
10	2.159	.4632	.06903	.14903	14.487	6.710	10
11	2.332	.4289	.06008	.14008	16.645	7.139	11
12	2.518	.3971	.05270	.13270	18.977	7.536	12
13	2.720	.3677	.04652	.12652	21.495	7.904	13
14	2.937	.3405	.04130	.12130	24.215	8.244	14
15	3.172	.3152	.03683	.11683	27.152	8.559	15
16	3.426	.2919	.03298	.11298	30.324	8.851	16
17	3.700	.2703	.02963	.10963	33.750	9.122	17
18	3.996	.2502	.02670	.10670	37.450	9.372	18
19	4.316	.2317	.02413	.10413	41.446	9.604	19
20	4.661	.2145	.02185	.10185	45.762	9.818	20
21	5.034	.1987	.01983	.09983	50.423	10.017	21
22	5.437	.1839	.01803	.09803	55.457	10.201	22
23	5.871	.1703	.01642	.09642	60.893	10.371	23
24	6.341	.1577	.01498	.09498	66.765	10.529	24
25	6.848	.1460	.01368	.09368	73.106	10.675	25
26	7.396	.1352	.01251	.09251	79.954	10.810	26
27	7.988	.1252	.01145	.09145	87.351	10.935	27
28	8.627	.1159	.01049	.09049	95.339	11.051	28
29	9.317	.1073	.00962	.08962	103.966	11.158	29
30	10.063	.0994	.00883	.08883	113.283	11.258	30
31	10.868	.0920	.00811	.08811	123.346	11.350	31
32	11.737	.0852	.00745	.08745	134.214	11.435	32
33	12.676	.0789	.00685	.08685	145.951	11.514	33
34	13.690	.0730	.00630	.08630	158.627	11.587	34
35	14.785	.0676	.00580	.08580	172.317	11.655	35
40	21.725	.0460	.00386	.08386	259.057	11.925	40
45	31.920	.0313	.00259	.08259	386.506	12.108	45
50	46.902	.0213	.00174	.08174	573.770	12.233	50
55	68.914	.0145	.00118	.08118	848.923	12.319	55
60	101.257	.0099	.00080	.08080	1,253.213	12.377	60
65	148.780	.0067	.00054	.08054	1,847.248	12.416	65
70	218.606	.0046	.00037	.08037	2,720.080	12.443	70
75	321.205	.0031	.00025	.08025	4,002.557	12.461	75
80	471.955	.0021	.00017	.08017	5,886.935	12.474	80
85	693.456	.0014	.00012	.08012	8,655.706	12.482	85
90	1,018.915	.0010	.00008	.08008	12,723.939	12.488	90
95	1,497.121	.0007	.00005	.08005	18,701.507	12.492	95
100	2,199.761	.0005	.00004	.08004	27,484.516	12.494	100

Table 1-14. Compound Interest Factors—(*Continued*)

n	Single payment		Uniform annual series				*n*
	Compound-amount factor	Present-worth factor	Sinking-fund factor	Capital-recovery factor	Compound-amount factor	Present-worth factor	
	Given *P*, to find *S* $(1+i)^n$	Given *S*, to find *P* $\frac{1}{(1+i)^n}$	Given *S*, to find *R* $\frac{i}{(1+i)^n-1}$	Given *P*, to find *R* $\frac{i(1+i)^n}{(1+i)^n-1}$	Given *R*, to find *S* $\frac{(1+i)^n-1}{i}$	Given *R*, to find *P* $\frac{(1+i)^n-1}{i(1+i)^n}$	
	10% Compound Interest Factors						
1	1.100	0.9091	1.00000	1.10000	1.000	0.909	1
2	1.210	.8264	0.47619	0.57619	2.100	1.736	2
3	1.331	.7513	.30211	.40211	3.310	2.487	3
4	1.464	.6830	.21547	.31547	4.641	3.170	4
5	1.611	.6209	.16380	.26380	6.105	3.791	5
6	1.772	.5645	.12961	.22961	7.716	4.355	6
7	1.949	.5132	.10541	.20541	9.487	4.868	7
8	2.144	.4665	.08744	.18744	11.436	5.335	8
9	2.358	.4241	.07364	.17364	13.579	5.759	9
10	2.594	.3855	.06275	.16275	15.937	6.144	10
11	2.853	.3505	.05396	.15396	18.531	6.495	11
12	3.138	.3186	.04676	.14676	21.384	6.814	12
13	3.452	.2897	.04078	.14078	24.523	7.103	13
14	3.797	.2633	.03575	.13575	27.975	7.367	14
15	4.177	.2394	.03147	.13147	31.772	7.606	15
16	4.595	.2176	.02782	.12782	35.950	7 824	16
17	5.054	.1978	.02466	.12466	40.545	8.022	17
18	5.560	.1799	.02193	.12193	45.599	8.201	18
19	6.116	.1635	.01955	.11955	51.159	8.365	19
20	6.727	.1486	.01746	.11746	57.275	8.514	20
21	7.400	.1351	.01562	.11562	64.002	8.649	21
22	8.140	.1228	.01401	.11401	71.403	8.772	22
23	8.954	.1117	.01257	.11257	79.543	8.883	23
24	9.850	.1015	.01130	.11130	88.497	8.985	24
25	10.835	.0923	.01017	.11017	98.347	9.077	25
26	11.918	.0839	.00916	.10916	109.182	9.161	26
27	13.110	.0763	.00826	.10826	121.100	9.237	27
28	14.421	.0693	.00745	.10745	134.210	9.307	28
29	15.863	.0630	.00673	.10673	148.631	9.370	29
30	17.449	.0573	.00608	.10608	164.494	9.427	30
31	19.194	.0521	.00550	.10550	181.943	9.479	31
32	21.114	.0474	.00497	.10497	201.138	9.526	32
33	23.225	.0431	.00450	.10450	222.252	9.569	33
34	25.548	.0391	.00407	.10407	245.477	9.609	34
35	28.102	.0356	.00369	.10369	271.024	9.644	35
40	45.259	.0221	.00226	.10226	442.593	9.779	40
45	72.890	.0137	.00139	.10139	718.905	9.863	45
50	117.391	.0085	.00086	.10086	1,163.909	9.915	50
55	189.059	.0053	.00053	.10053	1,880.591	9.947	55
60	304.482	.0033	.00033	.10033	3,034.816	9.967	60
65	490.371	.0020	.00020	.10020	4,893.707	9.980	65
70	789.747	.0013	.00013	.10013	7,887.470	9.987	70
75	1,271.895	.0008	.00008	.10008	12,708.954	9.992	75
80	2,048.400	.0005	.00005	.10005	20,474.002	9.995	80
85	3,298.969	.0003	.00003	.10003	32,979.690	9.997	85
90	5,313.023	.0002	.00002	.10002	53,120.226	9.998	90
95	8,556.676	.0001	.00001	.10001	85,556.760	9.999	95
100	13,780.612	.0001	.00001	.10001	137,796.123	9.999	100

Table 1-14. Compound Interest Factors—(*Concluded*)

Examples in Use of Tables

Given: $2500 is invested now at 5 per cent.
Required: Accumulated value in 10 years (*i.e.*, the amount of a given principal).
Solution:

$$S = P(1+i)^n = \$2500 \times 1.05^{10}$$
Compound-amount factor $= (1+i)^n = 1.05^{10} = 1.629$
$$S = \$2500 \times 1.629 = \$4062.50$$

Given: $19,500 will be required in 5 years to replace equipment now in use.
Required: With interest available at 3 per cent, what sum must be deposited in the bank at present to provide the required capital (*i.e.*, the principal which will amount to a given sum)?
Solution:

$$P = S\frac{1}{(1+i)^n} = \$19{,}500\frac{1}{1.03^5}$$
Present-worth factor $= 1/(1+i)^n = 1/1.03^5 = 0.8626$
$$P = \$19{,}500 \times 0.8626 = \$16{,}821$$

Given: $50,000 will be required in 10 years to purchase equipment.
Required: With interest available at 4 per cent, what sum must be deposited each year to provide the required capital (*i.e.*, the annuity which will amount to a given fund)?
Solution:

$$R = S\frac{i}{(1+i)^n - 1} = \$50{,}000\frac{0.04}{1.04^{10} - 1}$$
$$\text{Sinking-fund factor} = \frac{i}{(1+i)^n - 1} = \frac{0.04}{1.04^{10} - 1} = 0.08329$$
$$R = \$50{,}000 \times 0.08329 = \$4{,}164$$

Given: $20,000 is invested at 10 per cent interest.
Required: Annual sum that can be withdrawn over a 20-year period (*i.e.*, the annuity provided by a given capital).
Solution:

$$R = P\frac{i(1+i)^n}{(1+i)^n - 1} = \$20{,}000\frac{0.10 \times 1.10^{20}}{1.10^{20} - 1}$$
$$\text{Capital-recovery factor} = \frac{i(1+i)^n}{(1+i)^n - 1} = \frac{0.10 \times 1.10^{20}}{1.10^{20} - 1} = 0.11746$$
$$R = \$20{,}000 \times 0.11746 = \$2349.20$$

Given: $500 is invested each year at 8 per cent interest.
Required: Accumulated value in 15 years (*i.e.*, amount of an annuity).
Solution:

$$S = R\frac{(1+i)^n - 1}{i} = \$500\frac{1.08^{15} - 1}{0.08}$$
$$\text{Compound-amount factor} = \frac{(1-i)^n - 1}{i} = \frac{1.08^{15} - 1}{0.08} = 27.152$$
$$S = \$500 \times 27.152 = \$13{,}576$$

Given: $8,000 is required annually for 25 years.
Required: Sum that must be deposited now at 6 per cent interest.
Solution:

$$P = R\frac{(1+i)^n - 1}{i(1+i)^n} = \$8000\frac{1.06^{25} - 1}{0.06 \times 1.06^{25}}$$
$$\text{Present-worth factor} = \frac{(1+i)^n - 1}{i(1+i)^n} = \frac{1.06^{25} - 1}{0.06 \times 1.06^{25}} = 12.783$$
$$P = \$8000 \times 12.78 = \$102{,}264$$

Table 1-15. Ordinates and Areas between Abscissa Values $-z$ and $+z$ of the Normal Distribution Curve

z	X	Y	A	$1-A$	z	X	Y	A	$1-A$
0	μ	0.399	0.0000	1.0000	±1.50	$\mu \pm 1.50\sigma$	0.1295	0.8664	0.1336
±0.05	$\mu \pm 0.05\sigma$	.398	.0399	0.9601	±1.55	$\mu \pm 1.55\sigma$	.1200	.8789	.1211
± .10	$\mu \pm .10\sigma$	.397	.0797	.9203	±1.60	$\mu \pm 1.60\sigma$	.1109	.8904	.1096
± .15	$\mu \pm .15\sigma$	.394	.1192	.8808	±1.65	$\mu \pm 1.65\sigma$	.1023	.9011	.0989
± .20	$\mu \pm .20\sigma$	.391	.1585	.8415	±1.70	$\mu \pm 1.70\sigma$	.0940	.9109	.0891
± .25	$\mu \pm .25\sigma$	.387	.1974	.8026	±1.75	$\mu \pm 1.75\sigma$	.0863	.9199	.0801
± .30	$\mu \pm .30\sigma$	.381	.2358	.7642	±1.80	$\mu \pm 1.80\sigma$	.0790	.9281	.0719
± .35	$\mu \pm .35\sigma$	.375	.2737	.7263	±1.85	$\mu \pm 1.85\sigma$	.0721	.9357	.0643
± .40	$\mu \pm .40\sigma$	.368	.3108	.6892	±1.90	$\mu \pm 1.90\sigma$	.0656	.9426	.0574
± .45	$\mu \pm .45\sigma$	.361	.3473	.6527	±1.95	$\mu \pm 1.95\sigma$	.0596	.9488	.0512
± .50	$\mu \pm .50\sigma$	.352	.3829	.6171	±2.00	$\mu \pm 2.00\sigma$	.0540	.9545	.0455
± .55	$\mu \pm .55\sigma$	.343	.4177	.5823	±2.05	$\mu \pm 2.05\sigma$	.0488	.9596	.0404
± .60	$\mu \pm .60\sigma$	.333	.4515	.5485	±2.10	$\mu \pm 2.10\sigma$	.0440	.9643	.0357
± .65	$\mu \pm .65\sigma$	.323	.4843	.5157	±2.15	$\mu \pm 2.15\sigma$	.0396	.9684	.0316
± .70	$\mu \pm .70\sigma$	.312	.5161	.4839	±2.20	$\mu \pm 2.20\sigma$	.0355	.9722	.0278
± .75	$\mu \pm .75\sigma$	.301	.5467	.4533	±2.25	$\mu \pm 2.25\sigma$	.0317	.9756	.0244
± .80	$\mu \pm .80\sigma$	.290	.5763	.4237	±2.30	$\mu \pm 2.30\sigma$	.0283	.9786	.0214
± .85	$\mu \pm .85\sigma$	.278	.6047	.3953	±2.35	$\mu \pm 2.35\sigma$	.0252	.9812	.0188
± .90	$\mu \pm .90\sigma$	.266	.6319	.3681	±2.40	$\mu \pm 2.40\sigma$	.0224	.9836	.0164
± .95	$\mu \pm .95\sigma$	.254	.6579	.3421	±2.45	$\mu \pm 2.45\sigma$	.0198	.9857	.0143
±1.00	$\mu \pm 1.00\sigma$	.242	.6827	.3173	±2.50	$\mu \pm 2.50\sigma$	.0175	.9876	.0124
±1.05	$\mu \pm 1.05\sigma$	.230	.7063	.2937	±2.55	$\mu \pm 2.55\sigma$	.0154	.9892	.0108
±1.10	$\mu \pm 1.10\sigma$	.218	.7287	.2713	±2.60	$\mu \pm 2.60\sigma$	.0136	.9907	.0093
±1.15	$\mu \pm 1.15\sigma$	.206	.7499	.2501	±2.65	$\mu \pm 2.65\sigma$	.0119	.9920	.0080
±1.20	$\mu \pm 1.20\sigma$	.194	.7699	.2301	±2.70	$\mu \pm 2.70\sigma$	.0104	.9931	.0069
±1.25	$\mu \pm 1.25\sigma$	.183	.7887	.2113	±2.75	$\mu \pm 2.75\sigma$	.0091	.9940	.0060
±1.30	$\mu \pm 1.30\sigma$	.171	.8064	.1936	±2.80	$\mu \pm 2.80\sigma$	.0079	.9949	.0051
±1.35	$\mu \pm 1.35\sigma$	.160	.8230	.1770	±2.85	$\mu \pm 2.85\sigma$	.0069	.9956	.0044
±1.40	$\mu \pm 1.40\sigma$	.150	.8385	.1615	±2.90	$\mu \pm 2.90\sigma$	.0060	.9963	.0037
±1.45	$\mu \pm 1.45\sigma$	.139	.8529	.1471	±2.95	$\mu \pm 2.95\sigma$	.0051	.9968	.0032
±1.50	$\mu \pm 1.50\sigma$	.130	.8664	.1336	±3.00	$\mu \pm 3.00\sigma$	.0044	.9973	.0027
					±4.00	$\mu \pm 4.00\sigma$	.0001	.99994	.00006
					±5.00	$\mu \pm 5.00\sigma$	.000001	.9999994	.0000006
±0.000	μ	0.3989	0.0000	1.0000	±1.036	$\mu \pm 1.036\sigma$	0.2331	0.7000	0.3000
± .126	$\mu \pm 0.126\sigma$	.3958	.1000	0.9000	±1.282	$\mu \pm 1.282\sigma$	.1755	.8000	.2000
± .253	$\mu \pm .253\sigma$	.3863	.2000	.8000	±1.645	$\mu \pm 1.645\sigma$	.1031	.9000	.1000
± .385	$\mu \pm .385\sigma$	.3704	.3000	.7000	±1.960	$\mu \pm 1.960\sigma$	.0584	.9500	.0500
± .524	$\mu \pm .524\sigma$	3477	.4000	.6000	±2.576	$\mu \pm 2.576\sigma$	.0145	.9900	.0100
± .674	$\mu \pm .674\sigma$	.3178	.5000	.5000	±3.291	$\mu \pm 3.291\sigma$	.0018	.9990	.0010
± .842	$\mu \pm .842\sigma$	.2800	.6000	.4000	±3.891	$\mu \pm 3.891\sigma$	.0002	.9999	.0001

Table 1-16. Values of t

df	$t_{.60}$	$t_{.70}$	$t_{.80}$	$t_{.90}$	$t_{.95}$	$t_{.975}$	$t_{.99}$	$t_{.995}$
1	0.325	0.727	1.376	3.078	6.314	12.706	31.821	63.657
2	.289	.617	1.061	1.886	2.920	4.303	6.965	9.925
3	.277	.584	0.978	1.638	2.353	3.182	4.541	5.841
4	.271	.569	.941	1.533	2.132	2.776	3.747	4.604
5	.267	.559	.920	1.476	2.015	2.571	3.365	4.032
6	.265	.553	.906	1.440	1.943	2.447	3.143	3.707
7	.263	.549	.896	1.415	1.895	2.365	2.998	3.499
8	.262	.546	.889	1.397	1.860	2.306	2.896	3.355
9	.261	.543	.883	1.383	1.833	2.262	2.821	3.250
10	.260	.542	.879	1.372	1.812	2.228	2.764	3.169
11	.260	.540	.876	1.363	1.796	2.201	2.718	3.106
12	.259	.539	.873	1.356	1.782	2.179	2.681	3.055
13	.259	.538	.870	1.350	1.771	2.160	2.650	3.012
14	.258	.537	.868	1.345	1.761	2.145	2.624	2.977
15	.258	.536	.866	1.341	1.753	2.131	2.602	2.947
16	.258	.535	.865	1.337	1.746	2.120	2.583	2.921
17	.257	.534	.863	1.333	1.740	2.110	2.567	2.898
18	.257	.534	.862	1.330	1.734	2.101	2.552	2.878
19	.257	.533	.861	1.328	1.729	2.093	2.539	2.861
20	.257	.533	.860	1.325	1.725	2.086	2.528	2.845
21	.257	.532	.859	1.323	1.721	2.080	2.518	2.831
22	.256	.532	.858	1.321	1.717	2.074	2.508	2.819
23	.256	.532	.858	1.319	1.714	2.069	2.500	2.807
24	.256	.531	.857	1.318	1.711	2.064	2.492	2.797
25	.256	.531	.856	1.316	1.708	2.060	2.485	2.787
26	.256	.531	.856	1.315	1.706	2.056	2.479	2.779
27	.256	.531	.855	1.314	1.703	2.052	2.473	2.771
28	.256	.530	.855	1.313	1.701	2.048	2.467	2.763
29	.256	.530	.854	1.311	1.699	2.045	2.462	2.756
30	.256	.530	.854	1.310	1.697	2.042	2.457	2.750
40	.255	.529	.851	1.303	1.684	2.021	2.423	2.704
60	.254	.527	.848	1.296	1.671	2.000	2.390	2.660
120	.254	.526	.845	1.289	1.658	1.980	2.358	2.617
∞	.253	.524	.842	1.282	1.645	1.960	2.326	2.576
df	$-t_{.40}$	$-t_{.30}$	$-t_{.20}$	$-t_{.10}$	$-t_{.05}$	$-t_{.025}$	$-t_{.01}$	$-t_{.005}$

When the table is read from the foot, the tabled values are to be prefixed with a negative sign. Interpolation should be performed using the reciprocals of the degrees of freedom.

Table 1-17. Percentiles of the χ^2 Distribution

df	Per cent									
	0.5	1	2.5	5	10	90	95	97.5	99	99.5
1	0.000039	0.00016	0.00098	0.0039	0.0158	2.71	3.84	5.02	6.63	7.88
2	.0100	.0201	.0506	.1026	.2107	4.61	5.99	7.38	9.21	10.60
3	.0717	.115	.216	.352	.584	6.25	7.81	9.35	11.34	12.84
4	.207	.297	.484	.711	1.064	7.78	9.49	11.14	13.28	14.86
5	.412	.554	.831	1.15	1.61	9.24	11.07	12.83	15.09	16.75
6	.676	.872	1.24	1.64	2.20	10.64	12.59	14.45	16.81	18.55
7	.989	1.24	1.69	2.17	2.83	12.02	14.07	16.01	18.48	20.28
8	1.34	1.65	2.18	2.73	3.49	13.36	15.51	17.53	20.09	21.96
9	1.73	2.09	2.70	3.33	4.17	14.68	16.92	19.02	21.67	23.59
10	2.16	2.56	3.25	3.94	4.87	15.99	18.31	20.48	23.21	25.19
11	2.60	3.05	3.82	4.57	5.58	17.28	19.68	21.92	24.73	26.76
12	3.07	3.57	4.40	5.23	6.30	18.55	21.03	23.34	26.22	28.30
13	3.57	4.11	5.01	5.89	7.04	19.81	22.36	24.74	27.69	29.82
14	4.07	4.66	5.63	6.57	7.79	21.06	23.68	26.12	29.14	31.32
15	4.60	5.23	6.26	7.26	8.55	22.31	25.00	27.49	30.58	32.80
16	5.14	5.81	6.91	7.96	9.31	23.54	26.30	28.85	32.00	34.27
18	6.26	7.01	8.23	9.39	10.86	25.99	28.87	31.53	34.81	37.16
20	7.43	8.26	9.59	10.85	12.44	28.41	31.41	34.17	37.57	40.00
24	9.89	10.86	12.40	13.85	15.66	33.20	36.42	39.36	42.98	45.56
30	13.79	14.95	16.79	18.49	20.60	40.26	43.77	46.98	50.89	53.67
40	20.71	22.16	24.43	26.51	29.05	51.81	55.76	59.34	63.69	66.77
60	35.53	37.48	40.48	43.19	46.46	74.40	79.08	83.30	88.38	91.95
120	83.85	86.92	91.58	95.70	100.62	140.23	146.57	152.21	158.95	163.64

For large values of degrees of freedom the approximate formula

$$\chi_\alpha^2 = n\left(1 - \frac{2}{9n} + z_\alpha \sqrt{\frac{2}{9n}}\right)^3$$

where z_α is the normal deviate and n is the number of degrees of freedom, may be used. For example, $\chi_{.99}^2 = 60[1 - 0.00370 + 2.326(0.06086)]^3 = 60(1.1379)^3 = 88.4$ for the 99th percentile for 60 degrees of freedom.

Table 1-18. *F* Distribution

Upper 5% Points ($F_{.95}$)

Degrees of freedom for numerator (columns); Degrees of freedom for denominator (rows)

	1	2	3	4	5	6	7	8	9	10	12	15	20	24	30	40	60	120	∞
1	161	200	216	225	230	234	237	239	241	242	244	246	248	249	250	251	252	253	254
2	18.5	19.0	19.2	19.2	19.3	19.3	19.4	19.4	19.4	19.4	19.4	19.4	19.4	19.5	19.5	19.5	19.5	19.5	19.5
3	10.1	9.55	9.28	9.12	9.01	8.94	8.89	8.85	8.81	8.79	8.74	8.70	8.66	8.64	8.62	8.59	8.57	8.55	8.53
4	7.71	6.94	6.59	6.39	6.26	6.16	6.09	6.04	6.00	5.96	5.91	5.86	5.80	5.77	5.75	5.72	5.69	5.66	5.63
5	6.61	5.79	5.41	5.19	5.05	4.95	4.88	4.82	4.77	4.74	4.68	4.62	4.56	4.53	4.50	4.46	4.43	4.40	4.37
6	5.99	5.14	4.76	4.53	4.39	4.28	4.21	4.15	4.10	4.06	4.00	3.94	3.87	3.84	3.81	3.77	3.74	3.70	3.67
7	5.59	4.74	4.35	4.12	3.97	3.87	3.79	3.73	3.68	3.64	3.57	3.51	3.44	3.41	3.38	3.34	3.30	3.27	3.23
8	5.32	4.46	4.07	3.84	3.69	3.58	3.50	3.44	3.39	3.35	3.28	3.22	3.15	3.12	3.08	3.04	3.01	2.97	2.93
9	5.12	4.26	3.86	3.63	3.48	3.37	3.29	3.23	3.18	3.14	3.07	3.01	2.94	2.90	2.86	2.83	2.79	2.75	2.71
10	4.96	4.10	3.71	3.48	3.33	3.22	3.14	3.07	3.02	2.98	2.91	2.85	2.77	2.74	2.70	2.66	2.62	2.58	2.54
11	4.84	3.98	3.59	3.36	3.20	3.09	3.01	2.95	2.90	2.85	2.79	2.72	2.65	2.61	2.57	2.53	2.49	2.45	2.40
12	4.75	3.89	3.49	3.26	3.11	3.00	2.91	2.85	2.80	2.75	2.69	2.62	2.54	2.51	2.47	2.43	2.38	2.34	2.30
13	4.67	3.81	3.41	3.18	3.03	2.92	2.83	2.77	2.71	2.67	2.60	2.53	2.46	2.42	2.38	2.34	2.30	2.25	2.21
14	4.60	3.74	3.34	3.11	2.96	2.85	2.76	2.70	2.65	2.60	2.53	2.46	2.39	2.35	2.31	2.27	2.22	2.18	2.13
15	4.54	3.68	3.29	3.06	2.90	2.79	2.71	2.64	2.59	2.54	2.48	2.40	2.33	2.29	2.25	2.20	2.16	2.11	2.07
16	4.49	3.63	3.24	3.01	2.85	2.74	2.66	2.59	2.54	2.49	2.42	2.35	2.28	2.24	2.19	2.15	2.11	2.06	2.01
17	4.45	3.59	3.20	2.96	2.81	2.70	2.61	2.55	2.49	2.45	2.38	2.31	2.23	2.19	2.15	2.10	2.06	2.01	1.96
18	4.41	3.55	3.16	2.93	2.77	2.66	2.58	2.51	2.46	2.41	2.34	2.27	2.19	2.15	2.11	2.06	2.02	1.97	1.92
19	4.38	3.52	3.13	2.90	2.74	2.63	2.54	2.48	2.42	2.38	2.31	2.23	2.16	2.11	2.07	2.03	1.98	1.93	1.88
20	4.35	3.49	3.10	2.87	2.71	2.60	2.51	2.45	2.39	2.35	2.28	2.20	2.12	2.08	2.04	1.99	1.95	1.90	1.84
21	4.32	3.47	3.07	2.84	2.68	2.57	2.49	2.42	2.37	2.32	2.25	2.18	2.10	2.05	2.01	1.96	1.92	1.87	1.81
22	4.30	3.44	3.05	2.82	2.66	2.55	2.46	2.40	2.34	2.30	2.23	2.15	2.07	2.03	1.98	1.94	1.89	1.84	1.78
23	4.28	3.42	3.03	2.80	2.64	2.53	2.44	2.37	2.32	2.27	2.20	2.13	2.05	2.01	1.96	1.91	1.86	1.81	1.76
24	4.26	3.40	3.01	2.78	2.62	2.51	2.42	2.36	2.30	2.25	2.18	2.11	2.03	1.98	1.94	1.89	1.84	1.79	1.73
25	4.24	3.39	2.99	2.76	2.60	2.49	2.40	2.34	2.28	2.24	2.16	2.09	2.01	1.96	1.92	1.87	1.82	1.77	1.71
30	4.17	3.32	2.92	2.69	2.53	2.42	2.33	2.27	2.21	2.16	2.09	2.01	1.93	1.89	1.84	1.79	1.74	1.68	1.62
40	4.08	3.23	2.84	2.61	2.45	2.34	2.25	2.18	2.12	2.08	2.00	1.92	1.84	1.79	1.74	1.69	1.64	1.58	1.51
60	4.00	3.15	2.76	2.53	2.37	2.25	2.17	2.10	2.04	1.99	1.92	1.84	1.75	1.70	1.65	1.59	1.53	1.47	1.39
120	3.92	3.07	2.68	2.45	2.29	2.18	2.09	2.02	1.96	1.91	1.83	1.75	1.66	1.61	1.55	1.50	1.43	1.35	1.25
∞	3.84	3.00	2.60	2.37	2.21	2.10	2.01	1.94	1.88	1.83	1.75	1.67	1.57	1.52	1.46	1.39	1.32	1.22	1.00

Upper 1% Points ($F_{.99}$)

Degrees of freedom for numerator (columns); Degrees of freedom for denominator (rows)

	1	2	3	4	5	6	7	8	9	10	12	15	20	24	30	40	60	120	∞
1	4052	5000	5403	5625	5764	5859	5928	5982	6023	6056	6106	6157	6209	6235	6261	6287	6313	6339	6366
2	98.5	99.0	99.2	99.2	99.3	99.3	99.4	99.4	99.4	99.4	99.4	99.4	99.4	99.5	99.5	99.5	99.5	99.5	99.5
3	34.1	30.8	29.5	28.7	28.2	27.9	27.7	27.5	27.3	27.2	27.1	26.9	26.7	26.6	26.5	26.4	26.3	26.2	26.1
4	21.2	18.0	16.7	16.0	15.5	15.2	15.0	14.8	14.7	14.5	14.4	14.2	14.0	13.9	13.8	13.7	13.7	13.6	13.5
5	16.3	13.3	12.1	11.4	11.0	10.7	10.5	10.3	10.2	10.1	9.89	9.72	9.55	9.47	9.38	9.29	9.20	9.11	9.02
6	13.7	10.9	9.78	9.15	8.75	8.47	8.26	8.10	7.98	7.87	7.72	7.56	7.40	7.31	7.23	7.14	7.06	6.97	6.88
7	12.2	9.55	8.45	7.85	7.46	7.19	6.99	6.84	6.72	6.62	6.47	6.31	6.16	6.07	5.99	5.91	5.82	5.74	5.65
8	11.3	8.65	7.59	7.01	6.63	6.37	6.18	6.03	5.91	5.81	5.67	5.52	5.36	5.28	5.20	5.12	5.03	4.95	4.86
9	10.6	8.02	6.99	6.42	6.06	5.80	5.61	5.47	5.35	5.26	5.11	4.96	4.81	4.73	4.65	4.57	4.48	4.40	4.31
10	10.0	7.56	6.55	5.99	5.64	5.39	5.20	5.06	4.94	4.85	4.71	4.56	4.41	4.33	4.25	4.17	4.08	4.00	3.91
11	9.65	7.21	6.22	5.67	5.32	5.07	4.89	4.74	4.63	4.54	4.40	4.25	4.10	4.02	3.94	3.86	3.78	3.69	3.60
12	9.33	6.93	5.95	5.41	5.06	4.82	4.64	4.50	4.39	4.30	4.16	4.01	3.86	3.78	3.70	3.62	3.54	3.45	3.36
13	9.07	6.70	5.74	5.21	4.86	4.62	4.44	4.30	4.19	4.10	3.96	3.82	3.66	3.59	3.51	3.43	3.34	3.25	3.17
14	8.86	6.51	5.56	5.04	4.70	4.46	4.28	4.14	4.03	3.94	3.80	3.66	3.51	3.43	3.35	3.27	3.18	3.09	3.00
15	8.68	6.36	5.42	4.89	4.56	4.32	4.14	4.00	3.89	3.80	3.67	3.52	3.37	3.29	3.21	3.13	3.05	2.96	2.87
16	8.53	6.23	5.29	4.77	4.44	4.20	4.03	3.89	3.78	3.69	3.55	3.41	3.26	3.18	3.10	3.02	2.93	2.84	2.75
17	8.40	6.11	5.19	4.67	4.34	4.10	3.93	3.79	3.68	3.59	3.46	3.31	3.16	3.08	3.00	2.92	2.83	2.75	2.65
18	8.29	6.01	5.09	4.58	4.25	4.01	3.84	3.71	3.60	3.51	3.37	3.23	3.08	3.00	2.92	2.84	2.75	2.66	2.57
19	8.19	5.93	5.01	4.50	4.17	3.94	3.77	3.63	3.52	3.43	3.30	3.15	3.00	2.92	2.84	2.76	2.67	2.58	2.49
20	8.10	5.85	4.94	4.43	4.10	3.87	3.70	3.56	3.46	3.37	3.23	3.09	2.94	2.86	2.78	2.69	2.61	2.52	2.42
21	8.02	5.78	4.87	4.37	4.04	3.81	3.64	3.51	3.40	3.31	3.17	3.03	2.88	2.80	2.72	2.64	2.55	2.46	2.36
22	7.95	5.72	4.82	4.31	3.99	3.76	3.59	3.45	3.35	3.26	3.12	2.98	2.83	2.75	2.67	2.58	2.50	2.40	2.31
23	7.88	5.66	4.76	4.26	3.94	3.71	3.54	3.41	3.30	3.21	3.07	2.93	2.78	2.70	2.62	2.54	2.45	2.35	2.26
24	7.82	5.61	4.72	4.22	3.90	3.67	3.50	3.36	3.26	3.17	3.03	2.89	2.74	2.66	2.58	2.49	2.40	2.31	2.21
25	7.77	5.57	4.68	4.18	3.86	3.63	3.46	3.32	3.22	3.13	2.99	2.85	2.70	2.62	2.53	2.45	2.36	2.27	2.17
30	7.56	5.39	4.51	4.02	3.70	3.47	3.30	3.17	3.07	2.98	2.84	2.70	2.55	2.47	2.39	2.30	2.21	2.11	2.01
40	7.31	5.18	4.31	3.83	3.51	3.29	3.12	2.99	2.89	2.80	2.66	2.52	2.37	2.29	2.20	2.11	2.02	1.92	1.80
60	7.08	4.98	4.13	3.65	3.34	3.12	2.95	2.82	2.72	2.63	2.50	2.35	2.20	2.12	2.03	1.94	1.84	1.73	1.60
120	6.85	4.79	3.95	3.48	3.17	2.96	2.79	2.66	2.56	2.47	2.34	2.19	2.03	1.95	1.86	1.76	1.66	1.53	1.38
∞	6.63	4.61	3.78	3.32	3.02	2.80	2.64	2.51	2.41	2.32	2.18	2.04	1.88	1.79	1.70	1.59	1.47	1.32	1.00

Interpolation should be performed using reciprocals of the degrees of freedom.

SIGNS AND SYMBOLS

Table 1-19. Symbols and Nomenclature of Chemical Engineering*

Arranged alphabetically by symbols

Symbol	Term	Units
a	Acceleration	(ft./sec.)/sec., (ft./hr.)/hr.
	Activity	
	Aperture (also A)	in.
	Surface per unit volume	sq. ft./cu. ft.
A	Aperture (also a)	in.
	Area	sq. ft. (S is used for cross-sectional area available for flow)
	Free energy, Helmholtz ($U - TS$)	B.t.u., B.t.u./lb.-mole, p.c.u., p.c.u./lb.-mole
b	Breadth, width	ft.
B	Film thickness, effective	ft.
	Residue, waste, bottoms	lb.-moles/hr.
c	Concentration, volumetric	lb./cu. ft., lb.-moles/cu. ft.
	Specific heat	B.t.u./(lb.) (°F.), p.c.u./(lb.) (°C.)
c_p	Specific heat, at constant pressure	B.t.u./(lb.) (°F.), p.c.u./(lb.) (°C.)
c_s	Humid heat	B.t.u./(lb. dry air) (°F.), p.c.u. (lb. dry air) (°C.)
c_v	Specific heat, at constant volume	B.t.u./(lb.) (°F.), p.c.u./(lb.) (°C.)
C	Coefficient, of discharge, etc.	
	Coefficient of resistance	B.t.u./(hr.) (°F.), p.c.u./(hr.)(°C.)
	Conductance (see $1/R$)	B.t.u./(hr.) (°F.), p.c.u./(hr.)(°C.)
d	Differential operator	
D	Diameter	ft.
	Distillate rate	lb.-moles/hr.
D_v	Diffusivity of vapor	sq. ft./hr.
e	Base of natural logarithms	
E	Energy, in general	B.t.u., B.t.u./lb.-mole, p.c.u., p.c.u./lb.-mole
	Energy, internal	B.t.u., B.t.u./lb., p.c.u., p.c.u./lb.
	Entrainment ratio	lb./lb., lb.-moles/lb.-mole
	Evaporation	lb.
f	Coefficient of friction	
	Friction factor, Fanning	($F = 2fLV^2/g_cD$)
	Fugacity	lb. force/sq. ft., atm.
	Activity coefficient, molal basis, see γ (gamma)	
F	Feed rate	lb.-moles/hr.
	Force, total load	lb. force
	Friction in energy balance	(ft.) (lb. force)/lb.
	See G, Free energy, Gibbs	
g	Acceleration of gravity	(ft./sec.)/sec., (ft./hr.)/hr.
g_c	Newton law of motion, conversion factor in	(lb.)(ft.)/(sec.)²(lb. force)
g_0	Acceleration of gravity, standard value	(ft./sec.)/sec., (ft./hr.)/hr.
G	Free energy, Gibbs ($H - TS$)	(F also is used)
	Mass velocity,	lb./(hr.) (sq. ft.), lb./(sec.) (sq. ft.)
h	Coefficient of heat transfer, individual	B.t.u./(hr.) (sq. ft.) (°F.), p.c.u./(hr.) (sq. ft.) (°C.)
	Enthalpy, per unit weight	B.t.u./lb., p.c.u./lb. (i is used when necessary to distinguish)
h_{fg}	Latent heat. See λ (lambda)	B.t.u., B.t.u./lb., p.c.u., p.c.u./lb.
H	Enthalpy	B.t.u., B.t.u./lb.-mole p.c.u., p.c.u./lb.-mole
	Henry's law constant c/p	(lb.-moles/cu. ft.)/atm.
	Humidity	lb./lb. dry air
H_0	Solvent present	lb.
H_p	Height equivalent to a theoretical plate, "$H.E.T.P.$"	ft.
H_R	Humidity, relative	
H_t	Height of transfer unit, "$H.T.U.$"	ft.
i	See under Enthalpy, per unit weight	
I	Moment of inertia	(ft.)⁴
j	Heat transfer factor	$(h/cG)\phi(c\mu/k)$
J	Mechanical equivalent of heat	(ft.) (lb. force)/B.t.u., (ft.) (lb. force)/p.c.u.
k	Mass transfer coefficient, individual	lb.-moles/(hr.) (sq. ft.) (atm.)
	Specific heats, ratio of	c_p/c_v, κ (kappa) and γ (gamma) also are used
	Thermal conductivity	B.t.u./(hr.) (sq. ft.) (°F./ft.), p.c.u./(hr.) (sq. ft.) (°C./ft.)
k_G	Mass transfer coefficient, gas film	lb.-moles/(hr.) (sq. ft.) (atm.)
k_L	Mass transfer coefficient, liquid film	lb.-moles/(hr.) (sq. ft.) (lb.-mole/cu. ft.)
K	Equilibrium constant, $y = Kx$	
	Mass transfer coefficient, over-all	lb.-moles/(hr.) (sq. ft.) (atm.)
K_G	Mass transfer coefficient, on gas film basis	
K_L	Mass transfer coefficient, on liquid film basis	
L	Length	ft.
	Liquid rate	lb.-moles/hr.
	Mass velocity of liquid	(lb./(hr.) (sq. ft.)
L_m	Liquid rate, below feed	lb.-moles/hr.
L_n	Liquid rate, above feed	lb.-moles/hr.
m	Mass	lb.
	Mesh (also M)	1/in.
	Slope of equilibrium curve	dy^*/dx
M	Mesh (also m)	1/in.
	Molecular weight	
n	Rate of rotation	r.p.m.
N	Number in general	
	Rate of transfer	lb.-moles/hr.
	Radiation, intensity of	B.t.u./(hr.) (sq. ft.) p.c.u./(hr.) (sq. ft.)
N_p	Plates, number of	
N_t	"Transfer units," number of	
p	Pressure	lb. force/sq. ft., atm.
P	Power	(ft.) (lb. force)/sec.
q	Rate of flow, volumetric	cu. ft./sec., cu. ft./hr.
	Rate of heat transfer	B.t.u./hr., p.c.u./hr.
	Thermal condition of feed $(L_m - L_n)/F$	
Q	Quantity of heat transferred	B.t.u., p.c.u.
r	Equivalent resistance of cloth	
	Radius	ft.
R	Gas constant	Where necessary to distinguish, use R_0
	Production rate	lb./hr.
	Reflux ratio	Use R_D for L/D, and R_V for L/V
	Resistance, thermal	°F./(B.t.u./hr.), °C./(p.c.u./hr.)
R_H	Hydraulic radius	ft., sq. ft./ft.
R_R	Reduction ratio	
s	Entropy, per unit weight	B.t.u./(lb.)(°R.), p.c.u./(lb.) (°K.)
	Exponent of compressibility of cake	
	Specific surface	sq. ft./lb., sq. cm./g.
S	Cross section	sq. ft.
	Entropy	B.t.u./(lb.) (°R.) or B.t.u./(lb.-mole) (°R.), p.c.u./(°K.) or p.c.u./(lb.-mole) (°K.)
	Solubility	lb./100 lb. solvent
t	Temperature	°F. or °C. (θ is used in some lists)
	Time (see τ (tau))	sec., hr. (θ also has been used)

* From *Trans. Am. Inst. Chem. Engrs.*, Apr. 25, 1944.

Table 1-19. Symbols and Nomenclature of Chemical Engineering*—(*Concluded*)

T	Temperature, absolute	°K. or °R. (Rankine)
u	Velocity, local	ft./sec., ft./hr.
	Internal energy per unit weight	B.t.u./lb., p.c.u./lb.
U	Energy, in general	B.t.u., B.t.u./lb.-mole, p.c.u., p.c.u./lb.-mole
	Heat transfer coefficient, over-all	B.t.u./(hr.) (sq. ft.) (°F)., p.c.u./(hr.) (sq. ft.) (°C.)
	Internal energy	B.t.u., B.t.u./lb., p.c.u., p.c.u./lb.
v	Specific volume	cu. ft./lb.
v_H	Humid volume	cu. ft./lb. dry air
V	Vapor rate	lb.-moles/hr.
	Velocity, average	ft./sec., ft./hr.
	Volume, total or per mole	cu. ft., cu. ft./lb.-mole
V_a	Velocity, acoustic	ft./sec. (c is also used)
w	Mass flow rate	lb./sec., lb./hr.
W	Free moisture content	lb./lb.
	Residue, waste, bottoms	lb.-moles/hr.
	Work	B.t.u., p.c.u. Where necessary to distinguish, use W_k
	Weight, quantity of matter	lb.
W_e	Work, external	B.t.u., p.c.u.
W_k	See W	
x	Distance in direction of flow	ft.
	Mole fraction, in liquid	
x_v	Fraction by volume	
x_w	Fraction by weight	
X	Mole ratio, in liquid	
y	Depth	ft.
	Mole fraction, in vapor	
y^*	Mole fraction, in vapor, equilibrium value	
Y	Mole ratio, in vapor	
z	Compressibility	pV/RT
Z	Distance above datum plane	ft.
α (alpha)	Angle	Degrees, radians (θ and ϕ are also used)
	Coefficient of expansion, linear	(ft./ft.)/°F., (ft./ft.)/°C.
	Diffusivity, thermal	sq. ft./hr.
	Absorptivity (for radiation)	
	Relative volatility	
	Specific cake resistance	
β (beta)	Coefficient of expansion, volumetric	(cu. ft./cu. ft.)/°F., (cu. ft./cu. ft.)/°C.
γ (gamma)	Activity coefficient, molal basis. f also is used	
Γ (capital gamma)	Weight rate of flow per unit of breadth	lb./(sec.) (ft.), (lb./(hr.) (ft.)
Δ (capital delta)	Difference, finite; often that causing flow	
ϵ (epsilon)	Emissivity (for radiation)	
η (eta)	Efficiency	
θ (theta)	See τ (tau), α (alpha)	
κ (kappa)	Specific heats, ratio of: c_p/c_v	
λ (lambda)	Latent heat of evaporation	B.t.u./lb., p.c.u./lb.
μ (mu)	Viscosity, absolute	lb./(sec.) (ft.), lb./(hr.) (ft.)
$1/\mu$	Fluidity	(sec.) (ft.)/lb.
μ/μ_w	Viscosity, relative to water	
ν (nu)	Viscosity, kinematic η (eta) also is used	sq. ft./sec., sq. ft./hr.
ρ (rho)	Density	lb./cu. ft.
σ (sigma)	Surface tension	lb. force/ft., dynes/cm.
	Stefan-Boltzmann constant	
τ (tau)	See t (Time) [Θ (theta) also has been used]	sec., hr.
	Tractive force per unit area	lb. force/sq. ft.
ϕ, ψ, χ (phi, psi, chi)	Function	
	See α (alpha)	
ω (omega)	Solid angle	
	Velocity, angular	

Table 1-20. Mathematical Signs, Symbols, and Abbreviations

$\pm$ ($\mp$)	plus or minus (minus or plus)
$:$	divided by, ratio sign
$::$	proportional sign
$<$	less than
$\nless$	not less than
$>$	greater than
$\ngtr$	not greater than
$\cong$	approximately equals, congruent
$\sim$	similar to
$\Leftrightarrow$	equivalent to
$\neq$	not equal to
$\doteq$	approaches, is approximately equal to
$\propto$	varies as
∞	infinity
$\therefore$	therefore
$\sqrt{\ }$	square root
$\sqrt[3]{\ }$	cube root
$\sqrt[n]{\ }$	nth root
$\angle$	angle
$\perp$	perpendicular to
$\parallel$	parallel to
$\lvert x\rvert$	numerical value of x
log or $\log_{10}$	common logarithm or Briggsian logarithm
$\log_e$ or ln	natural logarithm or hyperbolic logarithm or Naperian logarithm
e	base (2.718) of natural system of logarithms
a°	an angle a degrees
a'	a prime, an angle a minutes
a''	a double prime, an angle a seconds, a second
sin	sine
cos	cosine
tan	tangent
ctn or cot	cotangent
sec	secant
csc	cosecant
vers	versed sine
covers	coversed sine
exsec	exsecant
$\sin^{-1}$	anti sine or angle whose sine is
sinh	hyperbolic sine
cosh	hyperbolic cosine
tanh	hyperbolic tangent
$\sinh^{-1}$	anti hyperbolic sine or angle whose hyperbolic sine is
$f(x)$ or $\phi(x)$	function of x
Δx	increment of x
Σ	summation of
dx	differential of x
dy/dx or y'	derivative of y with respect to x
d^2y/dx^2 or y''	second derivative of y with respect to x
d^ny/dx^n	nth derivative of y with respect to x
$\partial y/\partial x$	partial derivative of y with respect to x
$\partial^n y/\partial x^n$	nth partial derivative of y with respect to x
$\dfrac{\partial^n y}{\partial x\,\partial y}$	nth partial derivative with respect to x and y
$\int$	integral of
$\int_a^b$	integral between the limits a and b
$\dot{y}$	first derivative of y with respect to time
$\ddot{y}$	second derivative of y with respect to time
Δ or ∇^2	the "Laplacian" $\left(\dfrac{\partial^2}{\partial x^2}+\dfrac{\partial^2}{\partial y^2}+\dfrac{\partial^2}{\partial z^2}\right)$
δ	sign of a variation
$\oint$	sign for integration around a closed path

SECTION 2

MATHEMATICS

BY

Arthur E. Hoerl, M.A., Group Supervisor, Engineering Department, E. I. du Pont de Nemours & Company.

AND

William F. Ames, M.S., Associate Professor, Department of Mechanical Engineering, University of Delaware.

WITH

Robert J. Hunn, M.S., Senior Service Engineer, Engineering Department, E. I. du Pont de Nemours & Company. (Machine Computation)

John J. McKetta, Ph.D., Graduate Professor and Chairman, Department of Chemical Engineering, University of Texas. (Dimensional Analysis)

I. H. Silberberg, Ph.D., Assistant Professor, Department of Chemical Engineering, University of Texas. (Dimensional Analysis)

CONTENTS

DIFFERENTIAL EQUATIONS

DIFFERENCE EQUATIONS

INTEGRAL EQUATIONS

INTEGRAL TRANSFORMS

NUMERICAL APPROXIMATIONS

NUMERICAL AND APPROXIMATE METHODS

STATISTICAL ANALYSIS

MACHINE COMPUTATION

DIMENSIONAL ANALYSIS

MATHEMATICS

MISCELLANEOUS MATHEMATICAL CONSTANTS

π	$= 3.1415926536$	Pi
e	$= 2.7182818285$	Naperian logarithm base
γ	$= 0.5772156649$	Euler's constant
$\ln \pi$	$= 1.1447298858$	Naperian (natural) logarithm of pi
$\log \pi$	$= 0.4971498727$	Briggsian (common) logarithm of pi
$\log x$	$= 0.4342944819 \ln x$	Logarithm conversion
$\ln x$	$= 2.302585093 \log x$	Logarithm conversion

$\sqrt{e} = 1.6487217208$	$\log e = 0.4342944819$
$\sqrt{\pi} = 1.7724538510$	$\ln 10 = 2.3025850930$
$\sqrt{\pi/2} = 1.2533141371$	$\ln 2 = 0.6931471806$
$\sqrt{\pi/3} = 1.0233267080$	$\log (\log e) = 9.637784311 - 10$
$\sqrt{2\pi} = 2.5066282766$	$\sqrt{2} = 1.4142135624$
$\sqrt{0.1} = 0.3162277660$	$\sqrt{3} = 1.7320508076$
Radian $= 57.2957795131$ degrees	$\sqrt{5} = 2.2360679975$
Degree $= 0.0174532925$ radian	$\sqrt{6} = 2.4494897428$
Minute $= 0.0002908882$ radian	$\sqrt{7} = 2.6457513111$
Second $= 0.0000048481$ radian	$\sqrt{8} = 2.8284271247$
$\sqrt{\gamma} = 0.7597471058$	$\sqrt{10} = 3.1622776602$

POWERS, ROOTS, AND PROPORTIONS

	Indeterminants	Example*	
$a^0 = 1 (a \neq 0)$	$(\infty)(0)$	Xe^{-X}	$X \to \infty$
$0^a = 0 (a \neq 0)$	0^0	X^X	$X \to 0$
$a^\infty = 0 (a < 1)$	∞^0	$\left(\frac{1}{1-X}\right)^{1-X}$	$X \to 1$
$a^\infty = \infty (a > 1)$	1^∞	$(1-X)^{1/X}$	$X \to 0$
$\infty^a = \infty (a > 0)$	$(\infty - \infty)$	$\sec X - \tan X$	$X \to \frac{\pi}{2}$
$\infty^a = 0 (a < 0)$	0^∞	$(1-X)^{\frac{1}{1-X}}$	$X \to 1$
$1^0 = 1$	$0/0$	$\frac{1 - \sin X}{\cos X}$	$X \to \frac{\pi}{2}$
	∞/∞	$\frac{\ln (X - \pi/2)}{\tan X}$	$X \to \frac{\pi}{2}$

* See Limit, p. 2-23.

$a^{-n} = 1/a^n$

$(ab)^n = a^n b^n$

$(a^n)^m = a^{nm}$

$\sqrt[n]{a} = a^{1/n}$

$\sqrt[m]{\sqrt[n]{a}} = \sqrt[mn]{a}$

$a^{m/n} = (a^m)^{1/n} = \sqrt[n]{a^m}$

For $\boxed{\frac{a}{b} = \frac{c}{d}}$

Then $\frac{a+b}{b} = \frac{c+d}{d}$

$\frac{a-b}{b} = \frac{c-d}{d}$

$\frac{a-b}{a+b} = \frac{c-d}{c+d}$

$\frac{a+b}{a-b} = \frac{c+d}{c-d}$

$\log ab = \log a + \log b \qquad \log a^n = n \log a$

$\log \frac{a}{b} = \log a - \log b \qquad \log \sqrt[n]{a} = \frac{1}{n} \log a$

Computing Formula for Roots.

For $S = \sqrt[n]{X} = (X)^{1/n}$

Compute $S = \exp\left(\frac{\ln X}{n}\right)$

or **numerically**

Square Root. Find $S = \sqrt{155.96}$.

Direct.

```
     1 2 . 4  9
  1 √155.96 00        S = 12.49
    -1
   2̲2|55
      44
  24̲4|11 96
     -9 76
 248̲9|2 20 00
```

Iteration.

$$S_{i+1} = \frac{1}{2}\left(\frac{X}{S_i} + S_i\right)$$

Assume $S_1 = 12$. For $X = 155.96$

$$S_2 = \frac{1}{2}\left(\frac{155.96}{12} + 12\right) = 12.4983$$

$S_3 = 12.488398$

$S_4 = 12.48839461$

Correct to eight decimal places

Cube Root.

Direct for $S = (155.96)^{1/3}$.

```
                       5 .  3   8
                 25 ∛155.960 000
                     125
  30*(5)(53) + 3²  | 30 960
             = 7959 | 23 877
  30(53)(538) + 8² | 7 083 000
           = 855484 | 6 843 872
```

Iteration for $S = (X)^{1/3} = (15.596)^{1/3}$.

$$S_{i+1} = \frac{2}{3} S_i + \frac{X}{3S_i^2}$$

Use $S_1 = 1$ or let $\sqrt[3]{X} = \sqrt[3]{{}_\wedge NNN}\,(10^{P/3+R/3})$ where $P/3$ integer and $10^{1/3} = 2.154$, $10^{2/3} = 4.642$.

Then $\sqrt[3]{{}_\wedge NNN} = (0.15596)^{1/3}$ with $R = 2$.

The first approximation to $\sqrt[3]{{}_\wedge NNN}$ is

$0.349 + 1.387K - 1.236K^2 + 0.505K^3$, $K = {}_\wedge NNN$

* Always 30 for cube root.

For $S = (15.596)^{1/3} = (0.15596 \times 10^2)^{1/3}$

$$S_1 = \sqrt[3]{0.15596}\,(4.642) = 0.5372(4.642) = 2.494$$

$$S_2 = \frac{2}{3}(2.494) + \frac{1}{3}\left[\frac{15.596}{(2.494)^2}\right] = 2.49846$$

$$S_3 = \frac{2}{3}(2.49846) + \frac{1}{3}\left[\frac{15.596}{(2.49846)^2}\right] = 2.4984524$$

GENERAL

The basic problems of the sciences and engineering fall broadly into three categories:

1. "Equilibrium problems." These are problems of steady state. In such problems the configuration of the system is to be determined. This solution does not change with time but continues indefinitely in the same pattern, hence the name steady state. Typical chemical engineering examples include steady temperature distributions in heat conduction, equilibrium in chemical reactions, and steady diffusion problems.
2. "Eigenvalue problems." These are extensions of equilibrium problems in which critical values of certain parameters are to be determined in addition to the corresponding steady-state configurations. The determination of eigenvalues may also arise in propagation problems. Typical chemical engineering problems include those in heat transfer and resonance in which certain boundary conditions are prescribed.
3. "Propagation problems." These problems are concerned with predicting the subsequent behavior of a system from a knowledge of the initial state. For this reason they are often called the transient (time-varying) or unsteady-state phenomena. Chemical engineering examples include the transient state of chemical reactions (kinetics), the propagation of pressure waves in a fluid, transient behavior of an adsorption column, and the rate of approach to equilibrium of a packed distillation column.

The mathematical treatment of engineering problems involves four basic steps:

1. *Formulation.* The expression of the problem in mathematical language. That translation is based on the appropriate physical laws governing the process.
2. *Solution.* Appropriate mathematical operations are accomplished so that logical deductions may be drawn from the mathematical model.
3. *Interpretation.* Development of relations between the mathematical results and their meaning in the physical world.
4. *Refinement.* The recycling of the procedure to obtain better predictions as indicated by experimental checks.

Steps 1 and 2 are of primary interest here. The actual details are left to the various subsections, and only general approaches will be discussed here.

The formulation step may result in algebraic equations, difference equations, differential equations, integral equations, or combinations of these. In any event these mathematical models usually arise from statements of physical laws such as the laws of mass and energy conservation in the form

Input of conserved quantity − output of conserved quantity + conserved quantity produced = accumulation of conserved quantity

Rate of input of conserved quantity − rate of output of conserved quantity + rate of conserved quantity produced = rate of accumulation of conserved quantity

These statements may be abbreviated by the statement

Input − output + production = accumulation

When the basic physical laws are expressed in this form the formulation is greatly facilitated. These expressions are quite often given the name "material balance," "energy balance," and so forth. To be a little more specific, one could write the law of conservation of energy in the steady state as

Rate of energy in − rate of energy out + rate of energy produced = 0

Many general laws of the physical universe are expressible by differential equations. Specific phenomena are then singled out from the infinity of solutions of these equations by assigning the individual initial or boundary conditions which characterize the given problem. In mathematical language one such problem, the equilibrium problem, is called a *boundary-value* problem (Fig. 2-1). Schematically the problem is characterized by a

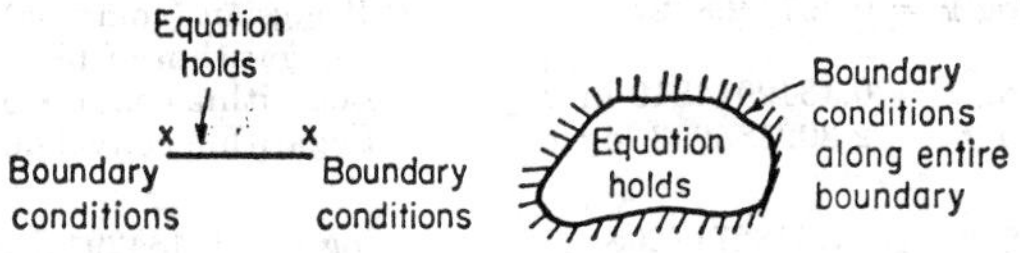

FIG. 2-1. Boundary conditions.

differential equation plus a closed region in which the equation holds, and on the boundaries of the region certain conditions (boundary conditions) are dictated by the physical problem. The solution of the equation must satisfy the differential equation inside the region and the prescribed conditions on the boundary.

In mathematical language the propagation problem is known as an initial-value problem (Fig. 2-2). Schematically the problem is characterized by a differential

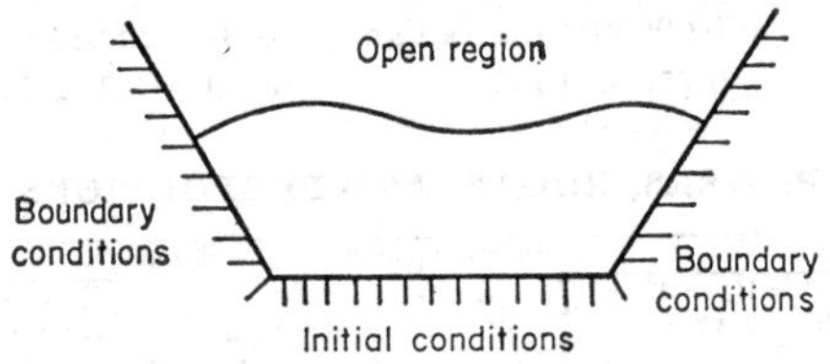

FIG. 2-2. Propagation problem.

equation plus an open region in which the equation holds. The solution of the differential equation must satisfy the initial conditions plus any "side" boundary conditions.

L. F. Richardson (1925) used descriptive phrases in illustrating the differences between these two problems. He called the equilibrium problem a *jury* problem and the propagation problem a *marching* problem. In the former the entire solution is examined and judged by a jury demanding simultaneous satisfaction of all the boundary conditions and all the internal requirements. In the latter the solution marches out from initial conditions guided in transit by "side" boundary conditions.

The description of phenomena in a "continuous" medium such as a gas or fluid leads oftentimes to partial differential equations. In particular, phenomena of "wave" propagation are described by a class of partial differential equations called "hyperbolic," and these are essentially different in their properties from other classes such as those which describe equilibrium ("elliptic") or diffusion and heat transfer ("parabolic"). *Prototypes* are:

Elliptic. Laplace's equation

$$\frac{\partial^2 u}{\partial x^2} + \frac{\partial^2 u}{\partial y^2} = 0$$

Poisson's equation

$$\frac{\partial^2 u}{\partial x^2} + \frac{\partial^2 u}{\partial y^2} = g(x, y)$$

These do not contain the variable t (time) explicitly; accordingly their solutions represent equilibrium configurations. Laplace's equation corresponds to a "natural" equilibrium, while Poisson's equation corresponds to an equilibrium under the influence of an external force of density proportional to $g(x, y)$.

Parabolic. The heat equation

$$\frac{\partial u}{\partial t} = \frac{\partial^2 u}{\partial x^2} + \frac{\partial^2 u}{\partial y^2}$$

describes non-equilibrium or propagation states of diffusion as well as heat transfer.

Hyperbolic. The wave equation

$$\frac{\partial^2 u}{\partial t^2} = \frac{\partial^2 u}{\partial x^2} + \frac{\partial^2 u}{\partial y^2}$$

describes wave propagation of all types, when the assumption is made that the wave amplitude is small and that interactions are linear.

The solution phase has been characterized in the past by a concentration on methods to obtain analytic solutions to the mathematical equations. These efforts have been most fruitful in the area of the linear equations such as those given directly above. However, many natural phenomena are non-linear and the present mathematical methods prove to be well-nigh unworkable. Thus formulation of the phenomena in the language generalized from the calculus does very little to help lessen our ignorance of the problem. When such situations arise, the only way open to us seems to be to retrace our steps to the time before calculus was invented. This represents the essence of an increasingly important area called numerical analysis. Thus the approach in solving a problem is to use the methods of the calculus when they represent a short cut but to avoid them by a recourse to algebra when they become unmanageable.

Numerical methods almost never fail to provide an answer to any particular situation but they can never furnish a general solution of any problem.

The mathematical details outlined here include both analytic and numerical techniques found to be useful in obtaining solutions to problems.

Our discussion to this point has been confined to those areas in which the governing laws are well known. However, in many areas, information is lacking on the governing laws, yet work must progress in these areas. Interest in the application of statistical methods to all types of problems has grown rapidly since World War II. Broadly speaking, statistical methods may be of use whenever conclusions are to be drawn or decisions made on the basis of experimental evidence. Since statistics could be defined as the technology of the scientific method it is primarily concerned with the first two aspects of the method, namely, the performance of experiments and the drawing of conclusions from experiments. Traditionally the field is divided into two areas:

1. *The Design of Experiments.* When conclusions are to be drawn or decisions made on the basis of experimental evidence statistical techniques are most useful where the experimental data are subject to errors. The design of experiments may then often be done in such a fashion as to avoid some of the sources of experimental error and make the necessary allowances for that portion which is unavoidable. Secondly the results can be presented in terms of probability statements which express the reliability of the results. Thirdly a statistical approach frequently forces a more complete and thorough evaluation of the experimental aims and leads to a more definitive experiment than would otherwise have been performed.

2. *Statistical Inference.* The broad problem of satistical inference is to provide measures of the uncertainty of conclusions drawn from experimental data. This area uses the theory of probability, enabling the scientist to assess the reliability of his conclusions in terms of probability statements.

Both these areas, the mathematical and the statistical, are intimately intertwined when applied to any given situation. The methods of one are often combined with the other. And both in order to be successfully used must result in the numerical answer to a problem—that is, they constitute the means to an end. Increasingly the numerical answer is being obtained from the mathematics with the aid of computing devices. These can be roughly divided into analog and digital computers.

The mathematics section is then broken up into three broad interrelated areas, mathematics, statistics, and computation devices.

MENSURATION FORMULAS

Let A denote areas and V volumes in the following:

PLANE GEOMETRIC FIGURES WITH STRAIGHT BOUNDARIES

Triangles (see also Trigonometry). $A = \frac{1}{2}bh$ where b = base, h = altitude.

Rectangle. $A = ab$ where a and b are the lengths of the sides.

Parallelogram (opposite sides parallel). $A = ah = ab \sin \alpha$ where a, b are the lengths of the sides, h the height, and α the angle between the sides.

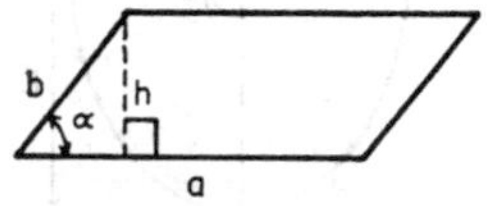

FIG. 2-3. Parallelogram.

Rhombus (equilateral parallelogram). $A = \frac{1}{2}ab$ where a, b are the lengths of the diagonals.

Trapezoid (four sides, two parallel). $A = \frac{1}{2}(a + b)h$ where the lengths of the parallel sides are a and b and h = height.

Quadrilateral (four-sided). $A = \frac{1}{2}ab \sin \theta$ where a, b are the lengths of the diagonals and the acute angle between them is θ.

Regular Polygon of n Sides.

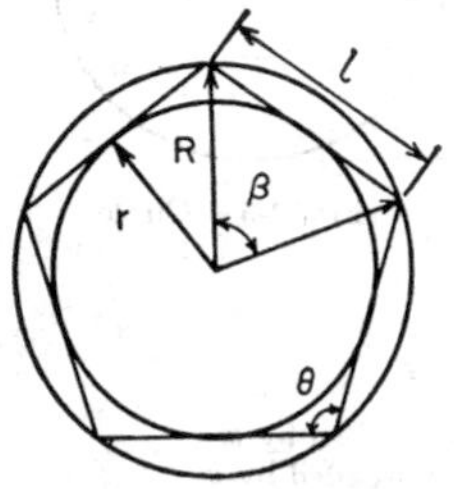

FIG. 2-4. Polygon.

$A = \frac{1}{4} nl^2 \cot \frac{180 \text{ deg.}}{n}$ where l = length of each side

$R = \frac{l}{2} \csc \frac{180 \text{ deg.}}{n}$ where R is the radius of the circumscribed circle

$r = \frac{l}{2} \cot \frac{180 \text{ deg.}}{n}$ where r is the radius of the inscribed circle

$\beta = \frac{360 \text{ deg.}}{n}$

$\theta = \frac{(n-2)\ 180 \text{ deg.}}{n}$

$l = 2r \tan \frac{\beta}{2} = 2R \sin \frac{\beta}{2}$

Inscribed and Circumscribed Circles with Regular Polygon of n Sides. Let l = length of one side.

Figure	n	Area	Radius of circumscribed circle	Radius of inscribed circle
Equilateral triangle	3	$0.4330\ l^2$	$0.5774\ l$	$0.2887\ l$
Square	4	$1.0000\ l^2$	$0.7071\ l$	$0.5000\ l$
Pentagon	5	$1.7205\ l^2$	$0.8507\ l$	$0.6882\ l$
Hexagon	6	$2.5981\ l^2$	$1.0000\ l$	$0.8660\ l$
Heptagon	7	$3.6339\ l^2$	$1.1523\ l$	$1.0383\ l$
Octagon	8	$4.8284\ l^2$	$1.3065\ l$	$1.2071\ l$
Nonagon	9	$6.1818\ l^2$	$1.4619\ l$	$1.3737\ l$
Decagon	10	$7.6942\ l^2$	$1.6180\ l$	$1.5388\ l$

Radius r of circle inscribed in triangle with sides a, b, c:

$$r = \sqrt{\frac{(s-a)(s-b)(s-c)}{s}} \qquad \text{where } s = \tfrac{1}{2}(a+b+c)$$

Radius R of circumscribed circle:

$$R = \frac{abc}{4\sqrt{s(s-a)(s-b)(s-c)}}$$

Area of polygon inscribed in a circle of radius r:

$$A = \frac{nr^2}{2} \sin \frac{360 \text{ deg.}}{n}$$

Perimeter of inscribed polygon:

$$P = 2nr \sin \frac{180 \text{ deg.}}{n}$$

Area of polygon circumscribed about a circle of radius r:

$$A = nr^2 \tan \frac{180 \text{ deg.}}{n}$$

PLANE GEOMETRIC FIGURES WITH CURVED BOUNDARIES

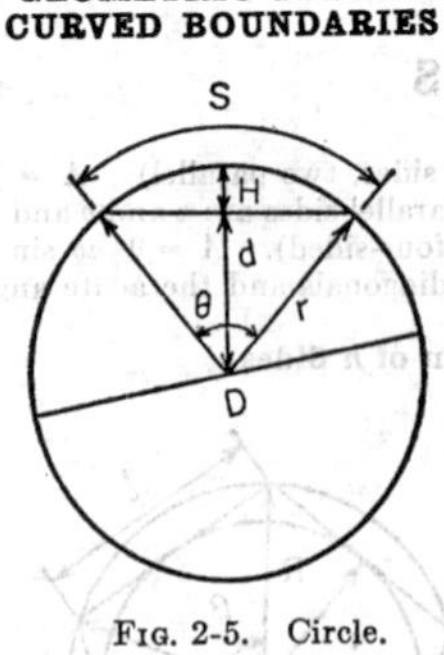

Fig. 2-5. Circle.

Circle. Let
C = circumference
r = radius
D = diameter
A = area
S = arc length subtended by θ
l = cord length subtended by θ
H = rise, $r - H = d$
θ = central angle, radians

$C = 2\pi r = \pi D \qquad (\pi = 3.14159\ \ldots)$

$S = r\theta = \tfrac{1}{2}D\theta$

$l = 2\sqrt{r^2 - d^2} = 2r \sin \frac{\theta}{2} = 2d \tan \frac{\theta}{2}$

$H = r - d$

$d = \frac{1}{2}\sqrt{4r^2 - l^2} = \frac{1}{2} l \cot \frac{\theta}{2}$

$\theta = \frac{S}{r} = 2 \cos^{-1} \frac{d}{r} = 2 \sin^{-1} \frac{l}{D}$

$A \text{ (circle)} = \pi r^2 = \tfrac{1}{4}\pi D^2$

$A \text{ (sector)} = \tfrac{1}{2} rS = \tfrac{1}{2} r^2\theta$

$A \text{ (segment)} = A \text{ (sector)} - A \text{ (triangle)} = \tfrac{1}{2} r^2(\theta - \sin\theta)$

$= r^2 \cos^{-1} \frac{r - H}{r} - (r - H)\sqrt{2rH - H^2}$

Ring (area between two circles of radius r_1 and r_2). (The circles need not be concentric but one of the circles must enclose the other.)

$$A = \pi(r_1 + r_2)(r_1 - r_2) \qquad r_1 > r_2$$

Ellipse. Let the semiaxes of the ellipse be a and b

$$A = \pi ab$$
$$C = 4aE(k)$$

where $k = 1 - (b^2/a^2)$ and $E(k)$ is the complete elliptic integral of the first kind (an approximation for the circumference $C = 2\pi\sqrt{\frac{a^2 + b^2}{2}}$).

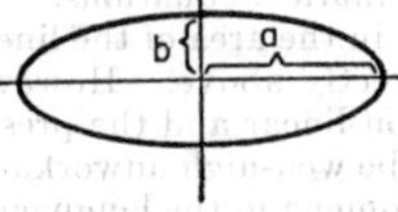

Fig. 2-6. Ellipse.

Parabola.

Length of arc $EFG = \sqrt{4x^2 + y^2} + \frac{y^2}{2x} \ln \frac{2x + \sqrt{4x^2 + y^2}}{y}$

Area of section $EFG = \tfrac{4}{3} xy$

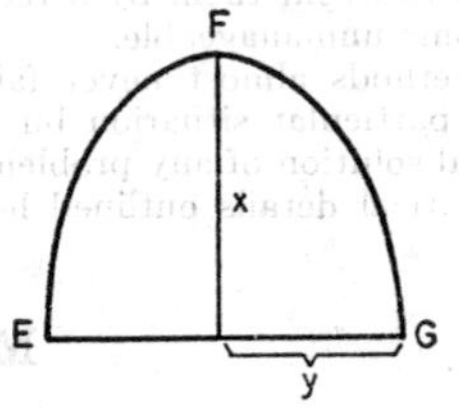

Fig. 2-7. Parabola.

Catenary (the curve formed by a cord of uniform weight suspended freely between two points).

$$y = a \cosh x$$

Length of arc s is approximately $L[1 + \tfrac{8}{3}(2B/L)^2]$ if $B \ll L$.

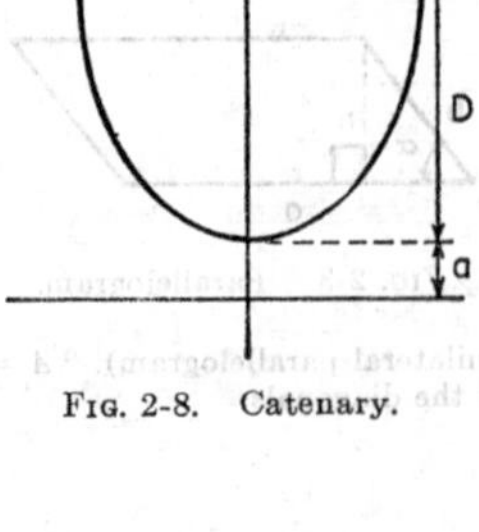

Fig. 2-8. Catenary.

SOLID GEOMETRIC FIGURES WITH PLANE BOUNDARIES

Cube. Volume $= a^3$; total surface area $= 6a^2$; diagonal $= a\sqrt{3}$, where a = length of one side of the cube.

Rectangular Parallelepiped. Volume $= abc$; surface area $= 2(ab + ac + bc)$; diagonal $= \sqrt{a^2 + b^2 + c^2}$ where a, b, c are the lengths of the sides.

Prism. Volume = (area of base) · (altitude); lateral surface area = (perimeter of right section) · (lateral edge).

Pyramid. Volume = ⅓ (area of base) · (altitude); lateral area of regular pyramid = ½ (perimeter of base) · (slant height) = ½ (number of sides) (length of one side) (slant height).

Frustum of Pyramid (formed from the pyramid by cutting off the top with a plane, usually parallel to the base).

$$V = \tfrac{1}{3}(A_1 + A_2 + \sqrt{A_1 \cdot A_2})h$$

where h = altitude and A_1, A_2 are the areas of the base; lateral area of a regular figure = ½ (sum of the perimeters of base) · (slant height).

Volume and Surface Area of Regular Polyhedra with Edge l.

Type of surface	Name	Volume	Surface area
4 equilateral triangles	Tetrahedron	$0.1179\ l^3$	$1.7321\ l^2$
6 squares	Hexahedron (cube)	$1.0000\ l^3$	$6.0000\ l^2$
8 equilateral triangles	Octahedron	$0.4714\ l^3$	$3.4641\ l^2$
12 pentagons	Dodecahedron	$7.6631\ l^3$	$20.6458\ l^2$
20 equilateral triangles	Icosahedron	$2.1817\ l^3$	$8.6603\ l^2$

SOLIDS BOUNDED BY CURVED SURFACES

Cylinders. V = (area of base) · (altitude); lateral surface area = (perimeter of right section) · (lateral edge).

Right circular cylinder. $V = \pi$ (radius)² · (altitude); Lateral surface area $= 2\pi$ (radius) · (altitude).

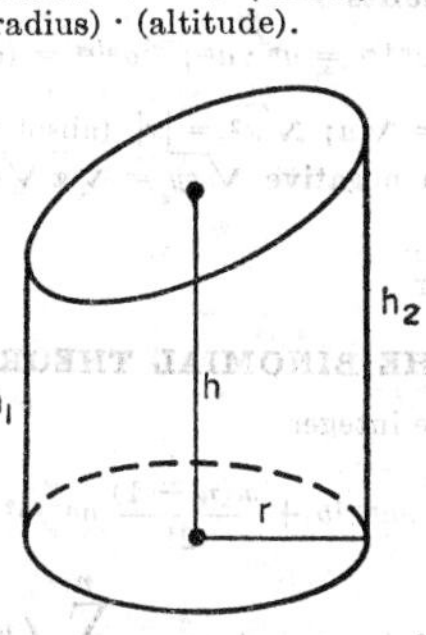

FIG. 2-9. Cylinder.

Truncated right circular cylinder.
$V = \pi r^2 h$; lateral area $= 2\pi rh$
$h = \tfrac{1}{2}(h_1 + h_2)$

Hollow cylinders. Volume $= \pi h(R^2 - r^2)$ where r and R are the internal and external radii and h is the height of the cylinder.

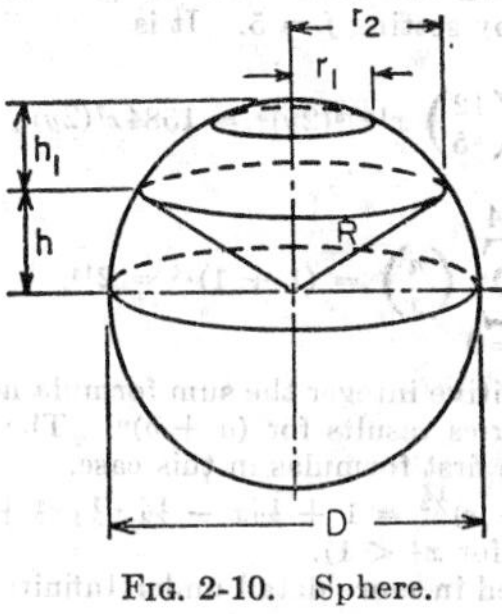

FIG. 2-10. Sphere.

Sphere.
V (sphere) $= \tfrac{4}{3}\pi R^3 = \tfrac{1}{6}\pi D^3$
V (spherical sector) $= \tfrac{2}{3}\pi R^2 h = \tfrac{1}{6}\pi D^2 h$
V (spherical segment of one base) $= \tfrac{1}{6}\pi h_1(3r_1^2 + h_1^2)$
V (spherical segment of two bases) $= \tfrac{1}{6}\pi h(3r_1^2 + 3r_2^2 + h^2)$
A (sphere) $= 4\pi R^2 = \pi D^2$
A (zone) $= 2\pi Rh = \pi Dh$
A (lune on the surface included between two great circles whose inclination is θ radians) $= 2R^2\theta$

Cone. V = ⅓ (area of base) · (altitude).

Right circular cone. $V = \dfrac{\pi}{3} r^2 h$ where h is the altitude and r is the radius of the base; curved surface area $= \pi r\sqrt{r^2 + h^2}$, curved surface of the *frustum of a right cone* $= \pi(r_1 + r_2)\sqrt{h^2 + (r_1 - r_2)^2}$ where r_1, r_2 are the radii of the base and top, respectively, and h is the altitude; volume of the frustum of a right cone $= \pi(h/3)(r_1^2 + r_1 r_2 + r_2^2) = \tfrac{1}{3}(A_1 + A_2 + \sqrt{A_1 A_2})$ where A_1 = area of base and A_2 = area of top.

Ellipsoid. $V = (\tfrac{4}{3})\pi abc$ where a, b, c are the lengths of the semiaxes.

Torus (obtained by rotating a circle of radius r about a line whose distance is $R > r$ from the center of the circle).

$$V = 2\pi^2 Rr^2 \qquad \text{Surface area} = 4\pi^2 Rr$$

Prolate Spheroid [formed by rotating an ellipse about its major axis $(2a)$]

$$\text{Surface area} = 2\pi b^2 + 2\pi(ab/e)\sin^{-1} e \qquad V = \tfrac{4}{3}\pi ab^2$$

where a, b are the major and minor axes and e = eccentricity $(e < 1)$.

Oblate Spheroid [formed by the rotation of an ellipse about its minor axis $(2b)$]. Data as above.

$$\text{Surface area} = 2\pi a^2 + \pi \frac{b^2}{e} \ln \frac{1+e}{1-e} \qquad V = \tfrac{4}{3}\pi a^2 b$$

MISCELLANEOUS FORMULAS (See also Calculus)

Volume of a Solid of Revolution (the solid generated by rotating a plane area about the x axis). $V = \pi \int_a^b [f(x)]^2\,dx$ where $y = f(x)$ is the equation of the plane curve and $a \leq x \leq b$.

Area of a Surface of Revolution.

$$S = 2\pi \int_a^b y\,ds$$

where $ds = \sqrt{1 + (dy/dx)^2}\,dx$ and $y = f(x)$ is the equation of the plane curve rotated about the x axis to generate the surface.

Area bounded by $f(x)$, the x axis, and the lines $x = a$, $x = b$.

$$A = \int_a^b f(x)\,dx$$

Length of Arc of a Plane Curve.

If $y = f(x)$

$$\text{Length of arc } s = \int_a^b \sqrt{1 + \left(\frac{dy}{dx}\right)^2}\,dx$$

If $x = g(y)$

$$\text{Length of arc } s = \int_c^d \sqrt{1 + \left(\frac{dx}{dy}\right)^2}\,dy$$

If $x = f(t)$, $y = g(t)$ $\quad s = \displaystyle\int_{t_0}^{t_1} \sqrt{\left(\frac{dx}{dt}\right)^2 + \left(\frac{dy}{dt}\right)^2}\,dt$

In general $(ds)^2 = (dx)^2 + (dy)^2$.

The Theorems of Pappus (for volumes and areas of surfaces of revolution).

1. If a plane area is revolved about a line which lies in its plane but does not intersect the area, then the volume generated is equal to the product of the area and the distance traveled by the area's center of gravity.

2. If an arc of a plane curve is revolved about a line which lies in its plane but does not intersect the arc, then the surface area generated by the arc is equal to the product of the length of the arc and the distance traveled by its center of gravity.

These theorems are useful for determining volumes V and surface areas S of solids of revolution if the centers of gravity are known. If S and V are known the centers of gravity may be determined.

IRREGULAR AREAS AND VOLUMES

Irregular Areas. Let $y_0, y_1, \ldots, y_n$ be the lengths of a series of equally spaced parallel chords and h be their distance

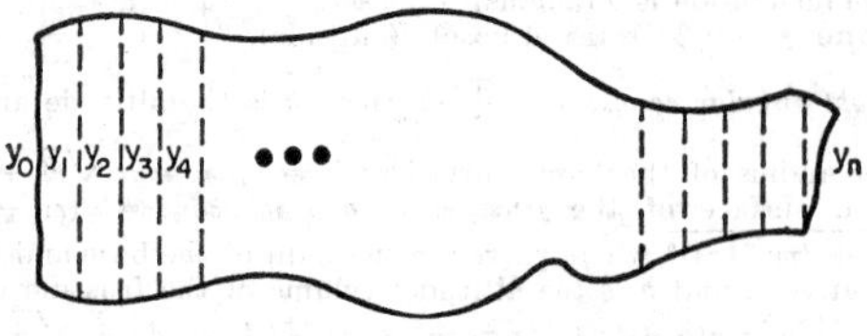

FIG. 2-11. Irregular area.

apart. The area of the figure is given approximately by any of the following:

$$A_T = \frac{h}{3}[(y_0 + y_n) + 2(y_1 + y_2 + \cdots + y_{n-1})]$$

(trapezoidal rule)

$$A_S = \frac{h}{3}[(y_0 + y_n) + 4(y_1 + y_3 + y_5 + \cdots + y_{n-1}) + 2(y_2 + y_4 + \cdots + y_{n-2})]$$

(n even, Simpson's rule)

$$A_W = \frac{3h}{8}[(y_0 + y_n) + 3(y_1 + y_2 + y_4 + y_5 + \cdots) + 2(y_3 + y_6 + \cdots)]$$

(Weddle's $\frac{3}{8}$ rule)

The greater the value of n, the greater the accuracy of approximation.

Irregular Volumes. To find the volume, replace the y's above by cross-sectional areas A_j and use the results in the above equations.

ALGEBRA

REFERENCES: Frazer, Duncan, and Collar, "Elementary Matrices," Cambridge, New York, 1938 (applications to dynamics and vibrations). MacDuffee, "The Theory of Matrices," Chelsea Publishing Co., New York, 1946 (mathematical theory). Zurmuhl, "Matrizen," Springer, Berlin, 1950 (theory and applications to electric circuits, differential equations, and numerical techniques). Bodewig, "Matrix Calculus," Interscience, New York, 1956 (exposition of numerical methods). Kaufman and Densi-Papin, "Course de calcul matricel," Albin Michel, Paris, 1951 (theory and applications).

OPERATIONS ON ALGEBRAIC EXPRESSIONS

An algebraic expression will here be denoted as a combination of letters and numbers such as

$$3ax - 3xy + 7x^2 + 7x^{3/2} - 2.8xy$$

Addition and Subtraction. Only like terms can be added or subtracted in two algebraic expressions.

Example 1. $(3x + 4xy - x^2) + (3x^2 + 2x - 8xy) = 5x - 4xy + 2x^2$.

Example 2. $(2^x + 3xy - 4x^{1/2}) + (3^x + 6x - 8xy) = 2^x + 3^x + 6x - 5xy - 4x^{1/2}$.

Multiplication. Multiplication of algebraic expressions is term by term and corresponding terms are combined.

Example. $(3xy + 6x + x^2 - y)(2x + 3y - 7) = 3xy(2x + 3y - 7) + 6x(2x + 3y - 7) + x^2(2x + 3y - 7) - y(2x + 3y - 7) = 2x^3 + 9x^2y + 9xy^2 + xy + 5x^2 - 42x - 3y^2 + 7y$.

Division. This operation is analogous to that in arithmetic.

Example. Divide $3e^{2x} + e^x + 1$ by $e^x + 1$.

```
                   Dividend
Divisor  e^x + 1 | 3e^2x + e^x + 1  | 3e^x - 2   Quotient
                   3e^2x + 3e^x
                          -2e^x + 1
                          -2e^x - 2
                                + 3   (Remainder)
```

Therefore, $3e^{2x} + e^x + 1 = (e^x + 1)(3e^x - 2) + 3$.

Operations with Zero. All numerical computations (except division) can be done with zero.

$a + 0 = 0 + a = a$; $a - 0 = a$; $0 - a = -a$; $(a)(0) = 0$; $a^0 = 1$; $0/a = 0$, $a \neq 0$.

$a/0$ and $0/0$ have no meaning.

Fractional Operations

$$-\frac{x}{y} = -\left(\frac{-x}{-y}\right) = \frac{x}{-y} = \frac{-x}{y};\ \frac{x}{y} = \frac{-x}{-y};\ \frac{x}{y} = \frac{ax}{ay};\ \left(\frac{x}{y}\right)^m = \frac{x^m}{y^m};\ \frac{x}{y} \pm \frac{z}{y} = \frac{x \pm z}{y};\ \left(\frac{x}{y}\right)\left(\frac{z}{t}\right) = \frac{xz}{yt};\ (x/y)/(z/t) = \left(\frac{x}{y}\right)\left(\frac{t}{z}\right) = \frac{xt}{yz}.$$

Factoring. That process of analysis consisting of reducing a given expression into the product of two or more simpler expressions is called *factoring*. The two or more simpler expressions are called *factors*. Some of the more common expressions are factored below:

(1) $(x^2 - y^2) = (x - y)(x + y)$
(2) $x^2 + 2xy + y^2 = (x + y)^2$
(3) $x^2 + ax + b = (x + ;)(x + d)$ where $c + d = a$, $cd = b$
(4) $by^2 + cy + d = (ey + f)(gy + h)$ where $eg = b$, $fg + eh = c$, $fh = d$
(5) $x^2 + y^2 + z^2 + 2xy + 2xz + 2yz = (x + y + z)^2$
(6) $x^2 - y^2 - z^2 - 2yz = (x - y - z)(x + y + z)$
(7) $x^2 + y^2 + z^2 - 2xy - 2xz + 2yz = (x - y - z)^2$
(8) $x^3 - y^3 = (x - y)(x^2 + xy + y^2)$
(9) $(x^3 + y^3) = (x + y)(x^2 - xy + y^2)$
(10) $(x^4 - y^4) = (x - y)(x + y)(x^2 + y^2)$
(11) $x^5 + y^5 = (x + y)(x^4 - x^3y + x^2y^2 - xy^3 + y^4)$
(12) $x^n - y^n = (x - y)(x^{n-1} + x^{n-2}y + x^{n-3}y^2 + \cdots + y^{n-1})$

Laws of Exponents

$(a^n)^m = a^{nm}$; $a^{n+m} = a^n \cdot a^m$; $a^{n/m} = (a^n)^{1/m}$; $a^{n-m} = \frac{a^n}{a^m}$; $a^{1/m} = \sqrt[m]{a}$; $a^{1/2} = \sqrt{a}$; $\sqrt{x^2} = |x|$ (absolute value of x). If x, y are not both negative $\sqrt{xy} = \sqrt{x}\sqrt{y}$; if $x > 0$ $\sqrt[n]{x^m} = x^{m/n}$; $\sqrt[n]{1/x} = \frac{1}{\sqrt[n]{x}}$.

THE BINOMIAL THEOREM

If n is a positive integer

$$(a + b)^n = a^n + na^{n-1}b + \frac{n(n-1)}{2!}a^{n-2}b^2 + \frac{n(n-1)(n-2)}{3!}a^{n-3}b^3 + \cdots + b^n = \sum_{j=0}^{n}\binom{n}{j}a^{n-j}b^j$$

where $\binom{n}{j} = \frac{n!}{j!(n-j)!}$ = number of combinations of n things taken j at a time. $n! = 1 \cdot 2 \cdot 3 \cdot 4 \cdots n$, $0! = 1$.

Example 1. Find the sixth term of $(x + 2y)^{12}$. The sixth term is obtained by setting $j = 5$. It is

$$\binom{12}{5}x^{12-5}(2y)^5 = 1584x^7(2y)^5$$

Example 2. $\sum_{j=0}^{14}\binom{n}{j} = (1 + 1)^{14} = 2^{14}$.

If n is not a positive integer the sum formula no longer applies and an infinite series results for $(a + b)^n$. The coefficients are obtained from the first formulas in this case.

Example. $(1 + x)^{1/2} = 1 + \frac{1}{2}x - \frac{1}{2} \cdot \frac{1}{4}x^2 + \frac{1}{2} \cdot \frac{1}{4} \cdot \frac{3}{6}x^3 \cdots$ (convergent for $x^2 < 1$).

These are discussed in more detail under Infinite Series.

PROGRESSIONS

An *arithmetic progression* is a succession of terms, such that each term, except the first, is derivable from the preceding by the addition of a quantity d called the common difference. All arithmetic progressions have the form a, $a + d$, $a + 2d$, $a + 3d$, ... With a = first term, l = last term, d = common difference, m = number of terms, and s = sum of the terms, the following relations hold:

$$l = a + (n-1)d = -\frac{d}{2} + \sqrt{2\,ds + \left(a - \frac{d}{2}\right)^2}$$

$$= \frac{s}{n} + \frac{(n-1)d}{2}$$

$$s = \frac{n}{2}[2a + (n-1)d] = \frac{n}{2}(a + l) = \frac{n}{2}[2l - (n-1)d]$$

$$a = l - (n-1)d = \frac{s}{n} - \frac{(n-1)d}{2} = \frac{2s}{n} - l$$

$$d = \frac{l-a}{n-1} = \frac{2(s-an)}{n(n-1)} = \frac{2(nl-s)}{n(n-1)}$$

$$n = \frac{l-a}{d} + 1 = \frac{2s}{l+a} = \frac{2l + d + \sqrt{(2+d)^2 - 8ds}}{2d}$$

The *arithmetic mean* of two numbers a, b is $\frac{a+b}{2}$; n numbers $a_1, \ldots, a_n$ is $\frac{a_1 + a_2 + \cdots + a_n}{n}$.

A *geometric* progression is a succession of terms such that each term, except the first, is derivable from the preceding by the multiplication of a quantity r called the *common ratio.* All such progressions have the form a, ar, ar^2, . . . , ar^{n-1}. With a = first term, l = last term, r = ratio, n = number of terms, s = sum of the terms, the following relations hold:

$$l = ar^{n-1} = \frac{[a + (r-1)s]}{r} = \frac{(r-1)sr^{n-1}}{r^n - 1}$$

$$s = \frac{a(r^n - 1)}{r - 1} = \frac{a(1 - r^n)}{1 - r} = \frac{rl - a}{r - 1} = \frac{lr^n - l}{r^n - r^{n-1}}$$

$$a = \frac{l}{r^{n-1}} = \frac{(r-1)s}{r^n - 1} \qquad r = \frac{s-a}{s-l} \qquad \log r = \frac{\log l - \log a}{n-1}$$

$$n = \frac{\log l - \log a}{\log r} + 1 = \frac{\log[a + (r-1)s] - \log a}{\log r}$$

The *geometric mean* between two numbers a, b is $\sqrt{ab}$; of n numbers is $(a_1a_2 \ldots a_n)^{1/n}$.

Example. Find the sum of $1 + \frac{1}{2} + \frac{1}{4} + \cdots + \frac{1}{64}$. Here $a = 1$, $r = \frac{1}{2}$, $n = 7$. Thus $s = \frac{\frac{1}{2}(\frac{1}{64}) - 1}{\frac{1}{2} - 1} = \frac{127}{64}$. $s = a + ar + ar^2 + \cdots + ar^{n-1} = \frac{a}{1-r} - \frac{ar^n}{1-r}$. If $|r| < 1$ then $\lim_{n \to \infty} s = \frac{a}{1-r}$, which is called the sum of the *infinite geometric progression.*

A progression of the form a, $(a + d)r$, $(a + 2d)r^2$, $(a + 3d)r^3$, etc., is a combined *arithmetic* and *geometric progression.* The sum of n such terms is

$$s = \frac{a - [a + (n-1)d]r^n}{1 - r} + \frac{rd(1 - r^{n-1})}{(1-r)^2}$$

If $|r| < 1$, $\lim_{n \to \infty} s = \frac{a}{1-r} + rd/(1-r)^2$. The terms a, b, c, etc., form a *harmonic progression* if their reciprocals $1/a$, $1/b$, $1/c$, etc., form an arithmetic progression.

Example. The progression 1, $\frac{1}{3}$, $\frac{1}{5}$, $\frac{1}{7}$, . . . , $\frac{1}{31}$ is harmonic since 1, 3, 5, 7, . . . , 31 form an arithmetic progression.

The *harmonic mean* of two numbers a, b is $\frac{2ab}{a+b}$.

PERMUTATIONS, COMBINATIONS, AND PROBABILITY

Each separate arrangement of all or a part of a set of things is called a *permutation.* The number of permutations of n things taken r at a time, written $P(n, r) = \frac{n!}{(n-r)!} = n(n-1)(n-2) \cdots (n - r + 1)$.

Example. The permutations of a, b, c two at a time are ab, ac, ba, ca, cb, bc, or 6. The formula is $P(3, 2) = \frac{3!}{1!} = 6$. The permutations of a, b, c three at a time are abc, bac, cab, acb, bca, and cba.

Each separate selection of objects that is possible irrespective of the order in which they are arranged is called a *combination.* The number of combinations of n things taken r at a time, written $C(n, r) = \frac{n!}{r!(n-r)!}$.

Example. The combinations of a, b, c taken 2 at a time are ab, ac, bc; taken 3 at a time is abc.

An important relation is $r!\,C(n, r) = P(n, r)$.

If an event can occur in p ways, and fail to occur in q ways, all ways being equally likely, the *probability* of its occurrence is $\frac{p}{p+q}$, and that of its failure $\frac{q}{p+q}$.

Example. Two dice may be thrown in 36 separate ways. What is the probability of throwing such that their sum is 7? Seven may arise in 6 ways: 1 and 6, 2 and 5, 3 and 4, 4 and 3, 5 and 2, 6 and 1. The probability of shooting 7 is $\frac{1}{6}$.

MISCELLANEOUS FORMULAS

Sums of Integers. $\sum_{j=1}^{n} j = 1 + 2 + \cdots + n = \frac{n(n+1)}{2}$;

$$\sum_{j=1}^{n} j^2 = \frac{n(n+1)(2n+1)}{6}; \quad \sum_{j=1}^{n} j^3 = \frac{n^2(n+1)^2}{4} = \left(\sum_{j=1}^{n} j\right)^2;$$

etc.

$$\sum_{j=1}^{n} j^p = \frac{n^{p+1}}{p+1} + \frac{n^p}{2} + \frac{p}{12}n^{p-1} - \frac{p(p-1)(p-2)}{720}n^{p-3} + \frac{p(p-1)(p-2)(p-3)}{30240}n^{p-5} + \cdots$$

where p is an integer.

Laws of Logarithms. If x, y, a are positive numbers, $a \neq 1$, then $\log_a xy = \log_a x + \log_a y$; $\log_a x/y = \log_a x - \log_a y$; $\log_a x^p = p \log_a x$; $\log_a a = 1$; $\log_a 1 = 0$. Let $b \neq 1$, the *change of base* formula is $\log_a x = \log_b x \log_a b = \frac{\log_b x}{\log_b a}$. From this result it follows that $\log_b a = \frac{1}{\log_a b}$.

Example. $\log_e x = \frac{\log_{10} x}{\log_{10} e} = (\log_{10} x)(\log_e 10)$.

Proportion. If $\frac{a}{b} = \frac{c}{d}$ then $\frac{a+b}{b} = \frac{c+d}{d}$, $\frac{a-b}{b} = \frac{c-d}{d}$, $\frac{a-b}{a+b} = \frac{c-d}{c+d}$.

Variation. If y is proportional to x or varies directly as x then $y = kx$. If y varies inversely as x then $y = k/x$. If y varies jointly as x and z then $y = kxz$. If y varies directly as x and inversely as z then $y = kx/z$.

THEORY OF EQUATIONS

Linear Equations. A *linear equation* is one of the first degree (*i.e.*, only the first powers of the variables are involved) and the process of obtaining definite values for the unknowns is called solving the equation. Every *linear equation* in *one variable* is written $Ax + B = 0$ or $x = -B/A$. Linear equations in n variables have the form

$$\begin{aligned} a_{11}x_1 + a_{12}x_2 + \cdots + a_{1n}x_n &= b_1 \\ a_{21}x_1 + a_{22}x_2 + \cdots + a_{2n}x_n &= b_2 \\ &\vdots \\ a_{n1}x_1 + a_{n2}x_2 + \cdots + a_{nn}x_n &= b_n \end{aligned}$$

Such a system has a unique solution (for $b_1, b_2, \ldots, b_n$ not all zero) if and only if the determinant of the system $\begin{vmatrix} a_{11} & \cdots & a_{1n} \\ a_{21} & \cdots & a_{2n} \\ \cdot & & \\ \cdot & & \\ a_{n1} & \cdots & a_{nn} \end{vmatrix}$ $\neq 0$. The solution of the system may then be found by *elimination*, *determinants*, or *matrix* methods (see Numerical Methods).

Example. Solution by the *elimination* method:

$$\begin{aligned} 3x_1 + 4x_2 - 5x_3 &= -2 \\ 9x_1 - 2x_2 + 3x_3 &= 1 \\ -6x_1 + 3x_2 - x_3 &= 3 \end{aligned} \qquad \begin{vmatrix} 3 & 4 & -5 \\ 9 & -2 & 3 \\ -6 & 3 & -1 \end{vmatrix} = -132 \neq 0$$

Multiply the first row by 2 and add to the third row, leaving the first row unchanged. The result is

$$\begin{aligned} 3x_1 + 4x_2 - 5x_3 &= -2 \\ 9x_1 - 2x_2 + 3x_3 &= 1 \\ 0x_1 + 11x_2 - 11x_3 &= -1 \end{aligned}$$

Multiply the first row by -3 and add to the second row.

$$\begin{aligned} 3x_1 + 4x_2 - 5x_3 &= -2 \\ 0x_1 - 14x_2 + 18x_3 &= 7 \\ 0x_1 + 11x_2 - 11x_3 &= -1 \end{aligned}$$

Multiply the second row by $^{11}\!/_{14}$ and add to the third row. The result is the triangular form

$$\begin{aligned} 3x_1 + 4x_2 - 5x_3 &= -2 \\ 0x_1 - 14x_2 + 18x_3 &= 7 \\ 0x_1 + 0x_2 + {}^{22}\!/_{7}x_3 &= {}^{9}\!/_{2} \end{aligned}$$

Then from the third equation $x_3 = {}^{63}\!/_{44}$; substituting this in the second equation yields $x_2 = {}^{59}\!/_{44}$. The first equation yields $x_1 = -{}^{9}\!/_{44}$. An alternate to this method, which is equivalent to it, is to solve one of the equations for x_3 in terms of x_1 and x_2, say the third equation, which gives $x_3 = -6x_1 + 3x_2 - 3$. This is then substituted in the second equation, yielding $-9x_1 + 7x_2 = 10$, which can then be solved for x_2, $x_2 = \dfrac{10 + 9x_1}{7}$. Substitution for x_3 and x_2 in the first equation gives an equation in x_1 alone.

Other methods for solving such systems will be given under Determinants and Matrices and Numerical Methods.

Quadratic Equations. Every *quadratic* equation in one variable is expressible in the form $ax^2 + bx + c = 0$, $a \neq 0$. This equation has two solutions, say x_1, x_2, given by $\left.\begin{matrix} x_1 \\ x_2 \end{matrix}\right\} = \dfrac{-b \pm \sqrt{b^2 - 4ac}}{2a}$. If a, b, c are real, the *discriminant* $b^2 - 4ac$ gives the character of the roots. If $b^2 - 4ac > 0$ the roots are *real* and *unequal*. If $b^2 - 4ac < 0$ the roots are *complex conjugates*. If $b^2 - 4ac = 0$ the roots are *real* and *equal*.

Two quadratic equations in *two variables* can in general be solved only by numerical methods (see Numerical Methods). If one equation is of the first degree, the other of the second degree, a solution may be obtained by solving the first for one unknown. This result is substituted in the second equation and the resulting quadratic solved.

Example. Solve $x^2 + 5xy - y^2 - 15 = 0$ and $x + 2y = 10$. The second equation yields $x = 10 - 2y$. Upon substitution into the first equation the quadratic $7y^2 - 10y - 85 = 0$ is obtained. The solutions of this equation are $\dfrac{5 \pm 2\sqrt{155}}{7}$.

Cubic Equations. A cubic equation, in one variable, has the form $x^3 + bx^2 + cx + d = 0$. Every cubic equation having complex coefficients has three complex roots. If the coefficients are real numbers then at least one of the roots must be real. The cubic equation $x^3 + bx^2 + cx + d = 0$ may be reduced by the substitution $x = y - \dfrac{b}{3}$ to the form $y^3 + py + q = 0$, where $p = {}^{1}\!/_{3}(3c - b^2)$, $q = {}^{1}\!/_{27}(27d - 9bc + 2b^3)$. This equation has the solutions $y_1 = A + B$, $y_2 = -{}^{1}\!/_{2}(A + B) + (i\sqrt{3}/2)(A - B)$, $y_3 = -{}^{1}\!/_{2}(A + B) - (i\sqrt{3}/2)(A - B)$ where $i^2 = -1$, $A = \sqrt[3]{-q/2 + \sqrt{R}}$, $B = \sqrt[3]{-q/2 - \sqrt{R}}$, and $R = (p/3)^3 + (q/2)^2$. If b, c, d are all real and if $R > 0$ there are one real root and two conjugate complex roots; if $R = 0$ there are three real roots, of which at least two are equal; if $R < 0$ there are three real unequal roots. If $R < 0$ the above formulas are impractical. In this case, the roots are given by $x_k = \mp 2\sqrt{-p/3}\cos[(\phi/3) + 120k]$, $k = 0, 1, 2$ where $\phi = \cos^{-1}\sqrt{\dfrac{q^2/4}{-p^3/27}}$ and the upper sign applies if $q > 0$, the lower if $q < 0$.

Example 1. $x^3 + 3x^2 + 9x + 9 = 0$ reduces to $y^3 + 6y + 2 = 0$ under $x = y - 1$. Here $p = 6$, $q = 2$, $R = 9$. Hence $A = \sqrt[3]{2}$, $B = \sqrt[3]{-4}$. The desired roots in y are $\sqrt[3]{2} - \sqrt[3]{4}$ and $-{}^{1}\!/_{2}(\sqrt[3]{2} - \sqrt[3]{4}) \pm \dfrac{i\sqrt{3}}{2}(\sqrt[3]{2} + \sqrt[3]{4})$. The roots in x are $x = y - 1$.

Example 2. $y^3 - 7y + 7 = 0$. $p = -7$, $q = 7$, $R < 0$. Hence $x_k = -\sqrt{\dfrac{28}{3}}\cos\left(\dfrac{\phi}{3} + 120k\right)$ where $\cos\phi = \sqrt{\dfrac{27}{28}}$, $\dfrac{\phi}{3} = 3°37'52''$. The roots are approximately -3.048916, 1.692020, and 1.356897.

Quartic Equations. The general quartic equation $x^4 + ax^3 + bx^2 + cx + d = 0$ may be reduced to the form $y^4 + py^2 + qy + r = 0$ by the substitution $x = y - (a/4)$. Let l, m, and n denote the roots of the resolvent cubic

$$t^3 + \left(\frac{p}{2}\right)t^2 + \frac{(p^2 - 4r)t}{16} - \frac{q^2}{64} = 0$$

found by the previous method. The required roots of the reduced quartic are

$$y_1 = \pm(-\sqrt{l} - \sqrt{m} - \sqrt{n});\ y_2 = \pm(-\sqrt{l} + \sqrt{m} + \sqrt{n});$$
$$y_3 = \pm(\sqrt{l} - \sqrt{m} + \sqrt{n});\ y_4 = \pm(\sqrt{l} + \sqrt{m} - \sqrt{n})$$

where the upper signs are used if $q > 0$ and the lower signs if $q < 0$.

General Polynomials of the *n*th Degree. Denote the general polynomial equation of degree n by $P(x) = a_0x^n + a_1x^{n-1} + \cdots + a_{n-1}x + a_n = 0$. If $n > 4$ there is no formula which gives the roots of the general equation. However, there are some general methods which may prove useful.

Remainder Theorems. When $P(x)$ is a polynomial, and $P(x)$ is divided by $x - a$ until a remainder independent of x is obtained, this remainder is equal to $P(a)$.

Example. $P(x) = 2x^4 - 3x^2 + 7x - 2$ when divided by $x + 1$ (here $a = -1$) results in $P(x) = (x + 1)(2x^3 - 2x^2 - x + 8) - 10$ where -10 is the remainder. It is easy to see that $P(-1) = -10$.

The Factor Theorem. If $P(a)$ is zero, the polynomial $P(x)$ has the factor $x - a$. In other words, if a is a root of $P(x) = 0$ then $x - a$ is a factor of $P(x)$.

If a number a is found to be a root of $P(x) = 0$ then division of $P(x)$ by $(x - a)$ leaves a polynomial of degree one less than that of the original equation, *i.e.*, $P(x) = Q(x)(x - a)$. Roots of $Q(x) = 0$ are clearly roots of $P(x) = 0$.

Example. $P(x) = x^3 - 6x^2 + 11x - 6 = 0$ has the root $+3$. Then $P(x) = (x - 3)(x^2 - 3x + 2)$. The roots of $x^2 - 3x + 2 = 0$ are 1 and 2. The roots of $P(x)$ are therefore 1, 2, 3.

Fundamental Theorem of Algebra. Every polynomial of degree n has exactly n roots, counting multiplicities. If the roots of $x^n + c_1x^{n-1} + c_2x^{n-2} + \cdots + c_{n-1}x + c_n = 0$ are $r_1, r_2, r_3, \ldots, r_n$ where multiplicities may occur then $c_1 = -\sum_{j=1}^{n} r_j$; $c_2 = \sum_{\substack{i,j=1 \\ i \neq j}}^{n} r_ir_j$ = sum of the product of the roots taken two at a time; $c_3 = -$(sum of the product of the roots taken three at a time); $\ldots$ $c_n = (-1)^n r_1r_2 \cdots r_n$.

This result allows a polynomial having given numbers as roots to be formed.

Example 1. Find a cubic equation whose roots are 1, 2, 3. $c_1 = -(1 + 2 + 3) = -6$; $c_2 = 1 \cdot 2 + 1 \cdot 3 + 2 \cdot 3 = 11$; $c_3 = -6$. The polynomial is $x^3 - 6x^2 + 11x - 6$.

Example 2. $x^4 - 12x^3 + 48x^2 - 80x + 48 = 0$ has a triple root. Solve the equation. Let r be the triple root and s be the other root. Then $3r + s = 12$; $3sr + 3r^2 = 48$. Subtract $9r^2 + 3rs = 36r$ from the second equation. There results $6r^2 - 36r + 48 = 0$ or $(r - 4)(r - 2) = 0$; $r = 2$, $r = 4$. If $r = 4$, $s = 0$, which is not possible. Since $r = 4$ is extraneous, $r = 2$ is the triple root. $s = 6$ is the other root.

Every polynomial equation $a_0x^n + a_1x^{n-1} + \cdots + a_n = 0$ with *rational coefficients* may be rewritten as a polynomial, of the same degree, with *integral coefficients* by multiplying each coefficient by the least common multiple of the denominators of the coefficients.

Example. The coefficients of $\frac{3}{2}x^4 + \frac{7}{3}x^3 - \frac{5}{6}x^2 + 2x - \frac{1}{6} = 0$ are rational numbers. The least common multiple of the denominators is $2 \cdot 3 = 6$. Therefore, the equation is equivalent to $9x^4 + 14x^3 - 5x^2 + 12x - 1 = 0$.

The Rational Root Theorem. If the polynomial equation $a_0x^n + \cdots + a_n = 0$ with integral coefficients has a rational root p/q (p and q integers having no common factor > 1) then p is an exact divisor of the constant term a_n and q is an exact divisor of the leading coefficient a_0.

This result allows the computation of all rational (and integral) roots of any polynomial having integral coefficients.

Example. Find all rational roots of $6y^3 + 7y^2 - 9y + 2 = 0$. The possibilities for the numerator are $\pm 1, \pm 2$. The possibilities for the denominator are $\pm 1, \pm 2, \pm 3, \pm 6$. Thus the possible rational roots are $\pm 1, \pm 2, \pm \frac{1}{2}, \pm \frac{1}{3}, \pm \frac{2}{3}, \pm \frac{1}{6}$. Trial of these values shows that -2 is a root. The depressed equation is $6y^2 - 5y + 1 = 0$, which has roots $\frac{1}{3}, \frac{1}{2}$.

Complex-root Theorem. If a polynomial equation with real coefficients has the root $a + ib$, it also has the root $a - ib$; that is, complex roots occur in conjugate pairs.

Example. $x^4 - 4x^2 + 8x - 4 = 0$ has one root $1 + i$. Another root is $1 - i$. Therefore, $(x - 1 - i)(x - 1 + i) = x^2 - 2x + 2$ is a factor of the polynomial. $x^4 - 4x^2 + 8x - 4 = (x^2 - 2x + 2)(x^2 + 2x - 2)$. The other roots are $1 \pm \sqrt{3}$.

Upper Bound for the Real Roots. Any number which exceeds all the roots is called an *upper bound* to the real roots. If the coefficients of a polynomial equation are all of like sign, there is no positive root. Such equations are excluded here since zero is the upper bound to the real roots. If the coefficient of the highest power of $P(x) = 0$ is negative, replace the equation by $-P(x) = 0$.

If in a polynomial $P(x) = c_0x^n + c_1x^{n-1} + \cdots + c_{n-1}x + c_n = 0$, with $c_0 > 0$, the first negative coefficient is preceded by k coefficients which are positive or zero, and if G denotes the greatest of the numerical values of the negative coefficients, then each real root is less than $1 + \sqrt[k]{G/c_0}$.

A lower bound to the negative roots of $P(x) = 0$ may be found by applying the rule to $P(-x) = 0$.

Example. $P(x) = x^7 + 2x^5 + 4x^4 - 8x^2 - 32 = 0$. Here $k = 5$ (since 2 coefficients are zero), $G = 32$, $c_0 = 1$. The upper bound is $1 + \sqrt[5]{32} = 3$. $P(-x) = -x^7 - 2x^5 + 4x^4 - 8x^2 - 32 = 0$. $-P(-x) = x^7 + 2x^5 - 4x^4 + 8x^2 + 32 = 0$. Here $k = 3, G = 4$, $c_0 = 1$. The lower bound is $-(1 + \sqrt[3]{4}) \approx -2.587$. Thus all real roots r lie in the range $-2.587 < r < 3$.

Descartes Rule of Signs. The number of positive real roots of a polynomial equation with real coefficients either is equal to the number v of its variations in sign or is less than v by a positive even integer. The number of negative roots of $P(x) = 0$ either is equal to the number of variations of sign of $P(-x)$ or is less than that number by a positive even integer.

Example 1. $P(x) = x^4 + 3x^3 + x - 1 = 0$. $v = 1$; so $P(x)$ has one positive root. $P(-x) = x^4 - 3x^3 - x - 1$. Here $v = 1$; so $P(x)$ has one negative root. The other two roots are complex conjugates.

Example 2. $P(x) = x^4 - x^2 + 10x - 4 = 0$. $v = 3$; so $P(x)$ has three or one positive roots. $P(-x) = x^4 - x^2 - 10x - 4$. $v = 1$; so $P(x)$ has exactly one negative root.

Numerical methods are often used to find the roots of polynomials. A detailed discussion of these techniques is given under Numerical Methods.

Determinants. Consider the system of two linear equations

$$a_{11}x_1 + a_{12}x_2 = b_1$$
$$a_{21}x_1 + a_{22}x_2 = b_2$$

If the first equation is multiplied by a_{22} and the second by $-a_{12}$ and the results added, we obtain

$$(a_{11}a_{22} - a_{21}a_{12})x_1 = b_1a_{22} - b_2a_{12}$$

The expression $a_{11}a_{22} - a_{21}a_{12}$ may be represented by the symbol

$$\begin{vmatrix} a_{11} & a_{12} \\ a_{21} & a_{22} \end{vmatrix} = a_{11}a_{22} - a_{21}a_{12}$$

This symbol is called a *determinant* of second order. The value of the square array of n^2 quantities a_{ij}, where $i = 1, \ldots, n$ is the row index, $j = 1, \ldots, n$ the column index, written in the form

$$A = |a_{ij}| = \begin{vmatrix} a_{11} & a_{12} & a_{13} & \cdots & a_{1n} \\ a_{21} & a_{22} & \cdots & \cdots & a_{2n} \\ \cdot & & & & \\ \cdot & & & & \\ \cdot & & & & \\ a_{n1} & a_{n2} & a_{n3} & \cdots & a_{nn} \end{vmatrix}$$

is called a *determinant.* The n^2 quantities a_{ij} are called the *elements* of the determinant. In the determinant A let the ith row and jth column be deleted and a new determinant formed having $n - 1$ rows and columns. This new determinant is called the *minor* of a_{ij} denoted M_{ij}.

Example. $\begin{vmatrix} a_{11} & a_{12} & a_{13} \\ a_{21} & a_{22} & a_{23} \\ a_{31} & a_{32} & a_{33} \end{vmatrix}$ The minor of a_{23} is $M_{23} = \begin{vmatrix} a_{11} & a_{12} \\ a_{31} & a_{32} \end{vmatrix}$

The *cofactor* A_{ij}, of the element a_{ij}, is the signed minor of a_{ij} determined by the rule $A_{ij} = (-1)^{i+j}M_{ij}$.

Example. $A_{23} = (-1)^5M_{23} = -M_{23}$.

The *value* of A is obtained by forming any of the equivalent expressions $\sum_{j=1}^{n} a_{ij}A_{ij}$, $\sum_{i=1}^{n} a_{ij}A_{ij}$ where the elements a_{ij} must be taken from a single row or a single column of A.

Example.

$$\begin{vmatrix} a_{11} & a_{12} & a_{13} \\ a_{21} & a_{22} & a_{23} \\ a_{31} & a_{32} & a_{33} \end{vmatrix} = a_{31}A_{31} + a_{32}A_{32} + a_{33}A_{33}$$
$$= a_{31}\begin{vmatrix} a_{12} & a_{13} \\ a_{22} & a_{22} \end{vmatrix} - a_{32}\begin{vmatrix} a_{11} & a_{13} \\ a_{21} & a_{23} \end{vmatrix} + a_{33}\begin{vmatrix} a_{11} & a_{12} \\ a_{21} & a_{22} \end{vmatrix}$$

where $\begin{vmatrix} a & b \\ c & d \end{vmatrix} = ad - bc$.

In general, A_{ij} will be determinants of order $n - 1$, but they may in turn be expanded by the rule.

It is easy to show that

$$\sum_{j=1}^{n} a_{ji}A_{jk} = \sum_{j=1}^{n} a_{ij}A_{jk} = \begin{cases} A & i = k \\ 0 & i \neq k \end{cases}$$

Fundamental Properties of Determinants.

1. The value of a determinant A is not changed if the rows and columns are interchanged.

2. If the elements of one row (or one column) of a determinant are all zero, the value of A is zero.

3. If the elements of one row (or column) of a determinant are multiplied by the same constant factor, the value of the determinant is multiplied by this factor.

4. If one determinant is obtained from another by interchanging any two rows (or columns), the value of either is the negative of the value of the other.

5. If two rows (or columns) of a determinant are identical the value of the determinant is zero.

6. If two determinants are identical except for one row (or column), the sum of their values is given by a single determinant obtained by adding corresponding elements of dissimilar rows (or columns) and leaving unchanged the remaining elements.

Example. $\begin{vmatrix} 3 & 2 \\ 1 & 5 \end{vmatrix} + \begin{vmatrix} 4 & 2 \\ 7 & 5 \end{vmatrix} = 13 + 6 = 19$

$\begin{vmatrix} 7 & 2 \\ 8 & 5 \end{vmatrix} = 35 - 16 = 19$

7. The value of a determinant is not changed if to the elements of any row (or column) are added a constant multiple of the corresponding elements of any other row (or column).

8. If all elements but one in a row (or column) are zero, the value of the determinant is the product of that element times its cofactor.

The evaluation of determinants using the definition is quite laborious. The labor can be reduced by applying the fundamental properties just outlined.

Example. Evaluate $\begin{vmatrix} 2 & 1 & 4 & 3 \\ -1 & 4 & 2 & 1 \\ 5 & 6 & 7 & 2 \\ 1 & 3 & 4 & 5 \end{vmatrix}$

The aim is to transform the determinant so that all elements but one in a given row (or column) are zero, *without changing the determinant* value. This may be done by utilizing property 7. Selecting the element 1 in the fourth column add −2 times the fourth column to the third column, then −4 times the fourth column to the second column; then add the fourth column to the first column; the result is

$$A = \begin{vmatrix} 5 & -11 & -2 & 3 \\ 0 & 0 & 0 & 1 \\ 7 & -2 & 3 & 2 \\ 6 & -17 & -6 & 5 \end{vmatrix} = 1 \begin{vmatrix} 5 & -11 & -2 \\ 7 & -2 & 3 \\ 6 & -17 & -6 \end{vmatrix}$$

by property 8. Property 7 is now used on this 3 × 3 determinant. Subtract the elements of the first row from the third row. The result is

$$A = \begin{vmatrix} 5 & -11 & -2 \\ 7 & -2 & 3 \\ 1 & -6 & -4 \end{vmatrix}$$

Now add −7 times the third row to the second row, then −5 times the third row to the first row, resulting in

$$A = \begin{vmatrix} 0 & 19 & 18 \\ 0 & 40 & 31 \\ 1 & -6 & -4 \end{vmatrix} = \begin{vmatrix} 19 & 18 \\ 40 & 31 \end{vmatrix} = -131$$

The solution of n linear equations (all b_i not zero)

$$\begin{aligned} a_{11}x_1 + a_{12}x_2 + \cdots + a_{1n}x_n &= b_1 \\ a_{21}x_1 + a_{22}x_2 + \cdots + a_{2n}x_n &= b_2 \\ \cdots \qquad\qquad & \cdot \\ \cdots \qquad\qquad & \cdot \\ \cdots \qquad\qquad & \cdot \\ a_{n1}x_1 + a_{n2}x_2 + \cdots + a_{nn}x_n &= b_n \end{aligned}$$

where $A = \begin{vmatrix} a_{11} & \cdots & a_{1n} \\ a_{21} & \cdots & a_{2n} \\ \cdot & & \\ \cdot & & \\ \cdot & & \\ a_{n1} & \cdots & a_{nn} \end{vmatrix} \neq 0$ has a unique solution given by

$x_1 = B_1/A$, $x_2 = B_2/A$, . . . , $x_n = B_n/A$ where B_k is the determinant obtained from A by replacing its kth column by b_1, b_2, . . . , b_n. This technique is called *Cramer's rule*. It usually requires more labor than the method of elimination or certain numerical techniques.

Example.

$$\begin{aligned} 5x + 3y + 3z &= 48 \\ 2x + 6y - 3z &= 18 \\ 8x - 3y + 2z &= 21 \end{aligned}$$

The solutions are $x = \dfrac{\begin{vmatrix} 48 & 3 & 3 \\ 18 & 6 & -3 \\ 21 & -3 & 2 \end{vmatrix}}{\begin{vmatrix} 5 & 3 & 3 \\ 2 & 6 & -3 \\ 8 & -3 & 2 \end{vmatrix}} = \dfrac{-693}{-231} = 3,$

$$y = \frac{\begin{vmatrix} 5 & 48 & 3 \\ 2 & 18 & -3 \\ 8 & 21 & 2 \end{vmatrix}}{-231} = \frac{-1155}{-231} = 5, \quad z = \frac{\begin{vmatrix} 5 & 3 & 48 \\ 2 & 6 & 18 \\ 8 & -3 & 21 \end{vmatrix}}{-231} = 6.$$

Matrices. A rectangular array of mn quantities, arranged in m rows and n columns

$$A = (a_{ij}) = \begin{bmatrix} a_{11} & \cdots & a_{1n} \\ a_{21} & \cdots & a_{2n} \\ \cdot & & \\ \cdot & & \\ \cdot & & \\ a_{m1} & \cdots & a_{mn} \end{bmatrix}$$

is called a *matrix*. The elements a_{ij} may be real or complex. The notation a_{ij} means the element in the ith row and jth column, i is called the *row index*, j the *column index*. If $m = n$ the matrix is said to be *square* and of *order n*. A matrix, even if it is square, *does not* have a *numerical value*, as a determinant does. However, if the matrix A is square, a determinant can be formed which has the same elements as the matrix A. This is called the *determinant of the matrix* and written det (A) or $|A|$. If A is square and det $(A) \neq 0$, A is said to be *non-singular*, if det $(A) = 0$, A is said to be *singular*. A matrix A has *rank r* if and only if it has a non-vanishing determinant of order r and no non-vanishing determinant of order $> r$.

Algebra of Matrices. Let $A = (a_{ij})$, $B = (b_{ij})$.

Equality. Two matrices A and B are *equal* (=) if and only if they are identical; that is, they have the same number of rows and the same number of columns and equal corresponding elements ($a_{ij} = b_{ij}$ for all i and j).

Addition and Subtraction. The operations of *addition* (+) and subtraction (−) of two or more matrices are possible if and only if they have the same number of rows and columns. Thus $A \pm B = (a_{ij} \pm b_{ij})$; *i.e.*, addition and subtraction are of corresponding elements.

Example.

$$\begin{bmatrix} 3 & 1 & 4 & -1 \\ 2 & 5 & 3 & 2 \\ 0 & 6 & 2 & -5 \end{bmatrix} + \begin{bmatrix} 2 & 6 & 1 & 4 \\ 1 & -1 & 0 & 1 \\ 3 & 2 & 1 & 0 \end{bmatrix} = \begin{bmatrix} 5 & 7 & 5 & 3 \\ 3 & 4 & 3 & 3 \\ 3 & 8 & 3 & -5 \end{bmatrix}$$

Transposition. The matrix obtained from A by interchanging the rows and columns of A is called the *transpose* of A, written A' or A^T.

Example.

$$A = \begin{bmatrix} 1 & 3 & 4 \\ 2 & 1 & 6 \end{bmatrix}, \quad A^T = \begin{bmatrix} 1 & 2 \\ 3 & 1 \\ 4 & 6 \end{bmatrix}$$

Note that $(A^T)^T = A$.

Multiplication. Let $A = (a_{ij})$, $i = 1, \ldots, m_1$; $j = 1, \ldots, m_2$. $B = (b_{ij})$, $i = 1, \ldots, n_1$; $j = 1, \ldots, n_2$. The *product AB* is defined if and only if the *number* of *columns* of A (m_2) equals the number of rows of $B(n_1)$, i.e., $n_1 = m_2$. For two such matrices the product $P = AB$ is *defined* by summing the element by element products of a row of A by a column of B. This is the *row* by *column rule.* Thus $p_{ij} = \sum_{k=1}^{n_1} a_{ik}b_{kj}$. The resulting matrix has m_1 rows and n_2 columns.

Example.

$$\begin{bmatrix} 3 & 2 \\ 1 & 1 \\ 5 & 4 \end{bmatrix} \begin{bmatrix} 0 & 1 & 5 & 6 \\ -2 & 0 & 1 & 3 \end{bmatrix} = \begin{bmatrix} -4 & 3 & 17 & 24 \\ -2 & 1 & 6 & 9 \\ -8 & 5 & 29 & 42 \end{bmatrix}$$

It is helpful to remember that the element p_{ij} is formed from the ith row of the first matrix and the jth column of the second matrix. The matrix product is *not commutative.* That is, $AB \neq BA$ in general.

Example.

$$\begin{bmatrix} 2 & 1 \\ 3 & -2 \end{bmatrix} \begin{bmatrix} 1 & 4 \\ 0 & 2 \end{bmatrix} = \begin{bmatrix} 2 & 10 \\ 3 & 8 \end{bmatrix} = AB$$

$$\begin{bmatrix} 1 & 4 \\ 0 & 2 \end{bmatrix} \begin{bmatrix} 2 & 1 \\ 3 & -2 \end{bmatrix} = \begin{bmatrix} 14 & -7 \\ 6 & -4 \end{bmatrix} = BA$$

Inverse of a Matrix. A *square* matrix A is said to have an *inverse* if there exists a matrix B such that $AB = BA = I$, where I is the *identity* matrix of order n.

$$\begin{bmatrix} 1 & 0 & \cdots & 0 \\ 0 & 1 & \cdots & \\ \cdot & & & \\ \cdot & & & \\ \cdot & & 1 & 0 \\ 0 & \cdots & 0 & 1 \end{bmatrix}$$

The inverse B is a square matrix of the order of A, designated by A^{-1}. Thus $AA^{-1} = A^{-1}A = I$. A square matrix A has an inverse if and only if A is *non-singular*.

Certain relations are important.

(*a*) $(AB)^{-1} = B^{-1}A^{-1}$

(*b*) $(AB)^T = B^TA^T$

(*c*) $(A^{-1})^T = (A^T)^{-1}$

(*d*) $(ABC)^{-1} = C^{-1}B^{-1}A^{-1}$

Scalar Multiplication. Let c be any real or complex number. $cA = (ca_{ij})$.

Example.

$$3\begin{bmatrix} 1 & 4 & 2 \\ 3 & 0 & -1 \end{bmatrix} = \begin{bmatrix} 3 & 12 & 6 \\ 9 & 0 & -3 \end{bmatrix}$$

The Adjoint Matrix of a Matrix. Let A_{ij} denote the cofactor of the element a_{ij} in the determinant of the matrix A. The matrix B^T where $B = (A_{ij})$ is called the adjoint matrix of A written adj $A = B^T$. Then $A^{-1} = \dfrac{\text{adj } A}{|A|}$. This definition may be used to calculate A^{-1}. However, it is very laborious and the inversion is usually accomplished by numerical techniques shown under Numerical Analysis.

Example.

$$\text{Let } A = \begin{bmatrix} 3 & 0 & -1 \\ -1 & 2 & 1 \\ 3 & 6 & 3 \end{bmatrix} \quad \text{Form } B = (A_{ij})$$

$$B = \begin{bmatrix} 0 & 6 & -12 \\ -6 & 12 & -18 \\ 2 & -2 & 6 \end{bmatrix}, \text{ adj } A = B^T = \begin{bmatrix} 0 & -6 & 2 \\ 6 & 12 & -2 \\ -12 & -18 & 6 \end{bmatrix};$$

$$|A| = 12. \quad A^{-1} = \frac{\text{adj } A}{|A|} = \begin{bmatrix} 0 & -\frac{1}{2} & \frac{1}{6} \\ \frac{1}{2} & 1 & -\frac{1}{6} \\ -1 & -\frac{3}{2} & \frac{1}{2} \end{bmatrix}.$$

Every set of n non-homogeneous linear equations in n unknowns

$$\begin{aligned} a_{11}x_1 + a_{12}x_2 + \cdots + a_{1n}x_n &= b_1 \\ a_{21}x_1 + a_{22}x_2 + \cdots + a_{2n}x_n &= b_2 \\ \cdot \qquad\qquad\qquad & \quad \cdot \\ \cdot \qquad\qquad\qquad & \quad \cdot \\ a_{n1}x_1 + a_{n2}x_2 + \cdots + a_{nn}x_n &= b_n \end{aligned}$$

can be written in matrix form as $AX = B$, where

$$A = (a_{ij}),\ X = \begin{bmatrix} x_1 \\ \cdot \\ \cdot \\ \cdot \\ x_n \end{bmatrix},\ B = \begin{bmatrix} b_1 \\ \cdot \\ \cdot \\ \cdot \\ b_n \end{bmatrix}.$$

The solution for the unknowns is $X = A^{-1}B$.

Example.

$$\begin{aligned} 3x_1 + 0x_2 - x_3 &= 4 \\ -x_1 + 2x_2 + x_3 &= -2 \\ 3x_1 + 6x_2 + 3x_3 &= 6 \end{aligned}$$

in matrix form is written

$$\begin{bmatrix} 3 & 0 & -1 \\ -1 & 2 & 1 \\ 3 & 6 & 3 \end{bmatrix} \begin{bmatrix} x_1 \\ x_2 \\ x_3 \end{bmatrix} = \begin{bmatrix} 4 \\ -2 \\ 6 \end{bmatrix}$$

The solution is

$$\begin{bmatrix} x_1 \\ x_2 \\ x_3 \end{bmatrix} = \begin{bmatrix} 0 & -\frac{1}{2} & \frac{1}{6} \\ \frac{1}{2} & 1 & -\frac{1}{6} \\ -1 & -\frac{3}{2} & \frac{1}{2} \end{bmatrix} \begin{bmatrix} 4 \\ -2 \\ 6 \end{bmatrix} = \begin{bmatrix} 2 \\ -1 \\ 2 \end{bmatrix};$$

that is, $x_1 = 2$, $x_2 = -1$, $x_3 = 2$.

Special Square Matrices.

(*a*) A *triangular* matrix is a matrix all of whose elements above or below the *main diagonal* (set of elements $a_{11}, \ldots, a_{nn}$) are zero. If A is triangular, $\det(A) = a_{11} \cdot a_{22} \cdot \ldots \cdot a_{nn}$.

(*b*) A *diagonal matrix* is one such that all elements both above and below the main diagonal are zero (*i.e.*, $a_{ij} = 0$ for all $i \neq j$). If all diagonal elements are equal the matrix is called scalar. If A is diagonal, $A = (a_{ii})$, $A^{-1} = \left(\dfrac{1}{a_{ii}}\right)$.

(*c*) If $a_{ij} = a_{ji}$ for all i and j (*i.e.*, $A = A^T$) the matrix is *symmetric*.

(*d*) If $a_{ij} = -a_{ji}$ for $i \neq j$ but the a_{ii} are not all zero the matrix is *skew*.

(*e*) If $a_{ij} = -a_{ji}$ for all i and j (*i.e.*, $a_{ii} = 0$) the matrix is *skew symmetric*.

(*f*) If $A^T = A^{-1}$ the matrix A is *orthogonal*.

(*g*) If the matrix $A^* = (\bar{a}_{ij})^T$, $\bar{a}_{ij}$ = complex conjugate of a_{ij}, A^* is the *associate* of A.

(*h*) If $A = A^{-1}$, A is *involutory*.

(*i*) If $A = A^*$, A is *hermitian*.

(*j*) If $A = -A^*$, A is *skew hermitian*.

(*k*) If $A^{-1} = A^*$, A is *unitary*.

If A is any matrix, then AA^T and A^TA are *square symmetric* matrices, usually of different order.

$$\textit{Example.} \quad \text{Let } A = \begin{bmatrix} 5 & 1 & 3 & 0 \\ 3 & 4 & 1 & 5 \\ 2 & -2 & 0 & 1 \end{bmatrix}, \quad A^T = \begin{bmatrix} 5 & 3 & 2 \\ 1 & 4 & -2 \\ 3 & 1 & 0 \\ 0 & 5 & 1 \end{bmatrix},$$

$$AA^T = \begin{bmatrix} 34 & 22 & 8 \\ 22 & 51 & 3 \\ 8 & 3 & 1 \end{bmatrix}, \qquad A^TA = \begin{bmatrix} 38 & 13 & 18 & 17 \\ 13 & 21 & 7 & 18 \\ 18 & 7 & 10 & 5 \\ 17 & 18 & 5 & 26 \end{bmatrix}.$$

Matrix Calculus.

Differentiation. Let the elements of $A = [a_{ij}(t)]$ be functions of t. Then $\dfrac{dA}{dt} = \left[\dfrac{da_{ij}(t)}{dt}\right]$.

$$\textit{Example.} \quad A = \begin{bmatrix} \sin t & \cos t \\ -\cos t & \sin t \end{bmatrix}, \quad \frac{dA}{dt} = \begin{bmatrix} \cos t & -\sin t \\ \sin t & \cos t \end{bmatrix}.$$

Integration. The integral $\int A\, dt = [\int a_{ij}(t)\, dt]$.

$$\textit{Example.} \quad A = \begin{bmatrix} t & 2 \\ t^2 & e^t \end{bmatrix}, \quad \int A\, dt = \begin{bmatrix} t^2/2 & 2t \\ t^3/3 & e^t \end{bmatrix}.$$

The matrix $B = \lambda I - A$ is called the *characteristic* (*eigen*) *matrix* of A. Here A is square of order n, λ is a scalar parameter, and I is the $n \times n$ identity. $\det B = \det(\lambda I - A) = 0$ is the characteristic (eigen) equation for A. In general the *characteristic equation* is of the same degree as the order of A. The roots of the characteristic equation are called the *eigenvalues* of A.

Example.

$$A = \begin{bmatrix} 1 & 2 \\ 3 & 8 \end{bmatrix} B = \begin{bmatrix} \lambda & 0 \\ 0 & \lambda \end{bmatrix} - \begin{bmatrix} 1 & 2 \\ 3 & 8 \end{bmatrix} = \begin{bmatrix} \lambda - 1 & -2 \\ -3 & \lambda - 8 \end{bmatrix}$$

is the characteristic matrix and

$$\begin{aligned} f(\lambda) = \det(B) = \det(\lambda I - A) &= (\lambda - 1)(\lambda - 8) - 6 \\ &= \lambda^2 - 9\lambda + 2 = 0 \end{aligned}$$

is the characteristic equation. The eigenvalues of A are the roots of $\lambda^2 - 9\lambda + 2 = 0$, which are $\dfrac{9 \pm \sqrt{73}}{2}$.

The matrix X_i, which has one column and n rows, called a *column vector* satisfying the equation

$$(\lambda I - A)X_i = 0$$

and associated with the ith characteristic root λ_i is called an eigenvector.

Matrices are quite useful in many applied problems, a few of which are listed here.

1. Distribution of the rate of flow in complex hydraulic systems.
2. The approximate solution of partial differential equations which arise in potential problems, vibrations, and radiation.
3. The solution of the normal equations for the least-squares applications.
4. Transmission-line characteristics.
5. The solution of large systems of linear differential equations.
6. Determination of approximate roots of algebraic equations.

ANALYTIC GEOMETRY

REFERENCES: Olmsted, "Solid Analytic Geometry," Appleton-Century, 1947. Thomas, "Calculus and Analytic Geometry," Addison-Wesley, Reading, Mass., 1953.

Analytic geometry uses algebraic equations and methods to study geometric problems. It also permits one to visualize algebraic equations in terms of geometric curves, which frequently clarifies abstract concepts.

PLANE ANALYTIC GEOMETRY

Coordinate Systems. The basic concept of analytic geometry is the establishment of a one to one correspondence between the points of the plane and number pairs (x, y). This correspondence may be done in a number of ways. The *rectangular* or *cartesian* coordinate system consists of two straight lines intersecting at right angles (Fig. 2-12). A point is designated by (x, y), where x (the abscissa) is the distance of the point from the y-axis measured parallel to the x-axis, positive if to the right, negative to the left. y(ordinate) is the distance of the point from the x-axis, measured parallel to the y-axis, positive if above, negative if below the x-axis. The *quadrants* are labeled 1, 2, 3, 4 in the drawing, the coordinates of points in the various

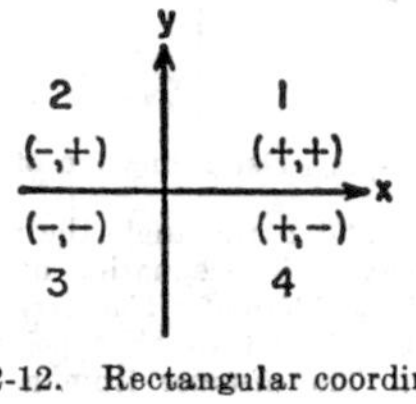

FIG. 2-12. Rectangular coordinates.

quadrants having the depicted signs. Another common coordinate system is the *polar* coordinate system (Fig. 2-13). In

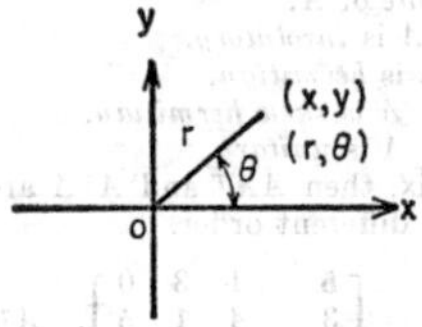

FIG. 2-13. Polar coordinates.

this system the position of a point is designated by the pair (r, θ), $r = \sqrt{x^2 + y^2}$ being the distance to the origin $0(0, 0)$ and θ being the angle the line r makes with the positive x-axis (polar axis). The *equations relating* the *polar* and *rectangular coordinate systems* are $x^2 + y^2 = r^2$, $x = r \cos \theta$, $y = r \sin \theta$, $\theta = \tan^{-1}(y/x)$. The *distance* between two points (x_1, y_1), (x_2, y_2) is defined by $d = \sqrt{(x_1 - x_2)^2 + (y_1 - y_2)^2}$ in rectangular coordinates or by $d = \sqrt{r_1^2 + r_2^2 - 2r_1r_2 \cos(\theta_1 - \theta_2)}$ in polar coordinates. Other coordinate systems are sometimes used. For example, on the *surface* of a *sphere latitude* and *longitude* prove useful.

The Straight Line. The *slope* m of a straight line is the tangent of the *inclination angle* θ made with the positive x-axis.

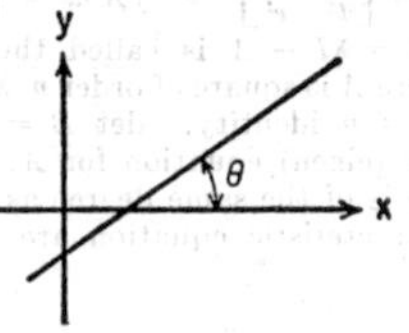

FIG. 2-14. Straight line.

If (x_1, y_1) and (x_2, y_2) are any two points on the line slope $= m = (y_2 - y_1)/(x_2 - x_1)$. The slope of a line parallel to the x-axis is zero, parallel to the y-axis is infinite. *Two lines are parallel* if and only if they have the same slope. *Two lines are perpendicular* if and only if the product of their slope is -1 (the exception being that case when the lines are parallel to the coordinate axes). *Every equation of the type $Ax + By + C = 0$ represents a straight line and every straight line has an equation of this form.* A straight line is determined by a variety of conditions:

Given Conditions	Equation of Line
(1) Parallel to x-axis	$y =$ constant
(2) Parallel to y-axis	$x =$ constant
(3) Point (x_1, y_1) and slope m	$y - y_1 = m(x - x_1)$
(4) Intercept on y-axs $(0, b)$, m	$y = mx + b$
(5) Intercept on x-axis $(a, 0)$, m	$y = m(x - a)$
(6) Two points (x_1, y_1), (x_2, y_2)	$y - y_1 = \dfrac{y_2 - y_1}{x_2 - x_1}(x - x_1)$
(7) Two intercepts $(a, 0)$, $(0, b)$	$\dfrac{x}{a} + \dfrac{y}{b} = 1$

The *angle β a line with slope m_1 makes with a line having slope m_2* is given by $\tan \beta = (m_2 - m_1)/(m_1m_2 + 1)$. A line is determined if the length and direction of the perpendicular to it (the *normal*) from the origin are given (see Fig. 2-15). Let $p =$ length

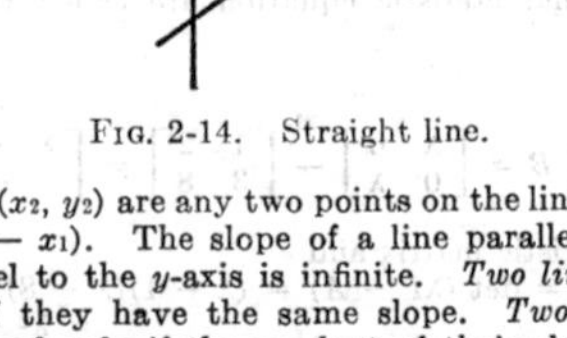

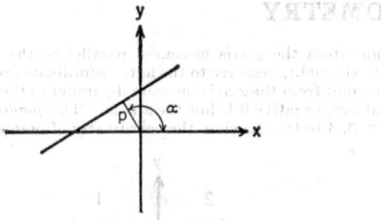

FIG. 2-15. Determination of line.

of the perpendicular and α the angle the perpendicular makes with the positive x-axis. The equation of the line is $x \cos \alpha + y \sin \alpha = p$. *The equation of a line perpendicular* to a given line of slope m and passing through a point (x_1, y_1) is $y - y_1 = -(1/m)(x - x_1)$. The *distance* from a point (x_1, y_1) to a line with equation $Ax + By + C = 0$ is $d = \dfrac{Ax_1 + By_1 + C}{\sqrt{A^2 + B^2}}$ and $d > 0$ if (x_1, y_1) and $(0, 0)$ are on the same side of the line; $d < 0$ if (x_1, y_1) and $(0, 0)$ are on opposite sides of the line.

Example 1. If it is known that centigrade C and Fahrenheit F are linearly related and when $C = 0°$, $F = 32°$; $C = 100°$, $F = 212°$, find the equation relating C and F and that point where $C = F$. Using the two-point form the equation is $F-32 = \dfrac{212-32}{100-0}(C-0)$ or $F = \frac{9}{5}C + 32$. Equivalently $C-0 = \dfrac{100-0}{212-32}(F-32)$ or $C = \frac{5}{9}(F-32°)$. Letting $C = F$ we have from either equation $F = C = -40$.

Example 2. Since the equation $Ax + By + C = 0$, $B \neq 0$ can be written in the form $y = -\dfrac{A}{B}x + \dfrac{C}{B}$ or $y = mx + D$ $\left(m = -\dfrac{A}{B},\ D = \dfrac{C}{B}\right)$ m and D can be determined from data and thus the line determined. Occasionally other equations can be reduced to this form. *Consider* $y = bx^n$. Taking logarithms $\log y = n \log x + \log b$. Let $Y = \log y$, $X = \log x$, $B = \log b$. The equation then has the form $Y = nX + B$, which is a linear equation. Consider $y = ka^{bx}$. Taking logarithms, this becomes $\log y = \log k + (b \log a)\, x$, which indicates that $\log y$ and x are linearly related with slope $b \log a$ and intercept on the y-axis $\log k$. Next consider $y = a + bx^n$. If the substitution $t = x^n$ is made, then the graph of $y = a + bt$ is a straight line.

Geometric Properties of a Curve When the Equation Is Given. The analysis of the properties of an equation is facilitated by the investigation of the equation using the following techniques:

(*a*) *Points of maximum, minimum, and inflection* may be investigated by means of the calculus.

(*b*) *Symmetry*. Let $F(x, y) = 0$ be the equation of the curve.

Condition on $F(x, y)$	Symmetry
$F(x, y) = F(-x, y)$	With respect to y-axis
$F(x, y) = F(x, -y)$	With respect to x-axis
$F(x, y) = F(-x, -y)$	With respect to origin
$F(x, y) = F(y, x)$	With respect to the line $y = x$

Example. $y^2 = x^2(x^2 - 1)$ is symmetric with respect to both axes and origin.

(*c*) *Extent*. Only real values of x and y are considered in obtaining the points (x, y) whose coordinates satisfy the equation. The *extent* may be limited by the condition that negative numbers do not have real square roots.

(*d*) *Intercepts*. Find those points where the curves of the function cross the coordinate axes.

(*e*) *Asymptotes*. An asymptote of a curve is a line or another curve such that the distance between the two approaches zero as $x, y \to \infty$. If the equation has the form $y = N(x)/D(x)$ where N, D are polynomials without common factors and $x = a$ is a root of $D(x) = 0$ then as $x \to a$ $y \to \infty$ and $x - a \to 0$. Hence $x = a$ is an asymptote.

(*f*) *Direction at a Point*. This may be found from the derivative of the function at a point. This concept is useful for distinguishing among a family of similar curves.

Example. $y^2 = (x^2 + 1)/(x^2 - 1)$ is symmetric with respect to the x and y axis and the origin. It has the vertical asymptotes $x = \pm 1$. When $x = 0$ $y^2 = -1$; so there are no y intercepts. If $y = 0$ $(x^2 + 1)/(x^2 - 1) = 0$; so there are no x intercepts. If $|x| < 1$, y^2 is negative; so $|x| > 1$. From $x^2 = (y^2 + 1)/(y^2 - 1)$, $y = \pm 1$ are horizontal asymptotes and $|y| > 1$. As $x \to 1^+$, $y \to +\infty$; as $x \to +\infty$, $y \to +1$. The graph is given in Fig. 2-16.

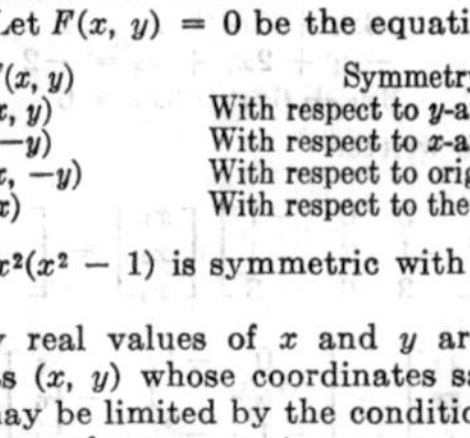

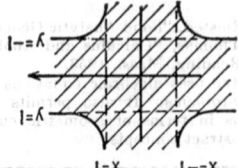

FIG. 2-16. Direction at a point.

Conic Sections. The curves included in this group are obtained from plane sections of the cone. They include the circle, ellipse, parabola, hyperbola, and degeneratively the point and straight line. A *conic* is the locus of a point whose distance from a fixed point called the *focus* is in a constant ratio to its distance from a fixed line, called the *directrix*. This ratio is the *eccentricity e.* If $e = 0$ the conic is a circle; if $0 < e < 1$ the conic is an ellipse; if $e = 1$ the conic is a parabola; if $e > 1$ the conic is a hyperbola. Every conic section is representable by an equation of second degree. Conversely every equation of second degree in two variables represents a conic. The general equation of the second degree is $Ax^2 + Bxy + Cy^2 + Dx + Ey + F = 0$. Let Δ be defined as the determinant

$$\Delta = \begin{vmatrix} 2A & B & D \\ B & 2C & E \\ D & E & 2F \end{vmatrix}$$

The table characterizes the curve represented by the equation.

	$B^2 - 4AC < 0$	$B^2 - 4AC = 0$	$B^2 - 4AC > 0$
$\Delta \neq 0$	$A\Delta < 0$ $A \neq C$, an ellipse $A\Delta < 0$ $A = C$, a circle $A\Delta > 0$, no locus	Parabola	Hyperbola
$\Delta = 0$	Point	2 parallel lines if $Q = D^2 + E^2 - 4(A + C)F > 0$ 1 straight line if $Q = 0$, no locus if $Q < 0$	2 intersecting straight lines

Example. $3x^2 + 4xy - 2y^2 + 3x - 2y + 7 = 0$.

$$\Delta = \begin{vmatrix} 6 & 4 & 3 \\ 4 & -4 & -2 \\ 3 & -2 & 14 \end{vmatrix} = -596 \neq 0, \quad B^2 - 4AC = 40 > 0;$$ the curve is therefore a hyperbola.

To *translate* the axes to a new origin at (h, k) substitute for x and y in the original equation $x + h$ and $y + k$. Translation of the axes can always be accomplished to eliminate the linear terms in the second-degree equation in two variables having no xy term.

Example. $x^2 + y^2 + 2x - 4y + 2 = 0$. Rewrite this as $x^2 + 2x + 1 + y^2 - 4y + 4 - 5 + 2 = 0$ or $(x + 1)^2 + (y - 2)^2 = 3$. Let $x^1 = x + 1$, $y^1 = y - 2$. Then $(x^1)^2 + (y^1)^2 = 3$. The axis has been translated to the new origin $(-1, 2)$.

To *rotate* the axes through an angle α, substitute for x the quantity $x \cos \alpha - y \sin \alpha$ and for y the quantity $x \sin \alpha + y \cos \alpha$. A rotation of the axes through $\alpha = \frac{1}{2} \cot^{-1} (A - C)/B$ will eliminate the cross-product term in the general second-degree equation.

Example. Consider $3x^2 + 2xy + y^2 - 2x + 3y = 7$. A rotation of axes through $\alpha = \frac{1}{2} \cot^{-1} 1 = 22\frac{1}{2}$ deg. eliminates the cross-product term.

Since a proper rotation of the axes will eliminate the term Bxy we need only consider equations of the form $Ax^2 + Cy^2 + Dx + Ey + F = 0$ where the coefficients are those which result after the axes are rotated. Investigation is facilitated by the following table.

Condition	Conic	Equation and properties
$A = C$	Circle	$(x - h)^2 + (y - k)^2 = r^2$, center at $(h, k) = \left(-\frac{D}{2A}, -\frac{E}{2A}\right)$, radius $r = \frac{1}{2A}\sqrt{D^2 + E^2 - 4AF}$. If $D^2 + E^2 - 4AF > 0$ real circle, $= 0$ point, < 0 no locus
$A \neq 0, C = 0$	Parabola	$(x - h)^2 = 4p(y - k)$, $h = -D/2A$, $4p = -\frac{E}{A}$, $k = \frac{D^2 - 4AF}{4AE}$. $p > 0$ opens upward, $p < 0$ opens downward. Focus $(h, p + k)$, directrix $y = -p + k$
$A = 0, C \neq 0$	Parabola	$(y - k)^2 = 4p(x - h)$, $h = \frac{E^2 - 4CF}{4CD}$, $4p = -\frac{D}{C}$, $k = -\frac{E}{2C}$ if $p > 0$ opens to right, $p < 0$ opens to left. Focus $(p + h, k)$, directrix $x = -p + h$
$AC > 0, A \neq C$ $C > A$	Ellipse	$\frac{(x - h)^2}{a^2} + \frac{(y - k)^2}{b^2} = 1$, $a > b$. Here $a^2 = \frac{G}{A}$, $b^2 = \frac{G}{C}$, $G = \frac{E^2}{4C} + \frac{D^2}{4A} - F$, $h = -\frac{D}{2A}$, $k = -\frac{E}{2C}$. Major axis the x-axis, foci at $(h \pm \sqrt{a^2 - b^2}, k)$, center (h, k)
$AC > 0, A \neq C$ $C < A$	Ellipse	$\frac{(x - h)^2}{b^2} + \frac{(y - k)^2}{a^2} = 1$, $a > b$. $a^2 = G/C$, $b^2 = G/A$, $G = \frac{E^2}{4C} + \frac{D^2}{4A} - F$, $h = -D/2A$, $k = -E/2C$. Major axis the y-axis, foci at $(h, k \pm \sqrt{a^2 - b^2})$, center (h, k)
$AC < 0$	Hyperbola	$\frac{(x - h)^2}{a^2} - \frac{(y - k)^2}{b^2} = 1$, $a^2 = G/A$, $b^2 = -G/C$, $G = \frac{E^2}{4C} + \frac{D^2}{4A} - F$, $h = -D/2A$, $k = -\frac{E}{2C}$. Intersects x-axis at $\left(h \pm \frac{a}{b}\sqrt{b^2 + k^2}, 0\right)$ or $\frac{(y - k)^2}{a^2} - \frac{(x - h)^2}{b^2} = 1$, $a^2 = G/C$, $b^2 = -G/A$, all others the same. Intersects y-axis at $\left(0, k \pm \frac{a}{b}\sqrt{a^2 + h^2}\right)$.

Example. $x^2 - 4y^2 + 2x + 8y - 7 = 0$ is equivalent to $(x + 1)^2/4 - (y - 1)^2 = 1$. This hyperbola opens out the x-axis with intercepts on the x-axis at $(-1 \pm 2\sqrt{2}, 0)$.

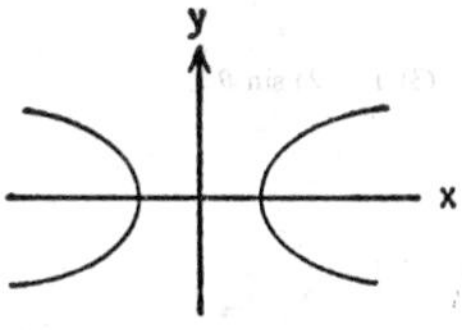

Fig. 2-17. Hyperbola.

Graphs of Polar Equations. The polar representation of a point in the plane is (r, θ) where $-\infty < r < \infty$ and θ is the angle with the positive x-axis (see under Coordinate System). $r = 0$ corresponds to $x = 0$, $y = 0$ regardless of θ. Positive values of r for fixed θ give points on the backward extension through the pole of the terminal side of θ. The same point may

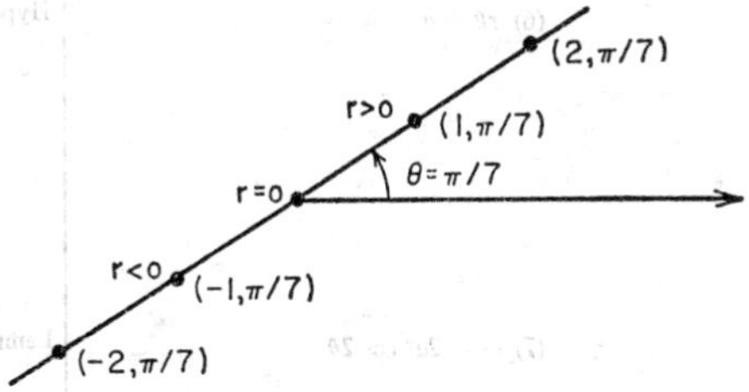

Fig. 2-18. Polar representation.

be represented in several different ways; thus the point $(2, \pi/3)$ or $(2, 60°)$ has the following representations: $(2, 60°)$, $(2, -300°)$ $(-2, 240°)$, $(-2, -120°)$. These are summarized in $(2, 60° + n\ 360°)$, $(-2, 240° + n\ 360°)$ $n = 0, \pm 1, \pm 2$, or in radian measure $[2, (\pi/3) + 2n\pi]$, $[-2, (4\pi/3) + 2n\pi]$ $n = 0, \pm 1, \pm 2$. Plotting of polar equations can be facilitated by the following steps:

1. Find those points where r is a maximum or minimum.
2. Find those values of θ where $r = 0$, if any.
3. Symmetry: The curve is symmetric about the origin if the equation is unchanged when r is replaced by $-r$, symmetric about the x-axis if the equation is unchanged when θ is replaced by $-\theta$, symmetric about the y-axis if the equation is unchanged when θ is replaced by $\pi - \theta$.

Parametric Equations. It is frequently useful to write the equations of a curve in terms of an auxiliary variable called a parameter. For example, a circle of radius a, center at $(0, 0)$, can be written in the equivalent form $x = a \cos \theta$, $y = a \sin \theta$

The tabulation below gives the form of the more common equations.

Polar equation	Type of curve	Representative graph
(1) $r = a$	Circle	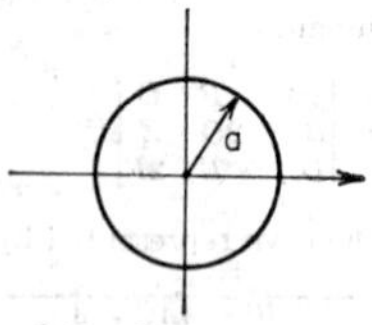 FIG. 2-19. Circle center (o, o).
(2) $r = 2a \cos \theta$	Circle	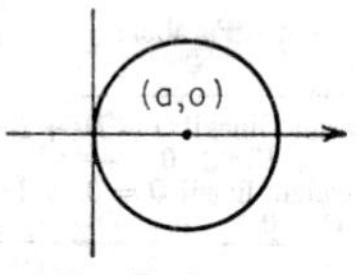 FIG. 2-20. Circle center (a, o).
(3) $r = 2a \sin \theta$	Circle	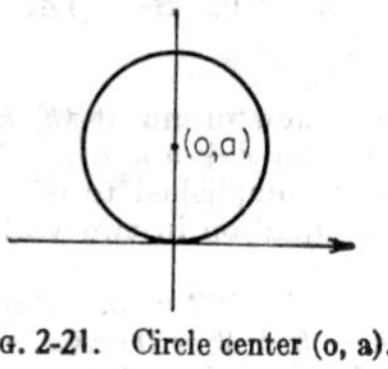 FIG. 2-21. Circle center (o, a).
(4) $r^2 - 2br \cos(\theta - \beta) + b^2 - a^2 = 0$	Circle center at (b, β), radius a	
(5) $r = \dfrac{ke}{1 - e \cos \theta}$	$e = 1$ Parabola $0 < e < 1$ Ellipse $e > 1$ Hyperbola	Focus at the pole, directrix $x = -k$
(6) $r\theta = a$	Hyperbolic spiral	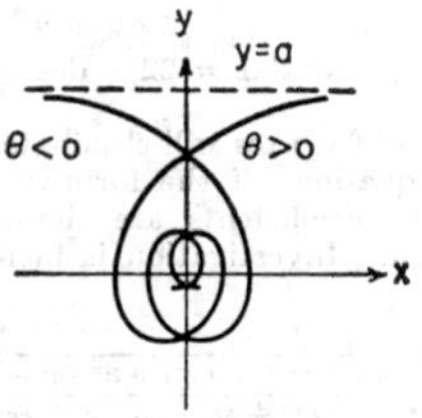 FIG. 2-22. Hyperbolic spiral.
(7) $r^2 = 2a^2 \cos 2\theta$	Lemniscate	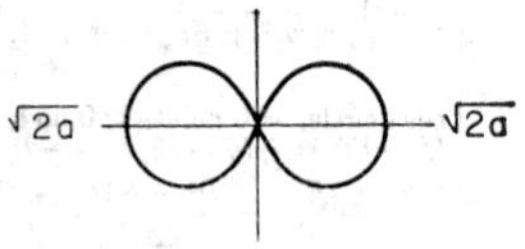 FIG. 2-23. Lemmscate.
(8) $r = a(1 - \cos \theta)$	Cardioid	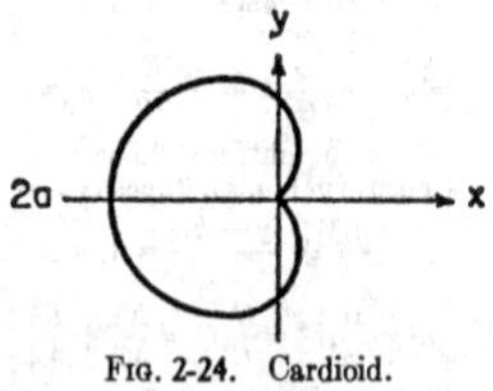 FIG. 2-24. Cardioid.
(9) $r = a \sec \theta$ $r = a \csc \theta$	Straight line parallel to y-axis Straight line parallel to x-axis	
(10) $r(a \cos \theta + b \sin \theta) = C$	General straight line	

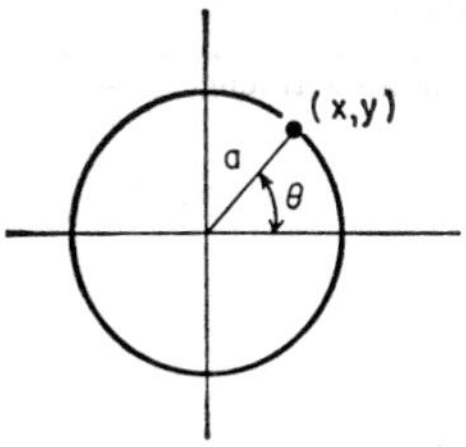

FIG. 2-25. Circle.

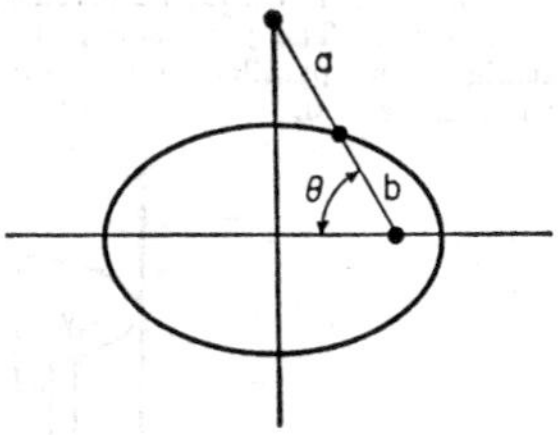

FIG. 2-26. Ellipse.

Some common equations in parametric form are given below.

(1) $(x-h)^2+(y-k)^2=a^2$	$x=h+a\cos\theta$ $y=k+a\sin\theta$	Circle
(2) $\frac{(x-h)^2}{a^2}+\frac{(y-k)^2}{b^2}=1$	$x=h+a\cos\phi$ $y=k+a\sin\phi$	Ellipse
(3) $x^2+y^2=a^2$	$x=\frac{-at}{\sqrt{t^2+1}}$	Parameter
	$y=\frac{a}{\sqrt{t^2+1}}$	$t=\frac{dy}{dx}=$ slope of tangent at (x, y)
(4) $y=a\cosh\frac{x}{a}$	$x=a\sinh^{-1}\frac{s}{a}$ $y=a^2+s^2$	Parameter s = arc length from $(0, a)$ to (x, y)
(5) Cycloid	$x=a(\phi-\sin\phi)$ $y=a(1-\cos\phi)$	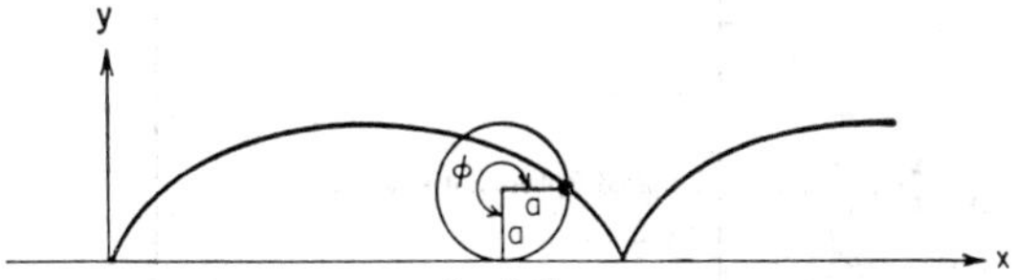

FIG. 2-27

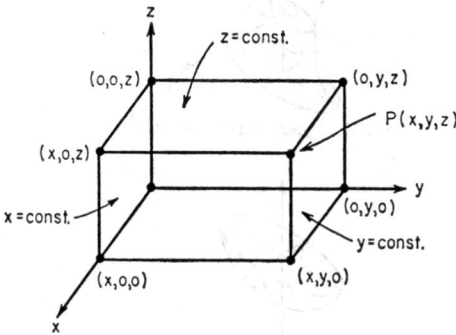

where θ is the parameter. Similarly $x = a\cos\phi$, $y = b\sin\phi$ are the parametric equations of the ellipse $\frac{x^2}{a^2}+\frac{y^2}{b^2}=1$ with parameter ϕ.

SOLID ANALYTIC GEOMETRY

Coordinate Systems. The commonly used coordinate systems are three in number. Others may be used in specific problems (see Morse and Feshbach, "Methods of Theoretical Physics"). The *rectangular* (cartesian) system consists of mutually orthogonal axes x, y, z. A triple of numbers (x, y, z)

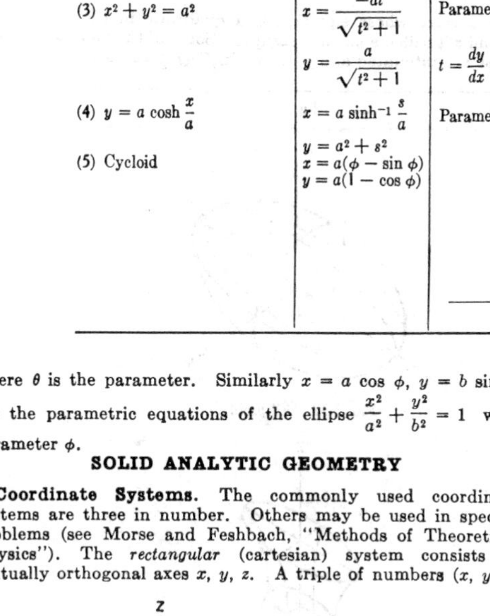

FIG. 2-28. Cartesian coordinates.

is used to represent each point. The *cylindrical* coordinate system (r, θ, z) is frequently used to locate a point in space. These are essentially the polar coordinates (r, θ) coupled with the z coordinate. As before, $x = r\cos\theta$, $y = r\sin\theta$, $z = z$ and $r^2 = x^2 + y^2$, $y/x = \tan\theta$. If r is held constant and θ and z are allowed to vary, the locus of (r, θ, z) is a right circular cylinder of radius r along the z-axis. The locus of $r = C$ is a circle

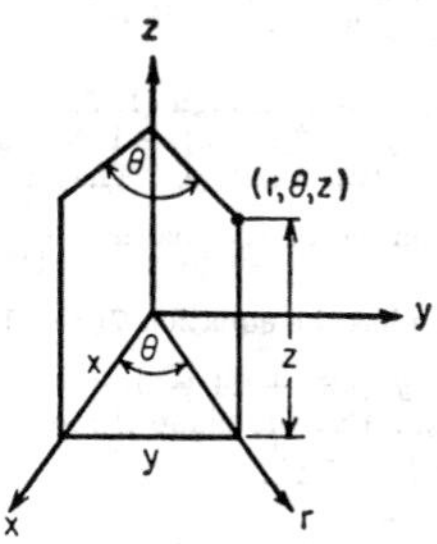

FIG. 2-29. Cylindrical coordinates.

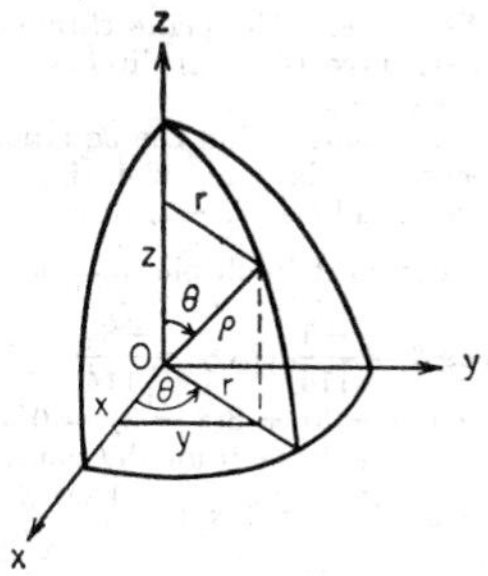

FIG. 2-30. Spherical coordinates.

and θ = constant is a plane containing the z-axis and making an angle θ with the xz plane. Cylindrical coordinates are convenient to use when the problem has an axis of symmetry.

The *spherical* coordinate system is convenient if there is a point of symmetry in the system. This point is taken as the origin and the coordinates (ρ, ϕ, θ) illustrated in Fig. 2-30. The relations are $x = \rho\sin\phi\cos\theta$, $y = \rho\sin\phi\sin\theta$, $z = \rho\cos\phi$ and $r = \rho\sin\phi$, $z = \rho\cos\phi$, $\theta = \theta$. θ = constant is a plane containing the z-axis and making an angle θ with the xz plane. ϕ = constant is a cone with vertex at 0. ρ = constant is the surface of a sphere of radius ρ, center at the origin 0. Every point in the space may be given spherical coordinates restricted to the ranges $0 \le \phi \le \pi$, $\rho \ge 0$, $0 \le \theta < 2\pi$.

Lines and Planes. The *distance* between two points (x_1, y_1, z_1), (x_2, y_2, z_2) is $d = \sqrt{(x_1-x_2)^2+(y_1-y_2)^2+(z_1-z_2)^2}$. There is nothing in the geometry of three dimensions quite analogous to the slope of a line in the plane case. Instead of specifying the direction of a line by a trigonometric function evaluated for one angle, a trigonometric function evaluated for three angles is used. The angles α, β, γ that a line segment makes with the x-, y-, and z-axes, respectively, are called the *direction angles* of the line and $\cos\alpha$, $\cos\beta$, $\cos\gamma$ are called the *direction cosines*. Let (x_1, y_1, z_1), (x_2, y_2, z_2) be on the line. Then $\cos\alpha = (x_2 - x_1)/d$, $\cos\beta = (y_2 - y_1)/d$, $\cos\gamma = (z_2 - z_1)/d$ where d = the distance between the two points. Clearly $\cos^2\alpha + \cos^2\beta + \cos^2\gamma = 1$. If two lines are specified by the direction cosines $(\cos\alpha_1, \cos\beta_1, \cos\gamma_1)$, $(\cos\alpha_2, \cos\beta_2, \cos\gamma_2)$ then the *angle θ between the lines* is $\cos\theta = \cos\alpha_1\cos\alpha_2 + \cos\beta_1\cos\beta_2 + \cos\gamma_1\cos\gamma_2$. Thus the *lines* are *perpendicular* if and only if θ = 90 deg. or $\cos\alpha_1\cos\alpha_2 + \cos\beta_1\cos\beta_2 + \cos\gamma_1\cos\gamma_2 = 0$. The *equation of a line* with direction cosines $(\cos\alpha, \cos\beta, \cos\gamma)$ passing through (x_1, y_1, z_1) is $(x - x_1)/\cos\alpha = (y - y_1)/\cos\beta = (z - z_1)/\cos\gamma$.

The *equation of every plane* is of the form $Ax + By + Cz + D = 0$. The numbers $\frac{A}{\sqrt{A^2+B^2+C^2}}$, $\frac{B}{\sqrt{A^2+B^2+C^2}}$, $\frac{C}{\sqrt{A^2+B^2+C^2}}$ are direction cosines of the *normal lines* to the plane. The plane through the point (x_1, y_1, z_1) whose normals have these as direction cosines is $A(x - x_1) + B(y - y_1) + C(z - z_1) = 0$.

Example. Find the equation of the plane through $(1, 5, -2)$ perpendicular to the line $(x + 9)/7 = (y - 3)/-1 = z/8$. The numbers $(7, -1, 8)$ are called *direction numbers.* They are a constant multiple of the direction cosines. $\cos\alpha = \frac{7}{114}$, $\cos\beta = \frac{-1}{114}$, $\cos\gamma = \frac{8}{114}$. The plane has the equation $7(x - 1) - 1(y - 5) + 8(z - 2) = 0$ or $7x - y + 8z + 14 = 0$.

The *distance* from the point (x_1, y_1, z_1) to the plane $Ax + By + Cz + D = 0$ is $d = \frac{|Ax_1 + By_1 + Cz_1 + D|}{\sqrt{A^2 + B^2 + C^2}}$.

Space Curves. Space curves are usually specified as the set of points whose coordinates are given parametrically by a system of equations $x = f(t)$, $y = g(t)$, $z = h(t)$ in the parameter t.

Example 1. The equation of a straight line in space is $(x - x_1)/a = (y - y_1)/b = (z - z_1)/c$. Since all these quantities must be equal (say to t) we may write $x = x_1 + at$, $y = y_1 + bt$, $z = z_1 + ct$, which represent the parametric equations of the line.

Example 2. The equations $x = a\cos\beta t$, $y = a\sin\beta t$, $z = bt$, a, β, b positive constants, represent a circular helix.

Surfaces. The locus of points (x, y, z) satisfying $f(x, y, z) = 0$ broadly speaking may be interpreted as a surface. The simplest of these is the *plane.* The next simplest is a *cylinder,* which is a surface generated by a straight line moving parallel to a given line and passing through a given curve.

Example. The parabolic cylinder $y = x^2$ is generated by a straight line parallel to the z-axis passing through $y = x^2$ in the plane $z = 0$.

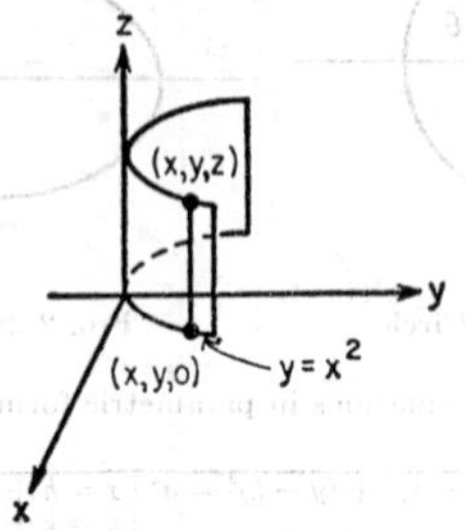

Fig. 2-31. Parabolic cylinder.

A surface whose equation is a quadratic in the variables x, y, and z is called a *quadric surface.* Some of the more common of these are tabulated and pictured in Figs. 2-32 to 2-41.

Equation	Name	Figure
(1) $\frac{x^2}{a^2} + \frac{y^2}{b^2} + \frac{z^2}{c^2} = 1$	Ellipsoid (sphere if $a = b = c$)	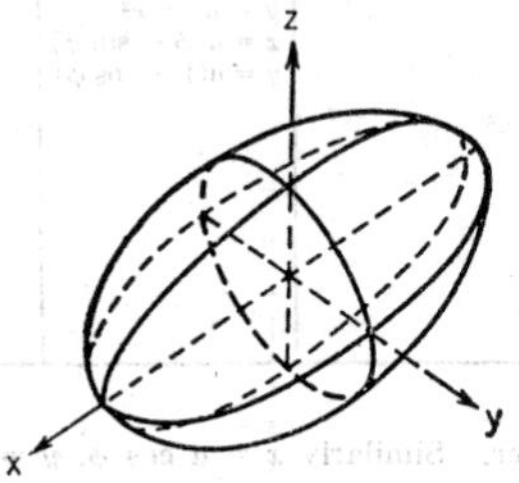 Fig. 2-32. Ellipsoid.
(2) $\frac{x^2}{a^2} + \frac{y^2}{b^2} - \frac{z^2}{c^2} = 1$	Hyperboloid of one sheet	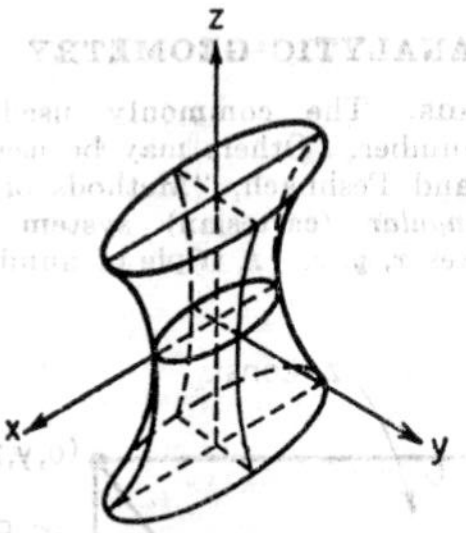 Fig. 2-33. Hyperboloid of one sheet.
(3) $\frac{x^2}{a^2} + \frac{y^2}{b^2} - \frac{z^2}{c^2} = -1$	Hyperboloid of two sheets	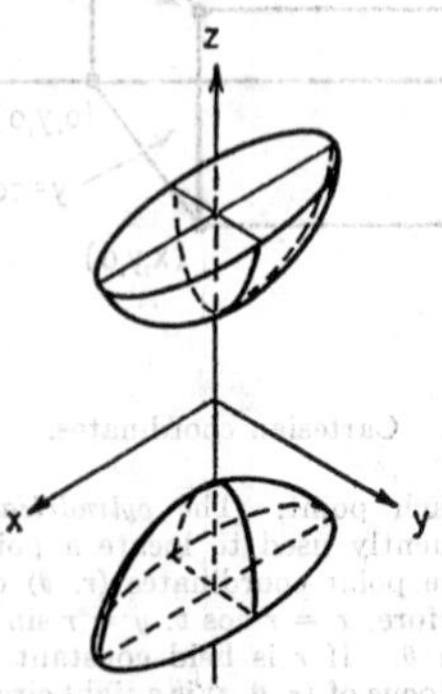 Fig. 2-34. Hyperboloid of two sheets.

Equation	Name	Figure
(4) $\frac{x^2}{a^2} + \frac{y^2}{b^2} - \frac{z^2}{c^2} = 0$	Cone	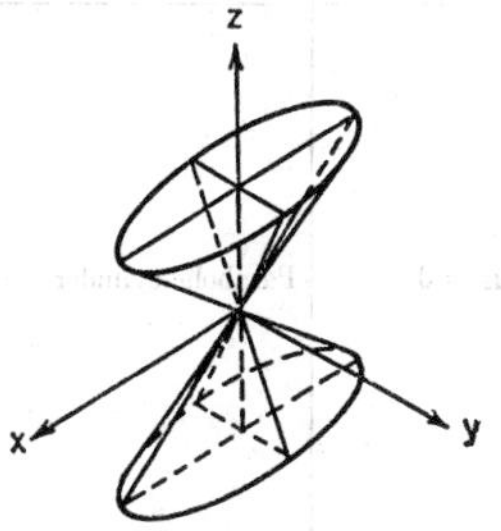 Fig. 2-35. Cone.
(5) $\frac{x^2}{a^2} + \frac{y^2}{b^2} + 2z = 0$	Elliptic paraboloid	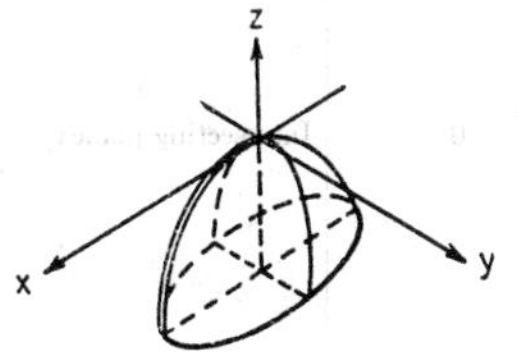 Fig. 2-36. Elliptic paraboloid.
(6) $\frac{x^2}{a^2} - \frac{y^2}{b^2} + 2z = 0$	Hyperbolic paraboloid (saddle)	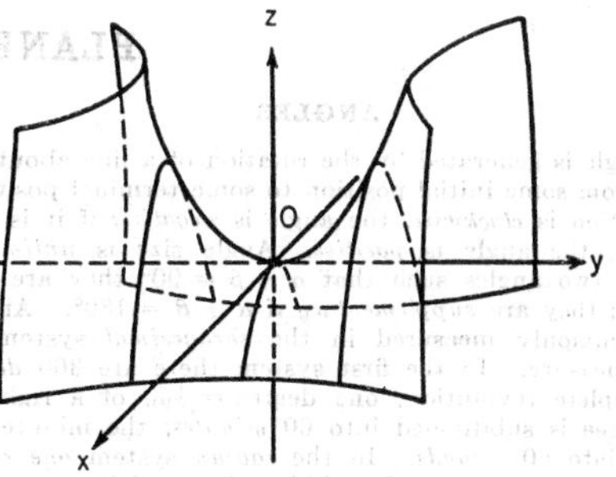 Fig. 2-37. Hyperbolic paraboloid.
(7) $\frac{x^2}{a^2} + \frac{y^2}{b^2} = 1$	Elliptic cylinder (circular cylinder if $a = b$)	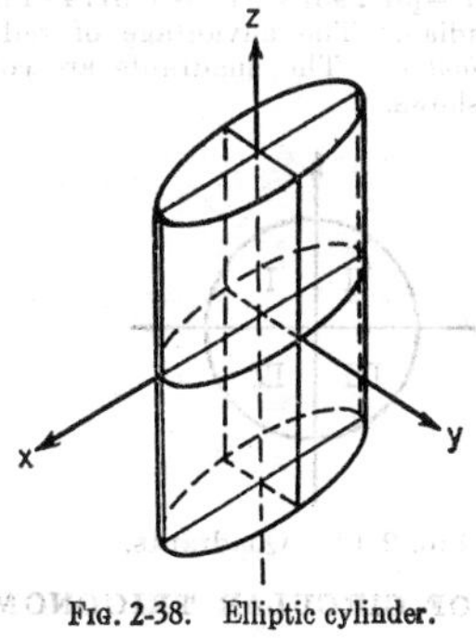 Fig. 2-38. Elliptic cylinder.
(8) $\frac{x^2}{a^2} - \frac{y^2}{b^2} = 1$	Hyperbolic cylinder	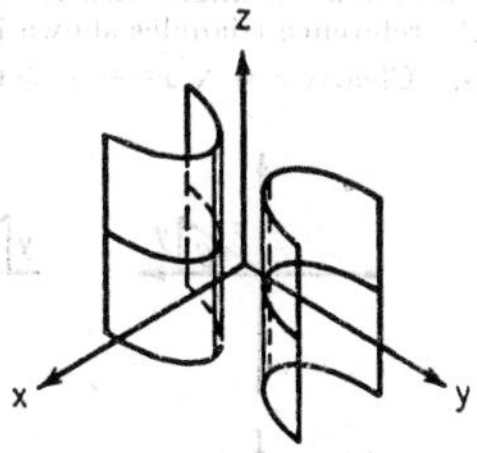 Fig. 2-39. Hyperbolic cylinder.

Equation	Name	Figure
(9) $x^2 + 2az = 0$	Parabolic cylinder	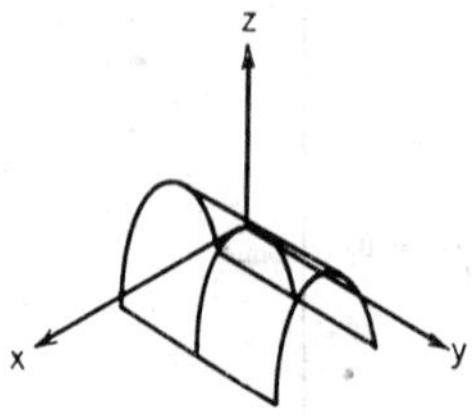 FIG. 2-40. Parabolic cylinder.
(10) $\frac{x^2}{a^2} - \frac{y^2}{b^2} = 0$	Intersecting planes	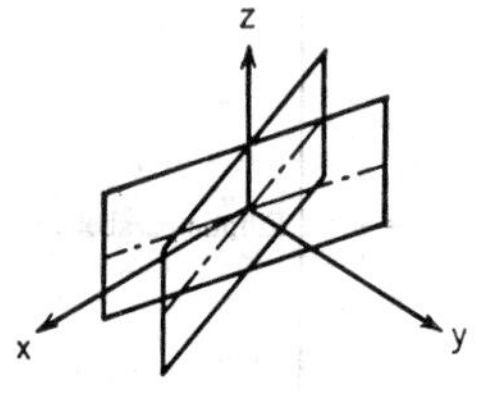 FIG. 2-41. Intersecting planes.

PLANE TRIGONOMETRY

ANGLES

An angle is generated by the rotation of a line about a fixed center from some initial position to some terminal position. If the rotation is *clockwise*, the angle is *negative;* if it is *counterclockwise*, the angle is *positive*. Angle size is *unlimited*. If α, β are two angles such that $\alpha + \beta = 90°$ they are complementary; they are *supplementary* if $\alpha + \beta = 180°$. Angles are most commonly measured in the *sexagesimal* system or by *radian* measure. In the first system there are 360 *degrees* in one complete revolution; one degree = $\frac{1}{90}$ of a right angle. The degree is subdivided into 60 *minutes;* the minute is subdivided into 60 *seconds*. In the *radian* system *one radian* is the angle at the center of a circle subtended by an arc whose length is equal to the radius of the circle. Thus 2π radians = 360°. One radian = 57.29578°; 1° = 0.01745 radian; 1 minute = 0.00029089 radian. The advantage of radian measure is that it is *dimensionless*. The quadrants are conventionally labeled as Fig. 2-42 shows.

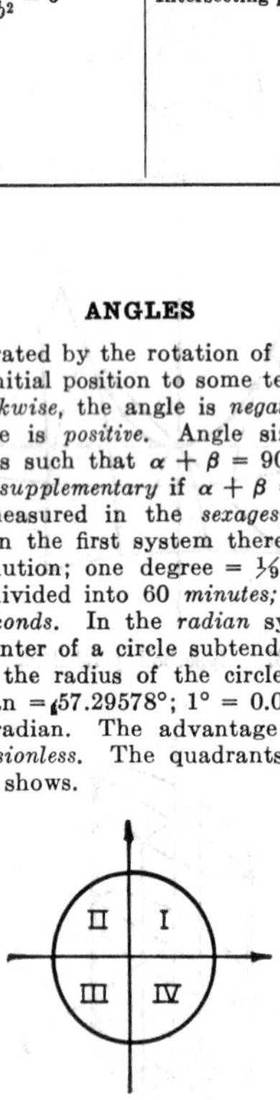

FIG. 2-42. Quadrants.

FUNCTIONS OF CIRCULAR TRIGONOMETRY

The trigonometric functions of angles are the ratios between the various sides of the reference triangles shown in Fig. 2-43 for the various quadrants. Clearly $r = \sqrt{x^2 + y^2} > 0$. The fundamental functions are

Sine of θ = $\sin\theta = \frac{y}{r}$ Secant of θ = $\sec\theta = \frac{r}{x}$

Cosine of θ = $\cos\theta = \frac{x}{r}$ Cosecant of θ = $\csc\theta = \frac{r}{y}$

Tangent of θ = $\tan\theta = y/x$ Cotangent of θ = $\cot\theta = \frac{x}{y}$

Magnitude and Sign of Trigonometric Functions. $0 \le \theta \le 360°$.

Function	0° to 90°	90° to 180°	180° to 270°	270° to 360°
$\sin\theta$	+0 to +1	+1 to +0	−0 to −1	−1 to −0
$\csc\theta$	+∞ to +1	+1 to +∞	−∞ to −1	−1 to −∞
$\cos\theta$	+1 to 0	−0 to −1	−1 to −0	+0 to +1
$\sec\theta$	+1 to +∞	−∞ to −1	−1 to −∞	+∞ to +1
$\tan\theta$	+0 to +∞	−∞ to −0	+0 to +∞	−∞ to −0
$\cot\theta$	+∞ to +0	−0 to −∞	+∞ to +0	−0 to −∞

Values of the Trigonometric Functions for Common Angles.

$\theta°$	θ, radians	$\sin\theta$	$\cos\theta$	$\tan\theta$
0	0	0	1	0
30	$\pi/6$	1/2	$\sqrt{3}/2$	$\sqrt{3}/3$
45	$\pi/4$	$\sqrt{2}/2$	$\sqrt{2}/2$	1
60	$\pi/3$	$\sqrt{3}/2$	1/2	$\sqrt{3}$
90	$\pi/2$	1	0	+∞

If $90° \le \theta \le 180°$, $\sin\theta = \sin(180° - \theta)$; $\cos\theta = -\cos(180° - \theta)$; $\tan\theta = -\tan(180° - \theta)$. If $180° \le \theta \le 270°$, $\sin\theta = -\sin(270° - \theta)$; $\cos\theta = -\cos(270° - \theta)$; $\tan\theta = \tan(270° - \theta)$. If $270° \le \theta \le 360°$, $\sin\theta = -\sin(360° - \theta)$; $\cos\theta = \cos(360° - \theta)$; $\tan\theta = -\tan(360° - \theta)$. The reciprocal properties may be used to find the values of the other functions.

If it is desired to *find* the *angle when a function of it is given* the

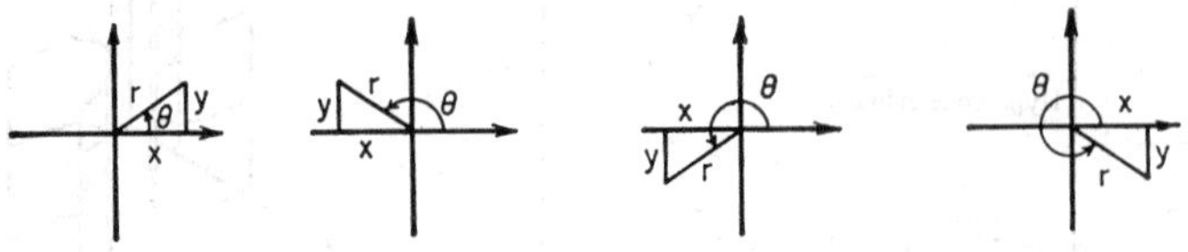

I II III IV

FIG. 2-43. Triangles.

procedure is as follows: There will in general be two angles between 0° and 360° corresponding to the given value of the function.

Given ($a > 0$)	Find an acute angle θ_0 such that	Required angles are
$\sin\theta = +a$	$\sin\theta_0 = a$	θ_0 and $(180° - \theta_0)$
$\cos\theta = +a$	$\cos\theta_0 = a$	θ_0 and $(360° - \theta_0)$
$\tan\theta = +a$	$\tan\theta_0 = a$	θ_0 and $(180° + \theta_0)$
$\sin\theta = -a$	$\sin\theta_0 = a$	$180° + \theta_0$ and $360° - \theta_0$
$\cos\theta = -a$	$\cos\theta_0 = a$	$180° - \theta_0$ and $180° + \theta_0$
$\tan\theta = -a$	$\tan\theta_0 = a$	$180° - \theta_0$ and $360° - \theta_0$

Relations between Functions of a Single Angle. $\sec\theta = \frac{1}{\cos\theta}$; $\csc\theta = \frac{1}{\sin\theta}$; $\tan\theta = \frac{\sin\theta}{\cos\theta} = \frac{\sec\theta}{\csc\theta} = \frac{1}{\cot\theta}$; $\sin^2\theta + \cos^2\theta = 1$; $1 + \tan^2\theta = \sec^2\theta$; $1 + \cot^2\theta = \csc^2\theta$. For $0 \le \theta \le 90°$ the following results hold: $\sin\theta = \frac{\cos\theta}{\cot\theta} = \sqrt{1 - \cos^2\theta} = \cos\theta\tan\theta = \frac{\tan\theta}{\sqrt{1 + \tan^2\theta}} = \frac{1}{\sqrt{1 + \cot^2\theta}} = 2\sin\frac{\theta}{2}\cos\frac{\theta}{2}$ and $\cos\theta = \sqrt{1 - \sin^2\theta} = \frac{1}{\sqrt{1 + \tan^2\theta}} = \frac{\cot\theta}{\sqrt{1 + \cot^2\theta}} = \frac{\sin\theta}{\tan\theta} = \cos^2\frac{\theta}{2} - \sin^2\frac{\theta}{2}$. The *cofunction property* is very important. $\cos\theta = \sin(90° - \theta)$, $\sin\theta = \cos(90° - \theta)$, $\tan\theta = \cot(90° - \theta)$, $\cot\theta = \tan(90° - \theta)$, etc.

Functions of Negative Angles. $\sin(-\theta) = -\sin\theta$, $\cos(-\theta) = \cos\theta$, $\tan(-\theta) = -\tan\theta$, $\sec(-\theta) = \sec\theta$, $\csc(-\theta) = -\csc\theta$, $\cot(-\theta) = -\cot\theta$.

Identities. *Sum and Difference Formulas.* Let x, y be two angles. $\sin(x \pm y) = \sin x\cos y \pm \cos x\sin y$; $\cos(x \pm y) = \cos x\cos y \mp \sin x\sin y$; $\tan(x \pm y) = \frac{\tan x \pm \tan y}{1 \mp \tan x\tan y}$; $\sin x + \sin y = 2\sin\frac{1}{2}(x + y)\cos\frac{1}{2}(x - y)$; $\sin x - \sin y = 2\cos\frac{1}{2}(x + y)\sin\frac{1}{2}(x - y)$; $\cos x + \cos y = 2\cos\frac{1}{2}(x + y)\cos\frac{1}{2}(x - y)$; $\cos x - \cos y = -2\sin\frac{1}{2}(x + y)\sin\frac{1}{2}(x - y)$; $\tan x \pm \tan y = \frac{\sin(x \pm y)}{\cos x\cos y}$; $\sin^2 x - \sin^2 y = \cos^2 y - \cos^2 x = \sin(x + y)\sin(x - y)$; $\cos^2 x - \sin^2 y = \cos^2 y - \sin^2 x = \cos(x + y)\cos(x - y)$; $\sin(45° + x) = \cos(45° - x)$; $\sin(45° - x) = \cos(45° + x)$; $\tan(45° \pm x) = \cot(45° \mp x)$. $A\cos x + B\sin x = \sqrt{A^2 + B^2}\sin(\alpha + x) = \sqrt{A^2 + B^2}\cos(\beta - x)$ where $\tan\alpha = A/B$, $\tan\beta = B/A$; both α and β are positive acute angles.

Multiple and Half Angle Identities. Let x = angle. $\sin 2x = 2\sin x\cos x$; $\sin x = 2\sin\frac{1}{2}x\cos\frac{1}{2}x$. $\cos 2x = \cos^2 x - \sin^2 x = 1 - 2\sin^2 x = 2\cos^2 x - 1$. $\tan 2x = \frac{2\tan x}{1 - \tan^2 x}$; $\sin 3x = 3\sin x - 4\sin^3 x$; $\cos 3x = 4\cos^3 x - 3\cos x$. $\tan 3x = \frac{3\tan x - \tan^3 x}{1 - 3\tan^2 x}$; $\sin 4x = 4\sin x\cos x - 8\sin^3 x\cos x$; $\cos 3x = 4\cos^3 x - 3\cos x$; $\cos 4x = 8\cos^4 x - 8\cos^2 x$. $\sin\left(\frac{x}{2}\right) = \sqrt{\frac{1}{2}(1 - \cos x)}$; $\cos\left(\frac{x}{2}\right) = \sqrt{\frac{1}{2}(1 + \cos x)}$; $\tan\left(\frac{x}{2}\right) = \sqrt{\frac{1 - \cos x}{1 + \cos x}} = \frac{\sin x}{1 + \cos x} = \frac{1 - \cos x}{\sin x}$.

Relations between Three Angles Whose Sum Is 180°. Let x, y, z be the angles. $\sin x + \sin y + \sin z = 4\cos\frac{x}{2}\cos\frac{y}{2}\cos\frac{z}{2}$; $\cos x + \cos y + \cos z = 4\sin\frac{x}{2}\sin\frac{y}{2}\sin\frac{z}{2} + 1$; $\sin x + \sin y - \sin z = 4\sin\frac{x}{2}\sin\frac{y}{2}\cos\frac{z}{2}$; $\sin^2 x + \sin^2 y + \sin^2 z = 2\cos x\cos y\cos z + 2$; $\tan x + \tan y + \tan z = \tan x\tan y\tan z$; $\sin 2x + \sin 2y + \sin 2z = 4\sin x\sin y\sin z$.

INVERSE TRIGONOMETRIC FUNCTIONS

$y = \sin^{-1} x = \arcsin x$ is the angle y whose sine is x. *Example.* $y = \sin^{-1}\frac{1}{2}$, y is 30°.

The complete solution of the equation $x = \sin y$ is $y = (-1)^n \sin^{-1} x + n\,(180°)$, $-\pi/2 \le \sin^{-1} x \le \pi/2$ where $\sin^{-1} x$ is the *principal value* of the angle whose sine is x. The range of *principal values* of the $\cos^{-1} x$ is $0 \le \cos^{-1} x \le \pi$ and $-\pi/2 \le \tan^{-1} x \le \pi/2$. If these restrictions are allowed to hold the following formulas result: $\sin^{-1} x = \cos^{-1}\sqrt{1 - x^2} = \tan^{-1}\frac{x}{\sqrt{1 - x^2}} = \cot^{-1}\frac{\sqrt{1 - x^2}}{x} = \sec^{-1}\frac{1}{\sqrt{1 - x^2}} = \csc^{-1}\frac{1}{x} = \frac{\pi}{2} - \cos^{-1} x$. $\cos^{-1} x = \sin^{-1}\sqrt{1 - x^2} = \tan^{-1}\frac{\sqrt{1 - x^2}}{x} = \cot^{-1}\frac{x}{\sqrt{1 - x^2}} = \sec^{-1}\frac{1}{x} = \csc^{-1}\frac{1}{\sqrt{1 - x^2}} = \frac{\pi}{2} - \sin^{-1} x$. $\tan^{-1} x = \sin^{-1}\frac{x}{\sqrt{1 + x^2}} = \cos^{-1}\frac{1}{\sqrt{1 + x^2}} = \cot^{-1}\frac{1}{x} = \sec^{-1}\sqrt{1 + x^2} = \csc^{-1}\frac{\sqrt{1 + x^2}}{x}$.

RELATIONS BETWEEN ANGLES AND SIDES OF TRIANGLES

Solutions of Triangles. Let a, b, c denote the sides and α, β, γ the angles opposite the sides in the triangle. Let $2s = a + b + c$, A = area, r = radius of the inscribed circle, R = radius of the circumscribed circle, and h = altitude. In any triangle $\alpha + \beta + \gamma = 180°$.

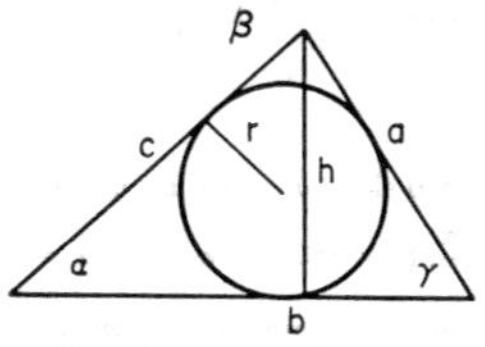

FIG. 2-44. Triangle.

The Law of Sines. $\frac{\sin\alpha}{a} = \frac{\sin\beta}{b} = \frac{\sin\gamma}{c}$.

The Law of Tangents. $\frac{a + b}{a - b} = \frac{\tan\frac{1}{2}(\alpha + \beta)}{\tan\frac{1}{2}(\alpha - \beta)}$; $\frac{b + c}{b - c} = \frac{\tan\frac{1}{2}(\beta + \gamma)}{\tan\frac{1}{2}(\beta - \gamma)}$; $\frac{a + c}{a - c} = \frac{\tan\frac{1}{2}(\alpha + \gamma)}{\tan\frac{1}{2}(\alpha - \gamma)}$.

The Law of Cosines. $a^2 = b^2 + c^2 - 2bc\cos\alpha$; $b^2 = a^2 + c^2 - 2ac\cos\beta$; $c^2 = a^2 + b^2 - 2ab\cos\gamma$.

Other Relations. In this section, where appropriate, two more formulas can be generated by replacing a by b, b by c, c by a, α by β, β by γ, and γ by α. $\cos\alpha = \frac{b^2 + c^2 - a^2}{2bc}$; $a = b\cos\gamma + c\cos\beta$; $\sin\alpha = \frac{2}{bc}\sqrt{s(s - a)(s - b)(s - c)}$; $\sin\frac{\alpha}{2} = \sqrt{\frac{(s - b)(s - c)}{bc}}$; $\cos\frac{\alpha}{2} = \sqrt{\frac{s(s - a)}{bc}}$; $A = \frac{1}{2}bh = \frac{1}{2}ab\sin\gamma = \frac{a^2\sin\beta\sin\gamma}{2\sin\alpha} = \sqrt{s(s - a)(s - b)(s - c)} = rs$ where $r = \sqrt{\frac{(s - a)(s - b)(s - c)}{s}}$. $R = \frac{a}{2\sin\alpha} = \frac{abc}{4A}$; $h = c\sin\alpha = a\sin\gamma = \frac{2rs}{b}$.

Example. $a = 5$, $b = 4$, $\alpha = 30°$. Use the law of sines. $\frac{\frac{1}{2}}{5} = \frac{\sin\beta}{4}$, $\sin\beta = \frac{2}{5}$, $\beta = 23°\ 35'$, $\gamma = 126°\ 25'$. So $c = \frac{\sin 126°\ 25'}{\frac{1}{10}} = 10(.8047) = 8.05$.

The relations given above suffice to solve any triangle. One method for each triangle is given.

Right Triangle. Given one side and any acute angle α, or any two sides the remaining parts can be obtained from the following formulas:

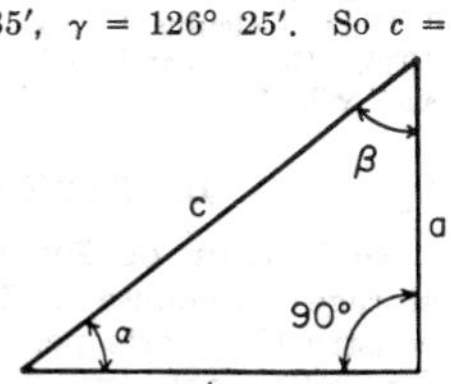

FIG. 2-45. Right triangle.

$a = \sqrt{(c + b)(c - b)} = c\sin\alpha = b\tan\alpha$

$b = \sqrt{(c + a)(c - a)} = c\cos\alpha = a\cot\alpha$

$c = \sqrt{a^2 + b^2}$, $\sin\alpha = \frac{a}{c}$, $\cos\alpha = \frac{b}{c}$, $\tan\alpha = \frac{a}{b}$, $\beta = 90° - \alpha$

$A = \frac{1}{2}ab = \frac{a^2}{2\tan\alpha} = \frac{b^2\tan\alpha}{2} = \frac{c^2\sin 2\alpha}{4}$

Oblique Triangles. There are four possible cases.

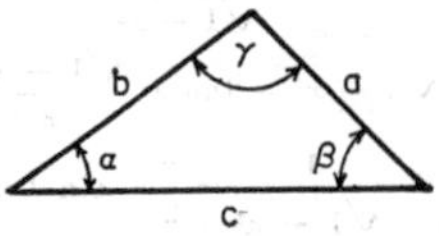

FIG. 2-46. Oblique triangle.

(*a*) Given *b*, *c* and the included angle α, $\frac{1}{2}(\beta + \gamma) = 90° - \frac{1}{2}\alpha$; $\tan\frac{1}{2}(\beta - \gamma) = \frac{b - c}{b + c}\tan\frac{1}{2}(\beta + \gamma)$; $\beta = \frac{1}{2}(\beta + \gamma) + \frac{1}{2}(\beta - \gamma)$; $\gamma = \frac{1}{2}(\beta + \gamma) - \frac{1}{2}(\beta - \gamma)$; $a = \frac{b \sin \alpha}{\sin \beta}$.

(*b*) Given the three sides *a*, *b*, *c*. $s = \frac{1}{2}(a + b + c)$; $r = \sqrt{\frac{(s - a)(s - b)(s - c)}{s}}$; $\tan\frac{1}{2}\alpha = \frac{r}{s - a}$; $\tan\frac{1}{2}\beta = \frac{r}{s - b}$; $\tan\frac{1}{2}\gamma = \frac{r}{s - c}$.

(*c*) Given any two sides *a*, *c* and an angle opposite one of them α. $\sin\gamma = \frac{c \sin \alpha}{a}$; $\beta = 180° - \alpha - \gamma$; $b = \frac{a \sin \beta}{\sin \alpha}$. There may be two solutions here. γ may have two values γ_1, γ_2; $\gamma_1 < 90°$, $\gamma_2 = 180° - \gamma_1 > 90°$. If $\alpha + \gamma_2 > 180°$, use only γ_1. This case may be *impossible* if $\sin\gamma > 1$.

(*d*) Given any side *c* and two angles α and β. $\gamma = 180° - \alpha - \beta$; $a = \frac{c \sin \alpha}{\sin \gamma}$; $b = \frac{c \sin \beta}{\sin \gamma}$.

HYPERBOLIC TRIGONOMETRY

The hyperbolic functions are certain combinations of exponentials e^x and e^{-x}. $\cosh x = \frac{e^x + e^{-x}}{2}$; $\sinh x = \frac{e^x - e^{-x}}{2}$; $\tanh x = \frac{\sinh x}{\cosh x} = \frac{e^x - e^{-x}}{e^x + e^{-x}}$. $\coth x = \frac{e^x + e^{-x}}{e^x - e^{-x}} = \frac{1}{\tanh x} = \frac{\cosh x}{\sinh x}$; $\operatorname{sech} x = \frac{1}{\cosh x} = \frac{2}{e^x + e^{-x}}$; $\operatorname{csch} x = \frac{1}{\sinh x} = \frac{2}{e^x - e^{-x}}$.

Fundamental Relationships. $\sinh x + \cosh x = e^x$; $\cosh x - \sinh x = e^{-x}$; $\cosh^2 x - \sinh^2 x = 1$; $\operatorname{sech}^2 x + \tanh^2 x = 1$; $\coth^2 x - \operatorname{csch}^2 x = 1$; $\sinh 2x = 2 \sinh x \cosh x$; $\cosh 2x = \cosh^2 x + \sinh^2 x = 1 + 2\sinh^2 x = 2\cosh^2 x - 1$. $\tanh 2x = \frac{2 \tanh x}{1 + \tanh^2 x}$; $\sinh(x \pm y) = \sinh x \cosh y \pm \cosh x \sinh y$; $\cosh(x \pm y) = \cosh x \cosh y \pm \sinh x \sinh y$; $2\sinh^2\frac{x}{2} = \cosh x - 1$; $2\cosh^2\frac{x}{2} = \cosh x + 1$; $\sinh(-x) = -\sinh x$; $\cosh(-x) = \cosh x$; $\tanh(-x) = -\tanh x$.

When $u = a \cosh x$, $v = a \sinh x$, then $u^2 - v^2 = a^2$, which is the equation for a hyperbola. In other words, the hyperbolic functions in the parametric equations $u = a \cosh x$, $v = a \sinh x$ have the same relation to the hyperbola $u^2 - v^2 = a^2$ that the equations $u = a \cos\theta$, $v = a \sin\theta$ have to the circle $u^2 + v^2 = a^2$.

Inverse Hyperbolic Functions. If $x = \sinh y$, then y is the inverse hyperbolic sine of x written $y = \sinh^{-1} x$ or arcsinh x. $\sinh^{-1} x = \log_e(x + \sqrt{x^2 + 1})$; $\cosh^{-1} x = \log_e(x + \sqrt{x^2 - 1})$; $\tanh^{-1} x = \frac{1}{2}\log_e\frac{1 + x}{1 - x}$; $\coth^{-1} x = \frac{1}{2}\log_e\frac{x + 1}{x - 1}$; $\operatorname{sech}^{-1} x = \log_e\left(\frac{1 + \sqrt{1 - x^2}}{x}\right)$; $\operatorname{csch}^{-1} = \log_e\left(\frac{1 + \sqrt{1 + x^2}}{x}\right)$.

Magnitude of the Hyperbolic Functions. $\cosh x \geq 1$ with equality only for $x = 0$; $-\infty < \sinh x < \infty$; $-1 < \tanh x < 1$. $\cosh x \sim e^x$ as $x \to \infty$; $\sinh x \to e^x$ as $x \to \infty$.

APPROXIMATIONS FOR TRIGONOMETRIC FUNCTIONS

For small values of θ (θ measured in radians) $\sin\theta \approx \theta$, $\tan\theta \approx \theta$, $\cos\theta \approx 1 - (\theta^2/2)$. The following relations actually hold: $\sin\theta < \theta < \tan\theta$; $\cos\theta < \frac{\sin\theta}{\theta} < 1$; $\sqrt{1 - \theta^2} < \frac{\sin\theta}{\theta} < 1$; $\theta\sqrt{1 - \theta^2} < \sin\theta < \theta$; $\cos\theta < \frac{\theta}{\tan\theta} < 1$; $\theta\left(1 - \frac{\theta^2}{2}\right) < \sin\theta < \theta$ and $\theta < \tan\theta < \frac{\theta}{\sqrt{1 - \theta^2}}$. The behavior ratios of the functions as $\theta \to 0$ is given by the following: $\lim_{\theta \to 0}\frac{\sin\theta}{\theta} = 1$; $\lim_{\theta \to 0}\frac{\sin\theta}{\tan\theta} = 1$.

DIFFERENTIAL AND INTEGRAL CALCULUS

REFERENCES: Kaplan, "Advanced Calculus," Addison-Wesley, Reading, Mass., 1956. Woods, "Advanced Calculus," Ginn, Boston, 1934. Whittaker and Watson, "Modern Analysis," Cambridge, New York, 1952. Hodgman, "Standard Mathematical Tables," 12th ed., Chemical Rubber Publishing Co., Cleveland, 1960. Dwight, "Tables of Integrals and Other Mathematical Data," Macmillan New York, 1947. Middlemiss, "Differential and Integral Calculus," 2d ed., McGraw-Hill, New York, 1946. Widder, "Advanced Calculus," Prentice-Hall, Englewood Cliffs, N.J., 1947. Courant, "Differential and Integral Calculus," vols. 1 and 2, Interscience, New York, 1936. Goursat and Hedrick, "A Course in Mathematical Analysis," vols. 1 and 2, Ginn, Boston, 1904.

DIFFERENTIAL CALCULUS

Definition of Functional Notation. Suppose a storage warehouse of 16,000 cu. ft. is required. The construction costs per square foot are $10, $3, and $2 for walls, roof, and floor, respectively. What are the minimum cost dimensions? Thus, with h = height, x = width, and y = length, the respective costs are

$$\begin{aligned} \text{Walls} &= 2 \times 10hy + 2 \times 10hx = 20h(y + x) \\ \text{Roof} &= 3xy \\ \text{Floor} &= 2xy \\ \text{Total cost} &= 2xy + 3xy + 20h(x + y) \\ &= 5xy + 20h(x + y) \end{aligned} \tag{2-1}$$

and the restriction

$$\text{Total volume} = xyh \tag{2-2}$$

Letting

$$h = \frac{\text{volume}}{xy} = \frac{16{,}000}{xy} \tag{2-3}$$

$$\begin{aligned} \text{Cost} &= 5xy + \frac{320{,}000}{xy}(y + x) \\ &= 5xy + 320{,}000\left(\frac{1}{x} + \frac{1}{y}\right) \end{aligned} \tag{2-4}$$

In this form it can be shown the minimum cost will occur for $x = y$; therefore

$$\text{Cost} = 5x^2 + 640{,}000\frac{1}{x}$$

By evaluation, the smallest cost will occur when $x = 40$

$$\text{Cost} = 5(1600) + \frac{640{,}000}{40} = \$24{,}000$$

The dimensions are then $x = 40$ ft., $y = 40$ ft., $h = \frac{16{,}000}{40 \times 40} = 10$ ft. Symbolically, the original cost relationship is written

$$\text{Cost} = f(x, y, h) = 5xy + 20h(y + x)$$

and the volume relation

$$\text{Volume} = g(x, y, h) = xyh$$

In terms of the derived general relationships (2-1) and (2-2), x, y, and h are *independent variables*—cost and volume *dependent variables*. That is, the cost and volume become fixed with the specification of dimensions. However, corresponding to the given restriction of the problem, relative to volume, the function $g(x, y, z) = xyh$ becomes a *constraint function*. In place of three independent and two dependent variables the problem reduces to two independent (volume has been constrained) and two dependent as in functions (2-3) and (2-4). Further, the requirement of minimum cost reduces the problem to three dependent variables (x, y, h) and no *degrees of freedom*, that is, freedom of independent selection.

Limit

Definition. It is stated the *limit* of function $f(x)$ as x approaches a (a is finite or else x is said to increase without bound) is the number N by writing

$$\lim_{x\to a} f(x) = N$$

This states that $f(x)$ can be calculated as close to N as desirable by making x sufficiently close to a. This does not put any restriction on $f(x)$ when $x = a$. More precisely, the former statement written

$$\lim_{x\to a} f(x) = N$$

implies a number δ can be found such that $0 < |a - x| < \delta$ for any given value of ϵ; so that $|N - f(x)| < \epsilon$.

Operations with Limits. The following operations with limits are valid:

(1) $$\lim_{x\to a} bf(x) = b \lim_{x\to a} f(x)$$

(2) $$\lim_{x\to a} [f(x) + g(x)] = \lim_{x\to a} f(x) + \lim_{x\to a} g(x)$$

(3) $$\lim_{x\to a} [f(x)g(x)] = \lim_{x\to a} f(x) \cdot \lim_{x\to a} g(x)$$

(4) $$\lim_{x\to a} \frac{f(x)}{g(x)} = \frac{\lim_{x\to a} f(x)}{\lim_{x\to a} g(x)} \qquad \text{if } \lim_{x\to a} g(x) \neq 0$$

Continuity

A function $f(x)$ is *continuous* at the point $x = a$ if

$$\lim_{h\to 0} [f(a + h) - f(a)] = 0$$

Rigorously, it is stated $f(x)$ is continuous for $x = a$ if for any positive ϵ there exists a $\delta > h$ such that $|f(a + h) - f(a)| < \epsilon$. For example, the function $(\sin x)/x$ is not continuous at $x = 0$ and therefore is said to be *discontinuous*. Discontinuities are classified into three types:

1. Finite $\quad y = \dfrac{\sin x}{x} \quad$ at $x = 0$
2. Infinite $\quad y = \dfrac{1}{x} \quad$ at $x = 0$
3. Jump $\quad y = \dfrac{10}{1 + e^{1/x}} \quad$ at $x = 0^+ \quad y = 0^+$; $\quad x = 0 \quad y = 0$; $\quad x = 0^- \quad y = 10$

Derivative

Definition. The function $f(x)$ has a derivative at $x = a$, which can be denoted as $f'(a)$, if

$$\lim_{h\to 0} \frac{f(a + h) - f(a)}{h} \text{ exists}$$

This requires continuity at $x = a$. Conversely, a function may be continuous but not have a derivative. The derivative function

$$f'(x) = \frac{df}{dx} = \lim_{h\to 0} \frac{f(x + h) - f(x)}{h}$$

Differentiation. Define $\Delta y = f(x + \Delta x) - f(x)$. Then dividing by Δx

$$\frac{\Delta y}{\Delta x} = \frac{f(x + \Delta x) - f(x)}{\Delta x}$$

Call $$\lim_{\Delta x\to 0} \frac{\Delta y}{\Delta x} = \frac{dy}{dx}$$

then $$\frac{dy}{dx} = \lim_{\Delta x\to 0} \frac{f(x + \Delta x) - f(x)}{\Delta x}$$

Example. Find the derivative of $y = \sin x$.

$$\begin{aligned} \frac{dy}{dx} &= \lim_{\Delta x\to 0} \frac{\sin (x + \Delta x) - f(x)}{\Delta x} \\ &= \lim_{\Delta x\to 0} \frac{2 \cos (x + \frac{1}{2} \Delta x) \sin \frac{1}{2} \Delta x}{\Delta x} \\ &= \lim_{\Delta x\to 0} \cos (x + \tfrac{1}{2} \Delta x) \lim_{\Delta x\to 0} \frac{\sin \frac{1}{2} \Delta x}{\frac{1}{2} \Delta x} \\ &= \cos x \qquad \text{since } \lim_{\Delta x\to 0} \frac{\sin \frac{1}{2} \Delta}{\frac{1}{2} \Delta x} x = 1 \end{aligned}$$

Differential Operations. The following differential operations are valid: $f, g, \ldots$ are functions of x, c is a constant; e is the base of the natural logarithms.

$$\frac{dc}{dx} = 0 \tag{2-5}$$

$$\frac{dx}{dx} = 1 \tag{2-6}$$

$$\frac{d}{dx}(f + g) = \frac{df}{dx} + \frac{dg}{dx} \tag{2-7}$$

$$\frac{d}{dx}(f \cdot g) = f\frac{dg}{dx} + g\frac{df}{dx} \tag{2-8}$$

$$\frac{dy}{dx} = \frac{1}{dx/dy} \tag{2-9}$$

$$\frac{d}{dx} f^n = nf^{n-1} \frac{df}{dx} \tag{2-10}$$

$$\frac{d}{dx}\left(\frac{f}{g}\right) = \frac{g(df/dx) - f(dg/dx)}{g^2} \tag{2-11}$$

$$\frac{df}{dx} = \frac{df}{dv}\frac{dv}{dx} \tag{2-12}$$

$$\frac{df^g}{dx} = gf^{g-1}\frac{df}{dx} + f^g \ln f \frac{dg}{dx} \tag{2-13}$$

$$\frac{da^x}{dx} = (\ln a)\, a^x \tag{2-14}$$

Example. Derive dy/dx for $x^2 + y^3 = x + xy + A$.

Here $$\frac{d}{dx}x^2 + \frac{d}{dx}y^3 = \frac{d}{dx}x + \frac{d}{dx}xy + \frac{d}{dx}A$$

$$2x + 3y^2\frac{dy}{dx} = 1 + y + x\frac{dy}{dx} + 0$$

by rules (2-9), (2-9), (2-6), (2-8), and (2-5), respectively].

Thus $$\frac{dy}{dx} = \frac{2x - 1 - y}{x - 3y^2}$$

Differentials.

$$de^x = e^x\,dx \quad (2\text{-}15)$$
$$d \ln x = \frac{1}{x}\,dx \quad (2\text{-}16)$$
$$d \log x = \frac{\log e}{x}\,dx \quad (2\text{-}17)$$
$$d \sin x = \cos x\,dx \quad (2\text{-}18)$$
$$d \cos x = -\sin x\,dx \quad (2\text{-}19)$$
$$d \tan x = \sec^2 x\,dx \quad (2\text{-}20)$$
$$d \cot x = -\csc^2 x\,dx \quad (2\text{-}21)$$
$$d \sec x = \tan x \sec x\,dx \quad (2\text{-}22)$$
$$d \csc x = -\cot x \csc x\,dx \quad (2\text{-}23)$$
$$d \sin^{-1} x = (1 - x^2)^{-1/2}\,dx \quad (2\text{-}24)$$
$$d \cos^{-1} = -(1 - x^2)^{-1/2}\,dx \quad (2\text{-}25)$$
$$d \tan^{-1} x = (1 + x^2)^{-1}\,dx \quad (2\text{-}26)$$
$$d \cot^{-1} x = -(1 + x^2)^{-1}\,dx \quad (2\text{-}27)$$
$$d \sec^{-1} x = x^{-1}(x^2 - 1)^{-1/2}\,dx \quad (2\text{-}28)$$
$$d \csc^{-1} x = -x^{-1}(x^2 - 1)^{-1/2}\,dx \quad (2\text{-}29)$$
$$d \sinh x = \cosh x\,dx \quad (2\text{-}30)$$
$$d \cosh x = \sinh x\,dx \quad (2\text{-}31)$$
$$d \tanh x = \text{sech}^2\,x\,dx \quad (2\text{-}32)$$
$$d \coth x = -\text{csch}^2\,x\,dx \quad (2\text{-}33)$$
$$d\,\text{sech}\,x = -\text{sech}\,x \tan h\,x\,dx \quad (2\text{-}34)$$
$$d\,\text{csch}\,x = -\text{csch}\,x \coth x\,dx \quad (2\text{-}35)$$
$$d \sinh^{-1} x = (x^2 + 1)^{-1/2}\,dx \quad (2\text{-}36)$$
$$d \cosh^{-1} = (x^2 - 1)^{-1/2}\,dx \quad (2\text{-}37)$$
$$d \tanh^{-1} x = (1 - x^2)^{-1}\,dx \quad (2\text{-}38)$$
$$d \coth^{-1} x = -(x^2 - 1)^{-1}\,dx \quad (2\text{-}39)$$
$$d\,\text{sech}^{-1} x = x(1 - x^2)^{-1/2}\,dx \quad (2\text{-}40)$$
$$d\,\text{csch}^{-1} x = -x^{-1}(x^2 + 1)^{-1/2}dx \quad (2\text{-}41)$$

Example 1 Find dy/dx for $y = \sqrt{x}\cos(1 - x^2)$.

Using

$$\frac{dy}{dx} = \sqrt{x}\frac{d}{dx}\cos(1 - x^2) + \cos(1 - x^2)\frac{d}{dx}\sqrt{x} \quad (2\text{-}8)$$

$$\frac{d}{dx}\cos(1 - x^2) = -\sin(1 - x^2)\frac{d}{dx}(1 - x^2) \quad (2\text{-}19)$$

$$= -\sin(1 - x^2)(0 - 2x) \quad (2\text{-}5), (2\text{-}10)$$

$$\frac{d\sqrt{x}}{dx} = \frac{1}{2}x^{-1/2}$$

$$\frac{dy}{dx} = 2x^{3/2}\sin(1 - x^2) + \frac{1}{2}x^{-1/2}\cos(1 - x^2) \quad (2\text{-}10)$$

Example 2. Find the derivative of $\tan x$ from that of $\sin x$.

$$v = \sin x$$
$$y = \tan x$$

Using

$$\frac{dy}{d \sin x} = \frac{dy}{dv} = \frac{dy}{dx}\frac{dx}{dv} \quad (2\text{-}12)$$

$$= \frac{d \tan x}{dx}\,\frac{1}{\dfrac{d \sin x}{dx}} \quad (2\text{-}9)$$

$$= \frac{\sec^2 x}{\cos x} \quad (2\text{-}18), (2\text{-}20)$$

Higher Differentials. The first derivative of $f(x)$ with respect to x is denoted by f' or df/dx. The derivative of the first derivative is called the second derivative of $f(x)$ with respect to x and is denoted by f'', $f^{(2)}$, or d^2f/dx^2; similarly for the higher-order derivatives.

Example. Given $f(x) = 3x^3 + 2x + 1$, calculate all derivative values at $x = 3$.

$$\frac{df(x)}{dx} = 9x^2 + 2, \qquad x = 3,\ f'(3) = 9(9) + 2 = 83$$

$$\frac{d^2f(x)}{dx} = 18x, \qquad x = 3,\ f''(3) = 18(3) = 54$$

$$\frac{d^3f(x)}{dx} = 18, \qquad x = 3,\ f'''(3) = 18$$

$$\frac{d^{(n)}f(x)}{dx^{(n)}} = 0, \qquad \text{for } n \geq 4$$

Indeterminate Forms—L'Hopital's Theorem. Forms of the type $0/0$, ∞/∞, $0 \cdot \infty$, etc., are called indeterminates. To find the limiting values that the corresponding functions approach, L'Hopital's theorem is useful: If two functions $f(x)$ and $g(x)$ both become zero at $x = a$ then the limit of their quotient is equal to the limit of the quotient of their separate derivatives, if the limit exists.

Example 1. Find $\lim_{x \to 0} \frac{\sin x}{x}$.

Here $$\lim_{x \to 0} \frac{\sin x}{x} = \lim_{x \to 0} \frac{d \sin x}{dx} = \lim_{x \to 0} \frac{\cos x}{1} = 1$$

Example 2. Find $\lim_{x \to \infty} \frac{1.1^x}{x^{1000}}$.

$$\lim_{x \to \infty} \frac{1.1^x}{x^{1000}} = \lim_{x \to \infty} \frac{d\,1.1^x}{dx^{1000}} = \lim_{x \to \infty} \frac{(\ln 1.1)1.1^x}{1000x^{999}}$$

Obviously $\lim_{x \to \infty} \frac{1.1^x}{x^{1000}} = \infty$ since repeated application of the rule will reduce the denominator to a finite number 1000! while the numerator remains infinitely large.

Example 3. Find $\lim_{x \to \infty} x^3 e^{-x}$.

$$\lim_{x \to \infty} x^3 e^{-x} = \lim_{x \to \infty} \frac{x^3}{e^x} = \lim_{x \to \infty} \frac{6}{e^x} = 0$$

Example 4. Find $\lim (1 - x)^{1/x}$.

Let
$$y = (1 - x)^{1/x}$$
$$\ln y = \frac{1}{x}\ln(1 - x)$$
$$\lim_{x \to 0} (\ln y) = \lim_{x \to 0} \frac{\ln(1 - x)}{x} = -1$$

Therefore, $$\lim_{x \to 0} y = e^{-1}$$

Example 5. Find $\lim_{x \to 1} \left(\frac{1}{x^2 - 1} - \frac{1}{x - 1}\right)$.

$$= \lim_{x \to 1} \frac{-x^2 + x}{x^3 - x^2 - x + 1} = \lim_{x \to 1} \frac{-2}{6x - 2} = -\frac{1}{2}$$

Partial Derivative

Definition. The abbreviation $z = f(x, y)$ means that z is a function of the two variables x and y. The derivative of z with respect to x, treating y as a constant, is called the partial derivative with respect to x and is usually denoted as $\partial z/\partial x$ or $\partial f(x,y)/\partial x$ or simply f_x. Partial differentiation, like full differentiation, is quite simple to apply. Conversely, the solution to partial differential equations is appreciably more difficult than that to differential equations.

Example. Find $\partial z/\partial x$ and $\partial z/\partial y$ for $z = ye^{x^2} + xe^y$.

$$\frac{\partial z}{\partial x} = y\frac{\partial e^{x^2}}{\partial x} + e^y\frac{\partial x}{\partial x} = 2xye^{x^2} + e^y \qquad \frac{\partial z}{\partial y} = e^{x^2}\frac{\partial y}{\partial y} + x\frac{\partial e^y}{\partial y} = e^{x^2} + xe^y$$

Order of Differentiation. It is generally true the order of differentiation is immaterial for any number of differentiations or variables provided the function and the appropriate derivatives are continuous. For $z = f(x, y)$ it follows:

$$\frac{\partial^3 f}{\partial y^2\,\partial x} = \frac{\partial^3 f}{\partial y\,\partial x\,\partial y} = \frac{\partial^3 f}{\partial x\,\partial y^2}$$

General Form for Differentiation. 1. Given $f(x, y) = 0$ and $x = g(t)$, $y = h(t)$.

$$\text{Then}\quad \frac{df}{dt} = \frac{\partial f}{\partial x}\frac{dx}{dt} + \frac{\partial f}{\partial y}\frac{dy}{dt}$$

$$\frac{d^2 f}{dt^2} = \frac{\partial^2 f}{\partial x^2}\left(\frac{dx}{dt}\right)^2 + 2\frac{\partial^2 f}{\partial x\,\partial y}\frac{dx}{dt}\frac{dy}{dt} + \frac{\partial^2 f}{\partial y^2}\left(\frac{dy}{dt}\right)^2 + \frac{\partial f}{\partial x}\frac{d^2x}{dt^2} + \frac{\partial f}{\partial y}\frac{d^2y}{dt^2}$$

Example. Find df/dt for $f = xy$, $x = \rho \sin t$, $y = \rho \cos t$.

$$\frac{df}{dt} = \frac{\partial(xy)}{\partial x}\left(\frac{d\,\rho \sin t}{dt}\right) + \frac{\partial(xy)}{\partial y}\left(\frac{d\,\rho \cos t}{dt}\right)$$
$$= y(\rho \cos t) + x(-\rho \sin t)$$
$$= \rho^2 \cos^2 t - \rho^2 \sin^2 t$$

2. Given $f(x, y) = 0$ and $x = g(t, s)$, $y = h(t, s)$.

$$\text{Then}\quad \frac{\partial f}{\partial t} = \frac{\partial f}{\partial x}\frac{\partial x}{\partial t} + \frac{\partial f}{\partial y}\frac{\partial y}{\partial t}$$
$$\frac{\partial f}{\partial s} = \frac{\partial f}{\partial x}\frac{\partial x}{\partial s} + \frac{\partial f}{\partial y}\frac{\partial y}{\partial s}$$

Differentiation of Composite Functions.

Rule 1. Given $f(x, y) = 0$ then $\dfrac{dy}{dx} = -\dfrac{\partial f/\partial x}{\partial f/\partial y}$ $\left(\dfrac{\partial f}{\partial y} \neq 0\right)$.

Example. Find dy/dx for $x^3 + y^3 = x + xy + A$. Let $f(x, y) = x^3 + y^3 - x - xy - A = 0$.

$$\frac{\partial f}{\partial x} = 2x - 1 - y \qquad \frac{\partial f}{\partial y} = 3y^2 - x$$
$$\frac{dy}{dx} = -\frac{2x - 1 - y}{3y^2 - x}$$

Rule 2. Given $f(u) = 0$ where $u = g(x)$ then

$$\frac{df}{dx} = f'(u)\frac{du}{dx}$$
$$\frac{d^2 f}{dx^2} = f''(u)\left(\frac{du}{dx}\right)^2 + f'(u)\frac{d^2u}{dx^2}$$

Example. Find df/dx for $f = \sin^2 u$ and $u = \sqrt{1 - x^2}$.

$$\frac{df}{dx} = \frac{d \sin^2 u}{du}\frac{d\sqrt{1 - x^2}}{dx}$$
$$= 2 \sin u \cos u \left(\frac{1}{2}\right)(-2x)(1 - x^2)^{-1/2}$$
$$= 2\frac{\sqrt{1 - u^2}}{u} \sin u \cos u$$

Rule 3. Given $f(u) = 0$ where $u = g(x, y)$ then

$$\frac{\partial f}{\partial x} = f'(u)\frac{\partial u}{\partial x} \qquad \frac{\partial f}{\partial y} = f'(u)\frac{\partial u}{\partial y}$$
$$\frac{\partial^2 f}{\partial x^2} = f''\left(\frac{\partial u}{\partial x}\right)^2 + f'\frac{\partial^2 u}{\partial x^2}$$
$$\frac{\partial^2 f}{\partial x\,\partial y} = f''\frac{\partial u}{\partial x}\frac{\partial u}{\partial y} + f'\frac{\partial^2 u}{\partial x\,\partial y}$$
$$\frac{\partial^2 f}{\partial y^2} = f''\left(\frac{\partial u}{\partial y}\right)^2 + f'\frac{\partial^2 u}{\partial y^2}$$

INTEGRAL CALCULUS

Indefinite Integral. If $f'(x)\,dx$ is the differential of $f(x)$, the integral of $f'(x)\,dx$ is $f(x)$. Symbolically

$$\int f'(x)\,dx = f(x) + c$$

where c is an arbitrary constant to be determined by the problem. By virtue of the known formulas for differentiation the following relationships hold:

$$\int (du + dv + dw) = \int du + \int dv + \int dw \qquad (2\text{-}42)$$

$$\int a\,dv = a\int dv \qquad (2\text{-}43)$$

$$\int v^n\,dv = \frac{v^{n+1}}{n+1} + c\,(n \neq -1) \qquad (2\text{-}44)$$

$$\int \frac{dv}{v} = \ln |v| + c \qquad (2\text{-}45)$$

$$\int a^v\,dv = \frac{a^v}{\ln a} + c \qquad (2\text{-}46)$$

$$\int e^v\,dv = e^v + c \qquad (2\text{-}47)$$

$$\int \sin v\,dv = -\cos v + c \qquad (2\text{-}48)$$

$$\int \cos v\,dv = \sin v + c \qquad (2\text{-}49)$$

$$\int \sec^2 v\,dv = \tan v + c \qquad (2\text{-}50)$$

$$\int \csc^2 v\,dv = -\cot v + c \qquad (2\text{-}51)$$

$$\int \sec v \tan v\,dv = \sec v + c \qquad (2\text{-}52)$$

$$\int \csc v \cot v\,dv = -\csc v + c \qquad (2\text{-}53)$$

$$\int \frac{dv}{v^2 + a^2} = \frac{1}{a}\tan^{-1}\frac{v}{a} + c \qquad (2\text{-}54)$$

$$\int \frac{dv}{\sqrt{a^2 - v^2}} = \sin^{-1}\frac{v}{a} + c \qquad (2\text{-}55)$$

$$\int \frac{dv}{v^2 - a^2} = \frac{1}{2a}\ln\left|\frac{v - a}{v + a}\right| + c \qquad (2\text{-}56)$$

$$\int \frac{dv}{\sqrt{v^2 \pm a^2}} = \ln |v + \sqrt{v^2 \pm a^2}| + c \qquad (2\text{-}57)$$

$$\int \sec v\,dv = \ln (\sec v + \tan v) + c \qquad (2\text{-}58)$$

$$\int \csc v\,dv = \ln (\csc v - \cot v) + c \qquad (2\text{-}59)$$

Example 1. Derive $\int a^v\,dv = \frac{a^v}{\ln a} + c$. By reference to the differentiation formula $\frac{da^v}{dv} = a^v \ln a$, or in the more usable form $d\left(\frac{a^v}{\ln a}\right) = a^v\,dv$, let $f' = a^v\,dv$; then $f = \frac{a^v}{\ln a}$ and hence $\int a^v\,dv = \frac{a^v}{\ln a} + c$.

Example 2. Find $\int (3x^2 + e^x - 10)\,dx$.

$$\begin{aligned}\int (3x^2 + e^x - 10)\,dx &= 3\int x^2\,dx + \int e^x\,dx - 10\int dx \qquad (2\text{-}42)\\ &= (x^3 + c_1) + (e^x + c_2) - (10x + c_3)\\ &= x^3 + e^x - 10x + c \qquad (2\text{-}44),(2\text{-}47)\end{aligned}$$

Example 3. Find $\int \frac{7x\,dx}{2 - 3x^2}$.

Let $v = 2 - 3x^2$

$dv = -6x\,dx$

$$\begin{aligned}\text{Thus}\quad \int \frac{7x\,dx}{2-3x^2} = 7\int \frac{x\,dx}{2-3x^2} &= -\frac{7}{6}\int \frac{-6x\,dx}{2-3x^2}\\ &= -\frac{7}{6}\int \frac{dv}{v}\\ &= -\frac{7}{6}\ln|v| + c\\ &= -\frac{7}{6}\ln|2 - 3x^2| + c\end{aligned}$$

Example 4. *Constant of Integration.* By definition the derivative of x^3 is $3x^2$, and x^3 is therefore the integral of $3x^2\,dx$. However, if $f = x^3 + 10$, it follows $f' = 3x^2\,dx$, and $x^3 + 10$ is therefore also the integral of $3x^2\,dx$. For this reason the constant c in $\int 3x^2\,dx = x^3 + c$ must be determined by the problem conditions, *i.e.*, the value of f for a specified x.

Methods of Integration. In practice it is rare when generally encountered functions can be directly integrated. For example, the integrand in $\int \sqrt{\sin x}\,dx$ which appears quite simple has no elementary function whose derivative is $\sqrt{\sin x}$. In general, there is no explicit way of determining whether a particular function can be integrated into an elementary form. As a whole, integration is a trial-and-error proposition which depends on the effort and ingenuity of the practitioner. The following are general procedures which can be used to find the elementary forms of the integral when they exist. When they do not exist or cannot be found either from tabled integration formulas or directly the only recourse is series expansion as illustrated below. Indefinite integrals cannot be solved numerically unless they are redefined as definite integrals (see Definite Integrals), *i.e.*, $F(x) = \int f(x)\,dx$ whereas $F(x) = \int_a^x f(t)\,dt$.

Direct Formula. Many integrals can be solved by transformation of the integrand to one of the forms given above.

Example. Find $\int x^2\sqrt{3x^3 + 10}\,dx$. Let $v = 3x^3 + 10$ for which $dv = 9x^2\,dx$. Thus

$$\begin{aligned}\int x^2\sqrt{3x^3+10}\,dx &= \int (3x^3+10)^{1/2}(x^2\,dx)\\ &= \frac{1}{9}\int (3x^3+10)^{1/2}(9x^2\,dx)\\ &= \frac{1}{9}\int v^{1/2}\,dv\\ &= \frac{1}{9}\frac{v^{3/2}}{3/2} + c \qquad \text{[by Eq. (2-44)]}\\ &= \frac{2}{27}(3x^3+10)^{3/2} + c\end{aligned}$$

Trigonometric Substitution. This technique is particularly well adapted to integrands in the form of radicals. For these the function is transformed into a trigonometric form. In the latter form they may be more easily recognizable relative to the identity formulas. These functions and their transformations are

$\sqrt{x^2 - a^2}$ Let $x = a\sec\theta$

$\sqrt{x^2 + a^2}$ Let $x = a\tan\theta$

$\sqrt{a^2 - x^2}$ Let $x = a\sin\theta$

Example. Find $\int \frac{\sqrt{4 - 9x^2}}{x^2}\,dx$. Let $x = \frac{2}{3}\sin\theta$; then $dx = \frac{2}{3}\cos\theta\,d\theta$.

$$\begin{aligned}3\int \frac{\sqrt{\left(\frac{2}{3}\right)^2 - x^2}}{x^2}\,dx &= 3\int \frac{\frac{2}{3}\sqrt{1-\sin^2\theta}}{\left(\frac{2}{3}\right)^2\sin^2\theta}\left(\frac{2}{3}\cos\theta\,d\theta\right)\\ &= 3\int \frac{\cos^2\theta}{\sin^2\theta}\,d\theta\\ &= 3\int \cot^2\theta\,d\theta\\ &= -3\cot\theta - \theta + c \quad \text{by trigonometric transform}\\ &= -\frac{\sqrt{4-9x^2}}{x} - 3\sin^{-1}\frac{3}{2}x + c \quad \text{in terms of } x\end{aligned}$$

Algebraic Substitution. Functions containing elements of the type $(a + bx)^{\frac{1}{n}}$ are best handled by the algebraic transformation $y^n = a + bx$.

Example. Find $\int \frac{x\,dx}{(3 + 4x)^{1/4}}$. Let $3 + 4x = y^4$; then $4dx = 4y^3\,dy$ and

$$\begin{aligned}\int \frac{x\,dx}{(3+4x)^{1/4}} &= \int \frac{\frac{y^4-3}{4}y^3\,dy}{y}\\ &= \frac{1}{4}\int y^2(y^4-3)\,dy\\ &= \frac{1}{4}\frac{y^7}{7} - \frac{3}{4}\frac{y^3}{3} + c\\ &= \frac{7}{4}(3+4x)^{7/4} - \frac{1}{4}(3+4x)^{3/4} + c\end{aligned}$$

General. The number of possible transformations one might use are unlimited. No specific over-all rules can be given. Success in handling integration problems depends primarily upon experience and ingenuity. The following example illustrates the extent to which alternative approaches are possible.

Example. Find $\int \frac{dx}{e^x - 1}$. Let $e^x = y$; then $e^x\,dx = dy$ or $dx = 1/y\,dy$.

$$\int \frac{dx}{e^x - 1} = \int \frac{(1/y)\,dy}{y - 1} = \int \frac{dy}{y^2 - y} = \ln\frac{y-1}{y} = \ln\frac{e^x - 1}{e^x}$$

Partial Fractions. Rational functions are of the type $f(x)/g(x)$ where $f(x)$ and $g(x)$ are polynomial expressions of degree m and n, respectively. If $m < n$ then $f(x)$ is of lower degree than $g(x)$. If not, perform the algebraic division—the remainder will then be at least one degree less than the denominator. Consider the following types:

Type 1. Reducible denominator to linear unequal factors. For example:

$$\frac{1}{x^3 - x^2 - 4x + 4} = \frac{1}{(x+2)(x-2)(x-1)}$$
$$= \frac{A}{x+2} + \frac{B}{x-2} + \frac{C}{x-1}$$
$$= \frac{A(x-2)(x-1) + B(x+2)(x-1) + C(x+2)(x-2)}{(x+2)(x-2)(x-1)}$$
$$= \frac{x^2(A+B+C) + x(-3A+B) + (2A-2B-4C)}{(x+2)(x-2)(x-1)}$$

or by equating
$$= \frac{1}{12(x+2)} + \frac{1}{4(x-2)} - \frac{1}{3(x-1)}$$

Hence
$$\int \frac{dx}{x^3 - x^2 - 4x + 4} = \int \frac{dx}{12(x+2)} + \int \frac{dx}{4(x-2)} - \int \frac{dx}{3(x-1)}$$

Type 2. Reducible denominator to linear but some equal factors. For example:

$$\frac{x^2 + 6x - 1}{(x-3)^2(x-1)} = \frac{A(x-3)(x-1) + B(x-1) + C(x-3)^2}{(x-3)^2(x-1)}$$

equating as above

$$= -\frac{1}{2(x-3)} + \frac{13}{13(x-3)^2} + \frac{3}{2(x-1)}$$

Type 3. Reducible denominator to quadratic factors.

$$\frac{8x^2 + 3}{(x^2 + x + 1)(x - 2)} = \frac{Ax + B}{x^2 + x + 1} + \frac{C}{x - 2}$$
$$= \frac{Ax(x-2) + B(x-2) + C(x^2 + x + 1)}{(x^2 + x + 1)(x - 2)}$$

by equating
$$= \frac{3x + 1}{x^2 + x + 1} + \frac{5}{x - 2}$$

Parts. An extremely useful formula for integration is the relation

$$d(uv) = u\,dv + v\,du$$

and $uv = \int u\,dv + \int v\,du$

or $\int u\,dv = uv - \int v\,du$

No general rule for breaking an integrand can be given. Experience alone limits the use of this technique. It is particularly useful for trigonometric and exponential functions.

Example 1. Find $\int xe^x\,dx$.

Let $u = x$ and $dv = e^x\,dx$

$du = dx$ $v = e^x$

Therefore $\int xe^x\,dx = xe^x - \int e^x\,dx$

$= xe^x - e^x + c$

Example 2. Find $\int e^x \sin x\,dx$.

Let $u = e^x$ $dv = \sin x\,dx$

$du = e^x\,dx$ $v = -\cos x$

$\int e^x \sin x\,dx = -e^x \cos x + \int e^x \cos x\,dx$

Again $u = e^x$ $dv = \cos x\,dx$

$du = e^x\,dx$ $v = \sin x$

$\int e^x \sin x\,dx = -e^x \cos x + e^x \sin x - \int e^x \sin x\,dx + c$

$= \frac{e^x}{2}(\sin x - \cos x) + c$

Series Expansion

When an explicit function cannot be found the integration can sometimes be carried out by a series expansion.

Example. Find $\int e^{-x^2}\,dx$.

Since $e^{-x^2} = 1 - x^2 + \frac{x^4}{2!} - \frac{x^6}{3!} + \cdots$

$$\int e^{-x^2}\,dx = \int dx - \int x^2\,dx + \int \frac{x^4}{2!}\,dx - \int \frac{x^6}{3!}\,dx + \cdots$$
$$= x - \frac{x^3}{3} + \frac{x^5}{5.2!} - \frac{x^7}{7.3!} + \cdots \qquad \text{for all } x$$

Definite Integral

Definition. The concept and derivation of the definite integral are completely different from those for the indefinite integral. These are by definition different types of operations. However, the formal operator $\int$ as it turns out treats the integrand in the same way for both.

Consider the function $f(x) = 10 - 10e^{-2x}$. Define $x_1 = a$ and $x_n = b$ and suppose it is desirable to compute the area between the curve and the coordinate axis $y = 0$ and bounded by $x_1 = a$, $x_n = b$. Obviously, by a sufficiently large number of rectangles this area could be approximated as closely as desired by the formula

$$\sum_{i=1}^{n-1} f(\xi_i)(x_{i+1} - x_i) = f(\xi_1)(x_2 - a) + f(\xi_2)(x_3 - x_2) + \cdots + f(\xi_n)(b - x_{n-1}) \qquad x_{i-1} \leq \xi_i \leq x_i$$

In this case the *definite integral* of $f(x)$ is defined as

$$\int_a^b f(x)\,dx = \lim_{n\to\infty} \sum_{i=1}^{n} f(\xi_i)(x_{i+1} - x_i)$$

For a rigorous definition of the definite integral the references should be consulted.

By definition, then, $F(x) \neq \int_a^b f(x)\,dx$ since $\int_a^b f(x)\,dx \equiv \int_a^b f(t)\,dt$. For the previous example then $\int_a^b (10 - 10e^{-2x})\,dx \equiv \int_a^b (10 - 10e^{-2t})\,dt$. Thus, the *value* of a definite integral depends on the limits a, b and any selected variable coefficients in the function but not on the *dummy variable* of integration x. Symbolically

$F(x) = \int f(x)\,dx$ indefinite integral where $\frac{dF}{dx} = f(x)$

$F(a, b) = \int_a^b f(x)\,dx$ definite integral

or $F(\alpha) = \int_a^b f(x, \alpha)\,dx$

There are certain restrictions of the integration definition, "The function $f(x)$ must be continuous in the finite interval (a, b) with at most a finite number of finite discontinuities," which must be observed before integration formulas can be generally applied. Two of these restrictions give rise to so-called *improper integrals* and require special handling. These occur when

1. The limits of integration are not both finite, *i.e.*, $\int_0^\infty e^{-x}\,dx$.
2. The function becomes infinite within the interval of integration, *i.e.*, $\int_0^1 \frac{1}{\sqrt{x}}\,dx$.

Techniques for determining when integration is valid under these conditions are available in the references. However, the following simplified rules will, in general, serve as a guide for most practical applications.

Rule 1. For the integral $\int_0^\infty \frac{\phi(x)}{x^n}\,dx$ if $\phi(x)$ is bounded the integral will converge for $n > 1$ and not converge for $n \leq 1$.

It is easily seen $\int_0^\infty e^{-x}\,dx$ converges by reference to the summation formula and noting $\frac{1}{x^2} > \frac{1}{e^x} > 0$ for large x.

Rule 2. For the integral $\int_a^b \frac{\phi(x)}{(a-x)^n}\,dx$ if $\phi(x)$ is bounded the integral will converge for $n < 1$ and diverge for $n \geq 1$. Thus $\int_0^1 \frac{1}{\sqrt{x}}\,dx$ will converge (exist) since $\frac{1}{2} < n < 1$.

Properties. The fundamental theorem of calculus states

$$\int_a^b f(x)\,dx = F(b) - F(a) \tag{2-60}$$

where

$$\frac{dF(x)}{dx} = f(x)$$

Other properties of the definite integral are

$$\int_a^b c[f(x)\,dx] = c\int_a^b f(x)\,dx \tag{2-61}$$

$$\int_a^b [f_1(x) + f_2(x)]\,dx = \int_a^b f_1(x)\,dx + \int_a^b f_2(x)\,dx \tag{2-62}$$

$$\int_a^b f(x)\,dx = -\int_b^a f(x)\,dx \tag{2-63}$$

$$\int_a^b f(x)\,dx = \int_a^c f(x)\,dx + \int_c^b f(x)\,dx \tag{2-64}$$

$$\int_a^b f(x)\,dx = (b-a)f(\xi) \qquad a \leq \xi \leq b \tag{2-65}$$

$$\frac{\partial}{\partial b}\int_a^b f(x)\,dx = f(b) \tag{2-66}$$

$$\frac{\partial}{\partial a}\int_a^b f(x)\,dx = -f(a) \tag{2-67}$$

$$\frac{d\phi}{d\alpha} = \int_a^b \frac{\partial f(x,\alpha)}{\partial \alpha}\,dx \tag{2-68}$$

$$\int_a^b dx \int_c^d f(x,\alpha)\,d\alpha = \int_c^d d\alpha \int_a^b f(x,\alpha)\,dx \tag{2-69}$$

Example 1. Find $\int_0^{\pi/2} \sin x\,dx$.

$$\int_0^{\pi/2} \sin x\,dx = [-\cos x]_0^{\pi/2} = -\left(\cos\frac{\pi}{2} - \cos 0\right) = 1$$

since

$$-\frac{d\cos x}{dx} = \sin x$$

Example 2. Find $\int_0^2 \frac{dx}{(x-1)^2}$. Direct application of the formula would yield the incorrect value

$$\int_0^2 \frac{dx}{(x-1)^2} = \left[-\frac{1}{x-1}\right] = -2$$

It should be noted $f(x) = 1/(x-1)^2$ becomes unbounded as $x \to 1$ and by Rule 2 the integral diverges and hence is said not to exist.

Methods of Integration. All the methods of integration available for the indefinite integral can be used for definite integrals. In addition, several others are available for the latter integrals and are indicated below.

Change of Variable. This substitution is basically the same as previously indicated for indefinite integrals. However, for definite integrals the limits of integration must also be changed; *i.e.*, for $x = \phi(t)$,

$$\int_a^b f(x)\,dx = \int_{t_0}^{t_1} f[\phi(t)]\phi'(t)\,dt$$

where $t = t_0$ when $x = a$
$t = t_1$ when $x = b$

Example. Find $\int_0^4 \sqrt{16 - x^2}\,dx$.

Let $x = 4\sin\theta$, $dx = 4\cos\theta$; $x = 0$, $x = 4$; $\theta = 0$, $\theta = \pi/2$

Then

$$\int_0^4 \sqrt{16-x^2}\,dx = 16\int_0^{\pi/2} \cos^2\theta\,d\theta = 16[\tfrac{1}{2}\theta + \tfrac{1}{4}\sin 2\theta]_0^{\pi/2} = 4\pi$$

Differentiation. Here the application of the general rules for differentiating under the integral sign may be useful.

Example. Find $\phi(\alpha) = \int_0^\infty \frac{e^{-\alpha x}\sin x}{x}\,dx\,(\alpha > 0)$. Since this is a continuous function of α it may be differentiated under the integral sign

$$\frac{d\phi}{d\alpha} = -\int_0^\infty e^{-\alpha x}\sin x\,dx = \frac{1}{1+\alpha^2}$$

$$\phi = -\tan^{-1}\alpha + c$$

and since $\phi(\alpha) \to 0$ as $\alpha \to \infty$

$$c = \frac{\pi}{2}$$

$$\phi(\alpha) = -\tan^{-1}\frac{1}{\alpha} + \frac{\pi}{2}$$

Integration. It is sometimes useful to generate a double integral to solve a problem. By this approach the fundamental theorem indicated by (2-69) can be used.

Example. Find $\int_0^1 \frac{x^b - x^a}{\ln x}\,dx$. Consider $\int_0^1 x^\alpha\,dx = \frac{1}{\alpha + 1}$ $(\alpha > -1)$. Then multiplying both sides by $d\alpha$ and integrating between a and b

$$\int_a^b d\alpha \int_0^1 x^\alpha\,dx = \int_a^b \frac{d\alpha}{\alpha + 1} = \ln\left|\frac{b+1}{a+1}\right|$$

But also

$$\int_a^b d\alpha \int_0^1 x^\alpha\,dx = \int_0^1 dx \int_a^b x^\alpha\,d\alpha = \int_0^1 \frac{x^b - x^a}{\ln x}\,dx$$

Therefore $$\int_0^1 \frac{x^b - x^a}{\ln x}\,dx = \ln\left|\frac{b+1}{a+1}\right|$$

Complex Variable. Certain definite integrals can be evaluated by the technique of complex variable integration. This is described in the references on Complex Variables.

Numerical. Because of the property of definite integrals another method for obtaining their solution is available which cannot be applied to indefinite integrals. This involves a numerical approximation based on the previously outlined summation definition:

$$\lim_{n\to\infty} \sum_{1}^{n-1} f(\xi_i)(x_{i+1} - x_i) = \int_a^b f(x)\,dx$$

where $x_1 = a$
$x_n = b$

Examples of this procedure are given under Numerical Methods, p. 2-51.

CALCULUS OF VARIATION

The calculus of variation is concerned with the determination of a functional form which minimizes or maximizes a specified mathematical form. For example, these include problems of the following type:

Find the equation of the curve $y = f(x)$:

1. Between the two points A and B which has a minimum length.
2. Between the two points A and B which generates a minimum area of revolution about $0\,X$.
3. Of given length which encloses the maximum area (this is called a *constrained* variational problem).

For problems of types 1 and 2 consider the integral

$$I = \int_a^b f\left(x, y, \frac{dy}{dx}\right) dx \qquad (2\text{-}70)$$

taken along the curve $y = g(x)$ between the points A and B in a plane. Then the integral I has a maximum or a minimum value along a curve c if $y = g(x)$ is a solution of the equation

$$\frac{\partial f}{\partial y} - \frac{d}{dx}\frac{\partial f}{\partial y'} = 0 \qquad (2\text{-}71)$$

Example 1. By elementary calculus the length of the curve $y = g(x)$ is given by

$$S = \int_A^B \sqrt{dx^2 + dy^2} = \int_A^B \sqrt{1 + \left(\frac{dy}{dx}\right)^2}\,dx$$

Here $f = \sqrt{1 + \left(\frac{dy}{dx}\right)^2}$, $\frac{\partial f}{\partial y} = 0$ $\quad \frac{\partial f}{\partial y'} = \frac{y'}{\sqrt{1 + y'^2}}$

By Eq. (2-71)

$$0 - \frac{d}{dx}\frac{y'}{\sqrt{1 + y'^2}} = 0$$

$$\frac{\sqrt{1 + y'^2}(y'') - y'(y'y''/\sqrt{1 + y'^2})}{1 + y'^2} = 0$$

or $y'' = 0$. For this $y = ax + b$ is the curve with minimum length between A and B. The constants a and b are used to make $y = f(x)$ pass through the points A and B.

Example 2. The area of revolution is given by

$$R = 2\pi \int_A^B y\,ds = 2\pi \int_A^B y\sqrt{1 + y'^2}\,dx$$

where $f = y\sqrt{1 + y'^2}$ $\quad \frac{\partial f}{\partial y} = \sqrt{1 + y'^2}$ $\quad \frac{\partial f}{\partial y'} = \frac{yy'}{\sqrt{1 + y'^2}}$

By Eq. (2-71)

$$\sqrt{1 + y'^2} - \frac{d}{dx}\frac{yy'}{\sqrt{1 + y'^2}} = 0$$

$$\sqrt{1 + y'^2} - \frac{\sqrt{1 + y'^2}(yy'' + y'^2) - yy'(y'y''/\sqrt{1 + y'^2})}{(1 + y'^2)} = 0$$

$$(1 + y'^2) - \frac{(1 + y'^2)(yy'' + y'^2) - yy'^2y''}{(1 + y'^2)} = 0$$

$$(1 + y'^2)^2 - y'^2 - yy'' - y'^4 = 0$$

$$1 + y'^2 - yy'' = 0$$

By setting $y' = \theta$ and $y'' = \theta(d\theta/dy)$ the equation reduces to

$$\frac{\theta\,d\theta}{1 + \theta^2} = \frac{dy}{y}$$

which has the solution $y = c\cosh(x - d)/c$. The constants c and d are used to pass the curve through the points A and B.

References should be consulted for solving constrained variational problems.

INFINITE SERIES

References: Bromwich, "An Introduction to the Theory of Infinite Series," Macmillan, New York, 1955. Hardy, "Divergent Series," Oxford, New York, 1949. Kaplan, "Advanced Calculus," Addison-Wesley, Reading, Mass., 1956. Woods, "Advanced Calculus," Ginn, Boston, 1934.

DEFINITIONS

A succession of numbers or terms which are formed according to some definite rule is called a *sequence.* The indicated sum of the terms of a sequence is called a *series.* If the terms of the sequence are variable then the series is called a *power series.*

Consider the sum of a finite number of terms in the geometric series (a special case of a power series).

$$S_n = a + ar + ar^2 + ar^3 + \cdots + ar^{n-1} \qquad (2\text{-}72)$$

It has been shown that for any number of terms n their sum is equal to the following:

$$S_n = a\frac{1 - r^n}{1 - r}$$

In the above form the geometric series is assumed finite. In the form (2-72) it can further be defined that the terms in the series be non-ending and therefore an infinite series.

$$S = a + ar + ar^2 + \cdots + ar^n + \cdots \qquad (2\text{-}73)$$

However, the defined sum of the terms (2-72)

$$S_n = a\frac{1 - r^n}{1 - r}$$

while valid for any finite value of r and n now takes on a different interpretation. In this sense it is necessary to consider the limit of S_n as n increases indefinitely:

$$S = \lim_{n\to\infty} S_n = a \lim_{n\to\infty} \frac{1-r^n}{1-r}$$

For this, it is stated the infinite series *converges* if the limit of S_n approaches a fixed finite value as n approaches infinity. Otherwise, the series is *divergent.*

On this basis an analysis of $S = a \lim_{n\to\infty} \frac{1-r^n}{1-r}$ shows if r is less than 1 but greater than -1 the infinite series is convergent. For values outside of the range $-1 < r < 1$ the series is divergent because the sum becomes unlimited. The range $-1 < r < 1$ is called the *region of convergence.*

Consider the divergence of (2-73) when $r = -1$ and $+1$. For the former case $r = -1$,

$$S = a + a(-1) + a(-1)^2 + a(-1)^3 + \cdots + a(-1)^n + \cdots$$
$$= a - a + a - a + a - \cdots$$

and for which

$$S = a \lim_{n\to\infty} \frac{1-r^n}{1-r} = a \lim_{n\to\infty} \frac{1-(-1)^n}{1+1} \qquad \text{undefined limit}$$

Since the limit sum does not exist the series is divergent. This is defined as a bounded or *oscillating divergent series.* Similarly for the value $r = +1$

$$S = a + a(1) + a(1)^2 + a(1)^3 + \cdots + a(1)^n + \cdots$$
$$S = a + a + a + a + \cdots + a + \cdots$$

The series is also divergent but defined as an *unbounded divergent series.*

There are also two types of convergent series. Consider the new series

$$S = 1 - \frac{1}{2} + \frac{1}{3} - \frac{1}{4} + \cdots + (-1)^{n+1}\frac{1}{n} + \cdots \tag{2-74}$$

It can be shown the series (2-74) does converge to the value $S = \log 2$. However, if each term is replaced by its absolute value the series becomes unbounded and therefore divergent (properly divergent):

$$S = 1 + \frac{1}{2} + \frac{1}{3} + \frac{1}{4} + \frac{1}{5} + \cdots \tag{2-75}$$

In this case the series (2-74) is defined as a *conditionally convergent* series. If the replacement series of absolute values also converges the series is defined to *converge absolutely.*

Series (2-74) is further defined as an *alternating series* while (2-75) is referred to as a *positive series.*

OPERATIONS WITH INFINITE SERIES

1. The convergence or divergence of an infinite series is unaffected by the removal of a finite number of finite terms.

This is a trivial theorem but useful to remember especially when using the comparison test to be described in the next section on tests.

2. If a series is conditionally convergent, its sum can be made to have any arbitrary value by a suitable rearrangement of the series; it can in fact be made divergent or oscillatory (Riemann's theorem).

This seemingly paradoxical theorem can be illustrated by the following example:

$$S = 1 - \frac{1}{2} + \frac{1}{3} - \frac{1}{4} + \frac{1}{5} - \frac{1}{6} + \cdots$$

The series is rearranged so that each positive term is followed by two negative terms:

$$t = 1 - \frac{1}{2} - \frac{1}{4} + \frac{1}{3} - \frac{1}{6} - \frac{1}{8} + \frac{1}{5} - \frac{1}{10} - \frac{1}{12} + \cdots$$

Define t_{3n} for the first $3n$ terms in the series

$$t_{3n} = \left(1 - \frac{1}{2}\right) - \frac{1}{4} + \left(\frac{1}{3} - \frac{1}{6}\right) - \frac{1}{8} + \cdots + \left(\frac{1}{2n-1} - \frac{1}{4n-2}\right) - \frac{1}{4n}$$
$$= \frac{1}{2} - \frac{1}{4} + \frac{1}{6} - \frac{1}{8} + \cdots + \frac{1}{4n-2} - \frac{1}{4n}$$
$$= \frac{1}{2}\left(1 - \frac{1}{2} + \frac{1}{3} - \frac{1}{4} + \cdots + \frac{1}{2n-1} - \frac{1}{2n}\right)$$
$$= \frac{1}{2} S_{2n}$$

where S_{2n} are the first $2n$ terms of the original series. Thus

$$\lim_{n\to\infty} t_{3n} = \lim_{n\to\infty} \frac{1}{2} S_{2n} = \frac{1}{2} S$$

and since $\lim t_{3n+2} = \lim t_{3n+1} = \lim t_{3n}$ it follows the sum of the series t is $\frac{1}{2} S$. Hence a derangement of the terms of an alternating series alters the sum of the series.

3. A series of positive terms, if convergent, has a sum independent of the order of its terms; but if divergent it remains divergent, however its terms are changed.

4. An oscillatory series can always be made to converge by grouping the terms in brackets.

For example, consider the series

$$1 - \frac{1}{2} + \frac{2}{3} - \frac{3}{4} + \frac{4}{5} - \frac{5}{6}$$

which oscillates between the values 0.306 and 1.306. However, the series

$$\left(1 - \frac{1}{2}\right) + \left(\frac{2}{3} - \frac{3}{4}\right) + \left(\frac{4}{5} - \frac{5}{6}\right) + \cdots = \frac{1}{2} - \frac{1}{12} - \frac{1}{30} - \frac{1}{56}$$
$$\cong 0.306 \cdots$$

and

$$1 - \left(\frac{1}{2} - \frac{2}{3}\right) - \left(\frac{3}{4} - \frac{4}{5}\right) - \left(\frac{5}{6} - \frac{6}{7}\right) + \cdots = 1 + \frac{1}{6} + \frac{1}{20} + \frac{1}{42}$$
$$= 1.306 \cdots$$

5. A power series can be inverted, provided the first-degree term is not zero.

Given:

$$y = b_1x + b_2x^2 + b_3x^3 + b_4x^4 + b_5x^5 + b_6x^6 + b_7x^7 + \cdots$$

then $x = B_1y + B_2y^2 + B_3y^3 + B_4y^4 + B_5y^5 + B_6y^6 + B_7y^7 + \cdots$

where

$$B_1 = \frac{1}{b_1}$$

$$B_2 = \frac{b_2}{b_1^3}$$

$$B_3 = \frac{1}{b_1^5}(2b_2^2 - b_1b_3)$$

$$B_4 = \frac{1}{b_1^7}(5b_1b_2b_3 - b_1^2b_4 - 5b_2^3)$$

Additional coefficients are available in the references.

6. Two series may be added or subtracted term by term provided each is a convergent series. The joint sum is equal to the sum (or difference) of the individuals.

7. The sum of two divergent series can be convergent. Similarly, the sum of a convergent series and a divergent series must be divergent.

Example. Given

$$\sum_{n=1}^{\infty}\left(\frac{1+n}{n^2}\right) = \frac{2}{1} + \frac{3}{4} + \frac{4}{9} + \frac{5}{16} + \cdots \qquad \text{a divergent series}$$

$$\sum_{n=1}^{\infty}\left(\frac{1-n}{n^2}\right) = -\frac{1}{4} - \frac{2}{9} - \frac{3}{16} + \cdots \qquad \text{a divergent series}$$

However

$$\sum\left(\frac{1+n}{n^2}\right) + \sum\left(\frac{1-n}{n^2}\right) = \sum\left(\frac{1+n+1-n}{n^2}\right) = 2\sum\frac{1}{n^2} \qquad \text{convergent}$$

8. A power series may be integrated term by term to represent the integral of the function within an interval of the region of convergence.

If $f(x) = a_0 + a_1x + a_2x^2 + \cdots$

Then

$$\int_a^b f(x)\,dx = \int_a^b a_0\,dx + \int_a^b a_1x\,dx + \int_a^b a_2x^2\,dx + \cdots$$

9. A power series may be differentiated term by term and represents the function $df(x)/dx$ within the same region of convergence as $f(x)$.

TESTS FOR CONVERGENCE AND DIVERGENCE

In general, the problem of determining whether a given series will converge or not can require a great deal of ingenuity and resourcefulness. There is no all-inclusive test which can be applied to all series. As the only alternative it is necessary to apply one or more of the developed theorems in an attempt to ascertain the convergence or divergence of the series under study. The following defined tests are given in relative order of effectiveness:

1. Comparison Test. A series will converge if the absolute value of each term (with or without a finite number of terms) is less than the corresponding term of a known convergent series. Similarly, a positive series is divergent if it is termwise larger than a known divergent series of positive terms.

Example 1a. **Need for comparison with a positive series.**

Given $1 - \frac{1}{1\times 2} + \frac{1}{2} - \frac{1}{2\times 3} + \frac{1}{3} - \frac{1}{3\times 4} + \cdots$

Comparison $1 - 1 + \frac{1}{2} - \frac{1}{2} + \frac{1}{3} - \frac{1}{3} + \cdots$

The reference series is known to converge to zero. Termwise, each term of the comparison series is numerically greater than or equal to the given series, and the former series converges to zero. However, the given series does diverge since

$$1 - \frac{1}{1\times 2} = \frac{1}{2}$$

$$\frac{1}{2} - \frac{1}{2\times 3} = \frac{1}{3}$$

$$\frac{1}{3} - \frac{1}{3\times 4} = \frac{1}{4} \qquad \text{etc.}$$

or

$$\frac{1}{2} + \frac{1}{3} + \frac{1}{4} + \frac{1}{5} + \cdots$$

Example 1b. **Convergent series.**

Given $1 + \frac{2}{3} + \frac{3}{3^2} + \frac{4}{3^3} + \frac{5}{3^4} + \cdots + \frac{n}{3^{n-1}} + \cdots$

Comparison $1 + \frac{1}{2} + \frac{1}{4} + \frac{1}{8} + \frac{1}{16} + \cdots + \frac{1}{2^{n-1}} \cdots$

(Geometrical series with $a = 1$, $r = \frac{1}{2}$)

Since the convergence or divergence of a series is unaffected by neglecting a finite number of terms the comparison test for the given series can be made without the first term:

$$\begin{array}{cccccccc} 1 & \frac{2}{3} & \frac{3}{3^2} & \frac{4}{3^3} & \frac{5}{3^4} & \cdots & \frac{n}{3^{n-1}} \\ & \updownarrow & \updownarrow & \updownarrow & \updownarrow & & \updownarrow \\ 1 & \frac{1}{2} & \frac{1}{4} & \frac{1}{8} & & \cdots & \frac{1}{2^{n-2}} \end{array}$$

In this case $\frac{2}{3} < 1$, $\frac{3}{9} < \frac{1}{2}$, $\frac{4}{27} < \frac{1}{4}$, $\frac{5}{81} < \frac{1}{8}$, and similarly for all higher-order terms since

$$\frac{n}{3^{n-1}} < \frac{1}{2^{n-2}} \qquad \text{for } n > 2$$

Therefore, since the comparison series converges, the given series must also converge. Further, the limit of the given series must be less than 3 as follows:

$$S = 1 + \frac{1}{2} + \frac{1}{4} + \frac{1}{8} + \cdots = \frac{1}{1-r} = 2$$

$$1 + \frac{2}{3} + \frac{3}{3^2} + \frac{4}{3^3} + \cdots < 1 + S < 3 \qquad \text{where } S = 2$$

2. *n*th Term Test. A series is divergent unless the *n*th term of the series approaches zero as *n* becomes increasingly large.

Example 2a. **Divergent series.**

Given $2 - \frac{2^2}{2^4} + \frac{2^3}{3^4} - \frac{2^4}{4^4} + \frac{2^5}{5^4} + \cdots + (-1)^{n+1}\frac{2^n}{n^4}$

A check calculation of the first few terms would indicate a rapid decrease in numerical value for the successive terms. This could lead to the false impression the series was convergent. The above theorem is a negative test (a test of whether the series is divergent only) but does show, as in this example, the divergence of a series, *i.e.*,

$$\lim_{n\to\infty}\frac{2^n}{n^4} = \lim_{n\to\infty}\frac{(d^4/dn^4)(2^n)}{(d^4/dn^4)(n^4)}$$

$$= \lim_{n\to\infty}\frac{(\ln 2)^4\,2^n}{24} \qquad \text{by L'Hopital's theorem (see p. 2-24)}$$

$$= \infty$$

Example 2*b*. Inconclusive test.

Given $\ln\frac{1}{2}+\ln\frac{2}{3}+\ln\frac{3}{4}+\ln\frac{4}{5}+\cdots+\ln\frac{n}{1+n}+\cdots$

Under the conditions of the nth term test, application to the above series is inconclusive. Although $\lim_{n\to\infty}\ln[n/(1+n)]$ does equal zero the converse conclusion based on the theorem cannot be inferred. In this example the series is actually divergent but cannot be demonstrated as divergent by this series test.

3. Ratio Test. If the absolute ratio of the $(n+1)$ term divided by the nth term as n becomes unbounded approaches

a. A number less than 1 the series is convergent.
b. A number greater than 1 the series is divergent.
c. A number equal to 1 the test is inconclusive.

Example 3*a*. Convergent series.

Given $1+\frac{2^5}{2!}+\frac{3^5}{3!}+\frac{4^5}{4!}+\cdots+\frac{n^5}{n!}+\frac{(n+1)^5}{(n+1)!}+\cdots$

Applying the ratio test

$$\begin{aligned}\lim_{n\to\infty}\frac{(n+1)^5/(n+1)!}{n^5/n!} &= \lim_{n\to\infty}\left(\frac{n+1}{n}\right)^5\frac{n!}{(n+1)!}\\ &= \lim_{n\to\infty}\left(\frac{n+1}{n}\right)^5\left(\frac{1}{n+1}\right)\\ &= \lim_{n\to\infty}\left(\frac{n+1}{n}\right)^5\lim_{n\to\infty}\frac{1}{n+1}\\ &= 1\times 0=0\end{aligned}$$

Therefore the series converges under statement *a*.

Example 3*b*. Divergent series.

Given $\frac{2}{1\times 2}+\frac{2^2}{2\times 3}+\frac{2^3}{3\times 4}+\cdots+\frac{2^n}{n(n+1)}+\frac{2^{n+1}}{(n+1)(n+2)}+\cdots$

By the ratio test

$$\begin{aligned}\lim_{n\to\infty}\frac{2^{n+1}/(n+1)(n+2)}{2^n/(n)(n+1)} &= \lim_{n\to\infty}\frac{2^{n+1}}{2^n}\frac{n(n+1)}{(n+2)(n+1)}\\ &= \lim_{n\to\infty}2\lim_{n\to\infty}\frac{n}{n+2}\\ &= 2\times 1=2\end{aligned}$$

Thus by statement *b* the series is divergent.

Example 3*c*. Inconclusive test.

Given $1+\frac{1}{2^r}+\frac{1}{3^r}+\frac{1}{4^r}+\cdots+\frac{1}{n^r}+\frac{1}{(n+1)}+\cdots$

Again

$$\begin{aligned}\lim_{n\to\infty}\frac{1/(n+1)^r}{1/n^r} &= \lim_{n\to\infty}\left(\frac{n}{n+1}\right)^r\\ &= 1 \text{ for any value of } r\end{aligned}$$

Under *c* the ratio test fails and no conclusion can be stated. However, as will be indicated, this series converges if $r>1$ and diverges if $r\le 1$.

4. Summation Test. If the partial summation S_n of a series converges as n becomes unbounded the series converges, and conversely, it diverges if S_n diverges.

Example 4*a*. Convergent series.

Given $1+\frac{2}{3}+\frac{2^2}{3^2}+\frac{2^3}{3^3}+\cdots+\frac{2^n}{3^n}+\cdots$

From the geometric-progression formula

$$\begin{aligned}S_n &= 1+\frac{2}{3}+\frac{2^2}{3^2}+\cdots+\frac{2^n}{3^n}\\ &= \frac{1-(2/3)^n}{1-2/3}\\ &= 3[1-(2/3)^n]\end{aligned}$$

and $\lim_{n\to\infty}S_n=3$

hence the series converges.

Example 4*b*. Divergent series (2-72).

Given

$$\ln\frac{1}{1+1}+\ln\frac{2}{2+1}+\ln\frac{3}{3+1}+\cdots+\ln\frac{n}{n+1}+\cdots$$

The partial sum S_n is given by

$$\begin{aligned}S_n &= \ln\frac{1}{1+1}+\ln\frac{2}{2+1}+\cdots+\ln\frac{n}{n+1}\\ &= \ln\left(\frac{1}{2+1}\cdot\frac{2}{2+1}\cdots\frac{n}{n+1}\right)\\ &= \ln\frac{1}{n+1}\end{aligned}$$

and since $\lim_{n\to\infty}S_n=-\infty$ the series diverges.

Example 4*c*. Divergent series (2-73).

Given $1+\frac{1}{2}+\frac{1}{3}+\frac{1}{4}+\frac{1}{5}+\cdots+\frac{1}{n}+\cdots$

It can be shown for

$$S_n=1+\frac{1}{2}+\frac{1}{3}+\cdots+\frac{1}{n}$$

that $S_n>\ln n+\frac{1}{2n}$ for all n

Therefore, since $\lim_{n\to\infty}[\ln n+(1/2n)]$ diverges the given series also diverges.

5. Alternating-series Test. If the terms of a series are alternately positive and negative, and never increase in numerical value, the series will converge, provided that the terms tend to zero as a limit.

6. Cauchy's Root Test. If the nth root of the nth absolute value term, as n becomes unbounded, approaches

a. A number less than 1 the series is convergent.
b. A number greater than 1 the series is divergent.
c. A number equal to 1 the test is inconclusive.

Example 6*a*. Convergent series.

Given

$$\frac{1}{2}+\left(\frac{2}{2+1}\right)^{2^2}+\left(\frac{3}{3+1}\right)^{3^2}+\cdots+\left(\frac{n}{n+1}\right)^{n^2}+\cdots$$

The application of the nth root test results in

$$\begin{aligned}\lim_{n\to\infty}\sqrt[n]{\left(\frac{n}{n+1}\right)^{n^2}} &= \lim_{n\to\infty}\left[\left(\frac{n}{n+1}\right)^{n^2}\right]^{1/n}\\ &= \lim_{n\to\infty}\left(\frac{n}{n+1}\right)^n\\ &= \frac{1}{e}\end{aligned}$$

Since $1/e$ is less than 1 the series converges.

Example 6*b*. Divergent series.

Given $1+\frac{3^2}{2^{10}}+\frac{3^3}{3^{10}}+\frac{3^4}{4^{10}}+\cdots\frac{3^n}{n^{10}}+\cdots$

By the root test the nth root limit of the nth term is taken as follows:

$$\lim_{n\to\infty} \sqrt[n]{\frac{3^n}{n^{10}}} = \lim_{n\to\infty} \left(\frac{3^n}{n^{10}}\right)^{1/n}$$
$$= \lim_{n\to\infty} (3) \lim_{n\to\infty} (n^{-10/n})$$
$$= 3$$

Therefore the series diverges. The fact that $\lim_{n\to\infty} (n^{-10/n}) = 1$ is easily verified by considering

$$X = n^{10/n}$$
$$\log X = \frac{10}{n} \log n$$
$$\lim_{n\to\infty} \log X = \lim_{n\to\infty} \frac{10}{n} \log n$$
$$= 0 \qquad X = 1 \text{ since } \lim_{n\to\infty} \log X = 0$$

Example 6c. Inconclusive test.

Given $\quad 1 + \frac{1}{2^r} + \frac{1}{3^r} + \frac{1}{4^r} + \cdots + \frac{1}{n^r} + \cdots$

By the root test

$$\lim_{n\to\infty} \sqrt[n]{1/n^r} = \lim_{n\to\infty} 1/n^{r/n}$$
$$= 1 \text{ for all } r$$

and therefore the test result is inconclusive. It will be shown the series does converge if $r > 1$.

7. Maclaurin's Integral Test. A series Σa_n converges or diverges with the integral $\int_1^\infty f(x)\,dx$ where $f(n) = a_n$ and $f(x)$ is defined and continuous for $1 \le x < \infty$ and $\lim_{x\to\infty} f(x) = 0$.

Example 7.

Given $\quad 1 + \frac{1}{2^r} + \frac{1}{3^r} + \frac{1}{4^r} + \cdots + \frac{1}{n^r} + \cdots$

For this example other tests are useful for certain regions of r but all break down when $r > 1$. The determination of the region of convergence in this case will be derived on this basis.

It follows that if $r \le 0$ then the criterion $\lim_{n\to\infty} a_n = 0$ is not met by test 2 and the series diverges for $r \le 0$.

Define $f(x) = 1/x^r$ which is continuous, decreasing, and the $\lim_{n\to\infty} 1/x^r = 0$ for $r > 0$. Thus, for $r \ne 1$*

$$\int_1^\infty \frac{1}{x^r}\,dx = \lim_{n\to\infty} \int_1^n \frac{1}{x^r}\,dx$$
$$= \lim_{n\to\infty} \left[\left(\frac{1/1-r}{x^{r-1}}\right)_1^n\right]^*$$
$$= \lim_{n\to\infty} \left[\frac{1}{1-r}\frac{1}{n^{r-1}} - \frac{1}{1-r}\right]$$
$$= \lim_{n\to\infty} \left[\frac{1}{r-1}\left(1 - \frac{1}{n^{r-1}}\right)\right]$$

The limit exists (finite) when $r > 1$ and therefore the series converges. For $0 < r < 1$ the limit does not exist and the series diverges. Further, when $r = 1$

$$\int_1^\infty \frac{1}{x}\,dx = \lim_{n\to\infty} \int_1^n \frac{1}{x}\,dx$$
$$= \lim_{n\to\infty} [\ln x]$$
$$= \infty \qquad \text{which implies divergence in the case } r = 1$$

Other tests of a more specialized and specific nature are available. However, these require more detailed mathematical definitions and recourse to advanced concepts such as upper and lower bounds. The indicated references should be consulted for details on their application and use.

* General integration identity not valid for $r = 1$.

SERIES SUMMATION AND IDENTITIES

Sums for the First n Numbers to Integer Powers.

$$\sum_{j=1}^{n} j = \frac{n(n+1)}{2} = 1 + 2 + 3 + 4 + \cdots + n$$

$$\sum_{j=1}^{n} j^2 = \frac{n(n+1)(2n+1)}{6} = 1^2 + 2^2 + 3^2 + 4^2 + \cdots + n^2$$

$$\sum_{j=1}^{n} j^3 = \frac{n^2(n+1)^2}{4} = 1^3 + 2^3 + 4^3 + \cdots + n^3$$

$$\sum_{j=1}^{n} j^4 = \frac{n(n+1)(2n+1)(3n^2+3n-1)}{30} = 1^4 + 2^4 + 3^4 + \cdots + n^4$$

Example 1. Find $1^4 + 2^4 + 3^4 + \cdots + 1000^4 = \Sigma n^4$.

$$\sum_1^{1000} n^4 = \frac{1000(1001)(2001)(3{,}000{,}000 + 3000 - 1)}{30}$$
$$= 200{,}500{,}333{,}333{,}300$$

Example 2. Find $1^4 + 3^4 + 5^4 + 7^4 + \cdots + 999^4 = \Sigma(2n-1)^4$.

$$\sum_1^{500} (2n-1)^4 = 1^4 + 3^4 + 5^4 + \cdots + 999^4$$
$$= 1^4 + 2^4 + 3^4 + 4^4 + 5^4 + \cdots + 1000^4 - (2^4 + 4^4 + 6^4 + \cdots + 1000^4)$$
$$= \sum_1^{1000} n^4 - \sum_1^{500} (2n)^4$$
$$= \sum_1^{1000} n^4 - 2^4 \sum_1^{500} n^4$$
$$= \frac{1000(1001)(2001)(3{,}000{,}000 + 3000 - 1)}{30} - 16\,\frac{500(501)(1001)(751{,}499)}{30}$$
$$= 99{,}999{,}666{,}666{,}900$$

Example 3. Find $1^4 + 1.25^4 + 1.50^4 + 1.75^4 + \cdots + 100^4$

$$= \sum\left(\frac{3}{4} + \frac{1}{4}n\right)^4.$$

$$\sum_1^{397} \left(\frac{3}{4} + \frac{1}{4}n\right)^4 = \sum_4^{400} \left(\frac{n}{4}\right)^4$$
$$= \frac{1}{4^4}\sum_4^{400} n^4 = \frac{1}{4^4}\sum_1^{400} n^4 - 1^4 - 2^4 - 3^4$$
$$= \frac{1}{256}\left[\frac{400(401)(801)(481{,}199)}{30} - 98\right]$$
$$= 8{,}050{,}083{,}332\,\frac{115}{128}$$

Arithmetic Progression.

$$\Sigma[a + (n-1)d] = a + (a+d) + (a+2d) + (a+3d) + \cdots + a + (n-1)d$$

$$= na + \frac{1}{2}n(n-1)d$$

Example. Find $1 + 6 + 11 + 16 + 21 + \cdots + 201$.

$$\sum_{1}^{41} [1 + (n-1)5] = 41(1) + \frac{1}{2}(41)(40)5$$

$$= 4141$$

Geometric Progression.

$$\Sigma(ar^n) = a + ar + ar^2 + ar^3 + \cdots + ar^{n-1}$$

$$= a\frac{1-r^n}{1-r}$$

Example. Find $\Sigma[ar^n]$ for $a = 2$, $r = \frac{1}{8}$, $n = 51$.

$$\sum_{1}^{51} 2\left(\frac{1}{8}\right)^{n-1} = 2\,\frac{1-(\frac{1}{8})^{50}}{1-\frac{1}{8}}$$

$$\cong 1\tfrac{9}{7}$$

Harmonic Progression.

$$\sum \frac{1}{a+nd} = \frac{1}{a} + \frac{1}{a+d} + \frac{1}{a+2d} + \frac{1}{a+3d} + \frac{1}{a+3d} + \cdots + \frac{1}{a+nd}$$

The reciprocals of the terms of the arithmetic-progression series are called a *harmonic progression.* No general summation formulas are available for this series.

Binomial Series.

$$(x+y)^n = x^n + nx^{n-1}y + \frac{n(n-1)}{2!}x^{n-2} + \frac{n(n-1)(n-2)}{3!}x^{n-3}y^3 + \cdots + \frac{n!}{(n-r)!r!}x^{n-r}y^r + \cdots + y^n$$

$$(1 \pm x)^n = 1 \pm nx + \frac{n(n-1)}{2!}x^2 \pm \frac{n(n-1)(n-2)}{3!}x^3 + \cdots \quad \begin{matrix} n > 0 \\ (x^2 < 1) \\ n < 0 \\ (x^2 \leq 1) \end{matrix}$$

Example 1. Find the coefficient of the term x^7y^{12} in $(x+y)^{19}$.

$$\frac{n!}{(n-r)!r!} = \frac{19!}{7!12!}$$

$$= \frac{19 \times 18 \times \cdots \times 13}{7 \times 6 \times 5 \times \cdots \times 1} = 50{,}388$$

Example 2. Find the sum of $1 - \frac{1}{3}x - \frac{1 \times 2}{3 \times 6}x^2 - \frac{1 \times 2 \times 5}{3 \times 6 \times 9}x^3 + \cdots$. By identification to the second form of the binomial series $n = \frac{1}{3}$; then

$$1 - \frac{1}{3}x - \frac{1 \times 2}{3 \times 6}x^2 - \frac{1 \times 2 \times 5}{3 \times 6 \times 9}x^3 + \cdots = (1-x)^{\frac{1}{3}}$$

which converges for $x^2 \leq 1$.

Example 3. Find $\sqrt{5}$ to 6 decimal places.

$$\sqrt{5} = 2\sqrt{1 + \tfrac{1}{4}} = 2\left(1 + \frac{1}{4}\right)^{\frac{1}{2}}$$

$$= 2\left[1 + \frac{1}{2(4)} - \frac{1}{8(16)} + \frac{1}{16(64)} - \frac{5}{128(256)} + \cdots\right]$$

1	1.00000000
1/2(4)	0.125
1/8(16)	−0.0078125
1/16(64)	0.00097656
5/128(256)	−0.00015259
7/256(1024)	0.00002670
21/1024(4096)	−0.00000501
33/2086(16384)	0.00000097
429/33376(65536)	−0.00000020
715/66752(262144)	0.00000001
	1.11803396 × 2 = 2.236068 = $\sqrt{5}$

Further,

$\sqrt{5}$ to 14 places is given by $\sqrt{5} = \frac{1}{2}\left(\frac{5}{2.2360679} + 2.2360679\right)$

$= 2.23606797749979$ (using the seven-place estimate of $\sqrt{5}$)

Taylor's Series.

$$f(x+h) = f(h) + xf'(h) + \frac{x^2}{2!}f''(h) + \frac{x^3}{3!}f'''(h) + \cdots$$

Example 1. Find $Y = 3 + 5x - 2x^2 - 2x^3$ for $x = 2$ given $Y(1) = 4$.

Set $x = 1$, $h = 1$

Then

$$\begin{aligned} f(h) &= 3 + 5 - 2 - 2 = 4 \\ f'(h) &= 5 - 4h - 6h^2 = -5 \\ f''(h) &= -4 - 12h = -16 \\ f'''(h) &= -12 = -12 \\ Y(2) &= 4 + 1(-5) + \tfrac{1}{2}(-16) + \tfrac{1}{6}(-12) \\ &= -11 \end{aligned}$$

Example 2. Find a series expansion for $\ln x$.

Set $h = 1$

Then

$$\begin{aligned} f(h) &= \ln 1 = 0 \\ f'(h) &= \frac{1}{x} = 1 \\ f''(h) &= -\frac{1}{x^2} = -1! \\ f'''(h) &= +1 \cdot 2/x^3 = 2! \\ f''''(h) &= -\frac{1 \cdot 2 \cdot 3}{x^4} = -3! \end{aligned}$$

etc.

and

$$\ln(x+1) = x - \frac{x^2}{2} + \frac{x^3}{3} - \frac{x^4}{4} + \cdots + (-1)^{n+1}\frac{x^n}{n} + \cdots$$

which converges for $-1 < x < 1$.

Maclaurin's Series.

$$f(x) = f(0) + xf'(0) + \frac{x^2}{2!}f''(0) + \frac{x^3}{3!}f'''(0) + \cdots$$

This is simply a special case of Taylor's series when h is set to zero.

Example. Compute $\sqrt[3]{e}$ to five places.

$$e^x = 1 + x + \frac{x^2}{2!} + \frac{x^3}{3!} + \cdots$$

$$e^{\frac{1}{3}} = 1 + \frac{1}{3} + \frac{1}{(3^2)2!} + \frac{1}{(3^3)3!} + \frac{1}{(3^4)4!} + \text{remainder}$$

$$= 1.39557 + R_5$$

The remainder R_5 can be estimated by a derived formula

$$R_n = \frac{x^n}{n!} f^{(n)}(x_0) \qquad x_0 \text{ such that } 0 < x_0 < x \text{ or } x < x_0 < 0 \text{ if } x < 0$$

which in this case

$$R_5 = \frac{(\frac{1}{3})^5}{5!} e^{\frac{1}{3}}$$

since $e^{\frac{1}{3}} < 3^{\frac{1}{3}}$

$$R_5 < \frac{\sqrt[3]{3}}{3^5 5!} \cong 0.00005$$

Therefore $e^{\frac{1}{3}} = 1.3956$ to 5 places

Exponential Series.

$$e^x = 1 + x + \frac{x^2}{2!} + \frac{x^3}{3!} + \cdots + \frac{x^n}{n!} + \cdots$$

region of convergence $-\infty < x < \infty$

Logarithmic Series.

$$\ln x = \frac{x-1}{x} + \frac{1}{2}\left(\frac{x-1}{x}\right)^2 + \frac{1}{3}\left(\frac{x-1}{x}\right)^3 + \cdots \qquad (x > \tfrac{1}{2})$$

$$\ln x = 2\left[\frac{x-1}{x+1} + \frac{1}{3}\left(\frac{x-1}{x+1}\right)^3 + \cdots\right] \qquad (x > 0)$$

Trigonometric Series.*

$$\sin x = x - \frac{x^3}{3!} + \frac{x^5}{5!} - \frac{x^7}{7!} + \cdots \qquad -\infty < x < \infty$$

* tan x series has awkward coefficients and should be computed as $\left[(\text{sign}) \dfrac{\sin x}{\sqrt{1 - \sin^2 x}}\right]$.

$$\cos x = 1 - \frac{x^2}{2!} + \frac{x^4}{4!} - \frac{x^6}{6!} + \cdots \qquad -\infty < x < \infty$$

$$\sin^{-1} x = x + \frac{x^3}{6} + \frac{1}{2}\cdot\frac{3}{4}\cdot\frac{x^5}{5} + \frac{1}{2}\cdot\frac{3}{4}\cdot\frac{5}{6}\cdot\frac{x^7}{7} + \cdots \qquad (x^2 < 1)$$

$$\tan^{-1} x = x - \frac{1}{3}x^3 + \frac{1}{5}x^5 - \frac{1}{7}x^7 + \cdots \qquad (x^2 < 1)$$

MISCELLANEOUS INFINITE SERIES*

$$e = 1 + \frac{1}{1} + \frac{1}{2!} + \frac{1}{3!} + \frac{1}{4!} + \cdots + \frac{1}{n!} + \cdots$$

$$\pi = 4\left(1 - \frac{1}{3} + \frac{1}{5} - \frac{1}{7} + \frac{1}{9} - \frac{1}{11} + \cdots + \frac{1}{2n-1} + \cdots\right)$$

$$\pi^2 = 6 + \frac{6}{2^2} + \frac{6}{3^2} + \frac{6}{4^2} + \frac{6}{5^2} + \cdots + \frac{6}{n^2} + \cdots$$

$$\ln 2 = 1 - \frac{1}{2} + \frac{1}{3} - \frac{1}{4} + \frac{1}{5} + \cdots + (-1)^n \frac{1}{n+1} + \cdots$$

$$\sqrt{2} = 1 + \frac{1}{2} + \frac{1}{2^2} + \frac{1}{2^3} + \frac{1}{2^4} + \cdots + \frac{1}{2^n} + \cdots$$

$$\sqrt{10} = 3\left[1 + \frac{1}{2(9)} \frac{1}{2!2^2 9^2} + \frac{3}{3!2^3 9^3} + \frac{3.5}{4!2^4 9^4} + \cdots\right]$$

$$2 = 1 + \frac{1}{2} + \frac{1}{4} + \frac{1}{8} + \frac{1}{16} + \cdots + \frac{1}{2^n} + \cdots$$

* These series are useful for testing general-purpose computer programs.

COMPLEX VARIABLE

REFERENCES: Churchill, "Complex Variables and Applications," 2d ed., McGraw-Hill, New York, 1960. Kaplan, "Advanced Calculus," Addison-Wesley, Reading, Mass., 1952. Whittaker and Watson, "A Course of Modern Analysis," 4th ed., Cambridge, New York, 1940. Guillemin, "The Mathematics of Circuit Analysis," Wiley, New York, 1949. van der Pol and Bremmer, "Operational Calculus," Cambridge, New York, 1950. Churchill, "Operational Mathematics," 2d ed., McGraw-Hill, New York, 1944.

Numbers of the form $z = x + iy$, where x and y are real, $i^2 = -1$, are called *complex numbers*. The numbers $z = x + iy$ are representable in the plane as shown in

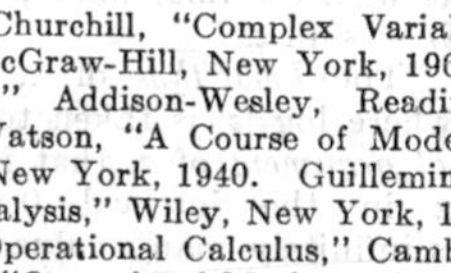

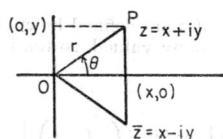

FIG. 2-47. Complex number.

Fig. 2-47. The following definitions and terminology are used:

1. Distance $OP = r =$ *absolute value* (*modulus*) of z written $|z|$. $|z| = \sqrt{x^2 + y^2}$.
2. x is the *real part* of z.
3. y is the *imaginary part* of z.
4. The angle θ, $0 \leq \theta \leq 2\pi$, measured counterclockwise from the positive x-axis to OP is the *argument* (*amplitude*) of z. $\theta = \arctan\ y/x = \arcsin\ y/r = \arccos x/r$.
5. The numbers r, θ are the *polar coordinates* of z.
6. $\bar{z} = x - iy$ is the *conjugate* of z.

ALGEBRA

Let $z_1 = x_1 + iy_1$, $z_2 = x_2 + iy_2$.

Equality. $z_1 = z_2$ if and only if $x_1 = x_2$ and $y_1 = y_2$.

Addition. $z_1 + z_2 = (x_1 + x_2) + i(y_1 + y_2)$.

Subtraction. $z_1 - z_2 = (x_1 - x_2) + i(y_1 - y_2)$.

Multiplication.

$$z_1 \cdot z_2 = (x_1x_2 - y_1y_2) + i(x_1y_2 + x_2y_1).$$

Division. $z_1/z_2 = \dfrac{x_1x_2 + y_1y_2}{x_2^2 + y_2^2} + i\dfrac{x_2y_1 - x_1y_2}{x_2^2 + y_2^2}$ $z_2 \neq 0$.

SPECIAL OPERATIONS

$z\bar{z} = x^2 + y^2 = |z|^2$; $\overline{z_1 \pm z_2} = \bar{z}_1 \pm \bar{z}_2$; $\bar{\bar{z}}_1 = z_1$; $\overline{z_1z_2} = \bar{z}_1\bar{z}_2$; $\overline{\left(\dfrac{z_1}{z_2}\right)} = \dfrac{\bar{z}_1}{\bar{z}_2}$; $|z_1 \cdot z_2| = |z_1| \cdot |z_2|$; $\arg\ (z_1 \cdot z_2) = \arg z_1 + \arg z_2$; $\arg\ (z_1/z_2) = \arg z_1 - \arg z_2$; $i^{4n} = 1$ for n any integer; $i^{2n} = -1$ where n is any odd integer; $z + \bar{z} = 2x$; $z - \bar{z} = 2iy$.

Every complex quantity can be expressed in the *form* $x + iy$.

Example 1. $(1 + i)^2 + (2 - i)^2 = 1 + 2i + i^2 + 4 - 4i + i^2 = 5 - 2i + 2i^2 = 3 - 2i$ since $i^2 = -1$.

Example 2. $\dfrac{1 + 2i}{3 - i} = \dfrac{(1 + 2i)(3 + i)}{(3 - i)(3 + i)} = \dfrac{3 + 7i + 2i^2}{9 - i^2} = \dfrac{1 + 7i}{10} = \dfrac{1}{10} + \dfrac{7}{10}i$.

Example 3. $\dfrac{3 + i}{i^3} = \dfrac{i(3 + i)}{i^4} = i(3 + i) = -1 + 3i$.

TRIGONOMETRIC REPRESENTATION

Referring to Fig. 2-47 there results $x = r\cos\theta$, $y = r\sin\theta$ so that $z = x + iy = r(\cos\theta + i\sin\theta)$, which is called the *polar form* of the complex number. $\cos\theta + i\sin\theta = e^{i\theta}$. Hence $z = x + iy = re^{i\theta}$. $\bar{z} = x - iy = re^{-i\theta}$. Two important results from this are $\cos\theta = \dfrac{e^{i\theta} + e^{-i\theta}}{2}$ and $\sin\theta = \dfrac{e^{i\theta} - e^{-i\theta}}{2i}$. Let $z_1 = r_1e^{i\theta_1}$, $z_2 = r_2e^{i\theta_2}$. This form is convenient for multiplication for $z_1z_2 = r_1r_2e^{i(\theta_1+\theta_2)}$ and for division for $z_1/z_2 = \dfrac{r_1}{r_2}e^{i(\theta_1-\theta_2)}$.

Example 1. $1 + 2i = \sqrt{5}(\cos 63°26' + i\sin 63°26') = \sqrt{5}e^{i(1.10713)}$ where 1.10713 radians = 63°26'.

Example 2. $\dfrac{1+i}{3i} = \dfrac{\sqrt{2}}{3}e^{i\left(\frac{\pi}{4}-\frac{\pi}{2}\right)} = \dfrac{\sqrt{2}}{3}e^{-i\frac{\pi}{4}}$.

POWERS AND ROOTS

If n is a positive integer $z^n = (re^{i\theta})^n = r^ne^{in\theta} = r^n(\cos n\theta + i\sin n\theta)$.

Example 1. $(1 + i)^8 = (\sqrt{2})^8e^{i8(\pi/4)} = 16e^{2\pi i} = 16$.

Example 2.
$$(\sqrt{3} - i)^5 = 2^5e^{i5\left(\frac{11\pi}{6}\right)} = 32\left(\cos\frac{55\pi}{6} + i\sin\frac{55\pi}{6}\right) = 32\left(-\frac{\sqrt{3}}{2} - \frac{i}{2}\right) = -16\sqrt{3} - 16i$$

If n is a positive integer $z^{1/n} = r^{1/n}e^{i\left(\frac{\theta+2k\pi}{n}\right)} = r^{1/n}\left[\cos\left(\dfrac{\theta + 2k\pi}{n}\right) + i\sin\left(\dfrac{\theta + 2k\pi}{n}\right)\right]$ and selecting values of $k = 0, 1, 2, 3, \ldots, n - 1$ give the n distinct values of $z^{1/n}$. The n roots of a complex quantity are spaced around a circle, with radius $r^{1/n}$, in the complex plane in a symmetric fashion.

Example. Find the three cube roots of -8. Here $r = 8$, $\theta = \pi$. The roots are $z_0 = 2(\cos\pi/3 + i\sin\pi/3) = 1 + i\sqrt{3}$, $z_1 = 2(\cos\pi + i\sin\pi) = -2$, $z_2 = 2(\cos 5\pi/3 + i\sin 5\pi/3) = 1 - i\sqrt{3}$.

ELEMENTARY COMPLEX FUNCTIONS

Polynomials. A *polynomial* in z, $a_nz^n + a_{n-1}z^{n-1} + \cdots + a_0$ where n is a positive integer is simply a sum of complex numbers times integral powers of z which have already been defined. Every polynomial of degree n has precisely n complex roots provided each multiple root of multiplicity m is counted m times.

Exponential Functions. The *exponential function* e^z is defined by the equation $e^z = e^{x+iy} = e^x \cdot e^{iy} = e^x(\cos y + i\sin y)$. Properties: $e^0 = 1$; $e^{z_1} \cdot e^{z_2} = e^{z_1+z_2}$; $e^{z_1}/e^{z_2} = e^{z_1-z_2}$; $e^{z+2k\pi i} = e^z$.

Trigonometric Functions. $\sin z = \dfrac{e^{iz} - e^{-iz}}{2i}$; $\cos z = \dfrac{e^{iz} + e^{-iz}}{2}$; $\tan z = \dfrac{\sin z}{\cos z}$; $\cot z = \dfrac{\cos z}{\sin z}$; $\sec z = \dfrac{1}{\cos z}$; $\csc z = \dfrac{1}{\sin z}$. Fundamental identities for these functions are the same as their real counterparts. Thus $\cos^2 z + \sin^2 z = 1$, $\cos(z_1 \pm z_2) = \cos z_1\cos z_2 \mp \sin z_1\sin z_2$, $\sin(z_1 \pm z_2) = \sin z_1\cos z_2 \pm \cos z_1\sin z_2$. The sine and cosine of z are *periodic functions* of *period* 2π; thus $\sin(z + 2\pi) = \sin z$. For computation purposes $\sin z = \sin(x + iy) = \sin x\cosh y + i\cos x\sinh y$ where $\sin x$, $\cosh y$, etc., are the real trigonometric and hyperbolic functions. Similarly $\cos z = \cos x\cosh y - i\sin x\sinh y$. If $x = 0$ in the above results $\cos iy = \cosh y$, $\sin iy = i\sinh y$.

Example 1. $\cos(1 + 2i) = \cos 1\cosh 2 - i\sin 1\sinh 2 = (0.54030)(3.7622) - i(0.84147)(3.6269) = 2.033 - i3.052$.

Example 2. Find all solutions of $\sin z = 3$. From above $\sin z = \sin x\cosh y + i\cos x\sinh y = 3$. Equating real and imaginary parts $\sin x\cosh y = 3$, $\cos x\sinh y = 0$. The second equation can hold for $y = 0$ or for $x = \pi/2, 3\pi/2, \ldots$. If $y = 0$, $\cosh 0 = 1$ and $\sin x = 3$ is impossible for real x. Therefore, $x = \pi/2, 3\pi/2, \ldots (2n + 1)\pi/2$, $n = 0, 1, 2, \ldots$. However, $\sin 3\pi/2 = -1$ and $\cosh y \geq 1$. Hence $x = \pi/2, 5\pi/2, \ldots$. The solution is $z = \dfrac{(4n + 1)\pi}{2} + i\cosh^{-1} 3$, $n = 0, 1, 2, 3, \ldots$.

Example 3. Find all solutions of $e^z = -i$. $e^z = e^x(\cos y + i\sin y) = -i$. Equating real and imaginary parts gives $e^x\cos y = \mathbf{0}$, $e^x\sin y = -1$. From the first $y = \pi/2, 3\pi/2, \ldots$. But $e^x > 0$. Therefore, $y = 3\pi/2, 7\pi/2, \ldots$. Then $x = 0$. The solution is $z = i\dfrac{(4n + 3)\pi}{2}$.

Two important facets of these functions should be recognized. First the *sin z* is *unbounded*, and second e^z takes *all* complex values *except* 0.

Hyperbolic Functions. $\sinh z = \dfrac{e^z - e^{-z}}{2}$; $\cosh z = \dfrac{e^z + e^{-z}}{2}$; $\tanh z = \dfrac{\sinh z}{\cosh z}$; $\coth z = \dfrac{\cosh z}{\sinh z}$; $\operatorname{csch} z = \dfrac{1}{\sinh z}$; $\operatorname{sech} z = \dfrac{1}{\cosh z}$. Fundamental identities for these functions are the same as for their real counterparts. $\cosh^2 z - \sinh^2 z = 1$; $\sinh(z_1 + z_2) = \sinh z_1\cosh z_2 + \cosh z_1\sinh z_2$; $\cosh(z_1 + z_2) = \cosh z_1\cosh z_2 + \sinh z_1\sinh z_2$; $\cosh z + \sinh z = e^z$; $\cosh z - \sinh z = e^{-z}$. The hyperbolic sine and hyperbolic cosine are *periodic functions* with the imaginary period $2\pi i$. That is, $\sinh(z + 2\pi i) = \sinh z$.

Logarithms. The *logarithm* of z, $\log z = \log|z| + i(\theta + 2n\pi)$, where $\log|z|$ is taken to the base e and *θ is the principal argument* of z, that is, the particular argument lying in the interval $0 \leq \theta < 2\pi$. The logarithm of z is infinitely many valued. If $n = 0$ the resulting logarithm is called the *principal value.* The familiar laws $\log z_1z_2 = \log z_1 + \log z_2$, $\log z_1/z_2 = \log z_1 - \log z_2$, $\log z^n = n\log z$ hold for this function.

Example. $\log(1 + i) = \log\sqrt{2} + i\left(\dfrac{\pi}{4} + 2n\pi\right)$.

General powers of z are defined by $z^\alpha = e^{\alpha\log z}$. Since $\log z$ is infinitely many valued, so too is z^α unless α is a rational number.

Example 1.
$$i^i = e^{i\log i} = e^{i\left[\log|i| + i\left(\frac{\pi}{2}+2n\pi\right)\right]} = e^{-\left(\frac{\pi}{2}+2n\pi\right)}.$$

Thus i^i is real with principal value $(n = 0) = e^{-\pi/2}$.

Example 2.
$$(\sqrt{2})^{1+i} = e^{(1+i)\log\sqrt{2}} = e^{\log\sqrt{2}}.\ e^{i\log\sqrt{2}} = \sqrt{2}\cdot$$
$$(\cos\log\sqrt{2} + i\sin\log\sqrt{2}) = \sqrt{2}[\cos(0.3466) + i\sin(0.3466)].$$

Inverse Trigonometric Functions. $\cos^{-1} z = -i\log(z \pm \sqrt{z^2 - 1})$; $\sin^{-1} z = -i\log(iz \pm \sqrt{1 - z^2})$; $\tan^{-1} z = \dfrac{i}{2}\log\left(\dfrac{i + z}{i - z}\right)$. These functions are infinitely many valued.

Inverse Hyperbolic Functions. $\cosh^{-1} z = \log (z \pm \sqrt{z^2 - 1})$; $\sinh^{-1} z = \log (z \pm \sqrt{z^2 + 1})$; $\tanh^{-1} z = \frac{1}{2} \log \left(\frac{1 + z}{1 - z}\right)$.

COMPLEX FUNCTIONS (ANALYTIC)

In the real-number system a greater than $b(a > b)$ and b less than $c(b < c)$ define an order relation. These relations have no meaning for complex numbers. The absolute value is used for ordering. Some important relations are given below: $|z| \geq x$; $|z| \geq y$; $|z_1 + z_2| \leq |z_1| + |z_2|$; $|z_1 - z_2| \geq ||z_1| - |z_2||$; $|z| \geq \frac{|x| + |y|}{\sqrt{2}}$. Parts of the complex plane, commonly called *regions* or *domains*, are described by using inequalities.

Example 1. $|z - 3| \leq 5$. This is equivalent to

$$\sqrt{(x - 3)^2 + y^2} \leq 5,$$

which is the set of all points within and on the circle, centered at $x = 3$, $y = 0$ of radius 5.

Example 2. $|z - 1| \leq x$ represents the set of all points inside and on the parabola $2x = y^2 + 1$.

Functions of a Complex Variable. If $z = x + iy$, $w = u + iv$ and if for each value of z in some region of the complex plane one or more values of w are defined then w is said to be a function of z, $w = f(z)$. Some of these functions have already been discussed, *e.g.*, $\sin z$, $\log z$. All functions are *reducible* to the *form* $w = u(x, y) + iv(x, y)$ where u, v are real functions of the real variables x and y.

Example 1. $z^3 = (x + iy)^3 = x^3 + 3x^2(iy) + 3x(iy)^2 + (iy)^3 = (x^3 - 3xy^2) + i(3x^2y - y^3)$.

Example 2. $\cos z = \cos x \cosh y - i \sin x \sinh y$.

Differentiation. The *derivative* of $w = f(z)$ is $\frac{dw}{dz} = \lim_{\Delta z \to 0} \frac{f(z + \Delta z) - f(z)}{\Delta z}$ and for the derivative to exist the limit must be the same no matter how Δz approaches zero. If w_1, w_2 are differentiable functions of z the following rules apply:

$$\frac{d(w_1 \pm w_2)}{dz} = \frac{dw_1}{dz} \pm \frac{dw_2}{dz} \qquad \frac{d(w_1 w_2)}{dz} = w_2 \frac{dw_1}{dz} + w_1 \frac{dw_2}{dz}$$

$$\frac{d(w_1/w_2)}{dz} = \frac{w_2(dw_1/dz) - w_1(dw_2/dz)}{w_2{}^2} \quad \text{and}$$

$$\frac{d(w_1{}^n)}{dz} = n w_1{}^{n-1} \frac{dw_1}{dz}$$

In order for $w = f(z)$ to be differentiable it is necessary that $\frac{\partial u}{\partial x} = \frac{\partial v}{\partial y}$ and $\frac{\partial v}{\partial x} = -\frac{\partial u}{\partial y}$. The last two equations are called the *Cauchy-Riemann* equations. The derivative $\frac{dw}{dz} = \frac{\partial u}{\partial x} + i \frac{\partial v}{\partial x} = \frac{\partial v}{\partial y} - i \frac{\partial u}{\partial y}$. If $f(z)$ possesses a derivative at z_0 and at *every point* in some neighborhood of z_0 then $f(z)$ is said to be *analytic* at z_0. If the Cauchy-Riemann equations are satisfied and u, v, $\frac{\partial u}{\partial x}, \frac{\partial u}{\partial y}, \frac{\partial v}{\partial x}, \frac{\partial v}{\partial y}$ are continuous in a region of the complex plane then $f(z)$ is analytic in that region.

Example 1. $w = z\bar{z} = x^2 + y^2$. Here $u = x^2 + y^2$, $v = 0$. $\frac{\partial u}{\partial x} = 2x$, $\frac{\partial u}{\partial y} = 2y$, $\frac{\partial v}{\partial x} = \frac{\partial v}{\partial y} = 0$. These are continuous everywhere, but the Cauchy-Riemann equations hold only at the origin. Therefore, w is nowhere analytic.

Example 2. $w = e^z = e^x \cos y + ie^x \sin y$. $u = e^x \cos y$, $v = e^x \sin y$. $\frac{\partial u}{\partial x} = e^x \cos y$, $\frac{\partial u}{\partial y} = -e^x \sin y$, $\frac{\partial v}{\partial x} = e^x \sin y$, $\frac{\partial v}{\partial y} = e^x \cos y$. The continuity and Cauchy-Riemann requirements are satisfied for all finite z. Hence e^z is analytic (except at ∞) and $\frac{dw}{dz} = \frac{\partial u}{\partial x} + i \frac{\partial v}{\partial x} = e^z$.

Example 3. $w = \frac{1}{z} = \frac{x - iy}{x^2 + y^2} = \frac{x}{x^2 + y^2} - i \frac{y}{x^2 + y^2}$. It is easy to see that dw/dz exists except at $z = 0$. Thus $1/z$ is analytic except at $z = 0$.

Singular Points. If $f(z)$ is analytic in a region except at certain points those points are called *singular* points.

Example 1. $1/z$ has a singular point at zero.

Example 2. $\tan z$ has singular points at $z = \pm(2n + 1)(\pi/2)$, $n = 0, 1, 2, \ldots$.

The derivatives of the common functions, given above, are the same as their real counterparts.

Example. $\frac{d}{dz} (\ln z) = \frac{1}{z}, \frac{d}{dz} (\sin z) = \cos z$.

Harmonic Functions. Both the *real* and *imaginary* parts of any analytic function $f = u + iv$ satisfy *Laplace's equation* $\partial^2\phi/\partial x^2 + \partial^2\phi/\partial y^2 = 0$. A function which possesses continuous second partial derivatives and satisfies Laplace's equation is called a *harmonic function.*

Example. $e^z = e^x \cos y + ie^x \sin y$. $u = e^x \cos y$, $\partial u/\partial x = e^x \cos y$, $\partial^2 u/\partial x^2 = e^x \cos y$, $\partial u/\partial y = -e^x \sin y$, $\partial^2 u/\partial y^2 = -e^x \cos y$. Clearly $\partial^2 u/\partial x^2 + \partial^2 u/\partial y^2 = 0$.

Similarly, $v = e^x \sin y$ is also harmonic. If $w = u + iv$ is analytic the curves $u(x, y) = c$ and $v(x, y) = k$ *intersect* at right *angles.*

Example. $z^3 = (x^3 - 3xy^2) + i(3x^2y - y^3)$. Set $u = x^3 - 3xy^2 = c$, $v = 3x^2y - y^3 = k$. By implicit differentiation there results, respectively, $\frac{dy}{dx} = \frac{x^2 - y^2}{2xy}$, $\frac{dy}{dx} = \frac{2xy}{y^2 - x^2}$, which are clearly negative reciprocals, the condition for perpendicularity.

Integration. In much of the work with complex variables a simple extension of integration called *line* or *curvilinear* integration is of fundamental importance. Since any complex line integral can be expressed in terms of real line integrals we define only *real line integrals.* Let $F(x, y)$ be a real, continuous function of x and y and c be any continuous curve of finite length joining the points A and B (Fig. 2-48). $F(x, y)$ is not related to the

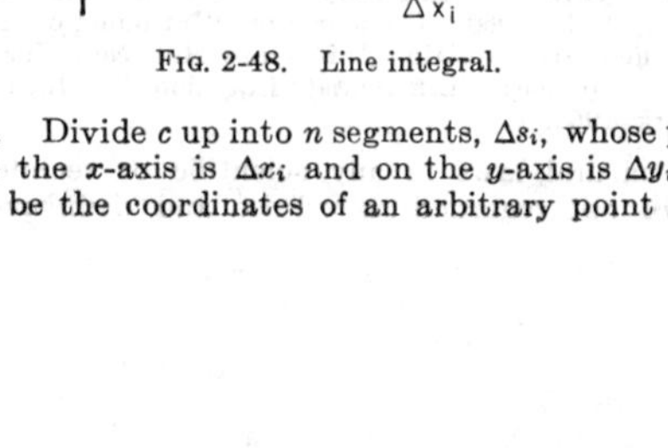

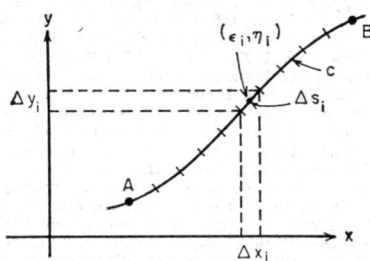

FIG. 2-48. Line integral.

curve c. Divide c up into n segments, Δs_i, whose projection on the x-axis is Δx_i and on the y-axis is Δy_i. Let (ϵ_i, η_i) be the coordinates of an arbitrary point in Δs_i,

The limits of the sums

$$\lim_{\text{all } \Delta s_i \to 0} \sum_{i=1}^{n} F(\epsilon_i, \eta_i)\,\Delta s_i = \int_c F(x, y)\,ds$$

$$\lim_{\text{all } \Delta s_i \to 0} \sum_{i=1}^{n} F(\epsilon_i, \eta_i)\,\Delta x_i = \int_c F(x, y)\,dx$$

$$\lim_{\text{all } \Delta s_i \to 0} \sum_{i=1}^{n} F(\epsilon_i, \eta_i)\,\Delta y_i = \int_c F(x, y)\,dy$$

are known as *line* integrals. Much of the initial strangeness of these integrals will vanish if it be observed that the ordinary definite integral $\int_a^b f(x)\,dx$ is just a line integral in which the curve c is the x-axis and $F(x, y)$ is a function of x alone. The evaluation of line integrals can be reduced to evaluation of ordinary integrals.

Example 1. $\int_c y(1 + x)\,dy$ where $c: y = 1 - x^2$ from $(-1, 0)$ to $(1, 0)$. Clearly $y = 1 - x^2$, $dy = -2x\,dx$. Thus $\int_c y(1 + x)\,dy = -2\int_{-1}^{1} (1 - x^2)(1 + x)\,x\,dx = -\tfrac{8}{15}$.

Example 2. $\int_c x^2y\,ds$, c is the square whose vertices are $(0, 0)$, $(1,0)$, $(1,1)$, $(0,1)$. $ds = \sqrt{dx^2 + dy^2}$. When $dx = 0$, $ds = dy$. From $(0, 0)$ to $(1, 0)$ $y = 0$, $dy = 0$. Similar arguments for the other sides give $\int_c x^2y\,ds = \int_0^1 0.x^2\,dx + \int_0^1 y\,dy + \int_1^0 x^2\,dx + \int_1^0 0.y\,dy = \tfrac{1}{2} - \tfrac{1}{3} = \tfrac{1}{6}$.

Let $f(z)$ be any function of z, analytic or not, and c any curve as above. The complex integral is calculated as $\int_c f(z)\,dz = \int_c (u\,dx - v\,dy) + i\int_c (v\,dx + u\,dy)$ where $f(z) = u(x, y) + iv(x, y)$. Properties of line integrals are the same as those for ordinary integrals. That is, $\int_c [f(z) \pm g(z)]\,dz = \int_c f(z)\,dz \pm \int_c g(z)\,dz$; $\int_c kf(z)\,dz = k\int_c f(z)\,dz$, etc.

Example. $\int_c (x^2 + iy)\,dz$ along $c: y = x$, 0 to $1 + i$. This becomes $\int_c (x^2 + iy)\,dz = \int_c (x^2\,dx - y\,dy) + i\int_c (y\,dx + x^2\,dy) = \int_0^1 x^2\,dx - \int_0^1 y\,dy + i\int_0^1 x\,dx + i\int_0^1 x^2\,dx = -\tfrac{1}{6} + 5i/6$.

Conformal Mapping. Every function of a complex variable $w = f(z) = u(x, y) + iv(x, y)$ transforms the x, y plane into the u, v plane in some manner. A *conformal* transformation is one in which angles between curves are preserved in *magnitude* and *sense.* Every analytic function, except at those points where $f'(z) = 0$, is a conformal transformation.

Example. $w = z^2$. $u + iv = (x^2 - y^2) + 2ixy$ or $u = x^2 - y^2$, $v = 2xy$. These are the transformation equations between the (x, y) and (u, v) planes. Lines parallel to the x-axis, $y = c_1$ map into curves in the u, v plane with parametric equations $u = x^2 - c_1^2$, $v = 2c_1x$. Eliminating x, $u = (v^2/4c_1^2) - c_1^2$, which represents a family of parabolas with the origin of the w plane as focus, the line $v = 0$ as axis and opening to the right. Similar arguments apply to $x = c_2$.

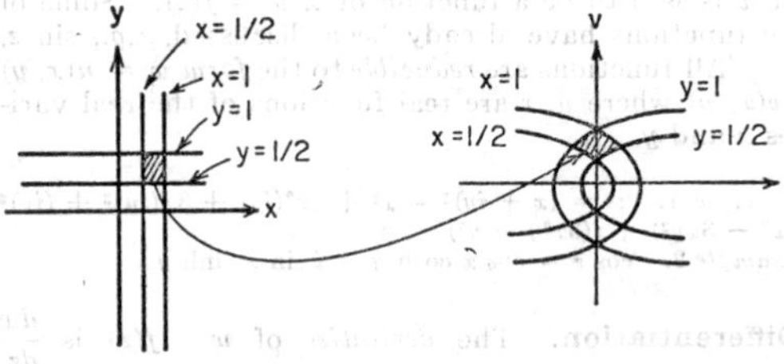

FIG. 2-49. Transformation.

The principles of complex variables are useful in the solution of a variety of applied problems. See the References for the details.

DIFFERENTIAL EQUATIONS

REFERENCES: Mickley, Sherwood, and Reed, "Applied Mathematics in Chemical Engineering," McGraw-Hill, New York, 1957. Marshall and Pigford, "The Application of Differential Equations to Chemical Engineering Problems," University of Delaware, Newark, Del., 1947. Wylie, "Advanced Engineering Mathematics," 3d ed., McGraw-Hill, New York, 1961. Kármán, and Biot, "Mathematical Methods in Engineering," McGraw-Hill, New York, 1940. Pipese, "Applied Mathematics for Engineering and Physicists," 2d ed., McGraw-Hill, New York, 1958. Ince, "Ordinary Differential Equations," Longmans, New York, 1927. Kamke, "Differentialgleichungen, Lesungsmethoden und Losungen," vols. 1 and 2, Leipzig, 1942. Miller, "Partial Differential Equations," Wiley, New York, 1941. Sneddon, "Fourier Transforms," McGraw-Hill, New York, 1951. Sneddon, "Partial Differential Equations," McGraw-Hill, New York, 1960. McLachlan, "Bessel Functions for Engineers," 2d ed., Oxford, New York, 1955. Bateman, "Partial Differential Equations of Mathematical Physics," Cambridge, New York, 1932. Courant and Hilbert, "Methods of Mathematical Physics," 2 vols., Interscience, New York, 1953. Moon and Spencer, "Field Theory for Engineers," Van Nostrand, Princeton, N.J., 1960. Cunningham, "Introduction to Nonlinear Differential Equations," McGraw-Hill, New York, 1960. Struble, "Nonlinear Differential Equations," McGraw-Hill, New York, 1962.

The natural laws in any scientific or technological field are not regarded as precise and definitive until they have been expressed in mathematical form. Such a form, usually an equation, is a relation between the quantity of interest, say product yield, and independent variables such as time and temperature upon which yield depends. When it happens that this equation involves, besides the function itself, one or more of its derivatives it is called a *differential equation.*

Example 1. The homogeneous bimolecular reaction $A + B \xrightarrow{k} C$ is characterized by the differential equation $dx/dt = k(a - x)(b - x)$ where a = initial concentration of A, b = initial concentration of B, and $x = x(t)$ = concentration of C as a function of time t.

Example 2. The differential equation of heat conduction in a moving fluid with velocity components v_x, v_y is

$$\frac{\partial u}{\partial t} + v_x\frac{\partial u}{\partial x} + v_y\frac{\partial u}{\partial y} = \frac{K}{\rho c_p}\left(\frac{\partial^2 u}{\partial x^2} + \frac{\partial^2 u}{\partial y^2}\right)$$

where $u = (x, y, t)$ = temperature, K = thermal conductivity, ρ = density, and c_p = specific heat at constant pressure.

ORDINARY DIFFERENTIAL EQUATIONS

When the function involved in the equation depends upon only one variable, its derivatives are ordinary derivatives and the differential equation is called an *ordinary differential equation*. When the function depends upon several independent variables then the equation is called a *partial differential equation*. The theories of ordinary and partial differential equations are quite different. In almost every respect the latter is more difficult.

Whichever the type, a differential equation is said to be of *n*th *order* if it involves derivatives of order n but no higher. The equation in Example 1 is of first order and in Example 2 of second order. The *degree* of a differential equation is the power to which the derivative of the highest order is raised after the equation has been cleared of fractions and radicals in the dependent variable and its derivatives.

A relation between the variables, involving no derivatives, is called a *solution* of the differential equation if this relation, when substituted in the equation, satisfies the equation. A solution of an ordinary differential equation which includes the maximum possible number of arbitrary constants is called the *general solution*. The maximum number of arbitrary constants is exactly equal to the order of the differential equation. If any set of specific values of the constants is chosen the result is still a solution called a *particular solution*.

Example. The general solution of $(d^2x/dt^2) + k^2x = 0$ is $x = A \cos kt + B \sin kt$ where A, B are arbitrary constants. A particular solution is $x = \frac{1}{2} \cos kt + 3 \sin kt$.

In the case of some equations still other solutions exist called *singular solutions*. A *singular* solution is any solution of the differential equation which is not included in the general solution.

Example. $y = x(dy/dx) - \frac{1}{4}(dy/dx)^2$ has the general solution $y = cx - \frac{1}{4}c^2$ where c is an arbitrary constant; $y = x^2$ is a singular solution, as is easily verified.

Ordinary Differential Equations of the First Order

Equations with Separable Variables. Every differential equation of the first order and of the first degree can be written in the form $M(x, y)\,dx + N(x, y)\,dy = 0$. If the equation can be transformed so that M does not involve y and N does not involve x then the variables are said to be *separated*. The solution can then be obtained by *quadrature*, which means that $y = \int f(x)\,dx + c$, which may or may not be expressible in simpler form.

Example. Two liquids A and B are boiling together in a vessel. Experimentally it is found that the ratio of the rates at which A and B are evaporating at any time is proportional to the ratio of the amount of A (say x) to the amount of B (say y) still in the liquid state. This physical law is expressible as $(dy/dt)/(dx/dt) = ky/x$ or $dy/dx = ky/x$, where k is a proportionality constant. This equation may be written $dy/y = k(dx/x)$ in which the variables are separated. The solution is $\ln y = k \ln x + \ln c$ or $y = cx^k$.

Exact Equations. The equation $M(x, y)dx + N(x, y)\,dy = 0$ is *exact* if and only if $\partial M/\partial y = \partial N/\partial x$. In this case there exists a function $w = f(x, y)$ such that $\partial f/\partial x = M$, $\partial f/\partial y = N$ and $f(x, y) = C$ is the required solution. $f(x, y)$ is found as follows: treat y as though it were constant and evaluate $\int M(x, y)\,dx$. Then treat x as though it were constant and evaluate $\int N(x, y)\,dy$. The sum of all unlike terms in these two integrals (including no repetitions) is $f(x, y)$.

Example. $(2xy - \cos x)dx + (x^2 - 1)\,dy = 0$ is exact for $\partial M/\partial y = 2x$, $\partial N/\partial x = 2x$. $\int M\,dx = \int (2xy - \cos x)dx = x^2y - \sin x$. $\int N\,dy = \int (x^2 - 1)\,dy = x^2y - y$. The solution is $x^2y - \sin x - y = C$, as may easily be verified.

Linear Equations. A differential equation is said to be *linear* when it is of first degree in the dependent variable and its derivatives. The general linear first-order differential equation has the form $dy/dx + P(x)y = Q(x)$. Its general solution is

$$y = e^{-\int P\,dx}\left[\int Qe^{\int P\,dx} + C\right]$$

Example. A tank initially holds 200 gal. of a salt solution in which 100 lb. is dissolved. Six gallons of brine containing 4 lb. of salt run into the tank per minute. If mixing is perfect and the output rate is 4 gal./min., what is the amount A of salt in the tank at time t? The differential equation of A is $\frac{dA}{dt} + \left(\frac{2}{100 + t}\right) A = 24$. Its general solution is $(100 + t)^2A = 8(100 + t)^3 + C$. At $t = 0$, $A = 100$; so the particular solution is $(100 + t)^2A = 8(100 + t)^3 - 7(100)^3$.

Equations Reducible to Linear Equations. The *Bernoulli* equation $(dy/dx) + P(x)y = y^nQ(x)$, $n \neq 0, 1$ is reducible to a linear equation by the substitution $z = y^{-n+1}$. The result of this is $[1/(1 - n)](dz/dx) + zP(x) = Q(x)$, which is readily integrated by techniques of the previous section. If $n = 0$ or 1 the equation is already linear.

Example. $\frac{dy}{dx} = \frac{xy^2 + 2y}{x}$. This is equivalent to $\frac{dy}{dx} - \frac{2}{x}y = y^2$. Set $z = y^{-1}$, $\frac{dy}{dx} = -y^2\frac{dz}{dx}$. The equation becomes $\frac{dz}{dx} + \frac{2}{x}z = -1$.

The "Riccati" equation in the form $(dy/dx) + ay^2 + Q(x)y + R(x) = 0$ can be reduced to the second-order linear differential equation $(d^2u/dx^2) + Q(x)(du/dx) + aR(x)u = 0$ by the substitution $u = e^{a\int y\,dx}$. The equation for u is then solved by techniques for higher-order equations.

Homogeneous Equations. A function $g(x, y)$ is said to be *homogeneous* of *degree m* if for any quantity $r, g(rx, ry) = r^m g(x, y)$, *e.g.*, $x^2y^2\,dx + xy^3\,dx = 0$ is homogeneous of degree 4 since x^2y^2 and xy^3 both have the required property. $\cos (xy)\,dx + x^2y^3\,dy = 0$ is not homogeneous. If the differential equation is homogeneous then either of the substitutions $y = vx$ or $x = vy$ will reduce the equation to the variables separable case. Let $y = vx$. Then $dy/dx = v + x(dv/dx)$; so that $dy/dx = f(x, y)$ becomes $v + x(dv/dx) = F(v)$ or $dv/[F(v) - v] = dx/x$.

Example. $(xe^{y/x} + y)\,dx - x\,dy = 0$ is equivalent to $dy/dx = e^{y/x} + (y/x)$. Let $y = vx$. Then $F(v) = e^v + v$ and $dv/v = dx/x$. The solution is $\ln x + e^{-y/x} = C$.

Equations Reducible to Homogeneous Equations. The differential equation of the form $\frac{dy}{dx} = f\left(\frac{ax + by + c}{dx + ey + g}\right)$ is reducible to a homogeneous equation by the substitution $u = ax + by + c$, $v = dx + ey + g$ for $ae - bd \neq 0$ and by $z = ax + by$, $w = dx + ey$ if $ae - bd = 0$.

Example. $\frac{dy}{dx} = \left(\frac{6x + 4y - 3}{3x + y - 1}\right)^2$. Since $ae - bd = -6 \neq 0$, set $u = 6x + 4y - 3$, $v = 3x + y - 1$. $du = 6dx + 4dy$, $dv = 3dx + dy$, $dx = \frac{2}{3}dv - \frac{1}{6}du$, $dy = +\frac{1}{2}du - dv$. Therefore, $(u^2 + 3v^2)\,du = (4u^2 + 6v^2)\,dv$, which is homogeneous.

Equations Linear in $f(y)$. $f'(y)(dy/dx) + Pf(y) = Q$, where P, Q are functions of x alone, is linear in $f(y)$.

Example. $e^y(dy/dx) - e^y = x$. Let $v = e^y$, $dv/dx = e^y(dy/dx)$. The equation becomes $(dv/dx) - v = x$, which is a linear equation with solution $v = ce^x - x - 1$ or $y = \ln(ce^x - x - 1)$. The last few pages have emphasized the importance of substitutions in solving differential equations.

Equations of the First Order but Not First Degree. A general differential equation of the first order is a relation $F(x, y, dy/dx) = 0$. If F is not of first degree in dy/dx this equation may be satisfied by several solution curves through a given point.

Equations Solvable for dy/dx. After solving for dy/dx, treat each of the solutions as it occurs under some case studied previously.

Example. $\left(\frac{dy}{dx}\right)^2 - x\frac{dy}{dx} - 2y\frac{dy}{dx} + 2xy = 0$. This is equivalent to $\left(\frac{dy}{dx} - 2y\right)\left(\frac{dy}{dx} - x\right) = 0$ or $\frac{dy}{dx} = x$, $\frac{dy}{dx} = 2y$. These equations have the solution $y = ce^{2x}$ and $y = \frac{x^2}{2} + c$.

Equations Solvable for y. Solution of the general equation for y gives one or more equations of the form $y = f(x, dy/dx)$. To solve this differentiate with respect to x and setting $p = dy/dx$ there results $p = \frac{\partial f}{\partial x} + \frac{\partial f}{\partial p}\frac{dp}{dx}$. The result is a differential equation of the first order and first degree in x and p. A solution may be found in the form $g(x, p, c) = 0$ and p eliminated between g and f to give the solution.

Example. *Clairaut's* equation written $y = xp + h(p)$ is an important case. Differentiating with respect to $x, p = p + [x + h'(p)]\,(dp/dx)$ and this is satisfied only if $x = -h'(p)$ or $dp/dx = 0$. The latter gives $p = c$, which substituted in the equation yields the solution $y = cx + f(c)$. Turning to $h'(p) = -x$ substitution in the original equation gives a parametric solution $y = -ph'(p) + h(p)$, $x = -h'(p)$. For example, $y = xp + p^2$ yields $(x + 2p)p = 0$ with solutions $y = cx + c^2$ and $y = -\frac{x^2}{4} + c$. Notice that the latter solution is singular.

Equations Solvable for x. The process for such equations is analogous to the preceding discussion except that there results $x = f(y, p)$ and $\frac{dx}{dy} = \frac{1}{p} = \frac{\partial f}{\partial y} + \frac{\partial f}{\partial p}\frac{dp}{dy}$.

Ordinary Differential Equations of Higher Order

The higher-order differential equations, especially those of order 2 are of great importance because of physical situations describable by them.

The Equation $y^{(n)} = f(x)$. Such a differential equation can be solved by n integrations. The solution will contain n arbitrary constants.

Second-order Equations. Dependent Variable Missing. Such an equation is of the form $F\left(x, \frac{dy}{dx}, \frac{d^2y}{dx^2}\right) = 0$. It can be reduced to a first-order equation by substituting $p = dy/dx$ and $dp/dx = d^2y/dx^2$.

Example. A body of weight w lb. falls from rest in a medium offering resistance proportional to the square of the velocity. If the limiting velocity (when acceleration = 0) is V and y acts positive downward the differential equation of motion is $\frac{d^2y}{dt^2} = g - \frac{g}{w}\lambda\left(\frac{dy}{dt}\right)^2$ by Newton's laws. If $p = dy/dt$ the equation becomes $\frac{dp}{dt} = g\left(1 - \frac{\lambda}{w}p^2\right)$. This equation is of the separable-variables type. Two integrations and the use of the limiting velocity give the solution $y = \frac{V^2}{g}\ln\cosh\frac{gt}{V}$.

Independent Variable Missing. Such an equation is of the form $F\left(y, \frac{dy}{dx}, \frac{d^2y}{dx^2}\right) = 0$. Set $\frac{dy}{dx} = p$, $\frac{d^2y}{dx^2} = p\frac{dp}{dy}$. The result is a first-order equation in p, $F\left(y, p, p\frac{dp}{dy}\right) = 0$.

Example 1. The capillary curve for one vertical plate is given by $\frac{d^2y}{dx^2} = \frac{4y}{c^2}\left[1 + \left(\frac{dy}{dx}\right)^2\right]^{3/2}$. Its solution by this technique is $x + \sqrt{c^2 - y^2} - \sqrt{c^2 - h_0^2} = \frac{c}{2}\left(\cosh^{-1}\frac{c}{y} - \cosh^{-1}\frac{c}{h_0}\right)$ where c, h_0 are physical constants.

Example 2. $yy'' + 2(y')^2 = 0$. $yp(dp/dy) + 2p^2 = 0$ or $y(dp/dy) + 2p = 0$ and $p = 0$. The first when integrated twice gives $y^3 = c_1x + c_2$. This solution clearly includes the second $y = x + c$ as a special case.

Linear Differential Equations with Constant Coefficients and Right-hand Member Zero (Homogeneous)

The solution of $y'' + ay' + by = 0$ depends upon the nature of the roots of the characteristic equation $m^2 + am + b = 0$ obtained by substituting the trial solution $y = e^{mx}$ in the equation.

Distinct Real Roots. If the roots of the characteristic equation are distinct real roots r_1 and r_2, say, the solution is $y = Ae^{r_1x} + Be^{r_2x}$ where A and B are arbitrary constants.

Example. $y'' + 4y' + 3 = 0$. The characteristic equation is $m^2 + 4m + 3 = 0$. The roots are -3 and -1, and the general solution is $y = Ae^{-3x} + Be^{-x}$.

Multiple Real Roots. If $r_1 = r_2$ the solution of the differential equation is $y = e^{r_1x}(A + Bx)$.

Example. $y'' + 4y + 4 = 0$. The characteristic equation is $m^2 + 4m + 4 = 0$ with roots -2 and -2. The solution is $y = e^{-2x}(A + Bx)$.

Roots Complex. If the characteristic roots are $p \pm iq$ then the solution is $y = e^{px}(A\cos qx + B\sin qx)$.

Example. The differential equation $My'' + Ay' + ky = 0$ represents the vibration of a linear system of mass M, spring constant k, and damping constant A. If $A < 2\sqrt{kM}$ the roots of the characteristic equation $Mm^2 + Am + k = 0$ are complex $-\frac{A}{2M} \pm i\sqrt{\frac{k}{M} - \left(\frac{A}{2M}\right)^2}$ and the solution is $y = e^{-\frac{At}{2M}}$ $\left\{c_1\cos\left(\sqrt{\frac{k}{M} - \left(\frac{A}{2M}\right)^2}\right)t + c_2\sin\left(\sqrt{\frac{k}{M} - \left(\frac{A}{2M}\right)^2}\right)t\right\}$. This solution is oscillatory representing *under critical damping.*

All these results generalize to homogeneous linear differential equations with constant coefficients of order higher than 2. These equations (especially of order 2) have been much used because of the ease of solution. Oscillations, electric circuits, diffusion processes, and heat-flow problems are a few examples where such equations are useful.

Linear Non-homogeneous Differential Equations

Linear Differential Equations Right-hand Member $f(x) \neq 0$. Again the specific remarks for $y'' + ay' + by = f(x)$ apply to differential equations of similar type but higher order. We shall discuss two general methods.

Method of Undetermined Coefficients. Use of this method is limited to equations exhibiting both constant coefficients and particular forms of the function $f(x)$.

In most cases $f(x)$ will be a sum or product of functions of the type constant, x^n (n a positive integer), e^{mx}, $\cos kx$, $\sin kx$. When this is the case the solution of the equation is $y = H(x) + P(x)$ where $H(x)$ is a solution of the homogeneous equations found by the method of the preceding section and $P(x)$ is a *particular integral* found by using the table below subject to the following: (1) When $f(x)$ consists of the sum of several terms, the appropriate form of $P(x)$ is the sum of the particular integrals corresponding to these terms individually. (2) When a term in any of the trial integrals listed is already a part of the homogeneous solution the indicated form of the particular integral is multiplied by x.

Form of Particular Integral

If $f(x)$ Is	then $P(x)$ Is
a (constant)	A (constant)
ax^n	$A_nx^n + A_{n-1}x^{n-1} + \cdots + A_1x + A_0$
ae^{rx}	Be^{rx}
$c \cos kx$, $d \sin kx$	$A \cos kx + B \sin kx$
$gx^ne^{rx} \cos kx$, $hx^ne^{rx} \sin kx$	$(A_nx^n + \cdots + A_0)e^{rx} \cos kx + (B_nx^n + \cdots + B_0)e^{rx} \sin kx$

Since the form of the particular integral is known, the constants may be evaluated by substitution in the differential equation.

Example. $y'' + 2y' + y = 3e^{2x} - \cos x + x^3$. The characteristic equation is $(m + 1)^2 = 0$ so that the homogeneous solution is $y = (c_1 + c_2x)e^{-x}$. To find a particular solution we use the trial solution from the table, $y = a_1e^{2x} + a_2 \cos x + a_3 \sin x + a_4x^3 + a_5x^2 + a_6x + a_7$. Substituting this in the differential equation, collecting and equating like terms, there results $a_1 = \frac{1}{3}$, $a_2 = 0$, $a_3 = -\frac{1}{2}$, $a_4 = 1$, $a_5 = -6$, $a_6 = 18$, and $a_7 = -24$. The solution is $y = (c_1 + c_2x)e^{-x} + \frac{1}{3}e^{2x} - \frac{1}{2} \sin x + x^3 - 6x^2 + 18x - 24$.

Method of Variation of Parameters. This method is applicable to any linear equation. The technique is developed for a second-order equation but immediately extends to higher order. Let the equation be $y'' + a(x)y' + b(x)y = R(x)$ and let the solution of the homogeneous equation, found by some method, be $y = c_1f_1(x) + c_2f_2(x)$. It is now assumed that a particular integral of the differential equation is of the form $P(x) = uf_1 + vf_2$ where u, v are functions of x to be determined by two equations. One equation results from the requirement that $uf_1 + vf_2$ satisfies the differential equation and the other is a degree of freedom open to the analyst. The best choice proves to be

$$u'f_1 + v'f_2 = 0 \quad \text{and} \quad u'f_1' + v'f_2' = R(x)$$

Then
$$u' = \frac{du}{dx} = -\frac{f_2}{f_1f_2' - f_2f_1'}R(x)$$
$$v' = \frac{dv}{dx} = \frac{f_1}{f_1f_2' - f_2f_1'}R(x)$$

and since f_1, f_2, and R are known u, v may be found by direct integration.

Example. $(1 - x^2)\dfrac{d^2y}{dx^2} - \dfrac{1}{x}\dfrac{dy}{dx} = x$. The homogeneous equation $(1 - x^2)\dfrac{d^2y}{dx^2} - \dfrac{1}{x}\dfrac{dy}{dx} = 0$ reduces to $\dfrac{dp}{p} = \dfrac{dx}{x(1 - x^2)}$ when we set $dy/dx = p$. Upon integrating twice $y = c_1\sqrt{x^2 - 1} + c_2$ is the homogeneous solution. Now assume the particular solution has the form $y = u\sqrt{x^2 - 1} + v$. The equations for u and v become

$$u' = \frac{du}{dx} = 1$$
$$v' = \frac{dv}{dx} = -\frac{1}{\sqrt{x^2 - 1}}$$

so that $u = x$ and $v = \ln(x + \sqrt{x^2 - 1})$. The complete solution is $y = c_1\sqrt{x^2 - 1} + c_2 + x\sqrt{x^2 - 1} + \ln(x + \sqrt{x^2 - 1})$.

SPECIAL DIFFERENTIAL EQUATIONS

The Euler Equation. The linear equation $x^ny^{(n)} + a_1x^{n-1}y^{(n-1)} + \cdots + a_{n-1}xy' + a_ny = R(x)$ can be reduced to a linear equation with constant coefficients by the change of variable $x = e^t$. To solve the homogeneous equation substitute x^r into it, cancel the powers of x, which are the same for all terms, and solve the resulting polynomial for r. In case of multiple or imaginary roots there results the form $y = x^r(\log x)^r$ and $y = x^\alpha[\cos(\beta \log x) + i \sin(\beta \log x)]$.

Example. Solve $x^2y'' - 2y = 0$. Setting $y = x^r$ $x^r[r(r - 1) - 2] = 0$. The roots of $r^2 - r - 2 = 0$ are $r = 2, -1$. The general solution is $y = Ax^2 + B/x$. The equation $(ax + b)^ny^{(n)} + a_1(ax + b)^{n-1}y^{(n-1)} + \cdots + a_ny = R(x)$ can be reduced to the Euler form by the substitution $ax + b = z$. It may be treated without change of variable, the homogeneous equation having solutions of the form $y = (ax + b)^r$.

Bessel's Equation. The linear equation $x^2\dfrac{d^2y}{dx^2} + (1 - 2\alpha)x\dfrac{dy}{dx} + [\beta^2\gamma^2x^{2\gamma} + (\alpha^2 - p^2\gamma^2)]y = 0$ is the general Bessel equation. By series methods, not to be discussed here, this equation can be shown to have the solution

$$y = Ax^\alpha J_p(\beta x^\gamma) + Bx^\alpha J_{-p}(\beta x^\gamma) \qquad p \text{ not an integer or zero}$$
$$y = Ax^\alpha J_p(\beta x^\gamma) + Bx^\alpha Y_p(\beta x^\gamma) \qquad p \text{ an integer}$$

where
$$J_p(x) = \left(\frac{x}{2}\right)^p \sum_{k=0}^{\infty} \frac{(-1)^k(x/2)^{2k}}{k!\Gamma(p + k + 1)}$$
$$J_{-p}(x) = \left(\frac{x}{2}\right)^{-p} \sum_{k=0}^{\infty} \frac{(-1)^k(x/2)^{2k}}{k!\Gamma(k + 1 - p)} \qquad p \text{ not an integer}$$

and
$$\Gamma(n) = \int_0^\infty x^{n-1}e^{-x}\,dx \qquad n > 0$$
$$= \frac{\Gamma(n + 1)}{n} \qquad 0 > n \neq -1, -2, \ldots$$

is the Gamma function. For p an integer

$$J_p(x) = \left(\frac{x}{2}\right)^p \sum_{k=0}^{\infty} \frac{(-1)^k(x/2)^{2k}}{k!(p + k)!}$$

(Bessel function of the *first kind of order* p)

$$Y_p(x) = \frac{2}{\pi}\left\{\left(\ln\frac{x}{2} + \gamma\right)J_p(x) - \frac{1}{2}\sum_{k=0}^{n-1}\frac{(p - k - 1)!(x/2)^{2k-p}}{k!} + \frac{1}{2}\sum_{k=0}^{\infty}(-1)^{k+1}[\phi(k) + \phi(k + p)]\frac{(x/2)^{2k+p}}{k!(p + k)!}\right\}$$

where $\gamma = 0.5772157 \cdots =$ Euler's constant and $\phi(k) = \sum_{m=1}^{k} 1/m$, $k \geq 1$, $\phi(0) = 0$. The series converge for all x. Much of the importance of Bessel's equation and Bessel functions lies in the fact that the solutions of numerous linear differential equations can be expressed in terms of them.

Example 1. $d^2y/dx^2 + [9x - (63/4x^2)]y = 0$. In general form this is $x^2(d^2y/dx^2) + (9x^3 - 63/4)y = 0$. Thus $\alpha = \frac{1}{2}$, $\gamma = \frac{3}{2}$, $\beta = 2$, $p = \frac{8}{3}$. The solution is (since $p \neq$ integer) $y = Ax^{1/2}J_{8/3}(2x^{3/2}) + Bx^{1/2}J_{-8/3}(2x^{3/2})$. Tables are available for the evaluation of many of these functions.

Example 2. The heat flow through a wedge-shaped fin is characterized by the equation $x^2(d^2y/dx^2) + x(dy/dx) - \alpha xy = 0$ where $y = T - T_{\text{air}}$, α is a combination of physical constants, and x = distance from fin end. Comparing this with the standard equation there results $\alpha = 0$, $p = 0$, $\gamma = \frac{1}{2}$, $\beta^2 = -4\alpha$ or $\beta = 2\alpha i$. The solution is $y = AJ_0(2\alpha i\sqrt{x}) + BY_0(2\alpha i\sqrt{x})$.

Legendre's Equation. The Legendre equation $(1 - x^2)y'' - 2xy' + n(n+1)y = 0 \quad n \geq 0$, has the solution $y = Au_n(x) + Bv_n(x)$ for n not an integer where $u_n(x) = 1 - \frac{n(n+1)}{2!}x^2 + \frac{n(n-2)(n+1)(n+3)}{4!}x^4 - \frac{n(n-2)(n-4)(n+1)(n+3)(n+5)}{6!}x^6 \cdots$ $v_n(x) = x - \frac{(n-1)(n+2)}{3!}x^3 + \frac{(n-1)(n+2)(n+4)}{5!}x^5 \cdots$. If n is an even integer or zero, u_n is a polynomial in x. If n is an odd integer then v_n is a polynomial. The interval of convergence for the series is $-1 < x < 1$. If n is an integer set $P_n(x) = \frac{u_n(x)}{u_n(1)}$ (n even or zero), $P_n = \frac{v_n(x)}{v_n(1)}$ (n odd). The polynomials P_n are the so-called Legendre polynomials, $P_0(x) = 1$, $P_1(x) = x$, $P_2(x) = \frac{1}{2}(3x^2 - 1)$, $P_3(x) = \frac{1}{2}(5x^3 - 3x)$, ... Designate by $Q_n(x)$ the *Legendre functions* of the *second kind* where $Q_n(x) = -v_n(1)\,u_n(x)$ for n odd and $Q_n(x) = u_n(1)\,v_n(x)$ for n even. The solution of Legendre's equation for integer n is $y = AP_n(x) + BQ_n(x)$.

Laguerre's Equation. The Laguerre equation $x(d^2y/dx^2) + (c - x)(dy/dx) - ay = 0$ is satisfied by the *confluent hypergeometric function* of Kummer, $M(a, c; x)$, if c is not an integer $y = AM(a, c; x) + Bx^{1-c}M(1 + a - c, 2 - c; x)$. If $c = 1$, $a = -n$, n a positive integer or zero, one solution is the *Laguerre polynomial* $AL_n(x)$; $L_0 = 1$, $L_1 = 1 - x$, $L_2 = 2 - 4x + x^2$, $L_3 = 6 - 18x + 9x^2 - x^3$, $L_4 = 24 - 96x + 72x^2 - 16x^3 + x^4$, $L_{r+1} = (1 + 2r - x)L_r - r^2L_{r-1}$. If $c = k + 1$, $a = k - n$ where k and n are integers; one solution is the associated Laguerre polynomial $y = A(d^k/dx^k)L_n(x)$ if $k \leq n$.

Example. $xy'' + (1 - x)y' + 3y = 0$. Here $c = 1$, $a = -3$. One solution is $y = AL_3 = A(6 - 18x + 9x^2 - x^3)$.

Hermite's Equation. The *Hermite equation* $y'' - 2xy' + 2ny = 0$ is satisfied by the *Hermite polynomial* of degree n, $y = AH_n(x)$ if n is a positive integer or zero. $H_0(x) = 1$, $H_1(x) = 2x$, $H_2(x) = 4x^2 - 2$, $H_3(x) = 8x^3 - 12x$, $H_4(x) = 16x^4 - 48x^2 + 12$, $H_{r+1}(x) = 2xH_r(x) - 2rH_{r-1}(x)$.

Example. $y'' - 2xy' + 6y = 0$. Here $n = 3$; so $y = AH_3 = A(8x^3 - 12x)$ is a solution.

Tschebyscheff's Equation. The equation $(1 - x^2)y'' - xy' + n^2y = 0$ for n a positive integer or zero is satisfied by the *nth Tschebyscheff polynomial* $y = AT_n(x)$. $T_0(x) = 1$, $T_1(x) = x$, $T_2(x) = 2x^2 - 1$, $T_3(x) = 4x^3 - 3x$, $T_4(x) = 8x^4 - 8x^2 + 1$; $T_{r+1}(x) = 2xT_r(x) - T_{r-1}(x)$.

Example. $(1 - x^2)y'' - xy' + 36y = 0$. Here $n = 6$. A solution is $y = AT_6(x) = 2xT_5(x) - T_4(x) = 2x(2xT_4 - T_3) - T_4 = 32x^6 - 48x^4 + 18x^2 - 1$. More detail on these special equations and others can be found in the literature.

PARTIAL DIFFERENTIAL EQUATIONS

The analysis of situations involving two or more independent variables frequently results in a partial differential equation.

Example 1. The equation $\frac{\partial T}{\partial t} = K\frac{\partial^2 T}{\partial x^2}$ represents the unsteady one-dimensional conduction of heat.

Example 2. The equation for the unsteady transverse motion of a uniform beam clamped at the ends is $\frac{\partial^4 y}{\partial x^4} + \frac{\rho}{EI}\frac{\partial^2 y}{\partial t^2} = 0$.

Example 3. The expansion of a gas behind a piston is characterized by the simultaneous equations $\frac{\partial u}{\partial t} + u\frac{\partial u}{\partial x} + \frac{c^2}{\rho}\frac{\partial \rho}{\partial x} = 0$ and $\frac{\partial \rho}{\partial t} + u\frac{\partial \rho}{\partial x} + \rho\frac{\partial u}{\partial x} = 0$.

Example 4. The heating of a diathermanous solid is characterized by the equation $\alpha\frac{\partial^2\theta}{\partial x^2} + \beta e^{-\gamma x} = \frac{\partial\theta}{\partial t}$.

The partial differential equation $\partial^2 f/\partial x\,\partial y = 0$ can be solved by two integrations yielding the solution $f = g(x) + h(y)$ where $g(x)$ and $h(y)$ are arbitrary differentiable functions. This result is an example of the fact that the general solution of partial differential equations involves arbitrary functions in contrast to the solution of ordinary differential equations which involve only arbitrary constants. A number of methods are available for finding the general solution of a partial differential equation. In most applications of partial differential equations the general solution is of limited use. In such applications the solution of a partial differential equation must satisfy both the equation and certain auxiliary conditions called *initial* and/or *boundary* conditions, which are dictated by the problem. Examples of these include the wall temperature is a fixed constant $T(x_0) = T_0$, there is no diffusion across a non-permeable wall, and the like. In ordinary differential equations these auxiliary conditions allow definite numbers to be assigned to the constants of integration. In partial differential equations the boundary conditions demand that the arbitrary functions resulting from integration assume specific forms. Except for a few cases (some first-order equations, D'Alembert's solution of the wave equation, and others) a procedure which first determines the arbitrary functions and then specializes them to fit the boundary conditions is usually not feasible. A more fruitful attack is to determine directly a set of particular solutions and then combine them so that the boundary conditions are satisfied. The only area in which much analysis has been accomplished is for linear homogeneous partial differential equations. Such equations have the property that, if $f_1, f_2, \ldots, f_n, \ldots$ are individually solutions, then the function $f = \sum_{i=1}^{\infty} f_i$ is also a solution provided the series converges and is differentiable up to the order (termwise) of the equation.

Partial Differential Equations of First Order

Linear. By linear in this case is meant that the partial derivatives appear to the first degree only, while the coefficients may be functions of all the independent variables plus the dependent variable. The general solution of the *linear partial* differential equation $P(x, y, z)(\partial z/\partial x) + Q(x, y, z)(\partial z/\partial y) = R(x, y, z)$ is $F(u, v) = 0$ where F is an arbitrary function arising from a relation $F(c_1, c_2) = 0$ and $u(x, y, z) = c_1$, $v(x, y, z) = c_2$ form a solution of the system $dx/P = dy/Q = dz/R$. If in addition it is desired to have the solution surface pass through a given curve (auxiliary condition), say C, whose parametric equations are $x = x(t)$, $y = y(t)$, $z = z(t)$, where t is a parameter, then the particular solution of $u = c_1$, $v = c_2$ must be such that $u[x(t), y(t), z(t)] = c_1$, $v[x(t), y(t), z(t)] = c_2$. From these two equations eliminate the variable t to obtain a relationship $F(c_1, c_2) = 0$. The solution is then $F(u, v) = 0$.

Example. Find the solution of $y(\partial z/\partial x) + zx(\partial z/\partial y) = 2xy$ passing through the circle $z = 0$, $x^2 + y^2 = 1$. The curve c in parametric form is $x = \cos t$, $y = \sin t$, $z = 0$. The equations $dx/y = dy/zx = dz/2xy$ have the solutions $u(x, y, z) = x^2 - z = c_1$, and $v(x, y, z) = y^2 - (z^2/2) = c_2$. Substituting the parametric equations for c into these results yields $c_1 + c_2 = 1$, upon elimination of t. The desired solution is then $x^2 - z + y^2 - (z^2/2) = 1$.

The general techniques applicable to the "Pfaffian" equation $P\,dx + Q\,dy + R\,dx = 0$ and $dx/P = dy/Q = dz/R$ may be found in the literature. Generalization of this method for non-linear partial differential equations of first order have been worked out. *Cauchy's method* of *characteristics*, *Charpit's* method, and *Jacobi's* method can be found in the literature.

Partial Differential Equations of Second and Higher Order

Many of the applications to scientific problems fall naturally into partial differential equations of second order, although there are important exceptions in elasticity, vibration theory, and elsewhere.

Phenomena of *propagation* such as vibrations are characterized by equations of "hyperbolic" type which are essentially different in their properties from other classes such as those which describe equilibrium (*elliptic*) or unsteady diffusion and heat transfer (*parabolic*). Prototypes are as follows:

Elliptic. *Laplace's equation* $\frac{\partial^2 u}{\partial x^2} + \frac{\partial^2 u}{\partial y^2} = 0$ and Poisson's equation $\frac{\partial^2 u}{\partial x^2} + \frac{\partial^2 u}{\partial y^2} = g(x, y)$. These do not contain the variable time explicitly and consequently represent equilibrium configurations. Laplace's equation is satisfied by the gravitational potential function at points in space not occupied by mass as well as by static electric or magnetic potential at points free from electric charges or magnetic poles. Other important functions satisfying Laplace's equation are the velocity potential of the irrotational motion of an incompressible fluid, used in hydrodynamics; the steady temperature at points in a homogeneous solid, and the steady state of diffusion through a homogeneous body. The gravitational potential V at points occupied by mass of density d satisfies Poisson's equation $\frac{\partial^2 V}{\partial x^2} + \frac{\partial^2 V}{\partial y^2} + \frac{\partial^2 V}{\partial z^2} = -4\pi d$.

Parabolic. The heat equation $\frac{\partial T}{\partial t} = \frac{\partial^2 T}{\partial x^2} + \frac{\partial^2 T}{\partial y^2}$ represents non-equilibrium or unsteady states of heat conduction and diffusion.

Hyperbolic. The wave equation $\frac{\partial^2 u}{\partial t^2} = c^2 \left(\frac{\partial^2 u}{\partial x^2} + \frac{\partial^2 u}{\partial y^2}\right)$ represents wave propagation of many varied types.

The solution of problems involving partial differential equations often revolves about an attempt to reduce the partial differential equation to one or more ordinary differential equations. The solutions of the ordinary differential equations are then combined (if possible) such that the boundary conditions as well as the original partial differential equation are simultaneously satisfied. Three of these techniques are illustrated.

The "Substitution" Method. The equation $\frac{\partial \theta}{\partial x} = \frac{A}{y}\frac{\partial^2 \theta}{\partial y^2}$ with the boundary conditions $\theta = 0$ at $x = 0$, $y > 0$; $\theta = 0$ at $y = \infty$, $x > 0$; $\theta = 1$ at $y = 0$, $x > 0$ represents the non-dimensional temperature θ of a fluid moving past an infinitely wide flat plate immersed in the fluid. Turbulent transfer is neglected as is molecular transport except in the y direction. It is now assumed that the equation and the boundary conditions can be satisfied by a solution of the form $\theta = f(y/x^n) = f(u)$ where $\theta = 0$ at $u = \infty$ and $\theta = 0$ at $u = 0$. The purpose here is to replace the independent variables x and y by the single variable u where it is hoped that a value of n exists which will allow x and y to be completely eliminated in the equation. In this case since $u = y/x^n$ there results after some calculation $\frac{\partial \theta}{\partial x} = -\frac{nu}{x}\frac{d\theta}{du}$, $\frac{\partial^2 \theta}{\partial y^2} = \frac{1}{x^{2n}}\frac{d^2\theta}{du^2}$ and when these are substituted in the equation $-\frac{1}{x} nu \frac{d\theta}{du} = \frac{1}{x^{3n}}\frac{A}{u}\frac{d^2\theta}{du^2}$. If this is to be a function of u only choose $n = \frac{1}{3}$. There results $\frac{d^2\theta}{du^2} + \frac{u^2}{3A}\frac{d\theta}{du} = 0$. Two integrations and use of the boundary conditions for this ordinary differential equation give the solution

$$\theta = \frac{\int_u^\infty \exp\left[-u^3/9A\right] du}{\int_0^\infty \exp\left[-u^3/9A\right] du}$$

Separation of Variables. This method is a powerful well-utilized method which is applicable in certain circumstances. It consists of assuming that the solution for a partial differential equation (illustrated for order 2) has the form $U = f(x)g(y)$. If it is then possible to obtain an ordinary differential equation on one side of the equation depending only on x and on the other side only on y the partial differential equation is said to be *separable* in the variables x, y. If this is the case one side of the equation is a function of x alone, the other of y alone. The two can be equal only if each is a constant, say λ. Thus the problem has again been reduced to the solution of ordinary differential equations.

Example. Laplace's equation $\frac{\partial^2 V}{\partial x^2} + \frac{\partial^2 V}{\partial y^2} = 0$ plus the boundary conditions $V(0, y) = 0$, $V(l, y) = 0$, $V(x, \infty) = 0$, $V(x, 0) = f(x)$ represents the *steady-state potential* in a thin plate (in z direction) of infinite extent in the y direction and of width l in the x direction. A potential $f(x)$ is impressed (at $y = 0$) from $x = 0$ to $x = l$ and the sides are grounded. To obtain a solution of this boundary-value problem assume $V(x, y) = f(x)g(y)$. Substitution in the differential equation yields $f''(x)g(y) + f(x)g''(y) = 0$, or $g''(y)/g(y) = -f''(x)/f(x) = \lambda^2$ (say). This system becomes $g''(y) - \lambda^2 g(y) = 0$ and $f''(x) + \lambda^2 f(x) = 0$. The solutions of these ordinary differential equations are, respectively, $g(y) = Ae^{\lambda y} + Be^{-\lambda y}$, $f(x) = C \sin \lambda x + D \cos \lambda x$. Then $f(x)g(y) = (Ae^{\lambda y} + Be^{-\lambda y})(C \sin \lambda x + D \cos \lambda x)$. Now $V(0, y) = 0$ so that $f(0)g(y) = (Ae^{\lambda y} + Be^{-\lambda y})\, D = 0$ for all y. Hence $D = 0$. The solution then has the form $\sin \lambda x(Ae^{\lambda y} + Be^{-\lambda y})$ where the multiplicative constant C has been eliminated. Since $V(l, y) = 0$, $\sin \lambda l(Ae^{\lambda y} + Be^{-\lambda y}) = 0$. Clearly the bracketed function of y is not zero, for the solution would then be the identically zero solution. Hence $\sin \lambda l = 0$ or $\lambda_n = n\pi/l$, $n = 1, 2, \ldots$ where λ_n = nth *eigenvalue*.

The solution now has the form $\sin \frac{n\pi x}{l}(Ae^{n\pi y/l} + Be^{-n\pi y/l})$. Since $V(x, \infty) = 0$, A must be taken to be zero since e^y becomes arbitrarily large as $y \to \infty$. The solution then reads B_n sin

$\frac{n\pi x}{l}\, e^{-n\pi y/l}$, where B_n is the multiplicative constant. The differential equation is linear and homogeneous so that $\sum_{n=1}^{\infty} B_n e^{-n\pi y/l}$ $\sin \frac{n\pi x}{l}$ is also a solution. Satisfaction of the last boundary condition is ensured by taking $B_n = \frac{2}{l}\int_0^l f(x) \sin \frac{n\pi x}{l}\, dx =$ Fourier sine coefficients of $f(x)$. Further, convergence and differentiability of this series are established quite easily. Thus the solution is

$$V(x, y) = \sum_{n=1}^{\infty} B_n e^{-n\pi y/l} \sin \frac{n\pi x}{l}$$

The Integral-transform Method. A number of integral transforms are used in the solution of differential equations. Only one, the *Laplace transform,* will be discussed here (for others, see p. 2-50). The one-sided Laplace transform indicated by $L[f(t)]$ is defined by the equation $L[f(t)] = \int_0^\infty f(t)e^{-st}\, dt$. It has numerous important properties. The ones of interest here are $L[f'(t)] = sL[f(t)] - f(0)$; $L[f''(t)] = s^2L[f(t)] - sf(0) - f'(0)$; $L[f^{(n)}(t)] = s^nL[f(t)] - s^{n-1}f(0) - s^{n-2}f'(0) - \cdots - f^{(n-1)}(0)$ for ordinary derivatives. For partial derivatives an indication of which variable is being transformed avoids confusion. Thus, if $y = y(x, t)$, $L_t\left[\frac{\partial y}{\partial t}\right] = sL[y(x, t)] - y(x, 0)$ whereas $L_t\left[\frac{\partial y}{\partial x}\right] = \frac{dL[y(x, t)]}{\partial x}$ since $L[y(x, t)]$ is "really" only a function of x. Otherwise the results are similar. These facts coupled with the *linearity* of the transform, *i.e.,* $L[af(t) + bg(t)] = aL[f(t)] + bL[g(t)]$, make it a useful device in solving some linear differential equations. Its use reduces the solution of ordinary differential equations to the solution of algebraic equations for $L[y]$. The solution of partial differential equations is reduced to the solution of ordinary differential equations. In both situations the inverse transform must be obtained either from tables, of which there are several, or by use of complex inversion methods.

Example 1. $y'' - 3y' + 2y = 0$. Initial conditions at $t = 0$, $y = 0$, $y' = 1$. $L[y''] = s^2L[y] - 1$. $L[y'] = sL[y]$. Hence $L[y'' - 3y' + 2y] = s^2L[y] - 1 - 3sL[y] + 2L[y] = 0$. Solving for $L[y]$ there results $L[y] = \frac{1}{(s-2)(s-1)} = \frac{1}{s-2} - \frac{1}{s-1}$. From the tables the function y having this transform is $y = e^{2t} - e^t$.

Example 2. The equation $\frac{\partial c}{\partial t} = D\frac{\partial^2 c}{\partial x^2}$ represents the diffusion in a semi-infinite medium, $x \geq 0$. Under the boundary conditions $c(0, t) = c_0$, $c(x, 0) = 0$ find a solution of the diffusion equation. Taking the Laplace transform of both sides with respect to t,

$$\int_0^\infty e^{-st}\frac{\partial^2 c}{\partial x^2}\, dt = \frac{1}{D}\int_0^\infty e^{-st}\frac{\partial c}{\partial t}\, dt$$

or

$$\frac{d^2F}{dx^2} = \frac{1}{D}sF - c(x, 0) = \frac{sF}{D}$$

where $F(x, s) = L_t[c(x, t)]$. Hence

$$\frac{d^2F}{dx^2} - \frac{s}{D}F = 0$$

The first boundary condition transforms into $F(0, s) = c_0/s$. Finally the solution of the ordinary differential equation for F subject to $F(0, s) = c_0/s$ and F remains finite as $x \to \infty$ is $F(x, s) = (c_0/s)e^{-\sqrt{\frac{s}{D}}x}$. Reference to a table shows that the function having this as its Laplace transform is

$$c(x, t) = c_0\left[1 - \frac{2}{\sqrt{\pi}}\int_0^{\frac{x}{2\sqrt{Dt}}} e^{-u^2}\, du\right]$$

DIFFERENCE EQUATIONS

REFERENCES: Batchelder, "An Introduction to Linear Difference Equations," Harvard University Press, Cambridge, Mass., 1927. Kármán and Biot, "Mathematical Methods in Engineering," Chap. 11, McGraw-Hill, New York, 1940. Marshall and Pigford, "The Application of Differential Equations to Chemical Engineering Problems," University of Delaware, Newark, Del., 1947. Mickley, Sherwood, and Reed, "Applied Mathematics in Chemical Engineering," McGraw-Hill, New York, 1957. Tiller and Tour, Stagewise Operations—Applications of the Calculus of Finite Differences to Chemical Engineering, *Trans. Am. Inst. Chem. Engrs.*, **40,** 317–332 (June, 1944).

Certain situations are such that the independent variable does not vary continuously but has meaning only for discrete values. Typical illustrations occur in the stagewise processes found in chemical engineering such as distillation, staged extraction systems, and absorption columns. In each of these the operation is characterized by a finite between-stage change of the dependent variable where the independent variable is the integral number of the stage. The importance of difference equations is twofold: (1) to analyze problems of the type described above and (2) to obtain approximate solutions of problems which lead, in their formulation, to differential equations. In this section only problems of analysis are considered; the application to approximate solutions is considered under Numerical Methods.

ELEMENTS OF THE CALCULUS OF FINITE DIFFERENCES

Let $y = f(x)$ be defined for discrete equidistant values of x, which will be denoted by x_n The corresponding value of y will be written $y_n = f(x_n)$. The *first forward difference* of $f(x)$ denoted by $\Delta f(x) = f(x + h) - f(x)$ where $h = x_n - x_{n-1} =$ interval length.

Example. Let $f(x) = x^2$. Then $\Delta f(x) = (x + h)^2 - x^2 = 2hx + h^2$.

The *second forward difference* is obtained by taking the difference of the first; thus $\Delta\Delta f(x) = \Delta^2 f(x) = \Delta f(x + h) - \Delta f(x) = f(x + 2h) - 2f(x + h) + f(x)$.

Example. $f(x) = x^2$, $\Delta^2 f(x) = \Delta[\Delta f(x)] = \Delta 2hx + \Delta h^2 = 2h(x + h) - 2h(x) + h^2 - h^2 = 2h^2$.

Similarly the *nth forward difference* is defined by the relation $\Delta^n f(x) = \Delta[\Delta^{n-1}f(x)]$. Other difference relations are also quite useful. Some of these are $\nabla f(x) = f(x) - f(x - h)$, which is called the *backward difference,* and $\delta f(x) = f[x + (h/2)] - f[x - (h/2)]$, called the *central difference.* Some properties of the *operator* Δ are quite important. If C is any constant $\Delta C = 0$; if $f(x)$ is any function of *period h,* $\Delta f(x) = 0$ (in fact, periodic functions of period h play the same role here as constants do in the differential calculus); $\Delta[f(x) + g(x)] = \Delta f(x)$

$+ \Delta g(x)$; $\Delta^m[\Delta^n f(x)] = \Delta^{m+n} f(x)$; $\Delta f(x)g(x) = f(x)\,\Delta g(x) + g(x+h)\,\Delta f(x)$; $\Delta\left[\frac{f(x)}{g(x)}\right] = \frac{g(x)\,\Delta f(x) - f(x)\,\Delta g(x)}{g(x)g(x+h)}$.

Example. $\Delta(x \sin x) = x\Delta \sin x + \sin (x+h)\,\Delta x = 2 \sin (h/2) \cos [x + (h/2)] + h \sin (x+h)$.

DIFFERENCE EQUATIONS

A *difference equation* is a relation between the differences and the independent variable, $\phi(\Delta^n y, \Delta^{n-1} y, \ldots, \Delta y, y, x) = 0$, where ϕ is some given function. The general case in which the interval between the successive points is any real number h, instead of 1, can be reduced to that with interval size 1 by the substitution $x = hx'$. Hence all further difference-equation work will assume the interval size between successive points is 1.

Example 1. $f(x+1) - (\alpha+1)f(x) + \alpha f(x-1) = 0$. Common notation usually is $y_x = f(x)$. This equation is then written $y_{x+1} - (\alpha+1)\,y_x + \alpha y_{x-1} = 0$.
Example 2. $y_{x+2} + 2y_x y_{x+1} + y_x = x^2$.
Example 3. $y_{x+1} - y_x = 2^x$.

The *order* of the difference equation is the difference between the largest and smallest arguments when written in the form of Example 2. Examples 1 and 2 are both of order 2, while Example 3 is of order 1. A *linear* difference equation involves no products or other non-linear functions of the dependent variable and its differences. Examples 1 and 3 are linear while Example 2 is non-linear.

A *solution* of a difference equation is a relation between the variables which satisfies the equation. If the difference equation is of order n the general solution involves n arbitrary constants. The techniques for solving difference equations resemble techniques used for differential equations.

The Equation $\Delta^n y = a$. The solution of $\Delta^n y = a$, where a is a constant, is a polynomial of degree n plus an arbitrary periodic function of period 1. That is, $y = (ax^n/n!) + c_1x^{n-1} + c_2x^{n-2} + \cdots + c_n + f(x)$, where $f(x+1) = f(x)$.

Example. $\Delta^3 y = 6$. The solution is $y = x^3 + c_1x^2 + c_2x + c_3 + f(x)$; c_1, c_2, c_3 are arbitrary constants and $f(x)$ is an arbitrary periodic function of period 1.

The Equation $y_{x+1} - y_x = \phi(x)$. This equation states that the first difference of the unknown function is equal to the given function $\phi(x)$. The solution by analogy with solving the differential equation $dy/dx = \phi(x)$ by integration is obtained by "finite integration" or summation. When there are only a *finite* number of data points this is easily accomplished by writing $y_x = \sum_{t=1}^{x} \phi(t)$ where the data points are numbered from 1 to x. This is the only situation considered here.

Examples. If $\phi(x) = 1$, $y_x = x$. If $\phi(x) = x$, $y_x = \frac{x(x-1)}{2}$. If $\phi(x) = a^x$, $a \neq 0$, $y_x = \frac{a^x}{a-1}$. If $\phi(x) = \sin x$, $y_x = -\cos \frac{(x - \frac{1}{2})}{2 \sin \frac{1}{2}}$.

Other examples may be evaluated by using summation, that is, $y_2 = y_1 + \phi(1)$, $y_3 = y_2 + \phi(2) = y_1 + \phi(1) + \phi(2)$, $y_4 = y_3 + \phi(3) = y_1 + \phi(1) + \phi(2) + \phi(3)$, $\ldots$, $y_x = y_1 + \sum_{t=1}^{x} \phi(t)$.

Example. $y_{x+1} - ry_x = 1$, r constant, $x > 0$ and $y_0 = 1$. $y_1 = 1 + r$, $y_2 = 1 + r + r^2, \ldots, y_x = 1 + r + \cdots + r^x = \frac{1 - r^{x+1}}{1-r}$ for $r \neq 1$ and $y_x = 1 + x$ for $r = 1$.

Linear Difference Equations

The linear difference equation of order n has the form $P_n y_{x+n} + P_{n-1}y_{x+n-1} + \cdots + P_1 y_{x+1} + P_0 y_x = Q(x)$ with $P_n \neq 0$ and $P_0 \neq 0$ and P_j; $j = 0, \ldots, n$ are functions of x.

Constant Coefficient and $Q(x) = 0$ (Homogeneous). The solution is obtained by trying a solution of the form $y_x = c\beta^x$. When this *trial solution* is substituted in the difference equation a polynomial of degree n results for β. If the solutions of this polynomial are denoted by $\beta_1, \beta_2, \ldots, \beta_n$ then the following cases result: (1) if all the β_j's are *real* and *unequal*, the solution is $y_x = \sum_{j=1}^{n} c_j\beta_j^x$ where the $c_1, \ldots, c_n$ are arbitrary constants; (2) if the roots are *real* and *repeated*, say β_j has multiplicity m, then the partial solution corresponding to β_j is $\beta_j^x(c_1 + c_2x + \cdots + c_mx^{m-1})$; (3) if the roots are *complex conjugates*, say, $a + ib = pe^{i\theta}$ and $a - ib = pe^{-i\theta}$, the partial solution corresponding to this pair is $p^x(c_1 \cos \theta x + c_2 \sin \theta x)$; (4) if the roots are *multiple complex conjugates*, say, $a + ib = pe^{i\theta}$ and $a - ib = pe^{-i\theta}$ are m-fold then the partial solution corresponding to these is $p^x[(c_1 + c_2x + \cdots + c_mx^{m-1}) \cos \theta x + (d_1 + d_2x + \cdots + d_mx^{m-1}) \sin \theta x]$.

Example 1. The equation $y_{x+1} - (\alpha+1)y_x + \alpha y_{x-1} = 0$, $y_0 = c_0$ and $y_{m+1} = \frac{x_{m+1}}{k}$ represents the steady-state composition of transferable material in the raffinate stream of a staged countercurrent liquid-liquid extraction system. Clearly y is a function of the stage number x. α is a combination of system constants. Using the trial solution $y_x = c\beta^x$ there results $\beta^2 - (\alpha+1)\beta + \alpha = 0$; so that $\beta_1 = 1$, $\beta_2 = \alpha$. The general solution is $y_x = c_1 + c_2\alpha^x$. Using the side conditions $c_1 = c_0 - c_2$, $c_2 = \frac{y_{m+1} - c_0}{\alpha^{m+1} + 1}$. The desired solution is

$$\frac{y_x - c_0}{y_{m+1} - c_0} = \frac{\alpha^x - 1}{\alpha^{m+1} - 1}$$

Example 2. $y_{x+3} - 3y_{x+2} + 4y_x = 0$. Setting $y_x = c\beta^x$ there results $\beta^3 - 3\beta^2 + 4 = 0$ or $\beta_1 = -1$, $\beta_2 = 2$, $\beta_3 = 2$. The general solution is $y_x = c_1(-1)^x + 2^x(c_2 + c_3x)$.

Example 3. $y_{x+1} - 2y_x + 2y_{x-1} = 0$. $\beta_1 = 1 + i$, $\beta_2 = 1 - i$. $p = \sqrt{1+1} = \sqrt{2}$, $\theta = \pi/4$. The solution is $y_x = 2^{x/2}[c_1 \cos (x\pi/4) + c_2 \sin (x\pi/4)]$.

Constant Coefficients and $Q(x) \neq 0$ (Non-homogeneous). In this case the general solution is found by first obtaining the homogeneous solution say y_x^H and adding to it any particular solution with $Q(x) \neq 0$ say y_x^P. There are several means of obtaining the particular solution.

The Method of Undetermined Coefficients. If $Q(x)$ is a product or linear combination of products of the functions e^{bx}, a^x, x^p (p a positive integer or zero) cox cx, and sin cx this method may be used. The "families" $[a^x]$, $[e^{bx}]$, [sin cx, cos cx] and $[x^p, x^{p-1}, \ldots, x, 1]$ are defined for each of the above functions in the following way: The "family" of a term f_x is the set of all functions of which f_x and all operations of the form a^{x+y}, cos $c(x+y)$, sin $c(x+y)$, $(x+y)^p$ on f_x and their linear combinations result in. The technique involves the following steps: (1) Solve the homogeneous system. (2) Construct the "family" of each term. (3) If the "family" has no representative in the homogeneous solution, assume y_x^P is a linear combination of the families of each term and determine the constants so that the equation is satisfied. (4) If a "family" has a representative in the homogeneous solution multiply each member of the family by the smallest integral power of x for which all such representatives are removed and revert to step (3).

Example 1. $y_{x+1} - 3y_x + 2y_{x-1} = 1 + a^x \quad a \neq 0$. The homogeneous solution is $y_x{}^H = c_1 + c_2 2^x$. The "family" of 1 is 1 and of a^x is a^x. However, 1 is a solution of the homogeneous system. Therefore, try $y_x{}^P = Ax + Ba^x$. Substituting in the equation there results $y_x = c_1 + c_2 2^x - x + \dfrac{a}{(a-1)(a-2)} a^x$, $a \neq 1$, $a \neq 2$. If $a = 1$, $y_x = c_1 + c_2 2^x - x$. If $a = 2$, $y_x = c_1 + c_2 2^x - x + x2^x$.

Example 2. The "family" of $x^2 3^x$ is $[x^2 3^x, x3^x, 3^x]$.

The Method of Variation of Parameters. This technique is applicable to general linear difference equations. It is illustrated for the second-order system $y_{x+2} + Ay_{x+1} + By_x = \phi(x)$. Assume the homogeneous solution has been found by some technique and write $y_x{}^H = c_1 u_x + c_2 v_x$. Assume a particular solution $y_x{}^P = D_x u_x + E_x v_x$. E_x and D_x can be found by solving the equations

$$E_{x+1} - E_x = \frac{u_{x+1}\phi(x)}{u_{x+1}v_{x+2} - u_{x+2}v_{x+1}}$$

$$D_{x+1} - D_x = \frac{v_{x+1}\phi(x)}{v_{x+1}u_{x+2} - v_{x+2}u_{x+1}}$$

by summation. The general solution is then $y_x = y_x{}^P + y_x{}^H$.

Example. $y_{x+2} - (2\cos\alpha)y_{x+1} + y_x = \sqrt{x} \quad x \geq 0$. The homogeneous solution is $y_x{}^H = c_1 \cos \alpha x + c_2 \sin \alpha x$. With $u_x = \cos \alpha x$, $v_x = \sin \alpha x$ it is found that $E_{x+1} - E_x = \dfrac{[\cos \alpha(x+1)]\sqrt{x}}{\sin \alpha}$, $D_{x+1} - D_x = \dfrac{-\sqrt{x}\sin \alpha(x+1)}{\sin \alpha}$. Thus for $\sin \alpha \neq 0$, $E_0 = 0$, $D_0 = 0$.

$$D_x = -\sum_{n=0}^{x} \frac{\sqrt{n}\sin n\alpha}{\sin \alpha} \qquad E_x = \sum_{n=0}^{x} \frac{\sqrt{n}\cos n\alpha}{\sin \alpha}$$

The general solution is $y_x = c_1 \cos \alpha x + c_2 \sin \alpha x - \cos \alpha x$

$$\sum_{n=0}^{x} \frac{\sqrt{n}\sin \alpha n}{\sin \alpha} + \sin \alpha x \sum_{n=0}^{x} \frac{\sqrt{n}\cos \alpha n}{\sin \alpha}.$$

Variable Coefficients. The method of variation of parameters applies equally well to the linear difference equation with *variable coefficients.* Techniques are therefore needed to solve the homogeneous system with variable coefficients.

Equation $y_{x+1} - a_x y_x = 0$. Assuming this equation valid for $x \geq 0$ and $y_0 = c$ the solution is $y_x = c \prod_{n=1}^{x} a_{x-1}$.

Example 1. $y_{x+1} + \dfrac{x+2}{x+1} y_x = 0$. The solution is $y_x = c \prod_{n=1}^{x} \left(-\dfrac{n+1}{n}\right) = c(-1)^x \dfrac{2}{1}\cdot\dfrac{3}{2}\cdot\cdots\dfrac{x+1}{x} = (-1)^x c(x+1)$.

Example 2. $y_{x+1} - xy_x = 0$. The solution is $y_x = c(x-1)!$

Reduction of Order. If one homogeneous solution, say u_x, can be found by inspection or otherwise, an equation of *lower* order can be obtained by the substitution $v_x = y_x/u_x$. The resultant equation must be satisfied by v_x = constant or $\Delta v_x = 0$. Thus the equation will be of reduced order if the new variable $U_x = \Delta(y_x/u_x)$ is introduced.

Example. $(x+2)y_{x+2} - (x+3)y_{x+1} + y_x = 0$. By observation $u_x = 1$ is a solution. Set $U_x = \Delta y_x = y_{x+1} - y_x$. There results $(x+2)U_{x+1} - U_x = 0$ which is of degree one lower than the original equation. The complete solution for y_x is finally

$$y_x = c_0 \sum_{n=0}^{x} \frac{1}{n!} + c_1.$$

Factorization. If the difference equation can be factored, then the general solution can be obtained by solving two or more successive equations of lower order. Consider $y_{x+2} + A_x y_{x+1} + B_x y_x = \phi(x)$. If there exists a_x, b_x such that $a_x + b_x = -A_x$ and $a_x b_x = B_x$ then the difference equation may be written $y_{x+2} - (a_x + b_x)y_{x+1} + a_x b_x y_x = \phi(x)$. First solve $U_{x+1} - b_x U_x = \phi(x)$ and then $y_{x+1} - a_x y_x = U_x$.

Example. $y_{x+2} - (2x+1)y_{x+1} + (x^2+x)y_x = 0$. Set $a_x = x$, $b_x = x+1$. Solve $u_{x+1} - (x+1)u_x = 0$ and then $y_{x+1} - xy_x = u_x$.

Substitution. If it is possible to rearrange a difference equation so it takes the form $af_{x+2}y_{x+2} + bf_{x+1}y_{x+1} + cf_x y_x = \phi(x)$ with a, b, c constants then the substitution $u_x = f_x y_x$ reduces the equation to one with constant coefficients.

Example. $(x+2)^2 y_{x+2} - 3(x+1)^2 y_{x+1} + 2x^2 y_x = 0$. Set $u_x = x^2 y_x$. The equation becomes $u_{x+2} - 3u_{x+1} + 2u_x = 0$, which is linear and easily solved by previous methods.

The substitution $u_x = y_x/f_x$ reduces $af_x f_{x+1} y_{x+2} + bf_x f_{x+2} y_{x+1} + cf_{x+1} f_{x+2} y_x = \phi(x)$ to an equation with constant coefficients.

Example. $x(x+1)y_{x+2} + 3x(x+2)y_{x+1} - 4(x+1)(x+2)y_x = x$. Set $u_x = y_x/f_x = y_x/x$. Then $y_x = xu_x$, $y_{x+1} = (x+1)u_{x+1}$ and $y_{x+2} = (x+2)u_{x+2}$. Substitution in the equation yields $x(x+1)(x+2)u_{x+2} + 3x(x+2)(x+1)u_{x+1} - 4x(x+1)(x+2)u_x = x$ or $u_{x+2} + 3u_{x+1} - 4u_x = \dfrac{1}{(x+1)}(x+2)$, which is a linear equation with constant coefficients.

The Riccati Difference Equation

The Riccati equation $y_{x+1}y_x + ay_{x+1} + by_x + c = 0$ is a non-linear difference equation which can be solved by reduction to linear form. Set $y = z + h$. The equation becomes $z_{x+1}z_x + (h+a)z_{x+1} + (h+b)z_x + h^2 + (a+b)h + c = 0$. If h is selected as a root of $h^2 + (a+b)h + c = 0$ and the equation is divided by $z_{x+1}z_x$ there results $\dfrac{(h+b)}{z_{x+1}} + \dfrac{(h+a)}{z_x} + 1 = 0$. This is a linear equation with constant coefficients. The solution is

$$y_x = h + \cfrac{1}{c\left[-\dfrac{a+h}{b+h}\right]^x - \dfrac{1}{(a+h)+(b+h)}}$$

Example. This equation is obtained in distillation problems, among others, where the number of theoretical plates is required. If the relative volatility is assumed constant, the plates are theoretically perfect, and the molal liquid and vapor rates are constant, then a material balance around the nth plate of the enriching section yields a Riccati difference equation.

INTEGRAL EQUATIONS

REFERENCES: Hildebrand, "Methods of Applied Mathematics," Chap. 4, Prentice-Hall, Englewood Cliffs, N.J., 1952. Lovitt, "Linear Integral Equations," McGraw-Hill, New York, 1924. Courant and Hilbert, "Methoden der mathematische Physik," Interscience, New York, 1943.

An *integral equation* is any equation in which the unknown function appears under the sign of integration and possibly outside the sign of integration. Such equations are important in mathematical applications to physical problems because it is often possible to restate a differential equation, together with its boundary conditions, as a single integral equation.

The simplest type of integral equation arises from the integration of the differential equation $dy/dx = f(x, y)$ with the initial condition $y = y_0$ when $x = x_0$. This is equivalent to $dy = f(x, y)\,dx$ or $\int_{y_0}^{y} dy = \int_{x_0}^{x} f(x, y)\,dx$. Upon integrating there results $y = y_0 + \int_{x_0}^{x} f(x, y)\,dx$. This type of equation can be solved by a process of *successive approximations*, often called the *Picard method*, which is useful for obtaining approximate solutions of differential equations. The iteration procedure is to select a first approximation for y, say $y = y_0$, then $y^{(1)} = y_0 + \int_{x_0}^{x} f(x, y_0)\,dx$. After integrating $y^{(2)} = y_0 + \int_{x_0}^{x} f(x, y^{(1)})\,dx$, and in general $y^{(n)} = y_0 + \int_{x_0}^{x} f(x, y^{(n-1)})\,dx$.

Example. $dy/dx = x^2 + y$, $x_0 = 0$, $y_0 = 1$. This problem is equivalent to the integral equation $y = 1 + \int_0^x (x^2 + y)\,dx$. Let the initial approximation for y be 1. Then $y^{(1)} = 1 + \int_0^x (x^2 + 1)\,dx = 1 + x + \frac{x^3}{3}$. $y^{(2)} = 1 + \int_0^x [x^2 + y^{(1)}]\,dx = 1 + \int_0^x \left[x^2 + 1 + x + \frac{x^3}{3}\right] dx = 1 + x + \frac{x^2}{2} + \frac{x^3}{3} + \frac{x^4}{12}$, etc.

CLASSIFICATION OF INTEGRAL EQUATIONS

$\int_a^b K(x, t)u(t)\,dt = f(x)$, where $f(x)$, $K(x, t)$, a and b are known and u is to be determined, is a *linear integral* equation of the *first kind* of *Fredholm type*. $K(x, t)$ is called the *kernel* function of the equation. If u, the unknown function, occurs only to the first power, the equation is said to be *linear*.

$\int_a^x K(x, t)u(t)\,dt = f(x)$ is a linear integral equation of the first kind of *Volterra type*.

An equation of the form $u(x) = f(x) + \int_a^b K(x, t)u(t)\,dt$ is said to be a *linear integral* equation of the *second kind*. If b is constant it is of *Fredholm type*. If $b = x$ it is of *Volterra type*. If $f(x)$ is identically zero, then $u(x) = \int_a^b K(x, t)u(t)\,dt$ is the *homogeneous* linear integral equation of the *second kind*. Sometimes a *parameter* λ is introduced; thus $u(x) = f(x) + \lambda\int_a^b K(x, t)u(t)\,dt$, which facilitates the solution and may take on various values in a particular problem.

The equation $\phi(x)u(x) = f(x) + \int_a^b K(x, t)u(t)\,dt$ is the linear integral equation of the *third kind*. If b = constant it is of Fredholm type and if $b = x$ it is of Volterra type.

If the unknown function u appears in the equation in any way except to the first power the integral equation is said to be *non-linear*. The equation $u(x) = f(x) + \int_a^b K(x, t)u^{3/2}(t)\,dt$ is non-linear. The differential equation $du/dx = g(x, u)$ is equivalent to the non-linear integral equation $u(x) = c + \int_a^x g[t, u(t)]\,dt$.

An integral equation is said to be *singular* when either one or both of the limits of integration become infinite or if $K(x, t)$ becomes infinite for one or more points of the interval under discussion.

Example. $u(x) = x + \int_0^\infty \cos(xt)\,u(t)\,dt$ and $f(x) = \int_0^x \frac{u(t)}{x - t}\,dt$ are both *singular*. The kernel of the first equation is $\cos(xt)$ and of the second $(x - t)^{-1}$.

RELATION TO DIFFERENTIAL EQUATIONS

The *Leibnitz rule* $\frac{d}{dx}\int_{a(x)}^{b(x)} F(x, t)\,dt = \int_{a(x)}^{b(x)} \frac{\partial F(x, t)}{\partial x}\,dt + F[x, b(x)]\frac{db}{dx} - F[x, a(x)]\frac{da}{dx}$ is frequently useful for *differentiation* of an *integral* involving a parameter. If $I_n(x) = \int_a^x (x - t)^{n-1}f(t)\,dt$ then $\frac{d^nI_n}{dx^n} = (n - 1)!\,f(x)$ and since $I_n(a) = 0$, $n \geq 1$, it follows that $I_n(a) = \frac{dI_n(a)}{dx} = \frac{d^2I_n(a)}{dx^2} = \cdots = \frac{d^{n-1}I_n(a)}{dx^{n-1}} = 0$. Hence $\frac{I_n(x)}{(n-1)!} = \frac{1}{(n-1)!}\int_a^x (x - t)^{n-1}f(t)\,dt = \underbrace{\int_a^x \cdots \int_a^x}_{n\text{ times}} f(x)\,\underbrace{dx \cdots dx}_{n\text{ times}}$. This result can be used to show the *equivalence* of the *initial-value* problem consisting of the second-order differential equation $\frac{d^2y}{dx^2} + A(x)\frac{dy}{dx} + B(x)y = f(x)$ together with the prescribed initial conditions $y(a) = y_0$, $y'(a) = y_0'$ to the integral equation

$$y(x) = -\int_a^x \{A(t) + (x - t)[B(t) - A'(t)]\}y(t)\,dt + \int_a^x (x - t)f(t)\,dt + [A(a)y_0 + y_0'](x - a) + y_0$$

or equivalently $y(x) = \int_a^x K(x, t)y(t)\,dt + F(x)$ where

$$K(x, t) = (t - x)[B(t) - A'(t)] - A(t)$$

and

$$F(x) = \int_a^x (x - t)f(t)\,dt + [A(a)y_0 + y_0'](x - a) + y_0$$

This integral equation is a *Volterra equation of the second kind*. Thus the *initial-value problem* is *equivalent* to a *Volterra integral equation of the second kind*.

Example. $\frac{d^2y}{dx^2} + x^2\frac{dy}{dx} + xy = x$, $y(0) = 1$, $y'(0) = 0$. Here $A(x) = x^2$, $B(x) = x$, $f(x) = x$. The equivalent integral equation is $y(x) = \int_0^x K(x, t)\, y(t)\, dt + F(x)$ where $K(x, t) = t(x - t) - t^2$ and $F(x) = \int_0^x (x - t)t\, dt + 1 = \frac{x^3}{6} + 1$. Combining these $y(x) = \int_0^x t[x - 2t]y(t)\, dt + \frac{x^3}{6} + 1$.

The expression for $I_n(x)/(n - 1)!$ can also be used to show the equivalence of *boundary-value problems* to *Fredholm integral* equations of the second kind. For example, the problem $(d^2y/dx^2) + \lambda y = 0$ with $y(0) = 0$, $y(a) = 0$ is equivalent to the integral equation $y(x) = \lambda \int_0^a K(x, t)\, y(t)\, dt$ where $K(x, t) = (t/a)(a - x)$ when $t < x$ and $K(x, t) = (x/a)(a - t)$ when $t > x$.

The differential equation may be recovered from the integral equation by differentiating the integral equation using the Leibnitz rule.

METHODS OF SOLUTION

To *solve* an integral equation of any type is to find the unknown function. In general the solution of integral equations by exact analytic methods is not easy. Oftentimes approximate or numerical methods must be resorted to. A few exact and approximate methods are considered here. Numerical methods are left for the discussion of numerical analysis.

Equations of Convolution Type. The equation $u(x) = f(x) + \lambda \int_0^x K(x - t)u(t)\, dt$ is a special case of the linear integral equation of the second kind of Volterra type. The integral part is the *convolution integral* discussed under Transforms; so the solution can be accomplished by Laplace transforms; $L[u(x)] = L[f(x)] + \lambda L[u(x)]L[K(x)]$ or $L[u(x)] = \frac{L[f(x)]}{1 - \lambda L[K(x)]}$, $u(x) = L^{-1}\left[\frac{L[f(x)]}{1 - \lambda L[K(x)]}\right]$. Equations of the type considered here occur quite frequently in practice in what can be called "cause-and-effect" systems.

Example. In a certain linear system, the effect $E(t)$ due to a cause $C = \lambda E$ at time τ is a function only of the elapsed time $t - \tau$. If the system has the activity level 1 at time $t < 0$ the cause λE and effect (E) relation is given by the integral equation $E(t) = 1 + \lambda \int_0^t K(t - \tau)E(\tau)\, d\tau$. Let $K(t - \tau) = t - \tau$. Then $E(t) = 1 + \lambda \int_0^t (t - \tau)E(\tau)\, d\tau$. Using the transform method $E(t) = L^{-1}\left[\frac{L[1]}{1 - \lambda L[K(t)]}\right] = L^{-1}\left[\frac{1/p}{1 - \lambda/p^2}\right] = L^{-1}\left[\frac{p}{p^2 - \lambda}\right] = \cosh \sqrt{\lambda}t$.

The General Abel Equation. The Volterra equation $F(x) = \int_0^x \frac{y(t)}{(x - t)^\alpha}\, dt$, $0 < \alpha < 1$ is known as "Abel's" equation. Its solution is $y(x) = \frac{\sin \alpha\pi}{\pi} \frac{d}{dx} \int_0^x \frac{F(t)\, dt}{(x - t)^{1-\alpha}}$.

Equations with Separable Kernels. The integral equation of second kind of Fredholm type $y(x) = f(x) + \int_a^b K(x, t)y(t)\, dt$ is said to have a *separable kernel* if $K(x, t) = u(x)v(t)$. The solution in this case is $y(x) = f(x) + \lambda \frac{\int_a^b K(x, t)f(t)\, dt}{1 - \lambda \int_a^b K(x, x)\, dx}$.

Example. $y(x) = x + \lambda \int_0^1 xty(t)\, dt$. The solution is

$$y(x) = f(x) + \lambda \frac{\int_0^1 (xt)t\, dt}{1 - \lambda \int_0^1 x^2\, dx} = x + \lambda \frac{x/3}{1 - (\lambda/3)} = \frac{3x}{3 - \lambda}$$

The Method of Successive Approximations. Consider the equation $y(x) = f(x) + \lambda \int_a^b K(x, t)y(t)\, dt$. In this method a unique solution is obtained in sequence form as follows: Substitute in the right-hand member of the equation $y_0(t)$ for $y(t)$. Upon integration there results $y_1(t) = f(x) + \lambda \int_a^b K(x, t)y_0(t)\, dt$. Continue in like manner by replacing y_0 by y_1, y_1 by y_2, etc. A series of functions $y_0(x)$, $y_1(x)$, $y_2(x)$, . . . are obtained which satisfy the equations

$$y_n(x) = f(x) + \lambda \int_a^b K(x, t)y_{n-1}(t)\, dt$$

Then $y_n(x) = f(x) + \lambda \int_a^b K(x, t)f(t)\, dt + \lambda^2 \int_a^b K(x, t) \int_a^b K(t, t_1)f(t_1)\, dt_1\, dt + \lambda^3 \int_a^b K(x, t) \int_a^b K(t, t_1) \int_a^b K(t_1, t_2)f(t_2)\, dt_2\, dt_1\, dt + \cdots + R_n$ where R_n is the remainder and $|R_n| \le |\lambda^n| \left(\begin{smallmatrix}\max.\ y_0 \\ a \le x \le b\end{smallmatrix}\right) M^n(b - a)^n$, where M = maximum value of $|K|$ in the rectangle $a \le t \le b$, $a \le x \le b$. If $|\lambda|M(b - a) < 1$, $\lim_{n\to\infty} R_n = 0$. Thus $y_n(x) \to y(x)$, which is the unique solution.

Example. Consider the equation $y(x) = 1 + \lambda \int_0^1 (1 - 3xt)\, y(t)\, dt$.

$$y(x) = 1 + \lambda \int_0^1 (1 - 3xt)\, dt + \lambda^2 \int_0^1 (1 - 3xt) \int_0^1 (1 - 3tt_1)\, dt_1\, dt + \cdots$$

$$= 1 + \lambda\left(1 - \frac{3}{2}x\right) + \lambda^2\frac{1}{4} + \frac{1}{4}\lambda^3\left(1 - \frac{3}{2}x\right) + \frac{\lambda^4}{16} + \frac{1}{16}\lambda^5\left(1 - \frac{3}{2}x\right) \cdots$$

$$= \left(1 + \frac{\lambda^2}{4} + \frac{\lambda^4}{16} + \cdots\right)\left(1 + \lambda\left(1 - \frac{3}{2}x\right)\right)$$

$$= \frac{1 + \lambda\left(1 - \frac{3}{2}x\right)}{1 - \frac{1}{4}\lambda^2} \qquad \lambda < 2$$

The Method of Successive Substitutions. This method obtains a solution by substituting the right-hand side of $y(x) = f(x) + \lambda \int_a^b K(x, t)y(t)\, dt$ for $y(t)$ in itself repeatedly. Thus $y(x) = f(x) + \lambda \int_a^b K(x, t)f(t)\, dt + \lambda^2 \int_a^b K(x, t) \int_a^b K(t, t_1)f(t_1)\, dt\, dt_1 + \cdots$. The method converges for $|\lambda| < \frac{1}{M(b - a)}$. It applies equally well to $y(x) = f(x) + \int_a^x K(x, t)y(t)\, dt$.

INTEGRAL TRANSFORMS (OPERATIONAL METHODS)

REFERENCES: McLachlan, "Complex Variable and Operational Calculus," Cambridge, New York, 1939. Pipes, "Applied Mathematics for Engineers and Physicists," 2d ed., McGraw-Hill, New York, 1958. Sneddon, "Fourier Transforms," McGraw-Hill, New York, 1951. Widder, "The Laplace Transform," Princeton University Press, Princeton, N.J., 1946. Campbell and Foster, Fourier Integrals for Practical Applications, *Bell System Tech. J.*, September, 1942. Tranter, "Integral Transforms in Mathematical Physics," Wiley, New York, 1951. Mickley, Sherwood, and Reed, "Applied Mathematics in Chemical Engineering," McGraw-Hill, New York, 1957. Churchill, "Operational Mathematics," 2d ed., McGraw-Hill, New York, 1958.

The term "operational method" implies a procedure of solving differential and difference equations whereby the boundary or initial conditions are automatically satisfied in the course of the solution. The technique offers a very powerful tool in the applications of mathematics.

All the integral transforms are special cases of the equation $g(s) = \int_a^b f(t)K(s, t)\,dt$ in which $g(s)$ is said to be the *transform* of $f(t)$ and $K(s, t)$ is called the *kernel* of the transform. A tabulation of the more important kernels and the interval (a, b) of applicability follows.

Name of transform	(a, b)	$K(s, t)$
Laplace	$(0, \infty)$	e^{-st}
Fourier	$(-\infty, \infty)$	$\frac{1}{\sqrt{2\pi}} e^{-ist}$
Fourier cosine	$(0, \infty)$	$\sqrt{\frac{2}{\pi}} \cos st$
Fourier sine	$(0, \infty)$	$\sqrt{\frac{2}{\pi}} \sin st$
Mellin	$(0, \infty)$	t^{s-1}
Hankel	$(0, \infty)$	$tJ_\nu(st),\ \nu \geq -\frac{1}{2}$

The first three transforms are considered here.

LAPLACE TRANSFORM

The Laplace transform of $f(t)$ is $g(s) = \int_0^\infty e^{-st}f(t)\,dt$. It may be thought of as transforming one class of functions into another. The advantage in the operation is that under certain circumstances it replaces complicated functions by simpler ones. The notation $L[f(t)] = g(s)$ is called the *direct transform* and $L^{-1}[g(s)] = f(t)$ is called the *inverse* transform. Both the direct and inverse transform are tabulated for many often occurring functions. In general $L^{-1}[g(s)] = \frac{1}{2\pi i}\int_{\alpha - i\infty}^{\alpha + i\infty} e^{st}g(s)\,ds$, and to evaluate this integral requires a knowledge of complex variables, the theory of residues, and contour integration.

Properties of the Laplace Transform. Let $L[f(t)] = g(s)$, $L^{-1}[g(s)] = f(t)$.

1. The Laplace transform may be applied to a function $f(t)$ if $f(t)$ is continuous or piecewise continuous; if $t^n|f(t)|$ is finite for all t, $t \to 0$, $n < 1$; and if $e^{-at}|f(t)|$ is finite as $t \to \infty$ for some value of a, $a > 0$.
2. L and L^{-1} are unique.
3. $L[af(t) + bh(t)] = aL[f(t)] + bL[h(t)]$ (linearity).
4. $L[e^{at}f(t)] = g(s - a)$ (shift theorem).
5. $L[(-t)^k f(t)] = d^kg/ds^k$; k a positive integer.

Example 1. $\int_0^\infty e^{-st} \sin at\,dt = \frac{a}{s^2 + a^2}$, $s > 0$. By property 5 $\frac{2as}{s^2 + a^2} = \int_0^\infty e^{-st}t \sin at\,dt$.

Example 2. $\int_0^\infty e^{-st}t\,dt = \frac{1}{s^2}$. Therefore, by property 4 $L[te^{-at}] = \frac{1}{(s + a)^2}$.

Example 3. Find $L^{-1}\left[\frac{1}{s^2 - 1}\right]$. $\frac{1}{s^2 - 1} = \frac{1}{2}\left[\frac{1}{s - 1} - \frac{1}{s + 1}\right] = \frac{1}{2}L[e^t] - \frac{1}{2}L[e^{-t}] = L\left[\frac{e^t - e^{-t}}{2}\right] = L[\sinh t]$. Therefore, $L^{-1}\left[\frac{1}{s^2 - 1}\right] = \sinh t$.

6. $L[f'(t)] = sL[f(t)] - f(0)$

$L[f''(t)] = s^2L[f(t)] - sf(0) - f'(0)$

$\cdot$

$\cdot$

$\cdot$

$L[f^{(n)}(t)] = s^nL[f(t)] - s^{n-1}f(0) - \cdots - sf^{(n-2)}(0) - f^{(n-1)}(0)$

Example. Solve $y'' + y = 2e^t$, $y(0) = y'(0) = 2$. $L[y''] = -y'(0) - sy(0) + s^2L[y] = -2 - 2s + s^2L[y]$. Thus $-2 - 2s + s^2L[y] + L[y] = 2L[e^t] = \frac{2}{s - 1}$. $L[y] = \frac{2s^2}{(s - 1)(s^2 + 1)} = \frac{1}{s - 1} + \frac{s}{s^2 + 1} + \frac{1}{s^2 + 1}$. Hence $y = e^t + \cos t + \sin t$.

A short table of very common Laplace transforms and inverse transforms is given below. The references include more detailed tables. Note: $\Gamma(n + 1) = \int_0^\infty x^ne^{-x}\,dx$ (gamma function); $J_n(t)$ = Bessel function of the first kind of order n.

$f(t)$	$g(s)$	$f(t)$	$g(s)$
1	$1/s$	$e^{-at}(1 - at)$	$\frac{s}{(s + a)^2}$
t^n, $(na + \text{integer})$	$\frac{n!}{s^{n+1}}$	$\frac{t \sin at}{2a}$	$\frac{s}{(s^2 + a^2)^2}$
t^n, $n \neq + \text{integer}$	$\frac{\Gamma(n + 1)}{s^{n+1}}$	$\frac{1}{2a^2} \sin at \sinh at$	$\frac{s}{s^4 + 4a^4}$
$\cos at$	$\frac{s}{s^2 + a^2}$	$\cos at \cosh at$	$\frac{s^3}{s^4 + 4a^4}$
$\sin at$	$\frac{a}{s^2 + a^2}$	$\frac{1}{2a}(\sinh at + \sin at)$	$\frac{s^2}{s^4 - a^4}$
$\cosh at$	$\frac{s}{s^2 - a^2}$	$\frac{1}{2}(\cosh at + \cos at)$	$\frac{s^3}{s^4 - a^4}$
$\sinh at$	$\frac{a}{s^2 - a^2}$	$\frac{\sin at}{t}$	$\tan^{-1} \frac{a}{s}$
e^{-at}	$\frac{1}{s + a}$	$J_0(at)$	$\frac{1}{\sqrt{s^2 + a^2}}$
$e^{-bt} \cos at$	$\frac{s + b}{(s + b)^2 + a^2}$	$\frac{n}{a^n}\frac{J_n(at)}{t}$	$\frac{1}{(\sqrt{s^2 + a^2} + s)^n}$
$e^{-bt} \sin a$	$\frac{a}{(s + b)^2 + a^2}$	$J_0(2\sqrt{at})$	$\frac{1}{s} e^{-a/s}$

7. $L\left[\int_a^t f(t)\,dt\right] = \frac{1}{s}L[f(t)] + \frac{1}{s}\int_a^0 f(t)\,dt.$

Example. Find $f(t)$ if $L[f(t)] = \frac{1}{s^2}\left[\frac{1}{s^2 - a^2}\right]$. $L\left[\frac{1}{a}\sinh at\right] = \frac{1}{s^2 - a^2}$. Therefore, $f(t) = \int_0^t \left[\int_0^t \frac{1}{a} \sinh at\,dt\right] dt = \frac{1}{a^2}\left[\frac{\sinh at}{a} - t\right]$.

8. $L\left[\frac{f(t)}{t}\right] = \int_s^\infty g(s)\,ds;\ L\left[\frac{f(t)}{t^k}\right]$
$$= \underbrace{\int_s^\infty \cdots \int_s^\infty}_{k \text{ integrals}} g(s)\,(ds)^k.$$

Example. $L\left[\frac{\sin at}{t}\right] = \int_s^\infty L[\sin at]\,ds = \int_s^\infty \frac{a\,ds}{s^2 + a^2} = \cot^{-1}\frac{s}{a}.$

9. The *unit step function* $u(t - a) = \begin{cases} 0 & t < a \\ 1 & t > a \end{cases}$. $L[u(t - a)] = \frac{e^{-as}}{s}$.

10. The *unit impulse function* is $\delta(a) = u'(t - a) = \begin{cases} 1 & \text{at } t = a \\ 0 & \text{elsewhere} \end{cases}$. $L[u'(t - a)] = e^{-as}$.

11. $L^{-1}[e^{-as}g(s)] = f(t - a)u(t - a)$ (second shift theorem).

12. If $f(t)$ is *periodic* of period b; *i.e.*, $f(t + b) = f(t)$, then $L[f(t)] = \left[\frac{1}{1 - e^{-bs}}\right]\int_0^b e^{-st}f(t)\,dt.$

Example. The partial differential equations relating the gas composition to position and time in a gas chromatograph are $\frac{\partial y}{\partial n} + \frac{\partial x}{\partial \theta} = 0$, $\frac{\partial y}{\partial n} = x - y$ where $x = mx'$, $n = \frac{k_G aP}{G_m} h$, $\theta = \left(\frac{mk_G aP}{\rho B}\right) t$ and G_M = molar velocity, y = mole fraction of the component in the gas phase, ρ_B = bulk density, h = distance from the entrance, P = pressure, k_G = mass-transfer coefficient, and m = slope of the equilibrium line. These equations are equivalent to $\frac{\partial^2 y}{\partial n\,\partial \theta} + \frac{\partial y}{\partial n} + \frac{\partial y}{\partial \theta} = 0$ where the boundary conditions considered here are $y(n, \theta) = y(0, \theta) = 0$ and $x(n, 0) = y(n, 0) + \frac{\partial y}{\partial n}(n, 0) = \delta(0)$ (see property 10). The problem is conveniently solved by using the Laplace transform of y with respect to n; write $g(s, \theta) = \int_0^\infty e^{-ns}y(n, \theta)\,dn$. Operating on the partial differential equation gives $s\frac{dg}{d\theta} - \frac{\partial y}{\partial \theta}(0, \theta) + sg - y(0, \theta) + \frac{dg}{d\theta} = 0$ or $(s + 1)\frac{dg}{d\theta} + sg = \frac{\partial y}{\partial \theta}(0, \theta) + y(0, \theta) = 0.$ The second boundary condition gives $g(s, 0) + sg(s, 0) - y(0, 0) = 1$ or $g(s, 0) + sg(s, 0) = 1$ $(L[\delta(0)] = 1)$. A solution of the ordinary differential equation for g consistent with this second condition is $g(s, \theta) = \frac{1}{s + 1} e^{-\frac{s\theta}{s+1}}$. Inversion of this transform gives the solution $y(n, \theta) = e^{-(n+\theta)} I_0(2\sqrt{n\theta})$ where I_0 = zero-order Bessel function of an imaginary argument. For large u, $I_n(u) \sim e^u/2\sqrt{\pi u}$. Hence for large n

$$y(n, \theta) \sim \frac{\exp.[-(\sqrt{\theta} - \sqrt{n})^2]}{2\pi^{1/2}(n\theta)^{1/4}}$$

or for sufficiently large n the peak concentration occurs near $\theta = n$.

Other applications of Laplace transforms are given under Differential Equations.

CONVOLUTION INTEGRAL

The *convolution integral (faltung)* of two functions $f(t)$, $r(t)$ is $x(t) = f(t)*r(t) = \int_0^t f(\tau)r(t - \tau)\,d\tau.$

Example. $t * \sin t = \int_0^t \tau \sin(t - \tau)\,d\tau = t - \sin t.$

13. $L[f(t)]L[h(t)] = L[f(t)*h(t)]$

FOURIER TRANSFORM

The *Fourier transform* is given by $F[f(t)] = \frac{1}{\sqrt{2\pi}}\int_{-\infty}^\infty f(t)e^{-ist}\,dt = g(s)$ and its *inverse* by $F^{-1}[g(s)] = \frac{1}{\sqrt{2\pi}}\int_{-\infty}^\infty g(s)e^{ist}\,dt = f(t)$. In brief, the condition for the Fourier transform to exist is that $\int_{-\infty}^\infty |f(t)|\,dt < \infty$, although certain functions may have a Fourier transform even if this is violated.

Example. The function in Fig. 2-50; $f(t) = \begin{cases} 1 & -a \le t \le a \\ 0 & \text{elsewhere} \end{cases}$ has $F[f(t)] = \int_{-a}^a e^{-ist}\,dt = \int_0^a e^{ist}\,dt + \int_0^a e^{-ist}\,dt = 2\int_0^a \cos st\,dt = \frac{2\sin sa}{s}.$

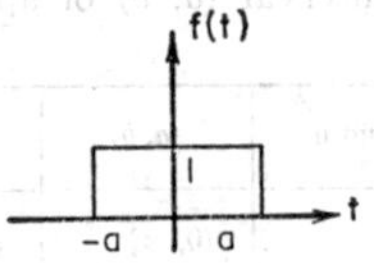

FIG. 2-50. Rectangular function.

Properties of the Fourier Transform. Let $F[f(t)] = g(s)$; $F^{-1}[g(s)] = f(t)$.

1. $F[f^{(n)}(t)] = (is)^n F[f(t)]$.
2. $F[af(t) + bh(t)] = aF[f(t)] + bF[h(t)]$.
3. $F[f(-t)] = g(-s)$.
4. $F[f(at)] = \frac{1}{a} g\left(\frac{s}{a}\right)$, $a > 0$.
5. $F[e^{-iwt}f(t)] = g(s + w)$.
6. $F[f(t + t_1)] = e^{ist_1}g(s)$.
7. $F[f(t)] = G(is) + G(-is)$ if $f(t) = f(-t)$ ($f(t)$ even)
   $F[f(t)] = G(is) - G(-is)$ if $f(t) = -f(-t)$ (f odd)

where $G(s) = L[f(t)]$. This result allows the use of the Laplace-transform tables to obtain the Fourier transforms.

Example. Find $F[e^{-a|t|}]$ by property 7. $e^{-a|t|}$ is even. So $L[e^{-at}] = \frac{1}{s + a}$. Therefore, $F[e^{-a|t|}] = \frac{1}{is + a} + \frac{1}{-is + a} = \frac{2a}{s^2 + a^2}$.

Tables of this transform may be found in "Tables of Integral Transforms," Bateman Manuscript Project, vol. 1, McGraw-Hill, New York, 1954.

FOURIER COSINE TRANSFORM

The *Fourier cosine transform* is given by $F_c[f(t)] = g(s) = \sqrt{\frac{2}{\pi}}\int_0^\infty f(t)\cos st\,dt$ and its *inverse* by $F_c^{-1}[g(s)] = f(t) = \sqrt{\frac{2}{\pi}}\int_0^\infty g(s)\cos st\,ds$. The *Fourier sine trans-*

form F_s is obtainable by replacing the cosine by the sine in the above integrals.

Example. $F_c[f(t)],\ f(t) = \begin{cases} 1 & 0 < t < a \\ 0 & a < t < \infty. \end{cases}$ $F_c[f(t)] = \sqrt{\frac{2}{\pi}} \int_0^a \cos st\, dt = \sqrt{\frac{2}{\pi}} \frac{\sin as}{s}.$

Properties of the Fourier Cosine Transform. $F_c[f(t)] = g(s)$.

1. $F_c[af(t) + bh(t)] = aF_c[f(t)] + bF_c[h(t)]$.
2. $F_c[f(at)] = \frac{1}{a} g\left(\frac{s}{a}\right)$.
3. $F_c[f(at) \cos bt] = \frac{1}{2a}\left[g\left(\frac{s+b}{a}\right) + g\left(\frac{s-b}{a}\right)\right]$, $a, b > 0$.
4. $F_c[t^{2n}f(t)] = (-1)^n \frac{d^{2n}g}{ds^{2n}}$.
5. $F_c[t^{2n+1}f(t)] = (-1)^n \frac{d^{2n+1}}{ds^{2n+1}} F_s[f(t)]$.

A short table of Fourier cosine transforms follows. More extensive tables can be found in the Bateman Series (*op. cit.*).

$f(t)$		$\frac{g(s)}{\sqrt{2/\pi}}$
t $2 - t$ 0	$0 < t < 1$ $1 < t < 2$ $2 < t < \infty$	$\frac{1}{s^2}[2 \cos s - 1 - \cos 2s]$
$t^{-1/2}$		$\pi^{1/2}(2s)^{-1/2}$
0 $(t - a)^{-1/2}$	$0 < t < a$ $a < t < \infty$	$\pi^{1/2}(2s)^{-1/2}[\cos as - \sin as]$
$(t^2 + a^2)^{-1}$		$\frac{1}{2}\pi a^{-1}e^{-as}$
e^{-at}	$a > 0$	$\frac{a}{s^2 + a^2}$
e^{-at^2}	$a > 0$	$\frac{1}{2}\pi^{1/2}a^{-1/2}e^{-s^2/4a}$
$\frac{\sin at}{t}$	$a > 0$	$\begin{cases} \pi/2 & s < a \\ \pi/4 & s = a \\ 0 & s > a \end{cases}$

Example. The temperature θ in the semi-infinite rod $0 \le x < \infty$ is determined by the differential equation $\frac{\partial \theta}{\partial t} = k \frac{\partial^2 \theta}{\partial x^2}$ and the condition $\theta = 0$ when $t = 0$, $x \ge 0$; $\frac{\partial \theta}{\partial x} = -\mu =$ constant when $x = 0$, $t > 0$. By using the Fourier cosine transform a solution may be found as $\theta(x, t) = \frac{2\mu}{\pi} \int_0^\infty \frac{\cos px}{p} (1 - e^{-kp^2t})\, dp$ (see Sneddon, *op. cit*).

NUMERICAL APPROXIMATIONS

IDENTITIES

For the following relationships the sign $\cong$ means approximately equal to, when X is small:

Approximation	Approximation
$\frac{1}{1 \pm X} \cong 1 \mp X$	$\sqrt{1 \pm X} \cong 1 \pm \frac{X}{2}$
$\frac{1 + Y}{1 \mp X} \cong 1 + Y \pm X$	$(1 \pm X)^{-n} \cong 1 \mp nX$
$(1 \pm X)^n \cong 1 \pm nX$	$(1 \pm X)^{-1/2} \cong 1 \mp \frac{X}{2}$
$(a \pm X)^2 \cong a^2 \pm 2aX$	$e^X \cong 1 + X$
$\sin X \cong X$ (X radians)	$\tan X \cong X$
$\sqrt{Y(Y + X)} \cong \frac{2Y + X}{2}$	$\sqrt{Y^2 + X^2} \cong Y + \frac{X^2}{2Y} \left(\frac{X}{Y} \text{ small}\right)$

SUMMATION AND APPROXIMATION

$$\sum_1^m \sqrt{n} \cong \tfrac{2}{3}m^{3/2} + \frac{\sqrt{m}}{2} - 0.245$$

$$\sum_1^m \frac{1}{n} \cong \ln m + C + \frac{b}{m} + \frac{c}{m^2} \qquad (m \ge 10)$$

m	True value	Formula value
10	2.928968254	2.9290
20	3.597739657	3.5976
30	3.994987131	3.9949
40	4.278543040	4.2785
50	4.499205338	4.4992
100	5.187377518	5.1875
1000	7.485470861	7.4857
10000	9.787606036	9.7878
50000	11.397003949	11.3972
100000	12.090146130	12.0903

$$n! \cong e^{-n}n^n \sqrt{2\pi n}$$

$$n! \cong \sqrt{2\pi} \left\{\frac{\sqrt{n^2 + n + \frac{1}{6}}}{e}\right\}^{n + 1/2}$$

$$\sqrt{X} \cong \frac{1}{2}\left[\frac{X}{S} + S\right] \qquad S = \sqrt{[X]}$$

$[X]$ = greatest integer in X, or S can be assumed as 1. Precision of $\sqrt{X}$ is roughly twice as many significant digits as $S \cong \sqrt{X}$. With a three-place square-root table the root of any number can be calculated to six places with one application of the above correction:

Given $X = 105.53196$ from $\sqrt{106} = 10.29563$ tabled

$$\sqrt{105.53196} \cong 0.5 \left[\frac{105.53196}{10.29563} + 10.29563\right] \cong 10.2729$$

A second application will give the root to eight decimal places.

NUMERICAL AND APPROXIMATE METHODS

REFERENCES: Hildebrand, "Introduction to Numerical Analysis," McGraw-Hill, New York, 1956. Scarborough, "Numerical Mathematical Analysis," Johns Hopkins Press, Baltimore, 1955. Booth, "Numerical Methods," Academic Press, New York, 1955. Hartree, "Numerical Analysis," Oxford, New York, 1952. Kopal, "Numerical Analysis," Wiley, New York, 1955. Householder, "Principles of Numerical Analysis," McGraw-Hill, New York, 1953. Lanczos, "Applied Analysis," Pitman, New York, 1957.

Introduction. The goal of approximate and numerical methods is to provide convenient techniques for obtaining useful information from mathematical formulations of physical problems. Often this mathematical statement is not solvable by analytical means. Or perhaps analytic solutions are available but in such a form that is inconvenient for direct interpretation numerically. In the first case it is necessary either to attempt to approximate the problem satisfactorily by one which will be amenable to analysis, to obtain an approximate solution to the original problem by numerical means, or to use the two techniques in combination.

Numerical techniques therefore do not yield exact

results in the sense of the mathematician. Since most numerical calculations are inexact the concept of error is an important feature. The error associated with an approximate value is defined as

$$\text{True value} = \text{approximate value} + \text{error}$$

The four sources of error are as follows:

1. "*Gross errors.*" These result from unpredictable human, mechanical, or electrical mistakes.

2. "*Round-off errors.*" These are the consequence of using a number specified by m correct digits to approximate a number which requires more than m digits for its exact specification. For example, approximate the irrational number $\sqrt{2}$ by 1.414. Such errors are often present in experimental data, in which case they may be called inherent errors, due either to empiricism or to the fact that the computer dictates the number of digits. Such errors may be especially damaging in areas such as matrix inversion or the numerical solution of partial differential equations where the number of algebraic operations is extremely large.

3. "*Truncation errors.*" These errors arise from the substitution of a finite number of steps for an infinite sequence of steps which would yield the exact result. To illustrate this error consider the infinite series for e^{-x}. $e^{-x} = 1 - x + \frac{x^2}{2} - \frac{x^3}{6} + E_T(x)$ where E_T is the truncation error, $E_T = \frac{1}{24} e^{-\epsilon} x^4$, $0 < \epsilon < x$. If x is positive, ϵ is also positive. Hence $e^{-\epsilon} < 1$. The approximation $e^{-x} \approx 1 - x + \frac{x^2}{2} - \frac{x^3}{6}$ is in error by a positive amount smaller than $\frac{1}{24} x^4$.

4. "*Inherited errors.*" These arise as a result of errors occurring in the previous steps of the computational algorithm.

The study of errors in a computation is related to the theory of probability. In what follows a relation for the error will be given in certain instances.

NUMERICAL SOLUTION OF LINEAR EQUATIONS AND ASSOCIATED PROBLEMS

The methods described here are concerned with a set of n linear equations in n unknowns $x_1, x_2, \ldots, x_n$ expressed in the form

$$\begin{aligned} a_{11}x_1 + a_{12}x_2 + a_{13}x_3 + \cdots + a_{1n}x_n &= b_1 \\ a_{21}x_1 + a_{22}x_2 + a_{23}x_3 + \cdots + a_{2n}x_n &= b_2 \\ \cdots\cdots\cdots\cdots\cdots\cdots\cdots\cdots \\ a_{n1}x_1 + a_{n2}x_2 + a_{n3}x_3 + \cdots + a_{nn}x_n &= b_n \end{aligned} \qquad (2\text{-}76)$$

where the n^2 coefficients a_{ij} and the n right-hand members are given. Equations (2-76) may be written in matrix form as

$$AX = B \qquad (2\text{-}77)$$

where

$$A = \begin{bmatrix} a_{11}a_{12} & \cdots & a_{1n} \\ a_{21}a_{22} & \cdots & a_{2n} \\ \cdots & \cdots & \cdots \\ a_{n1}a_{n2} & \cdots & a_{nn} \end{bmatrix} \qquad X = \begin{bmatrix} x_1 \\ x_2 \\ \cdot \\ \cdot \\ \cdot \\ x_n \end{bmatrix} \qquad B = \begin{bmatrix} b_1 \\ b_2 \\ \cdot \\ \cdot \\ \cdot \\ b_n \end{bmatrix}$$

and in the terminology a_{ij}, i = row index, j = column index. The problem of determining the values of $x_1, x_2, \ldots, x_n$ satisfying Eq. (2-76) may be accomplished numerically from the form (2-76) or from (2-77) by matrix-inversion techniques. In either case the methods are *direct* (meaning "once through") or *iterative* (repeated) procedures.

Direct Methods for Solving (2-76)

Suppose that the b_i's are not all zero and that the determinant of $A \neq 0$. Then (2-76) has a unique solution.

Gauss Reduction. This method is the simplest practical method for solving (2-76). It consists of dividing the first equation by a_{11} (if $a_{11} = 0$, reorder the equations) and using the result to eliminate x_1 from all succeeding equations. Next, the modified second equation is divided by a_{22}' (if $a_{22}' = 0$ a renumbering of equations and/or variables may again be necessary) and the resulting equation is used to eliminate x_2 from the succeeding equations. This elimination is done n times. The result is of the "triangular" form.

$$\begin{aligned} x_1 + a_{12}'x_2 + a_{13}'x_3 + \cdots + a_{1n}'x_n &= b_1' \\ x_2 + a_{23}'x_3 + \cdots + a_{2n}'x_n &= b_2' \\ \cdots\cdots\cdots\cdots\cdots\cdots\cdots\cdots \\ x_{n-1} + a'_{n-1,n}x_n &= b'_{n-1} \\ x_n &= b_n' \end{aligned}$$

where the a_{ij}' and b_i' represent the specific numerical values obtained by the above process. The solution is then obtained by working backward from the last equation. The procedure is illustrated as it would be done in practice in which only the coefficient array is recorded.

Example.

$$\begin{aligned} 18.7492x_1 + 6.0832x_2 - 4.8742x_3 &= 18.4666 \\ 6.0832x_1 + 12.3664x_2 + 2.4326x_3 &= 16.4098 \\ -4.8742x_1 + 2.4326x_2 + 16.8858x_3 &= 7.8678 \end{aligned}$$

or

18.7492	6.0832	−4.8742	18.4666
6.0832	12.3664	2.4326	16.4098
−4.8742	2.4326	16.8858	7.8678

Division by 18.7492 in the first row and then elimination of x_1 yields

1	0.32445	−0.25997	0.98493
	5.19635	2.00702	5.20914
	2.00702	7.80933	6.33427

Then division of the new second row by 5.19635 and elimination of x_2 in the third equation yields (writing down only the new second and third equations)

1	0.38624	1.00246
	7.03414	4.32234

Finally, dividing the last line by 7.03414 there results x_3 = 0.61448. Substitution of this into the previous line yields x_2 = 0.76512 and finally x_1 = 0.89643. The final result must be checked in each of the original equations.

The Gauss reduction is the basic procedure from which all other direct procedures have evolved. Its disadvantage is the recording of the new arrays and the possibility of gross errors. A modification using the kth equation, at the kth stage, to eliminate x_k from the preceding as well as the following equation gives a final diagonal form of the array. The solution is then obtained immediately. This procedure is called the Gauss-Jordan reduction. Another modification called the Gauss-Doolittle reduction is specifically for symmetric equations. These and the checks on the methods are outlined in the references; these are especially well done in Bodewig.

The Crout Reduction. A modification of the Gauss procedure which is well adapted for use on desk calculators and digital computers is a method devised by Crout. Recording of intermediate steps is minimized in this procedure. The Crout algorithm is summarized by the equations

$$a_{ij}' = a_{ij} - \sum_{k=1}^{j-1} a_{ik}'a_{kj}' \qquad i \geq j$$

$$a_{ij}' = \frac{1}{a_{ii}'}\left[a_{ij} - \sum_{k=1}^{i-1} a_{ik}'a_{kj}'\right] \qquad i < j \qquad (2\text{-}78)$$

$$b_i' = \frac{1}{a_{ii}'}\left[b_i - \sum_{k=1}^{i-1} a_{ik}'b_k'\right]$$

and finally the solution

$$x_i = b_i' - \sum_{k=i+1}^{n} a_{ik}'x_k \qquad (2\text{-}79)$$

and i and j run from 1 to n unless other restrictions are present. An excellent discussion of this technique is found in Hildebrand.

Example.

$$\begin{aligned} 2x_1 - 3x_2 + x_3 &= 1 \\ x_1 + 2x_2 + 3x_3 &= 3 \\ 4x_1 - x_2 - x_3 &= +1 \end{aligned}$$

From Eq. (2-78)

$$a_{11}' = a_{11} = 2 \qquad a_{12}' = \frac{1}{a_{11}'}[a_{12}] = -3/2$$

$$a_{21}' = a_{21} = 1 \qquad a_{22}' = a_{22} - a_{21}'a_{12}' = 7/2$$

$$a_{31}' = a_{31} = 4 \qquad a_{13}' = \frac{a_{13}}{a_{11}'} = 1/2$$

$$a_{23}' = \frac{1}{a_{22}'}[a_{23} - a_{21}'a_{13}'] = 5/7$$

$$a_{33}' = a_{33} - \sum_{k=1}^{2} a_{3k}'a_{k3}' = a_{33} - a_{31}'a_{13}' - a_{32}'a_{23}' = -46/7$$

$$b_1' = \frac{b_1}{a_{11}'} = 1/2 \qquad b_2' = \frac{1}{a_{22}'}[b_2 - a_{21}'b_1'] = 5/7$$

$$b_3' = \frac{1}{a_{33}'}[b_3 - a_{31}'b_1' - a_{32}'b_2'] = 16/23$$

$$a_{32}' = a_{32} - a_{31}'a_{12}' = +5$$

Hence by (2-79)

$$x_3 = b_3' = 16/23 \qquad x_2 = b_2' - a_{23}'x_3 = 5/23$$
$$x_1 = b_1' - a_{12}'x_2 - a_{13}'x_3 = 11/23$$

Iterative Methods for Solving (2-76)

In certain systems, for example, in the least-squares problems of statistics, it often happens that the diagonal elements (the elements a_{ii}) of (2-76) dominate strongly over the other elements. In these cases iterative methods may be used to solve the linear system (2-76). The more the diagonal terms dominate, the more rapidly the process converges and is in many cases superior to the direct processes.

Iteration in Total Steps. Referring to the linear system (2-76) the first set of approximate values is obtained by taking into account only the dominant diagonal terms in each equation. The approximate values are then inserted into the full system to obtain the second approximation. And so on. If the system has been rewritten so the diagonal terms dominate then the procedure is to rewrite it as

$$\begin{aligned} x_1 &= \frac{1}{a_{11}}(b_1 - a_{12}x_2 - a_{13}x_3 - \cdots - a_{1n}x_n) \\ x_2 &= \frac{1}{a_{22}}(b_2 - a_{21}x_1 - a_{23}x_3 - \cdots - a_{2n}x_n) \\ &\cdots\cdots\cdots\cdots\cdots\cdots \\ x_n &= \frac{1}{a_{nn}}(b_n - a_{n1}x_1 - a_{n2}x_2 - \cdots - a_{nn-1}x_{n-1}) \end{aligned} \qquad (2\text{-}80)$$

The initial approximation is

$$x_1^{(0)} = \frac{b_1}{a_{11}} \qquad x_2^{(0)} = \frac{b_2}{a_{22}} \qquad \cdots \qquad x_n^{(0)} = \frac{b_n}{a_{nn}} \qquad (2\text{-}81)$$

The next approximation is obtained by inserting the initial approximations in (2-80) and repeating until the successive approximations agree to within a specified tolerance.

Iteration in Single Steps. In this method a diagonal unknown, say x_4, is computed approximately, neglecting all others. This value is inserted into all other equations, and from one of them, an approximation for a second diagonal element is obtained. And so forth. Thus at every step all unknowns are computed by means of all components already known.

Example.

$$\begin{aligned} 10x_1 + x_2 - x_3 &= 2 \\ 2x_1 + 15x_2 - 3x_3 &= 6 \\ 3x_1 - x_2 + 20x_3 &= -4 \end{aligned}$$

$x_1^{(0)} = 2/10 = 1/5$ then $15x_2^{(0)} = 6 - 2/5$ $x_2^{(0)} = 28/75$ $20x_3^{(0)} = -4 - 3/5 + 28/75 = -347/75$ $x_3^{(0)} = -347/75 \cdot 20$ and so forth.

Relaxation. These procedures do not readily lend themselves to mechanization but are useful for hand computation. Their great facility is again concerned with linear systems having dominant diagonal elements. The ingenuity of the computer is important in this procedure, as will be seen below. The first step in the computation is to define *residuals* $R_1, R_2, \ldots, R_n$ from the system (2-76) by the equations

$$\begin{aligned} R_1 &= b_1 - a_{11}x_1 - a_{12}x_2 - \cdots - a_{1n}x_n \\ R_2 &= b_2 - a_{21}x_1 - a_{22}x_2 - \cdots - a_{2n}x_n \\ &\cdots\cdots\cdots\cdots\cdots\cdots \\ R_n &= b_n - a_{n1}x_1 - a_{n2}x_2 - \cdots - a_{nn}x_n \end{aligned} \qquad (2\text{-}82)$$

The unknowns are then estimated, say by the system (2-81), and the corresponding residuals are calculated, after which the estimated values of the unknowns are successively modified, one or more at a time, such that the magnitudes of all residuals are reduced approximately to zero. Since the residuals are known at each step one usually focuses attention on the residual of largest magnitude to reduce it to zero. A helpful hint here is to note in (2-82) that if x_i is increased by 1 and all other unknowns are held fixed then R_j decreases by a_{ji}.

Example. A typical sequence of relaxations is shown below for the system

$$\begin{aligned} 9.37x_1 + 3.04x_2 - 2x_3 &= 3 \\ 2.05x_1 + 7.22x_2 + 1.22x_3 &= 6 \\ -1.41x_1 + 1.83x_2 + 6.30x_3 &= -4 \end{aligned}$$

$$x_1^{(0)} = \frac{3}{9.37} = 0.32 \qquad R_1 = 3 - 9.37x_1 - 3.04x_2 + 2x_3$$

$$x_2^{(0)} = \frac{6}{7.22} = 0.83 \qquad R_2 = 6 - 2.05x_1 - 7.22x_2 - 1.22x_3$$

$$x_3^{(0)} = \frac{-4}{6.3} = -0.63 \qquad R_3 = -4 + 1.41x_1 - 1.83x_2 - 6.30x_3$$

Step No.	x_1	x_2	x_3	R_1	R_2	R_3
0	0.32	0.83	−0.63	−3.78	0.11	−1.07

The largest residual in magnitude, at this stage, is $R_1 = -3.78$. Thus we decrease x_1 by a convenient amount, usually of the size $\frac{R_1}{a_{11}} = -\frac{3.78}{9.37} \approx -0.4$, and recompute the residuals.

1	−0.08	0.83	−0.63	−0.03	0.93	−1.63

At this stage $R_3 = -1.63$ is largest. Decrease x_3 by $\frac{R_3}{a_{33}} = \frac{-1.63}{6.30} \approx -0.27$ and proceed.

2	−0.08	0.83	−0.9	−0.57	1.26	0.07

Iterative procedures are described in detail in Bodewig, "Matrix Calculus," Interscience, New York, 1956.

Matrix Inversion

In some problems, such as those encountered in statistical regression analysis, it is essential that the system (2-76) be solved by matrix inversion of (2-77). Thus $X = A^{-1}B$ where A^{-1} is the inverse of A, defined under Algebra.

The number of methods for inverting matrices are many and varied. The methods previously described may be continued to obtain the inverse of the matrix (see Bodewig, *op. cit.*). In addition two procedures which are admirably suited to use on large-scale digital computers are given.

The Modified-square-root Method (**Choleski**). This is a direct method for inverting symmetric matrices. As will be seen the division by the square root of the leading element reduces the round-off errors and the square rooting of all elements brings all matrix elements nearer in value, which is helpful. The matrix A is inverted by the following sequence of calculations where

$$A^{-1} = \begin{bmatrix} c_{11} & c_{12} & c_{13} & \cdots & c_{1n} \\ c_{21} & c_{22} & \cdots & \cdots & c_{2n} \\ \cdots & \cdots & \cdots & \cdots & \cdots \\ c_{n1} & c_{n2} & \cdots & \cdots & c_{nn} \end{bmatrix}$$

Since A is symmetric A^{-1} is also symmetric, so that $c_{ij} = c_{ji}$. Hence only c_{ij}, $i \geq j$ need be calculated. In general calculate

$$t_{ii} = \sqrt{a_{ii} - \sum_{k=1}^{i-1} t_{ki}^2}$$

$$t_{ij} = \frac{a_{ij} - \sum_{k=1}^{i-1} t_{ki}t_{kj}}{t_{ii}} \qquad i \neq j,\ i > j \tag{2-83}$$

$$c_{ii} = \frac{1}{t_{ii}^2} - \frac{\sum_{k=i+1}^{n} t_{ik}c_{ik}}{t_{ii}}$$

$$c_{ij} = -\frac{\sum_{k=j}^{n} t_{ik}c_{kj}}{t_{ii}} \qquad \text{and} \qquad c_{ij} = c_{ji}$$

These equations are illustrated below for a 4 × 4 matrix.

$$t_{11} = \sqrt{a_{11}} \qquad t_{12} = \frac{a_{12}}{t_{11}} \qquad t_{13} = \frac{a_{13}}{t_{11}} \qquad t_{14} = \frac{a_{14}}{t_{11}}$$

$$t_{22} = \sqrt{a_{22} - t_{12}^2} \qquad t_{23} = \frac{a_{23} - t_{12}t_{13}}{t_{22}}$$

$$t_{24} = \frac{a_{24} - t_{12}t_{14}}{t_{22}} \qquad t_{33} = \sqrt{a_{33} - t_{13}^2 - t_{23}^2}$$

$$t_{34} = \frac{a_{34} - t_{13}t_{14} - t_{23}t_{24}}{t_{33}} \qquad t_{44} = \sqrt{a_{44} - t_{14}^2 - t_{24}^2 - t_{34}^2}$$

and finally it is necessary to calculate the c_{ij} in reverse order. That is,

$$c_{44} = \frac{1}{t_{44}^2} \qquad c_{34} = \frac{-t_{34}c_{44}}{t_{33}} \qquad c_{24} = \frac{-t_{23}c_{34} - t_{24}c_{44}}{t_{22}}$$

$$c_{14} = \frac{-t_{12}c_{24} - t_{13}c_{34} - t_{14}c_{44}}{t_{11}} \qquad c_{33} = \frac{1}{t_{33}^2} - \frac{t_{34}c_{34}}{t_{33}}$$

$$c_{23} = \frac{-t_{23}c_{33} - t_{24}c_{34}}{t_{22}} \quad \cdots \quad \cdots$$

$$c_{11} = \frac{1}{t_{11}^2} - \frac{t_{12}c_{12} + t_{13}c_{13} + t_{14}c_{14}}{t_{11}}$$

The Smith Algorithm. This procedure is again a direct procedure which basically consists of a factorization of the matrix A until it is reduced to the identity by elementary row and column operations. The algorithm is outlined in Bodewig (*op. cit.*, p. 195).

NUMERICAL SOLUTION OF NON-LINEAR EQUATIONS IN ONE VARIABLE

Special Methods for Polynomials

Consider a polynomial equation of degree n

$$P(x) = a_0x^n + a_1x^{n-1} + a_2x^{n-2} + \cdots + a_{n-1}x + a_n = 0 \tag{2-84}$$

with real coefficients. $P(x)$ has exactly n roots, which may be real or complex. If all the coefficients of $P(x)$ are integers then any rational root say r/s (r, s integers, having no common divisors) of $P(x)$ must be such that r is an integral divisor of a_n and s is an integral divisor of a_0. Further, any polynomial with rational coefficients may be converted into one with integral coefficients by multiplying by the lowest common multiple of the denominators of the coefficients.

Example. $3x^4 - \frac{5}{3}x^2 + \frac{1}{5}x - 2 = 0$. The lowest common multiple of the denominator is 15. Thus multiplying by 15 (which does not change the roots) gives $45x^4 - 25x^2 + 3x - 30 = 0$. The only possible rational roots r/s are such that r may have the values ±30, ±15, ±10, ±6, ±3, ±2, ±1. s may have the values ±45, ±15, ±9, ±5, ±3, ±1. The possible rational roots may then be formed from all possible quotients, having no common factor.

In addition to these results one can obtain an upper and lower bound for the real roots by the following device: If $a_0 > 0$ in Eq. (2-84) and if in (2-84) the first negative coefficient is preceded by k coefficients which are positive or zero, and if G is the greatest of the absolute values of the negative coefficients then each real root is less than $1 + \sqrt[k]{G/c_0}$.

Example. $P(x) = x^5 + 3x^4 - 7x^2 - 40x + 2 = 0$. Here $a_0 = 1$, $G = 40$, and $k = 3$ since we must supply 0 as the coefficient for x^3. Thus $1 + \sqrt[3]{40} \approx 4.42$ is an upper bound for the real roots.

A lower bound to the real roots may be found by applying the criterion to the equation $P(-x)$.

Example. $P(-x) = -x^5 + 3x^4 - 7x^2 + 40x + 2 = 0$ which is equivalent to $x^5 - 3x^4 + 7x^2 - 40x - 2 = 0$ since a_0 must be +. Then $a_0 = 1$, $G = 40$, and $k = 1$. Hence $-(1 + 40) = -41$ is a lower bound. Thus all real roots $-41 < r < 4.42$.

One last result is helpful in getting an estimate of how many positive and negative real roots there are.

Descartes Rule. The number of positive real roots of a polynomial with real coefficients is either equal to the number of changes in sign v or is less than v by a positive even integer. The number of negative roots of $f(x)$ is either equal to the number of variations of sign of $f(-x)$ or is less than this by a positive even integer.

Example. $f(x) = x^4 - 13x^2 + 4x - 2 = 0$ has three changes in sign; therefore, there are either three or one positive roots. $f(-x) = x^4 - 13x^2 - 4x - 2$ has one change in sign. Therefore, there is one negative root.

More information on properties of polynomials and special techniques may be found in Dickson, "New First Course in the Theory of Equations," Wiley, New York, 1939, and MacDuffee, "Theory of Equations," Wiley, New York, 1954.

The Graeffe Root-squaring Technique. This is an iterative method for finding the roots of the algebraic equation

$$f(x) = a_0x^p + a_1x^{p-1} + \cdots + a_{p-1}x + a_p = 0 \qquad (2\text{-}85)$$

If the roots are $r_1, r_2, r_3, \cdots$ then one can write

$$S_p = r_1^p\left(1 + \frac{r_2^p}{r_1^p} + \frac{r_3^p}{r_1^p} + \cdots\right) \qquad (2\text{-}86)$$

and if one root is larger than all the others, say r_1, then for p large enough all terms (other than 1) would become negligible and thus

$$S_p \approx r_1^p$$

or

$$\lim_{p\to\infty} S_p^{1/p} = r_1$$

The Graeffe procedure provides an efficient way for computing S_p of (2-86) via a sequence of equations such that the roots of each equation are the squares of the roots of the preceding equations in the sequence. This serves the purpose of ultimately obtaining an equation whose roots are so widely separated in magnitude that they may be read approximately from the equation by inspection. The basic procedure is illustrated for a polynomial of degree 4

$$f(x) = a_0x^4 + a_1x^3 + a_2x^2 + a_3x + a_4 = 0 \qquad (2\text{-}87)$$

Rewrite (2-87) as

$$a_0x^4 + a_2x^2 + a_4 = -a_1x^3 - a_3x$$

and square both sides so that upon grouping

$$a_0^2x^8 + (2a_0a_2 - a_1^2)x^6 + (2a_0a_4 - 2a_1a_3 + a_2^2)x^4 + (2a_2a_4 - a_3^2)x^2 + a_4^2 = 0 \qquad (2\text{-}88)$$

Since this involves only even powers of x we may set $y = x^2$ and rewrite (2-38) as

$$a_0^2y^4 + (2a_0a_2 - a_1^2)y^3 + (2a_0a_4 - 2a_1a_3 + a_2^2)y^2 + (2a_2a_4 - a_3^2)y + a_4^2 = 0$$

whose roots are the squares of the original equation. If we repeat this process again the new equation has roots which are the fourth power, etc. After p such operations the roots are 2^p (original roots). If at any stage we write the coefficients of the unknown in sequence

$$a_0^{(p)} \quad a_1^{(p)} \quad a_2^{(p)} \quad a_3^{(p)} \quad a_4^{(p)}$$

then to get the new sequence $a_i^{(p+1)}$ write $a_i^{(p+1)} = 2a_0^{(p)}$ (times the symmetric coefficient with respect to $a_i^{(p)}$) $- 2a_1^{(p)}$ (times symmetric coefficient) $- \cdots (-1)^i a_i^{(p)2}$.

Now if the roots are r_1, r_2, r_3, r_4, then $a_1/a_0 = -\sum_{i=1}^{4} r_i$, $a_1^{(1)}/a_0^{(1)} = -\Sigma r_i^2, \ldots, a_1^{(p)}/a_0^{(p)} = -\Sigma r_i^{2^p}$. If the roots are all distinct and r_1 is the largest in magnitude then eventually

$$r_1^{2^p} \approx -\frac{a_1^{(p)}}{a_0^{(p)}}$$

And if r_2 is the next largest in magnitude then

$$r_2^{2^p} \approx -\frac{a_2^{(p)}}{a_1^{(p)}}$$

And in general $a_n^{(p)}/a^{(p)}_{n-1} \approx -r_n^{2^p}$. This procedure is easily generalized to polynomials of arbitrary degree and specialized to the case of multiple and complex roots. An excellent discussion of these ideas is found in Householder and Hildebrand. The signs of the roots are undetermined but these may be obtained by trial of both possibilities.

Example. $f(x) = x^4 - 7x^3 + 9x^2 + 7x - 10 = 0$.

Step p	$a_0^{(p)}$	$a_1^{(p)}$	$a_2^{(p)}$	$a_3^{(p)}$	$a_4^{(p)}$
0	1	−7	9	7	−10
1	1	−31	159	−229	100
2	1	−643	11,283	−20,641	10,000

Thus

$$r_1^4 \approx -\frac{a_1^{(2)}}{a_0^{(2)}} = 643 \qquad r_1 \approx +5.04$$

$$r_2^4 \approx -\frac{a_2^{(2)}}{a_1^{(2)}} = 17.6 \qquad r_2 \approx +2.05$$

and so forth. The actual roots are +5, +2, +1, and −1.

Other methods include Bernoulli iteration, Bairstow iteration, Lin iteration, and so forth. These may be found in the cited literature. In addition the methods given below may be used for the numerical solution of polynomials.

General Methods for Non-linear Equations in One Variable

Successive Substitutions. Let $f(x) = 0$ be the non-linear equation to be solved. If this is rewritten as $x = F(x)$ then an iterative scheme can be set up in the form $x_{k+1} = F(x_k)$. To start the iteration an initial guess must be obtained graphically or otherwise. The convergence or divergence of the procedure depends upon the method of writing $x = F(x)$, of which there will usually be several forms. A general rule to ensure convergence cannot be given. However, if a is a root of $f(x) = 0$, a necessary condition for convergence is that $|F'(x)| < 1$ in that interval about a in which the iteration proceeds. (This means the iteration cannot converge unless $|F'(x)| < 1$, but it does not ensure convergence.) This process is called *first order* because the error in x_{k+1} is proportional to the first power of the error in x_k.

Example. $f(x) = x^3 - x - 1 = 0$. A rough plot shows a real root of approximately 1.3. The equation can be written in the form $x = F(x)$ in several ways such as $x = x^3 - 1$, $x = \dfrac{1}{x^2 - 1}$, and $x = (1 + x)^{1/3}$. In the first case $F'(x) = 3x^2 = 5.07$ at $x = 1.3$; in the second $F(1.3) = 5.46$ and only in the third case is $F'(1.3) < 1$. Hence only the third iterative process has a chance to converge. This is illustrated below.

Iteration Table

Step k	$x = \dfrac{1}{x^2 - 1}$	$x = x^3 - 1$	$x = (1 + x)^{1/3}$
0	1.3	1.3	1.3
1	1.4493	1.197	1.32
2	0.9087	0.7150	1.3238
3	−5.737	−0.6345	1.3247
4	....	....	1.3247

Methods of Perturbation. Let $f(x) = 0$ be the equation. In general the iterative relation is

$$x_{k+1} = x_k - \frac{f(x_k)}{\alpha_k} \tag{2-89}$$

where the iteration begins with x_0 as an initial approximation and α_k as some functional.

The Newton-Raphson Procedure. This variant chooses $\alpha_k = f'(x_k)$ where $f' = df/dx$ and geometrically consists of replacing the graph of $f(x)$ by the tangent line at $x = x_k$ in each successive step. If $f'(x)$ and $f''(x)$ have the same sign throughout an interval $a \leq x \leq b$ containing the solution, with $f(a)$, $f(b)$ of opposite signs, then the process converges starting from any x_0 in the interval $a \leq x \leq b$. The process is second order.

Example
$$f(x) = x - 1 + \frac{(0.5)^x - 0.5}{0.3}$$
$$f'(x) = 1 - 2.3105[0.5]^x$$

An approximate root (obtained graphically) is 2.

Step k	x_k	$f(x_k)$	$f'(x_k)$
0	2	0.1667	0.4224
1	1.605	−0.002	0.2655
2	1.6125	−0.0005	......

The Method of False Position. This variant is commenced by finding x_0 and x_1 such that $f(x_0)$, $f(x_1)$ are of opposite signs. Then α_1 = slope of secant line joining $[x_0, f(x_0)]$ and $[x_1, f(x_1)]$ so that

$$x_2 = x_1 - \frac{x_1 - x_0}{f(x_1) - f(x_0)} f(x_1)$$

In each following step α_k is the slope of the line joining $[x_k, f(x_k)]$ to the most recently determined point where $f(x_j)$ has the opposite sign from that of $f(x_k)$. This method is of first order.

The Method of Wegstein. This is a variant of the method of successive substitutions which forces and/or accelerates convergence. The iterative procedure $x_{k+1} = F(x_k)$ is revised by setting $\hat{x}_{k+1} = F(x_k)$ and then taking $x_{k+1} = qx_k + (1 - q)\hat{x}_{k+1}$. Wegstein found that suitably chosen q's are related to the basic process as follows:

Behavior of Successive Substitution Process	Range of Optimum q
Oscillatory convergence..........	$0 < q < \frac{1}{2}$
Oscillatory divergence..........	$\frac{1}{2} < q < 1$
Monotonic convergence..........	$q < 0$
Monotonic divergence..........	$1 < q$

At each step q may be calculated to give a locally optimum value by setting

$$q = \frac{x_{k+1} - x_k}{x_{k+1} - 2x_k + x_{k-1}}$$

Numerical Solution of Simultaneous Non-linear Equations

The techniques illustrated here will be demonstrated for two simultaneous equations $f(x, y) = 0$, $g(x, y) = 0$. They immediately generalize to more than two simultaneous equations.

The Method of Successive Substitutions. The two simultaneous equations can be written in various ways in equivalent forms

$$x = F(x, y) \qquad y = G(x, y) \tag{2-90}$$

And the method of successive substitutions can be based on

$$x_{k+1} = F(x_k, y_k) \qquad y_{k+1} = G(x_k, y_k)$$

Again the procedure is of the first order and a necessary condition for convergence is

$$\left|\frac{\partial F}{\partial x}\right| + \left|\frac{\partial F}{\partial y}\right| < 1 \qquad \left|\frac{\partial G}{\partial x}\right| + \left|\frac{\partial G}{\partial y}\right| < 1$$

in the iteration neighborhood of the true solution.

The Newton-Raphson Procedure. Using (2-90) for the two simultaneous equations start from an approximation, say (x_0, y_0), obtained graphically or from a two-way table. Then solve successively the linear equations

$$\begin{aligned} \Delta x_k \frac{\partial f}{\partial x}(x_k, y_k) + \Delta y_k \frac{\partial f}{\partial y}(x_k, y_k) &= -f(x_k, y_k) \\ \Delta x_k \frac{\partial g}{\partial x}(x_k, y_k) + \Delta y_k \frac{\partial g}{\partial y}(x_k, y_k) &= -g(x_k, y_k) \end{aligned} \tag{2-91}$$

for Δx_k and Δy_k. Then the $k + 1$ approximation is given from $x_{k+1} = x_k + \Delta x_k$, $y_{k+1} = y_k + \Delta y_k$. A modification consists in solving equations (2-91) with (x_k, y_k) replaced by (x_0, y_0) (or other suitable pair later on in the iteration) in the derivatives. This means the derivatives (and therefore the coefficients of Δx_k, Δy_k) are independent of k. Hence the results become

$$\Delta x_k = \frac{-f(x_k, y_k)(\partial g/\partial y)(x_0, y_0) + g(x_k, y_k)(\partial f/\partial y)(x_0, y_0)}{(\partial f/\partial x)(x_0, y_0)(\partial g/\partial y)(x_0, y_0) - (\partial f/\partial y)(x_0, y_0)(\partial g/\partial x)(x_0, y_0)}$$
$$\Delta y_k = \frac{-g(x_k, y_k)(\partial f/\partial x)(x_0, y_0) + f(x_k, y_k)(\partial g/\partial x)(x_0, y_0)}{(\partial f/\partial x)(x_0, y_0)(\partial g/\partial y)(x_0, y_0) - (\partial f/\partial y)(x_0, y_0)(\partial g/\partial x)(x_0, y_0)} \tag{2-92}$$

and $x_{k+1} = \Delta x_k + x_k$, $y_{k+1} = \Delta y_k + y_k$. Such an alteration of the basic technique reduces the rapidity of convergence.

Example.
$$f(x, y) = 4x^2 + 6x - 4xy + 2y^2 - 3$$
$$g(x, y) = 2x^2 - 4xy + y^2$$

By plotting one of the approximate roots is found to be $x_0 = 0.4$, $y_0 = 0.3$. At this point there results $\partial f/\partial x = 8$, $\partial f/\partial y = -0.4$, $\partial g/\partial x = 0.4$, and $\partial g/\partial y = -1$. Hence from (2.92)

$$x_{k+1} = x_k + \Delta x_k = x_k + \frac{-f(x_k, y_k) - 0.4g(x_k, y_k)}{8(-1) - (-0.4)(0.4)}$$
$$= x_k - 0.12755f(x_k, y_k) - 0.05102g(x_k, y_k)$$

and $\quad y_{k+1} = y_k - 0.05102f(x_k, y_k) + 1.02041g(x_k, y_k)$

The first few iteration steps are shown below.

Step k	x_k	y_k	$f(x_k, y_k)$	$g(x_k, y_k)$
0	0.4	0.3	−0.26	0.07
1	0.43673	0.24184	0.078	0.0175
2	0.42672	0.25573	−0.0170	−0.007
3	0.42925	0.24943	0.0077	0.0010

The Method of Continuity. In the case of n equations in n unknowns, when n is large, determining the approximate solution may involve considerable effort. In such a case the method of continuity is admirably suited for use on either digital or analog computers. It consists basically of the introduction of an extra variable into the n equations

$$f_i(x_1, x_2, \ldots, x_n) = 0 \qquad i = 1, \ldots, n \qquad (2\text{-}93)$$

and replacing them by

$$f_i(x_1, x_2, \ldots, x_n, \lambda) = 0 \qquad i = 1, \ldots, n \qquad (2\text{-}94)$$

where λ is introduced in such a way that the functions (2-94) depend in a simple way upon λ and reduce to an easily solvable system for $\lambda = 0$ and to the original equations (2-93) for $\lambda = 1$. A system of ordinary differential equations, with independent variable λ, is then constructed by differentiating (2-94) with respect to λ. There results

$$\sum_{j=1}^{n} \frac{\partial f_i}{\partial x_j}\frac{dx_j}{d\lambda} + \frac{\partial f_i}{\partial \lambda} = 0 \qquad (2\text{-}95)$$

where $x_1, \ldots, x_n$ are considered as functions of λ. The equations (2-95) are integrated, with initial conditions obtained from (2-94) with $\lambda = 0$, from $\lambda = 0$ to $\lambda = 1$. If the solution can be continued to $\lambda = 1$ the values of $x_1, \ldots, x_n$ for $\lambda = 1$ will be a solution of the original equations. If the integration becomes infinite the parameter λ must be introduced in a different fashion. Integration of the differential equations (which are usually non-linear in λ) may be accomplished on an analog computer or by digital means using techniques described under Numerical Solution of Ordinary Differential Equations.

Example.

$$f(x, y) = 2 + x + y - x^2 + 8xy + y^3 = 0$$
$$g(x, y) = 1 + 2x + 3y + x^2 + xy - ye^x = 0$$

Introduce λ as

$$f(x, y, \lambda) = (2 + x + y) + \lambda(-x^2 + 8xy + y^3) = 0$$
$$g(x, y, \lambda) = (1 + 2x - 3y) + \lambda(x^2 + xy - ye^x) = 0$$

For $\lambda = 1$ these reduce to the original equations but for $\lambda = 0$ they are the linear system

$$x + y = -2$$
$$2x - 3y = -1$$

which has the unique solution $x = -1.4$, $y = -0.6$. The differential equations (2-95) become in this case

$$\begin{aligned}\frac{\partial f}{\partial x}\frac{dx}{d\lambda} + \frac{\partial f}{\partial y}\frac{dy}{d\lambda} &= -\frac{\partial f}{\partial \lambda}\\ \frac{\partial g}{\partial x}\frac{dx}{d\lambda} + \frac{\partial g}{\partial y}\frac{dy}{d\lambda} &= -\frac{\partial g}{\partial \lambda}\end{aligned} \qquad (2\text{-}96)$$

or

$$\frac{dx}{d\lambda} = \frac{\dfrac{\partial f}{\partial y}\dfrac{\partial g}{\partial \lambda} - \dfrac{\partial f}{\partial \lambda}\dfrac{\partial g}{\partial y}}{\dfrac{\partial f}{\partial x}\dfrac{\partial g}{\partial y} - \dfrac{\partial f}{\partial y}\dfrac{\partial g}{\partial x}}$$

$$\frac{dy}{d\lambda} = \frac{\dfrac{\partial f}{\partial \lambda}\dfrac{\partial g}{\partial x} - \dfrac{\partial f}{\partial x}\dfrac{\partial g}{\partial \lambda}}{\dfrac{\partial f}{\partial x}\dfrac{\partial g}{\partial y} - \dfrac{\partial f}{\partial y}\dfrac{\partial g}{\partial x}}$$

where

$$\frac{\partial f}{\partial x} = 1 - 2\lambda x + 8\lambda y$$
$$\frac{\partial f}{\partial y} = 1 + 8\lambda x + 3\lambda y^2$$
$$\frac{\partial g}{\partial x} = 2 + 2\lambda x + \lambda y - \lambda y e^x$$
$$\frac{\partial g}{\partial y} = -3 + \lambda x - \lambda e^x$$

Equations (2-96) are integrated in λ (starting with $x = -1.4$, $y = -0.6$ at $\lambda = 0$) to $\lambda = 1$. The values of x, y at $\lambda = 1$ constitute the solution.

Other Methods. Other methods can be found in the literature. To be especially mentioned are methods of steepest descent (see Householder) and relaxation methods (see Southwell, "Relaxation Methods in Theoretical Physics," Oxford, New York, 1946).

INTERPOLATION AND FINITE DIFFERENCES

The practicing engineer finds it constantly necessary to refer to tables as sources of information. Consequently interpolation, or that procedure of "reading between the lines of the table," is a necessary topic in numerical analysis.

Linear Interpolation. If a function $f(x)$ is approximately linear in a certain range then the ratio $\dfrac{f(x_1) - f(x_0)}{x_1 - x_0} = f[x_0, x_1]$ is approximately independent of x_0, x_1 in the range. The linear approximation to the function $f(x)$, $x_0 < x < x_1$ then leads to the interpolation formula

$$\begin{aligned} f(x) &\approx f(x_0) + (x - x_0)f[x_0, x_1]\\ &\approx f(x_0) + \frac{x - x_0}{x_1 - x_0}[f(x_1) - f(x_0)] \qquad (2\text{-}97)\\ &\approx \frac{1}{x_1 - x_0}[(x_1 - x)f(x_0) - (x_0 - x)f(x_1)]\end{aligned}$$

Example. Find cosh 0.83 by linear interpolation given cosh 0.8 and cosh 0.9.

x_i	$f(x_i)$	$x_i - 0.83$
0.8	1.33743	−0.03
0.9	1.43309	+0.07

$$f(0.83) \approx \frac{1}{0.10}[(0.07)(1.33743) - (-0.03)(1.43309)]$$
$$f(0.83) \approx 1.36613$$

Since the true five-place value is 1.36468, it is seen that here linear interpolation gives three significant figures.

Divided Differences of Higher Order and Higher-order Interpolation. The first-order divided difference $f[x_0, x_1]$ was defined above. Divided differences of second and higher order are defined iteratively by

$$f[x_0, x_1, x_2] = \frac{f[x_1, x_2] - f[x_0, x_1]}{x_2 - x_0}$$
$$\cdot$$
$$\cdot$$
$$\cdot \qquad (2\text{-}98)$$
$$f[x_0, x_1, \ldots, x_k] = \frac{f[x_1, \ldots, x_k] - f[x_0, x_1, \ldots, x_{k-1}]}{x_k - x_0}$$

and a convenient form for computational purposes is

$$f[x_0, x_1, \ldots, x_k] = \sum_{j=0}^{k}{}' \frac{f(x_j)}{(x_j - x_0)(x_j - x_1)\cdots(x_j - x_k)}$$

for any $k \geq 0$, where the $'$ means the term $(x_j - x_j)$ is omitted in the denominator. For example,

$$f[x_0, x_1, x_2] = \frac{f(x_0)}{(x_0 - x_1)(x_0 - x_2)} + \frac{f(x_1)}{(x_1 - x_0)(x_1 - x_2)} + \frac{f(x_2)}{(x_2 - x_0)(x_2 - x_1)}$$

If the accuracy afforded by a linear approximation is inadequate, a generally more accurate result may be based upon the assumption that $f(x)$ may be approximated by a polynomial of degree 2 or higher over certain ranges. This assumption leads to *Newton's fundamental interpolation formula* with divided differences

$$\begin{aligned} f(x) &\approx f(x_0) + (x - x_0)f[x_0, x_1] \\ &+ (x - x_0)(x - x_1)f[x_0, x_1, x_2] + \cdots \\ &+ (x - x_0)(x - x_1) \cdots (x - x_{n-1})f[x_0, x_1, \ldots, x_n] \\ &+ E_n(x) \qquad (2\text{-}99) \end{aligned}$$

where $E_n(x) = \text{error} = \dfrac{1}{(n+1)!} f^{(n+1)}(\epsilon)\pi(x)$ where min. $(x_0, \ldots, x) < \epsilon <$ max. $(x_0, x_1, \ldots, x_n, x)$ and $\pi(x) = (x - x_0)(x - x_1) \cdots (x - x_n)$. In order to use (2-99) most effectively one may first form a divided-difference table. For example, for third-order interpolation the difference table is

$$\begin{array}{c|lccc} x_0 & f(x_0) & & & \\ & & f[x_0, x_1] & & \\ x_1 & f(x_1) & & f[x_0, x_1, x_2] & \\ & & f[x_1, x_2] & & f[x_0, x_1, x_2, x_3] \\ x_2 & f(x_2) & & f[x_1, x_2, x_3] & \\ & & f[x_2, x_3] & & \\ x_3 & f(x_3) & & & \end{array}$$

where each entry is given by taking the difference between diagonally adjacent entries to the left, divided by the abscissas corresponding to the ordinates intercepted by the diagonals passing through the calculated entry.

Example. Calculate by third-order interpolation the value of cosh 0.83 given cosh 0.60, cosh 0.80, cosh 0.90, and cosh 1.10.

$$\begin{array}{r|lccc} x_0 = 0.60 & 1.18547 & & & \\ & & 0.7598 & & \\ x_1 = 0.80 & 1.33743 & & 0.6560 & \\ & & 0.9566 & & 0.1586 \\ x_2 = 0.90 & 1.43309 & & 0.7353 & \\ & & 1.1772 & & \\ x_3 = 1.10 & 1.66852 & & & \end{array}$$

From (2.99) with $n = 3$ we have

$$\begin{aligned} \cosh 0.83 &\approx 1.18547 + (0.23)(0.7598) + (0.23)(0.03)(0.6560) \\ &+ (0.23)(0.03)(-0.07)(0.1586) = 1.36464 \end{aligned}$$

which varies from the true value by 0.00004.

Equally Spaced Forward Differences. Formulas (2-98) and (2-99) are given in general form for unequally spaced ordinates. If the ordinates are *equally spaced*, *i.e.*, $x_j - x_{j-1} = \Delta x$ for all j, then the first differences are denoted by $\Delta f(x_0) = f(x_1) - f(x_0)$ or $\Delta y_0 = y_1 - y_0$ where $y = f(x)$. The differences of these first differences, called second differences, are denoted by $\Delta^2 y_0$, $\Delta^2 y_1, \ldots, \Delta^2 y_n$. Thus

$$\Delta^2 y_0 = \Delta y_1 - \Delta y_0 = y_2 - y_1 - y_1 + y_0 = y_2 - 2y_1 + y_0$$

And in general

$$\Delta^j y_0 = \sum_{n=0}^{j} (-1)^n \binom{j}{n} y_{j-n}$$

where $\dbinom{j}{n} = \dfrac{j!}{n!(j-n)!}$ = binomial coefficients.

Thus

$$\begin{aligned} \Delta^4 y_0 &= \sum_{n=0}^{4} (-1)^n \binom{4}{n} y_{4-n} = \binom{4}{0} y_4 - \binom{4}{1} y_3 \\ &+ \binom{4}{2} y_2 - \binom{4}{3} y_1 + \binom{4}{4} y_0 = y_4 - 4y_3 + 6y_2 \\ &- 4y_1 + y_0 \end{aligned}$$

A horizontal-difference table is convenient here. This is illustrated below for a particular example. Note that decimal points are often omitted.

Example.

x	y	Δy	$\Delta^2 y$	$\Delta^3 y$	$\Delta^4 y$	$\Delta^5 y$
1.5	2.129					
1.6	2.376	247				
1.7	2.645	269	22			
1.8	2.942	297	28	6		
1.9	3.268	326	29	1	−5	
2.0	3.627	359	33	4	3	8

If y = polynomial of degree n
$= a_n x^n + a_{n-1}x^{n-1} + \cdots + a_0 \qquad \Delta x = \text{constant}$
then Δy = polynomial of degree $n - 1$

.

.

.

$\Delta^j y$ = polynomial of degree $n - j \qquad j \le n$
$\Delta^n y = a_n(\Delta x)^n n!$

That is, if the values of the independent variable are all separated by equal intervals then the nth differences of a polynomial of the nth degree are constant. Conversely, if the nth differences of a tabulated function are constant when the independent variable is separated by equal intervals then the function is a polynomial of degree n. This result is quite useful, for it allows one to select a polynomial of appropriate degree to use to fit data.

Example. The data* below when differenced show that the approximate relation between x and y is a cubic, since the third differences are sensibly constant.

x	y	Δy	$\Delta^2 y$	$\Delta^1 y$
0	2.105			
0.2	2.808	703		
0.4	3.614	806	103	
0.6	4.604	990	184	81
0.8	5.857	1253	263	79
1.0	7.451	1594	341	78
1.2	9.467	2016	422	81
1.4	11.985	2518	502	80

Lagrange Interpolation Formulas. The Newton formulas (2-99) are expressed in terms of divided differences. It is often useful to have interpolation formulas expressed explicitly in terms of the ordinates involved. This is accomplished by the Lagrange interpolation polynomial of degree n

$$y(x) = \sum_{j=0}^{n} \frac{\pi(x)}{(x - x_j)\pi'(x_j)} f(x_j) \qquad (2\text{-}100)$$

where $\pi(x) = (x - x_0)(x - x_1) \cdots (x - x_n)$
$\pi'(x_j) = (x_j - x_0)(x_j - x_1) \cdots (x_j - x_n)$
where $(x_j - x_j)$ is the omitted factor. Thus

$$f(x) = y(x) + E_n(x)$$
$$E_n(x) = \frac{1}{(n+1)!} \pi(x) f^{(n+1)}(\epsilon)$$

Example. The interpolation polynomial of degree 3 is

$$\begin{aligned} y(x) &= \frac{(x - x_1)(x - x_2)(x - x_3)}{(x_0 - x_1)(x_0 - x_2)(x_0 - x_3)} f(x_0) \\ &+ \frac{(x - x_0)(x - x_2)(x - x_3)}{(x_1 - x_0)(x_1 - x_2)(x_1 - x_3)} f(x_1) \\ &+ \frac{(x - x_0)(x - x_1)(x - x_3)}{(x_2 - x_0)(x_2 - x_1)(x_2 - x_3)} f(x_2) \\ &+ \frac{(x - x_0)(x - x_1)(x - x_2)}{(x_3 - x_0)(x_3 - x_1)(x_3 - x_2)} f(x_3) \end{aligned}$$

* Reprinted by permission from I. S. and E. S. Sokolnikoff, "Higher Mathematics for Engineers and Physicists," McGraw-Hill, New York, 1941.

Thus directly from the data

x	0	1	3	4
$f(x)$	1	1	−1	2

we have as an interpolation polynomial $y(x)$ for $f(x)$

$$y(x) = 1 \cdot \frac{(x-1)(x-3)(x-4)}{(0-1)(0-3)(0-4)} + 1\,\frac{x(x-3)(x-4)}{(1-0)(1-3)(1-4)}$$
$$-1 \cdot \frac{x(x-1)(x-4)}{(3-0)(3-1)(3-4)} + 2\,\frac{(x-0)(x-1)(x-3)}{(4-0)(4-1)(4-3)}$$

Other Difference Methods (Equally Spaced Ordinates), Backward Differences. The backward differences denoted by

$$\nabla f(x) = f(x) - f(x-h)$$
$$\nabla^2 f(x) = \nabla f(x) - \nabla f(x-h) \quad \cdots$$
$$\nabla f^n(x) = \nabla^{n-1}f(x) - \nabla^{n-1}f(x-h)$$

are useful for calculation near the end of tabulated data.

Central Differences. The central difference denoted by

$$\delta f(x) = f\left(x+\frac{h}{2}\right) - f\left(x-\frac{h}{2}\right)$$
$$\delta^n f(x) = \delta^{n-1}f\left(x+\frac{h}{2}\right) - \delta^{n-1}f\left(x-\frac{h}{2}\right)$$

is useful for calculating at the interior points of tabulated data.

Also to be found in the literature already cited are Gaussian, Stirling, Bessel, Everett, Comrie differences, and so forth.

Inverse Interpolation. This is the process of finding the value of the independent variable or abscissa corresponding to a given value of the function when the latter is between two tabulated values of the abscissa. One method of accomplishing this is to use Lagrange's interpolation formula in the form

$$x = \psi(y) = \sum_{j=0}^{n} \frac{\pi(y)}{(y-y_j)\pi'(y_j)}\, x_j, \text{ where } x \text{ is expressed}$$

as a function of y. Other methods revolve about methods of iteration. These may be found in Scarborough (*op. cit.*).

NUMERICAL DIFFERENTIATION

Numerical differentiation should be avoided wherever possible, particularly when data are empirical and subject to appreciable observation errors. Errors in data can affect numerical derivatives quite strongly; *i.e.*, differentiation is a roughening process. When such a calculation must be made, it is usually desirable first to *smooth* the data to a certain extent.

The Use of Interpolation Formula. If the data are given over equidistant values of the independent variable x, an interpolation formula such as the Newton formula (see Hildebrand) may be used and the resulting formula differentiated analytically. If the independent variable is not at equidistant values then Lagrange's formulas must be used. By differentiating *three-* and *five-*point Lagrange interpolation formulas the following differentiation formulas result for equally spaced tabular points:

Three-point Formulas. Let x_0, x_1, x_2 be the three points.

$$f'(x_0) = \frac{1}{2h}[-3f(x_0) + 4f(x_1) - f(x_2)] + \frac{h^2}{3}f'''(\epsilon)$$
$$f'(x_1) = \frac{1}{2h}[-f(x_0) + f(x_2)] - \frac{h^2}{6}f'''(\epsilon) \qquad (2\text{-}101)$$
$$f'(x_2) = \frac{1}{2h}[f(x_0) - 4f(x_1) + 3f(x_2)] + \frac{h^2}{3}f'''(\epsilon)$$

where the last term is an error term $\min_j x_j < \epsilon < \max_j x_j$.

Five-point Formulas. Let x_0, x_1, x_2, x_3, x_4 be the five values of the equally spaced independent variable and $f_j = f(x_j)$.

$$f'(x_0) = \frac{1}{12h}[-25f_0 + 48f_1 - 36f_2 + 16f_3 - 3f_4] + \frac{h^4}{5}f^{(v)}(\epsilon)$$
$$f'(x_1) = \frac{1}{12h}[-3f_0 - 10f_1 + 18f_2 - 6f_3 + f_4] - \frac{h^4}{20}f^{(v)}(\epsilon)$$
$$f'(x_2) = \frac{1}{12h}[f_0 - 8f_1 + 8f_3 - f_4] + \frac{h^4}{30}f^{(v)}(\epsilon) \qquad (2\text{-}102)$$
$$f'(x_3) = \frac{1}{12h}[-f_0 + 6f_1 - 18f_2 + 10f_3 + 3f_4] - \frac{h^4}{20}f^{(v)}(\epsilon)$$
$$f'(x_4) = \frac{1}{12h}[3f_0 - 16f_1 + 36f_2 - 48f_3 + 25f_4] + \frac{h^4}{5}f^{(v)}(\epsilon)$$

and the last term is again an error term.

Smoothing Techniques. These techniques involve the approximation of the tabular data by a least-squares fit of the data using some known functional form, usually a polynomial (for the concept of least squares see Statistics). In place of approximating $f(x)$ by a single least-squares polynomial of degree n over the entire range of the tabulation, it is often desirable to replace each tabulated value by the value taken on by a least-squares polynomial of degree n relevant to a subrange of $2M + 1$ points centered, where possible, at the point for which the entry is to be modified. Thus each smoothed value replaces a tabulated value. Let $f_j = f(x_j)$ be the tabular points and y_j = smoothed values

First-degree Least Squares with Three Points.

$$y_0 = \tfrac{1}{6}[5f_0 + 2f_1 - f_2]$$
$$y_1 = \tfrac{1}{3}[f_0 + f_1 + f_2]$$
$$y_2 = \tfrac{1}{6}[-f_0 + 2f_1 + 5f_2]$$

First-degree Least Squares with Five Points.

$$y_0 = \tfrac{1}{5}[3f_0 + 2f_1 + f_2 - f_4]$$
$$y_1 = \tfrac{1}{10}[4f_0 + 3f_1 + 2f_2 + f_3]$$
$$y_2 = \tfrac{1}{5}[f_0 + f_1 + f_2 + f_3 + f_4]$$
$$y_3 = \tfrac{1}{10}[f_0 + 2f_1 + 3f_1 + 4f_3]$$
$$y_4 = \tfrac{1}{5}[-f_0 + f_2 + 2f_3 + 3f_4]$$

Thus, for example, if first-degree five-point least squares are used the central formula is used for all values except the first two and the last two, where the off-center formulas are used.

Third-degree Least Squares with Seven Points.

$$y_0 = \tfrac{1}{42}[39f_0 + 8f_1 - 4f_2 - 4f_3 + f_4 + 4f_5 - 2f_6]$$
$$y_1 = \tfrac{1}{42}[8f_0 + 19f_1 + 16f_2 + 6f_3 - 4f_4 - 7f_5 + 4f_6]$$
$$y_2 = \tfrac{1}{42}[-4f_0 + 16f_1 + 19f_2 + 12f_3 + 2f_4 - 4f_5 + f_6]$$
$$y_3 = \tfrac{1}{21}[-2f_0 + 3f_1 + 6f_2 + 7f_3 + 6f_4 + 3f_5 - 2f_6]$$
$$y_4 = \tfrac{1}{42}[f_0 - 4f_1 + 2f_2 + 12f_3 + 19f_4 + 16f_5 - 4f_6]$$
$$y_5 = \tfrac{1}{42}[4f_0 - 7f_1 - 4f_2 + 6f_3 + 16f_4 + 19f_5 + 8f_6]$$
$$y_6 = \tfrac{1}{42}[-2f_0 + 4f_1 + f_2 - 4f_3 - 4f_4 + 8f_5 + 39f_6] \qquad (2\text{-}103)$$

Additional smoothing formulas may be found in the references. After the data are smoothed any of the interpolation polynomials, or an appropriate least-squares polynomial, may be fitted and the results used to obtain the derivative.

Example.

x	0	1	2	3	4	5	6	7	8
$f(x)$	54	145	227	359	401	342	259	112	65

These data are smoothed with (2-103) as follows (two points are illustrated): To smooth the first point use the first formula of (2-103).

$$y_0 = \tfrac{1}{42}[39(54) + 8(145) - 4(227) - 4(359) + 401 + 4(342) - 2(259)]$$
$$= 51.7$$
$$y_2 = \tfrac{1}{42}[-4(54) + 16(145) + 19(227) + 12(359) + 2(401) - 4(342) + 259]$$
$$= 248.05$$

Least-squares Methods. *Parabolic.* For five evenly spaced neighboring abscissas labeled x_{-2}, x_{-1}, x_0, x_1, x_2 and their ordinates f_{-2}, f_{-1}, f_0, f_1, f_2 assume a parabola is fit by least squares. There results for all interior points, except the first and last two points of the data, the formula for the numerical derivative

$$f_0' = \frac{1}{10h}[-2f_{-2} - f_{-1} + f_1 + 2f_2]$$

For the first two data points designated by 0 and h

$$f'(0) = \frac{1}{20h}[-21f(0) + 13f(h) + 17f(2h) - 9f(3h)]$$
$$f'(h) = \frac{1}{20h}[-11f(0) + 3f(h) + 7f(2h) + f(3h)]$$

and for the last two given by $\alpha - h$, α

$$f'(\alpha - h) = \frac{1}{20h}[-11f(\alpha) + 3f(\alpha - h) + 7f(\alpha - 2h) + f(\alpha - 3h)]$$
$$f'(\alpha) = \frac{1}{20h}[-21f(\alpha) + 13f(\alpha - h) + 17f(\alpha - 2h) - 9f(\alpha - 3h)]$$

Quartic (Douglas-Avakian). A fourth-degree polynomial $y = a + bx + cx^2 + dx^3 + ex^4$ is fitted to seven adjacent equidistant points (spacing h) after a translation of coordinates has been made so that $x = 0$ corresponds to the central point of the seven. Thus these may be called $-3h$, $-2h$, $-h$, 0, h, $2h$, $3h$. Let k = coefficient of h for the seven points. That is, in $-3h$, $k = -3$. Then the coefficients for the polynomial are

$$a = \frac{524\sum f(kh) - 245\sum k^2f(kh) + 21\sum k^4f(kh)}{924}$$
$$b = \frac{397\sum kf(kh)}{1512h} - \frac{7\sum k^3f(kh)}{216h}$$
$$c = \frac{-840\sum f(kh) + 679\sum k^2f(kh) - 67\sum k^4f(kh)}{3168h^2}$$
$$d = \frac{-7\sum kf(kh) + \sum k^3f(kh)}{216h^3}$$
$$e = \frac{72\sum f(kh) - 67\sum k^2f(kh) + 7\sum k^4f(kh)}{3168h^4}$$

where all summations run from $k = -3$ to $k = +3$ and $f(kh)$ = tabular value at kh. The slope of the polynomial at $x = 0$ is $dy/dx = b$.

Example. Find the constants and dy/dz at $z = 3$ for the data*

$f(z)$	2	3	2	−1	−2	−2	−1
z	0	1	2	3	4	5	6

Here $h = 1$. Set $x = z - 3$, which moves the origin to the midpoint at $z = 3$. An aid to the hand calculation is given below.

z	y	x	k	$kf(kh)$	$k^2f(kh)$	$k^3f(kh)$	$k^4f(kh)$
0	2	−3	−3	−6	18	−54	162
1	3	−2	−2	−6	12	−24	48
2	2	−1	−1	−2	2	−2	2
3	−1	0	0	0	0	0	0
4	−2	1	1	−2	−2	−2	−2
5	−2	2	2	−4	−8	−16	−32
6	−1	3	3	−3	−9	−27	−81
Σ				−23	13	−125	97

Thus

$$a = \frac{524(1) - 245(13) + 21(97)}{924} = -0.68$$
$$b = \frac{397(-23)}{1{,}512} - \frac{7(-125)}{216} = -1.99$$

and so forth. The slope at $x = 0$ ($z = 3$) is

$$\frac{dy}{dx} = -1.99 = b$$

NUMERICAL INTEGRATION

A multitude of formulas have been developed to accomplish numerical integration which consists of computing the value of a definite integral from a set of numerical values of the integrand.

Newton-Cotes Integration Formulas (Equally Spaced Ordinates) for Functions Of One Variable

The definite integral $\int_a^b f(x)\,dx$ is to be evaluated.

Trapezoidal Rule. This formula consists of subdividing the interval $a \le x \le b$ into n subintervals a to $a + h$, $a + h$ to $a + 2h$, . . . and replacing the graph of $f(x)$ by the result of joining the ends of adjacent ordinates by line segments. If $f_j = f(x_j) = f(a + jh)$,

* Reprinted by permission from Mickley, Sherwood, and Reed, "Applied Mathematics in Chemical Engineering," McGraw-Hill, New York, 1957.

$f_0 = f(a)$, $f_n = f(b)$ the integration formula is

$$\int_a^b f(x)\,dx = \frac{h}{2}[f_0 + 2f_1 + 2f_2 + \cdots + 2f_{n-1} + f_n] + E_n$$

$$\text{where } |E_n| = \frac{nh^3}{12}|f''(\epsilon)| = \frac{(b-a)^3}{12n^2}|f''(\epsilon)| \qquad a < \epsilon < b$$

This procedure is not of high accuracy. However, if $f''(x)$ is continuous in $a < x < b$, the error goes to zero as $1/n^2$, $n \to \infty$.

Parabolic Rule (Simpson's Rule). This procedure consists of subdividing the interval $a < x < b$ into $n/2$ subintervals, each of length $2h$, where n is an *even* integer. Using the notation as above the integration formula is

$$\int_a^b f(x)\,dx = \frac{h}{3}[f_0 + 4f_1 + 2f_2 + 4f_3 + \cdots + 4f_{n-3} + 2f_{n-2} + 4f_{n-1} + f_n] + E_n$$

where

$$|E_n| = \frac{nh^5}{180}|f^{(\text{iv})}(\epsilon)| = \frac{(b-a)^5}{180n^4}|f^{(\text{iv})}(\epsilon)| \qquad a < \epsilon < b$$

This method approximates $f(x)$ by a parabola on each subinterval. This rule is generally more accurate than the trapezoidal rule. It is the most widely used integration formula.

Weddle's Rule. This procedure consists of subdividing the integral $a < x < b$ into $n/6$ subintervals, each of length $6h$, where n is a multiple of 6. Using the notation from the trapezoidal rule there results

$$\int_a^b f(x)\,dx = \frac{3h}{10}[f_0 + 5f_1 + f_2 + 6f_3 + f_4 + 5f_5 + 2f_6 + 5f_7 + f_8 + \cdots + 6f_{n-3} + f_{n-2} + 5f_{n-1} + f_n] + E_n$$

Note that the coefficients of f_j follow the rule 1, 5, 1, 6, 1, 5, 2, 5, 1, 6, 1, 5, 2, 5, etc. This procedure consists of approximating $f(x)$ by a polynomial of degree 6 on each subinterval. Here

$$E_n = \frac{nh^7}{1400}[10f^{(6)}(\epsilon_1) + 9h^2f^{(8)}(\epsilon_2)]$$

Two-dimensional Formula

Formulas for two-way integration over a rectangle, circle, ellipse, and so forth, may be developed by a double application of one-dimensional integration formulas. The two-dimensional generalization of the parabolic rule is given here. Consider the iterated integral

$\int_a^b \int_c^d f(x, y)\,dx\,dy$. Subdivide $c < x < d$ into m (even) subintervals of length $h = (d-c)/m$, and $a < y < b$ into n (even) subintervals of length $k = (b-a)/n$. This gives a subdivision of the rectangle $a \le y \le b$, $c \le x \le d$ into subrectangles. Let $x_j = c + jh$, $y_j = a + jk$, $f_{i,j} = f(x_i, y_j)$. Then

$$\int_a^b \int_c^d f(x, y)\,dx\,dy = \frac{hk}{9}[(f_{0,0} + 4f_{1,0} + 2f_{2,0} + \cdots + f_{m,0}) + 4(f_{0,1} + 4f_{1,1} + 2f_{2,1} + \cdots + f_{m,1}) + 2(f_{0,2} + 4f_{1,2} + 2f_{2,2} + \cdots + f_{m,2}) + \cdots + (f_{0,n} + 4f_{1,n} + 2f_{2,n} + \cdots + f_{m,n})] + E_{m,n}$$

$$\text{where } E_{m,n} = -\frac{hk}{90}\left[mh^4\frac{\partial^4 f(\epsilon_1\ \eta_1)}{\partial x^4} + nk^4\frac{\partial^4 f(\epsilon_2, \eta_2)}{\partial y^4}\right]$$

and ϵ_1, ϵ_2 lie in $c < x < d$, η_1, η_2 lie in $a < y < b$.

In addition the following literature is cited: Tyler, Numerical Integration of Functions of Several Variables [*Can. J. Math.*, 5, 393 (1953)]; Davis and Rabinowitz, Monte Carlo Experiments in Computing Multiple Integrals (*Math. Tables and Other Aids to Computation*, vol. 10, 1956).

Gaussian Integration Formulas (Unequally Spaced Abscissas)

These formulas are capable of yielding comparable accuracy with fewer ordinates than the equally spaced formulas. The ordinates are obtained by optimizing the distribution of the abscissas rather than by arbitrary choice. For the details of these formulas Hildebrand (*op. cit.*) is an excellent reference.

NUMERICAL SOLUTION OF ORDINARY DIFFERENTIAL EQUATIONS

A number of methods have been devised to solve ordinary differential equations numerically. The general references contain some information. A detailed reference is W. E. Milne, "Numerical Solution of Differential Equations" (Wiley, New York, 1953). By a numerical solution of a differential equation is meant a table of values of the function y and its derivatives over only a limited part of the range of the independent variable. Every differential equation of order n can be rewritten as n first-order differential equations. Therefore, the methods given below will be for first-order equations, and the generalization to simultaneous systems will be developed later.

The Modified Euler Method

This method is simple and yields modest accuracy. If extreme accuracy is desired a more sophisticated method should be selected. Let the first-order differential equation be $dy/dx = f(x, y)$ with the initial condition (x_0, y_0), that is, $y = y_0$ when $x = x_0$. The procedure is as follows:

Step 1. From the given initial conditions (x_0, y_0) compute $y_0' = f(x_0, y_0)$ and $y_0'' = \dfrac{\partial f(x_0, y_0)}{\partial x} + \dfrac{\partial f(x_0, y_0)}{\partial y}y_0'$. Then determine $y_1 = y_0 + hy_0' + \dfrac{h^2}{2}y_0''$ where h = subdivision of the independent variable.

Step 2. Determine $y_1' = f(x_1, y_1)$. $(x_1 = x_0 + h)$. These prepare us for:

Predictor Steps.

Step 3. For $n \ge 1$ calculate $(y_{n+1})_1 = y_{n-1} + 2hy_n'$.

Step 4. Calculate $(y'_{n+1})_1 = f[x_{n+1}, (y_{n+1})_1]$.

Corrector Steps.

Step 5. Calculate $(y_{n+1})_2 = y_n + \dfrac{h}{2}[(y'_{n+1})_1 + y_n']$

where y_n, y_n' without the subscripts are the previous values obtained by this process (or by steps 1 and 2).

Step 6. $(y'_{n+1})_2 = f[x_{n+1}, (y_{n+1})_2]$.

Step 7. Repeat the corrector steps 5 and 6 if necessary until the desired accuracy is produced in y_{n+1}, y'_{n+1}.

Example. Consider the equation $y' = 2y^2 + x$ with the initial conditions $y_0 = 1$ when $x_0 = 0$. Let $h = 0.1$. A few steps of the computation are illustrated.

Step No.	
1	$y_0' = 2y_0^2 + x_0 = 2$
	$y_0'' = 1 + 4y_0y_0' = 1 + 8 = 9$
	$y_1 = 1 + (0.1)(2) + \frac{(0.1)^2}{2}9 = 1.245$
2	$y_1' = 2y_1^2 + x_1 = 3.100 + 0.1 = 3.210$
3	$(y_2)_1 = y_0 + 2hy_1' = 1 + 2(0.1)3.210 = 1.642$
4	$(y_2')_1 = 2(y_2)_1^2 + x_2 = 5.592$
5	$(y_2)_2 = y_1 + \frac{0.1}{2}[(y_2')_1 + y_1'] = 1.685$
6	$(y_2')_2 = 2(y_2)_2^2 + x_2 = 5.878$
5 (repeat)	$(y_2)_3 = y_1 + (0.05)[(y_2')_2 + y_1'] = 1.699$
6 (repeat)	$(y_2')_3 = 2(y_2)_3^2 + x_2 = 5.974$

and so forth. This procedure may be programmed for a computer. A discussion of the truncation error of this process may be found in Milne.

Modified Adam's Method

The procedure given here was developed retaining third differences. It can then be considered as a more exact predictor-corrector method than the Euler method. The procedure is as follows for $dy/dx = f(x, y)$ and h = interval size:

Steps 1 *and* 2 are the same as in the Euler method.

Predictor Steps.

Step 3. $(y_{n+1})_1 = y_n + \frac{h}{24}[55y_n' - 59y'_{n-1} + 37y'_{n-2} - 9y'_{n-3}]$ where y_n', y'_{n-1}, etc., are calculated in step 1.

Step 4. $(y'_{n+1})_1 = f[x_{n+1}, (y_{n+1})_1]$.

Corrector Steps.

Step 5. $(y_{n+1})_2 = y_n + \frac{h}{24}[9(y'_{n+1})_1 + 19y_n' - 5y'_{n-1} + y'_{n-2}]$.

Step 6. $(y'_{n+1})_2 = f[x_{n+1}, (y_{n+1})_2]$.

Step 7. Iterate steps 5 and 6 if necessary.

Runge-Kutta Methods

These methods are self-starting and are inherently stable. Kopal (*op. cit.*) is the best reference for their derivation and discussion. Third- and fourth-order procedures are given below for $dy/dx = f(x, y)$, h = interval size.

Third Order (error $\approx h^4$).

$$k_0 = hf(x_n, y_n)$$
$$k_1 = hf(x_n + \tfrac{1}{2}h, y_n + \tfrac{1}{2}k_0)$$
$$k_2 = hf(x_n + h, y_n + 2k_1 - k_0)$$

and

$$y_{n+1} = y_n + \tfrac{1}{6}(k_0 + 4k_1 + k_2)$$

for all $n \geq 0$, with initial condition (x_0, y_0).

Fourth Order (error $\approx h^5$).

$$k_0 = hf(x_n, y_n)$$
$$k_1 = hf(x_n + \tfrac{1}{2}h, y_n + \tfrac{1}{2}k_0)$$
$$k_2 = hf(x_n + \tfrac{1}{2}h, y_n + \tfrac{1}{2}k_1)$$
$$k_3 = hf(x_n + h, y_n + k_2)$$
$$y_{n+1} = y_n + \tfrac{1}{6}(k_0 + 2k_1 + 2k_2 + k_3)$$

Example (third order). Let $dy/dx = x - 2y$ with initial condition $y_0 = 1$ when $x_0 = 0$ and let $h = 0.1$. Clearly $x_n = nh$. To calculate y_1 proceed as follows:

$$k_0 = 0.1[x_0 - 2y_0] = -0.2$$
$$k_1 = 0.1[0.05 - 2(1 - 0.1)] = -0.175$$
$$k_2 = 0.1[0.1 - 2(1 - 0.35 + 0.2)] = -0.16$$
$$y_1 = 1 + \tfrac{1}{6}(-0.2 - 0.7 - 0.16) = 0.8234$$

Equations of Higher Order and Simultaneous Differential Equations

Any differential equation of second or higher order can be reduced to a simultaneous system of first-order equations by the introduction of auxiliary variables. Consider the equations

$$\frac{d^2x}{dt^2} + xy\frac{dx}{dt} + z = e^z$$
$$\frac{d^2y}{dt^2} + zy\frac{dy}{dt} = 7 + t^2$$
$$\frac{d^2z}{dt^2} + xz\frac{dz}{dt} + x = e^x$$

If the new variables $x_1 = x$, $x_2 = y$, $x_3 = z$, $x_4 = dx_1/dt$ $x_5 = dx_2/dt$, $x_6 = dx_3/dt$ the equations become

$$\frac{dx_1}{dt} = x_4$$
$$\frac{dx_2}{dt} = x_5$$
$$\frac{dx_3}{dt} = x_6$$
$$\frac{dx_4}{dt} = -x_1x_2x_4 - x_3 + e^{x_3}$$
$$\frac{dx_5}{dt} = -x_3x_2x_5 + 7 + t^2$$
$$\frac{dx_6}{dt} = -x_1x_3x_6 - x_1 + e^{x_1}$$

which is a system of the general form

$$\frac{dx_i}{dt} = f_i(t, x_1, x_2, x_3, \ldots, x_n)$$

$i = 1, 2, \ldots, n$. Such systems may be solved by application simultaneously of any of the above numerical techniques. A Runge-Kutta method for

$$\frac{dx}{dt} = f(t, x, y)$$
$$\frac{dy}{dt} = g(t, x, y)$$

is given below. The fourth-order procedure is shown.

Starting at the initial conditions x_0, y_0, t_0 the next values x_1, y_1 are computed via the equations below (where $\Delta t = h$, $t_j = h + t_{j-1}$).

$$k_0 = hf(t_0, x_0, y_0) \qquad l_0 = hg(t_0, x_0, y_0)$$
$$k_1 = hf\left(t_0 + \frac{h}{2}, x_0 + \frac{k_0}{2}, y_0 + \frac{l_0}{2}\right)$$
$$l_1 = hg\left(t_0 + \frac{h}{2}, x_0 + \frac{k_0}{2}, y_0 + \frac{l_0}{2}\right)$$
$$k_2 = hf\left(t_0 + \frac{h}{2}, x_0 + \frac{k_1}{2}, y_0 + \frac{l_1}{2}\right)$$
$$l_2 = hg\left(t_0 + \frac{h}{2}, x_0 + \frac{k_1}{2}, y_0 + \frac{l_1}{2}\right)$$
$$k_3 = hf(t_0 + h, x_0 + k_2, y_0 + l_2)$$
$$l_3 = hg(t_0 + h, x_0 + k_2, y_0 + l_2)$$

and

$$x_1 = x_0 + \tfrac{1}{6}(k_0 + 2k_1 + 2k_2 + k_3)$$
$$y_1 = y_0 + \tfrac{1}{6}(l_0 + 2l_1 + 2l_2 + l_3)$$

To continue the computation, replace t_0, x_0, y_0, in the above formulas, by $t_1 = t_0 + h$, x_1, y_1 just calculated. Extension of this method to more than two equations follows precisely this same pattern.

NUMERICAL SOLUTION OF INTEGRAL EQUATIONS

In this section is considered a method of solving, numerically, the Fredholm integral equation of the second kind

$$u(x) = f(x) + \lambda \int_a^b k(x, t)u(t)\, dt \qquad \text{for } u(x) \qquad (2\text{-}104)$$

The method discussed arises because a definite integral can be closely approximated by any of several numerical integration formulas (each of which arises by approximating the function by some polynomial over an interval). Thus the definite integral in (2-104) can be replaced by an integration formula and (2-104) may be written

$$u(x) = f(x) + \lambda(b - a)\left[\sum_{i=1}^{n} c_i k(x, t_i)u(t_i)\right] \qquad (2\text{-}105)$$

where $t_1, \ldots, t_n$ are points of subdivision of the t-axis, $a \leq t \leq b$, and the c's are coefficients whose values depend upon the type of numerical integration formula used. Now (2-105) must hold for all values of x, $a \leq x \leq b$; so it must hold for $x = t_1$, $x = t_2, \ldots, x = t_n$. Substituting for x successively $t_1, t_2, \ldots, t_n$ and setting $u(t_i) = u_i$, $f(t_i) = f_i$ we get n linear algebraic equations for the n unknowns $u_1, \ldots, u_n$.
That is,

$$u_i = f_i + (b - a)[c_1 k(t_i, t_1)u_1 + c_2 k(t_i, t_2)u_2 + \cdots + c_n k(t_i, t_n)u_n] \qquad i = 1, 2, \ldots, n$$

These u_j may be solved for by the methods under Numerical Solution of Linear Equations and substituted into (2-105) to yield an approximate solution for (2-104).

Example. Solve numerically $u(x) = x + \frac{1}{3}\int_0^1 (t + x)\, u(t)\, dt$.

In this example $a = 0$, $b = 1$. Take $n = 3$, $t_1 = 0$, $t_2 = \frac{1}{2}$, $t_3 = 1$. Then (2-105) takes the form [where we have used the parabolic rule (see p. 2-61)]

$$u(x) = x + \frac{1}{3}\left[\frac{\frac{1}{2}}{3}(t_1 + x)u(t_1) + 4(t_2 + x)u(t_2) + (t_3 + x)u(t_3)\right]$$
$$= x + \frac{1}{18}[(t_1 + x)u(t_1) + 4(t_2 + x)u(t_2) + (t_3 + x)u(t_3)]$$

This must hold for all x, $0 \leq x \leq 1$. Hence take $x = t_1 = 0$, $x = t_2 = \frac{1}{2}$, $x = t_3 = 1$. Thus

$$u(t_1) = t_1 + \tfrac{1}{18}[2t_1 u(t_1) + 4(t_2 + t_1)u(t_2) + (t_3 + t_1)u(t_3)]$$
$$u(t_2) = t_2 + \tfrac{1}{18}[(t_1 + t_2)u(t_1) + 4(2t_2)u(t_2) + (t_3 + t_2)u(t_3)]$$
$$u(t_3) = t_3 + \tfrac{1}{18}[(t_1 + t_3)u(t_1) + 4(t_2 + t_3)u(t_2) + 2t_3 u(t_3)] \qquad (2\text{-}106)$$

Setting in the values of t_1, t_2, t_3 and $u(t_i) = u_i$ the equations (2.106) become

$$18u_1 - 2u_2 - u_3 = 0$$
$$-u_1 + 28u_2 - 3u_3 = 18$$
$$-u_1 - 6u_2 + 16u_3 = 18$$

with the solution $u_1 = \frac{12}{71}$, $u_2 = \frac{57}{71}$, $u_3 = \frac{102}{71}$.

Thus $u(x) = x + \frac{1}{18}[x\frac{12}{71} + 4(\frac{1}{2} + x)\frac{57}{71} + (1 + x)\frac{102}{71}]$
$= \frac{90}{71}x + \frac{12}{71}$

Because of the work involved in solving large systems of simultaneous linear equations it is desirable that only a small number of u's be computed. Thus the Gaussian integration formulas are useful because of the economy they offer. Scarborough (*op. cit.*) has a particularly readable section on these methods. In addition the following references are useful: Tricomi, "Integral Equation" (Interscience, New York, 1957); Buckner, "Die praktische Behandlung von Integral-Gleichungen" (Springer, Berlin, 1952).

NUMERICAL SOLUTION OF PARTIAL DIFFERENTIAL EQUATIONS

The numerical techniques for solving partial differential equations have evolved from finite difference approximations for the partial derivatives. In these methods the accuracy of the results can be estimated with difficulty in certain cases. If the numerical procedure satisfies two criteria named "convergence" and "stability" the accuracy is determined by the number of increments used and increased accuracy can be obtained at the cost of increased labor. The convergence criterion is concerned with the approach of the approximate numerical solution to the exact solution as the number of increments increases indefinitely. Unless the numerical solution converges to the exact solution the limit the numerical method is unsatisfactory. The stability criterion deals with the growth of errors in the calculation. Because any practical solution deals with a finite number of increments and finite number of significant figures errors are introduced into the calculation. These errors are not serious unless they increase as the solution proceeds.

In the case of linear partial differential equations with constant coefficients (and some with variable coefficients) conditions for convergence and stability have been developed for the numerical technique. We consider some techniques for propagation (non-steady-state problem usually) problems and for equilibrium problems (usually steady state). References which go into details are Milne (*op. cit.*); Southwell, "Relaxation Methods in Theoretical Physics," Oxford, New York, 1946; Mickley, Sherwood, and Reed, "Applied Mathematics in Chemical Engineering," McGraw-Hill, New York, 1957; Crandall, "Engineering Analysis," McGraw-Hill, New York, 1956; Richtmyer, "Difference Methods for Initial Value Problems," Interscience, New York, 1957.

The techniques are best illustrated by examples.

Example 1. *An Equilibrium Problem.* The partial differential equation

$$\frac{\partial^2 u}{\partial x^2} + \frac{\partial^2 u}{\partial y^2} = 0$$

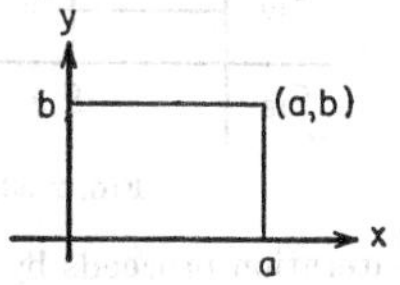

FIG. 2-51. Rectangular plate.

represents the temperature $u(x, y)$ under the steady flow of heat in a plate having a rectangular shape (Fig. 2-51) with the boundary conditions $u(x, 0) = x(a - x)$, $u(x, b) = 0$, $u(0, y) = 0$, $u(a, y) = 0$. If the region is subdivided into a lattice as indicated in Fig. 2-52, with h as the subdivision on both x and y, then the lattice points have values 1: (x, y); 2: $(x + h, y)$; 3: $(x + h, y + h)$; 4: $(x, y + h)$; 5: $(x - h, y + h)$; 6: $(x, y - h)$;

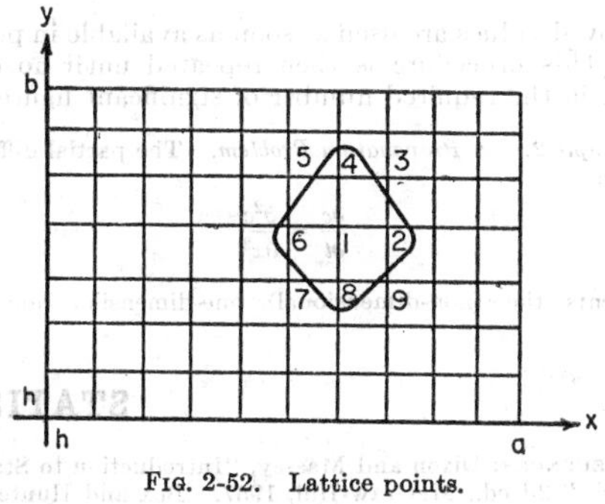

FIG. 2-52. Lattice points.

and so forth. One approximation for $\frac{\partial u}{\partial x}$, $\frac{\partial u}{\partial y}$ is

$$\frac{\partial u}{\partial x} = \frac{u(x + h, y) - u(x, y)}{h}$$
$$\frac{\partial u}{\partial y} = \frac{u(x, y + h) - u(x, y)}{h}$$

and for the second partials

$$\frac{\partial^2 u}{\partial x^2} = \frac{u(x + h, y) - 2u(x, y) + u(x - h, y)}{h^2}$$
$$\frac{\partial^2 u}{\partial y^2} = \frac{u(x, y + h) - 2u(x, y) + u(x, y - h)}{h^2}$$

Thus substituting these in the partial differential equation there results (after algebra)

$$u(x, y) = \frac{1}{4}[u(x + h, y) + u(x, y + h) + u(x - h, y) + u(x, y - h)] \quad (2\text{-}107)$$

which shows that the value at any interior lattice point is the average of the values of u at the four nearest surrounding points. Thus the value at 1 in the preceding diagram is computed from the grouping shown.

In practice the computation may be done by an *iteration method* as follows: the region is subdivided as below, the boundary values at the boundary lattice points are assigned (these are known; so they are designated by a's), and starting values of the temperature are inserted in the interior (these are unknown but rough values may be obtained by taking the values at the corners of the boundary and computing the value at the center of the mesh, by using the mean of these; then find the values for the centers of the four new squares by again taking the means of their corner values, etc.). Equation (2-107) is then used to continue the iteration. The

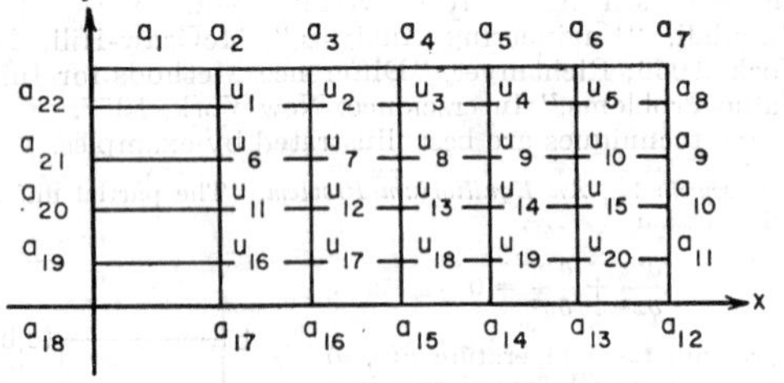

FIG. 2-53. Iteration mesh points.

iteration proceeds by calculating new values, *e.g.*,

$$u_1' = \frac{1}{4}[u_2 + a_2 + a_{22} + u_6]$$
$$u_2' = \frac{1}{4}[u_1' + a_3 + u_3 + u_7]$$

.
.
.

Improved values are used as soon as available in proceeding. This procedure is then repeated until no change occurs in the required number of significant figures.

Example 2. *A Propagation Problem.* The partial differential equation

$$\frac{\partial c}{\partial t} = \frac{\partial^2 c}{\partial x^2} \quad (2\text{-}108)$$

epresents the (non-dimensional) one-dimension non-steady-state diffusion of a fluid through a porous medium having a constant diffusion coefficient D. In this case our domain of integration is now (theoretically) of infinite extent in time. The domain in this case may not be subdivided arbitrarily, as we shall see below. Let the subdivision in the x direction be Δx and in the t direction Δt. We designate lattice points by $P_{-j,k}$ ($j = x$ index; k = time index).

Approximate $\dfrac{\partial^2 C}{\partial x^2} = \dfrac{C_{j-1,k} - 2C_{j,k} + C_{j+1,k}}{(\Delta x)^2}$

and $\dfrac{\partial C}{\partial t} = \dfrac{C_{j,k+1} - C_{j,k}}{\Delta t}$

where $C_{j,k}$ = value of C at $P_{j,k}$. Equation (2-108) becomes approximated by

$$\frac{C_{j-1,k} - 2C_{j,k} + C_{j+1,k}}{(\Delta x)^2} - \frac{C_{j,k+1} - C_{j,k}}{\Delta t} = 0$$

or upon solving for $C_{j,k+1}$ (*i.e.*, moving ahead in time) we have

$$C_{j,k+1} = \frac{\Delta t}{(\Delta x)^2} C_{j-1,k} + \left(1 - 2\frac{\Delta t}{(\Delta x)^2}\right) C_{j,k} + \frac{\Delta t}{(\Delta x)^2} C_{j+1,k}$$

The values at the necessary points to move ahead in time are illustrated in Fig. 2-54; *i.e.*, three points on the kth time line are

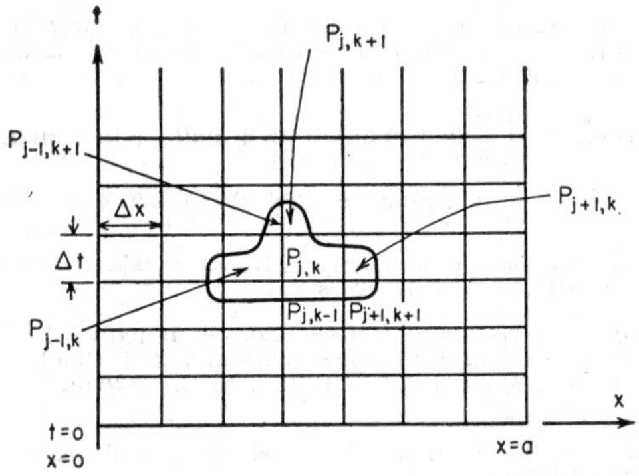

FIG. 2-54. Propagation problem.

used to calculate new values on the $k + 1$st time line. The value of $r = \Delta t/(\Delta x)^2$ (called the modulus) is important here. For stability of the procedure r must be $\leq \frac{1}{2}$. Milne has found that $r = \frac{1}{6}$ provides superior accuracy and thus is an optimum value.

The computation now proceeds upward from given initial conditions at $t = 0$ say $C(x, 0) = f(x)$ and utilizing the known boundary conditions at $x = 0$ and at $x = a$. Note that this procedure is not iterative as was the procedure in Example 1.

STATISTICAL ANALYSIS

REFERENCES: Dixon and Massey, "Introduction to Statistical Analysis," 2d ed., McGraw-Hill, 1957. Box and Hunter, *Ann. Math. Stat.*, March, 1957, pp. 195–241. Hoerl, *Chem. Eng. Progress*, November, 1959, pp. 69–78. Acton, "Analysis of Straight-line Data," Wiley, New York, 1959. Hald, "Statistical Theory with Engineering Applications," Wiley, New York, 1951. Davies, "Statistical Methods in Research and Production," Oliver & Boyd, Edinburgh and London 1947. Davies, "The Design and Analysis of Industrial Experiments," Oliver & Boyd, Edinburgh and London 1956. Mood, "Introduction to the Theory of Statistics," McGraw-Hill, New York, 1950. Bowker and Lieberman, "Engineering Statistics,' Prentice-Hall, Englewood Cliffs, N.J., 1959. Scheffé, "Analysis of Variance," Wiley, New York, 1959. Williams, "Regression Analysis," Wiley, New York, 1960. Chew, "Experimental Designs in Industry," Wiley, New York, 1958. National Bureau of Standards, "Fractional Factorial Experimental Designs for Factors at Two Levels," Applied Mathematics Series 48. "Fractional Factorial Experimental Designs for Factors at Three Levels," Applied Mathematics Series 54.

There is a difference to be recognized between *statistics* and *statistical analysis*. Statistics is a term sometimes employed in describing a large mass of figures: dollars, people, events, production quantities, industrial accidents, and the like. Increasingly, too, the term statistics is employed to imply some value derived from figures in volume, *e.g.*, the average, range, and so on. Statistical analysis, on the other hand, constitutes a body of techniques for deriving or organizing statistics, and for determining their essential significance.

There are two types of data to which statistical methods may be applied: variable and attribute. Data are of the variable type when they can be considered, from a practical standpoint, as having some continuously measurable characteristic. For example, the individual weights of a group of men can be considered to be a continuous characteristic although their weight would probably be measured only to the nearest pound or tenth of a pound. Attributes, on the other hand, are nonvariable classifications in that they are in the form of counts or number of things (called enumeration data). The numbers of males and females in the cities of the United States would, for example, be in the form of attributes.

The types of statistical analysis which can be applied to either variable or attribute data are the following:

1. To test a given hypothesis concerning some observed characteristic
2. To determine a reliable estimate of some factual value
3. To represent a physical situation functionally

The reason for such an analysis is the fact that all data are to some extent, one way or another, subject to chance error.* These chance errors may arise whether the problem involves an estimation—the testing of a hypothesis—or the development of a reliable model. For example, if a value is to be estimated by laboratory analysis, it would first appear that either the "true value" is obtained or it is not. However, since no experimentally determined value is absolute, it is frequently necessary to determine by statistical methods the reliability of scientific determination. This means that, in reporting the thermal conductivity of silver as 240 p.c.u./(hr.)(sq. ft.)(°C./ft.), based on n tests, we should indicate how precise an estimate this is. Are we 99 per cent confident that it is 240 in the sense of some value falling between 235 and 245? Or, on the other hand, are we 99 per cent confident that, corresponding to the purity of silver under study and our test conditions, the true thermal conductivity is between, say, 239.8 and 240.2? The use to which the determinations will be put really determines how confident we shall want to be concerning its absolute value. This is one illustration of the many applications in which statistical techniques can be utilized.

As a means of testing a hypothesis or determining the reliability of some factual value, a statistically designed experiment should be used. Basically, these designed experiments enable the analyst to determine, with a preassigned degree of confidence, the degree of variation in the experimental determinations which is due to chance and that which is the result of some possibly known or unknown influence. In addition, a statistical experiment is designed from the standpoint of being able to make a given number of reliable generalizations from a minimum number of experiments. It is for this reason that, in the modern design of experiments, the statistical approach is needed from the beginning.

The specific techniques of statistical design require extensive discussions and cannot be treated here for lack of space. However, several specific designs will be indicated later as an example of these techniques. For further details, the recommended books on the design of experiments, included in the References, should be consulted.

The objective of this discussion is primarily to describe and illustrate the concepts of statistical analysis.

* For example: Exactly 105 people might have died in New York City on a particular day; however, the next day 50 or possibly 200 people might die. While the observed number might be exact, its exact value is still due, to some extent, to chance.

VARIABILITY

Statistical methods are predicated on the single concept of variability. It is through this fundamental concept that a basis is determined for experimental design and analysis of data. In this sense statistical methods are concerned with deriving maximum information from a given set of data (analysis), and conversely, minimizing the amount of data (experimental design) to derive specific information.

Consider the following series of daily yields determined from a sulfuric acid reactor:

91.37	91.96
91.45	92.28
93.13	92.57
92.87	92.93
91.65	92.79

After obtaining these data the first thing which might be done would be to average them arithmetically. Symbolically, the arithmetic *average* or *mean* value is usually denoted as $\bar{x}$ where the individual values are indicated by $x_1, x_2, x_3, x_4, \ldots, x_{10}$, thus:

$$\begin{aligned}\bar{x} &= \tfrac{1}{10}(x_1 + x_2 + x_3 + \cdots + x_{10}) \\ &= \tfrac{1}{10}(91.37 + 91.45 + \cdots + 92.79) \\ &= 92.30 \text{ per cent}\end{aligned}$$

Mathematically, the average can be symbolized by

$$\bar{x} = \frac{1}{n}\sum_{i=1}^{n} x_i \quad \text{or} \quad \bar{x} = \frac{1}{n}\sum x_i$$

Having once obtained a measure of the average yield of the reactor many questions can now be asked. For example, a partial list of such questions would be

1. How well is it known the 10-day average of yield is 92.30 per cent?
2. How well is yield known based on one day of operation?
3. Did the reactor really operate one day at a yield of 93.13 per cent (the third day)?
4. Is there a daily trend in yield?

What gives rise to the above questions and makes this a problem of statistical analysis is the variability of the daily yields. Conversely, from this variability itself it is possible to determine the appropriate answers based on the theory of statistics. However, before describing how statistics is used to answer these questions it is necessary to define certain fundamental concepts which are utilized. These include

1. Standard deviation
2. True value
3. Degrees of freedom
4. Normal frequency distribution
5. Theoretical model distributions

STANDARD DEVIATION

There are obviously many ways in which to characterize the spread or variation in the original yield data. For example, the range (the largest value minus the smallest) or the average difference (without regard to algebraic sign) between the values and the calculated average would be ways in which this could be done. However, almost always the most efficient quantity for characterizing (the most reliable estimate) variability is called the *standard deviation* (also called the root mean square). This standard deviation is the square root of the average squared difference between the individual observations and the average value. The standard deviation, usually denoted by the symbol s, would be calculated for the given data as follows:

$$s = \sqrt{\frac{(91.37 - 92.30)^2 + \cdots + (92.79 - 92.30)^2}{(10 - 1)^*}}$$
$$= 0.65$$

Two other characteristic quantities are also of importance in their relation to the standard deviation:

1. *Variance or Mean Square.* The square of the standard deviation s, where $s^2 = \frac{1}{(n-1)} \sum_{i=1}^{n} (x_i - \bar{x})^2$.

2. *Sum of Squares.* The sum of squared differences before dividing by the number of observations minus 1 where sum of squares $= \sum_{i=1}^{n} (x_i - \bar{x})^2$.

For computational purposes the formula

$$s^2 = \frac{n\Sigma x^2 - (\Sigma x)^2}{n(n-1)}$$

is useful.

TRUE VALUE

For the previously indicated daily yields each is actually an average yield based on several analytic determinations. For this, a number of samples are taken from the batch production made during the day and analyzed. Yield is then based on the analytically determined product composition.

Because of analytic errors the yield varies from sample to sample even though the batch product is homogeneous. However, it is intuitively obvious that, if an increasingly large number of samples were taken (from the same homogeneous batch), the corresponding average yield determination for these would approach some fixed value.† This fixed value would be the *true value* of the batch. This is statistically denoted by the Greek letter mu (μ).

In a similar manner it would be possible to consider a homogeneous mixture of two days' product and refer to its true value yield. This concept can be extended then to any number of specific days of operation. Conversely, this number (the true yield) can only refer to production during a specific period of operation. The true yield is not relative to the reactor in the sense of being the reactor's true yield. Rather, it is a true yield during the specified period of operation. It is in this sense the material to follow is referred.

The estimated standard deviation s, between analytically determined yields, will also approach some fixed value which is denoted by sigma (σ).

DEGREES OF FREEDOM

In statistical analysis it is necessary to use a quantity called *degrees of freedom*. This quantity allows for a mathematical correction of the data for constraints placed upon the data. To illustrate what a constraint might be and how it is corrected consider the calculation for the variance:

$$s^2 = \frac{1}{n-1} \sum_{i=1}^{n} (x_i - \bar{x})^2 = \frac{n\Sigma x^2 - (\Sigma x)^2}{n(n-1)}$$

In estimating the true average μ from a sample, it can be shown that the best estimate is obtained by simply averaging the observed sample data $\bar{x} = (1/n)\Sigma x$.

Conversely, the variance formula used a divisor of $(n - 1)$ rather than n. The reason for this can be illustrated as follows:

Suppose instead of subtracting the calculated average $\bar{x}$ from each observation some other number, say A, were subtracted and the total of these differences divided by n. Thus

$$s^2 = \frac{1}{n} \sum (x_i - A)^2$$

The value of A which will make s^2 a minimum can be determined by differentiating s^2 in respect to A and setting the derivative equal to zero. Thus

$$\frac{d(s^2)}{dA} = \frac{d}{dA}\left[\frac{1}{n} \sum (x_i - A)^2\right]$$

$$0 = \frac{2}{n} \sum (x_i - A)$$

or $$0 = \sum x_i - \sum A$$

$$0 = \sum x_i - (A)(n)$$

$$\sum_{i=1}^{n} A = A + A + \cdots + A = nA$$

$$A = \frac{1}{n} \sum x_i$$

$$A = \bar{x}$$

Therefore, we see that s^2 will always have a minimum value when $\bar{x}$ is used. If μ were known and s^2 calculated by $s^2 = 1/n \sum_{i=1}^{n} (x_i - \mu)^2$, then s^2 would be larger in magnitude (on the average) than if $\bar{x}$ has been used. This is due to the fact that $\bar{x}$ is only an estimate of μ and will not therefore be exactly equal to it. $\bar{x}$ is the only value which makes s^2 a minimum; by necessity then any other number, say μ, will result in a larger value of s^2. Thus, by inverse deduction, since σ^2 is the true variance about μ and s^2 an estimate of σ^2, s^2 will be on the average underestimate σ^2 when $\bar{x}$ is used. To compensate for this bias, it can be shown mathematically that $(n - 1)$ should be used instead of n. The quantity $(n - 1)$ in this particular example is referred to as the degrees of freedom. In this sense it is stated that, since the given data have been used to calculate the average, one degree of freedom is lost for the calculation of the standard deviation; *i.e.*, a constraint has been placed on the data.

Symbolically, then,

$$s = \sqrt{\frac{\Sigma(x_i - \bar{x})^2}{(n-1)}}$$

Thus, the concept of degrees of freedom arises with a computation which is based on some other estimate. In this case the variance estimate is calculated relative to the data average, and therefore one sample, or degree of freedom of the data, has been used. Other applications and uses of degrees of freedom will be indicated.

* The reason for using $(10 - 1)$ is described under Degrees of Freedom.

† Mathematically this process of approaching some fixed value is called stochastic convergence—in opposition to convergence in the strict mathematical sense. For example, with a convergent series, by taking the sum of a sufficient number of terms, the absolute sum of the infinite series can be determined to any preassigned degree of accuracy. Stochastic convergence, on the other hand, implies that it cannot be specified with absolute assurance how close to the true average the estimated average is (regardless of the sample size). Rather the probability that it will approach some particular value which is the true value approaches 1, dependent, of course, on the satisfaction of certain mathematical conditions.

NORMAL FREQUENCY DISTRIBUTION

When dealing with large numbers of values it is convenient to form an *array* of the data in such a way the frequencies of occurrence of given values or ranges of values are tabulated and graphed. These frequency arrays are essentially a grouping of data. This grouping is accomplished by the designation of ranges which are called *class intervals.*

Table 2-1 is a summary distribution of 500 reactor yields. In speaking of tabulated data of this type several concepts are defined. The group or set of daily yields is called a *sample.* From this sample certain conclusions can be made concerning the *population* of daily yields. Although not practical the population is defined as the total entity of daily yields, that is, the ultimate final distribution of yields (collected on the same conditions) which would be determined if additional data were indefinitely added.

Table 2-1

Yields	No. of observations in interval	Cumulative frequency	Cumulative % frequency
No more than 90.50......	10	10	2.0
As much as 90.50 but no more than 90.88......	25	35	7.0
As much as 90.88 but no more than 91.25......	42	77	15.4
As much as 91.25 but no more than 91.63......	80	157	31.4
As much as 91.63 but no more than 92.00......	98	255	51.0
As much as 92.00 but no more than 92.37......	93	348	69.6
As much as 92.37 but no more than 92.75......	72	420	84.0
As much as 92.75 but no more than 93.12......	45	465	93.0
As much as 93.12 but no more than 93.50......	20	485	97.0
As much as 93.50..............................	15	500	100.0

The relative frequency of yields is called a distribution or the *frequency distribution.*

In presenting data, a table similar to Table 2-1 could be utilized or an arithmetic plot of the per cent frequencies used.

Another method of presenting the data can be accomplished by plotting the cumulative per cent frequency against the corresponding class interval. This method of graphing has the advantage of tending to smooth the data. In addition, for any particular level of yield this graph will indicate what percentage of the yields is less than the specified amount.

In many applications frequency data, of the type illustrated, follow very closely a theoretical mathematical distribution called the *normal frequency distribution.* In fact it has been found that the normal curve is the model of experimental errors for repeated measurements of the same thing, as, for example, the analytically determined yields from the same batch production.

Graph paper with the ordinate scaled (in a manner similar to the way logarithmic paper is scaled) to cumulative per cent frequency is available If the sample data are in fact normally distributed the resultant cumulative frequencies will plot on this graph paper in a straight line. Figure 2-55 includes the data for the yield figures of Table 2-1. Occasionally it is necessary to transform the class intervals into a form other than arithmetic. For this, log-normal paper (abscissa scale is logarithmic and the ordinate normal cumulative per cent frequency) is also available.

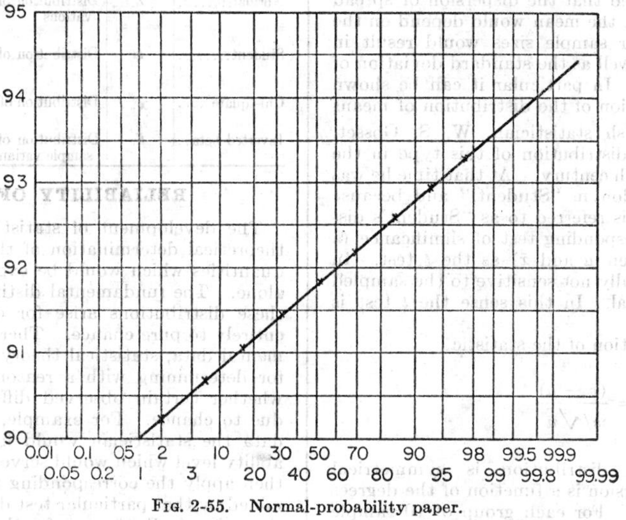

FIG. 2-55. Normal-probability paper.

Normal curve analysis is applicable to any situation wherein deviations from the mean in either direction are equally likely (symmetrical) and due to chance (experimental error) or to phenomena which are of the nature of chance. Another major significance of the theoretical normal curve lies in the fact the means of groups of samples taken from a population which is not necessarily characterized by the normal curve will result in a normal distribution (central-limit theorem). For example, given the frequency distribution in Fig. 2-56.

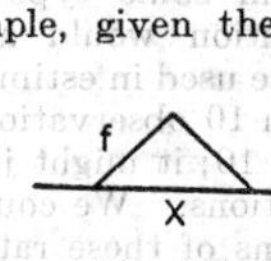

FIG. 2-56. Triangular frequency distribution.

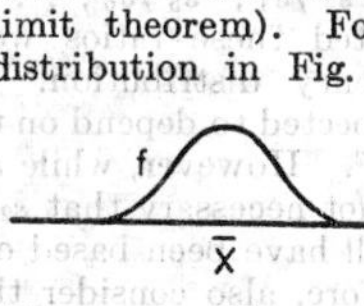

FIG. 2-57. Normal frequency distribution.

The distribution of five sample averages $\Sigma x/5$ will be normal with mean μ and a standard deviation equal to $\sigma/\sqrt{5}$.

THEORETICAL MODEL DISTRIBUTIONS

There are an appreciable number of statistical distributions which have for the most part been derived from the normal frequency distribution. However, the principles underlying only three of the more frequently used distributions will be discussed. These distributions form the basis for the most frequently used statistical tests of significance and will be discussed in the ensuing paragraphs.

It has been pointed out that, if the yield data contained only chance errors, the cumulative estimates $\bar{x}$ and s would gradually approach the limits μ and σ. In particular, the distribution of yields would also be, within practical limitations, normally distributed with mean μ and standard deviation σ. Suppose then that the true mean μ of the infinite population were known. In this case it would be expected that the averaged means for each group of say 10 yields would also have some symmetrical type of distribution centered around μ. However, it would be expected that the dispersion or spread of this distribution about the mean would depend on the sample size (since larger sample sizes would result in better estimate of μ) as well as the standard deviation of the original population. In particular it can be shown that the standard deviation of the distribution of means equals $\sigma/\sqrt{n}$. A British statistician, W. S. Gosset, originally formulated a distribution of this type in the early part of the twentieth century. At that time he was writing under the pseudonym "Student," and because of this, the distribution is referred to as "Student's distribution" and the corresponding test of significance (a measure of error between μ and $\bar{x}$) as the t test. In general the t test is actually not sensitive to the sampled distribution being normal. In this sense the t test is said to be *robust*.

Formally, the distribution of the statistic

$$t = \frac{(\bar{x} - \mu)}{s/\sqrt{n}}$$

was determined. This distribution is symmetrical about zero and its dispersion is a function of the degrees of freedom (d.f.) $n - 1$. For each group of 10 sample yields, a standard deviation could be individually calculated. It might then be expected that these estimates of σ would also have some type of distribution. For this mathematical formulation the distribution of $[s^2/(\sigma^2/\text{d.f.})]$ was determined. This particular distribution is called the chi-square (χ^2) distribution. Its form depends on the sample size used in calculating s^2.

Instead of considering the distribution of the individual variances themselves, we could consider another type of distribution also involving estimates of the true variance. With s_1^2 determined from a first group of 10 observations and s_2^2 from a second group of 10, the ratio s_1^2/s_2^2 can be calculated. This could then be carried on indefinitely with s_3^2/s_4^2, s_5^2/s_6^2, . . . , etc. Again it might be expected these ratios would also form some type of frequency distribution. This distribution would also be expected to depend on the sample size used in estimating s_i^2. However, while s_1^2 is based on 10 observations, it is not necessary that s_2^2 be based on 10; it might just as well have been based on 20 observations. We could, therefore, also consider the distributions of these ratios where all the numerators are based on sample sizes n_1 and the denominators on sample sizes n_2. The shape of these distributions would then depend on these respective sample sizes n_1 and n_2.

These particular distributions have been mathematically derived and tabulated. They have been denoted as the $F(\text{d.f.}_1, \text{d.f.}_2) = s_1^2/s_2^2$ distributions.

The utility of these various statistical distributions is in determining how large a difference between various quantities might be expected by chance. Basically, the purpose of utilizing statistical techniques is to determine whether various sets of data are different from other data or from some hypothesized value or values.

The basic assumption underlying the derivation of these distributions is that the individual observations are normally distributed and independent of each other. Therefore, when applying the corresponding statistical tests, caution should be observed with data suspected of appreciably differing from a normal distribution or where the observations are not independent.

In retrospect, the basic distributions which were discussed and will be utilized in this discussion are as follows:

Distribution	Symbol	Type	Symbolic form (non-dimensional)
Normal.	Z	Distribution of individual observations	$Z = \frac{x - \mu}{\sigma}$
Student.	t	Distribution of sample means	$t = \frac{(\bar{x} - \mu)}{s/\sqrt{n}}$
Chi-square.	χ^2	Distribution of sample variances	$\chi^2 = \frac{s^2}{\sigma^2/\text{d.f.}}$
Inverted beta. .	F	Distribution of the ratio of two sample variances	$F = \frac{s_1^2}{s_2^2}$

RELIABILITY OF ESTIMATES

The development of statistical analysis involves the theoretical determination of the distributions of certain quantities which would be expected to occur by chance alone. The fundamental distinction to be noted is that these distributions arise for conditions which are due entirely to pure chance. Therefore, in analyzing experimental data, statistical theory serves as a powerful tool for determining with a reasonable degree of assurance whether certain observed differences might have been due to chance. For example, before comparing sets of data the statistician would first select a chance probability level which would serve as a criterion. He would then apply the corresponding test of significance (determined by that particular test distribution) by calculating the value (t, F, χ^2, etc.) for that distribution of the data in question. If this calculated value could have occurred only by chance with a probability less than that selected, then the sets of data would be considered as being different.

In terms of the previously indicated normal distribution the probability that a randomly selected observation x (selected from the population) will be within so many units of the mean μ can be calculated. However, this leads to an integral which is very difficult to calculate. Because of this difficulty tables have been conveniently prepared in terms of $\mu \pm Z\sigma$ units as indicated in Table 1-15.

In terms of the yield problem assume that sufficient data are available so that μ and σ are known (for a period of say N days) and are respectively equal to 92 per cent and 0.75 (the variance between samples). The question could be asked as to what percentage of individual yields will be within ± 1.5 per cent of the average. For this it is necessary to convert the formula $x = \mu \pm Z\sigma$ as follows:

Since $x = 92 \pm 1.5$ is desired it follows, with $\sigma = 0.75$, $x = 92 \pm 1.5 = 92 \pm 0.75\ Z$ or $Z = 1.5/0.75 = 2$. That is, ± 1.5 per cent is 2 standard deviation units away from the mean. Thus, referring to Table 1-15, $\mu \pm 2\sigma$ will include an area of 0.9545. Therefore, 95.45 per cent of the daily yields will fall between 90.5 and 93.5 per cent.

In determining the degree of reliability associated with certain calculated characteristics, the chance range of difference between the true and estimated value (which vary by chance from sample to sample) can be determined. For the laboratory data previously discussed, the average of the first 10 determinations is an estimate of the true mean μ of the theoretically infinite number of such analyses. However, the question would certainly be asked as to just how good this sample of 10 is in estimating μ. If it is assumed that the difference between $\bar{x}$ and μ is only the result of chance and that the individual observations are normally distributed, then a measure of the reliability of $\bar{x}$ in estimating μ can be determined. This measure is referred to as a confidence interval. As previously indicated, if a distribution of individual observations is normally distributed with a standard deviation σ then the sample means (each based on n observations) randomly selected from that population will also be normally distributed about μ but with a standard deviation equal to $\sigma/\sqrt{n}$. Therefore, sample means can be thought of as individual observations but with a standard deviation of $\bar{\sigma} = \sigma/\sqrt{n}$. In other words, for

$$A = \frac{x - \mu}{\sigma}$$

it also follows that

$$A = \frac{\bar{x} - \mu}{\sigma/\sqrt{n}}$$

when $\bar{x}$ is the average of the n randomly selected observations $x_1, x_2, \ldots, x_n$.

Suppose then the true standard deviation σ of a particular normal distribution under study is known but the true mean μ is not known. In particular, a sample of n randomly selected observations might be obtained from which $\bar{x}$ would be calculated. The question might be raised, then, as to how precisely $\bar{x}$ might estimate μ. In other words, based on the sample value $\bar{x}$, what statement can be made concerning the value of μ? In any case, $\bar{x}$ is certainly the best single estimate of μ. However, what is desired is a range of values which will include, with a specified probability, the true value μ; *i.e.*, we would be this confident (corresponding to the selected probability level) that the value μ lies within this interval. The probability that $\bar{x}$ exactly equals μ is from a practical standpoint virtually zero—from a mathematical standpoint it is zero.

From
$$\pm Z = \frac{x - \mu}{\sigma}$$

it follows, by a simple rearrangement, that

$$\mu = x \pm Z\sigma$$

or in terms of $\bar{x}$

$$\mu = \bar{x} \pm Z\bar{\sigma} = \bar{x} \pm \frac{Z\sigma}{\sqrt{n}}$$

where $\bar{\sigma} = \sigma/\sqrt{n}$.

Therefore, corresponding to a selected probability level, which determines the value of Z, it can be stated

$$\bar{x} - \frac{Z\sigma}{\sqrt{n}} < \mu < \bar{x} + \frac{Z\sigma}{\sqrt{n}}$$

As an example, consider the first 10 observations for which $\bar{x} = 92.30$. If it were known that $\sigma = 0.75$ then a 95 per cent confidence interval for the true mean μ would be

$$92.30 - \frac{1.96 \times 0.75}{\sqrt{10}} < \mu < 92.30 + \frac{1.96 \times 0.75}{\sqrt{10}}$$
$$91.83 < \mu < 92.77$$

The value of 1.96 was obtained as follows: In Table 1-15 the cumulative probabilities from the mean for the normal distribution are tabulated in terms of $(Z\sigma)$ units. In this particular case the unit value which will include up to 47.5 per cent of the area on each side the mean was needed. Hence, ± 1.96 units from the mean will include 95 per cent of the area.

This analysis indicates that, based on 10 observations, there is 95 per cent expectation that the true average μ is between 91.83 and 92.77 (there is only 1 chance in 20 that we might be wrong).

If, in this particular case, σ were not known, a corresponding confidence interval could still be determined. This estimate must utilize the t instead of the Z distribution since t includes the additional variation introduced by the estimate s of σ. Again, for the first 10 observations, where it was calculated $s = 0.65$, there is a 95 per cent chance the following interval will include μ:

$$\bar{x} - \frac{ts}{\sqrt{n}} < \mu < \bar{x} + \frac{ts}{\sqrt{n}}$$
$$92.30 - \frac{2.26 \times 0.65}{\sqrt{10}} < \mu < 92.30 + \frac{2.26 \times 0.65}{\sqrt{10}}$$
$$91.82 < \mu < 92.76$$

The value of $t = 2.26$ was found in Table 1-16 corresponding to a probability of 95 per cent (2.5 per cent probability for each tail) and $(10 - 1)$ degrees of freedom.

The reliability of s^2, as an estimate of σ^2, can also be determined. Under these circumstances the χ^2 distribution will serve as a basis for evaluating the chance deviation of the estimated variance from the true variance. For the sample of 10 observations $s^2 = (0.65)^2$. Therefore, the 95 per cent confidence interval for the variance is given by

$$\frac{s^2}{\chi^2_{0.975}/(n-1)} < \sigma^2 < \frac{s^2}{\chi^2_{0.025}/(n-1)}$$
$$\frac{(.65)^2}{19.02/(10-1)} < \sigma^2 < \frac{(.65)^2}{2.70/(10-1)}$$
$$0.20 < \sigma^2 < 1.43$$

The values of χ^2 for various degrees of freedom and probabilities are indicated in Table 1-17. In this case, there are 9(10 minus 1 degree of freedom lost in determining $\bar{x}$) d.f. and for a probability level of 95 per cent, $\chi^2_{0.025} = 2.70$ and $\chi^2_{0.975} = 19.02$.

In other words, for a sample size of 10 only 1 time in 40 will $9s^2/\sigma^2$ be less than 2.70 by chance alone. Similarly, 1 time in 40, $9s^2/\sigma^2$ will be greater than 19.02. Jointly the probability of exceeding either is 5 per cent. Thus, even with the estimate $s^2 = (0.65)^2$ it is still not unlikely that $\sigma^2 = 0.75$.

Previously a statement was made concerning the range of values that would be expected when σ is known. However, it is also of interest to determine what percentage of observations can be expected to fall within some specified interval when the standard deviation is not known. For example, if the life expectancy of telephone poles is 20 years with a standard deviation of 3.5 years, it would be of interest to determine what percentage of the individual poles will last, say, from 15 to 25 years. Estimates of this type are called tolerance intervals.

If it were known for the previously indicated yields that $\mu = 92.0$ and $\sigma = 0.75$, then by definition of the normal distribution, it would be expected that, because of chance alone, 95 per cent of the observations would result in values between $(92.0 \pm 1.96\sigma)$ or that 90 per cent would be between $(92.0 \pm 1.65\sigma)$. However, μ and σ

are not usually known, and therefore, because of the lack in precision of the estimates, $\bar{x}$ and s, it will be known only within a certain probability what percentage of the individual observations will fall within a specified interval.

Tolerance intervals $\bar{x} \pm Ks$ are in a form similar to confidence intervals $\bar{x} \pm ts/\sqrt{n}$ but where K is determined so that it can be said with a confidence of $100 - \alpha$ (corresponding to an error of a α per cent) that the interval will cover at least a proportion P of the population.

In the case of the laboratory experiments, $\bar{x} = 92.30$ and $s = 0.65$; therefore, for $P = 90$ per cent and $100 - \alpha = 95$ per cent the corresponding interval is

$$92.30 \pm (2.84)^* \times (0.65)$$

or

$$[90.44, 94.16]$$

Therefore, there is a 95 per cent chance that the interval [90.44, 94.16] will include at least 90 per cent of the future determinations provided that they are obtained under the same conditions as those under which the samples were obtained.

Table 2-2

Type of interval	Conditions	Interval	Procedure	Reference
Cumulative	μ, σ known	$\mu \pm Z\sigma$ will include P% of the observations	1. Select P 2. Read Z from table	Table 1-15, P vs. Z
Tolerance	$\bar{x}$ estimate of μ s estimate of σ	The probability is $(100 - \alpha)$ that $\bar{x} \pm ks$ will include P% of the observations	1. Select $(100 - \alpha)$ 2. Select P 3. Read K from table corresponding to n sample size	$(100 - \alpha)$ vs. K vs. P for various n
Confidence mean	$\bar{x}$ estimate of μ σ known	There is a probability of $(100 - \alpha)$ that $\bar{x} \pm Z\sigma/\sqrt{n}$ will include μ	1. Select $(100 - \alpha)$ 2. Read Z from table	Table 1-15, $P = (100 - \alpha)$ vs. Z
Confidence mean	$\bar{x}$ estimate of μ	There is a probability of $(100 - \alpha)$ that $\bar{x} \pm ts/\sqrt{n}$ will include μ	1. Select $(100 - \alpha/2)$ 2. Read t from table corresponding to d.f.	Table 1-16, $P = (100 - \alpha/2)$ vs. t for d.f.
Confidence variance	s estimate of σ, no statement necessary for μ	There is a probability of $(100 - \alpha)$ that $\frac{s^2}{\chi_2^2/\text{d.f.}} < \sigma^2 < \frac{s^2}{\chi_1^2/\text{d.f.}}$	1. Select α 2. Read χ_1^2 for $\alpha/2$ corresponding to d.f. 3. Read χ_2^2 for $(100 - \alpha/2)$ corresponding to d.f.	Table 1-17, $\alpha/2$, $(100 - \alpha/2)$ vs. χ^2 for d.f.

Table 2-2 summarizes, for ready reference, the types of intervals which have been discussed. These intervals have been developed for populations which are normally distributed, and caution should therefore be exerted for situations suspected of deviating substantially from a normal distribution.

TESTING OF HYPOTHESIS

Comparison of Means

Quite frequently in research it is necessary to compare an average of a set of data to some hypothetical value or to the average of another set (or averages of other sets) of data to determine whether the observed differences between them might be due to chance. Under these circumstances the criterion for ascertaining whether an observed difference is real is to determine how large a difference might be due to chance alone. If the observed difference is larger than can be reasonably expected by chance alone then the difference is said to be statistically significant.

The three basic types of comparison are the following:

1. Between the mean $\bar{x}$ of a set of observed data and a hypothesized or assumed mean μ.

2. Between the mean $\bar{x}_1$ of one set of observed data and the mean $\bar{x}_2$ of some other set of observed data. (Subscripts 1, 2, 3, etc., will refer to the means of the individual groups 1, 2, 3, etc.)

3. Between the means $\bar{x}_1, \bar{x}_2, \bar{x}_3, \ldots, \bar{x}_n$ of n different sets of observed data.

It should be borne in mind that with these examples the statistical tests control only the probability of making one type of error (a type I error); *i.e.*, the probability of refuting the hypothesis, when in actuality it is true, has been controlled. However, the probability of indicating a difference, if it does exist, will not be specified. This is directly related to what is called a type II error, which determines the power of the test. This is discussed more fully under this heading.

First Comparison. Hypothesis $\mu = \mu_0$ (some given number), $\bar{x}$ estimate of μ. Before observing the previously discussed laboratory yields it might have been hypothesized that the true yield is $\mu = 92$. On this basis the question is whether, assuming these tests were performed under the same specifications, the observed average $\bar{x} = 92.30$ is consistent with this hypothesized value $\mu_0 = 92.0$. Under these circumstances the t test can be applied to determine whether a deviation as large as $(\bar{x} - \mu) = (92.30 - 92.00)$ could have reasonably been expected to occur by chance alone.

Before a statistical test is applied, the level of significance must first be selected. For this comparison, a theoretical frequency less than 1 time in 10 (90 per cent level) will be considered to be significant; *i.e.*, a smaller probability would indicate that the difference was not due entirely to chance. Therefore, if the calculated value of t is larger than that which would occur by chance alone 1 time in 10, the hypothesis would be assumed to be false (the true mean is probably not equal to 92.0).

For these particular data

$$t = \frac{\bar{x} - \mu}{s/\sqrt{n}} = \frac{92.30 - 92.0}{0.65\sqrt{10}} = 1.46$$

By Table 1-16 corresponding to a probability level of 90 per cent (read column headed 95 per cent for a two-tail test) and 9 degrees of freedom, the value of $t = 1.83$. Since the calculated value of t is less than 1.83 the hypothesis that $\mu = 92.0$ is not rejected.

In applying this test in the indicated fashion, a comparison of equality is made. Since the calculated average can be less than or greater than the hypothesized mean, a two-tail test must be used; *i.e.*, the observed difference $+0.30$ is treated as ± 0.30. If the test had been applied under a previous specification that the true mean is more than 92.0 ($\mu \geq 92.0$) then the above level of significance would have been 95 per cent.

Second Comparison. Hypothesis $\mu_1 = \mu_2$, assumed that $\sigma_1 = \sigma_2$. The previously indicated analysis was

* Values of K can be found in Eisenhart, Hastoy, and Wallis, "Techniques of Statistical Analysis," Chap. 2, McGraw-Hill, New York, 1947.

originally carried out for 10 tests, and some time later 10 additional tests were made. If it had been the case that, for the second set, a minor modification in the reactor had been made, the question might be asked as to whether this might affect the average yield. Under these circumstances it might reasonably be assumed that since the change was a minor modification the experimental error would remain substantially the same. On the other hand, it would still be reasonable to question whether the true mean remained the same.

For these conditions the t test can also be used to determine whether the observed differences could have been due to chance alone.

Again, the level of significance should be selected before applying the statistical test. The hypothesis for this test is that the two population means μ_1 and μ_2 are equal. In applying the test it is assumed that the standard deviations are equal. Under these specified conditions the value of t is calculated as follows:

$$t = \frac{\bar{x}_2 - \bar{x}_1}{s\sqrt{(1/n_1) + (1/n_2)}}$$

where $(s)^2$ is the pooled variance estimate of $\sigma^2 = \sigma_1^2 = \sigma_2^2$ given by

$$(s)^2 = \frac{(n_1 - 1)s_1^2 + (n_2 - 1)s_2^2}{n_1 + n_2 - 2}$$

Corresponding to the selected probability level $(100 - \alpha)$ the theoretical value of t can be found in the distribution table of t. If the calculated t is greater than this value, the hypothesis is refuted, and it is therefore assumed that $\mu_1 \neq \mu_2$.

The calculated means and standard deviations for the two groups of 10 observations were

$$\bar{x}_1 = 92.30 \qquad \bar{x}_2 = 92.59$$
$$s_1 = 0.65 \qquad s_2 = 0.37$$

With the hypothesis $\mu_1 = \mu_2$ and $\alpha = 5$ per cent, s^2 and t are calculated in the indicated way

$$s^2 = \frac{1}{2}(s_1^2 + s_2^2) \qquad (\text{where } n_1 = n_2)$$
$$= \frac{1}{2}[(0.65)^2 + (0.37)^2]$$
$$s^2 = 0.28 \qquad s = 0.53$$
$$t = \frac{\bar{x}_2 - \bar{x}_1}{s\sqrt{(2/n_1)}} \qquad (n_1 = n_2)$$
$$= \frac{92.59 - 92.30}{0.53\sqrt{2/10}}$$
$$= 1.22$$

To be significant at the 95 per cent probability level, with 18 degrees of freedom, t would have to be smaller than (-2.10) or larger than $(+2.10)$. Since the calculated value of t does not satisfy this condition, there is no statistical evidence for disputing the hypothesis $\mu_1 = \mu_2$.

Third Comparison. Hypothesis $\mu_1 = \mu_2$, where it is assumed or known $\sigma_1 \neq \sigma_2$. Under circumstances where the conditions of the experimental work, for the two groups of data, are different, and it is suggested the variances are probably not equal, another test is necessary. This condition might arise in several ways. For example, if new process-control equipment were added to the sulfuric acid reactor we might expect an increase in yield but additionally the day-by-day variation might be expected to decrease. Therefore, the respective standard deviations could not legitimately be assumed to be equal.

The calculations for one test of this type are substantially the same as the previous calculations. However, the degrees of freedom, d.f., are calculated from the variances and sample sizes. The statistic t and the quantity d.f. are given as follows:

$$t = \frac{\bar{x}_2 - \bar{x}_1}{\sqrt{s_1^2/n_1 + s_2^2/n_2}}$$
$$\text{d.f.} = \frac{[(s_1^2/n_1) + (s_2^2/n_2)]^2}{(s_1^2/n_1)^2/(n_1+1) + (s_2^2/n_2)^2/(n_2+1)} - 2$$

or if $n_1 = n_2$

$$\text{d.f.} = (n_1 + 1)\left[1 + \frac{2}{(s_1^2/s_2^2) + (s_2^2/s_1^2)}\right] - 2$$

The value of d.f. will not be an integer; however, it is sufficient to use the closest integral value.

For the two particular groups of data under study, this calculation results in the following:

$$t = \frac{92.59 - 92.30}{\sqrt{[(0.65)^2/10 + (0.37)^2/10]}}$$
$$= 1.22$$
$$\text{d.f.} = (11)\left[1 + \frac{2}{(0.65/0.37)^2 + (0.37/.065)^2}\right] - 2$$
$$= 15.45 \qquad \text{Use 15 d.f.}$$

Corresponding to a 90 per cent significance level and 15 degrees of freedom, t would have to be smaller than -1.75 or larger than $+1.75$ to be significant. Therefore, the hypothesis that the means are equal is accepted for lack of contrary evidence.

Fourth Comparison. Hypothesis $\mu_1 = \mu_2$, one experiment from each of two groups carried out under same conditions—no assumptions necessary in regard to σ_1 and σ_2.

If two experiments, one for each of two groups, are carried out simultaneously, and if it is suspected that extraneous factors might influence the individual determinations, still another type of analysis should be used. This might occur, for example, where a comparison is to be made between two different reactors and where it is not only convenient but also statistically expedient to carry out simultaneously two tests, one for each of the two reactors. The reason for this might be that only one or two experiments can be accomplished each day, and it is known that temperature and humidity, although of no particular interest in themselves, have a significant effect on the individual yields. The simplest remedy, of course, would be to control temperature and humidity; however, this is not always possible, especially if the tests are to be performed outdoors. Similarly, the extraneous factor might have been any one of a number of uncontrollable factors. An additional advantage in applying this analysis is that it is not necessary to assume that the variances for each of the two reactors are equal. On the other hand, however, if there is no pairwise correlation between yields (there are no common extraneous effects), information is actually lost by pairing. This loss results from a decrease in the total number of degrees of freedom.

These paired experiments and their differences are as follows:

Test No.	Reactor 1	Reactor 2	Difference
1	91.37	92.16	−0.79
2	91.45	92.17	−0.72
3	93.13	93.40	−0.27
4	92.87	92.80	0.07
5	91.65	92.27	−0.62
6	91.96	92.62	−0.66
7	92.28	92.42	−0.14
8	92.57	92.60	−0.03
9	92.93	92.75	0.18
10	92.79	92.66	0.13

The hypothesis is then set up that there is no difference between yields for the two reactors, *i.e.*, $\mu_1 = \mu_2$. Therefore, the observed difference between the two sample means should be due only to chance. If the hypothesis is true, the mean value of the differences should differ from zero only by chance.

The t test can again be utilized to determine whether the difference mean is substantially zero. In this case $\bar{x}_d = \bar{x}_1 - \bar{x}_2$. However, the difference values will, if there are extraneous factors, have a different variance than would be expected from the individual variances for reactors 1 and 2, which would be $(s_1^2 + s_2^2)$.

Since only the difference values are considered in this analysis, there are only $(n - 1) = 10 - 1 = 9$ degrees of freedom corresponding to a sample size of 10 differences.

$$\text{Diff.} = \bar{x}_1 - \bar{x}_2 \quad \text{(the order is immaterial)}$$
$$= 92.30 - 92.59$$
$$= -0.29$$

and

$$s^2 = \frac{n\Sigma d^2 - (\Sigma d)^2}{n(n-1)}$$
$$= 0.144$$

[If there were no extraneous factors s^2 would be an estimate of $s_1^2 + s_2^2 = (0.65)^2 + (0.37)^2 = 0.56$.] The value of t is then given by

$$t = \frac{\bar{x}_1 - \bar{x}_2}{s/\sqrt{n}}$$
$$= \frac{-0.29}{0.144/\sqrt{10}}$$
$$= -6.36$$

By chance alone the value of t (9 d.f.) will be larger than 1.83 (or smaller than −1.83) only 1 time in 10. Therefore, it may be concluded on the basis of this test that there is a significant difference between reactors 1 and 2.

The following is a summary of the first four comparisons that were made:

Comparison	Hypothesis	Assumption	Results	Remarks
First......	$\mu = \mu_0$	....	Not significant	$\bar{x}$ an estimate of μ
Second....	$\mu_1 = \mu_2$	$\sigma_1 = \sigma_2$	Not significant	Modification in equipment might change μ but probably not experimental error σ
Third.....	$\mu_1 = \mu_2$	$\sigma_1 \neq \sigma_2$	Not significant	Change in operators thus possibly changing experimental error σ
Fourth....	$\mu_1 = \mu_2$	None concerning σ_1, σ_2	Significant	Test the difference between two reactors. One test for each reactor carried out simultaneously. Extraneous effects

Comparison of Means. Suppose in the previous laboratory tests three or more reactors were utilized and 10 different tests carried out with each of them. Under these circumstances it would be desirable to determine whether there are any significant differences between the reactors. However, since the t distribution is valid only for the difference between two means, it would not be an efficient method of comparison. For example, with only 5 groups of data there are 10 different comparisons each with 8 degrees of freedom (in this sense they are not additive, *i.e.*, not 80 degrees of freedom) between any two of the groups; as a result, with a 90 per cent level of significance one of these comparisons can be expected to be significant by chance alone. On the other hand, a 99 per cent level of significance could be used to overcome this inherent difficulty. The disadvantage in using this approach is that the high level of significance makes it more difficult to exhibit smaller differences, if they do exist, between the means. More importantly, from a statistical basis, data should not usually be compared in more than one test. This difficulty is overcome by the use of the F test of significance.

Fifth Comparison: F Test between Means. It has been mentioned that, for a large number of individual tests, a relative frequency distribution, with an estimate $\bar{x}$ of μ and an estimate s of σ, will be defined. In particular it has been assumed that this distribution approaches a normal (Gaussian) distribution which, therefore, can be completely defined by μ and σ. Consider now the distribution of sample means.

Obviously, $\bar{x}$ based on 10 observations will in general be a better estimate of μ than any one particular determination. Similarly, $\bar{x}$ based on 20 observations would be better than the $\bar{x}$ which was based on 10. For this distribution of means, each of which is based on 10 observations, it would then be expected that the spread or dispersion would be less than the distribution of the individual observations. In particular, as has been indicated, the standard deviation σ of the means can be shown to be less by a proportion equal to the $\sqrt{n}$ (the sample size); that is, $\bar{\sigma} = \sigma/\sqrt{n}$. From this it can be concluded that a sample size m greater than n is more precise in estimating the true mean μ by a factor of $\sqrt{m/n}$.

On the basis of this distribution of means, a comparison can be made between several groups of estimated means to determine whether their corresponding true means are distinguishable. Consider the data previously indicated for reactors 1 and 2.

Reactor 1	Reactor 2
$\bar{x}_1 = 92.30$	$\bar{x}_2 = 92.59$
$s_1 = 0.65$	$s_2 = 0.37$

$$\frac{\bar{x}_1 + \bar{x}_2}{2} = 92.44$$

If there is no difference between the true variances of the two samples (but possibly a difference between their means) then their combined variance estimate is given by

$$s^2 = \frac{[\Sigma x_1^2 - (\Sigma x_1)^2/n_1] + [\Sigma x_2^2 - (\Sigma x_2)^2/n_2]}{n_1 + n_2 - 2}$$

For the sample data above

$$s^2 = \tfrac{1}{2}[(0.65)^2 + (0.37)^2] \qquad \text{when } n_1 = n_2$$
$$s^2 = 0.282 \qquad (s^2 \text{ based on 18 d.f.})$$

is the best estimate of the true error variance σ^2 of the individual tests.

Another type of variance can be calculated between the two estimated means; thus

$$\bar{s}^2 = \frac{1}{k-1}\sum(\bar{x}_i - \bar{\bar{x}})^2 \qquad (\text{two means: } k = 2,\ \bar{\bar{x}} = \text{average of means})$$
$$= [(92.30 - 92.44)^2 + (92.59 - 92.44)^2]/1$$
$$= 0.0421 \qquad \text{with 1 d.f.}$$

Now if there is in actuality *no difference* between the true means of the reactor then the above mean variance estimate (0.0421) is actually the basis for an *independent* estimate of the variance for individuals. As previously indicated, the true variance of the average for sample size n is given by σ^2/n where σ^2 is the variance of individuals. Hence, for the yield data $\bar{s}^2$ approximates $s^2/10$ or $10\bar{s}^2 \sim s^2$. Thus 10(0.0421) is an estimate of the previously but separately calculated value $s^2 = 0.280$. However, it should be observed this estimate does not have the precision of the previous value since this is now based on only 1 degree of freedom while the previous value was based on 18 d.f. Regardless of whether the individual means are equal or not, $\bar{s}^2$ will include an estimate of the error variance of the individual observations. If, however, there is a difference between the means this estimate will by necessity have to be larger (on the average) since it will also include a variance of the true difference between the means. Therefore, the F test can be applied to determine whether the difference between $(n\bar{s}^2)$ and s^2 is due to chance or is due to the fact $\mu_1 \neq \mu_2$. For this test

$$F(k-1, n-k) = \frac{s^2_1}{s^2_2}$$

With the previous yield data

$$F(1, 18) = \frac{0.406}{0.282} = 1.44$$

From Table 1-18, $F_{95}(1, 18) = 4.41$. To be significant the calculated value of F would have to be larger than 4.41; therefore, there is no indicated difference between the means.

For computational purposes there is a more convenient form for computing F tests. This is done through the use of an *analysis-of-variance* table. For this purpose the variance estimate based on the means is called a *between* (means) variance. Similarly, the combined variance estimate of the individuals is referred to as the *within* (individuals) or *residual* (error). Thus, with the previously indicated degrees of freedom:

	Mean square	d.f.
Between	0.421	1
Within	0.280	18

Multiplying the variance, which in the analysis-of-variance table is referred to as the *mean square*, by the degrees of freedom a quantity called *sum of squares* is obtained. Now, if all the original 20 yield values were combined in a single group their sum of squares about their average

$$\text{Sum of squares} = \sum_{1}^{20} (x_i - \bar{x})^2$$

would be equal to the combined sum of squares of the between and the within. Thus:

	Mean square	d.f.	Sum of squares
Between	0.421	1	0.421
Within	0.280	18	5.04
Total	.....	19	5.461

Ordinarily this analysis-of-variance table is listed in the reverse order, *i.e.*:

	Sum of squares	d.f.	Mean square	F
Between	0.421	1	0.421	1.50
Within	5.04	18	0.280	
Total	5.461	19		

From this it can be seen the calculation of any two sum of squares can be used to determine the third.

Sixth Comparison: Two Sources of Variation. By analogy the above analysis can be extended to the differences between any number of means. However, for the following it is assumed the error variance for individual observations is the same within each group. In particular, consider the following 5 groups of 10 analyses each:

Run No.	Reactors 1	2	3	4	5
1	91.37	92.16	90.87	91.30	91.54
2	91.45	92.17	90.83	91.51	91.93
3	93.13	93.40	91.70	93.35	92.52
4	92.87	92.80	91.71	92.98	92.27
5	91.65	92.27	90.92	91.63	91.73
6	91.96	92.62	90.83	91.45	91.76
7	92.28	92.42	92.79	91.99	92.71
8	92.57	92.60	92.67	91.86	92.94
9	92.93	92.75	91.79	90.08	90.22
10	92.79	92.66	91.51	90.12	90.66
Column total	923.00	925.85	915.62	916.27	918.28
Column mean	92.300	92.585	91.562	91.627	91.828
	Total sum = 4599.02				
	Total mean = 91.980				

In regard to these tabulated data a certain amount of variation of the individual runs within each column is indicated. Similarly, there are differences between the averages for each of the reactors. The question then is whether there is a significant difference between the reactors considering the degree of reliability of the five averages.

The method of calculation for the analysis follows directly from that previously indicated. Thus:

Between Reactors.

$$\text{Sum of squares} = 10[(92.300 - 91.980)^2 + (92.585 - 91.980)^2 + \cdots]$$

or more simply

$$= \tfrac{1}{10}[(923.00)^2 + (925.85)^2 + \cdots + (918.28)^2] - \frac{(4599.02)^2}{50}$$

$$= 7.909$$

Total.

$$\text{Sum of squares} = (91.37)^2 + (91.45)^2 + \cdots + (90.66)^2 - \frac{(4599.02)^2}{50}$$

$$= 34.325$$

Residual.

$$\text{Sum of squares} = (91.37 - 92.30)^2 + (91.45 - 92.30)^2 + \cdots + (90.22 - 91.828)^2 + (90.66 - 91.828)^2$$

or more simply

$$\text{Sum of squares} = 34.324 - 7.909 = 26.415$$

Therefore:

Source of variation	Sum of squares	d.f.	Mean square	F ratio
Between	7.909	4	1.977	3.37
Residual	26.415	45	0.587	
Total	34.324	49		

Corresponding to a 90 per cent level with 4 and 45 d.f. the F ratio would have to be larger than 2.57 (Table 1-18) to be significant (by chance alone F should be nearly equal to 1). This test states there is a significant difference between the reactors. However, the test does not state which specific one or more reactors are different from the others. For this another analysis is required.* As an example of this analysis consider the five reactor means ranked in increasing order

3	4	5	1	2
91.56	91.63	91.83	92.30	92.59

For this test the reactor yields can be pairwise compared by the calculation

$$s_{\bar{X}} = \left[s_R^2 \left(\frac{1}{n_1} + \frac{1}{n_2} \right) \right]^{1/2}$$
$$= \left[0.587 \left(\frac{1}{10} + \frac{1}{10} \right) \right]^{1/2}$$
$$= 0.34$$
$$A = [(k-1)F_{k-1,l}]^{1/2}$$
$$= [(5-1)2.08]^{1/2}$$
$$= 2.88$$

where s_R = residual standard deviation

n_1, n_2 = sample size for each reactor mean

l = residual d.f.

k = number of means

$F_{k-1,l} = F$ ratio at α probability level and $k-1$, l, d.f. (with a weak anal. of var. result, *i.e.*, small F, use lower probability level—90 per cent)

A contrast between two means is significant if

$$|\text{Diff.}| > As_R = 0.34 \times 2.88 = 0.98$$

Therefore, it may be concluded only reactor 3 can be distinguished from reactor 2 (see Power of the Test, p. 2-75).

Seventh Comparison. Three Sources of Variation. If two tests for each reactor had been carried out each day and it was suspected that temperature and humidity had influenced the yields, then a more complete analysis would have been justified. Under these circumstances the variation due to the days would have to be taken into account; *i.e.*, the effect of reactors and days would each be tested. This would result in a reduction of the residual sum of squares (if, of course, there is a difference between days) since part of the residual could not be explained in terms of a difference between days.

To test the significance of the differences between the reactors and the differences between the days, a similar analysis of variance is calculated. Corresponding to the previous calculations, the total and group sum of squares will remain the same. The sum of squares which the days account for is subtracted from the residual, which is in turn a more precise estimate of the true residual (if there is a difference between days).

The sums for the individual days are:

Day	Run No.	Sum of runs
I	1–2	915.13 = (91.37 + 91.45 + · · · + 91.54 + 91.93)
II	3–4	926.73 = (93.13 + 92.87 + · · · + 92.52 + 92.27)
III	5–6	916.82 = (91.65 + 91.96 + · · · + 91.73 + 91.76)
IV	7–8	924.83 = (92.28 + 92.57 + · · · + 92.71 + 92.94)
V	9–10	915.51 = (92.93 + 92.79 + · · · + 90.22 + 90.66)

In an analogous fashion the sum of squares accounted for by the days can be calculated as follows:

$$\text{Days} = \frac{(915.13)^2}{10} + \frac{(926.73)^2}{10} + \frac{(916.82)^2}{10} + \frac{(924.83)^2}{10} + \frac{(915.51)^2}{10} - \frac{(4599.02)^2}{50} = 12.242$$

* McCall, Linear Contrasts, *Quality Control*, 17 (1), (July, 1960). Scheffe, A Method for Judging All Contrasts in the Analysis of Variance, *Biometrics*, vol. 40, June, 1953.

Thus, the revised analysis of variance is:

Source of variation	Sum of squares	d.f.	Mean square	F test
Columns (reactors)....	7.909	4	1.977	5.71
Run (days)...........	12.242	4	3.060	8.84
Residual.............	14.173	41	0.346	
Total...............	34.324	49		

In this instance there are two comparisons to be made to determine if either has a significant influence on the analysis. It had originally been specified that a 95 per cent probability level would be used as the level of significance. Corresponding to this level with 4 and 41 degrees of freedom, by Table 1-18 F would have to be larger than 2.60 to be significant. Therefore, it may be concluded that there is sufficient evidence to indicate a difference between the reactors and the individual days. This example illustrates the necessity for taking into account, if possible, all the factors which might influence the values of the measured characteristic to better estimate the residual and determine other sources of variation.

COMPONENTS OF VARIANCE

One of the most useful and important concepts in statistical analysis is that of components of variance. In essence the latter two comparisons illustrated the components of variance principle through the partitioning of the sum of squares into their appropriate source. Referring to comparison seven it is stated, based on the analysis, that the variation in the observed yield, from test to test, was caused by three factors:

1. The unaccounted residual or experimental error σ_E^2
2. The differences between reactors σ_R^2
3. The differences between days σ_D^2

Therefore, corresponding to a single test under the same circumstances the expected yield x will deviate from μ with a standard deviation comprising the above three components.

To illustrate this point consider the five average yields for each reactor:

$$\bar{x}_1 = 92.300$$
$$\bar{x}_2 = 92.585$$
$$\bar{x}_3 = 91.562$$
$$\bar{x}_4 = 91.627$$
$$\bar{x}_5 = 91.828$$
$$\bar{\bar{x}} = 91.9804$$

for which

$$s^2 = \tfrac{1}{4} \sum_{1}^{5} (\bar{x}_i - 91.9804)^2 = 0.1977$$

The estimate $s^2 = 0.1977$ includes a component due to differences between the reactors and a component due to experimental error. If $\bar{x}_1$ were the true average of reactor 1 and $\bar{x}_2 = \mu_2$, and so on, then s^2 would be equal to σ_R^2. For the above, however, the variance s^2 is made up of the true differences between reactors and an error variance of each average:

$$s^2 = s_R^2 + \frac{s_E^2}{10} \quad \text{(since each average is based on 10 tests)}$$

$$\text{or} \quad 0.1977 = s_R^2 + \frac{0.346}{10} \quad \text{(0.346 from table above)}$$

$$\text{and} \quad s_R^2 = 0.1631$$

Similarly for the other three components. Therefore, the total variance of yields is made up of the estimates of

$$\sigma^2 = \sigma_E^2 + \sigma_R^2 + \sigma_D^2$$

Estimates of s_R^2, s_D^2, and s_E^2 are available from the analysis-of-variance table

Source of variation	Sum of squares	d.f.	Mean square	Estimate of
Reactors......	7.909	4	1.977	$\sigma_E^2 + 10\sigma_R^2$
Days.........	12.242	4	3.060	$\sigma_E^2 + 10\sigma_D^2$
Residual......	14.173	41	0.346	σ_E^2
Total.........	34.324	49		

Thus $s_E^2 = 0.346$

$$s_R^2 = \tfrac{1}{10}[1.977 - 0.346] = 0.1631$$
$$s_D^2 = \tfrac{1}{10}[3.060 - 0.346] = 0.2714$$

The total observed variance $s_1^2 = \dfrac{34.324}{49} = 0.700$ is *only approximated* by the alternate calculation

$$s_2^2 = 0.346 + 0.163 + 0.271 = 0.780$$

in specific applications. This difference occurs because of the errors of sampling and individual errors of estimation in σ_E^2, σ_R^2, and σ_D^2. However, the indicated values are the best estimates of these quantities.

POWER OF THE TEST

The previously discussed second comparison (p. 2-70) included a statistical test to determine whether the reactor yield has a significant (statistically speaking) change with a process modification. For this comparison a hypothesis was stated that they were equal. The statistical test of this hypothesis indicated there was not sufficient evidence to dispute the hypothesis. The statistical result simply implies any difference which might exist between the two is not large enough to distinguish from the experimental error. For example, assuming the true experimental error is $\sigma = 0.5$ per cent per test, it could not be expected that a true yield increase of only 0.01 per cent would be indicated by a sample of only 10 tests each. It is only known with 95 per cent confidence $\bar{x}_1 = 92.30 \pm \dfrac{0.5 \times 2.26^*}{\sqrt{10}} = 92.30 \pm 0.38$ and $\bar{x}_2 = 92.59 \pm \dfrac{0.5 \times 2.16^*}{\sqrt{10}} = 92.59 \pm 0.38$. Conversely, if another modification had been made which increased yield by 2.0 per cent, then it would have been expected the second 10 experiments would have an average yield of $(\mu + 2.0) \pm 0.38$. Under this circumstance it would be highly likely the statistical test would indicate a significant difference. Between comparisons of this type the effect of true differences on the statistical test and the nature of statistical inference are directly related to the concept of *power of the test.*

For a specific application the stated hypothesis is in actuality either true or false. Conversely, the statistical test based on a sample will *indicate* the hypothesis as either true or false. Symbolically, this can be represented in the following table:

		Actual hypothesis	
		True	False
Statistical indication of results	True......	✓	II(β)
	False.....	I(α)	✓

If the statistical analysis indicates a significant difference (rejects an hypothesis of equality) when the hypothesis is in fact true it is referred to as a *type* I *error* (probability of making this error is α). Conversely, the analysis can indicate no significant difference when there is a true difference—a *type* II *error* (probability of making this errors is β).

In testing the null hypothesis the probability of making a type I error is controlled. For example, in the second comparison the yield difference was tested at a 95 per cent probability level. For this, there was only a 5 per cent probability that a significant difference would be indicated when, in fact, no true difference existed. In statistical analysis the type I error ordinarily is the error which is controlled.

In practice, while the connotation is extremely important, the type II error is usually not computed except in special applications. The reasons for this are the computational work and conceptual complexities (for the experimenter or process engineer who is not a statistician but is interested in the results) which are involved. The type I error can be characterized by a single number (α). Conversely except in rare circumstances the type II error (β) must be characterized by a function. This arises because the probability of accepting a false hypothesis depends upon which alternative is actually true, that is, whether the true difference between reactor runs is 0.01 per cent, 2.0 per cent, or any other reasonable amount. Thus it is usually necessary to compute a curve to indicate the probability of showing specified differences based on different sample sizes.

As an example of this calculation, consider the previous comparison of the reactor before and after a modification. For this comparison the corresponding confidence interval is given by (see Hald)

$$\left(\frac{d}{2s}\right)^2 = \frac{F_{1-\alpha}(1, 2N-2)F_{1-\beta}(2N-2, 2N-2)}{N}$$

where $\mu_1 - \mu_2 = d$-true difference between means
s^2 = pooled error variance $(2N - 2)$d.f.
N = sample size of each comparison
$F_{1-\alpha}(1, 2N-2)$ = F table based on 1 and $2N-2$ degrees of freedom at a probability level of $(1-\alpha)$
$F_{1-\beta}(2N-2, 2N-2)$ = F table based on $2N-2$, $2N-2$ degrees of freedom at a probability level of $(1-\beta)$

Rewriting the equation and solving for d it can be computed that

$$d = 0.74 \text{ for } N = 10,\ 1-\alpha = 0.95,\ 1-\beta = 0.90$$
$$d = 0.44 \text{ for } N = 20,\ 1-\alpha = 0.95,\ 1-\beta = 0.90$$
$$d = 0.16 \text{ for } N = 100,\ 1-\alpha = 0.95,\ 1-\beta = 0.90$$

This states that if the true difference were as large as 0.74 there would be a 90 per cent probability of correctly rejecting the null hypothesis (when in fact it is false) when it is tested at a 95 per cent level. Thus, there is only one time in ten of making a type II error—accepting the hypothesis when the true difference is as large as 0.74. Similarly for the other differences corresponding to larger sample sizes.

Various alternative comparison tables and curves relating to sample size, probabilities, and specified differences are available in the References.

REGRESSION ANALYSIS

The statistical techniques which were previously discussed were primarily concerned with the testing of hypotheses. A more important and useful area of statistical analysis in engineering is the development of mathematical models to represent physical situations.

* $t = 2.26$ for 9 d.f. and 95 per cent confidence limit.

Considering the yield data for the previous sixth comparison (p. 2-73) suppose it had been further observed the average operating temperatures for the five reactors were different. These temperatures and the corresponding yields are:

Reactor	Average yield	Average temperature
1	92.30	207.1
2	92.58	210.3
3	91.56	200.4
4	91.63	201.1
5	91.83	203.4

Under this circumstance a simple plot of temperature vs. yield indicates a possible cause-and-effect relationship between these variables. In addition, this same trend is also indicated within each reactor for all 50 yield observations.

Conceptually the statistical interpretation for this type of application is different from the previous. For this it is more informative to develop a mathematical model to represent the indicated relationship, *i.e.*,

$$y = f(t)$$

This type of analysis is called regression analysis and is concerned with the development of a specific functional relationship—the mathematical model and its statistical significance and reliability. The application of regression analysis involves four steps:

1. Selection of a model
2. Calculation of the coefficients
3. Statistical test of the model to represent the physical situation
4. Evaluation of the model to determine direction for improvements

To illustrate these steps the previously indicated five yield and temperature averages will be used rather than the more correctly used individual runs.

As indicated by a plot the appropriate model to represent the relationship should be a straight line:

$$y = b_0 + b_1 t$$

For this the variable t is referred to as an *independent variable* and y—the yield, as a *response*.

For the second step it is necessary to determine the coefficients b_0 and b_1 of the model. The normal procedure for this calculation is the method of *least squares*. That is, the determination of the values b_0 and b_1 so that the sum

$$S = (92.30 - b_0 - 207.1b_1)^2 + (92.58 - b_0 - 210.3b_1)^2 + \cdots + (91.83 - b_0 - 203.4b_1)^2$$

is a minimum. In this sense this states those values of b_0 and b_1 which minimize the sum of squared differences between the observed and functional values. Mathematically the solution is computed by solving the differentiated form of the least-squares equation

$$S = \sum (y - b_0 - b_1 t)^2$$

$$\frac{\partial S}{\partial b_0} = \sum y - nb_0 - b_1 \sum t = 0$$

$$\frac{\partial S}{\partial b_1} = \sum yt - b_0 \sum t - b_1 \sum t^2 = 0$$

To carry out these calculations it is convenient to consider the variables scaled as

$$y = \text{yield} - 90$$
$$t = \text{temperature} - 200$$

Therefore:

t	t^2	y	ty
7.1	50.41	2.30	16.330
10.3	106.09	2.58	26.574
0.4	0.16	1.56	0.624
1.1	1.21	1.63	1.793
3.4	11.56	1.83	6.222
$\Sigma t = 22.3$	$\Sigma t^2 = 169.43$	$y = 9.90$	$\Sigma ty = 51.543$

or

$$5b_0 + 22.3b_1 = 9.90$$
$$22.3b_1 + 169.43b_1 = 51.543$$

The solution to these equations gives (see p. 2-52 for computing methods)

$$b_0 = 1.509$$
$$b_1 = 0.1056$$

and therefore

$$(\text{Yield} - 90) = 1.509 + 0.1056\ (\text{temperature} - 200)$$

or

$$\text{Yield} = 70.389 + 0.1056 \text{ temperature}$$

These calculations are readily carried out with a desk calculator (in which case the above sums are simply accumulated in the machine) or a computing machine depending upon the size of the problem.

For step 3 it is necessary to determine whether, and to what extent, yield can be predicted from a knowledge of the temperature. For this an analysis-of-variance calculation is performed.

With the model the expected yields corresponding to the observed temperatures can be calculated for each of the five data points:

No.	Temp.	Observed yield	Calculated yield	$Y_0 - Y_c$ error
1	207.1	92.30	92.26	0.04
2	210.3	92.58	92.60	−0.02
3	200.4	91.56	91.55	0.01
4	201.1	91.63	91.63	
5	203.4	91.83	91.87	−0.04

By definition, the sum of the errors is always zero except for round-off. The residual or error sum of squares is given by the sum of squared errors:

$$\text{Res. s.s.} = (0.04)^2 + (0.02)^2 + (0.01)^2 + (0.04)^2 = 0.0037$$

However, a more convenient form for computing the residual is given by the relationship [which can be derived from the equation $S = \Sigma(y - b_0 - b_1 t)^2$]:

$$\text{Residual} = \Sigma y^2 - b_0 \Sigma y - b_1 \Sigma ty$$
$$= 20.3858 - 1.509(9.90) - 0.1056(51.543)$$
$$= 0.0037592 \text{ or approximately } 0.0038$$

Assuming that temperature was not known the best estimate of yield for a sixth run would be the average of the five figures, *i.e.*, yield = 91.98. However, the expected variation from run to run is related to the total sum of squares of the individual yields about this average or

$$\text{Total s.s.} = \Sigma(\text{yield} - 91.98)^2 = 0.7838$$

Thus, to determine the significance of the model (or in other words how well can we expect to predict the sixth run given the temperature), it is only necessary to determine how much of the total variation has been accounted for by the temperature variable. This amount, in sum-of-square units, is called the regression sum of squares and is given by

$$\text{Regression s.s.} = \text{total} - \text{residual} = 0.7838 - 0.0038 = 0.7800$$

The following is the analysis of variance for the computed relationship:

Source	Sum of squares	d.f.	Mean square	F test
Regression......	0.7800	1	0.7800	600 significant
Residual........	0.0038	3	0.0013	
Total..........	0.7838	4		

In this case the degrees of freedom for regression is one since temperature is the only variable. The b_0 term is actually accounted for in the total d.f. since $b_0 = \bar{y}$ by virtue of the relation

$$\bar{y} = 91.98 = b_0 + b_1 t$$
$$= 70.398 + 0.1056\left(\frac{1022.3}{5}\right)$$
$$= 70.389 + 0.1056(204.46)$$
$$= 91.98$$

Step 4 in this example is the obvious conclusion that higher temperatures correspond to high yield runs. On the basis of this analysis further testing in a higher-temperature range should be carried out for additional confirmation of the model and the indicated appropriate action taken.

Regression analysis is basically the general application of the above principles. For more than one variable the same general rules of procedure follow and only the volume of calculation is changed. For example, if data were also available for feed rates during each run the assumed model might be

$$y = b_0 + b_1 t + b_2 f$$

The simultaneous equations for determining the coefficients would be

$$b_0 n + b_1 \Sigma t + b_2 \Sigma f = \Sigma y$$
$$b_0 \Sigma t + b_1 \Sigma t^2 + b_2 \Sigma tf = \Sigma ty$$
$$b_0 \Sigma f + b_1 \Sigma tf + b_2 \Sigma f^2 = \Sigma fy$$

Similarly, if preliminary analysis of the data indicated curvature between the temperature-yield relationship a model with a squared term might be appropriate:

$$y = b_0 + b_1 t + b_{11} t^2 + b_2 f$$

For purposes of classification all the above models are called *linear models*. In fact, any model which includes the coefficients (b_0, b_1, etc.) as linear terms is a linear model. Conversely, if the model includes a coefficient in a non-linear form it is called a *non-linear* model. For example,

$$y = a + be^{-ct}$$

would fall into this category because of the c term. The important point here is the computational difficulty associated with this latter type. For this, c cannot be calculated directly by the least-squares technique but rather an iterative method is required.

The appropriate model to be used for specific applications depends upon what is theoretically known about the process, the number of variables and data points, and the relative reliability of the data. There are no specific rules for selecting a model. Rather, only experience by the practitioner will dictate the appropriate course of selection. In general, however, for applications involving several variables the selection of non-linear models should be avoided unless there is a sound theoretical basis for selecting a particular type.

The use and benefits of regression analysis can be appreciable, especially in the evaluation of process data. In these applications, processes having as many as fifty variables, which are continuously changing over months of operation, can be evaluated by this technique. For these, the daily log records for say 150 to 500 data points are analyzed through the selected model (usually linear as a first approximation) to determine the relative effects of each variable on the response. This analysis in many situations has led to the quantitative determination of key operating variables whose effect had been camouflaged on individual point comparisons by the simultaneous changes in the other less (but unknown) important variables.

Corresponding confidence intervals for the regression coefficients and predicted values are available analogous to means and variances. For these,

1. The probability $(100 - \alpha)$ that b_0 is within a specified interval from the true value B_0 is given by

$$\left[b_0 - \frac{t}{\sqrt{n}} s < B_0 < b_0 + \frac{t}{\sqrt{n}} s\right]$$

where s is the residual standard deviation, n the total degrees of freedom, and t the Student distribution for the residual degrees of freedom at a level of $[100 - (\alpha/2)]$.

2. The true value B_1 is given by

$$\left[b_1 - t\frac{s}{s_X} < B_1 < b_1 - t\frac{s}{s_X}\right]$$

where s_X is the standard deviation of the corresponding independent variable.

3. The $(100 - \alpha)$ confidence interval for an individual y given X (temperature) is

$$[(b_0 + b_1 X) - tsk < y < (b_0 + b_1 X) + tsk]$$

where $$k = \sqrt{1 + \frac{1}{n} + \frac{(X - \bar{X})^2}{(n-1)s_X^2}}$$

DESIGN OF EXPERIMENTS

In the chemical industry experimental designs are particularly applied to the study of process variables and how they affect the product. For example, in the reactor problem the effect of operating temperature on yield was characterized by a regression analysis (p. 2-75). Similarly additional variables such as catalyst age, flow rate, and pressure could have been included in the regression analysis, that is, their quantitative effect on yield estimated by the regression coefficients.

Data which serve as the basis for the regression analysis can be obtained from either operating log data or from a specifically designed experiment. The latter includes the systematic and controlled procedure for developing the correct combinations of variable conditions to determine a reliable analysis. Conversely, log data frequently include anomalies due to the nature of collection. For example, the operator will frequently decrease flow rate when the reactor temperature is high. Thus, low flow rates occur with high temperatures, and conversely, and therefore neither of the variables can be distinguished from the other. Procedures for handling anomalies of this type are available;* however, it is still best to utilize designed experiments if possible.

Three basic types of experiments are most used in the chemical industry:

1. Factorial
2. Fractional factorial
3. Box-Wilson

* Hoerl, The Application of Ridge Analysis to Regression Problems, *Chem. Eng. Progress*, March, 1962.

For a process application which includes the study of three variables, say, temperature, flow rate, and pressure, on yield a factorial experiment could be effectively used. For this a reasonable number of operating levels of temperature, flow rate, and pressure would be selected. With the selected levels for each the factorial experiment would require all possible combinations. In the case where three levels were specified this would include $T_1F_1P_1$, $T_1F_1P_2$, $T_1F_1P_3$, . . . , $T_3F_3P_3$, or 27 tests. These tests would be randomly sequenced and augmented with two or three duplicate runs of $T_2F_2P_2$. The test results would be interpreted by a functional representation (regression analysis) and an analysis of variance.

For process applications including more than three variables the number of tests become excessive with a factorial experiment. For these fractional factorial or Box-Wilson experiments can be effectively used. The latter designs are described under Box-Wilson Experimental Designs.

Fractional factorials utilize some integer fraction (a multiple of the number of levels) of the corresponding total factorial experiments. For example, with five variables at three levels the factorial experiment would include a base of $3^5 = 243$ tests whereas a $\frac{1}{3}$ fractional would include a base of $\frac{1}{3}(3^5) = 81$, and a $\frac{1}{9}$ fractional $\frac{1}{9}(3^5) = 27$. These experiments are particularly useful in screening a large number of variables at two levels. For example, ten variables at two levels each can be analyzed with 32 tests. Various types of fractional experiments have been very effectively tabulated by the Department of Commerce.* Designs for mixed levels are not widely documented.

The indicated references should be consulted to determine the correct procedures for calculating the analysis of variance.

BOX-WILSON EXPERIMENTAL DESIGNS

Box-Wilson experimental designs are a series of tests for characterizing a physical mechanism. For this purpose a general series of experiments have been developed which efficiently serve as a basis for deriving the mathematical model of the process.

For a specific application suppose it is desirable to study the effects of operating temperature and pressure on the yield of a reactor. To achieve this statistically, experiments are carried out and their results reduced to a regression function by the methods of regression analysis. The generally used form of this model is

$$y = b_0 + b_1x_1 + b_2x_2 + b_{11}x_1^2 + b_{22}x_2^2 + b_{12}x_1x_2$$

for a two-variable system. In general the model, which is called a *response function*, includes three types of terms in addition to the constant b_0:

1. Linear terms in each of the variables $x_1, x_2, \ldots, x_p$
2. Squared terms in each of the variables $x_1^2, x_2^2, \ldots, x_p^2$
3. Cross-product or first-order interaction terms for each paired combination $x_1x_2, x_1x_3, \ldots, x_{p-1}x_p$

For a three-variable problem the response function would be

$$y = b_0 + b_1x_1 + b_2x_2 + b_3x_3 + b_{11}x_1^2 + b_{22}x_2^2 + b_{33}x_3^2 + b_{12}x_1x_2 + b_{13}x_1x_3 + b_{23}x_2x_3$$

The number of terms for p variables is therefore $\frac{(p+1)(p+2)}{2}$. While the general form of the model is not unique (for example, terms like $x_1^2x_2$ or $x_1x_2x_3$ could be included—however, this form does include the first $\frac{(p+1)(p+2)}{2}$ terms of the Taylor-series expansion in p variables (it does have convenient statistical, computational, and interpretive properties and is therefore convenient to use in this form.

One efficient technique (factorial experiments can also be used) for designing which specific experimental tests should be carried out to develop the coefficients of the model is the Box-Wilson composite rotatable designs. These experiments are especially applicable to industrial problems because they require a relatively small number of tests and have convenient computing properties.

For the purpose of the experiment the independent variables are each specified at five levels. The specific values of these five levels for each variable depend on the number of variables included in the experiment and the range over which they are to be studied.

Suppose one of the variables, say temperature, is to be studied between 200° to 300°F., which defines a range of 100°F. For convenience in the to-be-developed model, coded values for the operating levels of the variables are used. For this, a factor k = range/2 is defined for each variable where k is approximately equal to $\sqrt{p}$ (p = number of variables). For the indicated experiment the five levels of temperature which would be specified by the Box-Wilson design would be

Temperature	Coded Form
200	$-k$
$250 - \frac{50}{k}$	-1
250	0
$250 + \frac{50}{k}$	1
300	k

With three variables $k = 1.73$ and the corresponding temperatures for the two intermediate points would be $250 \pm 50/1.73$ or 221 and 279°F.

The specific combinations of levels for the variables can be illustrated by a three-variable design:

Axial points			Factorial points			Center point		
x_1	x_2	x_3	x_1	x_2	x_3	x_1	x_2	x_3
1.73	0	0	1	1	1	0	0	0
−1.73	0	0	1	1	−1			
0	1.73	0	1	−1	1			
0	−1.73	0	1	−1	−1	Total number of tests = 15 + replicates		
0	0	1.73	−1	1	1			
0	0	−1.73	−1	1	−1			
			−1	−1	1			
			−1	−1	−1			

The design principle includes three types of combinations, the axial, factorial, and center points. Thus axial points include each variable at its extreme levels with the others at their center-point level. The factorial points include all combinations of intermediate levels (or an mth replicate for a large number of variables; see p. 2-77). A center point is a single test at the average level of each variable. For the purposes of estimating experimental error the center point is usually repeated three to five times during the experiment. Designs for any number of variables can be readily laid out from these principles.

When the tests have been completed a regression analysis is carried out to determine the coefficients of the response function. For convenience the independent variables in the function are utilized in their coded form.

After the model has been developed an analysis of variance should be carried out to determine its significance. This computation follows the same principle of the previous chapter with a minor modification. In

* Fractional Factorial Experiment Designs for Factors at Two (Three) Levels, U.S. Department of Commerce, Applied Mathematics Series No. 48 (No. 54).

this situation, the previously indicated residual is called *lack of fit* and a new residual based on the mean square of center-point values is used. The lack of fit mean square estimates how well the functional form approximates the true trend of the response. An F test between this and the center-point residual will determine whether there is a significant deviation between them. If this is the case and the function also has a significant fit (relative to the residual) caution should be used in interpreting the function.

Having determined a model which significantly represents the system under study analysis can then be made of the function. This includes three possible alternatives depending upon the computing facilities available and potential value of the particular application:

1. Simple evaluations of the function for selected combinations of the variables to indicate the approximate magnitude of their effects
2. Contour plotting of the response in the $x_1 - x_2$ plane with selected levels of the other variables.
3 A ridge analysis* which characterizes the function's behavior in p dimensions

Most physical situations can usually be approximated by a quadratic function over a reasonable range of the variables. For this reason the Box-Wilson experimental designs are very useful in the study of industrial applications. More detailed information is available in the references.

ENUMERATION DATA

The previous discussion related to measurements of certain types of characteristics such as temperature, pressure, and yield. On the other hand, many problems arise in which counts, or simply the number of items falling into specified categories, are determined: specifically, the number of acceptable items in sample lots or the number of heads in 20 tosses of a coin. In other words, the classification has a particular characteristic or it does not. Such information is called *enumeration data.*

In analyzing enumeration data of this type a chi-square test is used to determine whether the observed frequencies are significantly different from so-called expected frequencies. In tossing a coin 50 times it would be expected that approximately 25 heads and 25 tails would be obtained. Similarly, corresponding to any comparable situation, the expected frequencies can be hypothesized and tested to determine whether sufficient evidence is indicated, in the sample, to refute the hypothesis.

While the chi-square distribution of frequency counts is mathematically different in theory from the previously indicated distribution of variances the resultant distribution function turns out to be the same. For this reason the same table of chi square can be used. However, it should be borne in mind that while chi square can be used in analyzing frequency data regardless of the distribution of the population frequencies it should not be used in variance analysis unless the population under study can be reasonably assumed to be normally distributed.

Let k be the number of different categories for which $f_1, f_2, \ldots, f_k$ are the observed individual counts within each category and where $f_1 + f_2 + \cdots + f_k = N$. Since the total number of counts N is not usually known ahead the hypothesis is stated on the basis of relative frequencies. As an example, in tossing a coin, it would be hypothesized that 50 per cent of the tosses will be heads and 50 per cent tails. The number of expected counts F_i are then determined for each category by multiplying the expected relative frequencies by N so that $F_1 + F_2 + \cdots + F_n = N$. Since this one restriction is placed on the frequencies F_i, one degree of freedom is lost.

* Hoerl, Optimization of Many Variable Equations, *Chem. Eng. Progress*, November, 1959.

The statistic which is used to measure the differences between the observed frequencies and the expected frequencies is

$$\chi^2 = \frac{(f_1 - F_1)^2}{F_1} + \frac{(f_2 - F_2)^2}{F_2} + \cdots + \frac{(f_k - F_k)^2}{F_k} = \sum_{i=1}^{k} \frac{(f_i - F_i)^2}{F_i}$$

The expected or mean value (by chance alone) of χ^2 is equal to the degrees of freedom $(k - 1)$.

In tossing a true coin it would be expected that 50 per cent of the tosses would be heads and 50 per cent tails. Therefore, in 500 tosses this would correspond to 250 tails and 250 heads. In testing a particular coin 275 tails and 225 heads were observed. On the basis of this information it is desirable to determine whether this particular coin is true. The corresponding table of analysis is as follows:

	Heads	Tails	Total
Observed........	225	275	500
Expected........	250	250	500

Since there are only two categories there is only one degree of freedom regardless of the total number of observations. This follows from the fact that with the total number of expected frequencies fixed only one category can be specified—the other being equal to the total frequency minus the specified frequency. By chance alone χ^2 would be larger than 3.84 only 1 time in 20; hence it may be concluded that the particular coin is probably unbalanced.

In the previous analysis a comparison was made to determine whether a series of observed frequencies differed significantly from expected values. This type of analysis, where the theoretical proportion of cases in each category is specified in advance, is called a single-classification problem. On the other hand, many problems involve two classifications such as eye and hair coloring of individuals. Problems of this type are called two-way classifications.

In analyzing data involving two classifications the purpose is to determine whether the two classifications are independent, *i.e.*, whether the two methods of classification are related in some way. For example, is it just as probable an individual's eyes are blue regardless of whether it is given that the hair is dark? If so, then these classifications are independent.

In particular consider the following frequencies of deaths of famous personalities in 1946:*

Occupation	Winter	Spring	Summer	Fall	Totals
Scientist........	9	8	10	19	46
Artist..........	49	32	36	50	167
Totals..........	58	40	46	69	213

If it is known that either a famous scientist or artist died in the winter, what is the probability that he or she will be in one field or the other, the hypothesis being that the probability is the same regardless of the season in which the death occurred? It is important to note that the relative frequencies of deaths by season or occupation have not been previously specified. It is from the row

* "The World Almanac and Book of Facts for 1947," New York World-Telegram, New York, 1947.

and column subtotals (marginal totals) that the expected frequencies are determined.

Given the indicated marginal totals the expected frequencies can be determined as follows:

Scientists

Winter: $46 \times 58/213 = 12.5$
Spring: $46 \times 40/213 = 8.7$
Summer: $46 \times 46/213 = 9.9$
Fall: $46 \times 69/213 = 14.9$

and similarly for the expected frequencies of artists' deaths. The final table of frequencies is therefore

Occupation	Winter		Spring		Summer		Fall		Total	
	Obs.	Exp.	Obs.	Exp.	Obs.	Exp.	Obs.	Exp.	Obs.	Exp.
Scientist....	9	12.5	8	8.7	10	9.9	19	14.9	46	46
Artist.......	49	45.5	32	31.3	36	36.1	50	54.1	167	167
Totals......	58	58	40	40	46	46	69	69	213	213

The value of χ^2 is computed in the same way.

$$\chi^2 = \frac{(9 - 12.5)^2}{12.5} + \frac{(8 - 8.7)^2}{8.7} + \cdots + \frac{(50 - 54.1)^2}{54.1} = 2.75$$

For this problem there are only three degrees of freedom since, with the marginal totals given, a maximum of only three observed frequencies can be freely specified, the others becoming fixed by these and the marginal totals. To be significant at a level of 95 per cent the value of χ^2 would have to be larger than 7.81. Therefore, it may be concluded that a famous artist is no more likely to die in any particular season than any one scientist.

A similar question might be asked as to the likelihood that an artist or scientist will die during any particular season: It is hypothesized that the deaths are equally likely for any season. In this case the analysis becomes a single-classification problem. The expected number of deaths has been corrected for the total number of days

	Winter	Spring	Summer	Fall	Totals
Observed....................	58	40	46	69	213
Expected....................	52	54	54	53	213
Number of days/year.........	89	93	93	90	

in the individual seasons. There are three degrees of freedom (4 − 1) since the total number of deaths has been specified. The calculated value of chi square is

$$\chi^2 = \frac{(58 - 52)^2}{52} + \frac{(40 - 54)^2}{54} + \frac{(46 - 54)^2}{54} + \frac{(69 - 53)^2}{53}$$

$$= 10.44$$

Corresponding to 3 d.f. and a 95 per cent probability level $\chi^2 = 7.81$ by Table 1-17; therefore, it may be concluded that the frequency of deaths of famous artists and scientists varies by season. It should not be concluded on the basis of this result that any unusual situation exists, since it is known that in general there are more deaths during the fall and winter than in the other two seasons.

MACHINE COMPUTATION

References: Alt, "Electronic Digital Computers," Wiley, New York, 1957. "Handbook of Automation and Control," vol. 2, "Computers and Data Processing," Wiley, New York, 1959. Wrubel, "A Primer for Programming for Digital Computers," McGraw-Hill, New York, 1959. Booth and Booth, "Automatic Digital Calculators," 2d ed., Academic Press, New York, 1956. Goode and Machol, "System Engineering," part 4, McGraw-Hill, New York, 1957. Johnson, "Analog Computer Techniques," McGraw-Hill, New York, 1956. Rogers and Connolly, "Analog Computation in Engineering Design," McGraw-Hill, New York, 1960. Hamming, *Science*, **85**, 169 (1957). Williams and coworkers, *J. Assoc. Computing Mach.*, **4**, 393 (1957). "Guide to Abstracts and Manuals for Computer Program Exchange," 2d ed., American Institute of Chemical Engineers, New York, 1960. McCracken, "A Guide to Fortran Programming, Wiley, New York, 1961.

Computing machines are divided into two broad classes, called analog and digital, although some hybrids exist (p. 2-86). Familiar examples, on a small scale, are the slide rule and the desk calculator, respectively.

Analog computers use some physical magnitude, such as a voltage or the position of a dial, to represent the variables in a problem. All the elements of an analog computer involved in a given problem are connected together and act simultaneously so as to behave in a manner *analogous* to the real situation being *simulated* by the analog machine.

Digital computers, by contrast, deal with *numbers* in a *sequential* fashion. The sequence of calculations performed results in a number or numbers which may be regarded as the answer; this answer in turn is interpreted in the context of the physical problem to which the calculations apply.

Each of these types of computer is discussed here separately. For each type, definitions of commonly used terms are followed by a discussion of the methodology applicable to computation with that type of machine.

These two types of machine are basically so different that generalizations as to their relative suitability can only be used as guides to be taken in conjunction with individual judgment. Analog machines bring the user in much closer contact with the process of computation than do digital machines. Hence analog machines should be considered when the problem is not clearly defined, for development work, when constant surveillance of the course of computation and of intermediate results is required or desirable, and when the choice of machines is in doubt. Problems should be transferred from the analog to the digital computer when the mechanics of data processing become burdensome or when the computations become routine.

DIGITAL MACHINES

Number Representation. The term *bit* is the formal name applied to the information contained in a basic element which is either on or off, one or zero, "yes" or "no." *Decimal digits*, or other symbols, may be represented by a group of bits by assigning varying combinations of bits to each number or letter. Two examples are given in Table 2-3.

Table 2-3. Typical Machine Equivalents
Decimal equivalents of each bit position are shown at the head of the column

Decimal	Biquinary	Binary
	05 01234	8421
0	10 10000	0000
1	10 01000	0001
2	10 00100	0010
3	10 00010	0011
4	10 00001	0100
5	01 10000	0101
6	01 01000	0110
7	01 00100	0111
8	01 00010	1000
9	01 00001	1001

Numbers (as contrasted to single characters) may be represented by stringing together the binary representations of the decimal digits which represent the number. They may also be represented as pure binary numbers by using more bit positions. In the binary system, positions to the right of the binary point indicate negative powers of 2, ½, ¼, ⅛, etc. The use of sufficient bit positions to the right of the binary point will permit representation of numbers between zero and unity to any desired accuracy.

Floating-point arithmetic is a formal procedure for keeping track of the position of the decimal point in computations involving numbers of widely different magnitudes. In everyday technical work, magnitudes are frequently represented by auxiliary powers of 10, *e.g.*, a Reynolds number of 1.5×10^6. Two numbers are required to express a single quantity. One is the numerical portion +1.5 (sometimes called the *argument* or mantissa); the other is the exponent +6. In the case of digital machines, it is customary to restrict the numerical portion to a number less than unity in absolute value. In decimal systems, the exponent indicates the power of 10 by which the (decimal) argument is to be multiplied to obtain the true quantity; in binary systems, the exponent indicates the power of 2 by which the (binary) argument is to be multiplied.

Normalization is the adjustment of the exponent so that the first digit of the argument is not zero.

Organization of Information. The *word* is the unit of internal transfer between the logical and arithmetical elements of a machine and its storage. The storage of most machines consists of several thousand or more words of fixed size. The average word consists of 30 to 48 bits or of 10 to 12 decimal digits. Words may contain information in the form of numerical magnitudes or of non-numeric data, such as the alphabetic characters comprising a name or title.

Characters, such as letters of the alphabet or punctuation marks, may be represented by a group of bits or by two decimal digits. This grouping is usually arranged so that there is a fixed number of characters per word. Some machines have provisions for independently moving individual characters within storage, in effect, a one-character word length.

A *block or record* is a group of words and is the unit of external transfer between the storage within a machine and the magnetic tapes or other input-output devices associated with the machine. Records and blocks are not necessarily of fixed length.

Fixed-point numbers are words, representing numerical magnitudes, in which the decimal point is understood to be in some fixed place, usually at one end or the other of the word.

Composed (or one-word) floating-point numbers may be represented in a single word by assigning part of the word to the exponent and part of the word to the argument. Each part requires a sign. In the excess-50, decimal, floating-point system, 50 is added to each exponent so that the numbers 00 to 99 represent the exponents −50 to +49, respectively. A common representation for excess-50 numbers places this exponent between the sign and the argument (Table 2-4). Binary representations with one bit for sign of the argument, 8 bits for excess-128 exponent, and 27 bits for argument are in common use. 2^{128} is approximately 10^{38}, which is therefore the largest number which can be so represented.

Table 2-4. Typical Excess-fifty Equivalents

Excess-fifty	Typical Equivalent
+4413200000	0.000 000132
+5712570000	1,257,000
−5110000000	−1.0
+4712700000	12.7×10^{-5}
−5292000000	-0.0092×10^4
+5033333333	⅓
−3792000000	-9.2×10^{-14}
+4542000000	0.00042×10^{-2}

Two-word floating-point representation, one word for the exponent and one for the argument, is more characteristic of programming systems than of machine hardware.

The *address* of a word is a distinguishing tag, usually a number of some sort, associated with each storage location. The instructions in a digital machine contain addresses although they deal with the information contained in the words of storage having these addresses. For example, the instruction, "Add 1," does not mean "Add 1 to the accumulator." To accomplish this, it would be necessary first to place the number 1 in some address, say 534, and then perform the instruction, "Add 534." However, in discussing instructions for a digital machine, it is customary to shorten the rather cumbersome phrase, "Clear the accumulator to zero and add the contents of storage location 23 to the accumulator and then add the contents of storage location 45 to the accumulator," to "Reset add 23; add 45."

Octal and *hexadecimal* numbering systems, having the radix 8 and 16, respectively, are often used as shorthand manual notation for addresses (and sometimes other numbers) which are basically binary numbers. Binary addresses are easily converted into octal or hexadecimal by subdividing them into groups of three or four bits, respectively.

Instructions to the machine may also be contained in the words of storage within the machine. Some machines have two instructions per word; most have only one. An instruction consists of (1) a coded number or letter, signifying an operation such as add, write on tape, or type out; (2) where pertinent, one or more addresses; and (3) possibly subsidiary information, such as the tape to be written on, the part of a word to be selected, or the size of record in a record transfer (*cf.* also index registers, p. 2-82).

Stored-program computers contain sequences of instructions within their internal storage. These instructions are indistinguishable from data except when actually being executed. Instructions may be transferred into the machine from external input devices, altered or moved about within the machine's storage, and otherwise manipulated, just as any other data would be. It is thus possible to have instructions for modifying instructions, and so on to any desired level of abstraction. Such a hierarchy of instructions can specify rather complex and involved operations using very simple basic instructions as elements. This reflexive property of stored-program machines is the key factor which differentiates them from other computing devices and makes them general-purpose computers. The other characteristics of stored-program machines, high speed, rapid input and output, and large storage capacity, are useful only if instructions for using these features can be given to the machine at comparable rates, *i.e.*, from within.

The *control unit* in a digital computer keeps track of the instruction being executed at any particular moment, decodes it, activates the other components of the computer required to carry out the instruction, and keeps track of where the next instruction will be found.

The basic *types of instructions* found in digital machines are:

1. Arithmetic—usually multiplication, division, addition, and subtraction
2. Transfer of information—including transfer within the machine (storage to storage), transfer into the machine (input to storage), and transfer out of the machine (storage to output)
3. Word manipulation—instructions dealing with parts of words
4. Control of special functions such as stop, jump to another point in the program, and manipulation of index registers (see p. 2-82)

Alphanumeric machines have provision for handling decimal digits and letters of the alphabet as logical entities within the machine.

Internally decimal machines have the logic of decimal carry built into them so that their arithmetic is done on a decimal basis (except for the addition of single digits).

Internally binary machines utilize a full binary representation of numbers and carry out their arithmetic with binary circuits operating on numbers of from 30 to 50 bits. Internally binary machines require some additional means, which may be part of the machine but is usually a program, to translate binary numbers into decimal numbers, which can be more readily understood. Such machines are sometimes termed *scientific* machines, as contrasted to alphanumeric machines, which are commonly used for data processing. This distinction is becoming blurred as improvements are made.

In an *integral* machine, the decimal point is at the right of the word. The arithmetic circuits of this type of machine produce integers as results.

In a *fractional* machine, the decimal point is at the left of the word. Two fractions multiplied together produce a fraction with possible truncation of the less significant portion.

Many machines have *double-length accumulators*, in which double-length products can be generated and then stored in pieces or otherwise operated upon.

Circuits for *floating-point* arithmetic are often included in a machine together with the basic fixed-point, integral, or fractional circuits.

In a *serial* machine, information is transferred along a single channel in the form of a series of pulses (or lack of same). The transmittal of information in a serial machine thus takes a time proportional to the length of the word. Similarly, arithmetical operations are performed one bit or digit at a time, followed by shift of the operands for consideration of the next bit or digit.

In a *parallel* machine, sufficient channels are provided to allow all bit positions to be transmitted at once.

In a *synchronous* machine, all operations are tied to a rigid timing schedule which synchronizes the operation of each component with the over-all operation of the machine.

Asynchronous machines have a variable cycle, so that the absence of information causes unnecessary parts of an operation to be skipped over. The next operation is then begun as soon as the previous one is completed, regardless of the time required.

A *multiprogrammed* machine can execute several strings of instructions simultaneously. In such a machine, storage and arithmetic units, as well as input-output equipment, are shared on a first-come, first-served basis. Simultaneous demands for the same unit cause delays in the lower-priority program. This mode of operation is accomplished by multiple control centers or by a control center capable of keeping track of several programs at once.

Address structure is also a basis for classifying digital machines. Typical address structures are $1 + 0$, $1 + 1$, $2 + 0$. The first number refers to the number of addresses of operands which can be associated with a single operation. The second number is either one or zero, depending on whether the address at which the machine is to find the next instruction is specified with every instruction or is understood to be the next instruction in sequence in storage.

Components. "*Hardware*" is the term applied to the elements of the machine itself, as opposed to the instructions to the machine, called "program."

Storage, sometimes called "memory," is the means by which data and instructions are retained within the machine so that both can be rapidly manipulated by it. Information is stored magnetically in the commonly available machines. Each bit of information is stored in a small portion of magnetic material.

Magnetic drums store information in small portions of the magnetic coating on the surface of a rapidly rotating drum. The typical drum is about 10 in. long and 10 in. in diameter and contains about 12,000 distinct locations on its surface. The state of magnetization on the drum surface is changed by a group of "write" heads. The state of magnetization is detected by a group of "read" heads. These heads are similar to those in an audio tape recorder. Because the drum rotates, each head serves a band or track of magnetizable locations on the drum. Although the drum rotates at high speed, the time required for a given location to come around under the head will be, on the average, quite long relative to the speed of electronic computing circuitry. Magnetic-drum storage is therefore relatively slow and is used in medium-sized machines or as auxiliary storage in the larger, high-speed machines.

Core storage is made up of small toroids of magnetic material less than ¼ in. in diameter, strung on wires. The state of magnetization of each core is detected or changed by current pulses through the wires. The cores are systematically strung on the wires in a gridlike formation in such a fashion that the number of magnetizing and detecting circuits required is much less than the number of cores served by these circuits. Although such a system is more complicated and costly than the magnetic drum, it has the advantage that information can be obtained from it at a speed limited only by the response time of the elements of the circuits. Storage in cores of 10^6 yes-or-no elements is not uncommon in big machines.

Access time is the time required to obtain a given piece of information, measured from the time that the location of that piece of information was determined. In the case of magnetic-drum storage, the access time depends on the position of the drum relative to the location on the drum of the desired information.

Random access is the term applied to storage, such as cores,in which the time to obtain or store information is independent of the location of the information. Core storage is 10^3 or more times as fast as drum storage when random locations are involved. The access times for drum and core are so different that, in a machine with both drum and core, it is impractical to transfer only one piece of information between them. Most large machines with both drum and core are equipped with means for transferring large blocks of sequential information from drum to core, or vice versa, in times comparing favorably with the random-access time for the core.

The circuits which transfer information from storage to other parts of the machine are arranged so that they duplicate the information at the destination while leaving the information intact in the original storage location.

In addition to the principal storage of a machine, be it core or drum, there is additional storage, much smaller in capacity but logically important, in the form of registers, counters, and buffers.

Registers are sometimes referred to as zero-access storage, indicating that operations can be performed immediately with the information in these registers.

The *accumulator* is the principal register in a digital machine. This register communicates directly with the arithmetic circuits; most arithmetical results are placed in it on completion of the operation.

The *program register*, or instruction register, is the register in which the instruction currently being executed is held.

The *program counter*, or control counter, is the counter in which the location of the next instruction to be executed is stored.

Index registers perform operations on addresses. By indexing, certain of the addresses in a sequence of instructions can be modified systematically each time the sequence of instructions is executed, the index register being similarly altered. When the index register reaches some preassigned limit, the repetitive execution of the modified sequence is terminated and the computer goes on to further instructions as provided by the program.

Auxiliary storage is provided as optional equipment on some machines. The principal types are disk storage ("juke box") and magnetic tape in multiple bins. The longer magnetic tapes on reels used as input and output are of course also a form of auxiliary storage. Disk and bin storage are intermediate in speed of access between core storage and magnetic-tape storage.

Input Devices. The keyboard is used for converting from human action to a representation by which information can be fed to a computer. Because typing is slow compared with the computer speed, intermediate accumulation of input information on some mechanical medium, such as punched cards, paper tape, or magnetic tape, is common practice. Console switches and direct-connected typewriters are sometimes used to put information into a digital machine. Usually, any given machine will have several alternate methods of receiving information.

Console switches provide for operator intervention, allowing for initiation and termination of operation, correction of minor malfunctions, and intervention when on-the-spot decisions can be made on the basis of the normal behavior of the program.

Direct-connected keyboards are the principal means of imput on small machines but are used on large machines only for inserting key pieces of data, not available at the time the main body of input was prepared.

Punched paper tape may have from four to eight channels. It is read by standard teletype equipment or similar mechanical devices using a pin-sensing device to detect holes. Punched-paper-tape readers of the mechanical type are limited to 10 or at most 20 characters per second.

Photoelectric readers for paper tape detect the holes in the tape by means of a bank of photocells, one for each channel. The tape is interposed between a light source and the photocells. Such readers are capable of speeds from 200 to 1000 characters per second. On small machines, the tape-reading speed is sometimes limited by the ability of the computer program to assimilate the information provided.

Punched cards, of the 12-row by 80-column type, are used as input by machines of various manufacturers. However, the card format is not always interpreted by the machine as 80 columns of 12 rows each. Other subdivisions of the 960 possible punch locations are used by individual machines. The interpretation which will be made by a given punch pattern is controlled in many machines by a plugboard. The plugboard is logically interposed between the card reader and the machine and permits rearrangement of the information on the card in transit to the machine, suppression or duplication of certain portions, and even some minor logical choices. Card readers usually accept 150 to 250 cards per minute and are available up to 2000 cards per minute. Punched cards with various other arrangements are also in use.

Magnetic tapes are the principal input medium for large machines. While a computer with more than one of each of the other types of input devices is unusual, large computers usually have about 10 tape units. Over 200 are theoretically possible on some models. Tape units customarily serve as both input and output devices, while the output devices corresponding to the other input media are usually separate and different from the input devices. The principal portion of a magnetic-tape unit consists of the mechanical device for getting from one part of the tape to the other. The addition of a write head near the read head permits the same transport mechanism to serve both the input and output functions. The magnetic tape used is a high-grade version of the familiar audio recording tape, usually somewhat wider.

Information is written on the tape in the form of *records* or *blocks*, which may consist of a fixed or variable number of characters. Most tape units write only in the forward direction and have an erase head, which precedes the write head by a few inches and cleans off any information which may be on the tape from its last use. Some designs of tape unit are capable of reading backward as well as forward; others can only read forward and must back-space or rewind to reach information which has already passed by. After use, tapes are customarily rewound onto the original reel and removed for storage or reuse, either at a later date or on auxiliary equipment. Pulse densities on tape range from 100 to the inch upward. Tape speeds are of the order of 100 to 150 in./sec. Most tape designs have a removable ring in the hub of the tape reel which engages a switch on the tape unit. The presence or absence of this ring ensures that the tape will not be written on and valuable information destroyed.

Buffers are provided in conjunction with the magnetic tapes of the more powerful machines. The transfer of information from tapes to storage ties up a portion of the logical and storage circuits during transfer. While the transfer operation itself is not particularly time-consuming, the speed of movement of the tape is relatively very slow. Time is wasted if the main logic and storage units are tied up during the time while the tape is moving physically by the read head. In a buffered machine, separate storage and control are employed to hold the information as it is accumulated from the tape. Meanwhile, the main computer circuits can be employed in arithmetic or other operations not involving the information coming from the tape in question. When the transfer of a record of information is complete, the contents of the buffer storage can be dumped into main storage at the machine's internal speed. The reverse of this process can be employed to transfer information to tape via the buffer.

Input auxiliaries are devices not attached to the main frame of a machine (*i.e.*, *off-line*). Among them are devices for converting information on punched cards to information on tape, for typing information onto tape from keyboards, for converting from paper to magnetic tape or from one type of magnetic tape to another, and for testing the magnetic uniformity and readability of tapes.

Verifiers for punched cards or magnetic tapes are input auxiliaries used to check the transcription manually from manuscript to input medium.

Output Devices. Output devices for digital computers include the following common types:

- Signal lights on the console
- On-line typewriters
- Paper-tape punches
- On-line card punches
- On-line printers
- On-line high-speed printers
- Magnetic-tape units

On-line typewriters and paper-tape punches are the principal output of many small machines. They usually limit the computing speed and are sparingly used on large machines. They are capable of speeds of about 10 characters per second; some paper-tape punches are available with speeds up to 60 characters per second.

On-line card punches are often connected to the machine through a plugboard which permits some editing and rearrangement of information en route from the machine to the punch. Punches have speeds of the order of 100 to 250 cards per minute.

On-line printers also frequently have plugboards interposed between the computer and the print format. Their print mechanism consists of a series of wheels, having type on their periphery. These wheels advance and rotate individually so as to present the proper letter to the face of the paper being printed. A whole line is printed at a time. *Line printers* of this type are limited in speed to about 150 lines per minute.

The name *high-speed printer* is applied to printers which use some other mechanism to get faster printing speed. The principal types are the rotating wheel, the wire matrix, and the chain printer.

Magnetic-tape output may be used again as input (thus acting as auxiliary storage) or it may be coded in such a way as to be interpreted by an off-line printer or an off-line tape-to-card converter.

Programs, Programming, and Programmers. In a stored-program machine, it is the *program*, written by a *programmer*, which keeps data and instructions separate, each assigned to its proper function. In the course of the development of the art of *programming*, other specialized terms have been employed to describe the various elements of this activity.

Coding is the most elementary of these terms and signifies simply an aggregate of instructions and addresses. The word is also used as a verb to signify the act of preparing coding.

A *subroutine* is a self-contained piece of coding which performs some definite function or calculation but which, in general, is not sufficient to cause the machine to carry out the computation of the solution to a problem from start to finish.

The noun *program* is used rather interchangeably with the terms *routine* and *code* to describe coding which is sufficiently self-contained to solve a problem. "Program" is also used as a verb.

Flow charts are the formal method for planning and presenting the logical structure of a computation. They are, in effect, block diagrams of the logical and of all possible temporal sequences which the computation may follow. A sequence of operations, be it arithmetic or information transfer, is usually summarized as a single block with reference for details to equations or other description, with the alternate sequence of computation resulting from each alternate of each choice clearly delineated. The flow-chart symbols approved by the Machine Computation Committee of the A.I.Ch.E. are given in "Guide to Abstracts and Manuals for Computer Program Exchange" (American Institute of Chemical Engineers, New York, 1960). The phrase "flow chart" is used sometimes as a verb.

An *algorithm* is the statement, in adequate detail, of the exact rules for making a given computation. A simple example is the grade-school method for calculating square roots. Algorithms may consist only of mathematical notation or algebraic formulas but they are usually more detailed, leaving nothing unspecified about the computation and including, in particular, the criterion for terminating the computation. Problems which have been reduced to algorithms by suitable formulation are then ready for coding.

Machine language is the special set of symbols for instructions, and the particular system of numbering for addresses which, when interpreted by a particular machine's circuitry, will cause that medium to perform the operation symbolized by the instructions.

The term *programming* is used to indicate a wide range of activities, ranging from the narrowest sense of preparing flow charts to that of including all activities related to the machine.

An *open shop* is a computing installation at which anyone who wishes may use the machine, assisted when necessary by an experienced programmer. By contrast, a *closed shop* is an installation at which problems are submitted to programmers, who in turn solve them by means of programs which they write and use on the machine; the results are then returned to the person submitting the problem. The terms have no reference to the employer of the persons using the machine. In a closed shop, both problem originator and programmer are usually members of the same organization.

Two *types of programming* are distinguished, that relating to *data processing* and that relating to *scientific computation.* Much programming related to the engineering field is of the latter type. However, this distinction on the basis of function cannot be carried over to distinguish between problem types. Statistical or mathematical concepts requiring much calculation could be applied to some aspects of marketing and other business problems, and a technical problem may involve considerable manipulation of intermediate results, i.e., data processing.

There are a number of *programming systems* which permit instructions for the machine to be written in a more convenient, understandable, or concise form than machine language. Associated with every programming system is a body of coding which is already prepared and which is used by the machine to interpret or extend the information fed as input to that system.

Utility programs include systems for correcting and merging the information on magnetic tapes and systems for listing or editing coding of various types.

Diagnostic programs are systems which assist in testing other programs. One of the most useful is the *follower* or *trace* program. When a program being tested is executed under the control of a follower program, a listing is obtained of the contents of the registers at each step in the program being tested. Other types of follower may list only certain key numbers or quantities during the execution of the program. From such listings, the action of the program under test may be followed and the point located where it is not operating as planned.

Special-purpose programming systems, larger and more general than a single program, exist for various machines to perform a wide variety of operations in some single field such as statistics, matrix algebra, differential equations, linear programming, maximization, and the like.

Pseudo code is the term usually applied to the information fed to a programming system which controls that system's action.

Assembly-language coding is the name applied to programming systems which have as their input a system of instructions resembling machine instructions but which is easier to write in some sense. *Automatic coding systems* produce machine-language coding or cause it to be executed.

A *library* of subroutines, already prepared to perform various functions, is frequently an adjunct of an automatic coding system. One such function is to supply floating-point arithmetic for those machines which do not have floating-point hardware. Subroutines for calculations of sines, cosines, logarithms, and exponentials are also often included in libraries.

An *assembly routine* is an automatic coding system which transforms pseudo code into machine code and assembles other coding as required from its library. The pseudo code for an assembler is usually similar in form to machine language but employs a more convenient notation. An assembler may also perform other functions, such as decimal-binary conversion.

The term *automatic programming* is usually applied to programming systems which accept a pseudo code which is not similar to machine language, for example, algebraic equations. The terms automatic coding and automatic programming are used somewhat interchangeably depending on local usage.

Algebraic translators produce machine code from algebraic equations, possibly by means of several translation steps, the lowest of which may be an assembly system. A number of such systems exist for different machines.

A *compiler* is a programming system which produces coding, usually in machine language, to be used later in the solution of a problem. The only function performed by a compiling program is to transform its input pseudo code into some other type of coding. While compiling, the compiler treats the program being compiled as data only. The resulting product (a program) is then saved and used to solve the original problem at any later time. The term compiler usually implies more sophisticated transformation of the input pseudo code than that done by an assembly routine.

An *interpreter* causes the machine-language instructions corresponding to the pseudo code to be executed as the pseudo code is being interpreted by the programming system. The pseudo code describing the procedure for solving the problem, the data required in the solution of the problem, and the interpretive program itself must all be contained in the storage of the machine at the same time. Problems which are repetitive cause the pseudo code to be reinterpreted for each repetition; interpreters therefore run more slowly than equivalent compilers. They compensate for this slowness by not taking the machine time required to compile the program. Interpretive pseudo code is frequently more concise than the corresponding machine-language instructions. The resulting saving of space is advantageous in long problems where program storage is at a premium.

Problem-oriented languages (POL) have a structure dependent on the type of problem which they are designed to express; the language structure is independent of the machine with which the problem is to be solved. Considerable research in programming theory is being devoted to the development of this type of programming language.

One such machine-independent language is *Algol*, the International algorithmic language. Algol is an internationally agreed upon standard notation for expressing algorithms. It is similar to and derives from the various algebraic automatic programming systems developed for specific machines. The specifications for Algol are published in the *Communications of the Association of Computing Machinery* [**6**, 1 (1963)]. Algorithms in Algol are being published in the *Communications;* a larger collection is to be published in a multivolume "Handbook for Automatic Computation" (Springer).

Although designed for stating algorithms clearly and concisely, Algol is also clearly a source language or pseudo code from which translation could be made to any machine for which a suitable compiler or translater is available. Translation programs for several specific machines have been developed.

One particular algebraic translator, *Fortran*, first written for one specific machine, has received widespread acceptance as a problem-oriented language for technical computations. Similar translators, also called Fortran, have been written for a number of other machines, including some made by other manufacturers. Minor differences between these various versions as well as differences in the configuration and computing power of the machines involved preclude using Fortran as an automatic translator from one machine to another. However, programs in Fortran are much easier to hand-translate for another machine than are programs in machine language.

Cobol is the business-oriented language now developed for data processing. It consists of selected English words or phrases which specify the operations to be performed.

Steps in Digital Computation. The steps in digital computation can be roughly divided into three parts: formulation, programming, and solution. In performing by machine the formerly entirely human function of computation, a number of new concepts have arisen at a wholly new level of abstraction. The best way found so far to gain a grasp of these concepts is to carry out personally the solution to a non-trivial problem by computation, despite the gross inefficiency of this method of learning.

Formulation is the analytical process which transforms a physical problem into a form suitable for solution by machine. Formulation is the most important of the three aspects of machine computation and the most likely to be slighted, since formulation does not directly involve the computer. However, in this area, the greatest gains (or losses) in computing effectiveness can be made. One of the first steps in formulation is to review the problem for suitability to computation, based on characteristics such as repetition, recursiveness, or reflexiveness. Other aspects of formulation are such matters as problem analysis and definition, review of basic assumptions, selection of mathematical models, selection of computing algorithms for standard parts of the calculation, algebraic rearrangement to remove redundant computation, and numerical analysis of errors and/or convergence, if required. The final result of formulation may be a high-level flow chart, an Algol statement, or a procedure written using conventional mathematical notation and English description.

Programming begins with the preparation of a detailed flow chart or its equivalent and includes the other steps in planning a program. Selection of machine and programming system is one of the first of these steps. This selection may be as much on the basis of availability, familiarity, and the existence of a completed program suitable for the problem as on the basis of the more obvious factors of size and speed. Other aspects of programming are planning input-output, coding, compiling, debugging (program testing), preparation of check solutions, and documentation. A.I.Ch.E. standards for documentation are given in "Guide to Abstracts and Manuals for Computer Program Exchange" (*op. cit.*). The growth of automatic programming and machine-independent languages is tending to reduce the importance of the coding phase of programming.

Problem *solution* comprises preparation of input data, supervision of running the computation (or preparation of instructions for others to do so), and review of the results for proper format, completeness, internal consistency, and reasonableness from an engineering standpoint.

Elapsed Time. Machines that do computation in seconds do not necessarily give answers in seconds. The difference between computing time and elapsed time is most marked when no program exists for the problem and one must proceed from formulation through computation of the final answer. Writing coding (or pseudo code) is slower than manual calculation; the advantage is gained when coding is reused because of the repetitive nature of the problem. Even use of a suitable finished program may consume several days of elapsed time for data preparation, data transcription, obtaining scheduled time, obtaining print-outs of results, and reviewing these for engineering suitability.

On the Subject of Errors. One of the advantages of computing machines is that they will perform complex calculations with an error frequency several orders of magnitude less than that obtained when the calculations are done manually, unchecked. In a long string of successive calculations, each depending on previous results, no progress will be made if the error frequency is high. Human beings make errors on the order of one every 200 operations. Thus it is necessary to look quite carefully at the portions of the problem solution involving human intervention while bearing in mind the remote possibility of machine malfunction. Formulation, data preparation, programming, and result interpretation are purely human functions and are subject to the highest error. Data transcription and result display involve interaction between man and machine; input-output and computation are purely mechanical operations.

Computing machines are not totally error-free. A few machines are self-checking; they stop and indicate when an error has been made by the machine so that it may be corrected or the calculation repeated. The input and output portions of digital machines make errors more frequently than the internal processors; input-output is more frequently routinely checked, either mechanically or as part of the program. Most machine errors result in eventual malfunction or in ridiculous answers; hence few pass unnoticed.

Commonly used methods of checking the human portions of the execution of a computation are proofreading (preferably by an individual different from the originator), duplication, back substitution (when the structure of the problem provides convenient equations), and review of the results for consistency, either internal or with other known facts about the problem.

A digital program which has been debugged and tested on a sample problem may be used to perform similar calculations with some confidence, provided an engineering review of the results is made after they have been calculated. However, no amount of testing will ever try out every possible sequence of execution of the instructions in a program of any consequence. Therefore, sooner or later, some combination of input data will cause untested instructions to be executed or some combination of instructions to be executed in an untested way. A hitherto undisclosed error may still remain in these untested instructions or in the original formulation which they represent. As a program is used and reused, there is an ever-decreasing but finite probability that the program contains an undetected error and will give erroneous results. The probability of such failure is much higher than the probability of machine error, if any care is taken with maintenance. This grim thesis does not negate the value of digital machines for engineering computation, but it does require that the machines be used in a manner somewhat different from that presented in the popular stereotype.

ANALOG MACHINES

Direct analogs are those in which electrical quantities, such as voltage and current, represent analogous quantities in some physical situation (*e.g.*, pressure and flow in fluid-flow calculations).

The Operational Analog. In the *operational analog* all quantities are represented by voltages, irrespective of their possible relationship to other electrical quantities. This type of analog computer can be connected to behave according to certain equations; these equations in turn are mathematical models of the physical situation under study.

Components. The *high-gain amplifier* is the principal component of the operational analog. These amplifiers are essentially micro-micro coulometers, devices which respond to very small changes in charge at their input. Their output is usually ±100 volts, delivered from a source of sufficiently low impedance that additional amplifiers and other equipment may be driven from this output without affecting it. The amplifiers are so sensitive that, in effect, they require (1) that there be no current flowing into or out of their input and (2) that the input voltage be zero for the output to be within its normal limits. The amplifiers are electronic in nature and usually chopper-stabilized so that they do not drift (change zero setting) over long periods of time. The symbol for the basic amplifier is given in Fig. 2-58*a*. Frequently, the ground-connection symbol is omitted as in Fig. 2-58*b*. Figure 2-58 also gives symbols for other elements of the analog computer.

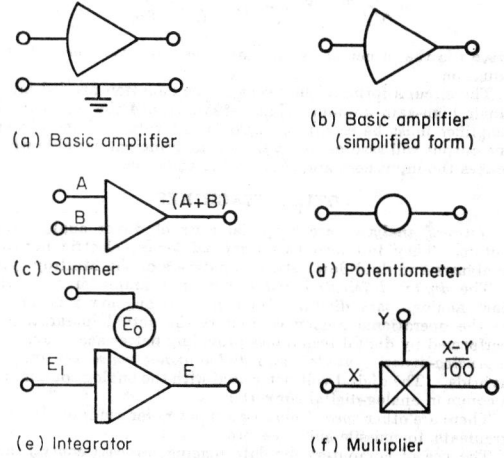

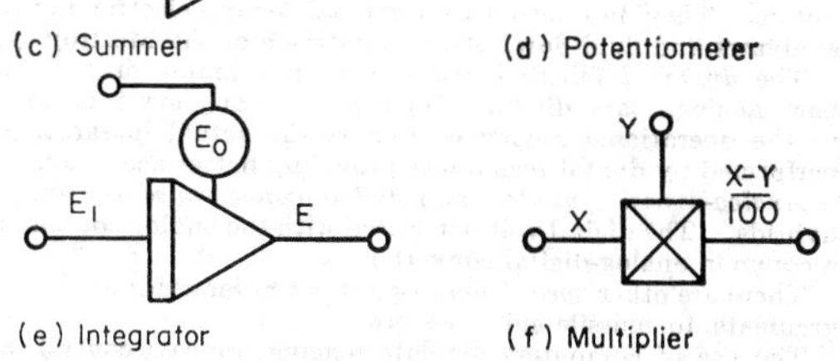

FIG. 2-58. Analog symbols.

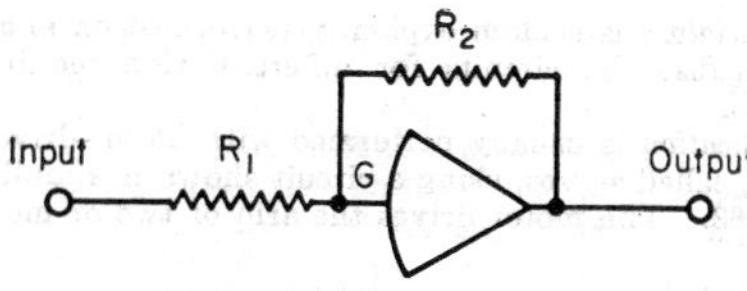

FIG. 2-59. Basic amplifier circuit.

The simplest use of an amplifier is to duplicate signals. Consider the amplifier connected as in Fig. 2-59, where resistance R_1 is the same as resistance R_2. Since current flowing from the input cannot flow into the amplifier without making very great changes in the output (because of the amplifier's infinite gain), it must flow out through R_2. Since the voltage at the input to the amplifier, point G, must also be zero and the two resistors are equal, the voltage at the output of the amplifier must be equal and opposite in sign to the voltage at the input.

A *summer* is an amplifier used to add two (or more) voltages, as shown in Fig. 2-60. If currents proportional to voltages A

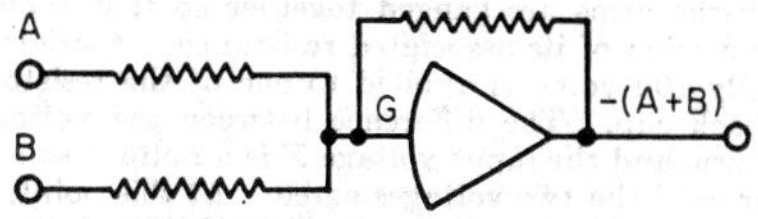

FIG. 2-60. Summer circuit.

and B flow toward the amplifier and all resistances are equal, the output voltage must be $-(A + B)$ to carry these currents away and maintain balance the input at essentially zero voltage. Variations in the input voltage can be neglected because it is so small compared with anything else in the circuit.

A *potentiometer* is used to multiply a voltage by a constant factor K (less than unity), as shown in Fig. 2-61.

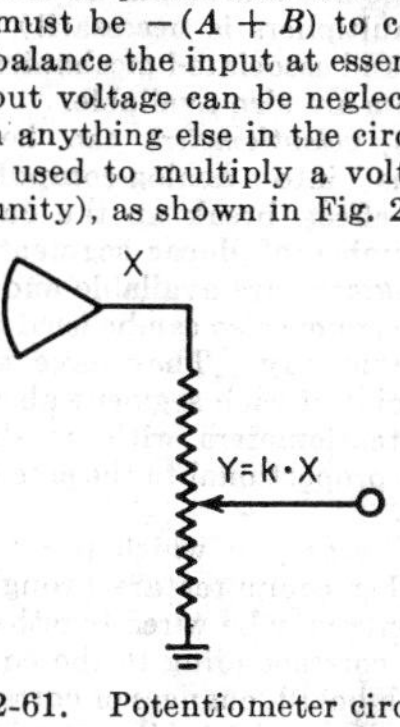

FIG. 2-61. Potentiometer circuit.

Multiplication by a constant, which may be greater than unity, can be done in another way with an amplifier. If, in the circuit of Fig. 2-59, R_1 is one-tenth of R_2, the output voltage must be ten times the input voltage to maintain the same current through both resistors.

Integration is performed by the circuit shown in Fig. 2-62; the feedback element is a capacitor rather than a resistor. The

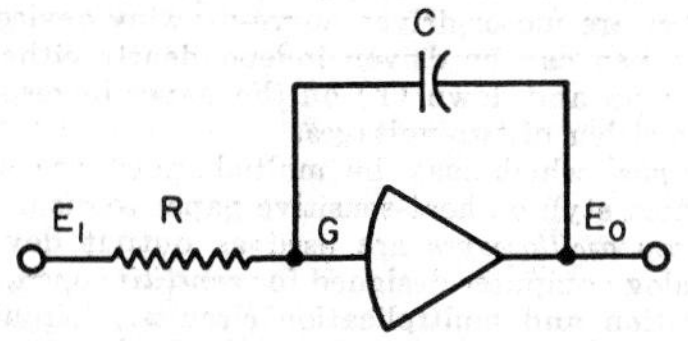

FIG. 2-62. Integrator circuit.

current to the amplifier is E_1/R, where E_1 is the input voltage. This current must be stored in the capacitor; it cannot flow into the amplifier. The fundamental equation defining a capacitor is

$$E = \frac{1}{C}\int_0^t I\,dt + E_0$$

where E_0 is the voltage at time $t = 0$. The end of the capacitor connected to point G must be at zero potential; hence the output voltage of the amplifier must be

$$E = \frac{-1}{R_1C}\int_0^t E_1\,dt + E_0$$

The time constant of the integrator is R_1C, measured in seconds.

Differentiation is seldom explicitly performed on analog computers because the circuits for differentiation require special techniques.

Multiplication is usually performed with motor-driven potentiometers, called servos, using a circuit shown in simplified form in Fig. 2-63. The motor drives the arm of two or more poten-

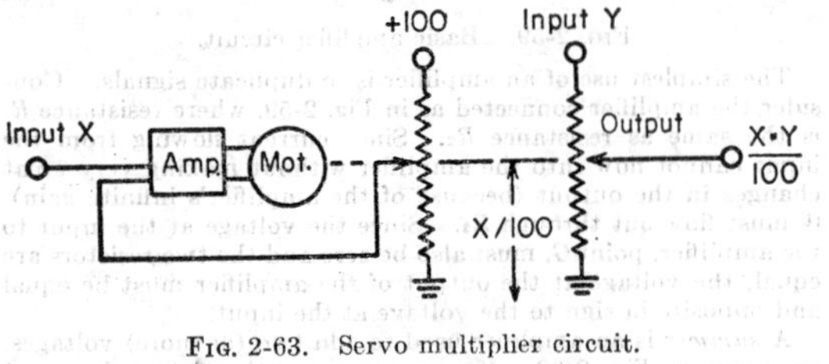

FIG. 2-63. Servo multiplier circuit.

tiometers; the arms are ganged together so that each taps off the same portion of its associated resistance. A reference voltage, usually 100 volts, is applied to one of the resistors, called the feedback cup. The difference between the voltage at the feedback arm and the input voltage X is amplified so as to drive the motor until the two voltages agree. At this point, the arms of the potentiometers are at a fraction $X/100$ of the total resistance. If another voltage Y is applied to the second potentiometer, the voltage at its arm will be $XY/100$. The speed of response of servomultipliers is necessarily limited to the drive speed of the motor and associated mechanical elements. Faster, electronic multipliers are also available.

Tapped (padded) potentiometers can be used to introduce arbitrary functions into analog-computer circuits. These potentiometers, in effect, break up the curve representing the function into a number of linear segments. Adjustments for the slope of each segment are available and can be preset.

Diode function generators also can be used to represent arbitrary functions in the same way. They have the added advantage that the starting point of each segment also can be preset.

Resolvers are potentiometers with non-linear windings such that their output is proportional to the sine or cosine of the angle of rotation (input).

Input. A *patch board,* to which the terminals of the components of an analog computer are brought, is the means by which the components may be wired together by plug-in jumpers to form the circuit corresponding to the equations to be solved. Because of the patch board, changes or corrections to the problem are relatively easy to make while running the computation. Setting of the dials of the coefficient potentiometers, diode function generators, and tapped potentiometers completes the input statement of a problem.

Output. Output from an analog computer is in the form of voltage readings or of curves.

Digital voltmeters have been developed which display voltages as digital quantities with four-digit precision.

XY plotters are motor-driven curve-drawing devices, so called because the pen can be driven independently either back and forth (X) or up and down (Y) on the paper in response to the variation in either of two voltages.

Oscillographs, which may be multichannel, use either inked pens or heated styli on heat-sensitive paper to display curves.

Cathode-ray oscilloscopes are used as output devices on the type of analog computer designed for *repetitive operation,* having fast integration and multiplication circuits. Circuitry is provided to repeat the problem often enough that the persistence of the cathode-ray screen makes display of the entire time behavior of key variables possible. The effect of variation of parameter settings on this display may then be easily observed.

Steps in Computation. *Formulation* is the first step in preparing a problem for an analog computer. Problems usually are formulated as one or more ordinary differential equations or as simultaneous non-linear equations. An important part of formulation is to include only those aspects of the problem which will have a major effect on the answer.

Algebraic manipulation is usually required once the problem has been stated in mathematical form. This includes isolation of similar functional groups which occur repeatedly, rearrangement to avoid division by zero or near-zero quantities, and the elimination, wherever possible, of explicit differentiation.

Mechanization is the drawing of a wiring diagram, using the symbols given in Fig. 2-58, to show the way in which physical components will be *connected* together to simulate the required equations. Although the digital flow chart (p. 2-83) is quite similar in appearance, it indicates the sequence *in time* in which the various computations are to be individually executed.

Scaling is required on nearly all analog problems. All voltages should lie between 1 and 100 per cent of full scale during the course of a problem; for best accuracy, they should lie between 10 and 100 per cent. This requires that the variables in the original problem statement be expressed in terms of scale factors.

Example. Pressure is to be used in a calculation as well as the square of the pressure; the pressure is of the order of 15 lb./sq. in; the machine is 100 volts full scale. A convenient scale factor for pressure P would be 5 volts/lb./sq. in. Having established this external scale, a scale of 0.25 volt/(lb./sq. in.)^2 should be used for P^2, to match the multiplier action. The voltage corresponding to the square of 15 lb./sq. in. would be 56.25 volts.

$$56.25 = \frac{(5 \times 15)(5 \times 15)}{100} = (15)^2 \times 0.25$$

Scaling also involves relating time within the analog to the independent variable of the problem, which may be real time or some other variable, such as the length of a pipe-line reactor. Each integration involves the introduction of this time-scale factor.

Selection of specific component identification numbers and addition of these to the scale diagram, together with indications of polarity where necessary, complete the wiring diagram. The patch board may now be wired in accordance with the diagram. Simultaneously, a listing of the scaled settings of the required coefficient potentiometers is prepared and used as a guide to setting their dials.

A *voltage check* is a manual calculation of the voltage at every point in the circuit for some single condition.

Special Applications. *Ordinary differential equations,* functions of a single independent variable, are the chief type of problem solved with an analog computer.

Partial differential equations can often be solved by breaking the second independent variable up into discrete intervals and expressing the derivatives with respect to this second variable in difference form. The result is a set of simultaneous equations in one independent variable. Such an arrangement will, in general, take as many times the amount of computer components as there are intervals in the formulation. Special devices are being developed for storing the profile of the values of the dependent variables as a function of one of the independent variables.

Implicit functions in which the principal variable (or its highest derivative) cannot be solved for explicitly can be solved by setting up the circuit corresponding to the function assuming, wherever necessary, that a voltage representing the principal variable will be available.

Example. The Colebrook equation, defining friction factor, can be rewritten as [J. Inst. C. E., **11**, 133 (1938)]

$$\frac{1}{\sqrt{f}} + 2 \log \left(\frac{E}{3.7D} + \frac{2.51}{\mathrm{Re}\sqrt{f}} \right) = 0$$

Here f is the principal variable and there are two terms to the equation.

The circuits forming the terms of the equation are fed into a single high-gain amplifier (Fig. 2-59*b*). Since the input to the amplifier must be essentially zero for all values of the output, the output will assume that value of the principal variable which makes the input zero and satisfies the equation.

OTHER MACHINES

Network analyzers are a special class of direct analog computers. They fall into two principal types, electric network analyzers and fluid-flow network analyzers of the McIlroy type.

The *digital differential analyzer* is an example of a hybrid, part analog, part digital. Its logical arrangement is similar to the operational analog computer; the actual integration is performed by digital techniques providing better accuracy.

Analog-digital converters and *digital-analog converters* are also hybrids. The digital voltmeter used with the analog computer is a common analog-digital converter.

There are other *special-purpose computers* for studying thermal gradients, for missile guidance, etc.

The use of computers for data logging, process control, and real-time simulation is described on pages 22–54 ff.

DIMENSIONAL ANALYSIS

Dimensional analysis is simply a mathematical tool, It is not necessary to be a mathematician, however, to be able to use and to understand dimensional analysis. A knowledge of its use will enable the engineer to save considerable time in planning experiments and in correlating results of an experiment or using correlations prepared by others.

In order to apply dimensional analysis to a situation, the engineer need know only the variables believed to be involved and their dimensions. He need use only these along with fundamental algebra to save time, trouble, and expense in experimental investigation or correlation of a problem. In some cases, without any experimental work at all, he can tell from dimensional analysis if a suspected variable is really involved in a particular problem.

In all cases, dimensional analysis will reduce the number of experimental variables to be correlated, and often it will point out the best experimental approach to the problem. It will not give quantitative information, however; experiment must still be relied upon for that purpose.

THE SIMPLEST PROBLEMS

When only two variables are to be correlated, a simple plot of one against the other results in a single curve. When the number of variables is increased to three, then values of the first are plotted against corresponding values of the second for several constant values of the third, producing a set of curves. The addition of a fourth or more variables greatly complicates both the experimental and the correlation work.

For an example of the value of dimensional analysis in a simple problem involving four variables, this hypothetical case is considered: Assume a problem exists wherein the only variables are two forces, F and P, and two lengths, X and Y.

Variable Correlation. The correlation of this simple problem by plotting one variable against another at constant values of the third and fourth variables would be anything but simple. In the experimental work F would have to be held constant at $F = F_1$ while the variation of Y with X was determined at constant values of $P(P = P_1, P_2, P_3$, etc.). Then F would have to be held at $F = F_2$ while the variation of Y with X was again determined for the various constant values of P. This procedure would have to be repeated again and again until the range of values of F had been covered.

Dimensional Analysis Correlations. Since in this simple problem the two variables F and P have the dimension of force and the two variables X and Y have the dimension of length, we would have two dimensionless groups F/P and X/Y. Application of the basic principle of dimensional analysis would show that the plot of F/P vs. X/Y would yield a single curve. It is then easily seen that the saving in experimental work would be tremendous since no single variable would have to be held constant. Only the dimensionless group X/Y would need to be varied, and the corresponding value of F/P would be measured.

Admittedly such simple problems are rare in chemical engineering studies. A more typical one would involve more variables with varying degrees of dimensional complexity in the individual variables. Such a problem is the one involving pressure drop accompanying the flow of a fluid through a closed conduit. In this problem suppose seven variables are considered: pressure drop, fluid velocity, fluid density, fluid viscosity, conduit length, conduit diameter, and conduit wall roughness. Application of dimensional analysis to this problem reduces the number of quantities to be correlated from seven variables to four dimensionless groups of variables, and a consideration of the mechanics of fluids further reduces the number to three dimensionless groups. A single chart then becomes sufficient for the general correlation of the seven original variables.

THE RAYLEIGH METHOD

Rayleigh's method is based upon the premise that if n quantities, $Q_1, Q_2, Q_3, \ldots, Q_n$, are involved in a certain physical phenomenon, for the purpose of the dimensional analysis their mutual dependence may be expressed as a power product of the following type:

$$Q_1 = KQ_2^{a_2}Q_3^{a_3} \cdots Q_n^{a_n} \qquad (2\text{-}109)$$

where K is a dimensionless constant.

In this equation, Q_1 might be construed to be the quantity which is of principal interest, although such an interpretation is entirely unessential to the method. The Q's would include all the variables known to enter into the particular phenomenon and, in addition, all dimensional constants either demanded by the dimensional system employed or otherwise known to be involved. The requirement of dimensional homogeneity places some restrictions upon the values that the $n - 1$ constants $a_2, a_3, \ldots, a_n$ may have. If the n variables and dimensional constants consist of r primary dimensions, then there exists a maximum of r conditions which the constant exponents of Eq. (2-109) must satisfy. The word "maximum" is advisedly used, for in some cases, depending upon the dimensional system used or the dimensional nature of the quantities involved, two or more of the r conditions may in effect be identical, thereby reducing the number of actual conditions to a value less than r. Consequently, of the $n - 1$ constants, a minimum of $n - 1 - r$ is not restricted by the requirement of dimensional homogeneity. The final result of dimensional analysis by the Rayleigh method is an arrangement of the n quantities into such a form that a dimensionless product or group containing Q_1 is equated to the product of a minimum of $n - 1 - r$ other dimensionless groups, each raised to the power represented by one of the $n - 1 - r$ unrestricted exponents. As a consequence, there results an arrangement of the n quantities into a minimum of $n - 1 - r + 1 = n - r$ dimensionless groups.

Example 1 (Rayleigh Method)

Pressure Drop by Friction in Fluid Flow. When a fluid is flowing in a small straight length dL of a pipe with internal diameter D, a pressure drop $-dp_f$ occurs as a result of friction. The variables believed to be involved and their dimensions in the engineering system* are given below.

Pressure drop $= -dp_f = (F/L^2)$
Pipe internal diameter $= D = (L)$
Pipe length $= dL = (L)$
Pipe roughness $= \epsilon = (L)$
Fluid linear velocity $= V = (L/\theta)$
Fluid absolute viscosity $= \mu = (M/L\theta)$
Fluid density $= \rho = (M/L^3)$
Dimensional constant $= g_c = (ML/F\theta^2)$

An inspection of the dimensions of these quantities indicates that all are dimensionally combinable and

* Any of the systems of dimensions could have been chosen. The engineering system is used here only because most readers are more familiar with it.

should appear in the result of the dimensional analysis. Therefore, since there are eight quantities and four primary dimensions, a minimum of three ($n - r - 1 = 3$) unrestricted exponents and a minimum of four ($n - r = 4$) dimensionless groups may be expected.

The basic equation relating the variables is

$$-dp_f = KD^a(dL)^b\epsilon^cV^d\rho^e\mu^hg_c^j \qquad (2\text{-}110)$$

The corresponding dimensional equation is

$$\frac{F}{L^2} = (L)^a(L)^b(L)^c\left(\frac{L}{\theta}\right)^d\left(\frac{M}{L^3}\right)^e\left(\frac{M}{L\theta}\right)^h\left(\frac{ML}{F\theta^2}\right)^j \qquad (2\text{-}111)$$

If the condition of dimensional homogeneity is applied, there results the following set of equations:

$$\begin{aligned} \Sigma F &= 0: 1 = -j \\ \Sigma M &= 0: 0 = e + h + j \\ \Sigma L &= 0: -2 = a + b + c + d - 3e - h + j \\ \Sigma\theta &= 0: 0 = -d - h - 2j \end{aligned} \qquad (2\text{-}112)$$

No two of these four equations are identical, nor may any be obtained from a linear combination of two others. Therefore, the number of conditions is the maximum ($r = 4$), and the minimum number of dimensionless groups may be expected ($n - r = 4$). Since there are four independent equations relating the seven constants, the values of four of the constants may be determined in terms of the remaining three. If we let these three unrestricted constants be b, c, and h, the solutions to Eqs. (2-112) then become

$$\begin{aligned} a &= -b - c - h \\ d &= 2 - h \\ e &= 1 - h \\ j &= -1 \end{aligned} \qquad (2\text{-}113)$$

The insertion of the solutions represented by Eqs. (2-113) into Eq. (2-111) results in the expression

$$-dp_f = KD^{-b-c-h}(dL)^b\epsilon^cV^{2-h}\rho^{1-h}\mu^hg_c^{-1} \qquad (2\text{-}114)$$

or

$$\frac{g_c(-dp_f)}{\rho V^2} = K(dL/D)^b(DV\rho/\mu)^{-h}(\epsilon/D)^c \qquad (2\text{-}115)$$

The seven variables plus g_c are now correlated in the form of four dimensionless groups. From theoretical considerations, it can be shown that the pressure drop $-dp_f$ must be directly proportional to the pipe length dL; consequently, the exponent b must have the value of unity. The dimensionless group $g_c(-dp_f)/\rho V^2$ is called the Euler number, N_{Eu}. The dimensionless group $DV\rho/\mu$ is called the Reynolds number, N_{Re}. Both these numbers have general application in fluid flow. The dimensionless group ϵ/D is called the roughness factor of the pipe.

For reasons which will be discussed briefly later, in place of Eq. (2-115) with $b = 1$ there may be written the more general functional equation

$$\frac{-dp_f}{\rho} = \frac{V^2}{g_c}\frac{dL}{D}\Phi(N_{Re}, \epsilon/D) \qquad (2\text{-}116)$$

If the function $\Phi(N_{Re}, \epsilon/D)$ is given the symbol $f/2$, Eq. (2-116) may be written as

$$\frac{-dp_f}{\rho} = f\frac{V^2}{2g_c}\frac{dL}{D} \qquad (2\text{-}116a)$$

The function of the Reynolds number and the roughness factor denoted by the symbol f is called the friction factor.

In this example the exponents b, c, and h were purposely selected as the unrestricted exponents in order to obtain the results in the conventional form. Three other exponents might have been so selected, with the obvious exception of j, which must have the value of -1 for this example. Inspection of the equations for ΣM and $\Sigma\theta$ also shows that, of the exponents d, e, and h, no more than one may be selected as an unrestricted exponent. For example, the selection of a, b, and d as the unrestricted exponents would have resulted in the following four dimensionless groups:

$$\frac{g_c(-dp_f)\epsilon^2\rho}{\mu^2} \qquad \frac{\epsilon}{D} \qquad \frac{dL}{D} \qquad \frac{\epsilon V\rho}{\mu}$$

The appearance of ϵ, a quantity which is difficult to determine with exactness, in three of these four dimensionless groups is undesirable. If $\epsilon V\rho/\mu$ is divided by ϵ/D, the Reynolds number $DV\rho/\mu$ results. If the group $g_c(-dp_f)\epsilon^2\rho/\mu^2$ is divided by $(\epsilon V\rho/\mu)^2$, the Euler number $g_c(-dp_f)/\rho V^2$ results. In this manner, the results of dimensional analysis may be converted from dimensionless groups that are not desired to groups that are more convenient and desirable.

The transformation of $(DV\rho/\mu)^{-h}(\epsilon/D)^c$ in Eq. (2-115) to an unspecified function of these two dimensionless groups $\Phi(N_{Re}, \epsilon/D)$ in Eq. (2-116) is a definite feature of the Rayleigh method. Solutions of the type of Eq. (2-115) may be regarded as special and may be summed up to give a more general solution. The requirement of dimensional homogeneity for the general solution is equivalent to a requirement of dimensional homogeneity for each special solution. Furthermore, since no restrictions are placed upon the constant K or the exponents in Eq. (2-115), the general solution may be regarded as a general function, as in Eq. (2-116).

The justification of the transition from a power-product equation to a general functional expression in the Rayleigh method implies a restriction upon the nature of the general function. If Rayleigh's method is to be taken at its face value, the function $\Phi(N_{Re}, \epsilon/D)$ in Example 1 must be representable as a *product* of two functions $\Phi_1(N_{Re})$ and $\Phi_2(\epsilon/D)$. In a more general case, suppose that an analysis by the Rayleigh method indicated that the dimensionless group P is a function of the dimensionless groups R and S, or

$$P = \Phi(R, S) \qquad (2\text{-}117)$$

The implicit restriction, however, is that the function be representable as

$$P = \Phi_1(R)\Phi_2(S) \qquad (2\text{-}117a)$$

and not as

$$P = \Phi_3(R) + \Phi_4(S) \qquad (2\text{-}117b)$$

nor as

$$P = [\Phi_5(R)]^{\Phi_6(S)} \qquad (2\text{-}117c)$$

If this apparent restriction in Rayleigh's method on the algebraic form in which the solution may be expressed were a general restriction in dimensional analysis, it would indeed be serious. Fortunately, Rayleigh's method may be rigorously regarded as nothing more than an algebraic procedure for determining the dimensionless groups that constitute a *complete* set for the group of quantities being considered. Any implication of restrictions on the nature of the functions of these groups is merely a trivial consequence of the algebraic procedure.

THE BUCKINGHAM Pi METHOD

Although this method was introduced in 1914, no rigorous proof was presented until Langhaar's contribution in 1951. He stated the Pi Theorem as follows:

If an equation is dimensionally homogeneous, it can be reduced to a relationship among a complete set of dimensionless products. . . . A set of dimensionless products of given variables is complete if each product in the set is independent of the others, and every other dimensionless product of the variables is a product of powers of dimensionless products in the set.

The dependence of n quantities may be expressed in the form of

$$Q_1^{a_1}Q_2^{a_2}Q_3^{a_3} \cdots Q_m^{a_m} \cdots Q_n^{a_n} = \pi_i \qquad i = 1, 2, 3, \ldots, p \qquad (2\text{-}118)$$

The significance of m and p will be explained shortly. No dimensionless constant is needed in Eq. (2-118). In the Rayleigh method, the *minimum* number of dimensionless groups possible from n quantities described by r dimensions was $n - r$. In the Buckingham method, it is necessary to know beforehand how many dimensionless groups will constitute a complete set. Consequently, the symbol m is introduced and defined as the number of *restrictions* placed upon Eq. (2-118) by virtue of the requirement of dimensional homogeneity. Furthermore, m will have as its maximum value the number of primary dimensions r. If there are m restrictions on the values of $a_1, a_2, a_3, \ldots, a_n$ in Eq. (2-118), there will be $n - m$ unrestricted exponents, and consequently $n - m$ dimensionless groups will result. Langhaar has proved that the number of dimensionless groups p constituting a complete set for n quantities is given by the equation

$$p = n - m \qquad (2\text{-}119)$$

According to Buckingham's theorem, the p dimensionless groups $\pi_1, \pi_2, \pi_3, \ldots, \pi_p$ are then related by the general functional equation

$$\phi(\pi_1, \pi_2, \pi_3, \ldots, \pi_p) = 0 \qquad (2\text{-}120)$$

This equation does no more than state that the particular phenomenon may now be described as rigorously and accurately in terms of the complete set of p dimensionless groups as it might be in terms of the n quantities involved in the phenomenon.

The evaluation of m has been the chief difficulty in the use of the Buckingham method. Van Driest stated that m could be considered as the maximum number of quantities involved in the problem that could be combined *without* forming a dimensionless group. Langhaar has rigorously proved this to be true and has further shown that m is in reality the rank of the matrix formed from the exponents of the dimensions of the quantities. This use of matrices in connection with Buckingham's method is convenient, but it is by no means essential to the method. The determination of m as the maximum number of variables that will not combine to form a dimensionless group is entirely satisfactory even though sometimes rather tedious. A simple demonstration of the fact that the maximum value of m is the number of primary dimensions results from a consideration of the five variables force, mass, length, time, and temperature with engineering-system dimensions. Obviously these five variables cannot possibly form a dimensionless group, but the inclusion of any other variable describable by the dimensions F, M, L, θ, and T will permit the formation of a dimensionless group.

Since there are by definition m restrictions upon the values of the constant exponents $a_1, a_2, a_3, \ldots, a_m, \ldots, a_n$ in Eq. (2-118), let the constants $a_1, a_2, a_3, \ldots, a_m$ be those so restricted. The constants $a_{m+1}, a_{m+2}, \ldots, a_n$ may be assigned any value, as they represent the $n - m$ unrestricted constants. To determine $\pi_1(i = 1)$ from Eq. (2-118), let $a_{m+1} = 1$ and $a_{m+2}, a_{m+3}, \ldots, a_n$ all equal zero. Similarly, to determine $\pi_2(i = 2)$, let $a_{m+2} = 1$ and $a_{m+1}, a_{m+3}, \ldots, a_n$ all equal zero. If this procedure is followed for all the $n - m$ unrestricted constants, the following set of equations will result:

$$\begin{aligned} \pi_1 &= Q_1^{a_1}Q_2^{a_2}Q_3^{a_3} \cdots Q_m^{a_m}Q_{m+1} \\ \pi_2 &= Q_1^{a_1}Q_2^{a_2}Q_3^{a_3} \cdots Q_m^{a_m}Q_{m+2} \\ &\cdot \\ &\cdot \\ &\cdot \\ \pi_p &= Q_1^{a_1}Q_2^{a_2}Q_3^{a_3} \cdots Q_m^{a_m}Q_n \end{aligned} \qquad (2\text{-}121)$$

This set of equations represents the equations that must be constructed from the quantities in any problem when Buckingham's method is used. The same m quantities appear in all p equations. In order to avoid difficulty or a complete impasse in the solutions of these equations, it is *essential* that these m repeating quantities be such that they alone are not capable of forming a dimensionless group.

Example 2 (Buckingham Pi Method)

Heat-transfer Film Coefficient. It is desired to determine a complete set of dimensionless groups with which to correlate experimental data on the film coefficient of heat transfer between the walls of a straight conduit with circular cross section and a fluid flowing in that conduit. The variables and the dimensional constant believed to be involved and their dimensions in the engineering system are given below:

Film coefficient $= h = (F/L\theta T)$
Conduit internal diameter $= D = (L)$
Fluid linear velocity $= V = (L/\theta)$
Fluid density $= \rho = (M/L^3)$
Fluid absolute viscosity $= \mu = (M/L\theta)$
Fluid thermal conductivity $= k = (F/\theta T)$
Fluid specific heat $= c_p = (FL/MT)$
Dimensional constant $= g_c = (ML/F\theta^2)$

The first step in the solution requires the determination of m. Since there are five primary dimensions $(FML\theta T)$ involved, the maximum value that m might have is 5. A few trials will show that there are several sets of five quantities which do not form dimensionless groups. Since m therefore has the value 5, the $n = 8$ quantities listed above should produce a complete set of $p = n - m = 3$ dimensionless groups according to Eq. (2-119).

Let the five repeating quantities that do not form a dimensionless group be D, V, μ, k, and g_c. According to Eq. (2-121), the following equations represent the three dimensionless groups:

$$\pi_1 = D^aV^b\mu^dk^eg_c^fh \qquad (2\text{-}122)$$
$$\pi_2 = D^aV^b\mu^dk^eg_c^fc_p \qquad (2\text{-}123)$$
$$\pi_3 = D^aV^b\mu^dk^eg_c^f\rho \qquad (2\text{-}124)$$

In these equations, h was included with the five repeating variables to form π_1. Similarly, c_p was included to form π_2, and ρ was included to form π_3.

The procedure from this point is identical to that in the Rayleigh method with the exception that no undetermined exponents will be found as the number of restrictions on each equation and the number of exponents are the same. This is a general characteristic of the Buckingham method. The dimensional equation corresponding to Eq. (2-122) is

$$F^\circ M^\circ L^\circ \theta^\circ T^\circ = (L)^a(L/\theta)^b(M/L\theta)^d(F/\theta T)^e (ML/F\theta^2)^f(F/L\theta T) \qquad (2\text{-}125)$$

Applying the condition of dimensional homogeneity, we have

$$\begin{aligned} \Sigma F &= 0: 0 = e - f + 1 \\ \Sigma M &= 0: 0 = d + f \\ \Sigma L &= 0: 0 = a + b - d + f - 1 \\ \Sigma \theta &= 0: 0 = -b - d - e - 2f - 1 \\ \Sigma T &= 0: 0 = -e - 1 \end{aligned} \qquad (2\text{-}126)$$

The solutions to Eqs. (2-126) are

$$\begin{aligned} a &= 1 \\ b &= 0 \\ d &= 0 \\ e &= -1 \\ f &= 0 \end{aligned} \tag{2-127}$$

Equation (2·122) then becomes

$$\pi_1 = D^1 V^0 \mu^0 k^{-1} g_c^{\,0} h$$

$$\pi_1 = \frac{hD}{k} \tag{2-128}$$

In a similar manner, the solutions to Eqs. (2-123) and (2-124) are found to be

$$\pi_2 = \frac{c_p \mu}{k} \tag{2-129}$$

$$\pi_3 = \frac{DV\rho}{\mu} \tag{2-130}$$

The dimensionless group hD/k is called the Nusselt number, N_{Nu}, and the group $c_p\mu/k$ is the Prandtl number, N_{Pr}. The group $DV\rho/\mu$ is the familiar Reynolds number, N_{Re}, encountered in fluid-friction problems. These three dimensionless groups are frequently used in heat-transfer film coefficient correlations. Functionally, their relation may be expressed as

$$\phi(N_{\text{Nu}}, N_{\text{Pr}}, N_{\text{Re}}) = 0 \tag{2-131}$$

or as

$$N_{\text{Nu}} = \phi_1(N_{\text{Pr}}, N_{\text{Re}}) \tag{2-132}$$

It has been found that these dimensionless groups may be correlated well by an equation of the type

$$\frac{hD}{k} = K(c_p\mu/k)^a (DV\rho/\mu)^b \tag{2-133}$$

in which K, a, and b are experimentally determined dimensionless constants. However, any other type of algebraic expression or perhaps simply a graphical relation among these three groups that accurately fits the experimental data would be an equally valid manner of expressing Eq. (2-131).

Naturally, other dimensionless groups might have been obtained in Example 2 by employing a different set of five repeating quantities that would not form a dimensionless group among themselves. Some of these groups may be found among those presented in Table 2-5. Such a complete set of three dimensionless groups might consist of Stanton, Reynolds, and Prandtl numbers, or of Stanton, Peclet, and Prandtl numbers. Also, such a complete set different from that obtained in Example 2 will result from a multiplication of appropriate powers of the Nusselt, Prandtl, and Reynolds numbers. For such a set to be complete, however, it must satisfy the condition that each of the three dimensionless groups be independent of the other two.

Although it is not directly necessary in the Buckingham method to know how many quantities are really involved (dimensionally combinable) in the problem, it is essential to the method that the correct estimation of the value of m be made. Since the inclusion of a quantity that is not dimensionally combinable will increase the value of m, thereby increasing the number of repeating quantities in the equations of the type of Eq. (2-121), some difficulty might be anticipated. However, all dimensionally non-combinable quantities must certainly be included in the largest sets of quantities characterized by the inability to form a dimensionless group among themselves. In such a case, when the equations of the type of Eqs. (2-121) are constructed, these quantities are included among the m repeating quantities, but being non-combinable, drop out from each dimensionless group being formed. This was the case with g_c in Example 2. Since both n and m are increased by one as a result of the inclusion of each non-combinable quantity, neither the prediction of the number of dimensionless groups nor the results of the analysis are affected in any way. Thus, the problem is handled automatically by the determination of m as the largest number of quantities that are not capable of forming a dimensionless group and by the use of this set of quantities as the m repeating quantities in Eqs. (2-121). Similarly, no difficulties arise when the method employing matrices is used.

By virtue of the inclusion of dimensionally non-combinable g_c in Example 2, the value of m resulting was the maximum value, the same as the number of primary dimensions ($FML\theta T$). Had g_c been omitted (an omission which the results of the analysis justified), the value of m would have been 4, one less than the number of primary dimensions. Inspection of Eqs. (2-126) for ΣF and ΣT shows that, if f is assigned the value of zero (equivalent to omission of g_c), these two equations become identical. Furthermore, inspection of the dimensions of the quantities excluding g_c shows that F/T is in reality a primary dimension for that set of variables. In other words, a four-dimensional system (F/T, M, L, θ) is adequate for the problem. Dimensions need not have physical significance, so that F/T is a perfectly permissible primary dimension for this problem, and actually the value of m was the number of primary dimensions. It would be misleading, however, not to stress the fact that all cases in which m is apparently less than the number of primary dimensions may not be so explained. The four quantities g_c, $-dp_f$, ρ, and V, as defined for Example 1, are described in the engineering system by the four dimensions F, M, L, and θ. However, $m = 3$ for this case, as these four quantities do combine to form the Euler number.

The lack of space necessarily limits the discussion on this important subject. It is suggested that beginners follow the comprehensive discussion of Silberberg and McKetta in the four-part article in *Petroleum Refiner* in 1953. Those more familiar with the subject should refer to Langhaar for a more complete and sophisticated treatment.

Table 2-5. Dimensionless Groups in the Engineering System of Dimensions*

Biot number	N_{Bi}	hL/k
Condensation number	N_{Co}	$(h/k)(\mu^2/\rho^2 g)^{1/3}$
Number used in condensation of vapors	N_{Cv}	$L^3\rho^2 g\lambda/k\mu\Delta t$
Euler number	N_{Eu}	$g_c(-dp)/\rho V^2$
Fourier number	N_{Fo}	$k\theta/\rho c L^2$
Froude number	N_{Fr}	V^2/Lg
Graetz number	N_{Gz}	wc/kL
Grashof number	N_{Gr}	$L^3\rho^2\beta g\Delta t/\mu^2$
Mach number	N_{Ma}	V/V_a
Nusselt number	N_{Nu}	hD/k
Peclet number	N_{Pe}	$DV\rho c/k$
Prandtl number	N_{Pr}	$c\mu/k$
Reynolds number	N_{Re}	$DV\rho/\mu$
Schmidt number	N_{Sc}	$\mu/\rho D_v$
Stanton number	N_{St}	$h/cV\rho$
Weber number	N_{We}	$LV^2\rho/\sigma g_c$

* For additional groups see work of Boucher and Alves.

REFERENCES: Bridgman, "Dimensional Analysis," Yale University Press, New Haven, Conn., 1937. Langhaar, "Dimensional Analysis and Theory of Models," Wiley, New York, 1951. Murphy, Dimensional Analysis, *Bull. V.P.I.* **42**(6), 1949. Porter, "The Method of Dimensions," Methuen, London, 1933. Boucher and Alves, Dimensionless Numbers, *Chem. Eng. Progress* **55**, 1960, pp. 55–64. Buckingham, On Physically Similar Systems: Illustrations of the Use of Dimensional Analysis, *Phys. Rev.* **4**, 1914, p. 345. Klinkenberg, *Chem. Eng. Science* **4**, 1955, pp. 130–140, 167–177. Rayleigh, The Principle of Similitude, *Nature*, **95**, 1915, p. 66. Silberberg and McKetta, Learning How to Use Dimensional Analysis, *Petrol. Refiner* **32**(4), p. 179; (5), p. 147; (6), p. 101; (7), p. 129, 1953. Van Driest, On Dimensional Analysis and the Presentation of Data in Fluid Flow Problems, *J. App. Mech.* **68**, A-34, March, 1946.

SECTION 3

PHYSICAL AND CHEMICAL DATA

BY

Peter E. Liley, Ph.D., D.I.C., A.R.C.S., Thermophysical Properties Research Center, School of Mechanical Engineering, Purdue University; Member, Institute of Physics, London.

WITH

Yeram S. Touloukian, Ph.D., Thermophysical Properties Research Center, School of Mechanical Engineering, Purdue University; Member, American Association for the Advancement of Science, American Rocket Society, American Society of Engineering Education, American Society of Heating, Refrigerating and Air-Conditioning Engineers, American Society of Mechanical Engineers.

AND

W. R. Gambill, B.S.Ch.E., Research Engineer, Oak Ridge National Laboratory, Union Carbide Nuclear Company. (Prediction and Correlation of Physical Properties)

CONTENTS

DENSITIES OF AQUEOUS ORGANIC SOLUTIONS

DENSITIES OF MISCELLANEOUS MATERIALS

SOLUBILITIES

THERMAL EXPANSION

JOULE-THOMSON EFFECT

CRITICAL CONSTANTS

COMPRESSIBILITIES

LATENT HEATS

SPECIFIC HEATS OF PURE COMPOUNDS

SPECIFIC HEATS OF AQUEOUS SOLUTIONS

SPECIFIC HEATS OF MISCELLANEOUS MATERIALS

HEATS AND FREE ENERGIES OF FORMATION

HEATS OF COMBUSTION

HEATS OF SOLUTION

THERMODYNAMIC PROPERTIES

TRANSPORT PROPERTIES

PREDICTION AND CORRELATION OF PHYSICAL PROPERTIES

PHYSICAL PROPERTIES OF PURE SUBSTANCES

Table 3-1. Physical Properties of the Elements and Inorganic Compounds*

Abbreviations Used in the Table

a., acid
A., specific gravity with reference to air = 1
abs., absolute
ac., acetic acid
act., acetone
al., 95 per cent ethyl alcohol
alk, alkali (*i.e.*, aq. NaOH or KOH)
am., amyl (C_5H_{11})
amor., amorphous
anh., anhydrous
aq., aqueous or water
aq. reg., aqua regia
atm., atmosphere or 760 mm. of mercury pressure
bk., black
brn., brown
bz., benzene
c., cold
cb., cubic
cc, cubic centimeter
chl., chloroform
col., colorless or white
conc., concentrated
cr., crystals or crystalline
d., decomposes
D., specific gravity with reference to hydrogen = 1
d. 50, decomposes at 50°C.; 50 d., melts at 50°C. with decomposition
delq., deliquescent
dil., dilute
dk., dark
eff., effloresces or efflorescent
et., ethyl ether
expl., explodes
gel., gelatinous
gly., glycerol, (glycerin)
gn., green
h., hot
hex., hexagonal
hyg., hygroscopic
i., insoluble
ign., ignites
lq., liquid
lt., light
m. al., methyl alcohol
mn., monoclinic
nd., needles
NH_3, liquid ammonia
NH_4OH, ammonium hydroxide solution
oct., octahedral
or., orange
pd., powder
pl., plates
pr., prisms or prismatic
pyr., pyridine
rhb., rhombic (orthorhombic)
s., soluble
satd., saturated
sl., slightly
soln., solution
subl., sublimes
sulf., sulfides
tart. a., tartaric acid
tet., tetragonal
tr., transition
tri., triclinic
trig., trigonal
v., very
vac., in vacuo
vl., violet
volt., volatile or volatilizes
wh., white
yel., yellow
∞, soluble in all proportions
<, less than
>, greater than
42±, about or near 42
$-3H_2O$, 100, loses 3 moles of water per formula weight at 100°C.

Formula weights are based upon the International Atomic Weights of 1941 and are computed to the nearest hundredth.

Refractive index, where given for a uniaxial crystal, is for the ordinary (ω) ray; where given for a biaxial crystal, the index given is for the median (β) value. Unless otherwise specified, the index is given for the sodium D-line (λ = 589.3 mμ).

Specific gravity values are given at room temperatures (15° to 20°C.) unless otherwise indicated by the small figures which follow the value: thus, "$5.6\frac{18°}{4}$" indicates a specific gravity of 5.6 for the substance at 18°C. referred to water at 4°C. In this table the values for the specific gravity of gases are given with reference to air (A) = 1, or hydrogen (D) = 1.

Melting point is recorded in a certain case as "82 d." and in some other case as "d. 82," the distinction being made in this manner to indicate that the former is a melting point with decomposition at 82°C., while in the latter decomposition only occurs at 82°C. Where a value such as "$-2H_2O$, 82" is given it indicates loss of 2 moles of water per formula weight of the compound at a temperature of 82°C.

Boiling point is given at atmospheric pressure (760 mm, of mercury) unless otherwise indicated; thus, "$82^{15 mm.}$" indicates the boiling point is 82°C. when the pressure is 15 mm.

Solubility is given in parts by weight (of the formula shown at the extreme left) per 100 parts by weight of the solvent; the small superscript indicates the temperature. In the case of gases the solubility is often expressed in some manner as "$5^{10°}$ cc" which indicates that at 10°C., 5 cc. of the gas are soluble in 100 g. of the solvent. The symbols of the common mineral acids: H_2SO_4, HNO_3, HCl, etc., represent dilute aqueous solutions of these acids. See also special tables on Solubility.

REFERENCES: The information given in this table has been collected mainly from the following sources: Mellor, "A Comprehensive Treatise on Inorganic and Theoretical Chemistry," Longmans, New York, 1922. Abegg, "Handbuch der anorganischen Chemie," S. Hirzel, Leipzig, 1905. Gmelin-Kraut, "Handbuch der anorganischen Chemie," 7th ed., Carl Winter, Heidelberg; 8th ed., Verlag Chemie, Berlin, 1924. Friend, "Textbook of Inorganic Chemistry," Griffin, London, 1914. Winchell, "Microscopic Character of Artificial Inorganic Solid Substances or Artificial Minerals," Wiley, New York, 1931. "International Critical Tables," McGraw-Hill, New York, 1926. "Tables annuelles internationales de constants et donnes numeriques," McGraw-Hill, New York. "Annual Tables of Physical Constants and Numerical Data," National Research Council, Princeton, N.J., 1943. Comey and Hahn, "A Dictionary of Chemical Solubilities," Macmillan, New York, 1921. Seidell, "Solubilities of Inorganic and Metal Organic Compounds," Van Nostrand, New York, 1940.

Name	Formula	Formula weight	Color, crystalline form and refractive index	Specific gravity	Melting point, °C.	Boiling point, °C.	Solubility in 100 parts		
							Cold water	Hot water	Other reagents
Aluminum	Al	26.97	silv., cb.	$2.70^{20°}$	660	2056	i.	i.	s. HCl, H_2SO_4, alk.
acetate, normal	$Al(C_2H_3O_2)_3$	204.10	wh. pd.	....	d. 200	....	s.	d.	
acetate, basic	$Al(OH)(C_2H_3O_2)_2$	162.07	wh., amor.	....	d.	....	i.	....	s.a.; i. NH_4 salts
bromide	$AlBr_3$	266.72	trig.	$3.01\frac{25°}{4}$	97.5	268	s.	....	s. al., act., CS_2
bromide	$AlBr_3.6H_2O$	374.82	col., delq. cr.	....	d. 100	....	s.	s.	s. al., CS_2
carbide	Al_4C_3	143.91	yel., hex., 2.70	2.95	d. >2200	....	d. to CH_4	....	s. a.; i. act.
chloride	$AlCl_3$	133.34	wh., delq., hex.	$2.44\frac{25°}{4}$	$194^{5.2 atm.}$	$182.7^{752 mm.}$; subl. 178	$69.87^{15°}$	s. d.	s. et., chl., CCl_4; i. bz.
chloride	$AlCl_3.6H_2O$	241.44	col., delq., trig., 1.560	....	....	....	400	v. s.	50 al.; s. et.
fluoride (fluellite)	$AlF_3.H_2O$	101.99	col., rhb., 1.490	2.17	d.		sl. s.		
fluoride	$Al_2F_6.7H_2O$	294.05	wh., cr. pd.	....	$-4H_2O$, 120	$-6H_2O$, 250	i.	sl. s.	
hydroxide	$Al(OH)_3$	77.99	wh., mn.	2.42	$-2H_2O$, 300	....	$0.000104^{18°}$	i.	s. a., alk.; i. a.
nitrate	$Al(NO_3)_3.9H_2O$	375.14	rhb., delq.	....	73	d. 134	v. s.	v. s. d.	s. al., CS_2
nitride	Al_2N_2	81.96	yel., hex.	$3.05\frac{25°}{4}$	$2150^{4 atm.}$	d. >1400	d. slowly	....	s. alk. d.
oxide	Al_2O_3	101.94	col., hex., 1.67-8	3.99	1999 to 2032	....	i.	i.	v. sl. s. a., alk.
oxide (corundum)	Al_2O_3	101.94	wh., trig., 1.768	4.00	1999 to 2032	2210	i.	i.	v. sl. s. a., alk.
phosphate	$AlPO_4$	121.95	col., hex.	2.59	....	....	i.	i.	s. a., alk.; i. ac.
potassium silicate (muscovite)	$3Al_2O_3.K_2O.6SiO_2.2H_2O$	796.40	mn., 1.590	2.9	d.	....	i.		
potassium silicate (orthoclase)	$Al_2O_3.K_2O.6SiO_2$	556.49	col., mn., 1.524	2.56	1450 (1150)		i.		

Aluminum potassium tartrate	$AlK(C_4H_4O_6)_2$	362.21	col.				s.	s.	
sodium fluoride (cryolite)	$AlF_3.3NaF$	209.96	wh., mn., 1.3389	2.90	1000		sl. s.		i. HCl
sodium silicate	$Al_2O_3.Na_2O.6SiO_2$	524 29	col., tri., 1.529	2.61	1100		i.	i.	d. a.
sulfate	$Al_2(SO_4)_3$	342.12	wh. cr.	2.71	d. 770		31.3$^{0°}$	89$^{100°}$	
Alum, ammonium (tschermigite)	$Al_2(SO_4)_3.(NH_4)_2SO_4.24H_2O$	906.64	col., oct., 1.4594	$1.64\frac{20°}{4}$	93.5	$-20H_2O$, 120; $-24H_2O$, 200	3.9$^{0°}$	∞ 100°	i. al.
ammonium chrome	$Cr_2(SO_4)_3.(NH_4)_2SO_4.24H_2O$	956.72	gn. or vl., oct., 1.4842	1.72	100 d.		21.2$^{25°}$		s. al.
ammonium iron	$Fe_2(SO_4)_3.(NH_4)_2SO_4.24H_2O$	964.40	vl., oct., 1.485	1.71	40		124$^{25°}$		i. al.
potassium (kalinite)	$Al_2(SO_4)_3.K_2SO_4.24H_2O$	948.76	col., mn., 1.4564	$1.76\frac{26°}{4}$	92	$-18H_2O$, 64.5	5.7$^{0°}$	∞ $^{93°}$	
potassium chrome	$Cr_2(SO_4)_3.K_2SO_4.24H_2O$	998.84	red or gn., cb., 1.4814	1.83	89		20	50	i. al.
sodium	$Al_2(SO_4)_3.Na_2SO_4.24H_2O$	916.56	col., oct., 1.4388	$1.675\frac{20°}{4}$	61		106.4$^{0°}$	121.7$^{45°}$	i. al.
Ammonia†	NH_3	17.03	col. gas, 1.325 (lq.)	0.817$^{-79°}$ 0.5971 (A)	−77.7	−33.4	89.9$^{0°}$	7.4$^{96°}$	14.8$^{20°}$ al.; s. et.
Ammonium acetate	$NH_4C_2H_3O_2$	77.08	wh., hyg. cr.	1.073	114	d.	148$^{4°}$		s. al.; sl. s. act.
auricyanide	$NH_4CN.Au(CN)_3.H_2O$	337.33	pl.		d. 200		s.	v. s.	i. al.
bicarbonate	NH_4HCO_3	79.06	mn. or rhb., 1.5358	1.573	d. 35–60		11.9$^{0°}$	27$^{30°}$	i. al.
bromide	NH_4Br	97.96	col., cb., 1.7108	$2.327\frac{15°}{4}$	subl. 542		68$^{10°}$	145.6$^{100°}$	s. al., et., act.
carbonate	$(NH_4)_2CO_3.H_2O$	114.11	col. pl.		d. 58		100$^{15°}$		i. al., CS_2, NH_3
carbonate, carbamate	$NH_4HCO_3.NH_2CO_2NH_4$‡	157.11	wh. cr.		subl.		25$^{15°}$	67$^{65°}$	
carbonate, sesqui-	$(NH_4)_2CO_3.2NH_4HCO_3.H_2O$	272.22	wh.		d.		20$^{15°}$	50$^{49°}$	
chloride (salammoniac)	NH_4Cl	53.50	wh., cb., 1.639, 1.6426	1.53$^{17°}$	d. 350	subl. 520	29.4$^{0°}$	77.3$^{100°}$	s. NH_3; sl. s. al., m. al.
chloroplatinate	$(NH_4)_2PtCl_6$	444.05	yel., cb.	3.065	d.		0.7$^{15°}$	1.25$^{100°}$	0.005 al.
chloroplatinite	$(NH_4)_2PtCl_4$	373.14	tet.		d.		s.	v. s.	
chlorostannate	$(NH_4)_2SnCl_6$	367.52	pink., cb.	2.4			33.3$^{15°}$		
chromate	$(NH_4)_2CrO_4$	152.09	yel., mn.	1.917$^{12°}$	d. 180		40.5$^{30°}$	d.	sl. s. act., NH_3; i. al.
cyanide	NH_4CN	44.06	col., cb.	0.79$^{100°}$ (A)	36		s.	v. s.	s. al.
dichromate	$(NH_4)_2Cr_2O_7$	252.10	or., mn.	2.15	d. 185		47.2$^{30°}$	v. s.	s. al.; i. act.
ferrocyanide	$(NH_4)_4Fe(CN)_6.6H_2O$	392.21	mn.		d.		s.		i. al.
fluoride	NH_4F	37.04	wh., hex.				v. s.	d.	s. al.; i. NH_3
fluoride, acid	$NH_4F.HF$	57.05	wh., rhb., 1.390	$2.21\frac{12°}{12}$			v. s.		
formate	HCO_2NH_4	63.06	col., mn., delq.	1.266	114–116	d. 180; subl. in vac.	102$^{0°}$	531$^{80°}$	s. al.
hydrosulfide	NH_4HS	51.11	col., rhb.		d.	subl. 120	v. s.		s. al.
hydroxide	NH_4OH	35.05	in soln. only				s.		
molybdate	$(NH_4)_2MoO_4$	196.03	mn.	2.27	d.		d.	d.	i. al., NH_3
molybdate, hepta-	$(NH_4)_6Mo_7O_{24}.4H_2O$‡	1235.95	col., mn.				44$^{25°}$		i. al.
nitrate (α), stable −16° to 32°	NH_4NO_3	80.05	col., tet., 1.611	$1.66\frac{25°}{4}$	169.6	d. 210	118.3$^{0°}$	241.8$^{30°}$	
nitrate (β), stable 32° to 84°	NH_4NO_3	80.05	col., rhb. or mn.	$1.725\frac{25°}{4}$		d. 210	365.8$^{35°}$	580$^{80°}$	3.8$^{20°}$ al., 17.1$^{20°}$ m. al.; v. s. NH_3
nitrite	NH_4NO_2	64.05	wh. nd.	1.69	expl.		s.	d.	s. al.
osmochloride	$(NH_4)_2OsCl_6$	439.02	cb.	$2.93\frac{20°}{4}$					
oxalate	$(NH_4)_2C_2O_4.H_2O$	142.12	col., rhb.	1.501			2.5$^{0°}$	11.8$^{50°}$	sl. s. al.; i. NH_3
oxalate, acid	$NH_4HC_2O_4.H_2O$	125.08	col., trimetric	1.556	d.		s.		
perchlorate	NH_4ClO_4	117.50	col., rhb., 1.4833	1.95	d.		10.9$^{0°}$	46.9$^{100°}$	2$^{20°}$ al.; s. act.; i. et.
persulfate	$(NH_4)_2S_2O_8$	228.20	wh., mn., 1.5016	1.98	d. 120		58.2$^{0°}$	d.	
phosphate, monobasic	$NH_4H_2PO_4$	115.04	col., tet., 1.5246	$1.803\frac{19°}{4}$			22.7$^{0°}$	173.2$^{100°}$	i. ac.
phosphate, dibasic	$(NH_4)_2HPO_4$	132.07	col., mn., 1.53	1.619			131$^{15°}$		i. act.
phosphate, meta-	$(NH_4)_4P_4O_{12}$	388.08	col., mn.	2.21			s.		

*By N. A. Lange, Ph.D., Handbook Publishers, Inc., Sandusky, Ohio. Abridged from table of Physical Constants of Inorganic Compounds in Lange, "Handbook of Chemistry."
† See special tables.
‡ Usual commercial form.

Table 3-1. Physical Properties of the Elements and Inorganic Compounds—(*Continued*)

Name	Formula	Formula weight	Color, crystalline form and refractive index	Specific gravity	Melting point, °C.	Boiling point, °C.	Solubility in 100 parts: Cold water	Hot water	Other reagents
Ammonium phosphomolybdate	$(NH_4)_3PO_4.12MoO_3.3H_2O$ (?)	1930.55	yel.		d.		$0.03^{15°}$	i.	s. alk.; i. al., HNO_3
silicofluoride	$(NH_4)_2SiF_6$	178.14	cb., 1.3696	2.01		subl.	$18.5^{17.5°}$	55.5	s. al.; i. act.
sulfamate	$NH_4.SO_3NH_2$	114.12	col. pl.		132	d. 160	$134^{0°}$	$357^{50°}$	
sulfate (mascagnite)	$(NH_4)_2SO_4$	132.14	col., rhb., 1.5230	$1.769\frac{20°}{4}$	513 d.		$70.6^{0°}$	$103.3^{100°}$	i. al., act., CS_2
sulfate, acid	NH_4HSO_4	115.11	col., rhb., 1.480	1.78	146.9	490	100		v. sl. s. al.; i. act.
sulfide	$(NH_4)_2S$	68.14	yel.-wh.		d.		v. s.		$120^{25°}$ NH_3
sulfide, penta-	$(NH_4)_2S_5$	196.38	or.-red pr.				s.		
sulfite	$(NH_4)_2SO_3.H_2O$	134.16	col., mn.	1.41	d.		$100^{12°}$		i. al., act.
sulfite, acid	NH_4HSO_3	99.11	rhb.	$2.03\frac{12°}{4}$	d.		s.		
tartrate	$(NH_4)_2C_4H_4O_6$	184.15	col., mn.	1.60	d.		$45^{0°}$	$87^{60°}$	sl. s. al.
thiocyanate	NH_4CNS	76.12	col., mn., 1.685±	1.305	149.6	d. 170	$120^{0°}$	$170^{20°}$	s. al., act., NH_3, SO_2
vanadate, meta-	NH_4VO_3	116.99	col. cr.	2.326	d.		$0.44^{13°}$	$3.05^{70°}$	i. al., NH_4Cl
Antimony	Sb	121.76	tin wh., trig.	$6.684^{25°}$	630.5	1380	i.	i.	s. aq. reg., h. conc. H_2SO_4
chloride, tri- (butter of antimony)*	$SbCl_3$	228.13	col., rhb., delq.	$3.14\frac{20°}{4}$	73.4	220.2	$601.6^{0°}$	$\infty^{72°}$	s. al., HCl, HBr, $H_2C_4H_4O_6$
oxide, tri- (valentinite)	Sb_2O_3	291.52	rhb., 2.35	5.67	656	1570	v. sl. s.	sl. s.	s. HCl, KOH, $H_2C_4H_4O_6$
oxide, tri- (senarmontite)	Sb_2O_3	291.52	cb., 2.087	5.2	652				
sulfide, tri- (stibnite)	Sb_2S_3	339.70	bk., rhb., 4.046	4.64	550		$0.00017^{18°}$	d.	s. HCl; alk., NH_4HS, K_2S; i. ac.
sulfide, penta-	Sb_2S_5	403.82	golden	$4.120^{0°}$	−2S, 135		i.	i.	s. HCl, alk., NH_4HS
telluride, tri-	Sb_2Te_3	626.35	gray		629				
Antimonyl potassium tartrate (tartar emetic)	$(SbO)KC_4H_4O_6.\frac{1}{2}H_2O$	333.94	wh., rhb.	2.60	$-\frac{1}{2}H_2O$, 100		$5.26^{8.7°}$	$35.7^{100°}$	s. gly.; i. al.
sulfate, normal	$(SbO)_2SO_4$	371.58	wh. pd.	4.89			d.	d.	
sulfate, basic	$(SbO)_2SO_4.Sb_2(OH)_4$	683.13	wh. pd.				i.	d.	$5.15^{15°}$ gly.
Argon	A	39.94	col. gas	$1.65^{-233°}$; $1.402^{-185.7°}$; 1.38 (A)	−189.2	−185.7	5.60° cc	$2.23^{50°}$ cc	$24^{25°}$ cc al.
Arsenic (crystalline)(α)	As_4	299.64	met., hex.	$5.727^{14°}$	$814^{36atm.}$	subl. 615	i.	i.	s. HNO_3
Arsenic (black)(β)	As_4	299.64	bk., amor.	$4.7^{20°}$			i.	i.	s. HNO_3, aq. reg.; aq. Cl_2, h. alk.
Arsenic (yellow)(γ)	As_4	299.64	yel., cb.	$2.0^{20°}$	d. 358				
acid, ortho-	$H_3AsO_4.\frac{1}{2}H_2O$	150.94	col., hyg.	2.0–2.5	35.5	$-H_2O$, 160	16.7	50	s. alk.
acid, meta-	$HAsO_3$	123.92	wh., hyg.		d.		d. to form	H_3AsO_4	
acid, pyro-	$H_4As_2O_7$	265.85	col.		d. 206		d. to form	H_3AsO_4	
pentoxide	As_2O_5	229.82	wh., amor.	4.086		d.	$59.5^{0°}$	$76.7^{100°}$	s. alk., al.
sulfide, di- (realgar)	As_2S_2	213.94	red, mn., 2.68	(α)$3.506^{19°}$; (β)$3.254^{19°}$	(α)tr. 267; (β)307	565	i.	d.	s. K_2S, $NaHCO_3$
sulfide, penta-	As_2S_5	310.12	yel.			d. 500	$0.00136^{0°}$	i.	s. HNO_3, alk.
Arsenious chloride (butter of arsenic)	$AsCl_3$	181.28	oily lq.	lq. 2.163	−18	130	d.	d.	s. HCl, HBr, PCl_3
hydride (arsine)	AsH_3	77.93	col. gas	2.695 (A)	−113.5	−55; d. 230	20 cc	sl. s.	sl. s. alk.
oxide (arsenolite)	As_2O_3	197.82	col., cb., fibrous, 1.755	$3.865\frac{25°}{4}$	subl.		sl. s.	sl. s.	i. al., et.
oxide (claudetite)	As_2O_3	197.82	col., mn., 1.92	3.85	subl.		sl. s.	sl. s.	i. al., et.
oxide	As_2O_3	197.82	amor. or vitreous	3.738	315		$1.2^{10°}$	$2.93^{40°}$	s. HCl, alk., Na_2CO_3; i. al., et.
Auric chloride	$AuCl_3.2H_2O$	339.60	or. cr.		d.		v. s.	v. s.	s. HCl, al., et.; sl. s. NH_3
cyanide	$Au(CN)_3.6H_2O$	383.35			d. 50		v. s.	v. s.	s. al.
Aurous chloride	AuCl	232.66	yel. cr.	7.4	$AuCl_3$, 170	d. 290	d.	d.	s. HCl, HBr; d. al.
cyanide	AuCN	223.22	yel. cr.		d.		i.	i.	s. KCN; i. al., et.
Cf. also under *Gold*									
Barium	Ba	137.36	silv. met.	3.5	850	1140	d.	d.	s. a.; d. al.
acetate	$Ba(C_2H_3O_2)_2$	255.45	col.	2.468			$58.8^{0°}$	$75.0^{100°}$	
acetate	$Ba(C_2H_3O_2)_2.H_2O$	273.46	wh., tri. pr., 1.517	2.19	$-H_2O$, 41		$75^{30°}$(anh.)	$79^{40°}$(anh.)	i. al.
bromide	$BaBr_2$	297.19	col.	$4.781\frac{24°}{4}$	847	d.	$98^{0°}$	$149^{100°}$	v. s. m. al.; v. sl. s. act.
bromide	$BaBr_2.2H_2O$	333.22	col., mn., 1.7266	3.69	$-2H_2O$, 100	d.	v. s.	v. s.	s. al.
carbonate (witherite)	$BaCO_3$	197.37	wh., rhb., 1.676	4.29	tr. 811 to α	d. 1450	$0.0022^{18°}$	$0.0065^{100°}$	s. a.; i. al.
carbonate (α)	$BaCO_3$	197.37	wh., hex.		tr. 982 to β				
carbonate (β)	$BaCO_3$	197.37	wh.		1740^{90atm}		$0.0022^{18°}$	$0.0065^{100°}$	s. a.; i. al.

Barium chlorate	$Ba(ClO_3)_2$	304.27	col.	...	414	...	$20.35^{0°}$	$84.8^{80°}$	
chlorate	$Ba(ClO_3)_2.H_2O$†	322.29	col., mn., 1.577	3.179	d. 120	...	s.	s.	sl. s. al., act.
chloride	$BaCl_2$	208.27	col., mn., 1.7361	$3.856\frac{24°}{4}$	tr. 925	1560	$31^{0°}$	$59^{100°}$	sl. s. HCl, HNO_3; i. al.
chloride	$BaCl_2$	208.27	col., cb.	...	962	1560			
chloride	$BaCl_2.2H_2O$†	244.31	col., mn., 1.646	$3.097\frac{24°}{4}$	$-2H_2O$, 100	...	$39.3^{0°}$	$76.8^{100°}$	sl. s. HCl, HNO_3; i. al.
hydroxide	$Ba(OH)_2$	171.38	col., mn.	4.495	...	...	$1.67^{0°}$	$101.4^{80°}$	
hydroxide	$Ba(OH)_2.8H_2O$	315.50	col., mn., 1.5017	$2.188^{16°}$	77.9	$-8H_2O$, 550	$5.6^{15°}$	...	v. sl. s. al.; i. et.
nitrate (nitrobarite)	$Ba(NO_3)_2$	261.38	col., cb., 1.572	$3.244^{23°}$	592	d.	$5.0^{0°}$	$34.2^{100°}$	sl. s. a.; i. al.
oxalate	BaC_2O_4	225.38	wh. cr.	2.658	...	...	$0.0016^{8°}$	$0.0024^{24°}$	s. a., NH_4Cl; i. al.
oxide	BaO	153.36	col., cb., 1.98	5.72	1923	2000±	$1.5^{0°}$	$90.8^{80°}$	s. HCl, HNO_3, abs. al.; i. NH_3, act.
peroxide	BaO_2†	169.36	gray or wh. pd.	4.958	−O, 800	...	v. sl. s.	d.	s. dil. a.; i. act.
peroxide	$BaO_2.8H_2O$	313.49	pearly sc.	...	$-8H_2O$, 100	...	0.168	d.	s. dil. a.; i. al., et., act.
phosphate, monobasic	$BaH_4(PO_4)_2$	331.35	tri.	$2.9^{4°}$	...	...	d.	d.	s. a.
phosphate, dibasic	$BaHPO_4$	233.35	wh., rhb. nd., 1.635	$4.165^{15°}$	...	...	0.015	...	s. a., NH_4 salts
phosphate, tribasic	$Ba_3(PO_4)_2$	602.04	wh., cb.	$4.1^{16°}$	...	...	i.	...	s. a.
phosphate, pyro-	$Ba_2P_2O_7$	448.68	wh., rhb.	$3.9^{20°}$	...	...	0.01	...	s. a., NH_4 salts
silicofluoride	$BaSiF_6$	279.42	pr.	$4.279^{15°}$	...	...	$0.026^{17°}$	$0.09^{100°}$	sl. s. HCl, NH_4Cl; i. al.
sulfate (barite, barytes)	$BaSO_4$	233.42	col., rhb., 1.636	$4.499^{15°}$	1580 d.	tr. to mn. 1149	$0.000115^{0°}$	$0.000285^{30°}$	s. conc. H_2SO_4; 0.006, 3% HCl
sulfide, mono-	BaS	169.42	col., cb., 2.155	$4.25^{15°}$	...	...	d.	d.	d. HCl; i. al.
sulfide, tri-	BaS_3	233.54	yel.-gn.	...	d. 400	...	s.	s.	
sulfide, tetra-	$BaS_4.2H_2O$	301.63	red, rhb.	$2.988^{20°}$	d. 200	...	$41^{15°}$	v. s.	i. al., CS_2
Beryllium (glucinum)	Be(Gl)	9.02	grav, met., hex.	1.816	1284	2767	i.	sl. s. d.	s. dil. a., alk.
Bismuth	Bi	209.00	silv. wh. or reddish, hex.	$9.80^{20°}$	271	1450	i.	i.	s. aq. reg., conc. H_2SO_4, HNO_3
carbonate, sub-	$Bi_2O_3.CO_2.H_2O$	528.03	wh. pd.	6.86	d.	...	i.	i.	s. a.
chloride, di-	$BiCl_2$(?)	279.91	bk. nd.	4.86	163	d. 300	d.		
chloride, tri-	$BiCl_3$†	315.37	wh. cr.	4.75	230	447	d.	...	s. al.
nitrate	$Bi(NO_3)_3.5H_2O$	485.10	col., tri.	2.82	d. 30	$-5H_2O$, 80	d.	...	$42^{19°}$ act.; s. a.; i. al.
nitrate, sub-	$BiONO_3.H_2O$	305.02	hex. pl.	$4.928^{15°}$	d. 260	...	i.	i.	s. a.
oxide, tri-	Bi_2O_3	466.00	yel., rhb.	8.9	820	1900±	i.	i.	s. a.
oxide, tri-	Bi_2O_3	466.00	yel., tet.	8.55	860	...	i.	i.	s. a.
oxide, tri-	Bi_2O_3	466.00	yel., cb.	8.20	tr. 704	...	i.	i.	s. a.
oxychloride	BiOCl	260.46	wh., amor.	$7.72^{15°}$	...	...	sl. s.	sl. s.	s. a.; i. act., NH_3, $H_2C_4H_4O_6$
Boric acid	H_3BO_3	61.84	wh., tri.	$1.435^{15°}$	185 d.	...	$2.66^{0°}$	$40.2^{100°}$	$22.2^{20°}$ gly., $0.24^{25°}$ et.; s. al.
Boron	B	10.82	gray or bk., amor. or mn.	2.32	2300	2550	i.	i.	s. HNO_3; i. al.
carbide	B_4C	55.29	bk. cr.	2.54	2450	>3500	i.	i.	i. a.
oxide	B_2O_3	69.64	col. glass, 1.459	1.85	577	>1500	$1.1^{0°}$	$15.7^{100°}$	s. a., al., gly.
oxide (sassolite)	$B_2O_3.3H_2O$	123.69	tri., 1.456	1.49	d.	...	sl. s.	s.	
Bromic acid	$HBrO_3$	128.92	col.; in soln. only	...	d. 100	...	v. s.	d.	
Bromine	Br_2	159.83	rhb., or red lq.	$3.119^{20°}$; 5.87 (A)	−7.2	58.78	$4.22^{0°}$	$3.13^{30°}$	s. al., et., alk., CS_2
hydrate	$Br_2.10H_2O$	339.99	red, oct.	...	d. 6.8	...	s.		
Cadmium	Cd	112.41	silv. met., hex.	$8.65^{20°}$	320.9	767	i.	i.	s. a., NH_4NO_3
acetate	$Cd(C_2H_3O_2)_2$	230.50	col.	2.341	256	d.	v. s.	...	s. m. al.
acetate	$Cd(C_2H_3O_2)_2.2H_2O$†	266.53	col., mn.	2.01	$-H_2O$, 130	...	v. s.	...	s. al.
carbonate	$CdCO_3$	172.42	wh., trig.	$4.258^{4°}$	d. <500	...	i.	i.	s. a., KCN, NH_4 salts; i. NH_3
chloride	$CdCl_2$	183.32	wh., cb.	$4.047\frac{25°}{4}$	568	960	$90^{0°}$	$147^{100°}$	$1.52^{15°}$ al.; i. et., act.
chloride	$CdCl_2.2\frac{1}{2}H_2O$	228.36	col., mn., 1.6513	3.327	tr. 34	...	$168^{20°}$	$180^{100°}$	$2.05^{15°}$ m. al.
cyanide	$Cd(CN)_2$	164.45	...	...	d. >200	...	$0.0247^{18°}$	...	s. a.; NH_4OH, KCN
hydroxide	$Cd(OH)_2$	146.43	wh., trig.	$4.79\frac{15°}{4}$	d. 300	...	$0.00026^{25°}$	...	s. a., NH_4 salts; i. alk.
nitrate	$Cd(NO_3)_2$	236.43	col.	...	350	...	$109.7^{0°}$	$326^{59.5°}$	v. s. a.
nitrate	$Cd(NO_3)_2.4H_2O$†	308.49	col. nd.	$2.455\frac{17°}{4}$	59.4	132	$215^{0°}$	...	s. al., NH_3; i. HNO_3
oxide	CdO	128.41	brn., cb.	8.15	...	...	i.	i.	s. a., NH_4 salts; i. alk.
oxide	CdO	128.41	brn., amor, 2.49	6.95	d. 900–1000	...	i.	i.	s. a., NH_4 salts; i. alk.
oxide, sub-	Cd_2O	240.82	gn., amor.	$8.192\frac{18°}{4}$	d.	...	...	...	d. a., alk.

* Usually the solution.
† Usual commercial form.

Table 3-1. Physical Properties of the Elements and Inorganic Compounds—(*Continued*)

Name	Formula	Formula weight	Color, crystalline form and refractive index	Specific gravity	Melting point, °C.	Boiling point, °C.	Solubility in 100 parts: Cold water	Hot water	Other reagents
Cadmium sulfate	$CdSO_4$	208.47	rhb.	$4.691\frac{24^\circ}{4}$	1000	...	$76.5^{0°}$	$60.8^{100°}$	i. act., NH_3
sulfate	$CdSO_4.H_2O$	226.49	mn.	$3.786^{20°}$	tr. 108	...	s.	s.	
sulfate	$3CdSO_4.8H_2O$*	769.54	col., mn., 1.565	3.09	tr. 41.5	...	$114.2^{0°}$	$127.6^{60°}$	i. al.
sulfate	$CdSO_4.4H_2O$	280.53	col.	3.05	...	...	s.	s.	i. al.
sulfate	$CdSO_4.7H_2O$	334.58	mn.	$2.48\frac{20^\circ}{4}$	tr. 4	...	$350^{-5°}$	...	i. al.
sulfide (greenockite)	CdS	144.47	yel.-or., hex., 2.506	4.58	1750^{100atm}	subl. in N_2, 980	0.000001	Colloidal	s. a.; v. s. NH_4OH
Calcium	Ca	40.08	silv. met., cb.	$1.55^{20°}$	810	1200 ± 30	d.	d.	s. a.; sl. s. al.
acetate	$Ca(C_2H_3O_2)_2.H_2O$	176.18	wh. nd.	...	d.	...	$52^{0°}$	$45.5^{80°}$	sl. s. al.
aluminate	$Ca(AlO_2)_2$	158.02	col., rhb. or mn.	$3.67^{20°}$	1600	...	d.	...	s. HCl
aluminum silicate (anorthite)	$CaO.Al_2O_3.2SiO_2$	278.14	tri., 1.5832	2.765	1551				
arsenate	$Ca_3(AsO_4)_2$	398.06	wh. pd.	...	...	...	$0.013^{25°}$	i.	s. dil. a.
bromide	$CaBr_2$	199.91	delq. nd.	$3.353\frac{25^\circ}{4}$	760	810	$125^{0°}$	$312^{105°}$	s. al., act.; sl. s. NH_3
carbonate (aragonite)	$CaCO_3$	100.09	col., rhb., 1.6809	2.93	d. 825	...	$0.0012^{20°}$†	$0.002^{100°}$	s. a., NH_4Cl
carbonate (calcite)	$CaCO_3$	100.09	col., hex., 1.550	$2.711\frac{25^\circ}{4}$	$1339^{103atm.}$	...	$0.0014^{25°}$	$0.002^{100°}$	s. a., NH_4Cl
chloride (hydrophilite)	$CaCl_2$*	110.99	wh., delq., cb, 1.52	$2.152\frac{15^\circ}{4}$	772	>1600	$59.5^{0°}$	$347^{260°}$	s. al.
chloride	$CaCl_2.H_2O$	129.01	col., delq.	...	...	...	s.	s.	s. al.
chloride	$CaCl_2.6H_2O$	219.09	col., trig., 1.417	$1.68^{17°}$	29.92	$-6H_2O$, 200	v. s.	v. s.	s. al.
citrate	$Ca_3(C_6H_5O_7)_2.4H_2O$	570.50	col. nd.	...	$-2H_2O$, 130	$-4H_2O$, 185	$0.085^{18°}$	$0.096^{25°}$	$0.0065^{18°}$ al.
cyanamide	$CaCN_2$	80.11	col., rhombohedral	...	...	...	s. d.	d.	
ferrocyanide	$Ca_2Fe(CN)_6.12H_2O$	508.31	yel., tri., 1.5818	1.7	...	...	s.	$150^{90°}$	i. al.
fluoride (fluorite)	CaF_2	78.08	wh., cb., 1.4339	$3.180^{20°}$	1330	...	$0.0016^{18°}$	$0.0017^{26°}$	sl. s. a.
formate	$Ca(HCO_2)_2$	130.12	col., rhb.	2.015	d.	...	$16.1^{0°}$	18.4^{100}	i. al., et.
hydride	CaH_2	42.10	wh. cr. or pd.	1.7	d. 675	...	d.	...	d. a.; i. bz.
hydroxide	$Ca(OH)_2$	74.10	col., hex., 1.574	2.2	$-H_2O$, 580	...	$0.185^{0°}$	$0.077^{100°}$	s. NH_4Cl
hypochlorite	$Ca(ClO)_2.4H_2O$	215.06	wh., feathery cr.	...	d.	...	delq.; d.	d.	d. a.
hypophosphate	$Ca_2P_2O_6.2H_2O$	274.15	granular	...	$-2H_2O$, 200	...	i.	...	s. HCl, $H_4P_2O_6$
lactate	$Ca(C_3H_5O_3)_2.5H_2O$	308.30	col., eff.	...	$-3H_2O$, 100	...	10.5	∞	∞ h. al.; i. et.
magnesium carbonate (dolomite)	$CaO.MgO.2CO_2$	184.42	trig., 1.68174	2.872	d. 730–760	...	$0.032^{18°}$		
magnesium silicate (diopside)	$CaO.MgO.2SiO_2$	216.52	wh., mn.	3.3	1391	...	i.	i.	
nitrate (nitrocalcite)	$Ca(NO_3)_2$	164.10	col., cb.	2.36	561	...	$102^{0°}$	$376^{151°}$	$14^{15°}$ al.; s. amyl al., NH_3
nitrate	$Ca(NO_3)_2.4H_2O$*	236.16	col., mn., 1.498	1.82	42.7	...	$266^{0°}$	v. s.	
nitride	Ca_3N_2	148.26	brn. cr.	$2.63^{17°}$	900	...	d.	d.	s. dil. a.; i. abs. al.
nitrite	$Ca(NO_2)_2.H_2O$	150.11	delq., hex.	$2.23^{34°}$	...	...	$77^{0°}$	$417^{90°}$	s. 90% al.
oxalate	CaC_2O_4	128.10	col., cb.	$2.2^{4°}$	d.	...	$0.00067^{13°}$	$0.0014^{95°}$	s. a.; i. ac.
oxalate	$CaC_2O_4.H_2O$	146.12	col.	2.2	$-H_2O$, 200	...	i.	i.	s. a.; i. ac
oxide	CaO	56.08	col., cb., 1.837	3.32	2570	2850	Forms $Ca(OH)_2$	...	s. a.; i. al.
peroxide	$CaO_2.8H_2O$	216.21	pearly, tet.	...	$-8H_2O$, 100	expl. 275	sl. s.	d.	s. a. d.; i. al., et.
phosphate, monobasic	$CaH_4(PO_4)_2.H_2O$	252.09	wh., tri.	$2.220\frac{16^\circ}{4}$	$-H_2O$, 100	d. 200	...	d.	
phosphate, dibasic	$CaHPO_4.2H_2O$	172.10	wh., mn. pl.	$2.306\frac{16^\circ}{4}$	d.	...	$0.02^{24.5°}$	$0.075^{100°}$	
phosphate, tribasic	$Ca_3(PO_4)_2$	310.20	wh., amor.	3.14	1670	...	0.0025	d.	s. a.; i. al., ac.
phosphate, meta-	$Ca(PO_3)_2$	198.04	wh., tet., 1.588	2.82	975	...	i.	i.	i. a.
phosphate, pyro-	$Ca_2P_2O_7$	254.12	col., biaxial, 1.60	3.09	1230	...	i.	...	s. a.
phosphate, pyro- (brushite)	$Ca_2P_2O_7.5H_2O$	344.20	wh., mn.	2.25	...	...	sl. s.	...	s. a.; i. NH_4Cl
phosphide	Ca_3P_2	182.20	red cr.	$2.51^{15°}$	>1600	...	d.	...	s. dil. a.; i. al., et.
silicate (α) (pseudowollastonite)	$CaSiO_3$	116.14	col., pseudo hex., 1.6150 or mn.(?)	2.905	1540	...	$0.0095^{17°}$	...	s. HCl
silicate (β) (wollastonite)	$CaSiO_3$	116.14	col., mn., 1.610	2.915	tr. 1190 to α				
sulfate (anhydrite)	$CaSO_4$	136.14	col., rhb., 1.576, or mn, 1.50	2.96	1450(mn.)	tr. 1193 to rhb.	$0.298^{20°}$	$0.1619^{100°}$	s. a., $Na_2S_2O_3$, NH_4 salts
sulfate (gypsum)	$CaSO_4.2H_2O$	172.17	col., mn., 1.5226	2.32	$-1\frac{1}{2}H_2O$, 128	$-2H_2O$, 163	$0.223^{0°}$	$0.257^{50°}$	s. a., gly., $Na_2S_2O_3$, NH_4 salts
sulfhydrate	$Ca(SH)_2.6H_2O$	214.31	col. pr.	...	d. 15	...	v. s.	v. s.	s. al.
sulfide (oldhamite)	CaS	72.14	col., cb.	$2.8^{15°}$	...	...	d.	d.	s. a.
sulfite	$CaSO_3.2H_2O$	156.17	wh., cr., 1.595	...	$-2H_2O$, 100	d. 650	$0.0043^{18°}$	$0.0027^{90°}$	s. H_2SO_3
tartrate	$CaC_4H_4O_6.4H_2O$	260.22	col., rhb.	...	d.	...	$0.037^{0°}$	$0.22^{85°}$	sl. s. al.
thiocyanate	$Ca(CNS)_2.3H_2O$	210.28	wh., delq. cr.	...	...	...	s.	v. s.	v. s. al.
thiosulfate	$CaS_2O_3.6H_2O$	260.30	col., tri., 1.56	$1.873^{16°}$	d.	...	$71.2^{9°}$	d.	i. al.
tungstate (scheelite)	$CaWO_4$	288.00	wh., tet., 1.9200	6.06	...	...	0.2	...	s. NH_4Cl; i. a.

Carbon, *Cf.* table of organic compounds									
Carbon, amorphous	C	12.01	bk., amor.	1.8–2.1	>3500	4200	i.	i.	i. a., alk.
Carbon, diamond	C	12.01	col., cb., 2.4195	$3.51^{20°}$	>3500	4200	i.	i.	i. a., alk.
Carbon, graphite	C	12.01	bk., hex.	$2.26^{20°}$	>3500	4200	i.	i.	i. a., alk.
dioxide	CO_2	44.01	col. gas	lq. $1.101^{-37°}$; 1.53 (A); solid $1.56^{-79°}$	$-56.6^{5.2atm.}$	subl. −78.5	$179.7^{0°}$ cc	$90.1^{20°}$ cc	s. a., alk.
disulfide	CS_2	76.13	col. lq.	lq. $1.261\frac{22}{20}°$; 2.63 (A)	−108.6	46.3	$0.2^{0°}$	$0.014^{50°}$	s. al., et.
monoxide	CO	28.01	col., poisonous, odorless gas	lq. $0.814^{-\frac{195}{4}°}$; 0.968 (A)	−207	−192	$0.0044^{0°}$; $3.5^{0°}$ cc	$0.0018^{50°}$; $2.32^{20°}$ cc	s. al., Cu_2Cl_2
oxychloride (phosgene)	$COCl_2$	98.92	poisonous gas	$1.392\frac{19}{4}°$	−104	8.2^{756mm}	v. s. sl. d.	d.	s. ac., CCl_4, bz.; d.a.
oxysulfide	COS	60.07	gas	lq. $1.24^{-87°}$; 2.10 (A)	−138.2	-50.2^{760mm}	$133^{0°}$ cc	$40.3^{30°}$ cc	v. s. alk., al.
suboxide	C_3O_2	68.03	gas	lq. $1.114^{0°}$	−107	7^{761mm}	d.	...	s. et.
thionyl chloride	$CSCl_2$	114.98	yel.-red lq.	$1.509^{15°}$	...	73.5			
Ceric hydroxide	$2CeO_2.3H_2O$	398.31	yel., gelatinous	...	...	...	...	...	s. a.; sl. s. alk. carb.; i. alk
hydroxynitrate	$Ce(OH)(NO_3)_3.3H_2O$	397.21	red, mn.	...	...	...	d.		
oxide	CeO_2	172.13	wh. or pa. yel., cb.	7.3	1950	...	i.	i.	s. H_2SO_4, HCl
sulfate	$Ce(SO_4)_2.4H_2O$	404.31	yel., rhb.	3.91	...	...	s. d.	...	s. dil. H_2SO_4
Cerium	Ce	140.13	steel gray, cb. or hex.	$6.9^{20°}$ cb.; 6.7 hex.	645	1400	i.	Slowly oxidized	s. dil. a.; i. al.
Cerous sulfate	$Ce_2(SO_4)_3$	568.44	wh., mn. or rhb.	3.91	...	...	$18.9^{0°}$	$0.4^{100°}$	
sulfate	$Ce_2(SO_4)_3.8H_2O$	712.57	tri.	$2.886^{17°}$	$-8H_2O$, 630	...	$25^{0°}$	$7.6^{40°}$	
Cesium	Ce	132.91	silv. met., hex.	$1.90^{20°}$	28.5	670	d.	...	s. a., al., NH_3
Chloric acid	$HClO_3.7H_2O$	210.58	lq.	$1.282^{14.2°}$	<−20	d. 40	v. s.		
Chlorine	Cl_2	70.91	rhb., or gn.-yel. gas	lq. $1.56^{-33.6°}$; $2.49^{0°}$ (A)	−101.6	−34.6	$1.46^{0°}$; $310^{10°}$ cc	$0.57^{30°}$; $177^{30°}$ cc	s. alk.
hydrate	$Cl_2.8H_2O$	215.04	rhb.	1.23	d. 9.6	...	s.	...	s. alk.
Chloroplatinic acid	$H_2PtCl_6.6H_2O$	518.08	red-brn., delq.	2.431	60	...	v. s.	v. s.	s. al., et.
Chlorostannic acid	$H_2SnCl_6.6H_2O$	441.55	delq.	$1.971^{28°}$	19.2	...	s.		
Chlorosulfonic acid	$HO.SO_2.Cl$	116.52	col. lq.	$1.787^{25°}$	−80	151.5^{765mm}	d.	...	d. al.; i. CS_2
Chromic acetate	$Cr_2(C_2H_3O_2)_6.2H_2O$	494.32	gn.	...	...	...	s.	...	$4.76^{15°}$ m. al.
chloride	$CrCl_3$	158.38	pink, trig.	$2.757^{15°}$	...	1200–1500 d.	i.§	sl. s.	i. a., act., CS_2
chloride	$CrCl_3.6H_2O$*	266.48	vl. or gn., hex. pl.	$1.835\frac{25}{4}°$	subl. 83	...	v. s. d.	...	s. al.; i. et.
fluoride	CrF_3	109.01	gn., rhb.	3.8	>1000	d.	i.	...	sl. s. a.; i. al., NH_3
hydroxide	$Cr(OH)_3$	103.03	gn. or blue, gelatinous	...	...	...	i.	...	s. a., alk.; sl. s. NH_3
hydroxide	$Cr(OH)_3.2H_2O$	139.07	gn.	...	$-2H_2O$, 100	...	i.	i.	s. a., alk.
nitrate	$Cr(NO_3)_3.9H_2O$*	400.18	purple pr.	...	36.5	d. 100	s.	s.	s. a., alk., al., act.
nitrate	$Cr(NO_3)_3.7\frac{1}{2}H_2O$	373.15	purple, mn.	...	100	d.	s.	s.	
oxide	Cr_2O_3	152.02	dark gn., hex.	5.21	1900	...	i.	i.	sl. s. a.
sulfate	$Cr_2(SO_4)_3$	392.20	rose pd.	3.012	...	...	i.§	...	i. a.
sulfate	$Cr_2(SO_4)_3.5H_2O$	482.28	gn.	...	...	...	s.	...	s. al., H_2SO_4
sulfate	$Cr_2(SO_4)_3.15H_2O$	662.44	vl.	$1.867^{17°}$	100	$-10H_2O$, 100	s.	d. 67°	sl. s. al.
sulfate	$Cr_2(SO_4)_3.18H_2O$	716.49	vl., cb., 1.564	$1.7^{22°}$	...	$-12H_2O$, 100	$120^{20°}$	d.	s. al.
sulfide	Cr_2S_3	200.02	brn.-bk. pd.	$3.77^{19°}$	−S, 1350	...	i.	d.	s. h. HNO_3
Chromium	Cr	52.01	gray, met., cb.	7.1	1615	2200	i.	i.	s. HCl, dil. H_2SO_4; i. HNO_3
trioxide (chromic acid)	CrO_3	100.01	red, rhb.	2.70	197 d.	...	$164.9^{0°}$	$206.7^{100°}$	s. H_2SO_4, al., et.
Chromous chloride	$CrCl_2$	122.92	wh., delq.	2.75	...	...	v. s.	v. s.	sl. s. al.; i. et.
hydroxide	$Cr(OH)_2$	86.03	yel.-brn.	...	d.	...	d.	...	s. conc. a.
oxide	CrO	68.01	bk. pd.	...	...	...	i.	i.	i. dil. HNO_3
sulfate	$CrSO_4.7H_2O$	274.18	blue	...	...	...	12.35^{0}	...	sl. s. al.
sulfide (daubrelite)	CrS	84.07	bk. pd.	3.97	1550	...	i.	...	v. s. a.
Chromyl chloride	CrO_2Cl_2	154.92	dark red lq.	1.92	−96.5	117.6	d.	...	s. et.
Cobalt	Co	58.94	silv. met., cb.	$8.9^{20°}$	1480	2900	i.	i.	s. a.
carbonyl	$Co(CO)_4$	170.98	or. cr.	$1.73^{18°}$	51	d. 52	i.	d.	s. al., et., CS_2
sulfide, di-	CoS_2	123.06	bk., cb.	4.269	...	...	i.	...	s. HNO_3, aq. reg.
Cobaltic chloride	$CoCl_3$	165.31	red cr.	2.94	subl.	...	s.	s.	
chloride, dichro	$Co(NH_3)_3Cl_3.H_2O$	234.42	...	...	...	...	s.	...	s. a., al.
chloride, luteo	$Co(NH_3)_6Cl_3$	267.50	or., mn.	$1.7016^{20°}$	...	...	$4.26^{0°}$	$12.74^{46.6°}$	i. al., NH_4OH
chloride, praseo	$Co(NH_3)_4Cl_3.H_2O$	251.46	gn., rhb.	1.847	...	...	v. s.	...	s. a.; i. al.

* Usual commercial form.
† The solubility of $CaCO_3$ in H_2O is greatly increased by increasing the amount of CO_2 in the H_2O.
§ Also a soluble modification.

Table 3-1. Physical Properties of the Elements and Inorganic Compounds—(*Continued*)

Name	Formula	Formula weight	Color, crystalline form and refractive index	Specific gravity	Melting point, °C.	Boiling point, °C.	Solubility in 100 parts: Cold water	Solubility in 100 parts: Hot water	Solubility in 100 parts: Other reagents
Cobaltic chloride, purpureo	$Co(NH_3)_5Cl_3$	250.47	rhb.	$1.819\frac{25^\circ}{25}$	...	...	0.232^{0°	$1.031^{46.5^\circ}$	i. al.
chloride, roseo	$Co(NH_3)_5Cl_3.H_2O$	268.49	brick red	...	d. 100	...	16.12^{0°	24.87^{16°	sl. s. HCl
hydroxide	$Co(OH)_3$	109.96	bk.	...	$-1\frac{1}{2}H_2O$, 100	...	i.	i.	s. a.; i. al.
oxide	Co_2O_3	165.88	bk.	5.18	d. 900	...	i.	i.	s. a.
sulfate	$Co_2(SO_4)_3$	406.06	blue cr.	...	...	...	d.	...	s. H_2SO_4
sulfide	Co_2S_3	214.06	bk. cr.	4.8	...	...	i.	...	d. a.
Cobalto-cobaltic oxide	Co_3O_4	240.82	bk., cb.	6.07	...	...	i.	i.	s. H_2SO_4; i. HCl, HNO_3
Cobaltous acetate	$Co(C_2H_3O_2)_2.4H_2O$	249.09	red-vl., mn., 1.542	$1.7053^{18.7^\circ}$	$-4H_2O$, 140	...	s.	s.	s. a., al.
chloride	$CoCl_2$	129.85	blue cr.	3.356	subl.	1049	45^{7°	105^{96°	31 al.; 8.6 act.
chloride	$CoCl_2.6H_2O$*	237.95	red, mn.	$1.924\frac{25^\circ}{25}$	86	$-6H_2O$, 110	116.5^{0°	177^{30°	v. s. et., act.
nitrate	$Co(NO_3)_2.6H_2O$	291.05	red, mn., 1.4	$1.883\frac{25^\circ}{25}$	<100	d.	84.03^{0°(anh.)	334.9^{90°(anh.)	$100^{12.5^\circ}$ al.; s. act.; sl. s. NH_3
oxide	CoO	74.94	brn., cb.	5.68	d. 1800	...	i.	i.	s. a., NH_4OH; i. al.
sulfate	$CoSO_4$	155.00	red pd.	3.710^{25°	d. 880	...	25.6^{0°	83^{100°	1.04^{18° m. al.; i. NH_3
sulfate	$CoSO_4.H_2O$	173.02	red pd., mn.(?), 1.639	3.13	d.	...	s.	s.	
sulfate (biebeorite)	$CoSO_4.7H_2O$*	281.11	red, mn., 1.483	$1.948\frac{25^\circ}{25}$	96.8	$-7H_2O$, 420	33^{20°	s.	2.5^{3° al.
sulfide (syeporite)	CoS	91.00	brn. nd.	5.45^{18°	>1100	...	0.00038^{18°	...	s. a., aq. reg.
Copper	Cu	63.57	yel.-red met., cb.	8.92^{20°	1083	2300	i.	i.	s. HNO_3, h. H_2SO_4
Cupric acetate	$Cu(C_2H_3O_2)_2$	181.66	...	$1.930\frac{20^\circ}{4}$	...	...	s.		
acetate	$Cu(C_2H_3O_2)_2.H_2O$	199.67	dark gn., mn.	1.882	115	240 d.	7.2	20	7 al.; s. et., gly.
aceto-arsenite (Paris green)	$(CuOAs_2O_3)_3.Cu(C_2H_3O_2)_2$*	1013.83	gn.	...	...	...	i.	...	s. a., NH_4OH
ammonium chloride	$CuCl_2.2NH_4Cl.2H_2O$	277.51	blue, tet., 1.670, 1.744	1.98	d. 110	...	33.8^{0°	99.3^{80°	s. a.
ammonium sulfate	$CuSO_4.4NH_3.H_2O$	245.77	blue, rhb.	1.81	d. 150	...	$18.05^{21.5^\circ}$	d.	i. al.
carbonate, basic (azurite)	$2CuCO_3.Cu(OH)_2$	344.75	blue, mn., 1.758	3.88	d. 220	...	i.	d.	s. NH_4OH, h. aq. $NaHCO_3$
carbonate, basic (malachite)	$CuCO_3.Cu(OH)_2$	221.17	dark gn., mn., 1.875	3.9	d.	...	i.	d.	s. KCN; 0.03 aq. CO_2
chloride (eriochalcite)	$CuCl_2$	134.48	brn.-yel. pd.	3.054	498	Forms Cu_2Cl_2 993	70.7^{0°	107.9^{100°	53^{15° al.; 68^{15° m. al.
chloride	$CuCl_2.2H_2O$	170.52	gn., rhb., 1.684	$2.39^{22.4^\circ}$	$-2H_2O$, 110	d.	110.4^{0°	192.4^{100°	s. al., et., NH_4Cl
chromate, basic	$CuCrO_4.2CuO.2H_2O$	374.75	yel.-brn.	...	$-2H_2O$, 260	...	i.	...	s. HNO_3, NH_4OH
cyanide	$Cu(CN)_2$	115.61	yel.-gn.	...	d.	...	i.	...	s. KCN, C_5H_5N
dichromate	$CuCr_2O_7.2H_2O$	315.62	bk., tri.	2.286^{18°	$-2H_2O$, 100	...	sl. s.	d.	s. a., NH_4OH
ferricyanide	$Cu_3[Fe(CN)_6]_2$	614.63	yel.-gn.	...	...	...	i.	...	s. NH_4OH; i. HCl
ferrocyanide	$Cu_2Fe(CN)_6.7H_2O$	465.21	red-brn.	...	...	...	i.	i.	s. NH_4OH; i. a., NH_3
formate	$Cu(HCO_2)_2$	153.61	blue, mn.	1.831	...	...	12.5	d.	0.25 al.
hydroxide	$Cu(OH)_2$	97.59	blue, gelatinous	3.368	$-H_2O$	...	i.	d.	s. a., NH_4OH, KCN, al.
lactate	$Cu(C_3H_5O_3)_2.2H_2O$	277.74	dark blue, mn.	...	...	...	16.7	45^{100°	sl. s. al.
nitrate	$Cu(NO_3)_2.3H_2O$*	241.63	blue, delq.	$2.047^{3.9^\circ}$	114.5	$-HNO_3$, 170	381^{40°	666^{80°	$100^{12.5^\circ}$ al.
nitrate	$Cu(NO_3)_2.6H_2O$	295.68	blue, rhb.	2.074	$-3H_2O$, 26.4	...	243.7^{0°	∞	s. al.
oxide (paramelaconite)	CuO	79.57	bk., cb..	6.40	d. 1026	...	i.	i.	s. a., KCN, NH_4Cl
oxide (tenorite)	CuO	79.57	bk., tri., 2.63	6.45	d. 1026	...	i.	i.	s. a., KCN, NH_4Cl
oxychloride	$CuCl_2.2CuO.4H_2O$	365.69	blue-gn.	...	$-3H_2O$, 140	...	i.	...	s. a.
phosphide	Cu_3P_2	252.67	bk.	6.35	d.	...	i.	...	s. HNO_3; i. HCl
sulfate (hydrocyanite)	$CuSO_4$	159.63	gn.-wh., rhb., 1.733	3.606^{15°	d. >600	Forms CuO, 650	14.3^{0°	75.4^{100°	i. al.
sulfate (blue vitriol or chalcanthite)	$CuSO_4.5H_2O$*	249.71	blue, tri., 1.5368	$2.286\frac{15.6^\circ}{4}$	$-4H_2O$, 110	$-5H_2O$, 250	24.3^{0°	205^{100°	1.1^{3° al.
sulfide (covellite)	CuS	95.63	blue, hex. or mn., 1.45	4.6	tr. 103	d. 220	0.000033^{18°	...	s. HNO_3, KCN
tartate	$CuC_4H_4O_6.3H_2O$	265.69	l+ gn. pd.	...	d.	...	0.02^{15°	0.14^{85°	s. a., KOH
Cuprous ammonium iodide	$CuI.NH_4I.H_2O$	353.47	rhb. pl.	...	...	...	d.	...	s. NH_4I
carbonate	Cu_2CO_3	187.15	yel.	4.4	d.	...	i.	i.	s. a., NH_4OH
chloride (nantokite)	Cu_2Cl_2	198.05	wh., cb., 1.973	3.53	422	1366	1.52^{25°	...	s. HCl, NH_4OH, al.
cyanide	$Cu_2(CN)_2$	179.16	wh., mn.	2.9	474.5	d.	i.	i.	s. KCN, HCl, NH_4OH; sl. s. NH_3
ferricyanide	$Cu_3Fe(CN)_6$	402.67	brn.-red	...	...	...	i.	...	s. NH_4OH; i. HCl
ferrocyanide	$Cu_4Fe(CN)_6$	466.24	brn.-red	...	...	...	i.	...	s. NH_4OH; i. NH_4Cl
fluoride	Cu_2F_2	165.14	red cr.	...	908	subl. 1100	i.	...	s. HF, HCl, HNO_3; i. al.
hydroxide	CuOH	80.58	yel.	3.4	$-\frac{1}{2}H_2O$, 360	...	i.	i.	s. a., NH_4OH
oxide (cuprite)	Cu_2O	143.14	red, cb., 2.705	6.0	1235	−O, 1800	i.	i.	s. HCl, NH_4Cl, NH_4OH

Cuprous phosphide	Cu_6P_2	443.38	gray-bk.	6.4 to 6.8	...	...	i.	...	s. HNO_3; i. HCl
sulfide (chalcocite)	Cu_2S	159.20	bk., rhb.	5.6	1100	...	$0.0005^{18°}$	...	s. HNO_3, NH_4OH; i. act.
sulfide	Cu_2S	159.20	bk., cb.	5.80	1130	...	$0.0005^{18°}$	...	s. HNO_3, NH_4OH; i. act.
Cyanogen	C_2N_2	52.02	poisonous gas	lq. $0.866^{-17.2°}$; 1.806 (A)	−34.4	−20.5	$450^{20°}$ cc	...	$2300^{20°}$ cc al.; $500^{18°}$ cc et.
Cyanogen compounds, *Cf.* table of organic compounds									
Ferric acetate, basic	$Fe(OH)(C_2H_3O_2)_2$	190.95	brn., amor.	...	...	...	i.	...	s. a., al.
ammonium sulfate, *Cf.* Alum									
chloride (molysite)	$FeCl_3$	162.22	bk.-brn., hex. delq.	$2.804^{11°}$	282	315	$74.4^{0°}$	$535.8^{100°}$	v. s. al., et. +HCl
chloride	$FeCl_3.6H_2O$*	270.32	red-yel., delq.	...	37	280	$246^{0°}$	∞	s. al., act., gly.
ferrocyanide (Prussian blue)	$Fe_4[Fe(CN)_6]_3$	859.27	dark blue	...	d.	...	i.	d.	s. HCl, conc. H_2SO_4; i. al., et.
hydroxide	$Fe(OH)_3$	106.87	red-brn.	3.4 to 3.9	−1½H_2O, 500	...	i.	i.	s. a.; i. al., et.
lactate	$Fe(C_3H_5O_3)_3$	323.06	brn., amor., delq.	...	...	...	v. s.	v. s.	i. et.
nitrate	$Fe(NO_3)_3.6H_2O$	349.97	rhb., delq.	$1.684^{20°}$	35	d.	$150^{0°}$	∞	s. al., act.
oxide (hematite)	Fe_2O_3	159.70	red or bk., trig., 3.042	5.12	1560 d.	...	i.	...	s. HCl
sulfate	$Fe_2(SO_4)_3$	399.88	rhb., 1.814	$3.097^{18°}$	d. 480	...	sl. s.	d.	i. H_2SO_4, NH_3
sulfate (coquimbite)	$Fe_2(SO_4)_3.9H_2O$	562.02	yel., trig.	2.1	...	...	440	d.	s. abs. al.
Ferroso-ferric chloride	$FeCl_2.2FeCl_3.18H_2O$	775.49	yel., delq.	...	d. 50	...	s.	s.	
ferricyanide (Prussian green)	$Fe'''_4Fe''_3[Fe(CN)_6]_6$	1662.70	gn.	...	d. 180	...	i.	...	s. d. h. HCl
oxide (magnetite; magnetic iron oxide)	Fe_3O_4	231.55	bk., cb., 2.42	5.2	1538 d.	...	i.	i.	i. al.
oxide, hydrated	$Fe_3O_4.4H_2O$	303.61	bk.	...	d.	...	i.	i.	s. a.
Ferrous ammonium sulfate	$FeSO_4.(NH_4)_2SO_4.6H_2O$	392.15	blue-gn., mn., 1.4915	1.864	d.	...	$18^{0°}$	$100^{75°}$	i. al.
chloride (lawrencite)	$FeCl_2$	126.76	gn.-yel., hex., 1.567	2.7	...	delq.	$64.4^{10°}$	$105.7^{100°}$	100 al.; s. act.; i. et.
chloroplatinate	$FePtCl_6.6H_2O$	571.92	yel., hex.	2.714	...	...	v. s.	v. s.	
ferricyanide (Turnbull's blue)	$Fe_3[Fe(CN)_6]_2$	591.47	dark blue	...	d.	...	i.	...	i. dil. a., al.
ferrocyanide	$Fe_2Fe(CN)_6$	323.66	blue-wh., amor.	...	...	...	i.		
formate	$Fe(HCO_2)_2.2H_2O$	181.92	...	...	d.	...	sl. s.		
hydroxide	$Fe(OH)_2$	89.87	lt. gn.	3.4	...	...	0.00067	...	s. a., NH_4Cl
nitrate	$Fe(NO_3)_2.6H_2O$	287.96	cr.	...	60.5	...	$200^{0°}$	$300^{25°}$	
oxide	FeO	71.85	bk.	5.7	1420	...	i.	i.	s. a.; i. alk.
phosphate (vivianite)	$Fe_3(PO_4)_2.8H_2O$	501.64	blue, mn., 1.592, 1.603	2.58	...	...	i.	i.	s. a.; i. ac.
silicate	$FeSiO_3$	131.91	mn.	3.5	1550				
sulfate (siderotilate)	$FeSO_4.5H_2O$	241.99	gn., tri., 1.536	2.2	...	−5H_2O, 300	s.	s.	i. al.
sulfate (copperas)	$FeSO_4.7H_2O$*	278.02	blue-gn., mn.	$1.899^{14.8°}$	64	−7H_2O, 300	$32.8^{0°}$	$149^{50°}$	i. al.
sulfide	FeS	87.91	bk., hex.	4.84	1193	d.	$0.000616^{18°}$	...	s. a.; i. NH_3
Cf. also under iron									
Fluoboric acid	HBF_4	87.83	col. lq.	...	...	130 d.	∞	∞	s. al.
Fluorine	F_2	38.00	gn.-yel. gas	lq. $1.11^{-187°}$; $1.31^{15°}$ (A)	−223	−187	d.		
Fluosilicic acid	H_2SiF_6	144.08	...	...	...	...	s.	s.	
Gadolinium	Gd	156.9		...	...	...			
Gallium bromide	$GaBr_3$	309.47	delq. cr.	...	...	...	s.	s.	
Glucinum *Cf.* Beryllium									
Gold	Au	197.20	yel. met., cb.	$19.3^{20°}$	1063	2600	i.	i.	s. aq. reg., KCN; i. a.
Gold, colloidal	Au	197.20	blue to vl.	...		...	s.	...	s. aq. reg., KCN; i. a.
Gold salts *Cf.* under Auric and Aurous									
Hafnium	Hf	178.6	hex.	12.1	>1700	>3200(?)			
Helium	He	4.00	col. gas	0.1368 (A)	<−272.2	−268.9	$0.97^{0°}$ cc	$1.08^{50°}$ cc	Absorbed by Pt
Hydrazine	N_2H_4	32.05	col. lq.	$1.011\frac{15°}{4}$	1.4	113.5	∞	∞	s. al.
formate	$N_2H_4.2HCO_2H$	124.10	cb.	...	128	...	s.		
hydrate	$N_2H_4.H_2O$	50.06	col.	$1.03^{21°}$	−40	$118.5^{739.5mm}$	∞	∞	∞ al.; i. et.
hydrochloride	$N_2H_4.HCl$	68.51	yel. lq.	...	...	...	v. s.	v. s.	sl. s. al.
hydrochloride, di-	$N_2H_4.2HCl$	104.98	wh., cb.	1.42	198	...	s.	v. s.	s. al.
nitrate	$N_2H_4.HNO_3$	95.06	cr.	...	70.7	subl. 140	$174.9^{10°}$	v. s.	
nitrate, di-	$N_2H_4.2HNO_3$	158.08	nd.	...	104	d.	v. s.		
sulfate	$N_2H_4.½H_2SO_4$	81.09	delq. pl.	...	85	...	v. s.	...	i. al.
sulfate	$N_2H_4.H_2SO_4$	130.12	rhb.	1.378	254	...	$3.055^{22°}$	$27.65^{60°}$	v. sl. s. abs. al.
Hydrazoic acid (azoimide)	HN_3	43.03	col. lq.	...	−80	37	∞	∞	∞ al.
Hydriodic acid	HI	127.93	col. gas	$4.4^{0°}$ (A)	−50.8	−35.5	$42500^{10°}$ cc	v. s.	s. al.
Hydriodic acid	$HI.H_2O$	145.94	col. lq.	$1.7^{15°}$	...	127^{774mm}	∞	...	∞ al.
Hydriodic acid	$HI.2H_2O$	163.96	col. lq.	...	−43	...	∞	...	s. al.
Hydriodic acid	$HI.3H_2O$	181.98	col. lq.	...	−48	...	∞	...	s. al.
Hydriodic acid	$HI.4H_2O$	199.99	col. lq.	...	−36.5	...	∞	...	s. al.
Hydrobromic acid	HBr	80.92	col. gas; 1.325 (lq.)	$2.71^{0°}$ (A)	−86	−67	$221^{0°}$	$130^{100°}$	s. al.

* Usual commercial form.

Table 3-1. Physical Properties of the Elements and Inorganic Compounds—(*Continued*)

Name	Formula	Formula weight	Color, crystalline form and refractive index	Specific gravity	Melting point, °C.	Boiling point, °C.	Solubility in 100 parts: Cold water	Hot water	Other reagents
Hydrobromic acid	$HBr.H_2O$	98.94	col. lq.	1.78	...	...	...	...	Stable at −15.5° and 1 atm., and at −11.3° and 2.5 atm.
Hydrobromic acid	HBr (47.8% in H_2O)	80.92	col. lq.	1.486	...	126	∞	...	s. al.
Hydrobromic acid	$HBr.2H_2O$	116.96	wh. cr.	$2.11^{-15°}$	−11	...	s.	s.	
Hydrochloric acid	HCl*	36.47	col. gas; 1.256 (lq.)	$1.268^{0°}$ (A)	−111	−85	$82.3^{0°}$	$56.1^{60°}$	s. al., et.
Hydrochloric acid	HCl (45.2% in H_2O)	36.47	col. lq.	1.48	−15.35	...	∞	...	s. al.
Hydrochloric acid	$HCl.2H_2O$	72.50	col. lq.	$1.46^{-18.3°/4}$	0	d.	∞	...	s. al.
Hydrochloric acid	$HCl.3H_2O$	90.51	col. lq.	...	−24.4	d.	∞	...	s. al.
Hydrocyanic acid (prussic acid)	HCN	27.03	poisonous gas or col. lq., 1.254	$0.697^{18°}$	−14	26	∞	...	∞ al., et.
Hydrofluoric acid	HF	20.01	gas or col. lq.	$0.988^{13.6°}$	−83	19.4	∞ 0° to 19.4°	v. s.	
Hydrofluoric acid	HF (35.35% in H_2O)	20.01	col. lq.	1.15	−35	120	v. s.		
Hydrogen	H_2	2.016	col. gas or cb.	lq. $0.0709^{-252.7°}$ 0.06948 (A)	−259.1	−252.7	$2.1^{0°}$ cc	$0.85^{80°}$ cc	sl. s. Fe, Pd, Pt
peroxide	H_2O_2†	34.02	col. lq., 1.333	$1.438^{20°/4}$	−0.89	151.4^{760mm}	∞	...	s. a., et.; i. petr. et
selenide	H_2Se	81.22	col. gas	$2.12^{-42°}$	−64	−42	$377^{4°}$ cc	$270^{22.5°}$ cc	s. CS_2, $COCl_2$
sulfide	H_2S	34.08	col. gas	1.1895 (A)	−82.9	−59.6	$437^{0°}$ cc	$186^{40°}$ cc	$9.54^{15°}$ cc al.; s. CS_2
Hydroxylamine	NH_2OH	33.03	rhb., delq.	$1.35^{18°}$	34	56.5^{22mm}	s.	d.	s. a., al.
hydrochloride	$NH_2OH.HCl$	69.50	col., mn.	$1.67^{17°}$	151	d.	$83.3^{17°}$	v. s.	s. al.; i. et.
nitrate	$NH_2OH.HNO_3$	96.05	col. cr.	...	48	d. <100	v. s.	d.	v. s. abs. al.
sulfate	$NH_2OH.\frac{1}{2}H_2SO_4$	82.07	col., mn.	...	170 d.	...	$32.9^{0°}$	$68.5^{90°}$	v. sl. s. al.; i. et., abs. al.
Hypobromous acid	HBrO	96.92	yel.	...	...	40^{50mm}	s.	d.	
Illinium	Il	146(?)							
Indium	In	114.76	soft, tet. met.	$7.3^{20°}$	155	1450	i.	i.	s. a.
Iodic acid	HIO_3	175.93	col., rhb.	$4.629^{0°}$	110 d.	...	$286^{0°}$	$576^{101°}$	v. s. 87% al.; i. abs. al, et., chl.
Iodine	I_2	253.84	blue-bk., rhb.	$4.93^{20°}$	113.5	184.35	$0.0162^{0°}$	$0.09566^{60°}$	s. al., KI, et.
oxide, penta-	I_2O_5	333.84	wh., trimetric	$4.799^{25°/4}$	d. 300	...	$187.4^{13°}$	...	i. abs. al., et., chl.
Iodoplatinic acid	$H_2PtI_6.9H_2O$	1120.91	brn., delq. mn.	...	...	...	s. d.		
Iridium	Ir	193.10	wh. met., cb.	$22.4^{20°}$	2350	>4800	i.	i.	sl. s. aq. reg., aq. Cl_2
Iron, cast‡	Fe	55.85	gray	7.03	1275	...	i.	i.	s. a.; i. alk.
pure	Fe	55.85	silv. met., cb.	$7.86^{20°}$	1535	3000	i.	i.	s. a.; i. alk.
steel	Fe	55.85	silv. gray	7.6 to 7.8	1375	...	i.	i.	s. a.; i. alk.
white pig	Fe	55.85	gray	7.6 to 7.8	1075	...	i.	i.	s. a.; i. alk.
wrought	Fe	55.85	gray	7.86	1505	...	i.	i.	s. a.; i. alk.
carbide (cementite)	Fe_3C	179.56	pseudo hex.	7.4	1837	...	i.	i.	s. a.
carbonyl	$Fe(CO)_5$	195.90	pa. yel. lq.	$1.457^{21°}$	−21	102.5^{760mm}	i.	...	s. al., H_2SO_4, alk.
nitride	Fe_2N	125.71	gray	6.35	d. >560	...	d.	...	s. HCl, H_2SO_4
silicide	FeSi	83.91	yel.-gray, oct.	$6.1^{20°/4}$	...	...	i.	i.	i. aq. reg.
sulfide, di- (marcasite)	FeS_2	119.97	yel., rhb.	4.87	tr. 450	d.	0.00049	...	i. dil. a.
sulfide, di- (pyrite)	FeS_2	119.97	yel., cb.	5.0	1171	d.	0.0005	...	i. dil. a.
sulfide (pyrrhotite)	Fe_7S_8	647.43	hex.	$4.6^{20°/4}$	d. >700	...	i.		
Cf. also under ferric and ferrous									
Krypton	Kr	83.70	col. gas	2.818 (A)	−169	−151.8	$11.05^{0°}$ cc	$3.57^{60°}$ cc	sl. s. al., bz.
Lanthanum	La	138.92	lead gray	$6.15^{20°}$	826	1800	d.	...	s. a.
Lead	Pb	207.21	silv. met., cb.	$11.337^{20°/20}$	327.5	1620	i.	i.	s. HNO_3; i. c. HCl, H_2SO_4
acetate	$Pb(C_2H_3O_2)_2$	325.30	wh. cr.	$3.251^{20°/4}$	280	...	$19.7^{0°}$	$221^{50°}$	s. gly.; v. sl. s. al.
acetate (sugar of lead)	$Pb(C_2H_3O_2)_2.3H_2O$§	379.35	wh., mn.	2.55	$-3H_2O$, 75	...	$45.64^{15°}$	$200^{100°}$	s. gly.; sl. s. al.
acetate	$Pb(C_2H_3O_2)_2.10H_2O$	505.46	wh., rhb.	1.689	22	...	s.	s.	
acetate, basic	$Pb_2(C_2H_3O_2)_3OH$	608.56	wh.	...	...	...	v. s.	...	sl. s. al.
acetate, basic	$Pb(C_2H_3O_2)_2.Pb(OH)_2.H_2O$	584.54	wh. nd.	...	...	...	v. s.	...	s. al.
acetate, basic	$Pb(C_2H_3O_2)_2.2Pb(OH)_2$	807.75	wh. nd.	...	...	...	5.55	18.2	s. al.
arsenate, monobasic	$PbH_4(AsO_4)_2$	489.06	tri., 1.82	$4.46^{15°}$	d. 140	...	d.	...	s. HNO_3
arsenate, dibasic (schultenite)	$PbHAsO_4$	347.13	wh., mn., 1.9097	5.94	d. >200	$-H_2O$, 280	i.	sl. s.	s. HNO_3, NaOH
arsenate, meta-	$Pb(AsO_3)_2$	453.03	hex.	$6.42^{15°}$	...	...	d.	...	s. HNO_3
arsenate, pyro-	$Pb_2As_2O_7$	676.24	rhb., 2.03	$6.85^{15°/15}$	802	...	i.	d.	s. HCl, HNO_3; i. ac.

Lead azide	PbN_6	291.26	col. nd.	...	expl. 350	...	i.	0.05_{100°	v. s. ac.; i. NH_4OH
bromide	$PbBr_2$	367.05	col., rhb.	6.66	373	918	0.4554_{0°	4.75_{100°	s. a., KBr.; sl. s. NH_3; i. al.
carbonate (cerussite)	$PbCO_3$	267.22	wh., rhb., 2.0763	6.6	d. 315	...	0.00011_{20°	d.	s. a., alk.; i. NH_3, al.
carbonate, basic (hydrocerussite; white lead)	$2PbCO_3.Pb(OH)_2$ §	775.67	wh., hex.	6.14	d. 400	...	i.	i.	s. ac.; sl. s. aq. CO_2
chloride (cotunnite)	$PbCl_2$	278.12	wh., rhb., 2.2172	5.80	501	954_{760mm}	0.673_{0°	3.34_{100°	sl. s. dil. HCl, NH_3; i. al.
chromate (crocoite)	$PbCrO_4$	323.22	yel., mn., 2.42	6.12	844	d.	0.000007_{20°	i.	s. a., alk.; i. NH_3, ac.
chromate, basic	$PbCrO_4.PbO$	546.43	or.-yel. nd.	...	...	...	i.	i.	s. a., alk.
formate	$Pb(HCO_2)_2$	297.25	wh., rhb.	4.56	d. 190	...	1.6_{16°	18_{100° d.	i. al.
hydroxide	$3PbO.H_2O$	687.65	cb.	7.592	$-H_2O$, 130	...	0.014	...	s. a., alk.
nitrate	$Pb(NO_3)_2$	331.23	col., cb. or mn., 1.7815	4.53	d. 470	...	38.8_{0°	138.8_{100°	8.8_{22° al.
oxide, sub-	Pb_2O	430.42	bk., amor.	8.34	d. red heat	...	i.	i.	s. a., alk.
oxide, mono- (litharge)	PbO	223.21	yel., tet.	9.53	888	...	0.0068_{18°	...	s. alk., PbAc, NH_4Cl, $CaCl_2$
oxide, mono (massicotite)	PbO	223.21	yel., rhb., 2.61	8.0					
oxide, mono-	PbO	223.21	amor.	9.2 to 9.5	...	...	i.	i.	s. alk., PbAc, NH_4Cl, $CaCl_2$
oxide, red (minium)	Pb_3O_4	685.63	red, amor.	9.1	d. 500	...	i.	i.	s. ac., h. HCl
oxide, sesqui-	Pb_2O_3	462.42	red-yel., amor.	...	d. 360	...	i.	i.	s. a., alk.
oxide, di- (plattnerite)	PbO_2	239.21	brn., tet., 2.229	9.375	d. 290	...	i.	i.	s. ac., h. alk.; i. al.
silicate	$PbSiO_3$	283.27	col., mn., 1.961	6.49	766	...	i.	...	s. a.
sulfate (anglesite)	$PbSO_4$	303.27	wh., mn. or rhb 1.8823	6.2	1170	...	0.0028_{0°	0.0056_{40°	s. conc. a., NH_4 salts; i. al.
sulfate, acid	$Pb(HSO_4)_2.H_2O$	419.36	cr.	...	d.	...	0.0001_{18°		sl. s. H_2SO_4
sulfate, basic (lanarkite)	$PbSO_4.PbO$	526.48	col., mn.	6.92	977	...	0.0044_{18°	...	sl. s. H_2SO_4
sulfide (galena)	PbS	239.27	lead gray, cb., 3.912	7.5	1120	...	0.00009_{18°	i.	s. a.; i. alk.
thiocyanate	$Pb(CNS)_2$	323.37	col., mn.	3.82	d. 190	...	0.05_{20°	s.	s. KCNS, HNO_3
Lithium	Li	6.94	silv. met. cb.	0.53_{20°	186	1336 ± 5	d.	d.	s. a., NH_3
benzoate	$LiC_7H_5O_2$	128.05	wh. leaflets	...	...	...	33_{25°	40_{100°	7.7_{25°, 10_{78° al.
bromide	LiBr	86.86	wh., delq., cb., 1.784	$3.464\frac{25^\circ}{4}$	547	1265	143_{0° $(2H_2O)$	266_{100° $(1H_2O)$	s. al., act.
bromide	$LiBr.2H_2O$	122.89	wh. pr.	...	44		246_{20°	...	s. al.
carbonate	Li_2CO_3	73.89	col., mn., 1.567	2.11_{0°	618	d.	1.54_{0°	0.72_{100°	s. dil. a.; i. al., act., NH_3
chloride	LiCl	42.40	wh., delq., cb., 1.662	$2.068\frac{25^\circ}{4}$	614	1360	67_{0°	127.5_{100°	2.48_{15° al.; s. et.
citrate	$Li_3C_6H_5O_7.4H_2O$	281.98	wh. cr.	...	d.		61.2_{15°	66.7_{100°	sl. s. al., et.
fluoride	LiF	25.94	wh., cb., 1.3915	$2.295_{21.5^\circ}$	870	1670	0.27_{18°	0.135_{35°	s. HF; i. act.
formate	$LiHCO_2.H_2O$	69.97	col., rhb.	1.46	$-H_2O$, 94	...	49.2_{0°	346.6_{104°	sl. s. al., et.
hydride	LiH	7.95	wh., cb.	0.820	680	...	d.	...	i. et.
hydroxide	LiOH	23.95	wh. cr.	2.54	445	925±	12.7_{0°	17.5_{100°	sl. s. al.
hydroxide	$LiOH.H_2O$	41.96	col., mn.	1.83	...	d.	22.3_{10°	26.8_{80°	sl. s. al.
nitrate	$LiNO_3$	68.95	col., trig., 1.735	2.38	261	...	53.4_{0°	194_{70°	s. al., NH_3
nitrate	$LiNO_3.3H_2O$	123.00	col.	...	29.88	...	v. s.	∞	
oxide	Li_2O	29.88	col., 1.644	$2.013\frac{25^\circ}{4}$	...	subl. <1000	forms LiOH		
phosphate, monobasic	LiH_2PO_4	103.94	col.	2.461	>100				
phosphate, tribasic	Li_3PO_4	115.80	wh., rhb.	$2.537_{17.5^\circ}$	837	...	0.034_{18°	v. sl. s.	s. a., NH_4Cl; i. act.
phosphate, tribasic	$Li_3PO_4.12H_2O$	331.99	wh., trig.	1.645	100	...	v. sl. s.	v. sl. s.	
salicylate	$LiC_7H_5O_3$	144.05	col.	...	d.	...	128_{25°	...	v. s. al.
sulfate	Li_2SO_4	109.94	col., mn., 1.465	2.22	860	...	35.34_{0°	29.9_{100°	i. act., 80% al.
sulfate	$Li_2SO_4.H_2O$ §	127.96	col., mn., 1.477	2.06	$-H_2O$, 130	...	43.6_{0°	35_{100°	i. 80% al.
sulfate, acid	$LiHSO_4$	104.01	pr.	2.123_{13°	170.5	...	d.		
Lutecium	Lu	174.99							
Magnesium	Mg	24.32	silv. met., hex.	1.74_{20°	651	1110	i.	sl. s. d.	s. a., NH_4 salts
acetate	$Mg(C_2H_3O_2)_2$	142.41	wh.	1.42	323	...	v. s.	v. s.	5.25_{15° m. al.
acetate	$Mg(C_2H_3O_2)_2.4H_2O$ §	214.47	wh., mn. pr., 1.491	1.454	80	...	v. s.	v. s.	v. s. al.
aluminate (spinel)	$MgO.Al_2O_3$	142.26	col. cb., 1.718–23	3.6	2135	...	i.	...	v. sl. s. dil. HCl; i. dil. HNO_3
ammonium chloride	$MgCl_2.NH_4Cl.6H_2O$	256.83	wh., rhb., delq.	1.456	$-4H_2O$, 195	...	16.7	s.	
ammonium phosphate (struvite)	$MgNH_4PO_4.6H_2O$	245.44	col., rhb., 1.496	1.715	d. 100	...	0.0231_{0°	0.0195_{80°	s. a.; i. al.
ammonium sulfate (boussingaultite)	$MgSO_4.(NH_4)_2SO_4.6H_2O$	360.62	col., mn.	1.72	>120	...	16.86_{0°	130_{100°	
benzoate	$Mg(C_7H_5O_2)_2.3H_2O$	320.59	wh. pd.	...	$-3H_2O$, 110	...	4.5_{25° (anh.)	s.	s. act.
carbonate (magnesite)	$MgCO_3$	83.43	wh., trig. 1.700	3.037	d. 350	...	0.0106	...	s. a., aq. CO_2; i. act., NH_3
carbonate (nesquehonite)	$MgCO_3.3H_2O$	138.38	col., rhb., 1.501	1.852	$-H_2O$, 100	...	0.1518_{19°	d.	s. a., aq. CO_2
carbonate, basic (hydromagnesite)	$3MgCO_3.Mg(OH)_2.3H_2O$	365.37	wh., rhb., 1.530	2.16	d.	...	0.04	0.011	s. a., NH_4 salts; i. al.

* Usual commercial form about 31 per cent.
† Usual commercial forms 3 or 30 per cent.
‡ See also a table of alloys.
§ Usual commercial form.

Table 3-1. Physical Properties of the Elements and Inorganic Compounds—*(Continued)*

Name	Formula	Formula weight	Color, crystalline form and refractive index	Specific gravity	Melting point, °C.	Boiling point, °C.	Solubility in 100 parts: Cold water	Hot water	Other reagents
Magnesium chloride (chloromagnesite)	$MgCl_2$	95.23	col., hex., 1.675	$2.325^{25°}$	712	1412	$52.8^{0°}$	$73^{100°}$	50 al.
chloride (bischofite)	$MgCl_2.6H_2O$*	203.33	wh., delq., mn., 1.507	1.56	118 d.	d.	$281^{0°}$	$918^{100°}$	50 al.
hydroxide (brucite)	$Mg(OH)_2$	58.34	wh., trig., 1.5617	2.4	d.	...	$0.0009^{18°}$	...	s. NH_4 salts, dil. a.
nitride	Mg_3N_2	100.98	gn.-yel., amor.	...	d.	...	i.	d.	s. a.; i. al.
oxide (magnesia; periclase)	MgO	40.32	col., cb., 1.7364	3.65	2800	3600	0.00062	...	s. a., NH_4 salts; i. al.
perchlorate	$Mg(ClO_4)_2$*	223.23	wh., delq.	$2.60^{25°}$	d.	...	$99.6^{25°}$	v. s.	24^{25} al., $51.8^{25°}$ m. al.; 0.29 et.
peroxide	MgO_2	56.32	wh. pd.	...	expl. 275	...	i.	i.	s. a.
phosphate, pyro-	$Mg_2P_2O_7$	222.60	col., mn., 1.604	$2.598^{22°}$	1383	...	i.	i.	s. a.; i. alk.
phosphate, pyro-	$Mg_2P_2O_7.3H_2O$	276.65	wh., amor.	2.56	$-3H_2O$, 100	...	i.	sl. s.	s. a.; i. al.
potassium chloride (carnallite)	$MgCl_2.KCl.6H_2O$	277.88	delq., rhb., 1.475	$1.60\frac{19.4°}{4}$	265	...	$64.5^{19°}$ d.	d.	d. al.
potassium sulfate (picromerite)	$MgSO_4.K_2SO_4.6H_2O$	402.73	mn., 1.4629	2.15	d. 72	...	$19.26^{0°}$	$81.7^{75°}$	
silicofluoride	$MgSiF_6.6H_2O$	274.48	col., trig., 1.3439	$1.788\frac{17.5°}{4}$	d.	...	$64.8^{17.5°}$	s.	d. HF
sodium chloride	$MgCl_2.NaCl.H_2O$	171.70	col.	...	...	...	s.	s.	
sulfate	$MgSO_4$	120.38	col.	2.66	1185	...	$26.9^{0°}$	$68.3^{100°}$	s. al.
sulfate (epsom salt; epsomite)	$MgSO_4.7H_2O$*	246.49	col., rhb., 1.4554	1.68	70 d.	...	$72.4^{0°}$	$178^{40°}$	s. al.
Manganese	Mn	54.93	gray-pink met.	$7.2^{20°}$	1260	1900	d.	...	s. dil. a.
acetate	$Mn(C_2H_3O_2)_2$	173.02	...	$1.74\frac{20°}{4}$	...	...	s.	s.	
acetate	$Mn(C_2H_3O_2)_2.4H_2O$*	245.08	pa. pink, mn.	1.589	...	...	s.	$64.5^{50°}$	s. al., m. al.
carbonate (rhodocrosite)	$MnCO_3$	114.94	rose, trig., 1.817	3.125	d.	...	$0.0065^{25°}$	...	s. aq. CO_2, dil. a., i. NH_3, al.
chloride (scacchite)	$MnCl_2$	125.84	rose, delq., cb.	$2.977\frac{25°}{4}$	650	1190	$63.4^{0°}$	$123.8^{106°}$	s. al.; i. et., NH_3
chloride	$MnCl_2.4H_2O$*	197.91	rose red, delq., mn. 1.575	2.01	58.0	$-H_2O$, 106; $-4H_2O$, 200	$151^{8°}$	∞	s. al.; i. et.
chloride, per-	$MnCl_4$	196.76	gn.	...	...	...	s.	s.	s. al., et.
hydroxide (ous) (pyrochroite)	$Mn(OH)_2$	88.95	wh., trig.	$3.258^{13°}$	d.	...	$0.002^{20°}$	i.	s. a., NH_4 salts; i. alk.
hydroxide (ic) (manganite)	$Mn_2O_3.H_2O$	175.88	brn., rhb., 2.24	3.258	d.	...	i.	i.	s. h. H_2SO_4
nitrate	$Mn(NO_3)_2.6H_2O$	287.04	rose red, mn.	$1.82^{21°}$	25.8	129.5	$426^{0°}$	∞	v. s. al.
oxide (ous) (manganosite)	MnO	70.93	gray-gn., cb., 2.16	5.18	1650	...	i.	i.	s. a., NH_4Cl
oxide (ic)	Mn_2O_3	157.86	brn.-bk., cb.	4.81	−O, 1080	...	i.	i.	s. a.; i. act.
oxide, di- (pyrolusite; polianite)	MnO_2*	86.93	bk., rhb.	5.026	−O, >230	...	i.	i.	s. HCl; i. HNO_3, act.
sulfate (ous)	$MnSO_4$	150.99	red-wh.	3.235	700	d. 850	$53^{0°}$	$73^{50°}$	s. al.; i. et.
sulfate (ous) (szmikite)	$MnSO_4.H_2O$	169.01	pa. pink, mn., 1.595	2.87	Stable 57 to 117	...	$98.47^{48°}$	$79.77^{100°}$	
sulfate (ous)	$MnSO_4.2H_2O$	187.02	...	$2.526^{15°}$	Stable 40 to 57	...	$85.27^{35°}$	$106.8^{55°}$	
sulfate (ous)	$MnSO_4.3H_2O$	205.04	...	$2.356^{15°}$	Stable 30 to 40	...	$74.22^{5°}$	$99.31^{57°}$	
sulfate (ous)	$MnSO_4.4H_2O$*	223.05	pink, rhb. or mn., 1.518	2.107	Stable 18 to 30	$-4H_2O$, 450	$136^{16°}$	$169^{50°}$	i. al.
sulfate (ous)	$MnSO_4.5H_2O$	241.07	pink, tri., 1.508	$2.103^{15°}$	Stable 8 to 18	...	$142^{5°}$	$200^{35°}$	
sulfate (ous)	$MnSO_4.6H_2O$	259.09	...	...	Stable −5 to +8	...	$204^{0°}$	$247^{9°}$	
sulfate (ous)	$MnSO_4.7H_2O$	277.10	pink, mn. or rhb.	2.092	Stable −10 to −5; 19 d.	$-7H_2O$, 280	$176^{0°}$	$251^{14°}$	
sulfate (ic)	$Mn_2(SO_4)_3$	398.04	gn., delq. cr.	3.24	d. 160	...	v. s.	d.	s. HCl, dil. H_2SO_4; i. conc. H_2SO_4, HNO_3
Masurium	Ma	98–99.5	...	11.5	2300 (?)				
Mercuric acetate	$Hg(C_2H_3O_2)_2$	318.70	wh. pl.	3.270	d.	...	$25^{10°}$	$100^{100°}$	s. al. sl. d.
bromide	$HgBr_2$	360.44	wh., rhb.	6.053	237	322	$0.5^{20°}$	$25^{100°}$	$25.2^{0°}$ al.; v. sl. s. et.
carbonate, basic	$HgCO_3.2HgO$	693.84	brn.-red	...	...	...	i.	...	s. aq. CO_2, NH_4Cl
chloride (corrosive sublimate)	$HgCl_2$	271.52	wh., rhb., 1.859	5.44	277	304	$3.6^{0°}$	$61.3^{100°}$	$33^{25°}$ 99% al.; 33 et.
fulminate	$Hg(CNO)_2$	284.65	cb.	4.42	expl.	...	sl. s.	...	s. NH_4OH, al.
hydroxide	$Hg(OH)_2$	234.63	...	...	$-H_2O$, 175	...	i.	i.	s. a.
oxide (montroydite)	HgO	216.61	yel. or red, rhb., 2.5	11.14	d. 100	...	$0.0052^{25°}$	$0.041^{100°}$	s. a.; i. al.
oxychloride (kleinite)	$HgCl_2.3HgO$	921.35	yel., hex.	7.93	d. 260	...	i.	d.	s. HCl
silicofluoride, basic	$HgSiF_6.HgO.3H_2O$	613.33	yel. nd.	...	...	...	d.	...	s. a.
sulfate	$HgSO_4$	296.67	wh., rhb.	6.47	d.	...	d.	...	s. a.; i. al., act., NH_3
sulfate, basic (turpeth)	$HgSO_4.2HgO$	729.89	yel., tet.	6.44	...	...	0.005	$0.167^{100°}$	s. a.; i. al.
Mercurous acetate	$HgC_2H_3O_2$	259.65	wh. sc.	...	d.	...	$0.75^{13°}$	d.	s. H_2SO_4, HNO_3; i. al.
bromide	HgBr	280.53	wh., tet.	7.307	subl. 345	...	7×10^{-9}	i.	s. a.; i. al., act.
carbonate	Hg_2CO_3	461.23	yel. pd.	...	d. 130	...	i.	d.	s. NH_4Cl
chloride (calomel)	HgCl	236.07	wh., tet., 1.9733	7.150	302	383.7	$0.0014^{0°}$	$0.0007^{43°}$	s. aq. reg., $Hg(NO_3)_2$; sl. s. HNO_3, HCl; i. al., et.
iodide	HgI	327.53	yel., tet.	7.70	290 d.	subl. 140; 310d.	2×10^{-8}	v. sl. s.	s. KI; i. al.
nitrate	$HgNO_3.H_2O$	280.63	wh. mn.	$4.785^{3.9°}$	70	expl.	v. s.	d.	s. HNO_3; i. al., et.

Mercurous oxide	Hg_2O	417.22	bk.	9.8	d. 100	....	i.	0.0007	s. h. ac.; i. alk., dil. HCl, NH_3
sulfate	Hg_2SO_4	497.28	wh., mn.	7.56	d.	....	$0.055^{16.5°}$	$0.092^{100°}$	s. H_2SO_4, HNO_3
Mercury†	Hg	200.61	silv. lq. or hex.(?)	$13.546^{20°}$	−38.87	356.9	i.	i.	s. HNO_3; i. HCl
Molybdenum	Mo	95.95	gray, cb.	10.2	2620 ± 10	3700	i.	i.	s. h. conc. H_2SO_4; i. HCl, HF, NH_3, dil. H_2SO_4, Hg
chloride, di-	$MoCl_2$	166.85	yel., amor.	$3.714^{25°}_{4}$	d.	....	i.	i.	s. HCl, H_2SO_4, NH_4OH, al., et.
chloride, tri-	$MoCl_3$	202.32	dark red pd.	$3.578^{25°}_{4}$	d.	....	i.	d.	s. HNO_3, H_2SO_4; v. sl. s. al., et.
chloride, tetra-	$MoCl_4$	237.78	brn., delq.	....	volt.	d.	s.	d.	s. HNO_3, H_2SO_4; sl. s. al., et.
chloride, penta-	$MoCl_5$	273.24	bk. cr.	$2.928^{25°}_{4}$	194	268	s.	d.	s. HNO_3, H_2SO_4; i. abs. al., et.
oxide, tri- (molybdite)	MoO_3	143.95	col., rhb.	$4.50^{19.5°}$	795	subl.	$0.107^{18°}$	$2.106^{70°}$	s. a., NH_4OH
sulfide, di- (molybdenite)	MoS_2	160.07	bk., hex., 4.7	$4.80^{14°}$	1185	....	i.	i.	s. H_2SO_4, aq. reg.
sulfide, tri-	MoS_3	192.13	red-brn.	....	d.	....	sl. s.	s.	s. alk. sulfides
sulfide, tetra-	MoS_4	224.19	brn. pd.	....	d.	....	i.	i.	s. alk. sulfides; i. NH_3
Molybdic acid	H_2MoO_4	161.97	yel-wh., hex.	....	d. 115	....	v. sl. s.	sl. s.	s. NH_4OH, H_2SO_4; i. NH_3
Molybdic acid	$H_2MoO_4.H_2O$	179.98	yel., mn.	$3.124^{15°}$	$-H_2O$, 70	$-2H_2O$, 200	$0.133^{18°}$	$2.13^{70°}$	s. a., NH_4OH, NH_4, salts
Neodymium	Nd	144.27	yellowish	$6.9^{20°}$	840	....	d.		
Neon	Ne	20.18	col. gas	lq. $1.204^{-245.9°}$ 0.674 (A)	−248.67	−245.9	2.6^{0°} cc	$1.1^{45°}$ cc	s. lq. O_2, al., act., bz.
Neptunium	Np^{239}	239	....	....	Produced by Neutron bombardment of U^{238}				
Nickel	Ni	58.69	silv. met., cb.	8.90^{20}	1452	2900	i.	i.	s. dil. HNO_3; sl. s. H_2SO_4, HCl; i. NH_3
acetate	$Ni(C_2H_3O_2)_2$	176.78	gn. pr.	1.798	d.	....	16.6	....	i. al.
ammonium chloride	$NiCl_2.NH_4Cl.6H_2O$	291.20	gn., delq., mn.	1.645	....	....	$150^{25°}$	v. s.	
ammonium sulfate	$NiSO_4.(NH_4)_2SO_4.6H_2O$	394.99	blue-gn., mn., 1.5007	1.923	....	....	$2.5^{3.5°}$	$39.2^{85°}$	v. sl. s. $(NH_4)_2SO_4$
bromate	$Ni(BrO_3)_2.6H_2O$	422.62	gn., cb.	2.575	d.	....	28	....	s. NH_4OH
bromide	$NiBr_2$	218.52	yel., delq.	$4.64^{28°}_{4}$	d.	....	$112.8^{0°}$	$156^{100°}$	s. al., et., NH_4OH
bromide	$NiBr_2.3H_2O$	272.57	gn., delq.	....	$-3H_2O$, 200	....	$199^{0°}$	$316^{100°}$	s. al., et., NH_4OH
bromide, ammonia	$NiBr_2.6NH_3$	320.71	vl. pd.	1.837	....	....	v. s.	d.	i. c. NH_4OH
bromoplatinate	$NiPtBr_6.6H_2O$	841.51	trig.	3.715					
carbonate	$NiCO_3$	118.70	lt. gn., rhb.	....	d.	....	$0.0093^{25°}$	i.	s. a.
carbonate, basic	$2NiCO_3.3Ni(OH)_2.4H_2O$	587.58	lt. gn.	....	d.	....	i.	d.	s. a., NH_4 salts
carbonyl	$Ni(CO)_4$	170.73	lq.	$1.31^{17°}$	−25	43^{751mm}	$0.018^{9.8°}$	i.	s. aq. reg., HNO_3, al., et
chloride	$NiCl_2$	129.60	yel., delq.	3.544	subl.	973	$53.8^{0°}$	$87.6^{100°}$	s. NH_4OH, al.; i. NH_3
chloride	$NiCl_2.6H_2O$*	237.70	gn., delq., mn., 1.57±	....	....	....	180	v. s.	v. s. al.
chloride, ammonia	$NiCl_2.6NH_3$	231.80	....	....	....	....	s.	d.	s. NH_4OH; i. al.
cyanide	$Ni(CN)_2.4H_2O$	182.79	gn. pl.	....	$-4H_2O$, 200	d.	i.	i.	s. KCN; i. dil. KCl
dimethylglyoxime	$NiC_8H_{14}O_4N_4$	288.91	scarlet red cr.	....	subl. 250	....	i.	i.	s. abs. al., a.; i. ac., NH_4OH
formate	$Ni(HCO_2)_2.2H_2O$	184.76	gn. cr.	2.154	d.	....	s.		
hydroxide (ic)	$Ni(OH)_3$	109.71	bk.	....	d.	....	i.	i.	s. a., NH_4OH, NH_4Cl
hydroxide (ous)	$Ni(OH)_2.\frac{1}{4}H_2O$	97.21	lt. gn.	4.36	d.	....	v. sl. s.	v. sl. s.	s. a., NH_4OH; i. alk.
nitrate	$Ni(NO_3)_2.6H_2O$	290.80	gn., mn.	2.05	56.7	136.7	$243.0^{0°}$	$\infty^{56.7°}$	s. NH_4OH; i. abs. al.
nitrate, ammonia	$Ni(NO_3)_2.4NH_3.2H_2O$	286.87	....	....	....	....	v. s.	....	i. al.
oxide, mono- (bunsenite)	NiO	74.69	gn.-bk., cb., 2.37	7.45	Forms Ni_2O_3 at 400		i.	i.	s. a., NH_4OH
potassium cyanide	$Ni(CN)_2.2KCN.H_2O$	258.97	red yel., mn.	$1.875^{11°}$	$-H_2O$, 100	....	s.	....	d. a.
sulfate	$NiSO_4$	154.75	yel., cb.	3.68	$-SO_3$, 840	....	$27.2^{0°}$	$76.7^{100°}$	i. al., et., act.
sulfate	$NiSO_4.6H_2O$*	262.85	gn. mn. or blue, tet., 1.5109	2.07	tr. 53.3	$-6H_2O$, 280	$131^{50°}$	$280^{100°}$	v. s. NH_4OH, al.
sulfate (morenosite)	$NiSO_4.7H_2O$	280.86	gn., rhb., 1.4893	1.948	98–100	$-6H_2O$, 103	$63.5^{0°}$	$117.8^{30°}$	s. al.
Nitric acid	HNO_3	63.02	col. lq.	1.502	−42	86	∞	∞	expl. with al.
Nitric acid	$HNO_3.H_2O$	81.03	col. lq.	....	−38	....	∞	∞	d. al.
Nitric acid	$HNO_3.3H_2O$	117.06	col. lq.	....	−18.5	....	$263^{-20°}$	∞	d. al.
Nitro acid sulfite	NO_2HSO_3	127.08	col., rhb.	....	73 d.	....	d.	....	s. H_2SO_4
Nitrogen	N_2	28.02	col. gas or cb. cr.	$1.026^{-252.5°}$ $0.808^{-195.8°}$ $12.5^{0°}$ (D)	−209.86	−195.8	$2.35^{0°}$ cc	$1.55^{20°}$ cc	sl. s. al.

* Usual commercial form.
† See also special table 48.

Table 3-1. Physical Properties of the Elements and Inorganic Compounds—*(Continued)*

Name	Formula	Formula weight	Color, crystalline form and refractive index	Specific gravity	Melting point, °C.	Boiling point, °C.	Solubility in 100 parts: Cold water	Hot water	Other reagents
Nitrogen oxide, mono- (ous)	N_2O	44.02	col. gas	lq. $1.226^{-89°}$ 1.530 (A)	−102.3	−90.7	$130.5^{20°}$ cc	$60.8^{24°}$ cc	s. H_2SO_4, al.
oxide, di- (ic)	NO or $(NO)_2$	30.01 (60.02)	col. gas	lq. $1.269^{-150.2°}$ 1.0367 (A)	−161	−151	$7.3^{40°}$ cc	$0.0^{100°}$	26.6 cc al.; 3.5 cc H_2SO_4; s. aq. $FeSO_4$
oxide, tri-	N_2O_3	76.02	red-brn. gas or blue lq. or solid	$1.447^{2°}$	−102	3.5	s.	...	s. a., et.
oxide, tetra- (per- or di-)	NO_2 or $(NO_2)_2$	46.01 (92.02)	yel. lq., col. solid, red-brn. gas	$1.448^{20°}$	−9.3	21.3	d.	...	s. HNO_3, H_2SO_4, chl., CS_2
oxide, penta-	N_2O_5	108.02	wh., rhb.	$1.63^{18°}$	30	47	s.	Forms HNO_3	
oxybromide	NOBr	109.92	brn. lq.	>1.0	−55.5	−2	d.		
oxychloride	NOCl	65.47	red-yel. lq. or gas	$1.417^{-12°}$ 2.31 (A)	−64.5	−5.5	d.	...	s. fuming H_2SO_4
Nitroxyl chloride	NO_2Cl	81.47	yel.-brn. gas	lq. $1.32^{14°}$	<−30	5	d		
Osmium	Os	190.2	blue, hex.	$22.48^{20°}$	2700	>5300	i.	i.	sl. s. aq. reg., HNO_3; i. NH_3
chloride, di-	$OsCl_2$	261.11	gn., delq.	...	...	...	s. d.	...	s. NaCl, al., et.
chloride, tri-	$OsCl_3$	296.57	brn., cb.	...	d. 560–600	...	sl. s.	...	s. a., alk., al.; sl. s. et.
chloride, tetra-	$OsCl_4$	332.03	red-yel. nd.	...	...	...	s. d.	...	s. HCl, al.
Oxygen	O_2	32.00	col. gas or hex. solid	$1.14^{-183°}$ $1.426^{-252.5°}$ 1.1053 (A)	−218.4	−183	$4.89^{0°}$ cc	$2.6^{80°}$ cc $1.7^{100°}$ cc	sl. s. al., s. fused Ag
Ozone	O_3	48.00	col. gas	$1.71^{-183°}$ $3.03^{-80°}$ 1.658 (A)	−251	−112	$0.49^{40°}$ cc	$0^{80°}$ cc	s. oil turp., oil cinn.
Palladium	Pd	106.70	silv. met., cb.	$12.0^{20°}$ $11^{1550°}$	1555	2200	i.	i.	s. aq. reg., h. H_2SO_4; i. NH_3
bromide (ous)	$PdBr_2$	266.53	brn.	...	...	...	i.	i.	s. HBr
chloride	$PdCl_2$	177.61	brn., cb.	...	500 d.	...	s.	s.	s. HCl, act., al.
chloride	$PdCl_2.2H_2O$	213.65	brn. pr.	...	...	...	s.	s.	s. HCl, act., al.
cyanide	$Pd(CN)_2$	158.74	yel.	...	d.	...	i.	i.	s. HCN, KCN, NH_4OH; i. dil. a.
hydride	Pd_2H	214.41	met.	11.06	d.				
Palladous dichlorodiammine	$Pd(NH_3)_2Cl_2$	211.68	red or yel., tet.	2.5	...	...	s.	...	s. a., NH_4OH
Perchloric acid	$HClO_4$	100.46	unstable, col. lq	$1.768\frac{22°}{4}$	−112	16^{18mm}	s.		
Perchloric acid	$HClO_4.H_2O$	118.48	fairly stable nd.	1.88	50	d.	s.		
Perchloric acid	$HClO_4.2H_2O$* 73.6% anh.	136.50	stable lq., col.	$1.71\frac{25°}{4}$	−17.8	200	v. s.	...	s. al.
Periodic acid	HIO_4	191.93	wh. cr.	...	d. 138	subl. 110	s.		
Periodic acid	$HIO_4.2H_2O$	227.96	delq., mn.	...	d. 110	...	v. s.	v. s.	sl. s. al., et.
Permanganic acid	$HMnO_4$	119.94	exists only in solution	...	...	...	v. s.	d.	d. al.
Permolybdic acid	$HMoO_4.2H_2O$	196.99	wh. cr.	...	...	...	v. s.	v. s.	
Persulfuric acid	$H_2S_2O_8$	194.14	hyg. cr.	...	<60	...	v. s.	d.	
Phosphamic acid	$PONH_2.(OH)_2$	97.02	cb.	...	d.	...	v. s.	v. s. d.	i. al.
Phosphatomolybdic acid	$H_7P(Mo_2O_7)_6.28H_2O$	2365.88	yel. cb.	...	78	−25H_2O, 140	s.	...	s. HNO_3
Phosphine	PH_3	34.00	col. gas	lq. $0.746^{-90°}$ 1.146 (A)	−132.5	−85	$26^{17°}$ cc	$i.^{100°}$	s. Cu_2Cl_2, al., et.
Phosphonium chloride	PH_4Cl	70.47	wh., cb.	...	28^{46atm}	subl.	d.		
Phosphoric acid, hypo-	$H_4P_2O_6$	161.99	cr.	...	55	d. 70	s.	$450^{62°}$	
Phosphoric acid, meta-	HPO_3	79.99	vitreous, delq.	2.2–2.5	subl.	...	s.	Forms H_3PO_4	i. lq. CO_2
Phosphoric acid, ortho-	H_3PO_4†	98.00	col., rhb.	$1.834^{18.2°}$	42.35	−½H_2O, 213	$2340^{26°}$	v. s.	s. al.
Phosphoric acid, pyro-	$H_4P_2O_7$	177.99	wh. nd.	...	61	...	$800^{23°}$	Forms H_3PO_4	v. s. al., et.
Phosphorous acid, hypo-	H_3PO_2	66.00	syrupy	$1.493^{18.8°}$	26.5	d.	∞	∞	
Phosphorous acid, ortho-	H_3PO_3	82.00	col.	$1.651^{21.2°}$	74	d. 200	$307.3^{0°}$	$730^{40°}$	
Phosphorous acid, pyro-	$H_4P_2O_5$	145.99	nd.	...	38	d. 130	d.		
Phosphorus, black	P_4	123.92	rhombohedral	2.69	...	ign. in air, 400	i.	i.	i. CS_2
Phosphorus, red	P_4	123.92	red, cb.	$2.20^{20°}$	590^{43atm}	ign. in air, 725	i.	i.	s. alk.; i. CS_2, NH_3, et.
Phosphorus, yellow	P_4	123.92	yel., hex., 2.1168	$1.82^{20°}$; lq. $1.745^{44.5°}$	44.1; ign. 34	280	0.0003	sl. s.	0.4 al.; $1000^{10°}$ CS_2; $1.5^{0°}$, $10^{81°}$ bz.; s. NH_3
chloride, tri-	PCl_3	137.35	col., fuming lq.	$1.574\frac{20.8°}{4}$	−111.8	75.95^{760mm}	d.	...	s. et., chl., CS_2
chloride, penta-	PCl_5	208.27	delq., tet.	solid 1.6; $3.60^{296°}$ (A)	148 under pressure	subl. 160	d.	...	s. CS_2, C_6H_5COCl
oxide, penta-	P_2O_5	141.96	wh., delq., amor.	2.387	subl. 250	...	Forms H_3PO_4	v. s.	s. H_2SO_4; i. NH_3, act.
oxychloride	$POCl_3$	153.35	col., fuming lq.	1.675	2	107.2^{760mm}	d.	...	d. al.

Phosphotungstic acid	$P_2O_5.2WO_3.42H_2O$	3681.67	yel.-gn. cr.				s.		s. al., et.
Platinum	Pt	195.23	silv. met., cb.	$21.45^{20°}$; lq. $19^{1755°}$	1755	4300	i.	i.	s. aq. reg., fused alk.
chloride (ic)	$PtCl_4$	337.06	brn.		d. 370		$140^{25°}$	v. s.	s. al., act.; sl. s. NH_3; i. et.
chloride (ous)	$PtCl_2$	266.14	brn.	$5.87^{11°}$	d. 581		i.	i.	s. HCl, NH_4OH; sl. s. NH_3; i. al., et.
chloride (ic)	$PtCl_4.8H_2O$	481.19	red, mn.	2.43	$-4H_2O$, 100		v. s.	v. s.	s. al., et.
cyanide (ous)	$Pt(CN)_2$	247.27	yel.-brn.				i.	i.	i. alk.
Plutonium	Pu	238		Produced by deuteron bombardment on U^{238}					
Plutonium	Pu	239		Produced by neutron bombardment on U^{238}					
Potassium	K	39.10	silv. met., cb.	$0.86^{20°}$; lq. $0.83^{62°}$	62.3	760	d.	Forms KOH	s. a., al., Hg
acetate	$KC_2H_3O_2$	98.14	wh. pd.	1.8	292		$217^{0°}$	$396^{90°}$	33 al.; i. et.
acetate, acid	$KH(C_2H_3O_2)_2$	158.19	delq. nd. or pl.		148	d. 200	d.		s. ac.
aluminate	$K_2(AlO_2)_2.3H_2O$	250.18	cr.				s.	d.	s. alk.; i al.
amide	KNH_2	55.12	yel.-grn.		338	subl. 400	d.		d. al.; $3.6^{25°}$ NH_3
arsenate (monobasic)	KH_2AsO_4	180.02	col., tet., 1.5674	2.867	288		$18.87^{6°}$	v. s.	i. al.
auricyanide	$KAu(CN)_4.1.5H_2O$	367.39	pl.		d. 200		s.	v. s.	s. al.
aurocyanide	$KAu(CN)_2$	288.33	rhb.				14.3	$200^{100°}$	sl. s. al.; i. et.
bicarbonate	$KHCO_3$	100.11	mn., 1.482	2.17	d. 100–200		$22.4^{0°}$	$60^{60°}$	i. satd. K_2CO_3, al.
bisulfate	$KHSO_4$	136.16	rhb., or mn., 1.480	2.35	210	d.	$36.3^{0°}$	$121.6^{100°}$	d. al.
bromate	$KBrO_3$	167.01	trig.	$3.27^{17.5°}$	370 d.		$3.11^{0°}$	$49.75^{100°}$	sl. s. al.; i. act.
bromide	KBr	119.01	col., cb., 1.5594	$2.75^{25°}$	730	1380	$53.5^{0°}$	$104^{100°}$	sl. s. al., et.
carbonate	K_2CO_3	138.20	wh., delq. pd., 1.531	2.29	891	d.	$105.5^{0°}$	$156^{100°}$	i. al.
carbonate	$K_2CO_3.2H_2O$	174.23	rhb.	2.043			$183^{0°}$	$331^{100°}$	
carbonate	$2K_2CO_3.3H_2O$	330.45	mn.	2.13			$129.4^{0°}$	$268^{100°}$	
chlorate	$KClO_3$	122.56	col., mn., 1.5167	2.32	368	d. 400	$3.3^{0°}$	$57^{100°}$	0.83 al.; s. alk.
chloride (sylvite)	KCl	74.56	col., cb., 1.4904	1.988	790	1500	$27.6^{0°}$	$56.7^{100°}$	s. al., alk.
chloroplatinate	K_2PtCl_6	486.16	yel., cb., 1.825±	3.499	d. 250		$0.74^{0°}$	$5.2^{100°}$	i. al., et.
chromate (tarapacaite)	K_2CrO_4	194.20	yel., rhb., 1.7261	$2.732^{18°}$	975		$58.0^{0°}$	$75.6^{100°}$	i. al.
cyanate	KCNO	81.11	wh., tet.	2.048			s.	d.	v. sl. s. al.
cyanide	KCN	65.11	wh., cb., delq., 1.410	$1.52^{16°}$	634.5		s.	$122.2^{103.3°}$	s. gly.; $0.9^{19.5°}$ al.; 1.3 h. al.
dichromate	$K_2Cr_2O_7$	294.21	red, tri.	2.69	398	d.	$4.9^{0°}$	$80^{100°}$	i. al.
ferricyanide	$K_3Fe(CN)_6$	329.25	red, mn. pr., 1.5689	1.84	d.		$33^{4.4°}$	$77.5^{100°}$	s. act.; sl. s. al.; i. NH_3
ferrocyanide	$K_4Fe(CN)_6.3H_2O$	422.39	yel., mn., 1.5772	$1.853^{17°}$	$-3HO_2$, 70		$27.8^{12.2°}$	$90.6^{96.3°}$	s. act.; i. NH_3, al., et.
formate	$KHCO_2$	84.11	col., rhb.	1.91	167.5	d.	$331^{18°}$	$657^{90°}$	sl. s. al.; i. et.
hydride	KH	40.10	cb., 1.453	0.80	d.		d.		i. et., bz., CS_2
hydrosulfide	KHS	72.16	wh., delq., rhb.	2.0	455		s.	s. d.	s. al.
hydroxide	KOH	56.10	wh., delq., rhb.	2.044	380	1320	$97^{0°}$	$178^{100°}$	v. s. al., et.; i. NH_3
iodate	KIO_3	214.02	col., mn.	3.89	560		$4.73^{0°}$	$32.2^{100°}$	s. KI; i. al., NH_3
iodide	KI	166.02	wh., cb., 1.6670	3.13	723	1330	$127.5^{0°}$	$208^{100°}$	$4^{20°}$ al.; s. NH_3; sl. s. et.
iodide, tri-	KI_3	419.86	dark blue, delq., mn.	3.498	45	d. 225	v. s.		s. KI, al.
iodoplatinate	K_2PtI_6	1034.94	cb.	5.18			s.		
manganate	K_2MnO_4	197.12	gn., rhb.		d. 190		d.		s. KOH
metabisulfite	$K_2S_2O_5$	222.31	mn., pl.		d. 150		$25^{0°}$	$120^{94°}$	sl. s. al.; i. et.
nitrate (saltpeter)	KNO_3	101.10	col., rhb., 1.5038	$2.11^{10.6°}$	tr. 129; 333	d. 400	$13.3^{0°}$	$246^{100°}$	$0.1^{30°}$ al.; i. et.
nitrite	KNO_2	85.10	pr.	1.915	297	d. 350	$281^{0°}$	$413^{100°}$	v. s. NH_3; sl. s. al.
oxalate	$K_2C_2O_4.H_2O$	184.23	wh., mn.	2.13	d.		$28.7^{0°}$	$83.2^{100°}$	
oxalate, acid	KHC_2O_4‡	128.12	mn., 1.545	2.0	d.		$14.3^{50°}$	$48.1^{100°}$	
oxalate, acid	$KHC_2O_4.\frac{1}{2}H_2O$	137.13	trimetric		d.		$2.2^{0°}$	$51.5^{100°}$	
oxide	K_2O	94.19	wh., cb.	$2.32\frac{20°}{4}$			Forms KOH	v. s.	s. al., et.
perchlorate	$KClO_4$	138.55	col., rhb., 1.4737	$2.524\frac{11°}{4}$	d. 400		$0.75^{0°}$	$21.8^{100°}$	$0.105^{20°}$ m. al.; i. et.
permanganate	$KMnO_4$	158.03	purple, rhb.	2.703	d. <240		$2.83^{0°}$	$32.35^{75°}$	s. H_2SO_4; d. al.
persulfate	$K_2S_2O_8$	270.31	wh., tri., 1.4669		d. <100		$1.77^{0°}$	$10^{40°}$	i. al.
phosphate, monobasic	KH_2PO_4	136.09	col., delq., tet., 1.5095	2.338	256		$14.8^{0°}$	$83.5^{90°}$	i. al.
phosphate, dibasic	K_2HPO_4	174.18	wh., delq.		d.		$33^{25°}$	v. s.	sl. s. al.
phosphate, tribasic	K_3PO_4	212.27	wh., rhb.	$2.564^{17°}$	1340		$193.1^{25°}$	v. s.	i. al.
phosphate, meta-	KPO_3	118.08	wh. pd.	$2.258^{14.5°}$	tr. 450; 798	1320	s.	s.	
phosphate, meta-	$K_4P_4O_{12}.2H_2O$	508.34	amor.	$2.264^{14.5°}$	$-2H_2O$, 100	d.	s.	83	s. a.
phosphate, pyro-	$K_4P_2O_7.3H_2O$	384.39	delq.	2.33	$-2H_2O$, 180	$-3H_2O$, 300	s.	v. s.	i. al.
phthalate, acid	$KHC_8H_4O_4$	204.22	wh. cr.	1.63	d.		$10.2^{25°}$	36	
platinocyanide	$K_2Pt(CN)_4.3H_2O$	431.54	yel., rhb., 1.62±	$2.45^{16°}$			sl. s.	v. s.	s. al., et.
silicate	K_2SiO_3	154.25	hyg. 1.521±		976		s.	s.	i. al.
silicate, tetra-	$K_2Si_4O_9.H_2O$	352.45	rhb., 1.530	2.417	d. 400		s.	s.	i. al.
sulfate (arcanite)	K_2SO_4	174.25	col., rhb., 1.4947	2.662	tr. 588		$7.35^{0°}$	$24.1^{100°}$	i. al., act., CS_2

* One commercial form 70 to 72 per cent.
† Common commercial form 85 per cent H_3PO_4 in aqueous solution.
‡ Usual commercial form.

Table 3-1. Physical Properties of the Elements and Inorganic Compounds—*(Continued)*

Name	Formula	Formula weight	Color, crystalline form and refractive index	Specific gravity	Melting point, °C.	Boiling point, °C.	Solubility in 100 parts: Cold water	Hot water	Other reagents
Potassium sulfate, pyro-	$K_2S_2O_7$	254.31	col.	2.277	300		s.	d.	
sulfide, mono-	$K_2S.5H_2O$	200.33	rhb., delq.		60	$-3H_2O$, 150	s.		s. al., gly.; i. et.
sulfite	$K_2SO_3.2H_2O$	194.28	wh., rhb.		d.		100	>100	sl. s. al.; i. NH_3
sulfite, acid	$KHSO_3$	120.16	wh., mn.		d. 190		$45.5^{15°}$	$91.5^{75°}$	i. abs. al.
tartrate	$K_2C_4H_4O_6.\frac{1}{2}H_2O$	235.27	col., mn., 1.526	1.98		d.	$12.5^{17.5°}$	$278^{100°}$	sl. s. al.
tartrate, acid	$KHC_4H_4O_6$*	188.18	col., rhb.	1.956			$0.37^{0°}$	$6.1^{100°}$	s. a., alk.; i. al., ac.
thiocyanate	KCNS	97.17	col.,delq., mn., 1.660±	1.886	172.3	d. 500	$177^{0°}$	$217^{20°}$	$20.8^{22°}$ act.; s. al.
thiosulfate	$K_2S_2O_3$	190.31	col., cb.		d. 400		$96.1^{0°}$	$311.2^{90°}$	
thiosulfate	$3K_2S_2O_3.H_2O$	588.95	delq., mn.	2.23	$-H_2O$, 180	d.			i. al.
Praseodymium	Pr	140.92	yel.	$6.5^{20°}$	940		d.		
Radium	Ra	226.05	wh., met.	5?	960	1140	d. $+H_2$		d. a.
bromide	$RaBr_2$	385.88	wh., mn.	5.79	728	subl. 900	$70^{20°}$	s.	s. al.
Radon (Niton)	Rn	222.0	gas	lq. 5.5; 111 (D)	−71	−62	$51^{0°}$ cc	$8.5^{50°}$ cc	
Rhenium	Re	186.31	hex.		3440				i. HF, HCl; s. H_2SO_4, HNO_3
Rhodium	Rh	102.91	gray-wh., cb.	12.5	1955	>2500	i.	i.	sl. s. aq. reg., a.
chloride	$RhCl_3$	209.28	red		d. 450	subl. 800±	i.	i.	v. sl. s. alk.; i. aq. reg., a.
chloride	$RhCl_3.4H_2O$	281.35	dark red				v. s.		s. HCl, al.; i. et.
Rubidium	Rb	85.48	silv. wh.	lq. $1.475^{38.5}$; $1.53^{20°}$	38.5	700	d.		s. a., al.
Ruthenium	Ru	101.70	bk., porous	8.6	>1950		i.	i.	sl. s. aq. reg., a.
Ruthenium	Ru	101.70	gray, hex.	$12.2^{20°}$	2450	>2700	i.	i.	
Samarium	Sm (also Sa)	150.43		7.7	>1300				
Scandium	Sc	45.10		2.5?	1200	2400			
Selenic acid	H_2SeO_4	144.98	hex. pr.	$2.950\frac{15°}{4}$	58	260	$1300^{30°}$	$\infty^{60°}$	s. H_2SO_4; d. al.; i. NH_3
Selenic acid	$H_2SeO_4.H_2O$	162.99	nd.	$2.627\frac{15°}{4}$	26	205	v. s.		
Selenium	Se_8	631.68	red pd., amor., 2.92	$4.26^{25°}$	50	688	i.	i.	s. CS_2, H_2SO_4, CH_2I_2
Selenium	Se_8	631.68	gray, trig., 3.00; red, hex.	4.80; 4.50	220	688	i.	i.	s. CS_2, H_2SO_4
Selenium	Se_8	631.68	steel gray	$4.8^{25°}$	217	688	i.	i.	i. CS_2; s. H_2SO_4
Selenous acid	H_2SeO_3	128.98	hex.	$3.004\frac{15°}{4}$	d.		$90^{0°}$	$400^{90°}$	v. s. al.; i. NH_3
Silicic acid, meta-	H_2SiO_3	78.08	amor., 1.41	2.1–2.3			i.	i.	s. alk.; i. NH_4Cl
Silicic acid, ortho-	H_4SiO_4	96.09	amor.	$1.576^{17°}$			sl. s.	sl. s.	s. alk.; i. NH_4Cl
Silicon, crystalline	Si	28.06	gray, cb., 3.736	$2.4^{20°}$	1420	2600	i.	i.	s. HNO_3 + HF, Ag; sl. s. Pb, Zn; i. HF
Silicon, graphitic	Si	28.06	cr.	2.0–2.5		2600	i.	i.	s. HNO_3 + HF, fused alk.; i. HF.
Silicon, amorphous	Si	28.06	brn., amor.	2		2600	i.	i.	s. HF, KOH
carbide	SiC	40.07	blue-bk., trig., 2.654	3.17	>2700	subl. 2200	i.	i.	s. fused alk.; i. a.
chloride, tri-	Si_2Cl_6	268.86	lf. or lq.	$1.58^{0°}$	−1	144^{760mm}	d.		d. alk.
chloride, tetra-	$SiCl_4$	169.89	col., fuming lq., 1.412	1.50	−70	57.6	d.		d. conc. H_2SO_4, al.
fluoride	SiF_4	104.06	gas	3.57 (A)	−95.7	-65^{1810mm}	v. s. d.		s. HNO_3, al., et.
hydride (silane)	SiH_4	32.09	col. gas	lq. $0.68^{-185°}$	−185	-112^{760mm}	i.		i. al., et.; d. KOH
oxide, di- (opal)	$SiO_2.xH_2O$	......	iridescent, amor.	2.2	1600–1750	subl. 1750	i.	i.	s. HF, h. alk., fused $CaCl_2$
oxide, di- (cristobalite)	SiO_2	60.06	col., cb. or tet., 1.487	2.32	1710	2230	i.	i.	s. HF; i. alk.
oxide, di- (lechatelierite)	SiO_2	60.06		2.20		2230	i.	i.	s. HF; i. alk.
oxide, di- (quartz)	SiO_2	60.06	hex., 1.5442	$2.650^{20°}$	tr. <1425	2230	i.	i.	s. HF; i. alk.
oxide, di- (tridymite)	SiO_2	60.06	trig., rhb., 1.469	2.26	tr. 1670	2230	i.		s. HF; i. alk.
Silver	Ag	107.88	silv. met., cb.	$10.5^{20°}$	960.5	1950	i.	i.	s. HNO_3, h. H_2SO_4; i. alk.
bromide (bromyrite)	AgBr	187.80	pa. yel., cb., 2.252	$6.473\frac{25°}{4}$	434	d. 700	$0.00002^{20°}$	$0.00037^{100°}$	$0.51^{18°}$ NH_4OH; s. KCN, $Na_2S_2O_3$
carbonate	Ag_2CO_3	275.77	yel. pd.	6.077	218 d.		$0.003^{20°}$	$0.05^{100°}$	s. NH_4OH, $Na_2S_2O_3$; i. al.
chloride (cerargyrite)	AgCl	143.34	wh., cb., 2.071	5.56	455	1550	$0.000089^{10°}$	$0.00217^{100°}$	s. NH_4OH, KCN; sl. s. HCl
cyanide	AgCN	133.90	wh., 1.685±	3.95	$-(CN)_2$, 320		$0.000022^{20°}$		s. NH_4OH, KCN, HNO_3
nitrate (lunar caustic)	$AgNO_3$	169.89	col., rhb., 1.744	$4.352\frac{19°}{4}$	212	444 d.	$122^{0°}$	$952^{100°}$	s. gly.; v. sl. s. al.
Sodium	Na	22.997	silv. met., cb.	$0.97^{20°}$	97.5	880	d., forms NaOH		i. bz.; d. al.
acetate	$NaC_2H_3O_2$	82.04	wh., mn., 1.464	1.528	324		$46.5^{20°}$	$170^{100°}$	$2.1^{18°}$ al.
acetate	$NaC_2H_3O_2.3H_2O$	136.09	wh., mn.	1.45	58	$-3H_2O$, 120	v. s.	v. s.	$7.8^{25°}$ abs. al.
aluminate	$NaAlO_2$	81.97	amor.		1650		s.	v. s.	i. al.
amide	$NaNH_2$	39.02	olive gn.		210	400	d.		d. al.

Sodium ammonium phosphate	$NaNH_4HPO_4.4H_2O$	209.09	col., mn.	1.574	79 d.	...	16.7	100	i. al.
antimonate, meta-	$2NaSbO_3.7H_2O$	511.63	cb.	...		...	$0.031^{12.3°}$	...	sl. s. al., NH_4 salts; i. ac.
arsenate	$Na_3AsO_4.12H_2O$	424.09	hex., 1.4589	1.759	86.3	...	$26.7^{17°}$	...	1.67 al., $50^{15°}$ gly.
arsenate, acid (monobasic)	$NaH_2AsO_4.H_2O$	181.94	rhb., 1.5535	2.535	d. 100	...	s.		
arsenate, acid (dibasic)	$Na_2HAsO_4.7H_2O$*	312.02	col., mn., 1.4658	1.871	125	$-7H_2O$, 100	$61^{15°}$	v. s.	sl. s. al.
arsenate, acid (dibasic)	$Na_2HAsO_4.12H_2O$	402.10	mn., 1.4496	1.72	28	$-12H_2O$, 100	$5.59^{0.1°}$	$140.7^{30°}$	sl. s. al.
arsenite, acid	Na_2HAsO_3	169.91	col.	1.87	...	...	v. s.		
benzoate	$NaC_7H_5O_2$	144.11	col. cr.	...	...	...	$62.5^{25°}$	$76.9^{100°}$	$2.3^{25°}$, $8.3^{78°}$ al.
bicarbonate	$NaHCO_3$	84.01	wh., mn., 1.500	2.20	$-CO_2$, 270	...	$6.9^{0°}$	$16.4^{60°}$	i. al.
bifluoride	$NaHF_2$	62.00	col. cr.	...	d.	...	$3.7^{20°}$	s.	
bisulfate	$NaHSO_4$	120.06	col., tri.	2.742	>315	d., $-H_2O$	$50^{0°}$	$100^{100°}$	d. al.; i. NH_3
bisulfite	$NaHSO_3$	104.06	col., mn., 1.526	1.48	d.	...	sl. s.	s.	i. al., act.
borate, tetra-	$Na_2B_4O_7$	201.27	...	2.367	741	...	$1.3^{0°}$	$8.79^{40°}$	i. al.
borate, tetra	$Na_2B_4O_7.5H_2O$	291.35	col., rhb., 1.461	1.815	...	...	$22^{62°}$ (anh.)	$52.3^{100°}$ (anh.)	
borate, tetra- (borax)	$Na_2B_4O_7.10H_2O$*	381.43	wh., mn., 1.4694	1.73	75	$-10H_2O$, 200	$1.3^{0.5}$ (anh.).	$20.3^{50°}$ (anh.)	s. gly.; i. abs. al.
bromate	$NaBrO_3$	150.91	col., cb.	$3.339^{17.5°}$	381	...	$27.5^{0°}$	$90.9^{100°}$	i. al.
bromide	$NaBr$	102.91	col., cb., 1.6412	$3.205^{17.5°}$	755	1390	$90^{20°}$	$121^{100°}$	sl. s. al.
bromide	$NaBr.2H_2O$	138.95	col., mn.	2.176	50.7	...	$79.5^{0°}$ (anh.)	$118.3^{80°}$ (anh.)	sl. s. al.
carbonate (soda ash)	Na_2CO_3	106.00	wh. pd., 1.535	2.533	851	d.	$7.1^{0°}$	$48.5^{104°}$	i. al., et.
carbonate	$Na_2CO_3.H_2O$	124.02	wh., rhb., 1.506–1.509	1.55	$-H_2O$, 100	...	s.	s.	s. gly.; i. al., et.
carbonate	$Na_2CO_3.7H_2O$	232.12	rhb. or trig.	1.51	d. 35.1	...	s.	s.	
carbonate (sal soda)	$Na_2CO_3.10H_2O$	286.16	wh., mn., 1.425	1.46	...	...	$21.5^{0°}$	$238^{30°}$	i. al.
carbonate, sesqui- (trona)	$Na_3H(CO_3)_2.2H_2O$	226.05	wh., mn., 1.5073	2.112	d.	...	$13^{0°}$	$42^{100°}$	
chlorate	$NaClO_3$	106.45	wh., cb., or trig., 1.5151	$2.490^{15°}$	248	d.	$79^{0°}$	$230^{100°}$	s. al.
chloride	$NaCl$	58.45	col., cb., 1.5443	2.163	800.4	1413	$35.7^{0°}$	$39.8^{100°}$	sl. s. al.; i. conc. HCl
chromate	Na_2CrO_4	162.00	yel., rhb.	2.723	392	...	$32^{0°}$	$126^{100°}$	
chromate	$Na_2CrO_4.10H_2O$	342.16	yel., delq., mn.	1.483	19.9	...	v. s.	∞	sl. s. al.
citrate	$2Na_3C_6H_5O_7.11H_2O$	714.36	wh., rhb.	$1.857\frac{23.5°}{4}$	$-11H_2O$, 150	d.	$91^{25°}$	$250^{100°}$	i. al.
cyanide	$NaCN$	49.02	wh., cb., 1.452	...	563.7	1496	$48^{10°}$	$82^{35°}$	s. NH_3; sl. s. al.
dichromate	$Na_2Cr_2O_7.2H_2O$	298.05	red, mn., 1.6994	$2.52^{13°}$	$-2H_2O$, 84.6; 356 (anh.)	d. 400	$238^{0°}$	$508^{80°}$	
ferricyanide	$Na_3Fe(CN)_6.H_2O$	298.97	red, delq.	...	...	...	$18.9^{0°}$	$67^{100°}$	i. al.
ferrocyanide	$Na_4Fe(CN)_6.10H_2O$	484.11	yel., mn.	1.458	...	...	$17.9^{20°}$ (anh.)	$63^{98.5°}$ (anh.)	i. al.
fluoride (villiaumite)	NaF	42.00	tet., 1.3258	2.79	992	...	$4^{0°}$	$5^{100°}$	v. sl. s. al.
formate	$NaHCO_2$	68.01	wh., mn.	1.919	253	...	$44^{0°}$	$160^{100°}$	sl. s. al.; i. et.
hydride	NaH	24.005	silv. nd., 1.470	0.92	d. 800	...	d.	...	i. bz., CS_2, CCl_4, NH_3; s. molten metal
hydrosulfide	$NaSH.2H_2O$	92.10	col., delq., nd.	...	d.	...	s.	s.	s. al.; d. a.
hydrosulfide	$NaSH.3H_2O$	110.11	rhb.	...	22	d.	s.	s.	s. al.; d. a.
hydrosulfite	$Na_2S_2O_4.2H_2O$	210.15	col. cr.	...	d.	...	$22^{20°}$	d.	i. al.
hydroxide	$NaOH$	40.00	wh., delq.	2.130	318.4	1390	$42^{0°}$	$347^{100°}$	v. s. al., et., gly.; i. act.
hydroxide	$NaOH.3\frac{1}{2}H_2O$	103.06	mn.	...	15.5	...	s.	v. s.	
hypochlorite	$NaOCl$	74.45	pa. yel., in soln. only	...	d.	...	$26^{0°}$	$158^{56°}$	
iodide	NaI*	149.92	col., cb., 1.7745	$3.667^{0°}$	651	1300	$158.7^{0°}$	$302^{100°}$	v. s. al., act.
iodide	$NaI.2H_2O$	185.95	col., mn.	2.448	...	...	v. s.	v. s.	v. s. NH_3
lactate	$NaC_3H_5O_3$	112.07	col., amor.	...	d.	...	v. s.	v. s.	s. al.; i. et.
nitrate (soda niter)	$NaNO_3$	85.01	col., trig., 1.5874	2.257	308	d. 380	$73^{0°}$	$180^{100°}$	s. NH_3; sl. s. gly., al.
nitrite	$NaNO_2$	69.01	pa. yel., rhb.	$2.168^{0°}$	271	d. 320	$72.1^{0°}$	$163.2^{100°}$	$0.3^{20°}$ et.; 0.3 abs. al.; $4.4^{20°}$ m. al.; v. s. NH_3
oxide	Na_2O	61.99	wh., delq.	2.27	subl.	...	Forms NaOH	...	d. al.
perborate	$NaBO_3.H_2O$	99.83	wh. pd.	...	d. 40	...	sl. s.	d.	s. gly., alk.
perchlorate	$NaClO_4$	122.45	rhb., 1.4617	...	482 d.	...	$170^{0°}$	$320^{100°}$	s. al.; 51 m. al.; 52 act.; i. et.
perchlorate	$NaClO_4.H_2O$	140.47	hex.	2.02	d. 130	...	$209^{15°}$	$284^{50°}$	s. al.
peroxide	Na_2O_2*	77.99	yel.-wh. pd.	2.805	d.	...	s. d.	d.	s. dil. a.
peroxide	$Na_2O_2.8H_2O$	222.12	wh., hex.	...	d. 30	...	s. d.	d.	
phosphate, monobasic	$NaH_2PO_4.H_2O$*	138.01	col., rhb., 1.4852	2.040	$-H_2O$, 100	d. 200	$71^{0°}$	$390^{83°}$	i. al.
phosphate, monobasic	$NaH_2PO_4.2H_2O$	156.03	col., rhb., 1.4629	1.91	60	...	$91.1^{0°}$	$308^{40°}$	
phosphate, dibasic	$Na_2HPO_4.7H_2O$	268.09	col., mn., 1.4424	1.679	d.	...	$185^{40°}$	$2000^{100°}$	
phosphate, dibasic	$Na_2HPO_4.12H_2O$	358.17	col., mn., 1.4361	1.52	34.6	$-12H_2O$, 180	$4.3^{0°}$	$76.7^{30°}$	i. al.
phosphate, tribasic	Na_3PO_4	163.97	wh.	$2.537^{17.5°}$	1340	...	$4.5^{0°}$	$77^{100°}$	
phosphate, tribasic	$Na_3PO_4.12H_2O$*	380.16	wh., trig., 1.4458	1.62	73.4	$-11H_2O$, 100	$28.3^{15°}$	∞	i. CS_2
phosphate, meta-	$Na_4P_4O_{12}$	407.91	col.	2.476	616 d.	...	s.	s.	s. a., alk.
phosphate, pyro-	$Na_4P_2O_7$*	265.95	wh.	2.45	988	...	$2.26^{0°}$	$45^{96°}$	d. a.
phosphate, pyro-	$Na_4P_2O_7.10H_2O$	446.11	mn., 1.4525	1.82	d.	...	$5.4^{0°}$	$93^{100°}$	i. al., NH_3
phosphate (pyrodisodium)	$Na_2H_2P_2O_7$	221.97	col., mn., 1.510	1.862	d. 220	...	$4.5^{0°}$	$21^{40°}$	
phosphate (pyrodisodium)	$Na_2H_2P_2O_7.6H_2O$	330.07	col., mn., 1.4645	1.848	...	...	$6.9^{0°}$	$36^{40°}$	
potassium tartrate	$NaKC_4H_4O_6.4H_2O$	282.23	rhb., 1.493	1.790	70 to 80	$-4H_2O$, 215	$26^{0°}$	$66^{26°}$	sl. s. al.
silicate, meta-	Na_2SiO_3	122.05	col., rhb., 1.520	...	1088	...	s.	s. d.	i. Na or K salts, al.

* Usual commercial form.

Table 3-1. Physical Properties of the Elements and Inorganic Compounds—*(Continued)*

Name	Formula	Formula weight	Color, crystalline form and refractive index	Specific gravity	Melting point, °C.	Boiling point, °C.	Solubility in 100 parts: Cold water	Hot water	Other reagents
Sodium silicate, meta-	$Na_2SiO_3.9H_2O$	284.20	rhb.	......	47	$-6H_2O$, 100	v. s.	v. s.	$29^{18°}$, ½N NaOH
silicate, ortho-	Na_4SiO_4	184.05	col., hex., 1.530	......	1018	......	s.	s.	
silicofluoride	Na_2SiF_6	188.05	wh., hex., 1.312	2.679	d.	......	$0.44^{0°}$	$2.45^{100°}$	i. al.
stannate	$Na_2SnO_3.3H_2O$	266.74	hex. tablets	......	d. 140	......	$50^{0°}$	$67^{50°}$	i. al., act.
sulfate (thenardite)	Na_2SO_4	142.05	col., rhb., 1.477	2.698	tr. 100 to mn.	......	$5^{0°}$	$42^{100°}$	i. al.
sulfate	Na_2SO_4	142.05	col., mn.	......	tr. 500 to hex.	......	$48.8^{40°}$	$42.5^{100°}$	d. HI; s. H_2SO_4
sulfate	Na_2SO_4	142.05	col., hex.	......	884	......	$19.4^{20°}$	$45.3^{60°}$	
sulfate	$Na_2SO_4.7H_2O$	268.17	tet.	......	......	......	$44.9^{0°}$	$202.6^{26°}$	
sulfate (Glauber's salt)	$Na_2SO_4.10H_2O$	322.21	col., mn., 1.396	1.464	32.4	$-10H_2O$, 100	$36^{15°}$	$412^{34°}$	i. al.
sulfide, mono-	Na_2S	78.05	pink or wh., amor.	1.856	......	......	$15.4^{10°}$	$57.3^{90°}$	sl. s. al.; i. et.
sulfide, tetra-	Na_2S_4	174.23	yel., cb.	......	275	......	s.	s.	s. al.
sulfide, penta-	Na_2S_5	206.29	yel.	......	251.8	......	s.	s.	s. al.
sulfite	Na_2SO_3	126.05	hex. pr., 1.565	$2.633\frac{15}{4}^{\circ}$	d.	......	$13.9^{0°}$	$28.3^{84°}$	i. al., NH
sulfite	$Na_2SO_3.7H_2O$	252.17	mn.	1.561	$-7H_2O$, 150	d.	$34.7^{2°}$	$67.8^{18°}$	i. al.
tartrate	$Na_2C_4H_4O_6.2H_2O$	230.10	rhb.	1.818	......	......	$29^{6°}$	$66^{43°}$	i. al.
thiocyanate	$NaCNS$	81.08	delq., rhb., 1.625±	......	287	......	$110^{10°}$	$225^{100°}$	v. s. al.
thiosulfate	$Na_2S_2O_3$	158.11	mn.	1.667	......	......	$50^{0°}$	$231^{80°}$	
thiosulfate (hypo)	$Na_2S_2O_3.5H_2O$*	248.19	mn. pr., 1.5079	1.685	d. 48.0	......	$74.7^{0°}$	$301.8^{60°}$	s. NH_3; v. sl. s. al.
tungstate	Na_2WO_4	293.91	wh., rhb.	4.179	692	......	$57.5^{80°}$	$97^{100°}$	
tungstate	$Na_2WO_4.2H_2O$*	329.95	wh., rhb.	3.245	$-2H_2O$, 100	......	$88^{0°}$	$123.5^{100°}$	sl. s. NH_3; i. a., al.
tungstate, para-	$Na_6W_7O_{24}.16H_2O$	2097.68	wh., tri.	$3.987^{14°}$	$-16H_2O$, 300	......	8	d.	
uranate	Na_2UO_4	348.06	yel.	......	......	......	i.	i.	s. alk. carb., dil. a.
vanadate	$Na_3VO_4.16H_2O$	472.20	col. nd.	......	866 (anh.)	......	v. s.	d.	i. al.
vanadate, pyro-	$Na_4V_2O_7$	305.89	hex.	......	654	......	s.	......	i. al.
Stannic chloride	$SnCl_4$	260.53	col., fuming lq.	2.226	−30.2	114.1	s.	d.	s. abs. al., act., NH_3; s. ∞ CS_2
oxide (cassiterite)	SnO_2	150.70	wh., tet., 1.9968	7.0	1127	......	i.	i.	s. conc. H_2SO_4; i. alk., NH_4OH, NH_3
sulfate	$Sn(SO_4)_2.2H_2O$	346.85	col., delq., hex.	......	......	......	v. s.	d.	s. dil. H_2SO_4, HCl; d. abs. al.
Stannous bromide	$SnBr_2$	278.53	yel., rhb.	$5.12^{17°}$	215.5	620	s.	d.	s. C_6H_5N
chloride	$SnCl_2$	189.61	wh., rhb.	......	246.8	623	$83.9^{0°}$	$269.8^{15°}$	s. alk., abs. al., et.
chloride (tin salt)	$SnCl_2.2H_2O$*	225.65	wh., tri.	$2.71^{15.5°}$	37.7	d.	$118.7^{0°}$	∞	s. tart. a., alk., al.
sulfate	$SnSO_4$	214.76	wh. cr.	......	$-SO_2$, 360	......	$19^{19°}$	$18^{100°}$	s. H_2SO_4
Strontium	Sr	87.63	silv. met.	2.6	800	1150	d.	Forms $Sr(OH)_2$	s. al., a.
acetate	$Sr(C_2H_3O_2)_2$	205.72	wh. cr.	2.099	......	d.	$36.9^{0°}$	$36.4^{97°}$	$0.26^{15°}$ m. al.
carbonate (strontianite)	$SrCO_3$	147.64	wh., rhb., 1.664	3.70	1497^{60atm}	$-CO_2$, 1350	$0.0011^{18°}$	$0.065^{100°}$	s. a., NH_4 salts, aq. CO_2
chloride	$SrCl_2$	158.54	wh., cb., 1.6499	3.052	873	......	$43.5^{0°}$	$100.8^{100°}$	v. sl. s. act., abs. al.; i. NH_3
chloride	$SrCl_2.6H_2O$*	266.64	wh., rhb., 1.5364	$1.933^{17°}$	$-4H_2O$, 61	$-6H_2O$, 100	$104^{0°}$	$198^{40°}$	
hydroxide	$Sr(OH)_2$	121.65	wh., delq.	3.625	375	......	$0.41^{0°}$	$21.83^{100°}$	s. NH_4Cl
hydroxide	$Sr(OH)_2.8H_2O$*	265.77	col., tet., 1.499	1.90	$-7H_2O$ in dry air	......	$0.90^{0°}$	$47.7^{100°}$	s. NH_4Cl; i. act.
nitrate	$Sr(NO_3)_2$*	211.65	col., cb., 1.5878	2.986	570	......	$40^{0°}$	$100^{89°}$	s. NH_3; 0.012 abs. al.
nitrate	$Sr(NO_3)_2.4H_2O$	283.71	wh., mn.	2.2	......	......	$62.2^{0°}$	$124^{20°}$	i. HNO_3
oxide (strontia)	SrO	103.63	col., cb., 1.870	4.7	2430	......	Forms $Sr(OH)_2$	......	sl. s. al.; i. et.
peroxide	SrO_2	119.63	wh. pd.	......	d.	......	$0.008^{20°}$	d.	s. al., NH_4Cl; i. act.
peroxide	$SrO_2.8H_2O$	263.76	wh. cr.	......	$-8H_2O$, 100	d.	$0.018^{20°}$	d.	s. al.; i. NH_4OH
sulfate (celestite)	$SrSO_4$	183.69	col., rhb., 1.6237	3.96	1580 d.	......	$0.0113^{0°}$	$0.0114^{32°}$	sl. s. a.; i. dil. H_2SO_4, al.
sulfate, acid	$Sr(HSO_4)_2$	281.77	col., granular	......	d.	......	d.	......	$14^{70°}$ H_2SO_4
Sulfamic acid	NH_2SO_3H	97.09	wh., rhb.	$2.03\frac{12}{4}^{\circ}$	205 d.	......	$20^{0°}$	$40^{70°}$	sl. s. al., act.; i. et.
Sulfur, amorphous	S	32.06	pa. yel. pd., 2.0–2.9	2.046	120	444.6	i.	i.	sl. s. CS_2
Sulfur, monoclinic	S_8	256.48	pa. yel., mn.	1.96	119.0	444.6	i.	i.	s. CS_2, al.
Sulfur, rhombic	S_8	256.48	pa. yel., rhb.	2.07	112.8	444.6	i.	i.	$24^{0°}$, $181^{55°}$ CS_2
Sulfur bromide, mono-	S_2Br_2	223.95	red, fuming lq.	2.635	−46	$54^{0.18mm}$	d.		
chloride, mono-	S_2Cl_2	135.03	red-yel. lq.	1.687	−80	138	d.	......	s. CS_2, et., bz.
chloride, di-	SCl_2	102.97	dark red fuming lq.	$1.621\frac{15}{15}^{\circ}$	−78	59	d.	......	d. al.
chloride, tetra-	SCl_4	173.89	yel.-brn. lq.	......	−30	d. > −20	d.		
oxide, di-	SO_2	64.06	col. gas	lq., $1.434^{0°}$; 2.264 (A)	−75.5	−10.0	$22.8^{0°}$	$4.5^{50°}$	s. H_2SO_4; al., ac.
oxide, tri-(α)	SO_3	80.06	col. pr.	lq., 1.923; 2.75 (A)	16.83	44.6	d.	......	s. H_2SO_4
oxide, tri-(β)	$(SO_3)_2$	160.12	col., silky, nd	$1.97^{20°}$	50	......	Forms H_2SO_4	......	s. H_2SO_4

Sulfuric acid	H_2SO_4*	98.08	col., viscous lq.	$1.834^{18°}_{4}$	10.49	d. 340	∞	∞	d. al.
Sulfuric acid	$H_2SO_4.H_2O$	116.09	pr. or lq.	$1.842^{15°}_{4}$	8.62	290	∞	∞	d. al.
Sulfuric acid	$H_2SO_4.2H_2O$	134.11	col. lq.	$1.650^{0°}_{4}$	−38.9	167	∞	∞	d. al.
Sulfuric acid, pyro-	$H_2S_2O_7$	178.14	cr.	$1.9^{20°}$	35	d.	d.	....	d. al.
Sulfuric oxychloride	SO_2Cl_2	134.97	col. lq.	$1.667^{20°}_{4}$	−54.1	69.1^{760mm}	d.	....	s. ac.; d. al.
Sulfurous oxybromide	$SOBr_2$	207.89	or.-yel. lq.	$2.68^{18°}$	−50	68^{40mm}	d.	....	s. bz., CS_2, CCl_4; d. act.
oxychloride	$SOCl_2$	118.97	col. lq.	1.638	−104.5	78.8	d.	....	s. bz., chl.
Tantalum	Ta	180.88	bk.-gray, cb.	16.6	2850	>4100	i.	i.	s. fused alk., HF; i. HCl, HNO_3, H_2SO_4
Tellurium	Te	127.61	met., hex.	(α) 6.24; (β) 6.00	452	1390	i.	i.	s. H_2SO_4, HNO_3, KCN, KOH, aq. reg.; i. CS_2
Terbium	Tb	159.20							
Thallium	Tl	204.39	blue-wh., tet.	11.85	303.5	1650	i.	i.	s. HNO_3, H_2SO_4; i. NH_3
acetate	$TlC_2H_3O_2$	263.43	silky nd.	3.68	110	....	v. s.	....	v. s. al.
chloride, mono-	TlCl	239.85	wh., cb.	7.00	430	806	$0.21^{0°}$	$1.8^{100°}$	sl. s. HCl; i. al., NH_4OH
chloride, sesqui-	Tl_2Cl_3	515.15	yel., hex.	5.9	400–500	d.	$0.26^{15°}$	$1.9^{100°}$	
chloride, tri-	$TlCl_3$	310.76	hex. pl.	....	25	d.	v. s.	....	s. al., et.
chloride, tri-	$TlCl_3.4H_2O$	382.83	nd.	....	37	$-4H_2O$, 100	$86.2^{17°}$	d.	s. al., et.
sulfate (ic)	$Tl_2(SO_4)_3.7H_2O$	823.07	lf.	....	$-6H_2O$, 200	d.	d.	d.	s. dil. H_2SO_4
sulfate (ous)	Tl_2SO_4	504.84	col., rhb., 1.8671	6.77	632	d.	$2.70^{0°}$	$18.45^{100°}$	
sulfate, acid	$TlHSO_4$	301.46	trimorphous	....	115 d.	....	....	....	v. sl. s. dil. H_2SO_4
Thio, *Cf.* sulfo or sulfur									
Thorium	Th	232.12	cb.	11.2	1845	>3000	i.	i.	s. HCl, H_2SO; sl. s. HNO_3; i. HF, alk.
oxide, di- (thorianite)	ThO_2	264.12	wh., cb.	9.69	>2800	4400	i.	....	s. h. H_2SO_4; i. alk.
sulfate	$Th(SO_4)_2$	424.24	....	$4.225^{17°}$	....	....	$0.74^{0°}$	$5.22^{50°}$	
sulfate	$Th(SO_4)_2.9H_2O$	586.38	mn. pr.	2.77	$-9H_2O$, 400	....	sl. s.	sl. s.	
Thulium	Tm	169.40	....	....	....	....	i.	i.	
Tin	Sn	118.70	silv. met., tet.	7.31	231.85	2260	i.	i.	s. HCl, H_2SO_4, dil. HNO_3, h. aq KOH
Tin	Sn	118.70	gray, cb.	5.750	Stable −163 to +18	2260	i.	i.	s. a., h. alk. solns.
Tin salts, *Cf.* stannic and stannous									
Titanic acid	H_2TiO_3	97.92	wh. pd.	....	....	....	i.	i.	s. alk.; v. sl. s. dil. a.; i. al.
Titanium	Ti	47.90	dark gray, cb.	$4.50^{17.5°}$	1800	>3000	i.	d.	s. a.
chloride, di-	$TiCl_2$	118.81	bk., delq.	....	Unstable in air	....	d.	....	i. CS_2, et., chl.
chloride, tri-	$TiCl_3$	154.27	vl., delq.	....	d. 440	....	s.	s.	
chloride, tetra-	$TiCl_4$*	189.73	col. lq.	lq., 1.726	−30	136.4	s.	d.	s. dil. HCl
oxide, di- (anatase)	TiO_2	79.90	brn. or bk., tet., 2.534–2.564	3.84	....		i.	i.	sl. s. alk.
oxide, di- (brookite)	TiO_2	79.90	brn. or bk., rhb., 2.586	4.17	....	....	i.	i.	
oxide, di- (rutile)	TiO_2	79.90	col. if pure, tet., 2.615	4.26	1640 d.	<3000	i.	i.	s. H_2SO_4, alk.
Tungsten	W	183.92	gray-bk., cb.	19.3	3370	5900	i.	i.	s. h. conc. KOH; sl. s. NH_3, HNO_3, aq. reg.
carbide	WC	195.93	gray pd., cb.	$15.7^{18°}$	2777	6000	i.	i.	s. F_2; i. a.
carbide	W_2C	379.85	iron gray	$16.06^{18°}$	2877	6000	i.	i.	s. h. HNO_3; sl. s. HCl, H_2SO_4
oxide, tri-	WO_3	231.92	yel., rhb.	7.16	>2130	....	i.	i.	s. alk.; i. a.
Tungstic acid (tungstite)	H_2WO_4	249.94	yel., rhb. 2.24	5.5	$-\frac{1}{2}H_2O$, 100; 1473	....	i.	sl. s.	s. HF, alk., NH_3
Uranic acid	H_2UO_4	304.09	yel. pd.	$5.926^{15°}$	$-H_2O$, 250 to 300	....	i.	i.	s. a., alk. carb.; i. alk.
Uranium	U	238.07	wh. cr.	$18.485^{13°}_{4}$	1133	3500	i.	i.	s. a.; i. alk.
carbide	U_2C_3	512.14	cr.	11.28	2400	....	d.	....	d. a.
oxide, di- (uraninite)	UO_2	270.07	bk., rhb.	10.9	2176	....	i.	i.	s. HNO_3, conc. H_2SO_4
oxide (pitchblende)	U_3O_8	842.21	olive gn.	7.31	d.	....	i.	i.	s. HNO_3, H_2SO_4
sulfate (ous)	$U(SO_4)_2.4H_2O$	502.25	gn., rhb.	....	$-4H_2O$, 300	....	$23^{11°}$	$96^{63°}$	s. dil. a.
Uranyl acetate	$UO_2(C_2H_3O_2)_2.2H_2O$	424.19	yel., rhb.	$2.89^{15°}$	$-2H_2O$, 110	....	$9.2^{17°}$	d.	s. al., act.
carbonate (rutherfordine)	UO_2CO_3	330.08	tet.	5.6					
nitrate	$UO_2(NO_3)_2.6H_2O$	502.18	yel., rhb., 1.4967	2.807	60.2	118	$170.3^{0°}$	$\infty^{60°}$	v. s. ac., al., et.; i. dil. alk.
sulfate	$UO_2SO_4.3H_2O$	420.18	yel. cr.	$3.28^{16.5°}$	d. 100	....	$18.9^{13.2°}$	$230^{25°}$	4 al.; s. a.
Vanadic acid, meta-	HVO_3	99.96	yel. scales	....	....	....	i.	....	s. a., alk.; i. NH_3

* Usual commercial form.

Table 3-1. Physical Properties of the Elements and Inorganic Compounds—(*Concluded*)

Name	Formula	Formula weight	Color, crystalline form and refractive index	Specific gravity	Melting point, °C.	Boiling point, °C.	Solubility in 100 parts: Cold water	Hot water	Other reagents
Vanadic acid, pyro-	$H_4V_2O_7$	217.93	pa. yel., amor.	...	...	...	i.	...	s. a., alk., NH_4OH
Vanadium	V	50.95	lt. gray, cb.	5.96	1710	3000	i.	i.	s. HNO_3, H_2SO_4; i. aq. alk.
chloride, di-	VCl_2	121.86	gn., hex., delq.	$3.23^{18°}$	...	...	s.	d.	s. al., et.
chloride, tri-	VCl_3	157.23	pink, tabular, delq.	$3.00^{18°}$	d.	...	s.	d.	s. abs. al., et.
chloride, tetra-	VCl_4	192.78	red lq.	$1.816^{30°}$	−109	148.5^{755mm}	s. d.	...	s. abs. al., et., chl., ac.
oxide, di-	V_2O_2	133.90	lt. gray cr.	3.64	ign.	...	i.	i.	s. a.
oxide, tri-	V_2O_3	149.90	bk. cr.	$4.87^{18°}_{4}$	1970	...	sl. s.	s.	s. HNO_3, HF, alk.
oxide, tetra-	V_2O_4	165.90	blue cr.	4.399	1967	...	i.	i.	s. a., alk.
oxide, penta-	V_2O_5	181.90	red-yel., rhb.	$3.357^{18°}_{4}$	800	d. 1750	$0.8^{20°}$	...	s. a., alk.; i. abs. al.
oxychloride, mono-	VOCl	102.41	brn. pd.	2.824	...	...	i.	...	v. s. HNO_3
Vanadyl chloride	$(VO)_2Cl$	169.36	yel. cr.	3.64	d. in air	...	i.	...	s. HNO_3
chloride, di-	$VOCl_2$	137.86	gn., delq.	$2.88^{13°}$	...	...	d.	...	s. abs. al., dil. HNO_3
chloride, tri-	$VOCl_3$	173.32	yel. lq.	1.829	<−15	127.19	s. d.	...	s. al., et., ∞ Br_2
Water†	H_2O	18.016	col. lq., $1.33300^{20°}$; hex. solid, 1.309	$1.004^{4°}$ (lq.); $0.915^{0°}$ (ice)	0	100	...	...	∞ al.; sl. s. et.
Water, heavy	D_2O	20.029	col. lq., $1.32844^{20°}$	$1.107^{20°}$	3.82	101.42	∞	∞	∞ al.; sl. s. et.
Xenon	Xe	131.30	col. gas	lq., $3.06^{-109.1}$; $2.7^{-140°}$; 4.53 (A)	−140	−109.1	$24.2^{0°}$ cc	$7.3^{50°}$ cc	
Ytterbium	Yb	173.04							
Yttrium	Y	88.92	dark gray, hex.	5.51	1490	2500	sl. d.	d.	v. s. dil. a., h. KOH
Zinc	Zn	65.38	silv. met., hex.	7.140	419.4	907	i.	i.	s. a., ac., alk.
acetate	$Zn(C_2H_3O_2)_2$	183.47	mn.	1.840	242	subl. in vac.	$30^{25°}$	$44.6^{100°}$	$2.8^{25°}$, $166^{79°}$ al.
acetate	$Zn(C_2H_3O_2)_2.2H_2O$*	219.50	wh., mn., 1.494	1.735	237	$-2H_2O$, 100	$40^{25°}$	$66.6^{100°}$	v. s. al.
bromide	$ZnBr_2$	225.21	rhb.	$4.219^{4°}$	394	650	$390^{0°}$	$670^{100°}$	v. s. NH_4OH, al., et.
carbonate	$ZnCO_3$	125.39	wh., trig., 1.818	4.42	$-CO_2$, 300	...	$0.001^{15°}$	...	s. a., alk., NH_4 salts; i. act., NH_3
chloride	$ZnCl_2$	136.29	wh., delq., 1.687, uniaxial	$2.91^{25°}_{4}$	283	732	$432^{25°}$	$615^{100°}$	$100^{12.5°}$ al.; v. s. et.; i. NH_3
cyanide	$Zn(CN)_2$	117.42	col., rhb.	...	d. 80	...	$0.0005^{18°}$	sl. s.	s. KCN, NH_3, alk.; i. al
hydroxide	$Zn(OH)_2$	99.40	col., rhb.	3.053	d. 125	...	$0.00052^{18°}$	...	s. a., alk., NH_4OH
iodide	ZnI_2	319.22	cb.	$4.666^{14.2°}_{4}$	446	624	$430^{0°}$	$510^{100°}$	s. a., al., NH_3, aq. $(NH_4)_2CO_3$
nitrate	$Zn(NO_3)_2.6H_2O$	297.49	col., tet.	$2.065^{14°}_{4}$	36.4	$-6H_2O$, 105	324.5	$∞^{36.4°}$	v. s. al.
oxide (zincite)	ZnO	81.38	wh., hex., 2.004	5.606	>1800	...	$0.00042^{18°}$	...	s. a., alk., NH_4Cl; i. NH_3
oxide	ZnO	81.38	wh., amor.	5.47	>1800	...	$0.00042^{18°}$		
peroxide	ZnO_2	97.38	yel.	1.571	expl. 212	...	0.0022	...	i. NH_4OH; d. a.
phosphide	Zn_3P_2	258.10	steel gray, cb.	$4.55^{13°}_{4}$	>420	1100	i.	...	s. dil. a.
silicate	$ZnSiO_3$	141.44	hex. or rhb.; glass, 1.650	3.52	1437	...	i.		
sulfate (zincosite)	$ZnSO_4$	161.44	wh., rhb., 1.669	$3.74^{15°}_{4}$	d. 740	...	$42^{0°}$	$61^{100°}$	sl. s al., s. gly.
sulfate	$ZnSO_4.H_2O$	179.46	col.	$3.28^{15°}_{4}$	d. 238	...	s.	$89.5^{100°}$	
sulfate	$ZnSO_4.6H_2O$	269.54	mn.	$2.072^{15°}_{4}$	$-5H_2O$, 70	...	s.	s.	sl. s. al.; i. act.; NH_3
sulfate (goslarite)	$ZnSO_4.7H_2O$*	287.55	rhb., 1.4801	$1.966^{16.5°}$	tr. 39	$-7H_2O$, 280	$115.2^{0°}$	$653.6^{100°}$	sl. s. al.; i. act.; NH_3
sulfide (α) (wurzite)	ZnS	97.44	wh., hex., 2.356	4.087	1850^{150atm}	subl. 1185	$0.00069^{18°}$	i.	v. s. a.; i. ac.
sulfide (β) (sphalerite)	ZnS	97.44	wh., cb.; glass (?) 2.18–2.25	$4.102^{25°}_{4}$	tr. 1020	...	i.	i.	s. a.
sulfide (blende)	ZnS	97.44	wh., granular	4.04	...	...	i.	i.	v. s. a.; i. ac.
sulfite	$ZnSO_3.2\frac{1}{2}H_2O$	190.48	mn.	...	$-2\frac{1}{2}H_2O$, 100	d. 200	0.16	d.	s. H_2SO_3, NH_4OH; i. al.
Zirconium	Zr	91.22	cb., pd. ign. easily	6.4	1700	>2900	i.	i.	s. HF, aq. reg.; sl. s. a.
oxide, di- (baddeleyite)	ZrO_2	123.22	yel. or brn., mn., 2.19	5.49	2700	...	i.	i.	s. H_2SO_4, HF
oxide, di- (free from Hf)	ZrO_2	123.22	wh., mn.	5.73	...	4300	i.	i.	s. H_2SO_4, HF

* Usual commercial form.

† *Cf.* special tables on water and steam, Nos. 3-3, 3-4, 3-5, 3-45, 3-46, 3-49, 3-259, 3-260, 3-261, 3-267, and 3-275.

Table 3-2. Physical Properties of Organic Compounds*

Abbreviations Used in the Table

(A), density referred to air
al., ethyl alcohol
amor., amorphous
aq., aqua, water
brn., brown
bz., benzene
c., cubic
cc., cubic centimeter
chl., chloroform
col., colorless
cr., crystalline
d., decomposes
d-, dextrorotatory
dl-, dextro-laevorotatory
et., ethyl ether
expl., explodes
gn., green
h., hot
hex., hexagonal
i-, iso-, containing the group $(CH_3)_2CH$-
i., insoluble
ign., ignites
l-, laevorotatory
lf., leaflets
lq., liquid
m-, meta
mn., monoclinic
n-, normal
nd., needles
o-, ortho
or., orange
p-, para
pd., powder
pet., petroleum ether
pl., plates
pr., prisms
rhb., rhombic
s., soluble
s-, sec-, secondary
silv., silvery
sl., slightly
subl., sublimes
sym., symmetrical
t-, tertiary
tet., tetragonal
tri., triclinic
uns., unsymmetrical
v., very
v. s., very soluble
v. sl. s., very slightly soluble
wh., white
yel., yellow
(+), right rotation
>, greater than
<, less than
∞, infinitely

This table of the physical properties includes the organic compounds of most general interest. For the properties of other organic compounds, reference must be made to larger tables in Lange's "Handbook of Chemistry" (Handbook Publishers), "Handbook of Chemistry and Physics" (Chemical Rubber Publishing Co.), Van Nostrand's "Chemical Annual," "International Critical Tables" (McGraw-Hill), and similar works.

The **molecular weights** are based on the 1941 atomic weight values. The **densities** are given for the temperature indicated and are usually referred to water at 4°C., *e.g.*, $1.028^{95/4}$ a density of 1.028 at 95°C. referred to water at 4°C., the 4 being omitted when it is not clear whether the reference is to water at 4°C. or at the temperature indicated by the upper figure. The melting and boiling points given have been selected from available data as probably the most accurate. The **solubility** is given in grams of the substance in 100 g. of the solvent. In the case of gases, the solubility is often expressed in some manner as "5^{10} cc." which indicates that, at 10°C., 5 cc. of the gas are soluble in 100 g. of the solvent.

Name	Synonym	Formula	Formula weight	Form and color	Specific gravity	Melting point, °C.	Boiling point, °C.	Solubility in 100 parts: Water	Alcohol	Ether
Abietic acid	sylvic acid, abietinic acid	$C_{20}H_{30}O_2$	302.44	lf.	....	182	....	i.	v. s.	v. s.
Acenaphthene	naphthylene ethylene	$C_{10}H_6(CH_2)_2$	154.20	rhb./al.	$1.069^{95/95}$	95	278–9	i.	s. h.	s. chl.
Acetal	acetaldehyde diethylacetal	$CH_3CH(OC_2H_5)_2$	118.17	lq.	$0.821^{22/4}$	....	102.2	6^{25}	∞	∞
Acet-aldehyde	ethanal	CH_3CHO	44.05	col. lq.	$0.783^{18/4}$	−123.5	20.2	∞	∞	∞
-aldehyde, par-	paraldehyde	$(C_2H_4O)_3$	132.16	col. cr.	$0.994^{20/4}$	10.5–12	124.4^{752}	12^{18}	∞	∞
-aldehyde ammonia	....	$CH_3CHOHNH_2$	61.08	col. cr.	....	97	100–10 d.	v. s.	v. s.	sl. s.
-amide	ethanamide	CH_3CONH_2	59.07	col. cr.	1.159	81(69.4)	222	s.	s.	v. sl. s.
-anilide	antifebrin	$C_6H_5NHCOCH_3$	135.16	rhb./al.	1.21^4	113–4	305	0.5^6	21^{20}	7^{25}
-phenetidide (o-)	o-ethoxyacetanilide	$CH_3CONHC_6H_4OC_2H_5$	179.21	lf./al.	....	79	>250	i.	s.	
(m-)	acetyl-m-phenetidine	$CH_3CONHC_6H_4OC_2H_5$	179.21	lf./al.	....	96–7	....	sl. s.	s.	
-toluidide (o-)	N-tolylacetamide	$CH_3C_6H_4NHCOCH_3$	149.19	rhb.	1.168^{15}	110	296	0.86^{19}	s.	s.
(p-)	N-tolylacetamide	$CH_3C_6H_4NHCOCH_3$	149.19	rhb. or mn.	1.212^{15}	153	306–7	0.09^{22}	10^{25}	s.
Acetic acid	ethanoic acid, vinegar acid	CH_3CO_2H	60.05	col. lq.	$1.049^{20/4}$	16.7	118.1	∞	∞	∞
anhydride	acetyl oxide, acetic oxide	$(CH_3CO)_2O$	102.09	col. lq.	$1.082^{20/4}$	−73	139.6	12 c.	∞	∞
nitrile	methyl cyanide	CH_3CN	41.05	col. lq.	$0.783^{20/4}$	−41	81.6–2.0	∞	∞	∞
Acetone dimethylketal	propanone, dimethyl ketone;	CH_3COCH_3	58.08	col. lq.	$0.792^{20/4}$	−94.6	56.5	∞	∞	∞
Acetonyl urea	dimethyl hydantoin	$<NHCONHCOC>(CH_3)_2$	128.13	tri./al.	....	175	subl.	s.	s.	s.
Acetophenone benzoyl hydride	methyl-phenyl ketone	$CH_3COC_6H_5$	120.14	lf.	$1.033^{15/15}$	20.5	202.3^{749}	i.	s.	s.
Acetyl-chloride	ethanoyl chloride	CH_3COCl	78.50	col. lq.	$1.105^{20/4}$	−112.0	51–2	d.	d.	∞
-phenylenediamine (-p)	amino-acetanilide (p)	$C_2H_3ONHC_6H_4NH_2$	150.18	nd./aq.	....	162	....	s. h.	v. s.	v. s.
Acetylene	ethyne; ethine	$HC{:}CH$	26.04	col. gas	(A) 0.906	-81.5^{891}	-84^{760}	100 $cc.^{18}$	600 $cc.^{18}$	
dichloride (cis)	1,2-dichloroethene	$CHCl{:}CHCl$	96.95	col. lq.	$1.291^{15/4}$	−80.5	60.3	0.35^{20}	∞	∞
(trans)	dioform	$CHCl{:}CHCl$	96.95	col. lq.	$1.265^{15/4}$	−50	48.4	0.63^{20}	∞	∞
Aconitic acid	equisetic acid; citridic acid	$C_3H_3(CO_2H)_3$	174.11	cr./aq.	....	192 d.	....	33^{15}	sl. s.	v. sl. s.
Acridine	....	$C_6H_4<(CH)(N)>C_6H_4$	179.21	rhb./aq. al.	....	110–1	346	sl. s. h.	s.	s.
Acrolein ethylene aldehyde	acrylic aldehyde, propenal	$CH_2{:}CH.CHO$	56.06	col. lq.	$0.841^{20/4}$	−87.7	52.5	40	s.	s.
Acrylic acid	propenoic acid	$CH_2{:}CH.CO_2H$	72.06	col. lq.	$1.062^{16/4}$	12–13	141–2	∞	∞	
nitrile	vinyl cyanide	$CH_2{:}CH.CN$	53.06	col. lq.	0.811^{20}	−82	78–9	s.		
Adipic acid	hexandioc acid, adipinic acid	$(CH_2CH_2CO_2H)_2$	146.14	mn. pr.	$1.360^{25/4}$	151–3	265^{10}	1.4^{15}	v. s.	0.6^{15}
amide		$(CH_2CH_2CONH_2)_2$	144.17	cr. pd.	....	226–7	....	0.4^{12}		
nitrile	tetramethylene	$(CH_2CH_2CN)_2$	108.14	col. oil	$0.951^{19/19}$	1	295	v. sl. s.	s.	v. sl. s.
Adrenaline (1-) (3,4,1)	1-suprarenine	$C_6H_3(OH)_2(CHOHCH_2NHCH_3)$	183.20	col. pd.	....	d. 207–11	....	0.03^{20}	v. sl. s.	i.
Alanine (α) (dl-)	....	$CH_3CH(NH_2)CO_2H$	89.09	nd./aq.	....	295 d.	subl. >200	22^{17}	v. sl. s.	i.
Aldol acetaldol,	2-hydroxybutyraldehyde	$CH_3CH(OH)CH_2CO_2H$	88.10	col. lq.	$1.103^{20/4}$	....	83^{20}	∞	∞	s.
Alizarin	Anthraquinoic acid,	$C_6H_4(CO)_2C_6H_2(OH)_2$	240.20	red rhb.	....	289–90	430	$0\ 03^{100}$	v. s.	v. s.
Allyl alcohol	propen-1-ol-3,propenyl alcohol	$CH_2{:}CH.CH_2OH$	58.08	col. lq.	$0.854^{20/4}$	−129	96.6	∞	∞	∞
bromide	3-bromo-propene-1	$CH_2{:}CH.CH_2Br$	120.99	lq.	$1.398^{20/4}$	−119.4	$70–1^{753}$	i.	∞	∞
chloride	3-chloro-propene-1	$CH_2{:}CH.CH_2Cl$	76.53	col. lq.	$0.938^{20/4}$	−136.4	44.6	<0.1	∞	∞
thiocyanate (i)	mustard oil	$CH_2{:}CH.CH_2NCS$	99.15	col. oil	$1.013^{20/4}$	−80	152	0.2	∞	∞
thiourea	thiosinamide	$CH_2{:}CH.CH_2NHCSNH_2$	116.18	col. pr.	$1.219^{20/20}$	77–8	....	3^0	s.	v. sl. s.
Aluminum ethoxide	....	$Al(OCH_2CH_3)_3$	164.15	pd.	$1.142^{20/0}$	150–60	$200–5^{10}$	d.	i.	v. sl. s.
Amino-anthraquinone (α)	....	$C_6H_4(CO)_2C_6H_3NH_2$	223.22	red nd.	....	256	subl.	i.	s.	s.
(β)	....	$C_6H_4(CO)_2C_6H_3NH_2$	223.22	red nd.	....	302	subl.	i.	s.	i.
-azobenzene	....	$C_6H_5.N{:}N.C_6H_4NH_2$	197.23	yel. mn.	....	126–7	225^{120}	sl. s. h.	s. h.	s.
-benzoic acid (m-)	....	$H_2N.C_6H_4CO_2H$	137.13	nd./aq.	$1.511^{4°}$	173–4	....	v. sl. s.	2^{10}	1.8^6
(p-)	aminodracylic acid	$H_2N.C_6H_4CO_2H$	137.13	mn. pr.	....	187–8	....	0.3^{13}	11^{10}	8.2^6

* By N. A. Lange, Ph.D , Handbook Publishers, Inc., Sandusky, Ohio. Abridged from table of Physical Constants of Organic Compounds in Lange's "Handbook of Chemistry."

Table 3-2. Physical Properties of Organic Compounds—(*Continued*)

Name	Synonym	Formula	Formula weight	Form and color	Specific gravity	Melting point, °C.	Boiling point, °C.	Solubility in 100 parts: Water	Alcohol	Ether
Amino-diphenylamine (p-)	....	$H_2N.C_6H_4NH.C_6H_5$	184.23	nd./aq. al.	....	67	354	sl. s.	s.	s.
-G-acid (2-)(6-,8-), Na₂ salt	....	$C_{10}H_5(NH_2)(SO_3Na)_2$	347.28	....	....	....	....	v. sl. s.		
-mono-potassium salt	....	$C_{10}H_5(NH_2)S_2O_6HK$	341.39	....	....	....	....	12.8^{20}		
-sodium salt	....	$C_{10}H_5(NH_2)S_2O_6HNa$	325.29	....	....	....	....	2.7^{13}		
-J-acid (2-)(5-,7-)	....	$C_{10}H_5(NH_2)(SO_3H)_2$	303.30	....	....	....	....	10.0^{20}		
-mono-potassium salt	....	$C_{10}H_5(NH_2)S_2O_6HK$	341.39	....	....	....	....	3.4^{18}		
-naphthol sulfonic (1-,2-,4-)(α-)	....	$C_{10}H_5OHNH_2SO_3H\frac{1}{2}H_2O$	248.25	....	....	....	....	v. s.		
(1-,8-,4-)	....	$NH_2(OH)C_{10}H_5SO_3H$	239.24	....	....	....	....	v. sl. s.		
-phenol (o-)	2-aminophenol	$H_2N.C_6H_4.OH$	109.12	col. nd.	....	173	subl.	1.7^{0}	4.3^{0}	v. s.
(m-)	3-aminophenol	$H_2N.C_6H_4.OH$	109.12	pr.	....	122–3	....	2.6^{0}	s.	sl. s.
(p-)	p-hydroxyaniline	$H_2N.C_6H_4.OH$	109.12	lf.	....	184–6 d.	subl.	1.1^{0}	4^{0}	i. bz.
-toluene sulfonic acid (1-,2-,3-)	....	$C_6H_3(CH_3)(NH_2)SO_3H$	187.21	nd.	....	....	....	0.97^{11}		
(1-,4-,2-)	....	$C_6H_3(CH_3)(NH_2)SO_3H.H_2O$	205.23	mn.	....	d.	....	0.5^{20}	i.	
(1-,4-,3-)	....	$C_6H_3(CH_3)(NH_2)SO_3H.\frac{1}{2}H_2O$	196.22	nd.	....	....	....	0.47		
(1-,2-,5-)	....	$C_6H_3(CH_3)(NH_2)SO_3H.H_2O$	205.23	tri./aq.	....	$-H_2O$, 120	....	3^{11}	i.	
Amyl acetate (n-)	....	$CH_3CO_2CH_2(CH_2)_3CH_3$	130.18	col. lq.	$0.879^{20/20}$	−70.8	148.4^{737}	v. sl. s.	∞	∞
(i-)	common amyl acetate	$CH_3CO_2CH_2CH_2CH(CH_3)_2$	130.18	col. lq.	$0.876^{15/4}$	....	142^{757}	0.3^{15}	∞	∞
		$CH_3CO_2CH_2CH(CH_3)C_2H_5$	130.18	col. lq.	0.880^{13}	....	141–2	v. sl. s.	∞	∞
(s-)	α-Me-Bu-acetate	$CH_3CO_2CH(CH_3)CH_2C_2H_5$	130.18	col. lq.	$0\ 922^{0}$	....	133.5	sl. s.	∞	∞
(s-)	di Et-carbinol acetate	$CH_3CO_2CH(C_2H_5)_2$	130.18	col. lq.	$0.871^{20/4}$	....	133	sl. s.	∞	∞
(t-)	....	$CH_3CO_2C(CH_3)_2C_2H_5$	130.18	col. lq.	$0\ 874^{19}$	....	124.5^{749}	v. sl. s.	∞	∞
alcohol (n-) fusel oil,	pentanol-1	$CH_3(CH_2)_3CH_2OH$	88.15	col. lq.	$0.817^{20/20}$	−78 5	137.9	2.7^{22}	∞	∞
(s-,n-) methyl-propyl carbinol,	pentanol-2	$C_2H_5CH_2CH(OH)CH_3$	88.15	col. lq.	$0.810^{20/20}$	....	119.5	4^{20}	∞	∞
(prim.-,i-) isobutyl carbinol,	2-methyl-butanol-4	$(CH_3)_2CHCH_2CH_2OH$	88.15	col. lq.	$0.813^{15/4}$	−117.2	132.0	2^{14}	∞	∞
		$(C_2H_5)_2CHOH$	88.15	col. lq.	$0.815^{25/4}$	....	115.6	5.5^{30}	∞	∞
(s-,i-)	2-methyl-butanol-3	$(CH_3)_2CHCH(OH)CH_3$	88.15	col. lq.	0.819^{19}	....	113–4	2.8^{30}	∞	∞
(t-)	2-methyl-butanol-2	$(CH_3)_2C(OH)C_2H_5$	88.15	col. lq.	$0\ 809^{20/4}$	−11.9	102	sl. s.	s.	s.
		$(CH_3)_3CCH_2OH$	88.15	cr.	....	52–3	113–4	sl. s.	∞	∞
(d-)	active amyl alcohol	$C_2H_5CH(CH_3)CH_2OH$	88.15	col. lq.	$0.816^{20/4}$	....	128	3.6^{30}	∞	∞
-amine (n-)	....	$CH_3(CH_2)_4NH_2$	87.16	col. lq.	0.766^{19}	−55	103–4	s.	s.	s.
(s-,n-)	....	$(C_3H_7)(CH_3)CHNH_2$	87.16	col. lq.	$0.749^{20/4}$	....	91–2	∞	∞	∞
(i-)	....	$(CH_3)_2CH(CH_2)_2NH_2$	87.16	col. lq.	$0.751^{18/4}$	....	95	∞	∞	∞
(t-)	....	$(C_2H_5)(CH_3)_2CNH_2$	87.16	col. lq.	$0.731^{25/4}$	−105	77–8	∞	∞	∞
....	1-NH₂-2-Me-butane	$C_2H_5CH(CH_3)CH_2NH_2$	87.16	col. lq.	0.755^{18}	....	95–6	∞	∞	∞
....	3-amino pentane	$(C_2H_5)_2CHNH_2$	87.16	col. lq.	$0.749^{20/4}$	....	90–1	∞	∞	∞
....	3-NH₂-2-Me-butane	$(CH_3)_2CHCH(CH_3)NH_2$	87.16	col. lq.	0.757^{18}	....	83–4	∞	∞	∞
aniline (i-)	....	$C_6H_5NHC_5H_{11}$	163.25	lq.	$0.928^{15/4}$	....	254.5	i.		
benzoate (i-)	....	$C_6H_5CO_2C_5H_{11}$	192.25	col. lq.	$0.992^{14/14}$	....	261^{746}	i.	∞	∞
bromide (n-)	1-bromopentane	$CH_3(CH_2)_3CH_2Br$	151.05	col. lq.	$1.218^{20/4}$	−95	129.7	i.	s.	
(i-)	4-Br-2-Me-butane	$(CH_3)_2CH(CH_2)_2Br$	151.05	col. lq.	$1.220^{17/15}$	....	120^{745}	0.02^{16}	s.	s.
(t-)	2-Br-2-Me-butane	$(CH_3)_2C(Br)C_2H_5$	151.05	lq.	$1.216^{19/0}$	....	108^{765}	i.	s.	s.
n-butyrate (n-)	....	$C_2H_5CH_2CO_2(CH_2)_4CH_3$	158.23	col. lq.	$0.871^{15/4}$	−73.2	186.4	0.05^{50}	∞	∞
(i-)	....	$C_2H_5CH_2CO_2.C_5H_{11}$	158.23	col. lq.	$0.866^{19/15}$	....	178.6	i.	∞	∞
(t-)	....	$C_3H_7CO_2C(CH_3)_2C_2H_5$	158.23	col. lq.	$0.865^{15/0}$	....	164	sl. s.	∞	∞
i-butyrate (i-)	....	$(CH_3)_2CHCO_2C_5H_{11}$	158.23	lq.	$0.876^{0/4}$	....	168.8	i.	s.	s.
chloride (n-)	1-chloropentane	$CH_3(CH_2)_3CH_2Cl$	106.60	col. lq.	$0.878^{20/4}$	−99	108.4	i.	s.	s.
(s-)	2-chloropentane	$C_2H_5CH_2CHClCH_3$	106.60	lq.	$0.870^{20/4}$	....	96.7	i.	s.	s.
(s-)	3-chloropentane	$(C_2H_5)_2CHCl$	106.60	col. lq.	0.895^{21}	....	97.3	i.	∞	∞
(i-)	4-Cl-2-Me-butane	$(CH_3)_2CH(CH_2)_2Cl$	106.60	col. lq.	$0.893^{20/4}$	....	99.7^{758}	i.	s.	∞
(s-,i-)	3-Cl-2-Me-butane	$(CH_3)CHCHClCH_3$	106.60	lq.	0.883^{0}	....	91^{753}	i.	s.	s.
(t-)	2-Cl-2-Me-butane	$(CH_3)_2CClC_2H_5$	106.60	lq.	$0.871^{20/4}$	−72.9	85.7	i.	s.	s.
....	1-Cl-2-Me-butane	$(CH_3)(C_2H_5)CHCH_2Cl$	106.60	lq.	$0.881^{17.5}$	....	98–9	i.	s.	s.
i-cyanide (i-)	iso-caproic iso-nitrile	$(CH_3)_2CH(CH_2)_2NC$	97.16	lq.	....	....	137–9	i.	s.	s.
formate (n-)	....	$HCO_2CH_2(CH_2)_3CH_3$	116.16	lq.	0.902^{0}	−73.5	132	v. sl. s.	∞	∞
(i-)	....	$HCO_2CH_2CH_2CH(CH_3)_2$	116.16	lq.	$0.882^{20/4}$	−93.5	123.5	0.3^{22}	∞	∞
iodide (n-)	1-iodopentane	$CH_3(CH_2)_3CH_2I$	198.06	lq.	$1.510^{20/4}$	−86	157.0	i.	s.	∞
(i-)	4-I-2-Me-butane	$(CH_3)_2CHCH_2CH_2I$	198.06	lq	$1.515^{18/4}$	....	147^{765}	i.	∞	∞
(s-,n-)	2-iodopentane	$C_2H_5CH_2CHICH_3$	198.06	lq.	$1.507^{17/4}$	....	144–5	i.	∞	∞
(t-)	2-I-2-Me-butane	$(CH_3)_2CIC_2H_5$	198.06	lq.	$1.471^{19/15}$	....	127^{765}	i.	∞	∞
		$C_2H_5CH(CH_3)CH_2I$	198.06	lq.	$1.524^{20/4}$	....	148	i.	∞	∞
mercaptan (n-)	pentanthiol-1	$CH_3(CH_2)_3CH_2SH$	104.21	lq.	0.857^{20}	....	126^{767}	i.	∞	∞
(n-)	pentanthiol-3	$(C_2H_5)_2CHSH$	104.21	col. lq.	....	....	105	i.	∞	∞
(i-)	2-Me-butanthiol-4	$(CH_3)_2CH(CH_2)_2SH$	104.21	lq.	$0.835^{20/4}$	....	120	i.	∞	∞
phenol (t-)(p-)	pentaphen	$C_5H_{11}.C_6H_4OH$	164.24	cr.	....	93	265–7	sl. s.	s.	s.

propionate (n-)	....	$C_2H_5CO_2(CH_2)_4CH_3$	144.21	lq.	$0.876^{15/4}$	−73.1	168.7	i.	∞	∞
(i-)	....	$C_2H_5CO_2(CH_2)_2CH(CH_3)_2$	144.21	col. lq.	$0.870^{20/4}$	....	160.2	0.1^{25}	∞	∞
(act.)	....	$C_2H_5CO_2C_5H_{11}$	144.21	col. lq.	$0.866^{20/4}$	....	58^{16}	v. sl. s.	∞	∞
salicylate (n-)	....	$HOC_6H_4CO_2C_5H_{11}$	208.25	lq.	1.065^{15}	....	265	i.	∞	∞
Amyl i-valerate (i)	....	$C_4H_9CO_2C_5H_{11}$	172.26	col. lq.	$0.858^{20/15}$	....	194	v. sl. s.	∞	∞
(t-)	....	$C_4H_9CO_2C_5H_{11}$	172.26	col. lq.	$0.861^{14/0}$	....	173–4	sl. s.	s.	s.
Amylene (n-)(α-)	pentene-1	$C_2H_5CH_2CH{:}CH_2$	70.13	lq.	0.644^{20}	....	30–1	i.	∞	∞
(i-)	2-methyl-butene-3	$(CH_3)_2CHCH{:}CH_2$	70.13	col. lq.	0.632^{15}	−135	20.5^{771}	i.	∞	∞
(α-)	2-methyl-butene-1	$(C_2H_5)(CH_3)C{:}CH_2$	70.13	col. lq.	$0.667^{0/0}$	....	$31–2^{758}$	i.	∞	∞
(-n)(β-)	pentene-2	$C_2H_5CH{:}CHCH_3$	70.13	col. lq.	$0.650^{20/4}$	−139	36.4	v. sl. s.	∞	∞
(i-)(β-)	2-methyl-butene-2	$(CH_3)_2C{:}CHCH_3$	70.13	col. lq.	$0.663^{19/4}$	−124	37–8	i.	s.	∞
Anethole (p-)	p-propenyl anisole	$CH_3CH{:}CH.C_6H_4OCH_3$	148.20	lf./al.	$0.991^{20/20}$	22.5	235.3	v. sl. s.	s.	∞
Anhydroformald-aniline	methylene aniline	$(CH_2NC_6H_5)_3$	315.40	pr./al.	....	143	185	i.	sl. s.	s.
Aniline	amino benzene, phenyl amine, cyanol	$C_6H_5NH_2$	93.12	col. oil	$1.022^{20/4}$	−6.2	184.4	3.6^{18}	∞	∞
hydrochloride	aniline salt, aniline chloride	$C_6H_5NH_2.HCl$	129.59	cr.	1.222^{4}	198	245	18^{15}	s.	i.
nitrate	....	$C_6H_5NH_2.HNO_3$	156.14	rhb.	1.356^{4}	d. 190	....	s.	s.	sl. s.
sulfate	....	$(C_6H_5NH_2)_2.H_2SO_4$	284.32	lf./al.	1.377^{4}	d.	....	5^{14}	sl. s.	i.
Anisal-acetone (p-)	MeO-benzalacetone	$CH_3OC_6H_4CH{:}CHCOCH_3$	176.22	lf./et.	....	73–4	....	i.	v. s.	v. s.
Anisic acid (p-)	....	$CH_3OC_6H_4CO_2H$	152.14	mn./aq.	1.385^{4}	184.2	275–80	0.03^{19}	v. s.	v. s.
aldehyde (p-)	....	$CH_3OC_6H_4CHO$	136.14	col. oil	$1.123^{20/4}$	2.5	247–8	v. sl. s.	∞	∞
Anisidine (o-)	2-amino-anisole	$CH_3OC_6H_4NH_2$	123.15	col. lq.	$1.098^{15/15}$	5.2	225	v. sl. s.	∞	∞
(m-)	MeO-aniline(m)	$CH_3OC_6H_4NH_2$	123.15	oil	$1.096^{20/4}$	< −12	251	v. sl. s.	s.	s.
(p-)	4-amino anisole	$CH_3OC_6H_4NH_2$	123.15	pl./aq.	$1.089^{55/55}$	57.2	243	s. h.	s.	s.
Anisole	methyl phenyl ether	$CH_3OC_6H_5$	108.13	col. lq.	$0.990^{22/4}$	−37.3	154–5	i.	s.	s.
Anthracene	paranaphthalene, anthracin green oil	$C_6H_4{:}(CH)_2{:}C_6H_4$	178.22	col. mn.	$1.25^{27/4}$	217–8	340–2	i.	1.5^{20}	
Anthramine (α)	α-amino-anthracene	$C_6H_4{:}(CH)_2{:}C_6H_3NH_2$	193.24	yel./al.	....	130±	....	i.	s.	
(β)	β-amino-anthracene	$C_6H_4{:}(CH)_2{:}C_6H_3NH_2$	193.24	yel./al.	....	238	subl.	i.	sl. s.	sl. s.
Anthranil	....	$C_6H_4{:}(NH)CO$	119.12	col. oil	$1.187^{15/4}$	< −18	d. >215	sl. s. h.	s.	s.
Anthranilic acid (o-)	....	$H_2NC_6H_4CO_2H$	137.13	col. rhb.	....	144–5	subl.	0.35^{14}	11^{10}	16^{7}
Anthrapurpurin (1-,2-,7-)	....	$C_{14}H_5O_2(OH)_3$	256.20	or. nd./al.	....	369	462	sl. s. h.	v. s. h.	sl. s.
Anthraquinone	diphenyleneketone, dihydrodiketoanthracene	$C_6H_4{:}(CO)_2{:}C_6H_4$	208.20	yel. rhb.	$1.438^{20/4}$	286	379–81	i.	0.05^{18}	v. sl. s.
disulfonate Na_2 (1-,5-)	p-anthraquinone disulfonate	$C_{14}H_6O_2(SO_3Na)_2.5H_2O$	502.38	yel. lf.	....	....	....	v. s.	i.	i.
(1-,8-)	x-anthraquinone disulfonate	$C_{14}H_6O_2(SO_3Na)_2.4H_2O$	484.37	yel. pr.	....	....	....	sl. s.		
(2-,6-)	....	$C_{14}H_6O_2(SO_3Na)_2.7H_2O$	538.41	col. cr.	....	....	....	3.9^{20}		
(2-,7-)	....	$C_{14}H_6O_2(SO_3Na)_2.4H_2O$	484.37	cr.	....	....	....	30.5^{20}	v. sl. s.	i.
sulfonate Na (1-)	....	$C_{14}H_7O_2SO_3Na$	310.25	yel. lf.	....	....	....	0.53^{20}	i.	i.
(2-)	....	$C_{14}H_7O_2SO_3Na$	310.25	silv. lf.	....	....	....	0.84^{25}	i.	i.
Anthrarufin (1-,5-)	....	$C_{14}H_6O_2(OH)_2$	240.20	yel. lf.	....	280	subl.	i.	sl. s.	s.
Antipyrene	1-ph-2,3-diMepyrazolone-5	$C_{11}H_{12}ON_2$	188.22	mn./aq.	$1.088^{113/4}$	113(109)	319^{174}	100^{25}	100	sl. s.
Apiole	1-allyl-2, 5-diMeO-3,4 methylenedioxybenzene	$C_{12}H_{14}O_2$	222.23	col. nd.	$1.02^{20/4}$	30	294	i	s.	s.
Arabinose (α)(d- or l-)	....	$CH_2OH(CHOH)_3CHO$	150.13	rhb. pr.	$1.585^{20/4}$	159.5	....	46^{0}	$0.5^{9°}$	i.
(dl-)	....	$CH_2OH(CHOH)_3CHO$	150.13	....	....	164.5	....	16.9^{10}		
Arachidic acid	eicosanoic acid	$CH_3(CH_2)_{18}CO_2H$	312.52	col. lf.	....	77	328	i.	s. h.	v. s.
Arsanilic acid (p-)	....	$H_2N.C_6H_4.AsO_3H_2$	217.04	nd./aq.	....	232	....	v. s. h.	v. s. h.	i.
Asparagine (l-)	....	$HO_2C.C_2H_3(NH_2).CONH_2$	132.12	rhb.	$1.543^{15/4}$	227–35	d. 235	3.1^{28}	i. c.	
Aspirin (o-)	....	$CH_3CO_2.C_6H_4.OH$	180.15	nd./aq.	....	135–6	....	1^{37}	s.	5^{20}
Atropic acid	α-phenyl acrylic acid	$C_6H_5C({:}CH_2).CO_2H$	148.15	nd./aq.	....	106–7	267 d.	0.1 c.	s.	s.
Auramine	4,4′-dimethylaminobenzophenomide	$[(CH_3)_2NC_6H_4]_2C{:}NH$	267.36	col./al.	....	136	....	i.	7^{20}	2.3^{20}
Aurine, coralline (4-,4′-)	....	$(HOC_6H_4)_2C{:}C_6H_4{:}O$	290.30	red	....	310 d.	....	i.	s.	s.
Azo-anisole (2-,2′-)	diMeO-azobenzene	$(CH_3O.C_6H_4N{:})2$	242.27	or. pr.	....	153	....	i.	s.	s.
benzene	diphenyldiimide	$C_6H_5N{:}N.C_6H_5$	182.22	or. mn.	$1.203^{20/4}$	68	297	i.	4.2^{20}	
Azoxybenzene	....	$(C_6H_5)_2N_2O$	198.22	yel. rhb.	$1.248^{20/20}$	36	d.	i.	11.4^{15}	
Barbituric acid	malonyl urea	$CO{:}(NHCO)_2{:}CH_2.2H_2O$	164.12	col./aq.	....	d. 245	....	s. h.	sl. s.	s.
Benzal acetone	Me-cinnamyl ketone	$C_6H_5CH{:}CHCOCH_3$	146.18	pl.	$1.035^{20/20}$	41–2	260–2	i.	s.	s.
Benzaldehyde	artificial almond oil	C_6H_5CHO	106.12	col. lq.	$1.046^{20/4}$	−26	179	0.3	∞	∞
Benzamide	....	$C_6H_5CONH_2$	121.13	col. pr.	1.341	130	290	1.35^{25}	17^{25}	sl. s.
Benzanilide	....	$C_6H_5CONHC_6H_5$	197.23	lf./al.	1.31^{4}	163	$117–9^{10}$	i.	4^{30}	sl. s.
Benzene	benzol, phenyl hydride, cyclohexatriene	C_6H_6	78.11	col. lq.	$0.879^{20/4}$	5.5	80.1	0.07^{22}	s.	∞
sulfinic acid	....	$C_6H_5SO_2H$	142.17	pr./aq.	....	83–4	d. >100	v. s. h.	v. s.	v. s.
sulfonic acid	....	$C_6H_5SO_3H$	158.17	col. nd.	....	65–6	d.	v. s.	v. s.	i.
sulfonic amide	benzene sulfonamide	$C_6H_5SO_2NH_2$	157.18	mn./aq.	....	156	....	0.43^{16}	v. s.	v. s.
sulfonic chloride	benzene sulfonyl chloride	$C_6H_5SO_2Cl$	176.62	cr.	$1.384^{15/15}$	14.5	251.5	i.	v. s.	s.
Benzidine (4-,4′-)	....	$NH_2.C_6H_4.C_6H_4.NH_2$	184.23	cr./aq.	....	128–9	400^{740}	1 h.	1 h.	2
disulfonic acid (2-,2′-)	....	$(.C_6H_3(NH_2)SO_3H)_2.3H_2O$	398.40	pr./aq.	....	d. >175	....	0.09^{25}	i.	i.
(3-,3′-)	....	$(.C_6H_3(NH_2)SO_3H)_2$	344.35	....	....	....	....	v. sl. s.		
Benzil	dibenzoyl	$C_6H_5CO.COC_6H_5$	210.22	pr.	1.23^{15}	95	348 d.	i.	v. s.	v. s.
Benzoic acid	....	$C_6H_5CO_2H$	122.12	mn. pr.	$1.266^{15/4}$	121.7	249.2	0.2^{17}	46^{15}	66^{15}
anhydride	....	$(C_6H_5CO)_2O$	226.22	rhb./et.	$1.199^{15/4}$	42	360	i.	s.	s.
nitrile	phenyl cyanide	C_6H_5CN	103.12	col. lq.	$1.001^{25/6}$	−12.9	190.7	1^{100}	∞	∞

Table 3-2. Physical Properties of Organic Compounds—(*Continued*)

Name	Synonym	Formula	Formula weight	Form and color	Specific gravity	Melting point, °C.	Boiling point, °C.	Solubility in 100 parts: Water	Alcohol	Ether
Benzoin (dl-)		$C_6H_5CO.CHOHC_6H_5$	212.24	mn.	....	133–7	344^{768}	v. sl. s.	s. h.	sl. s.
Benzophenone	diphenyl ketone	$C_6H_5COC_6H_5$	182.21	col. rhb.	1.083^{54}	48.5	305.4	i.	6.5^{15}	15^{13}
Benzotrichloride	phenyl chloroform	$C_6H_5CCl_3$	195.48	col. lq.	1.380^{14}	−4.75	220.7	i.	s.	s.
Benzoyl-benzoic acid (o-)		$C_6H_5COC_6H_4CO_2H.H_2O$	244.24	tri./aq.	....	93(128)	....	sl. s.		
-chloride		C_6H_5COCl	140.57	col. lq.	$1.212^{20/4}$	−0.5	197.2	d.	d. h.	∞
-peroxide		$(C_6H_5CO)_2O_2$	242.22	rhb./et.	....	108 d.	expl.	i.	s. h.	s.
Benzyl acetate		$CH_3CO_2CH_2C_6H_5$	150.17	col. lq.	1.057^{17}	−51.5	213.5	i.	∞	∞
alcohol	phenyl carbinol	$C_6H_5CH_2OH$	108.13	col. lq.	$1.043^{20/4}$	−15.3	204.7	4^{17}	∞	∞
amine	ω-amino toluene	$C_6H_5CH_2NH_2$	107.15	lq.	$0.982^{20/4}$	....	184.5	∞	∞	∞
aniline	phenyl-benzylamine	$C_6H_5CH_2NHC_6H_5$	183.24	mn. pr.	$1.065^{25/25}$	37–8	306^{759}	i.	....	s.
benzoate		$C_6H_5CO_2CH_2C_6H_5$	212.24	nd.	$1.12^{20/4}$	21	323–4	i.	∞	∞
butyrate		$C_2H_5CH_2CO_2CH_2C_6H_5$	178.22	col. lq.	$1.016^{16/18}$	....	238–40	i.	v. s.	v. s.
chloride	ω-chlorotoluene	$C_6H_5CH_2Cl$	126.58	col. lq.	$1.100^{20/20}$	−39	179.4	i.	∞	∞
ether	dibenzyl ether	$(C_6H_5CH_2)_2O$	198.25	lq.	1.036^{16}	....	295–8	i.	s. h.	s.
formate		$HCO_2CH_2C_6H_5$	136.14	col. lq.	1.081^{23}	3.6	$202–3^{747}$	i.	s.	∞
propionate		$C_2H_5CO_2CH_2C_6H_5$	164.20	lq.	$1.036^{16/17}$	....	220–2	i.		
Berberonic acid (2-,4-,5-)		$C_5H_2N(CO_2H)_3.2H_2O$	247.16	tri.	....	243	....	v. sl. s.	sl. s. h.	i.
Biuret	allophanamide	$NH(CONH_2)_2$	103.08	nd./al.	....	192–3 d.	....	1.3^{0}	s.	
Borneol (dl-)		$C_{10}H_{17}OH$	154.24	col. cr.	$1.011^{20/4}$	210.5	subl.	v. sl. s.		
(d- or l-)		$C_{10}H_{17}OH$	154.24	col. cr.	$1.011^{20/4}$	208–9	212–3	v. sl. s.	v. s.	v. s.
(iso-)		$C_{10}H_{17}OH$	154.24	col. cr.	....	212	....	i.		
Bornyl acetate (d-)		$CH_3CO_2C_{10}H_{17}$	196.28	rhb./pet.	0.991^{15}	29	226–7	i.	s.	s.
Bromo-aniline (p-)		$BrC_6H_4NH_2$	172.03	rhb.	1.8^{20}	63–4	....	i. c.	v. s.	v. s.
-benzene	phenyl bromide	C_6H_5Br	157.02	col. lq.	$1.495^{20/4}$	−30.6	156.2	i.	s.	∞
-camphor (3-)(d-)	α-bromocamphor	$BrC_{10}H_{15}O$	231.14	cr.	$1.449^{20/4}$	77–8	274	i.	20^{25}	v. s.
-diphenyl (p-)		$BrC_6H_4.C_6H_5$	233.11	cr./al.	....	90–1	310	i.	s.	34^{25}
-naphthalene (α-)	α-naphthyl bromide	$C_{10}H_7Br$	207.07	col. oil	$1.482^{20/4}$	5–6	281.1	i.	s.	∞
(β-)	β-naphthyl bromide	$C_{10}H_7Br$	207.07	lf./al.	1.605^{0}	59	281–2	i.	6^{20}	v. s.
-phenol (o-)		BrC_6H_4OH	173.02	col. lq.	1.553^{80}	5.6	194–5	s.	s.	∞
(m-)		BrC_6H_4OH	173.02	cr.	....	32–3	236–7	....	s.	s.
(p-)		BrC_6H_4OH	173.02	tet. cr.	1.588^{80}	63.5	238	1.4^{15}	v. s.	v. s.
-styrene (ω)(1)		$C_6H_5CH:CHBr$	183.05	lq.	$1.422^{20/4}$	7	221	i.	∞	∞
(2)		$C_6H_5CH:CHBr$	183.05	lq.	$1.427^{20/4}$	−7.5	108^{26}	i.	∞	∞
-toluene (o-)	o-tolyl bromide	$CH_3.C_6H_4Br$	171.04	col. lq.	$1.422^{20/4}$	−28	181.8	i.	s.	$∞^{25}$
(m-)		$CH_3.C_6H_4Br$	171.04	col. lq.	$1.410^{20/4}$	−39.8	183.7	i.	s.	s.
(p-)		$CH_3.C_6H_4Br$	171.04	cr./al.	$1.390^{20/4}$	28.5	184–5	i.	s.	$∞^{25}$
Bromoform	tribromo-methane	$CHBr_3$	252.77	col. lq.	$2.890^{20/4}$	8–9	150.5	0.1 c.	∞	∞
Butadiene (1-,2-)	methyl-allene	$CH_2CH:C:CH_2$	54.09	lq.	....	....	18–9	i.	∞	∞
(1-,3-)	erythrene	$CH_2:CHCH:CH_2$	54.09	col. gas	$0.621^{20/4}$	−108.9	−4.41	i.	∞	∞
Butadienyl acetylene		$CH_2:(CH)_2:CH.C:CH$	78.11	col. lq.	$0.773^{20/4}$	....	83–6	i.		
Butane	diethyl	$CH_3CH_2CH_2CH_3$	58.12	col. gas	0.60^{0}	−135	−0.6	i.	s.	s.
(i-)	trimethyl-methane	$(CH_3)_2CHCH_3$	58.12	col. gas	0.60^{0}	−145	−10	i.	s.	s.
Butyl acetate (n-)		$CH_3CO_2(CH_2)_2C_2H_5$	116.16	col. lq.	0.882^{20}	−76.3	125^{740}	0.7	∞	∞
(s-)		$CH_3CO_2CH(CH_3)C_2H_5$	116.16	col. lq.	$0.865^{25/4}$	....	112^{744}	i.	∞	∞
(i-)		$CH_3CO_2CH_2CH(CH_3)_2$	116.16	col. lq.	$0.871^{20/4}$	−98.9	118	0.6^{25}	∞	∞
(tert-)		$CH_3CO_2C(CH_3)_3$	116.16	col. lq.	$0.866^{20/4}$	....	$95–6^{750}$	i.	∞	∞
alcohol (n-)	butanol-1	$C_2H_5CH_2CH_2OH$	74.12	col. lq.	$0.810^{20/4}$	−79.9	117	9^{15}	∞	∞
(s-)	butanol-2	$C_2H_5CH(OH)CH_3$	74.12	col. lq.	$0.808^{20/4}$	−114.7	99.5	12.5^{20}	∞	∞
(i-)	2-methyl-propanol-1	$(CH_3)_2CHCH_2OH$	74.12	col. lq.	$0.805^{17.5}$	−108	107–8	10^{15}	∞	∞
(tert-)	2-methyl-propanol-2	$(CH_3)_3COH$	74.12	lq.	0.779^{26}	25.5	82.9	∞	∞	∞
amine (n-)		$C_2H_5CH_2CH_2NH_2$	73.14	col. lq.	$0.739^{25/4}$	−50	77.8	∞	∞	∞
(s-)		$C_2H_5CH(NH_2)CH_3$	73.14	col. lq.	$0.724^{20/4}$	−104	66^{772}	∞	∞	∞
(i-)		$(CH_3)_2CHCH_2NH_2$	73.14	col. lq.	$0.732^{20/20}$	−85	68–9	∞	∞	∞
(t-)		$(CH_3)_3CNH_2$	73.14	col. lq.	$0.698^{18/4}$	−67.5	45.2	....	∞	
p-aminophenol (N)(n)		$C_4H_9NH.C_6H_4.OH$	165.23	....	....	71	....	i.		
(N)(i-)		$C_4H_9NH.C_6H_4.OH$	165.23	....	....	79	....	i.		
aniline (n-)		$C_4H_9NHC_6H_5$	149.23	lq.	....	....	235^{720}	i.	v. s.	v. s.
(i-)		$C_4H_9NHC_6H_5$	149.23	oil	$0.940^{20/4}$	....	231–2	0.01^{15}	v. s.	v. s.
arsonic acid (n-)		$C_4H_9AsO(OH)_2$	182.04	col. lf.	....	158–9	....	s.	s.	i.
benzoate (n-)		$C_6H_5CO_2C_4H_9$	178.22	col. oil	$1.005^{25/25}$	−22	249–50	i.	s.	s.
(i-)		$C_6H_5CO_2C_4H_9$	178.22	col. oil	$0.997^{25/25}$	....	241.5	i.	∞	∞
bromide (n-)	1-bromo-butane	$C_2H_5CH_2CH_2Br$	137.03	lq.	$1.277^{20/4}$	−112.4	101.6	0.06^{16}	∞	∞
(s-)	2-bromo-butane	$C_2H_5CH(Br)CH_3$	137.03	lq.	$1.251^{25/4}$	−112	91.3	i.		
(i-)	1-Br-2-Me-propane	$(CH_3)_2CHCH_2Br$	137.03	lq.	$1.258^{25/4}$	−118.5	91.5	0.06^{18}	∞	∞
(t-)	2-Br-2-Me-propane	$(CH_3)_3CBr$	137.03	lq.	$1.211^{20/4}$	−16.2	73.3	i.	∞	∞

butyrate (n-)(n-)		$C_2H_5CH_2CO_2CH_2CH_2C_2H_5$	144.21	col. lq.	0.872$^{20/20}$	....	165.7^{736}	i.	∞	∞
(n-)(i-)		$C_2H_5CH_2CO_2CH_2CH(CH_3)_2$	144.21	col. lq.	0.863$^{18/4}$	....	156.9	i.	∞	∞
(i-)(i-)		$(CH_3)_2CHCO_2CH_2CH(CH_3)_2$	144.21	col. lq.	0.875$^{0/4}$	−80.7	148–9	i.	∞	∞
caproate		$CH_3(CH_2)_4CO_2C_4H_9$	172.26	col. lq.	0.882$^{0/0}$	....	204.3	i.		
carbamate (i-)		$NH_2CO_2CH_2CH(CH_3)_2$	117.15	col. lf.	0.956$^{76/4}$	65	206–7	i.	s.	s.
cellosolve (n-)	2-BuO-ethanol-1	$C_4H_9OCH_2CH_2OH$	118.17	col. lq.	0.903$^{20/4}$	....	171.2	∞	∞	∞
chloride (n-)	1-chloro-butane	$C_2H_5CH_2CH_2Cl$	92.57	col. lq.	0.887^{20}	−123.1	77.9^{763}	0.07^{18}	∞	∞
(s-)	2-chloro-butane	$C_2H_5.CHCl.CH_3$	92.57	col. lq.	0.871$^{20/4}$	−131	67.8^{767}	i.	∞	∞
(i-)	1-Cl₂-2-Me-propane	$(CH_3)_2CHCH_2Cl$	92.57	col. lq.	0.884^{15}	−131.2	68.9	i.	∞	∞
(t-)	2-Cl₂-2-Me-propane	$(CH_3)_3CCl$	92.57	col. lq.	0.847^{15}	−26.5	51–2	i.	∞	∞
dimethylbenzene (t-)(1-,3-,5-)		$(CH_3)_3C.C_6H_3:(CH_3)_2$	162.26	col. lq.	....	....	200–2^{147}	i.		
formate (n-)		$HCO_2CH_2CH_2C_2H_5$	102.13	lq.	0.911^{0}	....	106.9	v. sl. s.	∞	∞
(s-)		$HCO_2CH(CH_3)C_2H_5$	102.13	lq.	0.882$^{20/4}$	....	97	sl. s.	∞	∞
(i-)		$HCO_2CH_2CH(CH_3)_2$	102.13	lq.	0.885$^{20/4}$	−95.3	98.2	1.1^{22}	∞	∞
furoate (n-)		$OC_4H_3CO_2C_4H_9$	168.19	col. lq.	1.056$^{20/4}$	....	118–20^{25}	i.	∞	∞
iodide (n-)	1-iodo-butane	$C_2H_5CH_2CH_2I$	184.03	lq.	1.617$^{20/4}$	−103.5	129.9	i.	∞	∞
(s-)	2-iodo-butane	$C_2H_5CHICH_3$	184.03	lq.	1.595^{20}	−104	118–9	i.	∞	∞
(i-)	1-iodo-2-Me-propane	$(CH_3)_2CHCH_2I$	184.03	lq.	1.606$^{20/4}$	−90.7	120	i.	∞	∞
(t-)	2-iodo-2-Me-propane	$(CH_3)_3CI$	184.03	lq.	1.370$^{19/15}$	−34	99	i.	∞	∞
lactate (n-)		$CH_3CH(OH)CO_2C_4H_9$	146.18	col. lq.	0.968	....	75–6^{6}	sl. s.	∞	∞
mercaptan (n-)	butanthiol-1	$C_2H_5CH_2CH_2SH$	90.18	col. lq.	0.837$^{25/4}$	−116	97–8	sl. s.	v. s.	v. s.
(i-)	2-Me-propanthiol-1	$(CH_3)_2CHCH_2SH$	90.18	lq.	0.836$^{20/4}$	<−79	88	v. sl. s.	s.	s.
(t-)		$(CH_3)_3CSH$	90.18	lq	....	....	65–7			
methacrylate (n-)		$CH_2:C(CH_3)CO_2C_4H_9$	142.19	lq.	0.889$^{15.6}$	....	155	i		
(i-)		$CH_2:C(CH_3)CO_2C_4H_9$	142.19	lq.	0.889$^{15.6}$	....	155	i.		
phenol (p-)(t-)		$(CH_3)_3C.C_6H_4.OH$	150.21	nd./aq.	0.908$^{112/4}$	99	236–8	sl. s.	s.	s.
propionate (n-)		$C_2H_5CO_2C_4H_9$	130.18	col. lq.	0.883^{15}	−89.55	146	i.	∞	∞
(s-)		$C_2H_5CO_2C_4H_9$	130.18	col. lq.	0.866$^{20/4}$	....	132.5	i.	∞	∞
(i-)		$C_2H_5CO_2C_4H_9$	130.18	col. lq.	0.888$^{0/4}$	−71.4	136.8	i.	∞	∞
stearate (n-)		$CH_3(CH_2)_{16}CO_2C_4H_9$	340.57	col. lq.	0.855$^{25/25}$	27.5	220–5^{25}	0.3^{25}	s.	s.
(i-)		$CH_3(CH_2)_{16}CO_2C_4H_9$	340.57	wax	....	25	....	i.		
iso-thiocyanate (n-)	butyl mustard oil	$C_2H_5CH_2CH_2.N:CS$	115.19	lq.	0.956^{11}	....	165^{724}	i.	s.	s.
(i-)	iso-Bu mustard oil	$(CH_3)_2CHCH_2.N:CS$	115.19	lq.	0.964$^{14/4}$	....	162	i.	s.	s.
(s-)(d-)		$C_4H_9.N:CS$	115.19	lq.	0.943$^{20/4}$	....	159–63	i.	s.	s.
(t-)		$(CH_3)_3C.N:CS$	115.19	lq.	0.919^{10}	10.5	140^{770}	i.	s.	s.
valerate (n-)(n-)		$CH_3(CH_2)_3CO_2(CH_2)_3CH_3$	158.23	lq.	0.870$^{15/4}$	−93	186	v. sl. s.	∞	∞
(i-)(n-)		$(CH_3)_2CHCH_2CO_2(CH_2)_3CH_3$	158.23	lq.	0.862$^{25/4}$	....	168.8	i.	∞	∞
(i-)(s-)		$(CH_3)_2CHCH_2CO_2C_4H_9$	158.23	col. lq.	0.848$^{20/4}$	....	163–4^{752}	i.	∞	∞
(i-)(i-)		$C_4H_9CO_2C_4H_9$	158.23	col. lq.	0.874$^{0/4}$	....	168.7	i.	∞	∞
Butylene (α-)	butene-1	$C_2H_5CH:CH_2$	56.10	col. gas	0.6^{9}	−130	−5^{758}	i.	v. s.	v. s.
(β-)	butene-2	$CH_3CH:CHCH_3$	56.10	col. gas	....	−127	3^{746}			
Butyraldehyde (n-)		$CH_3CH_2CH_2CHO$	72.10	col. lq.	0.817$^{20/4}$	−99	75.7	4	∞	∞
(i-)	2-Me-propanol	$(CH_3)_2CHCHO$	72.10	col. lq.	0.794$^{20/4}$	−65.9	64^{757}	11^{20}	∞	∞
Butyric acid (n-)	butanoic acid	$C_2H_5CH_2CO_2H$	88.10	col. lq.	0.964$^{20/4}$	−4.7	163.5^{757}	∞	∞	∞
(i-)	2-Me-propanoic acid	$(CH_3)_2CHCO_2H$	88.10	col. lq.	0.949$^{20/4}$	−47	154.5	20^{20}	∞	∞
amide (n-)	n-butyramide	$C_2H_5CH_2CONH_2$	87.12	rhb.	1.032	115–6	216	16.3^{15}	s.	sl. s.
(i-)	iso-butyramide	$(CH_3)_2CHCONH_2$	87.12	mn. pl.	1.013	129–30	216–20	v. s.	s.	sl. s.
anhydride (n-)		$(C_2H_5CH_2CO)_2O$	158.19	col. lq.	0.968$^{20/20}$	−75	199.5	d.	d	∞
(i-)		$[(CH_3)_2CHCO]_2O$	158.19	col. lq.	0.950$^{25/4}$	−53.5	181.5^{734}	d.	d	∞
anilide (n-)	n-butyranilide	$C_3H_7CONHC_6H_5$	163.21	mn. pr.	1.134	92	189^{15}	i.	s.	s.
Caffeic acid (3-,4-)		$(HO)_2C_6H_3C_2H_2CO_2H$	180.15	yel./aq.	....	195–213	d.	s. h.	s.	sl. s.
Caffeine		$C_8H_{10}O_2N_4.H_2O$	212.21	nd./al.	1.23^{19}	237	subl.	2	2	0.3
Camphene (dl-)		$C_{10}H_{16}$	136.23	cr.	0.822^{78}	50	160	i.	s.	s.
(d- or l-)		$C_{10}H_{16}$	136.23	cr.	0.845$^{50/4}$	42.7	159.6	i.	s.	s.
Camphor (d-)		$C_{10}H_{16}O$	152.23	trig.	0.999$^{9/9}$	178–9	209.1^{759}	0.1	120^{12}	v. s.
Camphoric acid (d-)		$C_8H_{14}(CO_2H)_2$	200.23	mn.	1.186	187	....	0.6^{12}	s.	
Cantharidine		$C_{10}H_{12}O_4$	196.20	cr.	....	212	....	0.003		
Capric acid	decanoic acid	$CH_3(CH_2)_8CO_2H$	172.26	col. nd.	0.889^{37}	31.5	268–70	0.003	s.	s.
Caproic acid (n-)	hexanoic acid	$CH_3(CH_2)_4CO_2H$	116.16	oily lq.	0.922$^{20/4}$	−1.5	202^{761}	1.1^{20}	s.	s.
(i-)	2-Me-pentanoic-5 acid	$(CH_3)_2CH(CH_2)_2.CO_2H$	116.16	col. oil	0.925$^{20/4}$	−35	207.7	v. sl. s.	s.	s.
Caprylic acid (n-)	octanoic acid	$CH_3(CH_2)_6CO_2H$	144.21	col. lf.	0.910$^{20/4}$	16	237.5	0.07^{15}	s.	s.
Carbazole	diphenylenelimine, dibenzopyrrole	$(C_6H_4)_2NH$	167.20	lf.	....	244.8	354.8	i.	0.92^{14}	sl. s.
Carbitol	diethylene glycol mono-Et ether	$C_2H_5O(CH_2)_2O(CH_2)_2OH$	134.17	col. lq.	0.990$^{20/20}$	....	201.9	∞	v. s.	s.
Carbon disulfide		CS_2	76.13	col. lq.	1.263$^{20/4}$	−108.6	46.3	0.2^{0}	∞	∞
monoxide		CO	28.01	col. gas	0.81$^{-195/4}$	−207	−192	3.5^{0} cc.	s.	
suboxide		OC:C:CO	68.03	gas	1.114^{0}	−107	7^{761}	d.	....	s.
tetrabromide	tetrabromomethane	CBr_4	331.67	col. mn.	3.42	90.1(48)	189.5	0.02^{30}	s.	s.
tetrachloride	tetrachloromethane	CCl_4	153.84	col. lq.	1.595$^{20/4}$	−22.6	76.8	0.08^{20}	∞	∞
tetrafluoride	tetrafluoromethane	CF_4	88.01	gas	....	....	−128	sl. s.		

Table 3-2. Physical Properties of Organic Compounds—*(Continued)*

Name	Formula	Formula weight	Form and color	Specific gravity	Melting point, °C.	Boiling point, °C.	Solubility in 100 parts: Water	Alcohol	Ether
Carbonyl sulfide	COS	60.07	col. gas	1.24^{-87}	−138.2	-50.2^{760}	80^{14} cc.	s.	s.
Carminic acid	$C_{22}H_{20}O_{13}$	492.40	red pd.	....	d. 136	....	s.	s.	v. sl. s.
Carvacrol (1-,2-,4-)	$CH_3C_6H_3(OH)CH(CH_3)_2$	150.21	col. lq.	$0.977^{20/4}$	0.5	238	v. sl. s.	∞	∞
Carvacrylamine (2-,1-,4-)	$H_2NC_6H_3(CH_3)C_3H_7$	149.23	oil	0.994^{20}	−16	241	v. sl. s.	s.	s.
Carvone (d-)	$C_{10}H_{14}O$	150.21	col. lq.	$0.961^{20/4}$	....	230^{755}	i.	∞	∞
Cellosolve	$C_2H_5O(CH_2)_2OH$	90.12	col. lq.	$0.931^{20/4}$	−70	135.1	∞	∞	∞
acetate	$CH_3CO_2CH_2CH_2OC_2H_5$	132.16	col. lq.	$0.975^{20/4}$	....	156.3	22	∞	∞
Cellulose	$(C_6H_{10}O_5)x$	162.14	amor.	1.3–1.4	....	....	i.	i.	i.
Cetyl acetate	$CH_3CO_2(CH_2)_{15}CH_3$	284.47	nd.	0.858^{20}	22–3	200^{15}	i.	v. sl. s. c.	
alcohol	$CH_3(CH_2)_{14}CH_2OH$	242.43	lf.	$0.818^{50/4}$	49–50	189.5^{15}	i.	s.	s.
Chloral	$CCl_3.CHO$	147.40	col. lq.	$1.505^{25/4}$	−57±	97.6^{768}	v. s.	∞	∞
hydrate	$CCl_3.CH(OH)_2$	165.42	mn. pr.	$1.619^{50/4}$	51.7±	d. 98	474^{17}	v. s.	s.
Chloranil	$OC:(CCl.CCl)_2:CO$	245.89	yel./bz.	....	290	subl.	i.	i. c.	i. c.
Chloretone	$Cl_3C.C(OH)(CH_3)_2$	177.47	col. cr.	....	97	167	0.8 c.	111	s.
Chloro-acetanilide (p-)	$CH_3CO_2NHC_6H_4Cl$	169.61	rhb.	1.385^{22}	175–6	....	sl. s.	s.	v. s.
-acetic acid	$ClCH_2CO_2H$	94.50	col. cr.	$1.58^{20/20}$	61.2	189.5	v. s.	s.	s.
-acetone	CH_3COCH_2Cl	92.53	col. lq.	1.162^{16}	−44.5	121	∞	∞	∞
-acetophenone (ω-)	$C_6H_5COCH_2Cl$	154.59	rhb.	1.324^{15}	58–9	245–7	0.11	v. s.	v. s.
-acetyl chloride	$ClCH_2COCl$	112.95	col. lq.	$1.498^{20/20}$	....	105	d.	d.	
-aniline (o-)	$ClC_6H_4NH_2$	127.57	lq.	$1.213^{20/4}$	0	210.5	i.	....	s.
(m-)	$ClC_6H_4NH_2$	127.57	lq.	$1.216^{20/4}$	−10.4	230^{767}	i.	....	s.
(p-)	$ClC_6H_4NH_2$	127.57	rhb.	1.427^{19}	70–1	230–1	s. h.	s.	s.
-anthraquinone (1-)	$C_6H_4(CO)_2C_6H_3Cl$	242.65	yel. nd.	....	162	subl.	i.	sl. s. h.	
(2-)	$C_6H_4(CO)_2C_6H_3Cl$	242.65	nd./al.	....	208–9	....	i.		
-benzaldehyde (o-)	ClC_6H_4CHO	140.57	nd.	1.29^{8}	11	208^{748}	v. sl. s.	v. s.	v. s.
(m-)	ClC_6H_4CHO	140.57	pr.	1.250^{15}	17–8	213–4	v. sl. s.	v. s.	v. s.
(p-)	ClC_6H_4CHO	140.57	pr.	1.196^{61}	47.8	213^{748}	s. h.	v. s.	v. s.
-benzene	C_6H_5Cl	112.56	col. lq.	$1.107^{20/4}$	−45.2	132.1	0.049^{20}	∞	∞
-benzoic acid (o-)	$ClC_6H_4CO_2H$	156.57	mn./aq.	$1.544^{25/4}$	141–2	....	0.208^{25}	s.	s.
(m-)	$ClC_6H_4CO_2H$	156.57	pr.	$1.496^{25/4}$	158	....	0.041^{25}	s.	s.
(p-)	$ClC_6H_4CO_2H$	156.57	tri.	1.541^{24}	242–3	subl.	0.008^{25}	s.	s.
-buta-1,3-diene (2-)	$CH_2:CCl.CH:CH_2$	88.54	col. lq.	$0.958^{20/20}$	....	59.4	v. sl. s.	∞	∞
(1-)	$CH_2:CH.CH:CHCl$	88.54	col. lq.	$0.965^{20/20}$	....	69	v. sl. s.	∞	∞
-buta-1,2-diene (4-)	$CH_2:C:CH.CH_2Cl$	88.54	col. lq.	$0.991^{20/20}$	....	88	d.		
-dimethylhydantoin	$—C(CH_3)_2N(Cl)CON(Cl)CO—$	197.03	....	$1.5^{20/20}$	130	....	0.21^{25}		
-dinitrobenzene (α)(1-,2-)(4-)	$ClC_6H_3(NO_2)_2$	202.56	cr./et.	....	39(36)	315 d.	i.	v. s. h.	v. s.
(α)(1-,3-)(4-)	$ClC_6H_3(NO_2)_2$	202.56	rhb./et.	1.697^{22}	53(43)	315 d.	i.	s. h.	s.
-diphenyl (o-)	$C_6H_5.C_6H_4Cl$	188.65	cr.	....	34	267–8	i.		
(m-)	$C_6H_5.C_6H_4Cl$	188.65	cr.	....	89	284–5	i.		
(p-)	$C_6H_5.C_6H_4Cl$	188.65	lf.	....	77.5	282	i.		
-hydroquinone	$ClC_6H_3(OH)_2$	144.56	mn.	....	106	263 sl. d.	v. s.	v. s.	v. s.
-naphthalene (α-)	$C_{10}H_7Cl$	162.61	col. lq.	$1.194^{20/4}$	−20	259.3	i.	s.	∞
(β-)	$C_{10}H_7Cl$	162.61	lf./al.	1.266^{16}	56–7	264^{751}	i.	v. s.	v. s.
-nitrobenzene (o-)	$ClC_6H_4NO_2$	157.56	mn. nd.	$1.305^{80/4}$	32.5	245.5^{753}	i.	s. h.	s.
(m-)	$ClC_6H_4NO_2$	157.56	yel./al.	$1.343^{50/4}$	44.4(24)	235.6	i.	v. s. h.	v. s.
(p-)	$ClC_6H_4NO_2$	157.56	mn. pr.	1.298^{91}	83–4	242^{761}	i.	v. s. h.	v. s.
-nitrotoluene (2-,4-)	$CH_3C_6H_3(NO_2)(Cl)$	171.56	cr.	1.256^{80}	38.2	240^{718}	i.		
(2-,6-)	$CH_3C_6H_3(NO_2)(Cl)$	171.56	cr.	....	37.5	238	i.		
-phenol (o-)	ClC_6H_4OH	128.56	col. lq.	$1.241^{18/15}$	7(0)	175–6	2.85^{20}	s.	s.
(m-)	ClC_6H_4OH	128.56	nd.	1.268^{25}	32–3	214	2.60^{20}	s.	s.
(p-)	ClC_6H_4OH	128.56	nd.	$1.306^{20/4}$	41–3	217	2.71^{20}	v. s.	v. s.
-propionic acid (α)(dl-)	$CH_3.CHCl.CO_2H$	108.53	col. lq.	1.306^{9}	<−20	186	∞	∞	∞
-toluene (o-)	$CH_3.C_6H_4Cl$	126.58	col. lq.	$1.082^{20/4}$	−34	159.5	i.	s.	∞
(m-)	$CH_3.C_6H_4Cl$	126.58	col. lq.	$1.072^{20/4}$	−47.8	161.6	i.	s.	∞
(p-)	$CH_3.C_6H_4Cl$	126.58	col. lq.	$1.070^{20/4}$	7.5	162.2	i.	s.	∞
Chloroform	$CHCl_3$	119.39	col. lq.	1.489^{20}	−63.5	61.2	0.82^{20}	∞	∞
Chlorophyll (α-)	$C_{55}H_{72}O_5N_4Mg$	893.48	....	....	....	d.	i.	s.	
Chloropicrin	Cl_3CNO_2	164.39	lq.	$1.651^{23/4}$	−64	112.3^{766}	0.17^{18}	s.	s.
Cholesterol	$C_{27}H_{45}OH.H_2O$	404.65	rhb./al.	1.067	149–51	subl.	0.26^{20}	1.1^{17}	18
Chrysene	$C_{18}H_{12}$	228.28	col. rhb.	....	253–4	448	i.	0.1^{16}	v. sl. s.
Chrysoidine (2-,4-)	$C_6H_5.N:N.C_6H_3(NH_2)_2$	212.25	yel. cr.	....	117.5	....	sl. s. h.	s.	s.
Chrysophanic acid	$C_{14}H_5(OH)_2(CH_3)O_2$	254.23	yel./al.	....	195	subl.	i. c.	s. h.	sl. s.
Cinchomeronic acid (3-,4-)	$C_5H_3N(CO_2H)_2$	167.12	cr./HCl	....	258–9 d.	subl. d.	v. sl. s.	sl. s.	i.
Cineole, eucalyptole	$C_{10}H_{18}O$	154.24	col. oil	0.927^{20}	1.5	176–7	1.9^{15}	∞	∞
Cinnamic acid (cis-)	$C_6H_5CH:CHCO_2H$	148.15	mn. pr.	1.284^{4}	68	125^{19}			
(trans-)	$C_6H_5CH:CHCO_2H$	148.15	mn. pr.	1.245	133	300	0.04^{18}	24^{20}	v. s.

aldehyde	$C_6H_5CH{:}CHCHO$	132.15	lq.	$1.110^{20/20}$	−7.5	252 sl. d.	v. sl. s.	s.	∞
Cinnamyl alcohol	$C_6H_5CH{:}CHCH_2OH$	134.17	nd.	$1.040^{35/35}$	33	257.5	sl. s.	v. s.	v. s.
cinnamate	$C_8H_7CO_2C_9H_9$	264.31	nd. or pr.	$1.085^{16.5}$	44	....	i.	4 c.	33
Citraconic acid (cis-)	$CH_3C(CO_2H){:}CHCO_2H$	130.10	nd.	1.617	92–3	....	360^{25}	s.	s.
Citral (α)	$C_9H_{15}CHO$	152.23	col. oil	$0.890^{17/4}$	....	229	i.	∞	∞
Citric acid	$C_3H_4(OH)(CO_2H)_3$	192.12	cr.	$1.542^{20/4}$	153	d.	207.7^{25}	76^{15}	2^{15}
Citronellal (d-)	$C_9H_{17}.CHO$	154.24	col. oil	$0.855^{17.5}$	....	204–8	v. sl. s.	∞	∞
Citronellol (d-)	$C_{10}H_{20}O$	156.26	col. oil	$0.848^{20/4}$	....	224–5	v. sl. s.	∞	∞
Coniine (d-)(2-)	$C_3H_7.C_5H_{10}N$	127.22	col. lq.	0.847^{17}	−2	166–7	1.1	v. s.	v. s.
Coumaric acid (o-)	$HOC_6H_4CH{:}CHCO_2H$	164.15	nd./aq.	....	207–8	subl.	sl. s. c.	s.	v. sl. s.
(p-)	$HOC_6H_4CH{:}CHCO_2H$	164.15	cr./aq.	....	206–7 d.	....	s. h.	v. s. h.	v. s.
Coumarin	$C_9H_6O_2$	146.14	rhb./et.	$0.935^{20/4}$	70	290–1	0.3 c.	v. s.	s.
Coumarone	C_8H_6O	118.13	oil	$1.078^{15/15}$	< −18	173–4	i.	....	s.
Creatine	$C_4H_9N_3O_2.H_2O$	149.15	mn./aq.	....	295	....	1.4^{18}	0.01^{17}	i.
Creatinine	$C_4H_7N_3O$	113.12	mn.	....	260 d.	....	8.7^{16}	1^{16}	
Creosol (3-,1-,4-)	$CH_3O.C_6H_3(CH_3)OH$	138.16	pr.	$1.092^{20/20}$	5.5	$221–2^{765}$	v. sl. s.	∞	∞
Cresidine (1-,2-,4-)	$CH_3(NH_2)C_6H_3.OCH_3$	137.18	nd./pet.	....	93–4	235	v. sl. s.	s.	s.
Cresol (o-)	$CH_3C_6H_4OH$	108.13	cr.	$1.048^{20/4}$	30.8	190.8	2.5	$∞^{30}$	$∞^{30}$
(m-)	$CH_3C_6H_4OH$	108.13	lq.	$1.034^{20/4}$	10.9	202.8	0.5	∞	∞
(p-)	$CH_3C_6H_4OH$	108.13	pr.	$1.035^{20/4}$	35–6	202	1.8	$∞^{36}$	$∞^{36}$
Cresyl benzoate (o-)	$C_6H_5CO_2C_6H_4CH_3$	212.24	lq.	....	....	308	i.		
(m-)	$C_6H_5CO_2C_6H_4CH_3$	212.24	cr.	....	55	314	i.		
(p-)	$C_6H_5CO_2C_6H_4CH_3$	212.24	cr.	....	71.5	316	i.		
Crotonic acid (α-)	$CH_3CH{:}CHCO_2H$	86.09	col. mn.	$0.964^{79.7}$	72	189	8.3^{15}		
acid (β-)(cis-)	$CH_3CH{:}CHCO_2H$	86.09	nd.	$1.031^{15/4}$	15.5	170–1 d.	$∞^{25}$	s.	
aldehyde (α)	$CH_3CH{:}CHCHO$	70.09	col. lq.	$0.853^{20/20}$	−69	102.2	18	∞	∞
Cumene	$C_6H_5CH(CH_3)_2$	120.19	col. lq.	$0.862^{20/4}$	−96.9	152.5	i.	∞	∞
Cumic acid (p-)	$(CH_3)_2CH.C_6H_4CO_2H$	164.20	tri.	1.162^{4}	116–7	subl.	0.02^{25}	s.	s.
Cumidine (p-)	$(CH_3)_2CH.C_6H_4NH_2$	135.20	lq.	0.953	< −20	225^{761}	i.		
Cyanamide	$H_2N.CN$	42.04	col. nd.	$1.073^{48/4}$	44–5	140^{19}	v. s.	v. s.	v. s.
Cyanic acid	HOCN or HNCO	43.03	gas	1.140^{0}	−80	-64^{0}	sl. s.	....	s.
Cyanoacetic acid	$CH_2(CN)CO_2H$	85.06	col. lq.	....	65–6	$108^{0.2}$	s.	s.	s.
Cyanogen	$(CN)_2$	52.04	col. gas	0.866^{17}	−34.4	−21	450^{20} cc.	2300^{20} cc.	500^{20} cc.
bromide	BrCN	105.93	nd.	$2.015^{20/4}$	52	61.3^{750}	s.	s.	s.
chloride	ClCN	61.48	gas	1.222^{0}	−6.5	12.5–13	2500^{20} cc.	v. s.	5000^{20} cc.
Cyanuric acid	$C_3H_3O_3N_3.2H_2O$	165.11	mn./aq.	$1.768^{0/4}$	>360	d.	0.27^{17}	0.1^{22}	
Cyclo-butane	$CH_2 < (CH_2)_2 > CH_2$	56.10	col. gas	$0.703^{0/4}$	−50	$11–12^{726}$	i.	v. s.	
-heptane	$CH_2 < (CH_2CH_2CH_2)_2 >$	98.18	oil	$0.810^{20/4}$	−12	118–20	i.		
-hexane	$CH_2 < (CH_2CH_2)_2 > CH_2$	84.16	col. lq.	$0.779^{20/4}$	6.5	80–1	i.	∞	∞
-hexanol	$CH_2 < (CH_2CH_2)_2 > CHOH$	100.16	col. nd.	$0.962^{20/4}$	23.9	160–1	3.6^{20}	s.	s.
-hexanone	$CH_2 < (CH_2CH_2)_2 > CO$	98.14	col. oil	$0.947^{19/4}$	−45	155–6	s.	s.	s.
-hexene	$(.CH_2.CH_2CH{:})_2$	82.14	lq.	$0.810^{20/4}$	−103.7	83.3	v. sl. s.	v. s.	v. s.
-hexyl acetate	$CH_3CO_2C_6H_{11}$	142.19	oil	$0.985^{0/4}$	....	174^{750}	i.	∞	∞
amine	$CH_2 < (CH_2CH_2)_2 > CHNH_2$	99.17	col. lq.	$0.865^{20/0}$	....	134	i.	s.	
bromide	$CH_2 < (CH_2CH_2)_2 > CHBr$	163.06	col. lq.	$1.324^{20/20}$	....	165^{714}	i.	s.	s.
chloride	$CH_2 < (CH_2CH_2)_2 > CHCl$	118.61	col. lq.	$0.977^{18/4}$	−43.9	142	i.	....	∞
-pentadiene (1-,3-)	$CH_2 < (CH{:}CH)_2 >$	66.10	col. lq.	$0.805^{19/4}$	−85	41–2	i.	∞	∞
-pentane	$CH_2 < (CH_2CH_2)_2 >$	70.13	col. oil	$0.745^{20/4}$	−93.3	49–50	i.		
-pentanone	$<(CH_2CH_2)_2 > CO$	84.11	col. oil	0.948^{20}	−58.2	129–30	v. sl. s.		
-propane	$<CH_2CH_2CH_2>$	42.08	col. gas	0.720^{-79}	−126.6	-34^{749}	i.	s.	s.
Cymene (o-)	$CH_3.C_6H_4CH(CH_3)_2$	134.21	col. lq.	$0.875^{20/4}$	....	177	i.	s.	s.
(m-)	$CH_3.C_6H_4CH(CH_3)_2$	134.21	col. lq.	0.862^{20}	< −25	175–6	i.	s.	s.
(p-)	$CH_3.C_6H_4CH(CH_3)_2$	134.21	col. lq.	$0.857^{20/4}$	−73.5	176–7	i.	s.	s.
Cystine (l-)	$[.SCH_2CH(NH_2)CO_2H]_2$	240.29	pl.		d. 258–61	....	0.01^{19}	i.	
Dambose	$C_6H_6(OH)_6$	180.16	mn./aq.	1.752	253	319^{15}	2^{12}	i.	i.
Decahydronaphthalene (cis-)	$C_{10}H_{18}$	138.24	lq.	$0.895^{18/4}$	−51	193.3	i.	s.	s.
(trans-)	$C_{10}H_{18}$	138.24	lq.	$0.872^{20/4}$	−32	185.3	i.	s.	s.
Decane (n-)	$CH_3(CH_2)_8CH_3$	142.28	col. lq.	0.730^{2}	−29.7	174.0	i.	s.	∞
Decyl alcohol	$CH_3(CH_2)_8CH_2OH$	158.28	col. oil	$0.830^{20/4}$	7	232.9	i.	s.	
Dextrin	$(C_6H_{10}O_5)x$	162.14	amor.	1.038	....	....	s.	i.	i.
Diacetone alcohol	$(CH_3)_2C(OH).CH_2COCH_3$	116.16	lq.	0.931^{25}	−47	167.9	∞	∞	∞
Diamino-benzophenone (4-,4′-)	$H_2NC_6H_4COC_6H_4NH_2$	212.24	yel. nd.	....	237–9	....	sl. s. h.	s.	s.
-diphenylamine (4-,4′-)	$H_2NC_6H_4NHC_6H_4NH_2$	199.25	lf./aq.	....	158	d.	sl. s.	s.	s.
-diphenylmethane (4-,4′-)	$H_2NC_6H_4CH_2C_6H_4NH_2$	198.26	nd./aq.	....	93–4	$249–53^{15}$	sl. s. c.	s.	s.
-diphenylurea (4-,4′-)	$(H_2NC_6H_4NH)_2CO$	242.28	cr.	....	subl. 310	....	v. sl. s.		
Diamyl-amine (i-)	$[(CH_3)_2CHCH_2CH_2]_2NH$	157.29	col. lq.	$0.767^{21/4}$	−44	188–90	sl. s.	s.	∞
ether (n-)	$(C_2H_5CH_2CH_2CH_2)_2O$	158.28	col. lq.	$0.774^{20/4}$	−69	190	i.	∞	∞
(i-)	$[(CH_3)_2CH(CH_2)_2]_2O$	158.28	col. lq.	$0.777^{20/4}$	....	173.4	i.	∞	∞

Table 3-2. Physical Properties of Organic Compounds—*(Continued)*

Name	Formula	Formula weight	Form and color	Specific gravity	Melting point, °C.	Boiling point, °C.	Solubility in 100 parts: Water	Alcohol	Ether
Diamyl ketone (i-)	$[(CH_3)_2CHCH_2CH_2]_2CO$	170.29	yel. oil	$0.821^{25/4}$	14.6	228	i.	s.	s.
phthalate (n-)	$C_6H_4(CO_2C_5H_{11})_2$	306.39	col. lq.	....	....	$204\text{–}6^{11}$			
(i-)	$C_6H_4(CO_2C_5H_{11})_2$	306.39	col. lq.	1.03	....	225^{40}	i.	s.	s.
tartrate (i-)	$(HOCH.CO_2C_5H_{11})_2$	290.35	lq.	$1.063^{15/4}$	....	195^{16}	i.		
Dianisidine (o-)(4-,3-)$_2$	$[NH_2(OCH_3)C_6H_3]_2$	244.28	col. lf.	....	131.5	....	i.	s.	s.
Diazo-aminobenzene	$C_6H_5N{:}N.NHC_6H_5$	197.23	yel. lf.	....	96–8	expl.	i.	s. h.	v. s.
-aminotoluene (2-,2′-)	$C_7H_7N{:}N.NHC_7H_7$	225.28	or. cr.	....	51	....	0.05		
-methane	$CH_2{:}N_2$	42.04	gas	....	−145	−23	d.	....	s.
Dibenzothiazyl-disulfide (2-,2′-)	$(C_6H_4NSC)_2S_2$	232.46	cr.	1.50	180	d.	i.		
Dibenzoyl methane	$(C_6H_5CO)_2CH_2$	224.25	rhb./al.	....	78	$219\text{–}21^{18}$	i.	4.4^{20}	s.
Dibenzyl-amine	$(C_6H_5CH_2)_2NH$	197.27	col. oil	$1.028^{25/25}$	−26	$268\text{–}71^{250}$	i.	s.	s.
-aniline	$C_6H_5N(CH_2C_6H_5)_2$	273.36	pr./al.	....	70–1	>300	i.	v. s. h.	s.
ketone	$(C_6H_5CH_2)_2CO$	210.26	cr.	....	34–5	330.6	i.		
phthalate (o-)	$C_6H_4(CO_2CH_2C_6H_5)_2$	346.36	pr./al.	....	42–3	274^{12}	v. sl. s.	s.	s.
succinate	$(.CH_2CO_2CH_2C_6H_5)_2$	298.32	lf./al.	....	45–6	238^{14}	i.	s.	s.
Dibromo-benzene (o-)	$C_6H_4Br_2$	235.92	col. lq.	$1.956^{20/4}$	1.8	221–2	i.	s.	s.
(m-)	$C_6H_4Br_2$	235.92	col. lq.	$1.952^{20/4}$	−6.9	219^{755}	i.	s.	s.
(p-)	$C_6H_4Br_2$	235.92	pl./al.	2.261^{18}	87–8	218.6^{758}	i.	1.6	71^{25}
-diphenyl (4-,4′-)	$BrC_6H_4.C_6H_4Br$	312.02	mn. pr.	1.897	164–5	355–60	i.	v. sl. s. h.	
Dibutyl-adipate (n-)	$(.CH_2CH_2CO_2C_4H_9)_2$	258.35	col. lq.	$0.965^{20/4}$	−38	183^{14}	i.	∞	∞
(i-)	$(.CH_2CH_2CO_2C_4H_9)_2$	258.35	col. lq.	0.950^{25}	−20	278–80	i.		
-amine (n-)	$(C_2H_5CH_2CH_2)_2NH$	129.24	col. lq.	$0.768^{20/20}$	....	159^{761}	∞	∞	∞
(i-)	$[(CH_3)_2CHCH_2]_2NH$	129.24	col. lq.	$0.741^{25/4}$	−70	139–40	v. sl. s.	s.	s.
-p-aminophenol (s-)	$(C_4H_9)_2N.C_6H_4OH$	221.33	lq.	....	....	170^{10}	i.		
-aniline (n-)	$C_6H_5N(C_4H_9)_2$	205.33	lq.	....	....	262.8	i.	∞	∞
carbonate (n-)	$CO(OC_4H_9)_2$	174.23	col. lq.	$0.924^{20/4}$	....	207^{740}	i.	s.	
(i-)	$CO(OC_4H_9)_2$	174.23	col. lq.	0.919^{15}	....	190	i.		
(s-)	$CO(OC_4H_9)_2$	174.23	col. lq.	....	....	178–80			
ether (n-)	$(C_2H_5CH_2CH_2)_2O$	130.22	lq.	$0.769^{20/20}$	−98	142.4	<0.05	∞	∞
(i-)	$[(CH_3)_2CHCH_2]_2O$	130.22	lq.	0.762^{15}	....	122.5	i.	∞	∞
(s-)	$[C_2H_5(CH_3)CH]_2O$	130.22	lq.	0.756^{21}	....	121	i.	∞	∞
ketone (n-)	$(C_2H_5CH_2CH_2)_2CO$	142.23	lq.	$0.827^{13/4}$	−5.9	187.7	i.	s.	v. s.
(i-)	$[(CH_3)_2CHCH_2]_2CO$	142.23	oil	$0.805^{21/4}$	....	168.1	<0.06	∞	∞
malate (l-)(n-)	$C_2H_4O(CO_2C_4H_9)_2$	246.30	lq.	$1.038^{20/4}$	....	$170\text{–}1^{13}$	v. sl. s.		
oxalate (n-)	$(.CO_2C_4H_9)_2$	202.24	col. lq.	$0.986^{20/4}$	−29.6	245.5	i.	s.	s.
phthalate (n-)	$C_6H_4(CO_2C_4H_9)_2$	278.34	col. lq.	1.045^{21}	....	340	0.04^{25}	∞	∞
tartrate (d-)(n-)	$(CHOHCO_2C_4H_9)_2$	262.30	pr.	1.098^{15}	22–2.5	$200\text{–}3^{18}$	i.		
(d-)(i-)	$(CHOHCO_2C_4H_9)_2$	262.30	cr.	$1.031^{75/4}$	73–4	323–5	v. sl. s.		
Dichloro-acetic acid	$Cl_2CH.CO_2H$	128.95	lq.	$1.560^{25/25}$	9.7(−4)	194.4	∞	∞	∞
-acetone (αα-)	$Cl_2CHCOCH_3$	126.98	lq.	1.234^{15}	....	120	v. sl. s.	s.	s.
-aniline (2-,5-)	$Cl_2C_6H_3NH_2$	162.02	nd.	....	50	251	v. sl. s.	s.	s.
-anthraquinone (1-,3-)	$C_6H_4{:}(CO)_2{:}C_6H_2Cl_2$	277.10	yel. nd.	....	208–9	....	i.	i.	
(1-,4-)	$C_6H_4{:}(CO)_2{:}C_6H_2Cl_2$	277.10	yel. nd.	....	187.5	....	i.	v. sl. s.	v. sl. s.
(1-,5-)	$C_6H_3Cl{:}(CO)_2{:}C_6H_3Cl$	277.10	yel. nd.	....	251	....	i.	sl. s.	
(1-,6-)	$C_6H_3Cl{:}(CO)_2{:}C_6H_3Cl$	277.10	yel. nd.	....	203–4	....	i.		
(1-,8-)	$C_6H_3Cl{:}(CO)_2{:}C_6H_3Cl$	277.10	yel. nd.	....	202–3	....	i.	sl. s.	
(2-,3-)	$C_6H_4{:}(CO)_2{:}C_6H_2Cl_2$	277.10	yel. nd.	....	268–70	....	i.	sl. s.	
(2-,6-)	$C_6H_3Cl{:}(CO)_2{:}C_6H_3Cl$	277.10	yel. nd.	....	282	....	i.		
(2-,7-)	$C_6H_3Cl{:}(CO)_2{:}C_6H_3Cl$	277.10	yel. nd.	....	210–11	....	i.		
-benzene (o-)	$C_6H_4Cl_2$	147.01	col. lq.	$1.305^{20/4}$	−17.6	179	i.	∞	∞
(m-)	$C_6H_4Cl_2$	147.01	col. lq.	$1.288^{20/4}$	−24.8	172^{766}	i.	s.	s.
(p-)	$C_6H_4Cl_2$	147.01	col. mn.	1.458^{21}	53	174^{764}	i.	v. s.	v. s.
-butane (n-)(1-,4-)	$ClCH_2(CH_2)_2CH_2Cl$	127.02	lq.	....	−38.7	161–3			
-diphenyl (4-,4′-)	$ClC_6H_4.C_6H_4Cl$	223.10	pr.	$1.442^{0/4}$	148	315–9	i.	v. sl. s.	4^{25}
-ethane (1-,2-)	$ClCH_2.CH_2Cl$	98.97	col. lq.	$1.256^{20/20}$	−35.3	83.7	0.9^{0}	∞	∞
-naphthalene (β-)(1-,4-)	$C_{10}H_6Cl_2$	197.06	nd./al.	$1.300^{76/4}$	67–8	$286\text{–}7^{740}$	i.	v. sl. s.	
(γ-)(1-,5-)	$C_{10}H_6Cl_2$	197.06	lf./al.	....	107	subl.	i.	s.	s.
-nitrobenzene (2-,5-)	$Cl_2C_6H_3NO_2$	192.01	tri./al.	1.669^{22}	54.6	266	i.	v. s. h.	
-pentane (1-,5-)	$ClCH_2(CH_2)_3CH_2Cl$	141.04	col. lq.	$1.094^{25/4}$	....	180–1	i.	s.	s.
-phenol (2-,4-)	$Cl_2C_6H_3OH$	163.01	nd.	$1.383^{60/25}$	45	209–10	0.45^{20}	v. s.	v. s.
Dichloramine T (p-)	$CH_3C_6H_4SO_2NCl_2$	240.11	cr.	....	83	....	sl. s.		
Dicyandiamide	$H_2N.C({:}NH).NH.CN$	84.08	mn. pl.	1.40^{14}	207–8	d.	2.3^{13}	1.3^{13}	0.01^{13}
Diethanolamine	$HN(CH_2CH_2OH)_2$	105.14	pr.	$1.097^{20/4}$	28	270^{748}	∞	∞	v. sl. s.
Diethyl adipate	$(.CH_2CH_2CO_2C_2H_5)_2$	202.24	col. lq.	$1.009^{20/4}$	−21	$239\text{–}41^{761}$	0.43^{30}	s.	s.
-amine	$(C_2H_5)_2NH$	73.14	col. lq.	$0.712^{15/15}$	−38.9	55.5^{759}	v. s.	∞	∞
-aminophenol (m-)	$(C_2H_5)_2N.C_6H_4.OH$	165.23	rhb.	....	78	276–80	s.		

-aniline	$(C_2H_5)_2NC_6H_5$	149.23	oil	$0.934^{20/4}$	−34.4	216	1.4^{12}	s.	s.
sulfonic acid (m-)	$(C_2H_5)_2NC_6H_4SO_3H$	229.29	cr.	....	270 d.	....	s.		
carbonate	$OC(OC_2H_5)_2$	118.13	col. lq.	$0.975^{20/4}$	−43	126^{759}	i.	∞	∞
diethyl malonate	$(C_2H_5)_2C(CO_2C_2H_5)_2$	216.27	col. lq.	$0.985^{20/4}$	....	230	i.	∞	∞
Diethyl dimethyl malonate	$(CH_3)_2C(CO_2C_2H_5)_2$	188.22	col. lq.	$0.994^{25/25}$	....	196.7	i.	∞	∞
glutarate	$CH_2(CH_2CO_2C_2H_5)_2$	188.22	syrup	1.025^{21}	−24	237	0.88^{20}	v. s.	s.
ketone	$(C_2H_5)_2CO$	86.13	col. lq.	$0.816^{19/4}$	−42	101.7	4.7^{20}	∞	∞
malonate	$CH_2(CO_2C_2H_5)_2$	160.17	col. lq.	$1.055^{20/4}$	−49.8	198.9	2.08^{20}	∞	∞
-malonic acid	$(C_2H_5)_2C(CO_2H)_2$	160.17	pr./aq.	....	125	d. 170–80	65^{16}	v. s.	v. s.
-naphthylamine (α-)	$C_{10}H_7N(C_2H_5)_2$	199.28	col. oil	1.005	....	285–90	i.	∞	∞
(β-)	$C_{10}H_7N(C_2H_5)_2$	199.28	col. oil	1.026	....	318	i.	∞	∞
oxalate	$(.CO_2C_2H_5)_2$	146.14	col. lq.	$1.079^{20/4}$	−40.6	186	v. sl. s.	∞	∞
phthalate (o-)	$C_6H_4(CO_2C_2H_5)_2$	222.23	col. lq.	$1.121^{25/25}$	....	298–9	i.	∞	∞
sulfate	$O_2S(OC_2H_5)_2$	154.18	col. lq.	$1.172^{25/4}$	−25	210	i.	s.	∞
sulfide	$(C_2H_5)_2S$	90.18	col. lq.	$0.837^{20/4}$	−99.5	$92–3^{754}$	0.31^{20}	∞	∞
tartrate (d-)	$(CHOH.CO_2C_2H_5)_2$	206.19	lq.	$1.204^{20/4}$	17	280	sl. s.	∞	∞
-toluidine (o-)	$CH_3.C_6H_4.N(C_2H_5)_2$	163.25	lq.	....	....	$208–9^{755}$	i.	s.	s.
(m-)	$CH_3.C_6H_4.N(C_2H_5)_2$	163.25	lq.	....	....	231–2	i.	s.	s.
(p-)	$CH_3.C_6H_4.N(C_2H_5)_2$	163.25	lq.	$0.924^{15.5}$	....	228–9	i.		
Diethyleneglycol dinitrate	$O(CH_2CH_2ONO_2)_2$	196.12	lq.	$1.377^{25/4}$	−11.3	....	i.		
Difluorodichloromethane	F_2CCl_2	120.92	gas	1.486^{-30}	−155	−29.2	5.7 cc.^{26}	s.	s.
Diglycerol	$[(HO)_2C_3H_5]_2O$	166.17	lq.	....	....	$220–30^{10}$	s. h.	....	i.
Dihydroxy-dinaphthyl (α-)	$(HO.C_{10}H_6.)_2$	286.31	pl./al.	....	300	....	i.	s.	v. s.
(-2,-2′,-1,-1′)	$(HO.C_{10}H_6.)_2$	286.31	nd./al.	....	218	subl.	i.	s.	v. s.
-diphenyl (4-,4′-)	$(HO.C_6H_4.)_2$	186.20	rhb./al.	1.25	270–2	subl.	sl. s.	v. s.	v. s.
-ethyl formal (β-)	$CH_2(OCH_2CH_2OH)_2$	136.15	lq.	1.154^{25}	−5.3	264	∞		
-naphthalene (1-,5-)	$C_{10}H_6(OH)_2$	160.16	pr./aq.	....	258–60	d.	sl. s.	s.	v. s.
(1-,8-)	$C_{10}H_6(OH)_2$	160.16	nd.	....	140	....	sl. s. h.	....	v. s.
Dimethoxy-benzene (p-)	$(CH_3O)_2C_6H_4$	138.16	lf.	$1.053^{55/55}$	56	212.6	v. sl. s.	v. s.	v. s.
-diphenylamine (4-,4′-)	$HN(C_6H_4OCH_3)_2$	229.26	cr.	....	103	....	i.		
-ethyl adipate	$(CH_2)_4(CO_2C_2H_4OCH_3)_2$	262.30	lq.	$1.075^{15.6}$	....	$145–50^{2}$	5		
Dimethyl adipate	$[(CH_2)_2CO_2CH_3]_2$	174.19	col. lq.	$1.063^{20/4}$	10–1	115^{13}	i.		
-amine	$(CH_3)_2NH$	45.08	col. lq.	$0.680^{0/4}$	−96	7.4	v. s.	s.	s.
-aminoazobenzene (p-)	$C_6H_5N{:}N.C_6H_4N(CH_3)_2$	225.28	yel./al.	....	116–7	d.	i.	s.	s.
-aminoethanol	$(CH_3)_2NCH_2CH_2OH$	89.14	col. lq.	$0.887^{20/4}$	....	135^{758}	∞		
-aminophenol (m-)	$(CH_3)_2NC_6H_4OH$	137.18	nd.	....	85	265–8	sl. s. h.	s.	s.
-aniline	$(CH_3)_2NC_6H_5$	121.18	yel. lq.	$0.956^{20/4}$	2.5	193	i.	s.	s.
sulfonic acid (m-)	$(CH_3)_2NC_6H_4SO_3H$	201.24	cr.	....	d. 266	....	s.		
(p-)	$(CH_3)_2NC_6H_4SO_3H.H_2O$	219.25	pr.	....	257	....	s. h.	v. sl. s.	v. sl. s.
carbonate	$OC(OCH_3)_2$	90.08	col. lq.	$1.070^{20/4}$	0.5	89–90	i.	∞	∞
ether	CH_3OCH_3	46.07	gas	....	−138.5	−23.7	3700 cc.^{18}	s.	s.
-formamide	$HCON(CH_3)_2$	73.09	lq.	0.945^{25}	−58.3	152.8	∞		
fumarate	$(:CHCO_2CH_3)_2$	144.12	col. tri.	....	102	192	i.	sl. s.	sl. s.
glutarate	$(CH_2)_3(CO_2CH_3)_2$	160.17	lq.	$1.089^{15.6}$	−37	130^{50}			
glyoxime	$(CH_3.C{:}NOH)_2$	116.12	col. cr.	....	240–6	....	0.06^{20}	v. s.	v. s.
-naphthalene (1-,4-)	$C_{10}H_6(CH_3)_2$	156.22	lq.	$1.016^{20/4}$	<−18	264–6	i.		
(2-,3-)	$C_{10}H_6(CH_3)_2$	156.22	lf./al.	....	104	265^{767}	i.	sl. s.	
-naphthylamine (α-)	$C_{10}H_7N(CH_3)_2$	171.23	col. oil	1.042^{20}	....	274.5^{711}	i.	s.	s.
(β-)	$C_{10}H_7N(CH_3)_2$	171.23	col. cr.	$1.039^{70/70}$	46	304–5	i.	s.	s.
oxalate	$(.CO_2CH_3)_2$	118.09	col. mn.	1.148^{54}	54	163.3	6	s.	s.
phthalate (o-)	$C_6H_4(CO_2CH_3)_2$	194.18	col. lq.	$1.189^{25/25}$	....	280^{734}	0.43		
sulfate	$(CH_3O)_2SO_2$	126.13	col. oil	$1.352^{0/4}$	−26.8	188.3	v. sl. s.	∞	∞
sulfide	$(CH_3)_2S$	62.13	oil	$0.846^{21/4}$	−83.2	37.3	i.	s.	s.
tartrate (d-)	$(CHOH.CO_2CH_3)_2$	178.14	cr.	$1.328^{20/4}$	61.5	280	s.	200^{15}	
-vinyl-ethenyl carbinol	$(CH_3)_2COH.C{:}C.CH{:}CH_2$	110.15	lq.	$0.887^{20/4}$	....	150	6^{29}		
Dinaphthyl (αα-)	$C_{10}H_7.C_{10}H_7$	254.31	lf./al.	....	160	$240–4^{12}$	i.	s. h.	s.
-methane (αα′-)	$(C_{10}H_7)_2CH_2$	268.34	pr./al.	....	109	>360	i.	0.8 c.	v. s.
(β,β′-)	$(C_{10}H_7)_2CH_2$	268.34	nd./al.	....	92	....	i.	s.	
Dinitro-anisole (1-)(2-,4-)	$CH_3OC_6H_3(NO_2)_2$	198.13	col. mn.	1.341^{20}	94–5	....	sl. s. h.	1.5^{20}	
-benzene (o-)	$C_6H_4(NO_2)_2$	168.11	col. mn.	1.59^{18}	117–8	319^{774}	0.01 c.	1.9^{21}	
(m-)	$C_6H_4(NO_2)_2$	168.11	col. rhb.	$1.575^{20/4}$	89.8	300–2	0.3^{99}	3^{20}	
(p-)	$C_6H_4(NO_2)_2$	168.11	col. mn.	1.625^{18}	173–4	299^{777}	0.18^{100}	0.18^{21}	
sulfonic acid (2-,4-)(1-)	$(NO_2)_2C_6H_3SO_3H.3H_2O$	302.22	pr.	....	106–8	....	s.	s.	v. sl. s.
-benzoic acid (2-,4-)	$(NO_2)_2C_6H_3CO_2H$	212.12	cr./aq.	....	179–80	....	1.85^{25}	s.	
(3-,5-)	$(NO_2)_2C_6H_3CO_2H$	212.12	mn. pr.	....	204–5	subl.	s h.	v. s.	sl. s.
-benzophenone (4-,4′-)	$(NO_2C_6H_4)_2CO$	272.21	col. nd.	....	189	....	i.		
-diphenyl (4-,4′-)	$(NO_2C_6H_4)_2$	244.20	nd./al.	1.445	233	....	i.	1.5^{20}	
(2-,4′-)	$(NO_2C_6H_4)_2$	244.20	mn.	1.474	93.5	....	i.	v. s. h.	
-naphthalene (1-,5-)	$C_{10}H_6(NO_2)_2$	218.16	nd.	....	216	subl.	i.		
(1-,8-)	$C_{10}H_6(NO_2)_2$	218.16	rhb.	....	170–2	d.	i.	0.2 c.	

Table 3-2. Physical Properties of Organic Compounds—(*Continued*)

Name	Formula	Formula weight	Form and color	Specific gravity	Melting point, °C.	Boiling point, °C.	Solubility in 100 parts: Water	Alcohol	Ether
Dinitro-phenol (2-,3-)	$(NO_2)_2C_6H_3OH$	184.11	yel. mn.	1.681^{20}	144-5	....	sl. s.	v. s. h.	v. s.
(2-,4-)	$(NO_2)C_6H_3OH$	184.11	yel. rhb.	1.683^{24}	114-5	subl.	0.5 c.	4^{20}	v. s. h.
(2-,6-)	$(NO_2)C_6H_3OH$	184.11	yel. rhb.	....	63-4	....	s. h.	s. h.	s.
-salicylic acid (3-,5-)	$(NO_2)_2C_6H_2(OH)CO_2H.H_2O$	246.13	pl./aq.	....	173 d.	....	s. c.	v. s.	v. s.
-stilbene (4-,4′-)	$(NO_2C_6H_4CH:)_2$	270.24	yel. lf.	....	210-6	....	i.	v. sl. s.	v. sl. s.
-toluene (2-,4-)	$(NO_2)_2C_6H_3CH_3$	182.13	nd.	1.321^{71}	70	300	0.03^{22}	1.2^{15}	9^{15}
(3-,4-)	$(NO_2)_2C_6H_3CH_3$	182.13	nd.	1.259^{111}	60-1	....	i.		
(3-,5-)	$(NO_2)_2C_6H_3CH_3$	182.13	mn. pr.	1.277^{111}	92-3	subl.	sl. s.	s. h.	s.
Dioxane	$O < (CH_2.CH_2)_2 > O$	88.10	col. lq.	$1.033^{20/4}$	9.5-10.5	101.1	∞	s.	s.
Dipentene	$C_{12}H_{10}$	136.23	col. lq.	0.865^{18}	....	178	i.		
Diphenyl	$C_6H_5.C_6H_5$	154.20	col. mn.	$0.992^{73/4}$	69-70	254.9	i.	10^{20}	6.6^{20}
-amine	$C_6H_5NHC_6H_5$	169.22	col. mn.	$1.160^{20/20}$	52.9	302	0.03^{25}	$56^{19.5}$	s.
carbonate	$O(COC_6H_5)_2$	214.21	nd./al.	1.272^{14}	80	302-6	i.	v. s.	s.
-chloroarsine	$(C_6H_5)_2AsCl$	264.57	rhb.	1.583^{40}	43-4	d. 327	0.2 d.	20	s.
-ethane	$(C_6H_5CH_2.)_2$	182.25	col. pr.	$0.978^{50/50}$	52-3	284	i.	s.	v. s.
ether	$C_6H_5OC_6H_5$	170.20	col. rhb.	1.073^{20}	27	259	v. sl. s.	s.	∞
guanidine	$(C_6H_5NH)_2C:NH$	211.26	mn./al.	....	147-8	d. >170	v. sl. s.	9^{20}	sl. s.
-methane	$(C_6H_5)_2CH_2$	168.23	col. pr.	$1.001^{26/4}$	26-7	265	i.	v. s.	v. s.
phenylenediamine (p-)	$(C_6H_5NH)_2C_6H_4$	260.32	cr.	....	152	....	i.		
succinate	$(.CH_2CO_2C_6H_5)_2$	270.27	lf./al.	....	122-3	330	i.	....	s.
sulfide	$(C_6H_5)_2S$	186.26	col. lq.	$1.119^{15/15}$	<-40	296-7	i.	s. h.	∞
sulfone	$(C_6H_5)_2SO_2$	218.26	nd./aq.	$1.248^{25/4}$	128-9	379	sl. s. h.	s. h.	
urea (uns.)	$(C_6H_5)_2NCONH_2$	212.24	rhb.	1.276	189	....	v. sl. s.	s.	s.
Diphenylene oxide	$< (C_6H_4)_2O$	168.18	lf./al.	....	86-7	287-8	i.	s. h.	v. s.
Dipropyl adipate (n-)	$(.CH_2CH_2CO_2C_3H_7)_2$	230.30	col. lq.	$0.979^{20/4}$	-20.3	$143\text{-}5^{10}$	i.	s.	s.
-amine (n-)	$(C_2H_5CH_2)_2NH$	101.19	col. lq.	$0.739^{20/4}$	-39.6	110-1	s.	∞	∞
(i-)	$[(CH_3)_2CH]_2NH$	101.19	col. lq.	0.722^{22}	-61	83.5^{743}	s.	s.	
aniline (n-)	$C_6H_5N(C_3H_7)_2$	177.28	yel. oil	0.910^{20}	....	245.4	i.	s.	s.
carbonate (n-)	$O(COCH_2C_2H_5)_2$	146.18	col. lq.	0.968^{22}	....	168.2	v. sl. s.		
ether (n-)	$(C_2H_5CH_2)_2O$	102.17	col. lq.	$0.744^{21/0}$	-122	91	sl. s.	∞	∞
(i-)	$[(CH_3)_2CH]_2O$	102.17	col. lq.	$0.725^{21/0}$	-60	69	0.2	∞	∞
ketone (n-)	$(C_2H_5CH_2)_2CO$	114.18	col. lq.	$0.822^{20/4}$	-32.6	144.2	0.43	∞	∞
(i-)	$[(CH_3)_2CH]_2CO$	114.18	col. lq.	$0.806^{20/4}$	....	123.7	v. sl. s.	∞	∞
oxalate (n-)	$(CO_2CH_2C_2H_5)_2$	174.19	col. lq.	$1.038^{0/0}$	-51.7	213.5	d. h.		
(i-)	$[CO_2CH(CH_3)_2]_2$	174.19	col. lq.	....	....	190			
Disalicylal ethylenediamine	$[HOC_6H_4CH:NCH_2.]_2$	268.30	cr.	1.34	125-6	....	0.03^{28}		
Ditolyl guanidine (o-)	$(C_7H_7NH)_2C:NH$	239.31	cr.	$1.10^{20/4}$	178-9	....	v. sl. s.	s. h.	s.
Divinyl acetylene	$(H_2C:CH.C:)_2$	78.11	lq.	$0.776^{20/4}$	....	85	i.		
Docosane (n-)	$CH_3(CH_2)_{20}CH_3$	310.59	cr.	$0.778^{44/4}$	44.5	224.5^{15}	i.	4 h.	v. s.
Dodecane (n-)	$CH_3(CH_2)_{10}CH_3$	170.33	lq.	$0.751^{20/4}$	-9.6	214.5	i.	v. s.	v. s.
Dulcitol	$CH_2OH(CHOH)_4CH_2OH$	182.17	mn.	1.466^{15}	189	$290\text{-}5^{3}$	3.2^{15}	v. sl. s.	i.
Durene (1-,2-,4-,5-)	$(CH_3)_4C_6H_2$	134.21	mn.	$0.838^{81/4}$	79-80	193-5	i.	s.	s.
Elaidic acid	$C_8H_{17}CH:CH(CH_2)_7CO_2H$	282.45	lf./al.	$0.851^{79/4}$	51-2	288^{100}	i.	v. s.	v. s.
Eosine	$C_{20}H_8O_5Br_4$	647.93	col. cr.	....	....	....	i.	s.	
Ephedrine (l-)	$C_6H_5CHOHCH(CH_3)NHCH_3$	165.23	cr./et.	....	40	255	5	500	s.
Epichlorhydrin (α-)	$C_2H_3O.CH_2Cl$	92.53	lq.	$1.183^{25/25}$	-25.6	117^{756}	<5	∞	∞
Epidichlorohydrin (α-)	$CH_2:CCl.CH_2Cl$	110.98	col. lq.	1.204^{25}	....	94	i.	∞	∞
Erythritol (dl-)	$CH_2OH(CHOH)_2CH_2OH$	122.12	tet. pr.	$1.451^{20/4}$	126	329-31	60	sl. s. c.	i.
tetranitrate	$C_4H_6(ONO_2)_4$	302.12	lf./al.	....	61	expl.	i. c.	s.	s.
Ethane	CH_3CH_3	30.07	col. gas	0.546^{-88}	-172	-88.6	4.7 cc.[20]	150 cc.	1
Ethanol-amine	$HOCH_2CH_2NH_2$	61.08	col. oil	1.022^{20}	10.5	171^{757}	∞	∞	
formamide	$HCONHCH_2CH_2OH$	89.09	lq.	1.169^{25}	<-40	d.	∞		
Ether	$(CH_3CH_2)_2O$	74.12	col. lq.	$0.708^{25/4}$	-116.3	34.6	7.5^{20}	∞	
Ethyl abietate	$C_{19}H_{29}CO_2C_2H_5$	330.49	lq.	$1.020^{20/20}$	....	200^{4}	i.		
acetate	$CH_3CO_2C_2H_5$	88.10	col. lq.	$0.901^{20/4}$	-82.4	77.1	8.5^{15}	∞	∞
acetoacetate	$CH_3COCH_2CO_2C_2H_5$	130.14	col. lq.	$1.025^{20/4}$	-45	180^{755}	13^{17}	∞	∞
alcohol	CH_3CH_2OH	46.07	col. lq.	$0.789^{20/4}$	-112	78.4	∞	....	∞
-amine	$C_2H_5NH_2$	45.08	col. lq.	$0.689^{15/15}$	-80.6	16.6	∞	∞	∞
hydrochloride	$C_2H_5NH_2.HCl$	81.55	mn.	1.216	108-9	....	240^{17}	v. s.	i.
aniline	$C_6H_5NHC_2H_5$	121.18	lq.	$0.963^{20/4}$	-63.5	204	i.	∞	∞
sulfonic acid (m-)	$C_2H_5NHC_6H_4SO_3H$	201.24	nd./aq.	....	d. 294	....	2.15^{15}		
anisate (p-)	$CH_3OC_6H_4CO_2C_2H_5$	180.20	lq.	$1.103^{25/25}$	7-8	269-70	i.	s.	s.
anthranilate (o-)	$NH_2C_6H_4CO_2C_2H_5$	165.19	cr.	$1.117^{20/4}$	13	266-8	v. sl. s.	s.	s.
benzene	$C_6H_5.C_2H_5$	106.16	col. lq.	$0.867^{20/4}$	-94.4	136.2	0.01^{15}	∞	∞
benzoate	$C_6H_5CO_2C_2H_5$	150.17	col. lq.	$1.052^{15/15}$	-34.6	211-2	0.08^{20}	∞	∞
-benzyl-aniline	$C_6H_5N(C_2H_5)CH_2C_6H_5$	211.29	yel. oil	$1.034^{18.5}$	....	285^{10}	i.	18	∞

bromide	C_2H_5Br	108.98	col. lq.	$1.431^{20/4}$	−117.8	38.4	1.06^{0}	∞	∞
butyrate (n-)	$C_2H_5CH_2CO_2C_2H_5$	116.16	col. lq.	$0.879^{20/4}$	−93.3	120–1	0.68^{25}	∞	∞
(i-)	$(CH_3)_2CHCO_2C_2H_5$	116.16	col. lq.	$0.871^{20/4}$	−88.2	110–1	sl. s.	∞	∞
caprate (n-)	$CH_3(CH_2)_8CO_2C_2H_5$	200.31	lq.	0.859^{28}	−20	244.6^{753}	0.002^{20}	∞	∞
Ethyl caproate (n-)	$CH_3(CH_2)_4CO_2C_2H_5$	144.21	col. lq.	$0.873^{20/20}$	−67.5	$165–6^{736}$	i.	∞	∞
caprylate (n-)	$CH_3(CH_2)_6CO_2C_2H_5$	172.26	col. lq.	0.878^{17}	−45	$207–8^{753}$	i.	∞	∞
chloride	CH_3CH_2Cl	64.52	col. lq.	$0.917^{6/6}$	−139	13	0.45^{0}	∞	∞
chloroacetate	$ClCH_2CO_2C_2H_5$	122.55	col. lq.	$1.159^{20/4}$	−26	144	i.	∞	∞
chlorocarbonate	$ClCO_2CH_2CH_3$	108.53	col. lq.	$1.138^{20/4}$	−80.6	94–5	d.	∞	∞
cinnamate (trans-)	$C_6H_5CH{:}CHCO_2H$	176.21	col. lq.	$1.049^{20/4}$	12	271	i.	∞	∞
cyanoacetate	$CH_2(CN)CO_2C_2H_5$	113.11	col. lq.	$1.062^{20/4}$	−22.5	208^{753}	2^{25}	∞	∞
formate	$HCO_2CH_2CH_3$	74.08	col. lq.	$0.923^{20/4}$	−79	54^{760}	11^{18}	∞	∞
furoate (α)	$OC_4H_3CO_2C_2H_5$	140.13	lf.	$1.117^{21/4}$	34	195^{766}	i.	∞	∞
heptoate	$CH_3(CH_2)_5CO_2C_2H_5$	158.23	col. lq.	$0.872^{20/20}$	−66.1	187–8	0.029^{20}	∞	∞
hypochlorite	$ClOCH_2CH_3$	80.52	yel. lq.	$1.013^{-6/4}$	expl.	36^{752}	......	......	∞
iodide	CH_3CH_2I	155.98	col. lq.	$1.933^{20/4}$	−105	72.4	0.4^{20}	∞	∞
lactate	$CH_3CH(OH)CO_2C_2H_5$	118.13	oil	$1.030^{25/4}$	......	155	∞	∞	∞
laurate	$CH_3(CH_2)_{10}CO_2C_2H_5$	228.36	oil	$0.868^{13/4}$	−10.7	269	i.	s.	∞
mercaptan	CH_3CH_2SH	62.13	lq.	$0.839^{20/4}$	−121	36–7	1.5	s.	s.
methacrylate	$CH_2{:}C(CH_3)CO_2C_2H_5$	114.14	col. lq.	$0.913^{15.6}$	......	118	i.	s.	s.
naphthylamine (α-)	$C_{10}H_7NHC_2H_5$	171.23	oil	$1.060^{20/4}$	......	303^{723}	i.	s.	s.
naphthyl ether (α-)	$C_{10}H_7OC_2H_5$	172.22	cr.	$1.061^{20/20}$	5.5	276.4	i.	s.	s.
nitrate	$C_2H_5ONO_2$	91.07	col. lq.	$1.100^{25/4}$	−102	87–8	1.3^{55}	∞	∞
nitrite	C_2H_5ONO	75.07	lq.	$0.900^{15.5}$	......	17	v. sl. s.	∞	∞
oleate	$C_{17}H_{33}CO_2C_2H_5$	310.50	oil	0.867^{25}	<−15	$216–8^{15}$	i.	∞	∞
palmitate	$CH_3(CH_2)_{14}CO_2C_2H_5$	284.47	col. nd.	$0.858^{25/4}$	24–5	191^{10}	i.	s.	s.
pelargonate	$CH_3(CH_2)_7CO_2C_2H_5$	186.29	col. lq.	$0.866^{17.5}$	−44.5	$227–8^{757}$	i.	∞	∞
propionate	$CH_3CH_2CO_2C_2H_5$	102.13	col. lq.	$0.891^{20/4}$	−72.6	99.1	2.4^{20}	∞	∞
salicylate (o-)	$HOC_6H_4CO_2C_2H_5$	166.17	col. lq.	$1.136^{15/4}$	1.3	233–4	i.	∞	∞
stearate	$CH_3(CH_2)_{16}CO_2C_2H_5$	312.52	col. cr.	$0.848^{36.3}$	33.4(31)	201^{10}	i.	s.	s.
toluate (o-)	$CH_3.C_6H_4CO_2C_2H_5$	164.20	lq.	$1.032^{25/25}$	<−10	227	i.	∞	∞
(m-)	$CH_3.C_6H_4CO_2C_2H_5$	164.20	lq.	$1.030^{20/20}$	......	231^{750}	i.	∞	∞
toluene sulfonate (p-)	$CH_3.C_6H_4SO_3C_2H_5$	200.25	pr./al.	$1.166^{48/4}$	33–4	221.3	i.	s.	s.
toluidine (o-)	$CH_3.C_6H_4NHC_2H_5$	135.20	lq.	$0.948^{25/4}$	<−15	215–6	i.		
(p-)	$CH_3.C_6H_4NHC_2H_5$	135.20	lq.	$0.942^{25/4}$	......	217	i.		
urea	$C_2H_5NH.CO.NH_2$	88.11	nd.	1.213^{18}	92	......	v. s.	80	i.
valerate (n-)	$CH_3(CH_2)_3CO_2C_2H_5$	130.18	col. lq.	0.877^{20}	−91.2	145.5	0.24^{25}	∞	∞
(i-)	$(CH_3)_2CH(CH_2)_2CO_2C_2H_5$	130.18	col. lq.	$0.867^{20/4}$	−99.3	135	0.17^{20}	∞	∞
Ethylal	$CH_2(OC_2H_5)_2$	104.15	lq.	$0.824^{25/4}$	−66.5	89	9^{18}	∞	∞
Ethylene	$H_2C{:}CH_2$	28.05	col. gas	$0.57^{-102/4}$	−169	−103.9	26 cc.^{0}	360 cc.	s.
bromide	$BrCH_2.CH_2Br$	187.88	col. lq.	$2.180^{20/4}$	10	131.5	0.43^{30}	∞	∞
bromohydrin	$BrCH_2.CH_2OH$	124.98	col. lq.	$1.772^{20/4}$	......	150.3	sl. s.	s.	
chlorobromide	$ClCH_2.CH_2Br$	143.43	lq.	1.689^{19}	−16.6	106.7	0.69^{30}		
chlorohydrin	$ClCH_2.CH_2OH$	80.52	col. lq.	$1.213^{20/4}$	−69	128.8	∞	∞	∞
diamine	$H_2NCH_2.CH_2NH_2$	60.10	col. lq.	$0.900^{20/20}$	8.5	117.2	∞	∞	0.3
oxide	$<(CH_2)_2>O$	44.05	lq.	$0.887^{7/4}$	−111.3	13.5^{747}	∞	∞	v. s.
Ethylidene diacetate	$CH_3CH(O_2CCH_3)_2$	146.14	col. lq.	1.061^{12}	18.85	168^{740}	sl. s.	∞	
Eugenol (1-,4-,3-)	$C_3H_5.C_6H_3(OH)OCH_3$	164.20	oil	$1.070^{15/15}$	10.3	253.5	v. sl. s.	∞	∞
(i-)(1-,3-,4-)	$C_3H_5.C_6H_3(OCH_3)OH$	164.20	oil	$1.091^{15/15}$	−10	267.5	v. sl. s.	∞	∞
Fenchyl alcohol (dl-)	$C_{10}H_{17}OH$	154.24	col. cr.	0.935^{40}	35	201	sl. s.		
(d-)(α-)	$C_{10}H_{17}OH$	154.24	col. pr.	$0.964^{20/4}$	45–7	201–2	sl. s.	s.	s.
(i-)(l-)	$C_{10}H_{17}OH$	154.24	col. cr.	0.961	61–2	201–2	i.		
Ferric dimethyl-dithiocarbamate	$Fe[SSCN(CH_3)_2]_3$	416.47	cr.	......	d. 100–30	ign. >150	v. sl. s.		
Fluorene	$(C_6H_4)_2>CH_2$	166.21	cr./al.	$1.203^{0/4}$	115–6	293–5	i.	s. h.	s.
Fluorescein	$C_{20}H_{12}O_5$	332.30	yel. red	......	d. >290	......	v. sl. s. h.	s. h.	
Fluoro-dichloromethane	$FCHCl_2$	102.93	gas	1.426^{0}	−127	14.5	i.	s.	s.
-trichloromethane	Cl_3CF	137.38	col. lq.	$1.494^{17.2}$	......	24.9	i.	∞	∞
Formaldehyde	$HCHO$	30.03	gas	0.815^{-20}	−92	−21	v. s.	v. s.	v. s.
(m-)	$(CH_2O)_3$	90.08	wh.	1.17^{65}	64	114.5^{759}	21^{25}	s.	s.
(p-)	$(CH_2O)_x.xH_2O$	(30.03)	amor.	......	150–60	subl.	$20–30^{18}$	i.	i.
Formamide	$HCONH_2$	45.04	lq.	$1.139^{20/4}$	2	193	∞	∞	v. sl. s.
Formanilide	$HCONHC_6H_5$	121.13	mn.	$1.147^{15/15}$	47	216^{120}	sl. s.	v. s.	s.
Formic acid	HCO_2H	46.03	col. lq.	$1.220^{20/4}$	8.6	100.8	∞	∞	
Fructose	$CH_2OH(CHOH)_3COCH_2OH$	180.16	nd./aq.	$1.669^{17.5}$	95–105	......	v. s.	8^{18}	
Fuchsin	$C_{20}H_{19}N_3HCl$	337.84	red	1.22	d. >200	......	0.3	s.	i.
Fulminic acid	$C{:}NOH$	43.03							
Fumaric acid (trans-)	$HO_2CCH{:}CHCO_2H$	116.07	col. pr.	$1.635^{20/4}$	286–7	290	0.7^{17}	5.8^{30}	0.7^{25}
Furfural	$C_4H_3O.CHO$	96.08	lq.	$1.159^{20/4}$	−38.7	161.7^{760}	9.1^{13}	∞	∞
Furfuran	C_4H_4O	68.07	col. lq.	$0.937^{20/4}$	......	$31–2^{756}$	i.	s.	s.

Table 3-2. Physical Properties of Organic Compounds—(*Continued*)

Name	Formula	Formula weight	Form and color	Specific gravity	Melting point, °C.	Boiling point, °C.	Solubility in 100 parts		
							Water	Alcohol	Ether
Furfuryl acetate	$CH_3CO_2CH_2C_4H_3O$	140.13	col. oil	$1.118^{20/4}$	....	175–7	i.	s.	s.
alcohol	$C_4H_3O.CH_2OH$	98.10	oil	$1.129^{25/4}$	....	169.5^{752}	∞	s.	s.
butyrate	$C_3H_7CO_2CH_2.C_4H_3O$	168.19	col. lq.	$1.053^{20/4}$	....	212–3	v. sl. s.	s.	∞
propionate	$C_2H_5CO_2CH_2.C_4H_3O$	154.16	col. lq.	$1.109^{20/4}$	....	195–6	v. sl. s.	s.	∞
Furoic acid	$C_4H_3O.CO_2H$	112.08	mn. pr.	....	133–4	230–2	3.6^{15}	s.	s.
G-acid, K salt (2-)(6-,8-)	$HOC_{10}H_5(SO_3K)_2$	380.46	cr.	....	....	....	8^{25}		
Na salt (2-)(6-,8-)	$HOC_{10}H_5(SO_3Na)_2$	348.26	cr.	....	....	....	34^{20}		
Galactose (d-)(α-)	$C_5H_{11}O_5.CHO$	180.16	pr.	....	165.5	....	10.3^{0}	0.6^{40}	
Gallic acid (3-,4-,5-)	$(HO)_3C_6H_2CO_2H.H_2O$	188.13	mn./aq.	$1.694^{4/4}$	d. 220	....	1^{13}	28^{15}	2.5^{15}
Gamma acid (2-,8-,6-)	$C_{10}H_5(NH_2)(OH)SO_3H$	239.24	cr.						
Geraniol	$C_9H_{15}CH_2OH$	154.24	col. lq.	0.883^{15}	<−15	230	i.	∞	∞
Glucose (d-)(α-)	$C_5H_{11}O_5.CHO$	180.16	rhb.	1.544^{25}	146	....	$82^{17.5}$	sl. s.	i.
(d-)(β-)	$C_6H_{12}O_6.H_2O$	198.17	cr.	$1.562^{18/4}$	150	....	154^{15}		
Glucuronic acid	$CHO(CHOH)_4CO_2H$	194.14	cr.	....	154	d.	v. s.		
Glutam(in)ic acid (dl-)	$[.CHNH_2(CH_2)_2.](CO_2H)_2$	147.13	cr./aq.	1.460	199 d.	....	1.5^{20}	v. sl. s.	v. sl. s.
Glutaric acid	$CH_2(CH_2CO_2H)_2$	132.11	col. cr.	1.429^{15}	97.5	200^{20}	63.9^{20}	v. s.	v. s.
Glycerol	$CH_2OH.CHOH.CH_2OH$	92.09	col. lq.	$1.260^{50/4}$	17.9	290	∞	∞	i.
acetate (mono-)	$C_5H_{10}O_4$	134.13	col. oil	$1.20^{20/4}$	....	158^{165}	v. s.	v. s.	sl. s.
(di-)	$(CH_3CO_2)_2C_3H_5OH$	176.17	col. lq.	$1.178^{15/15}$	40	$175–6^{40}$	s.	s.	sl. s.
nitrate (mono-) (α-)	$CH_2OH.CHOH.CH_2NO_3$	137.09	col. pr.	1.40^{15}	58–9	155–60	70^{15}	v. s.	v. sl. s.
(β-)	$CH_2OH.CHNO_3.CH_2OH$	137.09	lf.	1.40^{15}	54	155–60	....	v. s.	sl. s.
dinitrate (1-,3-)	$CHOH(CH_2ONO_2)_2$	182.09	oil	1.47^{15}	<−30	$146–8^{15}$	....	v. s.	v. s.
Glyceryl triacetate	$(CH_3CO_2)_3C_3H_5$	218.20	col. lq.	$1.161^{17/4}$	−78	258–9	7.17^{15}	∞	∞
tribenzoate	$(C_6H_5CO_2)_3C_3H_5$	404.40	nd.	1.228^{12}	75–6	d.	i.	s. h.	s.
tributyrate	$(C_2H_5CH_2CO_2)_3C_3H_5$	302.36	col. lq.	$1.032^{20/4}$	<−75	305–9	i.	s.	s.
tricaprate	$[CH_3(CH_2)_8CO_2]_3C_3H_5$	554.83	col. cr.	$0.921^{40/4}$	31(25)	....	i.	s. h.	v. s.
tricaproate	$[CH_3(CH_2)_4CO_2]_3C_3H_5$	386.51	col. lq.	$0.987^{20/4}$	−25	....	i.	s.	s.
tricaprylate	$[CH_3(CH_2)_6CO_2]_3C_3H_5$	470.67	col. lq.	$0.954^{20/4}$	8.3(−21)	....	i.	s.	s.
trilaurate	$[CH_3(CH_2)_{10}CO_2]_3C_3H_5$	638.98	col. nd.	$0.894^{60/4}$	45–6	....	i.	sl. s. c.	v. s.
trimyristate	$[CH_3(CH_2)_{12}CO_2]_3C_3H_5$	723.14	lf.	$0.885^{60/6}$	56.5	....	i.	s.	
trinitrate	$CH_2NO_3.CHNO_3.CH_2NO_3$	227.09	yel. oil	1.601^{15}	13.3(2)	160^{15}	0.18^{20}	50^{20}	∞
trinitrite	$CH_2NO_2.CHNO_2.CH_2NO_2$	179.09	yel. lq.	$1.291^{10/16}$	....	150 sl. d.	d.	d.	s.
trioleate	$(C_{17}H_{33}CO_2)_3C_3H_5$	885.40	col. oil	0.915^{15}	−4	240^{18}	i.	sl. s.	v. s.
tripalmitate	$[CH_3(CH_2)_{14}CO_2]_3C_3H_5$	807.29	col. nd.	$0.866^{80/4}$	65.1	$310–20^{0.1}$	i.	0.004^{21}	v. s.
tristearate	$[CH_3(CH_2)_{16}CO_2]_3C_3H_5$	891.45	col. pr.	$0.862^{80/4}$	70.8(55)	....	i.	s. h.	s. h.
Glycide	$C_2H_3O.CH_2OH$	74.08	col. lq.	$1.114^{16/16}$	....	166 sl. d.	∞	∞	∞
Glycine, Glycocoll	$NH_2CH_2.CO_2H$	75.07	mn.	1.161	232–6 d.	....	23 c.	0.1 c.	i.
Glycol	$CH_2OH.CH_2OH$	62.07	col. lq.	$1.113^{19/4}$	−15.6	197.4	∞	∞	1.0
diacetate	$(CH_3CO_2CH_2.)_2$	146.14	col. lq.	$1.109^{14/4}$	−31	190.5	14.3^{22}	∞	∞
dibenzoate	$(C_6H_5CO_2CH_2.)_2$	270.27	rhb./et.	....	73–4	>360	i.	....	s.
dibutyrate	$(C_3H_7CO_2CH_2.)_2$	202.24	col. lq.	1.024^{0}	....	240	i.	v. s.	v. s.
dicaprylate	$(C_7H_{15}CO_2CH_2.)_2$	314.45	lq.	....	22	....	i.		
diformate	$(HCO_2CH_2.)_2$	118.09	lq.	....	....	174	v. sl. s.		
dilaurate	$(C_{11}H_{23}CO_2CH_2.)_2$	426.66	amor.	....	52–4	188^{20}	i.	v. s.	v. s.
dinitrate	$(O_2NO.CH_2.)_2$	152.07	yel. lq.	$1.482^{21/2}$	−20	expl. 114	0.92^{25}	s.	∞
dinitrite	$(ONO.CH_2.)_2$	120.07	lq.	1.216^{0}	<−15	96–8	i.	s. d.	s.
dipalmitate	$(C_{15}H_{31}CO_2CH_2.)_2$	538.87	nd.	....	71–2	$260^{0.1}$	i.	s.	s.
dipropionate	$(C_2H_5CO_2CH_2.)_2$	174.19	lq.	1.045^{25}	....	211–2	sl. s.	∞	∞
ether	$(HO.CH_2CH_2)_2O$	106.12	lq.	$1.118^{20/20}$	−10.5	244.8	∞	∞	i.
formal	$< O.CH_2CH_2OCH_2 >$	74.08	lq.	$1.060^{20/4}$	....	75–6	∞		
formate (mono-)	$HCO_2CH_2CH_2OH$	90.08	lq.	$1.199^{15/4}$	....	180	∞		
Glycolic acid	$HOCH_2CO_2H$	76.05	nd./aq.	....	79(63)	d.	∞	90^{25}	v. s.
Guaiacol (o-)	$CH_3O.C_6H_4OH$	124.13	pr.	$1.140^{15/15}$	28.3	205	1.7^{15}	v. s.	v. s.
Guanidine	$NH:C(NH_2)_2$	59.07	col. cr.	....	50	....	v. s.	s.	
H-acid, Na salt (1-,8-,3-,6-)	$C_{10}H_8O_7NS_2Na.1\frac{1}{2}H_2O$	368.31	cr.	....	....	....	0.17^{20}		
Heptacosane (n-)	$CH_3(CH_2)_{25}CH_3$	380.72	col. cr.	$0.780^{60/4}$	59.5	270^{15}	i.		
Heptane (n-)	$CH_3(CH_2)_5CH_3$	100.20	col. lq.	$0.684^{20/4}$	−90.6	98.4^{760}	0.005^{15}	sl. s.	∞
(i-)	$(CH_3)_2CH(CH_2)_3CH_3$	100.20	col. lq.	$0.679^{20/4}$	−118.2	90.0	i.	s.	∞
	$C_3H_7.CH(CH_3).C_2H_5$	100.20	col. lq.	$0.687^{20/4}$	−119.4	91.8	i.	s.	∞
	$(CH_3)_3C.CH_2.C_2H_5$	100.20	col. lq.	$0.674^{20/4}$	−125	79.1	i.	s.	∞
	$[(CH_3)_2CH]_2CH_2$	100.20	col. lq.	$0.675^{20/4}$	−119.4	80.8	i.	s.	∞
	$(CH_3)_2C(C_2H_5)_2$	100.20	col. lq.	$0.693^{20/4}$	−135.0	86.0	i.	s.	∞
	$(C_2H_5)_3CH$	100.20	col. lq.	$0.698^{20/4}$	−118.7	93.5	i.	s.	∞
	$(CH_3)_3C.CH(CH_3)_2$	100.20	col. lq.	$0.690^{20/4}$	−25	80.8	i.	s.	∞
Heptoic acid	$CH_3(CH_2)_5CO_2H$	130.18	col. lq.	0.918^{20}	−10	221–2	0.25^{15}	s.	s.
aldehyde	$CH_3(CH_2)_5CHO$	114.18	col. lq.	$0.850^{20/4}$	−42	155	0.02^{20}	∞	∞

Heptyl acetate (n-)	$CH_3CO_2CH_2(CH_2)_5CH_3$	158.24	col. lq.	$0.874^{16/16}$	....	191.5^{759}	i.	s.	s.
alcohol (n-)	$CH_3(CH_2)_5CH_2OH$	116.20	col. lq.	$0.824^{20/4}$	34.6	175^{756}	0.18^{25}	∞	∞
	$[(CH_3)_2CH]_2CHOH$	116.20	col. lq.	$0.829^{20/4}$	....	140	v. sl. s.	∞	∞
	$(C_2H_5.CH_2.CH_2)_2CHOH$	116.20	lq.	$0.820^{20/4}$	−37	156	i.	s.	s.
mercaptan	$CH_3CH(SH).C_5H_{11}$	132.26	lq.	0.835^{20}	....	$174–5^{765}$	i.		
Hexachloro-benzene	C_6Cl_6	284.80	mn.	2.044^{24}	228–31	309^{742}	i.	v. sl. s. h.	s. h.
-ethane	$CCl_3.CCl_3$	236.76	rhb.	$2.091^{20/4}$	186–7	186^{777}	0.005^{22}	v. s.	v. s.
Hexacosane (n-)	$CH_3(CH_2)_{24}CH_3$	366.69	cr.	$0.779^{57/4}$	56.6	262^{15}	i.	v. sl. s.	
Hexadecane (n-)	$CH_3(CH_2)_{14}CH_3$	226.43	lf.	$0.774^{20/4}$	18.5	287.5	i.	∞	∞
Hexaethylbenzene	$C_6(C_2H_5)_6$	246.42	pr./al.	$0.831^{130/4}$	130	298.3	i.	0.75^{25}	8^{25}
Hexamethylbenzene	$C_6(CH_3)_6$	162.26	pl./al.	....	166	265	i.	0.2^{0}	v. s.
Hexamethylene-diamine	$NH_2(CH_2)_6NH_2$	116.20	lf.	....	42	204–5	v. s.	s.	
-diisocyanate	$OCN(CH_2)_6NCO$	168.19	lq.	1.04^{28}	....	$143–4^{20}$	d.	d.	
-glycol	$HO(CH_2)_6OH$	118.17	nd./aq.	....	42	250	s.	s.	sl. s. h.
tetramine	$(CH_2)_6N_4$	140.19	col. rhb.	....	subl.	....	81^{12}	3	v. sl. s.
Hexane (n-)	$CH_3(CH_2)_4CH_3$	86.17	col. lq.	$0.659^{20/4}$	−94	69	0.014^{15}	50^{33}	∞
(i-)	$(CH_3)_2CH(CH_2)_2CH_3$	86.17	lq.	$0.654^{20/4}$	−153.7	60.2	i.	....	s.
(neo-)	$(CH_3)_3C.C_2H_5$	86.17	lq.	$0.649^{20/20}$	−98.2	49.7	i.	....	s.
	$(CH_3)_2CH.CH(CH_3)_2$	86.17	lq.	$0.662^{20/4}$	−129.8	58.0^{760}	i.	....	s.
	$(C_2H_5)_2CHCH_3$	86.17	lq.	$0.664^{20/4}$	−118	63.2	i.	....	s.
Hexyl acetate (n-)	$CH_3CO_2(CH_2)_5CH_3$	144.21	col. lq.	$0.890^{0/0}$	....	169.2	i.	v. s.	v. s.
alcohol (n-)	$CH_3(CH_2)_4CH_2OH$	102.17	col. lq.	$0.820^{20/20}$	−51.6	157.2	0.6^{20}	∞	∞
	$(CH_3)_2CH.C(CH_3)_2OH$	102.17	lq.	$0.821^{20/0}$	−14	120–1	v. sl. s.	∞	∞
	$(CH_3)_2COH.CH_2C_2H_5$	102.17	lq.	$0.809^{20/4}$	−107	123^{762}	v. sl. s.	∞	∞
formate (n-)	$HCO_2CH_2(CH_2)_4CH_3$	130.18	lq.	0.898^{0}	....	153.6	....	∞	∞
resorcinol (2-,4-)	$CH_3(CH_2)_5C_6H_3(OH)_2$	194.26	col. nd.	....	68–70	179^{7}	0.05	v. s.	s.
Hippuric acid	$C_6H_5CONHCH_2CO_2H$	179.17	rhb.	$1.371^{20/4}$	187–8	d.	0.4^{20}	s. h.	0.25^{18}
Histidine (l-)	$C_6H_9O_2N_3$	155.16	lf./aq.	....	d. 287	....	s.	v. sl. s.	i.
Homophthalic acid (o-)	$HO_2C.C_6H_4.CH_2CO_2H$	180.15	cr./aq.	....	175–80	....	s. h.	v. s.	sl. s.
Hydracrylic acid	$HOCH_2CH_2CO_2H$	90.08	syrup	....	....	d.			
Hydro-cyanic acid	HCN	27.03	lq.	0.697^{18}	−12	25–6	∞	∞	∞
-quinone (p-)	$C_6H_4(OH)_2$	110.11	cr.	1.332^{15}	170.3	285^{730}	6^{15}	v. s.	v. s.
Hydroxy-benzaldehyde (p-)	$HO.C_6H_4.CHO$	122.12	nd./aq.	1.129^{130}	116–7	subl.	1.38^{31}		
-benzanilide (o-)	$HO.C_6H_4.CONHC_6H_5$	213.23	pr./al.	....	135	d.	v. sl. s. h.	s.	s.
-quinoline (2-)(α-)	$C_9H_6N.OH$	145.15	pr./al.	....	199–200	subl.	s. h.	v. s.	v. s.
(8-)(o-)	$C_9H_6N.OH$	145.15	pr.	....	75–6	266.6^{752}	v. sl. s. c.	s.	sl. s.
Indigo	$[C_6H_4(CO)(NH)C:]_2$	262.26	cr.	1.35	390–2	subl.	i.	i.	i.
White	$C_{16}H_{12}O_2N_2$	264.27	gray	....	....	....	i.	s.	s.
Indole	C_8H_7N	117.14	lf./aq.	....	52	253–4	s. h.	s. h.	s.
Indoxyl	C_8H_6NOH	133.14	yel. pr.	....	85	110	s.	s.	s.
Iodo-benzene	C_6H_5I	204.02	col. lq.	$1.824^{25/4}$	−28.5	188.6	0.034^{20}	s.	∞
-phenol (p-)	IC_6H_4OH	220.02	nd./aq.	1.857^{112}	93–4	d.	sl. s.	v. s.	v. s.
Iodoform	HCI_3	393.78	yel. hex.	4.008^{17}	119	subl.	0.01^{25}	1.5^{17}	13.6^{25}
Ionone (α-)	$C_{10}H_{16}:CHCOCH_3$	192.29	col. oil	0.930^{20}	....	136.1^{17}	sl. s.	∞	∞
(β-)	$C_{10}H_{16}:CHCOCH_3$	192.29	col. oil	$0\ 944^{20}$	....	140^{18}	sl. s.	∞	∞
Irone (β-)	$C_{14}H_{22}O$	206.32	col. oil	0.939^{20}	....	144^{16}	v. sl. s.	v. s.	v. s.
Isatin	$C_6H_4 < (CO)(N) > COH$	147.13	yel. red	....	200–1	subl.	s. h.	v. s. h.	sl. s.
Isoprene	$CH_2:CH.C(CH_3):CH_2$	68.11	col. lq.	$0.681^{20/4}$	−120	34	i.	∞	∞
Ketene	$H_2C:CO$	42.04	col. gas	....	−151	−56	d.	d.	s.
Koch acid (1-)(3-,6-,8-)	$C_{10}H_4(NH_2)S_3O_9HNa_2$	427.34	cr.	....	....	....	7.2^{20}		
Lactic acid (dl-)	$CH_3CH(OH)CO_2H$	90.08	hyg.	$1.249^{15/4}$	16.8	122^{14}	∞	∞	∞
anhydride	$C_6H_{10}O_5$	162.14	yel. oil	....	....	d. 250	v. sl. s.	s.	s.
Lactide (dl-)	$C_6H_8C_4$	144.12	tri./al.	$0.862^{10/4}$	124.5	255^{757}	v. sl. s.	v. sl. s. c.	
Lactose	$C_{12}H_{22}O_{11}.H_2O$	360.31	col. rhb.	1.525^{20}	202	d.	17^{10}	i.	i.
Lauric acid	$CH_3(CH_2)_{10}CO_2H$	200.31	col. nd.	$0.869^{50/4}$	48(44)	225^{100}	i.	s.	s.
Laurone	$[CH_3(CH_2)_{10}]_2CO$	338.60	pl.	$0.809^{69/4}$	69–70	....	i.	i. c.	
Lauryl alcohol	$CH_3(CH_2)_{10}CH_2OH$	186.33	lf.	$0.831^{24/4}$	24	255–9	i.	s.	s.
Lead tetraethyl	$Pb(CH_2CH_3)_4$	323.45	col. lq.	$1.659^{18/4}$	−136	152^{291}	i.	sl. s.	∞
tetramethyl	$Pb(CH_3)_4$	267.35	col. lq.	$1.995^{20/4}$	−27.5	110^{760}	i.	∞	∞
Lecithin (protagon)	$C_{42}H_{48}O_9PN$	778.08	wax	....	150–200 d.	....	i.	s. h.	s. h.
Lepidine (py-4)	$C_9H_6N.CH_3$	143.18	lq.	1.086^{20}	9–10	261–3	sl. s.	∞	∞
Leucine (l-)	$(CH_3)_2CHCH_2CH(NH_2)CO_2H$	131.17	cr.	1.293^{18}	295	subl.	2.2^{18}		
Levulinic acid	$CH_3CO(CH_2)_2CO_2H$	116.11	lf.	$1.140^{20/20}$	33.5	245–6	v. s.	v. s.	v. s.
Limonene (d- or l-)	$C_{10}H_{16}$	136.23	lq.	$0.842^{20/4}$	−96.9	177	i.	∞	∞
Linalool (d- or l-)	$C_{10}H_{17}OH$	154.24	col. oil	0.868^{20}	....	198–200	v. sl. s.	s.	∞
Linalyl acetate	$CH_3CO_2C_{10}H_{17}$	196.28	col. lq.	0.895^{20}	....	220^{762} d.	v. sl. s.	∞	∞
Linoleic acid	$C_{17}H_{31}CO_2H$	280.44	yel. oil	$0.903^{18/4}$	−9.5	$229–30^{16}$	i.	∞	∞
Maleic acid	$HO_2C.CH:CH.CO_2H$	116.07	mn.	1.609	130.5	135 d.	79^{25}	70^{30}	8^{25}
anhydride	$< (.CHCO)_2 > O$	98.06	cr.	1.5	57–60	202	16.3^{30}		
Malic acid (dl-)	$HO_2CCH_2CH(OH)CO_2H$	134.09	col. cr.	$1.601^{20/4}$	128–9	150 d.	144^{26}	v. s.	v. s.
(d- or l-)	$HO_2CCH_2CH(OH)CO_2H$	134.09	col. cr.	$1.595^{20/4}$	99–100	140 d.	v. s.	v. s.	8.4^{15}
Malonic acid	$H_2C(CO_2H)_2$	104.06	col. tri.	1.631^{15}	130–5 d.	....	138^{16}	42^{25}	8^{15}

Table 3-2. Physical Properties of Organic Compounds—(*Continued*)

Name	Formula	Formula weight	Form and color	Specific gravity	Melting point, °C.	Boiling point, °C.	Solubility in 100 parts: Water	Alcohol	Ether
Maltose	$C_{12}H_{22}O_{11}.H_2O$	360.31	col. nd.	1.540^{17}	d.	......	108^{25}	v. sl. s. c.	i.
Mandelic acid (dl-)	$C_6H_5CH(OH)CO_2H$	152.14	rhb./aq.	$1.300^{20/4}$	118.1	d.	16^{20}	s.	s.
Mannitol (d-)	$CH_2OH(CHOH)_4CH_2OH$	182.17	col. rhb.	$1.489^{20/4}$	166	$290–5^{3}$	13^{14}	0.01^{14}	i.
Mannose (d-)	$CH_2OH(CHOH)_4CHO$	180.16	rhb.	$1.539^{20/4}$	132	......	248^{17}	v. sl. s.	i.
Margaric acid	$CH_3(CH_2)_{15}CO_2H$	270.44	col. pl.	0.853^{60}	60–1	227^{100}	i.	32^{28}	v. s.
Mellitic acid	$C_6(CO_2H)_6$	342.17	nd./al.	......	286–8	d.	v. s.	v. s.	
Menthol (l-)(α-)	$C_{10}H_{19}OH$	156.26	col. cr.	$0.890^{15/15}$	42–3	212	0.04 c.	v. s.	v. s.
Mercapto-benzothiazole (2-)	$< C_6H_4N:C(SH)S >$	167.24	nd.	$1.42^{20/4}$	179	d.	i.	s.	sl. s.
-thiazoline (2-)	$< CH_2N:C(SH)SCH_2 >$	119.20	cr.	1.50	106	......	1.6^{60}		
Mercuric cyanide	$Hg(CN)_2$	252.65	cr.	4.003^{22}	d. 320	......	12.5^{15}		
fulminate	$Hg(ONC)_2.\frac{1}{2}H_2O$	293.65	cr./aq.	4.4	expl.	......	0.07^{12}	s.	
Mesityl oxide	$(CH_3)_2C:CHCOCH_3$	98.14	lq.	$0.858^{20/4}$	−59	130^{750}	3^{20}	∞	∞
Mesitylene (1-,3-,5-)	$C_6H_3(CH_3)_3$	120.19	col. lq.	$0.865^{20/4}$	−45(−52)	164.8	i.	s.	∞
Metanilic acid (m-)	$H_2NC_6H_4SO_3H$	173.18	col. nd.	......	d.	......	2^{15}	v. sl. s.	v. sl. s.
Methane	CH_4	16.04	gas	0.415^{-164}	−182.6	−161.4	0.4^{20} cc.	47^{20} cc.	104^{10} cc.
Methoxy-methoxyethanol	$CH_3(OCH_2)_2CH_2OH$	106.12	lq.	1.038^{25}	<−70	167.5	∞		
Methyl acetate	$CH_3CO_2CH_3$	74.08	col. lq.	$0.924^{20/4}$	−98.7	57.1	33^{22}	∞	∞
acrylic acid (α-)	$CH_2:C(CH_3)CO_2H$	86.09	pr.	$1.015^{20/4}$	15–16	161–3	s. h.	∞	∞
alcohol	CH_3OH	32.04	col. lq.	$0.792^{20/4}$	−97–8	64.7	∞	∞	∞
-amine	CH_3NH_2	31.06	col. gas	0.699^{-11}	−92.5	-6.7^{758}	v. s.	v. s.	
-amine hydrochloride	$CH_3NH_2.HCl$	67.52	pl./al.	1.23	226–8	230^{15}	v. s.	23 h.	i.
aniline	$C_6H_5NHCH_3$	107.15	lq.	$0.989^{20/4}$	−57	195.5	0.01^{25}	s.	∞
anthracene (α-)	$C_6H_4:(CH)_2:C_6H_3CH_3$	192.25	lf./al.	$1.047^{99.4}$	86	......	i.		
(β-)	$C_6H_4:(CH)_2:C_6H_3CH_3$	192.25	col. lf.	$1.181^{0/4}$	207	......	i.	v. sl. s.	v. sl. s.
anthranilate (o-)	$NH_2C_6H_4CO_2CH_3$	151.16	col. lq.	$1.168^{19/4}$	24	135.5^{15}	sl. s.	s.	s.
anthraquinone (2-)	$C_6H_4:(CO)_2:C_6H_3CH_3$	222.23	col. nd.	......	176–7	subl.	i.	s.	s.
benzoate	$C_6H_5CO_2CH_3$	136.14	col. lq.	$1.087^{25/25}$	−12.5	198–9	0.02^{30}	∞	∞
benzylaniline	$C_6H_5N(CH_3)CH_2C_6H_5$	197.27	lq.	......	9.2	305–6	i.	s.	s.
bromide	CH_3Br	94.95	gas	$1.732^{0/0}$	−93	4.5^{758}	v. sl. s.	s.	s.
butyrate (n-)	$CH_3(CH_2)_2CO_2CH_3$	102.13	col. lq.	$0.898^{20/4}$	<−95	102.3	1.7	∞	∞
(i-)	$(CH_3)_2CHCO_2CH_3$	102.13	col. lq.	$0.891^{20/4}$	−84.7	92.6	v. sl. s.	∞	∞
caprate	$CH_3(CH_2)_8CO_2CH_3$	186.29	lq.	......	−18	223–4	i.	∞	∞
caproate (n-)	$CH_3(CH_2)_4CO_2CH_3$	130.18	col. lq.	$0.904^{0/0}$	......	149.5	i.	∞	∞
caprylate	$CH_3(CH_2)_6CO_2CH_3$	158.23	col. lq.	0.887^{18}	−40	192–4	i.	∞	∞
cellosolve	$CH_3OCH_2CH_2OH$	76.09	col. lq.	$0.965^{20/4}$	......	124–5	∞	∞	∞
chloride	CH_3Cl	50.49	gas	0.952^{0}	−97.7	−24	280^{16} cc.	v. s.	v. s.
chloroacetate	$ClCH_2CO_2CH_3$	108.53	col. lq.	$1.236^{20/4}$	−32.7	130^{740}	v. sl. s.	∞	∞
chloroformate	$ClCO_2CH_3$	94.50	col. lq.	1.236^{15}	......	71–2	d.	∞	∞
cinnamate	$C_6H_5CH:CHCO_2CH_3$	162.18	cr.	$1.042^{36/0}$	33.4	263	i.	v. s.	v. s.
cyclohexane	$CH_2 < (CH_2CH_2)_2 > CHCH_3$	98.18	col. lq.	$0.769^{20/4}$	−126.3	101	i.	s.	s.
ethyl carbonate	$CH_3O.CO.OC_2H_5$	104.10	lq.	1.002^{27}	−14.5	109.2	i.	∞	∞
ethyl ketone	$CH_3.CO.C_2H_5$	72.10	col. lq.	$0.805^{20/4}$	−85.9	79.6	35^{10}	∞	∞
ethyl oxalate	$CH_3OCO.CO_2C_2H_5$	132.11	lq.	$1.156^{0/0}$	......	173.7	i.	v. s.	v. s.
formate	HCO_2CH_3	60.05	lq.	$0.974^{20/4}$	−99.8	32	30^{20}	∞	
furoate	$C_4H_3O.CO_2CH_3$	126.11	col. lq.	$1.179^{21/4}$	......	181.3	i.	∞	∞
glucamine	$CH_2OH(CHOH)_4CH_2NHCH_3$	195.21							
glycolate	$HOCH_2CO_2CH_3$	90.08	lq.	1.168^{18}	......	151.2			
heptoate	$CH_3(CH_2)_5CO_2CH_3$	144.21	lq.	$0.881^{15/4}$	......	172–3	i.		
hypochlorite	$ClOCH_3$	66.49	gas	......	......	12^{726}			
iodide	CH_3I	141.95	col. lq.	$2.279^{20/4}$	−64.4	42.4	1.8^{15}	∞	∞
lactate	$CH_3CH(OH)CO_2CH_3$	104.10	lq.	1.090^{19}	......	144.8	∞	s.	s.
laurate	$CH_3(CH_2)_{10}CO_2CH_3$	214.34	lq.	......	5	148^{18}	i.		
mercaptan	CH_3SH	48.10	gas	0.896^{0}	−121	5.8^{752}	s.	v. s.	v. s.
methacrylate	$CH_2:C(CH_3)CO_2CH_3$	100.11	lq.	$0.950^{15.6}$	−48	100.3	i.		
myristate	$CH_3(CH_2)_{12}CO_2CH_3$	242.39	cr./al.	......	18–9	295^{715}	i.		
naphthalene (α-)	$C_{10}H_7CH_3$	142.19	oil	$1.025^{14/4}$	−19	244.6	i.	v. s.	v. s.
(β-)	$C_{10}H_7CH_3$	142.19	mn.	$0.994^{40/4}$	35–6	241–2	i.	v. s.	v. s.
nitrate	CH_3ONO_2	77.04	lq.	1.203^{25}	expl.	65	sl. s.	s.	s.
nitrite	CH_3ONO	61.04	gas	0.991^{15}	......	−12	......	s.	s.
nonyl ketone (n-)	$CH_3(CH_2)_8COCH_3$	170.29	col. oil	$0.828^{20/20}$	13.5	228	i.	s.	s.
oleate	$C_{17}H_{33}CO_2CH_3$	296.48	oil	0.879^{18}	......	$190–1^{10}$	i.	∞	∞
orange	$(CH_3)_2NC_6H_4N_2C_6H_4SO_3Na$	327.33	red pd.	......	......	......	0.2 c.		
palmitate	$CH_3(CH_2)_{14}CO_2CH_3$	270.44	col. cr.	......	30–1	196^{15}	i.	s.	s.
phosphine	CH_3PH_2	48.03	gas	......	......	-14^{759}	i.	sl. s.	
propionate	$CH_3CH_2CO_2CH_3$	88.10	col. lq.	$0.915^{20/4}$	−87.5	79.7	0.5^{20}	∞	∞
propyl ketone (n-)	$CH_3COCH_2CH_2CH_3$	86.13	col. lq.	$0.812^{15/15}$	−77.8	102	v. sl. s.	∞	∞
salicylate (o-)	$HO.C_6H_4CO_2CH_3$	152.14	col. lq.	$1.182^{25/25}$	−8.3	222.2	0.07^{30}	∞	∞

stearate	$CH_3(CH_2)_{16}CO_2CH_3$	298.49	col. cr.	...	38-9	215^{15}	i.	s.	s.
toluate (o-)	$CH_3.C_6H_4CO_2CH_3$	150.17	col. lq.	1.073^{15}	<−50	213	i.	∞	∞
(m-)	$CH_3.C_6H_4CO_2CH_3$	150.17	col. lq.	1.066^{15}	...	215	i.		
(p-)	$CH_3.C_6H_4CO_2CH_3$	150.17	cr.	...	33-4	217	i.	v. s.	v. s.
Methyl toluidine (o-)	$CH_3.C_6H_4NHCH_3$	121.18	lq.	0.973^{15}	...	206-7	i.	∞	∞
(m-)	$CH_3.C_6H_4NHCH_3$	121.18	lq.	...	...	206-7	i.	∞	∞
(p-)	$CH_3.C_6H_4NHCH_3$	121.18	lq.	$0.935^{55/4}$	...	211^{761}	i.	∞	∞
valerate (n-)	$CH_3(CH_2)_3CO_2CH_3$	116.16	lq.	$0.895^{15/4}$	−91	127.3	v. sl. s.	∞	∞
(i-)	$(CH_3)_2CHCH_2CO_2CH_3$	116.16	col. lq.	$0.881^{20/4}$	...	$116-7^{764}$	v. sl. s.	∞	∞
vinyl ketone	$CH_3COCH:CH_2$	70.09	lq.	$0.836^{20/4}$	...	81	>85		
Methylal	$HCH(OCH_3)_2$	76.09	col. lq.	$0.866^{15/4}$	−104.8	42-3	33	∞	∞
Methylene-bis-(phenyl-4-isocyanate)	$(OCN.C_6H_4)_2CH_2$	250.25	lq.	1.222^{30}	...	$210-2^{13}$	d.	d.	
bromide	CH_2Br_2	173.86	col. lq.	$2.495^{20/4}$	−52.8	98.5^{756}	1.17^{0}	∞	∞
chloride	CH_2Cl_2	84.94	col. lq.	$1.336^{20/4}$	−96.7	40-1	2^{20}	∞	∞
dianiline	$(C_6H_5NH)_2CH_2$	198.26	cr.	...	65	208-9 d.	i.	s.	s.
iodide	CH_2I_2	267.87	col. lq.	$3.325^{20/4}$	5.7	180 d.	1.4^{20}	∞	∞
Michler's hydrol (p-,p'-)	$[(CH_3)_2NC_6H_4]_2CHOH$	270.36	gn.	...	96-7	...	i.	s. h.	s.
ketone	$[(CH_3)_2NC_6H_4]_2CO$	268.35	lf./al.	...	174	>360 d.	i.	sl. s.	v. sl. s.
Morphine	$C_{17}H_{19}O_3N.H_2O$	303.35	pr./al.	1.317	254 d.	...	0.02^{20}	sl. s.	s.
Mucic acid	$(.CHOHCHOHCO_2H)_2$	210.14	pd.	...	206-14	...	0.33^{14}	i.	i.
Mustard gas	$(ClCH_2.CH_2)_2S$	159.08	oil	$1.275^{20/4}$	13-4	217	0.07^{25}	s.	s.
Myricyl alcohol	$C_{31}H_{63}OH(?)$	452.82	cr.	0.777^{95}	88	...	i.	v. sl. s.	v. s.
Myristic acid	$CH_3(CH_2)_{12}CO_2H$	228.36	col. lf.	$0.853^{70/4}$	57-8	250.5^{100}	i.	v. s.	v. s.
Myristyl alcohol	$CH_3(CH_2)_{12}CH_2OH$	214.38	cr.	$0.824^{38/4}$	38	167^{15}	<0.02	sl. s.	s.
Naphthalene	$C_{10}H_8$	128.16	pl./al.	$1.145^{20/4}$	80.2	217.9	0.003^{25}	9.5^{20}	v. s.
disulfonic acid (1-,5-)	$C_{10}H_6(SO_3H)_2$	288.28	lf.	...	d.	...	102^{20}	s.	i.
(1-,6-)	$C_{10}H_6(SO_3H)_2$	288.28	cr.	...	d. 125	...	164^{20}	s.	i.
sulfonic acid (α-)	$C_{10}H_7SO_3H.2H_2O$	244.26	cr.	...	90	...	v. s.	v. s.	sl. s.
(β-)	$C_{10}H_7SO_3H.H_2O$	226.24	cr.	...	125	...	77^{30}		
Naphthasultam (1-,8-)	$C_{10}H_7O_2NS$	205.22	nd.	...	177-8	...	s. h.	sl. s.	s.
disulfonate Na (1-,8-)	$C_{10}H_5O_8NS_3Na_2.2H_2O$	445.35	cr.	...	...	...	v. s.		
(2-,4-)	$C_{10}H_4O_8NS_3Na_3.8\frac{1}{2}H_2O$	584.45	lf.	...	...	...	v. s.	sl. s.	
Naphthoic acid (α-)	$C_{10}H_7CO_2H$	172.17	nd.	...	160-1	300	v. sl. s. h.	s. h.	s.
(β-)	$C_{10}H_7CO_2H$	172.17	mn.	$1.077^{100/4}$	184	>300	0.007^{25}	s.	s.
Naphthol (α-)	$C_{10}H_7OH$	144.16	mn.	1.224^{4}	96	278-80	sl. s. h.	v. s.	v. s.
(β-)	$C_{10}H_7OH$	144.16	mn.	1.217^{4}	122-3	285-6	0.074^{25}	v. s.	v. s.
sulfonic acid (α-)(1-,2-)	$HO.C_{10}H_6SO_3H$	224.22	pl./aq.	...	>250	...	v. s. h.	...	i.
(β-)(2-,6-)	$HO.C_{10}H_6SO_3H$	224.22	lf.	...	125	...	v. s.	v. s.	
Naphthyl acetate (α-)	$CH_3CO_2C_{10}H_7$	186.20	nd./al.	...	46-9	...	sl. s. h.	s.	s.
(β-)	$CH_3CO_2C_{10}H_7$	186.20	nd./al.	...	69-70	...	i.	s.	s.
amine (α-)	$C_{10}H_7NH_2$	143.18	rhb.	$1.123^{25/25}$	50	300.8	0.17 c.	v. s.	v. s.
(β-)	$C_{10}H_7NH_2$	143.18	lf./aq.	$1.061^{98/4}$	111-2	306.1	v. s. h.	s.	s.
amine hydrochloride (α-)	$C_{10}H_7NH_2.HCl$	179.65	nd.	...	...	subl.	3.8^{20}	s.	s.
(β-)	$C_{10}H_7NH_2.HCl$	179.65	lf.	...	...	...	v. s.	v. s.	
amine sulfonic acid (1-,4-)	$NH_2.C_{10}H_6.SO_3H$	223.24	nd.	...	d.	...	0.2^{100}	i.	i.
(1-,5-)	$NH_2.C_{10}H_6.SO_3H.H_2O$	241.26	cr.	...	...	...	sl. s.		
(1-,7-)	$NH_2.C_{10}H_6.SO_3H.H_2O$	241.26	cr.	...	...	...	0.46^{25}		
(1-,8-)	$NH_2.C_{10}H_6.SO_3H.H_2O$	241.26	cr.	...	...	...	0.42^{100}		
(2-,5-)	$NH_2.C_{10}H_6.SO_3H$	223.24	cr.	...	...	...	0.08		
(2-,6-)	$NH_2.C_{10}H_6.SO_3H.H_2O$	241.26	cr.	...	...	...	0.38^{100}		
(2-,7-)	$NH_2.C_{10}H_6.SO_3H.H_2O$	241.26	cr.	...	...	...	0.28^{100}		
isocyanate (α-)	$C_{10}H_7N:CO$	169.17	col. lq.	1.18	...	269-70	d.	s.	s.
Nicotine	$C_{10}H_{14}N_2$	162.23	oil	$1.009^{20/4}$	<−80	246^{730}	s.	∞	∞
Nicotinic acid (3-)	$C_5H_4NCO_2H$	123.11	nd./al.	...	235.2	subl.	s. h.	s. h.	v. sl. s.
(i-)(4-)	$C_5H_4NCO_2H$	123.11	nd./aq.	...	317	d.	s. h.	sl. s. h.	v. sl. s.
Nitro-acetanilide (p-)	$CH_3CONHC_6H_4NO_2$	180.16	rhb.	...	215-6	...	s. h.	s.	s.
-acetophenone (m-)	$CH_3COC_6H_4NO_2$	165.14	nd.	...	80-1	202	i.	s.	
-aminoanisole (4-,1-,2-)	$NO_2.C_6H_3(OCH_3)NH_2$	168.15	red nd.	1.207^{156}	118	...	i.	s.	
(5-,1-,2-)	$NO_2.C_6H_3(OCH_3)NH_2$	168.15	yel. nd.	1.211^{156}	139-40				
(3-,1-,4-)	$NO_2.C_6H_3(OCH_3)NH_2$	168.15	red	...	123	...	sl. s.	s.	s.
-aminophenol (4-,2-,1-)	$NO_2.C_6H_3(NH_2)OH$	154.12	or. pr.	...	142-3	...	sl. s. c.	v. s.	v. s.
-aniline (o-)	$NO_2.C_6H_4NH_2$	138.12	yel. rhb.	1.442^{15}	71.5	284.1	s. h.	v. s.	v. s.
(m-)	$NO_2.C_6H_4NH_2$	138.12	yel. rhb.	1.43	114	306.4	0.11^{20}	7.1^{20}	7.9^{20}
(p-)	$NO_2.C_6H_4NH_2$	138.12	yel. mn.	1.437^{14}	146-7	331.7	0.08^{19}	5.8^{20}	6.1^{20}
-anisole (o-)	$CH_3OC_6H_4NO_2$	153.13	col. cr.	$1.254^{20/4}$	9.4	272-3	0.17^{30}	∞	∞
(p-)	$CH_3OC_6H_4NO_2$	153.13	pr./al.	1.233^{20}	54	274	0.06^{30}	v. s.	v. s.
-anthraquinone (α-)	$C_6H_4:(CO)_2:C_6H_3NO_2$	253.20	nd.	...	230	270^{7}	i.	sl. s.	v. sl. s.
-anthraquinone sulfonic acid (1-,5-)	$NO_2.C_{14}H_6O_2.SO_3H$	333.26	yel. cr.	...	...	...	s	i.	i.
-benzal chloride (m-)	$NO_2.C_6H_4.CHCl_2$	206.03	mn.	...	65	...	i.	v. s. h.	v. s.
-benzaldehyde (m-)	$NO_2.C_6H_4CHO$	151.12	nd./aq.	...	58	164^{23}	1.95^{112}	v. s. h.	v. s.

Table 3-2. Physical Properties of Organic Compounds—*(Continued)*

Name	Formula	Formula weight	Form and color	Specific gravity	Melting point, °C.	Boiling point, °C.	Solubility in 100 parts: Water	Alcohol	Ether
Nitro-benzene	$C_6H_5NO_2$	123.11	yel. lq.	$1.205^{18/4}$	5.7	210.9	0.19^{20}	v. s.	∞
-benzidine (2-)	$NH_2C_6H_4C_6H_3(NH_2)NO_2$	229.23	red nd.	....	143	....	sl. s. h.		
-benzoic acid (o-)	$NO_2.C_6H_4.CO_2H$	167.12	tri./aq.	$1.575^{4/4}$	147.5	....	0.65^{20}	28^{11}	22^{11}
(m-)	$NO_2.C_6H_4.CO_2H$	167.12	mn.	$1.494^{4/4}$	140–1	....	0.24^{165}	3^{12}	25^{10}
(p-)	$NO_2.C_6H_4.CO_2H$	167.12	yel. mn.	$1.550^{32/4}$	240–2	subl.	0.02^{15}	0.9^{10}	2.2^{18}
-benzyl alcohol (m-)	$NO_2.C_6H_4.CH_2OH$	153.13	cr.	....	27	$175–80^{3}$			
-benzyl bromide (p-)	$NO_2.C_6H_4CH_2Br$	216.04	nd./al.	....	99–100	....	i.	2^{19}	v. s.
-chlorotoluene (1-,2-,6-)	$CH_3.C_6H_3(NO_2)Cl$	171.58	cr.	....	37.5	238	i.		
-cresol (1-,3-,4-)	$CH_3.C_6H_3(NO_2)OH$	153.13	yel.	$1.240^{39/4}$	32	125^{22}	v. sl. s.	v. s.	v. s.
-cymene (1-,2-,4-)	$CH_3.C_6H_3(NO_2)CH(CH_3)_2$	179.21	oil	$1.067^{20/4}$	....	152^{15}	i.		
-dimethylaniline (o-)	$NO_2.C_6N_4NHCH_3$	166.18	yel. oil	$1.179^{20/4}$	....	$151–3^{30}$	v. sl. s.	v. s.	v. s.
(m-)	$NO_2.C_6H_4NHCH_3$	166.18	red mn.	1.313^{17}	60–1	280–5	i.	s.	s.
(p-)	$NO_2.C_6H_4NHCH_3$	166.18	yel. nd.	....	163–4	....	i.	s. h.	
-diphenyl (o-)	$C_6H_5.C_6H_4NO_2$	199.20	rhb.	1.44	37	320	i.	s.	v. s.
(p-)	$C_6H_5.C_6H_4NO_2$	199.20	nd./al.	....	113–4	340	i.	sl. s. c.	v. s.
-diphenylamine (o-)	$C_6H_5.NH.C_6H_4NO_2$	214.22	or. cr.	....	75–6				
-guanidine	$H_2NC(NH)NHNO_2$	104.07	nd./aq.	....	246–7	....	9^{100}	sl. s.	v. sl. s.
-naphthalene (α-)	$C_{10}H_7NO_2$	173.16	yel./al.	1.223^{62}	59–60	304	i.	s.	s.
(β-)	$C_{10}H_7NO_2$	173.16	col./al.	....	79	165^{15}	i.	v. s.	v. s.
-phenol (o-)	$NO_2.C_6H_4.OH$	139.11	yel. mn.	1.295^{45}	44–5	214.5	1.08^{100}	v. s.	v. s.
(m-)	$NO_2.C_6H_4.OH$	139.11	col. mn.	1.485^{20}	96–7	194^{70}	1.35^{20}	v. s.	s.
(p-)	$NO_2.C_6H_4.OH$	139.11	yel. pr.	1.479^{20}	113–4	subl.	1.6^{25}	v. s.	v. s.
-phenol sulfonic acid (1-,4-,2-)	$HO.C_6H_3(NO_2)SO_3H.3H_2O$	273.22	nd.	....	d. 110	....	v. s.	v. s.	sl. s
(1-,2-,4-)	$HO.C_6H_3(NO_2)SO_3H.3H_2O$	273.22	nd./aq.	....	51.5	....	v. s.	v. s.	
-phthalic acid (3-)	$NO_2.C_6H_3(CO_2H)_2$	211.13	yel./aq.	....	222	....	2.05^{25}	v. s. h.	sl. s.
(4-)	$NO_2.C_6H_3(CO_2H)_2$	211.13	yel. cr.	....	164–5	....	v. s.	v. s.	s.
-toluene (o-)	$CH_3.C_6H_4NO_2$	137.13	yel. lq.	$1.163^{20/4}$	−4.1	222.3	0.07^{30}	∞	∞
(m-)	$CH_3.C_6H_4NO_2$	137.13	lq.	$1.160^{18/4}$	15–16	230–1	0.05^{30}	∞	∞
(p-)	$CH_3.C_6H_4NO_2$	137.13	rhb.	$1.139^{55/55}$	51.9	237.7	0.04^{30}	8.6^{15}	80.8^{15}
-toluene sulfonic acid (1-,4-,2-)	$CH_3.C_6H_3(NO_2)SO_3H.2H_2O$	253.23	pl./aq.	....	130	....	47.7^{23}	v. s.	v. s.
-toluidine (4-,1-,2-)	$NO_2.C_6H_3(CH_3)NH_2$	152.15	yel. mn.	1.365^{15}	105–7	....	v. sl. s.	s.	s.
(3-,1-,4-)	$NO_2.C_6H_3(CH_3)NH_2$	152.15	red mn.	1.312^{17}	116–7	....	sl. s. h.	s.	
Nitron	$C_{20}H_{16}N_4$	312.36	yel. lf.	....	189–90 d.	....	i.	s. h.	v. sl. s.
Nitroso-dimethylaniline (p-)	$ON.C_6H_4N(CH_3)_2$	150.18	gn. tri.	....	86–7	....	i.	s.	s.
-naphthol (β-)(1-)	$ON.C_{10}H_6OH$	173.16	brn. pr.	....	109.5	....	0.1^{20}	2.4^{18}	
Nonadecane (n-)	$CH_3(CH_2)_{17}CH_3$	268.51	cr.	$0.777^{32/4}$	32	330	i.	sl. s.	s.
Nonane (n-)	$CH_3(CH_2)_7CH_3$	128.25	col. lq.	$0.718^{20/4}$	−53.7	150.5^{759}	i.	sl. s.	s.
Octadecane (n-)	$CH_3(CH_2)_{16}CH_3$	254.48	cr.	$0.775^{28/4}$	28	317	i.	sl. s.	s.
Octane (n-)	$CH_3(CH_2)_6CH_3$	114.22	col. lq.	$0.703^{20/4}$	−56.5	125.7	0.002^{16}	sl. s.	s.
(iso-)	$(CH_3)_3CCH_2CH(CH_3)_2$	114.22	col. lq.	$0.692^{20/4}$	−107.4	99.3^{760}	i.	sl. s.	s.
Octyl acetate (n-)	$CH_3CO_2CH_2(CH_2)_6CH_3$	172.26	col. lq.	$0.885^{0/4}$	−38.5	210	i.	s.	s.
(sec-)	$CH_3CO_2CH(CH_3)C_6H_{13}$	172.26	col. lq.	$0.863^{14/4}$	....	195	i.	s.	s.
alcohol (n-)	$CH_3(CH_2)_6CH_2OH$	130.22	col. lq.	$0.827^{20/4}$	−16	194–5	0.054^{25}	∞	∞
(sec-)	$CH_3(CH_2)_5CH(OH)CH_3$	130.22	col. lq.	$0.822^{20/4}$	−38.6	179–80	0.096^{25}	∞	∞
Octylene (n-)	$CH_3(CH_2)_5CH{:}CH_2$	112.21	lq.	$0.721^{18/4}$	....	126	i.	∞	∞
Oleic acid	$C_8H_{17}CH{:}CH(CH_2)_7CO_2H$	282.45	col. nd.	$0.854^{78/4}$	14	$285–6^{100}$	i.	∞	∞
Orcinol (1-,3-,5-)	$(HO)_2C_6H_3.CH_3$	124.13	pr./bz.	1.290^{4}	107–8	287–90	v. s.	v. s.	v. s.
Oxalic acid	$HO_2C.CO_2H.2H_2O$	126.07	col. mn.	$1.653^{19/4}$	101.5	subl.	s.	s.	1.3
Palmitic acid	$CH_3(CH_2)_{14}CO_2H$	256.42	col. pl.	$0.849^{70/4}$	63–4	271.5^{100}	i.	9^{20}	s.
Pelargonic acid	$CH_3(CH_2)_7CO_2H$	158.23	col. oil	$0.906^{20/4}$	12.5	253–4	v. sl. s.	s.	s.
Penta-chloroethane	$CHCl_2.CCl_3$	202.31	col. lq.	$1.671^{25/4}$	−22	162	0.05^{20}	∞	∞
-decane (n-)	$CH_3(CH_2)_{13}CH_3$	212.41	col. lq.	$0.770^{20/4}$	10	270.5	i.	v. s.	v. s.
-erythritol	$C(CH_2OH)_4$	136.15	cr.	....	262	276^{30}	5.6^{15}	v. sl. s.	i.
Pentandiol	$HOCH_2(CH_2)_3CH_2OH$	104.15	lq.	$0.994^{20/4}$	....	239.4	∞		
Pentane (n-)	$CH_3(CH_2)_3CH_3$	72.15	col. lq.	$0.630^{18/4}$	−129.7	36.3	0.036^{16}	∞	∞
(i-)	$(CH_3)_2CHCH_2CH_3$	72.15	col. lq.	0.621^{19}	−160.0	27.95	i.	∞	∞
(neo-)	$(CH_3)_2C(CH_3)_2$	72.15	col. lq.	$0.613^{20/4}$	−20	9.5	i.	s.	s.
Phenacetin	$C_2H_5OC_6H_4NHCOCH_3$	179.21	col. mn.	....	134–5	d.	0.7^{20}	40 h.	1.6^{25}
Phenanthrene	$<(C_6H_4CH)_2>$	178.22	pl./al.	1.179^{25}	99–100	340	i.	10 h.	v. s.
Phenetidine (o-)	$C_2H_5O.C_6H_4.NH_2$	137.18	oil	....	<−21	228–9	i.	s.	s.
(p-)	$C_2H_5O.C_6H_4.NH_2$	137.18	lq.	1.061^{15}	3–4	254–5	i.	s.	s.
Phenetole	$C_2H_5O.C_6H_5$	122.16	col. lq.	$0.967^{20/4}$	−30.2	172	i.	∞	∞
Phenol	C_6H_5OH	94.11	col. nd.	$1.071^{25/4}$	42–3	181.4	8.2^{15}	∞	∞
-phthalein	$C_{20}H_{14}O_4$	318.31	col. rhb.	$1.299^{25/4}$	261–2	....	0.2^{20}	10^{25}	5.9 c.
-sulfonic acid (o-)	$HO.C_6H_4SO_3H.\frac{3}{4}H_2O$	187.68	cr.	....	50 d.	....	v. s.	v. s.	
Phenyl acetaldehyde	$C_6H_5CH_2CHO$	120.14	lq.	1.025^{20}	....	193–4	v. sl. s.	∞	∞
acetic acid	$C_6H_5CH_2CO_2H$	136.14	lf.	$1.081^{80/4}$	76–7	265.5	1.66^{20}	v. s.	v. s.

-acetylene	$C_6H_5C{:}CH$	102.13	col. lq.	$0.930^{20/4}$	−43	142–3	i.	∞	∞
aniline (o-)	$C_6H_5.C_6H_4.NH_2$	169.22	cr.	....	45–6	299^{760}	v. sl. s.	s.	s.
(p-)	$C_6H_5.C_6H_4.NH_2$	169.22	lf.	....	50–2	302	s. h.	s.	s.
Phenyl-ethyl alcohol	$C_6H_5CH_2CH_2OH$	122.16	col. oil	$1.023^{13/4}$	....	$219–21^{750}$	1.6^{20}	s.	∞
-glycine	$C_6H_5NHCH_2CO_2H$	151.16	cr.	....	127	....	s.	s.	sl. s.
-hydrazine	$C_6H_5NH.NH_2$	108.14	yel. oil	$1.097^{23/4}$	19.6	243.5	sl. s. h.	∞	∞
-hydrazine sulfonic acid (p-)	$H_2NNHC_6H_4SO_3H$	188.20	cr./al.	....	286	....	0.6^{12}	sl. s.	
isocyanate	$C_6H_5N{:}CO$	119.12	lq.	$1.096^{20/4}$	....	166^{769}	d.	d.	v. s.
-methylpyrazolone (3-)(N-)	$C_4H_5ON_2.C_6H_5$	174.20	pr./aq.	....	128	191^{17}	1^{20}	v. s. h.	v. sl. s.
-mustard oil	$C_6H_5N{:}CS$	135.18	col. lq.	$1.138^{15/15}$	−21	219–20	i.	s.	s.
naphthalene (α-)	$C_{10}H_7.C_6H_5$	204.26	waxy	....	45	336–7	i.	v. s.	v. s.
(β-)	$C_{10}H_7.C_6H_5$	204.26	lf./al.	....	102.5	345–6	i.	sl. s.	sl. s.
naphthylamine (α-)	$C_{10}H_7NHC_6H_5$	219.27	pr./al.	1.17	62	335^{258}	0.08^{60}	s.	s.
(β-)	$C_{10}H_7NHC_6H_5$	219.27	rhb.	1.18	107–8	399.5	0.4^{60}	v. s. h.	v. s. h.
phenol (o-)	$C_6H_5.C_6H_4OH$	170.20	nd.	....	56–7	275	i.	s.	s.
(p-)	$C_6H_5.C_6H_4OH$	170.20	nd.	....	164–5	305–8	i.	s.	s.
propyl alcohol (γ-)	$C_6H_5(CH_2)_3OH$	136.19	oil	$1.008^{20/4}$	< −18	235–7	sl. s.	∞	∞
quinoline (2-)(α-)	$C_6H_5.C_9H_6N$	205.25	nd.	....	86	363	sl. s.	s. h.	s.
(8-)(0-)	$C_6H_5.C_9H_6N$	205.25	lq.	....	....	283^{187}	sl. s.	s.	s.
salicylate, salol	$HO.C_6H_4CO_2C_6H_5$	214.21	rhb./al.	$1.250^{20/4}$	42–3	$172–3^{12}$	0.015^{25}	v. s. h.	s.
stearate	$CH_3(CH_2)_{16}CO_2C_6H_5$	360.56	cr.	....	52	267^{15}	i.		
urethane	$C_6H_5NHCO_2C_2H_5$	165.19	pl./al.	$1.106^{30/4}$	52–3	237–8	i. c.	s.	s.
Phenylene-diamine (o-)	$C_6H_4(NH_2)_2$	108.14	lf./aq.	....	103–4	256–8	73^{81}	v. s.	v. s.
(m-)	$C_6H_4(NH_2)_2$	108.14	rhb.	$1.139^{15/15}$	62.8	284–7	35.1^{25}	v. s.	s.
(p-)	$C_6H_4(NH_2)_2$	108.14	mn.	....	140	267	669^{107}	s.	s.
Phloroglucinol (1-,3-,5-)	$C_6H_3(OH)_3.2H_2O$	162.14	rhb.	....	117	subl.	1.13^{25}	v. s.	v. s.
Phorone	$[(CH_3)_2C{:}CH]_2CO$	138.20	yel. pr.	$0.885^{20/4}$	28	197.2^{743}	0.1^{50}	s.	s.
Phosgene	$OCCl_2$	98.92	gas	$1.392^{19/4}$	−104	8.2^{756}	v. sl. s.		
Phthalic acid (o-)	$C_6H_4(CO_2H)_2$	166.13	mn./aq.	$1.593^{20/4}$	208	d.	0.70^{25}	12^{18}	0.68^{15}
(m-)(iso-)	$C_6H_4(CO_2H)_2$	166.13	nd./aq.	....	330	subl.	0.2^{100}	s.	
anhydride (o-)	$C_6H_4 < (CO)_2 > O$	148.11	rhb.	1.527^{4}	130.8	284.5	v. sl. s.	s.	sl. s.
nitrile (o-)	$C_6H_4(CN)_2$	128.13	cr.	....	141	....	sl. s. c.		
Phthalide	$C_6H_4(CH_2)(CO) > O$	134.13	nd./aq.	$1.164^{99/4}$	73(65)	290	v. sl. s.	s.	
Phthalimide (o-)	$C_6H_4 < (CO)_2 > NH$	147.13	cr./et.	....	238	subl.	0.04^{25}	5	s. h.
Picoline (α-)	$C_5H_4N.CH_3$	93.12	col. lq.	$0.950^{15/4}$	−70	128.8	v. s.	∞	∞
(β-)	$C_5H_4N.CH_3$	93.12	col. lq.	$0.961^{15/4}$	....	143.5	∞	∞	∞
(γ-)	$C_5H_4N.CH_3$	93.12	lq.	$0.957^{15/4}$	....	143.1	∞	∞	∞
Picramic acid (1-,2-,4-,6-)	$HO.C_6H_2(NH_2)(NO_2)_2$	199.12	red nd.	....	169	....	0.14^{22}	s.	sl. s.
Picric acid (2-,4-,6-)	$HO.C_6H_2(NO_2)_3$	229.11	yel. rhb.	$1.763^{20/4}$	121.8	expl.	1.23^{20}	6^{20}	1^{13}
Picryl chloride (2-,4-,6-)	$ClC_6H_2(NO_2)_3$	247.56	yel. mn.	1.797^{20}	83	d.	0.018^{15}	4.8^{17}	7^{17}
Pinacol	$[(CH_3)_2C.OH]_2$	118.17	col. nd.	0.967^{15}	43(38)	$171–2^{739}$	sl. s. c.	v. s.	v. s.
Pinacoline	$CH_3COC(CH_3)_3$	100.16	col. lq.	0.800^{16}	−52.5	106.2	2.5^{15}	s.	s.
Pinene (α-)(dl-)	$C_{10}H_{16}$	136.23	col. lq.	$0.878^{20/4}$	−55	154–6	v. sl. s.	s.	∞
hydrochloride	$C_{10}H_{17}Cl$	172.69	lf.	....	131–2	207–8	i.	33	s.
Pinol (dl-)	$C_{10}H_{16}O$	152.23	lq.	$0.953^{20/20}$	....	183–4	....	s.	s.
Piperidine	$CH_2 < (CH_2CH_2)_2 > NH$	85.15	lq.	$0.860^{20/4}$	−9	106	∞	∞	
carboxylic acid (α-)(dl-)	$HO_2C.CH < (CH_2CH_2)_2 > NH$	129.16	cr.	....	264	....	s.		
Piperidinium pentamethylene dithiocarbamate	$(CH_2)_5CS_2H.HN(CH_2)_5$	232.41	cr.	1.13	175	....	6^{28}		
Propane	$CH_3CH_2CH_3$	44.09	gas	$0.585^{-45/4}$	−187.1	−42.2	6.5^{18} cc.	s.	v. s.
Propionic acid	$CH_3CH_2CO_2H$	74.08	col. lq.	$0.992^{20/4}$	−22	141.1	∞	∞	∞
aldehyde	CH_3CH_2CHO	58.08	col. lq.	$0.807^{20/4}$	−81	49.5^{740}	20^{20}	∞	∞
anhydride	$(CH_3CH_2CO)_2O$	130.14	col. lq.	$1.012^{20/4}$	−45	168.8^{780}	d.	d.	
Propyl acetate (n-)	$CH_3COCH_2CH_2CH_3$	102.13	col. lq.	$0.886^{20/4}$	−92.5	101.6	1.6^{16}	∞	∞
(i-)	$CH_3CO_2CH(CH_3)_2$	103.13	col. lq.	$0.874^{20/20}$	−73.4	88.4	3^{20}	∞	∞
alcohol (n-)	$CH_3CH_2CH_2OH$	60.09	col. lq.	$0.804^{20/4}$	−127	97.8	∞	∞	∞
(i-)	$(CH_3)_2CHOH$	60.09	col. lq.	$0.789^{20/4}$	−85.8	82.5	∞	∞	∞
amine (n-)	$CH_3CH_2CH_2NH_2$	59.11	col. lq.	$0.718^{20/20}$	−83	$49–50^{761}$	∞	∞	∞
(i-)	$(CH_3)_2CHNH_2$	59.11	col. lq.	$0.694^{15/4}$	−101	33–4	∞	∞	∞
aniline (n-)	$C_6H_5NHCH_2CH_2CH_3$	135.20	lq.	0.949^{18}	....	222	i.	v. s.	v. s.
benzoate (n-)	$C_6H_5CO_2CH_2CH_2CH_3$	164.20	col. lq.	$1.021^{25/25}$	−51.6	231	i.	s.	s.
(i-)	$C_6H_5CO_2CH(CH_3)_2$	164.20	col. lq.	$1.010^{25/25}$	....	218.5	i.	s.	s.
bromide (n-)	$CH_3CH_2CH_2Br$	123.00	col. lq.	$1.353^{20/4}$	−109.9	70.8	0.25^{20}	∞	∞
(i-)	$(CH_3)_2CHBr$	123.00	col. lq.	$1.310^{20/4}$	−89	60	0.32^{20}	∞	∞
n-butyrate (n-)	$C_2H_5CH_2CO_2CH_2C_2H_5$	130.18	col. lq.	0.879^{15}	−95.2	142.7	0.17^{17}	∞	∞
i-butyrate (n-)	$(CH_3)_2CHCO_2CH_2C_2H_5$	130.18	col. lq.	$0.884^{0/4}$	....	134–5	v. sl. s.		
n-butyrate (i-)	$C_2H_5CH_2CO_2CH(CH_3)_2$	130.18	col. lq.	0.865^{13}	....	128	v. sl. s.		
i-butyrate (i-)	$(CH_3)_2CHCO_2CH(CH_3)_2$	130.18	col. lq.	$0.869^{0/4}$	....	120.8	v. sl. s.		
chloride (n-)	$CH_3CH_2CH_2Cl$	78.54	col. lq.	$0.890^{20/4}$	−122.8	46.4	0.27^{20}	∞	∞
(i-)	$(CH_3)_2CHCl$	78.54	col. lq.	0.859^{20}	−117	36.5	0.31^{20}	∞	∞

Table 3-2. Physical Properties of Organic Compounds—(*Continued*)

Name	Formula	Formula weight	Form and color	Specific gravity	Melting point, °C.	Boiling point, °C.	Solubility in 100 parts: Water	Alcohol	Ether
Propyl formate (n-)	$HCO_2CH_2CH_2CH_3$	88.10	col. lq.	$0.901^{20/4}$	−92.9	81.3	2.2^{22}	∞	∞
(i-)	$HCO_2CH(CH_3)_2$	88.10	col. lq.	$0.873^{20/4}$	...	$68–71^{751}$	2.1^{22}	∞	∞
furoate (n-)	$C_4H_3O.CO_2C_3H_7$	154.16	col. lq.	$1.075^{26/4}$	...	211	v. sl. s.	s.	∞
lactate (n-)	$CH_3CH(OH)CO_2CH_2C_2H_5$	132.16	col. lq.	...	...	$122–3^{150}$	s.	s.	s.
(i-)	$CH_3CH(OH)CO_2CH(CH_3)_2$	132.16	col. lq.	...	...	167.5	s.	s.	s.
mercaptan (n-)	$CH_3CH_2CH_2SH$	76.15	lq.	$0.836^{25/4}$	−112	67–8	v. sl. s.	s.	s.
(i-)	$(CH_3)_2CHSH$	76.15	lq.	$0.809^{25/4}$	−130.7	58–60	v. sl. s.	∞	∞
propionate (n-)	$C_2H_5CO_2CH_2C_2H_5$	116.16	col. lq.	$0.883^{20/4}$	−76	122–3	0.56^{25}	∞	∞
(i-)	$C_2H_5CO_2CH(CH_3)_2$	116.16	col. lq.	0.893^{0}	...	$109–11^{750}$	0.6^{25}	∞	∞
thiocyanate (i-)	$(CH_3)_2CH.CNS$	101.16	lq.	0.963^{20}	...	$152–3^{754}$	i.	∞	∞
n-valerate (n-)	$CH_3(CH_2)_3CO_2CH_2C_2H_5$	144.21	lq.	0.874^{15}	−70.7	67.5	i.	∞	∞
i-valerate (n-)	$(CH_3)_2CHCH_2CO_2C_3H_7$	144.21	col. lq.	$0.863^{20/4}$	...	155.9	i.	∞	∞
i-valerate (i-)	$(CH_3)_2CHCH_2CO_2C_3H_7$	144.21	col. lq.	0.854^{17}	...	142^{756}			
Propylene	$CH_3CH:CH_2$	42.08	gas	$0.609^{-47/4}$	−185	-48^{749}	44.6 cc.	1200 cc.	
bromide	$CH_3CHBrCH_2Br$	201.91	col. lq.	$1.933^{20/4}$	−55.5	141.6	0.25^{20}	s.	v. s.
chlorohydrin	$CH_3CHClCH_2OH$	94.54	col. lq.	1.103^{20}	...	133–4	s.	s.	s.
chloride	$CH_3CHClCH_2Cl$	112.99	col. lq.	$1.159^{20/20}$	<−70	96.8	0.27^{20}	v. s.	v. s.
glycol	$CH_3CH(OH)CH_2OH$	76.09	col. oil	$1.040^{19.4}$	...	188–9	∞	∞	8
oxide	$CH_3(CHCH_2)O$	58.08	col. lq.	$0.831^{20/20}$	...	35	33^{20}	∞	∞
Protocatechuic acid (3-,4-)	$(HO)_2C_6H_3CO_2H.H_2O$	172.13	nd./aq.	$1.542^{4/4}$	199 d.	...	1.82^{14}	v. s.	s.
Pulegol (iso-)(d-)	$C_{10}H_{17}OH$	154.24	col. lq.	$0.911^{20/4}$	...	$86–9^{10}$	v. sl. s.		
Pulegone	$C_{10}H_{16}O$	152.23	col. lq.	$0.932^{20/20}$	...	224^{754}	i.	∞	∞
Pyrazole	—NH.N:CH.CH:CH—	68.08	nd./et.	...	70	186–8	s.	s.	s.
Pyrazoline	$—NH.N:CH.CH_2CH_2—$	70.09	lq.	...	...	144	∞	∞	sl. s.
Pyrazolone	$—NH.CO.CH_2CH:N—$	84.08	nd.	...	165	subl. d.	s.	v. s.	v. sl. s.
Pyrene	$C_{16}H_{10}$	202.24	yel. pr.	$1.277^{0/4}$	149–50	>360	i.	3 h.	v. s.
Pyridazine	$N_2 < (CHCH)_2 >$	80.09	lq.	$1.107^{20/4}$	−8	208	∞	s.	s.
Pyridine	$CH < (CHCH)_2 > N$	79.10	col. lq.	$0.982^{20/4}$	−42	115–6	∞	∞	s.
Pyrocatechol (o-)	$C_6H_4(OH)_2$	110.11	nd./aq.	1.344^{4}	104–5	240–5	45.1^{20}	v. s.	v. s.
Pyrogallol (1-,2-,3-)	$C_6H_3(OH)_3$	126.11	nd.	1.453^{4}	133–4	309	40^{13}	s.	s.
Pyrone	$CO < (CHCH)_2 > O$	96.08	cr.	$1.190^{40.3}$	32.5	215–7	v. sl. s.	s.	v. s.
Pyrrole	$< (CH:CH)_2 > NH$	67.09	lq.	$0.948^{20/4}$	...	131	i.	s.	s.
Pyrrolidine	$< (CH_2.CH_2)_2 > NH$	71.12	lq.	$0.852^{22.5}$	...	87–8	∞	∞	∞
Pyrroline	$< (CH.CH_2)_2 > NH$	69.10	lq.	$0.910^{20/4}$	...	90–1	v. s.	∞	∞
Pyruvic acid	CH_3COCO_2H	88.06	col. lq.	$1.267^{20/4}$	13.6	165	∞	∞	∞
Quercitrin	$C_{21}H_{20}O_{11}.2H_2O$	484.40	yel. nd.	...	182–5	...	0.04^{20}	s.	sl. s.
Quinaldine (py-2)	$CH_3.C_9H_6N$	143.18	lq.	$1.059^{20/4}$	−1	$244–5^{750}$	v. sl. s.	...	s.
Quinoline	C_9H_7N	129.15	lq.	1.095^{20}	−15	237.1^{747}	6	∞	∞
(iso-)	C_9H_7N	129.15	pl.	$1.099^{21/4}$	24.6	240.5^{763}	sl. s.	...	s.
-diol (1-,3-)	$—C_6H_4CH:C(OH)N:C(OH)—$	161.15	cr.	...	237	...	v. sl. s.		
Quinone (p-)	$CO < (CHCH)_2 > CO$	108.09	yel. mn.	$1.318^{20/4}$	115.7	subl.	sl. s. h.	s.	s.
R-acid Ca salt (2-)(3-,6-)	$HOC_{10}H_5(SO_3)_2Ca$	342.35	cr.	...	...	...	30.6^{25}		
K salt	$HOC_{10}H_5(SO_3K)_2$	380.46	cr.	...	...	...	29.5^{25}		
Na salt	$HOC_{10}H_5(SO_3Na)_2$	348.26	cr.	...	...	...	25.2^{25}		
Raffinose	$C_{18}H_{32}O_{16}.5H_2O$	594.52	cr./aq.	1.465^{0}	119	d. 130	14.3^{20}	0.1^{20}	
Resorcinol (m-)	$C_6H_4(OH)_2$	110.11	col. rhb.	1.272^{15}	110.7	276.5	147^{12}	v. s.	v. s.
Retene	$C_{18}H_{18}$	234.32	lf./al.	1.13^{16}	98–9	390–4	i.	69 h.	v. s. h.
Rhamnose (β-)	$CH_3(CHOH)_4CHO.H_2O$	182.17	col. mn.	$1.471^{20/4}$	126	...	60.8^{21}	...	i.
Ricinoleic acid	$C_{17}H_{32}(OH)CO_2H$	298.45	lq.	0.954^{16}	4–5	$226–8^{10}$	i.	∞	∞
Rosaniline	$C_{20}H_{21}ON_3$	319.39	col. nd.	...	186 d.	...	v. sl. s.	sl. s.	i.
Rosolic acid	$C_{20}H_{16}O_3$	304.33	red lf.	...	308–10 d.	...	0.12^{25}	v. s. h.	sl. s.
Saccharin	$C_6H_4(CO)(SO_2) > NH$	183.18	mn.	...	225–8	subl.	0.4^{25}	3.1 c.	1.05 c.
Safrole (1-,3-,4-)	$CH_2:CHCH_2.C_6H_3:O_2CH_2$	162.18	col. mn.	$1.100^{20/4}$	11.2	233–4	i.	s.	∞
(iso-)(1-,3-,4-)	$CH_3.CH:CH.C_6H_3:O_2CH_2$	162.18	col. lq.	$1.122^{20/4}$	6–7	252–3	i.	∞	∞
Salicylic acid (o-)	$HO.C_6H_4.CO_2H$	138.12	mn.	$1.443^{20/4}$	159	211^{20}	0.2^{23}	49^{15}	51^{15}
aldehyde (o-)	$HO.C_6H_4.CHO$	122.12	col. oil	$1.153^{25/4}$	−7	196.5	1.7^{86}	∞	∞
Saligenin	$HO.C_6H_4.CH_2OH$	124.13	rhb./aq.	1.161^{25}	86–7	subl.	6.6^{15}	v. s.	v.s.
Schaeffer's salt, Ca	$(HOC_{10}H_6SO_3)_2Ca.5H_2O$	576.59	cr.	...	...	...	4.76^{20}		
K	$HOC_{10}H_6SO_3K$	262.31	cr.	...	...	...	3.46^{25}		
Na	$HOC_{10}H_6SO_3Na$	246.21	cr.	...	...	...	6.29^{25}		
Semicarbazide	$NH_2.CO.NH.NH_2$	75.07	pr./al.	...	96	...	v. s.	v. s.	i.
hydrochloride	$NH_2.CO.NH.NH_3Cl$	111.54	pr.	...	173 d.	...	v. s.	sl. s.	i.
Skatole (3-)	$CH_3.C_8H_6N$	131.17	lf.	...	95	$265–6^{755}$	0.05 c.	s.	s.
Sodium methylate	CH_3ONa	54.03	pd.	...	d. 300	...	d.		
Sorbitol	$[CH_2OH(CHOH)_2]_2$	182.17	cr.	...	110–2	...	v. s.	v. s. h.	
Sorbose (d- or l-)	$C_6H_{12}O_6$	180.16	rhb.	1.654^{15}	165	...	55^{17}	sl. s.	
Starch	$(C_6H_{10}O_5)x$	162.14	amor.	1.50^{21}	d.	...	i.	i.	

Stearic acid	$CH_3(CH_2)_{16}CO_2H$	284.47	mn.	$0.847^{69.3}$	70–1	291^{110}	0.03^{25}	2^{20}	6
amide	$CH_3(CH_2)_{16}CONH_2$	283.48	col. cr.	....	108–9	251^{12}	i.	s. h.	s. h.
Styrene	$C_6H_5CH:CH_2$	104.14	col. lq.	$0.903^{20/4}$	−31	145–6	v. sl. s.	∞	∞
Suberic acid	$HO_2C(CH_2)_6CO_2H$	174.19	nd./aq.	$1.266^{25/4}$	140–4	279^{100}	0.14^{16}	s.	0.8^{15}
Succinic acid	$HO_2C(CH_2)_2CO_2H$	118.09	col. mn.	$1.572^{25/4}$	189–90	235 d.	6.8^{20}	9.9^{15}	1.2^{15}
Sucrose	$C_{12}H_{22}O_{11}$	342.30	col. mn.	1.588^{15}	170–86 d.	....	179^{0}	0.9	i.
Sulfanilic acid (p-)	$H_2N.C_6H_4.SO_3H$	173.18	col. cr.	....	d. >280	....	0.8^{10}	v. sl. s.	v. sl. s.
Sylvestrene (d-)	$C_{10}H_{16}$	136.23	lq.	$0.863^{20/4}$	....	176–7			
Tartaric acid (meso-)	$(CHOHCO_2H)_2$	150.09	cr.	1.737	159–60	....	120^{15}		
(racemic)	$(CHOHCO_2H)_2.H_2O$	168.10	tri.	$1.697^{20/4}$	205–6	....	20.6^{20}	2^{0}	0.09
(d- or l-)	$(CHOHCO_2H)_2$	150.09	mn.	$1.760^{20/4}$	168–70	d.	139^{20}	25^{15}	0.4^{15}
Tartronic acid	$CH(OH)(CO_2H)_2.\frac{1}{2}H_2O$	129.07	pr./aq.	....	d. 155–8	subl.	v. s.	v. s.	i.
Terephthalic acid (p-)	$C_6H_4(CO_2H)_2$	166.13	cr.	1.510	subl.	....	0.001 c.	sl. s. h.	i.
Terpin hydrate (cis-)	$C_{10}H_{20}O_2.H_2O$	190.28	rhb.	....	117	d.	0.4^{15}	10^{15}	1^{15}
Terpineol (α-)(d- or l-)	$C_{10}H_{18}O$	154.24	col. cr.	0.935^{15}	38–40	219–21	i.	v. s.	v. s.
(dl-)	$C_{10}H_{18}O$	154.24	col. cr.	$0.935^{20/20}$	35	$218–9^{752}$	i.	v. s.	v. s.
Terpinyl acetate (α-)(dl-)	$CH_3CO_2.C_{10}H_{17}$	196.28	lq.	$0.966^{20/4}$	<−50	220 d.	i.	20	
Tetrabromo-ethane (sym)	$Br_2CH.CHBr_2$	345.70	col. lq.	$2.964^{20/4}$	−1.0	151^{54}	i.	∞	∞
(uns)	$Br_3C.CH_2Br$	345.70	col. lq.	$2.875^{20/4}$	0	104^{13}	....	s.	
Tetrachloro-ethane (sym)	$Cl_2CH.CHCl_2$	167.86	col. lq.	$1.600^{20/4}$	−36	146.3	0.29^{20}	∞	∞
(uns)	$Cl_3C.CH_2Cl$	167.86	lq.	$1.588^{20/4}$	....	129–30	i.	∞	∞
-ethylene	$Cl_2C:CCl_2$	165.85	col. lq.	$1.624^{15/4}$	−19	120.8	0.02^{20}	∞	∞
Tetracosane (n-)	$CH_3(CH_2)_{22}CH_3$	338.64	cr.	$0.779^{51/4}$	51.1	324	....	....	s.
Tetradecane (n-)	$CH_3(CH_2)_{12}CH_3$	198.38	col. lq.	$0.765^{20/4}$	5.5	252.5	i.	v. s.	v. s.
Tetraethyl-thiuram disulfide	$[(C_2H_5)_2NCS]_2S_2$	296.52	cr.	1.17	70	....	i.		
Tetrafluoro-ethylene	$F_2C:CF_2$	100.02	gas	1.58^{-78}	−142.5	−76.3	0.01^{30}		
Tetrahydro-furan	$—CH_2(CH_2)_2CH_2.O—$	72.10	col. lq.	$0.888^{21/4}$	−65	65–6	s.	s.	s.
-furfuryl alcohol	$C_4H_7O.CH_2OH$	102.13	col. lq.	$1.050^{20/4}$	....	$177–8^{743}$	∞	∞	∞
-pyran	$—CH_2(CH_2)_3CH_2.O—$	86.13	lq.	$0.881^{20/4}$	....	88	s.		
Tetralin	$—C_6H_4CH_2(CH_2)_2CH_2—$	132.20	col. lq.	$0.973^{18/4}$	−31	206^{764}	i.	s.	s.
Tetramethyl-thiuram disulfide	$[(CH_3)_2NCS]_2S_2$	240.41	cr.	1.29	155–6	....	i.		
Tetryl (2-,4-,6-)	$(NO_2)_3C_6H_2.N(CH_3)NO_2$	287.15	yel. mn.	1.57^{19}	130.5	expl.	i.	s. h.	s.
Theobromine	$C_7H_8O_2N_4$	180.17	rhb.	....	330	....	0.06^{15}	0.06 c.	0.03 h.
Thio-acetic acid	$CH_3.CO.SH$	76.11	yel. lq.	1.074^{10}	<−17	93	s.	∞	∞
-aniline (4-, 4′-)	$(NH_2.C_6H_4)_2S$	216.29	nd./aq.	....	108	....	sl. s. h.	s.	s.
-carbanilide	$(C_6H_5.NH)_2CS$	228.30	rhb./al.	1.3^{24}	154	d.	i.	v. s.	v. s.
-naphthol (β-)	$C_{10}H_7.SH$	160.22	cr./al.	....	81	286–8	v. sl. s.	v. s.	v. s.
-phenol	$C_6H_5.SH$	110.17	col. lq.	$1.074^{23/4}$	....	168–9	v. sl. s.	v. s.	∞
-salicylic acid (o-)	$HS.C_6H_4.CO_2H$	154.18	yel. nd.	....	164	subl.	sl. s. h.	s.	
-urea	$NH_2.CS.NH_2$	76.12	rhb./al.	$1.405^{20/4}$	180–2	d.	9.2^{13}	s.	sl. s.
Thiophene	$<(CH:CH)_2>S$	84.13	col. lq.	$1.070^{15/4}$	−30	84	i.	s.	
Thymol (5-,2-,1-)	$(CH_3)(C_3H_7)C_6H_3OH$	150.21	cr.	$0.972^{25/25}$	51.5	232^{752}	0.09^{19}	v. s.	v. s.
Tolidine (0-)(3-,3′-,4-,4′-)	$[CH_3(NH_2)C_6H_3]_2$	212.28	lf.	....	128–9	....	v. sl. s.	s.	s.
Toluene	$C_6H_5.CH_3$	92.13	col. lq.	$0.866^{20/4}$	−95	110.8	0.05^{16}	s.	∞
sulfonic acid (o-)	$CH_3.C_6H_4SO_3H.2H_2O$	208.23	cr.	....	d.	128.8^{0}	v. s.	s.	
(p-)	$CH_3.C_6H_4SO_3H.H_2O$	190.21	mn.	....	104–5	$146–7^{0}$	v. s.	s.	
sulfonic amide (p-)	$CH_3.C_6H_4SO_2NH_2$	171.21	mn.	....	137	....	0.2^{9}	7.4^{5}	
sulfonic chloride (p-)	$CH_3.C_6H_4.SO_2Cl$	190.64	tri.	....	69	134.5^{10}	i.	s.	s.
Toluic acid (o-)	$CH_3.C_6H_4.CO_2H$	136.14	cr./aq.	$1.062^{115/4}$	104–5	259^{751}	2.17^{100}	v. s.	
(m-)	$CH_3.C_6H_4.CO_2H$	136.14	pr./aq.	$1.054^{112/4}$	110–1	263	1.6^{100}	v. s.	v. s.
(p-)	$CH_3.C_6H_4.CO_2H$	136.14	cr./aq.	....	179–80	274–5	1.3^{100}	v. s.	v. s.
Toluidine (o-)	$CH_3.C_6H_4.NH_2$	107.15	col. lq.	$0.999^{20/4}$	−16.3	199.7	1.5^{25}	∞	∞
(m-)	$CH_3.C_6H_4.NH_2$	107.15	col. lq.	$0.989^{20/4}$	−31.5	203.3	sl. s.	∞	∞
(p-)	$CH_3.C_6H_4.NH_2$	107.15	cr.	$1.046^{20/4}$	44–5	200.3	0.7^{21}	v s.	v. s.
hydrochloride (o-)	$CH_3.C_6H_4.NH_3Cl$	143.62	mn. pr.	....	218–20	242	s.	sl. s.	
sulfonic acid (1-,2-,3-)	$CH_3(NH_2)C_6H_3SO_3H$	187.21	cr.	....	....	....	0.97^{11}		
Toluylenediamine (1-,2-,4-)	$CH_3.C_6H_3(NH_2)_2$	122.17	rhb.	....	99	283–5	s. h.	s.	s.
Tolylene diisocyanate (1-,2-,4-)	$CH_3.C_6H_3(NCO)_2$	174.15	lq.	1.23^{28}	....	134.5^{20}	d.	d.	
Trehalose	$C_{12}H_{22}O_{11}.2H_2O$	378.33	rhb./al.	....	97	....	s. h.	sl. s. h.	i.
Triamylamine (n-)	$[CH_3(CH_2)_3CH_2]_3N$	227.42	lq.	....	....	240–5	i.		
(i-)	$[(CH_3)_2CH(CH_2)_2]_3N$	227.42	col. lq.	$0.786^{20/4}$	....	235	i.		
Tributyl-amine (n-)	$[CH_3(CH_2)_2CH_2]_3N$	185.34	col. lq.	$0.778^{20/20}$	....	216.5^{761}	i.	s.	∞
phosphite	$[CH_3(CH_2)_3O]_3P$	250.32	lq.	$0.925^{20/4}$	....	$122–3^{12}$	i.		
Trichloro-acetic acid	$Cl_3C.CO_2H$	163.40	cr.	$1.617^{46/15}$	58	195.5^{754}	120^{25}	s.	s.
-benzene (s-)(1-,3-,5-)	$C_6H_3Cl_3$	181.46	nd.	....	63.5	208.5^{764}	i.	sl. s.	
-ethane (1-,1-,1-)	$Cl_3C.CH_3$	133.42	lq.	$1.325^{26/4}$	....	74.1	i.	∞	∞
-ethylene	$Cl_2C:CHCl$	131.40	col. lq.	$1.466^{20/20}$	−73	87.2	0.1^{25}	∞	∞
-phenol	$Cl_3C_6H_2OH$	197.46	nd.	$1.490^{75/4}$	68–9	246	0.09^{25}	v. s.	v. s.
Tricosane (n-)	$CH_3(CH_2)_{21}CH_3$	324.61	lf.	$0.779^{48/4}$	47.7	234^{15}	i.		
Tricresyl phosphate (o-)	$OP(OC_6H_4CH_3)_3$	368.36	lq.	....	....	....	i.		
Tridecane (n-)	$CH_3(CH_2)_{11}CH_3$	184.35	col. lq.	$0.757^{20/4}$	−6.2	234	i.	v. s.	v. s.
Triethanol amine	$(HOCH_2CH_2)_3N$	149.19	col. lq.	$1.126^{20/20}$	20–1	$277–9^{150}$	∞	∞	sl. s.

Table 3-2. Physical Properties of Organic Compounds—(*Concluded*)

Name	Formula	Formula weight	Form and color	Specific gravity	Melting point, °C.	Boiling point, °C.	Solubility in 100 parts: Water	Alcohol	Ether
Triethyl-amine	$(CH_3CH_2)_3N$	101.19	col. oil	$0.729^{20/20}$	−114.8	89.4	$\infty > 19^{0}$	∞	∞
-benzene (1-,3-,5-)	$(C_2H_5)_3C_6H_3$	162.26	lq.	$0.861^{20/4}$	...	215	i.	s.	s.
(1-,2-,4-)	$(C_2H_5)_3C_6H_3$	162.26	lq.	$0.882^{17/4}$	...	$217–8^{755}$	i.	s.	s.
borate	$B(OCH_2CH_3)_3$	146.00	lq.	$0.864^{20/20}$	...	120	d.		
citrate	$HOC_3H_4(CO_2C_2H_5)_3$	276.28	oil	$1.137^{20/4}$	...	294	i.	∞	∞
Triethylene glycol	$(.CH_2OCH_2CH_2OH)_2$	150.17	col. lq.	$1.125^{20/20}$	−5	290	∞	∞	v. sl. s.
Trifluoro-chloromethane	CF_3Cl	104.47	gas	1.726^{-130}	−182	−80			
chloroethylene	$F_2C:CFCl$	116.48	gas	...	−157.5	−27.9	d.		
-trichloroethane	$Cl_2CF.CClF_2$	187.39	lq.	$1.576^{20/4}$	−35	47.6	i.	∞	∞
Trimethoxybutane (1-,3-,3-)	$CH_2(OCH_3)CH_2C(OCH_3)_2CH_3$	148.20	lq.	0.932	...	$63–5^{25}$	d.		
Trimethylamine	$(CH_3)_3N$	59.11	gas	0.662^{-5}	−124	3.5	41^{19}	s.	s.
Trimethylene bromide	$BrCH_2CH_2CH_2Br$	201.91	lq.	$1.987^{15/4}$	−34.4	167.5	0.17^{30}	s.	s.
chloride	$ClCH_2CH_2CH_2Cl$	112.99	lq.	1.201^{15}	...	123–5	0.27^{25}	s.	s.
glycol	$HOCH_2CH_2CH_2OH$	76.09	oil	$1.060^{20/4}$	...	214	∞	∞	
Trinitro-benzene (1-,3-,5-)	$C_6H_3(NO_2)_3$	213.11	col. rhb.	$1.688^{20/4}$	121	d.	0.03^{15}	1.9^{18}	1.5^{18}
-benzoic acid (2-,4-,6-)	$(NO_2)_3C_6H_2CO_2H$	257.12	rhb./aq.	...	210–20 d.	...	2.05^{24}		
-tert-butylxylene	$(NO_2)_3C_6(CH_3)_2C_4H_9$	297.26	nd./al.	...	110	...	i.	sl. s.	s.
-naphthalene (α-)(1-,3-,5-)	$C_{10}H_5(NO_2)_3$	263.16	rhb.	...	122–3	...	i.	s.	
(β-)(1-,3-,8-)	$C_{10}H_5(NO_2)_3$	263.16	cr./al.	...	218–9	...	0.02^{100}	0.05^{23}	0.13^{15}
(γ-)(1-,4-,5-)	$C_{10}H_5(NO_2)_3$	263.16	yel. cr.	...	148–9	...	i.	0.11^{19}	0.4^{19}
-phenol (2-,3-,6-)	$(NO_2)_3C_6H_2OH$	229.11	nd.		117–8	...	s. h.	v. s.	v. s.
-toluene (β-)(2-,3-,4-)	$CH_3C_6H_2(NO_2)_3$	227.13	cr.	$1.620^{20/4}$	112	expl.	i.	sl. s. c.	s.
(γ-)(2-,4-,5-)	$CH_3C_6H_2(NO_2)_3$	227.13	yel. pl.	$1.620^{20/4}$	104	expl.	i.	s. h.	v. s.
(α-)(2-,4-,6-)	$CH_3C_6H_2(NO_2)_3$	227.13	cr./al.	1.654	80.8	expl.	0.01^{20}	1.5^{22}	5^{38}
Trional	$C_2H_5(CH_3)C(SO_2C_2H_5)_3$	242.34	pl./al.	$1.199^{85/4}$	76	d.	0.3^{15}	5^{0}	6.6^{15}
Triphenyl-arsine	$(C_6H_5)_3As$	306.21	pl.	1.306	59–60	>360	i.	s.	v. s.
carbinol	$(C_6H_5)_3COH$	260.32	cr.	$1.188^{20/4}$	162.5	>360	i.	v. s.	v. s.
guanidine (α-)	$C_6H_5N:C(NHC_6H_5)_2$	287.35	rhb./al.	1.13	144–5	d.	i.	4^{0}	
methane	$(C_6H_5)_3CH$	244.32	cr.	$1.014^{99/4}$	93.4	359^{754}	i.	v. s. h.	v. s.
methyl	$(C_6H_5)_3C$ . . .	243.31	col. cr.	...	145–7	d.	i.	sl. s. h.	
phosphate	$OP(OC_6H_5)_3$	326.28	pr./al.	$1.206^{58/4}$	49–50	245^{11}	i.	155^{25}	v. s.
Tripropylamine (n-)	$(CH_3CH_2CH_2)_3N$	143.27	col. lq.	$0.757^{20/4}$	−93.5	156.5	v. sl. s.	∞	∞
Undecane (n-)	$CH_3(CH_2)_9CH_3$	156.30	col. lq.	$0.741^{20/4}$	−25.6	194.5	i.	∞	∞
Urea	$H_2N.CO.NH_2$	60.06	col. pr.	$1.335^{20/4}$	132.7	d.	100^{17}	20^{20}	sl. s.
nitrate	$CO(NH_2)_2.HNO_3$	123.07	col. mn.	...	152 d.	...	v. s. h.	s.	
Uric acid	$C_5H_4O_3N_4$	168.11	cr.	1.893^{20}	d.	...	0.06 h.	i.	i.
Valeric acid (n-)	$C_2H_5CH_2CH_2CO_2H$	102.13	col. lq.	$0.939^{20/4}$	−34.5	187	3.3^{16}	∞	∞
(i-)	$(CH_3)_2CHCH_2CO_2H$	102.13	col. lq.	$0.931^{20/20}$	−37.6	176	4.2^{20}	∞	∞
aldehyde (n-)	$C_2H_5CH_2CH_2CHO$	86.13	lq.	0.819^{11}	−92	103.4	v. sl. s.	s.	s.
(i-)	$(CH_3)_2CHCH_2CHO$	86.13	col. lq.	0.803^{17}	−51	92.5	sl. s.	s.	s.
amide (n-)	$C_2H_5CH_2CH_2CONH_2$	101.15	mn. pl.	1.023	106	...	v. s.	v. s.	v. s.
(i-)	$(CH_3)_2CHCH_2CONH_2$	101.15	mn.	$0.965^{20/4}$	135–7	232	s.	s.	s.
Vanillic acid (3-,4-,1-)	$CH_3O(OH)C_6H_3CO_2H$	168.14	nd./aq.	...	207	subl.	0.12^{14}	v. s.	v. s.
alcohol (3-,4-,1-)	$CH_3O(OH)C_6H_3CH_2OH$	154.16	mn./aq.	...	115	d.	v. s. h.	v. s.	v. s.
Vanillin (3-,4-,1-)	$CH_3O(OH)C_6H_3CHO$	152.14	mn.	1.056	81–2	285	1^{14}	v. s.	v. s.
Veratrole (o-)	$C_6H_4(OCH_3)_2$	138.16	cr.	$1.091^{15/15}$	22.5	207.1	v. sl. s.	s.	s.
Vinyl acetate	$CH_3CO_2CH:CH_2$	86.09	col. lq.	$0.932^{20/4}$	<−60	72–3	2^{20}	∞	∞
(poly-)	$(CH_3CO_2CH:CH_2)x$	(86.09)	...	1.19^{20}	100–25	...	i.		
acetic acid	$CH_2:CH.CH_2CO_2H$	86.09	col. lq.	$1.013^{15/15}$	−39	163	s.	∞	∞
acetylene	$CH_2:CH.C:CH$	52.07	gas	$0.705^{1.5}$	...	5.5	$0.67^{0.6}$		
alcohol	$CH_2:CHOH$	44.06							
(poly-)	$(CH_2:CHOH)x$	(44.06)	...	1.3^{20}	d. >200	...	s.		
chloride	$CH_2:CHCl$	62.50	gas	$0.908^{25/25}$	−160	−12	sl. s.	s.	v. s.
propionate	$C_2H_5CO_2CH:CH_2$	100.11	lq.	...		93–5	v. sl. s.		
Xylene (o-)	$C_6H_4(CH_3)_2$	106.16	col. lq.	$0.881^{20/4}$	−25	144	i.	s.	∞
(m-)	$C_6H_4(CH_3)_2$	106.16	col. lq.	$0.867^{17/4}$	−47.4	139.3	i.	s.	∞
(p-)	$C_6H_4(CH_3)_2$	106.16	col. lq.	$0.861^{20/4}$	13.2	138.5	i.	s.	v. s.
sulfonic acid (1-,4-,2-)	$(CH_3)_2C_6H_3SO_3H.2H_2O$	222.25	col. lf.	...	86	$149^{0.1}$	s.		
Xylidine (1:2)(3-)	$(CH_3)_2C_6H_3NH_2$	121.18	lq.	0.991^{15}	<−15	223	v. sl. s.	s.	s.
(1:2)(4-)	$(CH_3)_2C_6H_3NH_2$	121.18	pr.	$1.076^{17.5}$	49–50	224–6	v. sl. s.		
(1:3)(2-)	$(CH_3)_2C_6H_3NH_2$	121.18	lq.	0.980^{15}	...	216–7	v. sl. s.		
(1:3)(4-)	$(CH_3)_2C_6H_3NH_2$	121.18	lq.	$0.978^{20/4}$	...	213–4	v. sl. s.		
(1:3)(5-)	$(CH_3)_2C_6H_3NH_2$	121.18	oil	$0.972^{20/4}$	...	221–2	v. sl. s.		
(1:4)(2-)	$(CH_3)_2C_6H_3NH_2$	121.18	oil	$0.979^{21/4}$	15.5	215^{739}	v. sl. s.		
Xylose (l-)(+)	$CH_2OH(CHOH)_3CHO$	150.13	nd.	1.535^{0}	153–4	...	117^{20}	v. sl. s.	i.
Xylylene dichloride (p-)	$C_6H_4(CH_2Cl)_2$	175.06	mn.	1.417^{0}	100.5	240–5 d.	i.	s.	v. sl. s.
Zinc diethyl	$Zn(CH_2CH_3)_2$	123.50	col. lq.	1.182^{18}	−28	118	d.	d.	
dimethyl	$Zn(CH_3)_2$	95.45	col. lq.	1.386^{11}	−40	46	d.	d.	
dimethyl-dithiocarbamate	$Zn[S_2CN(CH_3)_2]_2$	305.79	...	$2.00^{40/4}$	248–50	...	i.		

VAPOR PRESSURES OF PURE SUBSTANCES

Table 3-3. Vapor Pressure of Water Ice from −15° to 0°C.*

Mm. Hg.

t, °C.	0.0	0.1	0.2	0.3	0.4	0.5	0.6	0.7	0.8	0.9
−14	1.361	1.348	1.336	1.324	1.312	1.300	1.288	1.276	1.264	1.253
−13	1.490	1.477	1.464	1.450	1.437	1.424	1.411	1.399	1.386	1.373
−12	1.632	1.617	1.602	1.588	1.574	1.559	1.546	1.532	1.518	1.504
−11	1.785	1.769	1.753	1.737	1.722	1.707	1.691	1.676	1.661	1.646
−10	1.950	1.934	1.916	1.899	1.883	1.866	1.849	1.833	1.817	1.800
− 9	2.131	2.112	2.093	2.075	2.057	2.039	2.021	2.003	1.985	1.968
− 8	2.326	2.306	2.285	2.266	2.246	2.226	2.207	2.187	2.168	2.149
− 7	2.537	2.515	2.493	2.472	2.450	2.429	2.408	2.387	2.367	2.346
− 6	2.765	2.742	2.718	2.695	2.672	2.649	2.626	2.603	2.581	2.559
− 5	3.013	2.987	2.962	2.937	2.912	2.887	2.862	2.838	2.813	2.790
− 4	3.280	3.252	3.225	3.198	3.171	3.144	3.117	3.091	3.065	3.039
− 3	3.568	3.539	3.509	3.480	3.451	3.422	3.393	3.364	3.336	3.308
− 2	3.880	3.848	3.816	3.785	3.753	3.722	3.691	3.660	3.630	3.599
− 1	4.217	4.182	4.147	4.113	4.079	4.045	4.012	3.979	3.946	3.913
− 0	4.579	4.542	4.504	4.467	4.431	4.395	4.359	4.323	4.287	4.252

* For data at 0(0.2)–30(2)–98°C. see p. 2324, "Handbook of Chemistry and Physics," 40th ed., Chemical Rubber Publishing Co.

Table 3-4. Vapor Pressure of Liquid Water from −16° to 0°C.*

Mm. Hg.

t, °C.	0.0	0.1	0.2	0.3	0.4	0.5	0.6	0.7	0.8	0.9
−15	1.436	1.425	1.414	1.402	1.390	1.379	1.368	1.356	1.345	1.334
−14	1.560	1.547	1.534	1.522	1.511	1.497	1.485	1.472	1.460	1.449
−13	1.691	1.678	1.665	1.651	1.637	1.624	1.611	1.599	1.585	1.572
−12	1.834	1.819	1.804	1.790	1.776	1.761	1.748	1.734	1.720	1.705
−11	1.987	1.971	1.955	1.939	1.924	1.909	1.893	1.878	1.863	1.848
−10	2.149	2.134	2.116	2.099	2.084	2.067	2.050	2.034	2.018	2.001
− 9	2.326	2.307	2.289	2.271	2.254	2.236	2.219	2.201	2.184	2.167
− 8	2.514	2.495	2.475	2.456	2.437	2.418	2.399	2.380	2.362	2.343
− 7	2.715	2.695	2.674	2.654	2.633	2.613	2.593	2.572	2.553	2.533
− 6	2.931	2.909	2.887	2.866	2.843	2.822	2.800	2.778	2.757	2.736
− 5	3.163	3.139	3.115	3.092	3.069	3.046	3.022	3.000	2.976	2.955
− 4	3.410	3.384	3.359	3.334	3.309	3.284	3.259	3.235	3.211	3.187
− 3	3.673	3.647	3.620	3.593	3.567	3.540	3.514	3.487	3.461	3.436
− 2	3.956	3.927	3.898	3.871	3.841	3.813	3.785	3.757	3.730	3.702
− 1	4.258	4.227	4.196	4.165	4.135	4.105	4.075	4.045	4.016	3.986
− 0	4.579	4.546	4.513	4.480	4.448	4.416	4.385	4.353	4.320	4.289

* Computed from the above table with the aid of the thermodynamic equation

$$\log_{10} \frac{p_w}{p_i} = \frac{-1.1489t}{273.1 + t} - 1.330 \times 10^{-5}t^2 + 9.084 \times 10^{-8}t^3$$

Table 3-5. Vapor Pressure of Liquid Water from 0° to 100°C.*

Mm. Hg.

t, °C.	0.0	0.1	0.2	0.3	0.4	0.5	0.6	0.7	0.8	0.9
0	4.579	4.613	4.647	4.681	4.715	4.750	4.785	4.820	4.855	4.890
1	4.926	4.962	4.998	5.034	5.070	5.107	5.144	5.181	5.219	5.256
2	5.294	5.332	5.370	5.408	5.447	5.486	5.525	5.565	5.605	5.645
3	5.685	5.725	5.766	5.807	5.848	5.889	5.931	5.973	6.015	6.058
4	6.101	6.144	6.187	6.230	6.274	6.318	6.363	6.408	6.453	6.498
5	6.543	6.589	6.635	6.681	6.728	6.775	6.822	6.869	6.917	6.965
6	7.013	7.062	7.111	7.160	7.209	7.259	7.309	7.360	7.411	7.462
7	7.513	7 565	7.617	7.669	7.722	7.775	7.828	7.882	7.936	7.990
8	8.045	8.100	8.155	8.211	8.267	8.323	8.380	8.437	8.494	8.551
9	8.609	8.668	8.727	8.786	8.845	8.905	8.965	9.025	9.086	9.147

Table 3-5. Vapor Pressure of Liquid Water from 0° to 100°C.*—*(Concluded)*

t, °C.	0.0	0.1	0.2	0.3	0.4	0.5	0.6	0.7	0.8	0.9
10	9.209	9.2 1	9.333	9.395	9.458	9.521	9.585	9.649	9.714	9.779
11	9.844	9.910	9.976	10.042	10.109	10.176	10.244	10.312	10.380	10.449
12	10.518	10.588	10.658	10.728	10.799	10.870	10.941	11.013	11.085	11.158
13	11.231	11.305	11.379	11.453	11.528	11.604	11.680	11 756	11.833	11.910
14	11.987	12.065	12.144	12.223	12.302	12.382	12.462	12.543	12.624	12.706
15	12.788	12.870	12.953	13.037	13.121	13.205	13.290	13.375	13.461	13.547
16	13.634	13.721	13.809	13.898	13.987	14.076	14.166	14.256	14.347	14.438
17	14.530	14.622	14.715	14.809	14.903	14.997	15.092	15.188	15.284	15.380
18	15.477	15.575	15.673	15.772	15.871	15.971	16.071	16.171	16.272	16.374
19	16.477	16.581	16.685	16.789	16.894	16.999	17.105	17.212	17.319	17.427
20	17.535	17.644	17.753	17.863	17.974	18.085	18.197	18.309	18.422	18.536
21	18.650	18.765	18.880	18.996	19.113	19.231	19.349	19.468	19.587	19.707
22	19.827	19.948	20.070	20.193	20.316	20.440	20.565	20.690	20.815	20.941
23	21.068	21.196	21.324	21.453	21.583	21.714	21.845	21.977	22.110	22.243
24	22.377	22.512	22.648	22.785	22.922	23.060	23.198	23.337	23.476	23.616
25	23.756	23.897	24.039	24.182	24.326	24.471	24.617	24.764	24.912	25.060
26	25.209	25.359	25.509	25.660	25.812	25.964	26.117	26.271	26.426	26.582
27	26.739	26.897	27.055	27.214	27.374	27.535	27.696	27.858	28.021	28.185
28	28.349	28.514	28.680	28.847	29.015	29.184	29.354	29.525	29.697	29.870
29	30.043	30.217	30.392	30.568	30.745	30.923	31.102	31.281	31.461	31.642
30	31.824	32.007	32.191	32.376	32.561	32.747	32.934	33.122	33 312	33.503
31	33.695	33.888	34.082	34.276	34.471	34.667	34.864	35.062	35.261	35.462
32	35.663	35.865	36.068	36.272	36.477	36.683	36.891	37.099	37.308	37.518
33	37 729	37.942	38.155	38.369	3 .584	38.801	39.018	39.237	39.457	39.677
34	39.898	40.121	40.344	40.569	40.796	41.023	41.251	41.480	41.710	41.942
35	42.175	42.409	42.644	42.880	43.117	43.355	43.595	43.836	44.078	44.320
36	44.563	44.808	45.054	45.301	45.549	45.799	46.050	46.302	46.556	46.811
37	47.067	47.324	47.582	47.841	48.102	48.364	48.627	48.891	49.157	49.424
38	49.692	49.961	50.231	50.502	50.774	51.048	51.323	51.600	51.879	52.160
39	52.442	52.725	53.009	53.294	53.580	53.867	54.156	54.446	54.737	55.030
40	55.324	55.61	55.91	56.21	56.51	56.81	57.11	57.41	57.72	58.03
41	58.34	58.65	58.96	59.27	59.58	59.90	60.22	60.54	60.86	61.18
42	61.50	61.82	62.14	62.47	62.80	63.13	63.46	63.79	64.12	64.46
43	64.80	65.14	65.48	65.82	66.16	66.51	66.86	67.21	67.56	67.91
44	68.26	68.61	68.97	69.33	69.69	70.05	70.41	70.77	71.14	71.51
45	71.88	72.25	72.62	72.99	73.36	73.74	74.12	74.50	74.88	75.26
46	75.65	76.04	76.43	76.82	77.21	77.60	78.00	78.40	78.80	79.20
47	79.60	80.00	80.41	80.82	81.23	81.64	82.05	82.46	82.87	83.29
48	83.71	84.13	84.56	84.99	85.42	85.85	86.28	86.71	87.14	87.58
49	88.02	88.46	88.90	89.34	89.79	90.24	90.69	91.14	91.59	92.05

t, °C.	0	1	2	3	4	5	6	7	8	9
50	92.51	97.20	102.09	107.20	112.51	118.04	123.80	129.82	136.08	142.60
60	149.38	156.43	163.77	171.38	179.31	187.54	196.09	204.96	214.17	223.73
70	233.7	243.9	254.6	265.7	277.2	289.1	301.4	314.1	327.3	341.0
80	355.1	369.7	384.9	400.6	416.8	433.6	450.9	468.7	487.1	506.1
90	525.76	527.76	529.77	531.78	533.80	535.82	537.86	539.90	541.95	544.00
91	546.05	548.11	550.18	552.26	554.35	556.44	558.53	560.64	562.75	564.87
92	566.99	569.12	571.26	573.40	575.55	577.71	579.87	582.04	584.22	586.41
93	588.60	590.80	593.00	595.21	597.43	599.66	601.89	604.13	606.38	608.64
94	610.90	613.17	615.44	617.72	620.01	622.31	624.61	626.92	629.24	631.57
95	633.90	636.24	638.59	640.94	643.30	645.67	648.05	650.43	652.82	655.22
96	657.62	660.03	662.45	664.88	667.31	669.75	672.20	674.66	677.12	679.69
97	682.07	684.55	687.04	689.54	692.05	694.57	697.10	699.63	702.17	704.71
98	707.27	709.83	712.40	714.98	717.56	720 15	722.75	725.36	727.98	730.61
99	733.24	735.88	738.53	741.18	743.85	746.52	749.20	751.89	754.58	757.29
100	760.00	762.72	765.45	768.19	770.93	773.68	776.44	779.22	782.00	784.78
101	787.57	790.37	793.18	796.00	798.82	801.66	804.50	807.35	810.21	813.08

* From the Physikalisch-technische Reichsanstalt, Holborn, Scheel, and Henning, "Wärmetabellen," Friedrich Vieweg & Sohn, Brunswick, 1909. By permission. For data at 50(0.2) 101.8°C., see "Handbook of Chemistry and Physics," 40th ed., p. 2326, Chemical Rubber Publishing Co. For a tabulation of temperature for pressures 700(1)779 mm. Hg, see Atack, "Handbook of Chemical Data," p. 117, Reinhold, New York, 1957. For a tabulation of pressure for 105(5)200(10)370°C., see Atack, p. 134, and for 100(1)374°C., see "Handbook of Chemistry and Physics," 40th ed., pp. 2328–2330, Chemical Rubber Publishing Co.

Table 3-6. Vapor Pressures of Inorganic Compounds, above 1 Atm.*

Compound		Pressure, atm.									Critical point	
Name	Formula	1	2	5	10	20	30	40	50	60	t_c, °C.	P_c, atm.
		Temperature, °C.										
Ammonia	NH_3	−33.6	−18.7	+4.7	25.7	50.1	66.1	78.9	89.3	98.3	132.4	111.5
Carbon monoxide	CO	−191.3	−183.5	−170.7	−161.0	−149.7	−141.9	......	......	......	−138.7	34.6
dioxide	CO_2	−78.2	−69.1	−56.7	−39.5	−18.9	−5.3	+5.9	14.9	22.4	31.1	73.0
disulfide	CS_2	46.5	69.1	104.8	136.3	175.5	201.5	222.8	240.0	256.0	273.0	72.9
Chlorine	Cl_2	−33.8	−16.9	+10.3	35.6	65.0	84.8	101.6	115.2	127.1	144.0	76.1
para-Hydrogen	H_2	−252.5	−250.2	−246.0	−241.8	......	......	......	......	......	−240.0	12.80
Hydrogen bromide	HBr	−66.5	−51.5	−29.1	−8.4	+16.8	33.9	48.1	60.0	70.6	90.0	84.4
chloride	HCl	−84.8	−71.4	−50.5	−31.7	−8.8	+5.9	17.8	27.9	36.2	51.4	81.6
cyanide	HCN	25.9	45.8	75.8	102.7	135.0	153.8	169.9	183.5	......	183.5	50.0
Water	H_2O	100.0	120.1	152.4	180.5	213.1	234.6	251.1	264.7	276.5	374.2	218.0
Hydrogen sulfide	H_2S	−60.4	−45.9	−22.3	−0.4	+25.5	41.9	55.8	66.7	76.3	100.3	88.9
Krypton	Kr	−152.0	−143.5	−130.0	−118.0	−101.7	−88.8	−78.4	−66.5	......	−63	54
Nitrogen	N_2	−195.8	−189.2	−179.1	−169.8	−157.6	−148.3	......	......	......	−147.2	33.5
Oxygen	O_2	−183.1	−176.0	−164.5	−153.2	−140.0	−130.7	−124.1	......	......	−118.9	49.7
Sulfur dioxide	SO_2	−10.0	+6.3	32.1	55.5	83.8	102.6	118.0	130.2	141.7	157.2	77.7
trioxide	SO_3	44.8	60.0	82.5	104.0	138.0	157.8	175.0	187.8	198.0	218.3	83.6

* Compiled from the extended tables published by D. R. Stull in *Ind. Eng. Chem.*, **39**, 517 (1947).

Table 3-7. Vapor Pressures of Inorganic Compounds, up to 1 Atm.*

Compound		Pressure, mm. Hg										Melting point, °C.
Name	Formula	1	5	10	20	40	60	100	200	400	760	
		Temperature, °C.										
Aluminum	Al	1284	1421	1487	1555	1635	1684	1749	1844	1947	2056	660
borohydride	$Al(BH_4)_3$	......	−52.2	−42.9	−32.5	−20.9	−13.4	−3.9	+11.2	28.1	45.9	−64.
bromide	$AlBr_3$	81.3	103.8	118.0	134.0	150.6	161.7	176.1	199.8	227.0	256.3	97.
chloride	Al_2Cl_6	100.0	116.4	123.8	131.8	139.9	145.4	152.0	161.8	171.6	180.2	192.4
fluoride	AlF_3	1238	1298	1324	1350	1378	1398	1422	1457	1496	1537	1040
iodide	AlI_3	178.0	207.7	225.8	244.2	265.0	277.8	294.5	322.0	354.0	385.5	
oxide	Al_2O_3	2148	2306	2385	2465	2549	2599	2665	2766	2874	2977	2050
Ammonia	NH_3	−109.1	−97.5	−91.9	−85.8	−79.2	−74.3	−68.4	−57.0	−45.4	−33.6	−77.7
heavy	ND_3	......	......	......	......	......	−74.0	−67.4	−57.0	−45.4	−33.4	−74.0
Ammonium bromide	NH_4Br	198.3	234.5	252.0	270.6	290.0	303.8	320.0	345.3	370.8	396.0	
carbamate	$N_2H_6CO_2$	−26.1	−10.4	−2.9	+5.3	14.0	19.6	26.7	37.2	48.0	58.3	
chloride	NH_4Cl	160.4	193.8	209.8	226.1	245.0	256.2	271.5	293.2	316.5	337.8	520
cyanide	NH_4CN	−50.6	−35.7	−28.6	−20.9	−12.6	−7.4	−0.5	+9.6	20.5	31.7	36
hydrogen sulfide	NH_4HS	−51.1	−36.0	−28.7	−20.8	−12.3	−7.0	0.0	+10.5	21.8	33.3	
iodide	NH_4I	210.9	247.0	263.5	282.8	302.8	316.0	331.8	355.8	381.0	404.9	
Antimony	Sb	886	984	1033	1084	1141	1176	1223	1288	1364	1440	630.5
tribromide	$SbBr_3$	93.9	126.0	142.7	158.3	177.4	188.1	203.5	225.7	250.2	275.0	96.6
trichloride	$SbCl_3$	49.2	71.4	85.2	100.6	117.8	128.3	143.3	165.9	192.2	219.0	73.4
pentachloride	$SbCl_5$	22.7	48.6	61.8	75.8	91.0	101.0	114.1	......	......		2.8
triiodide	SbI_3	163.6	203.8	223.5	244.8	267.8	282.5	303.5	333.8	368.5	401.0	167
trioxide	Sb_4O_6	574	626	666	729	812	873	957	1085	1242	1425	656
Argon	A	−218.2	−213.9	−210.9	−207.9	−204.9	−202.9	−200.5	−195.6	−190.6	−185.6	−189.2
Arsenic	As	372	416	437	459	483	498	518	548	579	610	814
Arsenic tribromide	$AsBr_3$	41.8	70.6	85.2	101.3	118.7	130.0	145.2	167.7	193.6	220.0	
trichloride	$AsCl_3$	−11.4	+11.7	+23.5	36.0	50.0	58.7	70.9	89.2	109.7	130.4	−18
trifluoride	AsF_3	......	......	......	......	−2.5	+4.2	13.2	26.7	41.4	56.3	−5.9
pentafluoride	AsF_5	−117.9	−108.0	−103.1	−98.0	−92.4	−83.5	−84.3	−75.5	−64.0	−52.8	−79.8
trioxide	As_2O_3	212.5	242.6	259.7	279.2	299.2	310.3	332.5	370.0	412.2	457.2	312.8
Arsine	AsH_3	−142.6	−130.8	−124.7	−117.7	−110.2	−104.8	−98.0	−87.2	−75.2	−62.1	−116.3
Barium	Ba	......	984	1049	1120	1195	1240	1301	1403	1518	1638	850
Beryllium borohydride	$Be(BH_4)_2$	+1.0	19.8	28.1	36.8	46.2	51.7	58.6	69.0	79.7	90.0	123
bromide	$BeBr_2$	289	325	342	361	379	390	405	427	451	474	490
chloride	$BeCl_2$	291	328	346	365	384	395	411	435	461	487	405
iodide	BeI_2	283	322	341	361	382	394	411	435	461	487	488
Bismuth	Bi	1021	1099	1136	1177	1217	1240	1271	1319	1370	1420	271
tribromide	$BiBr_3$	......	261	282	305	327	340	360	392	425	461	218
trichloride	$BiCl_3$	......	242	264	287	311	324	343	372	405	441	230
Diborane hydrobromide	B_2H_5Br	−93.3	−75.3	−66.3	−56.4	−45.4	−38.2	−29.0	−15.4	0.0	+16.3	−104.2
Borine carbonyl	BH_3CO	−139.2	−127.3	−121.1	−114.1	−106.6	−101.9	−95.3	−85.5	−74.8	−64.0	−137.0
triamine	$B_3N_3H_6$	−63.0	−45.0	−35.3	−25.0	−13.2	−5.8	+4.0	18.5	34.3	50.6	−58.2
Boron hydrides												
dihydrodecaborane	$B_{10}H_{14}$	60.0	80.8	90.2	100.0	117.4	127.8	142.3	163.8	......	......	99.6
dihydrodiborane	B_2H_6	−159.7	−149.5	−144.3	−138.5	−131.6	−127.2	−120.9	−111.2	−99.6	−86.5	−169
dihydropentaborane	B_5H_9	......	−40.4	−30.7	−20.0	−8.0	−0.4	+9.6	24.6	40.8	58.1	−47.0
tetrahydropentaborane	B_5H_{11}	−50.2	−29.9	−19.9	−9.2	+2.7	10.2	20.1	34.8	51.2	67.0	
tetrahydrotetraborane	B_4H_{10}	−90.9	−73.1	−64.3	−54.8	−44.3	−37.4	−28.1	−14.0	+0.8	16.1	−119.9
Boron tribromide	BBr_3	−41.4	−20.4	−10.1	+1.5	14.0	22.1	33.5	50.3	70.0	91.7	−45
trichloride	BCl_3	−91.5	−75.2	−66.9	−57.9	−47.8	−41.2	−32.4	−18.9	−3.6	+12.7	−107
trifluoride	BF_3	−154.6	−145.4	−141.3	−136.4	−131.0	−127.6	−123.0	−115.9	−108.3	−100.7	−126.8
Bromine	Br_2	−48.7	−32.8	−25.0	−16.8	−8.0	−0.6	+9.3	24.3	41.0	58.2	−7.3
pentafluoride	BrF_5	−69.3	−51.0	−41.9	−32.0	−21.0	−14.0	−4.5	+9.9	25.7	40.4	−61.4
Cadmium	Cd	394	455	484	516	553	578	611	658	711	765	320.9
chloride	$CdCl_2$	......	618	656	695	736	762	797	847	908	967	568
fluoride	CdF_2	1112	1231	1286	1344	1400	1436	1486	1561	1651	1751	520
iodide	CdI_2	416	481	512	546	584	608	640	688	742	796	385
oxide	CdO	1000	1100	1149	1200	1257	1295	1341	1409	1484	1559	
Calcium	Ca	......	926	983	1046	1111	1152	1207	1288	1388	1487	851
Carbon (graphite)	C	3586	3828	3946	4069	4196	4273	4373	4516	4660	4827	
dioxide	CO_2	−134.3	−124.4	−119.5	−114.4	−108.6	−104.8	−100.2	−93.0	−85.7	−78.2	−57.5
disulfide	CS_2	−73.8	−54.3	−44.7	−34.3	−22.5	−15.3	−5.1	+10.4	28.0	46.5	−110.8
monoxide	CO	−222.0	−217.2	−215.0	−212.8	−210.0	−208.1	−205.7	−201.3	−196.3	−191.3	−205.0
oxyselenide	$COSe$	−117.1	−102.3	−95.0	−86.3	−76.4	−70.2	−61.7	−49.8	−35.6	−21.9	
oxysulfide	COS	−132.4	−119.8	−113.3	−106.0	−98.3	−93.0	−85.9	−75.0	−62.7	−49.9	−138.8
selenosulfide	$CSeS$	−47.3	−26.5	−16.0	−4.4	+8.6	17.0	28.3	45.7	65.2	85.6	−75.2
subsulfide	C_3S_2	14.0	41.2	54.9	69.3	85.6	96.0	109.9	130.8	......	......	+0.4
tetrabromide	CBr_4	......	......	......	......	96.3	106.3	119.7	139.7	163.5	189.5	90.1
tetrachloride	CCl_4	−50.0	−30.0	−19.6	−8.2	+4.3	12.3	23.0	38.3	57.8	76.7	−22.6
tetrafluoride	CF_4	−184.6	−174.1	−169.3	−164.3	−158.8	−155.4	−150.7	−143.6	−135.5	−127.7	−183.7
Cesium	Cs	279	341	375	409	449	474	509	561	624	690	28.5
bromide	$CsBr$	748	838	887	938	993	1026	1072	1140	1221	1300	636
chloride	$CsCl$	744	837	884	934	989	1023	1069	1139	1217	1300	646
fluoride	CsF	712	798	844	893	947	980	1025	1092	1170	1251	683
iodide	CsI	738	828	873	923	976	1009	1055	1124	1200	1280	621
Chlorine	Cl_2	−118.0	−106.7	−101.6	−93.3	−84.5	−79.0	−71.7	−60.2	−47.3	−33.8	−100.7
fluoride	ClF	......	−143.4	−139.0	−134.3	−128.8	−125.3	−120.8	−114.4	−107.0	−100.5	−145
trifluoride	ClF_3	......	−80.4	−71.8	−62.3	−51.3	−44.1	−34.7	−20.7	−4.9	+11.5	−83
monoxide	Cl_2O	−98.5	−81.6	−73.1	−64.3	−54.3	−48.0	−39.4	−26.5	−12.5	+2.2	−116
dioxide	ClO_2	......	......	−59.0	−51.2	−42.8	−37.2	−29.4	−17.8	−4.0	+11.1	−59
heptoxide	Cl_2O_7	−45.3	−23.8	−13.2	−2.1	+10.3	+18.2	29.1	44.6	62.2	78.8	−91
Chlorosulfonic acid	HSO_3Cl	32.0	53.5	64.0	75.3	87.6	95.2	105.3	120.0	136.1	151.0	−80
Chromium	Cr	1616	1768	1845	1928	2013	2067	2139	2243	2361	2482	1615
carbonyl	$Cr(CO)_6$	36.0	58.0	68.3	79.5	91.2	98.3	108.0	121.8	137.2	151.0	
oxychloride	CrO_2Cl_2	−18.4	+3.2	13.8	25.7	38.5	46.7	58.0	75.2	95.2	117.1	
Cobalt chloride	$CoCl_2$	......	......	......	......	770	801	843	904	974	1050	735
nitrosyl tricarbonyl	$Co(CO)_3NO$	......	......	......	−1.3	+11.0	18.5	29.0	44.4	62.0	80.0	−11
Columbium fluoride	CbF_5	......	......	86.3	103.0	121.5	133.2	148.5	172.2	198.0	225.0	75.5
Copper	Cu	1628	1795	1879	1970	2067	2127	2207	2325	2465	2595	1083
Cuprous bromide	Cu_2Br_2	572	666	718	777	844	887	951	1052	1189	1355	504
chloride	Cu_2Cl_2	546	645	702	766	838	886	960	1077	1249	1490	422
iodide	Cu_2I_2	......	610	656	716	786	836	907	1018	1158	1336	605
Cyanogen	C_2N_2	−95.8	−83.2	−76.8	−70.1	−62.7	−57.9	−51.8	−42.6	−33.0	−21.0	−34.4
bromide	$CNBr$	−35.7	−18.3	−10.0	−1.0	+8.6	14.7	22.6	33.8	46.0	61.5	58
chloride	$CNCl$	−76.7	−61.4	−53.8	−46.1	−37.5	−32.1	−24.9	−14.1	−2.3	+13.1	−6.5
fluoride	CNF	−134.4	−123.8	−118.5	−112.8	−106.4	−102.3	−97.0	−89.2	−80.5	−72.6	

* Compiled from the extended tables published by D. R. Stull in *Ind. Eng. Chem.*, **39**, 517 (1947).

Table 3-7. Vapor Pressures of Inorganic Compounds, up to 1 Atm.—(*Continued*)

Compound		Pressure, mm. Hg										Melting point, °C.
Name	Formula	1	5	10	20	40	60	100	200	400	760	
		Temperature, °C.										
Deuterium cyanide	DCN	−68.9	−54.0	−46.7	−38.8	−30.1	−24.7	−17.5	−5.4	+10.0	26.2	−12
Fluorine	F_2	−223.0	−216.9	−214.1	−211.0	−207.7	−205.6	−202.7	−198.3	−193.2	−187.9	−223
oxide	F_2O	−196.1	−186.6	−182.3	−177.8	−173.0	−170.0	−165.8	−159.0	−151.9	−144.6	−223.9
Germanium bromide	$GeBr_4$	......	43.3	56.8	71.8	88.1	98.8	113.2	135.4	161.6	189.0	26.1
chloride	$GeCl_4$	−45.0	−24.9	−15.0	−4.1	+8.0	16.2	27.5	44.4	63.8	84.0	−49.5
hydride	GeH_4	−163.0	−151.0	−145.3	−139.2	−131.6	−126.7	−120.3	−111.2	−100.2	−88.9	−165
Trichlorogermane	$GeHCl_3$	−41.3	−22.3	−13.0	−3.0	+8.8	16.2	26.5	41.6	58.3	75.0	−71.1
Tetramethylgermane	$Ge(CH_3)_4$	−73.2	−54.6	−45.2	−35.0	−23.4	−16.2	−6.3	+8.8	26.0	44.0	−88
Digermane	Ge_2H_6	−88.7	−69.8	−60.1	−49.9	−38.2	−30.7	−20.3	−4.7	+13.3	31.5	−109
Trigermane	Ge_3H_8	−36.9	−12.8	−0.9	+11.8	26.3	35.5	47.9	67.0	88.6	110.8	−105.6
Gold	Au	1869	2059	2154	2256	2363	2431	2521	2657	2807	2966	1063
Helium	He	−271.7	−271.5	−271.3	−271.1	−270.7	−270.6	−270.3	−269.8	−269.3	−268.6	
para-Hydrogen	H_2	−263.3	−261.9	−261.3	−260.4	−259.6	−258.9	−257.9	−256.3	−254.5	−252.5	−259.1
Hydrogen bromide	HBr	−138.8	−127.4	−121.8	−115.4	−108.3	−103.8	−97.7	−88.1	−78.0	−66.5	−87.0
chloride	HCl	−150.8	−140.7	−135.6	−130.0	−123.8	−119.6	−114.0	−105.2	−95.3	−84.8	−114.3
cyanide	HCN	−71.0	−55.3	−47.7	−39.7	−30.9	−25.1	−17.8	−5.3	+10.2	25.9	−13.2
fluoride	H_2F_2	......	−74.7	−65.8	−56.0	−45.0	−37.9	−28.2	−13.2	+2.5	19.7	−83.7
iodide	HI	−123.3	−109.6	−102.3	−94.5	−85.6	−79.8	−72.1	−60.3	−48.3	−35.1	−50.9
oxide (water)	H_2O	−17.3	+1.2	11.2	22.1	34.0	41.5	51.6	66.5	83.0	100.0	0.0
sulfide	H_2S	−134.3	−122.4	−116.3	−109.7	−102.3	−97.9	−91.6	−82.3	−71.8	−60.4	−85.5
disulfide	HSSH	−43.2	−24.4	−15.2	−5.1	+6.0	12.8	22.0	35.3	49.6	64.0	−89.7
selenide	H_2Se	−115.3	−103.4	−97.9	−91.8	−84.7	−80.2	−74.2	−65.2	−53.6	−41.1	−64
telluride	H_2Te	−96.4	−82.4	−75.4	−67.8	−59.1	−53.7	−45.7	−32.4	−17.2	−2.0	−49.0
Iodine	I_2	38.7	62.2	73.2	84.7	97.5	105.4	116.5	137.3	159.8	183.0	112.9
heptafluoride	IF_7	−87.0	−70.7	−63.0	−54.5	−45.3	−39.4	−31.9	−20.7	−8.3	+4.0	5.5
Iron	Fe	1787	1957	2039	2128	2224	2283	2360	2475	2605	2735	1535
pentacarbonyl	$Fe(CO)_5$	......	−6.5	+4.6	16.7	30.3	39.1	50.3	68.0	86.1	105.0	−21
Ferric chloride	Fe_2Cl_6	194.0	221.8	235.5	246.0	256.8	263.7	272.5	285.0	298.0	319.0	304
Ferrous chloride	$FeCl_2$	......	......	700	737	779	805	842	897	961	1026	
Krypton	Kr	−199.3	−191.3	−187.2	−182.9	−178.4	−175.7	−171.8	−165.9	−159.0	−152.0	−156.7
Lead	Pb	973	1099	1162	1234	1309	1358	1421	1519	1630	1744	327.5
bromide	$PbBr_2$	513	578	610	646	686	711	745	796	856	914	373
chloride	$PbCl_2$	547	615	648	684	725	750	784	833	893	954	501
fluoride	PbF_2	......	861	904	950	1003	1036	1080	1144	1219	1293	855
iodide	PbI_2	479	540	571	605	644	668	701	750	807	872	402
oxide	PbO	943	1039	1085	1134	1189	1222	1265	1330	1402	1472	890
sulfide	PbS	852	928	975	1005	1048	1074	1108	1160	1221	1281	1114
Lithium	Li	723	828	881	940	1003	1042	1097	1178	1273	1372	186
bromide	LiBr	748	840	888	939	994	1028	1076	1147	1226	1310	547
chloride	LiCl	783	880	932	987	1045	1081	1129	1203	1290	1382	614
fluoride	LiF	1047	1156	1211	1270	1333	1372	1425	1503	1591	1681	870
iodide	LiI	723	802	841	883	927	955	993	1049	1110	1171	446
Magnesium	Mg	621	702	743	789	838	868	909	967	1034	1107	651
chloride	$MgCl_2$	778	877	930	988	1050	1088	1142	1223	1316	1418	712
Manganese	Mn	1292	1434	1505	1583	1666	1720	1792	1900	2029	2151	1260
chloride	$MnCl_2$	......	736	778	825	879	913	960	1028	1108	1190	650
Mercury	Hg	126.2	164.8	184.0	204.6	228.8	242.0	261.7	290.7	323.0	357.0	−38.9
Mercuric bromide	$HgBr_2$	136.5	165.3	179.8	194.3	211.5	221.0	237.8	262.7	290.0	319.0	237
chloride	$HgCl_2$	136.2	166.0	180.2	195.8	212.5	222.2	237.0	256.5	275.5	304.0	277
iodide	HgI_2	157.5	189.2	204.5	220.0	238.2	249.0	261.8	291.0	324.2	354.0	259
Molybdenum	Mo	3102	3393	3535	3690	3859	3964	4109	4322	4553	4804	2622
hexafluoride	MoF_6	−65.5	−49.0	−40.8	−32.0	−22.1	−16.2	−8.0	+4.1	17.2	36.0	17
oxide	MoO_3	734	785	814	851	892	917	955	1014	1082	1151	795
Neon	Ne	−257.3	−255.5	−254.6	−253.7	−252.6	−251.9	−251.0	−249.7	−248.1	−246.0	−248.7
Nickel	Ni	1810	1979	2057	2143	2234	2289	2364	2473	2603	2732	1452
carbonyl	$Ni(CO)_4$	......	......	......	......	−23.0	−15.9	−6.0	+8.8	25.8	42.5	−25
chloride	$NiCl_2$	671	731	759	789	821	840	866	904	945	987	1001
Nitrogen	N_2	−226.1	−221.3	−219.1	−216.8	−214.0	−212.3	−209.7	−205.6	−200.9	−195.8	−210.0
Nitric oxide	NO	−184.5	−180.6	−178.2	−175.3	−171.7	−168.9	−166.0	−162.3	−156.8	−151.7	−161
Nitrogen dioxide	NO_2	−55.6	−42.7	−36.7	−30.4	−23.9	−19.9	−14.7	−5.0	+8.0	21.0	−9.3
Nitrogen pentoxide	N_2O_5	−36.8	−23.0	−16.7	−10.0	−2.9	+1.8	7.4	15.6	24.4	32.4	30
Nitrous oxide	N_2O	−143.4	−133.4	−128.7	−124.0	−118.3	−114.9	−110.3	−103.6	−96.2	−85.5	−90.9
Nitrosyl chloride	NOCl	......	......	......	......	−60.2	−54.2	−46.3	−34.0	−20.3	−6.4	−64.5
fluoride	NOF	−132.0	−120.3	−114.3	−107.8	−100.3	−95.7	−88.8	−79.2	−68.2	−56.0	−134
Osmium tetroxide (yellow)	OsO_4	3.2	22.0	31.3	41.0	51.7	59.4	71.5	89.5	109.3	130.0	56
(white)	OsO_4	−5.6	+15.6	26.0	37.4	50.5	59.4	71.5	89.5	109.3	130.0	42
Oxygen	O_2	−219.1	−213.4	−210.6	−207.5	−204.1	−201.9	−198.8	−194.0	−188.8	−183.1	−218.7
Ozone	O_3	−180.4	−168.6	−163.2	−157.2	−150.7	−146.7	−141.0	−132.6	−122.5	−111.1	−251
Phosgene	$COCl_2$	−92.9	−77.0	−69.3	−60.3	−50.3	−44.0	−35.6	−22.3	−7.6	+8.3	−104
Phosphorus (yellow)	P	76.6	111.2	128.0	146.2	166.7	179.8	197.3	222.7	251.0	280.0	44.1
(violet)	P	237	271	287	306	323	334	349	370	391	417	590
tribromide	PBr_3	7.8	34.4	47.8	62.4	79.0	89.8	103.6	125.2	149.7	175.3	−40
trichloride	PCl_3	−51.6	−31.5	−21.3	−10.2	+2.3	10.2	21.0	37.6	56.9	74.2	−111.8
pentachloride	PCl_5	55.5	74.0	83.2	92.5	102.5	108.3	117.0	131.3	147.2	162.0	
Phosphine	PH_3	......	......	......	......	−129.4	−125.0	−118.8	−109.4	−98.3	−87.5	−132.5
Phosphonium bromide	PH_4Br	−43.7	−28.5	−21.2	−13.3	−5.0	+0.3	7.4	17.6	28.0	38.3	
chloride	PH_4Cl	−91.0	−79.6	−74.0	−68.0	−61.5	−57.3	−52.0	−44.0	−35.4	−27.0	−28.5
iodide	PH_4I	−25.2	−9.0	−1.1	+7.3	16.1	21.9	29.3	39.9	51.6	62.3	
Phosphorus trioxide	P_4O_6	......	39.7	53.0	67.8	84.0	94.2	108.3	129.0	150.3	173.1	22.5
pentoxide	P_4O_{10}	384	424	442	462	481	493	510	532	556	591	569
oxychloride	$POCl_3$	......	......	2.0	13.6	27.3	35.8	47.4	65.0	84.3	105.1	2
thiobromide	$PSBr_3$	50.0	72.4	83.6	95.5	108.0	116.0	126.3	141.8	157.8	175.0	38
thiochloride	$PSCl_3$	−18.3	+4.6	16.1	29.0	42.7	51.8	63.8	82.0	102.3	124.0	−36.2
Platinum	Pt	2730	3007	3146	3302	3469	3574	3714	3923	4169	4407	1755
Potassium	K	341	408	443	483	524	550	586	643	708	774	62.3
bromide	KBr	795	892	940	994	1050	1087	1137	1212	1297	1383	730
chloride	KCl	821	919	968	1020	1078	1115	1164	1239	1322	1407	790
fluoride	KF	885	988	1039	1096	1156	1193	1245	1323	1411	1502	880
hydroxide	KOH	719	814	863	918	976	1013	1064	1142	1233	1327	380
iodide	KI	745	840	887	938	995	1030	1080	1152	1238	1324	723
Radon	Rn	−144.2	−132.4	−126.3	−119.2	−111.3	−106.2	−99.0	−87.7	−75.0	−61.8	−71
Rhenium heptoxide	Re_2O_7	212.5	237.5	248.0	261.0	272.0	280.0	289.0	307.0	336.0	362.4	296

Table 3-7. Vapor Pressures of Inorganic Compounds, up to 1 Atm.—(*Concluded*)

Compound		Pressure, mm. Hg (Temperature, °C.)										Melting point, °C.
Name	Formula	1	5	10	20	40	60	100	200	400	760	
Rubidium	Rb	297	358	389	422	459	482	514	563	620	679	38.5
bromide	RbBr	781	876	923	975	1031	1066	1114	1186	1267	1352	682
chloride	RbCl	792	887	937	990	1047	1084	1133	1207	1294	1381	715
fluoride	RbF	921	982	1016	1052	1096	1123	1168	1239	1322	1408	760
iodide	RbI	748	839	884	935	991	1026	1072	1141	1223	1304	642
Selenium	Se	356	413	442	473	506	527	554	594	637	680	217
dioxide	SeO_2	157.0	187.7	202.5	217.5	234.1	244.6	258.0	277.0	297.7	317.0	340
hexafluoride	SeF_6	−118.6	−105.2	−98.9	−92.3	−84.7	−80.0	−73.9	−64.8	−55.2	−45.8	−34.7
oxychloride	$SeOCl_2$	34.8	59.8	71.9	84.2	98.0	106.5	118.0	134.6	151.7	168.0	8.5
tetrachloride	$SeCl_4$	74.0	96.3	107.4	118.1	130.1	137.8	147.5	161.0	176.4	191.5	
Silicon	Si	1724	1835	1888	1942	2000	2036	2083	2151	2220	2287	1420
dioxide	SiO_2	......	......	1732	1798	1867	1911	1969	2053	2141	2227	1710
tetrachloride	$SiCl_4$	−63.4	−44.1	−34.4	−24.0	−12.1	−4.8	+5.4	21.0	38.4	56.8	−68.8
tetrafluoride	SiF_4	−144.0	−134.8	−130.4	−125.9	−120.8	−117.5	−113.3	−170.2	−100.7	−94.8	−90
Trichlorofluorosilane	$SiFCl_3$	−92.6	−76.4	−68.3	−59.0	−48.8	−42.2	−33.2	−19.3	−4.0	+12.2	−120.8
Iodosilane	SiH_3I	......	−53.0	−47.7	−33.4	−21.8	−14.3	−4.4	+10.7	27.9	45.4	−57.0
Diiodosilane	SiH_2I_2	......	3.8	18.0	34.1	52.6	64.0	79.4	101.8	125.5	149.5	−1.0
Disiloxan	$(SiH_3)_2O$	−112.5	−95.8	−88.2	−79.8	−70.4	−64.2	−55.9	−43.5	−29.3	−15.4	−144.2
Trisilane	Si_3H_8	−68.9	−49.7	−40.0	−29.0	−16.9	−9.0	+1.6	17.8	35.5	53.1	−117.2
Trisilazane	$(SiH_3)_3N$	−68.7	−49.9	−40.4	−30.0	−18.5	−11.0	−1.1	+14.0	31.0	48.7	−105.7
Tetrasilane	Si_4H_{10}	−27.7	−6.2	+4.3	15.8	28.4	36.6	47.4	63.6	81.7	100.0	−93.6
Octachlorotrisilane	Si_3Cl_8	46.3	74.7	89.3	104.2	121.5	132.0	146.0	166.2	189.5	211.4	
Hexachlorodisiloxane	$(SiCl_3)_2O$	−5.0	17.8	29.4	41.5	55.2	63.8	75.4	92.5	113.6	135.6	−33.2
Hexachlorodisilane	Si_2Cl_6	+4.0	27.4	38.8	51.5	65.3	73.9	85.4	102.2	120.6	139.0	−1.2
Tribromosilane	$SiHBr_3$	−30.5	−8.0	+3.4	16.0	30.0	39.2	51.6	70.2	90.2	111.8	−73.5
Trichlorosilane	$SiHCl_3$	−80.7	−62.6	−53.4	−43.8	−32.9	−25.8	−16.4	−1.8	+14.5	31.8	−126.6
Trifluorosilane	$SiHF_3$	−152.0	−142.7	−138.2	−132.9	−127.3	−123.7	−118.7	−111.3	−102.8	−95.0	−131.4
Dibromosilane	SiH_2Br_2	−60.9	−40.0	−29.4	−18.0	−5.2	+3.2	14.1	31.6	50.7	70.5	−70.2
Difluorosilane	SiH_2F_2	−146.7	−136.0	−130.4	−124.3	−117.6	−113.3	−107.3	−98.3	−87.6	−77.8	
Monobromosilane	SiH_3Br	......	−85.7	−77.3	−68.3	−57.8	−51.1	−42.3	−28.6	−13.3	+2.4	−93.9
Monochlorosilane	SiH_3Cl	−117.8	−104.3	−97.7	−90.1	−81.8	−76.0	−68.5	−57.0	−44.5	−30.4	
Monofluorosilane	SiH_3F	−153.0	−145.5	−141.2	−136.3	−130.8	−127.2	−122.4	−115.2	−106.8	−98.0	
Tribromofluorosilane	$SiFBr_3$	−46.1	−25.4	−15.1	−3.7	+9.2	17.4	28.6	45.7	64.6	83.8	−82.5
Dichlorodifluorosilane	SiF_2Cl_2	−124.7	−110.5	−102.9	−94.5	−85.0	−78.6	−70.3	−58.0	−45.0	−31.8	−139.7
Trifluorobromosilane	SiF_3Br	......	......	......	......	......	......	......	−69.8	−55.9	−41.7	−70.5
Trifluorochlorosilane	SiF_3Cl	−144.0	−133.0	−127.0	−120.5	−112.8	−108.2	−101.7	−91.7	−81.0	−70.0	−142
Hexafluorodisilane	Si_2F_6	−81.0	−68.8	−63.1	−57.0	−50.6	−46.7	−41.7	−34.2	−26.4	−18.9	−18.6
Dichlorofluorobromosilane	$SiFCl_2Br$	−86.5	−68.4	−59.0	−48.8	−37.0	−29.0	−19.5	−3.2	+15.4	35.4	−112.3
Dibromochlorofluorosilane	$SiFClBr_2$	−65.2	−45.5	−35.6	−24.5	−12.0	−4.7	+6.3	23.0	43.0	59.5	−99.3
Silane	SiH_4	−179.3	−168.6	−163.0	−156.9	−150.3	−146.3	−140.5	−131.6	−122.0	−111.5	−185
Disilane	Si_2H_6	−114.8	−99.3	−91.4	−82.7	−72.8	−66.4	−57.5	−44.6	−29.0	−14.3	−132.6
Silver	Ag	1357	1500	1575	1658	1743	1795	1865	1971	2090	2212	960.5
chloride	AgCl	912	1019	1074	1134	1200	1242	1297	1379	1467	1564	455
iodide	AgI	820	927	983	1045	1111	1152	1210	1297	1400	1506	552
Sodium	Na	439	511	549	589	633	662	701	758	823	892	97.5
bromide	NaBr	806	903	952	1005	1063	1099	1148	1220	1304	1392	755
chloride	NaCl	865	967	1017	1072	1131	1169	1220	1296	1379	1465	800
cyanide	NaCN	817	928	983	1046	1115	1156	1214	1302	1401	1497	564
fluoride	NaF	1077	1186	1240	1300	1363	1403	1455	1531	1617	1704	992
hydroxide	NaOH	739	843	897	953	1017	1057	1111	1192	1286	1378	318
iodide	NaI	767	857	903	952	1005	1039	1083	1150	1225	1304	651
Strontium	Sr	......	847	898	953	1018	1057	1111	1192	1285	1384	800
Strontium oxide	SrO	2068	2198	2262	2333	2410	......	......	......	......	......	2430
Sulfur	S	183.8	223.0	243.8	264.7	288.3	305.5	327.2	359.7	399.6	444.6	112.8
monochloride	S_2Cl_2	−7.4	+15.7	27.5	40.0	54.1	63.2	75.3	93.5	115.4	138.0	−80
hexafluoride	SF_6	−132.7	−120.6	−114.7	−108.4	−101.5	−96.8	−90.9	−82.3	−72.6	−63.5	−50.2
Sulfuryl chloride	SO_2Cl_2	......	−35.1	−24.8	−13.4	−1.0	+7.2	17.8	33.7	51.3	69.2	−54.1
Sulfur dioxide	SO_2	−95.5	−83.0	−76.8	−69.7	−60.5	−54.6	−46.9	−35.4	−23.0	−10.0	−73.2
trioxide (α)	SO_3	−39.0	−23.7	−16.5	−9.1	−1.0	+4.0	10.5	20.5	32.6	44.8	16.8
trioxide (β)	SO_3	−34.0	−19.2	−12.3	−4.9	+3.2	8.0	14.3	23.7	32.6	44.8	32.3
trioxide (γ)	SO_3	−15.3	−2.0	+4.3	11.1	17.9	21.4	28.0	35.8	44.0	51.6	62.1
Tellurium	Te	520	605	650	697	753	789	838	910	997	1087	452
chloride	$TeCl_4$	......	......	233	253	273	287	304	330	360	392	224
fluoride	TeF_6	−111.3	−98.8	−92.4	−86.0	−78.4	−73.8	−67.9	−57.3	−48.2	−38.6	−37.8
Thallium	Tl	825	931	983	1040	1103	1143	1196	1274	1364	1457	3035
Thallous bromide	TlBr	......	490	522	559	598	621	653	703	759	819	460
chloride	TlCl	......	487	517	550	589	612	645	694	748	807	430
iodide	TlI	440	502	531	567	607	631	663	712	763	823	440
Thionyl bromide	$SOBr_2$	−6.7	+18.4	31.0	44.1	58.8	68.3	80.6	99.0	119.2	139.5	−52.2
Thionyl chloride	$SOCl_2$	−52.9	−32.4	−21.9	−10.5	+2.2	10.4	21.4	37.9	56.5	75.4	−104.5
Tin	Sn	1492	1634	1703	1777	1855	1903	1968	2063	2169	2270	231.9
Stannic bromide	$SnBr_4$	......	58.3	72.7	88.1	105.5	116.2	131.0	152.8	177.7	204.7	31.0
Stannous chloride	$SnCl_2$	316	366	391	420	450	467	493	533	577	623	246.8
Stannic chloride	$SnCl_4$	−22.7	−1.0	+10.0	22.0	35.2	43.5	54.7	72.0	92.1	113.0	−30.2
iodide	SnI_4	......	156.0	175.8	196.2	218.8	234.2	254.2	283.5	315.5	348.0	144.5
hydride	SnH_4	−140.0	−125.8	−118.5	−111.2	−102.3	−96.6	−89.2	−78.0	−65.2	−52.3	−149.9
Tin tetramethyl	$Sn(CH_3)_4$	−51.3	−31.0	−20.6	−9.3	+3.5	11.7	22.8	39.8	58.5	78.0	
trimethyl-ethyl	$Sn(CH_3)_3.C_2H_5$	−30.0	−7.6	+3.8	16.1	30.0	38.4	50.0	67.3	87.6	108.8	
trimethyl-propyl	$Sn(CH_3)_3.C_3H_7$	−12.0	+10.7	21.8	34.0	48.5	57.5	69.8	88.0	109.6	131.7	
Titanium chloride	$TiCl_4$	−13.9	+9.4	21.3	34.2	48.4	58.0	71.0	90.5	112.7	136.0	−30
Tungsten	W	3990	4337	4507	4690	4886	5007	5168	5403	5666	5927	3370
Tungsten hexafluoride	WF_6	−71.4	−56.5	−49.2	−41.5	−33.0	−27.5	−20.3	−10.0	+1.2	17.3	−0.5
Uranium hexafluoride	UF_6	−38.8	−22.0	−13.8	−5.2	+4.4	10.4	18.2	30.0	42.7	55.7	69.2
Vanadyl trichloride	$VOCl_3$	−23.2	+0.2	12.2	26.6	40.0	49.8	62.5	82.0	103.5	127.2	
Xenon	Xe	−168.5	−158.2	−152.8	−147.1	−141.2	−137.7	−132.8	−125.4	−117.1	−108.0	−111.6
Zinc	Zn	487	558	593	632	673	700	736	788	844	907	419.4
chloride	$ZnCl_2$	428	481	508	536	566	584	610	648	689	732	365
fluoride	ZnF_2	970	1055	1086	1129	1175	1207	1254	1329	1417	1497	872
diethyl	$Zn(C_2H_5)_2$	−22.4	0.0	+11.7	24.2	38.0	47.2	59.1	77.0	97.3	118.0	−28
Zirconium bromide	$ZrBr_4$	207	237	250	266	281	289	301	318	337	357	450
chloride	$ZrCl_4$	190	217	230	243	259	268	279	295	312	331	437
iodide	ZrI_4	264	297	311	329	344	355	369	389	409	431	499

Table 3-8. Vapor Pressures of Organic Compounds, up to 1 Atm.*

Compound		Pressure, mm. Hg										Melting point, °C.
Name	Formula	1	5	10	20	40	60	100	200	400	760	
		Temperature, °C.										
Acenaphthalene	$C_{12}H_{10}$	......	114.8	131.2	148.7	168.2	181.2	197.5	222.1	250.0	277.5	95
Acetal	$C_6H_{14}O_2$	−23.0	−2.3	+8.0	19.6	31.9	39.8	50.1	66.3	84.0	102.2	
Acetaldehyde	C_2H_4O	−81.5	−65.1	−56.8	−47.8	−37.8	−31.4	−22.6	−10.0	+4.9	20.2	−123.5
Acetamide	C_2H_5NO	65.0	92.0	105.0	120.0	135.8	145.8	158.0	178.3	200.0	222.0	81
Acetanilide	C_8H_9NO	114.0	146.6	162.0	180.0	199.6	211.8	227.2	250.5	277.0	303.8	113.5
Acetic acid	$C_2H_4O_2$	−17.2	+6.3	17.5	29.9	43.0	51.7	63.0	80.0	99.0	118.1	16.7
anhydride	$C_4H_6O_3$	1.7	24.8	36.0	48.3	62.1	70.8	82.2	100.0	119.8	139.6	−73
Acetone	C_3H_6O	−59.4	−40.5	−31.1	−20.8	−9.4	−2.0	+7.7	22.7	39.5	56.5	−94.6
Acetonitrile	C_2H_3N	−47.0	−26.6	−16.3	−5.0	+7.7	15.9	27.0	43.7	62.5	81.8	−41
Acetophenone	C_8H_8O	37.1	64.0	78.0	92.4	109.4	119.8	133.6	154.2	178.0	202.4	20.5
Acetyl chloride	C_2H_3OCl	−50.0	−35.0	−27.6	−19.6	−10.4	−4.5	+3.2	16.1	32.0	50.8	−112.0
Acetylene	C_2H_2	−142.9	−133.0	−128.2	−122.8	−116.7	−112.8	−107.9	−100.3	−92.0	−84.0	−81.5
Acridine	$C_{13}H_9N$	129.4	165.8	184.0	203.5	224.2	238.7	256.0	284.0	314.3	346.0	110.5
Acrolein (2-propenal)	C_3H_4O	−64.5	−46.0	−36.7	−26.3	−15.0	−7.5	+2.5	17.5	34.5	52.5	−87.7
Acrylic acid	$C_3H_4O_2$	+3.5	27.3	39.0	52.0	66.2	75.0	86.1	103.3	122.0	141.0	14
Adipic acid	$C_6H_{10}O_4$	159.5	191.0	205.5	222.0	240.5	251.0	265.0	287.8	312.5	337.5	152
Allene (propadiene)	C_3H_4	−120.6	−108.0	−101.0	−93.4	−85.2	−78.8	−72.5	−61.3	−48.5	−35.0	−136
Allyl alcohol (propen-1-ol-3)	C_3H_6O	−20.0	+0.2	10.5	21.7	33.4	40.3	50.0	64.5	80.2	96.6	−129
chloride (3-chloropropene)	C_3H_5Cl	−70.0	−52.0	−42.9	−32.8	−21.2	−14.1	−4.5	10.4	27.5	44.6	−136.4
isopropyl ether	$C_6H_{12}O$	−43.7	−23.1	−12.9	−1.8	+10.9	18.7	29.0	44.3	61.7	79.5	
isothiocyanate	C_4H_5NS	−2.0	+25.3	38.3	52.1	67.4	76.2	89.5	108.0	129.8	150.7	−80
n-propyl ether	$C_6H_{12}O$	−39.0	−18.2	−7.9	+3.7	16.4	25.0	35.8	52.6	71.4	90.5	
4-Allylveratrole	$C_{11}H_{14}O_2$	85.0	113.9	127.0	142.8	158.3	169.6	183.7	204.0	226.2	248.0	
iso-Amyl acetate	$C_7H_{14}O_2$	0.0	+23.7	35.2	47.8	62.1	71.0	83.2	101.3	121.5	142.0	
n-Amyl alcohol	$C_5H_{12}O$	+13.6	34.7	44.9	55.8	68.0	75.5	85.8	102.0	119.8	137.8	
iso-Amyl alcohol	$C_5H_{12}O$	+10.0	30.9	40.8	51.7	63.4	71.0	80.7	95.8	113.7	130.6	−117.2
sec-Amyl alcohol (2-pentanol)	$C_5H_{12}O$	+1.5	22.1	32.2	42.6	54.1	61.5	70.7	85.7	102.3	119.7	
tert-Amyl alcohol	$C_5H_{12}O$	−12.9	+7.2	17.2	27.9	38.8	46.0	55.3	69.7	85.7	101.7	−11.9
sec-Amylbenzene	$C_{11}H_{16}$	29.0	55.8	69.2	83.8	100.0	110.4	124.1	145.2	168.0	193.0	
iso-Amyl benzoate	$C_{12}H_{16}O_2$	72.0	104.5	121.6	139.7	158.3	171.4	186.8	210.2	235.8	262.0	
bromide (1-bromo-3-methylbutane)	$C_5H_{11}Br$	−20.4	+2.1	13.6	26.1	39.8	48.7	60.4	78.7	99.4	120.4	
n-butyrate	$C_9H_{18}O_2$	21.2	47.1	59.9	74.0	90.0	99.8	113.1	133.2	155.3	178.6	
formate	$C_6H_{12}O_2$	−17.5	+5.4	17.1	30.0	44.0	53.3	65.4	83.2	102.7	123.3	
iodide (1-iodo-3-methylbutane)	$C_5H_{11}I$	−2.5	+21.9	34.1	47.6	62.3	71.9	84.4	103.8	125.8	148.2	
isobutyrate	$C_9H_{18}O_2$	14.8	40.1	52.8	66.6	81.8	91.7	104.4	124.2	146.0	168.8	
Amyl isopropionate	$C_8H_{16}O_2$	+8.5	33.7	46.3	60.0	75.5	85.2	97.6	117.3	138.4	160.2	
iso-Amyl isovalerate	$C_{10}H_{20}O_2$	27.0	54.4	68.6	83.8	100.6	110.3	125.1	146.1	169.5	194.0	
n-Amyl levulinate	$C_{10}H_{18}O_3$	81.3	110.0	124.0	139.7	155.8	165.2	180.5	203.1	227.4	253.2	
iso-Amyl levulinate	$C_{10}H_{18}O_3$	75.6	104.0	118.8	134.4	151.7	162.6	177.0	198.1	222.7	247.9	
nitrate	$C_5H_{11}NO_3$	+5.2	28.8	40.3	53.5	67.6	76.3	88.6	106.7	126.5	147.5	
4-tert-Amylphenol	$C_{11}H_{16}O$	......	109.8	125.5	142.3	160.3	172.6	189.0	213.0	239.5	266.0	93
Anethole	$C_{10}H_{12}O$	62.6	91.6	106.0	121.8	139.3	149.8	164.2	186.1	210.5	235.3	22.5
Angelonitrile	C_5H_7N	−8.0	+15.0	28.0	41.0	55.8	65.2	77.5	96.3	117.7	140.0	
Aniline	C_6H_7N	34.8	57.9	69.4	82.0	96.7	106.0	119.9	140.1	161.9	184.4	−6.2
2-Anilinoethanol	$C_8H_{11}NO$	104.0	134.3	149.6	165.7	183.7	194.0	209.5	230.6	254.5	279.6	
Anisaldehyde	$C_8H_8O_2$	73.2	102.6	117.8	133.5	150.5	161.7	176.7	199.0	223.0	248.0	2.5
o-Anisidine (2-methoxyaniline)	C_7H_9NO	61.0	88.0	101.7	116.1	132.0	142.1	155.2	175.3	197.3	218.5	5.2
Anthracene	$C_{14}H_{10}$	145.0	173.5	187.2	201.9	217.5	231.8	250.0	279.0	310.2	342.0	217.5
Anthraquinone	$C_{14}H_8O_2$	190.0	219.4	234.2	248.3	264.3	273.3	285.0	314.6	346.2	379.9	286
Azelaic acid	$C_9H_{16}O_4$	178.3	210.4	225.5	242.4	260.0	271.8	286.5	309.6	332.8	356.5	106.5
Azelaldehyde	$C_9H_{18}O$	33.3	58.4	71.6	85.0	100.2	110.0	123.0	142.1	163.4	185.0	
Azobenzene	$C_{12}H_{10}N_2$	103.5	135.7	151.5	168.3	187.9	199.8	216.0	240.0	266.1	293.0	68
Benzal chloride (α,α-Dichlorotoluene)	$C_7H_6Cl_2$	35.4	64.0	78.7	94.3	112.1	123.4	138.3	160.7	187.0	214.0	−16.1
Benzaldehyde	C_7H_6O	26.2	50.1	62.0	75.0	90.1	99.6	112.5	131.7	154.1	179.0	−26
Benzanthrone	$C_{17}H_{10}O$	225.0	274.5	297.2	322.5	350.0	368.8	390.0	426.5	......	......	174
Benzene	C_6H_6	−36.7	−19.6	−11.5	−2.6	+7.6	15.4	26.1	42.2	60.6	80.1	+5.5
Benzenesulfonylchloride	$C_6H_5ClO_2S$	65.9	96.5	112.0	129.0	147.7	158.2	174.5	198.0	224.0	251.5	14.5
Benzil	$C_{14}H_{10}O_2$	128.4	165.2	183.0	202.8	224.5	238.2	255.8	283.5	314.3	347.0	95
Benzoic acid	$C_7H_6O_2$	96.0	119.5	132.1	146.7	162.6	172.8	186.2	205.8	227.0	249.2	121.7
anhydride	$C_{14}H_{10}O_3$	143.8	180.0	198.0	218.0	239.8	252.7	270.4	299.1	328.8	360.0	42
Benzoin	$C_{14}H_{12}O_2$	135.6	170.2	188.1	207.0	227.6	241.7	258.0	284.4	313.5	343.0	132
Benzonitrile	C_7H_5N	28.2	55.3	69.2	83.4	99.6	109.8	123.5	144.1	166.7	190.6	−12.9
Benzophenone	$C_{13}H_{10}O$	108.2	141.7	157.6	175.8	195.7	208.2	224.4	249.8	276.8	305.4	48.5
Benzotrichloride (α,α,α-Trichlorotoluene)	$C_7H_5Cl_3$	45.8	73.7	87.6	102.7	119.8	130.0	144.3	165.6	189.2	213.5	−21.2
Benzotrifluoride (α,α,α-Trifluorotoluene)	$C_7H_5F_3$	−32.0	−10.3	+0.4	12.2	25.7	34.0	45.3	62.5	82.0	102.2	−29.3
Benzoyl bromide	C_7H_5BrO	47.0	75.4	89.8	105.4	122.6	133.4	147.7	169.2	193.7	218.5	0
chloride	C_7H_5ClO	32.1	59.1	73.0	87.6	103.8	114.7	128.0	149.5	172.8	197.2	−0.5
nitrile	C_8H_5NO	44.5	71.7	85.5	100.2	116.6	127.0	141.0	161.3	185.0	208.0	33.5
Benzyl acetate	$C_9H_{10}O_2$	45.0	73.4	87.6	102.3	119.6	129.8	144.0	165.5	189.0	213.5	−51.5
alcohol	C_7H_8O	58.0	80.8	92.6	105.8	119.8	129.3	141.7	160.0	183.0	204.7	−15.3
Benzylamine	C_7H_9N	29.0	54.8	67.7	81.8	97.3	107.3	120.0	140.0	161.3	184.5	
Benzyl bromide (α-bromotoluene)	C_7H_7Br	32.2	59.6	73.4	88.3	104.8	115.6	129.8	150.8	175.2	198.5	−4
chloride (α-chlorotoluene)	C_7H_7Cl	22.0	47.8	60.8	75.0	90.7	100.5	114.2	134.0	155.8	179.4	−39
cinnamate	$C_{16}H_{14}O_2$	173.8	206.3	221.5	239.3	255.8	267.0	281.5	303.8	326.7	350.0	39
Benzyldichlorosilane	$C_7H_8Cl_2Si$	45.3	70.2	83.2	96.7	111.8	121.3	133.5	152.0	173.0	194.3	
Benzyl ethyl ether	$C_9H_{12}O$	26.0	52.0	65.0	79.6	95.4	105.5	118.9	139.6	161.5	185.0	
phenyl ether	$C_{13}H_{12}O$	95.4	127.7	144.0	160.7	180.1	192.6	209.2	233.2	259.8	287.0	
isothiocyanate	C_8H_7NS	79.5	107.8	121.8	137.0	153.0	163.8	177.7	198.0	220.4	243.0	
Biphenyl	$C_{12}H_{10}$	70.6	101.8	117.0	134.2	152.5	165.2	180.7	204.2	229.4	254.9	69.5
1-Biphenyloxy-2,3-epoxypropane	$C_{15}H_{14}O_2$	135.3	169.9	187.2	205.8	226.3	239.7	255.0	280.4	309.8	340.0	
d-Bornyl acetate	$C_{12}H_{20}O_2$	46.9	75.7	90.2	106.0	123.7	135.7	149.8	172.0	197.5	223.0	29
Bornyl n-butyrate	$C_{14}H_{24}O_2$	74.0	103.4	118.0	133.8	150.7	161.8	176.4	198.0	222.2	247.0	
formate	$C_{11}H_{18}O_2$	47.0	74.8	89.3	104.0	121.2	131.7	145.8	166.4	190.2	214.0	
isobutyrate	$C_{14}H_{24}O_2$	70.0	99.8	114.0	130.0	147.2	157.6	172.2	194.2	218.2	243.0	
propionate	$C_{13}H_{22}O_2$	64.6	93.7	108.0	123.7	140.4	151.2	165.7	187.5	211.2	235.0	
Brassidic acid	$C_{22}H_{42}O_2$	209.6	241.7	256.0	272.9	290.0	301.5	316.2	336.8	359.6	382.5	61.5
Bromoacetic acid	$C_2H_3BrO_2$	54.7	81.6	94.1	108.2	124.0	133.8	146.3	165.8	186.7	208.0	49.5
4-Bromoanisole	C_7H_7BrO	48.8	77.8	91.9	107.8	125.0	136.0	150.1	172.7	197.5	223.0	12.5

* Compiled from the extended tables published by D. R. Stull in *Ind. Eng. Chem.*, **39**, 517 (1947). For information on fuels see Hibbard, *N.A.C.A. Research Mem.* E56I21, 1956. For methane see Johnson (ed.), WADD-TR-60-56, 1960.

Table 3-8. Vapor Pressures of Organic Compounds, up to 1 Atm.—(*Continued*)

Compound: Name	Formula	1	5	10	20	40	60	100	200	400	760	Melting point, °C.
		Pressure, mm. Hg — Temperature, °C.										
Bromobenzene	C_6H_5Br	+2.9	27.8	40.0	53.8	68.6	78.1	90.8	110.1	132.3	156.2	−30.7
4-Bromobiphenyl	$C_{12}H_9Br$	98.0	133.7	150.6	169.8	190.8	204.5	221.8	248.2	277.7	310.0	90.5
1-Bromo-2-butanol	C_4H_9BrO	23.7	45.4	55.8	67.2	79.5	87.0	97.6	112.1	128.3	145.0	
1-Bromo-2-butanone	C_4H_7BrO	+6.2	30.0	41.8	54.2	68.2	77.3	89.2	107.0	126.3	147.0	
cis-1-Bromo-1-butene	C_4H_7Br	−44.0	−23.2	−12.8	−1.4	+11.5	19.8	30.8	47.8	66.8	86.2	
trans-1-Bromo-1-butene	C_4H_7Br	−38.4	−17.0	−6.4	+5.4	18.4	27.2	38.1	55.7	75.0	94.7	−100.3
2-Bromo-1-butene	C_4H_7Br	−47.3	−27.0	−16.8	−5.3	+7.2	15.4	26.3	42.8	61.9	81.0	−133.4
cis-2-Bromo-2-butene	C_4H_7Br	−39.0	−17.9	−7.2	+4.6	17.7	26.2	37.5	54.5	74.0	93.9	−111.2
trans-2-Bromo-2-butene	C_4H_7Br	−45.0	−24.1	−13.8	−2.4	+10.5	18.7	29.9	46.5	66.0	85.5	−114.6
1,4-Bromochlorobenzene	C_6H_4BrCl	32.0	59.5	72.7	87.8	103.8	114.8	128.0	149.5	172.6	196.9	
1-Bromo-1-chloroethane	C_2H_4BrCl	−36.0	−18.0	−9.4	0.0	+10.4	17.0	28.0	44.7	63.4	82.7	16.6
1-Bromo-2-chloroethane	C_2H_4BrCl	−28.8	−7.0	+4.1	16.0	29.7	38.0	49.5	66.8	86.0	106.7	−16.6
2-Bromo-4,6-dichlorophenol	$C_6H_3BrCl_2O$	84.0	115.6	130.8	147.7	165.8	177.6	193.2	216.5	242.0	268.0	68
1-Bromo-4-ethyl benzene	C_8H_9Br	30.4	42.5	74.0	90.2	108.5	121.0	135.5	156.5	182.0	206.0	−45.0
(2-Bromoethyl)-benzene	C_8H_9Br	48.0	76.2	90.5	105.8	123.2	133.8	148.2	169.8	194.0	219.0	
2-Bromoethyl 2-chloroethyl ether	C_4H_8BrClO	36.5	63.2	76.3	90.8	106.6	116.4	129.8	150.0	172.3	195.8	
(2-Bromoethyl)-cyclohexane	$C_8H_{15}Br$	38.7	66.6	80.5	95.8	113.0	123.7	138.0	160.0	186.2	213.0	
1-Bromoethylene	C_2H_3Br	−95.4	−77.8	−68.8	−58.8	−48.1	−41.2	−31.9	−17.2	−1.1	+15.8	−138
Bromoform (tribromomethane)	$CHBr_3$	.....	22.0	34.0	48.0	63.6	73.4	85.9	106.1	127.9	150.5	8.5
1-Bromonaphthalene	$C_{10}H_7Br$	84.2	117.5	133.6	150.2	170.2	183.5	198.8	224.2	252.0	281.1	5.5
2-Bromo-4-phenylphenol	$C_{12}H_9BrO$	100.0	135.4	152.3	171.8	193.8	207.0	224.5	251.0	280.2	311.0	95
3-Bromopyridine	C_5H_4BrN	16.8	42.0	55.2	69.1	84.1	94.1	107.8	127.7	150.0	173.4	
2-Bromotoluene	C_7H_7Br	24.4	49.7	62.3	76.0	91.0	100.0	112.0	133.6	157.3	181.8	−28
3-Bromotoluene	C_7H_7Br	14.8	50.8	64.0	78.1	93.9	104.1	117.8	138.0	160.0	183.7	39.8
4-Bromotoluene	C_7H_7Br	10.3	47.5	61.1	75.2	91.8	102.3	116.4	137.4	160.2	184.5	28.5
3-Bromo-2,4,6-trichlorophenol	$C_6H_2BrCl_3O$	112.4	146.2	163.2	181.8	200.5	213.0	229.3	253.0	278.0	305.8	
2-Bromo-1,4-xylene	C_8H_9Br	37.5	65.0	78.8	94.0	110.6	121.6	135.7	156.4	181.0	206.7	+9.5
1,2-Butadiene (methyl allene)	C_4H_6	−89.0	−72.7	−64.2	−54.9	−44.3	−37.5	−28.3	−14.2	+1.8	18.5	
1,3-Butadiene	C_4H_6	−102.8	−87.6	−79.7	−71.0	−61.3	−55.1	−46.8	−33.9	−19.3	−4.5	−108.9
n-Butane	C_4H_{10}	−101.5	−85.7	−77.8	−68.9	−59.1	−52.8	−44.2	−31.2	−16.3	−0.5	−135
iso-Butane (2-methylpropane)	C_4H_{10}	−109.2	−94.1	−86.4	−77.9	−68.4	−62.4	−54.1	−41.5	−27.1	−11.7	−145
1,3-Butanediol	$C_4H_{10}O_2$	22.2	67.5	85.3	100.0	117.4	127.5	141.2	161.0	183.8	206.5	77
1,2,3-Butanetriol	$C_4H_{10}O_3$	102.0	132.0	146.0	161.0	178.0	188.0	202.5	222.0	243.5	264.0	
1-Butene	C_4H_8	−104.8	−89.4	−81.6	−73.0	−63.4	−57.2	−48.9	−36.2	−21.7	−6.3	−130
cis-2-Butene	C_4H_8	−96.4	−81.1	−73.4	−64.6	−54.7	−48.4	−39.8	−26.8	−12.0	+3.7	−138.9
trans-2-Butene	C_4H_8	−99.4	−84.0	−76.3	−67.5	−57.6	−51.3	−42.7	−29.7	−14.8	+0.9	−105.4
3-Butenenitrile	C_4H_5N	−19.6	+2.9	14.1	26.6	40.0	48.8	60.2	78.0	98.0	119.0	
iso-Butyl acetate	$C_6H_{12}O_2$	−21.2	+1.4	12.8	25.5	39.2	48.0	59.7	77.6	97.5	118.0	−98.9
n-Butyl acrylate	$C_7H_{12}O_2$	−0.5	+23.5	35.5	48.6	63.4	72.6	85.1	104.0	125.2	147.4	−64.6
alcohol	$C_4H_{10}O$	−1.2	+20.0	30.2	41.5	53.4	60.3	70.1	84.3	100.8	117.5	−79.9
iso-Butyl alcohol	$C_4H_{10}O$	−9.0	+11.6	21.7	32.4	44.1	51.7	61.5	75.9	91.4	108.0	−108
sec-Butyl alcohol	$C_4H_{10}O$	−12.2	+7.2	16.9	27.3	38.1	45.2	54.1	67.9	83.9	99.5	−114.7
tert-Butyl alcohol	$C_4H_{10}O$	−20.4	−3.0	+5.5	14.3	24.5	31.0	39.8	52.7	68.0	82.9	25.3
iso-Butyl amine	$C_4H_{11}N$	−50.0	−31.0	−21.0	−10.3	+1.3	8.8	18.8	32.0	50.7	68.6	−85.0
n-Butylbenzene	$C_{10}H_{14}$	22.7	48.8	62.0	76.3	92.4	102.6	116.2	136.9	159.2	183.1	−88.0
iso-Butylbenzene	$C_{10}H_{14}$	14.1	40.5	53.7	67.8	83.3	93.3	107.0	127.2	149.6	172.8	−51.5
sec-Butylbenzene	$C_{10}H_{14}$	18.6	44.2	57.0	70.6	86.2	96.0	109.5	128.8	150.3	173.5	−75.5
tert-Butylbenzene	$C_{10}H_{14}$	13.0	39.0	51.7	65.6	80.8	90.6	103.8	123.7	145.8	168.5	−58
iso-Butyl benzoate	$C_{11}H_{14}O_2$	64.0	93.6	108.6	124.2	141.8	152.0	166.4	188.2	212.8	237.0	
n-Butyl bromide (1-bromobutane)	C_4H_9Br	−33.0	−11.2	−0.3	+11.6	24.8	33.4	44.7	62.0	81.7	101.6	−112.4
iso-Butyl n-butyrate	$C_8H_{16}O_2$	+4.6	30.0	42.2	56.1	71.7	81.3	94.0	113.9	135.7	156.9	
carbamate	$C_5H_{11}NO_2$	.....	83.7	96.4	110.1	125.3	134.6	147.2	165.7	186.0	206.5	65
Butyl carbitol (diethylene glycol butyl ether)	$C_8H_{18}O_3$	70.0	95.7	107.8	120.5	135.5	146.0	159.8	181.2	205.0	231.2	
n-Butyl chloride (1-chlorobutane)	C_4H_9Cl	−49.0	−28.9	−18.6	−7.4	+5.0	13.0	24.0	40.0	58.8	77.8	−123.1
iso-Butyl chloride	C_4H_9Cl	−53.8	−34.3	−24.5	−13.8	−1.9	+5.9	16.0	32.0	50.0	68.9	−131.2
sec-Butyl chloride (2-Chlorobutane)	C_4H_9Cl	−60.2	−39.8	−29.2	−17.7	−5.0	+3.4	14.2	31.5	50.0	68.0	−131.3
tert-Butyl chloride	C_4H_9Cl	.....	.....	.....	.....	−19.0	−11.4	−1.0	+14.6	32.6	51.0	−26.5
sec-Butyl chloroacetate	$C_6H_{11}ClO_2$	17.0	41.8	54.6	68.2	83.6	93.0	105.5	124.1	146.0	167.8	
2-tert-Butyl-4-cresol	$C_{11}H_{16}O$	70.0	98.0	112.0	127.2	143.9	153.7	167.0	187.8	210.0	232.6	
4-tert-Butyl-2-cresol	$C_{11}H_{16}O$	74.3	103.7	118.0	134.0	150.8	161.7	176.2	197.8	221.8	247.0	
iso-Butyl dichloroacetate	$C_6H_{10}Cl_2O_2$	28.6	54.3	67.5	81.4	96.7	106.6	119.8	139.2	160.0	183.0	
2,3-Butylene glycol (2,3-butanediol)	$C_4H_{10}O_2$	44.0	68.4	80.3	93.4	107.8	116.3	127.8	145.6	164.0	182.0	22.5
2-Butyl-2-ethylbutane-1,3-diol	$C_{10}H_{22}O_2$	94.1	122.6	136.8	151.2	167.8	178.0	191.9	212.0	233.5	255.0	
2-tert-Butyl-4-ethylphenol	$C_{12}H_{18}O$	76.3	106.2	121.0	137.0	154.0	165.4	179.0	200.3	223.8	247.8	
n-Butyl formate	$C_5H_{10}O_2$	−26.4	−4.7	+6.1	18.0	31.6	39.8	51.0	67.9	86.2	106.0	
iso-Butyl formate	$C_5H_{10}O_2$	−32.7	−11.4	−0.8	+11.0	24.1	32.4	43.4	60.0	79.0	98.2	−95.3
sec-Butyl formate	$C_5H_{10}O_2$	−34.4	−13.3	−3.1	+8.4	21.3	29.6	40.2	56.8	75.2	93.6	
sec-Butyl glycolate	$C_6H_{12}O_3$	28.3	53.6	66.0	79.8	94.2	104.0	116.4	135.5	155.6	177.5	
iso-Butyl iodide (1-iodo-2-methylpropane)	C_4H_9I	−17.0	+5.8	17.0	29.8	42.8	51.8	63.5	81.0	100.3	120.4	−90.7
isobutyrate	$C_8H_{16}O_2$	+4.1	28.0	39.9	52.4	67.2	75.9	88.0	106.3	126.3	147.5	−80.7
isovalerate	$C_9H_{18}O_2$	16.0	41.2	53.8	67.7	82.7	92.4	105.2	124.8	146.4	168.7	
levulinate	$C_9H_{16}O_3$	65.0	92.1	105.9	120.2	136.2	147.0	160.2	181.8	205.5	229.9	
naphthylketone (1-isovaleronaphthone)	$C_{15}H_{16}O$	136.0	167.9	184.0	201.6	219.7	231.5	246.7	269.7	294.0	320.0	
2-sec-Butylphenol	$C_{10}H_{14}O$	57.4	86.0	100.8	116.1	133.4	143.9	157.3	179.7	203.8	228.0	
2-tert-Butylphenol	$C_{10}H_{14}O$	56.6	84.2	98.1	113.0	129.2	140.0	153.5	173.8	196.3	219.5	
4-iso-Butylphenol	$C_{10}H_{14}O$	72.1	100.9	115.5	130.3	147.2	157.0	171.2	192.1	214.7	237.0	
4-sec-Butylphenol	$C_{10}H_{14}O$	71.4	100.5	114.8	130.3	147.8	157.9	172.4	194.3	217.6	242.1	
4-tert-Butylphenol	$C_{10}H_{14}O$	70.0	99.2	114.0	129.5	146.0	156.0	170.2	191.5	214.0	238.0	99
2-(4-tert-Butylphenoxy)ethyl acetate	$C_{14}H_{20}O_3$	118.0	150.0	165.8	183.3	201.5	212.8	228.0	250.3	277.6	304.4	
4-tert-Butylphenyl dichlorophosphate	$C_{10}H_{13}Cl_2O_2P$	96.0	129.6	146.0	164.0	184.3	197.2	214.3	240.0	268.2	299.0	
tert-Butyl phenyl ketone (pivalophenone)	$C_{11}H_{14}O$	57.8	85.7	99.0	114.3	130.4	140.8	154.0	175.0	197.7	220.0	
iso-Butyl propionate	$C_7H_{14}O_2$	−2.3	+20.9	32.3	44.8	58.5	67.6	79.5	97.0	116.4	136.8	−71
4-tert-Butyl-2,5-xylenol	$C_{12}H_{18}O$	88.2	119.8	135.0	151.0	169.8	180.3	195.0	217.5	241.3	265.3	
4-tert-Butyl-2,6-xylenol	$C_{12}H_{18}O$	74.0	103.9	119.0	135.0	152.2	163.6	176.0	196.0	217.8	239.8	
6-tert-Butyl-2,4-xylenol	$C_{12}H_{18}O$	70.3	100.2	115.0	131.0	148.5	158.2	172.0	192.3	214.2	236.5	
6-tert-Butyl-3,4-xylenol	$C_{12}H_{18}O$	83.9	113.6	127.0	143.0	159.7	170.0	184.0	204.5	226.7	249.5	
Butyric acid	$C_4H_8O_2$	25.5	49.8	61.5	74.0	88.0	96.5	108.0	125.5	144.5	163.5	−74.

Table 3-8. Vapor Pressures of Organic Compounds, up to 1 Atm.—(*Continued*)

Compound: Name	Formula	1 mm	5 mm	10 mm	20 mm	40 mm	60 mm	100 mm	200 mm	400 mm	760 mm	Melting point, °C.
		Temperature, °C.										
iso-Butyric acid	$C_4H_8O_2$	14.7	39.3	51.2	64.0	77.8	86.3	98.0	115.8	134.5	154.5	−47
Butyronitrile	C_4H_7N	−20.0	+2.1	13.4	25.7	38.4	47.3	59.0	76.7	96.8	117.5	
iso-Valerophenone	$C_{11}H_{14}O$	58.3	87.0	101.4	116.8	133.8	144.6	158.0	180.1	204.2	228.0	
Camphene	$C_{10}H_{16}$	......	......	47.2	60.4	75.7	85.0	97.9	117.5	138.7	160.5	50
Campholenic acid	$C_{10}H_{16}O_2$	97.6	125.7	139.8	153.9	170.0	180.0	193.7	212.7	234.0	256.0	
d-Camphor	$C_{10}H_{16}O$	41.5	68.6	82.3	97.5	114.0	124.0	138.0	157.9	182.0	209.2	178.5
Camphylamine	$C_{10}H_{19}N$	45.3	74.0	83.7	97.6	112.5	122.0	134.6	153.0	173.8	195.0	
Capraldehyde	$C_{10}H_{20}O$	51.9	78.8	92.0	106.3	122.2	132.0	145.3	164.8	186.3	208.5	
Capric acid	$C_{10}H_{20}O_2$	125.0	142.0	152.2	165.0	179.9	189.8	200.0	217.1	240.3	268.4	31.5
n-Caproic acid	$C_6H_{12}O_2$	71.4	89.5	99.5	111.8	125.0	133.3	144.0	160.8	181.0	202.0	−1.5
iso-Caproic acid	$C_6H_{12}O_2$	66.2	83.0	94.0	107.0	120.4	129.6	141.4	158.3	181.0	207.7	−35
iso-Caprolactone	$C_6H_{10}O_2$	38.3	66.4	80.3	95.7	112.3	123.2	137.2	157.8	182.1	207.0	
Capronitrile	$C_6H_{11}N$	9.2	34.6	47.5	61.7	76.9	86.8	99.8	119.7	141.0	163.7	
Capryl alcohol (2-octanol)	$C_8H_{18}O$	32.8	57.6	70.0	83.3	98.0	107.4	119.8	138.0	157.5	178.5	−38.6
Caprylaldehyde	$C_8H_{16}O$	73.4	92.0	101.2	110.2	120.0	126.0	133.9	145.4	156.5	168.5	
Caprylic acid (octanoic acid)	$C_8H_{16}O_2$	92.3	114.1	124.0	136.4	150.6	160.0	172.2	190.3	213.9	237.5	16
Caprylonitrile	$C_8H_{15}N$	43.0	67.6	80.4	94.6	110.6	121.2	134.8	155.2	179.5	204.5	
Carbazole	$C_{12}H_9N$	......	......	......	......	......	248.2	265.0	292.5	323.0	354.8	244.8
Carbon dioxide	CO_2	−134.3	−124.4	−119.5	−114.4	−108.6	−104.8	−100.2	−93.0	−85.7	−78.2	−57.5
disulfide	CS_2	−73.8	−54.3	−44.7	−34.3	−22.5	−15.3	−5.1	+10.4	28.0	46.5	−110.8
monoxide	CO	−222.0	−217.2	−215.0	−212.8	−210.0	−208.1	−205.7	−201.3	−196.3	−191.3	−205.0
oxyselenide (carbonyl selenide)	$COSe$	−117.1	−102.3	−95.0	−86.3	−76.4	−70.2	−61.7	−49.8	−35.6	−21.9	
oxysulfide (carbonyl sulfide)	COS	−132.4	−119.8	−113.3	−106.0	−98.3	−93.0	−85.9	−75.0	−62.7	−49.9	−138.8
tetrabromide	CBr_4	......	......	......	......	96.3	106.3	119.7	139.7	163.5	189.5	90.1
tetrachloride	CCl_4	−50.0	−30.0	−19.6	−8.2	+4.3	12.3	23.0	38.3	57.8	76.7	−22.6
tetrafluoride	CF_4	−184.6	−174.1	−169.3	−164.3	−158.8	−155.4	−150.7	−143.6	−135.5	−127.7	−183.7
Carvacrol	$C_{10}H_{14}O$	70.0	98.4	113.2	127.9	145.2	155.3	169.7	191.2	213.8	237.0	+0.5
Carvone	$C_{10}H_{14}O$	57.4	86.1	100.4	116.1	133.0	143.8	157.3	179.6	203.5	227.5	
Chavibetol	$C_{10}H_{12}O_2$	83.6	113.3	127.0	143.2	159.8	170.7	185.5	206.8	229.8	254.0	
Chloral (trichloroacetaldehyde)	C_2HCl_3O	−37.8	−16.0	−5.0	+7.2	20.2	29.1	40.2	57.8	77.5	97.7	−57
hydrate (trichloroacetaldehyde hydrate)	$C_2H_3Cl_3O_2$	−9.8	+10.0	19.5	29.2	39.7	46.2	55.0	68.0	82.1	96.2	51.7
Chloranil	$C_6Cl_4O_2$	70.7	89.3	97.8	106.4	116.1	122.0	129.5	140.3	151.3	162.6	290
Chloroacetic acid	$C_2H_3ClO_2$	43.0	68.3	81.0	94.2	109.2	118.3	130.7	149.0	169.0	189.5	61.2
anhydride	$C_4H_4Cl_2O_3$	67.2	94.1	108.0	122.4	138.2	148.0	159.8	177.8	197.0	217.0	46
2-Chloroaniline	C_6H_6ClN	46.3	72.3	84.8	99.2	115.6	125.7	139.5	160.0	183.7	208.8	0
3-Chloroaniline	C_6H_6ClN	63.5	89.8	102.0	116.7	133.6	144.1	158.0	179.5	203.5	228.5	−10.4
4-Chloroaniline	C_6H_6ClN	59.3	87.9	102.1	117.8	135.0	145.8	159.9	182.3	206.6	230.5	70.5
Chlorobenzene	C_6H_5Cl	−13.0	+10.6	22.2	35.3	49.7	58.3	70.7	89.4	110.0	132.2	−45.2
2-Chlorobenzotrichloride (2-α,α,α-tetrachlorotoluene)	$C_7H_4Cl_4$	69.0	101.8	117.9	135.8	155.0	167.8	185.0	208.0	233.0	262.1	28.7
2-Chlorobenzotrifluoride (2-chloro-α,α,α-trifluorotoluene)	$C_7H_4ClF_3$	0.0	24.7	37.1	50.6	65.9	75.4	88.3	108.3	130.0	152.2	−6.0
2-Chlorobiphenyl	$C_{12}H_9Cl$	89.3	109.8	134.7	151.2	169.9	182.1	197.0	219.6	243.8	267.5	34
4-Chlorobiphenyl	$C_{12}H_9Cl$	96.4	129.8	146.0	164.0	183.8	196.0	212.5	237.8	264.5	292.9	75.5
α-Chlorocrotonic acid	$C_4H_5ClO_2$	70.0	95.6	108.0	121.2	135.6	144.4	155.9	173.8	193.2	212.0	
Chlorodifluoromethane	$CHClF_2$	−122.8	−110.2	−103.7	−96.5	−88.6	−83.4	−76.4	−65.8	−53.6	−40.8	−160
Chlorodimethylphenylsilane	$C_8H_{11}ClSi$	29.8	56.7	70.0	84.7	101.2	111.5	124.7	145.5	168.6	193.5	
1-Chloro-2-ethoxybenzene	C_8H_9ClO	45.8	72.8	86.5	101.5	117.8	127.8	141.8	162.0	185.5	208.0	
2-(2-Chloroethoxy) ethanol	$C_4H_9ClO_2$	53.0	78.3	90.7	104.1	118.4	127.5	139.5	157.2	176.5	196.0	
bis-2-Chloroethyl acetacetal	$C_6H_{12}Cl_2O_2$	56.2	83.7	97.6	112.2	127.8	138.0	150.7	169.8	190.5	212.6	
1-Chloro-2-ethylbenzene	C_8H_9Cl	17.2	43.0	56.1	70.3	86.2	96.4	110.0	130.2	152.2	177.6	−80.2
1-Chloro-3-ethylbenzene	C_8H_9Cl	18.6	45.2	58.1	73.0	89.2	99.6	113.6	133.8	156.7	181.1	−53.3
1-Chloro-4-ethylbenzene	C_8H_9Cl	19.2	46.4	60.0	75.5	91.8	102.0	116.0	137.0	159.8	184.3	−62.6
2-Chloroethyl chloroacetate	$C_4H_6Cl_2O_2$	46.0	72.1	86.0	100.0	116.0	126.2	140.0	159.8	182.2	205.0	
2-Chloroethyl 2-chloroisopropyl ether	$C_5H_{10}Cl_2O$	24.7	50.1	63.0	77.2	92.4	102.2	115.8	135.7	156.5	180.0	
2-Chloroethyl 2-chloropropyl ether	$C_5H_{10}Cl_2O$	29.8	56.5	70.0	84.8	101.5	111.8	125.6	146.3	169.8	194.1	
2-Chloroethyl α-methylbenzyl ether	$C_{10}H_{13}ClO$	62.3	91.4	106.0	121.8	139.6	150.0	164.8	186.3	210.8	235.0	
Chloroform (trichloromethane)	$CHCl_3$	−58.0	−39.1	−29.7	−19.0	−7.1	+0.5	10.4	25.9	42.7	61.3	−63.5
1-Chloronaphthalene	$C_{10}H_7Cl$	80.6	104.8	118.6	134.4	153.2	165.6	180.4	204.2	230.8	259.3	−20
4-Chlorophenethyl alcohol	C_8H_9ClO	84.0	114.3	129.0	145.0	162.0	173.5	188.1	210.0	234.5	259.3	
2-Chlorophenol	C_6H_5ClO	12.1	38.2	51.2	65.9	82.0	92.0	106.0	126.4	149.8	174.5	7
3-Chlorophenol	C_6H_5ClO	44.2	72.0	86.1	101.7	118.0	129.4	143.0	164.8	188.7	214.0	32.5
4-Chlorophenol	C_6H_5ClO	49.8	78.2	92.2	108.1	125.0	136.1	150.0	172.0	196.0	220.0	42
2-Chloro-3-phenylphenol	$C_{12}H_9ClO$	118.0	152.2	169.7	186.7	207.4	219.6	237.0	261.3	289.4	317.5	+6
2-Chloro-6-phenylphenol	$C_{12}H_9ClO$	119.8	153.7	170.7	189.8	208.2	220.0	237.1	261.6	289.5	317.0	
Chloropicrin (trichloronitromethane)	CCl_3NO_2	−25.5	−3.3	+7.8	20.0	33.8	42.3	53.8	71.8	91.8	111.9	−64
1-Chloropropene	C_3H_5Cl	−81.3	−63.4	−54.1	−44.0	−32.7	−25.1	−15.1	+1.3	18.0	37.0	−99.0
2-Chloropyridine	C_5H_4ClN	13.3	38.8	51.7	65.8	81.7	91.6	104.6	125.0	147.7	170.2	
3-Chlorostyrene	C_8H_7Cl	25.3	51.3	65.2	80.0	96.5	107.2	121.2	142.2	165.7	190.0	
4-Chlorostyrene	C_8H_7Cl	28.0	54.5	67.5	82.0	98.0	108.5	122.0	143.5	166.0	191.0	−15.0
1-Chlorotetradecane	$C_{14}H_{29}Cl$	98.5	131.8	148.2	166.2	187.0	199.8	215.5	240.3	267.5	296.0	+0.9
2-Chlorotoluene	C_7H_7Cl	+5.4	30.6	43.2	56.9	72.0	81.8	94.7	115.0	137.1	159.3	
3-Chlorotoluene	C_7H_7Cl	+4.8	30.3	43.2	57.4	73.0	83.2	96.3	116.6	139.7	162.3	
4-Chlorotoluene	C_7H_7Cl	+5.5	31.0	43.8	57.8	73.5	83.3	96.6	117.1	139.8	162.3	+7.3
Chlorotriethylsilane	$C_6H_{15}ClSi$	−4.9	+19.8	32.0	45.5	60.2	69.5	82.3	101.6	123.6	146.3	
1-Chloro-1,2,2-trifluoroethylene	C_2ClF_3	−116.0	−102.5	−95.9	−88.2	−79.7	−74.1	−66.7	−55.0	−41.7	−27.9	−157.5
Chlorotrifluoromethane	$CClF_3$	−149.5	−139.2	−134.1	−128.5	−121.9	−117.3	−111.7	−102.5	−92.7	−81.2	
Chlorotrimethylsilane	C_3H_9ClSi	−62.8	−43.6	−34.0	−23.2	−11.4	−4.0	+6.0	21.9	39.4	57.9	
trans-Cinnamic acid	$C_9H_8O_2$	127.5	157.8	173.0	189.5	207.1	217.8	232.4	253.3	276.7	300.0	133
Cinnamyl alcohol	$C_9H_{10}O$	72.6	102.5	117.8	133.7	151.0	162.0	177.8	199.8	224.6	250.0	33
Cinnamylaldehyde	C_9H_8O	76.1	105.8	120.0	135.7	152.2	163.7	177.7	199.3	222.4	246.0	−7.5
Citraconic anhydride	$C_5H_4O_3$	47.1	74.8	88.9	103.8	120.3	131.3	145.4	165.8	189.8	213.5	
cis-α-Citral	$C_{10}H_{16}O$	61.7	90.0	103.9	119.4	135.9	146.3	160.0	181.8	205.0	228.0	
d-Citronellal	$C_{10}H_{18}O$	44.0	71.4	84.8	99.8	116.1	126.2	140.1	160.0	183.8	206.5	
Citronellic acid	$C_{10}H_{18}O_2$	99.5	127.3	141.4	155.6	171.9	182.1	195.4	214.5	236.6	257.0	
Citronellol	$C_{10}H_{20}O$	66.4	93.6	107.0	121.5	137.2	147.2	159.8	179.8	201.0	221.5	
Citronellyl acetate	$C_{12}H_{22}O_2$	74.7	100.2	113.0	126.0	140.5	149.7	161.0	178.8	197.8	217.0	
Coumarin	$C_9H_6O_2$	106.0	137.8	153.4	170.0	189.0	200.5	216.5	240.0	264.7	291.0	70

Table 3-8. Vapor Pressures of Organic Compounds, up to 1 Atm.—*(Continued)*

Compound		Pressure, mm. Hg (Temperature, °C.)										Melting point, °C.
Name	Formula	1	5	10	20	40	60	100	200	400	760	
o-Cresol (2-cresol; 2-methylphenol)	C_7H_8O	38.2	64.0	76.7	90.5	105.8	115.5	127.4	146.7	168.4	190.8	30.8
m-Cresol (3-cresol; 3-methylphenol)	C_7H_8O	52.0	76.0	87.8	101.4	116.0	125.8	138.0	157.3	179.0	202.8	10.9
p-Cresol (4-cresol; 4-methylphenol)	C_7H_8O	53.0	76.5	88.6	102.3	117.7	127.0	140.0	157.3	179.4	201.8	35.5
cis-Crotonic acid	$C_4H_6O_2$	33.5	57.4	69.0	82.0	96.0	104.5	116.3	133.9	152.2	171.9	15.5
trans-Crotonic acid	$C_4H_6O_2$	...	...	80.0	93.0	107.8	116.7	128.0	146.0	165.5	185.0	72
cis-Crotononitrile	C_4H_5N	−29.0	−7.1	+4.0	16.4	30.0	38.5	50.1	68.0	88.0	108.0	
trans-Crotononitrile	C_4H_5N	−19.5	+3.5	15.0	27.8	41.8	50.9	62.8	81.1	101.5	122.8	
Cumene	C_9H_{12}	+2.9	26.8	38.3	51.5	66.1	75.4	88.1	107.3	129.2	152.4	−96.0
4-Cumidene	$C_9H_{13}N$	60.0	88.2	102.2	117.8	134.2	145.0	158.0	180.0	203.2	227.0	
Cuminal	$C_{10}H_{12}O$	58.0	87.3	102.0	117.9	135.2	146.0	160.0	182.8	206.7	232.0	
Cuminyl alcohol	$C_{10}H_{14}O$	74.2	103.7	118.0	133.8	150.3	161.7	176.2	197.9	221.7	246.6	
2-Cyano-2-n-butyl acetate	$C_7H_{11}NO_2$	42.0	68.7	82.0	96.2	111.8	121.5	133.8	152.2	173.4	195.2	
Cyanogen	C_2N_2	−95.8	−83.2	−76.8	−70.1	−62.7	−57.9	−51.8	−42.6	−33.0	−21.0	−34.4
bromide	$CBrN$	−35.7	−18.3	−10.0	−1.0	+8.6	14.7	22.6	33.8	46.0	61.5	58
chloride	$CClN$	−76.7	−61.4	−53.8	−46.1	−37.5	−32.1	−24.9	−14.1	−2.3	+13.1	−6.5
iodide	CIN	25.2	47.2	57.7	68.6	80.3	88.0	97.6	111.5	126.1	141.1	
Cyclobutane	C_4H_8	−92.0	−76.0	−67.9	−58.7	−48.4	−41.8	−32.8	−18.9	−3.4	+12.9	−50
Cyclobutene	C_4H_6	−99.1	−83.4	−75.4	−66.6	−56.4	−50.0	−41.2	−27.8	−12.2	+2.4	
Cyclohexane	C_6H_{12}	−45.3	−25.4	−15.9	−5.0	+6.7	14.7	25.5	42.0	60.8	80.7	+6.6
Cyclohexaneethanol	$C_8H_{16}O$	50.4	77.2	90.0	104.0	119.8	129.8	142.7	161.7	183.5	205.4	
Cyclohexanol	$C_6H_{12}O$	21.0	44.0	56.0	68.8	83.0	91.8	103.7	121.7	141.4	161.0	23.9
Cyclohexanone	$C_6H_{10}O$	+1.4	26.4	38.7	52.5	67.8	77.5	90.4	110.3	132.5	155.6	−45.0
2-Cyclohexyl-4,6-dinitrophenol	$C_{12}H_{14}N_2O_5$	132.8	161.8	175.9	191.2	206.7	216.0	229.0	248.7	269.8	291.5	
Cyclopentane	C_5H_{10}	−68.0	−49.6	−40.4	−30.1	−18.6	−11.3	−1.3	+13.8	31.0	49.3	−93.7
Cyclopropane	C_3H_6	−116.8	−104.2	−97.5	−90.3	−82.3	−77.0	−70.0	−59.1	−46.9	−33.5	−126.6
Cymene	$C_{10}H_{14}$	17.3	43.9	57.0	71.1	87.0	97.2	110.8	131.4	153.5	177.2	−68.2
cis-Decalin	$C_{10}H_{18}$	22.5	50.1	64.2	79.8	97.2	108.0	123.2	145.4	169.9	194.6	−43.3
trans-Decalin	$C_{10}H_{18}$	−0.8	+30.6	47.2	65.3	85.7	98.4	114.6	136.2	160.1	186.7	−30.7
Decane	$C_{10}H_{22}$	16.5	42.3	55.7	69.8	85.5	95.5	108.6	128.4	150.6	174.1	−29.7
Decan-2-one	$C_{10}H_{20}O$	44.2	71.9	85.8	100.7	117.1	127.8	142.0	163.2	186.7	211.0	+3.5
1-Decene	$C_{10}H_{20}$	14.7	40.3	53.7	67.8	83.3	93.5	106.5	126.7	149.2	172.0	
Decyl alcohol	$C_{10}H_{22}O$	69.5	97.3	111.3	125.8	142.1	152.0	165.8	186.2	208.8	231.0	+7
Decyltrimethylsilane	$C_{13}H_{30}Si$	67.4	96.4	111.0	126.5	144.0	154.3	169.5	191.0	215.5	240.0	
Dehydroacetic acid	$C_8H_8O_4$	91.7	122.0	137.3	153.0	171.0	181.5	197.5	219.5	244.5	269.0	
Desoxybenzoin	$C_{14}H_{12}O$	123.3	156.2	173.5	192.0	212.0	224.5	241.3	265.2	293.0	321.0	60
Diacetamide	$C_4H_7NO_2$	70.0	95.0	108.0	122.6	138.2	148.0	160.6	180.8	202.0	223.0	78.5
Diacetylene (1,3-butadiyne)	C_4H_2	−82.5	−68.0	−61.2	−53.8	−45.9	−41.0	−34.0	−20.9	−6.1	+9.7	−34.9
Diallyldichlorosilane	$C_6H_{10}Cl_2Si$	+9.5	34.8	47.4	61.3	76.4	86.3	99.7	119.4	142.0	165.3	
Diallyl sulfide	$C_6H_{10}S$	−9.5	+14.4	26.6	39.7	54.2	63.7	75.8	94.8	116.1	138.6	−83
Diisoamyl ether	$C_{10}H_{22}O$	18.6	44.3	57.0	70.7	86.3	96.0	109.6	129.0	150.3	173.4	
oxalate	$C_{12}H_{22}O_4$	85.4	116.0	131.4	147.7	165.7	177.0	192.2	215.0	240.0	265.0	
sulfide	$C_{10}H_{22}S$	43.0	73.0	87.6	102.7	120.0	130.6	145.3	166.4	191.0	216.0	
Dibenzylamine	$C_{14}H_{15}N$	118.3	149.8	165.6	182.2	200.2	212.2	227.3	249.8	274.3	300.0	−26
Dibenzyl ketone (1,3-diphenyl-2-propanone)	$C_{15}H_{14}O$	125.5	159.8	177.6	195.7	216.6	229.4	246.6	272.3	301.7	330.5	34.5
1,4-Dibromobenzene	$C_6H_4Br_2$	61.0	79.3	87.7	103.6	120.8	131.6	146.5	168.5	192.5	218.6	87.5
1,2-Dibromobutane	$C_4H_8Br_2$	7.5	33.2	46.1	60.0	76.0	86.0	99.8	120.2	143.5	166.3	−64.5
dl-2,3-Dibromobutane	$C_4H_8Br_2$	+5.0	30.0	41.6	56.4	72.0	82.0	95.3	115.7	138.0	160.5	
meso-2,3-Dibromobutane	$C_4H_8Br_2$	+1.5	26.6	39.3	53.2	68.0	78.0	91.7	111.8	134.2	157.3	−34.5
1,2-Dibromodecane	$C_{10}H_{20}Br_2$	95.7	123.6	137.3	151.0	167.4	177.5	190.2	209.6	229.8	250.4	
Di(2-bromoethyl) ether	$C_4H_8Br_2O$	47.7	75.3	88.5	103.6	119.8	130.0	144.0	165.0	188.0	212.5	
α,β-Dibromomaleic anhydride	$C_4H_2Br_2O_3$	50.0	78.0	92.0	106.7	123.5	133.8	147.7	168.0	192.0	215.0	
1,2-Dibromo-2-methylpropane	$C_4H_8Br_2$	−28.8	−3.0	+10.5	25.7	42.3	53.7	68.8	92.1	119.8	149.0	−70.3
1,3-Dibromo-2-methylpropane	$C_4H_8Br_2$	14.0	40.0	53.0	67.5	83.5	93.7	107.4	117.8	150.6	174.6	
1,2-Dibromopentane	$C_5H_{10}Br_2$	19.8	45.4	58.0	72.0	87.4	97.4	110.1	130.2	151.8	175.0	
1,2-Dibromopropane	$C_3H_6Br_2$	−7.0	+17.3	29.4	42.3	57.2	66.4	78.7	97.8	118.5	141.6	−55.5
1,3-Dibromopropane	$C_3H_6Br_2$	+9.7	35.4	48.0	62.1	77.8	87.8	101.3	121.7	144.1	167.5	−34.4
2,3-Dibromopropene	$C_3H_4Br_2$	−6.0	+17.9	30.0	43.2	57.8	67.0	79.5	98.0	119.5	141.2	
2,3-Dibromo-1-propanol	$C_3H_6Br_2O$	57.0	84.5	98.2	113.5	129.8	140.0	153.0	173.8	196.0	219.0	
Diisobutylamine	$C_8H_{19}N$	−5.1	+18.4	30.6	43.7	57.8	67.0	79.2	97.6	118.0	139.5	−70
2,6-Ditert-butyl-4-cresol	$C_{15}H_{24}O$	85.8	116.2	131.0	147.0	164.1	175.2	190.0	212.8	237.6	262.5	
4,6-Ditert-butyl-2-cresol	$C_{15}H_{24}O$	86.2	117.3	132.4	149.0	167.4	179.0	194.0	217.5	243.4	269.3	
4,6-Ditert-butyl-3-cresol	$C_{15}H_{24}O$	103.7	135.2	150.0	167.0	185.3	196.1	211.0	233.0	257.1	282.0	
2,6-Ditert-butyl-4-ethylphenol	$C_{16}H_{26}O$	89.1	121.4	137.0	154.0	172.1	183.9	198.0	220.0	244.0	268.6	
4,6-Ditert-butyl-3-ethylphenol	$C_{16}H_{26}O$	111.5	142.6	157.4	174.0	192.3	204.4	218.0	241.7	264.6	290.0	
Diisobutyl oxalate	$C_{10}H_{18}O_4$	63.2	91.2	105.3	120.3	137.5	147.8	161.8	183.5	205.8	229.5	
2,4-Ditert-butylphenol	$C_{14}H_{22}O$	84.5	115.4	130.0	146.0	164.3	175.8	190.0	212.5	237.0	260.8	
Dibutyl phthalate	$C_{16}H_{22}O_4$	148.2	182.1	198.2	216.2	235.8	247.8	263.7	287.0	313.5	340.0	
sulfide	$C_8H_{18}S$	+21.7	51.8	66.4	80.5	96.0	105.8	118.6	138.0	159.0	182.0	−79.7
Diisobutyl d-tartrate	$C_{12}H_{22}O_6$	117.8	151.8	169.0	188.0	208.5	221.6	239.5	264.7	294.0	324.0	73.5
Dicarvacryl-mono-(6-chloro-2-xenyl) phosphate	$C_{32}H_{34}ClO_4P$	204.2	234.5	249.3	264.5	280.5	290.7	304.9	323.8	342.0	361.0	
Dicarvacryl-2-tolyl phosphate	$C_{27}H_{33}O_4P$	180.2	209.3	221.8	237.0	251.5	260.3	272.5	290.0	309.8	330.0	
Dichloroacetic acid	$C_2H_2Cl_2O_2$	44.0	69.8	82.6	96.3	111.8	121.5	134.0	152.3	173.7	194.4	9.7
1,2-Dichlorobenzene	$C_6H_4Cl_2$	20.0	46.0	59.1	73.4	89.4	99.5	112.9	133.4	155.8	179.0	−17.6
1,3-Dichlorobenzene	$C_6H_4Cl_2$	12.1	39.0	52.0	66.2	82.0	92.2	105.0	125.9	149.0	173.0	−24.2
1,4-Dichlorobenzene	$C_6H_4Cl_2$	...	...	54.8	69.2	84.8	95.2	108.4	128.3	150.2	173.9	53.0
1,2-Dichlorobutane	$C_4H_8Cl_2$	−23.6	−0.3	+11.5	24.5	37.7	47.8	60.2	79.7	100.8	123.5	
2,3-Dichlorobutane	$C_4H_8Cl_2$	−25.2	−3.0	+8.5	21.2	35.0	43.9	56.0	74.0	94.2	116.0	−80.4
1,2-Dichloro-1,2-difluoroethylene	$C_2Cl_2F_2$	−82.0	−65.6	−57.3	−48.3	−38.2	−31.8	−23.0	−10.0	+5.0	20.9	−112
Dichlorodifluoromethane	CCl_2F_2	−118.5	−104.6	−97.8	−90.1	−81.6	−76.1	−68.6	−57.0	−43.9	−29.8	
Dichlorodiphenyl silane	$C_{12}H_{10}Cl_2Si$	109.6	142.4	158.0	176.0	195.5	207.5	223.8	248.0	275.5	304.0	
Dichlorodiisopropyl ether	$C_6H_{12}Cl_2O$	29.6	55.2	68.2	82.2	97.3	106.9	119.7	139.0	159.8	182.7	
Di(2-chloroethoxy) methane	$C_5H_{10}Cl_2O_2$	53.0	80.4	94.0	109.5	125.5	135.8	149.6	170.0	192.0	215.0	
Dichloroethoxymethylsilane	$C_3H_8Cl_2OSi$	−33.8	−12.1	−1.3	+11.3	24.4	32.6	44.1	61.0	80.3	100.6	
1,2-Dichloro-3-ethylbenzene	$C_8H_8Cl_2$	46.0	75.0	90.0	105.9	123.8	135.0	149.8	172.0	197.0	222.1	−40.8
1,2-Dichloro-4-ethylbenzene	$C_8H_8Cl_2$	47.0	77.2	92.3	109.6	127.5	139.0	153.3	176.0	201.7	226.6	−76.4
1,4-Dichloro-2-ethylbenzene	$C_8H_8Cl_2$	38.5	68.0	83.2	99.8	118.0	129.0	144.0	166.2	191.5	216.3	−61.2
cis-1,2-Dichloroethylene	$C_2H_2Cl_2$	−58.4	−39.2	−29.9	−19.4	−7.9	−0.5	+9.5	24.6	41.0	59.0	−80.5
trans-1,2-Dichloro ethylene	$C_2H_2Cl_2$	−65.4	−47.2	−38.0	−28.0	−17.0	−10.0	−0.2	+14.3	30.8	47.8	−50.0

Table 3-8. Vapor Pressures of Organic Compounds, up to 1 Atm.—(*Continued*)

Compound: Name	Compound: Formula	Pressure, mm. Hg: 1	5	10	20	40	60	100	200	400	760	Melting point, °C.
		Temperature, °C.										
Di(2-chloroethyl) ether	$C_4H_8Cl_2O$	23.5	49.3	62.0	76.0	91.5	101.5	114.5	134.0	155.4	178.5	
Dichlorofluoromethane	$CHCl_2F$	−91.3	−75.5	−67.5	−58.6	−48.8	−42.6	−33.9	−20.9	−6.2	+8.9	
1,5-Dichlorohexamethyltrisiloxane	$C_6H_{18}Cl_2O_2Si_3$	26.0	52.0	65.1	79.0	94.8	105.0	118.2	138.3	160.2	184.0	−135
Dichloromethylphenylsilane	$C_7H_8Cl_2Si$	35.7	63.5	77.4	92.4	109.5	120.0	134.2	155.5	180.2	205.5	−53.0
1,1-Dichloro-2-methylpropane	$C_4H_8Cl_2$	−31.0	−8.4	+2.6	14.6	28.2	37.0	48.2	65.8	85.4	106.0	
1,2-Dichloro-2-methylpropane	$C_4H_8Cl_2$	−25.8	−4.2	+6.7	18.7	32.0	40.2	51.7	68.9	87.8	108.0	
1,3-Dichloro-2-methylpropane	$C_4H_8Cl_2$	−3.0	+20.6	32.0	44.8	58.6	67.5	78.8	96.1	115.4	135.0	
2,4-Dichlorophenol	$C_6H_4Cl_2O$	53.0	80.0	92.8	107.7	123.4	133.5	146.0	165.2	187.5	210.0	
2,6-Dichlorophenol	$C_6H_4Cl_2O$	59.5	87.6	101.0	115.5	131.6	141.8	154.6	175.5	197.7	220.0	45.0
α,α-Dichlorophenylacetonitrile	$C_8H_5Cl_2N$	56.0	84.0	98.1	113.8	130.0	141.0	154.5	176.2	199.5	223.5	
Dichlorophenylarsine	$C_6H_5AsCl_2$	61.8	100.0	116.0	133.1	151.0	163.2	178.9	202.8	228.8	256.5	
1,2-Dichloropropane	$C_3H_6Cl_2$	−38.5	−17.0	−6.1	+6.0	19.4	28.0	39.4	57.0	76.0	96.8	
2,3-Dichlorostyrene	$C_8H_6Cl_2$	61.0	90.1	104.6	120.5	137.8	149.0	163.5	185.7	210.0	235.0	
2,4-Dichlorostyrene	$C_8H_6Cl_2$	53.5	82.2	97.4	111.8	129.2	140.0	153.8	176.0	200.0	225.0	
2,5-Dichlorostyrene	$C_8H_6Cl_2$	55.5	83.9	98.2	114.0	131.0	142.0	155.8	178.0	202.5	227.0	
2,6-Dichlorostyrene	$C_8H_6Cl_2$	47.8	75.7	90.0	105.5	122.4	133.3	147.6	169.0	193.5	217.0	
3,4-Dichlorostyrene	$C_8H_6Cl_2$	57.2	86.0	100.4	116.2	133.7	144.6	158.2	181.5	205.7	230.0	
3,5-Dichlorostyrene	$C_8H_6Cl_2$	53.5	82.2	97.4	111.8	129.2	140.0	153.8	176.0	200.0	225.0	
1,2-Dichlorotetraethylbenzene	$C_{14}H_{20}Cl_2$	105.6	138.7	155.0	172.5	192.2	204.8	220.7	245.6	272.8	302.0	
1,4-Dichlorotetraethylbenzene	$C_{14}H_{20}Cl_2$	91.7	126.1	143.8	162.0	183.2	195.8	212.0	238.5	265.8	296.5	
1,2-Dichloro-1,1,2,2-tetrafluoroethane	$C_2Cl_2F_4$	−95.4	−80.0	−72.3	−63.5	−53.7	−47.5	−39.1	−26.3	−12.0	+3.5	
Dichloro-4-tolylsilane	$C_7H_8Cl_2Si$	46.2	71.7	84.2	97.8	113.2	122.6	135.5	153.5	175.2	196.3	−94
3,4-Dichloro-α,α,α-trifluorotoluene	$C_7H_3Cl_2F_3$	11.0	38.3	52.2	67.3	84.0	95.0	109.2	129.0	150.5	172.8	
Dicyclopentadiene	$C_{10}H_8$	......	34.1	47.6	62.0	77.9	88.0	101.7	121.8	144.2	166.6	−12.1
Diethoxydimethylsilane	$C_6H_{16}O_2Si$	−19.1	+2.4	13.3	25.3	38.0	46.3	57.6	74.2	93.2	113.5	32.9
Diethoxydiphenylsilane	$C_{16}H_{20}O_2Si$	111.5	142.8	157.6	174.3	193.2	205.0	220.0	243.8	259.7	296.0	
Diethyl adipate	$C_{10}H_{18}O_4$	74.0	106.6	123.0	138.3	154.6	165.8	179.0	198.2	219.1	240.0	
Diethylamine	$C_4H_{11}N$	......	......	−33.0	−22.6	−11.3	−4.0	+6.0	21.0	38.0	55.5	−21
N-Diethylaniline	$C_{10}H_{15}N$	49.7	78.0	91.9	107.2	123.6	133.8	147.3	168.2	192.4	215.5	−38.9
Diethyl arsanilate	$C_{10}H_{16}AsNO_3$	38.0	62.6	74.8	88.0	102.6	111.8	123.8	141.9	161.0	181.0	−34.4
1,2-Diethylbenzene	$C_{10}H_{14}$	22.3	48.7	62.0	76.4	92.5	102.6	116.2	136.7	159.0	183.5	
1,3-Diethylbenzene	$C_{10}H_{14}$	20.7	46.8	59.9	74.5	90.4	100.7	114.4	134.8	156.9	181.1	−31.4
1,4-Diethylbenzene	$C_{10}H_{14}$	20.7	47.1	60.3	74.7	91.1	101.3	115.3	136.1	159.0	183.8	−83.9
Diethyl carbonate	$C_5H_{10}O_3$	−10.1	+12.3	23.8	36.0	49.5	57.9	69.7	86.5	105.8	125.8	−43.2
cis-Diethyl citraconate	$C_9H_{14}O_4$	59.8	88.3	103.0	118.2	135.7	146.2	160.0	182.3	206.5	230.3	−43
Diethyl dioxosuccinate	$C_8H_{10}O_6$	70.0	98.0	112.0	126.8	143.8	153.7	167.7	188.0	210.8	233.5	
Diethylene glycol	$C_4H_{10}O_3$	91.8	120.0	133.8	148.0	164.3	174.0	187.5	207.0	226.5	244.8	
Diethyleneglycol-bis-chloroacetate	$C_8H_{12}Cl_2O_5$	148.3	180.0	195.8	212.0	229.0	239.5	252.0	271.5	291.8	313.0	
Diethylene glycol dimethyl ether Di(2-methoxyethyl) ether	$C_6H_{14}O_3$	13.0	37.6	50.0	63.0	77.5	86.8	99.5	118.0	138.5	159.8	
glycol ethyl ether	$C_6H_{14}O_3$	45.3	72.0	85.8	100.3	116.7	126.8	140.3	159.0	180.3	201.9	
Diethyl ether	$C_4H_{10}O$	−74.3	−56.9	−48.1	−38.5	27.7	−21.8	−11.5	+2.2	17.9	34.6	
ethylmalonate	$C_9H_{16}O_4$	50.8	77.8	91.6	106.0	122.4	132.4	146.0	166.0	188.7	211.5	−116.3
fumarate	$C_8H_{12}O_4$	53.2	81.2	95.3	110.2	126.7	137.7	151.1	172.2	195.8	218.5	
glutarate	$C_9H_{16}O_4$	65.6	94.7	109.7	125.4	142.8	153.2	167.8	189.5	212.8	237.0	+0.6
Diethylhexadecylamine	$C_{20}H_{43}N$	139.8	175.8	194.0	213.5	235.0	248.5	265.5	292.8	324.6	355.0	
Diethyl itaconate	$C_9H_{14}O_4$	51.3	80.2	95.2	111.0	128.2	139.9	154.3	177.5	203.1	227.9	
ketone (3-pentanone)	$C_5H_{10}O$	−12.7	+7.5	17.2	27.9	39.4	46.7	56.2	70.6	86.3	102.7	
malate	$C_8H_{14}O_5$	80.7	110.4	125.3	141.2	157.8	169.0	183.9	205.3	229.5	253.4	−42
maleate	$C_8H_{12}O_4$	57.3	85.6	100.0	115.3	131.8	142.4	156.0	177.8	201.7	225.0	
malonate	$C_7H_{12}O_4$	40.0	67.5	81.3	95.9	113.3	123.0	136.2	155.5	176.8	198.9	
mesaconate	$C_9H_{14}O_4$	62.8	91.0	105.3	120.3	137.3	147.9	161.6	183.2	205.8	229.0	−49.8
oxalate	$C_6H_{10}O_4$	47.4	71.8	83.8	96.8	110.6	119.7	130.8	147.9	166.2	185.7	
phthalate	$C_{12}H_{14}O_4$	108.8	140.7	156.0	173.6	192.1	204.1	219.5	243.0	267.5	294.0	−40.6
sebacate	$C_{14}H_{26}O_4$	125.3	156.2	172.1	189.8	207.5	218.4	234.4	255.8	280.3	305.5	
2,5-Diethylstyrene	$C_{12}H_{16}$	49.7	78.4	92.6	108.5	125.8	136.8	151.0	173.2	198.0	223.0	1.3
Diethyl succinate	$C_8H_{14}O_4$	54.6	83.0	96.6	111.7	127.8	138.2	151.1	171.7	193.8	216.5	
isosuccinate	$C_8H_{14}O_4$	39.8	66.7	80.0	94.7	111.0	121.4	134.8	155.1	177.7	201.3	−20.8
sulfate	$C_4H_{10}O_4S$	47.0	74.0	87.7	102.1	118.0	128.6	142.5	162.5	185.5	209.5	
sulfide	$C_4H_{10}S$	−39.6	−18.6	−8.0	+3.5	16.1	24.2	35.0	51.3	69.7	88.0	−25.0
sulfite	$C_4H_{10}O_3S$	10.0	34.2	46.4	59.7	74.2	83.8	96.3	115.8	137.0	159.0	−99.5
d-Diethyl tartrate	$C_8H_{14}O_6$	102.0	133.0	148.0	164.2	182.3	194.0	208.5	230.4	254.8	280.0	
dl-Diethyl tartrate	$C_8H_{14}O_6$	100.0	131.7	147.2	163.8	181.7	193.2	208.0	230.0	254.3	280.0	17
3,5-Diethyltoluene	$C_{11}H_{16}$	34.0	61.5	75.3	90.2	107.0	117.7	131.7	152.4	176.5	200.7	
Diethylzinc	$C_4H_{10}Zn$	−22.4	0.0	+11.7	24.2	38.0	47.2	59.1	77.0	97.3	118.0	
l-Dihydrocarvone	$C_{10}H_{16}O$	46.6	75.5	90.0	106.0	123.7	134.7	149.7	171.8	197.0	223.0	−28
Dihydrocitronellol	$C_{10}H_{22}O$	68.0	91.7	103.0	115.0	127.6	136.7	145.9	160.2	176.8	193.5	
1,4-Dihydroxyanthraquinone	$C_{14}H_8O_4$	196.7	239.8	259.8	282.0	307.4	323.3	344.5	377.8	413.0	450.0	
Dimethylacetylene (2-butyne)	C_4H_6	−73.0	−57.9	−50.5	−42.5	−33.9	−27.8	−18.8	−5.0	+10.6	27.2	194
Dimethylamine	C_2H_7N	−87.7	−72.2	−64.6	−56.0	−46.7	−40.7	−32.6	−20.4	−7.1	+7.4	−32.5
N,N-Dimethylaniline	$C_8H_{11}N$	29.5	56.3	70.0	84.8	101.6	111.9	125.8	146.5	169.2	193.1	−96
imethyl arsanilate	$C_8H_{12}AsNO_3$	15.0	39.6	51.8	65.0	79.7	88.6	101.0	119.8	140.3	160.5	+2.5
Di(α-methylbenzyl) ether	$C_{16}H_{18}O$	96.7	128.3	144.0	160.3	179.6	191.5	206.8	229.7	254.8	281.0	
2,2-Dimethylbutane	C_6H_{14}	−69.3	−50.7	−41.5	−31.1	−19.5	−12.1	−2.0	+13.4	31.0	49.7	
2,3-Dimethylbutane	C_6H_{14}	−63.6	−44.5	−34.9	−24.1	−12.4	−4.9	+5.4	21.1	39.0	58.0	−99.8
Dimethyl citraconate	$C_7H_{10}O_4$	50.8	78.2	91.8	106.5	122.6	132.7	145.8	165.8	188.0	210.5	−128.2
1,1-Dimethylcyclohexane	C_8H_{16}	−24.4	−1.4	+10.3	23.0	37.3	45.7	57.9	76.2	97.2	119.5	
cis-1,2-Dimethylcyclohexane	C_8H_{16}	−15.9	+7.3	18.4	31.1	45.3	54.4	66.8	85.6	107.0	129.7	−34
crans-1,2-Dimethylcyclohexane	C_8H_{16}	−21.1	+1.7	13.0	25.6	39.7	48.7	61.0	79.6	100.9	123.4	−50.0
crans-1,3-Dimethylcyclohexane	C_8H_{16}	−19.4	+3.4	14.9	27.4	41.4	50.4	62.5	81.0	102.1	124.4	−88.0
cis-1,3-Dimethylcyclohexane	C_8H_{16}	−22.7	0.0	+11.2	23.6	37.5	46.4	58.5	76.9	97.8	120.1	−92.0
cis-1,4-Dimethylcyclohexane	C_8H_{16}	−20.0	+3.2	14.5	27.1	41.1	50.1	62.3	80.8	101.9	124.3	−76.2
trans-1,4-Dimethylcyclohexane	C_8H_{16}	−24.3	−1.7	+10.1	22.6	36.5	45.4	57.6	76.0	97.0	119.3	−87.4
Dimethyl ether	C_2H_6O	−115.7	−101.1	−93.3	−85.2	−76.2	−70.4	−62.7	−50.9	−37.8	−23.7	−36.9
2,2-Dimethylhexane	C_8H_{18}	−29.7	−7.9	+3.1	15.0	28.2	36.7	48.2	65.7	85.6	106.8	−138.5
2,3-Dimethylhexane	C_8H_{18}	−23.0	−1.1	+9.9	22.1	35.6	44.2	56.0	73.8	94.1	115.6	
2,4-Dimethylhexane	C_8H_{18}	−26.9	−5.3	+5.2	17.2	30.5	39.0	50.6	68.1	88.2	109.4	
2,5-Dimethylhexane	C_8H_{18}	−26.7	−5.5	+5.3	17.2	30.4	38.9	50.5	68.0	87.9	109.1	−90.7

Table 3-8. Vapor Pressures of Organic Compounds, up to 1 Atm.—*(Continued)*

Compound		Pressure, mm. Hg										Melting point, °C.
Name	Formula	1	5	10	20	40	60	100	200	400	760	
		Temperature °C.										
3,3-Dimethylhexane	C_8H_{18}	−25.8	−4.4	+6.1	18.2	31.7	40.4	52.5	70.0	90.4	112.0	
3,4-Dimethylhexane	C_8H_{18}	−22.1	+0.2	11.3	23.5	37.1	45.8	57.7	75.6	96.0	117.7	
Dimethyl itaconate	$C_7H_{10}O_4$	69.3	94.0	106.6	119.7	133.7	142.6	153.7	171.0	189.8	208.0	38
l-Dimethyl malate	$C_6H_{10}O_5$	75.4	104.0	118.3	133.8	150.1	160.4	175.1	196.3	219.5	242.6	
Dimethyl maleate	$C_6H_8O_4$	45.7	73.0	86.4	101.3	117.2	127.1	140.4	160.0	182.2	205.0	
malonate	$C_5H_8O_4$	35.0	59.8	72.0	85.0	100.0	109.7	121.9	140.0	159.8	180.7	−62
trans-Dimethyl mesaconate	$C_7H_{10}O_4$	46.8	74.0	87.8	102.1	118.0	127.8	141.5	161.0	183.5	206.0	
2,7-Dimethyloctane	$C_{10}H_{22}$	+6.3	30.5	42.3	55.8	71.2	80.8	93.9	114.0	136.0	159.7	−52.8
Dimethyl oxalate	$C_4H_6O_4$	20.0	44.0	56.0	69.4	83.6	92.8	104.8	123.3	143.3	163.3	
2,2-Dimethylpentane	C_7H_{16}	−49.0	−28.7	−18.7	−7.5	+5.0	13.0	23.9	40.3	59.2	79.2	−123.7
2,3-Dimethylpentane	C_7H_{16}	−42.0	−20.8	−10.3	+1.1	13.9	22.1	33.3	50.1	69.4	89.8	−135
2,4-Dimethylpentane	C_7H_{16}	−48.0	−27.4	−17.1	−5.9	+6.5	14.5	25.4	41.8	60.6	80.5	−119.5
3,3-Dimethylpentane	C_7H_{16}	−45.9	−25.0	−14.4	−2.9	+9.9	18.1	29.3	46.2	65.5	86.1	−135.0
2,3-Dimethylphenol (2,3-xylenol)	$C_8H_{10}O$	56.0	83.8	97.6	112.0	129.2	139.5	152.2	173.0	196.0	218.0	75
2,4-Dimethylphenol (2,4-xylenol)	$C_8H_{10}O$	51.8	78.0	91.3	105.0	121.5	131.0	143.0	161.5	184.2	211.5	25.5
2,5-Dimethylphenol (2,5-xylenol)	$C_8H_{10}O$	51.8	78.0	91.3	105.0	121.5	131.0	143.0	161.5	184.2	211.5	74.5
3,4-Dimethylphenol (3,4-xylenol)	$C_8H_{10}O$	66.2	93.8	107.7	122.0	138.0	148.0	161.0	181.5	203.6	225.2	62.5
3.5-Dimethylphenol (3,5-xylenol)	$C_8H_{10}O$	62.0	89.2	102.4	117.0	133.3	143.5	156.0	176.2	197.8	219.5	68
Dimethylphenylsilane	$C_8H_{12}Si$	+5.3	30.3	42.6	56.2	71.4	81.3	94.2	114.2	136.4	159.3	
Dimethyl phthalate	$C_{10}H_{10}O_4$	100.3	131.8	147.6	164.0	182.8	194.0	210.0	232.7	257.8	283.7	
3,5-Dimethyl-1,2-pyrone	$C_7H_8O_2$	78.6	107.6	122.0	136.4	152.7	163.8	177.5	198.0	221.0	245.0	51.5
4,6-Dimethylresorcinol	$C_8H_{10}O_2$	49.0	76.8	90.7	105.8	122.5	133.2	147.3	167.8	192.0	215.0	
Dimethyl sebacate	$C_{12}H_{22}O_4$	104.0	139.8	156.2	175.8	196.0	208.0	222.6	245.0	269.6	293.5	38
2,4-Dimethylstyrene	$C_{10}H_{12}$	34.2	61.9	75.8	90.8	107.7	118.0	132.3	153.2	177.5	202.0	
2,5-Dimethylstyrene	$C_{10}H_{12}$	29.0	55.9	69.0	84.0	100.2	110.7	124.7	145.6	168.7	193.0	
α,α-Dimethylsuccinic anhydride	$C_6H_8O_3$	61.4	88.1	102.0	116.3	132.3	142.4	155.3	175.8	197.5	219.5	
Dimethyl sulfide	C_2H_6S	−75.6	−58.0	−49.2	−39.4	−28.4	−21.4	−12.0	+2.6	18.7	36.0	−83.2
d-Dimethyl tartrate	$C_6H_{10}O_6$	102.1	133.2	148.2	164.3	182.4	193.8	208.8	230.5	255.0	280.0	61.5
dl-Dimethyl tartrate	$C_6H_{10}O_6$	100.4	131.8	147.5	164.0	182.4	193.8	209.5	232.3	257.4	282.0	89
N,N-Dimethyl-2-toluidine	$C_9H_{13}N$	28.8	54.1	66.2	80.2	95.0	105.2	118.1	138.3	161.5	184.8	−61
N,N-Dimethyl-4-toluidine	$C_9H_{13}N$	50.1	74.3	86.7	100.0	116.3	126.4	140.3	161.6	185.4	209.5	
Di(nitrosomethyl) amine	$C_2H_5N_3O_2$	+3.2	27.8	40.0	53.7	68.2	77.7	90.3	110.0	131.3	153.0	
Diosphenol	$C_{10}H_{16}O_2$	66.7	95.4	109.0	124.0	141.2	151.3	165.6	186.2	209.5	232.0	
1,4-Dioxane	$C_4H_8O_2$	−35.8	−12.8	−1.2	+12.0	25.2	33.8	45.1	62.3	81.8	101.1	10
Dipentene	$C_{10}H_{16}$	14.0	40.4	53.8	68.2	84.3	94.6	108.3	128.2	150.5	174.6	
Diphenylamine	$C_{12}H_{11}N$	108.3	141.7	157.0	175.2	194.3	206.9	222.8	247.5	274.1	302.0	52.9
Diphenyl carbinol (benzhydrol)	$C_{13}H_{12}O$	110.0	145.0	162.0	180.9	200.0	212.0	227.5	250.0	275.6	301.0	68.5
chlorophosphate	$C_{12}H_{10}ClPO_3$	121.5	160.5	182.0	203.8	227.9	244.2	265.0	299.5	337.2	378.0	
disulfide	$C_{12}H_{10}S_2$	131.6	164.0	180.0	197.0	214.8	226.2	241.3	262.6	285.8	310.0	61
1,2-Diphenylethane (dibenzyl)	$C_{14}H_{14}$	86.8	119.8	136.0	153.7	173.7	186.0	202.8	227.8	255.0	284.0	51.5
Diphenyl ether	$C_{12}H_{10}O$	66.1	97.8	114.0	130.8	150.0	162.0	178.8	203.3	230.7	258.5	27
1,1-Diphenylethylene	$C_{14}H_{12}$	87.4	119.6	135.0	151.8	170.8	183.4	198.6	222.8	249.8	277.0	
trans-Diphenylethylene	$C_{14}H_{12}$	113.2	145.8	161.0	179.8	199.0	211.5	227.4	251.7	278.3	306.5	124
1,1-Diphenylhydrazine	$C_{12}H_{12}N_2$	126.0	159.3	176.1	194.0	213.5	225.9	242.5	267.2	294.0	322.2	44
Diphenylmethane	$C_{13}H_{12}$	76.0	107.4	122.8	139.8	157.8	170.2	186.3	210.7	237.5	264.5	26.5
Diphenyl sulfide	$C_{12}H_{10}S$	96.1	129.0	145.0	162.0	182.8	194.8	211.8	236.8	263.9	292.5	
Diphenyl-2-tolyl thiophosphate	$C_{18}H_{17}O_3PS$	159.7	179.8	201.6	215.5	230.6	240.4	252.5	270.3	290.0	310.0	
1,2-Dipropoxyethane	$C_8H_{18}O_2$	−38.8	−10.3	+5.0	22.3	42.3	55.8	74.2	103.8	140.0	180.0	
1,2-Diisopropylbenzene	$C_{12}H_{18}$	40.0	67.8	81.8	96.8	114.0	124.3	138.7	159.8	184.3	209.0	
1,3-Diisopropylbenzene	$C_{12}H_{18}$	34.7	62.3	76.0	91.2	107.9	118.2	132.3	153.7	177.6	202.0	−105
Dipropylene glycol	$C_6H_{14}O_3$	73.8	102.1	116.2	131.3	147.4	156.5	169.9	189.9	210.5	231.8	
Dipropyleneglycol monobutyl ether	$C_{10}H_{22}O_3$	64.7	92.0	106.0	120.4	136.3	146.3	159.8	180.0	203.8	227.0	
isopropyl ether	$C_9H_{20}O_3$	46.0	72.8	86.2	100.8	117.0	126.8	140.3	160.0	183.1	205.6	
Di-n-propyl ether	$C_6H_{14}O$	−43.3	−22.3	−11.8	0.0	+13.2	21.6	33.0	50.3	69.5	89.5	−122
Diisopropyl ether	$C_6H_{14}O$	−57.0	−37.4	−27.4	−16.7	−4.5	+3.4	13.7	30.0	48.2	67.5	−60
Di-n-propyl ketone (4-heptanone)	$C_7H_{14}O$	23.0	44.4	55.0	66.2	78.1	85.8	96.0	111.2	127.3	143.7	−32.6
Di-n-propyl oxalate	$C_8H_{14}O_4$	53.4	80.2	93.9	108.6	124.6	134.8	148.1	168.0	190.3	213.5	
Diisopropyl oxalate	$C_8H_{14}O_4$	43.2	69.0	81.9	95.6	110.5	120.0	132.6	151.2	171.8	193.5	
Di-n-propyl succinate	$C_{10}H_{18}O_4$	77.5	107.6	122.2	138.0	154.8	166.0	180.3	202.5	226.5	250.8	
Di-n-propyl d-tartrate	$C_{10}H_{18}O_6$	115.6	147.7	163.5	180.4	199.7	211.7	227.0	250.1	275.6	303.0	
Diisopropyl d-tartrate	$C_{10}H_{18}O_6$	103.7	133.7	148.2	164.0	181.8	192.6	207.3	228.2	251.8	275.0	
Divinyl acetylene (1,5-hexadiene-3-yne)	C_6H_6	−45.1	−24.4	−14.0	−2.8	+10.0	18.1	29.5	46.0	64.4	84.0	
1,3-Divinylbenzene	$C_{10}H_{10}$	32.7	60.0	73.8	88.7	105.5	116.0	130.0	151.4	175.2	199.5	−66.9
Docosane	$C_{22}H_{46}$	157.8	195.4	213.0	233.5	254.5	268.3	286.0	314.2	343.5	376.0	44.5
n-Dodecane	$C_{12}H_{26}$	47.8	75.8	90.0	104.6	121.7	132.1	146.2	167.2	191.0	216.2	−9.6
1-Dodecene	$C_{12}H_{24}$	47.2	74.0	87.8	102.4	118.6	128.5	142.3	162.2	185.5	208.0	−31.5
n-Dodecyl alcohol	$C_{12}H_{26}O$	91.0	120.2	134.7	150.0	167.2	177.8	192.0	213.0	235.7	259.0	24
Dodecylamine	$C_{12}H_{27}N$	82.8	111.8	127.8	141.6	157.4	168.0	182.1	203.0	225.0	248.0	
Dodecyltrimethylsilane	$C_{15}H_{34}Si$	91.2	122.1	137.7	153.8	172.1	184.2	199.5	222.0	248.0	273.0	
Elaidic acid	$C_{18}H_{34}O_2$	171.3	206.7	223.5	242.3	260.8	273.0	288.0	312.4	337.0	362.0	51.5
Epichlorohydrin	C_3H_5ClO	−16.5	+5.6	16.6	29.0	42.0	50.6	62.0	79.3	98.0	117.9	−25.6
1,2-Epoxy-2-methylpropane	C_4H_8O	−69.0	−50.0	−40.3	−29.5	−17.3	−9.7	+1.2	17.5	36.0	55.5	
Erucic acid	$C_{22}H_{42}O_2$	206.7	239.7	254.5	270.6	289.1	300.2	314.4	336.5	358.8	381.5	33.5
Estragole (p-methoxy allyl benzene)	$C_{10}H_{12}O$	52.6	80.0	93.7	108.4	124.6	135.2	148.5	168.7	192.0	215.0	
Ethane	C_2H_6	−159.5	−148.5	−142.9	−136.7	−129.8	−125.4	−119.3	−110.2	−99.7	−88.6	−183.2
Ethoxydimethylphenylsilane	$C_{10}H_{16}OSi$	36.3	63.1	76.2	91.0	107.2	127.5	131.4	151.5	175.0	199.5	
Ethoxytrimethylsilane	$C_5H_{14}OSi$	−50.9	−31.0	−20.7	−9.8	+3.7	11.5	22.1	38.1	56.3	75.7	
Ethoxytriphenylsilane	$C_{20}H_{20}OSi$	167.0	198.2	213.5	230.0	247.0	258.3	273.5	295.0	319.5	344.0	
Ethyl acetate	$C_4H_8O_2$	−43.4	−23.5	−13.5	−3.0	+9.1	16.6	27.0	42.0	59.3	77.1	−82.4
acetoacetate	$C_6H_{10}O_3$	28.5	54.0	67.3	81.1	96.2	106.0	118.5	138.0	158.2	180.8	−45
Ethylacetylene (1-butyne)	C_4H_6	−92.5	−76.7	−68.7	−59.9	−50.0	−43.4	−34.9	−21.6	−6.9	+8.7	−130
Ethyl acrylate	$C_5H_8O_2$	−29.5	−8.7	+2.0	13.0	26.0	33.5	44.5	61.5	80.0	99.5	−71.2
α-Ethylacrylic acid	$C_5H_8O_2$	47.0	70.7	82.0	94.4	108.1	116.7	127.5	144.0	160.7	179.2	
α-Ethylacrylonitrile	C_5H_7N	−29.0	−6.4	+5.0	17.7	31.8	40.6	53.0	71.6	92.2	114.0	
Ethyl alcohol (ethanol)	C_2H_6O	−31.3	−12.0	−2.3	+8.0	19.0	26.0	34.9	48.4	63.5	78.4	−112
Ethylamine	C_2H_7N	−82.3	−66.4	−58.3	−48.6	−39.8	−33.4	−25.1	−12.3	+2.0	16.6	−80.6
4-Ethylaniline	$C_8H_{11}N$	52.0	80.0	93.8	109.0	125.7	136.0	149.8	170.6	194.2	217.4	−4
N-Ethylaniline	$C_8H_{11}N$	38.5	66.4	80.6	96.0	113.2	123.6	137.3	156.9	180.8	204.0	−63.5

Table 3-8. Vapor Pressures of Organic Compounds, up to 1 Atm.—(*Continued*)

Compound		Pressure, mm. Hg										Melting point, °C.
Name	Formula	1	5	10	20	40	60	100	200	400	760	
		Temperature, °C.										
2-Ethylanisole	$C_9H_{12}O$	29.7	55.9	69.0	83.1	98.8	109.0	122.3	142.1	164.2	187.1	
3-Ethylanisole	$C_9H_{12}O$	33.7	60.3	73.9	88.5	104.8	115.5	129.2	149.7	172.8	196.5	
4-Ethylanisole	$C_9H_{12}O$	33.5	60.2	73.9	88.5	104.7	115.4	128.4	149.2	172.3	196.5	
Ethylbenzene	C_8H_{10}	−9.8	+13.9	25.9	38.6	52.8	61.8	74.1	92.7	113.8	136.2	−94.9
Ethyl benzoate	$C_9H_{10}O_2$	44.0	72.0	86.0	101.4	118.2	129.0	143.2	164.8	188.4	213.4	−34.6
benzoylacetate	$C_{11}H_{12}O_3$	107.6	136.4	150.3	166.8	181.8	191.9	205.0	223.8	244.7	265.0	
bromide	C_2H_5Br	−74.3	−56.4	−47.5	−37.8	−26.7	−19.5	−10.0	+4.5	21.0	38.4	−117.8
α-bromoisobutyrate	$C_6H_{11}BrO_2$	10.6	35.8	48.0	61.8	77.0	86.7	99.8	119.7	141.2	163.6	
n-butyrate	$C_6H_{12}O_2$	−18.4	+4.0	15.3	27.8	41.5	50.1	62.0	79.8	100.0	121.0	−93.3
isobutyrate	$C_6H_{12}O_2$	−24.3	−2.4	+8.4	20.6	33.8	42.3	53.5	71.0	90.0	110.0	−88.2
Ethylcamphoronic anhydride	$C_{11}H_{16}O_5$	118.2	149.8	165.0	181.8	199.8	211.5	226.6	248.5	272.8	298.0	
Ethyl isocaproate	$C_8H_{16}O_2$	11.0	35.8	48.0	61.7	76.3	85.8	98.4	117.8	139.2	160.4	
carbamate	$C_3H_7NO_2$	.....	65.8	77.8	91.0	105.6	114.8	126.2	144.2	164.0	184.0	49
carbanilate	$C_9H_{11}NO_2$	107.8	131.8	143.7	155.5	168.8	177.3	187.9	203.8	220.0	237.0	52.5
Ethylcetylamine	$C_{18}H_{39}N$	133.2	168.2	186.0	205.5	226.5	239.8	256.8	283.3	313.0	342.0	
Ethyl chloride	C_2H_5Cl	−89.8	−73.9	−65.8	−56.8	−47.0	−40.6	−32.0	−18.6	−3.9	+12.3	−139
chloroacetate	$C_4H_7ClO_2$	+1.0	25.4	37.5	50.4	65.2	74.0	86.0	103.8	123.8	144.2	−26
chloroglyoxylate	$C_4H_5ClO_3$	−5.1	+18.0	29.9	42.0	56.0	65.2	76.6	94.5	114.7	135.0	
α-chloropropionate	$C_5H_9ClO_2$	+6.6	30.2	41.9	54.3	68.2	77.3	89.3	107.2	126.2	146.5	
trans-cinnamate	$C_{11}H_{12}O_2$	87.6	108.5	134.0	150.3	169.2	181.2	196.0	219.3	245.0	271.0	12
3-Ethylcumene	$C_{11}H_{16}$	28.3	55.5	68.8	83.6	99.9	110.2	124.3	145.4	168.2	193.0	
4-Ethylcumene	$C_{11}H_{16}$	31.5	58.4	72.0	86.7	103.3	113.8	127.2	148.3	171.8	195.8	
Ethyl cyanoacetate	$C_5H_7NO_2$	67.8	93.5	106.0	119.8	133.8	142.1	152.8	169.8	187.8	206.0	
Ethylcyclohexane	C_8H_{16}	−14.5	+9.2	20.6	33.4	47.6	56.7	69.0	87.8	109.1	131.8	−111.3
Ethylcyclopentane	C_7H_{14}	−32.2	−10.8	−0.1	+11.7	25.0	33.4	45.0	62.4	82.3	103.4	−138.6
Ethyl dichloroacetate	$C_4H_6Cl_2O_2$	9.6	34.0	46.3	59.5	74.0	83.6	96.1	115.2	135.9	156.5	
N,N-diethyloxamate	$C_8H_{15}NO_3$	76.0	106.3	121.7	137.7	154.4	166.0	180.3	202.8	226.5	252.0	
N-Ethyldiphenylamine	$C_{14}H_{15}N$	98.3	130.2	146.0	162.8	182.0	193.7	209.8	233.0	258.8	286.0	
Ethylene	C_2H_4	−168.3	−158.3	−153.2	−147.6	−141.3	−137.3	−131.8	−123.4	−113.9	−103.7	−169
Ethylene-bis-(chloroacetate)	$C_6H_8Cl_2O_4$	112.0	142.4	158.0	173.5	191.0	201.8	215.0	237.3	259.5	283.5	
Ethylene chlorohydrin (2-chloroethanol)	C_2H_5ClO	−4.0	+19.0	30.3	42.5	56.0	64.1	75.0	91.8	110.0	128.8	−69
diamine (1,2-ethanediamine)	$C_2H_8N_2$	−11.0	+10.5	21.5	33.0	45.8	53.8	62.5	81.0	99.0	117.2	8.5
dibromide (1,2-dibromethane)	$C_2H_4Br_2$	−27.0	+4.7	18.6	32.7	48.0	57.9	70.4	89.8	110.1	131.5	10
dichloride (1,2-dichloroethane)	$C_2H_4Cl_2$	−44.5	−24.0	−13.6	−2.4	+10.0	18.1	29.4	45.7	64.0	82.4	−35.3
glycol (1,2-ethanediol)	$C_2H_6O_2$	53.0	79.7	92.1	105.8	120.0	129.5	141.8	158.5	178.5	197.3	−15.6
glycol diethyl ether (1,2-diethoxyethane)	$C_6H_{14}O_2$	−33.5	−10.2	+1.6	14.7	29.7	39.0	51.8	71.8	94.1	119.5	
glycol dimethyl ether (1,2-dimethoxyethane)	$C_4H_{10}O_2$	−48.0	−26.2	−15.3	−3.0	+10.7	19.7	31.8	50.0	70.8	93.0	
glycol monomethyl ether (2-methoxyethanol)	$C_3H_8O_2$	−13.5	+10.2	22.0	34.3	47.8	56.4	68.0	85.3	104.3	124.4	
oxide	C_2H_4O	−89.7	−73.8	−65.7	−56.6	−46.9	−40.7	−32.1	−19.5	−4.9	+10.7	−111.3
Ethyl α-ethylacetoacetate	$C_8H_{14}O_3$	40.5	67.3	80.2	94.6	110.3	120.6	133.8	153.2	175.6	198.0	
fluoride	C_2H_5F	−117.0	−103.8	−97.7	−90.0	−81.8	−76.4	−69.3	−58.0	−45.5	−32.0	
formate	$C_3H_6O_2$	−60.5	−42.2	−33.0	−22.7	−11.5	−4.3	−5.4	20.0	37.1	54.3	−79
2-furoate	$C_7H_8O_3$	37.6	63.8	77.1	91.5	107.5	117.5	130.4	150.1	172.5	195.0	34
glycolate	$C_4H_8O_3$	14.3	38.8	50.5	63.9	78.1	87.6	99.8	117.8	138.0	158.2	
3-Ethylhexane	C_8H_{18}	−20.0	+2.1	12.8	25.0	38.5	47.1	58.9	76.7	97.0	118.5	
2-Ethylhexyl acrylate	$C_{11}H_{20}O_2$	50.0	77.7	91.8	106.3	123.7	134.0	147.9	168.2	192.2	216.0	
Ethylidene chloride (1,1-dichloroethane)	$C_2H_4Cl_2$	−60.7	−41.9	−32.3	−21.9	−10.2	−2.9	+7.2	22.4	39.8	57.4	−96.7
fluoride (1,1-difluoroethane)	$C_2H_4F_2$	−112.5	−98.4	−91.7	−84.1	−75.8	−70.4	−63.2	−52.0	−39.5	−26.5	−117
Ethyl iodide	C_2H_5I	−54.4	−34.3	−24.3	−13.1	−0.9	+7.2	18.0	34.1	52.3	72.4	−105
Ethyl l-leucinate	$C_8H_{17}NO_2$	27.8	57.3	72.1	88.0	106.0	117.8	131.8	149.8	167.3	184.0	
Ethyl levulinate	$C_7H_{12}O_3$	47.3	74.0	87.3	101.8	117.7	127.6	141.3	160.2	183.0	206.2	
Ethyl mercaptan (ethanethiol)	C_2H_6S	−76.7	−59.1	−50.2	−40.7	−29.8	−22.4	−13.0	+1.5	17.7	35.0	−121
Ethyl methylcarbamate	$C_4H_9NO_2$	26.5	51.0	63.2	76.1	91.0	100.0	112.0	130.0	149.8	170.0	
Ethyl methyl ether	C_3H_8O	−91.0	−75.6	−67.8	−59.1	−49.4	−43.3	−34.8	−22.0	−7.8	+7.5	
1-Ethylnaphthalene	$C_{12}H_{12}$	70.0	101.4	116.8	133.8	152.0	164.1	180.0	204.6	230.8	258.1	−27
Ethyl α-naphthyl ketone (1-propionaphthone)	$C_{13}H_{12}O$	124.0	155.5	171.0	188.1	206.9	218.2	233.5	255.5	280.2	306.0	
Ethyl 3-nitrobenzoate	$C_9H_9NO_4$	108.1	140.2	155.0	173.6	192.6	205.0	220.3	244.6	270.6	298.0	47
3-Ethylpentane	C_7H_{16}	−37.8	−17.0	−6.8	+4.7	17.5	25.7	36.9	53.8	73.0	93.5	−118.6
4-Ethylphenetole	$C_{10}H_{14}O$	48.5	75.7	89.5	103.8	119.8	129.8	143.5	163.2	185.7	208.0	
2-Ethylphenol	$C_8H_{10}O$	46.2	73.4	87.0	101.5	117.9	127.9	141.8	161.6	184.5	207.5	−45
3-Ethylphenol	$C_8H_{10}O$	60.0	86.8	100.2	114.5	130.0	139.8	152.0	171.8	193.3	214.0	−4
4-Ethylphenol	$C_8H_{10}O$	59.3	86.5	100.2	115.0	131.3	141.7	154.2	175.0	197.4	219.0	46.5
Ethyl phenyl ether (phenetole)	$C_8H_{10}O$	18.1	43.7	56.4	70.3	86.6	95.4	108.4	127.9	149.8	172.0	−30.2
Ethyl propionate	$C_5H_{10}O_2$	−28.0	−7.2	+3.4	14.3	27.2	35.1	45.2	61.7	79.8	99.1	−72.6
Ethyl propyl ether	$C_5H_{12}O$	−64.3	−45.0	−35.0	−24.0	−12.0	−4.0	+6.8	23.3	41.6	61.7	
Ethyl salicylate	$C_9H_{10}O_3$	61.2	90.0	104.2	119.3	136.7	147.6	161.5	183.7	207.0	231.5	1.3
3-Ethylstyrene	$C_{10}H_{12}$	28.3	55.0	68.3	82.8	99.2	109.6	123.2	144.0	167.2	191.5	
4-Ethylstyrene	$C_{10}H_{12}$	26.0	52.7	66.3	80.8	97.3	107.6	121.5	142.0	165.0	189.0	
Ethylisothiocyanate	C_3H_5NS	−13.2	+10.6	22.8	36.1	50.8	59.8	71.9	90.0	110.1	131.0	−5.9
2-Ethyltoluene	C_9H_{12}	9.4	34.8	47.6	61.2	76.4	86.0	99.0	119.0	141.4	165.1	
3-Ethyltoluene	C_9H_{12}	7.2	32.3	44.7	58.2	73.3	82.9	95.9	115.5	137.8	161.3	−95.5
4-Ethyltoluene	C_9H_{12}	7.6	32.7	44.9	58.5	73.6	83.2	96.3	116.1	136.4	162.0	
Ethyl trichloroacetate	$C_4H_5Cl_3O_2$	20.7	45.5	57.7	70.6	85.5	94.4	107.4	125.8	146.0	167.0	
Ethyltrimethylsilane	$C_5H_{14}Si$	−60.6	−41.4	−31.8	−21.0	−9.0	−1.2	+9.2	25.0	42.8	62.0	
Ethyltrimethyltin	$C_5H_{14}Sn$	−30.0	−7.6	+3.8	16.1	30.0	38.4	50.0	67.3	87.6	108.8	
Ethyl isovalerate	$C_7H_{14}O_2$	−6.1	+17.0	28.7	41.3	55.2	64.0	75.9	93.8	114.0	134.3	−99.3
2-Ethyl-1,4-xylene	$C_{10}H_{14}$	25.7	52.0	65.6	79.8	96.0	106.2	120.0	140.2	163.1	186.9	
4-Ethyl-1,3-xylene	$C_{10}H_{14}$	26.3	53.0	66.4	80.6	97.2	107.4	121.2	141.8	164.4	188.4	
5-Ethyl-1,3-xylene	$C_{10}H_{14}$	22.1	48.8	62.1	76.5	92.6	103.0	116.5	137.4	159.6	183.7	
Eugenol	$C_{10}H_{12}O_2$	78.4	108.1	123.0	138.7	155.8	167.3	182.2	204.7	228.3	253.5	
iso-Eugenol	$C_{10}H_{12}O_2$	86.3	117.0	132.4	149.0	167.0	178.2	194.0	217.2	242.3	267.5	−10
Eugenyl acetate	$C_{12}H_{14}O_3$	101.6	132.3	148.0	164.2	183.0	194.0	209.7	232.5	257.4	282.0	295
Fencholic acid	$C_{10}H_{16}O_2$	101.7	128.7	142.3	155.8	171.8	181.5	194.0	215.0	237.8	264.1	19
d-Fenchone	$C_{10}H_{16}O$	28.0	54.7	68.3	83.0	99.5	109.8	123.6	144.0	166.8	191.0	5
dl-Fenchyl alcohol	$C_{10}H_{18}O$	45.8	70.3	82.1	95.6	110.8	120.2	132.3	150.0	173.2	201.0	35
Fluorene	$C_{13}H_{10}$	.....	129.3	146.0	164.2	185.2	197.8	214.7	240.3	268.6	295.0	113
Fluorobenzene	C_6H_5F	−43.4	−22.8	−12.4	−1.2	+11.5	19.6	30.4	47.2	65.7	84.7	−42.1

Table 3-8. Vapor Pressures of Organic Compounds, up to 1 Atm.—*(Continued)*

Compound		Pressure, mm. Hg										Melting point, °C.
		1	5	10	20	40	60	100	200	400	760	
Name	Formula	Temperature, °C.										
2-Fluorotoluene	C_7H_7F	−24.2	−2.2	+8.9	21.4	34.7	43.7	55.3	73.0	92.8	114.0	−80
3-Fluorotoluene	C_7H_7F	−22.4	−0.3	+11.0	23.4	37.0	45.8	57.5	75.4	95.4	116.0	−110.8
4-Fluorotoluene	C_7H_7F	−21.8	+0.3	11.8	24.0	37.8	46.5	58.1	76.0	96.1	117.0	
Formaldehyde	CH_2O	......	......	−88.0	−79.6	−70.6	−65.0	−57.3	−46.0	−33.0	−19.5	−92
Formamide	CH_3NO	70.5	96.3	109.5	122.5	137.5	147.0	157.5	175.5	193.5	210.5	
Formic acid	CH_2O_2	−20.0	−5.0	+2.1	10.3	24.0	32.4	43.8	61.4	80.3	100.6	8.2
trans-Fumaryl chloride	$C_4H_2Cl_2O_2$	+15.0	38.5	51.8	65.0	79.5	89.0	101.0	120.0	140.0	160.0	
Furfural (2-furaldehyde)	$C_5H_4O_2$	18.5	42.6	54.8	67.8	82.1	91.5	103.4	121.8	141.8	161.8	
Furfuryl alcohol	$C_5H_6O_2$	31.8	56.0	68.0	81.0	95.7	104.0	115.9	133.1	151.8	170.0	
Geraniol	$C_{10}H_{18}O$	69.2	96.8	110.0	125.6	141.8	151.5	165.3	185.6	207.8	230.0	
Geranyl acetate	$C_{12}H_{20}O_2$	73.5	102.7	117.9	133.0	150.0	160.3	175.2	196.3	219.8	243.3	
Geranyl n-butyrate	$C_{14}H_{24}O_2$	96.8	125.2	139.0	153.8	170.1	180.2	193.8	214.0	235.0	257.4	
Geranyl isobutyrate	$C_{14}H_{24}O_2$	90.9	119.6	133.0	147.9	164.0	174.0	187.7	207.6	228.5	251.0	
Geranyl formate	$C_{11}H_{18}O_2$	61.8	90.3	104.3	119.8	136.2	147.2	160.7	182.6	205.8	230.0	
Glutaric acid	$C_5H_8O_4$	155.5	183.8	196.0	210.5	226.3	235.5	247.0	265.0	283.5	303.0	97.5
Glutaric anhydride	$C_5H_6O_3$	100.8	133.3	149.5	166.0	185.5	196.2	212.5	236.5	261.0	287.0	
Glutaronitrile	$C_5H_6N_2$	91.3	123.7	140.0	156.5	176.4	189.5	205.5	230.0	257.3	286.2	
Glutaryl chloride	$C_5H_6Cl_2O_2$	56.1	84.0	97.8	112.3	128.3	139.1	151.8	172.4	195.3	217.0	
Glycerol	$C_3H_8O_3$	125.5	153.8	167.2	182.2	198.0	208.0	220.1	240.0	263.0	290.0	17.9
Glycerol dichlorohydrin (1,3-dichloro-2-propanol)	$C_3H_6Cl_2O$	28.0	52.2	64.7	78.0	93.0	102.0	114.8	133.3	153.5	174.3	
Glycol diacetate	$C_6H_{10}O_4$	38.3	64.1	77.1	90.8	106.1	115.8	128.0	147.8	168.3	190.5	−31
Glycolide (1,4-dioxane-2,6-dione)	$C_4H_4O_4$	......	103.0	116.6	132.0	148.6	158.2	173.2	194.0	217.0	240.0	97
Guaicol (2-methoxyphenol)	$C_7H_8O_2$	52.4	79.1	92.0	106.0	121.6	131.0	144.0	162.7	184.1	205.0	28.3
Heneicosane	$C_{21}H_{44}$	152.6	188.0	205.4	223.2	243.4	255.3	272.0	296.5	323.8	350.5	40.4
Heptacosane	$C_{27}H_{56}$	211.7	248.6	266.8	284.6	305.7	318.3	333.5	359.4	385.0	410.6	59.5
Heptadecane	$C_{17}H_{36}$	115.0	145.2	160.0	177.7	195.8	207.3	223.0	247.8	274.5	303.0	22.5
Heptaldehyde (enanthaldehyde)	$C_7H_{14}O$	12.0	32.7	43.0	54.0	66.3	74.0	84.0	102.0	125.5	155.0	−42
n-Heptane	C_7H_{16}	−34.0	−12.7	−2.1	+9.5	22.3	30.6	41.8	58.7	78.0	98.4	−90.6
Heptanoic acid (enanthic acid)	$C_7H_{14}O_2$	78.0	101.3	113.2	125.6	139.5	148.5	160.0	179.5	199.6	221.5	−10
1-Heptanol	$C_7H_{16}O$	42.4	64.3	74.7	85.8	99.8	108.0	119.5	136.6	155.6	175.8	34.6
Heptanoyl chloride (enanthyl chloride)	$C_7H_{13}ClO$	34.2	54.6	64.6	75.0	86.4	93.5	102.7	116.3	130.7	145.0	
2-Heptene	C_7H_{14}	−35.8	−14.1	−3.5	+8.3	21.5	30.0	41.3	58.6	78.1	98.5	
Heptylbenzene	$C_{13}H_{20}$	64.0	94.6	110.0	126.0	144.0	154.8	170.2	193.3	217.8	244.0	
Heptyl cyanide (enanthonitrile)	$C_7H_{13}N$	21.0	47.8	61.6	76.3	92.6	103.0	116.8	137.7	160.0	184.6	
Hexachlorobenzene	C_6Cl_6	114.4	149.3	166.4	185.7	206.0	219.0	235.5	258.5	283.5	309.4	230
Hexachloroethane	C_2Cl_6	32.7	49.8	73.5	87.6	102.3	112.0	124.2	143.1	163.8	185.6	186.6
Hexacosane	$C_{26}H_{54}$	204.0	240.0	257.4	275.8	295.2	307.8	323.2	348.4	374.6	399.8	56.6
Hexadecane	$C_{16}H_{34}$	105.3	135.2	149.8	164.7	181.3	193.2	208.5	231.7	258.3	287.5	18.5
1-Hexadecene	$C_{16}H_{32}$	101.6	131.7	146.2	162.0	178.8	190.8	205.3	226.8	250.0	274.0	4
n-Hexadecyl alcohol (cetyl alcohol)	$C_{16}H_{34}O$	122.7	158.3	177.8	197.8	219.8	234.3	251.7	280.2	312.7	344.0	49.3
n-Hexadecylamine (cetylamine)	$C_{16}H_{35}N$	123.6	157.8	176.0	195.7	215.7	228.8	245.8	272.2	300.4	330.0	
Hexaethylbenzene	$C_{18}H_{30}$	......	134.3	150.3	168.0	187.7	199.7	216.0	241.7	268.5	298.3	130
n-Hexane	C_6H_{14}	−53.9	−34.5	−25.0	−14.1	−2.3	+5.4	15.8	31.6	49.6	68.7	−95.3
1-Hexanol	$C_6H_{14}O$	24.4	47.2	58.2	70.3	83.7	92.0	102.8	119.6	138.0	157.0	−51.6
2-Hexanol	$C_6H_{14}O$	14.6	34.8	45.0	55.9	67.9	76.0	87.3	103.7	121.8	139.9	
3-Hexanol	$C_6H_{14}O$	+2.5	25.7	36.7	49.0	62.2	70.7	81.8	98.3	117.0	135.5	
1-Hexene	C_6H_{12}	−57.5	−38.0	−28.1	−17.2	−5.0	+2.8	13.0	29.0	46.8	66.0	−98.5
n-Hexyl levulinate	$C_{11}H_{20}O_3$	90.0	120.0	134.7	150.2	167.8	179.0	193.6	215.7	241.0	266.8	
n-Hexyl phenyl ketone (enanthophenone)	$C_{13}H_{18}O$	100.0	130.3	145.5	161.0	178.9	189.8	204.2	225.0	248.3	271.3	
Hydrocinnamic acid	$C_9H_{10}O_2$	102.2	133.5	148.7	165.0	183.3	194.0	209.0	230.8	255.0	279.8	48.5
Hydrogen cyanide (hydrocyanic acid)	CHN	−71.0	−55.3	−47.7	−39.7	−30.9	−25.1	−17.8	−5.3	+10.2	25.9	−13.2
Hydroquinone	$C_6H_6O_2$	132.4	153.3	163.5	174.6	192.0	203.0	216.5	238.0	262.5	286.2	170.3
4-Hydroxybenzaldehyde	$C_7H_6O_2$	121.2	153.2	169.7	186.8	206.0	217.5	233.5	256.8	282.6	310.0	115.5
α-Hydroxyisobutyric acid	$C_4H_8O_3$	73.5	98.5	110.5	123.8	138.0	146.4	157.7	175.2	193.8	212.0	79
α-Hydroxybutyronitrile	C_5H_9NO	41.0	65.8	77.8	90.7	104.8	113.9	125.0	142.0	159.8	178.8	
4-Hydroxy-3-methyl-2-butanone	$C_5H_{10}O_2$	44.6	69.3	81.0	94.0	108.2	117.4	129.0	146.5	165.5	185.0	
4-Hydroxy-4-methyl-2-pentanone	$C_6H_{12}O_2$	22.0	46.7	58.8	72.0	86.7	96.0	108.2	126.8	147.5	167.9	−47
3-Hydroxypropionitrile	C_3H_5NO	58.7	87.8	102.0	117.9	134.1	144.7	157.7	178.0	200.0	221.0	
Indene	C_9H_8	16.4	44.3	58.5	73.9	90.7	100.8	114.7	135.6	157.8	181.6	−2
Iodobenzene	C_6H_5I	24.1	50.6	64.0	78.3	94.4	105.0	118.3	139.8	163.9	188.6	−28.5
Iodononane	$C_9H_{19}I$	70.0	96.2	109.0	123.0	138.1	147.7	159.8	179.0	199.3	219.5	
2-Iodotoluene	C_7H_7I	37.2	65.9	79.8	95.6	112.4	123.8	138.1	160.0	185.7	211.0	
α-Ionone	$C_{13}H_{20}O$	79.5	108.8	123.0	139.0	155.6	166.3	181.2	202.5	225.2	250.0	
Isoprene	C_5H_8	−79.8	−62.3	−53.3	−43.5	−32.6	−25.4	−16.0	−1.2	+15.4	32.6	−146.7
Lauraldehyde	$C_{12}H_{24}O$	77.7	108.4	123.7	140.2	157.8	168.7	184.5	207.8	231.8	257.0	44.5
Lauric acid	$C_{12}H_{24}O_2$	121.0	150.6	166.0	183.6	201.4	212.7	227.5	249.8	273.8	299.2	48
Levulinaldehyde	$C_5H_8O_2$	28.1	54.9	68.0	82.7	98.3	108.4	121.8	142.0	164.0	187.0	
Levulinic acid	$C_5H_8O_3$	102.0	128.1	141.8	154.1	169.5	178.0	190.2	208.3	227.4	245.8	33.5
d-Limonene	$C_{10}H_{16}$	14.0	40.4	53.8	68.2	84.3	94.6	108.3	128.5	151.4	175.0	−96.9
Linalyl acetate	$C_{12}H_{20}O_2$	55.4	82.5	96.0	111.4	127.7	138.1	151.8	173.3	196.2	220.0	
Maleic anhydride	$C_4H_2O_3$	44.0	63.4	78.7	95.0	111.8	122.0	135.8	155.9	179.5	202.0	58
Menthane	$C_{10}H_{20}$	+9.7	35.7	48.3	62.7	78.3	88.6	102.1	122.7	146.0	169.5	
1-Menthol	$C_{10}H_{20}O$	56.0	83.2	96.0	110.3	126.1	136.1	149.4	168.3	190.2	212.0	42.5
Menthyl acetate	$C_{12}H_{22}O_2$	57.4	85.8	100.0	115.4	132.1	143.2	156.7	178.8	202.8	227.0	
benzoate	$C_{17}H_{24}O_2$	123.2	154.2	170.0	186.3	204.3	215.8	230.4	253.2	277.1	301.0	54.5
formate	$C_{11}H_{20}O_2$	47.3	75.8	90.0	105.8	123.0	133.8	148.0	169.8	194.2	219.0	
Mesityl oxide	$C_6H_{10}O$	−8.7	+14.1	26.0	37.9	51.7	60.4	72.1	90.0	109.8	130.0	−59
Methacrylic acid	$C_4H_6O_2$	25.5	48.5	60.0	72.7	86.4	95.3	106.6	123.9	142.5	161.0	15
Methacrylonitrile	C_4H_5N	−44.5	−23.3	−12.5	−0.6	+12.8	21.5	32.8	50.0	70.3	90.3	
Methane	CH_4	−205.9	−199.0	−195.5	−191.8	−187.7	−185.1	−181.4	−175.5	−168.8	−161.5	−182.5
Methanethiol	CH_4S	−90.7	−75.3	−67.5	−58.8	−49.2	−43.1	−34.8	−22.1	−7.9	+6.8	−121
Methoxyacetic acid	$C_3H_6O_3$	52.5	79.3	92.0	106.5	122.0	131.8	144.5	163.5	184.2	204.0	
N-Methylacetanilide	$C_9H_{11}NO$	......	103.8	118.6	135.1	152.2	164.2	179.8	202.3	227.4	253.0	102
Methyl acetate	$C_3H_6O_2$	−57.2	−38.6	−29.3	−19.1	−7.9	−0.5	+9.4	24.0	40.0	57.8	−98.7
acetylene (propyne)	C_3H_4	−111.0	−97.5	−90.5	−82.9	−74.3	−68.8	−61.3	−49.8	−37.2	−23.3	−102.7
acrylate	$C_4H_6O_2$	−43.7	−23.6	−13.5	−2.7	+9.2	17.3	28.0	43.9	61.8	80.2	
alcohol (methanol)	CH_4O	−44.0	−25.3	−16.2	−6.0	+5.0	12.1	21.2	34.8	49.9	64.7	−97.8
Methylamine	CH_5N	−95.8	−81.3	−73.8	−65.9	−56.9	−51.3	−43.7	−32.4	−19.7	−6.3	−93.5

Table 3-8. Vapor Pressures of Organic Compounds, up to 1 Atm.—(*Continued*)

Compound		Pressure, mm. Hg										Melting point, °C.
Name	Formula	1	5	10	20	40	60	100	200	400	760	
		Temperature, °C.										
N-Methylaniline	C_7H_9N	36.0	62.8	76.2	90.5	106.0	115.8	129.8	149.3	172.0	195.5	−57
Methyl anthranilate	$C_8H_9NO_2$	77.6	109.0	124.2	141.5	159.7	172.0	187.8	212.4	238.5	266.5	24
benzoate	$C_8H_8O_2$	39.0	64.4	77.3	91.8	107.8	117.4	130.8	151.4	174.7	199.5	−12.5
2-Methylbenzothiazole	C_8H_7NS	70.0	97.5	111.2	125.5	141.2	150.4	163.9	183.2	204.5	225.5	15.4
α-Methylbenzyl alcohol	$C_8H_{10}O$	49.0	75.2	88.0	102.1	117.8	127.4	140.3	159.0	180.7	204.0	
Methyl bromide	CH_3Br	−96.3	−80.6	−72.8	−64.0	−54.2	−48.0	−39.4	−26.5	−11.9	+3.6	−93
2-Methyl-1-butene	C_5H_{10}	−89.1	−72.8	−64.3	−54.8	−44.1	−37.3	−28.0	−13.8	+2.5	20.2	−135
2-Methyl-2-butene	C_5H_{10}	−75.4	−57.0	−47.9	−37.9	−26.7	−19.4	−9.9	+4.9	21.6	38.5	−133
Methyl isobutyl carbinol (2-methyl-4-pentanol)	$C_6H_{14}O$	−0.3	+22.1	33.3	45.4	58.2	67.0	78.0	94.9	113.5	131.7	
n-butyl ketone (2-hexanone)	$C_6H_{12}O$	+7.7	28.8	38.8	50.0	62.0	69.8	79.8	94.3	111.0	127.5	−56.9
isobutyl ketone (4-methyl-2-pentanone)	$C_6H_{12}O$	−1.4	+19.7	30.0	40.8	52.8	60.4	70.4	85.6	102.0	119.0	−84.7
n-butyrate	$C_5H_{10}O_2$	−26.8	−5.5	+5.0	16.7	29.6	37.4	48.0	64.3	83.1	102.3	
isobutyrate	$C_5H_{10}O_2$	−34.1	−13.0	−2.9	+8.4	21.0	28.9	39.6	55.7	73.6	92.6	−84.7
caprate	$C_{11}H_{22}O_2$	63.7	93.5	108.0	123.0	139.0	148.6	161.5	181.6	202.9	224.0	−18
caproate	$C_7H_{14}O_2$	+5.0	30.0	42.0	55.4	70.0	79.7	91.4	109.8	129.8	150	
caprylate	$C_9H_{18}O_2$	34.2	61.7	74.9	89.0	105.3	115.3	128.0	148.1	170.0	193.0	−40
chloride	CH_3Cl	......	−99.5	−92.4	−84.8	−76.0	−70.4	−63.0	−51.2	−38.0	−24.0	−97.7
chloroacetate	$C_3H_5ClO_2$	−2.9	19.0	30.0	41.5	54.5	63.0	73.5	90.5	109.5	130.3	−31.9
cinnamate	$C_{10}H_{10}O_2$	77.4	108.1	123.0	140.0	157.9	170.0	185.8	209.6	235.0	263.0	33.4
α-Methylcinnamic acid	$C_{10}H_{10}O_2$	125.7	155.0	169.8	185.2	201.8	212.0	224.8	245.0	266.8	288.0	
Methylcyclohexane	C_7H_{14}	−35.9	−14.0	−3.2	+8.7	22.0	30.5	42.1	59.6	79.6	100.9	−126.4
Methylcyclopentane	C_6H_{12}	−53.7	−33.8	−23.7	−12.8	−0.6	+7.2	17.9	34.0	52.3	71.8	−142.4
Methylcyclopropane	C_4H_8	−96.0	−80.6	−72.8	−64.0	−54.2	−48.0	−39.3	−26.0	−11.3	+4.5	
Methyl n-decyl ketone (n-dodecan-2-one)	$C_{12}H_{24}O$	77.1	106.0	120.4	136.0	152.4	163.8	177.5	199.0	222.5	246.5	
dichloroacetate	$C_3H_4Cl_2O_2$	3.2	26.7	38.1	50.7	64.7	73.6	85.4	103.2	122.6	143.0	
N-Methyldiphenylamine	$C_{13}H_{13}N$	103.5	134.0	149.7	165.8	184.0	195.4	210.1	232.8	257.0	282.0	−7.6
Methyl n-dodecyl ketone (2-tetradecanone)	$C_{14}H_{28}O$	99.3	130.0	145.5	161.3	179.8	191.4	206.0	228.2	253.3	278.0	
Methylene bromide (dibromomethane)	CH_2Br_2	−35.1	−13.2	−2.4	+9.7	23.3	31.6	42.3	58.5	79.0	98.6	−52.8
chloride (dichloromethane)	CH_2Cl_2	−70.0	−52.1	−43.3	−33.4	−22.3	−15.7	−6.3	+8.0	24.1	40.7	−96.7
Methyl ethyl ketone (2-butanone)	C_4H_8O	−48.3	−28.0	−17.7	−6.5	+6.0	14.0	25.0	41.6	60.0	79.6	−85.9
2-Methyl-3-ethylpentane	C_8H_{18}	−24.0	−1.8	+9.5	21.7	35.2	43.9	55.7	73.6	94.0	115.6	−114.5
3-Methyl-3-ethylpentane	C_8H_{18}	−23.9	−1.4	+9.9	22.3	36.2	45.0	57.1	75.3	96.2	118.3	−90
Methyl fluoride	CH_3F	−147.3	−137.0	−131.6	−125.9	−119.1	−115.0	−109.0	−99.9	−89.5	−78.2	
formate	$C_2H_4O_2$	−74.2	−57.0	−48.6	−39.2	−28.7	−21.9	−12.9	+0.8	16.0	32.0	−99.8
α-Methylglutaric anhydride	$C_6H_8O_3$	93.8	125.4	141.8	157.7	177.5	189.9	205.0	229.1	255.5	282.5	
Methyl glycolate	$C_3H_6O_3$	+9.6	33.7	45.3	58.1	72.3	81.8	93.7	111.8	131.7	151.5	
2-Methylheptadecane	$C_{18}H_{38}$	119.8	152.0	168.7	186.0	204.8	216.3	231.5	254.5	279.8	306.5	
2-Methylheptane	C_8H_{18}	−21.0	+1.3	12.3	24.4	37.9	46.6	58.3	76.0	96.2	117.6	−109.5
3-Methylheptane	C_8H_{18}	−19.8	+2.6	13.3	25.4	38.9	47.6	59.4	77.1	97.4	118.9	−120.8
4-Methylheptane	C_8H_{18}	−20.4	+1.5	12.4	24.5	38.0	46.6	58.3	76.1	96.3	117.7	−121.1
2-Methyl-2-heptene	C_8H_{16}	−16.1	+6.7	17.8	30.4	44.0	52.8	64.6	82.3	102.2	122.5	
6-Methyl-3-hepten-2-ol	$C_8H_{16}O$	41.6	65.0	76.7	89.3	102.7	111.5	122.6	139.5	156.6	175.5	
6-Methyl-5-hepten-2-ol	$C_8H_{16}O$	41.9	66.0	77.8	90.4	104.0	112.8	123.8	140.0	156.6	174.3	
2-Methylhexane	C_7H_{16}	−40.4	−19.5	−9.1	+2.3	14.9	23.0	34.1	50.8	69.8	90.0	−118.2
3-Methylhexane	C_7H_{16}	−39.0	−18.1	−7.8	+3.6	16.4	24.5	35.6	52.4	71.6	91.9	
Methyl iodide	CH_3I	......	−55.0	−45.8	−35.6	−24.2	−16.9	−7.0	+8.0	25.3	42.4	−64.4
laurate	$C_{13}H_{26}O_2$	87.8	117.9	133.2	149.0	166.0	176.8	190.8	......	......	......	5
levulinate	$C_6H_{10}O_3$	39.8	66.4	79.7	93.7	109.5	119.3	133.0	153.4	175.8	197.7	
methacrylate	$C_5H_8O_2$	−30.5	−10.0	+1.0	11.0	25.5	34.5	47.0	63.0	82.0	101.0	
myristate	$C_{15}H_{30}O_2$	115.0	145.7	160.8	177.8	195.8	207.5	222.6	245.3	269.8	295.8	18.5
α-naphthyl ketone (1-acetonaphthone)	$C_{12}H_{10}O$	115.6	146.3	161.5	178.4	196.8	208.6	223.8	246.7	270.5	295.5	
β-naphthyl ketone (2-acetonaphthone)	$C_{12}H_{10}O$	120.2	152.3	168.5	185.7	203.8	214.7	229.8	251.6	275.8	301.0	55.5
n-nonyl ketone (undecan-2-one)	$C_{11}H_{22}O$	68.2	95.5	108.9	123.1	139.0	148.6	161.0	181.2	202.3	224.0	15
palmitate	$C_{17}H_{34}O_2$	134.3	166.8	184.3	202.0	......	......	......	......	......	......	30
n-pentadecyl ketone (2-heptdecanone)	$C_{17}H_{34}O$	129.6	161.6	178.0	196.4	214.3	226.7	242.0	265.8	291.7	319.5	
2-Methylpentane	C_6H_{14}	−60.9	−41.7	−32.1	−21.4	−9.7	−1.9	+8.1	24.1	41.6	60.3	−154
3-Methylpentane	C_6H_{14}	−59.0	−39.8	−30.1	−19.4	−7.3	+0.1	10.5	26.5	44.2	63.3	−118
2-Methyl-1-pentanol	$C_6H_{14}O$	15.4	38.0	49.6	61.6	74.7	83.4	94.2	111.3	129.8	147.9	
2-Methyl-2-pentanol	$C_6H_{14}O$	−4.5	+16.8	27.6	38.8	51.3	58.8	69.2	85.0	102.6	121.2	−103
Methyl n-pentyl ketone (2-heptanone)	$C_7H_{14}O$	19.3	43.6	55.5	67.7	81.2	89.8	100.0	116.1	133.2	150.2	
phenyl ether (anisole)	C_7H_8O	+5.4	30.0	42.2	55.8	70.7	80.1	93.0	112.3	133.8	155.5	−37.3
2-Methylpropene	C_4H_8	−105.1	−96.5	−81.9	−73.4	−63.8	−57.7	−49.3	−36.7	−22.2	−6.9	−140.3
Methyl propionate	$C_4H_8O_2$	−42.0	−21.5	−11.8	−1.0	+11.0	18.7	29.0	44.2	61.8	79.8	−87.5
4-Methylpropiophenone	$C_{10}H_{12}O$	59.6	89.3	103.8	120.2	138.0	149.3	164.2	187.4	212.7	238.5	
2-Methylpropionyl bromide	C_4H_7BrO	13.5	38.4	50.6	64.1	79.4	88.8	101.6	120.5	141.7	163.0	
Methyl propyl ether	$C_4H_{10}O$	−72.2	−54.3	−45.4	−35.4	−24.3	−17.4	−8.1	+6.0	22.5	39.1	
n-propyl ketone (2-pentanone)	$C_5H_{10}O$	−12.0	+8.0	17.9	28.5	39.8	47.3	56.8	71.0	86.8	103.3	−77.8
isopropyl ketone (3-Methyl-2-butanone)	$C_5H_{10}O$	−19.9	−1.0	+8.3	18.3	29.6	36.2	45.5	59.0	73.8	88.9	−92
2-Methylquinoline	$C_{10}H_9N$	75.3	104.0	119.0	134.0	150.8	161.7	176.2	197.8	211.7	246.5	−1
Methyl salicylate	$C_8H_8O_3$	54.0	81.6	95.3	110.0	126.2	136.7	150.0	172.6	197.5	223.2	−8.3
α-Methyl styrene	C_9H_{10}	7.4	34.0	47.1	61.8	77.8	88.3	102.2	121.8	143.0	165.4	−23.2
4-Methyl styrene	C_9H_{10}	16.0	42.0	55.1	69.2	85.0	95.0	108.6	128.7	151.2	175.0	
Methyl n-tetradecyl ketone (2-hexadecanone)	$C_{16}H_{32}O$	109.8	151.5	167.3	184.6	203.7	215.0	230.5	254.4	279.8	307.0	
thiocyanate	C_2H_3NS	−14.0	+9.8	21.6	34.5	49.0	58.1	70.4	89.8	110.8	132.9	−51
isothiocyanate	C_2H_3NS	−34.7	−8.3	+5.4	20.4	38.2	47.5	59.3	77.5	97.8	119.0	35.5
undecyl ketone (2-tridecanone)	$C_{13}H_{26}O$	86.8	117.0	131.8	147.8	165.7	176.6	191.5	214.0	238.3	262.5	28.5
isovalerate	$C_6H_{12}O_2$	−19.2	+2.9	14.0	26.4	39.8	48.2	59.8	77.3	96.7	116.7	
Monovinylacetylene (butenyne)	C_4H_4	−93.2	−77.7	−70.0	−61.3	−51.7	−45.3	−37.1	−24.1	−10.1	+5.3	
Myrcene	$C_{10}H_{16}$	14.5	40.0	53.2	67.0	82.6	92.6	106.0	126.0	148.3	171.5	
Myristadehyde	$C_{14}H_{28}O$	99.0	132.0	148.3	166.2	186.0	198.3	214.5	240.4	267.9	297.8	23.5
Myristic acid (tetradecanoic acid)	$C_{14}H_{28}O_2$	142.0	174.1	190.8	207.6	223.5	237.2	250.5	272.3	294.6	318.0	57.5
Naphthalene	$C_{10}H_8$	52.6	74.2	85.8	101.7	119.3	130.2	145.5	167.7	193.2	217.9	80.2
1-Naphthoic acid	$C_{11}H_8O_2$	156.0	184.0	196.8	211.2	225.0	234.5	245.8	263.5	281.4	300.0	160.5
2-Naphthoic acid	$C_{11}H_8O_2$	160.8	189.7	202.8	216.9	231.5	241.3	252.7	270.3	289.5	308.5	184
1-Naphthol	$C_{10}H_8O$	94.0	125.5	142.0	158.0	177.8	190.0	206.0	229.6	255.8	282.5	96
2-Naphthol	$C_{10}H_8O$	......	128.6	145.5	161.8	181.7	193.7	209.8	234.0	260.6	288.0	122.5
1-Naphthylamine	$C_{10}H_9N$	104.3	137.7	153.8	171.6	191.5	203.8	220.0	244.9	272.2	300.8	50

Table 3-8. Vapor Pressures of Organic Compounds, up to 1 Atm.—(*Continued*)

Compound		Pressure, mm. Hg										Melting point, °C.
Name	Formula	1	5	10	20	40	60	100	200	400	760	
		Temperature, °C.										
2-Naphthylamine	$C_{10}H_9N$	108.0	141.6	157.6	175.8	195.7	208.1	224.3	249.7	277.4	306.1	111.5
Nicotine	$C_{10}H_{14}N_2$	61.8	91.8	107.2	123.7	142.1	154.7	169.5	193.8	219.8	247.3	
2-Nitroaniline	$C_6H_6N_2O_2$	104.0	135.7	150.4	167.7	186.0	197.8	213.0	236.3	260.0	284.5	71.5
3-Nitroaniline	$C_6H_6N_2O_2$	119.3	151.5	167.8	185.5	204.2	216.5	232.1	255.3	280.2	305.7	114
4-Nitroaniline	$C_6H_6N_2O_2$	142.4	177.6	194.4	213.2	234.2	245.9	261.8	284.5	310.2	336.0	146.5
2-Nitrobenzaldehyde	$C_7H_5NO_3$	85.8	117.7	133.4	150.0	168.8	180.7	196.2	220.0	246.8	273.5	40.9
3-Nitrobenzaldehyde	$C_7H_5NO_3$	96.2	127.4	142.8	159.0	177.7	189.5	204.3	227.4	252.1	278.3	58
Nitrobenzene	$C_6H_5NO_2$	44.4	71.6	84.9	99.3	115.4	125.8	139.9	161.2	185.8	210.6	+5.7
Nitroethane	$C_2H_5NO_2$	−21.0	+1.5	12.5	24.8	38.0	46.5	57.8	74.8	94.0	114.0	−90
Nitroglycerin	$C_3H_5N_3O_9$	127	167	188	210	235	251	......	......	......	......	11
Nitromethane	CH_3NO_2	−29.0	−7.9	+2.8	14.1	27.5	35.5	46.6	63.5	82.0	101.2	−29
2-Nitrophenol	$C_6H_5NO_3$	49.3	76.8	90.4	105.8	122.1	132.6	146.4	167.6	191.0	214.5	45
2-Nitrophenyl acetate	$C_8H_7NO_4$	100.0	128.0	142.0	155.8	172.8	181.7	194.1	213.0	233.5	253.0	
1-Nitropropane	$C_3H_7NO_2$	−9.6	+13.5	25.3	37.9	51.8	60.5	72.3	90.2	110.6	131.6	−108
2-Nitropropane	$C_3H_7NO_2$	−18.8	+4.1	15.8	28.2	41.8	50.3	62.0	80.0	99.8	120.3	−93
2-Nitrotoluene	$C_7H_7NO_2$	50.0	79.1	93.8	109.6	126.3	137.6	151.5	173.7	197.7	222.3	−4.1
3-Nitrotoluene	$C_7H_7NO_2$	50.2	81.0	96.0	112.8	130.7	142.5	156.9	180.3	206.8	231.9	15.5
4-Nitrotoluene	$C_7H_7NO_2$	53.7	85.0	100.5	117.7	136.0	147.9	163.0	186.7	212.5	238.3	51.9
4-Nitro-1,3-xylene (4-nitro-m-xylene)	$C_8H_9NO_2$	65.6	95.0	109.8	125.8	143.3	153.8	168.5	191.7	217.5	244.0	+2
Nonacosane	$C_{29}H_{60}$	234.2	269.8	286.4	303.6	323.2	334.8	350.0	373.2	397.2	421.8	63.8
Nonadecane	$C_{19}H_{40}$	133.2	166.3	183.5	200.8	220.0	232.8	248.0	271.8	299.8	330.0	32
n-Nonane	C_9H_{20}	+1.4	25.8	38.0	51.2	66.0	75.5	88.1	107.5	128.2	150.8	−53.7
1-Nonanol	$C_9H_{20}O$	59.5	86.1	99.7	113.8	129.0	139.0	151.3	170.5	192.1	213.5	−5
2-Nonanone	$C_9H_{18}O$	32.1	59.0	72.3	87.2	103.4	113.8	127.4	148.2	171.2	195.0	−19
Octacosane	$C_{28}H_{58}$	226.5	260.3	277.4	295.4	314.2	326.8	341.8	364.8	388.9	412.5	61.6
Octadecane	$C_{18}H_{38}$	119.6	152.1	169.6	187.5	207.4	219.7	236.0	260.6	288.0	317.0	28
n-Octane	C_8H_{18}	−14.0	+8.3	19.2	31.5	45.1	53.8	65.7	83.6	104.0	125.6	−56.8
n-Octanol (1-octanol)	$C_8H_{18}O$	54.0	76.5	88.3	101.0	115.2	123.3	135.2	152.0	173.8	195.2	−15.4
2-Octanone	$C_8H_{16}O$	23.6	48.4	60.9	74.3	89.8	99.0	111.7	130.4	151.0	172.9	−16
n-Octyl acrylate	$C_{11}H_{20}O_2$	58.5	87.7	102.0	117.8	135.6	145.6	159.1	180.2	204.0	227.0	
iodide (1-Iodooctane)	$C_8H_{17}I$	45.8	74.8	90.0	105.9	123.8	135.4	150.0	173.3	199.3	225.5	−45.9
Oleic acid	$C_{18}H_{34}O_2$	176.5	208.5	223.0	240.0	257.2	269.8	286.0	309.8	334.7	360.0	14
Palmitaldehyde	$C_{16}H_{32}O$	121.6	154.6	171.8	190.0	210.0	222.6	239.5	264.1	292.3	321.0	34
Palmitic acid	$C_{16}H_{32}O_2$	153.6	188.1	205.8	223.8	244.4	256.0	271.5	298.7	326.0	353.8	64.0
Palmitonitrile	$C_{16}H_{31}N$	134.3	168.3	185.8	204.2	223.8	236.6	251.5	277.1	304.5	332.0	31
Pelargonic acid	$C_9H_{18}O_2$	108.2	126.0	137.4	149.8	163.7	172.3	184.4	203.1	227.5	253.5	12.5
Pentachlorobenzene	C_6HCl_5	98.6	129.7	144.3	160.0	178.5	190.1	205.5	227.0	251.6	276.0	85.5
Pentachloroethane	C_2HCl_5	+1.0	27.2	39.8	53.9	69.9	80.0	93.5	114.0	137.2	160.5	−22
Pentachloroethylbenzene	$C_8H_5Cl_5$	96.2	130.0	148.0	166.0	186.2	199.0	216.0	241.8	269.3	299.0	
Pentachlorophenol	C_6HCl_5O	......	......	......	192.2	211.2	223.4	239.6	261.8	285.0	309.3	188.5
Pentacosane	$C_{25}H_{52}$	194.2	230.0	248.2	266.1	285.6	298.4	314.0	339.0	365.4	390.3	53.3
Pentadecane	$C_{15}H_{32}$	91.6	121.0	135.4	150.2	167.7	178.4	194.0	216.1	242.8	270.5	10
1,3-Pentadiene	C_5H_8	−71.8	−53.8	−45.0	−34.8	−23.4	−16.5	−6.7	+8.0	24.7	42.1	
1,4-Pentadiene	C_5H_8	−83.5	−66.2	−57.1	−47.7	−37.0	−30.0	−20.6	−6.7	+8.3	26.1	
Pentaethylbenzene	$C_{16}H_{26}$	86.0	120.0	135.8	152.4	171.9	184.2	200.0	224.1	250.2	277.0	
Pentaethylchlorobenzene	$C_{16}H_{25}Cl$	90.0	123.8	140.7	158.1	178.2	191.0	208.0	230.3	257.2	285.0	
n-Pentane	C_5H_{12}	−76.6	−62.5	−50.1	−40.2	−29.2	−22.2	−12.6	+1.9	18.5	36.1	−129.7
iso-Pentane (2-methylbutane)	C_5H_{12}	−82.9	−65.8	−57.0	−47.3	−36.5	−29.6	−20.2	−5.9	+10.5	27.8	−159.7
neo-Pentane (2,2-dimethylpropane)	C_5H_{12}	−102.0	−85.4	−76.7	−67.2	−56.1	−49.0	−39.1	−23.7	−7.1	+9.5	−16.6
2,3,4-Pentanetriol	$C_5H_{12}O_3$	155.0	189.3	204.5	220.5	239.6	249.8	263.5	284.5	307.0	327.2	
1-Pentene	C_5H_{10}	−80.4	−63.3	−54.5	−46.0	−34.1	−27.1	−17.7	−3.4	+12.8	30.1	
α-Phellandrene	$C_{10}H_{16}$	20.0	45.7	58.0	72.1	87.8	97.6	110.6	130.6	152.0	175.0	
Phenanthrene	$C_{14}H_{10}$	118.2	154.3	173.0	193.7	215.8	229.9	249.0	277.1	308.0	340.2	99.5
Phenethyl alcohol (phenyl cellosolve)	$C_8H_{10}O_2$	58.2	85.9	100.0	114.8	130.5	141.2	154.0	175.0	197.5	219.5	
2-Phenetidine	$C_8H_{11}NO$	67.0	94.7	108.6	123.7	139.9	149.8	163.5	184.0	207.0	228.0	
Phenol	C_6H_6O	40.1	62.5	73.8	86.0	100.1	108.4	121.4	139.0	160.0	181.9	40.6
2-Phenoxyethanol	$C_8H_{10}O_2$	78.0	106.6	121.2	136.0	152.2	163.2	176.5	197.6	221.0	245.3	11.6
2-Phenoxyethyl acetate	$C_{10}H_{12}O_3$	82.6	113.5	128.0	144.5	162.3	174.0	189.2	211.3	235.0	259.7	−6.7
Phenyl acetate	$C_8H_8O_2$	38.2	64.8	78.0	92.3	108.1	118.1	131.6	151.2	173.5	195.9	
Phenylacetic acid	$C_8H_8O_2$	97.0	127.0	141.3	156.0	173.6	184.5	198.2	219.5	243.0	265.5	76.5
Phenylacetonitrile	C_8H_7N	60.0	89.0	103.5	119.4	136.3	147.7	161.8	184.2	208.5	233.5	−23.8
Phenylacetyl chloride	C_8H_7ClO	48.0	75.3	89.0	103.6	119.8	129.8	143.5	163.8	186.0	210.0	
Phenyl benzoate	$C_{13}H_{10}O_2$	106.8	141.5	157.8	177.0	197.6	210.8	227.8	254.0	283.5	314.0	70.5
4-Phenyl-3-buten-2-one	$C_{10}H_{10}O$	81.7	112.2	127.4	143.8	161.3	172.6	187.8	211.0	235.4	261.0	41.5
Phenyl isocyanate	C_7H_5NO	10.6	36.0	48.5	62.5	77.7	87.7	100.6	120.8	142.7	165.6	
isocyanide	C_7H_5N	12.0	37.0	49.7	63.4	78.3	88.0	101.0	120.8	142.3	165.0	
Phenylcyclohexane	$C_{12}H_{16}$	67.5	96.5	111.3	126.4	144.0	154.2	169.3	191.3	214.6	240.0	+7.5
Phenyl dichlorophosphate	$C_6H_5Cl_2O_2P$	66.7	95.9	110.0	125.9	143.4	153.6	168.0	189.8	213.0	239.5	
m-Phenylene diamine (1,3-phenylenediamine)	$C_6H_8N_2$	99.8	131.2	147.0	163.8	182.5	194.0	209.9	233.0	259.0	285.5	62.8
Phenylglyoxal	$C_8H_6O_2$	......	75.0	87.8	100.7	115.5	124.2	136.2	153.8	173.5	193.5	73
Phenylhydrazine	$C_6H_8N_2$	71.8	101.6	115.8	131.5	148.2	158.7	173.5	195.4	218.2	243.5	19.5
N-Phenyliminodiethanol	$C_{10}H_{15}NO_2$	145.0	179.2	195.8	213.4	233.0	245.3	260.6	284.5	311.3	337.8	
1-Phenyl-1,3-pentanedione	$C_{11}H_{12}O_2$	98.0	128.5	144.0	159.9	178.0	189.8	204.5	226.7	251.2	276.5	
2-Phenylphenol	$C_{12}H_{10}O$	100.0	131.6	146.2	163.3	180.3	192.2	205.9	227.9	251.8	275.0	56.5
4-Phenylphenol	$C_{12}H_{10}O$	......	......	176.2	193.8	213.0	225.3	240.9	263.2	285.5	308.0	164.5
3-Phenyl-1-propanol	$C_9H_{12}O$	74.7	102.4	116.0	131.2	147.4	156.8	170.3	191.2	212.8	235.0	
Phenyl isothiocyanate	C_7H_5NS	47.2	75.6	89.8	115.5	122.5	133.3	147.7	169.6	194.0	218.5	−21.0
Phorone	$C_9H_{14}O$	42.0	68.3	81.5	95.6	111.3	121.4	134.0	153.5	175.3	197.2	28
iso-Phorone	$C_9H_{14}O$	38.0	66.7	81.2	96.8	114.5	125.6	140.6	163.3	188.7	215.2	
Phosgene (carbonyl chloride)	CCl_2O	−92.9	−77.0	−69.3	−60.3	−50.3	−44.0	−35.6	−22.3	−7.6	+8.3	−104
Phthalic anhydride	$C_8H_4O_3$	96.5	121.3	134.0	151.7	172.0	185.3	202.3	228.0	256.8	284.5	130.8
Phthalide	$C_8H_6O_2$	95.5	127.7	144.0	161.3	181.0	193.5	210.0	234.5	261.8	290.0	73
Phthaloyl chloride	$C_8H_4Cl_2O_2$	86.3	118.3	134.2	151.0	170.0	182.2	197.8	222.0	248.3	275.8	88.5
2-Picoline	C_6H_7N	−11.1	+12.6	24.4	37.4	51.2	59.9	71.4	89.0	108.4	128.8	−70
Pimelic acid	$C_7H_{12}O_4$	163.4	196.2	212.0	229.3	247.0	258.2	272.0	294.5	318.5	342.1	103
α-Pinene	$C_{10}H_{16}$	−1.0	+24.6	37.3	51.4	66.8	76.8	90.1	110.2	132.3	155.0	−55
β-Pinene	$C_{10}H_{16}$	+4.2	30.0	42.3	58.1	71.5	81.2	94.0	114.1	136.1	158.3	
Piperidine	$C_5H_{11}N$	......	−7.0	+3.9	15.8	29.2	37.7	49.0	66.2	85.7	106.0	−9

Table 3-8. Vapor Pressures of Organic Compounds, up to 1 Atm.—(*Continued*)

Compound		Pressure, mm. Hg										Melting point, °C.
Name	Formula	1	5	10	20	40	60	100	200	400	760	
		Temperature, °C.										
Piperonal	$C_8H_6O_3$	87.0	117.4	132.0	148.0	165.7	177.0	191.7	214.3	238.5	263.0	37
Propane	C_3H_8	-128.9	-115.4	-108.5	-100.9	-92.4	-87.0	-79.6	-68.4	-55.6	-42.1	-187.1
Propenylbenzene	C_9H_{10}	17.5	43.8	57.0	71.5	87.7	97.8	111.7	132.0	154.7	179.0	-30.1
Propionamide	C_3H_7NO	65.0	91.0	105.0	119.0	134.8	144.3	156.0	174.2	194.0	213.0	79
Propionic acid	$C_3H_6O_2$	4.6	28.0	39.7	52.0	65.8	74.1	85.8	102.5	122.0	141.1	-22
anhydride	$C_6H_{10}O_3$	20.6	45.3	57.7	70.4	85.6	94.5	107.2	127.8	146.0	167.0	-45
Propionitrile	C_3H_5N	-35.0	-13.6	-3.0	+8.8	22.0	30.1	41.4	58.2	77.7	97.1	-91.9
Propiophenone	$C_9H_{10}O$	50.0	77.9	92.2	107.6	124.3	135.0	149.3	170.2	194.2	218.0	21
n-Propyl acetate	$C_5H_{10}O_2$	-26.7	-5.4	+5.0	16.0	28.8	37.0	47.8	64.0	82.0	101.8	-92.5
iso-Propyl acetate	$C_5H_{10}O_2$	-38.3	-17.4	-7.2	+4.2	17.0	25.1	35.7	51.7	69.8	89.0	
n-Propyl alcohol (1-propanol)	C_3H_8O	-15.0	+5.0	14.7	25.3	36.4	43.5	52.8	66.8	82.0	97.8	-127
iso-Propyl alcohol (2-propanol)	C_3H_8O	-26.1	-7.0	+2.4	12.7	23.8	30.5	39.5	53.0	67.8	82.5	-85.8
n-Propylamine	C_3H_9N	-64.4	-46.3	-37.2	-27.1	-16.0	-9.0	+0.5	15.0	31.5	48.5	-83
Propylbenzene	C_9H_{12}	6.3	31.3	43.4	56.8	71.6	81.1	94.0	113.5	135.7	159.2	-99.5
Propyl benzoate	$C_{10}H_{12}O_2$	54.6	83.8	98.0	114.3	131.8	143.3	157.4	180.1	205.2	231.0	-51.6
n-Propyl bromide (1-bromopropane)	C_3H_7Br	-53.0	-33.4	-23.3	-12.4	-0.3	+7.5	18.0	34.0	52.0	71.0	-109.9
iso-Propyl bromide (2-bromopropane)	C_3H_7Br	-61.8	-42.5	-32.8	-22.0	-10.1	-2.5	+8.0	23.8	41.5	60.0	-89.0
n-Propyl n-butyrate	$C_7H_{14}O_2$	-1.6	+22.1	34.0	47.0	61.5	70.3	82.6	101.0	121.7	142.7	-95.2
isobutyrate	$C_7H_{14}O_2$	-6.2	+16.8	28.3	40.6	54.3	63.0	73.9	91.8	112.0	133.9	
iso-Propyl isobutyrate	$C_7H_{14}O_2$	-16.3	+5.8	17.0	29.0	42.4	51.4	62.3	80.2	100.0	120.5	
Propyl carbamate	$C_4H_9NO_2$	52.4	77.6	90.0	103.2	117.7	126.5	138.3	155.8	175.8	195.0	
n-Propyl chloride (1-chloropropane)	C_3H_7Cl	-68.3	-50.0	-41.0	-31.0	-19.5	-12.1	-2.5	+12.2	29.4	46.4	-122.8
iso-Propyl chloride (2-chloropropane)	C_3H_7Cl	-78.8	-61.1	-52.0	-42.0	-31.0	-23.5	-13.7	+1.3	18.1	36.5	-117
iso-Propyl chloroacetate	$C_5H_9ClO_2$	+3.8	28.1	40.2	53.9	68.7	78.0	90.3	108.8	128.0	148.6	
Propyl chloroglyoxylate	$C_5H_7ClO_3$	9.7	32.3	43.5	55.6	68.8	77.2	88.0	104.7	123.0	150.0	
Propylene	C_3H_6	-131.9	-120.7	-112.1	-104.7	-96.5	-91.3	-84.1	-73.3	-60.9	-47.7	-185
Propylene glycol (1,2-Propanediol)	$C_3H_8O_2$	45.5	70.8	83.2	96.4	111.2	119.9	132.0	149.7	168.1	188.2	
Propylene oxide	C_3H_6O	-75.0	-57.8	-49.0	-39.3	-28.4	-21.3	-12.0	+2.1	17.8	34.5	-112.1
n-Propyl formate	$C_4H_8O_2$	-43.0	-22.7	-12.6	-1.7	+10.8	18.8	29.5	45.3	62.6	81.3	-92.9
iso-Propyl formate	$C_4H_8O_2$	-52.0	-32.7	-22.7	-12.1	-0.2	+7.5	17.8	33.6	50.5	68.3	
4,4′-iso-Propylidenebisphenol	$C_{15}H_{16}O_2$	193.0	224.2	240.8	255.5	273.0	282.9	297.0	317.5	339.0	360.5	
n-Propyl iodide (1-iodopropane)	C_3H_7I	-36.0	-13.5	-2.4	+10.0	23.6	32.1	43.8	61.8	81.8	102.5	-98.8
iso-Propyl iodide (2-iodopropane)	C_3H_7I	-43.3	-22.1	-11.7	0.0	+13.2	21.6	32.8	50.0	69.5	89.5	-90
n-Propyl levulinate	$C_8H_{14}O_3$	59.7	86.3	99.9	114.0	130.1	140.6	154.0	175.6	198.0	221.2	
iso-Propyl levulinate	$C_8H_{14}O_3$	48.0	74.5	88.0	102.4	118.1	127.8	141.8	161.6	185.2	208.2	
Propyl mercaptan (1-propanethiol)	C_3H_8S	-56.0	-36.3	-26.3	-15.4	-3.2	+4.6	15.3	31.5	49.2	67.4	-112
2-iso-Propylnaphthalene	$C_{13}H_{14}$	76.0	107.9	123.4	140.3	159.0	171.4	187.6	211.8	238.5	266.0	
iso-Propyl β-naphthyl ketone (2-isobutyronaphthone)	$C_{14}H_{14}O$	133.2	165.4	181.0	197.7	215.6	227.0	242.3	264.0	288.2	313.0	
2-iso-Propylphenol	$C_9H_{12}O$	56.6	83.8	97.0	111.7	127.5	137.7	150.3	170.1	192.6	214.5	15.5
3-iso-Propylphenol	$C_9H_{12}O$	62.0	90.3	104.1	119.8	136.2	146.6	160.2	182.0	205.0	228.0	26
4-iso-Propylphenol	$C_9H_{12}O$	67.0	94.7	108.0	123.4	139.8	149.7	163.3	184.0	206.1	228.2	61
Propyl propionate	$C_6H_{12}O_2$	-14.2	+8.0	19.4	31.6	45.0	53.8	65.2	82.7	102.0	122.4	-76
4-iso-Propylstyrene	$C_{11}H_{14}$	34.7	62.3	76.0	91.2	108.0	118.4	132.8	153.9	178.0	202.5	
Propyl isovalerate	$C_8H_{16}O_2$	+8.0	32.8	45.1	58.0	72.8	82.3	95.0	113.9	135.0	155.9	
Pulegone	$C_{10}H_{16}O$	58.3	82.5	94.0	106.8	121.7	130.2	143.1	162.5	189.8	221.0	
Pyridine	C_5H_5N	-18.9	+2.5	13.2	24.8	38.0	46.8	57.8	75.0	95.6	115.4	-42
Pyrocatechol	$C_6H_6O_2$	.....	104.0	118.3	134.0	150.6	161.7	176.0	197.7	221.5	245.5	105
Pyrocaltechol diacetate (1,2-phenylene diacetate)	$C_{10}H_{10}O_4$	98.0	129.8	145.7	161.8	179.8	191.6	206.5	228.7	253.3	278.0	
Pyrogallol	$C_6H_6O_3$	.....	151.7	167.7	185.3	204.2	216.3	232.0	255.3	281.5	309.0	133
Pyrotartaric anhydride	$C_5H_6O_3$	69.7	99.7	114.2	130.0	147.8	158.6	173.8	196.1	221.0	247.4	
Pyruvic acid	$C_3H_4O_3$	21.4	45.8	57.9	70.8	85.3	94.1	106.5	124.7	144.7	165.0	13.6
Quinoline	C_9H_7N	59.7	89.6	103.8	119.8	136.7	148.1	163.2	186.2	212.3	237.7	-15
iso-Quinoline	C_9H_7N	63.5	92.7	107.8	123.7	141.6	152.0	167.6	190.0	214.5	240.5	24.6
Resorcinol	$C_6H_6O_2$	108.4	138.0	152.1	168.0	185.3	195.8	209.8	230.8	253.4	276.5	110.7
Safrole	$C_{10}H_{10}O_2$	63.8	93.0	107.6	123.0	140.1	150.3	165.1	186.2	210.0	233.0	11.2
Salicylaldehyde	$C_7H_6O_2$	33.0	60.1	73.8	88.7	105.2	115.7	129.4	150.0	173.7	196.5	-7
Salicylic acid	$C_7H_6O_3$	113.7	136.0	146.2	156.8	172.2	182.0	193.4	210.0	230.5	256.0	159
Sebacic acid	$C_{10}H_{18}O_4$	183.0	215.7	232.0	250.0	268.2	279.8	294.5	313.2	332.8	352.3	134.5
Selenophene	C_4H_4Se	-39.0	-16.0	-4.0	+9.1	24.1	33.8	47.0	66.7	89.8	114.3	
Skatole	C_9H_9N	95.0	124.2	139.6	154.3	171.9	183.6	197.4	218.8	242.5	266.2	95
Stearaldehyde	$C_{18}H_{36}O$	140.0	174.6	192.1	210.6	230.8	244.2	260.0	285.0	313.8	342.5	63.5
Stearic acid	$C_{18}H_{36}O_2$	173.7	209.0	225.0	243.4	263.3	275.5	291.0	316.5	343.0	370.0	69.3
Stearyl alcohol (1-octadecanol)	$C_{18}H_{38}O$	150.3	185.6	202.0	220.0	240.4	252.7	269.4	293.5	320.3	349.5	58.5
Styrene	C_8H_8	-7.0	+18.0	30.8	44.6	59.8	69.5	82.0	101.3	122.5	145.2	-30.6
Styrene dibromide [(1,2-dibromoethyl) benzene]	$C_8H_8Br_2$	86.0	115.6	129.8	145.2	161.8	172.2	186.3	207.8	230.0	254.0	
Suberic acid	$C_8H_{14}O_4$	172.8	205.5	219.5	238.2	254.6	265.4	279.8	300.5	322.8	345.5	142
Succinic anhydride	$C_4H_4O_3$	92.0	115.0	128.2	145.3	163.0	174.0	189.0	212.0	237.0	261.0	119.6
Succinimide	$C_4H_5NO_2$	115.0	143.2	157.0	174.0	192.0	203.0	217.4	240.0	263.5	287.5	125.5
Succinyl chloride	$C_4H_4Cl_2O_2$	39.0	65.0	78.0	91.8	107.5	117.2	130.0	149.3	170.0	192.5	17
α-Terpineol	$C_{10}H_{18}O$	52.8	80.4	94.3	109.8	126.0	136.3	150.1	171.2	194.3	217.5	35
Terpenoline	$C_{10}H_{16}$	32.3	58.0	70.6	84.8	100.0	109.8	122.7	142.0	163.5	185.0	
1,1,1,2-Tetrabromoethane	$C_2H_2Br_4$	58.0	83.3	95.7	108.5	123.2	132.0	144.0	161.5	181.0	200.0	
1,1,2,2-Tetrabromoethane	$C_2H_2Br_4$	65.0	95.5	110.0	126.0	144.0	155.1	170.0	192.5	217.5	243.5	
Tetraisobutylene	$C_{16}H_{32}$	63.8	93.7	108.5	124.5	142.2	152.6	167.5	190.0	214.6	240.0	
Tetracosane	$C_{24}H_{50}$	183.8	219.6	237.6	255.3	276.3	288.4	305.2	330.5	358.0	386.4	51.1
1,2,3,4-Tetrachlorobenzene	$C_6H_2Cl_4$	68.5	99.6	114.7	131.2	149.2	160.0	175.7	198.0	225.5	254.0	46.5
1,2,3,5-Tetrachlorobenzene	$C_6H_2Cl_4$	58.2	89.0	104.1	121.6	140.0	152.0	168.0	193.7	220.0	246.0	54.5
1,2,4,5-Tetrachlorobenzene	$C_6H_2Cl_4$	.....	.....	.....	.....	146.0	157.7	173.5	196.0	220.5	245.0	139
1,1,2,2-Tetrachloro-1,2-difluoroethane	$C_2Cl_4F_2$	-37.5	-16.0	-5.0	+6.7	19.8	28.1	38.6	55.0	73.1	92.0	26.5
1,1,1,2-Tetrachloroethane	$C_2H_2Cl_4$	-16.3	+7.4	19.3	32.1	46.7	56.0	68.0	87.2	108.2	130.5	-68.7
1,1,2,2-Tetrachloroethane	$C_2H_2Cl_4$	-3.8	+20.7	33.0	46.2	60.8	70.0	83.2	102.2	124.0	145.9	-36
1,2,3,5-Tetrachloro-4-ethylbenzene	$C_8H_6Cl_4$	77.0	110.0	126.0	143.7	162.1	175.0	191.6	215.3	243.0	270.0	
Tetrachloroethylene	C_2Cl_4	-20.6	+2.4	13.8	26.3	40.1	49.2	61.3	79.8	100.0	120.8	-19.0
2,3,4,6-Tetrachlorophenol	$C_6H_2Cl_4O$	100.0	130.3	145.3	161.0	179.1	190.0	205.2	227.2	250.4	275.0	69.5
3,4,5,6-Tetrachloro-1,2-xylene	$C_8H_6Cl_4$	94.4	125.0	140.3	156.0	174.2	185.8	200.5	223.0	248.3	273.5	
Tetradecane	$C_{14}H_{30}$	76.4	106.0	120.7	135.6	152.7	164.0	178.5	201.8	226.8	252.5	5.5

Table 3-8. Vapor Pressures of Organic Compounds, up to 1 Atm.—(*Continued*)

Compound		Pressure, mm. Hg										Melting point, °C.
		1	5	10	20	40	60	100	200	400	760	
Name	Formula	Temperature, °C.										
Tetradecylamine	$C_{14}H_{31}N$	102.6	135.8	152.0	170.0	189.0	200.2	215.7	239.8	264.6	291.2	
Tetradecyltrimethylsilane	$C_{17}H_{38}Si$	120.0	150.7	166.2	183.5	201.5	213.3	227.8	250.0	275.0	300.0	
Tetraethoxysilane	$C_8H_{20}O_4Si$	16.0	40.3	52.6	65.8	81.1	90.7	103.6	123.5	146.2	168.5	
1,2,3,4-Tetraethylbenzene	$C_{14}H_{22}$	65.7	96.2	111.6	127.7	145.8	156.7	172.4	196.0	221.4	248.0	11.6
Tetraethylene glycol	$C_8H_{18}O_5$	153.9	183.7	197.1	212.3	228.0	237.8	250.0	268.4	288.0	307.8	
Tetraethylene glycol chlorohydrin	$C_8H_{17}ClO_4$	110.1	141.8	156.1	172.6	190.0	200.5	214.7	236.5	258.2	281.5	
Tetraethyllead	$C_8H_{20}Pb$	38.4	63.6	74.8	88.0	102.4	111.7	123.8	142.0	161.8	183.0	−136
Tetraethylsilane	$C_8H_{20}Si$	−1.0	+23.9	36.3	50.0	65.3	74.8	88.0	108.0	130.2	153.0	
Tetralin	$C_{10}H_{12}$	38.0	65.3	79.0	93.8	110.4	121.3	135.3	157.2	181.8	207.2	−31.0
1,2,3,4-Tetramethylbenzene	$C_{10}H_{14}$	42.6	68.7	81.8	95.8	111.5	121.8	135.7	155.7	180.0	204.4	−6.2
1,2,3,5-Tetramethylbenzene	$C_{10}H_{14}$	40.6	65.8	77.8	91.0	105.8	115.4	128.3	149.9	173.7	197.9	−24.0
1,2,4,5-Tetramethylbenzene	$C_{10}H_{14}$	45.0	65.0	74.6	88.0	104.2	114.8	128.1	149.5	172.1	195.9	79.5
2,2,3,3-Tetramethylbutane	C_8H_{18}	−17.4	+3.2	13.5	24.6	36.8	44.5	54.8	70.2	87.4	106.3	−102.2
Tetramethylene dibromide (1,4-dibromobutane)	$C_4H_8Br_2$	32.0	58.8	72.4	87.6	104.0	115.1	128.7	149.8	173.8	197.5	−20
Tetramethyllead	$C_4H_{12}Pb$	−29.0	−6.8	+4.4	16.6	30.3	39.2	50.8	68.8	89.0	110.0	−27.5
Tetramethyltin	$C_4H_{12}Sn$	−51.3	−31.0	−20.6	−9.3	+3.5	11.7	22.8	39.8	58.5	78.0	
Tetrapropylene glycol monoisopropyl ether	$C_{15}H_{32}O_5$	116.6	147.8	163.0	179.8	197.7	209.0	223.3	245.0	268.3	292.7	
Thioacetic acid (mercaptoacetic acid)	$C_2H_4O_2S$	60.0	87.7	101.5	115.8	131.8	142.0	154.0	......	......	......	−16.5
Thiodiglycol (2,2′-thiodiethanol)	$C_4H_{10}O_2S$	42.0	96.0	128.0	165.0	210.0	240.5	285				
Thiophene	C_4H_4S	−40.7	−20.8	−10.9	0.0	+12.5	20.1	30.5	46.5	64.7	84.4	−38.3
Thiophenol (benzenethiol)	C_6H_6S	18.6	43.7	56.0	69.7	84.2	93.9	106.6	125.8	146.7	168.0	
α-Thujone	$C_{10}H_{16}O$	38.3	65.7	79.3	93.7	110.0	120.2	134.0	154.2	177.8	201.0	
Thymol	$C_{10}H_{14}O$	64.3	92.8	107.4	122.6	139.8	149.8	164.1	185.5	209.2	231.8	51.5
Tiglaldehyde	C_5H_8O	−25.0	−1.6	+10.0	23.2	37.0	45.8	57.7	75.4	95.5	116.4	
Tiglic acid	$C_5H_8O_2$	52.0	77.8	90.2	103.8	119.0	127.8	140.5	158.0	179.2	198.5	64.5
Tiglonitrile	C_5H_7N	−25.5	−2.4	+9.2	22.1	36.7	46.0	58.2	77.8	99.7	122.0	
Toluene	C_7H_8	−26.7	−4.4	+6.4	18.4	31.8	40.3	51.9	69.5	89.5	110.6	−95.0
Toluene-2,4-diamine	$C_7H_{10}N_2$	106.5	137.2	151.7	167.9	185.7	196.2	211.5	232.8	256.0	280.0	99
2-Toluic nitrile (2-tolunitrile)	C_8H_7N	36.7	64.0	77.9	93.0	110.0	120.8	135.0	156.0	180.0	205.2	−13
4-Toluic nitrile (4-tolunitrile)	C_8H_7N	42.5	71.3	85.8	101.7	109.5	130.0	145.2	167.3	193.0	217.6	29.5
2-Toluidine	C_7H_9N	44.0	69.3	81.4	95.1	110.0	119.8	133.0	153.0	176.2	199.7	−16.3
3-Toluidine	C_7H_9N	41.0	68.0	82.0	96.7	113.5	123.8	136.7	157.6	180.6	203.3	−31.5
4-Toluidine	C_7H_9N	42.0	68.2	81.8	95.8	111.5	121.5	133.7	154.0	176.9	200.4	44.5
2-Tolyl isocyanide	C_8H_7N	25.2	51.0	64.0	78.2	94.0	104.0	117.7	137.8	159.9	183.5	
4-Tolylhydrazine	$C_7H_{10}N_2$	82.4	110.0	123.8	138.6	154.1	165.0	178.0	198.0	219.5	242.0	65.5
Tribromoacetaldehyde	C_2HBr_3O	18.5	45.0	58.0	72.1	87.8	97.5	110.2	130.0	151.6	174.0	
1,1,2-Tribromobutane	$C_4H_7Br_3$	45.0	73.5	87.8	103.2	120.2	131.6	146.0	167.8	192.0	216.2	
1,2,2-Tribromobutane	$C_4H_7Br_3$	41.0	69.0	83.2	98.6	116.0	127.0	141.8	163.5	188.0	213.8	
2,2,3-Tribromobutane	$C_4H_7Br_3$	38.2	66.0	79.8	94.6	111.8	122.2	136.3	157.8	182.2	206.5	
1,1,2-Tribromoethane	$C_2H_3Br_3$	32.6	58.0	70.6	84.2	100.0	110.0	123.5	143.5	165.4	188.4	−26
1,2,3-Tribromopropane	$C_3H_5Br_3$	47.5	75.8	90.0	105.8	122.8	134.0	148.0	170.0	195.0	220.0	16.5
Triisobutylamine	$C_{12}H_{27}N$	32.3	57.4	69.8	83.0	97.8	107.3	119.7	138.0	157.8	179.0	−22
Triisobutylene	$C_{12}H_{24}$	18.0	44.0	56.5	70.0	86.7	96.7	110.0	130.2	153.0	179.0	
2,4,6-Tritertbutylphenol	$C_{18}H_{30}O$	95.2	126.1	142.0	158.0	177.4	188.0	203.0	226.2	250.6	276.3	
Trichloroacetic acid	$C_2HCl_3O_2$	51.0	76.0	88.2	101.8	116.3	125.9	137.8	155.4	175.2	195.6	57
Trichloroacetic anhydride	$C_4Cl_6O_3$	56.2	85.3	99.6	114.3	131.2	141.8	155.2	176.2	199.8	223.0	
Trichloroacetyl bromide	C_2BrCl_3O	−7.4	+16.7	29.3	42.1	57.2	66.7	79.5	98.4	120.2	143.0	
2,4,6-Trichloroaniline	$C_6H_4Cl_3N$	134.0	157.8	170.0	182.6	195.8	204.5	214.6	229.8	246.4	262.0	78
1,2,3-Trichlorobenzene	$C_6H_3Cl_3$	40.0	70.0	85.6	101.8	119.8	131.5	146.0	168.2	193.5	218.5	52.5
1,2,4-Trichlorobenzene	$C_6H_3Cl_3$	38.4	67.3	81.7	97.2	114.8	125.7	140.0	162.0	187.7	213.0	17
1,3,5-Trichlorobenzene	$C_6H_3Cl_3$	......	63.8	78.0	93.7	110.8	121.8	136.0	157.7	183.0	208.4	63.5
1,2,3-Trichlorobutane	$C_4H_7Cl_3$	+0.5	27.2	40.0	55.0	71.5	82.0	96.2	118.0	143.0	169.0	
1,1,1-Trichloroethane	$C_2H_3Cl_3$	−52.0	−32.0	−21.9	−10.8	+1.6	9.5	20.0	36.2	54.6	74.1	−30.6
1,1,2 Trichloroethane	$C_2H_3Cl_3$	−24.0	−2.0	+8.3	21.6	35.2	44.0	55.7	73.3	93.0	113.9	−36.7
Trichloroethylene	C_2HCl_3	−43.8	−22.8	−12.4	−1.0	+11.9	20.0	31.4	48.0	67.0	86.7	−73
Trichlorofluoromethane	CCl_3F	−84.3	−67.6	−59.0	−49.7	−39.0	−32.3	−23.0	−9.1	+6.8	23.7	
2,4,5-Trichlorophenol	$C_6H_3Cl_3O$	72.0	102.1	117.3	134.0	151.5	162.5	178.0	201.5	226.5	251.8	62
2,4,6-Trichlorophenol	$C_6H_3Cl_3O$	76.5	105.9	120.2	135.8	152.2	163.5	177.8	199.0	222.5	246.0	68.5
Tri-2-chlorophenylthiophosphate	$C_{18}H_{12}Cl_3O_3PS$	188.2	217.2	231.2	246.7	261.7	271.5	283.8	302.8	322.0	341.3	
1,1,1-Trichloropropane	$C_3H_5Cl_3$	−28.8	−7.0	+4.2	16.2	29.9	38.3	50.0	67.7	87.5	108.2	−77.7
1,2,3-Trichloropropane	$C_3H_5Cl_3$	+9.0	33.7	46.0	59.3	74.0	83.6	96.1	115.6	137.0	158.0	−14.7
1,1,2-Trichloro-1,2,2-trifluoroethane	$C_2Cl_3F_3$	−68.0	−49.4	−40.3	−30.0	−18.5	−11.2	−1.7	+13.5	30.2	47.6	−35
Tricosane	$C_{23}H_{48}$	170.0	206.3	223.0	242.0	261.3	273.8	289.8	313.5	339.8	366.5	47.7
Tridecane	$C_{13}H_{28}$	59.4	98.3	104.0	120.2	137.7	148.2	162.5	185.0	209.4	234.0	−6.2
Tridecanoic acid	$C_{13}H_{26}O_2$	137.8	166.3	181.0	195.8	212.4	222.0	236.0	255.2	276.5	299.0	41
Triethoxymethylsilane	$C_7H_{18}O_3Si$	−1.5	+22.8	34.6	47.2	61.7	70.4	82.7	101.0	121.8	143.5	
Triethoxyphenylsilane	$C_{12}H_{20}O_3Si$	71.0	98.8	112.6	127.2	143.5	153.2	167.5	188.0	210.5	233.5	
1,2,4-Triethylbenzene	$C_{12}H_{18}$	46.0	74.2	88.5	104.0	121.7	132.2	146.8	168.3	193.7	218.0	
1,3,4-Triethylbenzene	$C_{12}H_{18}$	47.9	76.0	90.2	105.8	122.6	133.4	147.7	168.3	193.2	217.5	
Triethylborine	$C_6H_{15}B$	......	......	−148.0	−140.6	−131.4	−125.2	−116.0	−101.0	−81.0	−56.2	
Triethyl camphoronate	$C_{15}H_{26}O_6$	......	150.2	166.0	183.6	201.8	213.5	228.6	250.8	276.0	301.0	135
citrate	$C_{12}H_{20}O_7$	107.0	138.7	144.0	171.1	190.4	202.5	217.8	242.2	267.5	294.0	
Triethyleneglycol	$C_6H_{14}O_4$	114.0	144.0	158.1	174.0	191.3	201.5	214.6	235.2	256.6	278.3	
Triethylheptylsilane	$C_{13}H_{30}Si$	70.0	99.8	114.6	130.3	148.0	158.2	174.0	196.0	221.0	247.0	
Triethyloctylsilane	$C_{14}H_{32}Si$	73.7	104.8	120.6	137.7	155.7	168.0	184.3	208.0	235.0	262.0	
Triethyl orthoformate	$C_7H_{16}O_3$	+5.5	29.2	40.5	53.4	67.5	76.0	88.0	106.0	125.7	146.0	
phosphate	$C_6H_{15}O_4P$	39.6	67.8	82.1	97.8	115.7	126.3	141.6	163.7	187.0	211.0	
Triethylthallium	$C_6H_{15}Tl$	+9.3	37.6	51.7	67.7	85.4	95.7	112.1	136.0	163.5	192.1	−63.0
Trifluorophenylsilane	$C_6H_5F_3Si$	−31.0	−9.7	+0.8	12.3	25.4	33.2	44.2	60.1	78.7	98.3	
Trimethallyl phosphate	$C_{12}H_{21}PO_4$	93.7	131.0	149.8	169.8	192.0	207.0	225.7	255.0	288.5	324.0	
2,3,5-Trimethylacetophenone	$C_{11}H_{14}O$	79.0	108.0	122.3	137.5	154.2	165.7	179.7	201.3	224.3	247.5	
Trimethylamine	C_3H_9N	−97.1	−81.7	−73.8	−65.0	−55.2	−48.8	−40.3	−27.0	−12.5	+2.9	−117.1
2,4,5-Trimethylaniline	$C_9H_{13}N$	68.4	95.9	109.0	123.7	139.8	149.5	162.0	182.3	203.7	234.5	67
1,2,3-Trimethylbenzene	C_9H_{12}	16.8	42.9	55.9	69.9	85.4	95.3	108.8	129.0	152.0	176.1	−25.5
1,2,4-Trimethylbenzene	C_9H_{12}	13.6	38.3	50.7	64.5	79.8	89.5	102.8	122.7	145.4	169.2	−44.1
1,3,5-Trimethylbenzene	C_9H_{12}	9.6	34.7	47.4	61.0	76.1	85.8	98.9	118.6	141.0	164.7	−44.8
2,2,3-Trimethylbutane	C_7H_{16}	......	......	−18.8	−7.5	+5.2	13.3	24.4	41.2	60.4	80.9	−25.0
Trimethyl citrate	$C_9H_{14}O_7$	106.2	146.2	160.4	177.2	194.2	205.5	219.6	241.3	264.2	287.0	78.5

Table 3-8. Vapor Pressures of Organic Compounds, up to 1 Atm.—(*Concluded*)

Compound		Pressure, mm. Hg										Melting point, °C.
Name	Formula	1	5	10	20	40	60	100	200	400	760	
		Temperature, °C.										
Trimethyleneglycol (1,3-propanediol)	$C_3H_8O_2$	59.4	87.2	100.6	115.5	131.0	141.1	153.4	172.8	193.8	214.2	
1,2,4-Trimethyl-5-ethylbenzene	$C_{11}H_{16}$	43.7	71.2	84.6	99.7	106.0	126.3	140.3	160.3	184.5	208.1	
1,3,5-Trimethyl-2-ethylbenzene	$C_{11}H_{16}$	38.8	67.0	80.5	96.0	113.2	123.8	137.9	158.4	183.5	208.0	
2,2,3-Trimethylpentane	C_8H_{18}	−29.0	−7.1	+3.9	16.0	29.5	38.1	49.9	67.8	88.2	109.8	−112.3
2,2,4-Trimethylpentane	C_8H_{18}	−36.5	−15.0	−4.3	+7.5	20.7	29.1	40.7	58.1	78.0	99.2	−107.3
2,3,3-Trimethylpentane	C_8H_{18}	−25.8	−3.9	+6.9	19.2	33.0	41.8	53.8	72.0	92.7	114.8	−101.5
2,3,4-Trimethylpentane	C_8H_{18}	−26.3	−4.1	+7.1	19.3	32.9	41.6	53.4	71.3	91.8	113.5	−109.2
2,2,4-Trimethyl-3-pentanone	$C_8H_{16}O$	14.7	36.0	46.4	57.6	69.8	77.3	87.6	102.2	118.4	135.0	
Trimethyl phosphate	$C_3H_9O_4P$	26.0	53.7	67.8	83.0	100.0	110.0	124.0	145.0	167.8	192.7	
2,4,5-Trimethylstyrene	$C_{11}H_{14}$	48.1	77.0	91.6	107.1	124.2	135.5	149.8	171.8	196.1	221.2	
2,4,6-Trimethylstyrene	$C_{11}H_{14}$	37.5	65.7	79.7	94.8	111.8	122.3	136.8	157.8	182.3	207.0	
Trimethylsuccinic anhydride	$C_7H_{10}O_3$	53.5	82.6	97.4	113.8	131.0	142.2	156.5	179.8	205.5	231.0	
Triphenylmethane	$C_{19}H_{16}$	169.7	188.4	197.0	206.8	215.5	221.2	228.4	239.7	249.8	259.2	93.4
Triphenylphosphate	$C_{18}H_{15}O_4P$	193.5	230.4	249.8	269.7	290.3	305.2	322.5	349.8	379.2	413.5	49.4
Tripropyleneglycol	$C_9H_{20}O_4$	96.0	125.7	140.5	155.8	173.7	184.6	199.0	220.2	244.3	267.2	
Tripropyleneglycol monobutyl ether	$C_{13}H_{28}O_4$	101.5	131.6	147.0	161.8	179.8	190.2	204.4	224.4	247.0	269.5	
Tripropyleneglycol monoisopropyl ether	$C_{12}H_{26}O_4$	82.4	112.4	127.3	143.7	161.4	173.2	187.8	209.7	232.8	256.6	
Tritolyl phosphate	$C_{21}H_{21}O_4P$	154.6	184.2	198.0	213.2	229.7	239.8	252.2	271.8	292.7	313.0	
Undecane	$C_{11}H_{24}$	32.7	59.7	73.9	85.6	104.4	115.2	128.1	149.3	171.9	195.8	−25.6
Undecanoic acid	$C_{11}H_{22}O_2$	101.4	133.1	149.0	166.0	185.6	197.2	212.5	237.8	262.8	290.0	29.5
10-Undecenoic acid	$C_{11}H_{20}O_2$	114.0	142.8	156.3	172.0	188.7	199.5	213.5	232.8	254.0	275.0	24.5
Undecan-2-ol	$C_{11}H_{24}O$	71.1	99.0	112.8	127.5	143.7	153.7	167.2	187.7	209.8	232.0	
n-Valeric acid	$C_5H_{10}O_2$	42.2	67.7	79.8	93.1	107.8	116.6	128.3	146.0	165.0	184.4	−34.5
iso-Valeric acid	$C_5H_{10}O_2$	34.5	59.6	71.3	84.0	98.0	107.3	118.9	136.2	155.2	175.1	−37.6
γ-Valerolactone	$C_5H_8O_2$	37.5	65.8	79.8	95.2	101.9	122.4	136.5	157.7	182.3	207.5	
Valeronitrile	C_5H_9N	−6.0	+18.1	30.0	43.3	57.8	66.9	78.6	97.7	118.7	140.8	
Vanillin	$C_8H_8O_3$	107.0	138.4	154.0	170.5	188.7	199.8	214.5	237.3	260.0	285.0	81.5
Vinyl acetate	$C_4H_6O_2$	−48.0	−28.0	−18.0	−7.0	+5.3	13.0	23.3	38.4	55.5	72.5	
2-Vinylanisole	$C_9H_{10}O$	41.9	68.0	81.0	94.7	110.0	119.8	132.3	151.0	172.1	194.0	
3-Vinylanisole	$C_9H_{10}O$	43.4	69.9	83.0	97.2	112.5	122.3	135.3	154.0	175.8	197.5	
4-Vinylanisole	$C_9H_{10}O$	45.2	72.0	85.7	100.0	116.0	126.1	139.7	159.0	182.0	204.5	
Vinyl chloride (1-chloroethylene)	C_2H_3Cl	−105.6	−90.8	−83.7	−75.7	−66.8	−61.1	−53.2	−41.3	−28.0	−13.8	−153.7
cyanide (acrylonitrile)	C_3H_3N	−51.0	−30.7	−20.3	−9.0	+3.8	11.8	22.8	38.7	58.3	78.5	−82
fluoride (1-fluoroethylene)	C_2H_3F	−149.3	−138.0	−132.2	−125.4	−118.0	−113.0	−106.2	−95.4	−84.0	−72.2	−160.5
Vinylidene chloride (1,1-dichloroethene)	$C_2H_2Cl_2$	−77.2	−60.0	−51.2	−41.7	−31.1	−24.0	−15.0	−1.0	+14.8	31.7	−122.5
4-Vinylphenetole	$C_{10}H_{12}O$	64.0	91.7	105.6	120.3	136.3	146.4	159.8	180.0	202.8	225.0	
2-Xenyl dichlorophosphate	$C_{12}H_9Cl_2PO$	138.2	171.1	187.0	205.0	223.8	236.0	251.5	275.3	301.5	328.5	
2,4-Xyaldehyde	$C_9H_{10}O$	59.0	85.9	99.0	114.0	129.7	139.8	152.2	172.3	194.1	215.5	75
2-Xylene (2-xylene)	C_8H_{10}	−3.8	+20.2	32.1	45.1	59.5	68.8	81.3	100.2	121.7	144.4	−25.2
3-Xylene (3-xylene)	C_8H_{10}	−6.9	+16.8	28.3	41.1	55.3	64.4	76.8	95.5	116.7	139.1	−47.9
4-Xylene (4-xylene)	C_8H_{10}	−8.1	+15.5	27.3	40.1	54.4	63.5	75.9	94.6	115.9	138.3	+13.3
2,4-Xylidine	$C_8H_{11}N$	52.6	79.8	93.0	107.6	123.8	133.7	146.8	166.4	188.3	211.5	
2,6-Xylidine	$C_8H_{11}N$	44.0	72.6	87.0	102.7	120.2	131.5	146.0	168.0	193.7	217.9	

Table 3-9. Vapor Pressures of Organic Compounds, above 1 Atm.*

Compound		Pressure, atm.									Critical point	
Name	Formula	1	2	5	10	20	30	40	50	60	t_c, °C.	P_c, atm.
		Temperature, °C.										
Acetic acid	$C_2H_4O_2$	118.1	143.5	180.3	214.0	252.0	276.5	297.0	312.5	......	321.6	57.2
anhydride	$C_4H_6O_3$	139.6	162.0	194.0	221.5	253.0	272.8	288.5	......	......	296	46
Acetone	C_3H_6O	56.5	78.6	113.0	144.5	181.0	205.0	214.5	......	......	235.0	47.0
Acetylene	C_2H_2	−84.0	−71.6	−50.2	−32.7	−10.0	+4.8	16.8	26.8	34.8	36.0	62.0
Allene (propadiene)	C_3H_4	−35.0	−18.4	+8.0	33.2	64.5	85.5	103.5	118.0	......	120.7	51.8
Aniline	C_6H_7N	184.4	212.8	254.8	292.7	342.0	375.5	400.0	422.4	......	426	52.4
Benzene	C_6H_6	80.1	103.8	142.5	178.8	221.5	249.5	272.3	290.3	......	290.5	50.1
Bromobenzene	C_6H_5Br	156.2	186.2	232.5	274.5	327.0	359.8	387.5	......	......	397	44.6
1,3-Butadiene	C_4H_6	−4.5	+15.3	47.0	76.0	114.0	139.8	158.0	......	......	161.8	42.6
iso-Butane (2-methylpropane)	C_4H_{10}	−11.7	+7.5	39.0	66.8	99.5	120.5	......	......	......	134.0	37.0
n-Butane	C_4H_{10}	−0.5	+18.8	50.0	79.5	116.0	140.6	......	......	......	152.8	36.0
iso-Butyl alcohol (2-methylpropanol-1)	$C_4H_{10}O$	108.0	127.3	156.2	182.0	212.5	232.0	251.0	......	......	265	48
n-Butyl alcohol (1-butanol)	$C_4H_{10}O$	117.5	139.8	172.5	203.0	237.0	259.0	277.0	......	......	287	48.4
sec-Butyl alcohol (2-butanol)	$C_4H_{10}O$	99.5	118.2	147.5	172.0	204.0	230.0	251.0	......	......	265	48
tert-Butyl alcohol (trimethyl carbinol)	$C_4H_{10}O$	82.9	102.0	130.0	154.2	184.5	207.0	222.5	......	......	235	49
iso-Butyl formate	$C_5H_{10}C_2$	98.2	121.8	157.8	192.4	234.0	261.0	......	......	......	278.0	38.0
Butyric acid	$C_4H_8O_2$	163.5	188.3	225.0	257.0	295.0	319.0	338.0	352.0	......	355	52.0
iso-Butyric acid	$C_4H_8O_2$	154.5	179.8	217.0	250.0	289.0	315.0	336.0	......	......	336	40.0
Carbon dioxide	CO_2	−78.2	−69.1	−56.7	−39.5	−18.9	−5.3	+5.9	14.9	22.4	31.1	73.0
disulfide	CS_2	46.5	69.1	104.8	136.3	175.5	201.5	222.8	240.0	256.0	273.0	72.9
monoxide	CO	−191.3	−183.5	−170.7	−161.0	−149.7	−141.9	......	......	......	−138.7	34.6
tetrachloride	CCl_4	76.7	102.0	141.7	178.0	222.0	251.2	276.0	......	......	283.1	45.0
Chlorobenzene	C_6H_5Cl	132.2	160.2	205.0	245.3	292.8	324.4	349.8	......	......	359.2	44.6
Chlorodifluoromethane	$CHClF_2$	−40.8	−24.7	+0.3	24.0	52.0	70.3	85.3	......	......	96	48.7
Chloroform (trichloromethane)	$CHCl_3$	61.3	83.9	120.0	152.3	191.8	216.5	237.5	254.0	......	260	54.9
1-Chloro-1,2,2-trifluoroethylene	C_2ClF_3	−27.9	−11.1	+15.5	40.0	71.1	91.9	......	......	......	107.0	39.0
Chlorotrifluoromethane	$CClF_3$	−81.2	−66.7	−42.7	−18.5	+12.0	34.8	52.8	......	......	53	40.3
Cyanogen	C_2N_2	−21.0	−4.4	+21.4	44.6	72.6	91.6	106.5	118.2	......	126.6	58.2
Cyclohexane	C_6H_{12}	80.7	106.0	146.4	184.0	228.4	257.5	......	......	......	279.9	39.8
1,2-Dibromoethane	$C_2H_4Br_2$	131.5	157.7	200.0	237.0	269.0	286.0	295.0	300.0	304.5	309.8	70.6
Dichlorodifluoromethane	CCl_2F_2	−29.8	−12.2	+16.1	42.4	74.0	95.6	......	......	......	111.5	39.6
1,1-Dichloroethane	$C_2H_4Cl_2$	57.3	80.2	117.3	150.3	192.7	220.0	243.0	261.5	......	261.5	50.0
1,2-Dichloroethane	$C_2H_4Cl_2$	83.7	108.1	147.8	183.5	226.5	254.0	272.0	285.0	......	288.4	53.0
cis-1,2-Dichloroethylene	$C_2H_2Cl_2$	59.0	82.1	119.3	152.3	194.0	221.5	244.5	260.0	......	271.0	57.9
trans-1,2-Dichloroethylene	$C_2H_2Cl_2$	47.8	69.8	104.0	135.7	174.0	199.8	220.0	236.5	......	243.3	54.5
Dichlorofluoromethane	$CHCl_2F$	8.9	28.4	59.0	87.0	121.2	144.0	162.6	177.5	......	178.5	51.0
1,2-Dichloro-1,1,2,2-tetrafluoroethane	$C_2Cl_2F_4$	3.5	22.8	54.0	82.3	117.5	140.9	......	......	......	145.7	32.3
Diethylamine	$C_4H_{11}N$	55.5	77.8	113.0	145.3	184.5	210.0	......	......	......	223.3	36.6
Diethyl ether	$C_4H_{10}O$	34.6	56.0	90.0	122.0	159.0	183.3	......	......	......	193.8	35.5
sulfide	$C_4H_{10}S$	88.0	112.0	153.8	190.2	234.0	263.0	......	......	......	283.8	39.1

* Compiled from the extended tables published by D. R. Stull in *Ind. Eng. Chem.*, **39**, 517 (1947). For data on gasoline and aircraft fuels see Hibbard, *N.A.C.A. Research Mem.* E56I21, 1956 (declassified 1958). Extensive data for aqueous solutions of ethylene glycol, diethylene glycol, triethylene glycol, and propylene glycol from −20° to 300°F. are contained in "Glycols," Union Carbide Corp. publication F4763F, 1958. See also Fig. 3-3, p. 3-64. For vapor-pressure curves of the Freon compounds to 300°F., 1000 lb./sq. in. abs., see E. I. du Pont De Nemours & Co., Inc., *Tech. Bull.* B-2, 1957; for methane data see Johnson (ed.), WADD-TR-56-60, 1960.

Table 3-9. Vapor Pressures of Organic Compounds, above 1 Atm.—(*Concluded*)

Compound		Pressure, atm.									Critical point	
Name	Formula	1	2	5	10	20	30	40	50	60	t_c, °C.	P_c, atm.
		Temperature, °C.										
Dimethylamine	C_2H_7N	7.4	25.0	53.9	80.0	111.7	132.2	149.8	162.6	......	164.5	52.4
2,3-Dimethylbutane	C_6H_{14}	58.0	82.0	120.3	155.7	198.7	225.5	......	......	......	227.4	30.7
Dimethyl ether	C_2H_6O	−23.7	−6.4	+20.8	45.5	75.7	96.0	112.1	125.2	......	126.9	52.0
oxalate	$C_4H_6O_4$	163.3	189.6	228.7	......	......	......	......	......	......	260	9.5
sulfide	C_2H_6S	36.0	57.8	92.3	124.5	163.8	188.5	209.0	224.5	......	229.9	54.6
n-Dodecane	$C_{12}H_{26}$	216.2	249.2	300.0	345.8	......	......	......	......	......	385	17.5
Ethane	C_2H_6	−88.6	−75.0	−52.8	−32.0	−6.4	+10.0	23.6	......	......	32.3	48.2
Ethyl acetate	$C_4H_8O_2$	77.1	100.6	136.6	169.7	209.5	235.0	......	......	......	250.1	37.9
alcohol (ethanol)	C_2H_6O	78.4	97.5	126.0	151.8	183.0	203.0	218.0	230.0	242.0	243.5	63.1
Ethylamine	C_2H_7N	16.6	35.7	65.3	91.8	124.0	146.0	163.0	176.0	......	183.2	55.5
Ethyl benzene	C_8H_{10}	136.2	163.5	207.5	246.3	294.5	326.5	......	......	......	346.4	38.1
bromide	C_2H_5Br	38.4	60.2	95.0	126.8	164.3	188.0	206.5	220.0	229.5	230.8	61.5
chloride	C_2H_5Cl	12.3	32.5	64.0	92.6	127.3	149.5	167.0	180.5	......	187.2	52.0
fluoride	C_2H_5F	−32.0	−16.7	+7.7	30.2	57.5	75.7	90.0	......	......	102.2	49.6
formate	$C_3H_6O_2$	54.3	76.0	110.5	142.2	180.0	205.0	225.0	......	......	235.3	46.8
isobutyrate	$C_6H_{12}O_2$	110.1	135.5	174.2	210.0	253.0	280.0	......	......	......	280.0	30.0
mercaptan (ethanethiol)	C_2H_6S	35.0	56.6	90.7	121.9	159.5	184.3	204.7	220.0	......	225.5	54.2
methyl ether	C_3H_8O	7.5	26.5	56.4	84.0	108.0	141.4	160.0	......	......	164.7	43.4
propionate	$C_5H_{10}O_2$	99.1	123.8	162.7	197.8	240.0	264.5	......	......	......	272.8	33.2
propyl ether	$C_5H_{12}O$	61.7	85.3	123.1	156.2	197.2	223.0	......	......	......	227.4	32.1
Ethylene	C_2H_4	−103.7	−90.8	−71.1	−52.8	−29.1	−14.2	−1.5	+8.9	......	9.6	50.7
Fluorobenzene	C_6H_5F	84.7	109.9	148.5	184.4	227.6	257.0	279.3	......	......	286.5	44.7
n-Heptane	C_7H_{16}	98.4	124.8	165.7	202.8	247.5	......	......	......	......	266.8	26.9
n-Hexane	C_6H_{14}	68.7	93.0	131.7	166.6	209.4	......	......	......	......	234.8	29.6
Hydrogen cyanide (hydrocyanic acid)	CHN	25.9	45.8	75.8	102.7	135.0	153.8	169.9	183.5	......	183.5	50.0
Iodobenzene	C_6H_5I	188.6	220.0	270.0	315.7	371.5	406.0	437.2			448	44.7
Methane	CH_4	−161.5	−152.3	−138.3	−124.8	−108.5	−96.3	−86.3	......	......	−82.1	45.8
Methyl acetate	$C_3H_6O_2$	57.8	79.5	113.1	144.2	181.0	205.0	225.0	......	......	233.7	46.3
acetylene (propyne)	C_3H_4	−23.3	−7.1	+19.5	43.8	74.0	94.0	111.5	125.0	......	128	52.8
alcohol	CH_4O	64.7	84.0	112.5	138.0	167.8	186.5	203.5	214.0	224.0	240.0	78.7
Methylamine	CH_5N	−6.3	+10.1	36.0	59.5	87.8	106.3	121.8	133.7	144.6	156.9	73.6
Methyl bromide	CH_3Br	3.6	23.3	54.8	84.0	121.7	147.5	170.2	190.0	......	194	51.6
butyrate	$C_5H_{10}O_2$	102.3	127.5	166.7	203.0	244.5	272.0	......	......	......	281.2	34.2
chloride	CH_3Cl	−24.0	−6.4	+22.0	47.3	77.3	97.5	113.8	126.0	137.5	143.8	65.8
fluoride	CH_3F	−78.2	−64.5	−42.0	−21.0	+2.6	15.5	26.5	36.0	43.5	44.9	62.0
formate	$C_2H_4O_2$	32.0	51.9	83.5	112.0	147.2	169.7	188.5	213.0	......	214.0	59.1
iodide	CH_3I	42.4	65.5	101.8	138.0	176.5	206.0	228.5	248.0	......	255	54.6
isobutyrate	$C_5H_{10}O_2$	92.6	116.7	155.2	190.2	232.0	259.5	......	......	......	267.5	33.9
mercaptan (methanethiol)	CH_4S	6.8	26.1	55.9	83.4	117.5	140.0	157.7	172.0	185.0	196.8	71.4
propionate	$C_4H_8O_2$	79.8	103.0	139.8	172.6	212.5	239.0	......	......	......	257.4	39.3
n-Octane	C_8H_{18}	125.6	152.7	196.2	235.8	281.4	......	......	......	......	296.2	24.7
iso Pentane (2-methylbutane)	C_5H_{12}	27.8	48.8	82.8	114.5	154.0	180.3	......	......	......	187.8	32.8
n-Pentane	C_5H_{12}	36.1	58.0	92.4	124.7	164.3	191.3	......	......	......	197.2	33.0
neo-Pentane (2,2-dimethylpropane)	C_5H_{12}	+9.5	29.5	61.1	90.7	127.6	152.5	......	......	......	159.0	33.0
Phenol	C_6H_6O	181.9	208.0	248.2	283.8	328.7	358.0	382.1	400.0	418.7	419	60.5
Phosgene (carbonyl chloride)	CCl_2O	8.3	27.3	57.2	85.0	119.0	141.8	159.8	174.0	......	181.7	56.0
Propane	C_3H_8	−42.1	−25.6	+1.4	26.9	58.1	78.7	94.8	......	......	96.8	42.0
Propionic acid	$C_3H_6O_2$	141.1	160.0	186.0	203.5	220.0	228.0	233.0	238.0	......	239.5	53.0
Propyl acetate	$C_5H_{10}O_2$	101.8	126.8	165.7	200.5	242.8	269.0	......	......	......	276.2	33.2
iso-Propyl alcohol (2-propanol)	C_3H_8O	82.5	101.3	130.2	155.7	186.0	205.0	220.2	232.0	......	235	53
n-Propyl alcohol (1-propanol)	C_3H_8O	97.8	117.0	149.0	177.0	210.8	232.3	250.0	......	......	263.7	49.9
Propylamine	C_3H_9N	48.5	69.8	102.8	133.4	170.0	194.3	214.5	......	......	223.8	46.8
Propyl formate	$C_4H_8O_2$	81.3	104.3	142.0	176.4	217.5	245.0	......	......	......	264.8	39.5
Propylene	C_3H_6	−47.7	−31.4	−4.8	+19.8	49.5	70.0	85.0	......	......	91.4	45.4
Tetramethylsilane	$C_4H_{12}Si$	27.0	48.0	82.0	113.0	152.0	178.0	......	......	......	185	33
Toluene	C_7H_8	110.6	136.5	178.0	215.8	262.5	292.8	319.0	......	......	320.6	41.6
Trichlorofluoromethane	CCl_3F	23.7	44.1	77.3	108.2	146.7	172.0	194.0	......	......	198.0	43.2
1,1,2-Trichloro-1,2,2-trifluoroethane	$C_2Cl_3F_3$	47.6	70.0	105.5	138.0	177.7	205.0	......	......	......	214.1	33.7

VAPOR PRESSURES OF SOLUTIONS*

Table 3-10. Partial Pressures of Water over Aqueous Solutions of HCl

$\log_{10} p\text{mm.} = A - \frac{B}{T}$, which, however, agrees only approximately with the table. The table is more nearly correct.

Partial pressure of H_2O, mm. Hg, °C.

% HCl	A	B	0°	5°	10°	15°	20°	25°	30°	35°	40°	45°	50°	60°	70°	80°	90°	100°	110°
6	8.99156	2282	4.18	6.04	8.45	11.7	15.9	21.8	29.1	39.4	50.6	66.2	86.0	139	220	333	492	715	
10	8.99864	2295	3.84	5.52	7.70	10.7	14.6	20.0	26.8	35.5	47.0	61.5	80.0	130	204	310	463	677	960
14	8.97075	2300	3.39	4.91	6.95	9.65	13.1	18.0	24.1	31.9	42.1	55.3	72.0	116	185	273	425	625	892
18	8.98014	2323	2.87	4.21	5.92	8.26	11.3	15.4	20.6	27.5	36.4	47.9	62.5	102	162	248	374	550	783
20	8.97877	2334	2.62	3.83	5.40	7.50	10.3	14.1	19.0	25.1	33.3	43.6	57.0	93.5	150	230	345	510	729
22	9.02708	2363	2.33	3.40	4.82	6.75	9.30	12.6	17.1	22.8	30.2	39.8	52.0	85.6	138	211	317	467	670
24	8.96022	2356	2.05	3.04	4.31	6.03	8.30	11.4	15.4	20.4	27.1	35.7	46.7	77.0	124	194	290	426	611
26	9.01511	2390	1.76	2.60	3.71	5.21	7.21	9.95	13.5	18.0	24.0	31.7	41.5	69.0	112	173	261	387	555
28	8.97611	2395	1.50	2.24	3.21	4.54	6.32	8.75	11.8	15.8	21.1	27.9	36.5	60.7	99.0	154	234	349	499
30	9.00117	2422	1.26	1.90	2.73	3.88	5.41	7.52	10.2	13.7	18.4	24.3	32.0	53.5	87.5	136	207	310	444
32	9.03317	2453	1.04	1.57	2.27	3.25	4.55	6.37	8.70	11.7	15.7	21.0	27.7	46.5	76.5	120	184	275	396
34	9.07143	2487	0.85	1.29	1.87	2.70	3.81	5.35	7.32	9.95	13.5	18.1	24.0	40.5	66.5	104	161	243	355
36	9.11815	2526	0.68	1.03	1.50	2.19	3.10	4.41	6.08	8.33	11.4	15.4	20.4	34.8	57.0	90.0	140	212	311
38	9.20783	2579	0.53	0.81	1.20	1.75	2.51	3.60	5.03	6.92	9.52	13.0	17.4	29.6	49.1	77.5	120	182	266
40	9.33923	2647	0.41	0.63	0.94	1.37	2.00	2.88	4.09	5.68	7.85	10.7	14.5	25.0	42.1	67.3	105	158	230
42	9.44953	2709	0.31	0.48	0.72	1.06	1.56	2.30	3.28	4.60	6.45	8.90	12.1	21.2	35.8	57.2	89.2	135	195

* Accuracy, *ca.* 2 per cent for solutions of 15 to 30 per cent HCl between 0 and 100°; for solutions of > 30 per cent HCl the accuracy is *ca.* 5 per cent at the lower temperatures and *ca.* 15 per cent at the higher temperatures. Below 15 per cent HCl, the accuracy is *ca.* 5 per cent at the lower temperatures and higher strengths to *ca.* 15 to 20 per cent at the lower strengths and perhaps 15 to 20 per cent at the higher temperatures and lower strengths.

Table 3-11. Partial Pressures of HCl over Aqueous Solutions of HCl

$\log_{10} p\text{mm.} = A - \frac{B}{T}$, which, however, agrees only approximately with the table. The table is more nearly correct.

Mm. Hg, °C.

%HCl	A	B	0°	5°	10°	15°	20°	25°	30°	35°	40°	45°	50°	60°	70°	80°	90°	100°	110°
2	11.8037	4736	....	....	0.0000117	0.000023	0.000044	0.000084	0.000151	0.000275	0.00047	0.00083	0.00140	0.00380	0.0100	0.0245	0.058	0.132	0.280
4	11.6400	4471	0.000018	0.000036	.000069	.000131	.00024	.00044	.00077	.00134	.0023	.00385	.0064	.0165	.0405	.095	.21	.46	.93
6	11.2144	4202	.000066	.000125	.000234	.000425	.00076	.00131	.00225	.0038	.0062	.0102	.0163	.040	.094	.206	.44	.92	1.78
8	11.0406	4042	.000118	.000323	.000583	.00104	.00178	.0031	.00515	.0085	.0136	.022	.0344	.081	.183	.39	.82	1.64	3.10
10	10.9311	3908	.00042	.00075	.00134	.00232	.00395	.0067	.0111	.0178	.0282	.045	.069	.157	.35	.73	1.48	2.9	5.4
12	10.7900	3765	.00099	.00175	.00305	.0052	.0088	.0145	.0234	.037	.058	.091	.136	.305	.66	1.34	2.65	5.1	9.3
14	10.6954	3636	.0024	.00415	.0071	.0118	.0196	.0316	.050	.078	.121	.185	.275	.60	1.25	2.50	4.8	9.0	16.0
16	10.6261	3516	.0056	.0095	.016	.0265	.0428	.0685	.106	.163	.247	.375	.55	1.17	2.40	4.66	8.8	16.1	28
18	10.4957	3376	.0135	.0225	.037	.060	.095	.148	.228	.345	.515	.77	1.11	2.3	4.55	8.6	15.7	28	48
20	10.3833	3245	.0316	.052	.084	.132	.205	.32	.48	.72	1.06	1.55	2.21	4.4	8.5	15.6	28.1	49	83
22	10.3172	3125	.0734	.119	.187	.294	.45	.68	1.02	1.50	2.18	3.14	4.42	8.6	16.3	29.3	52	90	146
24	10.2185	2995	.175	.277	.43	.66	1.00	1.49	2.17	3.14	4.5	6.4	8.9	16.9	31.0	54.5	94	157	253
26	10.1303	2870	.41	.64	.98	1.47	2.17	3.20	4.56	6.50	9.2	12.7	17.5	32.5	58.5	100	169	276	436
28	10.0115	2732	1.0	1.52	2.27	3.36	4.90	7.05	9.90	13.8	19.1	26.4	35.7	64	112	188	309	493	760
30	9.8763	2593	2.4	3.57	5.23	7.60	10.6	15.1	21.0	28.6	39.4	53	71	124	208	340	542	845	
32	9.7523	2457	5.7	8.3	11.8	16.8	23.5	32.5	44.5	60.0	81	107	141	238	390	623	970		
34	9.6061	2316	13.1	18.8	26.4	36.8	50.5	68.5	92	122	161	211	273	450	720				
36	9.5262	2229	29.0	41.0	56.4	78	105.5	142	188	246	322	416	535	860					
38	9.4670	2094	63.0	87.0	117	158	210	277	360	465	598	758	955						
40	9.2156	1939	130	176	233	307	399	515	627	830									
42	8.9925	1800	253	332	430	560	709	900											
44	8.8621	1681	510	655	840														
46	......	....	940																

Table 3-12. Partial Pressures of H_2O and SO_2 over Aqueous Solutions of Sulfur Dioxide*

Partial Pressures of H_2O and SO_2, mm. Hg, °C.

Grams SO_2 per 100 g. water	10°C.		20°C.		30°C.		40°C.		50°C.		60°C.	
	H_2O	SO_2	H_2O	SO_2	H_2O	SO_2	H_2O	SO_2	H_2O	SO_2	H_2O	SO_2
0.0	9.2	...	17.5	...	31.8	...	55.3	...	92.5	...	149.5	...
0.5	9.2	21	17.5	29	31.7	42	55.2	60	92.3	83	149.2	111
1.0	9.2	42	17.4	59	31.7	85	55.1	120	92.2	164	149.0	217
1.5	9.2	64	17.4	90	31.6	129	55.0	181	92.0	247	148.8	328
2.0	9.1	86	17.4	123	31.6	176	55.0	245	91.9	333	148.6	444
2.5	9.1	108	17.4	157	31.5	224	54.9	311	91.8	421	148.3	562
3.0	9.1	130	17.3	191	31.5	273	54.7	378	91.6	511	148.1	682
3.5	9.1	153	17.3	227	31.5	324	54.7	447	91.5	603	147.9	804
4.0	9.1	176	17.3	264	31.4	376	54.6	518	91.4	698		
4.5	9.1	199	17.3	300	31.4	428	54.5	588	91.2	793		
5.0	9.1	223	17.2	338	31.3	482	54.4	661				
5.5	9.0	247	17.2	375	31.3	536	54.4	733				
6.0	9.0	271	17.2	411	31.2	588	54.3	804				
6.5	9.0	295	17.2	448	31.2	642						
7.0	9.0	320	17.1	486	31.1	698						
7.5	9.0	345	17.1	524	31.1	752						
8.0	9.0	370	17.1	562	31.0	806						
8.5	9.0	395	17.0	600								
9.0	9.0	421	17.0	638								
9.5	8.9	447	17.0	676								
10.0	8.9	473	17.0	714								
10.5	8.9	499	17.0	751								
11.0	8.9	526	16.9	789								
11.5	8.9	553										
12.0	8.9	580										
12.5	8.9	608										
13.0	8.8	635										
13.5	8.8	662										
14.0	8.8	689										
14.5	8.8	716										
15.0	8.8	743										
15.5	8.8	771										
16.0	8.8	799										

Grams SO_2 per 100 g. water	70°C.		80°C.		90°C.		100°C.		110°C.		120°C.		130°C.	
	H_2O	SO_2	H_2O	SO_2	H_2O	SO_2	H_2O	SO_2	H_2O	SO_2	H_2O	SO_2	H_2O	SO_2
0.0	234	...	355	...	526	...	760	...	1074	...	1488	...	2026	
0.5	234	144	354	182	525	225	758	274	1072	326	1486	377	2024	420
1.0	233	281	354	356	524	445	757	548	1071	661	1484	775	2022	879
1.5	233	426	353	543	523	684	756	850	1070	1032				
2.0	233	581	353	746	523	940								
2.5	232	739	352	956										
3.0	232	897												

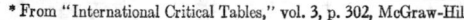

* From "International Critical Tables," vol. 3, p. 302, McGraw-Hill.

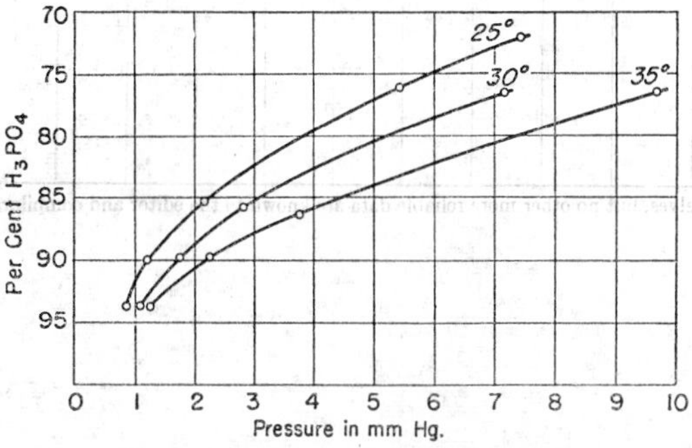

FIG. 3-1. Vapor pressures of H_3PO_4 aqueous. Partial pressure of H_2O vapor. (*Courtesy of Victor Chemical Works; measurements by W. H. Woodstock.*)

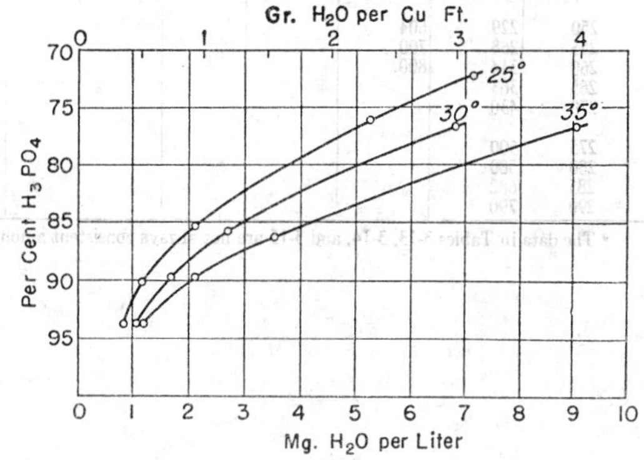

FIG. 3-2. Vapor pressures of H_3PO_4 aqueous. Weight of H_2O in saturated air. (*Courtesy of Victor Chemical Works; measurements by W. H. Woodstock.*)

Table 3-13. Vapor Pressures, Normal Boiling Points, and Latent Heats of Vaporization for Aqueous Solutions of H_2SO_4*

Percentages are wt. % H_2SO_4 in the solution

A and *B* are constants in the equation $\log_{10} p_{mm.} = A - \frac{B}{T}$

l = total heat of vaporization in g.-cal. per g. of water evaporated

B. P. = normal boiling point, °C.

For bibliography and discussion of data, see Greenewalt, *Ind. Eng. Chem.* **17**: 522, 1925.

Per cent	95	90	85	80	75	70	65	60	55	50	45	40	35	30	25	20	10
A	9.790	9.255	9.239	9.293	9.034	9.032	8.853	8.841	8.827	8.832	8.809	8.844	8.873	8.864		8.922	8.925
B	3888	3390	3175	3040	2810	2688	2533	2458	2400	2357	2322	2299	2286	2271		2268	2259
l	987	861	806	772	713	682	643	624	609	598	590	584	580	577		576	574
B. P.	290	255	225	202	182	165	151	140	130	123	118	114	110	108	106	104	102
°C.	Total vapor pressure, mm. Hg																
0	....	....	0.00418	0.0144	0.0550	0.154	0.377	0.686	1.08	1.55	2.07	2.55	3.06	3.43	3.72	4.02	4.38
5	....	0.00118	.00680	.0230	.0867	.235	.558	1.03	1.60	2.26	2.99	3.69	4.40	4.94	5.33	5.87	6.30
10	....	.00196	.0108	.0358	.128	.342	.800	1.46	2.26	3.19	4.19	5.22	6.23	6.91	7.46	8.05	8.80
15	....	.00318	.0169	.0555	.195	.506	1.15	2.05	3.19	4.50	5.85	7.27	8.65	9.65	10.5	11.3	12.3
20	....	.00497	.0257	.0835	.284	.723	1.61	2.87	4.43	6.20	8.10	9.95	11.8	13.2	14.3	15.4	16.6
25	....	.00765	.0390	.124	.408	1.03	2.24	3.97	6.15	8.45	10.9	13.5	15.8	17.8	19.4	20.8	22.4
30	....	.0117	.0585	.183	.580	1.44	3.09	5.41	8.29	11.3	14.7	18.0	21.2	23.8	26.0	27.8	30.0
35	0.00150	.0179	.0860	.265	.822	2.00	4.23	7.39	11.2	15.4	19.7	24.3	28.6	31.9	35.0	37.2	40.1
40	.00235	.0265	.125	.381	1.14	2.75	5.66	9.85	14.8	20.3	26.0	31.8	37.3	41.7	45.6	48.6	52.9
45	.00370	.0395	.181	.540	1.57	3.73	7.60	13.0	19.5	26.7	33.0	41.0	48.6	54.7	59.0	63.3	68.1
50	.00580	.0580	.260	.770	2.20	5.17	10.2	17.5	26.0	35.2	44.7	53.9	63.0	71.3	76.7	82.2	88.5
55	.00877	.0840	.367	1.06	2.95	6.89	13.4	22.7	33.7	45.5	57.5	69.0	80.2	91.0	98.2	106	113
60	.0133	.120	.411	1.47	3.98	9.12	18.6	29.3	43.0	58.0	73.0	87.3	102	116	124	133	143
65	.0196	.169	.707	2.00	5.30	10.2	22.7	37.7	55.1	73.7	92.3	110	127	145	156	167	178
70	.0288	.236	.960	2.68	7.02	15.6	29.0	48.0	69.6	92.5	116	138	159	180	195	207	223
75	.0415	.327	1.31	3.60	9.26	20.3	37.0	60.2	87.0	115	144	171	198	222	240	256	274
80	.0606	.450	1.77	4.77	12.0	26.0	47.0	75.3	108	143	179	211	244	273	295	314	337
85	.0879	.618	2.37	6.35	15.6	33.4	59.7	94.3	136	178	211	261	300	333	360	385	413
90	.123	.823	3.14	8.30	20.0	42.5	74.6	117	167	217	271	319	369	404	437	468	498
95	.172	1.12	4.18	10.8	25.7	53.9	92.7	144	205	268	335	390	450	493	531	580	608
100	.237	1.49	5.39	13.9	32.0	67.0	114	178	253	326	405	474	540	590	637	678	720
105	.321	1.93	6.95	17.6	40.0	82.3	140	213	302	393	484	568	642	702	758	812	
110	.437	2.52	9.00	22.5	50.0	103	172	260	367	471	580	679	768				
115	.590	3.23	11.4	28.3	62.0	126	207	313	435	562	684	800					
120	.788	4.19	14.5	35.6	76.5	153	251	377	522	670	812						
125	1.07	5.43	18.3	44.7	94.5	188	304	452	625	797							
130	1.42	6.97	23.2	56.0	117	230	370	544	744								
135	1.87	8.85	29.1	69.0	142	277	440	647									
140	2.40	11.2	36.3	85.5	173	332	525	760									
145	3.11	13.9	44.3	104	208	397	622										
150	4.02	17.5	54.6	127	248	471	730										
155	5.13	21.9	68.2	157	299	564											
160	6.47	27.7	82.0	188	354	665											
165	8.39	33.2	99.5	226	422	790											
170	10.3	39.8	119	267	496												
175	12.9	48.4	143	319	585												
180	15.9	59.0	169	378	685												
185	20.2	71.2	206	450	810												
190	24.8	85.0	245	535													
195	30.7	102	291	637													
200	36.7	120	340	735													
205	45.3	143	402														
210	55.0	170	472														
215	66.9	203	557														
220	79.8	240	647														
225	95.5	279	750														
230	115	326															
235	137	380															
240	164	450															
245	193	520															
250	229	604															
255	268	700															
260	314	800															
265	363																
270	430																
275	500																
280	580																
285	682																
290	790																

* The data in Tables 3-13, 3-14, and 3-15 are not always consistent among themselves, but no other more reliable data are known to the editor and compilers

Table 3-14. Partial Pressures of H_2SO_4 and H_2O over Sulfuric Acid Solutions

Mm. Hg

t, °C.	$p_{H_2SO_4}$	p_{H_2O}	t, °C.	$p_{H_2SO_4}$	p_{H_2O}	t, °C.	$p_{H_2SO_4}$	p_{H_2O}	t, °C.	$p_{H_2SO_4}$	p_{H_2O}	t, °C.	$p_{H_2SO_4}$	p_{H_2O}
89.25% H_2SO_4			91.26% H_2SO_4			95.06% H_2SO_4			98.06% H_2SO_4			99.23% H_2SO_4		
183.0	0.5	78.8	191.0	0.6	50.7	180.0	2.1	10.1	204.0	5.9	0.0	211.0	33.2	
197.5	1.3	116.9	205.0	1.9	84.7	200.0	4.8	21.2	218.5	9.8	1.5	225.0	49.9	
216.5	2.1	233.1	222.0	4.5	158.5	215.5	8.5	46.5	234.5	14.7	3.2	227.0	55.4	
230.0	3.6	306.3	242.5	6.4	271.6	232.0	13.4	91.9	249.0	28.5	2.6	244.0	84.1	<0.1
241.5	5.3	414.8	252.5	11.3	385.3	244.5	19.9	120.1	261.0	38.8	5.0	261.0	163.8	
			258.0	13.6	448.7	252.0	20.0	156.5	273.0	61.9	5.3	270.0	229.8	
			262.5	16.3	411.1	261.0	27.9	180.7	285.0	91.6	11.8	281.0	272.3	
						270.0	39.9	254.9	295.0	132.3	14.7	290.0	381.5	
						280.5	52.0	310.0						
						282.0	52.6	350.2						

Table 3-15. Partial Pressures of SO_3 over Fuming Sulfuric Acid

Mm. Hg, °C.

Total % H_2SO_4	% SO_3	20°	25°	30°	35°	40°	45°	50°	55°	60°	65°	70°	75°	80°	85°	90°
102.0	83.265	.....	.....	.....	0.4	0.6	1.0	1.6	2.5	3.8	5.7	8.5	12.5	18.2	26.3	37.5
103.0	84.081	.....	.....	.....	0.5	0.9	1.3	2.1	3.2	4.8	6.8	10.5	15.3	22.0	31.4	44.4
104.0	84.897	0.2	0.3	0.5	0.8	1.3	2.0	3.0	4.5	6.7	9.8	14.2	20.4	29.0	40.8	56.8
104.5	85.305	0.3	0.4	0.7	1.1	1.7	2.6	4.0	6.0	8.9	12.9	18.8	26.7	37.9	53.5	73.9
105.0	85.714	0.4	0.7	1.1	1.7	2.6	4.0	6.0	9.0	13.1	19.0	27.2	38.6	54.1	75.2	103.7
105.5	86.122	0.8	1.2	1.9	2.9	4.4	6.6	9.8	14.3	20.7	29.5	42.1	58.1	81.5	112.6	153.1
106.0	86.530	1.4	2.1	3.2	4.9	7.3	10.8	15.7	22.6	32.1	45.2	63.0	87.0	119.0	161.5	217.2
106.5	86.938	2.4	3.6	5.5	8.2	12.0	17.4	25.0	35.4	49.8	69.0	95.5	129.3	171.2	230.1	311.9
107.0	87.346	4.0	6.0	8.9	13.0	18.8	26.9	38.1	53.4	74.0	101.6	138.2	186.4	249.2	330.5	434.9
107.5	87.754	6.9	10.0	14.6	20.7	29.2	40.7	56.4	77.1	104.6	140.2	167.3	246.5	323.7	422.2	547.7
108.0	88.163	.....	15.9	22.4	31.4	43.4	59.4	80.6	108.3	144.2	190.4	249.4	324.2			
108.5	88.571	.....	.....	35.1	47.8	64.8	86.9	115.7	152.3	199.4	257.9	333.6	425.1			
109.0	88.979	.....	.....	.....	64.5	86.6	115.3	152.1	199.0	258.3	332.5	425.0	539.5			
110.0	89.795	.....	.....	.....	100.5	133.7	176.1	230.1	298.2	383.5	489.5					
111.0	90.612	.....	.....	105.2	140.5	185.7	243.4	316.3	407.9							
112.0	91.428	76.1	103.2	138.5	184.0	242.4	316.5	409.9	526.6							
113.0	92.244	96.9	130.9	175.1	232.1	304.9	397.1	512.9	657.4							
114.0	93.060	119.1	160.7	214.9	284.5	373.3	485.8	626.9	802.8							
115.0	93.877	144.2	194.3	259.2	342.6	448.8	583.0	751.2	960.4							

Table 3-16. Partial Pressures of HNO_3 and H_2O over Aqueous Solutions of HNO_3

Mm. Hg

Percentages are wt. % HNO_3 in solution

°C.	20%		25%		30%		35%		40%		45%		50%	
	HNO_3	H_2O	HNO_3	H_2O	HNO_3	H_2O	HNO_3	H_2O	HNO_3	H_2O	HNO_3	H_2O	HNO_3	H_2O
0	....	4.1	....	3.8	....	3.6	.....	3.3	.....	3.0	.....	2.6	.....	2.1
5	....	5.7	....	5.4	....	5.0	.....	4.6	.....	4.2	.....	3.6	.....	3.0
10	....	8.0	....	7.6	....	7.1	.....	6.5	.....	5.8	.....	5.0	0.12	4.2
15	.....	10.9	....	10.3	....	9.7	.....	8.9	.....	8.0	0.10	6.9	.18	5.8
20	....	15.2	....	14.2	....	13.2	.....	12.0	.....	10.8	.15	9.4	.27	7.9
25	....	20.6	....	19.2	....	17.8	.....	16.2	0.12	14.6	.23	12.7	.39	10.7
30	....	27.6	....	25.7	....	23.8	0.09	21.7	.17	19.5	.33	16.9	.56	14.4
35	....	36.5	....	33.8	....	31.1	.13	28.3	.25	25.5	.48	22.3	.80	19.0
40	....	47.5	....	44	0.11	41	.20	37.7	.36	33.5	.68	29.3	1.13	25.0
45	....	62	0.09	57.5	.17	53	.28	48	.52	43	.96	38.0	1.57	32.5
50	....	80	.13	75	.25	69	.42	63	.75	56	1.35	49.5	2.18	42.5
55	0.09	100	.18	94	.35	87	.59	79	1.04	71	1.83	62.5	2.95	54
60	.13	128	.28	121	.51	113	.85	102	1.48	90	2.54	80	4.05	70
65	.19	162	.40	151	.71	140	1.18	127	2.05	114	3.47	100	5.46	88
70	.27	200	.54	187	1.00	174	1.63	159	2.80	143	4.65	126	7.25	110
75	.38	250	.77	234	1.38	217	2.26	198	3.80	178	6.20	158	9.6	138
80	.53	307	1.05	287	1.87	267	3.07	243	5.10	218	8.15	195	12.5	170
85	.74	378	1.44	352	2.53	325	4.15	297	6.83	268	10.7	240	16.3	211
90	1.01	458	1.95	426	3.38	393	5.50	359	9.0	325	13.7	292	20.9	258
95	1.37	555	2.62	517	4.53	478	7.32	436	11.7	394	17.8	355	26.8	315
100	1.87	675	3.50	628	6.05	580	9.7	530	15.5	480	23.0	430	34.2	383
105	2.50	800	4.65	745	7.90	690	12.7	631	20.0	573	29.2	520	43.0	463
110	....	.....	....	.....	....	.....	16.5	755	25.7	688	37.0	625	54.5	560
115	....	.....	....	.....	....	.....	.....	.....	32.5	810	46	740	67	665
120	....	.....	....	.....	....	.....	.....	.....	.....	.....	.....	.....	84	785

Table 3-16. Partial Pressures of HNO_3 and H_2O over Aqueous Solutions of HNO_3—*(Concluded)*

°C.	55%		60%		65%		70%		80%		90%		100%
	HNO_3	H_2O	HNO_3	H_2O	HNO_3	H_2O	HNO_3	H_2O	HNO_3	H_2O	HNO_3	H_2O	HNO_3
0	......	1.8	0.19	1.5	0.41	1.3	0.79	1.1	2	....	5.5	....	11
5	0.14	2.5	.28	2.1	.60	1.8	1.12	1.6	3	....	8	....	15
10	.21	3.5	.41	3.0	.86	2.6	1.58	2.2	4	1.2	11	....	22
15	.31	4.9	.59	4.1	1.21	3.5	2.18	3.0	6	1.7	15	....	30
20	.45	6.7	.84	5.6	1.68	4.9	3.00	4.1	8	2.4	20	....	42
25	.66	9.1	1.21	7.7	2.32	6.6	4.10	5.5	10.5	3.2	27	1	57
30	.93	12.2	1.66	10.3	3.17	8.8	5.50	7.4	14	4	36	1.3	77
35	1.30	16.1	2.28	13.6	4.26	11.6	7.30	9.8	18.5	5.5	47	1.8	102
40	1.82	21.3	3.10	18.1	5.70	15.5	9.65	12.8	24.5	7	62	2.4	133
45	2.50	28.0	4.20	23.7	7.55	20.0	12.6	16.7	32	9.5	80	3	170
50	3.41	36.3	5.68	31	10.0	26.0	16.5	21.8	41	12	103	4	215
55	4.54	46	7.45	39	12.8	33.0	21.0	27.3	52	15	127	5	262
60	6.15	60	9.9	51	16.8	43.0	27.1	35.3	67	20	157	6.5	320
65	8.18	76	13.0	64	21.7	54.5	34.5	44.5	85	25	192	8	385
70	10.7	95	16.8	81	27.5	68	43.3	56	106	31	232	10	460
75	13.9	120	21.8	102	35.0	86	54.5	70	130	38	282	13	540
80	18.0	148	27.5	126	43.5	106	67.5	86	158	48	338	16	625
85	23.0	182	34.8	156	54.5	131	83	107	192	60	405	20	720
90	29.4	223	43.7	192	67.5	160	103	130	230	73	480	24	820
95	37.3	272	55.0	233	83.5	195	125	158	278	89	570	29	
100	47	331	69.5	285	103	238	152	192	330	108	675	35	
105	58.5	400	84.5	345	124	288	183	231	392	129	790	42	
110	73	485	103	417	152	345	221	270	465	155			
115	90	575	126	495	181	410	262	330	545	185			
120	110	685	156	590	218	490	312	393	640	219			
125	.....	.....	187	700	260	580	372	469					

Table 3-17. Partial Pressures of H_2O and HBr over Aqueous Solutions of HBr at 20° to 55°C.

Mm. Hg

% HBr	20°C.		25°C.		50°C.		55°C.	
	HBr	H_2O	HBr	H_2O	HBr	H_2O	HBr	H_2O
32	.....	...	0.0016					
34	.....	...	.0022					
36	.....	...	.0033					
38	.....	...	.0061					
40	.....	...	.011					
42	.....	...	.023					
44	.....	...	.048					
46	.....	...	.10					
48	0.09	6.2	.13	8.2	1.3	30.2	2.0	38
50	.23	4.5	.37	6.1	3.2	24.3	4.6	31
52	.71	3.3	1.1	4.5	7.2	19.3	10.2	25
54	2.2	2.4	3.2	3.3	17	16.0	23.0	21
56	6.8	1.7	9.3	2.4	40	13.3	51	18
58	21	1.3	27	1.9	91	10.4	115	14
60	.....	...	....	...	....	....	260	11.4

Table 3-18. Partial Pressures of HI over Aqueous Solutions of HI at 25°C.

Mm. Hg

%HI......	4	46	48	50	52	54	56
p_{HI}......	0.00064	0.0010	0.0022	0.0050	0.013	0.035	0.10

Table 3-19. Vapor Pressures of the System: Water—Sulfuric Acid—Nitric Acid

For these data, reference must be made to the graphs of "International Critical Tables," vol. 3, pp. 306–308.

Table 3-20. Total Vapor Pressures of Aqueous Solutions of CH_3COOH

Percentages are wt. % acetic acid in the solution

Mm. Hg

°C.	25%	50%	75%
20	16.3	15.7	15.3
25	22.1	21.4	20.8
30	29.6	28.8	27.8
35	39.4	38.3	36.6
40	51.7	50.2	48.1
45	67.0	65.0	62.0
50	87.2	85.0	80.1
55	110	107	102
60	141	138	130
65	178	172	162
70	223	216	203
75	277	269	251
80	342	331	310
85	419	407	376
90	510	497	458
95	618	602	550
100	743	725	666

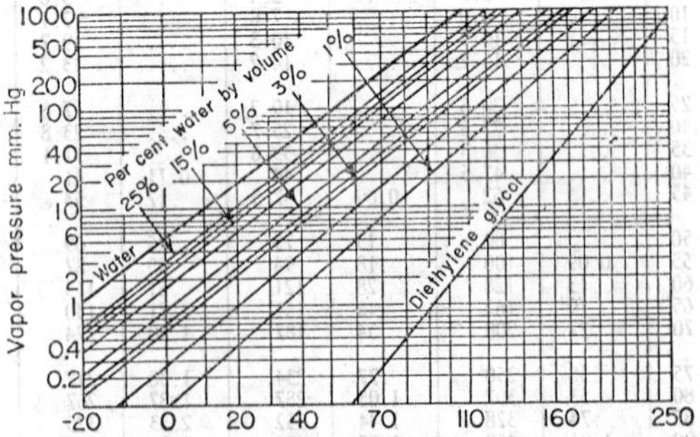

FIG. 3-3. Vapor pressure of aqueous diethylene glycol solutions. *(Courtesy of Carbide and Carbon Chemicals Corp.)*

Table 3-21. Partial Pressures of H_2O over Aqueous Solutions of NH_3*

Pressures are in pounds per square inch absolute

t, °F.	Molal concentration of ammonia in the solutions in percentages (Weight concentration of ammonia in the solution in percentages)																			
	0 (0)	5 (4.74)	10 (9.50)	15 (14.29)	20 (19.10)	25 (23.94)	30 (28.81)	35 (33.71)	40 (38.64)	45 (43.59)	50 (48.57)	55 (53.58)	60 (58.62)	65 (63.69)	70 (68.79)	75 (73.91)	80 (79.07)	85 (84.26)	90 (89.47)	95 (94.72)
32	0.09	0.084	0.079	0.074	0.070	0.065	0.060	0.056	0.051	0.047	0.042	0.038	0.034	0.030	0.025	0.021	0.017	0.013	0.008	0.004
40	.12	.115	.108	.101	.095	.089	.083	.076	.070	.064	.058	.052	.046	.040	.035	.029	.023	.015	.012	.006
50	.18	.17	.16	.15	.14	.13	.12	.11	.10	.094	.085	.076	.068	.059	.051	.042	.034	.025	.017	.008
60	.26	.24	.23	.21	.20	.19	.17	.16	.15	.13	.12	.11	.097	.085	.073	.061	.049	.037	.024	.012
70	.36	.34	.32	.30	.28	.26	.25	.23	.21	.19	.17	.15	.14	.12	.10	.086	.069	.052	.034	.017
80	.51	.48	.45	.42	.40	.37	.34	.32	.29	.27	.24	.22	.19	.17	.14	.12	.096	.072	.048	.024
90	.70	.66	.63	.58	.55	.51	.47	44	.40	.37	.33	.30	.26	.23	.20	.16	.13	.10	.066	.033
100	.95	.90	.85	.79	.74	.69	.64	.59	.55	.50	.45	.41	.36	.31	.27	.22	.18	.13	.090	.045
110	1.27	1.20	1.14	1.07	1.00	.93	.86	.80	.73	.67	.60	.54	.48	.42	.36	.30	.24	.18	.120	.061
120	1.69	1.60	1.51	1.42	1.33	1.24	1.15	1.06	.97	.89	.80	.72	.64	.56	.48	.40	.32	.24	.160	.081
130	2.22	2.10	1.98	1.86	1.74	1.62	1.51	1.39	1.28	1.17	1.05	.95	.84	.74	.63	.53	.42	.32	.210	.100
140	2.89	2.73	2.57	2.42	2.26	2.11	1.96	1.81	1.66	1.52	1.37	1.23	1.10	.96	.82	.69	.55	.41	.270	.140
150	3.72	3.51	3.31	3.11	2.91	2.72	2.52	2.33	2.14	1.95	1.76	1.59	1.41	1.24	1.06	.88	.71	.53	.350	.180
160	4.74	4.48	4.22	3.97	3.71	3.46	3.22	2.97	2.73	2.49	2.25	2.02	1.80	1.58	1.35	1.12	.90	.67	.450	.220
170	5.99	5.66	5.34	5.02	4.70	4.38	4.07	3.75	3.45	3.15	2.84	2.56	2.28	1.99	1.71	1.42	1.13	1.85	.570	.300
180	7.51	7.10	6.69	6.30	5.89	5.49	5.10	4.71	4.33	3.94	3.57	3.21	2.85	2.50	2.14	1.77	1.42	1.06		
190	9.34	8.83	8.32	7.82	7.32	6.83	6.34	5.86	5.38	4.91	4.44	3.99	3.55	3.10	2.65					
200	11.53	10.90	10.27	9.65	9.04	8.43	7.83	7.23	6.64	6.06	5.48	4.93	4.38	3.81						
210	14.12	13.35	12.58	11.82	11.07	10.32	9.59	8.86	8.13	7.42	6.71	6.04	5.34							
220	17.19	16.25	15.32	14.39	13.48	12.57	11.67	10.78	9.90	9.03	8.17	7.31								
230	20.78	19.64	18.51	17.40	16.29	15.19	14.11	13.03	11.97	10.91	9.87									
240	24.97	23.60	22.25	20.91	19.58	18.26	16.95	15.66	14.38	13.12	11.86									
250	29.83	28.20	26.58	25.00	23.39	21.82	20.25	18.71	17.18	15.67										

* Wilson, *Univ. Ill., Eng. Expt. Sta. Bull.* 146.,

Table 3-22. Mole Percentages of H_2O over Aqueous Solutions of NH_3*

t. °F.	Molal concentration of ammonia in the solutions in percentages (Weight concentration of ammonia in the solutions in percentages)																				
	0 (0)	5 (4.74)	10 (9.50)	15 (14.29)	20 (19.10)	25 (23.94)	30 (28.81)	35 (33.71)	40 (38.64)	45 (43.59)	50 (48.57)	55 (53.58)	60 (58.62)	65 (63.69)	70 (68.79)	75 (73.91)	80 (79.07)	85 (84.26)	90 (89.47)	95 (94.72)	100 (100.00)
32	100	24.3	13.2	7.63	4.43	2.50	1.43	0.856	0.514	0.335	0.216	0.151	0.109	0.0816	0.0585	0.0457	0.0345	0.0249	0.0146	0.00689	0.00
40	100	25.3	14.1	8.15	4.73	2.74	1.59	.943	.581	.372	.248	.172	.124	.0914	.0706	.0533	.0395	.0243	.0185	.00879	
50	100	26.6	15.2	9.09	5.24	3.03	1.78	1.060	.652	.434	.290	.202	.148	.1095	.0838	.0630	.0477	.0332	.0215	.00959	
60	100	27.9	16.2	9.50	5.69	3.42	1.97	1.210	.777	.481	.331	.238	.172	.1290	.0986	.0754	.0566	.0406	.0251	.01125	
70	100	29.1	17.4	10.30	6.14	3.65	2.27	1.390	.873	.569	.383	.266	.205	.1510	.112	.0882	.0656	.0474	.0296	.0135	
80	100	31.6	18.5	11.20	6.89	4.08	2.45	1.550	.978	.659	.444	.323	.230	.1750	.130	.103	.0772	.0528	.0351	.0167	
90	100	32.7	20.0	12.00	7.40	4.47	2.73	1.730	1.100	.742	.505	.366	.267	.2020	.157	.115	.0884	.0647	.0408	.0194	
100	100	34.4	21.0	12.90	7.92	4.85	3.00	1.890	1.250	.834	.574	.420	.307	.2290	.179	.135	.104	.0714	.0473	.0226	
110	100	35.9	22.2	13.80	8.59	5.29	3.30	2.110	1.370	.932	.644	.466	.347	.2640	.208	.157	.118	.0846	.0540	.0262	
120	100	37.5	23.4	14.70	9.22	5.75	3.63	2.320	1.520	1.044	.714	.529	.395	.3020	.233	.180	.135	.0970	.0619	.0300	
130	100	39.0	24.5	15.60	9.85	6.18	3.95	2.550	1.690	1.160	.811	.596	.444	.3430	.263	.205	.154	.1117	.0703	.0339	
140	100	40.7	25.8	16.50	10.50	6.69	4.28	2.790	1.860	1.286	.906	.663	.501	.3840	.297	.232	.175	.124	.0786	.0385	
150	100	42.3	27.1	17.50	11.20	7.19	4.63	3.080	2.040	1.410	1.004	.741	.558	.4320	.334	.257	.197	.140	.0892	.0439	
160	100	44.1	28.3	18.40	11.90	7.69	5.01	3.300	2.230	1.550	1.110	.818	.617	.4800	.372	.287	.218	.154	.1005	.0499	
170	100	45.6	29.6	19.40	12.70	8.22	5.38	3.580	2.430	1.700	1.220	.904	.689	.5300	.414	.320	.242	.174	.112	.0567	
180	100	47.3	30.9	20.40	13.40	8.76	5.78	3.870	2.640	1.850	1.340	.994	.756	.5860	.456	.352	.268	.192			
190	100	48.7	32.2	21.40	14.10	9.31	6.18	4.160	2.860	2.020	1.460	1.087	.830	.6420	.501						
200	100	50.4	33.4	22.30	14.90	9.88	6.59	4.470	3.080	2.190	1.580	1.187	.907	.7010							
210	100	52.1	34.7	23.40	15.70	10.45	7.03	4.780	3.310	2.360	1.720	1.272	.983								
220	100	53.7	36.1	24.40	16.40	11.05	7.48	5.100	3.560	2.540	1.860	1.390									
230	100	55.2	37.3	25.40	17.30	11.63	7.91	5.440	3.810	2.730	2.000										
240	100	56.8	38.6	26.50	18.00	12.24	8.36	5.780	4.060	2.920	2.150										
250	100	58.4	39.8	27.50	18.80	12.88	8.82	6.120	4.340	3.120											

* Wilson, *Univ. Ill., Eng. Expt. Sta. Bull.* 146.

Table 3-23. Partial Pressures of NH_3 over Aqueous Solutions of NH_3*

Pressures are in pounds per square inch absolute

t, °F.	Molal concentration of ammonia in the solutions in percentages (Weight concentration of ammonia in the solutions in percentages)																		
	5 (4.74)	10 (9.50)	15 (14.29)	20 (19.10)	25 (23.94)	30 (28.81)	35 (33.71)	40 (38.64)	45 (43.59)	50 (48.57)	55 (53.58)	60 (58.62)	65 (63.69)	70 (68.79)	75 (73.91)	80 (79.07)	85 (84.26)	90 (89.47)	95 (94.72)
32	0.26	0.52	0.90	1.51	2.67	4.27	6.54	8.93	14.13	19.36	25.12	31.13	36.74	42.69	45.92	49.26	52.13	54.89	58.05
40	.33	.66	1.14	1.92	3.16	5.13	7.98	11.98	17.14	23.33	30.15	37.15	43.69	49.56	54.40	58.31	61.62	64.77	68.38
50	.47	.89	1.50	2.53	4.16	6.63	10.24	15.24	21.56	29.17	37.46	45.86	53.79	60.82	66.63	71.26	75.22	79.05	83.40
60	.62	1.19	2.00	3.21	5.36	8.48	13.06	19.15	26.92	36.14	46.12	56.22	65.81	73.99	80.90	86.44	91.04	95.67	100.65
70	.83	1.52	2.60	4.28	6.87	10.76	16.33	23.84	33.20	44.25	56.29	68.32	79.42	89.26	97.42	104.01	109.55	114.83	120.61
80	1.04	1.98	3.34	5.45	8.69	13.52	20.29	29.40	40.69	53.84	67.97	82.36	95.52	107.06	116.42	124.20	130.57	136.35	143.70
90	1.36	2.52	4.25	6.88	10.89	16.76	25.04	35.94	49.45	64.99	81.61	98.35	113.79	127.22	138.18	147.02	154.46	161.74	169.73
100	1.72	3.20	5.34	8.60	13.53	20.68	30.57	43.57	59.49	77.85	97.27	116.81	134.70	150.23	162.94	173.22	181.97	190.13	199.17
110	2.14	4.00	6.65	10.64	16.65	25.21	37.01	52.43	71.20	92.59	115.16	137.62	158.42	176.18	190.85	203.02	212.71	222.22	232.79
120	2.67	4.95	8.21	13.09	20.30	30.54	44.56	62.62	84.44	109.40	135.48	161.44	185.14	205.81	222.28	236.05	247.14	258.24	270.02
130	3.28	6.09	10.05	15.93	24.58	36.74	53.16	74.27	99.69	128.45	158.45	188.16	215.14	238.70	257.87	272.88	286.08	298.46	311.80
140	3.97	7.41	12.21	19.23	29.43	43.77	62.97	87.53	116.72	149.93	184.17	218.18	248.70	275.33	297.12	314.45	328.99	342.93	358.46
150	4.78	8.92	14.70	23.09	35.09	51.91	74.28	102.51	136.15	173.64	212.91	251.24	286.00	316.24	340.82	360.39	376.57	392.45	409.62
160	5.68	10.70	17.57	27.45	41.56	61.03	86.91	119.37	157.71	200.45	244.98	288.38	327.82	361.75	389.08	411.30	429.73	447.35	466.38
170	6.75	12.67	20.85	32.41	48.89	71.48	101.09	138.30	181.95	230.36	280.54	329.42	373.61	411.59	442.28	466.67	487.85	507.63	528.50
180	7.90	14.96	24.56	38.13	57.19	83.07	116.97	159.37	208.66	263.43	319.89	374.25	424.10	466.26	500.63	528.08	551.24		
190	9.23	17.55	28.78	44.49	66.49	96.22	134.89	182.72	238.39	299.86	363.11	424.15	479.40	526.15					
200	10.70	20.45	33.49	51.58	76.90	110.85	154.58	208.56	270.94	340.02	410.17	478.62	539.79						
210	12.26	23.68	38.76	59.65	88.48	126.83	176.24	236.97	307.08	383.99	462.36	537.56							
220	14.02	27.15	44.61	68.43	101.24	144.74	200.46	268.30	346.07	431.43	518.19								
230	15.95	31.09	51.06	78.14	115.45	164.17	226.67	302.53	389.29	483.53									
240	17.92	35.40	58.00	89.02	130.94	185.79	255.26	339.72	435.78	540.44									
250	20.12	40.09	65.74	100.69	147.66	209.37	286.89	380.42	486.73										

* Wilson, *Univ. Ill., Eng. Expt. Sta. Bull.* 146.

Table 3-24. Total Vapor Pressures of Aqueous Solutions of NH_3*

Pressures are in pounds per square inch absolute

t, °F.	Molal concentration of ammonia in the solutions in percentages (Weight concentration of ammonia in the solutions in percentages)																				
	0 (0)	5 (4.74)	10 (9.50)	15 (14.29)	20 (19.10)	25 (23.94)	30 (28.81)	35 (33.71)	40 (38.64)	45 (43.59)	50 (48.57)	55 (53.58)	60 (58.62)	65 (63.69)	70 (68.79)	75 (73.91)	80 (79.07)	85 (84.26)	90 (89.47)	95 (94.72)	100 (100.00)
32	0.09	0.34	0.60	0.97	1.58	2.60	4.20	6.54	9.93	14.18	19.40	25.16	31.16	36.77	42.72	45.94	49.28	52.14	54.90	58.01	62.29
40	.12	.45	.77	1.24	2.01	3.25	5.21	8.06	12.05	17.20	23.39	30.20	37.20	43.73	49.60	54.43	58.33	61.64	64.78	68.32	73.32
50	.18	.64	1.05	1.65	2.67	4.29	6.75	10.35	15.34	21.65	29.26	37.54	45.93	53.85	60.87	66.67	71.29	75.25	79.07	83.41	89.19
60	.26	.86	1.42	2.21	3.51	5.55	8.65	13.22	19.30	27.05	36.26	46.23	56.32	65.90	74.06	80.96	86.49	91.08	95.69	100.66	107.6
70	.36	1.17	1.84	2.90	4.56	7.13	11.01	16.56	24.05	33.39	44.42	56.44	68.46	79.54	89.36	97.51	104.08	109.60	114.86	120.63	128.8
80	.51	1.52	2.43	3.76	5.85	9.06	13.86	20.61	29.69	40.96	54.08	68.19	82.55	95.69	107.20	116.54	124.30	130.64	136.40	143.72	153.0
90	.70	2.02	3.15	4.83	7.43	11.40	17.23	25.48	36.34	49.82	65.32	81.91	98.61	114.02	127.42	138.34	147.15	154.56	161.81	169.76	180.6
100	.95	2.62	4.05	6.13	9.34	14.22	21.32	31.16	44.12	59.99	78.30	97.68	117.17	135.01	150.50	163.16	173.40	182.10	190.22	199.22	211.9
110	1.27	3.34	5.14	7.72	11.64	17.58	26.07	37.81	53.16	71.87	93.19	115.7	138.10	158.84	176.54	191.15	203.26	212.89	222.34	232.85	247.0
120	1.69	4.27	6.46	9.63	14.42	21.54	31.69	45.62	63.59	85.33	110.2	136.2	162.08	185.70	206.29	222.68	236.37	247.38	258.40	270.1	286.4
130	2.22	5.38	8.07	11.91	17.67	26.20	38.25	54.55	75.55	100.86	129.5	159.	189.00	215.88	239.33	258.40	273.3	286.4	298.67	311.9	330.3
140	2.89	6.70	9.98	14.63	21.49	31.54	45.73	64.78	89.19	118.24	151.3	185.4	219.28	249.66	276.15	297.81	315.0	329.4	343.2	358.6	379.1
150	3.72	8.29	12.23	17.81	26.00	37.81	54.43	76.61	104.65	138.1	175.4	214.5	252.65	287.24	317.3	341.7	361.1	377.1	392.8	409.8	432.2
160	4.74	10.16	14.92	21.54	31.16	45.02	64.25	89.88	122.10	160.2	202.7	247.0	290.18	329.4	363.1	390.2	412.2	430.4	447.8	466.6	492.8
170	5.99	12.41	18.01	25.87	37.11	53.27	75.55	104.84	141.75	185.1	233.2	283.1	331.7	375.6	413.3	443.7	467.8	488.7	508.2	528.8	558.4
180	7.51	15.00	21.65	30.86	44.02	62.68	88.17	121.68	163.7	212.6	267.0	323.1	377.1	426.6	468.4	502.4	529.5	552.3			
190	9.34	18.06	25.87	36.60	51.81	73.32	102.56	140.75	188.1	243.3	304.3	367.1	427.7	482.5	528.8						
200	11.53	21.60	30.72	43.14	60.62	85.33	118.68	161.81	215.2	277.0	345.5	415.1	483.0	543.6							
210	14.12	25.61	36.26	50.58	70.72	98.80	136.42	185.10	245.1	314.5	390.7	468.4	542.9								
220	17.19	30.27	42.47	59.00	81.91	113.81	156.41	211.24	278.2	355.1	439.6	525.5									
230	20.78	35.59	49.60	68.46	94.43	130.64	178.28	239.70	314.5	400.2	493.4										
240	24.97	41.52	57.65	78.91	108.60	149.20	202.74	270.92	354.1	448.9	552.3										
250	29.83	48.32	66.67	90.74	124.08	169.48	229.62	305.60	397.6	502.4											

* Wilson, *Univ. Ill., Eng. Expt. Sta. Bull.* 146.

Table 3-25. Partial Pressures of H_2O over Aqueous Solutions of Sodium Carbonate

Mm. Hg

t, °C.	%Na_2CO_3						
	0	5	10	15	20	25	30
0	4.5	4.5					
10	9.2	9.0	8.8				
20	17.5	17.2	16.8	16.3			
30	31.8	31.2	30.4	29.6	28.8	27.8	26.4
40	55.3	54.2	53.0	57.6	50.2	48.4	46.1
50	92.5	90.7	88.7	86.5	84.1	81.2	77.5
60	149.5	146.5	143.5	139.9	136.1	131.6	125.7
70	239.8	235	230.5	225	219	211.5	202.5
80	355.5	348	342	334	325	315	301
90	526.0	516	506	494	482	467	447
100	760.0	746	731	715	697	676	648

Table 3-26. Partial Pressures of H_2O and CH_3OH over Aqueous Solutions of Methyl Alcohol*

Mole fraction CH_3OH	39.9°C. P_{H_2O}, mm. Hg	39.9°C. P_{CH_3OH}, mm. Hg	Mole fraction CH_3OH	59.4°C. P_{H_2O}, mm. Hg	59.4°C. P_{CH_3OH}, mm. Hg
0	54.7	0	0	145.4	0
14.99	39.2	66.1	22.17	106.9	210.1
17.85	38.5	75.5	27.40	102.2	240.2
21.07	37.2	85.2	33.24	96.6	272.1
27.31	35.8	100.6	39.80	91.7	301.9
31.06	34.9	108.8	47.08	84.8	335.6
40.1	32.8	127.7	55.5	76.9	373.7
47.0	31.5	141.6	69.2	57.8	439.4
55.8	27.3	158.4	78.5	43.8	486.6
68.9	20.7	186.6	85.9	30.1	526.9
86.0	10.1	225.2	100.0	0	609.3
100.0	0	260.7			

* "International Critical Tables," vol. 3, p. 290, McGraw-Hill.

Table 3-27. Partial Pressures of H_2O over Aqueous Solutions of Sodium Hydroxide

Mm. Hg

Conc. g. NaOH/ 100 g. H_2O	Temperature, °C.											
	0	20	40	60	80	100	120	160	200	250	300	350
0	4.6	17.5	55.3	149.5	355.5	760.0	1,489	4,633	11,647	29,771	64,200	123,600
5	4.4	16.9	53.2	143.5	341.5	730.0	1,430	4,450	11,200	28,600	61,800	118,900
10	4.2	16.0	50.6	137.0	325.5	697.0	1,365	4,260	10,750	27,500	59,300	114,100
20	3.6	13.9	44.2	120.5	288.5	621.0	1,225	3,860	9,800	25,300	54,700	105,400
30	2.9	11.3	36.6	101.0	246.0	537.0	1,070	3,460	8,950	23,300	50,800	98,000
40	2.2	8.7	28.7	81.0	202.0	450.0	920	3,090	8,150	21,500	47,200	91,600
50	...	6.3	20.7	62.5	160.5	368.0	770	2,690	7,400	19,900	44,100	85,800
60	...	4.4	15.5	47.0	124.0	294.0	635	2,340	6,750	18,400	41,200	80,700
70	...	3.0	10.9	34.5	94.0	231.0	515	2,030	6,100	17,100	38,700	76,000
80	...	2.0	7.6	24.5	70.5	179.0	415	1,740	5,500	15,800	36,300	71,900
90	...	1.3	5.2	17.5	53.0	138.0	330	1,490	5,000	14,700	34,200	68,100
100	...	0.9	3.6	12.5	38.5	105.0	262	1,300	4,500	13,650	32,200	64,600
120	...	....	1.7	6.3	20.5	61.0	164	915	3,650	11,800	28,800	58,600
140	...	....	....	3.0	11.0	35.5	102	765	2,980	10,300	25,900	53,400
160	...	....	....	1.5	6.0	20.5	63	470	2,430	8,960	23,300	49,000
180	...	....	....	.....	3.5	12.0	40	340	1,980	7,830	21,200	45,100
200	...	....	....	.....	2.0	7.0	25	245	1,620	6,870	19,200	41,800
250	...	....	....	.....	0.5	2.0	8	110	985	5,000	15,400	35,000
300	...	....	....	.....	0.1	0.5	2.7	50	610	3,690	12,500	29,800
350	...	....	....	.....	.....	.....	0.9	23	380	2,750	10,300	25,700
400	...	....	....	.....	.....	.....	.....	11	240	2,080	8,600	22,400
500	...	....	....	.....	.....	.....	.....	.....	100	1,210	6,100	17,500
700	...	....	....	.....	.....	.....	.....	.....	.....	440	3,300	11,500
1000	...	....	....	.....	.....	.....	.....	.....	.....	.....	1,470	6,800
2000	...	....	....	.....	.....	.....	.....	.....	.....	.....	150	1,760
4000	...	....	....	.....	.....	.....	.....	.....	.....	.....	.....	120
8000	...	....	....	.....	.....	.....	.....	.....	.....	.....	.....	7

WATER-VAPOR CONTENT OF GASES

CHARTS FOR GASES AT HIGH PRESSURES

The accompanying figures are useful in determining the water-vapor content of gases at high pressure in contact with liquid water. Data for air are given in Fig. 3-6. Figure 3-5 shows the water-vapor content of hydrogen and nitrogen in contact with liquid water at high pressures. For additional experimental values of the water content of compressed nitrogen in contact with water at 100, 200, and 300 atm. and up to 230°C., see Saddington and Krase, *J. Am. Chem. Soc.*, **56**, 360 (**1934**). Results to 100°C. are shown in Fig. 3-4, and comparisons with Bartlett's values at 50°C. are included. Figure 3-7 shows the water-vapor content of compressed gases in contact with liquid water. Figure 3-8 shows the volume percentage of water vapor in gases expanded from high-pressure contact with liquid water.

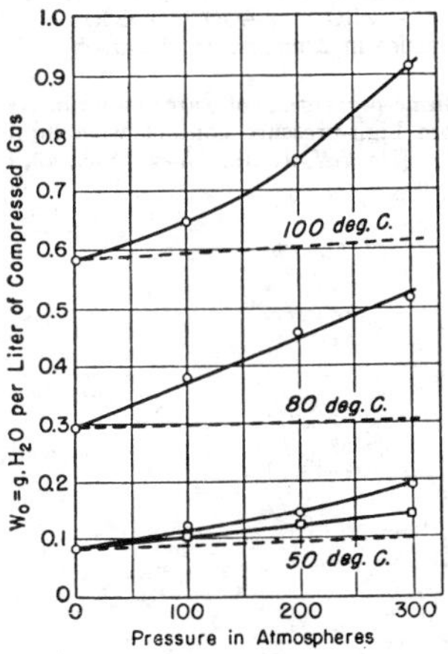

FIG. 3-4. Effect of pressure on the water-vapor content of compressed N_2 gas; ———, Poynting relation; □, Bartlett; ○, experimental. [*Saddington and Krase, J. Am. Chem. Soc.*, **56**, 360 (1934).]

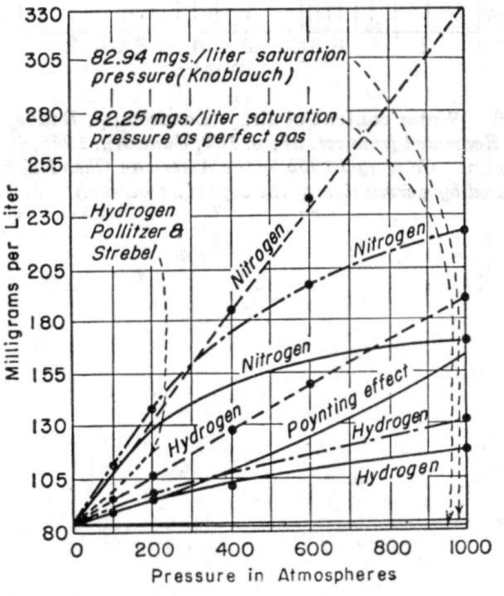

FIG. 3-5. Water-vapor content of hydrogen and nitrogen in contact with liquid water at high pressures at 50°C. — — —, calculated to perfect gas volume; ————, calculated to actual volume; —·—·—·, calculated to free space. [*Bartlett, J. Am. Chem. Soc.*, **49**, 65 (1927).]

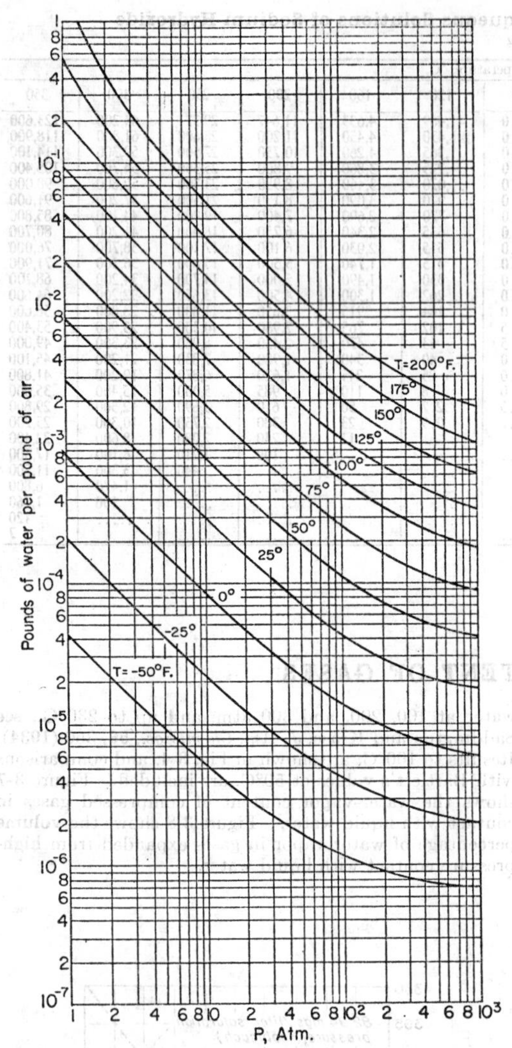

FIG. 3-6. Water content of air. (*Landsbaum, Dadds, and Stutzman. Reprinted from vol. 47, p. 102, January, 1955, issue of Ind. Eng. Chem. Copyright 1955 by the American Chemical Society and reproduced by permission of the copyright owner.*)

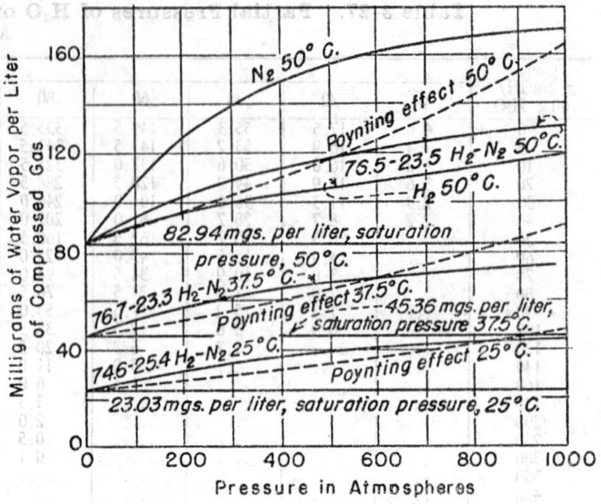

FIG. 3-7. Water-vapor content of $N_2 - H_2$ mixtures in contact with liquid water 25.0°, 37.5°, 50.0°C. [*Bartlett, J. Am. Chem. Soc.*, **49**, 65 (1927).]

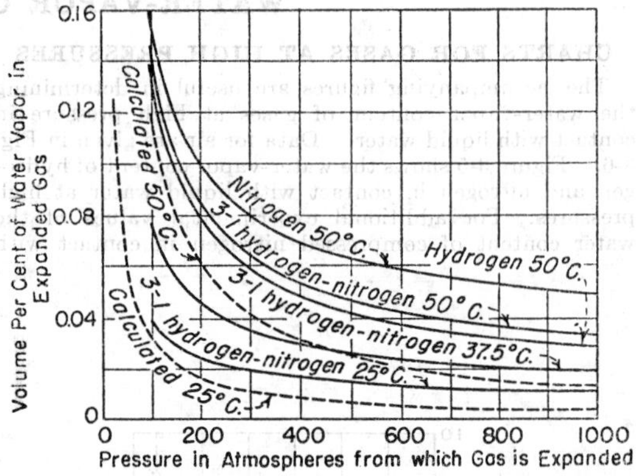

FIG. 3-8. Volume percentage of water vapor in $N_2 - H_2$ mixtures expanded from high-pressure contact with liquid water, 25.0°, 37.5°, 50.0°C. [*Bartlett, J. Am. Chem. Soc.*, **49**, 65 (1927).]

DISSOCIATION PRESSURES

From "International Critical Tables," vol. 7, pp. 224–313, where P is the pressure in atmospheres or millimeters and T is the temperature in degrees Kelvin (°C. + 273.1).

Table 3-28. Barium Hydroxide

$Ba(OH)_2(l) = BaO(s) + H_2O(g)$

T	P, atm.	T	P, atm.
903.1	0.0121	1187.1	0.507
1022.1	.072	1224.1	.692
1102.1	.196	1239.1	.764
1164.1	.429	1263.1	.921

Table 3-29. Barium Peroxide

$BaO_2(s) = BaO(s) + \frac{1}{2}O_2(g)$

T	P, atm.	T	P, atm.
891.1	0.0149	1108.1	0.945
970.1	.0861	1126.1	1.220
1010.1	.1855	1141.1	1.534

Table 3-30. Cadmium Carbonate

$CdCO_3(s) = CdO(s) + CO_2(g)$

T	P, atm.	T	P, atm.
523.1	0.00066	613.1	0.434
553.1	.0053	620.1	.536
581.1	.030	626.1	.691
595.1	.1324	633.1	1.349
603.1	.250	641.1	2.062

Table 3-31. Calcium Carbonate

$CaCO_3(s) = CaO(s) + CO_2(g)$

T	P, atm.	T	P, atm.
823.1	0.00054	1210.1	1.770
973.1	.0292	1355.6	8.892
1073.1	.220	1430.8	18.687
1170.1	1.000	1499.4	34.333
1179.6	1.151	1514.0	39.094

Table 3-32. Calcium Cyanamide

$CaCN_2$

t, °C.	P, mm.	t, °C.	P, mm.
950	5	1100	60
1050	26	1130	98
1080	40	1146	130

Table 3-33. Calcium Oxalate

$CaC_2O_4 = CaCO_3 + CO$

t, °C.	P, mm.	t, °C.	P, mm.
375	8.2	410	250.0
388	30.0	416	587.0
403	134.0	418	684.0

Table 3-34. Cobalt Sulfate

$CoSO_4 = CoO + SO_3$

t, °C.	P, mm.	t, °C.	P, mm.
755	8.8	920	346.0
825	37.0	950	592.0
880	144.0	970	826.0

Table 3-35. Ferrous Sulfate

$2FeSO_4 = Fe_2O_3 + SO_3 + SO_2$

t, °C.	P, mm.	t, °C.	P, mm.
235	1	631	296
316	10	654	546
482	73	698	1263

Table 3-36. Manganese Dioxide

MnO_2

t, °C.	P, mm.	t, °C.	P, mm.
281	2.4	385	82.7
333	18.4	393	86.2
368	59.3	423	150.3
382	60.2	486	359.7

Table 3-37. Mercuric Oxide

$HgO(red) = Hg(g) + \frac{1}{2}O_2(g)$

T	P, atm. ($Hg + O_2$)	T	P, atm. ($Hg + O_2$)
633.1	0.1185	713.1	0.8450
653.1	.1858	723.1	1.067
673.1	.3040	743.1	1.679
693.1	.5095	753.1	2.081

Table 3-38. Potassium Bicarbonate

$2KHCO_3(s) = K_2CO_3(s) + CO_2(g) + H_2O(g)$

T	P, atm.	T	P, atm.
340.8	0.0054	419.4	0.6203
389.5	.1463	424.9	.8034
400.3	.2527	429.1	.9645

Table 3-39. Potassium Carbonate

$K_2CO_3(s) = K_2O(s) + CO_2(g)$

T	P, atm.	T	P, atm.
1003.1	0.000	1243.1	0.012
1083.1	.0013	1273.1	.016
1163.1	.004	1363.1	.022

Table 3-40. Potassium Dihydrogen Phosphate*

$xKH_2PO_4 = (KPO_3)x + xH_2O$

t, °C.	P, mm.	t, °C.	P, mm.
170	6.3	254.5	715.8
200	68.3	256.5	733.6
220	188.3	258.5	739.1
240	467.9	264.0	751.0

* *J. Am. Chem. Soc.*, 49, 381 (1927).

Table 3-41. Potassium Hydride

$KH(s) = K(l) + \frac{1}{2}H_2(g)$

$\log P_{atm.} = -5850/T + 2.6 \log T + 1.014$, where P = atm.

Table 3-42. Silver Carbonate

$Ag_2CO_3 = Ag_2O + CO_2$

t, °C.	P, mm.	t, °C.	P, mm.
179.5	200	207.0	600
196.0	400	214.0	800

Table 3-43. Sodium Carbonate

$Na_2CO_3(s) = Na_2O(s) + CO_2(g)$

T	P, atm.	T	P, atm.
973.1	0.0013	1353.1	0.025
1153.1	.013	1473.1	.054

Table 3-44. Sodium Dihydrogen Phosphate

$2NaH_2PO_4 = Na_2H_2P_2O_7 + H_2O$

t, °C.	P, mm.	t, °C.	P, mm.
110.0	17.9	140.0	245.0
120.0	36.1	148.5	621.0
130.0	66.1	150.0	750.0

DENSITIES OF PURE SUBSTANCES*

Table 3-45. Density of Pure Water Free from Air, 0° to 41°C.*

°C.	Tenths of degrees: 0	1	2	3	4	5	6	7	8	9	Mean differences
0	0.999 8681	8747	8812	8875	8936	8996	9053	9109	9163	9216	+59
1	9267	9315	9363	9408	9452	9494	9534	9573	9610	9645	+41
2	9679	9711	9741	9769	9796	9821	9844	9866	9887	9905	+24
3	9922	9937	9951	9962	9973	9981	9988	9994	9998	0000	+8
4	1.000 0000	9999	9996	9992	9986	9979	9970	9960	9947	9934	−8
5	0.999 9919	9902	9884	9864	9842	9819	9795	9769	9742	9713	−24
6	9682	9650	9617	9582	9545	9507	9468	9427	9385	9341	−39
7	9296	9249	9201	9151	9100	9048	8994	8938	8881	8823	−53
8	8764	8903	8641	8577	8512	8445	8377	8308	8237	8165	−67
9	8091	8017	7940	7863	7784	7704	7622	7539	7455	7369	−81
10	7282	7194	7105	7014	6921	6826	6729	6632	6533	6432	−95
11	6331	6228	6124	6020	5913	5805	5696	5586	5474	5362	−108
12	5248	5132	5016	4898	4780	4660	4538	4415	4291	4166	−121
13	4040	3912	3784	3654	3523	3391	3257	3122	2986	2850	−133
14	2712	2572	2431	2289	2147	2003	1858	1711	1564	1416	−145
15	1266	1114	0962	0809	0655	0499	0343	0185	0026	9865	−156
16	.998 9705	9542	9378	9214	9048	8881	8713	8544	8373	8202	−168
17	8029	7856	7681	7505	7328	7150	6971	6791	6610	6427	−178
18	6244	6058	5873	5686	5498	5309	5119	4927	4735	4541	−190
19	4347	4152	3955	3757	3558	3358	3158	2955	2752	2549	−200
20	2343	2137	1930	1722	1511	1301	1090	0878	0663	0449	−211
21	0233	0016	9799	9580	9359	9139	8917	8694	8470	8245	−221
22	.997 8019	7792	7564	7335	7104	6873	6641	6408	6173	5938	−232
23	5702	5466	5227	4988	4747	4506	4264	4021	3777	3531	−242
24	3286	3039	2790	2541	2291	2040	1788	1535	1280	1026	−252
25	0770	0513	0255	9997	9736	9476	9214	8951	8688	8423	−261
26	.996 8158	7892	7624	7356	7087	6817	6545	6273	6000	5726	−271
27	5451	5176	4898	4620	4342	4062	3782	3500	3218	2935	−280
28	2652	2366	2080	1793	1505	1217	0928	0637	0346	0053	−289
29	.995 9761	9466	9171	8876	8579	8282	7983	7684	7383	7083	−298
30	6780	6478	6174	5869	5564	5258	4950	4642	4334	4024	−307
31	3714	3401	3089	2776	2462	2147	1832	1515	1198	0880	−315
32	0561	0241	9920	9599	9276	8954	8630	8304	7979	7653	−324
33	.994 7325	6997	6668	6338	6007	5676	5345	5011	4678	4343	−332
34	4007	3671	3335	2997	2659	2318	1978	1638	1296	0953	−340
35	0610	0267	9922	9576	9230	8883	8534	8186	7837	7486	−347
36	.993 7136	6784	6432	6078	5725	5369	5014	4658	4301	3943	−355
37	3585	3226	2866	2505	2144	1782	1419	1055	0691	0326	−362
38	.992 9960	9593	9227	8859	8490	8120	7751	7380	7008	6636	−370
39	6263	5890	5516	5140	4765	4389	4011	3634	3255	2876	−377
40	2497	2116	1734	1352	0971	0587	0203	9818	9433	9047	−384
41	.991 8661										

* According to P. Chappuis, Bureau International des Poids et Mesures. Under standard pressure (76 cm. Hg) at every tenth part of a degree from 0° to 41°C., in g./ml. Extracted from Table 287, "Smithsonian Physical Tables," 9th rev. ed., Washington, D.C., 1954.

Table 3-46. Density and Volume of Water −10° to +250°C.*

Temp., °C.	Density	Volume	Temp., °C.	Density	Volume	Temp., °C.	Density	Volume
−10	0.99815	1.00186	20	0.99823	1.00177	50	0.98807	1.01207
−9	843	157	21	802	198	51	762	254
−8	869	131	22	780	220	52	715	301
−7	892	108	23	757	244	53	669	349
−6	912	088	24	733	268	54	621	398
−5	.99930	1.00070	25	.99708	1.00293	55	.98573	1.01448
−4	945	055	26	682	320	60	324	705
−3	958	042	27	655	347	65	059	979
−2	970	031	28	627	375	70	.97781	1.02270
−1	979	021	29	598	404	75	489	576
0	.99987	1.00013	30	.99568	1.00434	80	.97183	1.02899
1	993	007	31	537	465	85	.96865	1.03237
2	997	003	32	506	497	90	534	590
3	999	001	33	473	530	95	192	959
4	1.00000	1.00000	34	440	563	100	.95838	1.04343
5	0.99999	1.00001	35	.99406	1.00598	110	.9510	1.0515
6	997	003	36	371	633	120	.9434	1.0601
7	993	007	37	336	669	130	.9352	1.0693
8	988	012	38	300	706	140	.9264	1.0794
9	981	019	39	263	743	150	.9173	1.0902
10	.99973	1.00027	40	.99225	1.00782	160	.9075	1.1019
11	963	037	41	187	821	170	.8973	1.1145
12	952	048	42	147	861	180	.8866	1.1279
13	940	060	43	107	901	190	.8750	1.1429
14	927	073	44	066	943	200	.8628	1.1590
15	.99913	1.00087	45	.99025	1.00985	210	.850	1.177
16	897	103	46	.98982	1.01028	220	.837	1.195
17	880	120	47	940	072	230	.823	1.215
18	862	138	48	896	116	240	.809	1.236
19	843	157	49	852	162	250	.794	1.259

* The mass of 1 cc. at 4°C. is taken as unity. Extracted from Table 290, "Smithsonian Physical Tables," 9th rev. ed., Washington, D.C., 1954.

* Gases have been listed (in Tables 3-48, 3-153) only for 0°C. and 1 atm. pressure. For all other temperatures use tabulated compressibility and volume data together with $\rho = MZ/V$ to obtain density data. For liquid air, argon, carbon monoxide, helium, methane, neon, nitrogen, and oxygen see Johnson (ed.), WADD-TR60-56, 1960. Extensive data for cryogenic fluids are given in Gersh, "Low Temperature Cooling," Part II, Moscow, 1949. Data on liquid helium and hydrogen are also given by Scott, "Cryogenic Engineering," Van Nostrand, Princeton, N.J., 1959. For liquid coolants see Weatherford, Tyler, and Ku, WADC-TR-59-598, 1959.

Table 3-47. Density and Volume of Mercury −10° to +360°C.*

Temp., °C.	Mass,† g./cc.	Volume of 1 g., cc.	Temp., °C.	Mass,† g./cc.	Volume of 1 g., cc.	Temp., °C.	Mass,† g./cc.	Volume of 1 g., cc.
−10	13.6198	0.0734225	20	13.5458	0.0738233	140	13.2563	0.0754354
− 9	6173	4358	21	5434	8367	150	2326	5708
− 8	6148	4492	22	5409	8501	160	2090	7064
− 7	6124	4626	23	5385	8635	170	1853	8422
− 6	6099	4759	24	5360	8768	180	1617	9784
− 5	13.6074	.0734893	25	13.5336	.0738902	190	13.1381	.0761149
− 4	6050	5026	26	5311	9036	200	1145	2516
− 3	6025	5160	27	5287	9170	210	0910	3886
− 2	6000	5293	28	5262	9304	220	0677	5260
− 1	5976	5427	29	5238	9437	230	0440	6637
− 0	13.5951	.0735560	30	13.5213	.0739572	240	13.0206	.0768017
1	5926	5694	31	5189	9705	250	12.9972	9402
2	5901	5828	32	5164	9839	260	9738	70900
3	5877	5961	33	5140	9973	270	9504	2182
4	5852	6095	34	5116	40107	280	9270	3579
5	13.5827	.0736228	35	13.5091	.0740241	290	12.9036	.0774979
6	5803	6362	36	5066	0374	300	8803	6385
7	5778	6496	37	5042	0508	310	8569	7795
8	5754	6629	38	5018	0642	320	8336	9210
9	5729	6763	39	4994	0776	330	8102	80630
10	13.5704	.0736893	40	13.4969	.0740910	340	12.7869	.0782054
11	5680	7030	50	4725	2250	350	7635	3485
12	5655	7164	60	4482	3592	360	7402	4921
13	5630	7298	70	4240	4936			
14	5606	7431	80	3998	6282			
15	13.5581	.0737565	90	13.3723	.0747631			
16	5557	7699	100	3515	8981			
17	5532	7832	110	3279	50305			
18	5507	7966	120	3040	1653			
19	5483	8100	130	2801	3002			

* For a table at 0(0.1)40.9°C. see Atack, "Handbook of Chemical Data," p. 14, Reinhold, New York, 1957. For a graph to 600°F. see Lubarsky and Kaufman, *N.A.C.A. Rept.* 1270, 1956; for data at −38.87, −30(10)0, etc., °C. see "American Institute of Physics Handbook," McGraw-Hill, New York, 1957.

† Density or mass in g./cc. and the volume of 1 g. of mercury. Reproduced from Table 291, "Smithsonian Physical Tables," 9th rev. ed., Washington, D.C., 1954.

Table 3-48. Densities of Gases at Standard Conditions (0°C., 1 atm.)*

Gas	Formula	Mol. wt.	Density G./l.	Density Lb./cu. ft.
Acetylene	C_2H_2	26.02	1.1708	0.0732
Air		....	1.2928	0.0808
Ammonia	NH_3	17.03	0.7708	0.0482
Argon	A	39.91	1.7828	0.1114
Bromine	Br_2	159.83	7.1388	0.4460
Butane	C_4H_{10}	58.08	2.5985	0.1623
Carbon dioxide	CO_2	44.00	1.9768	0.1235
Carbon monoxide	CO	28.00	1.2501	0.0781
Carbon oxychloride	$COCl_2$	98.91	4.5313	0.2830
Carbon oxysulfide	COS	60.06	2.7201	0.1700
Chlorine	Cl_2	70.91	3.2204	0.2011
Chlorine monoxide	Cl_2O	86.91	3.8874	0.2428
Cyanogen	C_2N_2	52.02	2.3348	0.1459
Ethane	C_2H_6	30.05	1.3567	0.0848
Ethyl chloride	C_2H_5Cl	64.50	2.8700	0.1793
Ethylene	C_2H_4	28.03	1.2644	0.0783
Fluorine	F_2	38.00	1.6354	0.1022
Helium	He	4.00	0.1769	0.0111
Hydrogen	H_2	2.016	0.0898	0.0056
Hydrogen chloride	HCl	36.47	1.6394	0.1024
Hydrogen fluoride	HF	20.01	0.9218	0.0576
Hydrogen iodide	HI	127.94	5.7245	0.3576
Hydrogen selenide	H_2Se	81.22	3.6134	0.2258
Hydrogen sulfide	H_2S	34.08	1.5392	0.0961
Hydrogen telluride	H_2Te	129.52	5.8034	0.3625
Krypton	Kr	82.90	3.6431	0.2275
Methane	CH_4	16.03	0.7167	0.0448
Methyl chloride	CH_3Cl	50.48	2.3044	0.1440
Neon	Ne	20.40	0.8713	0.0544
Nitric oxide	NO	30.01	1.3401	0.0837
Nitrogen	N_2	28.02	1.2507	0.0782
Nitrous oxide	N_2O	44.02	1.9781	0.1235
Nitrosyl chloride	NOCl	65.47	2.9864	0.1865
Oxygen	O_2	32.00	1.4289	0.0892
Phosphine	PH_4	34.05	1.5293	0.0955
Silicon fluoride	SiF_2	104.06	4.6541	0.2907
Sulfur dioxide	SO_2	64.06	2.9268	0.1828
Xenon	X	130.20	5.7168	0.3570

* For other tables see Atack, "Handbook of Chemical Data," pp. 90, 91, Reinhold, New York, 1957; "Smithsonian Physical Tables," 9th ed., Table 255, 1954; "American Institute of Physics Handbook," p. 2-200, McGraw-Hill, New York, 1957. See also Table 3-153, p. 3-101.

SPECIFIC VOLUMES OF PURE SUBSTANCES

Table 3-49. Volume in cc. at Various Temperatures of a cc. of Water Free from Air at the Temperature of Maximum Density, 0° to 36° C.*

Temp., °C.	0.0	0.1	0.2	0.3	0.4	0.5	0.6	0.7	0.8	0.9
0	1.000132	125	118	112	106	100	095	089	084	079
1	073	069	064	059	055	051	047	043	039	035
2	032	029	026	023	020	018	016	013	011	009
3	008	006	005	004	003	002	001	001	000	000
4	000	000	000	001	001	002	003	004	005	007
5	008	010	012	014	016	018	021	023	026	029
6	032	035	039	042	046	050	054	058	062	066
7	070	075	080	085	090	095	101	106	112	118
8	124	130	137	142	149	156	162	169	176	184
9	191	198	206	214	222	230	238	246	254	263
10	272	281	290	299	308	317	327	337	347	357
11	367	377	388	398	409	420	430	441	453	464
12	476	487	499	511	522	534	547	559	571	584
13	596	609	623	636	649	661	675	688	702	715
14	729	743	757	772	786	800	815	830	844	859
15	873	890	905	920	935	951	967	983	998	015
16	1.001031	047	063	080	097	113	130	147	164	182
17	198	216	233	252	269	287	305	323	341	358
18	378	396	415	433	452	471	490	510	529	548
19	568	588	606	626	646	667	687	707	728	748
20	769	790	811	832	853	874	895	916	938	960
21	981	002	024	046	068	091	113	135	158	181
22	1.002203	226	249	271	295	319	342	364	389	412
23	436	459	483	507	532	556	581	605	629	654
24	679	704	729	754	779	804	829	854	879	905
25	932	958	983	010	036	061	088	115	141	168
26	1.003195	221	248	275	302	330	357	384	412	439
27	467	495	523	550	579	607	635	663	692	720
28	749	776	806	836	865	893	922	951	981	011
29	1.004041	069	100	129	160	189	220	250	280	310
30	341	371	403	432	464	494	526	557	588	619
31	651	682	713	744	777	808	840	872	904	936
32	968	001	033	066	098	132	163	197	229	263
33	1.005296	328	361	395	427	461	496	530	562	597
34	631	665	698	732	768	802	836	871	904	940
35	975	009	044	078	115	150	185	219	255	290

* Extracted from Table 288, "Smithsonian Physical Tables," 9th rev. ed., Washington, D.C., 1954.

DENSITIES OF AQUEOUS INORGANIC SOLUTIONS

For more detailed data on densities see "International Critical Tables": tabular index, vol. 3, p. 1; abrasives, vol. 2, p. 87; air, moist, vol. 1, p. 71; building stones, vol. 2, p. 52; clays, vol. 2, p. 56; coals, vol. 2, p. 135; compounds, vol. 1 pp. 106, 176, 313, 341; elements, vol. 1, pp. 102, 340; fibers, vol. 2, p. 237; gases and vapors, vol. 3, pp. 3, 345; glass, vol. 2, p. 93; liquids and vitreous solids, vol. 3, p. 22; vol. 1, pp. 102, 340; vol. 2, pp. 456, 463; vol. 3, pp. 20, 35; liquid coolants and saturated vapors are available from WADC-TR-59-598, 1959; plastics are collected in the "Handbook of Chemistry and Physics," Chemical Rubber Publishing Co.; solid helium, neon, argon, fluorine, and methane data are given by Johnson (ed.) WADD-TR-60-56, 1960; temperatures of maximum solubility, vol. 3, p. 107; metals, vol. 2, p. 463; oils, fats, and waxes, vol. 2, p. 201; orthobaric, vol. 3, pp. 202, 228, 237, 244; petroleums, vol. 2, pp. 137, 144; plastics, vol. 2, p. 296; porcelains, vol. 2, pp. 68, 75; refrigerating brines, vol. 2, p. 327; rubber, vol. 2, pp. 255, 259; soaps, vol. 5, p. 447; metallic solid solutions, vol. 2, p. 358; solids, vol. 3, pp. 43, 45; vol. 2, p. 456; vol. 3, p. 21; solutions and mixtures, vol. 3, pp. 17, 51, 95, 104, 107, 111, 125, 130; woods, vol. 2, p. 1. Also see the "Handbook of Chemistry and Physics," Chemical Rubber Publishing Co., 40th ed., etc.

Table 3-50. Aluminum Sulfate [$Al_2(SO_4)_3$]

%	d_4^{15}	%	d_4^{15}
1	1.0093	16	1.1770
2	1.0195	20	1.2272
4	1.0404	24	1.2803
8	1.0837	26	1.3079
12	1.1293		

Table 3-51. Ammonia (NH_3)

%	−15°C.	−10°C.	−5°C.	0°C.	5°C.	10°C.	20°C.	25°C.	%	d_4^{15}
1	.....	0.9943	0.9954	0.9959	0.9958	0.9955	0.9939	0.993	32	0.889
2	.....	.9906	.9915	.9919	.9917	.9913	.9895	.988	36	.877
4	.....	.9834	.9840	.9842	.9837	.9832	.9811	.980	40	.865
8	0.970	.9701	.9701	.9695	.9686	.9677	.9651	.964	45	.849
12	.958	.9576	.9571	.9561	.9548	.9534	.9501	.948	50	.832
16	.947	.9461	.9450	.9435	.9420	.9402	.9362	.934	60	.796
20	.....	.9353	.9335	.9316	.9296	.9275	.9229		70	.755
24	.....	.9249	.9226	.9202	.9179	.9155	.9101		80	.711
28	.....	.9150	.9122	.9094	.9067	.9040	.8980		90	.665
30	.....	.9101	.9070	.9040	.9012	.8983	.8920		100	.618

Table 3-52. Ammonium Acetate* CH_3COONH_4

%	d_4^{25}
1	0.9992
2	1.0013
4	1.0055
8	1.0136
12	1.0216
16	1.0294
20	1.0368
24	1.0439
28	1.0507
30	1.0540
35	1.0618
40	1.0691
45	1.0760

* For data at 16°C. for 3(1)52 per cent see Atack "Handbook of Chemical Data," p. 33, Reinhold, New York, 1957.

Table 3-53. Ammonium Bichromate $(NH_4)_2Cr_2O_7$

%	d_4^{12}
1	1.0051
2	1.0108
4	1.0223
8	1.0463
12	1.0715
16	1.0981
20	1.1263

Table 3-54. Ammonium Chloride (NH_4Cl)

%	0°C.	10°C.	20°C.	30°C.	50°C.	80°C.	100°C.
1	1.0033	1.0029	1.0013	0.9987	0.9910	0.9749	0.9617
2	1.0067	1.0062	1.0045	1.0018	.9940	.9780	.9651
4	1.0135	1.0126	1.0107	1.0077	.9999	.9842	.9718
8	1.0266	1.0251	1.0227	1.0195	1.0116	.9963	.9849
12	1.0391	1.0370	1.0344	1.0310	1.0231	1.0081	.9975
16	1.0510	1.0485	1.0457	1.0422	1.0343	1.0198	1.0096
20	1.0625	1.0596	1.0567	1.0532	1.0454	1.0312	1.0213
24	1.0736	1.0705	1.0674	1.0641	1.0564	1.0426	1.0327

Table 3-55. Ammonium Chromate $(NH_4)_2CrO_4$

%	°C.	d_4^t
3.80	20	1.0219
10.52	13	1.0627
19.75	13.7	1.1189
28.04	19.6	1.1707

Table 3-56. Ammonium Nitrate (NH_4NO_3)

%	0°C.	10°C.	25°C.	40°C.	60°C.	80°C.
1.0	1.0043	1.0039	1.0011	0.9961	0.9870	0.9755
2.0	1.0088	1.0082	1.0051	1.0000	.9908	.9793
4.0	1.0178	1.0168	1.0132	1.0079	.9985	.9869
8.0	1.0358	1.0340	1.0297	1.0238	1.0142	1.0024
12.0	1.0539	1.0515	1.0464	1.0400	1.0301	1.0181
16.0	1.0721	1.0691	1.0633	1.0565	1.0462	1.0342
20.0	1.0905	1.0870	1.0806	1.0734	1.0627	1.0506
24.0	1.1090	1.1051	1.0982	1.0907	1.0796	1.0673
28.0	1.1277	1.1234	1.1161	1.1082	1.0968	1.0844
30.0	1.1371	1.1327	1.1252	1.1171	1.1055	1.0931
40.0	1.1862	1.1810	1.1727	1.1640	1.1515	1.1385
50.0	1.2380	1.2320	1.2229	1.2136	1.2006	1.1868

Table 3-57. Ammonium Sulfate $[(NH_4)_2SO_4]$

%	0°C.	20°C.	40°C.	80°C.	100°C.
1	1.0061	1.0041	0.9980	0.9777	0.9644
2	1.0124	1.0101	1.0039	.9836	.9705
4	1.0248	1.0220	1.0155	.9953	.9826
8	1.0495	1.0456	1.0387	1.0187	1.0066
12	1.0740	1.0691	1.0619	1.0421	1.0303
16	1.0980	1.0924	1.0849	1.0653	1.0539
20	1.1215	1.1154	1.1077	1.0883	1.0772
24	1.1448	1.1383	1.1304	1.1111	1.1003
28	1.1677	1.1609	1.1529	1.1338	1.1232
35	1.2072	1.2000	1.1919	1.1731	1.1629
40	1.2350	1.2277	1.2196	1.2011	1.1910
50	1.2899	1.2825	1.2745	1.2568	1.2466

Table 3-58. Arsenic Acid ($H_3A_3O_4$)

%	d_4^{15}	%	d_4^{15}
1	1.0057	20	1.1447
2	1.0124	30	1.2331
6	1.0398	40	1.3370
10	1.0681	50	1.4602
16	1.1128	60	1.6070
		70	1.7811

Table 3-59. Barium Chloride ($BaCl_2$)

%	0°C.	20°C.	40°C.	60°C.	80°C.	100°C.
2	1.0181	1.0159	1.0096	1.0004	0.9890	0.9755
4	1.0368	1.0341	1.0275	1.0181	1.0066	.9931
8	1.0760	1.0721	1.0648	1.0551	1.0434	1.0299
12	1.1178	1.1128	1.1047	1.0948	1.0827	1.0692
16	1.1627	1.1564	1.1478	1.1373	1.1249	1.1113
20	1.2105	1.2031	1.1938	1.1828	1.1702	1.1563
24	.....	1.2531	1.2430	1.2316	1.2186	1.2045
26	.....	1.2793	1.2688	1.2571	1.2440	1.2298

Table 3-60. Cadmium Nitrate $[Cd(NO_3)_2]$

%	d_4^{18}	%	d_4^{18}
2	1.0154	20	1.1904
4	1.0326	25	1.2488
8	1.0683	30	1.3124
12	1.1061	40	1.4590
16	1.1468	50	1.6356

Table 3-61. Calcium Chloride ($CaCl_2$)

%	−5°C.	0°C.	20°C.	30°C.	40°C.	60°C.	80°C.	100°C.	120°C.*	140°C.
2	......	1.0171	1.0148	1.0120	1.0084	0.9994	0.9881	0.9748	0.9596	0.9428
4	......	1.0346	1.0316	1.0286	1.0249	1.0158	1.0046	.9915	.9765	.9601
8	1.0708	1.0703	1.0659	1.0626	1.0586	1.0492	1.0382	1.0257	1.0111	.9954
12	1.1083	1.1072	1.1015	1.0978	1.0937	1.0840	1.0730	1.0610	1.0466	1.0317
16	1.1471	1.1454	1.1386	1.1345	1.1301	1.1202	1.1092	1.0973	1.0835	1.0691
20	1.1874	1.1853	1.1775	1.1730	1.1684	1.1581	1.1471	1.1352	1.1219	1.1080
25	......	1.2376	1.2284	1.2236	1.2186	1.2079	1.1965	1.1846		
30	......	1.2922	1.2816	1.2764	1.2709	1.2597	1.2478	1.2359		
35	......	......	1.3373	1.3316	1.3255	1.3137	1.3013	1.2893		
40	......	......	1.3957	1.3895	1.3826	1.3700	1.3571	1.3450		

* Corrected to atmospheric pressure.

Table 3-62. Calcium Hydroxide $[Ca(OH_2)]$

%	d_4^{15}	d_4^{25}
0.05	0.99979	0.99773
.10	1.00044	.99838
.15	1.00110	.99904

Table 3-63. Calcium Hypochlorite* ($CaOCl_2$)

% total salt	d_4^{15}
2	1.0169
4	1.0345
6	1.0520
8	1.0697
10	1.0876
12	1.1060

* $CaOCl_2$ = 89.15%;
$CaCl_2$ = 7.31%;
$Ca(ClO_3)_2$ = 0.26%;
$Ca(OH)_2$ = 2.92%.

Table 3-64. Calcium Nitrate $[Ca(NO_3)_2]$

%	6°C.	18°C.	25°C.	30°C.
2*	1.0157	1.0137	1.0120	1.0105
4	1.0316	1.0291	1.0272	1.0256
8	1.0641	1.0608	1.0585	1.0565
12	1.0979	1.0937	1.0911	1.0887
16	1.1330	1.1279	1.1250	1.1224
20	1.1694	1.1636	1.1602	1.1575
25	1.2168	1.2106	1.2065	1.2032
30	......	1.260		
35	......	1.311		
40	......	1.365		
45	......	1.422		
68*	......	1.747	1.741	1.736

* Supercooled tetrahydrate (m.p. 41.4°C.).

Table 3-65. Chromic Acid (CrO_3)

%	d_4^{15}	%	d_4^{15}
1	1.006	20	1.163
2	1.014	26	1.220
6	1.045	30	1.260
10	1.076	40	1.371
16	1.127	50	1.505
		60	1.663

Table 3-66. Chromium Chloride ($CrCl_3$)

%	d_4^{18} Violet	d_4^{18} Green	d_4^{18} Equilibrium mixture of violet and green
1	1.0076	1.0071	1.0075
2	1.0166	1.0157	1.0165
4	1.0349	1.0332	1.0347
8	1.0724	1.0691	1.0722
12	1.1114	1.1065	1.1111
14	1.1316		

Table 3-67. Copper Nitrate [$Cu(NO_3)_2$]

%	d_4^{20}	%	d_4^{20}
1	1.007	12	1.107
2	1.015	16	1.147
4	1.032	20	1.189
8	1.069	25	1.248

Table 3-68. Copper Sulfate ($CuSO_4$)

%	0°C.	20°C.	40°C
1	1.0104	1.0086	1.0024
4	1.0429	1.0401	1.0332
8	1.0887	1.084	1.0764
12	1.1379	1.1308	1.1222
16	......	1.180	
18	......	1.206	

Table 3-69. Cuprous Chloride (Cu_2Cl_2)

%	0°C.	20°C.	40°C.
1	1.0095	1.0072	1.002
4	1.0387	1.036	1.0305
8	1.0788	1.0754	1.0682
12	1.1208	1.1165	1.107
16	1.1653	1.1595	1.151
20	1.2121	1.2052	1.1953

Table 3-70. Ferric Chloride ($FeCl_3$)

%	0°C.	10°C.	20°C.	30°C.
1	1.0086	1.0084	1.0068	1.0040
2	1.0174	1.0168	1.0152	1.0122
4	1.0347	1.0341	1.0324	1.0292
8	1.0703	1.0692	1.0669	1.0636
12	1.1088	1.1071	1.1040	1.1006
16	1.1475	1.1449	1.1418	1.1386
20	1.1870	1.1847	1.1820	1.1786
25	1.2400	1.2380	1.2340	1.2290
30	1.2970	1.2950	1.2910	1.2850
35	1.3605	1.3580	1.3530	1.3475
40	1.4280	1.4235	1.4175	1.4115
45	......	1.4920	1.4850	
50	......	1.5610	1.5510	

Table 3-71. Ferric Sulfate [$Fe_2(SO_4)_3$]

%	$d_4^{17.5}$
1	1.0072
2	1.0157
4	1.0327
8	1.0670
12	1.1028
16	1.1409
20	1.1811
30	1.3073
40	1.4487
50	1.6127
60	1.7983

Table 3-72. Ferric Nitrate [$Fe(NO_3)_3$]

%	d_4^{18}
1	1.0065
2	1.0144
4	1.0304
8	1.0636
12	1.0989
16	1.1359
20	1.1748
25	1.2281

Table 3-73. Ferrous Sulfate ($FeSO_4$)

%	15°C.	18°C.	20°C.
0.2	......	1.00068	1.0002
0.4	......	1.00275	1.0022
0.8	......	1.00645	1.0062
1.0	1.0090	1.0085	1.0082
4.0	1.0380	1.0375	
8.0	1.0790	1.0785	
12.0	1.1235	1.1220	
16.0	1.1690	1.1675	
20.0	1.2150	1.2135	

Table 3-74. Hydrogen Bromide (HBr)

%	d_4^4	d_4^{10}	d_4^{25}
1.0	1.0073	1.0068	1.0041
2.0	1.0146	1.0139	1.0111
4.0	1.0295	1.0285	1.0255
6.0	1.0448	1.0435	1.0402
8.0	1.0604	1.0589	1.0552
10.0	1.0764	1.0747	1.0707
12.0	1.0928	1.0910	1.0867
14.0	1.1097	1.1078	1.1032
16.0	1.1272	1.1251	1.1202
18.0	1.1453	1.1430	1.1377
20.0	1.1640	1.1615	1.1557
22.0	1.1832	1.1806	1.1743
24.0	1.2030	1.2003	1.1935
26.0	1.2235	1.2206	1.2134
28.0	1.2446	1.2415	1.2340
30.0	1.2663	1.2630	1.2552
40.0	1.3877	1.3838	1.3736
50.0	1.5305	1.5257	1.5127
60.0	1.6950	1.6892	1.6731
65.0	1.7854	1.7792	1.7613

Table 3-75. Hydrogen Cyanide (HCN)

%	d_4^{18}
1	0.998
2	.996
4	.993
8	.984
12	.971
16	.956
82	.752
90	.724
100	.691

Table 3-76. Hydrogen Chloride (HCl)

%	−5°C.	0°C.	10°C.	20°C.	40°C.	60°C.	80°C.	100°C.
1	1.0048	1.0052	1.0048	1.0032	0.9970	0.9881	0.9768	0.9636
2	1.0104	1.0106	1.0100	1.0082	1.0019	.9930	0.9819	.9688
4	1.0213	1.0213	1.0202	1.0181	1.0116	1.0026	0.9919	.9791
6	1.0321	1.0319	1.0303	1.0279	1.0211	1.0121	1.0016	.9892
8	1.0428	1.0423	1.0403	1.0376	1.0305	1.0215	1.0111	.9992
10	1.0536	1.0528	1.0504	1.0474	1.0400	1.0310	1.0206	1.0090
12	1.0645	1.0634	1.0607	1.0574	1.0497	1.0406	1.0302	1.0188
14	1.0754	1.0741	1.0711	1.0675	1.0594	1.0502	1.0398	1.0286
16	1.0864	1.0849	1.0815	1.0776	1.0692	1.0598	1.0494	1.0383
18	1.0975	1.0958	1.0920	1.0878	1.0790	1.0694	1.0590	1.0479
20	1.1087	1.1067	1.1025	1.0980	1.0888	1.0790	1.0685	1.0574
22	1.1200	1.1177	1.1131	1.1083	1.0986	1.0886	1.0780	1.0668
24	1.1314	1.1287	1.1238	1.1187	1.1085	1.0982	1.0874	1.0761
26	1.1426	1.1396	1.1344	1.1290	1.1183	1.1076	1.0967	1.0853
28	1.1537	1.1505	1.1449	1.1392	1.1280	1.1169	1.1058	1.0942
30	1.1648	1.1613	1.1553	1.1493	1.1376	1.1260	1.1149	1.1030
32	......	......	......	1.1593				
34	......	......	......	1.1691				
36	......	......	......	1.1789				
38	......	......	......	1.1885				
40	......	......	......	1.1980				

Table 3-77. Hydrogen Fluoride (HF)

%	d_4^{20}	d_4^0
5	1.020	1.017
10	1.040	1.035
20	1.080	1.070
30	1.119	1.101
40	1.159	1.130
50	1.198	1.155
60	1.235	
70	1.258	
80	1.259	
90	1.178	
95	1.089	
100	1.0005	

Table 3-78. Hydrogen Peroxide (H_2O_2)

%	d_4^{18}	%	d_4^{18}
1	1.0022	26	1.0959
2	1.0058	28	1.1040
4	1.0131	30	1.1122
6	1.0204	35	1.1327
8	1.0277	40	1.1536
10	1.0351	45	1.1749
12	1.0425	50	1.1966
14	1.0499	55	1.2188
16	1.0574	60	1.2416
18	1.0649	70	1.2897
20	1.0725	80	1.3406
22	1.0802	90	1.3931
24	1.0880	100	1.4465

Table 3-79. Hydrofluosilic Acid (H_2SiF_6)

%	$d_4^{17.5}$	%	$d_4^{17.5}$
1	1.0080	16	1.1373
2	1.0161	20	1.1748
4	1.0324	25	1.2235
8	1.0661	30	1.2742
12	1.1011	34	1.3162

Table 3-80. Magnesium Chloride ($MgCl_2$)

%	0°C.	20°C.	40°C.	60°C.	80°C.	100°C.
2	1.0168	1.0146	1.0084	0.9995	0.9883	0.9753
4	1.0338	1.0311	1.0248	1.0159	1.0050	.9923
8	1.0683	1.0646	1.0580	1.0493	1.0388	1.0269
12	1.1035	1.0989	1.0921	1.0836	1.0735	1.0622
16	1.1395	1.1342	1.1272	1.1188	1.1092	1.0984
20	1.1764	1.1706	1.1635	1.1552	1.1460	1.1359
25	1.2246	1.2184	1.2111	1.2031	1.1942	1.1847
30	1.2754	1.2688	1.2614	1.2535	1.2451	1.2360

Table 3-81. Magnesium Sulfate ($MgSO_4$)

%	0°C.	20°C.	30°C.	40°C.	50°C.	60°C.	80°C.
2	1.0210	1.0186	1.0158	1.0123	1.0081	1.0032	0.9916
4	1.0423	1.0392	1.0362	1.0326	1.0283	1.0234	1.0118
8	1.0858	1.0816	1.0782	1.0743	1.0700	1.0650	1.0534
12	1.1309	1.1256	1.1220	1.1179	1.1135	1.1083	1.0968
16	1.1777	1.1717	1.1679	1.1637	1.1592		
20	1.2264	1.2198	1.2159	1.2117	1.2072		
26	1.3032	1.2961	1.2922	1.2879	1.2836		

Table 3-82. Nickel Chloride ($NiCl_2$)

%	d_4^{18}
1	1.0082
2	1.0179
4	1.0375
8	1.0785
12	1.1217
16	1.1674
20	1.2163
30	1.353

Table 3-83. Nickel Nitrate [$Ni(NO_3)_2$]

%	d_4^{20}
1	1.0065
2	1.0150
4	1.0325
8	1.0688
12	1.1070
16	1.1480
20	1.191
30	1.311
35	1.377

Table 3-84. Nickel Sulfate ($NiSO_4$)

%	d_4^{18}
1	1.0091
2	1.0198
4	1.0415
8	1.0852
12	1.1325
16	1.1825
18	1.2090

Table 3-85. Nitric Acid (HNO_3)

%	0°C.	5°C.	10°C.	15°C.	20°C.	25°C.	30°C.	40°C.	50°C.	60°C.	80°C.	100°C.
1	1.0058	1.00572	1.00534	1.00464	1.00364	1.00241	1.0009	0.9973	0.9931	0.9882	0.9767	0.9632
2	1.0117	1.01149	1.01099	1.01018	1.00909	1.00778	1.0061	1.0025	.9982	.9932	.9816	.9681
3	1.0176	1.01730	1.01668	1.01576	1.01457	1.01318	1.0114	1.0077	1.0033	.9982	.9865	.9730
4	1.0236	1.02315	1.02240	1.02137	1 02008	1.01861	1.0168	1.0129	1.0084	1.0033	.9915	.9779
5	1.0296	1.02904	1.02816	1.02702	1.02563	1.02408	1.0222	1.0182	1.0136	1.0084	.9965	.9829
6	1.0357	1.03497	1.03397	1.03272	1.03122	1.02958	1.0277	1.0235	1.0188	1.0136	1.0015	.9879
7	1.0418	1.0410	1.0399	1.0385	1.0369	1.0352	1.0333	1.0289	1.0241	1.0188	1.0066	.9929
8	1.0480	1.0471	1.0458	1.0443	1.0427	1.0409	1.0389	1.0344	1.0295	1.0241	1.0117	.9980
9	1.0543	1.0532	1.0518	1.0502	1.0485	1.0466	1.0446	1.0399	1.0349	1.0294	1.0169	1.0032
10	1.0606	1.0594	1.0578	1.0561	1.0543	1.0523	1.0503	1.0455	1.0403	1.0347	1.0221	1.0083
11	1.0669	1.0656	1.0639	1.0621	1.0602	1.0581	1.0560	1.0511	1.0458	1.0401	1.0273	1.0134
12	1.0733	1.0718	1.0700	1.0681	1.0661	1.0640	1.0618	1.0567	1.0513	1.0455	1.0326	1.0186
13	1.0797	1.0781	1.0762	1.0742	1.0721	1.0699	1.0676	1.0624	1.0568	1.0509	1.0379	1.0238
14	1.0862	1.0845	1.0824	1.0803	1.0781	1.0758	1.0735	1.0681	1.0624	1.0564	1.0432	1.0289
15	1.0927	1.0909	1.0887	1.0865	1.0842	1.0818	1.0794	1.0739	1.0680	1.0619	1.0485	1.0341
16	1.0992	1.0973	1.0950	1.0927	1.0903	1.0879	1.0854	1.0797	1.0737	1.0675	1.0538	1.0393
17	1.1057	1.1038	1.1014	1.0989	1.0964	1.0940	1.0914	1.0855	1.0794	1.0731	1.0592	1.0444
18	1.1123	1.1103	1.1078	1.1052	1.1026	1.1001	1.0974	1.0913	1.0851	1.0787	1.0646	1.0496
19	1.1189	1.1168	1.1142	1.1115	1.1088	1.1062	1.1034	1.0972	1.0908	1.0843	1.0700	1.0547
20	1.1255	1.1234	1.1206	1.1178	1.1150	1.1123	1.1094	1.1031	1.0966	1.0899	1.0754	1.0598
21	1.1322	1.1300	1.1271	1.1242	1.1213	1.1185	1.1155	1.1090	1.1024	1.0956	1.0808	1.0650
22	1.1389	1.1366	1.1336	1.1306	1.1276	1.1247	1.1217	1.1150	1.1083	1.1013	1.0862	1.0701
23	1.1457	1.1433	1.1402	1.1371	1.1340	1.1310	1.1280	1.1210	1.1142	1.1070	1.0917	1.0753
24	1.1525	1.1501	1.1469	1.1437	1.1404	1.1374	1.1343	1.1271	1.1201	1.1127	1.0972	1.0805
25	1.1594	1.1569	1.1536	1.1503	1.1469	1.1438	1.1406	1.1332	1.1260	1.1185	1.1027	1.0857
26	1.1663	1.1638	1.1603	1.1569	1.1534	1.1502	1.1469	1.1394	1.1320	1.1244	1.1083	1.0910
27	1.1733	1.1707	1.1670	1.1635	1.1600	1.1566	1.1533	1.1456	1.1381	1.1303	1.1139	1.0963
28	1.1803	1.1777	1.1738	1.1702	1.1666	1.1631	1.1597	1.1519	1.1442	1.1362	1.1195	1.1016
29	1.1874	1.1847	1.1807	1.1770	1.1733	1.1697	1.1662	1.1582	1.1503	1.1422	1.1251	1.1069
30	1.1945	1.1917	1.1876	1.1838	1.1800	1.1763	1.1727	1.1645	1.1564	1.1482	1.1307	1.1122
31	1.2016	1.1988	1.1945	1.1906	1.1867	1.1829	1.1792	1.1708	1.1625	1.1542	1.1363	1.1175
32	1.2088	1.2059	1.2014	1.1974	1.1934	1.1896	1.1857	1.1772	1.1687	1.1602	1.1419	1.1228
33	1.2160	1.2131	1.2084	1.2043	1.2002	1.1963	1.1922	1.1836	1.1749	1.1662	1.1476	1.1281
34	1.2233	1.2203	1.2155	1.2113	1.2071	1.2030	1.1988	1.1901	1.1812	1.1723	1.1533	1.1335
35	1.2306	1.2275	1.2227	1.2183	1.2140	1.2098	1.2055	1.1966	1.1876	1.1784	1.1591	1.1390
36	1.2375	1.2344	1.2294	1.2249	1.2205	1.2163	1.2119	1.2028	1.1936	1.1842	1.1645	1.1440
37	1.2444	1.2412	1.2361	1.2315	1.2270	1.2227	1.2182	1.2089	1.1995	1.1899	1.1699	1.1490
38	1.2513	1.2479	1.2428	1.2381	1.2335	1.2291	1.2245	1.2150	1.2054	1.1956	1.1752	1.1540
39	1.2581	1.2546	1.2494	1.2446	1.2399	1.2354	1.2308	1.2210	1.2112	1.2013	1.1805	1.1589
40	1.2649	1.2613	1.2560	1.2511	1.2463	1.2417	1.2370	1.2270	1.2170	1.2069	1.1858	1.1638
41	1.2717	1.2680	1.2626	1.2576	1.2527	1.2480	1.2432	1.2330	1.2229	1.2126	1.1911	1.1687
42	1.2786	1.2747	1.2692	1.2641	1.2591	1.2543	1.2494	1.2390	1.2287	1.2182	1.1963	1.1735
43	1.2854	1.2814	1.2758	1.2706	1.2655	1.2606	1.2556	1.2450	1.2345	1.2238	1.2015	1.1783
44	1.2922	1.2880	1.2824	1.2771	1.2719	1.2669	1.2618	1.2510	1.2403	1.2294	1.2067	1.1831
45	1.2990	1.2947	1.2890	1.2836	1.2783	1.2732	1.2680	1.2570	1.2461	1.2350	1.2119	1.1879
46	1.3058	1.3014	1.2955	1.2901	1.2847	1.2795	1.2742	1.2630	1.2519	1.2406	1.2171	1.1927
47	1.3126	1.3080	1.3021	1.2966	1.2911	1.2858	1.2804	1.2690	1.2577	1.2462	1.2223	1.1976
48	1.3194	1.3147	1.3087	1.3031	1.2975	1.2921	1.2867	1.2750	1.2635	1.2518	1.2275	1.2024
49	1.3263	1.3214	1.3153	1.3096	1.3040	1.2984	1.2929	1.2811	1.2693	1.2575	1.2328	1.2073
50	1.3327	1.3277	1.3215	1.3157	1.3100	1.3043	1.2987	1.2867	1.2748	1.2628	1.2377	1.2118
51	1.3391	1.3339	1.3277	1.3218	1.3160	1.3102	1.3045	1.2923	1.2802	1.2680	1.2425	1.2163
52	1.3454	1.3401	1.3338	1.3278	1.3219	1.3160	1.3102	1.2978	1.2856	1.2731	1.2473	1.2208
53	1.3517	1.3462	1.3399	1.3338	1.3278	1.3218	1.3159	1.3033	1.2909	1.2782	1.2521	1.2252
54	1.3579	1.3523	1.3459	1.3397	1.3336	1.3275	1.3215	1.3087	1.2961	1.2833	1.2568	1.2296
55	1.3640	1.3583	1.3518	1.3455	1.3393	1.3331	1.3270	1.3141	1.3013	1.2883	1.2615	1.2339
56	1.3700	1.3642	1.3576	1.3512	1.3449	1.3386	1.3324	1.3194	1.3064	1.2932	1.2661	1.2382
57	1.3759	1.3700	1.3634	1.3569	1.3505	1.3441	1.3377	1.3246	1.3114	1.2981	1.2706	1.2424
58	1.3818	1.3757	1.3691	1.3625	1.3560	1.3495	1.3430	1.3298	1.3164	1.3029	1.2751	1.2466
59	1.3875	1.3813	1.3747	1.3680	1.3614	1.3548	1.3482	1.3348	1.3213	1.3077	1.2795	1.2507
60	1.3931	1.3868	1.3801	1.3734	1.3667	1.3600	1.3533	1.3398	1.3261	1.3124	1.2839	1.2547
61	1.3986	1.3922	1.3855	1.3787	1.3719	1.3651	1.3583	1.3447	1.3308	1.3169	1.2881	1.2587
62	1.4039	1.3975	1.3907	1.3838	1.3769	1.3700	1.3632	1.3494	1.3354	1.3213	1.2922	1.2625
63	1.4091	1.4027	1.3958	1.3888	1.3818	1.3748	1.3679	1.3540	1.3398	1.3255	1.2962	1.2661
64	......	1.4078	1.4007	1.3936	1.3866	1.3795	1.3725					
65	......	1.4128	1.4055	1.3984	1.3913	1.3841	1.3770					
66	......	1.4177	1.4103	1.4031	1.3959	1.3887	1.3814					
67	......	1.4224	1.4150	1.4077	1.4004	1.3932	1.3857					
68	......	1.4271	1.4196	1.4122	1.4048	1.3976	1.3900					
69	......	1.4317	1.4241	1.4166	1.4091	1.4019	1.3942					
70	......	1.4362	1.4285	1.4210	1.4134	1.4061	1.3983					
71	......	1.4406	1.4328	1.4252	1.4176	1.4102	1.4023					
72	......	1.4449	1.4371	1.4294	1.4218	1.4142	1.4063					
73	......	1.4491	1.4413	1.4335	1.4258	1.4182	1.4103					
74	......	1.4532	1.4454	1.4376	1.4298	1.4221	1.4142					

Table 3-85. Nitric Acid (HNO_3)—*(Concluded)*

%	0°C.	5°C.	10°C.	15°C.	20°C.	25°C.	30°C.	40°C.	50°C.	60°C.	80°C.	100°C.
75	......	1.4573	1.4494	1.4415	1.4337	1.4259	1.4180					
76	......	1.4613	1.4533	1.4454	1.4375	1.4296	1.4217					
77	......	1.4652	1.4572	1.4492	1.4413	1.4333	1.4253					
78	......	1.4690	1.4610	1.4529	1.4450	1.4369	1.4288					
79	......	1.4727	1.4647	1.4565	1.4486	1.4404	1.4323					
80	......	1.4764	1.4683	1.4601	1.4521	1.4439	1.4357					
81	......	1.4800	1.4718	1.4636	1.4555	1.4473	1.4391					
82	......	1.4835	1.4753	1.4670	1.4589	1.4507	1.4424					
83	......	1.4869	1.4787	1.4704	1.4622	1.4540	1.4456					
84	......	1.4903	1.4820	1.4737	1.4655	1.4572	1.4487					
85	......	1.4936	1.4852	1.4769	1.4686	1.4603	1.4518					
86	......	1.4968	1.4883	1.4799	1.4716	1.4633	1.4548					
87	......	1.4999	1.4913	1.4829	1.4745	1.4662	1.4577					
88	......	1.5029	1.4942	1.4858	1.4773	1.4690	1.4605					
89	......	1.5058	1.4970	1.4885	1.4800	1.4716	1.4631					
90	......	1.5085	1.4997	1.4911	1.4826	1.4741	1.4656					
91	......	1.5111	1.5023	1.4936	1.4850	1.4766	1.4681					
92	......	1.5136	1.5048	1.4960	1.4873	1.4789	1.4704					
93	......	1.5156	1.5068	1.4979	1.4892	1.4807	1.4722					
94	......	1.5177	1.5088	1.4999	1.4912	1.4826	1.4741					
95	......	1.5198	1.5109	1.5019	1.4932	1.4846	1.4761					
96	......	1.5220	1.5130	1.5040	1.4952	1.4867	1.4781					
97	......	1.5244	1.5152	1.5062	1.4974	1.4889	1.4802					
98	......	1.5278	1.5187	1.5096	1.5008	1.4922	1.4835					
99	......	1.5327	1.5235	1.5144	1.5056	1.4969	1.4881					
100	......	1.5402	1.5310	1.5217	1.5129	1.5040	1.4952					

Table 3-86. Perchloric Acid ($HClO_4$)

%	d_4^{15}	d_4^{20}	d_4^{25}	d_4^{50}	%	d_4^{15}	d_4^{20}	d_4^{50}
1	1.0050	......	1.0020	0.9933	28	1.1900	1.1851	1.1645
2	1.0109	......	1.0070	0.9986	30	1.2067	1.2013	1.1800
4	1.0228	......	1.0169	0.9906	32	1.2239	1.2183	1.1960
6	1.0348	......	1.0270	1.0205	34	1.2418	1.2359	1.2130
8	1.0471	......	1.0372	1.0320	36	1.2603	1.2542	1.2310
10	1.0597	......	1.0475	1.0440	38	1.2794	1.2732	1.2490
12	1.0726	......	......	1.0560	40	1.2991	1.2927	1.2680
14	1.0589	......	......	1.0680	45	1.3521	1.3450	1.3180
16	1.0995	......	......	1.0810	50	1.4103	1.4018	1.3730
18	1.1135	......	......	1.0940	55	1.4733	1.4636	1.4320
20	1.1279	......	......	1.1070	60	1.5389	1.5298	1.4950
22	1.1428	......	......	1.1205	65	1.6059	1.5986	1.5620
24	1.1581	......	......	1.1345	70	1.6736	1.6680	1.6290
26	1.1738	1.1697	......	1.1490				

Table 3-87. Phosphoric Acid (H_3PO_4)

°C.	2%	6%	14%	20%	26%	35%	50%	75%	100%
0	1.0113	1.0339	1.0811	1.1192					
10	1.0109	1.0330	1.0792	1.1167	1.1567	1.221	1.341		
20	1.0092	1.0309	1.0764	1.1134	1.1529	1.216	1.335	1.579	1.870
30	1.0065	1.0279	1.0728	1.1094	1.1484	1.211	1.329	1.572	1.862
40	1.0029	1.0241	1.0685	1.1048					

Table 3-88. Potassium Bicarbonate ($KHCO_3$)

°C.	1%	2%	4%	6%	8%	10%
0	1.0066	1.0134	1.0270			
10	1.0064	1.0132	1.0268			
15	1.0058	1.0125	1.0260	1.0396	1.0534	1.0674
20	1.0049	1.0117	1.0252			
30	1.0024	1.0092	1.0228			
40	0.9990	1.0058	1.0195			
50	.9949	1.0017	1.0154			
60	.9901	0.9969	1.0106			
80	.9786	.9855	0.9993			
100	.9653	.9722	.9860			

Table 3-89. Potassium Bromide (KBr)

%	d_4^{20}
1	1.0054
2	1.0127
6	1.0426
12	1.0903
20	1.1601
30	1.2593
40	1.3746

Table 3-90. Potassium Carbonate (K_2CO_3)

%	0°C.	10°C.	20°C.	40°C.	60°C.	80°C.	100°C.
1	1.0094	1.0089	1.0072	1.0010	0.9919	0.9803	0.9670
2	1.0189	1.0182	1.0163	1.0098	1.0005	.9889	.9756
4	1.0381	1.0369	1.0345	1.0276	1.0180	1.0063	.9931
8	1.0768	1.0746	1.0715	1.0640	1.0538	1.0418	1.0291
12	1.1160	1.1131	1.1096	1.1013	1.0906	1.0786	1.0663
16	1.1562	1.1530	1.1490	1.1399	1.1290	1.1170	1.1049
20	1.1977	1.1941	1.1898	1.1801	1.1690	1.1570	1.1451
24	1.2405	1.2366	1.2320	1.2219	1.2106	1.1986	1.1869
28	1.2846	1.2804	1.2756	1.2652	1.2538	1.2418	1.2301
30	1.3071	1.3028	1.2979	1.2873	1.2759	1.2640	1.2522
35	1.3646	1.3600	1.3548	1.3440	1.3324	1.3206	1.3089
40	1.4244	1.4195	1.4141	1.4029	1.3913	1.3795	1.3678
45	1.4867	1.4815	1.4759	1.4644	1.4528	1.4408	1.4290
50	1.5517	1.5462	1.5404	1.5285	1.5169	1.5048	1.4928

Table 3-91. Potassium Chromate (K_2CrO_4)

%	d_4^{15}	d_4^{18}
1	1.0073	1.0066
2	1.0155	1.0147
4	1.0321	1.0311
8	1.0659	1.0647
12	1.1009	1.0999
16	......	1.1366
20	......	1.1748
24	......	1.2147
28	......	1.2566
30	......	1.2784

Table 3-92. Potassium Chlorate ($KClO_3$)

°C.	1%	2%	3%	4%
0	1.0061	1.0124	1.0189	1.0256
10	1.0059	1.0122	1.0187	1.0254
20	1.0045	1.0109	1.0174	1.0241
30	1.0020	1.0085	1.0151	1.0218
40	0.9986	1.0051	1.0116	1.0183
60	.9895	0.9959	1.0024	1.0091
80	.9781	.9845	0.9910	0.9977
100	.9646	.9709	.9774	.9840

Table 3-93. Potassium Chloride (KCl)

%	0°C.	20°C.	25°C.	40°C.	60°C.	80°C.	100°C.
1.0	1.00661	1.00462	1.00342	0.99847	0.9894	0.9780	0.9646
2.0	1.01335	1.01103	1.00977	1.00471	.9956	.9842	.9708
4.0	1.02690	1.02391	1.02255	1.01727	1.0080	.9966	.9834
8.0	1.05431	1.05003	1.04847	1.04278	1.0333	1.0219	1.0088
12.0	1.08222	1.07679	1.07506	1.06897	1.0592	1.0478	1.0350
16.0	1.11068	1.10434	1.10245	1.09600	1.0861	1.0746	1.0619
20.0	1.13973	1.13280	1.13072	1.12399	1.1138	1.1024	1.0897
24.0	....	1.16226	1.15995	1.15299	1.1425	1.1311	1.1185
28.0	....	....	....	1.18304	1.1723	1.1609	1.1483

%	110°C.	120°C.	130°C.	140°C.
3.79	0.9733	0.9663	0.9583	0.9502
7.45	.9978	.9899	.9827	.9745
13.62	1.0388	1.0313	1.0238	1.0159

Table 3-94. Potassium Chrome Alum [$K_2Cr_2(SO_4)_4$]

%	d_4^{15}
1	1.007
2	1.016
6	1.052
10	1.089
14	1.129
20	1.193
30	1.315
40	1.456
50	1.615

Table 3-95. Potassium Hydroxide (KOH)

%	d_4^{15}
1.0	1.0083
2.0	1.0175
4.0	1.0359
6.0	1.0544
8.0	1.0730
10.0	1.0918
15.0	1.1396
20.0	1.1884
25.0	1.2387
30.0	1.2905
35.0	1.3440
40.0	1.3991
45.0	1.4558
50.0	1.5143
51.7	1.5355 (sat'd. soln.)

Table 3-96. Potassium Nitrate (KNO_3)

%	0°C.	10°C.	20°C.	40°C.	60°C.	80°C.	100°C.
1	1.00654	1.00615	1.00447	0.99825	0.9890	0.9776	0.9641
2	1.01326	1.01262	1.01075	1.00430	.9949	.9834	.9699
4	1.02677	1.02566	1.02344	1.01652	1.0068	.9951	.9816
8	1.05419	1.05226	1.04940	1.04152	1.0313	1.0192	1.0056
12	1.08221	1.07963	1.07620	1.06740	1.0567	1.0442	1.0304
16	....	....	1.10392	1.09432	1.0831	1.0703	1.0562
20	....	....	1.13261	1.12240	1.1106	1.0974	1.0831
24	....	....	1.16233	1.15175	1.1391	1.1256	1.1110

Table 3-97. Potassium Dichromate ($K_2Cr_2O_7$)

%	d_4^{20}
1	1.0052
2	1.0122
4	1.0264
6	1.0408
8	1.0554
10	1.0703

Table 3-98. Potassium Sulfate (K_2SO_4)

%	d_4^{20}
1	1.0063
2	1.0145
4	1.0310
6	1.0477
8	1.0646
10	1.0817

Table 3-99. Potassium Sulfite (K_2SO_3)

%	d_4^{15}
1	1.0073
2	1.0155
4	1.0322
8	1.0667
12	1.1026
16	1.1402
20	1.1793
24	1.2197
26	1.2404

Table 3-100. Sodium Acetate ($NaC_2H_3O_2$)

%	d_4^{20}
1	1.0033
2	1.0084
4	1.0186
8	1.0392
12	1.0598
18	1.0807
20	1.1021
26	1.1351
28	1.1462

Table 3-101. Sodium Arsenate (Na_3AsO_4)

%	d_4^{17}
1	1.0097
2	1.0207
4	1.0431
8	1.0892
10	1.1130
12	1.1373

Table 3-102. Sodium Bichromate ($Na_2Cr_2O_7$)

%	d_4^{15}
1	1.006
2	1.013
4	1.027
8	1.056
12	1.084
16	1.112
20	1.140
24	1.166
28	1.193
30	1.207
35	1.244
40	1.279
45	1.312
50	1.342

Table 3-103. Sodium Bromide (NaBr)

%	d_4^{17}
1	1.0060
2	1.0139
4	1.0298
8	1.0631
10	1.0803
12	1.0981
20	1.1745
30	1.2841
40	1.4138

Table 3-104. Sodium Formate (HCOONa)

%	d_4^{25}
1	1.003
2	1.009
4	1.022
8	1.048
12	1.074
16	1.100
20	1.127
24	1.155
28	1.184
30	1.199
35	1.236
40	1.274

Table 3-105. Sodium Carbonate (Na_2CO_3)

%	0°C.	10°C.	20°C.	30°C.	40°C.	60°C.	80°C.	100°C.
1	1.0109	1.0103	1.0086	1.0058	1.0022	0.9929	0.9814	0.9683
2	1.0219	1.0210	1.0190	1.0159	1.0122	1.0027	.9910	.9782
4	1.0439	1.0423	1.0398	1.0363	1.0323	1.0223	1.0105	.9980
8	1.0878	1.0850	1.0816	1.0775	1.0732	1.0625	1.0503	1.0380
12	1.1319	1.1284	1.1244	1.1200	1.1150	1.1039	1.0914	1.0787
14	1.1543	1.1506	1.1463	1.1417	1.1365	1.1251	1.1125	1.0996
16	......	......	......	1.1636				
18	......	......	......	1.1859				
20	......	......	......	1.2086				
24	......	......	......	1.2552				
28	......	......	......	1.3031				
30	......	......	......	1.3274				

Table 3-106. Sodium Chlorate ($NaClO_3$)

%	d_4^{18}	%	d_4^{18}
1	1.0053	18	1.1288
2	1.0121	20	1.1449
4	1.0258	22	1.1614
6	1.0397	24	1.1782
8	1.0538	26	1.1953
10	1.0681	28	1.2128
12	1.0827	30	1.2307
14	1.0977	32	1.2491
16	1.1131	34	1.2680

Table 3-107. Sodium Chloride (NaCl)

%	0°C.	10°C.	25°C.	40°C.	60°C.	80°C.	100°C.
1	1.00747	1.00707	1.00409	0.99908	0.9900	0.9785	0.9651
2	1.01509	1.01442	1.01112	1.00593	.9967	.9852	.9719
4	1.03038	1.02920	1.02530	1.01977	1.0103	.9988	.9855
8	1.06121	1.05907	1.05412	1.04798	1.0381	1.0264	1.0134
12	1.09244	1.08946	1.08365	1.07699	1.0667	1.0549	1.0420
16	1.12419	1.12056	1.11401	1.10688	1.0962	1.0842	1.0713
20	1.15663	1.15254	1.14533	1.13774	1.1268	1.1146	1.1017
24	1.18999	1.18557	1.17776	1.16971	1.1584	1.1463	1.1331
26	1.20709	1.20254	1.19443	1.18614	1.1747	1.1626	1.1492

Table 3-108. Sodium Chromate (Na_2CrO_4)

%	d_4^{18}
1	1.0074
2	1.0164
4	1.0344
8	1.0718
12	1.1110
16	1.1518
20	1.1942
24	1.2383
26	1.2611

Table 3-109. Sodium Hydroxide (NaOH)

%	0°C.	15°C.	20°C.	40°C.	60°C.	80°C.	100°C.
1	1.0124	1.01065	1.0095	1.0033	0.9941	0.9824	0.9693
2	1.0244	1.02198	1.0207	1.0139	1.0045	.9929	.9797
4	1.0482	1.04441	1.0428	1.0352	1.0254	1.0139	1.0009
8	1.0943	1.08887	1.0869	1.0780	1.0676	1.0560	1.0432
12	1.1399	1.13327	1.1309	1.1210	1.1101	1.0983	1.0855
16	1.1849	1.17761	1.1751	1.1645	1.1531	1.1408	1.1277
20	1.2296	1.22183	1.2191	1.2079	1.1960	1.1833	1.1700
24	1.2741	1.26582	1.2629	1.2512	1.2388	1.2259	1.2124
28	1.3182	1.3094	1.3064	1.2942	1.2814	1.2682	1.2546
32	1.3614	1.3520	1.3490	1.3362	1.3232	1.3097	1.2960
36	1.4030	1.3933	1.3900	1.3768	1.3634	1.3498	1.3360
40	1.4435	1.4334	1.4300	1.4164	1.4027	1.3889	1.3750
44	1.4825	1.4720	1.4685	1.4545	1.4405	1.4266	1.4127
48	1.5210	1.5102	1.5065	1.4922	1.4781	1.4641	1.4503
50	1.5400	1.5290	1.5253	1.5109	1.4967	1.4827	1.4690

Table 3-110. Sodium Nitrate ($NaNO_3$)

%	0°C.	20°C.	40°C.	60°C.	80°C.	100°C.
1	1.0071	1.0049	0.9986	0.9894	0.9779	0.9644
2	1.0144	1.0117	1.0050	.9956	.9840	.9704
4	1.0290	1.0254	1.0180	1.0082	.9964	.9826
8	1.0587	1.0532	1.0447	1.0340	1.0218	1.0078
12	1.0891	1.0819	1.0724	1.0609	1.0481	1.0340
16	1.1203	1.1118	1.1013	1.0892	1.0757	1.0614
20	1.1526	1.1429	1.1314	1.1187	1.1048	1.0901
24	1.1860	1.1752	1.1629	1.1496	1.1351	1.1200
28	1.2204	1.2085	1.1955	1.1816	1.1667	1.1513
30	1.2380	1.2256	1.2122	1.1980	1.1830	1.1674
35	1.2834	1.2701	1.2560	1.2413	1.2258	1.2100
40	1.3316	1.3175	1.3027	1.2875	1.2715	1.2555
45	......	1.3683	1.3528	1.3371	1.3206	1.3044

Table 3-111. Sodium Nitrite ($NaNO_2$)

%	d_4^{15}
1	1.0058
2	1.0125
4	1.0260
8	1.0535
12	1.0816
16	1.1103
20	1.1394

Table 3-112. Sodium Silicate

	Concentration, %												
	1	2	4	8	10	14	20	24	30	36	40	45	50
	Density$_4^{20}$												
$Na_2O/3.9SiO_2$	1.006	1.014	1.030	1.063	1.080	1.116	1.172	1.211	1.275				
$Na_2O/3.36SiO_2$	1.006	1.014	1.030	1.065	1.083	1.120	1.179	1.222	1.290	1.365			
$Na_2O/2.40SiO_2$	1.007	1.016	1.034	1.071	1.090	1.130							
$Na_2O/2.44SiO_2$	.....	.....	.....	.....	.....	.....	.....	.....	1.309	1.387	1.445		
$Na_2O/2.06SiO_2$	1.007	1.016	1.035	1.073	1.093	1.134	1.200	1.247	1.321	1.397	1.450	1.520	1.594
$Na_2O/1.69SiO_2$	1.007	1.017	1.036	1.077	1.098	1.141	1.210	1.259	1.337	1.424			

Table 3-113. Sodium Sulfate (Na_2SO_4)

%	0°C.	20°C.	30°C.	40°C.	60°C.	80°C.	100°C.
1	1.0094	1.0073	1.0046	1.0010	0.9919	0.9805	0.9671
2	1.0189	1.0164	1.0135	1.0098	1.0007	.9892	.9758
4	1.0381	1.0348	1.0315	1.0276	1.0184	1.0068	.9934
8	1.0773	1.0724	1.0682	1.0639	1.0544	1.0426	1.0292
12	1.1174	1.1109	1.1062	1.1015	1.0915	1.0795	1.0661
16	1.1585	1.1506	1.1456	1.1406	1.1299	1.1176	1.1042
20	1.2008	1.1915	1.1865	1.1813	1.1696	1.1569	
24	1.2443	1.2336	1.2292	1.2237			

Table 3-114. Sodium Sulfide (Na_2S)

%	d_4^{18}
1	1.0098
2	1.0211
4	1.0440
8	1.0907
12	1.1388
16	1.1885
18	1.2140

Table 3-115. Sodium Sulfite (Na_2SO_3)

%	d_4^{19}
1	1.0078
2	1.0172
4	1.0363
8	1.0751
12	1.1146
16	1.1549
18	1.1755

Table 3-116. Sodium Thiosulfate ($Na_2S_2O_3$)

%	d_4^{20}
1	1.0065
2	1.0148
4	1.0315
8	1.0654
12	1.1003
16	1.1365
20	1.1740
24	1.2128
28	1.2532
30	1.2739
35	1.3273
40	1.3827

Table 3-117. Sodium Thiosulfate Pentahydrate ($Na_2S_2O_3.5H_2O$)

%	d_4^{19}
1	1.0052
2	1.0105
4	1.0211
8	1.0423
12	1.0639
16	1.0863
20	1.1087
24	1.1322
28	1.1558
30	1.1676
40	1.2297
50	1.2954

Table 3-118. Stannic Chloride ($SnCl_4$)

%	d_4^{15}
1	1.007
2	1.015
4	1.031
8	1.064
12	1.099
16	1.135
20	1.173
24	1.212
28	1.255
30	1.278
35	1.337
40	1.403
45	1.475
50	1.555
55	1.644
60	1.742
65	1.851
70	1.971

Table 3-119. Stannous Chloride ($SnCl_2$)

%	d_4^{15}
1	1.0068
2	1.0146
4	1.0306
8	1.0638
12	1.0986
16	1.1353
20	1.1743
24	1.2159
28	1.2603
30	1.2837
35	1.3461
40	1.4145
45	1.4897
50	1.5729
55	1.6656
60	1.7695
65	1.8865

Table 3-120. Sulfuric Acid (H_2SO_4)

%	0°C.	10°C.	15°C.	20°C.	25°C.	30°C.	40°C.	50°C.	60°C.	80°C.	100°C.
1	1.0074	1.0068	1.0060	1.0051	1.0038	1.0022	0.9986	0.9944	0.9895	0.9779	0.9645
2	1.0147	1.0138	1.0129	1.0118	1.0104	1.0087	1.0050	1.0006	.9956	.9839	.9705
3	1.0219	1.0206	1.0197	1.0184	1.0169	1.0152	1.0113	1.0067	1.0017	.9900	.9766
4	1.0291	1.0275	1.0264	1.0250	1.0234	1.0216	1.0176	1.0129	1.0078	.9961	.9827
5	1.0364	1.0344	1.0332	1.0317	1.0300	1.0281	1.0240	1.0192	1.0140	1.0022	.9888
6	1.0437	1.0414	1.0400	1.0385	1.0367	1.0347	1.0305	1.0256	1.0203	1.0084	.9950
7	1.0511	1.0485	1.0469	1.0453	1.0434	1.0414	1.0371	1.0321	1.0266	1.0146	1.0013
8	1.0585	1.0556	1.0539	1.0522	1.0502	1.0481	1.0437	1.0386	1.0330	1.0209	1.0076
9	1.0660	1.0628	1.0610	1.0591	1.0571	1.0549	1.0503	1.0451	1.0395	1.0273	1.0140
10	1.0735	1.0700	1.0681	1.0661	1.0640	1.0617	1.0570	1.0517	1.0460	1.0338	1.0204
11	1.0810	1.0773	1.0753	1.0731	1.0710	1.0686	1.0637	1.0584	1.0526	1.0403	1.0269
12	1.0886	1.0846	1.0825	1.0802	1.0780	1.0756	1.0705	1.0651	1.0593	1.0469	1.0335
13	1.0962	1.0920	1.0898	1.0874	1.0851	1.0826	1.0774	1.0719	1.0661	1.0536	1.0402
14	1.1039	1.0994	1.0971	1.0947	1.0922	1.0897	1.0844	1.0788	1.0729	1.0603	1.0469
15	1.1116	1.1069	1.1045	1.1020	1.0994	1.0968	1.0914	1.0857	1.0798	1.0671	1.0537
16	1.1194	1.1145	1.1120	1.1094	1.1067	1.1040	1.0985	1.0927	1.0868	1.0740	1.0605
17	1.1272	1.1221	1.1195	1.1168	1.1141	1.1113	1.1057	1.0998	1.0938	1.0809	1.0674
18	1.1351	1.1298	1.1271	1.1243	1.1215	1.1187	1.1129	1.1070	1.1009	1.0879	1.0744
19	1.1430	1.1375	1.1347	1.1318	1.1290	1.1261	1.1202	1.1142	1.1081	1.0950	1.0814
20	1.1510	1.1453	1.1424	1.1394	1.1365	1.1335	1.1275	1.1215	1.1153	1.1021	1.0885
21	1.1590	1.1531	1.1501	1.1471	1.1441	1.1410	1.1349	1.1288	1.1226	1.1093	1.0957
22	1.1670	1.1609	1.1579	1.1548	1.1517	1.1486	1.1424	1.1362	1.1299	1.1166	1.1029
23	1.1751	1.1688	1.1657	1.1626	1.1594	1.1563	1.1500	1.1437	1.1373	1.1239	1.1102
24	1.1832	1.1768	1.1736	1.1704	1.1672	1.1640	1.1576	1.1512	1.1448	1.1313	1.1176
25	1.1914	1.1848	1.1816	1.1783	1.1750	1.1718	1.1653	1.1588	1.1523	1.1388	1.1250
26	1.1996	1.1929	1.1896	1.1862	1.1829	1.1796	1.1730	1.1665	1.1599	1.1463	1.1325
27	1.2078	1.2010	1.1976	1.1942	1.1909	1.1875	1.1808	1.1742	1.1676	1.1539	1.1400
28	1.2160	1.2091	1.2057	1.2023	1.1989	1.1955	1.1887	1.1820	1.1753	1.1616	1.1476
29	1.2243	1.2173	1.2138	1.2104	1.2069	1.2035	1.1966	1.1898	1.1831	1.1693	1.1553
30	1.2326	1.2255	1.2220	1.2185	1.2150	1.2115	1.2046	1.1977	1.1909	1.1771	1.1630
31	1.2409	1.2338	1.2302	1.2267	1.2232	1.2196	1.2126	1.2057	1.1988	1.1849	1.1708
32	1.2493	1.2421	1.2385	1.2349	1.2314	1.2278	1.2207	1.2137	1.2068	1.1928	1.1787
33	1.2577	1.2504	1.2468	1.2432	1.2396	1.2360	1.2289	1.2218	1.2148	1.2008	1.1866
34	1.2661	1.2588	1.2552	1.2515	1.2479	1.2443	1.2371	1.2300	1.2229	1.2088	1.1946
35	1.2746	1.2672	1.2636	1.2599	1.2563	1.2526	1.2454	1.2383	1.2311	1.2169	1.2027
36	1.2831	1.2757	1.2720	1.2684	1.2647	1.2610	1.2538	1.2466	1.2394	1.2251	1.2109
37	1.2917	1.2843	1.2805	1.2769	1.2732	1.2695	1.2622	1.2550	1.2477	1.2334	1.2192
38	1.3004	1.2929	1.2891	1.2855	1.2818	1.2780	1.2707	1.2635	1.2561	1.2418	1.2276
39	1.3091	1.3016	1.2978	1.2941	1.2904	1.2866	1.2793	1.2720	1.2646	1.2503	1.2361
40	1.3179	1.3103	1.3065	1.3028	1.2991	1.2953	1.2880	1.2806	1.2732	1.2589	1.2446
41	1.3268	1.3191	1.3153	1.3116	1.3079	1.3041	1.2967	1.2893	1.2819	1.2675	1.2532
42	1.3357	1.3280	1.3242	1.3205	1.3167	1.3129	1.3055	1.2981	1.2907	1.2762	1.2619
43	1.3447	1.3370	1.3332	1.3294	1.3256	1.3218	1.3144	1.3070	1.2996	1.2850	1.2707
44	1.3538	1.3461	1.3423	1.3384	1.3346	1.3308	1.3234	1.3160	1.3086	1.2939	1.2796
45	1.3630	1.3553	1.3515	1.3476	1.3437	1.3399	1.3325	1.3251	1.3177	1.3029	1.2886
46	1.3724	1.3646	1.3608	1.3569	1.3530	1.3492	1.3417	1.3343	1.3269	1.3120	1.2976
47	1.3819	1.3740	1.3702	1.3663	1.3624	1.3586	1.3510	1.3435	1.3362	1.3212	1.3067
48	1.3915	1.3835	1.3797	1.3758	1.3719	1.3680	1.3604	1.3528	1.3455	1.3305	1.3159
49	1.4012	1.3931	1.3893	1.3854	1.3814	1.3775	1.3699	1.3623	1.3549	1.3399	1.3253
50	1.4110	1.4029	1.3990	1.3951	1.3911	1.3872	1.3795	1.3719	1.3644	1.3494	1.3348
51	1.4209	1.4128	1.4088	1.4049	1.4009	1.3970	1.3893	1.3816	1.3740	1.3590	1.3444
52	1.4310	1.4228	1.4188	1.4148	1.4109	1.4069	1.3991	1.3914	1.3837	1.3687	1.3540
53	1.4412	1.4329	1.4289	1.4248	1.4209	1.4169	1.4091	1.4013	1.3936	1.3785	1.3637
54	1.4515	1.4431	1.4391	1.4350	1.4310	1.4270	1.4191	1.4113	1.4036	1.3884	1.3735
55	1.4619	1.4535	1.4494	1.4453	1.4412	1.4372	1.4293	1.4214	1.4137	1.3984	1.3834
56	1.4724	1.4640	1.4598	1.4557	1.4516	1.4475	1.4396	1.4317	1.4239	1.4085	1.3934
57	1.4830	1.4746	1.4703	1.4662	1.4621	1.4580	1.4500	1.4420	1.4342	1.4187	1.4035
58	1.4937	1.4852	1.4809	1.4768	1.4726	1.4685	1.4604	1.4524	1.4446	1.4290	1.4137
59	1.5045	1.4959	1.4916	1.4875	1.4832	1.4791	1.4709	1.4629	1.4551	1.4393	1.4240
60	1.5154	1.5067	1.5024	1.4983	1.4940	1.4898	1.4816	1.4735	1.4656	1.4497	1.4344
61	1.5264	1.5177	1.5133	1.5091	1.5048	1.5006	1.4923	1.4842	1.4762	1.4602	1.4449
62	1.5375	1.5287	1.5243	1.5200	1.5157	1.5115	1.5031	1.4950	1.4869	1.4708	1.4554
63	1.5487	1.5398	1.5354	1.5310	1.5267	1.5225	1.5140	1.5058	1.4977	1.4815	1.4660
64	1.5600	1.5510	1.5465	1.5421	1.5378	1.5335	1.5250	1.5167	1.5086	1.4923	1.4766
65	1.5714	1.5623	1.5578	1.5533	1.5490	1.5446	1.5361	1.5277	1.5195	1.5031	1.4873
66	1.5828	1.5736	1.5691	1.5646	1.5602	1.5558	1.5472	1.5388	1.5305	1.5140	1.4981
67	1.5943	1.5850	1.5805	1.5760	1.5715	1.5671	1.5584	1.5499	1.5416	1.5249	1.5089
68	1.6059	1.5965	1.5920	1.5874	1.5829	1.5785	1.5697	1.5611	1.5528	1.5359	1.5198
69	1.6176	1.6081	1.6035	1.5989	1.5944	1.5899	1.5811	1.5724	1.5640	1.5470	1.5307
70	1.6293	1.6198	1.6151	1.6105	1.6059	1.6014	1.5925	1.5838	1.5753	1.5582	1.5417
71	1.6411	1.6315	1.6268	1.6221	1.6175	1.6130	1.6040	1.5952	1.5867	1.5694	1.5527
72	1.6529	1.6433	1.6385	1.6338	1.6292	1.6246	1.6155	1.6067	1.5981	1.5806	1.5637
73	1.6648	1.6551	1.6503	1.6456	1.6409	1.6363	1.6271	1.6182	1.6095	1.5919	1.5747
74	1.6768	1.6670	1.6622	1.6574	1.6526	1.6480	1.6387	1.6297	1.6209	1.6031	1.5857
75	1.6888	1.6789	1.6740	1.6692	1.6644	1.6597	1.6503	1.6412	1.6322	1.6142	1.5966
76	1.7008	1.6908	1.6858	1.6810	1.6761	1.6713	1.6619	1.6526	1.6435	1.6252	1.6074
77	1.7128	1.7026	1.6976	1.6927	1.6878	1.6829	1.6734	1.6640	1.6547	1.6361	1.6181
78	1.7247	1.7144	1.7093	1.7043	1.6994	1.6944	1.6847	1.6751	1.6657	1.6469	1.6286
79	1.7365	1.7261	1.7209	1.7158	1.7108	1.7058	1.6959	1.6862	1.6766	1.6575	1.6390

Table 3-120. Sulfuric Acid (H_2SO_4)—(*Concluded*)

%	0°C.	10°C.	15°C.	20°C.	25°C.	30°C.	40°C.	50°C.	60°C.	80°C.	100°C.
80	1.7482	1.7376	1.7323	1.7272	1.7221	1.7170	1.7069	1.6971	1.6873	1.6680	1.6493
81	1.7597	1.7489	1.7435	1.7383	1.7331	1.7279	1.7177	1.7077	1.6978	1.6782	1.6594
82	1.7709	1.7599	1.7544	1.7491	1.7437	1.7385	1.7281	1.7180	1.7080	1.6882	1.6692
83	1.7815	1.7704	1.7649	1.7594	1.7540	1.7487	1.7382	1.7279	1.7179	1.6979	1.6787
84	1.7916	1.7804	1.7748	1.7693	1.7639	1.7585	1.7479	1.7375	1.7274	1.7072	1.6878
85	1.8009	1.7897	1.7841	1.7786	1.7732	1.7678	1.7571	1.7466	1.7364	1.7161	1.6966
86	1.8095	1.7983	1.7927	1.7872	1.7818	1.7763	1.7657	1.7552	1.7449	1.7245	1.7050
87	1.8173	1.8061	1.8006	1.7951	1.7897	1.7842	1.7736	1.7632	1.7529	1.7324	1.7129
88	1.8243	1.8132	1.8077	1.8022	1.7968	1.7914	1.7809	1.7705	1.7602	1.7397	1.7202
89	1.8306	1.8195	1.8141	1.8087	1.8033	1.7979	1.7874	1.7770	1.7669	1.7464	1.7269
90	1.8361	1.8252	1.8198	1.8144	1.8091	1.8038	1.7933	1.7829	1.7729	1.7525	1.7331
91	1.8410	1.8302	1.8248	1.8195	1.8142	1.8090	1.7986	1.7883	1.7783	1.7581	1.7388
92	1.8453	1.8346	1.8293	1.8240	1.8188	1.8136	1.8033	1.7932	1.7832	1.7633	1.7439
93	1.8490	1.8384	1.8331	1.8279	1.8227	1.8176	1.8074	1.7974	1.7876	1.7681	1.7485
94	1.8520	1.8415	1.8363	1.8312	1.8260	1.8210	1.8109	1.8011	1.7914		
95	1.8544	1.8439	1.8388	1.8337	1.8286	1.8236	1.8137	1.8040	1.7944		
96	1.8560	1.8457	1.8406	1.8355	1.8305	1.8255	1.8157	1.8060	1.7965		
97	1.8569	1.8466	1.8414	1.8364	1.8314	1.8264	1.8166	1.8071	1.7977		
98	1.8567	1.8463	1.8411	1.8361	1.8310	1.8261	1.8163	1.8068	1.7976		
99	1.8551	1.8445	1.8393	1.8342	1.8292	1.8242	1.8145	1.8050	1.7958		
100	1.8517	1.8409	1.8357	1.8305	1.8255	1.8205	1.8107	1.8013	1.7922		

%	$d_4^{5.96}$	%	$d_4^{13.00}$	$d_4^{18.00}$
0.005	1.000 0140	0.05	0.999 810	0.999 028
.01	1.000 0576	.1	1.000 185	.999 400
.02	1.000 1434	.2	1.000 912	1.000 119
.03	1.000 2276	.3	1.001 623	1.000 820
.04	1.000 3104	.4	1.002 326	1.001 512
.05	1.000 3920	.5	1.003 023	1.002 197
.06	1.000 4726	.6	1.003 716	1.002 877
.07	1.000 5523	.8	1.005 090	1.004 227
.08	1.000 6313	1.0	1.006 452	1.005 570
.09	1.000 7098	1.2	1.007 807	1.006 909
.10	1.000 7880	1.4	1.009 159	1.008 247
.15	1.001 1732	1.6	1.010 510	1.009 583
.20	1.001 5514	1.8	1.011 860	1.010 918
.25	1.001 9254	2.0	1.013 209	1.012 252
.30	1.002 2961	2.2	1.014 557	1.013 586
.35	1.002 6639	2.4	1.015 904	1.014 919
.40	1.003 0292			
.45	1.003 3923			
.50	1.003 7534			

Table 3-121. Zinc Bromide ($ZnBr_2$)

%	0°C.	20°C.	40°C.	60°C.	80°C.	100°C.
2	1.0188	1.0167	1.0102	1.0008	0.9890	0.9751
4	1.0381	1.0354	1.0285	1.0187	1.0065	0.9921
8	1.0777	1.0738	1.0660	1.0554	1.0422	1.0270
12	1.1186	1.1135	1.1046	1.0932	1.0789	1.0629
16	1.1609	1.1544	1.1445	1.1320	1.1169	1.1000
20	1.2043	1.1965	1.1855	1.1720	1.1560	1.1382
30	1.3288	1.3170	1.3030	1.2868	1.2688	1.2489
40	1.477	1.462	1.445	1.427	1.406	1.385
50	1.661	1.643	1.623	1.602	1.579	1.555
60	1.891	1.869	1.845	1.822	1.797	1.771
65	2.026	2.002	1.976	1.951	1.924	1.898

Table 3-122. Zinc Chloride ($ZnCl_2$)

%	0°C.	20°C.	40°C.	60°C.	80°C.	100°C.
2	1.0192	1.0167	1.0099	1.0003	0.9882	0.9739
4	1.0384	1.0350	1.0274	1.0172	1.0044	.9894
8	1.0769	1.0715	1.0624	1.0508	1.0369	1.0211
12	1.1159	1.1085	1.0980	1.0853	1.0704	1.0541
16	1.1558	1.1468	1.1350	1.1212	1.1055	1.0888
20	1.1970	1.1866	1.1736	1.1590	1.1428	1.1255
30	1.3062	1.2928	1.2778	1.2614	1.2438	1.2252
40	1.4329	1.4173	1.4003	1.3824	1.3637	1.3441
50	1.5860	1.5681	1.5495	1.5300	1.5097	1.4892
60	......	1.749				
70	......	1.962				

Table 3-123. Zinc Nitrate [$Zn(NO_3)_2$]

%	18°C.	%	18°C.
2	1.0154	18	1.1652
4	1.0322	20	1.1865
6	1.0496	25	1.2427
8	1.0675	30	1.3029
10	1.0859	35	1.3678
12	1.1048	40	1.4378
14	1.1244	45	1.5134
16	1.1445	50	1.5944

Table 3-124. Zinc Sulfate ($ZnSO_4$)

%	20°C.
2	1.019
4	1.0403
6	1.0620
8	1.0842
10	1.1071
12	1.1308
14	1.1553
16	1.1806

DENSITIES OF AQUEOUS ORGANIC SOLUTIONS*

From "International Critical Tables," vol. 3, pp. 115–129. All compositions are in weight per cent *in vacuo*. All density values are d_4^t = g./ml. *in vacuo*.

Table 3-125. Formic Acid (HCOOH)

%	0°C.	15°C.	20°C.	30°C.	%	0°C.	15°C.	20°C.	30°C.	%	0°C.	15°C.	20°C.	30°C.	%	0°C.	15°C.	20°C.	30°C.
0	0.9999	0.9991	0.9982	0.9957	25	1.0706	1.0627	1.0609	1.0540	50	1.1349	1.1225	1.1207	1.1098	75	1.1953	1.1794	1.1769	1.1636
1	1.0028	1.0019	1.0019	0.9980	26	1.0733	1.0652	1.0633	1.0564	51	1.1374	1.1248	1.1223	1.1120	76	1.1976	1.1816	1.1785	1.1656
2	1.0059	1.0045	1.0044	1.0004	27	1.0760	1.0678	1.0656	1.0587	52	1.1399	1.1271	1.1244	1.1142	77	1.1999	1.1837	1.1801	1.1676
3	1.0090	1.0072	1.0070	1.0028	28	1.0787	1.0702	1.0681	1.0609	53	1.1424	1.1294	1.1269	1.1164	78	1.2021	1.1859	1.1818	1.1697
4	1.0120	1.0100	1.0093	1.0053	29	1.0813	1.0726	1.0705	1.0632	54	1.1448	1.1318	1.1295	1.1186	79	1.2043	1.1881	1.1837	1.1717
5	1.0150	1.0124	1.0115	1.0075	30	1.0839	1.0750	1.0729	1.0654	55	1.1472	1.1341	1.1320	1.1208	80	1.2065	1.1902	1.1806	1.1737
6	1.0179	1.0151	1.0141	1.0101	31	1.0866	1.0774	1.0753	1.0676	56	1.1497	1.1365	1.1342	1.1230	81	1.2088	1.1924	1.1876	1.1758
7	1.0207	1.0177	1.0170	1.0125	32	1.0891	1.0798	1.0777	1.0699	57	1.1523	1.1388	1.1361	1.1253	82	1.2110	1.1944	1.1896	1.1778
8	1.0237	1.0204	1.0196	1.0149	33	1.0916	1.0821	1.0800	1.0721	58	1.1548	1.1411	1.1381	1.1274	83	1.2132	1.1965	1.1914	1.1798
9	1.0266	1.0230	1.0221	1.0173	34	1.0941	1.0844	1.0823	1.0743	59	1.1573	1.1434	1.1401	1.1295	84	1.2154	1.1985	1.1929	1.1817
10	1.0295	1.0256	1.0246	1.0197	35	1.0966	1.0867	1.0847	1.0766	60	1.1597	1.1458	1.1424	1.1317	85	1.2176	1.2005	1.1953	1.1837
11	1.0324	1.0281	1.0271	1.0221	36	1.0993	1.0892	1.0871	1.0788	61	1.1621	1.1481	1.1448	1.1338	86	1.2196	1.2025	1.1976	1.1856
12	1.0351	1.0306	1.0296	1.0244	37	1.1018	1.0916	1.0895	1.0810	62	1.1645	1.1504	1.1473	1.1360	87	1.2217	1.2045	1.1994	1.1875
13	1.0379	1.0330	1.0321	1.0267	38	1.1043	1.0940	1.0919	1.0832	63	1.1669	1.1526	1.1493	1.1382	88	1.2237	1.2064	1.2012	1.1893
14	1.0407	1.0355	1.0345	1.0290	39	1.1069	1.0964	1.0940	1.0854	64	1.1694	1.1549	1.1517	1.1403	89	1.2258	1.2084	1.2028	1.1910
15	1.0435	1.0380	1.0370	1.0313	40	1.1095	1.0988	1.0963	1.0876	65	1.1718	1.1572	1.1543	1.1425	90	1.2278	1.2102	1.2044	1.1927
16	1.0463	1.0405	1.0393	1.0336	41	1.1122	1.1012	1.0990	1.0898	66	1.1742	1.1595	1.1565	1.1446	91	1.2297	1.2121	1.2059	1.1945
17	1.0491	1.0430	1.0417	1.0358	42	1.1148	1.1036	1.1015	1.0920	67	1.1766	1.1618	1.1584	1.1467	92	1.2316	1.2139	1.2078	1.1961
18	1.0518	1.0455	1.0441	1.0381	43	1.1174	1.1060	1.1038	1.0943	68	1.1790	1.1640	1.1604	1.1489	93	1.2335	1.2157	1.2099	1.1978
19	1.0545	1.0480	1.0464	1.0404	44	1.1199	1.1084	1.1062	1.0965	69	1.1813	1.1663	1.1628	1.1510	94	1.2354	1.2174	1.2117	1.1994
20	1.0571	1.0505	1.0488	1.0427	45	1.1224	1.1109	1.1085	1.0987	70	1.1835	1.1685	1.1655	1.1531	95	1.2372	1.2191	1.2140	1.2008
21	1.0598	1.0532	1.0512	1.0451	46	1.1249	1.1133	1.1108	1.1009	71	1.1858	1.1707	1.1677	1.1552	96	1.2390	1.2208	1.2158	1.2022
22	1.0625	1.0556	1.0537	1.0473	47	1.1274	1.1156	1.1130	1.1031	72	1.1882	1.1729	1.1702	1.1573	97	1.2408	1.2224	1.2170	1.2036
23	1.0652	1.0580	1.0561	1.0496	48	1.1299	1.1179	1.1157	1.1053	73	1.1906	1.1751	1.1728	1.1595	98	1.2425	1.2240	1.2183	1.2048
24	1.0679	1.0604	1.0585	1.0518	49	1.1324	1.1202	1.1185	1.1076	74	1.1929	1.1773	1.1752	1.1615	99	1.2441	1.2257	1.2202	1.2061
															100	1.2456	1.2273	1.2212	1.2073

Table 3-126. Acetic Acid (CH_3COOH)

%	0°C.	10°C.	15°C.	20°C.	25°C.	30°C.	40°C.	%	0°C.	10°C.	15°C.	20°C.	25°C.	30°C.	40°C.
0	0.9999	0.9997	0.9991	0.9982	0.9971	0.9957	0.9922	40	1.0621	1.0557	1.0522	1.0488	1.0450	1.0416	1.0338
1	1.0016	1.0013	1.0006	.9996	.9987	.9971	.9934	41	1.0633	1.0568	1.0532	1.0498	1.0460	1.0425	1.0346
2	1.0033	1.0029	1.0021	1.0012	1.0000	.9984	.9946	42	1.0644	1.0578	1.0542	1.0507	1.0469	1.0433	1.0353
3	1.0051	1.0044	1.0036	1.0025	1.0013	.9997	.9958	43	1.0656	1.0588	1.0551	1.0516	1.0477	1.0441	1.0361
4	1.0070	1.0060	1.0051	1.0040	1.0027	1.0011	.9970	44	1.0667	1.0598	1.0561	1.0525	1.0486	1.0449	1.0368
5	1.0088	1.0076	1.0066	1.0055	1.0041	1.0024	.9982	45	1.0679	1.0608	1.0570	1.0534	1.0495	1.0456	1.0375
6	1.0106	1.0092	1.0081	1.0069	1.0055	1.0037	.9994	46	1.0689	1.0618	1.0579	1.0542	1.0503	1.0464	1.0382
7	1.0124	1.0108	1.0096	1.0083	1.0068	1.0050	1.0006	47	1.0699	1.0627	1.0588	1.0551	1.0511	1.0471	1.0389
8	1.0142	1.0124	1.0111	1.0097	1.0081	1.0063	1.0018	48	1.0709	1.0636	1.0597	1.0559	1.0518	1.0479	1.0395
9	1.0159	1.0140	1.0126	1.0111	1.0094	1.0076	1.0030	49	1.0720	1.0645	1.0605	1.0567	1.0526	1.0486	1.0402
10	1.0177	1.0156	1.0141	1.0125	1.0107	1.0089	1.0042	50	1.0729	1.0654	1.0613	1.0575	1.0534	1.0492	1.0408
11	1.0194	1.0171	1.0155	1.0139	1.0120	1.0102	1.0054	51	1.0738	1.0663	1.0622	1.0582	1.0542	1.0499	1.0414
12	1.0211	1.0187	1.0170	1.0154	1.0133	1.0115	1.0065	52	1.0748	1.0671	1.0629	1.0590	1.0549	1.0506	1.0421
13	1.0228	1.0202	1.0184	1.0168	1.0146	1.0127	1.0077	53	1.0757	1.0679	1.0637	1.0597	1.0555	1.0512	1.0427
14	1.0245	1.0217	1.0199	1.0182	1.0159	1.0139	1.0088	54	1.0765	1.0687	1.0644	1.0604	1.0562	1.0518	1.0432
15	1.0262	1.0232	1.0213	1.0195	1.0172	1.0151	1.0099	55	1.0774	1.0694	1.0651	1.0611	1.0568	1.0525	1.0438
16	1.0278	1.0247	1.0227	1.0209	1.0185	1.0163	1.0110	56	1.0782	1.0701	1.0658	1.0618	1.0574	1.0531	1.0443
17	1.0295	1.0262	1.0241	1.0223	1.0198	1.0175	1.0121	57	1.0790	1.0708	1.0665	1.0624	1.0580	1.0536	1.0448
18	1.0311	1.0276	1.0255	1.0236	1.0210	1.0187	1.0132	58	1.0798	1.0715	1.0672	1.0631	1.0586	1.0542	1.0453
19	1.0327	1.0291	1.0269	1.0250	1.0223	1.0198	1.0142	59	1.0805	1.0722	1.0678	1.0637	1.0592	1.0547	1.0458
20	1.0343	1.0305	1.0283	1.0263	1.0235	1.0210	1.0153	60	1.0813	1.0728	1.0684	1.0642	1.0597	1.0552	1.0462
21	1.0358	1.0319	1.0297	1.0276	1.0248	1.0222	1.0164	61	1.0820	1.0734	1.0690	1.0648	1.0602	1.0557	1.0466
22	1.0374	1.0333	1.0310	1.0288	1.0260	1.0233	1.0174	62	1.0826	1.0740	1.0696	1.0653	1.0607	1.0562	1.0470
23	1.0389	1.0347	1.0323	1.0301	1.0272	1.0244	1.0185	63	1.0833	1.0746	1.0701	1.0658	1.0612	1.0566	1.0473
24	1.0404	1.0361	1.0336	1.0313	1.0283	1.0256	1.0195	64	1.0838	1.0752	1.0706	1.0662	1.0616	1.0571	1.0477
25	1.0419	1.0375	1.0349	1.0326	1.0295	1.0267	1.0205	65	1.0844	1.0757	1.0711	1.0666	1.0621	1.0575	1.0480
26	1.0434	1.0388	1.0362	1.0338	1.0307	1.0278	1.0215	66	1.0850	1.0762	1.0716	1.0671	1.0624	1.0578	1.0483
27	1.0449	1.0401	1.0374	1.0349	1.0318	1.0289	1.0225	67	1.0856	1.0767	1.0720	1.0675	1.0628	1.0582	1.0486
28	1.0463	1.0414	1.0386	1.0361	1.0329	1.0299	1.0234	68	1.0860	1.0771	1.0725	1.0678	1.0631	1.0585	1.0489
29	1.0477	1.0427	1.0399	1.0372	1.0340	1.0310	1.0244	69	1.0865	1.0775	1.0729	1.0682	1.0634	1.0588	1.0491
30	1.0491	1.0440	1.0411	1.0384	1.0350	1.0320	1.0253	70	1.0869	1.0779	1.0732	1.0685	1.0637	1.0590	1.0493
31	1.0505	1.0453	1.0423	1.0395	1.0361	1.0330	1.0262	71	1.0874	1.0783	1.0736	1.0687	1.0640	1.0592	1.0495
32	1.0519	1.0465	1.0435	1.0406	1.0372	1.0341	1.0272	72	1.0877	1.0786	1.0738	1.0690	1.0642	1.0594	1.0496
33	1.0532	1.0477	1.0446	1.0417	1.0382	1.0351	1.0281	73	1.0881	1.0789	1.0741	1.0693	1.0644	1.0595	1.0497
34	1.0545	1.0489	1.0458	1.0428	1.0392	1.0361	1.0289	74	1.0884	1.0792	1.0743	1.0694	1.0645	1.0596	1.0498
35	1.0558	1.0501	1.0469	1.0438	1.0402	1.0371	1.0298	75	1.0887	1.0794	1.0745	1.0696	1.0647	1.0597	1.0499
36	1.0571	1.0513	1.0480	1.0449	1.0412	1.0380	1.0306	76	1.0889	1.0796	1.0746	1.0698	1.0648	1.0598	1.0499
37	1.0584	1.0524	1.0491	1.0459	1.0422	1.0390	1.0314	77	1.0891	1.0797	1.0747	1.0699	1.0648	1.0598	1.0499
38	1.0596	1.0535	1.0501	1.0469	1.0432	1.0399	1.0322	78	1.0893	1.0798	1.0747	1.0700	1.0648	1.0598	1.0498
39	1.0608	1.0546	1.0512	1.0479	1.0441	1.0408	1.0330	79	1.0894	1.0798	1.0747	1.0700	1.0648	1.0597	1.0497

* For gasoline and aircraft fuels see Hibbard, *N.A.C.A. Research Mem.* E56I21, (declassified 1958).

Table 3-126. Acetic Acid (CH_3COOH)—(*Concluded*)

%	0°C.	10°C.	15°C.	20°C.	25°C.	30°C.	40°C.	%	0°C.	10°C.	15°C.	20°C.	25°C.	30°C.	40°C.
80	1.0895	1.0798	1.0747	1.0700	1.0647	1.0596	1.0495	90	1.0865	1.0766	1.0708	1.0661	1.0605	1.0549	1.0445
81	1.0895	1.0797	1.0745	1.0699	1.0646	1.0594	1.0493	91	1.0857	1.0758	1.0700	1.0652	1.0597	1.0541	1.0436
82	1.0895	1.0796	1.0743	1.0698	1.0644	1.0592	1.0490	92	1.0848	1.0749	1.0690	1.0643	1.0587	1.0530	1.0426
83	1.0895	1.0795	1.0741	1.0696	1.0642	1.0589	1.0487	93	1.0838	1.0739	1.0680	1.0632	1.0577	1.0518	1.0414
84	1.0893	1.0793	1.0738	1.0693	1.0638	1.0585	1.0483	94	1.0826	1.0727	1.0667	1.0619	1.0564	1.0506	1.0401
85	1.0891	1.0790	1.0735	1.0689	1.0635	1.0582	1.0479	95	1.0813	1.0714	1.0652	1.0605	1.0551	1.0491	1.0386
86	1.0887	1.0787	1.0731	1.0685	1.0630	1.0576	1.0473	96	1.0798	......	1.0632	1.0588	1.0535	1.0473	1.0368
87	1.0883	1.0783	1.0726	1.0680	1.0626	1.0571	1.0467	97	1.0780	......	1.0611	1.0570	1.0516	1.0454	1.0348
88	1.0877	1.0778	1.0721	1.0675	1.0620	1.0564	1.0460	98	1.0759	......	1.0590	1.0549	1.0495	1.0431	1.0325
89	1.0872	1.0773	1.0715	1.0668	1.0613	1.0557	1.0453	99	1.0730	......	1.0567	1.0524	1.0468	1.0407	1.0299
								100	1.0697	......	1.0545	1.0498	1.0440	1.0380	1.0271

Table 3-127. Oxalic Acid ($H_2C_2O_4$)

%	$d_4^{17.5}$	%	$d_4^{17.5}$
1	1.0035	8	1.0280
2	1.0070	10	1.0350
4	1.0140	12	1.0420

Table 3-128. Methyl Alcohol (CH_3OH)*

%	0°C.	10°C.	15.56°C.	20°C.	15°C.	%	0°C.	10°C.	15.56°C	20°C.	15°C.	%	0°C.	10°C.	15.56°C.	20°C.	15°C.
0	0.9999	0.9997	0.9990	0.9982	0.99913	35	0.9534	0.9484	0.9456	0.9433	0.94570	70	0.8869	0.8794	0.8748	0.8715	0.87507
1	.9981	.9980	.9973	.9965	.99727	36	.9520	.9469	.9440	.9416	.94404	71	.8847	.8770	.8726	.8690	.87271
2	.9963	.9962	.9955	.9948	.99543	37	.9505	.9453	.9422	.9398	.94237	72	.8824	.8747	.8702	.8665	.87033
3	.9946	.9945	.9938	.9931	.99370	38	.9490	.9437	.9405	.9381	.94067	73	.8801	.8724	.8678	.8641	.86792
4	.9930	.9929	.9921	.9914	.99198	39	.9475	.9420	.9387	.9363	.93894	74	.8778	.8699	.8653	.8616	.86546
5	.9914	.9912	.9904	.9896	.99029	40	.9459	.9403	.9369	.9345	.93720	75	.8754	.8676	.8629	.8592	.86300
6	.9899	.9896	.9889	.9880	.98864	41	.9443	.9387	.9351	.9327	.93543	76	.8729	.8651	.8604	.8567	.86051
7	.9884	.9881	.9872	.9863	.98701	42	.9427	.9370	.9333	.9309	.93365	77	.8705	.8626	.8579	.8542	.85801
8	.9870	.9865	.9857	.9847	.98547	43	.9411	.9352	.9315	.9290	.93185	78	.8680	.8602	.8554	.8518	.85551
9	.9856	.9849	.9841	.9831	.98394	44	.9395	.9334	.9297	.9272	.93001	79	.8657	.8577	.8529	.8494	.85300
10	.9842	.9834	.9826	.9815	.98241	45	.9377	.9316	.9279	.9252	.92815	80	.8634	.8551	.8503	.8469	.85048
11	.9829	.9820	.9811	.9799	.98093	46	.9360	.9298	.9261	.9234	.92627	81	.8610	.8527	.8478	.8446	.84794
12	.9816	.9805	.9796	.9784	.97945	47	.9342	.9279	.9242	.9214	.92436	82	.8585	.8501	.8452	.8420	.84536
13	.9804	.9791	.9781	.9768	.97802	48	.9324	.9260	.9223	.9196	.92242	83	.8560	.8475	.8426	.8394	.84274
14	.9792	.9778	.9766	.9754	.97660	49	.9306	.9240	.9204	.9176	.92048	84	.8535	.8449	.8400	.8366	.84009
15	.9780	.9764	.9752	.9740	.97518	50	.9287	.9221	.9185	.9156	.91852	85	.8510	.8422	.8374	.8340	.83742
16	.9769	.9751	.9738	.9725	.97377	51	.9269	.9202	.9166	.9135	.91653	86	.8483	.8394	.8347	.8314	.83475
17	.9758	.9739	.9723	.9710	.97237	52	.9250	.9182	.9146	.9114	.91451	87	.8456	.8367	.8320	.8286	.83207
18	.9747	.9726	.9709	.9696	.97096	53	.9230	.9162	.9126	.9094	.91248	88	.8428	.8340	.8294	.8258	.82937
19	.9736	.9713	.9695	.9681	.96955	54	.9211	.9142	.9106	.9073	.91044	89	.8400	.8314	.8267	.8230	.82667
20	.9725	.9700	.9680	.9666	.96814	55	.9191	.9122	.9086	.9052	.90839	90	.8374	.8287	.8239	.8202	.82396
21	.9714	.9687	.9666	.9651	.96673	56	.9172	.9101	.9065	.9032	.90631	91	.8347	.8261	.8212	.8174	.82124
22	.9702	.9673	.9652	.9636	.96533	57	.9151	.9080	.9045	.9010	.90421	92	.8320	.8234	.8185	.8146	.81849
23	.9690	.9660	.9638	.9622	.96392	58	.9131	.9060	.9024	.8988	.90210	93	.8293	.8208	.8157	.8118	.81568
24	.9678	.9646	.9624	.9607	.96251	59	.9111	.9039	.9002	.8968	.89996	94	.8266	.8180	.8129	.8090	.81285
25	.9666	.9632	.9609	.9592	.96108	60	.9090	.9018	.8980	.8946	.89781	95	.8240	.8152	.8101	.8062	.80999
26	.9654	.9618	.9595	.9576	.95963	61	.9068	.8998	.8958	.8924	.89563	96	.8212	.8124	.8073	.8034	.80713
27	.9642	.9604	.9580	.9562	.95817	62	.9046	.8977	.8936	.8902	.89341	97	.8186	.8096	.8045	.8005	.80428
28	.9629	.9590	.9565	.9546	.95668	63	.9024	.8955	.8913	.8879	.89117	98	.8158	.8068	.8016	.7976	.80143
29	.9616	.9575	.9550	.9531	.95518	64	.9002	.8933	.8890	.8856	.88890	99	.8130	.8040	.7987	.7948	.79859
30	.9604	.9560	.9535	.9515	.95366	65	.8980	.8911	.8867	.8834	.88662	100	.8102	.8009	.7959	.7917	.79577
31	.9590	.9546	.9521	.9499	.95213	66	.8958	.8888	.8844	.8811	.88433						
32	.9576	.9531	.9505	.9483	.95056	67	.8935	.8865	.8820	.8787	.88203						
33	.9563	.9516	.9489	.9466	.94896	68	.8913	.8842	.8797	.8763	.87971						
34	.9549	.9500	.9473	.9450	.94734	69	.8891	.8818	.8771	.8738	.87739						

* It should be noted that the values for 100 per cent do not agree with some data available elsewhere, *e.g.*, "American Institute of Physics Handbook," McGraw-Hill, New York, 1957. Also, see Atack, "Handbook of Chemical Data," Reinhold, New York, 1957.

Table 3-129. Ethyl Alcohol (C_2H_5OH)*

%	10°C.	15°C.	20°C.	25°C.	30°C.	35°C.	40°C.	%	10°C.	15°C.	20°C.	25°C.	30°C.	35°C.	40°C.
0	0.99973	0.99913	0.99823	0.99708	0.99568	0.99406	0.99225	50	0.92126	0.91776	0.91384	0.90985	0.90580	0.90168	0.89750
1	785	725	636	520	379	217	034	51	.91943	555	160	760	353	.89940	519
2	602	542	453	336	194	031	.98846	52	723	333	.90936	534	125	710	288
3	426	365	275	157	014	.98849	663	53	502	110	711	307	.89896	479	056
4	258	195	103	.98984	.98839	672	485	54	279	.90885	485	079	667	248	.88823
5	098	032	.98938	817	670	501	311	55	055	659	258	.89850	437	016	589
6	.98946	.98877	780	656	507	335	142	56	.90831	433	031	621	206	.88784	356
7	801	729	627	500	347	172	.97975	57	607	207	.89803	392	.88975	552	122
8	660	584	478	346	189	009	808	58	381	.89980	574	162	744	319	.87888
9	524	442	331	193	031	.97846	641	59	154	752	344	.88931	512	085	653
10	393	304	187	043	.97875	685	475	60	.89927	523	113	699	278	.87851	417
11	267	171	047	.97897	723	527	312	61	698	293	.88882	446	044	615	180
12	145	041	.97910	753	573	371	150	62	468	062	650	233	.87809	379	.86943
13	026	.97914	775	611	424	216	.96989	63	237	.88830	417	.87998	574	142	705
14	.97911	790	643	472	278	063	829	64	006	597	183	763	337	.86905	466
15	800	669	514	334	133	.96911	670	65	.88774	364	.87948	527	100	667	227
16	692	552	387	199	.96990	760	512	66	541	130	713	291	.86863	429	.85987
17	583	433	259	062	844	607	352	67	308	.87895	477	054	625	190	747
18	473	313	129	.96923	697	452	189	68	074	660	241	.86817	387	.85950	407
19	363	191	.96997	782	547	294	023	69	.87839	424	004	579	148	710	266
20	252	068	864	639	395	134	.95856	70	602	187	.86766	340	.85908	470	025
21	139	.96944	729	495	242	.95973	687	71	365	.86949	527	100	667	228	.84783
22	024	818	592	348	087	809	516	72	127	710	287	.85859	426	.84986	540
23	.96907	689	453	199	.95929	643	343	73	.86888	470	047	618	184	743	297
24	787	558	312	048	769	476	168	74	648	229	.85806	376	.84941	500	053
25	665	424	168	.95895	607	306	.94991	75	408	.85988	564	134	698	257	.83809
26	539	287	020	738	442	133	810	76	168	747	322	.84891	455	013	564
27	406	144	.95867	576	272	.94955	625	77	.85927	505	079	647	211	.83768	319
28	268	.95996	710	410	098	774	438	78	685	262	.84835	403	.83966	523	074
29	125	844	548	241	.94922	590	248	79	442	018	590	158	720	277	.82827
30	.95977	686	382	067	741	403	055	80	197	.84772	344	.83911	473	029	578
31	823	524	212	.94890	557	214	.93860	81	.84950	525	096	664	224	.82780	329
32	665	357	038	709	370	021	662	82	702	277	.83848	415	.82974	530	079
33	502	186	.94860	525	180	.93825	461	83	453	028	599	164	724	279	.81828
34	334	011	679	337	.93986	626	257	84	203	.83777	348	.82913	473	027	576
35	162	.94832	494	146	790	425	051	85	.83951	525	095	660	220	.81774	322
36	.94986	650	306	.93952	591	221	.92843	86	697	271	.82840	405	.81965	519	067
37	805	464	114	756	390	016	634	87	441	014	583	148	708	262	.80811
38	620	273	.93919	556	186	.92808	422	88	181	.82754	323	.81888	448	003	552
39	431	079	720	353	.92979	597	208	89	.82919	492	062	626	186	.80742	291
40	238	.93882	518	148	770	385	.91992	90	654	227	.81797	362	.80922	478	028
41	042	682	314	.92940	558	170	774	91	386	.81959	529	094	655	211	.79761
42	.93842	478	107	729	344	.91952	554	92	114	688	257	.80823	384	.79941	491
43	639	271	.92897	516	128	733	332	93	.81839	413	.80983	549	111	669	220
44	433	062	685	301	.91910	513	108	94	561	134	705	272	.79835	393	.78947
45	226	.92852	472	085	692	291	.90884	95	278	.80852	424	.79991	555	114	670
46	017	640	257	.91868	472	069	660	96	.80991	566	138	706	271	.78831	388
47	.92806	426	041	649	250	.90845	434	97	698	274	.79846	415	.78981	542	100
48	593	211	.91823	429	028	621	207	98	399	.79975	547	117	684	247	.77806
49	379	.91995	604	208	.90805	396	.89979	99	094	670	243	.78814	382	.77946	507
								100	.79784	360	.78934	506	075	641	203

* For data from −78° to 78°C., see "American Institute of Physics Handbook," p. 2-142, Table 2N-5, McGraw-Hill, New York, 1957.

Table 3-130. Densities of Mixtures of C_2H_5OH and H_2O at 20°C.

G./ml.

% alcohol by weight	Tenths of %: 0	1	2	3	4	5	6	7	8	9
0	0.99823	804	785	766	748	729	710	692	673	655
1	636	618	599	581	562	544	525	507	489	471
2	453	435	417	399	381	363	345	327	310	292
3	275	257	240	222	205	188	171	154	137	120
4	103	087	070	053	037	020	003	*987	*971	*954
5	.98938	922	906	890	874	859	843	827	811	796
6	780	765	749	734	718	703	688	673	658	642
7	627	612	597	582	567	553	538	523	508	493
8	478	463	449	434	419	404	389	374	360	345
9	331	316	301	287	273	258	244	229	215	201
10	187	172	158	144	130	117	103	089	075	061
11	047	033	019	006	*992	*978	*964	*951	*937	*923
12	.97910	896	883	869	855	842	828	815	801	788
13	775	761	748	735	722	709	696	683	670	657
14	643	630	617	604	591	578	565	552	539	526
15	514	501	488	475	462	450	438	425	412	400
16	387	374	361	349	336	323	310	297	284	272
17	259	246	233	220	207	194	181	168	155	142
18	129	116	103	089	076	063	050	037	024	010
19	.96997	984	971	957	944	931	917	904	891	877
20	864	850	837	823	810	796	783	769	756	742
21	729	716	702	688	675	661	647	634	620	606
22	592	578	564	551	537	523	509	495	481	467
23	453	439	425	411	396	382	368	354	340	326
24	312	297	283	269	254	240	225	211	196	182
25	168	153	139	124	109	094	080	065	050	035
26	020	005	*990	*975	*959	*944	*929	*914	*898	*883
27	.95867	851	836	820	805	789	773	757	742	726
28	710	694	678	662	646	630	613	597	581	565
29	548	532	516	499	483	466	450	433	416	400
30	382	365	349	332	315	298	281	264	247	230
31	212	195	178	161	143	126	108	091	074	056
32	038	020	003	*985	*967	*950	*932	*914	*896	*878
33	.94860	842	824	806	788	770	752	734	715	697
34	679	660	642	624	605	587	568	550	531	512
35	494	475	456	438	419	400	382	363	344	325
36	306	287	268	249	230	211	192	172	153	134
37	114	095	075	056	036	017	*997	*978	*958	*939
38	.93919	899	879	859	840	820	800	780	760	740
39	720	700	680	660	640	620	599	579	559	539
40	518	498	478	458	437	417	396	376	356	335
41	314	294	273	253	232	212	191	170	149	129
42	107	086	065	044	023	002	*981	*960	*939	*918
43	.92897	876	855	834	812	791	770	749	728	707
44	685	664	642	621	600	579	557	536	515	493
45	472	450	429	408	386	365	343	322	300	279
46	257	236	214	193	171	150	128	106	085	063
47	041	019	*997	*976	*954	*932	*910	*889	*867	*845
48	.91823	801	780	758	736	714	692	670	648	626
49	604	582	560	538	516	494	472	450	428	406

% alcohol by weight	Tenths of %: 0	1	2	3	4	5	6	7	8	9
50	0.91384	361	339	317	295	272	250	228	206	183
51	160	138	116	093	071	049	026	004	*981	*959
52	.90936	914	891	869	846	824	801	779	756	734
53	711	689	666	644	621	598	576	553	531	508
54	485	463	440	417	395	372	349	327	304	281
55	258	236	213	190	167	145	122	099	076	054
56	031	008	*985	*962	*939	*917	*894	*871	*848	*825
57	.89803	780	757	734	711	688	665	643	620	597
58	574	551	528	505	482	459	436	413	390	367
59	344	321	298	275	252	229	206	183	160	137
60	113	090	067	044	021	*998	*975	*951	*928	*905
61	.88882	859	836	812	789	766	743	720	696	673
62	650	626	603	580	557	533	510	487	463	440
63	417	393	370	347	323	300	277	253	230	206
64	183	160	136	113	089	066	042	019	*995	*972
65	.87948	925	901	878	854	831	807	784	760	737
66	713	689	666	642	619	595	572	548	524	501
67	477	454	430	406	383	359	336	312	288	265
68	241	218	194	170	147	123	099	075	052	028
69	004	*981	*957	*933	*909	*885	*862	*838	*814	*790
70	.86766	742	718	694	671	647	623	599	575	551
71	527	503	479	455	431	407	383	339	335	311
72	287	263	239	215	191	167	143	119	095	071
73	047	022	*998	*974	*950	*926	*902	*878	*854	*830
74	.85806	781	757	733	709	685	661	636	612	588
75	564	540	515	491	467	443	419	394	370	346
76	322	297	273	249	225	200	176	152	128	103
77	079	055	031	006	*982	*958	*933	*909	*884	*860
78	.84835	811	787	762	738	713	689	664	640	615
79	590	566	541	517	492	467	443	418	393	369
80	344	319	294	270	245	220	196	171	146	121
81	096	072	047	022	*997	*972	*947	*923	*898	*873
82	.83848	823	798	773	748	723	698	674	649	624
83	599	574	549	523	498	473	448	423	398	373
84	348	323	297	272	247	222	196	171	146	120
85	095	070	044	019	*994	*968	*943	*917	*892	*866
86	.82840	815	789	763	738	712	686	660	635	609
87	583	557	531	505	479	453	427	401	375	349
88	323	297	271	245	219	193	167	140	114	088
89	062	035	009	*983	*956	*930	*903	*877	*850	*824
90	.81797	770	744	717	690	664	637	610	583	556
91	529	502	475	448	421	394	366	339	312	285
92	257	230	203	175	148	120	093	066	038	010
93	.80983	955	928	900	872	844	817	789	761	733
94	705	677	649	621	593	565	537	509	480	452
95	424	395	367	338	310	281	253	224	195	166
96	138	109	080	051	022	*993	*963	*934	*905	*875
97	.79846	816	787	757	727	698	668	638	608	578
98	547	517	487	456	426	396	365	335	305	274
99	243	213	182	151	120	089	059	028	*997	*966
100	.78934									

* Indicates change in the first two decimal places.

Table 3-131. Specific Gravity (60°/60°F.) (15.56°/15.56°C.) of Mixtures by (Volume) of C_2H_5OH and H_2O

% alcohol by volume at 60°F.	Tenths of % 0	1	2	3	4	5	6	7	8	9	% alcohol by volume at 60°F.	Tenths of % 0	1	2	3	4	5	6	7	8	9
0	1.00000	*985	*970	*955	*940	*925	*910	*895	*880	865	50	0.93426	407	387	368	348	328	309	289	270	250
1	0.99850	835	820	806	791	776	761	747	732	717	51	230	210	190	171	151	131	111	091	071	051
2	703	688	674	659	645	630	616	602	587	573	52	031	011	*991	*971	*951	*931	*911	*890	*870	*850
3	559	545	531	516	502	488	474	460	446	432	53	.92830	810	789	769	749	728	708	688	667	647
4	419	405	391	378	364	350	336	323	309	296	54	626	605	585	564	544	523	502	482	461	440
5	282	269	255	242	228	215	202	189	176	163	55	419	398	377	357	336	315	294	273	252	231
6	150	137	124	111	098	085	073	060	047	035	56	210	189	168	147	126	105	084	062	041	020
7	022	009	*997	*984	*972	*960	*947	*935	*923	*911	57	.91999	978	956	935	914	892	871	849	827	806
8	.98899	887	875	863	851	838	826	814	803	791	58	784	762	741	719	697	675	653	631	610	588
9	779	767	755	743	731	720	708	696	684	672	59	565	543	521	499	477	455	433	410	388	366
10	661	649	637	625	614	602	590	579	567	556	60	344	322	299	277	255	232	210	188	165	143
11	544	532	521	509	498	487	475	464	452	441	61	120	097	075	052	030	007	*984	*962	*939	*916
12	430	419	408	396	385	374	363	352	341	330	62	.90893	870	847	825	802	779	756	733	710	687
13	319	308	297	286	275	264	254	243	232	221	63	664	641	618	595	572	549	526	503	480	457
14	210	200	190	179	168	157	147	136	125	115	64	434	411	388	365	341	318	295	272	249	225
15	104	093	083	072	062	051	040	030	019	009	65	202	179	155	132	108	085	061	038	014	*991
16	.97998	988	977	967	956	946	936	925	915	905	66	.89967	943	920	896	872	848	825	801	777	753
17	895	885	875	864	854	844	834	824	814	804	67	729	705	681	657	633	609	585	561	537	513
18	794	784	774	764	754	744	734	724	714	704	68	489	465	441	416	392	368	343	319	295	270
19	694	684	674	664	654	645	635	625	615	605	69	245	220	196	171	147	122	098	073	048	024
20	596	586	576	566	556	546	536	526	516	506	70	.88999	974	950	925	900	875	850	825	801	776
21	496	486	476	466	456	446	436	425	415	405	71	751	725	700	675	650	625	600	574	549	524
22	395	385	375	365	354	344	334	324	313	303	72	499	474	448	423	397	372	346	321	296	270
23	293	283	272	262	252	241	231	221	210	200	73	244	218	193	167	141	116	090	064	039	013
24	189	179	168	158	147	137	126	116	105	095	74	.87987	961	935	910	884	858	832	806	780	754
25	084	073	063	052	042	031	020	010	*999	*988	75	728	702	676	650	623	597	571	545	518	492
26	.96978	967	957	946	935	924	914	903	892	881	76	465	439	412	386	359	332	306	279	252	226
27	870	859	848	837	826	815	804	793	782	771	77	199	172	145	118	092	065	038	011	*984	*957
28	760	749	738	727	715	704	693	682	671	659	78	.86929	902	875	847	820	793	766	738	711	684
29	648	637	625	614	603	591	580	568	557	546	79	656	629	601	574	546	518	491	463	435	408
30	534	522	511	499	488	476	464	453	441	429	80	380	352	324	296	269	241	213	185	157	129
31	418	406	394	382	370	358	346	334	321	309	81	100	072	044	015	*987	*959	*931	*902	*874	*846
32	296	284	271	259	246	234	221	209	196	183	82	.85817	789	760	732	703	674	646	617	588	560
33	170	157	144	132	119	106	093	080	067	054	83	531	502	473	444	415	386	357	328	299	270
34	041	028	015	002	*988	*975	*962	*948	*935	*921	84	240	211	181	152	122	093	063	033	004	*974
35	.95908	894	881	867	854	840	826	812	798	784	85	.84944	914	884	854	824	794	764	734	703	673
36	770	756	742	728	714	700	685	671	657	643	86	642	612	581	551	520	490	459	428	398	367
37	628	614	599	585	570	556	541	526	512	497	87	336	305	274	243	212	181	150	119	088	056
38	482	467	452	437	423	408	393	378	362	347	88	025	*994	*962	*930	*899	*867	*835	*803	*771	*739
39	332	317	302	286	271	256	240	225	209	194	89	.83707	675	643	610	578	545	513	480	447	415
40	178	162	147	131	115	100	084	068	052	036	90	382	349	315	282	249	216	183	150	116	083
41	020	004	*988	*972	*956	*940	*923	*907	*891	*875	91	049	015	*981	*947	*913	*879	*845	*810	*776	*741
42	.94858	842	825	809	792	776	759	743	726	710	92	.82705	670	635	600	565	529	494	458	423	387
43	693	676	660	643	626	609	592	575	558	541	93	351	315	279	243	206	170	133	096	059	022
44	524	507	490	473	455	438	421	403	386	369	94	.81984	947	909	871	834	796	757	719	681	642
45	351	334	316	298	281	263	245	228	210	192	95	603	564	525	486	446	407	367	327	287	247
46	174	156	138	120	102	084	066	048	030	011	96	206	165	125	084	042	001	*960	*918	*876	*834
47	.93993	975	956	938	920	901	883	864	845	827	97	.80792	750	707	664	620	577	533	489	445	401
48	808	789	771	752	733	714	695	676	657	638	98	356	311	265	219	173	127	080	033	*985	*937
49	619	600	581	562	543	523	504	485	465	446	99	.79889	841	792	743	693	643	593	543	492	441
											100	389									

* Indicates change in first two decimal places.

Table 3-132. n-Propyl Alcohol (C_3H_7OH)

%	0°C.	15°C.	30°C.	%	0°C.	15°C.	30°C.	%	0°C.	15°C.	30°C.	%	0°C.	15°C.	30°C.	%	0°C.	15°C.	30°C.
0	0.9999	0.9991	0.9957	20	0.9789	0.9723	0.9643	40	0.9430	0.9331	0.9226	60	0.9033	0.8922	0.8807	80	0.8634	0.8516	0.8394
1	.9982	.9974	.9940	21	.9776	.9705	.9622	41	.9411	.9310	.9205	61	.9013	.8902	.8786	81	.8614	.8496	.8373
2	.9967	.9960	.9924	22	.9763	.9688	.9602	42	.9391	.9290	.9184	62	.8994	.8882	.8766	82	.8594	.8475	.8352
3	.9952	.9944	.9908	23	.9748	.9670	.9583	43	.9371	.9269	.9164	63	.8974	.8861	.8745	83	.8574	.8454	.8332
4	.9939	.9929	.9893	24	.9733	.9651	.9563	44	.9352	.9248	.9143	64	.8954	.8841	.8724	84	.8554	.8434	.8311
5	.9926	.9915	.9877	25	.9717	.9633	.9543	45	.9332	.9228	.9122	65	.8934	.8820	.8703	85	.8534	.8413	.8290
6	.9914	.9902	.9862	26	.9700	.9614	.9522	46	.9311	.9207	.9100	66	.8913	.8800	.8682	86	.8513	.8393	.8269
7	.9904	.9890	.9848	27	.9682	.9594	.9501	47	.9291	.9186	.9079	67	.8894	.8779	.8662	87	.8492	.8372	.8248
8	.9894	.9877	.9834	28	.9664	.9576	.9481	48	.9272	.9165	.9057	68	.8874	.8759	.8641	88	.8471	.8351	.8227
9	.9883	.9864	.9819	29	.9646	.9556	.9460	49	.9252	.9145	.9036	69	.8854	.8739	.8620	89	.8450	.8330	.8206
10	.9874	.9852	.9804	30	.9627	.9535	.9439	50	.9232	.9124	.9015	70	.8835	.8719	.8600	90	.8429	.8308	.8185
11	.9865	.9840	.9790	31	.9608	.9516	.9418	51	.9213	.9104	.8994	71	.8815	.8700	.8580	91	.8408	.8287	.8164
12	.9857	.9828	.9775	32	.9589	.9495	.9396	52	.9192	.9084	.8973	72	.8795	.8680	.8559	92	.8387	.8266	.8142
13	.9849	.9817	.9760	33	.9570	.9474	.9375	53	.9173	.9064	.8952	73	.8776	.8659	.8539	93	.8364	.8244	.8120
14	.9841	.9806	.9746	34	.9550	.9454	.9354	54	.9153	.9044	.8931	74	.8756	.8639	.8518	94	.8342	.8221	.8098
15	.9833	.9793	.9730	35	.9530	.9434	.9333	55	.9132	.9023	.8911	75	.8736	.8618	.8497	95	.8320	.8199	.8077
16	.9825	.9780	.9714	36	.9511	.9413	.9312	56	.9112	.9003	.8890	76	.8716	.8598	.8477	96	.8296	.8176	.8054
17	.9817	.9768	.9698	37	.9491	.9392	.9289	57	.9093	.8983	.8869	77	.8695	.8577	.8456	97	.8272	.8153	.8031
18	.9808	.9752	.9680	38	.9471	.9372	.9269	58	.9073	.8963	.8849	78	.8675	.8556	.8435	98	.8248	.8128	.8008
19	.9800	.9739	.9661	39	.9450	.9351	.9247	59	.9053	.8942	.8828	79	.8655	.8536	.8414	99	.8222	.8104	.7984
																100	.8194	.8077	.7958

Table 3-133. Isopropyl Alcohol (C_3H_7OH)

%	0°C.	15°C.*	15°C.*	20°C.	30°C
0	0.9999	0.9991	0.99913	0.9982	0.9957
1	.9980	.9973	.9972	.9962	.9939
2	.9962	.9956	.9954	.9944	.9921
3	.9946	.9938	.9936	.9926	.9904
4	.9930	.9922	.9920	.9909	.9887
5	.9916	.9906	.9904	.9893	.9871
6	.9902	.9892	.9890	.9877	.9855
7	.9890	.9878	.9875	.9862	.9839
8	.9878	.9864	.9862	.9847	.9824
9	.9866	.9851	.9849	.9833	.9809
10	.9856	.9838	.98362	.9820	.9794
11	.9846	.9826	.9824	.9808	.9778
12	.9838	.9813	.9812	.9797	.9764
13	.9829	.9802	.9800	.9876	.9750
14	.9821	.9790	.9788	.9776	.9735
15	.9814	.9779	.9777	.9765	.9720
16	.9806	.9768	.9765	.9754	.9705
17	.9799	.9756	.9753	.9743	.9690
18	.9792	.9745	.9741	.9731	.9675
19	.9784	.9730	.9728	.9717	.9658
20	.9777	.9719	.97158	.9703	.9642
21	.9768	.9704	.9703	.9688	.9624
22	.9759	.9690	.9689	.9669	.9606
23	.9749	.9675	.9674	.9651	.9587
24	.9739	.9660	.9659	.9634	.9569
25	.9727	.9643	.9642	.9615	.9549
26	.9714	.9626	.9624	.9597	.9529
27	.9699	.9608	.9605	.9577	.9509
28	.9684	.9590	.9586	.9558	.9488
29	.9669	.9570	.9568	.9540	.9467
30	.9652	.9551	.95493	.9520	.9446
31	.9634	......	.9530	.9500	.9426
32	.9615	......	.9510	.9481	.9405
33	.9596	......	.9489	.9460	.9383
34	.9577	......	.9468	.9440	.9361

%	0°C.	15°C.*	15°C.*	20°C.	30°C.
35	0.9557	......	0.9446	0.9419	0.9338
36	.9536	......	.9424	.9399	.9315
37	.9514	......	.9401	.9377	.9292
38	.9493	......	.9379	.9355	.9269
39	.9472	......	.9356	.9333	.9246
40	.9450	......	.93333	.9310	.9224
41	.9428	......	.9311	.9287	.9201
42	.9406	......	.9288	.9264	.9177
43	.9384	......	.9266	.9239	.9154
44	.9361	......	.9243	.9215	.9130
45	.9338	......	.9220	.9191	.9106
46	.9315	......	.9197	.9165	.9082
47	.9292	......	.9174	.9141	.9059
48	.9270	......	.9150	.9117	.9036
49	.9247	......	.9127	.9093	.9013
50	.9224	......	.91043	.9069	.8990
51	.9201	......	.9081	.9044	.8966
52	.9178	......	.9058	.9020	.8943
53	.9155	......	.9035	.8996	.8919
54	.9132	......	.9011	.8971	.8895
55	.9109	......	.8988	.8946	.8871
56	.9086	......	.8964	.8921	.8847
57	.9063	......	.8940	.8896	.8823
58	.9040	......	.8917	.8874	.8800
59	.9017	......	.8893	.8850	.8777
60	.8994	......	.88690	.8825	.8752
61	.8970	......	.8845	.8800	.8728
62	.8947	0.8829	.8821	.8776	.8704
63	.8924	.8805	.8798	.8751	.8680
64	.8901	.8781	.8775	.8727	.8656
65	.8878	.8757	.8752	.8702	.8631
66	.8854	.8733	.8728	.8679	.8607
67	.8831	.8710	.8705	.8656	.8583
68	.8807	.8686	.8682	.8632	.8559
69	.8784	.8662	.8658	.8609	.8535

%	0°C.	15°C.*	15°C.*	20°C.	30°C.
70	0.8761	0.8639	0.86346	0.8584	0.8511
71	.8738	.8615	.8611	.8560	.8487
72	.8714	.8592	.8588	.8537	.8464
73	.8691	.8568	.8564	.8513	.8440
74	.8668	.8545	.8541	.8489	.8416
75	.8644	.8521	.8517	.8464	.8392
76	.8621	.8497	.8493	.8439	.8368
77	.8598	.8474	.8470	.8415	.8344
78	.8575	.8450	.8446	.8391	.8321
79	.8551	.8426	.8422	.8366	.8297
80	.8528	.8403	.83979	.8342	.8273
81	.8503	.8379	.8374	.8317	.8248
82	.8479	.8355	.8350	.8292	.8224
83	.8456	.8331	.8326	.8268	.8200
84	.8432	.8307	.8302	.8243	.8175
85	.8408	.8282	.8278	.8219	.8151
86	.8384	.8259	.8254	.8194	.8127
87	.8360	.8234	.8229	.8169	.8201
88	.8336	.8209	.8205	.8145	.8078
89	.8311	.8184	.8180	.8120	.8053
90	.8287	.8161	.81553	.8096	.8029
91	.8262	.8136	.8130	.8072	.8004
92	.8237	.8110	.8104	.8047	.7979
93	.8212	.8085	.8079	.8023	.7954
94	.8186	.8060	.8052	.7998	.7929
95	.8160	.8034	.8026	.7973	.7904
96	.8133	.8008	.7999	.7949	.7878
97	.8106	.7981	.7972	.7925	.7852
98	.8078	.7954	.7945	.7901	.7826
99	.8048	.7926	.7918	.7877	.7799
100	.8016	.7896	.78913	.7854	.7770

* Two different observers; see "International Critical Tables," vol. 3, p. 120.

Table 3-134. Glycerol*

Glycerol, %	Density				
	15°C.	15.5°C.	20°C.	25°C.	30°C.
100	1.26415	1.26381	1.26108	1.15802	1.25495
99	1.26160	1.26125	1.25850	1.25545	1.25235
98	1.25900	1.25865	1.25590	1.25290	1.24975
97	1.25645	1.25610	1.25335	1.25030	1.24710
96	1.25385	1.25350	1.25080	1.24770	1.24450
95	1.25130	1.25095	1.24825	1.24515	1.24190
94	1.24865	1.24830	1.24560	1.24250	1.23930
93	1.24600	1.24565	1.24300	1.23985	1.23670
92	1.24340	1.24305	1.24035	1.23725	1.23410
91	1.24075	1.24040	1.23770	1.23460	1.23150
90	1.23810	1.23775	1.23510	1.23200	1.22890
89	1.23545	1.23510	1.23245	1.22935	1.22625
88	1.23280	1.23245	1.22975	1.22665	1.22360
87	1.23015	1.22980	1.22710	1.22400	1.22095
86	1.22750	1.22710	1.22445	1.22135	1.21830
85	1.22485	1.22445	1.22180	1.21870	1.21565
84	1.22220	1.22180	1.21915	1.21605	1.21300
83	1.21955	1.21915	1.21650	1.21340	1.21035
82	1.21690	1.21650	1.21380	1.21075	1.20770
81	1.21425	1.21385	1.21115	1.20810	1.20505
80	1.21160	1.21120	1.20850	1.20545	1.20240
79	1.20885	1.20845	1.20575	1.20275	1.19970
78	1.20610	1.20570	1.20305	1.20005	1.19705
77	1.20335	1.20300	1.20030	1.19735	1.19435
76	1.20060	1.20025	1.19760	1.19465	1.19170
75	1.19785	1.19750	1.19485	1.19195	1.18900
74	1.19510	1.19480	1.19215	1.18925	1.18635
73	1.19235	1.19205	1.18940	1.18650	1.18365
72	1.18965	1.18930	1.18670	1.18380	1.18100
71	1.18690	1.18655	1.18395	1.18110	1.17830
70	1.18415	1.18385	1.18125	1.17840	1.17565
69	1.18135	1.18105	1.17850	1.17565	1.17290
68	1.17860	1.17830	1.17575	1.17295	1.17020
67	1.17585	1.17555	1.17300	1.17020	1.16745
66	1.17305	1.17275	1.17025	1.16745	1.16470

Glycerol, %	Density				
	15°C.	15.5°C.	20°C.	25°C.	30°C.
65	1.17030	1.17000	1.16750	1.16475	1.16195
64	1.16755	1.16725	1.16475	1.16200	1.15925
63	1.16480	1.16445	1.16205	1.15925	1.15650
62	1.16200	1.16170	1.15930	1.15655	1.15375
61	1.15925	1.15895	1.15655	1.15380	1.15100
60	1.15650	1.15615	1.15380	1.15105	1.14830
59	1.15370	1.15340	1.15105	1.14835	1.14555
58	1.15095	1.15065	1.14830	1.14560	1.14285
57	1.14815	1.14785	1.14555	1.14285	1.14010
56	1.14535	1.14510	1.14280	1.14015	1.13740
55	1.14260	1.14230	1.14005	1.13740	1.13470
54	1.13980	1.13955	1.13730	1.13465	1.13195
53	1.13705	1.13680	1.13455	1.13195	1.12925
52	1.13425	1.13400	1.13180	1.12920	1.12650
51	1.13150	1.13125	1.12905	1.12650	1.12380
50	1.12870	1.12845	1.12630	1.12375	1.12110
49	1.12600	1.12575	1.12360	1.12110	1.11845
48	1.12325	1.12305	1.12090	1.11840	1.11580
47	1.12055	1.12030	1.11820	1.11575	1.11320
46	1.11780	1.11760	1.11550	1.11310	1.11055
45	1.11510	1.11490	1.11280	1.11040	1.10795
44	1.11235	1.11215	1.11010	1.10775	1.10530
43	1.10960	1.10945	1.10740	1.10510	1.10265
42	1.10690	1.10670	1.10470	1.10240	1.10005
41	1.10415	1.10400	1.10200	1.09975	1.09740
40	1.10145	1.10130	1.09930	1.09710	1.09475
39	1.09875	1.09860	1.09665	1.09445	1.09215
38	1.09605	1.09590	1.09400	1.09180	1.08955
37	1.09340	1.09320	1.09135	1.08915	1.08690
36	1.09070	1.09050	1.08865	1.08655	1.08430
35	1.08800	1.08780	1.08600	1.08390	1.08165
34	1.08530	1.08515	1.08335	1.08125	1.07905
33	1.08265	1.08245	1.08070	1.07860	1.07645
32	1.07995	1.07975	1.07800	1.07600	1.07380
31	1.07725	1.07705	1.07535	1.07335	1.07120

Glycerol, %	Density				
	15°C.	15.5°C.	20°C.	25°C.	30°C.
30	1.07455	1.07435	1.07270	1.07070	1.06855
29	1.07195	1.07175	1.07010	1.06815	1.06605
28	1.06935	1.06915	1.06755	1.06560	1.06355
27	1.06670	1.06655	1.06495	1.06305	1.06105
26	1.06410	1.06390	1.06240	1.06055	1.05855
25	1.06150	1.06130	1.05980	1.05800	1.05605
24	1.05885	1.05870	1.05720	1.05545	1.05350
23	1.05625	1.05610	1.05465	1.05290	1.05100
22	1.05365	1.05350	1.05205	1.05035	1.04850
21	1.05100	1.05090	1.04950	1.04780	1.04600
20	1.04840	1.04825	1.04690	1.04525	1.04350
19	1.04590	1.04575	1.04440	1.04280	1.04105
18	1.04335	1.04325	1.04195	1.04035	1.03860
17	1.04085	1.04075	1.03945	1.03790	1.03615
16	1.03835	1.03825	1.03695	1.03545	1.03370
15	1.03580	1.03570	1.03450	1.03300	1.03130
14	1.03330	1.03320	1.03200	1.03055	1.02885
13	1.03080	1.03070	1.02955	1.02805	1.02640
12	1.02830	1.02820	1.02705	1.02560	1.02395
11	1.02575	1.02565	1.02455	1.02315	1.02150
10	1.02325	1.02315	1.02210	1.02070	1.01905
9	1.02085	1.02075	1.01970	1.01835	1.01670
8	1.01840	1.01835	1.01730	1.01600	1.01440
7	1.01600	1.01590	1.01495	1.01360	1.01205
6	1.01360	1.01350	1.01255	1.01125	1.00970
5	1.01120	1.01110	1.01015	1.00890	1.00735
4	1.00875	1.00870	1.00780	1.00655	1.00505
3	1.00635	1.00630	1.00540	1.00415	1.00270
2	1.00395	1.00385	1.00300	1.00180	1.00035
1	1.00155	1.00145	1.00060	0.99945	0.99800
0	0.99913	0.99905	0.99823	0.99708	0.99568

* Bosart and Snoddy, *Ind. Eng. Chem.*, **20**, 1378 (1928).

Table 3-135. Hydrazine (N_2H_4)

%	d_4^{15}	%	d_4^{15}
1	1.0002	30	1.0305
2	1.0013	40	1.038
4	1.0034	50	1.044
8	1.0077	60	1.047
12	1.0121	70	1.046
16	1.0164	80	1.040
20	1.0207	90	1.030
24	1.0248	100	1.011
28	1.0286		

Table 3-136. Densities of Aqueous Solutions of Miscellaneous Organic Compounds*

d (resp., d_w, d_s) = density of the solution [resp., water; resp., the pure liquid solute] in g. per ml. p_s (resp., p_w) = weight % of solute (resp., water) in the solution. "Range" = range of applicability of the equation.

Section A. $d = d_w + Ap_s + Bp_s^2 + Cp_s^3$

Name	Formula	t, °C.	Range, p_s	A	B	C
Acetaldehyde	C_2H_4O	18	0– 30	$+0.0_3255$	-0.0_516	
Acetamide	C_2H_5NO	15	0– 6	$+0.0_3639$	$+0.0_4171$	
Acetone	C_3H_6O	0	0–100	-0.0_3856	-0.0_5449	-0.0_7588
		4	0–100	-0.0_37648	-0.0_41193	$+0.0_8272$
		15	0–100	-0.0_21009	-0.0_59682	-0.0_8624
		20	0–100	-0.0_21233	-0.0_53529	-0.0_75327
		25	0–100	-0.0_21171	-0.0_5904	-0.0_856
Acetonitrile	C_2H_3N	15	0– 16	-0.0_21175	-0.0_42024	
Allyl alcohol	C_3H_6O	0	0– 89	-0.0_33729	-0.0_41232	$+0.0_72984$
Benzenepentacarboxylic acid	$C_{11}H_6O_{10}$	25	0– 0.6	$+0.0_25615$	-0.0_2117	
Butyl alcohol (n-)	$C_4H_{10}O$	20	0– 7.9	-0.0_21651	$+0.0_4285$	
Butyric acid (n-)	$C_4H_8O_2$	18	0– 10	$+0.0_3414$	$+0.0_4131$	
		25	0– 62	$+0.0_35135$	-0.0_4166	$+0.0_611$
Chloral hydrate	$C_2H_3Cl_3O_2$	0	0– 70	$+0.0_24489$	$+0.0_42802$	-0.0_71291
		15	0– 78	$+0.0_24455$	$+0.0_42198$	$+0.0_74366$
		30	0– 90	$+0.0_24401$	$+0.0_41887$	$+0.0_76549$
Chloroacetic acid	$C_2H_3ClO_2$	20	0– 32	$+0.0_23648$	$+0.0_5302$	
		25	0– 86	$+0.0_23602$	$+0.0_5552$	$+0.0_722$
Citric acid (hydrate)	$C_6H_8O_7 + H_2O$	18	0– 50	$+0.0_23824$	$+0.0_41141$	$+0.0_717$
Dichloroacetic acid	$C_2H_2Cl_2O_2$	20	0– 30	$+0.0_24427$	$+0.0_5537$	$+0.0_77534$
		25	0– 97	$+0.0_24427$	$+0.0_5537$	$+0.0_77534$
Diethylamine hydrochloride	$C_4H_{12}ClN$	21	0– 36	$+0.0_334$	$+0.0_676$	
Ethylamine hydrochloride	C_2H_8ClN	21	0– 65	$+0.0_21193$	-0.0_5307	-0.0_747
Ethylene glycol	$C_2H_6O_2$	0	0–100	$+0.0_21483$	$+0.0_52992$	-0.0_75248
		15	0– 6	$+0.0_2133$	-0.0_5108	
Ethyl ether	$C_4H_{10}O$	20	0– 5	-0.0_2221	$+0.0_448$	
		25	0– 4.5	-0.0_2221	$+0.0_435$	
tartrate	$C_8H_{14}O_6$	15	0– 95	$+0.0_22367$	$+0.0_5358$	-0.0_76005
Formaldehyde	CH_2O	15	0– 40	$+0.0_22518$	-0.0_5658	$+0.0_6542$
Formamide	CH_3NO	25	22– 96	$+0.0_21217$	$+0.0_53199$	-0.0_72529
Furfural	$C_5H_4O_2$	20	0– 8	$+0.0_21827$	$+0.0_5366$	
		25	0– 8	$+0.0_21664$	$+0.0_421$	
Isoamyl alcohol	$C_5H_{12}O$	20	0– 2.5	$+0.0_2155$	$+0.0_43$	
Isobutyl alcohol	$C_4H_{10}O$	15	0– 8	-0.0_2146	$+0.0_56$	
		20	0– 8	-0.0_2169	$+0.0_438$	
Isobutyric acid	$C_4H_8O_2$	15	0– 9	$+0.0_352$		
		18	0– 9	$+0.0_345$		
		25	0– 12	$+0.0_337$		
Isovaleric acid	$C_5H_{10}O_2$	25	0– 5	$+0.0_3253$	-0.0_4282	
Lactic acid	C_3H_6O	25	0– 9	$+0.0_2231$	$+0.0_5186$	
Maleic acid	$C_4H_4O_4$	25	0– 40	$+0.0_234$	$+0.0_575$	
Malic acid	$C_4H_6O_5$	20	0– 40	$+0.0_23933$	$+0.0_5957$	
		25	0– 40	$+0.0_23736$	$+0.0_4175$	
Malonic acid	$C_3H_4O_4$	20	0– 40	$+0.0_2389$	$+0.0_41066$	
Methyl acetate	$C_3H_6O_2$	20	0– 20	$+0.0_340$	-0.0_574	
glucoside (α-)	$C_7H_{14}O_6$	0	26– 51	$+0.0_23336$	$+0.0_5996$	$+0.01544$
		30	26– 51	$+0.0_23151$	$+0.0_5975$	$+0.0_8978$
Nicotine	$C_{10}H_{14}N_2$	20	0– 60	$+0.0_3642$	$+0.0_5454$	-0.0_7687
Nitrophenol (p-)	$C_6H_5NO_3$	15	0– 1.5	$+0.0_23216$	-0.0_455	
Oxalic acid	$C_2H_2O_4$	0	0– 4	$+0.0_25898$	-0.0_33185	$+0.0_441$
		15	0– 4	$+0.0_2494$	-0.0_58	
		17.5	0– 9	$+0.0_2494$	-0.0_58	
		20	0– 4	$+0.0_25264$	-0.0_31996	$+0.0_4254$
		25	0– 4	$+0.0_25108$	-0.0_31607	$+0.0_4208$
Phenol	C_6H_6O	15	0– 5	$+0.0_2111$	-0.0_4283	
		80	0– 65	$+0.0_3462$	-0.0_686	
Phenylglycolic acid	$C_8H_8O_3$	25	0– 11	$+0.0_2207$	$+0.0_423$	
Picoline (α-)	C_6H_7N	25	0– 70	-0.0_4386	-0.0_51405	-0.0_74167
(β-)	C_6H_7N	25	0– 60	-0.0_4683	-0.0_513	
Propionic acid	$C_3H_6O_2$	18	0– 10	$+0.0_395$	-0.0_4172	
		25	0– 40	$+0.0_39245$	-0.0_599	$+0.0_7361$
Pyridine	C_5H_5N	25	0– 60	$+0.0_3229$	-0.0_5204	-0.0_828
Resorcinol	$C_6H_6O_2$	18	0– 52	$+0.0_2201$	$+0.0_5519$	-0.0_819
Succinic acid	$C_4H_6O_4$	25	0– 5.5	$+0.0_2304$		
Tartaric acid (d., l., or dl.)	$C_4H_6O_6$	15	0– 15	$+0.0_24482$	$+0.0_4185$	
		17.5	0– 50	$+0.0_24455$	$+0.0_4185$	
		20	0– 50	$+0.0_24432$	$+0.0_41837$	
		30	0– 50	$+0.0_24335$	$+0.0_4185$	
		40	0– 50	$+0.0_24265$	$+0.0_4185$	
		50	0– 50	$+0.0_24205$	$+0.0_4185$	
		60	0– 50	$+0.0_24155$	$+0.0_4185$	

* From "International Critical Tables," vol. 3, pp. 111–114.

Table 3-136. Densities of Aqueous Solutions of Miscellaneous Organic Compounds—(*Concluded*)

Name	Formula	t, °C.	Range, p_s	A	B	C
Tetraethyl ammonium chloride	$C_8H_{20}ClN$	21	0– 63	$+0.0_31884$	$+0.0_56$	$+0.0_7122$
Thiourea	CH_4N_2S	15	0– 7	$+0.0_22995$	$+0.0_5374$	
Trichloroacetic acid	$C_2HCl_3O_2$	12.5	0– 61	$+0.0_2499$	$+0.0_4153$	
		20	10– 30	$+0.0_25053$	$+0.0_41387$	
		25	0– 94	$+0.0_25051$	$+0.0_56119$	$+0.0_61038$
Triethylamine hydrochloride	$C_6H_{16}ClN$	21	0– 54	$+0.0_46$	$+0.0_5558$	-0.0_869
Trimethyl carbinol	$C_4H_{10}O$	20	0–100	-0.0_2117	-0.0_41908	$+0.0_7957$
		25	0–100	-0.0_21286	-0.0_4176	$+0.0_7887$
Urea	CH_4N_2O	14.8	0– 12	$+0.0_23213$	-0.0_44802	$+0.0_51216$
		18	0– 51	$+0.0_22718$	$+0.0_51552$	$+0.0_72573$
		20	0– 35	$+0.0_22702$	$+0.0_53712$	-0.0_72285
		25	0– 10	$+0.0_22728$	-0.0_41817	$+0.0_51379$
Urethane	$C_3H_7NO_2$	20	0–56	$+0.0_21278$	-0.0_5245	-0.0_73437
Valeric acid (n-)	$C_5H_{10}O_2$	25	0– 3	$+0.0_334$	-0.0_427	

Section B. $d = d_s + Ap_w + Bp_w^2 + Cp_w^3$

Name	Formula	d_s	t, °C.	Range, p_w	A	B	C
Butyl alcohol (n-)	$C_4H_{10}O$	0.8097	20	0–20	$+0.0_22103$	-0.0_4113	
Butyric acid (n-)	$C_4H_8O_2$	0.9534	25	0–38	$+0.0_21854$	-0.0_42314	
Ethyl ether	$C_4H_{10}O$	0.7077	25	0– 1.1	$+0.0_234$	$+0.0_336$	
Isobutyl alcohol	$C_4H_{10}O$	0.8170	0	0–14	$+0.0_22437$	-0.0_4285	
		0.8055	15	0–16	$+0.0_2224$	-0.0_4129	
Isobutyric acid	$C_4H_8O_2$	0.9425	26	0–80	$+0.0_21808$	-0.0_42358	$+0.0_61253$
Nicotine	$C_{10}H_{14}N_2$	1.0093	20	0–40	$+0.0_2199$	-0.0_4331	$+0.0_7315$
Picoline (α-)	C_6H_7N	0.9404	25	0–30	$+0.0_22715$	-0.0_4393	
(β-)	C_6H_7N	0.9515	25	0–40	$+0.0_21925$	-0.0_4352	$+0.0_625$
Pyridine	C_5H_5N	0.9776	25	0–40	$+0.0_21157$	-0.0_5536	-0.0_62
Trimethyl carbinol	$C_4H_{10}O$	0.7856	20	0–20	$+0.0_22287$	$+0.0_5275$	

Section C. $d_t = d_o + At + Bt^2$

Name	Formula	p_s	d_0	Range, °C.	A	B
Allyl alcohol	C_3H_6O	76.60	0.9122	0–45	-0.0_38	-0.0_527
Butyl alcohol (n-)	$C_4H_{10}O$	80.95	0.8614	0–43	-0.0_37292	-0.0_675
Chloral hydrate	$C_2H_3Cl_3O_2$	2.00	1.0094	7–80	-0.0_42597	-0.0_54313
		10.00	1.0476	7–80	-0.0_47955	-0.0_54253
Ethyl tartrate	$C_7H_{14}O_6$	5.00	1.0150	15–80	-0.0_32103	-0.0_52544
		10.00	1.0270	15–80	-0.0_32116	-0.0_62929
		25.00	1.0665	15–80	-0.0_3401	-0.0_523
Furfural	$C_5H_4O_2$	4.62	1.0125	22–74	-0.0_3232	-0.0_5254
		5.69	1.0140	22–74	-0.0_3221	-0.0_5268
		6.56	1.0155	22–74	-0.0_3211	-0.0_5290
Pyridine	C_5H_5N	9.34	1.0055	11–73	-0.0_3171	-0.0_53615
		21.20	1.0115	14–73	-0.0_3378	-0.0_5248
		29.50	1.0145	12–72	-0.0_3463	-0.0_5235
		40.40	1.0182	9–74	-0.0_3605	-0.0_5167

DENSITIES OF MISCELLANEOUS MATERIALS

Table 3-137. Approximate Specific Gravities and Densities of Miscellaneous Solids and Liquids*

Water at 4°C. and normal atmospheric pressure taken as unity
For more detailed data on any material, see the section dealing with the properties of that material.

Substance	Sp. gr.	Aver. weight lb./cu. ft.
Metals, Alloys, Ores		
Aluminum, cast-hammered	2.55–2.80	165
bronze	7.7	481
Brass, cast-rolled	8.4–8.7	534
Bronze, 7.9 to 14% Sn	7.4–8.9	509
phosphor	8.88	554
Copper, cast-rolled	8.8–8.95	556
ore, pyrites	4.1–4.3	262
German silver	8.58	536
Gold, cast-hammered	19.25–19.35	1205
coin (U.S.)	17.18–17.2	1073
Iridium	21.78–22.42	1383
Iron, gray cast	7.03–7.13	442
cast, pig	7.2	450
wrought	7.6–7.9	485
spiegeleisen	7.5	468
ferro-silicon	6.7–7.3	437
ore, hematite	5.2	325
ore, limonite	3.6–4.0	237
ore, magnetite	4.9–5.2	315
slag	2.5–3.0	172
Lead	11.34	710
ore, galena	7.3–7.6	465
Manganese	7.42	475
ore, pyrolusite	3.7–4.6	259
Mercury	13.6	849
Monel metal, rolled	8.97	555
Nickel	8.9	537
Platinum, cast-hammered	21.5	1330
Silver, cast-hammered	10.4–10.6	656
Steel, cold-drawn	7.83	489
machine	7.80	487
tool	7.70–7.73	481
Tin, cast-hammered	7.2–7.5	459
cassiterite	6.4–7.0	418
Tungsten	19.22	1200
Zinc, cast-rolled	6.9–7.2	440
blende	3.9–4.2	253
Various Solids		
Cereals, oats, bulk	0.51	26
barley, bulk	0.62	39
corn, rye, bulk	0.73	45
wheat, bulk	0.77	48
Cork	0.22–0.26	15
Cotton, flax, hemp	1.47–1.50	93
Fats	0.90–0.97	58
Flour, loose	0.40–0.50	28
pressed	0.70–0.80	47
Glass, common	2.40–2.80	162
plate or crown	2.45–2.72	161
crystal	2.90–3.00	184
flint	3.2–4.7	247
Hay and straw, bales	0.32	20
Leather	0.86–1.02	59
Paper	0.70–1.15	58
Potatoes, piled	0.67	44
Rubber, caoutchouc	0.92–0.96	59
goods	1.0–2.0	94
Salt, granulated, piled	0.77	48
Saltpeter	1.07	67
Starch	1.53	96
Sulfur	1.93–2.07	125
Wool	1.32	82

Substance	Sp. gr.	Aver. weight lb./cu. ft.
Timber, Air-dry		
Apple	0.66–0.74	44
Ash, black	0.55	34
white	0.64–0.71	42
Birch, sweet, yellow	0.71–0.72	44
Cedar, white, red	0.35	22
Cherry, wild red	0.43	27
Chestnut	0.48	30
Cypress	0.45–0.48	29
Elm, white	0.56	35
Fir, Douglas	0.48–0.55	32
balsam	0.40	25
Hemlock	0.45–0.50	29
Hickory	0.74–0.80	48
Locust	0.67–0.77	45
Mahogany	0.56–0.85	44
Maple, sugar	0.68	43
white	0.53	33
Oak, chestnut	0.74	46
live	0.87	54
red, black	0.64–0.71	42
white	0.77	48
Pine, Norway	0.55	34
Oregon	0.51	32
red	0.48	30
Southern	0.61–0.67	38–42
white	0.43	27
Poplar	0.43	27
Redwood, California	0.42	26
Spruce, white, red	0.45	28
Teak, African	0.99	62
Indian	0.66–0.88	48
Walnut, black	0.59	37
Willow	0.42–0.50	28
Various Liquids		
Alcohol, ethyl (100%)	0.789	49
methyl (100%)	0.796	50
Acid, muriatic, 40%	1.20	75
nitric, 91%	1.50	94
sulfuric, 87%	1.80	112
Chloroform	1.500	95
Ether	0.736	46
Lye, soda, 66%	1.70	106
Oils, vegetable	0.91–0.94	58
mineral, lubricants	0.88–0.94	57
Turpentine	0.861–0.867	54
Water, 4°C. max. density	1.0	62.428
100°C.	0.9584	59.830
ice	0.88–0.92	56
snow, fresh fallen	0.125	8
sea water	1.02–1.03	64
Ashlar Masonry		
Bluestone	2.3–2.6	153
Granite, syenite, gneiss	2.4–2.7	159
Limestone	2.1–2.8	153
Marble	2.4–2.8	162
Sandstone	2.0–2.6	143
Rubble Masonry		
Bluestone	2.2–2.5	147
Granite, syenite, gneiss	2.3–2.6	153
Limestone	2.0–2.7	147
Marble	2.3–2.7	156
Sandstone	1.9–2.5	137

Substance	Sp. gr.	Aver. weight lb./cu. ft.
Dry Rubble Masonry		
Granite, syenite, gneiss	1.9–2.3	130
Limestone, marble	1.9–2.1	125
Sandstone, bluestone	1.8–1.9	110
Brick Masonry		
Hard brick	1.8–2.3	128
Medium brick	1.6–2.0	112
Soft brick	1.4–1.9	103
Sand-lime brick	1.4–2.2	112
Concrete Masonry		
Cement, stone, sand	2.2–2.4	144
slag, etc.	1.9–2.3	130
cinder, etc.	1.5–1.7	100
Various Building Materials		
Ashes, cinders	0.64–0.72	40–45
Cement, Portland, loose	1.5	94
Lime, gypsum, loose	0.85–1.00	53–64
Mortar, lime, set	1.4–1.9	103
Portland cement	2.08–2.25	94–135
Portland cement	3.1–3.2	196
Slags, bank slag	1.1–1.2	67–72
bank screenings	1.5–1.9	98–117
machine slag	1.5	96
slag sand	0.8–0.9	49–55
Earth, etc., Excavated		
Clay, dry	1.0	63
damp plastic	1.76	110
and gravel, dry	1.6	100
Earth, dry, loose	1.2	76
dry, packed	1.5	95
moist, loose	1.3	78
moist, packed	1.6	96
mud, flowing	1.7	108
mud, packed	1.8	115
Riprap, limestone	1.3–1.4	80–85
Riprap, sandstone	1.4	90
Riprap, shale	1.7	105
Sand, gravel, dry, loose	1.4–1.7	90–105
gravel, dry, packed	1.6–1.9	100–120
gravel, wet	1.89–2.16	126
Excavations in Water		
Clay	1.28	80
River mud	1.44	90
Sand or gravel	0.96	60
and clay	1.00	65
Soil	1.12	70
Stone riprap	1.00	65
Minerals		
Asbestos	2.1–2.8	153
Barytes	4.50	281
Basalt	2.7–3.2	184
Bauxite	2.55	159
Bluestone	2.5–2.6	159
Borax	1.7–1.8	109
Chalk	1.8–2.8	143
Clay, marl	1.8–2.6	137
Dolomite	2.9	181
Feldspar, orthoclase	2.5–2.7	162
Gneiss	2.7–2.9	175
Granite	2.6–2.7	165
Greenstone, trap	2.8–3.2	187
Gypsum, alabaster	2.3–2.8	159
Hornblende	3.0	187
Limestone	2.1–2.86	155
Marble	2.6–2.86	170
Magnesite	3.0	187
Phosphate rock, apatite	3.2	200
Porphyry	2.6–2.9	172

* From Marks, "Mechanical Engineers' Handbook," McGraw-Hill.

Table 3-137. Approximate Specific Gravities and Densities of Miscellaneous Solids and Liquids—*(Concluded)*

Substance	Sp. gr.	Aver. weight lb./cu. ft.	Substance	Sp. gr.	Aver. weight lb./cu. ft.	Substance	Sp. gr.	Aver. weight lb./cu. ft.
Minerals (*Cont'd*)			Bituminous Substances			Bituminous Substances (*Cont'd*)		
Pumice, natural	0.37–0.90	40	Asphaltum	1.1–1.5	81	Petroleum	0.87	54
Quartz, flint	2.5–2.8	165	Coal, anthracite	1.4–1.8	97	refined (kerosene)	0.78–0.82	50
Sandstone	2.0–2.6	143	bituminous	1.2–1.5	84	benzine	0.73–0.75	46
Serpentine	2.7–2.8	171	lignite	1.1–1.4	78	gasoline	0.70–0.75	45
Shale, slate	2.6–2.9	172	peat, turf, dry	0.65–0.85	47	Pitch	1.07–1.15	69
						Tar, bituminous	1.20	75
Soapstone, talc	2.6–2.8	169	charcoal, pine	0.28–0.44	23			
Syenite	2.6–2.7	165	charcoal, oak	0.47–0.57	33	Coal and Coke, Piled		
			coke	1.0–1.4	75	Coal, anthracite	0.75–0.93	47–58
Stone, Quarried, Piled			Graphite	1.64–2.7	135	bituminous, lignite	0.64–0.87	40–54
Basalt, granite, gneiss	1.5	96	Paraffin	0.87–0.91	56	peat, turf	0.32–0.42	20–26
Greenstone, hornblende	1.7	107				charcoal	0.16–0.23	10–14
Limestone, marble, quartz	1.5	95				coke	0.37–0.51	23–32
Sandstone	1.3	82						
Shale	1.5	92						

SOLUBILITIES*

Table 3-138. Solubilities of Inorganic Compounds in Water at Various Temperatures*

This table shows the amount of anhydrous substance which is soluble in 100 g. of water at the temperature in degrees centigrade as indicated; where the formula is followed by † the value is expressed in grams of substance in 100 cc. of saturated solution. Solid phase gives the hydrated form in equilibrium with the saturated solution.

	Substance	Formula	Solid phase	0°C.	10°C.	20°C.	30°C.	40°C.	50°C.	60°C.	70°C.	80°C.	90°C.	100°C.	
1	Aluminum chloride	$AlCl_3$	$6H_2O$			$69.86^{15°}$									1
2	sulfate	$Al_2(SO_4)_3$	$18H_2O$	31.2	33.5	36.4	40.4	46.1	52.2	59.2	66.1	73.0	80.8	89.0	2
3	Ammonium aluminum sulfate	$(NH_4)_2Al_2(SO_4)_4$	$24H_2O$	2.1	4.99	7.74	10.94	14.88	20.10	26.70				$109.7^{95°}$	3
4	bicarbonate	NH_4HCO_3		11.9	15.8	21	27								4
5	bromide	NH_4Br		60.6	68	75.5	83.2	91.1	99.2	107.8	116.8	126	135.6	145.6	5
6	chloride	NH_4Cl		29.4	33.3	37.2	41.4	45.8	50.4	55.2	60.2	65.6	71.3	77.3	6
7	chloroplatinate	$(NH_4)_2PtCl_6$			0.7									1.25	7
8	chromate	$(NH_4)_2CrO_4$					40.4								8
9	chromium sulfate	$(NH_4)_2Cr_2(SO_4)_4$	$24H_2O$			$10.78^{25°}$									9
10	dichromate	$(NH_4)_2Cr_2O_7$					47.17								10
11	dihydrogen phosphite	$NH_4H_2PO_3$		171		$190^{14.5°}$	$260^{31°}$								11
12	hydrogen phosphate	$(NH_4)_2HPO_4$				131^{15}									12
13	iodide	NH_4I		154.2	163.2	172.3	181.4	190.5	199.6	208.9	218.7	228.8		250.3	13
14	magnesium phosphate	NH_4MgPO_4	$6H_2O$	0.023		0.052		0.036	0.030	0.040	0.016	0.019			14
15	manganese phosphate	NH_4MnPO_4	$7H_2O$			0		0		0	0.005	0.007			15
16	nitrate	NH_4NO_3		118.3		192	241.8	297.0	344.0	421.0	499.0	580.0	740.0	871.0	16
17	oxalate	$(NH_4)_2C_2O_4$	$1H_2O$	2.2	3.1	4.4	5.9	8.0	10.3						17
18	perchlorate†	NH_4ClO_4†		11.56		20.85		30.58		39.05		48.19		57.01	18
19	persulfate	$(NH_4)_2S_2O_8$		58.2											19
20	sulfate	$(NH_4)_2SO_4$		70.6	73.0	75.4	78.0	81.0		88.0		95.3		103.3	20
21	thiocyanate	NH_4CNS		119.8	144	170	207.7								21
22	vanadate (meta)	NH_4VO_3				0.48	0.84	1.32	1.78		3.05				22
23	Antimonious fluoride	SbF_3		384.7		444.7	563.6								23
24	sulfide	Sb_2S_3				$0.000175^{18°}$									24
25	Arsenic oxide	As_2O_5		59.5	62.1	65.8	69.5	71.2		73.0		75.1		76.7	25
26	Arsenious sulfide	As_2S_3		5.17×10^{-5} at 18°											26
27	Barium acetate	$Ba(C_2H_3O_2)_2$	$3H_2O$	59	63	71									27
28	acetate	$Ba(C_2H_3O_2)_2$	$1H_2O$				75	79	77	74	74			75	28
29	carbonate	$BaCO_3$			$0.0016^{8°}$	$0.0022^{18°}$	0.0024 at 24.2°								29
30	chlorate	$Ba(ClO_3)_2$	$1H_2O$	20.34	26.95	33.80	41.70	49.61		66.81		84.84		104.9	30
31	chloride	$BaCl_2$	$2H_2O$	31.6	33.3	35.7	38.2	40.7	43.6	46.4	49.4	52.4		58.8	31
32	chromate	$BaCrO_4$		0.0002	0.00028	0.00037	0.00046								32
33	hydroxide	$Ba(OH)_2$	$8H_2O$	1.67	2.48	3.89	5.59	8.22	13.12	20.94		101.4			33
34	iodide	BaI_2	$6H_2O$	170.2	185.7	203.1	219.6								34
35	iodide	BaI_2	$2H_2O$					231.9		247.3		261.0		271.7	35
36	nitrate	$Ba(NO_3)_2$		5.0	7.0	9.2	11.6	14.2	17.1	20.3		27.0		34.2	36
37	nitrite	$Ba(NO_2)_2$	$1H_2O$			67.5						205.8		300	37
38	oxalate	BaC_2O_4			$0.0016^{8°}$	$0.0022^{18°}$	0.0024 at 24.2°								38
39	perchlorate	$Ba(ClO_4)_2$	$3H_2O$	205.8		289.1		358.7	426.3		495.2		562.3		39
40	sulfate	$BaSO_4$		1.15×10^{-4}	2.0×10^{-4}	2.4×10^{-4}	2.85×10^{-4}								40
41	Beryllium sulfate	$BeSO_4$	$6H_2O$				52		60.67						41
42	sulfate	$BeSO_4$	$4H_2O$				43.78	46.74			62		83	100	42
43	sulfate	$BeSO_4$	$2H_2O$									84.76	98	110	43
44	Boric acid	H_3BO_3		2.66	3.57	5.04	6.60	8.72	11.54	14.81	16.73	23.75	30.38	40.25	44
45	Boron oxide	B_2O_3		1.1	1.5	2.2		4.0		6.2		9.5		15.7	45
46	Bromine	Br_2		4.22	3.4	3.20	3.13								46
47	Cadmium chloride	$CdCl_2$	$4H_2O$	97.59	125.1										47
48	chloride	$CdCl_2$	$2\frac{1}{2}H_2O$	90.01			132.1								48
49	chloride	$CdCl_2$	$1H_2O$		135.1	134.5		135.3		136.5		140.4		147.0	49
50	cyanide	$Cd(CN)_2$				$1.7^{15°}$									50
51	hydroxide	$Cd(OH)_2$					2.6×10^{-4} at 25°								51
52	sulfate	$CdSO_4$		76.48	76.00	76.60		78.54		83.68			63.13	60.77	52
53	Calcium acetate	$Ca(C_2H_3O_2)_2$	$2H_2O$	37.4	36.0	34.7	33.8	33.2		32.7		33.5			53
54	acetate	$Ca(C_2H_3O_2)_2$	$1H_2O$										31.1	29.7	54

* By N. A. Lange. Abridged from table of Solubilities of Inorganic Compounds in Water at Various Temperatures in Lange, "Handbook of Chemistry," 10th ed., McGraw-Hill, New York, 1961. For tables of the solubility of gases in water at various temperatures Atack ("Handbook of Chemical Data," Reinhold, New York, 1957) gives values at closer temperature intervals, usually 1° or 5°C., than are tabulated here. For the solubility of various hydrocarbons in water at high pressures see *J. Chem. Eng. Data*, 4, 212 (1959).

Table 3-138. Solubilities of Inorganic Compounds in Water at Various Temperatures—(*Continued*)

	Substance	Formula	Solid phase	0°C.	10°C.	20°C.	30°C.	40°C.	50°C.	60°C.	70°C.	80°C.	90°C.	100°C.	
1	Calcium bicarbonate	$Ca(HCO_3)_2$		16.15		16.60		17.05		17.50		17.95		18.40	1
2	chloride	$CaCl_2$	$6H_2O$	59.5	65.0	74.5	102								2
3	chloride	$CaCl_2$	$2H_2O$							136.8	141.7	147.0	152.7	159	3
4	fluoride	CaF_2				0.0016 (18°)	0.0017 (26°)								4
5	hydroxide	$Ca(OH)_2$		0.185	0.176	0.165	0.153	0.141	0.128	0.116	0.106	0.094	0.085	0.077	5
6	nitrate	$Ca(NO_3)_2$	$4H_2O$	102.0	115.3	129.3	152.6	195.9							6
7	nitrate	$Ca(NO_3)_2$	$3H_2O$					237.5	281.5						7
8	nitrate	$Ca(NO_3)_2$										358.7		363.6	8
9	nitrite	$Ca(NO_2)_2$	$4H_2O$	62.07		76.68									9
10	nitrite	$Ca(NO_2)_2$	$2H_2O$							132.6	151.9		244.8		10
11	oxalate	CaC_2O_4			6.7×10^{-4} at 13°	6.8×10^{-4} at 25°	9.5×10^{-4} at 50°	14×10^{-4} at 95°							11
12	sulfate	$CaSO_4$	$2H_2O$	0.1759	0.1928		0.2090	0.2097		0.2047	0.1966			0.1619	12
13	Carbon dioxide, 760 mm	CO_2		0.3346	0.2318	0.1688	0.1257	0.0973	0.0761	0.0576				0	13
14	monoxide, 760 mm	CO		0.0044	0.0035	0.0028	0.0024	0.0021	0.0018	0.0015	0.0013	0.0010	0.0006	0	14
15	Cesium chloride	$CsCl$		161.4	174.7	186.5	197.3	208.0	218.5	229.7	239.5	250.0	260.1	270.5	15
16	nitrate	$CsNO_3$		9.33	14.9	23.0	33.9	47.2	64.4	83.8	107.0	134.0	163.0	197.0	16
17	sulfate	Cs_2SO_4		167.1	173.1	178.7	184.1	189.9	194.9	199.9	205.0	210.3	214.9	220.3	17
18	Chlorine, 760 mm	Cl_2		1.46	0.980	0.716	0.562	0.451	0.386	0.324	0.274	0.219	0.125	0	18
19	Chromic anhydride	CrO_3		164.9				174.0	182.1				217.5	206.8	19
20	Cupric chloride	$CuCl_2$	$2H_2O$	70.7	73.76	77.0	80.34	83.8	87.44	91.2		99.2		107.9	20
21	nitrate	$Cu(NO_3)_2$	$6H_2O$	81.8	95.28	125.1									21
22	nitrate	$Cu(NO_3)_2$	$3H_2O$					159.8		178.8		207.8			22
23	sulfate	$CuSO_4$	$5H_2O$	14.3	17.4	20.7	25	28.5	33.3	40		55		75.4	23
24	sulfide	CuS				3.3×10^{-5} at 18°									24
25	Cuprous chloride	$CuCl$				1.52 (25°)									25
26	Ferric chloride	$FeCl_3$		74.4	81.9	91.8			315.1			525.8		535.7	26
27	Ferrous chloride	$FeCl_2$	$4H_2O$		64.5		73.0	77.3	82.5	88.7		100			27
28	chloride	$FeCl_2$											105.3	105.8	28
29	nitrate	$Fe(NO_3)_2$	$6H_2O$	71.02		83.8				165.6					29
30	sulfate	$FeSO_4$	$7H_2O$	15.65	20.51	26.5	32.9	40.2	48.6						30
31	sulfate	$FeSO_4$	$1H_2O$								50.9	43.6	37.3		31
32	Hydrobromic acid, 760 mm	HBr		221.2	210.3	198			171.5					130	32
33	Hydrochloric acid, 760 mm	HCl		82.3			67.3	63.3	59.6	56.1					33
34	Iodine	I_2				0.029	0.04	0.056	0.078						34
35	Lead acetate	$Pb(C_2H_3O_2)_2$	$3H_2O$				55.04 (25°)								35
36	bromide	$PbBr_2$		0.4554		0.85	1.15	1.53	1.94	2.36		3.34		4.75	36
37	carbonate	$PbCO_3$				0.00011									37
38	chloride	$PbCl_2$		0.6728		0.99	1.20	1.45	1.70	1.98		2.62		3.34	38
39	chromate	$PbCrO_4$				7×10^{-6}									39
40	fluoride	PbF_2			0.060	0.064	0.068								40
41	nitrate	$Pb(NO_3)_2$		38.8	48.3	56.5	66	75	85	95		115		38.8	41
42	sulfate	$PbSO_4$		0.0028	0.0035	0.0041	0.0049	0.0056							42
43	Magnesium bromide	$MgBr_2$	$6H_2O$	91.0	94.5	96.5	99.2	101.6	104.1	107.5		113.7		120.2	43
44	chloride	$MgCl_2$	$6H_2O$	52.8	53.5	54.5		57.5		61.0		66.0		73.0	44
45	hydroxide	$Mg(OH)_2$				0.0009 (18°)									45
46	nitrate	$Mg(NO_3)_2$	$6H_2O$	66.55				84.74					137.0		46
47	sulfate	$MgSO_4$	$7H_2O$		30.9	35.5	40.8	45.6							47
48	sulfate	$MgSO_4$	$6H_2O$	40.8	42.2	44.5	45.3		50.4	53.5	59.5	64.2	69.0	74.0	48
49	sulfate	$MgSO_4$	$1H_2O$									62.9		68.3	49
50	Manganous sulfate	$MnSO_4$	$7H_2O$	53.23	60.01										50
51	sulfate	$MnSO_4$	$5H_2O$		59.5	62.9	67.76								51
52	sulfate	$MnSO_4$	$4H_2O$			64.5	66.44	68.8	72.6						52
53	sulfate	$MnSO_4$	$1H_2O$						58.17	55.0	52.0	48.0	42.5	34.0	53
54	Mercurous chloride	$HgCl$		0.00014		0.0002		0.0007							54
55	Molybdic oxide	MoO_3	$2H_2O$			0.138	0.264	0.476	0.687	1.206	2.055	2.106			55
56	Nickel chloride	$NiCl_2$	$6H_2O$	53.9	59.5	64.2	68.9	73.3	78.3	82.2	85.2			87.6	56
57	nitrate	$Ni(NO_3)_2$	$6H_2O$	79.58		96.31		122.2							57
58	nitrate	$Ni(NO_3)_2$	$3H_2O$							163.1	169.1		235.1		58
59	sulfate	$NiSO_4$	$7H_2O$	27.22	32		42.46								59
60	sulfate	$NiSO_4$	$6H_2O$						50.15	54.80	59.44	63.17		76.7	60
61	Nitric oxide, 760 mm	NO		0.00984	0.00757	0.00618	0.00517	0.00440	0.00376	0.00324	0.00267	0.00199	0.00114	0	61
62	Nitrous oxide	N_2O			0.1705	0.1211									62

Table 3-138. Solubilities of Inorganic Compounds in Water at Various Temperatures—(*Continued*)

	Substance	Formula	Solid phase	0°C.	10°C.	20°C.	30°C.	40°C.	50°C.	60°C.	70°C.	80°C.	90°C.	100°C.	
1	Potassium acetate	$KC_2H_3O_2$	$1\frac{1}{2}H_2O$	216.7	233.9	255.6	283.8	323.3							1
2	acetate	$KC_2H_3O_2$	$\frac{1}{2}H_2O$						337.3	350	364.8	380.1	396.3		2
3	alum	$K_2SO_4.Al_2(SO_4)_3$	$24H_2O$	3.0	4.0	5.9	8.39	11.70	17.00	24.75	40.0	71.0	109.0		3
4	bicarbonate	$KHCO_3$		22.4	27.7	33.2	39.1	45.4		60.0					4
5	bisulfate	$KHSO_4$		36.3		51.4		67.3						121.6	5
6	bitartrate	$KHC_4H_4O_6$		0.32	0.40	0.53	0.90	1.32	1.83	2.46		4.6		6.95	6
7	carbonate	K_2CO_3	$2H_2O$	105.5	108	110.5	113.7	116.9	121.2	126.8	133.1	139.8	147.5	155.7	7
8	chlorate	$KClO_3$		3.3	5	7.4	10.5	14	19.3	24.5		38.5		57	8
9	chloride	KCl		27.6	31.0	34.0	37.0	40.0	42.6	45.5	48.3	51.1	54.0	56.7	9
10	chromate	K_2CrO_4		58.2	60.0	61.7	63.4	65.2	66.8	68.6	70.4	72.1	73.9	75.6	10
11	dichromate	$K_2Cr_2O_7$		5	7	12	20	26	34	43	52	61	70	80	11
12	ferricyanide	$K_3Fe(CN)_6$		31	36	43	50	60		66				82.6^{104}	12
13	hydroxide	KOH	$2H_2O$	97	103	112	126								13
14	hydroxide	KOH	$1H_2O$						140					178	14
15	nitrate	KNO_3		13.3	20.9	31.6	45.8	63.9	85.5	110.0	138	169	202	246	15
16	nitrite	KNO_2		278.8		298.4		334.9						412.8	16
17	perchlorate	$KClO_4$		0.75	1.05	1.80	2.6	4.4	6.5	9	11.8	14.8	18	21.8	17
18	permanganate	$KMnO_4$		2.83	4.4	6.4	9.0	12.56	16.89	22.2					18
19	persulfate†	$K_2S_2O_8$†	†	1.62	2.60	4.49	7.19	9.89							19
20	sulfate	K_2SO_4		7.35	9.22	11.11	12.97	14.76	16.50	18.17	19.75	21.4	22.8	24.1	20
21	thiocyanate	$KCNS$		177.0		217.5									21
22	Silver cyanide	$AgCN$				2.2×10^{-5}									22
23	nitrate	$AgNO_3$		122	170	222	300	376	455	525		669		952	23
24	sulfate	Ag_2SO_4		0.573	0.695	0.796	0.888	0.979	1.08	1.15	1.22	1.30	1.36	1.41	24
25	Sodium acetate	$NaC_2H_3O_2$	$3H_2O$	36.3	40.8	46.5	54.5	65.5	83	139					25
26	acetate	$NaC_2H_3O_2$		119	121	123.5	126	129.5	134	139.5	146	153	161	170	26
27	bicarbonate	$NaHCO_3$		6.9	8.15	9.6	11.1	12.7	14.45	16.4					27
28	carbonate	Na_2CO_3	$10H_2O$	7	12.5	21.5	38.8								28
29	carbonate	Na_2CO_3	$1H_2O$				50.5	48.5		46.4		45.8		45.5	29
30	chlorate	$NaClO_3$		79	89	101	113	126	140	155	172	189		230	30
31	chloride	$NaCl$		35.7	35.8	36.0	36.3	36.6	37.0	37.3	37.8	38.4	39.0	39.8	31
32	chromate	Na_2CrO_4	$10H_2O$	31.70	50.17	88.7									32
33	chromate	Na_2CrO_4	$4H_2O$				88.7	95.96	104	114.6					33
34	chromate	Na_2CrO_4									123.0	124.8		125.9	34
35	dichromate	$Na_2Cr_2O_7$	$2H_2O$	163.0		177.8			244.8		316.7	376.2			35
36	dichromate	$Na_2Cr_2O_7$												426.3	36
37	dihydrogen phosphate	NaH_2PO_4	$2H_2O$	57.9	69.9	85.2	106.5	138.2							37
38	dihydrogen phosphate	NaH_2PO_4	$1H_2O$						158.6						38
39	dihydrogen phosphate	NaH_2PO_4								179.3	190.3	207.3	225.3	246.6	39
40	hydrogen arsenate	Na_2HAsO_4	$12H_2O$	7.3	15.5	26.5	37	47		65		85			40
41	hydrogen phosphate	Na_2HPO_4	$12H_2O$	1.67	3.6	7.7	20.8								41
42	hydrogen phosphate	Na_2HPO_4	$7H_2O$					51.8							42
43	hydrogen phosphate	Na_2HPO_4	$2H_2O$						80.2	82.9	88.1	92.4	102.9		43
44	hydrogen phosphate	Na_2HPO_4												102.2	44
45	hydroxide	$NaOH$	$4H_2O$	42											45
46	hydroxide	$NaOH$	$3\frac{1}{2}H_2O$		51.5										46
47	hydroxide	$NaOH$	$1H_2O$			109	119	129	145	174					47
48	hydroxide	$NaOH$											313	347	48
49	nitrate	$NaNO_3$		73	80	88	96	104	114	124		148		180	49
50	nitrite	$NaNO_2$		72.1	78.0	84.5	91.6	98.4	104.1			132.6		163.2	50
51	oxalate	$Na_2C_2O_4$				3.7								6.33	51
52	phosphate, tri-	Na_3PO_4	$12H_2O$	1.5	4.1	11	20	31	43	55		81		108	52
53	pyrophosphate	$Na_4P_2O_7$	$10H_2O$	3.16	3.95	6.23	9.95	13.50	17.45	21.83		30.04		40.26	53
54	sulfate	Na_2SO_4	$10H_2O$	5.0	9.0	19.4	40.8								54
55	sulfate	Na_2SO_4	$7H_2O$	19.5	30	44									55
56	sulfate	Na_2SO_4						48.8	46.7	45.3		43.7		42.5	56
57	sulfide	Na_2S	$9H_2O$		15.42	18.8	22.5	28.5							57
58	sulfide	Na_2S	$5\frac{1}{2}H_2O$						39.82	42.69	45.73	51.40	59.23		58
59	sulfide	Na_2S	$6H_2O$						36.4	39.1	43.31	49.14	57.28		59
60	sulfite	Na_2SO_3	$7H_2O$	13.9	20	26.9	36								60
61	sulfite	Na_2SO_3						28	28.2	28.8		28.3			61
62	tetraborate	$Na_2B_4O_7$	$10H_2O$	1.3	1.6	2.7	3.9		10.5	20.3					62
63	tetraborate	$Na_2B_4O_7$	$5H_2O$								24.4	31.5	41	52.5	63
64	vanadate (meta)	$NaVO_3$	$2H_2O$			$15.3^{25°}$		30.2		68.4					64

Table 3-138. Solubilities of Inorganic Compounds in Water at Various Temperatures—(*Concluded*)

	Substance	Formula	Solid phase	0°C.	10°C.	20°C.	30°C.	40°C.	50°C.	60°C.	70°C.	80°C.	90°C.	100°C.	
1	Sodium vanadate (meta)	$NaVO_3$				21.1$^{25°}$		26.23		32.97	36.9	38.8$^{75°}$			1
2	Stannous chloride	$SnCl_2$		83.9		269.8$^{15°}$									2
3	sulfate	$SnSO_4$				19								18	3
4	Strontium acetate	$Sr(C_2H_3O_2)_2$	$4H_2O$	36.9	43.61										4
5	acetate	$Sr(C_2H_3O_2)_2$	$\frac{1}{2}H_2O$		42.95	41.6	39.5		37.35		36.24	36.10		36.4	5
6	chloride	$SrCl_2$	$6H_2O$	43.5	47.7	52.9	58.7	65.3	72.4	81.8					6
7	chloride	$SrCl_2$	$2H_2O$								85.9	90.5		100.8	7
8	nitrate	$Sr(NO_3)_2$	$1H_2O$	52.7		64.0			83.8	97.2			130.4	139	8
9	nitrate	$Sr(NO_3)_2$	$4H_2O$	40.1		70.5									9
10	nitrate	$Sr(NO_3)_2$					88.6	90.1		93.8	96	98	100		10
11	sulfate	$SrSO_4$		0.0113		0.0114	0.0114								11
12	Sulfur dioxide, 760 mm	SO_2		22.83	16.21	11.29	7.81	5.41	4.5						12
13	Thallium sulfate	Tl_2SO_4		2.70	3.70	4.87	6.16		9.21	10.92	12.74	14.61	16.53	18.45	13
14	Thorium sulfate	$Th(SO_4)_2$	$9H_2O$	0.74	0.98	1.38	1.995	2.998	5.22						14
15	sulfate	$Th(SO_4)_2$	$8H_2O$	1.0	1.25	1.62									15
16	sulfate	$Th(SO_4)_2$	$6H_2O$	1.50		1.90	2.45			6.64					16
17	sulfate	$Th(SO_4)_2$	$4H_2O$					4.04	2.54	1.63	1.09				17
18	Zinc chlorate	$ZnClO_3$	$6H_2O$	145.0	152.5										18
19	chlorate	$ZnClO_3$	$4H_2O$			200.3	209.2	223.2	273.1						19
20	nitrate	$Zn(NO_3)_2$	$6H_2O$	94.78		118.3									20
21	nitrate	$Zn(NO_3)_2$	$3H_2O$					206.9							21
22	sulfate	$ZnSO_4$	$7H_2O$	41.9	47	54.4									22
23	sulfate	$ZnSO_4$	$6H_2O$					70.1	76.8						23
24	sulfate	$ZnSO_4$	$1H_2O$									86.6	83.7	80.8	24

THERMAL EXPANSION

The tables given under this subject are reprinted by permission from the "Smithsonian Tables." For more detailed data on thermal expansion see "International Critical Tables": tabular index, vol. 3, p. 1; abrasives, vol. 2, p. 87; alloys, vol. 2, p. 463; building stones, vol. 2, p. 54; carbons, vol. 2, p. 303; elements, vol. 1, p. 102; enamels, vol. 2, p. 115; glass, vol. 2, p. 93; metals, vol. 2, p. 459; petroleums, vol. 2, p. 145; porcelains, vol. 2, pp. 70, 78; refractory materials, vol. 2, p. 83; solid insulators, vol. 2, p. 310.

Table 3-139. Coefficients of Thermal Expansion of Gases*

Coefficient at constant volume for temperatures from 0 to 100°C. $\alpha_p = \frac{1}{p_0}\left[\frac{dp}{dt}\right]_v$						Coefficient at constant pressure for temperatures from 0 to 100°C. $\alpha_v = \frac{1}{v_0}\left[\frac{dv}{dt}\right]_p$					
Substance	Initial pressure, mm. Hg	$10^6\alpha_p$	Substance	Initial pressure, mm. Hg	$10^6\alpha_p$	Substance	Initial pressure, mm. Hg	$10^6\alpha_p$	Substance	Initial pressure, mm. Hg	$10^6\alpha_p$
Air	760	3671.6	Hydrogen	760	3662.7	Air	760	3671.1	Hydrogen chloride	760	3734
Air	1000	3675	Hydrogen	1000	3662.6	Air	1000	3674	Krypton	862	3691.6
Ammonia	760	3767.8	chloride	760	3721	Ammonia	760	3790	Krypton	1000	3696.7
Argon	517	3668	Krypton	1000	3689.9	Argon	760	3672.4	Methane	760	3682
Argon	760	3672	Methane	760	3679	Argon	1000	3676	Neon	760	3660.6
Argon	1000	3675	Neon	760	3662.8	Carbon dioxide	760	3725	Neon	1007	3660.2
Carbon dioxide	760	3711	Neon	1362.8	3662.3	monoxide	760	3672	Nitrogen	760	3671
dioxide	1000	3726	Nitrogen	760	3672	Chlorine	760	3830	Nitrogen	994	3673.4
monoxide	760	3673	Nitrogen	994	3674	Cyanogen	760	3870	Nitrous oxide	760	3732
Chlorine	760	3803	Nitrous oxide	760	3719	Ethylene	760	3735	Nitrous oxide	1000	3706.7
Cyanogen	760	3830	Oxygen	760	3673.5	Helium	760	3659.1	Oxygen	760	3674
Ethylene	760	3722	Oxygen	1000	3675.7	Helium	994	3657.9	Oxygen	1000	3676.3
Helium	760	3661.3	Sulfur dioxide	760	3840	Hydrogen	760	3660.3	Sulfur dioxide	760	3880
Helium	1000	3660.7	Xenon	1000	3720	Hydrogen	1095	3659.0	Sulfur hexafluoride	760	3808
									Xenon	1000	3739.5

* The data were taken from collected and calculated values of Coppock, *Phil. Mag.*, (7) **19**, 446 (1935). For gas data prior to the year 1912 see "Handbook of Chemistry and Physics," 40th ed., pp. 2248–2249. Chemical Rubber Publishing Co. For data on carbon monoxide see Johnson (ed.), WADD-TR-60-56, 1960.

Table 3-140. Linear Expansion of the Solid Elements*

C is the true expansion coefficient at the given temperature; M is the mean coefficient between given temperatures; where one temperature is given, the true coefficient at that temperature is indicated; α and β are coefficients in formula $l_t = l_0(1 + \alpha t + \beta t^2)$; l_0 is length at 0°C. (unless otherwise indicated, when, if x is the reference temperature, $l_t = l_x[1 + \alpha(t - t_x) + \beta(t - t_x)^2]$; l_t is length at t°C.).

Element	Temp., °C.	$C \times 10^4$	Temp. range, °C.	$M \times 10^4$	Temp. range, °C.	$\alpha \times 10^4$	$\beta \times 10^6$
Aluminum	20	0.224	100	0.235	0, 500	0.22	0.009
Aluminum	300	0.284	500	0.311			
Antimony	20	0.136‖	20	0.080⊥			
Arsenic	20	0.05					
Bismuth	20	0.014‖	20	0.103⊥			
Cadmium	0	0.54‖	−180, −140	0.59‖	20, 100	0.526‖	
Cadmium	0	0.20⊥	−180, −140	0.117⊥	20, 100	0.214⊥	
Carbon, diamond	50	0.012					
graphite	50	0.06					
Chromium	....	....	20, 100	0.068	20, 500	0.086	
Cobalt	20	0.123	....	....	6, 121	0.121	0.0064
Copper	20	0.162	100	0.166	0, 625	0.161	0.0040
Copper	200	0.170	300	0.175			
Gold	20	0.140	17, 100	0.143	0, 520	0.142	0.0022
Gold	....	....	−191, 17	0.132			
Indium	40	0.417					
Iodine	....	....	−190, 17	0.837			
Iridium	20	0.065	....	....	0, 80	0.0636	0.0032
Iridium	....	....	....	....	1070, 1720	0.0679	0.0011
Iron, soft	40	0.1210	0, 100	0.11			
cast	20	0.118	....	....	0, 750	0.1158	0.0053
wrought	20	0.119	....	....	0, 750	0.1170	0.0053
steel	20	0.114	....	....	0, 750	0.1118	0.0053
Lead (99.9)	....	....	20, 100	0.291	100, 240	0.269	0.011
	100	0.291	20, 200	0.300			
	280	0.343					
Magnesium	20	0.254	−100, + 20	0.240	+ 20, 500	0.2480	0.0096
			20, 100	0.260			
Manganese	20	0.233	0, 100	0.228			
			−190, 0	0.159	20, 300	0.216	0.0121
Molybdenum†	20	0.053	0, 100	0.052	−142, 19	0.0515	0.0057
			25, 100	0.049	19, +305	0.0501	0.0014
			25, 500	0.055			
Nickel	20	0.126	0, 100	0.130	−190, + 20	0.1308	0.0166
					+ 20, +300	0.1236	0.0066
					500, 1000	0.1346	0.0033
Osmium	40	0.066					
Palladium	20	0.1173	....	....	−190, +100	0.1152	0.00517
					0, 1000	0.1167	0.0022
Platinum	20	0.0887	....	....	−190, −100	0.0875	0.00314
	20	0.0893	....	....	0, + 80	0.0890	0.00121
					0, 1000	0.0887	0.00132
Potassium	....	....	0, 50	0.83			
Rhodium	40	0.0850	6, 21	0.0876	− 75, −112	0.0746	
Ruthenium	40	0.0963					
Selenium	0	0.439	0, 100	0.660			

Table 3-140. Linear Expansion of the Solid Elements*—(*Concluded*)

Element	Temp., °C.	$C \times 10^4$	Temp. range, °C.	$M \times 10^4$	Temp. range, °C.	$\alpha \times 10^4$	$\beta \times 10^6$
Silicon	40	0.0763	− 3, + 18	0.0249	− 75, − 67	0.0182	
Silver	20	0.1846	0, 100	0.197	0, 875	0.1827	0.00479
	20	0.195			20, 500	0.1939	0.00295
Sodium	......	......	−190, −17	0.622	0, 50	0.72	
Steel, 36.4Ni	......	......	20, 260	0.031	260, 500	0.144	
			20, 340	0.055	340, 500	0.136	
Tantalum†	20	0.065	− 78, 0	0.059	20, 400	0.0646	0.0009
			0, 100	0.0655			
Tellurium	20	0.016‖	20	0.272⊥			
Thallium	40	0.302					
Tin	20	0.214	......	......	8, 95	0.2033	0.0263
	20	0.305‖	20	0.154⊥			
Tungsten†	27	0.0444	0, 100	0.045	−105, +502	0.0428	0.00058
Zinc	20‡	0.643‖	−140, −100	0.656‖	+ 0, 400	0.354	0.010
	20‡	0.125⊥	+ 20, 100	0.639‖			
	20	0.358	+ 20, 100	0.141⊥			

* "Smithsonian Tables." For more complete tabulations see Table 142, "Smithsonian Physical Tables," 9th ed., 1954; "Handbook of Chemistry and Physics," 40th ed., pp. 2239–2245, Chemical Rubber Publishing Co.; Goldsmith, and Waterman, WADC-TR-58-476, 1959; Johnson (ed.), WADD-TR-60-56, 1960, etc.

† Molybdenum, 300° to 2500°C.; $l_t = l_{300}[1 + 5.00 \times 10^{-6}(t - 300) + 10.5 \times 10^{-10}(t - 300)^2]$

Tantalum, 300° to 2800°C.; $l_t = l_{300}[1 + 6.60 \times 10^{-6}(t - 300) + 5.2 \times 10^{-10}(t - 300)^2]$

Tungsten, 300° to 2700°C.; $l_t = l_{300}[1 + 4.44 \times 10^{-6}(t - 300) + 4.5 \times 10^{-10}(t - 300)^2]$

Beryllium, 20° to 100°C.; 12.3×10^{-6} per °C.

Columbium, 0° to 100°C.; 7.2×10^{-6} per °C.

Tantalum, 20° to 100°C.; 6.6×10^{-6} per °C.

‡ Two errors in the data of zinc have been corrected. These values were taken from Grüneisen and Goens, *Z. Physik.*, 29, 141 (1924).

Table 3-141. Linear Expansion of Miscellaneous Substances*

The coefficient of cubical expansion may be taken as three times the linear coefficient. *t* is the temperature or range of temperature, *C* the coefficient of expansion.

Substance	t°C	$C \times 10^4$
Amber	0–30	0.50
	0–09	0.61
Bakelite, bleached	20–60	0.22
Brass:		
Cast	0–100	0.1875
Wire	0–100	0.1930
Wire	0–100	0.1783 to 0.193
71.5 Cu + 27.7 Zn + 0.3 Sn + 0.5 Pb	40	0.1859
71 Cu + 29 Zn	0–100	0.1906
Bronze:		
3 Cu + 1 Sn	16.6–100	0.1844
3 Cu + 1 Sn	16.6–350	0.2116
3 Cu + 1 Sn	16.6–957	0.1737
86.3 Cu + 9.7 Sn + 4 Zn	40	0.1782
97.6 Cu + 2.2 Sn + 0.2 P, hard	0–80	0.1713
97.6 Cu + 2.2 Sn + 0.2 P, soft	0–80	0.1708
Caoutchouc	....	0.657 to 0.686
Caoutchouc	16.7–25.3	0.770
Celluloid	20–70	1.00
Constantan	4–29	0.1523
Duralumin, 94Al	20–100	0.23
	20–300	0.25
Ebonite	25.3–35.4	0.842
Fluorspar. CaF_2	0–100	0.1950
German silver	0–100	0.1836
Gold-platinum, 2 Au + 1 Pt	0–100	0.1523
Gold-copper, 2 Au + 1 Cu	0–100	0.1552
Glass:		
Tube	0–100	0.0833
Tube	0–100	0.0828
Plate	0–100	0.0891
Crown (mean)	0–100	0.0897
Crown (mean)	50–60	0.0954
Flint	50–60	0.0788
Jena thermometer 16III normal	0–100	0.081

Substance	t°C	$C \times 10^4$
Jena thermometer 59III	0–100	0.058
Jena thermometer 59III	−191 to +16	0.424
Gutta percha	20	1.983
Ice	−20 to −1	0.51
Iceland spar:		
Parallel to axis	0–80	0.2631
Perpendicular to axis	0–80	0.0544
Lead tin (solder) 2 Pb + 1 Sn	0–100	0.2508
Limestone	25–100	0.09
Magnalium	12–39	0.238
Manganin	....	0.181
Marble	15–100	0.117
Monel metal	25–100	0.14
	25–600	0.16
Paraffin	0–16	1.0662
Paraffin	16–38	1.3030
Paraffin	38–49	4.7707
Platinum-iridium, 10 Pt + 1 Ir	40	0.0884
Platinum-silver, 1 Pt + 2 Ag	0–100	0.1523
Porcelain	20–790	0.0413
Porcelain Bayeux	1000–1400	0.0553
Quartz:		
Parallel to axis	0–80	0.0797
Parallel to axis	−190 to +16	0.0521
Perpend. to axis	0–80	0.1337
Quartz glass	−190 to +16	−0.0026
Quartz glass	16 to 500	0.0057
Quartz glass	16 to 1000	0.0058
Rock salt	40	0.4040
Rubber, hard	0	0.691
Rubber, hard	−160	0.300
Speculum metal	0–100	0.1933
Steel, 0.14 C, 34.5 Ni	25–100	0.037
	25–600	0.136

Substance	t°C	$C \times 10^4$
Topaz:		
Parallel to lesser horizontal axis	0–100	0.0832
Parallel to greater horizontal axis	0–100	0.0836
Parallel to vertical axis	0–100	0.0472
Tourmaline:		
Parallel to longitudinal axis	0–100	0.0937
Parallel to horizontal axis	0–100	0.0773
Type metal	16.6–254	0.1952
Vulcanite	0–18	0.6360
Wedgwood ware	0–100	0.0890
Wood:		
Parallel to fiber:		
Ash	0–100	0.0951
Beech	2.34	0.0257
Chestnut	2.34	0.0649
Elm	2.34	0.0565
Mahogany	2.34	0.0361
Maple	2.34	0.0638
Oak	2.34	0.0492
Pine	2.34	0.0541
Walnut	2.34	0.0658
Across the fiber:		
Beech	2.34	0.614
Chestnut	2.34	0.325
Elm	2.34	0.443
Mahogany	2.34	0.404
Maple	2.34	0.484
Oak	2.34	0.544
Pine	2.34	0.341
Walnut	2.34	0.484
Wax white	10–26	2.300
Wax white	26–31	3.120
Wax white	31–43	4.860
Wax white	43–57	15.227

* "Smithsonian Tables." For a more complete tabulation see Tables 143, 144, "Smithsonian Physical Tables," 9th ed., 1954, also reprinted in "American Institute of Physics Handbook," McGraw-Hill, New York, 1957; "Handbook of Chemistry and Physics," 40th ed., pp. 2239–2245, Chemical Rubber Publishing Co. For data on many solids prior to 1926 see Gruneisen, "Handbuch der Physik," vol. 10, pp. 1–52, 1926, translation available as *N.A.S.A.* RE 2-18-59W, 1959. For eight plastic solids below 300°K. see Scott, "Cryogenic Engineering," p. 331, Van Nostrand, Princeton, N.J., 1959. For 11 other materials to 300°K. see Scott, *loc. cit.*, p. 333. For quartz and silica see Cook, *Brit. J. Appl. Phys.*, 7, 285 (1956).

Table 3-142. Cubical Expansion of Liquids*

If V_0 is the volume at 0° then at t° the expansion formula is $V_t = V_0(1 + \alpha t + \beta t^2 + \gamma t^3)$. The table gives values of α, β, and γ and of C, the true coefficient of cubical expansion at 20° for some liquids and solutions. Δt is the temperature range of the observation.

Liquid	Range	$\alpha \times 10^3$	$\beta \times 10^6$	$\gamma \times 10^8$	$C \times 10^3$ at 20°
Acetic acid	16–107	1.0630	0.12636	1.0876	1.071
Acetone	0–54	1.3240	3.8090	− 0.87983	1.487
Alcohol:					
Amyl	−15–80	0.9001	0.6573	1.18458	0.902
Ethyl, 30% by volume	18–39	0.2928	10.790	−11.87	
Ethyl, 50% by volume	0–39	0.7450	1.85	0.730	
Ethyl, 99.3% by volume	27–46	1.012	2.20	....	1.12
Ethyl, 500 atm. pressure	0–40	0.866			
Ethyl, 3000 atm. pressure	0–40	0.524			
Methyl	0–61	1.1342	1.3635	0.8741	1.199
Benzene	11–81	1.17626	1.27776	0.80648	1.237
Bromine	0–59	1.06218	1.87714	− 0.30854	1.132
Calcium chloride:					
5.8% solution	18–25	0.07878	4.2742	....	0.250
40.9% solution	17–24	0.42383	0.8571	....	0.458
Carbon disulfide	−34–60	1.13980	1.37065	1.91225	1.218
500 atm. pressure	0–50	0.940			
3000 atm. pressure	0–50	0.581			
Carbon tetrachloride	0–76	1.18384	0.89881	1.35135	1.236
Chloroform	0–63	1.10715	4.66473	− 1.74328	1.273
Ether	−15–38	1.51324	2.35918	4.00512	1.656
Glycerin	......	0.4853	0.4895	....	0.505
Hydrochloric acid, 33.2% solution	0–33	0.4460	0.215	....	0.455
Mercury	0–100	0.18182	0.0078	....	0.18186
Olive oil	......	0.6821	1.1405	− 0.539	0.721
Pentane	0–33	1.4646	3.09319	1.6084	1.608
Potassium chloride, 24.3% solution	16–25	0.2695	2.080	....	0.353
Phenol	36–157	0.8340	0.10732	0.4446	1.090
Petroleum, 0.8467 density	24–120	0.8994	1.396	....	0.955
Sodium chloride, 20.6% solution	0–29	0.3640	1.237	....	0.414
Sodium sulfate, 24% solution	11–40	0.3599	1.258	....	0.410
Sulfuric acid:					
10.9% solution	0–30	0.2835	2.580	....	0.387
100.0%	0–30	0.5758	−0.432	....	0.558
Turpentine	− 9–106	0.9003	1.9595	− 0.44998	0.973
Water	0–33	−0.06427	8.5053	− 6.7900	0.207

* "Smithsonian Tables," Table 269. For a detailed discussion of mercury data see Cook, *Brit. J. Appl. Phys.*, 7, 285 (1956). For data on nitrogen and argon see Johnson (ed.), WADD-TR-60-56, 1960.

Bromoform[1] 7.7 − 50°C.
$V_t = 0.34204[1 + 0.00090411(t - 7.7) + 0.0000006766(t - 7.7)^2]$
0.34204 in the specific volume of bromoform at 7.7°C.
Glycerin[2] −62 to 0°C.
$V_t = V_0(1 + 4.83 \times 10^{-4}t - 0.49 \times 10^{-6}t^2)$
0 − 80°C.
$V_t = V_0(1 + 4.83 \times 10^{-4}t + 0.49 \times 10^{-6}t^2)$
Mercury[3] 0 − 300°C.
$V_t - V_0[1 + 10^{-8}(18153.8t + 0.7548t^2 + 0.001533t^2 + 0.00000536t^4)]$

[1] Sherman and Sherman, *J. Am. Chem. Soc.*, **50**, 1119 (1928). (An obvious error in their equation has been corrected.)
[2] Samsoen, *Ann. phys.*, (10) **9**, 91 (1928).
[3] Harlow, *Phil. Mag.*, (7) **7**, 674 (1929).

Table 3-143. Cubical Expansion of Solids*

If v_2 and v_1 are the volumes at t_2 and t_1, respectively, then $v_2 = v_1(1 + C\Delta t)$, C being the coefficient of cubical expansion and Δt the temperature interval. Where only a single temperature is stated, C represents the true coefficient of cubical expansion at that temperature.

Substance	t or Δt	$C \times 10^4$
Antimony	0–100	0.3167
Beryl	0–100	0.0105
Bismuth	0–100	0.3948
Copper†	0–100	0.4998
Diamond	40	0.0354
Emerald	40	0.0168
Galena	0–100	0.558
Glass, common tube	0–100	0.276
hard	0–100	0.214
Jena, borosilicate 59 III	20–100	0.156
pure silica	0–80	0.0129
Gold	0–100	0.4411
Ice	−20 to −1	1.1250
Iron	0–100	0.3550
Lead†	0–100	0.8399
Paraffin	20	5.88
Platinum	0–100	0.265
Porcelain, Berlin	20	0.0814
chloride	0–100	1.094
nitrate	0–100	1.967
sulfate	20	1.0754
Quartz	0–100	0.3840
Rock salt	50–60	1.2120
Rubber	20	4.87
Silver	0–100	0.5831
Sodium	20	2.13
Stearic acid	33.8–45.4	8.1
Sulfur, native	13.2–50.3	2.23
Tin	0–100	0.6889
Zinc†	0–100	0.8928

* "Smithsonian Tables," Table 268.
† See additional data below.

Aluminum[1] 100 − 530°C.
$V = V_0(1 + 2.16 \times 10^{-5}t + 0.95 \times 10^{-8}t^2)$
Cadmium[1] 130 − 270°C.
$V = V_0(1 + 8.04 \times 10^{-5}t + 5.9 \times 10^{-8}t^2)$
Copper[1] 110 − 300°C.
$V = V_0(1 + 1.62 \times 10^{-5}t + 0.20 \times 10^{-8}t^2)$
Colophony[2] 0 − 34°C.
$V = V_0(1 + 2.21 \times 10^{-4}t + 0.31 \times 10^{-6}t^2)$
34 − 150°C.
$V = V_{34}[1 + 7.40 \times 10^{-4}(t - 34) + 5.91 \times 10^{-6}(t - 34)^2]$
Lead[1] 100 − 280°C.
$V = V_0(1 + 1.60 \times 10^{-5}t + 3.2 \times 10^{-8}t^2)$
Shellac[2] 0 − 46°C.
$V = V_0(1 + 2.73 \times 10^{-4}t + 0.39 \times 10^{-6}t^2)$
46 − 100°C.
$V = V_{46}[1 + 13.10 \times 10^{-4}(t - 46) + 0.62 \times 10^{-6}(t - 46)^2]$
Silica (vitreous)[3] 0 − 300°C.
$V_t = V_0[1 + 10^{-8}(93.6t + 0.7776t^2 - 0.003315t^2 + 0.000005244t^4)$
Sugar (cane, amorphous)[2] 0 − 67°C.
$V_t = V_0(1 + 2.34 \times 10^{-4}t + 0.14 \times 10^{-6}t^2)$
67 − 160°C.
$V_t = V_{67}[1 + 5.02 \times 10^{-4}(t - 67) + 0.43 \times 10^{-6}(t - 67)^2]$
Zinc[1] 120 − 360°C.
$V_t = V_0(1 + 8.50 \times 10^{-5}t + 3.9 \times 10^{-8}t^2)$

[1] Uffelmann, *Phil. Mag.*, (7) **10**, 633 (1930).
[2] Samsoen, *Ann. phys.*, (10) **9**, 83 (1928).
[3] Harlow, *Phil. Mag.*, (7) **7**, 674 (1929).

JOULE-THOMSON EFFECT

Table 3-144. References Available for the Joule-Thomson Coefficient

Gas	Pressure range, atm.				Temp. range, °C.			Unclassified
	0–10	10–50	50–200	>200	<0	0–300	>300	
Air	12, 15, 16 19, 35	12, 15, 19 35	15, 19, 35	....	19, 35	12, 15, 16 19, 35	....	3, 4, 18
Ammonia	28	....	....	....	....	28	....	2, 3
Argon	39	39	39	....	39	39		
Benzene	31	31	31	....	....	31	31	
Butane	26	26	....	....	....	26		
Carbon dioxide	7, 8, 28 37	7, 8, 37	7, 8, 37	....	7, 8, 37	7, 8, 9, 10 37		
Carbon monoxide	17	17	....	....	17	17		
Deuterium	....	22, 24, 25 1*	1,* 22, 24 25	....	1,* 22, 24, 25			
Dowtherm A	46	46	....	....	....	46	46	
Ethane	45	45	....	....	....	45		
Ethylene	....	....	....	....	....	9, 10		
Helium	1, 38	1, 38	38	....	1, 38	38	....	48
Hydrogen	24, 30	22, 24, 25 30	24, 30	....	22, 24, 25 30	24		
Methane	....	6	6	....	....	6		
Mixtures	....	....	....	....	....	9, 11		
Natural gas	....	....	33	33	33	33		
Nitrogen	13, 28, 40	13, 40	13, 40	13	13, 40	9, 10, 13 28, 40	13	19
Nitrous oxide	....	....	....	....	....	9, 10		
Pentane	26, 34, 44	34	34	....	....	26, 34, 44		
Propane	41	43	....	....	....	43		
Steam	28, 29, 42	29, 42, 47	42, 47	....	....	28, 29, 42 45	29, 42, 47	29, 47

* See also 14 (generalized chart); 18 (review, to 1919); 20–22; 23 (review, to 1948); 27 (review, to 1905); 32, 36, 41, 50.

REFERENCES: 1. Baehr, *Z. Elektrochem.*, **60**, 515 (1956). 2. Beattie, *J. Math. Phys.*, **9**, 11 (1930). 3. Beattie, *Phys. Rev.*, **35**, 643 (1930). 4. Bradley and Hale, *Phys. Rev.*, **29**, 258 (1909). 5. Brown and Dean, *Bur. Standards J. Research*, **60**, 161 (1958). 6. Budenholzer, Sage, *et al.*, *Ind. Eng. Chem.*, **29**, 658 (1937). 7. Burnett, *Phys. Rev.*, **22**, 590 (1923). 8. Burnett, *Univ. Wisconsin Bull.* 9(No. 6), 1926. 9. Charnley, Ph.D. Thesis, University of Manchester, 1952. 10. Charnley, Isles, *et al.*, *Proc. Roy. Soc.* (*London*), **A217**, 133 (1953). 11. Charnley, Rowlinson, *et al.*, *Proc. Roy. Soc.* (*London*), **A230**, 354 (1955). 12. Dalton, *Commun. Phys. Lab. Univ. Leiden*, No. 109c, 1909. 13. Deming and Deming, *Phys. Rev.*, **48**, 448 (1935). 14. Edmister, *Petrol. Refiner*, **28**, 128 (1949). 15. Eucken, Clusius, *et al.*, *Z. tech. Physik.*, **13**, 267 (1932). 16 Eumorfopoulos and Rai, *Phil. Mag.*, **7**, 961 (1926). 17. Huang, Lin, *et al.*, *Z. Physik.*, **100**, 594 (1936). 18. Hoxton, *Phys. Rev.* **13**, 438 (1919). 19. Ishkin and Kaganev, *J. Tech. Phys. U.S.S.R.*, **26**, 2323 (1956). 20. Isles, Ph.D. Thesis, Leeds University. 21. Jenkin and Pye, *Phil. Trans. Roy. Soc.* (*London*), **A213**, 67 (1914); **A215**, 353 (1915). 22. Johnston, *J. Am. Chem. Soc.*, **68**, 2362 (1946). 23. Johnston, *Trans. Am. Soc. Mech. Engrs.*, **70**, 651 (1948). 24. Johnston, Bezman, *et al.*, *J. Am. Chem. Soc.*, **68**, 2367 (1946). 25. Johnston, Swanson, *et al.*, *J. Am. Chem. Soc.*, **68**, 2373 (1946). 26. Kennedy, Sage, *et al.*, *Ind. Eng. Chem.*, **28**, 718 (1936). 27. Kester, *Phys. Rev.*, **21**, 260 (1905). 28. Keyes and Collins, *Proc. Natl. Acad. Sci.*, **18**, 328 (1932). 29. Kleinschmidt, *Mech. Eng.*, **45**, 165 (1923); **48**, 155 (1926). 30. Koeppe, *Kältetechnik*, **8**, 275 (1956). 31. Lindsay and Brown, *Ind. Eng. Chem.*, **27**, 817 (1935). 32. Noell, Dissertation, Munich, 1914, Forschungs. 184, p. 1, 1916. 33. Palienko, *Trudy. Inst. Ispol' zovan. Gaza, Akad. Nauk. Ukr.*, No. 4, p. 87, 1956. 34. Pattee and Brown, *Ind. Eng. Chem.*, **26**, 511 (1934). 35. Roebuck, *Proc. Am. Acad. Arts Sci.*, **60**, 537 (1925); **64**, 287 (1930). 36. Roebuck, see 49 below. 37. Roebuck and Murrell, *Phys. Rev.*, **55**, 240 (1939). 38. Roebuck and Osterberg, *Phys. Rev.*, **37**, 110 (1931); **43**, 60 (1933). 39. Roebuck and Osterberg, *Phys. Rev.*, **46**, 785 (1934). 40. Roebuck and Osterberg, *Phys. Rev.*, **48**, 450 (1935). 41. Roebuck, Murrell, *et al.*, *J. Am. Chem. Soc.*, **64**, 400 (1942). 42. Sage, Unpublished data, California Institute of Technology, 1959. 43. Sage and Lacey, *Ind. Eng. Chem.*, **27**, 1484 (1934). 44. Sage, Kennedy, *et al.*, *Ind. Eng. Chem.*, **28**, 601 (1936). 45. Sage, Webster, *et al.*, *Ind. Eng. Chem.*, **29**, 658 (1937). 46. Ullock, Gaffert, *et al.*, *Trans. Am. Inst. Chem. Engrs.*, **32**, 73 (1936). 47. Yang, *Ind. Eng. Chem.*, **45**, 786 (1953). 48. Zelmanov, *J. Phys. U.S.S.R.*, **3**, 43 (1940). 49. Roebuck, recalculated data. 50. Michels, *et al.*, van der Waals laboratory publications.

Table 3-145. Joule-Thomson Data for Air*

P, atm.	Temp., °C.												
	−150	−100	−75	−50	−25	0	25	50	75	100	150	200	250
1	....	0.5895	0.4795	0.3910	0.3225	0.2745	0.2320	0.1956	0.1614	0.1355	0.0961	0.0645	0.0409
20	....	.5700	.4555	.3690	.3010	.2580	.2173	.1830	.1508	.1258	.0883	.0580	.0356
60	0.0450	.4820	.3835	.3195	.2610	.2200	.1852	.1571	.1293	.1062	.0732	.0453	.0254
100	.0185	.2775	.2880	.2505	.2130	.1820	.1550	.1310	.1087	.0884	.0600	.0343	.0165
140	− .0070	.1360	.1855	.1825	.1650	.1450	.1249	.1070	.0889	.0726	.0482	.0250	.0092
180	− .0255	.0655	.1136	.1270	.1240	.1100	.0959	.0829	.0707	.0580	.0376	.0174	.0027
200	− .0330	.0440	.0855	.1065	.1090	.0950							

* Free of water and CO_2. Extracted from Table 261, "Smithsonian Physical Tables," 9th rev. ed., Washington, D.C., 1954. These data are corrected from earlier publications. μ in °C./atm.

Table 3-146. Joule-Thomson Data for Argon*

Temp., °C.	Pressure, atm.						
	1	20	60	100	140	180	200
−150	1.812	......	−0.0025	−0.0277	−0.0403	−0.0595	−0.0640
−125	1.112	1.102	.1250	.0415	.0090	−.0100	− .0165
−100	0.8605	0.8485	.6900	.2820	.1137	.0560	.0395
−75	.7100	.6895	.5910	.4225	.2480	.1537	.1215
−50	.5960	.5720	.4963	.3970	.2840	.2037	.1860
−25	.5045	.4805	.4210	.3460	.2763	.2140	.1950
0	.4307	.4080	.3600	.3010	.2505	.2050	.1883
25	.3720	.3490	.3077	.2628	.2213	.1890	.1745
50	.3220	.3015	.2650	.2297	.1947	.1700	.1580
75	.2695	.2557	.2285	.1993	.1710	.1505	.1415
100	.2413	.2277	.1975	.1715	.1490	.1320	.1255
125	.2105	.1980	.1707	.1480	.1300	.1153	.1100
150	.1845	.1720	.1485	.1285	.1123	.0998	.0945
200	.1377	.1280	.1102	.0950	.0823	.0715	.0675
250	.0980	.0910	.0785	.0665	.0555	.0485	.0468
300	.0643	.0607	.0530	.0445	.0370	.0370	.0276

* Extracted from Table 263, "Smithsonian Physical Tables," 9th rev. ed., Washington, D.C., 1954. These data are corrected from an earlier publication. μ in °C./atm.

Table 3-147. Joule-Thomson Data for Carbon Dioxide*

Temp., °C.	Pressure, atm.							
	1	20	60	73	100	140	180	200
−75	......	−0.0200	−0.0200	−0.0232	−0.0228	−0.0240	−0.0250	−0.0290
−50	2.4130	− .0140	− .0150	− .0165	− .0160	− .0183	− .0228	− .0248
0	1.2900	1.4020	.0370	.0310	.0215	.0115	.0085	.0045
50	0.8950	.8950	.8800	.8225	.5570	.1720	.1025	.0930
100	.6490	.6375	.6080	.5920	.5405	.4320	.3000	.2555
125	.5600	.5450	.5160	.5068	.4750	.4130	.3230	.2915
150	.4890	.4695	.4430	.4380	.4155	.3760	.3102	.2910
200	.3770	.3575	.3400	.3325	.3150	.2890	.2600	.2455
250	.3075	.2885	.2625	.2565	.2420	.2235	.2045	.1975
300	.2650	.2425	.2080	.2002	.1872	.1700	.1540	.1505

* Extracted from Table 266, "Smithsonian Physical Tables," 9th rev. ed., Washington, D.C., 1954. These data are corrected from an earlier publication. μ in °C./atm.

Table 3-148. Ethyl Chloride*

μ = °C./atm.

°C.	0	20	40	60	80	100
μ	5.22	4.51	3.86	3.31	2.84	2.43

* For initial pressures of 3 atm. or less see Jenkin and Shorthose, "International Critical Tables," vol. 5, p. 146.

Table 3-149. Joule-Thomson Data for Helium*

t, °C.	$-\mu \times 10^2$	t, °C.	$-\mu \times 10^2$	t, °C.	$-\mu \times 10^2$	t, °C.	$-\mu \times 10^2$
−100	5.84	25	6.24	100	6.38	250	6.29
−50	6.05	50	6.31	150	6.45	300	5.97
0	6.16	75	6.35	200	6.41		

* Extracted from Table 262, Smithsonian Physical Tables," 9th rev. ed., Washington, D.C., 1954. These data are corrected from an earlier publication. μ in °C./atm. Below 200 atm. μ is independent of pressure.

Table 3-150. Joule-Thomson Data for Nitrogen*

Temp., °C.	Pressure, atm.							
	1	20	33.5	60	100	140	180	200
−150	1.2659	1.1246	0.1704	0.0601	0.0202	−0.0056	−0.0211	−0.0284
−125	0.8557	0.7948	.7025	.4940	.1314	.0498	.0167	.0032
−100	.6490	.5958	.5494	.4506	.2754	.1373	.0765	.0587
−75	.5033	.4671	.4318	.3712	.2682	.1735	.1026	.0800
−50	.3968	.3734	.3467	.3059	.2332	.1676	.1120	.0906
−25	.3224	.3013	.2854	.2528	.2001	.1506	.1101	.0932
0	.2656	.2494	.2377	.2088	.1679	.1316	.1015	.0891
25	.2217	.2060	.1961	.1729	.1400	.1105	.0874	.0779
50	.1855	.1709	.1621	.1449	.1164	.0915	.0732	.0666
75	.1555	.1421	.1336	.1191	.0941	.0740	.0583	.0543
100	.1292	.1173	.1100	.0975	.0768	.0582	.0462	.0419
125	.1070	.0973	.0904	.0786	.0621	.0459	.0347	.0326
150	.0868	.0776	.0734	.0628	.0482	.0348	.0248	.0228
200	.0558	.0472	.0430	.0372	.0262	.0168	.0094	.0070
250	.0331	.0256	.0230	.0160	.0071	.0009	−.0037	−.0058
300	.0140	.0096	.0050	−.0013	−.0075	−.0129	−.0160	−.0171

* Extracted from Table 264, "Smithsonian Physical Tables," 9th rev. ed., Washington, D.C., 1954. These data are corrected from an earlier publication. μ in °C./atm.

CRITICAL CONSTANTS*

Table 3-151. Critical Constants of Elements and Inorganic and Organic Compounds

For additional values of the critical temperature and pressure, see Table 3-6 p. 3-43, and Table 3-9, p. 3-59, on vapor pressures above 1 atm.

Name	Formula	t_c, °C.	P_c, atm.	d_c, g./cc.
Acetaldehyde	C_2H_4O	188.0		
Acetic acid	$C_2H_4O_2$	321.6	57.2	0.351
anhydride	$C_4H_6O_3$	296.0	46.0	
Acetone	C_3H_6O	235.0	47.0	0.268
Acetonitrile	C_2H_3N	274.7	47.7	0.240
Acetylene	C_2H_2	36.0	62.0	0.231
Air	.....	−140.7	37.2	0.35 (0.31)
Allyl alcohol	C_3H_6O	272.0		
Allylene	C_3H_4	128.0		
Allyl ethyl ether	$C_5H_{10}O$	245		
sulfide	$C_6H_{10}S$	380		
Ammonia	NH_3	132.4	111.5	0.235
Amyl alcohol (t-)	$C_5H_{12}O$	272		
Aniline	C_6H_7N	426	52.4	
Anisole	C_7H_8O	369	41.3	
Argon	A	−122	48.0	0.531
Arsenic	As	803	342.0	
Benzene	C_6H_6	288.5	47.7	0.304
Benzonitrile	C_7H_5N	426.0	41.6	
Boron tribromide	BBr_3	300	....	0.90
Bromine	Br_2	311	102	0.848
Bromobenzene	C_6H_5Br	397	44.6	0.486
Butadiene-1,3	C_4H_6	152	42.7	0.245
Butane (n-)	C_4H_{10}	153	36.0	
Butyl acetate (n-)	$C_6H_{12}O_2$	306.0		
alcohol (n-)	$C_4H_{10}O$	287	48.4	
alcohol (s-)	$C_4H_{10}O$	265		
alcohol (t-)	$C_4H_{10}O$	235		
Butyric acid (n-)	$C_4H_8O_2$	355	....	0.302
Butyronitrile	C_4H_7N	309	37.4	
Capronitrile	$C_6H_{11}N$	349.0	32.2	
Carbon dioxide	CO_2	31.1	73.0	0.460
disulfide	CS_2	273.0	76.0	0.441
monoxide	CO	−139.0	35.0	0.311
oxysulfide	COS	105.0	61.0	
tetrachloride	CCl_4	283.1	45.0	0.558
Chlorine	Cl_2	144.0	76.1	0.573
Chlorobenzene	C_6H_5Cl	359.0	44.6	0.365
Chloroform	$CHCl_3$	263.0	....	0.516
Cresol (o-)	$CH_3.C_6H_4OH$	422.0	49.4	
(m-)	$CH_3.C_6H_4OH$	432.0	45.0	
(p-)	$CH_3.C_6H_4OH$	426.0	50.8	
Cyanogen	$(CN)_2$	128.0	59.0	
Cyclohexane	C_6H_{12}	281.0	40.4	0.270
Deuterium	D_2	−234.4	17.4	
Dichlordifluormethane	CCl_2F_2	111.5	39.56	0.555
Diethylamine	$(C_2H_5)_2NH$	223.5	36.2	0.246
Di-isobutyl	$(CH_3)_2CH(CH_2)_2CH(CH_3)_2$	277.0	24.5	0.237
isopropyl	C_6H_{14}	227.4	30.6	0.241
Dimethylamine	$(CH_3)_2NH$	164.6	51.7	
Dimethyl aniline	$C_6H_5N(CH_3)_2$	415.0	35.8	
toluidine (o-)	$C_8H_{11}N$	395.0	30.8	
Dipropylamine	$(C_3H_7)_2NH$	277.0	31.0	
Ethane	C_2H_6	32.1	48.8	0.21
Ethyl acetate	$CH_3COOC_2H_5$	250.1	37.8	0.308
alcohol	C_2H_5OH	243.1	63.1	0.2755
allyl ether	$C_2H_5OCH_2CHCH_2$	245.0		
amine	$C_2H_5NH_2$	183.2	55.5	
bromide	C_2H_5Br	231.0	....	0.513
butyrate	$C_3H_7COOC_2H_5$	293.0	30.0	0.276
caprylate	$C_7H_{15}COOC_2H_5$	386.0		
chloride	C_2H_5Cl	187.2	52.0	0.33
chloroformate	$ClCOOC_2H_5$	<235.0		
crotonate	$C_6H_{10}O_2$	326.0		
disulfide	$(C_2H_5)_2S_2$	369.0		
Ethylene	C_2H_4	9.7	50.5	0.22
chloride	$C_2H_4Cl_2$	290	....	0.45
oxide	C_2H_4O	192.0		
Ethyl ether	$(C_2H_5)_2O$	194.6	35.5	0.2625
formate	$HCOOC_2H_5$	235.3	46.65	0.323
isobutyrate	$(CH_3)_2CHCOOC_2H_5$	280.0	30.0	0.276
isovalerate	$C_7H_{14}O_2$	315.0		
mercaptan	C_2H_5SH	225.5	54.2	0.301
methyl ether	$CH_3C_2H_5O$	164.7	43.4	0.270
sulfide	$C_2H_5CH_3S$	260.0	42.0	
nonylate	$C_{11}H_{22}O_2$	400.0		
propionate	$C_2H_5COOC_2H_5$	272.9	33.0	0.2965
propyl ether	$C_2H_5C_3H_7O$	227.4	32.1	0.258
sulfide	$(C_2H_5)_2S$	283.8	39.1	0.279
valerate	$C_7H_{14}O_2$	297.0		
Fluorobenzene	C_6H_5F	286.0	44.6	0.354
Fluorine	F	−155.0	25.0	
Germanium tetrachloride	$GeCl_4$	277.0	38.0	
Helium	He	−267.9	2.26	0.0693
Heptane (n-)	C_7H_{16}	266.8	26.8	0.234
Heptyl alcohol (n-)	$C_7H_{15}OH$	365.0		
Hexane (n-)	C_6H_{14}	234.8	29.5	0.234
Hydrazine	N_2H_4	380.0	145.0	
Hydrogen	H_2	−239.9	12.8	0.0310
bromide	HBr	90.0	84.0	
chloride	HCl	51.4	81.6	0.42
cyanide	HCN	183.5	53.2	0.20
fluoride	HF	230.2		
iodide	HI	151.0	82.0	
selenide	H_2Se	138.0	88.0	
sulfide	H_2S	100.4	88.9	2.86
Iodine	I_2	553.0		
Iodobenzene	C_6H_5I	448.0	44.6	0.581
Isoamyl acetate	$CH_3COOC_5H_{11}$	326.0		
alcohol	$C_5H_{11}OH$	307.0		
butyrate	$C_3H_7COOC_5H_{11}$	346.0		
formate	$HCOOC_5H_{11}$	303.0	34.0	0.282
mercaptan	$C_5H_{11}SH$	321.0		
propionate	$C_2H_5COOC_5H_{11}$	338.0		
sulfide	$(C_5H_{11})_2S$	391.0		
Isobutane	C_4H_{10}	134.0	37.0	
Isobutyl acetate	$CH_3COOC_4H_9$	288.0	31.0	0.281
alcohol	C_4H_9OH	265.0	48.0	
butyrate	$C_3H_7COOC_4H_9$	338.0		
formate	$HCOOC_4H_9$	278.0	38.0	0.288
isobutyrate	$C_3H_7COOC_4H_9$	329.0		
isovalerate	$C_9H_{18}O_2$	348.0		
propionate	$C_7H_{14}O_2$	319.0		
Isobutyric acid	C_3H_7COOH	336.0	....	0.304
Isopentane	C_5H_{12}	187.8	32.8	0.234
Isopropyl alcohol	C_3H_7OH	235.0	53.0	
Isovaleric acid	C_4H_9OH	361.0		
Krypton	Kr	−63.8	54.3	1.10
Mercury	Hg	>1550	>200	4–5
Methane	CH_4	−82.5	45.8	0.162
Methyl acetate	CH_3COOCH_3	233.7	46.3	0.325
Methylal	$CH_2(OCH_3)_2$	224.0		
Methyl alcohol	CH_3OH	240.0	78.7	0.272
amine	CH_3NH_2	156.9	73.6	
aniline	$C_6H_5NHCH_3$	429.0	51.3	
butyrate	$C_3H_7COOCH_3$	281.3	34.2	0.300
chloride	CH_3Cl	143.1	65.8	0.37
ether	$(CH_3)_2O$	126.9	52.0	0.271
ethyl ether	$CH_3OC_2H_5$	164.7	43.4	0.270
sulfide	$CH_3SC_2H_5$	260.0	42.0	
fluoride	CH_3F	44.9	62.0	
formate	$HCOOCH_3$	214.0	59.15	0.349
isobutyrate	$C_3H_7COOCH_3$	267.55	33.7	0.301
mercaptan	CH_3SH	196.8	71.4	0.323
oxalate	$(CH_3O_2C)_2$	260.0	9.48	
propionate	$C_2H_5COOCH_3$	257.4	39.3	0.312
sulfide	$(CH_3)_2S$	229.9	54.6	0.306
valerate	$C_6H_{12}O_2$	294.0(d)	32.0	0.279
Methyl diethyl ether	$C_6H_{12}O_2$	254.0		
Neon	Ne	−228.7	25.9	0.484
Niton	Nt	+104.5	62.5	
Nitric oxide	NO	−94.0	65.0	0.52
Nitrogen	N_2	−147.1	33.5	0.3110
tetroxide	N_2O_4	158.0	100	1.785
Nitrous oxide	N_2O	36.5	71.7	0.45
Octane (n-)	C_8H_{18}	296.0	24.6	0.234
Octyl alcohol (n-)	$C_8H_{17}OH$	385.0		
(s-)	$C_8H_{17}OH$	364.0		
Oxygen	O_2	−118.8	49.7	0.430
Paraldehyde	$(C_2H_4O)_3$	290.0		
Pentane (n-)	C_5H_{12}	197.2	33.0	0.232
Phenetole	$C_6H_5OC_2H_5$	374.0	33.8	
Phenol	C_6H_5OH	419.0	60.5	
Phosgene	$COCl_2$	182.0	56.0	0.52
Phosphine	PH	51.0	64.0	0.30
Phosphonium chloride	PH_4Cl	49.0	73.0	0.226
Propane (n-)	C_3H_8	96.8	42.0	0.220

* For additional data see "American Institute of Physics Handbook," McGraw-Hill, New York, 1957; Inatomi and Parrish, *A.E.C. Rept.* NAA-SR-62, 1950; Daunt, "Handbuch der Physik," vol. 14, p. 36, Springer, Berlin, 1956; Kobe and Lynn, *Chem. Revs.*, **52**, 117 (1953); Riedel, *Z. Elektrochem.*, **33**, 202 (1949); *Chem.-Ing.-Tech.*, **24**, 353 (1952); Rowlinson, *J. Chem. Phys.*, **19**, 831 (1951).

Table 3-151. Critical Constants of Elements and Inorganic and Organic Compounds—(*Concluded*)

Name	Formula	t_c, °C.	P_c, atm.	d_c, g./cc.
Propionic acid	C_2H_5COOH	339.5	53.0	0.315
Propyl alcohol (n-)	C_3H_7OH	263.7	49.95	0.273
acetate	$CH_3COOC_3H_7$	276.2	32.9	0.296
Propylamine	$C_3H_7NH_2$	223.8	46.3	
Propyl butyrate	$C_3H_7COOC_3H_7$	327.0		
chloride (n-)	C_3H_7Cl	230.0	45.2	
formate	$HCOOC_3H_7$	264.85	40.1	0.309
Propylene	C_3H_6	92.3	45.0	0.233
Propyl ethyl ether	$C_3H_7OC_2H_5$	227.4	32.1	0.258
isobutyrate	$C_3H_7COOC_3H_7$	316.0		
isovalerate	$C_8H_{16}O_2$	336.0		
Propionitrile	C_3H_5N	291.2	41.3	0.241
Propyl propionate	$C_2H_5COOC_3H_7$	305.0		
Pyridine	C_6H_5N	344.0	60.0	
Quinoline	C_9H_7N	520.0		
Radon	Rn	104.0	62.0	
Sodium	Na	2546	343	
Silicon tetrafluoride	SiF_4	−1.5	50.0	
tetrahydride	SiH_4	−3.5	48.0	
Stannic tetrachloride	$SnCl_4$	318.7	37.0	0.742
Steam	H_2O	374.0	217.7	0.4
Sulfur	S	1040		
dioxide	SO_2	157.2	77.7	0.52
trioxide	SO_3	218.3	83.6	0.630
Thiophene	C_4H_4S	317.0	48.0	
Thymol	$CH_3C_6H_3(OH)C_3H_7$	425.0		
Toluene	$C_6H_5CH_3$	320.6	41.6	0.292
Tolunitrile	$CH_3C_6H_4CN$	450.0		
Triethylamine	$(C_2H_5)_3N$	262.0	30.0	0.251
Trimethylamine	$(CH_3)_3N$	161.0	41.0	
Tritium	....	−229.5	20.8	
Valeric acid (n-)	$C_4H_{10}O_2$	379.0		
Water	H_2O	374.15	218.4	0.323
Xenon	Xe	16.6	58.2	1.155

Table 3-152. Critical Data for the Freon Compounds, etc.*

Name	Formula	t_c, °C.	P_c, atm.	V_c, cc./g.
Freon-12	CCl_2F_2	112	39.6	218
Freon-13	$CClF_3$	29	39	180
Freon-14	CF_4	−45	36.8	139
Freon-21	$CHCl_2F$			
Freon-22	$CHClF_2$	97	48.5	165
Freon-23	CHF_3	33	47	136
Freon-12-Bromine 1	$CBrClF_2$	154	41.2	232
Freon-115	CF_2CClF_2	60	30.8	260
Freon-C318	C_4F_8	117 est.		331 est.
Genetron 100	CH_3CHF_2	114	44.3	181
Genetron 101	CH_3CClF_2	138	40.7	232

* Compiled by D. R. Chapman, *N.A.C.A. Rept.* 1259, 1959. This report is recommended for other data.

COMPRESSIBILITIES

The tables given under this subject, with the exception of Tables 3-153, 3-154, 3-156, 3-157, 3-159, 3-160, 3-163, 3-167, and 3-168, were calculated and arranged by Dr. Richard Wiebe, of The Fixed Nitrogen Research Laboratory, Washington, D.C., for "Fixed Nitrogen" by Dr. Harry A. Curtis. The Chemical Catalog Company has kindly granted permission to reprint these data.

For more detailed data on Compressibilities see "Inter-

Table 3-153. Densities and Compressibilities of Gases at 0°C.*

Observer	Gas	$1 + \lambda$†	L_n/L_{lim}‡	Normal density	Mol. wt.	At. wt.
Moles and Clavera, 1927	N_2	1.00046	....	1.25049	28.0164	14.0082
Moles and Salazar						
Moles and Garrido	N_2	....	1.00043			
Heuse and Otto	N_2	1.00048				
Michels, Wouters, and de Boer, calc. by Cragoe from high pressure	N_2	1.000453	....	....	28.0149	14.0075
Baxter and Starkweather	N_2	....	1.00041	1.25036	28.0152	14.0076
Baxter and Starkweather, 1925–1928	A	....	1.00090	1.78364	39.944	
Baxter and Starkweather	Ne	....	0.99941	0.89990	20.183	
Baxter and Starkweather	He	....	....	0.17846	4.0002	
Heuse and Otto, 1930	He	0.99948				
Moles and Salazar, 1934	CO	....	1.00040	1.25001	28.0065	C = 12.0065
Batuecas, Maverick, and Schlatter, 1929	CO	1.00058				
Schlatter, 1930	CO	1.00048				
Moles and Toral, 1936	CO_2	....	1.00694	1.97693(8)	44.007	C = 12.007
Guye and Batuecas	CO^2	1.0070(9)	....	1.97686	43.999(5)	C = 12.000
Moles, Toral, and Escribano	C_2H_4	1	1.00730	1.26035(8)	28.046	C = 12.007
Batuecas, 1935	C_2H_4	1.0078(0)	....	1.26041	28.032	C = 12.000
Batuecas, 1934	C_3H_6	....	1.0203(0)	1.9148(5)	42.067	C = 12.006
Casado, 1943	$(CH_3)_2O$	1.02574	1.02520	2.1079	46.068	C = 12.010
					46.087	C = 12.019
Moles and Toral, 1936	N_2O	....	1.00737	1.97821(5)	44.016(7)	N = 14.0083
Casado, 1943	N_2O	1.00711	1.0070	1.9775	44.018	N = 14.009
Guye, 1905	NO	....	....	1.3402		
Gray, 1906	NO	....	....	1.34027		
Jaquerod and Scheuer	NO	1.00117	....	....	30.006	N = 14.006
Batuecas	NO	1.00111				
Moles, Sancho, and Roquero	NH_3	....	1.01521	0.77140(2)	17.0328	N = 14.009
Batuecas and Moles, 1930	NH_3	....	1.0155(7)	0.77170	17.0318	N = 14.0078
Moles, Toral, and Escribano	H_2S	....	1.01186	1.53842(6)	34.079	S = 32.063
Moles, Toral, and Escribano	SO_2	....	1.0240	2.92654(7)	64.062	S = 32.062
Moles and Toral	SiF_4	....	1.01004	4.69049	104.084	Si = 28.104
Whytlaw-Gray and Burt, 1909	HCl	1.00748	....	1.63915	36.469	
Scheuer	HCl	1.00737	....	1.63909	36.465	
Recalc. by Moles	HCl	....	....	1.63911	....	Cl = 35.457
Batuecas and Moles, 1926	CH_3Cl	....	1.0242	2.3070	50.4916	Cl = 35.458
Guye, Moles, and Rieman	HBr	1.00932	....	3.64421	80.962	Br = 79.918
Ritchie, 1930	PH_3	1.0091(2)	....	1.53072	34.000	P = 30.977

* From Whytlaw-Gray, *Quart. Revs.* (*London*), **IV**, 162 (1950). Copyrighted by the Chemical Society, London. Reproduced by permission. Some other density data are given in Table 3-48, p. 3-71.

† Isotherm data. Compressibility per atmosphere = $1 + \lambda$.

‡ Density data. L_n = normal density, L_{lim} = limiting density (as pressure → zero). $L_n/L_{lim} = 1/(1 + \lambda)$.

national Critical Tables": tabular index, vol. 3, p. 1; building stones, vol. 2, p. 54; compounds, vol. 3, p. 49; elements, vol. 3, pp. 35, 46; gases, vol. 3, pp. 3, 17, 435; glass, vol. 2, p. 93; liquids and vitreous solids, vol. 3, pp. 35, 40, 41; metals, vol. 3, p. 46; minerals and rocks, vol. 3, p. 49; animal and vegetable oils, vol. 2, p. 208; petroleum, vol. 2, p. 146; porcelains, vol. 2, p. 68; rubber, vol. 2, p. 269; solutions, vol. 3, p. 439; woods, vol. 2, p. 1. For Heats of Compression, see vol. 5, p. 144.

For values of the densities of gases at standard conditions, 0°C. and 1 atm., see Tables 3-48 and 3-153.

Table 3-154. Pressure-Volume Product for Acetylene*

$PV = 1.0000$ at 0°C. and 1 atm.

Pressure, atm.	pv at 0°C.	pv at 25°C.
0.5	1.0057	1.0989
1.0	1.0000	1.0937
2.0	0.9891	1.0841
4.0	.9708	1.0684
6.0	.9530	1.0531
8.0	.9360	1.0385
10.0	.9194	1.0255
12.0	.9026	1.0139

* Sameshima, *Bull. Chem. Soc. Japan*, **1**, 41 (1926).

Table 3-155. Pressure-Volume Product for Ammonia*,†

$PV = 1.0000$ at 1 atm. and 0°C.

Pressure, atm.	0°C.	25°C.	50°C.	100°C.	132.9°C.	150°C.	200°C.	250°C.	300°C.
1	1.000	1.095	1.191	1.379	1.503	1.567	1.754	1.940	2.126
2	0.986	1.085	1.182	1.373	1.498	1.563	1.750	1.937	2.124
5	.....	1.049	1.153	1.354	1.483	1.549	1.740	1.930	2.119
10	.....	.....	1.103	1.321	1.457	1.526	1.724	1.917	2.109
20	.....	.....	0.988	1.252	1.404	1.479	1.690	1.892	2.089
30	.....	.....	.....	1.176	1.349	1.430	1.656	1.867	2.071
40	.....	.....	.....	1.090	1.290	1.378	1.621	1.840	2.051
50	.....	.....	.....	0.995	1.227	1.326	1.586	1.816	2.032
60	.....	.....	.....	.....	1.160	1.272	1.551	1.791	2.013
80	.....	.....	.....	.....	.....	1.157	1.479	1.740	1.976
100	.....	.....	.....	.....	.....	.....	1.408	1.690	1.938
120	.....	.....	.....	.....	.....	.....	.....	.....	1.903

Pressure, atm.	0°C.‡	10°C.	20°C.	30°C.	40°C.	50°C.	60°C.	70°C.	80°C.	90°C.	100°C.
100	0.1196	0.1223	0.1250	0.1279	0.1305	0.1334	0.1373	0.1417	0.1465	0.1535	0.1606
200	.2437	.2457	.2484	.2526	.2570	.2628	.2693	.2769	.2859	.2963	.3081
300	.3533	.3594	.3657	.3722	.3796	.3886	.3980	.4082	.4190	.4309	.4441
400	.4720	.4777	.4843	.4913	.4998	.5094	.5206	.5322	.5449	.5593	.5705
500	.5839	.5914	.5995	.6084	.6186	.6300	.6419	.6552	.6696	.6853	.7019
600	.6942	.7027	.7113	.7213	.7321	.7443	.7576	.7728	.7898	.8076	.8261
700	.8060	.8137	.8222	.8330	.8453	.8608	.8754	.8916	.9094	.9279	.9472
800	.9171	.9256	.9340	.9441	.9564	.9711	.9873	1.0050	1.0243	1.0443	1.0659
900	1.0281	1.0351	1.0436	1.0544	1.0659	1.0814	1.0976	1.1168	1.1361	1.1577	1.1801
1000	1.1431	1.1489	1.1562	1.1654	1.1770	1.1917	1.2086	1.2279	1.2495	1.2719	1.2942
1100	1.2557	1.2603	1.2672	1.2757	1.2873	1.3012	1.3182	1.3382	1.3606	1.3829	1.4069

Pressure, atm.	110°C.	120°C.	130°C.	140°C.	150°C.	160°C.	170°C.	180°C.	190°C.	200°C.	210°C.
100	0.1724										
200	.3209	0.3363	0.3563	0.3845	0.4273	0.4921	0.5769	0.6841	0.8137	0.9680	
300	.4588	.4760	.4963	.5199	.5479	.5798	.6209	.6703	.7327	.8114	
400	.5917	.6097	.6308	.6541	.6801	.7090	.7421	.7790	.8237	.8700	
500	.7204	.7404	.7622	.7852	.8099	.8369	.8669	.8797	.9387	.9788	
600	.8469	.8677	.8901	.9132	.9379	.9634	.9927	1.0243	1.0567	1.0922	
700	.9680	.9896	1.0127	1.0366	1.0613	1.0875	1.1153	1.1423	1.1708	1.2001	
800	1.0875	1.1107	1.1346	1.1585	1.1839	1.2102	1.2372	1.2665	1.2958	1.3266	
900	1.2032	1.2271	1.2518	1.2773	1.3035	1.3297	1.3583	1.3868	1.4161	1.4477	1.4817
1000	1.3189	1.3436	1.3698	1.3961	1.4223	1.4493	1.4778	1.5056	1.5364	1.5673	1.5989
1100	1.4323	1.4585	1.4855	1.5118	1.5395	1.5673	1.5958	1.6259	1.6560	1.6861	1.7161

* Calculated from the Beattie-Bridgeman equation of state. See Beattie and Lawrence, *J. Am. Chem. Soc.*, **52**, 6 (1930).
† Calculated from experimental data of F. G. Keyes, *J. Am. Chem. Soc.*, **53**, 965 (1931).
‡ Data at 0° were extrapolated graphically.

Table 3-156. Compressibility Factors for Argon*

Temp., °K.	Pressure, atm. 1	4	7	10	40	70	100
100	0.9782	0.9079					
150	.9930	.9716	0.950	0.927			
200	.9971	.9882	.9792	.9702	0.8978	0.7838	0.6917
250	.9986	.9945	.9905	.9864	.9476	.9141	.8878
270	.9990	.9960	.9930	.9900	.9622	.9388	.9208
280	.9991	.9966	.9940	.9915	.9679	.9486	.9340
290	.9993	.9971	.9949	.9927	.9729	.9570	.9454
300	.9994	.9975	.9957	.9938	.9773	.9643	.9553
310	.9995	.9979	.9963	.9948	.9810	.9706	.9637
320	.9996	.9982	.9969	.9956	.9843	.9761	.9710
350	.9998	.9990	.9983	.9977	.9921	.9888	.9879
400	1.0000	.9999	.9999	.9998	1.0002	1.0022	1.0057
450	1.0001	1.0004	1.0007	1.0011	1.0050	1.0101	1.0162
500	1.0002	1.0007	1.0013	1.0018	1.0079	1.0147	1.0224
550	1.0002	1.0009	1.0016	1.0023	1.0095	1.0174	1.0259
600	1.0003	1.0010	1.0018	1.0026	1.0105	1.0190	1.0279
650	1.0003	1.0011	1.0019	1.0027	1.0111	1.0198	1.0289
700	1.0003	1.0011	1.0019	1.0028	1.0113	1.0201	1.0292
750	1.0003	1.0011	1.0020	1.0028	1.0114	1.0202	1.0292
800	1.0003	1.0011	1.0020	1.0028	1.0113	1.0199	1.0288
900	1.0003	1.0011	1.0019	1.0027	1.0110	1.0194	1.0279
1000	1.0003	1.0010	1.0018	1.0026	1.0105	1.0185	1.0265
1100	1.0003	1.0010	1.0017	1.0025	1.0100	1.0176	1.0252
1200	1.0002	1.0010	1.0017	1.0024	1.0095	1.0167	1.0239

* From Hilsenrath *et al.*, *N. B. S. Circ.* 564, 1955. These values have been rounded to four decimal places.

Table 3-157. Pressure-Volume Product for Carbon Dioxide

PV (bar-Amagat unit)

Pressure, bars†	Temp., °C. 200	300	400	500	600	700	800	900	1000
100	1.6181	2.0829	2.5088	2.9154	3.3134	3.7078	4.0950	4.4803	4.8638
200	1.5256	2.0578	2.5252	2.9529	3.3670	3.7736	4.1719	4.5652	4.9554
300	1.5174	2.0843	2.5685	3.0211	3.4479	3.8600	4.2614	4.6656	5.0573
400	1.5816	2.1438	2.6499	3.1177	3.5492	3.9643	4.3711	4.7750	5.1680
500	1.6943	2.2284	2.7436	3.2216	3.6630	4.0816	4.4924	4.8948	5.2843
600	1.8287	2.3343	2.8429	3.3280	3.7760	4.2032	4.6154	5.0184	5.4054
700	1.9774	2.4596	2.9536	3.4415	3.8965	4.3269	4.7425	5.1470	5.5292
800	2.1305	2.6025	3.0828	3.5627	4.0221	4.4519	4.8674	5.2701	5.6577
900	2.2843	2.7548	3.2258	3.6914	4.1475	4.5825	5.0011	5.3989	5.7803
1000	2.4372	2.9044	3.3738	3.8270	4.2790	4.7148	5.1282	5.5279	5.9067

* From Price, *Ind. Eng. Chem.* Reprinted from vol. 47, p. 1650, August, 1955. Copyright 1955 by the American Chemical Society and reprinted by permission of the copyright owner.
† atm. = 1.01325 bars.

Table 3-158. Pressure-Volume Product for Carbon Monoxide*

PV = 1.0000 at 1 atm. and 0°C.

Pressure, atm.	−70°C.	−50°C.	−25°C.	0°C.	25°C.	50°C.	100°C.	150°C.	200°C.
1	0.7427	0.8162	0.9082	1.0000	1.0918	1.1836	1.3671	1.5504	1.7336
10	.7275	.8061	.9025	0.9960	1.0885	1.1830	1.3700	1.5565	1.7423
20	.7115	.7947	.8960	.9912	1.0858	1.1827	1.3735	1.5630	1.7510
30	.6950	.7840	.8895	.9868	1.0836	1.1820	1.3769	1.5695	1.7595
40	.6792	.7730	.8833	.9825	1.0820	1.1821	1.3800	1.5755	1.7683
50	.6636	.7622	.8768	.9780	1.0814	1.1826	1.3837	1.5823	1.7758
60	.6495	.7530	.8712	.9755	1.0810	1.1842	1.3878	1.5880	1.7833
80	.6274	.7355	.8620	.9718	1.0820	1.1893	1.3967	1.6008	1.7985
100	.6147	.7264	.8592	.9725	1.0851	1.1955	1.4062	1.6151	1.8146
120	.6110	.7240	.8590	.9763	1.0917	1.2042	1.4176	1.6288	1.8310
140	.6142	.7270	.8627	.9832	1.1009	1.2139	1.4312	1.6450	1.8492
160	.6255	.7355	.8715	.9935	1.1125	1.2255	1.4456	1.6620	1.8683
180	.6431	.7485	.8856	1.0125	1.1255	1.2400	1.4615	1.6792	1.8883
200	.6631	.7656	.9022	1.0200	1.1415	1.2561	1.4794	1.6987	1.9090
250	.7247	.8205	.9520	1.0665	1.1885	1.3022	1.5280	1.7500	1.9632
300	.7955	.8872	1.0087	1.1211	1.2408	1.3521	1.5798	1.8054	2.0183
400	.9434	1.0285	1.1403	1.2487	1.3625	1.4716	1.6963	1.9178	2.1380
500	1.0920	1.1755	1.2831	1.3843	1.4940	1.6023	1.8235	2.0450	2.2627
600	1.2386	1.3225	1.4282	1.5256	1.6317	1.7378	1.9557	2.1757	2.3923
800	1.5236	1.6100	1.7153	1.8064	1.9115	2.0144	2.2244	2.4442	2.6602
1000	1.7992	1.8871	1.9935	2.0827	2.1857	2.2879	2.4935	2.7142	2.9264

* Bartlett, Hetherington, Kvalnes, and Tremearne, *J. Am. Chem. Soc.*, **52**, 1374 (1930); Goig, *Compt. rend.*, **189**, 246 (1929); Scott, *Proc. Roy. Soc., London*, **122A**, 283 (1929). For calculations of physical properties see Deming and Shupe, *Phys. Rev.* **38**, 2245 (1931); Deming and Deming, *ibid.*, **45**, 109 (1934).

Table 3-159. PVT Data for Ethane*

Density, moles/liter..	0.5	1.0	1.5	2.0	2.5	3.0	3.5	4.0	4.5	5.0
Temp., °C.	Pressures, atm.									
25	11.11	20.14	27.34	32.84	36.88	39.66	41.35			
50	12.24	22.58	31.24	38.41	44.27	49.02	52.87	55.97	58.49	60.56
75	13.34	24.95	35.08	43.80	51.37	57.98	63.78	68.89	73.52	77.79
100	14.43	27.28	38.79	49.03	58.29	66.68	74.36	81.50	88.25	94.73
125	15.52	29.64	42.49	54.25	65.13	75.26	84.81	93.91	102.73	111.46
150	16.60	31.89	46.08	59.31	71.78	83.61	94.99	106.06	117.00	127.98
175	17.67	34.17	49.66	64.36	78.40	91.93	105.13	118.16	131.20	144.41
200	18.71	36.44	53.25	69.38	84.97	100.19	115.20	130.18	145.30	160.77
225	19.80	38.64	56.73	74.27	91.38	108.24	125.02	141.90	159.08	176.73
250	20.89	40.87	60.23	79.16	97.81	116.30	134.84	153.59	172.87	192.77

Density, moles/liter..	5.5	6.0	6.5	7.0	7.5	8.0	9.0	10.0
Temp., °C.	Pressures, atm.							
50	62.40	63.99	65.52	67.08	68.82	70.88	76.90	87.76
75	81.97	85.95	90.00	94.29	99.01	104.38	118.32	139.23
100	101.36	107.86	114.60	121.83	129.74	138.64	160.77	191.98
125	120.56	129.64	139.19	149.41	160.60	173.10	203.63	244.97
150	139.68	151.38	163.70	176.99	191.52	207.66	246.57	298.02
175	158.68	172.98	188.20	204.54	222.44	242.24	289.49	350.95
200	177.62	194.53	212.59	232.03	253.29	276.76	332.56	
225	196.44	215.98	236.88	259.42	284.02	311.09		
250	215.21	237.38	261.13	286.74	314.67	345.38		
275	233.90	258.69	285.28	314.00	345.30			

* Data by Beattie, Hadlock, and Poffenberger, *J. Chem. Phys.*, **3**, 93 (1935); Beattie, Su, and Simard, *J. Am. Chem. Soc.*, **61**, 926 (1939). For thermal properties see Planck and Kambertz, *Ice and Cold Storage*, **39**, 159, 176 (1936).

For densities between 0.5 and 5.0 moles/liter and at temperatures from 25° to 250°C., the Beattie-Bridgman equation of state may be used:

$$P = \left[\frac{RT(1 - \epsilon)}{V^2}\right][V + B] - \frac{A}{V^2}$$

	$A = A_0(1 - a/V)$		$B = B_0(1 - b/V)$		$\epsilon = c/VT^3$	
R	A_0	a	B_0	b	c	Mol. wt.
Units: normal atmospheres, liters/mole, °K. (T°K. = t°C. + 273.13)						
0.08206	5.8800	0.05861	0.09400	0.01915	90.00×10^4	30.0462
Amagat units: normal atmospheres, V = 1 at 0°C. and 1 atm., °K.						
3.69658×10^{-3}	11.9320×10^{-3}	2.6402×10^{-3}	4.2344×10^{-3}	0.8627×10^{-3}	40.543×10^3	30.0462

Table 3-160. Pressure-Volume Product for Ethylene*

P, atm.	0°C.	20°C.	40°C.	60°C.	80°C.	100°C.
1	1.0000					
50	0.1755	0.6290	0.8140	0.9535	1.0770	1.1920
100	.3100	.3600	.4705	.6680	0.8465	1.0050
150	.4405	.4850	.5505	.6490	.7760	0.9240
200	.5650	.6095	66.90	7440	.8380	.9460
300	.8055	.8520	.9075	.9720	1.0475	1.1330
500	1.2555	1.3075	1.3670	1.4310	1.5000	1.5775
1000	2.2890	2.3535	2.4215	2.4925	2.5660	2.6425

* For more detailed data see "International Critical Tables," vol. 3, p. 15. See also data of Michels, De Gruyter, and Nilsen, *Physica*, **3**, 346 (1936).

Table 3-161. Pressure-Volume Product for Hydrogen*

$PV = 1.0000$ at 1 atm. and 0°C.

Pressure, atm.	−239.9 °C.	−207.9 °C.	−183 °C.	−150 °C.	−100 °C.	−70 °C.	−50 °C.	−25 °C.	0.0 °C.	20 °C.	50 °C.	100 °C.	200 °C.	300 °C.
1	......	0.2280	0.3297	0.4508	0.6340	0.7438	0.8170	0.9085	1.0000	1.0732	1.1830	1.3660	1.7317	2.0974
10	......	.2308	.3279	.4520	.6377	.7432	.8219	.9138	1.0057	1.0791	1.1891	1.3723	1.7380	2.1037
20	0.0286	.2239	.3265	.4541	.6421	.7535	.8275	.9187	1.0120	1.0855	1.1959	1.3792	1.7450	2.1108
30	.0389	.2183	.3260	.4564	.6466	.7583	.8331	.9257	1.0183	1.0920	1.2027	1.3862	1.7520	2.1178
40	.0595	.2144	.3262	.4591	.6513	.7642	.8389	.9318	1.0247	1.0985	1.2094	1.3931	1.7590	2.1249
50	.0717	.2126	.3271	.4623	.6562	.7695	.8447	.9378	1.0309	1.1051	1.2162	1.4001	1.7660	2.1319
60	......	.2127	.3289	.4658	.6613	.7752	.8506	.9441	1.0376	1.1116	1.2230	1.4070	1.7731	2.1392
80	......	.2187	.3346	.4740	.6720	.7870	.8628	.9567	1.0507	1.1249	1.2365	1.4209	1.7871	2.1530
100	......	.2301	.3434	.4839	.6834	.8003	.8754	.9700	1.0639	1.1388	1.2510	1.4356	1.8042	2.1733
200	......	......	......	......	......	.8640	.9411	1.0383	1.1336	1.2066	1.3203	1.5071	1.8756	2.2393
300	......	......	......	......	......	.9340	1.0112	1.1093	1.2045	1.2799	1.3915	1.5790		
400	......	......	......	......	......	1.0075	1.0832	1.1803	1.2775	1.3511	1.4635	1.6513	2.0206	2.3826
500	......	......	......	......	......	1.0804	1.1568	1.2542	1.3500	1.4240	1.5357	1.7235		
600	......	......	......	......	......	1.1555	1.2301	1.3272	1.4226	1.4958	1.6081	1.7955	2.1628	2.5246
800	......	......	......	......	......	1.3018	1.3755	1.4717	1.5665	1.6391	1.7512	1.9380	2.3043	2.6653
1000	......	......	......	......	......	1.4443	1.5185	1.6139	1.7101	1.7795	1.8917	2.0784	2.4568	2.8026

* Crommelin and Swallow, *Proc. 4th Intern. Congr. Refrig.*, **1**, 53*a* (1924); Holborn and Otto, *Z. Physik*, **23**, 77 (1924); *ibid.*, **33**, 1 (1925); Verschoyle, *Proc. Roy. Soc., London*, **111A**, 552 (1926); Holborn and Otto, *Z. Physik*, **38**, 359 (1926); Bartlett, Cupples, and Tremearne, *J. Am. Chem. Soc.*, **50**, 1275 (1928); Bartlett. Hetherington, Kvalnes, and Tremearne, *ibid.*, **52**, 1363 (1930). Michels, Niihoff, and Gerver, *Ann. Physik.*, **12**, 562 (1932); Wiebe and Gaddy, *J. Am. Chem. Soc.*, **60**, 2300 (1938). See also calculations of physical properties by Deming and Shupe, *Phys. Rev.*, **40**, 848 (1932); Deming and Deming, *ibid.*, **45**, 109 (1934).

Table 3-162. Pressure-Volume Product for a 3:1 Hydrogen-Nitrogen Mixture*

$PV = 1.0000$ at 1 atm. and 0°C

P, atm.	−70°C.	−50°C.	−25°C.	0°C.	25°C.	50°C.	100°C.	200°C.	300°C.
25	0.7506	0.8251	0.9187						
50	.7593	.8364	.9320	1.0263	1.1201	1.2133	1.4009	1.7704	2.1323
75	.7700	.8481	.9449						
100	.7816	.8615	.9601	1.0569	1.1527	1.2466	1.4377	1.8098	2.1759
125	.7947	.8750	.9760						
150	.8092	.8901	.9909						
200	.8430	.9256	1.0264	1.1273	1.2247	1.3207	1.5149	1.8912	2.2600
300	.9180	1.0003	1.1024						
400	1.0019	1.0833	1.1833	1.2864	1.3850	1.4825	1.6781	2.0601	2.4303
500	1.0897	1.1693	1.2679						
600	1.1771	1.2568	1.3561	1.4564	1.5549	1.6513	1.8472	2.2278	2.5993
800	1.3531	1.4306	1.5280	1.6295	1.7259	1.8217	2.0176	2.3962	2.7684
1000	1.5264	1.6024	1.6987	1.8009	1.8966	1.9916	2.1867	2.5654	2.9352

* From −70° to −25°C. smoothed values by Deming and Shupe from the work of Bartlett and Verschoyle (see Table 3-165). The other values were interpolated from Wiebe and Gaddy, *J. Am. Chem. Soc.*, **60**, 2300 (1938).

For data on some other hydrocarbons, see the following:
Propane: Sage, Schaafsma, and Lacey, *Ind. Eng. Chem.*, **26**, 1218 (1934). Beattie, Kay, and Kaminsky, *J. Am. Chem. Soc.*, **59**, 1589 (1937). For thermodynamic properties see Dana, Jenkins, Burdick, and Timm, *Refrig. Eng.*, **12**, 387 (1926).
Butane: (n- and isobutane) For thermodynamic properties see Dana, Jenkins, Burdick, and Timm, *Refrig. Eng.*, **12**, 387 (1926); Sage, Webster, and Lacey, *J. Ind. Eng. Chem.*, **29**, 1188 (1937).
n-Pentane: Young, *Sci. Proc. Roy. Dublin, Soc.*, **13**, 310 (1912).
n-Heptane: Smith, Beattie, and Kay, *J. Am. Chem. Soc.*, **59**, 1587 (1937).

Table 3-163. Pressure-Volume Product for Methane*

$PV = 1.0000$ at 1 atm. and 0°C.

Pressure, atm.	−70°C.	−50°C.	−25°C.	0.0°C.	25°C.	50°C.	100°C.	150°C.	200°C.
1	0.7410	0.8150	0.9075	1.0000	1.0922	1.1845	1.3686	1.5525	1.7363
10	.6985	.7795	.8803	0.9785	1.0733	1.1780	1.3595	1.5470	1.7348
20	.6473	.7402	.8493	.9543	1.0549	1.1590	1.3500	1.5422	1.7330
30	.5910	.6991	.8183	.9297	1.0373	1.1412	1.3411	1.5370	1.7311
40	.5244	.6547	.7873	.9061	1.0198	1.1275	1.3335	1.5345	1.7309
50	.4425	.6069	.7558	.8830	1.0034	1.1152	1.3268	1.5319	1.7307
60	.3366	.5551	.7243	.8607	0.9871	1.1017	1.3200	1.5292	1.7308
80	.2556	.4604	.6651	.8192	.9569	1.0799	1.3098	1.5248	1.7322
100	.2808	.4088	.6167	.7845	.9319	1.0624	1.3018	1.5237	1.7357
120	.3175	.4095	.5877	.7604	.9126	1.0487	1.2965	1.5241	1.7414
140	.3543	.4304	.5801	.7457	.9003	1.0399	1.2939	1.5272	1.7485
160	.3915	.4601	.5891	.7425	.8949	1.0367	1.2952	1.5325	1.7570
180	.4288	.4924	.6079	.7482	.8970	1.0373	1.2997	1.5398	1.7668
200	.4656	.5269	.6319	.7631	.9048	1.0437	1.3076	1.5500	1.7774
250	.5567	.6142	.7066	.8184	.9469	1.0776	1.3364	1.5867	1.8126
300	.6458	.7025	.7879	.8886	1.0062	1.1286	1.3785	1.6234	1.8534
400	.8185	.8750	.9561	1.0468	1.1499	1.2608	1.4929	1.7268	1.9586
500	.9867	1.0433	1.1221	1.2086	1.3064	1.4106	1.6277	1.8542	2.0803
600	1.1487	1.2071	1.2862	1.3709	1.4659	1.5653	1.7729	1.9935	2.2131
800	1.4631	1.5246	1.6046	1.6894	1.7801	1.8781	2.0744	2.2828	2.4949
1000	1.7656	1.8287	1.9110	2.0000	2.0892	2.1845	2.3757	2.5797	2,7861

* Keyes, Smith, and Joubert, *J. Math. Physics*, **1**, 191 (1922); Kvalnes and Gaddy, *J. Am. Chem. Soc.*, **53**, 394 (1931). For extension to 1675 atm. and 300°C. and for data on methane-ammonia mixtures, see Kazarnovskii and Levchenko, *J. Phys. Chem.* (U.S.S.R.), **18**, 380 (1944). Isotherms of methane-ethane mixtures at 0, 25, and 50 to 60 atm. were measured by Michels and Nederbragt, *Physica*, **6**, 656 (1939).

Table 3-164. Pressure-Volume Product for Methyl Chloride

P, atm.	PV	P, atm.	PV
69.9°C.		84.95°C.	
15.065	1.0251	16.19	1.0909
15.425	1.0190	16.586	1.0834
15.76	1.0115	17.09	1.0734
16.10	1.0062	17.61	1.0665
16.44	0.9966	18.13	1.0561
16°C.		18.74	1.0477
		19.36	1.0368
760 mm.	1.0000	19.40	1.0367
1200	0.9796	20.00	1.0239
1650	.9648	20.68	1.0106
2100	.9533	21.49	0.9969
2800	.9335	22.24	.9813

Table 3-165. Pressure-Volume Product for Nitrogen*,†

$PV = 1.0000$ at 1 atm. and 0°C.

Pressure, atm.	−146.3°C.	−130°C.	−100°C.	−70°C.	−50°C.	−25°C.	0.0°C.	20°C.	50°C.	100°C.	200°C.	300°C.	400°C.
1	......	0.5209	0.6319	0.7426	0.8162	0.9077	1.0000	1.0730	1.1835	1.3669	1.7335	2.1000	2.4663
10	......	.4873	.6109	.7292	.8060	.9010	.9962	1.0705	1.1836	1.3695	1.7398	2.1083	2.4758
20	0.3539	.4465	.5874	.7130	.7951	.8940	.9925	1.0690	1.1842	1.3728	1.7469	2.1175	2.4864
30	.2670	.4005	.5637	.7010	.7851	.8886	.9894	1.0677	1.1851	1.3765	1.7542	2.1271	2.4971
40	......	.3487	.5404	.6850	.7757	.8830	.9870	1.0668	1.1866	1.3805	1.7617	2.1366	2.5079
50	......	.2943	.5180	.6716	.7672	.8790	.9848	1.0669	1.1884	1.3849	1.7694	2.1462	2.5189
60	......	.2483	.4970	.6620	.7596	.8764	.9840	1.0670	1.1907	1.3896	1.7772	2.1559	2.5299
80	......	.2986	.4632	.6432	.7476	.8700	.9835	1.0687	1.1906	1.4002	1.7935	2.1755	2.5522
100	......	......	.4471	.6362	.7424	.8676	.9848	1.0749	1.2046	1.4121	1.8111	2.1973	2.5751
200	......	......	......	.6823	.7854	.9151	1.0355	1.1309	1.2742	1.4965	1.9119	2.3127	2.6971
300	......	......	......	.8053	.8986	1.0179	1.1335	1.2293	1.3711	1.5978	2.0216	2.4287	2.8193
400	......	......	......	.9477	1.0334	1.1445	1.2557	1.3467	1.4870	1.7119	2.1455	2.5506	2.9450
500	......	......	......	1.0914	1.1748	1.2798	1.3885	1.4782	1.6171	1.8388	2.2708	2.6774	3.0714
600	......	......	......	1.2331	1.3159	1.4186	1.5214	1.6698	1.7473	1.9657	2.3961	2.8042	3.1977
800	......	......	......	1.5111	1.5928	1.6958	1.7959	1.8817	2.0155	2.2279	2.6557	3.0623	3.4587
1000	......	......	......	1.7783	1.8573	1.9600	2.0641	2.1481	2.2825	2.4948	2.9212	3.3203	3.7224

* Holborn and Otto, *Z. Physik*, **23**, 77 (1924); *ibid.*, **33**, 1 (1925); Verschoyle, *Proc. Roy. Soc., London*, **111A**, 552 (1926); Holborn and Otto, *Z. Physik*, **38**, 359 (1926); Bartlett, Cupples, and Tremearne, *J. Am. Chem. Soc.*, **50**, 1275 (1928); Bartlett, Hetherington, Kvalnes, and Tremearne, *ibid.*, **52**, 1363 (1930); Amagat, *Ann. chim. phys.*, **29**, 68 (1893); Onnes and Urk, *Proc. 4th Intern. Congr. Refr.*, p. 69, *Comm. phys. Lab. Leyden*, No. 169*d*.

† Recent data show some disagreement, particularly in the high-pressure range at 50° and 100°C. (0.5 per cent). If more accurate data are needed between 0° and 150°C. to 400 atm., it is recommended to use the following equation taken from Otto, Michels, and Wouters, *Physik. Z.*, **35**, 97 (1934).

$$pv = A + Bp + Cp^2 + Dp^4 + Ep^6 + Fp^8$$

t, °C.	A	B10³	C10⁶	D10¹²	E10¹⁸	F10²⁴
0	1.00045	−0.45890	2.90964	23.1895	−587.22	4503.8
25	1.09201	−0.22110	2.65436	5.06187	−159.266	1008.8
50	1.18358	−0.01616	2.23372	2.64600	− 95.758	535.08
75	1.27515	+0.15299	1.92483	−0.46531	− 31.6196	163.97
100	1.36671	+0.28848	1.69106	−1.68806	− 8.2022	47.065
125	1.45828	+0.41812	1.37824	−0.56983	−11.4400	43.566
150	1.54985	+0.52421	1.19192	−0.91694	− 4.5638	18.788

The following equation taken from Michels, Wouters, and DeBoer, *Physica*, **3**, 585 (1936) may be used for values to 3000 atm. and at temperatures between 0° and 150°C. if a possible deviation of 3×10^{-4} is permissible. For higher accuracy, the authors recommend use of table giving $(pv_{calc.} - Pv_{exp.}) \times 10^5$.

$$p(v - \alpha) = A + \beta d + \gamma d^2 + \delta d^3 + \epsilon d^4$$

In this equation, *d* is the Amagat density defined as P/PV.

t, °C.	α10³	A	β10³	γ10⁶	δ10⁹	ε10¹²
0	0.48398	1.00045	−0.95241	3.38591	−2.22621	9.2040
25	.59626	1.09202	−0.88854	3.18775	−0.84709	6.6287
50	.54734	1.18358	−0.67607	3.24421	−0.58091	7.0958
75	.51846	1.27515	−0.48391	3.29668	−0.22363	7.2360
100	0.62860	1.36671	−0.47050	3.12708	+0.69591	4.8982
125	.65156	1.45828	−0.36509	3.17849	+0.84240	4.4999
150	.77424	1.54985	−0.39933	2.82427	+2.03012	1.4968

See also Deming and Shupe, *Phys. Rev.*, **37**, 638 (1931); Deming and Deming, *ibid.*, **45**, 109 (1934).

Table 3-166. Pressure-Volume Product for Oxygen*

$PV = 1.0000$ at 1 atm. and 0°C.

P, atm.	0°C.	50°C.	100°C.
1	1.0000	1.1838	1.3674
10	0.9913	1.1796	1.3661
25	.9776	1.1732	1.3644
50	.9569	1.1642	1.3630
75	.9388	1.1571	1.3632
100	.9234	1.1520	1.3651

* Calculated from equations given by Holborn and Otto, *Z. Physik*, **33**, 1 (1925). For additional data see "International Critical Tables," vol. 3, p. 8.

Table 3-167. Compressibilities of Liquids*

At the constant temperature t, the compressibility $\beta = (1/V_0)(dV/dP)$. In general as P increases, β decreases rapidly at first and then slowly; the change of β with t is large at low pressures but very small at pressures above 1000 to 2000 megabars. 1 megabar = 0.987 atm. = 10^6 dyne/cm.^{2}

Substance	Temp., °C.	Pressure, megabars	Compressibility per megabar $\beta \times 10^6$	Substance	Temp., °C.	Pressure, megabars	Compressibility per megabar $\beta \times 10^6$	Substance	Temp., °C.	Pressure, megabars	Compressibility per megabar $\beta \times 10^6$
Acetone	14	23	111	Ethyl acetate	20	400	75	Methyl alcohol	15	23	103
Acetone	20	500	61	alcohol	14	23	100	alcohol	20	200	95
Acetone	20	1,000	52	alcohol	20	500	63	alcohol	20	400	80
Acetone	40	12,000	9	alcohol	20	1,000	54	alcohol	20	500	65
Amyl alcohol	14	23	88	alcohol	20	12,000	8	alcohol	20	1,000	54
alcohol, iso	20	200	84	bromide	20	200	100	alcohol	20	12,000	8
alcohol, iso	20	400	70	bromide	20	400	82	Nitric acid	0	17	32
alcohol, n	20	500	61	bromide	20	500	70	Oils:			
alcohol, n	20	1,000	46	bromide	20	1,000	54	Almond	15	5	53
alcohol, n	20	12,000	8	bromide	20	12,000	8	Castor	15	5	46
alcohol, n	40	12,000	8	chloride	15	23	151	Linseed	15	5	51
Benzene	17	5	89	chloride	20	500	102	Olive	15	5	55
Benzene	20	200	77	chloride	20	1,000	66	Rapeseed	20	......	59
Benzene	20	400	67	chloride	20	12,000	8	Phosphorus trichloride	10	250	71
Bromine	20	200	56	ether	25	23	188	trichloride	20	500	63
Bromine	20	400	51	ether	20	500	84	trichloride	20	1,000	47
Butyl alcohol, iso	18	8	97	ether	20	1,000	61	trichloride	20	12,000	8
alcohol, iso	20	200	81	ether	20	12,000	10	Propyl alcohol (n)	20	200	77
alcohol, iso	20	400	64	iodide	20	200	81	alcohol (n)	20	400	67
alcohol, iso	20	500	56	iodide	20	400	69	alcohol (n?)	20	500	65
alcohol, iso	20	1,000	46	iodide	20	500	64	alcohol (n?)	20	1,000	47
alcohol, iso	20	12,000	8	iodide	20	1,000	50	alcohol (n?)	20	12,000	7
Carbon bisulfide	16	21	86	iodide	20	12,000	8	Toluene	20	200	74
bisulfide	20	500	57	Gallium	30	300	3.97	Toluene	20	400	64
bisulfide	20	1,000	48	Glycerol	15	5	22	Turpentine	20	.....	74
bisulfide	20	12,000	6	Hexane	20	200	117	Water	20	13	49
tetrachloride	20	200	86	Hexane	20	400	91	Water	20	200	43
tetrachloride	20	400	73	Kerosene	20	500	55	Water	20	400	41
Chloroform	20	200	83	Kerosene	20	1,000	45	Water	20	500	39
Chloroform	20	400	70	Kerosene	20	12,000	8	Water	40	500	38
Dichloroethylsulfide	32	1,000	34	Mercury	20	300	3.95	Water	40	1,000	33
Dichloroethylsulfide	32	2,000	24	Mercury	22	500	3.97	Water	40	12,000	9
Ethyl acetate	13	23	103	Mercury	22	1,000	3.91	Xylene, meta	20	200	69
acetate	20	200	90	Mercury	22	12,000	2.37	meta	20	400	60

* "Smithsonian Tables," Table 106.

Scott ("Cryogenic Engineering," Van Nostrand, Princeton, N.J., 1959) gives data for liquid nitrogen (p. 283), oxygen (p. 276), and hydrogen (p. 303). For a convenient index to the high-pressure work of Bridgman see "American Institute of Physics Handbook," p. 2-163, McGraw-Hill, New York, 1957.

Table 3-168. Compressibilities of Solids

Many data on the compressibility of solids obtained prior to 1926 are contained in Gruneisen, "Handbuch der Physik," vol. 10, pp. 1–52, Springer, Berlin, 1926, also available as translation *N.A.S.A.* RE 2-18-59W, 1959. See also Tables 271, 273, 276, 278, and other material in "Smithsonian Physical Tables," 9th ed., 1954. For a review of high-pressure work to 1946 see Bridgman, *Revs. Modern Phys.*, **18**, 1 (1946).

LATENT HEATS

Table 3-169. Heats of Fusion and Vaporization of the Elements and Inorganic Compounds*

Unless stated otherwise, the values have been taken from the compilations by K. K. Kelley on Heats of Fusion of Inorganic Compounds, *U. S. Bur. Mines Bull.* 393 (1936), and The Free Energies of Vaporization and Vapor Pressures of Inorganic Substances, *U. S. Bur. Mines Bull.* 383 (1935).

Substance	M.p., °C.	Heat of fusion,[a,b] cal./mole	B.p. at 1 atm., °C.	Heat of vaporization,[a,b] cal./mole
Aluminum:				
Al	660.0	2,550	2057	61,020
Al_2Br_6	97.5	5,420	256.4	10,920
Al_2Cl_6	192.5	16,960	180.2[c]	26,750[c]
$AlF_3.3NaF$	1000	16,380		
Al_2I_6	191.0	7,960	385.5	15,360
Al_2O_3	2045	(26,000)	3000	
Antimony:				
Sb	630.5	4,770	1440	46,670
$SbBr_3$	97	3,510		
$SbCl_3$	73.4	3,030	219	10,360
$SbCl_5$	4	2,400	172[d]	11,570
Sb_4O_6	655	(27,000)	1425	17,820
Sb_4S_6	546	11,200		
Argon:				
A	−189.3	290	−185.8	1,590
Arsenic:				
As	814	(6,620)	610[c]	31,000[c]
$AsBr_3$	31	2,810		
$AsCl_3$	− 16	2,420	122	7,570
AsF_5	− 80.7	2,800	− 52.8	4,980
As_4O_6	313	8,000	457.2	14,300
Barium:				
Ba	704	(1,400)[e]	1638	35,670
$BaBr_2$	847	6,000		
$BaCl_2$	960	5,370		
BaF_2	1287	3,000		
$Ba(NO_3)_2$	595	(5,900)		
$Ba_3(PO_4)_2$	1730	18,600		
$BaSO_4$	1350	9,700		
Beryllium:				
Be	1280	2,500[e]		
Bismuth:				
Bi	271.3	2,505	1420	
$BiBr_3$	....	....	461	18,020
$BiCl_3$	224	2,600	441	17,350
Bi_2O_3	817	6,800		
Bi_2S_5	747	8,900		
Boron:				
BBr_3	....	....	91.3	7,300
BCl_3	....	....	12.5	5,680
BF_3	−128	480	−100.9	4,620
B_2H_6	−165.5	....	− 92.4	3,685
B_3H_{10}	−119.8	....	16	6,470
B_5H_9	− 46.9	....	58	7,700
B_5H_{11}	....	....	67	8,500
$B_{10}H_{14}$	99.7	7,800	[f]	11,600
B_2H_5Br	−104	....	16	6,230
$B_3N_3H_6$	− 58	....	50.4	7,670
Bromine:				
Br_2	− 7.2	2,580	58.0	7,420
BrF_5	− 61.3	1,355	40.4	7,470
Cadmium:				
Cd	320.9	1,460	765	23,870
$CdBr_2$	568	(5,000)		
$CdCl_2$	568	5,300	967	29,860
CdF_2	1110	(5,400)		
CdI_2	387	3,660	796	25,400
CdO	....	....	1559[c]	53,820[c]
$CdSO_4$	1000	4,790		
Calcium:				
Ca	851	2,230	1487	36,580
$CaBr_2$	730	4,180		
$CaCO_3$	1282	(12,700)		
$CaCl_2$	782	6,100		
CaF_2	1392	4,100		
$Ca(NO_3)_2$	561	5,120		
CaO	2707	(12,240)		
$CaO.Al_2O_3.2SiO_2$	1550	29,400		
$CaO.MgO.2SiO_2$	1392	(18,200)		
$CaO.SiO_2$	1512	13,400		
$CaSO_4$	1297	6,700		
Carbon:				
C (graphite)	3600	11,000[e]		
CBr_4	90	1,050		
CCl_4	− 24.0	644	77	7,280
CF_4	....	....	−127.9	3,110
CH_4	−182.5	224	−161.4	2,040
C_2N_2	− 27.8	1,938[u]	− 21.1	5,576[u]
CNBr	52	....	....	11,010[c]
CNCl	− 5	2,240	13	6,300
Carbon (*Cont.*):				
CNF	....	....	− 72.8	5,780[c]
CNI	....	....	141	13,980[c]
CO	−205.0	200	−191.5	1,444
CO_2	− 57.5	1,900	− 78.4[c]	6,030[c,*]
COS	−138.8	1,129[k]	− 50.2	4,423[k]
$COCl_2$	....	....	8.0	5,990
CS_2	−112.0	1,049[l]		
Cerium:				
Ce	775	2,120		
Cesium:				
Cs	28.4	500	690	16,320
CsBr	....	....	1300	35,990
CsCl	642	3,600	1300	35,690
CsF	715	(2,450)	1251	34,330
CsI	....	....	1280	35,930
$CsNO_3$	407	3,250		
Chlorine:				
Cl_2	−101.0	1,531[m]	− 34.1	4,878[m]
ClF	....	....	−101	
ClF_3	....	....	11.3	5,890
Cl_2O	....	....	2.0	6,280
ClO_2	....	....	10.9	7,100
Cl_2O_7	....	....	79	8,480
Chromium:				
Cr	1550	3,930	2475	
CrO_2Cl_2	....	....	117	8,250
Cobalt:				
Co	1490	3,660		
$CoCl_2$	727	7,390	1050	27,170
Copper:				
Cu	1083.0	3,110	2595	72,810
Cu_2Br_2	....	....	1355	16,310
Cu_2Cl_2	430	4,890	1490	11,920
CuI	....	....	1336	15,940
$Cu_2(CN)_2$	473	(5,400)		
Cu_2O	1230	(13,400)		
CuO	1447	2,820		
Cu_2S	1127	5,500		
Fluorine:				
F_2	−223	....	−188.2	1,640
F_2O	....	....	−144.8	2,650
Gallium:				
Ga	29.8	1,336	2071	
Germanium:				
Ge	959	(8,300)		
GeH_4	−165	....	− 89.1	3,580
Ge_2H_6	−109	....	31.4	5,900
Ge_3H_8	−105.6	....	110.6	7,550
$GeHCl_3$	− 71	....	75[g]	8,000
$GeBr_4$	26.1	....	189	8,560
$GeCl_4$	− 49.5	....	84	7,030
$Ge(CH_3)_4$	− 88	....	44	6,460
Gold:				
Au	1063.0	3,030	2966	81,800
Helium:				
He	−271.4	....	−268.4	22
Hydrogen:				
H_2	−259.2	28	−252.7	216
HBr	− 86.9	575	− 66.7	4,210
HCl	−114.2	476	− 85.0	3,860
HCN	− 13.2	2,009[i]	25.7	6,027[i]
HF	− 83.0	1,094	33.3	7,460
$(HF)_6$	....	....	51.2	5,020
HI	− 50.8	686		
H_2O	0.0	1,436	100.0	9,729[h,q]
$H^2{}_2O$ (= D_2O)	3.8	1,501[s]	101.4	9,945[r,q]
H_2O_2	− 2	2,520[c]	158	10,270
HNO_3	− 47	600		
H_3PO_2	17.4	2,310		
H_3PO_3	74	3,070		
H_3PO_4	42.4	2,520		
$H_4P_2O_6$	55	8,300		
H_2S	− 85.5	568[t]	− 60.3	4,463[t]
H_2S_2	− 87.6	1,805		
H_2SO_4	10.5	2,360		
H_2Se	....	....	− 41.3	4,880
H_2SeO_4	58	3,450		
H_2Te	− 48.9	1,670	− 2.2	5,650
Indium:				
In	156.4	781		

* See also the section on engineering thermodynamic properties, Sec. 3, pp. 3-147ff. Data for helium [1.5(0.1) 4.2°K.] nitrogen (60° to 126°K.), and oxygen (67° to 155°K.) are given by Scott, "Cryogenic Engineering," Van Nostrand, Princeton, N.J., 1959. An extensive collection of data for air, argon, carbon monoxide, fluorine, helium, nitrogen, methane, and oxygen appears in Johnson (ed.), WADD-TR-60-56, 1960. For another tabulation see *N.B.S. Circ.* 500. A selection of these values appears in Table 4j-1, pp. 4-131 to 4-159, of "American Institute of Physics Handbook," McGraw-Hill, New York, 1957.

Table 3-169. Heats of Fusion and Vaporization of the Elements and Inorganic Compounds—(*Continued*)

Substance	M.p., °C.	Heat of fusion,[a,b] cal./mole	B.p. at 1 atm., °C.	Heat of vaporization,[a,b] cal./mole
Iodine:				
I_2	113.0	3,650	183	10,390
ICl(α)	17.2	2,660		
ICl(β)	13.9	2,270		
IF_7	......	......	4[c]	7,460[c]
Iron				
Fe	1530	3,560	2735	84,600
$FeCl_2$	677	7,800	1026	30,210
Fe_2Cl_6	304	20,590	319	12,040
$Fe(CO)_5$	− 21	3,250	105	9,000
FeO	1380	(7,700)		
FeS	1195	5,000		
Krypton:				
Kr	−157	360[e]	152.9	2,310[e]
Lead:				
Pb	327.4	1,224	1744	42,060
$PbBr_2$	488	4,290	914	27,700
$PbCl_2$	498	5,650	954	29,600
PbF_2	824	1,860	1293	38,300
PbI_2	412	5,970	872	24,850
$PbMoO_4$	1065	(25,800)		
PbO	890	2,820	1472	51,310
PbS	1114	4,150	1281	(50,000)
$PbSO_4$	1087	9,600		
$PbWO_4$	1123	(15,200)		
Lithium:				
Li	179	1,100	1372	32,250
$LiBO_2$	845	(5,570)		
LiBr	552	2,900	1310	35,420
LiCl	614	3,200	1382	35,960
LiF	847	(2,360)	1681	50,970
LiI	440	(1,420)	1171	40,770
LiOH	462	2,480		
Li_2MoO_4	705	4,200		
$LiNO_3$				
Li_2SiO_3	1177	7,210		
Li_4SiO_4	1249	7,430		
Li_2SO_4	857	3,040		
Li_2WO_4	742	(6,700)		
Magnesium:				
Mg	650	2,160	1107	32,520
$MgBr_2$	711	8,300		
$MgCl_2$	712	8,100	1418	32,690
MgF_2	1221	5,900		
MgO	2642	18,500		
$Mg_3(PO_4)_2$	1184	(11,300)		
$MgSiO_3$	1524	14,700		
$MgSO_4$	1127	3,500		
$MgZn_2$	589	(8,270)		
Manganese:				
Mn	1220	3,450	2152	55,150
$MnCl_2$	650	7,340	1190	29,630
$MnSiO_3$	1274	(8,200)		
$MnTiO_3$	1404	(7,960)		
Mercury:				
Hg	− 38.9	557	361	13,980
$HgBr_2$	241	3,960	319	14,080
$HgCl_2$	277	4,150	304	14,080
HgI_2	250	4,500	354	14,260
$HgSO_4$	850	(1,440)		
Molybdenum:				
Mo	2622	(6,660)	(4800)	(128,000)
MoF_6	17	2,500	36	6,000
MoO_3	745	(2,500)	1151	
Neon:				
Ne	−248.5	77	−246.0	440[e]
Nickel:				
Ni	1455	4,200	2730	87,300
$NiCl_2$	......	......	987[c]	48,360[c]
$Ni(CO)_4$	......	......	42.5	7,000
Ni_2S	645	(2,980)		
Ni_3S_2	790	5,800		
Nitrogen:				
N_2	−210.0	172	−195.8	1,336
NF_3	......	......	−129.0	3,000
NH_3	− 77.7	1,352[n]	− 33.4	5,581[n]
NH_4CNS	146	(4,700)		
NH_4NO_3	169.6	1,460		
N_2O	− 90.8	1,563	− 88.5	3,950
NO	−163.6	550	−151.7	3,307
N_2O_4	− 13	5,540	30	7,040
N_2O_5	......	......	32.4	13,800[c]
NOCl	......	......	− 6.4	6,140
Osmium:				
OsF_8	......	......	47.4	6,840
OsO_4(yellow)	56	4,060	130	9,450
OsO_4 (white)	42	2,340		
Oxygen				
O_2	−218.9	106	−183.0	1,629
O_3	......	......	−111	2,880
Palladium:				
Pd	1554	4,120		
Phosphorus:				
P_4 (yellow)	44.2	615	280	12,520
P_4 (violet)	......	......	417[c]	25,600[c]
P_4 (black)	......	......	453[c]	33,100
PCl_3	......	......	74.2	7,280
PH_3	−133.8	270[o]	− 87.7	3,489[o]
P_4O_6	23.8	3,360	174	10,380
$P_4O_{10}(\alpha)$	569	17,080	591	20,670
$P_4O_{10}(\beta)$	......	......	358[c]	
$POCl_3$	1.1	3,110	105.1	8,380
P_2S_3	......	......	508	
Platinum:				
Pt	1773.5	4,700	(4400)	(107,000)
Potassium:				
K	63.5	574	776	18,920
KBO_2	947	(5,700)		
KBr	742	5,000	1383	37,060
KCl	770	6,410	1407	38,840
KCN	623	(3,500)		
KCNS	179	2,250		
K_2CO_3	897	7,800		
K_2CrO_4	984	6,920		
$K_2Cr_2O_7$	398	8,770		
KF	857	6,500		
KI	682	4,100	1324	34,690
K_2MoO_4	922	(4,000)		
KNO_3	338	2,840		
KOH	360	(2,000)	1327	30,850
KPO_3	817	2,110		
K_3PO_4	1340	8,900		
$K_4P_2O_7$	1092	14,000		
K_2SO_4	1074	8,100		
K_2TiO_3	810	(10,600)		
K_2WO_4	927	(4,400)		
Praseodymium:				
Pr	932	2,700		
Radon:				
Rn	−71	......	− 61.8	4,010
Rhenium:				
Re	(3000)			
Re_2O_7	296	15,340	362.4	18,060
Re_2O_8	147	3,800		
Rubidium:				
Rb	39.1	525	679	18,110
RbBr	677	3,700	1352	37,120
RbCl	717	4,400	1381	36,920
RbF	833	4,130	1408	39,510
RbI	638	2,990	1304	35,960
$RbNO_3$	305	1,340		
Selenium:				
Se_2	217	1,220	753	25,490
Se_6	......	......	736	20,600
SeF_6	......	......	− 45.8[c]	6,350[c]
SeO_2	......	......	317[c]	20,900[f]
$SeOCl_2$	10	1,010	168	
Silicon:				
Si	1427	9,470	2290	
$SiCl_4$	− 67.6	1,845	56.8	6,860
Si_2Cl_6	− 1	......	139	
Si_3Cl_8	......	......	211.4	12,340
$(SiCl_3)_2O$	− 33	......	135.6	8,820
SiF_4	......	......	− 94.8[c]	6,130[c]
Si_2F_6	− 18.5	3,900	− 18.9[c]	10,400[c]
SiF_3Cl	−138	......	− 70.1	4,460
SiF_2Cl_2	−144	......	− 31.5	5,080
SiH_4	−185	......	−111.6	2,960
Si_2H_6	−132.5	......	− 14.3	5,110
Si_3H_8	−117	......	53.1	6,780
Si_4H_{10}	− 93.5	......	100	8,890
SiH_3Br	− 93.8	......	2.4	5,650
SiH_2Br_2	− 70.0	......	70.5	6,840
$SiHCl_3$	−126.5	......	31.8	6,360
$(SiH_3)_3N$	−105.6	......	48.7	6,850
$(SiH_3)_2O$	−144	......	− 15.4	5,350
SiO_2 (quartz)	1470	3,400	2230	
SiO_2 (cristobalite)	1700	2,100		
Silver:				
Ag	960.5	2,700	2212	60,720
AgBr	430	2,180		
AgCl	455	3,155	1564	42,520
AgCN	350	2,750		
AgI	557	2,250	1506	34,450
$AgNO_3$	209	2,755		
Ag_2S	842	3,360		
Ag_2SO_4	657	(4,300)		
Sodium:				
Na	97.7	630	914	23,120
$NaBO_2$	966	8,660		

Table 3-169. Heats of Fusion and Vaporization of the Elements and Inorganic Compounds—(*Concluded*)

Substance	M.p., °C.	Heat of fusion,[a,b] cal./mole	B.p. at 1 atm., °C.	Heat of vaporization,[a,b] cal./mole
Sodium (*Cont.*):				
NaBr	747	6,140	1392	37,950
NaCl	800	7,220	1465	40,810
$NaClO_3$	255	5,290		
NaCN	562	(4,400)	1500	37,280
NaCNS	323	4,450		
Na_2CO_3	854	7,000		
NaF	992	7,000	1704	53,260
NaI	662	5,240		
Na_2MoO_4	687	3,600		
$NaNO_3$	310	3,760		
NaOH	322	2,000	1378	
½Na_2O.½Al_2O_3.3SiO_2	1107	13,150		
$NaPO_3$	988	(5,000)		
$Na_4P_2O_7$	970	(13,700)		
Na_2S	920	(1,200)		
Na_2SiO_3	1087	10,300		
$Na_2Si_2O_5$	884	8,460		
Na_2SO_4	884	5,830		
Na_2WO_4	702	5,800		
Strontium:				
Sr	757	2,190	1384	33,610
$SrBr_2$	643	4,780		
$SrCl_2$	872	4,100		
SrF_2	1400	4,260		
$Sr_3(PO_4)_2$	1770	18,500		
Sulfur:				
S (rhombic)	112.8	....	444.6	2,200
S (monoclinic)	119.2			
S_2Cl_2	......	....	138	8,720
SF_6	......	....	− 63.5[c]	5,600[c]
SO_2	− 75.5	1,769[p]	− 5.0	5,960[p]
$SO_3(\alpha)$	17	2,060	44.8	10,190
$SO_3(\beta)$	32.4	2,890		
$SO_3(\gamma)$	62.2	6,310		
$SOBr_2$	......	....	139.5	9,920
$SOCl_2$	......	....	75.4	7,600
SO_2Cl_2	......	....	69.2	7,760
Tellurium:				
Te	453	3,230	1090	
$TeCl_4$	......	....	392	16,830
TeF_6	......	....	− 38.6[c]	6,700[c]
Thallium:				
Tl	302.5	1,030	1457	38,810
TlBr	460	5,990	819	23,800
TlCl	427	4,260	807	24,420
Tl_2CO_3	273	4,400		
TlI	440	3,125	823	25,030
$TlNO_3$	207	2,290		
Tl_2S	449	3,000		
Tl_2SO_4	632	5,500		
Tin:				
Sn_4	231.8	1,720	2270	68,000
$SnBr_2$	232	(1,700)		
$SnBr_4$	30	3,000		
$SnCl_2$	247	3,050	623	20,740
$SnCl_4$	− 33.2	2,190	113	8,330
$Sn(CH_3)_4$	......	....	78.3	7,320
SnH_4	−149.8	....	− 52.3	4,420
SnI_4	143.5	(4,300)		
Titanium:				
$TiBr_4$	38.2	(2,060)		
$TiCl_4$	− 23	2,240	136	8,350
TiO_2	1825	(11,400)		
Tungsten:				
W	3390	(8,400)	(5900)	(176,000)
WF_6	− 0.4	1,800	17.3	6,350
Uranium:				
UF_6	......	....	55.1[c]	9,990[c]
Xenon:				
Xe	−111.5	740	−108.0	3,110
Zinc:				
Zn	419.5	1,595	907	27,430
$ZnCl_2$	283	(5,500)	732	28,710
$Zn(C_2H_5)_2$	......	....	118	8,960
ZnO	1975	4,470		
ZnS	1645	(9,000)		
Zirconium:				
$ZrBr_4$	......	....	357[c]	25,800[c]
$ZrCl_4$	......	....	311[c]	25,290[c]
ZrI_4	......	....	431[c]	29,030[c]
ZrO_2	2715	20,800		

[a] Values in parentheses are uncertain.
[b] For the freezing point or the normal boiling point unless otherwise stated.
[c] Sublimation.
[d] Decomposes at about 75°C.; value obtained by extrapolation.
[e] Bichowsky and Rossini, "Thermochemistry of the Chemical Substances," Reinhold, New York (1936).
[f] Decomposes before the normal boiling point is reached.
[g] Decomposes at about 40°C.; value obtained by extrapolation.
[h] See also pp. 3-191ff. on steam table.
[i] Giauque and Ruehrwein, *J. Am. Chem. Soc.*, **61**, 2626 (1939).
[j] Giauque and Egan, *J. Chem. Phys.*, **5**, 45 (1937).
[k] Kemp and Giauque, *J. Am. Chem. Soc.*, **59**, 79 (1937).
[l] Brown and Manov, *J. Am. Chem. Soc.*, **59**, 500 (1937).
[m] Giauque and Powell, *J. Am. Chem. Soc.*, **61**, 1970 (1939).
[n] Overstreet and Giauque, *J. Am. Chem. Soc.*, **59**, 254 (1937).
[o] Stephenson and Giauque, *J. Chem. Phys.*, **5**, 149 (1937).
[p] Giauque and Stephenson, *J. Am. Chem. Soc.*, **60**, 1389 (1938).
[q] Osborne, Stimson, and Ginnings, *Bur. Standards J. Research*, **23**, 197, 261 (1939).
[r] Miles and Menzies, *J. Am. Chem. Soc.*, **58**, 1067 (1936).
[s] Long and Kemp, *J. Am. Chem. Soc.*, **58**, 1829 (1936).
[t] Giauque and Blue, *J. Am. Chem. Soc.*, **58**, 831 (1936).
[u] Ruehrwein and Giauque, *J. Am. Chem. Soc.*, **61**, 2940 (1939).

Table 3-170. Heats of Fusion of Organic Compounds

The values for the hydrocarbons are from the tables of the American Petroleum Institute Research Project 44 at the National Bureau of Standards, with some from Parks and Huffman, *Ind. Eng. Chem.*, **23**, 1138 (1931).

The values for the non-hydrocarbon compounds were recalculated from data in "International Critical Tables," vol. 5.

Hydrocarbon compounds	Formula	M.p., °C.	Heat of fusion, cal./g.
Paraffins:			
Methane	CH_4	−182.48	14.03
Ethane	C_2H_6	−183.23	22.712
Propane	C_3H_8	−187.65	19.100
n-Butane	C_4H_{10}	−138.33	19.167
2-Methylpropane	C_4H_{10}	−159.60	18.668
n-Pentane	C_5H_{12}	−129.723	27.874
2-Methylbutane	C_5H_{12}	−159.890	17.076
2,2-Dimethylpropane	C_5H_{12}	− 16.6	10.786
n-Hexane	C_6H_{14}	− 95.320	36.138
2-Methylpentane	C_6H_{14}	−153.680	17.407
2,2-Dimethylbutane	C_6H_{14}	− 99.73	1.607
2,3-Dimethylbutane	C_6H_{14}	−128.41	2.251
n-Heptane	C_7H_{16}	− 90.595	33.513
2-Methylhexane	C_7H_{16}	−118.270	21.158
3-Ethylpentane	C_7H_{16}	−118.593	22.555
2,2-Dimethylpentane	C_7H_{16}	−123.790	13.982
2,4-Dimethylpentane	C_7H_{16}	−119.230	15.968
3,3-Dimethylpentane	C_7H_{16}	−134.46	16.856
2,2,3-Trimethylbutane	C_7H_{16}	− 24.96	5.250
n-Octane	C_8H_{18}	− 56.798	43.169
2-Methylheptane	C_8H_{18}	−109.04	21.458
3-Methylpentane	C_8H_{18}	−120.50	23.795
4-Methylheptane	C_8H_{18}	−120.955	22.692
2,2-Dimethylhexane	C_8H_{18}	−121.18	24.226
2,5-Dimethylhexane	C_8H_{18}	− 91.200	26.903
3,3-Dimethylhexane	C_8H_{18}	−126.10	14.9
2-Methyl-3-ethylpentane	C_8H_{18}	−114.960	23.690
3-Methyl-3-ethylpentane	C_8H_{18}	− 90.870	22.657
2,2,3-Trimethylpentane	C_8H_{18}	−112.27	18.061
2,2,4-Trimethylpentane	C_8H_{18}	−107.365	19.278
2,3,3-Trimethylpentane	C_8H_{18}	−100.70	3.204
2,3,4-Trimethylpentane	C_8H_{18}	−109.210	19.392
2,2,3,3-Tetramethylbutane	C_8H_{18}	+100.69	14.900
n-Nonane	C_9H_{20}	− 53.9	41.2
n-Decane	$C_{10}H_{22}$	− 30.0	48.3
n-Undecane	$C_{11}H_{24}$	− 25.9	34.1
n-Dodecane	$C_{12}H_{26}$	− 9.6	51.3
Eicosane	$C_{20}H_{42}$	+ 36.4	52.0
Pentacosane	$C_{25}H_{52}$	+ 53.3	53.6
Tritriacontane	$C_{33}H_{68}$	+ 71.1	54.0
Aromatics:			
Benzene	C_6H_6	+ 5.533	30.100
Methylbenzene (Toluene)	C_7H_8	− 94.991	17.171
Ethylbenzene	C_8H_{10}	− 94.950	20.629
o-Xylene	C_8H_{10}	− 25.187	30.614
m-Xylene	C_8H_{10}	− 47.872	26.045
p-Xylene	C_8H_{10}	+ 13.263	38.526
n-Propylbenzene	C_9H_{12}	− 99.500	16.97
Isopropylbenzene	C_9H_{12}	− 96.028	19.22
1-Methyl-2-ethylbenzene	C_9H_{12}	− 80.833	21.13
Aromatics—(*Cont.*):			
1-Methyl-3-ethylbenzene	C_9H_{12}	− 95.55	15.14
1-Methyl-4-ethylbenzene	C_9H_{12}	− 62.350	25.29
1,2,3-Trimethylbenzene	C_9H_{12}	− 25.375	16.64
1,2,4-Trimethylbenzene	C_9H_{12}	− 43.80	24.54
1,3,5-Trimethylbenzene	C_9H_{12}	− 44.720	18.97
Naphthalene	$C_{10}H_8$	+ 80.0	36.0
Camphene	$C_{10}H_{12}$	+ 51	57
Durene	$C_{10}H_{14}$	+ 79.3	37.4
Isodurene	$C_{10}H_{14}$	− 24.0	23.0
Prehnitene	$C_{10}H_{14}$	− 7.7	20.0
p-Cymene	$C_{10}H_{14}$	− 68.9	17.1
n-Butyl benzene	$C_{10}H_{14}$	− 88.5	19.5
tert-Butyl benzene	$C_{10}H_{14}$	− 58.1	14.9
β-Methyl naphthalene	$C_{11}H_{10}$	+ 34.1	20.1
Diphenyl	$C_{12}H_{10}$	+ 68.6	28.8
Hexamethyl benzene	$C_{12}H_{18}$	+165.5	30.4
Diphenyl methane	$C_{13}H_{12}$	+ 25.2	26.4
Anthracene	$C_{14}H_{10}$	+216.5	38.7
Phenanthrene	$C_{14}H_{10}$	+ 96.3	25.0
Tolane	$C_{14}H_{10}$	+ 60	28.7
Stilbene	$C_{14}H_{12}$	+124	40.0
Dibenzil	$C_{14}H_{14}$	+ 51.4	30.7
Triphenyl methane	$C_{19}H_{16}$	+ 92.1	21.1
Alkyl cyclohexanes:			
Cyclohexane	C_6H_{12}	+ 6.67	7.569
Methylcyclohexane	C_7H_{14}	−126.58	16.429
Alkyl cyclopentanes:			
Cyclopentane	C_5H_{10}	− 93.80	2.068
Methylcyclopentane	C_6H_{12}	−142.445	19.68
Ethylcyclopentane	C_7H_{14}	−138.435	11.10
1,1-Dimethylcyclopentane	C_7H_{14}	− 69.73	3.36
cis-1,2-Dimethylcyclopentane	C_7H_{14}	− 53.85	3.87
trans-1,2-Dimethylcyclopentane	C_7H_{14}	−117.57	15.68
trans-1,3-Dimethylcyclopentane	C_7H_{14}	−133.680	17.93
Monoolefins:			
Ethene (Ethylene)	C_2H_4	−169.15	28.547
Propene (Propylene)	C_3H_6	−185.25	17.054
1-Butene	C_4H_8	−185.35	16.393
cis-2-Butene	C_4H_8	−138.91	31.135
trans-2-Butene	C_4H_8	−105.55	41.564
2-Methylpropene (isobutene)	C_4H_8	−140.35	25.265
1-Pentene	C_5H_{10}	−165.27	16.82
cis-2-pentene	C_5H_{10}	−151.363	24.239
trans-2-pentene	C_5H_{10}	−140.235	26.536
2-Methyl-1-butene	C_5H_{10}	−137.560	26.879
3-Methyl-1-butene	C_5H_{10}	−168.500	18.009
2-Methyl-2-butene	C_5H_{10}	−133.780	25.738
Acetylenes:			
Acetylene	C_2H_2	− 81.5	23.04
2-Butyne (dimethylacetylene)	C_4H_6	−132.23	40.808

Non-hydrocarbon compounds	Formula	M.p., °C.	Heat of fusion, cal./g.
Acetic acid	$C_2H_4O_2$	16.7	46.68
Acetone	C_3H_6O	−95.5	23.42
Acrylic acid	$C_3H_4O_2$	12.3	37.03
Allo-cinnamic acid	$C_9H_8O_2$	68	27.35
Aminobenzoic acid (o-)	$C_7H_7NO_2$	145	35.48
(m-)	$C_7H_7NO_2$	179.5	38.03
(p-)	$C_7H_7NO_2$	188.5	36.46
Amyl alcohol	$C_5H_{12}O$	−78.9	26.65
Anethole	$C_{10}H_{12}O$	22.5	25.80
Aniline	$C_6H_5NH_2$	−6.3	27.09
Anthraquinone	$C_{14}H_8O_2$	284.8	37.48
Apiol	$C_{12}H_{14}O_4$	29.5	25.80
Azobenzene	$C_{12}H_{10}N_2$	67.1	28.91
Azoxybenzene	$C_{12}H_{10}N_2O$	36	21.62
Benzil	$C_{14}H_{10}O_2$	95.2	22.15
Benzoic acid	$C_7H_6O_2$	122.45	33.90
Benzophenone	$C_{13}H_{10}O$	47.85	23.53
Benzylaniline	$C_{13}H_{13}N$	32.37	21.86
Bromocamphor	$C_{10}H_{15}BrO$	78	41.57
Bromochlorbenzene (o-)	C_6H_4BrCl	−12.6	15.41
(m-)	C_6H_4BrCl	−21.2	15.29
(p-)	C_6H_4BrCl	64.6	23.41
Bromoiodobenzene (o-)	C_6H_4BrI	21	12.18
(m-)	C_6H_4BrI	9.3	10.27
(p-)	C_6H_4BrI	90.1	16.60
Bromol hydrate	$C_2H_3Br_3O_2$	46	16.90
Bromophenol (p-)	C_6H_5BrO	63.5	20.50
Bromotoluene (p-)	C_7H_7Br	28	20.86
Butyl alcohol (n-)	$C_4H_{10}O$	−89.2	29.93
(t-)	$C_4H_{10}O$	25.4	21.88
Butyric acid (n-)	$C_4H_8O_2$	−5.7	30.04
Capric acid (n-)	$C_{10}H_{20}O_2$	31.99	38.87
Caprylic acid (n-)	$C_8H_{16}O_2$	16.3	35.40
Carbazole	$C_{12}H_9N$	243	42.05
Carbon tetrachloride	CCl_4	−22.8	41.57
Carvoxime (d-)	$C_{10}H_{15}NO$	71.5	23.29
(l-)	$C_{10}H_{15}NO$	71	23.41
(dl-)	$C_{10}H_{15}NO$	91	24.61
Cetyl alcohol	$C_{16}H_{34}O$	49.27	33.80
Chloracetic acid (α-)	$C_2H_3ClO_2$	61.2	31.06
(β-)	$C_2H_3ClO_2$	56	35.12
Chloral alcoholate	$C_4H_7Cl_3O_2$	9	24.03
hydrate	$C_2H_3Cl_3O_2$	47.4	33.18
Chloroaniline (p-)	C_6H_6ClN	71	37.15
Chlorobenzoic acid (o-)	$C_7H_5ClO_2$	140.2	39.30
(m-)	$C_7H_5ClO_2$	154.25	36.41
(p-)	$C_7H_5ClO_2$	239.7	49.21
Chloronitrobenzene (m-)	$C_6H_4ClNO_2$	44.4	29.38
(p-)	$C_6H_4ClNO_2$	83.5	31.51
Cinnamic acid	$C_9H_8O_2$	133	36.50
anhydride	$C_{18}H_{14}O_3$	48	28.14
Cresol (p-)	C_7H_8O	34.6	26.28
Crotonic acid (α-)	$C_4H_6O_2$	72	25.32
(cis-)	$C_4H_6O_2$	71.2	34.90
Cyanamide	CH_2N_2	44	49.81
Cyclohexanol	$C_6H_{12}O$	25.46	4.19

Table 3-170. Heats of Fusion of Organic Compounds—*(Concluded)*

Non-hydrocarbon compounds	Formula	M.p., °C.	Heat of fusion, cal./g.
Dibromobenzene (o-)	$C_6H_4Br_2$	1.8	12.78
(m-)	$C_6H_4Br_2$	−6.9	13.38
(p-)	$C_6H_4Br_2$	86	20.55
Dibromophenol (2, 4-)	$C_6H_4Br_2O$	12	13.97
Dichloroacetic acid	$C_2H_2Cl_2O_2$	−4(?)	14.21
Dichlorobenzene (o-)	$C_6H_4Cl_2$	−16.7	21.02
(m-)	$C_6H_4Cl_2$	−24.8	20.55
(p-)	$C_6H_4Cl_2$	53.13	29.67
Dihydroxybenzene (o-)	$C_6H_6O_2$	104.3	49.40
(m-)	$C_6H_6O_2$	109.65	46.20
(p-)	$C_6H_6O_2$	172.3	58.77
Di-iodobenzene (o-)	$C_6H_4I_2$	23.4	10.15
(m-)	$C_6H_4I_2$	34.2	11.54
(p-)	$C_6H_4I_2$	129	16.20
Dimethyl tartrate (dl-)	$C_6H_{10}O_6$	87	35.12
(d-)	$C_6H_{10}O_6$	49	21.50
pyrone	$C_7H_8O_2$	132	56.14
Dinitrobenzene (o-)	$C_6H_4N_2O_4$	116.93	32.25
(m-)	$C_6H_4N_2O_4$	89.7	24.70
(p-)	$C_6H_4N_2O_4$	173.5	39.99
Dinitrotoluene (2, 4-)	$C_7H_6N_2O_4$	70.14	26.40
Dioxane	$C_4H_8O_2$	11.0	34.85
Diphenyl amine	$C_{12}H_{11}N$	52.98	25.23
Elaidic acid	$C_{18}H_{34}O_2$	44.4	52.08
Ethyl acetate	$C_4H_8O_2$	83.8	28.43
alcohol	C_2H_6O	−114.4	25.76
Ethylene dibromide	$C_2H_4Br_2$	10.012	13.52
Ethyl ether	$C_4H_{10}O$	−116.3	23.54
Formic acid	CH_2O_2	8.40	58.89
Glutaric acid	$C_6H_8O_4$	97.5	37.39
Glycerol	$C_3H_8O_3$	18.07	47.49
Glycol, ethylene	$C_2H_6O_2$	−11.5	43.26
Hydrazo benzene	$C_{12}H_{12}N_2$	134	22.89
Hydrocinnamic acid	$C_9H_{10}O_2$	48	28.14
Hydroxyacetanilide	$C_8H_9NO_2$	91.3	33.59
Iodotoluene (p-)	C_7H_7I	34	18.75
Isopropyl alcohol	C_3H_8O	−88.5	21.08
ether	$C_6H_{14}O$	−86.8	25.79
Lauric acid (n-)	$C_{12}H_{24}O_2$	43.22	43.72
Levulinic acid	$C_5H_8O_3$	33	18.97
Menthol (l-) (α)	$C_{10}H_{20}O$	43.5	18.63
Methyl alcohol	CH_4O	−97.8	23.7
Myristic acid	$C_{14}H_{28}O_2$	53.86	47.49
Methyl cinnamate	$C_{10}H_{10}O_2$	36	26.53
fumarate	$C_6H_8O_4$	102	57.93
oxalate	$C_4H_6O_4$	54.35	42.64
phenylpropiolate	$C_{10}H_8O_2$	18	22.86
succinate	$C_6H_{10}O_4$	19.5	35.72

Non-hydrocarbon compounds	Formula	M.p., °C.	Heat of fusion, cal./g.
Naphthol (α-)	$C_{10}H_8O$	95.0	38.94
(β-)	$C_{10}H_8O$	120.6	31.30
Naphthylamine (α-)	$C_{10}H_9N$	50	22.34
Nitroaniline (o-)	$C_6H_6N_2O_2$	71.2	27.88
(m-)	$C_6H_6N_2O_2$	114.0	40.97
(p-)	$C_6H_6N_2O_2$	147.3	36.46
Nitrobenzene	$C_6H_5NO_2$	5.85	22.52
Nitrobenzoic acid (o-)	$C_7H_5NO_4$	145.8	40.06
(m-)	$C_7H_5NO_4$	141.1	27.59
(p-)	$C_7H_5NO_4$	239.2	52.80
Nitronaphthalene	$C_{10}H_7NO_2$	56.7	25.44
Nitrophenol (o-)	$C_6H_5NO_3$	45.13	26.76
Palmitic acid	$C_{16}H_{32}O_2$	61.82	39.18
Paraldehyde	$C_6H_{12}O_3$	10.5	25.02
Pelargic acid (n-) (β-)	$C_9H_{18}O_2$	....	39.04
Pelargonic acid (n-) (α-)	$C_9H_{18}O_2$	12.35	30.63
Phenol	C_6H_6O	40.92	29.03
Phenylacetic acid	$C_8H_8O_2$	76.7	25.44
Phenylhydrazine	$C_6H_8N_2$	19.6	36.31
Propyl ether (n)	$C_6H_{14}O$	−126.1	20.66
Quinone	$C_6H_4O_2$	115.7	40.85
Stearic acid	$C_{18}H_{30}O_2$	68.82	47.54
Succinic anhydride	$C_4H_4O_3$	119	48.74
Succinonitrile	$C_4H_4N_2$	54.5	11.71
Tetrachloroxylene (o-)	$C_8H_6Cl_4$	86	21.02
(p-)	$C_8H_6Cl_4$	95	22.10
Thiophene	C_4H_4S	−39.4	14.11
Thiosinamine	$C_4H_8N_2S$	77	33.45
Thymol	$C_{10}H_{14}O$	51.5	27.47
Toluic acid (o-)	$C_8H_8O_2$	103.7	35.40
(m-)	$C_8H_8O_2$	108.75	27.59
(p-)	$C_8H_8O_2$	179.6	39.90
Toluidine (p-)	C_7H_9N	43.3	39.90
Tribromophenol (2, 4, 6-)	$C_6H_3Br_3O$	93	13.38
Trichloroacetic acid	$C_2HCl_3O_2$	57.5	8.60
Trinitroglycerol	$C_3H_5N_3O_9$	12.3	23.02
Trinitrotoluene (2, 4, 6-)	$C_7H_5N_3O_6$	80.83	22.34
Tristearin	$C_{57}H_{110}O_6$	70.8, 54.5	45.63
Undecylic acid (α-) (n-)	$C_{11}H_{22}O_2$	28.25	32.20
(β-) (n-)	$C_{11}H_{22}O_2$	....	42.91
Urethane	$C_3H_7NO_2$	48.7	40.85
Veratrol	$C_8H_{10}O_2$	22.5	27.45
Xylene dibromide (o-)	$C_8H_8Br_2$	95	24.25
(m-)	$C_8H_8Br_2$	77	21.45
dichloride (o-)	$C_8H_8Cl_2$	55	29.03
(m-)	$C_8H_8Cl_2$	34	26.64
(p-)	$C_8H_8Cl_2$	100	32.73

Table 3-171. Heats of Vaporization of Organic Compounds

The values for the hydrocarbons are from the tables of the American Petroleum Institute Research Project 44 at the National Bureau of Standards.

The values for the non-hydrocarbon compounds were recalculated from data in "International Critical Tables," vol. 5.

Hydrocarbon compounds	Formula	Temperature, °C.	ΔHv, cal./g.
Paraffins:			
Methane	CH_4	−161.6	121.87
Ethane	C_2H_6	−88.9	116.87
Propane	C_3H_8	25	81.76
		−42.1	101.76
n-Butane	C_4H_{10}	25	86.63
		−0.50	92.09
2-Methylpropane (isobutane)	C_4H_{10}	25	78.63
		−11.72	87.56
n-Pentane	C_5H_{12}	25	87.54
		36.08	85.38
2-Methylbutane (isopentane)	C_5H_{12}	25	81.47
		27.86	80.97
2,2-Dimethylpropane (neopentane)	C_5H_{12}	25	72.15
		9.45	75.37
n-Hexane	C_6H_{14}	25	87.50
		68.74	80.48
2-Methylpentane	C_6H_{14}	25	82.83
		60.27	76.89
3-Methylpentane	C_6H_{14}	25	83.96
		63.28	78.42
2,2-Dimethylbutane	C_6H_{14}	25	76.79
		49.74	73.75
2,3-Dimethylbutane	C_6H_{14}	25	80.77
		57.99	76.53
n-Heptane	C_7H_{16}	25	87.18
		98.43	76.45
2-Methylhexane	C_7H_{16}	25	83.02
		90.05	73.4
3-Methylhexane	C_7H_{16}	25	83.68
		91.95	74.1
3-Ethylpentane	C_7H_{16}	25	84.02
		93.47	74.3
2,2-Dimethylpentane	C_7H_{16}	25	77.36
		79.20	69.7
2,3-Dimethylpentane	C_7H_{16}	25	81.68
		89.79	72.9
2,4-Dimethylpentane	C_7H_{16}	25	78.44
		80.51	70.9
3,3-Dimethylpentane	C_7H_{16}	25	78.76
		86.06	70.6
2,2,3-Trimethylbutane	C_7H_{16}	25	76.42
		80.88	69.3
n-Octane	C_8H_{18}	25	86.80
		125.66	73.19
2-Methylheptane	C_8H_{18}	25	83.02
		117.64	70.3
3-Methylheptane	C_8H_{18}	25	83.35
		118.92	71.3
4-Methylheptane	C_8H_{18}	25	83.01
		117.71	70.91
3-Ethylhexane	C_8H_{18}	25	82.95
		118.53	71.7
2,2-Dimethylhexane	C_8H_{18}	25	78.02
		106.84	67.7
2,3-Dimethylhexane	C_8H_{18}	25	81.17
		115.60	70.2
2,4-Dimethylhexane	C_8H_{18}	25	79.02
		109.43	68.5
2,5-Dimethylhexane	C_8H_{18}	25	79.21
		109.10	68.6
3,3-Dimethylhexane	C_8H_{18}	25	78.54
		111.97	68.5
3,4-Dimethylhexane	C_8H_{18}	25	81.55
		117.72	70.2
2-Methyl-3-ethylpentane	C_8H_{18}	25	80.60
		115.65	69.7
3-Methyl-3-ethylpentane	C_8H_{18}	25	79.49
		118.26	69.3
2,2,3-Trimethylpentane	C_8H_{18}	25	77.24
		109.84	67.3
2,2,4-Trimethylpentane	C_8H_{18}	25	73.50
		99.24	64.87
2,3,3-Trimethylpentane	C_8H_{18}	25	77.87
		114.76	68.1
2,3,4-Trimethylpentane	C_8H_{18}	25	78.90
		113.47	68.37
2,2,3,3-Tetramethylbutane	C_8H_{18}	106.30	66.2
Alkyl benzenes:			
Benzene	C_6H_6	25	103.57
		80.10	94.14
Methylbenzene (toluene)	C_7H_8	25	98.55
		110.62	86.8
Ethylbenzene	C_8H_{10}	25	95.11
		136.19	81.0
1,2-Dimethylbenzene (o-xylene)	C_8H_{10}	25	97.79
		144.42	82.9
1,3-Dimethylbenzene (m-xylene)	C_8H_{10}	25	96.03
		139.10	82.0
1,4-Dimethylbenzene (p-xylene)	C_8H_{10}	25	95.40
		138.35	81.2
n-Propylbenzene	C_9H_{12}	25	91.93
		159.22	76.0
Isopropylbenzene	C_9H_{12}	25	89.77
		152.40	74.6
1-Methyl-2-ethylbenzene	C_9H_{12}	25	94.9
		165.15	77.3
1-Methyl-3-ethylbenzene	C_9H_{12}	25	93.3
		161.30	76.6
1-Methyl-4-ethylbenzene	C_9H_{12}	25	92.7
		162.05	76.4
1,2,3-Trimethylbenzene	C_9H_{12}	25	97.56
		176.15	79.6
1,2,4-Trimethylbenzene (pseudocumene)	C_9H_{12}	25	95.33
		169.25	78.0
1,3,5-Trimethylbenzene (mesitylene)	C_9H_{12}	25	94.40
		164.70	77.6
Alkyl cyclopentanes:			
Cyclopentane	C_5H_{10}	25	97.1
		49.26	93.1
Methylcyclopentane	C_6H_{12}	25	89.83
		71.81	83.2
Ethylcyclopentane	C_7H_{14}	25	88.6
		103.45	78.3
1,1-Dimethylcyclopentane	C_7H_{14}	25	82.5
		87.5	74.6
cis-1,2-Dimethylcyclopentane	C_7H_{14}	25	86.4
		99.3	77.0
trans-1,2-Dimethylcyclopentane	C_7H_{14}	25	83.9
		91.9	75.5
trans-1,3-Dimethylcyclopentane	C_7H_{14}	25	83.6
		90.8	75.3
Alkyl cyclohexanes:			
Cyclohexane	C_6H_{12}	25	93.81
		80.74	85.6
Methylcyclohexane	C_7H_{14}	25	86.07
		100.94	76.9
Ethylcyclohexane	C_8H_{16}	25	86.21
		131.79	73.7
1,1-Dimethylcyclohexane	C_8H_{16}	25	80.9
		119.50	70.7
cis-1,2-Dimethylcyclohexane	C_8H_{16}	25	84.59
		129.73	72.9
trans-1,2-Dimethylcyclohexane	C_8H_{16}	25	81.70
		123.42	71.1
cis-1,3-Dimethylcyclohexane	C_8H_{16}	25	83.49
		124.45	72.1
trans-1,3-Dimethylcyclohexane	C_8H_{16}	25	81.42
		120.09	70.9
cis-1,4-Dimethylcyclohexane	C_8H_{16}	25	83.13
		124.32	71.9
trans-1,4-Dimethylcyclohexane	C_8H_{16}	25	80.67
		119.35	70.4
Monoolefins.			
Ethene (ethylene)	C_2H_4	−103.71	115.39
Propene (propylene)	C_3H_6	−47.70	104.62
1-Butene	C_4H_8	25	86.8
		−6.25	93.36
cis-2-Butene	C_4H_8	25	94.5
		3.72	99.46
trans-2-Butene	C_4H_8	25	91.8
		0.88	96.94
2-Methylpropene (isobutene)	C_4H_8	25	87.7
		−6.90	94.22

Non-hydrocarbon compounds	Formula	Temperature, °C.	ΔHv, cal./g.
Acetal	$C_6H_{14}O_2$	102.9	66.18
Acetaldehyde	C_2H_4O	21	136.17
Acetic acid	$C_2H_4O_2$	118.3	96.75
		140	94.37
		220	81.23
		321	0
anhydride	$C_4H_6O_3$	137	92.2
Acetone	C_3H_6O	0	134.74
		20	131.87
		40	128.05
		60	123.51
		80	118.26
		100	112.76
		235	0

Table 3-171. Heats of Vaporization of Organic Compounds—(*Concluded*)

Non-hydrocarbon compounds	Formula	Temperature, °C.	ΔHv, cal./g.
Acetonitrile	C_2H_3N	80	173.68
Acetophenone	C_8H_8O	203.7	77.16
Acetyl chloride	C_2H_3ClO	51	78.84
Air	....	....	51.0
Allyl alcohol	C_3H_6O	96	163.41
Amyl alcohol (n-)	$C_5H_{11}OH$	131	120.17
alcohol (t-)	$C_5H_{11}OH$	102	105.83
amine (n-)	$C_5H_{13}N$	95	98.67
bromide (n-)	$C_5H_{11}Br$	129	48.26
ether (n-)	$C_{10}H_{22}O$	170	69.52
iodide (n-)	$C_5H_{11}I$	155	47.54
methyl ketone (n-)	$C_7H_{14}O$	149.2	82.66
Amylene	C_5H_{10}	12.5	75.01
Anethole (p-)	$C_{10}H_{12}O$	232	71.43
Aniline	C_6H_7N	183	103.68
Benzaldehyde	C_7H_6O	179	86.48
Benzonitrile	C_7H_5N	189	87.68
Benzyl alcohol	C_7H_8O	204.3	112.28
Butyl acetate (n-)	$C_6H_{12}O_2$	124	73.82
alcohol (n-)	$C_4H_{10}O$	116.8	141.26
alcohol (s-)	$C_4H_{10}O$	98.1	134.38
alcohol (t-)	$C_4H_{10}O$	83	130.44
formate	$C_4H_{10}O_2$	105.1	86.74
methyl ketone (n-)	$C_6H_{12}O$	127	82.42
propionate (n-)	$C_7H_{14}O_2$	144.9	71.74
Butyric acid (n-)	$C_4H_8O_2$	163.5	113.96
Butyronitrile (n-)	C_4H_7N	117.4	114.91
Bromobenzene	C_6H_5Br	155.9	57.60
Capronitrile	$C_6H_{11}N$	156	88.15
Carbon disulfide	CS_2	0	89.35
		46.25	84.09
		100	75.49
		140	67.37
tetrachloride	CCl_4	0	52.06
		76.75	46.42
		200	32.73
Carvacrol	$C_{10}H_{14}O$	237	68.09
Chloral	C_2HCl_3O	....	53.99
hydrate	$C_2H_3Cl_3O_2$	96	131.87
Chlorobenzene	C_6H_5Cl	130.6	77.59
Chloroethyl alcohol (2-)	C_2H_5ClO	126.[illegible]	122.94
acetate (β-)	$C_4H_7ClO_2$	141.5	80.75
Chloroform	$CHCl_3$	0	64.74
		40	60.92
		61.5	59.01
		100	55.19
		260	0
Chlorotoluene (o-)	C_7H_7Cl	158.1	72.63
(p-)	C_7H_7Cl	160.4	73.13
Cresol (m-)	C_7H_8O	202	100.58
Cyanogen	$(CN)_2$	0	102.97
chloride	$CNCl$	13	134.98
Cyclohexanol	$C_6H_{12}O$	161.1	108.22
Cycohexyl chloride	$C_6H_{11}Cl$	142.0	74.78
Dichloroacetic acid	$C_2H_2Cl_2O_2$	194.4	77.16
Dichlorodifluormethane	CCl_2F_2	−29.8	40.40
Diethylamine	$C_4H_{11}N$	58	91.02
carbonate	$C_5H_{10}O_3$	126	73.10
ketone	$C_5H_{10}O$	101	90.78
oxalate	$C_6H_{10}O_4$	185	67.61
Di-isobutylamine	$C_8H_{19}N$	134	65.70
Dimethyl aniline	$C_8H_{11}N$	193	80.75
carbonate	$C_3H_6O_3$	90	88.15
Dipropyl ketone	$C_7H_{14}O$	143.5	75.73
Dipropylamine (n-)	$C_6H_{15}N$	108	75.73
Ethyl acetate	$C_4H_8O_2$	0.0	102.01
alcohol	C_2H_6O	78.3	204.26
Ethylamine	C_2H_7N	15	145.97
Ethyl benzoate	$C_9H_{10}O_2$	213	64.50
bromide	C_2H_5Br	38.4	59.92
butyrate (n-)	$C_6H_{12}O_2$	118.9	74.68
caprylate	$C_{10}H_{20}O_2$	207	60.44
chloride	C_2H_5Cl	4.7	92.93
		15.0	92.45
		20.0	92.22
		25.0	91.98
Ethylene bromide	$C_2H_4Br_2$	130.8	46.23
chloride	$C_2H_4Cl_2$	0	85.29
		82.3	77.33
glycol	$C_2H_6O_2$	197	191.12
oxide	C_2H_4O	13	138.56
Ethyl ether	$C_4H_{10}O$	34.6	83.85
formate	$C_3H_6O_2$	53.3	97.18
iodide	C_2H_5I	71.2	45.61
Ethylidine chloride	$C_2H_4Cl_2$	0.0	76.69
		60	67.13
Ethyl isobutyl ether	$C_6H_{14}O$	79.0	74.78
isobutyrate	$C_6H_{12}O_2$	109.2	72.05
isovalerate	$C_7H_{14}O_2$	144	67.85
methyl ketone	C_4H_8O	78.2	105.93
methyl ketoxime	C_4H_9NO	182	115.87

Non-hydrocarbon compounds	Formula	Temperature, °C.	ΔHv, cal./g.
Ethyl nonylate	$C_{11}H_{22}O_2$	227	58.05
propionate	$C_5H_{10}O_2$	97.6	80.08
propyl ether	$C_5H_{12}O$	60	82.66
valerate (n-)	$C_7H_{14}O_2$	98	77.16
Formic acid	CH_2O_2	101	119.93
Furane	C_4H_4O	31	95.32
Furfural	$C_5H_4O_2$	160.5	107.51
Heptyl alcohol (n-)	$C_7H_{16}O$	176	104.88
Hexylmethyl ketone	$C_8H_{16}O$	173	74.06
Hydrogen cyanide	HCN	20	210.23
Isoamyl acetate	$C_7H_{14}O_2$	143.6	69.04
alcohol	$C_5H_{12}O$	130.2	119.78
butyrate (n-)	$C_9H_{18}O_2$	169	61.88
formate	$C_6H_{12}O_2$	123	73.58
isobutyrate	$C_9H_{18}O_2$	168	57.57
propionate	$C_8H_{16}O_2$	161	65.22
valerate (n-)	$C_{10}H_{20}O_2$	187	56.14
Isobutyl acetate	$C_6H_{12}O_2$	115.3	73.75
alcohol	$C_4H_{10}O$	106.9	138.08
butyrate (n-)	$C_8H_{16}O_2$	157	64.50
formate	$C_5H_{10}O_2$	97	78.50
isovalerate	$C_9H_{18}O_2$	169	60.44
isobutyrate	$C_8H_{16}O_2$	148	63.31
propionate	$C_7H_{14}O_2$	137	65.94
valerate (n-)	$C_9H_{18}O_2$	169	57.81
Isobutyric acid	$C_4H_8O_2$	154	111.57
Isopropyl alcohol	C_3H_8O	82.3	159.35
methyl ketone	$C_5H_{10}O$	92	89.83
Isovaleric acid	$C_5H_{10}O_2$	176.3	101.05
Limonene	$C_{10}H_{16}$	165	69.52
Mesityl oxide	$C_6H_{10}O$	128	85.77
Methyl acetate	$C_3H_6O_2$	0.0	113.96
		56.3	98.09
Methylal	$C_3H_8O_2$	42	89.83
Methyl alcohol	CH_4O	0	284.29
		64.7	262.79
		100	241.29
		160	193.51
		200	148.12
		220	109.89
		240	0
amyl ketone (n-)	$C_7H_{14}O$	149.2	82.66
aniline	C_7H_9N	194	95.56
butyl ketone (n-)	$C_6H_{12}O$	127	82.42
butyrate (n-)	$C_5H_{10}O_2$	102.6	79.79
chloride	CH_3Cl	−23.8	102.25
		+15.0	96.04
		20.0	95.32
		25.0	94.60
ethyl ketone	C_4H_8O	78.2	105.93
ethyl ketoxime	C_4H_9NO	182	115.87
formate	$C_2H_4O_2$	31.3	112.35
hexyl ketone	$C_8H_{16}O$	173	74.06
iodide	CH_3I	42	45.87
isobutyrate	$C_5H_{10}O_2$	91.1	78.12
isopropyl ketone	$C_5H_{10}O$	92	89.83
isovalerate	$C_6H_{12}O_2$	116	72.39
phenyl ether	C_7H_8O	153	81.46
propionate	$C_4H_8O_2$	79.0	87.56
valerate (n-)	$C_6H_{12}O_2$	116	70.00
Naphthalene	$C_{10}H_8$	218	75.49
Nitrobenzene	$C_6H_5NO_2$	210	79.08
Nitromethane	CH_3NO_2	99.9	134.98
Octyl alcohol (n-)	$C_8H_{18}O$	196	97.47
alcohol (dl-) (sec-)	$C_8H_{18}O$	180	94.37
Phenyl methyl ether	C_7H_8O	153	81.46
Picoline (α-)	C_6H_7N	129	90.78
Piperidine	$C_5H_{11}N$	106	89.35
Propionic acid	$C_3H_6O_2$	139.3	98.81
Propionitrile	C_3H_5N	97	134.26
Propyl acetate (n-)	$C_5H_{10}O_2$	100.4	80.27
alcohol (n-)	C_3H_8O	97.2	164.36
butyrate (n-)	$C_7H_{14}O_2$	143.6	68.33
formate (n-)	$C_4H_8O_2$	80.0	88.13
isobutyrate (n-)	$C_7H_{14}O_2$	134	63.79
isovalerate (n-)	$C_8H_{16}O_2$	156	64.50
propionate (n-)	$C_6H_{12}O_2$	120.6	73.15
Pyridine	C_5H_5N	114.1	107.36
Salicylaldehyde	$C_7H_6O_2$	196	74.78
Tetrachloroethane (1,1,2,2-)	$C_2H_2Cl_4$	145	55.07
Tetrachloroethylene	C_2Cl_4	120.7	50.05
Toluidine (o-)	C_7H_9N	198	95.08
Trichloroethylene	C_2HCl_3	85.7	57.24
Valeronitrile (n-)	C_5H_9N	129	96.28

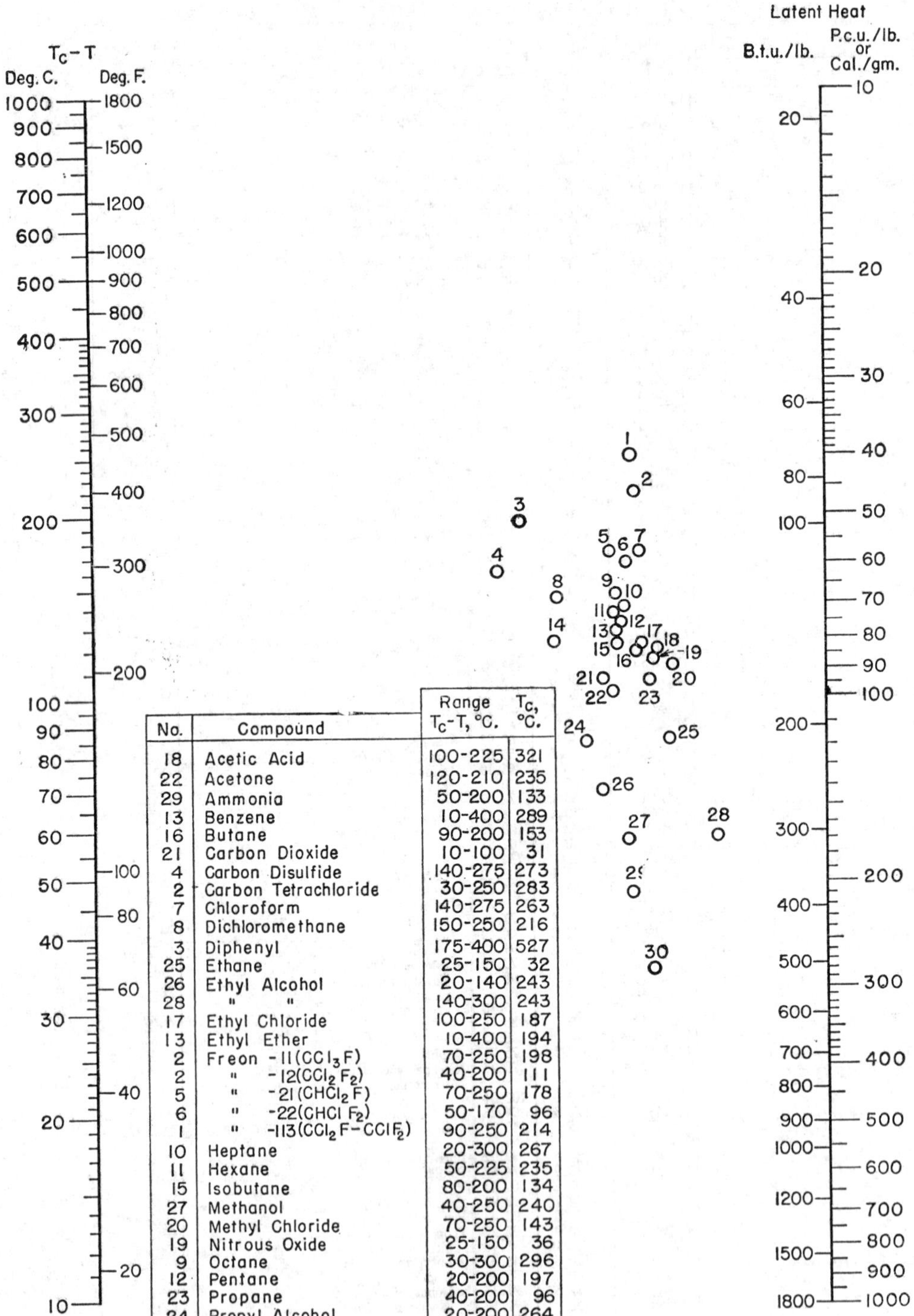

No.	Compound	Range T_c-T, °C.	T_c, °C.
18	Acetic Acid	100-225	321
22	Acetone	120-210	235
29	Ammonia	50-200	133
13	Benzene	10-400	289
16	Butane	90-200	153
21	Carbon Dioxide	10-100	31
4	Carbon Disulfide	140-275	273
2	Carbon Tetrachloride	30-250	283
7	Chloroform	140-275	263
8	Dichloromethane	150-250	216
3	Diphenyl	175-400	527
25	Ethane	25-150	32
26	Ethyl Alcohol	20-140	243
28	" "	140-300	243
17	Ethyl Chloride	100-250	187
13	Ethyl Ether	10-400	194
2	Freon -11(CCl_3F)	70-250	198
2	" -12(CCl_2F_2)	40-200	111
5	" -21($CHCl_2F$)	70-250	178
6	" -22($CHClF_2$)	50-170	96
1	" -113(CCl_2F-$CClF_2$)	90-250	214
10	Heptane	20-300	267
11	Hexane	50-225	235
15	Isobutane	80-200	134
27	Methanol	40-250	240
20	Methyl Chloride	70-250	143
19	Nitrous Oxide	25-150	36
9	Octane	30-300	296
12	Pentane	20-200	197
23	Propane	40-200	96
24	Propyl Alcohol	20-200	264
14	Sulfur Dioxide	90-160	157
30	Water	100-500	374

FIG. 3-9. Latent heat of vaporization. (*Chilton, Colburn, and Vernon, personal communication. Based mainly on data from "International Critical Tables."*)

Table 3-172. Heats of Fusion of Miscellaneous Materials

Material	M.p., °C.	Heat of fusion, cal./g.
Alloys		
30.5 Pb + 69.5 Sn	183	17
36.9 Pb + 63.1 Sn	179	15.5
63.7 Pb + 36.3 Sn	177.5	11.6
77.8 Pb + 22.2 Sn	176.5	9.54
1 Pb + 9 Sn	236	28
24 Pb + 27.3 Sn + 48.7 Bi	98.8	6.85
25.8 Pb + 14.7 Sn + 52.4 Bi + 7 Cd	75.5	8.4
Silicates		
Anorthite ($CaAl_2Si_2O_8$)	.....	100
Orthoclase ($KAlSi_2O_8$)	.....	100
Microcline ($KAlSi_3O_8$)	.....	83
Wollastonite ($CaSiO_3$)	.....	100
Malacolite ($Ca_3MgSi_4O_{12}$)	.....	94
Diopside ($CaMgSi_2O_6$)	.....	100
Olivine (Mg_2SiO_4)	.....	130
Fayalite (Fe_2SiO_4)	.....	85
Spermaceti	43.9	37.0
Wax (bees')	61.8	42.3

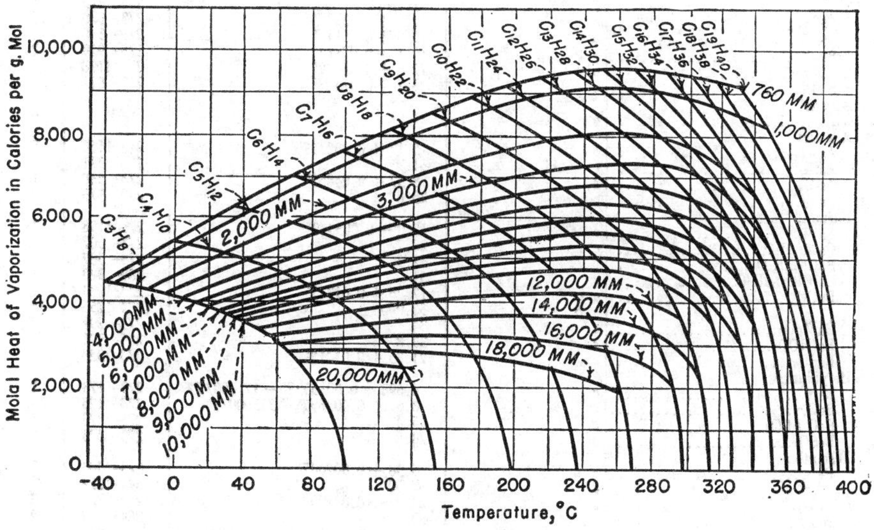

FIG. 3-10. Molal heats of vaporization of hydrocarbons. [*Schultz, Ind. Eng. Chem.*, **22**, 785 (1930).]

SPECIFIC HEATS OF PURE COMPOUNDS

Table 3-173. Heat Capacities of the Elements and Inorganic Compounds*

Substance	State†	Heat capacity at constant pressure (T = °K.; 0°C. = 273.1°K.), cal./deg. mol	Range of temperature, °K.	Uncertainty, %
Aluminum:[1]				
Al	c	$4.80 + 0.00322T$	273– 931	1
	l	7.00	931–1273	5
$AlBr_3$	c	$18.74 + 0.01866T$	273– 370	3
	l	29.5	370– 407	5
$AlCl_3$	c	$13.25 + 0.02800T$	273– 465	3
	l	31.2	465– 504	3
$AlCl_3.6H_2O$	c	76	288– 327	?
AlF_3	c	19.3	288– 326	?
$AlF_3.3\frac{1}{2}H_2O$	c	50.5	288– 326	?
$AlF_3.3NaF$	c	$38.63 + 0.04760T - 449200/T^2$	273–1273	2
	l	142	1273–1373	?
AlI_3	c	$16.88 + 0.02266T$	273– 464	3
	l	28.8	464– 480	5
Al_2O_3	c	$22.08 + 0.008971T - 522500/T^2$	273–1973	3
$Al_2O_3.SiO_2$	c, sillimanite	$40.79 + 0.004763T - 992800/T^2$	273–1573	3
	c, disthene	$41.81 + 0.005283T - 1211000/T^2$	273–1673	2
	c, andalusite	$43.96 + 0.001923T - 1086000/T^2$	273–1573	3
$3Al_2O_3.2SiO_2$	c, mullite	$59.65 + 0.0670T$	273– 576	5
$4Al_2O_3.3SiO_2$	c	$113.2 + 0.0652T$	273– 575	3
$Al_2(SO_4)_3$	c	63.5	273– 373	?
$Al_2(SO_4)_3.18H_2O$	c	235	288– 325	?
Antimony:				
Sb	c	$5.51 + 0.00178T$	273– 903	2
	l	7.15	903–1273	5
$SbBr_3$	c	$17.2 + 0.0293T$	273– 370	?
$SbCl_3$	c	$10.3 + 0.0511T$	273– 346	?
Sb_2O_3	c	$19.1 + 0.0171T$	273– 929	?
Sb_2O_4	c	$22.6 + 0.0162T$	273–1198	?
Sb_2S_3	c	$24.2 + 0.0132T$	273– 821	?
Argon:[2]				
A	g	4.97	All	0
Arsenic:				
As	c	$5.17 + 0.00234T$	273–1168	5
$AsCl_3$	l	31.9	286– 371	?
As_2O_3	c	$8.37 + 0.0486T$	273– 548	?
As_2S_3	c	25.8	293– 373	?
Barium:				
$BaCl_2$	c	$17.0 + 0.00334T$	273–1198	?
$BaCl_2.H_2O$	c	28.2	273– 307	?
$BaCl_2.2H_2O$	c	37.3	273– 307	?
$Ba(ClO_3)_2.H_2O$	c	51	289– 320	?
$BaCO_3$	c, α	$17.26 + 0.0131T$	273–1083	5
	c, β	30.0	1083–1255	15
$BaMoO_4$	c	34	273– 297	?
$Ba(NO_3)_2$	c	39.8	285– 371	?
$BaSO_4$	c	$21.35 + 0.0141T$	273–1323	5
Beryllium:[3]				
Be	c	$4.698 + 0.001555T - 121000/T^2$	273–1173	1
BeO	c	$8.69 + 0.00365T - 313000/T^2$	273–1175	5
$BeO.Al_2O_3$	c	25.4	273– 373	?
$BeSO_4$	c	20.8	273– 373	?
Bismuth:[4]				
Bi	c	$5.38 + 0.00260T$	273– 544	3
	l	7.60	544–1273	3
Bi_2O_3	c	$23.27 + 0.01105T$	273– 777	2
Bi_2S_3	c	30.4	284– 372	?
Boron:				
B	c	$1.54 + 0.00440T$	273–1174	5
B_2O_3	gls	$5.14 + 0.0320T$	273– 513	3
	gls	30.4	513– 623	3
BN	c	$1.61 + 0.00400T$	273–1173	5
Bromine:				
Br_2	g	9.00	300–2000	5
Cadmium:				
Cd	c	$5.46 + 0.002466T$	273– 594	1
	l	7.13	594– 973	5
CdO	c	$9.65 + 0.00208T$	273–2086	?
CdS	c	$12.9 + 0.00090T$	273–1273	?
$CdSO_4.8/3H_2O$	c	51.3	293	?
Calcium:				
Ca	c	$5.31 + 0.00333T$	273– 673	2
	c	$6.29 + 0.00140T$	673– 873	2
$CaCl_2$	c	$16.9 + 0.00386T$	273–1055	?
$CaCO_3$	c	$19.68 + 0.01189T - 307600/T^2$	273–1033	3
CaF_2	c	$14.7 + 0.00380T$	273–1651	?
$CaMg(CO_3)_2$	c	40.1	299– 372	?
$CaMoO_4$	c	33	273– 297	?
CaO	c	$10.00 + 0.00484T - 108000/T^2$	273–1173	2
$Ca(OH)_2$	c	21.4	276– 373	?
$CaO.Al_2O_3.2SiO_2$	c, anorthite	$63.13 + 0.01500T - 1537000/T^2$	273–1673	1
	gls	$67.41 + 0.01048T - 1874000/T^2$	273– 973	1

* From Kelley, *U.S. Bur. Mines Bull.* 371, 1934. For a revision see Kelley, *U.S. Bur. Mines Bull.* 477, 1948. Data for many elements and compounds are given by Johnson (ed.), WADD-TR-60-56, 1960, for cryogenic temperatures. For miscellaneous references to steels see Janis, International Nickel Co. bibliography. For empirical equations for 117 gases to 1000°K. or even higher temperatures see Spencer, *Ind. Eng. Chem.*, **40**, 2152 (1948). For a quadratic fit in terms of temperature for hydrocarbons see Vvedenskii, *Neftyanoe Khoz.*, **25**, 47 (1947). Tabulated data for gases can be obtained from many of the references cited in the Thermodynamic Properties Subsection and other tables in this section. For sources to more recent information see the footnote to Table 3-169, p. 3-107.

† The symbols in this column have the following meaning; *c*, crystal; *l*, liquid; *g*, gas; *gls*, glass.

Table 3-173. Heat Capacities of the Elements and Inorganic Compounds—(*Continued*)

Substance	State†	Heat capacity at constant pressure (T = °K.; 0°C. = 273.1°K.), cal./deg. mol	Range of temperature, °K.	Uncertainty, %
Calcium—(*Cont.*):				
$CaO.MgO.2SiO_2$	*c*, diopside	$54.46 + 0.005746T - 1500000/T^2$	273–1573	1
	gls	$51.68 + 0.009724T - 1308000/T^2$	273– 973	1
$CaO.SiO_2$	*c*, wollastonite	$27.95 + 0.002056T - 745600/T^2$	273–1573	1
	c, pseudowollastonite	$25.48 + 0.004132T - 488100/T^2$	273–1673	1
	gls	$23.16 + 0.009672T - 487100/T^2$	273– 973	1
CaP_2O_6	*c*	39.5	287– 371	?
$CaSO_4$	*c*	$18.52 + 0.02197T - 156800/T^2$	273–1373	5
$CaSO_4.2H_2O$	*c*	46.8	282– 373	?
$CaWO_4$	*c*	27.9	292– 322	?
Carbon:[5]				
C	*c*, graphite	$2.673 + 0.002617T - 116900/T^2$	273–1373	2
	c, diamond	$2.162 + 0.003059T - 130300/T^2$	273–1313	3
CH_4	*g*	$5.34 + 0.0115T$	273–1200	2
CO[6]	*g*	$6.60 + 0.00120T$	273–2500	1½
CO_2	*g*	$10.34 + 0.00274T - 195500/T^2$	273–1200	1½
CS_2	*l*	18.4	293	?
Cerium:				
Ce	*c*	$5.88 + 0.00123T$	273– 908	?
CeO_2	*c*	15.1	273– 373	?
$Ce_2(MoO_4)_3$	*c*	96	273– 297	?
$Ce_2(SO_4)_3$	*c*	66.4	273– 373	?
$Ce_2(SO_4)_3.5H_2O$	*c*	131.6	273– 319	?
Cesium:				
Cs	*c*	$1.96 + 0.0182T$	273– 301	3
	l	8.00	302	3
	g	4.97	All	0
CsBr	*c*	$12.6 + 0.00259T$	273– 909	?
CsCl	*c*	$11.7 + 0.00309T$	273– 752	?
CsF	*c*	$11.3 + 0.00285T$	273– 957	?
CsI	*c*	$11.6 + 0.00268T$	273– 894	?
Chlorine:				
Cl_2	*g*	$8.28 + 0.00056T$	273–2000	1½
Chromium:[7]				
Cr	*c*	$4.84 + 0.00295T$	273–1823	5
	l	9.70	1823–1923	10
$CrCl_3$	*c*	23	286– 319	?
Cr_2O_3	*c*	$26.0 + 0.00400T$	273–2263	?
CrSb	*c*	$12.3 + 0.00120T$	273–1383	?
$CrSb_2$	*c*	$19.2 + 0.00184T$	273– 949	?
$Cr_2(SO_4)_3$	*c*	67.4	273– 373	?
Cobalt:[8]				
Co	*c*	$5.12 + 0.00333T$	273–1763	5
	l	8.40	1763–1873	5
$CoAs_2.CoS_2$	*c*	32.9	283– 373	?
CoSb	*c*	$11.7 + 0.00156T$	273–1464	?
Co_2Sn	*c*	$15.83 + 0.00950T$	273– 903	2
CoS	*c*	$10.6 + 0.00251T$	273–1373	?
$CoSo_4.7H_2O$	*c*	96	286– 303	?
Copper:[9]				
Cu	*c*	$5.44 + 0.001462T$	273–1357	1
	l	7.50	1357–1573	3
CuAl	*c*	$9.88 + 0.00500T$	273– 733	2
$CuAl_2$	*c*	$16.78 + 0.00366T$	273– 773	2
Cu_3Al	*c*	$19.61 + 0.01054T$	273– 775	2
CuI	*c*	$12.1 + 0.00286T$	273– 675	?
CuI_2	*c*	20.1	274– 328	?
CuO	*c*	$10.87 + 0.003576T - 150600/T^2$	273– 810	2
$CuO.SiO_2.H_2O$	*c*	29	293– 323	?
CuS	*c*	$10.6 + 0.00264T$	273–1273	?
Cu_2S	*c*, α	$9.38 + 0.0312T$	273– 376	3
	c, β	20.9	376–1173	2
CuS.FeS	*c*	24	292– 321	?
Cu_2Sb	*c*	$13.73 + 0.01350T$	273– 573	2
Cu_2Sb	*c*	$21.79 + 0.00900T$	273– 693	2
Cu_2Se	*c*, α	20.85	273– 383	5
	c, β	20.35	383– 488	5
Cu_3Si	*c*	$21.3 + 0.00587T$	273–1135	?
$CuSO_4$	*c*	24.1	282	?
$CuSO_4.H_2O$	*c*	31.3	282	?
$CuSO_4.3H_2O$	*c*	49.0	282	?
$CuSO_4.5H_2O$	*c*	67.2	282	?
Fluorine:[10]				
F_2	*g*	$6.50 + 0.00100T$	300–3000	5
Gallium:				
Ga_2O_3	*c*	$18.2 + 0.0252T$	273– 923	?
$Ga_2(SO_4)_3$	*c*	62.4	273– 373	?
Germanium:[11]				
Ge	*c*			
Gold:				
Au	*c*	$5.61 + 0.00144T$	273–1336	2
	l	7.00	1336–1573	5
$AuSb_2$	*c*, α	$17.12 + 0.00465T$	273– 628	1
	c, βγ	$11.47 + 0.01756T$	628– 713	?
Helium:[12]				
He	*g*	4.97	All	0
Hydrogen:[13]				
H	*g*	4.97	All	0
H_2	*g*	$6.62 + 0.00081T$	273–2500	2
HBr	*g*	$6.80 + 0.00084T$	273–2000	2

Table 3-173. Heat Capacities of the Elements and Inorganic Compounds—(*Continued*)

Substance	State†	Heat capacity at constant pressure (T = °K.; 0°C. = 273.1°K.), cal./deg. mol	Range of temperature, °K.	Uncertainty, %
Hydrogen—(*Cont.*):				
HCl	g	$6.70 + 0.00084T$	273–2000	1½
HI	g	$6.93 + 0.00083T$	273–2000	2
H_2O	l	See Table 3-174		
	g	$8.22 + 0.00015T + 0.00000134T^2$	300–2500	?
H_2S	g	$7.20 + 0.00360T$	300– 600	8
$H_2S_2O_7$	c	27	281	?
	l	58	308	?
Indium:[14]				
In	c			
Iodine:				
I_2	g	9.00	300–2000	5
Iridium:				
Ir	c	$5.50 + 0.00148T$	273–1873	1
Iron:[15]				
Fe	c, α	$4.13 + 0.00638T$	273–1041	3
	c, β	$6.12 + 0.00336T$	1041–1179	3
	c, γ	8.40	1179–1674	5
	c, δ	10.0	1674–1803	5
	l	8.15	1803–1873	5
$FeAs_2$	c	17.8	283– 373	?
Fe_3C	c	$25.17 + 0.00223T$	273–1173	10
$FeCO_3$	c	22.7	293– 368	?
FeO	c	$12.62 + 0.001492T - 76200/T^2$	273–1173	2
Fe_2O_3	c	$24.72 + 0.01604T - 423400/T^2$	273–1097	2
Fe_3O_4	c	$41.17 + 0.01882T - 979500/T^2$	273–1065	2
$Fe_2O_3.3H_2O$	c	47.8	286– 373	?
FeS	c, α	$2.03 + 0.0390T$	273– 411	5
	c, β	$12.05 + 0.00273T$	411–1468	3
FeS_2	c	$10.7 + 0.01336T$	273– 773	?
FeSi	c	$10.54 + 0.00458T$	273– 903	2
Fe_2SiO_4	c	$33.57 + 0.01907T - 879700/T^2$	273–1161	2
$FeSO_4$	c	22	293– 373	?
$Fe_2(SO_4)_3$	c	66.2	273– 373	?
$FeSO_4.4H_2O$	c	63.6	282	?
$FeSO_4.7H_2O$	c	96	291– 319	?
Krypton:				
Kr	g	4.97	All	0
Lanthanum:[16]				
La	c	$5.91 + 0.00100T$	273–1009	?
La_2O_3	c	$22.6 + 0.00544T$	273–2273	?
$La_2(MoO_4)_3$	c	86	273– 307	?
$La_2(SO_4)_3$	c	66.9	273– 373	?
$La_2(SO_4)_3.9H_2O$	c	152	273– 319	?
Lead:[17]				
Pb	c	$5.77 + 0.00202T$	273– 600	2
	l	6.8	600–1273	5
$Pb_3(AsO_4)_2$	c	65.5	286– 370	?
PbB_2O_4	c	26.5	288– 371	?
PbB_4O_7	c	41.4	289– 371	?
$PbBr_2$	c	$18.13 + 0.00310T$	273– 761	2
	l	27.4	761– 860	10
$PbCl_2$	c	$15.88 + 0.00835T$	273– 771	2
	l	27.2	771– 851	10
$2PbCl_2.NH_4Cl$	c	53.1	293	?
$PbCO_3$	c	21.1	286– 320	?
$PbCrO_4$	c	29.1	292– 323	?
PbF_2	c	$16.5 + 0.00412T$	273–1091	?
PbI_2	c	$18.66 + 0.00293T$	273– 648	2
	l	32.3	648– 776	20
$PbMoO_4$	c	30.4	292– 322	?
$Pb(NO_3)_2$	c	36.4	286– 320	?
PbO	c	$10.33 + 0.00318T$	273– 544	2
PbO_2	c	$12.7 + 0.00780T$	273– ?	?
$Pb_2P_2O_7$	c	48.3	284– 371	?
PbS	c	$10.63 + 0.00401T$	273– 873	3
$PbSO_4$	c	26.4	293– 372	?
PbS_2O_3	c	29	293– 373	?
$PbWO_4$	c	35	273– 297	?
Lithium:				
Li	c	$0.68 + 0.0180T$	273– 459	10
	g	4.97	All	0
LiBr	c	$11.5 + 0.00302T$	273– 825	?
$LiBr.H_2O$	c	22.6	278– 318	?
LiCl	c	$11.0 + 0.00339T$	273– 887	?
$LiCl.H_2O$	c	23.6	279– 360	?
LiF	c	$8.20 + 0.00520T$	273–1117	?
LiI	c	$12.5 + 0.00208T$	273– 723	?
$LiI.H_2O$	c	23.6	277– 359	?
$LiI.2H_2O$	c	32.9	277– 345	?
$LiI.3H_2O$	c	43.2	277– 347	?
$LiNO_3$	c	$9.17 + 0.0360T$	273– 523	5
	l	26.8	523– 575	5
Magnesium:[18]				
Mg	c	$6.20 + 0.00133T - 67800/T^2$	273– 923	1
	l	7.4	923–1048	10
MgAg	c	$10.58 + 0.00412T$	273– 905	2
Mg_4Al_3	c	$34.4 + 0.0198T$	273– 736	?
MgAu	c	$11.3 + 0.00189T$	273–1433	?
Mg_2Au	c	$16.2 + 0.00451T$	273–1073	?

Table 3-173. Heat Capacities of the Elements and Inorganic Compounds—(*Continued*)

Substance	State†	Heat capacity at constant pressure (T = °K.; 0°C. = 273.1°K.), cal./deg. mol	Range of tempera-ture, °K.	Uncer-tainty, %
Magnesium—(*Cont.*):				
Mg_3Au	*c*	$21.2 + 0.00614T$	273–1103	?
$MgCl_2$	*c*	$17.3 + 0.00377T$	273– 991	?
$MgCl_2.6H_2O$	*c*	77.1	292– 342	?
$MgCO_3$	*c*	16.9	290	?
$MgCu_2$	*c*	$14.96 + 0.00776T$	273– 903	3
Mg_2Cu	*c*	$15.5 + 0.00652T$	273– 843	?
$MgNi_2$	*c*	$15.87 + 0.00692T$	273– 903	2
MgO	*c*	$10.86 + 0.001197T - 208700/T^2$	273–2073	2
$MgO.Al_2O_3$	*c*	28	288– 319	?
$MgO.SiO_2$	*c*, amphibole	$25.60 + 0.004380T - 674200/T^2$	273–1373	1
	c, pyroxene	$23.35 + 0.008062T - 558800/T^2$	273– 773	1
	gls	$23.30 + 0.007734T - 542000/T^2$	273– 973	1
$6MgO.MgCl_2.8B_2O_3$	*c*, α	$58.7 + 0.408T$	273– 538	5
	c, β	$107.2 + 0.2876T$	538– 623	5
$Mg(OH)_2$	*c*	18.2	292– 323	?
Mg_3Sb_2	*c*	$28.2 + 0.00560T$	273–1234	?
Mg_2Si	*c*	$15.4 + 0.00415T$	273–1343	?
$MgSO_4$	*c*	26.7	296– 372	?
$MgSO_4.H_2O$	*c*	33	282	?
$MgSO_4.6H_2O$	*c*	80	282	?
$MgSO_4.7H_2O$	*c*	89	291– 319	?
Manganese:				
Mn	*c*, α	$3.76 + 0.00747T$	273–1108	5
	c, β	$5.06 + 0.00395T$	1108–1317	5
	c, γ	$4.80 + 0.00422T$	1317–1493	5
	l	11.0	1493–1673	10
$MnCl_2$	*c*	$16.2 + 0.00520T$	273– 923	?
$MnCO_3$	*c*	$7.79 + 0.0421T + 0.0000090T^2$	273– 773	?
MnO	*c*	$7.43 + 0.01038T - 0.00000362T^2$	273–1923	?
Mn_2O_3	*c*	$10.33 + 0.0530T - 0.0000257T^2$	273–1173	?
Mn_3O_4	*c*	$19.25 + 0.0538T - 0.0000209T^2$	273–1773	?
MnO_2	*c*	$1.92 + 0.0471T - 0.0000297T^2$	273– 773	?
$Mn_2O_3.H_2O$	*c*	31	291– 322	?
MnS	*c*	$10.21 + 0.00656T - 0.00000242T^2$	273–1883	?
$MnSO_4$	*c*	27.5	293– 373	?
$MnSO_4.5H_2O$	*c*	78	290– 319	?
Mercury:[19]				
Hg	*l*	6.61	273– 630	1
	g	4.97	All	0
Hg_2	*g*	9.00	300–2000	5
$HgCl$	*c*	$11.05 + 0.00370T$	273– 798	?
$HgCl_2$	*c*	$15.3 + 0.0103T$	273– 553	?
$Hg(CN)_2$	*c*	25	285– 319	?
HgI	*c*	$11.4 + 0.00461T$	273– 563	?
HgI_2	*c*, α	$17.4 + 0.004001T$	273– 403	3
	c, β	20.2	403– 523	3
HgO	*c*	11.5	278– 371	?
HgS	*c*	$10.9 + 0.00365T$	273– 853	?
Hg_2SO_4	*c*	31.0	273– 307	?
Molybdenum:				
Mo	*c*	$5.69 + 0.00188T - 50300/T^2$	273–1773	5
MoO_3	*c*	$15.1 + 0.0121T$	273–1068	?
MoS_2	*c*	$19.7 + 0.00315T$	273– 729	?
Neon:[20]				
Ne	*g*	4.97	All	0
Nickel:[21]				
Ni	*c*, α	$4.26 + 0.00640T$	273– 626	2
	c, β	$6.99 + 0.000905T$	626–1725	5
	l	8.55	1725–1903	10
NiO	*c*	$11.3 + 0.00215T$	273–1273	?
NiS	*c*	$9.25 + 0.00640T$	273– 597	3
Ni_2Si	*c*	$15.8 + 0.00329T$	273–1582	?
$NiSi$	*c*	$10.0 + 0.00312T$	273–1273	?
Ni_3Sn	*c*	$20.78 + 0.0102T$	273– 904	2
$NiSO_4$	*c*	33.4	293– 373	?
$NiSO_4.6H_2O$	*c*	82	291– 325	?
$NiTe$	*c*	$11.00 + 0.00433T$	273– 700	2
Nitrogen:[22]				
N_2	*g*	$6.50 + 0.00100T$	300–3000	3
NH_3	*g*	$6.70 + 0.00630T$	300– 800	1½
NH_4Br	*c*	22.8	274– 328	?
NH_4Cl	*c*, α	$9.80 + 0.0368T$	273– 457	5
	c, β	$5.0 + 0.0340T$	457– 523	5
NH_4I	*c*	17.8	273– 328	?
NH_4NO_3	*c*	31.8	273– 293	?
$(NH_4)_2SO_4$	*c*	51.6	275– 328	?
NO	*g*	$8.05 + 0.000233T - 156300/T^2$	300–5000	2
Osmium:				
Os	*c*	$5.686 + 0.000875T$	273–1877	1
Oxygen:[23]				
O_2	*g*	$8.27 + 0.000258T - 187700/T^2$	300–5000	1
Palladium:[24]				
Pd	*c*	$5.41 + 0.00184T$	273–1822	2
Phosphorus:				
P	*c*, yellow	5.50	273– 317	5
	c, red	$0.21 + 0.0180T$	273– 472	10
	l	6.6	317– 373	10
PCl_3	*l*	28.7	284– 371	?
P_4O_{10}	*c*	$15.72 + 0.1092T$	273– 631	2
	g	73.6	631–1371	3

Table 3-173. Heat Capacities of the Elements and Inorganic Compounds—(*Continued*)

Substance	State†	Heat capacity at constant pressure (T = °K.; 0°C. = 273.1°K.), cal./deg. mol	Range of temperature, °K.	Uncertainty, %
Platinum:[25]				
Pt	*c*	$5.92 + 0.00116T$	273–1873	1
Potassium:				
K	*c*	$5.24 + 0.00555T$	273– 336	5
	l	7.7	336– 373	5
	g	4.97	All	0
K_2	*g*	9.00	300–2000	5
$KAsO_3$	*c*	25.3	290– 372	?
KBO_2	*c*	$12.6 + 0.0126T$	273–1220	?
$K_2B_4O_7$	*c*	51.3	290– 372	?
KBr	*c*	$11.49 + 0.00360T$	273– 543	2
KCl	*c*	$10.93 + 0.00376T$	273–1043	2
$KClO_3$	*c*	25.7	289– 371	?
$KClO_4$	*c*	26.3	287– 318	?
$2KCl.CuCl_2.2H_2O$	*c*	63	292– 323	?
$2KCl.PtCl_4$	*c*	55	286– 319	?
$2KCl.SnCl_4$	*c*	54.5	292– 323	?
$2KCl.ZnCl_2$	*c*	43.4	279– 319	?
$2KCN.Zn(CN)_2$	*c*	57.4	277– 319	?
K_2CO_3	*c*	29.9	296– 372	?
K_2CrO_4	*c*	35.9	289– 371	?
$K_2Cr_2O_7$	*c*	$42.80 + 0.0410T$	273– 671	5
	l	96.9	671– 757	5
KF	*c*	$10.8 + 0.00284T$	273–1129	?
$K_4Fe(CN)_6$	*c*	80.1	273– 319	?
$K_4Fe(CN)_6.3H_2O$	*c*	114.5	273– 310	?
KH_2AsO_4	*c*	32	289– 319	?
KH_2PO_4	*c*	28.3	290– 320	?
$KHSO_4$	*c*	30	292– 324	?
$KMnO_4$	*c*	28	287– 318	?
KNO_3	*c*	$6.42 + 0.0530T$	273– 401	10
	c	28.8	401– 611	5
	l	29.5	611– 683	10
$K_2O.Al_2O_3.3SiO_2$	*c*, orthoclase	$69.26 + 0.00821T - 2331000/T^2$	273–1373	1½
	gls, orthoclase	$69.81 + 0.01053 - 2403000/T^2$	273–1373	1½
	c, microcline	$65.65 + 0.01102T - 1748000/T^2$	273–1373	1½
	gls, microcline	$64.83 + 0.01438T - 1641000/T^2$	273–1373	1½
$K_4P_2O_7$	*c*	63.1	290– 371	?
K_2SO_4	*c*	33.1	287– 371	?
$K_2S_2O_8$	*c*	37	293– 373	?
$K_2SO_4.Al_2(SO_4)_3.24H_2O$	*c*	352	292– 322	?
$K_2SO_4.Cr_2(SO_4)_3.24H_2O$	*c*	324	292– 324	?
$K_2SO_4.MgSO_4.6H_2O$	*c*	106	292– 323	?
$K_2SO_4.NiSO_4.6H_2O$	*c*	107	289– 319	?
$K_2SO_4.ZnSO_4.6H_2O$	*c*	120	293– 317	?
Prometheum:[26]				
Pr	*c*			
Radon:				
Rn	*g*	4.97	All	0
Rhenium:				
Re	*c*	$6.30 + 0.00053T$	273–2273	?
Rhodium:				
Rh	*c*	$5.40 + 0.00219T$	273–1877	2
Rubidium:				
Rb	*c*	$3.27 + 0.0131T$	273– 312	2
	l	7.85	312– 373	5
RbBr	*c*	$11.6 + 0.00255T$	273– 954	?
RbCl	*c*	$11.5 + 0.00249T$	273– 987	?
Rb_2CO_3	*c*	28.4	291– 320	?
RbF	*c*	$11.3 + 0.00256T$	273–1048	?
RbI	*c*	$11.6 + 0.00263T$	273– 913	?
Scandium:				
Sc_2O_3	*c*	21.1	273– 373	?
$Sc_2(SO_4)_3$	*c*	62.0	273– 373	?
Selenium:				
Se	*c*	$4.53 + 0.00550T$	273– 490	2
	l	8.35	490– 570	3
Silicon:[27]				
Si	*c*	$5.74 + 0.000617T - 101000/T^2$	273–1174	2
SiC	*c*	$8.89 + 0.00291T - 284000/T^2$	273–1629	2
$SiCl_4$	*l*	32.4	293– 373	?
SiO_2	*c*, quartz, α	$10.87 + 0.008712T - 241200/T^2$	273– 848	1
	c, quartz, β	$10.95 + 0.00550T$	848–1873	3½
	c, cristobalite, α	$3.65 + 0.0240T$	273– 523	2½
	c, cristobalite, β	$17.09 + 0.000454T - 897200/T^2$	523–1973	2
	gls	$12.80 + 0.00447T - 302000/T^2$	273–1973	3½
Silver:[28]				
Ag	*c*	$5.60 + 0.00150T$	273–1234	1
	l	8.2	1234–1573	3
Ag_3Al	*c*	$22.56 + 0.00570T$	273– 902	2
Ag_2Al	*c*	$16.85 + 0.00450T$	273– 903	2
$AgAl_{12}$	*c*	$58.62 + 0.0575T$	273– 768	5
AgBr	*c*	$8.58 + 0.0141T$	273– 703	6
	l	14.9	703– 836	5
AgCl	*c*	$9.60 + 0.00929T$	273– 728	2
	l	14.05	728– 806	5
AgCNO	*c*	18.7	273– 353	?
AgI	*c*, α	$8.58 + 0.0141T$	273– 423	6
$AgNO_3$	*c*, α	$18.83 + 0.0160T$	273– 433	2
	c, β	25.7	433– 482	5
	l	30.2	482– 541	5

Table 3-173. Heat Capacities of the Elements and Inorganic Compounds—(*Continued*)

Substance	State†	Heat capacity at constant pressure (T = °K.; 0°C. = 273.1°K.), cal./deg. mol	Range of tempera-ture, °K.	Uncer-tainty, %
Silver—(*Cont.*):				
Ag_3PO_4	*c*	37.5	293- 325	?
Ag_2S	*c*, α	18.8	273- 448	5
	c, β	21.8	448- 597	5
Ag_3Sb	*c*	$19.53 + 0.0160T$	273- 694	5
Ag_2Se	*c*, α	20.2	273- 406	5
	c, β	20.4	406- 460	5
Sodium:[29]				
Na	*c*	$5.01 + 0.00536T$	273- 371	1½
	l	7.50	371- 451	2
	g	4.97	All	0
$NaBO_2$	*c*	$10.4 + 0.0199T$	273-1239	?
$Na_2B_4O_7$	*c*	47.9	289- 371	?
$Na_2B_4O_7.10H_2O$	*c*	147	292- 323	?
NaBr	*c*	$11.74 + 0.00233T$	273- 543	2
NaCl	*c*	$10.79 + 0.00420T$	273-1074	2
	l	15.9	1073-1205	3
$NaClO_3$	*c*	$9.48 + 0.0468T$	273- 528	3
	l	31.8	528- 572	5
NaCNO	*c*	13.1	273- 353	?
Na_2CO_3	*c*	28.9	288- 371	?
NaF	*c*	$10.4 + 0.00289T$	273-1261	?
$Na_2HPO_4.7H_2O$	*c*	86.6	275- 307	?
$Na_2HPO_4.12H_2O$	*c*	133.4	275- 307	?
NaI	*c*	$12.5 + 0.00162T$	273- 936	?
$NaNO_3$	*c*	$4.56 + 0.0580T$	273- 583	5
	l	37.2	583- 703	10
$Na_2O.Al_2O_3.3SiO_2$	*c*, albite	$63.78 + 0.01171T - 1678000/T^2$	273-1373	1
	gls	$61.25 + 0.01768T - 1545000/T^2$	273-1173	1
$NaPO_3$	*c*	22.1	290- 319	?
$Na_4P_2O_7$	*c*	60.7	290- 371	?
Na_2SO_4	*c*	32.8	289- 371	?
$Na_2S_2O_3$	*c*	34.9	273- 307	?
$Na_2S_2O_3.5H_2O$	*c*	86.2	273- 307	?
Sodium-potassium alloys[30]	*l*			
Strontium:				
$SrBr_2$	*c*	$18.1 + 0.00311T$	273- 923	?
$SrBr_2.H_2O$	*c*	28.9	277- 370	?
$SrBr_2.6H_2O$	*c*	82.1	276- 327	?
$SrCl_2$	*c*	$18.2 + 0.00244T$	273-1143	?
$SrCl_2.H_2O$	*c*	28.7	276- 365	?
$SrCl_2.2H_2O$	*c*	38.3	277- 366	?
$SrCO_3$	*c*	21.8	281- 371	?
SrI_2	*c*	$18.6 + 0.00304T$	273- 783	?
$SrI_2.H_2O$	*c*	28.5	276- 363	?
$SrI_2.2H_2O$	*c*	39.1	275- 336	?
$SrI_2.6H_2O$	*c*	84.9	275- 333	?
$SrMoO_4$	*c*	37	273- 297	?
$Sr(NO_3)_2$	*c*	38.3	290- 320	?
$SrSO_4$	*c*	26.2	293- 369	?
Sulfur:[31]				
S	*c*, rhombic	$3.63 + 0.00640T$	273- 368	3
	c, monoclinic	$4.38 + 0.00440T$	368- 392	3
S_2	*g*	$8.58 + 0.00030T$	300-2500	5
S_2Cl_2	*l*	27.5	273- 332	?
SO_2	*g*	$7.70 + 0.00530T - 0.00000083T^2$	300-2500	2½
Tantalum:[32]				
Ta	*c*	$5.91 + 0.00099T$	273-1173	2
Tellurium:				
Te	*c*	$5.19 + 0.00250T$	273- 600	3
Thallium:				
Tl	*c*, α	$5.32 + 0.00385T$	273- 500	1
	c, β	8.12	500- 576	1
	l	7.12	576- 773	3
TlBr	*c*	$12.53 + 0.00100T$	273- 733	10
	l	16.0	733- 800	10
TlCl	*c*	$12.56 + 0.00088T$	273- 700	5
	l	14.2	700- 803	10
Thorium:				
Th	*c*	6.40	273- 373	?
ThO_2	*c*	$14.6 + 0.00507T$	273-1273	?
$Th(SO_4)_2$	*c*	41.2	273- 373	?
Tin:[33]				
Sn	*c*	$5.05 + 0.00480T$	273- 504	2
	l	6.6	504-1273	10
SnAu	*c*	$11.79 + 0.00233T$	273- 581	1
$SnCl_2$	*c*	$16.2 + 0.00926T$	273- 520	?
$SnCl_4$	*l*	38.4	286- 371	?
SnO	*c*	$9.40 + 0.00362T$	273-1273	?
SnO_2	*c*	$13.94 + 0.00565T - 252000/T^2$	273-1373	?
SnPt	*c*	$11.49 + 0.00190T$	273-1318	1
SnS	*c*	$12.1 + 0.00165T$	273-1153	?
SnS_2	*c*	$20.5 + 0.00400T$	273- 873	?
Titanium:[34]				
Ti	*c*	$8.91 + 0.00114T - 433000/T^2$	273- 713	3
$TiCl_4$	*l*	35.7	285- 372	?
TiO_2	*c*	$11.81 + 0.00754T - 41900/T^2$	273- 713	3
Tungsten:				
W	*c*	$5.65 + 0.00866$	273-2073	1
WO_3	*c*	$16.0 + 0.00774T$	273-1550	?

Table 3-173. Heat Capacities of the Elements and Inorganic Compounds—(*Concluded*)

Substance	State†	Heat capacity at constant pressure (T = °K.; 0°C. = 273.1°K.), cal./deg. mol	Range of temperature, °K.	Uncertainty, %
Uranium:				
U	*c*	6.64	273–372	?
U_3O_8	*c*	59.8	276–314	?
Vanadium:				
V	*c*	$5.57 + 0.00097T$	273–1993	?
Xenon:				
Xe	*g*	4.97	All	0
Zinc:[35]				
Zn	*c*	$5.25 + 0.00270T$	273–692	1
	l	$7.59 + 0.00055T$	692–1122	3
$ZnCl_2$	*c*	$15.9 + 0.00800T$	273–638	?
ZnO	*c*	$11.40 + 0.00145T - 182400/T^2$	273–1573	1
ZnS	*c*	$12.81 + 0.00095T - 194600/T^2$	273–1173	5
ZnSb	*c*	$11.5 + 0.00313T$	273–810	?
$ZnSO_4$	*c*	28	293–373	?
$ZnSO_4.H_2O$	*c*	34.7	282	?
$ZnSO_4.6H_2O$	*c*	80.8	282	?
$ZnSO_4.7H_2O$	*c*	100.2	273–307	?
Zirconium:[36]				
ZrO_2	*c*	$11.62 + 0.01046T - 177700/T^2$	273–1673	5
$ZrO_2.SiO_2$	*c*	26.7	297–372	?

[1] See also Table 3-174. Data to 298°K. are also given by Scott, "Cryogenic Engineering," Van Nostrand, Princeton, N.J., 1959.
[2] For liquid and gas data see Johnson (ed.), WADD-TR-60-56, 1960.
[3] Stalder, *N.A.C.A. Tech. Note* **4141**, 1957 (Fig. 5) gives data from 400° to 2600°R.
[4] See also Table 3-174.
[5] For data from 400° to 5500°R. see Stalder, *N.A.C.A. Tech. Note* **4141**, 1957 (Fig. 4).
[6] For *s*, *l*, *g* data see Johnson (ed.), WADD-TR-60-56, 1960.
[7] See also Table 3-174.
[8] See also Table 3-174.
[9] For data from 400° to 2350°R. see Stalder, *N.A.C.A. Tech. Note* **4141**, 1957.
[10] For *s*, *l*, *g* data see Johnson (ed.), WADD-TR-60-56, 1960.
[11] See Table 3-174.
[12] For *l*, *g* data see Johnson (ed.), WADD-TR-60-56, 1960.
[13] For *s*, *l*, *g* data see Johnson (ed.), WADD-TR-60-56, 1960.
[14] See Table 3-174. [15] See also Table 3-174. [16] See also Table 3-174. [17] See also Table 3-174. [18] See also Table 3-174.
[19] See also Table 3-174; Douglas, Ball, *et al.*, *Bur. Standards J. Research*, **46**, 334 (1951); Busey and Giaque, *J. Am. Chem. Soc.*, **75**, 806 (1953); Sheldon, A.S.M.E Paper 49-A-30, 1949.
[20] For *s*, *l*, *g* data see Johnson (ed.), WADD-TR-56-60, 1960.
[21] See also Table 3-174.
[22] For *s*, *l*, *g* data see Johnson (ed.), WADD-TR-56-60, 1960.
[23] For *s*, *l*, *g* data see Johnson (ed.), WADD-TR-56-60, 1960.
Ozone: For liquid data see Brabets and Waterman, *J. Chem. Phys.*, **28**, 1212, 1958.
[24] See also Table 3-174. [25] See also Table 3-174. [26] See Table 3-174. [27] See also Table 3-174. [28] See also Table 3-174.
[29] See also Table 3-174. For data on liquid Na-K alloys to 1500°F. and for liquid NA to 1460°F. see Lubarsky and Kaufman, *N.A.C.A. Rept.* 1270, 1956.
[30] See footnote 29.
[31] See also Evans and Wagman, *Bur. Standards J. Research*, **49**, 141 (1952); Gratch, OTS PB 124957, 1950; Guthrie, Scott, *et al.*, *J. Am. Chem. Soc.*, **76**, 1488 (1954).
[32] See also Table 3-174. [33] See also Table 3-174. [34] See also Table 3-174. [35] See also Table 3-174. [36] See also Table 3-174.

Table 3-174. Heat Capacities of Some Elements below Room Temperature, cal./(g.-atom)(deg.)*

Element	Temp., °K.								
	1.0	1.5	2.0	4	10	25	50	100	200
Al	0.00036	0.00056	0.00076	0.0018	0.010	0.11	0.91	3.12	5.16
Bi	....	....	....	.027	.52	2.43	4.27	5.46	5.98
Cr	.00038	.00058	.00076	.0020	.010	0.06	0.47	2.39	4.81
Co	.0012	.0018	.0024	.0050	.017	.15	0.98	3.25	5.30
Ge	....	....	.00015	....	.018	.40	1.49	3.34	4.93
In	.0010	.0020	.0040	.025	.34				
In†	.00050	.00017	.004						
Fe	.0012	.0018	.0024	.0051	.017	.10	0.72	2.88	5.33
La	.0012	.0022	.0037	.014	.026	2.20	4.41	5.64	
Pb	.00080	.0029	.0051	.037	.67	3.36	5.11	5.83	6.20
Pb†	.0016	.0039	.0074	.048					
Mg	.00032	.00053	.00074	.0020	.01	0.19	1.41	3.77	5.38
Hg	....	....	....	.20	1.08	3.16	4.99	5.90	6.57
Ni	.0016	.0026	.0036	.0075	0.025	0.14	0.96	3.26	5.37
Nb	.0022	.0039	.0066	.010	.048				
Pd	.0031	.0047	.0066	.013	.054	0.41	1.97	4.27	5.79
Pt	.0016	.0026	.0035	.0088	.052	0.65	2.54	4.70	5.93
Pr	.0034	.0072	.014	.080	.99	4.36	6.18	6.22	
Si	.00004	.00007	.00011	.00054	.....	0.06	0.84	1.74	3.74
Ag	.00020	.00037	.00063	.0030	.048	0.75	2.78	4.82	5.80
Na	....	....	.0055	.014	.14	1.45	3.82	8.44	11.09
Ta	.0014	.0022	.0031	.0079	.05	0.59	2.60	4.78	5.77
Ta†	.00032	.0011	.0027	.016					
Sn	.00046	.00085	.0014	.0067	.22	1.65	3.68	5.35	6.08
Sn†	.00018	.00061	.0014						
Sn‡	....	....	....	....	.16	1.26	2.67	4.61	5.81
Ti	.00079	.0012	.0017	.0046	.....	0.16	1.08	3.37	5.31
Zn	.00017	.00028	.00043	.0017	.039	0.77	2.65	4.59	5.72
Zr	.00073	.0011	.0016	.0043	.030	0.48	2.21	4.45	5.72

* Extracted from General Electric Research Laboratory report dated October, 1952, by C. A. Shiffman. Reproduced by permission.
† Superconducting state.
‡ Gray allotropic form.

Table 3-175. Heat Capacity of Water*

Air-free, at a constant pressure of 1 atm.

Temperature, °C.	Heat capacity, constant pressure, 1 atm. cal./g. °C.†	Temperature, °C.	Heat capacity, constant pressure, 1 atm., cal./g. °C.†	Temperature, °C.	Heat capacity, constant pressure, 1 atm., cal./g. °C.†	Temperature, °C.	Heat capacity, constant pressure, 1 atm., cal./g. °C.†
0	1.00803	25	.99892	50	0.99919	75	1.00208
1	1.00717	26	.99885	51	.99926	76	1.00225
2	1.00636	27	.99878	52	.99935	77	1.00241
3	1.00564	28	.99873	53	.99943	78	1.00258
4	1.00495	29	.99869	54	.99950	79	1.00277
5	1.00433	30	.99866	55	.99959	80	1.00294
6	1.00378	31	.99864	56	.99969	81	1.00313
7	1.00325	32	.99861	57	.99978	82	1.00332
8	1.00277	33	.99861	58	.99988	83	1.00351
9	1.00234	34	.99859	59	.99998	84	1.00373
10	1.00194	35	.99859	60	1.00007	85	1.00392
11	1.00158	36	.99861	61	1.00019	86	1.00414
12	1.00124	37	.99861	62	1.00029	87	1.00435
13	1.00093	38	.99864	63	1.00041	88	1.00457
14	1.00067	39	.99866	64	1.00053	89	1.00480
15	1.00041	40	.99869	65	1.00065	90	1.00502
16	1.00019	41	.99871	66	1.00079	91	1.00526
17	0.99998	42	.99876	67	1.00091	92	1.00550
18	.99978	43	.99880	68	1.00105	93	1.00574
19	.99962	44	.99883	69	1.00117	94	1.00600
20	.99947	45	.99890	70	1.00131	95	1.00626
21	.99933	46	.99895	71	1.00146	96	1.00653
22	.99921	47	.99900	72	1.00160	97	1.00684
23	.99912	48	.99907	73	1.00177	98	1.00705
24	.99902	49	.99912	74	1.00191	99	1.00734
						100	1.00763

* From Osborne, Stimson, and Ginnings, *Bur. Standards J. Research*, **23**, 197 (1939). See also Benzler, *Allgem. Wärmetech.*, **5**, 222 (1954); Rasskazov and Sheindlin, *Doklady Akad.Nauk.S.S.S.R.*, **120**, 771 (1958); Gambill, *Chem. Eng.*, **53**, 139 (1959); "Handbook of Chemistry and Physics," 40th ed., Chemical Rubber Publishing Co. [p. 2259, below 0°C.; 0. 2263, 100(10)270°C.].

† 1 calorie = 4.1833 NBS int. j (National Bureau of Standards international joule).

Table 3-176. Specific Heats of Organic Liquids*

From "International Critical Tables," vol. 5, pp. 107–113 and a few data from other sources

Compound	Formula	Temperature, °C.	Sp. ht., cal./g. °C.
Acetal	$C_6H_{14}O_2$	0	0.467
		19–99	.520
Acetic acid*	$C_2H_4O_2$	26–95	.522
Acetone*	C_3H_6O	3–22.6	.514
		0	.506
		24.2–49.4	.538
Acetonitrile	C_2H_3N	21–76	.541
Acetophenone	C_8H_8O	20–196	.450
Acetyl chloride	C_2H_3ClO	0	.339
Allyl acetate	$C_5H_8O_2$	0	.430
alcohol	C_3H_6O	0	.386
		21–96	.665
benzoate	$C_{10}H_{10}O$	20	.388
butyrate	$C_7H_{12}O_2$	20	.451
chloride	C_3H_5Cl	0	.313
chloroacetate	$C_5H_7ClO_2$	20	.396
dichloroacetate	$C_5H_6Cl_2O_2$	20	.332
isobutyrate	$C_7H_{12}O_2$	20	.448
propionate	$C_6H_{10}O_2$	20	.451
trichloroacetate	$C_5H_5Cl_3O_2$	20	.288
valerate	$C_8H_{14}O$	20	.451
Aminobenzoic acid (o-)	$C_7H_7NO_2$	M. P.	.435
(m-)	$C_7H_7NO_2$	M. P.	.435
(p-)	$C_7H_7NO_2$	M. P.	.444
Amyl alcohol (d-primary)	$C_5H_{12}O$	22–125	.711
(t-)	$C_5H_{12}O$	20–99	.753
Amylene	C_5H_{10}	0	.282
Anethole	$C_{10}H_{12}O$	23–233	.511
		22.48	.551
		24.59	.564
		25.23	.612
Aniline	C_6H_7N	8–82	.512
Benzaldehyde	C_7H_6O	22–172	.428
Benzene*	C_6H_6	6–60	.419
		10	.340
		65	.482
Benzonitrile	C_7H_5N	22–186	.441
Benzophenone (β-)	$C_{13}H_{10}O$	3–40	.382
		0	.346
Benzyl alcohol	C_7H_8O	20–100	.511
		22–200	.540
chloride	C_7H_7Cl	0	.323
ethylene	C_9H_{10}	0	.393
Bromobenzene	C_6H_5Br	0	.215
		20–100	.231
		16.9–65	.239
Bromochlorobenzene (o-)	C_6H_4BrCl	0	.215
(m-)	C_6H_4BrCl	0	.212
Bromoiodobenzene (o-)	C_6H_4BrI	0	.153
		5–100	.160
		3.2–64.6	.157
		1.8–34	.157
(m-)	C_6H_4BrI	0	.152
		5–100	.158
		3.2–64.5	.156
		1.7–34.1	.154
		1.7–36.2	.149
Bromophenol	C_6H_5BrO	18–77	.316
Butane (n-)	C_4H_{10}	0	.549
Butyl alcohol (n-)	$C_4H_{10}O$	21–115	.687
		30	.582
		−76.2	.443
		−33.3	.453
		2.3	.526
		19.2	.563
chloride (n-)	C_4H_9Cl	20	.451
formate (n-)	$C_5H_{10}O_2$	20	.459
propionate	$C_7H_{14}O_2$	20	.459
valerate	$C_9H_{18}O_2$	20	.459
Butyric acid (n-)	$C_4H_8O_2$	0	.444
		40	.501
		20–100	.515
Butyronitrile (n-)	C_4H_7N	21–113	.547
Caproic acid	$C_6H_{12}O_2$	29–105	.531
Capronitrile	$C_6H_{11}N$	18–156	.541
Carbon tetrachloride*	CCl_4	0	.198
		20	.201
		30	.200
Carvacrol	$C_{10}H_{14}O$	24–233	.575
Chloral	C_2HCl_3O	17–53	.250
hydrate	$C_2H_3Cl_3O_2$	55–88	.470
Chlorobenzene*	C_6H_5Cl	0	.273
		10	.298
		20	.308
Chlorobenzoic acid (o-)	$C_7H_5ClO_2$	0	0.390
(m-)	$C_7H_5ClO_2$	0	.265
(p-)	$C_7H_5ClO_2$	M. P.	.545
Chloroform*	$CHCl_3$	0	.232
		15	.226
		30	.234
Chlorophenol	C_6H_5ClO	0–20	.399
Chlorotoluene	C_7H_7Cl	0	.315

* See line coordinate chart, Fig. 3-11, p. 3-126, for the specific heats of a number of substances as a function of the temperature. For additional data on the specific heat of liquid organic compounds see pp. 2278–2282 of "Handbook of Chemistry and Physics," 40th ed., Chemical Rubber Publishing Co. Extensive data on ethylene glycol, diethylene glycol, triethylene glycol, and propylene glycol solutions are contained in Union Carbide Corp. publication F4763F, 1958.

Table 3-176. Specific Heats of Organic Liquids.—(*Continued*)

Compound	Formula	Temperature, °C.	Sp. ht., cal./g. °C.
Cresol (o-)	C_7H_8O	0–20	.497
(m-)	C_7H_8O	21–197	.551
		0–20	.477
Cresyl methyl ether (p-)	$C_8H_{10}O$	0	.404
Crotonic acid	$C_4H_6O_2$	71.4	.500
Cyclohexanol	$C_6H_{12}O$	15–18	.416
Cyclohexanone	$C_6H_{10}O$	15–18	.431
o-Cymene	$C_{10}H_{14}$	0	.398
Decahydronaphthalene (cis-)	$C_{10}H_{18}$	15–18	.393
Decane	$C_{10}H_{22}$ b.p. = 159	21–154	.588
	$C_{10}H_{22}$ b.p. = 162	0–50	.493
	$C_{10}H_{22}$ b.p. = 172	0–50	.500
Decylene (γ-)	$C_{10}H_{20}$	0–50	.467
Diallyl oxalate	$C_8H_{10}O_4$	20	.424
succinate	$C_{10}H_{14}O_4$	20	.450
Diamylene	$C_{10}H_{20}$	20–130	.543
Dibromobenzene (o-)	$C_6H_4Br_2$	0	.179
(m-)	$C_6H_4Br_2$	0	.175
Dibutyl oxalate	$C_{10}H_{18}O_4$	20	.439
Dichlorodifluormethane	CCl_2F_2	−43	.21
Dichloroacetic acid	$C_2H_2Cl_2O_2$	{21–106	.349
		{21–196	.348
Dichlorobenzene (o-)	$C_6H_4Cl_2$	0	.269
(m-)	$C_6H_4Cl_2$	0	.269
(p-)	$C_6H_4Cl_2$	53–99	.297
Diethylamine	$C_4H_{11}N$	22.5	.516
Diethyl carbonate	$C_5H_{10}O_3$	0	.245
		20–100	.462
ether (see Ether)	$C_4H_{10}O$	20.2–123	.473
ketone	$C_5H_{10}O$	20–98.5	.555
malate	$C_8H_{14}O_5$	24–186	.473
malonate	$C_7H_{12}O_4$	20	.431
oxalate	$C_6H_{10}O_4$	20	.431
succinate	$C_8H_{14}O_4$	20	.450
Dihydronaphthalene	$C_{10}H_{10}$	18–28	.345
Di-iodobenzene (m-)	$C_6H_4I_2$	34.2–99.6	.139
Di-isoamyl	$C_{10}H_{22}$	21.5–155	.588
oxalate	$C_{12}H_{22}O_4$	20	.447
Di-isobutylamine	C_8H_9N	22–130	.569
Dimethyl aniline	$C_8H_{11}N$	{0–20	.416
		{0	.403
naphthalene (β-)	$C_{12}H_{12}$	0	.392
pyrone	$C_7H_8O_2$	166	.547
Dinitrobenzene (m-)	$C_6H_4N_2O_4$	M. P.	.404
Diphenylamine	$C_{12}H_{11}N$	54	.437
		56	.441
		66	.480
Dipropyl ketone	$C_7H_{14}O$	20–140	.550
malonate	$C_9H_{16}O_4$	20	.431
oxalate (n-)	$C_8H_{14}O_4$	20	.431
succinate	$C_{10}H_{18}O_4$	20	.450
Dodecane	$C_{12}H_{26}$	14–20	.505
		0–50	.498
Dodecylene	$C_{12}H_{24}$	0–50	.455
Ether*	$C_4H_{10}O$	−100	.511
		−50	.515
		−5	.525
		0	.521
		+30	.545
		80	.687
		120	.800
		140	.819
		180	1.037
Ethyl acetate*	$C_4H_8O_2$	20	0.457
		20	.476
acetoacetate	$C_6H_{10}O_3$	0	.428
		20–100	.475
alcohol*	C_2H_6O (100%)	−20	.505
		0–98	.680
benzene	C_8H_{10}	0	.392
		30	.407
benzoate	$C_9H_{10}O_2$	20	.387
bromide*	C_2H_5Br	−100	0.194
		−20	.206
		5–10	.216
		10–15	.213
		15–20	.214
butyrate	$C_6H_{12}O_2$	20	.457
chloride	C_2H_5Cl	−28 to +4	.426
		0	.367
chloroacetate	$C_4H_7ClO_2$	9–138	.416
		20	.397
cresyl ether (p-)	$C_9H_{12}O$	0	.427
dichloroacetate	$C_4H_6Cl_2O_2$	20	.328
ether	$C_4H_{10}O$	0	.521
formate	$C_3H_6O_2$	14–49	.508
		−20 to +14	.454

Compound	Formula	Temperature, °C.	Sp. ht., cal./g. °C.
Ethyl (*Cont.*):			
iodide*	C_2H_5I	−30	.156
		0	.161
		60	.171
isobutyrate	$C_6H_{12}O_2$	20	.457
propionate	$C_5H_{10}O_2$	20	.457
silicate	$C_8H_{20}SiO_4$	15–98	.424
sulfide	$C_4H_{10}S$	0	.468
		5–10	.470
		10–15	.473
		20–70	.477
trichloroacetate	$C_4H_5Cl_3O_2$	10–81	.294
		9–139	.305
		20	.284
valerate	$C_7H_{14}O_2$	20	.457
Ethylene bromide	$C_2H_4Br_2$	8–95	.182
		13–106	.175
		20	.173
chloride	$C_2H_4Cl_2$	−30	.278
		+20	.299
		30	.304
		50	.313
		60	.318
dichloroacetate	$C_6H_6Cl_4O_4$	0	.321
glycol*	$C_2H_6O_2$	−11.1	.535
		0	.542
		+ 2.5	.550
		5.1	.554
		14.9	.569
		19.9	.573
Formamide	CH_3NO	19	.549
Formic acid	CH_2O_2	0	.436
		15.5	.509
		20–100	.524
Furfural	$C_5H_4O_2$	0	.367
		20–100	.416
Glycerol*	$C_3H_8O_3$	15–50	.576
Glycol (ethylene)*	$C_2H_6O_2$	(see ethylene	glycol)
Heptaldehyde	$C_7H_{14}O$	0	.364
Heptane (n-)*	C_7H_{16}	0–50	.507
		20	.490
		30	.518
Heptylene	C_7H_{14}	0–50	.486
Heptylic acid	$C_7H_{14}O_2$	9	.556
Hexadecane (n-)	$C_{16}H_{34}$	0–50	.496
Hexadiene (1,5-)	C_6H_{10}	0	.405
Hexahydrocresol (o-)	$C_7H_{14}O$	15–18	.416
(m-)	$C_7H_{14}O$	15–18	.420
(p-)	$C_7H_{14}O$	15–18	.421
Hexane (n-)	C_6H_{14}	0–50	.527
		20–100	.600
Hexylene	C_6H_{12}	0–50	.504
Isoamyl acetate	$C_7H_{14}O_2$	20	.459
alcohol	$C_5H_{12}O$	0	.502
		20	.535
		30	.570
		47.9	.662
		10–117	.693
		21–130	.695
		75.5	.688
amine	$C_5H_{13}N$	22–91	.614
butyrate	$C_9H_{18}O_2$	20	.459
formate	$C_6H_{12}O_2$	16–65	.509
isobutyrate	$C_9H_{13}O_2$	20	.459
propionate	$C_8H_{16}O_2$	20	.459
succinate	$C_{14}H_{26}O_4$	0	.449
valerate	$C_{10}H_{20}O_2$	20	.459
Isobutane	C_4H_{10}	0	.549
Isobutyl acetate	$C_6H_{12}O_2$	20	.459
alcohol	$C_4H_{10}O$	21–109	.716
		30	.603
butyrate	$C_8H_{16}O_2$	20	0.459
succinate	$C_{12}H_{22}O_4$	0	.442
Isobutyric acid	$C_4H_8O_2$	20	.450
Isoheptane	C_7H_{16}	0–50	.501
Isopentane	C_5H_{12}	0	.512
		8	.527
Isovaleric acid	$C_5H_{10}O_2$	20	.463
		23–93	.590
Lauric acid	$C_{12}H_{24}O_2$	40–100	0.572
		57	.515
Mesitylene	C_9H_{12}	0	.393
Mesityl oxide	$C_6H_{10}O$	21–121	.521
Methyl acetate	$C_3H_6O_2$	15	.468
Methylal	$C_3H_8O_2$	15–41	.521

Table 3-176. Specific Heats of Organic Liquids.—(*Concluded*)

Compound	Formula	Temperature, °C.	Sp. ht., cal./g. °C.
Methyl alcohol*	CH_4O	5–10	.590
		15–20	.601
aniline	C_7H_9N	20–197	.512
benzoate	$C_8H_8O_2$	0	.363
butyl ketone	$C_6H_{12}O$	21–127	.553
butyrate (n-)	$C_5H_{10}O_2$	20	.459
chloroacetate	$C_3H_5ClO_2$	20	.382
cyclohexanone (o-)	$C_7H_{12}O$	15–18	.436
(m-)	$C_7H_{12}O$	15–18	.441
(p-)	$C_7H_{12}O$	15–18	.441
dichloroacetate	$C_3H_4Cl_2O_2$	20	.311
ethylketone	C_4H_8O	20–78	.549
ethylketoxime	C_4H_9NO	21.8–151.5	.650
formate	$C_2H_4O_2$	13–29	.516
hexyl ketone	$C_8H_{16}O$	22–168	.552
isobutyl ketone	$C_6H_{12}O$	20	.459
isopropyl ketone	$C_5H_{10}O$	20–91	.525
propionate	$C_4H_8O_2$	20	.459
trichloroacetate	$C_3H_3Cl_3O_2$	20	.267
valerate	$C_6H_{12}O_2$	20	.459
Methylene chloride	CH_2Cl_2	15–40	.288
Myristic acid	$C_{14}H_{28}O_2$	56–100	.539
Naphthalene	$C_{10}H_8$	87.5	.402
Naphthylamine (α-)	$C_{10}H_9N$	53.2	.475
		94.2	.476
Nitrobenzene	$C_6H_5NO_2$	10	.358
		30	.339
		50	.330
		70	.330
		90	.343
		120	.394
Nitrobenzoic acid (p-)	$C_7H_5NO_4$	M. P.	.449
Nitromethane	CH_3NO_2	17	.412
Nitronaphthalene (α-)	$C_{10}H_7NO_2$	58.6	.365
		61.4	.378
		94.3	.390
Nonane	C_9H_{20}	0–50	.503
Nonylene	C_9H_{18}	0–50	.485
Octane (n-)*	C_8H_{18}	0–50	.505
		20–123	.578
Octylene	C_8H_{16}	0–50	.486
Palmitic acid	$C_{16}H_{32}O_2$	65–104	.653
Paraldehyde	$C_6H_{12}O_3$	0	.436
Pentadecane	$C_{15}H_{32}$	0–50	.497
Pentadecylene	$C_{15}H_{30}$	0–50	.471
Phenetole	$C_8H_{10}O$	20	.446
Phenyl methyl ether	C_7H_8O	0	.405
		20–152	.483
Picoline (α-)	C_6H_7N	22–124	.434
Piperidine	$C_5H_{11}N$	20–98	.523
Propane	C_3H_8	0	.576
Propionaldehyde	C_3H_6O	0	.522
Propionic acid	$C_3H_6O_2$	0	.444
		20–137	.560
Propionitrile	C_3H_5N	0	.508
		19–95	.538
Propyl acetate (n-)	$C_5H_{10}O_2$	20	.459
benzene	C_9H_{12}	0	.400
benzoate	$C_{10}H_{12}O_2$	20	.398
butyrate	$C_7H_{14}O_2$	20	.459
Propyl (*Cont.*):			
chloroacetate	$C_5H_9ClO_2$	20	.414
dichloroacetate	$C_5H_8Cl_2O_2$	20	.341
formate (n-)	$C_4H_8O_2$	20	.459
isobutyrate	$C_7H_{14}O_2$	20	.459
phenyl ether	$C_9H_{12}O$	0	.429
propionate	$C_6H_{12}O_2$	20	.459
trichloroacetate	$C_5H_7Cl_3O_2$	20	.297
valerate	$C_8H_{16}O_2$	20	.459
Pseudocumene	C_9H_{12}	20	.414
Pyridine	C_5H_5N	20	.405
		21–108	.431
		0–20	.395
Quinoline	C_9H_7N	0–20	.352
Salicylaldehyde	$C_7H_6O_2$	18	382
Salol	$C_{13}H_{10}O_3$	44.1	.391
Stearic acid	$C_{18}H_{36}O_2$	75–137	.550
Tetrachloroethane	$C_2H_2Cl_4$	20	.268
Tetrachloroethylene	C_2Cl_4	20	.216
		24	.211
Tetradecane	$C_{14}H_{30}$	0–50	0.497
Thymol (m-)	$C_{10}H_{14}O$	50	.566
Toluene*	C_7H_8	{10	.364
		85	.534
		12–99}	.440
Toluidine (o-)	C_7H_9N	0	.454
		22–195	.598
		40.5	.498
(p-)	C_7H_9N	43	.524
		58	.634
		94	.533
Trichloroethane	$C_2H_3Cl_3$	20	0.266
Trichloroethylene	C_2HCl_3	20	.223
Tridecane	$C_{13}H_{28}$	0–50	.499
Tridecylene	$C_{13}H_{26}$	0–50	.457
Trinitrotoluene (2,4,6-)	$C_7H_5N_3O_6$	....	.335
Undecane	$C_{11}H_{24}$	0–50	.501
Undecylene	$C_{11}H_{22}$	0–50	.482
Valeronitrile	C_5H_9N	23–121	.520
Xylene (o-)*	C_8H_{10}	30	.411
		39	.450
(m-)*	C_8H_{10}	0	.383
		9–40	.400
		16–35	.387
		30	.401
(p-)*	C_8H_{10}	0	.383
		30	.397
		40.8	.428
dibromide (o-)	$C_8H_8Br_2$	15–40	.183
(m-)	$C_8H_8Br_2$	15–40	.184
(p-)	$C_8H_8Br_2$	15–40	.180
dichloride (o-)	$C_8H_8Cl_2$	15–40	.283
(m-)	$C_8H_8Cl_2$	15–40	.295
(p-)	$C_8H_8Cl_2$	15–40	.282
tetrachloride (o-)	$C_8H_6Cl_4$	15–40	.240
(p-)	$C_8H_6Cl_4$	15–40	.242
Xylyl ethyl ether (2,4-)	$C_{10}H_{14}O$	0	.417

Specific heat = P.c.u./(lb.)(deg. C.) = B.t.u./(lb.)(deg. F.)
= calories/(gm.)(deg. C.)

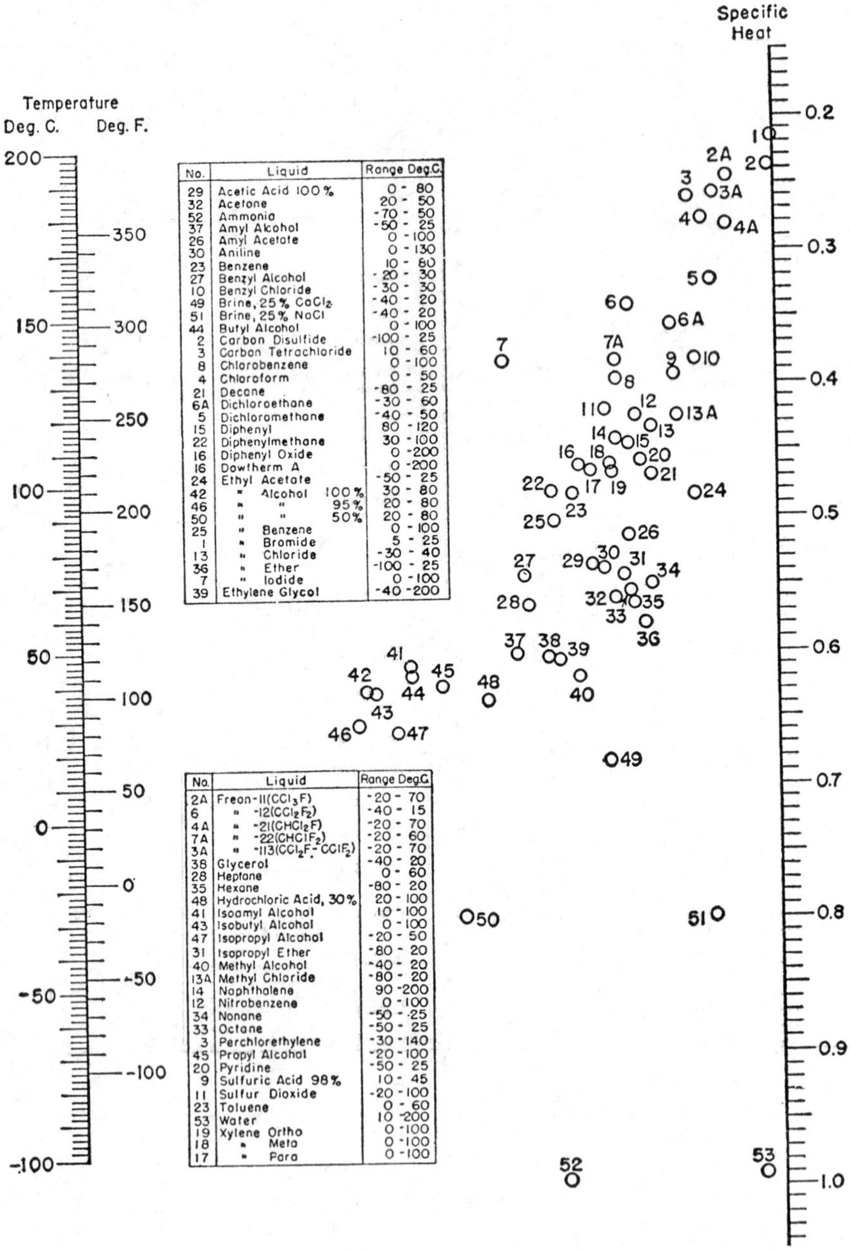

No.	Liquid	Range Deg.C.
29	Acetic Acid 100%	0 - 80
32	Acetone	20 - 50
52	Ammonia	-70 - 50
37	Amyl Alcohol	-50 - 25
26	Amyl Acetate	0 - 100
30	Aniline	0 - 130
23	Benzene	10 - 80
27	Benzyl Alcohol	-20 - 30
10	Benzyl Chloride	-30 - 30
49	Brine, 25% $CaCl_2$	-40 - 20
51	Brine, 25% NaCl	-40 - 20
44	Butyl Alcohol	0 - 100
2	Carbon Disulfide	-100 - 25
3	Carbon Tetrachloride	10 - 60
8	Chlorobenzene	0 - 100
4	Chloroform	0 - 50
21	Decane	-80 - 25
6A	Dichloroethane	-30 - 60
5	Dichloromethane	-40 - 50
15	Diphenyl	80 - 120
22	Diphenylmethane	30 - 100
16	Diphenyl Oxide	0 - 200
16	Dowtherm A	0 - 200
24	Ethyl Acetate	-50 - 25
42	" Alcohol 100%	30 - 80
46	" " 95%	20 - 80
50	" " 50%	20 - 80
25	" Benzene	0 - 100
1	" Bromide	5 - 25
13	" Chloride	-30 - 40
36	" Ether	-100 - 25
7	" Iodide	0 - 100
39	Ethylene Glycol	-40 - 200

No.	Liquid	Range Deg.C.
2A	Freon-11(CCl_3F)	-20 - 70
6	" -12(CCl_2F_2)	-40 - 15
4A	" -21($CHCl_2F$)	-20 - 70
7A	" -22($CHClF_2$)	-20 - 60
3A	" -113(CCl_2F-$CClF_2$)	-20 - 70
38	Glycerol	-40 - 20
28	Heptane	0 - 60
35	Hexane	-80 - 20
48	Hydrochloric Acid, 30%	20 - 100
41	Isoamyl Alcohol	10 - 100
43	Isobutyl Alcohol	0 - 100
47	Isopropyl Alcohol	-20 - 50
31	Isopropyl Ether	-80 - 20
40	Methyl Alcohol	-40 - 20
13A	Methyl Chloride	-80 - 20
14	Naphthalene	90 - 200
12	Nitrobenzene	0 - 100
34	Nonane	-50 - 25
33	Octane	-50 - 25
3	Perchlorethylene	-30 - 140
45	Propyl Alcohol	-20 - 100
20	Pyridine	-50 - 25
9	Sulfuric Acid 98%	10 - 45
11	Sulfur Dioxide	-20 - 100
23	Toluene	0 - 60
53	Water	10 - 200
19	Xylene Ortho	0 - 100
18	" Meta	0 - 100
17	" Para	0 - 100

FIG. 3-11. Specific heats of liquids. (*Chilton, Colburn, and Vernon, personal communication. Based mainly on data from "International Critical Tables."*)

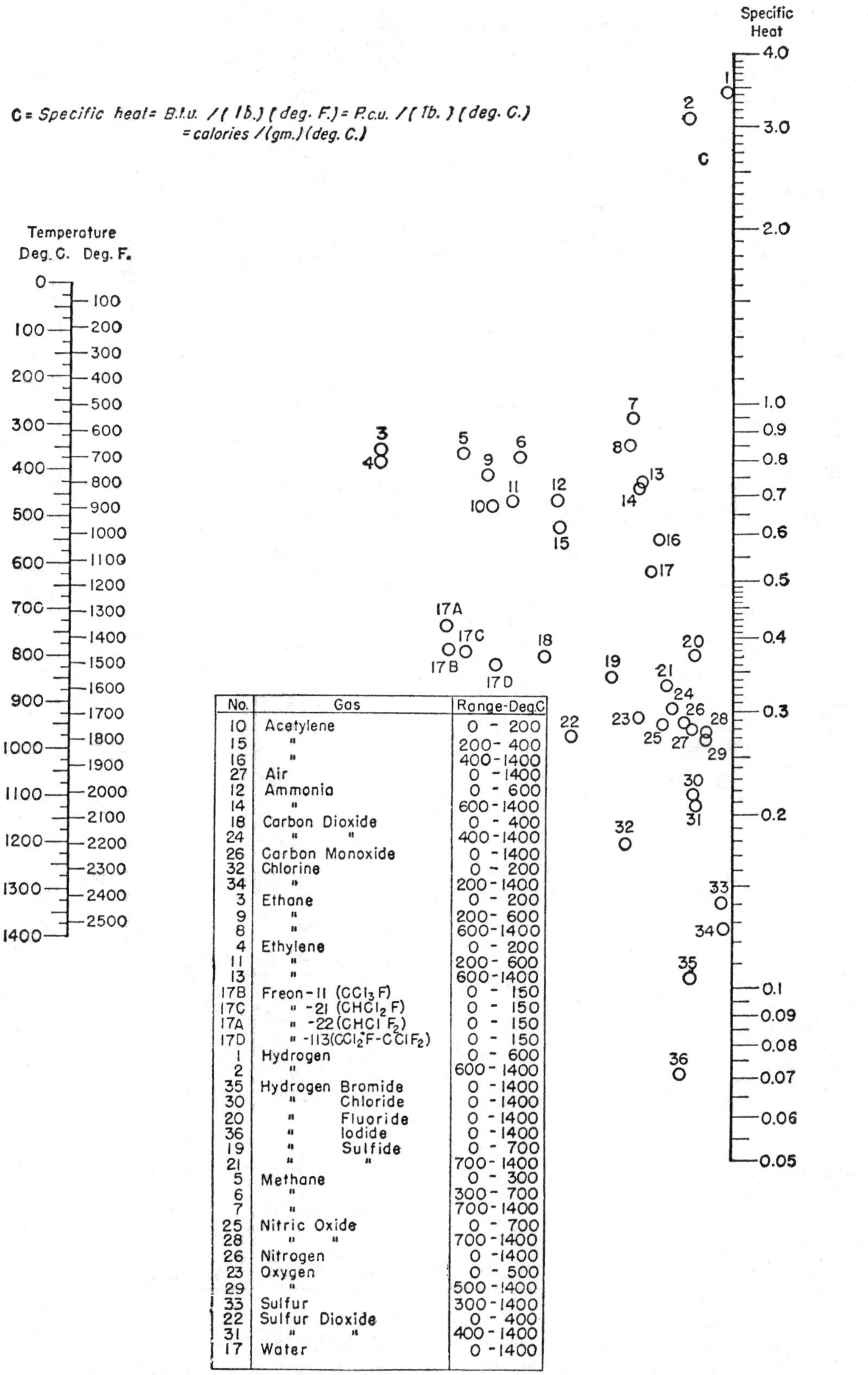

No.	Gas	Range-Deg.C
10	Acetylene	0 - 200
15	"	200 - 400
16	"	400 - 1400
27	Air	0 - 1400
12	Ammonia	0 - 600
14	"	600 - 1400
18	Carbon Dioxide	0 - 400
24	" "	400 - 1400
26	Carbon Monoxide	0 - 1400
32	Chlorine	0 - 200
34	"	200 - 1400
3	Ethane	0 - 200
9	"	200 - 600
8	"	600 - 1400
4	Ethylene	0 - 200
11	"	200 - 600
13	"	600 - 1400
17B	Freon-11 (CCl_3F)	0 - 150
17C	" -21 ($CHCl_2F$)	0 - 150
17A	" -22 ($CHClF_2$)	0 - 150
17D	" -113 (CCl_2F-$CClF_2$)	0 - 150
1	Hydrogen	0 - 600
2	"	600 - 1400
35	Hydrogen Bromide	0 - 1400
30	" Chloride	0 - 1400
20	" Fluoride	0 - 1400
36	" Iodide	0 - 1400
19	" Sulfide	0 - 700
21	" "	700 - 1400
5	Methane	0 - 300
6	"	300 - 700
7	"	700 - 1400
25	Nitric Oxide	0 - 700
28	" "	700 - 1400
26	Nitrogen	0 - 1400
23	Oxygen	0 - 500
29	"	500 - 1400
33	Sulfur	300 - 1400
22	Sulfur Dioxide	0 - 400
31	" "	400 - 1400
17	Water	0 - 1400

FIG. 3-12. Specific heats (C_p) of gases at 1 atm. pressure

Table 3-177. Specific Heats of Organic Solids

Recalculated from "International Critical Tables," vol. 5, pp. 101–105

Compound	Formula	Temperature, °C.	Sp. ht., cal./g. °C.
Acetic acid	$C_2H_4O_2$	−200 to +25	0.330 + 0.00080*t*
Acetone	C_3H_6O	−210 to −80	0.540 + 0.0156*t*
Aminobenzoic acid (o-)	$C_7H_7NO_2$	85 to m.p.	0.254 + 0.00136*t*
(m-)	$C_7H_7NO_2$	120 to m.p.	0.253 + 0.00122*t*
(p-)	$C_7H_7NO_2$	128 to m.p.	0.287 + 0.00088*t*
Aniline	C_6H_7N	....	0.741
Anthracene	$C_{14}H_{10}$	50	0.308
		100	0.350
		150	0.382
Anthraquinone	$C_{14}H_8O_2$	0 to 270	0.258 + 0.00069*t*
Apiol	$C_{12}H_{14}O_4$	10	0.299
Azobenzene	$C_{12}H_{10}N_2$	28	0.330
Benzene	C_6H_6	−250	0.0399
		−225	0.0908
		−200	0.124
		−150	0.170
		−100	0.227
		− 50	0.299
		0	0.375
Benzoic acid	$C_7H_6O_2$	20 to m.p.	0.287 + 0.00050*t*
Benzophenone	$C_{13}H_{10}O$	−150	0.115
		−100	0.172
		− 50	0.220
		0	0.275
		+ 20	0.303
Betol	$C_{17}H_{12}O_3$	−150	0.129
		−100	0.167
		0	0.248
		+ 50	0.308
Bromoiodobenzene (o-)	C_6H_4BrI	− 50 to 0	0.143 + 0.00025*t*
(m-)	C_6H_4BrI	− 75 to −15	0.143
(p-)	C_6H_4BrI	− 40 to 50	0.116 + 0.00032*t*
Bromonaphthalene (β-)	$C_{10}H_7Br$	41	0.260
Bromophenol	C_6H_5BrO	32	0.263
Camphene	$C_{10}H_{16}$	35	0.380
Capric acid	$C_{10}H_{20}O_2$	8	0.695
Caprylic acid	$C_8H_{16}O_2$	− 2	0.628
Carbon tetrachloride	CCl_4	−240	0.013
		−200	0.081
		−160	0.131
		−120	0.162
		− 80	0.182
		− 40	0.201
Cerotic acid	$C_{27}H_{54}O_2$	15	0.387
Chloral alcoholate	$C_4H_7Cl_3O_2$	78	0.509
hydrate	$C_2H_3Cl_3O_2$	32	0.213
Chloroacetic acid	$C_2H_3ClO_2$	60	0.363
Chlorobenzoic acid (o-)	$C_7H_5ClO_2$	80 to m.p.	0.228 + 0.00084*t*
(m-)	$C_7H_5ClO_2$	94 to m.p.	0.232 + 0.00073*t*
(p-)	$C_7H_5ClO_2$	180 to m.p.	0.242 + 0.00055*t*
Chlorobromobenzene (o-)	C_6H_4BrCl	− 34	0.192
(m-)	C_6H_4BrCl	− 52	0.150
(p-)	C_6H_4BrCl	− 40	0.150
Crotonic acid	$C_4H_6O_2$	38 to 70	0.520 + 0.00020*t*
Cyamelide	$C_3H_3N_3O_3$	40	0.263
Cyanamide	CH_2N_2	20	0.547
Cyanuric acid	$C_3H_3N_3O_3$	40	0.318
Dextrin	$(C_6H_{10}O_5)_x$	0 to 90	0.291 + 0.00096*t*
Dextrose	$C_6H_{12}O_6$	−250	0.016
		−200	0.077
		−100	0.160
		0	0.277
		20	0.300
Dibenzyl	$C_{14}H_{14}$	28	0.363
Dibromobenzene (o-)	$C_6H_4Br_2$	− 36	0.248
(m-)	$C_6H_4Br_2$	− 25	0.134
(p-)	$C_6H_4Br_2$	− 50 to +50	0.139 + 0.00038*t*
Dichloroacetic acid	$C_2H_2Cl_2O_2$	....	0.406
Dichlorobenzene (o-)	$C_6H_4Cl_2$	− 48.5	0.185
(m-)	$C_6H_4Cl_2$	− 52	0.186
(p-)	$C_6H_4Cl_2$	− 50 to +53	0.219 + 0.0021*t*
Dicyandiamide	$C_2H_4N_4$	0 to 204	0.456
Dihydroxybenzene (o-)	$C_6H_6O_2$	−163 to m.p.	0.278 + 0.00098*t*
(m-)	$C_6H_6O_2$	−160 to m.p.	0.269 + 0.00118*t*
(p-)	$C_6H_6O_2$	−250	0.025
		−240	0.038
		−220	0.061
		−200	0.081
		−150 to m.p.	0.268 + 0.00093*t*
Di-iodobenzene (o-)	$C_6H_4I_2$	− 50 to +15	0.109 + 0.00026*t*
(m-)	$C_6H_4I_2$	− 52 to −42	0.100 + 0.00026*t*
(p-)	$C_6H_4I_2$	− 50 to +80	0.101 + 0.00026*t*
Dimethyl oxalate	$C_4H_6O_4$	10 to 50	0.212 + 0.0044*t*
Dimethylpyrene	$C_7H_8O_2$	50	0.368
Dinitrobenzene (o-)	$C_6H_4N_2O_4$	−160 to m.p.	0.252 + 0.00083*t*
(m-)	$C_6H_4N_2O_4$	−160 to m.p.	0.248 + 0.00077*t*
(p-)	$C_6H_4N_2O_4$	119 to m.p.	0.259 + 0.00057*t*
Diphenyl	$C_{12}H_{10}$	40	0.385

Table 3-177. Specific Heats of Organic Solids—(*Continued*)

Compound	Formula	Temperature, °C.	Sp. ht., cal./g. °C.
Diphenylamine	$C_{12}H_{11}N$	26	0.337
Dulcitol	$C_6H_{14}O_6$	20	0.282
Erythritol	$C_4H_{10}O_4$	60	0.351
Ethyl alcohol	C_2H_6O (crystalline)	−190	0.232
		−180	0.248
		−160	0.282
		−140	0.318
		−130	0.376
	(vitreous)	−190	0.260
		−180	0.296
		−175	0.380
		−170	0.399
Ethylene glycol	$C_2H_6O_2$	−190 to −40	$0.366 + 0.00110t$
Formic acid	CH_2O_2	− 22	0.387
		0	0.430
Glutaric acid	$C_5H_8O_4$	20	0.299
Glycerol	$C_3H_8O_3$	−265	0.009
		−260	0.022
		−250	0.047
		−220	0.085
		−200	0.115
		−100	0.217
		0	0.330
Hexachloroethane	C_2Cl_6	25	0.174
Hexadecane	$C_{16}H_{34}$	....	0.495
Hydroxyacetanilide	$C_8H_9NO_2$	41 to m.p.	$0.249 + 0.00154t$
Iodobenzene	C_6H_5I	40	0.191
Isopropyl alcohol	C_3H_8O	−200 to −160	$0.051 + 0.00165t$
Lactose	$C_{12}H_{22}O_{11}$	20	0.287
	$C_{12}H_{22}O_{11}.H_2O$	20	0.299
Lauric acid	$C_{12}H_{24}O_2$	− 30 to +40	$0.430 + 0.000027t$
Levoglucosane	$C_6H_{10}O_5$	40	0.607
Levulose	$C_6H_{12}O_6$	20	0.275
Malonic acid	$C_3H_4O_4$	20	0.275
Maltose	$C_{12}H_{22}O_{11}$	20	0.320
Mannitol	$C_6H_{14}O_6$	0 to 100	$0.313 + 0.00025t$
Melamine	$C_3H_6N_6$	40	0.351
Myristic acid	$C_{14}H_{28}O_2$	0 to 35	$0.381 + 0.00545t$
Naphthalene	$C_{10}H_8$	−130 to m.p.	$0.281 + 0.00111t$
Naphthol (α-)	$C_{10}H_8O$	50 to m.p.	$0.240 + 0.00147t$
(β-)	$C_{10}H_8O$	61 to m.p.	$0.252 + 0.00128t$
Naphthylamine (α-)	$C_{10}H_9N$	0 to 50	$0.270 + 0.0031t$
Nitroaniline (o-)	$C_6H_6N_2O_2$	−160 to m.p.	$0.269 + 0.000920t$
(m-)	$C_6H_6N_2O_2$	−160 to m.p.	$0.275 + 0.000946t$
(p-)	$C_6H_6N_2O_2$	−160 to m.p.	$0.276 + 0.001000t$
Nitrobenzoic acid (o-)	$C_7H_5NO_4$	−163 to m.p.	$0.256 + 0.00085t$
(m-)	$C_7H_5NO_4$	66 to m.p.	$0.258 + 0.00091t$
(p-)	$C_7H_5NO_4$	−160 to m.p.	$0.247 + 0.00077t$
Nitronaphthalene	$C_{10}H_7NO_2$	0 to 55	$0.236 + 0.00215t$
Oxalic acid	$C_2H_2O_4$	−200 to +50	$0.259 + 0.00076t$
	$C_2H_2O_4.2H_2O$	−200	0.117
		−100	0.239
		0	0.338
		+ 50	0.385
		100	0.416
Palmitic acid	$C_{16}H_{32}O_2$	−180	0.167
		−140	0.208
		−100	0.251
		− 50	0.306
		0	0.382
		+ 20	0.430
Phenol	C_6H_6O	14 to 26	0.561
Phthalic acid	$C_8H_6O_4$	20	0.232
Picric acid	$C_6H_3N_3O_7$	−100	0.165
		0	0.240
		+ 50	0.263
		100	0.297
		120	0.332
Propionic acid	$C_3H_6O_2$	− 33	0.726
Propyl alcohol (n-)	C_3H_8O	−200	0.170
		−175	0.363
		−150	0.471
		−130	0.497
Pyrotartaric acid	$C_5H_8O_4$	20	0.301
Quinhydrone	$C_{12}H_{10}O_4$	−250	0.017
		−225	0.061
		−200	0.098
		−100	0.191
		0	0.256

Table 3-177. Specific Heats of Organic Solids—(*Concluded*)

Compound	Formula	Temperature, °C.	Sp. ht., cal./g. °C.
Quinone	$C_6H_4O_2$	−250	0.031
		−225	0.082
		−200	0.113
		−150 to m.p.	0.282 + 0.00083t
Salol	$C_{13}H_{10}O_3$	32	0.289
Stearic acid	$C_{18}H_{36}O_2$	15	0.399
Succinic acid	$C_4H_6O_4$	0 to 160	0.248 + 0.00153t
Sucrose	$C_{12}H_{22}O_{11}$	20	0.299
Sugar (cane)	$C_{12}H_{22}O_{11}$	22 to 51	0.301
Tartaric acid	$C_4H_6O_6$	36	0.287
Tartaric acid	$C_4H_6O_6.H_2O$	−150	0.112
		−100	0.170
		− 50	0.231
		0	0.308
		+ 50	0.366
Tetrachloroethylene	C_2Cl_4	− 40 to 0	0.198 + 0.00018t
Tetryl	$C_7H_5N_5O_8$	−100	0.182
		− 50	0.199
		0	0.212
		+100	0.236
1 Tetryl + 1 picric acid	$C_{13}H_8N_8O_{15}$	−100 to +100	0.253 + 0.00072t
1 Tetryl + 2 TNT	$C_{21}H_{15}N_{11}O_{20}$	−100	0.172
		0	0.280
		+ 50	0.325
Thymol	$C_{10}H_{14}O$	0 to 49	0.315 + 0.0031t
Toluic acid (o-)	$C_8H_8O_2$	54 to m.p.	0.277 + 0.00120t
(m-)	$C_8H_8O_2$	54 to m.p.	0.239 + 0.00195t
(p-)	$C_8H_8O_2$	130 to m.p.	0.271 + 0.00106t
Toluidine (p-)	C_7H_9N	0	0.337
		20	0.387
		40	0.440
Trichloroacetic acid	$C_2HCl_3O_2$	solid	0.459
Trimethyl carbinol	$C_4H_{10}O$	− 4	0.559
Trinitrotoluene	$C_7H_5N_3O_6$	−100	0.170
		− 50	0.253
		0	0.311
		+100	0.385
Trinitroxylene	$C_8H_7N_3O_6$	−185 to +23	0.241
		20 to 50	0.423
Triphenylmethane	$C_{19}H_{16}$	0 to 91	0.189 + 0.0027t
Urea	CH_4N_2O	20	0.320

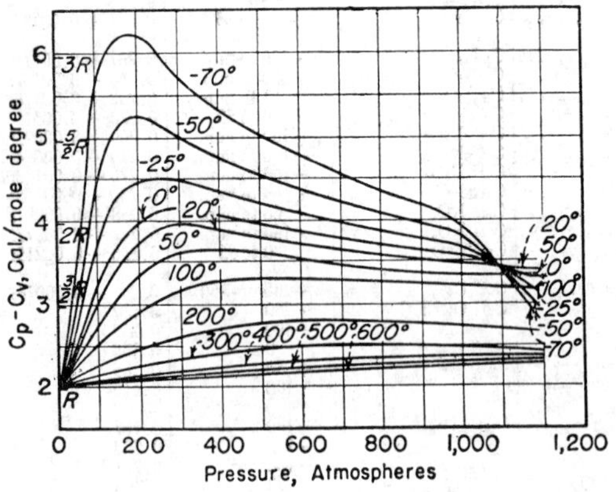

FIG. 3-13. The variation of $C_p - C_v$ for nitrogen with pressure at various temperatures. [*Deming and Shupe, Phys. Rev.*, **37**, 638 (1931).]

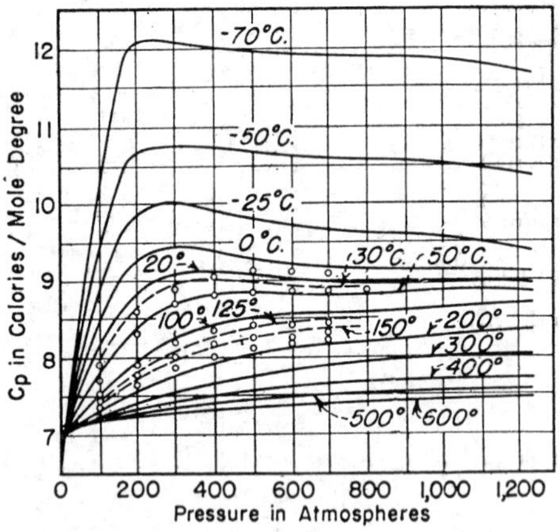

FIG. 3-14. The variation of heat capacity for nitrogen with pressure at various temperatures. [*Deming and Shupe, Phys. Rev.*, **37**, 638 (1931).]

Table 3-178. Liquefied Gases*

Substance (liquid)	Temperature or range of temperature, °C.	Specific heat, cal./g. °C.
Ammonia	−60	1.05
	0	1.10
	40	1.16
	80	1.29
	100	1.48
	110	1.61
Carbon dioxide (63 atm.)	−50 to −10	0.465 to 0.539
disulfide	−100 to 150	$0.235 + 0.00046t$
monoxide	−206 to −190	0.0615
Chlorine	−205	0.229
Hydrogen	−258 to −252	1.75 to 2.33
Nitric oxide	−158 to −156	0.580
Nitrogen	−209 to −197	.475
Oxygen	−216 to −200	.398
Sulfur dioxide	−20	.313
	0	.318
	20	.328
	60	.361
	100	.419
	150	.846

* For data on solid and liquid nitrogen (15° to 78°K.) see Scott "Cryogenic Engineering," p. 279, Van Nostrand, Princeton, N.J., 1959. For other gases see "Handbook of Chemistry and Physics," 40th ed., pp. 2273–2274, Chemical Rubber Publishing Co. For cryogenic data see also Johnson (ed.), WADD-TR-60-56, 1960; Gersh, "Low Temperature," vol. II, Moscow, 1949.

Table 3-179. Specific Heat of Air at High Pressures

Cal./g. °C.

Temp., °C.	Atmospheres					
	1	10	20	40	70	100
100	0.237	0.239	0.240	0.245	0.250	0.258
0	.238	.242	.247	.251	.277	.298
−50	.238	.246	.257	.279	.332	.412
−100	.239	.259	.285	.370	.846	
−150	.240	.311	.505			

For the specific heats of other materials as a function of the pressure, see "International Critical Tables," vol. 5, pp. 82–83. See Figs. 3-11 and 3-14.

Table 3-180. C_p/C_v: Ratios of Specific Heats of Gases at 1 Atm. Pressure*

Compound	Formula	Temperature, °C.	Ratio of specific heats, $(\gamma) = C_p/C_v$
Acetaldehyde	C_2H_4O	30	1.14
Acetic acid	$C_2H_4O_2$	136	1.15
Acetylene	C_2H_2	15	1.26
		−71	1.31
Air	....	925	1.36
		17	1.403
		−78	1.408
		−118	1.415
Ammonia	NH_3	15	1.310
Argon	A	15	1.668
		−180	1.76 (?)
		0–100	1.67
Benzene	C_6H_6	90	1.10
Bromine	Br_2	20–350	1.32
Carbon dioxide	CO_2	15	1.304
		−75	1.37
disulfide	CS_2	100	1.21
monoxide	CO	15	1.404
		−180	1.41
Chlorine	Cl_2	15	1.355
Chloroform	$CHCl_3$	100	1.15
Cyanogen	$(CN)_2$	15	1.256
Cyclohexane	C_6H_{12}	80	1.08
Dichlorodifluormethane	CCl_2F_2	25	1.139
Ethane	C_2H_6	100	1.19
		15	1.22
		−82	1.28
Ethyl alcohol	C_2H_6O	90	1.13
ether	$C_4H_{10}O$	35	1.08
		80	1.086
Ethylene	C_2H_4	100	1.18
		15	1.255
		−91	1.35
Helium	He	−180	1.660
Hexane (n-)	C_6H_{14}	80	1.08
Hydrogen	H_2	15	1.410
		−76	1.453
		−181	1.597
bromide	HBr	20	1.42
chloride	HCl	15	1.41
		100	1.40
cyanide	HCN	65	1.31
		140	1.28
		210	1.24

Compound	Formula	Temperature, °C.	Ratio of specific heats, $(\gamma) = C_p/C_v$
Hydrogen (*Cont.*):			
iodide	HI	20–100	1.40
sulfide	H_2S	15	1.32
		−45	1.30
		−57	1.29
Iodine	I_2	185	1.30
Isobutane	C_4H_{10}	15	1.11
Krypton	Kr	19	1.68
Mercury	Hg	360	1.67
Methane	CH_4	600	1.113
		300	1.16
		15	1.31
		−80	1.34
		−115	1.41
Methyl acetate	$C_3H_6O_2$	15	1.14
alcohol	CH_4O	77	1.203
ether	C_2H_6O	6–30	1.11
Methylal	$C_3H_8O_2$	13	1.06
		40	1.09
Neon	Ne	19	1.64
Nitric oxide	NO	15	1.400
		−45	1.39
		−80	1.38
Nitrogen	N_2	15	1.404
		−181	1.47
Nitrous oxide	N_2O	100	1.28
		15	1.303
		−30	1.31
		−70	1.34
Oxygen	O_2	15	1.401
		−76	1.415
		−181	1.45
Pentane (n-)	C_5H_{12}	86	1.086
Phosphorus	P	300	1.17
Potassium	K	850	1.77
Sodium	Na	750–920	1.68
Sulfur dioxide	SO_2	15	1.29
Xenon	Xe	19	1.66

* From "International Critical Tables," vol. 5, pp. 80–82.

Table 3-181. Ratios of Specific Heats of Air at High Pressures

Pressure, atm.	Ratio of specific heats, $(\gamma) = C_p/C_v$		Pressure, atm.	Ratio of specific heats, $(\gamma) = C_p/C_v$	
	0°C.	−79.4°C.		0°C.	−79.4°C.
25	1.47	1.57	125	1.69	2.40
50	1.53	1.77	150	1.74	2.47
75	1.59	2.00	175	1.78	2.41
100	1.65	2.20	200	1.83	2.33

For additional data, see "International Critical Tables," vol. 5, pp. 115–116, and pp. 122–125.

SPECIFIC HEATS OF AQUEOUS SOLUTIONS

For additional data see "International Critical Tables," vol. 5, pp. 115–116, and pp. 122–125

Table 3-182. Hydrochloric Acid

Mole % HCl	Specific heat, cal./g. °C.				
	0°C.	10°C.	20°C.	40°C.	60°C.
0.0	1.00				
9.09	0.72	0.72	0.74	0.75	0.78
16.7	.61	.605	.631	.645	.67
20.0	.58	.575	.591	.615	.638
25.9	.55	......			.61

Table 3-183. Sulfuric Acid*

$\%H_2SO_4$	C_p at 20°C., cal./g. °C.	$\%H_2SO_4$	C_p at 20°C., cal./g. °C.
0.34	0.9968	35.25	0.7238
0.68	.9937	37.69	.7023
1.34	.9877	40.49	.6770
2.65	.9762	43.75	.6476
3.50	.9688	47.57	.6153
5.16	.9549	52.13	.5801
9.82	.9177	57.65	.5420
15.36	.8767	64.47	.5012
21.40	.8339	73.13	.4628
22.27	.8275	77.91	.4518
23.22	.8205	81.33	.4481
24.25	.8127	82.49	.4467
25.39	.8041	84.48	.4408
26.63	.7945	85.48	.4346
28.00	.7837	89.36	.4016
29.52	.7717	91.81	.3787
30.34	.7647	94.82	.3554
31.20	.7579	97.44	.3404
33.11	.7422	100.00	.3352

* Vinal and Craig, *Bur. Standards J. Research*, **24**, 475 (1940).

Table 3-184. Nitric Acid Solutions

$\%HNO_3$ by Weight	Specific Heat at 20°C., Cal./g. °C.
0	1.000
10	0.900
20	.810
30	.730
40	.675
50	.650
60	.640
70	.615
80	.575
90	.515

Table 3-185. Phosphoric Acid*

$\%H_3PO_4$	C_p at 21.3°C. cal./g. °C.	$\%H_3PO_4$	C_p at 21.3°C. cal./g. °C.
2.50	0.9903	50.00	0.6350
3.80	.9970	52.19	.6220
5.33	.9669	53.72	.6113
8.81	.9389	56.04	.5972
10.27	.9293	58.06	.5831
14.39	.8958	60.23	.5704
16.23	.8796	62.10	.5603
19.99	.8489	64.14	.5460
22.10	.8300	66.13	.5349
24.56	.8125	68.14	.5242
25.98	.8004	69.97	.5157
28.15	.7856	69.50	.5160
29.96	.7735	71.88	.5046
32.09	.7590	73.71	.4940
33.95	.7432	75.79	.4847
36.26	.7270	77.69	.4786
38.10	.7160	79.54	.4680
40.10	.7024	80.00	.4686
42.08	.6877	82.00	.4593
44.11	.6748	84.00	.4500
46.22	.6607	85.98	.4419
48.16	.6475	88.01	.4359
49.79	.6370	89.72	.4206

* *Z. physik. Chem.*, **A167**, 42 (1933).

Table 3-186. Acetic Acid (at 38°C.)

Mole % acetic acid...........	0	6.98	30.9	54.5	100
Cal./g. °C..................	1.0	0.911	0.73	0.631	0.535

Table 3-187. Sodium Hydroxide (at 20°C.)

Mole % NaOH..	0	0.5	1.0	9.09	16.7	28.6	37.5
Cal./g. °C.......	1.0	0.985	0.97	0.835	0.80	0.784	0.782

Table 3-188. Potassium Hydroxide (at 19°C.)

Mole % KOH.....................	0	0.497	1.64	4.76	9.09
Cal./g. °C........................	1.0	0.975	0.93	0.814	0.75

Table 3-189. Ammonia

Mole % NH_3	Specific heat, cal./g. °C.			
	2.4°C.	20.6°C.	41°C.	61°C.
0	1.01	1.0	0.995	1.0
10.5	0.98	0.995	1.06	1.02
20.9	.96	.99	1.03	
31.2	.956	1.0		
41.4	.985			

Table 3-190. Sodium Carbonate*

$\%Na_2CO_3$ by weight	Temperature, °C.			
	17.6	30.0	76.6	98.0
0.000	0.9992	0.9986	1.0098	1.0084
1.498	.9807			
2.000	......	.9786		
2.901	.9597			
4.000	......	.9594		
5.000	.9428	......	0.9761	
6.000	......	.9392		
8.000	.9183			
10.000	.9086	......	.9452	
13.790	.8924			
13.840	......	.8881		
20.000	......	.8631	.8936	
25.000	......	......	.8615	0.8911

* *J. Chem. Soc.*, pp. 3062–3079 (1931).

Table 3-191. Sodium Chloride

Mole % NaCl	Specific heat, cal./g. °C.			
	6°C.	20°C.	33°C.	57°C.
0.249	.....	0.99		
.99	0.96	.97	0.97	
2.44	.91	.915	.915	0.923
9.09	.805	.81	.81	.82

Table 3-192. Potassium Chloride

Mole % KCl	Specific heat, cal./g. °C.			
	6°C.	20°C.	33°C.	40°C.
0.99	0.945	0.947	0.947	0.947
3.85	.828	.831	.835	.837
5.66	.77	.775	.778	.775
7.41	.....	.727		

Table 3-193. Zinc Sulfate

Composition	Temperature	Sp. ht., cal./g. °C.
$ZnSO_4 + 50H_2O$	20° to 52°C.	0.842
$ZnSO_4 + 200H_2O$	20° to 52°C.	.952

Table 3-194. Copper Sulfate

Composition	Temperature	Sp. ht., cal./g. °C.
$CuSO_4 + 50H_2O$	12° to 15°C.	0.848
$CuSO_4 + 200H_2O$	12° to 14°C.	.951
$CuSO_4 + 400H_2O$	13° to 17°C.	.975

Table 3-195. Methyl Alcohol

Mole % CH_3OH	Specific heat, cal./g. °C. 5°C.	20°C.	40°C.
5.88	1.02	1.0	0.995
12.3	0.975	0.982	.98
27.3	.877	.917	.92
45.8	.776	.811	.83
69.6	.681	.708	.726
100	.576	.60	.617

Table 3-196. Ethyl Alcohol

Mole % C_2H_5OH	Specific heat, cal./g. °C. 3°C.	23°C.	41°C.
4.16	1.05	1.02	1.02
11.5	1.02	1.03	1.03
37.0	0.805	0.86	0.875
61.0	.67	.727	.748
100.0	.54	.577	.621

Table 3-197. Normal Propyl Alcohol

Mole % C_3H_7OH	Specific heat, cal./g. °C. 5°C.	20°C.	40°C.
1.55	1.03	1.02	1.01
5.03	1.07	1.06	1.03
11.4	1.035	1.032	0.99
23.1	0.877	0.90	.91
41.2	.75	.78	.815
73.0	.612	.645	.708
100.0	.534	.57	.621

Table 3-198. Glycerol

Mole % $C_3H_5(OH)_3$	Specific heat, cal./g. °C. 15°C.	32°C.
2.12	0.961	0.960
4.66	.929	.924
11.5	.851	.841
22.7	.765	.758
43.9	.67	.672
100.0	.555	.576

NOTE.—For the specific heats of non-aqueous solutions, see "International Critical Tables," vol. 5, pp. 116, 125.

Table 3-199. Aniline (at 20°C.)

Mol % aniline	100	95	90.5	82.3	75.2
Cal./g. °C.	0.497	0.52	0.53	0.56	0.581

SPECIFIC HEATS OF MISCELLANEOUS MATERIALS

Table 3-200. Specific Heats of Miscellaneous Liquids and Solids

Material	Specific Heat, cal./g. °C.
Alumina	0.2 (100°C.); 0.274 (1500°C.)
Alundum	0.186 (100°C.)
Asbestos	0.25
Asphalt	0.22
Bakelite	0.3 to 0.4
Brickwork	About 0.2
Carbon	0.168 (26° to 76°C.)
	0.314 (40° to 892°C.)
	0.387 (56° to 1450°C.)
(gas retort)	0.204
(See under Graphite)	
Cellulose	0.32
Cement, Portland Clinker	0.186
Charcoal (wood)	0.242
Chrome brick	0.17
Clay	0.224
Coal	0.26 to 0.37
tar oils	0.34 (15° to 90°C.)
Coal tars	0.35 (40°C.); 0.45 (200°C.)
Coke	0.265 (21° to 400°C.)
	0.359 (21° to 800°C.)
	0.403 (21° to 1300°C.)
Concrete	0.156 (70° to 312°F.); 0.219 (72° to 1472°F.)
Cryolite	0.253 (16° to 55°C.)
Diamond	0.147
Fireclay brick	0.198 (100°C.); 0.298 (1500°C.)
Fluorspar	0.21 (30°C.)
Gasoline	0.53
Glass (crown)	0.16 to 0.20
(flint)	0.117
(pyrex)	0.20
(silicate)	0.188 to 0.204 (0 to 100°C.)
	0.24 to 0.26 (0 to 700°C.)
wool	0.157
Granite	0.20 (20° to 100°C.)
Graphite	0.165 (26° to 76°C.); 0.390 (56° to 1450°C.)
Gypsum	0.259 (16° to 46°C.)
Kerosene	0.47
Limestone	0.217
Litharge	0.055
Magnesia	0.234 (100°C.); 0.188 (1500°C.)
Magnesite brick	0.222 (100°C.); 0.195 (1500°C.)
Marble	0.21 (18°C.)
Pyrites (copper)	0.131 (19° to 50°C.)
(iron)	0.136 (15° to 98°C.)
Quartz	0.17 (0°C.); 0.28 (350°C.,
Sand	0.191
Silica	0.316
Steel	0.12
Stone	About 0.2
Turpentine	0.42 (18°C.)
Wood (oak)	0.570
Most woods vary between	0.45 and 0.65

Oils (animal, vegetable, mineral oils)

$$C_p(\text{cal./g. °C.}) = \frac{A}{\sqrt{d_4^{15}}} + B(t - 15)$$

Oils	A	B
Castor	0.500	0.0007
Citron	(0.438 at 54°C.)	
Fatty drying	0.440	0.0007
non-drying	0.450	0.0007
semidrying	0.445	0.0007
oils (except castor)	0.450	0.0007
Naphthene base	0.405	0.0009
Olive	(0.47 at 7°C.)	
Paraffin base	0.425	0.0009
Petroleum oils	0.415	0.0009

Porcelain	Average specific heat between 20°C. and 100°C.	300°C.	500°C.	1100°C.
Fired Berlin	0.189	0.203	0.222	0.337
Green Berlin	.185	.197	.228	
Fired Berlin (glaze)	.179	.189	.199	.245
Green Berlin (glaze)	.170	.183	.208	
Fired earthenware	.186	.203	.223	.324
Green earthenware	.181	.192	.215	

Material	Specific heat
Pyrex glass	0.20
Pyroxylin plastics	0.34 to 0.38
Rubber (vulcanized)	0.415
Silica brick	0.202 (100°C.); 0.195 (1500°C.)
Silicon carbide brick	0.202 (100°C.)
Silk	0.33
Stoneware (common)	0.185 to 0.191 (20° to 100°C.)
Wool	0.325
Zirconium oxide	0.11 (100°C.); 0.179 (1500°C.)

HEATS AND FREE ENERGIES OF FORMATION

Table 3-201. Heats and Free Energies of Formation of Inorganic and Organic Compounds

The values given in the following table for the heats and free energies of formation of inorganic compounds are derived from (*a*) Bichowsky and Rossini, "Thermochemistry of the Chemical Substances," Reinhold, New York, 1936; (*b*) Latimer, "Oxidation States of the Elements and Their Potentials in Aqueous Solution," Prentice-Hall, New York, 1938; (*c*) the tables of the American Petroleum Institute Research Project 44 at the National Bureau of Standards; and (*d*) the tables of Selected Values of Chemical Thermodynamic Properties of the National Bureau of Standards. The reader is referred to the preceding books and tables for additional details as to methods of calculation, standard states, etc.

The organic compounds in the following table are all given under the element carbon. The values for the non-hydrocarbons are largely from E. I. du Pont de Nemours & Co., Ammonia Department, Chemical Division, Experimental Station; and the values for the hydrocarbons are from the tables of the American Petroleum Institute Research Project 44 at the National Bureau of Standards.*

Compound	State†	Heat of formation‡§ ΔH (formation) at 25°C., kcal./mole	Free energy of formation‖¶ ΔF (formation) at 25°C., kcal./mole
Aluminum:			
Al	c	0.00	0.00
$AlBr_3$	c	−123.4	
	aq	−209.5	−189.2
Al_4C_3	c	−30.8	−29.0
$AlCl_3$	c	−163.8	
	aq, 600	−243.9	−209.5
AlF_3	c	−329	
	aq	−360.8	−312.6
AlI_3	c	−72.8	
	aq	−163.4	−152.5
AlN	c	−57.7	−50.4
$Al(NH_4)(SO_4)_2$	c	−561.19	−486.17
$Al(NH_4)(SO_4)_2.12H_2O$	c	−1419.36	−1179.26
$Al(NO_3)_3.6H_2O$	c	−680.89	−526.32
$Al(NO_3)_3.9H_2O$	c	−897.59	
Al_2O_3	c, corundum	−399.09	−376.87
$Al(OH)_3$	c	−304.8	−272.9
$Al_2O_3.SiO_2$	c, sillimanite	−648.7	
$Al_2O_3.SiO_2$	c, disthene	−642.4	
$Al_2O_3.SiO_2$	c, andalusite	−642.0	
$3Al_2O_3.2SiO_2$	c, mullite	−1874	
Al_2S_3	c	−121.6	
$Al_2(SO_4)_3$	c	−820.99	−739.53
	aq	−893.9	−759.3
$Al_2(SO_4)_3.6H_2O$	c	−1268.15	−1103.39
$Al_2(SO_4)_3.18H_2O$	c	−2120	
Antimony:			
Sb	c	0.00	0.00
$SbBr_3$	c	−59.9	
$SbCl_3$	c	−91.3	−77.8
$SbCl_5$	l	−104.8	
SbF_3	c	−216.6	
SbI_3	c	−22.8	
Sb_2O_3	c, I, orthorhombic	−165.4	−146.0
	c, II, octahedral	−166.6	
Sb_2O_4	c	−213.0	−186.6
Sb_2O_5	c	−230.0	−196.1
Sb_2S_3	c, black	−38.2	−36.9
Arsenic:			
As	c	0.00	0.00
$AsBr_3$	c	−45.9	
$AsCl_3$	l	−80.2	−70.5
AsF_3	l	−223.76	−212.27
AsH_3	g	43.6	37.7
AsI_3	c	−13.6	
As_2O_3	c	−154.1	−134.8
As_2O_5	c	−217.9	−183.9
As_2S_3	c	−20	−20
	amorphous	−34.76	
Barium:			
Ba	c	0.00	0.00
$BaBr_2$	c	−180.38	
	aq, 400	−185.67	−183.0
$BaCl_2$	c	−205.25	
	aq, 300	−207.92	−196.5
$Ba(ClO_3)_2$	c	−176.6	
	aq, 1600	−170.0	−134.4
$Ba(ClO_4)_2$	c	−210.2	
	aq, 800	....	−155.3
$Ba(CN)_2$	c	−48	
$Ba(CNO)_2$	c	−212.1	
	aq	....	−180.7
$BaCN_2$	c	−63.6	
$BaCO_3$	c, witherite	−284.2	−271.4
$BaCrO_4$	c	−342.2	
BaF_2	c	−287.9	
	aq, 1600	−284.6	−265.3
BaH_2	c	−40.8	−31.5
$Ba(HCO_3)_2$	aq	−459	−414.4
BaI_2	c	−144.6	
	aq, 400	−155.17	−158.52
$Ba(IO_3)_2$	c	−264.5	
	aq	−237.50	−198.35
$BaMoO_4$	c	−370	
Ba_3N_2	c	−90.7	
$Ba(NO_2)_2$	c	−184.5	
	aq	−179.05	−150.75
Barium (*Cont.*):			
$Ba(NO_3)_2$	c	−236.99	−189.94
	aq, 600	−227.74	
BaO	c	−133.0	
$Ba(OH)_2$	c	−225.9	
	aq, 400	−237.76	−209.02
$BaO.SiO_2$	c	−363	
$Ba_3(PO_4)_2$	c	−992	
$BaPtCl_6$	c	−284.9	
BaS	c	−111.2	
$BaSO_3$	c	−282.5	
$BaSO_4$	c	−340.2	−313.4
$BaWO_4$	c	−402	
Beryllium:			
Be	c	0.00	0.00
$BeBr_2$	c	−79.4	
	aq	−142	−127.9
$BeCl_2$	c	−112.6	
	aq	−163.9	−141.4
BeI_2	c	−39.4	
	aq	−112	−103.4
Be_3N_2	c	−134.5	−122.4
BeO	c	−145.3	−138.3
$Be(OH)_2$	c	−215.6	
BeS	c	−56.1	
$BeSO_4$	c	−281	
	aq	....	−254.8
Bismuth:			
Bi	c	0.00	0.00
$BiCl_3$	c	−90.5	−76.4
	aq	−101.6	
BiI_3	c	−24	
	aq	−27	
BiO	c	−49.5	−43.2
Bi_2O_3	c	−137.1	−117.9
$Bi(OH)_3$	c	−171.1	
Bi_2S_3	c	−43.9	−39.1
$Bi_2(SO_4)_3$	c	−607.1	
Boron:			
B	c	0.00	0.00
BBr_3	l	−52.7	
	g	−44.6	−50.9
BCl_3	g	−94.5	−90.8
BF_3	g	−265.2	−261.0
B_2H_6	g	7.5	19.9
BN	c	−32.1	−27.2
B_2O_3	c	−302.0	−282.9
	gls	−297.6	−280.3
$B(OH)_3$	c	−260.0	−229.4
B_2S_3	c	−56.6	
Bromine:			
Br_2	l	0.00	0.00
	g	7.47	0.931
BrCl	g	3.06	−0.63
Cadmium:			
Cd	c	0.00	0.00
$CdBr_2$	c	−75.8	−70.7
	aq, 400	−76.6	−67.6
$CdCl_2$	c	−92.149	−81.889
	aq, 400	−96.44	−81.2
$Cd(CN)_2$	c	36.2	
$CdCO_3$	c	−178.2	−163.2
CdI_2	c	−48.40	
	aq, 400	−47.46	−43.22
Cd_3N_2	c	39.8	
$Cd(NO_3)_2$	aq, 400	−115.67	−71.05
CdO	c	−62.35	−55.28
$Cd(OH)_2$	c	−135.0	−113.7
CdS	c	−34.5	−33.6
$CdSO_4$	c	−222.23	
	aq, 400	−232.635	−194.65
Calcium:			
Ca	c	0.00	0.00
$CaBr_2$	c	−162.20	
	aq, 400	−187.19	−181.86
CaC_2	c	−14.8	−16.0
$CaCl_2$	c	−190.6	−179.8
	aq	−209.15	−195.36

* For footnotes see p. 3-141.

Table 3-201. Heats and Free Energies of Formation of Inorganic and Organic Compounds—(*Continued*)

Compound	State†	Heat of formation‡§ ΔH (formation) at 25°C., kcal./mole	Free energy of formation‖¶ ΔF (formation) at 25°C., kcal./mole
Calcium (*Cont.*):			
$CaCN_2$	c	−85	
$Ca(CN)_2$	c	−43.3	
	aq	....	−54.0
$CaCO_3$	c, calcite	−289.5	−270.8
	c, aragonite	−289.54	−270.57
$CaCO_3.MgCO_3$	c	−558.8	
CaC_2O_4	c	−332.2	
$Ca(C_2H_3O_2)_2$	c	−356.3	
	aq	−364.1	−311.3
CaF_2	c	−290.2	
	aq	−286.5	−264.1
CaH_2	c	−46	−35.7
CaI_2	c	−128.49	
	aq, 400	−156.63	−157.37
Ca_3N_2	c	−103.2	−88.2
$Ca(NO_3)_2$	c	−224.05	−177.38
	aq, 400	−228.29	
$Ca(NO_3)_2.2H_2O$	c	−367.95	−293.57
$Ca(NO_3)_2.3H_2O$	c	−439.05	−351.58
$Ca(NO_3)_2.4H_2O$	c	−509.43	−409.32
CaO	c	−151.7	−144.3
$Ca(OH)_2$	c	−235.58	−213.9
	aq, 800	−239.2	−207.9
$CaO.SiO_2$	c, II, wollastonite	−377.9	−357.5
	c, I, pseudowollastonite	−376.6	−356.6
CaS	c	−114.3	−113.1
$CaSO_4$	c, insoluble form	−338.73	−311.9
	c, soluble form α	−336.58	−309.8
	c, soluble form β	−335.52	−308.8
$CaSO_4.\frac{1}{2}H_2O$	c	−376.13	
$CaSO_4.2H_2O$	c	−479.33	−425.47
$CaWO_4$	c	−387	
Carbon:			
C	c, graphite	0.00	0.00
	c, diamond	0.453	0.685
CO	g	−26.416	−32.808
CO_2	g	−94.052	−94.260
CH_4 methane	g	−17.889	−12.140
C_2H_6 ethane	g	−20.236	−7.860
C_3H_8 propane	g	−24.820	−5.614
C_4H_{10} n-butane	g	−29.812	−3.754
C_4H_{10} isobutane	g	−31.452	−4.296
C_5H_{12} n-pentane	g	−35.00	−1.96
	l	−41.36	−2.21
C_5H_{12} 2-methylbutane	g	−36.92	−3.50
	l	−42.85	−3.59
C_5H_{12} 2,2-dimethylpropane	g	−39.67	−3.64
C_6H_{14} n-hexane	g	−39.96	0.05
	l	−47.52	−0.91
C_6H_{14} 2-methylpentane	g	−41.66	−0.96
	l	−48.82	−1.73
C_6H_{14} 3-methylpentane	g	−41.02	−0.29
	l	−48.28	−1.12
C_6H_{14} 2,2-dimethylbutane	g	−44.35	−2.35
	l	−51.00	−2.88
C_6H_{14} 2,3-dimethylbutane	g	−42.49	−0.73
	l	−49.48	−1.44
C_7H_{16} n-heptane	g	−44.89	2.09
	l	−53.63	0.42
C_7H_{16} 2-methylhexane	g	−46.60	0.98
	l	−54.93	−0.47
C_7H_{16} 3-methylhexane	g	−45.96	1.10
	l	−54.35	−0.39
C_7H_{16} 3-ethylpentane	g	−45.34	2.59
	l	−53.77	1.06
C_7H_{16} 2,2-dimethylpentane	g	−49.29	0.09
	l	−57.05	−1.08
C_7H_{16} 2,3-dimethylpentane	g	−47.62	0.16
	l	−55.81	−1.27
C_7H_{16} 2,4-dimethylpentane	g	−48.30	0.72
	l	−56.17	−0.49
C_7H_{16} 3,3-dimethylpentane	g	−48.17	0.63
	l	−56.07	−0.69
C_7H_{16} 2,2,3-trimethylbutane	g	−48.96	0.76
	l	−56.63	−0.43
C_8H_{18} n-octane	g	−49.82	4.14
	l	−59.74	1.77
C_8H_{18} 2-methylheptane	g	−51.50	3.06
	l	−60.98	0.92
C_8H_{18} 3-methylheptane	g	−50.82	3.29
	l	−60.34	1.12
C_8H_{18} 4-methylheptane	g	−50.69	4.00
	l	−60.17	1.86
C_8H_{18} 3-ethylhexane	g	−50.40	3.95
	l	−59.88	1.80
Carbon (*Cont.*):			
C_8H_{18} 2,2-dimethylhexane	g	−53.71	2.56
	l	−62.63	−0.72
C_8H_{18} 2,3-dimethylhexane	g	−51.13	4.23
	l	−60.40	2.17
C_8H_{18} 2,4-dimethylhexane	g	−52.44	2.80
	l	−61.47	0.89
C_8H_{18} 2,5-dimethylhexane	g	−53.21	2.50
	l	−62.26	0.59
C_8H_{18} 3,3-dimethylhexane	g	−52.61	3.17
	l	−61.58	1.23
C_8H_{18} 3,4-dimethylhexane	g	−50.91	4.97
	l	−60.23	2.86
C_8H_{18} 2-methyl-3-ethylpentane	g	−50.48	5.08
	l	−59.69	3.03
C_8H_{18} 3-methyl-3-ethylpentane	g	−51.38	4.76
	l	−60.46	2.69
C_8H_{18} 2,2,3-trimethylpentane	g	−52.61	4.09
	l	−61.44	2.22
C_8H_{18} 2,2,4-trimethylpentane	g	−53.57	3.13
	l	−61.97	1.51
C_8H_{18} 2,3,3,-trimethylpentane	g	−51.73	4.52
	l	−60.63	2.54
C_8H_{18} 2,3,4-trimethylpentane	g	−51.97	4.32
	l	−60.98	2.34
C_8H_{18} 2,2,3,3,-tetramethylbutane	g	−53.99	4.88
	c	−64.23	2.74
C_2H_4 ethylene	g	12.496	16.282
C_3H_6 propylene	g	4.879	14.964
C_4H_8 1-butene	g	0.280	17.217
C_4H_8 cis-2-butene	g	−1.362	16.007
C_4H_8 trans-2-butene	g	−2.405	15.323
C_4H_8 2-methyl-2-propene	g	−3.343	14.574
C_5H_{10} 1-pentene	g	−5.000	18.787
C_5H_{10} cis-2-pentene	g	−6.710	17.173
C_5H_{10} trans-2-pentene	g	−7.590	16.575
C_5H_{10} 2-methyl-1-butene	g	−8.680	15.509
C_5H_{10} 3-methyl-1-butene	g	−6.920	17.874
C_5H_{10} 2-methyl-2-butene	g	−10.170	14.267
C_2H_2 acetylene	g	54.194	50.000
C_3H_4 methylacetylene	g	44.319	46.313
C_4H_6 1-butyne	g	39.70	48.52
C_4H_6 2-butyne	g	35.374	44.725
C_5H_8 1-pentyne	g	34.50	50.17
C_5H_8 2-pentyne	g	30.80	46.41
C_5H_8 3-methyl-1-butyne	g	32.60	49.12
C_6H_6 benzene	g	19.820	30.989
	l	11.718	29.756
C_7H_8 toluene	g	11.950	29.228
	l	2.867	27.282
C_8H_{10} ethylbenzene	g	7.120	31.208
	l	−2.977	28.614
C_8H_{10} o-xylene	g	4.540	29.177
	l	−5.841	26.370
C_8H_{10} m-xylene	g	4.120	28.405
	l	−6.075	25.730
C_8H_{10} p-xylene	g	4.290	28.952
	l	−5.838	26.310
C_9H_{12} n-propylbenzene	g	1.870	32.810
	l	−9.178	29.600
C_9H_{12} isopropylbenzene	g	0.940	32.738
	l	−9.848	29.708
C_9H_{12} 1-methyl-2-ethylbenzene	g	0.290	31.323
	l	−11.110	27.973
C_9H_{12} 1-methyl-3-ethylbenzene	g	−0.460	30.217
	l	−11.670	26.977
C_9H_{12} 1-methyl-4-ethylbenzene	g	−0.780	30.281
	l	−11.920	27.041
C_9H_{12} 1,2,3-trimethylbenzene	g	−2.290	29.319
	l	−14.013	25.679
C_9H_{12} 1,2,4-trimethylbenzene	g	−3.330	27.912
	l	−14.785	24.462
C_9H_{12} 1,3,5-trimethylbenzene	g	−3.840	28.172
	l	−15.184	24.832
C_5H_{10} cyclopentane	g	−18.46	9.23
	l	−25.31	8.70
C_6H_{12} methylcyclopentane	g	−25.50	8.55
	l	−33.08	7.53
C_7H_{14} ethylcyclopentane	g	−30.38	10.59
	l	−39.09	8.84

Table 3-201. Heats and Free Energies of Formation of Inorganic and Organic Compounds—(*Continued*)

Compound	State†	Heat of formation‡§ ΔH (formation) at 25°C., kcal./mole	Free energy of formation‖¶ ΔF (formation) at 25°C., kcal./mole
Carbon (*Cont.*):			
C_6H_{12} cyclohexane	g	−29.43	7.59
	l	−37.34	6.39
C_7H_{14} methylcyclohexane	g	−37.00	6.52
	l	−45.46	4.86
C_8H_{16} ethylcyclohexane	g	−41.06	9.38
	l	−50.73	6.96
CH_4O methanol	g	−48.08	−38.62
	l	−57.04	−39.80
C_2H_6O ethanol	g	−52.23	−40.23
	l	−66.35	−41.76
C_3H_8O *n*-propanol	g	−61.17	−38.83
	l	−71.87	−39.84
C_3H_8O isopropanol	g	−62.41	−38.20
	l	−74.32	−38.83
$C_4H_{10}O$ *n*-butanol	g	−67.81	−38.88
	l	−79.61	−40.37
$C_4H_{10}O$ isobutanol	g	−69.05	−38.25
	l	−81.06	−39.36
$C_2H_6O_2$ ethylene glycol	g	−92.53	−71.26
	l	−107.91	−76.44
$C_3H_8O_3$ glycerol	g		
	l	−159.16	−113.65
C_6H_6O phenol	g	−21.71	−6.26
	l	−37.80	−11.02
C_7H_8O cresol	g	....	−13.17
C_2H_4O ethylene oxide	g	−16.1	−6.94
C_2H_6O dimethyl ether	g	−43.06	−26.06
	l	−51.3	
$C_4H_{10}O$ diethyl ether	l	−65.2	−27.75
CH_2O formaldehyde	g	−28.29	−26.88
C_2H_4O acetaldehyde	g	−39.72	−31.46
C_3H_4O acrolein	g	−20.50	−15.57
	l	−27.97	−16.17
C_3H_6O propionaldehyde	g	−49.15	−33.96
C_4H_8O *n*-butyraldehyde	g	−52.40	−73.24
C_7H_6O benzaldehyde	g	−9.57	5.85
	l	−21.23	2.24
C_8H_8O *p*-toluic aldehyde	g	−17.78	4.09
	l	−29.79	0.97
C_2H_2O ketene	g	−14.78	−14.30
	l	−18.78	−13.32
C_3H_6O acetone	g	−51.79	−36.45
	l	−59.32	−37.16
$C_5H_{10}O$ diethylketone	l	−73.8	
CH_2O_2 formic acid	g	−86.67	−80.24
	l	−97.8	−82.7
½$(CH_2O_2)_2$ bimolecular formic acid	g	−93.85	−81.90
$C_2H_4O_2$ acetic acid	g	−104.72	−91.24
	l	−116.2	−93.56
$C_3H_6O_2$ propionic acid	g	−108.75	−88.27
	l	−121.7	−91.65
$C_2H_4O_3$ hydroxyacctic acid	l	−155.33	−125.57
$C_6H_{10}O_4$ adipic acid	g	−216.19	−163.96
	l	−235.51	−177.17
$C_2H_4O_2$ methyl formate	g	−84.69	−71.37
	l	−95.26	−71.53
$C_4H_6O_2$ methyl acrylate	g	−70.10	−56.78
	l	−82.76	−58.13
$C_4H_8O_2$ ethyl acetate	g	−102.02	−74.93
	l	−110.72	−76.11
$C_5H_{10}O_2$ ethyl propionate	g	−112.36	−77.37
	l	−122.16	−79.16
$C_4H_6O_3$ acetic anhydride	g	−148.82	−119.29
	l	−155.16	−121.75
$C_6H_{10}O_3$ propionic anhydride	g	−147.32	−109.78
	l	−161.53	−113.66
CS_2 carbon disulfide	g	28.11	16.13
COS carbonyl sulfide	g	−33.83	−40.85
C_2N_2 cyanogen	g	73.82	71.02
HCN hydrogen cyanide	g	31.1	27.94
	l	25.2	29.0
	aq, 100	25.2	26.8
C_2H_3N acetonitrile	g	19.81	
CH_5N methylamine	g	−6.7	6.6
C_2H_7N ethylamine	g	−12.24	10.01
C_3H_9N propylamine	g	−16.45	14.38
$C_4H_{11}N$ butylamine	g	−15.60	19.55
$C_6H_{13}N$ hexamethyleneimine	g	−14.37	31.52
	l	−24.90	28.84
CH_2N_2 cyanamide	l	11.18	24.30
	c	9.15	24.18
$C_6H_8N_2$ adiponitrile	g	33.34	61.43
	l	19.19	54.63
$C_6H_{16}N_2$ hexamethyienediamine	g	−30.57	28.91
CH_5N_3 guanidine	l	−27.48	7.34
	c	−30.68	6.33

Compound	State†	Heat of formation‡§ ΔH (formation) at 25°C., kcal./mole	Free energy of formation‖¶ ΔF (formation) at 25°C., kcal./mole
Carbon (*Cont.*):			
$C_3H_6N_6$ melamine	l	−19.33	40.80
CH_3NO formamide	g	−44.64	−36.60
C_2H_7NO ethanolamine	l	−62.52	27.50
CH_4N_2O urea	l	−77.55	−46.45
	c	−79.634	−47.118
Cerium:			
Ce	c	0.00	0.00
CeN	c	−78.2	−70.8
Cesium:			
Cs	c	0.00	0.00
CsBr	c	−97.64	
	aq, 500	−91.39	−94.86
CsCl	c	−106.31	
	aq, 400	−102.01	−101.61
Cs_2CO_3	c	−271.88	
CsF	c	−131.67	
	aq, 400	−140.48	−135.98
CsH	c	−12	−7.30
$CsHCO_3$	c	−230.6	
	aq, 2000	−226.6	−210.56
CsI	c	−83.91	
	aq, 400	−75.74	−82.61
$CsNH_2$	c	−28.2	
$CsNO_3$	c	−121.14	
	aq, 400	−111.54	−96.53
Cs_2O	c	−82.1	
CsOH	c	−100.2	
	aq, 200	−117.0	−107.87
Cs_2S	c	−87	
Cs_2SO_4	c	−344.86	
	aq	−340.12	−316.66
Chlorine:			
Cl_2	g	0.00	0.00
ClF	g	−25.7	
ClO	g	33	
ClO_2	g	24.7	29.5
ClO_3	g	37	
Cl_2O	g	18.20	22.40
Cl_2O_7	g	63	
Chromium:			
Cr	c	0.00	0.00
$CrBr_3$	aq	....	−122.7
Cr_3C_2	c	−21.008	−21.20
Cr_4C	c	−16.378	−16.74
$CrCl_2$	c	−103.1	−93.8
	aq	....	−102.1
CrF_2	c	−152	
CrF_3	c	−231	
CrI_2	c	−63.7	
	aq	....	−64.1
CrO_3	c	−139.3	
Cr_2O_3	c	−268.8	−249.3
$Cr_2(SO_4)_3$	aq	....	−626.3
Cobalt:			
Co	c	0.00	0.00
$CoBr_2$	c	−55.0	
	aq	−73.61	−61.96
Co_3C	c	9.49	7.08
$CoCl_2$	c	−76.9	−66.6
	aq, 400	−95.58	−75.46
$CoCO_3$	c	−172.39	−155.36
CoF_2	aq	−172.98	−144.2
CoI_2	c	−24.2	
	aq	−43.15	−37.4
$Co(NO_3)_2$	c	−102.8	
	aq	−114.9	−65.3
CoO	c	−57.5	
Co_3O_4	c	−196.5	
$Co(OH)_2$	c	−131.5	−108.9
$Co(OH)_3$	c	−177.0	−142.0
CoS	c	−22.3	−19.8
Co_2S_3	c	−40.0	
$CoSO_4$	c	−216.6	
	aq, 400	....	−188.9
Columbium:			
Cb	c	0.00	0.00
Cb_2O_5	c	−462.96	
Copper:			
Cu	c	0.00	0.00
CuBr	c	−26.7	−23.8
$CuBr_2$	c	−34.0	
	aq	−42.4	−33.25
CuCl	c	−31.4	−24.13
$CuCl_2$	c	−48.83	
	aq, 400	−64.7	
$CuClO_4$	aq	−28.3	1.34
$Cu(ClO_3)_2$	aq, 400	....	15.4
$Cu(ClO_4)_2$	aq	....	−5.5

Table 3-201. Heats and Free Energies of Formation of Inorganic and Organic Compounds—(*Continued*)

Compound	State†	Heat of formation‡§ ΔH (formation) at 25°C., kcal./mole	Free energy of formation‖¶ ΔF (formation) at 25°C., kcal./mole
Copper (*Cont.*):			
CuI	c	−17.8	−16.66
CuI_2	c	−4.8	
	aq	−11.9	−8.76
Cu_3N	c	17.78	
$Cu(NO_3)_2$	c	−73.1	
	aq, 200	−83.6	−36.6
CuO	c	−38.5	−31.9
Cu_2O	c	−43.00	−38.13
$Cu(OH)_2$	c	−108.9	−85.5
CuS	c	−11.6	−11.69
Cu_2S	c	−18.97	−20.56
$CuSO_4$	c	−184.7	−158.3
	aq, 800	−200.78	−160.19
Cu_2SO_4	c	−179.6	
	aq	....	−152.0
Erbium:			
Er	c	0.00	0.00
$Er(OH)_3$	c	−326.8	
Fluorine:			
F_2	g	0.00	0.00
F_2O	g	5.5	9.7
Gallium:			
Ga	c	0.00	0.00
$GaBr_3$	c	−92.4	
$GaCl_3$	c	−125.4	
GaN	c	−26.2	
Ga_2O	c	−84.3	
Ga_2O_3	c	−259.9	
Germanium:			
Ge	c	0.00	0.00
Ge_3N_4	c	−15.7	
GeO_2	c	−128.6	
Gold:			
Au	c	0.00	0.00
AuBr	c	−3.4	
$AuBr_3$	c	−14.5	
	aq	−11.0	24.47
AuCl	c	−8.3	
$AuCl_3$	c	−28.3	
	aq	−32.96	4.21
AuI	c	0.2	−0.76
Au_2O_3	c	11.0	18.71
$Au(OH)_3$	c	−100.6	
Hafnium:			
Hf	c	0.00	0.00
HfO_2	c	−271.1	−258.2
Hydrogen:			
H_3AsO_3	aq	−175.6	−153.04
H_3AsO_4	c	−214.9	
	aq	−214.8	−183.93
HBr	g	−8.66	−12.72
	aq, 400	−28.80	−24.58
HBrO	aq	−25.4	−19.90
$HBrO_3$	aq	−11.51	5.00
HCl	g	−22.063	−22.778
	aq, 400	−39.85	−31.330
HCN	g	31.1	27.94
	aq, 100	24.2	26.55
HClO	aq, 400	−28.18	−19.11
$HClO_3$	aq	−23.4	−0.25
$HClO_4$	aq, 660	−31.4	−10.70
$HC_2H_3O_2$	l	−116.2	−93.56
	aq, 400	−116.74	−96.8
$H_2C_2O_4$	c	−196.7	
	aq, 300	−194.6	−165.64
HCOOH	l	−97.8	−82.7
	aq, 200	−98.0	−85.1
H_2CO_3	aq	−167.19	−149.0
HF	g	−64.2	−64.7
	aq, 200	−75.75	
HI	g	6.27	0.365
	aq, 400	−13.47	−12.35
HIO	aq	−38	−23.33
HIO_3	c	−56.77	
	aq	−54.8	−32.25
HN_3	g	70.3	78.50
HNO_3	g	−31.99	−17.57
	l	−41.35	−19.05
	aq, 400	−49.210	
$HNO_3.H_2O$	l	−112.91	−78.36
$HNO_3.3H_2O$	l	−252.15	−193.70
H_2O	g	−57.7979	−54.6351
	l	−68.3174	−56.6899
H_2O_2	l	−45.16	−28.23
	aq, 200	−45.80	−31.47
H_3PO_2	c	−145.5	
	aq	−145.6	−120.0
H_3PO_3	c	−232.2	
	aq	−232.2	−204.0
Hydrogen (*Cont.*):			
H_3PO_4	c	−306.2	
	aq, 400	−309.32	−270.0
H_2S	g	−4.77	−7.85
	aq, 2000	−9.38	
H_2S_2	l	−3.6	
H_2SO_3	aq, 200	−146.88	−128.54
H_2SO_4	l	−193.69	
	aq, 400	−212.03	
H_2Se	g	20.5	17.0
	aq	18.1	18.4
H_2SeO_3	c	−126.5	
	aq	−122.4	−101.36
H_2SeO_4	c	−130.23	
	aq, 400	−143.4	
H_2SiO_3	c	−267.8	−247.9
H_4SiO_4	c	−340.6	
H_2Te	g	36.9	33.1
H_2TeO_3	c	−145.0	−115.7
	aq	−145.0	
H_2TeO_4	aq	−165.6	
Indium:			
In	c	0.00	0.00
$InBr_3$	c	−97.2	
	aq	−112.9	−97.2
$InCl_3$	c	−128.5	
	aq	−145.6	−117.5
InI_3	c	−56.5	
	aq	−67.2	−60.5
InN	c	−4.8	
In_2O_3	c	−222.47	
Iodine:			
I_2	c	0.00	0.00
	g	14.88	4.63
IBr	g	10.05	1.24
ICl	g	4.20	−1.32
ICl_3	c	−21.8	−6.05
I_2O_5	c	−42.5	
Iridium:			
Ir	c	0.00	0.00
IrCl	c	−20.5	−16.9
$IrCl_2$	c	−40.6	−32.0
$IrCl_3$	c	−60.5	−46.5
IrF_6	l	−130	
IrO_2	c	−40.14	
Iron:			
Fe	c, α	0.00	0.00
$FeBr_2$	c	−57.15	
	aq, 540	−78.7	−69.47
$FeBr_3$	aq	−95.5	−76.26
Fe_3C	c	5.69	4.24
$Fe(CO)_5$	l	−187.6	
$FeCO_3$	c, siderite	−172.4	−154.8
$FeCl_2$	c	−81.9	−72.6
	aq	−100.0	−83.0
$FeCl_3$	c	−96.4	
	aq, 2000	−128.5	−96.5
FeF_2	aq, 1200	−177.2	−151.7
FeI_2	c	−24.2	
	aq	−47.7	−45
FeI_3	aq	−49.7	−39.5
Fe_4N	c	−2.55	0.862
$Fe(NO_3)_2$	aq	−118.9	−72.8
$Fe(NO_3)_3$	aq, 800	−156.5	−81.3
FeO	c	−64.62	−59.38
Fe_2O_3	c	−198.5	−179.1
Fe_3O_4	c	−266.9	−242.3
$Fe(OH)_2$	c	−135.9	−115.7
$Fe(OH)_3$	c	−197.3	−166.3
$FeO.SiO_2$	c	−273.5	
Fe_2P	c	−13	
FeSi	c	−19.0	
FeS	c	−22.64	−23.23
FeS_2	c, pyrites	−38.62	−35.93
	c, marcasite	−33.0	
$FeSO_4$	c	−221.3	−195.5
	aq, 400	−236.2	−196.4
$Fe_2(SO_4)_3$	aq, 400	−653.3	−533.4
$FeTiO_3$	c, ilmenite	−295.51	−277.06
Lanthanum:			
La	c	0.00	0.00
$LaCl_3$	c	−253.1	
	aq	−284.7	
La_3H_8	c	−160	
LaN	c	−72.0	−64.6
La_2O_3	c	−539	
LaS_2	c	−148.3	
La_2S_3	c	−351.4	
$La_2(SO_4)_3$	aq	−972	

Table 3-201. Heats and Free Energies of Formation of Inorganic and Organic Compounds—(*Continued*)

Compound	State†	Heat of formation‡§ ΔH (formation) at 25°C., kcal./mole	Free energy of formation∥¶ ΔF (formation) at 25°C., kcal./mole
Lead:			
Pb	c	0.00	0.00
$PbBr_2$	c	−66.24	−62.06
	aq	−56.4	−54.97
$PbCO_3$	c, cerussite	−167.6	−150.0
$Pb(C_2H_3O_2)_2$	c	−232.6	
	aq, 400	−234.2	−184.40
PbC_2O_4	c	−205.3	
$PbCl_2$	c	−85.68	−75.04
	aq	−82.5	−68.47
PbF_2	c	−159.5	−148.1
PbI_2	c	−41.77	−41.47
$Pb(NO_3)_2$	c	−106.88	
	aq, 400	−99.46	−58.3
PbO	c, red	−51.72	−45.53
	c, yellow	−50.86	−43.88
PbO_2	c	−65.0	−52.0
Pb_3O_4	c	−172.4	−142.2
$Pb(OH)_2$	c	−123.0	−102.2
PbS	c	−22.38	−21.98
$PbSO_4$	c	−218.5	−192.9
Lithium:			
Li	c	0.00	0.00
LiBr	c	−83.75	
	aq, 400	−95.40	−95.28
$LiBrO_3$	aq	−77.9	−65.70
Li_2C_2	c	−13.0	
LiCN	aq	−31.4	−31.35
LiCNO	aq	−101.2	−94.12
$LiC_2H_3O_2$	aq	−183.9	−160.00
Li_2CO_3	c	−289.7	−269.8
	aq, 1900	−293.1	−267.58
LiCl	c	−97.63	
	aq, 278	−106.45	−102.03
$LiClO_3$	aq	−87.5	−70.95
$LiClO_4$	aq	−106.3	−81.4
LiF	c	−145.57	
	aq, 400	−144.85	−136.40
LiH	c	−22.9	
$LiHCO_3$	aq, 2000	−231.1	−210.98
LiI	c	−65.07	
	aq, 400	−80.09	−83.03
$LiIO_3$	aq	−121.3	−102.95
Li_3N	c	−47.45	−37.33
$LiNO_3$	c	−115.350	
	aq, 400	−115.88	−96.95
Li_2O	c	−142.3	
Li_2O_2	c	−151.9	−138.0
	aq	−159	
LiOH	c	−116.58	−106.44
	aq, 400	−121.47	−108.29
$LiOH.H_2O$	c	−188.92	
$Li_2O.SiO_2$	gls	−374	
Li_2Se	c	−84.9	
	aq	−95.5	−105.64
Li_2SO_4	c	−340.23	−314.66
	aq, 400	−347.02	
$Li_2SO_4.H_2O$	c	−411.57	−375.07
Magnesium:			
Mg	c	0.00	0.00
$Mg(AsO_4)_2$	c	−731.3	
	aq	−749	−630.14
$MgBr_2$	c	−123.9	
	aq, 400	−167.33	−156.94
$Mg(CN)_2$	aq	−39.7	−29.08
$MgCN_2$	c	−61	
$Mg(C_2H_3O_2)_2$	aq	−344.6	−286.38
$MgCO_3$	c	−261.7	−241.7
$MgCl_2$	c	−153.220	−143.77
	aq, 400	−189.76	
$MgCl_2.H_2O$	c	−230.970	−205.93
$MgCl_2.2H_2O$	c	−305.810	−267.20
$MgCl_2.4H_2O$	c	−453.820	−387.98
$MgCl_2.6H_2O$	c	−597.240	−505.45
MgF_2	c	−263.8	
MgI_2	c	−86.8	
	aq, 400	−136.79	−132.45
$MgMoO_4$	c	−329.9	
Mg_3N_2	c	−115.2	−100.8
$Mg(NO_3)_2$	c	−188.770	−140.66
	aq, 400	−209.927	−160.28
$Mg(NO_3)_2.2H_2O$	c	−336.625	
$Mg(NO_3)_2.6H_2O$	c	−624.48	−496.03
MgO	c	−143.84	−136.17
$MgO.SiO_2$	c	−347.5	−326.7
$Mg(OH)_2$	c, ppt.	−221.90	−200.17
	c, brucite	−223.9	−193.3
MgS	c	−84.2	
	aq	−108	
Magnesium (*Cont.*):			
$MgSO_4$	c	−304.94	−277.7
	aq, 400	−325.4	−283.88
MgTe	c	−25	
$MgWO_4$	c	−345.2	
Manganese:			
Mn	c, α	0.00	0.00
$MnBr_2$	c	−91	
	aq	−106	−97.8
Mn_3C	c	1.1	1.26
$Mn(C_2H_3O_2)_2$	c	−270.3	
	aq	−282.7	−227.2
$MnCO_3$	c	−211	−192.5
MnC_2O_4	c	−240.9	
$MnCl_2$	c	−112.0	−102.2
	aq, 400	−128.9	
MnF_2	aq, 1200	−206.1	−180.0
MnI_2	c	−49.8	
	aq	−76.2	−73.3
Mn_5N_2	c	−57.77	−46.49
$Mn(NO_3)_2$	c	−134.9	
	aq, 400	−148.0	−101.1
$Mn(NO_3)_2.6H_2O$	c	−557.07	−441.2
MnO	c	−92.04	−86.77
MnO_2	c	−124.58	−111.49
Mn_2O_3	c	−229.5	−209.9
Mn_3O_4	c	−331.65	−306.22
$MnO.SiO_2$	c	−301.3	−282.1
$Mn(OH)_2$	c	−163.4	−143.1
$Mn(OH)_3$	c	−221	−190
$Mn_3(PO_4)_2$	c	−736	
MnSe	c	−26.3	−27.5
MnS	c, green	−47.0	−48.0
$MnSO_4$	c	−254.18	−228.41
	aq, 400	−265.2	
$Mn_2(SO_4)_3$	c	−635	
	aq	−657	
Mercury:			
Hg	l	0.00	0.00
HgBr	g	23	18
$HgBr_2$	c	−40.68	−38.8
	aq	−38.4	−9.74
$Hg(C_2H_3O_2)_2$	c	−196.3	
	aq	−192.5	−139.2
$HgCl_2$	c	−53.4	−42.2
	aq	−50.3	−23.25
HgCl	g	19	14
Hg_2Cl_2	c	−63.13	
$Hg(CN)_2$	c	62.8	
	aq, 1110	66.25	
HgC_2O_4	c	−159.3	
HgH	g	57.1	52.25
HgI_2	c, red	−25.3	−24.0
HgI	g	33	23
Hg_2I_2	c	−28.88	−26.53
$Hg(NO_3)_2$	aq	−56.8	−13.09
$Hg_2(NO_3)_2$	aq	−58.5	−15.65
HgO	c, red	−21.6	−13.94
	c, yellow ppt.	−20.8	
Hg_2O	c	−21.6	−12.80
HgS	c, black	−10.7	−8.80
$HgSO_4$	c	−166.6	
Hg_2SO_4	c	−177.34	−149.12
Molybdenum:			
Mo	c	0.00	0.00
Mo_2C	c	4.36	2.91
Mo_2N	c	−8.3	
MoO_2	c	−130	−118.0
MoO_3	c	−180.39	−162.01
MoS_2	c	−56.27	−54.19
MoS_3	c	−61.48	−57.38
Nickel:			
Ni	c	0.00	0.00
$NiBr_2$	c	−53.4	
	aq	−72.6	−60.7
Ni_3C	c	9.2	8.88
$Ni(C_2H_3O_2)_2$	aq	−249.6	−190.1
$Ni(CN)_2$	aq	230.9	66.3
$NiCl_2$	c	−75.0	
	aq, 400	−94.34	−74.19
NiF_2	c	−157.5	
	aq	−171.6	−142.9
NiI_2	c	−22.4	
	aq	−42.0	−36.2
$Ni(NO_3)_2$	c	−101.5	
	aq, 200	−113.5	−64.0
NiO	c	−58.4	−51.7
$Ni(OH)_2$	c	−129.8	−105.6
$Ni(OH)_3$	c	−163.2	

Table 3-201. Heats and Free Energies of Formation of Inorganic and Organic Compounds—(*Continued*)

Compound	State†	Heat of formation‡§ ΔH (formation) at 25°C., kcal./mole	Free energy of formation‖¶ ΔF (formation) at 25°C., kcal./mole
Nickel (*Cont.*):			
NiS	c	−20.4	
$NiSO_4$	c	−216	
	aq, 200	−231.3	−187.6
Nitrogen:			
N_2	g	0.00	0.00
NF_3	g	−27	
NH_3	g	−10.96	−3.903
	aq, 200	−19.27	
NH_4Br	c	−64.57	
	aq	−60.27	−43.54
$NH_4C_2H_3O_2$	c	−148.1	
	aq, 400	−148.58	−108.26
NH_4CN	c	−0.7	
	aq	3.6	20.4
NH_4CNS	c	−17.8	
	aq	−12.3	4.4
$(NH_4)_2CO_3$	aq	−223.4	−164.1
$(NH_4)_2C_2O_4$	c	−266.3	
	aq	−260.6	−196.2
NH_4Cl	c	−75.23	−48.59
	aq, 400	−71.20	
NH_4ClO_4	c	−69.4	
	aq	−63.2	−21.1
$(NH_4)_2CrO_4$	c	−276.9	
	aq	−271.3	−209.3
NH_4F	c	−111.6	
	aq	−110.2	−84.7
NH_4I	c	−48.43	
	aq	−44.97	−31.3
NH_4NO_3	c	−87.40	
	aq, 500	−80.89	
NH_4OH	aq	−87.59	
$(NH_4)_2S$	aq, 400	−55.21	−14.50
$(NH_4)_2SO_4$	c	−281.74	−215.06
	aq, 400	−279.33	−214.02
N_2H_4	l	12.06	
$N_2H_4.H_2O$	l	−57.96	
$N_2H_4.H_2SO_4$	c	−232.2	
N_2O	g	19.55	24.82
NO	g	21.600	20.719
NO_2	g	7.96	12.26
N_2O_4	g	2.23	23.41
N_2O_5	c	−10.0	
NOBr	l	11.6	19.26
NOCl	g	12.8	16.1
Osmium:			
Os	c	0.00	0.00
OsO_4	c	−93.6	−70.9
	g	−80.1	−68.1
Oxygen:			
O_2	g	0.00	0.00
O_3	g	33.88	38.86
Palladium:			
Pd	c	0.00	0.00
PdO	c	−20.40	
Phosphorus:			
P	c, white ("yellow")	0.00	0.00
	c, red ("violet")	−4.22	−1.80
P	g	150.35	141.88
P_2	g	33.82	24.60
P_4	g	13.2	5.89
PBr_3	l	−45	
PBr_5	c	−60.6	
PCl_3	g	−70.0	−65.2
	l	−76.8	−63.3
PCl_5	g	−91.0	−73.2
PH_3	g	2.21	−1.45
PI_3	c	−10.9	
P_2O_5	c	−360.0	
$POCl_3$	g	−138.4	−127.2
Platinum:			
Pt	c	0.00	0.00
$PtBr_4$	c	−40.6	
	aq	−50.7	
$PtCl_2$	c	−34	
$PtCl_4$	c	62.6	
	aq	−82.3	
PtI_4	c	−18	
$Pt(OH)_2$	c	−87.5	−67.9
PtS	c	−20.18	−18.55
PtS_2	c	−26.64	−24.28
Potassium:			
K	c	0.00	0.00
K_3AsO_3	aq	−323.0	
K_3AsO_4	aq	−390.3	−355.7
KH_2AsO_4	c	−271.2	−236.7
KBr	c	−94.06	−90.8
	aq, 400	−89.19	−92.0
Potassium (*Cont.*):			
$KBrO_3$	c	−81.58	−60.30
	aq, 1667	−71.68	
$KC_2H_3O_2$	c	−173.80	
	aq, 400	−177.38	−156.73
KCl	c	−104.348	−97.76
	aq, 400	−100.164	−98.76
$KClO_3$	c	−93.5	−69.30
	aq, 400	−81.34	
$KClO_4$	c	−103.8	−72.86
	aq, 400	−101.14	
KCN	c	−28.1	
	aq, 400	−25.3	−28.08
KCNO	c	−99.6	
	aq	−94.5	−90.85
KCNS	c	−47.0	
	aq, 400	−41.07	−44.08
K_2CO_3	c	−274.01	
	aq, 400	−280.90	−264.04
$K_2C_2O_4$	c	−319.9	
	aq, 400	−315.5	−293.1
K_2CrO_4	c	−333.4	
	aq, 400	−328.2	−306.3
$K_2Cr_2O_7$	c	−488.5	
	aq, 400	−472.1	−440.9
KF	c	−134.50	
	aq, 180	−138.36	−133.13
$K_3Fe(CN)_6$	c	−48.4	
	aq	−34.5	
$K_4Fe(CN)_6$	c	−131.8	
	aq	−119.9	
KH	c	−10	−5.3
$KHCO_3$	c	−229.8	
	aq, 2000	−224.85	−207.71
KI	c	−78.88	−77.37
	aq, 500	−73.95	−79.76
KIO_3	c	−121.69	−101.87
	aq, 400	−115.18	−99.68
KIO_4	aq	−98.1	
$KMnO_4$	c	−192.9	−169.1
	aq, 400	−182.5	−168.0
K_2MoO_4	aq, 880	−364.2	−342.9
KNH_2	c	−28.25	
KNO_2	aq	−86.0	−75.9
KNO_3	c	−118.08	−94.29
	aq, 400	−109.79	−93.68
K_2O	c	−86.2	
$K_2O.Al_2O_3.4H_2O$	c, leucite	−1379.6	
	gls	−1368.2	
$K_2O.Al_2O_3.6H_2O$	c, adularia	−1810.7	
	c, microcline	−1784.5	
	gls	−1747	
KOH	c	−102.02	
	aq, 400	−114.96	−105.0
K_3PO_3	aq	−397.5	
K_3PO_4	aq	−478.7	−443.3
KH_2PO_4	c	−362.7	−326.1
K_2PtCl_4	c	−254.7	
	aq	−242.6	−226.5
K_2PtCl_6	c	−299.5	−263.6
	aq, 9400	−286.1	
K_2Se	c	−74.4	
	aq	−83.4	−99.10
K_2SeO_4	aq	−267.1	−240.0
K_2S	c	−121.5	
	aq, 400	−110.75	−111.44
K_2SO_3	c	−267.7	
	aq	−269.7	−251.3
K_2SO_4	c	−342.65	−314.62
	aq, 400	−336.48	−310.96
$K_2SO_4.Al_2(SO_4)_3$	c	−1178.38	−1068.48
$K_2SO_4.Al_2(SO_4)_3.24H_2O$	c	−2895.44	−2455.68
$K_2S_2O_6$	c	−418.62	
Rhenium:			
Re	c	0.00	0.00
ReF_6	g	−274	
Rhodium:			
Rh	c	0.00	0.00
RhO	c	−21.7	
Rh_2O	c	−22.7	
Rh_2O_3	c	−68.3	
Rubidium:			
Rb	c	0.00	0.00
RbBr	c	−95.82	
	g	−45.0	−52.50
	aq, 500	−90.54	−93.38
RbCN	aq	−25.9	
Rb_2CO_3	c	−273.22	
	aq, 220	−282.61	−263.78

Table 3-201. Heats and Free Energies of Formation of Inorganic and Organic Compounds—(*Continued*)

Compound	State†	Heat of formation‡§ ΔH (formation) at 25°C., kcal./mole	Free energy of formation‖¶ ΔF (formation) at 25°C., kcal./mole
Rubidium (*Cont.*):			
$RbCl$	c	−105.06	−98.48
	g	−53.6	−57.9
	aq, ∞	−101.06	−100.13
RbF	c	−133.23	
	aq, 400	−139.31	−134.5
$RbHCO_3$	c	−230.01	
	aq, 2000	−225.59	−209.07
RbI	c	−81.04	
	g	−31.2	−40.5
	aq, 400	−74.57	−81.13
$RbNH_2$	c	−27.74	
$RbNO_3$	c	−119.22	
	aq, 400	−110.52	−95.05
Rb_2O	c	−82.9	
Rb_2O_2	c	−107	
$RbOH$	c	−101.3	
	aq, 200	−115.8	−106.39
Ruthenium:			
Ru	c	0.00	0.00
RuS_2	c	−46.99	−44.11
Selenium:			
Se	c, I, hexagonal	0.00	0.00
	c, II, red, monoclinic	0.2	
Se_2Cl_2	l	−22.06	−13.73
SeF_6	g	−246	−222
SeO_2	c	−56.33	
Silicon:			
Si	c	0.00	0.00
$SiBr_4$	l	−93.0	
SiC	c	−28	−27.4
$SiCl_4$	l	−150.0	−133.9
	g	−142.5	−133.0
SiF_4	g	−370	−360
SiH_4	g	−14.8	−9.4
SiI_4	c	−29.8	
Si_3N_4	c	−179.25	−154.74
SiO_2	c, cristobalite, 1600° form	−202.62	
	c, cristobalite, 1100° form	−202.46	
	c, quartz	−203.35	−190.4
	c, tridymite	−203.23	
Silver:			
Ag	c	0.00	0.00
$AgBr$	c	−23.90	−23.02
Ag_2C_2	c	84.5	
$AgC_2H_3O_2$	c	−95.9	
	aq	−91.7	−70.86
$AgCN$	c	33.8	38.70
Ag_2CO_3	c	−119.5	−103.0
$Ag_2C_2O_4$	c	−158.7	
$AgCl$	c	−30.11	−25.98
AgF	c	−48.7	
	aq, 400	−53.1	−47.26
AgI	c	−15.14	−16.17
$AgIO_3$	c	−42.02	−24.08
$AgNO_2$	c	−11.6	3.76
	aq	−2.9	9.99
$AgNO_3$	c	−29.4	−7.66
	aq, 6500	−24.02	−7.81
Ag_2O	c	−6.95	−2.23
Ag_2S	c	−5.5	−7.6
Ag_2SO_4	c	−170.1	−146.8
	aq	−165.8	−139.22
Sodium:			
Na	c	0.00	0.00
Na_3AsO_3	aq, 500	−314.61	
Na_3AsO_4	c	−366	
	aq, 500	−381.97	−341.17
$NaBr$	c	−86.72	
	aq, 400	−86.33	−87.17
$NaBrO$	aq	−78.9	
$NaBrO_3$	aq, 400	−68.89	−57.59
$NaC_2H_3O_2$	c	−170.45	
	aq, 400	−175.450	−152.31
$NaCN$	c	−22.47	
	aq, 200	−22.29	−23.24
$NaCNO$	c	−96.3	
	aq	−91.7	−86.00
$NaCNS$	c	−39.94	
	aq, 400	−38.23	−39.24
Na_2CO_3	c	−269.46	−249.55
	aq, 1000	−275.13	−251.36
$NaCO_2NH_2$	c	−142.17	
$Na_2C_2O_4$	c	−313.8	
	aq, 600	−309.92	−283.42
$NaCl$	c	−98.321	−91.894
	aq, 400	−97.324	−93.92
Sodium (*Cont.*):			
$NaClO_3$	c	−83.59	
	aq, 400	−78.42	−62.84
$NaClO_4$	c	−101.12	
	aq, 476	−97.66	−73.29
Na_2CrO_4	c	−319.8	
	aq, 800	−323.0	−296.58
$Na_2Cr_2O_7$	aq, 1200	−465.9	−431.18
NaF	c	−135.94	−129.0
	aq, 400	−135.711	−128.29
NaH	c	−14	−9.30
$NaHCO_3$	c	−226.0	−202.66
	aq	−222.1	−202.87
NaI	c	−69.28	
	aq, ∞	−71.10	−74.92
$NaIO_3$	aq, 400	−112.300	−94.84
Na_2MoO_4	c	−364	
	aq	−358.7	−333.18
$NaNO_2$	c	−86.6	
	aq	−83.1	−71.04
$NaNO_3$	c	−111.71	−87.62
	aq, 400	−106.880	−88.84
Na_2O	c	−99.45	−90.06
Na_2O_2	c	−119.2	−105.0
$Na_2O.SiO_2$	c	−383.91	−361.49
$Na_2O.Al_2O_3.3SiO_2$	c, natrolite	−1180	
$Na_2O.Al_2O_3.4SiO_2$	c	−1366	
$NaOH$	c	−101.96	−90.60
	aq, 400	−112.193	−100.18
Na_3PO_3	aq, 1000	−389.1	
Na_3PO_4	c	−457	
	aq, 400	−471.9	−428.74
Na_2PtCl_4	aq	−237.2	−216.78
Na_2PtCl_6	c	−272.1	
	aq	−280.9	
Na_2Se	c	−59.1	
	aq, 440	−78.1	−89.42
Na_2SeO_4	c	−254	
	aq, 800	−261.5	−230.30
Na_2S	c	−89.8	
	aq, 400	−105.17	−101.76
Na_2SO_3	c	−261.2	−240.14
	aq, 800	−264.1	−241.58
Na_2SO_4	c	−330.50	−302.38
	aq, 1100	−330.82	−301.28
$Na_2SO_4.10H_2O$	c	−1033.85	−870.52
Na_2WO_4	c	−391	
	aq	−381.5	−345.18
Strontium:			
Sr	c	0.00	0.00
$SrBr_2$	c	−171.0	
	aq, 400	−187.24	−182.36
$Sr(C_2H_3O_2)_2$	c	−358.0	
	aq	−364.4	−311.80
$Sr(CN)_2$	aq	−59.5	−54.50
$SrCO_3$	c	−290.9	−271.9
$SrCl_2$	c	−197.84	
	aq, 400	−209.20	−195.86
SrF_2	c	−289.0	
$Sr(HCO_3)_2$	aq	−459.1	−413.76
SrI_2	c	−136.1	
	aq, 400	−156.70	−157.87
Sr_3N_2	c	−91.4	−76.5
$Sr(NO_3)_2$	c	−233.2	
	aq, 400	−228.73	−185.70
SrO	c	−140.8	−133.7
$SrO.SiO_2$	gls	−364	
SrO_2	c	−153.3	−139.0
Sr_2O	c	−153.6	
$Sr(OH)_2$	c	−228.7	
	aq, 800	−239.4	−208.27
$Sr_3(PO_4)_2$	c	−980	
	aq	−985	−881.54
SrS	c	−113.1	
	aq	−120.4	−109.78
$SrSO_4$	c	−345.3	
	aq, 400	−345.0	−309.30
$SrWO_4$	c	−393	
Sulfur:			
S	c, rhombic	0.00	0.00
	c, monoclinic	−0.071	−0.023
	l, λ	0.257	0.072
	l, λμ equilibrium	....	0.071
	g	53.25	43.57
S_2	g	31.02	19.36
S_6	g	27.78	13.97
S_8	g	27.090	12.770
S_2Br_2	l	−4	
SCl_4	l	−13.7	

Table 3-201. Heats and Free Energies of Formation of Inorganic and Organic Compounds—(*Concluded*)

Compound	State†	Heat of formation‡§ ΔH (formation) at 25°C., kcal./mole	Free energy of formation‖¶ ΔF (formation) at 25°C., kcal./mole
Sulfur (*Cont.*):			
S_2Cl_2	l	−14.2	−5.90
S_2Cl_4	l	−24.1	
SF_6	g	−262	−237
SO	g	19.02	12.75
SO_2	g	−70.94	−71.68
SO_3	g	−94.39	−88.59
	l	−103.03	−88.28
	c, α	−105.09	−88.22
	c, β	−105.92	−88.34
	c, γ	−109.34	−88.98
SO_2Cl_2	g	−82.04	−74.06
	l	−89.80	−75.06
Tantalum:			
Ta	c	0.00	0.00
TaN	c	−51.2	−45.11
Ta_2O_5	c	−486.0	−453.7
Tellurium:			
Te	c	0.00	0.00
$TeBr_4$	c	−49.3	
$TeCl_4$	c	−77.4	−57.4
TeF_6	g	−315	−292
TeO_2	c	−77.56	−64.66
Thallium:			
Tl	c	0.00	0.00
TlBr	c	−41.5	−39.43
	aq	−28.0	−32.34
TlCl	c	−49.37	−44.46
	aq	−38.4	−39.09
$TlCl_3$	c	−82.4	
	aq	−91.0	−44.25
TlF	aq	−77.6	−73.46
TlI	c	−31.1	−31.3
	aq	−12.7	−20.09
$TlNO_3$	c	−58.2	−36.32
	aq	−48.4	−34.01
Tl_2O	c	−43.18	
Tl_2O_3	c	−120	
TlOH	c	−57.44	−45.54
	aq	−53.9	−45.35
Tl_2S	c	−22	
Tl_2SO_4	c	−222.8	−197.79
	aq, 800	−214.1	−191.62
Thorium:			
Th	c	0.00	0.00
$ThBr_4$	c	−281.5	
	aq	−352.0	−295.31
ThC_2	c	−45.1	
$ThCl_4$	c	−335	
	aq	−392	−322.32
ThI_4	aq	−292.0	−246.33
Th_3N_4	c	−309.0	−282.3
ThO_2	c	−291.6	−280.1
$Th(OH)_4$	c, "soluble"	−336.1	
$Th(SO_4)_2$	c	−632	
	aq	−668.1	−549.2
Tin:			
Sn	c, II, tetragonal	0.00	0.00
	c, III, "gray," cubic	0.6	1.1
$SnBr_2$	c	−61.4	
	aq	−60.0	−55.43
$SnBr_4$	c	−94.8	
	aq	−110.6	−97.66
$SnCl_2$	c	−83.6	
	aq	−81.7	−68.94
$SnCl_4$	l	−127.3	−110.4
	aq	−157.6	−124.67
SnI_2	c	−38.9	
	aq	−33.3	−30.95
Tin (*Cont.*):			
SnO	c	−67.7	−60.75
SnO_2	c	−138.1	−123.6
$Sn(OH)_2$	c	−136.2	−115.95
$Sn(OH)_4$	c	−268.9	−226.00
SnS	c	−18.61	
Titanium:			
Ti	c	0.00	0.00
TiC	c	−110	−109.2
$TiCl_4$	l	−181.4	−165.5
TiN	c	−80.0	−73.17
TiO_2	c, III, rutile	−225.0	−211.9
	amorphous	−214.1	−201.4
Tungsten:			
W	c	0.00	0.00
WO_2	c	−130.5	−118.3
WO_3	c	−195.7	−177.3
WS_2	c	−84	
Uranium:			
U	c	0.00	0.00
UC_2	c	−29	
UCl_3	c	−213	
UCl_4	c	−251	
U_3N_4	c	−274	−249.6
UO_2	c	−256.6	−242.2
$UO_2(NO_3)_2.6H_2O$	c	−756.8	−617.8
UO_3	c	−291.6	
U_3O_8	c	−845.1	
Vanadium:			
V	c	0.00	0.00
VCl_2	c	−147	
VCl_3	l	−187	
VCl_4	l	−165	
VN	c	−41.43	−35.08
V_2O_2	c	−195	
V_2O_3	c	−296	−277
V_2O_4	c	−342	−316
V_2O_5	c	−373	−342
Zinc:			
Zn	c	0.00	0.00
ZnSb	c	−3.6	−3.88
$ZnBr_2$	c	−77.0	−72.9
	aq, 400	−93.6	
$Zn(C_2H_3O_2)_2$	c	−259.4	
	aq, 400	−269.4	−214.4
$Zn(CN)_2$	c	17.06	
$ZnCO_3$	c	−192.9	−173.5
$ZnCl_2$	c	−99.9	−88.8
	aq, 400	−115.44	
ZnF_2	aq	−192.9	−166.6
ZnI_2	c	−50.50	−49.93
	aq	−61.6	
$Zn(NO_3)_2$	aq, 400	−134.9	−87.7
ZnO	c, hexagonal	−83.36	−76.19
$ZnO.SiO_2$	c	−282.6	
$Zn(OH)_2$	c, rhombic	−153.66	
ZnS	c, wurtzite	−45.3	−44.2
$ZnSO_4$	c	−233.4	
	aq, 400	−252.12	−211.28
Zirconium:			
Zr	c	0.00	0.00
ZrC	c	−29.8	−34.6
$ZrCl_4$	c	−268.9	
ZrN	c	−82.5	−75.9
ZrO_2	c, monoclinic	−258.5	−244.6
$Zr(OH)_4$	c	−411.0	
$ZrO(OH)_2$	c	−337	−307.6

† The physical state is indicated as follows: *c*, crystal (solid); *l*, liquid; *g*, gas; *gls*, glass or solid supercooled liquid; *aq*, in aqueous solution. A number following the symbol *aq* applies only to the values of the heats of formation (not to those of free energies of formation); and indicates the number of moles of water per mole of solute; when no number is given, the solution is understood to be dilute. For the free energy of formation of a substance in aqueous solution, the concentration is always that of the hypothetical solution of unit molality.

‡ The increment in heat content, ΔH, in the reaction of forming the given substance from its elements in their standard states. When ΔH is negative, heat is evolved in the process, and, when positive, heat is absorbed.

§ The heat of solution in water of a given solid, liquid, or gaseous compound is given by the difference in the value for the heat of formation of the given compound in the solid, liquid, or gaseous state and its heat of formation in aqueous solution. The following two examples serve as an illustration of the procedure: (1) For NaCl(*c*) and NaCl(*aq*, 400H_2O), the values of ΔH(formation) are, respectively, −98.321 and −97.324 kg.-cal. per mole. Subtraction of the first value from the second gives $\Delta H = 0.998$ kg.-cal. per mole for the reaction of dissolving crystalline sodium chloride in 400 moles of water. When this process occurs at a constant pressure of 1 atm., 0.998 kg.-cal. of energy are absorbed. (2) For HCl(*g*) and HCl(*aq*, 400H_2O), the values for ΔH(formation) are, respectively, −22.06 and −39.85 kg.-cal. per mole. Subtraction of the first from the second gives $\Delta H = -17.79$ kg.-cal per mole for the reaction of dissolving gaseous hydrogen chloride in 400 moles of water. At a constant pressure of 1 atm. 17.79 kg.-cal. of energy are evolved in this process.

‖ The increment in the free energy, ΔF, in the reaction of forming the given substance in its standard state from its elements in their standard states. The standard states are: for a gas, fugacity (approximately equal to the pressure) of 1 atm.; for a pure liquid or solid, the substance at a pressure of 1 atm.; for a substance in aqueous solution, the hypothetical solution of unit molality, which has all the properties of the infinitely dilute solution except the property of concentration.

¶ The free energy of solution of a given substance from its normal standard state as a solid, liquid, or gas to the hypothetical one molal state in aqueous solution may be calculated in a manner similar to that described in footnote § for calculating the heat of solution.

HEATS OF COMBUSTION

Table 3-202. Hydrogen, Carbon, Carbon Monoxide, and Hydrocarbons

Heats of combustion of additional compounds may be calculated from the heats of formation given in Table 3-201, p. 3-134.

The following values are taken from the tables of the American Petroleum Institute Research Project 44 of the National Bureau of Standards on the Collection, Analysis, Calculation, and Compilation of Data on the Properties of Hydrocarbons.

Compound	Formula	State	Heat of combustion, $-\Delta Hc^\circ$, at 25°C. and constant pressure, to form: H_2O (liq.) and CO_2 (gas), Kcal./mole	H_2O (liq.) and CO_2 (gas), Cal./g.	H_2O (liq.) and CO_2 (gas), B.t.u./lb.	H_2O (gas) and CO_2 (gas), Kcal./mole	H_2O (gas) and CO_2 (gas), Cal./g.	H_2O (gas) and CO_2 (gas), B.t.u./lb.
Hydrogen	H_2	gas	68.3174	33,887.6	60,957.7	57.7979	28,669.6	51,571.4
Carbon	C	solid, graph.	94.0518	7,831.1	14,086.8			
Carbon monoxide	CO	gas	67.6361	2,414.7	4,343.6			
Paraffins								
Methane	CH_4	gas	212.798	13,265.1	23,861	191.759	11,953.6	21,502
Ethane	C_2H_6	gas	372.820	12,399.2	22,304	341.261	11,349.6	20,416
Propane	C_3H_8	gas	530.605	12,033.5	21,646	488.527	11,079.2	19,929
Propane	C_3H_8	liq.*	526.782	11,946.8	21,490	484.704	10,992.5	19,774
n-Butane	C_4H_{10}	gas	687.982	11,837.3	21,293	635.384	10,932.3	19,665
n-Butane	C_4H_{10}	liq.*	682.844	11,748.9	21,134	630.246	10,843.9	19,506
2-Methylpropane (Isobutane)	C_4H_{10}	gas	686.342	11,809.1	21,242	633.744	10,904.1	19,614
2-Methylpropane (Isobutane)	C_4H_{10}	liq.*	681.625	11,727.9	21,096	629.027	10,822.9	19,468
n-Pentane	C_5H_{12}	gas	845.16	11,714.6	21,072	782.04	10,839.7	19,499
n-Pentane	C_5H_{12}	liq.	838.80	11,626.4	20,914	775.68	10,751.5	19,340
2-Methylbutane (Isopentane)	C_5H_{12}	gas	843.24	11,688.0	21,025	780.12	10,813.1	19,451
2-Methylbutane (Isopentane)	C_5H_{12}	liq.	837.31	11,605.8	20,877	774.19	10,730.9	19,303
2,2-Dimethylpropane (Neopentane)	C_5H_{12}	gas	840.49	11,649.8	20,956	777.37	10,775.0	19,382
2,2-Dimethylpropane (Neopentane)	C_5H_{12}	liq.	835.18	11,576.2	20,824	772.06	10,701.4	19,250
n Hexane	C_6H_{14}	gas	1,002.57	11,634.5	20,928	928.93	10,780.0	19,391
n-Hexane	C_6H_{14}	liq.	995.01	11,546.8	20,771	921.37	10,692.2	19,233
2-Methylpentane	C_6H_{14}	gas	1,000.87	11,614.8	20,893	927.23	10,760.2	19,356
2-Methylpentane	C_6H_{14}	liq.	993.71	11,531.7	20,743	920.07	10,677.1	19,206
3-Methylpentane	C_6H_{14}	gas	1,001.51	11,622.2	20,906	927.87	10,767.6	19,369
3-Methylpentane	C_6H_{14}	liq.	994.25	11,538.0	20,755	920.61	10,683.4	19,218
2,2-Dimethylbutane	C_6H_{14}	gas	998.17	11,583.5	20,837	924.53	10,728.9	19,299
2,2-Dimethylbutane	C_6H_{14}	liq.	991.52	11,506.3	20,698	917.88	10,651.7	19,161
2,3-Dimethylbutane	C_6H_{14}	gas	1,000.04	11,605.2	20,876	926.40	10,750.6	19,338
2,3-Dimethylbutane	C_6H_{14}	liq.	993.05	11,524.0	20,730	919.41	10,669.5	19,192
n-Heptane	C_7H_{16}	gas	1,160.01	11,577.2	20,825	1,075.85	10,737.2	19,314
n-Heptane	C_7H_{16}	liq.	1,151.27	11,489.9	20,668	1,067.11	10,650.0	19,157
2-Methylhexane	C_7H_{16}	gas	1,158.30	11,560.1	20,795	1,074.14	10,720.2	19,284
2-Methylhexane	C_7H_{16}	liq.	1,149.97	11,477.0	20,645	1,065.81	10,637.0	19,134
3-Methylhexane	C_7H_{16}	gas	1,158.94	11,566.5	20,806	1,074.78	10,726.6	19,295
3-Methylhexane	C_7H_{16}	liq.	1,150.55	11,482.8	20,655	1,066.39	10,642.8	19,145
3-Ethylpentane	C_7H_{16}	gas	1,159.56	11,572.7	20,817	1,075.40	10,732.7	19,306
3-Ethylpentane	C_7H_{16}	liq.	1,151.13	11,488.6	20,666	1,066.97	10,648.6	19,155
2,2-Dimethylpentane	C_7H_{16}	gas	1,155.61	11,533.3	20,746	1,071.45	10,693.3	19,235
2,2-Dimethylpentane	C_7H_{16}	liq.	1,147.85	11,455.8	20,607	1,063.69	10,615.9	19,096
2,3-Dimethylpentane	C_7H_{16}	gas	1,157.28	11,549.9	20,776	1,073.12	10,710.0	19,265
2,3-Dimethylpentane	C_7H_{16}	liq.	1,149.09	11,468.2	20,629	1,064.93	10,628.3	19,118
2,4-Dimethylpentane	C_7H_{16}	gas	1,156.60	11,543.1	20,764	1,072.44	10,703.2	19,253
2,4-Dimethylpentane	C_7H_{16}	liq.	1,148.73	11,464.6	20,623	1,064.57	10,624.7	19,112
3,3-Dimethylpentane	C_7H_{16}	gas	1,156.73	11,544.4	20,766	1,072.57	10,704.5	19,255
3,3-Dimethylpentane	C_7H_{16}	liq.	1,148.83	11,465.6	20,625	1,064.67	10,625.7	19,114
2,2,3-Trimethylbutane	C_7H_{16}	gas	1,155.94	11,536.6	20,752	1,071.78	10,696.6	19,241
2,2,3-Trimethylbutane	C_7H_{16}	liq.	1,148.27	11,460.0	20,614	1,064.11	10,620.1	19,104
n-Octane	C_8H_{18}	gas	1,317.45	11,533.9	20,747	1,222.77	10,705.0	19,256
n-Octane	C_8H_{18}	liq.	1,307.53	11,447.1	20,591	1,212.85	10,618.2	19,100
2-Methylheptane	C_8H_{18}	gas	1,315.76	11,519.1	20,721	1,221.08	10,690.2	19,230
2-Methylheptane	C_8H_{18}	liq.	1,306.28	11,436.1	20,572	1,211.60	10,607.2	19,080
3-Methylheptane	C_8H_{18}	gas	1,316.44	11,525.1	20,732	1,221.76	10,696.2	19,240
3-Methylheptane	C_8H_{18}	liq.	1,306.92	11,441.7	20,582	1,212.24	10,612.8	19,091
4-Methylheptane	C_8H_{18}	gas	1,316.57	11,526.2	20,734	1,221.89	10,697.3	19,243
4-Methylheptane	C_8H_{16}	liq.	1,307.09	11,443.2	20,584	1,212.41	10,614.3	19,093
3-Ethylhexane	C_8H_{18}	gas	1,316.87	11,528.8	20,738	1,222.19	10,699.9	19,247
3-Ethylhexane	C_8H_{18}	liq.	1,307.39	11,445.8	20,589	1,212.71	10,616.9	19,098
2,2-Dimethylhexane	C_8H_{18}	gas	1,313.56	11,499.9	20,686	1,218.88	10,671.0	19,195
2,2-Dimethylhexane	C_8H_{18}	liq.	1,304.64	11,421.8	20,546	1,209.96	10,592.9	19,055
2,3-Dimethylhexane	C_8H_{18}	gas	1,316.13	11,522.4	20,727	1,221.45	10,693.5	19,236
2,3-Dimethylhexane	C_8H_{18}	liq.	1,306.86	11,441.2	20,581	1,212.18	10,612.3	19,090
2,4-Dimethylhexane	C_8H_{18}	gas	1,314.83	11,511.0	20,706	1,220.15	10,682.1	19,215
2,4-Dimethylhexane	C_8H_{18}	liq.	1,305.80	11,431.9	20,564	1,211.12	10,603.0	19,073
2,5-Dimethylhexane	C_8H_{18}	gas	1,314.05	11,504.2	20,694	1,219.37	10,675.3	19,203
2,5-Dimethylhexane	C_8H_{18}	liq.	1,305.00	11,424.9	20,551	1,210.32	10,596.0	19,060
3,3-Dimethylhexane	C_8H_{18}	gas	1,314.65	11,509.4	20,703	1,219.97	10,680.5	19,212
3,3-Dimethylhexane	C_8H_{18}	liq.	1,305.68	11,430.9	20,562	1,211.00	10,602.0	19,071
3,4-Dimethylhexane	C_8H_{18}	gas	1,316.36	11,524.4	20,730	1,221.68	10,695.5	19,239
3,4-Dimethylhexane	C_8H_{18}	liq.	1,307.04	11,442.8	20,583	1,212.36	10,613.9	19,092
2-Methyl-3-ethylpentane	C_8H_{18}	gas	1,316.79	11,528.1	20,737	1,222.11	10,699.2	19,246
2-Methyl-3-ethylpentane	C_8H_{18}	liq.	1,307.58	11,447.5	20,592	1,212.90	10,618.6	19,101
3-Methyl-3-ethylpentane	C_8H_{18}	gas	1,315.88	11,520.2	20,723	1,221.20	10,691.3	19,232
3-Methyl-3-ethylpentane	C_8H_{18}	liq.	1,306.80	11,440.7	20,580	1,212.12	10,611.8	19,089
2,2,3-Trimethylpentane	C_8H_{18}	gas	1,314.66	11,509.5	20,703	1,219.98	10,680.6	19,212
2,2,3-Trimethylpentane	C_8H_{18}	liq.	1,305.83	11,432.2	20,564	1,211.15	10,603.3	19,073
2,2,4-Trimethylpentane	C_8H_{18}	gas	1,313.69	11,501.0	20,688	1,219.01	10,672.1	19,197
2,2,4-Trimethylpentane	C_8H_{18}	liq.	1,305.29	11,427.5	20,556	1,210.61	10,598.6	19,065
2,3,3-Trimethylpentane	C_8H_{18}	gas	1,315.54	11,517.2	20,717	1,220.86	10,688.3	19,226
2,3,3-Trimethylpentane	C_8H_{18}	liq.	1,306.64	11,439.3	20,577	1,211.96	10,610.4	19,086
2,3,4-Trimethylpentane	C_8H_{18}	gas	1,315.29	11,515.0	20,713	1,220.61	10,686.1	19,222
2,3,4-Trimethylpentane	C_8H_{18}	liq.	1,306.28	11,436.1	20,572	1,211.60	10,607.2	19,080
2,2,3,3-Tetramethylbutane	C_8H_{18}	gas	1,313.27	11,497.3	20,682	1,218.59	10,668.4	19,191

Table 3-202. Hydrogen, Carbon, Carbon Monoxide, and Hydrocarbons—(*Continued*)

Compound	Formula	State	Heat of combustion, $-\Delta Hc°$, at 25°C. and constant pressure, to form: H_2O (liq.) and CO_2 (gas)			H_2O (gas) and CO_2 (gas)		
			Kcal./mole	Cal./g.	B.t.u./lb.	Kcal./mole	Cal./g.	B.t.u./lb.
2,2,3,3-Tetramethylbutane	C_8H_{18}	solid	1,303.03	11,407.7	20,520	1,208.35	10,578.8	19,029
n-Nonane	C_9H_{20}	gas	1,474.90	11,500.2	20,687	1,369.70	10,680.0	19,211
n-Nonane	C_9H_{20}	liq.	1,463.80	11,413.6	20,531	1,358.60	10,593.4	19,056
n-Decane	$C_{10}H_{22}$	gas	1,632.34	11,473.0	20,638	1,516.63	10,659.7	19,175
n-Decane	$C_{10}H_{22}$	liq.	1,620.06	11,386.7	20,483	1,504.35	10,573.4	19,020
n-Undecane	$C_{11}H_{24}$	gas	1,789.78	11,450.8	20,598	1,663.55	10,643.2	19,145
n-Undecane	$C_{11}H_{24}$	liq.	1,776.32	11,364.7	20,443	1,650.09	10,557.0	18,990
n-Dodecane	$C_{12}H_{26}$	gas	1,947.23	11,432.2	20,564	1,810.48	10,629.4	19,120
n-Dodecane	$C_{12}H_{26}$	liq.	1,932.59	11,346.3	20,410	1,795.84	10,543.4	18,966
n-Tridecane	$C_{13}H_{28}$	gas	2,104.67	11,416.5	20,536	1,957.40	10,617.6	19,099
n-Tridecane	$C_{13}H_{28}$	liq.	2,088.85	11,330.6	20,382	1,941.58	10,531.8	18,945
n-Tetradecane	$C_{14}H_{30}$	gas	2,262.11	11,402.9	20,512	2,104.32	10,607.5	19,081
n-Tetradecane	$C_{14}H_{30}$	liq.	2,245.11	11,317.2	20,358	2,087.32	10,521.8	18,927
n-Pentadecane	$C_{15}H_{32}$	gas	2,419.55	11,391.2	20,491	2,251.24	10,598.7	19,065
n-Pentadecane	$C_{15}H_{32}$	liq.	2,401.37	11,305.6	20,337	2,233.06	10,513.2	18,911
n-Hexadecane	$C_{16}H_{34}$	gas	2,577.00	11,380.9	20,472	2,398.17	10,591.1	19,052
n-Hexadecane	$C_{16}H_{34}$	liq.	2,557.64	11,295.4	20,318	2,378.81	10,505.6	18,898
n-Heptadecane	$C_{17}H_{36}$	gas	2,734.44	11,371.8	20,456	2,545.09	10,584.3	19,039
n-Heptadecane	$C_{17}H_{36}$	liq.	2,713.90	11,286.4	20,302	2,524.55	10,498.9	18,886
n-Octadecane	$C_{18}H_{38}$	gas	2,891.88	11,363.7	20,441	2,692.01	10,578.3	19,028
n-Octadecane	$C_{18}H_{38}$	liq.	2,870.16	11,278.4	20,288	2,670.29	10,493.0	18,875
n-Nonadecane	$C_{19}H_{40}$	gas	3,049.33	11,356.5	20,428	2,838.94	10,572.9	19,019
n-Nonadecane	$C_{19}H_{40}$	liq.	3,026.43	11,271.2	20,275	2,816.04	10,487.7	18,865
n-Eicosane	$C_{20}H_{42}$	gas	3,206.77	11,350.0	20,416	2,985.86	10,568.1	19,010
n-Eicosane	$C_{20}H_{42}$	liq.	3,182.69	11,264.7	20,263	2,961.78	10,482.8	18,857
	Alkyl benzenes							
Benzene	C_6H_6	gas	789.08	10,102.4	18,172	757.52	9,698.4	17,446
Benzene	C_6H_6	liq.	780.98	9,998.7	17,986	749.42	9,594.7	17,259
Methylbenzene (toluene)	C_7H_8	gas	943.58	10,241.4	18,422	901.50	9,784.7	17,601
Methylbenzene (toluene)	C_7H_8	liq.	934.50	10,142.8	18,245	892.42	9,686.1	17,424
Ethylbenzene	C_8H_{10}	gas	1,101.13	10,372.4	18,658	1,048.53	9,876.9	17,767
Ethylbenzene	C_8H_{10}	liq.	1,091.03	10,277.2	18,487	1,038.43	9,781.7	17,596
1,2-Dimethylbenzene (o-xylene)	C_8H_{10}	gas	1,098.54	10,348.0	18,614	1,045.94	9,852.5	17,723
1,2-Dimethylbenzene (o-xylene)	C_8H_{10}	liq.	1,088.16	10,250.2	18,438	1,035.56	9,754.7	17,547
1,3-Dimethylbenzene (m-xylene)	C_8H_{10}	gas	1,098.12	10,344.0	18,607	1,045.52	9,848.5	17,716
1,3-Dimethylbenzene (m-xylene)	C_8H_{10}	liq.	1,087.92	10,247.9	18,434	1,035.32	9,752.4	17,543
1,4-Dimethylbenzene (p-xylene)	C_8H_{10}	gas	1,098.29	10,345.6	18,610	1,045.69	9,850.1	17,719
1,4-Dimethylbenzene (p-xylene)	C_8H_{10}	liq.	1,088.16	10,250.2	18,438	1,035.56	9,754.7	17,547
n-Propylbenzene	C_9H_{12}	gas	1,258.24	10,469.1	18,832	1,195.12	9,943.9	17,887
n-Propylbenzene	C_9H_{12}	liq.	1,247.19	10,377.2	18,667	1,184.07	9,852.0	17,722
Isopropylbenzene (cumene)	C_9H_{12}	gas	1,257.31	10,461.4	18,818	1,194.19	9,936.2	17,873
Isopropylbenzene (cumene)	C_9H_{12}	liq.	1,246.52	10,371.6	18,657	1,183.40	9,846.4	17,712
1-Methyl-2-ethylbenzene	C_9H_{12}	gas	1,256.66	10,456.0	18,808	1,193.54	9,930.8	17,864
1-Methyl-2-ethylbenzene	C_9H_{12}	liq.	1,245.26	10,361.1	18,638	1,182.14	9,835.9	17,693
1-Methyl-3-ethylbenzene	C_9H_{12}	gas	1,255.92	10,449.8	18,797	1,192.80	9,924.6	17,853
1-Methyl-3-ethylbenzene	C_9H_{12}	liq.	1,244.71	10,356.5	18,630	1,181.59	9,831.3	17,685
1-Methyl-4-ethylbenzene	C_9H_{12}	gas	1,255.59	10,447.1	18,792	1,192.47	9,921.9	17,848
1-Methyl-4-ethylbenzene	C_9H_{12}	liq.	1,244.45	10,354.4	18,626	1,181.33	9,829.2	17,681
1,2,3-Trimethylbenzene (hemimellitene)	C_9H_{12}	gas	1,254.08	10,434.5	18,770	1,190.96	9,909.3	17,825
1,2,3-Trimethylbenzene (hemimellitene)	C_9H_{12}	liq.	1,242.36	10,337.0	18,594	1,179.24	9,811.8	17,650
1,2,4-Trimethylbenzene (pseudocumene)	C_9H_{12}	gas	1,253.04	10,425.8	18,754	1,189.92	9,900.7	17,809
1,2,4-Trimethylbenzene (pseudocumene)	C_9H_{12}	liq.	1,241.58	10,330.5	18,583	1,178.46	9,805.3	17,638
1,3,5-Trimethylbenzene (mesitylene)	C_9H_{12}	gas	1,252.53	10,421.6	18,747	1,189.41	9,896.4	17,802
1,3,5-Trimethylbenzene (mesitylene)	C_9H_{12}	liq.	1,241.19	10,327.2	18,577	1,178.07	9,802.1	17,632
n-Butylbenzene	$C_{10}H_{14}$	gas	1,415.44	10,546.3	18,971	1,341.80	9,997.6	17,984
n-Butylbenzene	$C_{10}H_{14}$	liq.	1,403.46	10,457.0	18,810	1,329.82	9,908.4	17,823
	Alkyl cyclopentanes							
Cyclopentane	C_5H_{10}	gas	793.39	11,313.1	20,350	740.79	10,563.1	19,001
Cyclopentane	C_5H_{10}	liq.	786.54	11,215.5	20,175	733.94	10,465.4	18,825
Methylcyclopentane	C_6H_{12}	gas	948.72	11,273.4	20,279	885.60	10,523.3	18,930
Methylcyclopentane	C_6H_{12}	liq.	941.14	11,183.3	20,117	878.02	10,433.2	18,768
Ethylcyclopentane	C_7H_{14}	gas	1,106.21	11,266.9	20,267	1,032.57	10,516.9	18,918
Ethylcyclopentane	C_7H_{14}	liq.	1,097.50	11,178.2	20,108	1,023.86	10,428.2	18,758
n-Propylcyclopentane	C_8H_{16}	gas	1,263.56	11,260.9	20,256	1,179.40	10,510.8	18,907
n-Propylcyclopentane	C_8H_{16}	liq.	1,253.74	11,173.4	20,099	1,169.58	10,423.3	18,750
n-Butylcyclopentane	C_9H_{18}	gas	1,421.10	11,257.7	20,250	1,326.42	10,507.6	18,901
n-Butylcyclopentane	C_9H_{18}	liq.	1,410.10	11,170.5	20,094	1,315.42	10,420.5	18,745
	Alkyl cyclohexanes							
Cyclohexane	C_6H_{12}	gas	944.79	11,226.7	20,195	881.67	10,476.7	18,846
Cyclohexane	C_6H_{12}	liq.	936.88	11,132.7	20,026	873.76	10,382.7	18,676
Methylcyclohexane	C_7H_{14}	gas	1,099.59	11,199.5	20,146	1,025.95	10,449.5	18,797
Methylcyclohexane	C_7H_{14}	liq.	1,091.13	11,113.3	19,991	1,017.49	10,363.3	18,642
Ethylcyclohexane	C_8H_{16}	gas	1,257.90	11,210.4	20,166	1,173.74	10,460.4	18,816
Ethylcyclohexane	C_8H_{16}	liq.	1,248.23	11,124.3	20,011	1,164.07	10,374.3	18,661
n-Propylcyclohexane	C_9H_{18}	gas	1,415.12	11,210.3	20,165	1,320.44	10,460.3	18,816
n-Propylcyclohexane	C_9H_{18}	liq.	1,404.34	11,124.9	20,012	1,309.66	10,374.9	18,663
n-Butylcyclohexane	$C_{10}H_{20}$	gas	1,572.74	11,213.0	20,170	1,467.54	10,463.0	18,821
n-Butylcyclohexane	$C_{10}H_{20}$	liq.	1,560.78	11,127.8	20,017	1,455.58	10,377.8	18,668
	Monoolefins							
Ethene (ethylene)	C_2H_4	gas	337.234	12,021.7	21,625	316.195	11,271.7	20,276
Propene (propylene)	C_3H_6	gas	491.987	11,692.3	21,032	460.428	10,942.3	19,683
1-Butene	C_4H_8	gas	649.757	11,581.3	20,833	607.679	10,831.3	19,484
cis-2-Butene	C_4H_8	gas	648.115	11,552.0	20,780	606.037	10,802.0	19,431
trans-2-Butene	C_4H_8	gas	647.072	11,533.4	20,747	604.994	10,783.4	19,397
2-Methylpropene (isobutene)	C_4H_8	gas	646.134	11,516.7	20,716	604.056	10,766.7	19,367
1-Pentene	C_5H_{10}	gas	806.85	11,505.1	20,696	754.25	10,755.1	19,346

Table 3-202. Hydrogen, Carbon, Carbon Monoxide, and Hydrocarbons—*(Concluded)*

Compound	Formula	State	Heat of combustion, $-\Delta Hc°$, at 25°C. and constant pressure, to form: H_2O (liq.) and CO_2 (gas), Kcal./mole	H_2O (liq.) and CO_2 (gas), Cal./g.	H_2O (liq.) and CO_2 (gas), B.t.u./lb.	H_2O (gas) and CO_2 (gas), Kcal./mole	H_2O (gas) and CO_2 (gas), Cal./g.	H_2O (gas) and CO_2 (gas), B.t.u./lb.
cis-2-Pentene	C_5H_{10}	gas	805.34	11,483.5	20,657	752.74	10,733.5	19,308
trans-2-Pentene	C_5H_{10}	gas	804.26	11,468.1	20,629	751.66	10,718.1	19,280
2-Methyl-1-butene	C_5H_{10}	gas	803.17	11,452.6	20,601	750.57	10,702.6	19,252
3-Methyl-1-butene	C_5H_{10}	gas	804.93	11,477.7	20,646	752.33	10,727.7	19,297
2-Methyl-2-butene	C_5H_{10}	gas	801.68	11,431.3	20,563	749.08	10,681.3	19,214
Acetylenes								
Ethyne (acetylene)	C_2H_2	gas	310.615	11,930.2	21,460	300.096	11,526.2	20,734
Propyne (methylacetylene)	C_3H_4	gas	463.109	11,559.8	20,794	442.070	11,034.6	19,849
1-Butyne (ethylacetylene)	C_4H_6	gas	620.86	11,478.7	20,648	589.302	10,895.2	19,599
2-Butyne (dimethylacetylene)	C_4H_6	gas	616.533	11,398.7	20,504	584.974	10,815.2	19,455
1-Pentyne	C_5H_8	gas	778.03	11,422.5	20,547	735.95	10,804.7	19,436
2-Pentyne	C_5H_8	gas	774.33	11,368.2	20,449	732.25	10,750.4	19,338
3-Methyl-1-butyne	C_5H_8	gas	776.13	11,394.6	20,497	734.05	10,776.8	19,386

* Saturation pressure.

HEATS OF SOLUTION

Table 3-203. Heats of Solution of Inorganic Compounds in Water

Heat evolved, in kilogram calories per gram formula weight, on solution in water at 18°C. Computed from data in Bichowsky and Rossini "Thermochemistry of Chemical Substances," Reinhold, New York, 1936

Substance	Dilution*	Formula	Heat, kg.-cal./g.-mole
Aluminum bromide	aq	$AlBr_3$	+85.3
chloride	600	$AlCl_3$	+77.9
	600	$AlCl_3.6H_2O$	+13.2
fluoride	aq	AlF_3	+31
	aq	$AlF_3.\frac{1}{2}H_2O$	+19.0
	aq	$AlF_3.3\frac{1}{2}H_2O$	−1.7
iodide	aq	AlI_3	+89.0
sulfate	aq	$Al_2(SO_4)_3$	+126
	aq	$Al_2(SO_4)_3.6H_2O$	+56.2
	aq	$Al_2(SO_4)_3.18H_2O$	+6.7
Ammonium bromide	aq	NH_4Br	−4.45
chloride	∞	NH_4Cl	−3.82
chromate	aq	$(NH_4)_2CrO_4$	−5.82
dichromate	600	$(NH_4)_2Cr_2O_7$	−12.9
iodide	aq	NH_4I	−3.56
nitrate	∞	NH_4NO_3	−6.47
perborate	aq	$NH_4BO_3.H_2O$	−9.0
sulfate	∞	$(NH_4)_2SO_4$	−2.75
sulfate, acid	800	NH_4HSO_4	+0.56
sulfite	aq	$(NH_4)_2SO_3$	−1.2
	aq	$(NH_4)_2SO_3.H_2O$	−4.13
Antimony fluoride	aq	SbF_3	−1.7
iodide	aq	SbI_3	−0.8
Arsenic acid	aq	H_3AsO_4	−0.4
Barium bromate	∞	$Ba(BrO_3)_2.H_2O$	−15.9
bromide	∞	$BaBr_2$	+5.3
	∞	$BaBr_2.H_2O$	−0.8
	∞	$BaBr_2.2H_2O$	−3.87
chlorate	∞	$Ba(ClO_3)_2$	−6.7
	∞	$Ba(ClO_3)_2.H_2O$	−10.6
chloride	∞	$BaCl_2$	+2.4
	∞	$BaCl_2.H_2O$	−2.17
	∞	$BaCl_2.2H_2O$	−4.5
cyanide	aq	$Ba(CN)_2$	+1.5
	aq	$Ba(CN)_2.H_2O$	−2.4
	aq	$Ba(CN)_2.2H_2O$	−4.9
iodate	∞	$Ba(IO_3)_2$	−9.1
	∞	$Ba(IO_3)_2.H_2O$	−11.3
iodide	∞	BaI_2	+10.5
	∞	$BaI_2.H_2O$	+2.7
	∞	$BaI_2.2H_2O$	+0.14
	∞	$BaI_2.2\frac{1}{2}H_2O$	−0.58
	∞	$BaI_2.7H_2O$	−6.61
nitrate	∞	$Ba(NO_3)_2$	−10.2
perchlorate	∞	$Ba(ClO_4)_2$	−2.8
	∞	$Ba(ClO_4)_2.3H_2O$	−10.5
sulfide	∞	BaS	+7.2
Beryllium bromide	aq	$BeBr_2$	+62.6
chloride	aq	$BeCl_2$	+51.1
iodide	aq	BeI_2	+72.6
sulfate	aq	$BeSO_4$	+18.1
	aq	$BeSO_4.H_2O$	+13.5
	aq	$BeSO_4.2H_2O$	+7.9
	aq	$BeSO_4.4H_2O$	+1.1
Bismuth iodide	aq	BiI_3	+3
Boric acid	aq	H_3BO_3	−5.4
Cadmium bromide	400	$CdBr_2$	+0.4
	400	$CdBr_2.4H_2O$	−7.3
chloride	400	$CdCl_2$	+3.1
	400	$CdCl_2.H_2O$	+0.6
	400	$CdCl_2.2\frac{1}{2}H_2O$	−3.00
nitrate	400	$Cd(NO_3)_2.H_2O$	+4.17
	400	$Cd(NO_3)_2.4H_2O$	−5.08
sulfate	400	$CdSO_4$	+10.69
	400	$CdSO_4.H_2O$	+6.05
	400	$CdSO_4.2\frac{2}{3}H_2O$	+2.51
Calcium acetate	∞	$Ca(C_2H_3O_2)_2$	+7.6
	∞	$Ca(C_2H_3O_2)_2.H_2O$	+6.5
bromide	∞	$CaBr_2$	+24.86
	∞	$CaBr_2.6H_2O$	−0.9
chloride	∞	$CaCl_2$	+4.9
	∞	$CaCl_2.H_2O$	+12.3
	∞	$CaCl_2.2H_2O$	+12.5
	∞	$CaCl_2.4H_2O$	+2.4
	∞	$CaCl_2.6H_2O$	−4.11
formate	400	$Ca(CHO_2)_2$	+0.7
iodide	∞	CaI_2	+28.0
	∞	$CaI_2.8H_2O$	+1.8
nitrate	∞	$Ca(NO_3)_2$	+4.1
	∞	$Ca(NO_3)_2.H_2O$	+0.7
	∞	$Ca(NO_3)_2.2H_2O$	−3.2
	∞	$Ca(NO_3)_2.3H_2O$	−4.2
	∞	$Ca(NO_3)_2.4H_2O$	−7.99
phosphate, mono-	aq	$Ca(H_2PO_4)_2.H_2O$	−0.6
dibasic	aq	$CaHPO_4.2H_2O$	−1
sulfate	∞	$CaSO_4$	+5.1
	∞	$CaSO_4.\frac{1}{2}H_2O$	+3.6
	∞	$CaSO_4.2H_2O$	−0.18
Chromous chloride	aq	$CrCl_2$	+18.6
		$CrCl_2.3H_2O$	+5.3
		$CrCl_2.4H_2O$	+2.0
iodide	aq	CrI_2	+5.7
Cobaltous bromide	aq	$CoBr_2$	+18.4
	aq	$CoBr_2.6H_2O$	−1.25
chloride	400	$CoCl_2$	+18.5
	400	$CoCl_2.2H_2O$	+9.8
	400	$CoCl_2.6H_2O$	−2.9
iodide	aq	CoI_2	+18.8
sulfate	400	$CoSO_4$	+15.0
	400	$CoSO_4.6H_2O$	−1.4
	400	$CoSO_4.7H_2O$	−3.6
Cupric acetate	aq	$Cu(C_2H_3O_2)_2$	+2.4
formate	aq	$Cu(CHO_2)_2$	+0.5
nitrate	200	$Cu(NO_3)_2$	+10.3
	200	$Cu(NO_3)_2.3H_2O$	−2.6
	200	$Cu(NO_3)_2.6H_2O$	−10.7
sulfate	800	$CuSO_4$	+15.9
		$CuSO_4.H_2O$	+9.3
		$CuSO_4.3H_2O$	+3.65
		$CuSO_4.5H_2O$	−2.85
Cuprous sulfate	aq	Cu_2SO_4	+11.6

* The numbers represent moles of water used to dissolve 1 g. formula weight of substance; ∞ means "infinite dilution"; and aq means "aqueous solution of unspecified dilution."

Table 3-203. Heats of Solution of Inorganic Compounds in Water—(*Continued*)

Substance	Dilution*	Formula	Heat, kg.-cal./g.-mole
Ferric chloride	1000	$FeCl_3$	+31.7
	1000	$FeCl_3.2\frac{1}{2}H_2O$	+21.0
	1000	$FeCl_3.6H_2O$	+5.6
nitrate	800	$Fe(NO_3)_3.9H_2O$	−9.1
Ferrous bromide	aq	$FeBr_2$	+18.0
chloride	400	$FeCl_2$	+17.9
	400	$FeCl_2.2H_2O$	+8.7
	400	$FeCl_2.4H_2O$	+2.7
iodide	aq	FeI_2	+23.3
sulfate	400	$FeSO_4$	+14.7
	400	$FeSO_4.H_2O$	+7.35
	400	$FeSO_4.4H_2O$	+1.4
	400	$FeSO_4.7H_2O$	−4.4
Lead acetate	400	$Pb(C_2H_3O_2)_2$	+1.4
	400	$Pb(C_2H_3O_2)_2.3H_2O$	−5.9
bromide	aq	$PbBr_2$	−10.1
chloride	aq	$PbCl_2$	−3.4
formate	aq	$Pb(CHO_2)_2$	−6.9
nitrate	400	$Pb(NO_3)_2$	−7.61
Lithium bromide	∞	$LiBr$	+11.54
	∞	$LiBr.H_2O$	+5.30
	∞	$LiBr.2H_2O$	+2.05
	∞	$LiBr.3H_2O$	−1.59
chloride	∞	$LiCl$	+8.66
	∞	$LiCl.H_2O$	+4.45
	∞	$LiCl.2H_2O$	+1.07
	∞	$LiCl.3H_2O$	−1.98
fluoride	∞	LiF	−0.74
hydroxide	∞	$LiOH$	+4.74
	∞	$LiOH.\frac{1}{8}H_2O$	+4.39
	∞	$LiOH.H_2O$	+9.6
iodide	∞	LiI	+14.92
	∞	$LiI.\frac{1}{2}H_2O$	+10.08
	∞	$LiI.H_2O$	+6.93
	∞	$LiI.2H_2O$	+3.43
	∞	$LiI.3H_2O$	−0.17
nitrate	∞	$LiNO_3$	+0.466
	∞	$LiNO_3.3H_2O$	−7.87
sulfate	∞	Li_2SO_4	+6.71
	∞	$Li_2SO_4.H_2O$	+3.77
Magnesium bromide	∞	$MgBr_2$	+43.7
	∞	$MgBr_2.H_2O$	+35.9
	∞	$MgBr_2.6H_2O$	+19.8
chloride	∞	$MgCl_2$	+36.3
	∞	$MgCl_2.2H_2O$	+20.8
	∞	$MgCl_2.4H_2O$	+10.5
	∞	$MgCl_2.6H_2O$	+3.4
iodide	∞	MgI_2	+50.2
nitrate	∞	$Mg(NO_3)_2.6H_2O$	−3.7
phosphate	aq	$Mg_3(PO_4)_2$	+10.2
sulfate	∞	$MgSO_4$	+21.1
	∞	$MgSO_4.H_2O$	+14.0
	∞	$MgSO_4.2H_2O$	+11.7
	∞	$MgSO_4.4H_2O$	+4.9
	∞	$MgSO_4.6H_2O$	+0.55
	∞	$MgSO_4.7H_2O$	−3.18
sulfide	aq	MgS	+25.8
Manganic nitrate	400	$Mn(NO_3)_2$	+12.9
	400	$Mn(NO_3)_2.3H_2O$	−3.9
	400	$Mn(NO_3)_2.6H_2O$	−6.2
sulfate	aq	$Mn_2(SO_4)_3$	+22
Manganous acetate	aq	$Mn(C_2H_3O_2)_2$	+12.2
	aq	$Mn(C_2H_3O_2)_2.4H_2O$	+1.6
bromide	aq	$MnBr_2$	+15
	aq	$MnBr_2.H_2O$	+14.4
	aq	$MnBr_2.4H_2O$	+16.1
chloride	400	$MnCl_2$	+16.0
	400	$MnCl_2.2H_2O$	+8.2
	400	$MnCl_2.4H_2O$	+1.5
formate	aq	$Mn(CHO_2)_2$	+4.3
	aq	$Mn(CHO_2)_2.2H_2O$	−2.9
iodide	aq	MnI_2	+26.2
	aq	$MnI_2.H_2O$	+24.1
	aq	$MnI_2.2H_2O$	+22.7
	aq	$MnI_2.4H_2O$	+19.9
	aq	$MnI_2.6H_2O$	+21.2
sulfate	400	$MnSO_4$	+13.8
	400	$MnSO_4.H_2O$	+11.9
	400	$MnSO_4.7H_2O$	−1.7
Mercuric acetate	aq	$Hg(C_2H_3O_2)_2$	−4.0
bromide	aq	$HgBr_2$	−2.4
chloride	aq	$HgCl_2$	−3.3
nitrate	aq	$Hg(NO_3)_2.\frac{1}{2}H_2O$	−0.7
Mercurous nitrate	aq	$Hg_2(NO_3)_2.2H_2O$	−11.5
Nickel bromide	aq	$NiBr_2$	+19.0
	aq	$NiBr_2.3H_2O$	+0.2
Nickel chloride	800	$NiCl_2$	+19.23
	800	$NiCl_2.2H_2O$	+10.4
	800	$NiCl_2.4H_2O$	+4.2
	800	$NiCl_2.6H_2O$	−1.15
iodide	aq	NiI_2	+19.4
nitrate	200	$Ni(NO_3)_2$	+11.8
	200	$Ni(NO_3)_2.6H_2O$	−7.5
sulfate	200	$NiSO_4$	+15.1
	200	$NiSO_4.7H_2O$	−4.2
Phosphoric acid, ortho-	400	H_3PO_4	+2.79
	400	$H_3PO_4.\frac{1}{2}H_2O$	−0.1
pyro-	aq	$H_4P_2O_7$	+25.9
	aq	$H_4P_2O_7.1\frac{1}{2}H_2O$	+4.65
Potassium acetate	∞	$KC_2H_3O_2$	+3.55
aluminum sulfate	600	$KAl(SO_4)_2$	+48.5
	600	$KAl(SO_4)_2.3H_2O$	+26.6
		$KAl(SO_4)_2.12H_2O$	−10.1
bicarbonate	2000	$KHCO_3$	−5.1
bromate	∞	$KBrO_3$	−10.13
bromide	∞	KBr	−5.13
carbonate	∞	K_2CO_3	+6.58
	∞	$K_2CO_3.\frac{1}{2}H_2O$	+4.25
	∞	$K_2CO_3.1\frac{1}{2}H_2O$	−0.43
chlorate	∞	$KClO_3$	−10.31
chloride	∞	KCl	−4.404
chromate	2185	K_2CrO_4	−4.9
chrome sulfate	600	$KCr(SO_4)_2$	+55
		$KCr(SO_4)_2.H_2O$	+42
		$KCr(SO_4)_2.2H_2O$	+33
		$KCr(SO_4)_2.6H_2O$	+7
		$KCr(SO_4)_2.12H_2O$	−9.5
cyanide	200	KCN	−3.0
dichromate	1600	$K_2Cr_2O_7$	−17.8
fluoride	∞	KF	+3.96
	∞	$KF.2H_2O$	−1.85
	∞	$KF.4H_2O$	−6.05
hydrosulfide	∞	KHS	+0.86
	∞	$KHS.\frac{1}{4}H_2O$	+1.21
hydroxide	∞	KOH	+12.91
	∞	$KOH.\frac{3}{4}H_2O$	+4.27
	∞	$KOH.H_2O$	+3.48
	∞	$KOH.7H_2O$	+0.86
iodate	∞	KIO_3	−6.93
iodide	∞	KI	−5.23
nitrate	∞	KNO_3	−8.633
oxalate	400	$K_2C_2O_4$	−4.6
		$K_2C_2O_4.H_2O$	−7.5
perchlorate	∞	$KClO_4$	−12.94
permanganate	400	$KMnO_4$	−10.4
phosphate, dihydrogen	aq	KH_2PO_4	+4.7
pyrosulfite	aq	$K_2S_2O_5$	−11.0
	aq	$K_2S_2O_5.\frac{1}{2}H_2O$	−10.22
sulfate	∞	K_2SO_4	−6.32
sulfate, acid	800	$KHSO_4$	−3.10
sulfide	∞	K_2S	−11.0
sulfite	aq	K_2SO_3	+1.8
	aq	$K_2SO_3.H_2O$	+1.37
thiocyanate	∞	$KCNS$	−6.08
thionate, di-	aq	$K_2S_2O_6$	−13.0
thiosulfate	∞	$K_2S_2O_3$	−4.5
Silver acetate	aq	$AgC_2H_3O_2$	−5.4
nitrate	200	$AgNO_3$	−4.4
Sodium acetate	∞	$NaC_2H_3O_2$	+4.085
	∞	$NaC_2H_3O_2.3H_2O$	−4.665
arsenate	500	Na_3AsO_4	+15.6
	500	$Na_3AsO_4.12H_2O$	−12.61
bicarbonate	1800	$NaHCO_3$	−4.1
borate, tetra-	900	$Na_2B_4O_7$	+10.0
	900	$Na_2B_4O_7.10H_2O$	−16.8
bromide	∞	$NaBr$	−0.58
	∞	$NaBr.2H_2O$	−4.57
carbonate	∞	Na_2CO_3	+5.57
	∞	$Na_2CO_3.H_2O$	+2.19
	∞	$Na_2CO_3.7H_2O$	−10.81
	∞	$Na_2CO_3.10H_2O$	−16.22
chlorate	∞	$NaClO_3$	−5.37
chloride	∞	$NaCl$	−1.164
chromate	800	Na_2CrO_4	+2.50
	800	$Na_2CrO_4.4H_2O$	−7.52
	800	$Na_2CrO_4.10H_2O$	−16.0
cyanide	200	$NaCN$	−0.37
	200	$NaCN.\frac{1}{2}H_2O$	−0.92
	200	$NaCN.2H_2O$	−4.41
fluoride	∞	NaF	−0.27
hydrosulfide	∞	$NaHS$	+4.62
	∞	$NaHS.2H_2O$	−1.49

Table 3-203. Heats of Solution of Inorganic Compounds in Water—(*Concluded*)

Substance	Dilution*	Formula	Heat, kg.-cal./g.-mole
Sodium hydroxide	∞	$NaOH$	+10.18
	∞	$NaOH.\frac{1}{2}H_2O$	+8.17
	∞	$NaOH.\frac{2}{3}H_2O$	+7.08
	∞	$NaOH.\frac{3}{4}H_2O$	+6.48
	∞	$NaOH.H_2O$	+5.17
iodide	∞	NaI	+1.57
	∞	$NaI.2H_2O$	−3.89
metaphosphate	600	$NaPO_3$	+3.97
nitrate	∞	$NaNO_3$	−5.05
nitrite	aq	$NaNO_2$	−3.6
perchlorate	∞	$NaClO_4$	−4.15
phosphate, di-	1600	Na_2HPO_4	+5.21
tri-	1600	Na_3PO_4	+13
phosphate	1600	$Na_3PO_4.12H_2O$	−15.3
di-	1600	$Na_2HPO_4.2H_2O$	−0.82
	1600	$Na_2HPO_4.7H_2O$	−12.04
	1600	$Na_2HPO_4.12H_2O$	−23.18
phosphite, mono-	600	NaH_2PO_3	+0.90
	600	$NaH_2PO_3.2\frac{1}{2}H_2O$	−5.29
di-	800	Na_2HPO_3	+9.30
	800	$Na_2HPO_3.5H_2O$	−4.54
pyrophosphate	1600	$Na_4P_2O_7$	+11.9
	1600	$Na_4P_2O_7.10H_2O$	−11.7
di-	1200	$Na_2H_2P_2O_7$	−2.2
	1200	$Na_2H_2P_2O_7.6H_2O$	−14.0
sulfate	∞	Na_2SO_4	+0.28
	∞	$Na_2SO_4.10H_2O$	−18.74
sulfate, acid	800	$NaHSO_4$	+1.74
	800	$NaHSO_4.H_2O$	+0.15
sulfide	∞	Na_2S	+15.2
	∞	$Na_2S.4\frac{1}{2}H_2O$	+0.09
	∞	$Na_2S.5H_2O$	−6.54
	∞	$Na_2S.9H_2O$	−16.65
sulfite	∞	Na_2SO_3	+2.8
	∞	$Na_2SO_3.7H_2O$	−11.1
thiocyanate	∞	$NaCNS$	−1.83
thionate, di-	aq	$Na_2S_2O_6$	−5.80
	aq	$Na_2S_2O_6.2H_2O$	−11.86

Substance	Dilution*	Formula	Heat, kg.-cal./g.-mole
Sodium thiosulfate	aq	$Na_2S_2O_3$	+2.0
	aq	$Na_2S_2O_3.5H_2O$	−11.30
Stannic bromide	aq	$SnBr_4$	+15.5
Stannous bromide	aq	$SnBr_2$	−1.6
iodide	aq	SnI_2	−5.8
Strontium acetate	∞	$Sr(C_2H_3O_2)_2$	+6.2
	∞	$Sr(C_2H_3O_2)_2.\frac{1}{2}H_2O$	+5.9
bromide	∞	$SrBr_2$	+16.4
	∞	$SrBr_2.H_2O$	+9.25
	∞	$SrBr_2.2H_2O$	+6.5
	∞	$SrBr_2.4H_2O$	+0.4
	∞	$SrBr_2.6H_2O$	−6.1
chloride	∞	$SrCl_2$	+11.54
	∞	$SrCl_2.H_2O$	+6.4
	∞	$SrCl_2.2H_2O$	+2.95
	∞	$SrCl_2.6H_2O$	−7.1
iodide	∞	SrI_2	+20.7
	∞	$SrI_2.H_2O$	+12.65
	∞	$SrI_2.2H_2O$	+10.4
	∞	$SrI_2.6H_2O$	−4.5
nitrate	∞	$Sr(NO_3)_2$	−4.8
	∞	$Sr(NO_3)_2.4H_2O$	−12.4
sulfate	∞	$SrSO_4$	+0.5
Sulfuric acid, pyro-	∞	$H_2S_2O_7$	−18.08
Zinc acetate	400	$Zn(C_2H_3O_2)_2$	+9.8
	400	$Zn(C_2H_3O_2)_2.H_2O$	+7.0
	400	$Zn(C_2H_3O_2)_2.2H_2O$	+3.9
bromide	400	$ZnBr_2$	+15.0
chloride	400	$ZnCl_2$	+15.72
iodide	aq	ZnI_2	+11.6
nitrate	400	$Zn(NO_3)_2.3H_2O$	−5
	400	$Zn(NO_3)_2.6H_2O$	−6.0
sulfate	400	$ZnSO_4$	+18.5
	400	$ZnSO_4.H_2O$	+10.0
	400	$ZnSO_4.6H_2O$	−0.8
	400	$ZnSO_4.7H_2O$	−4.3

Table 3-204. Heats of Solution of Organic Compounds in Water (at Infinite Dilution and Approximately Room Temperature)

(Recalculated and rearranged from "International Critical Tables," vol. 5, pp. 148–150)

Solute	Heat of Solution, G.-cal./g.-mole Solute*
Acetic acid (solid), $C_2H_4O_2$	−2,251
Acetylacetone, $C_5H_8O_2$	−641
Acetylurea, $C_3H_6N_2O_2$	−6,812
Aconitic acid, $C_6H_6O_6$	−4,206
Ammonium benzoate, $C_7H_9NO_2$	−2,700
picrate	−8,700
succinate (n-)	−3,489
Aniline, hydrochloride, C_6H_8ClN	−2,732
Barium picrate	−4,708
Benzoic acid, $C_7H_6O_2$	−6,501
Camphoric acid, $C_{10}H_{16}O_4$	−502
Citric acid, $C_6H_8O_7$	−5,401
Dextrin, $C_{12}H_{20}O_{10}$	268
Fumaric acid, $C_4H_4O_4$	−5,903
Hexamethylenetetramine, $C_6H_{12}N_4$	4,780
Hydroxybenzamide (m-), $C_7H_7NO_2$	−4,161
(m-), (HCl)	−7,003
(o-), $C_7H_7NO_2$	−4,340
(p-)	−5,392
Hydroxybenzoic acid (o-), $C_7H_6O_3$	−6,350
(p-), $C_7H_6O_3$	−5,781
Hydroxybenzyl alcohol (o-), $C_7H_8O_2$	−3,203
Inulin, $C_{36}H_{62}O_{31}$	−96
Isosuccinic acid, $C_4H_6O_4$	−3,420
Itaconic acid, $C_5H_6O_4$	−5,922
Lactose, $C_{12}H_{22}O_{11}.H_2O$	−3,705
Lead picrate	−7,098
($2H_2O$)	−13,193
Magnesium picrate	14,699
($8H_2O$)	−15,894
Maleic acid, $C_4H_4O_4$	−4,441
Malic acid, $C_4H_6O_5$	−3,150
Malonic acid, $C_3H_4O_4$	−4,493
Mandelic acid, $C_8H_8O_3$	−3,090
Mannitol, $C_6H_{14}O_6$	−5,260
Menthol, $C_{10}H_{20}O$	0
Nicotine dihydrochloride, $C_{10}H_{16}Cl_2N_2$	6,561
Nitrobenzoic acid (m-), $C_7H_5NO_4$	−5,593
(o-), $C_7H_5NO_4$	−5,306
(p-), $C_7H_5NO_4$	−8,891
Nitrophenol (m-), $C_6H_5NO_3$	−5,210
(o-), $C_6H_5NO_3$	−6,310
(p-), $C_6H_5NO_3$	−4,493
Oxalic acid, $C_2H_2O_4$	−2,290
($2H_2O$)	−8,485
Phenol (solid), C_6H_6O	−2,605
Phthalic acid, $C_8H_6O_4$	−4,871
Picric acid, $C_6H_3N_3O_7$	−7,098
Piperic acid, $C_{12}H_{10}O_4$	−10,492
Piperonylic acid, $C_8H_6O_4$	−9,106
Potassium benzoate	−1,506
citrate	2,820
tartrate (n-) (0.5 H_2O)	−5,562
Pyrogallol, $C_6H_6O_3$	−3,705
Pyrotartaric acid	−5,019
Quinone	−3,991
Raffinose, $C_{18}H_{32}O_{16}$ ($5H_2O$)	−9,703
Resorcinol, $C_6H_6O_2$	−3,960
Silver malonate (n-)	−9,799
Sodium citrate (tri-)	5,270
picrate	−6,441
potassium tartrate	−1,817
($4H_2O$)	−12,342
succinate (n-)	2,390
($6H_2O$)	−10,994
tartrate (n-)	−1,121
($2H_2O$)	−5,882
Strontium picrate	7,887
($6H_2O$)	−14,412
Succinic acid, $C_4H_6O_4$	−6,405
Succinimide, $C_4H_5NO_2$	−4,302
Sucrose, $C_{12}H_{22}O_{11}$	−1,319
Tartaric acid (d-)	−3,451
Thiourea, CH_4N_2S	−5,330
Urea, CH_4N_2O	−3,609
acetate	−8,795
formate	−7,194
nitrate	−10,803
oxalate	−17,806
Vanillic acid	−5,160
Vanillin	−5,210
Zinc picrate	−11,496
($8H_2O$)	−15,894

* + denotes heat evolved, and − denotes heat absorbed. All values are positive unless otherwise noted. The data in the "International Critical Tables" were calculated by E. Anderson.

THERMODYNAMIC PROPERTIES

EXPLANATION OF TABLES

The following subsection presents information on the thermodynamic properties of a number of fluids.

Notation

e = specific internal energy
h = enthalpy
p = pressure
s = specific entropy
t = temperature
T = absolute temperature
u = specific internal energy
v = specific volume
f = subscript, denoting saturated liquid
g = subscript, denoting saturated vapor

GENERAL INFORMATION ON THERMODYNAMIC PROPERTIES

A complete tabulation of the available information for the substances listed here would occupy many times the number of pages used. To provide the interested reader with further information references are given which either provide extensive numerical or graphical data or which extensively review the data for a particular fluid. In addition, the reader is reminded of other tables, such as for compressibility, appearing on other pages of this section which can be used to supplement the information presented here. In addition the following general references may be found of interest:

General References: Dodge, "Chemical Engineering Thermodynamics," McGraw-Hill, New York, 1944. Keenan, "Thermodynamics," Wiley, New York, 1941. Keenan and Keyes, "Thermodynamic Properties of Steam," Wiley, New York, 1936. Bosnjakovic, "Technische Thermodynamik," Theodor Steinkopf, Leipzig, 1935. Goff, "Notes on Thermodynamics," 3d ed., Swift, St. Louis, 1939. Sage and Lacey, "Volumetric and Phase Behavior of Hydrocarbons," Stanford University Press, Stanford, Calif., 1939. Weber, "Thermodynamics for Chemical Engineers," Wiley, New York, 1939. Martin, "Thermodynamic and Transport Properties of Gases, Liquids and Solids," p. 110, A.S.M.E., New York, 1959. Kroepelin *et al.*, "Thermodynamic and Transport Properties of Gases, Liquids and Solids," pp. 438, 453, A.S.M.E., New York, 1959. Bosnjakovic *et al.*, "Thermodynamic and Transport Properties of Gases, Liquids and Solids," p. 465, A.S.M.E., New York, 1959. Lydersen, Greenkorn, and Hougen, Generalized Thermodynamic Properties of Pure Fluids, *Univ. Wisconsin Eng. Expt. Sta. Rept.* 4, 1955. Reid and Sherwood, "The Properties of Gases and Liquids," McGraw-Hill, New York, 1958. Scott, "Cryogenic Engineering," Van Nostrand, Princeton, N.J., 1959. Rowlinson, "Handbuch der Physik," vol. XII, Springer, Berlin, 1958. For more specialized treatments appropriate entries in *Chemical Abstracts, Science Abstracts*, etc., may also be consulted. Such sources will prove particularly useful in enabling references dealing with the properties of a specific fluid to be ascertained.

Limitations of space have precluded the insertion of much information available on mixtures of variable composition. In appropriate cases references have been supplied and for further information the reader is also referred to:

General References for Mixtures: Dodge, "Chemical Engineering Thermodynamics," McGraw-Hill, New York, 1944. Merkel, *Z. Ver. deut. Ing.*, **72,** 109 (1928). Merkel, *Z. ges. Kälte-Ind.*, **35,** 130 (1928). Ponchon, *Tech. moderne*, **13,** 20, 55 (1921). Savarit, *Arts et métiers*, **65,** 142, 178, 241, 266, 307 (1922). Bosnjakovic, "Technische Thermodynamik," vols. 1, 2, Theodor Steinkopf, Leipzig, 1935. Hougen and Watson, "Chemical Process Principles," Wiley, New York, 1943. Reid and Sherwood, "The Properties of Gases and Liquids," McGraw-Hill, New York, 1958. A.I.Ch.E. Symposium Series, various volumes.

Table 3-205. Acetylene

For tabulated data and a T-S diagram see Din, "Thermodynamic Functions of Gases," vol. 2, Butterworth, London, 1956. A wall-sized T-S diagram is obtainable from Butterworth & Co. (Canada), Ltd. See also Maslov, *Zhur. Fiz. Khim.*, **27,** 237, (1953); Stull, *et al.*, *Ind. Eng. Chem.*, **35,** 639 (1943); Teranishi, *Rev. Phys. Chem. Japan*, **25,** 23 (1955).

Table 3-206. Saturated Air*

Absolute pressure, atm.	Temperature		Enthalpy, B.t.u./lb.		Entropy, B.t.u./(lb.)(°R.)		Absolute pressure, atm.	Temperature		Enthalpy, B.t.u./lb.		Entropy, B.t.u./(lb.)(°R.)	
p	Dew point, °R.	Bubble point, °R.	Liquid h_f	Vapor h_g	Liquid s_f	Vapor s_g	p	Dew point, °R.	Bubble point, °R.	Liquid h_f	Vapor h_g	Liquid s_f	Vapor s_g
1	147.17	141.70	46.33	134.55	0	0.6110	8	188.55	184.68	67.75	140.20	.1260	.5134
2	158.78	153.61	52.00	136.80	0.0363	0.5818	10	194.42	190.89	71.13	140.32	.1427	.5018
4	172.39	167.72	59.00	138.83	.0782	.5500	15	206.08	203.33	78.46	140.08	.1763	.4773
5	177.28	172.84	61.48	139.38	.0925	.5376	20	215.23	213.17	84.70	139.30	.2056	.4602
6	181.49	177.25	63.75	139.80	.1057	.5294	30	229.61	228.80	96.95	135.35	.2563	.4238
							37.25	238.34		118.75		0.3453	

* Williams, *Trans. Am. Inst. Chem. Engrs.*, **39,** 93 (1943).

Table 3-207. Superheated Air*

Temp., °K.	P = 1 atm.			P = 4 atm.			P = 7 atm.			P = 10 atm.			P = 40 atm.			P = 70 atm.			P = 100 atm.		
	Z	H	S	Z	H	S	Z	H	S	Z	H	S	Z	H	S	Z	H	S	Z	H	S
100	0.9808	1.2552	20.049																		
150	.9941	1.9036	21.486	0.9759	1.8736	20.062	0.9572	1.8421	19.465	0.9378	1.8112	19.069	0.6832								
200	.9977	2.5465	22.497	.9907	2.5281	21.091	.9837	2.5094	20.513	.9767	2.4908	20.139	.9080	2.2922	18.551	0.8481	2.0794	17.767	0.8105	1.8734	17.184
250	.9991	3.1879	23.278	.9963	3.1754	21.881	.9935	3.1631	21.308	.9908	3.1508	20.944	.9668	3.0274	19.449	.9498	2.9078	18.782	.9417	2.7972	18.324
300	.9997	3.8292	23.917	.9988	3.8204	22.524	.9980	3.8118	21.958	.9972	3.8034	21.594	.9914	3.7194	20.138	.9900	3.6411	19.513	.9933	3.5699	19.095
350	1.0000	4.4717	24.459	1.0001	4.4655	23.067	1.0002	4.4593	22.502	1.0004	4.4535	22.141	1.0033	4.3944	20.707	1.0090	4.3407	20.102	1.0176	4.2935	19.704
400	1.0002	5.1167	24.929	1.0008	5.1125	23.539	1.0014	5.1079	22.976	1.0021	5.1039	22.616	1.0095	5.0623	21.194	1.0188	5.0252	20.602	1.0299	4.9926	20.214
450	1.0003	5.7657	25.347	1.0012	5.7626	23.957	1.0021	5.7594	23.395	1.0030	5.7567	23.036	1.0128	5.7282	21.623	1.0239	5.7033	21.038	1.0362	5.6820	20.658
500	1.0003	6.4195	25.723	1.0014	6.4176	24.335	1.0024	6.4154	23.773	1.0035	6.4137	23.414	1.0145	6.3951	22.006	1.0265	6.3795	21.428	1.0393	6.3670	21.056
550	1.0004	7.0795	26.067	1.0015	7.0784	24.679	1.0026	7.0771	24.117	1.0037	7.0761	23.759	1.0154	7.0653	22.356	1.0277	7.0575	21.780	1.0406	7.0518	21.409
600	1.0004	7.7463	26.383	1.0015	7.7459	24.995	1.0027	7.7454	24.434	1.0039	7.7449	24.077	1.0157	7.7408	22.677	1.0281	7.7388	22.104	1.0408	7.7390	21.736
650	1.0004	8.4205	26.678	1.0015	8.4206	25.290	1.0027	8.4209	24.730	1.0039	8.4207	24.372	1.0158	8.4220	22.975	1.0280	8.4251	22.404	1.0405	8.4298	22.038
700	1.0004	9.1023	26.954	1.0015	9.1027	25.567	1.0027	9.1035	25.006	1.0039	9.1037	24.649	1.0156	9.1096	23.253	1.0275	9.1168	22.685	1.0397	9.1253	22.320
750	1.0004	9.7916	27.214	1.0015	9.7927	25.827	1.0026	9.7935	25.266	1.0038	9.7942	24.909	1.0153	9.8040	23.515	1.0270	9.8149	22.947	1.0389	9.8278	22.584
800	1.0004	10.489	27.460	1.0015	10.490	26.073	1.0026	10.491	25.512	1.0037	10.492	25.155	1.0149	10.505	23.762	1.0263	10.519	23.196	1.0379	10.534	22.833
850	1.0004	11.192	27.693	1.0014	11.192	26.306	1.0025	11.196	25.746	1.0036	11.197	25.388	1.0145	11.213	23.996	1.0256	11.230	23.432	1.0367	11.248	23.069
900	1.0004	11.904	27.915	1.0014	11.906	26.528	1.0025	11.908	25.968	1.0035	11.909	25.610	1.0141	11.928	24.219	1.0248	11.947	23.655	1.0356	11.968	23.293
950	1.0003	12.623	28.127	1.0014	12.625	26.741	1.0024	12.627	26.181	1.0034	12.628	25.822	1.0137	12.649	24.431	1.0240	12.670	23.867	1.0344	12.693	23.505
1000	1.0003	13.348	28.330	1.0013	13.350	26.944	1.0023	13.352	26.384	1.0033	13.354	26.025	1.0133	13.377	24.634	1.0233	13.400	24.071	1.0333	13.424	23.709

* Extracted from Hilsenrath *et al.*, *N.B.S. Circ.* 564, 1955. Compressibility data rounded to four decimals. For more detailed data see this source, also other references cited in the listing for Air. These data may be somewhat in error for the higher pressures at 150°K. and below as the recent Michels data were not considered in the preparation of these tables. Z = compressibility factor, PV/RT; H = enthalpy function, $(H - E)/RT$, and S = entropy, S/R. For pressure in atmospheres density in g./cc. and temperature in °K., $R = 2.83286$; for lb./sq. in., lb./cu. ft., and °F., respectively, $R = 0.0252098$. To convert enthalpy data into $H - E$ in cal./mole multiply values by 542.821; to convert into B.t.u./lb. multiply by 33.7098. To obtain entropy in cal./(g.)(°K.) multiply by 0.0686042; for entropy in B.t.u./(lb.)(°R.) multiply by 0.0685590. For other conversion factors see *N.B.S. Circ.* 564, p. 25, 1955, and Sec. 1.

Table 3-208. Air at High Temperatures*

T, °K.	Compressibility Z					Dimensionless enthalpy $\frac{ZH}{RT}$					Dimensionless entropy $\frac{ZS}{R}$					T, °K.
	Pressure, atm.															
	100	10	1.0	0.1	0.01	100	10	1.0	0.1	0.01	100	10	1.0	0.1	0.01	
500	1.000	1.000	1.000	1.000	1.000	3.52	3.52	3.52	3.52	3.52	21.1	23.4	25.7	28.0	30.3	500
1000	1.000	1.000	1.000	1.000	1.000	3.65	3.65	3.65	3.65	3.65	23.7	26.0	28.3	30.6	32.9	1000
1500	1.000	1.000	1.000	1.000	1.000	3.80	3.80	3.80	3.80	3.80	25.3	27.6	29.9	32.2	34.5	1500
2000	1.000	1.000	1.000	1.001	1.002	3.92	3.92	3.92	3.93	3.97	26.6	28.9	31.2	33.5	35.8	2000
2500	1.000	1.001	1.004	1.011	1.033	4.01	4.03	4.09	4.27	4.81	27.5	29.9	32.2	34.7	37.6	2500
3000	1.003	1.009	1.026	1.072	1.149	4.13	4.25	4.61	5.55	7.13	28.4	30.8	33.5	36.9	41.0	3000
3500	1.012	1.035	1.092	1.167	1.197	4.34	4.75	5.75	7.08	7.62	29.3	32.0	35.5	39.4	42.7	3500
4000	1.033	1.089	1.165	1.198	1.208	4.70	5.56	6.74	7.28	7.53	30.2	33.5	37.3	40.6	43.6	4000
4500	1.071	1.149	1.196	1.213	1.245	5.20	6.29	6.98	7.33	8.14	31.3	34.9	38.3	41.5	45.1	4500
5000	1.118	1.186	1.214	1.252	1.359	5.73	6.62	7.10	7.96	10.48	32.4	36.0	39.2	42.9	48.4	5000
5500	1.159	1.208	1.248	1.348	1.599	6.13	6.80	7.58	9.73	15.14	33.4	36.8	40.4	45.5	54.3	5500
6000	1.189	1.235	1.316	1.529	1.849	6.38	7.11	8.70	12.93	19.30	34.2	37.7	42.2	49.7	59.9	6000
6500	1.214	1.279	1.437	1.752	1.961	6.62	7.72	10.64	16.46	20.35	34.9	38.9	44.9	54.4	62.6	6500
7000	1.243	1.351	1.607	1.904	1.997	6.95	8.76	13.20	18.34	20.01	35.8	40.5	48.3	57.6	63.8	7000
7500	1.284	1.457	1.778	1.971	2.017	7.44	10.24	15.48	18.66	19.54	36.8	42.7	51.6	59.2	64.6	7500
8000	1.341	1.590	1.896	2.001	2.044	8.16	11.99	16.73	18.43	19.34	38.0	45.1	53.9	60.1	65.7	8000
8500	1.418	1.727	1.959	2.023	2.090	9.10	13.63	17.09	18.17	19.60	39.4	47.6	55.3	61.0	67.1	8500
9000	1.512	1.838	1.993	2.050	2.166	10.20	14.79	17.04	18.09	20.49	41.1	49.5	56.2	61.9	69.2	9000
9500	1.616	1.914	2.018	2.090	2.286	11.36	15.40	16.91	18.29	22.17	42.8	51.0	57.0	63.1	72.0	9500
10000	1.718	1.962	2.042	2.149	2.462	12.42	15.61	16.84	18.85	24.78	44.5	52.0	57.8	64.6	75.8	10000
10500	1.807	1.993	2.071	2.234	2.700	13.23	15.64	16.90	19.84	28.28	45.9	52.8	58.7	66.6	80.6	10500
11000	1.876	2.018	2.111	2.351	2.983	13.77	15.60	17.13	21.31	32.31	47.1	53.4	59.7	69.0	86.0	11000
11500	1.927	2.042	2.163	2.505	3.272	14.08	15.58	17.57	23.28	36.13	48.0	54.1	60.9	71.9	91.4	11500
12000	1.965	2.067	2.232	2.694	3.520	14.22	15.62	18.24	25.69	39.01	48.8	54.8	62.4	75.4	95.8	12000
12500	1.993	2.098	2.318	2.910	3.700	14.28	15.74	19.16	28.36	40.66	49.4	55.6	64.0	79.1	99.1	12500
13000	2.017	2.135	2.426	3.135	3.818	14.30	15.96	20.32	30.99	41.26	50.0	56.4	66.0	82.9	101.3	13000
13500	2.039	2.180	2.553	3.347	3.889	14.31	16.28	21.72	33.27	41.17	50.5	57.3	68.2	86.4	102.8	13500
14000	2.062	2.233	2.700	3.527	3.932	14.34	16.71	23.29	34.97	40.69	51.1	58.4	70.5	89.4	103.8	14000
14500	2.086	2.297	2.861	3.667	3.957	14.40	17.26	24.98	36.02	40.01	51.7	59.5	73.1	91.7	104.5	14500
15000	2.113	2.372	3.028	3.769	3.973	14.49	17.92	26.66	36.53	39.24	52.2	60.8	75.6	93.4	105.1	15000

* Extracted from Hansen, *N.A.S.A. Tech. Rept.* R-50, Table IV, p. 31, 1959.

For a *T-S* diagram, 75° to 455°K., 1 to 1200 atm., see Din, "Thermodynamic Functions of Gases," vol. 2, Butterworth, London, 1956. A wall-sized reproduction of this diagram is obtainable from Butterworth and Co. (Canada), Ltd. A modification of Hausen's 1926 diagram providing information from 70° to 325°K., 1 to 200 atm. (*T-S* diagram) and a *H-S* diagram from 90° to 330°K., 1 to 200 atm., is given by Daunt, "Handbuch der Physik," **14**, pp. 42, 45, Springer, Berlin, 1956. For a *T-S* diagram to 100 atm. and 2275°C. see Baker, "Technology of Heat," p. 54, Longmans, London, 1956. Values of thermodynamic functions of the standard atmosphere to 65,800 ft. are given in *N.A.C.A. Rept.* 1235, 1955. For a Mollier diagram of equilibrium air to 15,000°K. see Korobkin and Hastings, *NAVORD Rept.* 4446, 1957. A diagram also based on the same data has been given by Feldman, "Hypersonic Gas Dynamics Charts for Equilibrium Air," Avco Manufacturing Corp., 1957. Extensive tabulations of the properties of high-temperature air are available including Predvoditeley, Stupochenko, *et al.*, "Tables of Thermodynamic Functions of Air," Infosearch, London, 1958 (to 12,000°K. and 1000 atm.), Hilsenrath, Klein, *et al.*, AEDC-TR-59-20, 1959 (to 15,000°K. log ρ/ρ_0 from −7 to 2) etc. For a most extensive set of *H*-log *P*, *S*-log *P* charts (saturation to nearly 5000°K., 10^{-8} to 1000 atm.) see Erickson and Creekmore, *N.A.S.A. Tech. Note* D-231, 1960. An earlier set of diagrams from N.A.S.A. by Moeckel and Weston, *Tech. Note* 4265, 1958, was also based upon the same primary data. Logan and Treanor of Cornell Aeronautical Lab., Inc., have also produced extensive tables of thermodynamic properties for air.

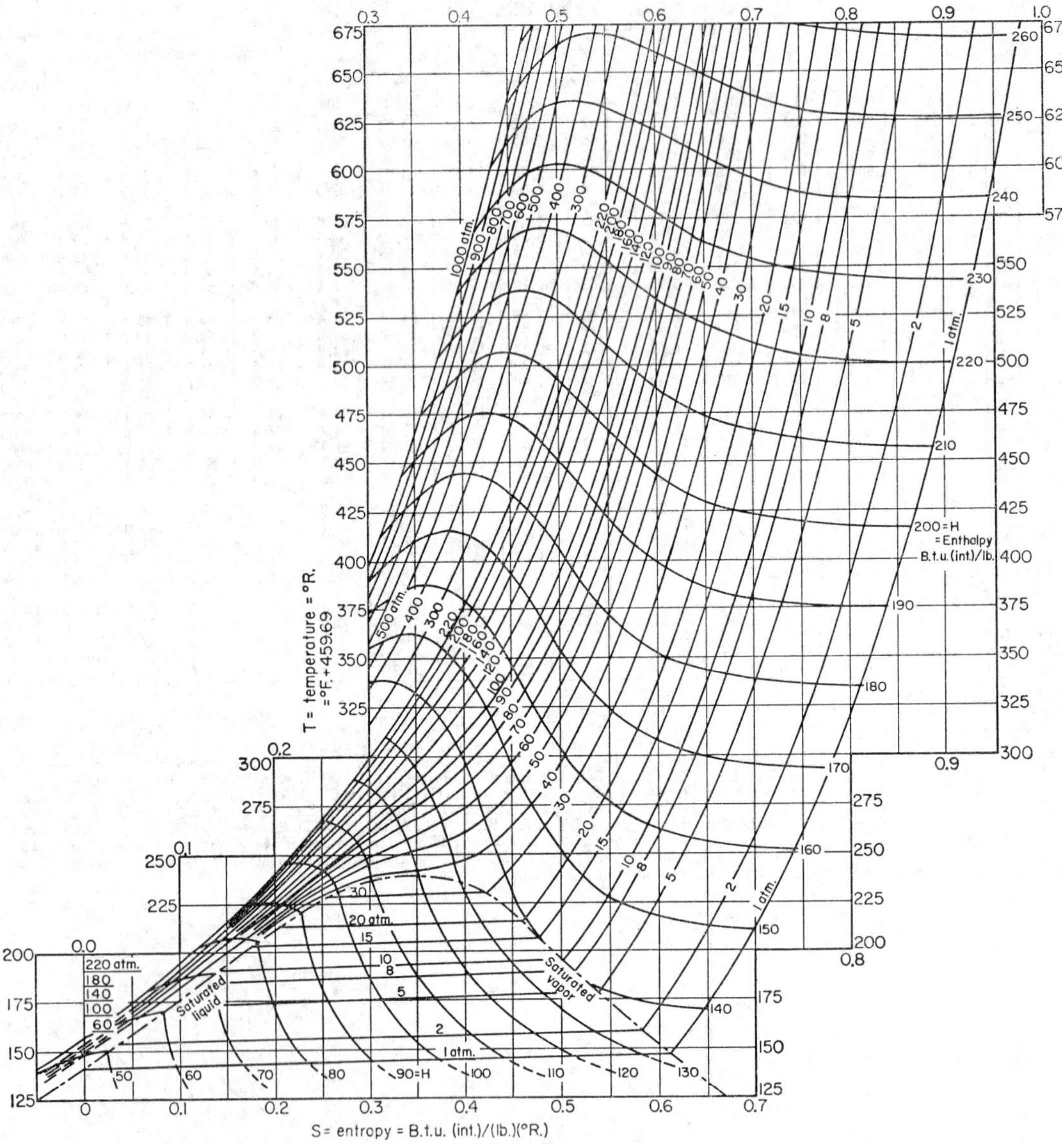

Fig. 3-15. Temperature-entropy diagram for air. [*Landsbaum, Dadds, Stevens, et al., Am. Inst. Chem. Engrs. J.*, **1** (3), 303 (1955). *Reproduced by permission of the authors and of the editor, Am. Inst. Chem. Engrs.*]

Table 3-209. Saturated Ammonia*

Temp., °F.	Abs. pressure, lb./sq. in.	Volume, cu. ft./lb.		Enthalpy, B.t.u./lb.		Entropy, B.t.u./(lb.)(°R.)		Temp., °F.	Abs. pressure, lb./sq. in.	Volume, cu. ft./lb.		Enthalpy, B.t.u./lb.		Entropy, B.t.u./(lb.)(°R.)	
		Liquid	Vapor	Liquid	Vapor	Liquid	Vapor			Liquid	Vapor	Liquid	Vapor	Liquid	Vapor
t	p	v_f	v_g	h_f	h_g	s_f	s_g	t	p	v_f	v_g	h_f	h_g	s_f	s_g
−60	5.55	0.02278	44.73	−21.2	589.6	−0.0517	1.4769	24	52.59	....	5.443	69.1	618.9	.1528	1.2897
−50	7.67	.02299	33.08	−10.6	593.7	− .0256	1.4497	28	57.28	....	5.021	73.5	619.9	.1618	1.2825
−40	10.41	.02322	24.86	0.0	597.6	.0000	1.4242	32	62.29	....	4.637	77.9	621.0	.1708	1.2755
−30	13.90	....	18.97	10.7	601.4	.0250	1.4001	36	67.63	....	4.289	82.3	622.0	.1797	1.2686
−20	18.30	.02369	14.68	21.4	605.0	.0497	1.3774	40	73.32	.02533	3.971	86.8	623.0	.1885	1.2618
−16	20.34	....	13.29	25.6	606.4	.0594	1.3686	50	89.19	.02564	3.294	97.9	625.2	.2105	1.2453
−12	22.56	....	12.06	30.0	607.8	.0690	1.3600	60	107.6	.02597	2.751	109.2	627.3	.2322	1.2294
− 8	24.97	....	10.97	34.3	609.2	.0786	1.3516	70	128.8	.02632	2.312	120.5	629.1	.2537	1.2140
− 4	27.59	....	9.991	38.6	610.5	.0880	1.3433	80	153.0	.02668	1.955	132.0	630.7	.2749	1.1991
0	30.42	.02419	9.116	42.9	611.8	.0975	1.3352	90	180.6	.02707	1.661	143.5	632.0	.2958	1.1846
4	33.47	....	8.333	47.2	613.0	.1069	1.3273	100	211.9	.02747	1.419	155.2	633.0	.3166	1.1705
8	36.77	....	7.629	51.6	614.3	.1162	1.3195	110	247.0	.02790	1.217	167.0	633.7	.3372	1.1566
12	40.31	....	6.996	56.0	615.5	.1254	1.3118	120	286.4	.02836	1.047	179.0	634.0	.3576	1.1427
16	44.12	....	6.425	60.3	616.6	.1346	1.3043	125	307.8	.02860	0.973	183.9	634.0	.3659	1.1372
20	48.21	.02474	5.910	64.7	617.8	.1437	1.2969								

* *U. S. Bur. Standards Circ.* 142, 1923.

Table 3-210. Superheated Ammonia*

v, volume, cu. ft./lb.; h, enthalpy, B.t.u./lb.; s, entropy, B.t.u./(lb.)(°R.)
Absolute pressure, lb. per sq. in. (saturation temperature, °F., in parentheses)

Temp., °F.	5 (−63.11)			7 (−52.88°)			10 (−41.34)			14 (−29.76)			18 (−20.61)		
	v	h	s	v	h	s	v	h	s	v	h	s	v	h	s
Sat.	49.31	588.5	1.4857	36.01	592.5	1.4574	25.81	597.1	1.4276	18.85	601.4	1.3996	14.90	604.8	1.3787
−50	51.05	595.2	1.5025	36.29	594.0	1.4611									
−40	52.36	600.3	1.5149	37.25	599.3	1.4739									
−30	53.67	605.4	1.5269	38.19	604.5	1.4861	26.58	603.2	1.4420						
−20	54.97	610.4	1.5385	39.13	609.6	1.4979	27.26	608.5	1.4542	19.33	606.8	1.4119	14.93	605.1	1.3795
−10	56.26	615.4	1.5498	40.07	614.7	1.5094	27.92	613.7	1.4659	19.82	612.2	1.4241	15.32	610.7	1.3921
0	57.55	620.4	1.5608	41.00	619.8	1.5206	28.58	618.9	1.4773	20.30	617.6	1.4358	15.70	616.2	1.4042
10	58.84	625.4	1.5716	41.93	624.9	1.5314	29.24	624.0	1.4884	20.78	622.8	1.4472	16.08	621.6	1.4158
20	60.12	630.4	1.5821	42.85	629.9	1.5421	29.90	629.1	1.4992	21.26	628.0	1.4582	16.46	626.9	1.4270
30	61.41	635.4	1.5925	43.77	635.0	1.5525	30.55	634.2	1.5097	21.73	633.2	1.4688	16.83	632.2	1.4380
40	62.69	640.4	1.6026	44.69	640.0	1.5627	31.20	639.3	1.5200	22.20	638.4	1.4793	17.20	637.5	1.4486
50	63.96	645.5	1.6125	45.61	645.0	1.5727	31.85	644.4	1.5301	22.67	643.6	1.4896	17.57	642.7	1.4590
60	65.24	650.5	1.6223	46.53	650.1	1.5825	32.49	649.5	1.5400	23.14	648.7	1.4996	17.94	647.9	1.4691
70	66.51	655.5	1.6319	47.44	655.2	1.5921	33.14	654.6	1.5497	23.60	653.9	1.5094	18.30	653.1	1.4790
80	67.79	660.6	1.6413	48.36	660.2	1.6016	33.78	659.7	1.5593	24.06	659.0	1.5191	18.67	658.4	1.4887

* *U. S. Bur. Standards Circ.* 142, 1923.

For a *T-S* diagram, 195° to 580°K., 1 to 1100 atm., see Davies, "Thermodynamic Functions of Gases," vol. 1, p. 88, Butterworth, London, 1956. A wall-sized reproduction of this diagram is obtainable from Butterworth & Co. (Canada), Ltd. The publication "Properties of Commonly Used Refrigerants," Air Conditioning & Refrigeration Institute, Washington, D.C., gives data for many more pressures and temperatures than can be tabulated here. For a *H-P* diagram, 5 to 200 lb./sq. in. abs., −40° to 160°F., see Baker, "Technology of Heat," Longmans, London, 1956. Kazarnowsky and Karapetyants, *J. Phys. Chem. U.S.S.R.*, **17**, 172 (1943) give data from 20 to 1000 atm., 150° to 300°C. For a bibliography of work on the thermodynamic, physical, and chemical properties as well as more applied studies see Phillips, White, *et al.*, *Ohio State Univ. Rept.*, August, 1952, p. 176.

Table 3-210. Properties of Superheated Ammonia*—(*Continued*)

Temp. °F.	5 (−63.11)			7 (−52.88°)			10 (−41.34)			14 (−29.76)			18 (−20.61)		
	v	h	s	v	h	s	v	h	s	v	h	s	v	h	s
90	69.06	665.6	1.6506	49.27	665.3	1.6110	34.42	664.8	1.5687	24.53	664.2	1.5285	19.03	663.6	1.4983
100	70.33	670.7	1.6598	50.18	670.4	1.6202	35.07	670.0	1.5779	24.99	669.4	1.5378	19.39	668.8	1.5077
110	71.60	675.8	1.6689	51.09	675.5	1.6292	35.71	675.1	1.5870	25.45	674.5	1.5470	19.75	674.0	1.5169
120	72.87	680.9	1.6778	52.00	680.7	1.6382	36.35	680.3	1.5960	25.91	679.7	1.5560	20.11	679.2	1.5260
130	74.14	686.1	1.6865	52.91	685.8	1.6470	36.99	685.4	1.6049	26.37	684.9	1.5649	20.47	684.4	1.5349
140	75.41	691.2	1.6952	53.82	691.0	1.6557	37.62	690.6	1.6136	26.83	690.1	1.5737	20.83	689.7	1.5438
150	76.68	696.4	1.7038	54.73	696.2	1.6643	38.26	695.8	1.6222	27.29	695.4	1.5824	21.19	694.9	1.5525
160	77.95	701.6	1.7122	55.63	701.4	1.6727	38.90	701.1	1.6307	27.74	700.6	1.5909	21.54	700.2	1.5610
170	79.21	706.8	1.7206	56.54	706.6	1.6811	39.54	706.3	1.6391	28.20	705.9	1.5993	21.90	705.5	1.5695
180	80.48	712.1	1.7289	57.45	711.9	1.6894	40.17	711.6	1.6474	28.66	711.2	1.6076	22.26	710.8	1.5778
190	.....	.....	.....	.....	.....	.....	40.81	716.9	1.6556	29.11	716.5	1.6159	22.61	716.1	1.5861
200	.....	.....	.....	.....	.....	.....	41.45	722.2	1.6637	29.57	721.8	1.6240	22.97	721.4	1.5943
220	.....	.....	.....	.....	.....	.....	.....	.....	.....	.....	.....	.....	23.68	732.2	1.6103

Temp., °F.	24 (−9.58)			30 (−0.57)			38 (9.42)			48 (19.80)		
	v	h	s	v	h	s	v	h	s	v	h	s
Sat.	11.39	608.6	1.3549	9.236	611.6	1.3364	7.396	614.7	1.3168	5.934	617.7	1.2973
0	11.67	614.1	1.3670	9.250	611.9	1.3371						
10	11.96	619.7	1.3791	9.492	617.8	1.3497	7.407	615.0	1.3175			
20	12.25	625.2	1.3907	9.731	623.5	1.3618	7.603	621.0	1.3301	5.937	617.8	1.2976
30	12.54	630.7	1.4019	9.966	629.1	1.3733	7.795	626.9	1.3422	6.096	624.0	1.3103
40	12.82	636.1	1.4128	10.20	634.6	1.3845	7.983	632.6	1.3538	6.251	630.0	1.3225
50	13.11	641.4	1.4234	10.43	640.1	1.3953	8.170	638.3	1.3650	6.404	635.9	1.3341
60	13.39	646.7	1.4337	10.65	645.5	1.4059	8.353	643.8	1.3758	6.554	641.6	1.3453
70	13.66	652.0	1.4438	10.88	650.9	1.4161	8.535	649.3	1.3863	6.702	647.3	1.3561
80	13.94	657.3	1.4537	11.10	656.2	1.4261	8.716	654.8	1.3965	6.848	652.9	1.3666
90	14.22	662.6	1.4634	11.33	661.6	1.4359	8.895	660.2	1.4065	6.993	658.5	1.3768
100	14.49	667.8	1.4729	11.55	666.9	1.4456	9.073	665.6	1.4163	7.137	664.0	1.3868
110	14.76	673.1	1.4822	11.77	672.2	1.4550	9.250	671.0	1.4258	7.280	669.5	1.3965
120	15.04	678.4	1.4914	11.99	677.5	1.4642	9.426	676.4	1.4352	7.421	675.0	1.4061
130	15.31	683.6	1.5004	12.21	682.9	1.4733	9.602	681.8	1.4444	7.562	680.5	1.4154
140	15.58	688.9	1.5093	12.43	688.2	1.4823	9.776	687.2	1.4534	7.702	685.9	1.4246
150	15.85	694.2	1.5180	12.65	693.5	1.4911	9.950	692.6	1.4623	7.842	691.4	1.4336
160	16.12	699.5	1.5266	12.87	698.8	1.4998	10.12	698.0	1.4711	7.981	696.8	1.4425
170	16.39	704.8	1.5352	13.08	704.2	1.5083	10.30	703.3	1.4797	8.119	702.3	1.4512
180	16.66	710.2	1.5436	13.30	709.6	1.5168	10.47	708.7	1.4883	8.257	707.7	1.4598
190	16.93	715.5	1.5518	13.52	714.9	1.5251	10.64	714.2	1.4966	8.395	713.2	1.4683
200	17.20	720.9	1.5600	13.73	720.3	1.5334	10.81	719.6	1.5049	8.532	718.7	1.4766
220	17.73	731.7	1.5761	14.16	731.1	1.5495	11.16	730.5	1.5212	8.805	729.6	1.4930
240	18.27	742.6	1.5919	14.59	742.0	1.5653	11.50	741.4	1.5371	9.077	740.6	1.5090
260	.....	.....	.....	15.02	753.0	1.5808	11.84	752.4	1.5526	9.348	751.7	1.5246
280	.....	.....	.....	.....	.....	.....	12.18	763.5	1.5678	9.619	762.9	1.5399
300	.....	.....	.....	.....	.....	.....	.....	.....	.....	9.888	774.1	1.5548

Temp., °F.	60 (30.21)			80 (44.40)			100 (56.05)			120 (66.02)		
	v	h	s	v	h	s	v	h	s	v	h	s
Sat.	4.805	620.5	1.2787	3.655	624.0	1.2545	2.952	626.5	1.2356	2.476	628.4	1.2201
30												
40	4.933	626.8	1.2913	.....	.....	.....	.....	.....	.....	.....	.....	.....
50	5.060	632.9	1.3035	3.712	627.7	1.2619	.....	.....	.....	.....	.....	.....
60	5.184	639.0	1.3152	3.812	634.3	1.2745	2.985	629.3	1.2409	.....	.....	.....
70	5.307	644.9	1.3265	3.909	640.6	1.2866	3.068	636.0	1.2539	2.505	631.3	1.2255
80	5.428	650.7	1.3373	4.005	646.7	1.2981	3.149	642.6	1.2661	2.576	638.3	1.2386
90	5.547	656.4	1.3479	4.098	652.8	1.3092	3.227	649.0	1.2778	2.645	645.0	1.2510
100	5.665	662.1	1.3581	4.190	658.7	1.3199	3.304	655.2	1.2891	2.712	651.6	1.2628
110	5.781	667.7	1.3681	4.281	664.6	1.3303	3.380	661.3	1.2999	2.778	658.0	1.2741
120	5.897	673.3	1.3778	4.371	670.4	1.3404	3.454	667.3	1.3104	2.842	664.2	1.2850
130	6.012	678.9	1.3873	4.460	676.1	1.3502	3.527	673.3	1.3206	2.905	670.4	1.2956
140	6.126	684.4	1.3966	4.548	681.8	1.3598	3.600	679.2	1.3305	2.967	676.5	1.3058
150	6.239	689.9	1.4058	4.635	687.5	1.3692	3.672	685.0	1.3401	3.029	682.5	1.3157
160	6.352	695.5	1.4148	4.722	693.2	1.3784	3.743	690.8	1.3495	3.089	688.4	1.3254
170	6.464	701.0	1.4236	4.808	698.8	1.3874	3.813	696.6	1.3588	3.149	694.3	1.3348
180	6.576	706.5	1.4323	4.893	704.4	1.3963	3.883	702.3	1.3678	3.209	700.2	1.3441
190	6.687	712.0	1.4409	4.978	710.0	1.4050	3.952	708.0	1.3767	3.268	706.0	1.3531
200	6.798	717.5	1.4493	5.063	715.6	1.4136	4.021	713.7	1.3854	3.326	711.8	1.3620
210	6.909	723.1	1.4576	5.147	721.3	1.4220	4.090	719.4	1.3940	3.385	717.6	1.3707
220	7.019	728.6	1.4658	5.231	726.9	1.4304	4.158	725.1	1.4024	3.442	723.1	1.3793
230	.....	.....	.....	5.315	732.5	1.4386	4.226	730.8	1.4108	3.500	729.2	1.3877
240	7.238	739.7	1.4819	5.398	738.1	1.4467	4.294	736.5	1.4190	3.557	734.9	1.3960
250	.....	.....	.....	5.482	743.8	1.4547	4.361	742.2	1.4271	3.614	740.7	1.4042
260	7.457	750.9	1.4976	5.565	749.4	1.4626	4.428	747.9	1.4350	3.671	746.5	1.4123
270	.....	.....	.....	.....	.....	.....	.....	.....	.....	3.727	752.2	1.4202
280	7.675	762.1	1.5130	5.730	760.7	1.4781	4.562	759.4	1.4507	3.783	758.0	1.4281
290	.....	.....	.....	.....	.....	.....	.....	.....	.....	3.839	763.8	1.4359
300	7.892	773.3	1.5281	5.894	772.1	1.4933	4.695	770.8	1.4660	3.895	769.6	1.4435

Table 3-210. Superheated Ammonia*—(*Concluded*)

Temp., °F.	140 (74.79)			160 (82.64)			180 (89.78)		
	v	*h*	*s*	*v*	*h*	*s*	*v*	*h*	*s*
Sat.	2.132	629.9	1.2068	1.872	631.1	1.1952	1.667	632.0	1.1850
80	2.166	633.8	1.2140						
90	2.228	640.9	1.2272	1.914	636.6	1.2055	1.668	632.2	1.1853
100	2.288	647.8	1.2396	1.969	643.9	1.2186	1.720	639.9	1.1992
110	2.347	654.5	1.2515	2.023	651.0	1.2311	1.770	647.3	1.2123
120	2.404	661.1	1.2628	2.075	657.8	1.2429	1.818	654.4	1.2247
130	2.460	667.4	1.2738	2.125	664.4	1.2542	1.865	661.3	1.2364
140	2.515	673.7	1.2843	2.175	670.9	1.2652	1.910	668.0	1.2477
150	2.569	679.9	1.2945	2.224	677.2	1.2757	1.955	674.6	1.2586
160	2.622	686.0	1.3045	2.272	683.5	1.2859	1.999	681.0	1.2691
170	2.675	692.0	1.3141	2.319	689.7	1.2958	2.042	687.3	1.2792
180	2.727	698.0	1.3236	2.365	695.8	1.3054	2.084	693.6	1.2891
190	2.779	704.0	1.3328	2.411	701.9	1.3148	2.126	699.8	1.2987
200	2.830	709.9	1.3418	2.457	707.9	1.3240	2.167	705.9	1.3081
210	2.880	715.8	1.3507	2.502	713.9	1.3331	2.208	712.0	1.3172
220	2.931	721.6	1.3594	2.547	719.9	1.3419	2.248	718.1	1.3262
230	2.981	727.5	1.3679	2.591	725.8	1.3506	2.288	724.1	1.3350
240	3.030	733.3	1.3763	2.635	731.7	1.3591	2.328	730.1	1.3436
250	3.080	739.2	1.3846	2.679	737.6	1.3675	2.367	736.1	1.3521
260	3.129	745.0	1.3928	2.723	743.5	1.3757	2.407	742.0	1.3605
270	3.179	750.8	1.4008	2.766	749.4	1.3838	2.446	748.0	1.3687
280	3.227	756.7	1.4088	2.809	755.3	1.3919	2.484	753.9	1.3768
290	3.275	762.5	1.4166	2.852	761.2	1.3998	2.523	759.9	1.3847
300	3.323	768.3	1.4243	2.895	767.1	1.4076	2.561	765.8	1.3926
320	3.420	780.0	1.4395	2.980	778.9	1.4229	2.637	777.7	1.4081
340	.....	.....	.....	3.064	790.7	1.4379	2.713	789.6	1.4231

Temp., °F.	200 (96.34)			220 (102.42)			240 (108.09)			260 (113.42)			300 (123.21)		
	v	*h*	*s*	*v*	*h*	*s*	*v*	*h*	*s*	*v*	*h*	*s*	*v*	*h*	*s*
Sat.	1.502	632.7	1.1756	1.367	633.2	1.1671	1.253	633.6	1.1592	1.155	633.9	1.1518	0.999	634.0	1.1383
110	1.567	643.4	1.1947	1.400	639.4	1.1781	1.261	635.3	1.1621						
120	1.612	650.9	1.2077	1.443	647.3	1.1917	1.302	643.5	1.1764	1.182	639.5	1.1617			
130	1.656	658.1	1.2200	1.485	654.8	1.2045	1.342	651.3	1.1898	1.220	647.8	1.1757	1.023	640.1	1.1487
140	1.698	665.0	1.2317	1.525	662.0	1.2167	1.380	658.8	1.2025	1.257	655.6	1.1889	1.058	648.7	1.1632
150	1.740	671.8	1.2429	1.564	669.0	1.2281	1.416	666.1	1.2145	1.292	663.1	1.2014	1.091	656.9	1.1767
160	1.780	678.4	1.2537	1.601	675.8	1.2394	1.452	673.1	1.2259	1.326	670.4	1.2132	1.123	664.7	1.1894
170	1.820	684.9	1.2641	1.638	682.5	1.2501	1.487	680.0	1.2369	1.359	677.5	1.2245	1.153	672.2	1.2014
180	1.859	691.3	1.2742	1.675	689.1	1.2604	1.521	686.7	1.2475	1.391	684.4	1.2354	1.183	679.5	1.2129
190	1.897	697.7	1.2840	1.710	695.5	1.2704	1.554	693.3	1.2577	1.422	691.1	1.2458	1.211	686.5	1.2239
200	1.935	703.9	1.2935	1.745	701.9	1.2801	1.587	699.8	1.2677	1.453	697.7	1.2560	1.239	693.5	1.2344
210	1.972	710.1	1.3029	1.780	708.2	1.2896	1.619	706.2	1.2773	1.484	704.3	1.2658	1.267	700.3	1.2447
220	2.009	716.3	1.3120	1.814	714.4	1.2989	1.651	712.6	1.2867	1.514	710.7	1.2754	1.294	706.9	1.2546
230	2.046	722.4	1.3209	1.848	720.6	1.3079	1.683	718.9	1.2959	1.543	717.1	1.2847	1.320	713.5	1.2642
240	2.082	728.4	1.3296	1.881	726.8	1.3168	1.714	725.1	1.3049	1.572	723.4	1.2938	1.346	720.0	1.2736
250	2.118	734.5	1.3382	1.914	732.9	1.3255	1.745	731.3	1.3137	1.601	729.7	1.3027	1.372	726.5	1.2827
260	2.154	740.5	1.3467	1.947	739.0	1.3340	1.775	737.5	1.3224	1.630	736.0	1.3115	1.397	732.9	1.2917
270	2.189	746.5	1.3550	1.980	745.1	1.3424	1.805	743.6	1.3308	1.658	742.2	1.3200	1.422	739.2	1.3004
280	2.225	752.5	1.3631	2.012	751.1	1.3507	1.835	749.8	1.3392	1.686	748.4	1.3285	1.447	745.5	1.3090
290	2.260	758.5	1.3712	2.044	757.2	1.3588	1.865	755.9	1.3474	1.714	754.5	1.3367	1.472	751.8	1.3175
300	2.295	764.5	1.3791	2.076	763.2	1.3668	1.895	762.0	1.3554	1.741	760.7	1.3449	1.496	758.1	1.3257
320	2.364	776.5	1.3947	2.140	775.3	1.3825	1.954	774.1	1.3712	1.796	772.9	1.3608	1.544	770.5	1.3419
340	2.432	788.5	1.4099	2.203	787.4	1.3978	2.012	786.3	1.3866	1.850	785.2	1.3763	1.592	782.9	1.3576
360	2.500	800.5	1.4247	2.265	799.5	1.4127	2.069	798.4	1.4016	1.904	797.4	1.3914	1.639	795.3	1.3729
380	2.568	812.5	1.4392	2.327	811.6	1.4273	2.126	810.6	1.4163	1.957	809.6	1.4062	1.686	807.7	1.3878
400	.....	.....	.....	.....	.....	.....	.....	.....	.....	2.009	821.9	1.4206	1.732	820.1	1.4024

* *U. S. Bur. Standards Circ.* 142, 1923.

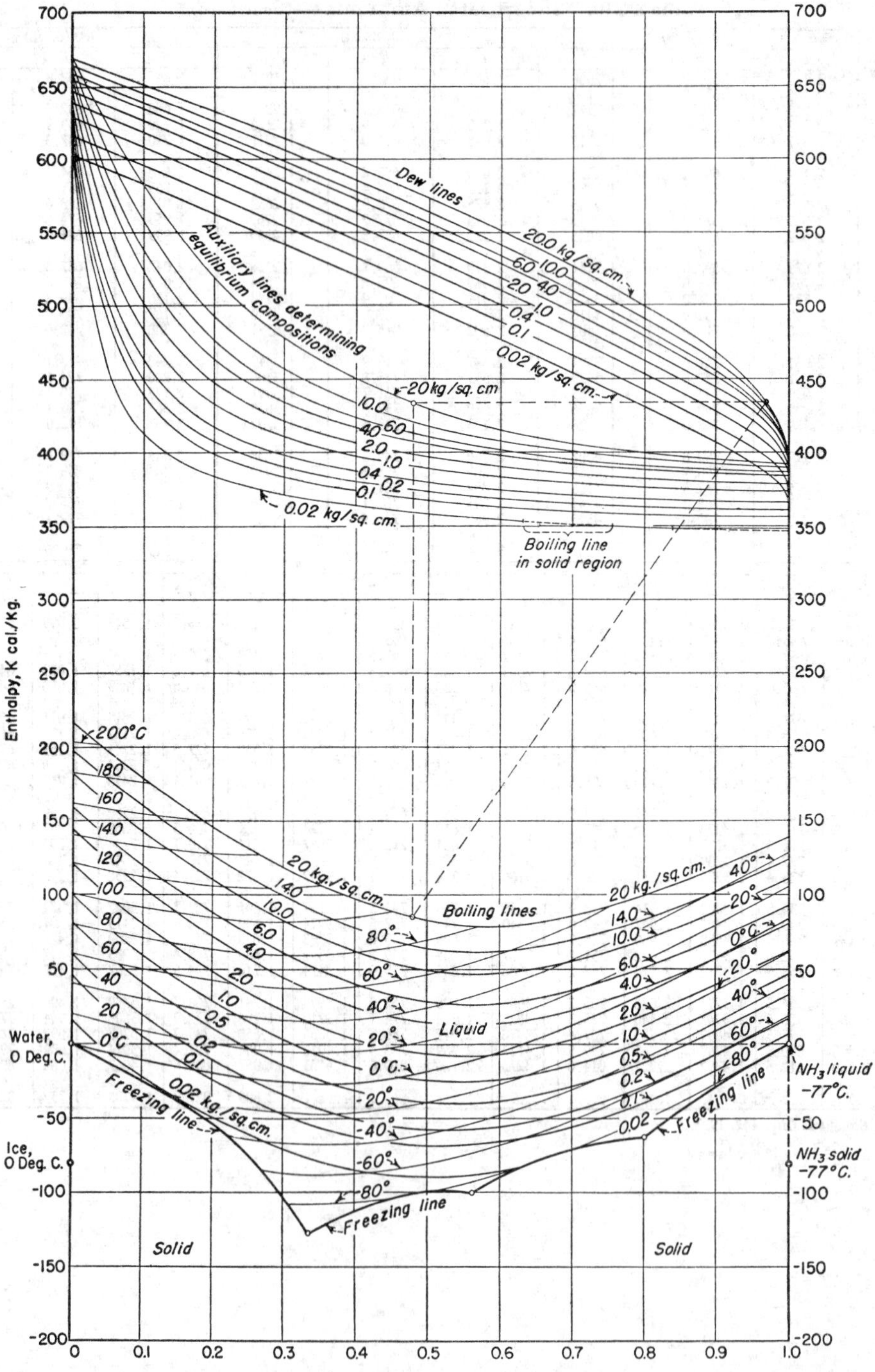

FIG. 3-16. Enthalpy-concentration diagram for aqueous ammonia. Reference states: Enthalpies of liquid water at 0°C. and liquid ammonia at −77°C. are zero. Note: In order to determine equilibrium compositions, a vertical may be erected from any liquid composition on any boiling line and its intersection with the appropriate auxiliary line determined. A horizontal from this intersection will establish the equilibrium vapor composition on the appropriate dew line. An example at 48 per cent ammonia and 20 kg./sq. cm. is indicated. (*Bosnjakovic, "Technische Thermodynamik," T. Steinkopff, Leipzig,* 1935.)

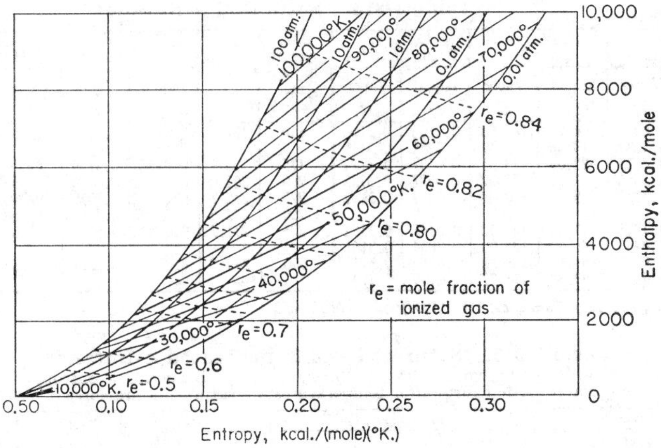

FIG. 3-17. Mollier diagram for argon in the plasma region. (*Bosnjakovic, Springe, et al., "Thermodynamic and Transport Properties of Gases, Liquids and Solids," p. 470, A.S.M.E., N.Y.*, 1959. *Reproduced by permission. Copyright* 1959, *McGraw-Hill Book Co., Inc.*) For a *T-S* diagram, 70° to 600°K., 0.1 to 6000 atm., see Din, "Thermodynamic Functions of Gases," vol. 2, p. 180, Butterworth, London, 1956. Tabulated data are also given for most of this range. A wall-sized reproduction of this diagram is available from Butterworth & Co. (Canada), Ltd. Tabulated data for the gas only are given by Hilsenrath *et al., N.B.S. Circ.* 564, 1955 (to 100 atm., 5000°K.). For ideal-gas functions to 6000°K. see Huff, Gordon, *et al., N.A.C.A. Rept.* 1037, 1951. Other tabulated data to 1050 atm., 0° to −140°C., are given by Michels, Levelt, *et al., Physica*, **24,** 769 (1958).

Table 3-211. Benzene

Bal' yan, *J. Appl. Chem. U.S.S.R.*, **13,** 1182 (1940); **18,** 12 (1941) (*T-S*, *H-T* diagrams, equations for properties). Kobe and Long, *Petrol. Refiner*, **28,** 145 (1949) (equations for C_p-*T*, *H-T*). Maxwell, "Data Book of Hydrocarbons," Van Nostrand, Princeton, N.J., 1951. Organick and Studhalter, *Chem. Eng. Progress*, **44,** 847 (1948) (calc. *dH/dP*, *dS/dP*). Riediger, *Chem.-Ing.-Tech.*, **23,** 272 (1951) (to 50 atm., 289°C.).

Table 3-212. Boron Compounds

For reviews of recent work on boron compounds see "Thermodynamic and Transport Properties of Gases, Liquids and Solids," A.S.M.E., New York, 1959.

Table 3-213. Saturated 1,3-Butadiene*

Temp., °F.	Abs. pressure, lb/sq. in.	Volume, cu. ft./lb.		Enthalpy, B.t.u./lb.		Entropy, B.t.u./(lb.)(°R)	
		Liquid	Vapor	Liquid	Vapor	Liquid	Vapor
t	p	v_f	v_g	h_f	h_g	s_f	s_g
−164.05	0.010	0.02097	5706.	122.61	341.8	0.5904	1.3317
−160	.013	.02104	4504.	124.44	342.7	.5973	1.3256
−140	.045	.02136	1406.	133.55	347.3	.6267	1.2953
−120	.130	.02170	516.5	142.72	352.0	.6546	1.2707
−100	.329	.02205	216.7	151.96	356.9	.6810	1.2509
− 90	.500	.02224	146.4	156.61	359.5	.6938	1.2425
− 80	.740	.02242	101.44	161.29	362.0	.7062	1.2350
− 70	1.071	.02261	71.88	165.99	364.7	.7184	1.2283
− 60	1.516	.02280	52.00	170.72	367.3	.7304	1.2223
− 50	2.103	.02300	38.33	175.49	370.0	.7422	1.2170
− 40	2.867	.02320	28.75	180.29	372.7	.7538	1.2123
− 30	3.841	.02341	21.91	185.14	375.5	.7652	1.2081
− 20	5.068	.02362	16.94	190.02	378.2	.7764	1.2045
− 10	6.592	.02384	13.27	194.96	381.0	.7875	1.2013
0	8.461	.02406	10.525	199.94	383.9	.7984	1.1985

Temp., °F.	Abs. pressure, lb/sq. in.	Volume, cu ft./lb.		Enthalpy, B.t.u./lb.		Entropy, B.t.u./(lb.)(°R)	
		Liquid	Vapor	Liquid	Vapor	Liquid	Vapor
t	p	v_f	v_g	h_f	h_g	s_f	s_g
10	10.728	0.02429	8.441	204.97	386.7	.8092	1.1962
20	13.45	.02453	6.840	210.05	389.6	.8199	1.1942
30	16.68	.02478	5.595	215.19	392.4	.8305	1.1925
40	20.49	.02503	4.617	220.40	395.3	.8410	1.1910
50	24.94	.02529	3.840	225.66	398.2	.8514	1.1899
60	30.11	.02557	3.218	231.00	401.1	.8617	1.1890
70	36.05	.02585	2.715	236.40	404.0	.8719	1.1883
80	42.84	.02614	2.305	241.88	406.8	.8821	1.1878
90	50.57	.02645	1.968	247.43	409.7	.8922	1.1874
100	59.30	.02678	1.689	253.0	412.5	.9023	1.1872
120	80.11	.02747	1.262	264.6	418.2	.9223	1.1873
140	105.93	.02823	0.9576	276.4	423.6	.9422	1.1877
160	137.4	.02909	.7362	288.6	428.9	.9620	1.1883
180	175.4	.03007	.5715	301.3	433.9	.9817	1.1891
200	220.5	.03121	.4465	315.	439.	1.001	1.190

* C. H. Meyers, C. S. Cragoe, and E. F. Mueller, *J. Research N. B. S.* **39,** 507 (1947).

Table 3-214. Saturated n-Butane*

Abs. pressure, lb./sq. in.	Temp., °F.	Volume, cu. ft./lb.		Enthalpy, B.t.u./lb.		Entropy, B.t.u./(lb.)(°R.)		Abs. pressure, lb./sq. in.	Temp., °F.	Volume, cu. ft./lb.		Enthalpy, B.t.u./lb.		Entropy, B.t.u./(lb.)(°R.)	
		Liquid	Vapor	Liquid	Vapor	Liquid	Vapor			Liquid	Vapor	Liquid	Vapor	Liquid	Vapor
p	t	v_f	v_g	h_f	h_g	s_f	s_g	p	t	v_f	v_g	h_f	h_g	s_f	s_g
30	67.6	0.02747	3.027	4.20	163.88	0.0106	0.3108	150	177.3	0.03183	0.6203	74.30	198.33	0.1267	0.3218
40	84.3	0.02802	2.301	13.80	169.11	0.0284	0.3116								
50	98.0	0.02850	1.8568	22.09	173.51	0.0407	0.3124	175	190.3	0.03264	0.5259	83.17	202.14	0.1408	0.3237
60	109.7	0.02891	1.5556	29.29	177.22	0.0527	0.3132	200	202.0	0.03342	0.4536	91.55	205.29	0.1534	0.3252
70	120.1	0.02926	1.3377	35.65	180.49	0.0639	0.3142	225	212.7	0.03422	0.3959	99.40	207.88	0.1646	0.3261
								250	222.5	0.03497	0.3489	106.68	209.97	0.1755	0.3267
80	129.3	0.02960	1.1728	41.50	183.38	0.0741	0.3152	275	231.7	0.03580	0.3095	113.63	211.68	0.1856	0.3270
90	137.7	0.02993	1.0433	46.80	186.00	0.0834	0.3161								
100	145.5	0.03025	0.9393	51.89	188.42	0.0919	0.3172	300	240.2	0.03671	0.2761	120.37	212.97	0.1950	0.3270
125	162.6	0.03104	0.7492	63.70	193.77	0.1105	0.3196								

* Sage, Webster, and Lacey, *Ind. Eng. Chem.*, **29**, 1188 (1937); with permission.

Table 3-215. Saturated and Superheated n-Butane*

p, absolute pressure, lb./sq. in.; v, volume, cu. ft./lb.; h, enthalpy, B.t.u./lb.; s, entropy, B.t.u./(lb.)(°R.)
Parenthetic figures after temperatures are saturation pressures

p	70°F. (31.30)			100°F. (51.62)			130°F. (80.78)			160°F. (120.99)		
	v	h	s	v	h	s	v	h	s	v	h	s
Satd. vapor	2.907	164.65	0.3109	1.7999	174.18	0.3125	1.1617	183.52	0.3152	0.7745	192.94	0.3192
Satd. liquid	0.02754	5.67	.01075	0.02856	23.32	.04295	0.02963	42.00	.07518	.03090	61.84	.10764
14.696	6.451	166.97	.3396	6.847	178.48	.3607	7.237	190.38	.3814	7.627	202.67	.4017
20	4.680	166.36	.3279	4.981	177.98	.3492	5.273	189.94	.3701	5.564	202.29	.3905
30	3.043	164.92	.3125	3.256	176.96	.3345	3.458	189.07	.3556	3.659	201.51	.3762
40	....	....	....	2.390	175.78	.3232	2.549	188.11	.3447	2.704	200.71	.3655
50	....	....	....	1.8669	174.45	.3139	2.003	187.07	.3359	2.131	199.87	.3570
60	....	....	....	....	....	....	1.6358	186.00	.3283	1.7477	198.97	.3497
70	....	....	....	....	....	....	1.3735	184.83	.3215	1.4742	189.05	.3433
80	....	....	....	....	....	....	1.1751	183.62	.3157	1.2681	197.10	.3376
90	....	....	....	....	....	....	....	....	....	1.1072	196.11	.3323
100	....	....	....	....	....	....	....	....	....	0.9783	195.11	.3274

p	190°F. (174.4)			220°F. (243.5)			250°F. (330.4)		
	v	h	s	v	h	s	v	h	s
Satd. vapor	0.5275	202.06	0.3237	0.3504	209.44	0.3266	0.2417	214.23	0.3267
Satd. liquid	.03262	82.94	.14033	.03476	105.11	.17311	.03797	128.21	.2055
14.696	8.013	215.33	.4217	8.398	228.38	.4414	8.780	241.82	.4607
20	5.851	215.00	.4105	6.136	228.10	.4302	6.419	241.59	.4496
30	3.855	214.35	.3964	4.048	227.54	.4163	4.240	241.10	.4358
40	2.855	213.65	.3859	3.003	226.96	.4060	3.149	240.59	.4256
50	2.255	212.94	.3776	2.377	226.35	.3978	2.4953	240.09	.4175
60	1.8548	212.18	.3706	1.9583	225.71	.3910	2.059	239.55	.4109
70	1.5688	211.38	.3647	1.6601	225.06	.3851	1.7485	238.98	.4051
80	1.3546	210.59	.3590	1.4365	224.37	.3799	1.5155	238.39	.4001
90	1.1867	209.76	.3541	1.2625	223.64	.3752	1.3340	237.78	.3955
100	1.0530	208.90	.3494	1.1232	222.89	.3708	1.1896	237.14	.3913
125	0.8095	206.68	.3390	0.8715	220.88	.3611	0.9286	235.45	.3819
150	.6461	204.36	.3305	.7022	218.72	.3525	.7535	233.62	.3740
175	....	....	....	.5791	216.42	.3445	.6270	231.61	.3669
200	....	....	....	.4844	213.99	.3370	.5303	229.41	.3600
225	....	....	....	.4082	211.41	.3306	.4530	227.03	.3533
250	....	....	....	....	....	....	.3901	224.46	.3468
275	....	....	....	....	....	....	.3366	221.66	.3405
300	....	....	....	....	....	....	.2904	218.56	.3343

* Sage, Webster, and Lacey, *Ind. Eng. Chem.*, **29**, 1188 (1937); with permission.

Prengle, Greenhaus, *et al.* *Chem. Eng. Progress*, **44**, 863 (1948) give data and a *H-P* diagram to 300 atm. 540°F. However, some of their entropy data are slightly in error and a revision was not available in time for insertion here.

Additional data for *n*-butane are contained in Benedict, Webb, *et al.*, *J. Chem. Phys.*, **8**, 334 (1940) (equation of state); Opfell, Schlinger, *et al.*, *Ind. Eng. Chem.*, vol. 46, 1954 (equation of state); Opfell, Sage, *et al.*, *Ind. Eng. Chem.*, **48**, 2069 (1956); Pitzer, *Ind. Eng. Chem.*, **36**, 829 (1944); Maxwell, "Data Book on Hydrocarbons," Van Nostrand, Princeton, N.J., 1951. "American Society of Refrigerating Engineers Data Book," 1955.

Table 3-216. Saturated Isobutane*

Abs. pressure, lb./sq. in.	Temp., °F.	Volume, cu. ft./lb.		Enthalpy, B.t.u./lb.		Entropy, B.t.u./(lb.)(°R.)		Abs. pressure, lb./sq. in.	Temp., °F.	Volume, cu. ft./lb.		Enthalpy, B.t.u./lb.		Entropy, B.t.u./(lb.)(°R.)	
		Liquid	Vapor	Liquid	Vapor	Liquid	Vapor			Liquid	Vapor	Liquid	Vapor	Liquid	Vapor
p	t	v_f	v_g	h_f	h_g	s_f	s_g	p	t	v	v	h	h	s	s
40	63.0	0.02838	2.210	1.64	146.4	0.0032	0.2803	200	178.3	.03412	.4305	73.94	181.0	.1259	.2938
50	76.5	.02888	1.7813	9.30	151.11	.0173	.2818	225	188.7	.03496	.3769	81.42	183.8	.1373	.2951
60	88.1	.02932	1.4904	16.01	154.82	.02957	.2831	250	198.3	.03578	.3327	88.51	185.8	.1478	.2957
70	98.2	.02973	1.2796	21.96	157.97	.0403	.2841	275	207.3	.03663	.2954	95.26	187.3	.1578	.2959
80	107.3	.03013	1.1198	27.34	160.81	.0499	.2852	300	215.6	.03748	.2633	101.7	188.7	.1671	.2959
90	115.5	.03049	0.9947	32.37	163.33	.0586	.2862	325	223.5	.03838	.2325	108.0	189.6	.1760	.2954
100	123.8	.03088	.8949	37.57	165.73	.0674	.2871	350	231.0	.03935	.2110	114.1	189.6	.1846	.2941
125	139.8	.03167	.7103	47.89	170.44	.0844	.2889	375	238.1	.04036	.1888	120.1	189.5	.1928	.2920
150	154.2	.03245	.5864	57.36	174.49	.0998	.2906	400	244.9	.04143	.1686	126.1	188.7	.2009	.2897
175	167.0	.03331	.4979	66.06	178.03	.1136	.2923								

* Sage and Lacey, *Ind. Eng. Chem.*, **30**, 673 (1938); with permission.

Table 3-217. Superheated Isobutane*

p, absolute pressure, lb./sq. in.; *v*, volume, cu. ft./lb.; *h*, enthalpy, B.t.u./lb.; *s*, entropy, B.t.u./(lb.)(°R.)
Parenthetic figures after temperatures are saturation pressures

p	70°F. (44.97)			100°F. (71.91)			130°F. (109.80)			160°F. (161.10)		
	v	*h*	*s*	*v*	*h*	*s*	*v*	*h*	*s*	*v*	*h*	*s*
Satd. vapor	1.975	148.94	0.2181	1.2463	158.51	0.2843	0.8123	167.57	0.2877	0.5437	176.10	0.2914
Satd. liquid	0.02863	5.58	.01040	0.02981	23.03	.04216	.03118	41.56	.07399	.03285	61.27	.10607
10	9.607	152.68	.3374	10.175	164.49	.3590	10.733	176.50	.3800	11.291	188.92	.4005
14.696	6.482	152.32	.3238	6.872	164.17	.3456	7.257	176.25	.3666	7.641	188.71	.3872
20	4.715	151.88	.3128	5.008	163.76	.3346	5.294	175.94	.3558	5.578	188.45	.3765
30	3.075	......	....	3.279	......	....	3.476	......	....	3.669	......	......
40	2.249	149.68	.2862	2.411	162.09	.3090	2.565	174.57	.3308	2.715	187.30	.3518
50	....	......	....	1.888	......	....	2.017	......	....	2.140	......	......
60	....	......	....	1.5379	159.93	.2945	1.6508	172.91	.3151	1.7575	185.91	.3366
80	....	......	....	....	......	....	1.1905	170.94	.3030	1.2781	184.30	.3251
100	....	......	....	....	......	....	0.9121	168.74	.2926	0.9888	182.64	.3154
125	....	......	....	....	......	....	....	......	....	.7558	180.28	.3048
150	....	......	....	....	......	....	....	......	....	.5983	177.48	.2953

p	190°F. (229.3)			220°F. (313.7)			250°F. (419.7)		
	v	*h*	*s*	*v*	*h*	*s*	*v*	*h*	*s*
Satd. vapor	0.3687	184.1	0.2953	0.2476	189.2	0.2958	0.154	187.9	0.2881
Satd. liquid	0.03506	82.37	.13867	.03799	105.2	.17207	.04228	130.4	.2072
10	11.854	201.70	.4207	12.410	214.85	.4404	12.965	228.39	.3600
14.696	8.023	201.52	.4074	8.403	214.71	.4273	8.783	228.28	.4468
20	5.860	201.30	.3968	6.141	214.53	.4167	6.422	228.14	.4363
30	3.861	......	....	4.051	......	....	4.240	......	......
40	2.861	200.35	.3724	3.006	213.66	.3925	3.150	227.49	.4123
50	2.260	......	....	2.379	......	....	2.497	......	......
60	1.8600	199.15	.3575	1.9619	212.66	.3779	2.061	226.66	.3979
80	1.3604	197.77	.3463	1.4404	211.49	.3670	1.5178	225.67	.3874
100	1.0600	196.23	.3371	1.1278	210.16	.3582	1.1925	224.54	.3788
125	0.8183	194.08	.3272	0.8771	208.31	.3487	0.9322	222.96	.3697
150	.6557	191.71	.3183	.7091	206.26	.3403	.7585	221.20	.3617
175	.5391	189.40	.3103	.5888	204.03	.3326	.6355	219.27	.3545
200	.4505	187.0	.3030	.4977	201.64	.3254	.5392	217.19	.3477
225	.3794	184.5	.2963	.4252	199.08	.3185	.4652	214.97	.3413
250	....	......	....	.3649	196.35	.3118	.4048	212.61	.3352
275	....	......	....	.3139	193.45	.3053	.3541	210.1	.3292
300	....	......	....	.2696	190.7	.2999	.3111	207.5	.3232
350	....	......	....	....	......	....	.2416	201.3	.3113
400	....	......	....	....	......	....	.187	192.6	.2963

* Sage and Lacey, *Ind. Eng. Chem.*, **30**, 673 (1938) with permission.
Beattie *et al.*, *J. Am. Chem. Soc.*, 64, 546 (1942) (*PVT*). Beattie, Marple, *et al.*, *J. Chem. Phys.*, **18**, 127, 1950 (*PVT*). Dana, Jenkins, *et al.*, *Refrig. Eng.*, **12**, 402 (1926) (vapor pressure, etc.). Curl and Pitzer, *Ind. Eng. Chem.*, **50**, 265 (1958) (calculated enthalpy values).

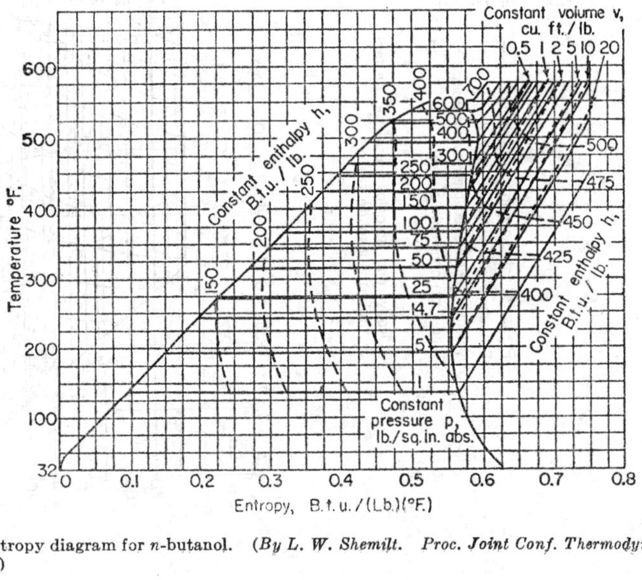

FIG. 3-18. Temperature-entropy diagram for *n*-butanol. (*By L. W. Shemilt. Proc. Joint Conf. Thermodynamic and Transport Properties of Fluids. London.* 1958.)

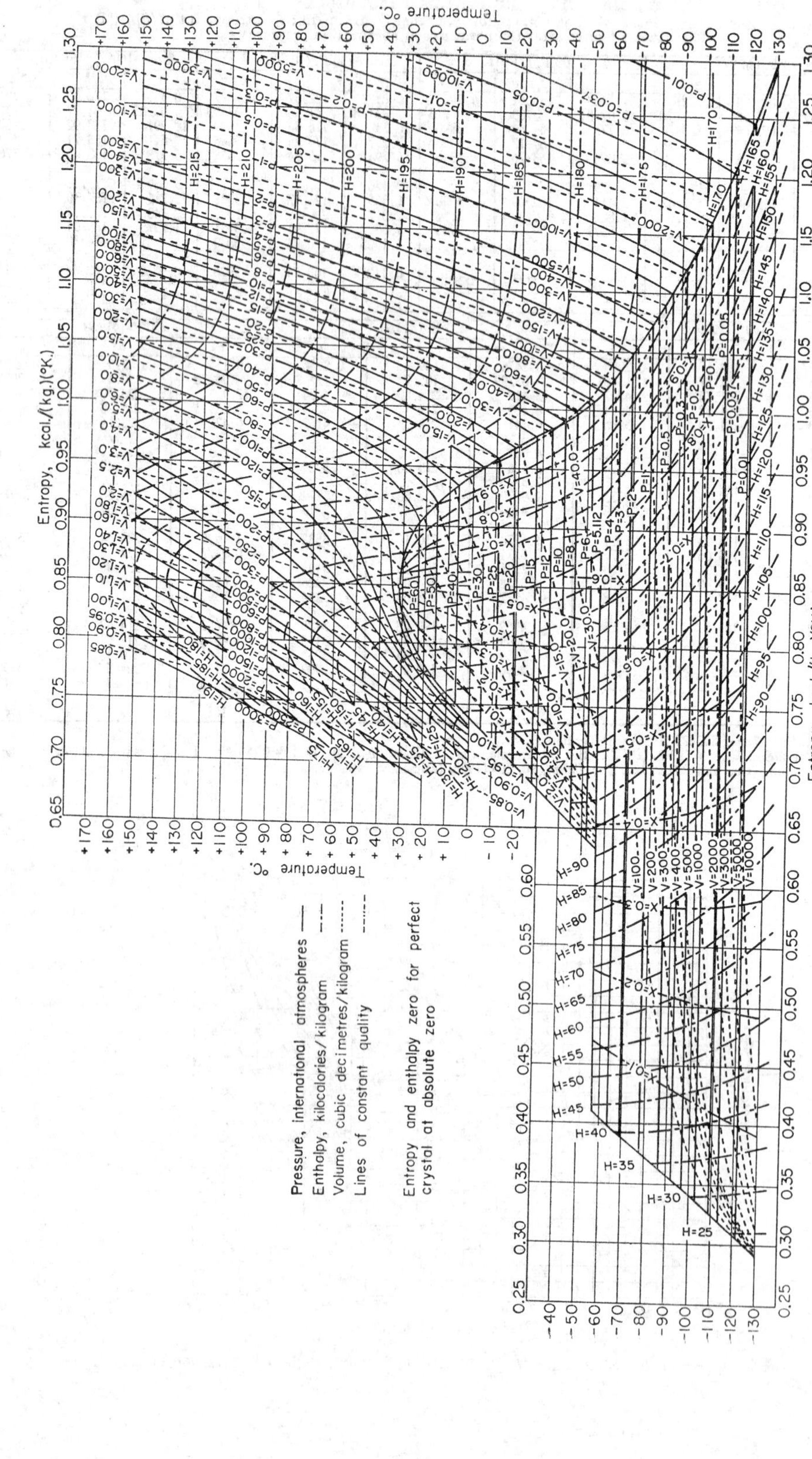

FIG. 3-19. Temperature-entropy diagram for carbon dioxide. [*From "Thermodynamic Functions of Gases," vol. 1, Butterworth, London,* 1956. *Copyright material. Reprinted by permission of the authors and publishers. A wall-sized reproduction of this diagram is obtainable from Butterworth & Co. (Canada), Ltd.*]

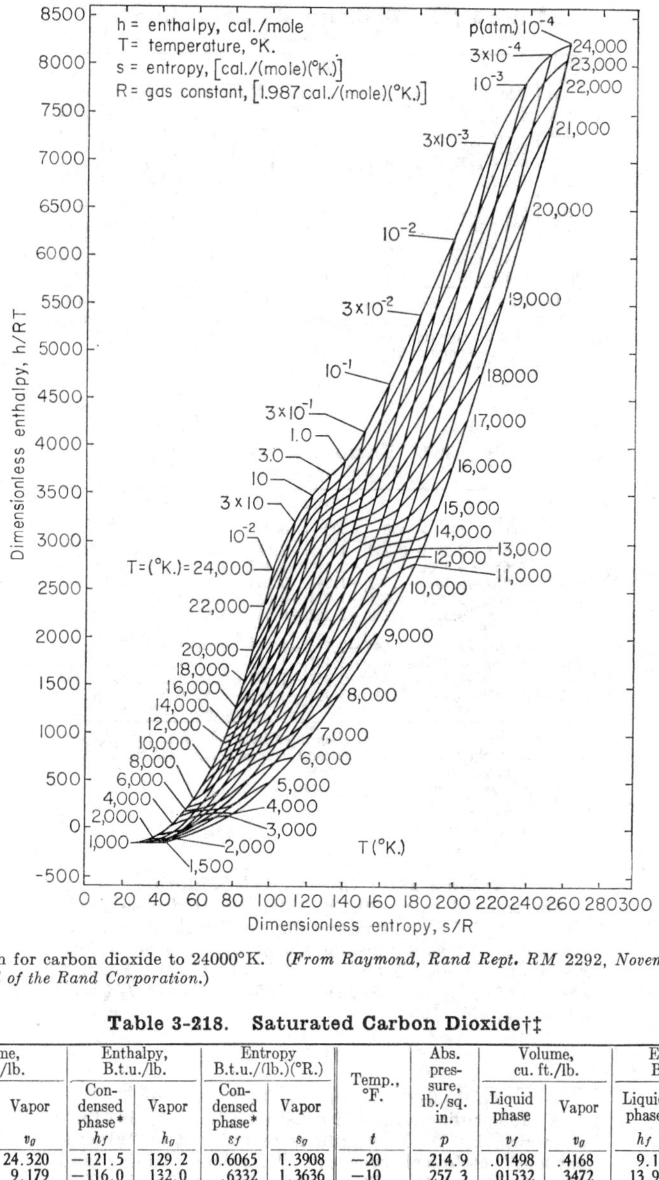

FIG. 3-20. Mollier diagram for carbon dioxide to 24000°K. *(From Raymond, Rand Rept. RM 2292, November, 1958. Reproduced by permission of the author and of the Rand Corporation.)*

Table 3-218. Saturated Carbon Dioxide†‡

Temp., °F.	Abs. pressure, lb./sq. in.	Volume, cu. ft./lb.		Enthalpy, B.t.u./lb.		Entropy B.t.u./(lb.)(°R.)	
		Condensed phase*	Vapor	Condensed phase*	Vapor	Condensed phase*	Vapor
t	p	v_f	v_g	h_f	h_g	s_f	s_g
−140	3.18	0.01008	24.320	−121.5	129.2	0.6065	1.3908
−120	8.90	.01018	9.179	−116.0	132.0	.6332	1.3636
−100	22.22	.01032	3.804	−110.1	134.3	.6403	1.3199
− 90	33.98	.01040	2.525	−106.7	135.1	.6499	1.3033
− 80	50.85	.01048	1.700	−102.5	135.7	.6607	1.2881
− 70	74.82	.01059	1.162	− 98.0	135.9	.6724	1.2726
− 69.9	75.10	.01059	1.157	− 97.9	135.9	.6725	1.2724
− 69.9	75.10	.01360	1.1570	− 13.7	135.7	.8885	1.2724
− 60	94.7	.01384	0.9270	− 9.2	136.6	.8997	1.2647
− 50	118.2	.01409	.7492	− 4.7	137.2	.9110	1.2572
− 40	145.8	.01437	.6113	.00	137.8	.9218	1.2503
− 30	177.8	.01466	.5029	4.5	138.2	.9325	1.2436

Temp., °F.	Abs. pressure, lb./sq. in.	Volume, cu. ft./lb.		Enthalpy, B.t.u./lb.		Entropy B.t.u./(lb.)(°R.)	
		Liquid phase	Vapor	Liquid phase	Vapor	Liquid phase	Vapor
t	p	v_f	v_g	h_f	h_g	s_f	s_g
−20	214.9	.01498	.4168	9.1	138.5	.9430	1.2372
−10	257.3	.01532	.3472	13.9	138.7	.9532	1.2303
0	305.5	0.1570	.2904	18.8	138.9	.9636	1.2247
10	360.2	.01614	.2437	24.0	138.7	.9744	1.2188
20	421.8	.01663	.2049	29.4	138.3	.9856	1.2127
30	490.8	.01719	.1722	35.4	137.8	.9976	1.2067
40	567.8	.01787	.1444	41.7	136.7	1.0092	1.1994
50	653.6	.01868	.1205	48.4	135.0	1.0218	1.1917
60	748.6	.01970	.0994	55.5	132.1	1.0353	1.1826
70	853.4	.02112	.08040	63.7	127.5	1.0500	1.1724
80	968.7	.02370	.06064	73.9	118.7	1.0694	1.1555
87.8	1069.4	.03454	.03454	97.0	97.0	1.1098	1.1098

* Above the solid line the condensed phase is solid; below the line it is liquid.
† "Refrigerating Data Book," 5th ed., American Society of Refrigerating Engineers, New York, 1942.
‡ $sf = 1.0$ at 32°F.
$hf = 36.7$ at 32°F.

For an extensive listing of work from 1935 to 1957 see Liley, *J. Chem. Eng. Data*, **4**, 238 (1959). In addition to the references listed there Cramer [*Chem.-Ing.-Tech.*, **27**, 484 (1955)] gives 44 references, a *T-S* diagram from −100° to 1000°C., to 12,000 atm., and a *H*-log *P* diagram from −50 to 175°C., to 3000 atm. Majumdar and Rustum [*Geochim. et Cosmochim. Acta*, **10**, 311 (1956)] give fugacities and free energies to 1000°K and 1400 bars. For ideal-gas functions to 6000°K. see Huff, Gordon, *et al.*, *N.A.C.A. Rept.* 1037, 1951. The data of Sweigert, Weber, and Allen appearing in the third edition of this handbook have been criticized by Granet and Kass, *Petrol. Refiner*, **31** (11), 137 (1952).

Table 3-219. Enthalpy of Carbon Dioxide*

H† (cal./mole)

Pressure, bars‡	Temp., °C.								
	200	300	400	500	600	700	800	900	1000
100	1546.8	2775.2	4001.5	5243.6	6512.7	7812.1	9135.6	10479.2	11841.4
200	1185.7	2552.5	3862.8	5151.9	6449.3	7770.9	9110.3	10466.2	11839.4
300	892.4	2367.2	3749.2	5081.2	6401.9	7740.6	9094.1	10461.9	11846.0
400	698.9	2221.1	3658.8	5029.5	6372.5	7726.2	9091.5	10470.3	11863.7
500	588.8	2112.0	3589.4	4989.8	6357.2	7725.9	9102.0	10489.9	11890.7
600	526.0	2040.2	3535.6	4958.6	6348.4	7733.6	9120.5	10518.5	11929.2
700	494.7	2000.0	3498.6	4938.7	6347.4	7747.5	9144.8	10554.5	11977.3
800	483.5	1982.2	3478.7	4928.4	6353.3	7766.7	9174.2	10595.7	12030.8
900	485.3	1978.5	3475.2	4929.3	6365.4	7790.9	9208.8	10641.0	12088.4
1000	496.7	1984.8	3484.3	4942.3	6384.3	7820.0	9248.0	10690.4	12149.4

* From Price, *Ind. Eng. Chem.* Reprinted from vol. 47, p. 1651, August, 1955. Copyright 1955 by the American Chemical Society and reprinted by permission of the copyright owner.

† Scale for zero point at 0°C. and 1 atm.

‡ 1 atm. = 1.01325 bars.

Table 3-220. Entropy of Carbon Dioxide*

S† (cal./mole-deg.)

Pressure, bars‡	Temp., °C.								
	200	300	400	500	600	700	800	900	1000
100	−4.617	−2.251	−0.289	1.429	2.977	4.384	5.674	6.871	7.987
200	−6.634	−4.000	−1.903	−0.118	1.466	2.896	4.201	5.410	6.535
300	−7.950	−5.107	−2.892	−1.047	0.566	2.015	3.334	4.553	5.687
400	−8.860	−5.927	−3.621	−1.723	−0.082	1.384	2.714	3.943	5.084
500	−9.503	−6.571	−4.200	−2.262	−0.590	0.892	2.233	3.470	4.617
600	−9.998	−7.084	−4.684	−2.715	−1.015	0.485	1.837	3.083	4.238
700	−10.394	−7.498	−5.093	−3.101	−1.377	0.139	1.501	2.757	3.923
800	−10.726	−7.843	−5.442	−3.437	−1.693	−0.162	1.210	2.476	3.652
900	−11.015	−8.142	−5.741	−3.730	−1.973	−0.428	0.954	2.229	3.415
1000	−11.271	−8.408	−6.002	−3.986	−2.222	−0.666	0.726	2.010	3.205

* From Price, *Ind. Eng. Chem.* Reprinted from vol. 47, p. 1651, August, 1955. Copyright 1955 by the American Chemical Society and reprinted by permission of the copyright owner.

† Scale for zero point at 0°C. and 1 atm.

‡ 1 atm. = 1.01325 bars.

Table 3-221. Carbon Tetrachloride

For some data at 20(10)120°F. see Hodgman (ed.), "Handbook of Chemistry and Physics," 40th ed., p. 2468, Chemical Rubber Publishing Co., 1958. For other data see Bernstein, *J. Chem. Phys.*, **24**, 911 (1956); Berring, *et al.*, *J. Chem. Phys.*, **23**, 1911 (1955); Spencer, *J. Chem. Phys.*, **25**, 357 (1956).

Table 3-222. Carbon Tetrafluoride

A Mollier diagram, −200°F. to 150°F., 5 to 594 lb./sq.in.abs., by W. F. Edgell, is reproduced in "Fluorocarbons" technical brochure, Minnesota Mining and Manufacturing Co., St. Paul, Minn., undated. This source also gives a small amount of other data.

Table 3-223. Carrene 7 (Azeotropic Mixture of CCl_2F_2 and $C_2H_4F_2$)

"Properties of Commonly-used Refrigerants," Air Conditioning & Refrigative Institute, Washington, D.C., 1957, lists thermodynamic properties and gives a H-log P diagram covering the range −40° to 450°F., 10 to 350 lb./sq.in.abs. Similar information, for −40° to 340°F., 10 to 260 lb./sq.in.abs., is given in the "American Society of Refrigerating Engineers Data Book," pp. 32.28–35, 1955. See also *World Refrig.*, **7**, 255, 369 (1956); and Gunther, "Refrigerating, Air Conditioning, and Cold Storage," Chilton, 1957, for further information.

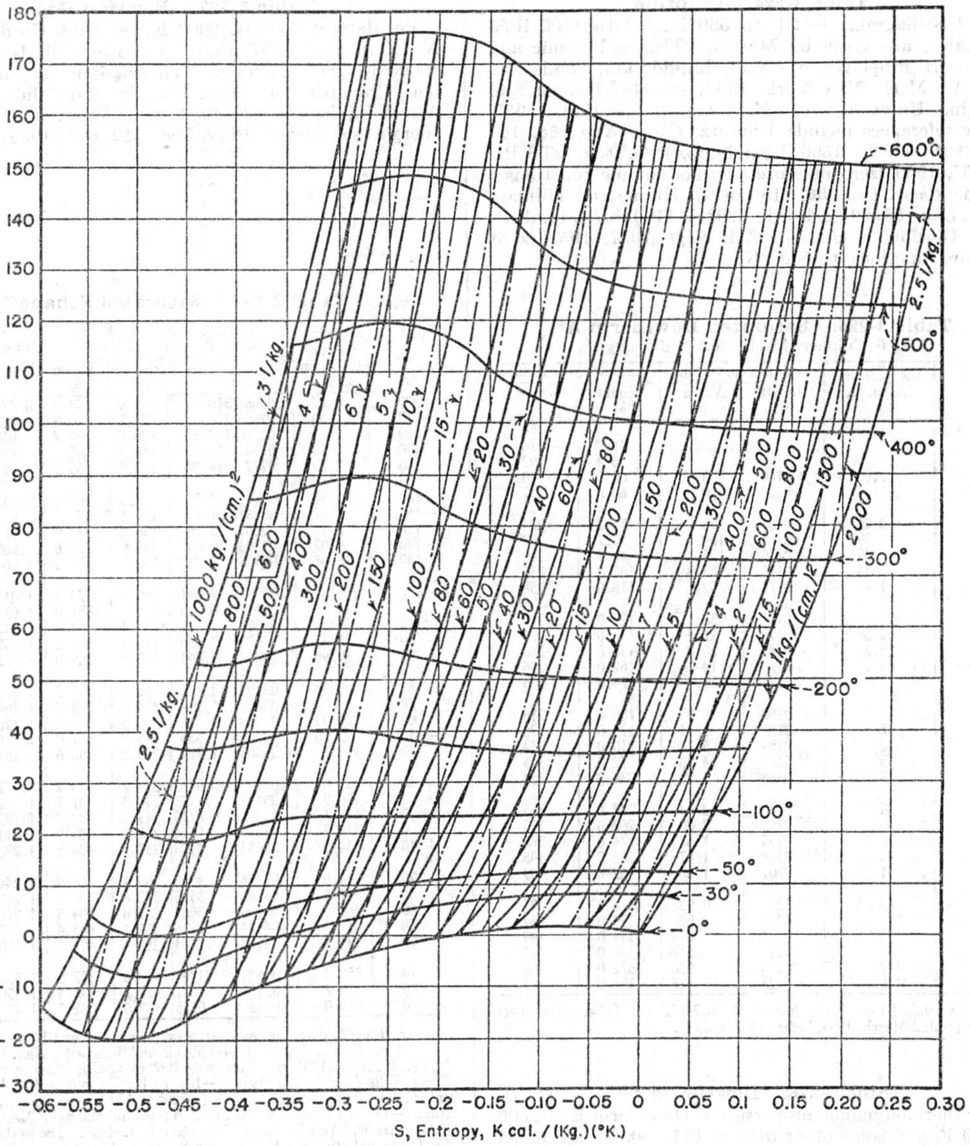

FIG. 3-21. Mollier chart for carbon monoxide. [*Guelpérine and Naiditch, Chimie & industrie*, **34**, 1011 (1935).] For a *T-S* diagram, −218° to 400°C., 0.005 to 1200 atm., see Leah, "Thermodynamic Functions of Gases," vol. 1, pp. 162, 163, Butterworth, London,1956. Two wall charts based on this diagram are obtainable from Butterworth & Co. (Canada), Ltd. See also Keesom, Bijl, *et al.*, *Appl. Sci. Research*, **A5**, 349 (1955) (*H-P*, −205° to 200°C., to 300 atm.); Michels, Lunbeck, *et al.*, *Appl. Sci. Research*, **A3**, 253 (1952); *Physica*, **18**, 128 (1952) (*H-P, H-S, T-S*, 0° to 150°C., to 3000 atm.); Hilsenrath *et al.*, *N.B.S. Circ.* 564, 1955 (tabulated data, to 100 atm. and 3000°K.); Huff, Gordon, *et al.*, *N.A.C.A.Rept.* 1037, 1951 (ideal-gas functions, to 6000°K.).

Table 3-224. Chlorine

A *T-S* diagram, −120° to 560°F., 0.2 to 1400 lb./sq.in.abs., was given by Martin, "Thermodynamic and Transport Properties of Gases, Liquids and Solids," p. 121, A.S.M.E., New York, 1959; see also Kapoor and Martin, University of Michigan publication, 1957. Other references include Dobratz, *Chem. Eng.*, **65**, 144 (1958) (to 500°F., 1500 lb./sq.in.abs.); Gratch, OTS PB 124957, 1950 (zero pressure thermodynamic functions); Hulme, *Chem. Eng.*, **56**, 118 (1949); Hulme and Tillman, *Chem. Eng.*, **56**, 99 (1949) (to 520°F., 1100 lb./sq.in.abs.); Huff, Gordon, *et al.*, *N.A.C.A. Rept.* 1037, 1951 (zero pressure functions, to 6000°K.).

Table 3-225. Saturated Dowtherm A*

(73.5 % diphenyloxide, 26.5 % diphenyl)

Temp., °F. t	Abs. pressure, lb./sq. in. p	Volume, cu. ft./lb. Liquid v_f	Vapor v_g	Enthalpy, B.t.u./lb. Liquid h_f	Vapor h_g
53.6	......	......	......	0	164
100	......	......	......	18.0	176
150	......	......	......	38.4	192
200	......	0.0160	833	60.0	210
220	......	.0162	500	69.0	217
240	0.20	.0163	294	78.2	224
260	.29	.0165	179	87.7	232
280	.49	.0166	125	97.5	240
300	.74	.0168	83.3	108.0	250
320	1.1	.0170	52.6	118.0	258
340	1.6	.0171	38.5	128.0	266
360	2.2	.0173	27.8	138.0	275
380	3.0	.0175	20.0	150.0	286
400	4.1	.0176	14.7	162.0	296
420	5.4	.0178	11.4	174.0	306
440	6.9	.0180	8.40	186.0	316
460	8.8	.0181	6.54	198.0	326
480	12	.0183	5.13	210.0	334
500	15	.0185	4.08	222.0	345
520	19	.0188	3.23	234.0	354
540	24	.0190	2.44	247.0	365
560	30	.0193	2.00	260.0	375
580	36	.0195	1.67	274.0	386
600	43	.0198	1.47	288.0	398
620	51	.0201	1.20	302.0	409
640	62	.0204	0.980	316.0	421
660	74	.0207	.826	330.0	432
680	88	.0211	.694	344.0	443
700	103	.0213	.617	358.0	455
720	120	.0218	.526	372.0	465
750	150	.0225	.417	393.0	482

* Dow Chemical Co. For values at 60(10)750°F. see Lefax Data Sheet 45-51, reprinted March, 1953, Lefax, Philadelphia.

Table 3-226. Dowtherm E*

For thermodynamic properties of Dowtherm E* at 300(5)500°F. and some other data at 0(10)500°F. see Lefax Data Sheet 49-7, reprinted 1954, Lefax, Philadelphia.

* Dow Chemical Co.

Table 3-227. Electron Gas

For data at 300(100)6000°K. see Huff, Gordon, *et al.*, *N.A.C.A. Rept.* 1037, 1951. For other data to 100 atm., 40000°K. see Martinek, "Thermodynamic and Transport Properties of Gases, Liquids, and Solids," p. 130, A.S.M.E., New York, 1959. For kinetic and potential energies see March, *Phys. Rev.*, **110**, 604 (1958).

Table 3-228. Saturated Ethane*

Temp., °F. t	Abs. pressure, lb./sq. in. p	Volume, cu. ft./lb. Liquid v_f	Vapor v_g	Enthalpy, B.t.u /lb. Liquid h_f	Vapor h_g	Entropy, B.t.u./(lb.)(°R.) Liquid s_f	Vapor s_g
−220	0.27	0.02669	310.5	117.6	353.9	0.8249	1.8107
−210	.50	.02694	179.2	123.1	356.8	.8474	1.7833
−200	.85	.02720	107.8	128.7	359.7	.8691	1.7587
−190	1.40	.02746	68.43	134.3	362.6	.8901	1.7366
−180	2.20	.02774	44.90	139.9	365.5	.9133	1.7201
−170	3.36	.02802	30.32	145.5	368.3	.9332	1.7025
−160	4.97	.02831	21.11	151.1	371.2	.9523	1.6865
−150	7.14	.02861	15.10	156.8	373.9	.9710	1.6720
−140	9.97	.02893	11.05	162.3	376.6	.9891	1.6593
−130	13.68	.02923	8.282	168.3	379.3	1.0065	1.6464
−127.55	14.696	.02931	7.741	169.9	379.9	1.0111	1.6435
−120	18.33	.02957	6.316	174.3	381.8	1.0240	1.6346
−110	24.17	.02991	4.876	180.3	384.3	1.0407	1.6241
−100	31.32	.03029	3.830	186.2	386.8	1.0570	1.6143
− 90	39.98	.03067	3.043	192.9	389.0	1.0731	1.6055
− 80	50.34	.03108	2.451	198.2	391.2	1.0890	1.5974
− 70	62.63	.03152	1.994	204.4	393.2	1.1047	1.5896
− 60	77.02	.03199	1.638	210.5	395.2	1.1205	1.5825
− 50	93.76	.03249	1.355	216.8	397.0	1.1362	1.5758
− 40	113.1	.03303	1.127	223.2	398.6	1.1519	1.5697
− 30	135.0	.03359	0.9452	229.7	400.2	1.1672	1.5639
− 20	159.9	.03422	.7983	236.3	401.7	1.1824	1.5583
− 10	188.1	.03494	.6775	243.2	402.9	1.1977	1.5530
0	219.7	.03570	.5754	250.3	403.9	1.2132	1.5476
+ 10	254.9	.03655	.4909	257.5	404.5	1.2289	1.5420
20	294.0	.03754	.4198	265.1	404.9	1.2445	1.5361
30	337.1	.03866	.3595	272.8	404.9	1.2604	1.5301
40	385.0	.03990	.3062	281.0	404.5	1.2762	1.5234
50	437.5	.04144	.2596	289.7	403.4	1.2926	1.5158
60	494.2	.04358	.2164	299.3	401.3	1.3100	1.5064
70	558.3	.04625	.1795	309.8	397.6	1.3284	1.4940
80	630.7	.05063	.1411	323.7	391.4	1.3505	1.4751
90.11	716.0	.0755	.0755	362.0	362.0	1.4234	1.4234

* For *H*-log *P* diagrams see Barkelew, Valentine, and Hurd, *Trans. Am. Inst. Chem. Engrs.*, 43, 25 (1947); Plank and Kambeitz, *Bull. Intern. Inst. Refrig.*, 17, A1-A24 (1936) (diagram, −100° to 32°C.); Plank and Kambeitz, *Z. ges. Kälte-Ind.*, 43, 209 (1936) (−100° to 150°C., to 80 atm.); Anon., *Bull. Intern. Inst. Refrig.*, 30, 132 (1950) (−100° to 150°C., to 70 atm.). *H-S* diagram, −140° to 400°F., to 60 atm., appears in Maxwell, "Data Book on Hydrocarbons," Van Nostrand, Princeton, N.J., 1951. For isotherms, 0° to 150°C., to 200 atm., see Michels, van Stratten, *et al.*, *Physica*, 20, 17 (1954). For other thermodynamic diagrams see Techo, M. S. Thesis, Chemical Engineering, Georgia Institute of Technology, 1958.

Table 3-229. Superheated Ethane*

v, volume, cu. ft./lb.; *h*, enthalpy, B.t.u./lb.; *s*, entropy, B.t.u./(lb.)(°R.)
Parenthetic figures under pressures are saturation temperatures

Temp., °F.	10 lb./sq. in. abs. (−140°F.)			20 lb./sq. in. abs. (−117.2°F.)			30 lb./sq. in. abs. (−102.0°F.)			40 lb./sq. in. abs. (−89.9°F.)			60 lb./sq. in. abs. (−72.0°F.)			80 lb./sq. in. abs. (−57.8°F.)			100 lb./sq. in. abs. (−46.0°F.)		
t	*v*	*h*	*s*	*v*	*h*	*s*	*v*	*h*	*s*	*v*	*h*	*s*	*v*	*h*	*s*	*v*	*h*	*s*	*v*	*h*	*s*
−140	11.05	376.6	1.6593	....	....	....	....	....	....	....	....	....	....	....	....	....	....	....	....	....	....
−120	11.82	383.5	1.6795	....	....	....	....	....	....	....	....	....	....	....	....	....	....	....	....	....	....
−100	12.58	390.4	1.6995	6.149	388.7	1.6491	4.010	386.9	1.6177	....	....	....	....	....	....	....	....	....	....	....	....
− 80	13.32	397.5	1.7186	6.542	396.0	1.6691	4.279	394.5	1.6382	3.151	392.8	1.6157	....	....	....	....	....	....	....	....	....
− 60	14.06	404.7	1.7373	6.926	403.4	1.6885	4.546	402.1	1.6579	3.356	400.7	1.6362	2.164	397.8	1.6039	....	....	....	....	....	....
− 40	14.80	412.0	1.7554	7.306	410.9	1.7072	4.808	409.7	1.6772	3.559	408.5	1.6558	2.305	406.0	1.6248	1.678	403.4	1.6015	1.298	400.6	1.5809
− 20	15.53	419.5	1.7732	7.682	418.5	1.7254	5.066	417.4	1.6959	3.757	416.4	1.6749	2.447	414.2	1.6449	1.790	412.0	1.6224	1.394	409.6	1.6031
0	16.26	427.1	1.7903	8.054	426.2	1.7428	5.320	425.3	1.7139	3.952	424.4	1.6932	2.583	422.5	1.6638	1.897	420.5	1.6419	1.484	418.4	1.6234
20	16.98	434.9	1.8069	8.425	434.1	1.7597	5.572	433.3	1.7310	4.145	432.4	1.7108	2.717	430.7	1.6817	2.002	429.0	1.6600	1.573	427.1	1.6425
40	17.71	442.9	1.8230	8.795	442.1	1.7763	5.822	441.4	1.7477	4.336	440.6	1.7279	2.849	439.1	1.6990	2.105	437.5	1.6777	1.658	435.8	1.6605
60	18.43	451.0	1.8389	9.163	450.3	1.7921	6.070	449.6	1.7641	4.525	448.9	1.7444	2.979	447.6	1.7157	2.206	446.1	1.6949	1.741	444.6	1.6778
80	19.16	459.3	1.8545	9.529	458.7	1.8079	6.319	458.1	1.7802	4.713	457.4	1.7606	3.108	456.2	1.7320	2.305	454.9	1.7116	1.823	453.5	1.6946
90.1	19.52	463.6	1.8624	9.713	463.0	1.8159	6.443	462.4	1.7883	4.808	461.8	1.7687	3.173	460.5	1.7402	2.354	459.3	1.7199	1.863	458.0	1.7030
100	19.89	467.9	1.8701	9.894	467.3	1.8236	6.565	466.7	1.7961	4.900	466.1	1.7765	3.236	464.9	1.7481	2.402	463.8	1.7278	1.902	462.5	1.7111
120	20.61	476.6	1.8854	10.26	476.0	1.8389	6.810	475.5	1.8118	5.086	475.0	1.7920	3.362	473.9	1.7637	2.499	472.8	1.7436	1.982	471.7	1.7274
140	21.33	485.5	1.9006	10.62	485.1	1.8542	7.055	484.6	1.8271	5.271	484.1	1.8074	3.487	483.0	1.7793	2.595	482.0	1.7593	2.060	481.0	1.7430
160	22.05	494.7	1.9160	10.98	494.2	1.8697	7.299	493.7	1.8425	5.456	493.3	1.8228	3.612	492.4	1.7951	2.690	491.5	1.7749	2.137	490.5	1.7587
180	22.77	504.0	1.9312	11.35	503.6	1.8849	7.542	503.1	1.8577	5.639	502.7	1.8382	3.736	501.9	1.8104	2.785	501.0	1.7905	2.214	500.3	1.7744
200	23.49	513.6	1.9460	11.71	513.3	1.8997	7.784	512.9	1.8727	5.822	512.5	1.8530	3.860	511.7	1.8254	2.879	510.9	1.8056	2.290	510.0	1.7897
220	24.20	523.5	1.9606	12.07	523.2	1.9144	8.026	522.8	1.8874	6.005	522.4	1.8678	3.984	521.6	1.8403	2.973	520.9	1.8205	2.366	520.2	1.8046
240	24.92	533.6	1.9751	12.43	533.2	1.9289	8.268	532.8	1.9019	6.187	532.5	1.8823	4.107	531.9	1.8549	3.066	531.2	1.8352	2.442	530.5	1.8194
260	25.64	543.9	1.9895	12.79	543.6	1.9433	8.511	543.2	1.9163	6.370	542.9	1.8967	4.229	542.2	1.8692	3.159	541.6	1.8497	2.517	540.9	1.8341
280	26.35	554.5	2.0037	13.15	554.2	1.9575	8.752	553.9	1.9305	6.552	553.6	1.9112	4.352	553.0	1.8836	3.252	552.3	1.8645	2.592	551.7	1.8485
300	27.07	565.3	2.0181	13.51	565.1	1.9721	8.992	564.7	1.9449	6.734	564.4	1.9256	4.474	563.9	1.8982	3.344	563.3	1.8786	2.666	562.7	1.8632
320	27.79	576.3	2.0323	13.87	576.0	1.9861	9.233	575.8	1.9591	6.917	575.5	1.9400	4.596	575.0	1.9127	3.436	574.4	1.8935	2.740	573.9	1.8776
340	28.50	587.6	2.0469	14.23	587.4	2.0007	9.474	587.1	1.9737	7.097	586.9	1.9544	4.717	586.3	1.9274	3.528	585.8	1.9078	2.815	585.3	1.8924
360	29.22	599.1	2.0609	14.59	598.9	2.0148	9.714	598.7	1.9878	7.278	598.4	1.9686	4.839	597.9	1.9412	3.620	597.4	1.9217	2.888	596.9	1.9064
380	29.93	610.9	2.0752	14.95	610.6	2.0292	9.954	610.4	2.0022	7.459	610.2	1.9828	4.960	609.7	1.9557	3.711	609.3	1.9362	2.962	608.8	1.9209
400	30.65	622.9	2.0891	15.31	622.6	2.0431	10.19	622.4	2.0161	7.639	622.2	1.9968	5.082	621.7	1.9697	3.803	621.3	1.9502	3.036	620.9	1.9350
420	31.37	635.0	2.1029	15.67	634.8	2.0569	10.43	634.5	2.0299	7.819	634.3	2.0108	5.202	633.9	1.9831	3.894	633.5	1.9641	3.109	633.1	1.9488
440	32.08	647.3	2.1166	16.03	647.1	2.0706	10.67	646.9	2.0437	7.999	646.7	2.0246	5.323	646.3	1.9973	3.985	645.8	1.9778	3.183	645.4	1.9626
460	32.80	659.8	2.1301	16.38	659.6	2.0841	10.91	659.4	2.0572	8.179	659.2	2.0382	5.444	658.8	2.0109	4.076	658.4	1.9914	3.256	658.0	1.9763
480	33.51	672.5	2.1440	16.74	672.3	2.0980	11.15	672.1	2.0711	8.359	671.9	2.0518	5.565	671.5	2.0249	4.168	671.2	2.0054	3.329	670.8	1.9900
500	34.23	685.4	2.1575	17.10	685.2	2.1115	11.39	685.0	2.0846	8.539	684.9	2.0655	5.686	684.5	2.0384	4.258	684.2	2.0189	3.402	683.8	2.0040

* Barkelew, Valentine, and Hurd, *Trans. Am. Inst. Chem. Engrs.* **43**, 25 (1947).

Temp., °F.	150 lb./sq. in. abs. (−24.2°F.)			200 lb./sq. in. abs. (−6.2°F.)			300 lb./sq. in. abs. (21.6°F.)			500 lb./sq. in. abs. (61.0°F.)			800 lb./sq. in. abs.			1000 lb./sq. in. abs.			1500 lb./sq. in. abs.		
t	*v*	*h*	*s*	*v*	*h*	*s*	*v*	*h*	*s*	*v*	*h*	*s*	*v*	*h*	*s*	*v*	*h*	*s*	*v*	*h*	*s*
−20	0.8639	403.0	1.5649	....	....	....	....	....	....	....	....	....	....	....	....	....	....	....	....	....	....
0	.9306	412.9	1.5870	0.6508	406.5	1.5582	....	....	....	....	....	....	....	....	....	....	....	....	....	....	....
20	.9964	422.3	1.6073	.7036	417.2	1.5805	....	....	....	....	....	....	....	....	....	....	....	....	....	....	....
40	1.059	431.6	1.6267	.7562	427.1	1.6013	0.4510	416.4	1.5586	....	....	....	....	....	....	....	....	....	....	....	....
60	1.120	440.9	1.6454	.8086	436.8	1.6208	.4921	427.9	1.5812	....	....	....	....	....	....	....	....	....	....	....	....
80	1.179	450.1	1.6633	.8578	446.5	1.6395	.5305	438.5	1.6019	0.2587	418.3	1.5386	....	....	....	....	....	....	....	....	....
90.1	1.207	454.8	1.6721	.8814	451.3	1.6487	.5489	443.9	1.6119	.2761	425.4	1.5526	0.05125	336.1	1.3687	0.04689	329.8	1.3535	0.04338	323.8	1.3282
100	1.235	459.5	1.6803	.9044	456.2	1.6574	.5662	449.3	1.6214	.2909	432.3	1.5648	.07366	362.4	1.4206	.05114	336.4	1.3694	.04488	326.8	1.3407
120	1.291	468.9	1.6966	.9481	466.0	1.6742	.5993	459.7	1.6396	.3169	445.3	1.5870	.1404	413.0	1.5103	.06852	375.9	1.4352	.04822	340.5	1.3651
140	1.346	478.2	1.7129	.9901	475.8	1.6909	.6310	470.2	1.6573	.3401	457.6	1.6077	.1691	432.9	1.5440	.1038	409.3	1.4964	.05401	360.2	1.4045
160	1.400	488.1	1.7289	1.032	485.7	1.7073	.6609	480.7	1.6746	.3625	469.3	1.6273	.1905	448.7	1.5705	.1302	431.5	1.5334	.0649	388.2	1.4497
180	1.454	497.9	1.7450	1.072	495.6	1.7235	.6903	491.0	1.6916	.3835	480.8	1.6459	.2089	463.0	1.5939	.1493	448.8	1.5615	.0779	413.2	1.4903
200	1.507	508.0	1.7606	1.112	505.9	1.7393	.7193	501.6	1.7080	.4039	492.4	1.6638	.2254	476.6	1.6149	.1652	464.8	1.5855	.0898	434.3	1.5223
220	1.559	518.2	1.7758	1.152	516.3	1.7547	.7480	512.3	1.7238	.4236	503.9	1.6808	.2405	489.7	1.6343	.1795	479.6	1.6076	.1007	453.1	1.5490
240	1.611	529.6	1.7909	1.192	526.9	1.7699	.7766	523.1	1.7393	.4433	515.2	1.6970	.2550	502.7	1.6528	.1925	493.5	1.6281	.1112	470.3	1.5735
260	1.662	539.2	1.8057	1.231	537.6	1.7849	.8048	534.1	1.7545	.4623	526.8	1.7135	.2687	515.3	1.6703	.2046	507.2	1.6472	.1210	486.4	1.5964
280	1.713	550.1	1.8204	1.270	548.6	1.7997	.8325	545.4	1.7698	.4804	538.6	1.7293	.2819	528.0	1.6877	.2161	520.7	1.6654	.1306	502.0	1.6182
300	1.763	561.1	1.8352	1.310	559.8	1.8145	.8593	556.8	1.7849	.4980	550.4	1.7450	.2949	540.6	1.7045	.2272	534.0	1.6830	.1398	517.0	1.6386
320	1.813	572.3	1.8496	1.350	571.0	1.8291	.8859	568.2	1.7998	.5156	562.4	1.7604	.3074	553.2	1.7206	.2382	547.0	1.7006	.1484	531.6	1.6573
340	1.863	583.8	1.8644	1.388	582.6	1.8441	.9124	580.0	1.8149	.5329	574.5	1.7760	.3196	565.9	1.7366	.2487	560.1	1.7170	.1564	545.9	1.6757
360	1.914	595.5	1.8785	1.427	594.4	1.8582	.9386	591.9	1.8292	.5499	586.8	1.7908	.3314	578.7	1.7524	.2589	573.3	1.7329	.1639	560.2	1.6928
380	1.964	607.4	1.8933	1.465	606.4	1.8731	.9650	603.9	1.8440	.5665	599.2	1.8061	.3428	591.6	1.7684	.2687	586.5	1.7480	.1712	574.3	1.7103
400	2.013	619.6	1.9073	1.503	618.7	1.8873	.9912	616.3	1.8584	.5830	611.6	1.8207	.3540	604.6	1.7833	.2783	599.9	1.7645	.1782	588.4	1.7269
420	2.063	631.8	1.9214	1.540	631.0	1.9013	1.017	628.7	1.8726	.5992	624.3	1.8352	.3653	617.6	1.7983	.2878	613.4	1.7797	.1853	602.5	1.7431
440	2.113	644.3	1.9352	1.577	643.5	1.9153	1.042	641.4	1.8867	.6152	637.2	1.8494	.3765	630.7	1.8130	.2973	626.8	1.7946	.1922	616.7	1.7588
460	2.162	657.0	1.9489	1.614	656.2	1.9290	1.067	654.2	1.9005	.6315	650.2	1.8634	.3877	644.0	1.8274	.3066	640.3	1.8092	.1992	630.8	1.7741
480	2.212	669.8	1.9629	1.651	669.1	1.9431	1.093	667.1	1.9147	.6475	663.5	1.8778	.3986	657.5	1.8421	.3160	653.9	1.8242	.2062	645.1	1.7895
500	2.261	682.9	1.9766	1.689	682.2	1.9568	1.119	680.2	1.9284	.6637	676.8	1.8918	.4095	671.6	1.8564	.3255	667.6	1.8387	.2132	659.6	1.8044

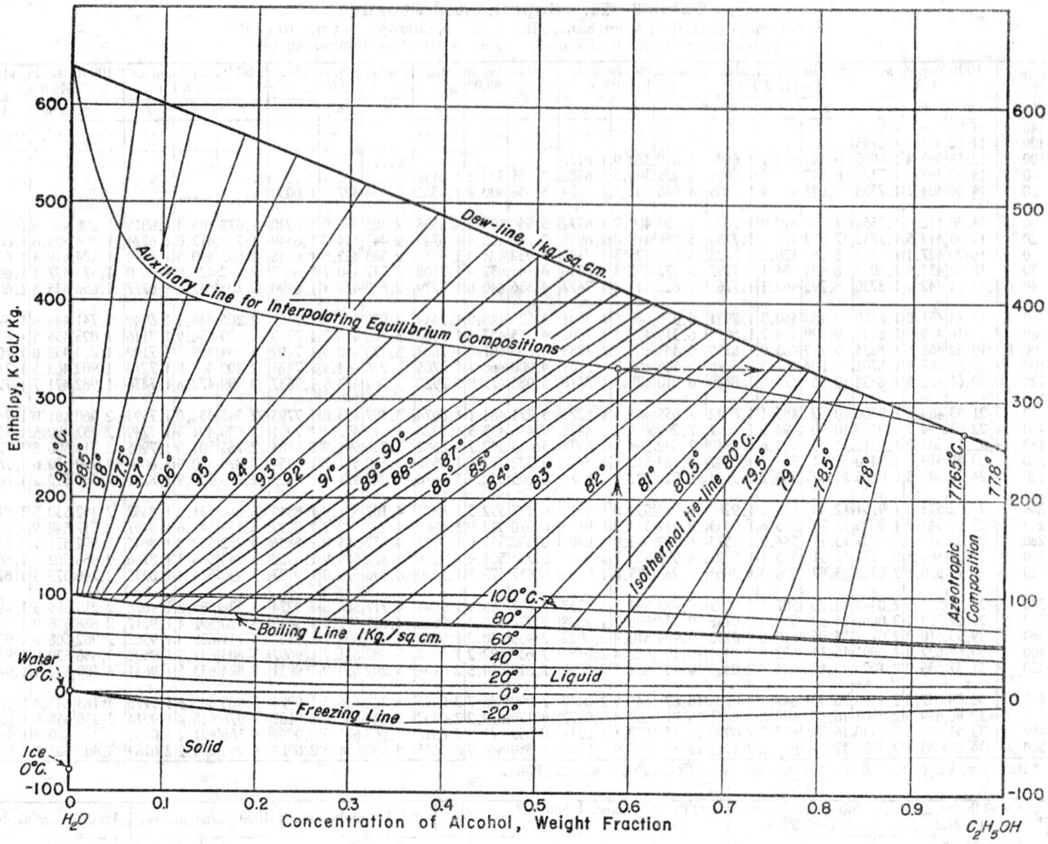

FIG. 3-22. Enthalpy-concentration diagram for aqueous ethyl alcohol. Reference states: Enthalpies of liquid water and ethyl alcohol at 0°C. are zero. Note: In order to interpolate equilibrium compositions, a vertical may be erected from any liquid composition on the boiling line and its intersection with the auxiliary line determined. A horizontal from this intersection will establish the equilibrium vapor composition on the dew line. (*Bosnjaković, "Technische Thermodynamik," T. Steinkopff, Leipzig, 1935.*)

Table 3-230. Saturated Ethylamine*
($C_2H_5NH_2$)

Temp., °F. t	Abs. Pressure, lb./sq. in. p	Volume, cu. ft./lb. vapor v_g	Enthalpy, B.t.u./lb. Liquid h_f	Enthalpy, B.t.u./lb. Vapor h_g	Entropy, B.t.u./(lb.)(°R.) Liquid s_f	Entropy, B.t.u./(lb.)(°R.) Vapor s_g
− 58	0.335	270.8	− 7.82	284.78	−0.0263	0.7094
− 40	.740	134.5	0.00	290.93	.0000	.6931
− 22	1.408	72.87	10.93	296.84	.0253	.6788
− 4	2.546	41.71	23.01	303.05	.0498	.6664
+ 5	3.342	32.32	27.61	306.04	0.619	.6609
23	5.590	20.00	38.91	311.92	.0857	.6512
41	8.960	12.88	50.36	317.50	.1091	.6430
68	16.896	7.156	68.18	326.50	.1437	.6332
86	24.72	5.039	80.50	332.46	.1664	.6281
113	41.49	3.136	99.52	341.44	.1999	.6223

* "Refrigerating Data Book," 5th ed., American Society of Refrigerating Engineers, New York, 1942.

Table 3-231. Saturated Ethyl Chloride*

Temp., °F. t	Abs. pressure, lb./sq. in. p	Volume, cu. ft./lb. Liquid v_f	Volume, cu. ft./lb. Vapor v_g	Enthalpy, B.t.u./lb. Liquid h_f	Enthalpy, B.t.u./lb. Vapor h_g	Entropy, B.t.u./(lb.)(°R.) Liquid s_f	Entropy, B.t.u./(lb.)(°R.) Vapor s_g
−22	2.20	0.01657	34.4	−23.1	158.2	−0.0497	0.3642
−13	2.85	.01669	26.95	−19.2	160.7	− .0410	.3615
− 4	3.66	.01682	21.33	−15.4	163.1	− .0324	.3591
+ 5	4.65	.01695	17.06	−11.6	165.4	− .0241	.3566
14	5.85	.01708	13.77	− 7.7	167.8	− .0159	.3543
23	7.28	.01721	11.21	− 3.8	170.2	− .0079	.3523
32	8.99	.01735	9.21	0.0	172.5	.0000	.3506
41	11.01	.01749	7.62	+ 3.8	174.7	+ .0077	.3488
50	13.37	.01763	6.36	7.7	177.0	.0154	.3475
59	16.11	.01777	5.34	11.6	179.3	.0228	.3459
68	19.29	.01792	4.51	15.4	181.4	.0302	.3446
77	22.94	.01807	3.84	19.2	183.5	.0374	.3433
86	27.10	.01822	3.29	23.1	185.7	.0445	.3423
95	31.82	.01838	2.83	26.9	187.7	.0515	.3412
104	37.17	.01854	2.44	30.8	189.9	.0583	.3402
113	43.16	.01870	2.13	34.6	191.8	.0651	.3394
122	49.88	.01887	1.86	38.5	193.8	.0718	.3386
131	57.36	.01904	1.63	42.3	195.6	.0783	.3377

* *Am. Soc. Refrigerating Eng. Circ. 9, 1926.*

Table 3-232. Saturated Ethylene*

Temp., °F.	Abs. pressure, atm.	Volume, cu. ft./lb.		Enthalpy, B.t.u./lb.		Entropy, B.t.u./(lb.)(°R.)	
		Liquid	Vapor	Liquid	Vapor	Liquid	Vapor
t	p	v_f	v_g	h_f	h_g	s_f	s_g
−272.47	0.0012	....	4064.0	− 68.19	176.5	−0.2826	1.024
−260.0	.0037	....	1405.0	− 60.84	180.1	− .2351	0.972
−240.0	.0177	....	328.6	− 49.16	185.7	− .1887	.880
−220.0	.0606	....	103.1	− 37.56	191.4	− .1382	.817
−200.0	.169	....	39.74	− 26.03	197.1	− .0922	.767
−180.0	.402	....	17.92	− 14.57	202.6	− .0498	.727
−160.0	.837	....	9.047	− 3.12	207.2	− .0103	.692
−154.66	1.0000	0.02818	7.6712	0.0	207.9	.0000	.6814
−140.00	1.5775	.02877	5.005	+ 8.6	210.5	+ .0249	.6563
−120.00	2.7376	.02964	2.987	20.8	214.2	.0648	.6340
−100.00	4.4616	.03122	1.879	32.8	217.2	.0995	.6121
− 80.00	6.8697	.03179	1.732	45.2	219.9	.1374	.5974
− 60.00	10.099	.03308	0.857	57.9	221.9	.1666	.5769
− 40.00	14.0338	.03468	.593	70.8	222.8	.1935	.5556
− 20.00	19.722	.03662	.419	84.7	222.7	.2245	.5383
0.00	26.397	.03912	.301	100.3	221.0	.2577	.5202
+ 20.00	34.55	.04292	.212	119.6	216.6	.2968	.4991
+ 40.00	44.54	.05035	.139	148.7	206.2	.3533	.4683
+ 49.82	50.50	.070	.070	171.8	171.8	.3964	.3964

* For data extracted from York and White, *Trans. Am. Inst. Chem. Engrs.*, **40**, 227 (1944) for the superheated vapor, −140° to 500°F., 1 to 300 atm., see Table 216, p. 259, 3d ed. of this handbook. The diagram of Benzler and Koch extends in the original to 10,000 kg./sq. cm. For a *T-S* diagram from 0° to 150°C., 1 to 2500 bars, see Dick and Hedley, "Thermodynamic Functions of Gases," vol. 2, p. 108, Butterworth, London, 1956. A wall-sized reproduction of the Dick and Hedley diagram is also available from Butterworth & Co. (Canada), Ltd. York and White, *loc. cit.*, also give a *H*-log *P* diagram, −140° to 520°F., 1 to 300 atm. For high-temperature data see Kroepelin, Neumann, *et al.*, *Abhandl. braunschweig wiss. Ges.*, **10**, 166 (1958).

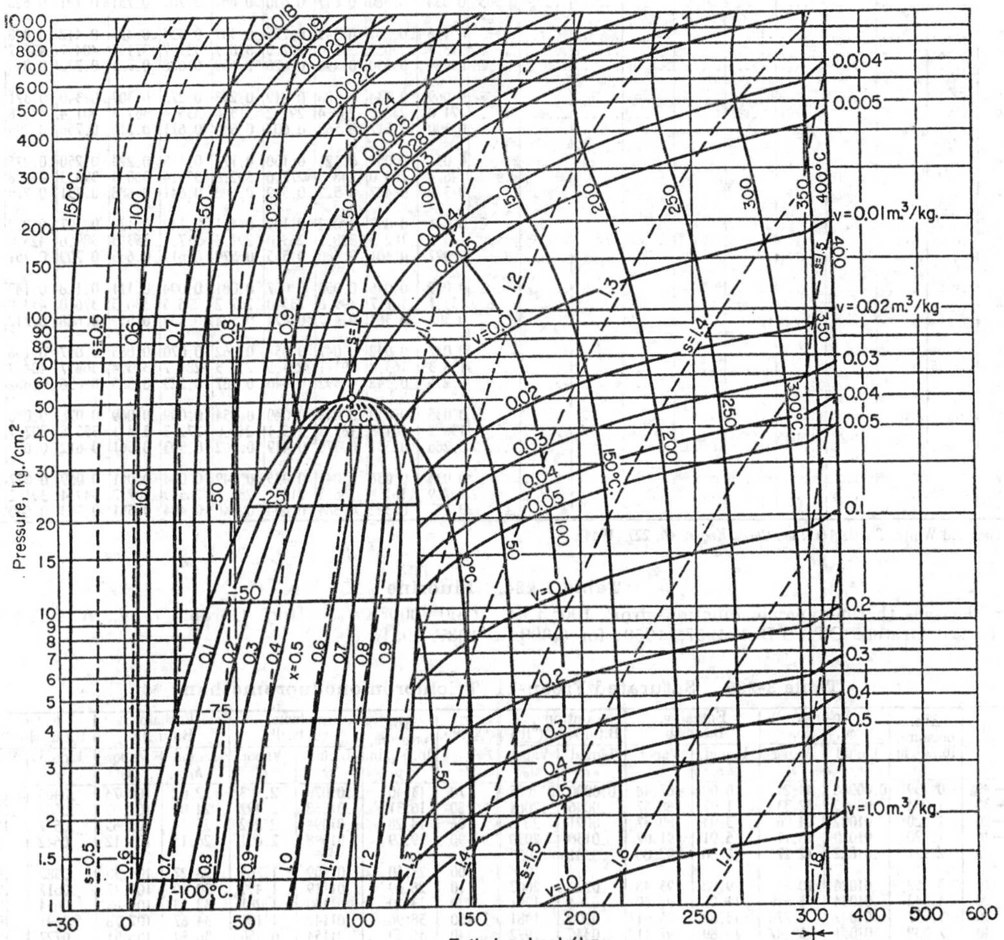

Fig. 3-23. Enthalpy-pressure diagram for ethylene. [*From Benzler and Koch, Chem.-Ing.-Tech.*, **27**, 71 (1955). *Copyright Verlag Chemie G.m.b.H., Weinheim, Bergstr., Germany.*]

Table 3-233. Superheated Ethylene*

v, volume, cu. ft./lb.; *h*, enthalpy, B.t.u./lb.; *s*, entropy, B.t.u./(lb.)(°R.)

Abs. pressure, atm.	Temperature, °F.																			
	−140°	−120°	−100°	−80°	−60°	−40°	−20°	0°	20°	40°	60°	100°	140°	180°	220°	260°	320°	380°	440°	500°
1 *v*	8.061	8.617	9.168	9.714	10.256	10.794	11.329	11.862	12.497	12.924	13.453	14.51	15.56	16.61	17.66	18.71	20.28	21.85	23.42	24.99
1 *h*	212.2	218.3	224.3	230.6	236.9	243.3	249.9	256.6	263.4	270.4	277.7	292.6	308.3	324.8	342.0	360.0	388.4	418.4	450.4	482.9
1 *s*	0.695	0.714	0.732	0.748	0.764	0.780	0.795	0.810	0.825	0.839	0.853	0.881	0.908	0.934	0.961	0.986	1.025	1.062	1.098	1.133
2 *v*	.....	4.190	4.479	4.765	5.047	5.324	5.599	5.873	6.144	6.414	6.683	7.217	7.749	8.280	8.808	9.34	10.12	10.91	11.70	12.48
2 *h*	.....	215.9	222.3	228.9	235.4	242.0	248.7	255.6	262.5	269.5	276.9	291.9	307.6	324.2	341.5	359.7	388.1	418.2	450.2	482.7
2 *s*	.....	0.659	0.677	0.693	0.710	0.726	0.741	0.756	0.771	0.785	0.799	0.828	0.855	0.881	0.909	0.934	0.974	1.011	1.048	1.083
4 *v*	.....	.....	2.130	2.287	2.439	2.588	2.733	2.878	3.019	3.159	3.297	3.571	3.843	4.113	4.380	4.647	5.046	5.443	5.838	6.234
4 *h*	.....	.....	218.2	225.5	232.4	239.3	246.3	253.4	260.6	267.8	275.3	290.6	306.6	323.3	340.6	358.9	387.4	417.6	449.7	482.3
4 *s*	.....	.....	0.623	0.641	0.658	0.675	0.691	0.706	0.722	0.737	0.751	0.780	0.807	0.833	0.860	0.886	0.925	0.963	1.000	1.035
6 *v*	.....	.....	.....	1.456	1.566	1.673	1.776	1.833	1.877	2.099	2.168	2.356	2.541	2.724	2.905	3.084	3.352	3.620	3.885	4.150
6 *h*	.....	.....	.....	221.6	229.1	236.6	243.9	251.2	258.6	266.0	273.7	289.3	305.4	322.3	339.8	358.1	386.8	417.0	449.2	481.8
6 *s*	.....	.....	.....	0.607	0.625	0.642	0.659	0.675	0.691	0.706	0.721	0.750	0.777	0.804	0.831	0.856	0.896	0.934	0.971	1.006
10 *v*	.....	.....	.....	.....	0.860	0.936	1.006	1.074	1.140	1.202	1.264	1.382	1.499	1.613	1.724	1.834	1.999	2.161	2.323	2.483
10 *h*	.....	.....	.....	.....	222.4	230.8	238.8	246.6	254.4	262.4	270.4	286.5	303.1	320.3	338.0	356.5	385.4	415.8	448.2	480.9
10 *s*	.....	.....	.....	.....	0.578	0.599	0.616	0.632	0.649	0.665	0.680	0.711	0.739	0.766	0.794	0.820	0.860	0.898	0.934	0.969
15 *v*	.....	.....	.....	.....	.....	.....	0.614	0.669	0.718	0.765	0.811	0.897	0.978	1.057	1.134	1.209	1.322	1.433	1.542	1.650
15 *h*	.....	.....	.....	.....	.....	.....	230.9	239.9	248.7	257.5	266.2	283.0	300.1	317.7	335.8	354.6	383.8	414.4	447.0	479.9
15 *s*	.....	.....	.....	.....	.....	.....	0.573	0.593	0.612	0.630	0.646	0.677	0.707	0.734	0.763	0.789	0.829	0.867	0.903	0.938
20 *v*	.....	.....	.....	.....	.....	.....	.....	0.459	0.503	0.545	0.583	0.652	0.717	0.778	0.838	0.897	0.983	1.068	1.151	1.233
20 *h*	.....	.....	.....	.....	.....	.....	.....	232.5	242.5	252.1	261.3	279.2	296.9	315.1	333.5	352.6	382.1	413.0	445.7	478.8
20 *s*	.....	.....	.....	.....	.....	.....	.....	0.560	0.582	0.591	0.618	0.651	0.682	0.710	0.740	0.766	0.807	0.845	0.882	0.917
30 *v*	.....	.....	.....	.....	.....	.....	.....	.....	0.282	0.318	0.350	0.405	0.454	0.498	0.543	0.585	0.645	0.704	0.760	0.817
30 *h*	.....	.....	.....	.....	.....	.....	.....	.....	226.9	239.5	250.8	271.2	290.2	309.5	328.7	348.3	378.6	410.1	443.3	476.7
30 *s*	.....	.....	.....	.....	.....	.....	.....	.....	0.528	0.552	0.574	0.613	0.646	0.676	0.706	0.734	0.775	0.814	0.851	0.887
40 *v*	.....	.....	.....	.....	.....	.....	.....	.....	.....	0.192	0.228	0.279	0.323	0.359	0.395	0.428	0.476	0.521	0.565	0.609
40 *h*	.....	.....	.....	.....	.....	.....	.....	.....	.....	221.1	237.3	262.3	283.4	303.7	323.8	344.1	375.1	407.2	440.8	474.5
40 *s*	.....	.....	.....	.....	.....	.....	.....	.....	.....	0.503	0.534	0.580	0.617	0.650	0.681	0.709	0.751	0.791	0.828	0.865
50 *v*	.....	.....	.....	.....	.....	.....	.....	.....	.....	.....	0.138	0.201	0.243	0.275	0.309	0.334	0.375	0.412	0.448	0.484
50 *h*	.....	.....	.....	.....	.....	.....	.....	.....	.....	.....	218.1	250.3	275.6	297.5	318.7	339.7	371.5	404.2	438.2	472.4
50 *s*	.....	.....	.....	.....	.....	.....	.....	.....	.....	.....	0.484	0.550	0.590	0.626	0.659	0.688	0.731	0.772	0.810	0.847
60 *v*	.....	.....	.....	.....	.....	.....	.....	.....	.....	.....	0.069	0.144	0.186	0.219	0.248	0.273	0.307	0.340	0.371	0.402
60 *h*	.....	.....	.....	.....	.....	.....	.....	.....	.....	.....	171.0	238.9	267.4	291.2	313.6	335.4	367.8	401.4	435.8	470.3
60 *s*	.....	.....	.....	.....	.....	.....	.....	.....	.....	.....	0.390	0.517	0.568	0.607	0.640	0.671	0.716	0.756	0.795	0.833
80 *v*	.....	.....	.....	.....	.....	.....	.....	.....	.....	.....	0.051	0.082	0.121	0.150	0.174	0.195	0.224	0.250	0.275	0.301
80 *h*	.....	.....	.....	.....	.....	.....	.....	.....	.....	.....	146.4	205.0	248.3	277.6	302.8	326.4	360.5	395.3	430.8	466.1
80 *s*	.....	.....	.....	.....	.....	.....	.....	.....	.....	.....	0.340	0.477	0.522	0.569	0.608	0.641	0.688	0.731	0.770	0.808
100 *v*	.....	.....	.....	.....	.....	.....	.....	.....	.....	.....	0.044	0.057	0.082	0.109	0.131	0.149	0.174	0.197	0.219	0.239
100 *h*	.....	.....	.....	.....	.....	.....	.....	.....	.....	.....	143.5	182.5	228.3	263.0	291.3	317.1	353.3	389.6	426.0	462.0
100 *s*	.....	.....	.....	.....	.....	.....	.....	.....	.....	.....	0.327	0.401	0.480	0.535	0.579	0.614	0.665	0.709	0.751	0.789
150 *v*	.....	.....	.....	.....	.....	.....	.....	.....	.....	.....	0.039	0.046	0.056	0.067	0.081	0.094	0.111	0.128	0.143	0.159
150 *h*	.....	.....	.....	.....	.....	.....	.....	.....	.....	.....	139.1	167.7	199.8	235.0	267.2	296.5	336.5	376.0	414.8	452.6
150 *s*	.....	.....	.....	.....	.....	.....	.....	.....	.....	.....	0.308	0.361	0.417	0.474	0.524	0.564	0.619	0.668	0.712	0.752
200 *v*	.....	.....	.....	.....	.....	.....	.....	.....	.....	.....	0.037	0.042	0.047	0.054	0.062	0.070	0.085	0.097	0.108	0.119
200 *h*	.....	.....	.....	.....	.....	.....	.....	.....	.....	.....	138.3	163.8	191.1	221.5	252.3	281.7	323.4	364.7	404.9	444.2
200 *s*	.....	.....	.....	.....	.....	.....	.....	.....	.....	.....	0.295	0.342	0.392	0.440	0.487	0.529	0.585	0.636	0.682	0.724
250 *v*	.....	.....	.....	.....	.....	.....	.....	.....	.....	.....	0.035	0.039	0.043	0.049	0.054	0.059	0.069	0.078	0.088	0.099
250 *h*	.....	.....	.....	.....	.....	.....	.....	.....	.....	.....	138.2	161.8	187.5	215.1	243.9	272.3	314.1	355.8	397.1	437.5
250 *s*	.....	.....	.....	.....	.....	.....	.....	.....	.....	.....	0.286	0.331	0.376	0.419	0.462	0.503	0.561	0.612	0.659	0.702
300 *v*	.....	.....	.....	.....	.....	.....	.....	.....	.....	.....	0.034	0.038	0.041	0.045	0.049	0.054	0.061	0.069	0.077	0.083
300 *h*	.....	.....	.....	.....	.....	.....	.....	.....	.....	.....	137.9	161.4	186.3	212.1	238.7	265.9	307.7	349.4	391.2	432.0
300 *s*	.....	.....	.....	.....	.....	.....	.....	.....	.....	.....	0.277	0.322	0.364	0.404	0.446	0.484	0.541	0.593	0.640	0.684

* York and White, *Trans. Am. Inst. Chem. Engrs.*, **40**, 227 (1944).

Table 3-234. Fluorine

For ideal-gas thermodynamic functions from 100° to 5000°R. see Gratch, OTS PB 124957, 1950; for 0,300 (100)6000°K. see Huff, Gordon, *et al.*, *N.A.C.A. Rept.* 1037, 1951.

Table 3-235. Saturated Freon-11 (Trichloromonofluoromethane)*

Temp., °F. *t*	Abs. pressure, lb./sq. in. *p*	Volume, cu. ft./lb. Liquid v_f	Volume, cu. ft./lb. Vapor v_g	Enthalpy, B.t.u./lb. Liquid h_f	Enthalpy, B.t.u./lb. Vapor h_g	Entropy, B.t.u./(lb.)(°R.) Liquid s_f	Entropy, B.t.u./(lb.)(°R.) Vapor s_g
−40	0.7391	0.00988	44.21	0.00	87.48	0.0000	0.2085
−30	1.034	.00995	32.33	1.97	88.67	.0046	.2064
−20	1.420	.01002	24.06	3.94	89.87	.0091	.2046
−10	1.920	.01010	18.17	5.91	91.07	.0136	.2030
5	2.931	.01022	12.27	8.88	92.88	.0201	.2009
10	3.352	.01026	10.83	9.88	93.48	.0222	.2003
20	4.342	.01034	8.519	11.87	94.69	.0264	.1991
30	5.557	.01042	6.776	13.88	95.91	.0306	.1981
40	7.032	.01051	5.447	15.89	97.11	.0346	.1972
50	8.804	.01060	4.421	17.92	98.32	.0386	.1964
60	10.90	.01069	3.626	19.96	99.53	.0426	.1958
70	13.40	.01079	2.993	22.02	100.73	.0465	.1951
80	16.31	.01088	2.492	24.09	101.93	.0504	.1947
86	18.28	.01094	2.242	25.34	102.65	.0527	.1944
90	19.69	.01098	2.091	26.18	103.12	.0542	.1942
100	23.60	.01109	1.765	28.27	104.30	.0580	.1938
110	28.09	.01119	1.499	30.40	105.47	.0617	.1935
120	33.20	.01130	1.281	32.53	106.63	.0654	.1933
130	38.96	.01142	1.101	34.67	107.78	.0691	.1931
140	45.50	.01154	0.9505	36.84	108.91	.0727	.1929
150	52.85	.01166	.8240	39.02	110.02	.0763	.1927
160	61.04	.01179	.7176	41.23	111.12	.0798	.1926

* Courtesy Kinetic Chemicals, Inc. For a *H*-log *P* diagram to 3000 lb./sq. in. abs., −20° to 800°F., see "Properties of Commonly-used Refrigerants," Air-Conditioning and Refrigerating Institute, Washington, D.C., 1957. No tabular data are given above 65 lb./sq. in. abs.

Table 3-236. Superheated Freon-11 (Trichloromonofluoromethane)*

v, volume, cu. ft./lb.; *h*, enthalpy, B.t.u./lb.; *s*, entropy, B.t.u./(lb.)(°R.)
Parenthetic figures after pressures are saturation temperatures

Temp., °F.	Abs. pressure 0.7 lb./sq. in. (−41.6°F.)		
t	*v*	*h*	*s*
Sat.	46.54	87.29	0.2090
−40	46.69	87.49	.2093
−30	47.81	88.69	.2121
−20	48.93	89.91	.2149
−10	50.06	91.14	.2177
0	51.18	92.38	.2204
10	52.30	93.63	.2231
20	53.42	94.89	.2258
30	54.54	96.16	.2284
40	55.66	97.44	.2310
50	56.77	98.73	.2335
60	57.89	100.03	.2361
70	59.01	101.34	.2386
80	60.13	102.67	.2411
90	61.25	104.00	.2435
100	62.37	105.34	.2459
110	63.49	106.69	.2483
120	64.60	108.06	.2507
130	65.72	109.43	.2531
140	66.84	110.82	.2554
150	67.96	112.22	.2577
160	69.08	113.62	.2600
170	70.20	115.04	.2622
180	71.32	116.47	.2645
190	72.43	117.90	.2667
200	73.55	119.35	.2689
210	74.67	120.81	.2711
220	75.79	122.27	.2733
230	76.90	123.75	.2754
240	78.02	125.24	.2776
250	79.14	126.74	.2797
260	80.26	128.25	.2818
270	.....	......	......

Temp., °F.	Abs. pressure 2.0 lb./sq. in. (−8.6°F.)		
t	*v*	*h*	*s*
Sat.	17.50	91.24	0.2028
0	17.83	92.31	.2052
10	18.23	93.56	.2079
20	18.62	94.82	.2105
30	19.02	96.09	.2131
40	19.41	97.37	.2157
50	19.81	98.66	.2183
60	20.20	99.97	.2208
70	20.59	101.28	.2233
80	20.99	102.61	.2258
90	21.38	103.94	.2282
100	21.77	105.28	.2307
110	22.17	106.64	.2331
120	22.56	108.01	.2354
130	22.95	109.38	.2378
140	23.35	110.76	.2401
150	23.74	112.17	.2424
160	24.13	113.57	.2447
170	24.52	114.98	.2470
180	24.92	116.41	.2492
190	25.31	117.85	.2515
200	25.70	119.30	.2537
210	26.10	120.76	.2559
220	26.49	122.22	.2581
230	26.88	123.70	.2602
240	27.27	125.19	.2624
250	27.66	126.69	.2645
260	28.06	128.21	.2666
270	28.45	129.73	.2687
280	28.84	131.26	.2708
290	29.23	132.80	.2728
300	29.62	134.35	.2749

Temp., °F.	Abs. pressure 5.0 lb./sq. in. (25.6°F.)		
t	*v*	*h*	*s*
Sat.	7.475	95.38	0.1985
30	7.543	95.94	.1997
40	7.703	97.22	.2023
50	7.863	98.51	.2048
60	8.023	99.82	.2074
70	8.182	101.14	.2099
80	8.341	102.47	.2124
90	8.500	103.80	.2148
100	8.659	105.16	.2173
110	8.818	106.51	.2197
120	8.977	107.88	.2220
130	9.135	109.26	.2244
140	9.294	110.65	.2267
150	9.452	112.05	.2290
160	9.610	113.45	.2313
170	9.769	114.87	.2336
180	9.927	116.30	.2359
190	10.09	117.74	.2381
200	10.25	119.19	.2403
210	10.40	120.65	.2425
220	10.56	122.12	.2447
230	10.72	123.60	.2469
240	10.88	125.09	.2490
250	11.04	126.59	.2511
260	11.19	128.11	.2533
270	11.35	129.63	.2554
280	11.51	131.16	.2574
290	11.67	132.71	.2595
300	11.82	134.27	.2616
310	11.98	135.83	.2636
320	12.14	137.40	.2656
330	12.30	138.98	.2677

Temp., °F.	Abs. pressure 10.0 lb./sq. in. (55.9°F.)		
t	*v*	*h*	*s*
Sat.	3.928	99.04	0.1960
60	3.961	99.57	.1970
70	4.042	100.89	.1996
80	4.123	102.23	.2021
90	4.204	103.57	.2045
100	4.285	104.93	.2070
110	4.366	106.29	.2094
120	4.447	107.67	.2118
130	4.528	109.05	.2141
140	4.609	110.44	.2165
150	4.690	111.85	.2188
160	4.771	113.26	.2211
170	5.851	114.69	.2234
180	4.932	116.12	.2257
190	5.012	117.56	.2279
200	5.092	119.01	.2301
210	5.171	120.48	.2323
220	5.251	121.95	.2345
230	5.331	123.43	.2367
240	5.411	124.92	.2388
250	5.491	126.43	.2409
260	5.571	127.95	.2431
270	5.650	129.48	.2452
280	5.730	131.01	.2473
290	5.809	132.56	.2494
300	5.889	134.12	.2514
310	5.969	135.68	.2535
320	6.048	137.26	.2555
330	6.127	138.84	.2575
340	6.206	140.43	.2595
350	6.285	142.04	.2615
360	6.365	143.66	.2635

Temp., °F.	Abs. pressure 20 lb./sq. in. (90.8°F.)		
t	*v*	*h*	*s*
Sat.	2.061	103.22	0.1942
100	2.099	104.47	.1964
110	2.140	105.84	.1989
120	2.182	107.23	.2013
130	2.224	108.63	.2036
140	2.266	110.03	.2060
150	2.307	111.44	.2083
160	2.349	112.87	.2107
170	2.390	114.31	.2130
180	2.431	115.75	.2152
190	2.473	117.19	.2175
200	2.514	118.65	.2197
210	2.555	120.12	.2219
220	2.596	121.60	.2241
230	2.637	123.09	.2263
240	2.678	124.59	.2285
250	2.719	126.11	.2306
260	2.760	127.63	.2328
270	2.800	129.16	.2349
280	2.841	130.70	.2370
290	2.881	132.25	.2391
300	2.922	133.82	.2411
310	2.962	135.39	.2432
320	3.003	136.97	.2452
330	3.043	138.56	.2472
340	3.084	140.16	.2493
350	3.124	141.77	.2513
360	3.164	143.40	.2532
370	3.205	145.03	.2552
380	3.245	146.68	.2572
390	3.286	148.33	.2592
400	3.326	149.99	.2611

Temp., °F.	Abs. pressure 40 lb./sq. in. (131.6°F.)		
t	*v*	*h*	*s*
Sat.	1.074	107.96	0.1930
140	1.092	109.17	.1950
150	1.115	110.60	.1974
160	1.137	112.04	.1997
170	1.159	113.49	.2021
180	1.181	114.95	.2044
190	1.202	116.42	.2067
200	1.224	117.89	.2089
210	1.246	119.38	.2112
220	1.268	120.88	.2134
230	1.289	122.39	.2156
240	1.311	124.91	.2178
250	1.332	125.44	.2199
260	1.353	126.97	.2221
270	1.374	128.52	.2242
280	1.396	130.08	.2263
290	1.417	131.64	.2284
300	1.438	133.22	.2305
310	1.459	134.80	.2326
320	1.480	136.40	.2347
330	1.501	138.00	.2367
340	1.522	139.61	.2387
350	1.543	141.24	.2407
360	1.564	142.88	.2427
370	1.584	144.52	.2447
380	1.605	146.18	.2467
390	1.626	147.83	.2487
400	1.647	149.51	.2506
410	1.668	151.19	.2526
420	1.688	152.89	.2545
430	1.709	154.59	.2564
440	1.729	156.30	.2583

Temp., °F.	Abs. pressure 60 lb./sq. in. (158.8°F.)		
t	*v*	*h*	*s*
Sat.	0.7297	110.99	0.1926
160	.7314	111.17	.1929
170	.7471	112.65	.1953
180	.7627	114.14	.1976
190	.7782	115.63	.1999
200	.7937	117.13	.2022
210	.8090	118.64	.2045
220	.8241	120.16	.2068
230	.8391	121.68	.2090
240	.8541	123.21	.2112
250	.8691	124.76	.2134
260	.8839	126.31	.2156
270	.8987	127.87	.2177
280	.9134	129.44	.2198
290	.9281	131.01	.2220
300	.9427	132.60	.2241
310	.9574	134.20	.2262
320	.9719	135.81	.2282
330	.9863	137.42	.2303
340	1.001	139.05	.2323
350	1.015	140.69	.2344
360	1.030	142.33	.2364
370	1.044	143.98	.2384
380	1.059	145.65	.2404
390	1.073	147.32	.2424
400	1.087	149.01	.2443
410	1.101	150.70	.2463
420	1.115	152.41	.2483
430	1.130	154.12	.2502
440	1.144	155.84	.2521
450	1.158	157.57	.2540
460	1.172	159.31	.2559

* Courtesy of Kinetic Chemicals, Inc. See footnote to Table 3-235. For other data see Pavlova, *Kholodil'naya Tekh.*, vol. 42, 1955 (−50° to 50°C.); "Properties of Commonly-used Refrigerants," Air-Conditioning and Refrigerating Institute, Washington, D.C. 1957.

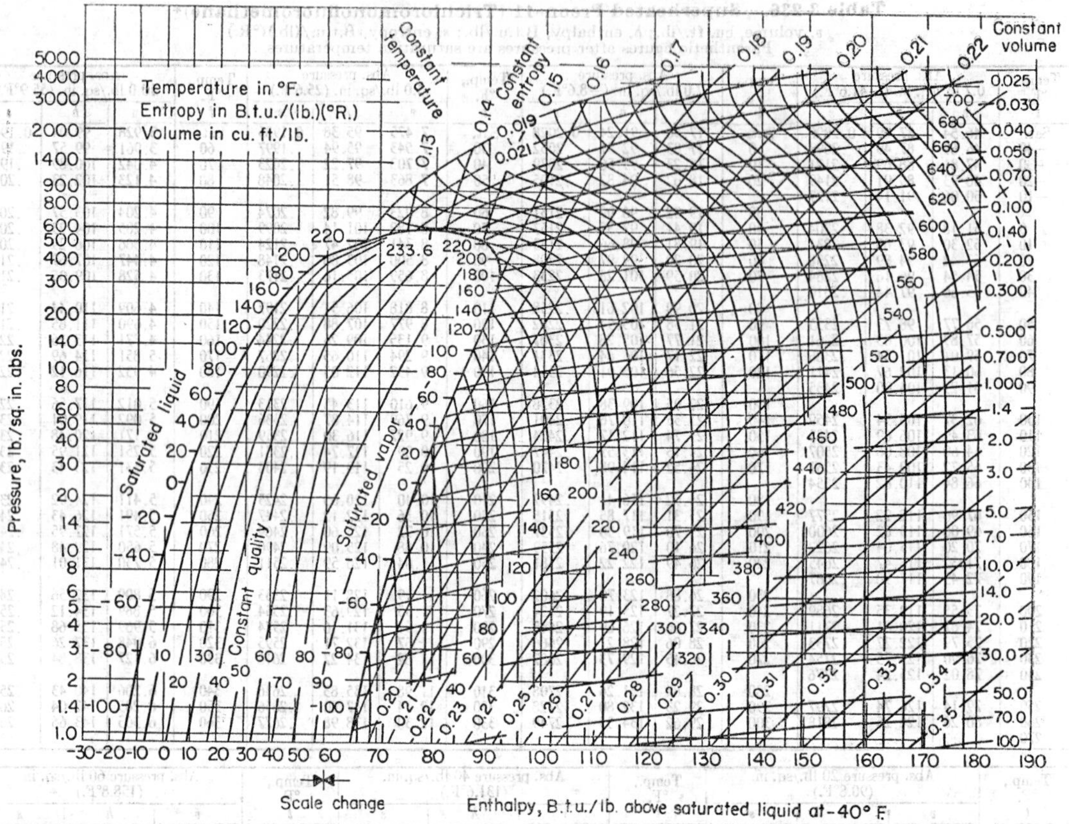

FIG. 3-24. Pressure-enthalpy diagram for Freon-12 refrigerant. (*Copyright 1956 by E. I. du Pont de Nemours & Co., Inc. Reprinted by permission.*) For a description of the experimental work and procedures used to calculate these data see McHarness, Eiseman, *et al.*, *Refrig. Eng.*, **63**, 31 (1955); see also Martin, "Thermodynamic and Transport Properties of Gases, Liquids and Solids," p. 110, A.S.M.E., New York, 1959. A publication "Thermodynamic Properties of Freon 12," E. I. du Pont de Nemours & Co., Inc., undated, reproduces the same diagram and tabular data to 600 lb./sq. in. abs. Apparently, tabular data above 600 lb./sq. in. abs. are not available.

Table 3-237. Saturated Freon-12 (Dichlorodifluoromethane)*

Temp., °F.	Abs. pressure, lb./sq. in.	Volume, cu. ft./lb.		Enthalpy, B.t.u./lb.		Entropy, B.t.u./(lb.)(°R.)		Temp., °F.	Abs. pressure, lb./sq. in.	Volume, cu. ft./lb.		Enthalpy, B.t.u./lb.		Entropy, B.t.u./(lb.)(°R.)	
		Liquid	Vapor	Liquid	Vapor	Liquid	Vapor			Liquid	Vapor	Liquid	Vapor	Liquid	Vapor
t	p	v_f	v_g	h_f	h_g	s_f	s_g	t	p	v_f	v_g	h_f	h_g	s_f	s_g
−40	9.32	0.0106	3.911	0	73.50	0	0.17517	32	44.77	.0115	.908	15.21	81.63	.03323	.16876
−30	12.02	.0107	3.088	2.03	74.70	0.00471	.17387	36	48.13	.0116	.848	16.10	82.27	.03502	.16854
−20	15.28	.0108	2.474	4.07	75.87	.00940	.17275	40	51.68	.0116	.792	17.00	82.71	.03680	.16833
−16	16.77	.0108	2.271	4.89	76.34	.01126	.17232	50	61.39	.0118	.673	19.27	83.78	.04126	.16785
−12	18.37	.0109	2.088	5.72	76.81	.01310	.17124	60	72.41	.0119	.575	21.57	84.82	.04568	.16741
− 8	20.08	.0109	1.922	6.57	77.29	.01496	.17158	70	84.82	.0121	.493	23.90	85.82	.05009	.16701
− 4	21.91	.0110	1.772	7.41	77.75	.01682	.17123	80	98.76	.0123	.425	26.28	86.80	.05446	.16662
0	23.87	.0110	1.637	8.25	78.21	.01869	.17091	90	114.3	.0125	.368	28.70	87.74	.05882	.16624
+ 4	25.96	.0111	1.514	9.10	78.67	.02052	.17060	100	131.6	.0127	.319	31.16	88.62	.06316	.16584
8	28.18	.0111	1.403	9.96	79.13	.02235	.17030	110	150.7	.0129	.277	33.65	89.43	.06749	.16542
12	30.56	.0112	1.301	10.82	79.59	.02419	.17001	120	171.8	.0132	.240	36.16	90.15	.07180	.16495
16	33.08	.0112	1.207	11.70	80.05	.02601	.16974	130	194.9	.0134	.208	38.69	90.76	.07607	.16438
20	35.75	.0113	1.121	12.55	80.49	.02783	.16949	140	220.2	.0138	.180	41.24	91.24	.08024	.16363
24	38.58	.0113	1.043	13.44	80.95	.02963	.16926								
28	41.59	.0114	0.973	14.32	81.39	.03143	.16900								

* From *Am. Soc. Refrig. Eng. Circ.* 12, by permission. Newer tables issued by E. I. du Pont de Nemours Co., Inc., show some differences.

Table 3-238. Saturated Freon-21 (Dichloromonofluoromethane)*

Temp., °F. t	Abs. pressure, lb./sq. in. p	Volume, cu. ft./lb. Liquid v_f	Volume, cu. ft./lb. Vapor v_g	Enthalpy, B.t.u./lb. Liquid h_f	Enthalpy, B.t.u./lb. Vapor h_g	Entropy, B.t.u./(lb.)(°R.) Liquid s_f	Entropy, B.t.u./(lb.)(°R.) Vapor s_g
−40	1.358	0.01058	32.09	0.00	114.56	0.0000	0.2730
−30	1.888	.01066	23.61	2.36	115.76	.0055	.2695
−20	2.578	.01075	17.66	4.71	116.96	.0109	.2663
−10	3.463	.01084	13.43	7.07	118.17	.0162	.2633
0	4.582	.01093	10.35	9.44	119.37	.0214	.2606
5	5.243	.01097	9.132	10.63	119.97	.0240	.2593
10	5.978	.01102	8.085	11.81	120.57	.0265	.2581
20	7.699	.01112	6.392	14.21	121.78	.0316	.2559
30	9.793	.01122	5.112	16.61	122.98	.0365	.2538
40	12.32	.01132	4.130	19.04	124.19	.0414	.2519
50	15.33	.01142	3.370	21.49	125.39	.0463	.2502
60	18.90	.01153	2.773	23.98	126.60	.0511	.2486
70	23.08	.01164	2.300	26.49	127.79	.0559	.2471
80	27.96	.01176	1.923	29.03	128.98	.0606	.2458
86	31.23	.01183	1.733	30.56	129.68	.0634	.2450
90	33.58	.01188	1.619	31.59	130.14	.0652	.2446
100	40.04	.01200	1.371	34.18	131.29	.0699	.2434
110	47.40	.01213	1.169	36.79	132.42	.0745	.2424
120	55.75	.01226	1.001	39.46	133.53	.0791	.2414
130	65.15	.01240	0.8623	42.13	134.61	.0837	.2405
140	75.72	.01254	.7457	44.86	135.66	.0882	.2396
150	87.51	.01269	.6476	47.62	136.68	.0927	.2388
160	100.6	.01284	.5646	50.43	137.69	.0972	.2381

* Courtesy Kinetic Chemicals, Inc.

Table 3-239. Superheated Freon-21 (Dichloromonofluoromethane)*

v, volume, cu. ft./lb.; h, enthalpy, B.t.u./lb.; s, entropy, B.t.u./(lb.)(°R.)
Parenthetic figures after pressures are saturation temperatures

Temp., °F. t	Abs. pressure 1.2 lb./sq. in. (−43.6°F.) v	h	s
Sat.	36.02	114.13	0.2744
−40	36.34	114.57	.2754
−30	37.21	115.80	.2783
−20	38.08	117.03	.2812
−10	38.95	118.28	.2840
0	39.83	119.54	.2867
10	40.70	120.80	.2894
20	41.57	122.08	.2921
30	42.44	128.38	.2948
40	43.32	124.69	.2975
50	44.19	126.01	.3001
60	45.06	127.35	.3027
70	45.93	128.71	.3053
80	46.80	130.09	.3079
90	47.67	131.48	.3104
100	48.54	132.88	.3129
110	49.42	134.29	.3154
120	50.29	135.71	.3179
130	51.16	137.14	.3203
140	52.03	138.59	.3228
150	52.90	140.06	.3252
160	53.77	141.55	.3276
170	54.64	143.05	.3300
180	55.51	144.56	.3324
190	56.38	146.08	.3348
200	57.25	147.61	.3371
210	58.12	149.16	.3394
220	58.99	150.73	.3418
230	59.86	152.31	.3441
240	60.73	153.90	.3464
250	61.60	155.51	.3486

Temp., °F. t	Abs. pressure 2 lb./sq. in. (−28.2°F.) v	h	s
Sat.	22.37	115.98	0.2689
−20	22.80	116.99	.2712
−10	23.33	118.24	.2740
0	23.85	119.49	.2768
10	24.38	120.76	.2795
20	24.90	122.04	.2822
30	25.43	123.34	.2849
40	25.95	124.65	.2876
50	26.47	125.98	.2902
60	27.00	127.33	.2928
70	27.52	128.69	.2954
80	28.05	130.07	.2979
90	28.57	131.45	.3005
100	29.09	132.85	.3030
110	29.62	134.26	.3055
120	30.14	135.68	.3080
130	30.66	137.12	.3104
140	31.19	138.57	.3129
150	31.71	140.03	.3153
160	32.23	141.52	.3177
170	32.76	143.02	.3201
180	33.28	144.53	.3225
190	33.80	146.05	.3249
200	34.33	147.59	.3272
210	34.85	149.14	.3296
220	35.37	150.71	.3319
230	35.89	152.29	.3342
240	36.42	153.88	.3365
250	36.94	155.59	.3388

Temp., °F. t	Abs. pressure 4 lb./sq. in. (−4.9°F.) v	h	s
Sat.	11.74	118.78	0.2619
0	11.87	119.40	.2633
10	12.14	120.66	.2660
20	12.40	121.95	.2687
30	12.66	123.25	.2714
40	12.93	124.57	.2741
50	13.19	125.90	.2767
60	13.45	127.25	.2793
70	13.72	128.61	.2819
80	13.98	129.99	.2845
90	14.24	131.37	.2870
100	14.51	132.77	.2895
110	14.77	134.18	.2920
120	15.03	135.61	.2945
130	15.29	137.04	.2970
140	15.56	138.49	.2994
150	15.82	139.96	.3019
160	16.08	141.45	.3043
170	16.35	142.95	.3067
180	16.61	144.46	.3091
190	16.87	145.98	.3114
200	17.13	147.52	.3138
210	17.39	149.08	.3161
220	17.66	150.65	.3184
230	17.92	152.23	.3207
240	18.18	153.82	.3230
250	18.44	155.43	.3253
260	18.70	157.05	.3276
270	18.97	158.68	.3298

Temp., °F. t	Abs. pressure 10 lb./sq. in. (30.9°F.) v	h	s
Sat.	5.014	123.10	0.2536
40	5.112	124.30	.2561
50	5.219	125.63	.2587
60	5.326	126.99	.2613
70	5.443	128.36	.2639
80	5.540	129.74	.2665
90	5.646	131.13	.2691
100	5.753	132.54	.2716
110	5.860	133.95	.2741
120	5.966	135.38	.2766
130	6.072	136.82	.2791
140	6.178	138.28	.2815
150	6.285	139.75	.2840
160	6.391	141.24	.2864
170	6.497	142.75	.2888
180	6.603	144.27	.2912
190	6.709	145.79	.2936
200	6.815	147.33	.2959
210	6.921	148.89	.2983
220	7.027	150.46	.3006
230	7.133	152.05	.3029
240	7.239	153.65	.3052
250	7.344	155.26	.3075
260	7.450	156.88	.3098
270	7.555	158.52	.3120
290	7.761	160.17	.3143
290	7.767	161.84	.3165
300	7.872	163.52	.3187
310	7.978	165.21	.3210

* Courtesy of Kinetic Chemicals, Inc.

Table 3-239. Superheated Freon-21 (Dichloromonofluoromethane)—(*Concluded*)

Temp., °F.	Abs. pressure 20 lb./sq. in. (62.8°F.)			Temp., °F.	Abs. pressure 50 lb./sq. in. (113.3°F.)			Temp., °F.	Abs. pressure 100 lb./sq. in. (159.6°F.)		
t	*v*	*h*	*s*	*t*	*v*	*h*	*s*	*t*	*v*	*h*	*s*
Sat.	2.630	126.94	0.2482	Sat.	1.111	132.79	0.2421	Sat.	0.5680	137.66	0.2381
60				120	1.127	133.78	.2438	160	.5685	137.72	.2382
70	2.670	127.94	.2501	130	1.150	135.26	.2463	170	.5815	139.32	.2408
80	2.725	129.33	.2527					180	.5945	140.92	.2433
90	2.780	130.73	.2552	140	1.173	136.75	.2488	190	.6073	142.53	.2458
				150	1.197	138.26	.2513				
100	2.834	132.14	.2578	160	1.220	139.79	.2538	200	.6200	144.16	.2483
110	2.889	133.56	.2603	170	1.243	141.33	.2563	210	.6326	145.80	.2508
120	2.943	135.00	.2628	180	1.265	142.88	.2587	220	.6540	147.45	.2532
130	2.998	136.45	.2653					230	.6574	149.10	.2556
140	3.052	137.91	.2678	190	1.288	144.43	.2612	240	.6698	150.76	.2580
				200	1.311	146.00	.2636				
150	3.106	139.39	.2702	210	1.334	147.59	.2659	250	.6820	152.44	.2604
160	3.160	140.90	.2727	220	1.356	149.19	.2683	260	.6942	154.13	.2628
170	3.214	142.41	.2751	230	1.379	150.80	.2707	270	.7063	155.83	.2651
180	3.268	143.93	.2775					280	.7183	157.54	.2674
190	3.322	145.46	.2799	240	1.401	152.42	.2730	290	.7303	159.26	.2698
				250	1.424	154.06	.2753				
200	3.376	147.01	.2822	260	1.446	155.71	.2776	300	.7423	161.00	.2721
210	3.430	148.58	.2846	270	1.469	157.37	.2799	310	.7542	162.75	.2743
220	3.484	150.16	.2869	280	1.491	159.05	.2822	320	.7660	164.51	.2766
230	3.537	151.75	.2892					330	.7777	166.28	.2789
240	3.591	153.36	.2915	290	1.513	160.74	.2845	340	.7894	168.06	.2811
				300	1.535	162.44	.2867				
250	3.645	154.97	.2938	310	1.558	164.16	.2890	350	.8011	169.85	.2833
260	3.698	156.60	.2961	320	1.580	165.89	.2912	360	.8128	171.66	.2856
270	3.752	158.24	.2984	330	1.602	167.63	.2934	370	.8244	173.48	.2878
280	3.805	159.90	.3007					380	.8360	175.31	.2900
290	3.859	161.57	.3029	340	1.624	169.38	.2956	390	.8475	177.16	.2922
				350	1.646	171.14	.2978				
300	3.912	163.25	.3051	360	1.668	172.92	.3000	400	.8590	179.02	.2943
310	3.965	164.95	.3074	370	1.690	174.72	.3022				
320	4.019	166.67	.3096	380	1.712	176.52	.3044				
330	4.072	168.40	.3118								
340	4.125	170.14	.3140	390	1.734	178.34	.3065				
...	.....	......	......								

Table 3-240. Fuels, Gasolines, and Hydrocarbon Mixtures

For *H-T* diagrams for fuels and gasoline see Hibbard, *N.A.C.A. Research Mem.* E56121, 1956 (declassified 1958); Edmister, *Ind. Eng. Chem.*, **30**, 352 (1938); *Petrol. Refiner*, **28**, 137, 149 (1949) (Mollier diagrams, etc.); Katz and Rzasa, "Bibliography for the Physical Behaviour of Hydrocarbons under Pressure and Related Phenomena," Edwards, Ann Arbor, Mich., 1946; Brown, *Petrol. Eng.*, **16**, 215 (1945) (Mollier diagrams for natural gases); Bauer and Middleton, *Petrol. Refiner*, **32**, 113 (1953) (enthalpy data); Scheibel and Jenny, *Ind. Eng. Chem.*, **37**, 990 (1954) (nomographs for enthalpy); Pitzer and Brattain, *Proc. Am. Petrol. Inst.*, **32**, 176 (1952) (hydrocarbons and related compounds); Lochmann, **32**, 301 (1951) (372 literature references to data on petroleum hydrocarbons, etc.); Sage and Lacey, *Chem. Eng.*, **62**, 396 (1955) (refers to 250-page A.P.I. publication). Van Winkle [*Petrol. Refiner*, **27**, 435 (1948)] gives the pressure coefficient of enthalpy for petroleum vapors.

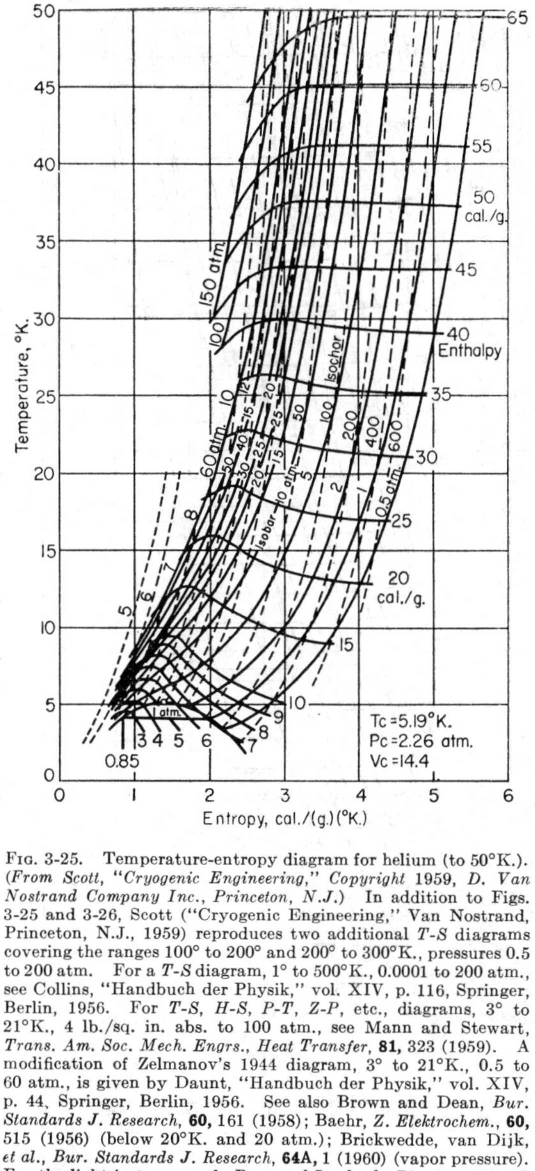

Fig. 3-25. Temperature-entropy diagram for helium (to 50°K.). (*From Scott, "Cryogenic Engineering," Copyright* 1959, *D. Van Nostrand Company Inc., Princeton, N.J.*) In addition to Figs. 3-25 and 3-26, Scott ("Cryogenic Engineering," Van Nostrand, Princeton, N.J., 1959) reproduces two additional *T-S* diagrams covering the ranges 100° to 200° and 200° to 300°K., pressures 0.5 to 200 atm. For a *T-S* diagram, 1° to 500°K., 0.0001 to 200 atm., see Collins, "Handbuch der Physik," vol. XIV, p. 116, Springer, Berlin, 1956. For *T-S*, *H-S*, *P-T*, *Z-P*, etc., diagrams, 3° to 21°K., 4 lb./sq. in. abs. to 100 atm., see Mann and Stewart, *Trans. Am. Soc. Mech. Engrs., Heat Transfer*, **81,** 323 (1959). A modification of Zelmanov's 1944 diagram, 3° to 21°K., 0.5 to 60 atm., is given by Daunt, "Handbuch der Physik," vol. XIV, p. 44, Springer, Berlin, 1956. See also Brown and Dean, *Bur. Standards J. Research*, **60,** 161 (1958); Baehr, *Z. Elektrochem.*, **60,** 515 (1956) (below 20°K. and 20 atm.); Brickwedde, van Dijk, *et al.*, *Bur. Standards J. Research*, **64A,** 1 (1960) (vapor pressure). For the light isotope see de Boer and Lunbeck, *Physica*, **14,** 510 (1948); Chenstov, *Uspekhi Fiz. Nauk*, **55,** 49 (1955); Dokoupil, *Physica*, **20,** 1181 (1954); Hammell, Sherman, *et al.*, *Physica*, **24,** 51 (1958). Cann and Ducati (Plasmadyne Corp. *Rept.* P-4TN069-54, 1959) give a Mollier diagram and tables from 6000° to 60,000°K. Hill and Lounasmaa [*Phil. Trans. Roy. Soc.*, **A252,** 357 (1960)] give data and diagrams for the range 3° to 20°K., 0 to 100 atm.

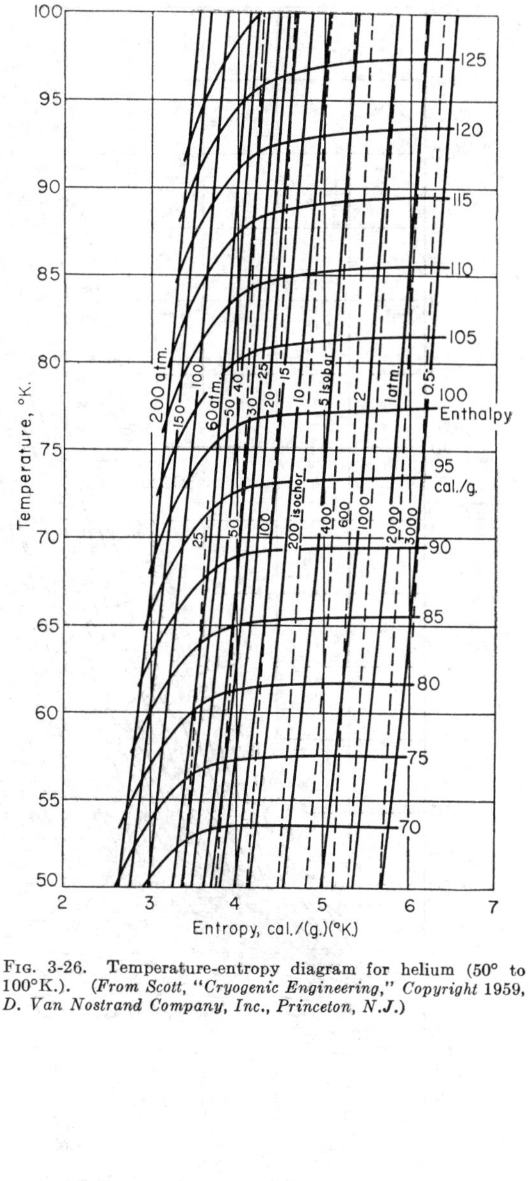

Fig. 3-26. Temperature-entropy diagram for helium (50° to 100°K.). (*From Scott, "Cryogenic Engineering," Copyright* 1959, *D. Van Nostrand Company, Inc., Princeton, N.J.*)

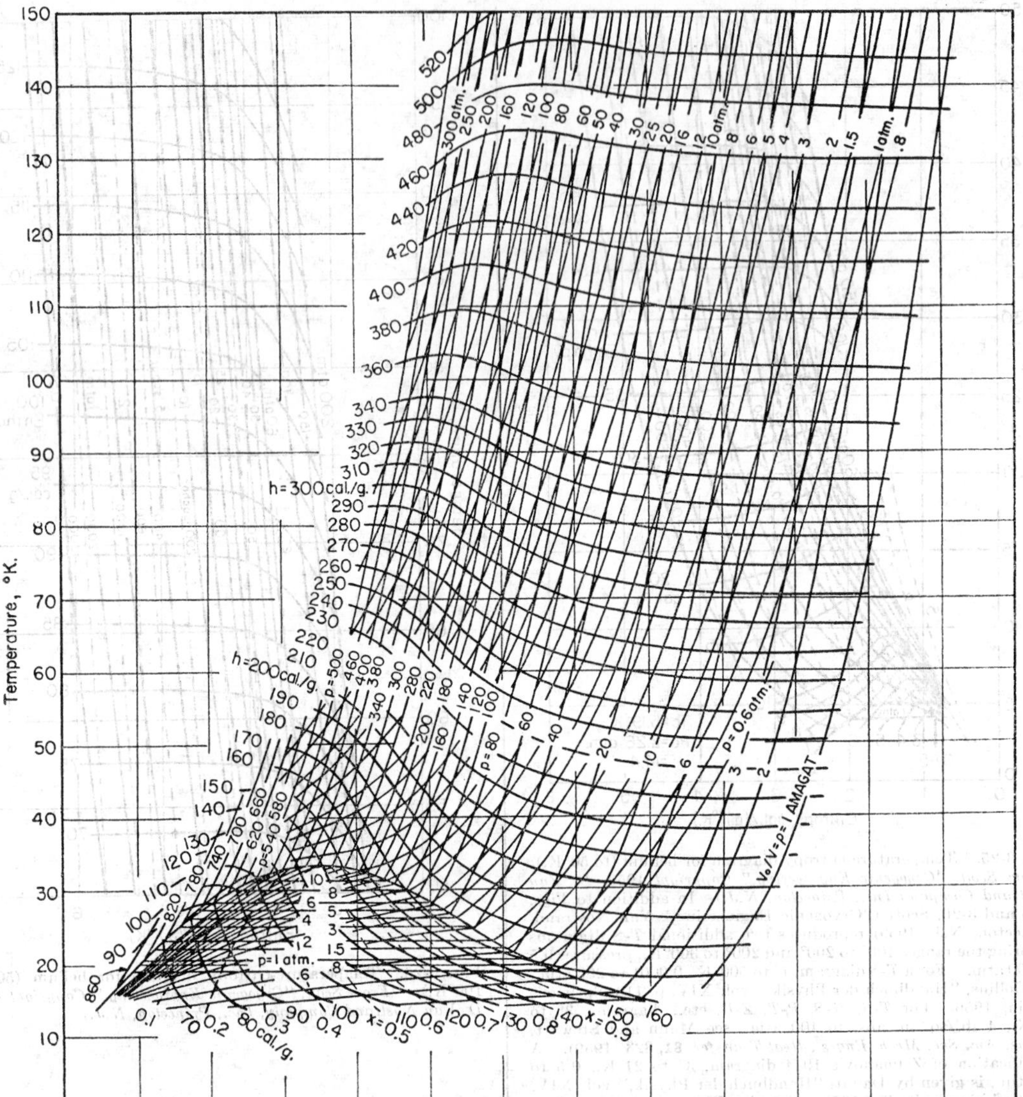

FIG. 3-27. Temperature-entropy diagram for hydrogen (0° to 150°K.). [*Woolley, Scott, and Brickwedde, Bur. Standards J. Research* **41**, 379 (1948). *Reproduced by permission of the authors.*] For tables of thermodynamic properties see Hilsenrath *et al., N.B.S. Circ.* 564, 1955. For other diagrams see Koeppe, *Kältetechnik,* **8,** 275 (1956) (*T-S,* to 120 atm.); Sanger-Bredt, *N.A.S.A.* TT Fl, 1959 (*H-S,* to 10 atm., 10,000°K.); King, *N.A.S.A. Tech. Note* D-275, 1960 (C_p-*T*, *H-T*, *S-T* graphs, to 5000°K., 100 atm.); Nicklin, *U. K. Atomic Energy Auth., Ind. Group Tech. Note* 36, 1956 (C_p, etc.).

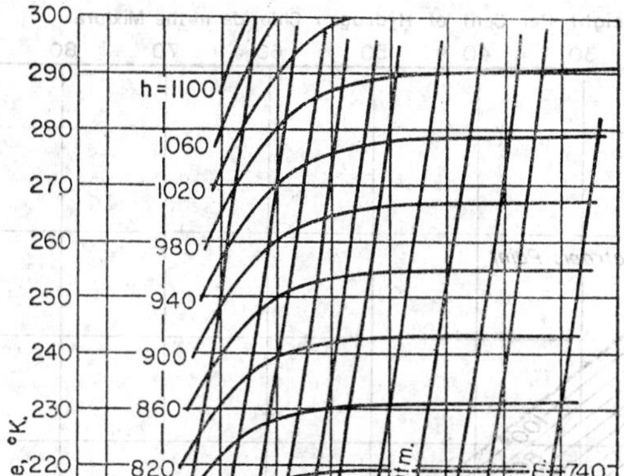

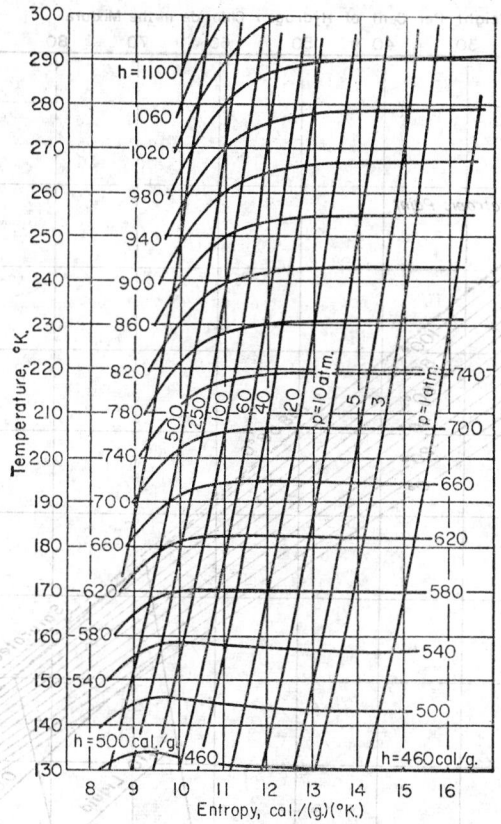

Fig. 3-28. Temperature-entropy diagram for hydrogen (130° to 300°K.). [*Woolley, Scott, and Brickwedde, Fig. 4h-3, p. 4-101, "American Institute of Physics Handbook," Gray (Ed.). Reproduced by permission. Copyright, 1957, by McGraw-Hill Book Company, Inc.*]

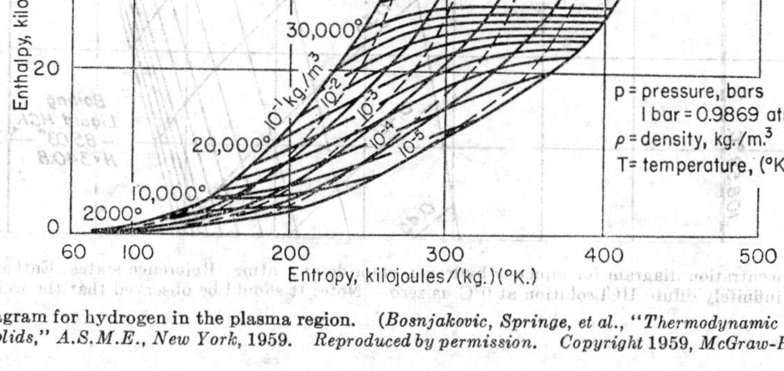

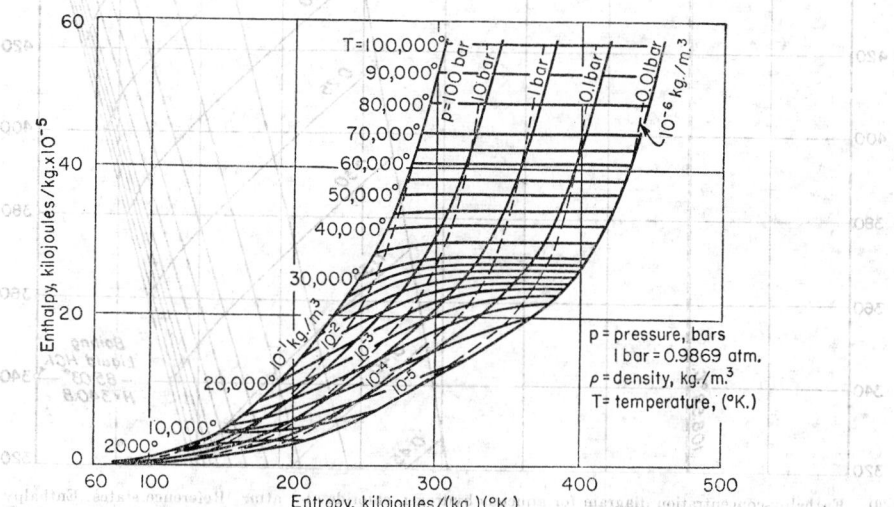

Fig. 3-29. Mollier diagram for hydrogen in the plasma region. (*Bosnjakovic, Springe, et al., "Thermodynamic and Transport Properties of Gases, Liquids and Solids," A.S.M.E., New York, 1959. Reproduced by permission. Copyright 1959, McGraw-Hill Book Company, Inc.*)

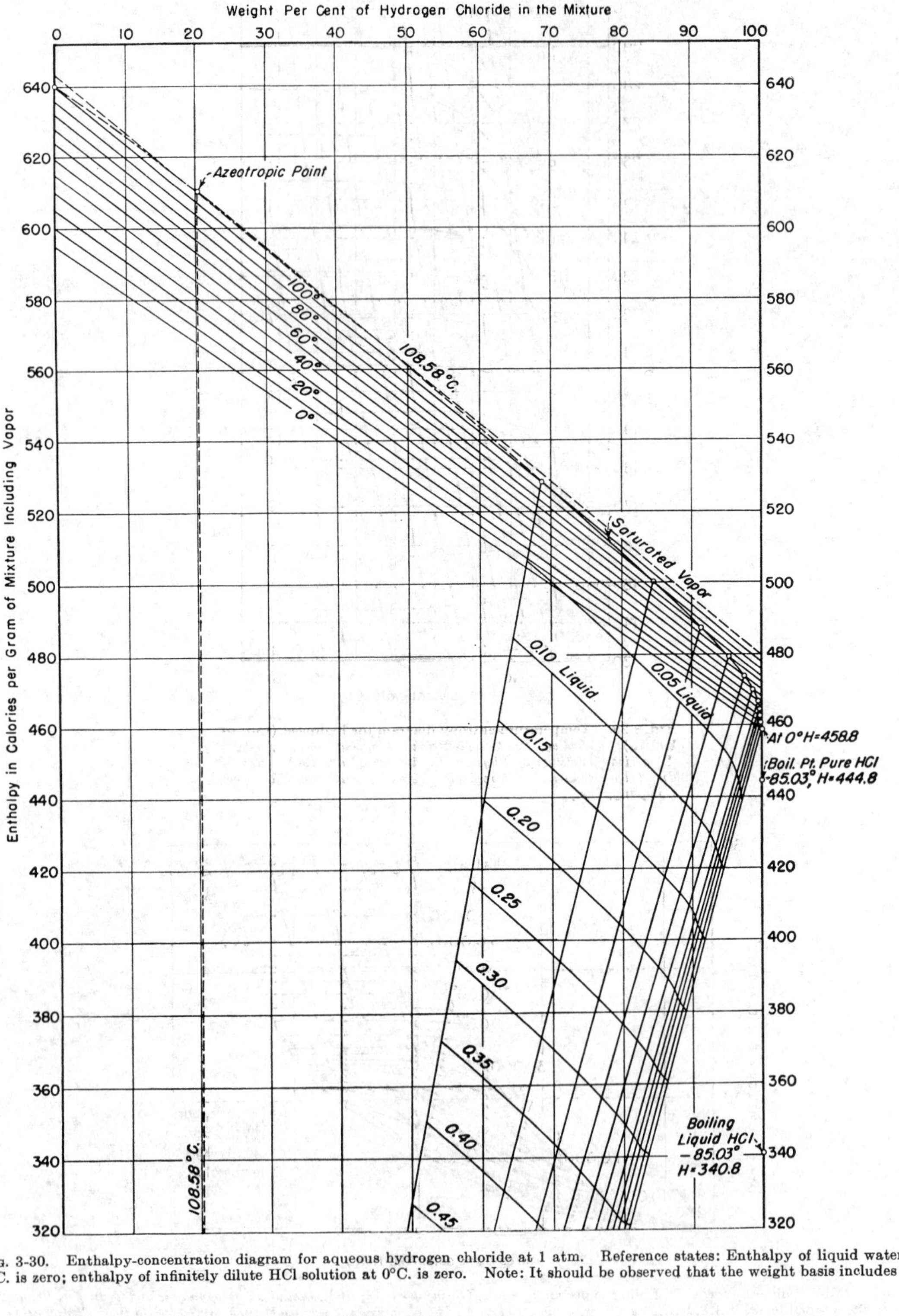

FIG. 3-30. Enthalpy-concentration diagram for aqueous hydrogen chloride at 1 atm. Reference states: Enthalpy of liquid water at 0°C. is zero; enthalpy of infinitely dilute HCl solution at 0°C. is zero. Note: It should be observed that the weight basis includes the

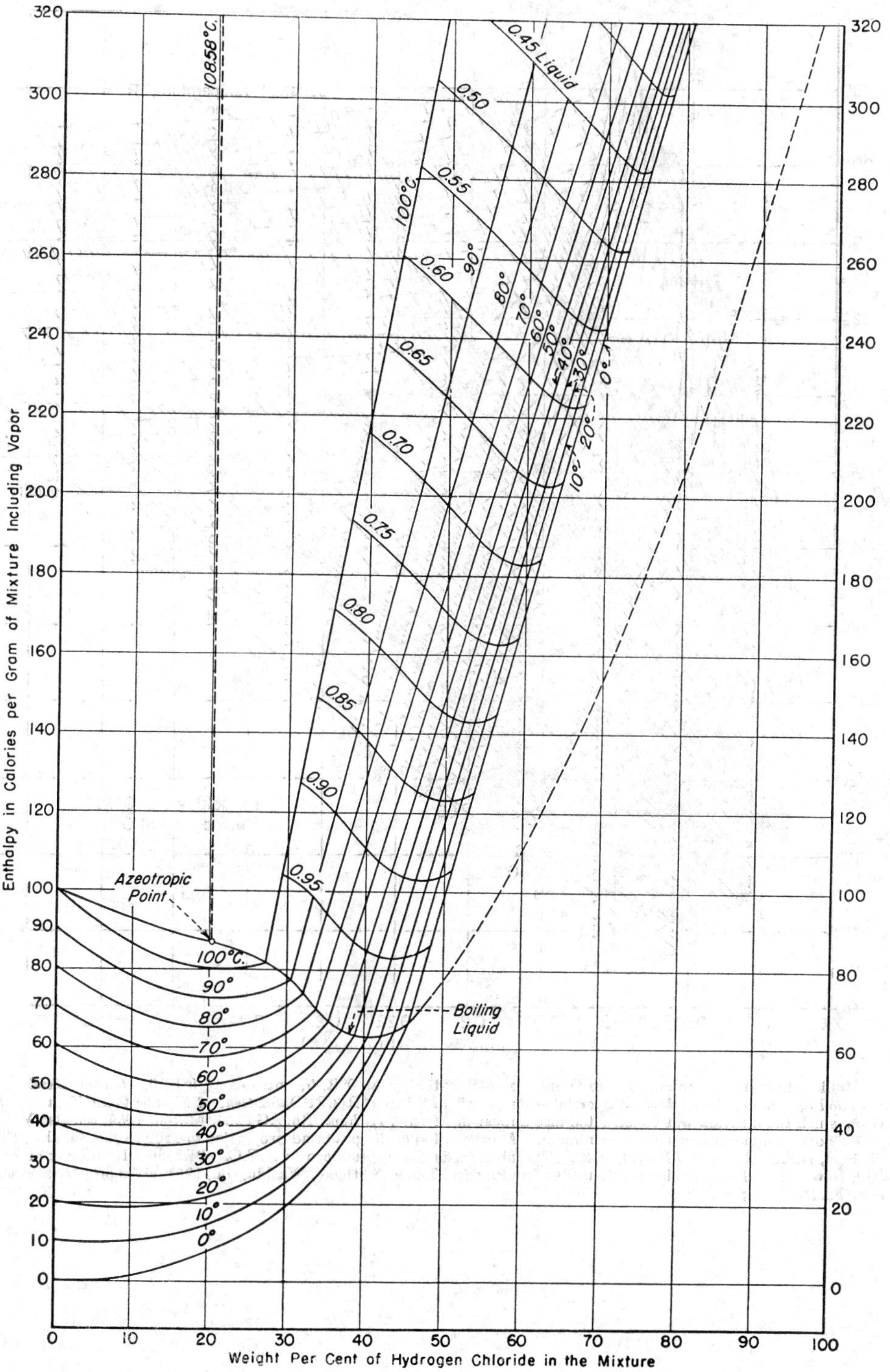

vapor, which is particularly important in the two-phase region. Saturation values may be read at the ends of the tie lines. [*Van Nuys. Trans. Am. Inst. Chem. Engrs.* **39**, 663 (1943).]

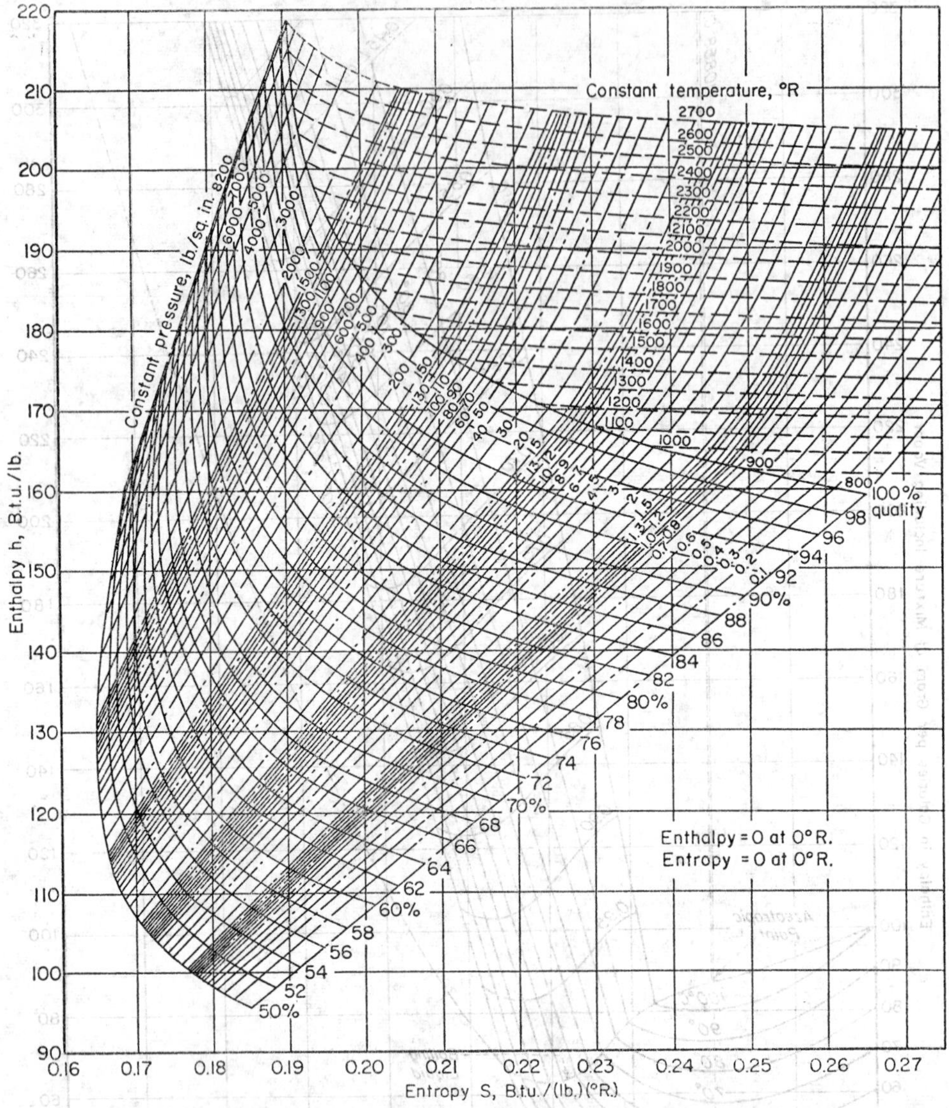

Fig. 3-31. Mollier diagram for mercury. Reference point: Enthalpy at 0°R.:0; entropy at 0°R.:0. (*From Meisl, and Shapiro, "Thermodynamic Properties of Alkali Metal Vapors and Mercury," TIS Report* R60FPD358, *General Electric Co., Cincinnati, June, 1960.*) The data from which the diagram was constructed also appear in Meisl, *TIS Rept.* R59AGT264, March, 1959; see also WADC-TR-59-598, 1959. This diagram is reproduced by permission. Another Mollier diagram and properties to 1100 lb./sq. in. abs., 1400°F., were given by Sheldon, A.S.M.E. Paper 49-A-30, 1949. The diagram is also reproduced in A.E.C. "Reactor Handbook of Engineering," McGraw-Hill, New York, 1955. Table 169, "Smithsonian Physical Tables," 9th ed., Washington, 1954, gives properties of the saturated vapor to 1100°F., 180 lb./sq. in. abs.

Table 3-241. Saturated Mercury*

Abs. pressure, lb./sq. in. p	Temp., °F. t	Volume, cu. ft./lb. Vapor v_f	Enthalpy, B.t.u./lb. Liquid h_f	Enthalpy, B.t.u./lb. Vapor h_g	Entropy, B.t.u./(lb.)(°R.) Liquid s_f	Entropy, B.t.u./(lb.)(°R.) Vapor s_g	Abs. pressure, lb./sq. in. p	Temp., °F. t	Volume, cu. ft./lb. Vapor v_f	Enthalpy, B.t.u./lb. Liquid h_f	Enthalpy, B.t.u./lb. Vapor h_g	Entropy, B.t.u./(lb.)(°R.) Liquid s_f	Entropy, B.t.u./(lb.)(°R.) Vapor s_g
0.4	402.3	114.5	13.81	141.9	0.02094	0.1696	25	730.4	2.429	26.05	146.9	.03297	.1345
.6	426.1	78.23	14.70	142.3	.02195	.1660	30	750.9	2.053	26.81	147.2	.03360	.1331
.8	443.8	59.71	15.36	142.6	.02269	.1635	35	769.0	1.781	27.49	147.5	.03416	.1319
1.0	458.1	48.45	15.89	142.8	.02328	.1615	40	784.8	1.576	28.08	147.8	.03464	.1308
1.5	485.1	33.14	16.90	143.2	.02436	.1580							
2	505.2	25.31	17.65	143.5	.02514	.1556	45	799.3	1.414	28.62	148.0	.03507	.1299
3	535.4	17.34	18.78	144.0	.02629	.1521	50	812.5	1.284	29.11	148.2	.03546	.1291
4	558.0	13.26	19.62	144.3	.02714	.1497	60	836.1	1.086	29.99	148.6	.03614	.1276
5	576.2	10.77	20.30	144.6	.02780	.1478	70	856.6	0.9436	30.75	148.9	.03672	.1264
6	591.4	9.096	20.87	144.8	.02834	.1462	80	874.8	0.8349	31.43	149.1	.03725	.1254
7	605.0	7.882	21.37	145.0	.02882	.1450	90	891.6	0.7497	32.06	149.4	.03771	.1245
8	616.8	6.963	21.81	145.2	.02923	.1439	100	906.9	0.6811	32.63	149.6	.03813	.1237
9	627.5	6.244	22.21	145.4	.02960	.1429	120	934.4	0.5767	33.60	150.1	.03887	.1224
10	637.3	5.661	22.58	145.5	.02993	.1420	140	958.3	0.5012	34.55	150.4	.03951	.1212
15	676.5	3.892	24.04	146.1	.03124	.1387	160	979.9	0.4438	35.35	150.8	.04007	.1202
20	706.2	2.983	25.15	146.6	.03220	.1363	180	999.6	0.3990	36.09	151.1	.04058	.1193

* Marks, "Mechanical Engineers' Handbook," 4th ed., McGraw-Hill, New York, 1941.

Table 3-242. Saturated Methane*

Temp., °F. t	Abs. pressure, lb./sq. in. p	Volume, cu. ft./lb. Liquid v_f	Volume, cu. ft./lb. Vapor v_g	Enthalpy, B.t.u./lb. Liquid h_f	Enthalpy, B.t.u./lb. Vapor h_g	Entropy B.t.u./(lb.)(°R.) Liquid s_f	Entropy B.t.u./(lb.)(°R.) Vapor s_g	Temp., °F. t	Abs. pressure, lb./sq. in. p	Volume, cu. ft./lb. Liquid v_f	Volume, cu. ft./lb. Vapor v_g	Enthalpy, B.t.u./lb. Liquid h_f	Enthalpy, B.t.u./lb. Vapor h_g	Entropy B.t.u./(lb.)(°R.) Liquid s_f	Entropy B.t.u./(lb.)(°R.) Vapor s_g
−280	4.90	0.03635	24.04	0	228.2	0	1.2699	−180	191.5	.04575	.773	87.8	257.0	.3767	.9816
−270	8.44	.03698	14.61	8.2	232.3	0.0423	1.2236	−170	240.0	.04745	.610	98.0	257.2	.4127	.9622
−260	13.80	.03766	9.31	16.6	236.4	.0823	1.1830	−160	297.0	.04944	.483	108.7	256.5	.4476	.9411
−250	21.71	.03839	6.13	25.0	240.3	.1201	1.1468	−150	364	.05197	.381	120.3	254.5	.4839	.9169
−240	32.4	.03915	4.24	33.3	243.9	.1578	1.1164	−140	440	.05224	.3008	133.2	251.2	.5214	.8905
−230	46.4	.03999	3.04	42.0	247.3	.1962	1.0900	−130	527	.05999	.2318	148.1	245.9	.5656	.8622
−220	64.5	.04092	2.23	50.6	250.2	.2333	1.0660	−120	627	.06961	.1613	171.8	231.4	.6329	.8083
−210	87.6	.04193	1.67	59.5	252.8	.2693	1.0434	−115.8	673	.0983	.0983	203.4	203.4	.7232	.7232
−200	115.7	.04306	1.281	68.8	254.8	.3062	1.0224								
−190	150.0	.04431	0.990	78.2	256.2	.3419	1.0019								

* Matthews and Hurd, *Trans. Am. Inst. Chem. Engrs.*, **42**, 55 (1946). For a tabulation of data for the superheated vapor see Table 227, pp. 270–271, 3d ed. of this handbook. Note that, for 320°F., 500 lb./sq. in. abs., h = 543.2 and not as printed. Tester, "Thermodynamic Properties of Methane," British Petroleum Co., publication undated and also published by Butterworth, London, gives *H*, *S*, *V*, *Z*, etc., for 1 to 1000 atm., 130(10)470°K. See also Corcoran, Bowles, *et al.*, *Ind. Eng. Chem.*, **37**, 825 (1945) (*T-S*, −230° to 70°F., 15 to 1400 lb./sq. in. abs.); Keesom, Bijl, *et al.*, *Appl. Sci. Research*, **A3**, 261 (1952) (*H*-log *P*, −100° to 475°C. to 300 atm.); Bloomer, Eakin, *et al.*, *Inst. Gas Technol. Research Bull.* 21, Chicago, 1955 (−260° to 500°F., 10 to 1500 lb./sq. in. abs.); Maxwell, "Data Book on Hydrocarbons," Van Nostrand, Princeton, N.J., 1951 (*H-T*, −200° to 1200°F., to 150 atm.; *H-S* to 480°F., 60 atm.); Levchenko, *J. Phys. Chem. U.S.S.R.*, **18**, 453 (1944) (to 200°K., 1000 atm.); Kroepelin, Neumann, *et al.*, *Abhandl. braunschweig. wiss. Ges.*, **10**, 166 (1958) (to 6000°K.).

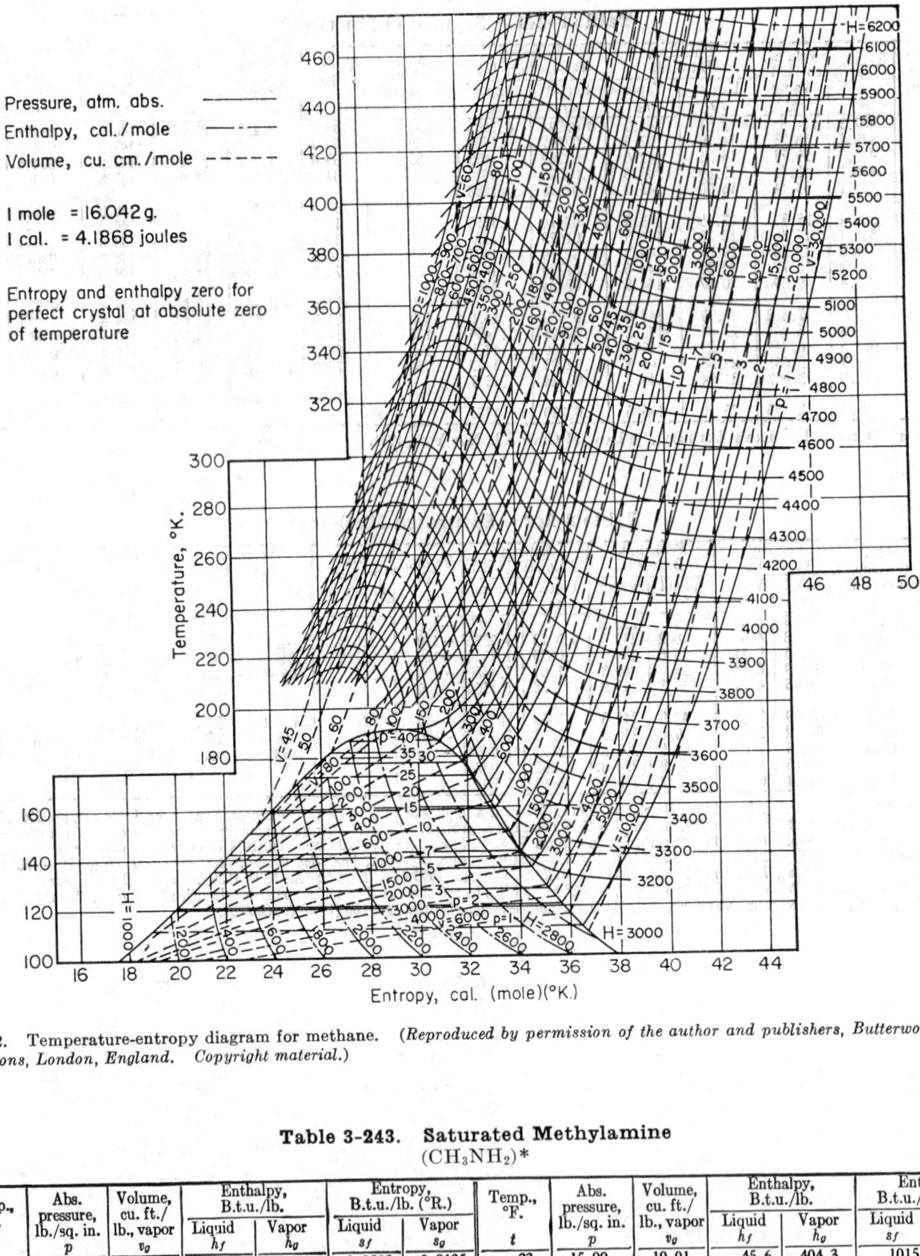

FIG. 3-32. Temperature-entropy diagram for methane. *(Reproduced by permission of the author and publishers, Butterworth Scientific Publications, London, England. Copyright material.)*

Table 3-243. Saturated Methylamine
(CH_3NH_2)*

Temp., °F.	Abs. pressure, lb./sq. in.	Volume, cu. ft./lb., vapor	Enthalpy, B.t.u./lb.		Entropy, B.t.u./lb. (°R.)		Temp., °F.	Abs. pressure, lb./sq. in.	Volume, cu. ft./lb., vapor	Enthalpy, B.t.u./lb.		Entropy, B.t.u./lb. (°R.)	
			Liquid	Vapor	Liquid	Vapor				Liquid	Vapor	Liquid	Vapor
t	p	v_g	h_f	h_g	s_f	s_g	t	p	v_g	h_f	h_g	s_f	s_g
− 58	1.322	98.93	−12.4	374.8	−0.0503	0.9135	23	15.99	10.01	45.6	404.3	.1015	.8443
− 40	2.532	56.72	0.0	381.7	.0000	.9092	41	24.49	6.796	59.2	410.1	.1292	.8300
− 22	4.551	32.56	12.7	388.4	.0294	.8877	68	43.52	3.985	80.2	418.8	.1698	.8115
− 4	7.78	19.84	25.7	395.0	.0586	.8689	86	61.53	2.962	94.5	424.4	.1963	.8008
+ 5	10.03	15.54	32.6	398.5	.0731	.8603	113	98.76	1.867	116.9	432.6	.2360	.7873

* "Refrigerating Data Book," 5th ed., American Society of Refrigerating Engineers, New York, 1942.

Table 3-244. Saturated Methyl Chloride*

Temp., °F. t	Abs. pressure, lb./sq. in. p	Volume, cu. ft./lb. Liquid v_f	Volume, cu. ft./lb. Vapor v_g	Enthalpy, B.t.u./lb. Liquid h_f	Enthalpy, B.t.u./lb. Vapor h_g	Entropy, B.t.u./(lb.)(°R.) Liquid s_f	Entropy, B.t.u./(lb.)(°R.) Vapor s_g
−40	6.878	0.01553	12.72	0.000	190.66	0.0000	0.4544
−30	9.036	.01568	9.873	3.562	192.08	.0084	.4472
−20	11.71	.01583	7.761	7.146	193.49	.0166	.4405
−10	14.96	.01598	6.176	10.75	194.87	.0247	.4343
0	18.90	.01613	4.969	14.39	196.23	.0327	.4284
5	21.15	.01622	4.471	16.21	196.92	.0367	.4257
10	23.60	.01631	4.038	18.04	197.58	.0406	.4229
20	29.16	.01647	3.312	21.73	198.84	.0484	.4177
30	35.68	.01665	2.739	25.44	200.03	.0560	.4126
40	43.25	.01684	2.286	29.17	201.17	.0636	.4079
50	51.99	.01704	1.920	32.93	202.28	.0710	.4034
60	62.00	.01724	1.624	36.71	203.33	.0784	.3991
70	73.41	.01744	1.382	40.52	204.34	.0856	.3950
80	86.26	.01764	1.183	44.36	205.27	.0928	.3910
86	94.70	.01778	1.081	46.47	205.80	.0970	.3887
90	100.6	.01786	1.018	48.21	206.13	.0998	.3872
100	116.7	.01808	0.8814	52.09	206.94	.1069	.3836
110	134.5	.01833	.7672	56.00	207.70	.1138	.3801
120	154.2	.01859	.6710	59.93	208.39	.1206	.3768
130	175.9	.01887	.5889	63.89	209.02	.1274	.3736
140	199.6	.01915	.5189	67.87	209.58	.1341	.3705
150	225.4	.01945	.4586	71.87	210.10	.1407	.3674
160	253.5	.01978	.4070	75.90	210.56	.1473	.3646
170	283.9	.02015	.3613	79.97	210.93	.1538	.3618

* Tanner, Banning, and Matthewson, *Ind. Eng. Chem.*, **31**, 878 (1939). Copyright, 1939, E. I. du Pont de Nemours & Co., Inc. For a du Pont *H*-log *P* diagram, −50° to 370°F., 3.5 to 270 lb./sq. in. gage, and data at closer pressure intervals to 140 lb./sq. in. abs., see "American Society of Refrigerating Engineers Data Book," pp. 32.82–84, 1955. For isotherms and thermodynamic tables, 0° to 150°C., to 150 atm., see Michels, Visser, *et al.*, *Physica*, **18**, 114 (1952). For a *H-P* diagram, −30° to 180°F., to 180 lb./sq. in. abs., see Baker, "Technology of Heat," Longmans, London, 1956.

Table 3-245. Superheated Methyl Chloride*

v, volume, cu. ft./lb.; h, enthalpy, B.t.u./lb.; s, entropy, B.t.u./(lb.)(°R.)
Parenthetic figures under pressures are saturation temperatures

Temp., °F.	Abs. pressure, 6 lb./sq. in. (−44.8°F.)			Temp., °F.	Abs. pressure, 10 lb./sq. in. (−26.1°F.)			Temp., °F.	Abs. pressure, 20 lb./sq. in. (2.5°F.)		
t	v	h	s	t	v	h	s	t	v	h	s
Sat.	14.45	189.96	0.4580	Sat.	8.993	192.64	0.4446	Sat.	4.710	196.58	0.4270
−40	14.62	190.77	.4599	−20	9.124	193.67	.4471	20	4.917	199.90	.4341
−20	15.36	194.27	.4681	0	9.567	197.32	.4552	40	5.146	203.75	.4420
0	16.09	197.84	.4760	20	10.01	201.04	.4630	60	5.373	207.66	.4496
20	16.82	201.48	.4838	40	10.45	204.78	.4707	80	5.599	211.65	.4572
40	17.55	205.19	.4914	60	10.89	208.62	.4782	100	5.823	215.69	.4645
60	18.27	209.01	.4989	80	11.33	212.53	.4856	120	6.046	219.80	.4717
80	18.99	212.88	.5061	100	11.77	216.50	.4928	140	6.268	223.99	.4788
100	19.71	216.82	.5133	120	12.21	220.54	.5000	160	6.489	228.24	.4858
120	20.42	220.84	.5204	140	12.65	224.67	.5069	180	6.709	232.56	.4927
140	21.14	224.94	.5274	160	13.08	228.86	.5138	200	6.929	236.94	.4994
160	21.86	229.11	.5342	180	13.52	233.13	.5206	220	7.147	241.40	.5061
180	22.57	233.36	.5410	200	13.95	237.47	.5273	240	7.365	245.96	.5127
200	23.29	237.69	.5476	220	14.38	241.89	.5339	260	7.583	250.55	.5192
220	24.00	242.09	.5542	240	14.81	246.42	.5045	280	7.801	255.23	.5256
240	24.71	246.60	.5607	260	15.24	250.98	.5469	300	8.019	259.96	.5319
260	25.42	251.15	.5672	280	15.67	255.66	.5532				

Temp., °F.	Abs. pressure, 50 lb./sq. in. (47.8°F.)			Temp., °F.	Abs. pressure, 100 lb./sq. in. (89.6°F.)			Temp., °F.	Abs. pressure, 200 lb./sq. in. (140.3°F.)		
t	v	h	s	t	v	h	s	t	v	h	s
Sat.	1.992	202.09	0.4043	Sat.	1.025	206.11	0.3872	Sat.	0.517	209.60	0.3702
60	2.054	204.65	.4094	100	1.055	208.58	.3920	160	.551	215.30	.3796
80	2.154	208.89	.4174	120	1.111	213.33	.4003	180	.582	220.87	.3886
100	2.252	213.18	.4252	140	1.165	218.15	.4084	200	.612	226.35	.3971
120	2.348	217.52	.4328	160	1.217	222.94	.4163	220	.641	231.75	.4052
140	2.443	221.88	.4402	180	1.268	227.71	.4239	240	.668	237.12	.4129
160	2.537	226.32	.4475	200	1.318	232.50	.4312	260	.695	242.39	.4204
180	2.630	230.79	.4546	220	1.367	237.32	.4384	280	.721	247.65	.4276
200	2.722	235.32	.4616	240	1.415	242.20	.4455	300	.747	252.93	.4346
220	2.813	239.90	.4684	260	1.463	247.06	.4523	320	.772	258.21	.4414

Temp., °F.	Abs. pressure, 50 lb./sq. in. (47.8°F.)			Temp., °F.	Abs. pressure, 100 lb./sq. in. (89.6°F.)			Temp., °F.	Abs. pressure, 200 lb./sq. in. (140.3°F.)		
t	v	h	s	t	v	h	s	t	v	h	s
240	2.903	244.58	.4752	280	1.511	251.96	.4591	340	.797	263.51	.4481
260	2.993	249.27	.4818	300	1.557	256.92	.4657	360	.822	268.84	.4547
280	3.083	254.02	.4884	320	1.603	261.93	.4722	380	.847	274.19	.4612
300	3.173	258.83	.4948	340	1.649	266.97	.4786	400	.870	279.59	.4676
320	3.261	263.71	.5011	360	1.695	272.07	.4849	420	.895	285.05	.4738
340	3.349	268.65	.5074	380	1.739	277.25	.4911	440	.918	290.52	.4800

* Tanner, Banning, and Matthewson, *Ind. Eng. Chem.*, **31**, 878 (1939). Copyright, 1939, E. I. du Pont de Nemours & Co., Inc.

Table 3-246. Saturated Methylene Chloride (CH_2Cl_2)*

Temp., °F. t	Abs. pressure, lb./sq. in. p	Volume, cu. ft./lb., vapor v_g	Enthalpy, B.t.u./lb. Liquid h_f	Enthalpy, B.t.u./lb. Vapor h_g	Entropy, B.t.u./(lb.)(°R.) Liquid s_f	Entropy, B.t.u./(lb.)(°R.) Vapor s_g
10	1.38	42.55	3.4	164.4	0.0072	0.3502
20	1.92	31.40	6.8	165.6	.0151	.3461
30	2.56	23.90	10.2	166.9	.0222	.3425
40	3.38	18.60	13.6	168.0	.0285	.3377
60	5.52	11.68	20.4	170.1	.0410	.3292
80	8.81	7.50	27.2	172.0	.0520	.3202
100	13.25	5.14	34.0	173.7	.0620	.3113
120	19.20	3.65	40.8	175.0	.0714	.3031
140	26.79	2.69	47.6	176.0	.0795	.2935

* "Refrigerating Data Book," 5th ed., American Society of Refrigerating Engineers, New York, 1942.

Table 3-247. Saturated Methyl Formate ($HCOOCH_3$)*

Temp., °F. t	Abs. pressure, lb./sq. in. p	Volume, cu. ft./lb., vapor v_g	Enthalpy, B.t.u./lb. Liquid h_f	Enthalpy, B.t.u./lb. Vapor h_g	Entropy, B.t.u./(lb.)(°R.) Liquid s_f	Entropy, B.t.u./(lb.)(°R.) Vapor s_g
0	1.50	54.0	0	232.5	0.0000	0.5055
20	2.70	31.0	10.3	236.6	.0219	.4934
40	4.66	18.9	20.6	240.7	.0432	.4837
60	7.61	12.0	30.9	244.8	.0633	.4748
80	12.07	7.98	41.2	248.8	.0825	.4670
100	18.26	5.38	51.5	252.9	.1015	.4615
120	27.24	3.74	61.8	257.0	.1192	.4559
140	38.41	2.65	72.1	261.0	.1375	.4525

* "Refrigerating Data Book," 5th ed., American Society of Refrigerating Engineers, New York, 1942.

Table 3-248. Neon

For a *H-T* diagram see Koeppe, *Z. angew. Phys.*, **8**, 581 (1956) (to 130°K., 120 atm.). For tables to 320°K., 200 atm., see Yendall, *Proc. 4th Cryogenic Eng. Conf.*, 1958. A new set of data has recently been produced by E. F. Yendall at Linde Tonawanda Research Labs., 1960. For high-temperature data see Amdur and Mason, *Phys. Fluids*, **1**, 370 (1958).

Table 3-249. Nitric Oxide

For ideal-gas thermodynamic functions see Beckett and Haar, *Proc. Joint Conf. Thermodynamic and Transport Props. Fluids, Inst. Mech. Engrs.*, London, 1958, p. 33; Fickett and Cowan, *A.E.C. Rept.* LA1727, 1954. For properties at higher pressures see Opfell, Schlinger, *et al.*, *Ind. Eng. Chem.*, **46**, 189 (1954) (−80° to 220°F., to 3000 lb./sq.in.abs.); Kobe and Pennington, *Petrol. Refiner*, **29**, 129 (1950) (H, C_p, etc., to 3500°).

Table 3-250. Saturated Nitrogen*

Temp., °K. T	Abs. pressure, atm. p	Volume, cc./g.-mole Liquid v_f	Volume, cc./g.-mole Vapor v_g	Enthalpy, cal./g.-mole Liquid h_f	Enthalpy, cal./g.-mole Vapor h_g	Entropy, cal./(g.-mole)(°K.) Liquid s_f	Entropy, cal./(g.-mole)(°K.) Vapor s_g
77.4	1.00	34.7	6190	0	1335	0.0	17.25
80	1.36	35.2	4640	39	1352	.42	16.83
85	2.25	36.3	2880	115	1381	1.18	16.08
90	3.54	37.5	1872	189	1402	1.90	15.38
95	5.31	39.0	1257	257	1412	2.56	14.72
100	7.67	40.6	875	326	1412	2.21	14.07
105	10.71	42.6	624	393	1402	3.81	13.43
110	14.54	45.0	452	460	1379	4.39	12.74
115	19.28	48.3	324	534	1338	5.01	11.99
120	25.04	53.2	227	625	1269	5.78	11.14
125	31.94	64.9	137	781	1112	7.02	9.64
126	33.47	90.1	90.1	952	952	8.67	8.67

* Millar and Sullivan, *U.S. Bur. Mines Tech. Paper* **424**, 1928.

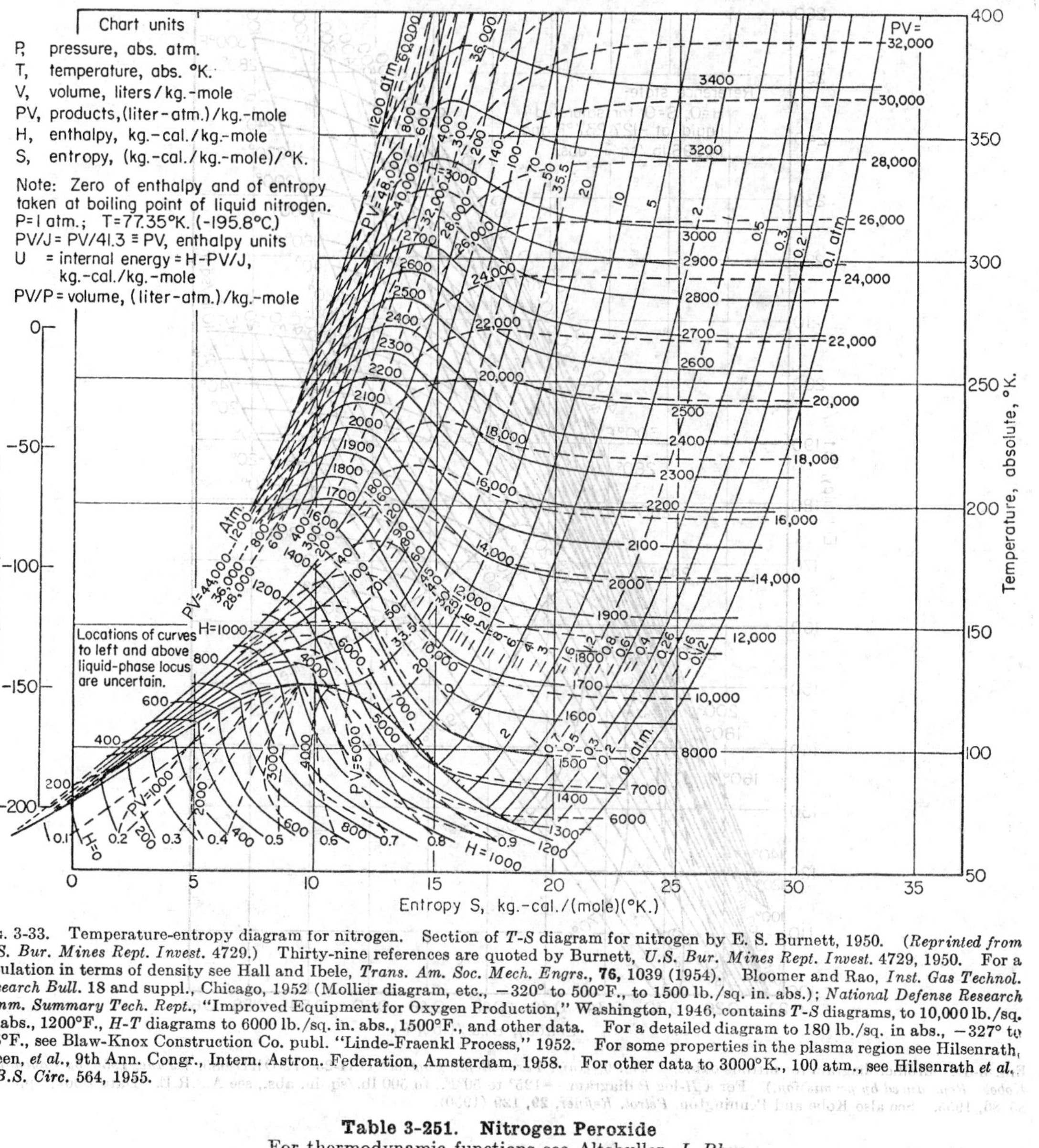

FIG. 3-33. Temperature-entropy diagram for nitrogen. Section of *T-S* diagram for nitrogen by E. S. Burnett, 1950. (*Reprinted from U.S. Bur. Mines Rept. Invest.* 4729.) Thirty-nine references are quoted by Burnett, *U.S. Bur. Mines Rept. Invest.* 4729, 1950. For a tabulation in terms of density see Hall and Ibele, *Trans. Am. Soc. Mech. Engrs.*, **76**, 1039 (1954). Bloomer and Rao, *Inst. Gas Technol. Research Bull.* 18 and suppl., Chicago, 1952 (Mollier diagram, etc., −320° to 500°F., to 1500 lb./sq. in. abs.); *National Defense Research Comm. Summary Tech. Rept.*, "Improved Equipment for Oxygen Production," Washington, 1946, contains *T-S* diagrams, to 10,000 lb./sq. in. abs., 1200°F., *H-T* diagrams to 6000 lb./sq. in. abs., 1500°F., and other data. For a detailed diagram to 180 lb./sq. in abs., −327° to 145°F., see Blaw-Knox Construction Co. publ. "Linde-Fraenkl Process," 1952. For some properties in the plasma region see Hilsenrath, Green, *et al.*, 9th Ann. Congr., Intern. Astron. Federation, Amsterdam, 1958. For other data to 3000°K., 100 atm., see Hilsenrath *et al.*, *N.B.S. Circ.* 564, 1955.

Table 3-251. Nitrogen Peroxide

For thermodynamic functions see Altshuller, *J. Phys. Chem.*, **61**, 251 (1957); Kobe and Pennington, *Petrol. Refiner*, **29**, 129 (1950).

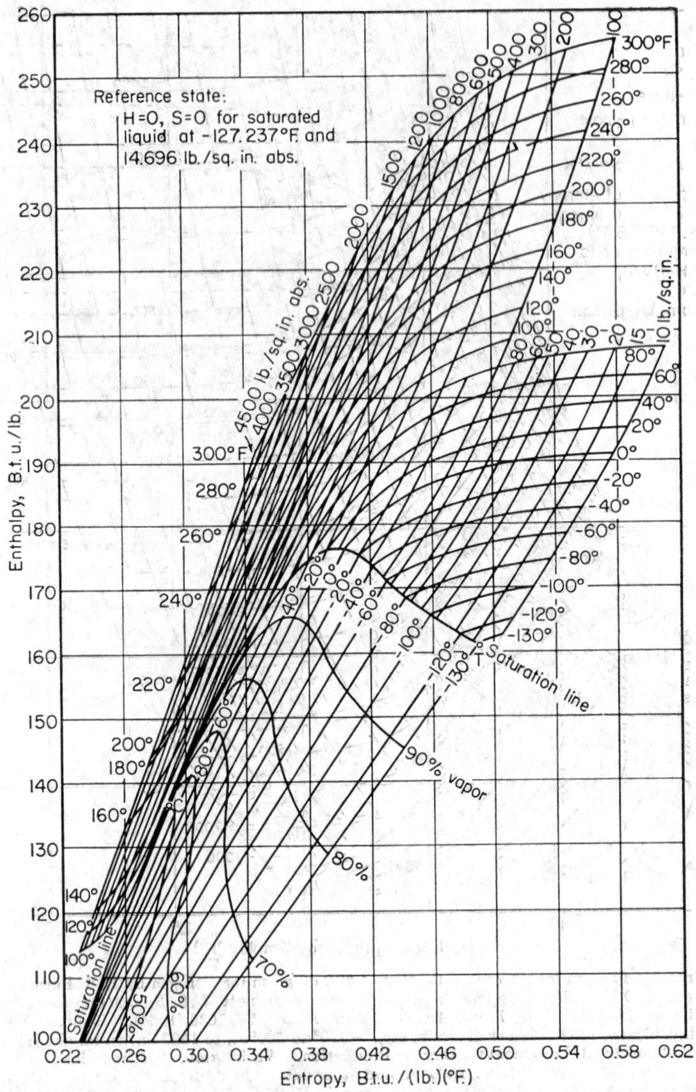

FIG. 3-34. Mollier diagram for nitrous oxide. (*Fig. 9, Univ. Texas Rept., Contract* DAI-23-072-ORD-685, 1 *June*, 1956, *by Couch and Kobe. Reproduced by permission.*) For a *H*-log *P* diagram, −125° to 50°F., to 500 lb./sq. in. abs., see A.S.R.E. "Data Book," pp. 33, 85–86, 1955. See also Kobe and Pennington, *Petrol. Refiner*, **29**, 129 (1950).

Table 3-252. Saturated Oxygen*

Temp., °K.	Abs. pressure, atm.	Volume, cc./g.-mole		Enthalpy, cal./g.-mole		Entropy, cal./(g.-mole)(°K.)		Temp., °K.	Abs. pressure, atm.	Volume, cc./g.-mole		Enthalpy, cal./g.-mole		Entropy, cal./(g.-mole)(°K.)	
		Liquid	Vapor	Liquid	Vapor	Liquid	Vapor			Liquid	Vapor	Liquid	Vapor	Liquid	Vapor
T	p	v_f	v_g	h_f	h_g	s_f	s_g	T	p	v_f	v_g	h_f	h_g	s_f	s_g
90.15	1.00	27.9	7223	158	1788	1.90	19.99	125	13.51	34.3	592	626	1864	6.13	16.02
95	1.60	28.6	4508	219	1800	2.55	19.21	130	17.52	35.7	460	700	1863	6.63	15.58
100	2.50	29.3	3028	284	1816	3.23	18.55	135	22.23	37.4	363	776	1854	7.19	15.18
105	3.73	30.1	2000	351	1831	3.86	17.96								
110	5.38	31.0	1456	420	1844	4.48	17.43	140	27.9	39.4	286	860	1833	7.78	14.73
								145	34.4	42.3	220	954	1783	8.41	14.13
115	7.51	32.0	1045	489	1854	5.08	16.95	150	42.2	47.9	157	1081	1682	9.24	13.25
120	10.20	33.1	784	557	1861	5.61	16.47	154.27	49.7	74.5	74.5	1393	1393	11.25	11.25

* Millar and Sullivan, *U.S. Bur. Mines Tech. Paper* 424, 1928.

Table 3-253. Superheated Oxygen*

v, volume, cc./g.-mole; h, enthalpy, cal./g.-mole; s, entropy, cal./(g.-mole)(°K.)
Pressure, atm.; saturation temperature, °K., in parentheses after pressure

Temp., °K.	1 atm. (90.15)			5 atm. (108.9)			10 atm. (119.7)			20 atm. (132.7)			40 atm. (148.7)			60 atm.		
T	v	h	s	v	h	s	v	h	s	v	h	s	v	h	s	v	h	s
95	7,630	1,824	20.38	....	....	.....	....	....	.....	...	....	.....	...	....	.....	...	....	.....
100	8,050	1,861	20.76	....	....	.....	....	....	.....	...	....	.....	...	....	.....	...	....	.....
110	8,890	1,933	21.44	1,560	1,853	17.66	....	....	.....	...	....	.....	...	....	.....	...	....	.....
120	9,730	2,005	22.07	1,790	1,947	18.48	805	1,865	16.53	...	....	.....	...	....	.....	...	....	.....
130	10,560	2,076	22.64	2,000	2,033	19.17	930	1,977	17.44	...	....	.....	...	....	.....	...	...	.....
140	11,400	2,146	23.16	2 210	2,113	19.76	1,040	2,069	18.13	455	1,961	16.10	...	....	.....	...	....	.....
150	12,240	2,216	23.65	2,400	2,188	20.28	1,150	2,151	18.69	516	2,072	16.86	184	1,780	13.90	...	....	.....
160	13,070	2,286	24.10	2,590	2,262	20.76	1,250	2,230	19.20	572	2,163	17.45	228	1,993	15.28	...	1,570	12.25
170	13,900	2,356	24.52	2,770	2,334	21.20	1,350	2,307	19.67	626	2,249	17.97	266	2,116	16.03	139	1,927	14.42
180	14,740	2,426	24.92	2,940	2,406	21.61	1,450	2,381	20.09	677	2,328	18.42	298	2,219	16.62	168	2,093	15.37
190	15,570	2,496	25.30	3,110	2,477	22.00	1,540	2,452	20.47	725	2,404	18.84	328	2,311	17.11	194	2,219	16.06
200	16,390	2,565	25.66	3,280	2,547	22.36	1,625	2,523	20.84	772	2,479	19.22	356	2,397	17.56	220	2,322	16.59
210	17,210	2,633	25.99	3,450	2,615	22.69	1,715	2,593	21.18	818	2,552	19.58	382	2,478	17.95	243	2,409	17.01
220	18,030	2,700	26.30	3,610	2,684	23.01	1,800	2,664	21.51	864	2,627	19.93	408	2,558	18.32	264	2,493	17.40
230	18,860	2,767	26.60	3,770	2,752	23.32	1,880	2,735	21.83	910	2,701	20.26	434	2,638	18.68	284	2,577	17.77
240	19,680	2,834	26.88	3,940	2,822	23.61	1,960	2,806	22.13	956	2 775	20.57	460	2,717	19.01	303	2,661	18.13
250	20,500	2,901	27.16	4,100	2,892	23.90	2,050	2,877	22.42	1,001	2,849	20.88	484	2,796	19.33	321	2,745	18.47
260	21,330	2,971	27.43	4,260	2,962	24.17	2,130	2,948	22.70	1,046	2,922	21.16	508	2,874	19.64	338	2,828	18.80
270	22,150	3,041	27.68	4,430	3,032	24.43	2,210	3,019	22.96	1,090	2,996	21.44	532	2,952	19.93	353	2,910	19.11
280	22,970	3,111	27.93	4,590	3,102	24.68	2,290	3,090	23.22	1,136	3,068	21.70	556	3,028	20.21	367	2,991	19.40
290	23,790	3,180	28.18	4,750	3,172	24.93	2,370	3,161	23.47	1,180	3,140	21.96	580	3,104	20.47	381	3,072	19.69
300	24,610	3,251	28.41	4,920	3,242	25.17	2,460	3,232	23.71	1,226	3,212	22.20	604	3,179	20.73	395	3,152	19.96

* Millar and Sullivan, *U.S. Bur. Mines Tech. Paper* 424, 1928.

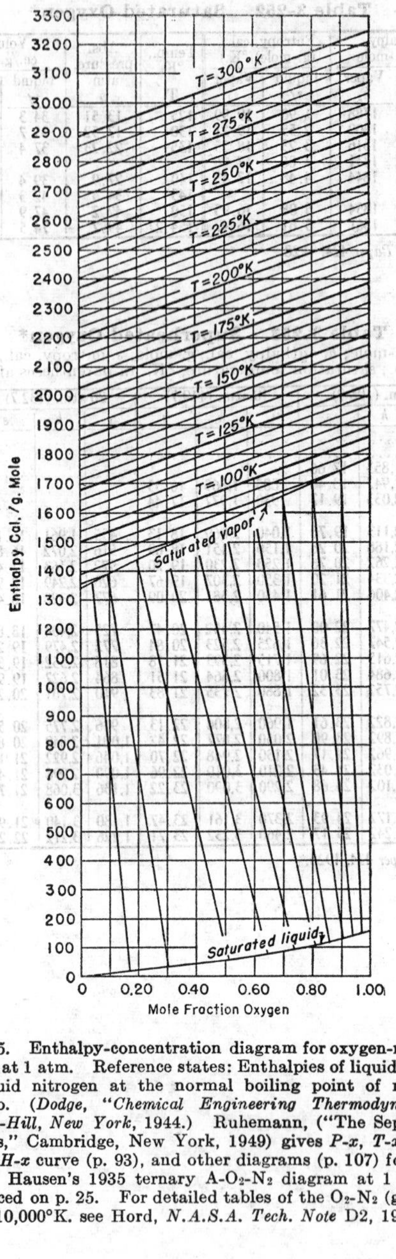

FIG. 3-35. Enthalpy-concentration diagram for oxygen-nitrogen mixture at 1 atm. Reference states: Enthalpies of liquid oxygen and liquid nitrogen at the normal boiling point of nitrogen are zero. (*Dodge, "Chemical Engineering Thermodynamics," McGraw-Hill, New York*, 1944.) Ruhemann, ("The Separation of Gases," Cambridge, New York, 1949) gives *P-x*, *T-x* curves (p. 46), *H-x* curve (p. 93), and other diagrams (p. 107) for 1 and 5 atm. Hausen's 1935 ternary A-O_2-N_2 diagram at 1 atm. is reproduced on p. 25. For detailed tables of the O_2-N_2 (gas) system to 10,000°K. see Hord, *N.A.S.A. Tech. Note* D2, 1959.

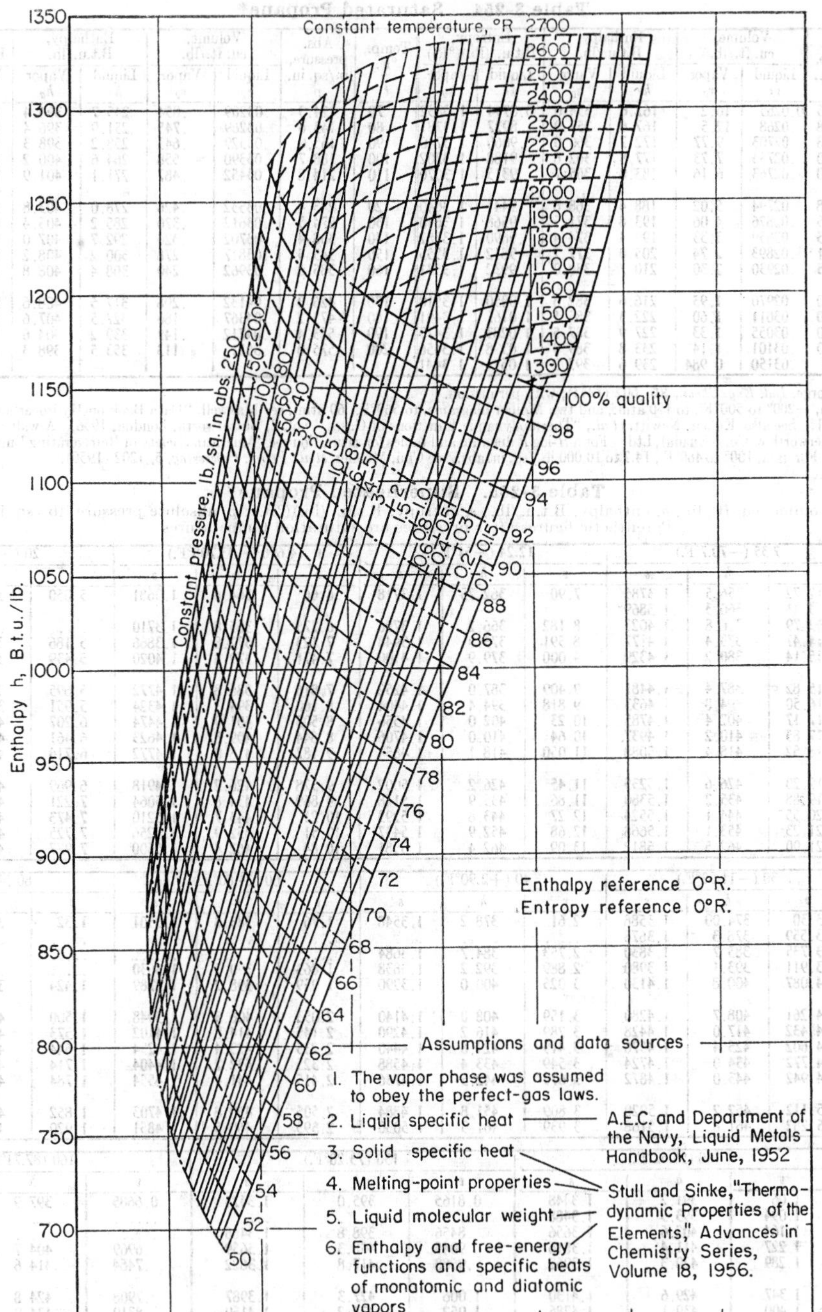

FIG. 3-36. Mollier diagram for potassium. Enthalpy reference −0°R.; entropy reference −0°R. (*From Meisl and Shapiro, "Thermodynamic Properties of Alkali Metal Vapors and Mercury," TIS Rept.* R60FPD358, *General Electric Co., Cincinnati, June,* 1960.) WADC-TR-59-598, 1959, contains an earlier diagram which was in error in the superheated region. This diagram is reproduced by permission.

Table 3-254. Saturated Propane*

Temp., °F. t	Abs. pressure, lb./sq.in. p	Volume, cu. ft./lb. Liquid v_f	Vapor v_g	Enthalpy, B.t.u./lb. Liquid h_f	Vapor h_g	Entropy, B.t.u./(lb.)(°R.) Liquid s_f	Vapor s_g	Temp., °F. t	Abs. pressure, lb./sq. in. p	Volume, cu. ft./lb. Liquid v_f	Vapor v_g	Enthalpy, B.t.u./lb. Liquid h_f	Vapor h_g	Entropy, B.t.u./(lb.)(°R.) Liquid s_f	Vapor s_g
−80	5.65	0.0265	16.2	162.6	354.0	0.8794	1.3832	70	124.3	.03209	.854	245.7	394.4	1.0624	1.3427
−70	7.48	.0268	12.5	167.6	357.0	.8927	1.3781	80	143.6	.03269	.745	251.9	396.4	1.0737	1.3413
−60	9.78	.02703	9.77	172.7	360.0	.9060	1.3740	90	165.0	.03329	.643	258.2	398.3	1.0850	1.3400
−50	12.60	.02733	7.73	177.8	362.8	.9188	1.3702	100	188.7	.03390	.558	264.6	400.2	1.0963	1.3388
−40	16.00	.02763	6.16	183.0	365.7	.9315	1.3670	110	214.8	.03452	.487	271.1	401.9	1.1080	1.3378
−30	20.18	.02794	5.02	188.4	368.6	.9441	1.3640	120	243.4	.03532	.426	278.0	403.8	1.1195	1.3368
−20	25.05	.02826	4.06	193.8	371.5	.9568	1.3610	130	274.5	.03612	.370	285.2	405.4	1.1310	1.3356
−10	30.95	.02859	3.33	199.4	374.4	.9690	1.3582	140	308.4	.03702	.320	292.7	407.0	1.1430	1.3347
0	37.81	.02893	2.74	205.0	377.2	.9812	1.3555	150	345.4	.03817	.278	300.2	408.2	1.1552	1.3326
10	45.85	.02930	2.30	210.7	380.0	.9932	1.3531	160	385.0	.03962	.240	308.4	408.8	1.1680	1.3303
20	55.00	.02970	1.93	216.6	382.6	1.0050	1.3510	170	426.0	.04132	.208	317.5	408.6	1.1816	1.3272
30	65.70	.03011	1.60	222.3	385.1	1.0167	1.3491	180	473.2	.04367	.180	327.5	407.6	1.1970	1.3223
40	77.80	.03055	1.33	227.9	387.5	1.0283	1.3473	190	523.4	.04712	.149	339.2	404.6	1.2140	1.3156
50	91.50	.03101	1.14	233.8	389.9	1.0398	1.3456	200	575.0	.0521	.113	353.5	398.3	1.2360	1.3040
60	106.9	.03150	0.984	239.6	392.2	1.0511	1.3441								

* Stearns and George, *Ind. Eng. Chem.*, **35**, 602 (1943); with permission.

For *H-T* diagram, −200° to 500°F., to 150 atm., and two Mollier diagrams, to 560°F., 60 atm., see Maxwell, "Data Book on Hydrocarbons," Van Nostrand, Princeton, N.J., 1951. See also Kuloor, Newitt, *et al.*, "Thermodynamic Functions of Gases," vol. 2, Butterworth, London, 1956. A wall-sized *T-S* diagram is obtainable from Butterworth & Co. (Canada), Ltd. For a *H*-log *P* diagram and tables for saturation see "American Society of Refrigerating Engineers Data Book," pp. 33, 87, 88, 1953. For data, 100° to 460°F., 14.7 to 10,000 lb./sq. in. abs., see Chu, Mueller, *et al.*, *Petrol. Processing*, **5**, 1202 (1950).

Table 3-255. Superheated Propane*

v, volume, cu. ft./lb.; h, enthalpy, B.t.u./lb.; s, entropy, B.t.u./(lb.)(°R.); p, absolute pressure, lb./sq. in.
Parenthetic figures after pressures are saturation temperatures

Temp., °F.	7.35 (−70.7°F.) v	h	s	12.24 (−51°F.) v	h	s	14.696 (−43.708°F.) v	h	s	20 (−30.30°F.) v	h	s
Sat.	12.72	356.5	1.3785	7.90	362.75	1.3718	6.66	364.6	1.3681	5.050	368.4	1.3640
−60	[illegible]	360.3	1.3869									
−40	13.79	366.8	1.4023	8.182	366.2	1.3796	6.775	365.8	1.3710	.....	.....	.....
−20	14.47	373.4	1.4177	8.591	373.0	1.3948	7.123	372.8	1.3866	5.186	372.2	1.3719
0	15.14	380.2	1.4329	9.000	379.9	1.4100	7.471	379.8	1.4020	5.439	379.3	1.3873
20	15.82	387.4	1.4481	9.409	387.0	1.4252	7.816	386.8	1.4772	5.695	386.5	1.4025
40	16.50	394.8	1.4633	9.818	394.4	1.4404	8.160	394.3	1.4324	5.951	393.9	1.4177
60	17.17	402.4	1.4785	10.23	402.0	1.4556	8.503	401.9	1.4474	6.207	401.6	1.4327
80	17.85	410.2	1.4937	10.64	410.0	1.4706	8.844	409.8	1.4623	6.461	409.4	1.4477
100	18.52	418.4	1.5088	11.050	418.1	1.4854	9.187	418.0	1.4772	6.716	417.6	1.4625
120	19.20	426.6	1.5235	11.45	426.2	1.5002	9.528	426.2	1.4918	6.969	425.9	1.4771
140	19.88	435.2	1.5380	11.86	435.9	1.5148	9.869	434.8	1.5064	7.221	434.6	1.4917
160	20.55	444.1	1.5524	12.27	443.8	1.5293	10.21	443.7	1.5210	7.473	443.5	1.5063
180	21.23	453.1	1.5668	12.68	452.9	1.5437	10.51	452.9	1.5256	7.725	452.6	1.5209
200	21.90	462.5	1.5812	13.09	462.4	1.5581	10.84	462.4	1.5500	7.977	461.9	1.5355

Temp., °F.	30 (−11.52°F.) v	h	s	40 (+2.90°F.) v	h	s	60 (24.80°F.) v	h	s	80 (41.69°F.) v	h	s
Sat.	3.30	374.00	1.3588	2.61	378.2	1.3548	1.76	383.8	1.3501	1.32	387.8	1.3470
0	3.559	378.3	1.3678	.....	.....	.....	.....	.....	.....	.....	.....	.....
20	3.735	385.7	1.3830	2.753	384.7	1.3684	.....	.....	.....	.....	.....	.....
40	3.911	393.1	1.3980	2.889	392.2	1.3838	1.863	390.1	1.3630	.....	.....	.....
60	4.087	400.8	1.4130	3.025	400.0	1.3990	1.959	398.2	1.3789	1.424	396.1	1.3624
80	4.261	408.7	1.4280	3.159	408.0	1.4140	2.053	406.3	1.3948	1.500	404.6	1.3785
100	4.432	417.0	1.4428	3.289	416.2	1.4290	2.145	414.8	1.4102	1.573	413.2	1.3940
120	4.602	425.4	1.4576	3.419	424.6	1.4440	2.235	423.4	1.4254	1.644	421.8	1.4094
140	4.772	434.0	1.4724	3.549	433.4	1.4588	2.325	432.2	1.4404	1.714	430.9	1.4248
160	4.942	443.0	1.4872	3.679	442.5	1.4736	2.415	441.4	1.4554	1.784	440.3	1.4402
180	5.112	452.2	1.5020	3.809	451.8	1.4884	2.505	450.8	1.4703	1.852	449.8	1.4554
200	5.282	461.8	1.5168	3.939	461.3	1.5030	2.593	460.5	1.4851	1.920	459.7	1.4704

Temp., °F.	100 (55.62°F.) v	h	s	130 (73.20°F.) v	h	s	160 (87.71°F.) v	h	s
Sat.	1.06	391.2	1.3448	0.8165	395.0	1.3424	0.6685	397.9	1.3404
60	1.094	393.5	1.3488	......	......	......	......	.....	......
80	1.164	402.6	1.3656	.8456	398.8	1.3486	......	.....	......
100	1.227	411.4	1.3816	.9045	408.3	1.3659	.6969	404.7	1.3521
120	1.289	420.3	1.3962	.9588	417.8	1.3822	.7464	414.6	1.3698
140	1.347	429.6	1.4130	1.006	427.3	1.3987	.7908	424.8	1.3867
160	1.400	439.1	1.4286	1.052	437.2	1.4150	.8319	434.9	1.4031
180	1.460	448.8	1.4440	1.098	447.0	1.4310	.8712	445.1	1.4195
200	1.516	458.8	1.4598	1.143	457.1	1.4468	.9093	455.4	1.4357

Temp., °F.	190 (100.50°F.) v	h	s	220 (111.85°F.) v	h	s	250 (122.12°F.) v	h	s	300 (137.55°F.) v	h	s
Sat.	0.5540	400.4	1.3388	0.4738	402.5	1.3375	0.4130	404.2	1.3355	0.3332	406.6	1.3345
120	.5995	411.6	1.3580	.4911	407.7	1.3460	......	.....	......	......	.....	......
140	.6415	422.1	1.3759	.5314	419.2	1.3650	.4473	415.9	1.3550	.3392	408.7	1.3372
160	.6792	432.4	1.3930	.5673	429.8	1.3827	.4816	427.1	1.3732	.3745	422.0	1.3580
180	.7144	443.0	1.4096	.5998	440.6	1.3999	.5121	438.0	1.3908	.4037	433.2	1.3765
200	.7472	453.4	1.4255	.6302	451.2	[illegible]	.5408	448.9	1.4074	.4303	444.9	1.3944

* Stearns and George, *Ind. Eng. Chem.*, **25**, 602 (1943); with permission.

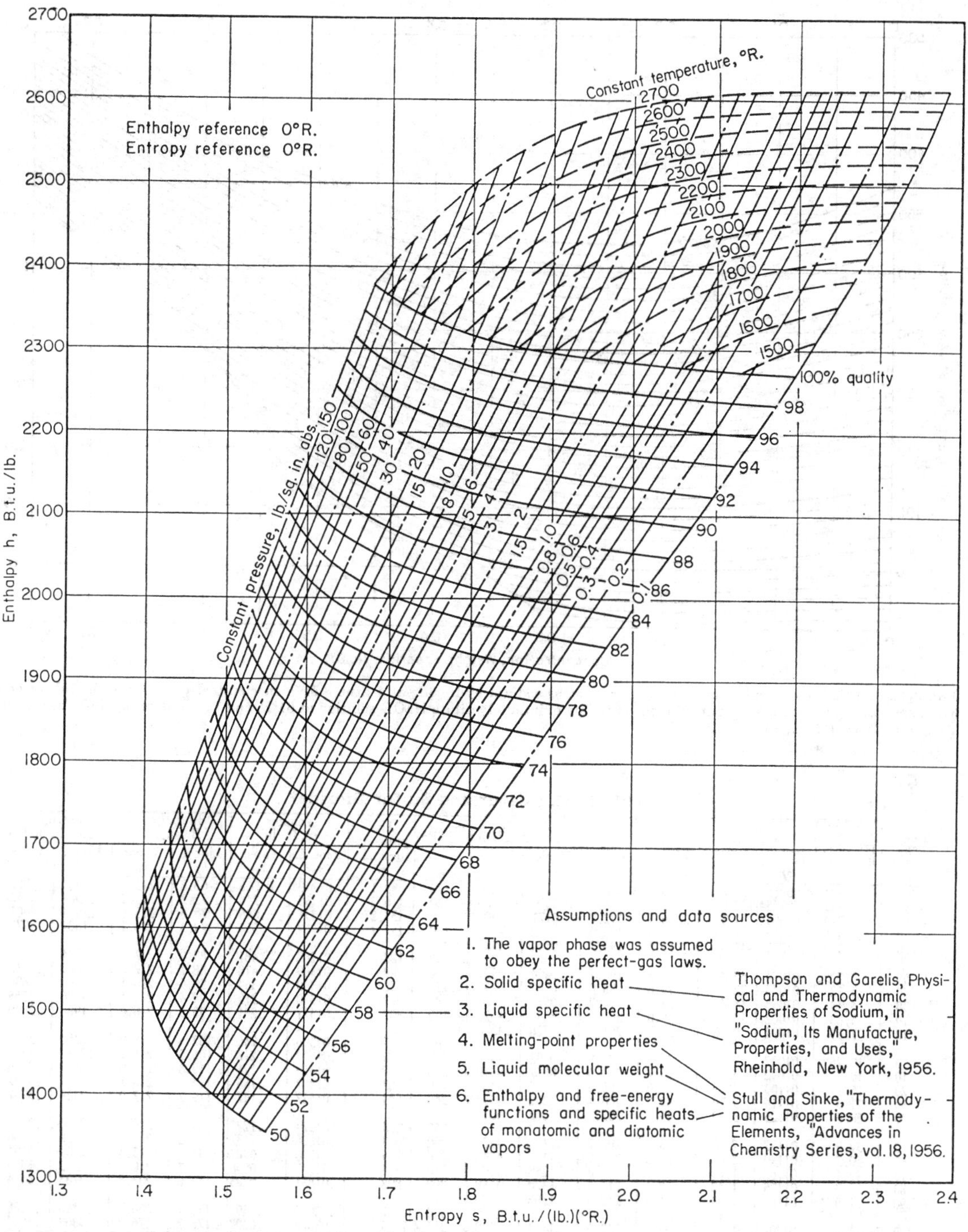

FIG. 3-37. Mollier diagram for sodium. Enthalpy reference −0°R.; entropy reference −0°R. (*From Meisl and Shapiro, "Thermodynamic Properties of Alkali Metal Vapors and Mercury," TIS Rept.* R60FPD358, *General Electric Co., Cincinnati, June,* 1960.) WADC-TR-598, 1959, contains an earlier diagram which was in error in the superheated region. This diagram is reproduced by permission. For properties of the vapor see also Inatomi and Benton, *A.E.C. Rept.* NAA-SR-141, 1951. A further report, Inatomi and Parrish, *A.E.C. Rept.* NAA-SR-62, 1950, gives properties and a *T-S* diagram to 5500°R., 1510 lb./sq. in. abs.

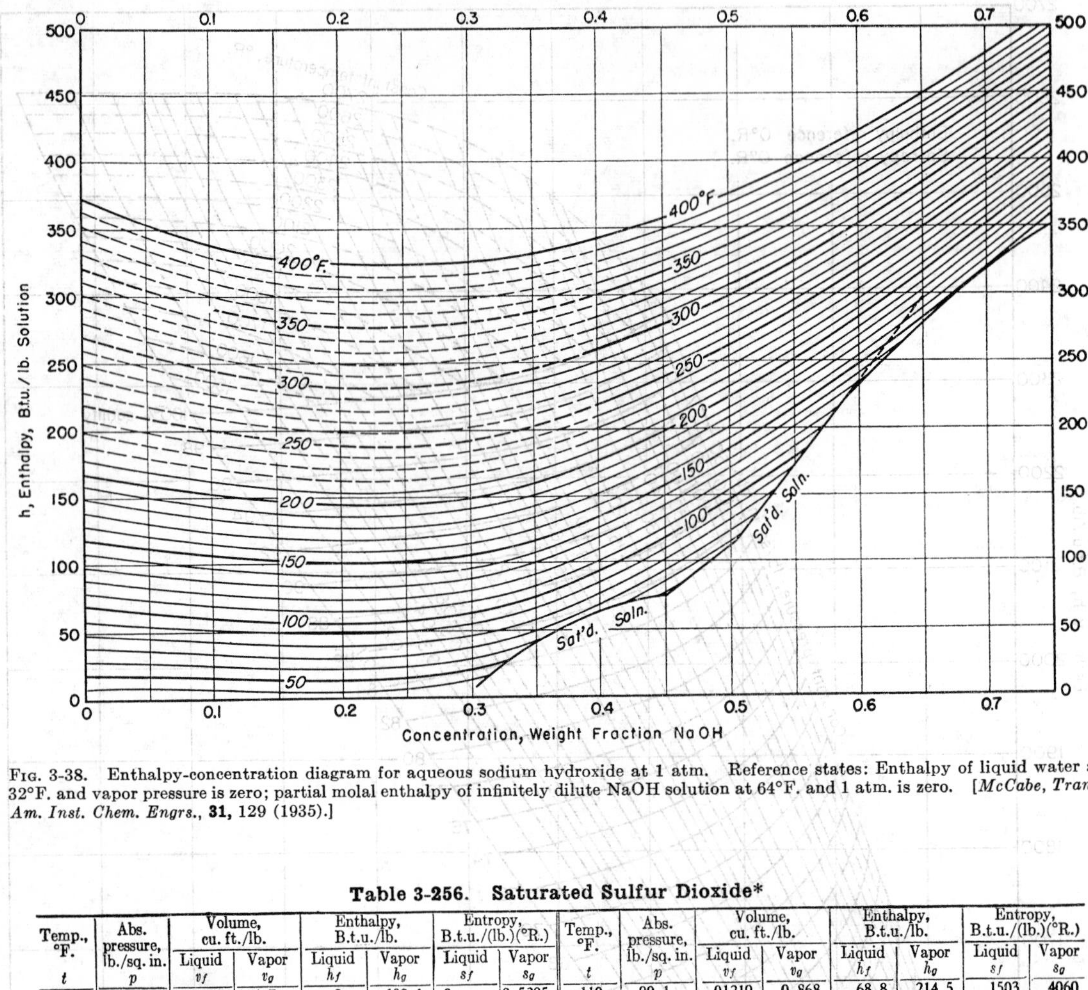

FIG. 3-38. Enthalpy-concentration diagram for aqueous sodium hydroxide at 1 atm. Reference states: Enthalpy of liquid water at 32°F. and vapor pressure is zero; partial molal enthalpy of infinitely dilute NaOH solution at 64°F. and 1 atm. is zero. [*McCabe, Trans. Am. Inst. Chem. Engrs.*, **31**, 129 (1935).]

Table 3-256. Saturated Sulfur Dioxide*

Temp., °F.	Abs. pressure, lb./sq. in.	Volume, cu. ft./lb.		Enthalpy, B.t.u./lb.		Entropy, B.t.u./(lb.)(°R.)		Temp., °F.	Abs. pressure, lb./sq. in.	Volume, cu. ft./lb.		Enthalpy, B.t.u./lb.		Entropy, B.t.u./(lb.)(°R.)	
		Liquid	Vapor	Liquid	Vapor	Liquid	Vapor			Liquid	Vapor	Liquid	Vapor	Liquid	Vapor
t	p	v_f	v_g	h_f	h_g	s_f	s_g	t	p	v_f	v_g	h_f	h_g	s_f	s_g
−100	0.294	0.009856	204.7	0	190.1	0	0.5285	110	99.1	.01219	0.868	68.8	214.5	.1503	.4060
− 90	.465	.009954	132.9	3.3	191.4	0.0090	.5179	120	116.3	.01235	.746	72.2	215.2	.1564	.4030
− 80	.710	.010054	89.3	6.5	192.7	.0177	.5081	130	135.8	.01251	.646	75.8	215.8	.1624	.4001
− 70	1.056	.01015	61.0	9.8	194.0	.0262	.4990	140	157.7	.01269	.554	79.3	216.4	.1684	.3972
− 60	1.550	.01025	42.6	13.0	195.3	.0344	.4905	150	182	.01288	.481	83.0	217.2	.1744	.3944
− 50	2.225	.01034	30.4	16.3	196.7	.0424	.4827	160	209	.01309	.418	86.7	217.6	.1805	.3917
− 40	3.12	.01044	22.2	19.6	198.0	.0502	.4753	170	238	.01330	.364	90.5	218.1	.1865	.3892
− 30	4.33	.01053	16.4	22.8	199.2	.0579	.4684	180	272	.01350	.319	94.4	218.4	.1926	.3865
− 20	5.88	.01062	12.5	26.0	200.4	.0654	.4620	190	307	.01371	.281	98.3	218.6	.1988	.3840
− 10	7.83	.01072	9.48	29.3	201.7	.0726	.4560	200	347	.01396	.246	102.4	218.9	.2050	.3815
0	10.26	.01082	7.35	32.5	202.8	.0797	.4503	210	390	.01422	.217	106.5	218.9	.2112	.3792
10	13.3	.01092	5.77	35.7	204.0	.0867	.4450	220	437	.01453	.191	110.8	218.8	.2175	.3764
20	16.9	.01103	4.59	39.0	205.3	.0935	.4402	230	487	.01487	.168	115.2	218.7	.2239	.3737
30	21.3	.01114	3.70	42.2	206.4	.1002	.4356	240	543	.01527	.147	119.7	217.9	.2304	.3707
40	26.6	.01125	3.02	45.5	207.7	.1067	.4313	250	604	.01574	.129	124.4	216.9	.2370	.3674
50	32.9	.01137	2.48	48.7	208.7	.1132	.4271	260	669	.01628	.113	129.2	215.4	.2438	.3636
60	40.3	.01149	2.05	52.0	209.8	.1195	.4232	270	739	.01690	.0987	134.3	213.3	.2509	.3591
70	49.1	.01162	1.70	55.3	210.8	.1258	.4194	280	816	.01767	.0848	139.7	210.6	.2582	.3543
80	59.3	.01175	1.42	58.6	211.7	.1320	.4158	290	898	.01861	.0723	148.6	203.8	.2703	.3434
90	71.0	.01189	1.20	61.9	212.6	.1382	.4123	300	987	.02002	.0599	152.1	200.7	.2746	.3386
100	84.1	.01204	1.02	65.3	213.5	.1443	.4090	315.4	1143	.03070	.0307	176.2	176.2	.3062	.3062

* Rynning and Hurd, *Trans. Am. Inst. Chem. Engrs.* **41**, 265 (1945).

Table 3-257. Superheated Sulfur Dioxide*

v, volume, cu. ft./lb.; h, enthalpy, B.t.u./lb.; s, entropy, B.t.u./(lb.)(°R.)
Parenthetic figures after pressures are saturation temperatures

Temp. °F.	10 lb./sq. in. abs. (−0.9°F.)			15 lb./sq. in. abs. (15.0°F.)			20 lb./sq. in. abs. (27.0°F.)			30 lb./sq. in. abs. (45.7°F.)			40 lb./sq. in. abs. (59.5°F.)			50 lb./sq. in. abs. (71.1°F.)		
t	v	h	s	v	h	s	v	h	s	v	h	s	v	h	s	v	h	s
0	7.57	202.9	0.4512	....	.....	......	....	.....	......	....	.....	......	....	.....	......	....	.....	......
20	7.90	205.9	.4576	5.22	205.4	0.4442	....	.....	......	....	.....	......	....	.....	......	....	.....	......
40	8.24	208.9	.4639	5.45	208.5	.4506	4.06	208.1	0.4409	....	.....	......	....	.....	......	....	.....	......
60	8.58	211.9	.4699	5.69	211.5	.4567	4.24	211.2	.4472	2.79	210.4	0.4334	2.06	209.7	0.4235	....	.....	......
80	8.93	215.0	.4758	5.92	214.6	.4626	4.41	214.4	.4534	2.91	213.7	.4396	2.15	213.1	.4298	1.70	212.3	0.4217
100	9.27	218.1	.4813	6.15	217.8	.4682	4.59	217.6	.4594	3.03	217.0	.4455	2.25	216.4	.4357	1.78	215.8	.4278
120	9.61	221.2	.4867	6.39	221.0	.4738	4.77	220.7	.4647	3.15	220.2	.4513	2.35	219.6	.4416	1.85	219.0	.4339
140	9.96	224.2	.4919	6.61	224.0	.4791	4.94	223.7	.4700	3.27	223.2	.4568	2.43	222.7	.4471	1.93	222.3	.4396
160	10.29	227.3	.4971	6.84	227.1	.4844	5.11	226.9	.4753	3.38	226.4	.4622	2.52	226.0	.4526	2.00	225.6	.4451
180	10.63	230.5	.5020	7.07	230.3	.4893	5.28	230.1	.4802	3.50	229.6	.4673	2.61	229.2	.4578	2.07	228.8	.4505
200	10.96	233.7	.5070	7.30	233.5	.4942	5.46	233.3	.4851	3.61	232.9	.4722	2.70	232.6	.4630	2.14	232.1	.4558
220	11.30	236.9	.5118	7.53	236.7	.4990	5.63	236.5	.4899	3.73	236.2	.4771	2.78	235.8	.4679	2.21	235.4	.4608
240	11.64	240.1	.5164	7.75	239.9	.5036	5.79	239.7	.4945	3.85	239.4	.4817	2.87	239.2	.4727	2.28	238.7	.4656
260	11.98	243.3	.5209	7.98	243.2	.5081	5.97	242.9	.4991	3.96	242.6	.4863	2.96	242.4	.4773	2.35	242.1	.4703
280	12.32	246.6	.5254	8.20	246.5	.5126	6.13	246.3	.5036	4.07	246.0	.4909	3.04	245.8	.4819	2.42	245.5	.4749
300	12.65	249.9	.5298	8.43	249.7	.5170	6.30	249.6	.5080	4.18	249.3	.4953	3.12	249.1	.4863	2.49	248.9	.4794
320	12.99	253.2	.5342	8.65	253.1	.5214	6.47	253.0	.5124	4.29	252.7	.4997	3.22	252.5	.4907	2.56	252.3	.4838
340	13.33	256.6	.5384	8.87	256.5	.5257	6.64	256.4	.5167	4.41	256.1	.5040	3.30	255.9	.4950	2.63	255.7	.4881
360	13.66	259.9	.5425	9.09	259.8	.5299	6.81	259.7	.5209	4.52	259.5	.5082	3.38	259.3	.4992	2.70	259.1	.4923
380	14.00	263.3	.5466	9.33	263.2	.5340	6.98	263.1	.5250	4.64	262.9	.5123	3.47	262.7	.5033	2.77	262.6	.4964
400	14.35	266.7	.5506	9.55	266.6	.5379	7.15	266.6	.5290	4.75	266.3	.5163	3.56	266.1	.5073	2.83	266.0	.5003
420	14.68	270.1	.5546	9.77	270.1	.5419	7.32	270.0	.5329	4.87	269.8	.5202	3.64	269.6	.5112	2.90	269.5	.5041
440	15.01	273.6	.5585	9.99	273.6	.5458	7.48	273.5	.5368	4.98	273.3	.5241	3.73	273.1	.5151	2.97	273.0	.5081
460	15.35	277.1	.5623	10.21	277.0	.5496	7.65	276.9	.5406	5.09	276.8	.5279	3.81	276.6	.5189	3.04	276.5	.5119
480	15.68	280.6	.5661	10.44	280.5	.5534	7.82	280.4	.5444	5.20	280.3	.5317	3.90	280.2	.5227	3.11	280.0	.5157
500	16.02	284.2	.5697	10.66	284.1	.5571	7.99	284.1	.5481	5.31	283.9	.5354	3.98	283.8	.5264	3.18	283.7	.5194

Temp. F.	60 lb./sq. in. abs. (80.7°F.)			80 lb./sq. in. abs. (96.9°F.)			100 lb./sq. in abs. (110.5°F.)			150 lb./sq. in. abs. (136.7°F.)			200 lb./sq. in. abs. (156.8°F.)			300 lb./sq. in. abs. (188.0°F.)		
t	v	h	s	v	h	s	v	h	s	v	h	s	v	h	s	v	h	s
100	1.46	215.1	0.4215	1.07	213.9	0.4110	....	.....	......	....	.....	......	....	.....	......	....	.....	......
120	1.53	218.5	.4276	1.13	217.4	.4172	0.882	216.0	0.4088	....	.....	......	....	.....	......	....	.....	......
140	1.59	221.7	.4334	1.17	220.8	.4232	.924	219.6	.4149	0.587	216.8	0.3993	....	.....	......	....	.....	......
160	1.65	225.0	.4391	1.22	224.1	.4290	.966	223.2	.4209	.617	220.7	.4054	0.441	218.1	0.3935	....	.....	......
180	1.71	228.4	.4447	1.27	227.5	.4346	1.004	226.6	.4267	.647	224.4	.4112	.464	222.0	.3998	....	.....	......
200	1.78	231.8	.4501	1.32	230.9	.4400	1.042	230.2	.4323	.677	228.1	.4172	.487	226.0	.4058	0.299	221.3	0.3883
220	1.83	235.1	.4553	1.36	234.3	.4452	1.080	233.6	.4376	.707	231.7	.4227	.509	229.7	.4116	.316	225.5	.3946
240	1.89	238.5	.4603	1.41	237.8	.4502	1.118	237.1	.4427	.735	235.3	.4280	.531	233.5	.4172	.333	229.7	.4005
260	1.95	241.8	.4650	1.45	241.2	.4550	1.154	240.5	.4476	.760	238.9	.4330	.551	237.3	.4226	.348	233.6	.4060
280	2.01	245.2	.4694	1.49	244.7	.4598	1.190	244.1	.4524	.786	242.5	.4379	.571	241.1	.4277	.364	237.8	.4123
300	2.07	248.6	.4736	1.54	248.1	.4643	1.226	247.5	.4570	.810	246.1	.4427	.590	244.8	.4325	.378	241.8	.4174
320	2.12	252.0	.4778	1.59	251.5	.4687	1.263	251.0	.4614	.834	249.8	.4473	.610	248.5	.4372	.392	246.0	.4223
340	2.18	255.5	.4820	1.63	255.1	.4731	1.298	254.6	.4656	.858	253.4	.4517	.629	252.2	.4418	.405	249.8	.4270
360	2.24	258.9	.4862	1.67	258.5	.4773	1.333	258.1	.4697	.882	257.0	.4561	.652	255.8	.4462	.419	253.5	.4316
380	2.30	262.4	.4903	1.71	262.0	.4814	1.367	261.6	.4737	.905	260.5	.4603	.667	259.4	.4505	.433	257.2	.4360
400	2.36	265.9	.4943	1.76	265.5	.4854	1.403	265.1	.4777	.929	264.1	.4645	.685	263.1	.4548	.446	261.0	.4404
420	2.41	269.4	.4983	1.80	269.0	.4893	1.439	268.6	.4817	.952	267.6	.4686	.704	266.7	.4589	.458	264.7	.4447
440	2.47	272.9	.5023	1.85	272.5	.4932	1.474	272.1	.4857	.974	271.2	.4726	.727	270.3	.4630	.471	268.4	.4489
460	2.53	276.4	.5061	1.89	276.0	.4970	1.509	275.7	.4896	.996	274.8	.4766	.740	273.9	.4670	.484	272.1	.4531
480	2.59	279.9	.5099	1.93	279.5	.5008	1.543	279.2	.4935	1.018	278.4	.4805	.759	277.6	.4710	.497	275.9	.4572
500	2.64	283.5	.5136	1.97	283.1	.5045	1.578	282.8	.4973	1.039	282.1	.4843	.776	281.3	.4748	.509	279.7	.4611

Temp. °F.	400 lb./sq. in. abs. (212.0°F.)			500 lb./sq. in. abs. (232.5°F.)			600 lb./sq. in. abs. (249.5°F.)			800 lb./sq. in. abs. (278.0°F.)			1000 lb./sq. in. abs. (301.5°F.)		
t	v	h	s	v	h	s	v	h	s	v	h	s	v	h	s
220	0.216	221.1	0.3810	.....	.....	......	.....	.....	......	.....	.....	......	.....	.....	......
240	.232	225.6	.3875	0.168	220.2	0.3753	.....	.....	......	.....	.....	......	.....	.....	......
260	.246	230.0	.3936	.182	225.2	.3820	0.138	220.4	0.3714	.....	.....	......	.....	.....	......
280	.255	234.4	.3994	.195	230.2	.3883	.150	226.3	.3783	0.0914	212.5	0.3560	.....	.....	......
300	.269	238.8	.4049	.206	235.0	.3944	.162	231.4	.3849	.1035	221.8	.3649	.....	.....	......
320	.282	243.1	.4102	.216	239.7	.4002	.172	236.5	.3913	.1140	229.1	.3734	0.0761	217.3	0.3504
340	.293	247.2	.4154	.226	244.2	.4059	.181	241.2	.3976	.1230	234.9	.3814	.0865	226.1	.3655
360	.305	251.0	.4203	.236	248.5	.4114	.189	245.8	.4035	.1308	240.0	.3887	.0944	232.7	.3760
380	.315	254.8	.4251	.244	252.6	.4165	.197	250.1	.4090	.1379	244.8	.3951	.1014	238.6	.3821
400	.325	258.8	.4298	.253	256.7	.4212	.205	254.4	.4138	.1446	249.5	.4004	.1076	244.2	.3888
420	.335	262.6	.4343	.261	260.6	.4257	.212	258.5	.4184	.1510	254.0	.4056	.1135	249.1	.3941
440	.346	266.4	.4386	.270	264.6	.4301	.220	262.5	.4229	.1572	258.3	.4106	.1190	253.9	.3998
460	.356	270.2	.4428	.279	268.5	.4345	.227	266.4	.4273	.1632	262.5	.4153	.1243	258.4	.4051
480	.366	274.1	.4469	.287	272.4	.4387	.234	270.5	.4317	.1691	266.8	.4200	.1296	262.8	.4101
500	.376	278.0	.4509	.295	276.3	.4428	.241	274.6	.4359	.1746	271.0	.4245	.1345	267.1	.4147

* Rynning and Hurd, *Trans. Am. Inst. Chem. Engrs.* **41**, 265 (1945).

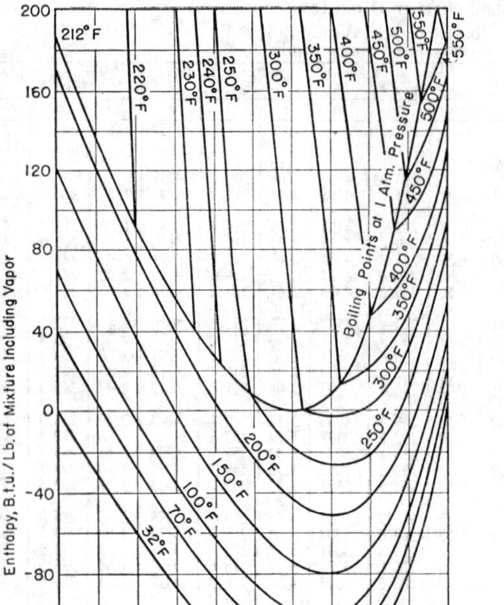

FIG. 3-39. Enthalpy-concentration diagram for aqueous sulfuric acid at 1 atm. Reference states: Enthalpies of pure liquid components at 32°F. and vapor pressures are zero. Note: It should be observed that the weight basis includes the vapor, which is particularly important in the two-phase region. The upper ends of the tie lines in this region are assumed to be pure water. (*Hougen and Watson, "Chemical Process Principles," Part I, Wiley, New York*, 1943.)

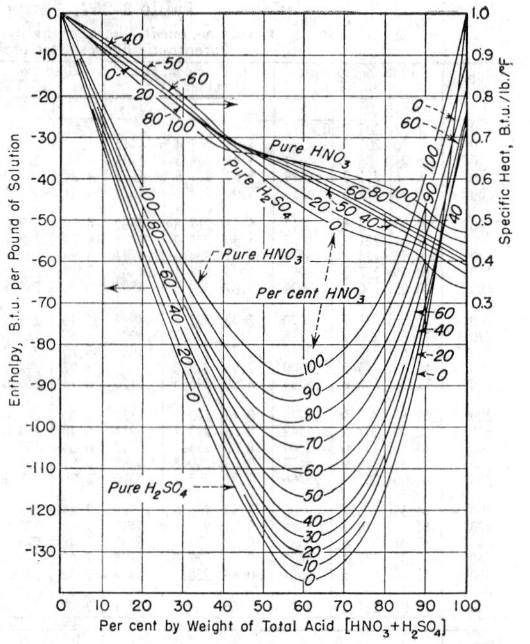

FIG. 3-40. Enthalpy-concentration diagram for aqueous sulfuric and nitric acids at 32°F. Reference states: Enthalpy of pure components at 32°F. is zero. Note: The per cent HNO_3 is computed on a water-free basis. Enthalpies at temperatures other than 32°F. may be computed by utilizing the specific-heat data given, which may be assumed independent of temperature as a first approximation. [*McKinley and Brown, Chem. & Met. Eng.*, **49**, 142 (1942).]

Table 3-258. Saturated Trichloroethylene (C_2HCl_3)*

Temp., °F.	Abs. pressure, lb./sq. in.	Volume, cu. ft./lb. vapor	Enthalpy, B.t.u./lb.		Entropy, B.t.u./(lb.)(°R.)		Temp., °F.	Abs. pressure, lb./sq. in.	Volume, cu. ft./lb. vapor	Enthalpy, B.t.u./lb.		Entropy, B.t.u./(lb.)(°R.)	
			Liquid	Vapor	Liquid	Vapor				Liquid	Vapor	Liquid	Vapor
t	p	v_g	h_f	h_g	s_f	s_g	t	p	v	h_f	h_g	s_f	s_g
0	0.150	261.3	0.0	112.60	0.0000	0.2451	80	1.56	28.00	19.84	129.62	.0374	.2414
10	.194	197.6	1.86	114.18	.0039	.2433	90	1.98	22.46	23.22	132.54	.0428	.2422
20	.252	153.3	3.90	116.00	.0081	.2429							
30	.352	114.5	6.12	117.92	.0127	.2411	100	2.45	18.54	26.60	135.41	.0480	.2428
40	.492	85.8	8.42	119.83	.0178	.2412	110	3.15	14.62	29.92	138.22	.0530	.2432
							120	3.98	11.73	33.60	141.38	.0581	.2440
50	.672	63.2	11.10	122.15	.0227	.2405	130	5.05	9.20	37.70	144.90	.0632	.2450
60	.900	47.53	13.80	124.43	.0278	.2404	140	6.31	7.70	42.00	148.57	.0680	.2459
70	1.20	36.00	16.80	127.02	.0324	.2407							

* "Refrigerating Data Book," 5th ed., American Society of Refrigerating Engineers, New York, 1942.

Table 3-259. Saturated Steam: Temperature Table*

Temp., °F.	Abs. pressure, lb./sq. in.	Volume, cu. ft./lb.		Enthalpy, B.t.u./lb.		Entropy, B.t.u./(lb.)(°R.)		Temp., °F.	Abs. pressure, lb./sq. in.	Volume, cu. ft./lb.		Enthalpy, B.t.u./lb.		Entropy, B.t.u./(lb.)(°R.)	
t	p	Liquid v_f	Vapor v_g	Liquid h_f	Vapor h_g	Liquid s_f	Vapor s_g	t	p	Liquid v_f	Vapor v_g	Liquid h_f	Vapor h_g	Liquid s_f	Vapor s_g
32	0.08854	0.01602	3306	0.00	1075.8	0.0000	2.1877	250	29.825	.01700	13.821	216.48	1164.0	.3675	1.6998
35	.09995	.01602	2947	3.02	1077.1	.0061	2.1770	260	35.429	.01709	11.763	228.64	1167.3	.3817	1.6860
40	.12170	.01602	2444	8.05	1079.3	.0162	2.1597	270	41.858	.01717	10.061	238.84	1170.6	.3958	1.6727
45	.14752	.01602	2036.4	13.06	1081.5	.0262	2.1429	280	49.203	.01726	8.645	249.06	1173.8	.4096	1.6597
50	.17811	.01603	1703.2	18.07	1083.7	.0361	2.1264	290	57.556	.01735	7.461	259.31	1176.8	.4234	1.6472
60	.2563	.01604	1206.7	28.06	1088.0	.0555	2.0948	300	67.013	.01745	6.466	269.59	1179.7	.4369	1.6350
70	.3631	.01606	867.9	38.04	1092.3	.0745	2.0647	310	77.68	.01755	5.626	279.92	1182.5	.4504	1.6231
80	.5069	.01608	633.1	48.02	1096.6	.0932	2.0360	320	89.66	.01765	4.914	290.28	1185.2	.4637	1.6115
90	.6982	.01610	468.0	57.99	1100.9	.1115	2.0087	330	103.06	.01776	4.307	300.68	1187.7	.4769	1.6002
100	.9492	.01613	350.4	67.97	1105.2	.1295	1.9826	340	118.01	.01787	3.788	311.13	1190.1	.4900	1.5891
110	1.2748	.01617	265.4	77.94	1109.5	.1471	1.9577	350	134.63	.01799	3.342	321.63	1192.3	.5029	1.5783
120	1.6924	.01620	203.27	87.92	1113.7	.1645	1.9339	360	153.04	.01811	2.957	332.18	1194.4	.5158	1.5677
130	2.2225	.01625	157.34	97.90	1117.9	.1816	1.9112	370	173.37	.01823	2.625	342.79	1196.3	.5286	1.5573
140	2.8886	.01629	123.01	107.89	1122.0	.1984	1.8894	380	195.77	.01836	2.335	353.45	1198.1	.5413	1.5471
150	3.718	.01634	97.07	117.89	1126.1	.2149	1.8685	390	220.37	.01850	2.0836	364.17	1199.6	.5539	1.5371
160	4.741	.01639	77.29	127.89	1130.2	.2311	1.8485	400	247.31	.01864	1.8633	374.97	1201.0	.5664	1.5272
170	5.992	.01645	62.06	137.90	1134.2	.2472	1.8293	410	276.75	.01878	1.6700	385.83	1202.1	.5788	1.5174
180	7.510	.01651	50.23	147.92	1138.1	.2630	1.8109	420	308.83	.01894	1.5000	396.77	1203.1	.5912	1.5078
190	9.339	.01657	40.96	157.95	1142.0	.2785	1.7932	430	343.72	.01910	1.3499	407.79	1203.8	.6035	1.4982
200	11.526	.01663	33.64	167.99	1145.9	.2938	1.7762	440	381.59	.01926	1.2171	418.90	1204.3	.6158	1.4887
210	14.123	.01670	27.82	178.05	1149.7	.3090	1.7598	450	422.6	.0194	1.0993	430.1	1204.6	.6280	1.4793
212	14.696	.01672	26.80	180.07	1150.4	.3120	1.7566	460	466.9	.0196	0.9944	441.4	1204.6	.6402	1.4700
220	17.186	.01677	23.15	188.13	1153.4	.3239	1.7440	470	514.7	.0198	.9009	452.8	1204.3	.6523	1.4606
230	20.780	.01684	19.382	198.23	1157.0	.3387	1.7288	480	566.1	.0200	.8172	464.4	1203.7	.6645	1.4513
240	24.969	.01692	16.323	208.34	1160.5	.3531	1.7140	490	621.4	.0202	.7423	476.0	1202.8	.6766	1.4419

Temp., °F.	Abs. pressure, lb./sq. in.	Volume, cu. ft./lb.		Enthalpy, B.t.u./lb.		Entropy, B.t.u./(lb.)(°R.)		Temp., °F.	Abs. pressure, lb./sq. in.	Volume, cu. ft./lb.		Enthalpy, B.t.u./lb.		Entropy, B.t.u./(lb.)(°R.)	
t	p	Liquid v_f	Vapor v_g	Liquid h_f	Vapor h_g	Liquid s_f	Vapor s_g	t	p	Liquid v_f	Vapor v_g	Liquid h_f	Vapor h_g	Liquid s_f	Vapor s_g
500	680.8	.0204	.6749	487.8	1201.7	.6887	1.4325	620	1786.6	.0247	.2201	646.7	1150.3	.8398	1.3062
520	812.4	.0209	.5594	511.9	1198.2	.7130	1.4136	640	2059.7	.0260	.1798	678.6	1130.5	.8679	1.2789
540	962.5	.0215	.4649	536.6	1193.2	.7374	1.3942	660	2365.4	.0278	.1442	714.2	1104.4	.8987	1.2472
560	1133.1	.0221	.3868	562.2	1186.4	.7621	1.3742	680	2708.1	.0305	.1115	757.3	1067.2	.9351	1.2071
580	1325.8	.0228	.3217	588.9	1177.3	.7872	1.3532								
								700	3093.7	.0369	.0761	823.3	995.4	.9905	1.1389
600	1542.9	.0236	.2668	617.0	1165.5	.8131	1.3307	705.4	3206.2	.0503	.0503	902.7	902.7	1.0580	1.0580

* Abridged from Keenan and Keyes, "Thermodynamic Properties of Steam," Wiley, New York, 1936.

Table 3-260. Saturated Steam: Pressure Table*

Abs. pressure lb./sq. in. p	Temp., °F. t	Volume, cu. ft./lb. Liquid v_f	Volume, cu. ft./lb. Vapor v_g	Enthalpy, B.t.u./lb. Liquid h_f	Enthalpy, B.t.u./lb. Vapor h_g	Entropy, B.t.u./(lb.)(°R.) Liquid s_f	Entropy, B.t.u./(lb.)(°R.) Vapor s_g	Internal energy, B.t.u./lb. Liquid u_f	Internal energy, B.t.u./lb. Vapor u_g
1.0	101.74	0.01614	333.6	69.70	1106.0	0.1326	1.9782	69.70	1044.3
2.0	126.08	.01623	173.73	93.99	1116.3	.1749	1.9200	93.98	1051.9
3.0	141.48	.01630	118.71	109.37	1122.6	.2008	1.8863	109.36	1056.7
4.0	152.97	.01636	90.63	120.86	1127.3	.2198	1.8625	120.85	1060.2
5.0	162.24	.01640	73.52	130.13	1131.1	.2347	1.8441	130.12	1063.1
6.0	170.06	.01645	61.98	137.96	1134.2	.2472	1.8292	137.94	1065.4
7.0	176.85	.01649	53.64	144.76	1136.9	.2581	1.8167	144.74	1067.4
8.0	182.86	.01653	47.34	150.79	1139.3	.2674	1.8057	150.77	1069.2
9.0	188.28	.01656	42.40	156.22	1141.4	.2759	1.7962	156.19	1070.8
10	193.21	.01659	38.42	161.17	1143.3	.2835	1.7876	161.14	1072.2
14.696	212.00	.01672	26.80	180.07	1150.4	.3120	1.7566	180.02	1077.5
15	213.03	.01672	26.29	181.11	1150.8	.3135	1.7549	181.06	1077.8
20	227.96	.01683	20.089	196.16	1156.3	.3356	1.7319	196.10	1081.9
25	240.07	.01692	16.303	208.42	1160.6	.3533	1.7139	208.34	1085.1
30	250.33	.01701	13.746	218.82	1164.1	.3680	1.6993	218.73	1087.8
35	259.28	.01708	11.898	227.91	1167.1	.3807	1.6870	227.80	1090.1
40	267.25	.01715	10.498	236.03	1169.7	.3919	1.6763	235.90	1092.0
45	274.44	.01721	9.401	243.36	1172.0	.4019	1.6669	243.22	1093.7
50	281.01	.01727	8.515	250.09	1174.1	.4110	1.6585	249.93	1095.3
55	287.07	.01732	7.787	256.30	1175.9	.4193	1.6509	256.12	1096.7
60	292.71	.01738	7.175	262.09	1177.6	.4270	1.6438	261.90	1097.9
65	297.97	.01743	6.655	267.50	1179.1	.4342	1.6374	267.29	1099.1
70	302.92	.01748	6.206	272.61	1180.6	.4409	1.6315	272.38	1100.2
75	307.60	.01753	5.816	277.43	1181.9	.4472	1.6259	277.19	1101.2
80	312.03	.01757	5.472	282.02	1183.1	.4531	1.6207	281.76	1102.1
85	316.25	.01761	5.168	286.39	1184.2	.4587	1.6158	286.11	1102.9
90	320.27	.01766	4.896	290.56	1185.3	.4641	1.6112	290.27	1103.7
95	324.12	.01770	4.652	294.56	1186.2	.4692	1.6068	294.25	1104.5
100	327.81	.01774	4.432	298.40	1187.2	.4740	1.6026	298.08	1105.2
110	334.77	.01782	4.049	305.66	1188.9	.4832	1.5948	305.30	1106.5
120	341.25	.01789	3.728	312.44	1190.4	.4916	1.5878	312.05	1107.6
130	347.32	.01796	3.455	318.81	1191.7	.4995	1.5812	318.38	1108.6
140	353.02	.01802	3.220	324.82	1193.0	.5069	1.5751	324.35	1109.6
150	358.42	.01809	3.015	330.51	1194.1	.5138	1.5694	330.01	1110.5
160	363.53	.01815	2.834	335.93	1195.1	.5204	1.5640	335.39	1111.2
170	368.41	.01822	2.675	341.09	1196.0	.5266	1.5590	340.52	1111.9
180	373.06	.01827	2.532	346.03	1196.9	.5325	1.5542	345.42	1112.5
190	377.51	.01833	2.404	350.79	1197.6	.5381	1.5497	350.15	1113.1
200	381.79	.01839	2.288	355.36	1198.4	.5435	1.5453	354.68	1113.7
250	400.95	.01865	1.8438	376.00	1201.1	.5675	1.5263	375.14	1115.8
300	417.33	.01890	1.5433	393.84	1202.8	.5879	1.5104	392.79	1117.1
350	431.72	.01913	1.3260	409.69	1203.9	.6056	1.4966	408.45	1118.0
400	444.59	.0193	1.1613	424.0	1204.5	.6214	1.4844	422.6	1118.5
450	456.28	.0195	1.0320	437.2	1204.6	.6356	1.4734	435.5	1118.7
500	467.01	.0197	0.9278	449.4	1204.4	.6487	1.4634	447.6	1118.6
550	476.94	.0199	.8424	460.8	1203.9	.6608	1.4542	458.8	1118.2
600	486.21	.0201	.7698	471.6	1203.2	.6720	1.4454	469.4	1117.7
650	494.90	.0203	.7083	481.8	1202.3	.6826	1.4374	479.4	1117.1
700	503.10	.0205	.6554	491.5	1201.2	.6925	1.4296	488.8	1116.3
750	510.86	.0207	.6092	500.8	1200.0	.7019	1.4223	598.0	1115.4
800	518.23	.0209	.5687	509.7	1198.6	.7108	1.4153	506.6	1114.4
850	525.26	.0210	.5327	518.3	1197.1	.7194	1.4085	515.0	1113.3
900	531.98	.0212	.5006	526.6	1195.4	.7275	1.4020	523.1	1112.1
950	538.43	.0214	.4717	534.6	1193.7	.7355	1.3957	530.9	1110.8
1000	544.61	.0216	.4456	542.4	1191.8	.7430	1.3897	538.4	1109.4
1100	556.31	.0220	.4001	557.4	1187.8	.7575	1.3780	552.9	1106.4
1200	567.22	.0223	.3619	571.7	1183.4	.7711	1.3667	566.7	1103.0
1300	577.46	.0227	.3293	585.4	1178.6	.7840	1.3559	580.0	1099.4
1400	587.10	.0231	.3012	598.7	1173.4	.7963	1.3454	592.7	1095.4
1500	596.23	.0235	.2765	611.6	1167.9	.8082	1.3351	605.1	1091.2
2000	635.82	.0257	.1878	671.7	1135.1	.8619	1.2849	662.2	1065.6
2500	668.13	.0287	.1307	730.6	1091.1	.9126	1.2322	717.3	1030.6
3000	695.36	.0346	.0858	802.5	1020.3	.9731	1.1615	783.4	972.7
3206.2	705.40	.0503	.0503	902.7	902.7	1.0580	1.0580	872.9	872.9

* Abridged from Keenan and Keyes, "Thermodynamic Properties of Steam," Wiley, New York, 1936.

Table 3-261. Superheated Steam*

v, volume, cu. ft./lb.; *h*, enthalpy, B.t.u./lb.; *s*, entropy, B.t.u./(lb.)(°R.)

Abs. pressure, lb./sq. in. (sat. temp.)		Temp., °F.												
		200	300	400	500	600	700	800	900	1000	1100	1200	1400	1600
	v	392.6	452.3	512.0	571.6	631.2	690.8	750.4	809.9	869.5	929.1	988.7	1107.8	1227.0
1	h	1150.4	1195.8	1241.7	1288.3	1335.7	1383.8	1432.8	1482.7	1533.5	1585.2	1637.7	1745.7	1857.5
(101.74)	s	2.0512	2.1153	2.1720	2.2233	2.2702	2.3137	2.3542	2.3923	2.4283	2.4625	2.4952	2.5566	2.6137
	v	78.16	90.25	102.26	114.22	126.16	138.10	150.03	161.95	173.87	185.79	197.71	221.6	245.4
5	h	1148.8	1195.0	1241.2	1288.0	1335.4	1383.6	1432.7	1482.6	1533.4	1585.1	1637.7	1745.7	1857.4
(162.24)	s	1.8718	1.9370	1.9942	2.0456	2.0927	2.1361	2.1767	2.2148	2.2509	2.2851	2.3178	2.3792	2.4363
	v	38.85	45.00	51.04	57.05	63.03	69.01	74.98	80.95	86.92	92.88	98.84	110.77	122.69
10	h	1146.6	1193.9	1240.6	1287.5	1335.1	1383.4	1432.5	1482.4	1533.2	1585.0	1637.6	1745.6	1857.3
(193.21)	s	1.7927	1.8595	1.9172	1.9689	2.0160	2.0596	2.1002	2.1383	2.1744	2.2086	2.2413	2.3028	2.3598
	v	.....	30.53	34.68	38.78	42.86	46.94	51.00	55.07	59.13	63.19	67.25	75.37	83.48
14.696	h	.....	1192.8	1239.9	1287.1	1334.8	1383.2	1432.3	1482.3	1533.1	1584.8	1637.5	1745.5	1857.3
(212.00)	s	.....	1.8160	1.8743	1.9261	1.9734	2.0170	2.0576	2.0958	2.1319	2.1662	2.1989	2.2603	2.3174
	v	.....	22.36	25.43	28.46	31.47	34.47	37.46	40.45	43.44	46.42	49.41	55.37	61.34
20	h	.....	1191.6	1239.2	1286.6	1334.4	1382.9	1432.1	1482.1	1533.0	1584.7	1637.4	1745.4	1857.2
(227.96)	s	.....	1.7808	1.8396	1.8918	1.9392	1.9829	2.0235	2.0618	2.0978	2.1321	2.1648	2.2263	2.2834
	v	.....	11.040	12.628	14.168	15.688	17.198	18.702	20.20	21.70	23.20	24.69	27.68	30.66
40	h	.....	1186.8	1236.5	1284.8	1333.1	1381.9	1431.3	1481.4	1532.4	1584.3	1637.0	1745.1	1857.0
(267.25)	s	.....	1.6994	1.7608	1.8140	1.8619	1.9058	1.9467	1.9850	2.0212	2.0555	2.0883	2.1498	2.2069
	v	.....	7.259	8.357	9.403	10.427	11.441	12.449	13.452	14.454	15.453	16.451	18.446	20.44
60	h	.....	1181.6	1233.6	1283.0	1331.8	1380.9	1430.5	1480.8	1531.9	1583.8	1636.6	1744.8	1856.7
(292.71)	s	.....	1.6492	1.7135	1.7678	1.8162	1.8605	1.9015	1.9400	1.9762	2.0106	2.0434	2.1049	2.1621
	v	.....	.....	6.220	7.020	7.797	8.562	9.322	10.077	10.830	11.582	12.332	13.830	15.325
80	h	.....	.....	1230.7	1281.1	1330.5	1379.9	1429.7	1480.1	1531.3	1583.4	1636.2	1744.5	1856.5
(312.03)	s	.....	.....	1.6791	1.7346	1.7836	1.8281	1.8694	1.9079	1.9442	1.9787	2.0115	2.0721	2.1303
	v	.....	.....	4.937	5.589	6.218	6.835	7.446	8.052	8.656	9.259	9.860	11.060	12.258
100	h	.....	.....	1227.6	1279.1	1329.1	1378.9	1428.9	1479.5	1530.8	1582.9	1635.7	1744.2	1856.2
(327.81)	s	.....	.....	1.6518	1.7085	1.7581	1.8029	1.8443	1.8829	1.9193	1.9538	1.9867	2.0484	2.1056
	v	.....	.....	4.081	4.636	5.165	5.683	6.195	6.702	7.207	7.710	8.212	9.214	10.213
120	h	.....	.....	1224.4	1277.2	1327.7	1377.8	1428.1	1478.8	1530.2	1582.4	1635.3	1743.9	1856.0
(341.25)	s	.....	.....	1.6287	1.6869	1.7370	1.7822	1.8237	1.8625	1.8990	1.9335	1.9664	2.0281	2.0854
	v	.....	.....	3.468	3.954	4.413	4.861	5.301	5.738	6.172	6.604	7.035	7.895	8.752
140	h	.....	.....	1221.1	1275.2	1326.4	1376.8	1427.3	1478.2	1529.7	1581.9	1634.9	1743.5	1855.7
(353.02)	s	.....	.....	1.6087	1.6683	1.7190	1.7645	1.8063	1.8451	1.8817	1.9163	1.9493	2.0110	2.0683
	v	.....	.....	3.008	3.443	3.849	4.244	4.631	5.015	5.396	5.775	6.152	6.906	7.656
160	h	.....	.....	1217.6	1273.1	1325.0	1375.7	1426.4	1477.5	1529.1	1581.4	1634.5	1743.2	1855.5
(363.53)	s	.....	.....	1.5908	1.6519	1.7033	1.7491	1.7911	1.8301	1.8667	1.9014	1.9344	1.9962	2.0535
	v	.....	.....	2.649	3.044	3.411	3.764	4.110	4.452	4.792	5.129	5.466	6.136	6.804
180	h	.....	.....	1214.0	1271.0	1323.5	1374.7	1425.6	1476.8	1528.6	1581.0	1634.1	1742.9	1855.2
(373.06)	s	.....	.....	1.5745	1.6373	1.6894	1.7355	1.7776	1.8167	1.8534	1.8882	1.9212	1.9831	2.0404
	v	.....	.....	2.361	2.726	3.060	3.380	3.693	4.002	4.309	4.613	4.917	5.521	6.123
200	h	.....	.....	1210.3	1268.9	1322.1	1373.6	1424.8	1476.2	1528.0	1580.5	1633.7	1742.6	1855.0
(381.79)	s	.....	.....	1.5594	1.6240	1.6767	1.7232	1.7655	1.8048	1.8415	1.8763	1.9094	1.9713	2.0287
	v	.....	.....	2.125	2.465	2.772	3.066	3.352	3.634	3.913	4.191	4.467	5.017	5.565
220	h	.....	.....	1206.5	1266.7	1320.7	1372.6	1424.0	1475.5	1527.5	1580.0	1633.3	1742.3	1854.7
(389.86)	s	.....	.....	1.5453	1.6117	1.6652	1.7120	1.7545	1.7939	1.8308	1.8656	1.8987	1.9607	2.0181
	v	.....	.....	1.9276	2.247	2.533	2.804	3.068	3.327	3.584	3.839	4.093	4.597	5.100
240	h	.....	.....	1202.5	1264.5	1319.2	1371.5	1423.2	1474.8	1526.9	1579.6	1632.9	1742.0	1854.5
(397.37)	s	.....	.....	1.5319	1.6003	1.6546	1.7017	1.7444	1.7839	1.8209	1.8558	1.8889	1.9510	2.0084
	v	.....	.....	.....	2.063	2.330	2.582	2.827	3.067	3.305	3.541	3.776	4.242	4.707
260	h	.....	.....	.....	1262.3	1317.7	1370.4	1422.3	1474.2	1526.3	1579.1	1632.5	1741.7	1854.2
(404.42)	s	.....	.....	.....	1.5897	1.6447	1.6922	1.7352	1.7748	1.8118	1.8467	1.8799	1.9420	1.9995
	v	.....	.....	.....	1.9047	2.156	2.392	2.621	2.845	3.066	3.286	3.504	3.938	4.370
280	h	.....	.....	.....	1260.0	1316.2	1369.4	1421.5	1473.5	1525.8	1578.6	1632.1	1741.4	1854.0
(411.05)	s	.....	.....	.....	1.5796	1.6354	1.6834	1.7265	1.7662	1.8033	1.8383	1.8716	1.9337	1.9912
	v	.....	.....	.....	1.7675	2.005	2.227	2.442	2.652	2.859	3.065	3.269	3.674	4.078
300	h	.....	.....	.....	1257.6	1314.7	1368.3	1420.6	1472.8	1525.2	1578.1	1631.7	1741.0	1853.7
(417.33)	s	.....	.....	.....	1.5701	1.6268	1.6751	1.7184	1.7582	1.7954	1.8305	1.8638	1.9260	1.9835
	v	.....	.....	.....	1.4923	1.7036	1.8980	2.084	2.266	2.445	2.622	2.798	3.147	3.493
350	h	.....	.....	.....	1251.5	1310.9	1365.5	1418.5	1471.1	1523.8	1577.0	1630.7	1740.3	1853.1
(431.72)	s	.....	.....	.....	1.5481	1.6070	1.6563	1.7002	1.7403	1.7777	1.8130	1.8463	1.9086	1.9663
	v	.....	.....	.....	1.2851	1.4770	1.6508	1.8161	1.9767	2.134	2.290	2.445	2.751	3.055
400	h	.....	.....	.....	1245.1	1306.9	1362.7	1416.4	1469.4	1522.4	1575.8	1629.6	1739.5	1852.5
(444.59)	s	.....	.....	.....	1.5281	1.5894	1.6398	1.6842	1.7247	1.7623	1.7977	1.8311	1.8936	1.9513

* Abridged from Keenan and Keyes, "Thermodynamic Properties of Steam," Wiley, New York, 1936. Copyright, 1937, by Joseph H. Keenan and Frederick G. Keyes.

Table 3-261. Superheated Steam*—(*Concluded*)

Abs. pressure, lb./sq. in. (sat. temp.)		Temp., °F.													
		500	550	600	620	640	660	680	700	800	900	1000	1200	1400	1600
	v	1.1231	1.2155	1.3005	1.3332	1.3652	1.3967	1.4278	1.4584	1.6074	1.7516	1.8928	2.170	2.443	2.714
450	h	1238.4	1272.0	1302.8	1314.6	1326.2	1337.5	1348.8	1359.9	1414.3	1467.7	1521.0	1628.6	1738.7	1851.9
(456.28)	s	1.5095	1.5437	1.5735	1.5845	1.5951	1.6054	1.6153	1.6250	1.6699	1.7108	1.7486	1.8177	1.8803	1.9381
	v	0.9927	1.0800	1.1591	1.1893	1.2188	1.2478	1.2763	1.3044	1.4405	1.5715	1.6996	1.9504	2.197	2.442
500	h	1231.3	1266.8	1298.6	1310.7	1322.6	1334.2	1345.7	1357.0	1412.1	1466.0	1519.6	1627.6	1737.9	1851.3
(467.01)	s	1.4919	1.5280	1.5588	1.5701	1.5810	1.5915	1.6016	1.6115	1.6571	1.6982	1.7363	1.8056	1.8683	1.9262
	v	0.8852	0.9686	1.0431	1.0714	1.0989	1.1259	1.1523	1.1783	1.3038	1.4241	1.5414	1.7706	1.9957	2.219
550	h	1223.7	1261.2	1294.3	1306.8	1318.9	1330.8	1342.5	1354.0	1409.9	1464.3	1518.2	1626.6	1737.1	1850.6
(476.94)	s	1.4751	1.5131	1.5451	1.5568	1.5680	1.5787	1.5890	1.5991	1.6452	1.6868	1.7250	1.7946	1.8575	1.9155
	v	0.7947	0.8753	0.9463	0.9729	0.9988	1.0241	1.0489	1.0732	1.1899	1.3013	1.4096	1.6208	1.8279	2.033
600	h	1215.7	1255.5	1289.9	1302.7	1315.2	1327.4	1339.3	1351.1	1407.7	1462.5	1516.7	1625.5	1736.3	1850.0
(486.21)	s	1.4586	1.4990	1.5323	1.5443	1.5558	1.5667	1.5773	1.5875	1.6343	1.6762	1.7147	1.7846	1.8476	1.9056
	v	......	0.7277	0.7934	0.8177	0.8411	0.8639	0.8860	0.9077	1.0108	1.1082	1.2024	1.3853	1.5641	1.7405
700	h	......	1243.2	1280.6	1294.3	1307.5	1320.3	1332.8	1345.0	1403.2	1459.0	1513.9	1623.5	1734.8	1848.8
(503.10)	s	......	1.4722	1.5084	1.5212	1.5333	1.5449	1.5559	1.5665	1.6147	1.6573	1.6963	1.7666	1.8299	1.8881
	v	......	0.6154	0.6779	0.7006	0.7223	0.7433	0.7635	0.7833	0.8763	0.9633	1.0470	1.2088	1.3662	1.5214
800	h	......	1229.8	1270.7	1285.4	1299.4	1312.9	1325.9	1338.6	1398.6	1455.4	1511.0	1621.4	1733.2	1847.5
(518.23)	s	......	1.4467	1.4863	1.5000	1.5129	1.5250	1.5366	1.5476	1.5972	1.6407	1.6801	1.7510	1.8146	1.8729
	v	......	0.5264	0.5873	0.6089	0.6294	0.6491	0.6680	0.6863	0.7716	0.8506	0.9262	1.0714	1.2124	1.3509
900	h	......	1215.0	1260.1	1275.9	1290.9	1305.1	1318.8	1332.1	1393.9	1451.8	1508.1	1619.3	1731.6	1846.3
(531.98)	s	......	1.4216	1.4653	1.4800	1.4938	1.5066	1.5187	1.5303	1.5814	1.6257	1.6656	1.7371	1.8009	1.8595
	v	......	0.4533	0.5140	0.5350	0.5546	0.5733	0.5912	0.6084	0.6878	0.7604	0.8294	0.9615	1.0893	1.2146
1000	h	......	1198.3	1248.8	1265.9	1281.9	1297.0	1311.4	1325.3	1389.2	1448.2	1505.1	1617.3	1730.0	1845.0
(544.61)	s	......	1.3961	1.4450	1.4610	1.4757	1.4893	1.5021	1.5141	1.5670	1.6121	1.6525	1.7245	1.7886	1.8474
	v	......	......	0.4532	0.4738	0.4929	0.5110	0.5281	0.5445	0.6191	0.6866	0.7503	0.8716	0.9885	1.1031
1100	h	......	......	1236.7	1255.3	1272.4	1288.5	1303.7	1318.3	1384.3	1444.5	1502.2	1615.2	1728.4	1843.8
(556.31)	s	......	......	1.4251	1.4425	1.4583	1.4728	1.4862	1.4989	1.5535	1.5995	1.6405	1.7130	1.7775	1.8363
	v	......	......	0.4016	0.4222	0.4410	0.4586	0.4752	0.4909	0.5617	0.6250	0.6843	0.7967	0.9046	1.0101
1200	h	......	......	1223.5	1243.9	1262.4	1279.6	1295.7	1311.0	1379.3	1440.7	1499.2	1613.1	1726.9	1842.5
(567.22)	s	......	......	1.4062	1.4243	1.4413	1.4568	1.4710	1.4843	1.5409	1.5879	1.6293	1.7025	1.7672	1.8263
	v	......	......	0.3174	0.3390	0.3580	0.3753	0.3912	0.4062	0.4714	0.5281	0.5805	0.6789	0.7727	0.8640
1400	h	......	......	1193.0	1218.4	1240.4	1260.3	1278.5	1295.5	1369.1	1433.1	1493.2	1608.9	1723.7	1840.0
(587.10)	s	......	......	1.3639	1.3877	1.4079	1.4258	1.4419	1.4567	1.5177	1.5666	1.6093	1.6836	1.7489	1.8083
	v	......	......	......	0.2733	0.2936	0.3112	0.3271	0.3417	0.4034	0.4553	0.5027	0.5906	0.6738	0.7545
1600	h	......	......	......	1187.8	1215.2	1238.7	1259.6	1278.7	1358.4	1425.3	1487.0	1604.6	1720.5	1837.5
(604.90)	s	......	......	......	1.3489	1.3741	1.3952	1.4137	1.4303	1.4964	1.5476	1.5914	1.6669	1.7328	1.7926
	v	......	......	......	......	0.2407	0.2597	0.2760	0.2907	0.3502	0.3986	0.4421	0.5218	0.5968	0.6693
1800	h	......	......	......	......	1185.1	1214.0	1238.5	1260.3	1347.2	1417.4	1480.8	1600.4	1717.3	1835.0
(621.03)	s	......	......	......	......	1.3377	1.3638	1.3855	1.4044	1.4765	1.5301	1.5752	1.6520	1.7185	1.7786
	v	......	......	......	......	0.1936	0.2161	0.2337	0.2489	0.3074	0.3532	0.3935	0.4668	0.5352	0.6011
2000	h	......	......	......	......	1145.6	1184.9	1214.8	1240.0	1335.5	1409.2	1474.5	1596.1	1714.1	1832.5
(635.82)	s	......	......	......	......	1.2945	1.3300	1.3564	1.3783	1.4576	1.5139	1.5603	1.6384	1.7055	1.7660
	v	......	......	......	......	......	......	0.1484	0.1686	0.2294	0.2710	0.3061	0.3678	0.4244	0.4784
2500	h	......	......	......	......	......	......	1132.3	1176.8	1303.6	1387.8	1458.4	1585.3	1706.1	1826.2
(668.13)	s	......	......	......	......	......	......	1.2687	1.3073	1.4127	1.4772	1.5273	1.6088	1.6775	1.7389
	v	......	......	......	......	......	......	......	0.0984	0.1760	0.2159	0.2476	0.3018	0.3505	0.3966
3000	h	......	......	......	......	......	......	......	1060.7	1267.2	1365.0	1441.8	1574.3	1698.0	1819.9
(695.36)	s	......	......	......	......	......	......	......	1.1966	1.3690	1.4439	1.4984	1.5837	1.6540	1.7163
	v	......	......	......	......	......	......	......	......	0.1583	0.1981	0.2288	0.2806	0.3267	0.3703
3206.2	h	......	......	......	......	......	......	......	......	1250.5	1355.2	1434.7	1569.8	1694.6	1817.2
(705.40)	s	......	......	......	......	......	......	......	......	1.3508	1.4309	1.4874	1.5742	1.6452	1.7080
	v	......	......	......	......	......	......	......	0.0306	0.1364	0.1762	0.2058	0.2546	0.2977	0.3381
3500	h	......	......	......	......	......	......	......	780.5	1224.9	1340.7	1424.5	1563.3	1689.8	1813.6
	s	......	......	......	......	......	......	......	0.9515	1.3241	1.4127	1.4723	1.5615	1.6336	1.6968
	v	......	......	......	......	......	......	......	0.0287	0.1052	0.1462	0.1743	0.2192	0.2581	0.2943
4000	h	......	......	......	......	......	......	......	763.8	1174.8	1314.4	1406.8	1552.2	1681.7	1807.2
	s	......	......	......	......	......	......	......	0.9347	1.2757	1.3827	1.4482	1.5417	1.6154	1.6795
	v	......	......	......	......	......	......	......	0.0276	0.0798	0.1226	0.1500	0.1917	0.2273	0.2602
4500	h	......	......	......	......	......	......	......	753.5	1113.9	1286.5	1388.4	1540.8	1673.5	1800.9
	s	......	......	......	......	......	......	......	0.9235	1.2204	1.3529	1.4253	1.5235	1.5990	1.6640
	v	......	......	......	......	......	......	......	0.0268	0.0593	0.1036	0.1303	0.1696	0.2027	0.2329
5000	h	......	......	......	......	......	......	......	746.4	1047.1	1256.5	1369.5	1529.5	1665.3	1794.5
	s	......	......	......	......	......	......	......	0.9152	1.1622	1.3231	1.4034	1.5066	1.5839	1.6499
	v	......	......	......	......	......	......	......	0.0262	0.0462	0.0880	0.1143	0.1516	0.1825	0.2106
5500	h	......	......	......	......	......	......	......	741.3	985.0	1224.1	1349.3	1518.2	1637.0	1788.1
	s	......	......	......	......	......	......	......	0.9090	1.1093	1.2930	1.3821	1.4908	1.5699	1.6369

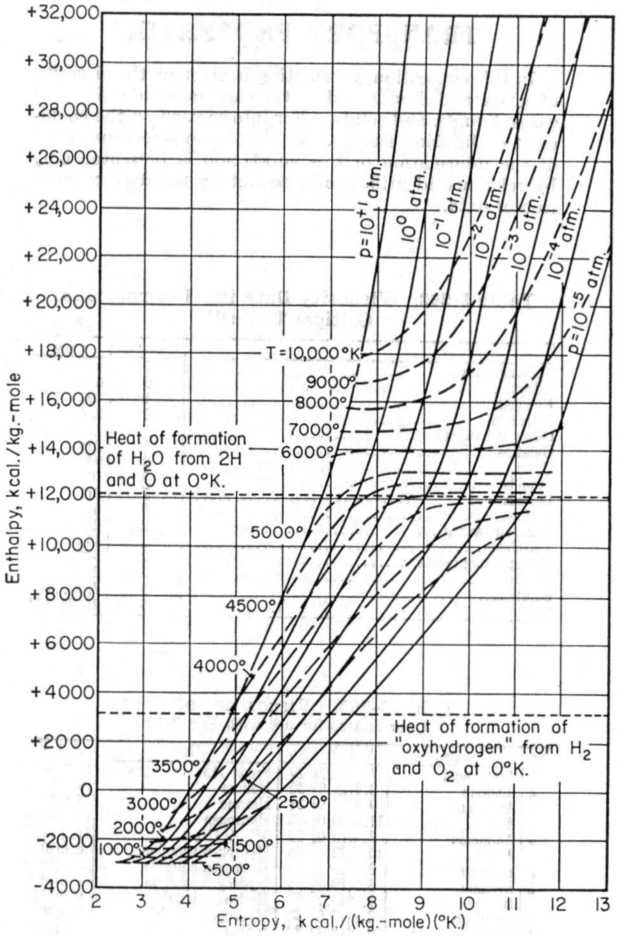

FIG. 3-41. Mollier diagram for water at equilibrium in the plasma region. [*Sanger-Bredt, Astronaut. Acta*, **3**, 250 (1959), Fig. **4**. *Copyright Springer, Vienna, 1957. Reproduced by permission.*) For similar material see Sanger-Bredt, *N.A.S.A.* TT Fl, 1959.

TRANSPORT PROPERTIES

In this subsection information is given on the viscosity of gases and liquids and on the thermal conductivity of gases, liquids, and solids. For information on the coefficient of diffusion see Sec. 14. For various reasons, much of the information of this subsection is presented only by reference identification and not by tabular presentation of data.

Table 3-262. Viscosity Data in "International Critical Tables"

	Volume	Page
Tabular index	5	1
Alloys	5	6
Elements	1	102
Elements	5	2, 6
Gases and vapors	5	1
Gelatins	2	233
Glass	2	94
Liquids	5	10
Liquids	7	211
Metals	5	6
Oils, fats, waxes	2	209
Petroleum	2	146
Refrigerating brines	2	328
Rubber	2	255, 259
Solutions	5	7, 12, 20
Solutions	5	21, 25, 447

Table 3-263. Viscosities of Gases
Coordinates for use with Fig. 3-42

No.	Gas	X	Y	No.	Gas	X	Y
1	Acetic acid	7.7	14.3	29	Freon-113	11.3	14.0
2	Acetone	8.9	13.0	30	Helium	10.9	20.5
3	Acetylene	9.8	14.9	31	Hexane	8.6	11.8
4	Air	11.0	20.0	32	Hydrogen	11.2	12.4
5	Ammonia	8.4	16.0	33	$3H_2 + 1N_2$	11.2	17.2
6	Argon	10.5	22.4	34	Hydrogen bromide	8.8	20.9
7	Benzene	8.5	13.2	35	Hydrogen chloride	8.8	18.7
8	Bromine	8.9	19.2	36	Hydrogen cyanide	9.8	14.9
9	Butene	9.2	13.7	37	Hydrogen iodide	9.0	21.3
10	Butylene	8.9	13.0	38	Hydrogen sulfide	8.6	18.0
11	Carbon dioxide	9.5	18.7	39	Iodine	9.0	18.4
12	Carbon disulfide	8.0	16.0	40	Mercury	5.3	22.9
13	Carbon monoxide	11.0	20.0	41	Methane	9.9	15.5
14	Chlorine	9.0	18.4	42	Methyl alcohol	8.5	15.6
15	Chloroform	8.9	15.7	43	Nitric oxide	10.9	20.5
16	Cyanogen	9.2	15.2	44	Nitrogen	10.6	20.0
17	Cyclohexane	9.2	12.0	45	Nitrosyl chloride	8.0	17.6
18	Ethane	9.1	14.5	46	Nitrous oxide	8.8	19.0
19	Ethyl acetate	8.5	13.2	47	Oxygen	11.0	21.3
20	Ethyl alcohol	9.2	14.2	48	Pentane	7.0	12.8
21	Ethyl chloride	8.5	15.6	49	Propane	9.7	12.9
22	Ethyl ether	8.9	13.0	50	Propyl alcohol	8.4	13.4
23	Ethylene	9.5	15.1	51	Propylene	9.0	13.8
24	Fluorine	7.3	23.8	52	Sulfur dioxide	9.6	17.0
25	Freon-11	10.6	15.1	53	Toluene	8.6	12.4
26	Freon-12	11.1	16.0	54	2, 3, 3-Trimethylbutane	9.5	10.5
27	Freon-21	10.8	15.3	55	Water	8.0	16.0
28	Freon-22	10.1	17.0	56	Xenon	9.3	23.0

Table 3-264. Viscosity of Steam*
Values in centipoises

Temp.		Pressure, lb. force/sq. in. abs.					
°C.	°F.	100	200	400	500	600	800
204	400	0.0198	0.0230				
260	500	.0213	.0236	0.0272	0.0289	0.0311	
316	600	.0228	.0246	.0279	.0294	.0314	0.0350
371	700	.0243	.0259	.0290	.0304	.0321	.0357
427	800	.0260	.0275	.0304	.0318	.0334	.0370
482	900	.0278	.0292	.0320	.0335	.0352	.0390
538	1000	.0296	.0310	.0338	.0354	.0372	.0414

* Data of Hawkins, Solberg, and Potter, *Trans. Am. Soc. Mech. Engrs.*, **62**, p. 677 (1940).

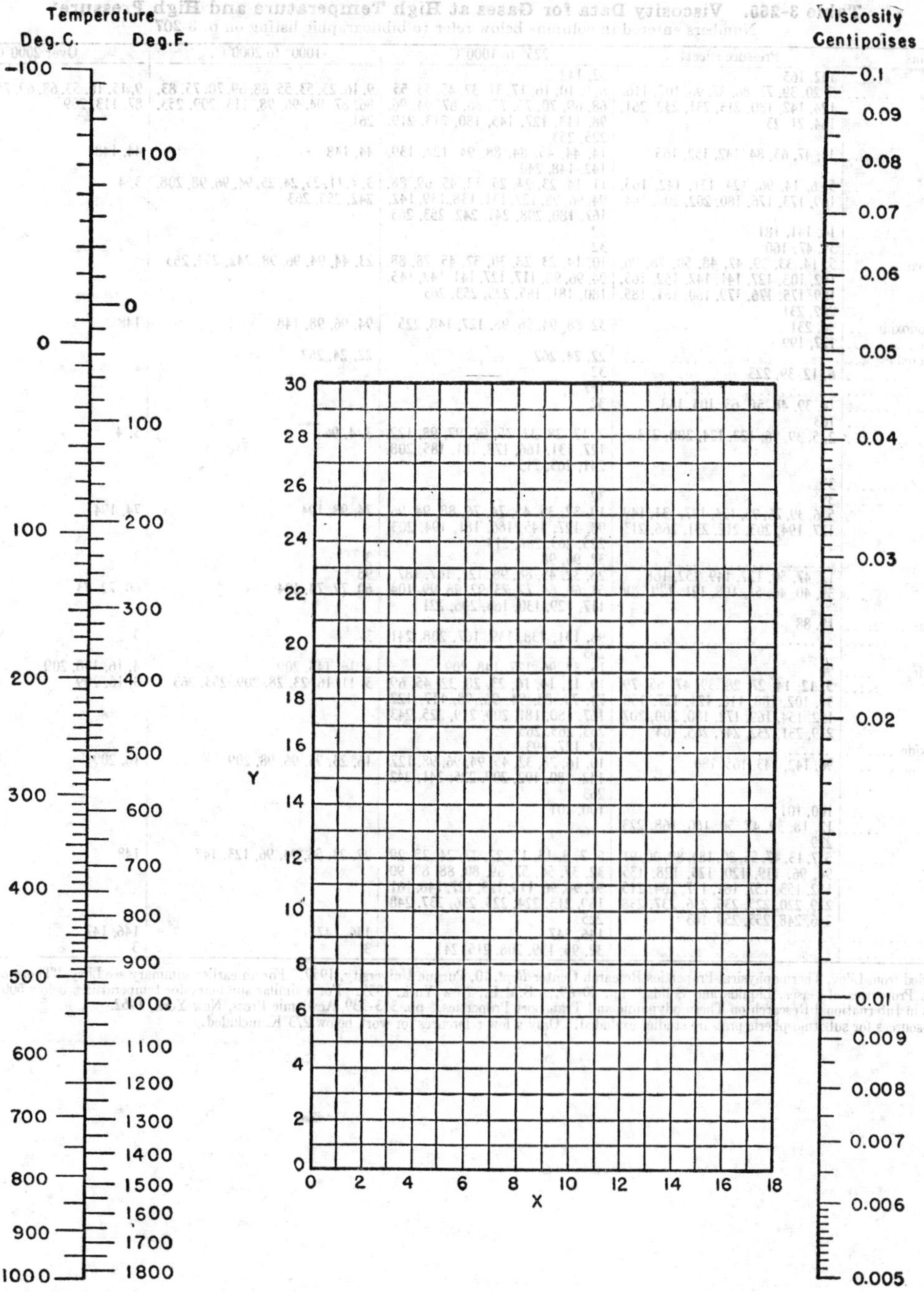

FIG. 3-42. Viscosities of gases at 1 atm. For coordinates, see Table 3-263.

Table 3-265. Viscosity Data for Gases at High Temperature and High Pressure*

Numbers entered in columns below refer to bibliographic listing on p. 3-207

Gas	Pressure effect†	225° to 1000°C.	1000° to 2000°C.	Over 2000°C.
Acetylene	142, 165	32, 142		
Air	5, 20, 39, 77, 86, 87, 96, 107, 116, 124, 142, 180, 213, 231, 232, 261, 164, 21, 23	8, 9, 10, 16, 17, 31, 32, 45, 53, 55, 68, 69, 70, 75, 77, 86, 87, 94, 96, 98, 113, 127, 145, 180, 213, 219, 225, 253	9, 16, 23, 53, 55, 68, 69, 70, 75, 83, 86, 87, 94, 96, 98, 113, 209, 253, 261	9, 15, 16, 53, 68, 69, 75, 81, 83, 86, 87, 113, 209
Ammonia	14, 47, 63, 84, 142, 152, 165	14, 44, 45, 84, 88, 94, 127, 139, 142, 148, 240	44, 148	44, 148
Argon	5, 6, 14, 96, 124, 131, 142, 165, 169, 173, 176, 180, 202, 208, 164	11, 14, 23, 24, 25, 32, 45, 69, 88, 94, 96, 98, 127, 131, 138, 139, 142, 167, 180, 208, 241, 242, 253, 263	3, 4, 11, 23, 24, 25, 94, 96, 98, 208, 242, 253, 263	3, 4
Benzene	14, 141, 181	32		
Butanes	39, 47, 160	32		
Carbon dioxide	5, 14, 33, 39, 47, 48, 50, 78, 96, 102, 103, 127, 141, 142, 152, 165, 169, 175, 176, 179, 180, 181, 185, 207, 231	10, 14, 23, 28, 30, 32, 45, 78, 88, 94, 96, 98, 117, 127, 141, 142, 145, 180, 181, 185, 225, 253, 263	23, 44, 94, 96, 98, 242, 253, 263	
Carbon monoxide	96, 231	32, 88, 94, 96, 98, 127, 148, 225	94, 96, 98, 148	148
Deuterium	177, 199			
Deuterium oxide	....	22, 24, 262	22, 24, 262	
Ethane	6, 12, 39, 223	32		
Ether	....	137		
Ethylene	14, 39, 48, 50, 63, 103, 168	32		
Freons	163			
Helium	2, 5, 39, 96, 122, 124, 200, 213	2, 17, 28, 32, 35, 96, 97, 98, 122, 127, 131, 166, 178, 181, 185, 208, 241, 263, 213	3, 4, 96	3, 4
Heptane	39			
Hexane	39	32		
Hydrogen	5, 6, 39, 76, 96, 124, 127, 131, 149, 177, 194, 203, 212, 231, 266, 213	10, 32, 35, 45, 74, 76, 88, 94, 96, 98, 127, 145, 166, 181, 194, 203, 225, 263, 266, 213	74, 98, 194	74, 194
Krypton	....	32, 96, 98	3	3
Methane	12, 47, 50, 127, 149, 152, 168	28, 32, 45, 88, 98, 127, 167, 187	98	
Mixtures	39, 40, 46, 51, 108, 121, 129, 206	51, 60, 64, 72, 73, 92, 98, 99, 104, 117, 129, 130, 166, 206, 221	60, 72, 73, 104	60, 72, 73
Natural gas	19, 88			
Neon	....	98, 131, 138, 139, 167, 208, 241, 263	3	3
Nitric oxide	96	16, 32, 96, 127, 148, 209	4, 16, 148, 209	4, 16, 148, 209
Nitrogen	5, 12, 14, 27, 28, 39, 47, 65, 79, 96, 102, 108, 118, 124, 127, 150, 152, 154, 169, 172, 180, 200, 207, 219, 231, 232, 247, 265, 164	10, 11, 14, 16, 23, 28, 32, 45, 69, 74, 79, 88, 94, 96, 98, 117, 127, 167, 180, 181, 209, 219, 225, 243, 253, 263, 265	3, 11, 16, 23, 28, 209, 253, 263	3, 16, 209
Nitrous oxide	....	32, 127, 193		
Oxygen	96, 142, 143, 165, 180	10, 16, 28, 32, 45, 94, 96, 98, 127, 142, 180, 192, 209, 225, 241, 242, 263	16, 23, 94, 96, 98, 209	16, 209
Pentane	100, 101	100, 101		
Propane	12, 18, 39, 47, 50, 160, 168, 223, 229			
Steam	5, 7, 13, 47, 56, 80, 184, 89, 90, 91, 94, 96, 119, 120, 123, 128, 135, 152, 153, 157, 161, 197, 204, 215, 219, 220, 225, 235, 236, 237, 238, 246, 248, 255, 259, 183	5, 7, 8, 13, 17, 22, 23, 24, 25, 29, 32, 37, 56, 57, 69, 80, 88, 89, 90, 91, 94, 96, 119, 123, 127, 148, 161, 189, 215, 224, 225, 236, 237, 248, 225	22, 23, 56, 94, 96, 123, 148	148
Sulfur	....	146, 147	146, 147	146, 147
Xenon	....	32, 95, 139, 208, 215, 241	3	3

* Modified from Liley, Thermophysical Properties Research Center *Rept.* 10, Purdue University, 1959. For an earlier summary see Liley, "Thermodynamic and Transport Properties of Gases, Liquids and Solids," pp. 40–69, A.S.M.E., New York, 1959. For a similar summary for temperatures below 500°K see Liley, "Progress in International Research on Thermodynamic and Transport Properties," pp. 313–339, Academic Press, New York, 1962.

† Data sources for subatmospheric pressure studies excluded. Only a few references for work below 273°K. included.

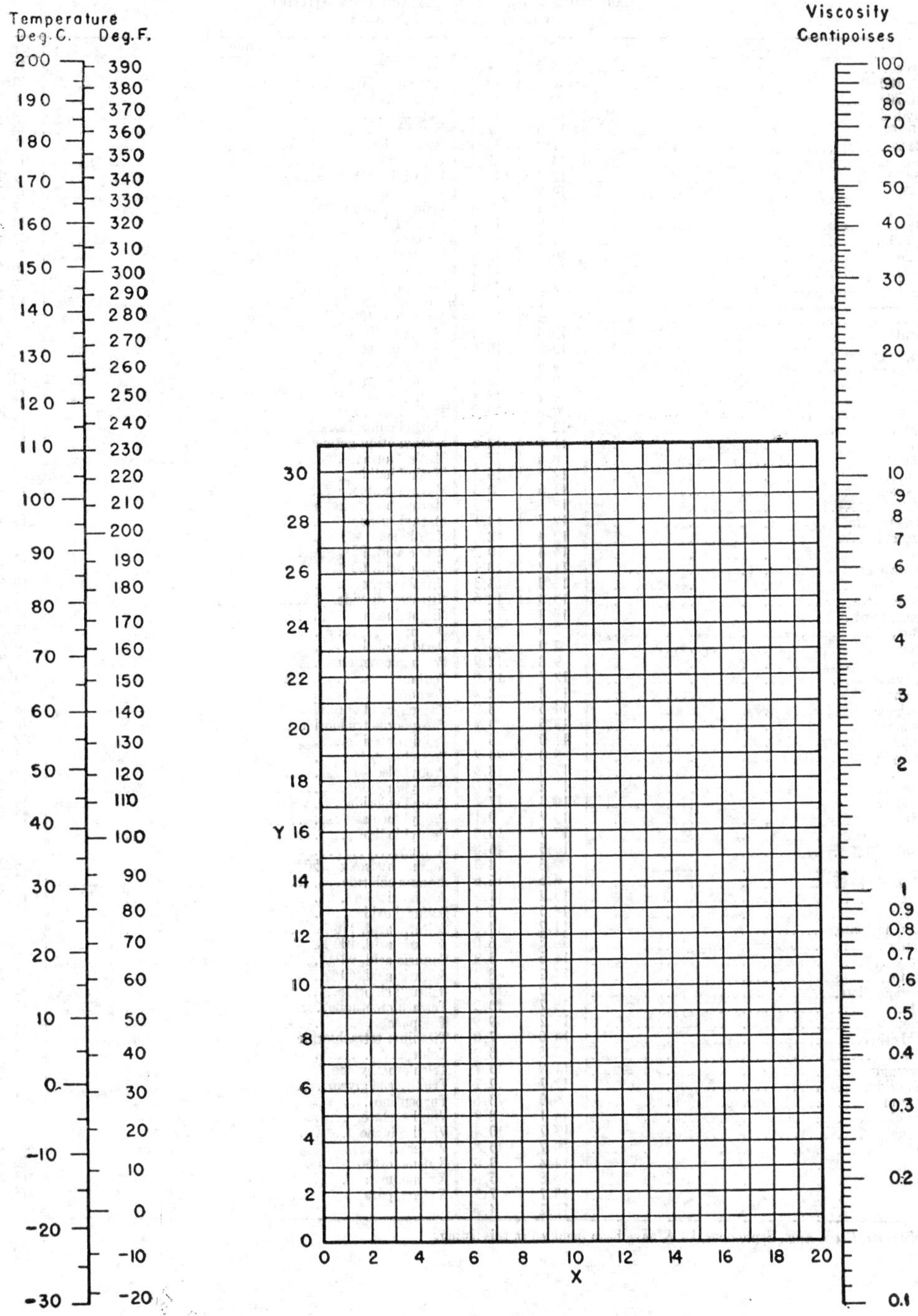

FIG. 3-43. Viscosities of liquids at 1 atm. For coordinates, see Table 3-266.

Table 3-266. Viscosities of Liquids

Coordinates for Fig. 3-43

Liquid	X	Y
Acetaldehyde	15.2	4.8
Acetic acid, 100%	12.1	14.2
Acetic acid, 70%	9.5	17.0
Acetic anhydride	12.7	12.8
Acetone, 100%	14.5	7.2
Acetone, 35%	7.9	15.0
Acetonitrile	14.4	7.4
Acrylic acid	12.3	13.9
Allyl alcohol	10.2	14.3
Allyl bromide	14.4	9.6
Allyl iodide	14.0	11.7
Ammonia, 100%	12.6	2.0
Ammonia, 26%	10.1	13.9
Amyl acetate	11.8	12.5
Amyl alcohol	7.5	18.4
Aniline	8.1	18.7
Anisole	12.3	13.5
Arsenic trichloride	13.9	14.5
Benzene	12.5	10.9
Brine, $CaCl_2$, 25%	6.6	15.9
Brine, NaCl, 25%	10.2	16.6
Bromine	14.2	13.2
Bromotoluene	20.0	15.9
Butyl acetate	12.3	11.0
Butyl acrylate	11.5	12.6
Butyl alcohol	8.6	17.2
Butyric acid	12.1	15.3
Carbon dioxide	11.6	0.3
Carbon disulfide	16.1	7.5
Carbon tetrachloride	12.7	13.1
Chlorobenzene	12.3	12.4
Chloroform	14.4	10.2
Chlorosulfonic acid	11.2	18.1
Chlorotoluene, ortho	13.0	13.3
Chlorotoluene, meta	13.3	12.5
Chlorotoluene, para	13.3	12.5
Cresol, meta	2.5	20.8
Cyclohexanol	2.9	24.3
Cyclohexane	9.8	12.9
Dibromomethane	12.7	15.8
Dichloroethane	13.2	12.2
Dichloromethane	14.6	8.9
Diethyl ketone	13.5	9.2
Diethyl oxalate	11.0	16.4
Diethylene glycol	5.0	24.7
Diphenyl	12.0	18.3
Dipropyl ether	13.2	8.6
Dipropyl oxalate	10.3	17.7
Ethyl acetate	13.7	9.1
Ethyl acrylate	12.7	10.4
Ethyl alcohol, 100%	10.5	13.8
Ethyl alcohol, 95%	9.8	14.3
Ethyl alcohol, 40%	6.5	16.6
Ethyl benzene	13.2	11.5
Ethyl bromide	14.5	8.1
2-Ethyl butyl acrylate	11.2	14.0
Ethyl chloride	14.8	6.0
Ethyl ether	14.5	5.3
Ethyl formate	14.2	8.4
2-Ethyl hexyl acrylate	9.0	15.0
Ethyl iodide	14.7	10.3
Ethyl propionate	13.2	9.9
Ethyl propyl ether	14.0	7.0
Ethyl sulfide	13.8	8.9
Ethylene bromide	11.9	15.7
Ethylene chloride	12.7	12.2
Ethylene glycol	6.0	23.6
Ethylidene chloride	14.1	8.7
Fluorobenzene	13.7	10.4
Formic acid	10.7	15.8
Freon-11	14.4	9.0
Freon-12	16.8	15.6
Freon-21	15.7	7.5
Freon-22	17.2	4.7
Freon-113	12.5	11.4
Glycerol, 100%	2.0	30.0
Glycerol, 50%	6.9	19.6
Heptane	14.1	8.4
Hexane	14.7	7.0
Hydrochloric acid, 31.5%	13.0	16.6
Iodobenzene	12.8	15.9
Isobutyl alcohol	7.1	18.0
Isobutyric acid	12.2	14.4
Isopropyl alcohol	8.2	16.0
Isopropyl bromide	14.1	9.2
Isopropyl chloride	13.9	7.1
Isopropyl iodide	13.7	11.2
Kerosene	10.2	16.9
Linseed oil, raw	7.5	27.2
Mercury	18.4	16.4
Methanol, 100%	12.4	10.5
Methanol, 90%	12.3	11.8
Methanol, 40%	7.8	15.5
Methyl acetate	14.2	8.2
Methyl acrylate	13.0	9.5
Methyl *i*-butyrate	12.3	9.7
Methyl *n*-butyrate	13.2	10.3
Methyl chloride	15.0	3.8
Methyl ethyl ketone	13.9	8.6
Methyl formate	14.2	7.5
Methyl iodide	14.3	9.3
Methyl propionate	13.5	9.0
Methyl propyl ketone	14.3	9.5
Methyl sulfide	15.3	6.4
Napthalene	7.9	18.1
Nitric acid, 95%	12.8	13.8
Nitric acid, 60%	10.8	17.0
Nitrobenzene	10.6	16.2
Nitrogen dioxide	12.9	8.6
Nitrotoluene	11.0	17.0
Octane	13.7	10.0
Octyl alcohol	6.6	21.1
Pentachloroethane	10.9	17.3
Pentane	14.9	5.2
Phenol	6.9	20.8
Phosphorus tribromide	13.8	16.7
Phosphorus trichloride	16.2	10.9
Propionic acid	12.8	13.8
Propyl acetate	13.1	10.3
Propyl alcohol	9.1	16.5
Propyl bromide	14.5	9.6
Propyl chloride	14.4	7.5
Propyl formate	13.1	9.7
Propyl iodide	14.1	11.6
Sodium	16.4	13.9
Sodium hydroxide, 50%	3.2	25.8
Stannic chloride	13.5	12.8
Succinonitrile	10.1	20.8
Sulfur dioxide	15.2	7.1
Sulfuric acid, 110%	7.2	27.4
Sulfuric acid, 100%	8.0	25.1
Sulfuric acid, 98%	7.0	24.8
Sulfuric acid, 60%	10.2	21.3
Sulfuryl chloride	15.2	12.4
Tetrachloroethane	11.9	15.7
Thiophene	13.2	11.0
Titanium tetrachloride	14.4	12.3
Toluene	13.7	10.4
Trichloroethylene	14.8	10.5
Triethylene glycol	4.7	24.8
Turpentine	11.5	14.9
Vinyl acetate	14.0	8.8
Vinyl toluene	13.4	12.0
Water	10.2	13.0
Xylene, ortho	13.5	12.1
Xylene, meta	13.9	10.6
Xylene, para	13.9	10.9

Values of Seiner, *Chem. Eng.*, September, 1958, have been included in this listing.

Table 3-267. Viscosity of Water*

Temp., °C.	Viscosity, centipoises	Temp., °C.	Viscosity, centipoises	Temp., °C.	Viscosity, centipoises
0	1.7921	33	0.7523	67	0.4233
1	1.7313	34	0.7371	68	0.4174
2	1.6728	35	0.7225	69	0.4117
3	1.6191	36	0.7085	70	0.4061
4	1.5674	37	0.6947	71	0.4006
5	1.5188	38	0.6814	72	0.3952
6	1.4728	39	0.6685	73	0.3900
7	1.4284	40	0.6560	74	0.3849
8	1.3860	41	0.6439	75	0.3799
9	1.3462	42	0.6321	76	0.3750
10	1.3077	43	0.6207	77	0.3702
11	1.2713	44	0.6097	78	0.3655
12	1.2363	45	0.5988	79	0.3610
13	1.2028	46	0.5883	80	0.3565
14	1.1709	47	0.5782	81	0.3521
15	1.1404	48	0.5683	82	0.3478
16	1.1111	49	0.5588	83	0.3436
17	1.0828	50	0.5494	84	0.3395
18	1.0559	51	0.5404	85	0.3355
19	1.0299	52	0.5315	86	0.3315
20	1.0050	53	0.5229	87	0.3276
20.20	*1.0000*	54	0.5146	88	0.3239
21	0.9810	55	0.5064	89	0.3202
22	0.9579	56	0.4985	90	0.3165
23	0.9358	57	0.4907	91	0.3130
24	0.9142	58	0.4832	92	0.3095
25	0.8937	59	0.4759	93	0.3060
26	0.8737	60	0.4688	94	0.3027
27	0.8545	61	0.4618	95	0.2994
28	0.8360	62	0.4550	96	0.2962
29	0.8180	63	0.4483	97	0.2930
30	0.8007	64	0.4418	98	0.2899
31	0.7840	65	0.4355	99	0.2868
32	0.7679	66	0.4293	100	0.2838

* Calculated by the formula:

$$1/\mu = 2.1482[(t - 8.435) + \sqrt{8078.4 + (t - 8.435)^2}] - 120.$$

From Bingham, "Fluidity and Plasticity," p. 340, McGraw-Hill, New York, 1922.

Table 3-268. Sucrose Solutions*

Viscosity in centipoises

Temp., °C.	Percentage sucrose by weight			Temp., °C.	Percentage sucrose by weight		
	20	40	60		20	40	60
0	3.818	14.82	......	50	0.974	2.506	14.06
5	3.166	11.60	......	55	0.887	2.227	11.71
10	2.662	9.830	113.9	60	0.811	1.989	9.87
15	2.275	7.496	74.9	65	0.745	1.785	8.37
20	1.967	6.223	56.7	70	0.688	1.614	7.18
25	1.710	5.206	44.02	75	0.637	1.467	6.22
30	1.510	4.398	34.01	80	0.592	1.339	5.42
35	1.336	3.776	26.62	85	0.552	1.226	4.75
40	1.197	3.261	21.30	90	.....	1.127	4.17
45	1.074	2.858	17.24	95	.....	1.041	3.73

* "International Critical Tables," vol. 5, p. 23. Bingham and Jackson, *Bur. Standards Bull.* 14, p. 59, 1919.

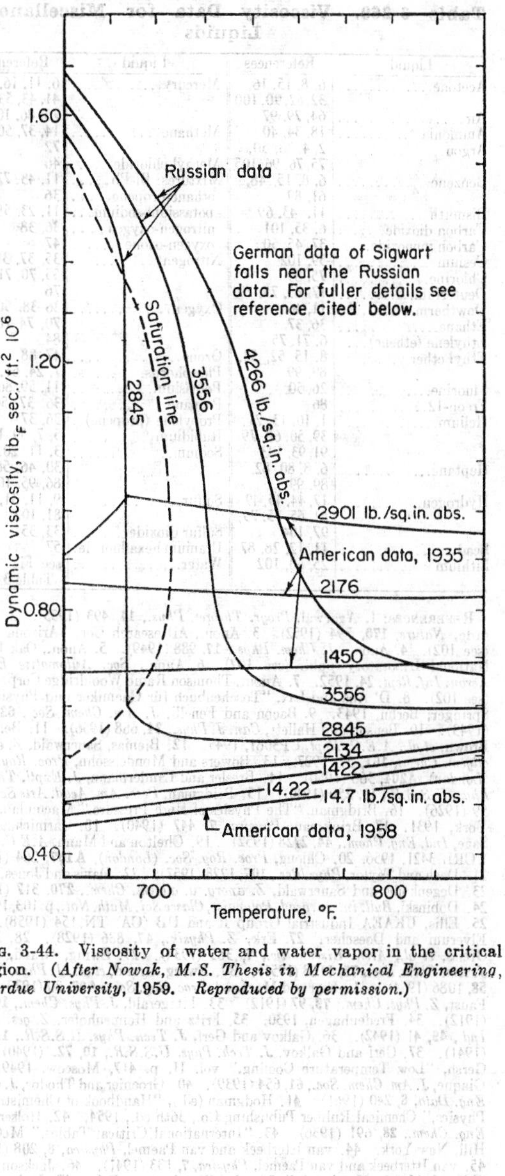

FIG. 3-44. Viscosity of water and water vapor in the critical region. (*After Nowak, M.S. Thesis in Mechanical Engineering, Purdue University, 1959. Reproduced by permission.*)

Table 3-269. Viscosity Data for Miscellaneous Liquids

Liquid	References	Liquid	References
Acetone	6, 8, 15, 16, 32, 62, 90, 100	Mercury	6, 11, 16, 27, 41, 43, 53, 58, 78, 86, 102
Air	64, 79, 97		
Ammonia	18, 34, 40	Methane	14, 37, 50, 70–72
Argon	2, 4, 38, 50, 75, 76, 96, 105	Methyl chloride	46
Benzene	6, 8, 15, 48, 61, 89	Mixtures: Bi-Pb	11, 43, 77
		ethane-propene	36
Bismuth	11, 43, 69	potassium-sodium	11, 23, 58, 86
Carbon dioxide	6, 35, 101	nitrogen-oxygen	36, 38
Carbon monoxide	37, 45, 50	oxygen-ozone	47
Cesium	59, 102	Nitrogen	35, 37, 38, 50, 55, 70, 71, 74–76
Chlorine	75, 83		
Deuterium	17, 65, 75, 79		
Dowtherm	11, 46	Oxygen	36–38, 50, 65, 70, 74–76, 79, 84
Ethane	36, 37		
Ethylene (ethene)	6, 71, 75		
Ethyl ether	8, 15, 52, 54, 89, 99	Ozone	47, 88
		Phosphorus	7, 24, 61, 102
Fluorine	26, 50	Potassium	11, 59, 86, 102
Freon-12	86	Propane	36, 37, 56, 66
Helium	1, 10, 13, 21, 39, 50, 68, 79, 91, 93, 103	Propylene (propene)	36, 37
		Rubidium	5, 7, 59, 102
		Sodium	3, 11, 20, 29, 30, 46, 58, 59, 86, 95, 102
Heptane	6, 8, 80, 82, 89, 99		
Hydrogen	17, 44, 45, 49–51, 65, 75, 79, 97, 104	Sulfur	9, 11, 31, 73, 81, 102
		Sulfur dioxide	33, 35
Lead	11, 12, 28, 87	Uranium hexafluoride	57
Lithium	25, 60, 102	Water	see Fig. 3-41, Table 3-267

REFERENCES: 1. Agarwal, *Progr. Theoret. Phys.*, **14**, 493 (1955). 2. Andrade, *Nature*, **170**, 794 (1952). 3. Anon., AiResearch Corp. Arizona publ. (see 102). 4. Anon., *J. Chem. Phys.*, **17**, 988 (1949). 5. Anon., Oak Ridge National Laboratory publ. (see 102). 6. Anon., *Soc. Automotive Engrs. Aeron. Inf. Rept.* 24, 1952. 7. Anon., Thomson Ramo Wooldridge Corp. publ. (see 102). 8. D' Ans and Lax, "Toschenbuch für Chemiker und Physiker," Springer, Berlin, 1943. 9. Bacon and Fenelli, *J. Am. Chem. Soc.*, **63**, 639 (1943). 10. Benson and Hallett, *Can. J. Phys.*, **34**, 668 (1956). 11. Bentley, Brown, *et al.*, *A.E.C. Rept.* CP3061, 1945. 12. Bienias, Sauerwald, *Z. anorg. allgem. Chem.*, **161**, 51, 1927. 13. Bowers and Mendelssohn, *Proc. Roy. Soc. (London)*, **A204**, 366 (1950). 14. Bresler and Landermann, *J. Exptl. Theoret. Phys. U.S.S.R.*, **10**, 250 (1940). 15. Bridgman, *Proc. Am. Acad. Arts Sci.*, **61**, 59 (1926). 16. Bridgman, "The Physics of High Pressure," Macmillan, New York, 1931. 17. Brinkman, *Physica*, **7**, 447 (1940). 18. Carmichael and Sage, *Ind. Eng. Chem.*, **44**, 2728 (1952). 19. Chelton and Mann, *A.E.C. Rept.* UCRL 3421, 1956. 20. Chiong, *Proc. Roy. Soc. (London)*, **A157**, 264 (1936). 21. Dash and Taylor, *Phys. Rev.*, **107**, 1228 (1957). 22. Davis and Jones, 1915. 23. Degenkolbe and Sauerwald, *Z. anorg. u. allgem. Chem.*, **270**, 317 (1952). 24. Dobinski, *Bull. intern. acad. Polonaise, Classe Sci. Math. Nat.*, p. 103, 1934A. 25. Ellis, UKAEA Industrial Group R and DB (CA) TN 154 (1958). 26. Elverum and Doescher. 27. Erk, *Z. Physik.*, **47**, 886 (1928). 28. Esser, Greiss, *et al.*, *Arch. Eisenhuttw.*, **7**, 385 (1934). 29. Ewing, Grand, *et al.*, *J. Am. Chem. Soc.*, **73**, 1168 (1951). 30. Ewing, Grand, *et al.*, *J. Phys. Chem.*, **58**, 1086 (1954). 31. Farr and MacLeod, *Proc. Roy. Soc.*, **A97**, 80 (1920). 32. Faust, *Z. Phys. Chem.*, **79**, 97 (1912). 33. Fitzgerald, *J. Phys. Chem.*, **16**, 621 (1912). 34. Fredenhagen, 1930, 35, Fritz and Hennenhofer, *Z. ges. Kalte-Ind.*, **49**, 41 (1942). 36. Galkov and Gerf, *J. Tech. Phys. U.S.S.R.*, **11**, 613 (1941). 37. Gerf and Galkov, *J. Tech. Phys. U.S.S.R.*, **10**, 72 (1940). 38. Gersh, "Low Temperature Cooling," vol. II, p. 417, Moscow, 1949. 39. Giaque, *J. Am. Chem. Soc.*, **61**, 654 (1939). 40. Groenier and Thodos, *J. Chem. Eng. Data*, **6**, 240 (1961). 41. Hodgman (ed.), "Handbook of Chemistry and Physics," Chemical Rubber Publishing Co., 36th ed., 1954. 42. Holser, *Ind. Eng. Chem.*, **28**, 691 (1936). 43. "International Critical Tables," McGraw-Hill, New York. **44**. van Itterbeek and van Paemel, *Physica*, **8**, 208 (1942). 45. van Itterbeek and van Paemel, *Physica*, **7**, 133 (1941). 46. Jackson (ed.), "Liquid Metals Handbook," 3d ed., Washington, D.C. 47. Jenkins and DiPaolo, *J. Chem. Phys.*, **25**, 296 (1956). 48. Jobling and Lawrence, *Proc. Roy. Soc. (London)*, **A206**, 257 (1951). 49. Johns, *Can. J. Research*, **17A**, 221 (1939). 50. Johnson (ed.), WADD-TR-60-56, 1960. 51. Keeson and MacWood, *Physica*, **5**, 745 (1938). 52. Khalilov, *Trudy. Inst. Fiz. i Mat. Akad. Nauk Azerbaidzhan S.S.R. Ser. Fiz.*, **5**, 48 (1951). 53. Koch, *Ann. Phys.*, **14**, 1 (1881). 54. Lewis, *J. Amer. Chem. Soc.*, **47**, 626 (1925). 55. "Technical Data on Liquid Nitrogen," Linde Air Products Bull., UCC, 1957. 56. Lipkin, Davison, *et al.*, *Ind. Eng. Chem.*, **34**, 976 (1942). 57. Llewellyn, *J. Chem. Soc. London*, vol. 28, 1953. 58. Lubarsky and Kaufman, *N.A.C.A. Tech. Rept.* **1270**, 1956. 59. Lyon (ed.), "Liquid Metals Handbook," 2d ed., Washington, D.C. 60. McGlothan, *A.E.C. Rept.* ORNL, Jan. 3, 1958. 61. Meyer, 1920, 62. Mitsukuri, 1927. 63. Monosson, 1931. 64. Naiki, Hanai, *et al.*, *Bull. Kyoto Univ.*, **31**, 56 (1953). 65. van Paemel, *Verhandel. Koninkl. Vlaam. Acad. Wetenschap.*, **3**, 3 (1941). 66. van Paemel and Mariens, *9th Intern. Congr. Refrig.*, Paris, **1**, 1048 (1955). 67. Partington, "An Advanced Treatise on Physical Chemistry," vol. **2**, Longmans, New York, 1951. 68. Pierre, *Kyltek. Tidskr.*, No. 5, 1953. 69. Plug, 1916. 70. Raw, *J. Chem. Phys.*, **22**, 1627 (1954). 71. Raw, *J. Chem. Phys.*, **22**, 1946 (1954). 72. Rossini, "Selected Values of Physical and Thermodynamic Properties of Hydrocarbons and Related Compounds," Carnegie Press, Pittsburgh (1953). 73. Rotinjanz, *Z. Phys. Chem.*, **62**, 609 (1908). 74. Rudenko, *J. Exptl. Theoret. Phys. U.S.S.R.*, **9**, 1078 (1939). 75. Rudenko, *J. Tech. Phys. U.S.S.R.*, **18**, 1123 1948). 76. Rudenko and Shubnikov, *Phys. Z. Sowjetunion*, **6**, 470 (1934). **77**. Saverwald and Topler, *Z. anorg. allgem. Chem.*, **157**, 117 (1926). 78. Schmidt, 1933. 79. Scott, "Cryogenic Engineering," Van Nostrand, Princeton, N.J., 1959. 80. Shepard, Henne, *et al.*, *J. Amer. Chem. Soc.*, **53**, 1948 (1931). 81. Singer, *Chem. Premsyl.*, **4**, 46 (1954). 82. Smyth and Stoops, *J. Amer. Chem. Soc.*, **50**, 1883 (1928). 83. Steacie and Johnson, *J. Amer. Chem. Soc.*, **47**, 754 (1925). 84. Sturat, Consolidated Vultee Aircraft Corp. *Rept.* GT771, 1948. 85. Sweeney, *Chem. Eng.*, **61**, 197 (1954). 86. Tables annuelles de constantes, Paris. 87. Taylor and Dash, *Phys. Rev.*, **106**, 398 (1957). 88. Thorpe, *First Int. Conf. Ozone*, ARF publ., 1957. 89. Thorpe and Roger, *Phil. Trans. Roy. Soc. London*, **185**, 397, 1984. 90. Timmermans and Martin, *J. Chim. Phys.*, **25**, 411 (1928). 91. Tjerkstra, *Physica*, **18**, 853 (1952). 92. Trautz, *Kolloid-Z.*, **100**, 405 (1942). 93. de Troyer, van Itterbeek, *et. al.*, *Physica*, **17**, 50 (1951). 94. Tuller (ed.), "The Sulfur Data Book," McGraw-Hill, New York, 1954. 95. University of Cincinnati TR GE ANP Project, May **6**, 1952. 96. Verkin and Rudenko, *Zhur. Eksptl. i Teoret. Fiz.*, **20**, 521 (1950). 97. Vershcaffelt and Nicaise, *Commun. Leiden*, 151g, 1917. 98. Volarovich, Moscow Peat Institute publ. 99. Vorlander, Fischer, 1932. 100. Walden, Uhlich, *et al.*, *Z. Physik. Chem.*, **123**, 429 (1926). 101. Warburg and Babo, *Ann. Phys.*, **17**, 390 (1882). 102. Weatherford Tyler, *et al.*, WADC-TR-59:598, 1959. 103. Woods and Hallett, *Can. J. Phys.*, **36**, 253 (1958). 104. Woolley, Scott, *et al.*, *Bur. Standards J. Research*, **41**, 379 (1948). 105. Zhadanova, *Zhur. Eksptl. i Theoret, Fiz.*, **13**, 724 (1956); *J. Exptl. Theoret. Phys., U.S.S.R.*, **4**, 19 (1957).

Table 3-270. Viscosity of Inhibited Ethylene Glycol*

3 per cent by weight of triethanolamine phosphate

Temp., °F	Dynamic viscosity lb./(hr.)(ft.)	Temp., °F.	Dynamic viscosity, lb./(hr.)(ft.)
50	88.572	210	5.539
60	67.688	220	4.987
70	52.708	230	4.513
80	41.745	240	4.102
90	33.614	250	3.744
100	27.370	260	3.432
110	22.632	270	3.156
120	18.917	280	2.911
130	15.982	290	2.693
140	14.238	300	2.563
150	11.732	310	2.328
160	10.179	320	2.176
170	8.898	330	2.038
180	7.831	340	1.909
190	6.938	350	1.798
200	6.181		

* From "Physical Properties of Aqueous Ethylene Glycol Solutions," report of the Physical Properties group, Aviation Fuels Division, Cooperative Fuel Research Committee, National Bureau of Standards, Washington, 1943.

Estimated effect of each 1 per cent by weight of triethanolamine phosphate: dynamic viscosity increased 3 per cent.

Table 3-271. Thermal Conductivities of Metals*

k = B.t.u./(hr.)(sq. ft.)(°F./ft.)

Substance	t, °F.	k
Metals		
Antimony	32	10.6
Antimony	212	9.7
Bismuth	64	4.7
Bismuth	212	3.9
Cadmium	64	53.7
Cadmium	212	52.2
Gold	64	169.0
Gold	212	170.0
Iron, pure	64	39.0
Iron, pure	212	36.6
Iron, wrought	64	34.9
Iron, wrought	212	34.6
Iron, cast	129	27.6
Iron, cast	216	26.8
Steel (1% C)	64	26.2
Steel (1% C)	212	25.9
Magnesium	32–212	92.0
Mercury	32	4.8
Nickel alloy (62 Ni, 12 Cr, 26 Fe)	68	7.8
Platinum	64	40.2
Platinum	212	41.9
Alloys		
Constantan (60 Cu, 40 Ni)	64	13.1
Constantan (60 Cu, 40 Ni)	212	15.5
Nickel silver	32	16.9
Nickel silver	212	21.5
Manganin {84 Cu, 4 Ni, 12 Mn}	64	12.8
	212	15.2
Platinoid (54 Cu, 25 Ni, 20 Zn)	64	14.5

* Marks, "Mechanical Engineers' Handbook," 4th ed., McGraw-Hill, New York, 1941. For A.I.S.I. 403 steel, Refractalloy 26, S816 alloy, porous 301 stainless steel, X40 alloy, Inconel X, N155 (low C) alloy, Nimonic 80, aluminum alloys 145, 245, 355, brass and silver from about 250° to 1100°F. see Evans, *N.A.C.A. Research Mem.* E50L07, 1951. For 23 solids from 2° to 300°K. see Scott, "Cryogenic Engineering," Van Nostrand, Princeton, N.J., 1959. For brass, nylon, beryllium, copper, soft solder, and Woods metal, 2° to 90°K., see Berman, Foster, *et al., Brit. J. Appl. Phys.*, **6**, 181 (1955). For 41 elements and binary alloys, 1° to 3500°K., see Purdue Univ. TPRC "Data Book," vol. I.

Table 3-272. Thermal Conductivity of Chromium Alloys

k = B.t.u./(hr.)(sq. ft.)(°F./ft.)

American Iron and Steel Institute Type No.	k at 212°F.	k at 932°F.
301, 302, 302B, 303, 304, 316†	9.4	12.4
308	8.8	12.5
309, 310	8.0	10.8
321, 347	9.3	12.8
403, 406, 410, 414, 416†	14.4	16.6
430, 430F†	15.1	15.2
442	12.5	14.2
501, 502†	21.2	19.5

NOTE. Table 3-272 is based on information from manufacturers.

† Shelton and Swanger (National Bureau of Standards), *Trans. Am. Soc. Steel Treating*, **21**, 1061–1078, (1933).

Table 3-273. Thermal Conductivity of Some Alloys at High Temperature*

°R.	Thermal conductivity, B.t.u./(ft.)(hr.)(°R.)					
	Kovar	Advance	Monel	Hastelloy A	Inconel	Nichrome V
500	7.8	....	9.0	5.6	6.0	5.5
600	8.3	11.4	10.2	6.2	6.5	6.1
700	8.6	12.6	11.2	6.8	7.0	6.7
800	8.7	13.9	12.3	7.3	7.6	7.3
900	8.7	15.1	13.4	7.8	8.1	7.8
1000	8.9	16.4	14.4	8.4	8.6	8.4
1100	9.2	17.6	15.4	9.0	9.1	9.0
1200	9.5	18.8	16.5	9.5	9.7	9.5
1300	9.8	20.0	17.6	10.1	10.2	10.1
1400	10.2	21.2	18.7	10.7	10.8	10.7
1500	10.5	22.5	19.8	11.3	11.3	11.3
1600	10.8	23.8	20.8	11.8	11.8	11.9
1700	11.1	25.0	21.9	12.3	12.4	12.4
1800	11.3	26.2	23.0	12.9	13.0	13.0
1900	11.5	27.4	24.0	13.4	13.6	13.5
2000	11.8	28.7	25.1	14.0	14.0	14.1
2100	12.1	30.0	26.1	14.6	14.5	14.7
2200	12.3	....	27.2	15.1	15.0	15.3

* Silverman, *J. Metals*, **5**, 631 (1953). Copyright American Institute of Mining, Metallurgical and Petroleum Engineers, Inc.

Table 3-274. Effect of Temperature upon Thermal Conductivity of Metals and Alloys*

Main body of table is k in B.t.u./(hr.)(sq. ft.)(°F./ft.)

t, °F / t, °C	32 / 0	212 / 100	392 / 200	572 / 300	752 / 400	932 / 500	1112 / 600	Melting point, °C.
Aluminum	117	119	124	133	144	155	...	660
Brass (70–30)	56	60	63	66	67	...	...	940
Cast iron	32	30	28	26	25	...	...	1275
Cast high silicon iron	30	...	...	...	...	...	...	1260
Copper (pure)	224	218	215	212	210	207	204	1083
Lead	20	19	18	18	...	...	...	327.5
Nickel	36	34	33	32	...	...	...	1452
Silver	242	238	...	...	...	...	...	960.5
Sodium	81	...	...	...	...	...	...	97.5
Steel (mild)	...	26	26	25	23	22	21	1375
Tantalum (at 18°C.)	32	...	...	...	...	...	...	2850
Tin	36	34	33	...	...	...	...	231.85
Wrought iron (Swedish)	...	32	30	28	26	23	...	1505
Zinc	65	64	62	59	54	...	...	419.4

* From "International Critical Tables," McGraw-Hill, New York, 1929, and other sources.

Table 3-275. Thermal Conductivity of Liquids

k = B.t.u./(hr.)(sq. ft.)(°F./ft.)

A linear variation with temperature may be assumed. The extreme values given constitute also the temperature limits over which the data are recommended.

Liquid	t, °F.	k
Acetic acid 100%[5]	68	0.099
50%[5]	68	.20
Acetone[4]	86	.102
	167	.095
Allyl alcohol[11]	77–86	.104
Ammonia[8]	5–86	.29
Ammonia, aqueous 26%[5]	68	.261
	140	.29
Amyl acetate[7]	50	.083
alcohol (n-)[6]	86	.094
	212	.089
(iso-)[12]	86	.088
	167	.087
Aniline[9]	32–68	.100
Benzene[12]	86	.092
	140	.087
Bromobenzene[12]	86	.074
	212	.070
Butyl acetate (n-)[11]	77–86	.085
alcohol (n-)[4]	86	.097
	167	.095
(iso-)[4]	50	.091
Calcium chloride brine 30%[5]	86	.32
15%[5]	86	.34
Carbon disulfide[4]	86	.093
	167	.088
tetrachloride[10]	32	.107
	154	.094
Chlorobenzene[12]	50	.083
Chloroform[10]	86	.080
Cymene (para-)[12]	86	.078
	140	.079
Decane (n-)[12]	86	.085
	140	.083
Dichlorodifluoromethane[12]	20	.057
	60	.053
	100	.048
	140	.043
	180	.038
Dichloroethane[10]	122	.082
Dichloromethane[10]	5	.111
	86	.096
Ethyl acetate[7]	68	.101
alcohol 100%[2]	68	.105
80%	68	.137
60%	68	.176
40%	68	.224
20%	68	.281
100%[2]	122	.087
benzene[12]	86	.086
	140	.082
bromide[4]	68	.070
ether[4]	86	.080
	167	.078
iodide[4,5]	104	.064
	167	.063
Ethylene glycol[7]	32	.153
Gasoline[6,12]	86	.078
Glycerol 100%[1]	68	.164
80%	68	.189
60%	68	.220
40%	68	.259
20%	68	.278
100%[1]	212	.164
Heptane (n-)[12]	86	.081
	140	.079
Hexane (n-)[12]	86	0.080
	140	.078
Heptyl alcohol (n-)[6]	86	.094
	167	.091
Hexyl alcohol (n-)[6]	86	.093
	167	.090
Kerosene[4]	68	.086
	167	.081
Mercury[7]	82	4.83
Methyl alcohol 100%[2]	68	0.124
80%	68	.154
60%	68	.190
40%	68	.234
20%	68	.284
100%	122	.114
chloride[3,10]	5	.111
	86	.089
Nitrobenzene[12]	86	.095
	212	.088
Nitromethane[12]	86	.125
	140	.120
Nonane (n-)[12]	86	.084
	140	.082
Octane (n-)[12]	86	.083
	140	.081
Oils[5,12]*	86	.079
Oils, castor[9]	68	.104
	212	.100
Oils, olive[9]	68	.097
	212	.095
Paraldehyde[12]	86	.084
	212	.078
Pentane (n-)[12]	86	.078
	167	.074
Perchloroethylene[10]	122	.092
Petroleum ether[4]	86	.075
	167	.073
Propyl alcohol (n-)[6]	86	.099
	167	.095
alcohol (iso-)[12]	86	.091
	140	.090
Sodium	212	49
	410	46
Sodium chloride brine 25.0%[5]	86	0.33
12.5%[5]	86	.34
Sulfuric acid 90%[5]	86	.21
60	86	.25
30	86	.30
Sulfur dioxide[8]	5	.128
	86	.111
Toluene[4,12]	86	.086
	167	.084
β-Trichloroethane[10]	122	.077
Trichloroethylene[10]	122	.080
Turpentine[7]	59	.074
Vaseline[7]	59	.106
Water[13]	32	.343
	100	.363
	200	.393
	300	.395
	420	.376
	620	.275
Xylene (ortho-)[7]	68	.090
(meta-)[7]	68	.090

* Thermal conductivity data for a number of oils are available from Reference 12. See also Table 3-276; for many oils an average value of 0.079 may be used.

1 Bates, *Ind. Eng. Chem.*, **28**, 494 (1936).
2 Bates, Hazzard, and Palmer, *Ind. Eng. Chem.*, **10**, 314 (1938).
3 Benning, A. F., private communication, 1940.
4 Bridgman, *Proc. Am. Acad. Arts Sci.*, **59**, 141 (1923).
5 Chilton and Genereaux, personal communication, 1939, based on data selected from the literature.
6 Daniloff, *J. Am. Chem. Soc.*, **54**, 1328 (1932).
7 "International Critical Tables," McGraw-Hill, New York, 1929.
8 Kardos, *Z. Ver. deut. Ing.* **77**, 1158 (1933); *Z. ges. Kälte-Ind.*, **41**, 1, 29 (1934).
9 Kaye and Higgins, *Proc. Roy. Soc.* (*London*), **A117**, 459 (1928).
10 DuPont Chlorinated Hydrocarbons, *Tech. Bull.*, Electrochemicals Dept., du Pont, Buffalo, N. Y., 1938.
11 Shiba, *Sci. Papers Inst. Phys. Chem. Research* (*Tokyo*), **16**, 205 (1931).
12 Smith, *Trans. Am. Soc. Mech. Engrs.*, **58**, 719 (1936).
13 Timrot and Vargaftik, *J. Tech. Phys.* (*U.S.S.R.*), **10**, 1063 (1940).

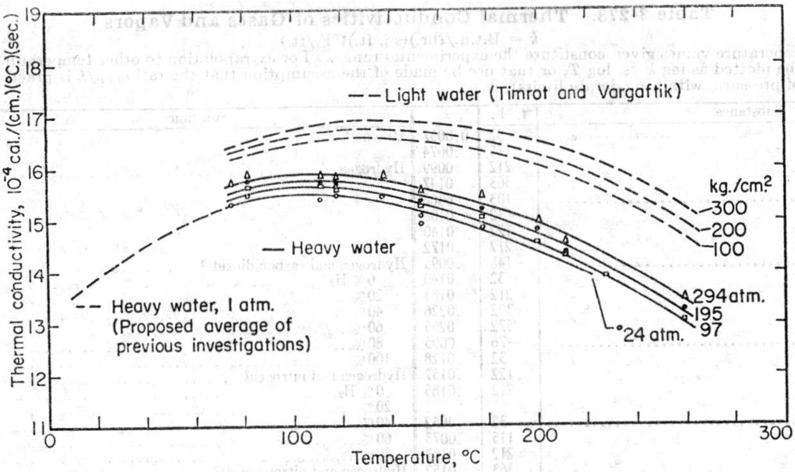

FIG. 3-45. Thermal conductivity of light and heavy water. *(From Ziebland and Burton, "Heat and Mass Transfer," vol. 1, 1960. Copyright 1960 Pergamon Press, Ltd., London. Reproduced by permission of the author, the Controller, H. M. Stationery Office, and Pergamon Press, Ltd.)*

Table 3-276. Thermal Conductivities of Petroleum Oils (*J. F. D. Smith*)

k = B.t.u./(hr.)(sq. ft.)(°F./ft.)

Designation of hydrocarbon oil	Aver. mol. wt.*	Viscosity, centipoises			k at 86°F.	k at 212°F.	Sp. gr. at 60°F.
		68°F.	140°F.	212°F.			
Light heat-transfer oil..	284	62.	9.5	3.2	0.0765	0.0748	0.925
Rabbeth spindle oil.....	303	24.5	5.7	2.37	.0825	.0805	.870
Velocite B oil.........	333	73.0	11.0	4.20	.0825	.0800	.897
Red oil....	418	....	44.0	9.90	.0815	.0796	.928

* H. O. Forrest and L. W. Cummings, personal communication.

Table 3-277. Thermal Conductivity of Inhibited Ethylene Glycol*

3 per cent by weight of triethanolamine phosphate

Temp., °F	Thermal conductivity, B.t.u./(hr.)(ft.)(°F.)
50	0.1718
75	.1646
100	.1598
125	.1523
150	.1477
175	.1402
200	.1356
225	.1282
250	.1234
275	.1161
300	.1112
325	.1040
350	.0992

* From "Physical Properties of Aqueous Ethylene Glycol Solutions," report of the Physical Properties group, Aviation Fuels Division, Cooperative Fuel Research Committee, National Bureau of Standards, Washington, 1943.

Estimated effect of each 1 per cent by weight of triethanolamine phosphate on thermal conductivity, negligible.

Table 3-278. Thermal Conductivities of Gases and Vapors

k = B.t.u./(hr.)(sq. ft.)(°F./ft.)

The extreme temperature values given constitute the experimental range. For extrapolation to other temperatures, it is suggested that the data given be plotted as log k vs. log T, or that use be made of the assumption that the ratio $c_p\mu/k$ is practically independent of temperature (or of pressure, within moderate limits).

Substance	t, °F.	k
Acetone[11]	32	0.0057
	115	.0074
	212	.0099
	363	.0147
Acetylene[3]	−103	.0068
	32	.0108
	122	.0140
	212	.0172
Air[1,11]	−148	.0095
	32	.0140
	212	.0183
	392	.0226
	572	.0265
Ammonia[3]	−76	.0095
	32	.0128
	122	.0157
	212	.0185
Benzene[11]	32	.0052
	115	.0073
	212	.0103
	363	.0152
	413	.0176
Butane (n-)[9]	32	.0078
	212	.0135
(iso-)[9]	32	.0080
	212	.0139
Carbon dioxide[12]	−58	.0068
	32	.0085
	212	.0133
	392	.0181
	572	.0228
disulfide[3]	32	.0040
	45	.0042
monoxide[1,3]	−312	.0041
	−294	.0046
	32	.0135
tetrachloride[11]	115	.0041
	212	.0052
	363	.0065
Chlorine[8]	32	.0043
Chloroform[11]	32	.0038
	115	.0046
	212	.0058
	363	.0077
Cyclohexane	216	.0095
Dichlorodifluoromethane	32	.0048
	122	.0064
	212	.0080
	302	.0097
Ethane[1,3]	−94	.0066
	−29	.0086
	32	.0106
	212	.0175
Ethyl acetate[11]	115	.0072
	212	.0096
	363	.0141
alcohol[11]	68	.0089
	212	.0124
chloride[11]	32	.0055
	212	.0095
	363	.0135
	413	.0152
ether[11]	32	.0077
	115	.0099
	212	.0131
	363	.0189
	413	.0209
Ethylene[3]	−96	.0064
	32	.0101
	122	.0131
	212	.0161
Heptane (n-)[11]	392	.0112
	212	.0103
Hexane (n-)[9]	32	.0072
	68	.0080

Substance	t, °F.	k
Hexene[11]	32	0.0061
	212	.0109
Hydrogen	−148	.065
	−58	.083
	32	.100
	122	.115
	212	.129
	572	.178
Hydrogen and carbon dioxide[7]	32	
0% H_2	....	.0083
20%	....	.0165
40%	....	.0270
60%	....	.0410
80%	....	.0620
100%	....	.10
Hydrogen and nitrogen[7]	32	
0% H_2	....	.0133
20%	....	.0212
40%	....	.0313
60%	....	.0438
80%	....	.0635
Hydrogen and nitrous oxide[7]	32	
0% H_2	....	.0092
20%	....	.0170
40%	....	.0270
60%	....	.0410
80%	....	.0650
Hydrogen sulfide[3]	32	.0076
Mercury[8]	392	.0197
Methane[1,3,9]	−148	.0100
	−58	.0145
	32	.0175
	122	.0215
Methyl alcohol[11]	32	.0083
	212	.0128
acetate[11]	32	.0059
	68	.0068
Methyl chloride[11]	32	.0053
	115	.0072
	212	.0094
	363	.0130
	413	.0148
Methylene chloride[11]	32	.0039
	115	.0049
	212	.0063
	413	.0095
Nitric oxide[3]	−94	.0103
	32	.0138
Nitrogen[2,3]	−148	.0095
	32	.0140
	122	.0160
	212	.0180
Nitrous oxide[2,3]	−98	.0067
	32	.0087
	212	.0128
Oxygen[1,2,6]	−148	.0095
	−58	.0119
	32	.0142
	122	.0164
	212	.0185
Pentane (n-)[9,11]	32	.0074
	68	.0083
(iso-)[11]	32	.0072
	212	.0127
Propane[9]	32	.0087
	212	.0151
Sulfur dioxide[3]	32	.0050
	212	.0069
Water vapor, zero pressure[10,14,*]	32	.0132
	200	.0159
	400	.0199
	600	.0256
	800	.0306
	1000	.0495

[1] Chilton and Genereaux, private communication, 1940.
[2] Dickens, *Proc. Roy. Soc. (London)*, **A143**, 517 (1934).
[3] Eucken, *Physik. Z.*, **12**, 1101 (1911); **14**, 324 (1913) (see footnote **17**).
[4] Gregory, *Proc. Roy. Soc. (London)*, **A149**, 324 (1935).
[5] Gregory and Archer, *Proc. Roy. Soc. (London)*, **A110**, 119 (1926).
[6] Gregory and Marshall, *Proc. Roy. Soc. (London)*, **A118**, 594 (1928).
[7] Ibbs and Hirst, *Proc. Roy. Soc. (London)*, **A123**, 134 (1929).
[8] "International Critical Tables," McGraw-Hill, New York, 1929.
[9] Mann and Dickens, *Proc. Roy. Soc. (London)*, **A134**, 77 (1931).
[10] Keenan and Keyes, "Thermodynamic Properties of Steam," Wiley, New York, 1944 (tenth impression).
[11] Moser, *Dissertation*, Berlin, 1913 (see footnote **17**).
[12] Sherrat and Griffiths, *Phil. Mag.*, **27**, 68 (1939).
[13] Spence and Dock, *Phil. Mag.*, **25**, 129 (1938).
[14] Varhaftik and Timrot, *J. Tech. Phys. (U.S.S.R.)*, 963(1939).
[15] Varhaftik and Parquenov, *J. Expt. Theoret. Phys. (U.S.S.R.)*, **8**, 189 (1938).
[16] Wüllner, *Ann. Physik*, **4**, 321 (1878).
[17] Data from Eucken and Moser are measurements relative to air. Data in this table from these sources are based on the thermal conductivity of air at 32°F. of 0.0140 B.t.u./(hr.)(sq. ft.)(°F./ft.).

* For saturated vapor (reference 10):

Lb./sq. in. abs.	250	500	1000	1500	2000
t, °F.	401	467	545	596	636
k	0.0748	0.0299	0.0395	0.0486	0.0578

Table 3-279. Thermal Conductivity of Gases at High Temperature and High Pressure*

Numbers entered in columns below refer to bibliographic listing below.

Gas	Pressure effect	225° to 1000°C.	1000° to 2000°C.	Over 2000°C.
Acetylene	....	66		
Air	63, 77, 86, 87, 96, 115, 127, 128, 180, 230, 232, 213	5, 10, 17, 21, 41, 53, 55, 67, 68, 77, 83, 86, 87, 94, 96, 127, 131, 180, 209, 217, 225, 226, 233, 254, 213	53, 55, 67, 68, 82, 83, 86, 87, 188, 209	53, 67, 68, 82, 83, 86, 87, 188, 209, 260
Ammonia	14, 63, 84, 126, 131, 133	62, 84, 127, 131		
Argon	14, 26, 38, 63, 96, 115, 126, 128, 131, 132, 158, 159, 169, 170, 174, 176, 180, 191, 201, 208, 244, 256, 268, 269	42, 43, 66, 94, 96, 114, 127, 131, 167, 180, 201, 202, 211, 214, 254	3, 211, 222	3, 222
Benzene	1, 63	1		
Carbon dioxide	14, 26, 58, 63, 78, 85, 96, 102, 115, 127, 129, 130, 131, 132, 144, 158, 201, 216, 230, 232, 247, 249	10, 42, 43, 62, 78, 94, 96, 102, 127, 130, 182, 185, 201, 202, 217, 225, 233, 254, 260, 267	96, 233	
Carbon monoxide	96, 127	94, 96, 127, 217, 225		
Chlorine	....	62		
Ethane	6, 131, 155, 159	42, 131		
Ethyl chloride	131			
Ethylene	14, 49, 63, 131, 158	42, 43		
Fluorine	....	62		
Freons	131			
Helium	63, 96, 158, 191, 256, 213	2, 17, 42, 43, 96, 114, 127, 131, 166, 185, 201, 267, 213	3	3
Hydrogen	6, 63, 76, 80, 96, 126, 131, 158, 190, 191, 203, 210, 230, 232, 257, 266, 213, 227	10, 76, 94, 96, 127, 131, 145, 225, 232, 234, 250, 266, 213		
Iodine	62			
Krypton	132	114, 167		
Methane	49, 63, 115, 126, 127, 131, 132, 133, 149, 158, 159, 187, 230, 232, 247	42, 43, 127, 131, 214		
Mixtures	46, 106, 112, 129, 130, 201	34, 52, 54, 72, 73, 104, 105 130, 136, 201, 202, 254	54, 58, 59, 60, 72, 73, 104, 105, 264	54, 58, 59, 60, 61, 72, 73, 193, 264
Neon	115, 131, 132	114, 131, 167	3	3
Nitric oxide	96, 195	66, 127		
Nitrogen	14, 26, 27, 38, 49, 58, 63, 79, 96, 109, 110, 111, 127, 129, 130, 131, 132, 136, 151, 158, 159, 169, 171, 180, 186, 201, 205, 230, 232, 244, 245, 247, 249, 269, 213	10, 11, 42, 43, 62, 79, 93, 94, 96, 109, 110, 127, 130, 131, 136, 180, 186, 201, 202, 214, 217, 225, 227, 232, 233, 254, 260, 265, 267, 213	3, 11, 36, 71, 93, 140, 162	3, 36, 71, 93, 140, 162
Nitrous oxide	115, 126, 131, 196	127		
Oxygen	26, 63, 96, 132, 180, 190, 191, 247, 269	10, 16, 42, 43, 62, 94, 96, 127, 131, 180, 225	16	16
Propane	49, 131	42, 43		
Propylene	1, 63, 131			
Steam	56, 63, 80, 84, 94, 96, 125, 134, 136, 144, 153, 161, 204, 235, 236, 238, 239, 245, 247, 248, 249, 251, 252, 258, 259, 183	17, 56, 94, 96, 125, 127, 131, 136, 153, 161, 189, 236, 239, 245, 248, 251, 254, 258		
Sulfur	....	146, 147	146, 147	146, 147
Toluene	1, 63	1		
Xenon	132, 213	114, 167, 213	3, 167, 213	3, 167, 213
Xylene	1, 63	1		

* Modified from Liley, Thermophysical Properties Research Center *Rept.* 10, Purdue University, 1959. For an earlier summary see Liley, "Thermodynamic and Transport Properties of Gases, Liquids and Solids," pp. 40–69, A.S.M.E., New York, 1959. For a similar summary for temperatures below 500°K see Liley, "Progress in International Research on Thermodynamic and Transport Properties," pp. 319–339, Academic Press, New York, 1962.

Bibliographic Listing for Tables 3-265 and 3-279: 1, Abas-Zade, *Doklady Akad. Nauk. S.S.S.R.*, **68**, 665 (1949). 2. Akin, *Trans. Am. Soc. Mech. Engrs.*, **72**, 751(1950). 3. Amdur and Mason, *Phys. Fluids*, **1** 370 (1958); ASTIA Documents AD 162222, AD 200968. 4. Amdur and Ross, ONR *Tech. Rept.* 2, Brown University, August, 1958; ASTIA Document AD 201120. 5. "American Institute of Physics Handbook," McGraw-Hill, New York, 1957. 6. Andrussow, *Z. Elektrochem.*, **61**, 253 (1957) and preceding papers. 7. Anon., *Brennstoff-Wärme-Kraft*, **3**, 120 (1951). 8. Anon., *Gen. Elec. Rev.*, **59**, 22 (1956). 9. Anon., NAVORD *Rept.* 1488 (vol. 5), 1953. 10. Anon., *Soc. Automotive Engrs. Aeronaut. Inf. Rept.* 24, 1952. 11. Bain, National Engineering Laboratory (East Kilbride, Scotland) *Rept.*, Heat 153, 1958. 12. Baron, Roof, and Wells, *J. Chem. Eng. Data*, **4**, 283 (1959). 13. Bartels, Tenbruggenoat, *et al.*, "Landolt-Bornstein Zahlenwerte und Funktionen aus Physik . . . und Technik," vol. 4, Part 1, Springer, Berlin, 1955. 14. Bateman, London Joint Conference, I.U.P.A.C./I.M.E., 1957.† 15. Bauer and Zlotnick, AVCO *Rept.* RAD-TR-58-12, September, 1958; *J. Am. Rocket Soc.*, **29**, 721 (1959). 16. Baulknight, "Transport Properties in Gases," pp. 89–95, Northwestern University Press, 1958. 17. Bentley, Brown, *et al.*, *A.E.C. Rept.* CP 3061, 1945. 18. Bicher and Katz, *Ind. Eng. Chem.*, **35**, 354 (1943). 19. Bicher and Katz, *Am. Inst. Mining Met. Eno. Publ.* 1599, 1953. 20. Biles and Putnam, *N.A.C.A. Tech. Note* 2783, 1952. 21. Boelter and Sharp, *N.A.C.A. Tech. Note* 1912, 1949. 22. Bonilla, *Columbia Univ. Rept.* CU-20-58; ASTIA Document AD 153026. 23. Bonilla, Brooks, and Walker, *Proc. General Disc. Heat Transfer*, vol. II, p. 167, Institution of Mechanical Engineers, London, 1951. 24. Bonilla, Wang, and Weiner, *Trans. Am. Soc. Mech. Engrs.*, **78**, 1285 (1956). 25. Bonilla, Wang, and Weiner, Document 4545, A.D.I. Auxiliary Publications, Library of Congress, Washington 25, D.C. 26. Borovik, *J. Exptl. Phys. U.S.S.R.*, **17**, 328 (1947); *J. Phys. U.S.S.R.*, **11**, 11 (1947). 27. Botzen, Ph.D. Thesis, Amsterdam, 1952; ASTIA Document AD 108543. 28. Brancker, *Ind. Chemist*, **30**, 307 (1954). 29. Braune and Linke, *Z. physik. Chem.*, **A148**, 195 (1930). 30. Breitenbach, *Ann. Physik*, **5**, 166 (1901). 31. Bremond, *Compt. rend.*, **196**, 1472 (1933). 32. Bromley, *A.E.C. Rept.* UCRL 525, November, 1949. 33. Brown, "Unit Operations," p. 147, Wiley, New York, 1950. 34. Brunot, *Trans. Am. Soc. Mech. Engrs.*, **62**, 613 (1940). 35. Buckingham, Davies, *et al.*, London Joint Conference, I.U.P.A.C./I.M.E., 1957. 36. Burhorn, *Z. Physik.*, **155**, 42 (1959). 37. Burlandt and Cannon, *Anal. Chem.*, **28**, 1801 (1956). 38. Burton and Ziebland, Explosives Research and Development Establishment (Waltham Abbey, England) *Rept.* 11/R/57. 39. Carr, *Bull. Inst. Gas. Technol.* 23, Chicago, 1953. 40. Carr, Paren, and Peck, *Chem. Eng. Progress*, *Symp. Ser.*, **51**, 506 (1955). 41. Chapman and Cowling, "The Mathematical Theory of Non Uniform Gases," Cambridge, New York, 1939. 42. Cheung, Ph.D. Thesis, University of California Radiation Laboratory, 1958; *A.E.C. Rept.* UCRL 8230, 1958. 43. Cheung, Bromley, *et al.*, *A.E.C. Rept.* UCRL 8230 rev., 1959. 44. Codegone, *Atti accad. sci. Torino Classe sci.*, **86**, 126 (1951–1952). 45. Codegone, *Ricerca sci.*, **22**, 1416 (1952). 46. Colburn, Drew, *et al.*, *Ind. Eng. Chem.*, **39**, 958 (1947). 47. Comings and Egly, *Ind. Eng. Chem.*, **32**, 714 (1940). 48. Comings and Egly, *Ind. Eng. Chem.*, **33**, 1224 (1941). 49. Comings and Nathan, *Ind. Eng. Chem.*, **39**, 964 (1947). 50. Comings, Mayland, and Egly, *Univ. Illinois Eng. Expt. Sta. Bull.* **42**, No. 15, 1944. 51. Dalin and West, *J. Phys. & Colloid Chem.*, **54**, 1215 (1950). 52. Daynes, "Gas Analysis by Measurement of Thermal Conductivity," Cambridge, New York, 1933. 53. Dommett, RAE (U.K.) *Tech. Note* GW 429; ASTIA Document AD 175386. 54. Edmonds, *Astrophys. J.*, **125**, 535 (1957). 55. Elenbaas, *Philips Research Repts.*, **3**, 450 (1948); *Ingenieur* (*Utrecht*), **60**, 021 (1948). 56. Fano, Hubbell, *et al.*, *N.A.C.A. Tech. Note* 3273, 1956; ASTIA Document AD 19904. 57. Faxen, "Thermodynamic Tables in the Metric System for Water and Steam," Nordisk Rotogravyr, Stockholm, 1953. 58. Filippov, *Vestnik Moskov. Univ.*, **8**, 109 (1953). 59. Finkelnburg, *Chem.-Ing.-Tech.*, **27**, 121 (1955). 60. Fortini and Huff, *N.A.C.A. Research Mem.* E56 L10a, 1957. 61. Fradkin, *Zhur. Eksp. i Teoret. Fiz.*, **32**, 1176 (1957); *J. Exptl. Theoret. Phys.* (*U.S.S.R.*), **5**, 956 (1957). 62. Franck, *Z. Elektrochem.*, **55**, 636 (1951). 63. Franck, *Chem.-Ing.-Tech.*, **25**, 238 (1952). 64. Friend, "Transport Properties in Gases," pp. 124–133, Northwestern

† Published as "Proceedings of the Conference on Thermodynamics and Transport Properties of Fluids," Institution of Mechanical Engineers, 1, Birdcage Walk, London, S. W. 1., England, 1958.

University Press, 1958. 65. Fritz and Hennenhofer, *Z. ges. Kälte-Ind.*, **49**, 41 (1942). 66. Gardiner and Schaefer, *Z. Elektrochem.*, **60**, 588 (1956). 67. Glassman and Bonilla, A.I.Ch.E. Symposium on Heat Transfer, A.I.Ch.E. Meeting, December, 1951. 68. Glassman and Bonilla, *Chem. Eng. Progress, Symp. Ser.*, **49**, 153, 388 (1953). 69. Glassman and Harris, *J. Phys. Chem.*, **56**, 797 (1952). 70. Glawe and Johnson, *N.A.C.A. Tech. Note* 3934, 1957. 71. Goldenberg, *Brit. J. Appl. Phys.*, **10**, 47 (1959). 72. Gordon, *N.A.C.A. Research Mem.* E57K22, 1958. 73. Gordon and Glueck, *N.A.C.A. Research Mem.* E58A21, 1958. 74. Gordon and Huff, *N.A.C.A. Research Mem.* E52L11, 1953. 75. Goulard, *Purdue Univ. Rept.* A-56-4, 1956. 76. Granet, *Petrol. Refiner*, **33**, 205 (1954). 77. Granet and Kass, *Petrol. Refiner*, **31**, 113 (October, 1952). 78. Granet and Kass, *Petrol. Refiner*, **31**, 137 (1952). 79. Granet and Kass, *Petrol. Refiner*, **32**, 149 (March, 1953). 80. Granet and Kass, *Petrol. Refiner*, **32**, 179 (May, 1953). 81. Green, N.B.S. Private Communication, December, 1957. 82. Green, N.B.S. Private Communication, December, 1957. 83. Greifinger, *Rand Corp. Rept.* RM 1797, 1956. 84. Groenier and Thodos, "The Viscosity and Thermal Conductivity of Ammonia: Gaseous and Liquid States," *J. Chem. Eng. Data*, **6**, 240 (1961.) 85. Guildner, *Proc. Natl. Acad. Sci.*, **44**, 1149 (1958). 86. Hansen, *N.A.C.A. Tech. Note* 4150, 1958. 87. Hansen and Heims, *N.A.C.A. Tech. Note* 4359, 1958. 88. Hawkins, *Trans. Am. Soc. Mech. Engrs.*, **70**, 655 (1948). 89. Hawkins, Sibbitt, and Solberg, *Trans. Am. Soc. Mech. Engrs.*, **70**, 19 (1948). 90. Hawkins, Solberg, and Potter, *Trans. Am. Soc. Mech. Engrs.*, **57**, 395 (1935). 91. Hawkins, Solberg, and Potter, *Trans. Am. Soc. Mech. Engrs.*, **62**, 677 (1940). 92. Heath, *Proc. Phys. Soc. (London)*, **66B**, 362 (1953). 93. Heil, *Brennstoff-Wärme-Kraft*, **10**, 298 (1958). 94. Hilsenrath *et al.*, *N.B.S. Circ.* 564, 1955. 95. Hilsenrath, AGARD Combustion Colloquium Liege, 1955; "Selected Combustion Problems," vol. II, Butterworth, London, 1956. 96. Hilsenrath and Touloukian, *Trans. Am. Soc. Mech. Engrs.*, **76**, 967 (1954). 97. Hirota, *Bull. Chem. Soc. Japan*, **22**, 16 (1949). 98. Hirschfelder, Bird, and Spotz, *Trans. Am. Soc. Mech. Engrs.* **71**, 929 (1949). 99. Hirschfelder, Curtiss, and Bird, "Molecular Theory of Gases and Liquids," Wiley, New York, 1954. 100. Hubbard and Brown, *Ind. Eng. Chem.*, **35**, 1276 (1943). 101. Hubbard and Brown, *Ind. Eng. Chem. Anal. Ed.*, **15**, 212 (1943). 102. Huggill and Weker, *Mech. Eng. Research Org., Dept. Sci. Ind. Research U.K., Rept.* 10, 1950. 103. Hulbert, *J. Phys. & Colloid Chem.*, **53**, 530 (1949). 104. Ibele and Irvine, A.S.M.E. Paper 59-A-102, 1959. 105. Ibrahim and Kabiel, *J. Appl. Phys.*, **23**, 1190 (1952). 106. Ishikawa and Yamaryo, *Bull. Inst. Phys. Chem. Research, Chem. Educ. (Tokyo)*, **23**, 311 (1944). 107. Iwasaki, *Sci. Repts. Research Insts. Tohoku Univ.*, **A3**, 247 (1951). 108. Iwasaki, *Sci. Repts. Research Insts. Tohoku Univ.*, **A6**, 296 (1954). 109. Johannin, London Joint Conference I.U.P.A.C./I.M.E., 1957. 110. Johannin, Ph.D. Thesis, Paris, France, 1958; *J. recherches centre natl. recherche sci.*, No. **43**, p. 116, 1958. 111. Johannin and Vodar, *Ind. Eng. Chem.*, **49**, 2040 (1957). 112. Junk and Comings, *Chem. Eng. Progress*, **49**, 263 (1953). 113. Kaeppeler and Krause, "Thermodynamic and Physical Properties of Air in Dissociation Equilibrium," Oldenburg, Munich. 114. Kannuluik and Carman, *Proc. Phys. Soc. (London)*, **65B**, 701 (1952). 115. Kannuluik and Donald, *Australian J. Sci. Research*, **3A**, 417 (1950). 116. Kellstrom, *Arkiv Mat. Astr. och Phys.*, **27A**, 1 (1941). 117. Kenney, Sarjant, *et al.*, *Brit. J. Appl. Phys.*, **7**, 324 (1956). 118. Kestin, "Transport Properties in Gases," pp. 27–50, Northwestern University Press, 1958. 119. Kestin, J., A.S.M.E. Annual Meeting Paper, Atlantic City, N.J., 1959. 120. Kestin and Leidenfrost, "Thermodynamic and Transport Properties of Gases, Liquids, and Solids," A.S.M.E., 1959. 121. Kestin and Leidenfrost, *Physica*, **25**, 525 (1959). 122. Kestin and Leidenfrost, *Physica*, **25**, 537 (1959). 123. Kestin and Moszvnski, *Brown Univ. Rept.* SPR-2, April, 1958. 124. Kestin and Wang, *Trans. Am. Soc. Mech. Engrs.*, **80**, 11 (1958); AFOSR *Tech. Note* 56-98; ASTIA Document AD82011. 125. Keyes, *J. Am. Chem. Soc.*, **72**, 433 (1950). 126. Keyes, Project Squid, Memo MIT-1, 1952; ASTIA Document AD 5117. 127. Keyes, Project Squid, *Tech. Rept.* 37, 1952. 128. Keyes, *Trans. Am. Soc. Mech. Engrs.*, **73**, 589 (1951). 129. Keyes, *Trans. Am. Soc. Mech. Engrs.*, **73**, 597 (1951). 130. Keyes, *Trans. Am. Soc. Mech. Engrs.*, **74**, 1303 (1952). 131. Keyes, *Trans. Am. Soc. Mech. Engrs.*, **76**, 809 (1954). 132. Keyes, *Trans. Am. Soc. Mech. Engrs.*, **77**, 1395 (1955). 133. Keyes, "Transport Properties in Gases," pp. 51–54, Northwestern University Press, 1958. 134. Keyes, A.S.M.E. Annual Meeting Paper, Atlantic City, N.J., 1959. 135. Keyes and Keenan, *Mech. Eng.*, **77**, 127 (1955). 136. Keyes and Sandell, *Trans. Am. Soc. Mech. Engrs.*, **72**, 767 (1950). 137. Khalilov, *Trudy Inst. Fiz. i Mat. Akad. Nauk. Azerbaĭdzhan*, **5**, 48 (1951). 138. Kihara, *Revs. Modern Phys.*, **25**, 831 (1953). 139. Kihara and Kotani, *Proc. Phys. Math. Soc. Japan*, **25**, 602 (1943). 140. King, "Theoretical Calculations of Arc Temperatures in Gases," p. 152, Pergamon Press, London, 1957. 141. Kiyama and Makita, *Rev. Phys. Chem. Japan*, **21**, 63 (1951). 142. Kiyama and Makita, *Rev. Phys. Chem. Japan*, **22**, 49 (1952). 143. Kiyama and Makita, *Rev. Phys. Chem. Japan*, **26**, 70 (1956). 144. Koch and Fritz, *Wärme-u. Kältetech.*, **42**, 113 (1940). 145. Kompaneets, *Sbornik Nauch Rabot Leningrad Inst. Mekl. Selsk. Khoz.*, **9**, 113 (1953). 146. Konowalow, Hirschfelder, and Lindner, *Univ. Wisconsin TCL Rept.* WIS-AEC-22, 1959. 147. Konowalow, Linder, and Hirschfelder, *Univ. Wisconsin NRL Rept.* WIS-AEC-17, 1958. 148. Krieger, *Rand Corp. Rept.* RM 646, 1951. 149. Kuss, *Z. angew. Phys.*, **4**, 203 (1952). 150. Lazarre and Vodar, *Compt. rend.*, **243**, 487 (1956). 151. Lazarre and Vodar, Joint Conference I.U.P.A.C./I.M.E., London, 1957. 152. Leipunski, *Acta Physicochim. U.R.S.S.*, **18**, 172 (1943). 153. Lemmon, Daniels, *et al.*, *Battelle Memorial Inst. Rept.* BMI 858, 1953. 154. Leng, Ph.D. Thesis, Purdue University, 1956. 155. Leng and Comings, *Ind. Eng. Chem.*, **49**, 2042 (1957). 156. Lenoir, *Univ. Arkansas Eng. Expt. Sta. Bull.* 16, 1952; Ph.D. Thesis, University of Illinois, 1949. 157. Lenoir, *Univ. Arkansas Eng. Expt. Sta. Bull.* 18, 1954. 158. Lenoir and Comings, *Chem. Eng. Progress*, **47**, 223 (1951). 159. Lenoir, Junk, and Comings, *Chem. Eng. Progress*, **49**, 539 (1953). 160. Lipkin, Davidson, *et al.*, *Ind. Eng. Chem.*, **34**, 976 (1942). 161. Lottes, "AEC Reactor Handbook Engineering," Chap. 1.3, pp. 34, 36, McGraw-Hill, New York, 1955. 162. Maecker, *Fortschr. Verfahrenstech.*, vol. 228, 1956–1957. 163. Makita, *Rev. Phys. Chem. Japan*, **24**, 74 (1954). 164. Makita, *Rev. Phys. Chem. Japan*, **27**, 16 (1957). 165. Makita, *Mem. Fac. Ind. Arts Kyoto Univ. Technol.*, No. 4, p. 19, 1955. 166. Mason and Rice, *J. Chem. Phys.*, **22**, 522 (1954). 167. Mason and Rice, *J. Chem. Phys.*, **22**, 843 (1954). 168. Mayland, Ph.D. Thesis, University of Illinois, 1943. 169. Michels, "Proceedings of the International Symposium on Statistical Mechanics," p. 365, Interscience, New York, 1958. 170. Michels and Botzen, *Physica*, **18**, 605 (1952). 171. Michels and Botzen, *Physica*, **19**, 585 (1953). 172. Michels and Gibson, *Proc. Roy. Soc. (London)*, **A134**, 288 (1931). 173. Michels, Botzen, *et al.*, *Physica*, **20**, 1141 (1954). 174. Michels, Botzen, *et al.*, *Physica*, **22**, 121 (1956). 175. Michels, Botzen, *et al.*, *Physica*, **23**, 95 (1957). 176. Michels, Cox, *et al.*, *J. Appl. Phys.*, **26**, 843 (1955). 177. Michels, Schipper, and Rintoul, *Physica*, **19**, 1011 (1953). 178. Mueller, *N.A.C.A. Tech. Note* 4063, 1947. 179. Naldrett and Maass, *Can. J. Research*, **18B**, 322 (1940). 180. National Defense Research Committee, Summary Technical Report, Division 11, "Improved Equipment for Oxygen Production," Washington, 1946. 181. Nicklin, U.K. Atomic Energy Authority, Ind. Group *Tech. Note* 36, 1956. 182. Novotry, M.S. Thesis, Mechanical Engineering, University of Minnesota, 1958. 183. Nowak, M.S. Thesis, Mechanical Engineering, Purdue University, 1959. 184. Nowak and Grosh, *A.E.C. Rept.* ANL 6064, 1959. 185. Nuttall, N.B.S.-N.A.C.A. "Tables of Thermal Properties of Gases," Tables 6.39, 6.42, and 13.39, 1950. 186. Nuttall and Ginning, *Bur. Standards J. Research*, **58**, 271 (1957). 187. Owens and Thodos, London Joint Conference I.U.P.A.C./I.M.E., 1957. 188. Patterson, AGARD *Rept.* 134, 1957; ASTIA Document AD 157313. 189. Perry, "Chemical Engineers' Handbook," McGraw-Hill, New York. 190. Prigogine and Waelbroeck, *Brit. Chem. Eng.*, **2**, 596 (1957). 191. Prigogine and Waelbroeck, London Joint Conference I.U.P.A.C./I.M.E., 1957. 192. Raw, *J. S. African Chem. Inst.*, **7**, 11, 20 (1954); **8**, 21, 25 (1955). 193. Raw and Ellis, *J. Chem. Phys.*, **28**, 1198 (1958). 194. Reisfeld, *A.E.C. Rept.* LA 2123, 1957; ASTIA Document AD 133360, 1957. 195. Richter and Sage, Project Squid *Rept.* CIT-2-P, 1957; ASTIA Document AD 139905. 196. Richter and Sage, Project Squid *Rept.* CIT-3-P, 1957; ASTIA Document AD 200655. 197. Richter, *Brennstoff-Wärme-Kraft*, **3**, 117 (1951). 198. de Rocco and Halford, *J. Chem. Phys.*, **28**, 1152 (1958). 199. Rosenbluth and Kaufman, *Phys. Rev.*, **109**, 1 (1958). 200. Ross and Brown, *Ind. Eng. Chem.*, **49**, 2026 (1957). 201. Rothman, Ph.D. Thesis, University of California, 1954; see also *A.E.C. Rept.* UCRL-2339, 1954. 202. Rothman and Bromley, *Ind. Eng. Chem.*, **47**, 899 (1955). 203. Rubin, *Petrol. Refiner*, **35**, 140 (1956). 204. Rudorff, *Eng. and Boiler House Rev.*, **60**, 100 (1946). 205. Ruthemann, *Atti. accad. sci. Torino*, **90**, 290 (1955–1956). 206. Satterfield, Wentworth, *et al.*, *Chem. Eng., Dept. Rept.* 39, M.I.T., 1953. 207. Savino and Sibbitt, *Ind. Eng. Chem.*, **51**, 551 (1959). 208. Saxena, *Indian J. Phys.*, **29**, 587 (1955). 209. Scala and Baulknight, *J. Am. Rocket Soc.*, **29**, 39 (1959). 210. Schaefer and Thodos, *Ind. Eng. Chem.*, **50**, 1585 (1958). 211. Schaefer and Reiter, *Naturwiss.*, **43**, 286 (1956). 212. Schipper, *Referat. Zhur. Khim.*, 1955. 213. Schirmer, *Tech. Wiss. Abhandl. Osram-Ges.*, **7**, 8 (1958). 214. Schottky, *Z. Elektrochem.*, **56**, 889 (1952). 215. Schugajew, *Physik. Z. Sowjetunion*, **5**, 659 (1934). 216. Sellschop, *Forsch. Gebiete Ingenieurw.*, **5B**, 162 (1934). 217. Sherratt and Griffiths, *Proc. Roy. Soc. (London)*, **A156**, 504 (1936). 218. Shilling and Laxton, *Phil. Mag.*, **10**, 721 (1930). 219. Sibbitt, Hawkins, and Solberg, *Trans. Am. Soc. Mech. Engrs.*, **65**, 401 (1943). 220. Sigwart, *Forsch. Gebiete Ingenieurw.*, **A7**, 310 (1936). 221. Sinanoglu, M.S. Thesis, Chemical Engineering, M.I.T., 1957. 222. Smiley, Ph.D. Thesis, Catholic University of America, 1957. 223. Smith and Brown, *Ind. Eng. Chem.*, **33**, 705 (1943). 224. Smith, *Proc. Roy. Soc. (London)*, **A106**, 83 (1924). 225. Society of Automotive Engineers, Inc., *Aeronaut. Inf. Rept.* 24, 1952. 226. Srivastava and Madan, *Proc. Natl. Acad. Sci., India*, **A21**, 254 (1952). 227. Srivastava, *Indian J. Phys.*, **31**, 404 (1957). 228. Srivastava, *J. Chem. Phys.*, **28**, 543 (1958). 229. Starling, Eakin, and Ellington, *Am. Inst. Chem. Engrs. J.*, **6**, 438 (1960). 230. Stolyarov, *Zhur. Fiz. Khim.*, **24**, 279 (1950). 231. Stolyarov, *Zhur. Fiz. Khim.*, **24**, 761 (1950). 232. Stolyarov, Ipateev, *et al.*, *Zhur. Fiz. Khim.*, **24**, 166 (1950). 233. Stops, *Nature*, **164**, 966 (1949); Ph.D. Thesis, University of London, 1949. 234. Strickler, *J. Chem. Phys.*, **17**, 427 (1949). 235. Timrot, *J. Phys. U.S.S.R.*, **2**, 419 (1940). 236. Timrot, "Tables of Thermal Properties of Water and Water Vapor Based on Experimental Data," Moscow, 1952. Viscosity data based on *J. Tech. Phys. U.S.S.R.*, **2**, 461 (1939). 237. Timrot, 5th Int. Conf. Props. Steam, London, 1956. 238. Timrot and Vargaftik, *J. Phys. U.S.S.R.*, **2**, 101 (1940). 239. Timrot and Vargaftik, *Zhur. Tekh. Fiz.*, **10**, 1063 (1940). 240. Trautz and Heberling, *Ann. Physik Lpz.*, **10**, 155 (1931). 241. Trautz and Zimmerman, *Ann. Physik*, **22**, 189 (1935). 242. Trautz and Zink, *Ann. Physik*, **7**, 427 (1930). 243. Tribus and Boelter, *N.A.C.A. Wartime Rept.* W9, 1942. 244. Uhlir, *J. Chem. Phys.*, **20**, 463 (1952). 245. Vargaftik, *Tech. Phys. U.S.S.R.*, **4**, 343 (1937). 246. Vargaftik, *Izvest. VTI*, **21**, 13 (1952). 247. Vargaftik, London Joint Conference I.U.P.A.C./I.M.E., 1957. 248. Vargaftik and Belyyakova, *Teploenergetika*, No. 5, p. 45, 1954. 249. Vargaftik and Oleschuk, *Izvest. VTI*, **15**, 7 (1946). 250. Vargaftik and Parfenov, *J. Exptl. Theoret. Phys. U.S.S.R.*, **8**, 189 (1938). 251. Vargaftik and Smirnova, *Zhur. Tech. Fiz.*, **26**, 1251 (1956); *Sovet. Phys. Tech. Phys.*, **1**, 1221 (1956). 252. Vargaftik and Timrot, *Zhur. Tech. Fiz.*, **2**, 63 (1939). 253. Vasilesco, *Ann. phys.*, **20**, 137, 292 (1945). 254. Vines, A.S.M.E. Paper 59-HT-12, 1959; ASTIA Document AD 205694; Squid *Rept.* MIT-20-P. 255. Vukalovitch, "Thermodynamic Properties of Water and Water Vapor," Moscow, 1951. 256. Waelbroeck and Zuckerbrodt, *J. Chem. Phys.*, **28**, 523 (1958). 257. Waelbroeck and Zuckerbrodt, *J. Chem. Phys.*, **28**, 524 (1958). 258. Wainwright and Alder, *Univ. California Rept.* UCRL 5251, 1958. 259. Wellmann, *Combustion*, **26**, 51 (1955). 260. Westenberg, *Combustion and Flame*, **1**, 346 (1957). 261. Westmoreland, *N.A.C.A. Tech. Note* 3180, 1954. 262. Whalley, London Joint Conference I.U.P.A.C./I.M.E., 1957. 263. Whalley and Schneider, *J. Chem. Phys.*, **20**, 657 (1952). 264. Wienecke, *Z. Physik*, **146**, 39 (1956). 265. Woolley, *N.A.C.A. Tech. Note* 3271, 1956. 266. Woolley, Scott, and Brickwedde, *Bur. Standards J. Research*, **41**, 379 (1948). 267. Wright, *A.E.C. Rept.* HW 21741, July 18, 1951. 268. Ziebland, *Dechema Monograph.*, vol. **32**, p. 74. 269. Ziebland and Burton, *Brit. J. Appl. Phys.*, **9**, 52 (1958).

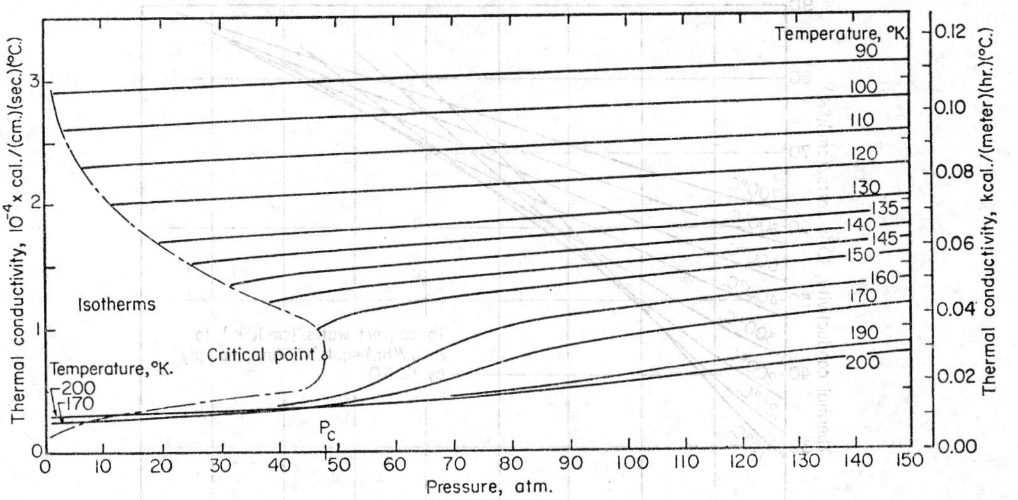

FIG. 3-46. Thermal conductivity of argon. [*From Ziebland, Dechema Monograph.* **32,** 74 (1959). *Crown copyright reserved. Reproduced by permission of the author, the Controller, H. M. Stationery Office, and the publisher.*]

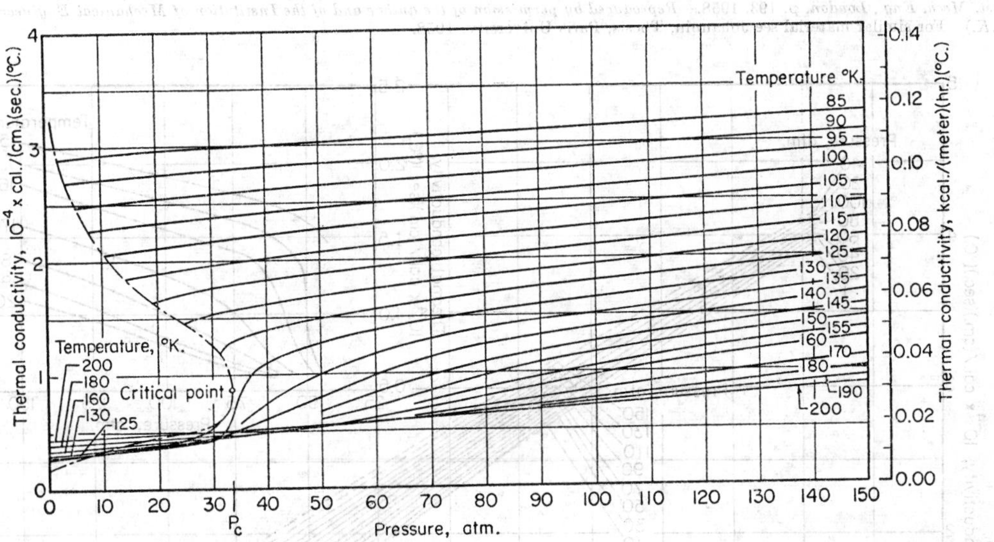

FIG. 3-47. Thermal conductivity of nitrogen (low temperature). (*Ziebland, private communication,* 1960. *Crown copyright reserved. Reproduced by permission of the author and the Controller, H.M. Stationery Office.*) For tabulated data and a graph of conductivity as a function of temperature see Ziebland and Burton, *Brit. J. Appl. Phys.,* **9,** 52 (1958).

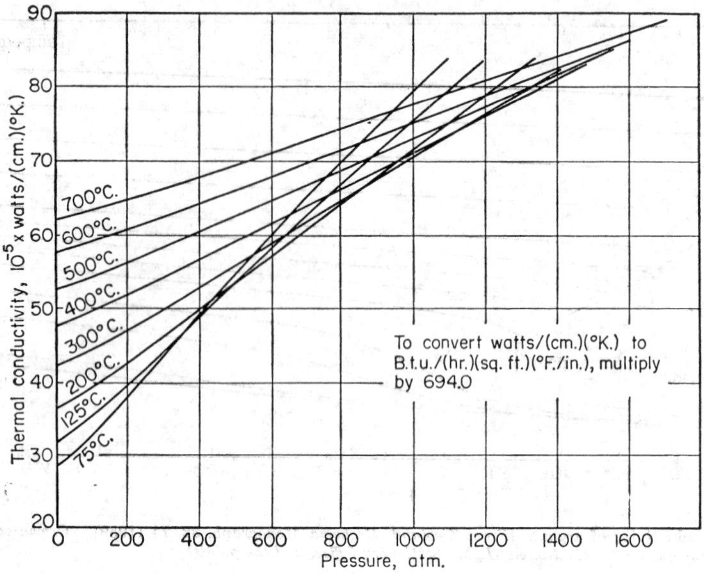

FIG. 3-48. Thermal conductivity of nitrogen (high temperatures). (*Johnannin, "Thermodynamic and Transport Properties of Fluids," Inst. Mech. Eng., London, p. 193, 1958. Reproduced by permission of the author and of the Institution of Mechanical Engineers, London, U.K.*) For similar material see Johannin, Thesis, Paris University, 1958.

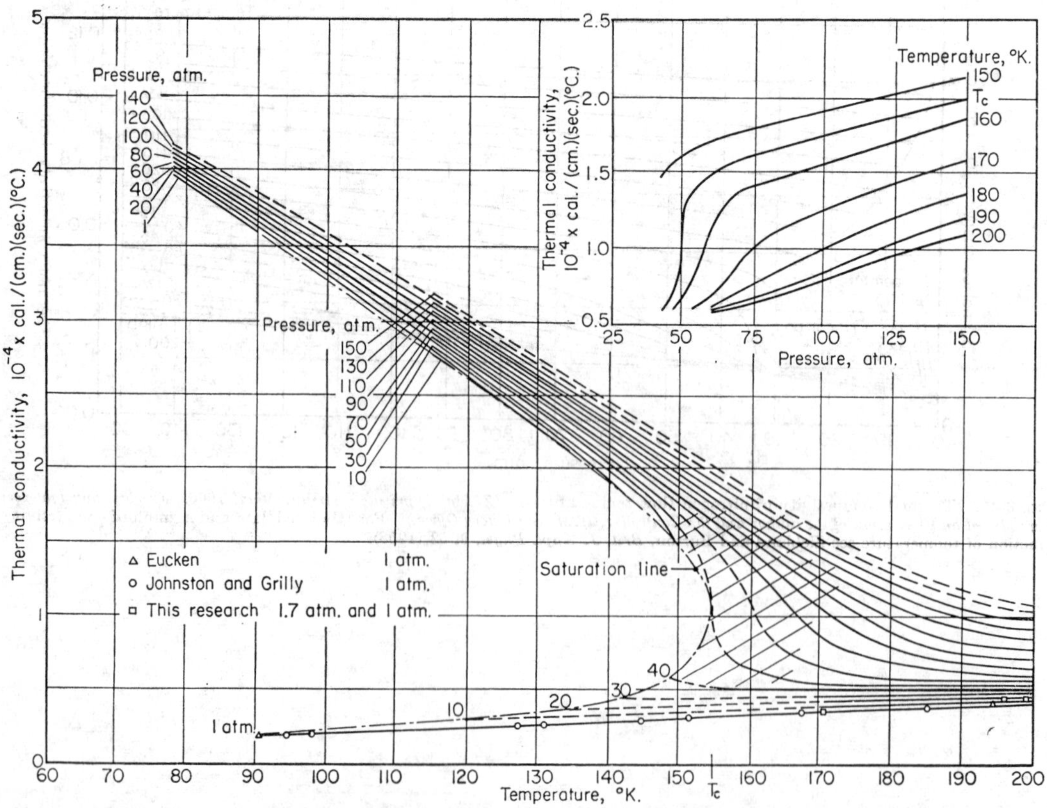

FIG. 3-49. Thermal conductivity of oxygen. [*From Ziebland and Burton, Brit. J. Appl. Phys.*, **6**, 416 (1955). *Crown copyright reserved. Reproduced by permission of the publishers and of the Controller, H.M. Stationery Office, England.*]

Table 3-280. Thermal Conductivities of Some Building and Insulating Materials*

k = B.t.u./(hr.)(sq. ft.)(°F./ft.)

Material	Apparent density ρ, lb./cu. ft. at room temperature	t, °C.	k
Aerogel, silica, opacified	8.5	120	0.013
		290	.026
Asbestos-cement boards	120	20	.43
Asbestos sheets	55.5	51	.096
Asbestos slate	112	0	.087
	112	60	.114
Asbestos	29.3	−200	.043
	29.3	0	.090
	36	0	.087
	36	100	.111
	36	200	.120
	36	400	.129
	43.5	−200	.090
	43.5	0	.135
Aluminum foil (7 air spaces per 2.5 in.)	0.2	38	.025
		177	.038
Ashes, wood	......	0–100	.041
Asphalt	132	20	.43
Boiler scale (Note 1)			
Bricks:			
Alumina (92–99% Al_2O_3 by wt.) fused	......	427	1.8
Alumina (64–65% Al_2O_3 by wt.)	......	1315	2.7
(See also Bricks, fire clay)	115	800	0.62
	115	1100	.63
Building brick work	......	20	.4
Carbon	96.7	...	3.0
Chrome brick (32% Cr_2O_3 by wt.)	200	200	.67
	200	650	.85
	200	1315	1.0
Diatomaceous earth, natural, across strata (Note 2)	27.7	204	0.051
	27.7	871	.077
Diatomaceous, natural, parallel to strata (Note 2)	27.7	204	.081
	27.7	871	.106
Diatomaceous earth, molded and fired (Note 2)	38	204	.14
	38	871	.18
Diatomaceous earth and clay, molded and fired (Note 2)	42.3	204	.14
	42.3	871	.19
Diatomaceous earth, high burn, large pores (Note 3)	37	200	.13
	37	1000	.34
Fire clay (Missouri)	......	200	.58
		600	.85
		1000	.95
		1400	1.02
Kaolin insulating brick (Note 3)	27	500	0.15
	27	1150	.26
Kaolin insulating firebrick (Note 4)	19	200	.050
	19	760	.113
Magnesite (86.8% MgO, 6.3% Fe_2O_3, 3% CaO, 2.6% SiO_2 by wt.)	158	204	2.2
	158	650	1.6
	158	1200	1.1
Silicon carbide brick, recrystallized (Note 3)	129	600	10.7
	129	800	9.2
	129	1000	8.0
	129	1200	7.0
	129	1400	6.3
Calcium carbonate, natural	162	30	1.3
White marble	......	....	1.7
Chalk	96	....	0.4
Calcium sulfate ($4H_2O$), artificial	84.6	40	.22
plaster (artificial)	132	75	.43
(building)	77.9	25	.25
Cambric (varnished)	......	38	.091
Carbon, gas	......	0–100	2.0
Carbon stock	94	−184	0.55
		0	3.6
Cardboard, corrugated	......	....	0.037
Celluloid	87.3	30	.12
Charcoal flakes	11.9	80	.043
	15	80	.051
Clinker (granular)	......	0–700	.27
Coke, petroleum	......	100	3.4
		500	2.9
Coke, petroleum (20–100 mesh)	62	400	0.55
Coke (powdered)	......	0–100	.11
Concrete (cinder)	......	....	.20
(stone)	......	....	.54
(1:4 dry)	......	....	.44

Material	Apparent density ρ, lb./cu. ft. at room temperature	t, °C.	k
Cotton wool	5	30	0.024
Cork board	10	30	.025
Cork (regranulated)	8.1	30	.026
(ground)	9.4	30	.025
Diatomaceous earth powder, coarse (Note 2)	20.0	38	.036
	20.0	871	.082
fine (Note 2)	17.2	204	.040
	17.2	871	.074
molded pipe covering (Note 2)	26.0	204	.051
	26.0	871	.088
4 vol. calcined earth and 1 vol. cement, poured and fired (Note 2)	61.8	204	.16
	61.8	871	.23
Dolomite	167	50	1.0
Ebonite	......	....	0.10
Enamel, silicate	38	....	0.5–0.75
Felt, wool	20.6	30	0.03
Fiber insulating board	14.8	21	.028
Fiber, red	80.5	20	.27
(with binder, baked)	......	20–97	.097
Gas carbon	......	0–100	2.0
Glass	......	....	0.2–0.73
Borosilicate type	139	30–75	0.63
Window glass	......	....	0.3–0.61
Soda glass	......	....	0.3–0.44
Granite	......	....	1.0–2.3
Graphite, longitudinal	......	20	95.
powdered, through 100 mesh	30	40	0.104
Gypsum (molded and dry)	78	20	.25
Hair felt (perpendicular to fibers)	17	30	.021
Ice	57.5	0	1.3
Infusorial earth, see diatomaceous earth			
Kapok	0.88	20	0.020
Lampblack	10	40	.038
Lava	......	....	.49
Leather, sole	62.4	....	.092
Limestone (15.3 vol. % H_2O)	103	24	.54
Linen	......	30	.05
Magnesia (powdered)	49.7	47	.35
Magnesia (light carbonate)	13	21	0.034
Magnesium oxide (compressed)	49.9	20	.32
Marble	......	....	1.2–1.7
Mica (perpendicular to planes)	......	50	0.25
Mill shavings	......	....	0.033–0.05
Mineral wool	9.4	30	0.0225
	19.7	30	.024
Paper	......	....	.075
Paraffin wax	......	0	.14
Petroleum coke	......	100	3.4
	......	500	2.9
Porcelain	......	200	0.88
Portland cement, see concrete	......	90	.17
Pumice stone	......	21–66	.14
Pyroxylin plastics	......	....	.075
Rubber (hard)	74.8	0	.087
(para)	......	21	.109
(soft)	......	21	0.075–0.092
Sand (dry)	94.6	20	0.19
Sandstone	140	40	1.06
Sawdust	12	21	0.03
Scale (Note 1)			
Silk	6.3	....	.026
varnished	......	38	.096
Slag, blast furnace	......	24–127	.064
Slag wool	12	30	.022
Slate	......	94	.86
Snow	34.7	0	.27
Sulfur (monoclinic)	......	100	0.09–0.097
(rhombic)	......	21	0.16
Wall board, insulating type	14.8	21	.028
Wall board, stiff paste board	43	30	.04
Wood shavings	8.8	30	.034
Wood (across grain):			
Balsa	7–8	30	0.025–0.03
Oak	51.5	15	0.12
Maple	44.7	50	.11
Pine, white	34.0	15	.087
Teak	40.0	15	.10
White fir	28.1	60	.062
Wood (parallel to grain):			
Pine	34.4	21	.20
Wool, animal	6.9	30	.021

* Marks, "Mechanical Engineers' Handbook," 4th ed., McGraw-Hill, New York, 1941. "International Critical Tables," McGraw-Hill, 1929, and other sources. For additional data, see pp. 458–459.

Note 1: B. Kamp [*Z. tech. Physik*, **12**, 30 (1931)] shows the effect of increased porosity in decreasing thermal conductivity of boiler scale. Partridge [University of Michigan, *Eng. Research Bull.* 15, 1930] has published a 170-page treatise on Formation and Properties of Boiler Scale.

Note 2: Townshend and Williams, *Chem. & Met.*, **39**, 219 (1932).

Note 3: Norton, "Refractories," 2d ed., McGraw-Hill, New York, 1942.

Note 4: Norton, private communication.

Table 3-281. Thermal Conductivities of Some Materials for Refrigeration and Building Insulation*

k = B.t.u./(hr.)(sq. ft.)(°F./ft) at approximately room temperature

Material	Apparent density, lb./cu. ft. room temp.	k
Soft flexible materials in sheet form:		
Chemically treated wood fiber	2.2	0.023
Eel grass between paper	3.4–4.6	0.021–0.022
Felted cattle hair	11–13	0.022
Flax fibers between paper	4.9	.023
Hair and asbestos fibers, felted	7.8	.023
Insulating hair, and jute	6.1–6.3	0.022–0.023
Jute and asbestos fibers, felted	10.0	0.031
Loose materials:		
Cork, regranulated, fine particles	8–9	.025
Charcoal, 6 mesh	15.2	.031
Diatomaceous earth, powdered	10.6	.026
Glass wool, curled	4–10	.024
Gypsum in powdered form	26–34	0.043–0.05
Mineral wool, fibrous	6	0.0217
	10	.0225
	14	.0233
	18	.0242
Sawdust	12	.034
Wood shavings, from planer	8.8	.034
Semiflexible materials in sheet form:		
Flax fiber	13.0	.026
Semirigid materials in board form:		
Corkboard	7.0	.0225
	10.6	.025
Mineral wool, block, with binder	16.7	.031
Stiff fibrous materials in sheet form:		
Wood pulp	16.2–16.9	.028
Sugar-cane fiber	13.2–14.8	.028
Cellular gypsum	8	.029
	12	.037
	18	.049
	24	.064
	30	.083

* Abstracted from *U.S. Bur. Standards Letter Circ.* 227, Apr. 19, 1927.

Table 3-282. Thermal Conductivities of Insulating Materials at High Temperatures*

k = B.t.u./(hr.)(sq. ft.)(°F./ft.)

Material	For temperatures, °F. up to	Mean temperatures, °F. 100	200	300	400	500	600	800	1000	1500	2000
Laminated asbestos felt (approx. 40 laminations per in.)	700	0.033	0.037	0.040	0.044	0.048					
Laminated asbestos felt (approx. 20 laminations per in.)	500	.045	.050	.055	.060	.065					
Corrugated asbestos (4 plies per in.)	300	.050	.058	.069							
85% magnesia (density, 13 lb./cu. ft.)	600	.034	.036	.038	.040						
Diatomaceous earth, asbestos and bonding material	1600	.045	.047	.049	.050	.053	0.055	0.060	0.065		
Diatomaceous earth brick	1600	.054	.056	.058	.060	.063	.065	.069	.073		
Diatomaceous earth brick	2000	.127	.130	.133	.137	.140	.143	.150	.158	0.176	
Diatomaceous earth brick	2500	.128	.131	.135	.139	.143	.148	.155	.163	.183	0.203
Diatomaceous earth powder (density, 18 lb./cu. ft.)	....	.039	.042	.044	.048	.051	.054	.061	.068		
Rock wool	....	.030	.034	.039	.044	.050	.057				

Asbestos cement, 1.2; 85% magnesia cement, 0.05; asbestos and rock wool cement, 0.075 approx.

* Marks, "Mechanical Engineers' Handbook," 4th ed., McGraw-Hill, New York, 1941.

Table 3-283. Thermal Conductivities of Insulating Materials at Moderate Temperatures (Nusselt)*

k = B.t.u./(hr.)(sq. ft.)(°F./ft.)

Material	Weight, lb./cu. ft.	Temperatures, °F. 32	100	200	300	400	600	800
Asbestos	36.0	0.087	0.097	0.110	0.117	0.121	0.125	0.130
Burned infusorial earth for pipe coverings	12.5	.043	.046	.052	.057	.062	.073	.085
Insulating composition (loose)	25.0	.040	.046	.050	.053	.055		
Cotton	5.0	.032	.035	.039				
Silk hair	9.1	.026	.030	.034				
Silk	6.3	.025	.028	.034				
Wool	8.5	.022	.027	.033				
Pulverized cork	10.0	.021	.026	.032				
Infusorial earth (loose)	22.0	.035	.039	.045	.047	.050	.053	

* Marks, "Mechanical Engineers' Handbook," 4th ed., McGraw-Hill, New York, 1941.

Table 3-284. Thermal Conductivities of Insulating Materials at Low Temperatures (Gröber)*

k = B.t.u./(hr.)(sq. ft.)(°F./ft.)

See also data in Sec. 12.

Material	Weight, lb./cu. ft.	Temperatures, °F. 32	−50	−100	−200	−300
Asbestos	44.0	0.135	0.132	0.130	0.125	0.100
Asbestos	29.0	.0894	.0860	.0820	.0720	.0545
Cotton	5.0	.0325	.0302	.0276	.0235	.0198
Silk	6.3	.0290	.0256	.0235	.0196	.0155

* Marks, "Mechanical Engineers' Handbook," 4th ed., McGraw-Hill, New York, 1941.

PREDICTION AND CORRELATION OF PHYSICAL PROPERTIES

Introduction. If available, reliable experimental physical-property data should be used. In the absence of such data, estimates sufficiently accurate for many engineering applications may be made with the methods outlined herein. These methods, which are also of value for interpolating, extrapolating, and correlating experimental data, have been selected as the best presently available when evaluated on the bases of over-all accuracy, generality, and simplicity. The error figures cited have generally been derived from extensive testing of a method with experimental data. Symbols are listed in the Notation, and applicable units are given individually with each equation. References, indicated by superscript numbers, are at the end of the subsection under Literature Cited.

Notation (appropriate units for each symbol are stated in the text following the equation in which it appears).

C_{ir} internal-rotational heat-capacity contribution
C_p heat capacity at constant pressure
C_v heat capacity at constant volume
k thermal conductivity
K defined by Fig. 3-51
ln denotes natural logarithm
log denotes common logarithm
L_f latent heat of fusion
L_v latent heat of vaporization
M molecular weight
n index of refraction
N_{Pr} Prandtl number
p porosity (volume fraction voids)
P absolute pressure
$[P]$ parachor
P_{cm} true critical pressure of a mixture
P_{Pc} pseudocritical pressure (for mixtures)
P_{Pr} pseudoreduced pressure $= P/P_{Pc}$
P_r reduced pressure $= P/P_c$
P_v vapor pressure
R universal gas constant
$[R_D]$ molar refraction
s specific gravity of fluid
t temperature, °F. or °C.
T absolute temperature, °R. or °K.
T_{cm} true critical temperature of a mixture
T_f melting point
T_{Pc} pseudocritical temperature (for mixtures)
T_{Pr} pseudoreduced temperature $= T/T_{Pc}$
T_r reduced temperature $= T/T_c$
V molar fluid volume
V_b molar liquid volume at T_b
V_c critical volume
w weight fraction of component
x mole fraction of component (usually in liquid phase)
y mole fraction of component in vapor phase
Z compressibility factor $= PV/RT$
β volumetric coefficient of thermal expansion
μ fluid viscosity; sub P, at pressure; sub 1, at one atmosphere; sub m, of a mixture; sub l, of the liquid in a liquid-solid suspension
ρ fluid density
ρ_e electrical resistivity
σ surface tension
σ_i interfacial tension
ϕ volume fraction of component or phase
ω liquid-phase expansion factor; acentric factor

Superscripts:
o at low pressure

Subscripts:
b at the normal boiling point
c at the critical point; of the continuous phase
d of the discontinuous or dispersed phase
i of the ith component
l of the liquid
m of a mixture
P,p at constant pressure
r reduced quantity
s in the saturated state; of solids in a fluid-solid mixture
T at constant temperature
v of the vapor (or gas)
x at constant composition
1,2, . . . denotes the components of a mixture or different levels of temperature or pressure

General References: Gambill, series of 33 articles, *Chem. Eng.*, February, 1957, through Jan. 11, 1960. Hirschfelder, Curtiss, and Bird, "Molecular Theory of Gases and Liquids," Wiley, New York, 1954. Partington, "An Advanced Treatise on Physical Chemistry," Longmans, London, vol. 1, 1949; vol. 2, 1951. Reid and Sherwood, "The Properties of Gases and Liquids," McGraw-Hill, New York, 1958. Scheibel, *Ind. Eng. Chem.*, **46**, 1569 (1954).

BOILING POINT

The normal boiling point T_b is usually known; when unavailable, it may be estimated with Meissner's equation[1]

$$T_b = \frac{637[R_D]^{1.47} + B}{[P]} \qquad (3\text{-}1)$$

wherein T_b is in °K. and both molar refraction $[R_D]$ and parachor $[P]$ are evaluated by summation of the additive contributions given in Table 3-285.[2] The constant B varies with chemical type as shown in Table 3-286. Equation (3-1) gives average and maximum errors (in T_b as °K.) of ~2 and 7 per cent. Evaluation of $[P]$ with Table 3-285 requires a check of the listed parachor strain constants. A more rapid method[3] involves summation of the additive constants of Table 3-287 and subtraction of 19 for every bond—single, double, or triple. This method gives $[P]$ within ~1½ per cent.

COEFFICIENT OF EXPANSION

The volumetric coefficient of thermal expansion, defined by

$$\beta = \frac{1}{V}\left(\frac{\partial V}{\partial T}\right)_P \qquad (3\text{-}2)$$

may be closely approximated, if density data are available, by

$$\beta = \frac{\rho_1^2 - \rho_2^2}{2(t_2 - t_1)\rho_1\rho_2} \qquad (3\text{-}3)$$

which is a finite-difference form of Eq. (3-2), and where β is the average coefficient for the indicated temperature range. In the absence of density data, Smith *et al.*[4] have shown that β may be estimated to within ~5 per cent for a large variety of liquid organic compounds according to

$$\beta = \frac{0.04314}{(T_c - T)^{0.641}} \qquad (3\text{-}4)$$

where the units of β and of T_c are (°K.)$^{-1}$ and °K., respectively. Polar liquids give the largest deviations.

Table 3-285. Atomic and Structural Contributions to Molar Refraction and Parachor[a]

Structure	Molar refraction $[R_D]$	Parachor $[P]$
C (singly bound)	2.418	9.2
H	1.100	15.4[b]
$—CH_2—$	4.618	40.0
O (hydroxyl)	1.525	20
O (in ethers, esters)	1.643	20
O (carboxyl)	2.211[c]	39[c]
F	0.95[d]	25.5
Cl	5.967	55
Br	8.865	69
I	13.900	90
N (primary amine)	2.322	17.5
N (secondary amine)	2.502	17.5
N (tertiary amine)	2.840	17.5
N (nitrile)	5.516[e]	55.5[e]
S	[f]	50
P	[g]	40.5
Other elements	[g]	[h]
3-member ring	0	12.5
4-member ring	0	6
5-member ring	0	3
6-member ring	0	0.8
7-member ring	0	−4.0
Double bond	1.733	19.0
Semipolar double bond	1.733	0
Triple bond	2.398	38
Singlet linkage	....	−9.5

Parachor Strain Constants: In the listings below, R is a hydrocarbon radical; X is a negative group; and when the negative group is Br, multiply the strain constant by 1.5.

Use +3 for carbonyl in the ring.

Use zero for RCH_2X, RCHO, RCOR, RCH_2R, RNH_2, NOR, NOOR, and R_2SeO.

Use −3 for $RCHX_2$, RCOOH, RCOOR, RCOCL, R_2CHX, R_2CHR, $RCONH_2$, ROCOOR, ROCOCl, RSOOR, ROSOOR, R_2NH, NOCl, NO_2R, NO_2OR, N_2O, azides, and RSeOOH.

Use −6 for RCX_3, R_3CX, ClCOCl, ClSOCl, RSO_2Cl, R_3CR, RSO_2R, $ROSO_2OR$, R_3N, NCl_3, NO_2Cl, PX_3, R_3P, $PO(OR)_3$, BX_3, AsX_3, SbX_3, and ClSeOCl.

Use −9 for CX_4, R_4C, SCl_4, SO_2Cl_2, $NOCl_3$, $POCl_3$, SiX_4, SnX_4, and CrO_2Cl.

Use −12 for $SOCl_4$, NCl, $SbCl_5$, and PCl_5.

Use −15 for SCl_6.

[a] Values in this table are taken from Herzog, *Ind. Eng. Chem.*, **36**, 998 (1944); Meissner, *Chem. Eng. Progress*, **45**, 151 (1949); and other sources.

[b] Hydrogen on bromine has a parachor of 16.4; on chlorine, 12.8; on oxygen, 10; on nitrogen, 12.5; on sulfur and carbon, 15.4.

[c] Includes allowance for double bond.

[d] Only for one fluorine atom attached to carbon. 1.1 for each F in polyfluorides.

[e] Includes allowance for triple bond.

[f] As SH, 7.69; as RSR, 7.97; as RCNS, 7.91; as RSSR, 8.11.

[g] Value depends on type of compound, apparently differing for various combining forms.

[h] As, 54; Sb, 68; Se, 63; B, 21.5; Si, 31; Be, 42; Al, 55; Cr, 58; Tl, 62; Sn, 64.5; Hg, 69; and Bi, 80.

Table 3-286. Constant B of Eq. (3-1) Related to Chemical Type

Compound Class	B
Acids (monocarboxylic)	28,000
Alcohols (monohydroxy), including phenol, cresols, etc.	16,500
Amines:	
Primary	6,500
Secondary	2,000
Tertiary	−3,000
Esters of monocarboxylic acids and monohydroxy alcohols	15,000
Esters of dibasic acids and monohydroxy alcohols	30,000
Ethers and mercaptans	4,000
Hydrocarbons:	
Acetylenic	−500
Aromatic	−2,500
Paraffinic and naphthenic	−2,500
Olefinic	−4,500
Ketones	15,000
Monochlorinated normal paraffins	4,000
Nitriles	20,000

Table 3-287. McGowan Parachor Contributions*

C	47.6	Be	59.1	Ge	93.3	Te	104.6
H	24.7	B	53.4	As	87.6	I	98.9
O	36.2	He	19.0	Se	81.9	Xe	93.2
N	41.9	F	30.5	Br	76.1	Pb	113.8
S	67.7	Ne	24.8	Kr	70.3	Bi	108.1
Cl	62.0	P	73.5	Sn	116.0	Po	102.4
Si	79.2	A	56.3	Sb	110.3	Rn	90.9
						Al	96.7

* $[P] = \Sigma$ (contributions) − (19) (number of bonds).

CRITICAL PROPERTIES

The **critical temperature** T_c of organic compounds may be accurately estimated by summing the additive contributions of Eduljee,[5] which are tabulated in Table 3-288. The sum of the contributions, denoted by $\Sigma\Delta_T$, is then substituted into

$$T_c = \frac{T_b}{\Sigma\Delta_T/100} \tag{3-5}$$

Equation (3-5) represents the critical temperatures of 239 compounds from 23 chemical groups within an average error of 1.0 per cent. For pure hydrocarbons, Nokay's simpler relation[6] gives errors < 2 per cent if $400° < T_b < 1400°$R. and $0.5 < s < 1.0$:

$$\log T_c = 1.2806 + 0.2985 \log s + 0.62164 \log T_b \tag{3-6}$$

where T_c and T_b are in °R. and s is the specific gravity of the liquid at 60°F./60°F. For normal paraffins only, of 4 to 20 carbon atoms per molecule, Eq. (3-6) gives T_c within a maximum error of $\sim \frac{1}{4}$ per cent. The critical temperatures of inorganic compounds have not been so well generalized but may be quickly estimated from the following modification of the Guldberg-Guye rule:

$$\frac{T_b}{T_c} = 0.613 \tag{3-7}$$

which showed deviations of 5.3 per cent (average) and 17.6 per cent (maximum) for 40 inorganic molecules. The critical temperatures of the elements may be approximated by the equation of Gates and Thodos:[7]

$$T_c = 1.4732 T_b^{1.0313} \tag{3-8}$$

with temperatures in °K. For 16 elements, the mean

Table 3-288. Atomic and Structural Contributions for Eduljee's T_c Method

	Δ_T	Remarks
Atomic values:		
Carbon	−55.32	
Hydrogen	28.52	
Oxygen	1.59	Etheric oxygen
Nitrogen	30.6	In amines
Nitrogen	−26.29	As member of a ring
Chlorine	29.89	
Bromine	31.15	
Fluorine	29.75	
Sulfur	1.31	
Silicon	−54.00	In silanes
Group values:		
OH	31.63	In phenols
	35.62	In alcohols, $n \leqq 3$*
	34.0	In alcohols, $n = 4$
	32.72	In alcohols, $n = 5$
	31.40	In alcohols, $n = 6$
	30.1	In alcohols, $n = 7$
	29	In alcohols, $n = 8$
	28.52	In alcohols, $n > 8$
C=O	31.63	Ketone group
—COOH	35.94	Carboxyl group
—COO—	4.12	In esters
—C≡N	33.83	Nitrile group
Bond values:		
(C)=(C)	56.61	For up to 3 carbon atoms per double bond
	55.21	For 4 or more carbon atoms per double bond
(C)≡(C)	112.9	
(N)—(C)	−19.17	In amines; value of zero when N—C bond is in a ring
(N)—(H)	−18.37	In amines
Ring-structure values:		
5-membered ring	54.28	
6-membered ring	53.52	
Fusion of two rings	0.25	
Position values:		
Single bonding or substitution on second carbon atom	−0.34	The position of the branch or substituent is counted conventionally from the right end of the chain
Two branches or substitutions on second carbon atom	−1.42	
Branching or substitution on number three or higher carbon atom	−0.96	

* n = number of carbon atoms per molecule.

deviation was 1.4 per cent. The true critical temperatures of mixtures are not used in generalized physical-property correlations because it has been found that use of the pseudocritical temperature T_{Pc} given by Kay[8] as

$$T_{Pc} = \Sigma x_i T_{ci} \tag{3-9}$$

results in a considerable improvement of correlation. Occasionally, however, knowledge of the true T_c is of value; it may be estimated by Edmister's equation,[9] which is specifically applicable to hydrocarbon mixtures:

$$T_{cm} = \Sigma w_i T_{ci} \tag{3-10}$$

For natural gas mixtures, Edmister[10] has given

$$T_{Pc} = 190 + 9.76M \tag{3-11}$$

where T_{Pc} = °R. Equation (3-11) is applicable for $16 < M < 26$. If the gas specific gravity (based on air = 1.0) is known, M is obtained from $M = 29s$.

The **critical pressure** P_c of organic compounds may be estimated by summing the additive contributions of Eduljee,[11] which are tabulated in Table 3-289. The

Table 3-289. Atomic and Structural Contributions for Eduljee's P_c Method

	Δ_P	Remarks
Atomic values:		
Carbon	−9.35	
Hydrogen	16.20	
Oxygen	17.20	Etheric oxygen
Nitrogen	0.0	
Chlorine	48.0	
Bromine	68.8	
Fluorine	39.9	
Sulfur	27.8	
Silicon	22.4	In silanes
Group values:		
OH	23.7	In alcohols and phenols
C=O	30.2	Ketone group
—COOH	57.7	Carboxyl group
C≡N	52.5	Nitrile group
Bond values:		
(C)=(C)	28.6 for $n = 2$	Value depends on number n of carbon atoms in chain
	27.9 for $n = 3$	
	25.2 for $n = 4$	
	21.2 for $n = 5$	
	16.4 for $n = 6$	
	11.0 for $n = 7$	
	5.3 for $n = 8$	
	0.0 for $n > 8$	
(C)≡(C)	51.1	As in acetylenes
(N)—(H)	−3.15	As in amines
Ring-structure values:		
5-membered ring	10.5	Homo- or heterocyclic saturated ring
6-membered ring	7.2	
Benzene ring	84.5	
Position values:		
Single branching or substitution on second carbon atom	−1.6	For multiple branching or substitution, use multiple values for Δ_P. The position of the branch is counted from both ends of the chain and the shorter distance taken
Single branching or substitution on third or higher carbon atom	−4.75	

sum of the contributions, denoted by $\Sigma\Delta_P$, is then used in the relation

$$P_c = \frac{10^4 M}{(\Sigma\Delta_P)^2} \tag{3-12}$$

where P_c is in atmospheres absolute. Equation (3-12) checks the critical pressures of 182 compounds from 23 chemical classes within an average error of 3.7 per cent. The critical pressure may be calculated more simply (but less accurately), if the critical volume is known, from one of Herzog's proposals:[12]

$$P_c = \frac{21.75 T_c}{V_c} \tag{3-13}$$

where P_c is in atmospheres absolute, T_c in °K., and V_c in cc./g.-mole. The maximum error associated with Eq. (3-13) is ~20 per cent. The true critical pressure of a hydrocarbon mixture may be estimated by the equation of Benedict:[13]

$$P_{cm} = P_{Pc}\left(9\left\{\frac{\Sigma x_i (T_{bi}/100)^2}{[\Sigma x_i (T_{bi}/100)]^2} - 1\right\} + 1\right) \tag{3-14}$$

where P_{Pc} is the pseudocritical pressure which is used in generalized property correlations. P_{Pc} is, in turn, given by Kay's rule[8] as

$$P_{Pc} = \Sigma x_i P_{ci} \tag{3-15}$$

For natural gas mixtures, one may use the equation[10]

$$P_{Pc} = 710 - 2.07M \tag{3-16}$$

where P_{Pc} = lb./sq. in. abs. Equation (3-16) is applicable for $16 < M < 26$. If the gas specific gravity (based on air = 1.0) is known, M is obtained from $M = 29s$.

The **critical volume** V_c may be estimated with Benson's simple relationship[14]

$$V_c = V_b(0.422 \log P_c + 1.981) \tag{3-17}$$

where V_c and V_b are in cc./g.-mole and P_c is in atmospheres absolute. Equation (3-17) predicts V_c with average and maximum errors of 2 to 3 and ~10 per cent, respectively. Errors are largest for nitriles and low-boiling gases. The molar liquid volume at the normal boiling point V_b may be obtained from

$$V_b = \frac{M}{\rho_{lb}} \tag{3-18}$$

if ρ_l at t_b is known, or it may be estimated within ~5 per cent by summation of the additive contributions[15] listed in Table 3-290. In cases where P_c is unknown and

Table 3-290. Structural Contributions to Liquid Molar Volume at the Normal Boiling Point*

Atomic Volumes

As	30.5	F	8.7	P	27.0	Sn	42.3
Bi	48.0	Ge	34.5	Pb	48.3†	Ti	35.7
Br	27.0	H	3.7	S	25.6	V	32.0
C	14.8	Hg	19.0	Sb	34.2‡	Zn	20.4
Cr	27.4	I	37.0	Si	32.0		

Cl, terminal, as in RCl	21.6	In acids	12.0
Medial, as in R—CHCl—R	24.6	In union with S, P, N	8.3
Nitrogen, double-bonded	15.6	3-membered ring, deduct	6.0
Triply bonded, as in nitriles	16.2§	4-membered ring, deduct	8.5
In primary amines, RNH_2	10.5	5-membered ring, deduct	11.5
In secondary amines, R_2NH	12.0	6-membered ring as in benzene, cyclohexane, pyridine, deduct	15.0
In tertiary amines, R_3N	10.8¶		
Oxygen, except as noted below	7.4		
In methyl esters	9.1	Naphthalene ring, deduct	30.0
In methyl ethers	9.9	Anthracene ring, deduct	47.5
In higher esters, ethers	11.0		

* Data are those of Le Bas as reported in "The Molecular Volumes of Liquid Chemical Compounds," Longmans, London, 1915. Units are cc./g.-mole.
† Average.
‡ Estimated.
§ Determined by author from available data.
¶ Determined by author from very limited data.

difficult to estimate, V_c may be directly estimated by the additive-contribution method of Lydersen.[16]

The **critical compressibility factor** $Z_c = P_cV_c/RT_c$ may be estimated with the equation of Lydersen:[16]

$$Z_c = \frac{1}{3.43 + 0.0067(L_v)_b^2} \tag{3-19}$$

where L_{vb} is expressed in units of kcal./g.-mole. Equation (3-19) may be expected to give an average deviation of ~4 per cent, the largest errors (up to 40 per cent) occurring with organic acids and nitriles.

Alternatively, if P_c and T_c are already known or have been calculated, use may be made of Edmister's suggestion.[17]

$$Z_c = 0.371 - 0.0343 \frac{\log P_c}{(T_c/T_b) - 1} \qquad (3\text{-}20)$$

where P_c is in atmospheres absolute. The **critical thermal conductivities** of the inert ("noble") gases have been represented by Owens and Thodos[18] by

$$k_c = \frac{0.0324 P_c^{0.223} T_c^{0.132}}{M^{0.586}} \qquad (3\text{-}21)$$

where the units of k_c, P_c, and T_c are B.t.u./(hr.)(ft.)(°F.), atmospheres absolute, and °K., respectively. For helium, it was necessary to use the pseudocritical constants $T_{Pc} = 20$°K. and $P_{Pc} = 9.60$ atm. For 11 diatomic gases, k_c was correlated within an average error of ~4 per cent by Schaefer and Thodos[19] according to

$$k_c = \frac{0.0228 P_c^{9/16}}{M^{1/3} T_c^{1/5}} \qquad (3\text{-}22)$$

where the units are the same as in Eq. (3-21). Though k_c may be approximated by Eq. (3-22), a more accurate result is obtainable by inserting a reliable experimental value of k into the generalized thermal-conductivity chart shown as Fig. 3-60. The **critical viscosities** of diatomic gases are well represented (2.4 per cent average error) by[20]

$$\mu_c = \frac{7.40 M^{1/2} P_c^{2/3}}{T_c^{1/6}} \qquad (3\text{-}23)$$

where the units are micropoise, atmospheres absolute, and °K. For all types of gases, Uyehara and Watson[21] found that Eq. (3-23), with a constant of 7.70, gives μ_c within average and maximum errors of 6.5 and 62.1 per cent. Somewhat better correlation (4.6 and 34.2 per cent average and maximum errors) results from use of the equation[21]

$$\mu_c = \frac{61.6 M^{1/2} T_c^{1/2}}{V_c^{2/3}} \qquad (3\text{-}24)$$

when V_c is known or calculable. Equation (3-24) is preferable for more complex molecules.

DENSITY

Liquid densities at the normal boiling point may be estimated within $\pm 2 - 3$ per cent by Benson's equation:[14]

$$\rho_b = \rho_c(1.981 + 0.422 \log P_c) \qquad (3\text{-}25)$$

where P_c is in atmospheres absolute. Errors are largest with low-boiling gases and nitriles. Alternatively, Eq. (3-18) may be rearranged to $\rho_{lb} = M/V_b$ and used with the additive V_b values of Table 3-290 to give ρ_b within $\pm 4 - 5$ per cent. A known or calculated liquid density may be extrapolated with reasonable accuracy to other temperatures with the equation[22]

$$\frac{(\rho_l - \rho_v)_2}{(\rho_l - \rho_v)_1} = \left(\frac{T_c - T_2}{T_c - T_1}\right)^{1/3} \qquad (3\text{-}26)$$

in which vapor density ρ_v may be neglected if P is small. Extrapolations may also be made with an Othmer reference-substance plot,[23] whereby a double-log graph is constructed of the known density values of the compound under consideration vs. density values of a similar reference substance at constant values of $(T_c - T)$, to obtain straight lines. The isothermal effect of pressure on ρ_l may be approximated with Fig. 3-50.[24] If all critical values—T_c, P_c, V_c, and Z_c—are known or have been calculated, Lu's generalized chart[25] (Fig. 3-51) should be used for ρ_l calculations. A liquid density may be estimated directly by calculation from the ordinate expression of Fig. 3-51. If a value of ρ is known, the chart is used with the equation

$$\frac{K_1}{\rho_1} = \frac{K_2}{\rho_2} \qquad (3\text{-}27)$$

where K_1 is read for the T_r and P_r of the known density value ρ_1, and K_2 is read at the T_r and P_r of the desired density ρ_2. This procedure, based on data, gives smaller deviations than does direct calculation. All densities and volumes in Fig. 3-51 are molar quantities. The chart is applicable for $Z_c \geq 0.24$ and may be expected to give results within ~3 per cent for direct calculation and within ~1 to 2 per cent when based on known data; these errors do not include uncertainties in the critical quantities if they are also calculated. Deviations are largest in the critical region (near T_r and $P_r = 1$).

Vapor densities or molar volumes may be calculated from the equation

$$V = \frac{ZRT}{P} \qquad (3\text{-}28)$$

with the compressibility factor Z obtained from the Nelson-Obert charts.[26] Also, recent work by Lydersen[16] has been plotted and appears as Fig. 3-52. Data for H_2 and He fit only for $T_r > 2.5$ and when their true

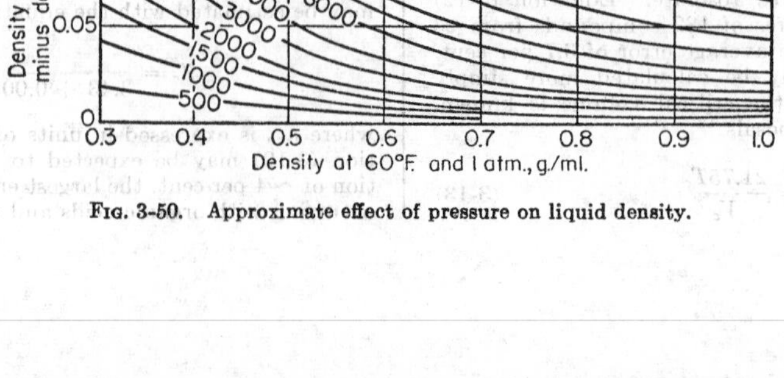

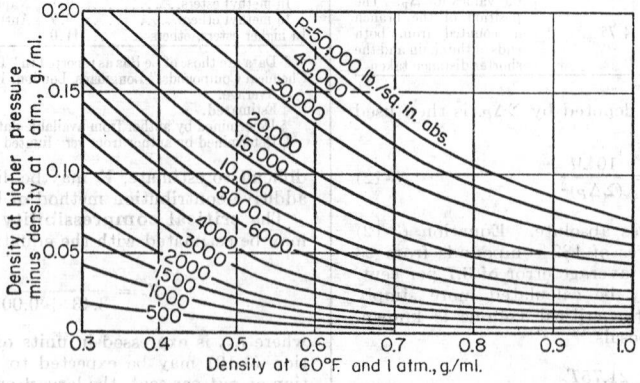

FIG. 3-50. Approximate effect of pressure on liquid density.

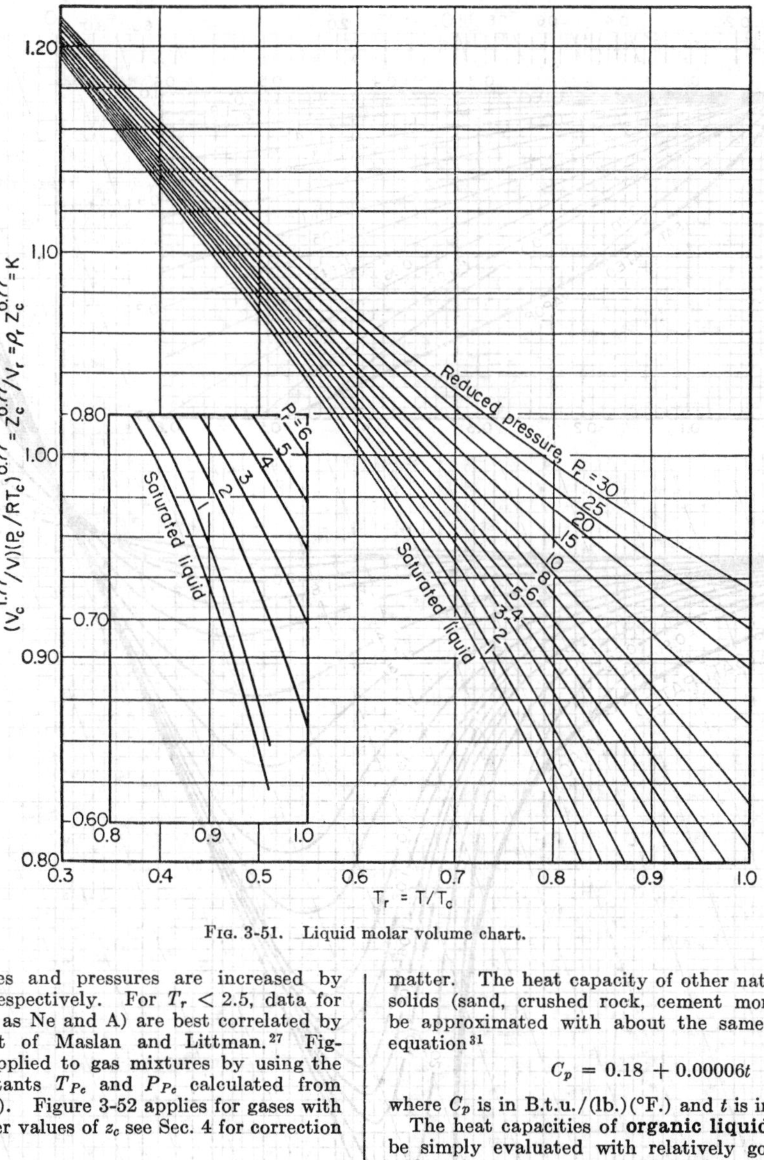

FIG. 3-51. Liquid molar volume chart.

critical temperatures and pressures are increased by 8°K. and 8 atm., respectively. For $T_r < 2.5$, data for H_2 and He (as well as Ne and A) are best correlated by the special Z-chart of Maslan and Littman.[27] Figure 3-52 may be applied to gas mixtures by using the pseudocritical constants T_{P_c} and P_{P_c} calculated from Eqs. (3-9) and (3-15). Figure 3-52 applies for gases with $z_c = 0.27$. For other values of z_c see Sec. 4 for correction methods.

DIFFUSION COEFFICIENTS

See Sec. 14 for details concerning the prediction of diffusivities.

HEAT CAPACITY

The heat capacities of **solids** may be roughly approximated with the empirical additive-contribution methods of Dulong and Petit[28] (solid elements), of Kopp[28] (solid compounds), and of Satoh[29] (solid organic compounds), but these methods are quite restricted and the values predicted are often seriously in error. Predictions for anthracitic and bituminous **coals** may be made within ±15 to 20 per cent with Clendenin's relation[30]

$$C_p = 0.20 + 0.00088t + 0.0015V \qquad (3\text{-}29)$$

where C_p is expressed as B.t.u./(lb.)(°F.)(ash-contained basis), t is in °C., and V is weight per cent volatile matter. The heat capacity of other naturally occurring solids (sand, crushed rock, cement mortars, etc.) may be approximated with about the same error with the equation[31]

$$C_p = 0.18 + 0.00006t \qquad (3\text{-}30)$$

where C_p is in B.t.u./(lb.)(°F.) and t is in °F.

The heat capacities of **organic liquids** at 20°C. may be simply evaluated with relatively good accuracy (5 and 14 per cent average and maximum errors) with the additive-contribution method of Johnson and Huang.[32] The values of Table 3-291 may be summed directly to obtain C_p in units of cal./(g.-mole)(°C.). The method is poor only for the first members of homologous series and for aldehydes. Heat capacities calculated in this manner at 20°C. may be extended to other temperatures with the Chow and Bright low-pressure temperature function[34]

$$C_p\omega^{2.8} = b \qquad (3\text{-}31)$$

where ω is the Watson liquid-phase expansion factor[35] and b is a constant which varies with the nature of the compound. For extrapolation of a known C_p value, Eq. (3-31) may be expressed as

$$C_{p2} = C_{p1}\left(\frac{\omega_1}{\omega_2}\right)^{2.8} \qquad (3\text{-}32)$$

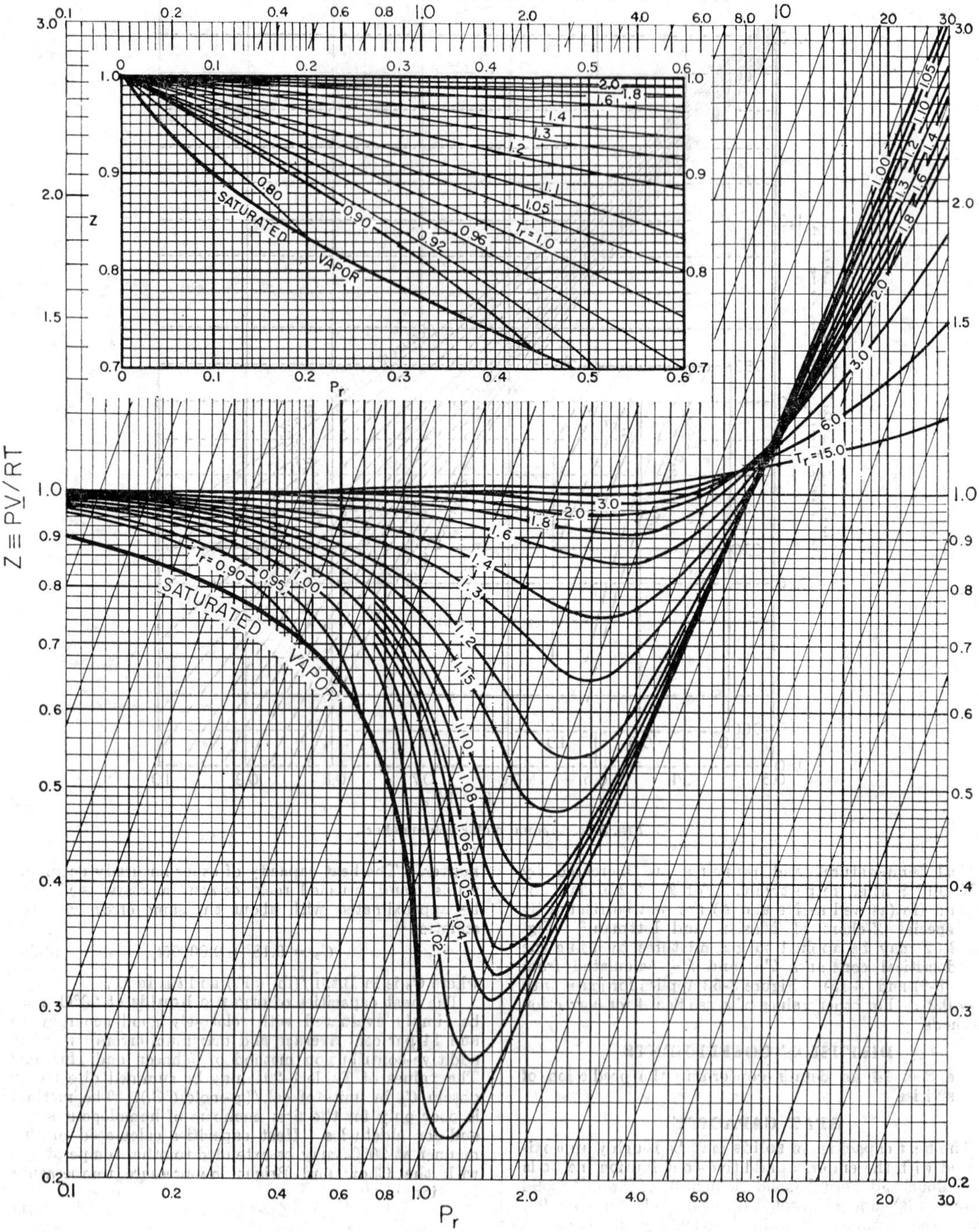

FIG. 3-52. Generalized compressibility charts. Pseudoreduced volume $V_r' = \frac{V}{RT_c/P_c}$.

Table 3-291. Group Heat Capacities for Organic Liquids

Group	Contribution,* cal./(g.-mole)(°C.)
CH_3—	9.9
—CH_2—	6.3
—C—H (with bonds above and below the C)	5.4
—COOH	19.1
—COO— (esters)	14.5
>CO (ketones)	14.7
—CN	13.9
—OH	11.0
—NH_2 (amines)	15.2
—Cl	8.6
—Br	3.7
—NO_2	15.3
—O—	8.4
—S—	10.6
C_6H_5—	30.5
H— (formic acid, formates)†	3.55
=CH— (allyl compounds)	5.4

* At 20°C. only. For certain atomic configurations, it may be necessary to use values for C alone and for H alone; values of −0.8 and 3.6, respectively, appear adequate.
† Value from ref. 33.

For the restricted range corresponding to $T_r \leq 0.65$ and $P \leq 10$ atm. absolute, ω is given by[35]

$$\omega = 0.1745 - 0.0838T_r \tag{3-33}$$

For **petroleum oils,** C_p may be estimated within 4 per cent with the equation[31]

$$C_p = \frac{0.388 + 0.00045t}{s^{0.5}} \tag{3-34}$$

where C_p is in B.t.u./(lb.)(°F.), t is in °F., and s is the liquid specific gravity at 60°F./60°F. Equation (3-34) is directly applicable for $32° < t < 400$°F. and for $0.75 < s < 0.96$. The average error is 5 per cent for the extended temperature range of 400° to 750°F.

The available data for the specific heats of **liquid metals and fused salts** have been partially generalized by Douglas,[36] whose conclusions are summarized in Table 3-292.

Table 3-292. Douglas's Predictions for the C_p of Liquid Metals and Fused Salts

Grouping	Number tested	Atomic C_p*	Deviation
Liquid metals and alloys:			
General	35	7.4	Three-fourths within 5%; maximum deviation of 12%
Transition metals†	5	9.6	Maximum of 15%
Fused salts:			
General	43	8.1	Three-fourths within 10%; maximum of 30%
Containing N‡	4	5.7	Maximum of 30%
Containing H‡	7	6.5	Maximum of 30%

* Units are B.t.u./(mean lb.-atom)(°F.). Divide by mean atomic weight to get B.t.u./(lb.)(°F.); where "mean atomic wt." equals chemical formula wt./number of atoms in formula. Values apply for a short range above the liquids' freezing points.
† Such as Ni and Cr. Electronic contributions to specific heat are unusually large for these elements.
‡ Nitrates and hydroxides have lower atomic specific heats than most other liquid salts because of hindered vibrations of the atoms in their tightly bound radicals.

More generalized and somewhat more accurate approaches to the estimation of liquid heat capacities include the thermodynamic method of Watson[35] and the bond-frequency method of Sakiadis and Coates,[37] but these correlations are considerably more complex than those treated here and generally require more data.

The heat capacities of **petroleum vapors** may be estimated from[38]

$$C_p{}^0 = \frac{(4.0 - s)(t + 670)}{6450} \tag{3-35}$$

where $C_p{}^0$ is in B.t.u/(lb.)(°F.), t is in °F., and s has the same meaning as in Eq. (3-34). Equation (3-35) exhibits an average deviation of ~2 per cent for the variable ranges: dew point $< t <$ 660°F. and $0.68 < s < 0.90$. Brooks[39] has presented graphical correlations of C_p and of C_p/C_v for natural gas.

The low-pressure heat capacities of **pure vapors and gases** may be estimated with good accuracy with Dobratz's equation[40]

$$C_p{}^0 = 4R + n_r'\frac{R}{2} + \Sigma q_i C_{\nu i} + \frac{3n - 6 - n_r' - \Sigma q_i}{\Sigma q_i}\Sigma q_i C_{\delta i} \tag{3-36}$$

in conjunction with Table 3-293,[33] which gives Meghreblian's recommendations[41] for the characteristic stretching- and bending-vibrational wave numbers (ν and δ), along with the corresponding constants of the heat-capacity equation

Table 3-293. Bond Frequencies and Heat-capacity Constants for Gases and Vapors

Bond	Stretching vibrations*				Bending vibrations*			
	ν, cm.$^{-1}$	A	$B \times 10^3$	$C \times 10^6$	δ, cm.$^{-1}$	A	$B \times 10^3$	$C \times 10^6$
C—C†	910	−0.339	3.564	−1.449	650	0.343	2.707	−1.150
C—C‡	1500	−0.836	3.288	−1.087	600	0.503	2.472	−1.058
C=C	1200	−0.740	3.730	−1.404	910	−0.339	3.564	−1.449
C≡C	2080	−0.606	1.861	−0.306	375	1.268	1.244	−0.544
C—H	3000	−0.139	0.168	0.447	1050	−0.579	3.741	−1.471
C—O	1030	−0.458	3.722	−1.471	1120	−0.665	3.757	−1.449
C=O	1740	−0.778	2.721	−0.759	780	−0.034	3.220	−1.341
C—N	1000	−0.501	3.695	−1.471	450	1.016	1.663	−0.723
C≡N	2220	−0.525	1.528	−0.141	240	1.665	0.566	−0.249
C—Cl	650	0.343	2.707	−1.150	260	1.613	0.656	−0.289
C—F	1050	−0.579	3.471	−1.471	1200	−0.740	3.730	−1.404
C—Br	610	0.471	2.519	−1.076	950	−0.415	3.630	−1.462
C—I	530	0.740	2.106	−0.908	880	−0.275	3.498	−1.431
O—H	3500	0.000	−0.240	0.560	1350	−0.819	3.563	−1.267
S—H	2570	−0.331	0.805	0.192	860	−0.230	3.450	−1.416
S=O	1250	−0.772	3.685	−1.363	520	0.774	2.051	−0.886
C—S	690	0.219	2.884	−1.218	280	1.558	0.750	−0.330
N—N§	1000	−0.501	3.695	−1.471	900	−0.320	3.547	−1.445
N—H	3300	−0.04	−0.12	0.53	1200	−0.740	3.730	−1.404
N—O	1270	−0.785	3.668	−1.347	660	0.311	2.754	−1.168
N=O	1470	−0.835	3.347	−1.125	650	0.343	2.707	−1.150

* The constants A, B, and C are for use in the equation $C_p{}^0 = A + BT + CT^2$, as illustrated in the text.
† Aliphatic.
‡ Aromatic or with conjugated double bonds.
§ Not for N_2O or N_2O_4.

$$C_p{}^0 = A + BT + CT^2 \tag{3-37}$$

as obtained from the analysis of Crawford and Parr.[42] In Eqs. (3-36) and (3-37), $C_p{}^0$ is low-pressure heat capacity, cal./(g.-mole)(°K.), R is the universal gas constant [1.987 cal./(g.-mole)(°K.)], n_r' is the number of single bonds about which internal rotation of groups can take place (*i.e.*, C—C or C—O in esters or ethers), q_i is the number of bonds of the ith type, n is the number of atoms in the molecule, Σq_i is the total number of bonds in the molecule, $C_{\nu i}$ and $C_{\delta i}$ are Einstein functions for bonds of the ith type, and T is in °K. To illustrate, we may apply Eqs. (3-36) and (3-37) and Table 3-293 as follows:

Example. Calculate the low-pressure C_p of C_3H_8 at 427°C. $n = 11$, $n_r' = 2$, $\Sigma q_i = 10$, $[(3n - 6 - n_r' - \Sigma q_i)/\Sigma q_i] = 1.5$, and $n_r'(R/2) = R$. Propane contains eight C—H bonds and two C—C bonds, and for the stretching vibrations (from Table 3-293):

$$\begin{aligned}\Sigma q_i C_{\nu i} &= 8(-0.139 + 0.168 \times 10^{-3}T + 0.447 \times 10^{-6}T^2) \\ &\quad + 2(-0.339 + 3.564 \times 10^{-3}T - 1.449 \times 10^{-6}T^2) \\ &= -1.789 + 8.471 \times 10^{-3}T + 0.68 \times 10^{-6}T^2\end{aligned}$$

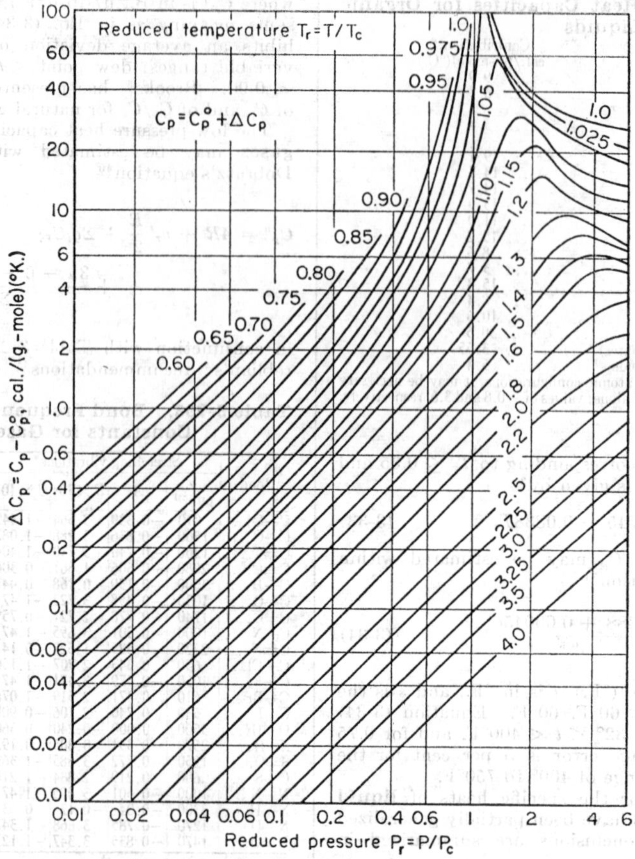

FIG. 3-53. Isothermal pressure correction to the molar heat capacity of gases.

$\Sigma q_i C_{\delta i}$ is evaluated in the same manner to give

$$\Sigma q_i C_{\delta i} = -3.940 + 35.364 \times 10^{-3}T - 14.09 \times 10^{-6}T^2$$

These terms are then combined according to Eq. (3-36) to yield

$$C_p{}^0 = 2.24 + 61.47 \times 10^{-3}T - 20.44 \times 10^{-6}T^2$$

At $T = 700$°K., the equation above gives $C_p{}^0 = 35.26$ cal./(g.-mole)(°K.). The experimental value is 34.20 cal./(g.-mole)(°K.), and the error is +3.1 per cent.

For all types of compounds over the recommended temperature interval of 300° to 1100°K., this method may be expected to give average and maximum deviations of ~5½ and 25 per cent. If the lowest homologs of a series and strained structures (*e.g.*, cyclopropane) are excluded, and if the temperature range is restricted to 500° $< T <$ 1100°K., average and maximum errors are ~4 and 10 per cent. Naphthenic-ring bondings should be treated as aromatic. A less generalized approach which will give more accurate estimates of $C_p{}^0$ for hydrocarbons only (from −250° to 3000°F.) is also available.[43]

The **effect of pressure** on the heat capacities of gases may be obtained from Edmister's graph,[44] shown as Fig. 3-53. The error in the calculated $\Delta C_p (= C_p - C_p{}^0)$ can be as large as 30 per cent, though 5 to 8 per cent is more normal. If $P > 50$ lb./sq. in. abs., approximately, the pressure correction may be significant.

The **heat-capacity ratio** C_p/C_v is easily obtained for an ideal gas, since $C_p - C_v = R$. Accordingly,

$$\left(\frac{C_p}{C_v}\right)_{\text{ideal}} = \frac{C_p}{C_p - R} = \frac{C_v + R}{C_v} \tag{3-38}$$

For a real gas, C_p/C_v may be calculated from

$$\frac{C_p}{C_v} = \frac{C_p}{C_p - (C_p - C_v)} \tag{3-39}$$

The quantity $(C_p - C_v)$, which is larger than R for a real gas, may be obtained from the generalized plot[45] shown as Fig. 3-54.

The only practical recourse at present for calculating the heat capacities of **mixtures** of solids, liquids, or gases—singly or in combination, miscible or immiscible—is to weight the pure-component or phase heat capacities by weight, mole, or volume fractions, the choice being dictated by the units of the heat capacities being weighted. For an immiscible mixture, this approach is entirely adequate. For miscible mixtures, the accuracy of such weighting varies from excellent in the case of low-density gases to quite poor for liquid mixtures with large heats of mixing. For liquids, the weighting rule will generally work well only for mixtures of chemically similar non-polar liquids (such as hydrocarbons or

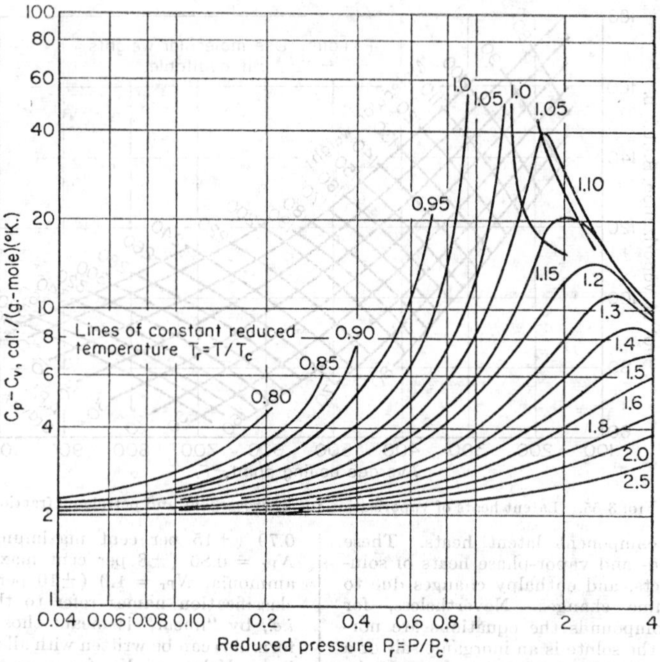

FIG. 3-54. Generalized heat-capacity differences, C_p-C_v vs. P_r and T_r.

liquid metals), or for aqueous solutions of non-electrolytes. Aqueous solutions of inorganic salts are a special class for which two rules of thumb are available: The weighted specific heat can be used, where the specific heat of the salt is for the crystalline state; or, alternatively, for solutions up to about 40 weight per cent solute, the assumption may be made that the dissolved salt has a negligible heat capacity. Thus a 30 weight per cent solution of NaCl in water would have a specific heat of ~0.7 cal./(g.)(°C.).

INTERFACIAL TENSION

The interfacial tension of immiscible liquids is less than the larger of the surface tensions of the component liquids. Quantitative prediction may be made with Antonoff's rule,[46] which states that, for two saturated-liquid layers in equilibrium, the interfacial tension is equal to the difference between the individual surface tensions of the two **mutually saturated** phases under a common vapor or gas

$$\sigma_i = \sigma_{1s} - \sigma_{2s} \tag{3-40}$$

If pure-component surface tensions are used in Eq. (3-40), the rule proves quite inaccurate, since $\sigma_i < (\sigma_1 - \sigma_2)$, and the error will often exceed 100 per cent. If, however, saturated-phase surface tensions are used, estimates within ~15 per cent may be made for both organic-water and organic-organic systems.

LATENT HEATS

For quick, but rough, estimates of the **latent heat of vaporization** of a liquid at its normal boiling point, Trouton's rule (*circa* 1884) may be used

$$L_{vb} = 21T_b \tag{3-41}$$

where L_{vb} is in cal./g.-mole and T_b is in °K. The error may be as large as ±30 per cent even with normally encountered liquids. If reliable data on vapor pressure and saturated liquid and vapor volumes are available, the strictly rigorous, thermodynamic Clapeyron equation may be applied. In the absence of such information, L_v at the normal boiling point may be estimated with average and maximum deviations of about 2½ and 10 per cent by Giacalone's equation[47]

$$L_{vb} = \frac{RT_cT_b \ln P_c}{T_c - T_b} \tag{3-42}$$

where P_c is expressed in atmospheres absolute.

A known or calculated latent heat may be accurately extrapolated to other temperatures with Watson's correlation[35]

$$\frac{L_{v2}}{L_{v1}} = \left(\frac{T_c - T_2}{T_c - T_1}\right)^{0.38} \tag{3-43}$$

which may be expected to give an average error in the change of latent heat of about 2 per cent to within ~10°K. of T_c. Equations (3-42) and (3-43) may be combined to give another dimensionless equation:

$$L_v = RT_cT_b \ln P_c \frac{(T_c - T)^{0.38}}{(T_c - T_b)^{1.38}} \tag{3-44}$$

which allows one to estimate L_v at any temperature without vapor-pressure data with an average error of about 4 per cent.

Latent heats of vaporization of liquid **mixtures** may be defined in various ways. The integral isobaric latent heat (pressure and composition constant) and the differential or equilibrium latent heat (pressure and temperature constant) may often be approximated to within ~ ±5 per cent with the simplified relations

$$(L_v)_{Px} = (L_v)_1x_1 + (L_v)_2x_2 + \cdots \tag{3-45}$$
$$(L_v)_{PT} = (L_v)_1y_1 + (L_v)_2y_2 + \cdots \tag{3-46}$$

where liquid and vapor component fractions x and y, respectively, are weight or molar fractions to correspond

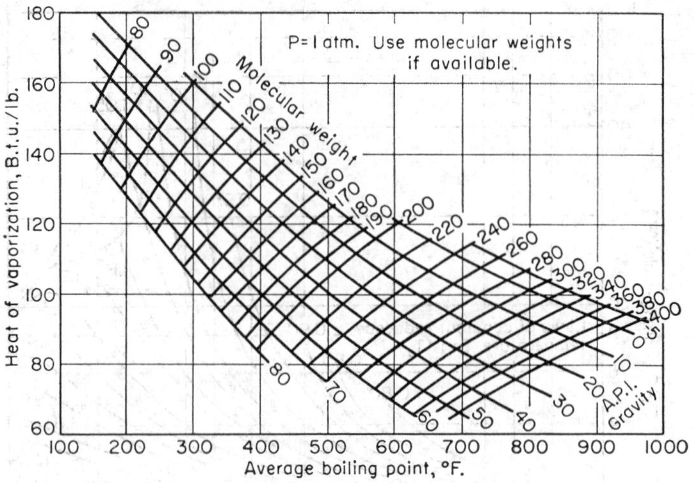

FIG. 3-55. Latent heats of vaporization for hydrocarbons and petroleum fractions.

to the units of the component latent heats. These equations neglect liquid- and vapor-phase heats of solution, sensible-heat effects, and enthalpy changes due to isothermal vapor-volume changes. Nevertheless, for mixtures of organic compounds the equations are normally adequate; but if the solute is an inorganic salt or a very soluble gas, the simplified equations cannot be used. A more complete general discussion of mixture L_v may be found in Dodge's text.[48] The latent heats of hydrocarbons and of petroleum fractions at 1 atm. may be read from Fig. 3-55, taken from Hougen and Watson.[49]

Latent heats of fusion cannot be estimated accurately. Average values of the molar entropy of fusion L_f/T_f are $\sim$2.2 for metallic elements, 5 to 7 for inorganic compounds, and 9 to 14 for organic compounds [when expressed as cal./(g.-atom)(°K.) or cal./(g.-mole) (°K.)], but the ranges are large and many exceptions are known to exist. For **inorganic compounds,** L_f may be approximated (within 10 per cent in some cases) with the correlation of Turkdogan and Pearson[50]:

$$L_f = (L_f/T_f)'T_f n \tag{3-47}$$

where L_f is in cal./g.-mole, T_f is in °K., and n is the number of atoms in the structural formula. The quantity $(L_f/T_f)'$ may be tabulated as follows, where $\Delta T = (T_f - 298)$:

ΔT, °K.	$(L_f/T_f)'$
0	1.9
300	2.5
700	3.0
≥1200	3.2

For organic compounds, the best average value of L_f/T_f is probably 13.5 cal./(g.-mole)(°K.), but as noted above, there are wide variations.

Latent heats of sublimation may be estimated with reasonable accuracy by summation of a latent heat of fusion and a latent heat of vaporization at the temperature of interest. Since L_f is often less than a fourth of the sum, the estimate may be fair even when the estimated latent heat of fusion is in large error.

PRANDTL NUMBER

The dimensionless Prandtl number is defined as $C_p\mu/k$. Low-pressure Prandtl numbers of gases and vapors have been assigned group-average values by Gambill[51] as follows: monatomic gases—$N_{Pr} = 0.67$ ($\pm$5 per cent maximum); linear non-polar gases—$N_{Pr} = 0.73$ ($\pm$15 per cent maximum); nonlinear non-polar gases—$N_{Pr} = 0.79$ ($\pm$15 per cent maximum); highly polar gases—$N_{Pr} = 0.86$ ($\pm$8 per cent maximum). For steam and ammonia, $N_{Pr} = 1.0$ ($\pm$10 per cent maximum). The classification names refer to the molecular structures; *i.e.*, by "linear" is meant those gases whose structural formulas can be written with all atoms on a single straight line. Values of N_{Pr} for gases at high pressures and for gas mixtures are best estimated by combination of separate estimates of C_p, μ, and k. Liquid-phase Prandtl numbers cannot be estimated accurately in the absence of data, but if an experimental value of μ is known, it may be combined with estimated values for C_p and k.

REFRACTIVE INDEX

For hydrocarbons only, Kurtz and coworkers[52] have shown that the simple empirical approximation

$$\Delta n = 0.6\Delta\rho_l \tag{3-48}$$

agrees with considerable data within an average deviation of about 2 per cent, where Δn and $\Delta\rho_l$ are corresponding changes in refractive index and liquid density. If one value of n and the liquid-density temperature dependence are known, values of n at other temperatures may be estimated. For most types of liquids, it has been shown[52] that the empirical Eykman equation

$$\rho_l = \frac{n^2 - 1}{C(n + 0.4)} \tag{3-49}$$

where C is a constant, is quite accurate over extended temperature ranges.

For organic liquids generally, refractive indices may be **roughly** estimated with the Lorentz-Lorenz expression which, solved for n, may be written as

$$n = \left(\frac{2[R_D] + V}{V - [R_D]}\right)^{1/2} \tag{3-50}$$

where molar refraction $[R_D]$ is evaluated by summation of the contributions of Table 3-285, and molar volume V is obtained from $V = M/\rho_l$; or, at t_b only, from Table 3-290.

SURFACE TENSION

If experimental values of refractive index are available, surface tensions may be estimated with an average error of 2 to 3 per cent with the relation[53,54]

$$\sigma = \left(\frac{[P]}{[R_D]}\frac{n^2 - 1}{n^2 + 2}\right)^4 \tag{3-51}$$

which gives σ in dynes/cm. and is limited to low-vapor-density conditions. In Eq. (3-51), evaluate $[R_D]$ from Table 3-285 and $[P]$ from Table 3-294, which lists Sugden's original parachor contribution values.[55]

Table 3-294. Contribution Values for Sugden's Parachor*

C	4.8
H (to O)	11.3
H (to C)	17.1
O (hydroxyl, ether)	20.0
O (carboxyl)	43.2†
O_2 (in esters, acids)	60.0†
F	25.7
Cl	54.3
Br	68.0
I	91.0
N (all amines)	12.5
N (nitrile)	29.1‡
S	48.2
P	37.7
3-membered ring	16.7
4-membered ring	11.6
5-membered ring	8.5
6-membered ring	6.1
Double bond	23.2
Triple bond	46.6

* For use in Eq. (3-51) only.
† Including double-bond allowance.
‡ Including triple-bond allowance.

In the absence of experimental refractive-index values, σ may be estimated from the definitive equation for parachor, as follows:

$$\sigma = \left(\frac{[P](\rho_l - \rho_v)}{M}\right)^4 \tag{3-52}$$

where the units of σ are dynes/cm. and of ρ, g./cc., and where the vapor density ρ_v should be evaluated under saturation conditions—*i.e.*, at the given temperature and the corresponding vapor pressure. At $t \lesssim t_b$, ρ_v is relatively small and may be neglected. Equation (3-52) will give values of σ to within about 30°C. of the critical temperature with an average error of 4 to 5 per cent. The convenient nomograph of Johnson *et al.*,[56] which represents Eq. (3-52), is shown as Fig. 3-56. Surface tensions at t_b only may be estimated within ~5 per cent with Walden's rule[57]

$$\sigma_b = \frac{L_{vb}\rho_{lb}}{364} \tag{3-53}$$

where L_{vb} is in cal./g.-mole, ρ_{lb} is in g./cc., and σ_b is in dynes/cm.

To **extrapolate** known or calculated values of σ to other temperatures within a moderate temperature range, use may be made of[58]

$$\frac{\sigma_2}{\sigma_1} = \left(\frac{T_c - T_2}{T_c - T_1}\right)^{1.2} \tag{3-54}$$

which is accurate within a few per cent in regions well removed from the critical point. Kharbanda's nomograph[59] representing Eq. (3-54) is shown as Fig. 3-57. Alternatively, Othmer's approach[60] may be utilized, whereby a log-log plot of σ vs. $(T_c - T)$ is made. Barring chemical changes, such a procedure produces a straight line over the complete liquid range of the compound.

For organic-organic liquid **mixtures,** Eqs. (3-51) and (3-52) may be used with good accuracy (~4 per cent average error) if mixture values of $[P]$, $[R_D]$, and n are evaluated[54,61] as follows

$$[P]_m = \Sigma[P]_i x_i \tag{3-55}$$
$$[R_D]_m = \Sigma[R_D]_i x_i \tag{3-56}$$
$$n_m = \Sigma n_i x_i \tag{3-57}$$

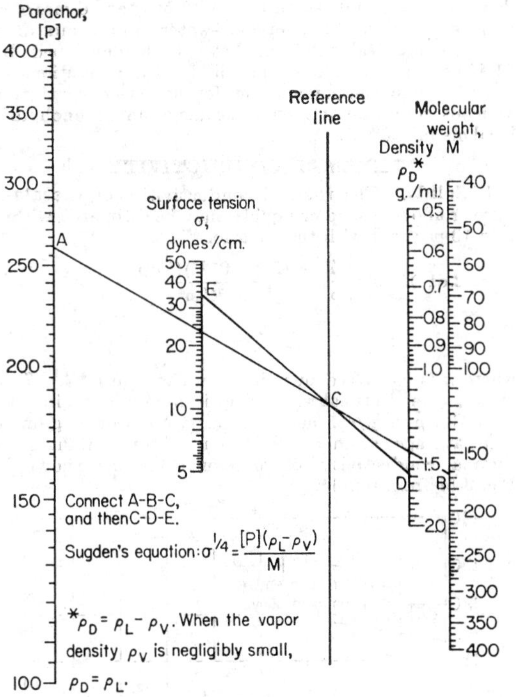

FIG. 3-56. Nomograph for estimating surface tension [Eq. (3-52)].

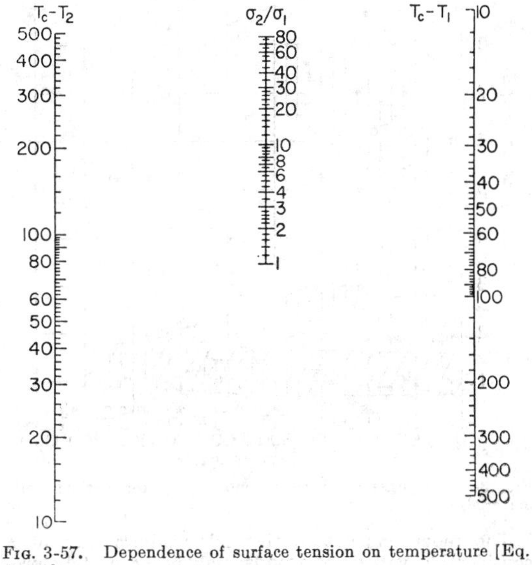

FIG. 3-57. Dependence of surface tension on temperature [Eq. (3-54)].

Such an approach is valid only under conditions of negligible vapor density; and at high pressures, the accurate relation of Katz and coworkers[62] is recommended:

$$(\sigma_m)^{1/4} = \sum [P]_i \left(\frac{\rho_l x_i}{M_l} - \frac{\rho_v y_i}{M_v}\right) \tag{3-58}$$

where ρ_l, ρ_v, M_l, and M_v are values for the mixture in the denoted phase and where the units of σ are dynes/cm. and of ρ, g./cc. For organic-water liquid mixtures, limited empirical relations have been developed by Meissner and Michaels[54] for dilute water solutions of some organic compounds and for higher-concentration aqueous solutions of monobasic acids and monohydric alcohols (at 20°C.).

THERMAL CONDUCTIVITY

1. **Solids.** The thermal conductivities of **metals**—pure or alloyed, solid or liquid—may be estimated within 5 to 10 per cent with the equation[63]

$$k = (2.61 \times 10^{-8}) \frac{T}{\rho_e} - \frac{(2 \times 10^{-17})(T/\rho_e)^2}{C_p\rho} + \frac{97C_p\rho^2}{MT} \quad (3\text{-}59)$$

where k is expressed in units of watts/(cm.)(°C.), T in °K., ρ_e (the electrical resistivity) in ohm-cm., C_p in cal./(g.)(°C.), ρ in g./cc., and M in g./g.-atom or g./g.-mole (use average atomic weight for alloys). Ranges of thermal conductivity for common solids are shown in Fig. 3-58 from ref. 64.

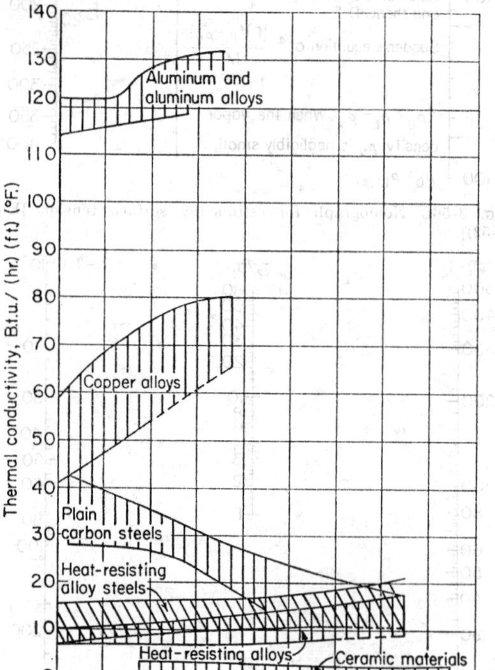

FIG. 3-58. Ranges of thermal conductivity for various solid materials.

The room-temperature thermal conductivities of a considerable variety of **woods** may be accurately predicted from[65]

$$k = \rho(0.1159 + 0.00233M) + 0.01375 \quad (3\text{-}60)$$

for a moisture content less than 40 weight per cent, where k is in units of B.t.u./(hr.)(ft.)(°F.), ρ is in g./cc. (based on weight when oven-dry and volume when green), and M is the average moisture content in weight per cent. For $M > 40$ weight per cent, use

$$k = \rho(0.1159 + 0.00316M) + 0.01375 \quad (3\text{-}61)$$

Values of k calculated from Eqs. (3-60) and (3-61) are for heat flow normal to the grain. The conductivities of solids with a grain structure, such as wood and quartz, are often two to four times larger parallel to the grain than in the transverse direction.

The thermal conductivities of **porous media** (solid + liquid or gas) are best correlated with Russell's equation[66]

$$\frac{k_{\text{comp}}}{k_{\text{cont}}} = \frac{\nu p^{2/3} + 1 - p^{2/3}}{\nu(p^{2/3} - p) + 1 - p^{2/3} + p} \quad (3\text{-}62)$$

where the subscripts "comp" and "cont" denote values for the composite mixture and for the continuous phase, respectively, and where p is the porosity (volume fraction of voids or obstacles), given, for a solid-gas mixture, by

$$p = \frac{\rho_{\text{solid}} - \rho_{\text{comp}}}{\rho_{\text{solid}} - \rho_{\text{gas}}} \quad (3\text{-}63)$$

The term ν is the ratio of the thermal conductivity of the porosities (or obstacles) to that of the continuous phase: $\nu = k_{\text{por}}/k_{\text{cont}}$. Equation (3-62) is applicable for $0 < p < 1$ when the particle size is reasonably uniform. For **cellular materials** (gas-solid with solid as the continuous phase, or solid-solid), average and maximum prediction errors appear to be ~6 and 15 per cent. If ν is large, Eq. (3-62) reduces to

$$\frac{k_{\text{comp}}}{k_{\text{cont}}} = \frac{1}{1 - p^{1/3}} \quad (3\text{-}64)$$

When a gas or liquid is the continuous phase of a solid-fluid mixture, as with **powders,** Eq. (3-62) does not give good agreement with experimental data, but Laubitz[67] has shown that doubling the right side of the equation restores its accuracy in this case. Russell's equation is predicated on conduction heat transfer alone, excluding mechanisms of convection (small for gas cavity diameters less than ~1 cm.), radiation (for which a correction expression is available,[67] but which is small at low temperature or if the average particle size is small), and vapor diffusion. The diffusion mechanism can be an important contribution in snow, *e.g.*, where it causes a transfer of latent heat of sublimation, a correction equation for which is given in ref. 68.

2. **Liquids.** The thermal conductivities of **pure liquids** may be estimated with Vargaftik's modification[69] of Palmer's expression,[70] as follows:

$$k = \frac{1.034C_p\rho^{4/3}}{\alpha M^{1/3}} \quad (3\text{-}65)$$

where k is in B.t.u./(hr.)(ft.)(°F.), C_p is in B.t.u./(lb.)(°F.), ρ is in g./cc., and α is an "abnormality factor" which may be taken as

$$\alpha = \frac{L_{vb}/T_b}{21} \quad (3\text{-}66)$$

at 30°C. for most liquids, or at $T_c/2$ for low boilers such as methane, N_2, and ethylene. In Eq. (3-66), the units of L_{vb}/T_b are cal./(g.-mole)(°K.). Calculated values of $\alpha < 1$ should be taken as unity, and at temperatures other than 30°C. (or $T_c/2$), α may be assumed to vary linearly between the value given by Eq. (3-66) at 30°C. and 1.0 at T_c. For 28 liquids tested, Eq. (3-65) gave average and maximum deviations of 8.7 and 31.6 per cent when this procedure was followed.

If one experimental value of k is available, the **temperature dependence** may be estimated within ~5 per cent with the relation

$$k = \frac{B}{\alpha} \rho^{4/3} \quad (3\text{-}67)$$

where B, a constant, is determined from the known k value. For most liquids, a curve of k vs. $\theta = (T - T_f)/(T_c - T_f)$ is linear from T_f to $\theta \approx 0.7$. Estimates of k may be made somewhat more quickly, but less accurately (13 and 50 per cent average and maximum errors), with Weber's original equation[71]

$$k = \frac{0.869 C_p \rho^{4/3}}{M^{1/3}} \tag{3-68}$$

where all units are the same as in Eq. (3-65).

The **effect of pressure** on the thermal conductivity of liquids is small* and may be neglected for pressures less than ~500 lb./sq. in. abs. At higher pressures, accurate estimates of the pressure effect may be made with Lenoir's generalized correlation,[72] according to which

$$\left(\frac{k_2}{k_1}\right)_T = \frac{\epsilon_2}{\epsilon_1} \tag{3-69}$$

where ϵ is a "conductivity factor" which is tabulated in Table 3-295 vs. P_r and T_r, and where subscripts 1 and 2 denote the lower and higher pressure levels (at the same temperature).

Table 3-295. Liquid-conductivity Factors vs. P_r and T_r

Reduced pressure	Reduced temperatures							
	0.4	0.5	0.6	0.7	0.8	0.9	0.96	1.0
0	14.25	13.39	12.42	11.40	10.14	8.10	6.98	
1	14.39	13.54	12.61	11.62	10.47	9.10	7.96	7.10
2	14.52	13.68	12.78	11.82	10.76	9.61	8.74	8.09
3	14.64	13.81	12.93	12.01	11.00	9.96	9.15	8.61
4	14.75	13.93	13.06	12.16	11.20	10.21	9.44	8.95
5	14.85	14.04	13.19	12.31	11.38	10.43	9.67	9.18
6	14.95	14.15	13.30	12.45	11.53	10.61	9.85	9.38
7	15.04	14.24	13.41	12.56	11.69	10.76	10.00	9.53
8	15.12	14.32	13.50	12.67	11.81	10.89	10.15	9.67
9	15.20	14.41	13.59	12.77	11.92	11.00	10.28	9.79
10	15.28	14.49	13.67	12.85	12.02	11.09	10.40	9.89
11	15.35	14.56	13.75	12.93	12.10	11.17	11.00	9.99
12	15.42	14.63	13.82	13.00	12.15	11.25	11.10	10.08

The thermal conductivities of **liquid mixtures** may in general be estimated with reasonable accuracy. For **petroleum** fractions and oil mixtures, *e.g.*, Smith's recommendation[73] of a single value of 0.079 B.t.u./(hr.)(ft.)(°F.) at 30°C. holds within ~13 per cent. At other temperatures, Cragoe's equation[74] appears satisfactory:

$$k = \frac{0.0677}{s}[1 - 0.0003(t - 32)] \tag{3-70}$$

where k is in B.t.u./(hr.)(ft.)(°F.), s is specific gravity at 60°F./60°F., and t is in °F. For $0.78 < s < 0.95$ and $32° < t < 392$°F., Eq. (3-70) gave average and maximum errors of 12 and 39 per cent.

For **miscible liquid mixtures,** the Barratt-Nettleton hyperbolic sine function[75]

$$k_m \sinh (100b) = \Sigma k_i \sinh (w_i b) \tag{3-71}$$

is quite accurate (~2 per cent average error), but it requires knowledge of one value of mixture conductivity in order to evaluate the constant b, which is specific to the constituents and only slightly dependent on temperature in the ranges investigated. In Eq. (3-71), w is the component weight percentage (100 × weight fraction). In the absence of even a single experimental value of mixture conductivity, use may be made of the correlation of Filippov and Novoselova[76] for binary non-polar liquid mixtures:

$$k_m = k_1 w_1 + k_2 w_2 - 0.72(k_2 - k_1)(w_1 w_2) \tag{3-72}$$

where the weight fraction w_2 refers to the component having the larger value of k.

Estimates of the thermal conductivities of **liquid-solid suspensions** may be made with the modification of Eq. (3-62) discussed in the text above, but Tareef's equation[77] has been more thoroughly tested[78] and gives excellent quantitative agreement with experimental data. Based on the analogy between a thermal field in a two-phase system and the electrical field in a similar system, Tareef's equation

$$k_m = k_c \frac{2k_c + k_d - 2\phi_d(k_c - k_d)}{2k_c + k_d + \phi_d(k_c - k_d)} \tag{3-73}$$

where subscripts c and d denote the continuous and discontinuous phases, respectively, and where ϕ is phase volume fraction, was found by Wang and Knudsen[79] also to apply with fair accuracy (deviation usually ≤20 per cent) to **liquid-liquid emulsions.**

3. **Gases.** Low-pressure thermal conductivities of **pure gases and vapors** may be most easily estimated by selecting a group-average Prandtl number (see p. 3-222) and calculating k^0 by use of known or calculated values for C_p and μ. Alternatively, one may use Eucken's approximation[80]

$$k^0 = \mu\left(C_v + \frac{9R}{4M}\right) \tag{3-74}$$

which, when combined with $(C_p - C_v) = R$, which is approximately true at low pressure, gives

$$k^0 = \mu\left(C_p + \frac{2.48}{M}\right) \tag{3-75}$$

where k^0 is in units of B.t.u./(hr.)(ft.)(°F.), μ is in lb./(hr.)(ft.), and C_p is in B.t.u./(lb.)(°F.). If μ and C_p are accurately known, Eq. (3-75) may be expected to give average errors of ~5, 8, and 13 per cent for non-polar linear, non-polar non-linear, and polar non-linear molecules, respectively.[33] Maximum errors of 25 to 30 per cent may be encountered.

With somewhat more effort, more accurate estimates of k^0 may be made with Bromley's correlation,[81] which may be summarized as follows:[33]

For monatomic gases:

$$\frac{Mk^0}{\mu C_v} = 2.4 + 0.016M^{1/2} \approx 2.5 \tag{3-76}$$

For non-polar linear molecules:

$$\frac{Mk^0}{\mu} = 1.32C_v + 3.40 - \frac{0.70}{T_r} \tag{3-77}$$

For non-polar or polar non-linear molecules:

$$\frac{Mk^0}{\mu} = 1.30C_v + 3.60 - 0.3C_{ir} - \frac{0.69}{T_r} - 3\alpha \tag{3-78}$$

In Eqs. (3-76) to (3-78), k^0 is expressed in units of cal./(sec.)(cm.)(°C.), μ in poise, and C_v, C_{ir}, and α in cal./(g.-mole)(°C.). The internal-rotational heat-capacity contribution C_{ir} may be approximated by summation of the group values[43,81] given in Table 3-296 as a function of temperature. The coefficient α may be estimated

* For many liquids, a pressure of ~12,000 atm. is required to double k_1.

with the equation

$$\alpha = \frac{3.0\rho_{lb}}{M}\left(\frac{L_{vb}}{T_b} - 8.75 - R\ln T_b\right) \tag{3-79}$$

where ρ_{lb} is in g./cc., L_{vb} in cal./g.-mole, T_b in °K., and where $R = 1.987$ cal./(g.-mole)(°K.). Equation (3-79) should not be used for the hydrogen halides. If μ and C_v are accurately known, this method will give errors of ~4, 3½, and 7½ per cent for non-polar linear, non-polar non-linear, and polar non-linear molecules, respectively.[33] Maximum errors may be as large as 20 per cent but seldom exceed 10 per cent.

The thermal conductivities of **gas mixtures** may be simply and accurately calculated from component conductivity values with the equation[82]

$$k_m = \frac{\Sigma y_i k_i (M_i)^{1/3}}{\Sigma y_i (M_i)^{1/3}} \tag{3-80}$$

which gave average and maximum errors of 2.7 and 9.5 per cent for 19 low-pressure binary mixtures at 273° < T < 353°K. The well-known Lindsay-Bromley correlation,[83] though much more involved, is only slightly more accurate.

The **effect of pressure** on the thermal conductivities of gases is often significant for pressures larger than a few atmospheres. Though the pressure effect cannot be calculated with a high degree of accuracy, it has been represented within about 20 per cent by the generalized chart of Lenoir, Junk, and Comings,[84] shown as Fig. 3-59. The thermal-conductivity ratio k/k^0 is the ratio of k

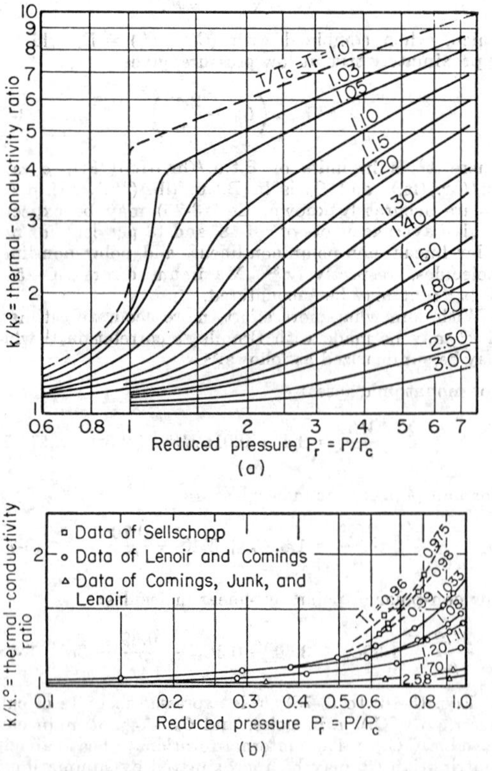

FIG. 3-59. Generalized correlation of the effect of pressure on gas-phase thermal conductivity. (a) High-pressure range; (b) low-pressure range.

Table 3-296. Internal-rotational Heat-capacity Contributions

C_{ir} in cal./(g.-mole)(°K.)

T, °K.	CH₃—C(=O)—R	CH₃—OH	RCH₂—O—CH₂R	—CH₂—CH₂—	CH₃—CH₂—	R—C(H)—H	R—C(—)—	R—CH=*	R—CH=†	=CH—CH=	≡C—C≡	R—C=
200	1.79	1.4	2.24	2.64	1.74	1.76	1.60	2.02	1.48	2.09	0.81	1.91
298	1.52	1.35	2.33	3.18	2.10	2.12	1.99	2.02	1.26	3.02	0.92	2.15
400	1.34	1.25	2.26	2.74	2.17	2.19	2.18	1.82	1.16	3.25	0.76	2.10
500	1.24	1.20	2.19	2.39	2.09	2.12	2.23	1.65	1.11	2.96	0.60	1.95
600	1.18	1.18	1.91	2.12	1.96	2.00	2.18	1.50	1.07	2.67	0.48	1.79
700	1.10	1.16	1.71	1.90	1.82	1.85	2.08	1.40	1.05	2.44	0.39	1.65
800	1.09	1.15	1.66	1.73	1.69	1.71	1.96	1.32	1.04	2.24	0.35	1.54
900	1.08	1.14	1.55	1.60	1.59	1.62	1.85	1.26	1.03	2.09	0.32	1.46
1000	1.06	1.13	1.47	1.51	1.51	1.55	1.76	1.21	1.02	1.96	0.31	1.38

* Based on propylene.
† Based on cis-2-butene.

at T and P to the conductivity k^0 of the same substance at the same temperature but at low pressure. A high-pressure k value is thus calculated from the relation $k = k^0(k/k^0)$, where the low-pressure k^0 value is experimental or calculated. Deviations associated with Fig. 3-59 are largest in the region of the critical point, and errors may be large for the more complicated and/or polar molecules. The k_m of **high-pressure gas mixtures** is probably best predicted by first estimating $k_m{}^0$ at low pressure with Eq. (3-80) and then employing Fig. 3-59 with pseudocritical temperatures and pressures from Eqs. (3-9) and (3-15).

A separate corresponding-states generalized correlation for the commonly encountered **diatomic gases** has been developed by Schaefer and Thodos[19] and is shown as Fig. 3-60. Note that k/k_c is used as ordinate, rather than k/k^0 as in Fig. 3-59. Figure 3-60 exhibited an average error of 1.4 per cent for the relatively extensive high-pressure N_2 data, and errors of 1.0 to 3.2 per cent for the other diatomics. For the 11 gases tabulated below the chart, k may be calculated directly at any T and P within its range. For other gases, k_c may be obtained if one experimental value of k is known. In the absence of any data, k_c may be approximated with Eq. (3-22).

VAPOR PRESSURE

If only the normal boiling point and the critical temperature and pressure are known, a linear two-point plot of ln P_v vs. $1/T_r$ is often surprisingly accurate. Alternatively, one may plot P_v of the compound vs. P_v of a reference substance (for which vapor-pressure data are known) at the same T_r as a straight line on log-log paper with good accuracy.[85]

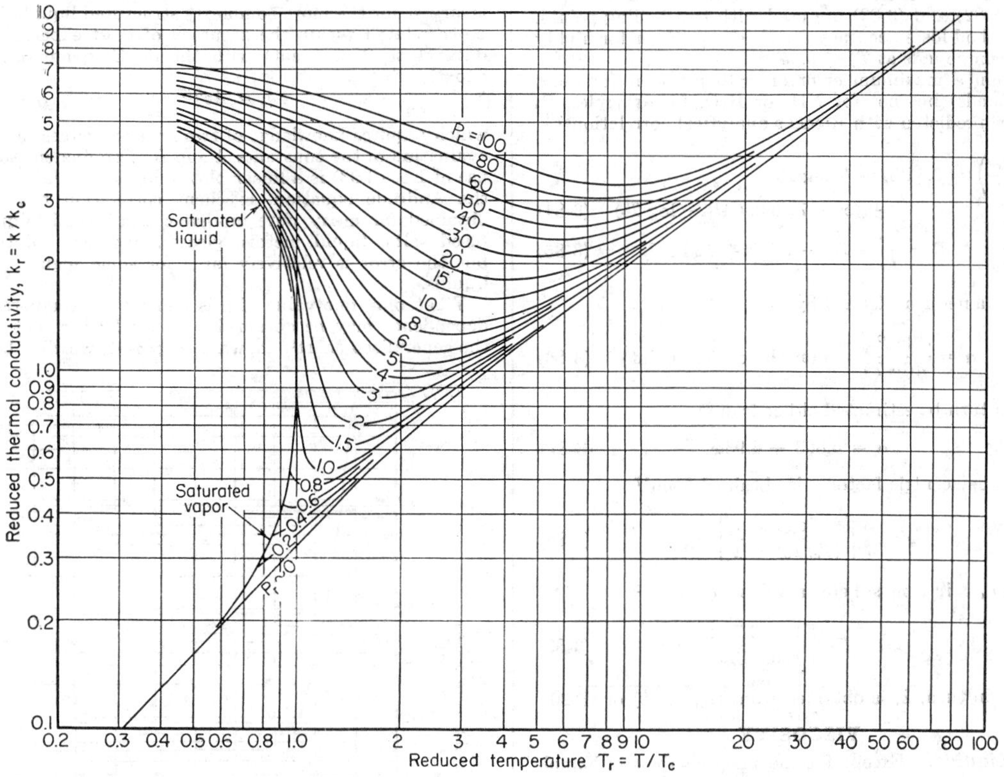

FIG. 3-60. Reduced thermal conductivity correlation for the diatomic gases.

	T_c,°K.	P_c,atm.	k_c, cal./(sec.)(cm.)(°K.)
Bromine, Br_2	584	102	6.79×10^{-5}
Carbon monoxide, CO	133	34.5	8.61
Chlorine, Cl_2	417	76.1	9.60
Fluorine, F_2	144	55.0	9.54
Hydrogen bromide, HBr	363.2	84	8.21
Hydrogen chloride, HCl	324.6	81.5	11.21
Hydrogen fluoride, HF	503.4	94.5	26.0
Iodine, I_2	785	116	6.33
Nitric oxide, NO	180	64	11.82
Nitrogen, N_2	126.2	33.5	8.55
Oxygen, O_2	154.8	50.1	10.40

The atmospheric isobar ($P \sim 0$) applies to pressures as low as 5 cm. of mercury.

The best of the simpler (three constant) vapor-pressure correlation equations is probably Antoine's[86]

$$\log P_v = A - \frac{B}{T + C} \qquad (3\text{-}81)$$

where A, B, and C are constants for a particular substance. If only two boiling points are known, let $C = 230$ and evaluate A and B from

$$A = \log P_v + \frac{B}{T + 230} \qquad (3\text{-}82)$$

$$\text{and} \quad B = \frac{[\log (P_{v1}/P_{v2})](T_1 + 230)(T_2 + 230)}{T_1 - T_2} \qquad (3\text{-}83)$$

wherein units of mm. Hg and °K. are most often used. One Antoine equation will accurately fit vapor-pressure data from T_f to $T_r = 0.85$ to 0.95. Accuracy is best when all three constants are evaluated from data; when Eqs. (3-82) and (3-83) are used with two boiling points, the method loses accuracy for $T_b < 250$°K. or for highly polar compounds at $T_r < 0.65$.[33]

Within a maximum error of ±10 per cent for most compounds (but not for NH_3 or H_2O, for example), P_v may be predicted with Riedel's analytical correlation[87]

$$\log\left(\frac{P_c}{P_v}\right) = 0.118B - 7 \log T_r + (\alpha - 7)(0.0364B - \log T_r) \qquad (3\text{-}84)$$

$$\text{where} \quad B = \frac{36}{T_r} - 35 - (T_r)^6 + 42 \ln T_r \qquad (3\text{-}85)$$

The parameter α, defined by

$$\alpha = \frac{d(\ln P_v)}{d(\ln T)} \quad \text{(at the critical point)} \qquad (3\text{-}86)$$

may in turn be estimated either from[88]

$$\alpha = 5.808 + 4.93\omega \qquad (3\text{-}87)$$

where the acentric factor ω is obtained from[17]

$$\omega = \frac{3}{7}\left[\frac{\log P_c}{(T_c/T_b) - 1}\right] - 1 \qquad (3\text{-}88)$$

where P_c is in atmospheres absolute, or from[89]

$$\alpha = 7 + \frac{1 - 3.72Z_c}{0.26Z_c} \qquad (3\text{-}89)$$

where, in turn, Z_c is obtained from Eq. (3-19) or (3-20).

VISCOSITY

1. **Liquids.** Except for the first members of homologous series, the viscosity of most **pure liquids** at their normal boiling points is ~0.29 centipoise (±25 to 30 per cent average).[90] Arrhenius's relation[91] permits a somewhat more accurate evaluation:

$$\mu_b = 0.275(\rho_{lb})^{1/2} \qquad (3\text{-}90)$$

where the units of μ and of ρ are cp. and g./cc. Equation (3-90) gives average and maximum deviations of ~21 and 52 per cent.

At temperatures other than t_b, liquid viscosity may best be estimated by Thomas's equation[92]

$$\mu = 0.1167\rho_l^{1/2}10^{\gamma} \qquad (3\text{-}91)$$

$$\text{where} \quad \gamma = \frac{B(1 - T_r)}{T_r} \qquad (3\text{-}92)$$

and where μ is in cp., ρ_l is in g./cc., and B is a viscosity constant to be calculated by summation of the atomic and group contributions of Table 3-297. Equation (3-91) is most valid when $t \leq t_b$ and the calculated viscosity is less than about 15 cp. Average and maximum errors of ~20 and 90 per cent may be expected.

Table 3-297. Structural Contributions for Calculating B in Eq. (3-92)

Carbon	−0.462
Hydrogen	+0.249
Oxygen	+0.054
Chlorine	+0.340
Bromine	+0.326
Iodine	+0.335
Sulfur	+0.043
C_6H_5	+0.385
Double bond	+0.478
CO (ketones, esters)	+0.105
CN (cyanides)	+0.381

The **effect of temperature** on liquid viscosity, which is largest for the more complexly structured liquids, may be correlated within the accuracy of most experimental data (1 to 2 per cent) with the de Guzman-Andrade equation[93]

$$\mu = Ae^{B/T} \qquad (3\text{-}93)$$

which requires knowledge of two or more values of μ for evaluation of the constants A and B. Equivalent to the use of Eq. (3-93) is a linear plot of log μ vs. $1/T$. With the Andrade equation, excellent correlation has been obtained for many pure inorganic and organic liquids, fused salts, liquid metals, glasses, and salt solutions, but the error is relatively large for some highly polar liquids.

When only one value of μ is known, the temperature dependence may be obtained within ~20 per cent with the generalized chart[94] shown as Fig. 3-61, which is based

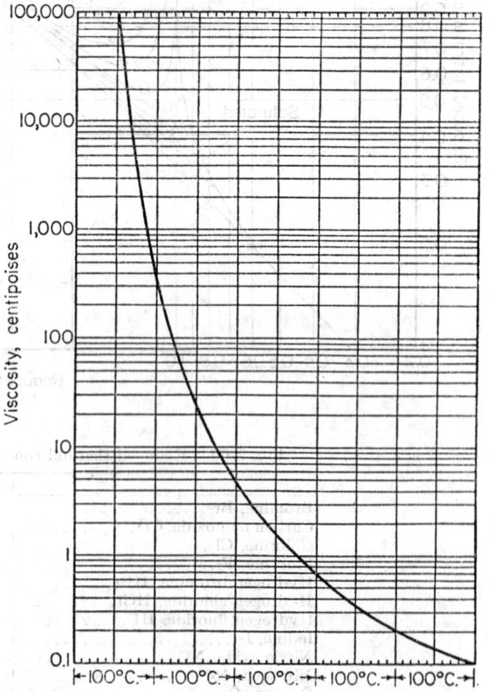

Fig. 3-61. Approximate temperature variation of liquid viscosity.

mainly on data for organic liquids and does not apply to mercury, suspensions, or emulsions. To use the chart, merely locate the known value of μ on the viscosity scale and then follow the curve the necessary amount—as indicated on the relative abscissa scale—to reach the temperature at which μ is desired.

Though liquid viscosity exhibits a greater **pressure variation** than almost any pure-liquid property, the effect is rarely significant for pressures less than about 40 atm. As with temperature sensitivity, the pressure dependence is largest for those liquids of complex molecular structure—for Hg, for example, the ratio of μ at pressure to μ at 1 atm., μ_P/μ_1, is only 1.32 at P = 11,700 atm., whereas for CH_3OH it is 10, and for eugenol (4-allyl-2-methoxy phenol), 10^7. Though Andrade's pressure-effect correlation[95] allows approximate estimates to be made, considerable auxiliary data are required. Bondi has observed[96] that, on the average, a pressure increase of 480 lb./sq. in. will increase the μ of liquid **oils** to the same extent as a temperature decrease of 1°C.

It is not possible, in the general case, to relate the viscosities of **miscible liquid mixtures** to the pure-component viscosities alone; but, on an empirical basis, the Kendall-Monroe equation[97] appears to be the most successful of this type:

$$\mu_m^{1/3} = x_1\mu_1^{1/3} + x_2\mu_2^{1/3} \qquad (3\text{-}94)$$

Equation (3-94) applies to non-electrolytic, non-associated similar liquid pairs whose component molecular weight and viscosity differences are small [say $(\mu_2 - \mu_1) < 15$ cp.]. Equation (3-94) has been shown to be accurate to within 2 to 3 per cent for oil blends. If at least one liquid-mixture viscosity is known, the Tamura-Kurata relation[98]

$$\mu_m = x_1\mu_1\phi_1 + x_2\mu_2\phi_2 + 2\mu_{12}(x_1x_2\phi_1\phi_2)^{1/2} \qquad (3\text{-}95)$$

relates mixture viscosity with composition within 5 to 10 per cent (maximum) even when a polar component is present. The interaction viscosity μ_{12} of Eq. (3-95) may be regarded as an adjustable constant to be determined from known μ_m data. μ_{12} is constant only at a given temperature level and may be considered to vary with temperature according to Eq. (3-93).

The viscosities of **immiscible liquid mixtures** may be calculated with Taylor's semitheoretical equation[99]

$$\frac{\mu_m}{\mu_c} = 1 + 2.5\phi_d \frac{u_d + 0.4\mu_c}{u_d + \mu_c} \qquad (3\text{-}96)$$

where subscripts c and d denote the continuous and dispersed phases, respectively. Equation (3-96) is based on the existence of small spherical droplets and probably does not apply for ϕ_d greater than about 0.03. For larger values of ϕ_d, Olney and Carlson[100] have suggested use of Arrhenius's equation[101] for certain applications:

$$\mu_m = (\mu_1)^{x_1}(\mu_2)^{x_2} \qquad (3\text{-}97)$$

The viscosities of **liquid-solid suspensions** may be estimated roughly for ϕ_s (volume fraction solids) less than 0.5 with Kunitz's relation[102,103]

$$\frac{\mu_m}{\mu_l} = \frac{1 + 0.5\phi_s}{(1 - \phi_s)^4} \qquad (3\text{-}98)$$

Equation (3-98) is most accurate for $\phi_s \leq 0.1$. Estimates are roughly correct only when the solids are free-flowing when wet (*e.g.*, metal powders and glass beads). For solids such as clay, chalk, starch, and graphite, which are usually not free-flowing, the viscosities are nearly always larger than those calculated. The best method for this case is probably the proposal of Ting and Luebbers,[104] which also requires density data and may be summarized as follows:

For suspensions of constant-diameter spherical particles:

$$\frac{\mu_m}{\mu_l} = \frac{1}{1 - \dfrac{\phi_s}{0.460 - 0.00158(\mu_l/R)^{0.469}}} \qquad (3\text{-}99)$$

where $R = \rho_l/\rho_s$ (or the reverse for $R < 1$), and μ's are in cp. This equation was very satisfactory up to $\phi_s = 0.3$.

For monodisperse suspensions of isodimensional (equiaxed) cubical particles (*e.g.*, salt), or rounded particles (*e.g.*, blasting sand):

$$\frac{\mu_m}{\mu_l} = \frac{0.403}{0.403 - \phi_s} \qquad (3\text{-}100)$$

For suspensions of spheres of unequal diameters:

$$\frac{\mu_l\phi_s}{\mu_m - \mu_l} = 0.460 - 0.00158\left(\frac{\mu_l}{R}\right)^{0.469} - 0.79\phi_s \qquad (3\text{-}101)$$

The free-flowing criterion applies to this method as wel as to the one discussed earlier.

2. **Gases.** The Bromley and Wilke modification[105] of the theoretical Hirschfelder method[106] for computing the viscosities of low-pressure **pure gases and vapors** gives excellent results (3 and 15 per cent average and maximum errors) if the critical volume is known or can be accurately calculated. In the equation

$$\mu^\circ = \frac{33.3(MT_c)^{1/2}}{V_c^{2/3}}[f(1.33T_r)] \qquad (3\text{-}102)$$

μ^0 is expressed in micropoise, T_c in °K., and V_c in cc./g.-mole. The variation of the function $[f(1.33T_r)]$ is shown in Table 3-298 and has been represented analytically with accuracy by Scheibel[107] with the equation

Table 3-298. Gas-viscosity Temperature Function for Eqs. (3-102) and (3-107)

$(1.33\ T_r)$	$f(1.33\ T_r)$	$(1.33\ T_r)$	$f(1.33\ T_r)$	$(1.33\ T_r)$	$f(1.33\ T_r)$
0.30	0.1969	1.65	1.0174	4.0	2.0719
.35	.2252	1.70	1.0453	4.1	2.1090
.40	.2540	1.75	1.0729	4.2	2.1457
.45	.2834	1.80	1.0999	4.3	2.1820
.50	.3134	1.85	1.1264	4.4	2.2180
.55	.3440	1.90	1.1529	4.5	2.2536
.60	.3751	1.95	1.1790	4.6	2.2888
.65	.4066	2.00	1.2048	4.7	2.3237
.70	.4384	2.1	1.2558	4.8	2.3583
.75	.4704	2.2	1.3057	4.9	2.3926
.80	.5025	2.3	1.3547	5.0	2.4264
.85	.5346	2.4	1.4028	6.0	2.751
.90	.5666	2.5	1.4501	7.0	3.053
.95	.5985	2.6	1.4962	8.0	3.337
1.00	.6302	2.7	1.5417	9.0	3.607
1.05	.6616	2.8	1.5861	10	3.866
1.10	.6928	2.9	1.6298	20	6.063
1.15	.7237	3.0	1.6728	30	7.880
1.20	.7544	3.1	1.7154	40	9.488
1.25	.7849	3.2	1.7573	50	10.958
1.30	.8151	3.3	1.7983	60	12.324
1.35	.8449	3.4	1.8388	70	13.615
1.40	.8744	3.5	1.8789	80	14.839
1.45	.9036	3.6	1.9186	90	16.010
1.50	.9325	3.7	1.9576	100	17.137
1.55	.9611	3.8	1.9962	200	26.80
1.60	.9894	3.9	2.0343	400	41.90

$$f(1.33T_r) = 1.058T_r^{0.645} - \frac{0.261}{(1.9T_r)^{0.9\log(1.9T_r)}} \qquad (3\text{-}103)$$

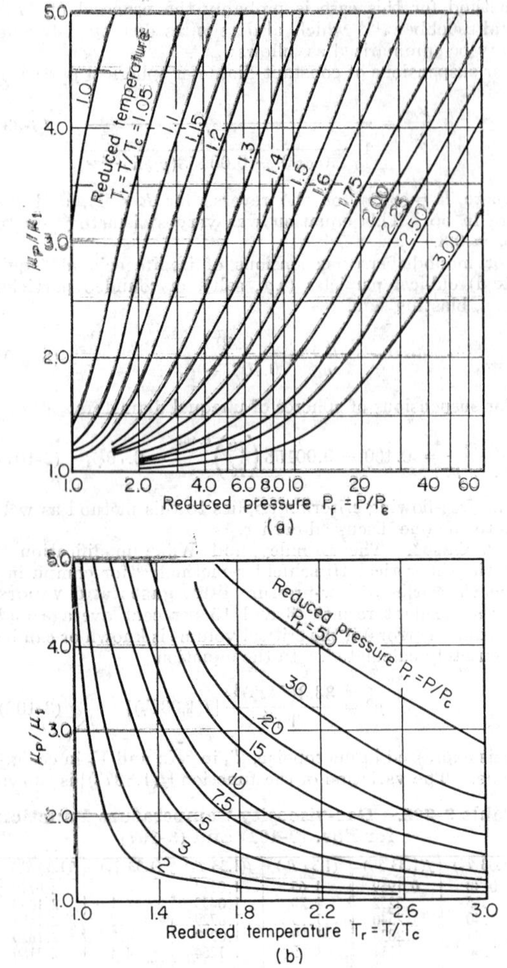

FIG. 3-62. (a) Effect of pressure on gas viscosity; (b) plotted for easier interpolation.

which is applicable for $T_r > 0.3$. If V_c is unknown, slightly less accurate estimates of μ^0 may be made with Arnold's correlation[108,109]

$$\mu^0 = \frac{27.0 M^{1/2} T^{3/2}}{V_b^{2/3}(T + 1.47 T_b)} \tag{3-104}$$

where μ^0 is in micropoise, T and T_b are in °K., and V_b is in cc./g.-mole. The molar volume V_b may be calculated from Eq. (3-18) or evaluated by summation of the additive contributions of Table 3-290. Equation (3-104) may be expected to give average and maximum deviations of 5 to 6 and 15 per cent, respectively.

The **effect of temperature** on gas viscosity may be taken from Eq. (3-104) as

$$\mu^0 \propto \frac{T^{3/2}}{T + 1.47 T_b} \tag{3-105}$$

which may be written as

$$\frac{\mu_2^0}{\mu_1^0} = \left(\frac{T_2}{T_1}\right)^{3/2} \frac{(T_1 + 1.47 T_b)}{(T_2 + 1.47 T_b)} \tag{3-106}$$

Similarly, Eq. (3-102) may be written to show temperature dependence as follows:

$$\frac{\mu_2^0}{\mu_1^0} = \frac{f(1.33 T_{r2})}{f(1.33 T_{r1})} \tag{3-107}$$

Equation (3-107) is probably preferable for extrapolations over very broad temperature ranges.

The **effect of pressure** on gas viscosity is well represented by the generalized charts of Carr and coworkers,[110] shown as Fig. 3-62a and b. These charts represent the pressure dependence of gas viscosity within average and maximum deviations of ~2 and 10 per cent in most cases. In the region of the critical point, errors may be serious. Presentation of Fig. 3-62 as two plots, with parametric curves and abscissa scales reversed in one, allows more accurate interpolation. If, for example, $T_r = 1.67$ and $P_r = 23$, one may read (μ_P/μ_1) values from Fig. 3-62a at $P_r = 23$ and at $T_r = 1.60$ and 1.75, straddling the desired but unplotted isotherm. One may then plot these points (of μ_P/μ_1 vs. T_r) on Fig. 3-62b to construct the desired isobar for $P_r = 23$, from which μ_P/μ_1 at $T_r = 1.67$ may be read. Figure 3-63 is an

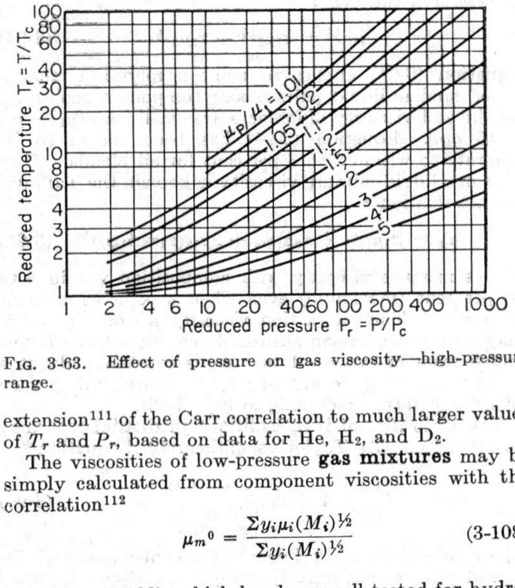

FIG. 3-63. Effect of pressure on gas viscosity—high-pressure range.

extension[111] of the Carr correlation to much larger values of T_r and P_r, based on data for He, H_2, and D_2.

The viscosities of low-pressure **gas mixtures** may be simply calculated from component viscosities with the correlation[112]

$$\mu_m^0 = \frac{\Sigma y_i \mu_i (M_i)^{1/2}}{\Sigma y_i (M_i)^{1/2}} \tag{3-108}$$

Equation (3-108), which has been well tested for hydrocarbon mixtures and for industrial multicomponent mixtures, uniformly represents the data within ~2 per cent. A known exception[82] is gas mixtures containing H_2, which often exhibit maxima in their viscosity-composition curves. For small H_2 contents, errors are small but may reach 10 per cent for H_2-rich mixtures. If the H_2 content is in excess of ~25 per cent, Wilke's much more involved correlation[113] is preferable to Eq. (3-108). The viscosities of high-pressure gas mixtures may be estimated by applying Eq. (3-108) to known or calculated low-pressure component viscosities, and then using Fig. 3-62 with pseudoreduced temperatures $(T_{P_r} = T/T_{P_c})$ and pseudoreduced pressures $(P_{P_r} = P/P_{P_c})$, with T_{P_c} and P_{P_c} obtained from Eqs. (3-9) and (3-15).

LITERATURE CITED: 1. Meissner, *Chem. Eng. Progress*, **45** (2), 149–153 (1949). 2. Gambill, *Chem. Eng.*, July, 1957, p. 267. 3. McGowan, *Chem. & Ind. (London)*, vol. 495, May 31, 1952. 4. Smith, Greenbaum, and Rutledge, *J. Phys. Chem.*, **58**, 443–447

(1954). 5. Gambill, *Chem. Eng.*, June 15, 1959, pp. 182–183. 6. Nokay, *Chem. Eng.*, Feb. 23, 1959, p. 146. 7. Gates and Thodos, *Am. Inst. Chem. Engrs. J.*, **6** (1), 50–54 (1960). 8. Kay, *Ind. Eng. Chem.*, **28,** 1014 (1936). 9. Edmister, *Petrol. Refiner*, September, 1949, pp. 95–102. 10. Edmister, *Petrol. Refiner*, April, 1948, p. 213. 11. Gambill, *Chem. Eng.*, July 13, 1959, pp. 157, 160. 12. Herzog, *Ind. Eng. Chem.*, **36,** 997 (1944). 13. Benedict (1939), as given by Edmister, *Petrol. Refiner*, September, 1949, pp. 95–102. 14. Benson, *J. Phys. & Colloid Chem.*, **52,** 1060 (1948). 15. LeBas, "The Molecular Volumes of Liquid Chemical Compounds," Longmans, London, 1915. 16. Lydersen, *Univ. Wisconsin Eng. Expt. Sta. Rept.* 3 and 4, 1955. 17. Edmister, *Petrol. Refiner*, April, 1958, p. 178. 18. Owens and Thodos, *Am. Inst. Chem. Engrs. J.*, December, 1957, pp. 454–461. 19. Schaefer and Thodos, *Am. Inst. Chem. Engrs. J.*, September, 1959, pp. 367–372. 20. Brebach and Thodos, *Ind. Eng. Chem.*, **50,** 1095–1100 (1958). 21. Uyehara and Watson, *Natl. Petrol. News (Tech. Sec.)*, **36,** R-764 (1944). 22. Goldhammer, *Z. physik Chem.*, **71,** 577 (1910). 23. Othmer, Josefowitz, and Schmutzler, *Ind. Eng. Chem.*, **40,** 883–885 (1948). 24. N.G.S.M.A. "Data Book," 6th ed., 1951. 25. Lu, *Chem. Eng.*, May 4, 1959, pp. 137–138. 26. Nelson and Obert, *Chem. Eng.*, July, 1954, pp. 203–208. 27. Maslan and Littman, *Ind. Eng. Chem.*, **45,** 1566–1568 (1953). 28. Wenner, "Thermochemical Calculations," McGraw-Hill, New York, 1941. 29. Satoh, *J. Sci. Research Inst. (Tokyo)*, **43,** 79 (1948); also given in ref. 33. 30. Clendenin, *Pa. State College Mineral Industries Exptl. Sta. Tech. Paper* 160, 1949. 31. Cragoe, *N.B.S. Misc. Publ.* 97, 1929. 32. Johnson and Huang, *Can. J. Technol.*, **33,** 421 (1955). 33. Reid and Sherwood, "The Properties of Gases and Liquids," McGraw-Hill, New York, 1958. 34. Chow and Bright, *Chem. Eng. Progress*, **49,** 175 (1953). 35. Watson, *Ind. Eng. Chem.*, **35,** 398 (1943). 36. Douglas, *Trans. Am. Soc. Mech. Engrs.*, **79,** 23 (1957). 37. Sakiadis and Coates, *Am. Inst. Chem. Engrs. J.*, **2,** 88 (1956). 38. Bahlke and Kay, *Ind. Eng. Chem.*, **21,** 942 (1929). 39. Brooks, *Oil Gas J.*, May 4, 1953, pp. 139–140. 40. Dobratz, *Ind. Eng. Chem.*, **33,** 759 (1941). 41. Meghreblian, *J. Am. Rocket Soc.*, **21,** 127 (1951). 42. Crawford and Parr, *J. Chem. Phys.*, **16,** 233 (1948). 43. Souders, Matthews, and Hurd, *Ind. Eng. Chem.*, **41,** 1037 (1949). 44. Edmister, *Petrol. Engr.*, December, 1950, p. C-16. 45. Edmister, *Petrol. Refiner*, November, 1948, p. 613. 46. Antonoff, *J. Russ. Phys. Chem. Soc.*, **39,** 342 (1907); *J. Chim. Phys.*, **5,** 372 (1907). 47. Giacalone, *Gazz. chim. ital.*, **81,** 180 (1951). 48. Dodge, "Chemical Engineering Thermodynamics," pp. 392–394, McGraw-Hill, New York, 1944. 49. Hougen and Watson, "Chemical Process Principles," Part 1, p. 337, Wiley, New York, 1943. 50. Turkdogan and Pearson, *J. Appl. Chem.*, **3,** 495 (1953). 51. Gambill, *Chem. Eng.*, Aug. 25, 1958, pp. 121–124. 52. Ward and Kurtz, *Ind. Eng. Chem., Anal. Ed.*, **10,** 573 (1938); Kurtz *et al.*, *Ind. Eng. Chem.*, **42,** 174 (1950). 53. Tripathi, *J. Indian Chem. Soc.*, **18,** 411 (1941). 54. Meissner and Michaels, *Ind. Eng. Chem.*, **41,** 2782 (1949). 55. Sugden, "The Parachor and Valency," Routledge, London, 1930. 56. Johnson *et al.*, *Chem. in Can.*, August, 1954, p. 28. 57. Walden, *Z. Elektrochem.*, **14,** 712 (1908). 58. Lövgren *Svensk Kem. Tidskr.*, **53,** 359 (1941). 59. Kharbanda, *Ind. Chemist*, April, 1955, p. 187. 60. Othmer *et al.*, *Ind. Eng. Chem.*, **40,** 886 (1948). 61. Hammick and Andrew, *J. Chem. Soc.*, 754 (1929). 62. Weinaug and Katz, *Ind. Eng. Chem.*, **35,** 239 (1943); Reno and Katz, *Ind. Eng. Chem.*, **35,** 1091 (1943). 63. Ewing, Walker, Grand, and Miller, *Chem. Eng. Progress, Symp. Ser.*, **53** (20), 19–24 (1957). 64. Freche, *N.A.C.A. Research Mem.* E51A03, Mar. 9, 1951. 65. Forest Products Lab., U.S, Department of Agriculture, *Tech. Note* 248, Madison, Wis., December, 1952. 66. Russell, *J. Am. Ceram. Soc.*, **18,** 1 (1935), 67. Laubitz, *Can. J. Phys.*, **37,** 798 (1959). 68. Woodside, *Can. J. Phys.*, **36,** 815 (1958). 69. Vargaftik, "Proceedings of the Conference on Thermodynamic and Transport Properties of Fluids (London, July, 1957)," pp. 142–149, Institution of Mechanical Engineers, London, 1958. 70. Palmer, *Ind. Eng. Chem.*, **40,** 89 (1948). 71. Weber, *Wied. Ann., Ann. phys. Chem.*, **10,** 103 (1880). 72. Lenoir, *Petrol. Refiner*, **36** (8), 162 (1957). 73. Smith, *Trans. Am. Soc. Mech. Engrs.*, **58,** 719 (1936). 74. Cragoe, *N.B.S. Misc. Publ.* 97, 1929. 75. Barratt and Nettleton, "International Critical Tables," vol. V, p. 227, McGraw-Hill, New York, 1929. 76. Filippov and Novoselova, *Vestnik Moskov. Univ., Ser. Fiz.-Mat. i Estestven. Nauk*, No. 2, **10** (3), 37 (1955). 77. Tareef, *J. Colloid (U.S.S.R.)*, **6,** 545 (1940). 78. Orr and Dalla Valle, Heat Transfer Studies for 1954, *Chem. Eng. Progress, Symp. Ser.*, No. 9, **50,** 29–31 (1954). 79. Wang and Knudsen, *Ind. Eng. Chem.*, **50,** 1667 (1958). 80. Eucken, *Physik. Z.*, **14,** 324 (1913). 81. Bromley, *Univ. Calif. Radiation Lab. Rept.* UCRL-1852, June 12, 1952. 82. Friend and Adler, "Transport Properties in Gases," pp. 128–131, Cambel and Fenn (Ed.), Northwestern University Press, Evanston, Ill., 1958. 83. Lindsay and Bromley, *Ind. Eng. Chem.*, **42,** 1508 (1950). 84. Lenoir, Junk, and Comings, *Chem. Eng. Progress*, **49,** 539 (1953). 85. Gordon, *Ind. Eng. Chem.*, **35,** 851 (1943). 86. Antoine, *Compt. rend.*, **107,** 681, 836 (1888). 87. Riedel, *Chem.-Ing.-Tech.*, **26,** 83 (1954). 88. Hirschfelder *et al.*, *Ind. Eng. Chem.*, **50,** 375 (1958). 89. Riedel, *Chem.-Ing.-Tech.*, **26,** 679 (1954). 90. Gambill, *Chem. Eng.*, Jan. 12, 1959, p. 130. 91. See Partington, "An Advanced Treatise on Physical Chemistry," vol. II, Longmans, London, 1949. 92. Thomas, *J. Chem. Soc.*, Part II, pp. 573–579, 1946. 93. Andrade, *Nature*, **125,** 309, 582 (1930). 94. Lewis and Squires, *Oil Gas J.*, Nov. 15, 1934, pp. 92–96. 95. Andrade, *Endeavour*, **13,** 117 (July, 1954). 96. Bondi, *Petrol. Refiner*, **25,** 269 (1946). 97. Kendall and Monroe, *J. Am. Chem. Soc.*, **39,** 1787 (1917); **43,** 115 (1921). 98. Tamura and Kurata, *Bull. Chem. Soc. Japan*, **25,** 32 (1952). 99. Taylor, *Proc. Roy. Soc. (London)*, **138A,** 41 (1932). 100. Olney and Carlson, *Chem. Eng. Progress*, **43,** 473 (1947). 101. Arrhenius, *Z. physik. Chem.*, **1,** 285 (1887). 102. Kunitz, *J. Gen. Physiol.*, **9,** 715 (1926). 103. Gambill, *Chem. Eng.*, Mar. 9, 1959, pp. 151–152. 104. Ting and Luebbers, *Am. Inst. Chem. Engrs. J.*, **3** (1), 111 (1957). 105. Bromley and Wilke, *Ind. Eng. Chem.*, **43,** 1641 (1951). 106. Hirschfelder, Curtiss, and Bird, "Molecular Theory of Gases and Liquids," Wiley, New York, 1954. 107. Scheibel, *Ind. Eng. Chem.*, **46,** 1574, 2007 (1954). 108. Arnold, *J. Chem. Phys.*, **1,** 170 (1933). 109. Gambill, *Chem. Eng.*, December, 1955, pp. 207–210. 110. Carr, Parent, and Peck, *Chem. Eng. Progress, Symp. Ser.*, **51** (16), 91 (1955). 111. Ross and Brown, *Ind. Eng. Chem.*, **49,** 2026 (1957). 112. Herning and Zipperer, *Gas-u. Wasserfach*, **79,** 49, 69 (1936). 113. Wilke, *J. Chem. Phys.*, **18,** 517 (1950).

SECTION 4

REACTION KINETICS, REACTOR DESIGN, AND THERMODYNAMICS

BY

Robert H. Perry, Ph.D., Professor, Department of Chemical Engineering, University of Rochester; Member, American Society for Engineering Education, American Association for the Advancement of Science. (Section Coeditor, Reaction Kinetics and Reactor Design)

C. M. Sliepcevich, Ph.D., Associate Dean of Engineering, University of Oklahoma; Member, American Institute of Chemical Engineers, American Chemical Society, American Society for Engineering Education, American Association for the Advancement of Science; Registered Professional Engineer in Michigan and Oklahoma. (Section Coeditor, Thermodynamics)

Don W. Green, Ph.D., Research Engineer, Continental Oil Company; Member, American Institute of Chemical Engineers. (Reaction Kinetics, Reactor Design)

Riki Kobayashi, Ph.D., Associate Professor of Chemical Engineering, Rice University; Member, American Institute of Chemical Engineers, American Chemical Society, American Institute of Physics, American Institute of Mining and Metallurgical Engineers. (Thermodynamics)

Thomas W. Leland, Ph.D., Associate Professor of Chemical Engineering, Rice University; Member, American Institute of Chemical Engineers, American Chemical Society. (Thermodynamics)

WITH

Donald Finn, Ph.D., Graduate Fellow, University of Oklahoma. (Thermodynamics)

ACKNOWLEDGING

J. M. Smith, Sc.D., Professor of Engineering, University of California (Davis), (For Comments on Reaction Kinetics and Reactor Design)

CONTENTS

REACTION KINETICS AND REACTOR DESIGN

THERMODYNAMICS

REACTION KINETICS AND REACTOR DESIGN

Introduction. The rates at which chemical processes proceed are of both theoretical and practical importance in chemical engineering. Marked progress has been made in recent years toward developing and establishing rate equations as well as design procedures for constructing chemical reactors. At present, chemical kinetics is not, however, an exact science. From a practical standpoint it is not yet possible to formulate generalized mathematical relations for the rate of a chemical reaction. Quantitative treatment of reaction velocities rests largely on an empirical basis, especially for the majority of industrially important reactions. The interpretation of experimental data and kinetic analysis is in most cases an individual problem.

HOMOGENEOUS REACTIONS

Rate of Reaction. The rate of a chemical reaction is defined herein as the moles of a particular component converted per unit time and per unit volume of reactor.

$$r_A = -\frac{dN_A}{V d\theta} \qquad (4\text{-}1a)$$

For a constant-volume (batch) system, the rate expression may be simplified.

$$r_A = -\frac{dC_A}{d\theta} \qquad (4\text{-}1b)$$

Equation (4-1*b*) is applicable in batch reactors where the reactants are enclosed in a vessel with no provision made for flow in or out during the course of the reaction. For gaseous systems of this type, the constant-volume restraint is exactly met. In liquid systems, changes in density during the course of the reaction may cause changes in volume, but these are generally small.

In contrast to the batch case, consider the dynamic system (flow reactor) where reactants flow continuously into a reaction vessel and products are continuously removed. At steady state there is no change in any of the system properties with time at a fixed position, but properties do change as the reaction mixture flows through the vessel. For this case, the rate expression is commonly written as

$$r_A = \frac{F dx_A}{dV} \qquad (4\text{-}1c)$$

where F is the total feed rate in moles/sec. and x is the moles of reactant A converted per mole of total feed.

Order of Reaction. Reactions are classified into first, second, third, and higher orders according to the number of molecules which appear to enter into the reaction as determined by the relationship between the rate and the reactant concentrations. Mathematical rate equations for reactions of various orders are presented later.

The stoichiometric chemical equation does not necessarily determine the order of reaction. This can be decided only by experiment. Measurement of the rate of a reaction supplies practical information for determining the influence of operating variables and the optimum conditions for carrying out a reaction in practice.

While the kinetic behavior of some simple systems is satisfactorily represented by integral-order rate equations, many reactions have been found to follow more complex rate equations. This is so in many cases of industrial importance.

The reaction mechanism may involve intermediate products which subsequently decompose and react among themselves or with the original reactants to form the final products. Also, either the reactants or the intermediate products may undergo side reactions in addition to the principal reaction.

Determination of Order. The rate of reaction has been found to be proportional to the concentrations of the reacting components.

$$r_A = kC_A{}^a C_B{}^b C_C{}^c \qquad (4\text{-}2)$$

where k = specific reaction rate constant (or simply rate constant) empirically determined and a strong function of temperature

C_A, C_B, C_C, = concentration of reacting components (moles per cubic foot)

a, b, c = empirically determined exponents

The order of a reaction is the sum of the exponents a, b, and c, or the order may be expressed with respect to individual components as "of order a with respect to component A, etc. . . ."

Substitution of Eq. (4-2) for r_A in Eq. (4-1) and subsequent integration at constant temperature yields different results depending on the order of the reaction. Also, the integration depends upon whether the reaction is to be carried out in a batch system where the composition changes with time, or in a steady-state flow system where the composition changes with position in the reactor. Results for simple orders are given in Table 4-1 for the constant-volume process.

Either the differential or integral equations listed in Table 4-1 may be used to test the order of the reaction. As an example, the following expression for the second-order mechanism will be used:

$$2A \rightarrow \text{products}$$

The differential equation of this reaction has the following form for a constant-volume process:

$$\frac{-dC_A}{d\theta} = kC_A{}^2$$

therefore, a plot of $\ln(\Delta C_A/\Delta\theta)$ vs. $\ln C_A$ will yield a straight line of slope 2.

In the integral method the differential equation is integrated as follows:

$$-\int_{C_A{}^0}^{C_A} \left(\frac{dC_A}{C_A{}^2}\right) = k\int_0^\theta d\theta$$

$$\frac{1}{C_A} - \frac{1}{C_A{}^0} = k\theta$$

or

$$\frac{1}{C_A} = k\theta + \frac{1}{C_A{}^0} \qquad (4\text{-}3)$$

Equation (4-3) may be used to solve for k at various values

Table 4-1. Rate Equations for Reactions of Simple Order

Order	Differential equation	Constant-volume process
Zero	$-\frac{dN_A}{Vd\theta} = k$	$k(\theta - \theta_0) = C_A{}^0 - C_A$
One-half	$-\frac{dN_A}{Vd\theta} = kC_A{}^{1/2}$	$k(\theta - \theta_0) = 2(C_A{}^{0\,1/2} - C_A{}^{1/2})$
First	$-\frac{dN_A}{Vd\theta} = kC_A$	$k(\theta - \theta_0) = \ln \frac{C_A{}^0}{C_A}$
Second	$-\frac{dN_A}{Vd\theta} = kC_A{}^2$	$k(\theta - \theta_0) = \frac{1}{C_A} - \frac{1}{C_A{}^0}$
	$-\frac{dN_A}{Vd\theta} = kC_AC_B$	$k(\theta - \theta_0) = \frac{1}{C_B{}^0 - C_A{}^0} \ln \frac{C_AC_A{}^0 + C_A{}^0C_B{}^0 - C_A{}^{02}}{C_AC_B{}^0}$; $C_A{}^0 \neq C_B{}^0$*
Third	$-\frac{dN_A}{Vd\theta} = kC_A{}^3$	$2k(\theta - \theta_0) = \frac{1}{C_A{}^2} - \frac{1}{C_A{}^{02}}$
	$-\frac{dN_A}{Vd\theta} = kC_AC_BC_C$	$k(\theta - \theta_0) = \frac{1}{(C_B{}^0 - C_A{}^0)(C_C{}^0 - C_A{}^0)} \ln \frac{C_A{}^0}{C_A} + \frac{1}{(C_B{}^0 - C_C{}^0)(C_B{}^0 - C_A{}^0)} \ln \left(\frac{C_B{}^0}{C_A + C_B{}^0 - C_A{}^0}\right) + \frac{1}{(C_C{}^0 - C_B{}^0)(C_C{}^0 - C_A{}^0)} \ln \left(\frac{C_C{}^0}{C_A + C_C{}^0 - C_A{}^0}\right)$; $C_B{}^0 \neq C_C{}^0 \neq C_A{}^0$†

C^0 and θ_0 are initial conditions for time and concentration, respectively.

* $C_A{}^0 = C_B{}^0$. Use expression for $-\frac{dN_A}{Vd\theta} = kC_A{}^2$.

† $C_A{}^0 = C_B{}^0 = C_C{}^0$. Use expression for $-\frac{dN_A}{Vd\theta} = kC_A{}^3$.

of C_A and θ. Constancy of k values indicates a second-order reaction.

A third slightly different method would involve plotting the appropriate integral functions for assumed orders and choosing the one in which a straight line is obtained (in this case presumably the second-order expression). To do this values of concentration are chosen as a function of time at constant temperature. $(1/C_A) - (1/C_A{}^0)$ is then plotted vs. time; the slope is equal to k. It is best then to take all the experimental values individually and calculate k. There should be only the normal experimental scatter of the data with no tendency apparent for k to "drift" up or down as a function of conversion.

The foregoing equations for concentration as a function of time apply to constant-volume, batch reaction systems. The order of a reaction can also be evaluated from data obtained in a flow reactor using Eq. (4-1*c*). Experimental data consist of a degree of conversion versus values of V/F which can be compared with the integrated forms of Eq. (4-1*c*) for different mechanisms to determine the order and k value.

Analysis of Complex Reactions. The simple kinetic equations previously presented apply strictly only to irreversible reactions proceeding by a single mechanism with the formation of a single group of products. Many industrially important systems involve a much more complex reaction process, a considerable number of reactions taking place simultaneously.

Where a series of reactions proceed simultaneously, each may be assumed to take place at its own specific rate independently of the others and to follow the simple reaction-rate equation for its own particular order. The net total rate of change is then the summation of the rates of all the independent reactions taking place. Certain definitive classes of simultaneous reactions are commonly recognized: reversible reactions, consecutive reactions, and concurrent or side reactions.

Many industrially important cases are encountered in which the reaction proceeds only partially to completion in the desired direction, and the effect of the reverse reaction on the net rate of formation of product cannot be neglected. In this case the net velocity of reaction is given by the difference of the velocities of forward and reverse reactions.

In other industrially important cases the initial reaction between the original reactants is followed by one or more subsequent or consecutive reactions, *e.g.*,

$$A \rightarrow B \rightarrow D + E$$

in which the products first formed decompose or react with each other or the original substances to form the final products. The measured rate of formation of the final products depends upon the relative rates of the consecutive reactions and is frequently expressed by a complicated kinetic equation. Intermediate products are often difficult to isolate. If the velocity of one of the series of consecutive reactions is relatively much slower than those of the others, which is frequently the case, the rate of this slow reaction determines the rate of formation of the final products and the order of the entire reaction.

In still other important cases a given set of substances react in more than one way by different mechanisms giving rise to a series of concurrent or side reactions which form different sets of final products, *e.g.*,

$$2A \rightarrow B + D$$
$$A \rightarrow R + S$$

Each of these side reactions has its own characteristic rate. The total rate of disappearance of the reactants is then the sum of the rates of the individual side reactions. The relative rates of such side reactions are determined by reaction conditions, and it is frequently possible to alter the relative amounts of the various sets of products by altering the conditions. This can often be accomplished with the aid of a selective catalyst.

Unless the situation is unusually complicated, if the reactions taking place and their respective orders are known or can be determined, it is usually possible to derive reaction-rate equations to express the kinetic behavior of the system. The general procedure is to set up the simple differential-rate equations of the proper order for each separate reaction in terms of the rate of disappearance of reactants and the rate of formation of products and then to combine these to express the net reaction rate.

Treatment of the numerous possible cases is outside the scope of this handbook.

In a complex case, the exact reaction mechanisms involved and their orders are not known; so that a kinetic analysis of rate data offers the only method of approach.

A common procedure is to postulate a number of hypothetical reaction mechanisms, assigning appropriate simple integral reaction orders to the several steps, and then to analyze the experimental rate data in terms of the demands of the kinetic rate relations developed for each. It is not always possible to differentiate between the validity of two or more assumed possible mechanisms. A few of many possible examples may be useful in illustrating methods of attack.

Reversible Reactions. The simplest case occurs when both forward and reverse reactions are of the same order, either first or second, and the products are initially absent from the reacting mixture. If both reactions are second-order, according to the scheme

$$A + B \underset{k_R}{\overset{k_F}{\rightleftarrows}} D + E \tag{4-4}$$

the net rate of disappearance of A (which is equal to the net rate of formation of product, *i.e.*, $-dn_A/d\theta = +dn_D/d\theta$) is

$$\frac{-dN_A}{V\,d\theta} = k_F C_A C_B - k_R C_D C_E \tag{4-5}$$

Equation (4-5) is readily integrated at constant volume (or, since no volume change is involved, also at constant pressure). In the general case where volume changes are involved, integration is most readily accomplished numerically (see Sec. 2).

In the case of reversible reactions of this type, at the equilibrium state, $dn_A/d\theta = 0$. Then

$$k_F C_A C_B = k_R C_D C_E \tag{4-6}$$

and

$$\frac{C_D C_E}{C_A C_B} = \frac{k_F}{k_R} \tag{4-7}$$

If the reacting substances constitute an ideal solution, *i.e.*, conditions such that activities are proportional to concentrations,

$$\frac{C_D C_E}{C_A C_B} = \frac{k_F}{k_R} = K \tag{4-8}$$

where K is the equilibrium constant. From Eq. (4-8) and the expression resulting from integration of Eq. (4-5) both the velocity constants can be calculated.

Consecutive Reactions. Consider the simple consecutive reaction scheme

$$A \xrightarrow{k_1} B \xrightarrow{k_2} D$$

in which an intermediate group of products represented by B is formed from the reactant A in an irreversible first step and subsequently changes in a consecutive irreversible reaction into the final products D. For simplicity, consider the case where volume is constant. If the two reactions are of the general mth and nth orders, respectively, we may write the kinetic equations for the rate of disappearance of A

$$\frac{-dC_A}{d\theta} = k_1 C_A{}^m \tag{4-9}$$

for the rate of formation of D

$$\frac{+dC_D}{d\theta} = k_2 C_B{}^n \tag{4-10}$$

for the net rate of appearance of B

$$\frac{+dC_B}{d\theta} = k_1 C_A{}^m - k_2 C_B{}^n \tag{4-11}$$

Equation (4-9) is readily integrated and arranged in form suitable for the calculation of the constant k_1 from experimental data. The others are not so readily handled, but in such cases it is often possible to utilize numerical methods to permit the integration and calculation of the several velocity constants.

If k_1 and k_2 are of the same relative order of magnitude, the concentration of B in the reaction mixture continually increases in the early stages, passes through a maximum at some intermediate time, diminishes, and eventually vanishes leaving the substance D as the final product of reaction. The course of such consecutive reactions with respect to the concentration-time relation of the several substances is illustrated in Fig. 4-1. The exact shape of

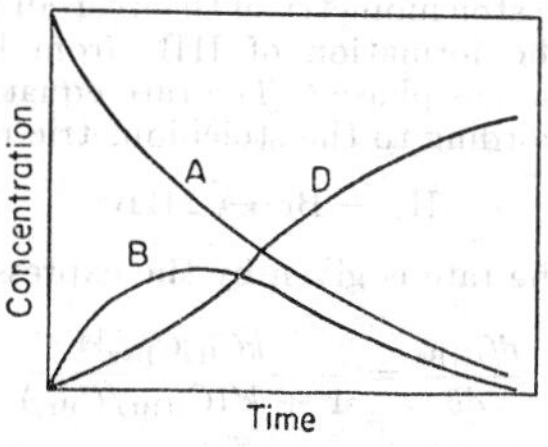

FIG. 4-1. Schematic representation of the relationship of the concentration of reactants and products to reaction time in consecutive reactions.

each curve depends upon the orders of the several reactions. The concentration of B at its maximum and the position of the maximum depend also upon the relative values of the velocity constants. If B is a desired product, it is evidently important to stop the reaction at a time near the maximum.

Side Reactions. The scheme

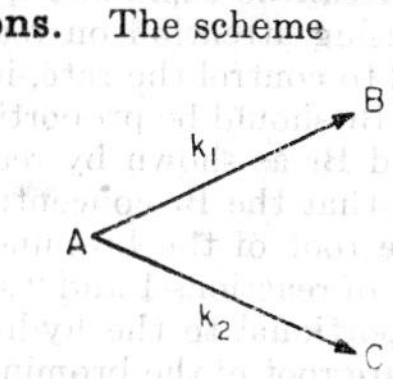

in which both reactions are irreversible is a simple example of this case. For general reactions of the mth and nth order at constant volume the kinetic relations are

$$\frac{+dC_B}{d\theta} = k_1 C_A{}^m \tag{4-12}$$

$$\frac{+dC_D}{d\theta} = k_2 C_A{}^n \tag{4-13}$$

$$\frac{-dC_A}{d\theta} = k_1 C_A{}^m + k_2 C_A{}^n \tag{4-14}$$

Also from Eqs. (4-12) and (4-13)

$$\frac{dC_B}{dC_D} = \frac{k_1}{k_2} C_A{}^{m-n} \tag{4-15}$$

Except in the simple case that both reactions are of the same order, integration is complicated. If, however, m does equal n,

$$\frac{-dC_A}{d\theta} = (k_1 + k_2) C_A{}^n \tag{4-16}$$

and

$$\frac{dC_B}{dC_D} = \frac{k_1}{k_2} \tag{4-17}$$

If the initial values of C_B and C_D are zero, Eq. (4-17) can be integrated to the form

$$\frac{C_B}{C_D} = \frac{k_1}{k_2} = \text{const.}$$

From these relations and the appropriate experimental data k_1 and k_2 can then be calculated.

Chain Reactions. It has been mentioned that the order of a rate equation may not correspond to the stoichiometry of the over-all reaction. In such cases it is helpful to look for a sequence of simple, individual steps leading to rates in agreement with the experimentally determined results. Often reactions between free radicals or atoms can explain cases where the kinetics do not agree with the stoichiometry of the over-all reaction. An example is the formation of HBr from hydrogen and bromine in the gas phase. The rate equation is not second-order according to the stoichiometric reaction

$$H_2 + Br_2 \rightarrow 2HBr$$

but instead the rate is given by the expression

$$\frac{dC_{HBr}}{d\theta} = \frac{kC_{H_2}C_{Br_2}{}^{1/2}}{1 + k'(C_{HBr}/C_{Br_2})} \tag{4-18}$$

This expression can be explained by assuming that the reaction occurs by the following series of steps:

1: $Br_2 \rightarrow 2Br$
2: $H_2 + Br \rightarrow HBr + H$
3: $H + Br_2 \rightarrow HBr + Br$
4: $H + HBr \rightarrow H_2 + Br$
5: $2Br \rightarrow Br_2$

Considering the rate equation for the formation of HBr, the numerator can be explained qualitatively in a simple way by focusing attention on reactions 1 and 2. If both are assumed to control the rate, it is evident that the production of HBr should be proportional to the concentration of H_2 and Br as shown by reaction 2. From reaction 1 it is seen that the Br concentration is proportional to the square root of the bromine concentration. Thus a combination of reactions 1 and 2 suggests that the rate should be proportional to the hydrogen concentration and to the square root of the bromine concentration, in agreement with the experimental result. Reactions 4 and 5 are chain-breaking steps in the process. Reaction 5 removes Br atoms and tends to prevent reaction 2. This effect gives rise to the denominator term in the rate equation. As the product concentration (HBr) builds up, reaction 4 becomes more important, and the over-all rate should be reduced. This is indicated by the denominator term in the rate equation. Similarly, high bromine concentrations tend to reduce reaction 5 and in so doing increase the rate of the over-all reaction. This explains the presence of the bromine concentration in the denominator of Eq. (4-18).

The acceptance of the chain theory for explaining some complex reactions has been aided by (1) the establishment of the presence of free radicals and atoms by spectroscopic measurements and (2) the observation that known means of destroying free radicals result in a decreased rate of the over-all reaction.

Many combustion reactions are believed to occur by a chain mechanism involving free atoms. The available evidence strongly suggests that chain reactions forming and destroying free radicals are necessary to explain the thermal cracking of hydrocarbons. Lewis and von Elbe have summarized recent experimental work and modern theoretical developments for chain reactions (Lewis and von Elbe, "Combustion, Flames, and Explosions of Gases," Academic Press, Inc., New York, 1951).

Effect of Temperature. Chemical-reaction rates are markedly influenced by temperature. Several kinds of behavior occur. Complex reactions or those limited by physical factors such as diffusion or adsorption or by the special behavior of catalysts exhibit differing behavior. Some comments may be made about the various types.

1. Normal behavior, that is, a comparatively rapid increase in rate with rising temperature
2. The behavior of certain heterogeneous reactions dominated by resistance to diffusion between phases, a rather slow increase in rate with rising temperature
3. Typical of explosions, where a very rapid rise takes place at the ignition temperature
4. Catalytic reactions controlled by the rate of adsorption (in which the amount of adsorption decreases at elevated temperatures) and enzyme reactions (where high temperatures destroy the enzyme) causing a decrease in rate above certain temperatures following an initial rise in rate with temperature
5. Diminishing rate with increasing temperature, for example, the reaction between oxygen and nitric oxide where the equilibrium conversion is favored by lower temperatures and the rate appears to depend on the displacement from equilibrium

To emphasize, behavior of type 1 is characteristic of simple reactions; the others are behaviors of composite reactions or of reactions influenced by physical rate processes.

The striking effect of temperature on rate was noted at an early date, with relations of the form $r = aT^m$, where m ranged from 6 to 8, and also the form $r = ae^{-b/T}$ being proposed. Arrhenius in 1889 was able to rationalize the simple exponential form, which is still regarded as generally adequate. In an attempt to explain the effect of temperature on rate he was led to assume an equilibrium situation to which he applied the van't Hoff thermodynamic equation

$$\frac{d(\ln K)}{dT} = \frac{\Delta E}{RT^2}$$

where K is the equilibrium constant and is equal to the ratio of the forward and reverse reaction-rate constants; thus $K = k_1/k_2$. Consequently,

$$\frac{d(\ln k_1)}{dT} - \frac{d(\ln k_2)}{dT} = \frac{E_1}{RT^2} - \frac{E_2}{RT^2} \tag{4-19}$$

Arrhenius noted from experimental data that the individual specific reaction rates followed relations of the form suggested by Eq. (4-19), or

$$\frac{d(\ln k)}{dT} = \frac{E}{RT^2}$$

This may be integrated to the following form when E is constant over the temperature range of interest:

$$k = Ae^{-E/RT}$$

This is called the Arrhenius equation; E is the energy of activation and A the frequency factor. It represents the effect of temperature so accurately that when deviations occur they are usually taken as evidence that the reaction is a composite one or that physical processes are important.

The frequency factor has the units of specific reaction rate, usually based on the units of concentration, and is thus dependent on the order of the reaction.

Other equations have been proposed, some empirical, some theoretical. For all practical purposes, the Arrhenius equation is a sufficiently accurate representation of data.

Typical activation energies which can be used in the Arrhenius-type equation in the prediction of the dependence of the specific reaction-rate constant on temperature are given in Table 4-2.

Table 4-2. Some Energies of Activation*

System	Energy of Activation, kcal./g.-mole
First-order gaseous decompositions:	
Nitrogen tetroxide	13.9
Ethyl chlorocarbonate	29.1
Ethyl peroxide	31.5
Ethyl nitrite	37.7
Methyl iodide	43.0
Nitromethane	50.6
Dimethylethyl acetic acid	60.0
Trimethyl acetic acid	65.5
Second-order gaseous reactions between stable molecules:	
$NO + O_3 \rightarrow NO_2 + O_2$	2.5
$i\text{-}C_4H_8 + HBr \rightarrow$	22.5
$2NOCl \rightarrow 2NO + Cl_2$	24.0
$i\text{-}C_4H_8 + HCl \rightarrow$	28.8
$H_2 + I_2 \rightarrow 2HI$	40.0
$2HI \rightarrow H_2 + I_2$	44.0
$C_2H_4 + H_2 \rightarrow$	43.2
Second-order reactions involving atoms or radicals:	
$H + HBr \rightarrow H_2 + Br$	1.2
$H + Br_2 \rightarrow HBr + Br$	1.2
$CH_3 + i\text{-}C_4H_{10} \rightarrow$	7.6
$CH_3 + n\text{-}C_4H_{10} \rightarrow$	8.3
$CH_3 + C_2H_6 \rightarrow$	10.4
Third-order gaseous reactions:	
$2NO + O_2 \rightarrow 2NO_2$	0 or negative
$H + H + H \rightarrow H_2 + H$	0
$2NO + Br_2 \rightarrow 2NOBr$	~4
$2NO + Cl_2 \rightarrow 2NOCl$	~4

* From Frost and Pearson, "Kinetics and Mechanism," Wiley, New York, 1953.

Theoretical Hypotheses. Collision Theory. The Arrhenius theory requires that, before reaction can occur, the molecules of reactants must have an energy of activation E above their normal, or average, energy. The possibility of some molecules possessing this excess exists because of the statistical distribution of energy over a wide range in the large number of molecules making up the system. Thus according to the classical kinetic theory some gaseous molecules will possess much larger amounts of translational energy than others, owing to variations in molecular velocities. It is logical to suppose that a collision between these molecules of reactants would provide a means of making available the activation energy necessary for the reaction to occur. By assuming that the molecules behave as hard spheres it is possible to develop simple expressions for the rate. This approach has become known as the collision theory. This theory offers a simple and clear picture of the mechanism of reactions and predicts reasonably good results for a few gas- and liquid-phase reactions involving simple molecules.

According to the collision theory the number of molecules of product formed per unit time per unit volume, *i.e.*, the rate, is equal to the number of collisions multiplied by a factor f. This factor takes into account the fact that only a fraction of the collisions involve molecules that possess the necessary excess energy (activation energy). For a simple gaseous reaction such as $A + B \rightarrow C + D$ and based on the kinetic theory of gases, the number of collisions is given by the expression

$$z = c_A c_B \sigma_{AB}^2 \left(8\pi RT \frac{M_A + M_B}{M_A M_B}\right)^{1/2} \qquad (4\text{-}20)$$

where c = concentration, molecules/cc. (not moles/cc.)
σ_{AB} = effective diameter of A and B upon collision
M = molecular weight
R = gas constant = $k_B n$, the product of Boltzmann's constant and Avogadro's number, ergs/(°K.) (g.-mole)

Then the rate equation (4-1) may be written

$$r_A = f c_A c_B \sigma_{AB}^2 \left(8\pi RT \frac{M_A + M_B}{M_A M_B}\right)^{1/2} \qquad (4\text{-}21)$$

or it may be expressed in terms of concentration

$$r_A = k c_A c_B \qquad (4\text{-}22)$$

Using the Arrhenius equation for k, this last expression becomes

$$r_A = A e^{-E/RT} c_A c_B \qquad (4\text{-}23)$$

Combining (4-21) and (4-23) gives the following result for A:

$$A e^{-E/RT} = f \sigma_{AB}^2 \left(8\pi RT \frac{M_A + M_B}{M_A M_B}\right)^{1/2} \qquad (4\text{-}24)$$

The fraction of the molecules that possess the required excess energy for reaction should depend not upon the number of collisions but instead on the magnitude of the energy itself. Assuming a Maxwellian distribution, the fraction of the total molecules having an energy E can be shown to be $e^{-E/RT}$. Hence f may be taken as $e^{-E/RT}$, and then the frequency factor A is given by

$$A = \sigma_{AB}^2 \left(8\pi RT \frac{M_A + M_B}{M_A M_B}\right)^{1/2} \qquad (4\text{-}25)$$

Finally, substitution of this value of A in the Arrhenius equation gives the collision-theory expression for the specific reaction rate, *i.e.*,

$$k = \sigma_{AB}^2 \left(8\pi RT \frac{M_A + M_B}{M_A M_B}\right)^{1/2} e^{-E/RT}$$

cc./(molecule)(sec.) (4-26)

In summary, these principal interrelations exist between reaction kinetics and the kinetic theory of gases:

1. Equation (4-21) resembles the law of mass action, in so far as the effect of concentration is concerned.
2. Since the effect of temperature on the exponential in Eq. (4-26) is much greater than on the $T^{1/2}$ term, this equation resembles the Arrhenius equation for the dependence of reaction rate on temperature.

Thus the kinetic theory provides a reasonable interpretation of some important features of the mechanics of reaction, but it is of limited utility with regard to specific reactions. More modern theories are able to predict more accurately the rates of some specific reactions. Values of effective diameters for certain molecules are given in Table 4-3. For molecules not listed, the effective diameter may be approximated by the equation

$$\sigma = 1.18\, V_b$$

where V_b is the LeBas atomic volume (see Sec. 18 for calculation of V_b).

The collision diameter to be used in Eq. (4-26) for unlike molecules may be taken as the mean of the individual diameters.

Theory of Absolute Reaction Rates (Activated-complex Theory). The collision theory has been found to give results in reasonably good agreement with experimental data for a number of simple gas reactions. The theory has also been satisfactory for several reactions in solution involving simple ions. However, for many other reactions, in both the gas and the liquid phase, the predicted rates are much too large. Predicted frequency factors lie in the rather narrow range of 10^9 to 10^{11}, while measured values may be as low as 10^5. The deviation appears to increase with the complexity of the reactant

Table 4-3. Effective Diameters of Certain Diatomic and Triatomic Molecules*

Molecule	A.†
H_2	0.7416_6
HD	0.7413_6
D_2	0.7416_1
Li_2	2.672_5
Na_2	3.078_6
K_2	3.923
LiH	1.5949
NaH	1.8873
KH	2.244
Cl_2	1.988
Br_2	2.283_6
I_2	2.666_6
FCl	1.62813_1
ICl	2.32069_6
HCl	1.27460
HBr	1.413_8
HI	1.604_1
NaI	(2.90)
CsF	2.34
CsI	(3.41)
CH	1.1198
OH	0.9706
O_2	1.20739_8
CO	1.1281_9
NO	1.1508
N_2	1.094
P_2	1.894_3
CO_2	2.326
CS_2	3.108
H_2O	1.52
D_2O	1.52
H_2S	2.014
F_2O	2.14
Cl_2O	2.71
SO_2	2.56
NO_2	2.01
N_2O	2.317
O_3	2.180
HCN	2.216
ClCN	2.793
BrCN	2.949
ICN	3.154

* From Moelwyn-Hughes, "Physical Chemistry," Pergamon, New York, 1957.

† A. = angstrom units, 1×10^{-8} cm.

molecules. As a means of recognizing this disagreement it has been customary to introduce a probability factor having a value less than unity. This factor is sometimes called a "stearic factor" based on the supposition that for complex molecules the orientation on collision is important. To still retain the hard-sphere concept it is then necessary to explain why all the collisions supplying the necessary energy do not result in reaction.

The principles of quantum mechanics were applied to this problem, and there resulted what has become known as the absolute theory of reaction rates. In this theory reaction is still presumed to occur as a result of collisions between reacting molecules, but what happens after collision is examined in more detail.

Table 4-4. Calculated Frequency Factors*

Reaction	Frequency-factor Value†
2 atoms	10^{-10}–10^{-9}
Atom + linear molecule, linear complex	10^{-12}–10^{-11}
Atom + linear molecule, non-linear complex	10^{-11}–10^{-10}
Atom + non-linear molecule, linear complex	10^{-12}–10^{-11}
2 linear molecules, linear complex	10^{-14}–10^{-13}
2 linear molecules, non-linear complex	10^{-13}–10^{-12}
1 linear + 1 non-linear molecule, non-linear complex	10^{-14}–10^{-13}
2 non-linear molecules, non-linear complex	10^{-15}–10^{-14}
3 atoms, linear complex	10^{-33}

* From Frost and Pearson, "Kinetics and Mechanism," Wiley, New York, 1953.

† Concentrations are in molecules/cc., and time is in seconds.

The essential feature of the theory is the postulation of an activated complex, which is an intermediate unstable substance formed from the reactants and decomposing into the products. A basic assumption that is made regarding this activated complex is that it is in thermodynamic equilibrium with the reactants. This means that the rate-controlling step in the over-all reaction is the rate of decomposition of the activated complex into the products. This concept of an equilibrium activation step followed by a slow decomposition is equivalent to assuming a time lag between activation and decomposition into the products of reaction. It is the answer proposed by the absolute-rate theory to the question of why all collisions supplying the necessary energy are not effective in producing a reaction.

These ideas may be illustrated by considering the reaction

$$aA + bB \rightleftarrows AB^* \rightarrow cC + dD$$

where the lower-case letters represent the number of moles of each component involved. The intermediate activated complex is represented as AB^* and its concentration is that defined by the thermodynamic equilibrium constant expressed in terms of activities:

$$K_a^* = \frac{a_{AB}^*}{a_A{}^a a_B{}^b} \tag{4-27}$$

The rate of decomposition of the activated complex is proportional to the concentration of this unstable compound and also equal to the over-all rate of reaction. Thus

$$r_A = \alpha C_{AB}^* \tag{4-28}$$

The proportionality constant α can be shown, from statistical mechanics, to be

$$\alpha = \frac{k_B T}{h} \tag{4-29}$$

where k_B = Boltzmann's constant = 1.38×10^{-16} erg/°K.

h = Planck's constant = 6.624×10^{-27} erg-sec.

For liquid system, unit activity is defined at unit mole fraction

$$C_{AB}^* = \frac{a_{AB}^*}{\gamma_{AB}^* v_m} \tag{4-30}$$

where γ_{AB}^* = activity coefficient for the complex, AB^*

v_m = average molal volume of the system

For gaseous systems, unit activity is defined at a unit fugacity of one atmosphere. If this is not assumed, standard state fugacities should be included in definitions of concentration.

$$C_{AB}^* = \frac{a_{AB}^*}{\nu_{AB}^* ZRT} \tag{4-31}$$

where ν_{AB}^* = fugacity coefficient for the complex, AB^*

Z = average compressibility factor for the system

Assuming a gaseous system (the derivation is exactly analogous for liquid systems) and using Eq. (4-27)

$$r_A = \frac{k_B T}{h} C_{AB}^* = \frac{k_B a_{AB}^*}{\nu_{AB}^* ZRh} = \frac{k_B K_a^* a_A{}^a a_B{}^b}{\nu_{AB}^* ZRh} \tag{4-32}$$

From thermodynamics it is known that

$$\Delta F^* = -RT \ln K_a^* = \Delta H^* - T\Delta S^* \tag{4-33}$$

where ΔF^* is the free-energy change for the formation of the activated complex from compounds A and B. ΔH^* and ΔS^* are the enthalpy and entropy changes for the same step. Thus:

$$K_a^* = e^{(-\Delta H^*/RT + \Delta S^*/R)}$$

Substituting in Eq. (4-32)

$$r_A = \frac{k_B a_A{}^a a_B{}^b}{\nu_{AB}^* ZRh} e^{-(\Delta H^*/RT + \Delta S^*/R)} \tag{4-34}$$

As

$$C_i = a_i/(\nu_i ZRT)$$

$$r_A = \frac{k_B C_A{}^a C_B{}^b \nu_A{}^a \nu_B{}^b (ZRT)^{a+b}}{\nu_{AB}^* ZRh} e^{(-\Delta H^*/RT + \Delta S^*/R)} \tag{4-35}$$

Since r_A has been defined

$$r_A = kC_A{}^aC_B{}^b \qquad (4\text{-}35a)$$

then the specific reaction-rate constant k may be shown by comparison of Eqs. (4-35) and (4-35a) to be:

$$k = \frac{k_B\nu_A{}^a\nu_B{}^b}{\nu_{AB}{}^*ZRh}(ZRT)^{a+b}\,e^{(-\Delta H^*/RT+\Delta S^*/R)} \qquad (4\text{-}36)$$

Simplifying by assuming that the fugacity coefficients are unity (and $Z = 1$), then for a bimolecular reaction where $a = b = 1$:

$$k = \frac{k_BRT^2}{h}\,e^{(-\Delta H^*/RT+\Delta S^*/R)} \qquad (4\text{-}37)$$

Comparing this expression to that formulated by Arrhenius

$$k = Ae^{-E/RT}$$

it can be seen that

$$E = \Delta H^*$$

$$A = \frac{k_BRT^2}{h}\,e^{\Delta S^*/R}$$

The entropy of activation ΔS^* is calculated through use of partition functions. Prediction of ΔH^* from a theoretical basis is not certain, and experimental data must be relied upon.

Ordinarily in the application of Eqs. (4-33) and (4-37) the enthalpy and entropy of activation are assumed to be independent of temperature since the change in heat capacity which accompanies the activation is small. For unimolecular reactions this change is negligible, and ΔH^* and ΔS^* may be treated as constants over wide ranges of temperature. This assumption is also satisfactory for other reactions over moderate ranges of temperature. In such cases the values of ΔH^* and ΔS^* are average values for the temperature range involved.

Where rate data are to be extended over wide temperature ranges the effect of $\Delta C_p{}^*$, the change in heat capacity accompanying the formation of the activated complex, should be considered. Where $\Delta C_p{}^*$ is constant,

$$\Delta H^* = I_H{}^* + \Delta C_p{}^*T \qquad (4\text{-}38)$$

$$\Delta S^* = I_S{}^* + \Delta C_p{}^*\ln T \qquad (4\text{-}39)$$

$I_H{}^*$ and $I_S{}^*$ are constants of integration.

Equations (4-38) and (4-39) are ordinarily used only where rate data are extrapolated to a widely different temperature range, as, for example, if low-temperature rate data in a forward reaction are combined with thermodynamic data in order to estimate rates of the reverse reaction at a high temperature. For rate equations within either temperature range ΔS^* and ΔH^* may be taken as constant at average values.

If these equations are used for the interpretation of experimental data it is necessary that rate measurements be available at two temperatures in order to evaluate ΔH^* and ΔS^*. If ΔS^* can be approximated by theoretical calculations, rate measurements at one temperature suffice to evaluate reaction rates at other temperatures.

The status of the problem of predicting a rate of reaction may be summarized in the following manner: The absolute-reaction-rate theory firmly relates the rate to chemical structure. It needs more development before accurate numerical values can be predicted for most reactions. From an engineering viewpoint this means that experimental kinetic studies must still form the bases for the development of commercial reactors. Finally, the Arrhenius equation adequately predicts the effect of temperature on the rate when single-step chemical processes are involved.

HETEROGENEOUS REACTIONS—CATALYZED

Introduction. Heterogeneous-phase reactions occur either because the reactants themselves are of different phase or because the catalyst (usually solid) is of a phase different from the fluid reactants. The latter case is considered in this subsection. For a discussion of reactions involving reactants of different phase, see the subsection following. One method of analyzing solid catalyzed reactions is to postulate that, of the several mechanistic steps that occur, a single one will control the over-all rate of reaction. In more sophisticated analyses it may be supposed that two or more are relatively slow, and of the same order of magnitude in rate, thus combining in their effect to set the over-all rate. The individual steps in the process are:

Diffusion of reactants to and diffusion of products away from the outside surface of the catalyst

Diffusion of either reactants or products within pores in the catalyst pellets

Adsorption of reactants or desorption of products at the catalyst surface

The actual reaction on the catalyst surface involving adsorbed reactants

The definition of rate [Eq. (4-1c)] for heterogeneously catalyzed reactions taking place in dynamic (flow reactor) systems is usually written as

$$r_A{}' = \frac{Fdx_A}{dW}$$

where $r_A{}'$ is expressed as moles of reactant A converted per unit time per unit weight of catalyst. W is the weight of catalyst, and F and x are as defined for Eq. (4-1c).

In the analysis of laboratory or plant data, one may test for the rate-controlling step in the over-all process. This is done to allow scale-up of laboratory data or prediction of the effect of a change in operating variables beyond the range of available data for the reaction. The techniques are outlined below in brief form. However, it cannot be emphasized too strongly that the mechanism chosen among the several postulated in such an analysis only fits the experimental data and is not proof that the chosen mechanism and controlling step describe the way the reaction actually occurs. Extrapolation of a rate expression so derived beyond the range of experimental data can be done, therefore, with only slightly more confidence than with use of a purely empirical rate expression. It should be remembered, too, that mechanistic analysis—or empirical correlation of the data—is applied only after the effects of the diffusional steps have been taken into account.

External Diffusion. The effects of diffusional resistances are kept to a minimum by using a high velocity through the catalyst bed. These effects may be tested for in the experimental reactor by varying the feed rate and weight of catalyst at the same time (to give the same value of W/F, weight of catalyst divided by flow rate, at different velocities) and then noting the conversion.

The conversion is measured at a value of W/F at which the gas velocity is low. Then it is measured again at a high velocity, but with more catalyst to keep the ratio W/F constant. The two values of conversion will coincide if the effect of diffusion is negligible. If the conversions are different, there is a diffusion effect.

There are two ways to test this effect. One is to make a series of runs at different velocities with the amount of catalyst adjusted to a constant W/F ratio. These data are then plotted as conversion vs. velocity. If diffusion

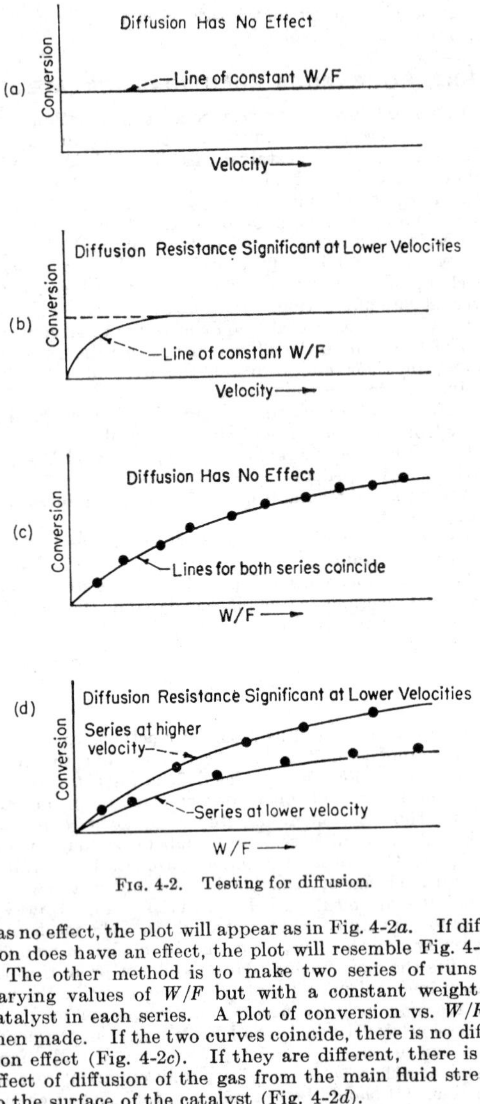

FIG. 4-2. Testing for diffusion.

has no effect, the plot will appear as in Fig. 4-2*a*. If diffusion does have an effect, the plot will resemble Fig. 4-2*b*.

The other method is to make two series of runs at varying values of W/F but with a constant weight of catalyst in each series. A plot of conversion vs. W/F is then made. If the two curves coincide, there is no diffusion effect (Fig. 4-2*c*). If they are different, there is an effect of diffusion of the gas from the main fluid stream to the surface of the catalyst (Fig. 4-2*d*).

If diffusion does significantly affect the over-all rate of reaction, formulation of the rate expression and estimation of the mass-transfer coefficient is done in the following manner (for supplementary information on diffusional processes, see Sec. 14):

The transport of reactants and products to and from the surface of the catalyst is by the mechanisms of molecular and turbulent diffusion. When the fluid velocities are large with respect to the solid, molecular diffusion will play a small role in determining the rate of mass transfer. This is usually the situation in fixed-bed reactors, where the mass velocity of fluid past the surface of catalyst particles is high. At the other extreme is the batch reactor with little or no provision made for agitation. In this case molecular diffusion may be the predominant transport process.

The rate of mass transfer from a bulk-gas phase to the solid surface is described by the expression

$$N = k_g a'(p_g - p_i) \tag{4-40}$$

where N = rate of mass transfer, lb.-moles/(hr). (lb. of catalyst)

p_g = partial pressure of diffusing gas in bulk stream, atm.

p_i = partial pressure of diffusing gas at solid surface, atm.

k_g = mass-transfer coefficient, lb.-moles/(hr.)(atm.)(sq. ft.)

a' = external area of catalyst particle per unit mass, sq. ft./lb. (see Table 4-5) ($a' = a/\rho_B$)

ρ_B = bulk density of catalyst bed, lb./cu. ft.

For flow reactors, at steady-state conditions, the rate of reaction is equal to the rate of diffusion when both are expressed in terms of the same component.

Table 4-5. Values of *a*, Sq. Ft. of External Surface/Cu. Ft. of Catalyst Bed

To use in Eq. (4-42) divide by the bulk density of the bed, lb./cu. ft. of bed

D_p, in.	Mesh-size opening (Tyler)	Values of *a*			
		% void space			
		26	30	40	50
0.5	.....	107	101	86.4	72
0.4	2	133	126	108	90
0.3	2.5	178	168	144	120
0.2	3.5	266	252	216	180
0.1	7–8	533	504	432	360
0.05	12–14	1066	1008	864	720
0.01	60	5330	5040	4320	3600

Once the mass-transfer coefficient is known, Eq. (4-40) can be employed to determine the difference in partial pressure between the bulk of the gas and at the solid surface. This value of $(p_g - p_i)$ determines the importance of external diffusion in the list of seven series steps constituting the over-all reaction. For example, if $(p_g - p_i)$ is but a few per cent of p_g, diffusion resistances can be neglected. Then bulk partial pressures can be used in studying the remaining processes. On the other hand, if $(p_g - p_i)$ is a large fraction of p_g, serious errors result unless interface values of partial pressure are employed in studying the surface processes.

For liquid-phase reaction mixtures Eq. (4-40) becomes

$$r = k_L a(C_g - C_i) \tag{4-41}$$

where the driving force is expressed in concentrations and k_L is the corresponding liquid-phase diffusion coefficient. Less is known about diffusivities in the liquid phase; so that it is more difficult to predict satisfactory values for k_L than for k_g.

The following correlations for mass-transfer coefficients are applicable:

$$j_D = \frac{k_g M_m p_f}{G}\left(\frac{\mu}{\rho D}\right)^{2/3} = 0.989\left(\frac{d_p G}{\mu}\right)^{-0.41} \tag{4-42}$$

$$j_D = \frac{k_g M_m p_f}{G}\left(\frac{\mu}{\rho D}\right)^{2/3} = 1.82\left(\frac{d_p G}{\mu}\right)^{-0.51} \tag{4-43}$$

The first expression applies for $d_p G/\mu$ greater than 350 and the second for lower Reynolds numbers. In these equations D is the molecular diffusivity, sq. ft./sec.; p_f the pressure film factor, atm. (analogous to the mean partial pressure of the inert gas in a single diffusing component in a stagnant gas); M_m the mean molecular weight, d_p the average particle diameter, ft.; and G the mass velocity, lb./(hr.)(sq. ft.).

By combining equations to eliminate k_g an expression for $p_g - p_i$ can be developed in terms of the rate of reaction r_A. This has been done by Yang and Hougen [*Chem. Eng. Progress.*, **46,** 146 (1950)], who carried the problem further by developing convenient charts for estimating the value of $p_g - p_i$ at various levels of rate of reaction and mass velocity G.

Pore Diffusion. Even with a high enough fluid velocity through the catalyst bed to keep external diffusion resistances at a minimum, it is still possible that the catalyst may not be used to its fullest capacity. This is the case when diffusion within the pores of the catalyst particle is an important rate-controlling step.

If diffusion is fast compared with the rate of reaction, the reactants will be able to diffuse into the innermost parts of the pellet. The entire internal surface will "see" a concentration of reactants in the fluid phase approximately equal to $C_A{}^0$, the reactant concentration at the catalyst surface. If, however, the chemical reaction is fast compared with diffusion, the reactants will be converted before diffusing very far into the catalyst pellet. Reaction will thus occur mainly in the outer periphery of the pellet and part of the interior surface will not be utilized.

As size of the catalyst decreases, the resistance to pore diffusion decreases because the path of diffusion becomes shorter. A test for pore-diffusion effects can therefore be made. At the same ratio of catalyst weight to feed rate, experimental runs with different-sized pellets will give the same reaction rate if pore resistance is negligible. If pore diffusion is significant, the rate will increase with decreasing pellet size. Once the pore resistance is small enough that another step becomes controlling, further decrease in pellet size will not increase the reaction rate. This has been done by Wakao, Selwood, and Smith (*Am. Inst. Chem. Engrs. J.*, to be published).

In analyzing kinetic data in porous catalysts, falsification of the "order" of the reaction, the specific reaction-rate constant, and the magnitude of the activation energy may result if pore-diffusion effects are not recognized [Wheeler, *Advances in Catalysis*, **III,** 281 (1951). Weisz and Prater, *Advances in Catalysis*, **VI,** 176 (1954)]. In fact, if unusually low activation energies are obtained for a reaction, this may be taken as an indication that pore diffusion is controlling.

To characterize the effects of pore diffusion an "effectiveness factor" η has been introduced and is used in conjunction with an estimated catalyst area per unit volume of reactor. The effectiveness factor is defined as the ratio of actual reaction rate per unit mass of catalyst to the rate which would result if no diffusional resistance or catalyst-poison effects were present. The reaction rate may then be expressed as

$$r_A = kf(C_i{}^0)S_v\eta$$

where r_A = as defined in Eq. (4-1)
k = specific reaction-rate constant
$f(C_i{}^0)$ = concentration-dependent term evaluated at external catalyst surface
S_v = catalyst surface area per unit volume of reactor (see Table 4-6)
η = effectiveness factor

For simple cases, η may be calculated by solution of the differential equations describing a system in which simultaneous diffusion and chemical reaction are occurring. A few such solutions are given in Fig. 4-3. The modulus m in Fig. 4-3 is

$$m = l\sqrt{\frac{k'}{D_i}(C_i{}^0)^{n-1}}$$

where l = characteristic pore length, for spherical pellets l = radius of the sphere, for flat plates $l = \frac{1}{2}$ catalyst width
$k' = 2k/\bar{r}$
$\bar{r}$ = average pore radius $2V_g/S_g$ (see Table 4-6)
D_i = fluid-phase diffusion coefficient
$C_i{}^0$ = concentration of reactant at external catalyst surface
n = true order of the chemical reaction
V_g = pore volume/g.
S_g = surface area/g.

It has been assumed there are no heat effects, *i.e.*, no temperature gradients in the pellets. The reactions are considered to be irreversible and there is no volume change on reaction [Thiele, *Ind. Eng. Chem.*, **31,** 917 (1939)]. It should be emphasized that the effectiveness factors presented in Fig. 4-3 have been derived assuming isothermal simple first- and second-order reaction-rate equations. In any real heterogeneous reaction system with a combined adsorption–surface reaction–desorption mechanism the possibility of representing the data by such a simple rate expression is rare. However, these curves can be used as an approximation for real cases by techniques given in the literature [Wheeler, *Advances in Catalysis*, **III,** 299 (1951). Weisz and Prater, *Advances*

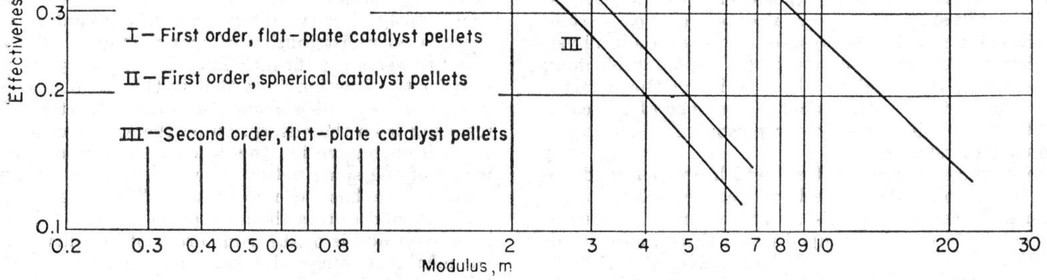

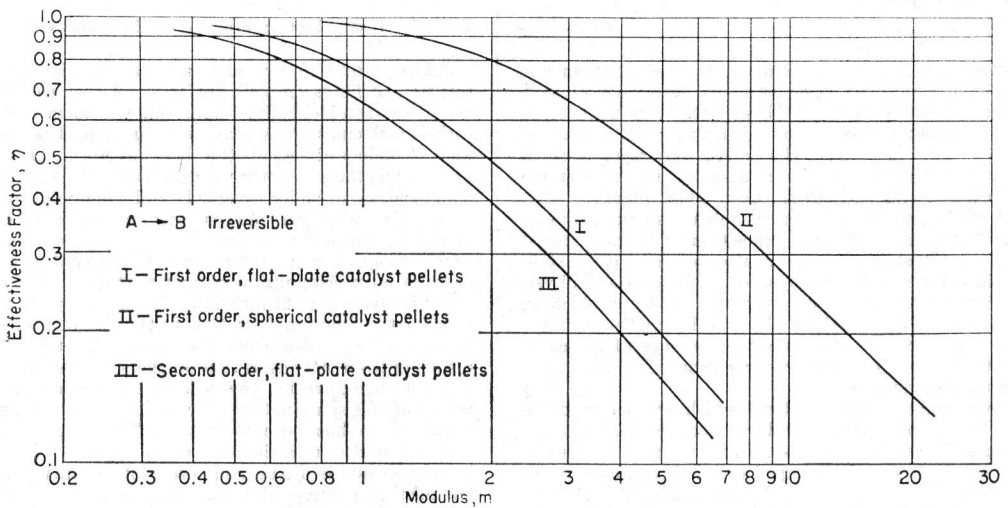

FIG. 4-3. Effectiveness factor for reactions of simple order.

in Catalysis, **VI**, 169 (1954). Hougen and Watson, *Chem. Process Principles*, **III**, 999 (1949)].

Since the rate of reaction is usually a strong function of temperature, temperature gradients within the catalyst particle can have a pronounced effect on the average rate for the particle. For example, in an exothermic reaction, the temperature will increase from the surface of the particle inward, reaching a maximum value at the center. If the heat of reaction is large, the increase in temperature within the particle may be large enough to more than offset the decrease in rate due to pore-diffusion resistance. Under these circumstances the effectiveness factor may be greater than unity.

Physical properties for several catalysts are given in Table 4-6.

Table 4-6. Values of Internal Surface Area, Pore Volume, and Average Pore Radius for Typical Catalysts

Catalyst	S_g, sq. m./g.	V_g, cc./g.	$\bar{r} = 2V_g/S_g$, A.
Activated carbons	500–1500	0.6–0.8	10–20
Silica gels	200–700	0.4	15–100
Silica-alumina cracking catalysts ~ 10–20% Al_2O_3	200–700	0.2–0.7	15–150
Silica-alumina (steam deactivated)	67	0.519	155
Silica-magnesia microsphere:			
Nalco, 25% MgO	630	0.451	14.3
Nalco, steam treated, 621°C., 400 lb./sq. in. gage for 24 hr	322	0.283	17.6
Da-5 silica-magnesia	656	0.365	11.1
Activated clays	150–225	0.4–0.52	~100
TCC clay pellets (MgO, CaO, Fe_2O_3, SO_4) = ~ 10%	276	0.363	26.3
Clays:			
Montmorillonite (raw)	214	0.297–0.306	~28
Montmorillonite (heated 550°C.)	212	0.268	25.2
Vermiculite	35	0.063–0.057	~314
Activated alumina (Alorico)	175	0.388	45
CoMo on alumina	168–251	0.261–0.331	20–40
Kieselguhr (Celite 296)	4.2	1.14	11,000
Fe-synthetic NH_3 catalyst	4–13	0.12	200–1000
Co-ThO_2-Kieselguhr 100:18:100 (reduced) pellets	42.3	0.73	345
Co-ThO_2-MgO (100:6:12) (reduced) granular	84.1	0.80	190
Co-Kieselguhr 100:200 (reduced) granular	22.8	2.31	2030
Porous plate (Coors No. 760)	1.6	0.172	2150
Pumice	0.38		
Fused copper catalyst	0.23		
Ni film	8.4		
Ni on pumice, 91.8% pumice	1.27		

S_g = catalyst surface area.
V_g = catalyst pore volume.
$\bar{r}$ = average radius of pore.
A. = angstrom unit = 1×10^{-8} cm.

Catalyst Poisoning. Some substances exert an appreciable inhibitive effect on catalysis, even when present in very small amounts. These are termed poisons. They act most frequently by adsorbing on the catalyst surface. This may mask the active centers or cause a change in selectivity of the catalyst or, in the extreme case, catalyze an undesirable by-product reaction (*e.g.*, small quantities of nickel in petroleum stocks promote dehydrogenation). Simple deposition of inert material on the catalyst surface may also occur (*e.g.*, carbon deposition on cracking catalysts). This results in physically covering the active-catalyst sites and/or in blocking off the pores, thus making the interior of the catalyst inaccessible. Other poisons cause a change of the catalyst structure (*e.g.*, water-vapor poisoning of platinum-alumina catalyst).

The principal metal catalysts which are poisoned because of a strong adsorptive bond between catalyst and poison are given in Table 4-7. The common poisons of these catalysts may be grouped under three major headings [Maxted, *Advances in Catalysis*, **III**, 129 (1951)]. These are (1) compounds of elements in group Vb or VIb

Table 4-7. Catalysts Poisoned*

Fe (26)	Co (27)	Ni (28)	Cu (29)
Ru (44)	Rh (45)	Pd (46)	Ag (47)
Os (76)	Ir (77)	Pt (78)	Au (79)

* From Maxted, *Advances in Catalysis*, vol. III, Academic Press, Inc., New York, 1951.

of the periodic series, (2) compounds of a large number of catalytically toxic metals (Cu^+, Zn^{++}, Cu^{++}), and (3) multiple-bond molecules (CO_2, C_2H_4).

For some catalysts, over the major portion of the poisoning curve (catalyst activity vs. poison concentration), activity decreases linearly as poison concentration on the catalyst increases. When poisons are present in a catalyst system, the effectiveness factor η (discussed above with regard to pore diffusion) will be a function of time until the poison concentration reaches an equilibrium value. For simple cases, curves of η vs. time have been derived. Plots showing the form of the curves for a first-order irreversible chemical reaction in flat-plate catalysts are presented in Fig. 4-4

where $m = l\sqrt{\dfrac{k'}{D_i}}$ (defined as above)

k_p = poisoning-rate constant
Θ = dimensionless time, $k'\theta$
θ = time

The initial rise of η is due to the initial diffusion into the catalyst pores.

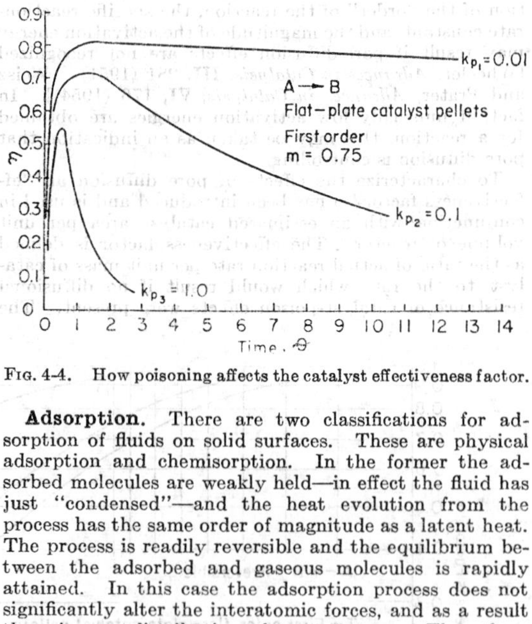

FIG. 4-4. How poisoning affects the catalyst effectiveness factor.

Adsorption. There are two classifications for adsorption of fluids on solid surfaces. These are physical adsorption and chemisorption. In the former the adsorbed molecules are weakly held—in effect the fluid has just "condensed"—and the heat evolution from the process has the same order of magnitude as a latent heat. The process is readily reversible and the equilibrium between the adsorbed and gaseous molecules is rapidly attained. In this case the adsorption process does not significantly alter the interatomic forces, and as a result there is no redistribution of energy states. Thus there could not be a significant change in the energy of activation for the reaction from that in the gaseous phase, for instance; i.e., there could be little catalytic behavior resulting from the adsorption on the solid surface.

With chemisorption the adsorbed material is held by forces of the same nature as exists between atoms. In effect, there has been a "reaction" between the fluid and the solid during the adsorption process. Hence the heat evolution is of the same order of magnitude as in a chemical reaction and bond energies have been redistributed altering the activation energy of the desired reaction from that existing when neither reactant is adsorbed. If the activation energy has been reduced—an increase in rate, *i.e.*, catalytic behavior, results from the adsorption process.

Thus chemisorption is of primary interest in the study of heterogeneous catalysis. (Note that physical adsorption is of value in studying physical properties of the porous catalyst, such as surface area.) A quantitative treatment of the adsorption process is needed. It is necessary to have available an expression relating the rate and amount of adsorption to the concentration of the adsorbed material in the fluid adjacent to the catalyst surface. At equilibrium and constant temperature, such a relation is known as an adsorption isotherm. In developing an idealized model for such an analysis, several assumptions are necessary. The Langmuir concept of adsorption is based upon the following postulates:

1. It is assumed that all the "active centers," with respect to catalytic effect, have the same capacity for adsorption and that the rest of the surface has none.
2. There is no interaction between adsorbed molecules; *i.e.*, the amount of adsorption does not affect the specific rate.
3. All adsorption occurs by the same mechanism.

The analysis, and resulting mathematical formulation, is most easily followed by study of a specific assumed example. Assume that the reactant A is a diatomic molecule which dissociates on adsorption according to the reaction

$$2s + A \underset{k_r}{\overset{k_f}{\rightleftarrows}} 2A_{\frac{1}{2}}s$$

where s is a catalyst site and $A_{\frac{1}{2}}s$ may be considered a compound resulting from the "reaction" of a dissociated A molecule and the site during the chemisorption process.

The rate of adsorption is therefore proportional to the bulk-phase reactant concentration and to the square of the concentration of unoccupied active-catalyst sites. It is important to recall that the concentration of A in the fluid phase will be the same as the bulk-phase concentration only if both external and pore diffusional resistances are small compared with the resistance of the adsorption step. The rate of adsorption is given by the equation

$$r_f = k_f C_A (1 - \theta)^2 \tag{4-44}$$

where θ is fraction of total sites occupied by adsorbed A and k_f includes a conversion factor to allow for the total number of active sites per unit weight of catalyst. Thus k_f not only is temperature-dependent but is also a function of the catalyst involved and its physical form, in so far as this latter characteristic affects the number of sites per unit weight of catalyst.

Similarly, the rate of desorption of A is given by

$$r_r = k_r(\theta)^2 \tag{4-45}$$

At equilibrium between adsorbed dissociated A and the A molecules in the fluid phase, the rates of adsorption and desorption are equal:

$$r_f = r_r = k_f C_A (1 - \theta)^2 = k_r(\theta)^2$$

$$K_A = \frac{k_f}{k_r} = \frac{\theta^2}{C_A(1 - \theta)^2} \tag{4-46}$$

where K_A is an equilibrium constant for the adsorption process and is a function of temperature, the catalyst involved, and the catalyst's physical configuration.

Solution of Eq. (4-46) for θ yields

$$\theta = \frac{\sqrt{K_A C_A}}{1 + \sqrt{K_A C_A}} \tag{4-47}$$

This same development may be followed for more complicated postulated adsorption mechanisms. For instance, if two gases are simultaneously adsorbed and one, B, dissociates on adsorption, the resulting rate equations become

$$r_{fA} = k_{fA} C_A (1 - \theta_A - \theta_B)$$
$$r_{fB} = k_{fB} C_B (1 - \theta_A - \theta_B)^2$$
$$r_{rA} = k_{rA} \theta_A$$
$$r_{rB} = k_{rB} \theta_B^2$$

where θ_A and θ_B are the fraction of the surface covered by adsorbed A and B, respectively. In terms of equilibrium constants they are

$$\theta_A = \frac{K_A C_A}{1 + K_A C_A + \sqrt{K_B C_B}}$$

$$\theta_B = \frac{\sqrt{K_B C_B}}{1 + K_A C_A + \sqrt{K_B C_B}}$$

K_A and K_B are adsorption equilibrium constants for the separate processes involving adsorption of each type of molecule.

The derivation of expressions for the fraction of total catalyst sites occupied by a particular species will prove of value when the steps of chemisorption and desorption are considered as part of a sequence of steps which also includes the surface reaction of adsorbed molecules. This step is considered in the next section.

Surface Reaction. As mentioned above, "adsorption" and "desorption" are most usefully thought of as individual steps in a series of chemical reactions occurring sequentially in the conversion of reactants to products. One of these steps may be assumed to determine the over-all rate of reaction, in which case the others are assumed to be occurring at near equilibrium conditions.

The procedure involved in testing whether a step in a postulated mechanism may be controlling is as follows:

1. Correct the fluid-phase concentration adjacent to the catalyst surface for the effect of external diffusion. Consider the influence of pore diffusion on the over-all rate.
2. Postulate an adsorption–surface reaction–desorption mechanism and derive a rate expression assuming one of the steps in this mechanism to be rate-controlling and the others to occur at near equilibrium conditions.
3. Test to see if the experimental data can be predicted with reasonable accuracy by the derived rate expression.

The data and analysis procedure described provides little insight into the true mechanism of the reaction. All that can be said is that a mathematical equation has been developed which agrees with the experimental data over the range studied.

An example of the procedure outlined above will best serve to make the method clear.

The reaction to be considered is

$$A + B \rightleftarrows R$$

1. An adsorption–surface reaction–desorption mechanism is assumed (where s represents a catalyst site)

1: $A + s \rightleftarrows As$ 2: $B + s \rightleftarrows Bs$	Adsorption of A and B molecules
3: $As + B \rightleftarrows Rs$	Adsorbed A reacts with B in the fluid. There is no reaction of A with adsorbed B. Adsorbed B serves only to block catalyst sites
4: $Rs \rightleftarrows R + s$	Desorption of product R

2. For each of these reactions it is possible to formulate a rate expression involving both forward and reverse reactions. If the reaction occurs at near equilibrium

conditions the concentrations are related by an equilibrium constant.

1: $$r_1 = k_{1_f}C_A(1 - \theta_A - \theta_B - \theta_R) - k_{1_r}\theta_A$$

$$K_1 = \frac{\theta_A}{C_A(1 - \theta_A - \theta_B - \theta_R)}$$

2: $$r_2 = k_{2_f}C_B(1 - \theta_A - \theta_B - \theta_R) - k_{2_r}\theta_B$$

$$K_2 = \frac{\theta_B}{C_B(1 - \theta_A - \theta_B - \theta_R)}$$

3: $$r_3 = k_{3_f}(\theta_A)C_B - k_{3_r}\theta_R$$

$$K_3 = \frac{\theta_R}{\theta_A C_B}$$

4: $$r_4 = k_{4_f}\theta_R - k_{4_r}C_R(1 - \theta_A - \theta_B - \theta_R)$$

$$K_4 = \frac{C_R(1 - \theta_A - \theta_B - \theta_R)}{\theta_R}$$

In these equations K_1, K_2, K_3, and K_4 are equilibrium constants for the individual steps. Note that K_4 is written for a desorption step and is the reciprocal of the usual adsorption equilibrium constant.

3. One of these steps is now assumed to be rate-controlling and the others to occur at near equilibrium. Let us assume, for now, that step 3, the surface reaction between adsorbed A and B in the fluid, is rate-controlling. The appropriate rate expression would then be that given for r_3; however, it involves the fraction of total catalyst sites occupied by A and by $R(\theta_A$ and $\theta_R)$. Available experimental data will be in terms of C_A, C_B, and C_R. Making use of the assumption that steps 1, 2, and 4 occur at near equilibrium will allow determination of θ_A and θ_R in terms of known quantities

$$\theta_A = K_1C_A(1 - \theta_A - \theta_B - \theta_R)$$

$$\theta_R = \frac{C_R(1 - \theta_A - \theta_B - \theta_R)}{K_4}$$

and $$K_3 = \frac{k_{3f}}{k_{3r}} \quad \text{or} \quad k_{3r} = \frac{k_{3f}}{K_3}$$

Thus

$$r_3 = k_{3f}K_1C_AC_B(1 - \theta_A - \theta_B - \theta_R) - \frac{k_{3f}C_R}{K_3}\frac{(1 - \theta_A - \theta_B - \theta_R)}{K_4}$$

$$\text{or } r_3 = k_{3f}(1 - \theta_A - \theta_B - \theta_R)\left(K_1C_AC_B - \frac{C_R}{K_3K_4}\right) \tag{4-48}$$

The fraction of total catalyst sites vacant has been defined as $(1 - \theta_A - \theta_B - \theta_R) = \theta_v$. Therefore,

$$1 - K_1C_A\theta_v - K_2C_B\theta_v - \frac{C_R}{K_4}\theta_v = \theta_v \tag{4-49}$$

Solving for $\theta_v = (1 - \theta_A - \theta_B - \theta_R)$ in Eq. (4-49) and substituting in Eq. (4-48) yields with simplification:

$$r_3 = \frac{k_{3f}K_1(C_AC_B - C_R/K_3K_4K_1)}{K_1C_A + K_2C_B + C_R/K_4 + 1} \tag{4-50}$$

The product $K_1K_3K_4$ is equivalent to the over-all equilibrium constant for all the productive steps in the assumed mechanism. Equation (4-50) may be rewritten as

$$r_3 = \frac{k(C_AC_B - C_R/K)}{K_AC_A + K_BC_B + K_RC_R + 1}$$

where $k = k_{3f}K_1$, $K = K_1K_3K_4$, $K_A = K_1$, $K_B = K_2$, and $K_R = 1/K_4$. Derived rate expressions of this type for several different postulated reaction mechanisms are presented in Table 4-8.

4. Experimental rate data are used to evaluate the constants k_{3f}, K_1, K_2, and K_4 in Eq. (4-50); bulk-fluid-phase concentrations can be used only if there are no diffusional resistances.

A summary of rate expressions resulting for many assumed mechanisms, with different further assumptions as to the rate-controlling steps, is presented as Table 4-8.

It is appropriate to mention the utility of "initial rate" data in the test for a fit of the proposed rate equation against experimental results. It should be emphasized though that this technique is useful only for a preliminary screening for the validity of alternate proposed equations. If one can obtain the experimental rate when the conversion of A has been negligible (*i.e.*, negligible formation of R), then C_R in Eq. (4-50) is zero and the equation simplifies to

$$r_0 = \frac{kC_AC_B}{K_1C_A + K_2C_B + 1} \tag{4-51}$$

where r_0 is used to denote the initial rate and $k = k_{3f}K_1$. The utility of Eq. (4-51) over Eq. (4-50) is its increased simplicity for preliminary comparison with experimental data.

It may be shown (see subsections on Reactor Design and Interpretation of Laboratory Kinetic Data) that a flow reactor is described mathematically by

$$\int_0^x \frac{dx}{r_A} = \frac{V_R}{F} \tag{4-52}$$

where x = moles of A converted per mole of feed
r_A = rate expression, moles of A converted per unit time per unit volume
V_R = reactor volume
F = molal feed rate to the reactor

With catalytic reactors it is sometimes convenient to express r_A in terms of a unit mass of catalyst rather than unit volume and therefore V_R is replaced by W, the total mass of catalyst in the reactor. Presentation of catalytic-reactor data is often made then as a plot of x vs. W/F. It is apparent that the slope of such a plot at $x = 0$ will be the initial rate r_0.

Several methods are possible for determining the initial rate from the x vs. W/F curve. For example,

1. Measure the slope of the tangent to the curve at the point $x = 0$, $W/F = 0$.
2. Measure slopes of tangents at several values of W/F, plot slopes vs. W/F, and then extrapolate to $W/F = 0$.
3. Fit an empirical equation to the x vs. W/F curve and differentiate the equation.

HETEROGENEOUS REACTIONS—UNCATALYZED

Many non-catalyzed industrial processes involve reactants in more than one phase. Such reactions are complicated by the fact that, before substances in different phases can react, they must diffuse to at least the interface. Consequently, in addition to chemical reaction-rate kinetics, certain physical factors which affect the rate of mass transfer between phases also affect the over-all rate of a heterogeneous reaction. These factors are:

1. Amount of interfacial surface.
2. Rate of diffusion of fluids to and across the interfacial film, which is influenced principally by the relative velocities of the two phases, the pressure of the gas phase, and to a minor extent the temperature of the system, in addition to the physical properties of the reactants and the geometry of the system.
3. Rate of diffusion of the products away from the reaction zone. This is of importance only with reversible

Table 4-8. Mechanisms and Their Corresponding Rate Equations

Chemical equation	Catalytic steps	Rate equation*
$A \rightleftharpoons R$	$A + s \rightleftharpoons As$	$r = \frac{k(C_A - C_R/K)}{1 + K_R C_R}$
	$As \rightleftharpoons Rs$	$r = \frac{k(C_A - C_R/K)}{1 + K_A C_A + K_R C_R}$
	$Rs \rightleftharpoons R + s$	$r = \frac{k(C_A - C_R/K)}{1 + K_A C_A}$
$A \rightleftharpoons R$	$2A + s \rightleftharpoons A_2s$	$r = \frac{k(C_A^2 - C_R^2/K^2)}{1 + K_R C_R + K_R C_R^2}$
	$A_2s + s \rightleftharpoons 2As$	$r = \frac{k(C_A^2 - C_R^2/K^2)}{(1 + K_R C_R + K_A C_A^2)^2}$
	$As \rightleftharpoons Rs$	$r = \frac{k(C_A - C_R/K)}{1 + K_A C_A^2 + K_A' C_A + K_R C_R}$
	$Rs \rightleftharpoons R + s$	$r = \frac{k(C_A - C_R/K)}{1 + K_A C_A^2 + K_A' C_A}$
$A \rightleftharpoons R$	$A + 2s \rightleftharpoons 2A_{\frac{1}{2}}s$	$r = \frac{k(C_A - C_R/K)}{(1 + \sqrt{K_R C_R} + K_R' C_R)^2}$
	$2A_{\frac{1}{2}}s \rightleftharpoons Rs + s$	$r = \frac{k(C_A - C_R/K)}{(1 + \sqrt{K_A C_A} + K_R C_R)^2}$
	$Rs \rightleftharpoons R + S$	$r = \frac{k(C_A - C_R/K)}{1 + \sqrt{K_A C_A} + K_A' C_A}$
$A \rightleftharpoons R + S$	$A + s \rightleftharpoons As$	$r = \frac{k(C_A - C_R C_S/K)}{1 + K_{RS} C_R C_S + K_R C_R + K_S C_S}$
	$As + s \rightleftharpoons Rs + Ss$	$r = \frac{k(C_A - C_R C_S/K)}{(1 + K_A C_A + K_R C_R + K_S C_S)^2}$
	$Rs \rightleftharpoons R + s$ $Ss \rightleftharpoons S + s$	$r = \frac{k(C_A - C_R C_S/K)}{C_S(1 + K_A C_A + (K_{AS} C_A/C_S) + K_S C_S)}$
$A \rightleftharpoons R + S$	$A + s \rightleftharpoons As$	$r = \frac{k(C_A - C_R C_S/K)}{1 + K_R C_R + K_{RS} C_R C_S}$
	$As \rightleftharpoons Rs + S$	$r = \frac{k(C_A - C_R C_S/K)}{1 + K_A C_A + K_R C_R}$
	$Rs \rightleftharpoons R + s$	$r = \frac{k(C_A - C_R C_S/K)}{C_S(1 + K_A C_A + K_{AS} C_A/C_S)}$
$A + B \rightleftharpoons R$	$A + s \rightleftharpoons As$	$r = \frac{k(C_A - C_R/KC_B)}{1 + (K_{RB} C_R/C_B) + K_B C_B + K_R C_R}$
	$B + s \rightleftharpoons Bs$	$r = \frac{kC_B - C_R/KC_A)}{1 + K_A C_A + (K_{RA} C_R/C_A) + K_R C_R}$
	$As + Bs \rightleftharpoons Rs + s$	$r = \frac{k(C_A C_B - C_R/K)}{(1 + K_A C_A + K_B C_B + K_R C_R)^2}$
	$Rs \rightleftharpoons R + s$	$r = \frac{k(C_A C_B - C_R/K)}{1 + K_A C_A + K_B C_B + K_{AB} C_A C_B}$
$A + B \rightleftharpoons R + S$	$A + s \rightleftharpoons As$	$r = \frac{k(C_A - C_R C_S/KC_B)}{1 + (K_{RS} C_R C_S/C_B)^{\frac{1}{2}} + K_B C_B + K_R C_R + K_S C_S}$
	$B + s \rightleftharpoons Bs$	$r = \frac{k(C_B - C_R C_S/KC_A)}{1 + (K_{RS} C_R C_S/C_A) + K_A C_A + K_R C_R + K_S C_S}$
	$As + Bs \rightleftharpoons Rs + Ss$	$r = \frac{k(C_A C_B - C_R C_S/K)}{(1 + K_A C_A + K_B C_B + K_R C_R + K_S C_S)^2}$
	$Rs \rightleftharpoons R + s$ $Ss \rightleftharpoons S + s$	$r = \frac{k[(C_A C_B/C_S) - C_R/K]}{1 + K_A C_A + K_B C_B + K_S C_S + K_{AB} C_A C_B/C_S}$
$A + B \rightleftharpoons R + S$	$A + 2s \rightleftharpoons 2A_{\frac{1}{2}}s$	$r = \frac{k(C_A - C_R C_S/KC_B)}{[1 + K_{RS} C_R C_S/C_B + K_B C_B + K_R C_R + K_S C_S]^2}$
	$B + s \rightleftharpoons Bs$	$r = \frac{k(C_B - C_R C_S/KC_A)}{1 + \sqrt{K_A C_A} + (K_{RS} C_R C_S/C_A) + K_R C_R + K_S C_S}$
	$2A_{\frac{1}{2}}s + Bs \rightleftharpoons Rs + Ss + s$	$r = \frac{k(C_A C_B - C_R C_S/K)}{(1 + \sqrt{K_A C_A} + K_B C_B + K_R C_R + K_S C_S)^3}$
	$Rs \rightleftharpoons R + s$	$r = \frac{k(C_A C_B/C_S - C_R/K)}{1 + K_A \sqrt{C_A} + K_B C_B + (K_{AB} C_A C_B/C_S) + K_S C_S}$
	$Ss \rightleftharpoons S + s$	$r = \frac{k(C_A C_B/C_R - C_S/K)}{1 + \sqrt{K_A C_A} + K_B C_B + K_R C_R + K_{AB} C_A C_B/C_R}$
$A + B \rightleftharpoons R + S$	$B + s \rightleftharpoons Bs$	$r = \frac{k(C_B - C_S C_R/KC_A)}{1 + K_R C_R + K_{RS} C_R C_S/C_A}$
	$A + Bs \rightleftharpoons Rs + S$	$r = \frac{k(C_A C_B - C_R C_S/K)}{1 + K_R C_R + K_B C_B}$
	$Rs \rightleftharpoons R + s$	$r = \frac{k[(C_A C_B/C_S) - C_R/K]}{1 + (K_{AB} C_A C_B/C_S) + K_B C_B}$

$K_{AB} \ldots$ = combined equilibrium constants.
K = over-all equilibrium constant for the chemical equation.
k = constant.
* The rate equation is opposite the catalytic step assumed to be rate-controlling.

reactions, unless the concentrations of the products are sufficient to influence the diffusivities of the reactants.

Of importance is turbulence resulting from agitation or other means. Not only may this control the amount of surface available for reaction, but it may reduce diffusional resistances.

A complete formulation of the rate equation must therefore take into account both the mass-transfer and chemical-reaction resistances. In some instances, one of the rates, mass transfer or reaction, is so much smaller than the other that it becomes controlling. Experimentally, the dominant step can be detected by observing the effects of certain changes in operating conditions. For example, if the over-all rate increases markedly with temperature in accordance with the Arrhenius law, the chemical resistance is likely to be of considerable significance. Or, the rate may change when the flow rate is varied, in a way predicted by correlations for the rate of mass transfer.

When a reaction is studied experimentally, it may be desirable to seek the conditions under which one step at a time is controlling. Though with this information it will not be possible to calculate rigorously the rate for any intermediate condition, in many instances an adequate estimate can be made from the extreme conditions. If the rate of mass transfer is controlling, other sections of this handbook present adequate methods for handling the problem (see Sec. 14, in particular). For the case where chemical-reaction kinetics alone controls, earlier portions of this section provide applicable methods. Instances where both rates are of the same order of magnitude are discussed briefly below.

Heterogeneous uncatalyzed reactions of industrial significance occur between all combinations of gas, liquid, and solid phases.

Gas-Liquid Reactions. This classification constitutes that one most thoroughly studied both experimentally and theoretically. For a complete discussion of the general case where both chemical kinetics and mass-transfer rates influence the over-all rate, see Sec. 14. This treats the common industrial case in which one of the reactants is absorbed by the liquid where reaction occurs.

Liquid-Liquid Reactions. If chemical reaction occurs in only one of two partially miscible liquid phases which have been intimately intermixed, and if both reaction kinetics and rate of mass transfer of one of the reactants to the phase of reaction contribute to fixing the over-all rate, an analysis for simultaneous absorption and chemical reaction as discussed in Sec. 14 is appropriate.

However, if the reaction proceeds in both phases, the over-all reaction rate is influenced by the rates of diffusion to the interface, reaction at the interface, and the individual homogeneous reactions in each of the two separate phases. If agitation of the system is sufficient to maintain an equilibrium distribution of the components between the phases, the relation between the concentration of a particular component in each phase is given by the distribution coefficient. The over-all rate is the sum of the rates in the individual phases. As an example of the mathematical analysis, consider the second-order reaction between the partially miscible components A and B:

$$A + B \rightarrow \text{products}$$

Then, the rates of disappearance of A by reaction are stated for each phase as

$$r_{A_1} = k_1 C_{A_1} C_{B_1} = -\frac{1}{V_1}\frac{dn_{A_1}}{d\theta}$$

and

$$r_{A_2} = k_2 C_{A_2} C_{B_2} = -\frac{1}{V_2}\frac{dn_{A_2}}{d\theta}$$

where the subscripts 1 and 2 refer to the individual phases. At phase equilibrium, the distribution coefficients apply:

$$K_A = \frac{C_{A_1}}{C_{A_2}} \quad \text{and} \quad K_B = \frac{C_{B_1}}{C_{B_2}}$$

The total rate of disappearance of A by reaction is r_A.

$$r_A = \frac{-1}{V_1 + V_2}\frac{dn_A}{d\theta}$$

and

$$\frac{dn_A}{d\theta} = \frac{dn_{A_1}}{d\theta} + \frac{dn_{A_2}}{d\theta} = -(k_1 C_{A_1} C_{B_1} V_1 + k_2 C_{A_2} C_{B_2} V_2)$$

or substituting,

$$r_A = \frac{1}{V_1 + V_2}\left(k_1 C_{A_1} C_{B_1} V_1 + k_2 \frac{C_{A_1}}{K_A}\frac{C_{B_1}}{K_B} V_2\right)$$

$$r_A = \left(\bar{V}_1 k_1 + \bar{V}_2 \frac{k_2}{K_A K_B}\right) C_{A_1} C_{B_1} \quad (4\text{-}53)$$

where $\bar{V}_1$ and $\bar{V}_2$ are the volume fractions of each of the phases.

In applying a relation such as Eq. (4-53), it would be convenient to assume that $k_1 = k_2$. If these reaction-rate constants are indeed independent of concentration and functions only of temperature, this would be valid. However, this simple approach is seldom justified, for usually the functional relation between concentrations is different in each phase, implying a different mechanism with, of course, different constants. In general, the dependence of the reaction-rate constant upon concentration is large for liquid-phase reactions.

In a liquid-liquid, non-catalyzed reaction, if agitation is insufficient to maintain miscibility equilibrium between the two phases, the rate expression must include a mass-transfer term. Consider the same reaction as that postulated in the illustration assuming phase equilibrium, and stipulate further that phase 1 is predominantly component A and that phase 2 consists for the most part of component B. The diffusional resistance for A is then largely in phase 2, and for B in phase 1. Finally, assume that phase equilibrium exists at the interface, and that the rate of chemical reaction in both phases is limited by mass transfer. This means that the rate of mass transfer of A to phase 2 equals the rate of disappearance of A in that phase by reaction. This will occur when C_{A_2} drops to a level $C_{A_2}^0$ which balances these rates. Thus $C_{A_2}^0$ is a steady-state value as is $C_{B_1}^0$.

By reaction

$$-\frac{dn_{A_1}}{d\theta} = r_{A_1} V_1 = k_1 C_{A_1} C_{B_1}^0 V_1$$

By mass transfer

$$\frac{dn_{A_1}}{d\theta} = -k_2'a\left(\frac{C_{A_1}}{K_A} - C_{A_2}^0\right)(V_1 + V_2)$$

where $k_2'a$ is a mass-transfer coefficient for phase 2 per unit volume of both phases. In these equations, k' = moles/(sq. ft.)(hr.)(moles/cu. ft. driving force), a = sq. ft. of interfacial surface per unit volume of both phases, and C_{A_1}/K_A is the equilibrium interfacial value of C_{A_2}. If the rate of transfer of A to phase 2 equals its rate of disappearance in that phase,

$$r_{A_2} V_2 = k_2'a(V_1 + V_2)\left(\frac{C_{A_1}}{K_A} - C_{A_2}^0\right) \quad (4\text{-}54)$$

also $r_{A_1}V_1 + r_{A_2}V_2 = r_A(V_1 + V_2)$, the total rate of disappearance of A from the system. Hence,

$$r_A = \left[k_1\bar{V}_1 C_{A_1} C_{B_1} + k_2'a \left(\frac{C_{A_1}}{K_A} - C_{A_2} \right) \right]$$

Also,

$$V_2 r_{A_2} = k_2 C_{B_2} C_{A_2}{}^0 V_2 \tag{4-55}$$

By equating Eqs. (4-54) and (4-55), $C_{A_2}{}^0$ can be defined in an expression involving only known concentrations. $C_{B_2}{}^0$ may be analogously treated. These resulting expressions are

$$C_{A_2}{}^0 = \frac{k_2'a(C_A/K_A)(V_1 + V_2)}{k_2 V_2 C_{B_2} + k_2'a(V_1 + V_2)}$$

$$C_{B_1}{}^0 = \frac{k_1'a(C_{B_2}/K_B)(V_1 + V_2)}{k_1 V_1 C_{A_1} + k_1'a(V_1 + V_2)}$$

Approximations for $k'a$ may be made utilizing empirical correlations; however, these are strongly dependent on the physical configuration of the contacting system (see Secs. 14 and 21). It is probably best to use experimentally determined empirical expressions for scale-up purposes.

Gas-Solid and Liquid-Solid Reactions. In general, non-catalyzed reactions in these classifications occur at the solid surface, as is the case in catalytic heterogeneous reactions. Therefore, the method of analysis already presented for catalytic reactions is appropriate in this case as well. However, a chemisorption step is not necessarily involved, as is invariably the case with catalytic behavior, and attention needs to be focused only on the diffusional processes and reaction at the surface. Should reaction occur in the fluid phase after either solution or sublimation of the solid, a treatment analogous to that for homogeneous reaction is appropriate. The concentration of the solid-phase reactant in the fluid phase may be postulated as equal to one of two possible values. If there is good agitation and resultant complete intermixing, the solid-phase reactant may be assumed to be at its equilibrium concentration as fixed by solubility or vapor-pressure considerations. Alternately, the mass-transfer rate may be controlling and the fluid-phase concentration falls below the equilibrium value to some point where the rate of mass transfer to the fluid phase equals the rate of chemical reaction in that phase.

The intermediate case, wherein the fluid-phase concentration of the solid is transient—rising slowly toward the equilibrium value—has not been generally treated. In this instance, both chemical kinetics and diffusional rates affect the over-all rate. The treatment presented for simultaneous absorption and chemical reaction in Sec. 14 may be of assistance in analyzing this type of problem after suitable adaptation for interfacial conditions.

DESIGN OF KINETIC EXPERIMENTS AND INTERPRETATION OF LABORATORY KINETIC DATA

Introduction. To design full-scale chemical plants involving chemical reactions, one must have available laboratory or pilot-plant kinetic data. It is not possible to predict the mechanism of even simple homogeneous reactions. The science of predicting reaction-rate constants as well as the temperature dependence of these constants from the properties of the reacting molecules is in its infancy. What must be derived from laboratory data is, then, a rate expression involving the concentrations of reactants and products in a functional relationship accurate over a reasonable range of operating variables. This relationship may be entirely empirical in nature or may be of a form derivable from fundamental theoretical analyses. In the case of heterogeneous catalyzed reactions, the latter technique leads to expressions which are difficult to integrate in design use and involve several temperature-dependent constants which must be evaluated independently. This requires more extensive experimental data. There is justification for this procedure. First, the difficulty of integration has been largely done away with by the application of digital computers. Secondly, the more theoretical form of the rate equation may be extrapolated outside the range of the experimental data with more confidence.

Weller [*Am. Inst. Chem. Engrs. J.*, **2**, 61 (1956)] presents arguments for the use of an empirical equation such as

$$r_A = kC_A{}^a C_B{}^b C_C{}^c C_D{}^d \cdots$$

where a, b, c, and d are empirically derived exponents. For ease in applying the derived rate equation, Weller suggests limiting values for these exponents to integral or half integral values. For a large variety of reactions examined, it is pointed out that (1) such an equation represents the data as well as the more theoretical form, (2) the exponents are temperature-independent over a reasonable temperature range, and (3) use of such an empirical form protects the investigator from the tendency to assume that he has discovered the actual mechanism, while in fact, he has only postulated one of perhaps several mechanisms which empirically fit the data.

Chemical Similitude. It is still advisable to build and operate a prototype pilot-scale reactor to ensure satisfactory operation of the full-scale unit. Walas ("Reaction Kinetics for Chemical Engineers," McGraw-Hill, New York, 1959) presents a useful discussion of the technique used in designing the prototype reactor to ensure similitude on scale-up. This discussion is summarized below.

Consideration of the appropriate differential equations at steady state for the conservation of mass, momentum, and thermal energy leads to seven dimensionless groups which must be equal for both model and prototype in order for complete similitude to exist. These groups are shown as items a to g in Table 4-9.

Table 4-9. Dimensionless Groups in Chemical Reaction*

Homogeneous reaction	Heterogeneous reaction	Name of group
(a) $\frac{rL}{uC}$	(h) $\frac{r}{SC}$	Damkohler
(b) $\frac{rR^2}{DC}$	(i) $\frac{rD_p{}^2}{DC}$	
(c) $\frac{u}{rL\,\Delta V}$	(j) $\frac{S}{r\,\Delta V}$	
(d) $\frac{Ru\rho}{\mu}$	(k) $\frac{D_p SL\rho}{\mu}$	Reynolds
(e) $\frac{C_p uR^2\rho}{kL}$	(l) $\frac{c_p S\rho R^2}{k + 4/3D_p\rho\sigma T^3}$	Peclet
(f) $\frac{QrR^2}{k\,\Delta T}$	(m) $\frac{QrR^2}{(k + 4/3D_p\rho\sigma T^3)\,\Delta T}$	
(g) $\frac{Qr}{T(4a\epsilon\sigma T^3 - C_p\rho r\,\Delta V)}$	(n) $\frac{Qr}{C_p\rho r\,\Delta V\,\Delta T}$	

* From Walas, "Reaction Kinetics for Chemical Engineers," McGraw-Hill, New York, 1959.

The behavior of a reaction may be compared in two vessels whose radii are in the ratio λ. For simplicity, the conditions in the two reactors will be taken so nearly similar that all important physical properties such as viscosity and density are substantially the same in both. Accordingly, comparison of the dimensionless groups yields these relations, where the primes designate the prototype:

$$R' = \lambda R \tag{4-56}$$
$$L' = \lambda L \tag{4-57}$$
$$u' = \lambda^{-1} u \tag{4-58}$$
$$T' = \lambda^{-2/3} T \tag{4-59}$$
$$r' = \lambda^{-2} r \tag{4-60}$$
$$e^{-b/T'} = \lambda^{-2} e^{-b/T} \tag{4-61}$$

The last of these follows from the Arrhenius equation. When radiant-heat transfer is not a factor, Eq. (4-59) is ignored. From these equations it appears, for example, that greater flow rates and faster reaction rates are needed in the smaller reactor when complete similitude is to hold.

Similar relations hold for heterogeneous system. As a linear dimension, the particle diameter is used instead of the radius of the reactor, and the space velocity S instead of the linear velocity u. Seven dimensionless groups for heterogeneous reactions are also listed in Table 4-9, items h to n, though only six of these are independent. The term $\frac{4}{3D_p \sigma T^3}$ is the contribution of thermal radiation to the thermal conductivity.

Comparing two heterogeneous reactors whose radii are in the ratio λ and making the same assumptions regarding physical properties that were made in the derivation of Eq. (4-56), two corresponding sets of relations are obtained, depending on the dominant mode of heat transfer. When conductive heat flow is dominant,

$$R' = \lambda R \tag{4-62}$$
$$L' = \lambda L \tag{4-63}$$
$$D_p' = \lambda D_p \tag{4-64}$$
$$S' = \lambda^{-2} S \tag{4-65}$$
$$r' = \lambda^{-2} r \tag{4-66}$$
$$\Delta T' = \lambda \, \Delta T \tag{4-67}$$

When radiant heat flow dominates and the temperatures of the two reactors are equal,

$$R' = \lambda R \tag{4-68}$$
$$L' = \lambda^{2/3} L \tag{4-69}$$
$$D_p' = \lambda^{2/3} D_p \tag{4-70}$$
$$S' = \lambda^{-4/3} S \tag{4-71}$$
$$r' = \lambda^{4/3} r \tag{4-72}$$
$$\Delta T' = \lambda^{2/3} \, \Delta T \tag{4-73}$$

The conditions of similitude in heterogeneous catalytic reactors require, for example, that the prototype be relatively shorter and that the particle diameter increase more slowly than the vessel diameter. Also, the catalyst activity must be different in the two sizes of reactors.

On the whole, the requirements for complete dimensional similitude are impractical. Whether chemical, dynamic, thermodynamic, or geometric similitude, individually or in partial combination, is adequate depends on the characteristics of each reaction mixture and the operating conditions. Table 4-10 lists the dimensionless groups that may be ignored in certain special cases. Changes in operating conditions, notably temperature,

Table 4-10. Special Cases Requiring Limited Similitude*

Condition	Dimensionless groups of Table 4-9 that may be ignored	
	Homogeneous	Heterogeneous
Batch, or low flow rate	a, c, d, e	h, j, k, l
Small diffusional resistance	b	i
Constant volume	c, g	j, n
Small radiation heat transfer	g	n
Adiabatic, with small heat of reaction	f, g	m, n

* From Walas, "Reaction Kinetics for Chemical Engineers," McGraw-Hill, New York, 1959.

may alter the relative importance of the dimensionless groups.

When the controlling condition is either heat transfer or diffusive mass transfer, dynamical similitude is required, since the coefficients of both processes depend on the Reynolds number. Chemical similitude alone is required when the chemical reaction rate controls the operation; equality of the Damkohler group rL/uC is then sufficient. In this group, the term L/u is the mean reaction time. Thus chemical similitude is achieved when the reaction rates, the reaction times, and the initial concentrations are the same in both model and prototype.

When chemical similitude is preserved, the geometry and the heat-transfer behavior are also fixed, but not necessarily as required by dynamical similitude. Table 4-11 shows the geometrical relations for homogeneous reactions and for heterogeneous ones with two different particle-size to reactor-volume relationships. Similarly, Table 4-12 shows the behavior of heat transfer through the walls of the vessels of model and prototype whose volumes are in the ratio $1/\lambda^3$. Diffusive mass transfer is neglected in both tables.

Table 4-11. Geometrical Relations in Chemical Similitude*

Item	Ratio of prototype to model		
	Homogeneous	Heterogeneous	
Particle diameter	...	λ	1
Reactor volume	λ^3	λ^3	λ^3
Catalyst surface/volume	...	λ	1
Volumetric rate of flow	λ^3	λ^2	λ^3
Reactor volume/volumetric rate of flow	1	λ	1

* From Walas, "Reaction Kinetics for Chemical Engineers," McGraw-Hill New York, 1959.

Table 4-12. Heat-transfer Relations in Chemical Similitude*

Item	Ratio of prototype to model		
	Homogeneous	Heterogeneous	
Particle diameter	...	λ	1
Heat-transfer surface	λ^2	λ^2	λ^2
Volumetric flow rate	λ^3	λ^2	λ^3
Heat transfer per unit of surface	1	λ^2	λ^2
Heat transfer per unit of through-put	λ^{-1}	1	λ^{-1}

* From Walas, "Reaction Kinetics for Chemical Engineers," McGraw-Hill, New York, 1959.

All nomenclature is consistent with the prior discussion. C is concentration in moles/cu. ft.; L is reactor length in feet; u is velocity in ft./sec.; r is the rate of reaction expressed as moles/(cu. ft.)(sec.); R equals reactor radius in feet; D is diffusivity in sq. ft./sec.; ΔV is the volume change per unit disappearance of the reactant for which r is written in cu. ft./mole; ρ is the density in lb./cu. ft.; μ is the viscosity in lb./(ft.)(sec.); C_p is the heat capacity in B.t.u./(lb.)(°F.); k is the thermal conductivity in B.t.u./(sec.)(sq. ft.)(°F./ft.); ΔT is the temperature in excess of the wall temperature in °F.; Q is the heat generated by reaction in B.t.u./mole reacted; D_p is the particle diameter in feet; S is the space velocity with units of sec.$^{-1}$; a is the wall surface area per unit of reactor volume in ft.$^{-1}$; σ is a proportionality constant of 0.484 B.t.u./sec. (sq. ft.)(°F.)^4; ϵ is the emissivity or absorptivity of the reactor wall and is dimensionless.

Batch Reactors and Integral-flow Reactors. The basic design equation applicable to either experimental or full-scale reactors of any type is

$$\int_0^\theta V_R \, d\theta = -\int_{n_{A_1}}^{n_{A_2}} \frac{dn_A}{r_A} \tag{4-74}$$

where n_{A_1} and n_{A_2} are the number of moles of reactant A present at time zero and at time equal to θ (sec.). V_R is the reactor volume in cubic feet and r_A is the rate of disappearance of A expressed as moles/(cu. ft.)(sec.). This equation is generally applicable and will describe any system or reaction if the proper expression for r_A is used. However, the form of equation for r_A may depend upon the type of reactor because of the effects of mixing. If the system is non-isothermal, the temperature dependence of the constants must be included in the expression for r_A. A heat balance is then also required to relate the system temperature to the amount of A converted, the heat of reaction, the specific heat of the system, and the heat losses to the surroundings. However, in experimental analysis, one should attempt to obtain isothermal operation.

Equation (4-74) may be simplified somewhat for constant-volume batch processes to

$$V_R\theta = -\int_{n_{A_1}}^{n_{A_2}} \frac{dn_A}{r_A} \tag{4-75}$$

If r_A is expressed in terms of molal concentrations, these can be converted to expressions involving n_A by noting that $C_iV_R = n_i$ and n_i at any time may be related to n_A using the initial number of moles of that component and the stoichiometry of the reaction. If a non-constant-volume (constant-pressure) process is involved, V_R must be stated as a function of the conversion and included in the integration of the right-hand term:

$$\theta = \int_{n_{A_1}}^{n_{A_2}} \frac{dn_A}{r_AV_R} \tag{4-76}$$

For flow reactors Eq. (4-75) is usually expressed as

$$\frac{V_R}{F} = -\int_0^{x_{A_2}} \frac{dx}{r_A} \tag{4-77}$$

where x_A is the moles of A converted per mole of total feed and F is the total feed rate in moles/sec.

For catalytic heterogeneous reactors, it is convenient to modify Eq. (4-77) again and express the design equation as

$$\frac{W}{F} = \int_0^{x_{A_2}} \frac{dx_A}{r_A'} \tag{4-78}$$

where r_A' is now expressed as moles of A converted per unit time per unit weight of catalyst [*i.e.*, $r_A' = r_A(1/\rho_c)$ where ρ_c is the pounds of catalyst per unit of reactor volume].

The laboratory and pilot-plant data on which reactor designs must be based are in general of three types:

1. Measurements of composition as a function of time in a batch reactor of constant volume operated at various temperatures and pressures
2. Measurements of composition as a function of feed rate to a flow reactor of constant volume operated at various pressure and temperature levels
3. Measurements of composition as a function of time in a variable-volume batch reactor operated at constant temperature and substantially constant pressure

The third type of data is much less common than the other two, and the experimental technique is more difficult. Data of the second type are generally the most dependable and simple to obtain. This method has the advantage of direct applicability to flow-type reactors. Data of the first type should not be used for the design of flow reactors unless it is certain that the extent of mixing is the same in both the batch and flow systems. In all cases it is important that the temperature does not vary with time in the batch reactor, or with position in the flow reactor

If a simple order is suspected and data at constant volume and temperature are available the equations of Table 4-1 are used. If one of these equations properly represents the experimental data a plot of θ against the variable expression on the right side of the equation will yield a straight line having a slope equal to $1/k$. Equations based on plausible mechanisms are tested in this manner to confirm the mechanism and the order of reaction. For flow reactors the same procedure is followed, the equations of Table 4-1 being used and V_R/F being plotted instead of θ.

In any case it is desirable to secure data for a wide range of pressures and concentrations for positive determination of the proper rate equation. Such data are obtained by varying the initial compositions of reactants and, in gaseous systems, by operation at different pressures. From determinations of reaction-velocity constants at several temperatures, the activation energy and temperature dependence of the rate may be established.

Many processes involve simultaneous and consecutive reactions, or such a complex mechanism that the development of integrated rate equations for the over-all reaction is difficult. The analysis of data on such processes may be handled by determining differential rates of reaction, r_A, by graphical differentiation of curves relating conversions to time for non-flow reactions or to V_R/F for flow reactions. The differential rates of the individual reactions may be determined in this manner from data on the over-all process. The individual rates are correlated with the corresponding concentrations to determine the proper rate equation.

However, graphical differentiation is difficult to apply satisfactorily in a realistic case because of the scatter in most kinetic measurements. Small changes in the shape of the curve drawn through such data have large effects on the predicted rates. It is best to consider such a method for the prediction of rates as only a screening device or first approximation which is then tested against integral expressions. An alternate technique for preliminary evaluation of a proposed mechanism is the use of initial rates (*i.e.*, at $x = 0$) discussed earlier. As mentioned there, this has the further value of simplifying the rate expression by elimination of product concentrations.

Other techniques for employing rate data at finite conversions have been presented by Corrigan in a series of articles in *Chemical Engineering*, July, 1954, to July, 1956. His development is summarized below. The first two methods described, like those above, are primarily useful for screening of alternate mechanisms.

There are several methods for using the data to establish the rate equation. Briefly, they are:

1. Put the rate equation for each mechanism in the linear form

$$f(r) = a + bC_A + cC_R + \cdots$$

and solve for the rate constants.

2. Plot $f(r)$, a function of rate, vs. C_A and observe the shape of the curve.
3. Evaluate the constants by trial and error until an equation is obtained which fits the data.
4. Use the equation in the integrated form

$$\frac{W}{F} = af_1(x) + bf_2(x) + \cdots$$

and solve for the constants directly from the experimental data using the method of least squares. In this equation the terms $f_1(x)$, $f_2(x)$ are functions of x that can be evaluated separately by either numerical or graphical integration.

Each method is considered in detail as it applies to the reaction of A going reversibly to R and S.

Method 1. If the rate equation were

$$r = \frac{k[C_A - (C_R C_S/K)]}{1 + K_A C_A + K_R C_R + K_S C_S} \quad (4\text{-}79)$$

$$r = \frac{C_A - (C_R C_S/K)}{a + bC_A + cC_R + dC_S}$$

it could be arranged to the form

$$\frac{C_A - (C_R C_S/K)}{r} = a + bC_A + cC_R + dC_S \quad (4\text{-}80)$$

Here the unknown constants appear only in the linear terms on the right side and $[C_A - (C_R C_S/K)]/r$ is the function of rate.

We assume that K, the equilibrium constant, is also known. If not, it can be obtained from the x vs. W/F curves since x becomes asymptotic to the equilibrium value. The rate and the corresponding concentrations can be evaluated from the x vs. W/F curves and the constants obtained by the method of least squares.

This is done for each mechanism. If any of the constants for a given mechanism is negative, that mechanism is rejected. This is a basic criterion of the Langmuir-Hinshelwood approach to adsorption; however, negative constants are not unknown. For this method to be valid the terms C_A, C_R, and C_S must be independent variables. Therefore, a series of x vs. W/F curves must be obtained in which some R or S or both are introduced into the feed. If only a feed of pure A is used, C_R and C_S are not independent variables, and c and d cannot be determined separately.

This method is probably the least desirable one for integral-reactor data because of the tedious calculations involved.

Method 2. Another way of indicating the mechanism is to write the rate equation for each mechanism as

$$f(r) = a' + b'C_A \quad (4\text{-}81)$$

If a plot of $f(r)$ vs. C_A is not a straight line, probably the particular mechanism for which the equation was derived does not apply.

As an example, consider the mechanism for which the single-site surface reaction is the controlling step:

$$Al \rightleftarrows Rl + S$$

The rate equation for this mechanism is

$$r = \frac{k[C_A - (C_R C_S/K)]}{1 + K_A C_A + K_R C_R} \quad (4\text{-}82)$$

This may be put into the form

$$\frac{C_A - (C_R C_S/K)}{r} = a + bC_A + cC_R \quad (4\text{-}83)$$

If all the data had been obtained with the use of pure A in the feed, these relations would hold:

$$C_T = C_A + C_R + C_S \qquad \text{and} \qquad C_R + C_S = 2C_R$$

since $C_R = C_S$. C_T = total concentration. Concentrations in this rate expression can be readily converted to partial pressures using the perfect gas law and compressibility factor—if the pressure is sufficiently high, fugacities should be used. Therefore,

$$C_R = \frac{C_T - C_A}{2}$$

Thus Eq. (4-83) will reduce to

$$\frac{C_A - (C_R C_S/K)}{r} = a' + b'C_A$$

where $a' = a + \frac{1}{2}cC_T$; and $b' = b - \frac{1}{2}c$.

Plots of $[C_A - (C_R C_S/K)]/r$ vs. C_A for a series of values of total pressure will give a set of straight parallel lines. If we plot the intercepts of these lines against pressure, we get a straight line of intercept a and slope equal to $\frac{1}{2}c$. The constant b may be obtained from the slope of the original family of curves and the value of c, since $b' = b - \frac{1}{2}c$.

Method 3. Determine the constants by trial and error. After the less likely possibilities are eliminated, the one or two possible equations that remain may be tested against the original x vs. W/F curves by graphical integration.

$$\frac{W}{F} = \int_0^x \frac{dx}{r'} \quad (4\text{-}84)$$

and r' is calculated from the selected rate equation.

If the calculated curve does not fit the data exactly, the constants may be adjusted one at a time and the curve replotted after each adjustment until a close fit is obtained. This method is not recommended except as a final adjustment because it is tedious.

Method 4. Graphically integrate tables of integrated functions. After a mechanism is assumed and the rate equation is derived it is then necessary to establish the constants of this rate equation. The method of f tables rather than the old and more familiar method of slopes can be used. The derivation for calculating the constants by this method is outlined.

This rate equation is postulated:

$$r' = \frac{k[C_A C_B - (C_R C_S/K)]}{1 + K_A C_A + K_R C_R} \quad (4\text{-}85)$$

and the general expression for finding W/F:

$$\frac{W}{F} = \int_0^x \frac{dx}{r'} \quad (4\text{-}86)$$

We can then obtain an expression for W/F by substituting Eq. (4-85) in Eq. (4-86).

$$\frac{W}{F} = \int_0^x \frac{1 + K_A C_A + K_R C_R}{k[C_A C_B - (C_R C_S/K)]} dx$$

By setting $1/k = a$, $K_A/k = b$, $K_R/k = c$ and inverting the denominator, we obtain a set of three integrals:

$$\frac{W}{F} = a\int_0^x \frac{dx}{C_A C_B - (C_R C_S/K)} + b\int_0^x \frac{C_A\,dx}{C_A C_B - (C_R C_S/K)} + c\int_0^x \frac{C_R\,dx}{C_A C_B - (C_R C_S/K)}$$

This may be abbreviated to read

$$\frac{W}{F} = af_1 + bf_2 + cf_3$$

If the inlet composition and total pressure are known as well as the stoichiometry of the reaction, the values of the concentrations or partial pressures can be expressed in terms of conversion. For the reaction,

$$A + B \rightleftarrows R + S$$

using an inlet composition of 50 per cent A, 50 per cent B, and a total pressure of 1 atm., the above equation becomes

$$\frac{W}{F} = 4a(RT)^2 \int_0^x \frac{dx}{(1-2x)^2 - 4x^2/K} + 2bRT \int_0^x \frac{(1-2x)\,dx}{(1-2x)^2 - 4x^2/K} + 4cRT \int_0^x \frac{x\,dx}{(1-2x)^2 - 4x^2/K}$$

where x is in moles of A converted per mole of feed. Similar expressions can be found for any feed ratio and total pressure.

The values of these integrals are found by plotting the various functions against conversion and taking the area under the curve from zero to the experimental values of conversion. With W/F and the values of the integrals known at the various experimental points, one can then find the values of the constants.

One technique is the method of least squares, operating upon the method of f tables.

Since the terms in the integral can be calculated for corresponding values of x, the integrals can be evaluated graphically and tabulated or plotted against x. We can then use the experimental conversion and W/F values directly to solve for the constants. The necessity of taking tangents is eliminated.

The method of f tables is not applicable to all mechanism equations but it is quite useful for those in which the adsorption terms are to the first power.

Once one decides upon the correct rate equation and evaluates the constants, the equation must be checked against the experimental data. To do this:

Calculate r' for a series of values of x.

Calculate W/F for a series of values of x.

Plot $1/r'$ against x.

Take the areas under the curve for successive values of x, since

$$\frac{W}{F} = \int_0^x \frac{dx}{r'}$$

A plot of x vs. W/F is then compared with the original data. The rate equation should be checked not only with the experimental data that were used in obtaining the equation but also with the data that have not been used previously in the correlation.

Since the constants are temperature-dependent, they must be evaluated at several temperatures. They can usually be correlated by a plot of their logarithms against reciprocal temperatures.

In some cases it may be possible to measure the equilibrium adsorption constants by an independent study. These should agree reasonably well with those evaluated from the rate equations by the methods described above. If they do not, the constants in the rate equation should be considered empirical.

Differential Reactors. If a flow reactor is operated at constant temperature and at very low conversions resulting from very short residence times, all the concentrations for both reactants and products are essentially constant at the levels in the feed. Further, the temperature variation within the reactor is small enough that an average value can be employed without serious error. Therefore, r_A may be factored outside the integral sign in the design equation regardless of the complexity of the concentration-dependent expression which may eventually develop for the rate. Using the "catalytic reactor form" of the design equation as an example,

$$\frac{W}{F} = \int_0^x \frac{dx}{r_A} = \frac{1}{r_A}\int_0^x dx = \frac{x}{r_A} \tag{4-87}$$

For any particular concentration of reactants and products in the feed, weight of catalyst bed, feed rate, and temperature, a certain experimental conversion of A will result. The rate for those conditions may be calculated from Eq. (4-87), or

$$r_A = \frac{Fx}{W} = f(C_A, C_B, C_R, \ldots) \tag{4-88}$$

The rates so obtained may be tested for alternate postulated dependencies on concentration of reactants and products. Methods 1 and 2 (listed previously for integral rate data) are also applicable for differential rate data.

It is evident that differential reactor data can be analyzed much more easily and provide more reliable results than integral reactor results.

REACTOR DESIGN

It is assumed that, at the point of undertaking a reactor design, whether it be a batch or flow system, rate expressions have been derived. This means that the rate has been related functionally to the concentration of reactants and products, that the temperature dependence of all constants in the rate expressions has been determined, and that these rate expressions have been established for all simultaneous or consecutive reactions which will occur. If the heat- and mass-transfer characteristics of the system can be predicted, the necessary differential equations describing the performance of the reactor can be formulated. The discussion that follows will be limited to the formulation of these equations. Their solution can sometimes be accomplished analytically. Approximate methods, both numerical and graphical, are available (see Sec. 2) and digital computers are applicable. Depending on the background of the engineer and the time and facilities available, different methods will be used.

At the end of this section, a discussion of heat transfer in reactors is presented.

Back Mixing. Before proceeding with a discussion of specific types of reactors, a general discussion concerning the effect of varying degrees of mixing is in order. In theory, the integration of the design equation for a non-flow batch reactor (complete mixing) and for a longitudinal-flow reactor (in which no longitudinal mixing but complete radial mixing is assumed) yields the same result. The time that it takes an element of fluid to flow through the longitudinal reactor is the same as the contact time in a batch reactor. For this reason the same integral equations that hold for a batch reactor will also be true for a longitudinal-flow reactor.

However, these equations do not hold for reactors such as stirred tanks, packed towers, and baffled tanks, where there is back mixing within the reactor.

As a matter of fact, since the concept of plug flow is a hypothetical one, there is some back mixing in all flow reactors. That is, even in long tubular or coil reactors there is some mixing in the direction of flow. Also in batch reactors there is a distribution of residence time among the elements of fluid leaving the reactor tank. When complete mixing occurs, as in some reactors, the rate is constant throughout the reactor and a differential equation is not needed to express the change in concentration or conversion between the inlet and outlet streams.

Assume that an equation represented stoichiometrically as $A + B \rightarrow R + S$ (irreversibly) is also second-order in the rate expression, *i.e.*,

$$-\frac{dn_A}{V_R d\theta} = kC_A C_B$$

As listed earlier, the integration of this equation for the non-flow batch or longitudinal reactor yields

$$k(\theta - \theta_0) = \frac{1}{C_B{}^0 - C_A{}^0} \ln \frac{C_A C_A{}^0 + C_A{}^0 C_B{}^0 - C_A{}^{02}}{C_A C_B{}^0} \quad (4\text{-}89)$$

For the stirred (completely back-mixed) tank flow reactor, a material balance on component A gives

$$\frac{FC_A{}^0}{\rho_F} = \frac{F}{\rho_F} C_A + kC_A C_B V_R$$

where $C_A{}^0$ is the feed concentration of A, F is the total feed rate in moles/sec., and ρ_F is the molar density of the feed in moles/cu. ft. C_A and C_B are the concentrations of A and B in the tank and are the same as in the outlet stream. Solution of this equation for C_A yields

$$C_A = \frac{C_A{}^0}{1 + (kC_B V_R \rho_F / F)}$$

Since $V_R \rho_F / F$ is the residence time θ_b for the stirred-tank reactor operation,

$$C_A = \frac{C_A{}^0}{1 + kC_B \theta_b} \quad (4\text{-}90)$$

From stoichiometry $C_A{}^0 - C_A = C_B{}^0 - C_B$. Substitution of C_B from this expression into Eq. (4-90) allows solution for θ_b in terms of the feed concentrations of A and B and the fraction of A converted $1 - (C_A/C_A{}^0)$. The feed concentration of B is most generally expressed as a ratio to the feed concentration of A, *i.e.*, $M = C_B{}^0/C_A{}^0$.

Equations (4-89) and (4-90) express the concentration-time relationship for the two types of reactors—the non-flow batch and non-mixing tubular flow reactor on one hand, and the completely mixed stirred-tank reactor on the other. A comparison of these two times is shown in Fig. 4-5 with parametric values of M as presented by Corrigan (*Chem. Eng.*, November, 1955).

Such an analysis is possible for any expression for r_A and will allow comparison of residence times required to achieve the same conversion as a function of feed rates. It should be noted that complete mixing in the radial direction is assumed for the tubular reactor along with no mixing in the longitudinal direction.

A reverse question to that answered by Fig. 4-5 is: Given a specified reactor volume, what conversion can be expected with a stirred-tank reactor as compared with a longitudinal reactor? For the same reaction, the same analysis, but plotting variables differently, yields Fig. 4-6 (Corrigan, *loc. cit.*), which answers this question for one molar feed ratio, *i.e.*, 1 to 1.

Corrigan (*loc. cit.*) presents analyses of this type for more complicated series and consecutive reactions.

In preliminary calculations the reactor can be evaluated for two extreme cases—longitudinal flow and complete mixing. Any reactor will fall within these limits.

One can assume with a fair degree of certainty that a small-diameter pipe will fall at one extreme and a stirred tank at the other. Unfortunately, there is no exact way to evaluate other types of reactors (packed towers, large-diameter pipes, baffled tanks) although experimental information is beginning to accumulate on the degree of mixing in such intermediate cases.

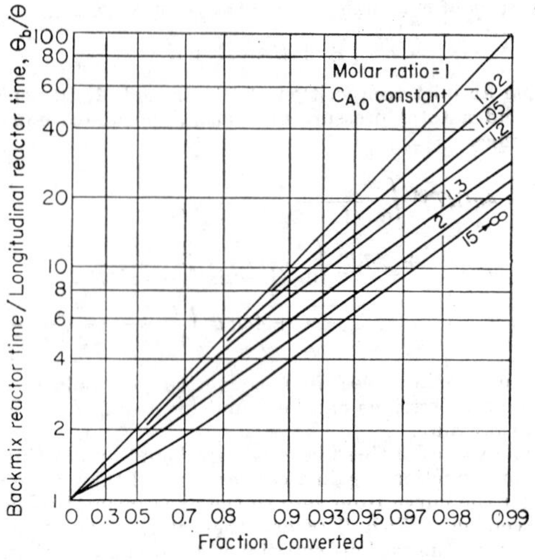

FIG. 4-5. Holding-time ratios for second-order reactions.

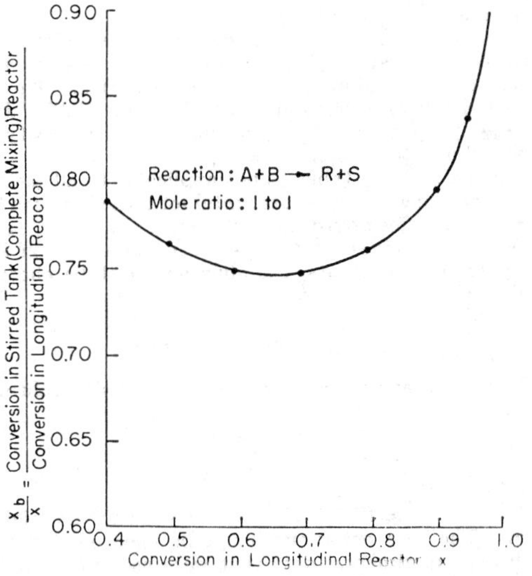

FIG. 4-6. How back mixing affects conversion at constant volume.

Mass and Energy-balance Design Equations. The differential equations applying to various types of reactors and operating methods will be formulated for the case of a reaction whose stoichiometry may be represented by

1: $\quad A + B \rightleftarrows C$

2: $\quad C + B \rightleftarrows D$

r_1 represents the net forward rate of reaction 1 and r_2 for reaction 2. The mechanism is not specified and therefore the functional relationship between the rate and concentrations is not specified. It is further assumed that no C or D is present in the feed.

In the general case, non-isothermal and/or non-adiabatic, the temperature-dependent expressions for specific heat, reaction-rate constants, and heat of reaction should be substituted in these equations.

The nomenclature is consistent for all equations and may be defined as:

A_w = heat-transfer area, sq. ft.
C_A^0, C_B^0 = feed concentration of component A and B, moles/cu. ft.
C_{p_f} = molar heat capacity of the feed, B.t.u./(mole)(°F.)
C_{p_i} = molar heat capacity of ith component, B.t.u./(mole)(°F.)
D = reactor diameter, ft.
F = feed rate, moles/sec.
H_i^0 = enthalpy of ith component in feed stream, B.t.u./mole
H_i = enthalpy of ith component, B.t.u./mole
ΔH_1, ΔH_2 = heat of reaction for reactions 1 and 2, respectively, B.t.u./mole
l = length along tubular reactor, ft.
$n_{A \cdots D}$ = number of moles of component $A \cdots D$
r = reaction rate, moles/(sec.)(cu. ft.)
r' = reaction rate, moles/(sec.)(lb. of catalyst)
T = temperature of reacting mixture, °F.
T_0 = reference temperature, °F.
T_f = temperature of the feed, °F.
T_w = temperature of heat source or sink to or from which reaction mixture is transferring heat, °F.
U = over-all heat-transfer coefficient, B.t.u./(hr.)(sq. ft)(°F.)
V_R^0 = initial volume of reaction mixture, cu. ft.
V_R = reactor volume, cu. ft.
v = reaction-mixture velocity, ft./sec.
$x_{A \cdots D}$ = mole fraction of component $A \cdots D$
ρ = molal density of reacting mixture at any point in tube, moles/cu. ft.
ρ_c = catalyst density (as packed), lb./cu. ft.
ρ_F = molar density of feed, moles/cu. ft.
θ = time, sec.

1. *Batch Reactors.*

Design Equations

$$\frac{dn_C}{d\theta} = (r_1 - r_2)V_R$$
$$\frac{dn_D}{d\theta} = r_2 V_R \qquad \text{Mass balance}$$
$$\frac{d[\Sigma n_i C_{p_i}(T - T_0)]}{d\theta} = UA(T_w - T) - (r_1\,\Delta H_1 + r_2\,\Delta H_2)V_R \qquad \text{Energy balance}$$

Omit left side of energy-balance equation if isothermal. Omit $(T_w - T)$ if adiabatic. In addition, from the stoichiometry of the reaction

$$n_A = C_A^0 V_R - n_C - n_D$$
$$n_B = C_B^0 V_R - n_C - 2n_D$$

Applications. In small-scale or complicated processes that manufacture expensive products.

Advantages: General versatility combined with a high yield of the desired product.

Disadvantages: Small-scale production. High labor cost.

2. *Semibatch Reactor—Non-constant Volume* (an initial charge of A is made to the reactor and B is then continuously added).

$$V_R = V_R^0 + \frac{F}{\rho_F}\theta$$

Volume in reactor at any time is assumed to be the initial volume plus volume of feed added.

$$A = \frac{4V_R}{D}$$

Design Equations

$$\frac{dn_C}{d\theta} = (r_1 - r_2)\left(V_R^0 + \frac{F\theta}{\rho_F}\right)$$
$$\frac{dn_B}{d\theta} = \frac{F}{\rho_F}C_B^0 - (r_1 + r_2)\left(V_R^0 + \frac{F\theta}{\rho_F}\right) \qquad \text{Mass balance}$$
$$\frac{d[\Sigma n_i C_{p_i}(T - T_0)]}{d\theta} = \frac{F}{\rho_F}C_B^0 H_B^0 + \frac{4}{D}U\left(V_R^0 + \frac{F\theta}{\rho_F}\right)(T_w - T) - (r_1\,\Delta H_1 + r_2\,\Delta H_2)\left(V_R^0 + \frac{F\theta}{\rho_F}\right) \qquad \text{Energy balance}$$

Omit left side of energy-balance equation if isothermal. Omit $(T_w - T)$ if adiabatic. Expressions for n_A and n_D may be obtained from stoichiometry.

Applications. For carrying out homogeneous-flow reactions with addition of one reactant.

Advantages: The concentration of one reactant is kept low. Good temperature control.

Disadvantages: Small-scale production. High labor cost.

3. *Semibatch Reactor—Constant Overflow* (an initial charge of A fills the reactor and B is added continuously; overflow volume is assumed equal to feed volume, usually applicable when neither reactant is a gas and no gaseous products are formed).

Design Equations

$$\frac{dn_C}{d\theta} = -\frac{Fn_c}{\rho_F V_R} + (r_1 - r_2)V_R$$
$$\frac{dn_D}{d\theta} = -\frac{F n_D}{\rho_F V_R} + r_2 V_R$$
$$\frac{dn_B}{d\theta} = -\frac{F}{\rho_F V_R}(n_B - C_B^0 V_R) - (r_1 + r_2)V_R \qquad \text{Mass balance}$$
$$\frac{dn_A}{d\theta} = -\frac{F}{\rho_F V_R}n_A - r_1 V_R$$
$$\frac{d[\Sigma n_i C_{p_i}(T - T_0)]}{d\theta} = \frac{F}{\rho_F}\sum C_i^0 H_i^0 - \frac{F}{\rho_F V_R}\sum n_i H_i + UA(T_w - T) - (r_1\,\Delta H_1 + r_2\,\Delta H_2)V_R \qquad \text{Energy balance}$$

Omit left side of energy-balance equation if isothermal. Omit $(T_w - T)$ if adiabatic.

4. *Semibatch Reactor—Constant Volume—No Overflow* (an initial charge of A is made to the reactor and B is added continuously—usually applies when B is a gas). Same as Case 2, except replace term $\left(V_R^0 + \frac{F\theta}{\rho_F}\right)$ with V_R.

5. *Flow Reactor—Complete Mixing* (such as a stirred-tank continuous-flow reactor). Same as Case 3, except all differentials with respect to time equal zero and there is one additional term in the equations for component A, C, D if these are present in the feed stream, *i.e.*, for component A,

$$\frac{dn_A}{d\theta} = 0 = -\frac{F}{\rho_F V_R}(n_A - C_A^0 V_R) - r_1 V_R$$

These reactors are usually used in series and the equations apply to any single one.

Applications. Where agitation is required and where a single tank would be excessively large to obtain the required degree of conversion.

Advantages: See usage above.

Disadvantages: Back mixing in system. More expensive than a single tank.

6. *Flow Reactor—No Longitudinal Mixing, Complete Radial Mixing.* For a catalytic fixed-bed reactor:

Design Equations

$$\frac{d(v\rho x_C)}{dl} = (r_1' - r_2')\rho_c \qquad \frac{d(v\rho x_D)}{dl} = r_2'\rho_c \qquad \text{Mass balance}$$

$$\frac{d[v\rho \Sigma x_i C_{p_i}(T - T_0)]}{dl} = \frac{4}{D} U(T_w - T) - (r_1' \Delta H_1 + r_2' \Delta H_2)\rho_c \qquad \text{Energy balance}$$

Omit left side of energy-balance equation if isothermal. Omit $(T_w - T)$ if adiabatic. Expressions for n_A and n_B may be obtained from the stoichiometry of the reacting system.

Applications. If system homogeneous:

Advantages: High through-put with little or no back mixing in the system.

Disadvantages: Holding time fixed for a given through-put. Very expensive for reactions that require high holding time.

If catalytic fixed-bed system:

Advantages: Little back mixing.

Disadvantages: Possibility of hot spots within bed. Difficult to replace catalyst.

HEAT TRANSFER IN REACTORS

In the heat-balance equations of the previous subsection, the over-all transfer coefficient, U, was included. It is the purpose of this subsection to review, briefly, procedures for estimating this quantity. Reference should also be made to Secs. 10 and 11 where prediction methods and empirical values may be found for certain physical situations. The temperature differences between process fluid and surroundings in the equations of the prior subsection were assumed to be constant and equal throughout the reactor for batch reactors and radially for longitudinal reactors.

If there is substantial back mixing in a longitudinal reactor, this type of analysis is invalid, as the assumption is that a slug of material moving through the tube is mixed completely in the radial direction but not at all longitudinally. This permits easy formulation of a heat balance on this slug taking into account heat of reaction, heat transfer to the surroundings, and sensible-heat effects.

With tubular reactors containing a bed of solid-catalyst particles, it is sometimes not justified to assume a uniform reaction temperature across the tube. Under these circumstances the rate of heat transfer and the variation in temperature within the reaction mixture must be studied. This situation is considered in detail in Smith ("Chemical Engineering Kinetics," McGraw-Hill, New York, 1956).

Such conditions of nonuniform temperature may also be encountered in batch and semibatch reactors when the degree of mixing is poor, as with a poorly designed agitation device. At present there is insufficient information on the relationship between the agitator design and the non-uniformity of temperatures to be able to handle this problem in an exact way analytically.

In summary, for batch reactors, only the case of perfect mixing can be handled with confidence. For flow reactors only the case of no longitudinal mixing can be treated. Fortunately, these requirements are close to fulfillment in many cases, *i.e.*, in batch reactors with efficient mixing and in flow cases with long reactors operated at moderate or high fluid velocities.

Batch Reactors

Kettle-side Coefficient. For well-agitated kettles Chilton, Drew, and Jebens [*Ind. Eng. Chem.*, **36**, 510 (1944)] have correlated considerable data for both jacket and coil heat-transfer coefficients. Their results may be represented by the following dimensionless equations.

For jacket heat transfer

$$\frac{h_k d}{k}\left(\frac{\mu_s}{\mu}\right)^{0.14} = 0.36\left(\frac{P^2N\rho}{\mu}\right)^{2/3}\left(\frac{c\mu}{k}\right)^{1/3} \tag{4-91}$$

For coil heat transfer

$$\frac{h_k d}{k}\left(\frac{\mu_s}{\mu}\right)^{0.14} = 0.87\left(\frac{P^2N\rho}{\mu}\right)^{2/3}\left(\frac{c\mu}{k}\right)^{1/3} \tag{4-92}$$

where d = diameter of kettle, ft.

h_k = kettle-side film coefficient at inside kettle surface in Eq. (4-91) and at outside surface of coil for Eq. (4-92), B.t.u./(hr.)(sq. ft.)(°F.)

μ_s = viscosity of kettle mixture at temperature of kettle or coil surface, lb./(ft.)(hr.)

μ = viscosity at bulk temperature of kettle mixture, lb./(ft.)(hr.)

P = length of paddle agitator, ft.

N = agitator shaft speed, revolutions per unit time

ρ = density of kettle mixture at bulk temperature, lb./cu. ft.

c = specific heat of kettle fluid at bulk temperature, B.t.u./(lb)(°F.)

k = thermal conductivity of kettle mixture at bulk temperature, B.t.u./(hr.)(sq. ft.)(°F./ft.)

Cummings and West [*Ind. Eng. Chem.*, **42**, 2303 (1950)] obtained data in a kettle equipped with more intense agitation and obtained a coefficient of 1.01 in Eq. (4-92), instead of 0.87.

Jacket-side Coefficients. There are very few data available. Often this coefficient is relatively high compared with the over-all resistance to heat transfer. Some empirical values are given in Sec. 11.

Coil-side Coefficients. The heat-transfer coefficient inside a coiled tube is increased over that for a straight tube because of the turbulence induced by the turning of the coil. By comparing data for the two cases it has been suggested that the straight-tube coefficient be multiplied by $(1 + 3.5\, d_t/d_c)$ to obtain the value for the coil arrangement. d_t/d_c is the ratio of the inside diameter of the tube to the diameter of the coil.

Homogeneous-flow Reactors

For tubular reactors, the generalized correlations for laminar and turbulent flow in conventional heat exchangers are applicable as presented in Sec. 10.

Heterogeneous-flow Reactors

Fixed Bed. Wall Coefficient. Jakob ("Heat Transfer," vol. II, Wiley, New York, 1957) gives

$$\frac{hD_t}{k_G} = fD_t^{0.17}\left(\frac{D_pG}{\mu}\right)^{0.83}\frac{C_p\mu}{k_g} \tag{4-93}$$

where f is as given in Fig. 4-7 (D_p in inches and D_t in feet)

h = wall coefficient, B.t.u./(hr.)(sq. ft)(°F.)
D_t = vessel diameter, ft.
k_g = thermal conductivity of the fluid, B.t.u./(hr.)(sq. ft)(°F./ft.)
D_p = particle diameter, ft.
G = fluid velocity, lb./(hr.)(sq. ft.)
μ = fluid viscosity, lb./(ft.)(hr.)
C_p = fluid specific heat, B.t.u./(lb.)(°F.)

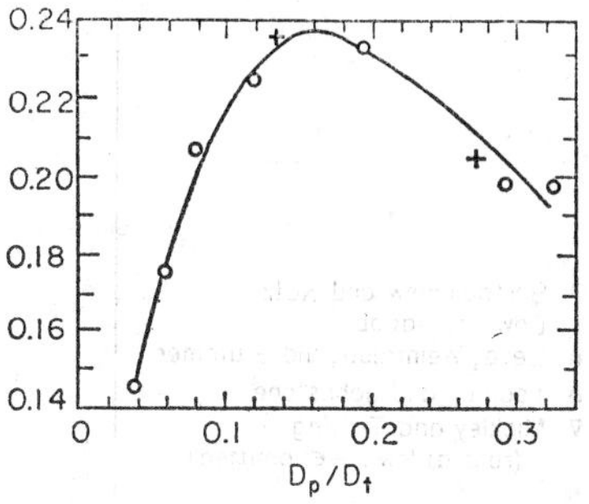

FIG. 4-7. Coefficient f for Eq. (4-93).

Other correlations which have been proposed include those of Leva [*Ind. Eng. Chem.*, **42**, 2498 (1950)]

$$h = 0.813\frac{k_g}{D_t}e^{-6D_p/D_t}\left(\frac{D_pG}{\mu}\right)^{0.90} \quad \text{for } \frac{D_p}{D_t} < 0.35 \tag{4-94}$$

$$h = 0.125\frac{k_g}{D_t}\left(\frac{D_pG}{\mu}\right)^{0.75} \quad \text{for } 0.35 < \frac{D_p}{D_t} < 0.60 \tag{4-95}$$

and Calderbank and Pogorski [*Trans. Inst. Chem. Engrs.* (*London*), **35**, 195 (1957)]

$$\frac{hD_p}{k_g} = 3.6\left(\frac{D_pG}{\mu\epsilon}\right)^{.365} \tag{4-96}$$

where ϵ = fraction voids in the bed

For a technique allowing calculation of radial temperature gradients in a packed bed, see Smith ("Chemical Engineering Kinetics," McGraw-Hill, New York, 1956).

Fluidized Beds. Wall Coefficient. For external walls see Wen and Fau (*Chem. Eng.*, July, 1957)

$$h_e = 11.6k_g(C_s\rho_p)^{0.4}\left(\frac{G\eta}{\mu N_f}\right)^{0.36} \tag{4-97}$$

where C_s = heat capacity of solid, B.t.u./(lb.)(°F.)
ρ_p = particle density, lb./cu. ft.
η = fluidization efficiency, see Fig. 4-8
N_f = bed expansion ratio, see Fig. 4-9

For internal walls

$$h_i = 9h_eG^{-0.37} \tag{4-98}$$

In Fig. 4-7 G_{mf} is the minimum fluidizing velocity and is defined by

$$G_{mf} = \frac{5.23(10^5)\rho^{1.1}(\rho_p - \rho_g)^{0.9}D_p^2}{\mu} \tag{4-99}$$

and G_f is the actual mass velocity in the bed.

Wender and Cooper [*Am. Inst. Chem. Engrs. J.*, **4**, 15 (1958)] approached the problem of correlation from a largely empirical position. Some commercial hydroformer data were included in this survey. At internal surfaces,

$$\frac{h_iD_p/k_g}{1-\epsilon}\left(\frac{k_g}{C_g\rho_g}\right)^{0.43} = 0.033C_R\left(\frac{D_pG}{\mu}\right)^{0.23}\left(\frac{C_s}{C_g}\right)^{0.80}\left(\frac{\rho_p}{\rho_g}\right)^{0.66} \tag{4-100}$$

where C_R is a correction for the displacement of the immersed tube from the axis of the vessel (see the reference). The group $k_g/C_g\rho_g$ has the dimensions of square feet per

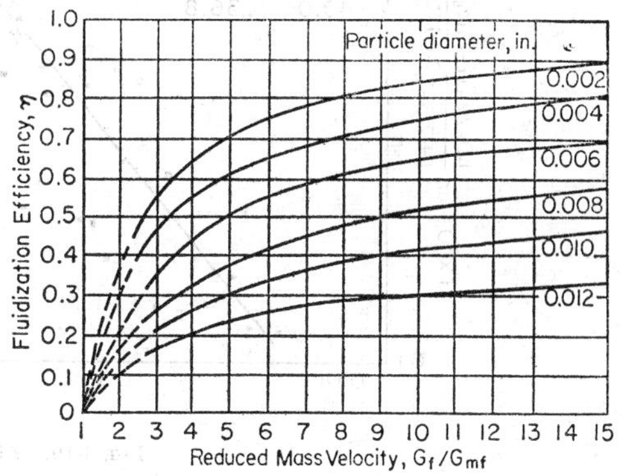

FIG. 4-8. Fluidization efficiency.

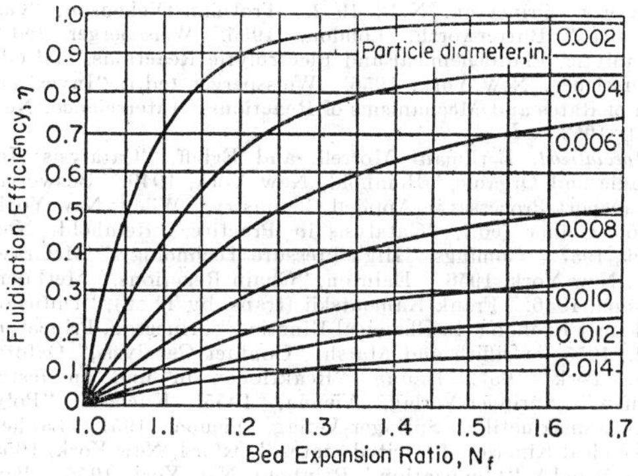

FIG. 4-9. Bed expansion ratio.

hour; all other groups in this and the following equation are dimensionless. At external surfaces,

$$\frac{h_eD_p}{k_g(1-\epsilon)(C_s\rho_p/C_g\rho_g)} = f(1 + 7.5e^{-0.44L_HC_s/D_tC_g}) \tag{4-101}$$

where f is given by Fig. 4-10. An important feature of this equation is inclusion of the ratio of bed depth to vessel diameter L_H/D_t.

BOOKS AND REVIEWS: *Chemical engineering:* Corrigan, Young, and Mills, Reaction Kinetics, *Chem. Eng.*, July, 1954–October, 1956. Hougen, "Reaction Kinetics in Chemical Engineering," American Institute of Chemical Engineers, New York, 1951. Hougen and Watson, "Kinetics and Catalysis," Wiley, New York, 1947. Smith, "Chemical Engineering Kinetics," McGraw-Hill, New York, 1956.

General: Amis, "Kinetics of Chemical Change in Solution," Macmillan, New York, 1949. Frost and Pearson, "Kinetics and Mechanism," Wiley, New York, 1953. Hinshelwood, "Kinetics of Chemical Change," Oxford, New York, 1940. Laidler, "Chemical Kinetics," McGraw-Hill, New York, 1950. Moelwyn-Hughes, "Kinetics of Reactions in Solution," Oxford, New York,

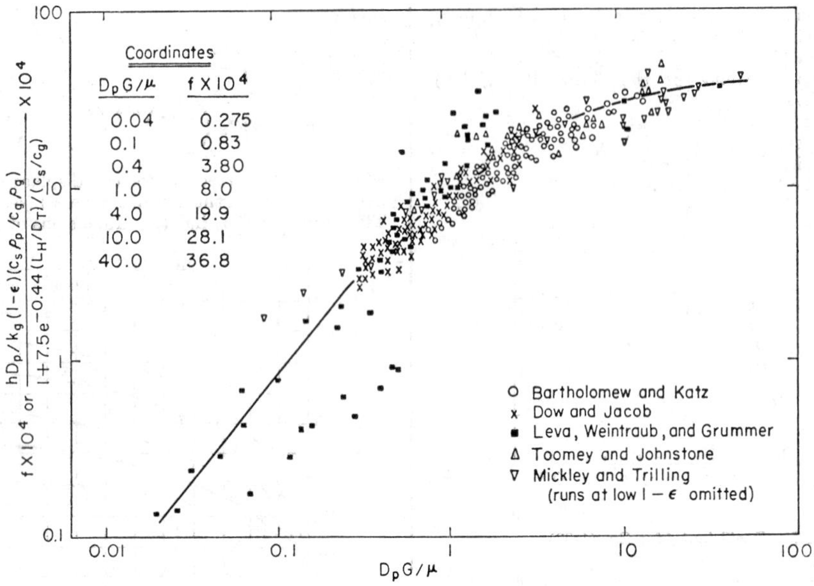

FIG. 4-10. *f* factor for Eq. (4-101).

1947. Pease, "Equilibrium and Kinetics in Gaseous Systems," Princeton, Princeton, N.J., 1942. Trotman-Dickenson, "Gas Kinetics," Butterworth, London, 1955. Weissberger (ed.), "Catalytic, Photochemical and Electrolytic Reactions," 2d ed., Interscience, New York, 1956. Weissberger (ed.), "Investigation of Rates and Mechanisms of Reactions," Interscience, New York, 1953.

Specialized: Berkman, Morrell, and Egloff, "Catalysis: Inorganic and Organic," Reinhold, New York, 1940. Bosworth, "Transport Processes in Applied Chemistry," Wiley, New York, 1956. Collier (ed.), "Catalysis in Practice," Reinhold, New York, 1957. Comings, "High Pressure Technology," McGraw-Hill, New York, 1956. Dainton, "Chain Reactions," Methuen, London, 1956. Frank-Kamentskii (trans. by Thon), "Diffusion and Heat Exchange in Chemical Kinetics," Princeton, Princeton, N.J., 1955. Griffith and Marsh, "Contact Catalysis," Oxford, New York, 1957. Hauffe, "Reaktionen in und an festen Stoffen," Springer-Verlag, Vienna, 1955. Kuchler, "Polymerisationskinetik," Springer-Verlag, Vienna, 1951. Laidler, "Chemical Kinetics of Excited States," Oxford, New York, 1955. Othmer (ed.), "Fluidization," Reinhold, New York, 1956. Penner, "Introduction to the Study of Chemical Reactions in Flow Systems," Butterworth, London, 1955. Ramm, "Absorptionsprozesse in der chemischen Technik," 2d German ed., Verlag Technik, Berlin, 1953. Rietema (ed.), "Chemical Reaction Engineering," Pergamon, London, 1958. Schwab, Taylor, and Spence, "Catalysis from the Standpoint of Chemical Kinetics," Van Nostrand, Princeton, N.J., 1937. Sherwood and Pigford, "Absorption and Extraction," 2d ed., McGraw-Hill, New York, 1952. Trapnell, "Chemisorption," Butterworth, London, 1955.

Serial works: Advances in Catalysis, Academic Press, Inc., New York, annually since 1948. Emmett (ed.), "Catalysis," 6 vols. thus far, Reinhold, New York, 1954–1958. Schwab, "Handbuch der Katalyze," Springer-Verlag, Vienna, 1940 to date.

Data: Tables of Chemical Kinetics: Homogeneous Reactions, *N.B.S. Circ.* 510, 1951. Basic Manual, 1951. Supplement 1, 1956. Supplement 2, Alphabetical Index, 1960.

Literature reviews in Ind. Eng. Chem.: Rate Theory and Homogeneous Reactions, **45,** 894 (1953); **46,** 880 (1954); **47,** 594 (1955); **48,** 570 (1956). Heterogeneous Reactions, **45,** 898 (1953); **46,** 884 (1954); **48,** 562 (1956); **49,** 486 (1957); **50,** 486 (1958).

THERMODYNAMICS

DEFINITIONS

The definition of the various terms and functions in thermodynamics has almost become standardized, but there is still considerable variation in the symbols used (Guggenheim, "Thermodynamics," p. 20, Interscience, New York, 1949). It is imperative in thermodynamic analyses that the definitions not only be stated unambiguously but also be used precisely (Obert, "Concepts of Thermodynamics," McGraw-Hill, 1960).

Energy. It has been most frequently defined as the capacity for doing work. However, it should be clear that energy also includes heat. In reality energy is a development or concept of the human mind; in the broad sense it is that which accompanies or causes a change in state or condition. The amount of energy is related to the identifiable characteristics of matter which are observable and which can be measured either directly or indirectly. These characteristics are called *properties;* examples are mass, pressure, temperature, volume, chemical potential, surface potential, surface area, height, velocity, etc. It will be noted that some of these properties, such as pressure, temperature, chemical and surface potential, height, and velocity, are independent of the mass of matter; they are classed as *intensive* properties. Other properties which depend on the mass such as volume, surface area, and all kinds of energy are known as *extensive* properties. It is apparent that extensive properties evaluated on a unit mass basis (*specific* values such as volume per unit mass) become intensive properties.

It should be noted further that the above properties represent or identify the gross characteristics or state of matter. They involve no assumptions concerning the structure of matter; they are known to exist through our sense perceptions (hot vs. cold); they can be observed, measured, and described by relatively few dimensions. For this reason they are called *macroscopic* coordinates; it is this viewpoint with which thermodynamics is primarily concerned. On the other hand, it is possible to derive or evaluate, but not measure directly, these properties by the use of statistical mechanics. In this case our sense perceptions are of no value; a structure of matter, such as the existence of molecules, must be first assumed. The position and velocity coordinates of each molecule (a total of six quantities in Cartesian coordinates) must be specified. Such a detailed description is thus in terms of *microscopic* coordinates. For example, from the microscopic viewpoint temperature is related to the average kinetic energy of all the molecules, whereas from the macroscopic viewpoint temperature is a consequence of our sense perceptions. It had been observed, long before the concept of molecular structure was advanced, that if a hot body is placed in contact with a cold body, the hotter one becomes colder and vice versa until both bodies exhibit the same degree of hotness or coldness (*thermal equilibrium*) as perceived by our senses. In fact, this observation is the basis for the *Zeroth law of thermodynamics:*

Two bodies, each in thermal equilibrium with a third body, are in thermal equilibrium with each other.

The most serious limitation to the microscopic viewpoint is that it is constantly subject to change since it depends on assumptions regarding the structure of matter. The validity of these assumptions must always be verified by comparison with results obtained from the macroscopic viewpoint (Zemansky, "Heat and Thermodynamics," McGraw-Hill, New York, 1957).

As was stated above energy includes both heat and work. The two are quantitatively related by the so-called mechanical equivalent of heat. The actual unit of heat energy is the electrical joule. Between 1910 and 1948 all electrical measurements are in terms of the international joule, which differs from the absolute joule by only a small amount (Rossini, "Chemical Thermodynamics," Wiley, New York, 1950):

1 international joule = 1.000165 absolute joules

Since all measurements today are in terms of absolute joules and since the most common unit of heat energy in practice is the thermochemical calorie, the following conversion units are convenient:

1 cal. = 0.99935 I.T. cal.
1 I.T. cal. = 4.1860 international joules = 4.1868 absolute joules

(The I.T. calorie is the International Steam Table calorie, which is defined as 1/860 international watt-hr.)

1 cal. = 0.0039657 B.t.u.
1 cal. = 3.08595 ft.-lb. (wt.)

$$1\ \frac{\text{I.T. cal.}}{^\circ\text{K g.}} = \frac{\text{I.T. B.t.u.}}{^\circ\text{R. lb.}}$$

1 I.T. B.t.u. = 778.16 ft.-lb. = J.

A complete set of fundamental constants and conversion factors is given in Sec. 1.

System. In the most general sense a *system* is any portion of the universe set apart for study. Physically, it is any collection of matter within prescribed boundaries. These boundaries may be real or imaginary, stationary or movable. Systems are classified as being closed (batch) or open (flow). In a closed system matter does not cross the boundaries (system of constant mass) whereas in the open system matter does cross the boundaries (system of either variable or constant mass). Whatever is not included in the system constitutes the *surroundings*, although usually it is only the immediate surroundings that are of importance in thermodynamic analyses.

Nomenclature. Following is a list of fundamental definitions and symbols to be used throughout this section:

1. Q is that form of energy in *transition* between the system and surroundings as a result of a temperature difference. Purely by convention, it is *positive* when the system *receives* the heat energy and *negative* when it *loses* heat energy. Heat ceases to exist when it crosses the boundaries of the system; *it cannot be stored as such.*

2. W is any form of energy other than heat which is in *transition* between the system and the surroundings as a result of a difference in mechanical, electrical, chemical, etc., forces. *As defined here, W does not include energy associated with a transfer of mass across the boundaries of the system.* It is *positive* (again purely by convention) when the system *loses* work energy and *negative* when it *receives* work energy. (Note that W has the opposite sense of Q.) Work ceases to exist when it crosses the boundaries of the system; like Q it cannot be stored as such.

3. U is the internal (first defined by Clausius) or intrinsic energy of a system; it includes all forms of energy contained within the system (thermostatic property) except the energy due to position (potential) or motion (kinetic) of the system. Potential and kinetic energy are external or mechanical properties of the system. U is a *fundamental property.*

4. C_v is the rate of increase of internal energy per unit increase in temperature when all other independent properties of the system such as volume, mass, and surface are held constant. Thus,

$$C_v = \left(\frac{dU}{dT}\right)_{v,m,\text{ etc.}}$$

C_v is commonly called heat capacity or specific heat as a holdover from the old caloric theory. In reality the so-called heat capacities can be measured in the laboratory without any heat being transferred between the system and the surrounding (Keenan, "Thermodynamics," pp. 20–22, Wiley, New York, 1941). It would be more precise to call C_v the energy capacity at constant volume.

5. H is the enthalpy. It is purely a convenient *derived* (rather than fundamental like U) property relating internal energy and the product of pressure and volume as follows:

$$H = U + PV$$

For the same reasons as given above in the case of C_v, H has been *miscalled* heat content or sensible heat.

6. C_p is the rate of increase of enthalpy per unit increase in temperature when all other independent properties of the system such as pressure, mass, and surface are held constant. Thus,

$$C_p = \left(\frac{dH}{dT}\right)_{P,m,\text{ etc.}}$$

Similarly to C_v, C_p is more precisely the energy capacity at constant pressure rather than heat capacity.

7. A is the Helmholtz "free" energy. It is purely a convenient derived property relating the fundamental properties internal energy, temperature, and entropy (to be explained later) as follows:

$$A = U - TS$$

8. G is the Gibbs "free" energy. It also is a convenient derived property relating the fundamental properties

internal energy, pressure, volume, temperature, and entropy as follows:

$$G = U + PV - TS = H - TS$$

9. ΔY represents the difference in any property of the system Y between a second state and a first state. Thus,

$$(\Delta Y) = Y_2 - Y_1$$
$$-(\Delta Y) = Y_1 - Y_2$$

This sign convention is very important.

10. Extensive properties such as V, S, U, H, A, and G can be expressed as *specific* or *intensive* properties by dividing the extensive property by the mass. Thus in shorthand notation:

a. For *pure* substances

$$\frac{V}{m} = \mathbf{V} \qquad \frac{U}{m} = \mathbf{U} \qquad \text{etc.}$$

b. But for *substances* in a homogeneous mixture or solution it is necessary to differentiate between the specific property of a substance in the pure state and that same substance in the presence of other substances. Denoting the total volume, for example, of a solution by V_{solu}, then by *definition* the specific volume of component A in the solution is given by

$$\left(\frac{dV_{\text{solu}}}{dm_A}\right)_{P,T,m_B,\text{etc.}} = \bar{V}_A$$

$\bar{V}_A$ is the *partial* specific volume at constant pressure, temperature, mass of component B and all other components, etc. In general $\bar{V}_A \neq \mathbf{V}_A$, as will be shown later. Similarly, other partial specific properties such as $\bar{H}_A$, $\bar{G}_A$, and $\bar{S}_A$ can be derived.

Kinds of Energy. Thus far, nothing has been said about the various kinds of energy which contribute to the internal energy of the system. It is convenient for the purposes of quantitative analysis to subdivide the internal energy into several categories. Figure 4-11 is

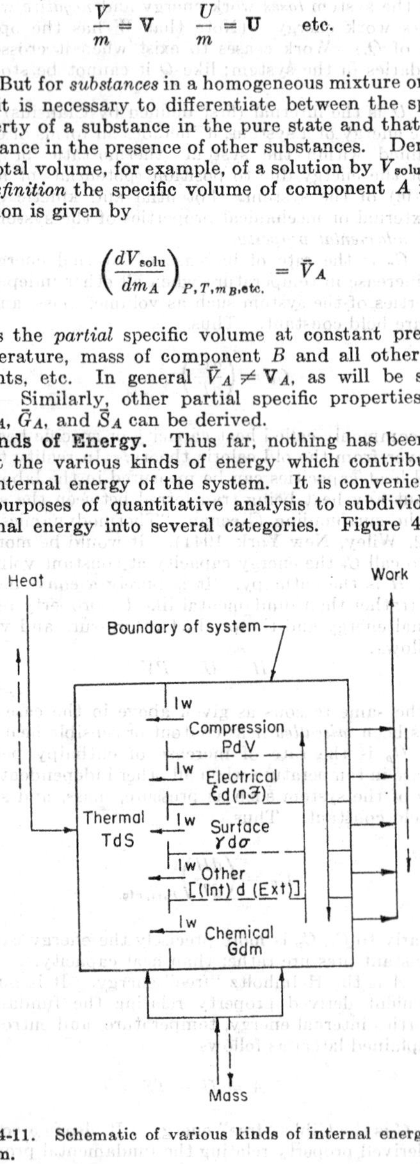

FIG. 4-11. Schematic of various kinds of internal energy in a system.

an oversimplified attempt to illustrate this classification of internal energy schematically. There are several important features in this diagram which should be noted.

1. All heat added to the system becomes a part of the thermal energy.
2. All work delivered to the system (negative sense) becomes a part of either the compression, electrical, surface, chemical, or "other," or any combination of these.
3. Part of the energy introduced into the system by the addition of mass identifies itself with the thermal energy, the remainder with the chemical energy.
4. The vertical arrows (dual direction) on the right, but within the boundaries of the system, indicate that a rearrangement of the energy within the system (other than thermal) is theoretically possible, such as a conversion of chemical to electrical energy.
5. The unidirectional horizontal arrows pointing only to the left and labeled lw (discussed later) indicate that all forms of energy, other than thermal energy, can be converted into thermal energy but not vice versa. Although not evident in the diagram, lw can be generated or produced by virtue of temperature gradients which may exist *within* the system. (Refer to the discussion of the second law which follows.)
6. All various kinds of energy are mathematically expressed as the product of an intensive property and the derivative of a corresponding extensive property, abbreviated as [(Int)d(Ext)]. Thus:

Kind of energy	Intensive property	Extensive property
Compression	Pressure P	Volume V
Electrical	Electromotive force $\mathcal{E}$	Quantity of electricity $n\mathcal{F}$
Surface	Surface tension γ	Surface area σ
Chemical	Chemical potential G	Mass m
Thermal	Temperature T	Entropy S

At this point it will suffice to define entropy S as simply the extensive property associated with thermal energy (this concept will be developed later) in the same respect that volume V is the extensive property associated with compression energy.

7. If the system undergoes a decrease in compression energy $\int P\,dV$ it does not necessarily mean that this amount of energy represents the work delivered to the surrounding. According to Fig. 4-11,

$$W_{\text{compression}} = \int P\,dV - (lw)_{\text{compression}} \tag{4-102}$$

Similar expressions can be written for other kinds of work energy listed in the above table. An equivalent form of Eq. (4-102) is

$$W = W_{\text{rev}} - lw' \tag{4-103}$$

where lw' is due to all potentials except temperature and where W_{rev} (reversible work) is defined as the work obtained when $lw' = 0$. It should be apparent from Eq. (4-103) that the term lw' represents energy that might have done work (as a result of either potential gradients within the system or potential differences between the system and the surroundings) but did not; therefore it is appropriately called "lost work." The term lw' either can be evaluated by means of Eq. (4-103) or else it must be evaluated from other theoretical considerations (such as in the case of laminar flow) or empirical correlations (turbulent flow). In the case of a change in compression energy, W is simply the product of the force exerted on the surroundings and the distance through which the force moves $\int F_{\text{surr}}\,dS$. Since $F = PA$, it follows that

$$W = \int P_{\text{surr}} A\,dS = \int P_{\text{surr}}\,dV \tag{4-104}$$

and

$$(lw)_{\text{compression}} = \int P\,dV - \int P_{\text{surr}}\,dV \tag{4-102a}$$

Similar expressions can be developed for all the other forms of energy. Note in the case of thermal energy, *if the mass of the system is held constant and the temperature is uniform,*

$$(\int T\,dS)_m = (Q + lw)_m \qquad (4\text{-}105)$$

8. By reference to Fig. 4-11, it is now possible to write the following differential equation for the total internal energy of the system (more will be said about this point later):

$$dU = T\,dS - P\,dV + \mathbf{G}\,dm + \mathcal{E}d(n\mathfrak{F}) + \gamma\,d\sigma + \text{etc.} \qquad (4\text{-}106)$$

Note that this equation as written does not require that lw be equal to zero; however, because the quantities on the right-hand side of the equation are inexact differentials, *i.e.*, dependent on the path of integration, they can only be evaluated, term by term, for the case in which $lw = 0$. Despite this fact, Eq. (4-106) holds whether lw is equal to or different from zero.

Equation (4-106), when solved explicitly for $T\,dS$, is frequently referred to as the defining equation for entropy.

Kinds of Processes. Whenever a system undergoes a change in state, with or without an exchange of energy with the surroundings, a process is said to occur. Whether or not an exchange of energy occurs between the system and surroundings (interaction) will depend entirely on the existence of an imbalance in corresponding intensive properties of the system and the surroundings provided the boundary itself does not provide the restraint. For example, if the temperature of the system is higher than the temperature of the surroundings, heat will tend to flow from the system to the surroundings. However, if the system is surrounded by a perfect heat insulator, there will be no flow of heat and the temperature of the system will remain constant provided no other effects take place.

Because of the many different possible variations and constraints that can be imposed on a system, it has become convenient to develop a shorthand terminology to describe various kinds of processes which take place under particular restricted conditions, some of which are:

1. Isothermal, constant temperature
2. Isobaric or isopiestic, constant pressure
3. Isochoric or isometric, constant volume
4. Isenthalpic, constant enthalpy
5. Isentropic, constant entropy
6. Adiabatic, $Q = 0$
7. Anergic, $W = 0$
8. Isolated, $Q = 0$, $W = 0$, constant mass (adiabatic, anergic, and closed)
9. Reversible, $lw = 0$

Molal Quantities. A mole of any substance is that quantity of the substance whose weight in pounds, grams, etc., is numerically equal to its molecular weight. If expressed in pounds, it is called the pound-mole; if in grams, the gram-mole.

The molal volume of any gas which behaves ideally ($PV = nRT$) at standard temperature and pressure (S.T.P. = 0°C. and 760 mm. Hg or 32°F. and 29.92 in. Hg) is 22,412 cc./g.-mole or 359 cu. ft./lb.-mole. Although the molal volume of any ideal gas at a particular pressure and temperature is the same, the molal volume of liquids and solids varies depending on their specific chemical nature and their density.

The mole fraction of any component in a homogeneous mixture is obtained by dividing the number of moles of that component by the sum of the number of moles of all components. The number of moles of any component is equal to the mass of that component divided by its molecular weight. In the case of an ideal gaseous mixture the mole fraction is numerically equal to the volume fraction. The volume fraction of a component in a mixture is equal to the volume of that component at the total pressure and temperature of the mixture divided by the volume of the mixture at the same temperature and pressure.

TECHNIQUES FOR DERIVING EQUATIONS IN THERMODYNAMICS

Although the laws of thermodynamics are based on empirical observations, the real utility of the science of thermodynamics is that it is amenable to rigorous mathematical analyses which lead to equations which permit a quantitative evaluation of the behavior of matter. The principal difficulty arises from the fact that thermodynamics deals with so many variables almost an infinite number of equations can be developed. The problem is to select the appropriate equation to fit the circumstances; the only reliable approach is to derive the specialized equation needed from the relatively few, completely generalized equations and dimensions. It is beyond the scope of this treatment to elaborate on the details; only a few pertinent points will be reviewed in the following. Many excellent references are available (for example, Obert, "Concepts of Thermodynamics," McGraw-Hill, New York, 1960; Lee and Sears, "Thermodynamics," Addison-Wesley, Reading, Mass., 1956; Hall and Ibele, "Engineering Thermodynamics," Prentice-Hall, Englewood Cliffs, N.J., 1960; Hougen, Watson, and Ragatz, "Chemical Process Principles," Part 2, Thermodynamics, 2d ed., Wiley, New York, 1959).

Properties as Exact Differentials. As was implied before, the thermodynamic properties are fixed by the state of the system. This state can be represented *implicitly* by an "equation of state" which in its most general form is

$$\phi(P, V, T, m_A, \ldots) = 0 \qquad (4\text{-}107)$$

If the function given by Eq. (4-107) is single-valued in n variables, then by assigning arbitrary values to $(n - 1)$ variables (independent), the nth variable (dependent) is determined. Thus Eq. (4-107) can be just as well written in *explicit* form; for example, if P is chosen as the dependent variable,

$$P = F(V, T, m_A, \ldots) = P(V, T, m_A, \ldots) \qquad (4\text{-}108)$$

where the functional notation F has been now replaced by the same symbol as used for the dependent variable P purely for convenience.

Equation (4-108) can be written as a total differential in terms of its partial derivatives with respect to its different independent variables as follows:

$$dP = \left(\frac{dP}{dV}\right)_{T,m_A,\text{etc.}} dV + \left(\frac{dP}{dT}\right)_{V,m_A,\text{etc.}} dT + \left(\frac{dP}{dm_A}\right)_{V,T,\text{etc.}} dm_A + \cdots \qquad (4\text{-}109)$$

Equation (4-109) is typical of a general class of equations which are termed *complete* or *exact* differential equations. They have the important property that the value of the integral (in this case, of dP) is dependent only on the value of P at the initial and final states and is independent of the path followed between these two states. Thus,

$$\int_{P_1}^{P_2} dP = P_2 - P_1 = \Delta P = \Delta[P(V, T, m_A, \ldots)] \qquad (4\text{-}110)$$

Equation (4-109) can be written in a variety of equivalent

forms. For example, if all independent variables other than V and T are held constant, as denoted by the subscripts on the dependent and independent variables,

$$[dP]_{m_A,\text{etc.}} = \left(\frac{dP}{dV}\right)_{T,m_A,\text{etc.}} [dV]_{m_A,\text{etc.}} + \left(\frac{dP}{dT}\right)_{V,m_A,\text{etc.}} [dT]_{m_A,\text{etc.}} \quad (4\text{-}111)$$

It should be noted that the coefficients of the independent variables dV and dT are the partial derivatives $(dP/dV)_{T,m_A,\text{etc.}}$ and $(dP/dT)_{V,m_A,\text{etc.}}$

Equation (4-110) can be further specialized for the case of constant pressure; thus,

$$[dP]_{P,m_A,\text{etc.}} = 0 = \left(\frac{dP}{dV}\right)_{T,m_A,\text{etc.}} [dV]_{P,m_A,\text{etc.}} + \left(\frac{dP}{dT}\right)_{V,m_A,\text{etc.}} [dT]_{P,m_A,\text{etc.}} \quad (4\text{-}112)$$

It is permissible to divide through Eq. (4-112) by either dV or dT; selecting dV, rearranging, and noting that a partial derivative can be inverted,

$$\left(\frac{dP}{dV}\right)_{T,m_A,\text{etc.}} = -\left(\frac{dP}{dT}\right)_{V,m_A,\text{etc.}} \left(\frac{dT}{dV}\right)_{P,m_A,\text{etc.}} \quad (4\text{-}113)$$

An equivalent form of Eq. (4-113) is

$$-1 = \left(\frac{dP}{dT}\right)_{V,m_A,\text{etc.}} \left(\frac{dT}{dV}\right)_{P,m_A,\text{etc.}} \left(\frac{dV}{dP}\right)_{T,m_A,\text{etc.}} \quad (4\text{-}113a)$$

It is a further property of an exact differential, such as Eq. (4-111), in the two independent variables V and T that

$$\left[\frac{d}{dT}\left(\frac{dP}{dV}\right)_{T,m_A,\text{etc.}}\right]_V = \left[\frac{d}{dV}\left(\frac{dP}{dT}\right)_{V,m_A,\text{etc.}}\right]_T \quad (4\text{-}114)$$

or in a partial notation, where all subscripts can be dropped

$$\frac{\partial^2 P}{\partial T\,\partial V} = \frac{\partial^2 P}{\partial V\,\partial T} \quad (4\text{-}114a)$$

Equation (4-114*a*) is just another way of saying that the order of differentiation does not affect the final result.

If more than two independent variables are involved, such as Eq. (4-109), relationships similar to Eq. (4-114) or (4-114*a*) may be obtained with respect to *any pair* of independent variables.

Maxwell Relations. By making use of the property of an exact differential [Eq. (4-114*a*)] and the definition of the energy functions given before, four important thermodynamic equations are obtained.

Restricting Eq. (4-106) to constant, m, $n\mathfrak{F}$, σ, etc.,

$$[dU]_{m,\text{etc.}} = T[dS]_{m,\text{etc.}} - P[dV]_{m,\text{etc.}} \quad (4\text{-}115)$$

Thus,
$$\left(\frac{dT}{dV}\right)_{S,m,\text{etc.}} = -\left(\frac{dP}{dS}\right)_{V,m,\text{etc.}} \quad (4\text{-}116)$$

$$[dH]_{m,\text{etc.}} = T[dS]_{m,\text{etc.}} + V[dP]_{m,\text{etc.}} \quad (4\text{-}117)$$

$$\left(\frac{dT}{dP}\right)_{S,m,\text{etc.}} = \left(\frac{dV}{dS}\right)_{P,m,\text{etc.}} \quad (4\text{-}118)$$

$$[dA]_{m,\text{etc.}} = -S[dT]_{m,\text{etc.}} - P[dV]_{m,\text{etc.}} \quad (4\text{-}119)$$

$$\left(\frac{dS}{dV}\right)_{T,m,\text{etc.}} = \left(\frac{dP}{dT}\right)_{V,m,\text{etc.}} \quad (4\text{-}120)$$

$$[dG]_{m,\text{etc.}} = -S[dT]_{m,\text{etc.}} + V[dP]_{m,\text{etc.}} \quad (4\text{-}121)$$

$$\left(\frac{dS}{dP}\right)_{T,m,\text{etc.}} = -\left(\frac{dV}{dT}\right)_{P,m,\text{etc.}} \quad (4\text{-}122)$$

Equations (4-116), (4-118), (4-120), and (4-122) are called the Maxwell relations. Note that Eq. (4-116) is *not* the inverse of Eq. (4-122). The former gives the variation in pressure with entropy at constant V, m, etc., whereas the latter gives the variation of entropy with pressure at constant T, m, etc. Equations (4-118) and (4-120) are unlike for similar reasons. It should be apparent now why it is so necessary to label each partial derivative with the variables that are being held constant rather than simply use partial notations.

Other Relations. It has been pointed out before that the thermodynamic properties are functions of the state of matter; in other words, they can be expressed in terms of the state variables or an equation of state such as Eq. (4-107) or (4-108). Only a few examples will be given below. More complete listings are available elsewhere (Bridgman, "Condensed Collection of Thermodynamics Formulas," Harvard University Press, Cambridge, Mass., 1926; Hougen, Watson, and Ragatz. "Chemical Process Principles," Part 2, Thermodynamics, 2d ed., Wiley, New York, 1959).

1. Isothermal effect of volume on internal energy: Let $U = U(V, T, m, \ldots)$; then

$$[dU]_{m,\text{etc.}} = \left(\frac{dU}{dT}\right)_{V,m,\text{etc.}} [dT]_{m,\text{etc.}} + \left(\frac{dU}{dV}\right)_{T,m,\text{etc.}} [dV]_{m,\text{etc.}} \quad (4\text{-}123)$$

or
$$[dU]_{m,\text{etc.}} = C_V[dT]_{m,\text{etc.}} + \left(\frac{dU}{dV}\right)_{T,m,\text{etc.}} [dV]_{m,\text{etc.}} \quad (4\text{-}123a)$$

but
$$[dU]_{m,\text{etc.}} = T[dS]_{m,\text{etc.}} - P[dV]_{m,\text{etc.}} \quad (4\text{-}115)$$

and since $S = S(V, T, m, \ldots)$

$$[dS]_{m,\text{etc.}} = \left(\frac{dS}{dT}\right)_{V,m,\text{etc.}} [dT]_{m,\text{etc.}} + \left(\frac{dS}{dV}\right)_{T,m,\text{etc.}} [dV]_{m,\text{etc.}} \quad (4\text{-}124)$$

substituting Eq. (4-124) into Eq. (4-115), setting T equal to a constant, and dividing through by $[dV]_{T,m,\text{etc.}}$

$$\left(\frac{dU}{dV}\right)_{T,m,\text{etc.}} = T\left(\frac{dS}{dV}\right)_{T,m,\text{etc.}} - P \quad (4\text{-}125)$$

Combining Eqs. (4-120) and (4-125)

$$\left(\frac{dU}{dV}\right)_{T,m,\text{etc.}} = T\left(\frac{dP}{dT}\right)_{V,m,\text{etc.}} - P \quad (4\text{-}126)$$

Equation (4-126) permits the calculation of the isothermal effect of volume on internal energy from a knowledge of directly measurable properties P, V, and T.

$$\int_{U_1}^{U_2} [dU]_{T,m,\text{etc.}} = \int_{V_1}^{V_2} \left[T\left(\frac{dP}{dT}\right)_{V,m,\text{etc.}} - P\right] [dV]_{T,m,\text{etc.}} \quad (4\text{-}126a)$$

In order to evaluate the right-hand side of Eq. (4-126*a*), the precise relationship among P, V, and T must be known. If an analytical expression is not available (particularly one which cannot be solved explicitly for P) use will have to be made of experimental data. The first step will be to prepare a graph of a family of curves of P vs. T for several different values of V which at least encompass the values of V_1 and V_2. For the particular temperature in question, the slope of the P vs. T curves at each value of V is measured, which gives $(dP/dT)_{V,m,\text{etc.}}$.

A cross plot is then made of $(dP/dT)_{V,m,\text{etc.}}$ vs. V and the area underneath this curve between V_1 and V_2 is determined, thus

$$\text{Area} = \int_{V_1}^{V_2} \left(\frac{dT}{dP}\right)_{V,m,\text{etc.}} [dV]_{T,m,\text{etc.}}$$

The area is then multiplied by the absolute temperature in question to give the numerical value of the first term on the right-hand side of Eq. (4-126*a*). Another plot is then made of P vs. V at the same temperature, and the area under the curve is determined graphically. A numerical solution to Eq. (4-126*a*) is thus obtainable by this rather tedious process.

If Eq. (4-126) is combined with the equation for an ideal gas, $\mathbf{PV} = RT$,

$$\left[\left(\frac{dU}{dV}\right)_{T,m,\text{etc.}}\right]_{PV=RT} = 0 \qquad (4\text{-}127)$$

By combining Eqs. (4-123*a*) and (4-126),

$$[dU]_{m,\text{etc.}} = C_V[dT]_{m,\text{etc.}} + \left[T\left(\frac{dP}{dT}\right)_{V,m,\text{etc.}} - P\right][dV]_{m,\text{etc.}} \qquad (4\text{-}123b)$$

2. Isothermal effect of pressure on enthalpy: In this case, let $H = (P, T, m, \ldots)$ and $S = S(P, T, m, \ldots)$. With the use of Eq. (4-122) and a development similar to the one immediately above,

$$\left(\frac{dH}{dP}\right)_{T,m,\text{etc.}} = V - T\left(\frac{dV}{dT}\right)_{P,m,\text{etc.}} \qquad (4\text{-}128)$$

$$\left[\left(\frac{dH}{dP}\right)_{T,m,\text{etc.}}\right]_{PV=RT} = 0 \qquad (4\text{-}129)$$

$$[dH]_{m,\text{etc.}} = C_p[dT]_{m,\text{etc.}} + \left[V - T\left(\frac{dV}{dT}\right)_{P,m,\text{etc.}}\right][dP]_{m,\text{etc.}} \qquad (4\text{-}130)$$

3. The effect of temperature, pressure, and volume on entropy: From Eqs. (4-115) and (4-123*a*)

$$T[dS]_{m,\text{etc.}} - P[dV]_{m,\text{etc.}} = C_V[dT]_{m,\text{etc.}} + \left(\frac{dU}{dV}\right)_{T,m,\text{etc.}}[dV]_{m,\text{etc.}} \qquad (4\text{-}131)$$

Equation (4-131) becomes at constant volume

$$\left[\frac{dS}{dT}\right]_{V,m,\text{etc.}} = \frac{C_V}{T} \qquad (4\text{-}132)$$

By similar procedures

$$\left[\frac{dS}{dT}\right]_{P,m,\text{etc.}} = \frac{C_P}{T} \qquad (4\text{-}133)$$

Therefore, by Eqs. (4-120), (4-124), and (4-132)

$$[dS]_{m,\text{etc.}} = \frac{C_V}{T}[dT]_{m,\text{etc.}} + \left(\frac{dP}{dT}\right)_{V,m,\text{etc.}}[dV]_{m,\text{etc.}} \qquad (4\text{-}134)$$

and, by Eqs. (4-122), (4-133), and analogous reasoning

$$[dS]_{m,\text{etc.}} = \frac{C_p}{T}[dT]_{m,\text{etc.}} - \left(\frac{dV}{dT}\right)_{P,m,\text{etc.}}[dP]_{m,\text{etc.}} \qquad (4\text{-}135)$$

An extremely important difference is to be noted here. Although

$$\left[\left(\frac{dU}{dV}\right)_{T,m,\text{etc.}}\right]_{PV=RT} = 0 \qquad (4\text{-}127)$$

and

$$\left[\left(\frac{dH}{dP}\right)_{T,m,\text{etc.}}\right]_{PV=RT} = 0 \qquad (4\text{-}129)$$

$$\left[\left(\frac{dS}{dV}\right)_{T,m,\text{etc.}}\right]_{PV=RT} = \frac{R}{V} \qquad (4\text{-}136)$$

$$\left[\left(\frac{dS}{dP}\right)_{T,m,\text{etc.}}\right]_{PV=RT} = -\frac{R}{P} \qquad (4\text{-}137)$$

Because the definitions for the derived properties A and G include the property S it can be anticipated in the light of Eqs. (4-136) and (4-137) that the partials of A or G with respect to V or P for the case of the ideal gas will *not* vanish.

4. The effect of temperature, pressure and volume on the specific heats: Both C_V and C_p vary with temperature; the analytical expressions can assume a variety of forms. A common form for gases over moderate ranges of temperature is

$$\mathbf{C}_v = A + BT + CT^2$$

(More complete information and data on specific heats are given in Sec. 3.)

If the property of an exact differential [Eq. (4-114)] is applied to Eqs. (4-123*b*) and (4-130), the following results are obtained:

$$\left(\frac{dC_v}{dV}\right)_{T,m,\text{etc.}} = T\left[\frac{d^2P}{dT^2}\right]_{V,m,\text{etc.}} \qquad (4\text{-}138)$$

$$\left(\frac{dC_p}{dP}\right)_{T,m,\text{etc.}} = -T\left[\frac{d^2V}{dT^2}\right]_{P,m,\text{etc.}} \qquad (4\text{-}139)$$

If Eqs. (4-123*b*) and (4-130) are combined with the defining equation $H = U + PV$, then

$$(C_p - C_v)[dT]_{m,\text{etc.}} = T\left(\frac{dP}{dT}\right)_{V,m,\text{etc.}}[dV]_{m,\text{etc.}} + T\left(\frac{dV}{dT}\right)_{P,m,\text{etc.}}[dP]_{m,\text{etc.}}$$

Note that, by setting *either* dV *or* dP equal to zero and dividing through by dT, the following equation results:

$$(C_p - C_v) = T\left(\frac{dV}{dT}\right)_{P,m,\text{etc.}}\left(\frac{dP}{dT}\right)_{V,m,\text{etc.}} \qquad (4\text{-}140)$$

For the case of an ideal gas

$$[(\mathbf{C}_p - \mathbf{C}_v)]_{PV=RT} = R \qquad (4\text{-}141)$$

As will be shown later, the ratio of C_p and C_v is a useful quantity. From Eqs. (4-132) and (4-133)

$$\frac{C_p}{C_v} = \frac{(dS/dT)_{P,m,\text{etc.}}}{(dS/dT)_{V,m,\text{etc.}}} \qquad (4\text{-}142)$$

Both the numerator and denominator of Eq. (4-412) can be transposed. Utilizing a procedure similar to the derivation of Eq. (4-113) except that the starting point [Eq. (4-109)] is replaced by Eq. (4-124), the following is obtained:

$$\left(\frac{dS}{dT}\right)_{V,m,\text{etc.}} = -\left(\frac{dS}{dV}\right)_{T,m,\text{etc.}}\left(\frac{dV}{dT}\right)_{S,m,\text{etc.}} \qquad (4\text{-}143)$$

By similar manipulations, but starting with $S = S(P, T, m, \ldots)$,

$$\left(\frac{dS}{dT}\right)_{P,m,\text{etc.}} = -\left(\frac{dS}{dP}\right)_{T,m,\text{etc.}}\left(\frac{dP}{dT}\right)_{S,m,\text{etc.}} \tag{4-144}$$

Combining Eqs. (4-142), (4-143), and (4-144) with Eqs. (4-120) and (4-122),

$$\frac{C_p}{C_v} = \left(\frac{dP}{dV}\right)_{S,m,\text{etc.}}\left(\frac{dV}{dP}\right)_{T,m,\text{etc.}} \tag{4-145}$$

It is significant to note that Eq. (4-145) differs from all the previous relations (which were expressed in terms of P, V, and T *alone*) in that the additional term, entropy, is required.

5. Joule-Thomson coefficient: Another very useful partial derivative is the rate of change of temperature with pressure at constant enthalpy. A practical example is a throttling valve in a flow system; as will be shown later, the enthalpy upstream and downstream from the valve is approximately the same. It is quite obvious that the important variables in this case are T, P, and H; therefore, reference will be made to Eq. (4-130) under the conditions that $dH = 0$.

$$\left(\frac{dT}{dP}\right)_{H,m,\text{etc.}} = \frac{T(dV/dT)_{P,m,\text{etc.}} - V}{C_p} \tag{4-146}$$

The partial derivative on the left-hand side is known as the Joule-Thomson coefficient; from Eqs. (4-128) and (4-129) it follows that the coefficient is equal to zero for an ideal gas, $PV = RT$. For real gases, the coefficient can be equal to, less than, or greater than zero. Where it equals zero is known as the inversion point; that is, above this point the substance "cools" upon expansion; below, it "heats up" on expansion. *The inversion point is not a unique point;* it is a locus of points on a P vs. T diagram at constant enthalpy (Dodge, "Chemical Engineering Thermodynamics," McGraw-Hill, New York, 1944).

6. Compressibility coefficients: Because solids and liquids show relatively small variations in volumes with changes in temperature, as compared with gases, it is convenient to define:

a. Isothermal-compressibility coefficient

$$\kappa = -\frac{1}{V}\left(\frac{dV}{dP}\right)_{T,m,\text{etc.}} \tag{4-147}$$

b. Isobaric-expansion coefficient

$$\beta = -\frac{1}{V}\left(\frac{dV}{dT}\right)_{P,m,\text{etc.}} \tag{4-148}$$

Homogeneous Functions. Extensive properties have been previously defined as being dependent on the mass of matter involved. This definition is perfectly adequate for a pure substance or a solution that does not undergo a change in composition. If any particular extensive property of a system changes in direct proportion to the mass, that extensive property is said to be a homogeneous function of the first degree in mass. Thus, if U is expressed completely in terms of *independent, extensive* variables, such as Eq. (4-106), then it can be shown by a mathematical proposition known as Euler's theorem (Gibbs, "The Collected Works of J. Willard Gibbs," vol. I, Yale University Press, New Haven, 1948) that the integrated form will always be

$$U = TS - PV + \mathbf{G}m + \text{etc.} \tag{4-149}$$

The significance of homogeneous functions will be demonstrated later in the discussion on solutions.

THE FIRST LAW OF THERMODYNAMICS AND THE ENTROPY BALANCE

The following treatment of the first law is based entirely on the generalized open-system concept [Brown and Sliepcevich, *Chem. Eng. Progress*, **48**, 493 (1952). Van Wylen, "Thermodynamics," Wiley, New York, 1959]. In this respect it differs from the classical development, which is based on closed systems. However, this difference is not so fundamental as it may first appear. The definition of a system is purely arbitrary and subject to the whims of the observer. It is always possible (although not readily apparent) to define a so-called flow system by juggling the boundaries of the system and allowing them to move such that the mass of the system remains constant, in which case the system is closed.

Energy Balance. The first-law energy balance is simply a statement of the principle of the conservation of energy. Thus,

$$\text{Input} - \text{output} = \text{accumulation} \tag{4-150}$$

An illustration of the generalized open system is given in Fig. 4-12. Although the system boundaries appear to be

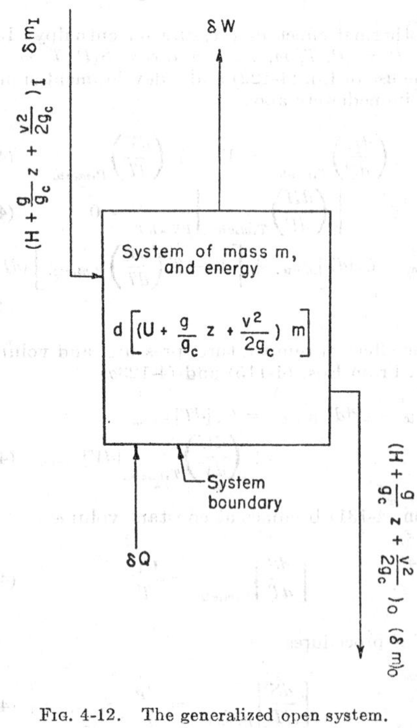

FIG. 4-12. The generalized open system.

fixed in space, it should be understood that they are free to move (such as the expansion of a cold steam line).

1. The energy *added* to the system consists of all the net heat transferred $\Sigma(\delta Q)$ and the energy brought into the system as a result of mass entering,

$$\sum\left(\mathbf{U} + P\mathbf{V} + \frac{g}{g_c}z + \frac{v^2}{2g_c}\right)_I (\delta m)_I$$

where $\mathbf{U}$ = internal energy of the mass at the inlet-state conditions per unit mass ($U/m = \mathbf{U}$) relative to some reference level

PV = energy per unit mass over and above the internal energy as a result of flow; commonly called flow energy

$\frac{g}{g_c} z$ = potential energy of unit mass relative to some datum plane

$\frac{v^2}{2g_c}$ = kinetic energy of unit mass relative to some reference body. This term is precise only if there is no variation in velocity across the flow channel, but it is sufficiently accurate if the mean linear velocity is used (Dodge, "Chemical Engineering Thermodynamics," p. 311, McGraw-Hill, New York, 1944).

$(\delta m)_I$ = quantity of mass that enters the system

Σ = a summation which takes into account any variations of the energy content of the mass that enters as well as multiple inlet streams

2. The energy that *leaves* the system is given by $\Sigma(\delta W)$, which includes all forms of work whether it be motion of the boundaries of the system against the surroundings, "shaft" work as in the case of a pump or turbine, electrical work as in the case of a battery, etc.

$$\sum\left(\mathbf{U} + P\mathbf{V} + \frac{g}{g_c}z + \frac{v^2}{2g_c}\right)_0 (\delta m)_0$$

which is the energy associated with the mass leaving the system as indicated by the subscript 0. The individual terms in this expression have the same definitions as given above.

3. The energy that is *accumulated* in the system is given

$$\int_{(\ )_B}^{(\ )_E} d\left[\left(\mathbf{U} + \frac{g}{g_c}z + \frac{v^2}{2g_c}\right)(m)\right]$$

where the limits on the integral denote the appropriate property at the beginning B and the end E of the accumulation period. Note that, if the properties of the system are not uniform throughout (homogeneous) it may be necessary to subdivide the system into a sufficient number of parts such that for each part the assumption of homogeneity is valid. In this case the above integral can be applied to each part and a summation made over all the integrals.

Combining Eq. (4-150) with the definition $\mathbf{H} = \mathbf{U} + P\mathbf{V}$,

$$\left\{\left[\sum\left(\mathbf{H} + \frac{g}{g_c}z + \frac{v^2}{2g_c}\right)_0 (\delta m)_0\right] - \left[\sum\left(\mathbf{H} + \frac{g}{g_c}z + \frac{v^2}{2g_c}\right)_I (\delta m)_I\right]\right\} + \int_{(\ )_B}^{(\ )_E} d\left[\left(\mathbf{U} + \frac{g}{g_c}z + \frac{v^2}{2g_c}\right)(m)\right] = \sum(\delta Q) - \sum(\delta W) \quad (4\text{-}151)$$

Equation (4-151) is perfectly general and is equally applicable for all types of systems whether they be closed, steady state, unsteady state, etc. *However, there is one very important exception* in the intraconversion of mass and energy as given by Einstein's theory of relativity in the form of the mass-energy equation

$$E = \frac{m}{g_c}c^2 \quad (4\text{-}152)$$

where c is the velocity of light. Although Eq. (4-151) clearly demonstrates that only the differences in energy rather than the absolute values are of importance, Eq. (4-152) provides a theoretical basis for calculating absolute energies.

The important point is that Eq. (4-151) can be "corrected" to account for such phenomena.

Mass Balance. Equation (4-150) can be simply applied to the mass balance for Fig. 4-12. Thus,

$$\delta m_I - \delta m_0 = dm \quad (4\text{-}153)$$

Equation (4-153) is a statement of the law of conservation of mass. It is generally valid except for the special case where relativity effects are significant, as stated above in connection with Eq. (4-152). However, it should be noted that the mass in Eq. (4-152) does not remain constant; it increases with velocity according to the Lorentz-Fitzgerald equation

$$m = m_0\left(\frac{1}{\sqrt{1 - v^2/c^2}}\right) \quad (4\text{-}154)$$

where m_0 = mass at rest

v = velocity relative to the observer

For most practical purposes (even in present-day space flight), v is so much smaller than c that m can be taken equal to m_0. Furthermore, the change in mass accompanying a change in energy, according to Eq. (4-152), is usually undetectable; it can be neglected in all cases except in nuclear reactions. In nuclear reactions, the mass balance [Eq. (4-153)] can be "corrected" if need be, just as the energy balance [Eq. (4-151)] would have to be modified. For most cases, it is permissible to write separate balance equations for energy and mass. The other alternative would be to write a single equation for a combined accounting of mass and energy.

Entropy Balance. By using the same procedures employed in the development of the energy and mass balances, and with particular reference to Figs. 4-11 and 4-12, it is possible to write a generalized entropy balance as follows:

$$dS = \delta\left(\frac{Q_i}{T_i}\right) + \left(\frac{\delta lw}{T}\right) + \mathbf{S}_I\delta m_I - \mathbf{S}_0\delta m_0 \quad (4\text{-}155)$$

where dS = increase in entropy of the system

$\delta\left(\frac{Q_i}{T_i}\right)$ = heat transferred to the system divided by the local absolute temperature T_i of the system at the point on the boundary of the system where this heat transfer Q_i takes place

$\left(\frac{\delta lw}{T}\right)$ = "lost work" divided by the absolute temperature of the system at which this "lost work" occurs. The quantity $(\delta lw/T)$ is variously called entropy production S_p (or irreversibility I) to emphasize that it can never be less than zero. The lost work arises from all potential gradients or discontinuities within the system whether they be temperature, pressure, chemical potential, etc., or any combination of these

$\mathbf{S}_I\delta m_I$ and $\mathbf{S}_0\delta m_0$ account for the entropy changes in the system resulting from a transfer of mass into or out of the system

Equation (4-155) is also sometimes written as

$$dS = d_eS + d_iS \quad (4\text{-}156)$$

where d_eS includes all transfers external to the system such as $\delta(Q_i/T_i)$, $\mathbf{S}_I\ \delta m_I$, and $\mathbf{S}_0\ \delta m_0$ and d_iS is $(\delta lw/T)$.

It is apparent that the evaluation of the terms $\delta(Q_i/T_i)$ and $(\delta lw/T)$ in Eq. (4-155) will pose certain difficulties either if the temperature of the system is not uniform throughout or if the temperature, even though uniform throughout, changes during the process. The saving grace is that dS is a perfect differential which is dependent only on the initial and final states and frequently can be evaluated from the equations developed previously if the end states are known. The calculation procedures should become more evident by some of the examples which follow. The important point to remember is that for any particular process the sum of $\delta(Q_i/T_i)$ and $(\delta lw/T)$ will always give a unique value regardless of how the detailed analysis is performed. All that is required is a precise definition of what constitutes the boundaries of the system (Sliepcevich and Powers, "An Introduction to Thermodynamics," University of Oklahoma Bookstore, Norman, Okla., 1959. Hall and Ibele, "Engineering Thermodynamics," Prentice-Hall, Englewood Cliffs, N.J., 1960).

Specialized Equations for Closed and Open Systems. Although it is possible to treat all thermodynamic systems as closed (simply by defining the boundaries of the system properly and observing the conditions of restraint) it is convenient to derive specialized equations which are applicable to particular kinds of systems (Brown and Sliepcevich, *Chem. Eng. Progress*, vol. 48, 1952). The following classifications will be used:

1. Closed, including both unsteady and steady state
2. Unsteady-state or transient flow
3. Steady-state flow

In reality, these subdivisions are somewhat arbitrary but common.

1. *Closed Systems.* No mass enters or leaves the system. Therefore, Eq. (4-153) becomes

$$\delta m_I = \delta m_O = dm = 0 \tag{4-157}$$

and Eq. (4-151) becomes

$$\int_{(\ )_B}^{(\ )_E} d\left[\left(\mathbf{U} + \frac{g}{g_c}z + \frac{v^2}{2g_c}\right)(m)\right] = \sum(\delta Q) - \sum(\delta w) \tag{4-158}$$

or integrating and substituting, $\mathbf{U}m = U$,

$$(U_E - U_B) + m\frac{g}{g_c}(z_E - z_B) + \frac{m}{2g_c}(v_E^2 - v_B^2) = Q - W \tag{4-158a}$$

or

$$\Delta U + m\frac{g}{g_c}\Delta z + \frac{m}{2g_c}\Delta v^2 = Q - W \tag{4-158b}$$

Likewise, Eq. (4-155) becomes

$$dS = \delta\left(\frac{Q_i}{T_i}\right) + \left(\frac{\delta lw}{T}\right) \tag{4-159}$$

and upon integrating

$$S_E - S_B = \sum \delta\left(\frac{Q_i}{T_i}\right) + \sum\left(\frac{\delta lw}{T}\right) = \Delta S \tag{4-159a}$$

where the summation signs are retained to emphasize that the temperature of the system need not be uniform throughout or constant during the process.

Example 1. An ideal gas at a pressure P_1 and a temperature T_1 is contained in a perfectly insulated reservoir of V_R cu. ft. capacity. A valve, located at the top of the reservoir, is opened slowly so that no pressure or temperature gradients exist in the reservoir at any time, and the gas is allowed to escape into the surrounding atmosphere. What are the final conditions of the gas remaining in the tank when the pressure has fallen to P_2?

Solution. The first step is to define the system as one of constant mass. The gas initially in the reservoir is separated into two parts by an imaginary (diathermic) membrane such that the gas below the membrane in Fig. 4-13 remains at all times in the

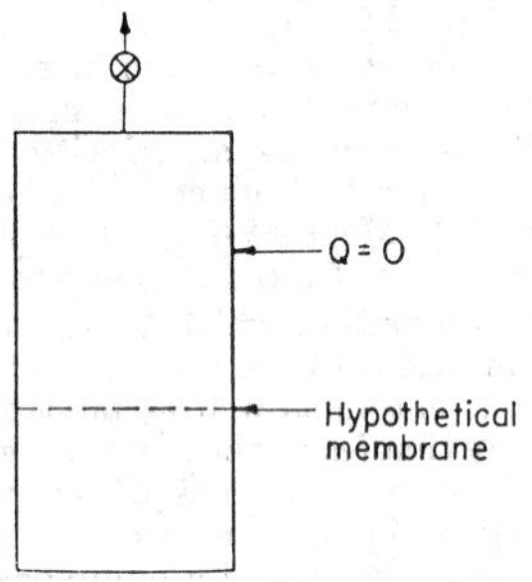

FIG. 4-13. Gas escaping into the atmosphere from a pressurized, insulated reservoir.

reservoir and the gas above escapes. The gas which remains in the reservoir is defined as the system.

1. The process is adiabatic ($Q = 0$) and reversible ($lw = 0$). Neglecting the potential-energy effect and since the gas is ideal, $(dU/dV)_{T,m,\text{etc.}} = 0$, combining Eqs. (4-158), (4-102), and (4-123a), and restricting to unit mass,

$$\mathbf{C}_v\,dT = -P\,d\mathbf{V} = -\frac{RT}{\mathbf{V}}\,d\mathbf{V} \tag{4-160}$$

2. Assuming $\mathbf{C}_v/R$ is independent of temperature, substituting $\mathbf{V} = RT/P$ and Eq. (4-141), Eq. (4-160) becomes

$$C_p d\ln T = R d\ln P \tag{4-161}$$

Defining

$$\frac{\mathbf{C}_p}{\mathbf{C}_v} = K \tag{4-162}$$

Combining Eqs. (4-160), (4-161), and (4-162) and integrating,

$$\frac{T_2}{T_1} = \left(\frac{P_2}{P_1}\right)^{\frac{K-1}{K}} \tag{4-163}$$

Example 2. The valve to an insulated, completely evacuated tank is slowly opened to the atmosphere until the pressure in the tank has risen to P, whereupon the valve is closed. Assuming that

1. Heat losses, the heat capacity of the tank walls, potential and kinetic energy are all negligible
2. Heat capacity of the gas is independent of temperature
3. Air is an ideal gas

derive an expression for the temperature of the gas in the tank at any instant in terms of the temperature of the atmosphere, T_{ats}.

Solution. The system is defined as shown in Fig. 4-14 to include the tank and the perfectly elastic, impermeable balloon which contains only sufficient gas to raise the pressure in the tank to P when the balloon is completely collapsed.

Denote the properties of the gas in the tank by subscript t and in the balloon by subscript b. Applying Eq. (4-158a)

$$(m_t\mathbf{U}_t + m_b\mathbf{U}_b)_E - (m_t\mathbf{U}_t + m_b\mathbf{U}_b)_B = -P_b[(\mathbf{V}_b m_b)_E - (\mathbf{V}_b m_b)_B] \tag{4-164}$$

Since $(m_t)_E = (m_b)_B$; $(m_t)_B = 0 = (m_b)_E$;

$$(\mathbf{U}_t)_E = (\mathbf{U}_b + P_b\mathbf{V}_b)_B = (\mathbf{U}_b + RT_b)_B \tag{4-165}$$

But

$$\mathbf{U} = \mathbf{C}_v(T - T_{\text{ref}}) \tag{4-166}$$

if $\mathbf{C}_v \neq f(T)$ and T_{ref} is an arbitrary reference temperature. Thus,

$$(T_t)_E = \frac{\mathbf{C}_v + R}{\mathbf{C}_v}(T_b)_B \tag{4-167}$$

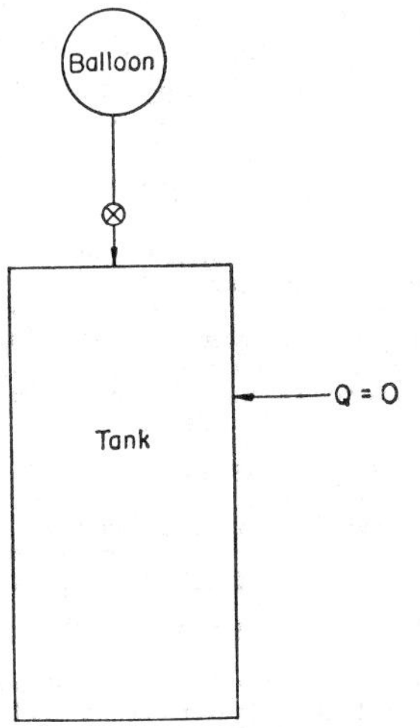

FIG. 4-14. Gas entering an evacuated, insulated tank from a balloon which is at pressure and temperature equilibrium with the atmosphere.

Since $(T_b)_B = T_{\text{ats}}$ and since $\mathbf{C}_p = \mathbf{C}_v + R$

$$(T_i)_E = \frac{\mathbf{C}_p}{\mathbf{C}_v}(T_{\text{ats}}) \qquad (4\text{-}168)$$

Note that the temperature of the gas upon entering the tank will rise. For example, if $(T_b)_B$ is taken to be 70°F. and the ratio of specific heats is 1.4 (ideal, diatomic gas)

$$(T_i)_E = 1.4(70 + 460) = 742°\text{R.} = 282°\text{F.}$$

However, in actual practice the temperature will rise several degrees only because the tank walls do not have negligible heat capacity. The reason for the temperature rise is that the atmosphere does work on the gas, thus adding energy to it which is reflected by an increase in temperature. Equation (4-165) demonstrates this point clearly: thus

$$(\mathbf{U}_i)_E = (\mathbf{H}_b)_B \qquad (4\text{-}165a)$$

Example 3. Compute the entropy production in a rod that is transferring heat at a *steady state* along the direction of its long axis only if the ends are maintained at T_1 and T_2, respectively, by thermal sources of infinite capacity (Fig. 4-15).

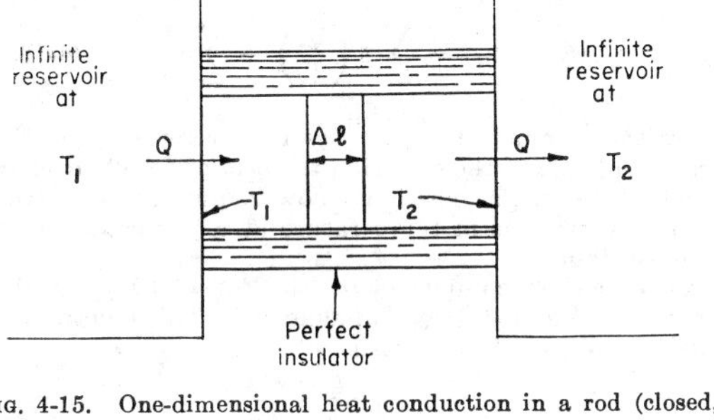

FIG. 4-15. One-dimensional heat conduction in a rod (closed, steady-state system).

Solution. Because the net $Q(Q_1 = -Q_2)$ and W are zero, if the rod itself is taken as the system, Eq. (4-158) becomes

$$\int dU = 0 \qquad (4\text{-}169)$$

Combining Eq. (4-169) with Eq. (4-106) and noting that V, m, etc., are all constant, it follows that

$$dS = 0 \qquad (4\text{-}170)$$

Apply Eq. (4-170) to (4-159)

$$-\delta\left(\frac{Q_i}{T_i}\right) = \frac{\delta lw}{T} = \delta S_p \qquad (4\text{-}171)$$

Since all the heat that enters the system is transferred at a local boundary temperature T_1 and that which leaves at a boundary temperature of T_2, it follows that

$$-\sum\left(\frac{Q_i}{T_i}\right) = -\left(\frac{Q_1}{T_1} + \frac{Q_2}{T_2}\right) = \sum \delta S_p = S_p \qquad (4\text{-}172)$$

but $Q_2 = -Q_1$

$$S_p = Q_1\left(\frac{1}{T_2} - \frac{1}{T_1}\right) \qquad (4\text{-}173)$$

Since $Q_1 > 0$ and $T_1 > T_2$,

$$S_p > 0 \qquad (4\text{-}174)$$

The same result as Eq. (4-173) can be obtained by "integrating" along the length of the rod. Thus, if a small element of length Δl is temporarily removed from the system and placed in contact at its extremities with two infinite reservoirs at temperatures T_i and $T_i + \Delta T_i$ and a quantity of heat Q_1 is transferred from one reservoir to the other through this small element,

$$\delta S_p = -Q_1\left[\frac{1}{T_i} - \frac{1}{(T_i + \Delta T_i)}\right]$$

Letting ΔT approach zero for an infinitesimal element and integrating over the entire length of the rod,

$$S_p = \sum(\delta S_p) = -Q_1\int_{T_1}^{T_2}\frac{dT}{T_2} = Q_1\left(\frac{1}{T_2} - \frac{1}{T_1}\right) \qquad (4\text{-}174a)$$

The analysis above in which the integration was performed over the entire rod has the advantage over the previous analysis in that it clearly demonstrates that entropy is produced along the whole length of the rod.

2. *Unsteady-state or Transient Flow.* In the most general case, Eq. (4-151) holds. However, it is frequently difficult to apply if none of the terms can be canceled since very rarely is enough information available for the process. For example, the mass-balance equation [Eq. (4-153)] can be used to interrelate δm_I, δm_O, and dm, but since two of the variables are independent, a further restriction or relation between these two independent variables must be specified before Eq. (4-151) is tractable. A major application of Eq. (4-151) is for the case in which either δm_I or δm_O is equal to zero.

a. For the case in which $\delta m_I = 0$. Ignore potential- and kinetic-energy effects purely to simplify the resulting equations. Then Eq. (4-153) becomes

$$-\delta m_O = dm \qquad (4\text{-}175)$$

and Eq. (4-151) reduces to

$$\Sigma(\mathbf{H}_O\,\delta m_O) + (U_E - U_B) = \Sigma(\delta Q) - \Sigma(\delta W) \qquad (4\text{-}176)$$

Likewise, Eq. (4-155) becomes

$$dS = \delta\left(\frac{Q_i}{T_i}\right) + \left(\frac{\delta lw}{T}\right) - \mathbf{S}_O\,\delta m_O \qquad (4\text{-}177)$$

Example 4. Example 1, which was solved by the closed-system analysis, can be treated as an open system. Referring to Fig. 4-13, and removing the membrane, define the system as the gas present in the entire reservoir at any instant. Obviously, the mass of the system will not be constant during the process. Again in this case, $Q = 0$, as before. However, $W = 0$ in the open system (remember that W does not include energy associated with the transfer of mass), whereas $W \neq 0$ for the closed-system analysis. Applying Eq. (4-175) and remembering $U = \mathbf{U}m$ Eq. (4-176) becomes

$$(\mathbf{H}_0 - \mathbf{U})\, dm = m\, d\mathbf{U} \tag{4-178}$$

But since it was assumed that there were no potential gradients in the system, the specific properties of the mass leaving are always the same as the specific properties of the mass in the system (the reservoir); thus

$$\mathbf{H}_0 = \mathbf{H} \tag{4-179}$$

Substituting Eq. (4-179) in (4-178) and noting that $\mathbf{H} - \mathbf{U} = P\mathbf{V} = RT$ for an ideal gas,

$$\frac{RT\, dm}{m} = \mathbf{C}_v\, dT \tag{4-180}$$

The volume of the reservoir V_R remains constant and is equal to

$$V_R = \text{const.} = m\mathbf{V} \tag{4-181}$$

Differentiating and rearranging,

$$\frac{d\mathbf{V}}{\mathbf{V}} = -\frac{dm}{m} \tag{4-182}$$

Substituting Eq. (4-182) in (4-180),

$$\frac{-RT\, d\mathbf{V}}{\mathbf{V}} = \mathbf{C}_V\, dT \tag{4-160}$$

which is identical to the equation derived for the closed-system analysis in Example 1.

b. For the case in which $\delta m_0 = 0$. Ignore potential- and kinetic-energy effects. Then Eqs. (4-153) and (4-151) become

$$\delta m_I = dm \tag{4-183}$$

$$-\Sigma(\mathbf{H}_I \delta m_I) + (U_E - U_B) = \Sigma(\delta Q) - \Sigma(\delta W) \tag{4-184}$$

Likewise Eq. (4-155) reduces to

$$dS = \delta\left(\frac{Q_i}{T_i}\right) + \frac{\delta lw}{T} + \mathbf{S}_I\, \delta m_I \tag{4-185}$$

Example 5. Example 2, which was solved by the closed-system analysis, can be treated as an open system. Referring to Fig. 4-14 define the system as the tank and valve, excluding the balloon. As was explained in Example 4, $Q = 0$, as before in Example 2, but $W = 0$ in the open system. Applying Eq. (4-183) and since only one stream is entering, Eq. (4-184) becomes

$$-\mathbf{H}_I\, \delta m_I + dU = 0 \tag{4-186}$$

Integrating Eq. (4-186)

$$U_E - U_B = H_I \tag{4-186a}$$

Since the tank was evacuated at the beginning, $U_B = 0$, and U_E is identically equal to $(U_t)_E$ in Eq. (4-165*a*). Likewise, $H_I = (H_b)_B$. Noting that the masses involved in Examples 2 and 5 are identical, Eq. (4-186*a*) becomes

$$(\mathbf{U}_t)_E = (\mathbf{H}_b)_B \tag{4-165a}$$

Example 6. In Example 4 the analysis was somewhat simplified because the properties of the material leaving the system were identical to the properties of the system at that same instance. However, the equivalence of these properties need not be the case. For example, consider the case of a perfectly insulated accumulator filled with superheated steam at elevated pressure and temperature. If the valve to the accumulator is opened slowly, and steam is allowed to escape, the properties of the steam leaving can be assumed to be the same as the properties of the steam remaining in the accumulator up to the point of condensation. If this process is treated as an open system, and since $Q = 0$ and $lw = 0$, Eq. (4-177) becomes

$$dS = -\mathbf{S}_0\, \delta m_0 \tag{4-187}$$

but since $S = \mathbf{S}m$ and $\delta m_0 = -dm$

$$dS = (\mathbf{S}_0 - \mathbf{S})\frac{dm}{m}$$

and since $\mathbf{S}_0 = \mathbf{S}$ in this case,

$$d\mathbf{S} = 0 \tag{4-188}$$

Once the steam in the accumulator reaches the condensation point, three alternatives are possible:

a. If the mixture of steam and water is thoroughly mixed, such that properties of the material leaving are the same as the properties remaining, $\mathbf{S}_0 = \mathbf{S}$ and Eq. (4-188) applies.

b. If only the saturated vapor is withdrawn from the accumulator, then $\mathbf{S}_0 > \mathbf{S}$ and $dm < 0$; therefore

$$d\mathbf{S} < 0 \tag{4-189}$$

for the remaining material in the accumulator.

c. If only saturated liquid is withdrawn, such as by a drain on the bottom of the tank, $\mathbf{S}_0 < \mathbf{S}$ and $dm < 0$; consequently

$$d\mathbf{S} > 0 \tag{4-190}$$

The significant point to observe is that, although the above processes are all adiabatic and reversible, $d\mathbf{S}$ can be greater than, equal to, or less than zero if $d\mathbf{S}$ is evaluated for an open system.

3. *Steady-state Flow.* A large class of practical applications can be treated from the standpoint of steady-state flow. A necessary and sufficient condition for steady-state flow is that dU, dz, and $d(v^2)$ in Eq. (4-151) and dm in Eq. (4-153) all be equal to zero. Although these conditions imply that the states of the fluid at any point within the system will be the same at all times, these conditions have to be qualified to the extent that it is only necessary and sufficient that the states of the fluid at all points within the open system periodically and simultaneously become identical with states previously existing at those points. A typical example is a reciprocating pump that is discharging water through a pipe line at a constant rate (Keenan, "Thermodynamics," p. 35, Wiley, New York, 1941). Thus, Eq. (4-153) becomes

$$\delta m_I = \delta m_0 \quad (\text{since } dm = 0) \tag{4-191}$$

and Eq. (4-151) becomes, on a unit-mass basis,

$$(\mathbf{H}_0 - \mathbf{H}_I) + \frac{g}{g_c}(z_0 - z_I) + \frac{1}{2g_c}(v_0^2 - v_I^2) = \sum(\delta\mathbf{Q}) - \sum(\delta\mathbf{W}) \tag{4-192}$$

and Eq. (4-155) becomes

$$(\mathbf{S}_0 - \mathbf{S}_I) = \sum \delta\left(\frac{\mathbf{Q}_i}{T_i}\right) + \sum \frac{\delta\mathbf{lw}}{T} \tag{4-193}$$

where the summation sign is essentially retained on the right-hand side of the equation to account for changes in temperature with position (not required with true periodic variations in temperature at a particular point in the system).

An equation comparable with Eq. (4-192) can be derived from a closed-system analysis. This equation is usually expressed in the form

$$d\mathbf{H} + \frac{g}{g_c}\,dz + \frac{d(v^2)}{2g_c} = \delta\mathbf{Q} - \delta\mathbf{W}_s \tag{4-194}$$

It should be noted that δW_s in Eq. (4-194) is identically equal to δW in Eq. (4-192) since in the latter δW, by definition, does not include energy associated with the transfer of mass into or out of the system. The distinction between Eq. (4-192), which results from an open-system analysis, and Eq. (4-194), which represents the closed-system analysis, is fundamentally important.

Equation (4-192) can be expressed in a familiar form by appropriate combination with Eq. (4-193). Note that the latter cannot be solved explicitly for (δQ_i) or (δlw) unless the temperature of the system T is constant and uniform throughout, in which case $T_i = T = T_I = T_0$. For this *very special case*, Eq. (4-193) yields

$$[(TS)_0 - (TS)_I]_T = [\Sigma(\delta \mathbf{Q}) + \Sigma(\delta \mathbf{lw})]_T \quad (4\text{-}195)$$

Substituting Eq. (4-195) in Eq. (4-191) gives

$$\left[(\mathbf{G}_0 - \mathbf{G}_I) + \frac{g}{g_c}(z_0 - z_I) + \frac{v_0^2 - v_I^2}{2g_c}\right]_T = -(\mathbf{W} + \mathbf{lw})_T \quad (4\text{-}196)$$

The difference $(\mathbf{G}_0 - \mathbf{G}_I)$ can be expressed in differential form as

$$(\mathbf{G}_0 - \mathbf{G}_I)_T = \int_{\mathbf{G}_I}^{\mathbf{G}_0} d\mathbf{G}_T = \int_{P_I}^{P_0} \mathbf{V}\, dP_T \quad (4\text{-}197)$$

Combining Eqs. (4-197) and (4-196),

$$\left[\int_{P_I}^{P_0} \mathbf{V}\, dP + \frac{g}{g_c}(z_0 - z_I) + \frac{v_0^2 - v_I^2}{2g_c}\right]_T = -(\mathbf{W} + \mathbf{lw})_T \quad (4\text{-}198)$$

If $\mathbf{V}$ does not vary appreciably with pressure, such as for liquids and solids, Eq. (4-198) can be written (since $\mathbf{V} = 1/\rho$)

$$\left[\frac{P_0 - P_I}{\rho} + \frac{g}{g_c}(z_0 - z_I) + \frac{v_0^2 - v_I^2}{2g_c}\right]_{T,\rho} = -(\mathbf{W} - \mathbf{lw})_{T,\rho} \quad (4\text{-}199)$$

Equation (4-199) is "related" to the Bernoulli equation in fluid mechanics. Equation (4-199) has been "forced" for steady-state systems which are not at constant temperature by resorting to empirical approximations.

A form similar to Eq. (4-198) can be derived for the case of adiabatic reversible flow in which Eq. (4-193) reduces to a zero identity since $Q = 0 = lw$. Since

$$(\mathbf{H}_0 - \mathbf{H}_I)_S = \int_{\mathbf{H}_I}^{\mathbf{H}_0} (d\mathbf{H})_S = \int_{P_I}^{P_0} (\mathbf{V}\, dP)_S \quad (4\text{-}200)$$

Eq. (4-192) becomes

$$\left[\int_{P_I}^{P_0} \mathbf{V}\, dP + \frac{g}{g_c}(z_0 - z_I) + \frac{v_0^2 - v_I^2}{2g_c}\right]_S = -(\mathbf{W})_S \quad (4\text{-}201)$$

Note that Eq. (4-201) differs from Eq. (4-198) in that it does not contain the lw term ($lw = 0$), and it is restricted to steady-state flow at constant entropy. On the other hand, Eq. (4-198) is restricted to constant temperature and holds whether $lw = 0$ or $lw > 0$. These differences and restrictions are frequently overlooked in fluid mechanics.

Example 7. A single-stage turboblower is taking 1000 standard cu. ft. of dry air per minute from a large room where the temperature is 70°F. and the pressure is 14.7 lb./sq. in. abs. The axis of the horizontal discharge pipe is 50 ft. above that of the intake, and the air is discharged at a pressure of 0.5 lb./sq. in. gage and 70°F. The velocity of the air at the point of exhaust is 75 ft./sec. The power input to the drive shaft of the exhauster is 5 hp. Compute the lost work, the heat transferred, and the entropy increase, per pound of air passing through the exhauster system.

Solution. Assume that air is an ideal gas with a molecular weight of 29 and that the flow through the system can be considered isothermal. Then Eq. (4-198) applies.

$$\left[\int_{P_I}^{P_0} \mathbf{V}\, dP + \frac{g}{g_c}(z_0 - z_I) + \frac{1}{2g_c}(v_0^2 - v_I^2)\right]_T = (-\mathbf{W} - \mathbf{lw})_T \quad (4\text{-}198)$$

Upon substituting the ideal gas law and integrating,

$$\left[RT \ln \frac{P_0}{P_I} + \frac{g}{g_c}(z_0 - z_I) + \frac{1}{2g_c}(v_0^2 - z_I^2)\right]_T = (-\mathbf{W} - \mathbf{lw})_T \quad (4\text{-}202)$$

Since $\mathbf{W} = \dfrac{-33{,}000 \times 5}{(1000/378) \times 29} = -2160$ ft.-lb./lb., then

$$(1/29)(1.987 \times 778)(530) \ln \frac{15.2}{14.7} + (50 - 0) + \frac{75^2 - 0}{64.4} = 2160 - \mathbf{lw}$$

$$\mathbf{lw} = 1131 \text{ ft.-lb./lb.} = 1.45 \text{ B.t.u./lb.}$$

To calculate $\mathbf{Q}$, use Eq. (4-192). Since the flow is isothermal and the gas is ideal, $(\mathbf{H}_0 - \mathbf{H}_I) = 0$; thus

$$\mathbf{Q} = \mathbf{W} + \frac{g}{g_c}(z_0 - z_I) + \frac{1}{2g_c}(v_0^2 - v_I^2)$$

$$= -2160 + 50 + \frac{75^2 - 0}{64.4} = -2023 \text{ ft.-lb./lb.}$$

$$= -2.6 \text{ B.t.u./lb.} \quad (4\text{-}203)$$

To calculate $(\mathbf{S}_0 - \mathbf{S}_I)$, use Eq. (4-195) and divide through by the constant temperature T.

$$(\mathbf{S}_0 - \mathbf{S}_I) = \frac{\mathbf{Q}}{T} + \frac{\mathbf{lw}}{T}$$

$$= \frac{-2023 + 1131}{530} = -1.68 \text{ ft.-lb./°R./lb.}$$

$$= -0.0022 \text{ B.t.u./lb./°R.} \quad (4\text{-}195a)$$

A number of useful equations can be derived for the flow of fluids through nozzles. According to the open-system analysis for nozzles $W = 0$; furthermore since the wall surface of a nozzle is so small in comparison with the rate of flow through the nozzle, it can be assumed that $Q = 0$. In the study of nozzles, the steady-state rate of flow is defined as

$$\frac{v}{\mathbf{V}} = \frac{\dot{m}}{A}$$

where $\dot{m}$ is the mass flow per unit time and A is the cross-sectional area of flow.

a. For a horizontal nozzle, Eq. (4-192) can be specialized for the general case,

$$\frac{\dot{m}}{A} = \frac{v_0}{\mathbf{V}_0} = \frac{\sqrt{2g_c(\mathbf{H}_I - \mathbf{H}_0) + v_I^2}}{\mathbf{V}_0} \quad (4\text{-}204)$$

b. For a horizontal nozzle in which it is permissible to assume $lw = 0$, $\mathbf{C}_p \neq f(T)$ and substituting Eq. (4-163) in Eq. (4-204)

$$\frac{\dot{m}}{A} = \frac{v_0}{\mathbf{V}_0} = \frac{\sqrt{2g_c\mathbf{C}_pT_I[1 - (P_0/P_I)^{\frac{K-1}{K}}] + v_I^2}}{\mathbf{V}_0} \quad (4\text{-}205)$$

Another form of Eq. (4-205) can be derived from Eq. (4-201)

$$\frac{\dot{m}}{A} = \frac{v_0}{\mathbf{V}_0} = \frac{\sqrt{-2g_c\left(\int_{P_I}^{P_0} \mathbf{V}\, dP\right)_S + v_I^2}}{\mathbf{V}_0} \quad (4\text{-}206)$$

The $\int \mathbf{V}\, dP$ in Eq. (4-206) can be integrated by use of

$$P_I \mathbf{V}_I{}^K = P_0 \mathbf{V}_0{}^K = P\mathbf{V}^K \tag{4-207}$$

and setting $v_I = 0$, the following results:

$$\frac{\dot{m}}{A} = \frac{v_0}{\mathbf{V}_0} = \sqrt{2g_c \frac{P_I}{\mathbf{V}_I} \frac{K}{K-1} \left(\frac{P_0}{P_I}\right)^{2/K} \left[1 - \left(\frac{P_0}{P_I}\right)^{\frac{K-1}{K}}\right]} \tag{4-208}$$

The maximum rate of mass flow per unit area can be found by differentiating Eq. (4-208) with respect to the pressure ratio P_0/P_I, where P_0 is treated as a variable. Setting this derivative equal to zero and substituting the so-called critical-flow pressure P_{CF} for P_0,

$$\frac{P_{CF}}{P_I} = \left(\frac{2}{K+1}\right)^{\frac{K}{K-1}} \tag{4-209}$$

for air, Eq. (4-209) becomes

$$P_{CF} = 0.528\, P_I \tag{4-210}$$

Equation (4-209) states that when the downstream pressure reaches P_{CF} the mass velocity $\dot{m}/A$ is a maximum; any further decrease in the downstream pressure cannot increase the mass velocity. For any expansion of the gas from P_I to any pressure down to the critical pressure P_{CF} the nozzle must be converging. If the nozzle consists simply of an orifice at the outlet of the conduit, the pressure at the outlet boundary cannot be less than P_{CF} as given by Eq. (4-209); such a device is known as a critical-flow prover.

For any reversible expansion to a pressure below the critical-flow pressure, the nozzle must be converging and diverging. Any decrease in pressure below P_{CF} cannot increase the mass velocity $\dot{m}/A$ but only increases the linear velocity v. At the throat of the nozzle (the point of minimum cross-sectional area of flow) the linear velocity is equal to the velocity of sound in that fluid; linear velocities in the diverging part are greater than the velocity of sound.

A number of other equations pertinent to the thermodynamics of fluid flow, such as the Rayleigh and Fanno lines, high-velocity flow, and shock analysis, can be derived but are beyond the scope of the present treatment (Keenan, "Thermodynamics," Wiley, New York, 1941; Kiefer, Kinney, and Stuart, "Principles of Engineering Thermodynamics," Wiley, New York, 1954; Hall, "Thermodynamics of Fluid Flow," Prentice-Hall, Englewood Cliffs, N.J., 1951).

One other point merits brief consideration in steady-state flow processes. By its very nature, the compression of gas occurs adiabatically, and thus the temperature rises. The allowable temperature rise is limited to not exceeding the allowable operating temperature for the materials of construction. Furthermore, the work required to compress a gas is a maximum for an adiabatic compression and a minimum for an isothermal compression; therefore, it is desirable to have the compression approach isothermal conditions. Since it is impractical in any compression device to attain isothermal conditions, compression is usually carried out in stages with intercooling between stages if the over-all compression ratio exceeds 3 to 5. It can be shown that, in a two-stage compression, the minimum work is achieved by operating each stage at a pressure ratio which is the *square root* of the over-all pressure ratio; for a three-stage compression each stage should operate at a pressure ratio which is the *cube root* of the over-all pressure ratio, etc. (Soo, "Thermodynamics of Engineering Science," Prentice-Hall, Englewood Cliffs, N.J., 1958).

THE SECOND LAW OF THERMODYNAMICS AND THE CONCEPT OF THE AVAILABILITY OF ENERGY

In the mathematical statement of the first law of thermodynamics, the law of conservation of energy [Eq. (4-151)], a precise differentiation between heat and work was made. This difference is a consequence of the second law of thermodynamics, which actually preceded a precise statement of the first law by some 50 years, primarily because of the continued adherence (even today) to the old caloric theory of heat.

In an attempt to attach some practical or physical significance to entropy, the concept of availability or unavailability of energy has been very useful. However, this principle has evolved in such a manner that its inherent relationship to the entropy concept and the classical Carnot cycle is not always appreciated, as evidenced even in recent literature [Denbigh, *Chem. Eng. Sci.*, **6**, 1 (1956)].

Presumedly the first complete and precise treatment of the availability of energy and its relationship to the entropy concept is due to Bryan ("Thermodynamics," Stechert, New York, 1907). Bryan ascribed two definitions to entropy: (1) that arising from reversible heat transfer, and (2) that arising from any increases in the unavailable energy of the system. Dodge ("Chemical Engineering Thermodynamics," p. 74, McGraw-Hill, New York, 1944) has objected to the practice of defining entropy in terms of unavailable energy because ". . . there is no definite and unambiguous definition of unavailable energy that is applicable to all the various processes with which we shall be concerned." However, as pointed out by Bryan, the second definition of entropy places no restrictions on the nature of the transformations which take place since it considers the unavailable energy resulting from a transfer of heat as well as the irreversible changes which increase the unavailable energy at the expense of the available energy. Bryan's viewpoint, nevertheless, is supported on the basis that available energy or maximum work is an exact differential whereas classical reversible work is not exact, as will be shown later.

The Generalized Work Balance. Equation (4-151) can be solved explicitly for W, giving

$$W = \sum\left[\left(\mathbf{H} + \frac{g}{g_c}z + \frac{v^2}{2g_c}\right)(\delta m)\right]_I - \sum\left[\left(\mathbf{H} + \frac{g}{g_c}z + \frac{v^2}{2g_c}\right)(\delta m)\right]_0 - \int_{(\ )_B}^{(\ )_E} d\left[\left(\mathbf{U} + \frac{g}{g_c}z + \frac{v^2}{2g_c}\right)(m)\right] + \sum(\delta Q) \tag{4-151a}$$

Equation (4-151a) states that work may be obtained by a transfer of mass into or out of the system, by a variation of the energy within the boundaries of the system, and by a transfer of heat with the surroundings. In a process which occurs without any losses arising from irreversibilities Eq. (4-151a) gives the value for W_{rev}. The extent to which W_{rev} is realized in any given process, *subject to the specified end conditions*, is essentially a statement of the second law in its more practical form and constitutes the basis for engineering applications. All the terms on the right-hand side of Eq. (4-151a) express properties possessed by matter with the exception of Q. Therefore, it would be very useful to relate Q to some property of matter, which indeed is part of the duty that the entropy term performs as well as accounting for irreversibilities and mass transfers according to Eq. (4-155):

$$dS = \delta\left(\frac{Q_i}{T_i}\right) + \left(\frac{\delta lw}{T}\right) + \mathbf{S}_I\,\delta m_I - \mathbf{S}_0\,\delta m_0 \quad (4\text{-}155)$$

Conversion of Heat into Work. The extent to which heat may be converted into work is one of the most important aspects of the second law. The basic concepts involved can be easily demonstrated schematically by reference to the ordinary elevator in Fig. 4-16. The

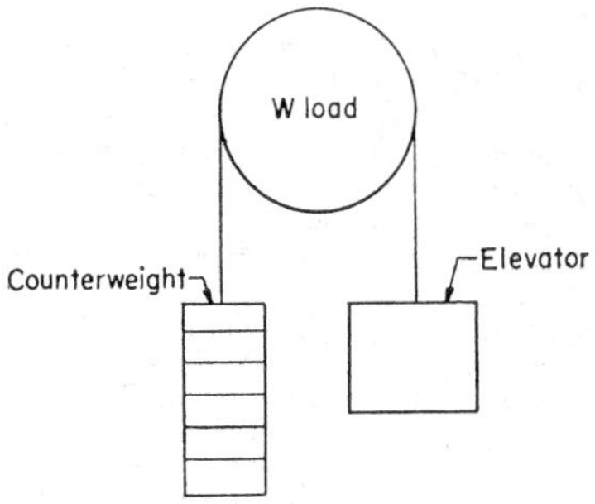

FIG. 4-16. Ordinary mechanical elevator.

empty elevator is counterweighted over a pulley. The only work required to raise the elevator is that required to overcome friction in the pulley. If the pulley is frictionless, no external work is required to raise the elevator because of the counterweights; in other words, the elevator and counterweights exchange gravitational potential. If a load is placed on the elevator, the external work required to raise the elevator is simply the product of the load and the change in elevation. If the load is discharged at the higher elevation and the elevator is returned to the original level, a cycle has been completed, the net result of which is the transfer of a load from a lower elevation to a higher elevation by means of a net amount of work delivered to the elevator pulley.

Figure 4-17 is a schematic of an elevator which operates between a datum level z_D as indicated by the line *beh* and an arbitrary level indicated by the line *cdg*. The weight of the elevator is indicated by the length of

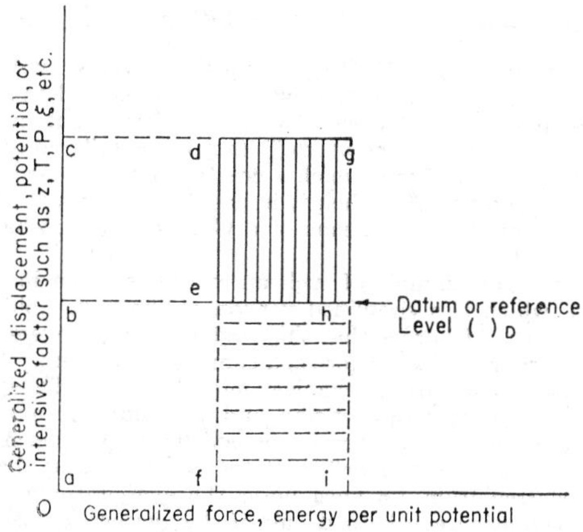

FIG. 4-17. Generalized force, energy per unit potential, vs. extensive factor such as m, $\delta\,(Q/T)$, $\delta\,V$, $\delta\,\mathfrak{F}$, etc.

the line *be*, the load added to the elevator by the length of line *eh*. The potential energy of the load at the datum level referred to the absolute level is given by the horizontally shaded area *fehi*. As the load is raised to level *cdg*, an amount of external work indicated by the vertically shaded area *edgh* is delivered to the pulley. This amount of work is exactly equal to the increase in potential energy of the load; the total potential energy of the load is given by the sum of the two shaded areas. Theoretically, the total potential energy referred to the absolute zero of elevation (center of the earth) represents energy which is capable of doing work. However, if the elevator shaft does not extend below the datum level *beh*, then the load at elevation *cdg* has only potential energy *edgh available* for doing work, and the potential energy represented by *fehi* is unavailable for doing work unless the elevator shaft is lowered. It should be noted in the foregoing that no mention was made of the mass, material of construction, or other properties of the empty elevator. It merely acts as the working substance and operates in a cycle. The principal object of interest is the load that rides on the elevator. The external work required depends only on the load being elevated and the difference in levels; it is completely independent of the nature of the working substance (an important corollary of the second law.)

It is not difficult to visualize that the above development will apply equally well if the elevator is loaded and unloaded at several levels. Figure 4-18 indicates that the

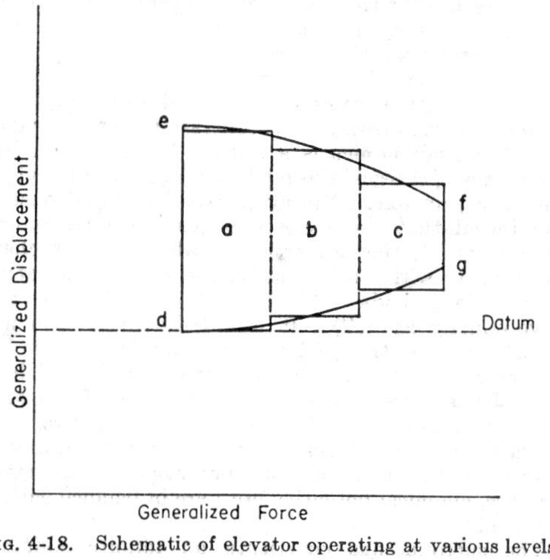

FIG. 4-18. Schematic of elevator operating at various levels.

external work required will be the sum of areas $a + b + c$. It can be further visualized that, if the loadings, unloadings, and levels are reduced to infinitesimal increments, the operation can be schematically represented by the continuous curved lines *ef* and *dg*. The external work required is then given by the area enclosed between these two curves, area *defg*.

Figure 4-17 can be transformed into a thermal elevator simply by labeling the ordinate at T and the abscissa $\delta(Q/T)$. This thermal elevator is nothing but the classical Carnot cycle operating between two fixed temperature limits, which will be denoted by T_i and T_D. The reversible work required to elevate a quantity of $\delta(Q/T)$ from T_D to T_i is given by

$$-\delta W_C = \left[\delta\left(\frac{Q_D}{T_D}\right)\right](T_i - T_D) \qquad (4\text{-}211)$$

where W_C denotes reversible Carnot work. Similarly,

the work delivered when $\delta(Q_i/T_i)$ is lowered from T_i to T_D is given by

$$-\delta W_C = \left[\delta\left(\frac{Q_i}{T_i}\right)\right](T_D - T_i) \qquad (4\text{-}212)$$

It is apparent from Eqs. (4-211) and (4-212) or Fig. 4-18 that

$$\delta\left(\frac{Q_D}{T_D}\right) = -\delta\left(\frac{Q_i}{T_i}\right) \qquad (4\text{-}213)$$

for a reversible cycle.

Example 1. Saturated benzene vapor at atmospheric pressure is being condensed continuously to a saturated liquid by means of an atmospheric air condenser. Compute the theoretical reversible work that could be obtained from this process.

Boiling point of benzene = 176°F.

Latent heat of vaporization = 170 B.t.u./lb.

Atmospheric temperature = 70°F.

Solution. If the air condenser is replaced by a reversible Carnot engine which absorbs heat at T_i = 176°F. and delivers it to T_D = 70°F., Eq. (4-212) applies. Thus,

$$-W_C = \frac{170}{460 + 176}[(70 + 460) - (176 + 460)]$$

$$W_C = 28 \text{ B.t.u./lb.}$$

The Dead State or Datum Level. In classical reversible thermodynamics, it is customary to visualize that all heat transfers take place between the system and infinite reservoirs having the same temperature as the system. Since all levels of temperature can be encountered in the various processes that might be considered, classical reversible thermodynamics requires at its disposal an infinite number of reservoirs of infinite capacity. The existence of such reservoirs is contrary to experience; and since thermodynamics is a science based on empirical observations, classical thermodynamics appears to violate this very principle. However, experience and observation reveal that there exists at least one reservoir of infinite extent, the properties of which do not change significantly with time, namely, the surrounding atmosphere (a large body of water or the earth's crust could serve equally as well). It would therefore seem more logical to base thermodynamic analyses on one real infinite reservoir than on an infinite number of hypothetical reservoirs. Another valid argument for choosing the surrounding atmosphere as the reference reservoir is the fact that any system under no restraint will undergo changes until eventually its potentials (temperature, pressure, chemical potential, etc.) are in balance with the surroundings.

The surroundings constitute an infinite source of energy (low level) which is "freely available." To be useful, it is only necessary to load this energy on a thermal elevator and elevate it to the desired temperature level. Only the work energy that is used in operating the elevator will have to be "paid for"; the energy taken from the surroundings is "free." An example might clarify this point.

Example 2. Find the least amount of power required to maintain a building at a constant temperature of 65°F. when the outdoors temperature is 0°F. Heat losses from the building amount to 780,000 B.t.u./hr.

Solution. The total amount of energy that must be delivered at 65°F. is 780,000 B.t.u./hr. Referring to Fig. 4-17, this requirement means that the area under *dg* down to the absolute zero of temperature (*fedghi*) must equal 780,000 B.t.u. Therefore, the quantity of $\delta(Q/T)$ that must be loaded on the elevator is given by the length of the line *dg* or *eh*,

$$-\delta\left(\frac{Q_i}{T_i}\right) = \delta\left(\frac{Q_D}{T_D}\right) = \frac{780{,}000}{460 + 65}$$

Substituting in Eq. (4-211)

$$-W_C = \frac{780{,}000}{460 + 65}(65 - 0)$$

$$W_C = -96{,}600 \text{ B.t.u./hr.}$$

The amount of energy extracted from the surroundings at 0°F. is simply 780,000 − 96,600 = 683,400 B.t.u./hr. Thus, to deliver 780,000 B.t.u., approximately 87 per cent is "freely" available from the surroundings and the remainder has to be "paid for" in elevating this energy. It is this advantage that makes the "heat pump" for heating buildings so attractive. However, other complications, such as capital equipment and power costs, tend to make this device uneconomical in certain regions and climates.

On the other hand, the surroundings serve as a reservoir or "dump" of infinite capacity to which energy is freely rejected. Suppose in Example 2 above it were desired to deliver 96,600 B.t.u./hr. of work to some external device. It would be necessary to extract 780,000 B.t.u. at 65°F., lower it on a thermal elevator to 0°F., in which case 683,400 B.t.u. represents energy that is unavailable for doing further work.

It is apparent from the foregoing that heat cannot be completely converted into work (in a cyclic or self-sustaining process). Only a fraction of the heat energy is available for doing work; in fact it is given by Eq. (4-212) as being equal to $[(T_D - T_i)/T_i]$. Unless T_D is equal to the absolute zero of temperature, the fraction will always be less than 1. Since T_D is usually about 460° to 560°R., and maximum operating temperatures for heat transfer rarely exceed 1500°R. (metallurgical limit), the best that can be expected (at least for the present) is a fractional conversion of (1500 − 460)/1500 ≅ 0.75.

The above fraction has been designated as the efficiency of a heat engine and is defined from Eq. (4-212), where $T_i > T_D$, as

$$\text{Eff.} = +\frac{W_C}{Q_i} = \frac{T_i - T_D}{T_i} \qquad (4\text{-}214)$$

On the other hand, for a refrigeration machine a coefficient of performance has been defined from Eq. (4-211), where $T_i > T_D$, as

$$\text{C.O.P.} = \frac{Q_D}{-W_C} = \frac{T_D}{T_i - T_D} \qquad (4\text{-}215)$$

Availability of Energy. Returning to the generalized work balance [Eq. (4-151*b*)] and simplifying it by ignoring potential- and kinetic-energy effects,

$$W = \Sigma \mathbf{H}_I\, \delta m_I - \Sigma \mathbf{H}_0\, \delta m_0 - \int dU + \Sigma(\delta Q) \qquad (4\text{-}216)$$

Referring to Fig. 4-19, it is evident that, even though the system as defined by the dashed envelope undergoes a reversible process, if the heat is transferred out of the system at some temperature T_i (not necessarily constant with time or position) which is greater than the surrounding temperature T_D, then it is possible to recover additional work W_C by means of a Carnot-type engine, as indicated.

A typical example of such an engine is given in Fig. 4-20, which is a simplified version of the household refrigerator. In order that this engine may be reversible, it is necessary that *lw* for each component be zero. The possible losses are mechanical and thermal. Thus the compressor, expansion engine, and flow conduits must all be frictionless. No extraneous heat losses are permissible; all equipment is well insulated. All the heat that is transferred from T_D must enter the evaporator at T_D; this condition can be met only if the evaporator has infinite heat-exchange surface with infinite heat conductivity. Similar conditions must exist in the condenser,

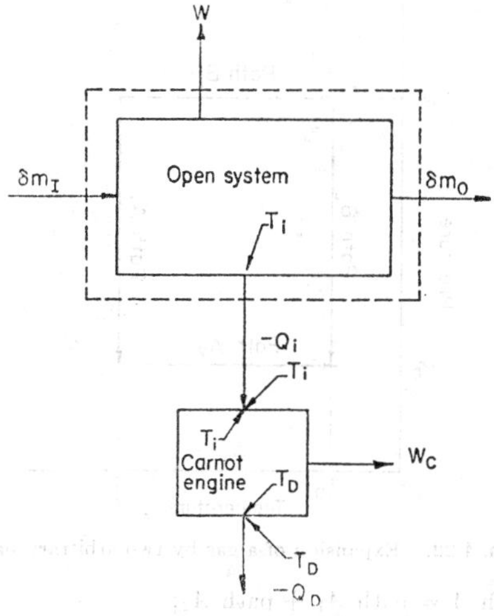

FIG. 4-19. Open system transferring heat to a Carnot engine located in the surroundings.

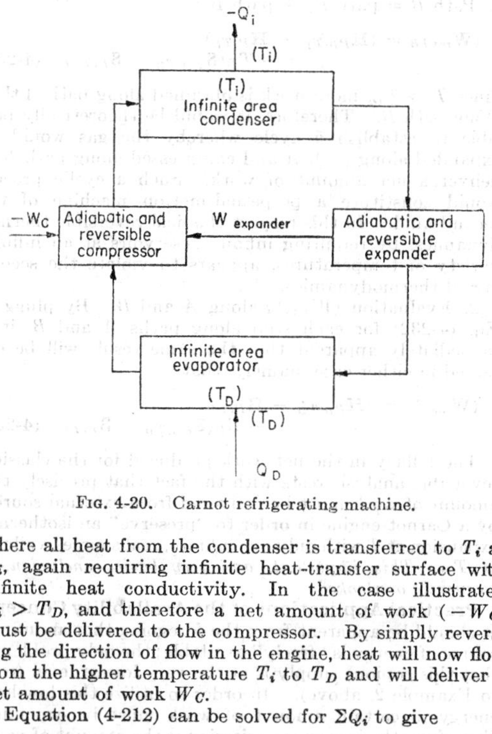

FIG. 4-20. Carnot refrigerating machine.

where all heat from the condenser is transferred to T_i at T_i, again requiring infinite heat-transfer surface with infinite heat conductivity. In the case illustrated $T_i > T_D$, and therefore a net amount of work $(-W_C)$ must be delivered to the compressor. By simply reversing the direction of flow in the engine, heat will now flow from the higher temperature T_i to T_D and will deliver a net amount of work W_C.

Equation (4-212) can be solved for ΣQ_i to give

$$(\Sigma Q_i)_C = T_D \sum \delta \left(\frac{Q_i}{T_i}\right)_C + W_C \qquad (4\text{-}212a)$$

Substituting in Eq. (4-216) and since $(\Sigma Q_i)_{\text{Carnot}} = -(\Sigma Q_i)_{\text{system}} = -[\Sigma(\delta Q)]_{\text{system}}$

$$-\sum (W + W_C) = \sum \mathbf{H}_O \, \delta m_O - \sum \mathbf{H}_I \, \delta m_I + \Delta U - T_D \sum \delta \left(\frac{Q_i}{T_i}\right) \qquad (4\text{-}217)$$

Solving Eq. (4-155) for $\delta(Q_i/T_i)$, integrating, and multiplying through by T_D yields

$$T_D \sum \delta \left(\frac{Q_i}{T_i}\right) = T_D \, \Delta S = T_D \sum \left(\frac{\delta lw}{T}\right) + T_D \sum \mathbf{S}_O \, \delta m_O - T_D \sum \mathbf{S}_I \, \delta m_I \qquad (4\text{-}218)$$

Combining Eqs. (4-217) and (4-218)

$$-\left[\sum W + T_D \sum \left(\frac{\delta lw}{T}\right) + \sum W_C\right] = \sum [(\mathbf{H}_O - T_D \mathbf{S}_O)(\delta m_O)] - \sum [(\mathbf{H}_I - T_D \mathbf{S}_I)(\delta m_I)] + (\Delta U - T_D \, \Delta S) \qquad (4\text{-}219)$$

If lw for the system as defined in Fig. 4-19 equals zero, then $W = W_{\text{rev}}$ and the left-hand side of Eq. (4-219) can be replaced by

$$W_{\max} = W_{\text{rev}} + W_C \qquad (4\text{-}220)$$

Substituting Eq. (4-220) in Eq. (4-219)

$$-(W_{\max}) = \Sigma[(\mathbf{H}_O - T_D \mathbf{S}_O)(\delta m_O)] - \Sigma[(\mathbf{H}_I - T_D \mathbf{S}_I)(\delta m_I)] + (\Delta U - T_D \, \Delta S) \qquad (4\text{-}221)$$

If any of the work done by the system is expended in "pushing back" the surroundings $(P_D \, \Delta V)$ this amount is usually not considered useful work. Therefore, subtracting $(P_D \, \Delta V)$ from $W_{\max}$, we define useful maximum work as

$$(W_{\max})_u = W_{\max} - P_D \, \Delta V \qquad (4\text{-}222)$$

Substituting Eq. (4-222) in (4-221)

$$-(W_{\max})_u = \Sigma[(\mathbf{H}_O - T_D \mathbf{S}_O)(\delta m_O)] - \Sigma[(\mathbf{H}_I - T_D \mathbf{S}_I)(\delta m_I)] + (\Delta U - T_D \, \Delta S + P_D \, \Delta V) \qquad (4\text{-}223)$$

There are four important observations that should be noted regarding Eq. (4-223):

1. It is perfectly general except that the potential- and kinetic-energy terms associated with $\mathbf{H}_O$, $\mathbf{H}_I$, and U were dropped out in order to simplify the equation. For complete generality these terms should be reinstated.
2. T_D is a fixed "dead-state" temperature and has nothing to do with the temperatures at which $\mathbf{S}_O$, $\mathbf{S}_I$, and ΔS are evaluated.
3. The system as defined in Fig. 4-19 does not include the Carnot engine; however, the heat is transferred from the system to the surroundings by a reversible Carnot engine and the work obtained W_C is included in $W_{\max}$.
4. The system as defined is assumed to undergo a reversible process, that is, lw for the system is zero.

Equation (4-223) can be derived by including the Carnot engine as part of the system as shown in Fig. 4-21. In this case the work of the system is

$$W_{\text{system}} = W + W_C \qquad (4\text{-}224)$$

and the heat transferred from the system is

$$Q_{\text{system}} = Q_D \qquad (4\text{-}225)$$

Thus, instead of using Eq. (4-216) as the starting point, it should be modified as follows by Eqs. (4-224) and (4-225):

$$-(W + W_C) = \Sigma \mathbf{H}_O \, \delta m_O - \Sigma \mathbf{H}_I \, \delta m_I + \int dU - Q_D \qquad (4\text{-}226)$$

The generalized entropy balance [Eq. (4-155)] must be

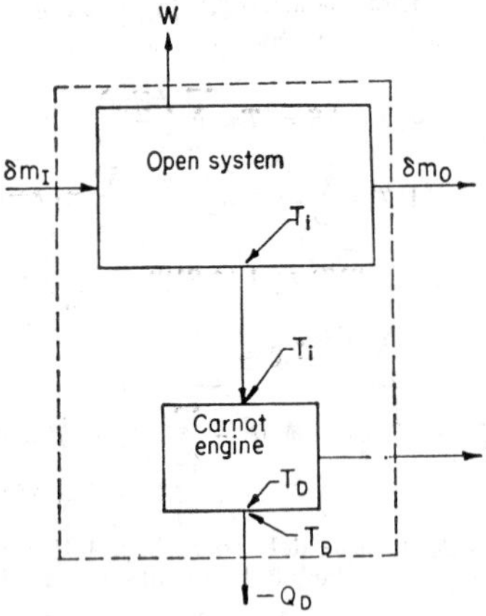

FIG. 4-21. Combined open system and Carnot engine.

modified by replacing $\delta(Q_i/T_i)$ by $\delta(Q_D/T_D)$; thus

$$dS = \delta\left(\frac{Q_D}{T_D}\right) + \left(\frac{\delta lw}{T}\right) + \mathbf{S}_I\,\delta m_I - \mathbf{S}_0\,\delta m_0 \quad (4\text{-}227)$$

which upon integrating and noting that T_D is a constant,

$$-Q_D = -T_D\,\Delta S + T_D\sum\left(\frac{\delta lw}{T}\right) + \left(\sum \mathbf{S}_I\,\delta m_I - \sum \mathbf{S}_0\,\delta m_0\right)T_D \quad (4\text{-}228)$$

Equations (4-226) and (4-228) combine to give Eq. (4-219). Equation (4-223) then follows as before. Equation (4-223) can be easily specialized as follows:

Closed systems:

$$-(W_{\max})_u = (\Delta U - T_D\,\Delta S + P_D\,\Delta V) \quad (4\text{-}229)$$

Unsteady-state flow:

For $\delta m_I = 0$

$$-(W_{\max})_u = \Sigma(\mathbf{H}_0 - T_D\mathbf{S}_0)\,\delta m_0 + (\Delta U - T_D\,\Delta S + P_D\,\Delta V) \quad (4\text{-}230)$$

For $\delta m_0 = 0$

$$-(W_{\max})_u = -\Sigma(\mathbf{H}_I - T_D\mathbf{S}_I)\,\delta m_I + (\Delta U - T_D\,\Delta S + P_D\,\Delta V) \quad (4\text{-}231)$$

Steady-state flow:

$$-(\mathbf{W}_{\max})_u = (\mathbf{H}_0 - \mathbf{H}_I) - T_D(\mathbf{S}_0 - \mathbf{S}_I) \quad (4\text{-}232)$$

Maximum Work as an Exact Differential. The most important aspect of the maximum-work principle is that like other thermodynamic functions *it is an exact differential (dependent only on the end states) whereas W_{rev} is an inexact differential (dependent on the path of integration).* To prove this point, consider a gas initially at an elevated P and T being continuously expanded down to a final state P_D, T_D. To test for exactness, it is only necessary to select two arbitrary reversible paths connecting the two states. It is convenient to select the two paths indicated in Fig. 4-22.

1. Evaluate $\mathbf{W}_{rev} = \int \mathbf{V}\,dP$ along path A and B, neglecting potential and kinetic energies.

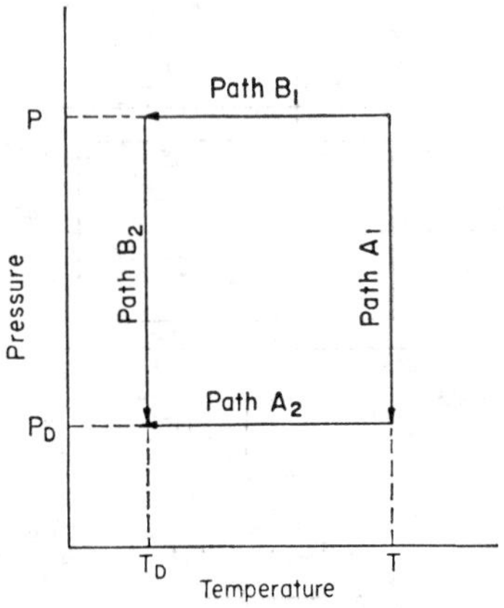

FIG. 4-22. Expansion of a gas by two arbitrary paths.

a. Path A = path A_1 + path A_2:

$$-(\mathbf{W}_{rev})_A = (\mathbf{H}_{P_D,T} - \mathbf{H}_{P,T}) - T(\mathbf{S}_{P_D,T} - \mathbf{S}_{P,T}) \quad (4\text{-}233)$$

b. Path B = path B_1 + path B_2:

$$-(\mathbf{W}_{rev})_B = (\mathbf{H}_{P_D,T_D} - \mathbf{H}_{P,T_D}) - T_D(\mathbf{S}_{P_D,T_D} - \mathbf{S}_{P,T_D}) \quad (4\text{-}234)$$

Since $T > T_D$, more work is obtained along path A than along path B. Therefore, it would be theoretically possible to establish a cycle whereby the gas would be expanded along path A and compressed along path B to deliver a net amount of work. Such a cyclic process would constitute a perpetual-motion machine of the second kind. In this respect classical reversible thermodynamics, by requiring infinite reservoirs at an infinite variety of temperatures, appears to violate the second law of thermodynamics.

2. Evaluation $(W_{\max})_u$ along A and B. By plugging Eq. (4-232) for each step along paths A and B, it is immediately apparent that the same result will be obtained in either case, namely, that

$$-(\mathbf{W}_{\max})_u = (\mathbf{H}_{P_D,T_D} - \mathbf{H}_{P,T}) - T_D(\mathbf{S}_{P_D,T_D} - \mathbf{S}_{P,T}) \quad (4\text{-}235)$$

The fallacy in the net work produced for the classical reversible analysis rests with the fact that precisely this amount of work must be delivered from external sources by a Carnot engine in order to "preserve" an isothermal expansion at T with only one infinite, real source available at T_D. *This important, and very basic conclusion, is frequently overlooked.*

Practical Applications of the Availability Concept. It should be apparent from the foregoing that an infinite source of energy is "freely" available; the only problem is that this copious supply is at the very lowest level (refer to Example 2, above). In order to utilize this low-level energy, a certain amount of work must be expended. Therefore, the important criterion is the amount of work, rather than the amount of heat energy. To illustrate the point, compare the maximum amount of useful work that can be obtained from condensing saturated steam at 100°F. and at 212°F. if the ambient temperature is 70°F. From the steam tables:

1. Condensing at 100°F., Eq. (4-232) gives

$$-(\mathbf{W}_{\max})_u = (-1037) - 530(-1.853) = 54 \text{ B.t.u./lb.}$$

2. Condensing at 212°F., Eq. (4-232) gives

$$-(\mathbf{W}_{\max})_u = (-970.3) - 530(-1.445) = 204 \text{ B.t.u./lb.}$$

Even though the enthalpies in the two cases are almost identical, the energy available for doing work $(W_{max})_u$ differs by a factor of 4. For this reason, when process steam is used successively in an industrial plant, it has become customary in assessing costs to the individual departments to base them on the decrease in availability rather than "heat content."

Another practical application of the maximum-work principle is in the analysis of the performance of turbines. By definition,

$$\text{Efficiency} = \frac{W}{(W_{rev})_{Q=0}} \tag{4-236}$$

where W is the actual work delivered and $(W_{rev})_{Q=0}$ represents the work that can be obtained if the working fluid is expanded adiabatically and reversibly from the same initial conditions, but not to the same final conditions, that exist in the actual process. Another criterion of the performance of a turbine is as follows:

$$\text{Effectiveness} = \frac{W}{W_{max}} \tag{4-237}$$

where in this case W_{max} is evaluated for the same initial and final conditions as in the actual process. For this reason, Eq. (4-237) is a more realistic evaluation of the performance of a turbine than Eq. (4-236).

The availability-of-energy or maximum-work equations, such as Eq. (4-223), provide a rapid and convenient means for evaluating the performance of an industrial process. This equation can be applied over various subdivisions of the process to obtain the maximum (or minimum) work. This figure is then compared with the actual work being delivered or expended. The parts of the process where the differences between W_{actual} and W_{max} are unexpectedly large should be investigated closely in order to determine the reasons for the low efficiency and the corrective action needed.

It is also helpful to make a second-law analysis of a proposed new process in order to establish performance limits.

Example 3. It is desired to liquefy 100 million standard cu. ft. of dry natural gas per day. The gas can be delivered to the liquefaction plant at 1000 lb./sq. in. abs. and 100°F. The liquid is to leave the plant at −258°F. and 1 atm. How much horsepower will be required?

Solution. To obtain the theoretical minimum work, Eq. (4-232) will be used. For purposes of calculation treat the natural gas as pure methane and assume an ambient temperature of 100°F. = T_D.

$$\begin{aligned} -(\mathbf{W}_{max})_u &= (\mathbf{H}_0 - \mathbf{H}_I) - T_D(\mathbf{S}_0 - \mathbf{S}_I) \qquad (4\text{-}232)\\ &= (18.3 - 395) - 560(0.0899 - 1.1513)\\ &= (-376.7) - 650(-1.0614)\\ &= (-376.7) + (594.4) = 217.7 \text{ B.t.u./lb.}\\ &\cong 15{,}000 \text{ hp.} \end{aligned}$$

This figure is the theoretical minimum as could be obtained from an ideal or Carnot-type refrigeration machine. A better estimate for the power requirements can be made by adding to this theoretical value the unavoidable losses in actual practice such as temperature approaches in the heat exchangers, mechanical efficiencies of compressors and expanders, throttle valves, mixing of streams of different temperatures, and pressure losses in lines. The total of these losses is estimated at about 150 per cent of the theoretical work; so that the realistic minimum-work requirement becomes 37,500 hp. This figure represents the one to "shoot for" in an actual plant; it is unlikely that it can be bettered by any economical process.

In the process design of heat exchangers, it is possible to violate the second law of thermodynamics if only terminal temperature differences are considered. For example, consider the countercurrent methane heat exchanger shown in Fig. 4-23. The terminal temperatures of

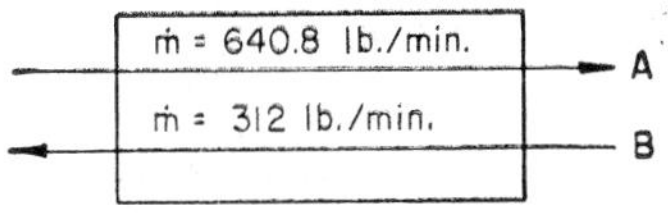

Fig. 4-23. Countercurrent methane heat exchanger.

stream B are greater than of stream A. A heat balance around the heat exchanger checks:

$$\begin{aligned} 640.8(407 - 240) &= 312(394 - 52)\\ 107{,}000 &= 107{,}000 \end{aligned}$$

Thus far, the heat exchanger appears to be operable. However, it is necessary to check the temperature differences between the two streams at each point in the exchanger to determine if any temperature crosses occur. The temperature of each stream is plotted against the heat transferred in Fig. 4-24. It can be seen that, in the

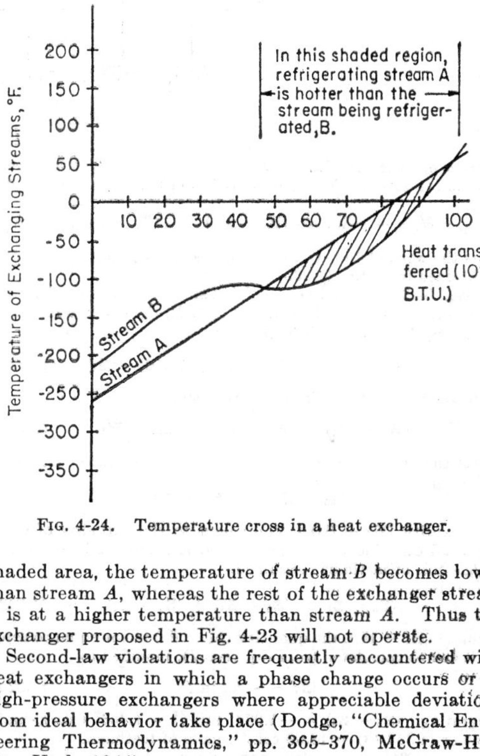

Fig. 4-24. Temperature cross in a heat exchanger.

shaded area, the temperature of stream B becomes lower than stream A, whereas the rest of the exchanger stream B is at a higher temperature than stream A. Thus the exchanger proposed in Fig. 4-23 will not operate.

Second-law violations are frequently encountered with heat exchangers in which a phase change occurs or in high-pressure exchangers where appreciable deviations from ideal behavior take place (Dodge, "Chemical Engineering Thermodynamics," pp. 365–370, McGraw-Hill, New York, 1944).

The complete generality of Eq. (4-223) can be demonstrated by a process involving heat transfers, expansions, chemical reactions, etc.

Example 4. A mixture consisting of one-third by volume of methane and two-thirds oxygen at 25°C. and 9 atm. total pressure is fed continuously to a combustion chamber where the methane is burned completely at 1800°C. The combustion products are then cooled and expanded at constant composition to 25°C. and 1 atm. pressure.

1. What is the maximum work obtainable from this process?

Solution. The process can be visualized as shown in Fig. 4-25, where the system is indicated by the envelope (dashed line).

$$W_{max} = (W_C)_1 + (W_C)_2 + (W_E) + (W_C)_3 + (W_X) \tag{4-238}$$

$(W_C)_1$, $(W_C)_2$, and $(W_C)_3$ can be evaluated by Eqs. (4-211) and (4-212). W_E is the reversible work which can be obtained by

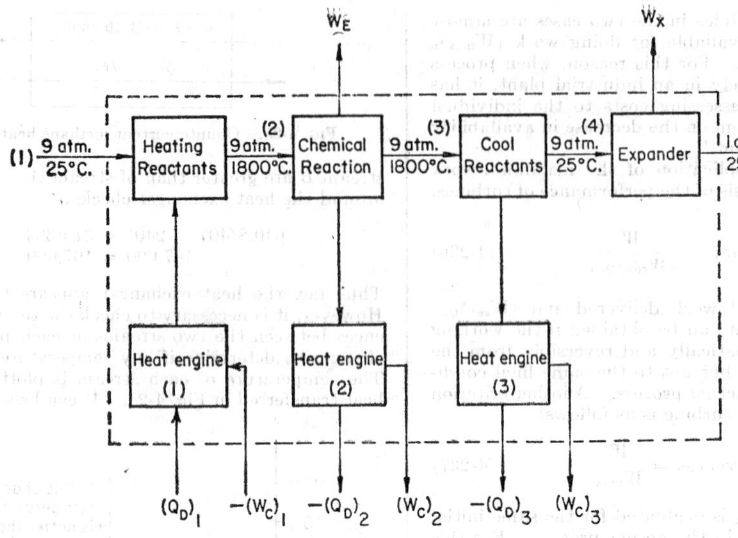

FIG. 4-25. Combustion process.

carrying out the chemical reaction in a reversible galvanic cell. Equation (4-196), neglecting potential- and kinetic-energy effects, gives

$$-\mathbf{W}_{rev} = -\mathbf{W}_E = [(\mathbf{H}_3 - \mathbf{H}_2) - T(\mathbf{S}_3 - \mathbf{S}_2)]_T \qquad (4\text{-}239)$$

W_X is the work of the expander. Since it is isothermal, W_X can be obtained from Eq. (4-239).

If Eq. (4-238) is now summed for all the work quantities by means of Eqs. (4-211), (4-212), and (4-239), the result is identical to Eq. (4-232) as would be expected:

$$-(\mathbf{W}_{max})_u = (\mathbf{H}_5 - \mathbf{H}_1) - T_D(\mathbf{S}_5 - \mathbf{S}_1) \qquad (4\text{-}232a)$$

where $\mathbf{H}_5 = \mathbf{H}_0$, $\mathbf{H}_1 = \mathbf{H}_I$, etc. Note that

$$(\mathbf{H}_5 - \mathbf{H}_1) = (\mathbf{H}_5 - \mathbf{H}_4) + (\mathbf{H}_4 - \mathbf{H}_1) \qquad (4\text{-}240)$$

but for the isothermal expansion of an ideal gas, $(\mathbf{H}_5 - \mathbf{H}_4) = 0$, so that

$$(\mathbf{H}_5 - \mathbf{H}_1) = (\mathbf{H}_4 - \mathbf{H}_1) \qquad (4\text{-}241)$$

The quantity $(\mathbf{H}_4 - \mathbf{H}_1)$ is equivalent to the enthalpy of reaction at 25°C. The value reported in the literature is −208,500 cal./g.-mole of methane consumed.

Likewise,

$$(\mathbf{S}_5 - \mathbf{S}_1) = (\mathbf{S}_5 - \mathbf{S}_4) + (\mathbf{S}_4 - \mathbf{S}_1) \qquad (4\text{-}242)$$

Unlike $(\mathbf{H}_5 - \mathbf{H}_4)$, the quantity $(\mathbf{S}_5 - \mathbf{S}_4)$ is not equal to zero, but it can be calculated from Eq. (4-137), modified to

$$d\mathbf{S}_T = -Rd \ln P \qquad (4\text{-}137a)$$

Integrating, $(\mathbf{S}_5 - \mathbf{S}_4) = -1.987 \ln(\frac{1}{9}) = 4.363$ cal./g.-mole of gas or $(4.363)(3) = 13.09$ cal./g.-mole of methane.

In Eq. (4-242), $(\mathbf{S}_4 - \mathbf{S}_1)$ represents the entropy of reaction at 25°C. The value reported in the literature is −1.23 cal./g.-mole CH_4/°K.

Thus, from Eq. (4-242),

$$(\mathbf{S}_5 - \mathbf{S}_1) = -1.23 + 13.09 = 11.86$$

Substituting these values in Eq. (4-232*a*)

$$-(\mathbf{W}_{max})_u = -208{,}500 - 298(11.86)$$
$$= 212{,}035 \text{ cal./g.-mole } CH_4$$

2. What would be the maximum work obtainable if the combustion reaction were carried out irreversibly at 1800°C. but all other steps in the process were reversible? The lost work arising from irreversible reaction at 1800° is identically equal to (W_E) as given by Eq. (4-239). From the literature, values are obtained for the enthalpy and entropy of reaction at 1800°C. Thus,

$$-\mathbf{lw} = -\mathbf{W}_E = (-211{,}110) - (1800 + 273)(-4.07)$$
$$\mathbf{lw} = 202{,}690 \text{ cal./g.-mole } CH_4$$

When the reaction occurs irreversibly, the lost work is transferred into heat engine 2 in Fig. 4-25 in addition to the energy transferred in the reversible reaction so that actually

$$(W_{C_2})_{case2} > (W_{C_2})_{case1}$$

but

$$(W_E)_{case1} \gg (W_E)_{case2} = 0$$

Only a portion of the lw generated in the combustion chamber can be converted into work; the fraction

$$T_D \frac{lw}{T} = (273 + 25)\frac{202{,}690}{273 + 1800} = 29{,}200 \text{ cal.}$$

is "irretrievably lost." Therefore, for Case 2,

$$(\mathbf{W}_{max})_u = 212{,}035 - 29{,}200$$
$$= 182{,}835 \text{ cal./g.-mole } CH_4$$

The significance of the term $T_D\Sigma\left(\frac{\delta lw}{T}\right)$ on the left-hand side of Eq. (4-219) should now be obvious in view of the example above.

The Potential Concept of Availability. From the generalized elevator principle illustrated in Fig. 4-17, and specialized for the case of T and $\delta(Q_i/T_i)$, W_C was found to be of the form

$$-\delta W_C = \left[\delta\left(\frac{Q_D}{T_D}\right)\right](T_i - T_D) \qquad (4\text{-}211)$$

For very small differences between T_i and T_D, Eq. (4-211) can be expressed as

$$-\delta W_C = \left[\left(\frac{Q_D}{T_D}\right)\right][dT] \qquad (4\text{-}211a)$$

Brown [Brown, *Trans. Am. Inst. Chem. Engrs.*, **34**, 489 (1938)] extended Eq. (4-211*a*) to include all potentials by summing up the individual work effects. Thus*

$$\delta\left(\frac{Q}{T}\right) dT - \delta V\, dP + \delta\left(\frac{mg}{g_c}\right) dz + \delta(n\mathfrak{F})d\mathcal{E}$$
$$+ \delta m_A\, d\bar{G}_A + \delta M_B\, d\bar{G}_B + \delta\sigma\, d\gamma$$
$$+ \text{etc.} = -\delta W_{max} \qquad (4\text{-}243)$$

As will be shown later, Eq. (4-243) has generalized utility.

*Sign in front of the term $\delta V\, dP$ has been changed from original reference to make consistent with rest of terms.

CONCEPT OF EQUILIBRIUM

A system is said to be in complete thermodynamic equilibrium if for all possible variations from the original state of the system there is no "tendency" for a spontaneous change to take place. Although a spontaneous change is frequently associated with processes in which no useful work is performed, W_{rev} is nevertheless greater than zero. However, even though W_{rev} has a positive value, it does not guarantee that a change will take place either "spontaneously" or even after long periods of time. Take, for example, a mixture composed of 2 moles of hydrogen and 1 mole of oxygen contained in a "perfectly elastic and impermeable" balloon at atmospheric pressure and temperature. The gaseous mixture is in pressure and temperature equilibrium with the surroundings. If hydrogen and oxygen combined to form water at atmospheric temperature and pressure, a tremendous amount of energy (57.8 kcal./mole of H_2O formed) would be released. Yet a mixture of hydrogen and oxygen has been observed in the laboratory without a detectable trace of water being formed even after many years. The mixture appears to be dormant, and there is no tendency to change to a more stable state, H_2O, even if the temperature is raised over rather wide limits. However, if a source of very high temperature is introduced into the mixture, such as an electric spark, the combination takes place with explosive violence. The same result can be achieved by the introduction of a catalyst such as platinum. The release of this dormant or latent chemical energy seems to be prevented by a "passive resistance." It is obvious that, in applying the test for stable equilibrium, complications arise because of the element of time or passive resistance. To circumvent such difficulties, it is necessary either to qualify completely every statement made regarding equilibrium or to establish certain ground rules within which the test for equilibrium must be made.

Kinds of Equilibrium. The foregoing implies that various "degrees" of equilibrium are possible. The classical example of marble located in a series of depressions and elevations is represented in Fig. 4-26. For this discussion, assume that points a and g represent the lowest

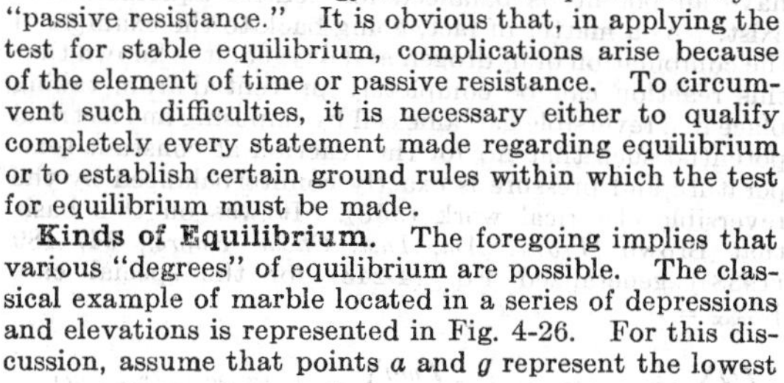

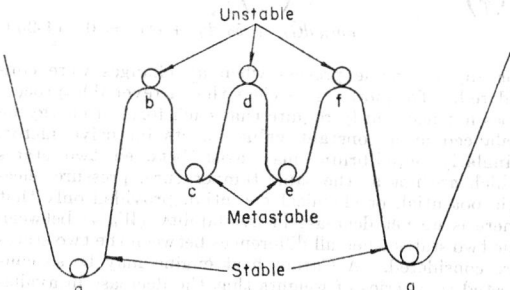

FIG. 4-26. Kinds of equilibrium in a gravitational field.

elevations to be considered. Therefore, for all displacements of the marble from positions a and g, the marble will have a tendency to return to this elevation. The marble is then said to be in its most "stable" position. Consider next a displacement of the marble to the left from position b. The slightest disturbance causes a major change in elevation from position b to a. Position b thus represents an "unstable" elevation. Now consider a displacement to the left from position c. If the displacement is not of sufficient magnitude to push the marble over the hump at b, the marble will come back to rest at c. However, if the displacement is sufficiently large, the marble will come to rest eventually at a. The position of the marble at c is stable to disturbances of modest magnitude but unstable to disturbances beyond this magnitude. The degree of stability at c is called "metastable." Note that this situation is similar to the above case of combining hydrogen and oxygen to form water. It is characteristic of both stable and metastable equilibrium (preserved by passive resistance) that they are found to exist in nature; unstable equilibrium does not exist because of the ever-present disturbances of all magnitudes.

Since in many cases the determination of the ultimate state of matter is not so important as a comparison between two states, the concept of "neutral" equilibrium has been introduced. Essentially, the test for neutral equilibrium requires that the comparison be made only with respect to the two positions under consideration without any concern for all possible positions. To this extent, it is not necessary to select arbitrarily an ultimate or zero point, and therefore, this complication is avoided. Neutral equilibrium thus represents a more practical basis for evaluation and analysis in many cases.

Criteria for Stable Equilibria. Various mathematical criteria which represent the necessary and sufficient conditions for stable equilibrium were first advanced by Gibbs; a complete exposition is beyond the present scope. Classically, these conditions were developed for closed systems; however, it should be apparent from the foregoing discussion of the first and second laws that it is immaterial whether a closed or open system is selected for study just so long as the definition of the system is precisely observed.

For a closed system, Eq. (4-158a) holds: On a unit-mass basis

$$(\mathbf{U}_E - \mathbf{U}_B) + \frac{g}{g_c}(z_E - z_B) + \frac{1}{2g_c}(v_E^2 - v_B^2) = \mathbf{Q} - \mathbf{W} \quad (4\text{-}158c)$$

or its equivalent

$$\Delta\mathbf{U} + \Delta\left(\frac{g}{g_c}\right)z + \Delta\left(\frac{v^2}{2g_c}\right) = \mathbf{Q} - \mathbf{W} \quad (4\text{-}158d)$$

Remembering that the test for a spontaneous change requires that W_{rev} be greater than, or in the limit equal to, zero, setting lw equal to zero; and restricting to a closed system, at a uniform temperature T, the generalized entropy balance [(Eq. (4-155)] becomes on a unit-mass basis

$$\int T\,d\mathbf{S} = \mathbf{Q}_{rev} \quad (4\text{-}244)$$

If the work of expansion against the surroundings ($P_{surr}\,\Delta V$)is separated out from W (which includes work of all kinds) according to the following definition:

$$W_{rev} = W_{net\,rev} + P_{surr}\,\Delta V \quad (4\text{-}245)$$

Substituting Eqs. (4-244) and (4-245) in Eq. (4-158d) and restricting the result to *constant* U, z, v, and V,

$$\mathbf{W}_{net\,rev} = [\int T\,d\mathbf{S}]_{\mathbf{U},z,v,\mathbf{V}} \quad (4\text{-}246)$$

Obviously, if $\mathbf{W}_{net\,rev}$ is to be greater than zero—the condition for a spontaneous change—the entropy must increase for any variation in which $\mathbf{U}$, z, v, and $\mathbf{V}$ are held constant. Thus the condition for a spontaneous change is, when comparing two states,

$$[\Delta\mathbf{S}]_{\mathbf{U},z,v,\mathbf{V}} > 0 \quad \text{(unstable or metastable)} \quad (4\text{-}247)$$

Obviously, at the other extreme which completely negates the possibility of a spontaneous change, the necessary and sufficient condition for stable equilibrium becomes

$$[\Delta \mathbf{S}]_{U,z,v,V} < 0 \qquad \text{(stable)} \qquad (4\text{-}248)$$

If the two states under consideration lead to the conclusion that

$$[\Delta \mathbf{S}]_{U,z,v,V} = 0 \qquad \text{(neutral)} \qquad (4\text{-}249)$$

then the two states are said to be in neutral equilibrium.

The conditions of restraint imposed on Eqs. (4-247), (4-248), and (4-249) (constant **U**, z, v, and **V**) are quite severe and not conveniently applicable to most cases of interest. A more useful but nonetheless equivalent set of criteria can be developed in a similar manner by remembering that

$$G = H = TS \qquad \text{or} \qquad G = U + PV - TS$$

and

$$[\int P\,dV]_P = [\int d(PV)]_P$$

It then follows that

$$[\Delta G]_{P,T,z,v} < 0 \qquad \text{(unstable or metastable)} \qquad (4\text{-}250)$$

$$[\Delta G]_{P,T,z,v} > 0 \qquad \text{(stable)} \qquad (4\text{-}251)$$

$$[\Delta G]_{P,T,z,v} = 0 \qquad \text{(neutral)} \qquad (4\text{-}252)$$

It is implicit that all the foregoing criteria are restricted to a closed system for which the mass remains constant. As mentioned before, it is possible to develop the necessary and sufficient conditions for equilibrium by considering an open system. Take the special case of the two states at the same temperature connected by a steady-flow reversible process; Eq. (4-196) becomes

$$\left[(\mathbf{G}_0 - \mathbf{G}_I) + \frac{g}{g_c}(z_0 - z_I) + \frac{1}{2g_c}(v_0^2 - v_I^2)\right]_T = -\mathbf{W}_{rev} \qquad (4\text{-}253)$$

For neutral equilibrium between these two states, it is necessary and sufficient that $W_{rev} = 0$, or

$$\left[(\mathbf{G}_0 - \mathbf{G}_I) + \frac{g}{g_c}(z_0 - z_I) + \frac{1}{2g_c}(v_0^2 - v_I^2)\right]_{T,W_{rev}=0} = 0 \qquad (4\text{-}254)$$

A simple illustration will serve to illustrate the use of the above equation. Consider a lake as shown in Fig. 4-27. Assume the lake to be at a uniform temperature.

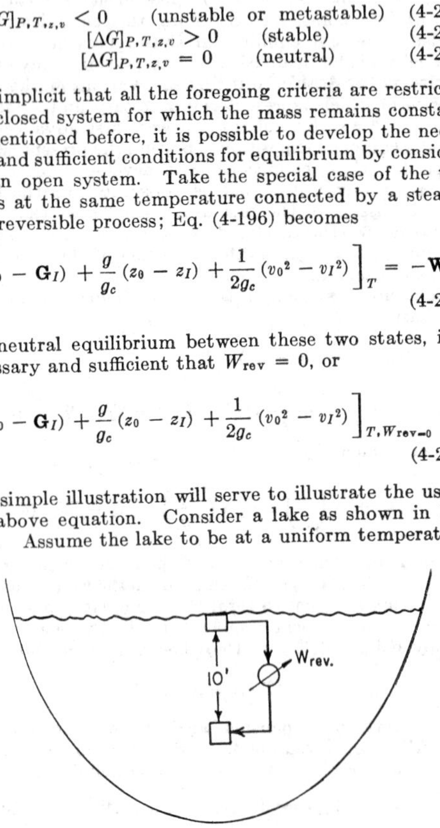

FIG. 4-27. Neutral equilibrium in a body of water.

Imagine that 1 lb. of water at the top of the lake is connected by a flow pipe to a point 10 ft. below the surface of the lake through a reversible turbine. Comparing these two levels, Eq. (4-253) reduces to

$$\left[(\mathbf{G}_0 - \mathbf{G}_I) + \frac{g}{g_c}(z_0 - z_I)\right]_{T,v} = -\mathbf{W}_{rev} \qquad (4\text{-}255)$$

but

$$(\mathbf{G}_0 - \mathbf{G}_I)_T = \int_{P_I}^{P_0} \mathbf{V}\,dP \cong \frac{P_0 - P_I}{\rho} \qquad (4\text{-}256)$$

and

$$\frac{g}{g_c}(z_0 - z_I) \cong z_0 - z_I \qquad (4\text{-}257)$$

However, it is to be noted that

$$-\frac{P_0 - P_I}{\rho} = z_0 - z_I \qquad (4\text{-}258)$$

and $W_{rev} = 0$. Therefore, the 1 lb. of water at the surface is in neutral equilibrium with the 1 lb. of water 10 ft. below the surface, and there is no tendency for a transfer to take place even though the pressures are not balanced. The situation here can be likened to a system of equal weights suspended freely over a frictionless pulley as shown in Fig. 4-28, where the elevation on one side is

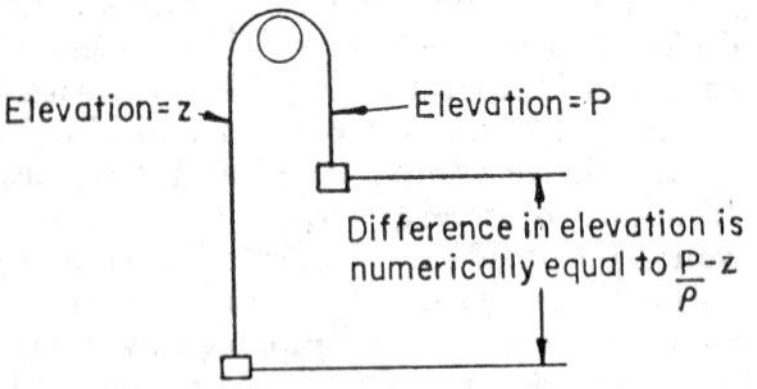

FIG. 4-28. Neutral equilibrium in a system of unequal potentials.

measured in terms of height in a gravitational field and on the other side by pressure in a "pressure" field.

Generalized Criteria for Complete Thermodynamic Equilibrium. The above rather trivial example serves to illustrate the point that it is not necessary to have all potentials balanced for neutral equilibrium to exist. As a matter of fact, going back to the example of the combination of hydrogen and oxygen, it is known that this reaction can be completely prevented from taking place in a reversible galvanic cell by imposing an electrical potential such that ΔG for the reaction at constant temperature and pressure is exactly counterbalanced by the reversible electrical work ($n\mathfrak{F}\mathcal{E}$). It was on this basis that Brown [*Trans. Am. Inst. Chem. Engrs.*, **34**, 489 (1938)] generalized Eq. (4-243) for the special case $W_{max} = 0$,

$$\delta\left(\frac{Q}{T}\right) dT - \delta V\,dP + \delta\left(\frac{mg}{g_c}\right) dz + \delta\mathfrak{F}\,d\mathcal{E} + \delta m_A\,d\bar{G}_A + \delta m_B\,d\bar{G}_B + \delta\sigma\,d\gamma + \text{etc.} = 0 \qquad (4\text{-}259)$$

for any reversible process when *all* changes were considered. To quote, "it is clear that a reversible process does not necessarily require that each form of energy be balanced at a constant value for its intensive factor. Similarly, equilibrium may exist between two states which are not at the same temperature, pressure, electric potential, or chemical potential, provided only that there is no net decrease in availability (W_{max}) between the two states when all differences between the two states are considered. A Carnot heat engine may be so connected to a series of weights that the decrease in availability of the heat energy in the Carnot cycle is exactly balanced by the increase in availability or potential energy in the weight. Such an operation represents a reversible process, and under the conditions, the initial and final states are in (neutral) equilibrium." Similar analyses hold for other potentials, for example, the reversible galvanic cell in which the two potentials, electrical and chemical, are balanced.

THERMODYNAMIC PROPERTIES OF PURE FLUIDS

The quantitative estimation of the thermodynamic properties of pure fluids under a given pressure and temperature implies that the phase behavior of the pure substance be understood under the stated conditions. The phase behavior of pure fluids can be best summarized by the pressure-temperature projection of univariant equilibria: gas-liquid, liquid-solid, gas-solid, or solid-solid. The pressure-temperature projection giving the locus of conditions for the transition from one phase to another is complicated by the occurrence of several solid phases and the inclusion of metastable univariant equilibria (Ricci, "The Phase Rule and Heterogeneous Equilibria," Van Nostrand, Princeton, N.J., 1951).

For pure substances, triple points involving the vapor phase are restricted by thermodynamics to the two cases shown in Fig. 4-29*a* and *b*, with the first case being far more prevalent. Of the elements which exist as gases at room temperature, only helium does not possess a solid-liquid-gas triple point.

In Fig. 4-29, if phase 1 is designated as a solid, and phase 2 as a liquid phase, then the transition condition

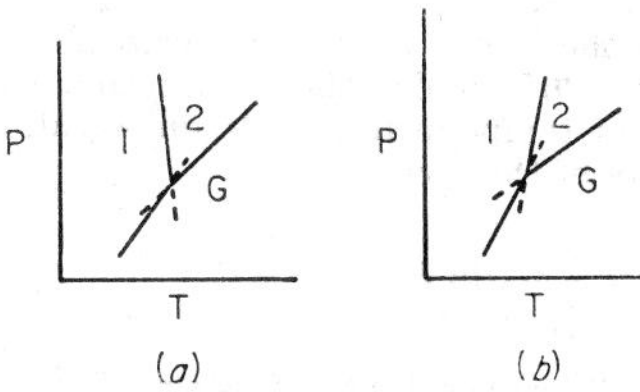

FIG. 4-29. Systems whose triple point involves the vapor phase *G*.

for 2-G becomes the well-known vapor-pressure curve which terminates as a triple point at its lower end and as the critical point at the upper extremity.

The pressure-volume-temperature (*PVT*) surfaces for a given mass of a simple substance are given in Fig. 4-30*a* with the corresponding pressure-temperature (*PT*) projection of the loci for the coexistence of two phases given in Fig. 4-30*b*. Phase transitions occur when a line in Fig. 4-30*b* is traversed. The vapor pressure terminates at the critical point *C*.

The critical temperature and pressure is that state at which the densities of the gas and liquid phases and all other intensive properties of these phases become identical. At the critical point, $(dP/dV)_T$ is zero. A further condition shown by careful experimental work along the critical isotherm in the vicinity of the critical is $(d^2P/dV^2)_T = 0$, as evidenced by Fig. 4-31. The dashed

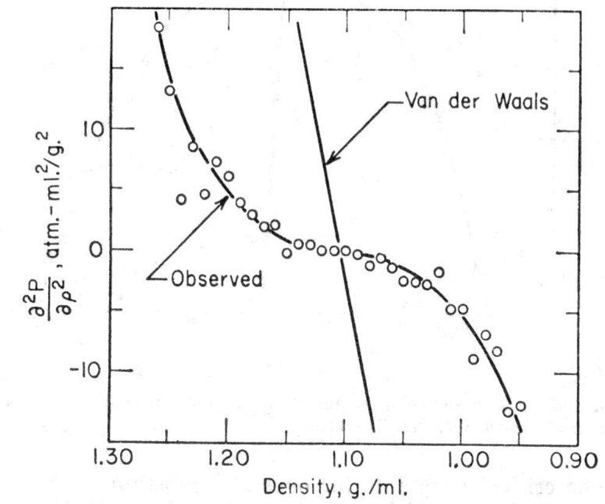

FIG. 4-31. The second derivative of pressure with respect to density along the critical isotherm. [*Habgood and Schneider, Can. J. Chem.*, **32**, 98, 164 (1954).]

line is the curve predicted by van der Waals' equation (discussed later).

The conditions at critical point among others must be fulfilled by theoretically sound equations of states. The difficulties attending the measurement of critical constants have been summarized by Rowlinson ("Liquids and Liquid Mixtures," Academic Press, Inc., New York, 1959). The critical density is the most difficult critical property to determine experimentally. It is most commonly determined by applying the law of rectilinear

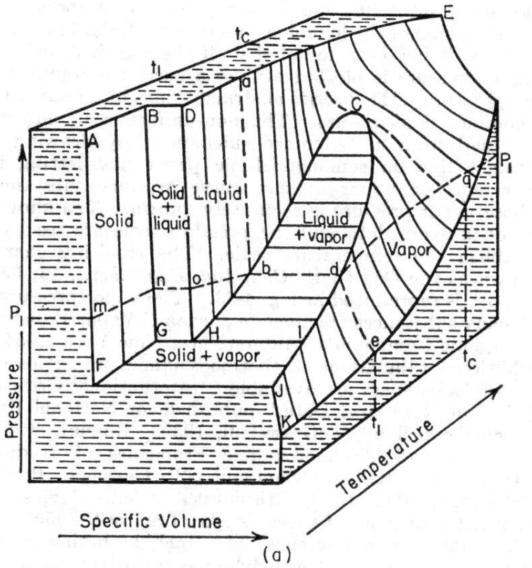

FIG. 4-30*a*. Pressure-volume-temperature surface for a given mass of a pure substance. [*Sherborne, Trans. Am. Inst. Mech. Engrs.*, **136**, 119 (1940).]

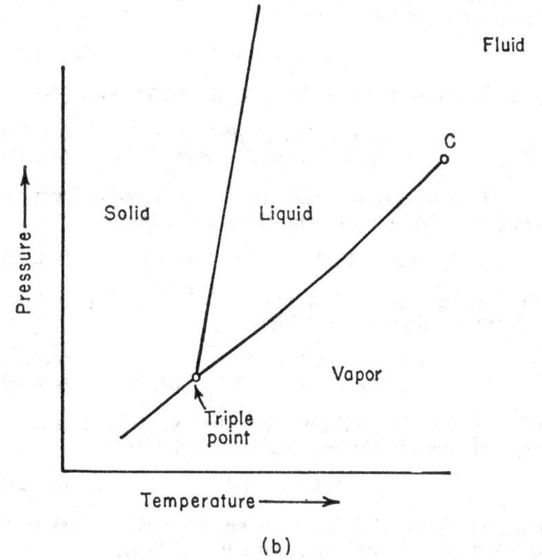

FIG. 4-30*b*. Pressure-temperature projection of univariant two-phase equilibrium.

diameters introduced by Cailletet and Mathias [*Compt. rend.*, **102**, 1202 (1886)] who discovered that the mean of the orthobaric densities passed through the critical density as illustrated in Fig. 4-32.

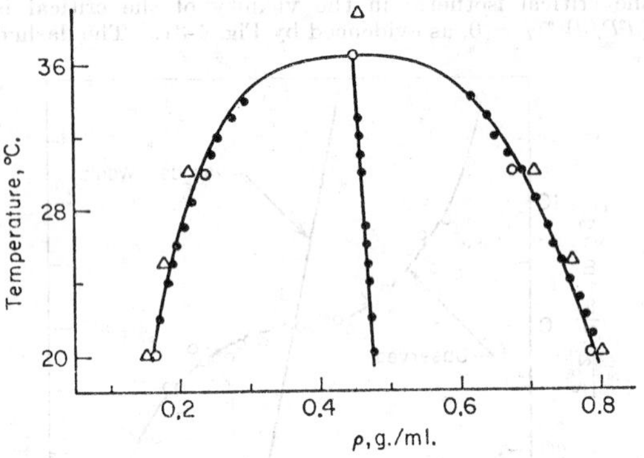

FIG. 4-32. The orthobaric densities of nitrous oxide. [*Cook, Trans. Faraday Soc.*, **49**, 716 (1953).]

The critical constants for over 200 substances are reported by Kobe and Lynn [*Chem. Revs.*, **52**, 117 (1953)]. A comprehensive tabulation of the critical properties of hydrocarbons and related compounds is included in the A.P.I. 44 compilation (Rossini *et al.*, "Selected Values of Physical and Thermodynamic Properties of Hydrocarbons and Related Compounds," Carnegie Press, Pittsburgh, Pa., 1953). Critical data on pure substances are presented in the "International Critical Tables." A comprehensive review of empirical methods for the estimation of pure-component criticals has been made (Reid and Sherwood, "The Properties of Gases and Liquids," McGraw-Hill, 1958) and some of these methods are discussed in Sec. 3.

Vapor Pressure of Pure Liquids. The slopes of the univariant equilibrium lines are governed by the Clapeyron equation. For two phases of the same pure substance in neutral equilibrium at constant temperature and pressure, Eq. (4-252) applies,

$$dG_{T,P} = 0 \tag{4-252}$$

For a closed system, applying Eqs. (4-252) and (4-157)

$$dG_{T,P} = dG'_{T,P} + dG''_{T,P} = 0 \tag{4-260}$$

and

$$dm = 0 = dm' + dm'' \tag{4-261}$$

where the primes denote the two phases, liquid and vapor. Combining the definition for G with Eq. (4-106),

$$dG = V\,dP - S\,dT + \mathbf{G}\,dm \tag{4-262}$$

Substituting Eqs. (4-262) and (4-261) into Eq. (4-260) gives the equilibrium condition

$$\mathbf{G}' = \mathbf{G}'' \tag{4-263}$$

or

$$\Delta\mathbf{G}_{T,P} = 0 = (\mathbf{G}'' - \mathbf{G}') \tag{4-263a}$$

Furthermore, if equilibrium is to be maintained as a result of changes in the independent variables

$$d\mathbf{G}' = d\mathbf{G}'' \tag{4-264}$$

Substituting the definition for an extensive property in Eq. (4-262) and combining with Eq. (4-264),

$$\mathbf{V}'\,dP - \mathbf{S}'\,dT = \mathbf{V}''\,dP - \mathbf{S}''\,dT \tag{4-265}$$

Since $\Delta G_{T,P} = \Delta H - T\,\Delta S$, applying Eq. (4-263$a$) and solving for the slope dP/dT gives the Clapeyron equation

$$\frac{dP}{dT} = \frac{\mathbf{S}'' - \mathbf{S}'}{\mathbf{V}'' - \mathbf{V}'} = \frac{\Delta\mathbf{S}}{\Delta\mathbf{V}} = \frac{\Delta\mathbf{H}}{T\,\Delta\mathbf{V}} \tag{4-266}$$

Equation (4-266) relates the slope of the univariant lines in Fig. 4-29 to the entropy and volume changes in the phase transition or to the enthalpy and volume changes in the transition. The corresponding Clapeyron equation for any number of components has been discussed by Li [*J. Chem. Phys.*, **25**, 572 (1956)].

When one of the phases is assumed to be a vapor behaving as a perfect gas and the molal volume of the denser phase is assumed to be negligible in relation to the vapor phase, Eq. (4-266) reduces to

$$\frac{d \ln P}{dT} = \frac{\Delta\mathbf{H}}{RT^2} \tag{4-267}$$

where $\Delta\mathbf{H}$ is the latent heat of vaporization. Integration of Eq. (2-267) under the assumption that $\Delta\mathbf{H}$ is independent of temperature yields an equation for the vapor pressure of the form

$$\ln P = \frac{A}{T} + B \tag{4-268}$$

where A and B are constants of integration. Equation (4-268) gives a good approximation of the vapor pressure of a pure substance over considerable ranges of pressure when A and B are determined empirically. The graphical representation of the vapor pressure may be further improved by plotting the logarithm of the vapor pressure as a function of $1/(T + C)$ where T is the absolute temperature and C is a characteristic constant which is determined empirically, as, for example, the equation of Antoine [Antoine, *Compt. rend.*, **107**, 681, 778 (1888)]:

$$\log_{10} P = a - \frac{b}{T + C} \tag{4-269}$$

where a, b, C, are empirically determined constants for a particular substance and T is the absolute temperature.

In the case of the homologous series of aliphatic hydrocarbons, it has been found that, if the logarithm of the vapor pressure is plotted against a special non-uniform temperature scale, a series of straight lines intersecting at a common point results. This non-uniform scale may be obtained from a "reference substance" by drawing a straight line on semilogarithmic paper and letting it represent the vapor-pressure curve of some substance whose vapor pressure is accurately known. The known vapor-pressure data and the pressure scale are used to establish the temperature scale. The resulting chart, known as the Cox chart [Cox, *Ind. Eng. Chem.*, **15**, 592 (1923)], is reproduced in Fig. 4-33. The vapor pressures of many substances are given in Jordan ("Vapor Pressure of Organic Compounds," Interscience, New York, 1954). Additional tabulations of thermodynamic properties of specific substances are available ("International Critical Tables of Numerical Data," published for National Research Council by McGraw-Hill, 1930. Rossini, *et al.*, "Physical and Thermodynamic Properties of Hydrocarbons and Related Compounds," Carnegie Press, Pittsburgh, Pa., 1953. Hilsenrath *et al.*, Tables of Thermal Properties of Gases, *N.B.S. Circ.* 564, 1955).

The latter two references also include both fundamental and derived thermodynamic properties such as enthalpy $\mathbf{H}$, entropy $\mathbf{S}$, internal energy $\mathbf{U}$, fugacity f, and specific heat $\mathbf{C}_p$ or $\mathbf{C}_v$. The thermodynamic properties of pure substances (and mixtures) may be presented over

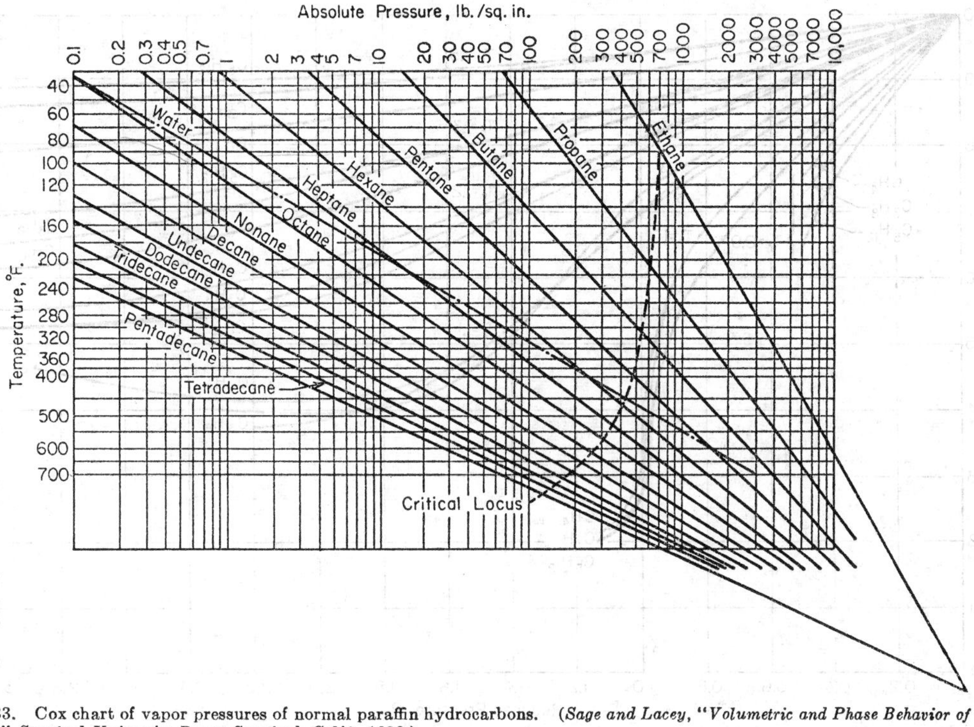

FIG. 4-33. Cox chart of vapor pressures of normal paraffin hydrocarbons. *(Sage and Lacey, "Volumetric and Phase Behavior of Hydrocarbons," Stanford University Press, Stanford, Calif., 1939.)*

wide ranges of pressures and temperatures with some loss of accuracy by the application of the principle of corresponding states.

THE GENERALIZED PROPERTIES OF PURE FLUIDS

Since the possibilities of using actual experimental data for a given engineering problem are usually readily exhausted, it is necessary to rely upon generalized methods of estimating the properties of fluids. One of the most useful ways in which to represent the behavior of pure substances and mixtures is through the application of the principle of corresponding states.

The principle states that two substances should have similar properties at corresponding conditions with reference to some basic properties such as the critical temperature and pressure. The principle of corresponding states has been applied to many thermodynamic and transport properties since its inception for both pure components and mixtures [Brown, Souders, and Smith, *Ind. Eng. Chem.*, **24**, 513 (1932). Brock and Bird, *Am. Inst. Chem. Engrs. J.*, **1**, 174 (1955). Comings, Mayland, and Egly, *Univ. Illinois Eng. Expt. Sta. Bull.* 35, 1944. Kay, *Ind. Eng. Chem.*, **28**, 1014 (1936). Leland and Mueller, *Ind. Eng. Chem.*, **51**, 597 (1959)].

The principle of corresponding states has been placed on a sound theoretical basis through its statistical derivation for gases [de Boer and Michels, *Physica*, **5**, 945 (1938)], liquids [Pitzer, *J. Chem. Phys.*, **7**, 583 (1939)], and gases, liquids, and solids [Guggenheim, *J. Chem. Phys.*, **13**, 253 (1945)].

The application of the corresponding-states principle to argon, krypton, and xenon (spherical, monatomic, inert gases) confirms the soundness of the principle when all the conditions assumed in its statistical derivation are substantially fulfilled in nature (Rowlinson, "Liquids and Liquid Mixtures," Academic Press, Inc., New York, 1959).

The corresponding conditions most frequently utilized are the reduced temperature, pressure, volume, density, and compressibility factors, which are defined by

$$T_r = \frac{T}{T_c} \qquad P_r = \frac{P}{P_c} \qquad V_r = \frac{\mathbf{V}}{\mathbf{V}_c}$$

$$\rho_r = \frac{\rho}{\rho_c} \qquad z_r = \frac{z}{z_c} \tag{4-270}$$

where the absolute values of temperature, pressure, volume, density, and the compressibility factor are divided respectively by their critical values.

The Corresponding-states Principle and Fluid Compressibility. The most familiar example of the corresponding-states principle is a plot of the compressibility factor $z = P\mathbf{V}/RT$ as a function of the reduced pressure and temperature to give a function of the form

$$z = f(P_r, T_r) \tag{4-271}$$

However, as indicated in Fig. 4-34, the relationship for complex molecules is only approximately true and especially inadequate in the neighborhood of the critical when good precision is desired. Accordingly, a third parameter has been introduced [Meissner and Seferian, *Chem. Eng. Progress*, **45**, 579 (1951). Lydersen, Greenkorn, and Hougen, *Univ. Wisconsin Eng. Sta. Rept.* 4, 1955] to give a compressibility-factor correlation of the form

$$z = f(P_r, T_r, z_c) \tag{4-272}$$

where the critical compressibility is defined as

$$z_c = \frac{P_c\mathbf{V}_c}{RT_c} \tag{4-273}$$

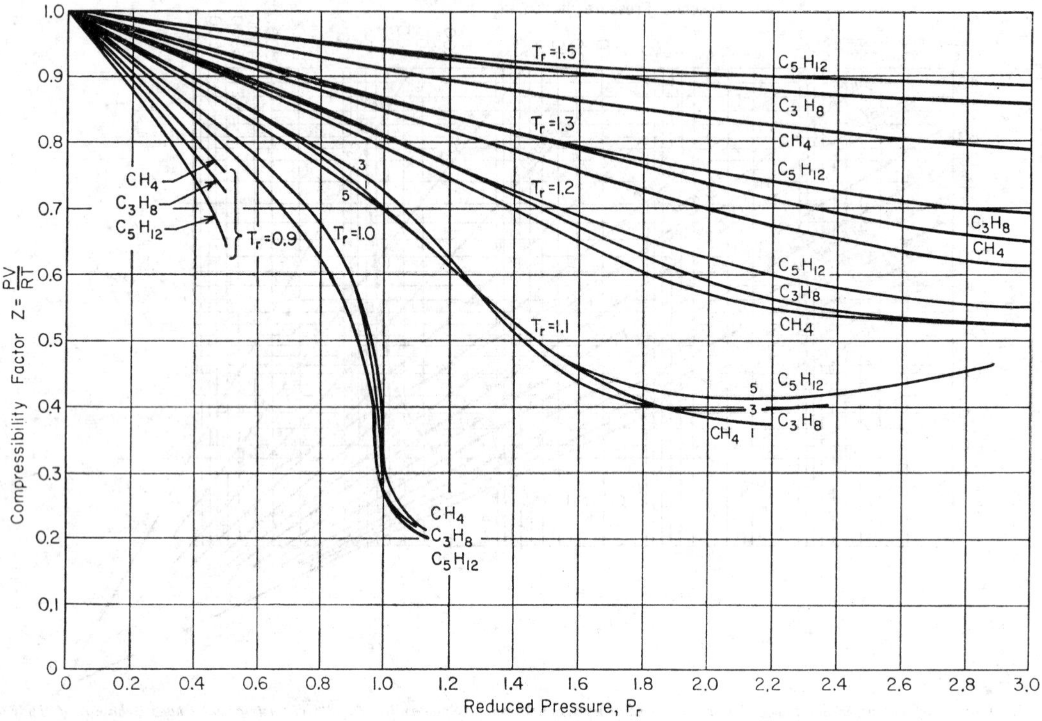

FIG. 4-34. Compressibility factor as a function of reduced pressure and temperature for methane, propane, and *n*-pentane. [*Brown, Sonders, and Smith, Ind. Eng. Chem.*, **24**, 515 (1932).]

The introduction of the third parameter z_c is justified by the observation that z_c varies from 0.20 to 0.30 as evidenced by plots of the type shown in Fig. 4-35.

Other third parameters have been introduced with comparable effectiveness [Reidel, *Chem.-Ing.-Tech.* **26**, 83, 257, 679 (1954). Pitzer, *J. Am. Chem. Soc.*, **77**, 3433 (1955)].

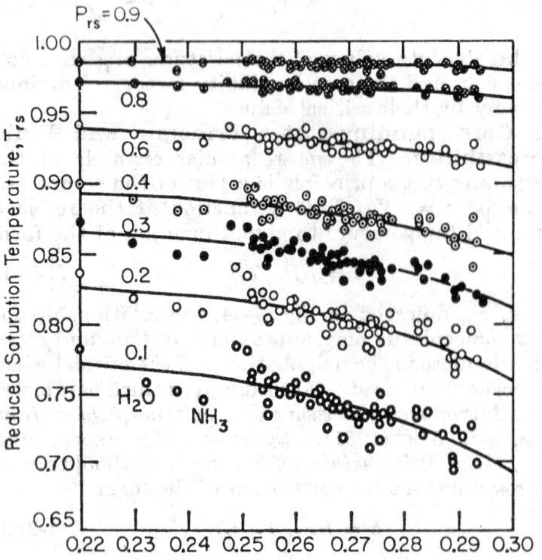

FIG. 4-35. Effect of z_c on reduced saturation temperatures at various reduced pressures. (*Lydersen, Greenkorn, and Hougen, Univ. Wisconsin Eng. Expt. Sta. Rept.* 4, 1955.)

The generalized thermodynamic properties given by Lydersen *et al.* were in tabular form for critical compressibilities z_c of 0.23, 0.25, 0.27, and 0.29. The choice of the particular values of z_c is based upon the distribution of z_c values in nature as given below (Hougen, Watson, and Ragatz, "Chemical Process Principles," Part 2, Thermodynamics, p. 574, Wiley, New York, 1959).

Grouping of Compounds According to Range of Variation of Critical Compressibilities

z_c	Representative compound	Remarks
0.232	Water	Forms 3-dimensional hydrogen bonds
0.24–0.26	Acetone, ammonia, esters, alcohols, *n*-decane	Oxygenated compounds, many of which form hydrogen bonds, long-chained hydrocarbons
0.26–0.28	60% of compounds, mostly hydrocarbons	Non-associating molecules
0.28–0.30	O_2, N_2, CO, H_2S, CH_4, C_2H_6, A, Ne	Simple, nearly spherical molecules

It should be noted that close packing of the molecules resulting from intermolecular association such as hydrogen-bond formation exhibits low z_c's while non-associating, simple, spherical molecules tend to give high z_c's.

Figure 3-52 shows the compressibility-factor tables of Lydersen *et al.* for $z_c = 0.27$ as presented by Hougen, Watson, and Ragatz ("Chemical Process Principles," Part 2, Wiley, New York, 1959). The compressibility factors are tabulated at frequent intervals of reduced temperature T_r and reduced pressure P_r for $z_c = 0.27$ in the above reference (pp. 588–591). Properties of z_c other than 0.27 may be readily calculated by the use of correction terms D which are tabulated adjacent to the property being evaluated. The value of a property B' (includes enthalpy, entropy, and internal-energy departures from ideal-gas behavior, compressibility factor, and reduced density) at z_c other than 0.27 is calculated from the relation

$$B' = B + D(z_c - 0.27) \tag{4-274}$$

where B = property at $z_c = 0.27$
D_a = correction term for use when $z_c > 0.27$
D_b = correction term for use when $z_c < 0.27$

It should be noted that hydrogen and helium *do not* fit the generalized correlations in their saturation ranges.

Density of Pure Liquids and the Reduced-density Correlation. Using the data of Riedel [*Chem.-Ing.-Tech.*, **26**, 259 (1954)], Lydersen *et al.* prepared a reduced-density correlation of the form

$$\rho_r = \frac{\rho}{\rho_c} = f(P_r, T_r, z_c) \tag{4-275}$$

The reduced-density correlation has the advantage that it is relatively sensitive to pressure changes, whereas the compressibility-factor correlation is insensitive to relatively large changes in pressure. The reduced densities of liquids are tabulated in Hougen, Watson, and Ragatz for $z_c = 0.27$ together with the correction terms D_a and D_b for values of z_c other than 0.27. The recommended procedure for use of the tabulated data is to select a reference state at which an accurate density measurement is available (usually at atmospheric pressure). This value is used in conjunction with the reduced-density table by the following relation:

$$\frac{\rho_2}{\rho_{r_2}} = \frac{\rho_1}{\rho_{r_1}} = \rho_c' = \frac{P_c}{z_c' R T_c} \tag{4-276}$$

where ρ_1 = accurate measurement of density at T_{r_1} and P_{r_1}
ρ_2 = desired density at T_{r_2} and P_{r_2}
ρ_c', z_c' = corrected values of ρ_c and z_c

Liquid densities may also be predicated using Lu's generalized chart, Fig. 3-50 (see Sec. 3 for procedure).

Effect of Pressure on Enthalpy. The isothermal effect of pressure on the enthalpy of a pure substance is given by Eq. (4-128),

$$\left(\frac{d\mathbf{H}}{dP}\right)_T = \mathbf{V} - T\left(\frac{d\mathbf{V}}{dT}\right)_P \tag{4-128}$$

Combining Eq. (4-128) with the definition for z, placing in reduced form, and integrating at constant temperature between the limits of zero and the existing pressure

$$\left(\frac{\mathbf{H}^* - \mathbf{H}}{T_c}\right)_T = \left[RT_r^2 \int_0^{P_r} \left(\frac{dz}{dT_r}\right)_{P_r} \frac{dP_r}{P_r}\right]_T \tag{4-277}$$

where H^* is defined as

$$\lim_{p \to 0} \mathbf{H} = \mathbf{H}^* \tag{4-278}$$

Since every substance at a finite temperature has a finite vapor pressure, then if the pressure upon a substance is decreased without limit, the substance will eventually vaporize and the vapor will approach the condition of a perfect or ideal gas as the pressure approaches zero. $\mathbf{H}^*$ therefore represents the specific enthalpy of a substance in the ideal-gas state at the temperature in question.

Values of $(\mathbf{H}^* - \mathbf{H})/T_c$ in conjunction with the correction terms D are tabulated for $z_c = 0.27$ for both gases and liquids in Hougen, Watson, and Ragatz and are plotted in Fig. 4-36.

Fugacity. The fugacity function was introduced by G. N. Lewis [*Proc. Acad. Sci. Wash.*, **37**, 49 (1901)] primarily for application to the analysis of isothermal processes involving solution behavior, phase changes, and chemical reactions.

Fugacity is defined in terms of the Gibbs free energy for a *pure substance* as

$$d\mathbf{G}_T = (RT\, d \ln f)_T \tag{4-279}$$

At constant temperature Eq. (4-262) reduces to

$$d\mathbf{G}_T = \mathbf{V}\, dP_T \tag{4-280}$$

Thus
$$\mathbf{V}\, dP_T = (RT\, d \ln f)_T \tag{4-281}$$

Equation (4-281) gives a relationship for evaluating the fugacity from experimental PVT data or from an equation of state.

Combining the definition of the compressibility factor z with Eq. (4-281) yields

$$(d \ln f)_T = (z\, d \ln P)_T \tag{4-282}$$

Subtracting $d \ln P$ from both sides of the equation and integrating, noting that by definition

$$\lim_{P \to 0} \frac{f}{P} = 1 \tag{4-283}$$

i.e., the fugacity equals the pressure for an ideal gas,

$$\ln \frac{f}{P} = \int_0^P \frac{z-1}{P}\, dP \tag{4-284}$$

In terms of the reduced properties Eq. (4-284) becomes

$$\ln \frac{f}{P} = \int_0^{P_r} \frac{z-1}{P_r}\, dP_r \tag{4-285}$$

Values of the fugacity coefficient f/P which have been evaluated for $z_c = 0.27$ are tabulated in Hougen, Watson, and Ragatz and plotted in Fig. 4-37. Also included are the values of the correction term D, which provides a means of obtaining values of f/P other than at $z_c = 0.27$ from the equation

$$\left(\frac{f}{P}\right)' = \frac{f}{P} 10^{D(z_c - 0.27)} \tag{4-286}$$

For a pure liquid and its vapor in equilibrium, the Gibbs free energy of vaporization $\mathbf{G}_V - \mathbf{G}_l = 0$ [(Eq. (4-263*a*)]. Therefore,

$$(\Delta\mathbf{G})_{T,P} = (\mathbf{G}_V - \mathbf{G}_l)_{T,P} = \left[RT \ln \left(\frac{f_v}{f_l}\right)\right]_{T,P} = 0 \tag{4-287}$$

and
$$f_l = f_v \tag{4-288}$$

The fugacity of a pure liquid and its vapor at equilibrium are identical.

Effect of Temperature on Fugacity. The fugacity of a pure component, defined by Eq. (4-279), may be expressed in integrated form as

$$\mathbf{G} = RT \ln f + \varphi(T) \tag{4-289}$$

where φ is a function of temperature only. Rearranging Eq. (4-289), dividing by T, and differentiating with respect to T holding pressure constant

$$\left(\frac{d[(\mathbf{G}/T) - (\varphi/T)]}{dT}\right)_P = R\left(\frac{d \ln f}{dT}\right)_P \tag{4-290}$$

But
$$\left(\frac{d(\mathbf{G}/T)}{dT}\right)_P = \frac{T(d\mathbf{G}/dT)_P - \mathbf{G}}{T^2} = \frac{-(\mathbf{G} + T\mathbf{S})}{T^2} = \frac{-\mathbf{H}}{T^2} \tag{4-291}$$

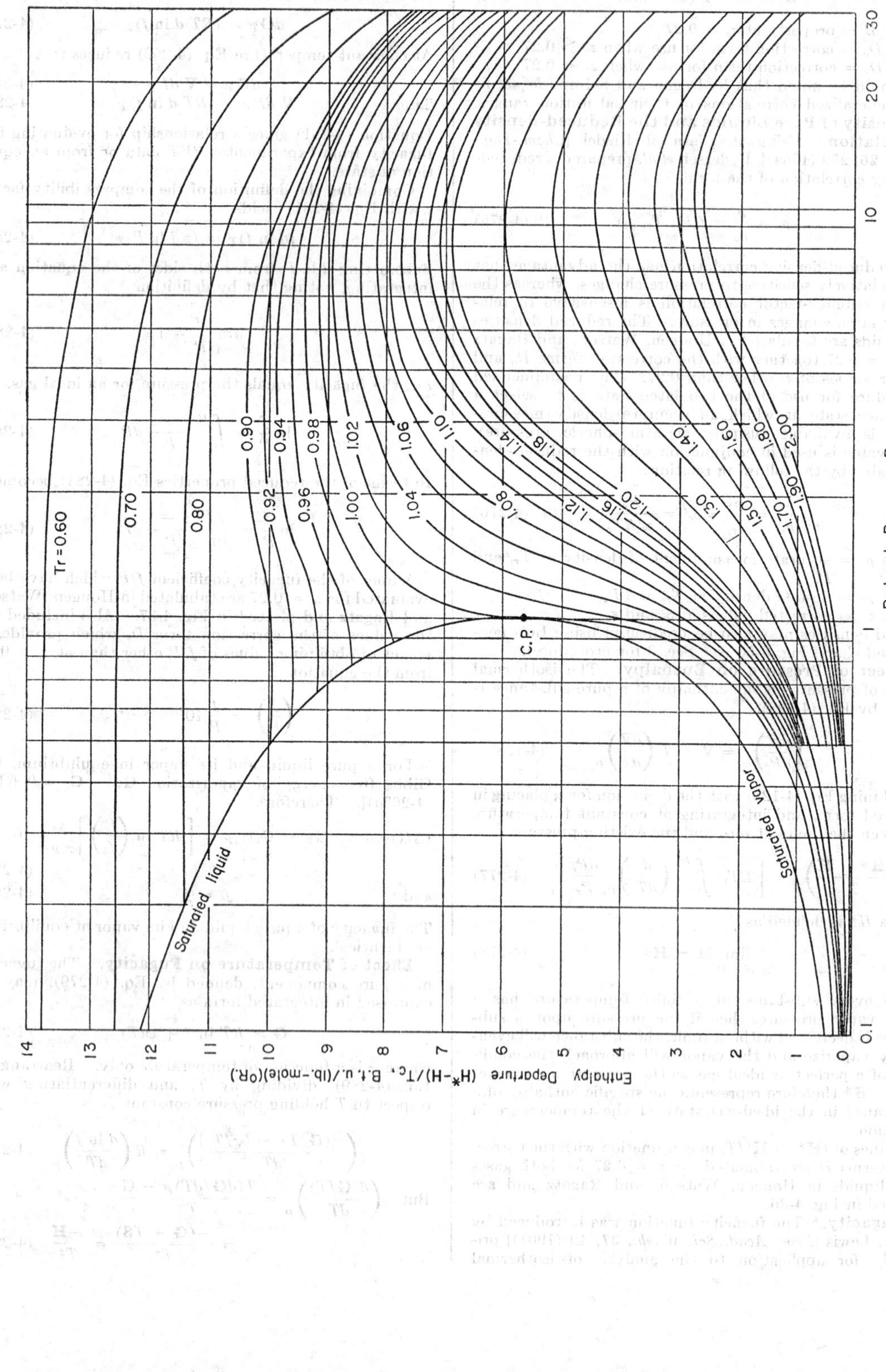

FIG. 4-36. Enthalpy departure of gases and liquids; z_c = 0.27. (*Based on Table 50, "Chemical Process Principles," Part 2, Wiley, New York, 1959.*)

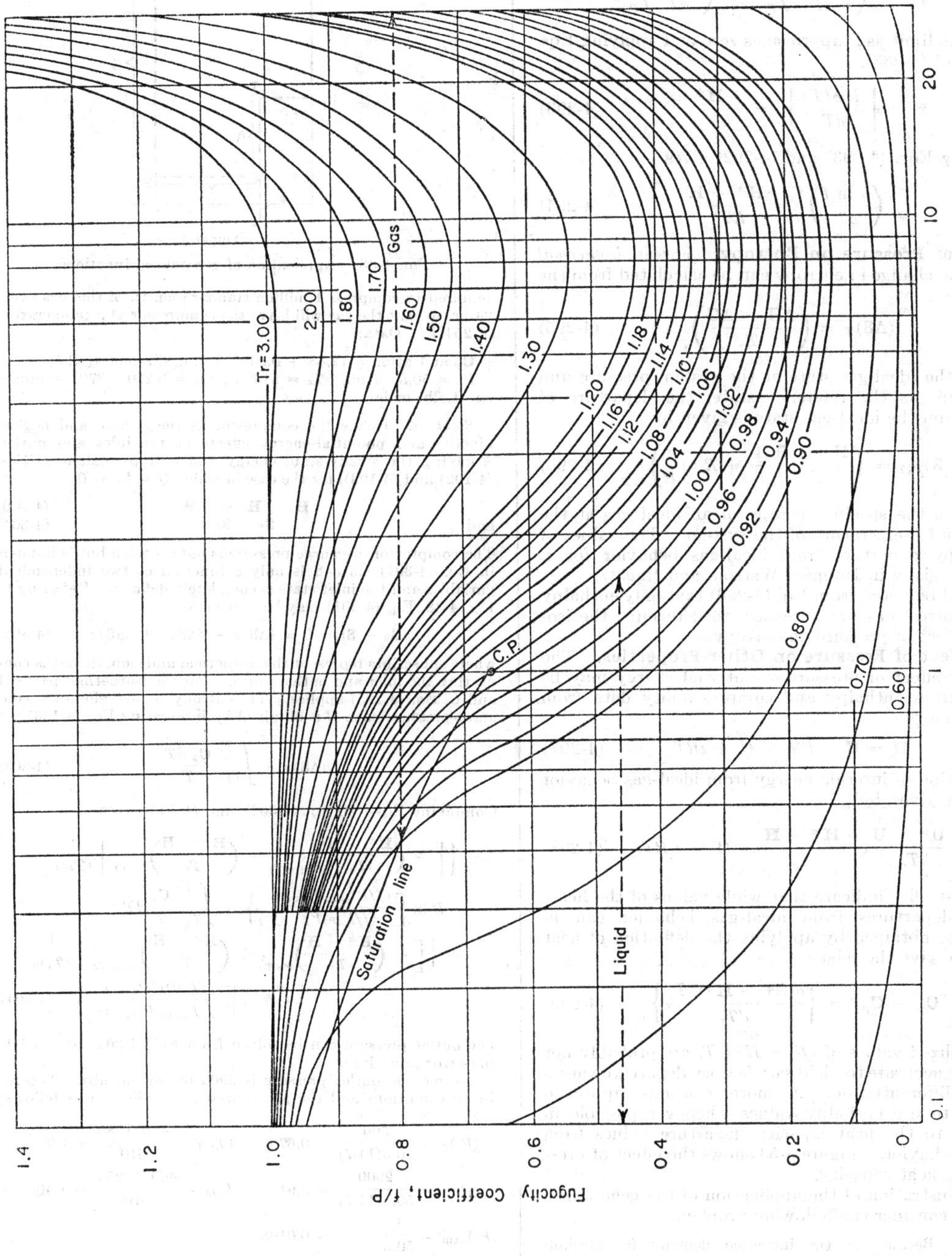

FIG. 4-37. Fugacity coefficients of gases and liquids; z_c = 0.27. (*Based on Table 51, "Chemical Process Principles," Part 2, Wiley, New York, 1959.*)

therefore, Eq. (4-290) becomes

$$\frac{-\mathbf{H}}{T^2} - \left(\frac{d(\varphi/T)}{dT}\right)_P = R\left(\frac{d \ln f}{dT}\right)_P \qquad (4\text{-}292)$$

Taking the limit as P approaches zero and applying Eqs. (4-278) and (4-283),

$$\left[\frac{d(\varphi/T)}{dT}\right]_P = \frac{-\mathbf{H}^*}{T^2} \qquad (4\text{-}293)$$

Combining Eqs. (4-293) and (4-292) gives

$$\left(\frac{d \ln f}{dT}\right)_P = \frac{\mathbf{H}^* - \mathbf{H}}{RT^2} \qquad (4\text{-}294)$$

Effect of Pressure on Entropy. For an *isothermal process*, the change in entropy can be calculated from the relation

$$(\Delta\mathbf{S})_T = \left(\frac{\Delta\mathbf{H} - \Delta\mathbf{G}}{T}\right)_T \qquad (4\text{-}295)$$

Selecting the ideal-gas state at the system pressure and temperature as the reference state, the departure of entropy from the ideal-gas state is given by

$$(\mathbf{S}^* - \mathbf{S})_{P,T} = \left(\frac{\mathbf{H}^* - \mathbf{H}}{T_c}\frac{1}{T_r} + R \ln \frac{f}{P}\right)_{P,T} \qquad (4\text{-}296)$$

where $\mathbf{S}^*$ is the specific entropy of an ideal gas at the pressure and temperature of the system. The values of the entropy departure from ideal-gas behavior for $z_c = 0.27$ are given in Hougen, Watson, and Ragatz.

It should be noted from Eq. (4-296) that only enthalpy and f/P corrections are necessary to determine the isothermal effect of pressure on entropy.

The Effect of Pressure on Other Properties. The isothermal effect of pressure on internal energy may be obtained from enthalpy and compressibility data from the definition

$$\mathbf{H} = \mathbf{U} + P\mathbf{V} = U + zRT \qquad (4\text{-}297)$$

The deviation of internal energy from ideal-gas behavior is therefore given by

$$\frac{\mathbf{U}^* - \mathbf{U}}{T_c} = \frac{\mathbf{H}^* - \mathbf{H}}{T_c} - (1 - z)RT_r \qquad (4\text{-}298)$$

Recent studies indicate that while values of the heat-capacity departures from ideal-gas behavior can in principle be obtained by applying the definition of heat capacity to give the relation

$$\mathbf{C}_p - \mathbf{C}_p^* = \left\{\frac{d[(\mathbf{H} - \mathbf{H}^*)/T_c]}{dT_r}\right\}_P \qquad (4\text{-}299)$$

the generalized values of $(H - H^*)/T_c$ are probably not sufficiently accurate to yield satisfactory departure values through differentiation. A more cautious approach would be to use enthalpy values whenever possible in preference to the heat-capacity departure values from ideal-gas behavior. Figure 3-53 shows the effect of pressure on the heat capacity.

As an illustration of the application of the generalized properties consider the following problem.

Example. Because of the increased demand for alcohols during World War II, extensive research was devoted to the production of alcohols from petroleum "waste" gases. One reaction in particular consisted in the catalytic hydration of ethylene to ethyl alcohol at elevated temperatures and pressures

$$C_2H_4 + H_2O \rightleftarrows C_2H_5OH$$

If a supply of ethylene is available at 500 lb./sq. in. abs. and 80°F., compute the reversible adiabatic work in horsepower

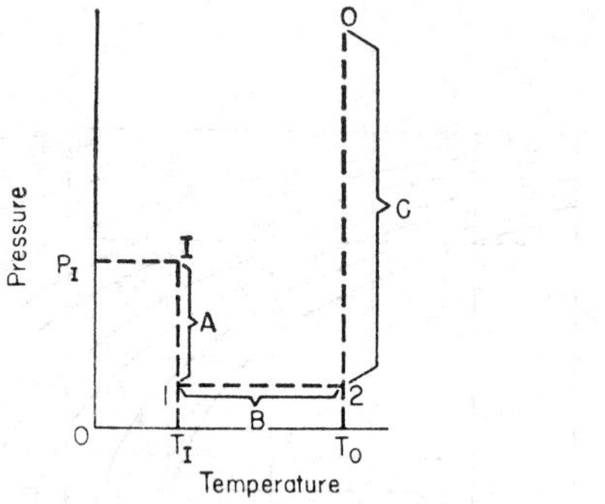

Fig. 4-38. Application of generalized functions.

required to compress 1 million standard cu. ft. of this gas every 24 hr. so that the gas will leave the compressor at a temperature of 254°F. Data:

$\mathbf{C}_p$ at 1 atm. = 12.88 + 0.006T B.t.u./(lb.-mole)(°R.)
P_c = 50.5 atm., T_c = 510°R., z_c = 0.270, 379 standard cu. ft./lb.-mole

Solution. Define the compressor as the system and neglect kinetic- and potential-energy effects at the inlet and outlet. Applying the steady-state energy and entropy balances [Eqs. (4-192) and (4-193)] for the case in which $Q = lw = 0$,

$$\mathbf{H}_0 - \mathbf{H}_I = -\mathbf{W} \qquad (4\text{-}300)$$

and

$$\mathbf{S}_0 = \mathbf{S}_I \qquad (4\text{-}301)$$

The compressor discharge pressure is not specified but is implicit in Eq. (4-301) since $\mathbf{S}$ is only a function of two independent variables and the inlet state is completely defined. Referring to Fig. 4-38, Eq. (4-301) may be written as

$$\mathbf{S}_0 - \mathbf{S}_I = 0 = (\Delta\mathbf{S})_A + (\Delta\mathbf{S})_B + (\Delta\mathbf{S})_C \qquad (4\text{-}302)$$

where subscripts represent the isothermal and isobaric paths connecting the inlet and outlet states. For the isothermal paths A and C, Eq. (4-295) applies. The entropy change along the constant-pressure path B is obtained by integrating Eq. (4-133).

$$(\Delta\mathbf{S})_B = \int_{T_I}^{T_0} \frac{\mathbf{C}_p\, dT}{T} \qquad (4\text{-}303)$$

Combining Eqs. (4-295), (4-302), and (4-303) gives

$$0 = \left\{\left[-\left(\frac{\mathbf{H}^* - \mathbf{H}}{T_c}\right)_{\text{atm},T_I} + \left(\frac{\mathbf{H}^* - \mathbf{H}}{T_c}\right)_{P_I,T_I}\right]\frac{1}{(T_r)_I} - R \ln \left[\frac{(f/P)_{\text{atm}}P_{\text{atm}}}{(f/P)_{P_I}P_I}\right]_{T_I}\right\} + \int_{T_I}^{T_0} \frac{\mathbf{C}_p}{T}\, dT + \left\{\left[-\left(\frac{\mathbf{H}^* - \mathbf{H}}{T_c}\right)_{P_0,T_0} + \left(\frac{\mathbf{H}^* - \mathbf{H}}{T_c}\right)_{\text{atm},T_0}\right]\frac{1}{(T_r)_0} - R \ln \left[\frac{(f/P)_{P_0}P_0}{(f/P)_{\text{atm}}P_{\text{atm}}}\right]_{T_0}\right\} \qquad (4\text{-}304)$$

The outlet pressure can be solved from Eq. (4-304) by a trial-and-error procedure.

Assume the outlet pressure is 2900 lb./sq. in. abs. The reduced conditions and the generalized properties are as follows;

$$(P_r)_I = \frac{500}{50.5(14.7)} = 0.673 \qquad (T_r)_I = \frac{460 + 80}{510} = 1.06$$

$$(P_r)_0 = \frac{2900}{50.5(14.7)} = 3.91 \qquad (T_r)_0 = \frac{460 + 254}{510} = 1.40$$

$$(P_r)_{\text{atm}} = \frac{1}{50.5} = 0.0198$$

P_r, T_r	$\frac{\mathbf{H}^* - \mathbf{H}}{T_c}$	$\frac{f}{P}$
$(P_r)_I$, $(T_r)_I$	1.57	0.829
$(P_r)_{\text{atm}}$, $(T_r)_I$	0.036	0.998
$(P_r)_0$, $(T_r)_0$	4.18	0.706
$(P_r)_{\text{atm}}$, $(T_r)_0$	0.02	0.999

Substituting these quantities in the right-hand side of Eq. (4-304) gives −0.05. This number is sufficiently close to zero so that additional assumptions for P_0 are not warranted.

The work of compression is determined by the energy balance [Eq. (4-300)]. Expanding the enthalpy difference in the same manner as for the entropy change,

$$\mathbf{H}_0 - \mathbf{H}_I = (\Delta\mathbf{H})_A + (\Delta\mathbf{H})_B + (\Delta\mathbf{H})_C \qquad (4\text{-}305)$$

The enthalpy changes along paths A and C are identical with those used in Eq. (4-304) while that along path B can be obtained from the definition of $\mathbf{C}_p$. Thus

$$(\Delta\mathbf{H})_B = \int_{T_I}^{T_0} \mathbf{C}_p\, dT \qquad (4\text{-}306)$$

Combining Eqs. (4-305) and (4-306),

$$\mathbf{H}_0 - \mathbf{H}_I = \left\{\left[-\left(\frac{\mathbf{H}^* - \mathbf{H}}{T_c}\right)_{\text{atm},T_I} + \left(\frac{\mathbf{H}^* - \mathbf{H}}{T_c}\right)_{P_I,T_I}\right]T_c\right\} + \int_{T_I}^{T_0} \mathbf{C}_p\, dT + \left\{\left[-\left(\frac{\mathbf{H}^* - \mathbf{H}}{T_c}\right)_{P_0,T_0} + \left(\frac{\mathbf{H}^* - \mathbf{H}}{T_c}\right)_{\text{atm},T_0}\right]T_c\right\} \qquad (4\text{-}307)$$

$$\mathbf{H}_0 - \mathbf{H}_I = (-0.036 + 1.57 - 4.18 + 0.02)510 + \int_{540}^{714} (12.88 + 0.006T)\, dT$$

$$= -1339 + 2244 + 656 = 1561 \text{ B.t.u./lb.-mole}$$

$$\mathbf{W} = -1561 \text{ B.t.u./lb.-mole ethylene}$$

$$\text{hp.} = \frac{10^6}{379}\,\frac{1561}{(24)(60)}\,\frac{778}{33{,}000} = 67.5$$

Construction of Thermodynamic Charts by Generalized Methods. Tables and charts of thermodynamic relationships such as enthalpy-temperature, temperature-entropy, and pressure-enthalpy are frequently desired for specific substances. For the construction of such specific tables and figures, reference is given to Hougen, Watson, and Ragatz ("Chemical Process Principles," Part 2, Thermodynamics, pp. 619–635, Wiley, New York, 1959).

EQUATIONS OF STATE

The thermodynamic properties of a pure fluid may be represented by an equation of state which gives the relation between the pressure P, the molar volume $\mathbf{V}$, and the absolute thermodynamic temperature T, with a functional form:

$$f(P, \mathbf{V}, T) = 0 \qquad (4\text{-}107a)$$

Alternatively Eq. (4-107a) may be given explicitly in terms of P:

$$P = \varphi(\mathbf{V}, T) \qquad (4\text{-}108a)$$

or explicitly in terms of V or T.

The simplest equation of state would be that for a perfect gas

$$PV = nRT \qquad (4\text{-}308)$$

where P = pressure
V = volume
R = gas constant per mole
T = absolute temperature
n = moles of gas

From a molecular standpoint, a perfect gas would require that the interaction between the molecules be so weak that it can be neglected. In nature, perfect-gas behavior is approached when the gas is sufficiently rarefied since all gas molecules show strong interaction at close distances.

Virial Equation of State. The virial equation of state expresses the product of pressure and volume in a power series in $1/\mathbf{V}$ or as a power series in P. The two forms of the virial equation of state are

$$\frac{P\mathbf{V}}{RT} = 1 + \frac{\beta(T)}{\mathbf{V}} + \frac{\gamma(T)}{\mathbf{V}^2} + \cdots \qquad (4\text{-}309)$$

and

$$\frac{P\mathbf{V}}{RT} = 1 + \beta'(T)P + \gamma'(T)P^2 + \cdots \qquad (4\text{-}310)$$

in which $\beta(T), \beta'(T)$ are called the second virial coefficients and $\gamma(T)$, $\gamma'(T)$ are the third virial coefficients. Equations (4-309) and (4-310) may be applied using measured or theoretical values of the coefficients. It may be shown that the coefficients of the two expansions bear the simple relation (Hirschfelder, Curtiss, and Bird, "Molecular Theory of Gases and Liquids," p. 131, Wiley, New York, 1954)

$$\beta'(T) = \frac{\beta(T)}{T} \qquad (4\text{-}311)$$

and

$$\gamma'(T) = \frac{[\gamma(T) - \beta^2(T)]}{RT^2} \qquad (4\text{-}312)$$

The virial equations of state are significant from a theoretical standpoint because the virial coefficients may be expressed as integrals involving the intermolecular potential functions and in many cases can be solved for numerically when the parameters of the intermolecular potential functions are assigned. From statistical mechanical considerations, it becomes evident that the second, third, fourth, . . . virial coefficients represent the deviations from ideal-gas behavior when collisions involving two, three, four, . . . molecules become important in the gas. At low and moderate densities the deviations from ideal gas may be adequately described by using the second virial coefficient only to give

$$P\mathbf{V} = RT + \beta'(T)RTP \qquad (4\text{-}313)$$

Numerous engineering applications of the virial form of the equation of state to moderate dense gases have become evident in recent years [Prausnitz, *Chem. Eng. Sci.*, **6**, 112 (1957); *Am. Inst. Chem. Engrs. J.*, **4**, 430 (1958). Connolly and Kandalic, *Physics of Fluids*, **3**, 463 (1960)].

The rigorous application of the virial equation of state is hampered by the difficulty of measuring the virial coefficients beyond the second virial and of calculating the third and higher virial coefficients for realistic intermolecular potentials. The relative contributions of the successive virial coefficients is a function of the density, the higher virials becoming extremely significant at higher densities. Accordingly, the convergence of the series becomes poorer at the higher densities and in fact *diverges* for densities approaching that of liquids (Hirschfelder, Curtiss, and Bird, "Molecular Theory of Gases and Liquids," p. 132, Wiley, New York, 1954)

Classical Equations of States. Three classical equations of state that have received considerable attention are

$$P = \frac{RT}{\mathbf{V} - b} - \frac{a}{\mathbf{V}^2} \qquad \text{(van der Waals)} \qquad (4\text{-}314)$$

$$P = \frac{RT}{\mathbf{V} - b}\, e^{-a/\mathbf{V}RT} \qquad \text{(Dieterici)} \qquad (4\text{-}315)$$

$$P = \frac{RT}{\mathbf{V} - b} - \frac{a}{T\mathbf{V}^2} \qquad \text{(Berthelot)} \qquad (4\text{-}316)$$

While these equations of state do not give a good representation of the compressibility of gases over wide ranges of conditions, they do qualitatively represent the salient features of the pressure-volume-temperature surface. All three equations of state provide for a liquid-gas critical point and a vapor-liquid envelope. The van der Waals equation requires linear isometrics, Dieterici's isometrics of positive curvature, and Berthelot's isometrics with negative curvature. Applying the two conditions which apply to a pure substance at its critical

$$\left(\frac{dP}{d\mathbf{V}}\right)_T = 0 \qquad (4\text{-}317)$$

$$\left(\frac{d^2P}{d\mathbf{V}^2}\right)_T = 0 \qquad (4\text{-}318)$$

it is possible to solve for the two constants of each equation in terms of the critical constants P_c, $\mathbf{V}_c$, and T_c. Thus each equation can be written in terms of reduced parameters containing no constants characteristic of a particular gas. Van der Waals' equation of state in terms of reduced variables becomes

$$\left(P_r + \frac{3}{V_r^2}\right)\left(3V_r - 1\right) = 8T_r \qquad (4\text{-}319)$$

The Dieterici equation gives a critical compressibility which is in excellent agreement with the average values for 25 non-polar gases and is the best all-around analytical two-constant equation of state [Beattie and Stockmayer, *Reports and Projects in Physics*, **7**, 195 (1940)].

Few equations of state give negative curvature at low densities, positive at intermediate densities, and negative curvature at high densities in agreement with the observed behavior of gases. Among the equations of state showing all three of these characteristics is the one developed by Benedict, Webb, and Rubin [*J. Chem. Phys.*, **8**, 334 (1940)] which contains eight empirical constants. Even so, the latter does not provide for a maximum in the second virial coefficient.

The Benedict-Webb-Rubin equation of state like the Beattie-Bridgman equation of state [Beattie and Bridgman, *J. Am. Chem. Soc.*, **49**, 1665 (1927)] is based upon a hard-sphere molecular model.

The Benedict-Webb-Rubin equation of state has the form

$$P = RT\rho + \left(B_0RT - A_0 - \frac{C_0}{T^2}\right)\rho^2 + (bRT - a)\rho^3 + a\alpha\rho^6 + \frac{c\rho^3}{T^2}(1 + \gamma\rho^2)e^{-\gamma\rho^2} \qquad (4\text{-}320)$$

where $\rho = 1/\mathbf{V}$ and A_0, B_0, C_0, a, b, c, α, and γ are eight constants which are determined empirically for each substance. Combining rules for the constants have been devised to permit application of the equation to multicomponent mixtures [Benedict, Webb, and Rubin, *Chem. Eng. Progress*, **47**, 419, 571, 609 (1951)].

Two other equations of state that show promise but have not been applied to mixtures are those of Martin and Hou [*Am. Inst. Chem. Engrs. J.*, **1**, 142 (1955)] and Hirschfelder, Beuhler, McGee, and Sutton [*Ind. Eng. Chem.*, **50**, 375 (1958)].

THERMODYNAMICS OF SOLUTIONS

Solutions of gases and liquids are far more predominant than pure substances in chemical, petroleum, and metallurgical processes, hence the treatment of the thermodynamics of homogeneous mixtures. This area of thermodynamics encompasses such a large spectrum of topics that it is beyond the scope of this treatment to present more than a limited discussion of some of the basic principles. For a more comprehensive treatment of the fundamentals, the reader is referred to Dodge ("Chemical Engineering Thermodynamics," McGraw-Hill, New York, 1944) and Lewis, Randall, Pitzer, and Brewer ("Thermodynamics," 2d ed., McGraw-Hill, New York, 1961).

Partial Molal Functions. Let the function ψ represent *any extensive property* of a homogeneous phase, such as V, H, G, and S, which is a function of temperature, pressure, and amounts of the various constituents. The total differential of ψ is given by the expression

$$d\psi = \left(\frac{d\psi}{dT}\right)_{P,n_A,n_B,\ldots} dT + \left(\frac{d\psi}{dP}\right)_{T,n_A,n_B,\ldots} dP + \left(\frac{d\psi}{dn_A}\right)_{T,P,n_B,\ldots} dn_A + \left(\frac{d\psi}{dn_B}\right)_{T,P,n_A,\ldots} dn_B + \cdots \qquad (4\text{-}321)$$

Recalling that the partial molal quantity is defined as

$$\bar{\psi}_i = \left(\frac{d\psi}{dn_i}\right)_{T,P,n_j} \qquad (4\text{-}322)$$

where all the n's are constant except n_i, Eq. (4-321) becomes

$$d\psi = \left(\frac{d\psi}{dT}\right)_{P,n_A,n_B,\ldots} dT + \left(\frac{d\psi}{dP}\right)_{T,n_A,n_B,\ldots} dP + \bar{\psi}_A\,dn_A + \bar{\psi}_B\,dn_B + \cdots \qquad (4\text{-}321a)$$

Imposing the restraints of constant temperature and pressure,

$$d\psi_{T,P} = (\bar{\psi}_A\,dn_A + \bar{\psi}_B\,dn_B + \cdots)_{T,P} \qquad (4\text{-}321b)$$

It is evident from the definition of the partial molal quantity that $\bar{\psi}_i$ is an intensive property and as such is a function of temperature, pressure, and composition.

The extensive property ψ is a single-valued homogeneous function of the first degree in the number of moles of the components of the system. From Euler's theorem on homogeneous functions, it follows that

$$\psi = n_A\bar{\psi}_A + n_B\bar{\psi}_B + \cdots \qquad (4\text{-}323)$$

and therefore

$$d\psi_{T,P} = [\bar{\psi}_A\,dn_A + \bar{\psi}_B\,dn_B + \cdots + n_A\,d\bar{\psi}_A + n_B\,d\bar{\psi}_B + \cdots]_{T,P} \qquad (4\text{-}324)$$

Subtracting Eq. (4-321b) from Eq. (4-324) gives

$$[n_A\,d\bar{\psi}_A + n_B\,d\bar{\psi}_B + \cdots]_{T,P} = 0 \qquad (4\text{-}325)$$

which is commonly referred to as the Gibbs-Duhem equation. If the moles of one constituent are regarded as the main variable, Eq. (4-325) takes the form

$$n_A\left(\frac{d\bar{\psi}_A}{dn_A}\right)_{T,P} + n_B\left(\frac{d\bar{\psi}_B}{dn_A}\right)_{T,P} + \cdots = 0 \qquad (4\text{-}326)$$

or in terms of mole fractions

$$x_A\left(\frac{d\bar{\psi}_A}{dx_A}\right)_{T,P} + x_B\left(\frac{d\bar{\psi}_B}{dx_A}\right)_{T,P} + \cdots = 0 \qquad (4\text{-}327)$$

The Gibbs-Duhem equation in various forms has been frequently applied to each phase of a binary liquid-vapor system at equilibrium for the calculation of the composition of the coexisting phases. In the case of a two-phase system at equilibrium, this expression *does not* represent an equilibrium relation, since according to the phase rule, equilibrium between the phases cannot be maintained at constant temperature and pressure with only variations

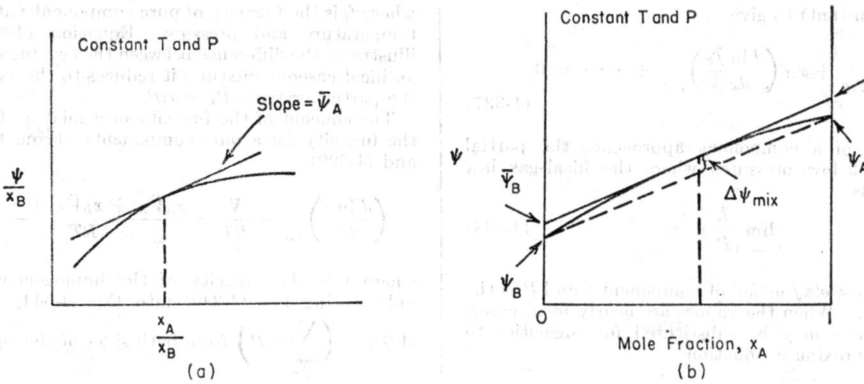

FIG. 4-39. Determination of partial quantities by graphical methods.

in composition. One of the conditions must be dropped (constant T or P); hence expressions of the form of Eq. (4-327) *do not* apply. [Ibl and Dodge, *Chem. Eng. Sci.*, **2**, 120 (1953), have derived the exact relationships which are valid at T constant and P variable or P constant and T variable.] These equations will be discussed later.

Methods for Determining Partial Molal Quantities. Several methods are available for determining partial molal quantities for binary solutions; only two graphical methods are presented here.

1. *Tangent-slope Method.* If ψ, any extensive property containing a *fixed amount of component A*, is plotted as a function of n_B, the slope of the curve at any point is $\bar{\psi}_B$

$$\bar{\psi}_B = \left(\frac{d\psi}{dn_B}\right)_{T,P,n_A} \tag{4-322a}$$

This method is particularly useful when the composition is expressed as molality. If the composition is given in terms of the ratios of moles or mass fractions, Eq. (4-322*a*) can be expressed as

$$\bar{\psi}_B = \left(\frac{d\psi}{dn_B}\right)_{T,P,n_A} = \left[\frac{d(\psi/n_A)}{d(n_B/n_A)}\right]_{T,P,n_A} = \left[\frac{d(\psi/x_A)}{d(x_B/x_A)}\right]_{T,P} \tag{4-328}$$

where ψ is the molal or specific property of the solution. The slope of the plot of ψ/x_A vs. x_B/x_A at any point is $\bar{\psi}_B$ (see Fig. 4-39*a*). The value for $\bar{\psi}_A$ can be calculated from Eq. (4-323) or from an expression similar to Eq. (4-328).

2. *Tangent-intercept Method.* The specific property ψ of a binary solution is given by

$$\psi = x_A\bar{\psi}_A + x_B\bar{\psi}_B = x_A(\bar{\psi}_A - \bar{\psi}_B) + \bar{\psi}_B \tag{4-329}$$

If a line is drawn tangent to the curve of ψ vs. x_A at any point, the intercept of tangent on the ordinate at $x_A = 1$ is $\bar{\psi}_A$ and at $x_A = 0$, $\bar{\psi}_B$ (see Fig. 4-39*b*).

The proof of this theorem is as follows: The equation of the tangent line is

$$\psi = x_A\left(\frac{d\psi}{dx_A}\right)_{T,P} + B \tag{4-330}$$

where B is the intercept at $x_A = 0$. Differentiating Eq. (4-329) with respect to x_A at constant T and P and applying the Gibbs-Duhem relation [Eq. (4-327)]

$$\left(\frac{d\psi}{dx_A}\right)_{T,P} = \bar{\psi}_A - \bar{\psi}_B \tag{4-331}$$

Combining Eqs. (4-330) and (4-331) and subtracting from Eq. (4-329) gives the intercept of the tangent line at $x_A = 0$ as $B = \bar{\psi}_B$. In a similar fashion, it can be shown that $\bar{\psi}_A$ is the intercept at $x_A = 1$.

It should be evident that the equations developed for partial quantities are applicable on both a mole or mass basis. If the latter is the case, the x_i's represent the mass fractions of the various components.

Gibbs-Duhem Relation for Binary Solutions. Applying Eq. (4-327) to a binary system,

$$\frac{(d\bar{\psi}_A/dx_A)_{T,P}}{(d\bar{\psi}_B/dx_A)_{T,P}} = -\frac{x_B}{x_A} \tag{4-332}$$

If $\bar{\psi}_A$ and $\bar{\psi}_B$ are plotted as functions of x_A, then according to Eq. (4-332) the slope of one curve is determined by the slope of the other curve and the composition. For the limiting case of an infinitely dilute solution of component B, $(d\bar{\psi}_A/dx_A)_{T,P}$ must equal zero or $(d\bar{\psi}_B/dx_A)_{T,P}$ is infinite. Partial molal volumes, enthalpies, internal energies, and heat capacities constitute examples of the first type while all partial quantities involving entropy, such as S, G, and A, follow the second type of behavior. Because of the characteristic behavior of the partial Gibbs free energy in dilute solutions, it is more convenient to use related functions such as fugacity, activity, and activity coefficients.

Fugacity of a Component in a Mixture. The fugacity of component i in solution $\bar{f}_i$ is defined similar to the fugacity of the pure component, *i.e.*,

$$(d\bar{G}_i)_T = (RT\, d\ln \bar{f}_i)_T \tag{4-333}$$

or integrated form

$$\bar{G}_i = RT\ln \bar{f}_i + \varphi_i(T) \tag{4-334}$$

where $\bar{G}_i$ is the partial Gibbs free energy, where $\bar{f}_i$ is a function of pressure, temperature, and composition and where φ_i is a function of temperature only. Hence

$$\left(\frac{d\bar{G}_i}{dP}\right)_{T,x_k} = RT\left(\frac{d\ln \bar{f}_i}{dP}\right)_{T,x_k} \tag{4-335}$$

and

$$\left(\frac{d\bar{G}_i}{dx_j}\right)_{T,P,x_{k-2}} = RT\left(\frac{d\ln \bar{f}_i}{dx_j}\right)_{T,P,x_{k-2}} \tag{4-336}$$

where k is the number of constituents in the mixture of which i and j are members and the subscript x_{k-2} indicates that $(k - 2)$ mole fractions are held constant.

The Gibbs-Duhem relation in terms of fugacities is obtained by combining Eq. (4-327) with Eq. (4-333) (holding P constant) to give

$$x_A \left(\frac{d \ln \bar{f}_A}{dx_A}\right)_{T,P} + x_B \left(\frac{d \ln \bar{f}_B}{dx_A}\right)_{T,P} + \cdots = 0 \tag{4-337}$$

The fugacity of a component approaches the partial pressure $\bar{P}_i$ at low pressures where the ideal-gas law applies. Thus

$$\lim_{P \to 0} \frac{\bar{f}_i}{P} = x_i \tag{4-338}$$

where x_i is the *mole fraction* of component i and P is the total pressure. When the vapors are nearly ideal gases, partial pressures may be substituted for fugacities to obtain the approximate equation

$$x_A \left(\frac{d \ln \bar{P}_A}{dx_A}\right)_{T,P} + x_B \left(\frac{d \ln \bar{P}_B}{dx_A}\right)_{T,P} + \cdots = 0 \tag{4-339}$$

Equation (4-339) (called the Duhem-Margules equation) has been frequently used to check the consistency of vapor-liquid equilibrium data for systems in which the vapor phase is nearly an ideal gas. However, as indicated previously, this equation may be in serious error for certain systems (see discussion of partial molal quantities).

The effect of pressure and temperature on the fugacity can be determined by methods identical with those used in deriving Eqs. (4-280) and (4-294). Thus

$$\left(\frac{d \ln \bar{f}_i}{dP}\right)_{T,x} = \frac{\bar{V}_i}{RT} \tag{4-340}$$

and

$$\left(\frac{d \ln \bar{f}_i}{dT}\right)_{P,x} = \frac{\mathbf{H}_i^* - \bar{H}_i}{RT^2} \tag{4-341}$$

where $(\mathbf{H}_i^* - \bar{H}_i)$ is the difference between the enthalpy of pure component i in the ideal-gas state and the partial enthalpy of component i in solution.

The fugacity of a component in a homogeneous mixture is essential for the prediction of phase and chemical equilibria and transport phenomena. The fugacity can be determined from experimental PVT-composition data, from equations of state for mixtures such as the Benedict-Webb-Rubin equation [*Chem. Eng. Progress*, **47**, 419 (1951)], or from generalized correlations using pseudo-reduced temperatures and pressures [Joffe, *Ind. Eng. Chem.*, **40**, 1738 (1948). Kay, *Ind. Eng. Chem.*, **28**, 1014 (1936). Mueller and Leland, *Ind. Eng. Chem.*, **51**, 597 (1959)].

The relationship between the fugacity and the volumetric properties of the solution can be obtained from Eq. (4-340). Subtracting $1/P$ from both sides of the equation and integrating to the system pressure P yields

$$\ln \frac{\bar{f}_i}{x_i P} = \frac{1}{RT} \int_0^P \left(\bar{V}_i - \frac{RT}{P}\right) dP \tag{4-342}$$

where Eq. (4-338) has been applied to determine the lower limit of integration. The ratio $\bar{f}_i/x_iP$ is called the fugacity coefficient for a component in solution. If Eq. (4-342) is expressed in terms of the molal volume of the pure component instead of the ideal-gas molal volume RT/P, a relationship is obtained between the fugacity of a component in solution and the fugacity of the pure component, *i.e.*,

$$\ln \bar{f}_i = \ln x_i f_i + \frac{1}{RT} \int_0^P (\bar{V}_i - \mathbf{V}_i)\, dP \tag{4-343}$$

where f_i is the fugacity of pure component i at the system temperature and pressure. Equation (4-343) clearly illustrates the difference between the two fugacities. For an ideal gaseous mixture, it reduces to the expression for the partial pressure $\bar{P}_i = x_iP$.

The concept of the fugacity of a mixture follows from the fugacity for a pure component. From Eqs. (4-281) and (4-329),

$$\left(\frac{d \ln f}{dP}\right)_{T,x} = \frac{\mathbf{V}}{RT} = \frac{x_A\bar{V}_A + x_B\bar{V}_B + \cdots}{RT} \tag{4-344}$$

where f is the fugacity of the homogeneous mixture. Substituting Eq. (4-340) into Eq. (4-344), subtracting $(1/P) = \left(\sum_i x_i/P\right)$ from both sides of the equation, and integrating gives

$$\ln f = x_A \ln \frac{\bar{f}_A}{x_A} + x_B \ln \frac{\bar{f}_B}{x_B} + \cdots \tag{4-345}$$

Mixing Processes. The relationship between the properties of the pure components and those in solution can best be understood by considering the energy, volume, and entropy changes associated with mixing phenomena. The mixing of two or more components to form a homogeneous solution is totally irreversible; that is, no work is recovered from the process.

For a steady-state mixing process at constant temperature and pressure, the energy and entropy balances [Eqs. (4-192) and (4-193)] become

$$\mathbf{H} - (\mathbf{H}_A x_A + \mathbf{H}_B x_B + \cdots) = \mathbf{Q} \tag{4-346}$$

and

$$\mathbf{S} - (\mathbf{S}_A x_A + \mathbf{S}_B x_B + \cdots) = \frac{\mathbf{Q}}{T} + \frac{\mathbf{lw}}{T} \tag{4-347}$$

where $\mathbf{H}$ and $\mathbf{S}$ represent the specific or molal enthalpy and entropy of the mixture and $x_A, x_B, \ldots$ the mass or mole fractions of components $A, B, \cdots$. Solving Eq. (4-347) for $\mathbf{Q}$, substituting in Eq. (4-346), and applying Eq. (4-103) yields the relation

$$(\mathbf{W}_{\text{rev}})_{T,P} = \mathbf{lw}_{T,P} = -[\mathbf{G} - (x_A\mathbf{G}_A + x_B\mathbf{G}_B + \cdots)] \tag{4-348}$$

Since $lw > 0$, it may be concluded that there is always a decrease in the Gibbs free energy on mixing.

Let ψ represent any extensive property of a homogeneous mixture. Then by definition

$$(\Delta\psi_{\text{mix}})_{T,P} = \psi - \sum_i x_i\psi_i \tag{4-349}$$

where $\Delta\psi_{\text{mix}}$ is the change in the extensive property on mixing per unit mass or mole of solution. Combining Eq. (4-349) with Eq. (4-323),

$$(\Delta\psi_{\text{mix}})_{T,P} = \sum_i x_i(\bar{\psi}_i - \psi_i) \tag{4-350}$$

Although it should be obvious from Eq. (4-350), the determination of $\Delta\psi_{\text{mix}}$ for properties where only relative values are used, such as H, U, G, and S, both $\bar{\psi}_i$ and ψ_i *must be* referred to the same reference state. However, different reference states may be used for different components in the mixture. It follows from Eqs. (4-346) through (4-350) that

$$(\Delta \mathbf{H}_{\text{mix}})_{T,P} = \sum_i x_i(\bar{H}_i - \mathbf{H}_i) = \mathbf{Q} \qquad (4\text{-}351)$$

$$(\Delta \mathbf{S}_{\text{mix}})_{T,P} = \sum_i x_i(\bar{S}_i - \mathbf{S}_i) = \frac{\mathbf{Q} + \mathbf{lw}}{T} \qquad (4\text{-}352)$$

$$(\Delta \mathbf{G}_{\text{mix}})_{T,P} = \sum_i x_i(\bar{G}_i - \mathbf{G}_i) = -\mathbf{lw}_{T,P} = -(\mathbf{W}_{\text{rev}})_{T,P} \qquad (4\text{-}353)$$

and $(\Delta \mathbf{G}_{\text{mix}})_{T,P} = (\Delta \mathbf{H}_{\text{mix}})_{T,P} - T(\Delta \mathbf{S}_{\text{mix}})_{T,P}$ (4-354)

The Gibbs free energy of mixing as given by Eq. (4-353) is frequently expressed in terms of fugacities. Since by Eq. (4-333)

$$(\bar{G}_i - \mathbf{G}_i)_{T,P} = \int_{\text{pure component}}^{\text{solution}} dG_{iT,P} = RT \int_{\text{pure}}^{\text{solution}} (d \ln \bar{f}_i)_{T,P} = RT \ln \frac{\bar{f}_i}{f_i} \qquad (4\text{-}355)$$

then

$$(\Delta \mathbf{G}_{\text{mix}})_{T,P} = RT \sum_i x_i \ln \frac{\bar{f}_i}{f_i} \qquad (4\text{-}353a)$$

Multicomponent Phase Equilibria. The Gibbs free energy of a homogeneous phase is an extensive property. Therefore, by Euler's theorem,

$$G = \sum_i n_i \bar{G}_i$$

and

$$dG = \sum_i n_i \, d\bar{G}_i + \sum_i \bar{G}_i \, dn_i \qquad (4\text{-}356)$$

From Eq. (4-107) and the definition for G,

$$dG = V \, dP - S \, dT + \sum_i \bar{G}_i \, dn_i \qquad (4\text{-}357)$$

Equating Eqs. (4-356) and (4-357) and dividing by the total moles of the given phase yields the Gibbs equation, which is valid for any open phase at variable T and P,

$$\mathbf{V} \, dP - \mathbf{S} \, dT - \sum_i x_i \, d\bar{G}_i = 0 \qquad (4\text{-}358)$$

If more than one phase is present in a system at equilibrium, the variations of the independent variables dT. dP, $d\bar{G}_1$, $d\bar{G}_2$, · · · must be equal in all phases. Thus

$$\begin{aligned} \bar{G}_{A}' &= \bar{G}_{A}'' = \bar{G}_{A}''' = \cdots \\ \bar{G}_{B}' &= \bar{G}_{B}'' = \bar{G}_{B}''' = \cdots \end{aligned} \qquad (4\text{-}359)$$

etc.

where the primes denote the various phases. Equation (4-359) implies that, for a system of two or more multicomponent phases in equilibrium at a given temperature and pressure, the criterion for equilibrium is given by the equality of the partial Gibbs free energy of each component in all phases. Applying Eq. (4-334), the condition for equilibrium in terms of fugacities is

$$\begin{aligned} \bar{f}_{A}' &= \bar{f}_{A}'' = \bar{f}_{A}''' = \cdots \\ \bar{f}_{B}' &= \bar{f}_{B}'' = \bar{f}_{B}''' = \cdots \end{aligned} \qquad (4\text{-}360)$$

etc.

These relations are fundamental in calculations of multicomponent phase equilibria.

Vapor-Liquid Equilibrium Relationships. As indicated previously, Ibl and Dodge [*Chem. Eng. Sci.*, **2**, 120 (1953)] have shown that the Gibbs-Duhem equation *does not apply rigorously* to either constant-pressure systems in which the temperature varies to preserve equilibrium, or isothermal systems in which the pressure varies. Their expression for a constant-pressure system in equilibrium with its vapor is

$$\left(x_A \frac{d \ln \bar{f}_A}{dx_A} + x_B \frac{d \ln \bar{f}_B}{dx_A}\right)_P = \left[\frac{\sum_{i=A}^{B} x_i(\mathbf{H}_i^* - \bar{H}_i')}{RT^2} \frac{dT}{dx_A}\right]_P \qquad (4\text{-}361)$$

where the prime denotes the liquid phase, (dT/dx_A) represents the slope of the curve of the boiling point vs. the liquid-phase composition, x_i the mole fraction in the liquid phase, and $\bar{f}_i$ the fugacity of i in the equilibrium phase.

A similar expression results for an isothermal system,

$$\left(x_A \frac{d \ln \bar{f}_A}{dx_A} + x_B \frac{d \ln \bar{f}_B}{dx_A}\right)_T = \left(\frac{\mathbf{V}'}{RT} \frac{dP}{dx_A}\right)_T \qquad (4\text{-}362)$$

where $\mathbf{V}'$ is the molal volume of the liquid phase and (dP/dx_A) is the slope of the curve of total pressure vs. liquid-phase composition.

Ideal Solutions. The concept of an ideal solution is fundamental to the study of the thermodynamics of mixtures. Physically, an ideal solution may be defined as one in which the molecules of a component in solution are affected by their environment in exactly the same manner as they are in the pure state at the same temperature and pressure as the solution. In reality, there are no such solutions because this definition would be fulfilled only by mixtures of molecular types which are exactly alike yet are still distinguishable from each other. The value of the ideal-solution concept lies in the fact that it is a limit which many solutions approach closely.

The mathematical expression of the ideal solution is given by the Lewis and Randall fugacity rule,

$$\bar{f}_i = x_i f_i \qquad (4\text{-}363)$$

where f_i is the fugacity of pure component i at the temperature and pressure of the solution and x_i is the *mole fraction* of component i. At pressures low enough for the vapor phase to be considered as an ideal gas, $\bar{f}_i = \bar{P}_i$ and the fugacity of the pure component is equal to its vapor pressure, P_i^0. The ideal-solution law thus reduces to Raoult's law,

$$\bar{P}_i = x_i P_i^0 \qquad (4\text{-}364)$$

Solutions which obey the ideal-solution rule are completely predictable and all their thermodynamic properties may be determined from the properties of the pure components. Of course, it must be remembered that this condition is in reality a limit and no actual solution obeys the rule perfectly over all ranges of temperature, pressure, and composition.

Properties of an Ideal Solution. The properties of an ideal solution can be determined by numerous methods. If Eq. (4-363) is written in logarithmic form and differentiated with respect to pressure holding temperature and composition constant,

$$\left(\frac{d \ln \bar{f}_i}{dP}\right)_{T,x} - \left(\frac{d \ln f_i}{dP}\right)_T = 0 = \frac{\bar{V}_i - \mathbf{V}_i}{RT} \qquad (4\text{-}365)$$

Since by definition Eq. (4-363) holds for all temperatures, pressures, and compositions, it follows from Eq. (4-350) that

$$(\Delta \mathbf{V}_{mix})_{T,P} = 0 \quad (4\text{-}366)$$

and therefore the volume of the solution follows the additive-volume rule,

$$\mathbf{V} = \sum_i x_i \mathbf{V}_i \quad (4\text{-}367)$$

In a similar fashion, differentiating with respect to temperature,

$$\left(\frac{d \ln \bar{f}_i}{dT}\right)_{P,x} - \left(\frac{d \ln f_i}{dT}\right)_P = 0 = \frac{\mathbf{H}_i - \bar{H}_i}{RT^2} \quad (4\text{-}368)$$

which yields the condition

$$(\Delta \mathbf{H}_{mix})_{T,P} = 0 \quad (4\text{-}369)$$

Hence the enthalpy of the solution also follows the linear-addition rule and is given by the expression

$$\mathbf{H} = \sum_i x_i \mathbf{H}_i \quad (4\text{-}370)$$

From the definition of the heat capacity C_p, it is easily shown that for ideal solutions,

$$\mathbf{C}_p = \sum_i x_i (\mathbf{C}_p)_i \quad (4\text{-}371)$$

Since $(\Delta \mathbf{H}_{mix})_{T,P} = (\Delta \mathbf{U}_{mix})_{T,P} + P(\Delta \mathbf{V}_{mix})_{T,P}$, then from Eqs. (4-366) and (4-369),

$$(\Delta \mathbf{U}_{mix})_{T,P} = 0 \quad (4\text{-}372)$$

The decrease in the Gibbs free energy of mixing per mole of ideal solution is obtained by combining Eq. (4-353*a*) with Eq. (4-363) to give

$$(\Delta \mathbf{G}_{mix})_{T,P} = RT \sum_i x_i \ln x_i \quad (4\text{-}373)$$

It follows from the other properties of mixing that the entropy of 1 mole of an ideal solution exceeds that of the pure components by

$$(\Delta \mathbf{S}_{mix})_{T,P} = -R \sum_i x_i \ln x_i \quad (4\text{-}374)$$

Frequently in solution theory the concept of the excess property of mixing is employed. The excess-mixing property is defined as

$$(\Delta \psi^E{}_{mix})_{T,P} = [\Delta \psi_{mix} - (\Delta \psi_{mix})_{\text{ideal solution}}]_{T,P} \quad (4\text{-}375)$$

Applying this definition to the property G, the excess Gibbs free energy of mixing is

$$(\Delta \mathbf{G}^E{}_{mix})_{T,P} = RT \sum_i x_i \ln \frac{\bar{f}_i}{x_i f_i} \quad (4\text{-}376)$$

A more complete discussion of the ideal-solution concept and its relation to the physical properties of solutions may be found in a number of references (Denbigh, "The Principles of Chemical Equilibrium," Cambridge, New York, 1955; Prigogine, "The Molecular Theory of Solutions," North Holland Publishing Co., Amsterdam, 1957. Lewis, Randall, Pitzer, and Brewer, "Thermodynamics," 2d ed., McGraw-Hill, New York, 1961).

Activity, Activity Coefficients, and Standard States. It is often impossible or impractical because of the lack of thermodynamic data to determine the fugacity of a component in solution. It is therefore advantageous to use the ratio between the fugacity $\bar{f}_i$ of component i in a given state and its fugacity $f_i{}^0$ in some other *arbitrary state but at the same temperature.* This arbitrary reference state is called the standard state and will be designated by the superscript zero. The ratio of fugacities is called activity and is defined as

$$\bar{a}_i = \frac{\bar{f}_i}{f_i{}^0} \quad (4\text{-}377)$$

where $\bar{a}_i$ is the activity of component i in solution and $f_i{}^0$ is standard-state fugacity.

The change in the Gibbs free energy of component i in transferring 1 mole from the standard state to any given state at the same temperature is obtained by integrating Eq. (4-333) to yield

$$\bar{G}_i = RT \ln \bar{f}_i + (G_i{}^0 - RT \ln f_i{}^0) \quad (4\text{-}378)$$

or in terms of activity

$$\bar{G}_i = G_i{}^0 + RT \ln \bar{a}_i \quad (4\text{-}379)$$

Comparing Eq. (4-378) with Eq. (4-334)

$$\varphi_i(T) = G_i{}^0 - RT \ln f_i{}^0 \quad (4\text{-}380)$$

It is stated by some authors that $f_i{}^0$ must be defined at a fixed pressure. However, this statement is *not true* since from Eq. (4-335)

$$\left(\frac{dG_i{}^0}{dP}\right)_{T,x} - RT\left(\frac{d \ln f_i{}^0}{dP}\right)_{T,x} = 0 \quad (4\text{-}381)$$

this condition is automatically satisfied.

The selection of the standard-state pressure and composition is purely arbitrary and hence the activity is also arbitrary. For this reason it is *imperative that the standard state for each component in solution be clearly and precisely defined.*

Standard States. The standard state for a pure gas is almost always defined as the fugacity of the ideal-gas state at 1 atm. pressure and the temperature in question. Since for ideal gases $f = P$, the standard-stage fugacity f^0 is 1 atm. This state is hypothetical to the extent that real gases deviate from ideal-gas behavior at 1 atm. The character of the standard-state definition for gases is illustrated in Fig. 4-40.

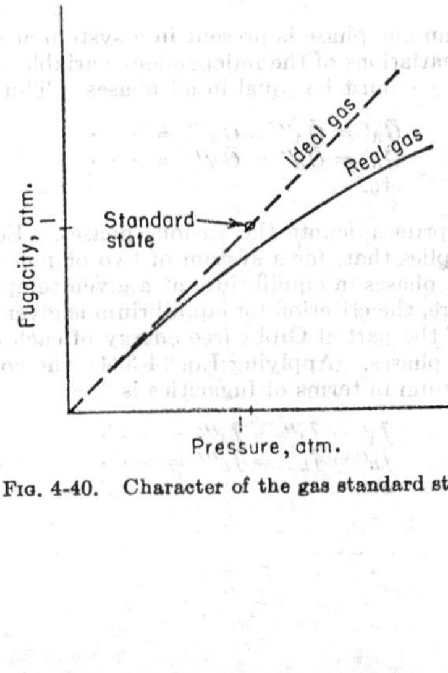

FIG. 4-40. Character of the gas standard state.

The arbitrary nature of the choice of the standard-state fugacity f_i^0 can be illustrated by considering a typical fugacity-composition relation for a non-ideal solution at constant temperature and pressure as shown in Fig. 4-41. The actual fugacity behavior is represented

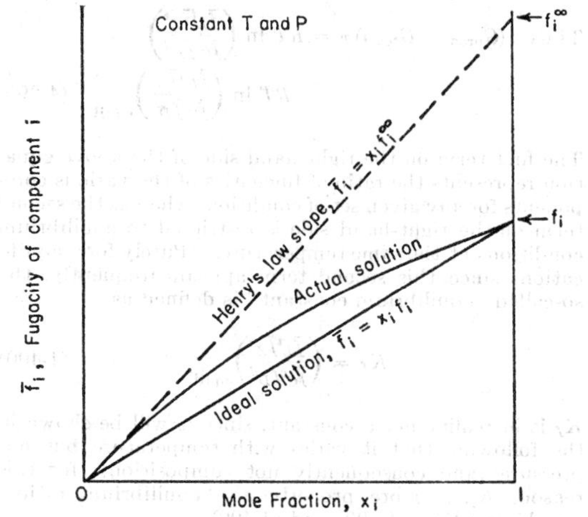

FIG. 4-41. Fugacity as a function of composition.

by the curved solid line, while the ideal-solution locus is given by the straight line with the equation $\bar{f}_i = x_i f_i$.

There are several important characteristics of the actual-solution locus. In a region near the pure-component state, $\bar{f}_i$ approaches the ideal-solution locus, *i.e.*,

$$\lim_{x_i \to 1} \frac{\bar{f}_i}{f_i} = 1 \tag{4-382}$$

In other words, as the solution becomes richer in component i, its environment in the solution will naturally approach its environment in the pure state. Therefore, if one is dealing with concentrated solutions of component i (frequently called the solvent) the selection of $f_i^0 = f_i$ is an obvious one, particularly if extrapolation of data is required. The activity for this standard state is given by

$$\bar{a}_i = \frac{\bar{f}_i}{f_i^0} = \frac{\bar{f}_i}{f_i} \tag{4-383}$$

If the solution obeys the ideal-solution law over the whole range of compositions [Eq. (4-363)] *and if* $f_i^0 = f_i$, then, and only then,

$$\bar{a}_i = \frac{\bar{f}_i}{f_i^0} = \frac{x_i f_i}{f_i} = x_i \tag{4-384}$$

In very dilute solutions of component i, the choice of $f_i^0 = f_i$, although still permissible, would be poor especially from the standpoint of the prediction of $\bar{f}_i$ since large differences may exist between actual- and ideal-solution behavior even at low concentrations. If a line is drawn tangent to the actual curve at $x_i = 0$, its equation would be represented by $\bar{f}_i = x_i f_i^\infty$ where f_i^∞ is the intercept at $x_i = 1$ (Fig. 4-41). The definition of f_i^∞ can be defined mathematically as

$$\lim_{x_i \to 0} \frac{\bar{f}_i}{x_i} = f_i^\infty \tag{4-385}$$

Since the actual curve approaches asymptotically to the limiting slope at infinite dilution, f_i^∞ represents the fugacity of a hypothetical pure component which has all the properties of component i when it is present in the solution at an infinitely dilute concentration. At low pressures, f_i^∞ becomes simply the Henry's-law constant for the component. In the neighborhood of $x_i = 0$, the fugacity of component i is approximated by

$$\bar{f}_i \simeq x_i f_i^\infty \tag{4-386}$$

This region may extend to appreciable concentrations for certain systems and may apply essentially only to infinitely dilute solutions for others. If the standard-state fugacity is defined as f_i^∞, the activity is given by

$$\bar{a}_i = \frac{\bar{f}_i}{f_i^0} = \frac{\bar{f}_i}{f_i^\infty} \tag{4-387}$$

For the region in which the solution has a Henry's-law type of behavior and for which $f_i^0 = f_i^\infty$,

$$\bar{a}_i = \frac{\bar{f}_i}{f_i^0} = \frac{x_i f_i^\infty}{f_i^\infty} = x_i \tag{4-388}$$

If the standard state $f^0 = f_i$ is used, Eq. (4-388) becomes

$$\bar{a}_i = \frac{\bar{f}_i}{f_i^0} = \frac{x_i f_i^\infty}{f_i} = \left(\frac{f_i^\infty}{f_i}\right) x_i \tag{4-389}$$

It is apparent from Eqs. (4-388) and (4-389) that the value of the activity depends entirely on the choice of the standard state. Its utility lies in the fact that absolute values for fugacity are not required.

Another derived thermodynamic function which is frequently encountered in solution theory is the activity coefficient $\bar{\gamma}$ which is defined as

$$\bar{\gamma}_i = \frac{\bar{a}_i}{x_i} \tag{4-390}$$

The major advantage of the activity coefficient is that its variations are much smaller than those for activity; so that interpolation and extrapolation of data are considerably more accurate. Deviations of the activity coefficient about a fixed value (dependent on the standard-state definition) are a measure of the non-ideality of the component in solution.

Effect of Temperature and Pressure on the Activity and the Activity Coefficient. The variations of the activity and the activity coefficient with pressure and temperature can be obtained from their definitions and the effect of these variables on fugacity to yield

$$\left(\frac{d \ln \bar{a}_i}{dP}\right)_{T,x} = \left(\frac{d \ln \bar{\gamma}_i}{dP}\right)_{T,x} = \frac{\bar{V}_i - V_i^0}{RT} \tag{4-391}$$

and
$$\left(\frac{d \ln \bar{a}_i}{dT}\right)_{P,x} = \left(\frac{d \ln \bar{\gamma}_i}{dT}\right)_{P,x} = \frac{H_i^0 - \bar{H}_i}{RT^2} \tag{4-392}$$

where V_i^0 and H_i^0 are the partial molal volume and enthalpy, respectively, of component i in the standard state. If the standard-state pressure is defined as a fixed pressure, for example, at 1 atm., then $V_i^0 = 0$. However, if the standard state is defined by $f_i^0 = f_i$, the fugacity of pure component i at the temperature and pressure of the system, then $V_i^0 = \mathbf{V}_i$ and $H_i^0 = \mathbf{H}_i$.

Types of Non-ideality. The simplest method of classification of non-ideal solutions is in regard to the direction of deviation from Raoult's law or the Lewis and Randall rule. If the actual partial vapor pressure is greater than that predicted by Raoult's law, the deviation is positive, and if less than, the deviation is negative. These deviations are the result of changes in molecular sizes, shapes, and intermolecular forces when the solution is formed from its components. An excellent discussion of these factors is available [Margeneau, *Revs. Modern Phys.*, **11**, 1 (1939). Hildebrand and Scott, "The Solubility of Non-Electrolytes," 3d ed., Reinhold, New York, 1950. Hirschfelder, Curtiss, and Bird, "Molecular Theory of Gases and Liquids," Wiley, New York, 1954].

Many non-ideal solutions have sufficient translational energy to overcome any tendency to segregation due to different molecular fields and thus possess nearly an ideal entropy of mixing. Such solutions are referred to as regular solutions. Other solutions form with essentially no heat or volume change. These solutions are called athermal (no heat). The prediction of properties of these solutions is discussed in the above references.

CHEMICAL EQUILIBRIA

Because engineers are primarily concerned with the work requirements for any given process, it is desirable to have a convenient method for calculating the work on chemical reacting systems. In most cases, the net reversible work as defined by Eq. (4-245) is of more interest than the reversible work simply because any work done against the surroundings in order to maintain the pressure constant is considered as non-useful work.

For a *closed system*, combining Eqs. (4-244) and (4-158*d*) with the basic definition $G = U + PV - TS$, and restricting to constant temperature and pressure,

$$\mathbf{W}_{\text{net rev}} = -(\Delta \mathbf{G})_{P,T} \tag{4-393}$$

By similar procedures, *in steady-state flow*, for which $P_{\text{surr}}\,\Delta V = 0$,

$$\mathbf{W}_{\text{rev}} = \mathbf{W}_{\text{net rev}} = -(\mathbf{G}_0 - \mathbf{G}_I)_T \tag{4-394}$$

Equations (4-393) and (4-394) demonstrate the utility of the property G in evaluating reversible work in particular for processes in which chemical reactions take place. Consider the typical chemical reaction:

$$cC + dD \rightleftharpoons lL + zZ \tag{4-395}$$

where c, d, l, and z represent the stoichiometric numbers for components C, D, L, and Z. By definition, for a particular temperature,

$$(d\bar{G}_i)_T = (RT\, d \ln \bar{f}_i)_T \tag{4-333}$$

and integrating

$$\bar{G}_i = RT \ln \bar{f}_i + \varphi_i(T) \tag{4-334}$$

where $\varphi_i(T)$ is used rather than a constant of integration for the sake of complete generality.

It will be recalled that the "total" G of a *homogeneous* mixture of components is given by

$$G = \sum_i n_i \bar{G}_i \tag{4-323}$$

where n_i denotes the quantities (moles or masses) of each component. If in Eq. (4-395) the products are arbitrarily denoted by L and Z and the reactants by C and D, applying Eqs. (4-323) and (4-334) to Eq. (4-395),

$$(G_{\text{prod}} - G_{\text{react}})_T = \Delta G_T = RT \ln \frac{\bar{f}_L{}^l \bar{f}_Z{}^z}{\bar{f}_C{}^c \bar{f}_D{}^d} + \sum_i \varphi_i(T) \tag{4-396}$$

where $(G_{\text{prod}} - G_{\text{react}})_T = [(l\bar{G}_L + z\bar{G}_Z) - (c\bar{G}_C + d\bar{G}_D)]_T$ (4-397)

Equation (4-396) is not very useful because of the undetermined function $\Sigma\varphi_i(T)$. However, at neutral equilibrium, from Eq. (4-252) the left-hand side of Eq. (4-396) is zero; therefore,

$$\sum_i \varphi_i(T) = -RT \ln \left(\frac{\bar{f}_L{}^l \bar{f}_Z{}^z}{\bar{f}_C{}^c \bar{f}_D{}^d}\right)_{\text{equil}} \tag{4-398}$$

Thus

$$(G_{\text{prod}} - G_{\text{react}})_T = RT \ln \left(\frac{\bar{f}_L{}^l \bar{f}_Z{}^z}{\bar{f}_C{}^c \bar{f}_D{}^d}\right) - RT \ln \left(\frac{\bar{f}_L{}^l \bar{f}_Z{}^z}{\bar{f}_C{}^c \bar{f}_D{}^d}\right)_{\text{equil}} \tag{4-399}$$

The first term on the right-hand side of the above equation represents the ratio of fugacities of the various components for any given set of conditions whereas the second term on the right-hand side is restricted to equilibrium conditions at the same temperature. Purely for simplification, since this second term appears frequently, the so-called "equilibrium constant" is defined as

$$K_f = \left(\frac{\bar{f}_L{}^l \bar{f}_Z{}^z}{\bar{f}_C{}^c \bar{f}_D{}^d}\right)_{\text{equil}} \tag{4-400}$$

K_f is in reality not a constant, since it will be shown in the following that it varies with temperature but not pressure (and consequently not composition); for this reason, K_f is more properly an "equilibrium ratio." Combining Eqs. (4-399) and (4-400)

$$(G_{\text{prod}} - G_{\text{react}})_T = RT \ln \left(\frac{\bar{f}_L{}^l \bar{f}_Z{}^z}{\bar{f}_C{}^c \bar{f}_D{}^d}\right) - RT \ln K_f \tag{4-401}$$

Equation (4-401) is perfectly general and is applicable to all chemical reaction systems, *whether at equilibrium or not.* At any particular temperature, if $(G_{\text{prod}} - G_{\text{react}})_T < 0$, it can be concluded that the reaction has a "tendency" to proceed spontaneously. However, as pointed out in the discussion of the concept of equilibrium, the reaction may or may not take place depending on passive resistance (hydrogen and oxygen). If $(G_{\text{prod}} - G_{\text{react}})_T > 0$, it simply means that work energy must be supplied from some external source in order to cause the reaction to take place. A good example is the electrolytic decomposition of aluminum or magnesium oxide, both of which are *commercially* feasible.

A corresponding equation can be derived in terms of the activities as defined previously,

$$\bar{a}_i = \frac{\bar{f}_i}{f_i{}^0} \tag{4-377}$$

If Eq. (4-379) is applied to each species in the chemical reaction [Eq. (4-395)] the following results:

$$[(G - G^0)_{\text{prod}} - (G - G^0)_{\text{react}}]_T = RT \ln \frac{\bar{a}_L{}^l \bar{a}_Z{}^z}{\bar{a}_C{}^c \bar{a}_D{}^d} \tag{4-402}$$

or

$$(G_{\text{prod}} - G_{\text{react}})_T = RT \ln \frac{\bar{a}_L{}^l \bar{a}_Z{}^z}{\bar{a}_C{}^c \bar{a}_D{}^d} + (G^0{}_{\text{prod}} - G^0{}_{\text{react}})_T \tag{4-402a}$$

Again, applying the condition of equilibrium, *i.e.*, setting the left-hand side of Eq. (4-402*a*) equal to zero,

$$(G^0{}_{\text{prod}} - G^0{}_{\text{react}})_T = -RT \ln \left(\frac{\bar{a}_L{}^l \bar{a}_Z{}^z}{\bar{a}_C{}^z \bar{a}_D{}^d}\right)_{\text{equil}} \equiv -RT \ln K_a \tag{4-403}$$

Thus

$$(G_{\text{prod}} - G_{\text{react}})_T = RT \ln \frac{\bar{a}_L{}^l \bar{a}_Z{}^z}{\bar{a}_C{}^c \bar{a}_D{}^d} - RT \ln K_a \tag{4-404}$$

The relationship between K_f and K_a can be obtained by combining Eqs. (4-400) and (4-403):

$$K_f = K_a \frac{(f^0)_L{}^l (f^0)_Z{}^z}{(f^0)_C{}^c (f^0)_D{}^d} \tag{4-405}$$

It is apparent from Eq. (4-405) that, depending on how the standard states are defined, K_f may or may not be identically equal to K_a. For example, in the special case where all products and reactants are in the gaseous state and if the standard state for each gaseous component is taken as unit fugacity, then $K_f = K_a$.

It should also be noted that the value of K_a is completely arbitrary in the sense that it is dependent on the standard states chosen. Fortunately, by convention, the most common standard states used are as follows:

1. For pure gases at the temperature in question, f^0 is always taken to be unit fugacity, *i.e., one atmosphere* (see discussion in Solutions).
2. For pure liquids and solids under 1 atm. pressure and the temperature in question, the activity is *most frequently* (*but not always*) assumed to be unity. An alternative definition is the pure liquid or solid at the temperature in question and under its own vapor pressure. However, if the effect of external pressure on the vapor pressure is negligible, it is immaterial whether the standard-state pressure is taken at 1 atm. or the vapor pressure.

Example 1. Consider the heterogeneous reaction

$$CaCO_3(s) = CaO(s) + CO_2(g)$$

$$K_f = \frac{\bar{f}_{CO_2}\bar{f}_{CaO}}{\bar{f}_{CaCO_3}}$$

If it is assumed that there are no mutual solubilities of any of the constituents in the solid phases and that the fugacities of the solids are so low that the quantities of CaO and $CaCO_3$ in the vapor phases are undetectable, then the fugacities of the components in the mixture, $\bar{f}$'s, can be replaced by the fugacities of the pure components. Thus

$$K_f = \frac{f_{CO_2} f_{CaO}}{f_{CaCO_3}}$$

If the fugacities of the pure solids are so low that it is difficult to measure, the above equation can be transposed as follows:

$$K_f \left(\frac{f_{CaCO_3}}{f_{CaO}}\right) = f_{CO_2}$$

Now at any particular temperature and pressure, the ratio of the fugacities of $CaCO_3$ and CaO is fixed and constant, regardless of the nature of the other components present in the reacting mixture provided the assumption of the existence of pure solid phases of $CaCO_3$ and CaO is still valid. Then,

$$K_f \left(\frac{f_{CaCO_3}}{f_{CaO}}\right) = K_f' = f_{CO_2}$$

where K_f' is a modified or pseudo equilibrium ratio proportional to the true equilibrium ratio K_f.

The above example can be more conveniently analyzed in terms of K_a.

$$K_a = \left(\frac{\bar{a}_{CO_2}\bar{a}_{CaO}}{\bar{a}_{CaCO_3}}\right)_{\text{equil}}$$

Again, assuming that the solid phases exist in only the pure state, and selecting for them the standard state of unit activity,

$$K_a = \bar{a}_{CO_2}$$

But, remembering that it was assumed that the gaseous phase was made up essentially of pure CO_2, and selecting $f^0_{CO_2} = 1$ atm.,

$$K_a = f_{CO_2} = K_f'$$

If the pressure is sufficiently low to permit the assumption of ideal-gas behavior, then the f_{CO_2} can be replaced by the equilibrium pressure. In general, it can be concluded that

For homogeneous gaseous reactions

$$K_a = K_f$$

For heterogeneous reactions

$$K_a = K_f' = \alpha K_f$$

where α is a proportionality constant.

The real convenience in defining and utilizing the standard-state concept is that it permits the tabulation of thermodynamic data in a compact form. It will be recalled that functions such as H, G, S are perfect or exact differentials and are dependent only on the initial and final states. Because standard states are usually defined specifically, as indicated above, values for ΔH^0, ΔG^0, etc., can be tabulated without a detailed description of the standard state assumed. For example, the so-called heat of reaction ΔH^0 (irreversible heat of reaction) is simply the differences in enthalpy between the products and reactants when each product and each reactant is in its standard state. From this value, it is possible to calculate ΔH for any other set of conditions by applying the thermodynamic relations for the effect of temperature and pressure on enthalpy. On occasion, however, particularly for heterogeneous reactions where mutual solubilities occur in the liquid and solid phases, it is not always clear what standard states are applicable unless the original source of data is consulted. Neglect to examine such cases in detail has resulted in erroneous applications and conclusions in the literature. Along these same lines, needless confusion and wasted effort have arisen from the failure to appreciate that, in dilute solutions where the assumption of a linear (Henry's) solution law is valid, the activity coefficient $\bar{\gamma}$ (defined as $\bar{a}/x$) is equal to unity ($\bar{a} = x$) only if the standard state is selected as the hypothetical state of infinite dilution. For all other standard states, including the frequently assumed state of unit activity for the pure component, *the activity is not equal to the concentration* ($\bar{\gamma} \neq 1$). The most that can be said in this case is that activity is proportional to concentration.

Effect of Temperature on K_f and K_a. It has been previously shown that fugacity is a function of temperature; therefore, it would be expected that both K_f and K_a are temperature-dependent. If Eqs. (4-401) and (4-404) are differentiated *term by term* with respect to temperature and with only the restriction of constant pressure (but not the restriction of constant composition) and remembering that

$$\left(\frac{d \ln \bar{f}_i}{dT}\right)_{P,x} = \frac{\mathbf{H}_i{}^* - \bar{H}_i}{RT^2} \tag{4-341}$$

$$\left(\frac{d \ln \bar{a}_i}{dT}\right)_{P,x} = \frac{H_i{}^0 - \bar{H}_i}{RT^2} \tag{4-392}$$

and

$$H = \sum_i n_i \bar{H}_i \tag{4-323}$$

it follows that

$$\left(\frac{d \ln K_f}{dT}\right)_P = \frac{H^*_{\text{prod}} - H^*_{\text{react}}}{RT^2} = \frac{\Delta H_T{}^*}{RT^2} \tag{4-406}$$

where

$$H^*_{prod} - H^*_{react} = (lH_L^* + zH_Z^*) - (cH_C^* + dH_D^*)$$

and
$$\left(\frac{d \ln K_a}{dT}\right)_P = \frac{H^0_{prod} - H^0_{react}}{RT^2} = \frac{\Delta H_T^0}{RT^2} \quad (4\text{-}407)$$

where

$$H^0_{prod} - H^0_{react} = (lH_L^0 + zH_Z^0) - (cH_C^0 + dH_D^0)$$

The difference between Eqs. (4-406) and (4-407) should be noted. Whereas H^* refers to the products and reactants each at zero pressure (ideal-gas state), H^0 refers to the products and reactants each in their standard state (usually 1 atm.). The two quantities $(\Delta H)_T^*$ and $(\Delta H)_T^0$ are identically equal only for gaseous systems in which $f^0 = 1$ atm. (ideal-gas state).

Effect of Pressure on K_f and K_a. The equilibrium ratio K_f is defined in terms of fugacities which take into account deviations from ideal-gas behavior. Yet, according to Eq. (4-406), the temperature dependence of K_f is related to the enthalpy of reaction in the ideal-gas state. It can therefore be anticipated that K_f is independent of pressure. If Eq. (4-401) is differentiated *term by term* with respect to pressure, holding the temperature constant, and remembering that

$$\left(\frac{d \ln \bar{f}_i}{dP}\right)_{T,x} = \frac{\bar{V}_i}{RT} \quad (4\text{-}340)$$

and
$$V = \sum_i n_i \bar{V}_i \quad (4\text{-}323)$$

it follows that
$$\left(\frac{d \ln K_f}{dP}\right)_T = 0 \quad (4\text{-}408)$$

A similar procedure in which Eq. (4-404) is differentiated term by term with respect to pressure at constant temperature can be utilized to obtain the pressure dependence of K_a. However, the result can be obtained immediately by converting Eq. (4-405) into logarithmic form and differentiating with respect to pressure at constant temperature to give, using the result of Eq. (4-408),

$$\left(\frac{d \ln K_a}{dP}\right)_T = \left[\frac{d \ln \dfrac{(f^0)_L{}^l (f^0)_Z{}^z}{(f^0)_C{}^c (f^0)_D{}^d}}{dP}\right]_T \quad (4\text{-}409)$$

It should be noted that, if the standard-state fugacity f^0 is defined to be independent of pressure, *i.e.*, at a fixed pressure, then, *and only then*,

$$\left(\frac{d \ln K_a}{dP}\right)_T = 0$$

If f^0 is defined so as to vary with the pressure such as at the pressure of the reaction, then and only then

$$\left(\frac{d \ln K_a}{dP}\right)_T = -\frac{V^0_{prod} - V^0_{react}}{RT} \quad (4\text{-}410)$$

where

$$V^0_{prod} - V^0_{react} = (lV_L^0 + zV_Z^0) - (cV_C^0 + dV_D^0)$$

An excellent example of the *convenience* of defining f^0 as a function of pressure is the liquid-phase hydration of ethylene to ethanol (Dodge, "Chemical Engineering Thermodynamics," pp. 505–508, McGraw-Hill, New York, 1944). For a 1½-fold variation in pressure, the K_a shows a variation of almost 5-fold.

Smoothing Equilibrium Data. Since it is very difficult to obtain consistent equilibrium data experimentally, a very useful method for checking the thermodynamic consistency of such data should be apparent from Eq. (4-406) or Eq. (4-407).

$$\left(\frac{d \ln K_f}{dT}\right)_P = \frac{H^*_{prod} - H^*_{react}}{RT^2} = \frac{\Delta H_T^*}{RT^2}$$

In order to integrate the above expression, the variation of the enthalpy or "heat" of reaction with temperature must be known. Recalling the definition of C_p, it follows that the variation of the heat of reaction with temperature is given by

$$\Delta H_T^* = \Delta H_{T_0}^* + \int_{T_0}^{T} (\Delta C_p^*)\, dT \quad (4\text{-}411)$$

where the T subscript refers to ΔH at temperature T and

$$\Delta C_p^* = l(\mathbf{C}_p)_L^* + z(\mathbf{C}_p)_Z^* - c(\mathbf{C}_p)_C^* - d(\mathbf{C}_p)_D^* \quad (4\text{-}412)$$

If the molal heat capacity of each substance in the ideal-gas state $\mathbf{C}_p^*$ is represented by an equation of the form

$$\mathbf{C}_p^* = \alpha + \beta T + \gamma T^2 \quad (4\text{-}413)$$

then integration of Eq. (4-411) yields

$$\Delta H_T^* = I_1 + (\Delta\alpha)T + \left(\frac{\Delta\beta}{2}\right)T^2 + \left(\frac{\Delta\gamma}{3}\right)T^3 \quad (4\text{-}14)$$

where $I_1 = \Delta H_{T_0}^* + (\Delta\alpha)T_0 + \left(\dfrac{\Delta\beta}{2}\right)T_0^2 + \left(\dfrac{\Delta\gamma}{3}\right)T_0^3$ (4-415)

and $\Delta\alpha = l\alpha_L + z\alpha_Z - c\alpha_C - d\alpha_D$

with similar expressions for $\Delta\beta$ and $\Delta\gamma$. Substituting Eq. (4-414) in Eq. (4-406), integrating without limits at constant pressure, and rearranging gives

$$\frac{I_1}{T} + I_2 = -R \ln K_f + (\Delta\alpha) \ln T + \left(\frac{\Delta\beta}{2}\right)T + \left(\frac{\Delta\gamma}{6}\right)T^2 = \sum \quad (4\text{-}416)$$

where I_2 is an integration constant. A plot of the right-hand side of Eq. (4-416), Σ, vs. $1/T$ should yield a straight line if the data are thermodynamically consistent (Dodge, "Chemical Engineering Thermodynamics," McGraw-Hill, pp. 489–492, New York, 1944).

Generalized Approximation for Non-ideal Gases Which Obey the Ideal-solution Law. It will be recalled that the definition of an ideal solution is given by

$$\bar{f}_i = x_i f_i \quad (4\text{-}363)$$

which can be written in terms of the generalized f/p correlation as

$$\bar{f}_i = x_i \frac{f_i}{P} P \quad (4\text{-}417)$$

An approximate equilibrium constant can be defined using the f/P correlation as follows:

$$K_f' = (K_f)_{\text{ideal solution}} = \frac{x_L{}^l x_Z{}^z\, (f/P)_L{}^l (f/P)_Z{}^z}{x_C{}^c x_D{}^d\, (f/P)_C{}^c (f/P)_D{}^d} P^{l+z-b-c} \quad (4\text{-}418)$$

Since, by definition, the partial pressure is given by

$$\bar{P}_i = x_i P$$

then Eq. (4-418) may be written as

$$K_f' = \frac{K_P K_f}{P} = K_P \frac{(f/P)_L{}^l (f/P)_Z{}^z}{(f/P)_C{}^c (f/P)_D{}^d} \tag{4-419}$$

Both K_P and $K_{f/P}$ vary with pressure, but K_f' is fairly constant with pressure up to moderately high pressures, indicating that the ideal-solution assumption is generally valid for gaseous mixtures.

Example 2. For the reaction

$$CO + 2H_2 \rightleftharpoons CH_3OH$$

the following expression has been reported for K_a:

$$-RT \ln K_a = -17{,}660 + 17.5T \ln T - 57.2T - 0.0136T^2$$

where T is in °K.

It is permissible to assume that the gaseous mixture forms an ideal solution and that the law of corresponding states applies.

a. Calculate the composition of the equilibrium mixture in mole per cent at 325°C. and 300 atm. (Assume that stoichiometric portions of CO and H_2 are used.)

b. How much heat, in calories per mole of methanol formed, would be given off if the above reaction were carried out irreversibly at 1 atm. pressure and 325°C.?

Critical Properties

	T_c, °K.	P_c, atm.	Molal heat capacities at 1 atm., cal./g.-mole °K.
CH_3OH	513	78.7	$2.0 + 0.03T$
CO	134	35.0	$6.5 + 0.001T$
H_2	33.1	12.8	$6.5 + 0.0009T$

Solution. For the gaseous system, the standard state for each component is $f^0 = 1$ atm.; therefore, $K_a = K_f$. The equilibrium composition can be obtained from the expression

$$K_f' = (K_f)_{\text{ideal solution}}$$

$$= \frac{x_{CH_3OH}}{x_{CO} x_{H_2}{}^2} \left[\frac{(f/P)_{CH_3OH}}{(f/P)_{CO} (f/P)_{H_2}{}^2} \right]^{P^{1-1-2}} \tag{4-420}$$

where x_i is the mole fraction of the ith component and P is the system pressure in atmospheres.

Assume as a basis initially 1 mole of CO. Let u represent the moles of CO converted to methanol. From a mole balance the equilibrium composition is

	Moles	Mole fraction x
CH_3OH	u	$\frac{u}{3-2u}$
CO	$1-u$	$\frac{1-u}{3-2u}$
H_2	$2-2u$	$\frac{2(1-u)}{3-2u}$

(4-421)

The fugacity coefficients f/P for CH_3OH and CO are obtained from Table 51, Hougen, Watson, and Ragatz. The f/P value for H_2 is obtained from Fig. 4-37 after adjusting the critical constants by adding 8°K. and 8 atm.

	T_c, °K.	P_c, atm.	P_r	T_r	f/p
CH_3OH	513	78.7	3.38	1.164	0.435
CO	134	35.0	8.56	4.46	1.16
H_2	(33 + 8)	(12.8 + 8)	14.4	14.55	1.12

The equilibrium constant K_f' at 325°C. can be obtained from the expression for K_a and is found to be

$$K_f' = K_a = 1.884(10^{-4})$$

Substituting the values in the expression for K_a [Eq. (4-420)].

$$\frac{u(3-2u)^2}{(1-u)^3} = 226.9$$

Solving for u by trial and error gives $u = 0.81$. The equilibrium composition at 325°C. and 300 atm. is

Part *a*

		Mole %
CH_3OH	$= \frac{0.81}{1.38}(100) =$	58.69
CO	$= \frac{0.19}{1.38}(100) =$	13.77
H_2	$= \frac{0.38}{1.38}(100) =$	27.54
		100.00

Part *b.* The heat given off if the reaction is carried out irreversibly is the enthalpy of reaction at 1 atm. and 325°C. From Eq. (4-407) $\Delta H^\circ_{\text{reaction}}$ is the enthalpy ("heat") of reaction at the standard-state pressure of 1 atm. Differentiating the expression for $\ln K_a$ with respect to temperature gives $\Delta H^\circ_{\text{reaction}} = -17{,}660 - 17.5T + 0.0136T^2$.

The "heat" evolved at 325°C. and 1 atm. is

$$\Delta H^\circ_{\text{reaction}} = Q_{\text{irrev}} = -23{,}270 \text{ cal./g.-mole } CH_3OH \text{ formed}$$

Chemical Equilibria for Simultaneous Reactions. In the previous discussion, consideration was given only to equilibrium for a single chemical reaction. When several reactions occur, the composition of the equilibrium mixture depends on the simultaneous equilibria of all possible reactions. In the chemical, petroleum, and metallurgical fields, it is more common to find simultaneous rather than single reactions. If many products are formed, such as in the cracking of hydrocarbons, the resulting composition cannot ordinarily be calculated because, strictly speaking, all possible reactions involved must be considered, which in some cases is impractical. However, in many processes the number of reactions of significance are reduced to a minimum by the application of selective catalysts or by considering only the products which occur in appreciable proportions. For such cases, the assumptions involved in the reduction of the number of reactions are implicit in all chemical-equilibria calculations. It is important therefore to recognize that these assumptions are valid only when they are supplemented by knowledge of the actual course of reaction.

For example, consider the reaction of carbon monoxide with hydrogen. The number of products theoretically possible is almost unlimited, as is evidenced industrially by the Fischer-Tropsch synthesis. It is possible, however, with the application of a selective catalyst to exclude essentially all products except methanol. Thus a pseudoequilibrium yield can be determined by considering only the reaction in Example 2 and ignoring all other reactions. Consequently calculations of the true equilibrium are of no practical importance, and therefore, equilibrium calculations are ordinarily limited to the relatively fast reactions.

Various procedures for the determination of the equilibrium composition for a set of simultaneous reactions have been reported in the literature. Only a few are listed here. [Hougen and Watson, "Chemical Process Principles," Part 2, Wiley, New York, 1950. Dodge, "Chemical Engineering Thermodynamics," McGraw-Hill, New York, 1944. Kandiner and Brinkley, *Ind. Eng. Chem.*, **42,** 850 (1950). Martin and Yachter, *Ind. Eng. Chem.*, **43,** 2446 (1951). Smith, *J. Am. Inst. Chem. Engrs.*, **5,** 26 (1959).] These procedures differ primarily in the method in which the set of simultaneous equilibrium and balance equations are solved, *i.e.*, by trial and error, graphical, matrix, relaxation, and other techniques.

The generalized procedure for equilibrium calculations

for simultaneous reactions can be illustrated by considering the following simple example (Wenner, "Thermochemical Calculations," pp. 223–227, McGraw-Hill, New York, 1941).

Example 3. Butadiene, an important raw material for the manufacture of certain types of synthetic rubber, may be produced by the dehydrogenation of 1-butene over chromium, molybdenum, and vanadium oxide catalysts.

Assume that the external conditions may be controlled so that the following reactions are the only ones occurring to any appreciable extent:

1: $C_4H_8 \rightleftharpoons C_4H_6 + H_2$
2: $C_4H_8 + H_2 \rightleftharpoons C_4H_{10}$
3: $C_4H_6 \rightleftharpoons 4C_{(S)} + 3H_2$

Compute the composition of the final equilibrium mixture for the following conditions:

a. Pressure = 1 atm.
b. Temperature = 600°C.
c. Ratio of moles of inert to moles of 1-butene feed = 0.05
d. Assume that 2 per cent of the original butenes fed to the reactor are irreversibly cracked to carbon and hydrogen according to reaction 3.

It is permissible to assume ideal-gas behavior.

Data:

For reaction 1

$$RT \ln K_a = -24{,}760 + 5T \ln T - 3.09T$$

For reaction 2

$$RT \ln K_a = 28{,}600 - 5T \ln T + 5.64T$$

where T is in °K.

Solution. Assume as a basis 1 mole of 1-butene feed. Let x represent the moles of 1-butene converted by reaction 1, y the moles converted by reaction 2, and z the moles of butadiene converted by reaction 3. According to condition *d* above, z equals 0.02 mole. This condition in effect reduces the number of simultaneous reactions which must be considered to reactions 1 and 2 only. At equilibrium, a mole balance for each constituent in the two reactions gives

$$\begin{aligned} \text{Moles } C_4H_8 &= 1 - x - y \\ \text{Moles } C_4H_6 &= x - 0.02 \\ \text{Moles } C_4H_{10} &= y \\ \text{Moles } H_2 &= x - y + 0.06 \\ \text{Moles of inerts} &= 0.05 \\ \text{Total moles} &= 1.09 + x - y \end{aligned}$$

At 600°C. the equilibrium constants are

$$(K_a)_1 = 3.43$$
$$(K_a)_2 = 9.55$$

Since the gases are ideal and the system pressure is 1.0 atm., substitution in Eq. (4-418) yields

$$(K_a)_1 = 3.43 = \frac{(x - 0.02)(x - y + 0.06)}{(1.09 + x - y)(1 - x - y)} \tag{4-422}$$

and $$(K_a)_2 = 9.55 = \frac{y(1.09 + x - y)}{(1 - x - y)(x - y + 0.06)} \tag{4-423}$$

The two equilibrium equations [Eqs. (4-422) and (4-423)] must be solved simultaneously to yield the equilibrium composition. Solving by a graphical technique

$$x = 0.714$$
$$y = 0.234$$

which gives the equilibrium composition:

Component	Mole %
C_4H_8	3.5
C_4H_6	46.9
C_4H_{10}	15.8
H_2	36.5
Inerts	3.3

It is readily apparent from the above example that, for systems with several reactions, the solution of the set of simultaneous equations becomes involved because of the large number of unknowns and also (in general) because of the non-linearity of the equations. Goldwasser has developed a method for determining the equilibrium composition regardless of the non-linearity in the system of equilibrium equations [Goldwasser, *Ind. Eng. Chem.*, **51**, 595 (1959)]. The method employed is a relaxation technique in which the initial estimated equilibrium concentrations are continually adjusted by means of a simple correction equation until the desired degree of accuracy is obtained. The method is primarily intended for use with a digital computer but is also applicable to hand calculation.

THIRD LAW OF THERMODYNAMICS

Nernst in 1906 and Planck in 1911, by examining experimental data of questionable precision, observed that the entropy of a substance appeared to approach zero at the absolute zero of temperature. They generalized this observation into what is essentially the third law of thermodynamics. It was, however, left to G. N. Lewis to give the first fully satisfactory statement of this principle (Lewis and Randall, "Thermodynamics and the Free Energy of Chemical Substances," 1st ed., McGraw-Hill, New York, 1923).

"*If the entropy of each element in some crystalline state be taken as zero at the absolute zero of temperature, every substance has a positive entropy; but at the absolute zero of temperature the entropy may become zero, and does so become in the case of perfect crystalline substances.*"

The third law implies that the change in entropy from absolute zero to any temperature T must be finite and positive, *i.e.*,

$$\int_0^T \frac{\mathbf{C}}{T}\, dT > 0 \tag{4-424}$$

where $\mathbf{C}$ represents the heat capacity, either $\mathbf{C}_p$ or $\mathbf{C}_v$. Thus the heat capacity must approach zero as the temperature decreases.

$$\lim_{T \to 0} \mathbf{C} = 0 \tag{4-425}$$

and the ratio $\mathbf{C}/T$ remains finite. According to the Debye theory, the heat capacity due to atomic vibrations is proportional to the cube of the absolute temperature, which leaves $\mathbf{C}/T$ proportional to T^2.

The third law implies that the entropy of a perfect crystalline solid is zero at the absolute zero of temperature regardless of the pressure or volume. From Eqs. (4-120), (4-122), (4-147), and (4-148),

$$\left(\frac{d\mathbf{S}}{dP}\right)_T = -\left(\frac{d\mathbf{V}}{dT}\right)_P = \beta\mathbf{V} \tag{4-122a}$$

$$\left(\frac{d\mathbf{S}}{d\mathbf{V}}\right)_T = \left(\frac{dP}{dT}\right)_V = -\frac{(d\mathbf{V}/dT)_P}{(d\mathbf{V}/dP)_T} = \frac{\beta\mathbf{V}}{\kappa\mathbf{V}} \tag{4-120a}$$

it follows that the coefficient of thermal expansion β, as shown in Eq. (4-122*a*), must also approach zero since $(d\mathbf{S}/dP)_T$ approaches zero with decreasing temperature. Experimental data indicate that β approaches zero asymptotically with zero slope.

Absolute Entropies. Absolute entropies are obtained by experimental measurements down to temperatures in the range 1° to 15°K. and extrapolation to absolute zero by the Debye theory of heat capacities for solids. On this basis, the entropy of a substance which is perfectly crystalline at absolute zero is given by the relation

$$\mathbf{S} = \int_0^T \frac{\mathbf{C}_p}{T}\, dT + \sum \Delta\mathbf{S}_{\text{trans}} \tag{4-426}$$

where ΔS_{trans} represents the entropy change of any transition, such as for liquids and gases the entropies of fusion and vaporization.

Several effects have been noted which indicate that randomness still exists in the state which is taken as the standard of zero entropy. Entropies of mixing of isotopes and of random orientation of nuclear spins are still present at temperatures of 1° to 15°K. and the extrapolation procedures do not consider these effects. In general, they are not important since their entropy contributions cancel in the calculation of ΔS for the changes which ordinarily arise.

Heat capacities for most of the elements and many compounds have been measured to very low temperatures and the absolute entropies calculated by Eq. (4-426). The entropies of substances are tabulated in standard-state values as is done for other thermodynamic properties. The standard state for solids and liquids is taken as the pure component at 1 atm. pressure. The standard state for entropies of gases is the hypothetical ideal-gas state at 1 atm. pressure. The standard-state values are indicated by the superscript zero. Kelly (*U.S. Bur. Mines Bull.* 447, 1950; and Kelley and King, *U.S. Bur. Mines Bull.* 592, 1960) has tabulated values of S^0 and $S_T{}^0 - S^0{}_{298}$ at 100°C. intervals for many elements and inorganic compounds.

The great utility of the third law is in the prediction of chemical equilibria and therefore the direction of chemical reactions. It provides a means of obtaining from heat-capacity measurements the absolute entropy of each substance in a reaction and therefore $\Delta S_T{}^0$ of reaction. $\Delta S_T{}^0$ of a reaction is defined similar to $\Delta G_T{}^0$ and $\Delta H_T{}^0$, *i.e.*, for any reaction as presented by Eq. (4-395),

$$\Delta S_T{}^0 = (S^0{}_{prod} - S^0{}_{react})_T = lS_L{}^0 + zS_Z{}^0 - cS_C{}^0 - dS_D{}^0 \quad (4\text{-}427)$$

where $\Delta S_T{}^0$ represents the change in entropy between the products and the reactants each in their standard state at the same temperature. If the absolute entropy values are known for each reactant and product in their standard state, then $\Delta S_T{}^0$ may be calculated and combined with $\Delta H_T{}^0$ to determine $\Delta G_T{}^0$ from the expression

$$\Delta G_T{}^0 = \Delta H_T{}^0 - T\,\Delta S_T{}^0 \quad (4\text{-}428)$$

The standard-state Gibbs free-energy change $\Delta G_T{}^0$ is related to the equilibrium constant K_a by Eq. (4-403); hence the third law provides a method for the prediction of chemical equilibrium.

ELECTRICAL EFFECTS

The intraconversion of chemical and electrical energy has widespread industrial applications in the production of metals and chemicals such as aluminum, magnesium, and bromine, and as a source of electrical energy (dry cells, storage batteries, fuel cells, etc.). An excellent discussion of the electrochemical industry, its fundamental principles, operating and design characteristics, and economics, is given by Mantell ("Electrochemical Engineering," 4th ed., McGraw-Hill, New York, 1960).

In order to determine the quantitative relationships for these electrochemical effects consider a reaction occurring in a galvanic cell operating at constant temperature and pressure. The maximum electrical work which the cell is capable of performing is, as for any process, the net reversible work

$$(W_{rev\ net})_{T,P} = W_{E\max} = -(\Delta G)_T = -(G_{prod} - G_{react})_T \quad (4\text{-}429)$$

Recalling from previous definitions, electrical energy is given by

$$W_E = -\int \mathcal{E}\, d(n\mathfrak{F}) \quad (4\text{-}430)$$

where $\mathcal{E}$ is the electromotive force of the cell, n the number of chemical equivalents transferred, and $\mathfrak{F}$ is the Faraday equivalent (approximately 96,500 coulombs per equivalent). For a reversible process which yields $(-n\mathfrak{F})$ coulombs, the e.m.f. is constant and positive. Integrating Eq. (4-430)

$$W_E = n\mathfrak{F}\mathcal{E} \quad (4\text{-}431)$$

Combining Eqs. (4-429) and (4-431) gives

$$(\Delta G)_T = (G_{prod} - G_{react})_T = -n\mathfrak{F}\mathcal{E} \quad (4\text{-}432)$$

From Eq. (4-432) and other derived identities, the entropy and irreversible heat of reaction (ΔS and ΔH) can be obtained from the e.m.f. and its temperature coefficient.

Example. If the reaction

$$MgO_{(sat.\ solution)} \rightarrow Mg_{(liq.)} + \tfrac{1}{2}O_{2(gas)}$$

takes place in a reversible galvanic cell with oxygen at 1 atm. pressure, the following voltages are required:

Voltage by Potentiometer	Temperature of Reaction, °C.
2.50	1150
2.60	960
2.75	690

1. Compute for the reaction at 1000°C. $(\Delta G)_T$, $(\Delta S)_T$, and $(\Delta H)_T$.
2. If the solution at 1000°C. were ideal and the concentration of MgO were one-half that of a saturated solution, what voltage would be required?
3. What is the pressure of O_2 required to make the reaction reversible, without applying an e.m.f., from a saturated solution at 1000°C.?

Solution. For the reaction above, the number of equivalents transferred per mole of Mg is given by the cathode or anode reactions

$$Mg^{++} + 2\epsilon \rightarrow Mg$$
$$O^{=} \rightarrow \tfrac{1}{2}O_2 + 2\epsilon$$

Hence two equivalents are transferred per mole of magnesium produced. A plot of the reversible voltage vs. the temperature gives, at 1000°C.,

$$\mathcal{E} = 2.578 \text{ volts}$$
$$\left(\frac{d\mathcal{E}}{dT}\right)_P = 0.000533 \text{ volt/°C.}$$

Part 1. The free energy of reaction is calculated from Eq. (4-432) as

$$(\Delta G)_T = -2(23{,}062)(-2.758) = 118{,}910 \text{ cal./g.-mole Mg}$$

From Eqs. (4-121) and (4-432), it follows that ΔS is given by

$$(\Delta S)_T = -\left(\frac{d(\Delta G)_T}{dT}\right)_P = n\mathfrak{F}\left(\frac{d\mathcal{E}}{dT}\right)_P \quad (4\text{-}433)$$

$$(\Delta S)_T = 2(23{,}062)(0.000533) = 24.58 \text{ cal./g.-mole Mg °K.}$$

In a similar manner, substituting Eqs. (4-432) and (4-433) in the expression $(\Delta H)_T = (\Delta G)_T + T(\Delta S)_T$ yields the Gibbs-Helmholtz relation

$$(\Delta H)_T = n\mathfrak{F}\left[-\mathcal{E} + T\left(\frac{d\mathcal{E}}{dT}\right)_P\right] \quad (4\text{-}434)$$

$$= 2(23{,}062)[2.578 + 1273(0.000533)]$$
$$(\Delta H)_T = 150{,}230 \text{ cal./g.-mole Mg}$$

Part 2. In a saturated solution of MgO in Mg (limited solubility) $\bar{f}_{MgO} = f_{MgO}$. If MgO follows a linear-solution law in its solubility range,

$$\bar{f} = x\left(\frac{f_{sat}}{x_{sat}}\right)$$

Thus, considering the reaction

$$MgO_{(50\%\ sat)} \rightarrow MgO_{(sat)}$$

$$(\Delta G)_T = RT \ln \left[\frac{\bar{f}_{sat}}{\bar{f}_{(50\%\ sat)}}\right] = RT \ln \left(\frac{x_{sat}}{x}\right)$$

$$= 1.987(1273) \ln 2 = 1752 \text{ cal./g.-mole MgO}$$

Combining this result with part 1, the free-energy change for the reaction

$$MgO_{(50\%\ sat)} \rightarrow Mg_{(liq)} + \tfrac{1}{2}O_{2(gas\ 1\ atm)}$$

is $(\Delta G)_T = -2(23{,}062)\mathcal{E} = 1752 + 118{,}910$

which yields $\mathcal{E} = -2.61$ volts

Part 3. In part 1 each product and reactant is in its standard state, *i.e.*, $\bar{a} = 1$ or $f^0 = f$ for MgO and Mg and $f^0 = 1$ atm. for O_2. Therefore, from Eq. (4-404),

$$(\Delta G)_T = RT \ln \frac{(\bar{a}_{O_2})^{1/2}\bar{a}_{Mg}}{\bar{a}_{MgO}} + 118{,}910$$

But $\bar{a}_{Mg} = \bar{a}_{MgO} = 1$ and $\Delta G = 0$ for the reversible process. Substituting into the above equation,

$$\ln \bar{a}_{O_2} = -\frac{118{,}910(2)}{1987(1273)}$$

which for ideal-gas behavior gives

$$P_{O_2} = (f^0\bar{a})_{O_2} = 1.75 \times 10^{-41} \text{ atm.}$$

A comprehensive discussion of the thermodynamics of electrical effects as applied to galvanic cells, electrolyte solutions, and polarizable materials can be found in Lewis and Randall ("Thermodynamics," 2d ed., McGraw-Hill, New York, 1961).

MISCELLANEOUS EFFECTS

It is beyond the scope of this treatment to present all the useful equations of thermodynamics; the emphasis thus far has been to develop and present only the more basic equations from which an unlimited number of specialized equations can be derived. However, there are several other important relations which merit inclusion.

The Effect of Inert-gas Pressure on the Vapor Pressure of a Pure Substance. Consider a pure liquid A in equilibrium with its own vapor at a particular temperature. If an inert gas, which does not dissolve in the liquid, is added to the vapor such as to increase the pressure in the vapor space (and consequently on the liquid) while holding the temperature constant, additional liquid will vaporize so as to maintain equilibrium according to

$$(d\mathbf{G}_A')_T = (d\bar{G}_A'')_T \tag{4-264a}$$

where $\bar{G}_A''$ represents the partial molal free energy of A in the vapor phase and $\mathbf{G}_A'$ the molal free energy in the pure-liquid phase. Therefore,

$$(\mathbf{V}_A'\, dP)_T = (RT\, d \ln \bar{f}_A'')_T \tag{4-435}$$

where P refers to the total pressure (inert gas plus vapor of A).

$$\left(\frac{d \ln \bar{f}_A''}{dP}\right)_T = \frac{\mathbf{V}_A'}{RT} \tag{4-435a}$$

where $\mathbf{V}_A'$ is the molal volume of the liquid at the total pressure P. Equation (4-435a) is rigorous and involves no assumptions. If ideal gases are assumed, then Eq. (4-435a) becomes the well-known Poynting or Le Châtelier equation.

$$\left(\frac{d\bar{P}_A''}{dP}\right)_{T,PV=RT} \cong \frac{(\mathbf{V}_A')_{atP}}{(\mathbf{V}_A'')_{at\bar{P}_A''}} \tag{4-435b}$$

where $\bar{P}_A''$ is the partial pressure of component A in the vapor phase at total pressure P. If the liquid is assumed to be incompressible then it is immaterial whether $\mathbf{V}_A'$ is evaluated at P or $\bar{P}_A''$. Equation (4-435b) can be integrated between the limits of the vapor pressure of the pure component $P_A{}^0$ and any arbitrary partial pressure of component A in the vapor mixture $\bar{P}_A''$ to give

$$\ln \frac{\bar{P}_A''}{P_A{}^0} \cong \frac{\mathbf{V}_A'}{RT}(P - P_A{}^0) \tag{4-435c}$$

The Effect of Radius of Curvature on the Vapor Pressure. Consider a small droplet of liquid in equilibrium with its own vapor. If the radius r of the droplet is varied at constant pressure and temperature by adding mass to the droplet, the change in the Gibbs free energy of the liquid is given by

$$(d\mathbf{G}_A')_{P,T} = 2\mathbf{V}'\gamma\, d\frac{1}{r} \tag{4-436}$$

if it is assumed that the surface tension γ does not vary with radius of curvature (not quite true; γ decreases with radius). Since

$$(d\mathbf{G}')_T = (d\mathbf{G}'')_T = \mathbf{V}''\, dP \tag{4-264b}$$

Combining Eqs. (4-436) and (4-264b) and integrating by assuming that the vapor behaves as an ideal gas,

$$RT \ln \frac{P}{P^0} \cong \frac{2\mathbf{V}'\gamma}{r} \tag{4-437}$$

where P represents the equilibrium pressure of the vapor surrounding a droplet of radius r, and P^0 represents the vapor pressure of the liquid above a flat surface (r = infinity). The effect of radius of curvature on the vapor pressure as given by Eq. (4-437) can be ignored in most cases for drops having a radius greater than 10^{-5} cm or 0.1 micron, which is substantially below the range of droplet sizes produced by even the most efficient atomization devices.

Preferential Adsorption of a Component at an Interface. In a binary liquid the composition of the components at the surface is different from the composition of the components in the bulk of the liquid. The concentration difference of component A can be obtained as follows:

$$dG = \bar{G}_A\, dm_A + \gamma\, d\sigma \tag{4-438}$$

where γ represents the surface tension of the binary liquid. By making use of the fact that dG is a perfect differential and applying the restriction that at equilibrium $dG = 0$,

$$(\Delta M)_A = -\int \left(\frac{d\gamma}{dG}\right) d\sigma \tag{4-439}$$

where $(\Delta M)_A$ represents the difference in composition between component A in the surface layer and the bulk of the liquid. It can be reasoned from Eq. (4-439) that, if the surface tension of the binary liquid increases with increased concentration of component A, then the composition of component A in the bulk of the liquid will be greater than at the surface, and vice versa. It is interesting to note that Eq. (4-439) can be obtained directly by inspection of Eq. (4-259).

IRREVERSIBLE THERMODYNAMICS

The principal basic equations of irreversible thermodynamics can be summarized as follows:

$$\frac{d_iS}{d\theta} = J_1X_1 + J_2X_2 \tag{4-440}$$

$$J_1 = L_{11}X_1 + L_{12}X_2 \tag{4-441}$$

$$J_2 = L_{21}X_1 + L_{22}X_2 \tag{4-442}$$

$$L_{12} = L_{21} \qquad \text{(Onsager relations)} \tag{4-443}$$

where $\frac{d_iS}{d\theta}$ represents the entropy production arising from irreversibilities

J_1, J_2 represent fluxes of energy and/or mass

X_1, X_2 represent the potential differences or driving forces which give rise to the fluxes J_1 and J_2

L_{11}, L_{12}, etc., are rate constants or phenomenological coefficients

For example, consider the simultaneous *irreversible* transfer of heat and mass. Then, if the driving force for heat transfer alone is taken as ΔT and for mass transfer alone as $\Delta\bar{G}$, Eqs. (4-441) and (4-442) can be specialized:

$$J_Q = L_{11}\frac{\Delta T}{T} + L_{12}\frac{\Delta\bar{G}}{T} \tag{4-441a}$$

$$J_M = L_{21}\frac{\Delta T}{T} + L_{22}\frac{\Delta\bar{G}}{T} \tag{4-442a}$$

Equations (4-441*a*) and (4-442*a*) state that the rates of simultaneous transfer of mass and heat are influenced by both potential differences, temperature and chemical potential. These equations are believed to hold true in general so long as the potential differences are small and the fluxes are properly selected to constitute *conjugate flows.*

Starting with Eq. (4-243), differentiating with respect to time, expanding to only the first-power terms in a Taylor series (since the potential differences are assumed to be small), applying the criterion that W_{max} is a perfect differential, and then setting $W_{max} = lw$, it can be shown that Eqs. (4-441*a*) and (4-442*a*) can be written as follows:

$$J_Q = \frac{\partial\, l\dot{w}^2}{\partial T^2}\frac{\Delta T}{T} + \frac{\partial^2\, l\dot{w}}{\partial T\,\partial\bar{G}}\frac{\Delta\bar{G}}{T} \tag{4-441b}$$

$$J_M = \frac{\partial^2\, l\dot{w}}{\partial\bar{G}\,\partial T}\frac{\Delta T}{T} + \frac{\partial^2\, l\dot{w}}{\partial\bar{G}^2}\frac{\Delta\bar{G}}{T} \tag{4-442b}$$

where $l\dot{w}$ represents the *rate* of production of lost work. The rate constants are then given by

$$L_{11} = \frac{\partial^2\, l\dot{w}}{\partial T^2} \tag{4-444}$$

$$L_{22} = \frac{\partial^2\, l\dot{w}}{\partial\bar{G}^2} \tag{4-445}$$

$$L_{12} = \frac{\partial^2\, l\dot{w}}{\partial T\,\partial\bar{G}} = \frac{\partial^2\, l\dot{w}}{\partial\bar{G}\,\partial T} = L_{21} \tag{4-446}$$

Equation (4-446) states that the Onsager relations given by Eq. (4-443) are a consequence of the fact that W_{max} is a perfect differential.

The fact that the coefficients L are third-order mixed partial derivatives (θ, T, G), coupled with the requirement that the potential differences must be small, probably accounts for the limited success thus far in verifying the above equations experimentally.

It is beyond the present scope to continue this interesting development into more specialized applications. It will suffice to say that the generalized treatment of the first and second laws as presented herein is adequate to handle irreversible thermodynamics. This approach differs from the conventional found in numerous references.

SECTION 5

FLUID AND PARTICLE MECHANICS

BY

Donald F. Boucher, Ph.D., Chemical Engineer, Engineering Research Laboratory, E. I. du Pont de Nemours & Co., Wilmington, Del.; Member, American Institute of Chemical Engineers, American Chemical Society, Society of Rheology; Registered Professional Engineer (Delaware).

George E. Alves, M.S., Chemical Engineer, Engineering Research Laboratory, E. I. du Pont de Nemours & Co., Wilmington, Del.; Member, American Institute of Chemical Engineers, American Society of Mechanical Engineers, American Chemical Society, Society of Rheology; Registered Professional Engineer (Delaware).

CONTENTS

FLUID STATICS AND PRESSURE MEASUREMENT

FLOW MEASUREMENT

FLUID DYNAMICS

PARTICLE DYNAMICS

FLUID STATICS AND PRESSURE MEASUREMENT

REFERENCES: *Fluid statics.* Dodge and Thompson, "Fluid Mechanics," McGraw-Hill, New York, 1937. Schoder and Dawson, "Hydraulics," McGraw-Hill, New York, 1934. Vennard, "Elementary Fluid Mechanics," 4th ed., Wiley, New York, 1961.

Pressure measurement, general. Addison, "Hydraulic Measurements," Wiley, New York, 1949. Considine, "Process Instruments and Controls Handbook," McGraw-Hill, New York, 1957. Dean, "Aerodynamic Measurements," Gas Turbine Laboratory, M.I.T., Cambridge, Mass., 1953. Diederichs and Andrae, "Experimental Mechanical Engineering," vol. I, Wiley, New York, 1930.

Pressure measurement, specific. For absolute pressures below 0.5 lb. force/sq. in. (about 1 in. Hg): Dushman and Lafferty, "Scientific Foundations of Vacuum Technique," 2d ed., Wiley, New York, 1962. Leck, "Pressure Measurement in Vacuum Systems," Institute of Physics, London, 1957. Pirani and Yarwood, "Principles of Vacuum Engineering," Reinhold, New York, 1961. For pressures over 20,000 lb. force/sq. in.: Bridgman, "The Physics of High Pressure," G. Bell, London, 1949.

DEFINITIONS

Fluid statics is concerned with the static properties and behavior of fluids. In the case of liquids, this subject is known as **hydrostatics**; in the case of gases it is called **pneumatics.**

A body of fluid in static equilibrium is being acted upon only by compressive forces. The intensity of this force, expressed in terms of pounds force per square inch or dynes per square centimeter, is known as **static pressure.** It is normal to any surface on which it acts, and at any given point it has the same magnitude irrespective of the orientation of the surface. This is one way of stating **Pascal's law.** Another way is that the pressure at any point in a fluid at rest acts with equal intensity in all directions.

Gage pressure is the difference between a given fluid pressure and that of the atmosphere. The readings of pressure gages are commonly positive gage pressures. A vacuum gage may be used to show negative gage pressures, *i.e.*, fluid pressures less than atmospheric. **Absolute pressure** is the true total pressure and is equal to gage pressure (taken with the proper sign) plus atmospheric pressure.

The term **static head** generally denotes the pressure in a fluid due to the head of fluid above the point in question. Its magnitude is given by the application of Newton's law (force = mass × acceleration). In the case of **liquids** (constant density), the static head p_h (lb. force/sq. ft.) is given by

$$p_h = \frac{h\rho g}{g_c} \qquad (5\text{-}1)$$

where h = head of liquid above the point, ft.; ρ = liquid density, lb./cu. ft.; g = local acceleration due to gravity, ft./sec.^{2}; g_c = dimensional constant, 32.17 (lb.) (ft.)/(lb. force)(sec.^{2}).

Dynamic pressure is the difference between **impact pressure** and **static head.** In the case of a moving fluid, a physical interpretation of the gage readings cannot be given without specific knowledge as to the position and orientation of the pressure tap relative to the flow. Specifications of pressure or piezometer taps are given on p. 5-5.

LIQUID-COLUMN MANOMETERS

The **height, or head** [Eq. (5-1)], to which a fluid rises in an open vertical tube attached to an apparatus containing a liquid is a direct measure of the pressure at the point of attachment and is frequently used to show the level of liquids in tanks and vessels. This same principle can be applied with U-tube gages (Fig. 5-1*a*) and equivalent devices (such as that shown in Fig. 5-1*b*) to measure

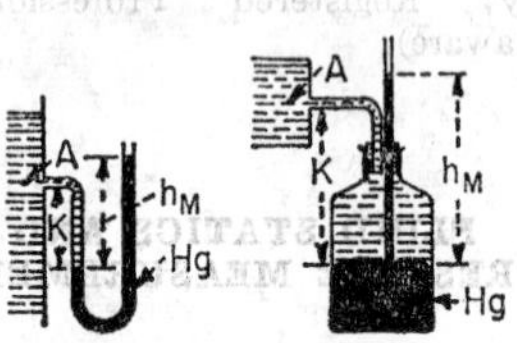

FIG. 5-1. Open manometers.

pressure in terms of the head of a fluid other than the one under test. Most of these gages may be used either as **open** or as **differential manometers.** The manometric fluid that constitutes the measured liquid column of these gages may be any liquid immiscible with the fluid under pressure. For high vacuums or for high pressures and large pressure differences, the gage liquid is a high-density liquid, generally mercury; for low pressures and small pressure differences, a low-density liquid (*e.g.*, alcohol, water, carbon tetrachloride) is used.

The **open U-tube** (Fig. 5-1*a*) and the **open gage** (Fig. 5-1*b*) each show a reading h_M ft. of manometric fluid. If the interface of the manometric fluid and the fluid of which the pressure is wanted is K ft. below the point of attachment A, ρ_A lb./cu. ft. is the density of the latter fluid at A, and ρ_M lb./cu. ft. is that of the manometric fluid, then gage pressure p_A lb. force/sq. ft. at A is

$$p_A = (h_M\rho_M - K\rho_A)\frac{g}{g_c} \qquad (5\text{-}2)^*$$

where g = local acceleration due to gravity, approximately 32.2 ft./sec.^{2}; g_c = dimensional constant, 32.17 (ft.)(lb.)/(lb. force)(sec.^{2}). The head h_A at A as feet of the fluid at that point is

$$h_A = h_M\left(\frac{\rho_M}{\rho_A}\right) - K \qquad (5\text{-}3)^*$$

When a gas pressure is measured, unless it is very high, ρ_A is so much smaller than ρ_M that the terms involving K in the above formulas are negligible.

The **differential U-tube** (Fig. 5-2) shows the pressure difference between taps A and B to be

$$p_A - p_B = [h_M(\rho_M - \rho_A) + K_A\rho_A - K_B\rho_B]\frac{g}{g_c} \qquad (5\text{-}4)$$

* The line leading from the pressure tap to the gage is assumed to be filled with fluid of the same density as that in the apparatus at the location of the pressure tap; if this is not the case, ρ_A is the density of the fluid actually filling the gage line, and the value given for h_A must be multiplied by ρ_A/ρ, where ρ is the density of the fluid whose head is being measured.

where h_M ft. is the difference in height of the manometric fluid in the U-tube; K_A and K_B ft. are the vertical distances of the upper surface of the manometric fluid above A and B, respectively; ρ_A and ρ_B lb./cu. ft. are the densities of the fluids at A and B, respectively, and ρ_M lb./cu. ft. is the density of the manometric fluid. If either pressure tap is above the higher level of manometric fluid, the corresponding K is taken to be negative. Valve D, which is kept closed when the gage is in use, is used to vent off gas which may accumulate at these high points.

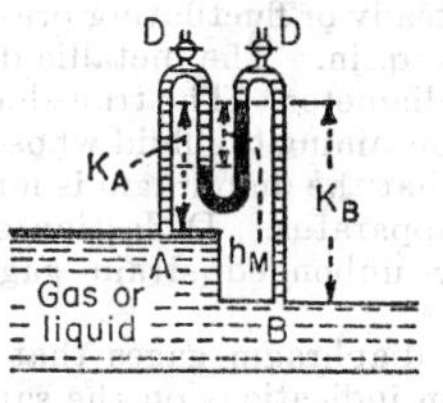

FIG. 5-2. Differential U-tube.

The **inverted differential U-tube,** in which the manometric fluid may be a gas or a light liquid, can be used to measure liquid pressure differentials, especially for the flow of slurries where solids tend to settle out. Additional details on the use of this manometer can be obtained from Addison, *op. cit.*, p. 19.

Closed U-tubes (Fig. 5-3) using mercury as the manometric fluid serve to measure directly the absolute pressure p (lb. force/sq. ft. abs.) of a fluid, provided that the space between the closed end and the mercury is substantially a perfect vacuum.

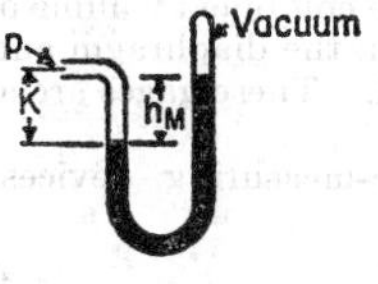

FIG. 5-3. Closed U-tube.

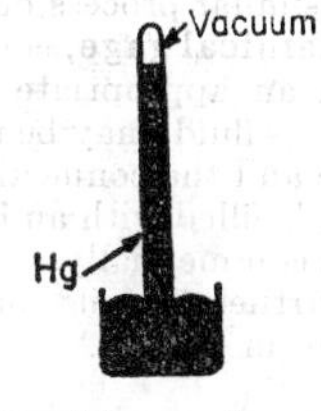

FIG. 5-4. Mercury barometer.

The **mercury barometer** (Fig. 5-4) indicates directly the absolute pressure of the atmosphere in terms of height of the mercury column. Normal (standard) barometric pressure is 760 mm. mercury (at 0°C.) by definition. Equivalents of this pressure in other units are 29.921 in. Hg (at 0°C.); 14.696 lb. force/sq. in.; and 1 atm. For those cases where barometer readings, when expressed by the height of a mercury column, must be corrected to standard temperature (usually 0°C.), appropriate temperature correction factors are given in Hodgman, Weast, and Selby, "Handbook of Chemistry and Physics," 43d ed., pp. 2518–2522, Chemical Rubber, Cleveland, 1961–1962.

Tube Size for Manometers. To avoid capillary error, tube diameter should be sufficiently large and the manometric fluids of such densities that the effect of capillarity is negligible in comparison with the gage reading. Minimum inside diameters consonant with good practice are ¼ in. for U-tubes and ½ in. for devices such as that shown in Fig. 5-1*b* (see A.S.M.E. Power Test Code PTC 19.2; 5, 1942). Smaller diameters are generally permissible for U-tubes because the capillary displacement in one leg tends to cancel that in the other.

The capillary rise in feet in a small vertical open tube of circular cross section dipping into a pool of liquid is given by

$$h = \frac{4\sigma \cos \theta}{gD(\rho_1 - \rho_2)} \tag{5-5}$$

Here σ = surface tension, lb. force/ft. [(dynes/cm.) times (6.85×10^{-5})]; D = inside diameter, ft.; ρ_1 and ρ_2 are the densities in lb./cu. ft. of the liquid and gas (or light liquid), respectively; g = local acceleration due to gravity, approximately 32.2 ft./sec.²; θ is the contact angle subtended by the heavier fluid. For most organic liquids and water, the contact angle θ is zero against glass, provided the glass is wet with a film of the liquid; for mercury against glass, θ = 140 deg. ("International Critical Tables," vol. IV, pp. 434–435, McGraw-Hill, New York, 1928). For further discussion of contact angles and an extensive bibliography, see Partington, "An Advanced Treatise on Physical Chemistry," vol. 2, pp. 166–168, Longmans, London, 1951.

MULTIPLYING GAGES

To attain the requisite precision in measurement of small pressure differences by liquid-column manometers, means must often be devised to magnify the readings. Of the schemes that follow, the second and third may give tenfold multiplication; the fourth as much as thirtyfold. In general, the greater the multiplication, the more elaborate must be the precautions in the use of the gage if the gain in precision is not to be illusory.

1. **Change of Manometric Fluid.** In open manometers, choose a fluid of lower density. In differential manometers, choose a fluid such that the difference between its density and that of the fluid being measured is as small as possible.

2. **Inclined U-Tube** (Fig. 5-5). If the reading R ft. is taken as shown and R_0 ft. is the zero reading, by making the substitution $h_M = (R - R_0) \sin \theta$, the formulas of preceding paragraphs give $(p_A - p_B)$ when

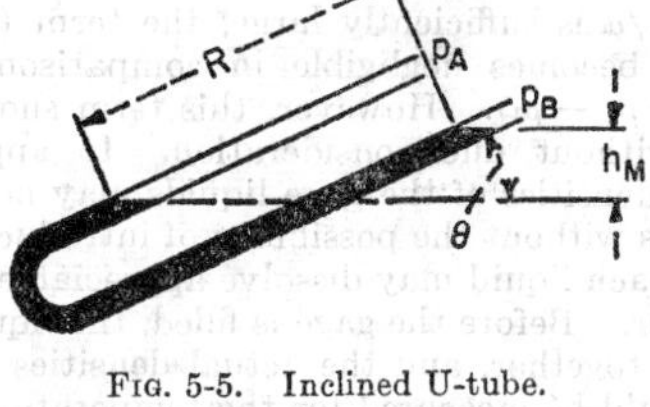

FIG. 5-5. Inclined U-tube.

the corresponding upright U-tube is replaced by one inclined. For precise work, the gage should be calibrated because of possible variations in tube diameter and slope.

3. **The Draft Gage** (Fig. 5-6). Commonly used for low gas heads, this has for one leg of the U a reservoir of much larger bore than the tubing that forms the inclined

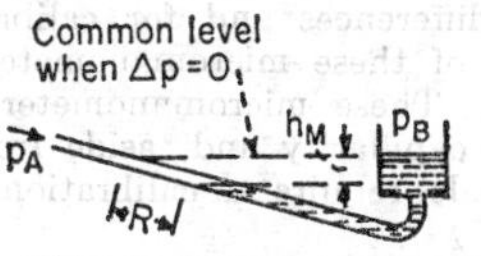

FIG. 5-6. Draft gage.

leg. Hence variations of level in the inclined tube produce little change in level in the reservoir. Although h_M may be readily computed in terms of reading R and the dimensions of the tube, calibration of the gage (p. 5-4) is preferable; often the changes of level in the reservoir not negligible, and also variations in tube diameter may introduce serious error into the computation. Commercial gages are often provided with a scale giving h_M directly in inches of water (sometimes expressed as in. WG), provided a particular liquid (often not water) fills the tube; failure to appreciate that the scale is incorrect unless the gage is filled with the specified liquid is a frequent source of error. If the scale reads correctly when density of the gage liquid is ρ_0, then the reading must be multiplied by ρ/ρ_0 if density of the fluid actually in use is ρ.

4. **Two-fluid U-tube** (Fig. 5-7). This is a highly sensitive device for measuring small gas heads. Let A sq. ft. be the cross-sectional area of each of the reservoirs,

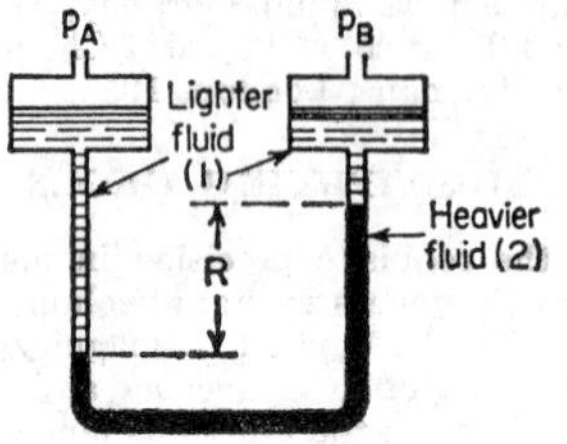

FIG. 5-7. Two-fluid U-tube.

a sq. ft. that of the tube forming the U; let ρ_1 be the density of the lighter fluid, ρ_2 that of the heavier fluid, both in lb./cu. ft.; and if R ft. is the reading and R_0 ft. is its value with zero pressure difference, then the pressure difference in lb. force/sq. ft. is

$$p_A - p_B = (R - R_0)\left(\rho_2 - \rho_1 + \frac{a}{A}\rho_1\right)\frac{g}{g_c} \qquad (5\text{-}6)$$

where g = local acceleration due to gravity, approximately 32.2 ft./sec.^{2}; g_c = dimensional constant, 32.17 (ft.)(lb.)/(lb. force)(sec.^{2}).

When A/a is sufficiently large, the term $(a/A)\ \rho_1$ in Eq. (5-6) becomes negligible in comparison with the difference $(\rho_2 - \rho_1)$. However, this term should not be omitted without due consideration. In applying Eq. (5-6), the densities of the gage liquids may not be taken from tables without the possibility of introducing serious error, for each liquid may dissolve appreciable quantities of the other. Before the gage is filled, the liquids should be shaken together, and the actual densities of the two layers should be measured for the temperature at which the gage is to be used. When high magnification is being sought, the U-tube may have to be enclosed in a constant-temperature bath so that $(\rho_2 - \rho_1)$ may be accurately known. In general, if highest accuracy is desired, the gage should be calibrated.

Several **micromanometers,** based on the liquid-column principle, and of extreme precision and sensitivity, have been developed for measuring minute gas-pressure differences and for calibrating low-range gages. Some of these micromanometers are available commercially. These micromanometers are free from errors due to capillarity and, aside from checking the micrometer scale, require no calibration.

MECHANICAL PRESSURE GAGES

The **Bourdon-tube gage** indicates pressure by the amount of flection under internal pressure of an oval tube bent in an arc of a circle and closed at one end. These gages are commercially available for all pressures below atmospheric and for pressures up to 100,000 lb. force/sq. in. above atmospheric.

A **diaphragm gage** depends for its indication on the deflection of a diaphragm, usually metallic, when subjected to a difference of pressure between the two faces. These gages are available for the same general purposes as Bourdon gages but are not usually employed for high pressures. The aneroid barometer is a type of diaphragm gage.

Small **pressure transducers with flush-mounted diaphragms** are commercially available for the measurement of either steady or fluctuating pressures up to about 15,000 lb. force/sq. in. The metallic diaphragms are as small as 3/16 in. diameter. The transducer is mounted on the apparatus containing the fluid whose pressure is to be measured such that the diaphragm is flush with the inner surface of the apparatus. Deflection of the diaphragm is measured by unbonded strain gages and recorded electrically.

Bourdon and diaphragm gages that show both pressure and vacuum indications on the same dial are called **compound gages.**

Conditions of Use. Bourdon tubes should not be exposed to temperatures over about 150°F. (about 65°C.), because above this temperature the tubes lose part of their elasticity. When the pressure of a hotter fluid is to be measured, some type of liquid seal should be used to keep the hot fluid from the tube. In using either a Bourdon or diaphragm gage to measure gas pressure, if the gage is below the pressure tap of the apparatus so that liquid can collect in the lead, the gage reading will be too high by an amount equal to the hydrostatic head of the accumulated liquid.

For measuring pressures of corrosive fluids, slurries and similar process fluids which may foul Bourdon tubes, a **chemical gage,** consisting of a Bourdon gage equipped with an appropriate flexible diaphragm to seal off the process fluid, may be used. The combined volume of the tube and the connection between the diaphragm and the tube is filled with an inert liquid. These gages are available commercially.

Further details on pressure-measuring devices are found in Sec. 22.

CALIBRATION OF GAGES

Simple **liquid-column manometers** do not require calibration if they are so constructed as to minimize errors due to capillarity (see p. 5-3). If the scales used to measure the readings have been checked against a standard, the accuracy of the gages depends solely upon the precision of determining the position of the liquid surfaces. Hence liquid-column manometers are primary standards used to calibrate other gages.

For **high pressures** and, with commercial mechanical gages, even for quite moderate pressures, a dead-weight gage (see Addison, *op. cit.*, p. 28, or Diederichs and Andrae, *op. cit.*, p. 97) is commonly used as the primary standard because it is safer and more convenient than use of manometers. When manometers are used as high-pressure standards, an extremely high mercury column may be avoided by connecting a number of the usual U-tubes in series. Multiplying gages are standardized by comparing them with a micromanometer. Procedure in the calibration of a gage consists merely of connecting it, in parallel with a standard gage, to a reservoir wherein constant pressure may be maintained. Readings of the unknown gage are then made for various reservoir pressures as determined by the standard.

FLOW MEASUREMENT

References: Addison, "Hydraulic Measurements," 2d ed., Wiley, New York, 1949. A.S.M.E. Research Committee on Fluid Meters Report, "Fluid Meters—Their Theory and Application," 5th ed., 1959. A.S.M.E. Power Test Codes, Part 5, "Measurement of Quantity of Materials," 1959. Considine, "Process Instruments and Controls Handbook," McGraw-Hill, New York, 1957. Dean, "Aerodynamic Measurements," M.I.T., Cambridge, Mass., 1953. Diederichs and Andrae, "Experimental Mechanical Engineering," vol. I, Wiley, New York, 1930. Goldstein, "Modern Developments in Fluid Dynamics," Oxford, London, 1938. Ladenburg, Lewis, Pease, and Taylor, "Physical Measurements in Gas Dynamics and Combustion," Princeton University Press, Princeton, N.J., 1954. Ower, "The Measurement of Air Flow," Chapman & Hall, London, 1949. Rhodes, "Industrial Instruments for Measurement and Control," McGraw-Hill, New York, 1941. Schoder and Dawson, "Hydraulics," McGraw-Hill, New York, 1934.

This subsection summarizes the techniques available for measuring static pressures, point velocities, and flow rates of flowing fluids. Coverage is generally limited to the primary, or actuating, elements. Secondary elements (*e.g.*, pressure gages or manometers) are, for a given primary device, more or less interchangeable. They are described elsewhere in this section and in Sec. 22.

STATIC PRESSURE

Local Static Pressure. In a moving fluid, the local static pressure is equal to the pressure on a surface which moves with the fluid, or to the normal pressure (for Newtonian fluids) on a stationary surface which parallels the flow. The pressure on such a surface is measured by making a small hole perpendicular to the surface and connecting the opening to a pressure-sensing element (Fig. 5-8*a*). The hole is known as a piezometer opening or pressure tap.

Measurement of local static pressure is frequently difficult or impractical. If the channel is so small that introduction of any solid object disturbs the flow pattern

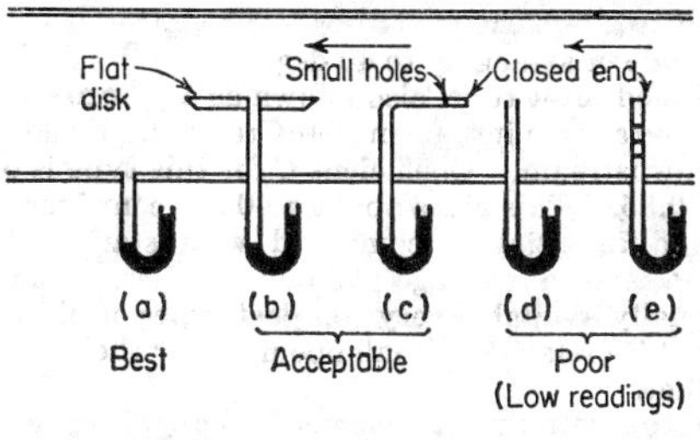

Fig. 5-8. Measurement of static pressure.

and increases the velocity, there will be a reduction and redistribution of the static pressure. If the flow is in straight parallel lines, aside from the fluctuations of normal turbulence, the **flat disk** (Fig. 5-8*b*) and the **bent tube** (Fig. 5-8*c*) give satisfactory results when properly aligned with the stream. Slight misalignments can cause serious errors. Diameter of the disk should be twenty times its thickness and forty times the static opening; the face must be flat and smooth, with the knife-edges made by beveling the underside. The piezometer tube, such as that in Fig. 5-8*c*, should have openings with size and spacing as specified for a pitot tube (Fig. 5-10).

Readings given by open straight tubes (Fig. 5-8*d*) are too low. Readings of closed tubes oriented perpendicular to the axis of the stream and provided with side openings (Fig. 5-8*e*) may be low by as much as two velocity heads.

Average Static Pressure. In most cases, the object of a static-pressure measurement is to obtain a suitable average value for substitution in Bernoulli's theorem or in an equivalent flow formula. This can be done simply only when the flow is in straight lines parallel to the confining walls, such as in straight ducts at sufficient distance downstream from bends or other disturbances. For such streams, the sum of static head and gravitational potential head is the same at all points in a cross section taken perpendicular to the axis of flow. Thus the exact location of a piezometer opening about the periphery of such a cross section is immaterial, provided its elevation is known. However, in stating the static pressure, the custom is to give the value at the elevation corresponding to the center line of the stream.

With flow in curved passages or with swirling flow, determination of a true average static pressure is, in general, impractical. In metering, straightening vanes are often placed upstream of the pressure tap to eliminate swirl.

Specifications for Piezometer Taps. The size of a static opening should be small compared with the diameter of the pipe and yet large compared with the scale of surface irregularities. For reliable results, it is essential that (1) the surface in which the hole is made be substantially smooth and parallel to the flow for some distance on either side of the opening, and (2) the opening be flush with the surface and possess no "burr" or other irregularity around its edge. Rounding of the edge is often employed to ensure absence of a burr. Pressure readings will be high if the tap is inclined upstream, is rounded excessively on the upstream side, has a burr on the downstream side, or has an excessive countersink or recess. Pressure readings will be low if the tap is inclined downstream, is rounded excessively on the downstream side, has a burr on the upstream side, or protrudes into the flow stream. Errors resulting from these faults can be large.

Recommendations for **pressure-tap dimensions,** as given by the American Society of Mechanical Engineers and the American Gas Association, are summarized in Table 5-1. The length of a pressure-tap opening prior to any enlargement in the tap channel should be at least two tap diameters, preferably three or more.

Table 5-1. Pressure-tap Holes

Nominal inside pipe diam., in.	Max. diam. of pressure tap, in.	Radius of hole-edge rounding, in.
1	1/8	<1/64
2	1/4	1/64
3	3/8	1/64–1/32
4	1/2	1/32
8	1/2	1/32–1/16
16	3/4	1/32–1/16

A **piezometer ring** is a toroidal manifold into which are connected several side-wall static taps located around the perimeter of a common cross section. Its intent is to give an average pressure, in case differences in pressure exist around the perimeter other than those due to static head. However, there is generally no assurance that a true average is provided thereby. Principal advantage of the ring is that use of several holes in place of a single hole reduces the possibility of completely plugging the static openings.

Flush-mounted diaphragm pressure-sensing elements are used primarily with fluids which degrade or decompose upon standing. They are discussed in more detail in Sec. 22.

VELOCITY METERS

Pitot tubes measure local or point velocities by measuring the difference between impact pressure and static pressure. The pitot tube shown in Fig. 5-9 consists of an impact tube whose opening faces directly into the stream to measure impact pressure, plus one or more

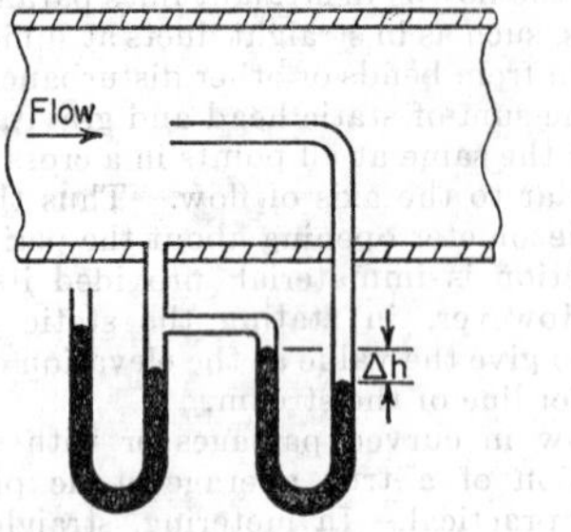

FIG. 5-9. Pitot tube with side-wall static tap.

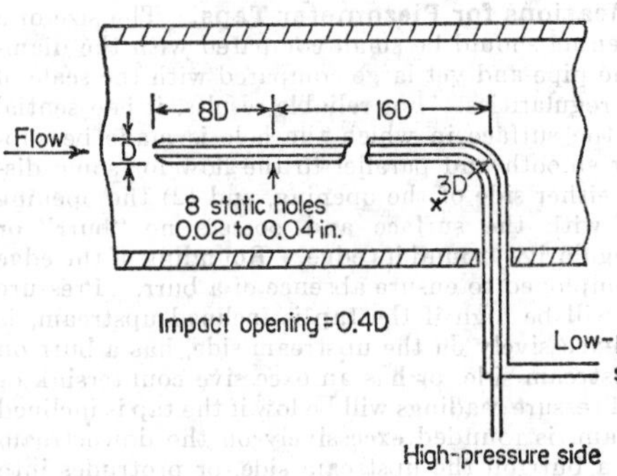

FIG. 5-10. Pitot-static tube.

side-wall taps to measure local static pressure. The combined pitot-static tube shown in Fig. 5-10 consists of a jacketed impact tube with one or more rows of holes in the jacket to measure the static pressure. Velocity V_0 (ft./sec.) at the point where the tip is located is given by

$$V_0 = C\sqrt{2g_c\,\Delta h} = C\sqrt{2g_c(p_i - p_0)/\rho_0} \qquad (5\text{-}7)$$

where C = coefficient, dimensionless; g_c = dimensional constant, 32.17 (ft.)(lb.)/(lb. force)(sec.^{2}); Δh = differential pressure as shown in Fig. 5-9, expressed in feet of fluid flowing [(ft.)(lb. force)/lb.]; p_i = impact pressure, lb. force/sq. ft.; p_0 = local static pressure, lb. force/sq. ft.; ρ_0 = fluid density, lb./cu. ft., measured at pressure p_0 and the local temperature. With gases at velocities above 200 ft./sec., compressibility becomes important, and the following equation should be used:

$$V_0 = C\sqrt{\frac{2g_ck}{k-1}\left(\frac{p_0}{\rho_0}\right)\left[\left(\frac{p_i}{p_0}\right)^{(k-1)/k} - 1\right]} \qquad (5\text{-}8)$$

where k is the ratio of specific heat at constant pressure to that at constant volume. (See A.S.M.E. Research Report on Fluid Meters, *op. cit.*, p. 84.) Coefficient C is usually close to 1.00 ($\pm$0.01) for simple pitot tubes (Fig. 5-9) and generally ranges between 0.98 and 1.00 for pitot-static tubes (Fig. 5-10).

There are certain **limitations** on the range of usefulness of pitot tubes. With **gases,** the differential is very small at low velocities; *e.g.*, at 15 ft./sec. the differential is only about 0.045 in. water for air at 1 atm., which represents a lower limit for 1 per cent error even when one uses a micromanometer with a precision of 0.001 in. water. Equation (5-8) does not apply for Mach numbers greater than 0.7, because of the interference of shock waves. For supersonic flow, local Mach numbers can be calculated from a knowledge of the impact and true static pressures; see Ladenburg *et al.*, *op. cit.*, pp. 111–112.

With **liquids** at low velocities, the effect of Reynolds number upon the coefficient is important. The coefficients are appreciably less than unity for Reynolds numbers less than 500 for pitot tubes and for Reynolds numbers less than 2300 for pitot-static tubes [see Folsom, *Trans. Am. Soc. Mech. Engrs.*, **78**, 1447–1460 (1956)]. Reynolds numbers here are based on the probe outside diameter. Operation at low Reynolds numbers requires prior calibration of the probe.

The pitot-static tube is more sensitive to **yaw** or **angle of attack** than is the simple pitot tube because of the sensitivity of the static taps to orientation. The error involved is strongly dependent upon the exact probe dimensions. In general, angles greater than 10 deg. should be avoided if the velocity error is to be 1 per cent or less.

Disturbances upstream of the probe can cause large errors, in part because of the turbulence generated and its effect on the static-pressure measurement. A calming section of at least 50 pipe diameters is desirable. If this is not possible, the use of straightening vanes or a honeycomb is advisable.

Effect of **pulsating flow** on pitot-tube accuracy is treated by Ower, *op. cit.*, pp. 75–77. For sinusoidal velocity fluctuations of $\pm$25 per cent about the mean, the indicated velocity would be 1.5 per cent high, and for $\pm$50 per cent, it would be 6 per cent high. Thus, in general, to avoid errors greater than 1 per cent, pulsations greater than $\pm$20 per cent should be damped.

Special Tubes. A variety of special forms of the pitot tube have been evolved. Folsom (*loc. cit.*) gives a description of many of these special types, together with a comprehensive bibliography. Included therein are the impact tube for **boundary-layer** measurements and **shielded total-pressure tubes.** The latter are insensitive to angle of attack up to 40 deg.

A reversed pitot tube, also known as a **pitometer,** has one pressure opening facing upstream and the other facing downstream. Coefficient C for this type is on the order of 0.85. This gives about a 40 per cent increase in pressure differential as compared with standard pitot tubes and is an advantage at low velocities. There are commercially available very compact types of pitometers which require relatively small openings for their insertion into a duct.

The **pitot-venturi** flow element is capable of developing a pressure differential five to ten times that of a standard pitot tube. This is accomplished by employing a pair of concentric venturi elements in place of the pitot probe. The low-pressure tap is connected to the throat of the inner venturi which, in turn, discharges into the throat of the outer venturi. For a discussion of performance and application of this flow element, see Stoll [*Trans. Am. Soc. Mech. Engrs.*, **73**, 963–969 (1951)].

Anemometers. An anemometer may be any instrument for measurement of gas velocity, *e.g.*, a pitot tube, but usually the term refers to one of the types below.

The **vane anemometer** is a delicate revolution counter with jeweled bearings, actuated by a small windmill (usually 3 to 4 in. diameter) constructed of flat, or slightly curved, radially disposed vanes. Gas velocity is determined by using a stop watch to find the time interval required to pass a given number of feet of gas as indicated by the counter. The velocity so obtained is inversely proportional to gas density. If the original calibration was carried out in a gas of density ρ_0 and the density of the gas stream being metered is ρ_1, the true gas velocity can be found as follows: From the calibration curve for the instrument, find $V_{t,0}$ corresponding to the quantity $V_m \sqrt{\rho_1/\rho_0}$, where V_m = measured velocity. Then the actual velocity $V_{t,1}$ is equal to $V_{t,0} \sqrt{\rho_0/\rho_1}$. In general, when working with air, the effects of atmospheric-density changes can be neglected for all velocities above 5 ft./sec. In all cases, care must be taken to hold the anemometer well away from one's body or from any object not normally present in the stream.

The instrument has a useful velocity range of about 2 to 40 ft./sec. Below about 2 ft./sec., accuracy is poor because of the increased effect of bearing friction. Velocities over about 40 ft./sec. impose an excessive strain on the standard instrument. Vane anemometers are sensitive to shock and cannot be used in corrosive atmospheres. Therefore, accuracy is questionable unless a recent calibration has been made and the history of the instrument subsequent to calibration is known. For additional information, see Ower, *op. cit.*, Chap. VII.

The term **current meter** is applied to any of a variety of mechanical devices for measuring the velocity of liquids in open and closed channels. Most of these meters are substantially the same in principle as the vane anemometer, but their construction is more rugged. For further information, see Diederichs and Andrae, *op. cit.*, pp. 490–496; Addision, *op. cit.*, pp. 89–98; Holzbach, "Instruments for Measurement and Control," pp. 153–157, Reinhold, New York, 1955.

A special **swinging-vane** type of velocity meter is produced commercially. It is especially adapted to ventilation work and to the measurement of moderately low velocities—down to 50 ft./min. For information, see "A.S.H.R.A.E. Guide and Data Book," p. 245, and Manufacturers Catalog Data Section, p. 237, American Society of Heating, Refrigerating, and Air-conditioning Engineers, New York, 1961.

The **hot-wire anemometer** consists essentially of an electrically heated, fine wire (generally platinum) exposed to the gas stream whose velocity is being measured. An increase in fluid velocity, other things being equal, increases the rate of heat flow from the wire to the gas, thereby tending to cool the wire and alter its electrical resistance. In a constant-current anemometer, gas velocity is determined by measuring the resulting wire resistance; in the constant-resistance type, gas velocity is determined from the current required to maintain the wire temperature, and thus the resistance, constant. Difference in the two types is primarily in the electric circuits and instruments employed.

The hot-wire anemometer can, with suitable calibration, accurately measure velocities from about 0.5 ft./sec. to supersonic velocities and detect velocity fluctuations with frequencies up to 200,000 cycles/sec. Fairly rugged, inexpensive units can be built for the measurement of mean velocities in the range of 0.5 to 100 ft./sec. More elaborate, compensated units are commercially available for use in unsteady flow and turbulence measurements. The hot-wire anemometer is treated in considerable detail in Dean, *op. cit.*, Chap. VI, and in Ladenburg *et al.*, *op. cit.*, Art. F-2.

The hot-wire anemometer can be modified for liquid measurements, although difficulties are encountered because of bubbles and dirt adhering to the wire. See Stevens, Borden, and Strausser [David Taylor Model Basin Report 953, December, 1956]; Middlebrook and Piret [*Ind. Eng. Chem.*, **42**, 1511–1513 (1950)]; Piret *et al.* [*Ind. Eng. Chem.*, **39**, 1098–1103 (1947)].

The **heated-thermocouple anemometer** measures gas velocity from the cooling effect of the gas stream flowing across the hot junctions of a thermopile supplied with constant electrical power input. Alternate junctions are maintained at ambient temperature, thus compensating for the effect of ambient temperature. For details see Bunker [*Proc. Instr. Soc. Am.*, **9**, Paper 54-43-2 (1954)].

Traversing for Mean Velocity. Mean velocity in a duct can be obtained by dividing the cross section into a number of equal areas, finding the local velocity at a representative point in each, and averaging the results. In the case of **rectangular passages,** the cross section is usually divided into small squares or rectangles and the velocity is found at the center of each. In **circular pipes,** the cross section is divided into several equal annular areas and a central circle. Readings of velocity are made at the intersections of a diameter and the set of circles which bisect the annuli and the central circle.

For an N-point traverse on a circular cross section, make readings on each side of the cross section at

$$100 \times \sqrt{\frac{2n-1}{N}} \text{ per cent} \qquad \left(n = 1, 2, 3 \text{ to } \frac{N}{2}\right)$$

of the pipe radius from the center. Traversing several diameters spaced at equal angles about the pipe is required if the velocity distribution is unsymmetrical. With a normal velocity distribution in a circular pipe, a 10-point traverse theoretically gives a mean velocity 0.3 per cent high, and a 20-point traverse, 0.1 per cent high.

For normal velocity distribution in straight circular pipes at locations preceded by runs of at least 50 diameters without pipe fittings or other obstructions, the graph shown in Fig. 5-11 shows the ratio of mean velocity V to velocity at the center u_{max} plotted against Reynolds number, where D = inside pipe diameter, ρ = fluid density, and μ = fluid viscosity, all in consistent units. Mean velocity is readily determined from this chart and a pitot reading at the center of the pipe if the quantity $Du_{max}\,\rho/\mu$ is less than 2000 or greater than 5000. The method is unreliable at intermediate values of Reynolds number.

Flow Visualization. A great many techniques have been developed for the visualization of velocity patterns, particularly for use in water-tunnel and wind-tunnel studies. In the case of **liquids,** the more common methods of revealing flow lines involve the use of dye traces, the addition of aluminum flake, and the use of polarized light with a doubly refractive liquid or suspension. For the latter, see Prados and Peebles [*Am. Inst. Chem. Engrs. J.*, **5**, 225–234 (1959)]. The velocity pattern for viscous flow in a two-dimensional system can be quantitatively mapped using an electrolytic-tank analog or a conductive-paper analog with a suitable combination of resistances, sources, and sinks.

In the case of **gases,** flow lines can be revealed through the use of smoke traces or the addition of a lightweight powder such as balsa dust to the stream. One of the best smoke generators is the reaction of titanium tetrachloride with moisture in the air. Tufts of wool or nylon attached at one end to a solid surface can be used to reveal flow phenomena in the vicinity of the surface. Optical methods commonly employed depend upon changes in refractive index resulting from the presence of heated wires or secondary streams in the flow field or upon changes in density in the primary gas as a result of compressibility effects. The three common techniques are the shadowgraph, the schlieren, and the interferometer. All three theoretically can give quantitative information on the velocity profiles in a two-dimensional system but in practice, only the interferometer is commonly so used. The optical methods are described by

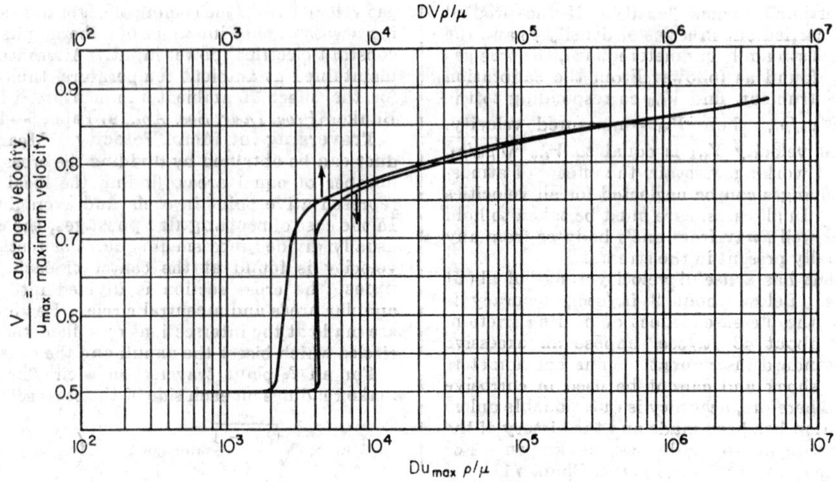

FIG. 5-11. Velocity ratio vs. Reynolds number for smooth circular pipes. [*Based on data from Rothfus, Archer, Klimas, and Sikchi, Am. Inst. Chem. Engrs. J.*, **3**, 208 (1957).]

Ladenburg *et al.*, *op. cit.*, pp. 3–108. For additional information on other methods, see Goldstein, *op. cit.*, vol. I, pp. 280–296.

HEAD METERS

General Principles. If a constriction is placed in a closed channel carrying a stream of fluid, there will be an increase in velocity, and hence an increase in kinetic energy, at the point of constriction. From an energy balance, as given by Bernoulli's theorem (p. 5-16), there must be a corresponding reduction in pressure. Rate of discharge from the constriction can be calculated knowing this pressure reduction, the area available for flow at the constriction, density of the fluid, and the coefficient of discharge C. The latter is defined as the ratio of actual flow to the theoretical flow and makes allowance for stream contraction and frictional effects.

Venturi Meters. The standard, Herschel-type venturi meter consists of a short length of straight tubing connected at either end to the pipe line by conical sections (see Fig. 5-12). Recommended proportions (A.S.M.E.

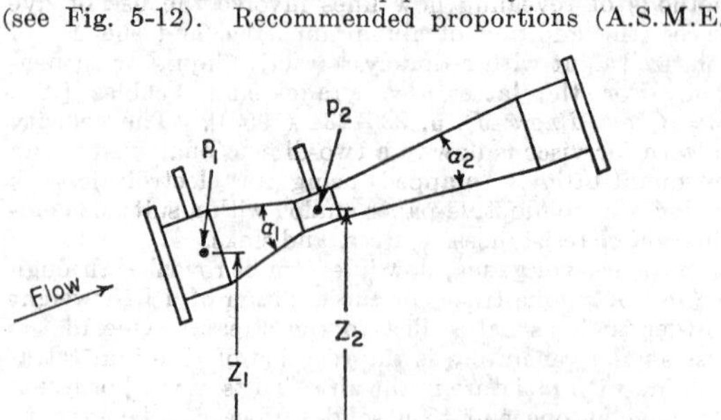

FIG. 5-12. Herschel-type venturi tube.

PTC, *op. cit.*, p. 17) are entrance cone angle $\alpha_1 = 21 \pm 2$ deg.; exit cone angle $\alpha_2 = 5$ to 15 deg.; throat length = one throat diameter; upstream tap located 0.25 to 0.5 pipe diameter upstream of the entrance cone. The straight and conical sections should be joined by smooth curved surfaces for best results.

The practical working equation for weight rate of discharge, adopted by A.S.M.E. Research Committee on Fluid Meters for use with either gases or liquids, is

$$w = q_1\rho_1 = CYA_2\sqrt{\frac{2g_c(p_1 - p_2)\rho_1}{1 - \beta^4}} = KYA_2\sqrt{2g_c(p_1 - p_2)\rho_1} \quad (5\text{-}9)$$

where A_2 = cross-sectional area of throat, sq. ft.; C = coefficient of discharge, dimensionless; g_c = dimensional constant, 32.17 (lb.)(ft.)/(lb. force)(sec.^{2}); $K = C/\sqrt{1 - \beta^4}$, dimensionless; p_1, p_2 = pressure at upstream and downstream static pressure taps, respectively, lb. force/sq. ft.; q_1 = volumetric rate of discharge measured at upstream pressure and temperature, cu. ft./sec.; w = weight rate of discharge, lb./sec.; Y = expansion factor (see below), dimensionless; β = ratio of throat diameter to pipe diameter, dimensionless; ρ_1 = density at upstream pressure and temperature, lb./cu. ft.

For the flow of **gases,** expansion factor Y, which allows for the change in gas density as it expands adiabatically from p_1 to p_2, is given by

$$Y = \sqrt{r^{2/k}\left(\frac{k}{k-1}\right)\left(\frac{1 - r^{(k-1)/k}}{1 - r}\right)\left(\frac{1 - \beta^4}{1 - \beta^4 r^{2/k}}\right)} \quad (5\text{-}10)$$

for venturi meters and flow nozzles, where $r = p_2/p_1$ and k = specific heat ratio c_p/c_v. Values of Y computed from Eq. (5-10) are given in Fig. 5-13 as a function of r, k, and β.

For the flow of **liquids,** expansion factor Y is unity. The change in potential energy in the case of an inclined or vertical venturi meter must be allowed for. Equation (5-9) is accordingly modified to give

$$w = q_1\rho = CA_2\sqrt{\frac{[2g_c(p_1 - p_2) + 2g\rho(Z_1 - Z_2)]\rho}{1 - \beta^4}} \quad (5\text{-}11)$$

where g = local acceleration due to gravity, 32.2 ft./sec.^{2}; Z_1, Z_2 = vertical heights, ft., above an arbitrary datum plane corresponding to the center-line pressure-reading locations for p_1 and p_2, respectively.

Value of the **discharge coefficient** C for a **Herschel-**

type venturi meter depends upon the Reynolds number and to a minor extent upon the size of the venturi, increasing with diameter. A plot of C vs. pipe Reynolds number is given in A.S.M.E. PTC, *op. cit.*, p. 19. A value of 0.984 can be used for pipe Reynolds numbers larger than 200,000.

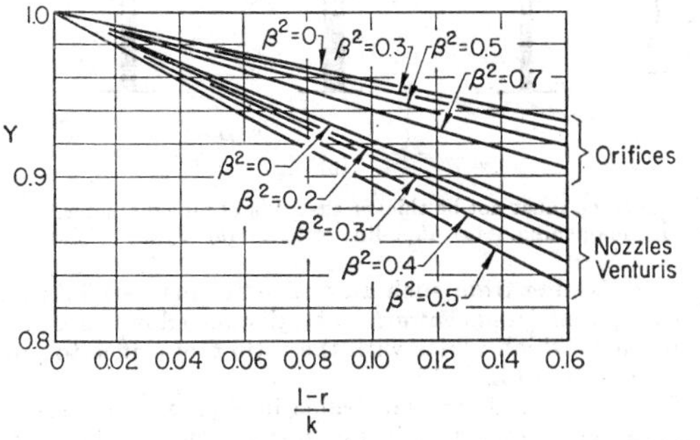

FIG. 5-13. Values of expansion factor Y for orifices, nozzles, and venturis.

Permanent pressure loss for a Herschel-type venturi tube depends upon diameter ratio β and discharge cone angle α_2. It ranges from 10 to 15 per cent of the pressure differential $(p_1 - p_2)$ for small angles (5 to 7 deg.) and from 10 to 30 per cent for large angles (15 deg.), with the larger losses occurring at low values of β (see p. 12 of the preceding reference).

A variety of **short-tube** venturi meters are available commercially. They require less space for installation and are generally (although not always) characterized by a greater pressure loss than the corresponding Herschel-type venturi meter. Discharge coefficients vary widely for different types, and individual calibration is recommended if the manufacturer's calibration is not available. Results of tests on the Dall flow tube are given by Miner [*Trans. Am. Soc. Mech. Engrs.*, **78,** 475–479 (1956)] and Dowdell [*Instr. and Control Systems,* **33,** 1006–1009 (1960)]; and on the Gentile flow tube (also called Beth flow tube or Foster flow tube) by Hooper [*Trans. Am. Soc. Mech. Engrs.*, **72,** 1009–1110 (1950)].

Flow Nozzles. A simple form of flow nozzle is shown in Fig. 5-14. It consists essentially of a short cylinder

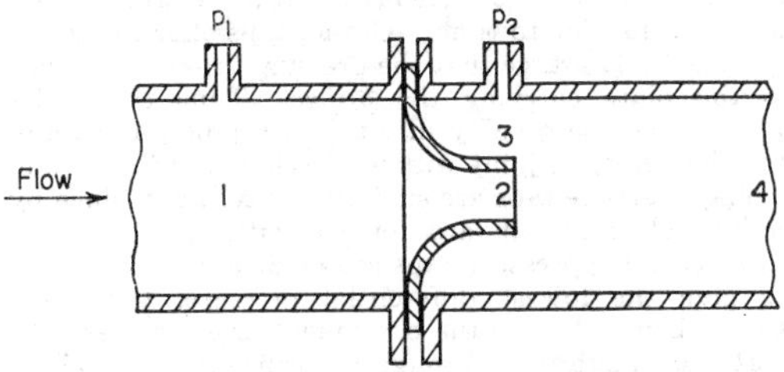

FIG. 5-14. Flow nozzle assembly.

with a flared approach section. The approach cross section is preferably elliptical in shape but may be conical. Recommended contours for long-radius flow nozzles are given in A.S.M.E. PTC, *op. cit.*, p. 13. In general, the length of the straight portion of the throat is about 0.5 throat diameter, the upstream pressure tap is located about one pipe diameter from the nozzle inlet face, and the downstream pressure tap about 0.5 pipe diameter from the inlet face. For subsonic flow, the pressures at points 2 and 3 will be practically identical. If a conical inlet is preferred, the inlet and throat geometry specified for a Herschel-type venturi meter can be used, omitting the expansion section.

Rate of discharge through a flow nozzle for subcritical flow can be determined by the equations given for venturi meters, Eq. (5-9) for gases and Eq. (5-11) for liquids. The expansion factor Y for nozzles is the same as that for venturi meters [Eq. (5-10), Fig. 5-13]. Value of the discharge coefficient C depends primarily upon the pipe Reynolds number and to a lesser extent upon the diameter ratio β. Curves of recommended coefficients for long-radius flow nozzles with pressure taps located one pipe diameter upstream and one-half pipe diameter downstream of the inlet face of the nozzle are given on p. 15 of the preceding reference. In general, coefficients range from 0.95 at a pipe Reynolds number of 10,000 to 0.99 at 1,000,000.

Permanent pressure loss across a subsonic flow nozzle is approximated by

$$p_1 - p_4 = \frac{1 - \beta^2}{1 + \beta^2}(p_1 - p_2) \tag{5-12}$$

where p_1, p_2, p_4 = static pressures measured at the locations shown in Fig. 5-14, lb. force/sq. ft.; β = ratio of nozzle throat diameter to pipe diameter, dimensionless. Equation (5-12) is based on a momentum balance assuming constant fluid density (see Lapple *et al.*, "Fluid and Particle Mechanics," p. 13, University of Delaware, Newark, 1951).

Critical Flow Nozzle. For a given set of upstream conditions, the rate of discharge of a **gas** from a nozzle will increase for a decrease in the absolute pressure ratio p_2/p_1, until the linear velocity in the throat reaches that of sound in the gas at that location. The value of p_2/p_1 for which the acoustic velocity is just attained is called the critical pressure ratio r_c. The actual pressure in the throat will not fall below p_1r_c, even if a much lower pressure exists downstream.

The **critical pressure ratio** r_c can be obtained from the following theoretical equation, which assumes a perfect gas and a frictionless nozzle:

$$r_c^{(1-k)/k} + \left(\frac{k-1}{2}\right)\beta^4 r_c^{2/k} = \frac{k+1}{2} \tag{5-13}$$

This reduces, for $\beta \leq 0.2$, to

$$r_c = \left(\frac{2}{k+1}\right)^{k/(k-1)} \tag{5-14}$$

where k = ratio of specific heats c_p/c_v; β = diameter ratio. A table of values of r_c as a function of k and β is given in A.S.M.E. Research Report on Fluid Meters, *op. cit.*, p. 82. For small values of β, r_c = 0.487 for k = 1.667; 0.528 for k = 1.40; 0.546 for k = 1.30; 0.574 for k = 1.15.

Under **critical flow conditions,** only the upstream conditions p_1, v_1, and T_1 need be known to determine flow rate, which, for $\beta \leq 0.2$, is given by

$$w_{\max} = CA_2\sqrt{g_c k\left(\frac{p_1}{v_1}\right)\left(\frac{2}{k+1}\right)^{(k+1)/(k-1)}} \tag{5-15}$$

For a **perfect gas,** this corresponds to

$$w_{\max} = CA_2 p_1\sqrt{g_c k\left(\frac{M}{RT_1}\right)\left(\frac{2}{k+1}\right)^{(k+1)/(k-1)}} \tag{5-16}$$

For **air,** Eq. (5-15) reduces to

$$w_{\max} = \frac{0.533CA_2p_1}{\sqrt{T_1}} \tag{5-17}$$

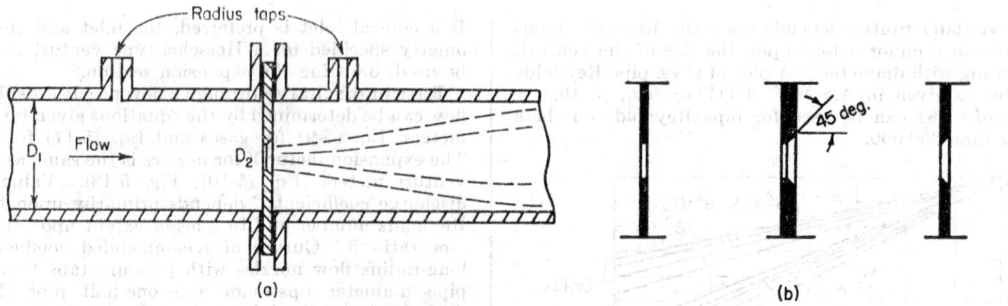

FIG. 5-15. Square-edged or sharp-edged orifices. The plate at the orifice opening must not be thicker than 1/30 of pipe diameter, 1/8 of the orifice diameter, or 1/4 of the distance from the pipe wall to the edge of the opening. (a) Pipe-line orifice. (b) Types of plates.

where A_2 = cross-sectional area of throat, sq. ft.; C = coefficient of discharge, dimensionless; g_c = dimensional constant, 32.17 (lb.)(ft.)/(lb. force)(sec.²); k = ratio of specific heats, c_p/c_v; M = molecular weight, lb./lb.-mole; p_1 = pressure on upstream side of nozzle, lb. force/sq. ft.; R = gas constant, 1546 (ft.)(lb. force)/(lb.-mole)(°F.); T_1 = absolute temperature on upstream side of nozzle, °R., (°F. + 460); v_1 = specific volume on upstream side of nozzle, cu. ft./lb.; and w_{max} = maximum flow rate, lb./sec.

Discharge coefficients for critical flow nozzles are, in general, the same as those for subsonic nozzles. See Grace and Lapple [*Trans. Am. Soc. Mech. Engrs.*, **73**, 639–647 (1951)].

Orifice Meters. A **square-edged** or **sharp-edged** orifice, as shown in Fig. 5-15, is a clean-cut square-edged hole with straight walls perpendicular to the flat upstream face of a thin plate placed crosswise of the channel. The

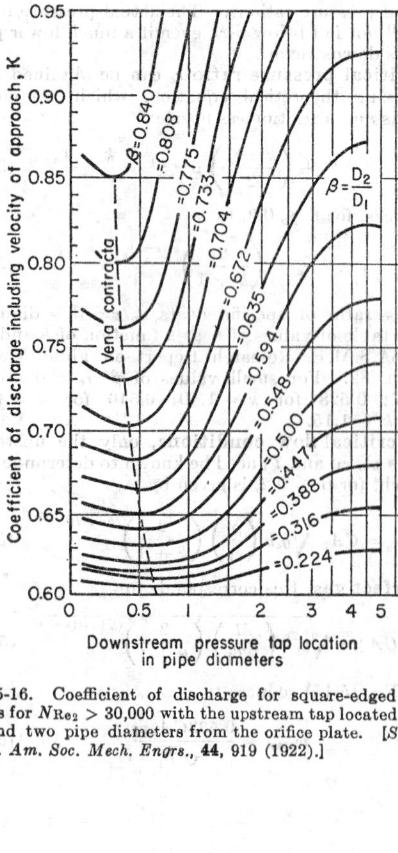

FIG. 5-16. Coefficient of discharge for square-edged circular orifices for $N_{Re_2} > 30{,}000$ with the upstream tap located between one and two pipe diameters from the orifice plate. [*Spitzglass, Trans. Am. Soc. Mech. Engrs.*, **44**, 919 (1922).]

stream issuing from such an orifice attains its minimum cross section (*vena contracta*) at a distance downstream of the orifice which varies with the ratio β of orifice to pipe diameter (see Fig. 5-16).

For a centered circular orifice in a pipe, the pressure differential is customarily measured between one of the following pressure-tap pairs. Except in the case of flange taps, all measurements of distance from the orifice are made from the upstream face of the plate.

1. **Corner Taps.** Static holes drilled one in the upstream and one in the downstream flange, with the openings as close as possible to the orifice plate.
2. **Radius Taps.** Static holes located 1 pipe diameter upstream and 1/2 pipe diameter downstream from the plate.
3. **Pipe Taps.** Static holes located 2 1/2 pipe diameters upstream and 8 pipe diameters downstream from the plate.
4. **Flange Taps.** Static holes located 1 in. upstream and 1 in. downstream from the plate.
5. **Vena Contracta Taps.** The upstream static hole is 1/2 to 2 pipe diameters from the plate. The downstream tap is located at the position of minimum pressure (see Fig. 5-16).

Radius taps are best from a practical standpoint; the downstream pressure tap is located at about the mean position of the *vena contracta*, and the upstream tap is sufficiently far upstream to be unaffected by distortion of the flow in the immediate vicinity of the orifice (in practice, the upstream tap can be as much as 2 pipe diameters from the plate without affecting the results). *Vena contracta* taps give the largest differential head for a given rate of flow but are inconvenient if the orifice size is changed from time to time. Corner taps offer the sometimes great advantage that the pressure taps can be built into the plate carrying the orifice. Thus the entire apparatus can be quickly inserted in a pipe line at any convenient flanged joint without having to drill holes in the pipe. Flange taps are similarly convenient, since by merely replacing standard flanges with special orifice flanges, suitable pressure taps are made available. Pipe taps give the lowest differential pressure, the value obtained being close to the permanent pressure loss.

Rate of discharge through an orifice meter is given by Eq. (5-9) for either liquids or gases. For the case of **gases**, expansion factor Y for orifices is approximated (for $r_c \leq r \leq 1.0$) by

$$Y = 1 - \frac{1 - r}{k}(0.41 + 0.35\beta^4) \tag{5-18}$$

where r = ratio of downstream to upstream static pressure p_2/p_1; k = ratio of specific heats c_p/c_v; β = diameter ratio. Values of Y can also be obtained from Fig. 5-13. For the case of **liquids**, expansion factor Y is unity, and Eq. (5-11) should be used, since it allows for any difference in elevation between the upstream and downstream taps.

Coefficient of discharge C for a given orifice type is a function of Reynolds number N_{Re} and diameter ratio β. At Reynolds numbers (based on orifice diameter and velocity) greater than about 30,000, the coefficients are substantially constant. For square-edged or sharp-edged concentric circular orifices, the value will fall between 0.595 and 0.620 for *vena contracta* or radius taps for β up to 0.8 and for flange taps for β up to 0.5. Figure 5-16 gives the coefficient of discharge K, including the velocity-of-approach factor $(1/\sqrt{1 - \beta^4})$, as a function of β and the location of the downstream tap. Precise values of K are given in A.S.M.E. PTC, *op. cit.*, pp. 20–39, for flange taps, radius taps, *vena contracta* taps, and corner taps.

In the transition region (N_{Re} between 50 and 30,000), the coefficients are generally higher than the above values (the larger the β, the higher the coefficient). In the laminar-flow region ($N_{Re} < 50$), C drops rapidly with decreasing N_{Re}. Calibration is nearly always advisable at Reynolds numbers below 30,000. The results of a survey of literature data on orifice coefficients for corner taps in the pipe Reynolds number range of 4 to 50,000 were given by Iversen [*Trans. Am. Soc. Mech. Engrs.*, **78**, 359–364 (1956)]; and for flange taps in the orifice Reynolds-number range of 40 to 10,000, original data on coefficients are presented by Ambrosius and Spink [*ibid.*, **69**, 805–812 (1947)].

Permanent pressure loss across a concentric circular orifice with radius or *vena contracta* taps can be approximated by

$$\frac{p_1 - p_4}{p_1 - p_2} = 1 - \beta^2 \qquad (5\text{-}19)$$

where p_1, p_2 = upstream and downstream pressure-tap readings, respectively; p_4 = fully recovered pressure (4 to 8 pipe diameters downstream of the orifice); β = diameter ratio. See A.S.M.E. PTC, *op. cit.*, Fig. 5.

For the case of **critical flow** through a square- or sharp-edged concentric circular orifice (where $r \leq r_c$, see p. 5-9), use Eqs. (5-15), (5-16), and (5-17) as given for critical flow nozzles. However, unlike nozzles, the flow through a sharp-edged orifice continues to increase as the downstream pressure drops below that corresponding to the critical pressure ratio r_c. This is due to an increase in the cross section of the *vena contracta* as the downstream pressure is reduced, giving a corresponding increase in the coefficient of discharge. At $r = r_c$, C is about 0.75, while at $r \cong 0$, C has increased to about 0.84. See Grace and Lapple (*loc. cit.*).

Segmental and **eccentric orifices** are frequently used for gas metering where there is a possibility that entrained liquids or solids would otherwise accumulate in front of a concentric circular orifice. This can be avoided if the opening is placed on the lower side of the pipe. For liquid flow with entrained gas, the opening is placed on the upper side. The pressure taps should be located on the opposite side of the pipe from the opening.

Coefficient C for a square-edged eccentric circular orifice (with opening tangent to pipe wall) varies from about 0.61 to 0.63 for β's from 0.3 to 0.5, respectively, and pipe Reynolds numbers > 10,000, for either *vena contracta* or flange taps (where β = diameter ratio). For square-edged segmental orifices, the coefficient C falls generally between 0.63 and 0.64 for $0.3 \leq \beta \leq 0.5$ and pipe Reynolds numbers > 10,000, for *vena contracta* or flange taps, where β = diameter ratio for an equivalent circular orifice = $\sqrt{\alpha}$ (α = ratio of orifice to pipe cross-sectional areas). Values of expansion factor Y are slightly higher than for concentric circular orifices, and location of the *vena contracta* is moved farther downstream as compared with concentric circular orifices. For further details, see A.S.M.E. Research Report on Fluid Meters, *op. cit.*, pp. 178–181.

Annular orifices can also be used to advantage for gas metering where there is a possibility of entrained liquids or solids and for liquid metering with entrained gas present in small concentrations. Coefficient K was found by Bell and Bergelin [*Trans. Am. Soc. Mech. Engrs.*, **79**, 593–601 (1957)] to range from about 0.63 to 0.67 for annulus Reynolds numbers in the range of 100 to 20,000, respectively, for values of $2L/(D - d)$ less than 1; where L = thickness of orifice at outer edge, ft.; D = inside pipe diameter, ft.; d = diameter of orifice disk, ft. The annulus Reynolds number is defined as

$$N_{Re} = (D - d)\frac{G}{\mu} \qquad (5\text{-}20)$$

where G = mass velocity through orifice opening, lb./(sec.) (sq. ft.); μ = fluid viscosity, lb./(ft.)(sec.). The above coefficients were determined for β's ($= d/D$) in the range of 0.95 to 0.996 and with pressure taps located ¾ in. upstream of the disk and 9 in. downstream in a 5.25-in.-diameter pipe.

Elbow Meters. A pipe elbow can be used as a flowmeter for liquids if the differential centrifugal head generated between the inner and outer radii of the bend is measured by means of pressure taps so located midway around the bend. Equation (5-11) can be used, except that the pressure-difference term ($p_1 - p_2$) is now taken to be the differential centrifugal pressure. The discharge coefficient C should preferably be determined by calibration. According to Rouse ("Engineering Hydraulics," p. 206, Wiley, New York, 1950), the coefficient can be estimated within 10 per cent for circular pipe for well-developed turbulent flow from $C = \sqrt{R_c/2D}$; where R_c = radius of curvature and D = inside pipe diameter in consistent units. See also Addison, *op. cit.*, pp. 174–176.

Accuracy. Square-edged orifices and venturi tubes have been so extensively studied and standardized that reproducibilities within 1 to 2 per cent can be expected between standard meters when new and clean. This is therefore the order of reliability to be had, assuming (1) accurate measurement of meter differential, (2) selection of the coefficient of discharge from recommended published literature, (3) accurate knowledge of fluid density, (4) accurate measurement of critical meter dimensions, (5) smooth upstream face of orifice, and (6) proper location of the meter with respect to other flow-disturbing elements in the system. Care must also be taken to avoid even slight corrosion or fouling during use.

Presence of **swirling flow** or an **abnormal velocity distribution** upstream of the metering element can cause serious metering error unless calibration in place is employed or sufficient straight pipe is inserted between the meter and the source of disturbance. Table 5-2 gives the minimum lengths of straight pipe required to avoid appreciable error due to the presence of certain fittings and valves either upstream or downstream of an orifice or nozzle. These values were extracted from plots presented by Sprenkle [*Trans. Am. Soc. Mech. Engrs.*, **67**, 345–360 (1945)]. Table 5-2 also shows the reduction in spacing made possible by use of straightening vanes between the fittings and the meter. Entirely adequate straightening vanes can be provided by fitting a bundle of thin-wall tubes within the pipe. The center-to-center distance between tubes should not exceed one-fourth the pipe diameter, and the bundle length should be at least eight times this distance.

Table 5-2. Locations of Orifices and Nozzles Relative to Pipe Fittings

Distances in pipe diameters, D_1

Type of fitting upstream	$\frac{D_2}{D_1}$	Distance, upstream fitting to orifice: Without straightening vanes	Distance, upstream fitting to orifice: With straightening vanes	Distance, vanes to orifice	Distance, nearest downstream fitting from orifice
Single 90-deg. ell, tee, or cross used as ell	0.2	6			2
	0.4	6			
	0.6	8	10		
	0.8	20	12	8	4
2 short-radius 90-deg. ells in form of S	0.2	7			2
	0.4	8	8		
	0.6	13	10	6	
	0.8	25	15	11	4
2 long- or short-radius 90-deg. ells in perpendicular planes	0.2	15	9	5	2
	0.4	18	10	6	
	0.6	25	11	7	
	0.8	40	13	9	4
Contraction or enlargement	0.2	8	Vanes have no advantage		2
	0.4	9			
	0.6	10			
	0.8	15			4
Globe valve or stop check	0.2	9	9	5	2
	0.4	10	10	6	
	0.6	13	10	6	
	0.8	21	13	9	4
Gate valve, wide open, or plug cocks	0.2	6	Same as globe valve		2
	0.4	6			
	0.6	8			
	0.8	14			4

The distances specified in Table 5-2 will be conservative if applied to venturi meters. For specific information on requirements for venturi meters, see a discussion by Pardoe appended to the preceding reference. Extensive data on the effect of installation on the coefficients of venturi meters is given elsewhere by Pardoe [*Trans. Am. Soc. Mech. Engrs.*, **65**, 337–349 (1943)].

In the presence of **flow pulsations,** the indications of head meters such as orifices, nozzles, and venturis will often be undependable for several reasons. First, the measured pressure differential will tend to be high, since the pressure differential is proportional to the square of flow rate for a head meter, and the square root of the mean differential pressure is always greater than the mean of the square roots of the differential pressures. Second, there is a phase shift as the wave passes through the metering restriction which can affect the differential. Third, pulsations can be set up in the manometer leads themselves. Frequency of the pulsation also plays a part. At low frequencies, the meter reading can generally faithfully follow the flow pulsations, but at high frequencies it cannot. This is due to inertia of the fluid in the manometer leads or of the manometric fluid, whereupon the meter would give a reading intermediate between the maximum and minimum flows but having no predictable relation to the mean flow. Pressure transducers with flush-mounted diaphragms can be used together with high-speed recording equipment to provide accurate records of the pressure profiles at the upstream and downstream pressure taps, which can then be analyzed and translated into a mean flow rate.

The rather general practice of producing a steady differential reading by placing restrictions in the manometer leads can result in a reading which, under a fixed set of conditions, may be useful in control of an operation but which has no predictable relation to the actual average flow. If calibration is employed to compensate for the presence of pulsations, complete reproduction of operating conditions, including source of pulsations and wave form, is necessary to ensure reasonable accuracy.

According to Head [*Trans. Am. Soc. Mech. Engrs.*, **78**, 1471–1479 (1956)], a pulsation-intensity limit of $\Gamma = 0.1$ is recommended as a practical pulsation threshold below which the performance of all types of flowmeters will differ negligibly from steady-flow performance (an error of less than 1 per cent in flow due to pulsation). Γ is the peak-to-trough flow variation expressed as a fraction of the average flow rate. According to A.S.M.E. Research Report on Fluid Meters (*op. cit.*), a meter can read 1 to 2 per cent high when $\Gamma = 0.4$ for a sinusoidal pulsation, 10 to 20 per cent high when $\Gamma = 1.3$, and 25 to 50 per cent high when $\Gamma = 2.0$. When the pulsation amplitude is such as to result in a greater-than-permissible metering error, consideration should be given to installation of a pulsation damper between the source of pulsations and the flowmeter. References to methods of pulsation-damper design are given on p. 5-56.

Pulsations are most likely to be encountered in discharge lines from reciprocating pumps or compressors and in lines supplying steam to reciprocating machinery. For **gas flow,** a combination involving a surge chamber and a constriction in the line can be used to damp out the pulsations to an acceptable level. The surge chamber is generally located as close to the pulsation source as possible, with the constriction located between the surge chamber and the metering element. This arrangement can be used for either a suction or discharge line. For such an arrangement, the metering error has been found to be a function of the Hodgson number N_H, which is defined as

$$N_H = \frac{Qn\,\Delta p_s}{qp_s} \tag{5-21}$$

where Q = volume of surge chamber and pipe between metering element and pulsation source, cu. ft.; n = pulsation frequency, 1/sec.; Δp_s = permanent pressure drop between metering element and surge chamber, lb. force/sq. ft.; q = average volume flow rate, cu. ft./sec., based on gas density in the surge chamber; p_s = pressure in surge chamber, lb. force/sq. ft.

Herning and Schmid [*Z. Ver. deut. Ing.*, **82**, 1107–1114 (1938)] presented charts for a simplex double-acting compressor for the prediction of metering error as a function of Hodgson number and s, the ratio of piston discharge time to total time per stroke. Table 5-3 gives the minimum Hodgson numbers required to reduce the metering error to 1 per cent as given by the charts (for specific heat ratios between 1.28 and 1.37). Schmid [*Z. Ver. deut. Ing.*, **84**, 596–598 (1940)] presented similar charts for a duplex double-acting compressor and a triplex double-acting compressor for a specific heat ratio of 1.37. Table 5-4 gives the minimum Hodgson numbers corresponding to a 1 per cent metering error for these cases. The value of $Q\,\Delta p_s$ can be calculated from the appropriate Hodgson number, and appropriate values of Q and Δp_s selected so as to satisfy this minimum requirement.

Table 5-3. Minimum Hodgson Numbers

Simplex double-acting compressor

s	N_H	s	N_H
0.167	1.31	0.667	0.60
0.333	1.00	0.833	0.43
0.50	0.80	1.00	0.34

Table 5-4. Minimum Hodgson Numbers

Duplex double-acting compressor: s	Duplex double-acting compressor: N_H	Triplex double-acting compressor: s	Triplex double-acting compressor: N_H
0.167	1.00	0.167	0.85
0.333	0.70	0.333	0.30
0.50	0.30	0.50	0.15
0.667	0.10	0.667	0.06
0.833	0.05	0.833	0.00
1.00	0.00	1.00	0.00

AREA METERS

General Principles. The underlying principle of an ideal area meter is the same as that of a head meter of the orifice type (see p. 5-10). The stream to be measured is throttled by a constriction, but instead of observing the variation with flow of the differential head across an orifice of fixed size, the constriction of an area meter is so arranged that its size is varied to accommodate the flow while the differential head is held constant.

A simple example of an area meter is a gate valve of the rising-stem type provided with static-pressure taps before and after the gate and a means for measuring the stem position. In most common types of area meters, the variation of the opening is automatically brought about by the motion of a weighted piston or float supported by the fluid. Two different cylinder- and piston-type area meters are described in the A.S.M.E. Research Report on Fluid Meters, *op. cit.*, p. 87.

Rotameters. The rotameter, an example of which is shown in Fig. 5-17, has become one of the most popular flowmeters in the chemical process industries. It consists essentially of a plummet or "float" which is free to move up or down in a vertical, slightly tapered tube having its small end down. The fluid enters the lower end of the tube and causes the float to rise until the annular area between the float and the wall of the tube is such that the pressure drop across this constriction is just sufficient to support the float. Typically, the tapered tube is of glass and carries etched upon it a nearly linear scale on which the position of the float may be visually noted as an indication of the flow.

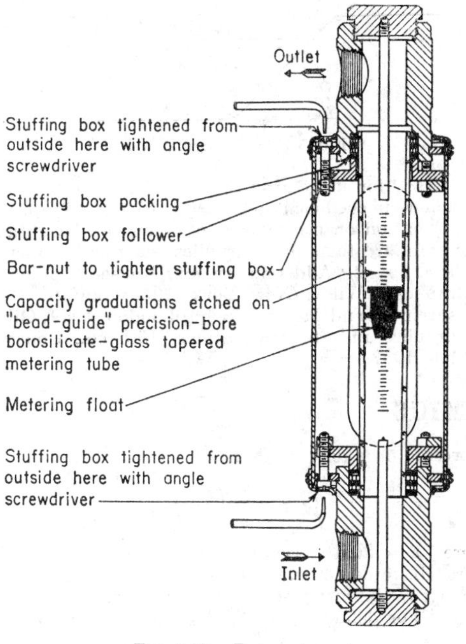

FIG. 5-17. Rotameter.

Interchangeable precision-bore glass tubes and metal metering tubes are available. Rotameters have proved satisfactory both for gases and for liquids at high and at low pressures. A single instrument can readily cover a tenfold range of flow, and by providing "floats" of different densities, a two-hundredfold range is practicable. Rotameters are available with pneumatic, electric, and electronic transmitters for actuating remote recorders, integrators, and automatic flow controllers (see Considine, *op. cit.*, pp. 4-63 to 4-66, and Sec. 22, this handbook).

Rotameters require no straight runs of pipe before or after the point of installation. Pressure losses are substantially constant over the whole flow range. In experimental work, for greatest precision, a rotameter should be calibrated with the fluid which is to be metered. However, most modern rotameters are precision-made such that their performance closely corresponds to a master calibration plot for the type in question. Such a plot is supplied with the meter upon purchase.

According to Head [*Trans. Am. Soc. Mech. Engrs.*, **76,** 851–862 (1954)], flow rate through a rotameter can be obtained from

$$w = q\rho = KD_f \sqrt{\frac{W_f(\rho_f - \rho)\rho}{\rho_f}} \tag{5-22}$$

and

$$K = \phi\left[\frac{D_t}{D_f}, \frac{\mu}{\sqrt{\frac{W_f(\rho_f - \rho)\rho}{\rho_f}}}\right] \tag{5-23}$$

where w = flow rate, lb./sec.; q = volumetric flow rate, cu. ft./sec.; ρ = fluid density, lb./cu. ft.; K = flow parameter, (ft.$^{1/2}$)/sec.; D_f = float diameter at constriction, ft.; W_f = float weight, lb.; ρ_f = float density, lb./cu. ft.; D_t = tube diameter at point of constriction, ft.; μ = fluid viscosity, lb./(ft.)(sec.). The appropriate value of K is obtained from a composite correlation of K vs. the parameters shown in Eq. (5-23) corresponding to the float shape being used. The relation of D_t to rotameter reading is also required for the tube taper and size being used.

The ratio of flow rates for two different fluids A and B at the same rotameter reading is given by

$$\frac{w_A}{w_B} = \frac{K_A}{K_B}\sqrt{\frac{(\rho_f - \rho_A)\rho_A}{(\rho_f - \rho_B)\rho_B}} \tag{5-24}$$

A measure of self-compensation, with respect to weight rate of flow, for fluid-density changes can be introduced through the use of a float with a density twice that of the fluid being metered, in which case an increase of 10 per cent in ρ will produce a decrease of only 0.5 per cent in w for the same reading. The extent of immunity to changes in fluid viscosity depends upon shape of the float.

Additional information on rotameter theory is presented by Fischer [*Chem. Eng.*, **59** (6), 180–184 (1952)]; by Coleman [*Trans. Inst. Chem. Engrs.*, **34,** 339–350 (1956)]; by McCabe and Smith ("Unit Operations of Chemical Engineering," pp. 117–123, McGraw-Hill, New York, 1956).

WEIRS

General Principles. Liquid flow in an open channel may be metered by means of a weir, which consists of a dam over which, or through a notch in which, the liquid flows. The terms "rectangular weir," "triangular weir," etc., generally refer to the shape of the notch in a notched weir. All weirs considered here have flat upstream faces that are perpendicular to the bed and walls of the channel.

Sharp-edged weirs have edges like those of square or sharp-edged orifices (see p. 5-10). Notched weirs are ordinarily sharp-edged. Weirs not in the sharp-edged class are, for the most part, those described as **broad-crested weirs.** For a detailed description of the latter type and their performance, see Schoder and Dawson, *op. cit.*, pp. 175–181.

The head h_0 on a weir is the liquid-level height above the crest or base of the notch. The head must be measured sufficiently far upstream to avoid the drop in level occasioned by the overfall which begins at a distance about $2h_0$ upstream from the weir. Surface-level measurements should be made a distance of $3h_0$ or more upstream, preferably using a stilling box equipped with a high-precision level gage, *e.g.*, a hook gage or float gage.

With sharp-edged weirs, the sheet of discharging liquid, called the *nappe*, contracts as it leaves the opening and free discharge occurs. Rounding the upstream edge will reduce the contraction and increase the flow rate for a given head. A clinging nappe may result if the head is very small, if the edge is well rounded, or if air cannot flow in beneath the nappe. This, in turn, results in an increase in the discharge rate for a given head as compared with that for a free nappe. For further information on the effect of the nappe, see Gibson, "Hydraulics and Its Applications," 5th ed., Constable, London, 1952.

Flow through a **rectangular weir** (Fig. 5-18) is given by

$$q = 0.415(L - 0.2h_0)h_0^{1.5}\sqrt{2g} \qquad (5\text{-}25)$$

where q = volumetric flow rate, cu. ft./sec.; L = crest length, ft.; h_0 = weir head, ft.; g = local acceleration

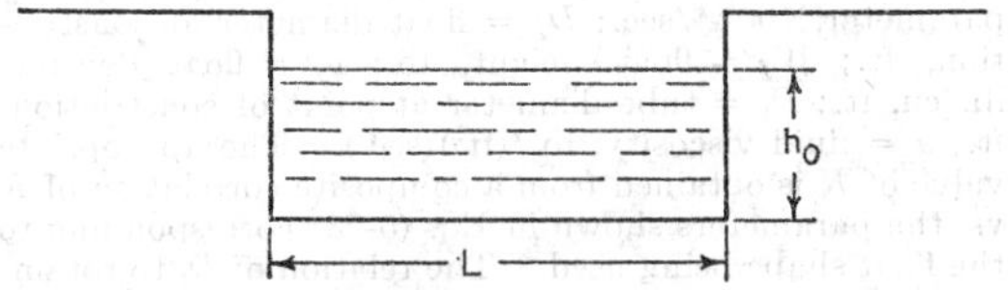

FIG. 5-18. Rectangular weir.

due to gravity, approximately 32.2 ft./(sec.^{2}). This is known as the modified Francis formula for a rectangular sharp-edged weir with two end corrections; it applies where the velocity-of-approach correction is small. The Francis formula agrees with experiments within 3 per cent if (1) L is greater than $2h_0$, (2) velocity of approach is 2 ft./sec. or less, (3) height of crest above bottom of channel is at least $3h_0$, and (4) h_0 is not less than 0.3 ft.

Narrow rectangular notches ($h_0 > L$) have been found to give about 93 per cent of the discharge predicted by the Francis formula. Thus

$$q = 0.386Lh_0^{1.5}\sqrt{2g} \qquad (5\text{-}26)$$

In this case, no end corrections are applied, even though the formula applies only for sharp-edged weirs. See Schoder and Dawson, *op. cit.*, p. 175, for further details.

The **triangular-notch weir** has the advantage that a single notch can accommodate a wide range of flow rates, although this in turn reduces its accuracy. The discharge for sharp- or square-edged weirs is given by

$$q = \frac{0.31h_0^{2.5}\sqrt{2g}}{\tan\phi} \qquad (5\text{-}27)$$

See Eq. (5-25) for nomenclature. Angle ϕ is illustrated in Fig. 5-19. See Lenz [*Trans. Am. Soc. Civil Engrs.*, **108**,

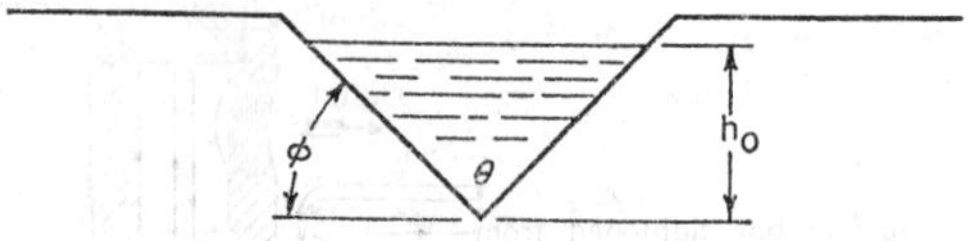

FIG. 5-19. Triangular weir.

759 (1943)] for effect of viscosity and surface tension on V-notch weir coefficients; also Venard (*op. cit.*, p. 438).

Information on other types of weirs can be obtained from standard texts on hydraulics, such as Schoder and Dawson, *op. cit.;* Addisson, *op. cit.;* Rouse, "Engineering Hydraulics," Wiley, New York, 1950; Linford, "Flow Measurement and Meters," Spon, London, 1949; Gibson, "Hydraulics and Its Applications," 5th ed., Constable, London, 1952.

FLUID DYNAMICS

REFERENCES: Coulson and Richardson, "Chemical Engineering," McGraw-Hill, New York, 1955. Cremer and Davies, "Chemical Engineering Practice," Academic Press, New York, 1956–1959. Dodge, "Chemical Engineering Thermodynamics," McGraw-Hill, New York, 1944. Dodge and Thompson, "Fluid Mechanics," McGraw-Hill, New York, 1937. Goldstein, "Modern Developments in Fluid Dynamics," Oxford, London, 1938. Knudsen and Katz, "Fluid Dynamics and Heat Transfer," McGraw-Hill, New York, 1958. Lapple *et al.*, "Fluid and Particle Mechanics," University of Delaware, Newark, 1951. Rouse, "Engineering Hydraulics," Wiley, New York, 1950. Streeter, "Handbook of Fluid Dynamics," McGraw-Hill, New York, 1961. Vennard, "Elementary Fluid Mechanics," 4th ed., Wiley, New York, 1961.

NATURE OF FLUIDS

A **fluid** is a substance which undergoes continuous deformation when subjected to a shear stress. The resistance offered by a real fluid to such deformation is called its **consistency**. For gases and for simple (or Newtonian) liquids, the consistency is constant if static pressure and temperature are fixed; and for such materials, the consistency is called the **viscosity**.

Consider two layers of fluid y ft. apart, as shown in Fig. 5-20, with the top layer moving parallel to the bottom layer at a velocity u ft./sec. relative to the bottom layer. With a gas or a Newtonian liquid, a force F is required to maintain this motion, the magnitude of which is given by

$$F = \frac{\mu u A}{y} \quad \text{lb. force} \qquad (5\text{-}28)$$

Expressed on a differential basis

$$\tau = \frac{\mu}{g_c}\left(\frac{du}{dy}\right) \qquad (5\text{-}29)$$

where μ = fluid viscosity, lb./(ft.)(sec.); τ = shear stress, lb. force/sq. ft.; g_c = dimensional constant, 32.17 (lb.) (ft.)/(lb. force)(sec.^{2}); du/dy = velocity gradient, 1/sec. For definitions of F, A, u, and y, see Fig. 5-20.

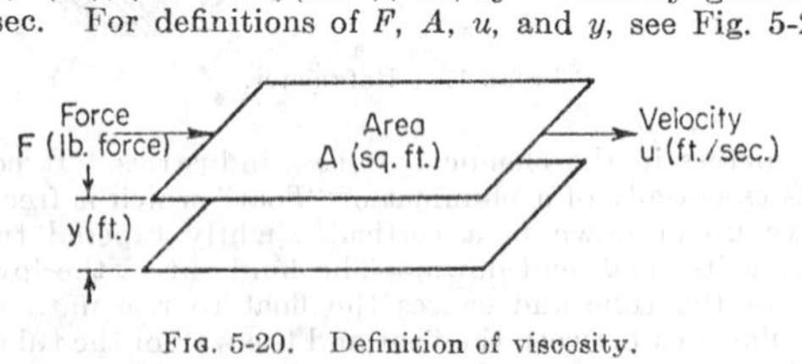

FIG. 5-20. Definition of viscosity.

Viscosity can thus be considered to be a momentum conductivity analogous to thermal conductivity in heat transfer by conduction and to the diffusion coefficient in mass transfer by diffusion.

If the consistency of a fluid is a function of shear stress as well as of temperature and pressure, the fluid is called a **non-Newtonian fluid.** Such phenomena are observed only in certain classes of liquids and semisolids. Characteristics of these materials are described under Non-Newtonian Flow, pp. 5-35 to 5-38.

An **ideal** or **perfect fluid** is a hypothetical gas or

liquid which offers no resistance to shear and therefore has zero consistency. The imaginary perfect fluid is not to be confused with a "perfect gas" (*cf.* p. 4-55). In most flow problems, highly incorrect results are obtained if viscosity is neglected, although in the same problem, the pressure-volume-temperature relations for perfect gases may often be safely used.

The unit of viscosity (*i.e.*, absolute viscosity) in the c.g.s. system is the **poise** (p.) = 1 g./(cm.)(sec.). Viscosities are usually tabulated in **centipoise** (cp.) = 0.01 poise. Conversion factors from centipoise to other units are given in Table 5-5.

Table 5-5. Conversion of Units for Viscosity

To Convert Centipoise to	Multiply by
lb./(ft.)(sec.)	$0.672 \times 10^{-3} = 1/1488$
lb./(ft.)(hr.)	2.42
kg./(m.)(sec.)	0.001

Kinematic viscosity of a fluid of density ρ lb./cu. ft. and viscosity μ lb./(ft.)(sec.) is $\nu = \mu/\rho$, ft.^{2}/sec. The c.g.s. unit of kinematic viscosity is known as the **stoke** and equals 1 cm.^{2}/sec.

Fluidity is the reciprocal of viscosity. In the c.g.s. system, the unit is known as the **rhe** = 1/poise.

A wide variety of viscometers is available for measurement of viscosity, such as capillary, rotational, orifice, falling ball, and oscillatory types. They are described in Barr, "A Monograph of Viscometry," Oxford, New York, 1931.

In several common commercial viscometers, the kinematic viscosity is determined from the time of efflux (seconds) of a fixed volume of liquid through a standard capillary tube or orifice. In such instruments, the entrance and kinetic effects often constitute an important part of the resistance to flow. Consequently, the relation between time of efflux and kinematic viscosity is empirically determined.

The following special terminology is now commonly used in connection with **polymer solution viscosities:**

Relative viscosity $\mu_r = \mu/\mu_0$, ratio of solution viscosity to solvent viscosity at the same temperature.

Specific viscosity $\mu_{sp} = \mu_r - 1$.

Reduced viscosity $\mu_{red} = \mu_{sp}/c$, where c = concentration, g./100 ml.

Inherent viscosity $\mu_{inh} = (\ln \mu_r)/c$.

Intrinsic viscosity $[\mu] = [(\ln \mu_r)/c]_{c \to 0}$. This is also called the limiting viscosity number. Intrinsic viscosity $[\mu]$, being independent of concentration by virtue of extrapolation to $c = 0$, is the quantity usually correlated with molecular weight. For additional information see Billmeyer, "Textbook of Polymer Chemistry," pp. 128–139, Interscience, New York, 1957.

Viscosity data are given in Sec. 3, Tables 3-262 *ff.* See also "International Critical Tables," McGraw-Hill, New York, 1926–1933; Hodgman *et al.*, "Handbook of Chemistry and Physics," 43d ed., pp. 2209–2227, Chemical Rubber, Cleveland, 1961–1962; Lange, "Handbook of Chemistry," 10th ed., pp. 1657–1669, McGraw-Hill, New York, 1961. Reasonable estimates of viscosity can often be made when no data are available. Methods available for estimation are summarized in Sec. 3.

TERMINOLOGY IN FLUID DYNAMICS

A flow is said to be **steady** if it is invariant with time, *i.e.*, the mass flow rate is constant and all other quantities (temperature, pressure, cross-sectional area) are independent of time. Conversely, the flow is said to be **unsteady** if the mass flow rate and/or other quantities vary with time. Unsteady flow can result from control-valve action, from the action of reciprocating machinery, or from unstable two-phase flow.

A stream is said to be **uniform** if the shape and size of its cross section are the same throughout the channel. A temperature or velocity is said to be uniform throughout a region when it has the same value at all parts of the region at a given instant.

The **mean mass velocity** G of a stream past a given cross section, taken perpendicular to the general direction of flow through the apparatus, is the weight rate of flow divided by the area of the given cross section. Throughout a channel of uniform cross-sectional area, the mean mass velocity is constant unless there is an accumulation or depletion of material within the channel. When considering the flow through a bank of tubes or a bed of solids, the term **superficial mass velocity** is given to the quantity obtained on dividing the weight rate by the total cross-sectional area of the enclosing chamber (without subtracting that part of the cross section occupied by the obstructions).

The **mean linear velocity** V of a stream past any given cross section is commonly taken to be the quantity obtained when the corresponding mean mass velocity is divided by the average density at the given cross section. Unless the flow is isothermal, the term mean linear velocity cannot be interpreted unless the rule chosen for determination of the average density is stated definitely. Consequently it is preferable, when possible, to treat non-isothermal flow in terms of the mass velocity. **Superficial linear velocity** corresponds to the superficial mass velocity.

The **acoustic velocity,** or **velocity of sound,** in a fluid of large extent or contained in a rigid-walled vessel, is given by

$$V_a = \sqrt{g_c\left(\frac{\partial p}{\partial \rho}\right)_s} = \sqrt{g_c k\left(\frac{\partial p}{\partial \rho}\right)_T} = \sqrt{\frac{Kg_c}{\rho}} \quad \text{ft./sec.} \tag{5-30}$$

where g_c = dimensional constant, 32.17 (lb.)(ft.)/(lb. force)(sec.^{2}); p = absolute pressure, lb. force/sq. ft.; ρ = fluid density, lb./cu. ft.; k = ratio of specific heats c_p/c_v, dimensionless; K = fluid bulk modulus of elasticity, lb. force/sq. ft. Subscript s denotes constancy of entropy, and subscript T, constancy of temperature. For perfect gases, $(\partial p/\partial \rho)_T = p/\rho = RT/M$, where T = absolute temperature, °R. (= °F. + 460), R = gas constant, 1546 (ft.)(lb. force)/(°R.)(lb.-mole), M = molecular weight, lb./lb.-mole. Consequently, for a perfect gas, $V_a = \sqrt{g_c kRT/M}$. See Dodge and Thompson, *op. cit.*, pp. 362–366; Keenan, "Thermodynamics," pp. 318–321, 332, Wiley, New York, 1941.

The **velocity head** $V^2/2g_c$, (ft.)(lb. force)/lb., is the static head equivalent of the kinetic energy in a stream of uniform velocity V.

For definitions of thermodynamic terms, such as internal energy, enthalpy, total heat, entropy, etc., see Sec. 4 (pp. 4-26 to 4-28).

A **Reynolds number** N_{Re} is any of several dimensionless quantities of the form $LV\rho/\mu$ which are all proportional to the ratio of inertial force to viscous force in a flow system. Here L = a characteristic linear dimension of the flow channel, ft.; V = linear velocity, ft./sec.; ρ = fluid density, lb./cu. ft.; μ = fluid viscosity, lb./(ft.)(sec.). The **critical** Reynolds number corresponds to the transition from turbulent flow to laminar flow as the velocity is reduced. Its value depends upon the channel geometry, being in the range of 2000 to 3000 for circular pipe (see Fig. 5-25).

The **mean hydraulic radius** R_H of a channel is equal to the cross-sectional area of that part of the channel which is filled with fluid divided by the length of the wetted perimeter. The hydraulic radius of a circular pipe is one-fourth the diameter; hence for a non-circular duct, the **hydraulic diameter** is said to be four times the hydraulic radius. For various cross-sectional shapes, see Table 5-10.

A **streamline** is defined as a line which lies in the direction of flow at every point at a given instant. **Laminar flow** is defined as that in which the streamlines remain distinct from one another over their entire length. The streamlines need not be straight or the flow steady, as long as the above criterion is fulfilled. This type of motion is also called **streamline flow** or **viscous flow.**

If the Reynolds number in a system exceeds the critical Reynolds number, the motion is generally found not to be laminar throughout the channel. Eddies generated in the initial zone of instability spread rapidly throughout the fluid, thereby producing a disruption of the entire flow pattern. The result is fluid turbulence superimposed upon the primary motion of translation, producing what is called **turbulent flow**. For additional information on turbulence and turbulent flow, see Hinze, "Turbulence," McGraw-Hill, New York, 1959; Rouse, *op. cit.*, pp. 83–99; Schlichting, "Boundary-layer Theory," 4th ed., pp. 457–611, McGraw-Hill, New York, 1960.

ENERGY BALANCE

Total Energy Balance. Consider a unit weight (1 lb.) of fluid in a flow system, and let

G = mass velocity, lb./(sec.)(sq. ft. of cross section)
g = local acceleration due to gravity, ft./sec.^{2}
g_c = dimensional constant, 32.17 (lb.)(ft.)/(lb. force)(sec.^{2})
i = enthalpy, B.t.u./lb.
J = mechanical equivalent of heat, 778 (ft.)(lb. force)/B.t.u.
p = absolute static pressure, lb. force/sq. ft.
s = entropy, B.t.u./(°R.)(lb.)
u = internal (or intrinsic) energy, B.t.u./lb.
V = linear velocity, ft./sec.
v = specific volume, cu. ft./lb.
Z = height above any arbitrary horizontal datum plane, ft.

Then the potential energy relative to the chosen reference level is Zg/g_c, the kinetic energy is $V^2/2g_c$, and the total energy of the pound of fluid is $(Ju + Zg/g_c + V^2/2g_c)$, all in units of (ft.)(lb. force)/lb. For steady flow of the fluid, there will be no accumulation or depletion of either fluid or energy within the system, and the total energy of the system can be altered only by adding or subtracting heat from the system or by external work on the system. Thus

$$\left(Ju_2 + \frac{Z_2g}{g_c} + \frac{V_2^2}{2g_c}\right) - \left(Ju_1 + \frac{Z_1g}{g_c} + \frac{V_1^2}{2g_c}\right) = JQ + W \tag{5-31}$$

where subscripts 1 and 2 indicate conditions at inlet and outlet, respectively; Q is the heat added, B.t.u./lb., from sources external to the system; W is the net external work, (ft.)(lb. force)/lb., done on the pound of fluid while in the apparatus. The term W may be subdivided as

$$W = p_1v_1 - p_2v_2 + W_e \tag{5-32}$$

where W_e = work delivered by external source, such as a blower or pump, (ft.)(lb. force)/lb.

Combining Eqs. (5-31) and (5-32) gives

$$Ju_1 + \frac{Z_1g}{g_c} + \frac{V_1^2}{2g_c} + p_1v_1 + JQ + W_e = Ju_2 + \frac{Z_2g}{g_c} + \frac{V_2^2}{2g_c} + p_2v_2 \tag{5-33}$$

This expression of the first law of thermodynamics is often known as the **over-all energy balance** form of **Bernoulli's theorem.** No friction term occurs in this expression, since friction represents a conversion of mechanical energy into heat, with no change in the over-all energy content of the system.

The kinetic-energy terms in the foregoing equations apply strictly only for a uniform velocity across a given cross section. For turbulent flow in circular pipes, the term $V^2/2g_c$ is 3 to 8 per cent too low; while for laminar flow in circular pipes, the proper kinetic-energy term is V^2/g_c, which makes due allowance for the parabolic velocity distribution.

If $i\,[= u + (pv/J)$, B.t.u./lb.] is the enthalpy (total heat or heat content), Eq. (5-33) takes a form convenient for use with steam or other fluids for which the thermal properties are tabulated or calculable:

$$(Z_1 - Z_2)\frac{g}{g_c} + J(i_1 - i_2) + JQ + W_e = \frac{V_2^2 - V_1^2}{2g_c} \tag{5-34}$$

For adiabatic, frictionless flow through a horizontal nozzle, Eq. (5-34) reduces to

$$J(i_1 - i_2) = \frac{G^2(v_2^2 - v_1^2)}{2g_c} \tag{5-35}$$

For perfect gases [*i.e.*, if pv = (constant)(T)], Eq. (5-35) becomes

$$J(i_1 - i_2) = J\int_{T_2}^{T_1} c_p\,dT = J(c_p)_{\text{avg}}(T_1 - T_2) = \frac{k}{k-1}(p_1v_1 - p_2v_2) \tag{5-36}$$

where $k = c_p/c_v$, ratio of specific heats at constant pressure and volume, respectively; T = absolute temperature °R. (= °F. + 460).

Mechanical Energy Balance. The change in internal energy $J\,du$ of a pound of fluid may be expressed as $JT\,ds - p\,dv$. If other forms of energy, such as electrical, are present and undergoing change, they should also be included. The presence of friction renders the process irreversible, whence $JT\,ds = J\,dQ + dF$, where F = friction loss, (ft.)(lb. force)/lb. With this consideration of friction loss and irreversibility, Eq. (5-33) becomes

$$\frac{Z_1g}{g_c} + \frac{V_1^2}{2g_c} - \int_1^2 v\,dp - F + W_e = \frac{Z_2g}{g_c} + \frac{V_2^2}{2g_c} \tag{5-37}$$

Eq. (5-37) is known as the **mechanical energy** form of **Bernoulli's theorem.**

For **liquids**, the integral $\int_1^2 v\,dp$ becomes simply $(p_2 - p_1)v$ where v is substantially constant. For **gases,** the exact value of the integral depends upon the path followed by the expansion. For **isothermal flow** of a perfect gas

$$\int_1^2 v\,dp = -\frac{RT}{M}\ln\frac{v_2}{v_1} = -\frac{RT}{M}\ln\frac{p_1}{p_2} \tag{5-38}$$

For **adiabatic flow,** see Compressible Flow, p. 5-22.

System Pressure-drop Evaluation. There is a real distinction between pressure drop and friction loss. Pressure drop represents a conversion of pressure energy into any other form of energy, whereas friction loss represents a net loss in the total available work energy of the fluid. The two terms are related by Eq. (5-37).

There are two methods of evaluating the over-all pressure drop for a system having a number of resistances in series. The first method involves calculation of the **pressure drop** for each individual resistance with due regard for algebraic sign and then summing up all such items for the entire system. The second method involves the calculation of **friction loss** for each individual resistance, summing up all such items, and applying Eq. (5-37) to obtain the over-all pressure drop. The pressure-drop summation should be used in systems involving branching lines. For the case of compressible flow with large pressure drops, see Compressible Flow, p. 5-22.

MOMENTUM BALANCE

The **principle of conservation of momentum** states that the total momentum within a system remains constant during the exchange of momentum between two or more masses of the system. This is illustrated by the case of two masses m_M and m_N moving in the same direction, which impact and then travel together in the same direction with a common velocity V:

$$\frac{m_M V_M}{g_c} + \frac{m_N V_N}{g_c} = \frac{(m_M + m_N)V}{g_c} \tag{5-39}$$

In this illustration there is a loss in kinetic energy through the exchange of momentum.

For flowing fluids, the **equation of momentum** is

$$F = \frac{w\,\Delta V}{g_c} = \frac{\rho q\,\Delta V}{g_c} \tag{5-40}$$

where F = force acting on the fluid, lb. force; w = weight rate of flow, lb./sec.; ΔV = change in velocity, ft./sec.; ρ = fluid density, lb./cu. ft.; q = volumetric flow rate, cu. ft./sec.; g_c = dimensional constant, 32.17 (lb.)(ft.)/(lb. force)(sec.^{2}). This equation is applied to several practical problems in the following subsections.

Jet Impact on a Plate. For an open jet impinging upon a **stationary oblique flat plate** (Dodge and Thompson, *op. cit.*, pp. 114–115), as shown in Fig. 5-21, force F acting normal to the plate is given by

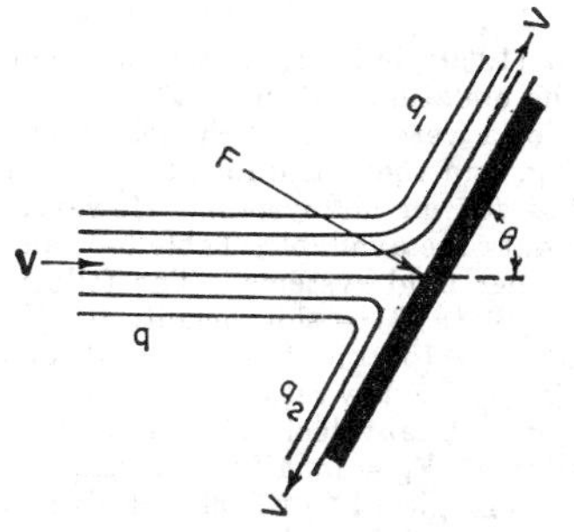

FIG. 5-21. Jet impact on stationary oblique flat plate.

$$F = \frac{\rho q V}{g_c} \sin\theta \tag{5-41}$$

This force is a vector quantity, and its components can be determined from vector addition. The division of flow is given by

$$q_1 = \frac{q}{2}(1 + \cos\theta) \tag{5-42}$$

$$q_2 = \frac{q}{2}(1 - \cos\theta) \tag{5-43}$$

where θ = angle of inclination of the plate; other symbols as given above.

The above equations assume that there is no loss of energy (thus the velocity must be unchanged), and that the plate is smooth (thus there is no tangential force).

For jet impact on a **stationary normal flat plate**, θ = 90 deg. and

$$F = \frac{\rho q V}{g_c} \tag{5-44}$$

$$q_1 = q_2 = \frac{q}{2} \tag{5-45}$$

Forces on Bends. The forces exerted by a flowing fluid on a bend (Fig. 5-22) can be computed from a force balance on the bend (Dodge and Thompson, *op. cit.*, pp. 122–123; and Vennard, *op. cit.*, p. 175). From a balance of the forces due to pressure, momentum change, and weight along directions x and y, the forces F_x and F_y exerted **by the bend on the flowing fluid** are

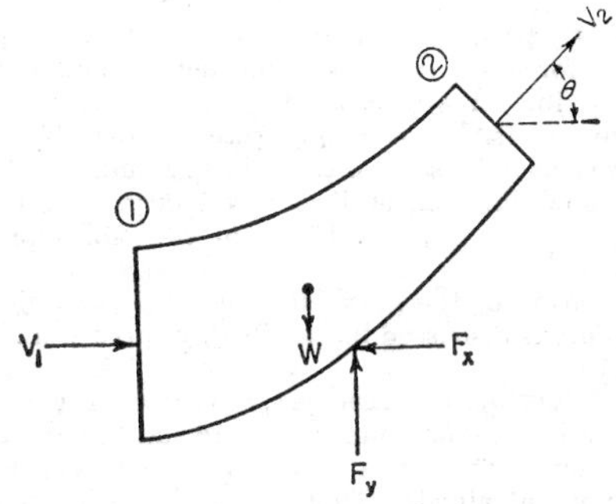

FIG. 5-22. Forces on a bend.

$$F_x = p_1A_1 - p_2A_2\cos\theta + \frac{\rho q}{g_c}(V_1 - V_2\cos\theta) \tag{5-46}$$

$$F_y = \frac{Wg}{g_c} + \left(p_2A_2 + \frac{\rho q V_2}{g_c}\right)\sin\theta \tag{5-47}$$

where F_x = force in horizontal direction exerted by the bend on the flowing fluid, lb. force; F_y = force in vertical direction exerted by the bend on the flowing fluid, lb. force; p_1 = pressure, lb. force/sq. ft., A_1 = area, sq. ft., and V_1 = velocity, ft./sec., at the inlet to the bend; p_2 = pressure, lb. force/sq. ft., A_2 = area, sq. ft., and V_2 = velocity, ft./sec., at the outlet of the bend; q = fluid volumetric flow rate, cu. ft./sec.; ρ = fluid density, lb./cu. ft.; g = local acceleration due to gravity, approximately 32.2 ft./sec.^{2}; g_c = dimensional constant, 32.17 (lb.)(ft.)/(lb. force)(sec.^{2}); W = weight of fluid in the bend, lb.; θ = angle subtended by the outlet.

The forces exerted **by the flowing fluid on the bend** are equal and opposite to those given by Eqs. (5-46) and (5-47).

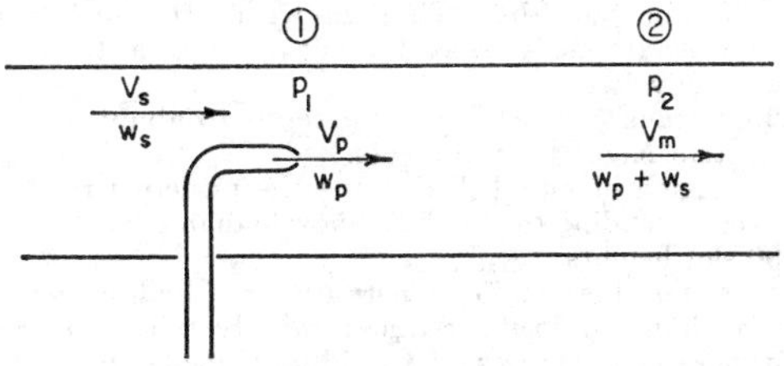

FIG. 5-23. Draft-tube ejector.

Ejectors. An ejector is a device in which the kinetic energy of one fluid (primary fluid) is used to pump another fluid (secondary fluid). The performance of this device can be computed by application of the momentum equation. The method will be illustrated for a draft-tube ejector (Fig. 5-23). The primary, high-velocity fluid enters at 1 and mixes with the secondary, low-velocity fluid; mixing is assumed to be complete at 2. Through this mixing, a major portion of the momentum of the primary fluid is imparted to the secondary fluid, resulting in a static pressure at 2 greater than that at 1. This increase in static pressure is given by equating the pressure and momentum forces along the draft tube. For incompressible fluids, this increase $p_2 - p_1$ is given by

$$(p_2 - p_1)g_cA = w_p(V_p - V_m) + w_s(V_s - V_m) \qquad (5\text{-}48)$$

where p_1 = pressure at 1, lb. force/sq. ft.; p_2 = pressure at 2, lb. force/sq. ft.; g_c = dimensional constant, 32.17 (lb.)(ft.)/(lb. force)(sec.²); A = cross-sectional area of the tube, sq. ft.; w_p = weight rate of flow, lb./sec., and V_p = velocity, ft./sec., of the primary fluid; w_s = weight rate of flow, lb./sec., and V_s = velocity, ft./sec., of the secondary fluid; V_m = velocity of the combined fluids, ft./sec.

Application of the momentum equation to ejectors of other types is discussed in detail by Lapple *et al.*, *op. cit.*, Chap. 5.

Jet Behavior. A **free jet,** upon leaving an outlet, will entrain the surrounding fluid and expand. The momentum of the jet is transferred to the surrounding fluid being entrained. There is some loss in momentum due to turbulence and to static-pressure gradients across the jet. A jet is considered free when its cross-sectional area is less than one-fifth of the total cross-sectional flow area of the region through which it is flowing [Elrod, *Heating, Piping Air Conditioning,* **26** (3), 149–155 (1954)].

A **turbulent jet** is considered in this discussion to be a free jet whose jet Reynolds number is greater than 2,000. Additional discussion on the relation between Reynolds number and turbulence in jets is given by Elrod (*loc. cit.*). A turbulent free jet (Fig. 5-24) has four flow regions

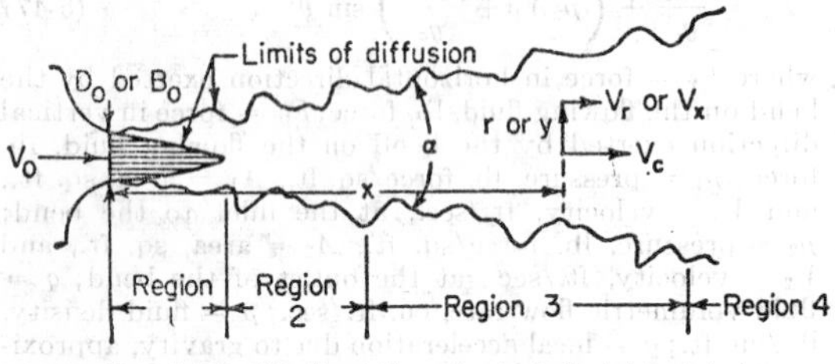

FIG. 5-24. Configuration of a turbulent free jet.

[Tuve, *Heating, Piping Air Conditioning,* **25** (1), 181–191 (1953)]:

1. Region of flow establishment—a short region whose length is about 5 nozzle diameters or slot heights (for a slot of infinite width). The fluid within the cone or core of same length has a velocity about the same as the initial discharge velocity.
2. A transition region that extends to about 8 nozzle diameters, slightly less for slots.
3. Region of established flow—the principal region of the jet, extending to about 100 nozzle diameters or about 2000 slot heights.
4. A terminal region where the residual center-line or maximum velocity reduces rapidly within a short distance. For air jets, the residual velocity will reduce to less than 1 ft./sec., usually regarded as still air.

Table 5-6 gives characteristics of **rounded-inlet circular jets and of rounded-inlet infinitely wide slot jets** (aspect ratio or width-to-height ratio > 15). Information in the table is for a homogeneous air system under isothermal conditions, *i.e.,* where both the jet fluid and the entrained fluid are air and of the same temperature. Data of Donald and Singer [*Trans. Inst. Chem. Engrs.,*

Table 5-6. Turbulent Free-jet Characteristics
Where both jet fluid and entrained fluid are air

Rounded-inlet Circular Jet

Longitudinal distribution of velocity along jet center line†·‡

$$\frac{V_c}{V_0} = K\frac{D_0}{x} \qquad \text{for } 7 < \frac{x}{D_0} < 100$$

$$K = 5 \qquad \text{for } V_0 = 8 \text{ to } 16 \text{ ft./sec.}$$
$$K = 6.2 \qquad \text{for } V_0 = 33 \text{ to } 170 \text{ ft./sec.}$$

Radial distribution of longitudinal velocity‡

$$\log\left(\frac{V_c}{V_r}\right) = 40\left(\frac{r}{x}\right)^2 \qquad \text{for } 7 < \frac{x}{D_0} < 100$$

Jet angle†·‡

$$\alpha \simeq 20° \qquad \text{for } \frac{x}{D_0} < 100$$

Entrainment of surrounding fluid*

$$\frac{q}{q_0} = 0.32\frac{x}{D_0} \qquad \text{for } 7 < \frac{x}{D_0} < 100$$

Rounded-inlet, Infinitely Wide, Slot Jet

Longitudinal distribution of velocity along jet center line*

$$\frac{V_c}{V_0} = 2.28\left(\frac{B_0}{x}\right)^{0.5} \qquad \text{for } 5 < \frac{x}{B_0} < 2000 \text{ and } V_0 = 40 \text{ to } 180 \text{ ft./sec.}$$

Transverse distribution of longitudinal velocity*

$$\log\left(\frac{V_c}{V_x}\right) = 18.4\left(\frac{y}{x}\right)^2 \qquad \text{for } 5 < \frac{x}{B_0} < 2000$$

Jet angle*

α is slightly larger than that for a circular jet

Entrainment of surrounding fluid*

$$\frac{q}{q_0} = 0.62\left(\frac{x}{B_0}\right)^{0.5} \qquad \text{for } 5 < \frac{x}{B_0} < 2000$$

† Nottage, Slaby, and Gojsza, *Heating, Piping Air Conditioning,* **24** (1), 165–176 (1952).
‡ Tuve, *Heating, Piping Air Conditioning,* **25** (1), 181–191 (1953).
* Albertson, Dai, Jensen, and Rouse, *Proc. Am. Soc. Civil Engrs.,* **74**, 1571–1596 (1948).

37, 255–267 (1959)] indicate that jet angle and the coefficients in the equations given in Table 5-6 depend upon the fluids; for a water system, the jet angle for a circular jet is 14 deg. and the entrainment ratio is about 70 per cent of that for an air system. However, until more conclusive data are available, Table 5-6 can be used as a guide for other fluid systems. The following **nomenclature** is used: B_0 = slot height, ft.; D_0 = opening diameter, ft.; q = total jet flow rate at distance x, cu. ft./sec.; q_0 = initial jet flow rate, cu. ft./sec.; r = radius, ft.; V_c = jet center-line velocity, ft./sec.; V_0 = initial jet velocity, ft./sec.; V_r = longitudinal velocity at radius r, ft./sec.; V_x = longitudinal velocity at distance y, ft./sec.; x = distance from jet discharge, ft.; y = distance from jet center line, ft.

Characteristics of **rectangular jets** of various aspect ratios are given by Elrod (*loc. cit.*). Characteristics of **slot jets** discharging into a moving surrounding fluid are given by Weinstein, Osterle and Forstall [*J. Appl. Mech.,* **23**, 437–443 (1956)] and of **coaxial gas jets** by Forstall and Shapiro [*J. Appl. Mech.,* **17**, 399–408 (1950)].

Density gradients will affect the rate of spread of a single-phase free jet. A jet of lower density than the surroundings spreads more rapidly than a jet of the same density as the surroundings, and conversely, a jet of higher density than the surroundings spreads less rapidly. Additional details are given by Keagy and Weller (*Proc. Heat Transfer and Fluid Mech. Inst., A.S.M.E.,* June 22–24, 1949, pp. 89–98) and Cleeves and Boelter [*Chem. Eng. Progress,* **43**, 123–134 (1947)].

Laminar Jets. Few experimental data exist on laminar jets; however, theoretical analyses for velocity distributions and entrainment ratios are available (see Schlichting, "Boundary Layer Theory," 4th ed., pp. 164–168, 181–184, McGraw-Hill, New York, 1960).

FLOW IN PIPES AND CHANNELS

Velocity Distribution, Circular Pipes. For **laminar flow** in circular pipes, the velocity pattern is parabolic in shape with a maximum velocity at the center equal to two times the average velocity V. The local velocity u at any point in the cross section is given by

$$\frac{u}{V} = 2\left(1 - \frac{r^2}{r_w^2}\right) \tag{5-49}$$

where r = radius at the point in question and r_w = radius of the pipe. See Knudsen and Katz, *op. cit.*, p. 86.

The corresponding **distribution of residence time** for **laminar flow** is given by

$$F(\theta) = 1 - \frac{1}{4}\left(\frac{\theta_{avg}}{\theta}\right) \quad \text{for } \frac{\theta_{avg}}{\theta} < 2 \tag{5-50}$$

where $F(\theta)$ = fraction of material in system for less than time θ; θ_{avg} = average residence time in system. See Danckwerts [*Chem. Eng. Sci.*, **2**, 1–12 (February, 1953)].

In the transition region (N_{Re} from 2000 to 3000), the velocity profile becomes more blunt and the ratio V/u_{max} increases (see Fig. 5-11). At higher Reynolds numbers the flow is generally turbulent, and the velocity profile in smooth-wall pipes is characterized by a laminar boundary layer, a turbulent core, and a buffer layer in between. For **turbulent flow** in rough-wall pipes, the local velocity in the turbulent core is given by

$$u^+ = 8.5 + 2.5 \ln \frac{y}{e} \tag{5-51}$$

where $u^+ = u/u^*$; u = local velocity, ft./sec., at distance y ft. from the pipe wall; $u^* = \sqrt{\tau_0 g_c/\rho}$ (called friction velocity); τ_0 = wall shear stress ($\Delta p D/4L$), lb. force/sq. ft.; g_c = dimensional constant, 32.17 (lb.)(ft.)/(lb. force)(sec.^{2}); ρ = fluid density, lb./cu. ft.; Δp = pressure drop, lb. force/sq. ft.; D = inside pipe diameter, ft.; L = pipe length, ft.; e = height of wall roughness, ft. For further details, see Knudsen and Katz, *op. cit.*, pp. 154–169, and Cremer and Davies, *op. cit.*, vol. 4, p. 401.

Equations describing the distribution of residence time for turbulent flow in pipes are given by Danckwerts, *loc. cit.*

Velocity Distribution, Other Shapes. For velocity profiles under laminar- and turbulent-flow conditions in annuli, between infinite parallel planes, and in other noncircular cross sections, see Knudsen and Katz, *op. cit.*; Purday, "Mechanics of Viscous Flow," Chap. II, Dover, New York, 1949; Rouse, "Advanced Mechanics of Fluids," p. 219, Wiley, New York, 1959; Goldstein, *op. cit.*, vol. 2, pp. 359–360.

Analytically derived equations are presented by Straub, Silberman, and Nelson [*Trans. Am. Soc. Civil Engrs.*, **123**, 685–714 (1958)] for **laminar flow** through a variety of **open-channel** cross sections, including semicircular, rectangular, triangular, elliptical, trapezoidal, etc.

Experimentally determined velocity profiles are also presented by Straub *et al.* for **turbulent flow** in triangular troughs. Profiles for channels of various cross sections are given in O'Brien and Hickox, "Applied Fluid Mechanics," pp. 268–270, McGraw-Hill, New York, 1937, and Chow, "Open-channel Hydraulics," pp. 24–29, McGraw-Hill, New York, 1959.

Incompressible Flow. The flow can be considered to be incompressible if (1) the substance flowing is a liquid or (2) if it is a gas whose density changes within the system no more than 10 per cent. In this event, if the inlet density is employed, the resulting error in computed pressure drop will generally not exceed the uncertainty limits in the friction factor. In the event of larger changes in fluid density, *e.g.*, gases with large pressure drops, the more exact methods described under Compressible Flow (pp. 5-22 to 5-28) should be used.

General Formulas and Methods. The problem of finding one of the three quantities—rate of discharge, size of channel, pressure or head loss—when the other two are given is solved by substituting the data of the problem in an appropriate form of the mechanical energy balance (p. 5-16) after the term F, frictional loss of mechanical energy, has been evaluated. That part of F which arises from friction within the channel proper is considered below. The part due to fittings, bends, and the like, which often constitutes a major part of the friction, is discussed on pp. 5-30 to 5-35.

The **Fanning,** or **Darcy, equation,** Eq. (5-52), for steady flow in uniform **circular pipes** running full of liquid under **isothermal conditions**

$$F = \left(\frac{4fL}{D}\right)\frac{V^2}{2g_c} = \left(\frac{4fL}{D}\right)h_v = \left(\frac{4fL}{D}\right)\frac{G^2}{2g_c\rho^2} = \frac{32fLw^2}{\pi^2\rho^2 g_c D^5} = \frac{32fLq^2}{\pi^2 g_c D^5} \tag{5-52}$$

gives the friction loss F in (ft.)(lb. force)/lb. of fluid flowing (or ft. of fluid flowing), where D = duct diameter, ft.; L = duct length, ft.; ρ = fluid density, lb./cu. ft.; V = fluid velocity, ft./sec.; h_v = velocity head ($V^2/2g_c$), ft. of fluid flowing; G = mass velocity, lb./(sec.)(sq. ft.); w = weight rate of flow, lb./sec.; q = volumetric rate of flow, cu. ft./sec.; g_c = dimensional constant, 32.17 (lb.)(ft.)/(lb. force)(sec.^{2}); f = **Fanning friction factor** (see below), dimensionless.

The pressure drop due to friction is $\Delta p = F\rho$, lb. force/sq. ft.

The **Fanning friction factor** f is a function of the Reynolds number N_{Re} and the roughness of the channel inside surface ϵ. One widely used correlation [Moody, *Trans. Am. Soc. Mech. Engrs.*, **66**, 671–684 (1944)], as shown in Fig. 5-25, is a plot of Fanning friction factor as a function of Reynolds number and relative roughness ϵ/D or ϵ''/D'', where ϵ = surface roughness, ft.; D = pipe inside diameter, ft.; ϵ'' = surface roughness, in.; and D'' = pipe inside diameter, in. Values of ϵ or ϵ'' for various materials are given in Table 5-7. Substitution of the equation for curve A, Fig. 5-25, into Eq. (5-52) yields Poiseuille's law for laminar flow ($N_{Re} \leq 2000$); see Table 5-11. Care must be exercised when values of f are taken from the literature, because the same name and symbol are sometimes used to denote various multiples of the f given by Fig. 5-25.

A rapid method of solving Eq. (5-52) for turbulent flow ($N_{Re} > 2000$) is to use the **alignment chart** in Fig. 5-26, which is based on curve D of Fig. 5-25 [Genereaux, *Chem. & Met. Eng.*, **44**, 241–248 (1937)]. If, for the value of N_{Re}, obtaining some other value of f, say f', is pre-

Table 5-7. Values of Surface Roughness for Various Materials*

Material	Surface roughness	
	ϵ, ft.	ϵ'', in.
Drawn tubing (brass, lead, glass, and the like)	0.000005	0.00006
Commercial steel or wrought iron	0.00015	0.0018
Asphalted cast iron	0.0004	0.0048
Galvanized iron	0.0005	0.006
Cast iron	0.00085	0.010
Wood stave	0.0006–0.003	0.0072–0.036
Concrete	0.001–0.01	0.012–0.12
Riveted steel	0.003–0.03	0.036–0.36

* Moody, *Trans. Am. Soc. Mech. Engrs.*, **66**, 671–684 (1944); *Mech. Eng.*, **69**, 1005–1006 (1947).

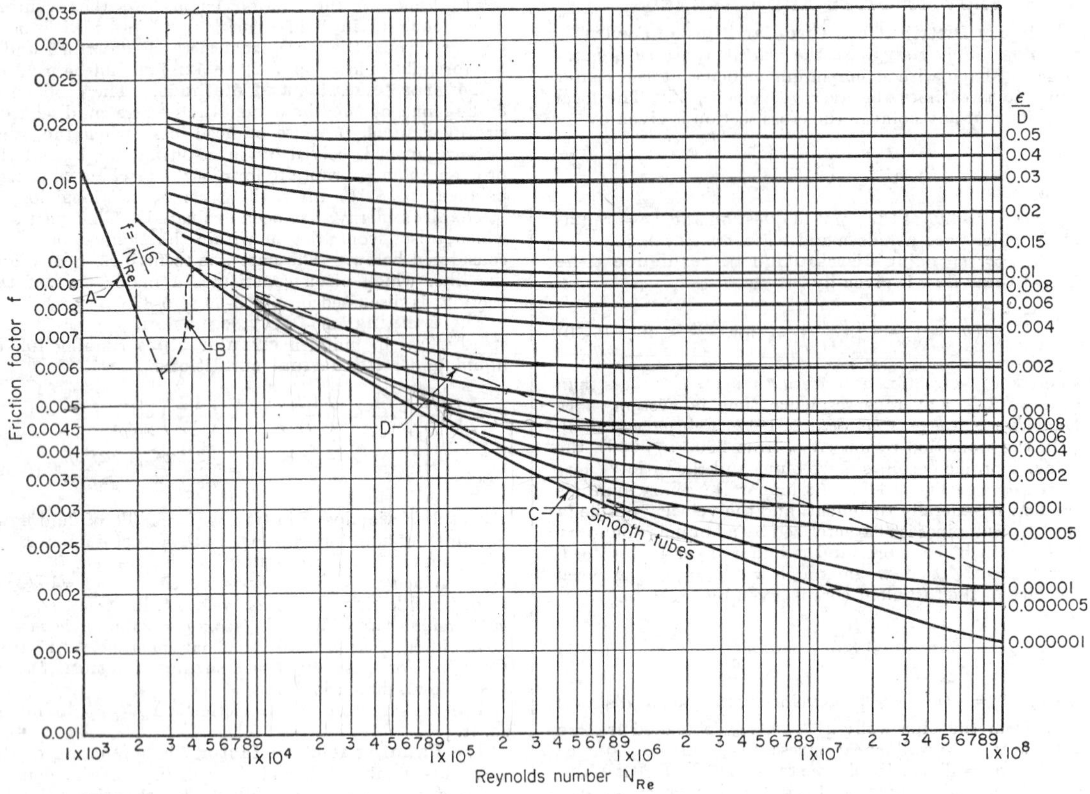

FIG. 5-25. Fanning friction factors. [*Based on Moody, Trans. Am. Soc. Mech. Engrs.*, **66**, 671 (1944).]

Table 5-8. Correction Factors for Fig. 5-26

Quantity sought	$\frac{\Delta p}{L}$ or $\frac{\Delta h}{L}$	D_i	w or G
Factor	f'/f	$(f'/f)^{1/5}$	$\sqrt{f/f'}$

ferred, the quantity sought, as given by the chart, should be multiplied by the factors given in Table 5-8. A nomograph to find pressure drop, taking into account pipe surface roughness, and a nomograph to determine flow rate or pipe size if either is unknown and if the pressure drop is known, are given by Arnold [*Chem. Eng.*, **66** (11), 103–106 (1959)].

For **rough estimates** or **checks,** the velocity-head concept [Lapple, *Chem. Eng.*, **56** (5), 96–104 (1949)] can be applied to the first two forms of Eq. (5-52). The velocity head is $V^2/2g_c = h_v$ and the number of velocity-head losses in straight pipe is $4fL/D$. Typical values of h_v and L/D for 1 velocity-head loss are given in Table 5-9.

Table 5-9. Approximate Values of Velocity Head and Pipe Length Equivalent to One Velocity-head Loss

Fluid	Fluid velocity, ft./sec.	Velocity head, various units
Any fluid	8	1.0 ft. fluid
Water	4	0.1 lb. force/sq. in.
	12	1.0 lb. force/sq. in.
Air (125°F., 1 atm.)	50	0.5 in. water
	70	1.0 in. water
	100	2.0 in. water

Pipe length equivalent to 1 velocity-head loss

Fluid	L/D
Water	45 ($f = 0.0055$)
Air	55 ($f = 0.0045$)

Table 5-10. Values of Hydraulic Radius R_H for Various Cross Sections

$$R_H = \frac{\text{area of stream cross section}}{\text{wetted perimeter}}; \text{ hydraulic diameter} = 4R_H$$

Shape of Cross Section	R_H
Pipes and ducts, running full:	
Circle, diam. = D	$\frac{D}{4}$
Annulus, inner diam. = d, outer diam. = D	$\frac{(D-d)}{4}$
Square, side = D	$\frac{D}{4}$
Rectangle, sides a, b	$\frac{ab}{2(a+b)}$
Ellipse, major axis = $2a$, minor axis = $2b$	$\frac{ab}{K(a+b)}$ See Note
Open channels or partly filled ducts:	
Rectangle, depth = y, width = b	$\frac{by}{b+2y}$
Semicircle, free surface on a diam. D	$\frac{D}{4}$
Wide shallow stream on flat plate, depth = y	y
Triangular trough, ∠ = 90 deg., bisector vertical, depth = y, slant depth = d	$\frac{d}{4} = \frac{y}{2\sqrt{2}}$
Trapezoid (depth = y, bottom width = b): Side slope 60 deg. from horizontal	$y\left(\frac{b + y/\sqrt{3}}{b + 4y/\sqrt{3}}\right)$
Side slope 45 deg.	$\frac{yb + y^2}{b + 2\sqrt{2}y}$
Film (thickness = t) on wall of vertical wetted wall tower of diameter = D	$t - t^2/D = t$ (approx.)

NOTE: Values of K. If $S = (a - b)/(a + b)$,

S =	0.1	0.2	0.3	0.4	0.5	0.6	0.7	0.8	0.9	1.0
K =	1.002	1.010	1.023	1.040	1.064	1.092	1.127	1.168	1.216	1.273

For **cross sections other than circular** of **ducts running full** or for **open channels** when the variation in depth is negligible, where the flow is in the **turbulent-flow region,** the first three forms of the Fanning equation, Eq. (5-52), are applicable if D, wherever it occurs, is replaced by the hydraulic diameter (four times the hydraulic radius, $4\,R_H$). Values of R_H for some common cross sections are given in Table 5-10. Friction factors for annuli which contain various types of inner fin tubes and annuli which are eccentric are given by Knudsen and Katz, *op. cit.*, pp. 193–205. In the **laminar-flow region,** for **ducts running full,** the formulas given in Table 5-11 should be used. These formulas do not include end corrections. The pressure drop $p_1 - p_2$ is that measured between static pressure taps L ft. apart in the wall of a continuous duct when sufficient distance is allowed between the inlet and the upstream pressure tap to ensure the existence of the normal velocity distribution at the latter point (see p. 5-31). When short tubes are involved, these formulas will give highly incorrect results if the pressure drop is measured between terminal reservoirs without applying end corrections. For these corrections, see pp. 5-30 to 5-32.

In **non-isothermal flow of liquids,** f is sensibly increased if the liquid is being cooled and is decreased if the liquid is being heated. The available data, which are largely for oils, are approximated by first finding f as for isothermal flow of the liquid at the main-stream temperature and then dividing the result, in the case of cooling, by $(\mu_a/\mu_w)^{0.23}$ if in the laminar region, or by $(\mu_a/\mu_w)^{0.11}$ if in the turbulent region; or, in the case of heating, by $(\mu_a/\mu_w)^{0.38}$ if in the laminar region, or by $(\mu_a/\mu_w)^{0.17}$ if in the turbulent region. Here μ_a is the viscosity at the main-stream temperature, and μ_w is that at the wall temperature [see Sieder and Tate, *Ind. Eng. Chem.*, **28**, 1429–1435 (1936)]. In addition, $\rho = 1/v$ varies with temperature but, owing to incompressibility, not with p. Thus the following equation, Eq. (5-54) for pressure drop for ducts running full, such as heat-exchanger tubes, can be obtained by substituting the differential form of Eq. (5-52) into Eq. (5-37), dividing throughout by v, expressing ρ as a function of length because temperature is a function of length, and integrating,

$$p_1 - p_2 = \frac{G^2(v_2 - v_1)}{g_c} + \int_0^L \left(\frac{fG^2v}{2g_cR_H} + K\rho\right) dx \qquad (5\text{-}53)$$

$$p_1 - p_2 = \frac{G^2(v_2 - v_1)}{g_c} + \frac{fG^2v_{\text{avg}}L}{2g_cR_H} + K\rho_{\text{avg}}L \qquad (5\text{-}54)$$

where p_1 = upstream static pressure, lb. force/sq. ft.; p_2 = downstream static pressure, lb. force/sq. ft.; G = mass velocity, lb./(sec.)(sq. ft.); v_1 = specific volume at

Table 5-11. Laminar-flow Formulas

Ducts Running Full

For liquids, let $N = \frac{\rho g_c}{\mu}\left(\rho \sin \alpha + \frac{p_1 - p_2}{L}\right)$; for gases, let $N^{(a)} = \frac{g_cM}{2zRT\mu}\left(\frac{p_1^2 - p_2^2}{L}\right)$

Duct cross section	Theoretical equation for weight rate of flow
Circle,(b),(c) diam. = D	$w = \frac{\pi D^4N}{128}$ [for liquids this reduces to $p_1 - p_2 = \frac{32\mu LV}{g_cD^2}$ (*i.e.*, Poiseuille's law) if tube is horizontal]
Ellipse,(c) semiaxes = a,b	$w = \frac{\pi a^3b^3}{a^2 + b^2}\left(\frac{N}{4}\right)$
Rectangle,(d) width = a, height = b	$w = \frac{ab^3N}{K}$
where a/b = 1, 2, 3, 4, 5, 10, ∞ (broad parallel plates); K = 28.6, 17.5, 15.3, 14.2, 13.7, 12.8, 12	
Broad parallel plates,(b),(d) spacing = b; *i.e.*, rectangle with $a/b = \infty$	$w = \frac{b^3N}{12}$ per unit width
Annulus,(c) outer diam. = D_2, inner diam. = D_1	$w = \frac{\pi(D_2^2 - D_1^2)N}{128}\left[D_2^2 + D_1^2 - \frac{(D_2^2 - D_1^2)}{2.3 \log_{10}(D_2/D_1)}\right]$

Open Channels

Let $N = \frac{\rho^2 g_c \sin \alpha}{\mu}$, since necessarily $p_1 = p_2$; the following equations are valid only when the variation in depth is negligible

Channel cross section	Theoretical equation for weight rate of flow
Rectangle,(e) width = a, depth = $\frac{b}{2}$	$w = \frac{ab^3N}{2K}$
where a/b = 1, 2, 3, 4, 5, 10, ∞ (broad stream); K = 28.6, 17.5, 15.3, 14.2, 13.7, 12.8, 12	
Broad stream on flat plate,(e) depth = $\frac{b}{2}$	$w = \frac{b^3N}{24}$ per unit breadth
V-trough,(f) vertical ∠ = 90 deg., bisector vertical, slant depth = a	$w = \frac{a^4N}{57}$

Notation used in Table 5-11:

a, b, D = characteristic lengths, ft.
g_c = dimensional constant, 32.17 (lb.)(ft.)/(lb. force)(sec.²)
L = length of passage, ft.
M = molecular weight, lb./lb.-mole
p_1, p_2 = upstream and downstream static pressures, lb. force/sq. ft. abs.
R = gas constant, 1543 (ft.)(lb. force)/(°R.) (lb.-mole)
T = absolute temperature, °R. (°F. + 460)
w = weight rate of flow, lb./sec.
z = compressibility factor, dimensionless
α = angle between duct axis and horizontal, deg.
ρ = fluid density, lb./cu. ft.
μ = absolute viscosity, lb./(ft.)(sec.)

(a) If the pressure drop is less than 10 per cent of the downstream absolute pressure, the approximate expression $N = \frac{\rho g_c(p_1 - p_2)}{\mu L}$ may be used in case of gases.

(b) Dryden, Murnaghan, and Bateman, "Hydrodynamics," pp. 178, 184–185, Dover, New York, 1956.
(c) Lamb, "Hydrodynamics," 6th ed., p. 587, Cambridge, New York, 1932.
(d) Purday, "An Introduction to the Mechanics of Viscous Flow," pp. 16–18, Dover, New York, 1949.
(e) Owen, *Trans. Am. Soc. Civil Engrs.*, **119**, 1157–1175 (1954).
(f) Straub *et al.*, *Trans. Am. Soc. Civil Engrs.*, **123**, 685–714 (1958).

upstream conditions, cu. ft./lb.; v_2 = specific volume at downstream conditions, cu. ft./lb.; g_c = dimensional constant, 32.17 (lb.)(ft.)/(lb. force)(sec.²); f = Fanning friction factor, dimensionless; x = distance from inlet to a point downstream, ft.; L = duct length, ft.; v_{avg} = average specific volume, cu. ft./lb.; ρ_{avg} = average density, lb./cu. ft.; R_H = hydraulic radius, ft.; $K = \sin\theta$ where θ = angle of inclination to horizontal. Note that $v_{avg} \neq 1/\rho_{avg}$ and that both are here averaged with respect to length, not with respect to p.

For **open channels,** the data are largely based on experiments with water in **turbulent flow,** and the results are usually given in terms of Chézy coefficients used in the Chézy formula (see Rouse, *op. cit.*, p. 591):

$$V = C\sqrt{R_H S} \tag{5-55}$$

where V = velocity, ft./sec.; C = Chézy coefficient ($= \sqrt{2g_c/f}$), [(lb.)(ft.)/(lb. force)(sec.²)]$^{1/2}$; R_H = hydraulic radius, ft.; S = slope of the channel for small changes in flow depth, also $= F/L$. The Chézy coefficient is computed from the Manning formula:

$$C = \frac{1.49(R_H)^{0.167}}{n} \tag{5-56}$$

where n = roughness factor given in Table 5-12. For the turbulent flow of **other fluids** in open channels, Eq. (5-52) and Table 5-10 should be used, or else C should be computed from the corresponding values of f. For the

Table 5-12. Average Values of n for Manning Formula, Eq. (5-56)

Surface	n*
Cast-iron pipe, fair condition	0.014
Riveted steel pipe	0.017
Vitrified sewer pipe	0.015
Concrete pipe	0.015
Wood-stave pipe	0.012
Planed plank flume	0.013
Semicircular metal flumes, smooth	0.013
Semicircular metal flumes, corrugated	0.028
Canals and ditches:	
Earth, straight and uniform	0.023
Winding sluggish canals	0.028
Dredged earth channels	0.030
Natural-stream channels:	
Clean, straight bank, full stage	0.030
Winding, some pools and shoals	0.040
Same, but with stony sections	0.055
Sluggish reaches, very deep pools, very weedy	0.070–0.125

* King, "Handbook of Hydraulics," 4th ed., p. **7**-20, McGraw-Hill, New York, 1954. For detailed information, see Chow, "Open-channel Hydraulics," pp. 110–123, McGraw-Hill, New York, 1959.

laminar flow of fluids in open channels, the equations given in Table 5-11 are recommended. For other cross sections, such as semicircular channels, V-troughs of various angles, elliptical channels, and trapezoidal channels, and for rough channels, see Straub, Silberman, and Nelson [*Trans. Am. Soc. Civil Engrs.*, **123**, 685–714 (1958)]. The lower critical Reynolds number, $N_{Re} = 4R_H V\rho/\mu$, for transition between laminar and turbulent flow in smooth channels is somewhat higher than that for smooth circular pipes, varying from 2000 to 4000, depending upon the cross-sectional shape [Straub *et al.*, *loc. cit.*; Owen, *Trans. Am. Soc. Civil Engrs.*, **119**, 1157–1175 (1954)].

Pipe-flow Chart, Fig. 5-26.

Gas Example. Air at a pressure of 120 lb. force/sq. in. gage and a temperature of 30°C. is flowing at the rate of 500 lb./hr. through a 2-in. Sch. 40 steel pipe. What is the pressure drop per foot of pipe?

Actual inside diameter is 2.067 in. Pressure of the air is (120 + 14.7)/14.7 = 9.16 atm. abs. Connect D_i' = 2.067 with w' = 0.5 and extend the line to intersect the reference line at A = 6.15. Connect 30°C. on the gas-temperature scale with molecular weight = 29 and intersect the $\mu_c^{0.16}/\rho$ line at 7.1. Join this last intersection with point A, intersecting the $\Delta p_F'(P_G)/L$ line at 0.008. The pressure drop is then 0.008/9.16 = 0.00087 lb. force/(sq. in.)(ft. of pipe).

Liquid Example. A 25 per cent calcium chloride brine is to be pumped through a line at 250 gal./min. at a temperature of 0°C. If the allowable pressure drop is 0.006 lb. force/(sq. in.)(ft. of pipe), what size pipe is required?

Connect 0°C. on the liquid-temperature scale with the intersection of grid values X = 2.6 and Y = 4.2 shown in Table 5-13. Extend the line to $\mu_c^{0.16}/\rho$ = 0.0179 and connect that point to $\Delta p_F'/L$ = 0.006 and extend to the reference line at point B = 11.65. Connect point B through w' = 147 (since at density of 73.3 lb./cu. ft., 250 gal./min. = 147,000 lb./hr.) to intersect at D_i' = 5.5 in., indicating a 6-in. pipe.

Allowance for Viscosity and Density. Gases. Temperature and molecular-weight scales are given in Fig. 5-26 in the form of a line-coordinated chart by which values of $\mu_c^{0.16}/\rho$ at atmospheric pressure are determined directly. Though the viscosities of gases and gas mixtures are not exactly proportional to molecular weight, the error is small because viscosity enters the calculation to only the 0.16 power.

Liquids. A separate temperature scale and grid are given on the chart. Coordinates given in Table 5-13

Table 5-13. Coordinates for Liquids and Aqueous Solutions

	X	Y		X	Y
Acetaldehyde	−0.3	3.7	Formic acid	1.5	4.5
Acetic acid, 100%	1.0	4.0	Glycerol, 100%	6.9	1.8
Acetic acid, 77%	2.6	3.8	Glycerol, 50%	3.0	3.7
Acetic anhydride	0.7	4.3	Hydrochloric acid, 31.5%	1.1	4.2
Acetone, 100%	0.9	3.4	Linseed oil, raw	3.4	1.8
Acetone, 35%	2.7	3.7	Mercury	See chart	
Ammonia, anhydrous	0.9	3.6	Methanol, 100%	0.8	3.3
Ammonia, 26%	1.9	3.6	Methanol, 40%	2.8	3.6
Aniline	2.5	3.4	Methyl acetate	0.0	4.2
Benzene	0.6	3.6	Methyl chloride	−0.8	4.3
Butanol	2.6	2.6	Nitric acid, 95%	0.8	5.8
Calcium chloride brine, 25%	2.6	4.2	Nitric acid, 60%	1.5	4.8
Carbon disulfide	0.0	5.6	Nitrobenzene	1.7	4.4
Carbon tetrachloride	0.7	6.0	Octane	0.4	2.7
Chloroform	0.0	6.0	Phenol	2.4	3.4
Chlorosulfonic acid	1.5	5.8	Propionic acid	0.6	3.8
Cyclohexanol	5.3	2.2	Sodium chloride brine, 25%	2.1	4.4
Diphenyl	0.0	3.5	Sodium hydroxide, 50%	5.3	3.7
Ethyl acetate	0.2	3.9	Sulfur dioxide	−0.2	6.1
Ethyl alcohol, 95%	1.9	3.0	Sulfuric acid, 110%	3.7	4.7
Ethyl alcohol, 45%	3.6	3.4	Sulfuric acid, 98%	3.5	4.8
Ethyl chloride	0.2	4.3	Sulfuric acid, 78%	3.2	4.8
Ethyl ether	−0.3	3.2	Tetrachlorethylene	0.3	6.2
Ethylene glycol	3.5	2.9	Toluene	0.4	3.6
Fluorocarbon F-11	0.0	6.2	Trichlorethylene	0.1	5.9
Fluorocarbon F-12	−1.2	5.9	Turpentine	1.1	3.1
Fluorocarbon F-21	−0.4	5.9	Vinyl acetate	0.4	4.2
Fluorocarbon F-22	−1.7	5.5	Water	2.0	4.2
Fluorocarbon F-113	0.9	6.2			

locate the point for a given liquid on the grid; a line through the point and the given temperature determines $\mu_c^{0.16}/\rho$ directly. Coordinates for liquids not given in the table may be determined by calculating values of $\mu_c^{0.16}/\rho$ for two temperatures and noting the intersection of lines connecting corresponding values of $\mu_c^{0.16}/\rho$ and temperature.

Compressible Flow. If the pressure drop due to the flow of a gas through a system is large enough, compared with the inlet pressure, to occasion a 10 per cent or greater decrease in gas density, then the flow is considered to be "compressible." In this event, formulas must be used which make proper allowance for this change in both density and velocity.

The flow of gases at atmospheric pressure and above is generally either laminar or turbulent in character, the transition between the two generally occurring somewhere in the Reynolds-number range of 2,000 to 3,000. **Turbulent flow** occurs above the transition, while **lami-**

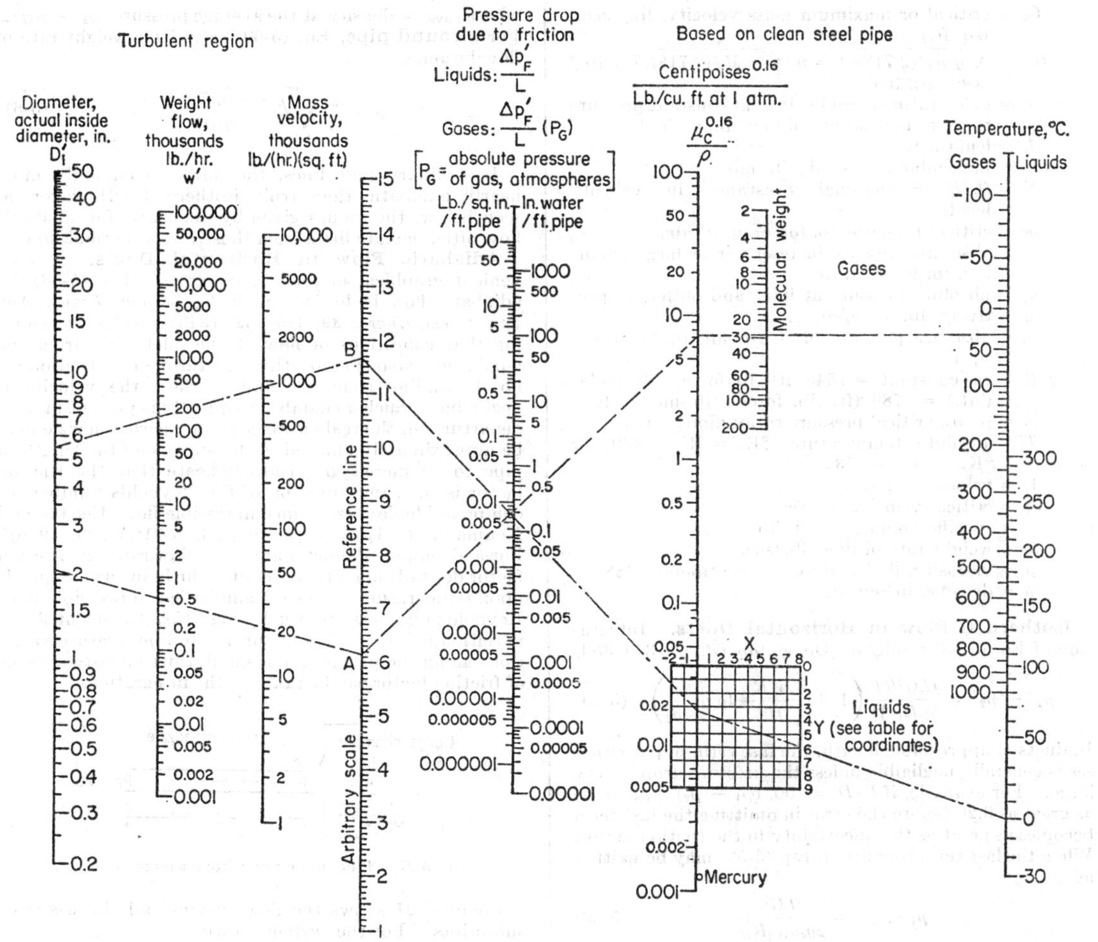

FIG. 5-26. Pipe-flow chart. [*Genereaux, Chem. & Met. Eng.*, **44**, 241 (1937).]

nar flow occurs below the transition. However, at low pressures or in very small channels, another flow phenomenon, **molecular flow**, is encountered. This occurs when the mean free path [see Eq. (5-76)] is of the same order of magnitude as the channel diameter. In this type of flow, a gas molecule migrates along the channel independently of other gas molecules.

When mean free path of the gas is less than about 65 per cent but greater than about 1 per cent of the channel diameter, the gas layer next to the channel wall assumes a certain velocity of slip. This is known as **slip flow** and may be taken to be a combination of laminar and molecular flows. Slip flow and molecular flow are most often encountered in high-vacuum technology.

Turbulent Flow. The general formulas and methods under Incompressible Flow will apply only to a differential length of duct dx throughout which the density may be considered constant. Thus, in general, the Fanning equation, Eq. (5-52), must be used in differential form:

$$\frac{dF}{dx} = \frac{4fV^2}{2g_cD} = \frac{fV^2}{2g_cR_H} = \frac{fG^2}{2g_c\rho^2R_H} \tag{5-57}$$

Substitution of Eq. (5-57) in the differential form of the mechanical energy balance [Eq. (5-37)] gives

$$v\,dp + \frac{V\,dV}{g_c} = -\left(\frac{fV^2}{2g_cR_H} + \sin\theta\right)dx \tag{5-58}$$

where $v = 1/\rho$ = fluid specific volume, cu. ft./lb.; $(\sin\theta)\,dx = dz$ = vertical distance, ft., through which the fluid is raised when it moves distance dx along the pipe; W_e in Eq. (5-37) has been taken to be zero on the supposition that no pump is in the line. In a uniform duct, mass velocity $G = V/v$ is constant so that, if p is known as a function of v only, $v\,dp$ can be written $\phi(v)\,dv$. Then, when $\sin\theta$ is constant, the variables in Eq. (5-58) are separable and exact integration is possible, although graphical procedures may be needed. The results below are obtained from Eq. (5-58) in the case of perfect gases ($pv = RT/M$).

Nomenclature for Perfect-gas Equations and Charts.

- A = area, sq. ft.
- A_c = area for critical flow, sq. ft.
- D = diameter, ft.
- f = Fanning friction factor, dimensionless
- g_c = dimensional constant, 32.17 (lb.)(ft.)/(lb. force)(sec.^{2})
- $G = V\rho = V/v$ = mass velocity, lb./(sec.)(sq. ft.)

G_c = critical or maximum mass velocity, lb./(sec.)(sq. ft.)
G_{ci} = $\sqrt{g_c p_0/(2.718 v_0)} = p_0 \sqrt{g_c M/(2.718 R T_0)}$, lb./(sec.)(sq. ft.)
k = c_p/c_v, ratio of specific heat at constant pressure to that at constant volume, dimensionless
L = length, ft.
M = molecular weight, lb./lb.-mole
N = fL/R_H = frictional resistance in velocity heads
p_c = critical pressure, lb. force/sq. ft. abs.
p_0 = absolute pressure in reservoir or large chamber, lb. force/sq. ft.
p_1, p_2 = absolute pressure at inlet and outlet, respectively, lb. force/sq. ft.
p_3 = absolute pressure of surroundings, lb. force/sq. ft.
R = gas constant = 1546 (ft.)(lb. force)/(lb.-mole)(°R.) = 2780 (ft.)(lb. force)/(lb.-mole)(°K.)
r_c = p_c/p_0, critical pressure ratio, dimensionless
T = absolute temperature, °R. = °F. + 460; or °K. = °C. + 273
V = velocity, ft./sec.
V_c = critical velocity, ft./sec.
v = specific volume, cu. ft./lb.
w = weight rate of flow, lb./sec.
μ = viscosity, lb./(ft.)(sec.) = centipoise/1488
ρ = density, lb./cu. ft.

Isothermal Flow in Horizontal Ducts. Integration of Eq. (5-58) results in (Dodge, *op. cit.*, pp. 349–350)

$$p_1^2 - p_2^2 = \frac{fLG^2RT}{g_c R_H M}\left(1 + \frac{4.61 R_H}{fL}\log_{10}\frac{p_1}{p_2}\right) \quad (5\text{-}59)$$

In ducts of appreciable length, the last term in parentheses is generally negligible unless the pressure drop is very large. For example, if $L/D = 100$, $(p_1 - p_2)/p_1$ may be as great as 0.20 before the error in omitting the last term becomes as great as the uncertainty in the friction factor. When the last term is omitted, Eq. (5-59) may be written as

$$p_1 - p_2 = \frac{fLG^2}{2 g_c \rho_{avg} R_H} \quad (5\text{-}60)$$

where ρ_{avg} = density at the average pressure $(p_1 + p_2)/2$. For a **round pipe,** Eq. (5-60) solved for weight rate of flow becomes

$$w = \frac{\pi}{8}\sqrt{\frac{(p_1^2 - p_2^2) g_c D^5 M}{fLRT}} \quad (5\text{-}61)$$

In ordinary pipe lines, the flow is commonly more nearly adiabatic than truly isothermal. However, as seen below, the values given by the charts for adiabatic flow often deviate little from those for isothermal flow.

Adiabatic Flow in Horizontal Ducts. A convenient graphical method of integrating Eq. (5-58) for adiabatic flow in horizontal ducts [Lapple, *Trans. Am. Inst. Chem. Engrs.*, **39**, 385–432 (1943)] results by assuming that conditions of flow at the inlet arise from the adiabatic expansion of the gas through a frictionless nozzle leading from a chamber where the velocity is negligible. Such a chamber frequently is present in fact; departures of the real entrance from a perfect nozzle may be approximately allowed for by supposing the length of pipe to be increased. Data indicate that the friction factor is the same function of the Reynolds number for compressible flow as for incompressible flow [Keenan and Neumann, *J. Appl. Mechanics*, **13**, A-91–A-100 (1946)]. For a given pipe diameter and mass flow rate, the friction factor depends upon the viscosity which, in turn, depends upon temperature. Since in adiabatic compressible flow, Reynolds numbers are usually high (*i.e.*, turbulent flow), variation of the friction factor due to temperature variations along the pipe length is small; thus a constant value of friction factor can be taken in the integrations.

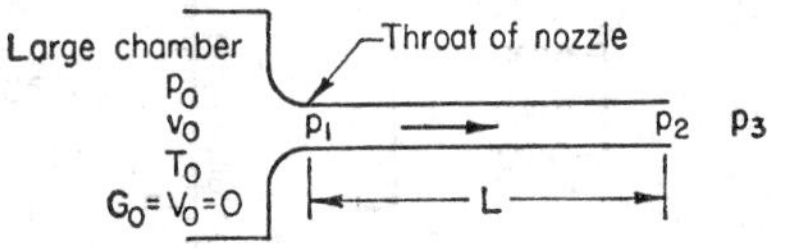

FIG. 5-27. Pipe discharging from a large chamber.

Figure 5-27 shows the flow system and the usage of subscripts. For the system shown,

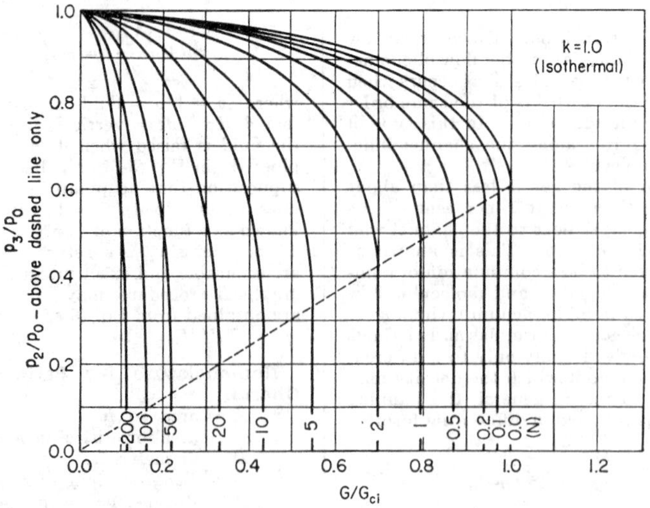

FIG. 5-28*a*. Design chart for isothermal and adiabatic flow of compressible fluids through pipes at high pressure drops. [Lapple, *Trans. Am. Inst. Chem. Engrs.*, **39**, 385 (1943).]

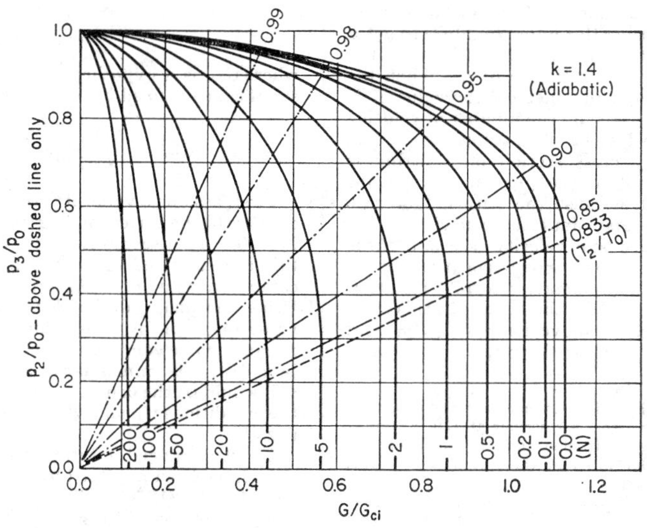

b

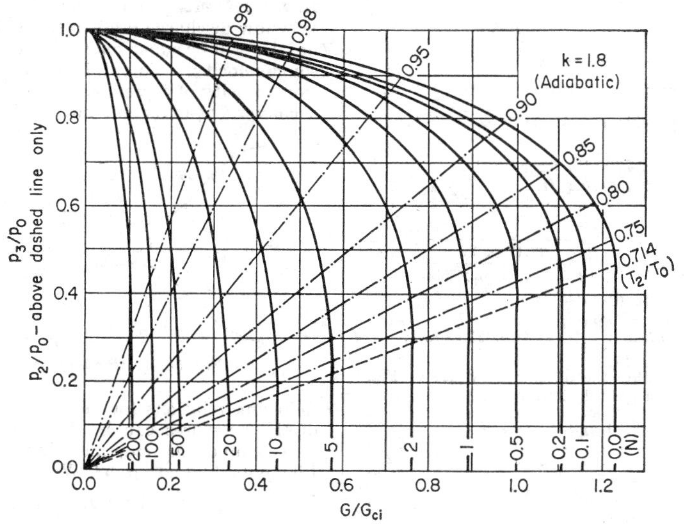

c

FIG. 5-28*b* and *c*. Design charts for adiabatic flow of compressible fluids through pipes at high pressure drops. [*Lapple, Trans. Am. Inst. Chem. Engrs.*, **39,** 385 (1943).]

$$\frac{v_1}{v_0} = \left(\frac{p_0}{p_1}\right)^{1/k} \tag{5-62}$$

$$\frac{T_1}{T_0} = \left(\frac{p_1}{p_0}\right)^{(k-1)/k} \tag{5-63}$$

$$\frac{p_0}{p_1} = \left[1 + \frac{G^2}{2g_c}\left(\frac{k-1}{k}\right)\frac{RT_1}{Mp_1^2}\right]^{k/(k-1)} \tag{5-64}$$

$$\frac{T_2}{T_1} = \left(\frac{p_2}{p_1}\right)\left(\frac{v_2}{v_1}\right) \tag{5-65}$$

The charts of Fig. 5-28*a*, *b*, and *c* show, for three values of *k*, ratio of specific heats, and for various values of frictional resistance *N*, number of velocity heads in the duct, the relation between p_2/p_0 or p_3/p_0 and the ratio of mass velocity *G* in the duct to a parameter

$$G_{ci} = \sqrt{\frac{g_c p_0}{2.718 v_0}} = p_0\sqrt{\frac{g_c M}{2.718RT_0}} \tag{5-66}$$

The quantity G_{ci} is the maximum mass velocity hypothetically attainable on isothermal expansion through the system of Fig. 5-27, when $N = 0$. Such an isothermal expansion is not physically realizable. The ratios p_2/p_0 and p_3/p_0 are identical if, for a given *N*, the mass velocity is less than a certain maximum or critical value G_c; this is true above the dashed line on the charts. If p_3/p_0 is less than the value of p_2/p_0 corresponding to G_c, the flow is then independent of p_3 (see p. 5-9). The dashed line is a plot of p_2/p_0 at critical flow vs. G_c/G_{ci}.

Use of the charts is most easily understood by studying the illustrative example given below. Interpolation between charts is permissible for other values of *k*.

When G is being sought, assume $f = 0.0045$ to determine a trial value of G; then, using this approximate G to get a Reynolds number, find f from Fig. 5-25 and repeat the calculation using this revised estimate of f. When fittings are present in the pipe line, increase the value of N calculated for the straight pipe by the number of velocity heads equivalent to the loss in the fittings (see Table 5-19). If, however, any cross section of a fitting is appreciably less than that of the pipe line, erroneous results may be obtained, because the critical flow rate through the constriction may limit the capacity of the line; this occurs if the acoustic velocity (see p. 5-15) is approached at the constriction. For a sharp or abrupt inlet, the charts lead to approximately correct results if 0.5 is added to the value of N for the duct. In this case, however, the formulas given above for v_1/v_0, p_0/p_1, and T_1/T_0 are inapplicable, because they apply only to a rounded entrance.

Illustrative Example. It is desired to calculate the discharge rate of air to the atmosphere from a reservoir at 150 lb. force/sq. in. gage and 70°F. through 35 ft. of straight 2-in. Sch. 40 steel pipe (inside diameter = 2.067 in.) and three standard 90 deg. elbows. The pipe inlet is abrupt.

To solve the problem, it is necessary to assume a value of the friction factor f and express all resistance in terms of N as follows:

Resistance	(L/D)	(N)
Inlet	...	0.50*
Straight pipe	203	3.65†
Elbows (three)	...	2.25
		6.40

* Assumed an abrupt inlet.
† Calculated, assuming $f = 0.0045$.

From the conditions of the problem,

$$T_0 = 530°\text{R.}$$
$$p_0 = (150 + 14.7)(144) = 23{,}700 \text{ lb. force/sq. ft.}$$
$$p_3 = (14.7)(144) = 2120 \text{ lb. force/sq. ft.}$$
$$p_3/p_0 = 0.0893$$
$$M = 29$$

$$G_{ci} = p_0 \sqrt{\frac{g_c M}{2.718 R T_0}} = 23{,}700 \sqrt{\frac{32.17 \times 29}{2.718 \times 1546 \times 530}}$$
$$G_{ci} = 486 \text{ lb./(sec.)(sq. ft.)}$$
$$\text{Pipe cross section} = (0.785)\left(\frac{2.067}{12}\right)^2 = 0.0233 \text{ sq. ft.}$$

It is now possible to calculate the discharge by use of Fig. 5-28*b* as shown by the following tabulation:

k	1.4
(G/G_{ci}), from curve for $N = 6.40$ and $(p_3/p_0) = 0.0893$	0.53
G, lb./(sec.)(sq. ft.)	257
Discharge rate, lb./sec	5.99
(T_2/T_0), from dashed line, since (p_3/p_0) is below dashed line	0.833
T_2, °R	442
Average gas temp. in pipe, °F	26
Viscosity μ at average gas temp., lb./(ft.)(sec.)	1.14×10^{-5}
N_{Re} or (DG/μ)	3,880,000
f	0.0047

Since the value of f so obtained checks the assumed value reasonably well, it is not necessary in this case to repeat the determination of G.

Figure 5-28*a*, *b*, and *c* can also be used to compute the **pressure drop between two locations along a pipe line.** For example, if the conditions at a given location and the flow rate are known, and if the pressure at a location downstream is desired, let the known conditions be T_1 and p_1. Thus the ratios G/G_{1ci}, p_2/p_1, and T_2/T_1 are referred to the known conditions and can be related to G/G_{ci}, p_1/p_0, and T_1/T_0 by

$$\frac{G}{G_{1ci}} = \frac{G}{G_{ci}}\left(\frac{\sqrt{T_1/T_0}}{p_1/p_0}\right) \tag{5-67}$$

$$\frac{p_2}{p_1} = \frac{p_2/p_0}{p_1/p_0} \tag{5-68}$$

$$\frac{T_2}{T_1} = \frac{T_2/T_0}{T_1/T_0} \tag{5-69}$$

where G_{1ci} is a hypothetical quantity of no real physical significance defined by

$$G_{1ci} = \sqrt{\frac{g_c p_1}{2.718 v_1}} = p_1 \sqrt{\frac{g_c M}{2.718 R T_1}} \tag{5-70}$$

First, assume a value of G/G_{ci}, and from the appropriate chart read the corresponding values of p_1/p_0 and T_1/T_0 for $N = 0$. Then compute G/G_{ci} from Eq. (5-67). Using this new assumed value, repeat the procedure until the computed value of G/G_{ci} equals the last assumed value. Using the final value of G/G_{ci}, read from the chart the value of p_1/p_0 for $N = 0$ and of p_2/p_0 for $N = 4fL/D$; p_2 can then be computed from Eq. (5-68). The values of p_0 and T_0 determined above are, in general, hypothetical and would be the conditions in a chamber required to give the conditions p_1 and T_1 in the throat of a frictionless nozzle.

Charts arranged in terms of known downstream conditions have been prepared by Powley [*Can. J. Chem. Eng.*, **36,** 241–245 (1958)]. These charts facilitate prediction of upstream conditions when flow rate and downstream conditions are known.

Flow through Convergent-divergent Nozzles (De Laval Nozzle). For very high chamber pressures or very low discharge pressures, the discharge velocity from nozzles will be supersonic, *i.e.*, greater than the critical or sonic velocity. To obtain the ultimate adiabatic expansion velocity of a gas, *i.e.*, the highest discharge velocity, a convergent-divergent nozzle (Fig. 5-29) is used. The

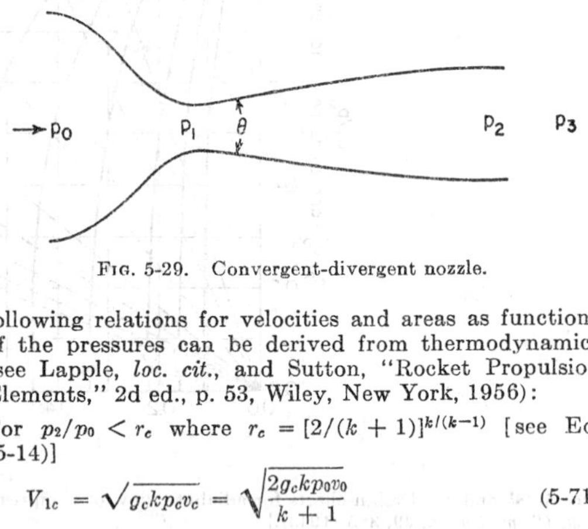

FIG. 5-29. Convergent-divergent nozzle.

following relations for velocities and areas as functions of the pressures can be derived from thermodynamics (see Lapple, *loc. cit.*, and Sutton, "Rocket Propulsion Elements," 2d ed., p. 53, Wiley, New York, 1956):

For $p_2/p_0 < r_c$ where $r_c = [2/(k+1)]^{k/(k-1)}$ [see Eq. (5-14)]

$$V_{1c} = \sqrt{g_c k p_c v_c} = \sqrt{\frac{2 g_c k p_0 v_0}{k+1}} \tag{5-71}$$

$$G_{1c} = \left(\frac{2}{k+1}\right)^{(k+1)/2(k-1)} \sqrt{\frac{g_c k p_0}{v_0}} \tag{5-72}$$

$$p_{1c} = p_0 \left(\frac{2}{k+1}\right)^{k/(k-1)} \tag{5-73}$$

$$\left(\frac{A_{1c}}{A_2}\right)^2 = \left(\frac{2}{k-1}\right)\left(\frac{k+1}{2}\right)^{(k+1)/(k-1)}\left(\frac{p_2}{p_0}\right)^{2/k}\left[1 - \left(\frac{p_2}{p_0}\right)^{(k-1)/k}\right] \tag{5-74}$$

$$\left(\frac{V_2}{V_{1c}}\right)^2 = \left(\frac{k+1}{k-1}\right)\left[1 - \left(\frac{p_2}{p_0}\right)^{(k-1)/k}\right] \tag{5-75}$$

Only for $p_2 = p_3$ is the ultimate adiabatic expansion velocity realized in the nozzle. The expansion will be incomplete within the nozzle if $p_2 > p_3$, or a compression shock will result if $p_2 < p_3$.

The shape of the converging section is similar to that of a simple converging nozzle. The shape of the diverging section to obtain a uniform, parallel, shock-free supersonic stream of the discharge must be of a special shape; methods of design are given by Liepmann and Roshko ("Elements of Gasdynamics," p. 284, Wiley, New York, 1957). If the nozzle is to be used as a thrust device, the diverging section can be a simple conical diverging section with a total angle $\theta = 30$ deg. (Sutton, *loc. cit.*, p. 75). Note that, if $p_2/p_0 > [2/(k+1)]^{k/(k-1)}$, the discharge velocity will be subsonic; for such cases, a simple converging nozzle can be used.

For **laminar flow** of gases under isothermal conditions, Eq. (5-60) for various duct shapes can be reduced to the forms given in Table 5-11. Note that p_1 and p_2 are the absolute pressures, lb. force/sq. ft. abs., at the upstream and downstream locations, respectively.

Slip flow exists for practical purposes for values of X between 0.014 and 1.0, where X is given by Brown *et al.* [*J. Appl. Phys.*, **17**, 802–813 (1946)] as

$$X = \frac{\lambda}{D}\sqrt{\frac{8}{\pi}} = \frac{2\mu}{p_m'D}\sqrt{\frac{R'T}{Mg_c'}} \tag{5-76}$$

where λ = mean free path, ft.; D = channel diameter, ft.; μ = gas viscosity at atmospheric pressure and temperature T, lb./(ft.)(sec.) = cp./1488; p_m' = arithmetic mean absolute pressure, microns Hg; R' = universal gas constant, 5.56×10^5 (microns Hg)(cu. ft.)/(lb.-mole)(°R.); T = absolute gas temperature, °R. = (°F. + 460); M = molecular weight of gas, lb./(lb.-mole); g_c' = dimensional constant, 0.0896 lb./(ft.)(sec.^{2})(microns Hg). Thus for $X = 0.014$ (the approximate boundary between laminar flow and slip flow), the mean free path λ is about 1 per cent of the channel diameter.

In vacuum technology, it is common practice to refer to the **conductance,** or "speed," of a given pipe, pump, or system. The conductance of a pipe or system is the inverse of the resistance and is defined by

$$C = \frac{q'}{\Delta p'} \quad \text{cu. ft./sec.} \tag{5-77}$$

where $q' = w/\rho'$ = volumetric flow rate referred to a pressure of 1 micron Hg, (micron)(cu. ft.)/sec.; $\Delta p'$ = pressure drop, microns Hg; w = weight rate of flow, lb./sec.; $\rho' = M/R'T$ = gas density at a pressure of 1 micron Hg. For resistances in **series,** the system conductance is given by

$$\frac{1}{C} = \frac{1}{C_1} + \frac{1}{C_2} + \frac{1}{C_3} + \cdots \tag{5-78}$$

For resistances in **parallel,** the system conductance is given by

$$C = C_1 + C_2 + C_3 + \cdots \tag{5-79}$$

If the system contains a pump of speed S_p cu. ft./sec., the speed of the system S_0 is given by

$$\frac{1}{S_0} = \frac{1}{S_p} + \frac{1}{C} \tag{5-80}$$

where C is the conductance of the system (cu. ft./sec.) as determined from the individual conductances by Eqs. (5-78) and (5-79).

The **conductance** of a **pipe line** is most conveniently obtained for the slip-flow region by the method of Brown *et al.* (*loc. cit.*) which involves the use of Fig. 5-30. Conductance of the pipe line is first calculated as for laminar flow:

$$C_{\text{lam}} = \frac{q'_{\text{lam}}}{\Delta p'} = \frac{g_c'D^2Ap_m'}{32\mu L} \tag{5-81}$$

where C_{lam} = pipe-line conductance for laminar flow, cu. ft./sec.; q'_{lam} = volumetric flow rate (referred to a pressure of 1 micron Hg) computed for laminar flow, (micron)(cu. ft.)/sec.; $\Delta p'$ = pressure drop, microns Hg; A = cross-sectional area, sq. ft.; L = pipe-line length, ft.; other variables as defined following Eq. (5-76). True conductance C of the pipe line is then obtained from

$$C = FC_{\text{lam}} \quad \text{cu. ft./sec.} \tag{5-82}$$

where correction factor F is obtained from Fig. 5-30 as a function of X.

Experimental data on the **conductance** of **sharp-edged orifices** in the slip-flow region is given by Knudsen [*Ann. Physik*, **28**, 999–1016 (1909)].

For **elbows** and **tees,** few data are available. For design, conductance can be computed as for a straight pipe, using the path length through the fitting.

For additional information on slip flow, see Dushman and Lafferty, "Scientific Foundations of Vacuum Technique," 2d ed., pp. 104–111, Wiley, New York, 1962;

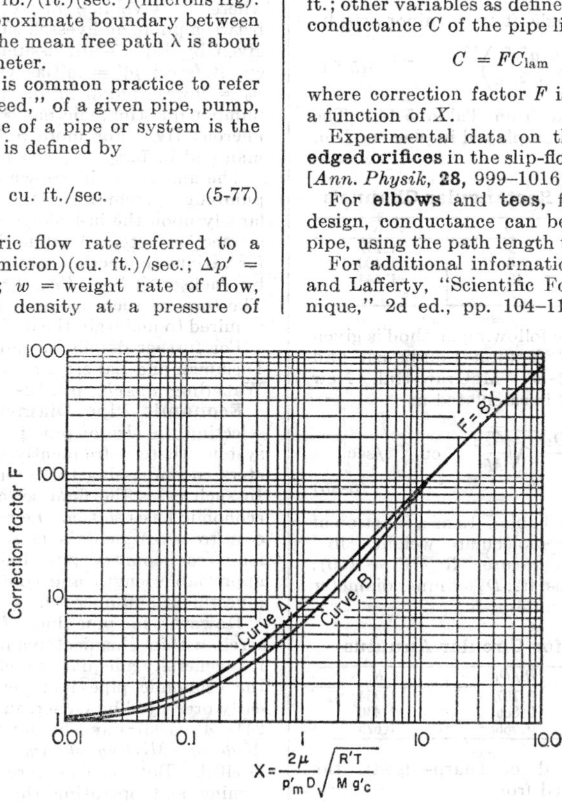

FIG. 5-30. Correction factor for Poiseuille's equation at low pressures. Curve A: experimental curve for glass capillaries and smooth metal tubes. [*From Brown et al., J. Appl. Phys.*, **17**, 802 (1946).] Curve B: experimental curve for iron pipe. (*Courtesy of E. I. du Pont de Nemours & Co.*)

Lawrance, 1954 *Vacuum Symposium Trans.*, pp. 55–62, Committee on Vacuum Techniques, Boston.

Molecular flow exists for practical purposes for values of X greater than 1.0, where X is defined by Eq. (5-76). This boundary between molecular flow and slip flow corresponds to a mean free path λ equal to about 65 per cent of the channel diameter. The over-all system conductance or speed for molecular flow is obtained from the individual conductances as indicated by Eqs. (5-78), (5-79), and (5-80).

For **circular pipe,** conductance can be obtained most conveniently by the method of Brown *et al.* (*loc. cit.*) which involves the use of Fig. 5-30. Conductance of the pipe line is first calculated as for laminar flow, using Eq. (5-81). Parameter X is computed, using Eq. (5-76), and the corresponding value of the correction factor F obtained from Fig. 5-30. The molecular-flow conductance is then computed as the product of F and the laminar-flow conductance, as given by Eq. (5-82). Note that the curve for glass and smooth metal pipe is a straight line in the molecular-flow region and is described by the equation $F = 8.0X$. For short pipes ($L/D < 100$), allowance should be made for entrance effects (see paragraph below on "short pipes").

For **rectangular channels,** the following method is given by Normand [*Ind. Eng. Chem.*, **40,** 783–787 (1948)]. Treat the channel as though it were a round pipe having an equivalent diameter D_e determined as follows:

(1) If $a/b < 3$
$$D_e = 2\sqrt{\frac{ab}{\pi}} \qquad (5\text{-}83)$$

where a = major axis of rectangle, ft.; b = minor axis, ft.

(2) If $a/b > 3$
$$D_e = \left(2.55K\frac{a^2b^2}{a+b}\right)^{1/3} \qquad (5\text{-}84)$$

where K = constant obtained from Table 5-14. The value of D_e so obtained is then employed in place of D in Eqs. (5-76) and (5-81).

Table 5-14. Constants for Rectangular Channels

a/b	K	a/b	K
1.0	1.108	5	1.297
1.5	1.126	8	1.400
2.0	1.151	10	1.444
3.0	1.198		

For a **circular annulus,** the following method is given by Guthrie and Wakerling ("Vacuum Equipment and Techniques," pp. 37–38, 52–53, McGraw-Hill, New York, 1949). Conductance C is calculated as

$$C = 165K\frac{(D_1 - D_2)^2(D_1 + D_2)}{L}\sqrt{\frac{T}{M}} \quad \text{cu. ft./sec.} \qquad (5\text{-}85)$$

where K = a constant given in Table 5-15 as a function of D_2/D_1, dimensionless; M = molecular weight, lb./(lb.-mole); T = absolute temperature, °R. (°F. + 460); D_1 = outer diameter of annulus, ft.; D_2 = inner diameter of annulus, ft.; L = length of annulus, ft.

Table 5-15. Constants for Circular Annulus

D_2/D_1	K	D_2/D_1	K
0	1.00	0.707	1.254
0.259	1.072	0.866	1.430
0.500	1.154	0.966	1.675

For an **orifice** (thin-walled or sharp-edged), the conductance C can be computed from

$$C = 161A\sqrt{\frac{T}{M}} \quad \text{cu. ft./sec.} \qquad (5\text{-}86)$$

where T = absolute temperature, °R. (°F. + 460); M = molecular weight, lb./(lb.-mole); A = area of opening, sq. ft. See Guthrie and Wakerling, *op. cit.*, pp. 19, 52–53.

For a **short pipe** of circular cross section, the conductance as calculated for the orifice via Eq. (5-86) is multiplied by a correction factor K, which is a function of the length-to-diameter ratio. K can be approximated as follows (Kennard, "Kinetic Theory of Gases," pp. 306–308, McGraw-Hill, New York, 1938):

For $0 \leq L/D \leq 0.75$
$$K = \frac{1}{1 + (L/D)} \qquad (5\text{-}87)$$

For $L/D > 0.75$
$$K = \frac{1 + 0.8(L/D)}{1 + 1.90(L/D) + 0.6(L/D)^2} \qquad (5\text{-}88)$$

where L = length of tube, ft.; D = diameter, ft. More precise values of K can be obtained from Dushman and Lafferty, *op. cit.*, pp. 94–95. For values of $L/D > 100$, the error due to neglecting the "end correction" (using the long-pipe formulas) will be less than 2 per cent.

For **elbows** and **tees,** conductance can be computed as for a straight pipe, using an equivalent length equal to the actual path length plus 1.33 pipe diameters. See Guthrie and Wakerling, *op. cit.*, pp. 41–43.

Pump-down time θ for evacuating a vessel in the absence of in-leakage is given approximately by

$$\theta = 2.303\frac{V_t}{S_0}\log\frac{p_1' - p_0'}{p_2' - p_0'} \quad \text{sec.} \qquad (5\text{-}89)$$

where V_t = volume of vessel plus volume of piping between pump and vessel, cu. ft.; S_0 = speed of system as given by Eq. (5-80), assumed independent of pressure, cu. ft./sec.; p_1' = initial vessel pressure, microns Hg; p_0' = lowest pump intake pressure attainable with the pump in question, microns Hg; p_2' = final vessel pressure, microns Hg. For more precise calculations, see Dushman and Lafferty (*op. cit.*, pp. 111–116).

The amount of inerts which have to be removed by a pumping system after the pump-down stage depends largely upon the in-leakage of air at the various fittings, connections, etc. A tabulation of average air in-leakages for various connections and pipe-line components is given by Jackson [*Chem. Eng. Progress*, **44,** 347–352 (1948)]. The total of such leakages determines the size of pump required to maintain the desired vacuum.

For further details on molecular-flow phenomena, see Dushman and Lafferty, *op. cit.*, pp. 87–104; Guthrie and Wakerling, *op. cit.*, pp. 12–58.

Economic Pipe Diameter, Turbulent Flow. In selecting the size of pipe to be used for a fluid-handling system, there is frequently a range of permissible diameters encompassing two or more standard sizes of pipe. In such cases the final selection should be made on an economic basis so that the relationship of total operating cost to investment is most favorable. In the case of long cross-country pipe lines or of alloy pipe lines of appreciable length and complexity, detailed analyses of investment and operating costs are warranted.

However, for pipe lines of the lengths usually encountered within chemical plants and petroleum refineries, it is generally adequate to select the diameter from one of the economic pipe-diameter charts. Such charts were early presented by Genereaux [*Chem. & Met. Eng.*, **44** (5), 241–248 (1937)] and by Johnson and Maker [*Proc. Tenth Mid-year Meeting of Am. Petrol. Inst.*, Sec. III, 7–23 (1940)]. Both charts were based on minimum cost of owning and operating the pipe line. The Genereaux chart requires only a knowledge of flow rate and fluid density for selection of the economic pipe diameter, whereas the Johnson-Maker chart requires in addition a

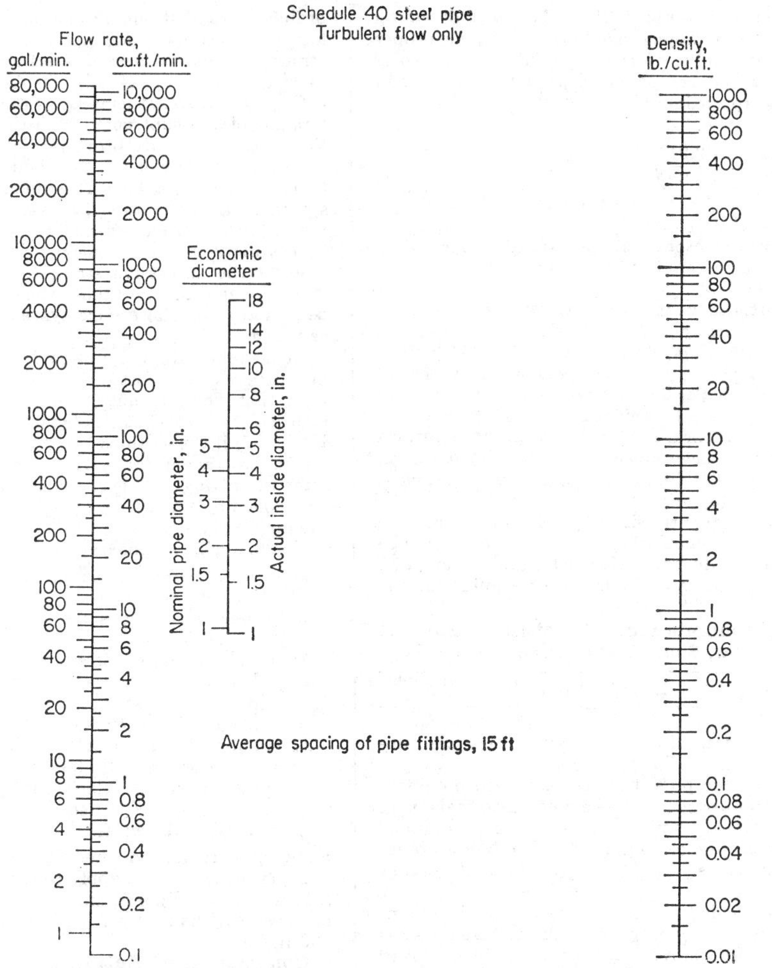

FIG. 5-31. Economic pipe diameter; chart constructed from Eq. (5-90). Connect values of flow rate and density to obtain economic diameter. (*Courtesy of E. I. du Pont de Nemours & Co.*)

knowledge of a number of cost factors plus the friction factor. However, the latter procedure is relatively ageless, since up-to-date cost data can be employed.

The **economic pipe-diameter chart** for steel pipe given in Fig. 5-31 is furnished by courtesy of E. I. du Pont de Nemours & Co. It is based on the following equation:

$$\frac{D^{4.84+n}}{1 + 0.794L_e'D} = \frac{\left[(1 + M)(1 - \phi) + ZM/(a' + b')\right](0.000189YKw^{2.84}\mu'^{0.16})}{n(1 + F)X[Z + (a + b)(1 - \phi)]E\rho^2} \qquad (5\text{-}90)$$

where D = economic pipe diameter, ft.; n = exponent in pipe-cost equation $[C = (1 + F)XD^n]$, dimensionless; C = installed cost of pipe line, including fittings, dollars per foot; F = factor for installation and fittings, dimensionless; X = cost of 1 ft. of 1-ft.-diameter pipe, dollars; L_e' = factor for friction in fittings, equivalent length in pipe diameters per unit length of pipe, 1/ft.; M = factor to express cost of pumping installation in terms of yearly cost of power delivered to the fluid, dollars per dollar; ϕ = factor for taxes and other expense, dimensionless; Z = fractional rate of return on incremental investment, dimensionless; a' = fractional annual depreciation on pumping installation, dimensionless; b' = fractional annual maintenance on installation, dimensionless; a = fractional annual depreciation on pipe line, dimensionless; b = fractional annual maintenance on pipe line, dimensionless; E = combined fractional efficiency of pump and motor, dimensionless; ρ = fluid density, lb./cu. ft.; Y = days of operation per year (in terms of 24-hr. days); K = cost of power delivered to motor, dollars per kilowatt-hour; w = weight rate of flow, lb./sec.; μ' = fluid viscosity, centipoise. Table 5-16 gives the values em-

Table 5-16. Factors Employed in Constructing Fig. 5-31

Variable	Value used	Variable	Value used
$a + b$	0.2	M	0.8
$a' + b'$	0.4	X	2.91
E	0.5	Y	328
F	Variable	Z	0.20
K	0.0085	μ'	1.0
L_e'	2.35	ϕ	0.39
n	1.5		

ployed in constructing Fig. 5-31. The effect of values other than those employed can be obtained by proper ratioing. For example, if the pipe in question costs \$5.82 per linear foot compared with \$2.91 employed in the chart, then approximately

$$\frac{D'}{D_c'} = \left(\frac{2.91}{5.82}\right)^{\frac{1}{6.34}} = (0.50)^{0.157}$$

or

$$D' = 0.90D_c'$$

assuming the other factors were unchanged. Here D' = economic pipe diameter, in.; D_c' = pipe diameter from chart (Fig. 5-31), in.

Pipe- and fitting-cost information has been given by Dickson [*Chem. Eng.*, **57** (1), 123–135 (1950)]; Braca and Happel [*Chem. Eng.*, **60** (1), 180–187 (1953)]; Zimmerman and Lavine ["Chemical Engineering Costs," Industrial Research Service, Dover, N.H., 1950]; Aries and Newton ["Chemical Engineering Cost Estimation," McGraw-Hill, New York, 1955]. **Cost information on prime movers** has been given by Chilton [*Chem. Eng.*, **56** (6), 97–106 (1949)]; Zimmerman and Lavine (*op. cit.*); Aries and Newton (*op. cit.*).

Pipe lines are frequently sized by selecting a "reasonable" velocity and calculating the corresponding pipe diameter. **Economic velocities** determined from Fig. 5-31 are given in Table 5-17 for use as a guide for the

Table 5-17. Economic Fluid Velocities, Turbulent Flow, Sch. 40 Steel Pipe

Density, lb./cu. ft.	100	50	10	1	0.1	0.01
Economic velocity, ft./sec.	5.1	6.2	10.1	19.5	39	78

case of Sch. 40 steel pipe. These velocities are substantially independent of diameter.

After the economic pipe diameter has been obtained, the Reynolds number should be calculated to make sure that the flow is actually turbulent. (See p. 5-15 for information on critical Reynolds number.) If the flow proves not to be turbulent, see below on economics of laminar flow.

The above methods for obtaining economic pipe diameter can obviously apply only where the motive power is supplied by a prime mover such as a pump or blower within the system under study. They cannot apply to steam lines, since the value of pressure lost in the line depends upon temperature and pressure level. They also cannot apply where the source of fluid is a main under a fixed pressure or a head tank. In the case of a pump suction line, a check has to be made after selecting the economic pipe diameter to see if the resulting net positive suction head meets requirements (see p. 6-3). If not, a larger diameter will be required. In the case of a pipe line handling suspended solids, the velocity employed has to be sufficient to keep the solids from settling out and yet not high enough to cause excessive erosion.

Economic Pipe Diameter, Laminar Flow. Pipe lines for transport of high-viscosity liquids in chemical plants or petroleum refineries are seldom designed purely on the basis of economics. More often, the size is dictated by available pressure drop or by residence-time considerations.

An economic pipe-diameter chart for laminar flow was given by Sarchet and Colburn [*Ind. Eng. Chem.*, **32**, 1249–1252 (1940)]. It can be used as a guide for those cases where the chart for turbulent flow (Fig. 5-31) gives a pipe diameter that corresponds to laminar flow with the given flow rate, or where the viscosity is of the order of 1000 centipoise or more.

Miscellaneous Pressure Losses. Experimental determinations of the resistance of fittings and valves are ordinarily carried out by measuring the over-all friction loss in a system made up of two or more lengths of straight pipe connected in series by a suitable number of identical fittings or valves. To obtain the loss due to the fittings or valves themselves, the friction loss in the straight pipe is subtracted from the over-all or total friction loss. There are three distinct conventions for computing the length of the "straight pipe" in the test system: (1) the actual length of the center line of the entire system is taken; (2) the lengths of the individual pieces of pipe that are actually straight are summed; (3) the distances between the intersections of the extended center lines of the successive straight pipes are added. The first convention, *i.e.*, taking the **actual length of the center line of the entire system,** is used here, except as noted.

In the following compilation, F (ft.)(lb. force)/lb. is the mechanical energy lost through friction by each pound of fluid that flows through the fitting in question. F is identically the quantity designated by the same symbol in Eq. (5-37) if the sections 1 and 2, to which that equation refers, are taken, respectively, immediately before and after the fitting. Hence, to calculate the pressure drop occasioned by the fitting, Eq. (5-37) must be solved using the appropriate F.

The following symbols are used here:

A = cross-sectional area, sq. ft.
D = inside diameter, ft.
g_c = dimensional constant, 32.17 (lb.)(ft.)/(lb. force)(sec.^{2})
G = average mass velocity, lb./(sq. ft.)(sec.)
K = coefficient expressed as number of velocity heads, dimensionless
L = length of pipe or duct, ft.
L_e = equivalent length of straight pipe, ft.
p = static pressure, lb. force/sq. ft.
V = average linear velocity, ft./sec.
μ = viscosity, lb./(ft.)(sec.)
ρ = density, lb./cu. ft.

Subscripts are defined where they are used.

Equations and data apply to the flow of **incompressible fluids,** *i.e.*, liquids, and gases and vapors for density changes less than 10 per cent or for velocities less than 200 ft./sec.

Contraction or Entrance Losses. For a **sudden contraction** at a sharp-edged entrance to a pipe line or a sudden reduction in the cross-sectional area of a duct

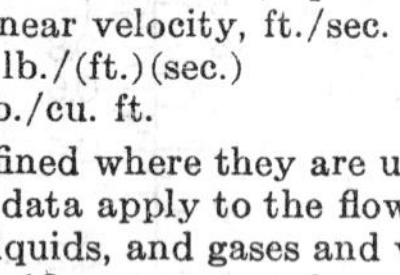

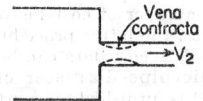

FIG. 5-32. Sudden contraction.

(Fig. 5-32), the loss of mechanical energy due to friction for **turbulent flow** is

$$F = K_c \frac{V_2^2}{2g_c} \quad \text{ft. of fluid} \qquad (5\text{-}91)$$

where V_2 = average velocity in the smaller pipe, ft./sec.; K_c = coefficient, function of the ratio of the smaller cross-sectional area A_2 to the larger cross-sectional area A_1, and of the Reynolds numbers in both pipes. Values of K_c for turbulent flow (see Rouse, *op. cit.*, p. 415) are given in Table 5-18. For **laminar flow,** the sudden

Table 5-18. Sudden Contraction-loss Coefficient for Turbulent Flow

A_2/A_1	0	0.2	0.4	0.6	0.8	1.0
K_c	0.5	0.45	0.36	0.21	0.07	0

contraction loss may be small. For additional information, see below on "entrance length."

For a **trumpet-shaped** or **rounded entrance** (Fig. 5-33) with a radius of rounding greater than about 15 per

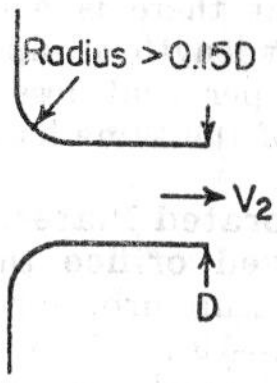

FIG. 5-33. Rounded entrance.

cent of the pipe diameter, the contraction coefficient K_c for **turbulent flow** is about 0.04 (see Vennard, *op. cit.*, pp. 315–317). Rounding of the inlet prevents formation of the *vena contracta* (see Fig. 5-32), thereby resulting in a smaller loss. For **laminar flow,** this entrance loss is negligible (see below).

Even though contraction or entrance losses for **laminar flow** are small or negligible, there is an abnormally high rate of pressure drop for a distance along the tube. This distance, known as the **entrance length,** was computed by Langhaar [*J. Appl. Mechanics,* **9,** A55–A58 (1942)] to be $0.057N_{Re}$ pipe diameters for the case of a circular pipe [see also Shapiro, Siegel, and Kline, *Proc. 2d U.S. Natl. Cong. Appl. Mech.*, A.S.M.E., 1954, pp. 733–741]. Cause of the abnormality lies in the work required to set up the parabolic velocity distribution for the laminar flow through a pipe. An increased frictional resistance near the pipe inlet arises from the same cause in **turbulent flow** also [Prandtl and Tietjens, "Applied Hydro- and Aero-mechanics," pp. 48–52, McGraw-Hill, New York, 1934; Ross, *Trans. Am. Soc. Mech. Engrs.*, **78,** 915–923 (1956)]. The effect appears to be of less importance in the turbulent region than in the laminar region; however, this effect may be an important cause for discrepancies among various sets of pipe-friction measurements. For a Reynolds number $DG/\mu = 2000$, the entrance effect would persist for about 115 diameters. Since, in a straight pipe with a rounded entrance leading from a quiet tank, laminar flow may be maintained without great difficulty up to very high Reynolds numbers, the deviation from Poiseuille's law near the inlet may be important (see Goldstein, *op. cit.*, vol. I, p. 321; Prandtl and Tietjens, *op. cit.*, pp. 33–35).

For circular tubes, the **pressure drop for laminar flow in the entrance length** following a rounded inlet in a horizontal pipe can be estimated from the curve given in Fig. 5-34. With an abrupt or square-edge inlet, for Reynolds numbers less than about 500, Fig. 5-34 applies; for Reynolds numbers greater than about 500, the pressure drop will be greater because of the *vena contracta* and eddies which are found behind the inlet. For further data, see Kreith and Eisenstadt, [*Trans. Am. Soc. Mech. Engrs.*, **79,** 1070 (1957)]. In Fig. 5-34, p_0 = static pressure in the reservoir, lb. force/sq. ft.; p_L = static pressure in the pipe at distance L, lb. force/sq. ft.; L = distance from the beginning of the straight pipe, *i.e.*, from exit of the inlet, ft. The equivalent length L_e of a rounded inlet for laminar flow is probably between 0 and 0.5 discharge diameter D [see Rivas and Shapiro, *Trans. Am. Soc. Mech. Engrs.*, **78,** 489–497 (1956); Shapiro and Smith, Friction Coefficients in the Inlet Length of Smooth Round Tubes, *N.A.C.A. Tech. Note* 1785, (November, 1948)].

Enlargement or Exit Losses. For ducts of any cross section, the frictional loss for a **sudden enlargement**

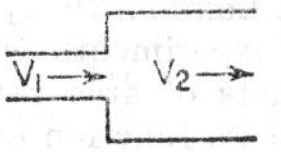

FIG. 5-35. Sudden enlargement.

(Fig. 5-35) with **turbulent flow** is given by the simple Borda-Carnot equation,

$$F = \frac{(V_1 - V_2)^2}{2g_c} = \frac{V_1^2}{2g_c}\left(1 - \frac{A_1}{A_2}\right)^2 \quad (5\text{-}92)$$

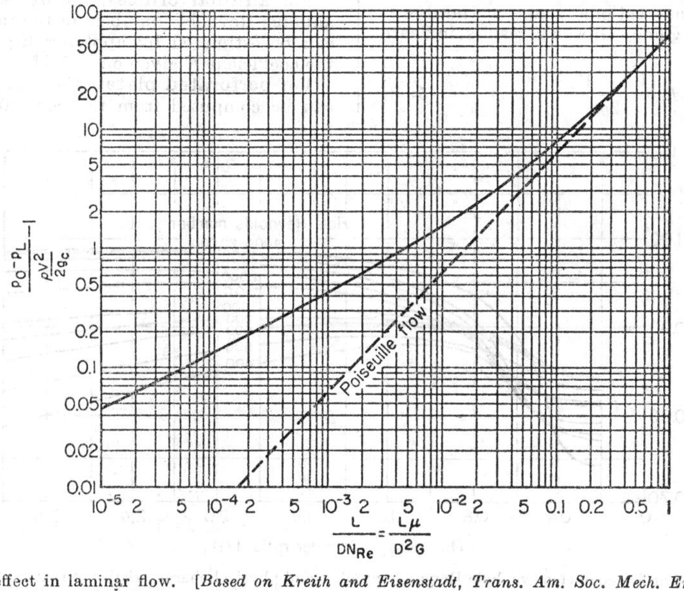

FIG. 5-34. Entrance effect in laminar flow. [*Based on Kreith and Eisenstadt, Trans. Am. Soc. Mech. Engrs.*, **79,** 1070 (1957); *and Shapiro, Siegel, and Kline, Proc. 2d Natl. Congr. Appl. Mech.*, p. 733, *A.S.M.E.*, 1954.]

where V_1 = velocity in smaller duct, ft./sec.; V_2 = velocity in larger duct, ft./sec.; A_1 = cross-sectional area of smaller duct, sq. ft.; A_2 = cross-sectional area of larger duct, sq. ft. Equation (5-92) has been shown by Schutt to be exact for water in fully turbulent flow [*Trans. Am. Soc. Mech. Engrs.*, **51,** Paper Hyd.-51-10 (1929)] and to apply fairly well to the turbulent flow of gases and vapors with velocities less than 200 ft./sec. [Kays, *Trans. Am. Soc. Mech. Engrs.*, **72,** 1067–1074 (1950)]. For **laminar flow** in the smaller tube, the result obtained by Eq. (5-92) should probably be doubled. At least, such a procedure appears to give the proper exit loss for the limiting case where the velocity in the discharge or downstream reservoir is negligible [see Kreith and Eisenstadt, *loc. cit.;* Philippoff and Gaskins, *Trans.Soc. Rheology*, **2,** 263–284 (1958)].

If the transition from a small to a large duct of any cross-sectional shape is accomplished by a **uniformly diverging duct** (Fig. 5-36) with a straight axis, the total

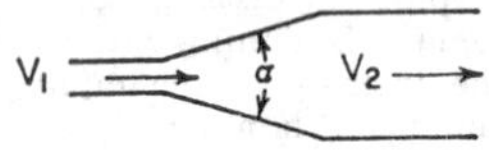

FIG. 5-36. Uniformly diverging duct.

pressure change Δp between the ends of the diverging section may be estimated by integrating the differential form of Eq. (5-52), provided that the total angle α between the diverging walls is not greater than about 7 deg. Gibson ["Hydraulics and Its Applications," 5th ed., p. 93, Constable, London, 1952] found for **turbulent flow,** based on his experiments with water flowing in conical diverging ducts of area ratios from 1-to-2.5 to 1-to-9, that the loss as a function of α decreases as α increases up to about 5 to 7 deg. and then increases rapidly with increasing α. For α above 35 deg., the loss often exceeds considerably that accompanying a sudden expansion, reaching a maximum at around 60 deg.; it then gradually decreases to that for a sudden expansion at α = 180 deg. A general and simple formulation for $\alpha > 7$ deg. cannot be given, since the measured losses are influenced by angle of divergence and ratio of expansion, the value of N_{Re}, nature of the initial velocity distribution, and length and cross-sectional shape of the downstream passage. As a guide, Gibson's results indicate that

$$\Delta h = K\frac{(V_1 - V_2)^2}{2g_c} \tag{5-93}$$

where Δh = total head loss, ft. of fluid flowing

$K \cong 0.13$ for $\alpha \cong 5$ to 7 deg.

$K = 0.0110\,\alpha^{1.22}$ for 7.5 deg. $< \alpha <$ 35 deg.

and where α is in degrees.

Trumpet-shaped enlargements for **turbulent flow** so designed that there is a constant decrease in velocity head per unit length of pipe axis were found to give from 20 to 60 per cent less frictional loss than straight taper pipes of the same length (Gibson, *op. cit.*, p. 95).

Orifices and Perforated Plates. For a **concentric circular square-edged orifice** the over-all frictional loss or permanent pressure drop for **turbulent flow** can be estimated by Eq. (5-19), p. 5-11. If the flow is **laminar** in the upstream channel, data on short tubes (Kreith and Eisenstadt, *loc. cit.*, p. 1074) indicate that the over-all frictional loss F (ft.)(lb. force)/lb. is equal to the orifice differential expressed in feet of fluid flowing.

For **sharp-edged,** ***i.e.,*** **knife-edged, circular orifices** when

$$\frac{D_2G_2}{\mu} \text{ or } \left(\frac{D_1G_1}{\mu}\right)\left(\frac{1}{\beta}\right) < 10$$

the equivalent length L_e of straight pipe of diameter D_1 corresponding to the over-all frictional loss is

$$\frac{L_e}{D_2} = \frac{\alpha^2}{64}(1 - \beta^4) \tag{5-94}$$

where $\alpha = 6.38 + 2.33\beta^2$ for $\beta \leq 0.8$ and where L_e = equivalent length, ft.; $\beta = D_2/D_1$, dimensionless; D_1 = upstream pipe diameter, ft.; D_2 = orifice diameter, ft.; G_1 = mass velocity in upstream pipe, lb./(sec.)(sq. ft.); G_2 = mass velocity in orifice, lb./(sec.)(sq. ft.); μ = viscosity, lb./(ft.)(sec.) (Johansen, *Aero. Res. Comm., Gt. Brit., Reports and Memoranda* 1252, 1929).

For a **rounded orifice** or **well-shaped nozzle** placed in a pipe line, the over-all frictional loss for **turbulent flow** can be estimated by applying Eq. (5-12). For **laminar flow,** the over-all frictional loss can be estimated from Fig. 5-34, taking the equivalent length L_e of a rounded inlet as about $0.2D_2$ (see p. 5-31), where D_2 = orifice or nozzle exit diameter, ft.

For **annular orifices,** the over-all frictional loss for annulus Reynolds numbers in the range of 100 to 20,000 can be estimated by applying Eq. (5-9) together with the coefficient K given on p. 5-11.

For **perforated plates,** the permanent pressure drop can be computed from the correlation by Van Winkle

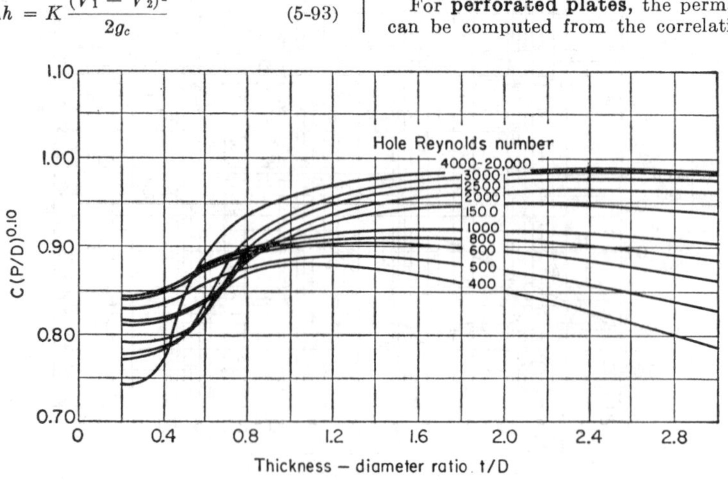

FIG. 5-37. Perforated-plate orifice coefficient vs. hole Reynolds number and physical characteristics of plate. [*Smith and Van Winkle, Am. Inst. Chem. Engrs. J.*, **4,** 266 (1958).]

et al. They correlated within ±5 per cent the pressure-drop data of their own and of others for the flow of gases **through perforated plates with square-edged holes** on an equilateral triangular spacing for a **hole Reynolds number range of 400 to 20,000.** The basic equation is

$$w = CA_fY\sqrt{\frac{2g_c\rho_1\,\Delta p}{1-(A_f/A_p)^2}} \qquad (5\text{-}95)$$

where w = weight rate of flow, lb./sec.; C = orifice coefficient described below, dimensionless; A_f = total free area of holes, sq. ft.; A_p = total cross-sectional area of perforated plate, sq. ft.; Y = expansion factor [Eq. (5-18), p. 5-10], dimensionless; g_c = dimensional constant, 32.17 (lb.)(ft.)/(lb. force)(sec.^{2}); ρ_1 = fluid density at upstream pressure and temperature, lb./cu. ft.; Δp = pressure drop across the plate, lb. force/sq. ft. Orifice coefficient C as a function of Reynolds number and physical characteristics of the plate is given in Fig. 5-37 [Smith and Van Winkle, *Am. Inst. Chem. Engrs. J.*, **4**, 266–268 (1958); see also Kolodzie and Van Winkle, *Am. Inst. Chem. Engrs. J.*, **3**, 305–312 (1957)], where P = hole pitch (center-to-center distance), ft.; D = hole diameter, ft.; t = plate thickness, ft.; N_{Re} = Reynolds number based on hole diameter = $wD/A_f\mu$, dimensionless; μ = fluid viscosity, lb./(ft.)(sec.). If the inlet edge of the hole is slightly rounded, as may be the case for punched holes, the coefficient can be considerably higher than that given by Fig. 5-37. An indication of the effect of rounding can be seen from preceding information on entrance losses.

Fittings and Valves. For **turbulent flow,** the additional frictional loss for fittings and valves can be allowed for by expressing the loss either as an equivalent length of straight pipe in pipe diameter, L_e/D, or as a number of velocity heads K lost in a pipe of the same size. K is defined as

$$K = \frac{\Delta h_f}{V^2/2g_c} \qquad (5\text{-}96)$$

where Δh_f = additional frictional loss (total frictional loss less frictional loss for center-line length of straight pipe), ft. of fluid flowing; V = average fluid velocity, ft./sec.; g_c = dimensional constant, 32.17 (lb.)(ft.)/(lb. force)(sec.^{2}). Quantities L_e/D and K are not entirely comparable, but both are accurate within the limits of available data or differences in details of available com-

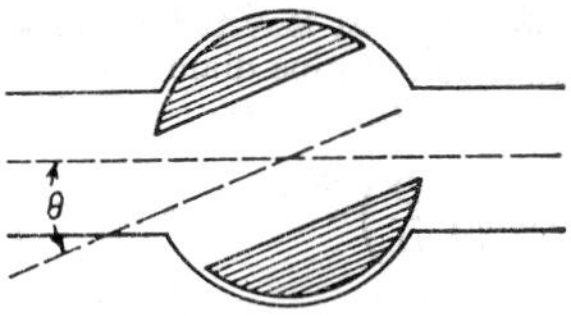

FIG. 5-38. Plug cock.

mercial fittings and valves. Theoretically K would be constant for all sizes of a given design of fitting or valve if all sizes were geometrically similar; however, geometric similarity is seldom achieved [De Craene, *Heating, Piping Air Conditioning,* **27** (10), 90–95 (1955)]. Data indicate that resistance K tends to decrease with increasing fitting or valve size [De Craene, *loc. cit.*, and Pigott, *Trans. Am. Soc. Mech. Engrs.*, **72**, 679–688 (1950)].

Representative values of K and of L_e expressed in pipe diameters for many types of fittings and valves are given in Table 5-19. Most of the values given are for standard screwed fittings and are probably accurate within ±30 per cent. The difference in frictional loss between screwed, flanged, and welded ends has been found to be

Table 5-19. Additional Frictional Loss for Turbulent Flow through Fittings and Valves[k]

Type of Fitting or Valve	Additional Friction Loss, Equivalent No. of Velocity Heads, K[s]
45-deg. ell, standard[a,b,e,g,i]	0.35
45-deg. ell, long radius[b]	0.2
90-deg. ell, standard[a,b,d,g,i,m]	0.75
Long radius[a,b,e,g]	0.45
Square or miter[m]	1.3
180-deg. bend, close return[a,b,g]	1.5
Tee, standard, along run, branch blanked off[g]	0.4
Used as ell, entering run[d,g]	1.3
Used as ell, entering branch[b,d,g]	1.5
Branching flow[f,h,l]	1[o]
Coupling[b,g]	0.04
Union[g]	0.04
Gate valve,[a,g,j] open	0.17
¾ open[p]	0.9
½ open[p]	4.5
¼ open[p]	24.0
Diaphragm valve,[n] open	2.3
¾ open[p]	2.6
½ open[p]	4.3
¼ open[p]	21.0
Globe valve,[g,j] bevel seat, open	6.4
½ open[p]	9.5
Composition seat, open	6.0
½ open[p]	8.5
Plug disk, open	9.0
¾ open[p]	13.0
½ open[p]	36.0
¼ open[p]	112.0
Angle valve,[a,g] open	3.0
Y or blowoff valve,[g,j] open	3.0
Plug cock (Fig. 5-38)[c] θ = 5°	0.05
10°	0.29
20°	1.56
40°	17.3
60°	206.0
Butterfly valve[c] (Fig. 5-39) θ = 5°	0.24
10°	0.52
20°	1.54
40°	10.8
60°	118.0
Check valve,[a,g,j] swing	2.0[q]
Disk	10.0[q]
Ball	70.0[q]
Foot valve[g]	15.0
Water meter,[m] disk	7.0[r]
Piston	15.0[r]
Rotary (star-shaped disk)	10.0[r]
Turbine-wheel	6.0[r]

[a] Flow of Fluids through Valves, Fittings, and Pipe, *Tech. Paper* 410, Crane Co., 1957.

[b] Freeman, "Experiments upon the Flow of Water in Pipes and Pipe Fittings," American Society of Mechanical Engineers, New York, 1941.

[c] Gibson, "Hydraulics and Its Applications," 5th ed., p. 250, Constable, London, 1952.

[d] Giesecke and Badgett, *Heating, Piping Air Conditioning*, **4** (6), 443–447 (1932).

[e] Giesecke, *J. Am. Soc. Heat. Vent. Engrs.*, **32**, 461 (1926).

[f] Gilman, *Heating, Piping Air Conditioning*, **27** (4), 141–147 (1955).

[g] "Standards of Hydraulic Institute—Tentative Standards, Pipe Friction," Hydraulic Institute, New York, 1948.

[h] Hoopes, Isakoff, Clarke, and Drew, *Chem. Eng. Progress*, **44**, 691–696 (1948).

[i] Ito, *Trans. Am. Soc. Mech. Engrs.*, **82**, Series D, 131–143 (1960).

[j] Lansford, Loss of Head in Flow of Fluids through Various Types of 1½-in. Valves, *Univ. Illinois Eng. Expt. Sta. Bull. Series* 340, 1943.

[k] Lapple, *Chem. Eng.*, **56** (5), 96–104 (1949), general survey reference.

[l] McNown, *Proc. Am. Soc. Civil Engrs.*, **79**, Separate 258, pp. 1–22 (1953); discussion, *ibid.*, **80**, Separate 396, pp. 19–45 (1954).

[m] Schoder and Dawson, "Hydraulics," 2d ed., p. 213, McGraw-Hill, New York, 1934.

[n] Streeter, *Prod. Eng.*, **18** (7), 89–91 (1947).

[o] This is pressure drop (including friction loss) between run and branch, based on velocity in the main stream before branching. Actual value depends on the flow split, ranging from 0.5 to 1.3 if main stream enters run and from 0.7 to 1.5 if main stream enters branch.

[p] The fraction open is directly proportional to stem travel or turns of hand wheel. Flow direction through some types of valves has a small effect on pressure drop (see Freeman, *op. cit.*). For practical purposes this effect may be neglected.

[q] Values apply only when check valve is fully open, which is generally the case for velocities more than 3 ft./sec. for water.

[r] Values should be regarded as approximate because there is much variation in equipment of the same type from different manufacturers.

[s] Equivalent length in pipe diameter depends upon Reynolds number; see p. 5-20. For rough estimates, L_e/D can be obtained by multiplying K by 45 for liquids similar to water and by 55 for gases similar to air.

insignificant (De Craene, *loc. cit.*). Manufacturers and users of valves, especially control valves, have found it convenient to express valve capacity in terms of a flow coefficient C_v. This coefficient is related to K by

$$C_v = \frac{29.9d^2}{\sqrt{K}} \qquad (5\text{-}97)$$

where C_v = valve-flow coefficient, gal./min. of water at 60°F. flowing under a valve pressure drop of 1 lb. force/sq. in.; d = inside diameter of valve, in.

For **laminar flow,** data for the frictional loss of fittings and valves are meager [Beck and Miller, *J. Am. Soc. Naval Engrs.*, **56**, 62–83 (1944); Beck, *ibid.*, **56**, 235–271, 366–388, 389–395 (1944); De Craene, *loc. cit.;* Karr and Schutz, *J. Am. Soc. Naval Engrs.*, **52**, 239–256 (1940); Kittredge and Rowley, *Trans. Am. Soc. Mech. Engrs.*, **79**, 1759–1766 (1957)]. The data of Kittredge and Rowley (*loc. cit.*) indicate that the additional frictional loss expressed as number of velocity heads K is constant for Reynolds numbers from over 2000 (turbulent flow) down to about 500; then K increases rapidly with decreasing Reynolds number. Typical values of K [Eq. (5-96)] for laminar-flow Reynolds numbers N_{Re} are given in Table 5-20.

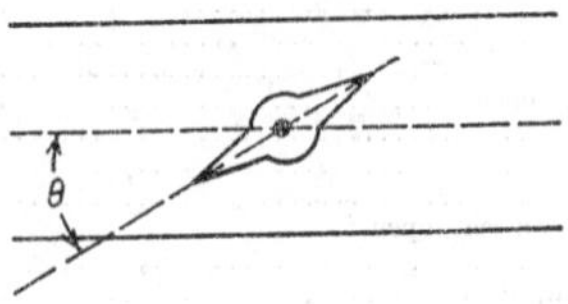

FIG. 5-39. Butterfly valve.

Table 5-20. Additional Frictional Loss for Laminar Flow through Fittings and Valves*

Type of fitting or valve	Additional frictional loss expressed as K			
	N_{Re} = 1000	500	100	50
90-deg. ell, short radius	0.9	1.0	7.5	16
Tee, standard, along run	0.4	0.5	2.5	
Branch to line	1.5	1.8	4.9	9.3
Gate valve	1.2	1.7	9.9	24
Globe valve, composition disk	11	12	20	30
Plug	12	14	19	27
Angle valve	8	8.5	11	19
Check valve, swing	4	4.5	17	55

* From curves by Kittredge and Rowley, *Trans. Am. Soc. Mech. Engrs.*, **79**, 1759–1766 (1957).

Bends and Curved Pipe. For **turbulent flow** in **smooth 90-deg. bends** (Fig. 5-40*a*) and **segmental 90-deg. bends** (Fig. 5-40*b*), total friction loss expressed as the ratio of equivalent length of straight pipe L_e to pipe diameter D as a function of the ratio of radius of curvature R to pipe diameter D, all in consistent units, is given in Fig. 5-41. The curve for smooth bends is based on various published data (see Fig. 5-41 for references) and represents most of the data with an uncertainty of probably ±25 per cent. The curves for segmental bends are based on few data. For a 45-deg. bend, total friction loss is about 65 per cent of the loss for a 90-deg. bend of a proportional number of segments and, similarly, for a 180-deg. bend, the loss is about 140 per cent of that for a 90-deg. bend, based on information presented by Conn, Colborne, and Brown [*Heating, Piping Air Conditioning,* **25** (1), 201–205 (1953)]; Hydraulic Institute ("Tentative Standards—Pipe Friction," Hydraulic Institute, New York, 1948); Ito, *loc. cit.;* Madison ("Fan Engineering," 5th ed., pp. 151–152, 157, Buffalo Forge Co., Buffalo, 1948); Snyder, *loc. cit.*

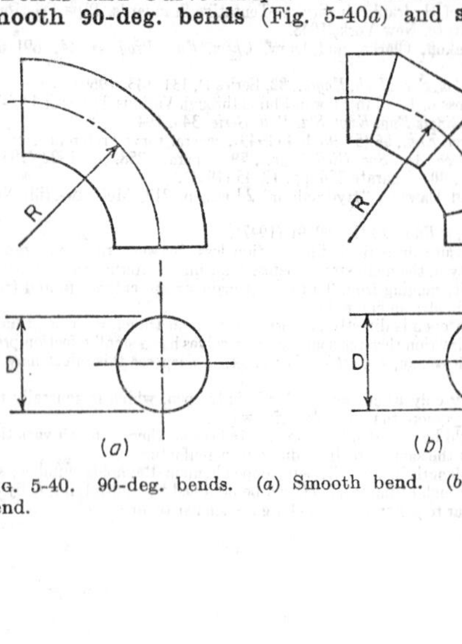

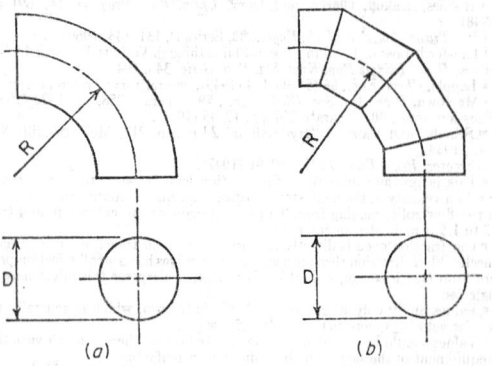

FIG. 5-40. 90-deg. bends. (*a*) Smooth bend. (*b*) Segmental bend.

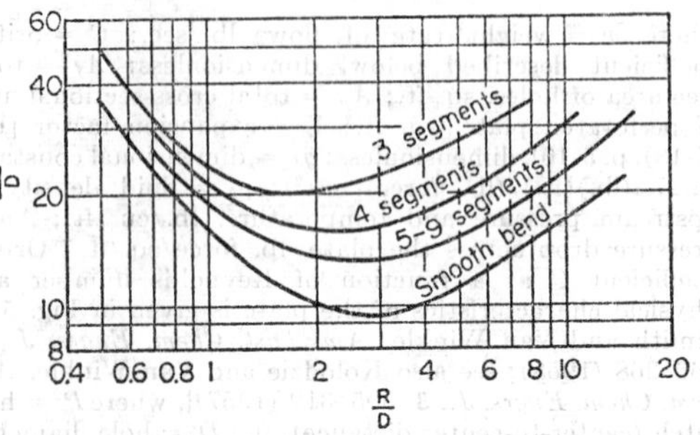

FIG. 5-41. Total friction loss in 90-deg. bends. [*Smooth bend: based on information from Freeman, "Experiments upon the Flow of Water in Pipes and Pipe Fittings," p. 173, A.S.M.E., New York, 1941; Ito, Trans. Am. Soc. Mech. Engrs.*, **82**, *Series D*, 131 (1960); *Locklin, Trans. Am. Soc. Heating Ventilating Engrs.*, **56**, 479 (1950); *Snyder, Heating, Piping & Air Conditioning*, **7** (1), 5 (1935). *Segmental bends: from Locklin (loc. cit.).*]

For flow through a **curved pipe or coil,** a secondary circulation of fluid called the double-eddy or Dean effect takes place in a plane at right angles to the main flow. Because of this circulation the friction loss in the curved pipe is greater than in an equal length of straight pipe. This circulation also stabilizes laminar flow, thus increasing the critical Reynolds number. The maximum Reynolds number, or **critical Reynolds number,** for laminar flow as a function of pipe diameter and coil diameter is given by Ito (*loc. cit.*):

$$(N_{Re})_{crit} = 20{,}000\left(\frac{D}{D_c}\right)^{0.32} \qquad \text{for } 15 < \frac{D_c}{D} < 860 \qquad (5\text{-}98)$$

where $(N_{Re})_{crit} = (DG/\mu)_{crit}$ = critical Reynolds number, dimensionless; D = pipe diameter, ft.; D_c = coil diameter, ft.; G = mass velocity, lb./(sec.)(sq. ft.); μ = fluid viscosity, lb./(ft.)(sec.). For $(D_c/D) > 860$, the critical Reynolds number for curved pipe is about the same as that for straight pipe.

Total friction loss for **laminar flow** in **curved pipe** can be expressed in terms of an equivalent length L_e of straight pipe. Ratio of the equivalent to actual coil center-line length L_e/L is a function of the Dean number or $(N_{Re})(D/D_c)^{1/2}$ as shown in Fig. 5-42 (see also Ito, *loc. cit.*, and Goldstein, *op. cit.*, vol. I, p. 312). This curve is accurate to within ±5 per cent. The **friction loss** for **turbulent flow** can be computed from the Fanning friction equation, Eq. (5-52), where for curved pipe the

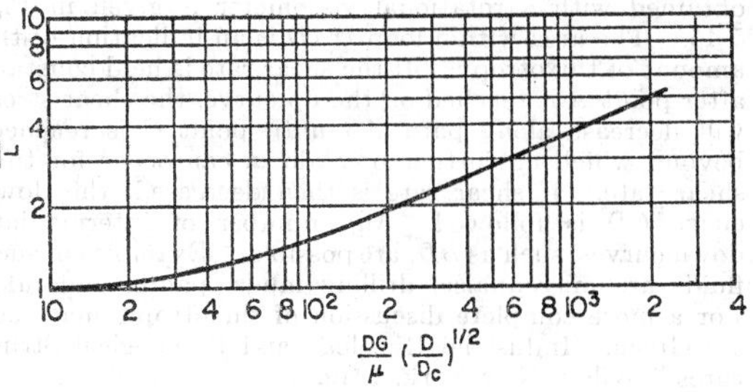

FIG. 5-42. Equivalent length for curved pipe in laminar flow. [*White, Proc. Roy. Soc. (London)*, **A123,** 645 (1929).] $\frac{L_e}{L} = 1$ for $\frac{DG}{\mu}\left(\frac{D}{D_c}\right)^{1/2} < 10.$

friction factor f_c is given by the empirically determined equation (Ito, *loc. cit.*):

$$f_c\left(\frac{D_c}{D}\right)^{1/2} = 0.0073 + 0.076\left[N_{\text{Re}}\left(\frac{D}{D_c}\right)^2\right]^{-1/4}$$

$$\text{for } 0.034 < N_{\text{Re}}\left(\frac{D}{D_c}\right)^2 < 300 \quad (5\text{-}99)$$

For $N_{\text{Re}}\ (D/D_c)^2 < 0.034$, the friction factor for curved pipe is practically the same as that for straight pipe. Equation (5-99) is probably accurate within ± 5 per cent.

Screens. The flow through a screen can be considered as flow through a number of orifices or nozzles in parallel. Thus the pressure drop or head loss across a screen can be computed from an orifice-type equation. The resulting equation for head loss is

$$\Delta h = \left(\frac{n}{C^2}\right)\left(\frac{1-\alpha^2}{\alpha^2}\right)\left(\frac{V^2}{2g_c}\right) \quad (5\text{-}100)$$

where Δh = head loss, ft. of fluid flowing; n = number of screens in series, dimensionless; C = screen discharge coefficient, dimensionless; α = fractional free projected area of screen, dimensionless; V = superficial velocity ahead of screen, ft./sec.; g_c = dimensional constant, 32.17 (lb.)(ft.)/(lb. force)(sec.^{2}). Experimental data [Volokhov, *Vestnik. Ing. Techn.*, (4), 149–152 (1930)] indicate that for a series of screens the over-all head loss is directly proportional to the number of screens in series, as given by Eq. (5-100), and is not affected by either the spacing between successive screens or by their orientation with respect to one another.

Screen discharge coefficient C is a function of screen Reynolds number, $N_{\text{Re}} = D_sV\rho/\alpha\mu$, where D_s = aperture width, ft.; ρ = fluid density, lb./cu. ft.; μ = fluid viscosity, lb./(ft.)(sec.). For **plain rectangular-mesh screens,** Lapple's plot of C vs. N_{Re} is given in Fig. 5-43 (courtesy of E. I. du Pont de Nemours & Co.). This curve represents most of the data to within ± 20 per cent. Coefficients greater than 1 probably indicate that the effective free area is larger than that of the projected area and that there is partial recovery of head due to the downstream rounding of the wires.

Other methods of correlating over-all frictional losses across screens are given by Cornell [*Trans. Am. Soc. Mech. Engrs.*, **80,** 791–799 (1958)] and Grootenhuis [*Proc. Inst. Mech. Engrs.*, **168A,** 837–846 (1954)].

Baffles. For **segmental baffles,** such as tube-bundle baffles in heat exchangers, the over-all friction loss for **turbulent flow** can be computed from

$$\Delta h = 2n_B\frac{V_B{}^2}{2g_c} = \frac{n_Bw^2}{g_c\rho^2A_B{}^2} \quad (5\text{-}101)$$

where Δh = over-all friction loss, ft. of fluid flowing; n_B = number of baffles in series, dimensionless; V_B = fluid velocity through baffle opening (based on A_B), ft./sec.; w = weight rate of flow, lb./sec.; A_B = net free area of baffle opening, sq. ft.; ρ = fluid density, lb./cu. ft.; g_c = dimensional constant, 32.17 (lb.)(ft.)/(lb. force) (sec.^{2}). Equation (5-101) is equivalent to treating the baffle opening as a segmental orifice with an over-all discharge coefficient of about 0.7. No allowance is made for leakage, such as that between baffle and shell or between baffle and tubes.

NON-NEWTONIAN FLOW

General Description. Non-Newtonian fluids are usually divided into three general classes: (1) those whose properties are independent of time or duration of shear, (2) those whose properties are dependent upon duration of shear, and (3) those which exhibit many characteristics of a solid. See Metzner, "Non-Newtonian Technology," in Drew and Hoopes, "Advances in Chemical Engineer-

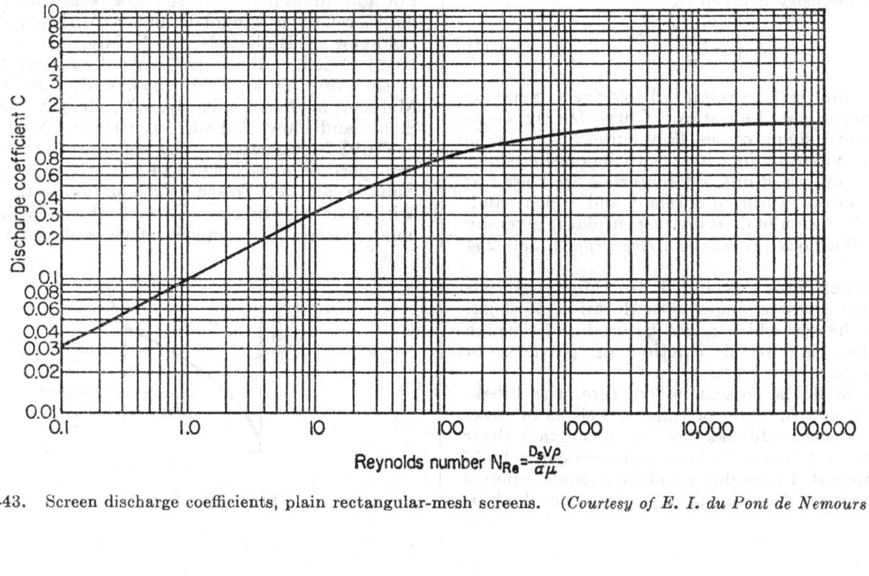

FIG. 5-43. Screen discharge coefficients, plain rectangular-mesh screens. (*Courtesy of E. I. du Pont de Nemours & Co.*)

ing," vol. I, Academic Press, New York, 1956; Metzner, "Flow Behavior of Thermoplastics," in Bernhardt, "Processing of Thermoplastic Materials," Reinhold, New York, 1959; Wilkinson, "Non-Newtonian Fluids," Pergamon Press, New York, 1960.

1. **Time-independent.** The following three types of materials are in this class:

a. Bingham plastic fluids are probably the simplest non-Newtonian fluids because they differ from Newtonian fluids only in that their linear relationship between shear stress and shear rate does not go through the origin. This is illustrated by curve *B* in Fig. 5-44. This curve

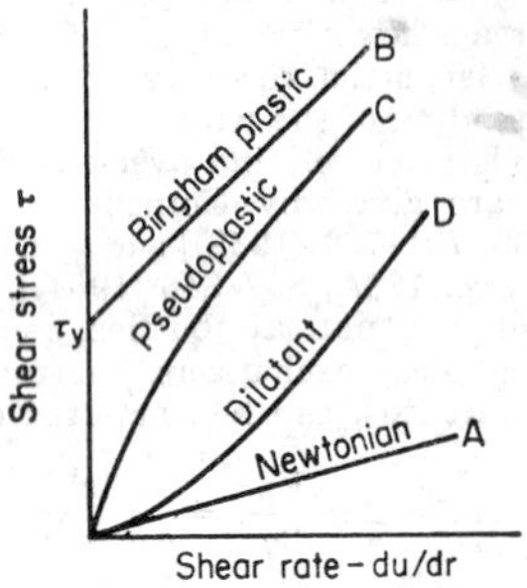

FIG. 5-44. Shear diagrams.

shows that a finite shear stress τ_y is required to initiate flow. For comparison, a Newtonian fluid has a curve similar to curve *A*. Examples of fluids exhibiting Bingham-plastic behavior include water suspensions of rock [Wilhelm, Wroughton, and Loeffel, *Ind. Eng. Chem.*, **31**, 622–629 (1939)] or grains [Binder and Busher, *J. Appl. Mechanics*, **13**, A101–A105 (1946)] and sewage sludge [Caldwell and Babbitt, *Ind. Eng. Chem.*, **33**, 249–256 (1941)].

b. Pseudoplastic materials include the majority of non-Newtonian fluids. They include polymeric solutions or melts, and suspensions of paper pulp or pigments. Shape of the flow curve is shown as curve *C*, Fig. 5-44. In general the flow curve is a straight line on a logarithmic plot and can be defined by

$$\tau = K\left(-\frac{du}{dr}\right)^n \quad \text{where } n < 1 \tag{5-102}$$

The apparent viscosity is given by

$$\mu_a = K\left(-\frac{du}{dr}\right)^{n-1} \tag{5-103}$$

c. Dilatant materials exhibit rheological behavior opposite to that of pseudoplastics. Curve *D* (Fig. 5-44) shows the typical shape of the flow curve. As can be seen, apparent viscosity increases with increasing shear rate. Some examples of dilatant materials are starch or mica suspensions in water, quicksand and beach sand. An excellent discussion of dilatant suspensions is given by Metzner and Whitlock [*Trans. Soc. Rheology*, **2**, 239–254 (1958)].

2. **Time-dependent.** Included are those materials for which shear stress changes with duration of shear. Excluded are changes which might be produced through mechanical breaking or destruction of particles or molecular bonds.

a. Thixotropic fluids possess a structure, the breakdown of which is a function of time as well as of shear rate. As the structure breaks down with constant shear rate, shear stress decreases. This structure can rebuild itself if not prevented from doing so by externally applied forces. The shear diagram of a thixotropic fluid as obtained with a rotational viscometer is given in Fig. 5-45. The area within loop *DAD* is an indication of the amount of thixotropy. If the shear rate is held constant after point *A* is reached on the up curve, the shear stress will decrease along path *AB* until point *C* is reached, beyond which no further breakdown can occur for that shear rate. If shear rate is then decreased, the down curve *CD* is followed. Any number of intermediate down curves, such as *BD*, are possible. Examples of such fluids are mayonnaise, drilling muds, paints and inks. For a more complete discussion of thixotropic materials see Green, "Industrial Rheology and Rheological Structures," Wiley, New York, 1949.

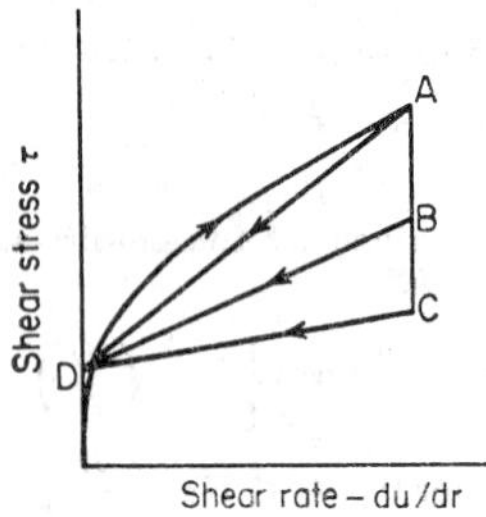

FIG. 5-45. Shear diagram for thixotropic fluid.

b. Rheopectic materials will set up or build up, *i.e.*, increase in apparent viscosity very rapidly upon being rhythmically shaken or tapped. Examples of these materials are bentonite sols, vanadium pentoxide sols and gypsum suspensions in water. This phenomenon has been observed under constant shear rate [Yannas and Gonzalez, *Nature*, **191**, 1384 (1961)].

3. **Viscoelastic Fluids.** These fluids exhibit elastic recovery from deformations which occur during flow. Polymeric liquids comprise the largest group of fluids in this class. In the flow of these fluids, normal stresses (*i.e.*, stresses perpendicular to direction of flow) in addition to the usual tangential stresses are built up. These normal stresses give rise to several unusual phenomena; for example, the "Weissenberg effect," in which the fluid has a tendency to climb up a shaft rotating in the fluid. For the steady-state flow of viscoelastic fluids, the equations developed for pseudoplastic fluids apply; the elastic properties are generally manifested as "end effects." For additional details on the flow behavior of viscoelastic fluids, reference should be made to Alfrey, "Mechanical Behavior of High Polymers," Interscience, New York, 1948; Eirich, "Rheology," vols. 1, 2, and 3, Academic Press, New York, 1956, 1958, and 1960, respectively; Metzner in Bernhardt, *op. cit.*; Reiner, "Deformation, Strain and Flow," 2d ed., Interscience, New York, 1960.

Fluid Mechanics. The scaleup of pipe lines for the transport of non-Newtonian materials can be done by using a plot of Poiseuille's equation, *i.e.*, plotting on arithmetic coordinates $8V/D$ vs. $D\,\Delta p/4L$ for the particular material. A typical curve is shown in Fig. 5-46.

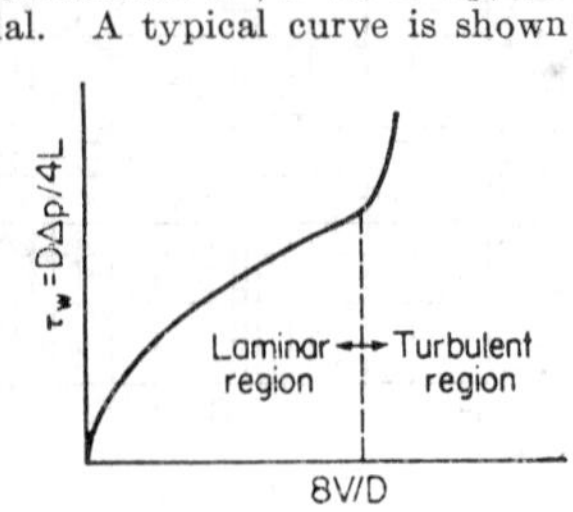

FIG. 5-46. General flow curve.

$D\,\Delta p/4L$ is the shear stress at the pipe wall τ_w, and $8V/D$ is proportional to shear rate at the wall; where D = pipe diameter, ft.; Δp = pressure drop, lb. force/sq. ft.; L = length of pipe, ft.; V = velocity, ft./sec.

In the **laminar region** the curve (Fig. 5-46) is independent of pipe diameter for time-independent non-Newtonians. Thus such a curve, determined for the flow of a non-Newtonian in a small pipe, can be used to scale up to a larger pipe. If the fluid is time-dependent, a separate curve will be obtained for each pipe diameter and pipe length. For additional details see Alves, Boucher, and Pigford, *Chem. Eng. Progress*, **48**, 385–393 (1952).

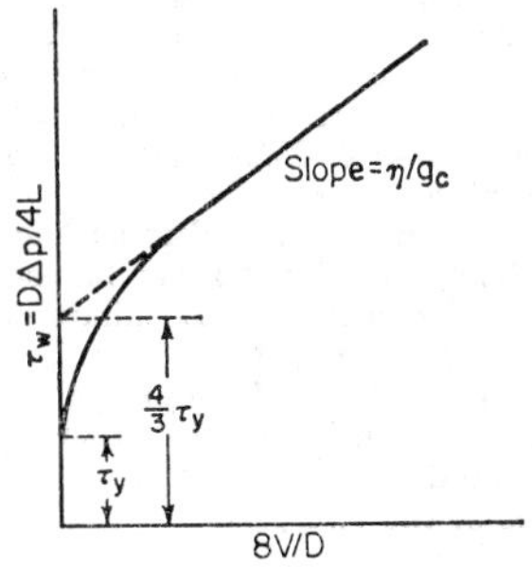

FIG. 5-47. Bingham plastic-flow curve.

For **Bingham plastics**, a typical curve is shown in Fig. 5-47. The theoretical flow equation (see Caldwell and Babbitt, *loc. cit.*) is

$$\frac{8V}{D} = \frac{g_c\tau_w}{\eta}\left[1 - \frac{4}{3}\frac{\tau_y}{\tau_w} + \frac{1}{3}\left(\frac{\tau_y}{\tau_w}\right)^4\right] \tag{5-104}$$

Since $(\tau_y/\tau_w)^4$ is relatively small except at large values of τ_y/τ_w, *i.e.*, at small shear stresses or pressure drops, Eq. (5-104) may be approximated by

$$\frac{8V}{D} = \frac{g_c}{\eta}\left(\tau_w - \frac{4}{3}\tau_y\right) \tag{5-105}$$

The error in omitting the last term in Eq. (5-104) is less than 2 per cent for τ_y/τ_w less than 0.4. The apparent viscosity μ_a can be obtained from substituting Eq. (5-105) into Poiseuille's equation,

$$\mu_a = \frac{g_c\tau_y D}{6V} + \eta \tag{5-106}$$

In the above equations, D = pipe inside diameter, ft.; g_c = dimensional constant, 32.17 (lb.)(ft.)/(lb. force)(sec.^{2}); L = pipe length, ft.; Δp = static pressure drop, lb. force/sq. ft.; V = velocity, ft./sec.; η = coefficient of rigidity, lb./(ft.)(sec.); μ_a = apparent viscosity, lb./(ft.)(sec.); τ_w = wall shear stress = $D\,\Delta p/4L$, lb. force/sq. ft.; τ_y = yield stress, lb. force/sq. ft.

For those fluids where the power law, Eq. (5-102), applies:

$$\frac{D\,\Delta p}{4L} = K'\left(\frac{8V}{D}\right)^{n'} \tag{5-107}$$

$$\left(-\frac{du}{dr}\right)_w = \text{shear rate at wall} = \left(\frac{3n'+1}{4n'}\right)\left(\frac{8V}{D}\right) \tag{5-108}$$

where
$$n' = \frac{d[\ln(D\,\Delta p/4L)]}{d[\ln(8V/D)]} \tag{5-109}$$

n' is the slope of the line from plotting $D\,\Delta p/4L$ vs. $8V/D$ on logarithmic coordinates. For $n' = 1$, the fluid is Newtonian; for $n' < 1$, pseudoplastic or Bingham plastic; and for $n' > 1$, dilatant. K', consistency index, is the value of $D\,\Delta p/4L$ for $8V/D = 1$. For Newtonian fluids, $K' = \mu/g_c$. For the above equations, nomenclature is the same as that given after Eq. (5-106).

The **limit of stable laminar flow** is usually taken as N_{Re} = 2100, where

$$N_{\text{Re}} = \text{generalized Reynolds number} = \frac{D^{n'}V^{2-n'}\rho}{\gamma} \tag{5-110}$$

and
$$\gamma = g_c K' 8^{n'-1} \tag{5-111}$$

or
$$N_{\text{Re}} = \frac{DV\rho}{\mu_a} \quad \text{for Bingham plastics} \tag{5-112}$$

where ρ = density, lb./cu. ft.; other symbols defined following Eq. (5-106). For additional details, see Metzner in Drew and Hoopes, *op. cit.;* Metzner and Reed [*Am. Inst. Chem. Engrs. J.*, **1**, 434–440 (1955)].

In **turbulent flow,** the curve (Fig. 5-46) will break off sharply. The point of breakoff will be different for different pipe diameters. To size pipe lines, two general methods are available. In the first method, the generalized Reynolds number, Eq. (5-110), is computed and then the friction factor determined from Fig. 5-25 and the pressure drop from the Fanning equation, Eq. (5-52) (see Metzner and Reed, *loc. cit.*). In the second method, the "turbulent viscosity" is computed from pressure-drop data in the turbulent region (Fig. 5-46) and the friction-factor vs. Reynolds-number plot (Fig. 5-25). This is done as follows: From values of $D\,\Delta p/4L$, V, and D, the friction factor f is computed from Eq. (5-52); from this value of f, the corresponding N_{Re} is obtained from Fig. 5-25, and from $N_{\text{Re}} = DV\rho/\mu_T$, the "turbulent viscosity" μ_T is computed. This value of μ_T can then be used for other pipe diameters. Pressure drop computed by this procedure should be accurate within ± 25 per cent. See Alves *et al.* (*loc. cit.*) for additional details. A theoretical analysis for turbulent flow of non-Newtonian fluids is given by Dodge and Metzner [*Am. Inst. Chem. Engrs. J.*, **5**, 189–204 (1959)].

For those fluids where Eq. (5-107) applies, K' and n can be determined from rotational viscometer data (Metzner in Drew and Hoopes, *op. cit.*). The method is as follows: For values of torque at various rotational speeds of the cup or bob, shear stress at the wall of the cylindrical bob is computed from

$$\tau_i = \frac{2T}{\pi D_i^2 h} \tag{5-113}$$

where τ_i = shear stress at wall, lb. force/sq. ft.; T = torque, (lb. force)(ft.); D_i = diameter of bob, ft.; h = height of bob, ft. The shear rate at the wall of a cylindrical bob is given as [Krieger and Maron, *J. Appl. Phys.*, **25**, 72–75 (1954), see also Metzner in Drew and Hoopes, *op. cit.*]

$$\left(-\frac{du}{dr}\right)_i = \frac{4\pi N}{1-(1/s^2)}\left[1 + k_1\left(\frac{1}{n''}-1\right) + k_2\left(\frac{1}{n''}-1\right)^2\right] \quad \text{for } s < 1.2 \tag{5-114}$$

$$k_1 = \frac{s^2-1}{2s^2}\left(1 + \frac{2}{3}\ln s\right) \tag{5-115}$$

and
$$k_2 = \frac{s^2-1}{6s^2}\ln s \tag{5-116}$$

where $(-du/dr)_i$ = shear stress at wall of bob, 1/sec.; N = rotational speed, rev./sec.; n'' = slope of logarithmic plot of torque vs. rotational speed; s = ratio of cup diameter to bob diameter, dimensionless. From Eq.

(5-102) values of K and n are obtained. Metzner and Reed (*loc. cit.*) have shown that, for many fluids,

$$n' = n \tag{5-117}$$

and
$$K' = K\left(\frac{3n'+1}{4n'}\right)^{n'} \tag{5-118}$$

An excellent discussion of theories for various viscometers is given by Oka (in Eirich, "Rheology," vol. 3, Chap. 2, Academic Press, New York, 1960). Practical aspects of viscometry are given by Bowen [*Chem. Eng.*, **68** (17), 119; (18), 131 (1961)].

TWO-PHASE FLOW

Liquids and Gases. For **cocurrent flow with constant liquid-gas ratios,** considerable experimental and theoretical work has been done on prediction of pressure drop, volume fractions, and flow pattern for flow in pipes. A reliable general correlation has not as yet been developed, although correlations for specific flow systems have been published. Presented here are **guides** for the estimation of flow pattern, pressure drop and volume fractions for flow in horizontal and vertical pipes.

In horizontal pipe, flow patterns have been reported in the literature and correlated empirically as functions of flow rates and flow properties. The boundaries between flow patterns, however, are not sharply defined, because the transitions are gradual and the mean boundaries depend upon interpretations of individual investigators and upon piping configurations and fluids under study. The following general types of **flow pattern** have been reported, where the values of the superficial velocities given are representative values for liquids with viscosities less than about 100 centipoise and gases of densities about that of air:

1. **Bubble or froth flow,** in which bubbles of gas are dispersed throughout the liquid, occurs for liquid superficial velocities from about 5 to 15 ft./sec. and gas superficial velocities from about 1 to 10 ft./sec. (See p. 5-15 for definition of superficial velocity.)

2. **Plug flow,** in which alternate plugs of liquid and gas move along the upper part of the pipe, occurs for liquid superficial velocities less than 2 ft./sec. and gas superficial velocities less than 3 ft./sec.

3. **Stratified flow,** in which the liquid flows along the bottom of the pipe and the gas flows over a smooth liquid-gas interface, occurs for liquid superficial velocities less than 0.5 ft./sec. and gas superficial velocities from about 2 to about 10 ft./sec.

4. **Wavy flow** is similar to stratified flow except the interface has waves traveling in the direction of flow. This occurs for liquid superficial velocities less than about 1 ft./sec. and gas superficial velocities about 15 ft./sec.

5. **Slug flow,** in which a wave is picked up periodically by the rapidly moving gas to form a frothy slug which passes along the pipe at a greater velocity than the average liquid velocity. In this type of flow, slugs can cause severe and, in some cases, dangerous vibrations in equipment because of impact of the high-velocity slugs against such fittings as return bends.

6. **Annular flow,** in which the liquid flows as a film around the pipe inside wall and the gas flows as a core. A portion of the liquid is entrained as a spray by the central gas core. This type of flow occurs for gas superficial velocities greater than about 20 ft./sec. Determinations of entrainment are reported by Wicks and Dukler [*Am. Inst. Chem. Engrs. J.*, **6**, 463–468 (1960)].

7. **Spray** or **dispersed flow,** in which nearly all the liquid is entrained as fine droplets by the gas, probably occurs for gas superficial velocities greater than 200 ft./sec. The interaction between an air stream and a moving horizontal water surface is described by Hanratty and Engen [*Am. Inst. Chem. Engrs. J.*, **3**, 299–304 (1957)].

For additional details on flow patterns see Alves [*Chem. Eng. Progress*, **50**, 449–456 (1954)] for 1-in., four-pass pipe-line contactor; Baker [*Oil Gas J.*, **53** (12), 185–190, 192, 195 (1954)] for a correlation of published data from 1- to 4-in. pipes; Bergelin and Gazley (*Proc. Heat Transfer and Fluid Mech. Inst.*, A.S.M.E., June 22–24, 1949, pp. 7–18) for 1-in. pipe; Hoogendoorn [*Chem. Eng. Sci.*, **9**, 205–217 (1959); *Ingenieur*, **71** (46), 081–087 (1959)] for 1- to 5½-in. pipes; Hughes, Evans, and Sternling [*Chem. Eng. Progress*, **49**, 78–87 (1953)] for a correlation of published data from 1- to 4-in. pipe; Johnson and Abou-Sabe [*Trans. Am. Soc. Mech. Engrs.*, **74**, 977–987 (1952)] for 1-in. pipe; Reid *et al.* [*Am. Inst. Chem. Engrs. J.*, **3**, 321–324 (1957)] for data from 4- and 6-in. pipe; White and Huntington [*Petrol. Engr.*, **27** (9), D40–D45 (1955)] for 1- to 2-in. pipe.

Two-phase pressure drop due to friction for cocurrent flow in **horizontal pipe** can be estimated by the semiempirical correlation of Lockhart and Martinelli [*Chem. Eng. Progress*, **45**, 39–48 (1949)]. Basis of the correlation is that the two-phase pressure drop is equal to the single-phase pressure drop for either phase multiplied by a factor found to be a function of the single-phase pressure drops of the two phases:

$$\left(\frac{\Delta p}{\Delta L}\right)_{TP} = Y_L\left(\frac{\Delta p}{\Delta L}\right)_L \tag{5-119}$$

or
$$\left(\frac{\Delta p}{\Delta L}\right)_{TP} = Y_G\left(\frac{\Delta p}{\Delta L}\right)_G \tag{5-120}$$

where $Y_L = F_1(X)$ and $Y_G = F_2(X)$ (5-121)

$$X = \left[\frac{(\Delta p/\Delta L)_L}{(\Delta p/\Delta L)_G}\right]^{1/2} \tag{5-122}$$

Note that
$$Y_G = X^2 Y_L \tag{5-123}$$

The single-phase pressure-drop gradients $(\Delta p/\Delta L)_L$ and $(\Delta p/\Delta L)_G$ are computed from the Fanning equation, Eq. (5-52), assuming that each phase is flowing alone in the pipe; that is, superficial velocities are used. The superficial velocities are based on the full cross-sectional area of the pipe:

$$V_L = \frac{q_L}{A} \quad \text{and} \quad V_G = \frac{q_G}{A} \tag{5-124}$$

where V_L = liquid-phase superficial velocity, ft./sec.; V_G = gas-phase superficial velocity, ft./sec.; q_L = liquid-phase volumetric flow rate, cu. ft./sec.; q_G = gas-phase volumetric flow rate, cu. ft./sec.; A = pipe cross-sectional area, sq. ft.

Functions F_1 and F_2, Eq. (5-121), are shown as curves in Fig. 5-48. Separate curves are required for each flow regime; liquid in viscous* flow and gas in viscous flow (*vv*); liquid viscous-gas turbulent (*vt*); and similarly (*tv*) and (*tt*). In Fig. 5-48, however, only one curve is given for liquid viscous-gas turbulent and liquid turbulent-gas viscous because the difference between the experimental curves is small compared with the uncertainty of the correlation. The transition criterion between viscous flow and turbulent flow is not definitely known. However, for design purposes, the transition can be taken as that for single-phase flow; that is, the flow can be considered viscous for $N_{Re} \leq 2000$ and turbulent for $N_{Re} > 2000$, where N_{Re} is based on superficial velocity. Lockhart and Martinelli (*loc. cit.*) correlated their pressure-drop data on flows in pipes 1 in. or less in diameter within about ±50 per cent. In general,

* The term "viscous" is customarily used, rather than "laminar," in reference to two-phase flow.

the predictions are high for stratified, wavy and slug flows and low for annular flow. The correlations can be applied to pipe diameters up to 4 in. with about the same accuracy. Several investigators have studied flows in larger pipes (up to 10 in.) and have developed equations for pressure drop in their particular system; however, a better general correlation has not been developed. For other correlations, see Baker *(loc. cit.)*; Chenoweth and

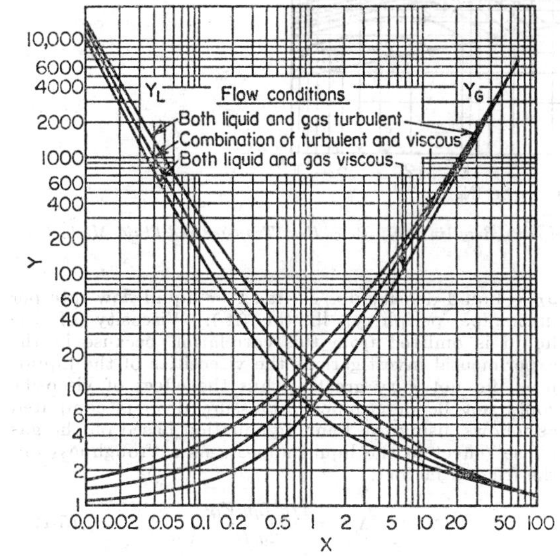

FIG. 5-48. Parameters for pressure drop in liquid-gas flow through horizontal pipes. [*Based on Lockhart and Martinelli, Chem. Eng. Progress*, **45**, 39 (1949).]

Martin [*Petrol. Refiner*, **34** (10), 151–155 (1955)]; Hoogendoorn *(loc. cit.)*; Reid *et al.* *(loc. cit.)*.

Volume fraction or **hold up** of a phase for cocurrent flow in **horizontal pipe** can be predicted from the following correlation developed by Lockhart and Martinelli *(loc. cit.)*:

$$R_L = F_3(X) \quad \text{and} \quad R_G = F_4(X) \tag{5-125}$$

where

$$R_L + R_G = 1 \tag{5-126}$$

R_L = fraction of pipe volume occupied by the liquid phase, dimensionless; R_G = fraction occupied by gas phase, dimensionless; X = parameter defined by Eq. (5-122), dimensionless. Function F_3 as a curve of R_L vs. X is given in Fig. 5-49. Lockhart and Martinelli correlated data for pipe diameters 1 in. and less within ±50 per cent of the curve shown. Indications are that liquid-volume fractions may be less than those predicted by Fig. 5-49 for liquid viscosities greater than 1 centipoise (see Alves, *loc. cit.*) and greater than predicted for larger pipe diameters (see Baker, *loc. cit.*).

Pressure-drop data for a 1-in. **inlet or feed tee,** with the liquid entering the run and the gas entering the branch, are given by Alves *(loc. cit.)*. For **fittings** and **valves,** results of Chenoweth and Martin *(loc. cit.)* indicate that single-phase data can be used in their correlation for two-phase pressure drop.

For **upflow** in **vertical pipe,** most of the work has been done on gas lifts, a type of liquid pump. A gas lift consists simply of a vertical pipe, open at both ends, part of which is submerged below the surface of the liquid to be pumped. Compressed gas is admitted to the bottom of the pipe, forming a mixture of liquid and gas within the pipe. The gas reduces the average density of the mixture to a value where the weight of the mixture is less than equivalent to the submergence or pressure at the air inlet. Thus at the proper rates of liquid and gas, the mixture rises upward through the pipe and is discharged at the upper end. The submergence is the distance from the liquid surface to the air inlet. The lift is the distance from the liquid surface to the discharge. The submergence ratio is defined as

$$R_s = \frac{\text{submergence}}{\text{submergence} + \text{lift}} \tag{5-127}$$

For **upflow** the following general types of **flow pattern** have been observed where the values of the superficial velocities given are representative for liquids with viscosities less than about 100 centipoise and gas densities about that of air:

1. **Bubble** or **aerated flow,** in which the gas is dispersed as fine bubbles throughout the liquid, occurs for gas superficial velocities below about 2 ft./sec.
2. **Piston, plug,** or **slug flow,** in which the gas flows as large plugs, occurs for gas superficial velocities from about 2 to about 30 ft./sec.
3. **Annular** or **film flow,** in which the liquid flows up the pipe as an annulus and the gas flows as a core, occurs for liquid superficial velocities less than 2 ft./sec. and gas superficial velocities over 30 ft./sec.
4. **Mist flow,** in which the liquid is carried as fine drops by the gas phase. Data indicate that this probably occurs for superficial gas velocities over about 70 ft./sec. [Yagi and Sasaki, *Chem. Eng. (Japan)*, **17**, 216–223 (1953)].

For additional details on flow-pattern types and for correlation of flow pattern with flow rates, pressure

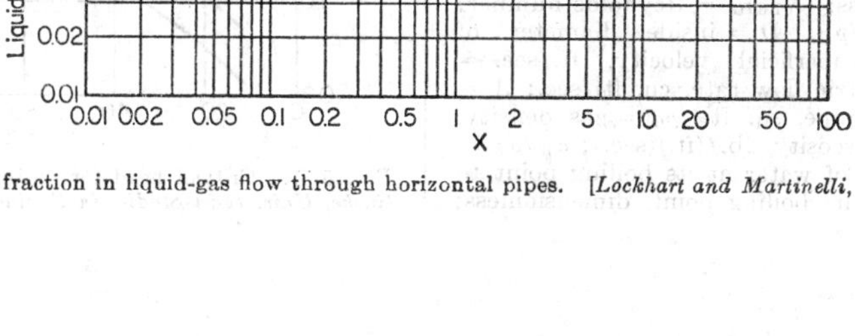

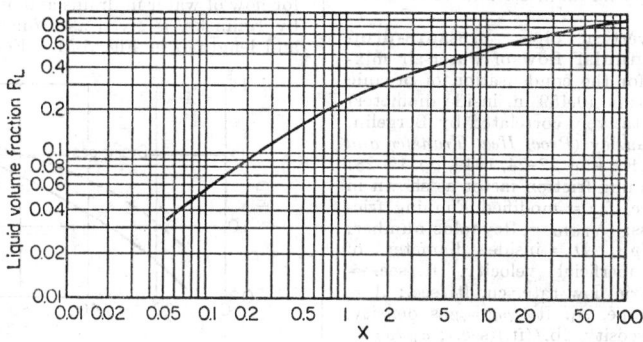

FIG. 5-49. Liquid volume fraction in liquid-gas flow through horizontal pipes. [*Lockhart and Martinelli, Chem. Eng. Progress*, **45**, 39 (1949).]

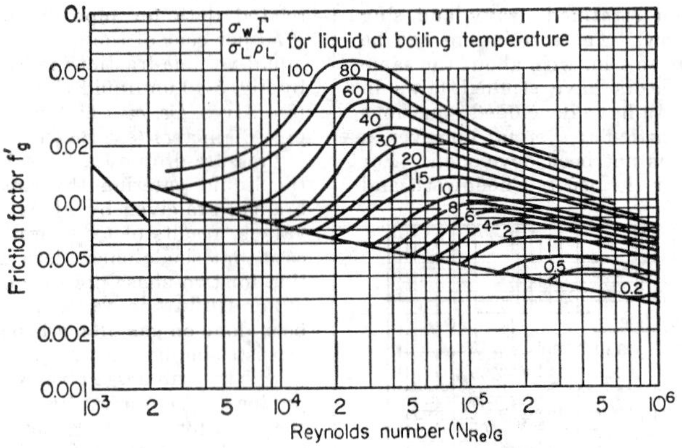

FIG. 5-50. Friction factors for liquid-gas flow downward in vertical pipe. (*Bergelin et al., Proc. Heat Transfer and Fluid Mech. Inst., A.S.M.E.*, p. 19, 1949.)

drops and pipe sizes, reference should be made to Gosline [*Trans. Am. Inst. Mining Met. Engrs.* (*Petrol. Development and Technol.*), **118,** 56–70 (1936)]; Govier *et al.* [*Can. J. Chem. Eng.*, **35,** 58–70 (1957); **36,** 195–202 (1958); **38,** 62–66 (1960)]; Huntington *et al.* [*Trans. Am. Inst. Mining Met. Engrs.* (*Petrol. Development and Technol.*), **136,** 79–90 (1940); *Petrol. Refiner,* **33** (11), 208–211 (1954)].

During upflow, there is considerable slippage between the liquid and the gas; thus the **ratio of liquid to gas** within the pipe is greater than that at the inlet. Experimental data for the flow of water-air and kerosene-air mixtures in ½- and 2-in. pipes are presented by Galegar, Stovall, and Huntington [*Petrol. Refiner,* **33** (11), 208–211 (1954)]; experimental data and a correlation for the flow of water-air mixtures in ½- to 2.5-in. pipes are given by Govier and Short [*Can. J. Chem. Eng.*, **36,** 195–202 (1958)] and by Brown, Sullivan, and Govier [*ibid.*, **38,** 62–66 (1960)]. Until further confirmation, this correlation should be used only for systems similar to those investigated. Some data on liquid entrainment are given by Anderson and Mantzouranis [*Chem. Eng. Sci.*, **12,** 233 (1960)].

For prediction of **pressure drop** in **upflow,** no satisfactory general method has been developed. Tentative correlations are given by Govier and Short (*loc. cit.*), Brown *et al.* (*loc. cit.*), and Hughmark and Pressburg [*Am. Inst. Chem. Engrs. J.*, **7,** 677 (1961)], but they should be used only for conditions similar to those studied. To predict the **operation of gas lifts** see data of Shaw (*Texas Eng. Expt. Sta. Bull.* 113, 1949) on air-water and air-oil lifts of 1 to 2½ in. diameter and 10 to 80 ft. high.

For **downflow** in vertical pipes, **pressure-drop** measurements for the **annular flow** of water-air mixtures in 1-in. pipe and for the condensation of organic vapors inside a vertical tube (0.459 in. inside diameter) condenser have been tentatively correlated by Bergelin, Kegel, Carpenter, and Gazley (*Proc. Heat Transfer and Fluid Mech. Inst.*, A.S.M.E., June 22–24, 1949, pp. 19–28) based on a modified Fanning friction factor as shown in Fig. 5-50. In this figure, f_G' = modified Fanning friction factor, dimensionless; $(N_{Re})_G$ = Reynolds number, dimensionless = $DV_G\rho_G/\mu_G$; D = inside diameter of pipe, ft.; V_G = gas superficial velocity, ft./sec. = q_G/A; q_G = gas volumetric flow rate, cu. ft./sec.; A = cross-sectional area of pipe, sq. ft.; ρ_G = gas density, lb./cu. ft.; μ_G = gas viscosity, lb./(ft.)(sec.); σ_W/σ_L = ratio of surface tension of water at its boiling point to that of other liquid at its boiling point, dimensionless; ρ_L = liquid density, lb./cu. ft.; Γ = liquid flow rate per unit pipe periphery, lb./(hr.)(ft.). Viscosity of the liquid is omitted from this correlation because in the experimental investigations the viscosities of the liquids used did not vary greatly; thus the effect of viscosity could not be determined. Pressure drop is computed as follows, using the Fanning equation based on the gas phase (effect of the liquid appears as a "roughness" in the friction factor):

$$\Delta p = \frac{4f_G' L\rho_G V_G^2}{2g_c D} \tag{5-128}$$

where Δp = pressure drop, lb. force/sq. ft.; L = pipe length, ft.; g_c = dimensional constant, 32.17 (lb.)(ft.)/(lb. force)(sec.²). Application of Eq. (5-128) to condensing flow in vertical condensers is described below, p. 5-42.

Also involving **downflow** are **drain** and **overflow** pipes. The entrance to a drain pipe is flush with a horizontal surface; the entrance to an overflow pipe is above the horizontal surface, *i.e.*, the pipe extends through and above the horizontal surface. When such pipes do not run full, considerable amounts of gas can be drawn down by the flowing liquid. The amount of gas entrained is a function of pipe diameter, pipe length and liquid flow rate. Extensive data on air entrainment and head above the entrance as a function of water flow rate for pipe diameters from 1.73 to 5.84 in. and lengths from about 4 to 17 ft. are reported by Kalinske (*Univ. Iowa Studies in Engineering, Bull.* 26, pp. 26–40, 1939–1940). For heads greater than the critical, the pipes will run full and no gas will be entrained. The critical head h for flow of water in drains and overflow pipes, as reported by Kalinske, is given as a function of pipe diameter D and length L in Fig. 5-51. From Kalinske's investiga-

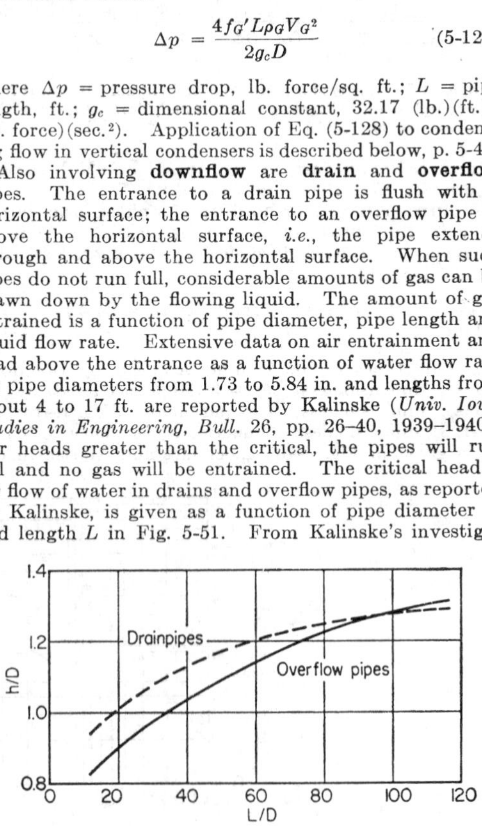

FIG. 5-51. Critical head for drain and overflow pipes. (*Kalinske, Univ. Iowa Studies in Engineering, Bull.* 26, 1939–1940.)

velocities used are generally less than 25 ft./sec. and are approximately equal to twice the actual solids velocities (Wen and Simons, *loc. cit.*).

Total **pressure drop** in **horizontal pipe** may be considered as the sum of the following individual pressure drops [Mehta, Smith, and Comings, *Ind. Eng. Chem.*, **49**, 986–992 (1957)]:

1. For acceleration of gas to the carrying velocity

$$\Delta p_{a,G} = \frac{G_G V_G}{2g_c} \qquad (5\text{-}135)$$

2. For acceleration of solid particles

$$\Delta p_{a,s} = \frac{G_s V_s}{g_c} \qquad (5\text{-}136)$$

3. For friction between gas and pipe wall

$$\Delta p_{f,G} = \frac{4f_G L \rho_{dG} V_G^2}{2g_c D_t} = \frac{4f_G L G_G V_G}{2g_c D_t} \qquad (5\text{-}137)$$

4. For combined friction between particles and pipe wall, between gas and particles, and between particles, assuming that this friction can be expressed by a type of friction factor equation

$$\Delta p_{f,s} = \frac{4f_s L \rho_{ds} V_s^2}{2g_c D_t} = \frac{4f_s L G_s V_s}{2g_c D_t} \qquad (5\text{-}138)$$

Friction factor f_s can be related to the particle drag coefficient by a force balance on the particles in the pipe as follows:

$$4f_s = \frac{3\rho_G D_t C}{2\rho_s D_s}\left(\frac{V_G - V_s}{V_s}\right)^2 \qquad (5\text{-}139)$$

In the above equations, Δp = pressure drop, lb. force/sq. ft.; C = drag coefficient, dimensionless, obtained from Fig. 5-70, p. 5-60, for N_{Re} Reynolds number = $D_s(V_G - V_s)\rho_G/\mu_G$; D_s = diameter of solid particle, ft.; D_t = diameter of tube or pipe, ft.; f_G = Fanning friction factor, dimensionless, obtained from Fig. 5-25, p. 5-20; f_s = solids friction factor, dimensionless; $G_G = \rho_{dG}V_G$ = gas mass velocity, lb./(sec.)(sq. ft.); $G_s = \rho_{ds}V_s$ = solids mass velocity, lb./(sec.)(sq. ft.); g_c = dimensional constant, 32.17 (lb.)(ft.)/(lb. force)(sec.^{2}); L = length of pipe, ft.; V_G = actual velocity of gas, ft./sec.; V_s = actual velocity of solids, ft./sec.; ρ_{dG} = dispersed gas density, weight of gas/unit volume of pipe, lb./cu. ft.; ρ_{ds} = dispersed solids density, weight of solids/unit volume of pipe, lb./cu. ft.; ρ_G = gas density, lb./cu. ft.; ρ_s = solids density, lb./cu. ft.; μ_G = gas viscosity, lb./(ft.)(sec.).

For **solids-to-gas weight-rate ratios less than 5** in **horizontal pipes,** such as those usually employed in conventional pneumatic conveying systems, Hinkle (Ph.D. Thesis, Chemical Engineering, Georgia Institute of Technology, Atlanta, 1953) found experimentally (for flow of air and solid particles 0.014 to 0.33 in. diameter in 2- and 3-in. glass pipe) that

$$V_s = V_G'\left[1 - 1.41 D_s^{0.3}\left(\frac{\rho_s}{62.3}\right)^{0.5}\right] \qquad (5\text{-}140)$$

where for this case $V_G' = G_G/\rho_G$ = superficial gas velocity, ft./sec. In such systems with low solids-to-gas ratios, $V_G \simeq V_G'$. For **solids-to-gas weight-rate ratios over 50,** such as those used in dense-phase transport, the particles tend to settle and move along the bottom of the pipe, and the flow pattern is therefore considerably different from that in the conventional dilute-phase pneumatic conveyor. Wen and Simons (*loc. cit.*) obtained the following empirical pressure-drop correlation for conditions where the particles were considered to have reached their terminal velocity. Their experiments involved the flow of glass beads (<0.01 in. diameter) and coal powder (<0.03 in. diameter) with air in a ¼-in. steel pipe and in ½- to 1-in. glass pipes.

$$\left(\frac{\Delta p_f}{L\rho_{ds}}\right)\left(\frac{D_t}{D_s}\right)^{0.25} = 2.5V_s^{0.45} \qquad (5\text{-}141)$$

where Δp_f = sum of the pressure drops due to friction, lb. force/sq. ft.; L = length of pipe, ft.; $\rho_{ds} = G_s/V_s$ = dispersed solids density, weight of solids/unit volume of pipe, lb./cu. ft.; $G_s = w_s/A_t$ = superficial mass velocity of the solids, lb./(sec.)(sq. ft.); w_s = solids flow rate, lb./sec.; A_t = cross-sectional area of pipe, sq. ft.; D_t = diameter of pipe, ft.; D_s = diameter of solid particle, ft.; V_s = average actual velocity of solid particles, ft./sec., determined from Fig. 5-53. Average actual velocity of

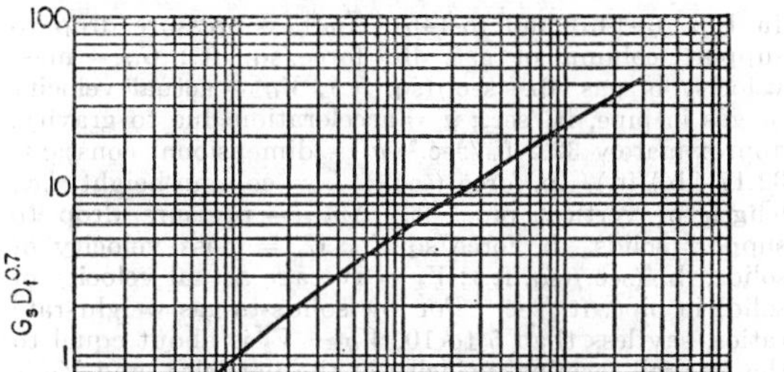

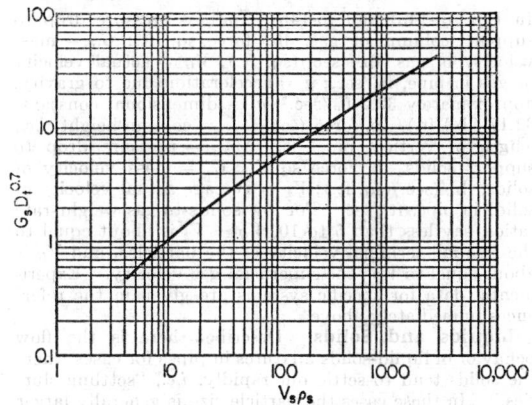

FIG. 5-53. Average velocity of solid particles. [*Wen and Simons, Am. Inst. Chem. Engrs. J.*, **5**, 263 (1959).]

the air can be determined from the slippage between the air and the solids. Wen and Simons (*loc. cit.*) found that $V_a \simeq 2V_s$. Mass velocity of the air is given by

$$G_a = \rho_{da}V_a \qquad (5\text{-}142)$$

where

$$\rho_{da} = \frac{\rho_a}{\rho_s}(\rho_s - \rho_{ds}) \qquad (5\text{-}143)$$

and where G_a = mass velocity of air, lb./(sec.)(sq. ft.); V_a = average actual velocity of air, ft./sec.; ρ_{da} = dispersed air density, weight of air/unit volume of pipe, lb./cu. ft.; ρ_a = air density, lb./cu. ft.; ρ_s = solids particle density, lb./cu. ft.; ρ_{ds} = dispersed solids density, weight of solids/unit volume of pipe, lb./cu. ft. The pressure drop correlation, Eq. (5-141), is not dimensionless because only one gas, namely, air, was used. Its uncertainty appears to be on the order of ±35 per cent. Additional investigation is needed to develop a general correlation.

For **upflow** of gases and solids in **vertical pipes,** the **minimum carrying velocity** for low solids-to-gas weight-rate ratios can be estimated by the following equation proposed by DallaValle (*loc. cit.*):

$$V_{C,v} = 910\left(\frac{\rho_s}{\rho_s + 62.3}\right)D_s^{0.60} \qquad (5\text{-}144)$$

where $V_{C,v}$ = minimum carrying velocity, ft./sec.; ρ_s = density of solids particle, lb./cu. ft.; D_s = diameter of largest particle to be conveyed, ft. For high solids-to-gas weight-rate ratios, data on carrying velocities are not readily available.

Total **pressure drop** in **vertical pipe** may be considered as the sum of the following individual pressure drops [Hariu and Molstad, *Ind. Eng. Chem.*, **41**, 1148–1160 (1949); Mehta, Smith, and Comings, *loc. cit.*]:

1. For acceleration of gas to the carrying velocity, Eq. (5-135)
2. For acceleration of solid particles, Eq. (5-136)
3. For friction between gas and pipe wall, Eq. (5-137)
4. For combined friction between particles and pipe wall, and the like, Eqs. (5-138) and (5-139)
5. For support of the column of gas,

$$\Delta p_{h,G} = \frac{G_G g L}{V_G g_c} \qquad (5\text{-}145)$$

6. For support of solids,

$$\Delta p_{h,s} = \frac{G_s g L}{V_s g_c} \qquad (5\text{-}146)$$

In Eqs. (5-145) and (5-146), $\Delta p_{h,G}$ = pressure drop to support column of gas, lb. force/sq. ft.; G_G = mass velocity of gas, lb./(sec.)(sq. ft.); V_G = actual velocity of gas in pipe, ft./sec.; g = acceleration due to gravity, approximately 32.2 ft./sec.^{2}; g_c = dimensional constant, 32.17 (lb.)(ft.)/(lb. force)(sec.^{2}); L = column height, *i.e.*, length of vertical pipe, ft.; $\Delta p_{h,s}$ = pressure drop to support solids, lb. force/sq. ft.; G_s = mass velocity of solids, lb./(sec.)(sq. ft.); V_s = average actual velocity of solids in pipe, ft./sec. For low solids-to-gas weight-rate ratios, say less than 5 to 10, $V_G - V_s$ is about equal to the free-fall terminal velocity of the particles, and V_G is about equal to V_G', the superficial gas velocity. Experimental data for specific systems are given in the references immediately above.

Liquids and Solids. Described here is the flow behavior of liquid-solids mixtures in pipes for cases where the solids tend to settle out rapidly, *i.e.*, "settling slurries." In these cases the particle size is generally larger than 0.01 in. (0.25 mm.). For those cases where the solids readily remain in suspension, such as with solids of particle size less than 0.002 in. (50 microns), the discussion given on pp. 5-35 to 5-38 applies.

In **horizontal pipe,** gravity tends to stratify the mixture, the solids settling to the bottom. However, the solids can remain suspended in the liquid as a result of turbulence in the liquid due to high velocities, or where the particles are relatively small (less than about ⅛ in.). Settling of the solids has a pronounced effect upon pressure drop. At high velocities, the pressure gradient along the pipe is slightly greater than that for liquid alone flowing at the same velocity. With finely divided solids, the pressure gradient at high velocities may be less than that for the liquid alone because the solids tend to damp the turbulence [see Wilson, *Trans. Am. Soc. Civil Engrs.*, **107,** 1576–1594 (1942)]. As velocity is reduced, the pressure gradient for the slurry will decrease, but it becomes increasingly greater than that for the liquid alone; a minimum pressure gradient is then reached, after which the pressure gradient increases with further reduction in velocity because of settling of the solids.

Transport velocity is a function of pipe diameter, particle size, particle density, solids concentration, and fluid properties. For particle sizes under 0.04 in. (1 mm.), Spells [*Trans. Inst. Chem. Engrs.*, **33,** 79–84 (1955)] gives the following correlations on the flow of water suspensions of sands, ash, and lime in **horizontal pipes** of 1 to 12 in. diameter:

1. Velocity to keep particles in suspension, V_1 ft./sec.,

$$\frac{V_1^2}{gD_s}\frac{\rho_L}{(\rho_s - \rho_L)} = 0.0251\left(\frac{V_1 D_t \rho_m}{\mu_L}\right)^{0.775} \qquad (5\text{-}147)$$

2. Velocity when pressure gradient for slurry becomes identical to that for a liquid with a density equal to the slurry and a viscosity the same as water, V_2 ft./sec.,

$$\frac{V_2^2}{gD_s}\frac{\rho_L}{(\rho_s - \rho_L)} = 0.074\left(\frac{V_2 D_t \rho_m}{\mu_L}\right)^{0.775} \qquad (5\text{-}148)$$

where, in Eqs. (5-147) and (5-148), g = acceleration due to gravity, approximately 32.2 ft./sec.^{2}; D_s = particle diameter, ft., such that 85 per cent by weight of particles are smaller than D_s; ρ_s = particle density, lb./cu. ft.; ρ_L = liquid density, lb./cu. ft.; D_t = pipe diameter, ft.; ρ_m = slurry density, lb./cu. ft.; μ_L = liquid viscosity, lb./(ft.)(sec.).

For large particles (diameter up to about one-third the pipe diameter), Worster and Denny [*Proc. Inst. Mech. Engrs. (London)*, **169**, 563–586 (1955)] give approximate values of the velocity for minimum pressure gradient for the flow of water suspensions of about 25 per cent by volume of coal or gravel as listed in Table 5-21. Additional velocity data for the flow of sand or similar suspensions are given by Howard [*Trans. Am. Soc. Civil Engrs.*, **104**, 1334–1380 (1939)]; Newitt, Richardson, Abbott, and Turtle [*Trans. Inst. Chem. Engrs.*, **33,** 93–110 (1955)]; Smith [*ibid.*, **33,** 85–92 (1955)]; Wilson (*loc. cit.*). A general correlation for particles in the 40-micron to 2-mm. range has been proposed by Hughmark [*Ind. Eng. Chem.*, **53,** 389 (1961)].

Table 5-21. Velocity for Minimum Pressure Gradient, Water Suspensions of Coal or Gravel*

Pipe diam., in.	Velocity, ft./sec.†	
	Coal‡	Gravel§
1	1.5	3
3	3.5	7
6	5	10
9	6.3	13
12	7.3	15
18	8.8	17.5

* Worster and Denny, *Proc. Inst. Mech. Engrs. (London)*, **169**, 563–586 (1955).
† For concentrations about 25 per cent by volume.
‡ Specific gravity = 1.4.
§ Specific gravity = 2.6.

Although there are considerable data on **pressure drop** for flow of water suspensions of sand, gravel, coal, and the like in **horizontal** pipes, no single correlation has been found to be entirely satisfactory for all particle sizes, particle densities, concentrations, and pipe sizes. As a guide, the modified Durand equation can be used (see Smith, *loc. cit.*):

$$\frac{i_m - i_L}{i_L} = 121\, c\left\{\frac{D_t g(\rho_s - \rho_L)}{V^2 \rho_L}\,\frac{V_s}{\sqrt{D_s g(\rho_s - \rho_L)/\rho_L}}\right\}^{3/2} \qquad (5\text{-}149)$$

where i_m = pressure gradient for mixture = $(\Delta h_m/L)(\rho_m/\rho_L)$, ft. of liquid L per ft. of pipe; i_L = pressure gradient for liquid L flowing alone at velocity V, ft. of liquid L per ft. of pipe; Δh_m = head loss for mixture, ft. of mixture; L = length of pipe, ft.; ρ_m = mixture density, lb./cu. ft.; ρ_L = liquid density, lb./cu. ft.; ρ_s = solid particle density, lb./cu. ft.; D_t = pipe diameter, ft.; D_s = solid particle diameter, ft.; c = concentration as volume fraction of solids, dimensionless; g = acceleration due to gravity, approximately 32.2 ft./sec.^{2}; V = mixture velocity, ft./sec.; V_s = free-fall velocity of solids particle in liquid L, ft./sec.

Equation (5-149) is based on the flow of water suspensions of various solids of particle diameters of about 0.01 to about 1 in. with concentrations up to around 30 volume per cent in pipe diameters from 1½ to 23 in. The equation is applicable for closely sized particles and for liquid velocities greater than 3 ft./sec. (see Smith, *loc. cit.*). For mixed particle sizes, the equation will be in error; the amount of error depends upon the amount of fines and the spread in particle size (see Smith, *loc. cit.*, and discussion by Durand and Condolios of the paper by Worster and Denny, *loc. cit.*). Pressure-drop data for the flow of various solids-water mixtures, such as sands, gravels, and coal in water, are presented by Howard (*loc. cit.*), Newitt *et al.* (*loc. cit.*), Smith (*loc. cit.*), Wilson (*loc. cit.*), and Worster and Denny (*loc. cit.*). Pressure-drop data for the flow of paper stock in pipes are given in the Data Section of "Standards of Hydraulic Institute," Hydraulic Institute, New York, 1951.

In **upflow** in **vertical pipes** the concentration of solids will increase, and in **downflow** the concentration will decrease because of the slip between the liquid and the solids. The **slip velocity,** *i.e.*, difference between liquid and solids velocities, can be taken as equal to the free-fall velocity of the solids in the liquid. The **pressure drop** for flows where the nominal mixture velocity is greater than four or five times the free-fall velocity of the solids may be estimated by

$$i_m = i_L \pm \left[c\left(\frac{\rho_s}{\rho_L} - 1\right) + 1\right] \qquad (5\text{-}150)$$

where + is for upflow and − is for downflow. Nomenclature is the same as for Eq. (5-149). Additional details are given by Worster and Denny (*loc. cit.*).

FLUID DISTRIBUTION

Uniform fluid distribution is essential for efficient operation of chemical processing equipment such as contactors and reactors, mixers, burners, heat exchangers, extrusion dies, and textile-spinning chimneys. To obtain optimum distribution, proper consideration must be given to flow behavior in the distributor, flow conditions upstream of the distributor, and flow conditions downstream of the distributor. Guides for the design of various types of fluid distributors are described below. These procedures take into account only the flow behavior in the distributor.

Perforated-pipe Distributors. The simple perforated pipe or sparger (Fig. 5-54), used in a wide variety of piping configurations, is a common type of distributor.

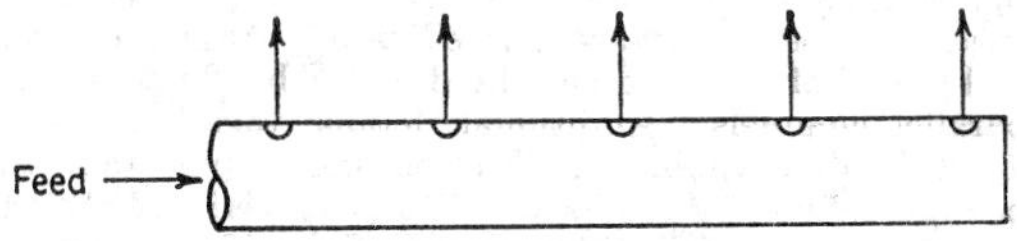

FIG. 5-54. Perforated-pipe distributor.

As shown, the flow distribution is uniform; this is the case when there is a proper balance between (1) kinetic energy and momentum force of the inlet stream, (2) friction losses along the length of pipe, and (3) pressure drop across the outlet holes. When inlet-stream kinetic energy and momentum force predominate, increasing amounts of fluid will be discharged as the flow travels toward the closed end; when friction losses along the pipe predominate, decreasing amounts of fluid will be discharged as the flow travels toward the closed end. When an upstream disturbance, such as produced by a bend, is superimposed upon a case of predominant inlet-stream kinetic energy and momentum force, the flow from the outlet holes near the distributor inlet and near the closed end can be greater than in the middle.

A **rule of thumb for design** of perforated-pipe distributors for turbulent flow such that the maldistribution is less than ±5 per cent is this: The ratios of kinetic energy of the inlet stream to pressure drop across the outlet hole and of friction loss in the pipe to pressure drop across the outlet hole should be equal to or less than one-tenth [Senecal, *Ind. Eng. Chem.*, **49**, 993–997 (1957)]. From a knowledge of the velocity distribution at the inlet to the distributor, the kinetic energy can be computed from

$$\text{Kinetic energy} = \frac{\alpha V_i^2}{2g_c} \quad \text{ft. of fluid flowing} \qquad (5\text{-}151)$$

where V_i = average inlet velocity, ft./sec.; g_c = dimensional constant, 32.17 (lb.)(ft.)/(lb. force)(sec.^{2}); α = correction factor to compensate for use of the average velocity, dimensionless. As a guide, α is 1.00 for plug flow (uniform velocity distribution), about 1.05 to 1.10 for turbulent flow in long straight ducts, 2 for laminar flow [Stoker, *Ind. Eng. Chem.*, **38**, 622–624 (1946)]. For other velocity distributions, the method of computing α is given by Rouse, *op. cit.*, pp. 399–401.

Generally, an orifice coefficient of 0.60 to 0.63 is used; however, for perforated pipes, the orifice coefficient is a function of hole size relative to pipe diameter and wall thickness, flow rate through the hole, flow rate in the pipe across the hole, and the like, and thus the value of the orifice coefficient could be considerably different from the values generally used (Senecal, *loc. cit.*). Additional experimental data are needed to define the above function. In general, if the component of the hole outlet velocity normal to the pipe wall is larger than the velocity along the pipe, the effect of the pipe velocity on the orifice coefficient would appear to be small [Grobman, Dittrich, and Graves, *Trans. Am. Soc. Mech. Engrs.*, **79**, 1601–1607 (1957)].

The **pressure change** due to friction and to momentum recovery over the length of the perforated-pipe distributor can be shown by theory to be (Lapple *et al.*, "Fluid and Particle Mechanics," p. 15, University of Delaware, Newark, 1951)

$$\Delta h_p = \left(\frac{4fL}{3D} - 2\right)\frac{V_i^2}{2g_c} \qquad (5\text{-}152)$$

where Δh_p = net loss in head between the inlet and closed end of the pipe, ft. of flowing fluid; f = Fanning friction factor, dimensionless; L = pipe length, ft.; D = pipe diameter, ft.; V_i = average fluid velocity at inlet to pipe, ft./sec.; g_c = dimensional constant, 32.17 (lb.)(ft.)/(lb. force)(sec.^{2}). Experimental investigations have shown that the factor 2 for momentum recovery may be high, the actual value being closer to 1 [Van der Hegge Zijnen, *Appl. Sci. Research*, **A3**, 144–162 (1951–1953)]. Assuming a constant orifice coefficient, the percentage of maldistribution between the first and last outlets can be given by

$$\text{Per cent maldistribution} = 100\left[1 - \sqrt{\frac{\Delta h_{0_1} - \Delta h_p}{\Delta h_{0_1}}}\right] \qquad (5\text{-}153)$$

where Δh_{0_1} = difference in head across the first outlet, ft. of fluid flowing.

Slot-type distributors are generally used in sheeting dies for extrusion of films and coatings and in air knives for control of thickness of a material applied to a moving sheet.

A simple slotted pipe (Fig. 5-55) for turbulent flow conditions can give severe maldistribution, because this

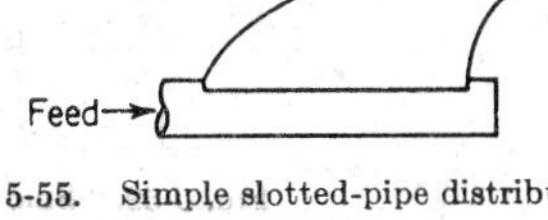

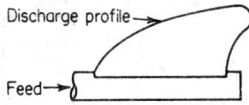

FIG. 5-55. Simple slotted-pipe distributor.

type of distributor does not readily give a discharge perpendicular to the slot [Koestel and Tuve, *Heating, Piping Air Conditioning*, **20** (1), 153–157 (1948); Koestel and Young, *Heating, Piping Air Conditioning*, **23** (7), 111–115 (1951)]. The discharge angle will vary along the length of pipe. However, for slots in tapered ducts where the duct cross-sectional area decreases linearly to zero at the far end, the discharge angle will be constant along the length of duct (Koestel and Young, *loc. cit.*). One way to ensure an almost perpendicular discharge is to have the ratio of the area of the slot to the cross-sectional area of the pipe equal to or less than 0.1. As in the case of the perforated-pipe distributor, for good performance a proper balance has to be made of kinetic energy and momentum changes, friction and discharge losses, and upstream and downstream flow conditions. Another way to improve the discharge angle is to use turning vanes as described below.

In practice, the following methods may be used to keep the diameter of the pipe to a minimum consistent with good performance (Senecal, *loc. cit.*):

1. Feed from both ends; this reduces the kinetic-energy term.
2. Modify cross-sectional design (Fig. 5-56); the slot is thus farther away from the influence of feed-stream velocity.

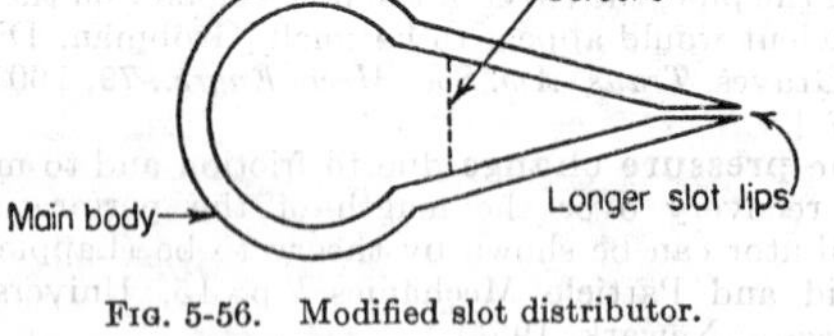

FIG. 5-56. Modified slot distributor.

3. Increase pressure drop across the slot; this can be accomplished by lengthening the lips (see Fig. 5-56).
4. Use of screens (see Fig. 5-56); screens upstream of the slot will increase the over-all pressure drop across the slot.

Considerations needed to be taken into account when designing and using an air knife are discussed by Senecal (*loc. cit.*).

Design procedures for extrusion dies, wherein the flow is laminar as with highly viscous fluids, are presented by Bernhardt ("Processing of Thermoplastic Materials," pp. 248–281, Reinhold, New York, 1959).

Turning Vanes. In applications such as in ventilation work, the discharge profile from slots (see Fig. 5-55) can be improved through the use of turning vanes. The tapered duct design is the most amenable for turning vanes because the discharge angle remains constant. One way of installing the vanes is shown in Fig. 5-57. The vanes should have a depth twice the spacing ["Heating, Ventilating, Air Conditioning Guide," vol. 38, pp. 282–283, American Society of Heating, Refrigerating, and Air-Conditioning Engineers, 1960] and a curvature of a circular arc which is tangent to the discharge angle θ of a

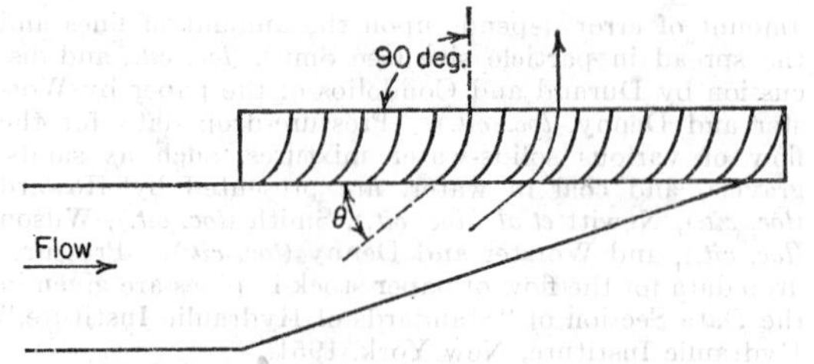

FIG. 5-57. Turning vanes in a slot distributor.

slot without vanes at the upstream end of the vanes and perpendicular to the slot at the downstream or discharge end (Koestel and Young, *loc. cit.*). Angle θ can be estimated from

$$\cot \theta = \frac{C_d A_s}{A_d} \tag{5-154}$$

where A_s = slot area, sq. ft.; A_d = duct cross-sectional area at upstream end, sq. ft.; C_d = discharge coefficient of slot, dimensionless.

Vanes may be used also to improve velocity distribution and to reduce friction loss in bends. For a miter bend with low-velocity flows, simple circular arcs (Fig. 5-58) can be used, and with high-velocity flows, vanes of

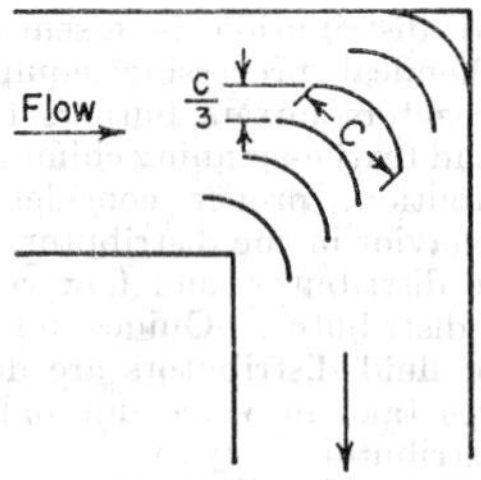

FIG. 5-58. Miter bend with vanes.

special airfoil shapes are required (see Rouse, *op. cit.*, pp. 422–423). For a sweep bend, splitter vanes are used. These vanes are curved vanes extending from end to end of the bend and dividing the bend into several parallel channels. Additional details, together with a chart for determining the location of the splitters in the bend, are given by Madison ("Fan Engineering," 5th ed., pp. 152–156, Buffalo Forge Co., Buffalo, 1948).

Perforated Plates and Screens. A non-uniform velocity profile of **turbulent flow** through channels or process equipment can be smoothed out to any desired degree by adding sufficient uniform resistance, such as perforated plates or screens across the flow channel.

Referring to Fig. 5-59, the amount of resistance required to smooth out a specific non-uniform velocity profile to a desired degree can be estimated from the following equations (Stoker, *loc. cit.*):

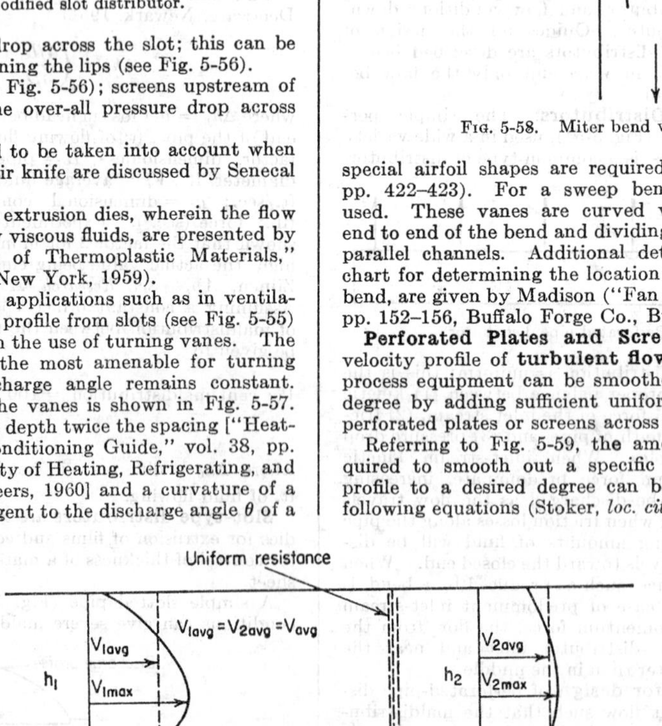

FIG. 5-59. Smoothing out a non-uniform velocity profile in a channel.

$$\frac{V_{2\max}}{V_{\text{avg}}} = \sqrt{\frac{(V_{1\max}/V_{\text{avg}})^2 + \alpha_2 - \alpha_1 + \alpha_2 K}{1+K}} \quad (5\text{-}155)$$

$$h_1 - h_2 = K\left(\frac{V^2_{\text{avg}}}{2g_c}\right) \quad (5\text{-}156)$$

where V = velocity, ft./sec.; h = static head, ft. of fluid flowing; α = correction factor to compensate for use of the average velocity, dimensionless; K = equivalent resistance of the uniform resistance expressed as number of velocity heads based on velocity V, dimensionless; g_c = dimensional constant, 32.17 (lb.)(ft.)/(lb. force)(sec.^{2}); subscripts are defined in Fig. 5-59. Typical values of α are given on p. 5-45. Values of $V_{\max}/V_{\text{avg}}$ are given in Fig. 5-11, p. 5-8. K as computed from Eq. (5-155) will generally be on the order of 10. From the value of $h_1 - h_2$ the characteristics of the perforated plates or screens can be determined, using Eq. (5-95) or (5-100), respectively.

Beds of Solids. A suitable depth of solids can be employed as a fluid distributor. The depth should be such that the pressure drop across the bed is at least 10 velocity heads, based upon the superficial velocity through the bed. Methods of computing the pressure drop are given on pp. 5-49 to 5-53.

If a single liquid stream is fed to the top of a bed of solids with no gas flow, the flow will not become uniform until four or five bed diameters have been traversed [Baker, Chilton, and Vernon, *Trans. Am. Inst. Chem. Engrs.*, **31**, 296–315 (1935)]. For the flow of a liquid downward through a bed of solids, where the liquid was initially distributed uniformly, Akehata and Sato [*Chem. Eng. (Japan)*, **22**, 430–435 (1958)] found that the flow can become maldistributed in a distance of three to six bed diameters for either laminar or turbulent flow when the ratio of bed diameter to particle diameter is less than 15.

Velocity distribution of gas flow through beds of solids has been studied by Schwartz and Smith [*Ind. Eng. Chem.*, **45**, 1209–1218 (1953)]. They found that the velocity profile has a maximum value approximately one particle diameter from the wall, and the variation in the velocity profile was less than 20 per cent for ratios of bed diameter to particle diameter of more than 30. The above observations of velocity profile were confirmed by Calderbank and Pogorski [*Trans. Inst. Chem. Engrs.*, **35**, 195–207 (1957)].

TUBE BANKS

It is not possible to obtain a fundamental correlation of data on pressure drop across tube banks by means of a single, simple friction factor–Reynolds number curve. This is due to lack of geometric similarity among the large number of tube configurations and spacings encountered. A degree of correlation was early obtained by Chilton and Genereaux [*Trans. Am. Inst. Chem. Engrs.*, **29**, 161–173 (1933)] for turbulent flow by use of a friction factor–modified Reynolds number relationship, with separate curves for staggered and in-line arrangements. Friction factor was based on the number of rows normal to the flow and on $V_{\max}$, the maximum velocity through the clearances; Reynolds number was based on $V_{\max}$ and on D_c, the transverse tube clearance (see Fig. 5-60). Judicious choice of D_c for the diameter term made at least partial allowance for the effect of transverse spacing, although no allowance was made for longitudinal spacing. Later investigators have made allowance for configuration and spacing by incorporating spacing correction factors in their friction-factor expressions or by use of multiple friction-factor plots. The best of these representations are described below.

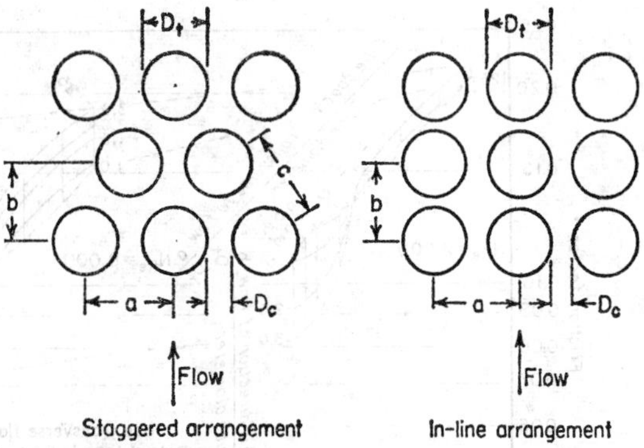

FIG. 5-60. Tube-bank configurations.

Turbulent Region. The correlation given by Grimison [*Trans. Am. Soc. Mech. Engrs.*, **59**, 583–594 (1937)] is recommended for predicting pressure drop for turbulent flow [$(N_{\text{Re}})_t \geq 2{,}000$] across staggered or in-line tube banks for tube spacings [(a/D_t), (b/D_t)] ranging from 1.25 to 3.0. The pressure drop is given by

$$\Delta p = \frac{4fN_r\rho V^2_{\max}}{2g_c} \quad \text{lb. force/sq. ft.} \quad (5\text{-}157)$$

where f = friction factor, dimensionless; N_r = number of rows of tubes in the direction of flow, dimensionless; ρ = fluid density, lb./cu. ft.; $V_{\max}$ = fluid velocity through the minimum area available for flow, ft./sec.; g_c = dimensional constant, 32.17 (lb.)(ft.)/(lb. force)(sec.^{2}).

For banks of **staggered tubes,** the friction factor for isothermal flow is obtained from Fig. 5-61*a*. Each "fence" (group of parametric curves) represents a particular Reynolds number defined as

$$N_{\text{Re}} = \frac{D_t V_{\max}\rho}{\mu} \quad (5\text{-}158)$$

where D_t = tube outside diameter, ft.; μ = fluid viscosity, lb./(ft.)(sec.) = centipoise/1488. The numbers along each "fence" represent the transverse and horizontal spacings. The upper chart is for the case where the minimum area for flow is in the transverse openings, while the lower chart is for the case where the minimum area is in the diagonal openings. In the latter case, $V_{\max}$ must be based upon the area of the diagonal openings and N_r taken as the number of rows in the direction of flow less 1. A critical comparison of this method with all available data showed an average deviation from the data of the order of ±15 per cent [Boucher and Lapple, *Chem. Eng. Progress*, **44**, 117–134 (1948)]. For the case of tube spacings greater than three tube diameters, the correlation given by Gunter and Shaw [*Trans. Am. Soc. Mech. Engrs.*, **67**, 643–660 (1945)] can be used as an approximation. As an **approximation,** the pressure drop can be taken as 0.72 superficial velocity heads per row of tubes for tube spacings commonly encountered in practice (Lapple *et al.*, *op. cit.*, p. 40).

For banks of **in-line tubes,** the friction factor for isothermal flow is obtained from Fig. 5-61*b*. Each "fence" represents a particular Reynolds number as defined in the preceding paragraph. Average deviation of this method from available data is on the order of ±15 per cent. For tube spacings greater than three tube diameters, the charts given by Gram, Mackey, and Monroe [*Trans. Am. Soc. Mech. Engrs.*, **80**, 25–35 (1958)] can be used. As an **approximation,** the pressure drop can

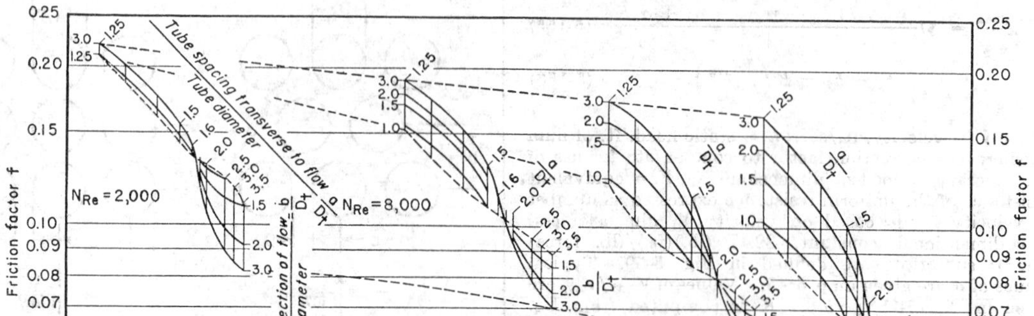

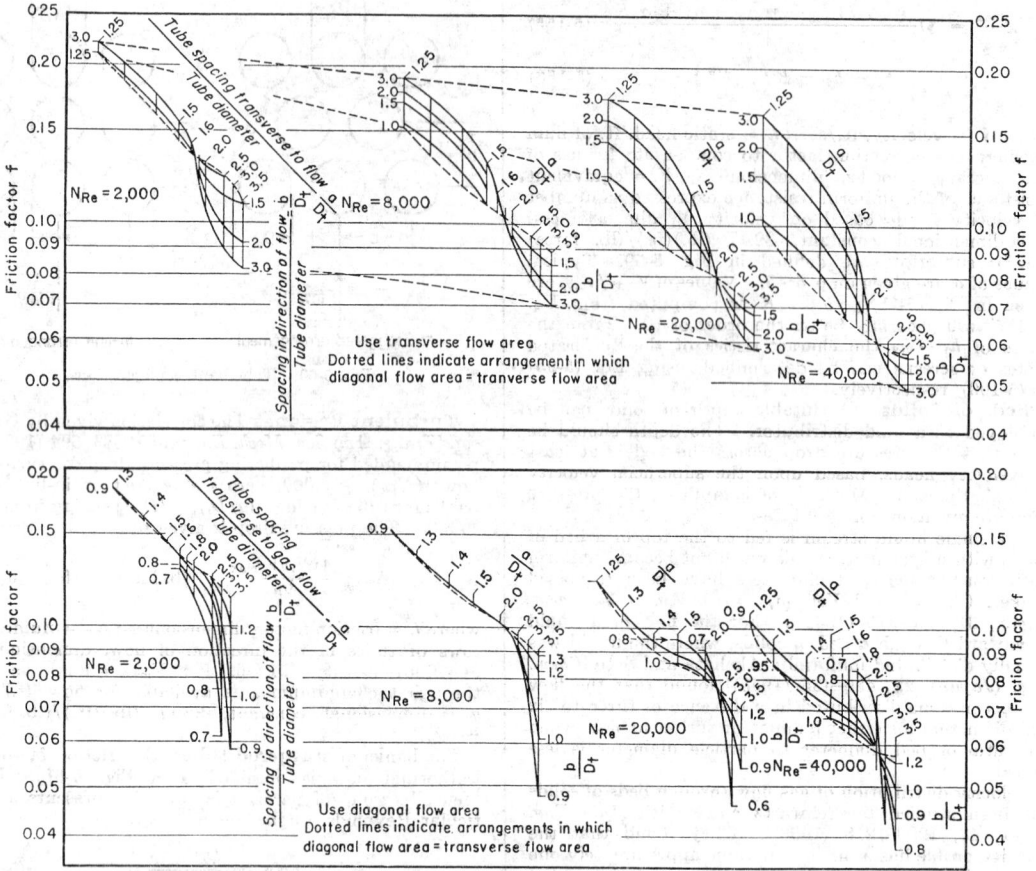

FIG. 5-61*a*. (Upper chart) Friction factors for staggered tube banks with minimum gas-flow area in transverse openings. (Lower chart) Friction factors for staggered tube banks with minimum gas-flow area in diagonal openings. [*Grimison, Trans. Am. Soc. Mech. Engrs.*, **59**, 583 (1937).]

be taken as 0.32 superficial velocity heads per row of tubes [Lapple *et al.*, *op. cit.*, p. 40].

In the case of turbulent flow through **shallow banks** of tubes, the average friction factor per row will be somewhat higher than indicated by Fig. 5-61, which is based on banks ten or more rows deep. The magnitude of this increase depends upon tube spacing and arrangement. A 30 per cent increase per row for two rows, 15 per cent per row for three rows, and 7 per cent per row for four rows can be taken as about the maximum likely to be encountered (Boucher and Lapple, *loc. cit.*).

For a **single row** of tubes, the friction factor is given by curve *B* in Fig. 5-62 as a function of tube spacing. This curve is based on the data of several experimenters, all adjusted to a Reynolds number [Eq. (5-158)] of 10,000. The values should be substantially independent of Reynolds number in the range of 1,000 to 100,000.

For the case of **extended surfaces,** which include fins mounted perpendicular to the tubes or spiral-wound fins, pin fins, plate fins, etc., friction data for the specific surface involved should be used. See Jameson [*Trans. Am. Soc. Mech. Engrs.*, **67,** 633–642 (1945)] for helical fins on round tubes; Kays and London [*ibid.*, **72,** 1087–1097 (1950)] for 13 different surfaces, including plate fins and finned flat tubes; Kays (American Society of Mechanical Engineers, Paper 53-A-211) for pin fins. In case specific data are not available, the correlation given by Gunter and Shaw (*loc. cit.*) can be used as an approximation.

For the case where a large temperature change occurs in a gas flowing across a tube bundle, it is necessary to select a suitable mean temperature upon which to base the gas properties. This is given by

$$t_m = t_t + K\,\Delta t_m \qquad \text{°F. or °C.} \tag{5-159}$$

where t_t = average tube-wall temperature, °F or °C.; K = a constant, dimensionless; Δt_m = log mean temperature difference between the gas and the tubes, °F. or °C. Values of K averaged from the recommendations of Chilton and Genereaux (*loc. cit.*) and Grimison (*loc. cit.*) are as follows: for in-line tubes, 0.9 for cooling and −0.9 for heating; for staggered tubes, 0.75 for cooling and −0.8 for heating.

In the case of non-isothermal flow of **liquids** across tube bundles, the friction factor is appreciably increased if the liquid is being cooled and decreased if the liquid is being heated. The factors given for non-isothermal flow of liquids in pipes (p. 5-21) are recommended for use in this case.

A method for computing pressure drop for two-phase, gas-liquid, horizontal cross flow through tube banks is

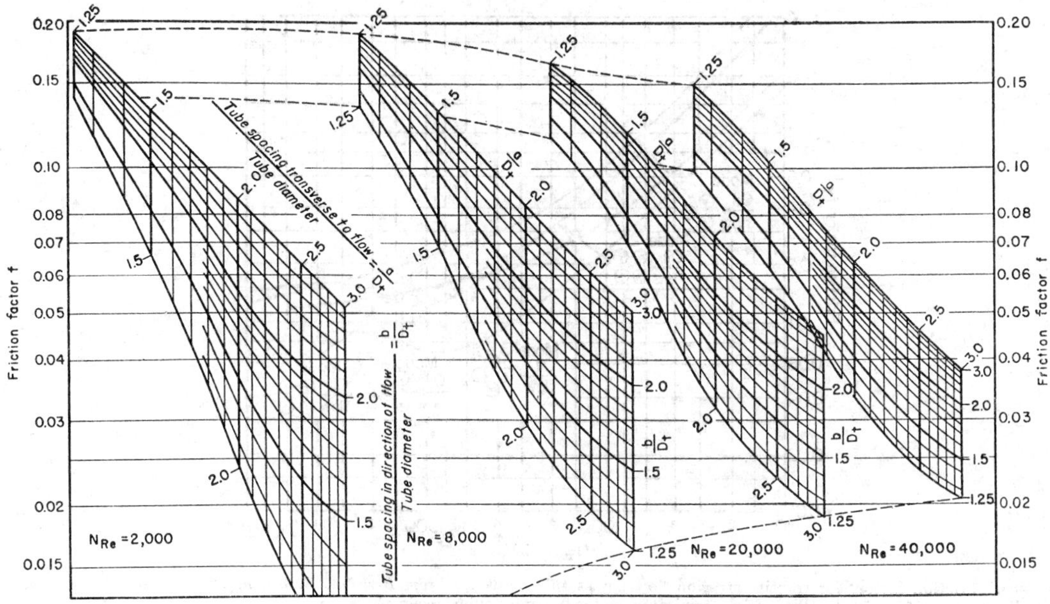

FIG. 5-61*b*. Friction factors for in-line tube banks.

given by Diehl and Unruh (American Society of Mechanical Engineers, Paper 58-HT-20).

The **transition region** for flow across tube banks extends approximately over the Reynolds-number [Eq. (5-158)] range of 200 to 2,000. The friction-factor curves shown in Fig. 5-63 for five different configurations were obtained from Bergelin, Brown, and Doberstein [*Trans. Am. Soc. Mech. Engrs.*, **74**, 953–960 (1952)]. Pressure drop is given by

$$\Delta p = \frac{4 f_T N_r \rho V^2_{\max}}{2 g_c} \left(\frac{\mu_s}{\mu_b}\right)^{0.14} \quad \text{lb. force/sq. ft.} \qquad (5\text{-}160)$$

where f_T = friction factor obtained from Fig. 5-63, dimensionless; N_r = number of major restrictions encountered in flow through the bank (equal to number of rows where minimum free-flow area occurs in transverse openings, and to number of rows less 1 where it occurs in the diagonal openings), dimensionless; ρ = fluid density, lb./cu. ft.; $V_{\max}$ = fluid velocity through minimum free-flow area, ft./sec.; g_c = dimensional constant, 32.17 (lb.)(ft.)/(lb. force)(sec.^{2}); μ_s = fluid viscosity at tube surface temperature, lb./(ft.)(sec.); μ_b = fluid viscosity at average bulk temperature, lb./(ft.)(sec.).

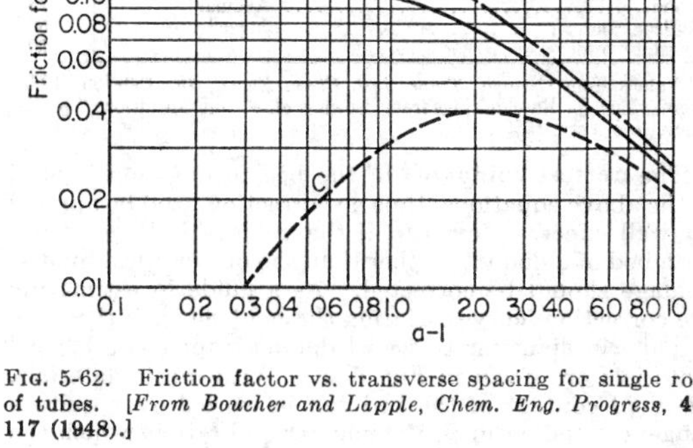

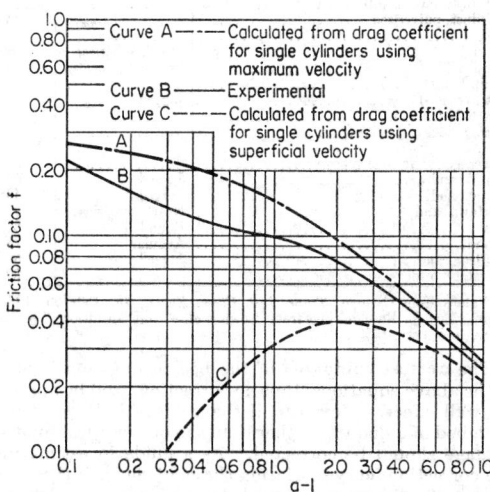

FIG. 5-62. Friction factor vs. transverse spacing for single row of tubes. [*From Boucher and Lapple, Chem. Eng. Progress*, **44**, 117 (1948).]

Laminar Region. Bergelin, Colburn, and Hull (*Univ. Deleware Eng. Expt. Sta. Bull.* 2, 1950) recommend the following equations for pressure drop with laminar flow [$(N_{\text{Re}})_v < 100$] across banks of plain tubes with pitch ratios P/D_t of 1.25 and 1.50:

$$\Delta p = \frac{280 N_r}{(N_{\text{Re}})_v} \left(\frac{D_t}{P}\right)^{1.6} \left(\frac{\mu_s}{\mu_b}\right)^m \left(\frac{\rho V^2_{\max}}{2 g_c}\right) \quad \frac{\text{lb. force}}{\text{sq. ft.}} \qquad (5\text{-}161)$$

$$m = \frac{0.57}{(N_{\text{Re}})_v^{0.25}} \qquad (5\text{-}162)$$

where $(N_{\text{Re}})_v = D_v V_{\max} \rho/\mu$, dimensionless; D_v = volumetric hydraulic diameter [(4 × free-bundle volume)/(exposed surface area of tubes)], ft.; P = pitch (= a for in-line arrangements, = a or c, whichever is smaller, for staggered arrangement), ft.; other quantities as defined following Eq. (5-160). Bergelin *et al.* show that pressure drop per row is independent of the number of rows in the bank with laminar flow.

The validity of extrapolating Eq. (5-161) to pitch ratios larger than 1.50 is not known. The correlation of Gunter and Shaw (*loc. cit.*) can be used as an approximation for such cases.

BEDS OF SOLIDS

Fixed Beds of Granular Solids. Pressure-drop data on the flow of fluids through beds of granular solids are not readily correlated because of the variety of granular materials and of their packing arrangement. For the flow of a **single incompressible fluid** through a bed of granular solids, the pressure drop or other flow

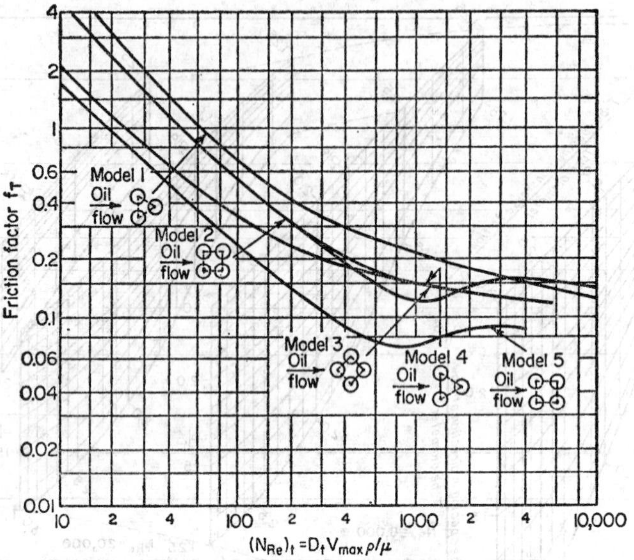

FIG. 5-63. Friction factors for transition-region flow across tube banks. [*From Bergelin, Brown, and Doberstein, Trans. Am. Soc. Mech. Engrs.*, **74**, 953 (1952).] (Pitch is the minimum center-to-center tube spacing.)

Model	Rows	D_t, in.	Pitch/D_t
1	10	3/8	1.25
2	10	3/8	1.25
3	14	3/8	1.25
4	10	3/8	1.50
5	10	3/8	1.50

characteristics can be predicted from the correlation given by Leva [*Chem. Eng.*, **56** (5), 115–117 (1949), or "Fluidization," McGraw-Hill, New York, 1959]. In this correlation,

$$\Delta p = \frac{2 f_m G^2 L (1 - \epsilon)^{3-n}}{D_p g_c \rho \phi_s^{3-n} \epsilon^3} \quad (5\text{-}163)$$

where Δp = pressure drop, lb. force/sq. ft.; L = depth of bed, ft.; g_c = dimensional constant, 32.17 (lb.)(ft.)/(lb. force)(sec.^{2}); D_p = average particle diameter, defined as the diameter of a sphere of the same volume as the particle, ft.; ϵ = voidage (fractional free volume), dimensionless; n = exponent, a function of the modified Reynolds number N_{Re}' given in Fig. 5-64, dimensionless; ϕ_s = shape factor of the solid, defined as the quotient of the area of a sphere equivalent to the volume of the particle divided by the actual surface of the particle, dimensionless; G = fluid superficial mass velocity based on empty chamber cross section, lb./(sec.)(sq. ft.); ρ = fluid density, lb./cu. ft.; f_m = friction factor, a function of N_{Re}' given in Fig. 5-64. The modified Reynolds number N_{Re}' is defined as

$$N_{Re}' = \frac{D_p G}{\mu} \quad (5\text{-}164)$$

where μ = fluid viscosity, lb./(ft.)(sec.).

For non-spherical particles,

$$D_p = \frac{6(1 - \epsilon)}{\phi_s S} \quad (5\text{-}165)$$

where S = specific surface, or area of particle surface per unit volume of bed = $S_0(1 - \epsilon)$, sq. ft./cu. ft.; S_0 = area of particle surface per unit volume of solids, sq. ft./cu. ft.

Values of the **shape factor** ϕ_s for a number of materials are tabulated in Table 5-22. This tabulation will serve as a guide in the estimation of shape factors for other materials.

Table 5-22. Shape Factors for Non-spherical Particles*

Material	Nature of grain	ϕ_s
Arnould's wire spirals		0.2
Berl saddles		.3
Coal dust, natural (up to 3/8 in.)		.65
Coal dust, pulverized		.73
Cork		.69
Flue dust	Fused, spherical	.89
Flue dust	Fused, aggregates	.55
Fusain fibers		.38
Glass, crushed	Jagged	.65
Mica flakes		.28
Raschig rings		.3
Sand:		
Average for various types		.75
Flint sand	Jagged	.65
Flint sand	Jagged flakes	.43
Ottawa sand	Nearly spherical	.95
Sand	Rounded	.83
Sand	Angular	.73
Wilcox sand	Jagged	.60
Tungsten powder		.89

* Values from Carman *Trans. Inst. Chem. Engrs.*, **15**, 150–166 (1937), except value for Raschig rings from Brown *et al.* ("Unit Operations," p. 214, Wiley, New York, 1950).

The **actual voidage** ϵ of the bed in question is used in the above equations; thus no correction need be applied for wall effect. However, if the voidage is known only for a bed of a diameter other than the one in question, the voidage should be corrected. As a guide in estimating the correction, curves relating the voidage with the ratio of particle diameter to vessel diameter for some typical materials are given in Fig. 5-65. With most materials, the void content of the bed can be varied over quite a range, depending upon the manner and rate in which the

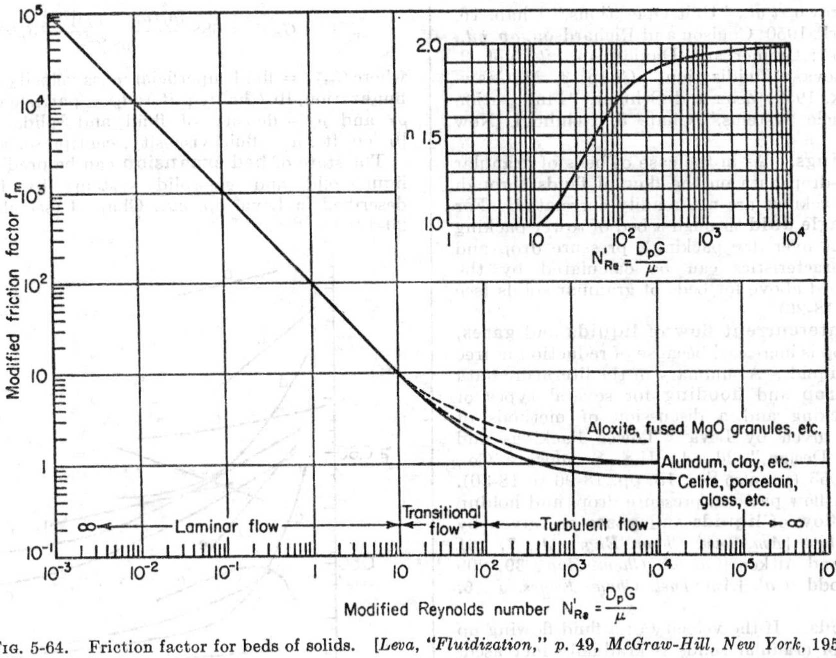

FIG. 5-64. Friction factor for beds of solids. [*Leva, "Fluidization," p. 49, McGraw-Hill, New York,* 1959.]

material is introduced into the vessel. Thus the values of the voidage given in Fig. 5-65 should be used as a guide only.

For granular solids of **mixed sizes**, the average particle diameter D_p can be calculated as

$$\frac{1}{D_p} = \sum \frac{x}{D_{p,x}} \tag{5-166}$$

where x = weight fraction, dimensionless, of particle diameter $D_{p,x}$, ft.

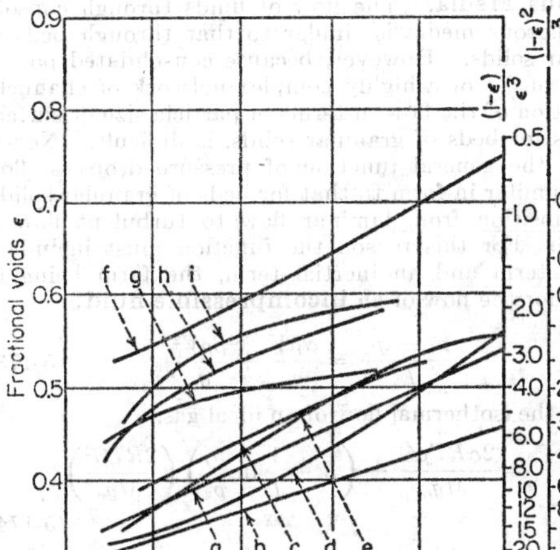

FIG. 5-65. Voidage in packed beds. Spherical: *a*, smooth, uniform; *b*, smooth, mixed; *c*, clay. Cylindrical: *d*, smooth, uniform; *e*, alundum, uniform; *f*, clay Raschig rings. Granules: *g*, fused magnetite (synthetic ammonia catalyst); *h*, fused alundum; *i*, Aloxite. (*Leva, "Fluidization," p. 54, McGraw-Hill, New York,* 1959.)

Based on studies with flow of gases through beds of sands by Leva, Grummer, Weintraub, and Pollchik [*Chem. Eng. Progress,* **44,** 511–520 (1948)], the flow parameters for flow up through a bed do not differ from those for flow down through the bed, provided the bed voidage remains the same, *i.e.*, no bed expansion.

For the flow of a **single compressible fluid** through a bed of granular solids, the following equation can be derived (see, for example, Cremer and Davies, *op. cit.*, vol. 2, pp. 436–437) from the mechanical-energy-balance equation, Eq. (5-37), and Leva's correlation, Eq. (5-163):

$$p_1^2 - p_2^2 = \frac{2zRG^2T}{g_cM}\left[\ln\frac{v_2}{v_1} + \frac{2f_mL(1-\epsilon)^{3-n}}{\phi_s^{3-n}\epsilon^3 D_p}\right] \tag{5-167}$$

where p_1 = absolute upstream pressure, lb. force/sq. ft.; p_2 = absolute downstream pressure, lb. force/sq. ft.; z = gas compressibility factor, dimensionless; R = gas constant = 1546 (ft.) (lb. force)/(lb.-mole) (°R.) = 2780 (ft.)(lb. force)/(lb.-mole)(°K.); T = temperature, °R. or °K; M = molecular weight, lb./lb.-mole; v_1 = upstream specific volume of gas, cu. ft./lb.; v_2 = downstream specific volume of gas, cu. ft./lb.

For an **approximation** of the pressure drop across beds of solids, the velocity-head concept can be employed. Equation (5-163) can be rewritten as

$$\frac{\Delta p}{\rho} = \Delta h = \left[\frac{4f_m(1-\epsilon)^{3-n}}{\phi_s^{3-n}\epsilon^3}\right]\left(\frac{L}{D_p}\right)\left(\frac{V^2}{2g_c}\right) \tag{5-168}$$

where Δh = pressure-head loss, ft. of fluid flowing; $V^2/2g_c$ = velocity head, ft. of fluid flowing; $V = G/\rho$ = superficial fluid velocity, ft./sec. The pressure-head loss for a bed depth of one particle diameter ($L/D_p = 1$) for turbulent flow ($N_{Re}' > 100$) through a bed of spherical, or nearly so, particles can be shown from Eq. (5-168) and Figs. 5-64 and 5-65 to be

$$\Delta h \simeq 50\left(\frac{V^2}{2g_c}\right) \tag{5-169}$$

Other methods of correlation of pressure-drop data

are given by Brown *et al.*, "Unit Operations," Chap. 16, Wiley, New York, 1950; Coulson and Richardson, *op. cit.*, vol. 2, Chap. 11; Cremer and Davies, *op. cit.*, vol. 2, pp. 376–421; Leva, "Fluidization," Chap. 3, McGraw-Hill, New York, 1959; Zenz and Othmer, "Fluidization and Fluid-particle Systems," Chap. 5, Reinhold, New York, 1960.

Tower Packings. As in the case of beds of granular solids, pressure-drop data on the flow of fluids through beds of tower packings are not readily correlated. For the flow of a **single fluid** through a bed of tower packing (*e.g.*, flow of gas over dry packing), pressure drop and other flow characteristics can be calculated by the methods described above for beds of granular solids (see also Sec. 18, p. 18-26).

For the **countercurrent flow** of **liquids** and **gases**, the pressure drop is increased because of reduction in free volume by the liquid. A summary of the literature data on **pressure drop** and **flooding** for several types of commercial packing and a discussion of methods of correlation are given by Leva, "Tower Packings and Packed Tower Design," 2d ed., U.S. Stoneware Co., Akron, Ohio, 1953 (see also Sec. 18, pp. 18-26 to 18-30).

Some data on flow pattern, pressure drop, and holdup for **cocurrent flow** of **liquids** and **gases** are given by Larkins and White [*Am. Inst. Chem. Engrs. J.*, **7**, 231 (1961)], Gunn and Aitken [*Can. J. Chem. Eng.*, **39**, 209 (1961)], and Dodd *et al.* [*Am. Inst. Chem. Engrs. J.*, **6**, 390 (1960)].

Fluidized Beds. If the velocity of a fluid flowing up through a bed of granular solids is gradually increased, conditions will be met in which the fluid drag force, *i.e.*, pressure drop × vessel cross-sectional area, will just equal the weight of the solids, and the particles will just begin to be in motion. This will be the onset of fluidization, or minimum fluidization. Since for most gas-solid systems, fluidization will begin for $N_{Re}' = D_p G_{mf}/\mu < 10$, values of mass velocity and voidage for onset of fluidization can be related by (Leva, "Fluidization," p. 63, McGraw-Hill, New York, 1959)

$$G_{mf} = \frac{0.005 D_p^2 g_c \rho_f (\rho_s - \rho_f) \phi_s^2 \epsilon_{mf}^3}{\mu(1 - \epsilon_{mf})} \qquad (5\text{-}170)$$

where G_{mf} = fluid superficial mass velocity for minimum fluidization, lb./(sec.)(sq. ft.); D_p = particle diameter, ft.; g_c = dimensional constant, 32.17 (lb.)(ft.)/(lb. force)(sec.^{2}); ρ_f = fluid density, lb./cu. ft.; ρ_s = solids density, lb./cu. ft.; ϕ_s = particle shape factor, dimensionless; ϵ_{mf} = voidage at minimum fluidization, dimensionless; μ = fluid viscosity, lb./(ft.)(sec.).

The **minimum voidage** can be determined by passing the fluid up through the bed and noting the bed height at incipient particle motion or minimum fluidization, and thus

$$\epsilon_{mf} = 1 - \frac{W}{L_{mf} A (\rho_s - \rho_f)} \qquad (5\text{-}171)$$

where W = weight of solids in bed, lb.; L_{mf} = height of bed at minimum fluidization, ft.; A = cross-sectional area of vessel, sq. ft. This and other methods of determining the minimum voidage are described by Leva, *op. cit.*, pp. 20–21, 63. Typical values of minimum voidage as reported in the literature have been collected by Leva and are shown as a function of particle diameter in Fig. 5-66.

To improve the usefulness of Eq. (5-170), Leva and coworkers found (see Leva, *op. cit.*, pp. 63–64) that variables ϕ_s and ϵ_{mf} could be related to N_{Re}', thus reducing Eq. (5-170) to the following equation (in mixed units) for $N_{Re}' < 5.0$:

$$G_{mf}' = 688 \frac{[\rho_f(\rho_s - \rho_f)]^{0.94}}{\mu^{0.88}} d_p^{1.82} \qquad (5\text{-}172)$$

where G_{mf}' = fluid superficial mass velocity for minimum fluidization, lb./(hr.)(sq. ft.); d_p = particle diameter, in.; ρ_f and ρ_s = density of fluid and solids, respectively, lb./cu. ft.; μ = fluid viscosity, centipoise.

The state of **bed expansion** can be predicted for both liquid-solid and gas-solid systems by the methods described in Leva, *op. cit.*, Chap. 4 (see also Sec. 20, p. 20-42).

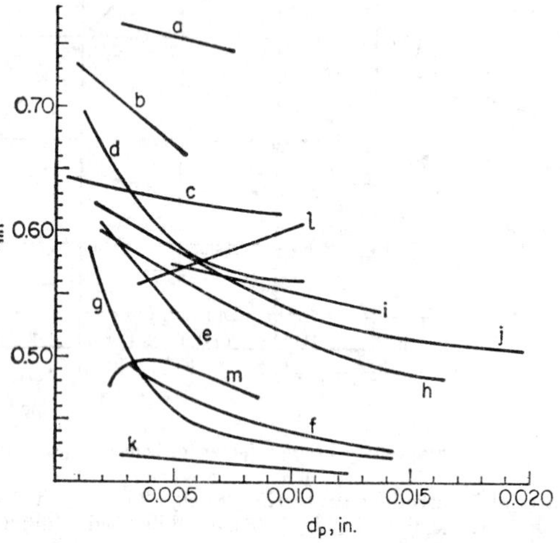

FIG. 5-66. Typical values of minimum voidage. (*a*) Soft brick; (*b*) adsorption carbon; (*c*) broken Raschig rings; (*d*) coal and glass powder; (*e*) silicon carbide; (*f*) sand; (*g*) round sand, $\phi_s = 0.86$; (*h*) sharp sand, $\phi_s = 0.67$; (*i*) Fischer-Tropsch catalyst, $\phi_s = 0.58$; (*j*) anthracite coal, $\phi_s = 0.63$; (*k*) mixed round sand, $\phi_s = 0.86$; (*l*) coke; (*m*) silicon carbide. (*For references, see Leva, "Fluidization," p. 21, McGraw-Hill, New York, 1959.*)

Porous Media. The flow of fluids through consolidated porous media is similar to that through beds of granular solids. However, because consolidated porous media consist of a highly complex network of channels, description of the flow in terms of particle size or surface area, as for beds of granular solids, is difficult. Nevertheless, the general function of pressure drop vs. flow rate is similar in form to that for beds of granular solids, *i.e.*, transition from laminar flow to turbulent flow is gradual. For this reason the function must include a viscous term and an inertial term, the form being as follows for the flow of an **incompressible fluid**:

$$\frac{p_1 - p_2}{L} = \frac{\alpha \mu V}{g_c} + \frac{\beta \rho V^2}{g_c} \qquad (5\text{-}173)$$

and for the isothermal flow of an ideal gas,

$$\frac{p_1^2 - p_2^2}{L} = \frac{2\alpha RT\mu G}{Mg_c} + \left(\beta + \frac{1}{L}\ln\frac{p_1}{p_2}\right)\left(\frac{2RTG^2}{Mg_c}\right) \qquad (5\text{-}174)$$

where p_1 = absolute upstream pressure, lb. force/sq. ft.; p_2 = absolute downstream pressure, lb. force/sq. ft.; L = thickness of the medium, ft.; V = superficial velocity of fluid (based on total cross section), ft./sec.; G = superficial mass velocity of fluid, lb./(sec.)(sq. ft.); ρ = fluid density, lb./cu. ft.; μ = fluid viscosity, lb./(ft.)(sec.); g_c = dimensional constant, 32.17 (lb.)(ft.)/(lb. force)(sec.^{2}); M = molecular weight of gas, lb./lb.-mole; R = gas constant, 1546 (ft.)(lb. force)/(lb.-mole)

(°R.) = 2780 (ft.)(lb. force)/(lb.-mole)(°K.); T = absolute temperature, °R. or °K.; α = viscous resistance coefficient, ft.$^{-2}$; β = inertial resistance coefficient, ft.$^{-1}$. For additional details, see Green and Duwez [*J. Appl. Mechanics*, **18**, 39–45 (1951)].

For purely viscous flow, the second term (involving V^2) on the right-hand side of Eq. (5-173) becomes negligible and the resulting equation is known as **Darcy's equation** of flow through porous media. The quantity $1/\alpha$ is referred to as the **permeability coefficient,** the unit of which is the **darcy,** defined as the permeability of a porous medium to viscous flow for the flow of 1 ml./sec./sq. cm. of surface of a liquid of 1 centipoise viscosity under a pressure gradient of 1 atm./cm. For further information on the Darcy equation, see Muskat, "Physical Principles of Oil Production," Chap. 3, McGraw-Hill, New York, 1949; Cremer and Davies, *op. cit.*, vol. 2, pp. 406–414; Rouse, *op. cit.*, Chap. V.

Values of α and β are determined experimentally for each type of porous medium. Data on pressure drop as a function of flow rate for various fluids are generally available from the manufacturer of such porous media as sintered metals. As a guide, values of α and β for specimens of sintered stainless steel, iron, and bronze are given by Green and Duwez (*loc. cit.*), and of sandstones by Cremer and Davies (*op. cit.*, vol. 2, p. 417). Pressure-drop data for flow of air and of liquids of various viscosities through specimens of sintered stainless steel and bronze are presented by Langhammer and Glick [*Prod. Eng.*, **24** (4), 179–182 (1953)].

Capillary diameters of porous media may be of the same order of magnitude as the mean free path of the molecules of the diffusing gas, even at several atmospheres pressure. For these cases, the slip-flow and molecular-flow equations (see pp. 5-27, 5-28) may be modified to apply to the flow of gases through porous media [see Monet and Vermeulen, *Chem. Eng. Prog. Symp. Ser.*, **55**, No. 25 (1959)].

FLOW AROUND OBJECTS

Vortex Shedding. In the flow of fluids past objects and through orifices or similar restrictions, fluid vortices are shed periodically downstream from the object or other initiating element. Objects such as smokestacks, chemical processing columns, suspended pipe lines, and electrical transmission lines can be subjected to damaging vibrations and forces due to the vortices, especially if the frequency of vortex shedding is close to the natural vibration frequency of the object. Also, such vortex shedding can produce sound, such as in the "Aeolian harp" or singing wires.

Development of the **vortex street,** commonly called "von Kármán vortex street," behind a cylindrical object in a flowing fluid is shown in Fig. 5-67 (see Rouse, *op. cit.*, pp. 129–130). Velocity of the vortex street is given by

$$V_v = 0.86V \qquad (5\text{-}175)$$

where V_v = velocity of vortex street, ft./sec.; V = free-stream velocity of the fluid, ft./sec.

Investigations have shown that the **frequency of vortex shedding** may be computed from the Strouhal number N_S, which in turn is a function of the Reynolds number N_{Re} [for references, see Krzywoblocki, *Appl. Mechanics Revs.*, **6**, 393–397 (1953)]. Over a wide range of Reynolds numbers, the Strouhal number is approximately constant (see Rouse, *op. cit.*, pp. 129–130, or Goldstein, *op. cit.*, vol. 2, p. 419):

$$N_S = \frac{fD}{V} = 0.19 \qquad \text{for } 500 < N_{Re} < 10^5 \qquad (5\text{-}176)$$

where f = frequency, cycles/sec.; D = diameter of cylinder or effective width of object, ft.; V = free-stream velocity, ft./sec.; N_{Re} = Reynolds number = $VD\rho/\mu$, dimensionless; ρ = fluid density, lb./cu. ft.; μ = fluid viscosity, lb./(ft.)(sec.). For $N_{Re} < 500$, the Strouhal number decreases with decreasing Reynolds number. Below $N_{Re} = 40$, the vortices are difficult to detect. For $N_{Re} > 10^5$, the Strouhal number increases rapidly with increasing Reynolds number. Above $N_{Re} = 4 \times 10^5$, the vortices are weak and aperiodic [Steidel, *J. Appl. Mechanics*, **23**, 649–650 (1956)]. However, there may be cases where vibration of the object will be evident for Reynolds number well above 4×10^5 [see Farquharson's discussion, pp. 1386–1387, of Ozker and Smith, *Trans. Am. Soc. Mech. Engrs.*, **78**, 1381–1391 (1956); Den Hartog, *Proc. Natl. Acad. Sci.*, **40**, 155–157 (1954)]. Frequency of vibration of the object is equal to the frequency of vortex shedding.

Because of the flow behavior in the vicinity of the location of vortex shedding, an **alternating lateral force** F_K acting on the cylinder results. (Note that this force is perpendicular to the direction of flow.) The maximum lateral force F_K is in the direction away from the last vortex, and for any object, this force is given by [see Den Hartog, "Mechanical Vibrations," 4th ed., pp. 305–309, McGraw-Hill, New York, 1956]

$$F_K = C_K A \frac{\rho V^2}{2g_c} \qquad (5\text{-}177)$$

where F_K = lateral force (sometimes called von Kármán force), lb. force; C_K = von Kármán coefficient, dimensionless; A = projected area (perpendicular to the direction of flow), sq. ft.; ρ = fluid density, lb./cu. ft.; V = free-stream velocity of fluid, ft./sec.; g_c = dimensional constant, 32.17 (lb.)(ft.)/(lb. force)(sec.^{2}). C_K is dependent upon shape of the object and upon flow characteristics. For a cylinder, C_K = 1.7 and A = diameter × length, sq. ft. [see Rouse, *op. cit.*, pp. 129–130, or Steinman, *Am. Scientist*, **42**, 397–438, 460 (1954)]. Thus this force is about twice that due to fluid drag alone. If the cylinder is vibrating, the diameter term is replaced by an effective diameter which will never exceed twice the cylinder diameter (see Rouse, *op. cit.*, pp. 129–130).

The following references pertain to discussions of vortex shedding in specific engineering structures: steel stacks (Ozker and Smith, *loc. cit.*); chemical processing columns [Freese, *Trans. Am. Soc. Mech. Engrs.*, **81**, Series B, 77–91 (1959)]; suspended pipe lines [Baird, *Trans. Am. Soc. Mech. Engrs.*, **77**, 797–804 (1955)]; suspended cable (Steidel, *loc. cit.*); heat exchangers [Putnam, *Trans. Am. Soc. Mech. Engrs.*, **81**, Series A, 417–422 (1959)]; suspension bridges (Steinman, *loc. cit.*).

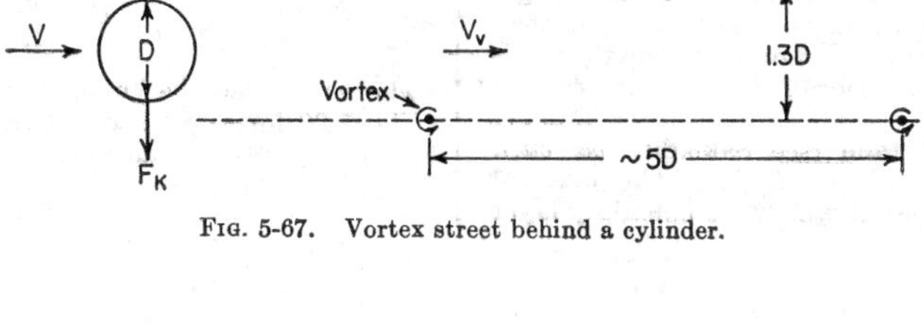

FIG. 5-67. Vortex street behind a cylinder.

Boundary-layer Behavior. When a fluid of low viscosity flows with an initial uniform velocity over a surface, such as a flat plate, the velocity decreases until it is zero at the surface of the plate. This decrease in velocity takes place in a small layer of fluid called the "boundary layer." The flow in this layer may be laminar or turbulent; the transition can be estimated from the length Reynolds number.

Following are presented equations for **boundary-layer thickness** and **drag** for flow around finite flat plates (Prandtl, "Essentials of Fluid Dynamics," Hafner, New York, 1952; Prandtl and Tietjens, "Applied Hydro- and Aero-mechanics," McGraw-Hill, New York, 1934; Schlichting, "Boundary Layer Theory," 4th ed., McGraw-Hill, New York, 1960) and continuous flat and cylindrical surfaces [Sakiadis, *Am. Inst. Chem. Engrs. J.*, **7**, 26, 221, 467 (1961)]. Nomenclature common to these equations is: b = width of flat plate, ft.; D = total drag, lb. force; g_c = dimensional constant, 32.17 (lb.)(ft.)/(lb. force)(sec.^{2}); L = exposed length of surface, ft.; q = total quantity of fluid entrained, cu. ft./sec.; r = radius of continuous cylindrical surface, ft.; V = velocity of finite flat plate in stationary fluid, or free-stream velocity of fluid approaching stationary finite flat plate, or velocity of continuous surface, ft./sec.; x = distance from leading edge or from orifice or slot to a point along the surface, ft.; $(N_{Re})_x = V\rho x/\mu$ = Reynolds number based on axial length, dimensionless; $(N_{Re})_L$ = length Reynolds number where $x = L$, dimensionless; δ = boundary-layer thickness where local velocity equals $0.99V$, ft.; μ = fluid viscosity, lb./(ft.)(sec.); ρ = fluid density, lb./cu. ft.

Finite Flat Plate. For the case of the finite plate parallel with the fluid stream, the **critical length Reynolds number** at which the boundary layer becomes turbulent is

$$(N_{Re})_x = \frac{V\rho x}{\mu} = 500{,}000 \tag{5-178}$$

For a **laminar boundary layer,** the boundary-layer thickness along the plate is given by (Prandtl, *op. cit.*, p. 109; Schlichting, *op. cit.*, p. 122)

$$\delta = 5(x)(N_{Re})_x^{-0.5} \tag{5-179}$$

Total drag on the plate, *i.e.*, drag on both surfaces of the plate, is given by (Prandtl, *op. cit.*, p. 193; Schlichting, *op. cit.*, p. 120)

$$D = 1.328bLV^2\left(\frac{\rho}{g_c}\right)(N_{Re})_L^{-0.5} \tag{5-180}$$

For a **turbulent boundary layer,** the boundary-layer thickness is given by (Prandtl and Tietjens, *op. cit.*, p. 76; Schlichting, *op. cit.*, p. 537)

$$\delta = 0.37(x)(N_{Re})_x^{-0.2} \tag{5-181}$$

and the total drag on both sides of the plate is given by (Prandtl and Tietjens, *op. cit.*, p. 77; Schlichting, *op. cit.*, p. 537):

$$D = 0.072bLV^2\left(\frac{\rho}{g_c}\right)(N_{Re})_L^{-0.2} \tag{5-182}$$

When this laminar boundary layer is a large part of the total length of the surface, the total drag can be computed by the following method (Schlichting, *op. cit.*, p. 538): Total drag for length L is computed, assuming a turbulent boundary layer from the leading edge; then from this total drag the turbulent drag for length x_{crit} is subtracted; then to this total drag the laminar drag for the length x_{crit} is added.

Continuous Flat Surface (see Sakiadis, *loc. cit.*). This case is illustrated in Fig. 5-68*a*. The **critical length Reynolds number** at which the boundary layer becomes turbulent is given by Eq. (5-178). For a **laminar boundary layer,** its thickness is given by

$$\delta = 6.37(x)(N_{Re})_x^{-0.5} \tag{5-183}$$

and the total drag on both sides of the surface is given by

$$D = 1.776bLV^2\left(\frac{\rho}{g_c}\right)(N_{Re})_L^{-0.5} \tag{5-184}$$

Total quantity of fluid entrained or pumped by the surface is given by

$$q = 3.232bLV(N_{Re})_L^{-0.5} \tag{5-185}$$

For a **turbulent boundary layer,** thickness is given by

$$\delta = 1.01(x)(N_{Re})_x^{-0.2} \tag{5-186}$$

Total drag on both sides of the surface is given by

$$D = 0.056bLV^2\left(\frac{\rho}{g_c}\right)(N_{Re})_L^{-0.2} \tag{5-187}$$

and total quantity of fluid entrained or pumped by the surface is given by

$$q = 0.252bLV(N_{Re})_L^{-0.2} \tag{5-188}$$

When the laminar boundary layer is a large part of the total length of the surface, the total drag can be computed by the method described for the finite flat plate.

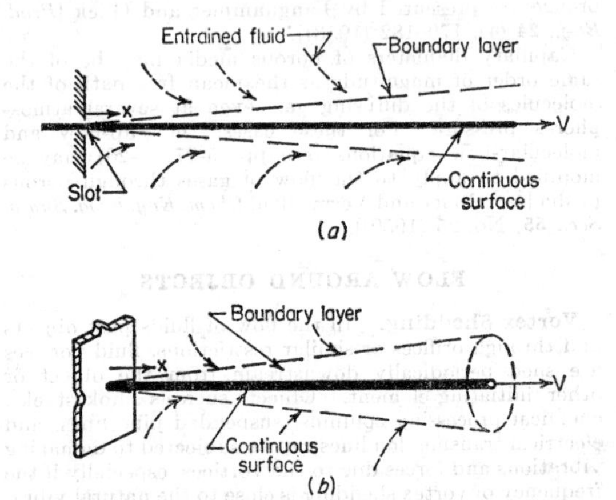

FIG. 5-68. Continuous surfaces. (*a*) Continuous flat surface. (*b*) Continuous cylindrical surface. [*Sakiadis, Am. Inst. Chem. Engrs. J.*, **7**, 221, 467 (1961).]

Continuous Cylindrical Surface (see Sakiadis, *loc. cit.*). This case is illustrated in Fig. 5-68*b*. The **critical length Reynolds number** at which the boundary layer becomes turbulent is given by

$$(N_{Re})_{x,crit} = \frac{V\rho x}{\mu} = 250{,}000 \tag{5-189}$$

For a **laminar boundary layer,** boundary-layer thickness δ can be determined from Fig. 5-69; total drag on the surface is given by

$$D = \frac{\rho}{g_c}V^2\Theta \tag{5-190}$$

where Θ, called the "momentum area," is obtained from Fig. 5-69 for $x = L$; total quantity of fluid entrained or pumped by the surface is given by

$$q = V\Delta \tag{5-191}$$

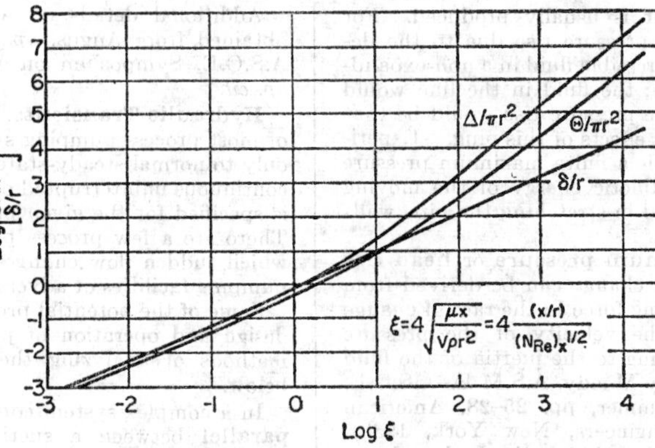

FIG. 5-69. Boundary-layer parameters for continuous cylindrical surfaces. [*Sakiadis, Am. Inst. Chem. Engrs. J.*, **7**, 467 (1961).]

where Δ, called the "displacement area," is obtained from Fig. 5-69 for $x = L$. For a **turbulent boundary layer**, results to date are inconclusive.

FALLING FILMS

Laminar Flow. Theoretical equations describing **laminar flow** of liquid films on **flat surfaces**, as presented by Cooper, Drew, and McAdams [*Ind. Eng. Chem.*, **26**, 428–431 (1934)] and by Fallah, Hunter, and Nash [*J. Soc. Chem. Ind.*, **53**, 369T–379T (1934)], are as follows:

$$m = \left[\frac{3\Gamma\mu}{g\rho_f(\rho_f - \rho_c)\sin\phi}\right]^{1/3} \quad (5\text{-}192)$$

$$u = \frac{g(\rho_f - \rho_c)\sin\phi}{\mu}\left(mx - \frac{x^2}{2}\right) \quad (5\text{-}193)$$

$$V = \frac{\Gamma}{m\rho_f} = \frac{g(\rho_f - \rho_c)m^2\sin\phi}{3\mu} \quad (5\text{-}194)$$

$$\frac{u_{max}}{V} = 1.50 \quad (5\text{-}195)$$

where m = film thickness, ft.; Γ = liquid loading per unit width of plate, lb./(sec.)(ft.); μ = film liquid viscosity, lb./(ft.)(sec.); g = acceleration due to gravity, ft./sec.²; ρ_f = density of film liquid, lb./cu. ft.; ρ_c = density of surrounding fluid, lb./cu. ft.; ϕ = angle of inclination with the horizontal; u = local film velocity, ft./sec.; x = distance from plate, ft.; V = average film velocity, ft./sec. These equations assume no surface tractive force is present.

A number of investigators have shown that Eq. (5-192) accurately predicts the **film thickness** for laminar flow of low-viscosity liquids (<5 centipoise) up to a critical Reynolds number ($4\Gamma/\mu$) generally found to be in the range of 1,000 to 2,000. However, Jackson [*Am. Inst. Chem. Engrs. J.*, **1**, 231–240 (1955)] found that higher-viscosity liquids (10 to 20 centipoise) gave film thicknesses appreciably below the predictions of Eq. (5-192) following the inception of surface wave motion. The latter was found to start at a Froude number ($N_{Fr} = V^2/gm$) of about 1.0. From this it follows that the volumetric flow rate at which waves start depends only upon the kinematic viscosity for the case of a vertical plate and a surrounding fluid of negligible density (*i.e.*, a gas). Then $\Gamma/\rho_f = 3(\mu/\rho_f)$, which corresponds to $N_{Re} = 12$.

Presence of **surface waves** affects the velocity distributions given by Eqs. (5-193) and (5-195). Friedman and Miller [*Ind. Eng. Chem.*, **33**, 885–891 (1941)] found u_{max}/V to be 1.5 up to $N_{Re} \simeq 25$, after which it increased to about 2.2 at $N_{Re} \simeq 100$. Jackson (*loc. cit.*) found u_{max}/V to be 1.5 up to $N_{Fr} \simeq 1.0$ ($N_{Re} = 12$), increasing rapidly to 2.2 at $N_{Fr} = 9.0$ ($N_{Re} = 108$), and dropping slowly to about 1.8 at $N_{Fr} = 200$ ($N_{Re} = 2400$).

Jackson (*loc. cit.*) has rederived Eqs. (5-192) through (5-195) for the case of films flowing on the inside wall of a **circular tube** for the case of a negligible surface tractive force. In this case, u_{max}/V is not a constant but varies from 1.5 up to 2.0 as film thickness increases from zero up to the pipe radius.

Turbulent Flow. An equation for estimating **film thickness** in the **turbulent-flow** regime ($N_{Re} > 2000$) was derived by Belkin *et al.* [*Am. Inst. Chem. Engrs. J.*, **5**, 245–248 (1959)] by analogy with turbulent flow between parallel plates, as follows:

$$m = \frac{0.315\mu^{2/3}}{g^{1/3}\rho_f^{2/3}}(N_{Re}\sqrt{f})^{2/3} \quad (5\text{-}196)$$

From the friction data of Walker, Whan, and Rothfuss [*Am. Inst. Chem. Engrs. J.*, **3**, 484–489 (1957)] for parallel plates,

$$f = 0.079(N_{Re})^{-0.25} \quad (5\text{-}197)$$

in the N_{Re} range of 3000 to 100,000. Equations (5-196) and (5-197) combined give

$$m = 0.304\left(\frac{\Gamma^{1.75}\mu^{0.25}}{g\rho_f^2}\right)^{1/3} \quad (5\text{-}198)$$

The derivation assumes negligible surface tractive force, a surrounding fluid of negligible density (*i.e.*, a gas), and vertical orientation of the plate. This correlation was found to compare favorably with experimental data over the N_{Re} range of 3000 to 30,000.

Effect of Surface Traction. If a drag is exerted on the surface of the film because of motion in the surrounding fluid, the film thickness will be reduced or increased, depending upon whether the drag is in parallel or counter, respectively, to the action of gravity. Thomas and Portalski [*Ind. Eng. Chem.*, **50**, 1081–1088 (1958)] and Dukler [*Chem. Eng. Progress*, **55** (10), 62–67 (1959)] both employed the Nikuradse generalized velocity-distribution equations in developing procedures for computing film thickness and velocity distribution both with and without a surface tractive force. Dukler (*loc. cit.*) presented graphical solutions for the case of tractive force parallel with the action of gravity.

UNSTEADY-STATE BEHAVIOR

Water Hammer. When a column of flowing fluid is suddenly stopped, a pounding of the line commonly known as **water hammer** is usually produced. For sudden flow stoppage, the pressure rise due to the deceleration of a truly incompressible fluid in a non-expandable pipe would be infinite; the fluid in the line would behave as a "plug" and the pressure rise would be that corresponding to the inertia effects of this plug. Experience has shown that there is a finite maximum pressure rise, because part of the kinetic energy of the moving fluid in the pipe is expended in stretching the pipe walls and compressing the fluid.

The equation for **maximum pressure** or **head rise** produced by a sudden flow change can be derived from Newton's second law, relating force to the rate of change of momentum, utilizing the velocity of the pressure waves which are set up owing to the inertia of the fluid in the line (see derivation by Moody, A.S.M.E.–A.S.C.E. Symposium on Water Hammer, pp. 25–28, American Society of Mechanical Engineers, New York, 1933). The resulting equation is referred to as the Joukowsky or water-hammer equation:

$$h_{wh} = \frac{a(\Delta V)}{g_c} \tag{5-199}$$

where

$$a = \sqrt{\frac{1}{\left[\frac{\rho}{g_c}\left(\frac{1}{k} + \frac{D}{bE}\right)\right]}} \tag{5-200}$$

and h_{wh} = water-hammer head, ft. of fluid; a = velocity of wave propagation, ft./sec.; ΔV = change in velocity, ft./sec.; g_c = dimensional constant, 32.17 (lb.)(ft.)/(lb. force)(sec.^{2}); ρ = fluid density, lb./cu. ft.; k = bulk modulus of elasticity of the fluid, lb. force/sq. ft.; D = pipe inside diameter, ft.; b = pipe-wall thickness, ft.; E = modulus of elasticity of pipe-wall material, lb. force/sq. ft. The maximum head rise given by Eq. (5-199) can also be developed if the flow is changed within the time it takes the pressure wave to travel from the point of stoppage to the end of the pipe or to the location of total wave reflection and return; that is, within one period as given by

$$\tau = \frac{2L}{a} \tag{5-201}$$

where τ = pipe period, sec.; L = length of pipe, ft.; a = velocity of wave propagation, ft./sec.

For **standard steel pipe**, the value of the wave velocity is about 3000 ft./sec.; therefore, from Eq. (5-199),

$$h_{wh} \simeq 95(\Delta V) \quad \text{for standard steel pipe} \tag{5-202}$$

If the time of flow stoppage is somewhat longer than one pipe period τ, the pressure rise will not be so great as that given by Eq. (5-199), since part of the direct pressure waves will be canceled by the reflected pressure waves. The actual pressure rise can be determined by use of the Allievi equations or charts [see Angus, "Hydraulics for Engineers," 3d ed., pp. 283–284, 291–292, Pitman, Toronto, 1943; Kerr and Strowger, A.S.M.E.–A.S.C.E. Symposium on Water Hammer, pp. 15–24, 1933; Rich, "Hydraulic Transients," pp. 24–27, McGraw-Hill, New York, 1951].

The above analysis also applies to the pressure reduction for the reflected wave or on acceleration of flow. If the pressure reduction results in a static pressure at any point in the line below the vapor pressure of the fluid, the fluid in the line will separate or pull apart as the pressure wave passes that location. To keep the pipe from collapsing or bursting, provision must be made for protective devices such as relief valves to admit air when the fluid separates and to release air and some fluid when the fluid rejoins.

Additional details on water-hammer theory can be obtained from Angus, *op. cit.*, Chap. XIV; A.S.M.E.–A.S.C.E. Symposium on Water Hammer, 1933; Rich, *op. cit.*

Hydraulic Transients. In the design and operation of most process pumping systems, consideration is given only to normal steady-state conditions; that is, based on continuous uninterrupted operation, the pumping system is specified for the given process flow rate and pressure. There are a few process pumping systems, however, in which sudden flow changes would cause damage to the pumping facilities or adversely affect the process.

Some of the potential problems to be considered in the design and operation of process pumping systems and methods of analyzing these systems are pointed out below.

In a complex system consisting of **several pumps in parallel** between a suction header and a discharge header, failure of power to one of the pumps could produce one of the following situations: (1) If there were no check valve in the failed pump discharge line, a considerable backflow could follow the failure, thus producing a further decrease in flow through the discharge header and producing a high reverse rotation of the pump which could cause damage to the motor. Experience indicates that a pump impeller could attain almost the design forward speed in the reverse direction in less than 1 sec. [Alves, *Am. Inst. Chem. Engrs. J.*, **2**, 143–147 (1956)]. A flywheel installed on the pump shaft could be used to extend the pumping time while the individual system was being shut down. (2) If there were a check valve, the sudden backflow could slam the disk on the seat, possibly damaging the valve or setting up a dangerous pressure surge, or the disk could "hang up" for a time, allowing backflow to build up and then slam shut, thus setting up dangerous pressure surges. A flywheel on the pump shaft will extend the pumping time to permit a check valve to operate properly [for example, see *Power*, **84** (1), 57 (1940)].

Methods of analyzing pumping systems with possible hydraulic transients are described in the literature by several investigators, including Rich, *op. cit.*; Parmakian, "Water Hammer Analysis," Prentice-Hall, Englewood Cliffs, N.J., 1955; Knapp, *Trans. Am. Soc. Mech. Engrs.*, **59**, 683–689 (1937); Angus, *Proc. Inst. Mech. Engrs.* (*London*), **136**, 245–331 (1937); Alves, *loc. cit.* For the quick estimation of various hydraulic transients in pumping systems, Parmakian (*op. cit.*, pp. 87–91) presents charts based upon experience with large pumping installations.

Pulsating Flow. Flow pulsations in piping systems most often result from the presence of reciprocating machinery (compressors or pumps) in the system. Such pulsations generally adversely affect the performance of flowmeters and process-control elements and can cause vibration and ultimately equipment failure. The preferred solution is to minimize the problem by employing multipiston double-acting units. If this is not practical, then a pulsation damper should be installed.

Gas-phase Pulsation Damping. A general description of methods available for damping of gas-phase flow pulsations is given by the M. W. Kellogg Co., "Design of Piping Systems," 2d ed., pp. 279–283, 333–335, Wiley, New York, 1956. A tabulation of six different types of pulsation dampers and wave filters is given in Campbell, "Process Dynamics," pp. 102–103, Wiley, New York, 1958, together with applicable formulas and attenuation characteristics. Included therein are the in-line surge chamber, closed-end resonator, low-pass filter, high-pass filter, band-pass filter, and band-elimination filter. Chilton and Handley [*Trans. Am. Soc. Mech. Engrs.*, **74**, 931–943 (1952)] present charts for predicting the

Table 5-23. Dimensionless Groupings and Their Significance

Name	Symbol	Formula	Special nomenclature*	Proportional to†	Where used
Bingham No.	N_{Bm}	$\tau_y g_c L/\mu_p V$	L = width of channel, ft. μ_p = coeff. of rigidity, lb./(ft.)(sec.) τ_y = yield stress, lb. force/sq. ft.	$\frac{\text{Yield stress}}{\text{Viscous stress}}$	Flow of Bingham plastics
Blake No.	B	$V\rho/[\mu(1-e)s]$	e = voidage, dimensionless s = particle area/particle volume, 1/ft.	$\frac{\text{Inertial force}}{\text{Viscous force}}$	Beds of solids
Bond No.	N_{Bo}	$(\rho-\rho')L^2 g_L/g_c\sigma$	L = diam. of droplet, ft. ρ = density of droplet, lb./cu. ft. ρ' = density of surrounding fluid, lb./cu. ft. σ = surface tension, lb. force/ft.	$\frac{\text{Gravitational force}}{\text{Surface-tension force}}$	Atomization
Capillary No.	Ca	$\mu V/g_c\sigma$	σ = surface tension, lb. force/ft.	$\frac{\text{Viscous force}}{\text{Surface-tension force}}$	Atomization; two-phase flow in beds of solids
Cauchy No.	N_C	$\rho V^2/g_c E_b$	E_b = bulk modulus of fluid, lb. force/sq. ft.	$\frac{\text{Inertial force}}{\text{Compressibility force}}$	Compressible flow
Cavitation No.	σ_c	$[(p-p_v)/\rho]/(V^2/2g_c)$	p = local absolute static pressure, lb. force/sq. ft. p_v = vapor pressure, lb. force/sq. ft.	$\frac{\text{Excess of local static head over vapor-pressure head}}{\text{Velocity head}}$	Cavitation
Dean No.	N_D	$(VL\rho/\mu)(L/2R)^{1/2}$	L = diam. of pipe, ft. R = radius of curvature, ft.	$N_{\text{Re}}\left(\frac{\text{centrifugal force}}{\text{inertial force}}\right)$	Flow in curved channels
Drag coefficient	C_d	$(\rho-\rho')Lg_L/\rho V^2$	L = characteristic dimension of object, ft. ρ = density of object, lb./cu. ft. ρ' = density of surrounding fluid, lb./cu. ft.	$\frac{\text{Gravitational force}}{\text{Inertial force}}$	Free settling velocities
Elasticity No.	N_{El}	$\theta_r\mu/\rho L^2$	L = radius of pipe, ft. θ_r = relaxation time, sec.	$\frac{\text{Elastic force}}{\text{Inertial force}}$	Viscoelastic flow
Euler No.	N_{Eu}	$g_c(\Delta p_F/\rho)/V^2$	N = number of velocity heads, dimensionless $\Delta p_F/\rho$ = friction head, ft.-lb. force/lb.	$\frac{\text{Friction head}}{2\times\text{velocity head}}$	Fluid friction in conduits
Fanning friction factor	f	$g_c D(\Delta p_F/\rho)/2V^2L$	D = characteristic diam. of cross section, ft. L = length of pipe, ft. $\Delta p_F/\rho$ = friction head, ft.-lb. force/lb.	Shear stress at pipe wall expressed as number of velocity heads	Fluid friction in conduits
Froude No.	N_{Fr}	$V^2/g_L L$	L = characteristic dimension of system, ft.	$\frac{\text{Inertial force}}{\text{Gravitational force}}$	Wave and surface behavior
Hodgson No.	N_H	$V'f'\Delta p_F/\bar{q}\bar{p}$	f' = frequency, 1/sec. $\bar{p}$ = average static pressure, lb. force/sq. ft. Δp_F = pressure drop due to friction, lb. force/sq. ft. $\bar{q}$ = average volumetric flow rate, cu. ft./sec. V' = volume of system, cu. ft.	$\frac{\text{Time constant of system}}{\text{Period of pulsation}}$	Pulsating gas flow
Ohnesorge No.	Z	$\mu/(\rho g_c L\sigma)^{1/2}$	L = characteristic dimension of system, ft. σ = surface tension, lb. force/ft.	$\frac{\text{Viscous force}}{(\text{Inertial force}\times\text{surface-tension force})^{1/2}}=\frac{(N_{\text{We}})^{1/2}}{N_{\text{Re}}}$	Atomization
Pipe-line parameter	ρ_n	$aV_0/2g_cH$	a = water-hammer wave velocity, ft./sec. H = static head, ft.-lb. force/lb. V_0 = initial velocity, ft./sec.	$\frac{\text{Max. water-hammer pressure rise}}{2\times\text{static pressure}}$	Water hammer (hydraulic transients)
Power No.	N_P	$Pg_c/L^5\rho n^3$	P = power to agitator, ft.-lb. force/sec. L = characteristic dimension of agitator paddle, ft. n = rate of rotation, 1/sec.	$\frac{\text{Drag force on paddle}}{\text{Inertial force}}$	Power consumption in agitated vessels
Prandtl velocity ratio	u^+	$u/(\tau_w g_c/\rho)^{1/2}$	u = local velocity, ft./sec. τ_w = shear stress at wall, lb. force/sq. ft.	$\left(\frac{\text{Inertial force}}{\text{Wall shear force}}\right)^{1/2}=\frac{u}{V}\left(\frac{f}{2}\right)^{1/2}$	Turbulence
Reynolds No.	N_{Re}	$LV\rho/\mu$	L = characteristic dimension of the system, ft.	$\frac{\text{Inertial force}}{\text{Viscous force}}$	Dynamic similarity
Strouhal No.	N_{Sl}	$f'L/V$	f' = frequency, 1/sec. L = characteristic dimension of obstacle, ft.	Reciprocal of vortex spacing expressed as number of obstacle diameters	Von Kármán vortex streets
Weber No.	N_{We}	$V^2\rho L/g_c\sigma$	L = characteristic dimension of system, ft. σ = surface tension, lb. force/ft.	$\frac{\text{Inertial force}}{\text{Surface-tension force}}$	Bubble formation, break-up of liquid jet

* See General Nomenclature in Table 5-24.
† See Force Proportionalities in Table 5-24.

performance of a single-tank damper (in-line surge chamber) and a π-type filter (low-pass filter). Isakoff [*Ind. Eng. Chem.*, **47**, 413–421 (1955)] showed how a low-pass electrical filter could be used as an analog for a low-pass gas-pulsation damper, thereby facilitating design of the latter.

Liquid-phase Pulsation Damping. For liquid systems the custom is to employ gas-filled surge chambers attached to the pipe line on both the suction and discharge sides of the pump and located as close to the pump as possible. Sizing of such surge chambers is discussed by Chilton and Handley [*Trans. Am. Soc. Mech. Engrs.*, **77**, 225–230 (1955)]. Diaphragms or bellows are frequently used to separate the surge-chamber gas from the process liquid and thereby prevent gradual depletion of the gas. Equations for sizing such units are given by

Greer Hydraulics, *Bull.* 500, 1957, and by Cook Electric Co., *Tech. Rev.*, **2** (2), 1955.

Cavitation. A practical definition of cavitation is the formation and collapse of vapor cavities in a flowing liquid. Such a vapor cavity can form anywhere in the flowing liquid where the local pressure is reduced to that of the liquid vapor pressure at the temperature of the flowing liquid. At these locations, some of the liquid vaporizes to form bubbles or cavities of vapor. Low-pressure zones can be produced by a local increase in velocity (in accordance with Bernoulli's equation, see p. 5-16) as in eddies or vortices, or over boundary contours; by rapid vibration of the boundary; by separation or parting of a liquid column owing to "water hammer"; or by an over-all reduction in static pressure.

Collapse of the bubbles will begin when they are moved into regions where the local pressure is higher than the vapor pressure. Collapse of these cavities may produce objectionable noise and vibration, and extensive erosion or pitting of the boundary materials in the regions of bubble collapse. An exceedingly important effect of cavitation in liquid-handling facilities is the decrease in performance and efficiency of the equipment; for examples, valves used as flow regulators [Ball, *Trans. Am. Soc. Mech. Engrs.*, **79**, 1275–1283 (1957)] and pumps [Salemann, *Trans. Am. Soc. Mech. Engrs.*, **81**, Series D, 167–180 (1959)]. Additional information can be obtained on the mechanism of cavitation from Knapp and Hollander [*Trans. Am. Soc. Mech. Engrs.*, **70**, 419–435 (1948)] and Knapp [*Proc. Inst. Mech. Engrs. (London)*, **166**, 150–163 (1952); *Trans. Am. Soc. Mech. Engrs.*, **77**, 1045–1054 (1955)], and on damage by cavitation from Vennard [*Proc. Am. Soc. Civil Engrs.*, **71**, 1000–1013 (1945)] and Knapp [*Trans. Am. Soc. Mech. Engrs.*, **77**, 1045–1054 (1955)].

In correlating equipment performance data, a useful parameter is the dimensionless grouping called the cavitation number σ_c (or K):

$$\sigma_c = \frac{p - p_v}{\rho V^2/2g_c} \tag{5-203}$$

where p = static pressure (absolute) in undisturbed flow, lb. force/sq. ft.; p_v = liquid vapor pressure (absolute), lb. force/sq. ft.; ρ = liquid density, lb./cu. ft.; V = free-stream velocity of liquid, ft./sec.; g_c = dimensional constant, 32.17 (lb.)(ft.)/(lb. force)(sec.^{2}). The cavitation number can be considered as the ratio of the net static pressure available to collapse the bubble to the dynamic pressure available to initiate the formation of the bubble. The value of the cavitation number for incipient cavitation $\sigma_{c,i}$ for a specific boundary condition or item of equipment is a characteristic of the geometry. Incipient cavitation numbers for various head forms (blunt, rounded, conical, ellipsoidal) of cylinders are given by Rouse and McNown (Cavitation and Pressure Distribution—Head Forms at Zero Angle of Yaw, *Univ. Iowa Studies in Eng. Bull.* 32, 1948); and for various shapes of surface irregularities by Holl [*Trans. Am. Soc. Mech. Engrs.*, **82**, Series D, 169–183 (1960)].

Scaling up cavitation data obtained for a model must be done with caution. Investigations by Knapp [*Proc. Inst. Mech. Engrs. (London)*, **166**, 150–163 (1952)] and Kermeen, McGraw, and Parkin [*Trans. Am. Soc. Mech. Engrs.*, **77**, 533–541 (1955)] indicate that the cavitation number for incipient cavitation depends upon the free-stream velocity and the characteristic dimension or size. Additional details are given by Holl and Wislicenus [*Trans. Am. Soc. Mech. Engrs.*, **83**, Series D, 385 (1961)].

MODEL STUDIES

A **model** is a device or means which is so constituted that it can be used to predict accurately the performance of a "prototype." The **prototype** in turn is the full-scale physical system which is to be modeled. There are two general types of models:

1. Physically similar models which differ only in scale from the prototype
2. Physically dissimilar models such as mathematical models and electrical analogs

The principle of similarity must be observed in planning model studies. Four types of similarities are important in most chemical engineering studies, namely:

1. Geometric similarity (dimensional proportionality)
2. Mechanical similarity
   a. Static similarity (deformation proportionality)
   b. Kinematic similarity (time proportionality)
   c. Dynamic similarity (force proportionality)
3. Thermal similarity (temperature proportionality)
4. Chemical similarity (concentration proportionality)

Selection of dimensions and operating conditions so as to satisfy geometric, thermal, and chemical similarity requirements is usually relatively straightforward. Satisfaction of mechanical similarity requirements, however, generally involves proportionality control of certain critical groups of variables that are selected either by dimensional analysis or by inspection. The latter procedure, in particular, requires familiarity with known dimensionless numbers and their significance.

Table 5-24. Force Proportionalities

Buoyancy force $\propto L^3\rho\beta\Delta t g/g_c$
Centrifugal force $\propto \rho L^3V^2/g_cR$
Compressibility force $\propto E_bL^2$
Coriolis force $\propto 2(\rho/g_c)L^3\omega V \sin \alpha$
Elastic force $\propto \Theta_r\mu V^2$
Gravitational force $\propto L^3(\rho - \rho')g/g_c$
Inertial force $\propto L^2\rho V^2/g_c$
Surface-tension force $\propto L\sigma$
Viscous force $\propto L\mu V/g_c$
Wall shear force $\propto \tau_w L^2$

General Nomenclature:
E_b = bulk modulus, lb. force/sq. ft.
g = local acceleration due to gravity, ft./sec.^{2}
g_c = dimensional constant, 32.17 (lb.)(ft.)/(lb. force)(sec.^{2})
L = characteristic dimension of system, ft.
R = radius of curvature, ft.
V = velocity, ft./sec.
α = angle, dimensionless
β = coefficient of expansion, 1/°F.
Δt = temperature difference, °F.
Θ_r = relaxation time, sec.
μ = viscosity, lb./(ft.)(sec.)
ρ = density, lb./cu. ft.
σ = surface tension, lb. force/ft.
τ_w = shear stress at wall, lb. force/sq. ft.
ω = angular velocity, radians/sec.

Table 5-23 gives a list of dimensionless numbers frequently encountered in fluid mechanics together with their formulas, significance, area of use, and literature references. This is part of a more extensive tabulation given by Boucher and Alves [*Chem. Eng. Progress*, **55** (9), 55–64 (1959)]. Table 5-24 gives a tabulation of force proportionalities.

Detailed treatments of the subject of model studies can be found in Johnstone and Thring, "Pilot Plants, Models, and Scale-up Methods in Chemical Engineering," McGraw-Hill, New York, 1957; Langhaar, "Dimensional Analysis and Theory of Models," Wiley, New York, 1951; Murphy, "Similitude in Engineering," Ronald, New York, 1950.

PARTICLE DYNAMICS

REFERENCES: Brown *et al.*, "Unit Operations," Wiley, New York, 1950. Knudsen and Katz, "Fluid Dynamics and Heat Transfer," McGraw-Hill, New York, 1958. Lapple *et al.*, "Fluid and Particle Mechanics," University of Delaware, Newark, 1951. Zenz and Othmer, "Fluidization and Fluid-particle Systems," Reinhold, New York, 1960.

Whenever relative motion exists between a particle and a surrounding fluid, the fluid will exert a **drag** upon the particle. The drag force on the particle is given by

$$F_d = \frac{CA_p\rho u^2}{2g_c} \quad \text{lb. force} \qquad (5\text{-}204)$$

where C = drag coefficient, dimensionless; A_p = projected area of particle in direction of motion, sq. ft.; ρ = density of surrounding fluid, lb./cu. ft.; u = relative velocity between particle and fluid, ft./sec.; g_c = dimensional constant, 32.17 (lb.)(ft.)/(lb. force)(sec.^{2}).

Except for extraneous effects, such as turbulence, it makes no difference whether the fluid moves past the particle or the particle moves through the fluid. A particle falling under the action of gravity will accelerate until drag force just balances gravitational force, after which it will continue to fall at a constant velocity known as the **terminal** or **free-settling velocity** u_t, as given by

$$u_t = \sqrt{\frac{2gm_p(\rho_p - \rho)}{\rho\rho_pA_pC}} \quad \text{ft./sec.} \qquad (5\text{-}205)$$

where g = local acceleration due to gravity, ft./sec.^{2}; m_p = mass of particle, lb.; ρ_p = density of particle, lb./cu. ft.; remainder of symbols defined above. The drag coefficient C has been found to be a function of the shape of the particle and the Reynolds number $D_p\rho u/\mu$, where D_p = diameter of particle, ft., and μ = fluid viscosity, lb./(ft.)(sec.).

Spherical Rigid Particles. For the case of spherical particles, Eq. (5-205) becomes

$$u_t = \sqrt{\frac{4gD_p(\rho_p - \rho)}{3\rho C}} \quad \text{ft./sec.} \qquad (5\text{-}206)$$

A plot of drag coefficient C vs. N_{Re} is given as the solid curve in Fig. 5-70. For $N_{\mathrm{Re}} < 0.3$,

$$C = \frac{24}{N_{\mathrm{Re}}} \qquad (5\text{-}207)$$

This corresponds to **Stokes's law**, which is usually written

$$F_d = 3\pi\mu u D_p/g_c \quad \text{lb. force} \qquad (5\text{-}208)$$

The **terminal** settling velocity in the Stokes's-law region becomes

$$u_t = \frac{gD_p^2(\rho_p - \rho)}{18\mu} \quad \text{ft./sec.} \qquad (5\text{-}209)$$

In the **Newton's-law** region, which covers the Reynolds-number range of 1000 to 200,000, drag coefficient C has an approximately constant value of 0.44 for spheres. In this region, Eq. (5-205) becomes

$$u_t = 1.74\sqrt{gD_p(\rho_p - \rho)/\rho} \quad \text{ft./sec.} \qquad (5\text{-}210)$$

In the **intermediate region** ($0.3 < N_{\mathrm{Re}} < 1000$), the drag-coefficient relationship for spheres can be approximated by

$$C = \frac{18.5}{N_{\mathrm{Re}}^{0.6}} \qquad (5\text{-}211)$$

It is generally more satisfactory to employ the curve in Fig. 5-70 for this region.

Non-spherical Rigid Particles. The drag on a **non-spherical** particle depends upon its shape and its orientation with respect to the direction of motion. In the Stokes's-law region a particle will generally retain its initial orientation during settling, whereas in the Newton's-law region it will assume a position of maximum resistance. The drag coefficients for **disks** (flat side perpendicular to the direction of motion) and for **cylinders** (infinite length with axis perpendicular to the direction of motion) are given in Fig. 5-70 as a function of Reynolds number. The effect of length-to-diameter ratio for cylinders in the Newton's-law region is reported by Knudsen and Katz (*op. cit.*, p. 301).

Pettyjohn and Christiansen [*Chem. Eng. Progress*, **44**, 157–172 (1948)] present correlations which allow for the effect of particle shape on free-settling velocities for **isometric particles.** For $N_{\mathrm{Re}} < 0.05$, the terminal or free-settling velocity is given by

$$u_t = K_1\frac{gD_s^2(\rho_p - \rho)}{18\mu} \quad \text{ft./sec.} \qquad (5\text{-}212)$$

$$K_1 = 0.843 \log\frac{\psi}{0.065} \qquad (5\text{-}213)$$

where ψ = sphericity (area of a sphere divided by the area of the non-spherical particle having the same volume as the sphere), dimensionless; g = local acceleration due to gravity, ft./sec.^{2}; D_s = "spherical" diameter (diameter of a sphere of equal volume), ft.; ρ_p = particle density, lb./cu. ft.; ρ = fluid density, lb./cu. ft.; μ = fluid viscosity, lb./(ft.)(sec.).

In the **Newton's-law** region, the terminal velocity is given by

$$u_t = \sqrt{\frac{4D_s(\rho_p - \rho)g}{3K_2\rho}} \quad \text{ft./sec.} \qquad (5\text{-}214)$$

$$K_2 = 5.31 - 4.88\psi \qquad (5\text{-}215)$$

Equations (5-213) and (5-215) are based on experiments on cube-octahedrons, octahedrons, cubes, and tetrahedrons for which the sphericity ψ ranges from 0.906 to 0.670, respectively.

For particles having sphericities less than 0.67, the correlations presented by Becker [*Can. J. Chem. Eng.*, **37**, 85–91 (1959)] should be employed. Reference to this paper is also recommended for the **intermediate-law region.** The settling characteristics of **non-spherical particles** are also discussed at some length by Zenz and Othmer (*op. cit.*, Chap. 6) and by Brown *et al.* (*op. cit.*, pp. 76–78).

Drag coefficients for various two- and three-dimensional bodies are given by Hoerner, "Fluid-dynamic Drag," Chaps. III and IV, published by author, Midland Park, N.J., 1958. Drag coefficients for flow normal to two-dimensional cylinders with a variety of cross sections are listed in Knudsen and Katz (*op. cit.*, pp. 302–304).

Gas Bubbles. Fluid particles differ from solid particles in that internal circulation and particle deformation can occur, both of which affect drag coefficient and terminal velocity. Bubbles retain a spherical shape up to some Reynolds number between 1 and 100, but internal circulation results in a reduction in drag or an increase in terminal velocity (up to 50 per cent in the Stokes's-law region) for liquids of higher viscosity than water, as shown by Garner and Hammerton [*Chem. Eng. Sci.*, **3**, 1 (Feb., 1954)]. At higher Reynolds numbers the bubbles assume a flattened shape normal to the direction of flow; this is accompanied by an increase in drag. Motion of such deformed bubbles is generally unstable

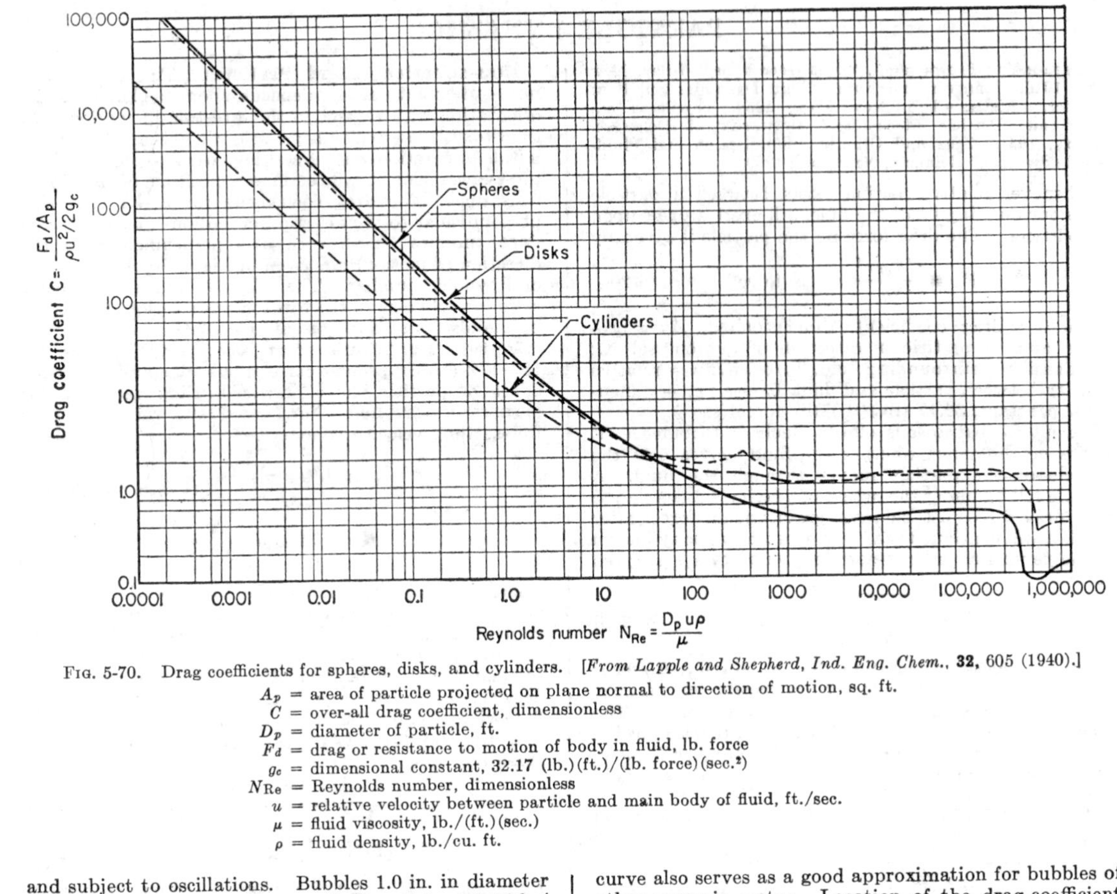

FIG. 5-70. Drag coefficients for spheres, disks, and cylinders. [*From Lapple and Shepherd, Ind. Eng. Chem.*, **32**, 605 (1940).]

A_p = area of particle projected on plane normal to direction of motion, sq. ft.
C = over-all drag coefficient, dimensionless
D_p = diameter of particle, ft.
F_d = drag or resistance to motion of body in fluid, lb. force
g_c = dimensional constant, 32.17 (lb.)(ft.)/(lb. force)(sec.^{2})
N_{Re} = Reynolds number, dimensionless
u = relative velocity between particle and main body of fluid, ft./sec.
μ = fluid viscosity, lb./(ft.)(sec.)
ρ = fluid density, lb./cu. ft.

and subject to oscillations. Bubbles 1.0 in. in diameter or larger will reach a maximum velocity of about 1.25 ft./sec. in water, the larger bubbles being deformed to a greater extent or ruptured (see Lapple *et al.*, *op. cit.*, p. 289.)

The **drag-coefficient** curve for air bubbles rising in water as given by Haberman and Morton (*David W. Taylor Model Basin Report* 802, 1953) is shown in Fig. 5-71. Diameter of the bubble is taken to be the diameter of a sphere having the same volume as the bubble. This

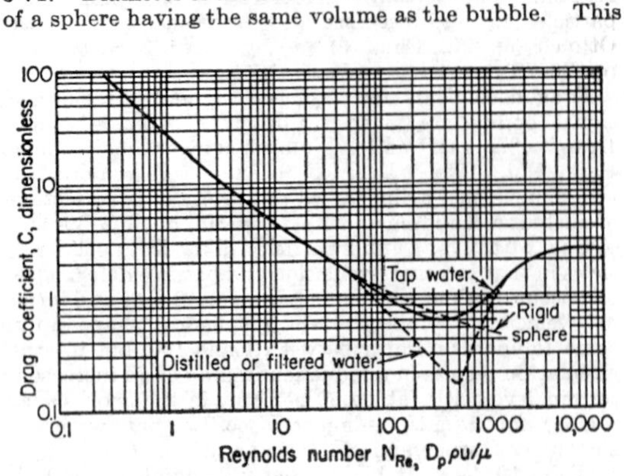

FIG. 5-71. Drag coefficient for air bubbles rising in water at room temperature. (*Haberman and Morton, David W. Taylor Model Basin Report* 802, 1953.)

curve also serves as a good approximation for bubbles of other gases in water. Location of the drag-coefficient curve for a given system depends on the physical properties of the system, including liquid viscosity and interfacial tension. For liquids having properties appreciably different from water, see Haberman and Morton (*op. cit.*). For additional information on the effect of interfacial tension, see Harmathy [*Am. Inst. Chem. Engrs. J.*, **6**, 281 (1960)].

Liquid Drops in Liquids. Liquid drops will either rise or settle in a separate immiscible liquid medium, depending upon whether the drop density is less or greater, respectively, than the liquid medium density. According to Warshay *et al.* [*Can. J. Chem. Eng.*, **37**, 29–36 (1959)], the **terminal velocity** can be approximated by use of the drag-coefficient curve for solid spheres up to a Reynolds number of about 10. The actual terminal velocity will be somewhat greater than the one so predicted.

For systems characterized by low liquid viscosities (~1 centipoise), the correlation of Hu and Kintner [*Am. Inst. Chem. Engrs. J.*, **1**, 42–48 (1955)] as given in Fig. 5-72 is recommended. Here the dimensionless parameter $C(N_{We})(P^{0.15})$ is correlated with another dimensionless parameter $N_{Re}/P^{0.15}$; where C = drag coefficient, dimensionless; N_{We} = Weber number ($u_t^2 D_p \rho/\sigma_i$), dimensionless; u_t = relative terminal velocity between the drop and the liquid medium, ft./sec.; D_p = drop diameter, ft.; ρ = density of medium, lb./cu. ft.; σ_i = interfacial tension, lb. force/ft. (dynes/cm. times 6.85×10^{-5}); $P = 3(N_{Re})^4/4C(N_{We})^3$, dimen-

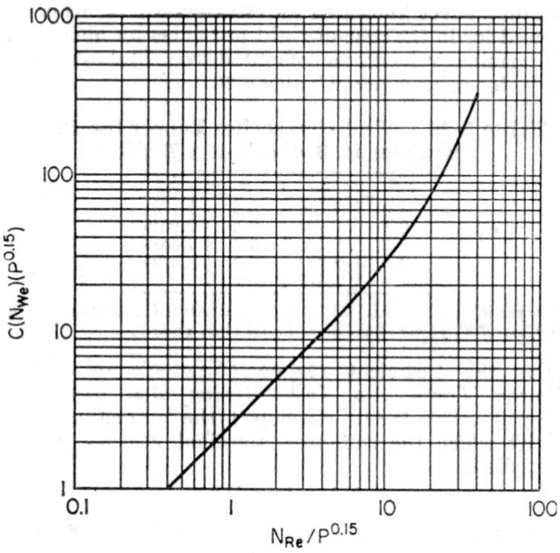

FIG. 5-72. Liquid drops in liquid media. [*From Hu and Kintner, Am. Inst. Chem. Engrs. J.*, **1**, 42 (1955).]

sionless; N_{Re} = Reynolds number ($D_p u_t \rho/\mu$), dimensionless; μ = viscosity of medium, lb./(ft.)(sec.) = centipoise/1488. Figure 5-72 can be used together with Eq. (5-205) or Eq. (5-206) in computing terminal velocity.

Klee and Treybal [*Am. Inst. Chem. Engrs. J.*, **2**, 444–447 (1956)] have also presented correlations relating to the rise or fall of liquid drops in liquid media. In the systems tested, the interfacial tension ranged from 0.3 to 42 dynes/cm. and liquid medium viscosities from 0.9 to 1.5 centipoise.

Liquid Drops in Gases. Liquid drops falling in gases appear to remain spherical and follow the same drag relationships as solid spherical particles up to a Reynolds number of about 100. Large drops will deform, with a resulting increase in drag, and in some cases will shatter. The largest water drop which will fall in air at its terminal velocity is about 5/16 in. diameter. The corresponding maximum velocity is about 30 ft./sec.

Hughes and Gilliland [*Chem. Eng. Progress*, **48**, 497–504 (1952)] correlated terminal-settling-velocity data for a variety of liquids in air on the basis of a drag coefficient–Reynolds number chart with lines of constant Su as given in Fig. 5-73, where Su = (1/Ohnesorge number)^2 = $g_c \sigma_i \rho D_p/\mu^2$; g_c = dimensional constant, 32.17 (lb.)(ft.)/(lb. force)(sec.^{2}); σ_i = interfacial tension, lb. force/ft.;

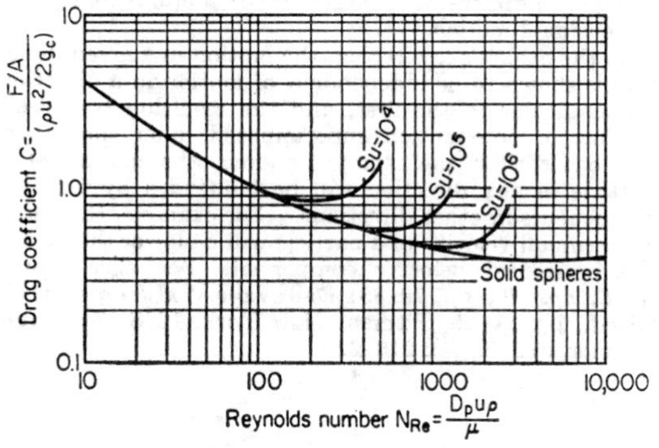

FIG. 5-73. Drag coefficient for liquid drops in gases. [*From Hughes and Gilliland, Chem. Eng. Progress*, **48**, 497 (1952).]

ρ = gas density, lb./cu. ft.; D_p = drop diameter, ft.; μ = gas viscosity, lb./(ft.)(sec.).

Application. The use of a simple C vs. N_{Re} plot for prediction of either **terminal velocity** or **particle diameter** involves trial and error, since both terms are involved in both the ordinate and abscissa. However, the terms CN_{Re}^2 and C/N_{Re} do not include u_t or D_p, respectively. Thus, to eliminate trial and error, values of these quantities can be calculated and plotted against each other or against N_{Re}. Then, depending upon whether u_t or D_p is unknown, the value of CN_{Re}^2 or C/N_{Re}, respectively, can be calculated, and the unknown obtained from the corresponding term. For spherical particles,

$$CN_{Re}^2 = \frac{4g\rho D_p^3(\rho_p - \rho)}{3\mu^2} \tag{5-216}$$

$$\frac{C}{N_{Re}} = \frac{4g\mu(\rho_p - \rho)}{3\rho^2 u_t^3} \tag{5-217}$$

Values of C, N_{Re}, CN_{Re}^2, and C/N_{Re} are given in Table 5-25 for spherical particles.

Table 5-25. Drag Coefficient and Related Functions for Spherical Particles*

N_{Re}	C	CN_{Re}^2	C/N_{Re}
0.1	240	2.4	2,400
0.2	120	4.8	600
0.3	80	7.2	267
0.5	49.5	12.4	99.0
0.7	36.5	17.9	52.1
1.0	26.5	26.5	26.5
2	14.6	58.4	7.3
3	10.4	93.7	3.47
5	6.9	173	1.38
7	5.3	260	0.757
10	4.1	410	0.410
20	2.55	1.02×10^3	0.1275
30	2.00	1.80	0.0667
50	1.50	3.75	0.0300
70	1.27	6.23	0.0181
100	1.07	1.07×10^4	0.0107
200	0.77	3.08	3.85×10^{-3}
300	0.65	5.85	2.17
500	0.55	1.38×10^5	1.10
700	0.50	2.45	7.14×10^{-4}
1,000	0.46	4.60	4.60
2,000	0.42	1.68×10^6	2.10
3,000	0.40	3.60	1.333
5,000	0.385	9.60	7.70×10^{-5}
7,000	0.390	1.91×10^7	5.57
10,000	0.405	4.05	4.05
20,000	0.45	1.80×10^8	2.25
30,000	0.47	4.26	1.57
50,000	0.49	1.23×10^9	9.80×10^{-6}
70,000	0.50	2.45	7.14
100,000	0.48	4.8	4.80
200,000	0.42	1.68×10^{10}	2.10
300,000	0.20	1.80	6.67×10^{-7}
400,000	0.084	1.34	2.10
600,000	0.10	3.60	1.667
1,000,000	0.13	1.30×10^{11}	1.300
3,000,000	0.20	1.80×10^{12}	6.67×10^{-8}

For values of N_{Re} less than 0.3, $C = 24/N_{Re}$.

* From Lapple and Shepherd, *Ind. Eng. Chem.*, **32**, 605–617 (1940).

Figure 5-74 gives the terminal settling velocities of spherical particles of different densities settling in air and water at 70°F. under the action of gravity. These curves should be useful for ready reference in practical applications. They are based on the drag-coefficient values given in Table 5-25.

Limitations. The relationships presented thus far have dealt with the motion of particles present in relatively dilute concentration and in bodies of fluid of relatively large cross section. When the concentration

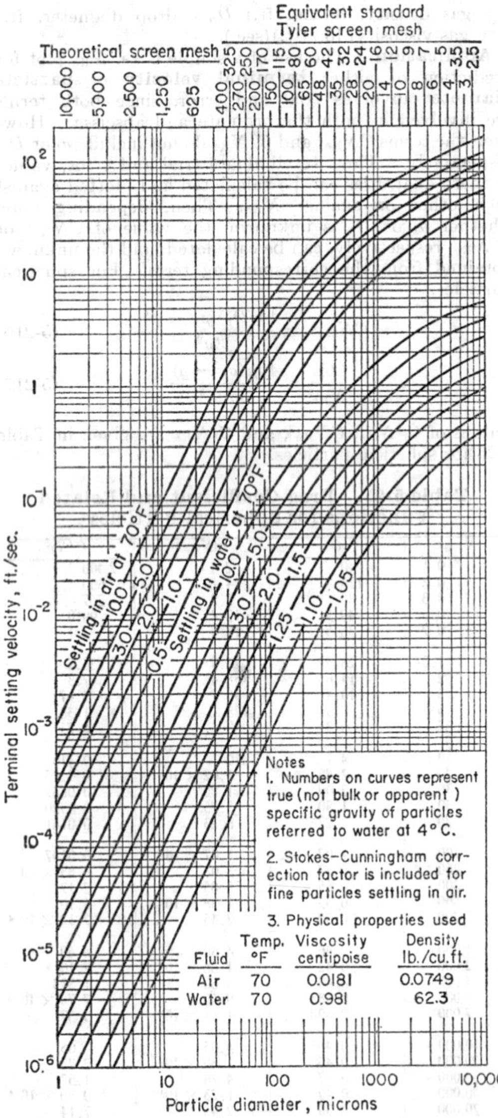

FIG. 5-74. Terminal velocities of spherical particles of different densities settling in air and water at 70°F. under the action of gravity. (*From Lapple et al., op. cit., p. 292.*)

becomes high, the particles will be close enough to exert a mutual retarding effect on the settling. This condition is often referred to as **"hindered" settling.** The effect is not significant at volumetric concentrations below 0.1 per cent. For the effect at higher concentrations, see Lapple *et al.* (*op. cit.*, p. 289) and Brown *et al.* (*op. cit.*, pp. 78–79).

When the diameter of the particle becomes appreciable with respect to the diameter of the container in which it is settling, the container walls will exert an additional retarding effect known as the **wall effect.** This can be allowed for in the case of **rigid particles** by multiplying the terminal velocity as computed from Stokes's law by the factor k_w as given in Table 5-26.

Table 5-26. Wall Correction Factor for Rigid Particles in Stokes's-law Region

β	k_w	β	k_w
0.0	1.000	0.5	0.170
0.1	0.792	0.6	0.0945
0.2	0.596	0.7	0.0468
0.3	0.422	0.8	0.0205
0.4	0.279		

β = particle diameter divided by vessel diameter. (From Haberman and Sayre, *David W. Taylor Model Basin Report* 1143, 1958).

For the turbulent regime (Newton's-law region), Munroe [*Trans. Am. Inst. Mining Met. Engrs.*, **17**, 637–659 (1888–1889)] developed the correction factor k_w' by which the computed terminal velocity may be multiplied:

$$k_w' = 1 - \beta^{1.5} \quad (5\text{-}218)$$

where β = particle diameter divided by vessel diameter.

Stokes's law is subject to a lower limit in the case of rigid particles settling in a gas. When the particle size approaches the mean free path of the fluid molecules, the settling velocity will be greater than that computed from Stokes's law. The correction known as the **Stokes-Cunningham correction** is less than 1 per cent for particles larger than 16 microns settling in air. Particles smaller than this are also subject to **Brownian motion** because of impact of the fluid molecules. For particles finer than 0.1 micron, this random motion is far greater in magnitude than any directed particle motion due to gravitational settling. For additional information on the magnitude of these two effects, see Lapple *et al.* (*op. cit.*, pp. 285–286) and Zenz and Othmer (*op. cit.*, Chap. 6).

For the case of **bubbles in liquids,** a wall effect will be encountered for bubble diameters larger than 1/100 of the vessel diameter. Information on this effect is given by Harmathy (*loc. cit.*) and Uno and Kintner [*Am. Inst. Chem. Engrs. J.*, **2**, 420 (1956)].

For the case of **liquid drops in liquids,** information on the wall effect is given by Harmathy (*loc. cit.*) and Strom and Kintner [*Am. Inst. Chem. Engrs. J.*, **4**, 153 (1958)].

Particle Trajectories. In the treatment up to this point, only one-dimensional steady-state motion has been considered, vertically up or down, under the action of gravity. Equations have been developed by Lapple and Shepherd [*Ind. Eng. Chem.*, **32**, 605–617 (1940)] for calculating the position-time histories for particles undergoing one-dimensional accelerated motion and two-dimensional motion.

In the Stokes's law region, the motion in a given direction is shown to be independent of motion in a direction perpendicular to the first, and the resulting trajectory is that of one motion superimposed upon the other. For other than the laminar regime, the motion of a particle in any direction will be influenced by velocity components in other directions. For example, the vertical terminal velocity of a particle will be lower the higher the horizontal velocity component. See also Brown *et al.*, *op. cit.*, pp. 79–83; DallaValle, "Micromeritics," 2d ed., pp. 24–29, Pitman, New York, 1948; Zenz and Othmer, *op. cit.*, pp. 216–220.

SECTION 6

TRANSPORT AND STORAGE OF FLUIDS

BY

Raymond P. Genereaux, Ch.E., Chemical Engineer, E. I. du Pont de Nemours & Co.; Member, American Chemical Society, American Institute of Chemical Engineers; Registered Professional Engineer (Delaware). (Section Editor)

Philip P. O'Neill, M.S., Mechanical Equipment Consultant, E. I. du Pont de Nemours & Co.; Member, American Society of Mechanical Engineers; Registered Professional Engineer (Pennsylvania). (Pumping of Liquids and Gases)

Joseph C. Thompson, B.S., District Manager, General American Transportation Corp.; Member, American Petroleum Institute, American Society of Mechanical Engineers; Registered Professional Engineer (Illinois). (Storage and Bulk Transport of Fluids)

William D. Webb, Development Engineer, E. I. du Pont de Nemours & Co.; Member, American Society of Mechanical Engineers; Registered Professional Engineer (Delaware). (Pipe and Fittings)

CONTENTS

PUMPING OF LIQUIDS AND GASES

Means of Producing Fluid Flow.* There are six methods by which fluids can be made to move through a conduit or channel: (1) by action of centrifugal force; (2) by volumetric displacement, accomplished either mechanically or with other fluids; (3) by mechanical impulse; (4) by transfer of momentum from another fluid; (5) by electromagnetic force; (6) by gravity. Regardless of the physical nature of a fluid, whether it is compressible or incompressible, these six methods include all available means for fluid transport.

Centrifugal Force. Though the physical appearance of the many types of centrifugal pumps and compressors varies greatly, the basic function of each is the same, *i.e.*, to produce kinetic energy by the action of centrifugal force and then to convert this energy partially to pressure by efficiently reducing its velocity.

A device which combines the use of centrifugal force with mechanical impulse to produce an increase in pressure is the axial-flow compressor or pump. In this device the fluid travels roughly parallel to the shaft through a series of alternately rotating and stationary radial blades having airfoil cross sections. The fluid is accelerated in the axial direction by mechanical impulses from the rotating blades; concurrently, a positive pressure gradient in the radial direction is established in each stage by centrifugal force. The net pressure rise per stage results from both effects.

In general, centrifugal fluid-transport devices have these characteristics: (1) discharge is relatively free of pulsation; (2) mechanical design lends itself to high through-puts, which means that capacity limitations are rarely a problem; (3) they are capable of efficient performance over a wide range of pressures and capacities even at constant-speed operation; (4) discharge pressure is a function of fluid density.

Displacement. Discharge of a fluid from a vessel by partially or completely displacing its internal volume with a second fluid or by mechanical means is the principle upon which a great many fluid-transport devices operate. Included in this group are reciprocating piston and diaphragm machines, rotary vane and gear types, fluid piston compressors, acid eggs, and air lifts.

The large variety of displacement-type fluid-transport devices makes it difficult to list characteristics common to each. However, for most types it is correct to state that (1) they are adaptable to high-pressure operation, (2) discharge of many will pulsate unless an auxiliary damping system is employed, (3) mechanical considerations limit maximum through-puts, and (4) they are capable of efficient performance at extremely low-volume through-put rates.

Mechanical Impulse. The principle of mechanical impulse when applied to fluids is usually combined with one of the other means of imparting motion. As mentioned above, this is the case in axial-flow compressors and pumps. The turbine or regenerative-type pump is another device which functions partially by mechanical impulse.

Transference of Momentum. Acceleration of one fluid in order to transfer its momentum to a second is a principle commonly used in the handling of corrosive materials, in pumping from inaccessible depths, or for evacuation. Jets and eductors are in this category.

These are normally relatively inefficient performers. In cases where the motivating fluid is air or steam, operating costs are apt to be several times that of other types of fluid-transport equipment. On the other hand, absence of moving parts and simplicity of construction often justify their use in severe services or inaccessible locations.

Electromagnetic Force. When the fluid is a good electrical conductor, as is the case with molten metals, it is possible to impress an electromagnetic field around the fluid conduit in such a way that a driving force is created that will cause flow. Such pumps have been developed for the handling of heat-transfer liquids, especially for nuclear reactors.

Measurement of Performance. The amount of useful work that any fluid-transport device performs is the product of (1) the rate at which the fluid passes through it and (2) the height of column of fluid equivalent under adiabatic conditions to the total pressure differential measured immediately before and after the device. The first of these quantities is normally referred to as **capacity** while the second is known as **head.**

Capacity is expressed in various units, depending upon the type of device. It is common practice to use gallons per minute for most types of liquid pumps. With machines handling compressible fluids (gases), the capacity term must be related to a defined set of temperature and pressure conditions. Usually capacities are stated in cubic feet per minute at inlet conditions to the machine.

Efficiency. The ratio of useful hydraulic work performed to the actual work input, regardless of the type of drive, is known as **over-all efficiency.** In addition, there are several other efficiencies which serve as useful yardsticks in measuring the effectiveness of a machine's design. These are dealt with in detail below.

Work Performed in Pumping. To move a liquid against gravity with a pump, work must be expended. A pump may actually raise the liquid, or force it into a pressure vessel, or merely give it enough head to overcome pipe friction. No matter what the service required of a pump, all forms of energy imparted to the liquid in performing this service must be accounted for in establishing the work performed. To add algebraically all these forms of energy, it is customary to express them all in terms of head measured in feet of liquid.

To determine the theoretical work required of a pump, known as **hydraulic horsepower,** it is necessary to know total dynamic head and weight of liquid to be pumped in a given time. Usually weight is expressed in terms of volume and density or specific gravity.

$$\text{Hydraulic hp.} = \frac{8.33Hs(\text{gal./min.})}{33{,}000} \qquad (6\text{-}1)$$

$$= \frac{Hs(\text{gal./min.})}{3960} \qquad (6\text{-}2)$$

$$= \frac{H_p(\text{gal./min.})}{1714} \qquad (6\text{-}3)$$

* Acknowledgment is made of the contribution of F. L. Lucker to the third edition. Substantial portions of his work, especially relating to reciprocating compressors, have been reused here.

where H = total dynamic head, ft. liquid; H_p = total dynamic head, lb./sq. in.; s = specific gravity.

The actual or **brake horsepower** of a pump is greater than the theoretical or hydraulic horsepower by the amount of losses incurred in the pump through friction, leakage, etc. The efficiency of a pump is therefore defined as

$$\text{Pump efficiency} = \frac{\text{hydraulic hp.}}{\text{brake hp.}} \qquad (6\text{-}4)$$

In pumping devices where the power input is not supplied through a mechanical linkage, *i.e.*, acid eggs, jets, etc., the pump efficiency is equal to the hydraulic horsepower delivered to the liquid pumped divided by the hydraulic horsepower available in the driving fluid.

Total dynamic head H of a pump is the difference between total discharge head h_d and total suction head h_s. **Total suction head** is the reading h_{sg} of a gage at the suction flange of a pump (corrected to the pump center line* and converted to feet of liquid) plus the barometer reading in feet of liquid, plus the velocity head h_{vs} (feet) at the point of gage attachment:

$$h_s = h_{sg} + \text{atm.} + h_{vs} \qquad (6\text{-}5)$$

If the static pressure at the suction flange is less than atmospheric, requiring use of a vacuum gage, this reading, converted to feet of liquid, is used for h_{sg} in Eq. (6-5) with a negative sign.

Before installation it is possible to estimate the total suction head as follows:

$$h_s = h_{ss} - h_{fs} \qquad (6\text{-}6)$$

where h_{ss} = static suction head and h_{fs} = suction friction head, both in ft. liquid.

Total discharge head h_d is the reading h_{dg} of a gage at the discharge flange of a pump (corrected to the pump center line* and converted to feet of liquid) plus the barometer reading in feet of liquid, plus the velocity head h_{vd} (feet) at the point of gage attachment:

$$h_d = h_{dg} + \text{atm.} + h_{vd} \qquad (6\text{-}7)$$

Again, if the discharge gage pressure is below atmospheric, the vacuum-gage reading in feet of liquid is used for h_{dg} with a negative sign.

Before installation it is possible to estimate the total discharge head from the static discharge head h_{sd} and the discharge friction head h_{fd} as follows:

$$h_d = h_{sd} + h_{fd} \qquad (6\text{-}8)$$

Static suction head h_{ss} on a pump is the vertical distance (feet) between the free level of the source of supply and the pump center line, plus the absolute pressure at this level converted to feet of liquid. **Total static head** h_{ts} is the difference of discharge and suction static heads.

Velocity. Since most liquids are practically incompressible, there is a definite relation between the quantity flowing past a given point in a given time and the velocity of flow. This relation is expressed as

$$Q = Av \qquad (6\text{-}9)$$

$$v \text{ (for circular conduits)} = \frac{0.409(\text{gal./min.})}{d^2} \qquad (6\text{-}10)$$

where Q = quantity of flow, cu. ft./sec.; A = cross-sectional area of conduit, sq. ft.; v = velocity of flow, ft./sec.; d = inside diameter, in.

* On vertical pumps, the correction should be made to the eye of the suction impeller.

Velocity head is the vertical distance a body would have to fall to acquire the velocity v. It corresponds to the static or pressure head that would cause that velocity.

Viscosity (see Sec. 5 for further information). In flowing liquids the existence of internal friction or the internal resistance to relative motion of the fluid particles must be considered. This resistance is called viscosity. Usually viscosity decreases with rising temperature. Viscous liquids tend to increase the horsepower required by a pump, to reduce pump efficiency, head, and capacity, and increase friction in pipe lines.

Friction head is the pressure (feet of liquid) required to overcome the resistance to flow in pipe and fittings. This is dealt with in detail in Sec. 5.

Suction Limitations on a Pump. The maximum theoretical deviation between the pump center line and level of a suction source exposed to atmosphere would be a distance equivalent in feet of liquid to the atmospheric pressure, less the head equivalent to the vapor pressure p of the liquid, less the head equivalent to the pressure of any gas in solution, less the friction head h_{fs}, and less the head equivalent to the entrance loss. We see then that for each pump there is a certain minimum suction head required for it to operate; this is always less than the equivalent barometric height of the liquid being handled. This value varies with pump throughput and is known as the required **net positive suction head** $(\text{NPSH})_R$. Manufacturers publish curves relating this value to capacity and speed for each pump. To use this information properly, it is necessary to calculate the net positive suction head that will be available $(\text{NPSH})_A$ to the pump suction. This can be calculated from the formula

$$(\text{NPSH})_A = h_{ss} - h_{fs} - p \qquad (6\text{-}11)$$

If $(\text{NPSH})_A$ is to be checked on an existing installation, it can be determined as follows:

$$(\text{NPSH})_A = \text{atm.} + h_{sg} - p + h_{vs} \qquad (6\text{-}12)$$

Practically, the NPSH required for operation without cavitation and vibration in the pump is somewhat greater than the theoretical. The actual $(\text{NPSH})_R$ depends on the characteristics of the liquid, the total head, and the pump speed, capacity, and impeller design. Any suction condition which reduces $(\text{NPSH})_A$ below that required to prevent cavitation can lead to serious mechanical difficulty.

Net Positive Suction Head Curves for Centrifugal Hot-water Pumps. Figures 6-1 and 6-2 are typical

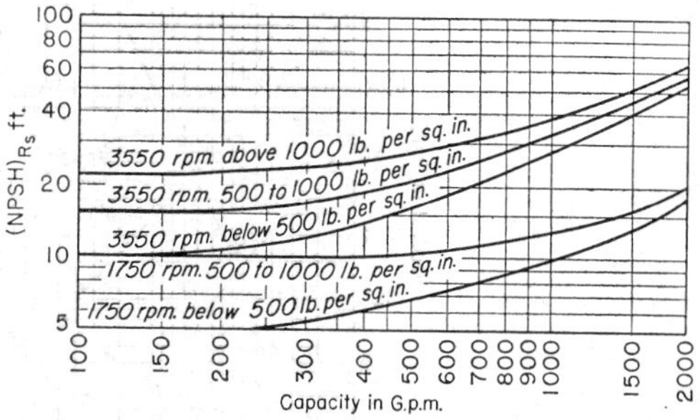

FIG. 6-1. Net positive suction head, centrifugal hot-water pumps, single suction. Compiled from data by representative companies. Curves apply to water temperatures up to 212°F. For temperatures above 212°F. use temperature correction chart, Fig. 6-2. For speeds within ±25 per cent of those shown, correct capacity according to: r.p.m. $\sqrt{\text{gal./min.}}$ = constant. *(By permission of Hydraulic Institute.)*

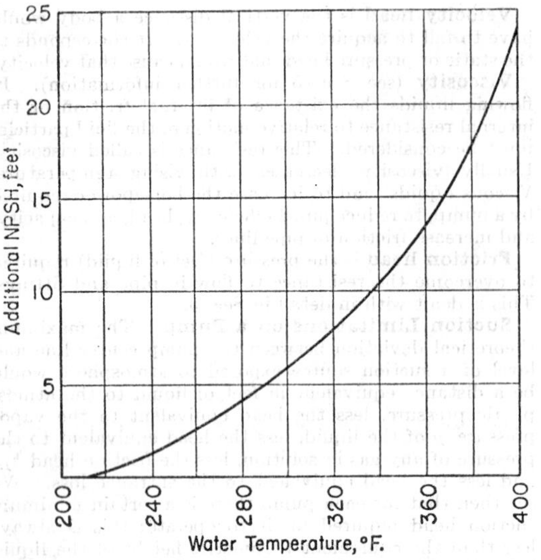

FIG. 6-2. Temperature correction chart, centrifugal hot-water pumps, single and double suction. Additional suction head to be added to values given on Fig. 6-1. (*By permission of Hydraulic Institute.*)

of suction limitations on hot-liquid pumps. NPSH required above the vapor pressure for different capacities and speeds, including additional NPSH required in case the water temperature exceeds 212°F., is shown. The addition is necessitated by air entrainment.

For hot-liquid pumps taking suction from a source where the prevailing pressure is equivalent to the vapor pressure corresponding to its temperature, the net positive suction head available is the difference between the liquid level at the source and the pump center line minus the entrance and friction losses in the suction piping.

Example. If a pump handles water at 350°F. temperature with 150 lb./sq. in. gage pressure at the suction nozzle and with 12 ft./sec. velocity, what is the net positive suction head available?

Solution. The vapor pressure for 350°F. water = 134.6 lb./sq. in. abs.

Specific gravity of 350°F. water = 0.89

Velocity head $v^2/2g$ = 2.22 ft. (g = 32.17 ft./sec.²)

$$\text{Thus } (\text{NPSH})_A = \frac{(150 + 14.7 - 134.6)2.31}{0.89} + 2.22 = 80.32 \text{ ft.}$$

Pump Selection. When selecting pumps for any service, it is necessary to know the liquid to be handled, total dynamic head, suction and discharge heads, and in most cases, the temperature, viscosity, vapor pressure, and specific gravity. In the chemical industry the task of pump selection is frequently further complicated by the presence of solids and corrosion characteristics demanding special materials. Solids may accelerate erosion, have a tendency to agglomerate, or may require delicate handling to prevent undesirable degradation.

Range of Operation. Because of the wide variety of pump types and the number of factors which determine the selection of any for a specific installation, the designer must first eliminate all but those of reasonable possibility. Since range of operation is always an important consideration, Fig. 6-3 should be of assistance. The boundaries shown for each pump type are at best only approximate, as unusual applications will arise where the best selection contradicts the chart. In most cases, however, Fig. 6-3 will prove useful in limiting consideration to two or three types of pumps.

Pump Materials. In the chemical industry the selection of pump materials is dictated by considerations of corrosion, erosion, personnel safety, and liquid contamination. The experience of pump manufacturers is often valuable in selecting materials. See also Sec. 23.

Presence of Solids. Adequate hydraulic performance and use of the most durable materials may not always be sufficient to produce the most satisfactory pump selection. When solids are present there are other considerations of equal importance. All internal passages must have adequate dimensions. Pockets and dead spots where solids could accumulate must be avoided. If the solids are abrasive, close internal clearances between stationary and moving parts are undesirable. Means should also be available for flushing with a clean liquid before shutdown.

Installations requiring the gentle handling of suspended

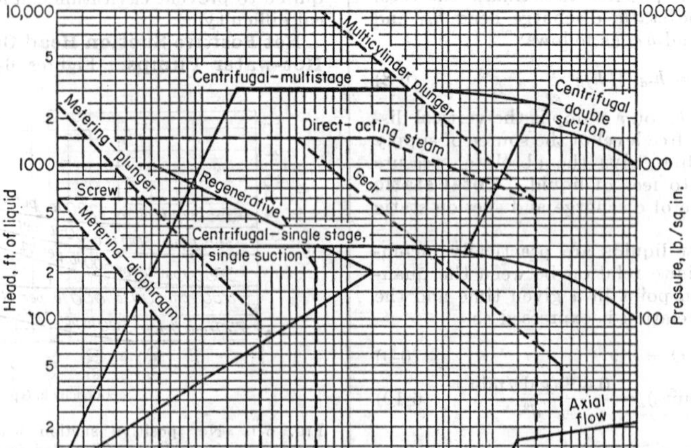

FIG. 6-3. Pump coverage chart based on normal ranges of operation of commercially available types. Solid lines—use left ordinate, head scale. Broken lines—use right ordinate, pressure scale.

solids, such as pumps feeding filter presses, demand special attention.

Adaptability to easy maintenance is a feature of increasing importance in today's economy. Chemical pump installations requiring annual maintenance of two or three times the original investment are not uncommon. In most cases this is the result of improper selection.

The **centrifugal pump** is the type most widely used in the chemical industry for transferring liquids of all types—raw materials, materials in manufacture, and finished products—as well as for general services of water supply, boiler feed, condenser circulation, condensate return, etc. They are available through a vast range of sizes; in capacities from 2 or 3 gal./min. up to 100,000 gal./min.; and for discharge heads (pressures) from a few feet up to several thousand lb./sq. in. The size and type best suited to a particular application can be determined only by an engineering study of the problem.

The primary advantages of a centrifugal pump are simplicity, low first cost, uniform (non-pulsating) flow, small floor space, low maintenance expense, quiet operation, and adaptability to use with motor or turbine drive.

A centrifugal pump, in its simplest form, consists of an impeller rotating within a casing. The **impeller** consists of a number of blades, either open or shrouded, mounted on a shaft that projects outside the casing. Impellers may have their axis of rotation either horizontal or vertical, to suit the work to be done. Closed-type or shrouded impellers are generally most efficient. Open- or semiopen-type impellers are used for viscous liquids or liquids containing solid materials and on many small pumps for general service. Impellers may be of the single-suction type or double-suction type—single if the liquid enters from one side, double if it enters from both sides.

Casings are of three general types but in any case consist of a chamber in which the impeller rotates, provided with inlet and exit for the liquid being pumped. The simplest form of casing is the circular casing, consisting of an annular chamber around the impeller, no attempt being made to overcome the losses that will arise from eddies and shock when the liquid leaving the impeller at relatively high velocities enters this chamber. Such casings are seldom used.

Volute casings take the form of a volute, increasing in cross-sectional area as the outlet is approached. The volute converts the velocity energy imparted to the liquid by the impeller into pressure energy, with comparatively low losses.

A third type of casing is used in diffuser-type or turbine pumps. In this type, guide vanes or diffusers are interposed between the impeller and the casing chamber. Losses are kept to a minimum in a well-designed pump of this type. This construction is often used in multistage, high-head pumps.

Action of a Centrifugal Pump. Briefly the action of a centrifugal pump may be shown by Fig. 6-4. Power

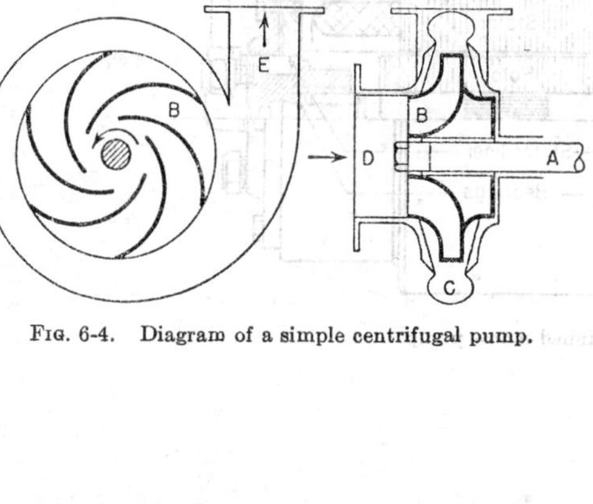

FIG. 6-4. Diagram of a simple centrifugal pump.

from an outside source is applied to shaft *A*, rotating the impeller *B* within the stationary casing *C*. The blades of the impeller in revolving produce a reduction in pressure at the entrance or eye of the impeller. This causes liquid to flow into the impeller from the suction pipe *D*. This liquid is forced outward along the impeller blades at an increasing velocity. The velocity head it has acquired when it leaves the blade tips is changed to pressure head as the liquid passes into the volute chamber and thence out the discharge *E*.

Centrifugal-pump Characteristics. Figure 6-5 shows a typical characteristic curve of a centrifugal pump.

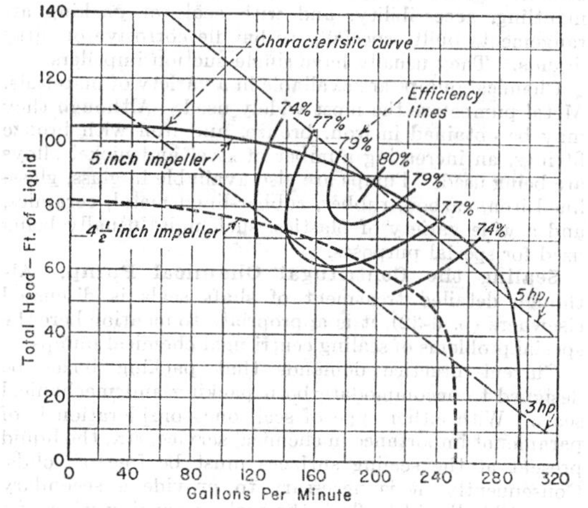

FIG 6-5. Characteristic curve of centrifugal pump of constant speed.

It is important to note that at any fixed speed the pump will operate along this curve and at no other points. For instance, on the curve shown at 200 gal./min., the pump will generate 87 ft. head. If the head is increased to 100 ft., 120 gal./min. will be delivered. It is not possible to reduce the capacity to 120 gal./min. at 87 ft. head, unless the discharge is throttled so that 100 ft. head is actually generated within the pump. On pumps with variable-speed drivers such as steam turbines, it is possible to change the characteristic curve, as shown by Fig. 6-6.

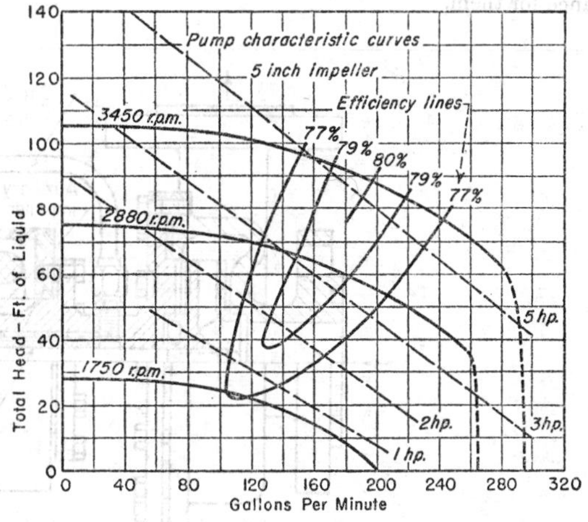

FIG. 6-6. Characteristic curve of centrifugal pump of various speeds.

It is important to remember that the head produced will be the same for any clean liquid of the same viscosity. The pressure rise, however, will vary in proportion to the specific gravity. Viscosities of less than 50 centipoises do not affect the head materially.

Single-stage centrifugal pumps are available in capacities up to and over 50,000 gal./min., for heads (pressures) up to 1600 ft. They are available in a variety of designs for particular services (see Fig. 6-3).

Process Pumps. This term is usually applied to single-stage pedestal-mounted units of simple design for capacities up to 1000 gal./min. and heads up to about 300 ft. These pumps are designed for ease in dismantling, accessibility, and with seals or packing arrangements built especially to handle corrosive or dirty liquids. They usually have single-suction impellers.

Chemical pumps are available in a variety of materials. Metal pumps are the most widely used. Although they may be obtained in iron, bronze, and iron with bronze fittings, an increasing number of steel and nickel alloys are being used. Pumps are also available in glass, glass-lined iron, carbon, rubber, rubber-lined metal, ceramics, and a wide variety of plastics, such units usually being used for special purposes.

Sealing the Centrifugal Chemical Pump. Although detailed treatment of shaft seals is discussed elsewhere (p. 6-32), it is appropriate to mention here the special problems of sealing centrifugal chemical pumps.

Current practice demands that packing boxes be designed to accommodate both packing and mechanical seals. With either type of seal, one consideration is of paramount importance in chemical service, *viz.*, the liquid present at the sealing surfaces must be free of solids. Consequently, it is necessary to provide a secondary compatible liquid to flush the seal or packing whenever the process liquid is not absolutely clean.

The use of **packing** necessarily results in the continuous escape of a small amount of liquid past the seal, as its operation depends upon the maintenance of wetted surfaces to minimize generation of heat. If the effluent is toxic or corrosive, quench glands or catch pans are usually employed. Mechanical seals observed to be leaking cannot be adjusted without shutting down the pump, whereas packing can be tightened while operating. On the other hand, mechanical seals pass only infinitesimal quantities of fluid, usually in the form of vapor. In general, the more effective performance of mechanical seals when properly applied is gaining increased acceptance for them.

Double-suction single-stage pumps are used for general water-supply and circulating service and for chemical service when handling liquids that are noncorrosive to iron or bronze. They are available for capacities from about 25 gal./min. up to as high as 50,000 gal./min. and heads up to 1600 ft. Such units are available in iron, bronze, and iron with bronze fittings. Other materials increase the cost; where they are required, a standard chemical pump is usually more economical.

Close-coupled Pumps (see Fig. 6-7). Pumps with built-in electric motor or sometimes steam-turbine-driven (*i.e.*, with pump impeller and driver on the same

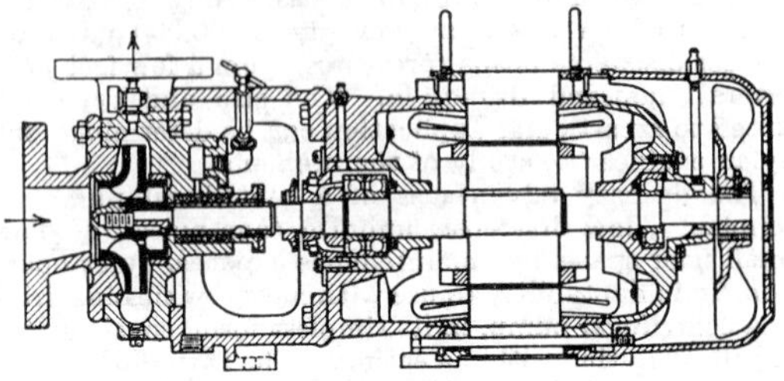

FIG. 6-7. A close-coupled pump.

shaft) are known as close-coupled pumps. Such units are extremely compact and are suitable for a variety of services where standard iron and bronze materials are satisfactory. They are available in capacities up to about 2000 gal./min. for heads up to about 240 ft. Two-stage units in the smaller sizes are available for heads to around 500 ft.

The **canned-motor pump** (Fig. 6-8) is commanding increasing attention in the chemical industry. These units are close-coupled designs in which the cavity housing the motor rotor and the pump casing are interconnected. As a result, the motor bearings run in the process liquid and all seals are eliminated. Because the process liquid is the bearing lubricant, abrasive solids cannot be tolerated. Standard single-stage canned-motor pumps are available for flows up to 700 gal./min. and heads up to 250 ft. Two-stage units are also available for heads up to 600 ft. Canned-motor pumps are being widely used for handling organic solvents, organic heat-transfer liquids, and light oils, as well as many clean toxic or hazardous liquids, or where leakage is an economic problem.

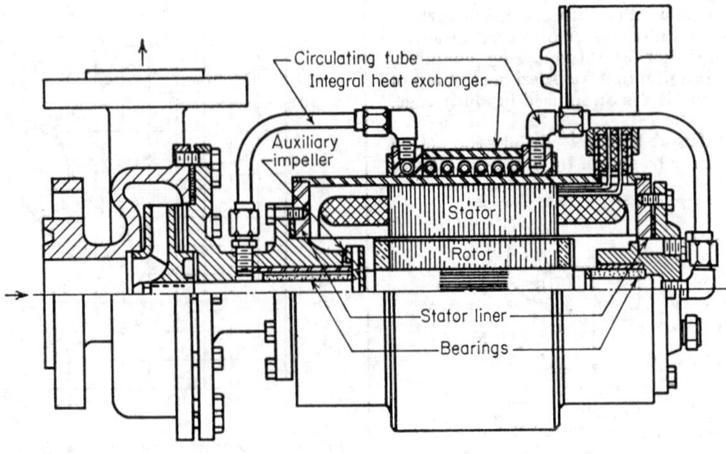

FIG. 6-8. Chempump canned-motor pump.

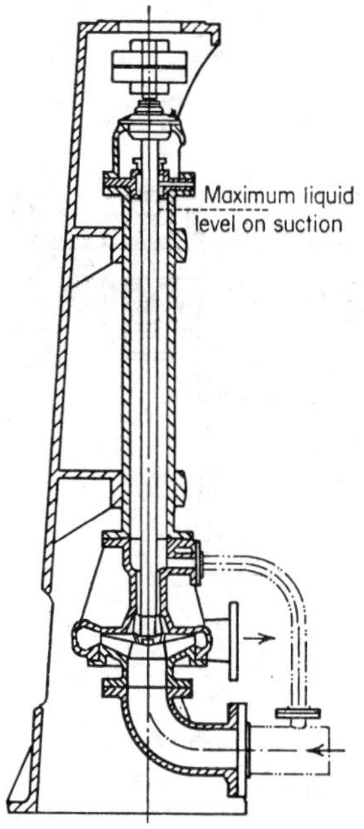

FIG. 6-9. Lawrence vertical process pump for dry-pit mounting.

Vertical Process Pumps. When taking suction from a tank containing corrosive, solids-bearing, or toxic liquid, it is often advisable to use a vertical pump with the packing box located above the highest liquid level. Figure 6-9 shows a **dry-pit mounting,** so called because the pump column and casing are not submerged in the tank. In a **wet-pit** installation, the pump drive is mounted on the tank cover, with the column and casing actually immersed.

These pumps have the advantage of (1) not having to seal against the liquid and (2) being self-draining when the tank is drained. When the variation of the tank liquid level is considerable, the shaft length required often demands intermediate and foot bearings. If gritty solids are present, these bearings can sometimes be avoided by using tapered shafts and double discharge volutes to balance the hydraulic radial thrust.

Sump pumps are small single-stage vertical pumps used to drain shallow pits or sumps. They have the same general construction as vertical process pumps but are not designed for severe operating conditions.

Multistage centrifugal pumps are in general used for services requiring higher heads (pressures) than can be generated by single-stage pumps. Such services include high-pressure water-supply pumps, fire pumps, boiler-feed pumps, and charge pumps for refinery processes. Such pumps are available for pressures as high as 3000 lb./sq. in. at capacities up to 3000 gal./min. and above.

Multistage pumps may be of the volute type or of the diffuser type. Volute-type pumps (see Fig. 6-10) usually have single-suction impellers arranged with half of the impeller inlets facing one direction and half in the opposite direction to balance thrust. Some two-, three-, and four-stage (see Fig. 6-11) units have double-suction impellers; but this construction, except for special-purpose units, makes the casings of impractical size for more stages.

Diffuser-type pumps (see Fig. 6-12) usually have single-suction impellers arranged with all impeller inlets facing in the same direction and impeller thrust neutralized by a differential-pressure device known as a balancing drum.

Pumps for very high pressures often have an inner volute-type casing or assembly of diffuser units placed within a forged-steel shell or barrel.

Axial-flow (propeller) pumps (Fig. 6-13) are essentially very high capacity, low head units. Normally they are designed for flows in excess of 2000 gal./min. against heads of 50 ft. or less. They are used to great

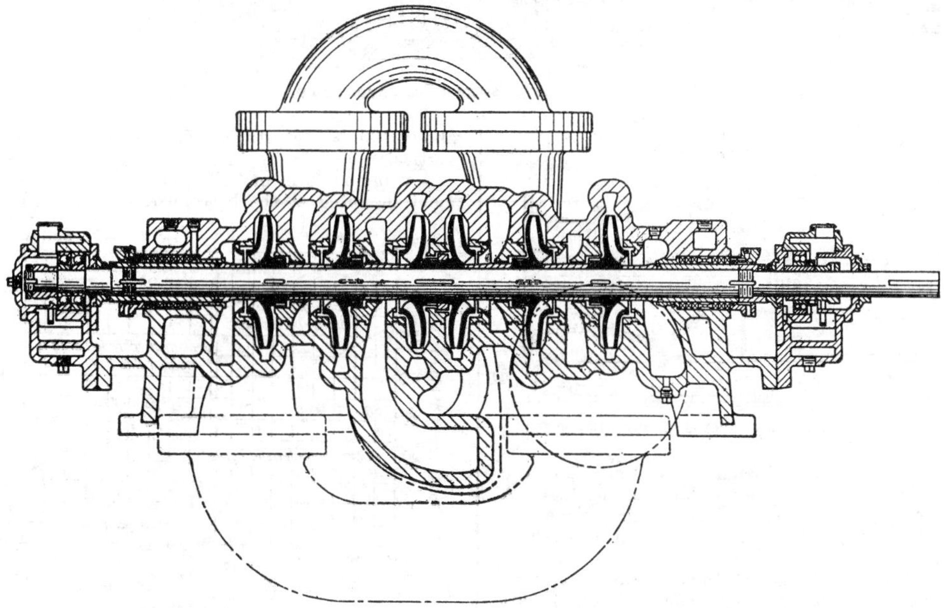

FIG. 6-10. A six-stage volute-type pump.

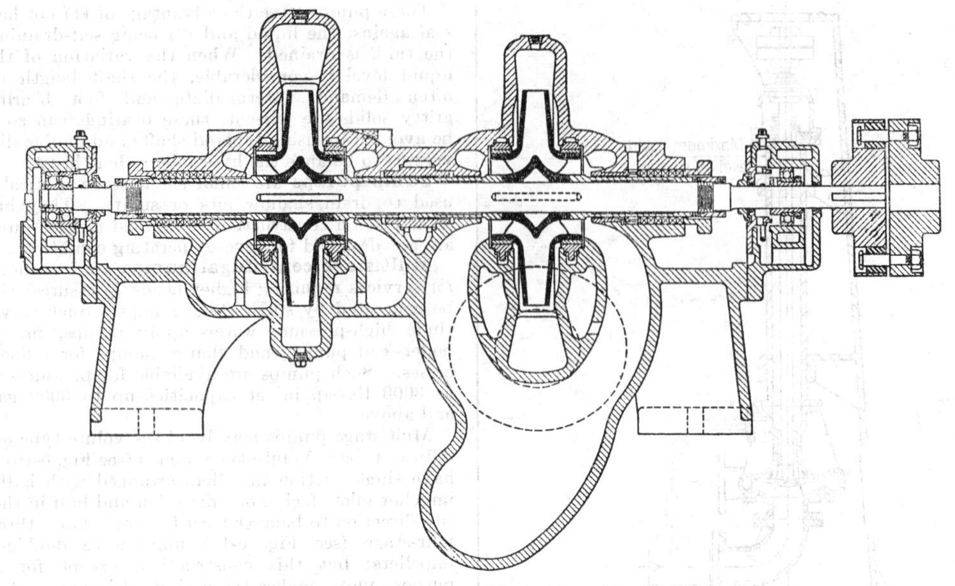

FIG. 6-11. Two-stage pump with double-suction impellers.

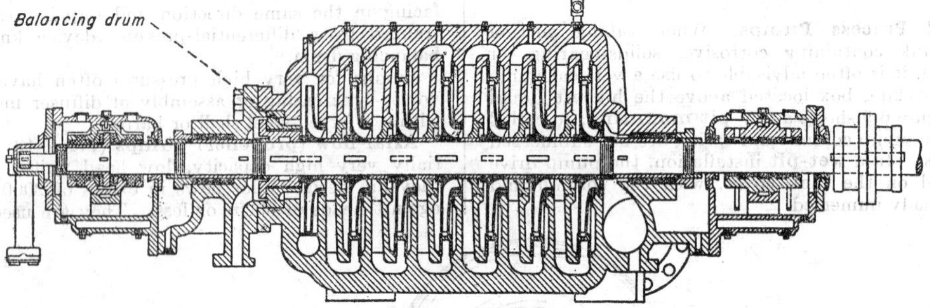

FIG. 6-12. A seven-stage diffuser-type pump.

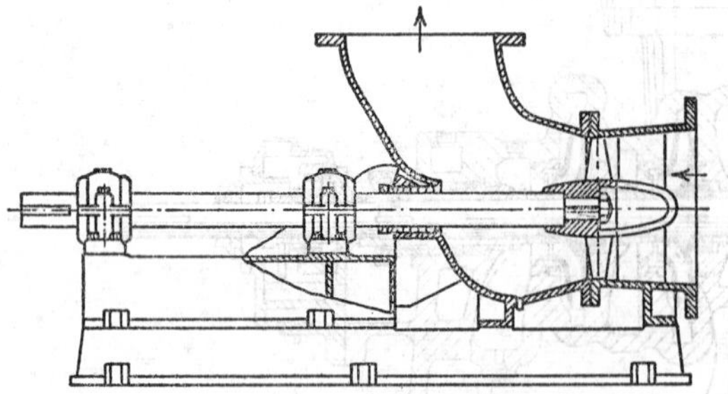

FIG. 6-13. Lawrence axial-flow elbow-type propeller pump.

advantage in closed-loop circulation systems where the pump casing merely becomes an elbow in the line. A common installation is for calandria circulation. A characteristic curve of an axial-flow pump is given in Fig. 6-14.

Turbine Pumps. The term turbine pump is applied to units with **mixed-flow** (*i.e.*, part axial and part centrifugal) impellers. Such units are available in capacities from 100 gal./min. upward for heads up to about 100 ft. per stage. Turbine pumps are usually vertical.

A common form of turbine pump has the pump element mounted at the bottom of a column that serves

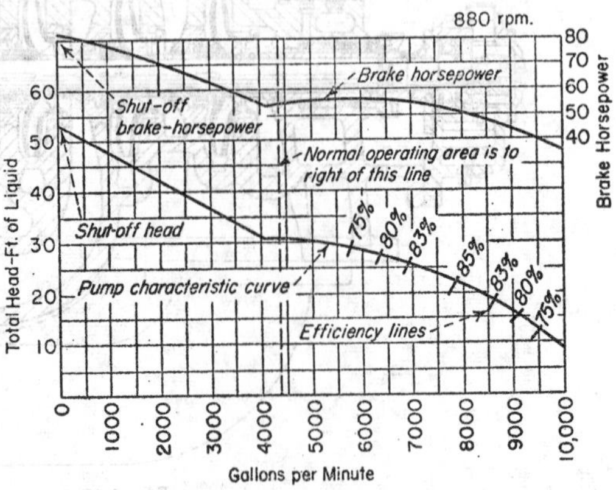

FIG. 6-14. Characteristic curve of axial-flow pump.

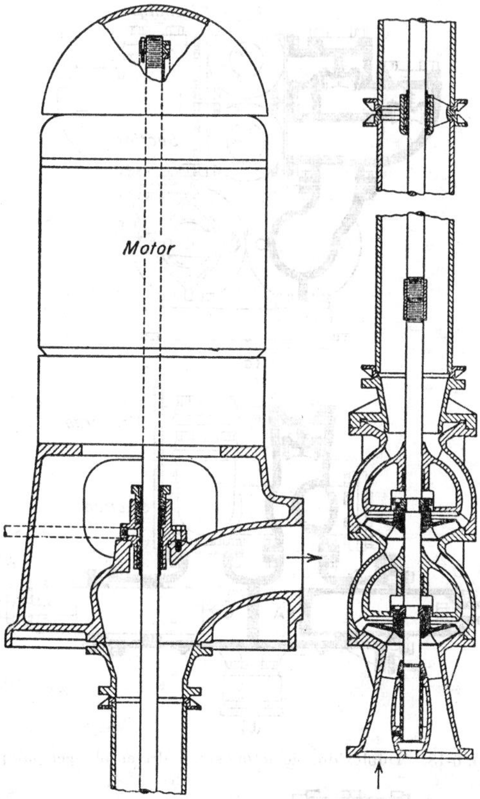

FIG. 6-15. A propeller, or mixed-flow, pump.

as the discharge pipe (see Fig. 6-15). Such units are immersed in the liquid to be pumped and are commonly used for wells, condenser circulating water, large volume drainage, etc. Another form of the pump has a shell surrounding the pumping element which is connected to the intake pipe. In this form the pump is used on condensate service in power plants and for process work in oil refineries and elsewhere.

Regenerative pumps, also sometimes referred to as **turbine** pumps because of the shape of the impeller, employ a combination of mechanical impulse and centrifugal force to produce heads of several hundred feet at low volumes (usually less than 100 gal./min.). The impeller, which rotates at high speed with small clearances, has many short radial passages milled on each side at the periphery. Similar channels are milled in the mating surfaces of the casing. Upon entering, the liquid is directed into the impeller passages and proceeds in a spiral pattern around the periphery, passing alternately from impeller to the casing, receiving successive impulses as it does so. Figure 6-16 illustrates a typical performance-characteristic curve.

These pumps are particularly useful where it is required to handle low volumes of low-viscosity liquids at higher pressures than are normally available with centrifugal pumps. Close clearances limit their use to clean liquids. For very high heads multiple-stage units are available.

Positive-displacement Pumps. Whereas the total dynamic head developed by a centrifugal, mixed-flow, or axial-flow pump is uniquely determined for any given flow by the speed at which it rotates, positive-displacement pumps and those which approach positive displacement will ideally produce whatever head is impressed upon them by the restrictions to flow on the discharge side. Actually, neglecting slippage, the maximum head obtainable is determined by the power available in the drive and the strength of the pump parts.

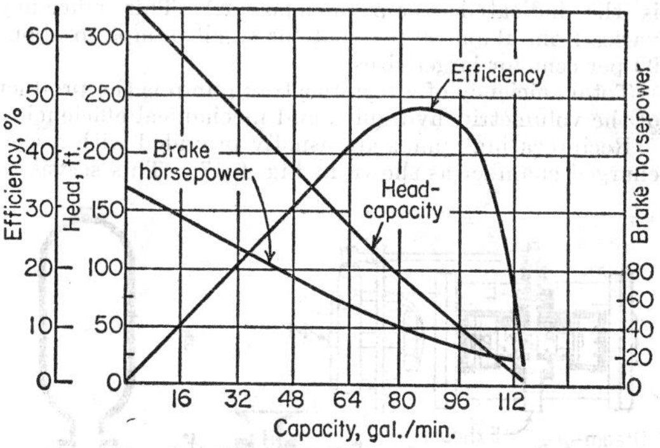

FIG. 6-16. Performance curves of regenerative pump.

In general, over-all efficiencies of positive-displacement pumps are higher than with centrifugal equipment because internal losses are minimized. On the other hand, the flexibility of each piece of equipment in handling a wide range of capacities is somewhat limited.

Reciprocating Pumps. There are three classes of reciprocating pumps, *viz.*, **piston pumps, plunger pumps,** and **diaphragm pumps.** In general the action of the liquid-transferring parts of these pumps is the same, a cylindrical piston, plunger, or bucket, or round diaphragm being caused to pass or flex back and forth in a chamber. The device is equipped with valves for inlet and discharge of the liquid being pumped, and the operation of these valves is related in a definite manner to the motions of the piston.

In considering the operation of a reciprocating pump, several efficiencies must be taken into account. These are volumetric efficiency, hydraulic efficiency, indicated efficiency, and mechanical efficiency.

Volumetric efficiency is the relation of the liquid actually pumped to that which theoretically should be moved on a basis of the piston displacement. It indicates the percentage loss and, when stated as 1 − volumetric efficiency, is called the slip. In good practice, slip should not be over 5 per cent. In new pumps, or those kept in good condition, it will be as low as 1 per cent.

Hydraulic efficiency is the ratio of the actual head pumped to the theoretical head and is expressed by the equation

$$\text{Efficiency}_{\text{hyd}} = \frac{H}{H + \text{hydraulic losses}} \tag{6-13}$$

The hydraulic losses are the losses in head in the suction and discharge lines. In the suction line, these consist of (1) velocity head, (2) entrance head, (3) friction in suction pipe, (4) losses in bends, and (5) losses in suction valves. The loss in the discharge line consists of (6) loss in discharge valves, (7) velocity head, and (8) friction in discharge pipe.

Indicated efficiency is the relation of the horsepower required to move the liquid actually pumped against the total head to the horsepower calculated from the indicator card of the liquid end.

Mechanical efficiency is the relation of the indicated liquid horsepower of the pump to the actual power input from the drive. (For steam-driven pumps the input is the indicated steam horsepower.) This efficiency varies from about 50 per cent for small pumps to about 90 per cent for larger sizes.

Total efficiency of a reciprocating pump is the product of the volumetric, hydraulic, and mechanical efficiencies.

Reciprocating pumps are usually provided with a gas-charged chamber as shown in Fig. 6-17. This serves to

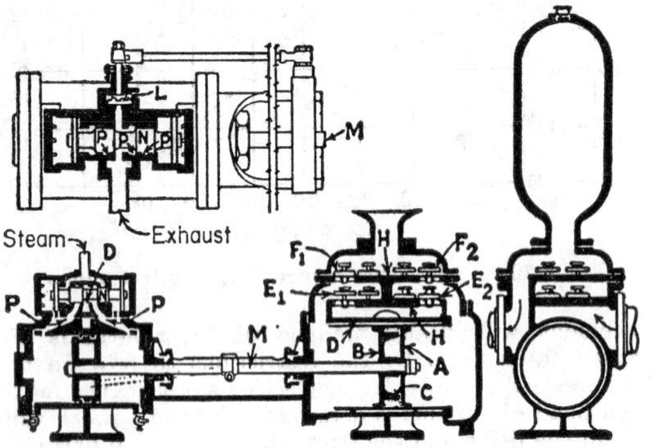

Fig. 6-17. Water end of a double-acting steam-driven reciprocating pump.

smooth out irregularities in the discharge of the pump and gives a uniform flow. In many installations surge chambers are required on the suction side. Piping layouts should be studied to determine the most effective size and location. The following list arranges reciprocating pumps in the order of their relative smoothness of flow: single single-acting, single double-acting, duplex single-acting, duplex double-acting, triplex single- and double-acting, and quintuplex single- and double-acting. Similarly for steam pumps the order is: single double-acting and duplex double-acting. Where surge chambers are used, provision should be made to keep the chamber charged with gas. A surge chamber filled with liquid is of no value. A water-level gage is desirable to permit a check on the amount of gas in the chamber.

Piston Pumps. There are two ordinary types of piston pumps:

Simplex Double-acting. These may be direct-acting (*i.e.*, direct-connected to a steam cylinder) or power-driven (through crank and flywheel from the cross-head of a steam engine). Figure 6-17 is a pump of this type, designed for use at heads up to 200 ft. In this figure, the piston consists of disks *A* and *B*, with packing rings *C* between. A bronze liner for the water cylinder is shown at *D*. Suction valves are E_1 and E_2. Discharge valves are F_1 and F_2. In the steam end, pilot valve *L* is operated by a rod, actuated by piston rod *M*. This pilot operates main valve *N* to cover or uncover steam ports *P*.

Duplex Double-acting. These pumps differ primarily from those of the simplex type in having two water cylinders whose operation is coordinated. These pumps may be direct-acting, steam-driven, or power-driven with crank and flywheel.

A duplex outside-end-packed plunger pump with pot valves, of the type used with hydraulic presses and for similar service, is shown in Fig. 6-18. In this drawing, plunger *A* is direct-connected to rod *B*, while plunger *C* is operated from the rod by means of yoke *D* and tie rods.

Plunger pumps differ from piston pumps in that they have one or more constant-diameter plungers reciprocating through packing glands displacing liquid from cylinders in which there is considerable radial clearance. They are always single-acting in the sense that only one end of the plunger is used in pumping the liquid.

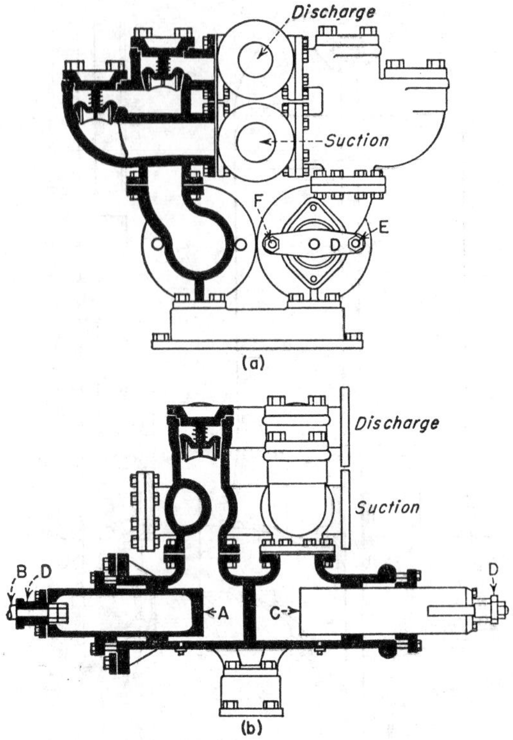

Fig. 6-18. Duplex double-acting steam-driven plunger pump.

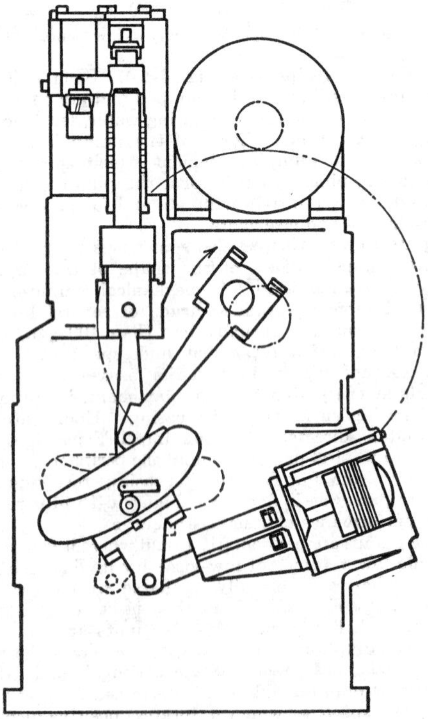

Fig. 6-19. Aldrich-Groff variable-stroke power pump

Plunger pumps are available with one, two, three, four, five, or even more cylinders. Simplex and duplex units are often built in a horizontal design. Those with three or more cylinders are usually of vertical design. The driver may be an electric motor, steam or gas engine, or steam turbine. This is the common type of **power pump.** An example, arranged for belt drive, is shown in Fig. 6-19, from which the action may be readily traced.

Occasionally plunger pumps are constructed with opposed cylinders and plungers connected by yokes and tie rods; this arrangement, in effect, constitutes a double-acting unit.

Simplex plunger pumps mounted singly or in gangs with a common drive are used quite commonly as **metering** or **proportioning pumps** (Fig. 6-20). Frequently

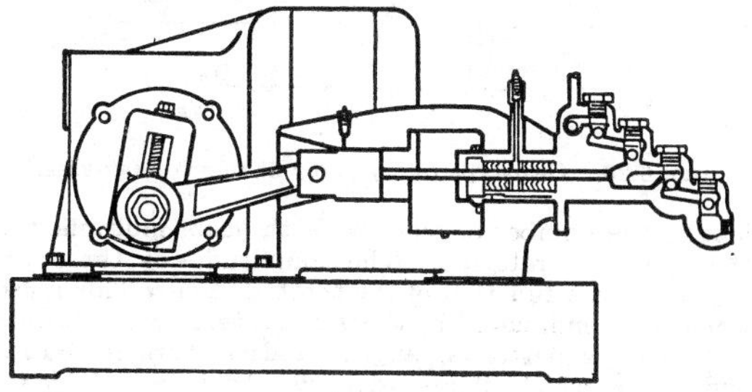

Fig. 6-20. Milton Roy plunger-type metering pump.

a variable-speed drive or stroke-adjusting mechanism is provided to vary the flow as desired. These pumps are designed to measure or control the flow of liquid within a deviation of plus or minus 2 per cent with capacities up to 50 gal./min. and pressures as high as several thousand lb./sq. in.

Diaphragm pumps perform similarly to piston and plunger pumps. Their construction differs in that the reciprocating driving member is a flexible diaphragm fabricated of metal, rubber, or plastic. Chief advantage of this arrangement is elimination of all packing and seals exposed to the liquid pumped. This, of course, is an important asset to equipment required to handle hazardous or toxic liquids.

A common type of low-capacity diaphragm pump designed for metering service employs a plunger working in oil to actuate a metallic or plastic diaphragm. Built for pressures in excess of 1000 lb./sq. in. with flow rates up to about 5 gal./min. per cylinder, such pumps possess all the characteristics of plunger-type metering pumps with the added advantage that it is possible to mount the pumping head in a remote, even submerged, location entirely separate from the drive.

Figure 6-21 shows a high-capacity (100 gal./min.) diaphragm pump with actuation provided by a mechanical linkage.

Pneumatically actuated diaphragm pumps (Fig. 6-22) require no power source other than plant compressed

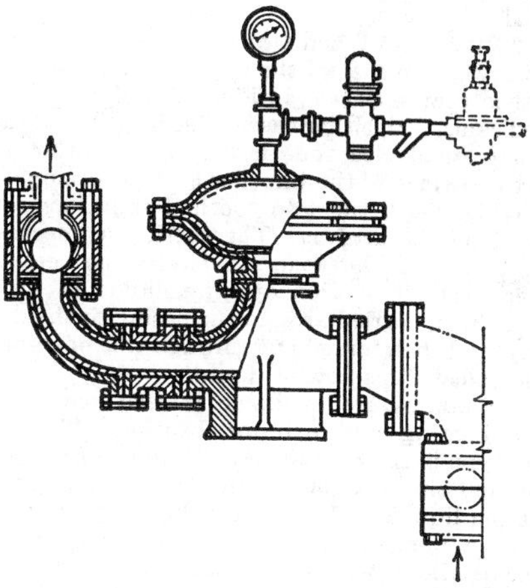

Fig. 6-22. Dorr-Oliver pneumatically actuated diaphragm pump for slurry service.

air. Such pumps must have a flooded suction and the pressure is, of course, limited to the available air pressure. Because of their slow speed and large valves, this type is well suited to the gentle handling of liquids where the degradation of suspended solids is undesirable.

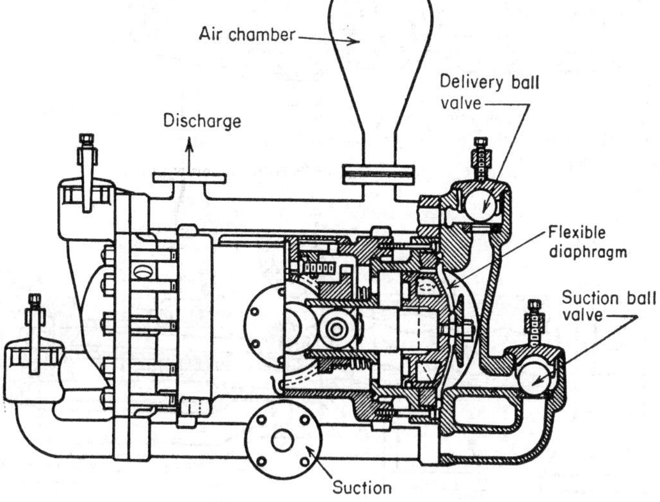

Fig. 6-21. Shriver mechanically actuated diaphragm pump.

A major consideration in the application of diaphragm pumps is the realization that diaphragm failure will probably occur eventually. The consequences of such failure should be realistically appraised before selection, and maintenance procedures should be established accordingly.

Rotary Pumps. In rotary pumps mechanical displacement of the liquid is produced by rotation of one or more members within a stationary housing. Because internal clearances, although small, are a necessity in all but a few special types, these pumps cannot truly be called positive-displacement pumps. However, in many respects, they can be considered as such.

When built of the proper materials, these pumps will handle any liquid that does not contain grit or abrasive material.

Gear Pumps. When two or more impellers are used in a rotary-pump casing, the impellers will take the form of toothed-gear wheels as in Fig. 6-23, of helical gears, or of lobed cams. In either case, these impellers rotate with extremely small clearance between each other and between the surface of the impeller and the casing. Referring to Fig. 6-23, the two toothed impellers rotate as indicated by the arrows. The suction connection is at the bottom. As the spaces between the teeth of the impeller pass the suction opening, liquid is impounded between them, carried around the casing to the discharge opening, and then forced out through this opening. The arrows indicate this flow of liquid.

Rotary pumps are available in two general classes, interior bearing and exterior bearing. The interior-bearing type is used for handling liquids of a lubricating nature, and the exterior-bearing type is used with non-lubricating liquids. The interior-bearing pump is lubricated by a part of the liquid being pumped, and the exterior-bearing type is oil-lubricated.

The use of straight teeth in gear pumps will produce pulsations in the discharge having a frequency equivalent to the number of teeth on both gears multiplied by the speed of rotation. The amplitude of these disturbances is a function of the tooth design. This pulsation can be eliminated by the use of rotors having **helical** teeth with a particular angle. This in turn introduces end thrust which, if excessive, can be balanced by the use of **double helical** or **herringbone** teeth.

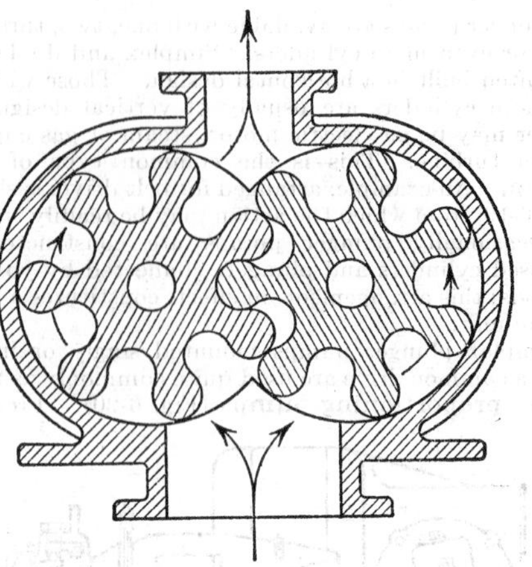

Fig. 6-23. Gear-type rotary pump having two impellers.

Screw Pumps. A modification of the helical gear pump is the screw pump. Figure 6-24 illustrates a two rotor version in which the liquid is fed to either the center or ends, depending upon the direction of rotation, and progresses axially in the cavities formed by the meshing threads or teeth. In three rotor versions, the center one is the driving member while the other two are driven. Figure 6-25 shows still another arrangement in which a

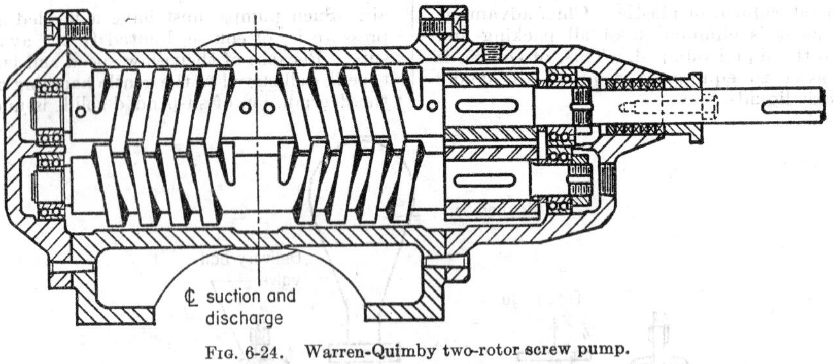

Fig. 6-24. Warren-Quimby two-rotor screw pump.

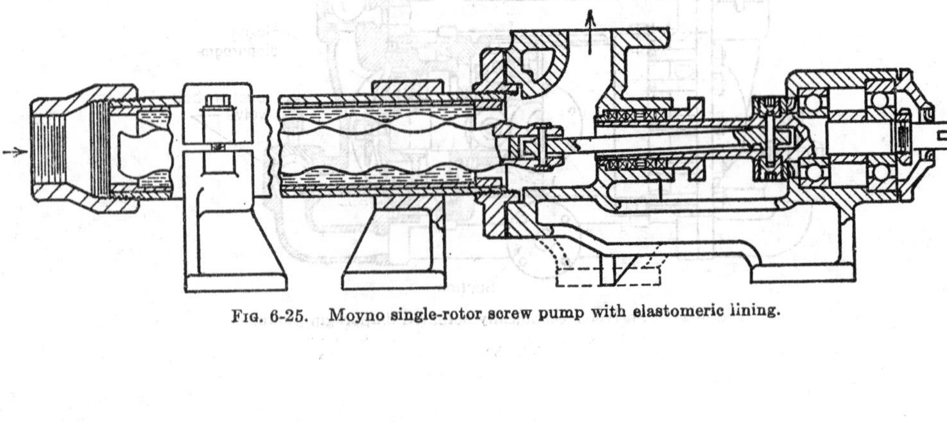

Fig. 6-25. Moyno single-rotor screw pump with elastomeric lining.

male metal rotor of unique design rotates without clearance in an elastomeric stationary female sleeve.

Screw pumps, because of multiple dams preventing slip, are well adapted for producing pressure rises of several hundred lb./sq. in. especially when handling viscous liquids such as heavy oils. The all-metal pumps are generally subject to the same limitations on handling abrasive solids as the conventional gear pumps. In addition, the wide bearing spans usually demand that the liquid have considerable lubricity to prevent metal-to-metal contact.

Among the liquids handled by rotary pumps are mineral oils, vegetable oils, animal oils, greases, glucose, viscose, molasses, paints, varnish, shellac, lacquers, alcohols, catsup, brine, mayonnaise, sizing, soap, tanning liquors, vinegar, and ink. Some screw-type units are specially designed for the gentle handling of large solids suspended in the liquid.

Handling Liquids by Fluid Displacement. In addition to liquid pumps that depend on the mechanical action of pistons, plungers, or impellers to move the material, other devices for this purpose employ displacement by a secondary fluid. This group includes air lifts and acid eggs.

The **air lift** is a device for raising liquid by means of compressed air. In the past it was widely used for pumping wells, but it has been less widely used since the development of efficient centrifugal pumps. It operates by introducing compressed air into the liquid near the bottom of the well. The air and liquid mixture, being lighter than liquid alone, rises in the well casing. The advantages of this system of pumping lie in the fact that there are no moving parts in the well. The pumping equipment is an air compressor, which can be located on the surface.

A simplified sketch of an air lift is shown in Fig. 6-26. Referring to this sketch, the running submergence H_s is

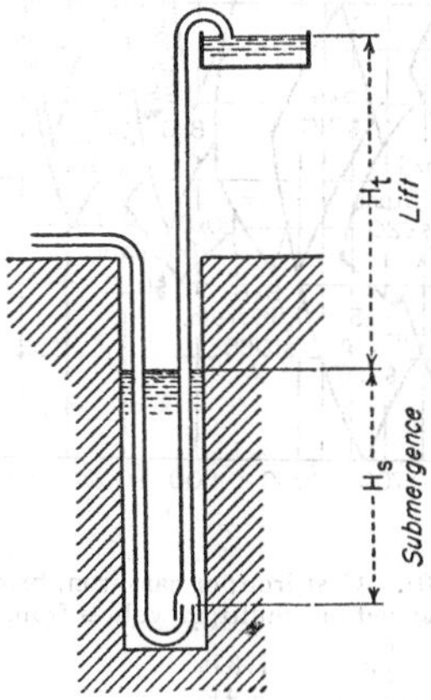

FIG. 6-26. Simplified sketch of an air lift, showing submergence and total head.

the distance from the water level to the point of an air inlet, and the total head H_t is the distance from the working surface of the water to the point of discharge. An empirical formula to express the volume of free air required to lift 1 gal. water has been developed by the Ingersoll-Rand Co. from practice. According to this formula,

$$V_a = 0.8 \frac{H_t}{C \log_{10}[(H_s + 34)/34]} \tag{6-14}$$

where V_a is the volume of free air, cu. ft., and C is a constant, values for which, varying with the total head, are

H_t, Ft.	C
10- 60	245
61-200	233
201-500	216
501-650	185
651-750	156

In the design of an air lift, the submergence as expressed by the ratio $H_s/(H_t + H_s)$ should vary from 0.66 for a head of 20 ft. to 0.41 for a head of 500 ft. The results given by this formula approximate those found in practice, but variations occur caused by the design of the foot pieces. The air pressure required to operate an air lift is given by

$$p = B + 0.434s \tag{6-15}$$

where p is in lb./sq. in. abs., B is the barometric pressure, lb./sq. in., and s is the submergence, ft.

The efficiency of an air lift, *i.e.*, the ratio of the water horsepower to the indicated air horsepower of the compressor, is about 70 per cent, except at starting, when it is considerably lower. Higher air pressure is also required for starting, when the pressure must be equivalent to the height of the water level, at rest, above the end of the air pipe.

An **acid egg** or **blowcase** consists of an egg-shaped container which can be filled with a charge of liquid that is to be pumped. This container is fitted with an inlet pipe for the charge, an outlet pipe for the discharge, and a pipe for the admission of compressed air or gas, as illustrated in Fig. 6-27. Pressure of air or gas on the

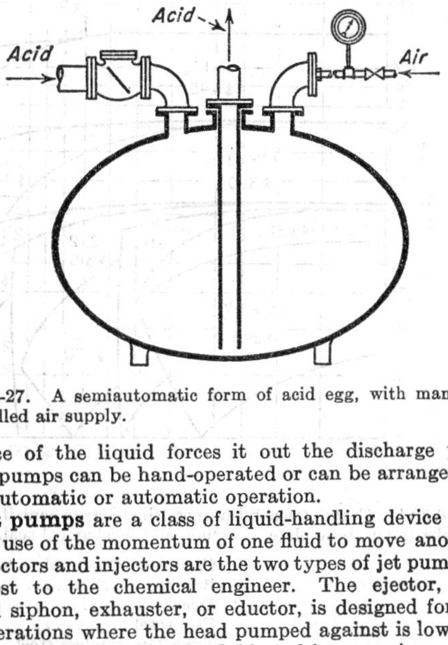

FIG. 6-27. A semiautomatic form of acid egg, with manually controlled air supply.

surface of the liquid forces it out the discharge pipe. Such pumps can be hand-operated or can be arranged for semiautomatic or automatic operation.

Jet pumps are a class of liquid-handling device that make use of the momentum of one fluid to move another.

Ejectors and injectors are the two types of jet pumps of interest to the chemical engineer. The **ejector**, also called siphon, exhauster, or eductor, is designed for use in operations where the head pumped against is low and is less than the head of the fluid used for pumping. The injector is a special type of jet pump, operated by steam and used for boiler feed and similar services, in which the fluid being pumped is discharged into a space under the same pressure as that of the steam that is used to operate the injector.

Figure 6-28 shows a simple design of jet pump of the ejector type. The pumping fluid enters through the nozzle at the left and passes through the venturi nozzle at the center and out the discharge opening at the right. As it passes into the venturi nozzle, it develops a suction that causes some of the fluid in the suction chamber to be taken into the venturi nozzle and, entraining with the stream passing through the discharge, be delivered through this discharge.

The efficiency of an ejector or jet pump is low, being only a few per cent. The head developed by the ejector is also low, except in special types. The device has the disadvantage of diluting the fluid pumped by mixing it

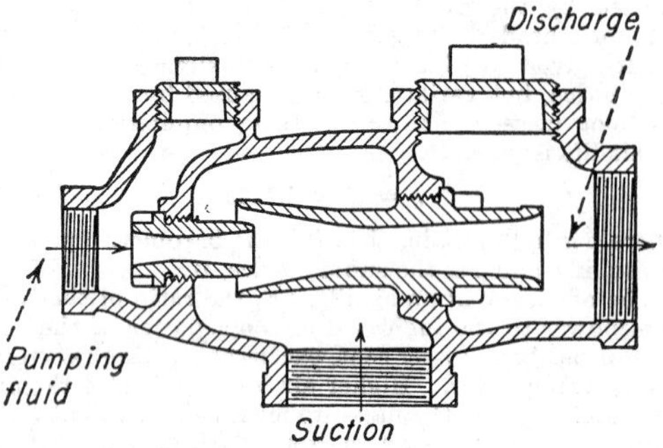

Fig. 6-28. Simple type of ejector for water service.

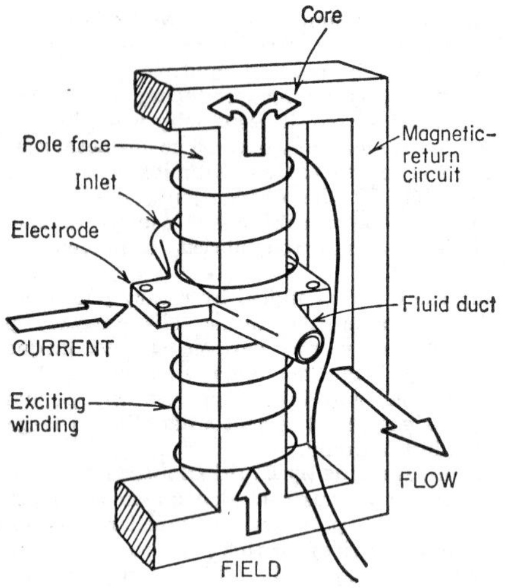

Fig. 6-29. Schematic diagram of d.c. electromagnetic pump.

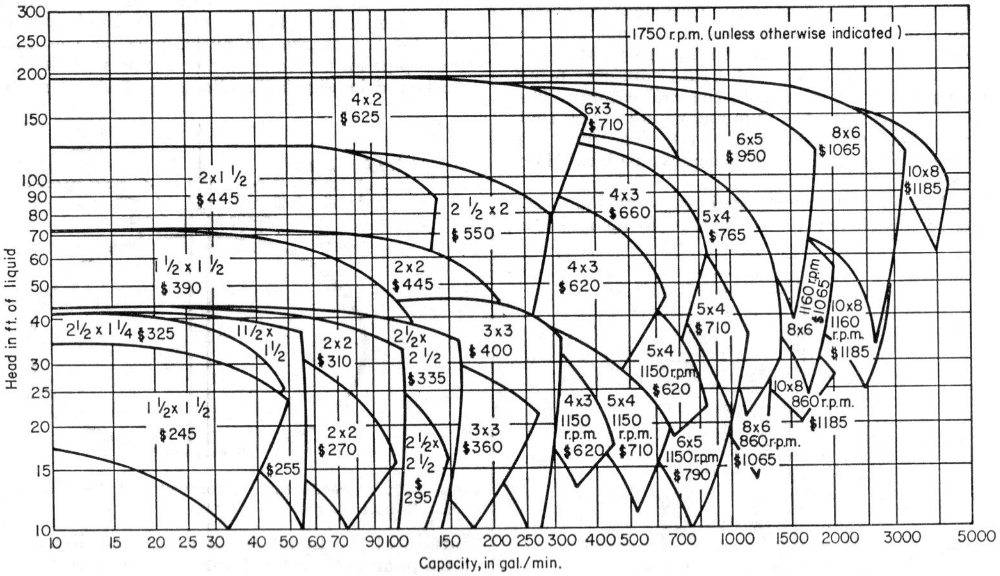

Fig. 6-29A. Costs of general-purpose single-stage centrifugal pumps (first quarter 1960). Cast iron; or cast iron, bronze-fitted. Cost includes pump, base plate, coupling, and mechanical seal. For other materials of construction, multiply values from the chart by:

Cast iron, 316 stainless-fitted	1.34
Bronze	1.44
Ductile iron	1.44
Cast steel	1.72
Type 316 stainless steel	1.85
Carpenter 20	1.93
Worthite	2.00
Elcomet K	2.00
R-55	3.00

Adjust above costs for the following:

Type 316 stainless shaft	Add $ 50–$100
Trap and separator (for self-priming pumps)	Add $300–$500
Stainless drip pan	Add $ 80–$150
Ferroxyl test	Add $ 60–$100
Halide test	Add $ 40–$ 50

(*Courtesy of E. I. du Pont de Nemours & Co.*)

with the pumping fluid. In steam injectors for boiler feed and similar services, where the heat of the steam is recovered, the efficiency is close to 100 per cent.

The simple ejector or siphon is widely used, in spite of its low efficiency, for transferring liquids from one tank to another, for lifting acids, alkalies, or solid-containing liquids of an abrasive nature, and for emptying sumps.

Electromagnetic Pumps. The necessity of circulating liquid-metal heat-transfer media in nuclear-reactor systems has led to development of electromagnetic pumps. All electromagnetic pumps utilize the motor principle—that a conductor in a magnetic field, carrying a current which flows at right angles to the direction of the field, has a force exerted on it, the force being mutually perpendicular to both the field and the current. In all electromagnetic pumps, the fluid is the conductor. This force, suitably directed in the fluid, manifests itself as a pressure if the fluid is suitably contained. The field and current can be produced in a number of different ways and the force utilized variously.

Both a.c. and d.c. units are available. D.c. pumps (Fig. 6-29) are simpler but the high current requirement is a definite limitation. A.c. pumps can readily obtain high currents by making use of transformers. Multipole induction a.c. pumps have been built in **helical** and **linear** configurations. Helical units are effective for relatively high heads and low flows, while linear induction pumps are best suited for large flows at moderate heads. Electromagnetic pumps are available for flow rates up to 10,000 gal./min., and pressures up to 300 lb./sq. in. are practical. Performance characteristics resemble those of centrifugal pumps.

Pump Costs. Space does not permit presentation of adequate cost data on the many types of pumps discussed

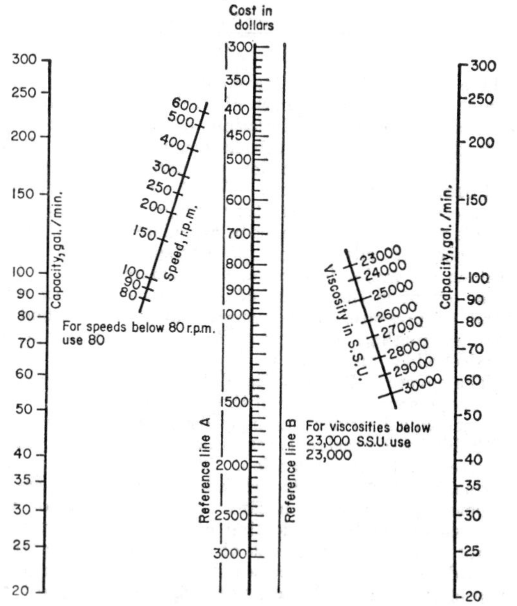

FIG. 6-29*B*. Costs of positive-displacement gear pumps (third quarter 1958). Cast iron or steel. Cost includes pump, base plate, and coupling. For bronze, multiply values from chart by 1.40; for type 316 stainless steel, multiply by 1.50. Directions: Pass a line through capacity scale at left and speed scale and mark intersection on reference line *A*. Pass a line through capacity scale at right and viscosity scale and mark intersection on reference line *B*. Connect points on reference lines *A* and *B* and read cost on center scale. (*Courtesy of E. I. du Pont de Nemours & Co.*)

in this section. For two of the most common varieties, however, it is possible to give representative values. Figure 6-29*A* is a plot of costs for single-stage, pedestal-mounted, **centrifugal pumps,** with a tabulation of factors to be applied when there is a departure from standard materials. Figure 6-29*B* may be used to approximate costs for **gear pumps** of conventional design.

Theory of Compression. In any continuous compression process the relation of absolute pressure p to volume V is expressed by the formula

$$pV^n = K \tag{6-16}$$

The plot of pressure vs. volume for each value of exponent n is known as a **polytropic** curve. Since the work W performed in proceeding from p_1 to p_2 along any polytropic curve (Fig. 6-30) is

$$W = \int_1^2 p\,dV \tag{6-17}$$

it follows that the amount of work required is dependent upon the polytropic curve involved and increases with increasing values of n. The path requiring the least

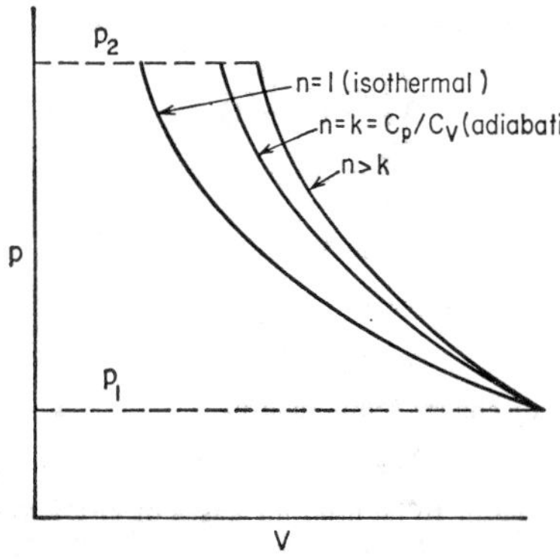

FIG. 6-30. Polytropic compression curves.

amount of input work is $n = 1$, which is equivalent to **isothermal** compression. For **adiabatic** compression, *i.e.*, no heat added or taken away during the process, $n = k$ = ratio of specific heat at constant pressure to that at constant volume.

As it is usually impractical to build sufficient heat-transfer equipment into the design of most compressors to carry away the bulk of the heat of compression, most machines tend to operate along a polytropic path which approaches the adiabatic. Most compressor calculations are therefore based on the adiabatic curve.

Some formulas based upon the adiabatic equation and useful in compressor work are as follows:

Pressure, volume, and **temperature** relations for perfect gases:

$$\frac{p_2}{p_1} = \left(\frac{V_1}{V_2}\right)^k \tag{6-18}$$

$$\frac{T_2}{T_1} = \left(\frac{V_1}{V_2}\right)^{k-1} \tag{6-19}$$

$$\frac{p_2}{p_1} = \left(\frac{T_2}{T_1}\right)^{k/(k-1)} \tag{6-20}$$

Adiabatic head:

$$H_{ad} = \frac{k}{k-1} RT_1 \left[\left(\frac{p_2}{p_1}\right)^{(k-1)/k} - 1\right] \tag{6-21}$$

where R = gas constant and T = absolute temperature, °R.

Since the work performed on the gas is equal to the product of the head and the weight of gas handled, the **adiabatic horsepower** is

$$\text{hp.} = \frac{wH_{ad}}{550} = \frac{k}{k-1}\,\frac{wRT_1}{550}\left[\left(\frac{p_2}{p_1}\right)^{(k-1)/k} - 1\right] \quad (6\text{-}22)$$

$$\text{or hp.} = 0.00436\,Q_1p_1\left(\frac{k}{k-1}\right)\left[\left(\frac{p_2}{p_1}\right)^{(k-1)/k} - 1\right] \quad (6\text{-}23)$$

where w = weight of gas, lb./sec.; H_{ad} = adiabatic head, ft.; Q = flow rate, cu. ft./min.

Adiabatic discharge temperature is

$$T_2 = T_1\left(\frac{p_2}{p_1}\right)^{(k-1)/k} \quad (6\text{-}24)$$

Air and a number of other gases have a value of k = 1.39 to 1.41. To simplify calculations for these gases, tables have been made of the bracketed expression in the above equations for a value of k = 1.395. These are known as X factors, and they are given in Table 6-1. Using X factors, the adiabatic formulas for k = 1.395 read as follows:

Adiabatic temperature, pressure, and volume relations:

$$\frac{V_1}{V_2} = \frac{p_2}{(X+1)p_1} \quad (6\text{-}25)$$

$$\frac{T_2}{T_1} = X + 1 \quad (6\text{-}26)$$

$$T_2 - T_1 = T_1X = T_2\frac{X}{X+1} \quad (6\text{-}27)$$

Adiabatic horsepower:

$$\text{hp.} = 0.0154Q_1p_1X \quad (6\text{-}28)$$

Adiabatic discharge temperature:

$$T_2 = T_1(X+1) \quad (6\text{-}29)$$

For the X factor to be used for gases of any k value, the curve in Fig. 6-31 has been developed. Values of X_G/X may be found from this curve. Values of X_G are therefore obtained by multiplying X_G/X from the curve by values of X found in Table 6-1.

Adiabatic horsepower for gases other than air:

$$\text{hp.} = \frac{0.01Q_1p_1X}{d} \quad (6\text{-}30)$$

where $d = 2.292\,(k-1)/k$.

If the compression cycle approaches the isothermal condition pV = const., as is the case when several stages with intercoolers are used, a simple approximation of the horsepower is obtained from the formula

$$\text{hp.} = 0.0044p_1Q_1 \ln\frac{p_2}{p_1} \quad (6\text{-}31)$$

For **multistage compressors** of N_S number of stages with adiabatic compression in each stage, equal division of work between the stages and intercooling back to the intake temperature, the following formulas are helpful:

$$\text{hp.}_{ad} = \frac{0.01N_SQ_1p_1}{d}\left[\left(\sqrt[N_S]{X_G+1}\right) - 1\right] \quad (6\text{-}32)$$

$$T_2 = T_1\sqrt[N_S]{X_G+1} \quad (6\text{-}33)$$

Piston displacement of reciprocating compressors with single-acting cylinders:

$$\text{P.D.} = \frac{ASN(\text{r.p.m.})}{1728} \quad (6\text{-}34)$$

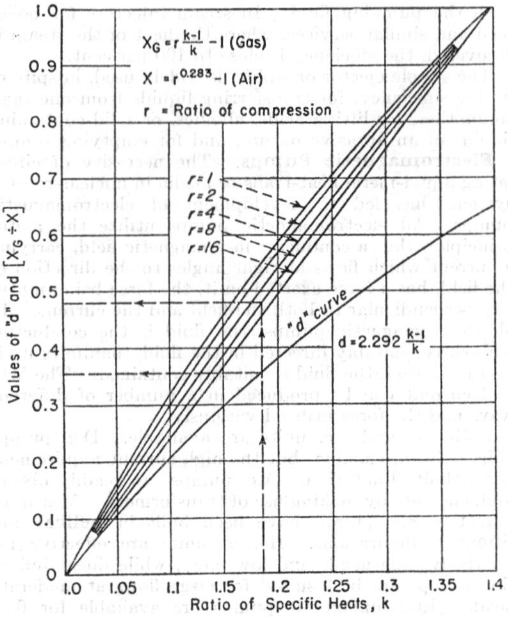

FIG. 6-31. Factors for use in adiabatic formula. Values of X to be used in finding X_G may be obtained from Table 6-1. (*By permission of Compressed Air Data.*)

For double-acting cylinders:

$$\text{P.D.} = \frac{ASN(\text{r.p.m.})}{874} \quad (6\text{-}35)$$

where P.D. = piston displacement, cu. ft./min.; A = piston area, sq. in.; S = length of stroke, in.; N = number of first-stage pistons. Equation (6-35) makes a reasonable deduction for the volume occupied by the piston rod. Without this deduction, the divisor would be 864.

Compressor Selection. For the chemical engineer to select the most satisfactory compression equipment, a wide variety of types must be considered, each of which has peculiar advantages for particular applications. Among the major factors to be considered, arranged to some extent in their order of importance, are flow rate, head or pressure, temperature limitations, method of sealing, method of lubrication, power consumption, serviceability, and cost.

The coverage chart in Fig. 6-32 will assist in defining the range of performance of the common types.

In chemical service, the plant designer must often cope with highly corrosive gases which may in turn carry erosive solids in suspension. Temperatures of gases, normally quite acceptable when handling air, may create a potential explosion hazard. Contamination of the process stream by lubricating oil, water, etc., even in minute quantities, may not be permissible. The trend toward continuous processes does not allow frequent inspection or maintenance, necessitating the utmost reliability in all mechanical equipment.

Fans are used for low pressures, in general, for pressure heads of less than 0.5 lb./sq. in. They are usually classified as of the centrifugal type or the axial-flow type. Both types are used for ventilating work, supplying draft to boilers and furnaces, moving large volumes of air or gas through ducts, supplying air for drying, conveying material suspended in the gas stream, removing fumes, etc.

Table 6-1. Values of X for Normal Air and Perfect Diatomic Gases*

$$X = r^{0.283} - 1$$

r	0	1	2	3	4	5	6	7	8	9	r	0	1	2	3	4	5	6	7	8	9
1.00	0.00 000	028	057	085	113	141	169	198	226	254	1.75	0.17 160	179	198	217	236	255	274	292	311	330
1.01	.00 282	310	338	366	394	422	450	478	506	534	1.76	.17 349	368	387	406	425	443	462	481	500	519
1.02	.00 562	590	618	646	673	701	729	757	785	812	1.77	.17 538	556	575	594	613	631	650	669	688	706
1.03	.00 840	868	895	923	951	978	006	034	061	089	1.78	.17 725	744	762	781	800	818	837	856	874	893
1.04	.01 116	144	171	199	226	253	281	308	336	363	1.79	.17 912	930	949	968	986	005	023	042	061	079
1.05	.01 390	418	445	472	500	527	554	581	608	636	1.80	.18 098	116	135	153	172	191	209	228	246	265
1.06	.01 663	690	717	744	771	798	825	852	879	906	1.81	.18 283	302	320	339	357	376	394	412	431	449
1.07	.01 933	960	987	014	041	068	095	122	148	175	1.82	.18 468	486	505	523	541	560	578	596	615	633
1.08	.02 202	229	255	282	309	336	362	389	416	442	1.83	.18 652	670	688	707	725	743	762	780	798	816
1.09	.02 469	495	522	549	575	602	628	655	681	708	1.84	.18 835	853	871	890	908	926	944	962	981	999
1.10	.02 734	760	787	813	840	866	892	919	945	971	1.85	.19 017	035	054	072	090	108	126	144	163	181
1.11	.02 997	024	050	076	102	129	155	181	207	233	1.86	.19 199	217	235	253	271	289	308	326	344	362
1.12	.03 259	285	311	337	363	389	415	441	467	493	1.87	.19 380	398	416	434	452	470	488	506	524	542
1.13	.03 519	545	571	597	623	649	675	700	726	752	1.88	.19 560	578	596	614	632	650	668	686	704	722
1.14	.03 778	804	829	855	881	906	932	958	983	009	1.89	.19 740	758	776	794	811	829	847	865	883	901
1.15	.04 035	060	086	111	137	162	188	213	239	264	1.90	.19 919	937	954	972	990	008	026	044	061	079
1.16	.04 290	315	341	366	391	417	442	467	493	518	1.91	.20 097	115	133	150	168	186	204	221	239	257
1.17	.04 543	569	594	619	644	670	695	720	745	770	1.92	.20 275	292	310	328	345	363	381	399	416	434
1.18	.04 796	821	846	871	896	921	946	971	996	021	1.93	.20 452	469	487	504	522	540	557	575	593	610
1.19	.05 046	071	096	121	146	171	196	221	245	270	1.94	.20 628	645	663	681	698	716	733	751	768	786
1.20	.05 295	320	345	370	394	419	444	469	493	518	1.95	.20 804	821	839	856	874	891	909	926	944	961
1.21	.05 543	567	592	617	641	666	691	715	740	764	1.96	.20 979	996	013	031	048	066	083	101	118	135
1.22	.05 789	813	838	862	887	911	936	960	985	009	1.97	.21 153	170	188	205	222	240	257	275	292	309
1.23	.06 034	058	082	107	131	155	180	204	228	253	1.98	.21 327	344	361	379	396	413	431	448	465	482
1.24	.06 277	301	325	350	374	398	422	446	470	495	1.99	.21 500	517	534	552	569	586	603	620	638	655
1.25	.06 519	543	567	591	615	639	663	687	711	735	2.00	.21 672	689	707	724	741	758	775	792	810	827
1.26	.06 759	783	807	831	855	879	903	927	951	974	2.01	.21 844	861	878	895	913	930	947	964	981	998
1.27	.06 998	022	046	070	094	117	141	165	189	212	2.02	.22 015	032	049	066	084	101	118	135	152	169
1.28	.07 236	260	283	307	331	354	378	402	425	449	2.03	.22 186	203	220	237	254	271	288	305	322	339
1.29	.07 472	496	520	543	567	590	614	637	661	684	2.04	.22 356	373	390	407	424	441	458	474	491	508
1.30	.07 708	731	754	778	801	825	848	871	895	918	2.05	.22 525	542	559	576	593	610	627	644	660	677
1.31	.07 941	965	988	011	035	058	081	104	128	151	2.06	.22 694	711	728	745	762	778	795	812	829	846
1.32	.08 174	197	220	243	267	290	313	336	359	382	2.07	.22 863	879	896	913	930	946	963	980	997	013
1.33	.08 405	428	451	474	497	520	543	566	589	612	2.08	.23 030	047	064	080	097	114	130	147	164	181
1.34	.08 635	658	681	704	727	750	773	795	818	841	2.09	.23 197	214	231	247	264	281	297	314	331	347
1.35	.08 864	887	910	932	955	978	001	023	046	069	2.10	.23 364	380	397	414	430	447	463	480	497	513
1.36	.09 092	114	137	160	182	205	228	250	273	295	2.11	.23 530	546	563	579	596	613	629	646	662	679
1.37	.09 318	341	363	386	408	431	453	476	498	521	2.12	.23 695	712	728	745	761	778	794	811	827	844
1.38	.09 543	566	588	611	633	655	678	700	723	745	2.13	.23 860	877	893	909	926	942	959	975	992	008
1.39	.09 767	790	812	834	857	879	901	923	946	968	2.14	.24 024	041	057	074	090	106	123	139	155	172
1.40	.09 990	012	035	057	079	101	123	145	168	190	2.15	.24 188	204	221	237	253	270	286	302	319	335
1.41	.10 212	234	256	278	300	322	344	366	389	411	2.16	.24 351	368	384	400	416	433	449	465	481	498
1.42	.10 433	455	477	499	521	542	564	586	608	630	2.17	.24 514	530	546	563	579	595	611	627	644	660
1.43	.10 652	674	696	718	740	761	783	805	827	849	2.18	.24 676	692	708	724	741	757	773	789	805	821
1.44	.10 871	892	914	936	958	979	001	023	045	066	2.19	.24 838	854	870	886	902	918	934	950	966	983
1.45	.11 088	110	131	153	175	196	218	239	261	283	2.20	.24 999	015	031	047	063	079	095	111	127	143
1.46	.11 304	326	347	369	390	412	433	455	476	498	2.21	.25 159	175	191	207	223	239	255	271	287	303
1.47	.11 520	541	562	584	605	627	648	669	691	712	2.22	.25 319	335	351	367	383	399	415	431	447	463
1.48	.11 734	755	776	798	819	840	862	883	904	925	2.23	.25 479	495	511	526	542	558	574	590	606	622
1.49	.11 947	968	989	010	032	053	074	095	116	138	2.24	.25 638	654	669	685	701	717	733	749	765	780
1.50	.12 159	180	201	222	243	264	286	307	328	349	2.25	.25 796	812	828	844	859	875	891	907	923	938
1.51	.12 370	391	412	433	454	475	496	517	538	559	2.26	.25 954	970	986	001	017	033	049	064	080	096
1.52	.12 580	601	622	643	664	685	706	726	747	768	2.27	.26 112	127	143	159	175	190	206	222	237	253
1.53	.12 789	810	831	852	872	893	914	935	956	977	2.28	.26 269	284	300	316	331	347	363	378	394	409
1.54	.12 997	018	039	060	080	101	122	142	163	184	2.29	.26 425	441	456	472	488	503	519	534	550	566
1.55	.13 205	225	246	266	287	308	328	349	370	390	2.30	.26 581	597	612	628	643	659	675	690	706	721
1.56	.13 411	431	452	472	493	513	534	554	575	595	2.31	.26 737	752	768	783	799	814	830	845	861	876
1.57	.13 616	636	657	677	698	718	739	759	780	800	2.32	.26 892	907	923	938	954	969	984	000	015	031
1.58	.13 820	841	861	881	902	922	942	963	983	003	2.33	.27 046	062	077	092	108	123	139	154	169	185
1.59	.14 024	044	064	085	105	125	145	165	186	206	2.34	.27 200	216	231	246	262	277	292	308	323	338
1.60	.14 226	246	267	287	307	327	347	367	387	408	2.35	.27 354	369	384	400	415	430	446	461	476	492
1.61	.14 428	448	468	488	508	528	548	568	588	608	2.36	.27 507	522	538	553	568	583	599	614	629	644
1.62	.14 628	648	668	688	708	728	748	768	788	808	2.37	.27 660	675	690	705	721	736	751	766	781	797
1.63	.14 828	848	868	888	908	928	948	968	988	007	2.38	.27 812	827	842	857	873	888	903	918	933	948
1.64	.15 027	047	067	087	107	126	146	166	186	206	2.39	.27 964	979	994	009	024	039	054	070	085	100
1.65	.15 225	245	265	284	304	324	344	363	383	403	2.40	.28 115	130	145	160	175	190	205	220	236	251
1.66	.15 423	442	462	481	501	521	540	560	580	599	2.41	.28 266	281	296	311	326	341	356	371	386	401
1.67	.15 619	638	658	678	697	717	736	756	775	795	2.42	.28 416	431	446	461	476	491	506	521	536	551
1.68	.15 814	834	853	873	892	912	931	951	970	990	2.43	.28 566	581	596	611	626	641	656	671	686	701
1.69	.16 009	028	048	067	087	106	125	145	164	184	2.44	.28 716	730	745	760	775	790	805	820	835	850
1.70	.16 203	222	242	261	280	299	319	338	357	377	2.45	.28 865	879	894	909	924	939	954	969	984	998
1.71	.16 396	415	434	454	473	492	511	531	550	569	2.46	.29 013	028	043	058	073	087	102	117	132	147
1.72	.16 588	607	626	646	665	684	703	722	741	760	2.47	.29 162	176	191	206	221	235	250	265	280	295
1.73	.16 780	799	818	837	856	875	894	913	932	951	2.48	.29 309	324	339	353	368	383	398	412	427	442
1.74	.16 970	989	008	027	046	065	084	103	122	141	2.49	.29 457	471	486	501	515	530	545	559	574	589

* Printed by permission of Compressed Air Data.

Table 6-1. Values of *X* for Normal Air and Perfect Diatomic Gases*—(*Continued*)

r	0	1	2	3	4	5	6	7	8	9	r	0	1	2	3	4	5	6	7	8	9
2.50	0.29 604	618	633	647	662	677	691	706	721	735	2.75	0.33 147	161	174	188	202	215	229	243	256	270
2.51	.29 750	765	779	794	808	823	838	852	867	881	2.76	.33 284	297	311	325	338	352	366	379	393	407
2.52	.29 896	911	925	940	954	969	984	998	013	027	2.77	.33 420	434	448	461	475	488	502	516	529	543
2.53	.30 042	056	071	085	100	114	129	144	158	173	2.78	.33 556	570	584	597	611	624	638	651	665	679
2.54	.30 187	202	216	231	245	260	274	289	303	318	2.79	.33 692	706	719	733	746	760	773	787	801	814
2.55	.30 332	346	361	375	390	404	419	433	448	462	2.80	.33 828	841	855	868	882	895	909	922	936	949
2.56	.30 476	491	505	520	534	548	563	577	592	606	2.81	.33 963	976	990	003	017	030	044	057	070	084
2.57	.30 620	635	649	663	678	692	707	721	735	750	2.82	.34 097	111	124	138	151	165	178	191	205	218
2.58	.30 764	778	793	807	821	836	850	864	879	893	2.83	.34 232	245	259	272	285	299	312	326	339	352
2.59	.30 907	921	936	950	964	979	993	007	021	036	2.84	.34 366	379	393	406	419	433	446	459	473	486
2.60	.31 050	064	079	093	107	121	136	150	164	178	2.85	.34 500	513	526	540	553	566	580	593	606	620
2.61	.31 193	207	221	235	249	264	278	292	306	320	2.86	.34 633	646	660	673	686	700	713	726	739	753
2.62	.31 335	349	363	377	391	405	420	434	448	462	2.87	.34 766	779	793	806	819	832	846	859	872	886
2.63	.31 476	490	505	519	533	547	561	575	589	603	2.88	.34 899	912	925	939	952	965	978	991	005	018
2.64	.31 618	632	646	660	674	688	702	716	730	744	2.89	.35 031	044	058	071	084	097	110	124	137	150
2.65	.31 759	773	787	801	815	829	843	857	871	885	2.90	.35 163	176	190	203	216	229	242	255	269	282
2.66	.31 899	913	927	941	955	969	983	997	011	025	2.91	.35 295	308	321	334	347	361	374	387	400	413
2.67	.32 039	053	067	081	095	109	123	137	151	165	2.92	.35 426	439	452	466	479	492	505	518	531	544
2.68	.32 179	193	207	221	235	249	262	276	290	304	2.93	.35 557	570	584	597	610	623	636	649	662	675
2.69	.32 318	332	346	360	374	388	402	416	429	443	2.94	.35 688	701	714	727	740	753	767	780	793	806
2.70	.32 457	471	485	499	513	527	540	554	568	582	2.95	.35 819	832	845	858	871	884	897	910	923	936
2.71	.32 596	610	624	637	651	665	679	693	707	720	2.96	.35 949	962	975	988	001	014	027	040	053	066
2.72	.32 734	748	762	776	789	803	817	831	845	858	2.97	.36 079	092	105	118	131	144	157	169	182	195
2.73	.32 872	886	900	913	927	941	955	968	982	996	2.98	.36 208	221	234	247	260	273	286	299	312	324
2.74	.33 010	023	037	051	065	078	092	106	119	133	2.99	.36 337	350	363	376	389	402	415	428	440	453

r	0	1	2	3	4	5	6	7	8	9
3.0	0.3647	0.3659	0.3672	0.3685	0.3698	0.3711	0.3723	0.3736	0.3749	0.3761
3.1	.3774	.3786	.3799	.3811	.3824	.3836	.3849	.3861	.3874	.3886
3.2	.3898	.3911	.3923	.3935	.3947	.3959	.3971	.3984	.3996	.4008
3.3	.4020	.4032	.4044	.4056	.4068	.4080	.4091	.4103	.4115	.4127
3.4	.4139	.4150	.4162	.4174	.4186	.4197	.4209	.4220	.4232	.4244
3.5	.4255	.4267	.4278	.4290	.4301	.4313	.4324	.4335	.4347	.4358
3.6	.4369	.4380	.4392	.4403	.4414	.4425	.4437	.4448	.4459	.4470
3.7	.4481	.4492	.4503	.4514	.4525	.4536	.4547	.4558	.4569	.4580
3.8	.4591	.4602	.4612	.4623	.4634	.4645	.4656	.4666	.4677	.4688
3.9	.4698	.4709	.4720	.4730	.4741	.4752	.4762	.4773	.4783	.4794
4.0	.4804	.4815	.4825	.4835	.4846	.4856	.4867	.4877	.4887	.4898
4.1	.4908	.4918	.4928	.4939	.4949	.4959	.4970	.4980	.4990	.5000
4.2	.5010	.5020	.5030	.5040	.5050	.5060	.5070	.5080	.5090	.5100
4.3	.5110	.5120	.5130	.5140	.5150	.5160	.5170	.5179	.5189	.5199
4.4	.5209	.5219	.5228	.5238	.5248	.5258	.5267	.5277	.5287	.5296
4.5	.5306	.5316	.5325	.5335	.5344	.5354	.5363	.5373	.5382	.5392
4.6	.5401	.5411	.5420	.5430	.5439	.5449	.5458	.5467	.5477	.5486
4.7	.5495	.5505	.5514	.5523	.5533	.5542	.5551	.5560	.5570	.5579
4.8	.5588	.5597	.5606	.5616	.5625	.5634	.5643	.5652	.5661	.5670
4.9	.5679	.5688	.5697	.5706	.5715	.5724	.5733	.5742	.5751	.5760
5.0	.5769	.5778	.5787	.5796	.5805	.5814	.5822	.5831	.5840	.5849
5.1	.5858	.5867	.5875	.5884	.5893	.5902	.5910	.5919	.5928	.5936
5.2	.5945	.5954	.5962	.5971	.5980	.5988	.5997	.6006	.6014	.6023
5.3	.6031	.6040	.6048	.6057	.6065	.6074	.6082	.6091	.6099	.6108
5.4	.6116	.6125	.6133	.6142	.6150	.6159	.6167	.6175	.6184	.6192
5.5	.6200	.6209	.6217	.6225	.6234	.6242	.6250	.6258	.6267	.6275
5.6	.6283	.6291	.6300	.6308	.6316	.6324	.6332	.6340	.6349	.6357
5.7	.6365	.6373	.6381	.6389	.6397	.6405	.6413	.6421	.6430	.6438
5.8	.6446	.6454	.6462	.6470	.6478	.6486	.6494	.6502	.6509	.6517
5.9	.6525	.6533	.6541	.6549	.6557	.6565	.6573	.6581	.6588	.6596
6.0	.6604	.6612	.6620	.6628	.6635	.6643	.6651	.6659	.6666	.6674
6.1	.6682	.6690	.6697	.6705	.6713	.6721	.6729	.6736	.6744	.6752
6.2	.6759	.6767	.6774	.6782	.6789	.6797	.6805	.6812	.6820	.6827
6.3	.6835	.6843	.6850	.6858	.6865	.6873	.6880	.6888	.6895	.6903
6.4	.6910	.6918	.6925	.6933	.6940	.6948	.6955	.6963	.6970	.6978
6.5	.6985	.6992	.7000	.7007	.7014	.7021	.7028	.7036	.7043	.7050
6.6	.7058	.7065	.7073	.7080	.7087	.7095	.7102	.7110	.7117	.7124
6.7	.7131	.7138	.7145	.7153	.7160	.7167	.7174	.7181	.7189	.7196
6.8	.7203	.7210	.7217	.7224	.7232	.7239	.7246	.7253	.7260	.7267
6.9	.7274	.7281	.7288	.7295	.7302	.7309	.7316	.7323	.7330	.7338
7.0	.7345	.7352	.7359	.7366	.7373	.7380	.7386	.7393	.7400	.7407
7.1	.7414	.7421	.7428	.7435	.7442	.7449	.7456	.7463	.7470	.7477
7.2	.7483	.7490	.7497	.7504	.7511	.7518	.7524	.7531	.7538	.7545
7.3	.7552	.7559	.7565	.7572	.7579	.7586	.7592	.7599	.7606	.7613
7.4	.7620	.7626	.7633	.7640	.7646	.7653	.7660	.7666	.7673	.7680
7.5	.7687	.7693	.7700	.7706	.7713	.7720	.7726	.7733	.7740	.7746
7.6	.7753	.7760	.7766	.7773	.7779	.7786	.7792	.7799	.7806	.7812
7.7	.7819	.7825	.7832	.7838	.7845	.7851	.7858	.7864	.7871	.7877
7.8	.7884	.7890	.7897	.7903	.7910	.7916	.7923	.7929	.7936	.7942
7.9	.7949	.7955	.7961	.7968	.7974	.7981	.7987	.7993	.8000	.8006

* Printed by permission of Compressed Air Data.

Table 6-1. Values of X for Normal Air and Perfect Diatomic Gases*—(*Concluded*)

r	0	1	2	3	4	5	6	7	8	9
8.0	0.8013	0.8019	0.8025	0.8032	0.8038	0.8044	0.8051	0.8057	0.8063	0.8070
8.1	.8076	.8082	.8089	.8095	.8101	.8108	.8114	.8120	.8126	.8133
8.2	.8139	.8145	.8151	.8158	.8164	.8170	.8176	.8183	.8189	.8195
8.3	.8201	.8207	.8214	.8220	.8226	.8232	.8238	.8245	.8251	.8257
8.4	.8263	.8269	.8275	.8281	.8288	.8294	.8300	.8306	.8312	.8318
8.5	.8324	.8330	.8336	.8343	.8349	.8355	.8361	.8367	.8373	.8379
8.6	.8385	.8391	.8397	.8403	.8409	.8415	.8421	.8427	.8433	.8439
8.7	.8445	.8451	.8457	.8463	.8469	.8475	.8481	.8487	.8493	.8499
8.8	.8505	.8511	.8517	.8523	.8529	.8535	.8541	.8547	.8552	.8558
8.9	.8564	.8570	.8576	.8582	.8588	.8594	.8600	.8605	.8611	.8617
9.0	.8623	.8629	.8635	.8641	.8646	.8652	.8658	.8664	.8670	.8676
9.1	.8681	.8687	.8693	.8699	.8705	.8710	.8716	.8722	.8728	.8734
9.2	.8739	.8745	.8751	.8757	.8762	.8768	.8774	.8779	.8785	.8791
9.3	.8797	.8802	.8808	.8814	.8819	.8825	.8831	.8837	.8842	.8848
9.4	.8854	.8859	.8865	.8871	.8876	.8882	.8888	.8893	.8899	.8905
9.5	.8910	.8916	.8921	.8927	.8933	.8938	.8944	.8949	.8955	.8961
9.6	.8966	.8972	.8977	.8983	.8989	.8994	.9000	.9005	.9011	.9016
9.7	.9022	.9028	.9033	.9039	.9044	.9050	.9055	.9061	.9066	.9072
9.8	.9077	.9083	.9088	.9094	.9099	.9105	.9110	.9116	.9121	.9127
9.9	.9132	.9138	.9143	.9149	.9154	.9159	.9165	.9170	.9176	.9181
10.0	.9187	.9192	.9198	.9203	.9208	.9214	.9219	.9225	.9230	.9235
10.1	.9241	.9246	.9252	.9257	.9262	.9268	.9273	.9278	.9284	.9289
10.2	.9295	.9300	.9305	.9311	.9316	.9321	.9327	.9332	.9337	.9343
10.3	.9348	.9353	.9358	.9364	.9369	.9374	.9380	.9385	.9390	.9396
10.4	.9401	.9406	.9411	.9417	.9422	.9427	.9432	.9438	.9443	.9448
10.5	.9453	.9459	.9464	.9469	.9474	.9480	.9485	.9490	.9495	.9500
10.6	.9506	.9511	.9516	.9521	.9526	.9532	.9537	.9542	.9547	.9552
10.7	.9558	.9563	.9568	.9573	.9578	.9583	.9589	.9594	.9599	.9604
10.8	.9609	.9614	.9619	.9625	.9630	.9635	.9640	.9645	.9650	.9655
10.9	.9660	.9665	.9671	.9676	.9681	.9686	.9691	.9696	.9701	.9706
11.0	.9711	.9716	.9721	.9726	.9732	.9737	.9742	.9747	.9752	.9757
11.1	.9762	.9767	.9772	.9777	.9782	.9787	.9792	.9797	.9802	.9807
11.2	.9812	.9817	.9822	.9827	.9832	.9837	.9842	.9847	.9852	.9857
11.3	.9862	.9867	.9872	.9877	.9882	.9887	.9892	.9897	.9902	.9907
11.4	.9912	.9916	.9921	.9926	.9931	.9936	.9941	.9946	.9951	.9956
11.5	.9961	.9966	.9971	.9975	.9980	.9985	.9990	.9995	1.0000	1.0005
11.6	1.0010	1.0015	1.0019	1.0024	1.0029	1.0034	1.0039	1.0044	1.0049	1.0054
11.7	1.0058	1.0063	1.0068	1.0073	1.0078	1.0083	1.0087	1.0092	1.0097	1.0102
11.8	1.0107	1.0112	1.0116	1.0121	1.0126	1.0131	1.0136	1.0140	1.0145	1.0150
11.9	1.0155	1.0160	1.0164	1.0169	1.0174	1.0179	1.0184	1.0188	1.0193	1.0198
12.0	1.0203	1.0207	1.0212	1.0217	1.0222	1.0226	1.0231	1.0236	1.0241	1.0245

* Printed by permission of Compressed Air Data.

NOTE: Taken from Moss and Smith, Engineering Computations for Air and Gases, *Trans. Am. Soc. Mech. Engrs.*, vol. 52, 1930, paper APM-52-8. For nozzles $r = p_1/p_2$. For compressors and exhausters $r = p_2/p_1$.

r	x	r	x	r	x	r	x	r	x	r	x	r	x	r	x	r	x
12.5	1.0428	15.0	1.1520	17.5	1.2479	20.0	1.3345	22.5	1.4136	25.0	1.4867	27.5	1.5546	30.0	1.6183	32.5	1.6783
13.0	1.0666	15.5	1.1720	18.0	1.2659	20.5	1.3509	23.0	1.4287	25.5	1.5006	28.0	1.5678	30.5	1.6306	33.0	1.6899
13.5	1.0887	16.0	1.1916	18.5	1.2835	21.0	1.3669	23.5	1.4435	26.0	1.5144	28.5	1.5794	31.0	1.6434	33.5	1.7014
14.0	1.1103	16.5	1.2108	19.0	1.3008	21.5	1.3828	24.0	1.4581	26.5	1.5280	29.0	1.5933	31.5	1.6547	34.0	1.7127
14.5	1.1314	17.0	1.2295	19.5	1.3189	22.0	1.3983	24.5	1.4725	27.0	1.5414	29.5	1.6059	32.0	1.6666	34.5	1.7240

Values of X from 12.5 to 34.5 calculated by Ingersoll-Rand Co.

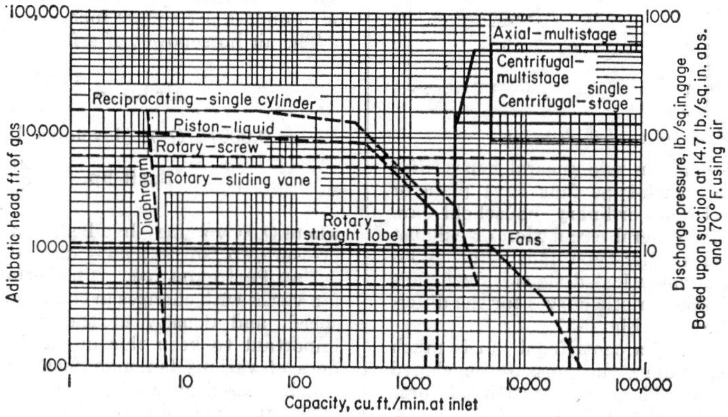

FIG. 6-32. Compressor coverage chart based on normal range of operation of the commercially available types shown. Solid lines—use left ordinate, head. Broken lines—use right ordinate, pressure.

Centrifugal Fans. These are made in three general types, the *straight-blade*, or *steel-plate, fan*, the *forward-curved-blade fan*, and the *backward-curved-blade fan*.

Straight-blade fans (Fig. 6-33) have rotors of comparatively large diameter with a few (5 to 12) radial

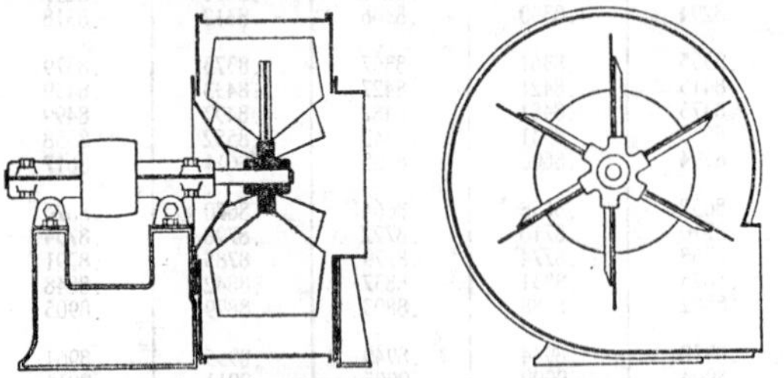

FIG. 6-33. Straight-blade, or steel-plate, fan.

blades resembling paddle wheels. These operate at comparatively low speed. They are often used in exhaust work, particularly where wastes are carried in the air stream.

Forward-curved-blade fans (Fig. 6-34) are usually of the multiblade (20 to 64) "Sirocco" type. The rotors

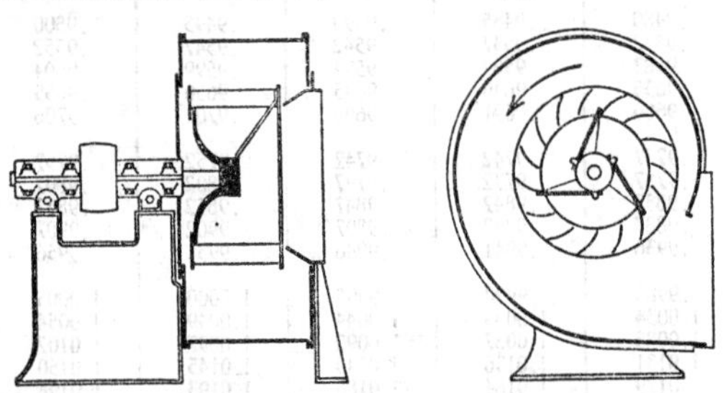

FIG. 6-34. Forward-curved-blade, or "Sirocco"-type, fan.

are of smaller diameter, and they operate at higher speeds than straight-blade units.

Backward-curved-blade fans (Fig. 6-35) are of the multiblade (10 to 50) type. Such fans have a wide range of usefulness.

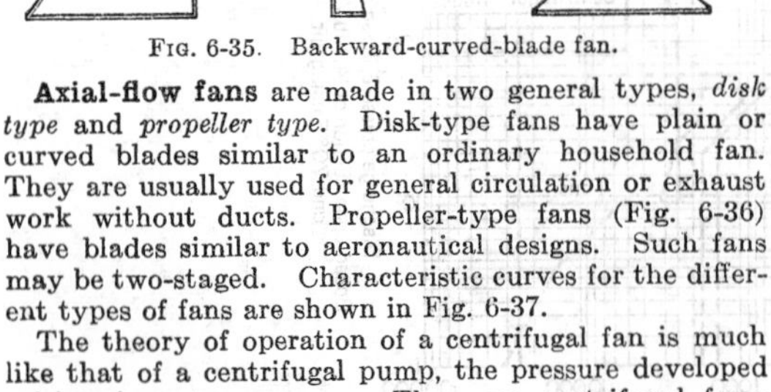

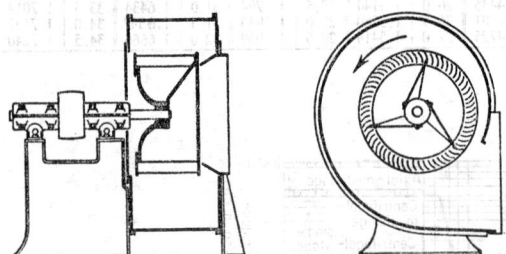

FIG. 6-35. Backward-curved-blade fan.

Axial-flow fans are made in two general types, *disk type* and *propeller type.* Disk-type fans have plain or curved blades similar to an ordinary household fan. They are usually used for general circulation or exhaust work without ducts. Propeller-type fans (Fig. 6-36) have blades similar to aeronautical designs. Such fans may be two-staged. Characteristic curves for the different types of fans are shown in Fig. 6-37.

The theory of operation of a centrifugal fan is much like that of a centrifugal pump, the pressure developed arising from two sources. These are centrifugal force due to the rotation of an enclosed volume of air or gas, and velocity imparted to the air or gas by the blades and partly converted to pressure by the volute or scroll-shaped fan casing.

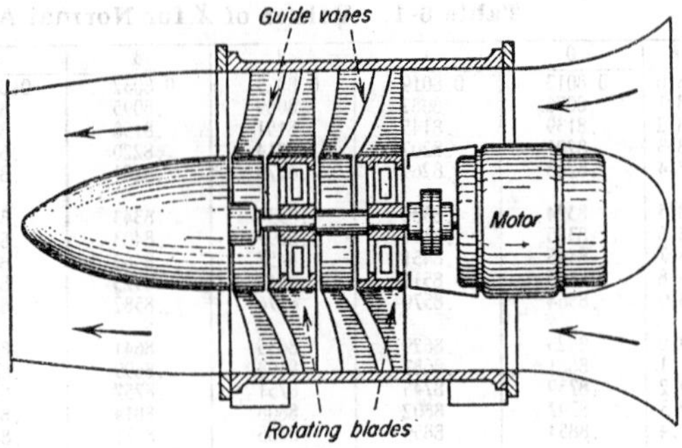

FIG. 6-36. A two-stage axial-flow fan.

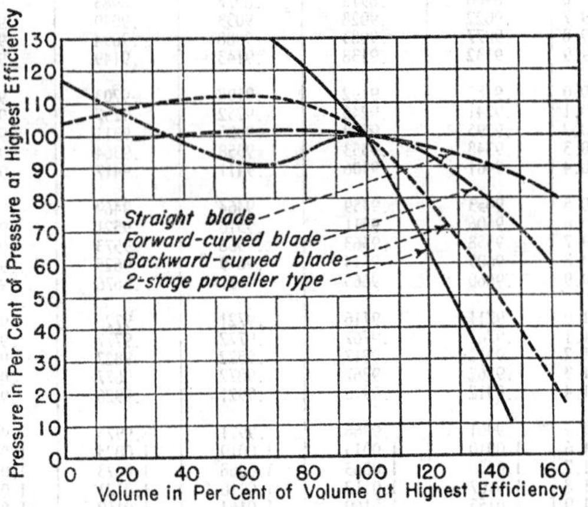

FIG. 6-37. Approximate characteristics of various types of fans.

The centrifugal force developed by the rotor produces a compression of the air or gas which, in fan engineering, is called the *static pressure.* The amount of this static pressure developed depends upon the ratio of the velocity of the air leaving the tips of the blades to the velocity of the air entering the fan at the heel of the blades. Therefore, the longer the blades, the greater the static pressure developed by the fan.

Operating efficiencies of fans are in the range of 40 to 70 per cent. Operating pressure is the sum of the static pressure and the velocity head of the air leaving the fan. It is generally expressed in inches of water gage, or in ounces per square inch.

The air horsepower of a fan is given by

$$\text{Air hp.} = \frac{144Q(p_2 - p_1)}{33{,}000}$$

$$= 0.000157Q \times (\text{developed head, in. water}) \qquad (6\text{-}36)$$

$$\text{Shaft hp.} = \frac{\text{air hp.}}{\text{efficiency}} \qquad (6\text{-}37)$$

where Q = volume handled, cu. ft./min; p_1 = inlet pressure, lb./sq. in.; p_2 = discharge pressure, lb./sq. in.

Fan Performance. The performance of a centrifugal fan varies with changes in conditions such as temperature, speed, and density of the gas being handled. It is important to keep this in mind in using the catalogue data of various fan manufacturers, since such data are usually based on assumed standard conditions, such as 70°F. and 29.92 in. barometric pressure, or 68°F. and 50 per cent relative humidity. Corrections must be made for variations from these assumed standards. The usual variations are as follows:

When speed varies:

1. Capacity varies directly as the speed ratio.
2. Pressure varies as the square of the speed ratio.
3. Horsepower varies as the cube of the speed ratio.

When temperature of air or gas varies:

Horsepower and pressure vary inversely as the absolute temperature (speed and capacity being constant).

When density of air or gas varies:

Horsepower and pressure vary directly as the density (speed and capacity being constant).

Selection of Fans. It is a common practice among fan manufacturers to publish complete data in tabular form showing capacities, pressures, speeds, and horsepowers of their fans under standard conditions of temperature and air density. These tables are of great use to the heating and ventilating engineer and to others who specialize in fan engineering. Those who do not specialize along these lines, including the chemical engineer, should not attempt to select fans from these tables. The proper course to follow is to put full data concerning the job to be done in the hands of fan manufacturers and allow them to specify the fan they are willing to guarantee to do the required work at the best obtainable economy. A comparison of several such proposals from manufacturers will indicate the best choice.

Centrifugal compressors, or **turboblowers,** are widely used to handle large volumes of gas at pressure rises from 0.5 up to several hundred lb./sq. in. The most important criterion, more so than pressure rise, is the pressure ratio, as pointed out below. For pressures below 0.5 lb./sq. in. one of the several types of fans is ordinarily selected.

Turboblowers are used for a wide variety of services, including cooling and drying; supplying combustion air to furnaces and ovens; for blowing blast furnaces, cupolas, and converters; for transporting solid materials; for flotation processes; for agitation and aeration; for ventilation; as exhausters; and for boosting and compressing gas or steam.

The principle of a turboblower is the same as that of a centrifugal pump, the main difference being that the air or gas handled in a blower is compressible while the liquids handled in a pump are practically incompressible. Inasmuch as the pressure is developed by centrifugal force, it is very important to know the density of the gas to be compressed. Since turboblowers develop a pressure within themselves dependent upon the nature and condition of the gas being handled and virtually independent of the process load, in selecting a proper size of blower, the combination of the most adverse conditions occurring simultaneously must be determined. The conditions to be considered are as follows:

Lowest barometric pressure
Lowest intake pressure
Maximum intake temperature
Highest ratio of specific heats (*k* value)
Lowest specific gravity
Maximum intake volume
Maximum discharge pressure

Most turboblowers operate at speeds of 3500 r.p.m. or higher, a limiting factor being impeller stress considerations. Recent advances in machine design and thermodynamic technology have resulted in production of some units running at speeds in excess of 30,000 r.p.m. Turboblower drives are usually electric motors, or steam or gas turbines with or without speed-increasing gears.

In a turboblower, as in a centrifugal pump, the head in feet is independent of the fluid handled. It is evident from an examination of the formulas previously listed in this section that the pressure ratio is dependent upon the inlet temperature, molecular weight, and the ratio of specific heats *k*. With air, having a molecular weight of 29, pressure ratios per stage when taking suction at room temperature are limited to about 1.4. With hydrogen, molecular weight of 2, pressure ratios are limited to about 1.025. For gases heavier than air, such as carbon dioxide, considerably higher pressure ratios than 1.4 are obtainable. Single casings (Fig. 6-38) do not usually

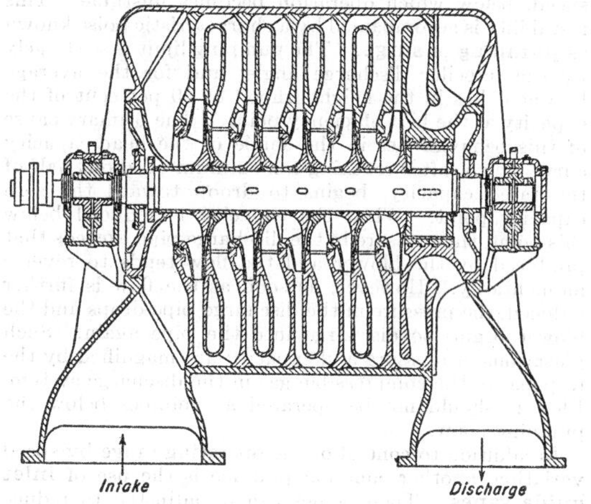

Fig. 6-38. A five-stage turboblower.

contain more than six or seven stages. If this number is not sufficient to produce the required pressure rise, two or more casings can be used in series, often with intercoolers.

Typical **characteristic curves** of a multistage blower are shown in Fig. 6-39. From these curves it will be

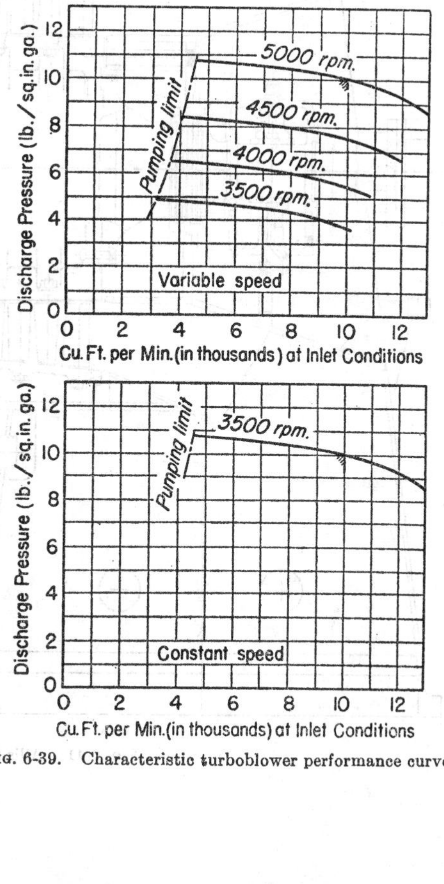

Fig. 6-39. Characteristic turboblower performance curves.

seen that a turboblower is essentially a **constant-pressure** machine and that the power consumption is almost **directly** proportional to the volume delivered. For motor-driven blowers various devices such as hydraulic couplings, magnetic couplings, or wound-rotor motors may be used to obtain efficient operation at part loads or under adverse operating conditions.

There is a minimum capacity for each blower, at every speed, below which operation becomes unstable. This instability is accompanied by a characteristic noise known as **pumping** or **surge**. The pumping limit is set largely by the impeller discharge angle, and for the average blower it lies in the neighborhood of 50 per cent of the capacity at the best efficiency point. The primary cause of this behavior lies in the shape of the head-capacity curve which, after reaching a maximum at about half of the rated capacity, begins to droop toward the zero capacity point. When the capacity is reduced below this point, the pressure in the discharge pipe exceeds that produced by the blower and the flow tends to reverse momentarily. However, as soon as the flow is further reduced, the pressure in the discharge pipe drops and the blower begins to discharge into the pipe again. Such pulsations in pressure and capacity are magnified by the response of the compressible gas in the discharge system. Blowers should not be operated at volumes below the pumping point.

In addition to control of the operating range by speed variation, another common practice is the use of **inlet guide vanes.** These vanes can be adjusted to reduce

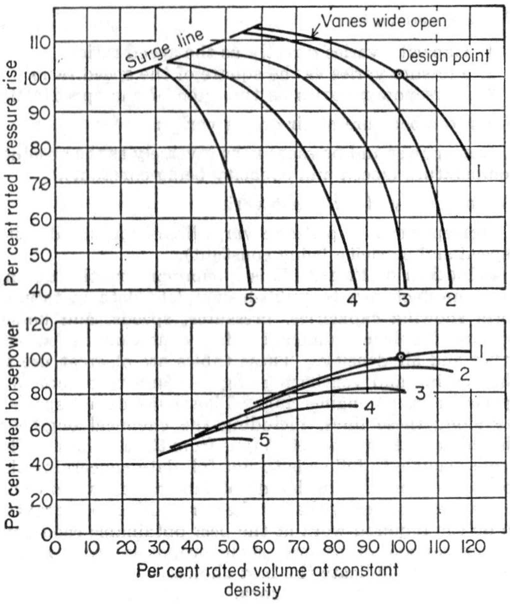

FIG. 6-40. Performance curves showing effects of inlet guide vanes.

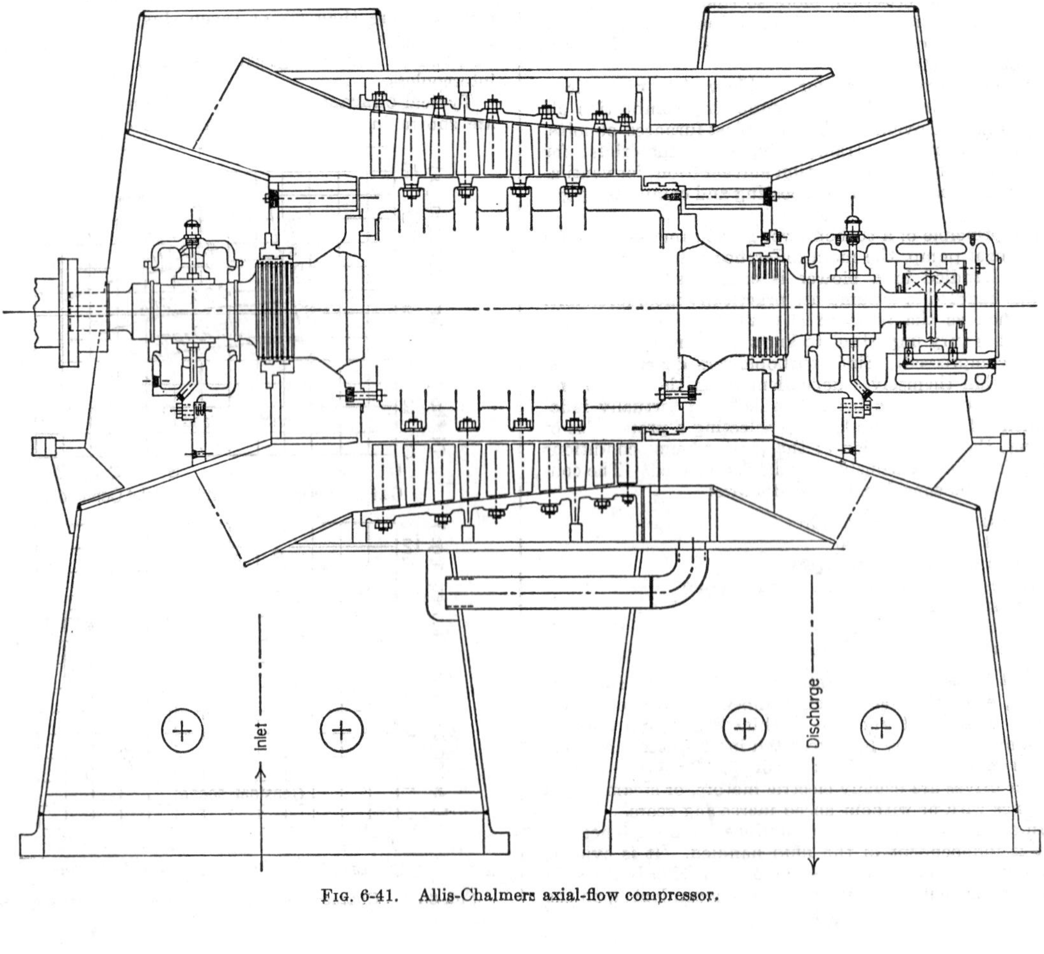

FIG. 6-41. Allis-Chalmers axial-flow compressor.

the capacity and to increase the stable operating range (Fig. 6-40). Although the primary role of the guide vanes is to provide prerotation ahead of the impeller and thus to reduce the entrance losses, the same vanes act as a throttle to reduce the flow rate by reducing the gas density.

A less efficient method than guide vanes for accomplishing nearly the same result is the use of a **blast gate** in the suction line. Discharge pressures can also be varied with a blast gate in the discharge line, although the latter will not affect the range of performance.

By proper use of one or more of the above methods of control, together with adequate instrumentation, turboblowers can be equipped to deliver gas at constant discharge pressure, constant suction pressure, constant volume, or constant weight.

The **axial compressor** has been developed for use with gas turbines and possesses several advantages for aircraft jet-engine service. Its acceptance by industry for stationary installations has been slow, but several large-capacity units have been constructed for blast-furnace, gas-booster, and wind-tunnel service. **High efficiency** and higher capacity are the only important advantages of axial-flow compressors over centrifugal machines for stationary installations. Their smaller size and weight are not of much value, particularly in view of the fact that prices are comparable with centrifugal machines designed for the same conditions. The disadvantages are a limited operating range, greater vulnerability to corrosion and erosion, and susceptibility to deposits.

Figure 6-41 shows a typical axial-flow machine. The rotating element consists of a single drum to which are attached several rows of blades of decreasing height having cross sections of airfoil shape. Between each row is a stationary row which redirects the flow and accomplishes some degree of conversion of velocity head to pressure. Pressure ratios per casing are comparable with centrifugal equipment, although flow rates are considerably higher for a given casing diameter because of the greater area of the flow path.

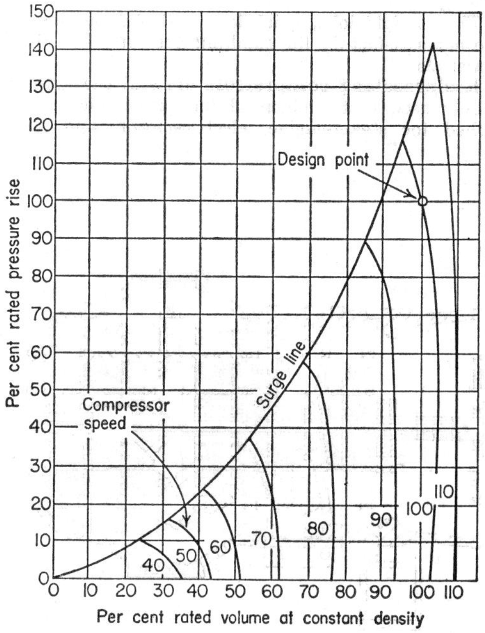

FIG. 6-42. Typical performance characteristics of an axial-flow compressor.

Because of the relatively steep head-capacity-characteristic curve, the pumping point may be within 10 per cent of the design flow as is illustrated in Fig. 6-42.

Rotary compressors, blowers, and vacuum pumps are machines of the positive-displacement type. Such units are essentially constant-volume machines with variable discharge pressure. Volume can be varied only by changing the speed or by by-passing or wasting some of the capacity of the machine. The discharge pressure will vary with the resistance on the discharge side of the system. A characteristic curve typical of the form produced by these rotary units is shown in Fig. 6-43. Rotary compressors are generally classified as straight-lobe

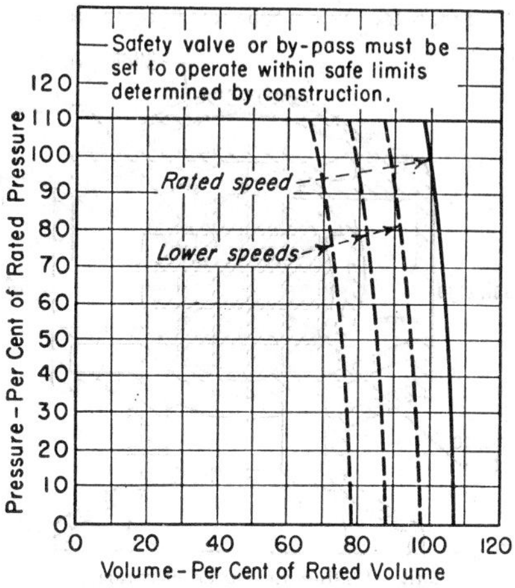

FIG. 6-43. Approximate type of performance curve for rotary compressors.

type, screw type, sliding-vane type, and liquid-piston type.

The **straight-lobe** type is illustrated in Fig. 6-44. Such units are available for pressure differentials up to

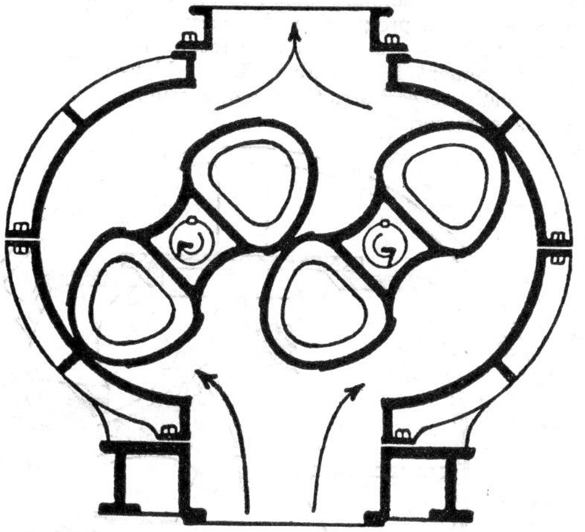

FIG. 6-44. Two-impeller type of positive rotary blower.

about 12 lb./sq. in. and capacities up to 15,000 cu. ft./min. Sometimes multiple units are operated in series to produce higher pressures; individual-stage pressure differentials are limited by the shaft deflection, which must necessarily be kept small to maintain rotor and casing clearance.

The **screw**-type rotary compressor as shown in Fig.

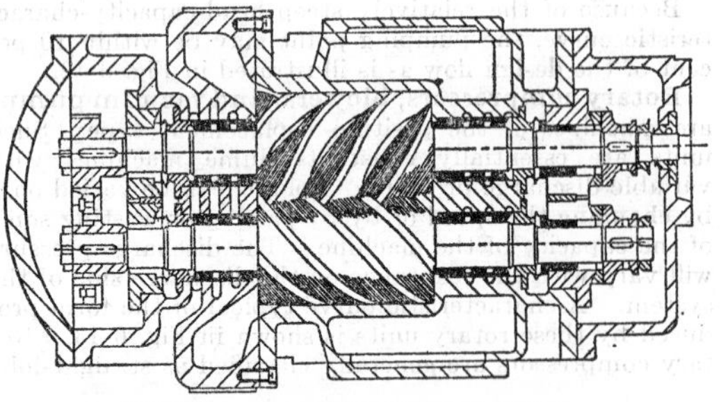

FIG. 6-45. Screw-type rotary compressor.

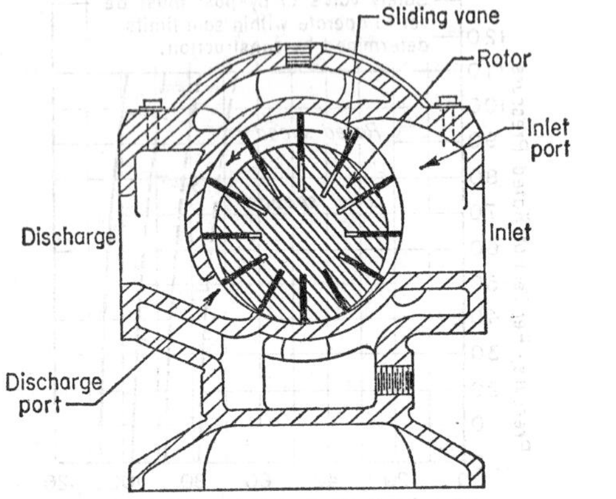

FIG. 6-46. Sliding-vane type of rotary blower.

6-45 is capable of handling capacities up to about 25,000 cu. ft./min. at pressure ratios of 4 to 1 and higher. As there is no unbalanced radial load on the rotor shafts, the magnitude of the pressure rise is not a limiting feature. Relatively small diameter rotors allow rotative speeds of several thousand r.p.m. Unlike the straight-lobe rotary machines, the rotors are male and female whose rotation causes the axial progression of successive sealed cavities. These machines are staged with intercoolers when such an arrangement is advisable. Their high-speed operation usually necessitates the use of suction and discharge noise suppressors.

The **sliding-vane** type is illustrated in Fig. 6-46. These units are offered for operating pressures up to 125 lb./sq. in. and in capacities up to 2000 cu. ft./min. Generally, pressure ratios per stage are limited to 4 to 1.

The **liquid-piston** type is illustrated in Fig. 6-47. They are offered as single-stage units for pressure differentials up to about 75 lb./sq. in. in the smaller sizes

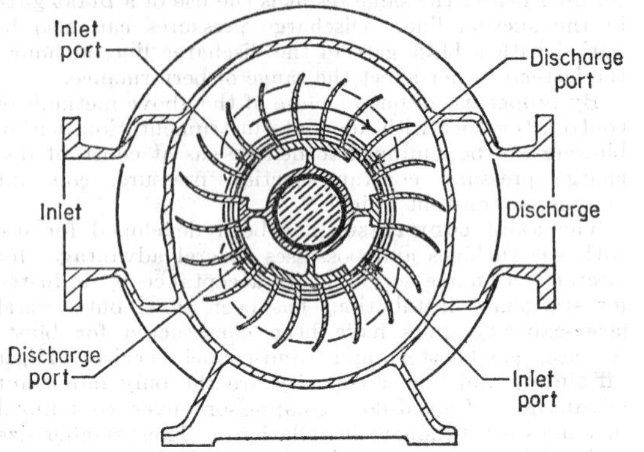

FIG. 6-47. Liquid-piston type of rotary blower.

and capacities up to 4000 cu. ft./min. when used with a few lb./sq. in. differential. Staging is used for higher pressure differentials. These units have found wide application as vacuum pumps on wet-vacuum service. Inlet and discharge ports are located in the impeller hub. As the vaned impeller rotates, centrifugal force drives the sealing liquid against the walls of the elliptical housing, causing the air to be successively drawn in the vane cavities and expelled against discharge pressure. Constant replacement or external recirculation of the sealing liquid is necessary to prevent overheating. A separator is usually used in the discharge line to minimize carryover of entrained liquid. Compressor capacity can be considerably reduced if the gas is highly soluble in the sealing liquid.

The straight-lobe, axial-flow, and sliding-vane types are not satisfactory for handling dust or other abrasive materials.

Reciprocating compressors are still the type most widely used in the chemical industry. They are furnished for steam-engine, electric-motor, and gas- or

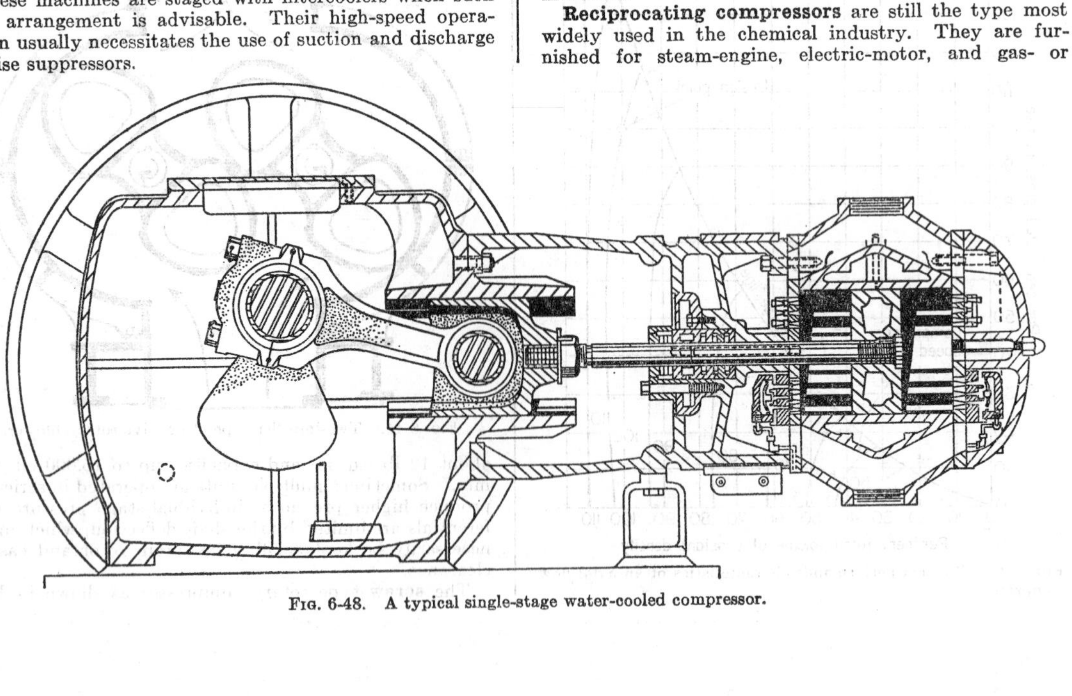

FIG. 6-48. A typical single-stage water-cooled compressor.

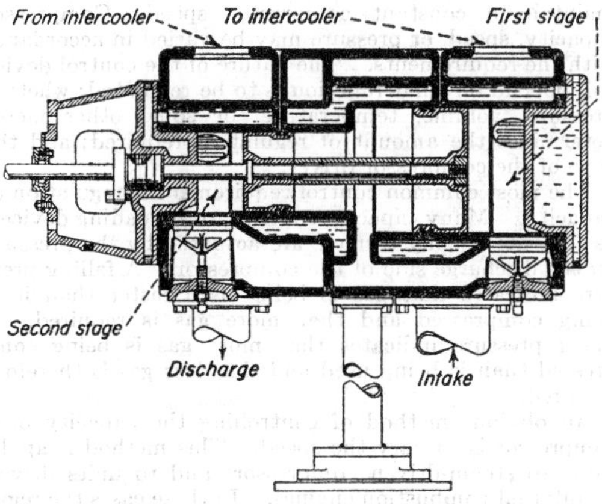

FIG. 6-49. Two-stage single-acting opposed piston in a single-step-type cylinder.

diesel-engine drive; and, in a few cases, for turbine drive through reduction gears.

Reciprocating compressors are furnished either *single-stage* or *multistage*. The number of stages is determined by the compression ratio p_2/p_1. The compression ratio per stage is generally limited to 4, although small-sized units are furnished with a compression ratio as high as 8 and even higher.

Single-acting air-cooled and water-cooled compressors are available in sizes up to about 100 hp. Such units are available in one, two, three, or four stages for pressures as high as 3500 lb./sq. in. These machines are seldom used for gas compression because of the difficulty of preventing gas leakage and contamination of lubricating oil.

The compressors most commonly used for compressing gases have a crosshead to which the connecting rod and piston rod are connected. This provides a straight-line motion for the piston rod and permits simple packing to be used. Figure 6-48 illustrates a simple single-stage machine of this type having a double-acting piston.

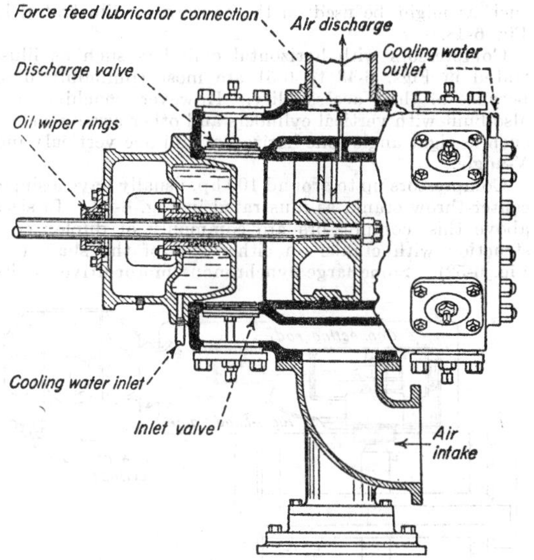

FIG. 6-50. Typical double-acting piston and compressor cylinder.

Either single-acting (Fig. 6-49) or double-acting pistons (Fig. 6-50) may be used, depending on the size of the machine and the number of stages. In some machines double-acting pistons are used in the first stages and single-acting in the later stages.

On **multistage** machines, intercoolers are provided between stages. These are essentially heat exchangers which remove the heat of compression from the gas and reduce its temperature to approximately the temperature existing at the compressor intake. Such cooling reduces the volume of gas going to the high-pressure cylinders, reduces the horsepower required for compression, and, at high pressures, keeps the temperature within safe operating limits.

Figure 6-51 illustrates a two-stage compressor end

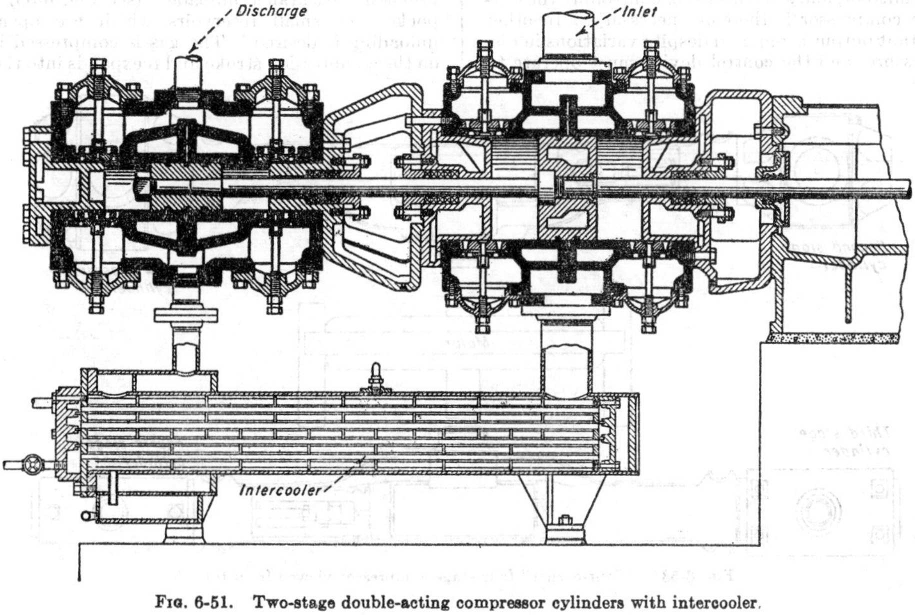

FIG. 6-51. Two-stage double-acting compressor cylinders with intercooler.

such as might be used on the compressor illustrated in Fig. 6-48.

Compressors with horizontal cylinders such as illustrated in Figs. 6-48 to 6-51 are most commonly used because of their accessibility. However, machines are also built with vertical cylinders and other arrangements such as right angle (one horizontal and one vertical) and V-angle.

Compressors up to around 100 hp. usually have a single center-throw crank, as illustrated in Fig. 6-48. In sizes above this, compressors are commonly of duplex construction with cranks on either end of the shaft (see Fig. 6-52). Some large synchronous motor-driven units

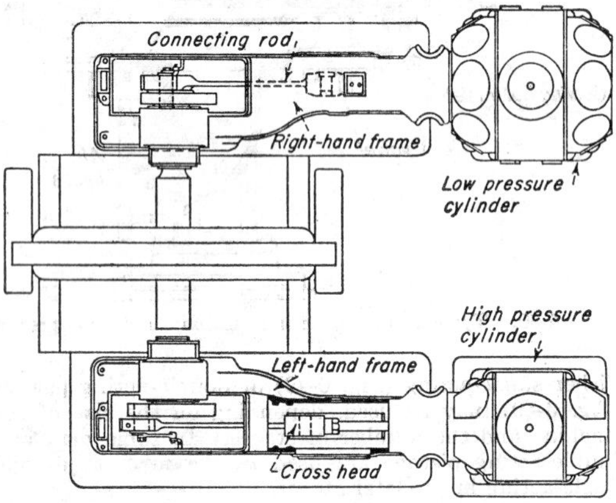

Fig. 6-52. Duplex two-stage compressor looking down from the top.

are of four-corner construction, *i.e.*, they are of double-duplex construction with two connecting rods from each of the two crank throws (see Fig. 6-53). Steam-driven compressors have one or more steam cylinders which are connected directly by piston rod or tie rods to the gas cylinder piston or crosshead.

Control Devices. In many installations the use of gas is intermittent, and some means of controlling the output of the compressor is therefore necessary. In other cases constant output is required despite variations in discharge pressure, and the control device must operate to maintain a constant compressor speed. Compressor capacity, speed, or pressure may be varied in accordance with the requirements. The nature of the control device will depend on what function is to be regulated; whether pressure, volume, temperature, or some other factor determines the amount of regulation required; and the type of the compressor driver.

The most common control requirement is regulation of capacity. Many capacity controls, or unloading devices, as they are usually termed, are actuated by the pressure on the discharge side of the compressor. A falling pressure indicates that gas is being used faster than it is being compressed and that more gas is required. A rising pressure indicates that more gas is being compressed than is being used and that less gas is therefore required.

An obvious method of controlling the capacity of a compressor is to vary the speed. This method is applicable to steam-driven compressors and to units driven by internal-combustion engines. In these cases the regulator actuates the steam-admission or fuel-admission valve on the compressor driver and thus controls the speed.

Motor-driven compressors usually operate at constant speed, and other methods of controlling the capacity are necessary. On reciprocating compressors up to about 100 hp., two types of control are usually available. These are automatic-start-and-stop control and constant-speed control.

Automatic-start-and-stop control, as its name implies, stops or starts the compressor by means of a pressure-actuated switch as the gas demand varies. It should be used only when the demand for gas will be intermittent.

Constant-speed control should be used when gas demand is fairly constant. With this type of control, the compressor runs continuously, until shut down, but compresses only when gas is needed. Three methods of unloading the compressor with this type of control are in common use: (1) *closed suction unloaders*, (2) *open inlet-valve unloaders*, and (3) *clearance unloaders*. The closed suction unloader consists of a pressure-actuated valve which shuts off the compressor intake. Open inlet-valve unloaders (see Fig. 6-54) operate to hold the compressor inlet valves open and thereby prevent compression. Clearance unloaders (see Fig. 6-55) consist of pockets or small reservoirs which are opened when unloading is desired. The gas is compressed into them on the compression stroke and reexpands into the cylinder

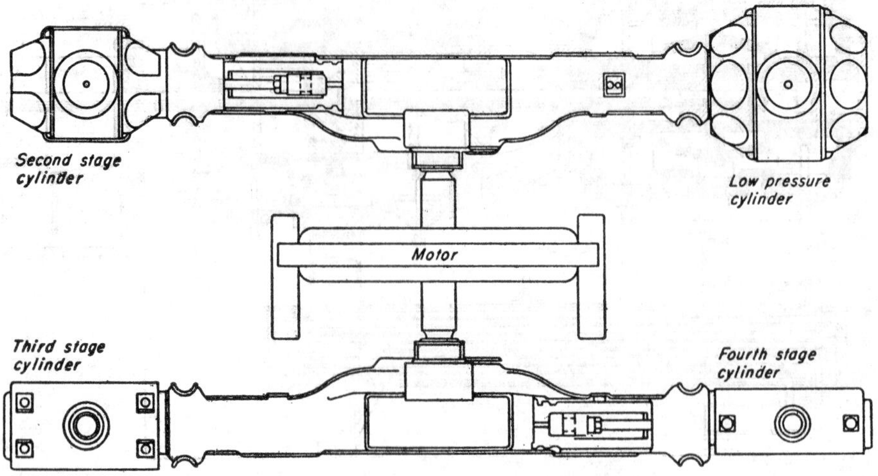

Fig. 6-53. "Four-corner" four-stage compressor viewed from top.

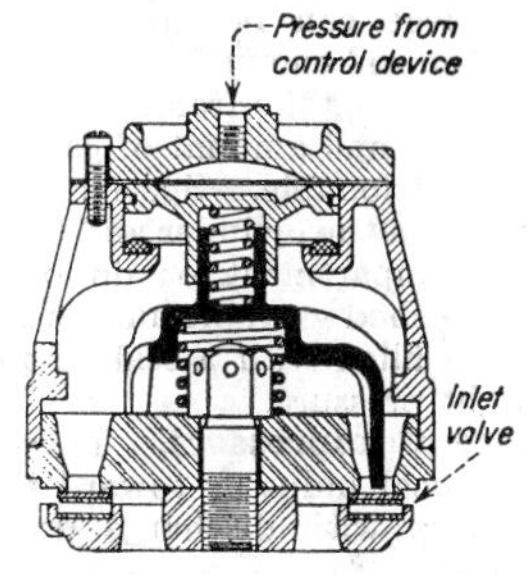

FIG. 6-54. Inlet valve unloader.

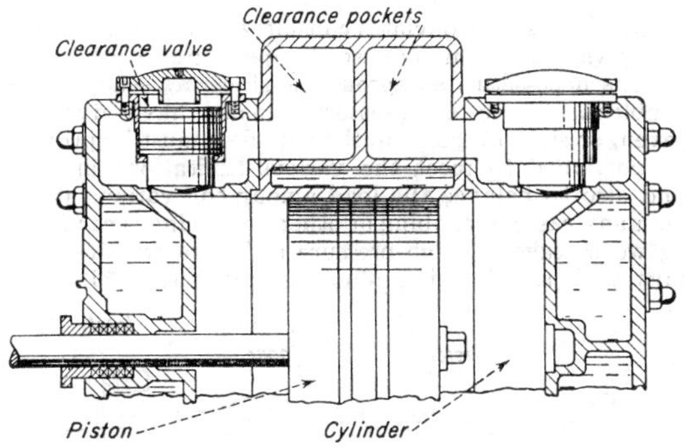

FIG. 6-55. Ingersoll-Rand "clearance control" cylinder.

on the return stroke, thus preventing the compression of additional gas.

It is sometimes desirable to have a compressor equipped with both constant-speed and automatic-start-and-stop control. When this is done, a switch allows immediate selection of either type.

Motor-driven reciprocating compressors above about 100 hp. in size are usually equipped with a **step control.** This is in reality a variation of constant-speed control in which unloading is accomplished in a series of steps, varying from full load down to no load. *Three-step control* (full load, one-half load, and no load) is usually accomplished with inlet-valve unloaders. *Five-step control* (full load, three-fourths load, one-half load, one-fourth load, and no load) is accomplished by means of clearance

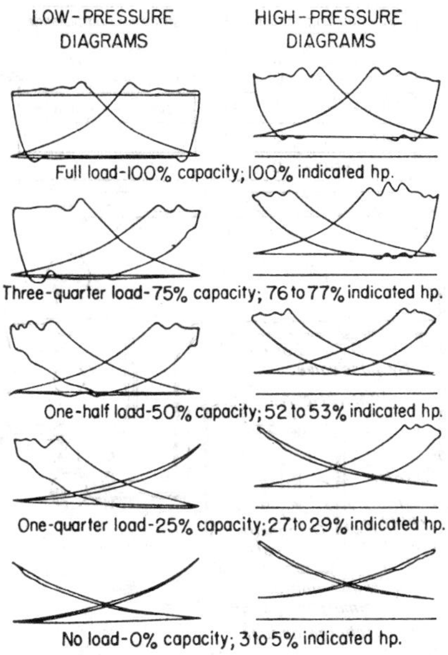

FIG. 6-56. Actual indicator diagram showing operation of clearance control at five load points of a two-stage compressor.

pockets (see Fig. 6-56). On some makes of machines, inlet-valve and clearance control unloading are used in combination.

Although such control devices are usually automatically operated, manual operation is satisfactory for some services. Where manual operation is provided, it often consists of a valve or valves to open and close clearance pockets. In some cases, a movable cylinder head is provided for variable clearance in the cylinder (see Fig. 6-57).

Where no capacity control or unloading device is provided, it is necessary to provide by-passes between the inlet and discharge in order that the compressor can be started against no load (see Fig. 6-58).

Non-lubricated Cylinders. Most compressors use oil to lubricate the cylinder. In some processes, however, the slightest oil contamination is objectionable.

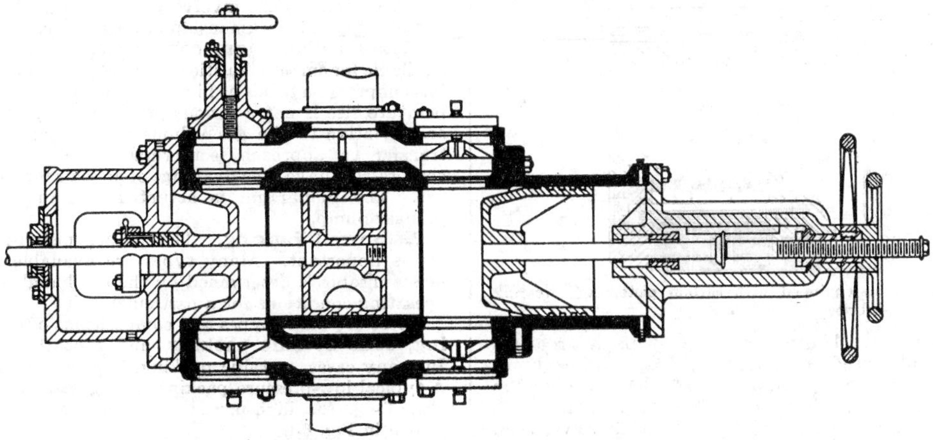

FIG. 6-57. Sectional view of a cylinder equipped with a hand-operated valve lifter on one end and a variable-volume clearance pocket at the other end.

Starting compressor	Stopping compressor
Start with A and D open	Close ---- C
Close ------ D	Close --- B
Close ------- A	Open ---- A and D
Open ------- B	
Slowly open --- C	

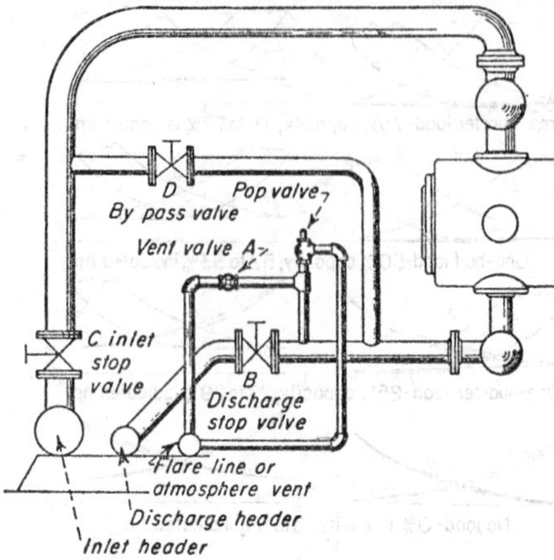

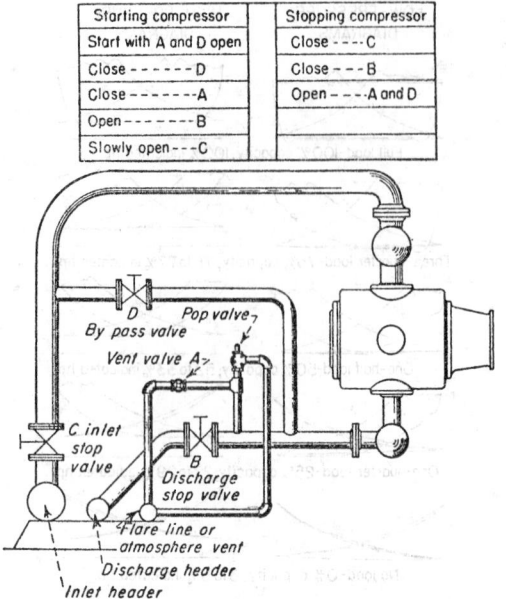

Fig. 6-58. Starting by-pass arrangement for a single-stage compressor. On multistage machines each stage is by-passed in a similar manner.

For such cases a number of manufacturers furnish a "non-lubricated" cylinder (see Fig. 6-59). The piston on these cylinders is equipped with piston rings of graphitic carbon or Teflon* as well as pads or rings of the same material to maintain the proper clearance between the piston

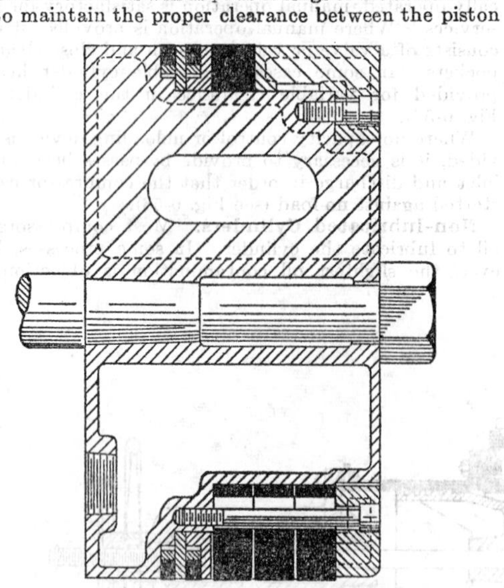

Fig. 6-59. Piston equipped with carbon piston and wearing rings for a "non-lubricated" cylinder.

and the cylinder. Plastic packing of a type that requires no lubricant is used on the stuffing box. Although oil-wiper rings are used on the piston rod where it leaves the compressor frame, minute quantities of oil might conceivably enter the cylinder on the rod. Where even such small amounts of oil are objectionable, an extended cylinder connecting piece can be furnished. This simply lengthens the piston rod enough so that no portion of the rod can alternately enter the frame and cylinder.

In many cases, a small amount of gas leaking through the packing is objectionable. Special connecting pieces are furnished between the cylinder and frame, which may be either single-compartment or double-compartment. These may be furnished gastight and vented back to the suction or may be filled with a sealing gas or fluid and held under a slight pressure.

High-pressure Compressors. There is a definite trend in the chemical industry toward the use of *high-pressure compressors* with discharge pressures of from 5000 to 25,000 lb./sq. in. These require special design, and a complete knowledge of the characteristics of the gas is necessary.

The gas usually deviates considerably from the perfect gas laws, and in many cases temperature or other limitations necessitate a thorough engineering study of the problem. These compressors usually have five, six, seven, or eight stages, and the cylinders must be properly proportioned to meet the various limitations involved and also to balance the load among the various stages. In many cases, scrubbing or other processing is carried on between stages. High-pressure cylinders are steel forgings with single-acting plungers (see Fig. 6-60). The

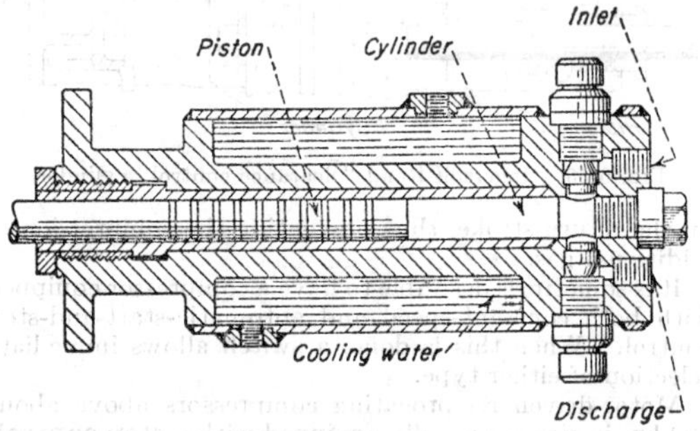

Fig. 6-60. Forged-steel single-acting high-pressure cylinder.

compressors are usually designed so that the pressure load against the plunger is opposed by one or more single-acting pistons of the lower pressure stages. Piston-rod packing is usually the segmental-ring metallic type. Accurate fitting and correct lubrication are very important. High-pressure compressor valves are designed for the conditions involved. Extremely high-grade engineering and workmanship are necessary.

Metallic diaphragm compressors (Fig. 6-61) are available for small quantities (up to about 10 cu. ft./min.) for compression ratios as high as 10 to 1 per stage. Temperature rise is not a serious problem, as the large wall area relative to the gas volume permits sufficient heat transfer to approach isothermal compression. These compressors have the advantage of no seals for the process gas. The diaphragm is actuated hydraulically by a plunger pump.

Piston-rod Packing. The proper piston-rod packing is important. Many types are available, and the most suitable is determined by the gas handled and the operating conditions for a particular unit.

There are many types and compositions of **soft packing, semimetallic packing,** and **metallic packing.** In many cases, metallic packing is to be recommended. A typical low-pressure packing arrangement is shown in Fig. 6-62. A high-pressure packing arrangement is shown in Fig. 6-63.

Where wet, volatile, or hazardous gases are handled or where the service is intermittent, an auxiliary packing

*Du Pont TFE fluorocarbon resin.

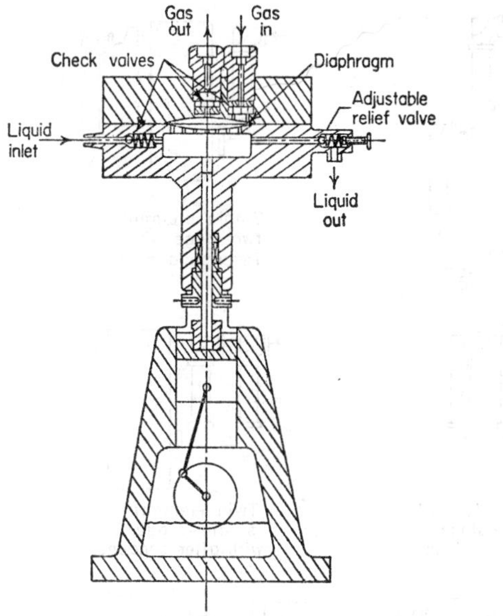

FIG. 6-61. Pressure Products Industries high-pressure diaphragm compressor.

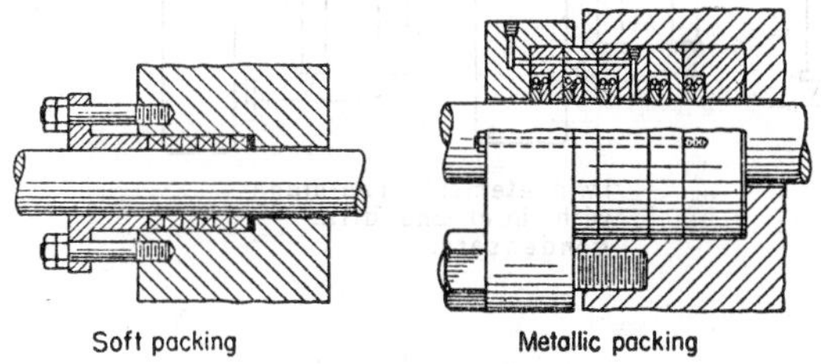

FIG. 6-62. Typical packing arrangements for low-pressure stuffing boxes.

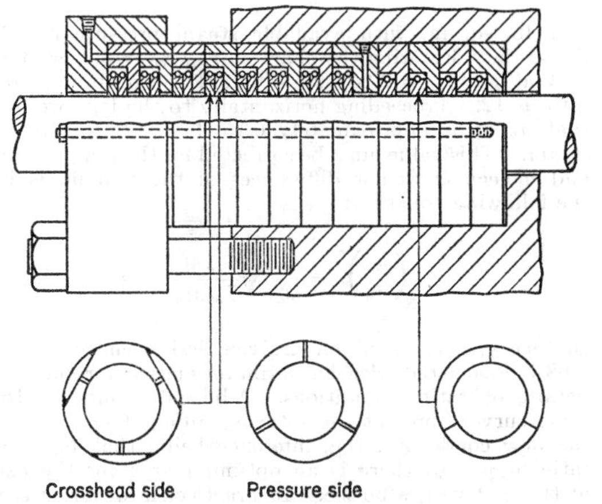

FIG. 6-63. A typical high-pressure stuffing box using metallic packing.

gland and soft packing are usually employed (see Fig. 6-64).

Ejectors. An ejector is a simplified type of vacuum pump or compressor which has no pistons, valves, rotors, or other moving parts. Figure 6-65 illustrates a **steam-jet ejector.** It consists essentially of a steam nozzle

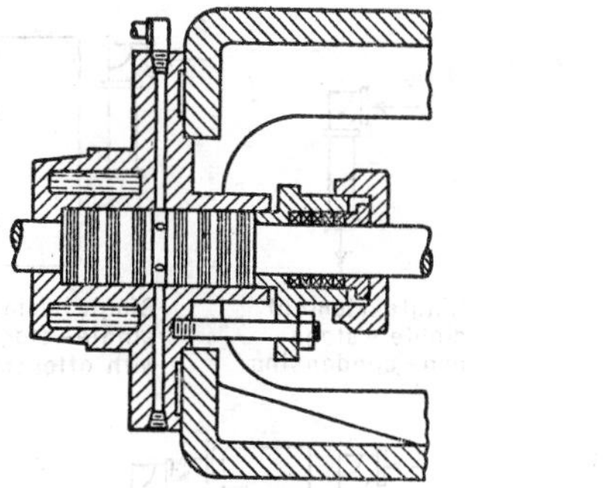

FIG. 6-64. Stuffing box with auxiliary soft packing for handling gases.

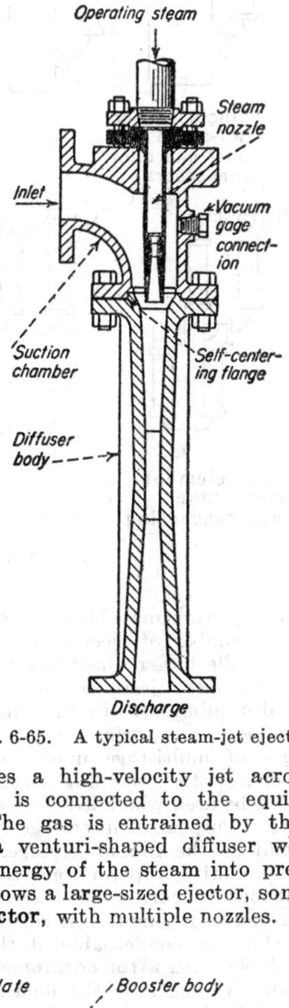

FIG. 6-65. A typical steam-jet ejector.

that discharges a high-velocity jet across a suction chamber that is connected to the equipment to be evacuated. The gas is entrained by the steam and carried into a venturi-shaped diffuser which converts the velocity energy of the steam into pressure energy. Figure 6-66 shows a large-sized ejector, sometimes called a **booster ejector,** with multiple nozzles.

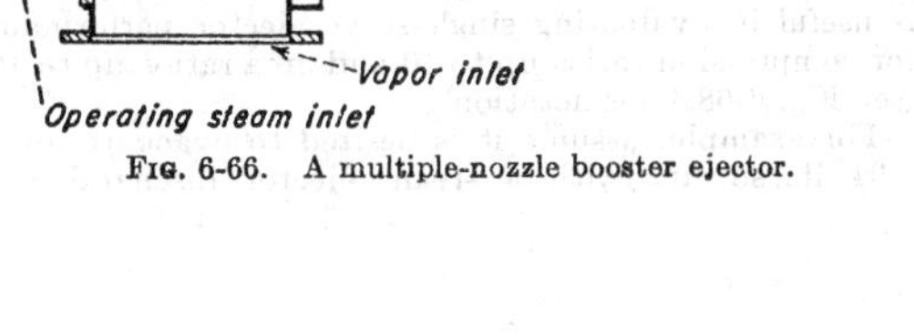

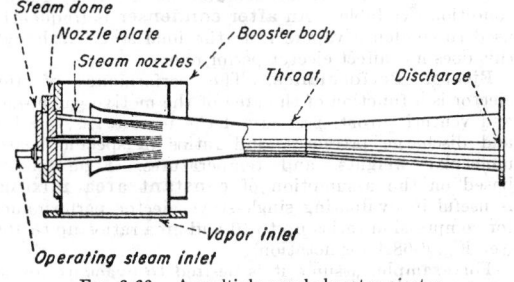

FIG. 6-66. A multiple-nozzle booster ejector.

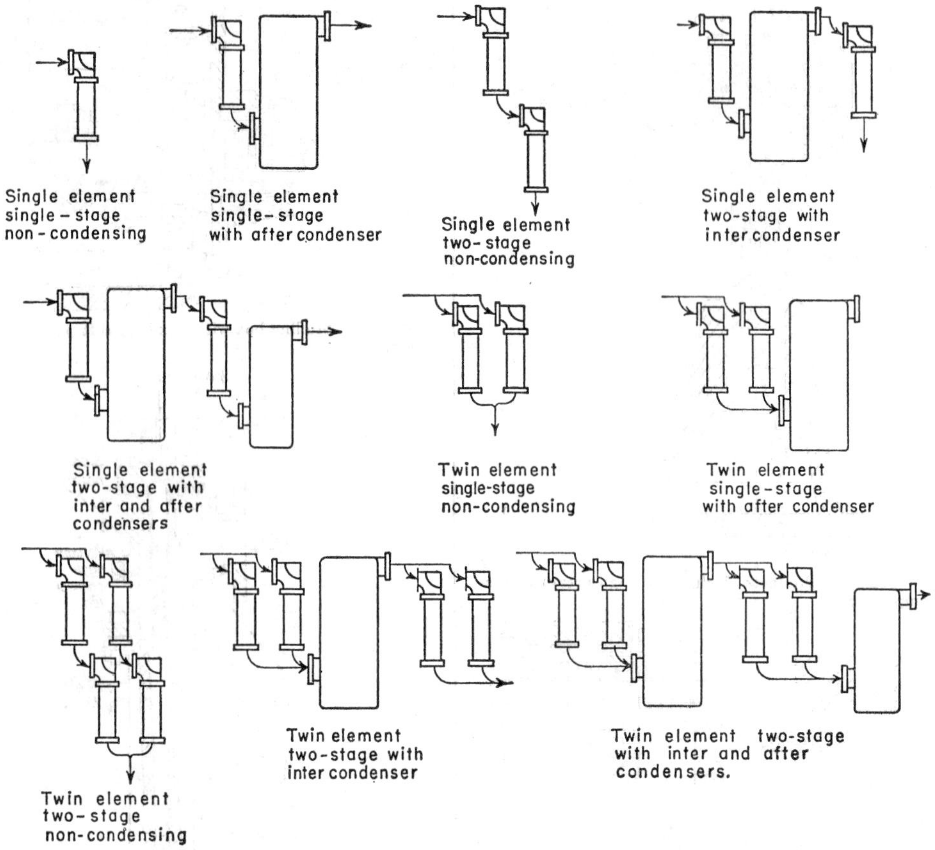

FIG. 6-67. Common ejector arrangements.

Two or more ejectors may be connected in series or stages. Also a number of ejectors may be connected in parallel to handle larger quantities of gas or vapor. See Fig. 6-67 for typical ejector arrangements.

Liquid-cooled **condensers** of either the direct-contact (barometric) type or the surface type usually are used between stages of multistage units to condense the operating vapor from the preceding stage. Surface-type condensers must be used where it is necessary to reclaim the condensate. Purpose of interstage condensers is to reduce the load on the following stage, thus reducing consumption of motive vapor or gas and ejector size. Likewise, a **precondenser** installed ahead of an ejector reduces its size and consumption if the suction gas contains vapors that are condensable at the temperature condition available. An **after condenser** is frequently used to condense vapors from the final stage, although this does not affect ejector performance.

Ejector Performance. The performance of any ejector is a function of the area of the motive gas nozzle and venturi throat, pressure of the motive gas, suction and discharge pressures, and ratios of specific heats, molecular weights, and temperatures. Figure 6-68, based on the assumption of **constant area mixing,** is useful in evaluating single-stage ejector performance for compression ratios up to 10 and area ratios up to 100 (see Fig. 6-68*A* for notation).

For example, assume it is desired to evacuate air at 2.94 lb./sq. in. with a steam ejector discharging to 14.7 lb./sq. in. with available steam pressure of 100 lb./sq. in. Entering the chart at $p_{o3}/p_{ob} = 5.0$, we find that at $p_{ob}/p_{oa} = 2.94/100 = 0.0294$ the optimum area ratio is 12. Proceeding horizontally to the left, we find that w_b/w_a is approximately 0.15 lb. of air per lb. of steam. This value must be corrected for the temperature and molecular weight differences of the two fluids by the following equation:

$$\left(\frac{w_b}{w_a}\right)' = \frac{w_b}{w_a}\sqrt{\frac{T_{oa}M_b}{T_{ob}M_a}} \tag{6-38}$$

In theory, each point on a given design curve of Fig. 6-68 is associated with an optimum ejector for the prevailing operating conditions. Adjacent points on the same curve represent theoretically different ejectors for the new conditions, the difference being that for each ratio of p_{ob}/p_{oa} there is an optimum area for the exit of the motive gas nozzle. In practice, however, a segment of a given curve for constant A_2/A_t represents the performance of a single ejector satisfactorily for estimating purposes, provided that the suction pressure lies within 20 to 130 per cent of the design suction pressure and the motive pressure within 80 to 120 per cent of design motive pressure. Thus the curves can be used to select an optimum ejector for the design point and to estimate its performance at off-design conditions, within the limits noted. Final ejector selection should, of course,

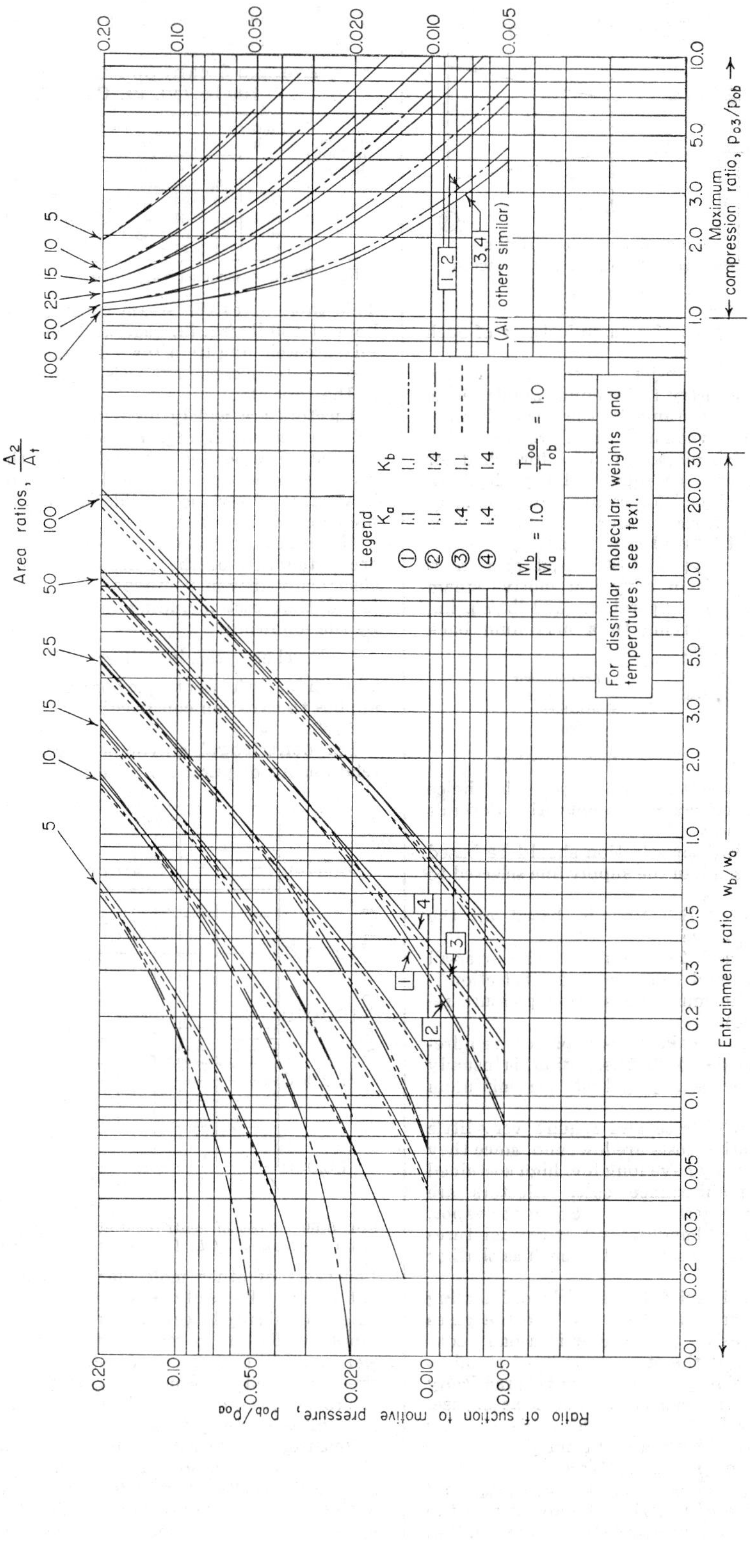

FIG. 6-68. Optimum design curves for single-stage ejectors. [*DeFrate and Hoerl, Chem. Eng. Progress Symp. Ser.*, **55** (21), 46 (1959).]

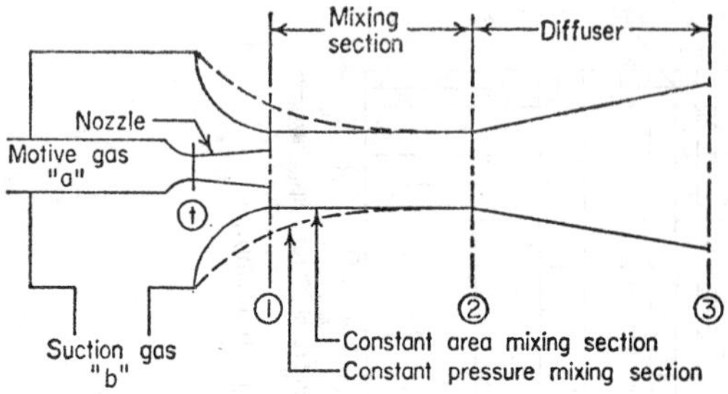

FIG. 6-68A. Notation for Fig. 6-68.

be made with the assistance of a manufacturer of such equipment.

Uses of Ejectors. Steam-jet ejectors are widely used in the chemical industry for vacuum applications. They are in general more suitable for the lower absolute pressures, *i.e.*, higher vacuum, than reciprocating vacuum pumps, although ejectors can be furnished for any suction and discharge pressure and capacity. In some cases they are designed for compressing steam at pressures above atmospheric pressure. In such cases they are usually called **thermal compressors.**

The range of popular types of steam-jet ejectors is shown below on the basis of a typical motive steam pressure and cooling-water temperature (100 lb./sq. in., 85°F.), with ejector discharging to a maximum back pressure of 1 lb./sq. in. gage.

Range of Design Suction Pressure, In. or Mm. Hg Abs.	Arrangement of Ejector
30 –3.0 in.	Single-stage
5.0–0.5 in.	Two-stage
50 –1 mm.	Three-stage
5 –0.05 mm.	Four- or five-stage

Note that there is some overlap in range. The choice of the most suitable type for a given application depends upon the following factors:

1. *Steam Pressure.* Ejector selection should be based upon the minimum pressure in the supply line selected to serve the unit.

2. *Water Temperature.* Selection is based on the maximum water temperature.

3. *Suction Pressure and Temperature.* The over-all process requirements should be considered. Selection is usually governed by the minimum suction pressure required (highest vacuum).

4. *Capacity Required.* Again over-all process requirements should be considered, but selection is usually governed by the capacity required at the minimum process pressure.

Ejectors are easy to operate and require very little maintenance. Installation costs are low; and, since they have no moving parts, they have long life, high sustained efficiency, and low maintenance cost. Ejectors are suitable for handling practically any type of gas or vapor. They are also suitable for handling wet or dry mixtures or gases containing sticky or solid matter such as chaff or dust.

Ejectors are available in suitable materials for handling high temperature or corrosive gases. Where the gases or vapors are not corrosive, the diffuser is usually constructed of cast iron and the steam nozzle of stainless steel. For more corrosive gases and vapors, practically any combination of metals can be used such as bronze, various stainless-steel alloys, etc. Besides this, ejectors are constructed from solid carbon and from glass.

The capacity of ejectors is usually expressed as pounds per hour. This has proved less subject to confusion and error than the practice of referring to capacity on the volumetric basis. Typical average steam consumption of ejectors having various suction pressures is shown in the table below:

Average Steam Consumption, lb./hr. at 100 lb./sq. in. Gage Pressure

Weight mixture, lb./hr.	% net dry air by weight	Suction pressure, in. Hg abs.									
		0.5		1.0		1.5	2.0	3.0	4.0		6.0
		3 stage	2 stage	3 stage	2 stage	2 stage	2 stage	2 stage	2 stage	1 stage	1 stage
10	100	73	99	59	70	58	50	42	38	58	36
10	70	59	84	47	60	49	42	35	31	63	39
10	40	45	68	33	47	38	32	26	23	68	41
10	10	24	45	16	28	21	17	14	12	74	42

NOTE: Steam consumption is approximately proportional to capacity.

This table gives the steam consumption in pounds per hour at 100 lb./sq. in. gage while handling the gas-vapor mixture weighing 10 lb./hr. For larger or smaller capacities, the steam consumption is approximately proportional to the capacity.

Ejectors are widely used in condensation, batch distillation, shelf drying, evaporation, cooling, and impregnating processes. In addition, their use in compressing process gases instead of compression machinery is worthy of serious consideration where suitable economic conditions prevail.

Compressor Costs. In general, compressor costs are a function of the horsepower required. For large electrically driven **reciprocating** machines it has been found that cost including motor can be approximated by the following:

$$\text{Purchase price in dollars} = 7740 + 99.5\ \text{hp.}_{is}$$

where hp._{is} is the isentropic horsepower. This expression applies to cast-iron construction as of the second quarter of 1962.

For **centrifugal** air compressors, Fig. 6-69 shows the relationship of purchase price to isentropic horsepower.

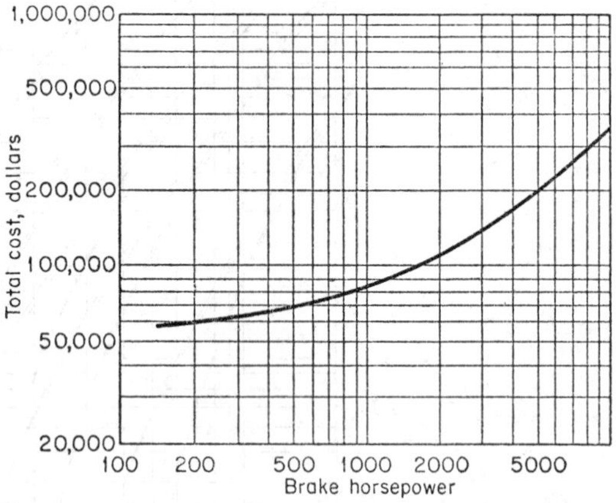

FIG. 6-69. Cost of centrifugal air compressors (second quarter 1962). (*Courtesy of E. I. du Pont de Nemours & Co.*)

For gases of other molecular weights, these values do not apply. Basically, lower molecular weights necessitate a physically larger machine for the same horsepower input, while the reverse is true for higher molecular weights. It is difficult to establish a quantitative expression for effect of molecular weight, since the handling of process gases often entails use of special materials and elaborate sealing systems.

Sealing of Rotating Shafts. As rotating shafts in pumps, fans, compressors, agitators, etc., are usually displaced radially when in operation by varying amounts depending upon the loads transmitted, their seals must have flexibility. As shaft lengths are normally limited by such items as critical speed and allowable deflection, it is essential that the seals be compact. In the chemical industry especially, corrosion resistance of the materials is of great importance. It is frequently necessary to provide secondary flushing mediums to prevent erosion or abrasion of critical sealing faces by solids in the process fluid, as well as to carry away excessive heat. As sealing problems constitute a large percentage of chemical plant maintenance expense, proper initial selection of shaft seals is an essential factor of process design.

Packing. The most common type of rotating shaft seal consists of packing composed of fibers which are first woven, twisted, or braided into strands, and then formed into coils, spirals, or rings. To ensure initial lubrication and to facilitate installation, the basic materials are often impregnated. Common materials are asbestos fabric, braided and twisted asbestos, rubber and duck, flax, jute, and metallic braids. The so-called **plastic** packings can be made up with varying amounts of fiber combined with a binder and lubricant for high-speed applications. Maximum temperatures that base materials of packings withstand and still give good service are:

	°F.
Flax	100
Cotton	200
Duck and rubber	300
Rubber	350
Metallic (lead-based)	425
Asbestos 1003	500
Asbestos 204	700
Metallic (aluminum-based)	1025
Metallic (copper-based)	1525

Application of Packing. Coils and spirals are cut to form closed or nearly closed rings in the stuffing box. Clearance between ends should be sufficient to allow for fitting and possible expansion due to swelling of the packing while in operation.

Correct form of the ring joint depends on materials and service requirements. Braided and flexible metallic packings usually have butt or square joints (Fig. 6-70*a*).

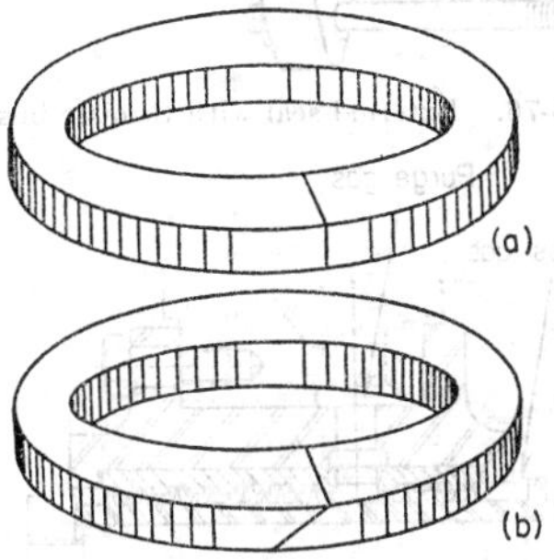

FIG. 6-70. Butt and skive joints for compression packing rings.

With other packing material, service experience indicates that rings cut with bevel or skive joints (Fig. 6-70*b*) are more satisfactory. A slight advantage of the bevel joint over the butt joint is that the bevel permits a certain amount of sliding action, thus absorbing a portion of ring expansion.

In the manufacture of packings, the proper grade and type of **lubricant** is usually impregnated for each service for which the packing is recommended. However, it is impossible to provide sufficient lubrication to last the normal life of the packing. Lack of lubrication causes packing to become hard and lose its resiliency, thus increasing friction, shortening packing life, and increasing operating costs.

An effective means of renewing packing lubrication is to provide a lubricating **lantern ring.** The ring provides an opening for the forced feeding of oil, grease, sealed or secondary medium into the packing set, giving a constant supply of lubricant. This method is particularly effective on pumps handling volatile liquids and for the exclusion of solids from the sealing faces.

Lantern rings are also employed for cooling, to provide an additional seal against leakage of liquid being pumped, and to prevent infiltration of air through the stuffing box on the pump suction side.

In pumps where no lantern ring is used, **a small amount of leakage through the packing is essential.**

The chief advantage of packing over other types of seals is the ease with which it can be adjusted or replaced. Most equipment is designed so that disassembly of major components is not required to remove or add packing rings. The major disadvantages of a packing-type seal are the necessity for frequent adjustment and the quantity of fluid flow required to lubricate it.

Mechanical Seals. The term mechanical seal designates a prefabricated or packaged assembly that forms a running seal between flat, precision-finished surfaces. Except in a few special designs, sealing surfaces are oriented at right angles to the axis of shaft rotation. The direction of forces holding the sealing faces in contact is parallel to the shaft. All mechanical seals contain four basic elements—a rotating seal ring, a stationary seal ring, a spring-loading section for maintaining seal-face contact, and static seals. These components are pointed out in Fig. 6-71.

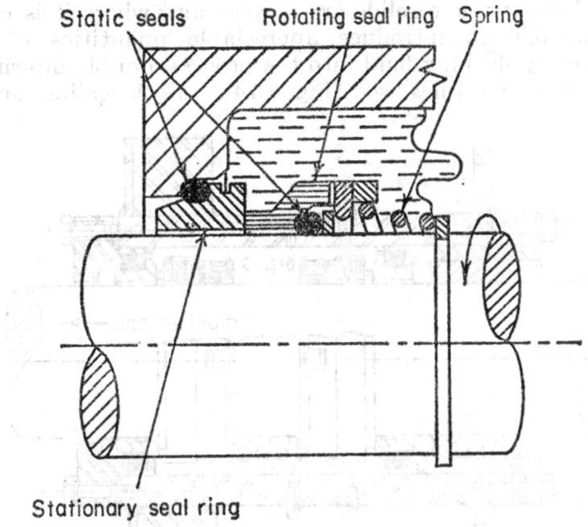

FIG. 6-71. Mechanical seal components.

Types. Mechanical seals are classified broadly as internal or external. **Internal seals** (Fig. 6-72) are

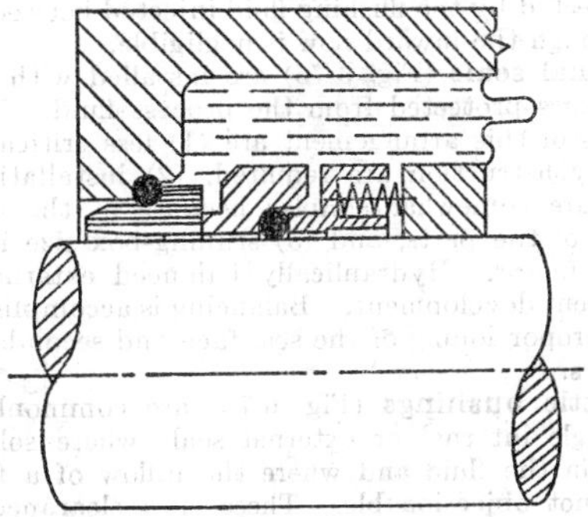

FIG. 6-72. Internal mechanical seal.

installed with all seal components exposed to the fluid sealed. The advantages of this arrangement are (1) the ability to seal against high pressures since the hydrostatic force is normally in the same direction as the spring force, (2) protection of seal parts from external mechanical damage, and (3) reduction in shaft length required.

For high-pressure installations, it is possible to partially or fully balance the hydrostatic force on the rotating member of an internal seal by using a stepped shaft or shaft sleeve (Fig. 6-73). This method of relieving face

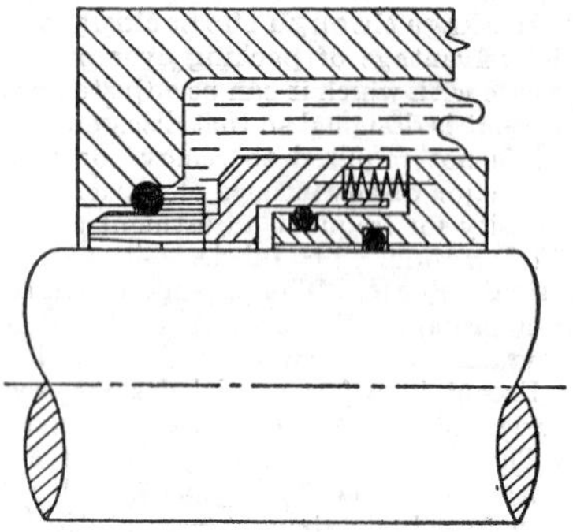

FIG. 6-73. Balanced internal mechanical seal.

pressure is an effective way of decreasing power consumption and extending seal life.

Where abrasive solids are present and where it is not permissible to introduce appreciable quantities of a secondary flushing fluid into the process, double internal seals are sometimes used (Fig. 6-74). Both sealing faces

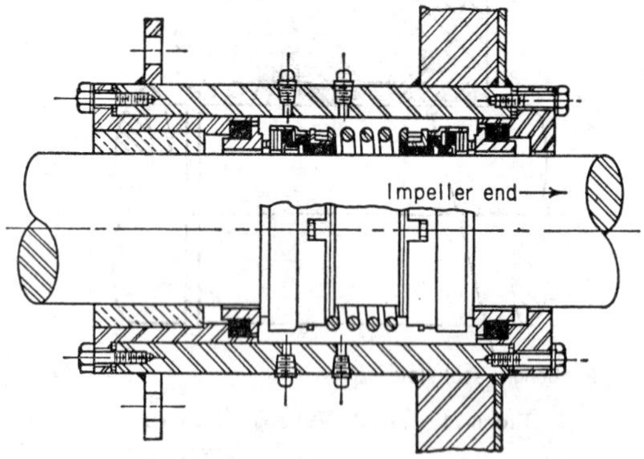

FIG. 6-74. Double mechanical seal.

are protected by the flushing fluid injected between them even though the inward flow is negligible.

External seals (Fig. 6-75) are installed with all seal components protected from the process fluid. The advantages of this arrangement are (1) less critical materials of construction are required, (2) installation and setting are somewhat simpler because of the exposed position of the parts, and (3) stuffing-box size is not a limiting factor. Hydraulically balanced external seals are a recent development. Balancing is accomplished by proper proportioning of the seal face and secondary seal diameters.

Throttle bushings (Fig. 6-76) are commonly used with single internal or external seals where solids are present in the fluid and where the inflow of a flushing fluid is not objectionable. These close-clearance bushings are intended to serve as flow restrictions through which the maintenance of a small inward flow of flushing fluid prevents the entrance of a process fluid into the stuffing box.

Application. Mechanical seals find their best applications where fluids must be contained under substantial pressures. In such services, advantages of mechanical seals, as compared with conventional packed

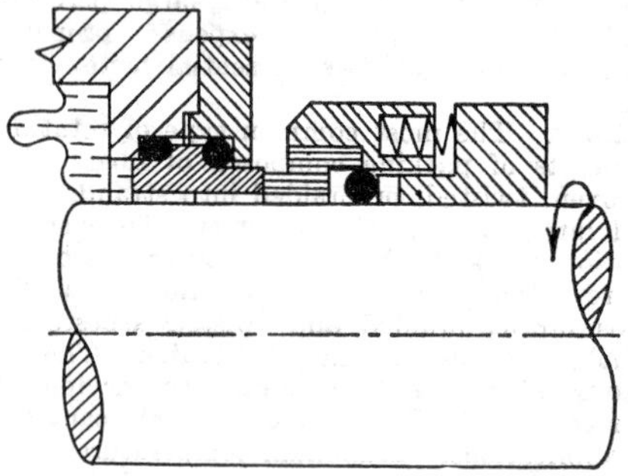

FIG. 6-75. External mechanical seal.

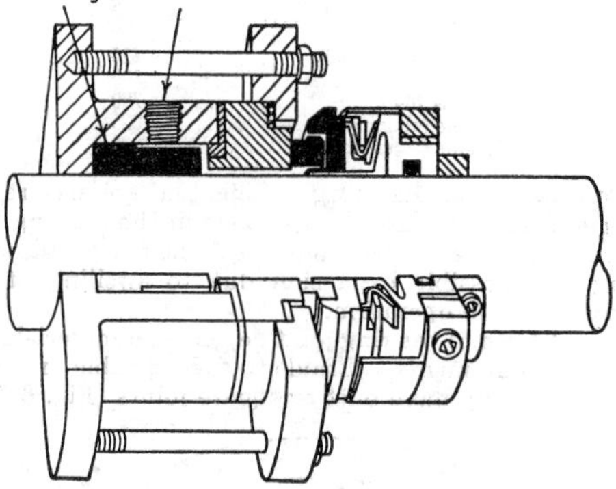

FIG. 6-76. External seal with throttle bushing.

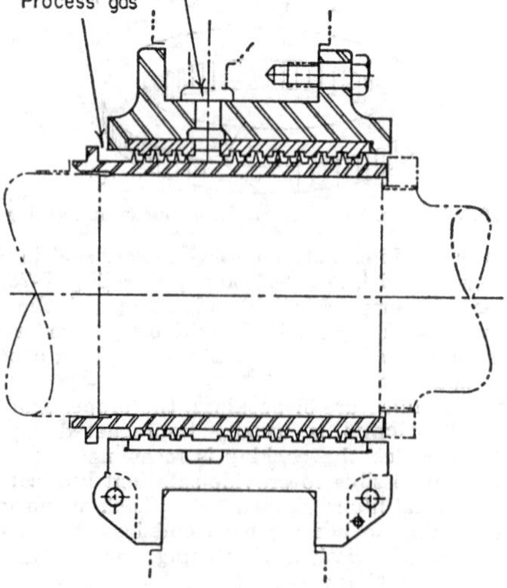

FIG 6-77. Labyrinth seal for centrifugal compressor.

stuffing boxes, are reduced friction-power loss, elimination of wear on shaft or shaft sleeve, negligible leakage over a long service life, and freedom from periodic maintenance. On the other hand mechanical seals are precision components and demand careful handling and installation.

Materials. Springs and other metallic components are available in a wide variety of alloys and are usually selected on the basis of temperature and corrosion conditions. The use of a particular mechanical seal is frequently restricted by the temperature limitations of the organic materials used in the static seals. Most elastomers are limited to about 250°F. Teflon will withstand temperatures of 500°F. but softens appreciably above 400°F. Glass-filled Teflon is dimensionally stable up to 450° to 500°F.

One of the most common elements used for seal faces is carbon. Although compatible with most process media, carbon is affected by strong oxidizing agents, including fuming nitric acid, hydrogen chloride, and high-temperature air (above 600°F.). Normal mating-face materials for carbon are hard steel, stainless steel, or one of the cast irons.

Other sealing-face combinations that have been satisfactory in corrosive service are ceramic against ceramic, ceramic against carbon, and carbon against glass. The ceramics have also been mated with the various hard-facing alloys. When selecting seal materials the possibility of galvanic corrosion must also be considered.

Gas Seals. Face-type seals are generally not acceptable for gas service because of the difficulty of dissipating the heat generated. The most common gas seal is a **labyrinth** consisting of a number of circumferential knives or touch points arranged in series to provide successive expansion of the fluid (Fig. 6-77). As the differential pressure across any individual restriction is small, the total leakage is minimized. In cases where no external leakage of the process gas is permissible, a purge of some non-toxic gas is usually provided at an intermediate bleed point.

In some installations where the presence of liquids in the gas stream is not undesirable, a liquid-buffered seal is used. This consists of a close-fitting bushing into which oil, water, etc., is injected. In refrigeration centrifugal compressors the bearings and the oil-buffered seals are located in a single enclosed housing.

PIPE AND FITTINGS

Pipe and tube are divided into two main classes—seamless and welded. **Seamless pipe,** as a trade designation, refers to pipe made by forging a solid round, piercing it by simultaneously rotating and forcing it over a piercer point and further reducing it by rolling and drawing. However, seamless pipe and tube are also produced by extrusion, casting into static or centrifugal molds, and by forging and boring. Seamless pipe has the same pounds per square inch strength throughout the wall. Pierced seamless pipe frequently has the inside surface eccentric to the outside surface, resulting in non-uniform wall thickness.

Welded pipe is made from rolled strips formed into cylinders and seam-welded by various methods. The welds are credited with 60 to 100 per cent of the strength of the pipe wall, depending on welding and inspection procedures. Larger diameters and lower ratios of wall thickness to diameter can be obtained in welded pipe than can be obtained in seamless pipe (other than cast pipe). Uniform wall thickness is obtained. Hydrostatic testing does not reveal very short lengths of partially completed weld. This presents a possibility that small leaks may develop prematurely when handling corrosive fluids or when exposed to external corrosion. The weld must be taken into account in developing procedures for bending, flaring, and expanding the welded pipe.

Bends and Elbow Fittings. Directional changes in piping systems require bends and elbow fittings. **Bends** may be made cold or hot. The outside wall is thinned by an amount that varies with the procedure used. Subsequent annealing is required for some materials. To prevent wrinkling and excessive flattening, sand packing is required for hot bending, and sand packing or flexible mandrels may be necessary for cold bending, depending on the ratios of the outside diameter of the pipe to the center-line radius of the bend and to the wall thickness of the pipe. For bends with a center-line radius of 5 nominal pipe diameters, internal support is not required when the wall thickness is at least 6 per cent of the outside diameter of the pipe. Wrinkled bends are made by progressively heating the pipe only on the side which will be the inside of the bend.

Elbow fittings may be cast, forged, or hot or cold formed from short pieces of pipe, or made by welding together pieces of miter-cut pipe. Thinning of pipe during forming of elbows is compensated for by starting with heavier walls.

Flow in bends and elbow fittings is more turbulent than in straight pipe, thus increasing corrosion and erosion. This can be countered by selecting a component with greater radius of curvature, thicker wall, or smoother interior contour, but this is seldom economical in miter elbows.

Compared with elbow fittings, bends with a center-line radius of 5 nominal pipe diameters save the cost of joints and reduce pressure drop. Such bends are not suited for installation in a bank of pipes of unequal size where the bends are in the same plane as the bank.

Tees may be cast, forged, or hot or cold formed from short pieces of pipe. Though it is impossible to have the same flow simultaneously through all three end connections, it is not economical to produce or stock the great variety of tees which accurate sizing of end connections requires. It is customary to stock only tees with the two end (run) connections the same size and the branch connection either the same size as the run connections or one, two, or three sizes smaller. Adjacent reducers or reducing elbow fittings are used for other size reductions. Branch connections (see joints) are often more economical than tees, particularly where the ratio of branch to run is small.

Reducers may be cast, forged, or hot or cold formed from short pieces of pipe. End connections may be concentric; or eccentric, that is, tangent to the same plane at one point on their circumference. For pipe supported by hangers, concentric reducers permit maintenance of the same hanger length; for pipe laid on structural steel, eccentric reducers permit maintaining the same elevation of top of steel. Eccentric reducers with the common tangent plane below permit complete drainage of branched horizontal piping systems through branches smaller than the main. With the common tangent plane above, they permit liquid flow in horizontal lines to sweep the line free of gas or vapor.

Reducing elbow fittings permit change of direction and concentric size reduction in the same fitting.

Valves. Valve bodies may be cast, forged, machined from bar stock, or fabricated from welded plate. Valves serve not only to regulate the flow of fluids but also to isolate piping or equipment for maintenance without interrupting other connected units. Valve design should keep pressure, temperature changes, and strain from connected piping from distorting or misaligning the sealing surfaces. The sealing surfaces should be of such material and design that the valve will remain tight over a reasonable service period. The principal types are named, described, compared, and illustrated with line diagrams, below. In the line diagrams, the operating stem is shown in solid black, direction of flow by arrows on a thin solid line, motion of valve parts by arrows on a dotted line. Moving parts are drawn with solid lines in the nearly closed position and dotted lines in the fully open position. Packing is represented by an X in a square.

Gate valves (Fig. 6-78) are designed in two types. The wedge-shaped gate, **inclined-seat** type is most

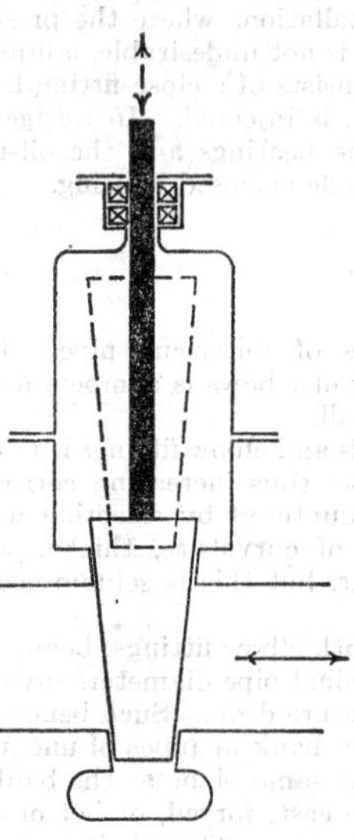

Fig. 6-78. Gate valve.

commonly used. The wedge gate is usually solid but may be flexible (partly cut into halves by a plane at right angles to the pipe), or split (completely cleft by such a plane). Flexible and split wedges minimize galling of the sealing surfaces by distorting more easily to match angularly misaligned seats. In the double-disk, **parallel-seat** type, an inclined-plane device mounted between the disks converts stem force to axial force, pressing the disks against the seats, after the disks are positioned for closing. This gate assembly distorts automatically to match both angular misalignment of the seats and longitudinal shrinkage of the valve body on cooling.

When shearing high-velocity flow of dense fluids, the gate assemblies shake violently, and for this service the solid-wedge or flexible-wedge valves are preferred. Where valve operation is manual, small by-pass valves installed in parallel with the main valve may be used to eliminate the shake problem and to minimize manual effort in opening and closing the valves. Double-disk parallel-seat valves should be installed with the stem essentially vertical. All wedge gate valves are equipped with tongue-and-groove guides to keep the gate sealing surfaces from clattering on the seats and marring them during opening and closing. Depending on the velocity and density of the fluid stream being sheared, these guiding surfaces may be as-cast, machined, or hard surfaced and ground.

Gate valves may have non-rising stems, inside-screw rising stems, or outside-screw rising stems, listed in order of decreasing exposure of the stem threads to the fluid handled. Rising-stem valves require more space, but the position of the stem visually indicates the position of the gate. Indication is clearest on the outside-screw rising-stem valves, and on these the stem threads and thrust collars may be lubricated, reducing operating effort. The stem connection to the gate assembly prevents the stem from rotating.

Gate valves are used to minimize pressure drop in the open position and to stop the flow of fluid rather than to regulate it. The problem, when the valve is closed, of pressure build-up in the bonnet from cold liquids expanding or chemical action between fluid and bonnet should be solved by a relief valve or by notching the upstream seat ring.

Globe valves (Fig. 6-79) are designed as either inside-screw rising stem or outside-screw rising stem.

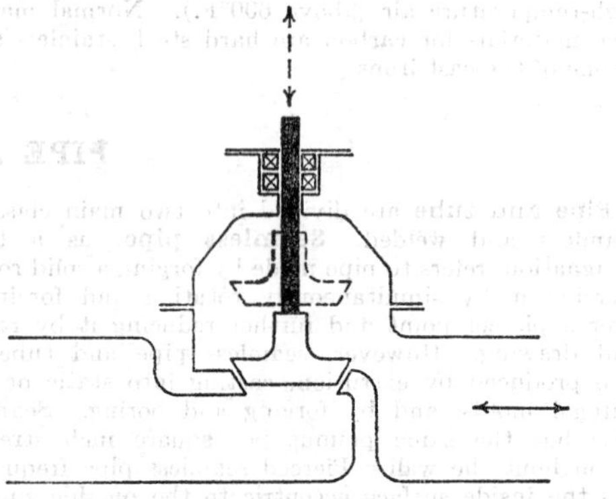

Fig. 6-79. Globe valve.

Small valves generally are of the inside-screw type, while in larger sizes the outside-screw type is preferred. In most designs the disks are free to rotate on the stems; this prevents galling between the disk and the seat.

In the larger sizes, with conical seats, this swivel may permit enough misalignment to prevent proper sealing between the disk and the seat. Where the valve is close to an elbow on the upstream side, the swivel also permits uneven distribution of the fluid to spin the disk on the stem. Guides above the disks, below the disk, or both are used to prevent misalignment and spinning. Misalignment can also be prevented by use of spherical seats and designing the disk so that the pressure point of the stem on the disk is at the center of the sphere. In some designs, spinning and misalignment are prevented by rigidly attaching the disk to the stem, preventing rotation of the stem by lugs which ride along the yoke, and using a yoke bushing as in outside-screw-and-yoke gate valves.

Large globe valves should be installed with stems vertical. Globe valves are preferably installed with the higher-pressure side connected to the top of the disk. Exceptions are (1) where blocked flow caused by separation of the disk from the stem would damage equipment, or (2) where the valve is installed in seldom-used vertical drain lines in which accumulation of rust, scale, or sludge might prevent opening the valve.

Pressure drop through globe valves is much greater than that for gate valves. In Y-type globe valves, the stem and seat are at about 45 deg. to the pipe instead of 90 deg. This reduces pressure drop but impairs alignment of seat and disk.

Globe valves in horizontal lines prevent complete drainage. Seat wiper valves in which the disk may be rotated by a separate stem inside and concentric with the main stem are used to clear the seats of solid deposits.

Angle valves (Fig. 6-80) are similar to globe valves; the same bonnet, stem, and disk are used for both.

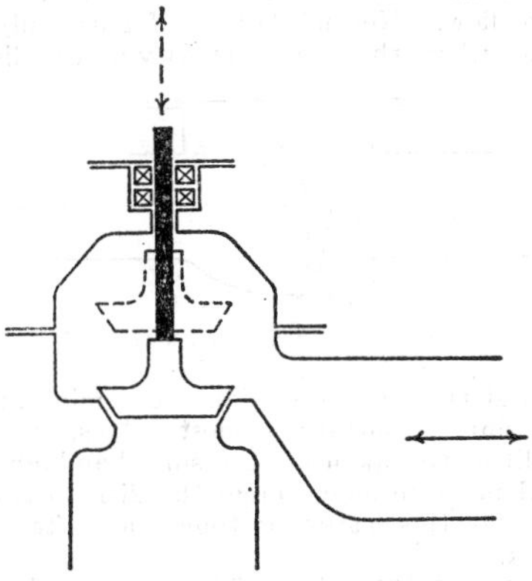

FIG. 6-80. Angle valve.

They combine an elbow fitting and a globe valve into one component with a substantial saving in pressure drop. Flanged angle valves are easier to remove and replace than flanged globe valves.

Diaphragm valves (Fig. 6-81) are limited to pressures of approximately 50 lb./sq. in. The fabric-reinforced

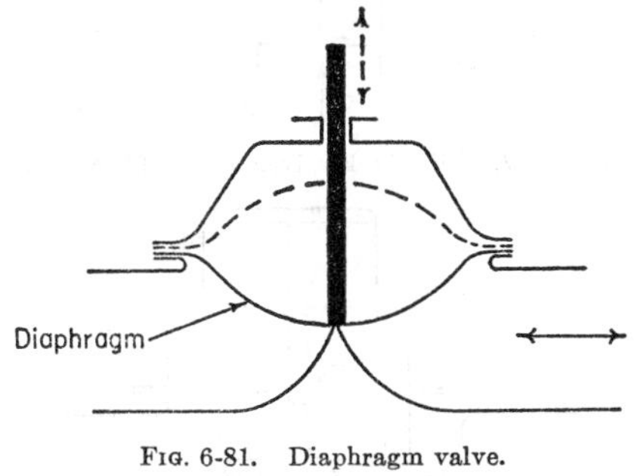

FIG. 6-81. Diaphragm valve.

diaphragms may be made from natural rubber, from a synthetic rubber, or from natural or synthetic rubbers faced with Teflon fluorocarbon resin. The simple shape of the body makes lining it economical. Elastomers have shorter lives as diaphragms than as linings because of flexing but still provide satisfactory service. Plastic bodies, which have low moduli of elasticity compared with metals, are practical in diaphragm valves since alignment and distortion are minor problems.

These valves are excellent for fluids containing suspended solids and can be installed in any position. Models are available in which the dam is very low, reducing pressure drop to a negligible quantity and permitting complete drainage in horizontal lines. However, drainage can be obtained with any model simply by installing with stem horizontal. The only maintenance required is replacement of the diaphragm, which can be done very quickly without removing the valve from the line.

Plug cocks (Fig. 6-82) are limited to temperatures below 500°F. since differential expansion between the plug and the body results in seizure. Size and shape of

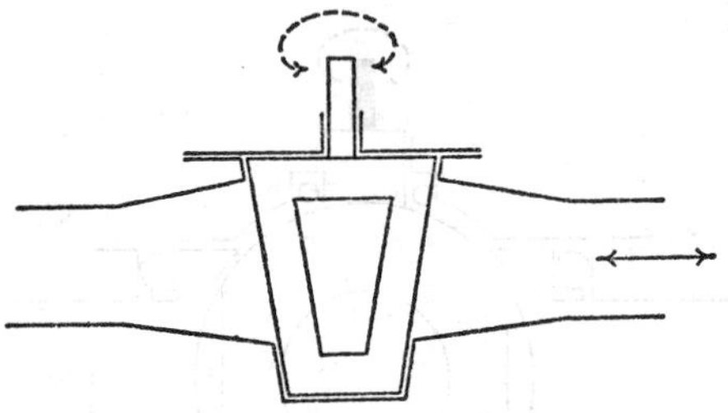

FIG. 6-82. Plug cock.

the port divide these valves into different types. In order of increasing cost they are: short venturi, reduced rectangular port; long venturi, reduced rectangular port; full rectangular port; and full round port.

In **lever-sealed** plug cocks, tapered plugs are used. The plugs are raised by turning one lever, rotated by another lever, and reseated by the first lever. **Lubricated** plug cocks may use straight or tapered plugs. The tapered plugs may be raised slightly, to reduce turning effort, by injection of the lubricant, which also acts as a seal. Plastic is used in non-lubricated plug cocks as a body liner, or a plug coating, or as port seals in the body or on the plug.

In plug cocks other than lever-sealed plug cocks, the contact area between plug and body is large, and gearing is usually used in sizes 6 in. and larger to minimize operating effort. There are several lever-sealed plug cocks incorporating mechanisms which convert rotary motion of a handwheel into sequenced motion of the two levers.

For lubricated plug cocks, the lubricant must have limited viscosity change over the range of operating temperature, must have low solubility in the fluid handled, and must be applied regularly. There must be no chemical reaction between the lubricant and the fluid which would harden or soften the lubricant or contaminate the fluid. For these reasons, lubricated plug cocks are most often used where there are a large number handling the same or closely related fluids at approximately the same temperature.

Lever-sealed plug cocks are used for throttling service. Because of the large contact area between plug and body, if a plug cock is operable, there is little likelihood of leakage when closed, and the handle position is a clearly visible indication of the valve position.

Ball valves (Figs. 6-83 and 6-84) are limited to temperatures which have little effect on their plastic seats. Since the sealing element is a ball, its alignment is not essential to tight shutoff. In free-ball valves, the ball is

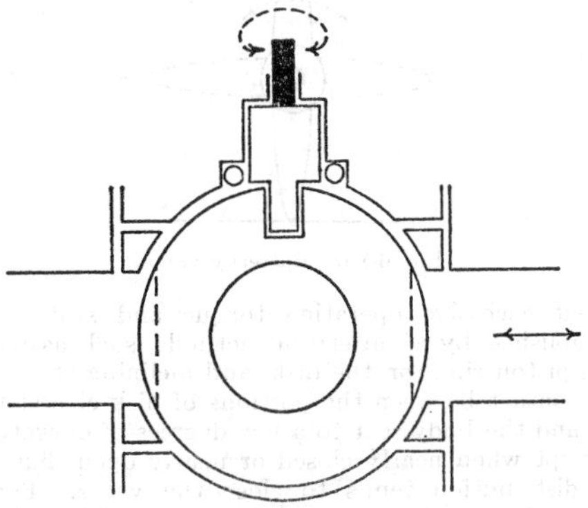

FIG. 6-83. Ball valve Free ball, compressed seats, split body, three piece.

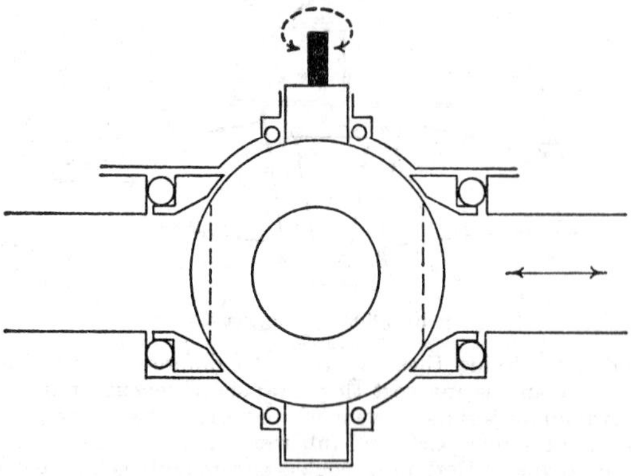

FIG. 6-84. Ball valve. Fixed ball, O-ring seal seats, top entry.

free to move axially. Pressure differential across the valve forces the ball in the closed position against the downstream seat and the latter against the body. In fixed-ball valves, the ball rotates on stem extensions, with the bearings sealed with O-rings. Plastic seats may be compressed or spring-loaded against the ball and the body by the assembly of the valves, or they may be forced against the ball by pressure across the valve acting against O-rings which seal between the seat and the body.

Ball valves in which the ball and seats are inserted from above are known as top-entry ball valves. Replacement of seats is easiest in this type. The others are known as split-body valves. Some of these incorporate bolted assembly which permits their use as joints for assembly of the piping. Replacement of seats in this type is easiest where the body consists of three pieces with the ball and the seats contained in the middle piece.

For the larger sizes in high-pressure service, the fixed-ball type with O-ring seat seals requires less operating effort. However, these require two different plastic materials with resistance to the fluid and its temperature. Like plug cocks, ball valves may be either restricted port or full port, but the ports are always round and pressure drop is low.

Butterfly valves (Fig. 6-85) occupy less space in the line than any other valves. Relatively tight sealing

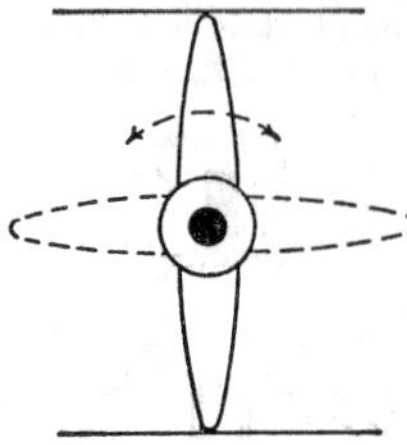

FIG. 6-85. Butterfly valve.

without excessive operating torque and seat wear is accomplished by a variety of methods, such as resilient seats, piston rings on the disk, and inclining the stem to limit contact between the portions of disk closest to the stem and the body seat to a few degrees of curvature.

Except when nearly closed or nearly open, fluid-pressure distribution tends to close the valve. For this reason, the smaller manually operated valves have a latching device on the handle, and the larger manually operated valves use worm gearing on the stem. This hydraulic unbalance is proportional to the pressure drop and is the principal component in the torque required to operate the valves. Compared with other valves for low pressure drops, they can be operated by smaller hydraulic cylinders. Pressure drop is quite high compared with gate valves.

Swing check valves (Fig. 6-86) are used to prevent reversal of flow. Normal design is for use only in horizontal lines where the force of gravity on the disk is at a

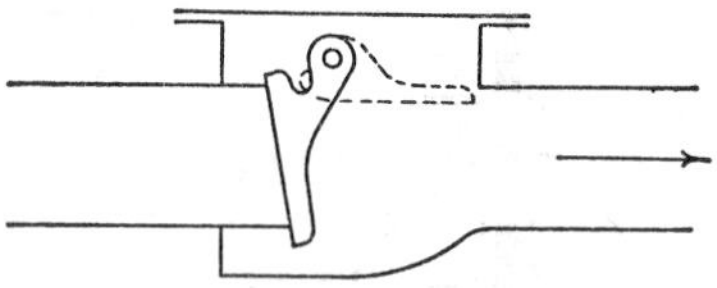

FIG. 6-86. Swing check valve.

maximum at the start of closing and a minimum at the end of closing. Contrary to most valves, check valves are more likely to leak at low pressure than high pressure, since fluid pressure alone forces the disk to conform to the seat. For this reason elastomers are often mounted on the disk.

Lift check valves (Figs. 6-87, 6-88, and 6-89) are made in three styles. Vertical lift check valves are for installation in vertical lines where the flow is normally upward; globe check valves are for use in horizontal

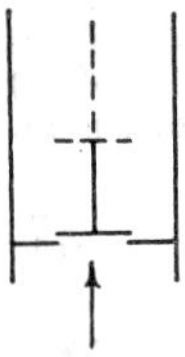

FIG. 6-87. Lift check valve, vertical lift check.

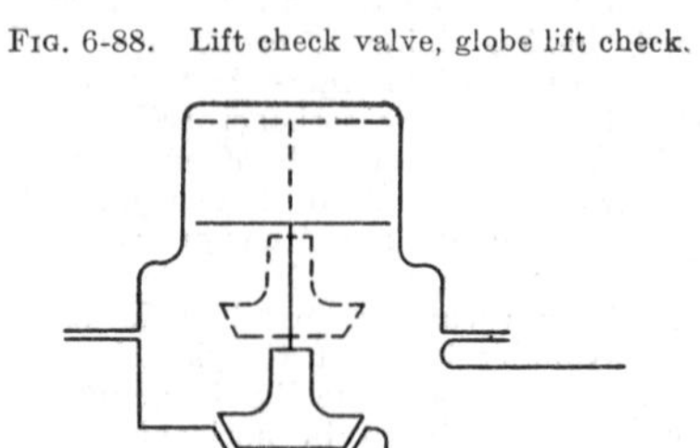

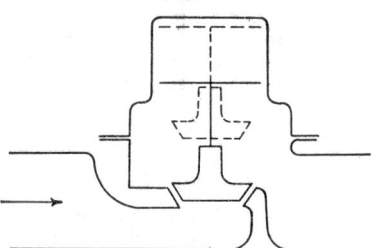

FIG. 6-88. Lift check valve, globe lift check.

FIG. 6-89. Lift check valve, angle lift check.

lines; angle check valves are for installation where a vertical line with upward flow turns horizontal. Globe and angle check valves normally incorporate an integral dashpot above the disk to slow the motion of the disk and reduce wear. In vertical lift check valves, this feature is found only in the larger sizes. Springs may be incorporated in the dashpots to speed up closing, but this increases the pressure drop. Lift checks should not be used where the fluid contains suspended solids.

Tilting-disk check valves (Fig. 6-90) may be installed in a horizontal line or in lines in which the flow

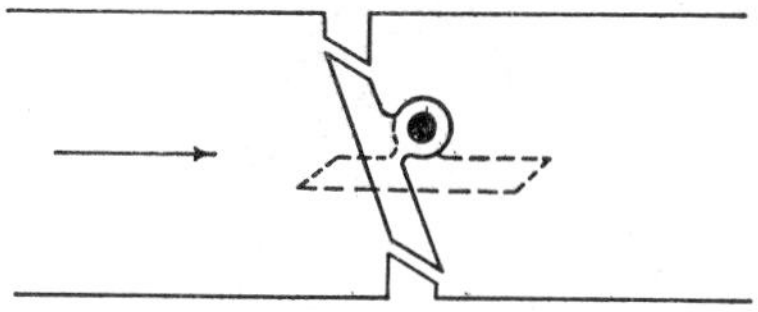

FIG. 6-90. Tilting-disk check valve.

is vertically upward. Location of the pivot point is selected so that the distribution of pressure in the fluid handled speeds the closing but arrests slamming. Compared with swing check valves of the same size, pressure drop is less at low velocities but greater at high velocities.

Closure at the instant of reversal of flow is most nearly attained in this valve. This timing of closure is not the whole solution to noise and shock at check valves. For example, if cessation of pressure at the inlet of the valve produces flashing of the decelerating stream downstream from the valve, or if stoppage of flow is caused by a sudden closure of a valve some distance downstream from the check valve, and the stoppage is followed by returning water hammer, slower closure may be necessary. For these applications, tilting-disk check valves are equipped with external dashpots.

Valve Trim. Various alloys are available for valve parts such as seats, disks, and stems which must retain smooth finish for successful operation. The problem in seat materials is fivefold: (1) resistance to corrosion by the fluid handled and to oxidation at high temperatures; (2) resistance to erosion by suspended solids in the fluid; (3) prevention of galling (seizure at point of contact) by differences in material or hardness or both; (4) maintenance of high strength at high temperature; (5) avoidance of distortion.

All valve trim materials have coefficients of thermal expansion which exceed those of cast or forged carbon steel by 24 to 45 per cent and tend to cause distortion of seats and disks. To some extent leakage from this cause is prevented by closing the valve more tightly. Inserting a ring of high-temperature elastomer, either in or alongside the trim metal in the seat or disk, prevents leakage from this cause.

Joints. Pipe must be joined to pipe and to other components. Optimum design requires a minimum of assembly labor and provides the same resistance possessed by the pipe to (1) internal pressure as regards both rupture and leakage, (2) bending moments arising from spanning long distances between supports or from thermal expansion in piping containing offsets, (3) axial strain arising from internal pressure acting on changes in direction, blanks or closed valves, or from thermal contraction in straight runs, (4) rupture or leakage in event of fire.

However, joints in pipe buried in the soil, where position of each length and component is fixed, need provide the same resistance as the pipe to internal pressure only; in event of earth settlement, the joints may be required to yield to resulting bending moments without leakage. Also, in piping subject to thermal expansion and contraction, some joints may be required to yield to resulting bending moments and axial strains without leakage.

The ideal pipe joint is free from changes in any dimension of the flow passage or direction of flow which would increase pressure drop or prevent complete drainage. It is free from crevices in which corrosion might be accelerated. It would require a minimum of labor to disassemble. Required frequency for disassembling the joint must be considered in making the selection. Generally speaking, joints which are easy to disassemble are deficient in one or more of the other requirements of the ideal joint.

Most joints involve modifications of the components being joined, and components with the desired modifications can usually be purchased.

The most widely used joint in piping systems is the **butt-welded joint** (Fig. 6-91). In all ductile pipe

FIG. 6-91. Butt weld.

metals which can be welded, pipe, elbows, tees, laterals, reducers, caps, valves, flanges, and V-clamp joints are available in all sizes and wall thicknesses with ends prepared for butt welding. Joint strength equal to the original pipe (except for work-hardened pipes which are annealed by the welding), unimpaired flow pattern, and generally unimpaired corrosion resistance more than compensate for the necessary careful alignment, skilled labor, and equipment required.

Plain-end pipe used for **socket-weld joints** (Fig. 6-92) is available in all sizes, but fittings and valves

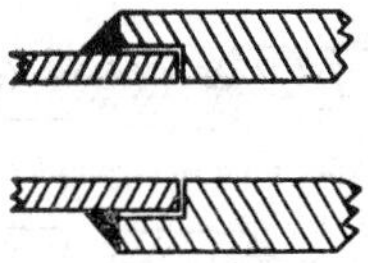

FIG. 6-92. Socket weld.

with socket-weld ends are limited to sizes 3 in. and smaller, where the extra cost of the socket is outweighed by much easier alignment and less skill needed in welding. The joint is not so resistant to bending stress as the butt-welded joint but is otherwise equal, except that, for some fluids, the crevice between the pipe and the socket may promote corrosion.

Branch welds (Fig. 6-93) eliminate the purchase of tees and require no more weld metal than tees. Where

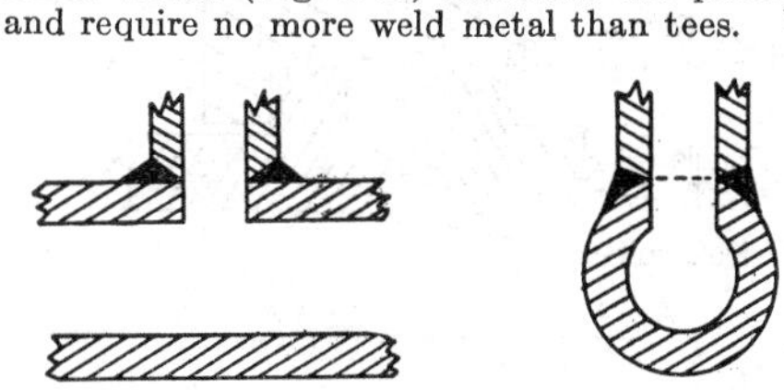

FIG. 6-93. Branch weld.

the branch approaches the size of the run, careful end preparation of the branch pipe is required and the run pipe is weakened by the branch weld. Pressure piping codes provide rules for reinforcement of the run where required (see Sec. 24). Reinforcing pads and fittings are commercially available. Use of the fittings facilitates visual inspection of the branch weld.

Pipe with **taper pipe thread** ends (Fig. 6-94) per A.S.A. B2.1 is available 12 in. and smaller, subject to minimum wall limitations. Fittings and valves with taper pipe thread ends are available in most pipe metals.

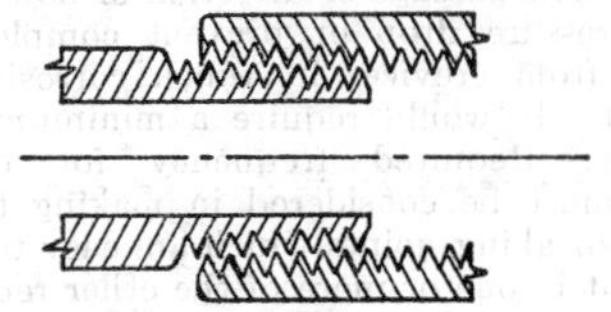

FIG. 6-94. Taper pipe thread.

Principal use of threaded joints is in sizes 2 in. and smaller, in metals where the most economically produced walls are thick enough to withstand considerable pressure and corrosion after reduction in thickness due to threading. For threaded joints over 2 in., assembly labor and size and cost of tools increase rapidly. Careful alignment is required at the start of assembly, and rotation of the components, as well as variation in length produced by diametral tolerances in the threads, severely limits preassembly of the components. Threading is not a precise machining operation, and filler materials known as "pipe dope" are necessary to block the spiral leakage path.

Threads notch the pipe and cause loss of strength and fatigue resistance. Enlargement and contraction of the flow passage at threaded joints creates turbulence; sometimes corrosion and erosion are aggravated at the point where the pipe has already been thinned by threading.

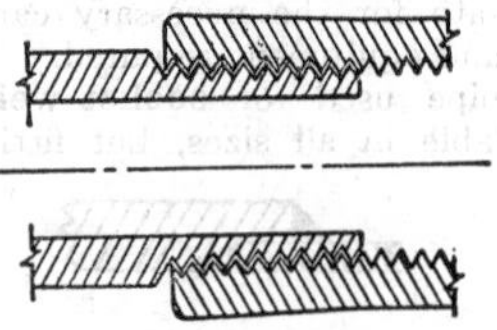

FIG. 6-95. Taper pipe to straight coupling thread.

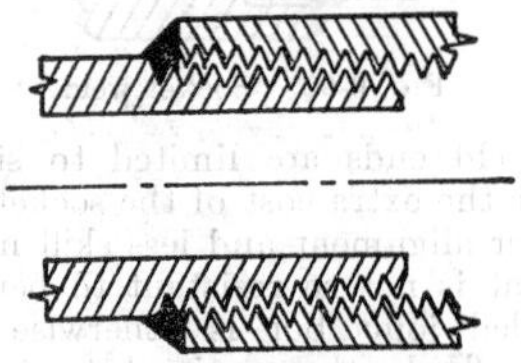

FIG. 6-96. Taper pipe thread, seal-welded.

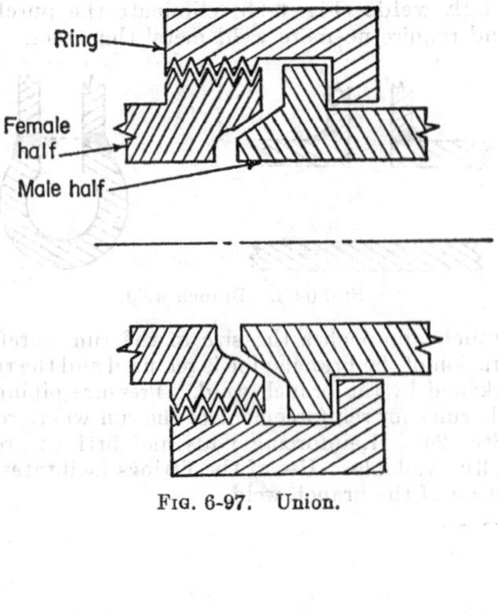

FIG. 6-97. Union.

The tendency of pipe wrenches to crush pipe and fittings limits the torque available for tightening threaded joints. For low-pressure systems, a slight rotation in the joint may be used to impart flexibility to the system, but this same rotation, unwanted, may cause leaks to develop in higher-pressure systems. In some metals, galling occurs when threaded joints are disassembled.

Straight pipe threads (Fig. 6-95) are confined to lightweight couplings sizes 2 in. and smaller. Manufacturers of threaded pipe ship it with such couplings

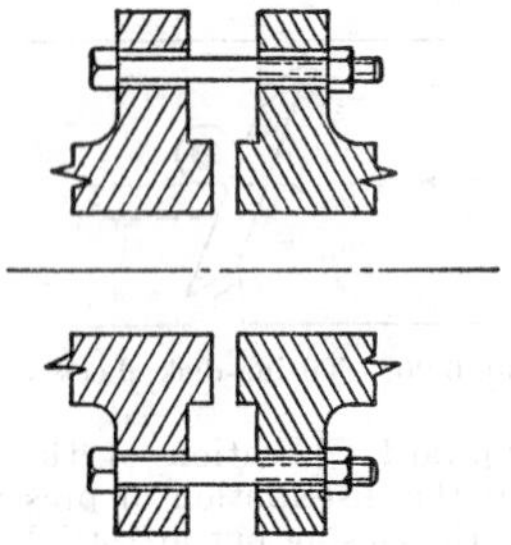

FIG. 6-98. Flanged joint.

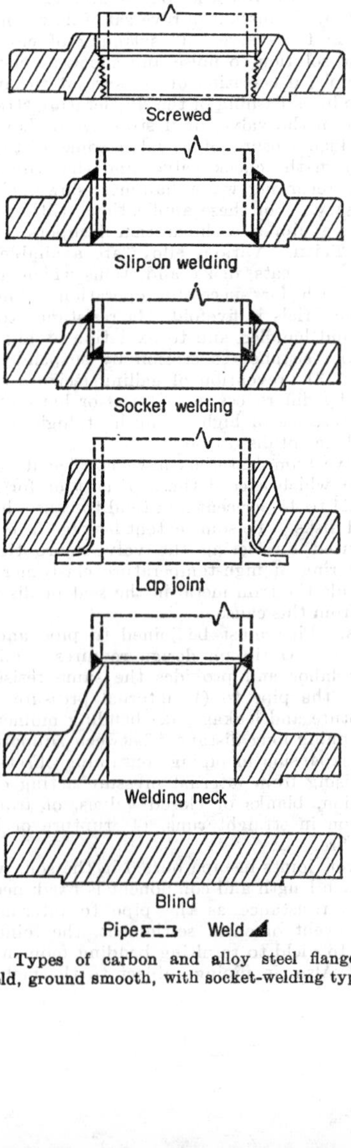

FIG. 6-99. Types of carbon and alloy steel flanges. (Note internal weld, ground smooth, with socket-welding type.)

installed on one end of each pipe. The joint obtained is inferior to that obtained with taper threads.

Where both components of a threaded joint are of weldable metal, the joint may be seal-welded as shown in Fig. 6-96. This is limited to new construction and is not suitable as a repair procedure, since pipe dope in the threads would interfere with welding. This method provides tight joints with a minimum of welding labor. Where threaded joints used to join materials with widely different coefficients of thermal expansion are subject to temperature cycling, seal welding may be necessary to prevent leakage.

To assist in assembly and disassembly of both threaded and welded systems, **union joints** (Fig. 6-97) are used. They comprise metal-to-metal seats drawn together by a shouldered straight thread nut and are available both in couplings for joining two lengths of pipe and on the ends of some fittings. On threaded piping systems where disassembly is not contemplated, union joints installed at intervals permit future further tightening of threaded joints. Tightening of heavy unions yields tight joints even if the pipe is slightly misaligned at the start of tightening.

For sizes larger than 2 in., where disassembly is contemplated, the **flanged joint** (Fig. 6-98) is the most widely used. Figures 6-99 and 6-100 illustrate the wide variety of types and facings available. Though flanged joints consume a large volume of metal, precise machining is required only on the facing. Flanged joints do not impose severe diametral tolerances on the pipe. Careful alignment prior to assembly of flat-face and raised-face flanges is not required, and the necessary wrenches are far smaller than those for screwed assembly for the same size of pipe.

Manufacturers offer **flanged-end pipe** in only a few metals. Otherwise, flanges are attached to pipe by various types of joints (Fig. 6-99). The lap joint involves a modification of the pipe which may be formed from the pipe itself or by welding a ring or a lap joint stub end to it. **Flanged end fittings** and **valves** are available in all sizes of most pipe metals.

Welding-neck flanges provide joints as strong as the pipe under all types of static and cycling loading. Slip-on, socket-weld, and lap-joint flanges provide joints as strong as the pipe under static loading but have lower resistance to cyclic stresses. Lap-joint flanges avoid the necessity of orienting flanges so that vertical and horizontal center lines are halfway between bolt holes and permit orientation of the stems of flanged valves at any angle needed to provide clearance. The tolerance is 1/8 in. in the bolt holes; the necessity of making sure that the gasket does not protrude into the flow channel results in some disturbance of the flow pattern when flat-face and raised-face flanges are used. This can be eliminated by using welding-neck or socket-weld flanges with male-and-female or tongue-and-groove facings.

Gaskets must resist corrosion by the fluids handled. The more expensive male-and-female or tongue-and-groove facings may be required to seat hard gaskets adequately. With these facings the gasket cannot blow out. Flanged joints, by placing the gasket material under heavy compression and permitting only edge

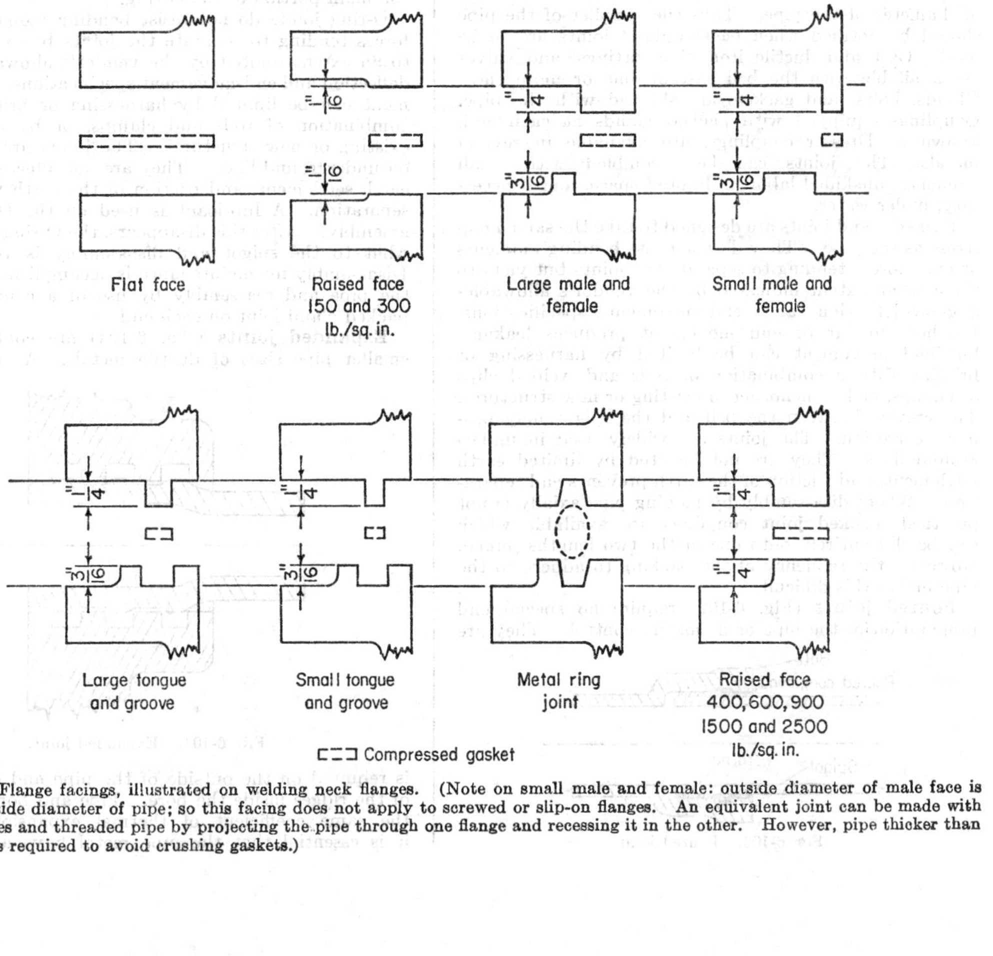

FIG. 6-100. Flange facings, illustrated on welding neck flanges. (Note on small male and female: outside diameter of male face is less than outside diameter of pipe; so this facing does not apply to screwed or slip-on flanges. An equivalent joint can be made with screwed flanges and threaded pipe by projecting the pipe through one flange and recessing it in the other. However, pipe thicker than Schedule 40 is required to avoid crushing gaskets.)

attack by the fluid handled, can use gasket materials which, in other joints, might not satisfactorily resist the fluid handled.

Metal-ring-joint facing is the most costly facing. The ring must be softer than the flange and is usually a softer grade of the same metal as the flange. It is used where other gasket materials are destroyed by the fluid handled. In event of fire, it does not leak. Because the surfaces the gasket contacts are below the flange face, it is the least likely facing to be damaged in handling. Compared with raised or smooth faces, it is more difficult to disassemble because the flanges can be separated only in the axial direction.

Packed-gland joints (Fig. 6-101) require no special end preparation of pipe but do require careful control

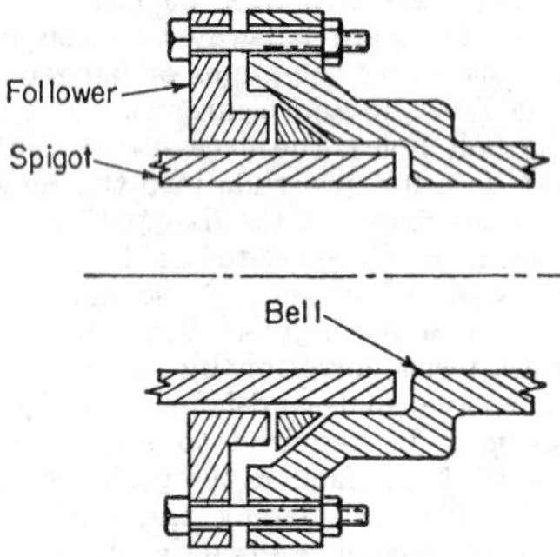

Fig. 6-101. Packed-gland joint.

of diameter of the pipe. Thus the supplier of the pipe should be notified when packed-gland joints are to be used. Cast and ductile iron pipe, fittings, and valves are available with the bell cast on one or more ends. Glands, bolts, and gaskets are shipped with the pipe. Couplings equipped with packed glands at each end, known as Dresser couplings, are available in several metals. The joints can be assembled with small wrenches, unskilled labor, in limited space, and if necessary, under water.

Packed-gland joints are designed to take the same hoop stress as the pipe. They do not resist bending moments or axial forces tending to separate the joints but yield to them to an extent indicated by the vendor's allowable-angular-deflection and end-movement specifications. Further angular or end movement produces leakage, but end movement can be limited by harnessing or bridling with a combination of rods and welded clips or clamps, or by anchoring to existing or new structures. The crevice between the bell and the spigot may promote corrosion. The joints are widely used in underground lines. They are not affected by limited earth settlement, and friction of the earth prevents end separation. Where disassembly by moving pipe axially is not practical, packed joint couplings are available which can be slid entirely onto one of the two lengths joined. However, the tendency of the packing to adhere to the pipe makes this difficult.

Poured joints (Fig. 6-102) require no special end preparation of the pipe or diametral control. They are

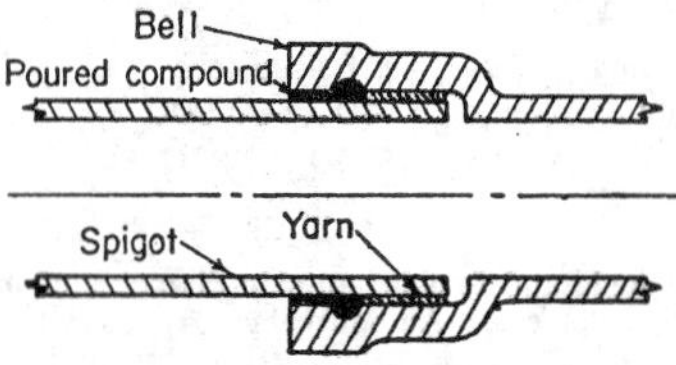

Fig. 6-102. Poured joint

used for brittle materials. Pipe, fittings, and valves are furnished with the bells cast on one or more ends. The pouring compound may be molten, or chemical setting, or merely compacted; these are listed in descending order of ability to hold pressure. These joints cannot absorb angular or axial movement without leaking. Disassembly for maintenance is accomplished by cutting the pipe and reassembly by the use of a coupling with a bell on each end.

O-ring joints (Fig. 6-103) require diametral control of the end of the pipe. They are used for brittle materials. Pipe, fittings and valves are furnished with the

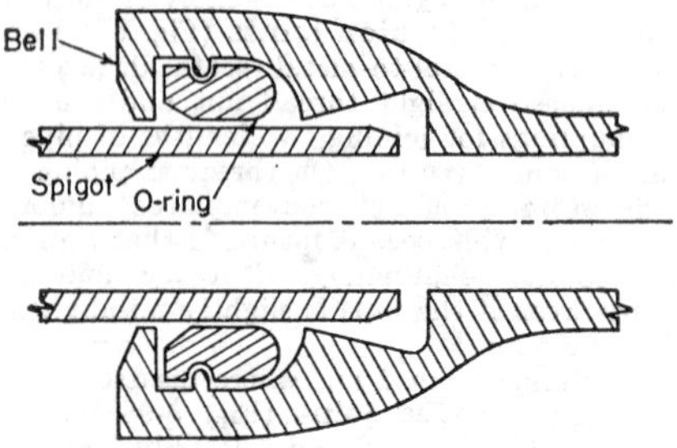

Fig. 6-103. O-ring joint.

bells cast on one or more ends. Considerable force is required to push the spigot through the O-ring; this is reduced by the extension on the O-ring, which causes the friction of the pipe to elongate the cross section of the main portion of the O-ring.

O-ring joints do not resist bending moments or axial forces tending to separate the joints but yield to them to an extent limited by the vendor's allowable-angular-deflection and end-movement specifications. End movement can be limited by harnessing or bridling with a combination of rods and clamps, or by anchoring to existing or new structures. The joints are widely used on underground lines. They are not affected by limited earth settlement, and friction of the earth prevents end separation. A lubricant is used on the O-ring during assembly. After this disappears, the O-ring bonds somewhat to the spigot and disassembly is very difficult. Disassembly for maintenance is accomplished by cutting the pipe and reassembly by use of a coupling with a packed gland joint on each end.

Expanded joints (Fig. 6-104) are confined to the smaller pipe sizes of ductile metals. A smooth finish

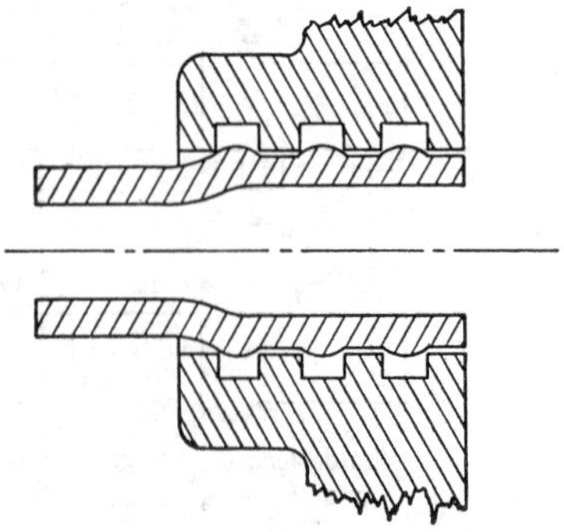

Fig. 6-104. Expanded joint.

is required on the outside of the pipe and on the faces of the ridges inside the bore. Pipe and bore must have the same coefficient of thermal expansion. Further, it is essential that the pipe metal have a lower yield point than the metal into which it is expanded, except in cases where the metal into which it is expanded is a thin cylinder temporarily backed by clamped heavy semicylindrical metal shells with a high yield point. An expanding tool is required, one for each size of pipe.

After completion of the joint, it is difficult to determine whether the increase in the inside diameter of the pipe represents permanent stretch of the bore of the mating part or flow of metal into the grooves of the bore. An excess of the latter results in excessive thinning of the tube, while an insufficiency of the latter may cause the pipe to pull out of the bore under axial loading. In a variation, the expanded joint is combined with a flared joint to increase resistance to axial load. These joints are used to attach unions and Lovekin flanges to pipe. For alloy piping, composite Lovekin flanges are available in which the bore and raised face portion are made of the alloy, retained in the steel balance of the flange by an offset.

Grooved joints (Fig. 6-105) are divided into two classes, cut groove and rolled groove. Rolled grooves are preferred because, compared with cut grooves, they are easier to form and reduce the metal wall less. However, they slightly reduce the flow area. They are limited to thin walls of ductile material, while cut grooves, because of their reduction of the pipe wall, are limited to thick walls. In the larger pipe sizes, some commonly used wall thicknesses are too thick for rolled grooves but too thin for cut grooves. The thinning of the walls impairs resistance to corrosion and erosion but not to internal pressure, because the thinned area is reinforced by the coupling.

Control of outside diameter is important. Permissible minus tolerance is limited, since it impairs the grip of the couplings. Plus tolerance makes it necessary to cut the cut grooves deeper, increasing the thinning of the wall. Plus tolerance is not a problem with rolled grooves, since they are confined to walls thin enough so that the couplings can compress the pipe. Pipe is available from vendors already grooved and also with heavier-wall grooved ends welded on.

Grooved joints resist axial forces tending to separate the joints. Angular deflection, up to the limit specified by the vendor, may be used to absorb thermal expansion and to permit the piping to be laid on uneven ground. Compared with flanged joints, grooved joints will not pull misaligned pipe into alignment and thus they require more support, but otherwise they require less labor for handling, assembly, and disassembly.

Gaskets are self-sealing against both internal and external pressure and are available in a wide variety of elastomers. However, successful performance of an elastomer as a flange gasket does not necessarily mean equally satisfactory performance in a grooved joint, since exposure to the fluid in the latter is much greater and hardening has a greater unfavorable effect. It is customary to use couplings which are resistant to corrosion by the fluid in the pipe, but couplings which would contaminate the fluid may be used.

V-clamp joints (Fig. 6-106) are attached to the pipe by butt-weld or expanded joints. Theoretically, there is only one relative position of the parts in which the conical surfaces of the clamp are completely in contact with the conical surfaces of the stub ends. In actual practice, there is considerable flexing of the stub ends and the clamp; also complete contact is not required. This permits use of elastomeric gaskets as well as metal gaskets. Fittings are also available with integral conical shouldered ends.

Conical ends vary from machined forgings to roll-formed tubing, and clamps vary from machined forgings to bands to which several roll-formed channels are attached at their centers by spot welding. A hinge may be inserted in the band as a substitute for one of

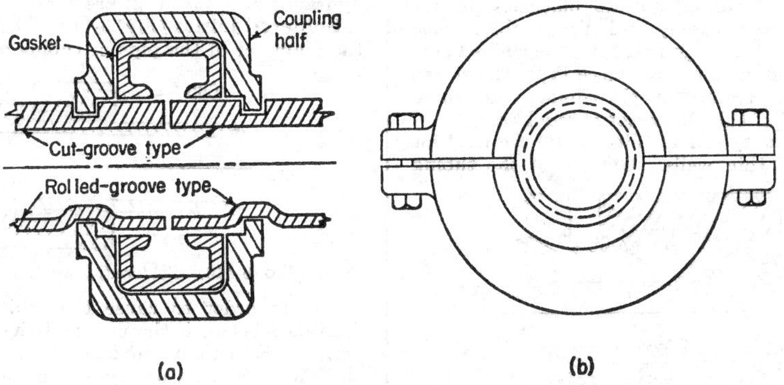

Fig. 6-105. Grooved joint. (a) Section. (b) End view.

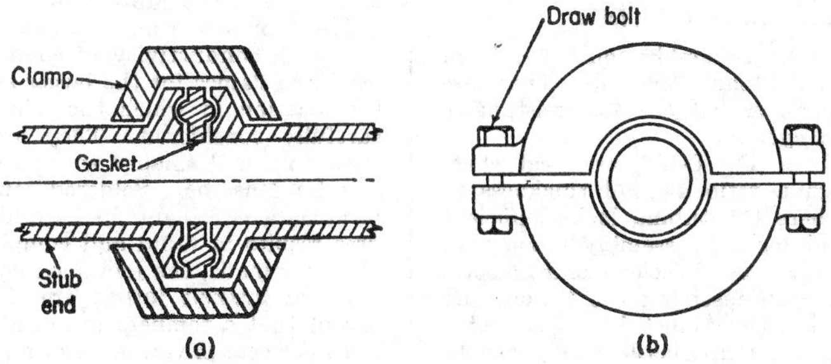

Fig. 6-106. V-clamp joint. (a) Section. (b) End view.

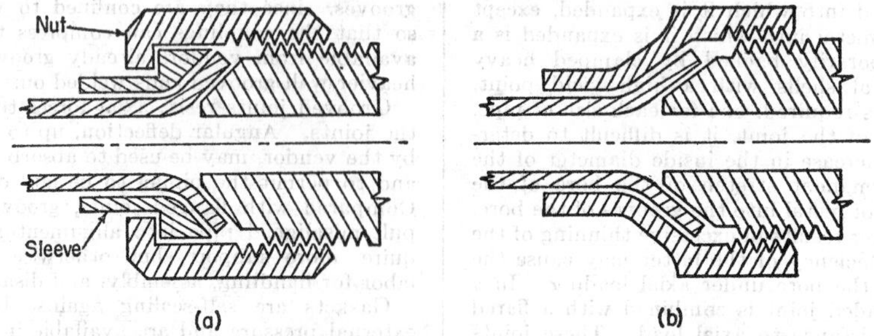

FIG. 6-107. Flared-fitting joint. (a) Three-piece. (b) Two-piece.

the draw bolts. Latches may also be substituted for draw bolts.

Compared with flanges, V-clamp joints use less metal, require less labor for assembly, and are less likely to leak under wide-range rapid temperature cycling. However, they are more susceptible to failure or damage from overtightening. They are widely used for high-alloy piping subject to periodic cleaning or relocation. Manufactured as forgings, they are used in carbon steel with metal gaskets for very high pressures. They resist both axial strain and bending moments. Each size of each type of joint is customarily rated by the vendor for both internal pressure and bending moment.

Flared-fitting joints (Fig. 6-107) are used for ductile tubing for which the ratio of wall thickness to diameter is small enough to permit flaring without cracking the inside surface. The tubing must have a smooth interior surface. The three-piece type avoids torsional strain on the tubing and minimizes vibration fatigue on the flared portion of the tubing. More labor is required for assembly, but it is more resistant to temperature cycling than other tubing fittings, is unlikely to be damaged by overtightening, and its efficiency is not impaired by repeated assembly and disassembly. Size is limited because of the large number of machined surfaces. The nut and, in the three-piece type, the sleeve need not be the same material as the tubing. For these fittings, less control of tube diameter is required.

Compression-fitting joints (Fig. 6-108) are used for ductile tubing with thin walls. Outside of the tubing

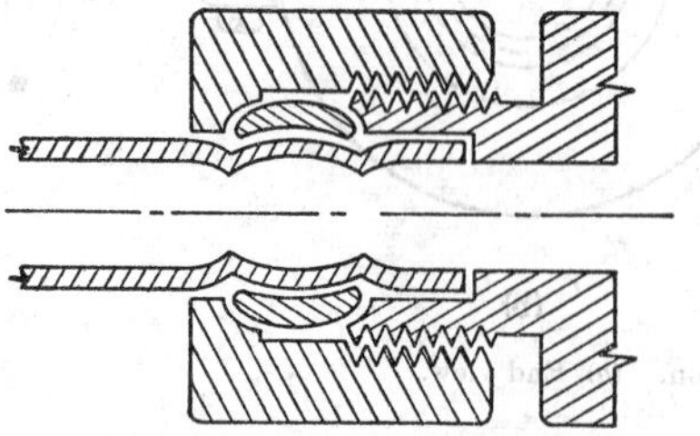

FIG. 6-108. Compression-fitting joint.

must be clean and smooth. Assembly consists only of inserting the tubing and tightening the nut. These are the least costly tubing fittings but are not resistant to vibration or temperature cycling.

Bite-type-fitting joints (Fig. 6-109) are used where the tubing has too high a ratio of wall thickness to diameter for flaring, where the tubing lacks sufficient ductility for flaring, and for low assembly labor cost. The outside of the tubing must be clean and smooth. Assembly consists in merely inserting the tubing and tightening the nut. The sleeve must be considerably harder than the tubing yet still ductile enough to be diametrally compressed and must be as resistant to corrosion by the fluid handled as the tubing. The

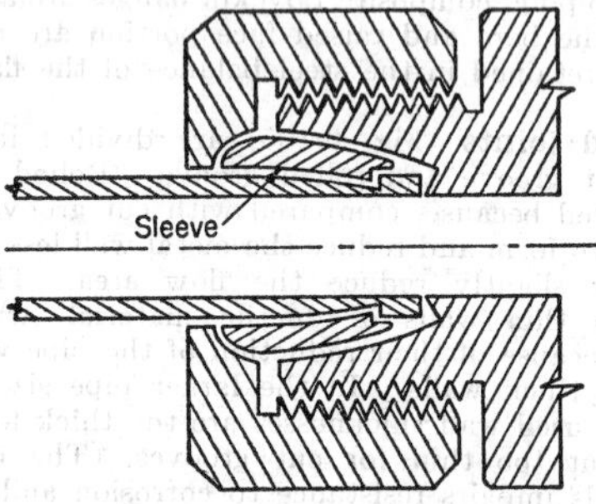

FIG. 6-109. Bite-type fitting joint.

fittings are resistant to vibration but not to wide-range rapid temperature cycling. Compared with flared fittings they are less suited for repeated assembly and disassembly, require closer diametral control of the tubing, and are more susceptible from damage from overtightening. They are widely used for oil-filled hydraulic systems at all pressures.

Soldered joints (Fig. 6-110) require precise control of the diameter of the pipe or tubing and of the cup in the

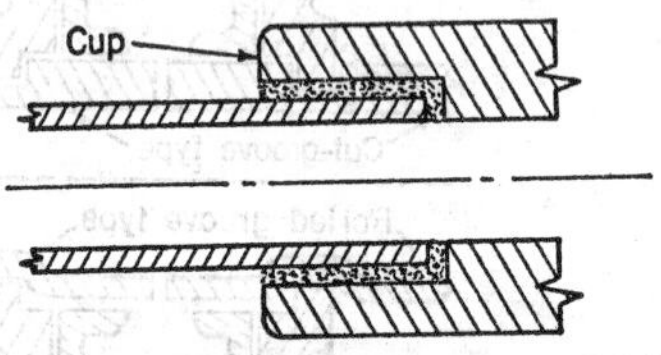

FIG. 6-110. Soldered, brazed, or cemented joint.

fitting in order to cause the solder to draw into the clearance between the cup and the tubing by capillary action. Extrusion provides this diametral control, and the joints are most widely used in copper. A 50 per cent lead, 50 per cent tin solder is used for temperatures up to 200°F. Careful cleaning of the outside of the tubing and inside of the cup is required.

Heat for soldering is usually obtained from torches. The high conductivity of copper makes it necessary to use large flames for the larger sizes, and for this reason, the location in which the joint will be made must be carefully considered. They are most widely used in sizes 2 in. and smaller where the heat requirements are less burdensome. Soldered joints should not be used in areas where plant fires are likely because exposure to fires results in rapid and complete failure of the joints. Properly made, the joints are completely impervious.

Silver-brazed joints are similar to soldered joints except that a temperature of about 1100°F. is required. A 15 per cent silver, 80 per cent copper, 5 per cent phosphorus solder is used for copper and copper alloys, while 45 per cent silver, 15 per cent copper, 16 per cent zinc,

Table 6-2. Properties of Ferrous Pipe

Nominal pipe size, in.	Outside diam., in.	Schedule No.	Wall thickness, in.	Inside diam., in.	Cross-sectional area		Circumference, ft., or surface, sq. ft./ft. of length		Capacity at 1 ft./sec. velocity		Weight of plain-end pipe, lb./ft.
					Metal, sq. in.	Flow, sq. ft.	Outside	Inside	U.S. gal./min.	Lb./hr. water	
⅛	0.405	10S	0.049	0.307	0.055	0.00051	0.106	0.0804	0.231	115.5	0.19
		40ST, 40S	.068	.269	.072	.00040	.106	.0705	.179	89.5	.24
		80XS, 80S	.095	.215	.093	.00025	.106	.0563	.113	56.5	.31
¼	0.540	10S	.065	.410	.097	.00092	.141	.107	.412	206.5	.33
		40ST, 40S	.088	.364	.125	.00072	.141	.095	.323	161.5	.42
		80XS, 80S	.119	.302	.157	.00050	.141	.079	.224	112.0	.54
⅜	0.675	10S	.065	.545	.125	.00162	.177	.143	.727	363.5	.42
		40ST, 40S	.091	.493	.167	.00133	.177	.129	.596	298.0	.57
		80XS, 80S	.126	.423	.217	.00098	.177	.111	.440	220.0	.74
½	0.840	5S	.065	.710	.158	.00275	.220	.186	1.234	617.0	.54
		10S	.083	.674	.197	.00248	.220	.176	1.112	556.0	.67
		40ST, 40S	.109	.622	.250	.00211	.220	.163	0.945	472.0	.85
		80XS, 80S	.147	.546	.320	.00163	.220	.143	0.730	365.0	1.09
		160	.188	.464	.385	.00117	.220	.122	0.527	263.5	1.31
		XX	.294	.252	.504	.00035	.220	.066	0.155	77.5	1.71
¾	1.050	5S	.065	.920	.201	.00461	.275	.241	2.072	1036.0	0.69
		10S	.083	.884	.252	.00426	.275	.231	1.903	951.5	0.86
		40ST, 40S	.113	.824	.333	.00371	.275	.216	1.665	832.5	1.13
		80XS, 80S	.154	.742	.433	.00300	.275	.194	1.345	672.5	1.47
		160	.219	.612	.572	.00204	.275	.160	0.917	458.5	1.94
		XX	.308	.434	.718	.00103	.275	.114	0.461	230.5	2.44
1	1.315	5S	.065	1.185	.255	.00768	.344	.310	3.449	1725	0.87
		10S	.109	1.097	.413	.00656	.344	.287	2.946	1473	1.40
		40ST, 40S	.133	1.049	.494	.00600	.344	.275	2.690	1345	1.68
		80XS, 80S	.179	0.957	.639	.00499	.344	.250	2.240	1120	2.17
		160	.250	0.815	.836	.00362	.344	.213	1.625	812.5	2.84
		XX	.358	0.599	1.076	.00196	.344	.157	0.878	439.0	3.66
1¼	1.660	5S	.065	1.530	0.326	.01277	.435	.401	5.73	2865	1.11
		10S	.109	1.442	0.531	.01134	.435	.378	5.09	2545	1.81
		40ST, 40S	.140	1.380	0.668	.01040	.435	.361	4.57	2285	2.27
		80XS, 80S	.191	1.278	0.881	.00891	.435	.335	3.99	1995	3.00
		160	.250	1.160	1.107	.00734	.435	.304	3.29	1645	3.76
		XX	.382	0.896	1.534	.00438	.435	.235	1.97	985	5.21
1½	1.900	5S	.065	1.770	0.375	.01709	.497	.463	7.67	3835	1.28
		10S	.109	1.682	0.614	.01543	.497	.440	6.94	3465	2.09
		40ST, 40S	.145	1.610	0.800	.01414	.497	.421	6.34	3170	2.72
		80XS, 80S	.200	1.500	1.069	.01225	.497	.393	5.49	2745	3.63
		160	.281	1.338	1.429	.00976	.497	.350	4.38	2190	4.86
		XX	.400	1.100	1.885	.00660	.497	.288	2.96	1480	6.41
2	2.375	5S	.065	2.245	0.472	.02749	.622	.588	12.34	6170	1.61
		10S	.109	2.157	0.776	.02538	.622	.565	11.39	5695	2.64
		40ST, 40S	.154	2.067	1.075	.02330	.622	.541	10.45	5225	3.65
		80ST, 80S	.218	1.939	1.477	.02050	.622	.508	9.20	4600	5.02
		160	.344	1.687	2.195	.01552	.622	.436	6.97	3485	7.46
		XX	.436	1.503	2.656	.01232	.622	.393	5.53	2765	9.03
2½	2.875	5S	.083	2.709	0.728	.04003	.753	.709	17.97	8985	2.48
		10S	.120	2.635	1.039	.03787	.753	.690	17.00	8500	3.53
		40ST, 40S	.203	2.469	1.704	.03322	.753	.647	14.92	7460	5.79
		80XS, 80S	.276	2.323	2.254	.02942	.753	.608	13.20	6600	7.66
		160	.375	2.125	2.945	.02463	.753	.556	11.07	5535	10.01
		XX	.552	1.771	4.028	.01711	.753	.464	7.68	3840	13.70
3	3.500	5S	.083	3.334	0.891	.06063	.916	.873	27.21	13,605	3.03
		10S	.120	3.260	1.274	.05796	.916	.853	26.02	13,010	4.33
		40ST, 40S	.216	3.068	2.228	.05130	.916	.803	23.00	11,500	7.58
		80XS, 80S	.300	2.900	3.016	.04587	.916	.759	20.55	10,275	10.25
		160	.438	2.624	4.213	.03755	.916	.687	16.86	8430	14.31
		XX	.600	2.300	5.466	.02885	.916	.602	12.95	6475	18.58
3½	4.0	5S	.083	3.834	1.021	.08017	1.047	1.004	35.98	17,990	3.48
		10S	.120	3.760	1.463	.07711	1.047	0.984	34.61	17,305	4.97
		40ST, 40S	.226	3.548	2.680	.06870	1.047	0.929	30.80	15,400	9.11
		80XS, 80S	.318	3.364	3.678	.06170	1.047	0.881	27.70	13,850	12.51
4	4.5	5S	.083	4.334	1.152	.10245	1.178	1.135	46.0	23,000	3.92
		10S	.120	4.260	1.651	.09898	1.178	1.115	44.4	22,200	5.61
		40ST, 40S	.237	4.026	3.17	.08840	1.178	1.054	39.6	19,800	10.79
		80XS, 80S	.337	3.826	4.41	.07986	1.178	1.002	35.8	17,900	14.98
		120	.438	3.624	5.58	.07170	1.178	0.949	32.2	16,100	19.01
		160	.531	3.438	6.62	.06647	1.178	0.900	28.9	14,450	22.52
		XX	.674	3.152	8.10	.05419	1.178	0.825	24.3	12,150	27.54
5	5.563	5S	.109	5.345	1.87	.1558	1.456	1.399	69.9	34,950	6.36
		10S	.134	5.295	2.29	.1529	1.456	1.386	68.6	34,300	7.77
		40ST, 40S	.258	5.047	4.30	.1390	1.456	1.321	62.3	31,150	14.62
		80XS, 80S	.375	4.813	6.11	.1263	1.456	1.260	57.7	28,850	20.78
		120	.500	4.563	7.95	.1136	1.456	1.195	51.0	25,500	27.04
		160	.625	4.313	9.70	.1015	1.456	1.129	45.5	22,750	32.96
		XX	.750	4.063	11.34	.0900	1.456	1.064	40.4	20,200	38.55

Table 6-2. Properties of Ferrous Pipe—*(Continued)*

Nominal pipe size, in.	Outside diam., in.	Schedule No.	Wall thickness, in.	Inside diam., in.	Cross-sectional area		Circumference, ft., or surface, sq. ft./ft. of length		Capacity at 1 ft./sec. velocity		Weight of plain-end pipe, lb./ft.
					Metal, sq. in.	Flow, sq. ft.	Outside	Inside	U.S. gal./min.	Lb./hr. water	
6	6.625	5S	0.109	6.407	2.23	0.2239	1.734	1.677	100.5	50,250	7.60
		10S	.134	6.357	2.73	.2204	1.734	1.664	98.9	49,450	9.29
		40ST, 40S	.280	6.065	5.58	.2006	1.734	1.588	90.0	45,000	18.97
		80XS, 80S	.432	5.761	8.40	.1810	1.734	1.508	81.1	40,550	28.57
		120	.562	5.501	10.70	.1650	1.734	1.440	73.9	36,950	36.42
		160	.719	5.187	13.34	.1467	1.734	1.358	65.9	32,950	45.34
		XX	.864	4.897	15.64	.1308	1.734	1.282	58.7	29,350	53.16
8	8.625	5S	.109	8.407	2.915	.3855	2.258	2.201	173.0	86,500	9.93
		10S	148	8.329	3.941	.3784	2.258	2.180	169.8	84,900	13.40
		20	.250	8.125	6.578	.3601	2.258	2.127	161.5	80,750	22.36
		30	.277	8.071	7.260	.3553	2.258	2.113	159.4	79,700	24.70
		40ST, 40S	.322	7.981	8.396	.3474	2.258	2.089	155.7	77,850	28.55
		60	.406	7.813	10.48	.3329	2.258	2.045	149.4	74,700	35.66
		80XS, 80S	.500	7.625	12.76	.3171	2.258	1.996	142.3	71,150	43.39
		100	.594	7.437	14.99	.3017	2.258	1.947	135.4	67,700	50.93
		120	.719	7.187	17.86	.2817	2.258	1.882	126.4	63,200	60.69
		140	.812	7.001	19.93	.2673	2.258	1.833	120.0	60,000	67.79
		XX	.875	6.875	21.30	.2578	2.258	1.800	115.7	57,850	72.42
		160	.906	6.813	21.97	.2532	2.258	1.784	113.5	56,750	74.71
10	10.75	5S	.134	10.842	4.47	.5993	2.814	2.744	269.0	134,500	15.23
		10S	.165	10.420	5.49	.5922	2.814	2.728	265.8	132,900	18.70
		20	.250	10.250	8.25	.5731	2.814	2.685	257.0	128,500	28.04
		30	.307	10.136	10.07	.5603	2.814	2.655	252.0	126,000	34.24
		40ST, 40S	.365	10.020	11.91	.5475	2.814	2.620	246.0	123,000	40.48
		80S, 60XS	.500	9.750	16.10	.5185	2.814	2.550	233.0	116,500	54.74
		80	.594	9.562	18.95	.4987	2.814	2.503	223.4	111,700	64.40
		100	.719	9.312	22.66	.4729	2.814	2.438	212.3	106,150	77.00
		120	.844	9.062	26.27	.4479	2.814	2.372	201.0	100,500	89.27
		140, XX	1.000	8.750	30.63	.4176	2.814	2.291	188.0	94,000	104.13
		160	1.125	8.500	34.02	.3941	2.814	2.225	177.0	88,500	115.65
12	12.75	5S	0.156	12.438	6.17	.8438	3.338	3.26	378.7	189,350	22.22
		10S	0.180	12.390	7.11	.8373	3.338	3.24	375.8	187,900	24.20
		20	0.250	12.250	9.82	.8185	3.338	3.21	367.0	183,500	33.38
		30	0.330	12.090	12.88	.7972	3.338	3.17	358.0	179,000	43.77
		ST, 40S	0.375	12.000	14.58	.7854	3.338	3.14	352.5	176,250	49.56
		40	0.406	11.938	15.74	.7773	3.338	3.13	349.0	174,500	53.56
		XS, 80S	0.500	11.750	19.24	.7530	3.338	3.08	338.0	169,000	65.42
		60	0.562	11.626	21.52	.7372	3.338	3.04	331.0	165,500	73.22
		80	0.688	11.374	26.07	.7056	3.338	2.98	316.7	158,350	88.57
		100	0.844	11.062	31.57	.6674	3.338	2.90	299.6	149,800	107.29
		120, XX	1.000	10.750	36.91	.6303	3.338	2.81	283.0	141,500	125.49
		140	1.125	10.500	41.09	.6013	3.338	2.75	270.0	135,000	139.68
		160	1.312	10.126	47.14	.5592	3.338	2.65	251.0	125,500	160.33
14	14	5S	0.156	13.688	6.78	1.0219	3.665	3.58	459	229,500	22.76
		10S	0.188	13.624	8.16	1.0125	3.665	3.57	454	227,000	27.70
		10	0.250	13.500	10.80	0.9940	3.665	3.53	446	223,000	36.71
		20	0.312	13.376	13.42	0.9750	3.665	3.50	438	219,000	45.68
		30, ST	0.375	13.250	16.05	0.9575	3.665	3.47	430	215,000	54.57
		40	0.438	13.124	18.66	0.9397	3.665	3.44	422	211,000	63.37
		XS	0.500	13.000	21.21	0.9218	3.665	3.40	414	207,000	72.09
		60	0.594	12.812	25.02	0.8957	3.665	3.35	402	201,000	85.01
		80	0.750	12.500	31.22	0.8522	3.665	3.27	382	191,000	106.13
		100	0.938	12.124	38.49	0.8017	3.665	3.17	360	180,000	130.79
		120	1.094	11.812	44.36	0.7610	3.665	3.09	342	171,000	150.76
		140	1.250	11.500	50.07	0.7213	3.665	3.01	324	162,000	170.22
		160	1.406	11.188	55.63	0.6827	3.665	2.93	306	153,000	189.12
16	16	5S	0.165	15.670	8.18	1.3393	4.189	4.10	601	300,500	27.87
		10S	0.188	15.624	9.34	1.3314	4.189	4.09	598	299,000	31.62
		10	0.250	15.500	12.37	1.3104	4.189	4.06	587	293,500	42.05
		20	0.312	15.376	15.38	1.2985	4.189	4.03	578	289,000	52.36
		30, ST	0.375	15.250	18.41	1.2680	4.189	3.99	568	284,000	62.58
		40, XS	0.500	15.000	24.35	1.2272	4.189	3.93	550	275,000	82.77
		60	0.656	14.688	31.62	1.1766	4.189	3.85	528	264,000	107.54
		80	0.844	14.312	40.19	1.1171	4.189	3.75	501	250,500	136.58
		100	1.031	13.938	48.48	1.0596	4.189	3.65	474	237,000	164.86
		120	1.219	13.562	56.61	1.0032	4.189	3.55	450	225,000	192.40
		140	1.438	13.124	65.79	0.9394	4.189	3.44	422	211,000	223.57
		160	1.594	12.812	72.14	0.8953	4.189	3.35	402	201,000	245.22
18	18	5S	0.165	17.670	9.25	1.7029	4.712	4.63	764	382,000	31.32
		10S	0.188	17.624	10.52	1.6941	4.712	4.61	760	379,400	35.48
		10	0.250	17.500	13.94	1.6703	4.712	4.58	750	375,000	47.39
		20	0.312	17.376	17.34	1.6468	4.712	4.55	739	369,500	59.03
		ST	0.375	17.250	20.76	1.6230	4.712	4.52	728	364,000	70.59
		30	0.438	17.124	24.16	1.5993	4.712	4.48	718	359,000	82.06
		XS	0.500	17.000	27.49	1.5763	4.712	4.45	707	353,500	93.45
		40	0.562	16.876	30.79	1.5533	4.712	4.42	697	348,500	104.76
		60	0.750	16.500	40.64	1.4849	4.712	4.32	666	333,000	138.17
		80	0.938	16.124	50.28	1.4180	4.712	4.22	636	318,000	170.75
		100	1.156	15.688	61.17	1.3423	4.712	4.11	602	301,000	208.00
		120	1.375	15.250	71.82	1.2684	4.712	3.99	569	284,500	244.14
		140	1.562	14.876	80.66	1.2070	4.712	3.89	540	270,000	274.30
		160	1.781	14.438	90.75	1.1370	4.712	3.78	510	255,000	308.55

Table 6-2. Properties of Ferrous Pipe—(*Concluded*)

Nominal pipe size, in.	Outside diam., in.	Schedule No.	Wall thickness, in.	Inside diam., in.	Cross-sectional area: Metal, sq. in.	Cross-sectional area: Flow, sq. ft.	Circumference, ft., or surface, sq. ft./ft. of length: Outside	Circumference: Inside	Capacity at 1 ft./sec. velocity: U.S. gal./min.	Capacity: Lb./hr. water	Weight of plain-end pipe, lb./ft.
20	20	5S	0.188	19.624	11.70	2.1004	5.236	5.14	943	471,500	39.76
		10S	.218	19.564	13.55	2.0878	5.236	5.12	937	467,500	45.98
		10	.250	19.500	15.51	2.0740	5.236	5.11	930	465,000	52.73
		20, ST	.375	19.250	23.12	2.0211	5.236	5.04	902	451,000	78.60
		30, XS	.500	19.000	30.63	1.9689	5.236	4.97	883	441,500	104.13
		40	.594	18.812	36.21	1.9302	5.236	4.92	866	433,000	123.06
		60	.812	18.376	48.95	1.8417	5.236	4.81	826	413,000	166.50
		80	1.031	17.938	61.44	1.7550	5.236	4.70	787	393,500	208.92
		100	1.281	17.438	75.33	1.6585	5.236	4.57	744	372,000	256.15
		120	1.500	17.000	87.18	1.5763	5.236	4.45	707	353,500	296.37
		140	1.750	16.500	100.3	1.4849	5.236	4.32	665	332,500	341.10
		160	1.969	16.062	111.5	1.4071	5.236	4.21	632	316,000	379.14
24	24	5S	0.218	23.564	16.29	3.0285	6.283	6.17	1359	679,500	55.08
		10, 10S	0.250	23.500	18.65	3.012	6.283	6.15	1350	675,000	63.41
		20, ST	0.375	23.250	27.83	2.948	6.283	6.09	1325	662,500	94.62
		XS	0.500	23.000	36.90	2.885	6.283	6.02	1295	642,500	125.49
		30	0.562	22.876	41.39	2.854	6.283	5.99	1281	640,500	140.80
		40	0.688	22.624	50.39	2.792	6.283	5.92	1253	626,500	171.17
		60	0.969	22.062	70.11	2.655	6.283	5.78	1192	596,000	238.29
		80	1.219	21.562	87.24	2.536	6.283	5.64	1138	569,000	296.53
		100	1.531	20.938	108.1	2.391	6.283	5.48	1073	536,500	367.45
		120	1.812	20.376	126.3	2.264	6.283	5.33	1016	508,000	429.50
		140	2.062	19.876	142.1	2.155	6.283	5.20	965	482,500	483.24
		160	2.344	19.312	159.5	2.034	6.283	5.06	913	456,500	542.09
30	30	5S	0.250	29.500	23.37	4.746	7.854	7.72	2130	1,065,000	79.43
		10, 10S	0.312	29.376	29.10	4.707	7.854	7.69	2110	1,055,000	99.08
		ST	0.375	29.250	34.90	4.666	7.854	7.66	2094	1,048,000	118.65
		20, XS	0.500	29.000	46.34	4.587	7.854	7.59	2055	1,027,500	157.53
		30	0.625	28.750	57.68	4.508	7.854	7.53	2020	1,010,000	196.08

5S, 10S, and 40S are taken from A.S.A. B16.19, "Stainless Steel Pipe." ST = standard wall, XS = extra strong wall, XX = double extra strong wall are all taken from Table 4 of A.S.A. B16.10, "Wrought-steel and Wrought Iron Pipe." Wrought-iron pipe has slightly thicker walls, approximately 3 per cent, but the same weight per foot, because of lower density. 10, 20, 30, 40, 60, 80, 100, 120, 140, and 160 are taken from Table 2 of A.S.A. B16.10, "Wrought Steel and Wrought Iron Pipe," and apply to steel pipe only. Decimal thicknesses for respective pipe sizes represent their nominal or average wall dimensions. Mill tolerances as high as 12½ per cent are permitted.

Plain-end pipe is produced by a square cut. Pipe is also shipped from the mills threaded, with a threaded coupling on one end, or with the ends beveled for welding, or grooved or sized for patented couplings. Weights per foot for threaded and coupled pipe are slightly greater because of the weight of the coupling, but it is not available larger than 12 in., or lighter than Schedule 30 sizes 8 through 12 in., or Schedule 40 6 in. and smaller.

24 per cent cadmium solders are used for copper, copper alloys, carbon steel, and alloy steel. Silver-brazed joints are used for temperatures up to 400°F. Cast-bronze fittings and valves with preinserted rings of 15 per cent silver, 80 per cent copper, 5 per cent phosphorous brazing alloy are available.

Silver-brazed joints are used where temperature or the combination of temperature and pressure is beyond the range of soldered joints. They are also more reliable in event of plant fires.

Cemented joints also require precise control of the diameter of the pipe and of the cup in the fitting. They are used in rigid plastic piping, with the cement being a modification of the plastic.

Clamped-insert joints (Fig. 6-111) are used for flexible plastic pipe up through the 2-in. size. Friction

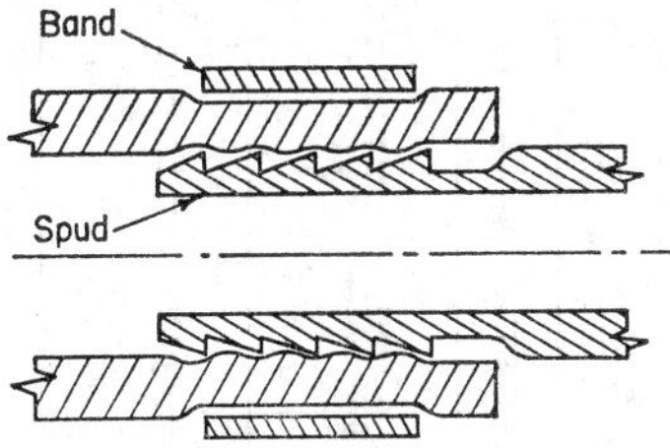

FIG. 6-111. Clamped-insert joint.

between the pipe and the spud is developed both by forcing the spud into the pipe and by tightening the clamp. For the larger sizes, which have thicker walls, these methods cannot develop adequate friction. The joints also have high pressure drop. Stainless-steel bands are available, also spuds in a variety of plastics and metals.

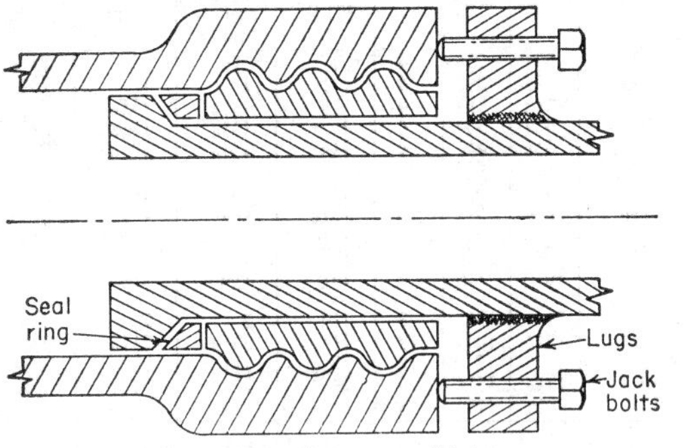

FIG. 6-112. Pressure-seal joint.

Pressure-seal joints (Fig. 6-112) are used for pressures 600 lb./sq. in. and higher. They use less metal than flanged joints but require much more machining of surfaces. There are several designs, in all of which increasing fluid pressure increases the force holding the sealing surfaces against each other. They are widely used as the bonnet joint in carbon- and alloy-steel valves.

Ferrous-metal Piping Systems. Wrought ferrous pipe systems are the most widely used and the most completely covered by national standards. For these reasons, and because of the continuing extension of ferrous pipe standards to other piping materials, **wrought steel and iron** pipe systems are presented here in greater detail than systems made of other materials.

Table 6-2 gives standard size-wall thickness combinations, together with capacity and weight. Additional thicknesses and additional size-wall thickness

Table 6-3. Dimensions of 150-lb. Flanges for Use with Ferrous Pipe
All dimensions in inches

Nominal pipe size	Outside diam. flange	Diam. of bolt circle	No. of bolts	Length through hub: A.S.A. B16.1 screwed (125-lb.)	A.S.A. B16.5 screwed, slip-on, socket-weld	A.S.A. B16.5 lap-joint	A.S.A. B16.5 welding-neck
½	3½	2⅜	4	.....	⅝	⅝	1⅞
¾	3⅞	2¾	4	.....	⅝	⅝	2 1/16
1	4¼	3⅛	4	11/16	11/16	11/16	2 3/16
1¼	4⅝	3½	4	13/16	13/16	13/16	2¼
1½	5	3⅞	4	⅞	⅞	⅞	2 7/16
2	6	4¾	4	1	1	1	2½
2½	7	5½	4	1⅛	1⅛	1⅛	2¾
3	7½	6	4	1 3/16	1 3/16	1 3/16	2¾
3½	8½	7	8	1¼	1¼	1¼	2 13/16
4	9	7½	8	1 5/16	1 5/16	1 5/16	3
5	10	8½	8	1 7/16	1 7/16	1 7/16	3½
6	11	9½	8	1 9/16	1 9/16	1 9/16	3½
8	13½	11¾	8	1¾	1¾	1¾	4
10	16	14¼	12	1 15/16	1 15/16	1 15/16	4
12	19	17	12	2 3/16	2 3/16	2 3/16	4½
14 o.d.	21	18¾	12	2¼	2¼	3⅛*	5
16 o.d.	23½	21¼	16	2½	2½	3 7/16	5
18 o.d.	25	22¾	16	2 11/16	2 11/16	3 13/16	5½
20 o.d.	27½	25	20	2⅞	2⅞	4 1/16	5 11/16
24 o.d.	32	29½	20	3¼	3¼	4⅜	6

* Lap-joint flanges are also available in this and larger sizes with same length through hub as slip-on flanges.

Table 6-4. Dimensions of 300-lb. Flanges for Use with Ferrous Pipe
All dimensions in inches

Nominal pipe size	Outside diam. flange	Diam. of bolt circle	No. of bolts	Length through hub: A.S.A. B16.2 screwed (250-lb.)	A.S.A. B16.5 screwed, slip-on, socket-weld*	A.S.A. B16.5 lap-joint	A.S.A. B16.5 welding-neck
½	3¾	2⅝	4	.....	⅞	⅞	2 1/16
¾	4⅝	3¼	4	.....	1	1	2¼
1	4⅞	3½	4	⅞	1 1/16	1 1/16	2 7/16
1¼	5¼	3⅞	4	1	1 1/16	1 1/16	2 9/16
1½	6⅛	4½	4	1⅛	1 3/16	1 3/16	2 11/16
2	6½	5	8	1¼	1 5/16	1 5/16	2¾
2½	7½	5⅞	8	1 7/16	1½	1½	3
3	8¼	6⅝	8	1 9/16	1 11/16	1 11/16	3⅛
3½	9	7¼	8	1⅝	1¾	1¾	3 3/16
4	10	7⅞	8	1¾	1⅞	1⅞	3⅜
5	11	9¼	8	1⅞	2	2	3⅞
6	12½	10⅝	12	1 15/16	2 1/16	2 1/16	3⅞
8	15	13	12	2 3/16	2 7/16	2 7/16	4⅜
10	17½	15¼	16	2⅜	2⅝	3¾†	4⅝
12	20½	17¾	16	2 9/16	2⅞	4	5⅛
14 o.d.	23	20¼	20	2 11/16	3	4⅜	5⅝
16 o.d.	25½	22½	20	2⅞	3¼	4¾	5¾
18 o.d.	28	24¾	24	.....	3½	5⅛	6¼
20 o.d.	30½	27	24	.....	3¾	5½	6⅜
24 o.d.	36	32	24	.....	4 3/16	6	6⅝

* A.S.A. B16.5 does not show 300-lb. socket-weld flanges larger than 3 in., but 4 in. is available.
† Lap-joint flanges are also available in this and larger sizes with same length through hub as slip-on flanges.

combinations are available as tubing. Two common classifications of tubing are "pressure" and "mechanical." Wall thickness (gage) is specified as either "average wall" or "minimum wall." Minimum wall is more costly than average wall, and because of closer wall thickness and diametral tolerance, both gage systems make pressure tubing more costly than pipe. However, average-wall carbon-steel electric-resistance-welded tubing, sizes 2⅜, 2⅞, 3½, and 4½ in. outside diameter produced from coiled strip on progressive forming rolls and electromagnetically rather than pressure tested, competes vigorously with pipe.

Ferrous pipe and tubing (other than cast iron) can be bent hot or cold. Cast iron, malleable iron, cast ferrous, forged ferrous, and wrought ferrous fittings are available. Welded, threaded, flanged, packed gland, expanded, and grooved joints are used for pipe, and welded, flared fitting and bite-type fitting joints are used for tubing.

Dimensions of alloy, carbon-steel, and cast-iron pipe **flanges** with flat and raised faces are given in Tables 6-3 to 6-9 (see Fig. 6-99). Against cast-iron flanged fittings or valves, steel pipe flanges are often preferred to cast-iron pipe flanges because they permit welded rather than screwed assembly to the pipe and because cast-iron pipe flanges, not being reinforced by the pipe, are not so

Table 6-5. Dimensions of 400-lb. Flanges for Use with Ferrous Pipe
All dimensions in inches

Nominal pipe size	Outside diam. flange	Diam. of bolt circle	No. of bolts	Length through hub: A.S.A. B16.5 screwed, slip-on*	A.S.A. B16.5 lap-joint	A.S.A. B16.5 welding-neck
½	3¾	2⅝	4	⅞	⅞	2 1/16
¾	4⅝	3¼	4	1	1	2¼
1	4⅞	3½	4	1 1/16	1 1/16	2 7/16
1¼	5¼	3⅞	4	1⅛	1⅛	2⅝
1½	6⅛	4½	4	1¼	1¼	2¾
2	6½	5	8	1 7/16	1 7/16	2⅞
2½	7½	5⅞	8	1⅝	1⅝	3⅛
3	8¼	6⅝	8	1 13/16	1 13/16	3¼
3½	9	7¼	8	1 15/16	1 15/16	3⅜
4	10	7⅞	8	2	2	3½
5	11	9¼	8	2⅛	2⅛	4
6	12½	10⅝	12	2¼	2¼	4 1/16
8	15	13	12	2 11/16	2 11/16	4⅝
10	17½	15¼	16	2⅞	4†	4⅞
12	20½	17¾	16	3⅛	4¼	5⅜
14 o.d.	23	20¼	20	3 5/16	4⅝	5⅞
16 o.d.	25½	22½	20	3 11/16	5	6
18 o.d.	28	24¾	24	3⅞	5⅜	6½
20 o.d.	30½	27	24	4	5¾	6⅝
24 o.d.	36	32	24	4½	6¼	6⅞

* A.S.A. B16.5 does not show 400-lb. socket-weld flanges and they are not available.
† Lap-joint flanges are also available in this and larger sizes with same length through hub as slip-on flanges.

Table 6-6. Dimensions of 600-lb. Flanges for Use with Ferrous Pipe
All dimensions in inches

Nominal pipe size	Outside diam. flange	Diam. of bolt circle	No. of bolts	Length through hub: A.S.A. B16.5 screwed, slip-on, socket-weld*	A.S.A. B16.5 lap-joint	A.S.A. B16.5 welding-neck
½	3¾	2⅝	4	⅞	⅞	2 1/16
¾	4⅝	3¼	4	1	1	2¼
1	4⅞	3½	4	1 1/16	1 1/16	2 7/16
1¼	5¼	3⅞	4	1⅛	1⅛	2⅝
1½	6⅛	4½	4	1¼	1¼	2¾
2	6½	5	8	1 7/16	1 7/16	2⅞
2½	7½	5⅞	8	1⅝	1⅝	3⅛
3	8¼	6⅝	8	1 13/16	1 13/16	3¼
3½	9	7¼	8	1 15/16	1 15/16	3⅜
4	10¾	8½	8	2⅛	2⅛	4
5	13	10½	8	2⅜	2⅜	4½
6	14	11½	12	2⅝	2⅝	4⅝
8	16½	13¾	12	3	3	5¼
10	20	17	16	3⅜	4⅜†	6
12	22	19¼	20	3⅝	4⅝	6⅛
14	23¾	20¾	20	3 11/16	5	6½
16	27	23¾	20	4 3/16	5½	7
18	29¼	25¾	20	4⅝	6	7¼
20	32	28½	24	5	6½	7½
24	37	33	24	5½	7¼	8

* A.S.A. B16.5 does not show 600-lb. socket-weld flanges larger than 3 in. but 3½ in. is available.
† Lap-joint flanges are also available in this and larger sizes with same length through hub as slip-on flanges.

Table 6-7. Dimensions of 900-lb. Flanges for Use with Ferrous Pipe

All dimensions in inches

Nominal pipe size	Outside diam. flange	Diam. of bolt circle	No. of bolts	Length through hub: A.S.A. B16.5 screwed, slip-on*	A.S.A. B16.5 lap-joint	A.S.A. B16.5 welding-neck
½	4¾	3¼	4	1¼	1¼	2⅜
¾	5⅛	3½	4	1⅜	1⅜	2¾
1	5⅞	4	4	1⅝	1⅝	2⅞
1¼	6¼	4⅜	4	1⅝	1⅝	2⅞
1½	7	4⅞	4	1¾	1¾	3¼
2	8½	6½	8	2¼	2¼	4
2½	9⅝	7½	8	2½	2½	4⅛
3	9½	7½	8	2⅛	2⅛	4
4	11½	9¼	8	2¾	2¾	4½
5	13¾	11	8	3⅛	3⅛	5
6	15	12½	12	3⅜	3⅜	5½
8	18½	15½	12	4	4½†	6⅜
10	21½	18½	16	4¼	5	7¼
12	24	21	20	4⅝	5⅝	7⅞
14	25¼	22	20	5⅛	6⅛	8⅜
16	27¾	24¼	20	5¼	6½	8½
18	31	27	20	6	7½	9
20	33¾	29½	20	6¼	8¼	9¾
24	41	35½	20	8	10½	11½

* A.S.A. B16.5 does not show 900-lb. socket-weld flanges and they are not available.

† Lap-joint flanges are also available in this and larger sizes with same length through hub as slip-on flanges.

Table 6-8. Dimensions of 1500-lb. Flanges for Use with Ferrous Pipe

All dimensions in inches

Nominal pipe size	Outside diam. flange	Diam. of bolt circle	No. of bolts	Length through hub: A.S.A. B16.5 screwed, slip-on,* socket-weld*	A.S.A. B16.5 lap-joint	A.S.A. B16.5 welding-neck
½	4¾	3¼	4	1¼	1¼	2⅜
¾	5⅛	3½	4	1⅜	1⅜	2¾
1	5⅞	4	4	1⅝	1⅝	2⅞
1¼	6¼	4⅜	4	1⅝	1⅝	2⅞
1½	7	4⅞	4	1¾	1¾	3¼
2	8½	6½	8	2¼	2¼	4
2½	9⅝	7½	8	2½	2½	4⅛
3	10½	8	8	2⅞	2⅞	4⅝
4	12¼	9½	8	3 9/16	3 9/16	4⅞
5	14¾	11½	8	4⅛	4⅛	6⅛
6	15½	12½	12	4 11/16	4 11/16	6¾
8	19	15½	12	5⅝	5⅝	8⅜
10	23	19	12	6¼	7†	10
12	26½	22½	16	7⅛	8⅝	11⅛
14	29½	25	16	.....	9½	11¾
16	32½	27¾	16	.....	10¼	12¼
18	36	30½	16	.....	10⅞	12⅞
20	38¾	32¾	16	.....	11½	14
24	46	39	16	.....	13	16

* A.S.A. B16.5 does not show 1500-lb. slip-on or socket-weld flanges over 2½ in. but slip-on are available through 24 in.

† Lap-joint flanges are also available in this and larger sizes with same length through hub as slip-on flanges.

resistant to abuse as flanges cast integral on cast-iron fittings.

Facing of alloy and carbon steel pipe and fitting flanges is shown in Fig. 6-100; 125-lb. cast-iron pipe and fitting flanges have flat faces, which with full-face gaskets minimize bending stresses; 250-lb. cast-iron pipe and fitting flanges have 1/16-in. raised faces (wider than on steel flanges) for the same purpose. For use against 125-lb. cast-iron flanges with gaskets harder than rubber, 150-lb. steel flanges should be purchased flat-face and full-face gaskets should be used to minimize bending stresses in the cast-iron flanges. Carbon steel and ductile (nodular) iron lap-joint flanges are widely used in austenitic stainless-steel systems to reduce costs.

Table 6-9. Dimensions of 2500-lb. Flanges for Use with Ferrous Pipe

All dimensions in inches

Nominal pipe size	Outside diam. flange	Diam. of bolt circle	No. of bolts	Length through hub: A.S.A. B16.5 screwed, slip-on,* lap-joint	A.S.A. B16.5 welding-neck
½	5¼	3½	4	1 9/16	2⅞
¾	5½	3¾	4	1 11/16	3⅛
1	6¼	4¼	4	1⅞	3½
1¼	7¼	5⅛	4	2 1/16	3¾
1½	8	5¾	4	2⅜	4⅜
2	9¼	6¾	8	2¾	5
2½	10½	7¾	8	3⅛	5⅝
3	12	9	8	3⅝	6⅝
4	14	10¾	8	4¼	7½
5	16½	12¾	8	5⅛	9
6	19	14½	8	6	10¾
8	21¾	17¼	12	7	12½
10	26½	21¼	12	9	16½
12	30	24⅜	12	10	18¼

* A.S.A. B16.5 does not show 2500-lb. slip-on flanges but they are available through 12 in.

Dimensions of carbon-steel, alloy-steel, and cast-iron **flanged fittings** are given in Table 6-10 for flat- and raised-face flanges. Where other facings, except for metal-ring-joint, are used, Fig. 6-100 gives values to correct length through hub dimensions for flanges and center-to-contact-surface-of-face dimensions for flanged fittings. Flanged fittings are used where pipe is likely to be dismantled for frequent cleaning or extensive revision, for lined piping systems, for seasonal insertion of blanks as a substitute for valves, and in some low-pressure systems with high corrosion rates to get a combination of heavy wall and torsional yielding by rotation of fittings on the gaskets. They are also used in areas where welding is not permitted.

Dimensions of carbon- and alloy-steel **butt-welding fittings** are shown in Table 6-11. Butt-welding fittings are available in the wall thicknesses shown in Table 6-2. Butt-welding elbows with short straight pipe extensions at the ends are also available for insertion in slip-on flanges. Schedule 5 and Schedule 10 stainless-steel butt-welding fittings are also available with such extensions for expanding into stainless-steel hubs mechanically locked in carbon-steel A.S.A. B16.5 dimension flanges. Branch welds (Fig. 6-93) are frequently used instead of welding tees.

Forged fittings made by boring out solid forgings are available with socket-weld (Fig. 6-92) or with screwed ends in sizes through 4 in., but 2 in. is the usual upper size limit for use. Below the socket, socket-weld fittings are bored the same inside diameter as the pipe. A.S.A. B16.11 gives minimum dimensions for socket-weld fittings for Schedule 40, Schedule 80, and Schedule 160 pipe in sizes through 3 in. These are sold as 2000 lb., 3000 lb., and 4000 lb. socket-weld fittings. Socket-weld fittings are also available bored for double-extra-heavy pipe as 6000 lb. class. MSS SP-49 gives dimensions for screwed forged fittings in 2000-lb., 3000-lb., and 6000-lb. classes. It also gives pressure-temperature ratings of forged carbon-steel screwed fittings. One set of forging blanks is used for 2000- and 3000-lb. socket-weld and 2000-lb. screwed fittings, a second set for 4000- and 6000-lb. socket-weld and 3000-lb. screwed, and a third set for 6000-lb. screwed fittings. All these pressure classes are the ratings at atmospheric temperature.

Ferrous forged fittings with **screwed** ends may be installed without pipe dope in the threads and seal-welded (Fig. 6-96) to secure bottle-tight joints with a minimum of welders' labor. They are not subject to deformation by pipe wrenches, and such couplings,

Table 6-10. Center-to-contact-surface-of-face Dimensions of Ferrous Flanged Fittings

All dimensions in inches

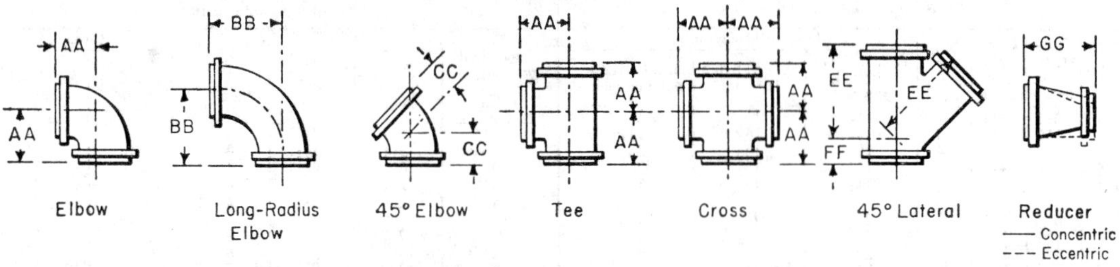

Nominal pipe size	A.S.A. B16.5 150-lb. standard A.S.A. B16.1						A.S.A. B16.5 300-lb. standard A.S.A. B16b					
	AA	BB	CC	EE	FF	GG	AA	BB	CC	EE	FF	GG
½												
¾												
1	3½	5	1¾	5¾	1¾	4½	4	5	2¼	6½	2	4½
1¼	3¾	5½	2	6¼	1¾	4½	4¼	5½	2½	7¼	2¼	4½
1½	4	6	2¼	7	2	4½	4½	6	2¾	8½	2½	4½
2	4½	6½	2½	8	2½	5	5	6½	3	9	2½	5
2½	5	7	3	9½	2½	5½	5½	7	3½	10½	2½	5½
3	5½	7¾	3	10	3	6	6	7¾	3½	11	3	6
3½	6	8½	3½	11½	3	6½	6½	8½	4	12½	3	6½
4	6½	9	4	12	3	7	7	9	4½	13½	3	7
5	7½	10¼	4½	13½	3½	8	8	10¼	5	15	3½	8
6	8	11½	5	14½	3½	9	8½	11½	5½	17½	4	9
8	9	14	5½	17½	4½	11	10	14	6	20½	5	11
10	11	16½	6½	20½	5	12	11½	16½	7	24	5½	12
12	12	19	7½	24½	5½	14	13	19	8	27½	6	14
14 o.d.	14	21½	7½	27	6	16	15	21½	8½	31	6½	16
16 o.d.	15	24	8	30	6½	18	16½	24	9½	34½	7½	18
18 o.d.	16½	26½	8½	32	7	19	18	26½	10	37½	8	19
20 o.d.	18	29	9½	35	8	20	19½	29	10½	40½	8½	20
24 o.d.	22	34	11	40½	9	24	22½	34	12	47½	10	24

Nominal pipe size	400-lb. standard					600-lb. standard				
	AA	CC	EE	FF	GG	AA	CC	EE	FF	GG
½	3¼	2	5¾	1¾	5	3¼	2	5¾	1¾	5
¾	3¾	2½	6¾	2	5	3¾	2½	6¾	2	5
1	4¼	2½	7¼	2¼	5	4¼	2½	7¼	2¼	5
1¼	4½	2¾	8	2½	5	4½	2¾	8	2½	5
1½	4¾	3	9	2¾	5	4¾	3	9	2¾	5
2	5¾	4¼	10¼	3½	6	5¾	4¼	10¼	3½	6
2½	6½	4½	11½	3½	6¾	6½	4½	11½	3½	6¾
3	7	5	12¾	4	7¼	7	5	12¾	4	7¼
3½	7½	5½	14	4½	7¾	7½	5½	14	4½	7¾
4	8	5½	16	4½	8¼	8½	6	16½	4½	8¾
5	9	6	16¾	5	9¼	10	7	19½	6	10¼
6	9¾	6¼	18¾	5¼	10	11	7½	21	6½	11¼
8	11¾	6¾	22¼	5¾	12	13	8½	24½	7	13¼
10	13¼	7¾	25¾	6¼	13½	15½	9½	29½	8	15¾
12	15	8¾	29¾	6½	15¼	16½	10	31½	8½	16¾
14 o.d.	16¼	9¼	32¾	7	16½	17½	10¾	34¼	9	17¾
16 o.d.	17¾	10¼	36¼	8	18½	19½	11¾	38½	10	19¾
18 o.d.	19¼	10¾	39¼	8½	19½	21½	12¼	42	10½	21¾
20 o.d.	20¾	11¼	42¾	9	21	23½	13	45½	11	23¾
24 o.d.	24¼	12¾	50¼	10½	24½	27½	14¾	53	13	27¾

Nominal pipe size	A.S.A. B16.5 900-lb. standard					A.S.A. B16.5 1500-lb. standard					A.S.A. B16.5 2500-lb. standard				
	AA	CC	EE	FF	GG	AA	CC	EE	FF	GG	AA	CC	EE	FF	GG
½	4¼	3				4¼	3				5³⁄₁₆				
¾	4½	3¼				4½	3¼				5⅜				
1	5	3½	9	2½	5	5	3½	9	2½	5	6¹⁄₁₆	4			
1¼	5½	4	10	3	5¾	5½	4	10	3	5¾	6⅞	4¼			
1½	6	4¼	11	3½	6¼	6	4¼	11	3½	6¼	7⁹⁄₁₆	4¾			
2	7¼	4¾	13¼	4	7¼	7¼	4¾	13¼	4	7¼	8⅞	5¾	15¼	5¼	9½
2½	8¼	5¼	15¼	4½	8¼	8¼	5¼	15¼	4½	8¼	10	6¼	17¼	5¾	10½
3	7½	5½	14½	4½	7¾	9¼	5¾	17¼	5	9¼	11⅜	7¼	19¾	6¾	11¾
4	9	6½	17½	5½	9¼	10¾	7¼	19¼	6	10¾	13¼	8½	23	7¾	13½
5	11	7½	21	6½	11¼	13¼	8¾	23¼	7½	13¾	15⅝	10	27¼	9¼	15¾
6	12	8	22½	6½	12¼	13⅞	9⅜	24⅞	8⅛	14½	18	11½	31¼	10½	18
8	14½	9	27½	7½	14¾	16⅜	10⅞	29⅞	9⅛	17	20⅛	12¾	35¼	11¾	20½
10	16½	10	31½	8½	16¾	19½	12	36	10¼	20¼	25	16	43¼	14¾	25½
12	19	11	34½	9	17¾	22¼	13¼	40¾	12	23	28	17¾	49¼	16¼	29
14 o.d.	20¼	11½	36½	9½	19	24¾	14¼	44	12½	25¾					
16 o.d.	22¼	12½	40¾	10½	21	27¼	16¼	48¼	14¾	28¼					
18 o.d.	24	13¼	45½	12	24½	30¼	17¾	53¼	16½	31½					
20 o.d.	26	14½	50¼	13	20½	32¾	18¾	57¾	17¾	34					
24 o.d.	30½	18	60	15½	30½	38¼	20¾	67¼	20½	39¾					

NOTE: Outline drawings show ¼-in. raised face machined onto flange, as for A.S.A. B16.5 400 lb. and higher. A.S.A. B16b and A.S.A. B16.5 150 and 300 lb. have ¹⁄₁₆-in. raised face; A.S.A. B16.1 has no raised face.

See Tables 6-3 to 6-9 for flange drillings.

Dimensions for 400- and 600-lb. fittings are identical for sizes ½ to 3½ in., inclusive.

A.S.A. Standards B16.5, 1957; A.S.A. B16.1, 1953; A.S.A. B16b, 1953. Dimensions for 900- and 1500-lb. fittings are identical for sizes ½ to 2½ in., inclusive.

bushings, and plugs are often used with the screwed fittings below.

A.S.A. B16.3 gives dimensions of 150-lb. **malleable-iron screwed fittings** through the 6-in. size for 150 lb./sq. in. saturated steam and 300 lb./sq. in. at room temperature. A.S.A. B16.19 gives dimensions of 300-lb. malleable-iron screwed fittings through the 3-in. size for 300 lb./sq. in. steam at 550°F. or 1000 lb./sq. in. at room temperature. These fittings are available with male threads or unions on one end for installation in confined spaces. Major use is in 150-lb. elbows, tees, and reducers in sizes 2 in. and smaller. They are less costly than forged fittings but cannot be seal-welded.

A.S.A. B16.4 gives dimensions of 125-lb. **cast-iron screwed fittings** through the 12-in. size for 125 lb./sq. in. saturated steam and 175 lb./sq. in. at 150°F. and of 250-lb. cast-iron screwed fittings through the 12-in. size for 250 lb./sq. in. saturated steam and for 400 lb./sq. in. at 150°F. The 125-lb. fittings are made in regular 90- and 45-deg. elbows, reducing elbows, regular and reducing tees, and crosses. The 250-lb. fittings are made only in straight sizes. Major use is in 125-lb. elbows, tees, and reducers in low-pressure non-critical service.

Ferrous valves are available with screwed or socket-weld ends in the smaller sizes. Bronze and brass

Table 6-11. Ferrous Butt-welding Fittings
All dimensions in inches

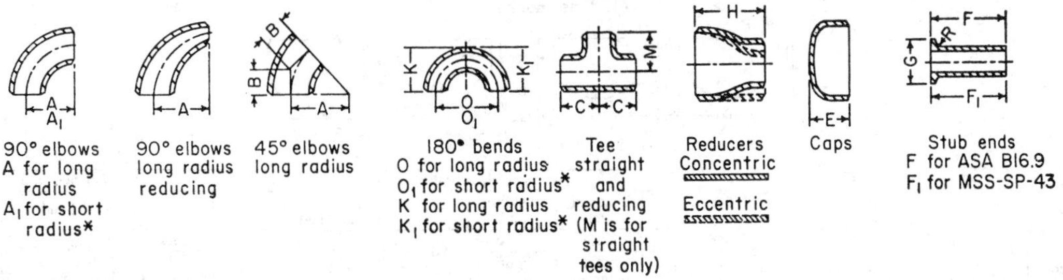

Pipe size	A	K	A_1	K_1	B	O	O_1	M, C	H	E†	G	F	F_1	R‡
½*	1½	1⅞	....	....	⅝	3	....	1		1	1⅜	3	2	⅛
¾*	1⅛	1 11/16	....	....	7/16	2¼	....	1	1½	1¼	1 11/16	3	2	⅛
1	1½	2 3/16	1	1⅝	⅞	3	2	1½	2	1½	2	4	2	⅛
1¼	1⅞	2¾	1¼	2 1/16	1	3¾	2½	1⅞	2	1½	2½	4	2	3/16
1½	2¼	3¼	1½	2 7/16	1⅛	4½	3	2¼	2½	1½	2⅞	4	2	¼
2	3	4 3/16	2	3 3/16	1⅜	6	4	2½	3	1½	3⅝	6	2½	5/16
2½	3¾	5 3/16	2½	3 15/16	1¾	7½	5	3	3½	1½	4⅛	6	2½	5/16
3	4½	6¼	3	4¾	2	9	6	3⅜	3½	2	5	6	2½	⅜
3½	5¼	7¼	3½	5½	2¼	10½	7	3¾	4	2½	5½	6	3	⅜
4	6	8¼	4	6¼	2½	12	8	4⅛	4	2½	6 3/16	6	3	7/16
5	7½	10 5/16	5	7¾	3⅛	15	10	4⅞	5	3	7 5/16	8	3	7/16
6	9	12 5/16	6	9 5/16	3¾	18	12	5⅝	5½	3½	8½	8	3½	½
8	12	16 5/16	8	12 5/16	5	24	16	7	6	4	10⅝	8	4	½
10	15	20⅜	10	15⅜	6¼	30	20	8½	7	5	12¾	10	5	½
12	18	24⅜	12	18⅜	7½	36	24	10	8	6	15	10	6	½
14	21	28	14	21	8¾	42	28	11	13	6½	16¼	12	7	½
16	24	32	16	24	10	48	32	12	14	7	18½	12	8	½
18	27	36	18	27	11¼	54	36	13½	15	8	21	12	9	½
20	30	40	20	30	12½	60	40	15	20	9	23	12	10	½
22	33	44	22	....	13½	66	....	16½	20	10	25¼	12	....	½
24	36	48	24	36	15	72	48	17	20	10½	27¼	12	12	½

* Not included in A.S.A. B16.9 but commercially available.
† For wall thicknesses greater than extra-heavy, E is greater than shown here for sizes 2 in. and larger.
‡ For MSS SP-43 type B stub ends, which are designed to be backed up by slip-on flanges, $R = 1/32$ in. for 4 in. and smaller and 1/16 in. for 6 through 12 in.

screwed-end valves are widely used for low-pressure service in ferrous systems. Table 6-12 gives contact-surface-of-face to contact-surface-of-face dimensions for **flanged ferrous valves** and end-to-end dimensions for **butt-welding ferrous valves.** Drilling of end flanges is shown in Tables 6-3 to 6-9. Bolt holes are located so that the stem is equidistant from the center line of two bolt holes. Even where removal for maintenance is not anticipated, flanged valves are frequently used instead of butt-welding-end valves because they permit insertion of blanks for isolating sections of a loop piping system.

Ferrous valves are also available in nodular (ductile) iron which has tensile strength and yield point approximately equal to cast carbon steel at temperatures 650°F. and below and only slightly less elongation.

Cast-iron piping systems provide more metal for less cost than steel piping systems and are widely used in low-pressure service where internal and external corrosion cause a considerable loss of metal. Cast iron is widely used for underground water distribution in sizes 4 through 24 in. in firm soil. Cement lining is available at nominal cost for handling tuberculating water. Most cast-iron pipe is centrifugally cast (in rapidly revolving molds), which increases tensile strength and reduces porosity. The required wall thickness for underground installation increases with internal pressure, depth of bury, and weight of vehicles operating over the pipe. It is reduced by the degree to which the soil surrounding the pipe provides support uniform along the pipe and around the lower 180 deg.

The poured joint (Fig. 6-102) has largely been superseded by the mechanical joint (Fig. 6-101) and the O-ring joint (Fig. 6-103) which are better suited to wet trenches, bad weather, and unskilled labor and minimize strain on the pipe from ground settlement. The latter two joints use the same gasket for all pressures of any one size and consequently the same outside diameter of pipe. They differ from cast-iron pipe for poured joints, for which the outside diameter increases in irregular steps as the wall thickness is increased to resist increasing internal pressure.

Table 6-13 gives wall thicknesses and diameters for **centrifugally cast pipe** with mechanical or O-ring joints for pipe laid without blocks underneath it in a flat-bottom trench with tamped backfill under 5 ft. of cover. Identical thicknesses are used where principal stress is other than from internal pressure. Larger sizes are available.

Lengths vary between 16 and 20 ft. according to the supplier. Table 6-14 gives allowable deflection for the far end of one length from the center line of the preceding length and minimum radius of circular layout for mechanical joint pipe. Approximately the same deflections are possible with O-ring joint pipe.

Cast-iron pipe is also supplied with **flanged ends** A.S.A. B16.4 125 lb. or A.S.A. B16b 250 lb. (see Tables 6-3 and 6-4). On pit-cast pipe the flanges are cast integral; on centrifugally cast pipe they are assembled by threaded joints. Cast-iron flanged pipe systems must be laid out so that thermal expansion is absorbed by rotation of one flange face on the other.

The center-to-bottom-of-bell dimensions for **mechanical joint fittings** is the same as the center-to-face

Table 6-12. Contact-surface-of-face-to-contact-surface-of-face and End-to-end Dimensions of Ferrous Valves

All dimensions in inches

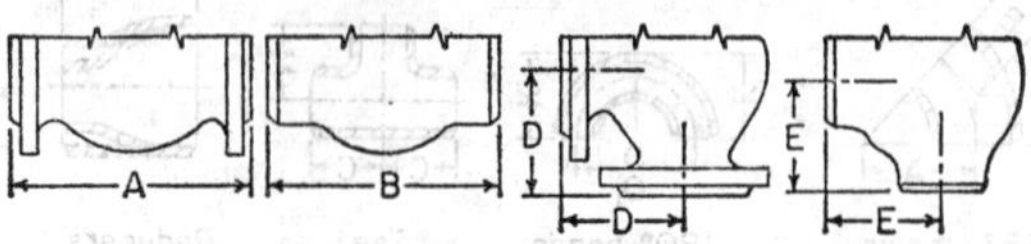

Nominal valve size	Class 125 cast iron, Flanged end, Gate, Solid wedge	Class 125, Gate, Double disk	Class 125, Globe and lift check	Class 125, Angle and lift check	Class 125, Swing check	Class 150 steel, MSS-SP-42 through 12-in. size, Flanged end, Gate, Solid wedge and double disk	Class 150, Welding end, Gate, Solid wedge and double disk	Class 150, Flanged end and welding end, Globe and lift check	Class 150, Flanged end and welding end, Angle and lift check	Class 150, Flanged end and welding end, Swing check	Class 250 cast iron, Flanged end, Gate, Solid wedge and double disk	Class 250, Globe, lift check, and swing check	Class 250, Angle and lift check
	A	*A*	*A*	*D*	*A*	*A*	*B*	*A* and *B*	*D* and *E*	*A* and *B*	*A*	*A*	*D*
¼	....	....	....	....	....	4	4	4	2	4			
⅜	....	....	....	....	....	4	4	4	2	4			
½	....	....	....	....	....	4¼	4¼	4¼	2¼	4¼			
¾	....	....	....	....	....	4⅝	4⅝	4⅝	2½	4⅝			
1	....	....	....	....	....	5	5	5	2¾	5			
1¼	....	....	....	....	....	5½	5½	5½	3	5½			
1½	....	....	....	....	....	6½	6½	6½	3¼	6½			
2	7	7	8	4	8	7	8½	8	4	8	8½	10½	5¼
2½	7½	7½	8½	4¼	8½	7½	9½	8½	4¼	8½	9½	11½	5¾
3	8	8	9½	4¾	9½	8	11⅛	9½	4¾	9½	11⅛	12½	6¼
3½	8½	8½	....	....	....	*	....	....	....	....	12	14	7
4	9	9	11½	5¾	11½	9	12	11½	5¾	11½	15	15¾	7⅞
5	10	10	13	6½	13	10	15	14	7	13	15⅞	17½	8¾
6	10½	10½	14	7	14	10½	15⅞	16	8	14	16½	21	10½
8	11½	11½	19½	9¾	19½	11½	16½	19½	9¾	19½	18	24½	12¼
10	13	13	24½	12¼	24½	13	18	24½	12¼	24½	19¾	28	14
12	14	14	27½	13¾	27½	14	19¾	27½	13¾	27½	22½	*	
14	15	*	31	15½	31	15	22½	31	15½	31	24	*	
16	16	*	36	18	*	16	24	36	18	*	26		
18	17	*	....	....	*	17	26	....	....	*	28		
20	18	*	....	....	*	18	28	....	....	*			
24	20	*	....	....	*	20	32	....	....	*	31		

Nominal valve size	Class 300 steel, Flanged end and welding end, Gate, Solid wedge and double disk	Class 300, Globe and lift check	Class 300, Angle and lift check	Class 300, Swing check	Class 400 steel, Flanged end and welding end, Gate, Solid wedge	Class 400, Gate, Double disk	Class 400, Globe, lift check, and swing check	Class 400, Angle and lift check	Class 600 steel, Flanged end and welding end, Gate, Solid wedge	Class 600, Gate, Double disk	Class 600, Gate, Short pattern†	Class 600, Regular globe, regular lift check, swing check	Class 600, Short pattern† globe, short pattern lift check	Class 600, Angle and lift check, Regular	Class 600, Angle and lift check, Short pattern
	A and *B*	*A* and *B*	*D* and *E*	*A* and *B*	*A* and *B*	*A* and *B*	*A* and *B*	*D* and *E*	*A* and *B*	*A* and *B*	*B*	*A* and *B*	*B*	*D* and *E*	*E*
½	....	6	3	....	6½	....	6½	3¼	6½	....	....	6½	....	3¼	
¾	....	7	3½	....	7½	....	7½	3¾	7½	....	....	7½	....	3¾	
1	....	8	4	8½	8½	8½	8½	4¼	8½	8½	5¼	8½	5¼	4¼	
1¼	....	8½	4¼	9	9	9	9	4½	9	9	5¾	9	5¾	4½	
1½	7½	9	4½	9½	9½	9½	9½	4¾	9½	9½	6	9½	6	4¾	
2	8½	10½	5¼	10½	11½	11½	11½	5¾	11½	11½	7	11½	7	5¾	4¼
2½	9½	11½	5¾	11½	13	13	13	6½	13	13	8½	13	8½	6½	5
3	11⅛	12½	6¼	12½	14	14	14	7	14	14	10	14	10	7	6
4	12	14	7	14	16	16	16	8	17	17	12	17	12	8½	7
5	15	15¾	7⅞	15¾	18	18	18	9	20	20	15	20	15	10	8½
6	15⅞	17½	8¾	17½	19½	19½	19½	9¾	22	22	18	22	18	11	10
8	16½	22	11	21	23½	23½	23½	11¾	26	26	23	26	23	13	
10	18	24½	12¼	24½	26½	26½	26½	13¼	31	31	28	31	28	15½	
12	19¾	28	14	28	30	30	30	15	33	33	32	33	32	16½	
14	30	....	....	*	32½	30½	*	....	35	35	35	*			
16	33	....	....	*	35½	35½	*	....	39	39	39	*			
18	36	....	....	*	38½	38½	*	....	43	43	43	*			
20	39	....	....	*	41½	41½	*	....	47	47	47	*			
22	43	....	....	*	45	45	*	....	51	51	....	*			
24	45	....	....	*	48½	48½	*	....	55	55	55	*			

Nominal valve size	Class 900 steel							Class 1500 steel					Nominal valve size	Class 2500 steel				
	Flanged end and welding end							Flanged end and welding end						Flanged end and welding end				
	Gate			Regular globe, regular lift check, swing check	Short pattern† globe, short pattern lift check	Angle and lift check		Gate			Globe, lift check, swing check	Angle and lift check		Gate			Globe, lift check, swing check	Angle and lift check
	Solid wedge	Double disk	Short pattern†			Regular	Short pattern	Solid wedge	Double disk	Short pattern†				Solid wedge	Double disk	Short pattern†		
	A and *B*	*A* and *B*	*B*	*A* and *B*	*B*	*D* and *E*	*E*	*A* and *B*	*A* and *B*	*B*	*A* and *B*	*D* and *E*		*A* and *B*	*A* and *B*	*B*	*A* and *B*	*B*
¾	....	....	....	9	...	4½	....	....	....	....	9	4½	½	10⅜	....	....	10⅜	5 3/16
1	10	....	5½	10	...	5	....	10	....	5½	10	5	¾	10¾	....	....	10¾	5⅜
1¼	11	....	6½	11	...	5½	....	11	....	6½	11	5½	1	12⅛	....	7 5/16	12⅛	6 1/16
1½	12	....	7	12	...	6	....	12	....	7	12	6	1¼	13¾	....	9⅛	13¾	6⅞
2	14½	14½	8½	14½	...	7¼	....	14½	14½	8½	14½	7¼	1½	15⅛	....	9⅛	15⅛	7 9/16
2½	16½	16½	10	16½	...	8¼	....	16½	16½	10	16½	8¼	2	17¾	17¾	11	17¾	8⅞
3	15	15	12	15	12	7½	6	18½	18½	12	18½	9¼	2½	20	20	13	20	10
4	18	18	14	18	14	9	7	21½	21½	16	21½	10¾	3	22¾	22¾	14½	22¾	11⅜
5	22	22	17	22	17	11	8½	26½	26½	19	26½	13¼	4	26½	26½	18	26½	13¼
6	24	24	20	24	20	12	10	27¾	27¾	22	27¾	13⅞	5	31¼	31¼	21	31¼	15⅝
8	29	29	26	29	26	14½	13	32¾	32¾	28	32¾	16⅜	6	36	36	24	36	18
10	33	33	31	33	31	16½	15½	39	39	34	39	19½	8	40¼	40¼	30	40¼	20⅛
12	38	38	36	38	36	19	18	44½	44½	39	44½	22¼	10	50	50	36	50	25
14	40½	40½	39	40½	39	20¼	19½	49½	49½	42	49½	24¾	12	56	56	41	56	28
16	44½	44½	43	....	...	....	...	54½	54½	47			14	....	....	44		
18	48	48	*	....	...	....	....	60½	60½	53			16	....	....	49		
20	52	52	*	....	...	....	....	65½	65½	58			18	....	....	55		
24	61	61	*	....	...	....	....	76½	76½									

NOTE: Outline drawings for flanged valves show ¼-in. raised face machined onto flange, as for 400-lb. cast-steel valves. 150- and 300-lb. cast-steel valves and 250-lb. cast-iron valves have 1/16-in. raised faces. 125-lb. cast-iron and 150-lb. corrosion-resistant valves covered by MSS-SP-42 have no raised faces.
* Not shown in A.S.A. B16.10 but commercially available.
† These dimensions apply to pressure seal or flangeless bonnet valves only.

Table 6-13. Dimensions of Cast-iron Pipe

All dimensions in inches

Pipe size	Outside diam.*		Wall thickness†						
	Pipe	Mech. joint bell	Class 50 50 lb./sq.in.	Class 100 100 lb./sq.in.	Class 150 150 lb./sq.in.	Class 200 200 lb./sq.in.	Class 250 250 lb./sq.in.	Class 300 300 lb./sq.in.	Class 350 350 lb./sq.in.
3	3.96	7.62	0.32	0.32	0.32	0.32	0.32	0.32	0.32
4	4.80	9.06	.35	.35	.35	.35	.35	.35	.35
6	6.90	11.06	.38	.38	.38	.38	.38	.38	.38
8	9.05	13.31	.41	.41	.41	.41	.41	.41	.41
10	11.10	15.62	.44	.44	.44	.44	.44	.48	.52
12	13.20	17.88	.48	.48	.48	.48	.52	.52	.56
14	15.30	20.25	.48	.51	.51	.55	.59	.59	.64
16	17.40	22.50	.54	.54	.54	.58	.63	.68	.68
18	19.50	24.75	.54	.58	.58	.63	.68	.73	.79
20	21.60	27.00	.57	.62	.62	.67	.72	.78	.84
24	25.80	31.50	.63	.68	.73	.79	.79	.85	.92

* From A.S.A. A21.11-1952.
† From A.S.A. A21.6-1962, Table 6.3, and A.S.A. A21.8-1962, Table 8.3.

Table 6-14. Deflections and Curves, Cast-iron Pipe*

Pipe size	Bend in one joint, angle	Deflection, in.				Approx. radius, ft., of curve produced by succession of joints			
		12-ft. length	16-ft. length	18-ft. length	20-ft. length	12-ft. length	16-ft. length	18-ft. length	20-ft. length
3	8°18′	21	28	31	...	85	100	125	
4	8°18′	21	28	31	...	85	110	125	
6	7°7′	18	24	27	...	100	130	145	
8	5°21′	13	18	20	...	130	170	195	
10	5°21′	13	18	20	...	130	170	195	
12	5°21′	13	18	20	22	130	170	195	220
14	3°35′	9	12	13½	15	190	250	285	320
16	3°35′	9	12	13½	15	190	250	285	320
18	3°0′	7½	10	11	12	230	300	340	380
20	3°0′	7½	10	11	12	230	300	340	380
24	2°23′	6	8	9	10	300	400	450	500

* "Handbook of Cast Iron Pipe," 2d ed., Cast Iron Pipe Research Association, Chicago. (Mechanical joint pipe.)

dimension for A.S.A. B16.4 125-lb. flanged fittings (see Table 6-10). Stock fittings are designed for 250 lb./sq. in. in sizes through 12 in. and 150 lb./sq. in. in sizes 14 through 48 in. Higher-pressure fittings are available in the larger sizes; in the case of tees they may contain strengthening bolts located on a diameter of the water passage. Stock fittings include 22½- and 11¼-deg. bends.

Cast-iron piping components are also available in nodular (ductile) iron at increased cost. Ductile iron has an elongation of 10 per cent or more, which permits its use in applications where cast iron would be unsuitable.

High-silicon Iron. Duriron is a high-silicon iron and contains approximately 14.5 per cent silicon and 0.85 per cent carbon. It is resistant to most chemicals, such as sulfuric, nitric, and acetic acids at any strength and temperature. Durichlor is a special high-silicon iron, containing 3 per cent molybdenum. It is resistant to the same corrosives for which Duriron is recommended and in addition is almost entirely resistant to hydrochloric acid at all concentrations and at all temperatures up to the boiling point.

These alloys are available in the cast form only. Pipe and fittings are cast with upset ends being joined by malleable-iron split flanges. (To resist external corrosion, split flanges made from 25 per cent Cr, 25 per cent Ni iron are available.) Allowable working pressures cannot be stated in the manner customary for other types of pipe because of such variables as thermal shock, pulsating pressures, and the corrosive being handled. Although rupture does not occur below 400 lb./sq. in. pressure in sizes up to and including 6 in., 50 lb./sq. in. is a normal recommendation even though the pipe has been used for pressure considerably in excess of that figure.

Table 6-15 lists sizes 1 to 12 in., and larger sizes can be obtained. Bell-and-spigot pipe is produced in the weights and dimensions shown in Table 6-15; fittings are available. Since these alloys have practically no elasticity, it is necessary to use expansion joints in relatively short pipe lines. Connections for Duriron-flanged pipe, fittings, valves, and pumps are made to 125-lb. American Standard drilling.

Table 6-15. Duriron and Durichlor Pipe*

Size, inside diam., in.	Split flanged ends				Bell-and-spigot ends			
	Outside diam., in.	Wall thickness, in.	Standard† length, ft.	Weight per piece, lb.	Outside diam., in.	Wall thickness, in.	Standard† length, ft.	Weight per piece, lb.
1	1¾	⅜	3	15				
1½	2¼	⅜	3	18	2⅛	5/16	3	20
2	2¾	⅜	4	32	2⅝	5/16	4	30
2½	3¼	⅜	5	45				
3	3⅞	7/16	5	62	3 11/16	11/32	5	68
4	4⅞	7/16	5	100	4⅝	5/16	5	89
6	7	½	5	180	6 11/16	11/32	5	133
8	9¼	⅝	6	265	9	½	5	232
10	11½	¾	6	433	11¼	⅝	5	341
12	14	1	6	694	13¼	⅝	5	463
15	....	....	...	...	16¾	⅞	5	680

* The Duriron Co.
† Laying lengths; lengths less than standard are available.

Non-ferrous-metal Piping Systems. Aluminum. Seamless aluminum pipe and tube are produced by extrusion in essentially pure aluminum and in several alloys; 20-, 30-, and 40-ft. lengths are available. Alloying and mill treatment improve the physical properties but welding reduces them. Essentially pure aluminum has an ultimate tensile strength of 9500 lb./sq. in., subject to a slight increase by mill treatment which is lost during welding. Alloy 6061, which contains 0.25 per cent copper, 0.6 per cent silicon, 1 per cent magnesium, and 0.25 per cent chromium, has an ultimate tensile strength of 18,000 lb./sq. in. in the annealed condition, 38,000 lb./sq. in., mill treated as 6061-T6, and 24,000 lb./sq. in. at welded joints. Extensive use is made of alloy 1060, which is 99.6 per cent pure aluminum, for hydrogen peroxide; of alloy 3003, which contains 1.2 per cent manganese, for high-purity chemicals; and of alloys 6063 and 6061 for many other services. Alloy 6063 is the same as 6061 minus the chromium and has slightly lower mechanical properties.

Aluminum is not embrittled by low temperatures and is not subject to external corrosion when exposed to normal atmospheres. At 400°F. strength is less than half that at room temperature. It is attacked by alkalies, by traces of copper, nickel, mercury, and other heavy-metal ions, and by prolonged contact with wet insulation. It suffers from galvanic corrosion when coupled to copper, nickel, or lead-base alloys but not when coupled to galvanized iron or austenitic stainless steel.

Aluminum pipe is stocked in 3003, 6061, and 6063 Schedule 40 through 10 in., Schedule 30 8 through 10 in., and standard-weight 12-in. size. It is also stocked in 6063 as Schedule 5 through 6 in. and Schedule 10 through 8 in. (see Table 6-2).

Threaded **aluminum fittings** are seldom recommended for process piping. Wrought fittings with welding ends (see Table 6-11 for dimensions) and with grooved joint ends are available. Wrought 6061-T6 flanges with dimensions per Table 6-3 are also available. Cast flanges and flanged fittings, sand-cast as alloy B214, 3.8 per cent magnesium alloy with 13,000 lb./sq. in. yield strength, or permanent mold cast as alloy 356-T6, 7 per cent silicon, 0.3 per cent magnesium alloy with 27,000 lb./sq. in. yield strength are available, but consideration must be given to the fact that the modulus of elasticity of aluminum is only slightly more than one-third that of ferrous alloys. See Table 6-10 for dimensions.

Aluminum-body diaphragm and ball valves are used extensively.

Aluminum's ability to be formed by extrusion permits production of double-channel pipe consisting of a large channel for the process fluid and a small channel for steam or hot water to keep the process fluid from freezing. Cast welding and flanged fittings for such systems are also available.

Copper and Copper Alloys. Seamless copper, bronze, brass, copper-nickel alloy, and copper-silicon alloy pipe and tube are produced by extrusion. **Tube** is available in outside diameter sizes from 1/16 to 16 in. and in a range of wall thickness varying from 0.005 in. for the smallest tube to 0.75 in. for the 16-in. size. Tube is usually specified by outside diameter and wall thickness. Table 11-2 (p. 11-11) gives dimensions of condenser and heat-exchanger tube.

Seamless copper is sold with water tube outside diameter (outside diameter ⅛ in. greater than nominal), as outside diameter tube, and as pipe with pipe outside diameter. As tube it is available as annealed (soft) temper coils where the ratio of wall thickness to diameter is high enough to permit straightening without kinking or excessive flattening. It is available in all size-wall combinations as drawn (hard) temper in 20-ft. lengths. Copper tube is widely used for piping in offices and laboratories, for steam tracing, and for pneumatic control systems. Flared-fitting joints (Fig. 6-107), compression-fitting joints (Fig. 6-108), bite-type-fitting joints (Fig. 6-109), and soldered or brazed joints (Fig. 6-110) are used for the tube. Figure 6-110 is most economical for ¾ in. size and larger. Ease of handling

Table 6-16. Copper Water Tube—Types K, L, M*
For tubing or soldered fittings
All tolerances plus and minus except as otherwise indicated

Nominal size	Actual outside diam., in.	Mean outside diam. tolerances, in.		Wall thickness, in.						Theoretical weight, lb./ft		
				Type K		Type L		Type M				
		Soft annealed	Hard drawn	Nominal	Tolerance	Nominal	Tolerance	Nominal	Tolerance	Type K	Type L	Type M
¼	0.375	0.002	0.001	0.035	0.004	0.030	0.0035	.....	......	0.145	0.126	
⅜	.500	.0025	.001	.049	.004	.035	.0035	0.025	0.0025	.269	.198	0.145
½	.625	.0025	.001	.049	.004	.040	.0035	.028	.0025	.344	.285	.204
⅝	.750	.0025	.001	.049	.004	.042	.0035	.....	......	.418	.362	
¾	.875	.003	.001	.065	.0045	.045	.004	.032	.003	.641	.455	.328
1	1.125	.0035	.0015	.065	.0045	.050	.004	.035	.0035	.839	.655	.465
1¼	1.375	.004	.0015	.065	.0045	.055	.0045	.042	.0035	1.04	.884	.682
1½	1.625	.0045	.002	.072	.005	.060	.0045	.049	.004	1.36	1.14	.940
2	2.125	.005	.002	.083	.007	.070	.006	.058	.006	2.06	1.75	1.46
2½	2.625	.005	.002	.095	.007	.080	.006	.065	.006	2.93	2.48	2.03
3	3.125	.005	.002	.109	.007	.090	.007	.072	.006	4.00	3.33	2.68
3½	3.625	.005	.002	.120	.008	.100	.007	.083	.007	5.12	4.29	3.58
4	4.125	.005	.002	.134	.010	.110	.009	.095	.009	6.51	5.38	4.66
5	5.125	.005	.002	.160	.010	.125	.010	.109	.009	9.67	7.61	6.66
6	6.125	.005	.002	.192	.012	.140	.011	.122	.010	13.9	10.2	8.92
			+ −									
8	8.125	.006	.002 .004	.271	.016	.200	.014	.170	.014	25.9	19.3	16.5
10	10.125	.008	.002 .006	.338	.018	.250	.016	.212	.015	40.3	30.1	25.6
12	12.125	.008	.002 .006	.405	.020	.280	.018	.254	.016	57.8	40.4	36.7

Weight tolerance: Tube shall not vary in weight by more than 7 per cent from the nominal weight given above.
* Copper & Brass Research Association Standard Tube 6, 1959, corresponds to theNational Bureau of Standards simplified practice recommendations R217-49 amendent, 6/22/50.

and bending favors the use of copper; it will survive freeze-ups without failure.

Copper tube with **water tube outside diameter** is available per A.S.T.M. B-88 with dimensions and tolerance as given in Table 6-16. Types K and L soft temper are available in 60- and 100-ft. coils, sizes 1 in. and smaller, and in 60-ft. coils, sizes 1¼ and 1½ in. Type K soft temper is available in 45-ft. coils, size 2 in. Sizing and rounding tools are used on cut ends of soft copper tube ¾ in. and larger prior to making solder or braze joints. Type M is available only in hard temper in straight lengths. Copper tube with water tube outside diameter is also available per A.S.T.M. B-306 for nonpressure applications. Size-wall combinations are 1¼ in., 0.040-in. wall; 1½ in., 0.042-in. wall; 2 in., 0.042-in. wall; 3 in., 0.045-in. wall; 4 in., 0.058-in. wall; 5 in., 0.072-in. wall; 6 in., 0.083-in. wall. Otherwise, it is the same as type M except wall-thickness tolerances are slightly less.

Outside diameter copper tube, soft temper, for refrigeration field service and automotive and general service is available per A.S.T.M. B280 with dimensions and tolerances per Table 6-17. Standard length of

Table 6-17. Copper O.D. Tube for Refrigeration Field, Automotive and General Service*
For mechanical or soldered fittings
All tolerances plus and minus

Nominal size	Actual outside diam., in.	Mean outside diam. tolerances, in.	Wall thickness, in.	Wall-thickness tolerances, in.	Nominal wt., lb./ft.
⅛	0.125	0.002	0.030	0.003	0.0347
3⁄16	.188	.002	.030	.0025	.0575
¼	.250	.002	.030	.0025	.0804
5⁄16	.312	.002	.032	.0025	.109
⅜	.375	.002	.032	.0025	.134
½	.500	.002	.032	.0025	.182
⅝	.625	.002	.035	.003	.251
¾	.750	.0025	.035	.003	.305

* Copper & Brass Research Association Tube 11, 3/2/59.

coils is 25 ft. for automotive and general service and 50 ft. for refrigeration service tube, but longer coils are available on special order.

Too high a temperature or too long a heating period when silver brazing ruins red brass solder-joint fittings faster than wrought-copper fittings. The former are available in larger sizes. Yellow brass fails from dezincification in some waters.

Red brass and bronze valves are available with female solder-joint ends for soldered copper-tube piping systems.

Table 6-18 shows pressure-temperature ratings for soldered and silver-brazed copper-tubing systems, reflecting strength of fitting and tube, composition of solder, and temperature of fluid conveyed.

Table 6-18. Ratings of Soldered and Silver-brazed Joints

Solder used in joints	Service temp., °F.	Max. service pressure, lb./sq. in.				
		Water-tube size, in.				
		¼ through 1	1¼ through 2	2½ through 4	5 through 8	10 through 12
50% tin, 50% lead (A.S.T.M. B32 alloy 50A)	100	200	175	150	130	100
	150	150	125	100	90	70
	200	100	90	75	70	50
	250	85	75	50	50	40
95% tin, 5% antimony	100	500	400	300	150	150
	150	400	350	275	150	150
	200	300	250	200	150	140
	250	200	175	150	140	110
5% phosphorus, 15% silver, 80% copper (A.S.T.M. B260 B CuP-5) or 45% silver, 15% copper, 16% zinc, 24% cadmium (A.S.T.M. B260 B Ag-1)	250	250	300	210	150	150
	350	270	190	155	150	150

Copper **pipe** is available per A.S.T.M. B42 with dimensions per Table 6-19. Butt-welding fittings (Table 6-11) are available to fit it, also screwed fittings per A.S.A. B16.15 and A.S.A. B16.17, but solder-end fittings of approximately the same dimensions as the screwed fittings and silver brazing alloy are the usual method of assembly. Red brass or bronze valves with ends identical to the fittings are available. Flanges and flanged fittings are seldom used, since soldered or silver-brazed joints can be melted apart and reassembled.

Threadless copper pipe, thinner than A.S.T.M. B42, is available with dimensions per Table 6-20. Solder-end fittings similar to A.S.A. B16.15 screwed fittings and solder-end valves are used with this pipe.

Table 6-19. Copper and Red Brass Pipe*

A. Dimensions and Weights of Regular Pipe

Nominal pipe size, in.	Nominal dimensions, in.			Cross-sectional area of bore, sq. in.	Lb./ft.		Nominal pipe size, in.	Nominal dimensions, in.			Cross-sectional area of bore, sq. in.	Lb./ft.	
	Outside diam.	Inside diam.	Wall Thickness		Red brass	Copper		Outside diam.	Inside diam.	Wall thickness		Red brass	Copper
1/8	0.405	0.281	0.062	0.062	0.253	0.259	2½	2.875	2.501	0.187	4.91	5.99	6.12
¼	.540	.376	.082	.110	.447	.457	3	3.500	3.062	.219	7.37	8.56	8.75
3/8	.675	.495	.090	.192	.627	.641	3½	4.000	3.500	.250	9.62	11.2	11.4
½	.840	.626	.107	.307	.934	.955	4	4.500	4.000	.250	12.6	12.7	12.9
¾	1.050	.822	.114	.531	1.27	1.30	5	5.562	5.062	.250	20.1	15.8	16.2
1	1.315	1.063	.126	.887	1.78	1.82	6	6.625	6.125	.250	29.5	19.0	19.4
1¼	1.660	1.368	.146	1.47	2.63	2.69	8	8.625	8.001	.312	50.3	30.9	31.6
1½	1.900	1.609	.150	2.01	3.13	3.20	10	10.750	10.020	.365	78.8	45.2	46.2
2	2.375	2.063	.156	3.34	4.12	4.22	12	12.750	12.000	.375	113.	55.3	56.5

B. Dimensions and Weights of Extra Strong Pipe

Nominal pipe size, in.	Nominal dimensions, in.			Cross-sectional area of bore, sq. in.	Lb./ft.		Nominal pipe size, in.	Nominal dimensions, in.			Cross-sectional area of bore, sq. in.	Lb./ft.	
	Outside diam.	Inside diam.	Wall Thickness		Red brass	Copper		Outside diam.	Inside diam.	Wall thickness		Red brass	Copper
1/8	0.405	0.205	0.100	0.033	0.363	0.371	2½	2.875	2.315	0.280	4.21	8.66	8.85
¼	.540	.294	.123	.068	.611	.625	3	3.500	2.892	.304	6.57	11.6	11.8
3/8	.675	.421	.127	.139	.829	.847	3½	4.000	3.358	.321	8.86	14.1	14.4
½	.840	.542	.149	.231	1.23	1.25	4	4.500	3.818	.341	11.5	16.9	17.3
¾	1.050	.736	.157	.425	1.67	1.71	5	5.562	4.812	.375	18.2	23.2	23.7
1	1.315	.951	.182	.710	2.46	2.51	6	6.625	5.751	.437	26.0	32.2	32.9
1¼	1.660	1.272	.194	1.27	3.39	3.46	8	8.625	7.625	.500	45.7	48.4	49.5
1½	1.900	1.494	.203	1.75	4.10	4.19	10	10.750	9.750	.500	74.7	61.1	62.4
2	2.375	1.933	.221	2.94	5.67	5.80							

C. Weight and Wall Thickness Tolerances

Standard pipe size	Weight per ft. tolerances	Wall thickness tolerances to nearest 0.001 in.	
	Plus or minus, %	Minus, %	Plus
Up to 6 in., inclusive	5	5	Limited only by weight tolerances
Over 6–8 in., inclusive	7	7	
Over 8 in.	8	8	

Length tolerances: Standard length 12 ft. plus or minus ½ in.

* Copper & Brass Research Association Standard Tube 8, 3/2/59, corresponds to the National Bureau of Standards simplified practice recommendations R217-49 amendment, 6/22/50.

Table 6-20. Copper Threadless Pipe (Hard-drawn)*

Conforms with A.S.T.M. Designation B302 for working pressures up to 200 lb./sq. in.

Standard pipe size, in.	Actual outside diam., in.	Average outside diam. tolerances, all minus	Wall thickness, in.	Wall thickness tolerances, plus and minus	Nominal wt., lb./ft.	Inside diam., in.	Cross-sectional area of bore, sq. in.
¼	0.540	0.004	0.065	0.0035	0.376	0.410	0.132
3/8	.675	.004	.065	.004	.483	.545	.233
½	.840	.005	.065	.004	.613	.710	.396
¾	1.050	.005	.065	.004	.780	.920	.665
1	1.315	.005	.065	.004	.989	1.185	1.10
1¼	1.660	.006	.065	.004	1.26	1.530	1.84
1½	1.900	.006	.065	.004	1.45	1.770	2.46
2	2.375	.007	.065	.006	1.83	2.245	3.96
2½	2.875	.007	.065	.006	2.22	2.745	5.92
3	3.500	.008	.083	.007	3.45	3.334	8.73
3½	4.000	.008	.095	.007	4.52	3.810	11.4
4	4.500	.010	.107	.009	5.72	4.286	14.4
5	5.562	.012	.132	.010	8.73	5.298	22.0
6	6.625	.014	.158	.010	12.4	6.309	31.3
8	8.625	.018	.205	.014	21.0	8.215	53.0
10	10.750	.018	.256	.016	32.7	10.238	82.3
12	12.750	.018	.313	.020	47.4	12.124	115

Length and tolerance: Standard length furnished straight, 20 ft. plus 1 in. minus zero.

Squareness of cut: Same as for round seamless tube; see Tube 2b.

Roundness tolerances: Same as for round seamless tube; see Tube 2b.

* Copper & Brass Research Association Tube 9, 3/2/59.

Copper pipe is attacked by water originating in granite substrata and for this reason red brass pipe per A.S.T.M. B43 is used in its place, with red brass screwed or solder-end fittings.

70 per cent copper, 30 per cent nickel and 90 per cent copper, 10 per cent nickel are available as seamless pipe and welding fittings for handling brackish water in Schedule 10 and regular copper pipe thicknesses.

Copper-silicon alloy (96 per cent copper, 3 per cent silicon, 1 per cent manganese), per A.S.T.M. B315, is furnished as seamless pipe and welding fittings in Schedule 10 and regular and extra-strong copper pipe thicknesses.

Lead and lead-lined steel pipe are widely used for handling sulfuric acid at moderate temperatures. Because of the low physical strength of the metal, it is customary to lay lead pipe in steel angles or wood troughs. Chemical lead per A.S.T.M. B29-55, which is 99.9 per cent lead, 0.04 to 0.08 per cent copper, and bismuth not over 0.005 per cent, has the greatest corrosion resistance; 6 per cent antimonial lead has greater strength at temperatures below 225°F., and more resistance to abrasion and erosion; 0.04 per cent tellurium lead has the same strength as chemical lead but withstands vibration better. There is no national dimensional standard for chemical-lead **pipe**. Table 6-21 gives dimensions usually available. Maximum allowable fiber stresses are shown in Fig. 6-113.

Lead pipe is usually delivered in 12-ft. lengths. The most common field jointing method is "lead burning," a form of welding using a hydrogen flame. Antimonial lead flanges with drilling per Table 6-3 are also used. Lead crosses, straight and reducing tees, true Ys, straight and reducing laterals, and elbows are also available, or can be fabricated in the field from the pipe. Solid

Table 6-21. Lead Pipe for Chemical Use

Inside diam., in.	Wall, in.	Outside diam., in.	Wt., lb./ft.
1/4	1/16	3/8	0.30
	1/8	1/2	0.73
	3/16	5/8	1.27
	1/4	3/4	1.93
3/8	1/16	1/2	0.43
	1/8	5/8	0.97
	3/16	3/4	1.63
	1/4	7/8	2.42
1/2	1/8	3/4	1.20
	3/16	7/8	1.99
	1/4	1	2.89
	5/16	1 1/8	3.92
	3/8	1 1/4	5.07
5/8	1/8	7/8	1.45
	3/16	1	2.35
	1/4	1 1/8	3.38
	5/16	1 1/4	4.53
	3/8	1 3/8	5.80
3/4	1/8	1	1.69
	3/16	1 1/8	2.72
	1/4	1 1/4	3.87
	5/16	1 3/8	5.14
	3/8	1 1/2	6.52
	1/2	1 3/4	9.66
1	1/8	1 1/4	2.18
	3/16	1 3/8	3.45
	1/4	1 1/2	4.83
	5/16	1 5/8	6.34
	3/8	1 3/4	7.97
	1/2	2	11.60
1 1/4	1/8	1 1/2	2.65
	3/16	1 5/8	4.16
	1/4	1 3/4	5.79
	5/16	1 7/8	7.54
	3/8	2	9.42
	1/2	2 1/4	13.52
1 1/2	1/8	1 3/4	3.14
	3/16	1 7/8	4.89
	1/4	2	6.77
	5/16	2 1/8	8.76
	3/8	2 1/4	10.87
	1/2	2 1/2	15.46
1 3/4	1/8	2	3.63
	3/16	2 1/8	5.62
	1/4	2 1/4	7.73
	5/16	2 3/8	9.97
	3/8	2 1/2	12.32
	1/2	2 3/4	17.37
2	1/8	2 1/4	4.10
	3/16	2 3/8	6.34
	1/4	2 1/2	8.69
	5/16	2 5/8	11.16
	3/8	2 3/4	13.76
	1/2	3	19.32
2 1/2	1/8	2 3/4	5.07
	3/16	2 7/8	7.78
	1/4	3	10.63
	5/16	3 1/8	13.59
	3/8	3 1/4	16.69
	1/2	3 1/2	23.18
3	1/8	3 1/4	6.06
	3/16	3 3/8	9.25
	1/4	3 1/2	12.55
	5/16	3 5/8	15.99
	3/8	3 3/4	19.54
	1/2	4	27.06
3 1/2	1/8	3 3/4	6.99
	3/16	3 7/8	10.68
	1/4	4	14.51
	5/16	4 1/8	18.40
	3/8	4 1/4	22.48
	1/2	4 1/2	30.90
4	1/8	4 1/4	7.96
	3/16	4 3/8	12.11
	1/4	4 1/2	16.39
	5/16	4 5/8	20.82
	3/8	4 3/4	25.34
	1/2	5	34.79
4 1/2	1/8	4 3/4	8.95
	3/16	4 7/8	13.63
	1/4	5	18.50
	5/16	5 1/8	23.27
	3/8	5 1/4	28.29
	1/2	5 1/2	38.67
5	1/8	5 1/4	9.89
	3/16	5 3/8	15.00
	1/4	5 1/2	20.27
	5/16	5 5/8	25.63
	3/8	5 3/4	31.14
	1/2	6	42.47
5 1/2	1/8	5 3/4	10.87
	3/16	5 7/8	16.47
	1/4	6	22.20
	5/16	6 1/8	28.06
	3/8	6 1/4	34.04
	1/2	6 1/2	46.36
6	1/8	6 1/4	11.84
	3/16	6 3/8	17.94
	1/4	6 1/2	24.10
	5/16	6 5/8	30.50
	3/8	6 3/4	36.96
	1/2	7	50.24
7	1/8	7 1/4	13.77
	3/16	7 3/8	20.83
	1/4	7 1/2	28.02
	5/16	7 5/8	35.32
	3/8	7 3/4	42.75
	1/2	8	57.96
8	1/8	8 1/4	15.70
	3/16	8 3/8	23.73
	1/4	8 1/2	31.89
	5/16	8 5/8	40.17
	3/8	8 3/4	48.55
	1/2	9	65.70
10	1/8	10 1/4	19.58
	3/16	10 3/8	29.52
	1/4	10 1/2	39.60
	5/16	10 5/8	49.79
	3/8	10 3/4	60.12
	1/2	11	81.13
12	3/16	12 3/8	35.33
	1/4	12 1/2	47.33
	5/16	12 5/8	59.48
	3/8	12 3/4	71.74
	1/2	13	96.58

antimonial lead valves are available for pressures up through 65 lb./sq. in., and are preferred where spillage is frequent.

Lead-lined pipe withstands greater pressure and requires far less support than lead pipe. It is available in two types: expanded, in which chemical lead is hydraulically expanded inside flanged steel pipe and carried out on the flange faces; and homogeneous, in which chemical lead is poured in as a lining. Expanded lead-lined steel pipe has lower cost and is manufactured to ordered length or shipped in random lengths of approximately 20 ft. Several thicknesses of lining are available for each size and range from 5/64 through 1/4 in. for 1 in. size to 3/16 through 3/8 in. for 12 in. size. Homogeneous lead-lined steel pipe is used for vacuum, for high or cycling temperatures, and for high pressure. It is normally shipped flanged with lead-faced flanges in ordered or random lengths of about 20 ft. Thickness of lining is 1/8, 3/16, or 1/4 in. for sizes 1 through 6 in. and 3/16 or 1/4 in. for sizes 8 through 12 in. For both types of lining, pipe and extra flanges can be shipped separately. The pipe is cut, threaded, and end-faced in the field, the flanges are screwed on, and the lead flange face is bonded to the lining by lead burning. Flanged lead-lined fittings and valves are available. They and the flanges are normally 125 lb. cast iron but 250 lb. cast iron or steel in any pressure class may be obtained.

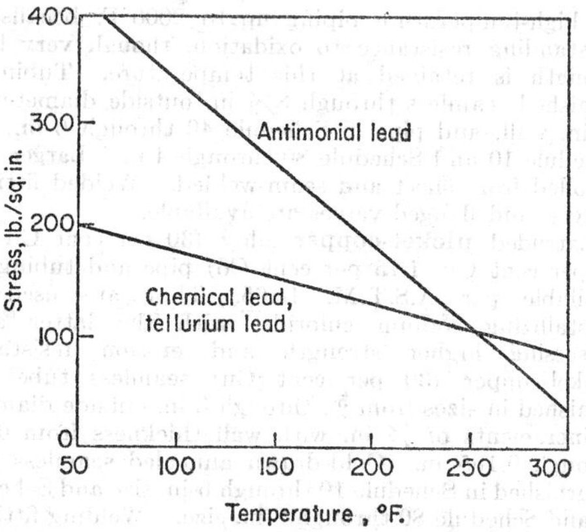

Fig. 6-113. Maximum allowable fiber stresses in lead pipe.

Magnesium. Extruded magnesium tubing resists attack by most alkalies and many organic chemicals including aldehydes, alcohols, phenols, amines, and esters. It is available per A.S.T.M. B217-58 alloyed with aluminum, manganese, or zinc. Ultimate and yield strength at 400°F. are about one-half those at room temperature. Outside diameter range is 1/4 through 8 in. Wall thickness ranges from a minimum of 0.028 in. to a maximum of 0.031 in. for the 1/4 in. diameter and from a minimum of 0.250 in. to a maximum of 1.0 in. for the 8 in. diameter.

Nickel and Nickel Alloys. Extruded **nickel** pipe and tubing is available in two grades: 99 per cent nickel, 0.06 per cent carbon is used for halogen acids at high temperatures and sodium chloride solutions; 99 per cent nickel, 0.01 per cent carbon is used for fused caustic soda. They are available per A.S.T.M. B161 as tubing in sizes from 3/8 to 3 in. outside diameter in increments of 1/8 in. with wall thickness 0.049 through 0.165 in., and as pipe, Schedule 10, 1/8 through 6 in., and Schedule 40 and 80, 1/8 through 8 in. Larger pipe is rolled from sheet and seam-welded. Welding fittings are available. Cast-nickel flanged valves are available. Because of low strength, lap joints backed up with other metal flanges are used instead of nickel flanges.

Carbon-steel pipe and welding fittings internally plated with 0.008- to 0.015-in. nickel are sometimes used as a substitute. Nickel-phosphorus internal coatings are also available.

Extruded **nickel-chromium-iron** (14 per cent Cr, 7 per cent Fe, 79 per cent Ni) pipe and tubing are used for high-temperature piping up to 2000°F. because of outstanding resistance to oxidation, though very little strength is retained at this temperature. Tubing is furnished seamless through 8½ in. outside diameter by ⅝-in. wall, and pipe in Schedule 40 through 6 in., and Schedule 10 and Schedule 80 through 4 in. Larger pipe is rolled from sheet and seam-welded. Welded fittings, flanges, and flanged valves are available.

Extruded **nickel-copper** alloy (30 per cent Cu and 29 per cent Cu, 1.75 per cent Co) pipe and tubing are available per A.S.T.M. B165. They are used for crystallizing sodium chloride, with the latter alloy possessing higher strength and erosion resistance. Nickel-copper (30 per cent Cu) seamless tubes are furnished in sizes from ⅝ through 3 in. outside diameter in increments of ⅛ in. with wall thickness from 0.049 through 0.165 in. Cold-drawn annealed seamless pipe is furnished in Schedule 10 through 6-in. size and Schedule 40 and Schedule 80 through 8-in. size. Welding fittings, flanges, and flanged valves are available. Nickel copper (29 per cent Cu, 1.75 per cent Co) seamless tubes are furnished in sizes through 3¼ in. outside diameter. Seamless pipe is furnished in Schedule 40 and 80 through 2½-in. size.

Nickel-molybdenum-iron alloy (30 per cent Mo, 5 per cent Fe, 65 per cent Ni) is used for wet hydrogen chloride gas and boiling hydrochloric acid. It retains over two-thirds of its room-temperature yield strength at 1600°F. **Nickel-molybdenum-chromium-tungsten-iron** alloy (17 per cent Mo, 15 per cent Cr, 5 per cent W, 5 per cent Fe, 58 per cent Ni) is resistant to oxidizing and reducing atmospheres up to 2100°F. and has exceptional resistance to strong oxidizing agents such as ferric chloride and cupric chloride. Both alloys are weldable and are furnished as welded pipe, Schedule 5, 1½ through 4 in.; Schedule 10, 1 through 4 in.; Schedule 40, ¼ through 4 in. (except for the ¾- and 1-in. sizes of the latter alloy); and Schedule 80, 1½ through 4 in. The latter alloy is available as wrought seamless pipe in sizes ¾ through 1½ in. Both alloys are available as cast pipe Schedule 80, 1 through 8 in. Cast welding elbows, sizes ¼ through 4 in., and stub ends, ½ through 6 in., are stocked, but intersection welds (Fig. 6-93) are used instead of welding tees. Cast flanged fittings 1 through 4 in. and cast 150-lb. welding-neck and slip-on flanges ½ through 12 in. are also available. Welded pipe larger than 4 in. is made from rolled-up plate, seam-welded. Cast valves are available.

Nickel-chromium-molybdenum-copper-iron (29 per cent Ni, 20 per cent Cr, 3 per cent Mo, 4 per cent Cu, 44 per cent Fe) has excellent resistance to sulfuric acid at temperatures and concentrations outside the range for carbon steel. It is weldable and is alloyed with columbium for welded construction. Welded pipe is furnished Schedule 5, ½ through 4 in.; Schedule 10, ⅛ through 4 in.; and Schedule 40, ⅛ through 2 in. Wrought welding fittings, forged welding flanges, and cast valves to match the pipe are also available.

Tin. Pure high-grade block tin is made into pipe and tubing in straight lengths, coils, or on reels; the dimensions of the usual sizes are given in Table 6-22. The longest length of pipe is one weighing 50 lb. Because of the relative inactivity of tin, it is used principally for handling fluids intended for human consumption, and others of which contamination is undesirable. The allowable working fiber stress is 150 lb./sq. in.

Table 6-22. Block Tin Pipe*
Approximate Sizes and Weights

Inside diam., in.	Outside diam., in.	Weight per ft., oz.	Inside diam., in.	Outside diam., in.	Weight per ft., oz.	Inside diam., in.	Outside diam., in.	Weight per ft., oz.
1/16	1/8	1/2	3/8	17/32 F	6	5/8	25/32 S	8
				9/16	7		25/32	9
1/8	3/16	3/4		19/32 S	8		13/16 S	10
				19/32 F	9		7/8 S	14
3/16	1/4 F	1 1/2		5/8	10			
	5/16	2 1/2		21/32	12	3/4	7/8	8
							29/32	10
1/4	3/8	3	7/16	17/32 F	4		29/32 F	11
	13/32	4		19/32 S	6		15/16 S	12
	7/16	5		5/8	8		31/32 F	16
	15/32 S	6					1	17
	1/2 S	7	1/2	19/32 F	4 1/2		1 1/32	20
	1/2 F	8		5/8 S	5			
				5/8	5 1/2	1	1 3/32 F	9
5/16	7/16 F	4		5/8 F	6		1 5/32 F	14
	1/2 S	5 1/2		21/32	7		1 3/16	16
	17/32	7 1/2		21/32 F	8		1 3/16 F	18
	17/32 F	8		23/32 S	10		1 7/32 F	20
				3/4 S	12		1 1/4	22
3/8	1/2 S	4						
	1/2	4 1/2						
	17/32 S	5						

F = full; S = scant.
* National Lead Co.

Titanium. Unalloyed titanium of commercial purity is resistant to oxidizing acids such as nitric, chromic, and aqua regia and is particularly resistant to corrosion by sea water in processes for extracting fresh water from it. Pipe per A.S.T.M. B337-58T is available welded or seamless via one of the following processes: extrusion, centrifugal casting, machining of bar stock, or powder compaction; Schedule 5S, Schedule 160, and double extra heavy, ½- through 8-in. size; and Schedule 10S, 40S, and 80S, ⅛- through 8-in. size. Extruded and drawn tubing per A.S.T.M. B338-58T is available from ¼ in. outside diameter, 0.028- through 0.065-in. wall, up through 3½ in. outside diameter, 0.065- through ¼-in. wall. Cast welding fittings, flanges, and valves are also available. Titanium is used at temperatures up to 600°F. It is extremely notch-sensitive. Titanium alloys are available, such as 6 Al-4V, with higher tensile strengths than straight titanium. Unfortunately, they lack the corrosion resistance and weldability of the unalloyed material.

Zirconium (**tin 1.2 to 1.7 per cent**) has excellent resistance to dilute and concentrated nitric acid at 212°F. Tubing is available **seamless** ranging from ½ in. outside diameter by 0.030-in. wall to 8 in. outside diameter by 0.4-in. wall, and **welded** up through 30 in. outside diameter by ⅛-in. wall. Cast valves and fittings are also available.

Flexible Metal Hose. Deeply corrugated thin brass, bronze, Monel, aluminum, and steel tubes are covered with flexible braided-wire jackets to form flexible metal hose. Both tube and braid are brazed or welded to pipe thread, union, or flanged ends. Inside diameters range from ⅛ to 12 in. Maximum recommended temperature for bronze hose is approximately 450°F. Metal thickness is much less than for straight tube for the same pressure-temperature conditions; so accurate data on corrosion and erosion are required to make proper selection.

Non-metallic Piping Systems. Asbestos-cement pipe is seamless pipe made of silica and portland cement, compacted under heavy pressure, uniformly reinforced with asbestos fiber, and thoroughly cured. The interior surface is smooth, does not corrode, and does not tuberculate. Under normal conditions of operation, asbestos cement will handle solutions within a pH range of 4.5 to 14. It is a brittle material and undergoes expansion on wetting. The most widely used joints are O-ring joints. Poured joints are also used to bond serrated pipe ends to the serrated bore of flanges. It is used extensively for underground water systems, for paper-mill slurries and wastes, and for mine water. The O-ring joints limit the temperature to 150°F. The light weight of the pipe minimizes handling labor but careful handling is required to avoid damage.

Table 6-23. Asbestos-cement Pressure Pipe*

Nominal size	Length, ft.	Class 100†			Class 150†			Class 200†		
		Inside diam., in.	Wall, in.‡	Wt., lb./ft.§	Inside diam., in.	Wall, in.‡	Wt., lb./ft.§	Inside diam., in.	Wall, in.‡	Wt., lb./ft.§
4	13	3.95	0.35	6.3	3.95	0.43	7.6	3.95	0.43	9.3
6	13	5.85	.42	10.6	5.85	.53	13.0	5.70	.60	15.4
8	13	7.85	.47	15.8	7.85	.63	19.9	7.60	.75	23.9
10	13	9.85	.52	21.8	10.00	.83	32.0	9.63	1.01	37.2
12	13	11.70	.64	29.7	12.00	.96	43.8	11.56	1.18	51.7
14	13	13.59	.74	38.9	14.00	1.11	58.5	13.59	1.31	69.0
16	13	15.50	.83	48.8	16.00	1.23	73.0	15.50	1.48	89.2

* Johns-Manville Co.
† Equivalent to working pressure, lb./sq. in.
‡ Minimum thickness of machined end; balance of pipe is thicker.
§ Pipe plus O-ring joint coupling.

Table 6-24. Asbestos-cement Gravity Sewer Pipe*

Nominal size	Inside diam., in.	Class 1500†		Class 2400†		Class 3300†		Class 4000†		Class 5000†	
		Wall, in.‡	Wt., lb./ft.	Wall, in.‡	Wt., lb./ft.	Wall, in.†	Wt., lb./ft.	Wall, in.‡	Wt., lb./ft.	Wall, in.‡	Wt., lb./ft.
6	6.00	0.46	8.5	0.49	9.5	0.57	11.1				
8	8.00	.51	12.6	.52	13.3	.61	15.6				
10	10.00	.56	17.6	.58	18.9	.68	22.0	0.75	24.3	0.85	27.6
12	12.05	.61	22.8	.63	24.3	.75	28.8	.82	31.5	0.93	35.8
14	14.05	....	....	.68	30.3	.81	35.8	.89	39.3	1.00	44.3
16	16.05	....	....	.73	37.0	.86	43.1	.95	47.6	1.07	53.7
18	18.05	....	....	.77	43.6	.91	50.9	1.01	56.5	1.13	63.3
20	20.05	....	....	.81	50.7	.96	59.2	1.06	65.4	1.19	73.6
24	24.05	....	....	.89	66.4	1.05	77.2	1.16	85.3	1.30	95.8
30	30.05	....	....	....	....	1.17	106.8	1.30	118.8	1.45	132.7
36	36.05	....	....	....	....	....	.....	1.42	155.0	1.59	173.8

Standard pipe length is 13 ft. except 6 in. Class 1500 is 10 ft. and 8 in. Class 1500 may also be 10 ft.
* Johns-Manville Co.
† Crushing strength per A.S.T.M. three-edge bearing method.
‡ Thickness of wall of pipe excluding machined ends. Same coupling is used for all classes; it protects the machined ends from crushing loads.

Asbestos-cement fittings and valves are not available, but flanged fabricated-steel fittings lined with segments of asbestos-cement pipe and cement-lined cast-iron fittings with end bells for O-ring joint to asbestos-cement pipe can be obtained. Adapters to regular cast-iron fittings are also available. When installed above ground, two guided supports per length of pipe are recommended, and where O-ring joints are used, internal pressure thrusts at changes in direction, at reducers, at dead ends, and at valves must be resisted by braces. When poured flanges are used, expansion joints must be used also with braces to resist corresponding pressure thrust.

Pressure pipe is made in three classes corresponding to working pressures of 100, 150, and 200 lb./sq. in. (Table 6-23).

Gravity sewer pipe is made in five classes for varying depths of bury, trench dimension, soil, and vehicular loading (Table 6-24).

Ventilating duct is available as shown in Table 6-25.

Table 6-25. Asbestos-cement Ducts*

Inside diam., in.	Length, ft.	Wall thickness, in.	Outside diam., in.	Weight† per ft., lb.
3	10	0.32	3.64	2.7
4	10	.32	4.64	3.5
5	10	.35	5.70	4.7
6	10	.35	6.70	5.5
7	10	.40	7.80	7.4
8	10	.40	8.80	9.7
10	13	.40	10.80	12.5
12	13	.45	12.90	16.6
14	13	.45	14.90	19.3
16	13	.50	17.00	24.2
18	13	.50	19.00	27.1
20	13	.55	21.10	32.9
24	13	.60	25.20	42.6
30	13	.67	31.34	58.8
36	13	.75	37.50	81.0

* Johns-Manville Co.
† Weights given are exclusive of couplings and fittings.

Impervious graphite pipe, fittings, and valve bodies are made of electric-furnace graphite which, after extruding or molding, is rendered impervious by impregnation with synthetic resins. When impregnated with phenolic resin, it is resistant to most acids (including hydrofluoric), salts, and organic compounds. When impregnated with modified phenolic resin, it is resistant to strong alkalies and highly oxidizing materials. Ultimate tensile strength is low (2500 lb./sq. in.) and the material is brittle, but the modulus of elasticity is only 2,200,000 lb./sq. in. It is highly resistant to thermal shock and is available with glass-cloth and resin armor for protection against physical abuse. Maximum continuous operating temperature is 340°F. Components are designed for operating pressure which increases from 50 lb./sq. in. at 340°F. to 75 lb./sq. in. at 70°F.

Table 6-26 lists standard sizes of pipe; ½-, ¾-, and ⅞-in. sizes are heat-exchanger tubing, and standard fittings are not available for these sizes. Pipe is shipped

Table 6-26. Standard Sizes of Impervious Graphite Pipe*

Nominal pipe size, in.	Inside diam., in.	Outside diam., in.	Wall thickness, in.	Max. length, ft.	Average weight, lb./ft.	Inside cross-sectional area, sq. ft.	Circumference, ft., or surface, sq. ft./ft. of length	
							Inside	Outside
½	½	¾	⅛	6	0.19	0.00136	0.131	0.196
¾	¾	1	⅛	6	.27	.00307	.196	.262
⅞	⅞	1¼	3/16	9	.48	.00417	.229	.327
1	1	1½	¼	9	.74	.00545	.262	.393
1½	1½	2	¼	9	1.1	.01227	.393	.524
2	2	2¾	⅜	9	1.7	.0218	.524	.687
2½	2⅜	3	5/16	9	2.0	.0308	.622	.785
3	3	4	½	9	5.4	.0491	.785	1.047
4	4	5¼	⅝	9	8.1	.0873	1.047	1.374
6	6	7½	¾	9	15.6	.1965	1.571	1.964
8	7¾	9¾	1	6	24.3	.328	2.029	2.553
10	10	13	1½	6	45.1	.545	2.618	3.403

* National Carbon Co.

threaded on request. National Form straight threads are used. Fittings made from the same material with the same thread form are available and include laps which can be screwed on the ends of pipe and stub ends which can be screwed into the fittings, both for the purpose of making flanged lap joints. All threaded joints are permanently bonded by special cements. Flanged joints use split cast-iron backup flanges which have 150-lb. A.S.A. B16.5 bolting in sizes 6 in. and smaller and 300-lb. A.S.A. B16.5 bolting in sizes 8 in. and larger. Asbestos sheet packing is used between the flange and the back of the lap to equalize bearing. Pipe can be sawed to length in the field and threaded with special tools. Synthetic elastomeric and Teflon gaskets are available. Diaphragm valves with impervious graphite bodies are available in sizes 1 through 6 in. Maximum recommended support spacing is 9 ft., and valves should be supported independently.

Cement-lined pipe is made by lining iron or steel pipe with special cement. Its use prevents pick-up of iron by the fluid handled and corrosion of the metal by brackish water. Threaded pipe in sizes from ¾ to 4 in. are stocked.

Threaded fittings are generally lead- or tin-lined to avoid chipping the lining in making up a joint and to provide smooth flow through the fitting. The coefficients of expansion of iron and cement are nearly alike. Table 6-27 gives dimensions of cement-lined pipe.

Table 6-27. Cement-lined Carbon-steel Pipe*

Standard pipe size, in.	Inside diam. after lining, in.	Thickness of lining, in.	Weight, per ft., lb.	Standard pipe size, in.	Inside diam. after lining, in.	Thickness of lining, in.	Weight per ft., lb.
¾	0.70	0.06	1.3	3	2.70	0.13	8.3
1	.90	.07	1.9	4	3.60	.16	12.0
1¼	1.20	.08	2.5	6	5.40	.25	24.0
1½	1.40	.09	3.0	8	7.40	.25	32.0
2	1.80	.10	4.1	10	9.40	.30	43.0
2½	2.20	.10	6.6	12	11.40	.30	55.0

* Cement Lined Pipe Co.

Cement-lined carbon-steel pipe larger than 4 in. is shipped with flanged or welding ends. Welding does not damage the lining, which forms a slag protecting the weld. Shop cement lining of carbon-steel pipe larger than 12 in. is covered by A.W.W.A. 7A.7. Cement-lined carbon-steel butt-welding fittings and flanged cast-iron fittings are available. Shop cement lining of cast-iron pipe is covered by A.S.A. A21.4. A.W.W.A. C602-54T includes cement lining of both cast-iron and carbon-steel water lines in place.

Acidproof chemical-stoneware pipe and fittings withstand most acid, alkali, or other corrosives, the main exception being hydrofluoric acid. The widest range of sizes is made with the bell-and-spigot joint and with plain butt ends (Table 6-28), while the conical flanged joint can be obtained in the "low-pressure" class in sizes from 1 to 10 in. (Table 6-29).

Table 6-29. Chemical Ware—Flanged Pressure Pipe*

Inside diam., in.	Outside diam., in.	Wall thickness, in.	Max. length, ft.	Inside diam., in.	Outside diam., in.	Wall thickness, in.	Max. length, ft.
1	1¾	⅜	5	4	5	½	5
1½	2½	½	5	5	6¼	⅝	5
2	3	½	5	6	7¼	⅝	5
2½	3½	½	5	8	9½	¾	5
3	4	½	5	10	11¾	⅞	5

* U.S. Stoneware Co.

Plain butt-end pipe is furnished with cemented-on flanges with A.S.A. B16.1 drilling, or (for use in ventilating work where the space is too limited for bell-and-spigot pipe) with a ring for joining with a steel band. Medium-pressure chemical-ware pipe armored with glass fiber reinforced with furan resin can be obtained. Flanges with A.S.A. B16.1 drilling bear against hubs formed from the armor.

Fittings and plug valves with ends to match the various types of pipe are available.

Table 6-30 gives dimensions of chemical-ware rectangular ventilating duct.

Table 6-30. Chemical Ware—Rectangular Ventilating Pipe

Inside width, in.	Inside length, in.	Wall thickness, in.	Max. length, ft.	Wt. per ft., lb.	Inside width, in.	Inside length, in.	Wall thickness, in.	Max. length, ft.	Wt. per ft., lb.
8	12	⅞	5	33	18	24	1½	5	140
10	15	1⅛	5	45	20	30	1⅝	4	165
12	18	1¼	5	60					
20	20	1⅜	5	95					

Table 6-28. Chemical Ware—Bell-and-spigot and Plain Butt-end Pipe

Low pressure*				Medium pressure†					High pressure*				
Inside diam., in.	Outside diam., in.	Wall thickness, in.	Working pressure, lb./sq. in.	Inside diam., in.	Outside diam., in.	Wall thickness, in.	Max. length, ft.	Weight per ft., lb.	Nominal size, in.	Inside diam., in.	Outside diam., in.	Wall thickness, in.	Working pressure, lb./sq. in.
1	1¾	⅜							1	½	1¾	⅝	
1½	2½	½	30	1½	2¼	⅜	5	3¼	1½	1	2½	¾	60
2	3	½	30	2	2¾	⅜	5	4	2	1½	3	¾	60
3	4	½	25	3	4	½	5	5½	3	2	4	⅞	50
4	5	½	25	4	5	½	5	8½	4	3	5	1	50
5	6¼	⅝	20	5	6	½	5	11					
6	7¼	⅝	20	6	7¼	⅝	6	15	6	5	7¼	1⅛	45
8	9½	¾	20	8	9½	¾	6	20	8	7	9½	1¼	45
9	10¾	⅞											
10	11¾	⅞		10	11¾	⅞	6	28	10	9	11¾	1⅜	
12	13¾	⅞		12	13¾	⅞	6	36	12	10¾	13¾	1½	
14	16	1							14	12¾	16	1⅝	
15	17¼	1⅛		15	17	1	5	45					
16	18½	1¼							16	15	18½	1¾	
18	20½	1¼		18	20	1	5	70	18	16¾	20½	1⅞	
20	22¾	1⅜		20	22	1	5	80	20	18¾	22¾	2	
22	25	1½											
24	27	1½		24	26½	1¼	4	95	24	22¾	27	2⅛	
				27	29½	1¼	4	110					
30	33¼	1⅝		30	32½	1¼	4	120	30	28¼	33¼	2½	
36	39½	1¾											

* Standard lengths up to 5 ft. for 1- to 18 in. pipe; above 18 in., 3 ft.; U.S. Stoneware Co.

† Maurice A. Knight Co.

Ordinary chemical stoneware is sensitive to changes of temperature, and pipe of more than 3 or 4 in. inside diameter made of ordinary chemical ware should not be used when temperatures of more than 140°F. are involved. Special "heat-shock-resistant" stoneware (such as U.S. Stoneware Co. Ceratherm-500 or General Ceramics Co. SP-22) should be used above 130°F. and especially where pipe lines carry alternatively hot and cold gases or liquids.

Vitrified-clay sewer pipe is resistant to all chemicals except hydrofluoric acid and is produced as standard strength (A.S.T.M. C-13) and extra strength (A.S.T.M. C-200). It is used for sewage, industrial waste, and storm water at atmospheric pressure. Elbows, Y-branches, tees, reducers, and increasers are available. Assembly is by poured joints which allow for ample angular deflection. Joint compounds are of the hot-pour type or the cold mastic type; both adhere tightly to the scored clay surfaces but remain flexible enough to prevent leakage in event of earth settlement. Pipe is also available with bituminous or plastic material die-cast on the outside of the spigot and the inside of the bell. The interfaces are a snug fit cemented by applying a solvent to them at the time of assembly. Dimensions of pipe are given in Table 6-31. Choice between standard and extra strength is based on earth and vehicular loading.

Table 6-31. Vitrified Clay Sewer Pipe

Nominal size	Min. laying length, ft.	Min. outside diam. of barrel, in.	Min. wall thickness	
			Standard strength, in.	Extra strength, in.
4	2	4⅞	7/16	
6	2	7 1/16	½	9/16
8	2	9¼	9/16	¾
10	2	11½	11/16	⅞
12	2	13¾	13/16	1 1/16
16	3	17 3/16	15/16	1⅜
18	3	20⅝	1⅛	1¾
21	3	24⅛	1 5/16	2
24	3	27½	1½	2¼
27	3	31	1 11/16	2½
30	3	34⅜	1⅞	2¾
33	3	37⅝	2	3
36	3	40¾	2 1/16	3¼

Concrete. Unreinforced-concrete sewer pipe is made with poured joint ends in sizes from 4 to 24 in. conforming to A.S.T.M. C14-59T. Reinforced-concrete culvert, storm drain, and sewer pipe is made with poured joint or O-ring joint ends conforming to A.S.T.M. C76-57T in five classes of reinforcement area and wall thickness in sizes from 12 through 108 in. Essentially the same pipe, except with O-ring joint ends only, is available for water pressures up to 45 lb./sq. in. in sizes 12 through 96 in. and lengths up through 16 ft. conforming to A.W.W.A. C302-57.

For higher water pressures, a steel cylinder approximately 1/16 in. thick is embedded in the wall of the pipe, which prevents leakage through cracks, and to this, there may be added prestressed (approximately 100,000 lb./sq. in.) circumferential reinforcing wire applied after the cylinder has been stiffened by cement lining. Such pipe is available in accordance with A.W.W.A. C300-57, sizes 20 through 96 in. for pressures 40 through 260 lb./sq. in., and in accordance with A.W.W.A. C301-57, sizes 16 through 72 in. for pressures 50 through 350 lb./sq. in. O-ring joints are used. Pipe is also available with steel lugs welded to the reinforcing cages and projecting through the outside surface of the pipe for "bridling." This is known as "subaqueous pipe." **Concrete** fittings are also available. Concrete piping systems can be lined with special salt-glazed vitrified-clay liner plates, joined with a die-cast asphalt joint.

Glass pipe and tubing are made from heat- and chemical-resistant borosilicate glass (*e.g.*, Corning Glass Works No. 774). This glass is highly stable in acids and resists attack by alkalies in solutions where pH is 8 or less. It is attacked by hydrofluoric acid and glacial phosphoric acid. Some important physical properties are:

Modulus of elasticity, lb./sq. in.	9,750,000
Specific gravity	2.23
Specific heat	0.20
Thermal conductivity at 75°F., B.t.u./(hr.)(sq. ft.) (°F./in.)	8.1

Conical flanged glass pipe is made in the sizes shown in Table 6-32 and in lengths from 6 in. to 10 ft. Maximum recommended working pressure is 50 lb./sq. in. through 3-in. size, 35 lb./sq. in. for 4-in. size, and 20 lb./sq. in. for 6-in. size. Maximum sudden temperature differential is 200°F. through 3-in. size, 175°F. for 4-in. size and 160°F. for 6-in. size. Maximum operating temperature is 450°F. A complete line of fittings is available, and special parts are made to order. Thermal-expansion stresses should be completely relieved by tied Teflon corrugated expansion joints and offsets. Hangers should be padded to avoid scratching pipe,

Table 6-32. Glass Pipe and Tubing*
A. Pipe, Conical Flanged Joint
(See Fig. 6-114)

Inside diam., in.	Outside diam., in.	Wall thickness, in.	Weight per ft., lb.
1	1.31	0.156	0.55
1.5	1.84	.171	.87
2	2.34	.171	1.13
3	3.41	.202	1.97
4	4.50	.264	3.41
6	6.66	.328	6.30

B. Industrial Tubing, Plain Ends

Outside diameter, in.	Medium wall		Heavy wall	
	Wall thickness, in.	Weight per ft., lb.	Wall thickness, in.	Weight per ft., lb.
¼	3/64	0.029		
½	1/16	.083	3/32	0.11
¾	1/16	.131	⅛	.24
1	3/32	.26	5/32	.40
1¼	3/32	.33	5/32	.53
1½	3/32	.41	5/32	.64
1¾	3/32	.48	5/32	.76
2	⅛	.72	3/16	1.05
2¼	⅛	.82	3/16	1.19
2½	⅛	.91	3/16	1.33
2¾	⅛	1.01	3/16	1.48
3	⅛	1.10	3/16	1.60
3¼	⅛	1.20	3/16	1.77
3½	⅛	1.30	3/16	1.91
4	3/16	2.17	¼	2.85
4½	3/16	2.45	¼	3.20

* Corning Glass Works.

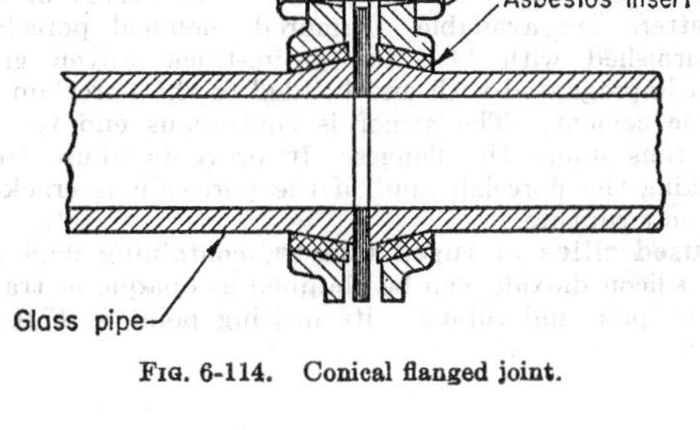

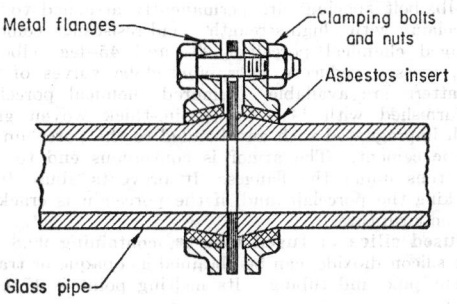

FIG. 6-114. Conical flanged joint.

should fit loosely, and should be located 1 ft. from each end of each 10-ft. length.

Glass pipe can be furnished with an epoxy-resin coating reinforced with woven glass fiber to protect it from abuse.

Bell-and-spigot pipe is used where large-diameter corrosion-resistant pipe is required for low-pressure gas lines, fume ducts, or packed columns. Industrial glass tubing is available in medium and heavy wall in stock lengths of 60 in. ± 1/4 in.; dimensions are shown in Table 6-32.

Glass-lined steel pipe is fully resistant at temperatures up to 212°F. to all acids except hydrofluoric and to all alkaline solutions up to pH 12. It can be used at temperatures up to 450°F., provided that there are no excessive sudden temperature changes, and at pressures up to 150 lb./sq. in. for standard pipe and 300 lb./sq. in. for special pipe. The glass lining is usually 1/32 in. thick. Dimensions of 1 1/2- to 12-in. pipe are shown in Table 6-33. Larger sizes can be made to order. Complete fittings are available as glass-lined ductile-iron

Table 6-33. Glass-lined Steel Pipe*

Size, in.	Inside diam., in.	Outside diam., in.	Max. length, ft.	Weight per ft., lb.
1 1/2	1.500	1.875	6	3.38
2	2.000	2.375	10	4.38
3	3.000	3.500	10	8.68
4	4.000	4.500	10	11.35
5	5.000	5.500	10	14.0
6	6.000	6.625	10	21.1
8	7.981	8.625	10	27.7
10	10.020	10.75	10	
12	12.020	12.75	10	

* Pfaudler Co.

castings for pressures up to 150 lb./sq. in. and as glass-lined steel for higher pressures. Modified lap-joint flanged joints are used for assembly of the system.

Chemical porcelain pipe, fittings, and valves, made of dense, non-porous material and fired at 2250°F., are inert to all acids except hydrofluoric but are not usually recommended for alkalies. Surfaces, except where ground for gasketing, are usually glazed for easy cleaning. Working pressures of 50 to 100 lb./sq. in. are recommended for valves and piping. Temperatures of 400°F. or more can be used, but sudden thermal shocks must be avoided. Table 6-34 lists standard pipe dimensions.

Table 6-34. Chemical Porcelain Pipe

Inside diam., in.	Outside diam., in.	Wall thickness, in.	Wt. per ft., lb.
1/2	1 3/8	7/16	1.84
1	2 1/8	9/16	3.55
1 1/2	2 3/4	5/8	5.24
2	3 1/4	5/8	6 68
3	4 3/8	11/16	10.45
4	5 1/2	3/4	15.15
6	7 7/8	15/16	24.4
8	10	1	36.0

Malleable- or ductile-iron flanges (A.S.A. B16.1, 125-lb. bolt spacing) are permanently attached to the porcelain with high-strength acid-resistant cement. Flanged chemical porcelain 90- and 45-deg. elbows, tees, crosses, reducers, caps, and globe valves of the Y-pattern are available. Armored chemical porcelain is furnished with 1/16- to 3/32-in.-thick woven glass cloth impregnated with and bonded to the porcelain by plastic cement. The armor is continuous end to end and runs under the flanges. It prevents abuse from cracking the porcelain and, if the porcelain is cracked, prevents rupture.

Fused silica or **fused quartz,** containing 99.8 per cent silicon dioxide, can be obtained as opaque or transparent pipe and tubing. Its melting point is 1710°C. Tensile strength is approximately 7000 lb./sq. in.; specific gravity is about 2.2. The pipe and tubing can be used continuously at temperatures up to 1000°C. and intermittently up to 1500°C. Its chief assets are non-contamination of most chemicals in high-temperature service, thermal-shock resistance, and high-temperature electrical insulating characteristics.

Transparent tubing is available in inside diameters from 1 to 125 mm. in a range of wall thicknesses. Satin-surface tubing is available in inside diameters from 1/16 to 2 in., and sand-surface pipe and tubing are available in 1/2 to 24 in. inside diameters and lengths up to 20 ft. Sand-surface pipe and tubing are obtainable in wall thicknesses varying from 1/8 to 1 in. Pipe and tubing sections in both opaque and transparent fused silica or fused quartz can be readily machine-ground to special tolerances for pressure joints or other purposes. Also, fused silica piping and tubing can be reprocessed to meet special-design requirements. Manufacturers should be consulted for specific details.

Wood Pipe. Douglas fir, white pine, redwood, and cypress are the most common woods used for wood pipe. Dimensions are given in Table 6-35. Wood-lined steel pipe is suitable for temperatures up to 180°F.

Table 6-35. Wood Pipe*

Wood-lined steel pipe			Machine-banded wood stave pipe				Square wood pipe	
Inside diam., in.	Outside diam. in.	Usual metal wall thickness, B. & S. gage	Inside diam., in.	Outside† diam., in.	Wood wall thickness, in.	Weight per ft., lb.‡	Inside diam., in.	Outside dimensions. in.
4	5 5/8	14	2	5	1 1/2	8	2	4 × 4
5	6 5/8	14	3	6	1 1/2	10	2	5 × 5
6	7 5/8	14	4	7 1/4	1 5/8	13	3	6 × 6
8	10	14	6	9 1/2	1 3/4	19	3	7 × 7
10	12	14	8	11 1/2	1 3/4	22	3	8 × 8
12	14	14	10	13 1/2	1 3/4	26	4	8 × 8
14	16	14	12	15 1/2	1 3/4	32	4	9 × 9
16	18	12	14	17 1/2	1 3/4	35	5	9 × 9
18	20 1/2	12	16	19 1/2	1 3/4	40	5	10 × 10
20	22 3/4	10	18	21 1/2	1 3/4	44	6	10 × 10
21 1/2	24 1/4	10	20	23 1/2	1 3/4	50	6	12 × 12
23 1/2	26 3/4	10	24	27 1/2	1 3/4	55		
25 1/2	29	10	24	29 1/2	2 3/4	80		
			30	35 1/2	2 3/4	100		
			36	41 1/2	2 3/4	130		
			48	53 1/2	2 3/4	175		

* Michigan Pipe Co.
† Dimension does not include banding and coating.
‡ Weights vary with types of wood.

and for pressures from 200 lb./sq. in. for the 4-in. size, through 125 lb./sq. in. for the 10-in. size, to 100 lb./sq. in. for larger than 10 in. For fume stacks and similar uses, wood-stave pipe with rods on 1-ft. centers is most satisfactory because it permits periodic tightening.

For underground installation, machine-banded wood-stave pipe is generally suitable. The staves have double tongues and grooves on lateral edges and are wound with 1-in.-wide steel strips of adequate gage and spacing to provide four pressure classes—43, 86, 130, and 172 lb./sq. in.—although it is recommended that working pressure be limited to 60 per cent of class pressure. The pipe is usually coated heavily with asphalt and sawdust. Lengths are random and up to 16 ft.; joints are mortise and tenon. Galvanized or copper wire or stainless-steel bands can be supplied with or without the asphalt coating.

Square wood pipe is usually made of white pine with mortise-and-tenon joints. There is also steam-pipe casing for covering and insulating underground steam lines.

Fittings for wood pipe are made of cast iron, of wood, and of wood-lined steel.

Plastic and Fiber-plastic Piping Systems. In contrast to other piping materials, plastic pipe is free from internal and external corrosion, is easily cut and joined, and does not cause galvanic corrosion when coupled to other materials. Allowable stresses and upper temperature limits are low. Normal operation is in the creep range. Fluids for which a plastic is not suited penetrate and soften it rather than dissolve surface layers. Coefficients of thermal expansion are high.

Acrylonitrile-butadiene-styrene (ABS) plastic has excellent resistance to sulfuric and hydrochloric acids at room temperature but is not resistant to oxidizing acids. It is also resistant to acid, alkaline, and neutral salts. It is pigmented black to resist ultraviolet light and is supplied in 20-ft. lengths. Usual assembly is by solvent welded joints (Fig. 6-110). The pipe is produced by extrusion. Service pressures recommended by vendors are **at 75°F.**, although 160°F. is considered to be the maximum permissible operating temperature for type I ABS resin and 180°F. is the corresponding limit for type II. Recommended service pressures at maximum temperature are 50 per cent of those at 75°F.

Pipe in accordance with A.G.A. Specification DCM-56-15 has iron pipe size outside diameters, is available in sizes ½ through 6 in., has wall thicknesses about 75 per cent that of Schedule 40 (Table 6-2) and, with cemented joints, is recommended for pressures ranging from 250 lb./sq. in. for the ½-in. size down to 80 lb./sq. in. for the 6-in. size when manufactured from type I ABS resin.

Pipe in accordance with A.S.T.M. D1527 has iron pipe size outside diameters, is available in sizes ½ through 6 in., has wall thicknesses conforming with Schedule 80 (Table 6-2). With cemented joints, when manufactured from type I ABS resin, it is recommended for pressures ranging from 350 lb./sq. in. for the ½-in. size down to 155 lb./sq. in. for the 6-in. size. With threaded joints, when manufactured from type I ABS resins, it is recommended for pressures ranging from 240 lb./sq. in. for the ½-in. size down to 120 lb./sq. in. in the 6-in. size.

Pipe in accordance with A.S.T.M. D1528 has outside diameters slightly less than iron pipe size. This is the solvent-welded-pipe (SWP) dimensional system. It is available in sizes ½ through 6 in. in two pressure classes. With cemented joints, the recommended pressure for one class is 150 lb./sq. in. for all sizes; for the second class, it is 100 lb./sq. in. for all sizes. For sizes 2 in. and larger, a modified material, type II ABS, with considerably higher allowable stress and slightly lower impact strength, is used. Fittings are available for all classes. The distance between supports should be only one-third the spacing used for steel pipe.

Cellulose acetate–butyrate plastic has excellent resistance to all chloride salts. It is pigmented black to resist ultraviolet light and is supplied in 20-ft. lengths. A.S.T.M. D1503 applies to solvent-welded (SWP size) cellulose acetate–butyrate pipe. Assembly is by solvent-welded joints (Fig. 6-110). The pipe is produced by extrusion. Service pressures recommended by vendors are at 60°F., with 140°F. considered to be the maximum permissible operating temperature. At 140°F., recommended service pressures are 60 per cent of those at 60°F. The pipe is available in sizes ½ through 6 in. Outside diameters are less than iron pipe size; this is the SWP dimensional system. Recommended service pressures range from 105 lb./sq. in. for the ½-in. size down to 80 lb./sq. in. for the 6-in. size. A full line of fittings is available.

Glass fiber–epoxy resin has good resistance to nonoxidizing acids, alkalies, salt water, and corrosive gases. The glass fibers are many times stronger at room temperature than plastics, do not lose strength with increasing temperature, and reinforce the plastic effectively up to 260°F. The glass fibers are located near the outside wall, protected from the contents by a thick wall of plastic and protected from the atmosphere by a thin wall of plastic. Stock sizes are 2 through 12 in. A typical design, using wall thicknesses of Schedule 40 and Schedule 80 steel pipe, closely approaches the allowable pressure of butt-welded steel pipe at 80°F. but drops to one-half this allowable pressure at 180°F.

Pipe is supplied in 21-ft. lengths. It is intended for long straight runs rather than systems containing numerous fittings, and lengths are supplied with male threads which are superimposed on the outside diameter. Normal assembly is with screwed couplings or screwed flanges. When the pipe is sawed to non-factory lengths, the teeth should cut from the inside of the pipe toward the outside to preserve the structure of the interior plastic zone. A two-component cement may be used to bond-cut unthreaded lengths into threaded couplings or flanges or cemented joint fittings. Curing of the cement is temperature-sensitive; it sets to full strength in 45 min. at 200°F., 12 hr. at 100°F., and 24 hr. at 50°F. Extensive use is made of shop-fabricated flanged preassemblies. Only flanged joints are used to bond to metallic piping systems. Compared with other plastics, the ratio of fitting cost to pipe cost is high. Screwed fittings, cemented-joint fittings, and flanged fittings are available. Flanged, lined, metallic valves are used.

Glass fabric–furan resin, which resists acids, alkalies, and chlorinated organic solvents up to 280°F., is furnished as pressure pipe in sizes 1½ through 12 in. and as fume duct 4 through 36 in. Fittings are also available and both are normally furnished with plain ends. Assembly is normally made by butting plain ends together in an alignment device, wrapping the joint with glass fabric, and brush-coating each layer with resin furnished by the supplier of the pipe. The resin sets in 24 hr. at room temperature. Pipe and fittings are also available from the factory with bell ends, and with enlarged tapered ends on which split cast-iron flanges with A.S.A. B16.5 150-lb. drilling may be mounted. Allowable pressures for the pipe and fittings are 60 lb./sq. in. for sizes 1½ through 4 in.; 45 lb./sq. in. for sizes 6 through 8 in., and 30 lb./sq. in. for sizes 10 through 12 in. The inside diameter of the pipe, fume duct, and fittings is the nominal size. Wall thicknesses are ½ in. for pipe sizes 1½ through 4 in. and fume duct size 4 through 18 in., ⅝ in. for pipe size 6 in. and fume duct size 20 and 24 in., and ¾ in. for pipe size 8 through 12 in. and fume duct 30 and 36 in.

Haveg 41 asbestos-filled phenolic resin is furnished as pipe and fittings with several types of joints and is resistant to most acidic chemicals, especially hydrochloric acid. The standard joint uses split cast-iron flanges set in tapered grooves machined in the outside of the pipe near the ends. A facing and grooving tool can be obtained. Standard lengths are 4 ft. in the ½- and ¾-in. sizes and 10 ft. in all other sizes. Table 6-36 gives dimensions. Flanges are drilled per A.S.A. B16.5.

Figure 6-115 shows pressure-temperature ratings for standard-wall pipe with standard joints. Pipe and fittings with bell-and-spigot joints and with screwed joints are also available for use where external corrosion might destroy the cast-iron flanges. Fume duct is furnished with split-flange or bell-and-spigot joints. Drainage pipe is available with taper-sleeve-cemented joints for pipe, fittings, and hubs for split flanges. Y-type globe valves, diaphragm valves, and foot and check valves are available.

In Haveg 31, the phenolic resin is modified to improve resistance to wet chlorine. It is furnished in the same

Table 6-36. Haveg Pipe*

Pressure pipe			Fume duct			
Size, actual inside diam., in.	Outside diam., in.	Wall thickness, in.	Size, in.	Actual inside diam., in.	Outside diam., in.	Wall thickness, in.
½	1¼	⅜	2	2	2¾	⅜
¾	1½	⅜	3	3	3¾	⅜
1	1¾	⅜	4	4	4¾	⅜
1¼	2	⅜	5	5	6	½
1½	2½	½	6	6	7	½
2	3	½	8	8	9	½
2½	3½	½	10	10	11	½
3	4¼	⅝	12	12	13	½
3½	4¾	⅝	14	14½	15½	½
4	5¼	⅝	16	16½	17½	½
5	6½	¾	18	18¼	19¼	½
6	7½	¾	20	20½	21½	½
8	9¾	⅞	24	24	25¼	⅝
10	12	1	30	30¼	31½	⅝
12	14	1	36	36	37¼	⅝

* Haveg Corp.

forms as Haveg 41 but pressure-temperature ratings of the standard-wall pipe with the standard joints are 75 per cent of those shown in Fig. 6-115 and maximum temperature is 265°F.

Haveg 61 asbestos-filled furan resin is highly resistant to most acids and bases, interchangeably, as well as to many hydrocarbons, halogenated organic compounds, and organic acids. Its pressure-temperature ratings are the same as those shown in Fig. 6-115, and maximum temperature is 265°F.

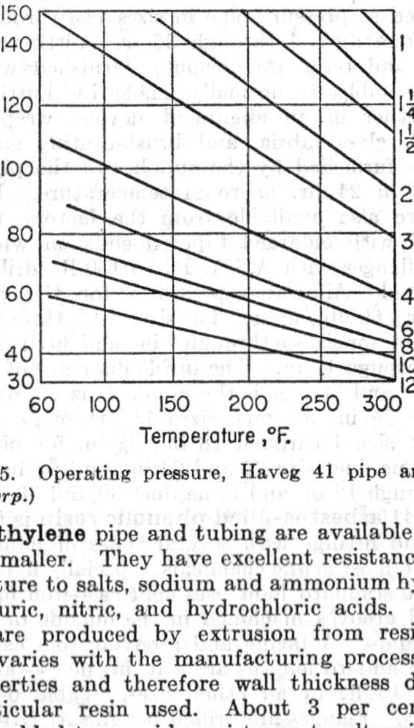

FIG. 6-115. Operating pressure, Haveg 41 pipe and fittings. (*Haveg Corp.*)

Polyethylene pipe and tubing are available in sizes 6 in. and smaller. They have excellent resistance at room temperature to salts, sodium and ammonium hydroxides, and sulfuric, nitric, and hydrochloric acids. Pipe and tubing are produced by extrusion from resins whose density varies with the manufacturing process. Physical properties and therefore wall thickness depend on the particular resin used. About 3 per cent carbon black is added to provide resistance to ultraviolet light. Use of higher-density resin reduces splitting and pinholing in service and increases the strength of the material and the maximum service temperature.

A.S.T.M. D1248 establishes types and grades of polyethylene resin based on mechanical properties. Temperature range is from 0° to about 140°F., but at the upper limit the allowable pressure is less than half the value at 73.4°F. Polyethylene water piping is not damaged by freezing. Pipe and tubing 2 in. and smaller are shipped in coils several hundred feet in length. Schedule 40 iron pipe size inside diameters are standard. In sizes 2 in. and smaller, clamped insert joints (Fig. 6-111) are widely used. Inserts are available in nylon, polypropylene, high-impact styrene, and a variety of metals. For the larger sizes, on which insert fittings are impractical, automated butt fusion joining equipment is available which aligns the ends, and faces, heats, and presses them together. Department of Commerce Commercial Standard CS197 includes dimensional and material standards for one schedule (Schedule 40) and two pressure-rated series (75 and 100 lb./sq. in. at 73.4°F.).

For pressures below 100 lb./sq. in., polyethylene competes vigorously with steel for buried piping.

For drainage systems a complete line of components, including pipe in 20-ft. lengths, which can easily be field-assembled is commercially available. Socket joints, heat-fused without use of flame, solvents, or cements, are stronger than the pipe, smooth on the interior, and do not involve any change in size, shape, or direction of the flow channel.

Polyvinyl chloride (PVC) is used both as pipe and as linings for pipe. A.S.T.M. D1785 applies to polyvinyl chloride pipe in sizes ⅛ through 6 in. in Schedule 40 and 80 iron pipe size and ½ through 6 in. in Schedule 120 iron pipe size. Fittings are available in sizes 6 in. and smaller. They have excellent resistance at room temperatures to salts, alcohol, gasoline, ammonium hydroxide, and sulfuric, nitric, acetic, and hydrochloric acids. Type I, which is unplasticized, is the most widely used. Temperature range is from 0° to 150°F.

Solvent cemented joints (Fig. 6-110) are standard but screwed joints are sometimes used with Schedule 80 pipe. Cemented joints must not be disturbed for 5 min. and achieve full strength in one day. Because of the difference in thermal expansion, joints between PVC pipe and metal pipe should be flanged, using a PVC flange on the PVC pipe and a full-face gasket. Flanges are available with A.S.A. B16.5 150-lb. drilling. Table 6-37 gives working pressures. Ball valves, Y-type globe valves, and diaphragm valves are available in PVC.

Table 6-37. Continuous Working Pressures for PVC Pipe, lb./sq. in.

Iron pipe size	Solvent cemented joints						Threaded joints		
	Schedule 40			Schedule 80			Schedule 80		
	Working temp.			Working temp.			Working temp.		
	100°F.	120°F.	150°F.	100°F.	120°F.	150°F.	100°F.	120°F.	150°F.
½	220	145	75	290	195	100	180	120	65
¾	180	120	65	245	165	90	155	105	55
1	170	115	60	230	155	80	140	95	50
1½	130	90	45	175	120	65	115	80	40
2	110	75	40	155	105	55	105	70	35
3	105	70	35	145	95	50	95	65	35
4	90	60	30	130	85	45	90	60	30
6	70	55	25	110	75	40	85	55	30

In iron pipe sizes 2 through 4 in., electric resistance welded mechanical tubing with rigid PVC liners is available with ends roll-grooved for groove joint couplings (Fig. 6-105).

Rubber is used both as pipe and as lining for pipe. **Hard-rubber piping systems** are available in two classes—natural rubber and nitrile synthetic rubber (Buna N). Components are designed for 50 lb./sq. in. with the upper temperature limit 120°F. for natural and 260°F. for nitrile synthetic. They are brittle materials with an ultimate tensile strength of 7500 lb./sq. in. They are widely used for fluids containing the chloride radical. Pipe is available as shown in Table 6-38.

Taper pipe threads are used to join pipe to flanges and fittings. Use of a thread dope supplied by the vendor is required. Cutting of threads by the vendor rather than in the field is recommended. Threaded fittings are available through the 6-in. size and flanges and flanged fittings with A.S.A. B16.5 150-lb. drilling are available

Table 6-38. Hard-rubber Pipe*

Nominal size	Length, ft.	Outside diam., in.	Wall, in.	Inside diam., in.	Wt. per ft., lb.	
					Natural	Nitrile
¼	10	0.540	0.145	0.250	0.094	0.100
⅜	10	.675	.150	.375	.141	.150
½	10	.840	.170	.500	.172	.183
¾	10	1.050	.181	.687	.258	.275
1	10	1.315	.189	.937	.344	.367
1¼	10	1.660	.205	1.250	.540	.576
1½	10	1.900	.231	1.437	.641	.684
2	10	2.375	.250	1.875	.883	.938
2½	10	2.875	.312	2.250	1.134	1.209
3	10	3.500	.375	2.750	1.985	2.116
4	10	4.500	.375	3.750	2.875	3.065
5	10	5.563	.406	4.750	3.900	4.158
6	10	6.625	.500	5.625	5.200	5.543
8	10	8.625	.812	7.000	10.800	11.514

* American Hard Rubber Co.

through the 8-in. size, but the flanges must be backed up with metal rings about ⅛ in. thick. Check valves are available through the 3-in. size. Rubber-lined gate, diaphragm, and globe valves are used. Supports should be spaced every 6 ft. and valves should be supported independently.

Rubber-lined pipe is made in lengths up to 20 ft. with seamless, straight seam-welded, and some types of spiral-welded pipe using various types of natural and synthetic adhering rubber. The type of rubber is selected to provide the most suitable lining for the specific service. In general, soft rubber is used for abrasion resistance, semihard for general service, and hard for the more severe service conditions. Multiple-ply lining combinations of hard and soft rubber are available. The thickness of lining ranges from ⅛ to ¼ in. depending on the service, the type of rubber, and the method of lining. Cast-steel, ductile-iron, and cast-iron flanged fittings are available rubber-lined. The fittings are usually purchased by the vendor since absence of porosity on the inner surface is essential. Pipe is flanged before rubber lining and welding elbows and tees may be incorporated at one end of the length of pipe, subject to the conditions that the size of the pipe and the location of the fittings are such that the operator doing the lining can place a hand on any point on the interior surface of the fitting. Welds must be ground smooth on the inside and a radius is required at the inner edge of the flange face.

The rubber lining is extended out over the face of flanges. With hard-rubber lining, a gasket is required. With soft-rubber lining, coating or a polyethylene sheet is required in place of a gasket to avoid bonding of the lining on one flange to the lining on the other and to permit disassembly of the flanged joint. Also, for pressures over 125 lb./sq. in., the tendency of soft-rubber linings to extrude out between the flanges may be prevented by terminating the lining inside the bolt holes and filling the balance of the space between the flange faces with a Masonite spacer of the proper thickness. Hard-rubber-lined gate, diaphragm, and swing check valves are available. In the gate valves, stem, wedge assembly, and seat rings, and in the check valves, hinge pin, flapper arm, disk, and seat ring must be made of metal resistant to the solution handled.

Teflon-lined carbon-steel pipe Schedule 40 or heavier is available in pipe sizes 1 through 8 in. in lengths up to 10 ft. Teflon is not affected by any concentration of acids, alkalies or solvents. Normal construction is Schedule 40 pipe with 150-lb. flanges. It may be used at temperatures up to 500°F. and pressures up to 150 lb./sq. in. The non-adhesive properties of the liner make it ideal for handling sticky or viscous substances. Thickness of the lining varies from 60 to 150 mils depending on pipe size. Only flanged joints are used and the lining extends across the face nearly to the bolt holes. Cast-steel or ductile-iron flanges and flanged fittings with A.S.A. B16.5 150-lb. drilling are used. Lined pipe spacers from 1 to 3 in. in ½-in. increments are available for length adjustments in the field. The pipe cannot be cut to length in the field. The wall of the carbon-steel pipe is perforated with tell-tale holes. Glass-lined valves with Teflon or Teflon-faced diaphragms are available for Teflon-lined piping systems.

Saran-lined carbon-steel pipe is available in sizes 1 through 8 in. It has excellent resistance to hydrochloric acid. The temperature range is from minus 40° to 200°F. in continuous service. It is manufactured by inserting a rigid polyvinylidene chloride liner into an oversize approximately Schedule 40 carbon-steel seamless pipe and swaging the assembly to produce iron pipe size outside diameter, firmly engaging the liner with $\frac{3}{16}$ in. of the liner projecting at each end. The pressure rating is 300 lb./sq. in. at 200°F. Pipe is furnished in 10-ft. lengths threaded at both ends. It may be cut to length in the field in a lathe using a parting tool.

Saran-lined screwed malleable-iron fittings sizes 2 in. and smaller and cast-iron flanges and saran-lined flanged fittings 8 in. and smaller are available with a rating of 150 lb./sq. in. at 200°F. Cast-steel flanges and polyvinylidene chloride-lined flanged fittings are available with a rating of 300 lb./sq. in. at 200°F. The linings on the fittings are carried around onto the raised face. The flanges are specially machined to receive a triangular gasket which is compressed against the outside of the abutting ends of the liner.

The inside diameters of saran-lined pipe and fittings are as follows:

Size	1	1¼	1½	2	2½	3	4	6	8
Inside diam., in.	1$\frac{1}{16}$	1	1$\frac{5}{16}$	1¾	2$\frac{3}{32}$	2$\frac{11}{16}$	3⅝	5$\frac{9}{16}$	7½

Pipe Supports. A number of the more common methods of supporting pipes are illustrated in Fig. 6-116. For lead and polyethylene pipe, the use of angles and channels has met with success.

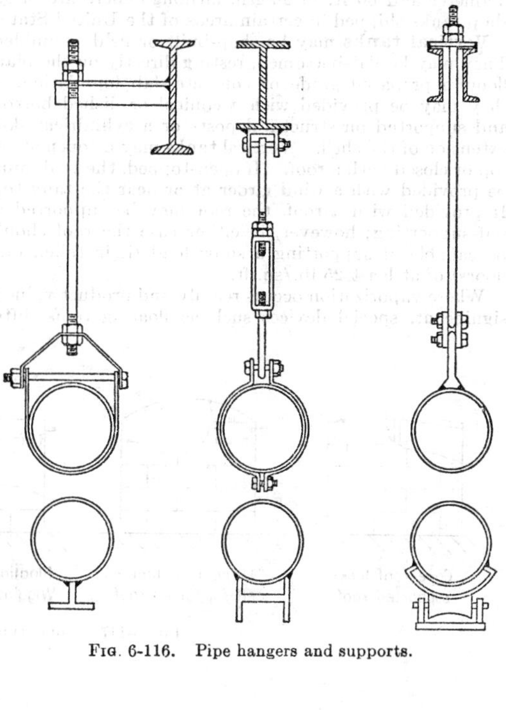

FIG. 6-116. Pipe hangers and supports.

STORAGE AND BULK TRANSPORT OF FLUIDS

Storage of Liquids. Selection of type of storage container for liquid materials should be based on ambient-temperature conditions, absolute vapor pressure of the liquid at storage conditions, toxicity and/or corrosiveness of the liquid. Liquid storage can be discussed according to three major pressure divisions: atmospheric-pressure storage, which ranges from open reservoirs to storage tanks with a maximum design pressure of 0.5 lb./sq. in. gage; low-pressure tanks, with maximum design pressures of 15 lb./sq. in. gage; and pressure tanks, with design pressures over 15 lb./sq. in. gage.

Atmospheric storage employs reservoirs, where the liquid can be exposed to the elements, or some type of tank for all other purposes. Opportunities for using **reservoirs** are few, because most liquids must be protected from contamination or dilution. Water is the liquid most commonly stored this way in chemical process industries. Where the quantities are large, reservoir design lies in the domain of the civil engineer. For small reservoirs, concrete-walled excavations or concrete tanks without tops, either sunken in the ground or raised above it, are in common use. Such tanks should be constructed with reinforced walls adequate to hold the contents when the reservoir is completely filled. The concrete should be waterproofed so as to prevent leakage.

Atmospheric tanks are used for liquids whose vapor pressure is atmospheric or below at storage conditions. The common types of atmospheric tanks are rectangular or cylindrical, the latter subdivided into horizontal and vertical. **Rectangular tanks,** as the name implies, are flat-sided and usually flat-bottomed tanks of smaller sizes. This type of tank in larger capacities is uneconomical, because it requires extensive reinforcement of the flat sides against the hydrostatic pressure of the stored product. **Horizontal tanks** are used where adequate ground or floor area is available. These tanks are usually shop-built and are thus restricted in size to practical shipping limits, usually about 11 to 12 ft. in diameter and 60 ft. in length, although there are larger shop tanks shipped in certain areas of the United States.

Vertical tanks may be shop-built or field-assembled. They may be flat-bottomed, resting directly on the plant floor, a prepared grade or concrete-slab foundation, or they may be provided with a conical or dished bottom and supported on structural posts or a cylindrical skirt extension of the shell. Vertical tanks may be open at the top or closed with a roof. If open-topped, the tank must be provided with a wind girder at or near the tank top. If provided with a roof, the roof may be supported or self-supporting; however, in either case the roof should be capable of supporting a snow load (if installed outdoors) of at least 25 lb./sq. ft.

Where vaporization occurs readily and product value is significant, special devices such as floating roofs, lifter roofs, or a variable vapor space on top of the tank may be used to reduce the loss of vapor. This vapor loss occurs as a result of displacement during filling operations, also as a result of slight pressure changes due to ambient temperature changes and, in the case of outdoor storage, as a result of solar-energy absorption. **Floating-roof tanks** are open-topped or closed tanks with a panlike or pontoon-type structure floating directly on the stored liquid. Clearance between the tank shell and the roof, which moves with the liquid level, is closed by a seal available in a variety of designs. There is no appreciable vapor space; thus corrosion caused by oxygen or water vapor present in air is virtually eliminated and, in the case of flammable liquids, the fire hazard is greatly reduced.

Lifter or expansion roofs are vertically movable roofs sealed to the tank shell by either a flexible synthetic membrane or by liquid in a launder near the tank top. As the vapor volume above the stored liquid expands because of thermal changes or tank filling, the roof rises to accommodate the changes. Vapor space is always present; thus not all the advantage of the floating roof is attained. However, it is possible to manifold a lifter-roof tank to other tanks, extending the benefits of vapor conservation at little additional cost.

Vapor tanks may be mounted atop vertical tanks when larger capacity requirements are necessary because of extensive tank manifolding for vapor conservation or vapor recycling in an inert-gas blanketing system. Such a vapor tank may be isolated from the tank upon which it is mounted.

Proper application of floating roofs, lifter roofs, or vapor tanks requires extensive study. The principles involved are set forth in the American Petroleum Institute manual on evaporation losses (*A.P.I. Bull.* 2513, 1959).

Low-pressure tanks are used to store higher-vapor-pressure liquids and are usually limited to pressures below 15 lb./sq. in. gage. While this limitation is arbitrary, many states have regulations which require more expensive design and construction considerations above 15 lb./sq. in. These tanks may be horizontal, vertical, or spherical. Horizontal tanks may be installed on concrete saddles, or the tanks may be provided with a reinforcing band at each point of support integral with the support system. Tanks in this category must be provided with hemispherical, dished, or elliptical heads.

High-pressure tanks may be horizontal or vertical cylinders (commonly called "bullets") or spheres.

In the design of liquid-storage tanks, certain rules have evolved which are fairly well accepted **industry standards.** These rules comprehensively cover all design considerations, as follows:

Flat-bottomed carbon-steel tanks to 0.5 lb./sq. in.

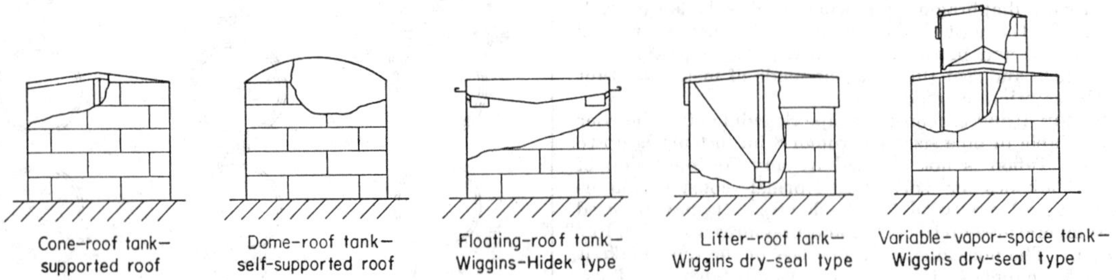

Fig. 6-117. Some types of atmospheric storage tanks.

gage, A.P.I. Code 650; aluminum alloy atmospheric tanks, A.P.I. Code 12G; steel tanks, standpipes, reservoirs, and elevated tanks for water storage, A.W.W.A. Code D100; carbon-steel tanks for pressures between 0.5 and 15 lb./sq. in. gage, A.P.I. Code 620; for pressures above 15 lb./sq. in. gage, also for full vacuum, A.S.M.E. Pressure Vessel Code; for hazardous (flammable) liquids, National Board of Fire Underwriters Pamphlet No. 30.

Materials for tank construction are varied. All weldable carbon steels, many grades of stainless steels, aluminum, many copper and brass alloys are used. Some tanks for certain services permit the use of wood staves. Recent developments in plastics open new fields with materials such as polyesters, epoxies, and polyethylenes available for special applications. Special materials or linings may be used to solve problems in corrosion or product contamination.

Tanks must be protected from pressure or vacuum excess by means of **vents.** Analysis of venting requirements must consider not only pumping rates but liquid-body temperature changes and the resulting effect on liquid-surface vapor pressure. Solar-energy absorption and ambient-temperature changes must be considered.

Field tanks involving flammable liquids require **grounding.** This usually consists of lugs on the tank connected by heavy copper cable to a rod driven into the ground. Discharging hazardous liquids into tanks should be carefully considered to avoid static build-up. Fire-protection equipment, such as foam connections or systems, steam snuffing lines, water fog, or spray installations may be required. Flame arrestors and/or snuffers may be combined with tank vents.

Useful tank **accessories** include manways for internal access, inlet and outlet nozzles, stairways or ladders, internal sumps to facilitate complete emptying, thermometers, and gaging apparatus. Gaging may be accomplished through a simple direct-opening hatch installed in the roof or ground, or remote-reading apparatus may be installed. Tanks may be provided with internal or external heaters for materials tending to solidify or become viscous at ambient temperatures. Refrigeration may be used to reduce vapor pressure of volatile liquids.

Insulation of heated or refrigerated tanks may be broken into two categories: (1) −150° to +40°F., where the principal problem is vapor penetration, and thus insulation must be designed to present a vapor barrier; (2) +40°F. to practical limits for conventional materials of construction, where the proper choice of insulation is a function of environment and economics. In this temperature range special attention should be paid to methods of fastening of insulation, finish, or weatherproofing.

Cryogenic tanks are a fairly recent development for the temperature range below −150°F. In the typical case, the liquid is contained in a tank fabricated of special materials chosen for low-temperature ductility. Surrounding this tank is another, larger vessel. The annular space between the two vessels is filled with a powdered insulation such as perlite. This annular space may be evacuated to a high vacuum. Such construction permits storage of liquid oxygen, nitrogen, etc., with relatively low boil-off due to heat leaks.

Quantities stored in tanks can be readily determined from the dimensions of the tank and the depth of the liquid in the tank. Capacities of rectangular tanks are given in Table 6-39 and of vertical tanks in Table 6-40. The contents of horizontal cylindrical tanks will be influenced by the shape of the tank ends, which may be convex, straight, or concave. For rough estimating, the effect of the ends may be neglected.

When a horizontal cylindrical tank is only partly filled, a deduction must be made from the total contents of the tank equal to the unfilled portion above the liquid level.

Table 6-39. Capacities (U.S. Gallons) of Rectangular Tanks for Each Foot of Liquid

231 cu. in. = 1 U.S. gal.;* 1 cu. ft. = 1728 cu. in. = 7.4805 U.S. gal.

Tank width, in.	Tank length													
	6″ 0.5′	12″ 1′	18″ 1′-6″	24″ 2′	30″ 2′-6″	36″ 3′	42″ 3′-6″	48″ 4′	54″ 4′-6″	60″ 5′	66″ 5′-6″	72″ 6′	78″ 6′-6″	84″ 7′
6	1.87	3.74	5.61	7.48	9.35	11.22	13.09	14.96	16.83	18.70	20.57	22.44	24.31	26.18
12	3.74	7.48	11.22	14.96	18.70	22.44	26.18	29.92	33.66	37.40	41.14	44.88	48.62	52.36
18	5.61	11.22	16.83	22.44	28.05	33.66	39.27	44.88	50.49	56.10	61.71	67.32	72.93	78.55
24	7.48	14.96	22.44	29.92	37.40	44.88	52.36	59.84	67.32	74.81	82.29	89.77	97.25	104.73
30	9.35	18.70	28.05	37.40	46.75	56.10	65.45	74.81	84.16	93.51	102.86	112.21	121.56	130.91
36	11.22	22.44	33.66	44.88	56.10	67.32	78.55	89.77	100.99	112.21	123.43	134.65	145.87	157.09
42	13.09	26.18	39.27	52.36	65.45	78.55	91.64	104.73	117.82	130.91	144.00	157.09	170.18	183.27
48	14.96	29.92	44.88	59.84	74.81	89.77	104.73	119.69	134.65	149.61	164.57	179.53	194.49	209.45
54	16.83	33.66	50.49	67.32	84.16	100.99	117.82	134.65	151.48	168.31	185.14	201.97	218.81	235.64
60	18.70	37.40	56.10	74.81	93.51	112.21	130.91	149.61	168.31	187.01	205.71	224.42	243.12	261.82
66	20.57	41.14	61.71	82.29	102.86	123.43	144.00	164.57	185.14	205.71	226.29	246.86	267.43	288.00
72	22.44	44.88	67.32	89.77	112.21	134.65	157.09	179.53	201.97	224.42	246.86	269.30	291.74	314.18
78	24.31	48.62	72.94	97.25	121.56	145.87	170.18	194.49	218.81	243.12	267.43	291.74	316.05	340.36
84	26.18	52.36	78.55	104.73	130.91	157.09	183.27	209.45	235.64	261.82	288.00	314.18	340.36	366.55
90	28.05	56.10	84.16	112.21	140.26	168.31	196.36	224.42	252.47	280.52	308.58	336.62	364.68	392.73
96	29.92	59.84	89.77	119.69	149.61	179.53	209.45	239.38	269.30	299.22	329.14	359.06	388.99	418.91

Tank width, in.	Tank length													
	90″ 7′-6″	96″ 8′	102″ 8′-6″	108″ 9′	114″ 9′-6″	120″ 10′	126″ 10′-6″	132″ 11′	138″ 11′-6″	144″ 12′	150″ 12′-6″	156″ 13′	162″ 13′-6″	168″ 14′
6	28.05	29.92	31.79	33.66	35.53	37.40	39.27	41.14	43.01	44.88	46.75	48.62	50.49	52.36
12	56.10	59.84	63.58	67.32	71.06	74.81	78.55	82.29	86.03	89.77	93.51	97.25	100.99	104.73
18	84.16	89.77	95.38	100.99	106.60	112.21	117.82	123.43	129.04	134.65	140.26	145.87	151.48	157.09
24	112.21	119.69	127.17	134.65	142.13	149.61	157.09	164.57	172.05	179.53	187.01	194.49	201.97	209.45
30	140.26	149.61	158.96	168.31	177.66	187.01	196.36	205.71	215.06	224.42	233.77	243.12	252.47	261.82
36	168.31	179.53	190.75	201.97	213.19	224.42	235.64	246.86	258.08	269.30	280.52	291.74	302.96	314.18
42	196.36	209.45	222.55	235.64	248.73	261.82	274.91	288.00	301.09	314.18	327.27	340.36	353.45	366.55
48	224.42	239.38	254.34	269.30	284.26	299.22	314.18	329.14	344.10	359.07	374.03	388.99	403.95	418.91
54	252.47	269.30	286.13	302.96	319.79	336.62	353.45	370.29	387.12	403.95	420.78	437.61	454.44	471.27
60	280.52	299.22	317.92	336.62	355.32	374.03	392.73	411.43	430.13	448.83	467.53	486.23	504.94	523.64
66	308.57	329.14	349.71	370.29	390.86	411.43	432.00	452.57	473.14	493.71	514.29	534.86	555.43	576.00
72	336.62	359.06	381.51	403.95	426.39	448.83	471.27	493.71	516.16	538.60	561.04	583.48	605.92	628.36
78	364.68	388.99	413.30	437.61	461.92	486.23	510.55	534.86	559.17	583.48	607.79	632.10	656.42	680.73
84	392.73	418.91	445.09	471.27	497.45	523.64	549.82	576.00	602.18	628.36	654.55	680.73	706.91	733.09
90	420.78	448.83	476.88	504.94	532.99	561.04	589.09	617.14	645.19	673.25	701.30	729.35	757.40	785.45
96	448.83	478.75	508.68	538.60	568.52	598.44	628.36	658.29	688.21	718.13	748.05	777.97	807.90	837.82

* For Imperial gallons, multiply above capacities by 1.2.

Table 6-40. Capacities of Vertical Cylindrical Tanks in U.S. Gallons

Diameter Ft.	Diameter In.	Gal./ft. depth	Diameter Ft.	Diameter In.	Gal./ft. depth	Diameter Ft.	Diameter In.	Gal./ft. depth
0	0		10	0	587.52	20	0	2350.1
	3	0.37		3	617.26		3	2409.2
	6	1.47		6	647.74		6	2469.1
	9	3.31		9	678.95		9	2529.6
1	0	5.88	11	0	710.90	21	0	2591.0
	3	9.18		3	743.58		3	2653.0
	6	13.22		6	776.99		6	2715.8
	9	17.99		9	811.14		9	2779.3
2	0	23.50	12	0	846.03	22	0	2843.6
	3	29.74		3	881.64		3	2908.6
	6	36.72		6	918.00		6	2974.3
	9	44.43		9	955.08		9	3040.8
3	0	52.88	13	0	992.91	23	0	3108.0
	3	62.06		3	1031.5		3	3175.9
	6	71.97		6	1070.8		6	3244.6
	9	82.62		9	1110.8		9	3314.0
4	0	94.00	14	0	1151.5	24	0	3384.1
	3	106.12		3	1193.0		3	3455.0
	6	118.97		6	1235.3		6	3526.6
	9	132.56		9	1278.2		9	3598.9
5	0	146.88	15	0	1321.9	25	0	3672.0
	3	161.93		3	1366.3		3	3745.8
	6	177.72		6	1411.5		6	3820.3
	9	194.25		9	1457.4		9	3895.6
6	0	211.51	16	0	1504.1	26	0	3971.6
	3	229.50		3	1551.4		3	4048.4
	6	248.23		6	1599.5		6	4125.9
	9	267.69		9	1648.4		9	4204.1
7	0	287.88	17	0	1697.9	27	0	4283.0
	3	308.81		3	1748.2		3	4362.7
	6	330.48		6	1799.3		6	4443.1
	9	352.88		9	1851.1		9	4524.3
8	0	376.01	18	0	1903.6	28	0	4606.1
	3	399.88		3	1956.8		3	4688.8
	6	424.48		6	2010.8		6	4772.1
	9	449.82		9	2065.5		9	4856.2
9	0	475.89	19	0	2120.9	29	0	4941.0
	3	502.70		3	2177.1		3	5026.6
	6	530.24		6	2234.0		6	5112.9
	9	558.51		9	2291.7		9	5199.9

If the tank is filled to a point above the axis, then subtract from the total contents an amount equal to the contents of a space having the same length as the tank and an end area equal to the unwetted segment of the tank end. If the tank is filled to a point below the axis, then the contents become equal to that obtained by multiplying the length of the tank by the area of the wetted segment of the end of the tank.

Table 6-41 will be useful in estimating the contents of partially filled horizontal cylindrical tanks with flat ends. For computing values not found in the table, use the procedure of the following example, referring to Fig. 6-118:

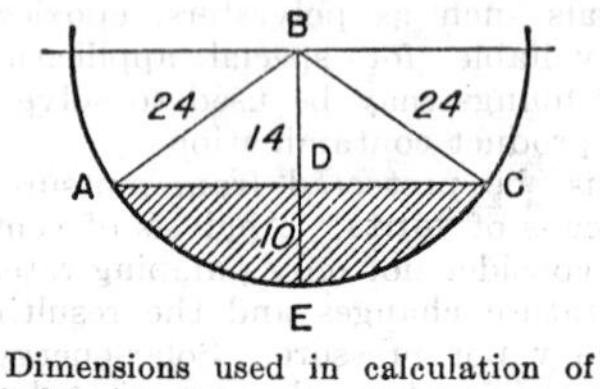

FIG. 6-118. Dimensions used in calculation of capacities of horizontal cylindrical tanks.

Assume tank diameter = 48 in., filled with liquid to a depth of 10 in. Find the volume in U.S. gallons per foot of tank length.

Area ACE = area $ABCE$ − area ABC.

$$\text{Area } ABCE = \left(\frac{2\angle ABD}{360}\right) \times \text{area of circle, and } \angle ABD$$

is found from its cosine which is $^{14}/_{24}$.

$$\therefore \angle ABD = 54.25°$$

$$\text{Area } ABC = 14 \times 24 \times \sin \angle ABD$$

or $14 \times 24 \times \sin 54.25 = 14 \times 24 \times .8116 = 272.7$

$$\text{Area } ABCE = \frac{108.50}{360} \times \pi \times (24)^2 = 545.4.$$

$$\therefore \text{Area } ACE = 545.4 - 272.7 = 272.7$$

$$\therefore \text{Vol. (U.S. gal.) per ft. of length} = \frac{272.7 \times 12}{231} = 14.17$$

Table 6-41. Capacities of Horizontal Cylindrical Tanks
Contents given in U.S. gallons for 1 ft. of length
Flat ends

Diameter of tank, in.	Depth of liquid, in. 3	6	9	12	15	18	21	24	27	30	33	36	39	42	45	48	51
12	1.15	2.94	4.73	**5.88**													
18	1.45	3.86	6.61	9.36	11.77	**13.22**											
24	1.70	4.60	8.05	11.75	15.45	18.90	21.80	**23.50**									
30	1.91	5.23	9.27	13.72	18.36	23.00	27.45	31.49	34.81	**36.72**							
36	2.12	5.79	10.34	15.43	20.85	26.44	32.03	37.45	42.54	47.09	50.76	**52.88**					
42	2.28	6.31	11.31	16.97	23.07	29.46	35.99	42.51	48.90	55.00	60.66	65.66	69.69	**71.97**			
48	2.45	6.78	12.20	18.38	25.10	32.20	39.54	47.01	54.47	61.81	68.91	75.63	81.81	87.23	91.56	**94.01**	
54	2.60	7.22	13.04	19.68	26.97	34.72	42.80	51.08	59.49	67.90	76.18	84.26	92.01	99.30	105.94	111.76	116.38
60	2.75	7.64	13.82	20.91	28.72	37.06	45.82	54.88	64 11	73.45	82.78	92.01	101.07	109.83	118.17	125.98	133.07
66	2.89	8.04	14.56	22.07	30.37	39.28	48.65	58.39	68.42	78.59	88.87	99.14	109.31	119.34	129.08	138.45	147.36
72	3.02	8.42	15.26	23.17	31.92	41.36	51.32	61.71	72.45	83.41	94.54	105.76	116.98	128.11	139.07	149.81	160.20
78	3.15	8.78	15.94	24.21	33.41	43.34	53.86	64.87	76.27	87.97	99.90	111.97	124.12	136.27	148.34	160.27	171.97
84	3.26	9.12	16.57	25.24	34.85	45.24	56.29	67.87	79.91	92.30	104.98	117.85	130.87	143.95	157.03	170.05	182.92
90	3.43	9.46	17.20	26.20	36.21	47.05	58.61	70.75	83.39	96.43	109.81	123.46	137.28	151.22	165.25	179.27	193.21
96	3.50	9.79	17.80	27.13	37.52	48.81	60.84	73.52	86.73	100.39	114.44	128.79	143.40	158.17	173.07	188.01	202.95
102	3.61	10.10	18.37	28.01	39.00	50.49	62.99	76.18	89.94	104.20	118.89	133.92	149.25	164.81	180.53	196.36	212.25
108	3.71	10.39	18.94	28.90	40.03	52.14	65.09	78.74	93.04	107.87	123.17	138.87	154.89	171.19	187.71	204.37	221.15

Diameter of tank, in.	Depth of liquid, in. 54	57	60	63	66	69	72	75	78	81	84	87	90	93	96	102	108
54	**118.98**																
60	139.25	144.14	**146.89**														
66	155.66	163.17	169.69	174.84	**177.73**												
72	170.16	179.60	188.35	196.26	203.10	208.50	**211.52**										
78	183.37	194.38	204.90	214.83	224.03	232.30	239.46	245.09	**248.24**								
84	195.60	207.99	220.03	231.61	242.66	253.05	262.66	271.33	278.78	284.64	**287.90**						
90	207.03	220.68	234.06	247.10	259.74	271.88	283.44	294.28	304.29	313.29	321.03	327.06	**330.49**				
96	217.85	232.62	247.23	261.58	275.63	289.29	302.50	315.18	327.21	338.50	348.89	358.22	366.23	372.52	**376.02**		
102	228.12	243.95	259.67	275.23	290.56	305.59	320.28	334.54	348.30	361.49	373.99	385.48	396.47	406.11	414.38	**424.48**	
108	238.05	254.75	271.53	288.19	304.71	321.01	337.03	352.73	368.03	382.86	397.16	410.81	423.76	435.87	447.00	465.51	**475.90**

For computing the contents of horizontal cylindrical tanks with **bulged or dished ends,** Fig. 6-119 will be

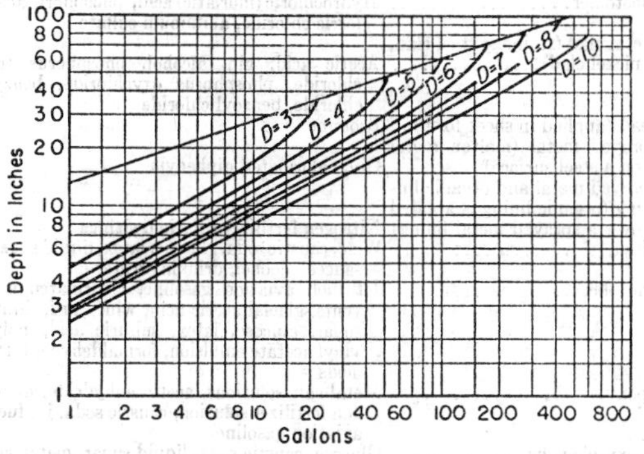

FIG. 6-119. Volumes of (two) bulged or dished ends of horizontal cylindrical tanks. Constructed from Doolittle formula (*Ind. Eng. Chem., March,* 1928):

$$V \text{ (both ends)} = 0.00093h^2(3r - h) \text{ gal.}$$

where h = depth, in.
r = radius of tank, in.
In curves, D = diameter of tank, ft.

useful. This chart gives the volumes of the bulged or dished ends for tanks of diameters of 3, 4, 5, 6, 7, 8, and 10 ft. corresponding to various depths. The volumes read from Fig. 6-119 must be added to (or subtracted from) the volumes computed for tanks with flat ends.

When it is desired to figure the contents of an existing horizontal tank with curved ends more accurately, the alternative method of calibration is recommended. This consists in completely filling the tank with water, then drawing off the contents in steps, reducing the depth of the liquid by even amounts, and accurately measuring the quantity of liquid withdrawn for each of these unit reductions in depth. In this way a table can be compiled giving the tank contents for each unit of depth of liquid in the tank. In practice, with such a table and a liquid-level gage, the quantity in a tank can be readily obtained.

Liquid materials **stored in containers** are generally packed in barrels, kegs, drums, cans, or glass containers. The storage of the barrels, kegs, and drums will be the same as that described in Sec. 7 for solids packed in similar containers. For cans, one of the most convenient methods is to stack the cans several tiers high on pallets or skid platforms and then handle them into and out of storage by means of electric or hand-operated industrial lift trucks. Where small cans are to be stacked to a considerable height, machinery developed for service in food canneries will be found useful for both stacking and reclaiming.

Storage for glass containers, such as carboys or bottles, may be either on skids or pallets, or directly on the floor. Movement into and out of storage is best carried out by means of hand-operated or electrical industrial trucks. Special bodies are available for these trucks for handling carboys efficiently.

Storage of Gases. Gases may be stored in gasometers at pressures up to about 0.5 lb./sq. in. These structures are classified by type of seal and may be divided into two classes—fluid seal and dry seal.

Fluid-seal gasholders may be built in any capacity. They consist of a tub or seal tank and movable bell. Seals are usually water, although special fluids such as oils may be used. Fluid-sealed holders usually require massive foundations with the attendant high costs, particularly in the larger sizes.

Dry-seal holders consist of a tank with a vertically moving piston connected to the tank side wall by a special flexible synthetic-rubber-impregnated fabric chemically inert to the gas being stored (Fig. 6-120). Since the piston freely floats on the gas, means of guiding and leveling this piston must be used.

Gases may be stored at pressures above 0.5 lb./sq. in. in horizontal or vertical pressure tanks, in spheres, or in spheroids.

Bulk storage of gas is usually carried out in tanks of the types just described, which permit the pressure to be maintained fairly constant. Where storage is carried out in ordinary tanks, arrangement must be made to prevent the gas from becoming diluted with air, and also to prevent too great a pressure from building up within the tank. Ordinarily, such tanks are used only for compressed air, in which case they are called *air receivers.*

Gas storage in holders or tanks is accomplished by means of compressors or blowers, taking the gas from its source and feeding to the storage through pipe lines. Reclaiming of gas from storage is also done by means of a compressor or blower, or by utilizing the gas pressure in the storage when this is great enough. Such reclaiming is done through piping systems. Frequently the gas pressure in the storage tank is sufficient to serve partly, and it can then be supplemented by additional pressure imparted to the gas by means of a blower or compressor.

Quantities of gas stored in holders must be calculated for some standard conditions, because of the changes that occur in gas volumes with variations in pressure and temperature. The gas placed in storage and that removed from storage may be metered in one of many types of gas meters available, and in this way a running check may be kept on the quantity stored.

Gas stored in containers is usually stored in what are called gas "cylinders." These are heavily constructed tanks of drum or bottle shape. Heavy construction is used in order that the gas may be stored under considerable pressure, thus permitting a relatively large amount of gas (when considered from the standpoint of its volume under ordinary pressures) to be stored in a relatively small container. Container storage for gas is usually employed for the storage and shipment of such gases as oxygen, carbon dioxide, acetylene, propane, butane, and hydrogen. It provides a convenient method for gas shipment. When such gas cylinders are stored in the plant, their relatively great weight, due to the heavy construction used, should be kept in mind so that storage floors will not be overloaded.

Bulk Transport of Fluids. Commodities (all liquids, chemicals, gases, meltable solids, slurries, and emulsions handled) can be divided into two basic classes —regulatory and non-regulatory. A **regulatory commodity** is one that has been classified as dangerous by the Interstate Commerce Commission. These commodities fall into such categories as poisonous, flammable, oxidizing, corrosive, explosive, or compressed gas.

These dangerous commodities are listed either by name or by general category in a book entitled "Agent T. C. George's Tariff No. 13 Publishing the I.C.C. Regulations" (T. C. George, New York, 1960).

For a new commodity that may be dangerous, the Bureau of Explosives will recommend type of car and fittings to be required for this particular commodity to the Interstate Commerce Commission. The Bureau's recommendations are based upon chemical, physical, and toxicological data submitted by the proposed shipper.

The majority of fluids transported today do not fall in the dangerous category. These **non-regulatory commodities** may be transported in almost any type of tank car, and more latitude is allowed in loading and unloading fittings, construction of car, etc.

More than 1000 commodities are being transported in **tank cars** in the United States. These commodities range from hydrogen and oxygen to sulfur and high-melt pitches. Tank-car capacities vary from 2200 to 30,300 gal. The majority are one-compartment tanks; however, based upon requirements, a tank may be divided into as many as six compartments. This means six different commodities, or different grades of one commodity, may be shipped in one car. Each compartment has its own individual safety relief, loading, and unloading system.

High-pressure removable cylinders are also mounted on underframes; these are referred to as **multiunit tank cars.** These tanks normally transport high-pressure compressed or liquefied gases. Some gases are also transported in a high-pressure cylindrical tank mounted within a special boxcar.

In 1961 there were approximately 71 classes of cars, of which five were multiunit cars. Types of cars differ in many variables, such as materials of construction, loading and unloading fittings, pressure-relief systems, coils, and insulation. These variables are illustrated as follows:

Most tanks are constructed of boiler-plate steel, flange quality; plate thickness varies with the type of car and also the maximum working pressure of the tank. If commodity purity requirements, corrosive properties, or I.C.C. regulation are involved, tanks may be made of stainless steel, nickel, aluminum, or clad steel. In some cases, because of the economics involved, a steel car with an organic, inorganic, elastomer, or sprayed-metal lining may be used. Typical commodities that may be transported in various linings are listed in Table 6-42. The type of lining required for a special commodity is usually determined by special laboratory tests, because most corrosion occurs on the return trip, when a residual amount of commodity is present in the bottom of the tank, and the corrosion factors are not the same as those the manufacturer encounters.

Table 6-42. Typical Commodities Transported in Tank Cars with Various Linings

Type of Lining	Commodities
Elastomer	Hydrochloric (muriatic) acid, phosphoric acid, ferric chloride, aluminum sulfate
Metal clad (stainless steel clad, nickel clad)	Acetic acid, gin, alcohol, phosphorus trichloride, phosphorus oxychloride, benzyl chloride, benzoyl chloride
Lead (applied in sheet form)	Bromine
Sprayed metal (molten metal on a steel surface)	Gin, chlorinated diphenyls
Sprayed metal and organic lining (organic lining is applied over a sprayed metal lining)	Nitrogen fertilizer solution, sizings
Vinyl	Wine, caustic soda, glucose, latex, liquid sugar sauces, alcohol, drinking water
Phenolic	Jet fuel, aviation gasoline, chlorinated solvents, glacial acetic acid, wine, lard, liquid sugar, glucose, latex, sulfuric acid, polyvinyl acetate emulsion, formaldehyde, fatty acids
Epoxy	Metal salt solutions, acetic anhydride, nitrogen fertilizer solution, caustic soda, jet fuel, aviation gasoline
Epoxy-phenolic	Glucose, caustic soda, liquid sugar, metal salt solution
Latex (spray applied in multiple coats)	Caustic soda
Asphalt	Tannic acid
Glass	Milk, grape juice, blood, cherries, orange juice
Electroless nickel	Caustic soda, fatty acid, glucose, liquid sugar
Alkyd	Glucose, liquid sugar, light oils

Type of car is determined by certain physical characteristics, such as vapor pressure, corrosivity, and toxicity. For a regulatory commodity, type is specified by the Interstate Commerce Commission. **High-pressure tank car** is a term normally applied to those cars having a safety-valve setting of 75 lb./sq. in. (except all groups of the I.C.C. 111A100-W series with the exception of I.C.C. 111A100-W-4) and higher (*i.e.*, A.R.A. V, I.C.C. 105A100-W, I.C.C. 105A300-W, I.C.C. 109A300-W, etc.). Commodities that must be shipped in these cars are non-flammable compressed gases, flammable compressed gases, certain flammable liquids, and highly toxic commodities. The class of high-pressure car used to

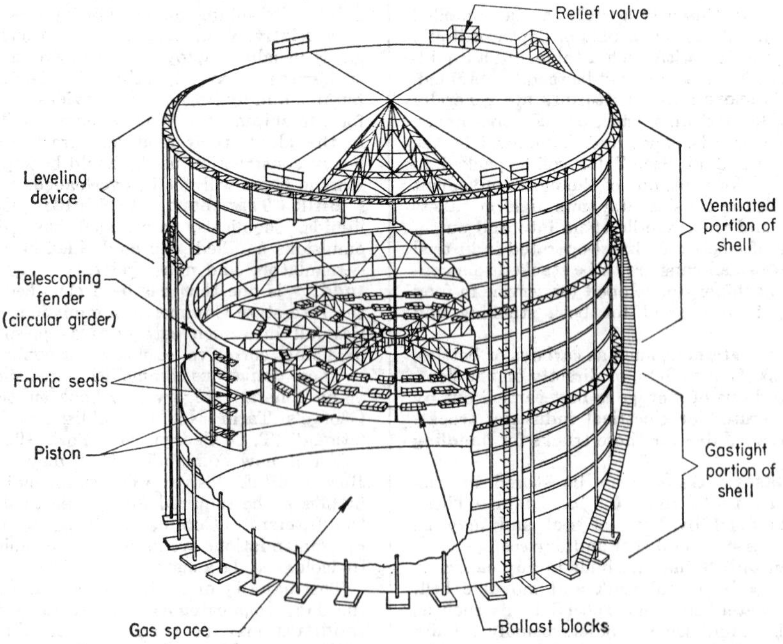

FIG. 6-120. Cutaway view of Wiggins gasholder.

transport a commodity normally depends upon its vapor pressure at 100°, 105°, or 130°F. **Low-pressure tank car** is a term normally applied to those cars having a safety-valve or vent setting at or under 75 lb./sq. in. (except I.C.C. 111A100-W-4) and are normally equipped with one safety vent set to rupture at 45 lb./sq. in. or with one or two safety valves set to release at 35 lb./sq. in. (except the I.C.C. 111A100-W series cars, which are equipped with one safety valve set to release at 75 lb./sq. in.).

The majority of tank cars in service in the United States are **general-service cars,** the "work horses" of the industry. Low vapor-pressure and most non-regulatory commodities are transported in these cars.

Acid cars, as the name implies, are specially designed low-pressure tanks for the transportation of acids. For safety reasons, no bottom outlet is permitted, and all unloading is done from the top.

Several commodities are shipped in Wet-Flo cars. The commodity is loaded in a dry form, and at the unloading point, water or other solvent is injected into the car in order to unload the commodity in solution form.

All tank cars are equipped with some type of pressure-relief system to prevent the build-up of pressure above the maximum limitations of the tank. A general-service car is normally loaded through the dome and is unloaded through an outlet located in the bottom of the tank. For unloading a high-pressure tank car, or if it is desired to unload a general-service car from the top, unloading fittings are located on the top of the car. They consist of at least one dip pipe running from top of the tank down to the bottom and a separate connection located in the top of the tank. Air or an inert gas is applied to the connection in order to pressurize the tank, and the commodity is then unloaded through the dip pipe. A pump may be used to assist in the unloading of the car.

Tank cars generally are not heated during transit; so if the melting point of the commodity is above the ambient temperature, some means of either heating the commodity or preventing heat loss during transit must be employed. Coils can be installed either inside the tank or attached to the outside of the tank (outside coils are used if a high-pressure car is involved or if the commodity being transported in the tank is difficult to clean and requires manual scraping and chipping). As certain commodities can be damaged by either excessive heat loss or gain in transit, insulation can be used to control the rate of heat transfer. Insulation is also employed to prevent a pressure build-up due to temperature increase of a compressed gas.

Frequently, tank cars are changed from the transportation of one commodity to another. In many cases, complete removal of all traces of the prior commodity is required to prevent contamination of the subsequent commodity. Other times, all traces of the commodity must be removed after every load or every few loads.

Through improvement in design and changes in regulations, the maximum size of a tank has been increased from 12,000 up to over 30,000 gal. Highly specialized cars and a wider variety of linings are constantly being perfected to meet the ever-increasing demands of various industries.

Truck tank trailers for the transportation of bulk liquids are available in capacities from 2600 to 8500 gal. Determining factor in truck-trailer hauling is the weight limitation in the states of travel. Tank-trailer movements are governed by Interstate Commerce Commission regulations for hauling hazardous commodities, covering flowable- and corrosive-liquid pressure requirements and other safety considerations.

Trailers are available in virtually all grades of carbon steel, aluminum, and stainless steel. For various purposes and commodities, trailers can be insulated or non-insulated, refrigerated or heated, single or multiple compartmented, non-pressure or pressure, and equipped with various methods of discharge. Recent years have seen a tremendous increase in special trailer designs, for a variety of purposes. Cryogenic trailers are hauling liquid oxygen, nitrogen, and even hydrogen.

Containers or **portable tanks** designed to facilitate transfer from truck trailer to rail car or ship are becoming increasingly important. These containers are usually custom-designed to meet the requirements of the governing regulatory bodies (such as Interstate Commerce Commission, Association of American Railroads, U.S. Coast Guard). Some progress in standardization of container sizes has been made by American Standards Association MH-5 Committee for Shipping Containers.

Such containers reduce the need for transfer operations, with a resulting decrease in handling costs. It is possible for an inland plant not located on a railroad to load such a container and deliver to a foreign user without product transfer.

Water Transportation. Vessels used for water transportation in the United States are built to the requirements of the American Bureau of Shipping and the U.S. Coast Guard. The design of vessels used for water transportation must be cleared by these agencies.

Ocean shipping by the chemical industry is accomplished in many types of conventional containers, ranging from small cans up through drums, special ship containers capable of transfer to rail or truck trailer, and finally barges and ships. While some special ships have been built, many wartime T-2 tankers are being used. The latter are 10,000 tons gross capable of transporting approximately 140,000 bbl. of cargo in tanks so arranged to provide 26 individual tanks.

Inland-water transportation other than by ship or conventional small container is accomplished by barges. There are many types and sizes of barges of four general classes: single-skin compartmented, double-skin compartmented, tank, and open hopper. Single- and double-skin barges are used for atmospheric-pressure liquids. Tank barges are equipped with pressure tanks for both low- and high-pressure commodities. Open-hopper barges are mainly used for bulk solids and other types of material capable of exposure to the elements without spoilage.

River locks determine the size limits of barges. Usually barges are 35 or 52½ ft. wide and are combined two or three side by side in long tows. Barge lengths must be uniform to permit operation in tows, and there are a great number of 195-ft. barges. Depths of barges are usually about 10 to 14 ft., depending on the weight of material being handled and the depth of waterway the barge will travel.

SECTION 7
SOLIDS TRANSPORT AND STORAGE

BY

Robert G. Zilly, M.S., Editor, *Building Construction;* Member, American Society of Mechanical Engineers.

CONTENTS

TRANSPORT OF SOLIDS IN BULK

STORAGE OF SOLIDS IN BULK

TRANSPORT OF SOLIDS IN CONTAINERS

TRANSPORT OF SOLIDS IN BULK

Selection of the correct conveyor for a specific bulk material in a specific situation is complicated by the large number of interrelated factors which must be considered. Standardized equipment designs and complete engineering data are available for many common types of conveyors. When used with materials having well-known conveying characteristics, performance for these conveyors can be accurately predicted. However, even the best-known conveyors can give disappointing performance if material characteristics are unfavorable. It is often true that conveyor engineering is more art than science, and problems involving unusual materials or equipment should be approached with caution.

Many pre-engineered conveyor components can be purchased on a merchandise basis. They are economical, easy to assemble, and perform well on conventional applications for which they are designed. However, it is advisable to use such equipment only after checking with its manufacturer to be sure the application is proper.

Capacity requirement is a prime factor in conveyor selection. Belt conveyors can be manufactured in relatively large sizes to operate at high speeds, and hence deliver large tonnages economically. On the other hand, screw conveyors become extremely cumbersome as they get larger and cannot be operated at high speeds without creating serious abrasion problems.

Length of travel for certain types of conveyors is definitely limited. With high-tensile-strength belting, the length limit on belt conveyors is a matter of miles. Air conveyors are limited to thousands of feet, vibrating conveyors to hundreds of feet. In general, as length of travel increases, the variety of conveyors that can be used decreases.

Lift can usually be handled most economically by vertical or slightly inclined bucket elevators. However, when lift and horizontal travel are combined, other conveyors should be considered. Conveyors which combine several directions of travel in a single unit are generally more expensive, but the fact that they require only a single drive may often compensate for this added cost.

Material characteristics should be considered—both chemical and physical. Abrasiveness, friability, and lump size are just a few of the physical characteristics that may influence conveyor selection. Chemical effects, such as those due to oil on rubber or acids on metal, may dictate the structural materials out of which conveyor components are fabricated. On the other hand, moisture or oxidation effects from exposure to the atmosphere may be harmful to the material being conveyed. In these cases, total enclosure of the conveyor, or even an artificial atmosphere, may be necessary. Obviously, certain types of conveyors lend themselves to such requirements better than others.

Processing requirements can be met by some conveyors with little or no change in design. For example, the continuous-flow conveyor may provide sufficient process cooling simply because it puts the conveyed material in direct contact with good heat-conducting metals. Screen decks can be easily attached to vibrating conveyors for simple sizing and scalping operations, and special screw flights or casings on screw conveyors are available for a wide variety of processing operations such as mixing, dewatering, heating, and cooling.

Initial cost of a conveyor system is usually related to life expectancy. The first really long-distance belt conveyor system was designed and fabricated to extremely high standards of quality. After 35 years it was still in operation with almost all the original machinery. However, had this operation been planned for only 10 years' life, this particular conveyor system would represent a case of gross overdesign. While there is a market for

Table 7-1. Conveyors for Bulk Materials

Function	Conveyor Type
Conveying materials horizontally	Apron, belt, continuous flow, drag flight, screw, vibrating, bucket, pivoted bucket, air
Conveying materials up or down an incline	Apron, belt, continuous flow, flight, screw, skip hoist, air
Elevating materials	Bucket elevator, continuous flow, skip hoist, air
Handling materials over a combination horizontal and vertical path	Continuous flow, gravity-discharge bucket, pivoted bucket, air
Distributing materials to or collecting materials from bins, bunkers, etc.	Belt, flight, screw, continuous flow, gravity-discharge bucket, pivoted bucket, air
Removing materials from rail cars, trucks, etc.	Car dumper, grain-car unloader, car shaker, power shovel, air

Table 7-2. Feeders for Bulk Materials*

Material Characteristics	Feeder Type
Fine, free-flowing materials	Bar flight, belt, oscillating or vibrating, rotary vane, screw
Non-abrasive and granular materials, materials with some lumps	Apron, bar flight, belt, oscillating or vibrating, reciprocating, rotary plate, screw
Materials difficult to handle because of being hot, abrasive, lumpy, or stringy	Apron, bar flight, belt, oscillating or vibrating, reciprocating
Heavy, lumpy, or abrasive materials similar to pit-run stone and ore	Apron, oscillating or vibrating, reciprocating

* Link-Belt Co.

Table 7-3. Classification System for Bulk Solids*

Material characteristics		Class
Size	Very fine —minus 100 mesh	A
	Fine—100 mesh to ⅛ in.	B
	Granular—⅛ to ½ in.	C
	Lumpy—containing lumps ½ in. and over	D
	Irregular—being fibrous, stringy, or the like	H
Flowability	Very free flowing—angle of respose up to 30 deg.	1
	Free flowing—angle of repose 30 deg. to 45 deg.	2
	Sluggish—angle of repose 45 deg. and up	3
Abrasiveness	Non-abrasive	6
	Mildly abrasive	7
	Very abrasive	8
Special characteristics	Contaminable, affecting use or salability	K
	Hygroscopic	L
	Highly corrosive	N
	Mildly corrosive	P
	Gives off dust or fumes harmful to life	R
	Contains explosive dust	S
	Degradable, affecting use or salability	T
	Very light and fluffy	W
	Interlocks or mats to resist digging	X
	Aerates and becomes fluid	Y
	Packs under pressure	Z

Example: A material which is granular, very free flowing, mildly abrasive, and mildly corrosive would fall in classes C, 1, 7, and P, making its classification C17P.

* Link-Belt Co.

used conveyor equipment, it is extremely limited. Thus it is important to gear conveyor quality to expected length of use.

Comparative costs for conveyor systems can be based only on studies of a specific problem. For example, belt-conveyor idlers are available in a range of qualities that may put the best unit in a price range three times as high as the cheapest. Bearing quality, steel thickness, and diameter of rolls all affect cost, as does design for easy maintenance and repair. This situation is typical of most conveyor equipment. Hence it is necessary for the user to make his own cost comparisons on the basis of a specific study for each conveyor application.

As a general **guide to conveyor selection,** Table 7-1 indicates conveyor choices on the basis of some common functions. Table 7-2 is designed to aid in **feeder selection** on the basis of the physical characteristics of material. Table 7-3 is a coded listing of **material characteristics** for use with Table 7-4, which describes the **conveying qualities** of some common materials. While these tables may serve as valuable guides, conveyor selection must be based on the "as-conveyed" characteristics of a material. For example, if packing or aerating can occur in the conveyor, its performance will not meet expectations if calculations are based on an average weight per cubic foot. Storage conditions,

Table 7-4. Material Classes and Weights*

Material	Average weight, lb./cu. ft.†	Class‡
Alum, lumpy	50–60	D26§
Alum, fine	45–50	B26§
Alumina	60	B28
Alumina gel	45	B27
Aluminum hydrate	18	C26
Ammonium chloride, crystalline	52	B26
Ammonium sulfate	45–58	§
Antimony powder		B27
Asbestos shred	20–25	H37WZ
Ashes, coal, dry, 3 in. and under	35–40	D37
Asphalt, crushed, ½ in. and under	45	C26
Bagasse	7–10	H36WXZ
Baking powder	41	A26
Bark, wood, refuse	10–20	H37X§
Bauxite, crushed, 3 in. and under	75–85	D28§
Bentonite, 100 mesh and under	50–60	A27Y§
Bicarbonate of soda	41	A26
Boneblack, 100 mesh and under	20–25	A27§
Bonechar, ⅛ in. and under	27–40	B27
Bonemeal	55–60	B27
Borate of lime		A26§
Borax, fine	53	B26
Boric acid, fine	55	B26
Calcium carbide	70–80	D27
Carbon black, pelletized	20–25	B16TZ§
Carbon black, powder	4–6	§
Casein	36	B27§
Cast-iron chips	130–200	C37
Cement, portland	65–85	A27Y
Cement clinker	75–80	D28§
Chalk, lumpy	85–90	D37Z
Chalk, 100 mesh and under	70–75	A37YZ
Charcoal	18–25	D37T
Cinders, coal	40	D28§
Clay (see bentonite, fuller's earth, kaolin, and marl)		
Coal, anthracite	60	C27P
Coal, bituminous, mined, 50 mesh and under	50	B36P
Coal, bituminous, mined, sized	50	D26PT
Coal, bituminous, mined, slack, ½ in. and under	50	C36P
Coke, loose	23–32	D38TX§
Coke, petroleum, calcined	35–45	D28X
Coke breeze, ¼ in. and under	25–35	C38
Copper sulfate		D26
Cork, fine ground	12–15	B36WY
Cork, granulated	12–15	C36
Cryolite	110	D27
Cullet	80–120	D28§
Dicalcium phosphate	43	A36
Dolomite, lumpy	90–100	D27§
Ebonite, crushed, ½ in. and under	63–70	C26
Epsom salts	40–50	B26
Feldspar, ground, ⅛ in. and under	65–70	B27
Ferrous sulfate	50–75	C27
Flour, wheat	35–40	A36K§
Fluorspar	82	C37
Fly ash, dry	35–45	A18Y§
Fuller's earth, oil filter, burned	40	B28
Fuller's earth, oil filter, raw	35–40	B27
Fuller's earth, oil filter, spent	60–65	§
Glass batch	90–100	D28§
Glue, ground, ⅛ in. and under	40	B27
Graphite, flake	40	C26
Graphite, flour	28	A16Y
Gypsum, calcined, ½ in. and under	55–60	C27
Gypsum, raw, 1 in. and under	90–100	D27
Gypsum, calcined, powdered	60–80	A37
Ice, crushed	35–45	D16
Ilmenite	140	B28
Kaolin clay, 3 in. and under	163	D27
Lead arsenate	72	B36R
Lignite, air dried	45–55	D26
Lime, ground, ⅛ in. and under	60	B36Z
Lime, hydrated, ⅛ in. and under	40	B26YZ
Lime, hydrated, pulverized	32–40	A26YZ
Lime, pebble	53–56	D36
Limestone, agricultural, ⅛ in. and under	68	B27§
Limestone, crushed	85–90	D27§
Limestone dust	75	A37Y§
Magnesium chloride	33	C36
Manganese sulfate	70	C28
Marl	80	D27§
Mica, ground	13–15	B27
Mica, pulverized	13–15	A27Y
Mica, flakes	17–22	B17WY
Muriate of potash	77	B28
Naphthalene flakes	45	§
Oxalic acid crystals	60	B36L
Oyster shells, ground, ½ in. and under	53	C27
Oyster shells, whole		D27X
Phenol-formaldehyde molding powder	30–40	A36
Phosphate rock	75–85	D27§
Phosphate sand	90–100	B28
Potassium nitrate	76	C17P
Pumice, ⅛ in. and under	42–45	B38§
Salt, common dry, coarse	45–50	C37PL§
Salt, common dry, fine	70–80	B27PL§
Salt cake, dry, coarse	85	D27
Salt cake, dry, pulverized	65–85	B27
Saltpeter	80	B26S
Sand, bank, dry	90–110	B28
Sand, silica, dry	90–100	B18
Sawdust	10–13	§
Shale, crushed	85–90	C27
Shellac, powdered or granulated	31	B26K§
Silica gel	45	B28
Slag, furnace, granulated	60–65	C28
Slate, crushed, ½ in. and under	80–90	C27
Slate, ground, ⅛ in. and under	82	B27
Soap beads or granules		B26T
Soap chips	15–25	C26T§
Soap flakes	5–15	B26T§
Soap powder	20–25	B26§
Soapstone talc, fine	40–50	A37Z
Soda ash, heavy	55–65	B27
Soda ash, light	20–35	A27W
Sodium nitrate	70–80	§
Sodium sulfate (see salt cake)		
Starch	25–50	§
Steel chips, crushed	100–150	D38
Sugar, granulated	50–55	B26KT
Sugar, raw, cane, or beet	55–65	B36Z§
Sugar-beet pulp, dry	12–15	§
Sugar-beet pulp, wet	25–45	§
Sulfur, crushed, ½ in. and under	50–60	C26S§
Sulfur, lumpy, 3 in. and under	80–85	D26S§
Sulfur, powdered	50–60	B26SY§
Talcum powder	40–60	A27Y
Trisodium phosphate	60	B27
Vermiculite, expanded	16	C37W
Vermiculite ore	80	D27
Wood chips	10–30	H36WX§
Wood flour	16–36	§
Zinc oxide, heavy	30–35	A36Z§
Zinc oxide, light	10–15	A36WZ§

* Link-Belt Co.

† Weights of material, loose or slightly agitated. Weights are usually different when materials are settled or packed as in bins or containers.

‡ These classes represent observations under general conditions. Specific conditions may vary because of manufacturing processes and handling.

§ Class may vary considerably because of conditions.

variations in ambient temperature and humidity, discharge methods—all may affect the conveying characteristics of a material. All such factors should be carefully considered before making a final conveyor selection.

Conveyor Drives. Depending on specific job requirements, a conveyor drive may cost from 10 to 30 per cent of the total cost of the conveyor system. Since it is good practice to maintain a selected inventory of spare parts for drives, economy can be achieved by standardizing conveyor drives throughout the plant. For example, use of intermediate-speed reduction via V-belts and sheaves or chains and sprockets can frequently permit use of the same speed-reducer size for several drives. Thus it may be possible to keep only one speed reducer in repair stock for a number of conveyors.

Classification of conveyor drives falls naturally into fixed speed and adjustable speed. **Fixed-speed drives** may be altered by simple sheave or sprocket changes for minor speed alterations. However, for major adjustments motor or speed-reducer changes are required. In any event, the conveyor must be shut down while the change is made. **Adjustable-speed drives** are designed for changing speed by either manual or automatic adjustment while the conveyor is in operation, to meet variations in processing requirements.

Conveyor drives can be further classified by the number of speed reductions. Most common is a two-step system: the motor is coupled to a speed reducer and the slow-speed shaft of the reducer is connected to the conveyor drive shaft by V-belt or roller chain. The second reduction not only allows for a simpler speed reducer but gives the added benefit of allowing a more flexible layout of the motor and reducer mounting plate. On many installations this eliminates the necessity for a specially designed drive mount.

Motors for conveyor drives are generally three-phase, 60-cycle, 220-volt. However, there is a definite trend toward higher service voltages which should be considered for both long-term consequences and immediate economy. Although there are many adjustable-speed drives which use a.c. induction motors powered by a.c. alternators or a.c.-driven eddy-current clutches, there is strong preference for d.c. motors where speed adjustments are required over a wide range and at extremely accurate settings. In the larger horsepower range a motor-generator set is generally used; in the smaller, electronic conversion.

The squirrel-cage motor is most commonly used with belt conveyors, and with drives up to 10 hp., across-the-line starting is generally specified. Between 10 and 50 hp., squirrel-cage motors are generally started by means of a manual reduced-voltage starter or a magnetic primary-resistance starter. Normal torque motors are generally specified with the assumption that, if power is sufficient to drive the belt, sufficient starting torque can be developed. Motor selection for large conveyors should be based on careful study with particular emphasis on starting conditions.

Chain conveyors usually require a high-slip, high-torque motor because of their high static friction which demands a high starting torque. Since chain conveyors of any appreciable length, as in warehouse tow conveyors, require multiple drives, they introduce the problem of synchronization. With high slip, the lightly loaded motor will tend to pick up speed and load, while the overloaded motor will tend to slow down and relieve itself. Many devices are available to maintain proper synchronization on multiple-drive conveyors (see also Sec. 25).

Speed reducers are generally classified according to shaft arrangement and type of gearing. Helical or spur gears are most commonly used on speed reducers because of their relatively high efficiency, although in a single reduction they are limited to ratios of about 10 to 1. Bevel gears are often used because they allow for a right-angled transfer of power, but a single reduction is limited to a ratio of around 6 to 1. The worm gear can achieve a 100 to 1 speed reduction in a single step. However, power losses are high and overheating may occur if selection is not made carefully.

Because of their compact arrangement, gear motors and motor reducers are used quite widely. Shaft-mounted reducers, first used on belt conveyors almost exclusively, are now widely used on other types of conveyors and are available in an ample range of horsepowers and reduction ratios. Motorized-head pulleys, popular in Europe, are gradually finding acceptance in the United States.

Adjustable-speed mechanical drives use either V-belts and variable-pitch sheaves with a limit of about 60 hp., or self-tooth-forming chain and radially grooved conical sheaves, or driver and driven cones connected by metal rings with beveled surfaces to match the cones. All these mechanically adjustable speed-reduction units are available with a wide variety of manual and automatic control arrangements.

Since almost any conveyor can jam for some reason, provision should be made for cutting off power from the drive motor when this occurs. Since the motor rotor has a relatively high inertia, the shear-pin hub is a good device because it cuts out power to the conveyor but allows the motor rotor to continue to rotate. However, because replacement of shear pins is sometimes rather time-consuming, electrical controls or controlled-torque couplings are sometimes used instead.

Interlocking controls in a conveyor system are obviously important in a multiple-conveyor system because of the fact that, if one conveyor stops, the whole system behind it will jam up if power is not cut off. It is also important to install a device on the head shaft which will prevent back travel (see also Sec. 24).

Screw Conveyors. This is one of the oldest and most versatile conveyor types. It consists of a helicoid (helix rolled from flat steel bar) or sectional (individual sections blanked and formed into a helix from flat plate) flight, mounted on a pipe or shaft and turning in a trough. Power to convey must be transmitted through the pipe or shaft and is limited by the allowable size of this member. Screw-conveyor capacities are generally limited to around 10,000 cu. ft./hr.

In addition to their conveying ability, screw conveyors can be adapted to a wide variety of **processing operations.** Almost any degree of mixing can be achieved with screw-conveyor flights cut, cut and folded, or replaced by a series of paddles. Use of ribbon flights allows sticky materials to be handled. Variable-pitch, tapered-flight, or stepped-flight units can give excellent control for feeder applications or on conveyors where precise control of transport rate is required. Short-pitch screws are used for inclined and vertical conveying applications, and double-flight short-pitch units effectively deter flushing action. In addition to a wide variety of designs for components, screw conveyors may be fabricated in a variety of materials ranging from cast iron to stainless steel.

Use of hollow screws and pipes for circulating hot or cold fluids allows the screw conveyor to be used for heating, cooling, and drying operations. Jacketed casings may be used for the same purpose. It is relatively easy to seal a screw conveyor from the outside atmosphere so that it can operate outdoors without special protection. In fact, it can be completely sealed to operate in its own atmosphere at positive or negative pressure, and the casing can be insulated to maintain internal temperatures in areas of high or low ambient temperature. A further advantage is the fact that the casing can be designed with a drop bottom for easy cleaning to avoid contamination when different materials are to be run through the same system.

Since screw conveyors are usually made up of standard sections coupled together, special attention should be given to bending stresses in the couplings. Hanger bearings supporting the flights obstruct flow of material when the trough is loaded above their level. Thus, with difficult materials, the load in the trough must be kept below this level, or special hanger bearings which minimize obstruction should be selected. Since screw conveyors operate at relatively low rotational speeds, the fact that the outer edge of the flight may be moving at a relatively high linear speed is often neglected. This may create a wear problem; if too severe, it can be reduced by use of hard-surfaced edges, detachable hardened flight segments, rubber covering, or high-carbon steels.

Horsepower calculations for screw conveyors are well standardized. However, each manufacturer has grouped numerical constants in a different fashion and assigned slightly different values on the basis of individual design variations. Thus, in comparing screw-conveyor horsepower requirements it is advisable to use a specific formula for specific equipment.

Required horsepower is made up of two components: that necessary to drive the screw empty and that necessary to move the material. The first component is a function of conveyor length, speed of rotation, and friction in the conveyor bearings. The second is a function of the total weight of material conveyed per unit of time, conveyed length, and depth to which the trough is loaded. The latter power item is in turn a function of the internal friction and friction on metal of the conveyed material.

Table 7-5 indicates screw-conveyor performance on the basis of material classifications as listed in Table 7-4 and defined in Table 7-3. Table 7-6 gives a wide range of capacities and horsepower requirements for various sizes of screws handling 50 lb./cu. ft. material of average conveyability. Within reasonable limits, values from Tables 7-5 and 7-6 can be interpolated for preliminary estimates and designs.

Typical **feed arrangements** are shown in Fig. 7-1. Plain spouts (Fig. 7-1*a*) may be used where feed rate is

Table 7-5. Screw-conveyor Capacities and Loading Conditions*

Material class†	Screw diam., in.	Max. lump size, in.		Capacity, cu. ft./hr.‡		Approx. area occupied by material¶
		25% lumps	100% lumps	At 1 r.p.m.	At max. r.p.m.§	
A, B, C, D, and H 16, 26, 36	6	¾	½	2.27	375	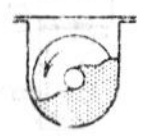
	9	1½	¾	8.0	1,200	
	12	2	1	19.3	2,700	
	14	2½	1¼	30.8	4,000	
	16	3	1½	46.6	5,600	
	18	3	2	66.1	7,600	
	20	3½	2	95.0	10,000	45%
A, B, C, D, and H 17, 27, 37	6	¾	½	1.5	75	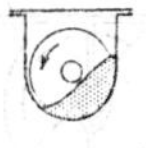
	9	1½	¾	5.6	280	
	12	2	1	13.3	665	
	14	2½	1¼	21.1	1,055	
	16	3	1½	31.4	1,570	
	18	3	2	45.4	2,270	
	20	3½	2	62.1	3,105	30%
A, B, C, D, and H 18, 28, 38	6	¾	½	0.75	25	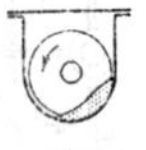
	9	1½	¾	2.8	90	
	12	2	1	6.7	200	
	14	2½	1¼	10.5	300	
	16	3	1½	15.7	425	
	18	3	2	22.7	590	
	20	3½	2	31.1	780	15%

* Link-Belt Co.

† These classifications cover a broad list of materials that generally can be handled in a screw conveyor. Special consideration must be given to applications handling materials with the following characteristics:
Highly corrosive, Class N
Degradable, affecting use or salability, Class T
Interlocks or mats, Class X
Highly aerated or of fluid nature, Class Y

‡ Capacity for horizontal conveyor uniformly fed. Volumetric capacity based on material slightly agitated or fluffed. Material highly fluffed or aerated will decrease in weight and increase in volume.

§ Maximum capacity for economical service.

¶ Percentages higher than those indicated will result in excessive wear on hanger bearings and couplings.

fairly uniform and controlled by preceding equipment. Capacity of the conveyor should be well above the maximum rate of feed from either single or multiple feed points. The rotary cutoff valve (Fig. 7-1*b*) is an enclosed dust-tight quick-acting valve for free-flowing materials. The rotary-vane feeder (Fig. 7-1*c*) delivers a uniform predetermined volume of material and may be driven from the screw or independently by constant or variable-speed drive. Rack-and-pinion gates (Fig. 7-1*d*) are well suited to free-flowing materials in bins, hoppers, tanks, or silos, and are also used as side inlet gates (Fig. 7-1*e*) for heavy or lumpy materials.

Typical **discharge arrangements** are shown in Fig. 7-2. Plain discharge openings (Fig. 7-2*a*) equipped

Table 7-6. Screw-conveyor Data for 50 Lb./Cu. Ft. Material and Pipe-mounted Sectional Spiral Flights*

Capacity†		Diam. of flights, in.	Diam. of pipe, in.‡	Diam. of shafts, in.	Hanger centers, ft.	Max. size lumps			Speed, r.p.m.	Max. torque capacity, in.-lb.	Feed section diam., in.	Hp. at motor§					Max. hp. capacity at speed listed
Tons/hr.	Cu. ft./hr.					All lumps	Lumps 20 to 25%	Lumps 10% or less				15 ft. max. length	30 ft. max. length	45 ft. max. length	60 ft. max. length	75 ft. max. length	
5	200	9	2½	2	10	¾	1½	2¼	40	7,600	6	0.43	0.85	1.27	1.69	2.11	4.8
10	400	10	2½	2	10	¾	1½	2½	55	7,600	9	0.85	1.69	2.25	3.00	3.75	6.6
15	600	10	2½	2	10	¾	1½	2½	80	7,600	9	1.27	2.25	3.38	3.94	4.93	9.6
		12	2½	2	12	1	2	3	45	7,600	10	1.27	2.25	3.38	3.94	4.93	5.4
		12	3½	3						16,400		1.27	2.25	3.38	3.94	4.93	11.7
20	800	12	2½	2	12	1	2	3	60	7,600	10	1.69	3.00	3.94	4.87	5.63	7.2
			3½	3						16,400		1.69	3.00	3.94	4.87	5.63	15.6
25	1000	12	2½	2	12	1	2	3	75	7,600	10	2.12	3.75	4.93	5.63	6.55	9.0
			3½	3						16,400		2.12	3.75	4.93	5.63	6.55	19.5
		14	3½	3		1¼	2½	3½	45	16,400	12	2.12	3.75	4.93	5.63	6.55	11.7
30	1200	14	3½	3	12	1¼	2½	3½	55	16,400	12	2.25	3.94	5.05	6.75	7.50	14.3
35	1400	14	3½	3	12	1¼	2½	3½	65	16,400	12	2.62	4.58	5.90	7.00	8.75	16.9
40	1600	16	3½	3	12	1½	3	4	50	16,400	14	3.00	4.50	6.75	8.00	10.00	13.0

* Fairfield Engineering Co.

† Capacities are based on screws carrying 31 per cent of their cross section, and in the case of feed sections with half pitch flights based on 100 per cent of their cross section.

‡ Pipe sizes given are for ¼-in. flights.

§ Horsepowers listed are calculated for average conditions and are proper motor size with factors for length of conveyor, momentary overloads, etc., taken into consideration.

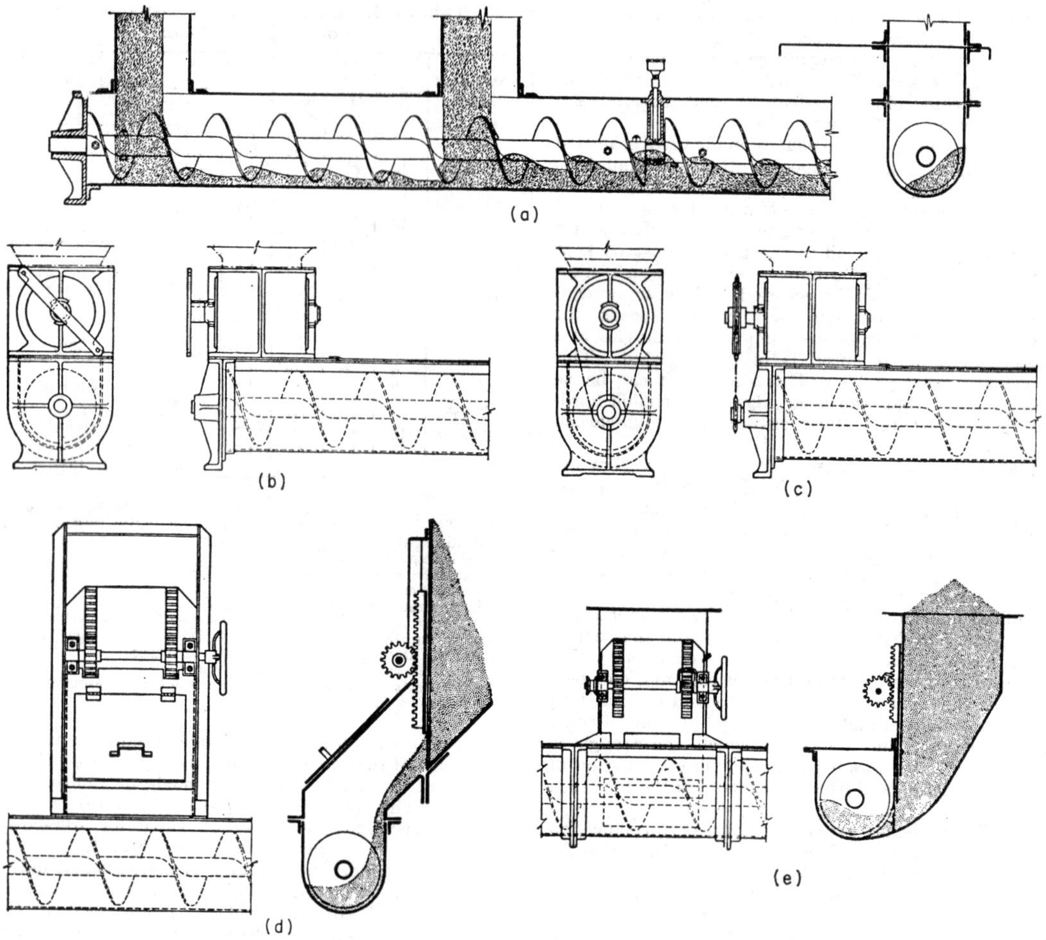

FIG. 7-1. Typical feed arrangements for screw conveyors. (*a*) Plain spouts or chutes. (*b*) Rotary cutoff valve. (*c*) Rotary-vane feeder. (*d*) Bin gate. (*e*) Side inlet gate. (*Link-Belt Co.*)

with a discharge spout (Fig. 7-2*b*) are most common, although the open-end trough (Fig. 7-2*c*) is frequently used, as is the discharge-trough end (Fig. 7-2*e*). Open-bottom troughs (Fig. 7-2*g*) are often used for spreading material uniformly over a storage area. Flat-bottomed rack-and-pinion gates (Fig. 7-2*f*) allow selective discharge, as do hand slide gates (Fig. 7-2*d*). However, for perishable materials, the curved slide gate (Fig. 7-2*h*) eliminates the dead-storage pocket. Enclosed rack-and-pinion gates (Fig. 7-2*j*) give dust-tight operation and rotary cutoff valves (Fig. 7-2*i*) allow quick shutoff and are readily adaptable to remote control.

Belt Conveyors. This device is almost universal in application. It can travel for miles at speeds up to 1000 ft./min. and handle up to 5000 tons/hr. It can also operate over short distances at speeds slow enough for manual picking, with a capacity of only a few pounds per hour. However, it is not normally applicable to processing operations, except under unusual conditions.

Belt-conveyor slopes are limited to a maximum of about 30 deg., with those in the 18- to 20-deg. range more common. Direction changes can occur only in the vertical plane of the belt path and must be carefully designed as vertical curves or relatively flat bends. Belt conveyors inside the plant may have higher initial cost than some other types of conveyors and, depending on idler design, may or may not require more maintenance. However, a belt conveyor given good routine maintenance can be expected to outlast almost any other type of conveyor. Thus, in terms of cost per ton handled, outstanding economy records have been established by belt conveyors.

Belt-conveyor design begins with study of the material to be handled. Since weight per cubic foot is an important factor, it should be accurately determined with the material in an "as-handled" condition. It is not wise to rely solely on published tables of weight per cubic foot for various materials, since many processing operations will affect this by fluffing or compacting the material. Lump size is important, too. For a 24-in. belt, uniform lump size can range up to about 4 in. For each 6-in. increase in belt width, lump size can increase about 2 in. If material contains around 90 per cent fines, lump size can be increased around 50 per cent. However, care should be taken to maintain uniform flow of material, with fine material reaching the belt first to protect it from impact damage. The larger the lump, the more danger of its falling off the belt or rolling back

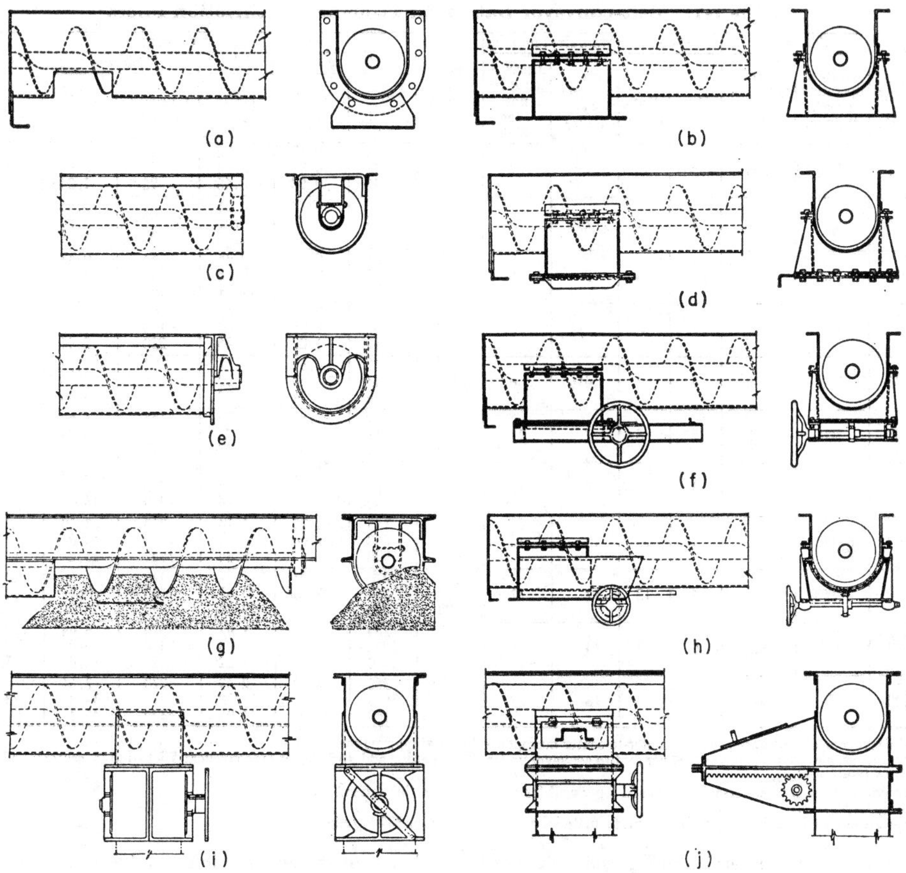

FIG. 7-2. Typical discharge arrangements for screw conveyors. (*a*) Plain discharge opening. (*b*) Discharge spout. (*c*) Open-end trough. (*d*) Hand slide gate. (*e*) Discharge trough end. (*f*) Rack-and-pinion flat slide gate. (*g*) Open-bottom trough. (*h*) Rack-and-pinion curved slide gate. (*i*) Rotary cutoff valve. (*j*) Enclosed rack-and-pinion gate. (*Link-Belt Co.*)

on inclines. With the belt running horizontally or sloping only slightly at the feed point, the problem of lumps falling off is minimized, especially if particular care is taken with feed-chute design.

Temperature and chemical activity of the conveyed material play important roles in belt selection. For example, natural rubber should be avoided with oily materials, even when the material does not present an obviously oily surface. Special rubber, cotton, and asbestos-fiber belts are available to meet varying degrees of material temperature, and they should be used wherever high temperatures exist. Belts can be seriously and quickly damaged by high temperature, and the investment in what at first glance seems to be an extremely high-priced belt may prove most economical in the long run.

Moisture may create poor discharge conditions because of material sticking to the belt and to chutes, or it may even reduce capacity if it is present in enough quantity to give the material fluid properties. Even though abrasion may create problems with belt conveyors, they are easier to solve with properly designed belt systems than with most other conveyors.

In establishing belt-conveyor tonnage requirements it is important to work with peak rather than average loads. Only occasionally are these two figures identical, because of intentional or accidental variations in production rates. The belt that runs empty half the time must carry twice the average load when it is working.

When a belt conveyor must change direction it is often easier to use more than one conveyor. However, vertical curves can be designed and upward changes of direction can be accomplished with a pair of snub pulleys. If the belt pull is downward on the idlers a simple flat pulley can be used for minor directional changes. In any case, using a single continuous belt eliminates the need for more than one drive. With a pair of snub pulleys, the carrying face of the belt is brought in contact with the pulley; hence special care must be taken to get a good discharge. When bending the belt over a flat pulley, belt speed must be slow enough to keep material from flying off the belt. In many situations the smooth curve, either concave or convex, is preferable. For a 24-in. belt the minimum curve radius is about 200 ft., but for best operating conditions it should be carefully designed.

Operating conditions which affect belt-conveyor design include climate, surroundings, and hours of continuous service. Temperature and humidity extremes may dictate total enclosure of the belt; surroundings which involve such conditions as high temperature or corrosive atmosphere can affect belt, machinery, and

Table 7-7. Belt-conveyor Data with Troughed Antifriction Idlers*

Belt width, in.	Cross-sectional area of load, sq. ft.	Belt speed: Normal operating speed, ft./min.	Belt speed: Max. advisable speed, ft./min.	Belt plies: Min.	Belt plies: Max.	Max. size lump, in.: Sized material 80% under	Max. size lump, in.: Unsized material not over 20%	Belt speed, ft./min.	50 lb./cu. ft. material: Capacity, tons/hr.	50 lb./cu. ft. material: Hp./10-ft. lift	50 lb./cu. ft. material: Hp./100-ft. centers	100 lb./cu. ft. material: Capacity, tons/hr.	100 lb./cu. ft. material: Hp./10-ft. lift	100 lb./cu. ft. material: Hp./100-ft. centers	Add hp. for tripper†
14	0.11	200	300	3	5	2	3	100	16	0.17	0.22	32	0.34	0.44	1.00
								200	32	0.34	0.44	64	0.68	0.88	
								300	48	0.52	0.66	96	1.04	1.32	
16	0.14	200	300	3	5	2½	4	100	22	0.23	0.28	44	0.46	0.56	1.25
								200	44	0.45	0.56	88	0.90	1.12	
								300	66	0.68	0.84	132	1.36	1.68	
18	0.18	250	350	4	6	3	5	100	27	0.29	0.35	54	0.58	0.7	1.50
								250	67	0.71	0.88	134	1.42	1.76	
								350	95	1.00	1.21	190	2.00	2.42	
20	0.22	250	350	4	6	3½	6	100	33	0.35	0.42	66	0.70	0.84	1.60
								250	82	0.86	1.03	164	1.72	2.06	
								350	115	1.22	1.45	230	2.44	2.9	
24	0.33	300	400	4	7	4½	8	100	49	0.51	0.51	98	1.02	1.02	1.75
								300	147	1.53	1.52	294	3.06	3.04	
								400	196	2.04	2.02	392	4.08	4.04	
30	0.53	300	450	4	8	7	12	100	79	0.80	0.75	158	1.60	1.5	2.50
								300	237	2.40	2.25	474	4.80	4.5	
								450	355	3.60	3.37	710	7.20	6.74	
36	0.78	400	600	4	9	8	15	100	115	1.22	0.80	230	2.44	1.59	3.53
								400	460	4.87	3.18	920	9.74	6.36	
								600	690	7.30	4.76	1380	14.6	9.52	
42	1.09	400	600	4	10	10	18	100	165	1.75	1.14	330	3.50	2.28	4.79
								400	660	7.00	4.56	1320	14.0	9.12	
								600	990	11.6	6.84	1980	23.2	13.68	
48	1.46	400	600	4	12	12	21	100	220	2.33	1.52	440	4.66	3.04	6.42
								400	880	9.35	6.07	1760	18.7	12.14	
								600	1320	14.0	9.10	2640	28.0	18.2	
54	1.90	450	600	6	12	14	24	100	285	3.02	1.97	570	6.04	3.94	10.56
								450	1282	13.6	8.85	2564	27.2	17.7	
								600	1710	18.1	11.82	3420	36.2	23.6	
60	2.40	450	600	6	13	16	28	100	360	3.82	2.49	720	7.64	4.98	
								450	1620	17.2	11.20	3240	34.4	22.4	
								600	2160	22.9	14.95	4320	45.8	29.9	

For inclined conveyors add lift horsepower to center-to-center horsepower for total horsepower.
For horsepower consumed by terminals add 20 per cent to conveyor under 50-ft. centers; add 10 per cent for conveyors 51- to 100-ft. centers; add 5 per cent for conveyors 101- to 150-ft. centers.
For horsepower consumed by countershaft drive, add 5 per cent for each reduction through cut gears.
* Fairfield Engineering Co.
† Horsepower given for tripper is based on 50 lb./cu. ft. material and a belt speed of 300 ft./min.

structure; and continuous service may require extremely high-quality components and even specially designed equipment for servicing while the belt is in operation. For example, idlers may be obtained with tilting stands which allow them to be tipped out of the way for service while the belt is running.

Belt width and speed are functions of bulk density of the material and lump size. Lowest first cost can often be obtained by using the narrowest possible belt for a given lump size and operating it at maximum speed. However, speed often may be limited by dusting, and sometimes it may be better economy to use a wider belt with fewer plies to combine the necessary tensile strength with good belt-troughing characteristics. Abrasiveness of the material can strongly affect speed and also lump size, for at higher speeds abrasive wear is increased and there is greater danger of lumps rolling off the belt. Ideally a belt should run with lump size, slope, and load of less than recommended maximums, and with uniform feed introduced to the belt centrally as nearly as possible in the direction and speed of belt travel.

Horsepower to drive a belt conveyor is made up of five components: power to drive the empty belt, to move the load against friction of the rotating parts, to raise or lower the load, to overcome inertia in putting material into motion, and to operate a belt-driven tripper if required. As with most other conveyor problems, it is advisable to work with formulas and constants from a specific manufacturer in making these calculations. For estimating purposes, typical data are given in Table 7-7.

Belt selection depends on horsepower and development of the required tensile strength. Knowing drive-shaft horsepower, belt tension can be calculated and a belt selected. However, since various combinations of width and ply thickness will develop the required strength, final selection is influenced by lump size, troughability of the belt, and ability of the belt to support the load between idlers. Thus it is necessary to use a "cut-and-try" system to arrive at a belt selection which meets all requirements.

Once final belt selection has been made, **idlers and return rolls** can also be selected. Figure 7-3 indicates the wide variety of belt supports for bulk-handling applications. Figure 7-3*a* and *b* are flat-belt arrangements of rollers or plate which allow material to be discharged by simple V-shaped plows. The flat plate-supported belt allows side walls to be erected to prevent dribble or to build up larger loads on the flat belt. As in Fig. 7-3*f*, larger capacity can also be achieved by troughing the plate. The 20-deg. troughing idler with equal-length rolls (Fig. 7-3*c*) is the most common, with lighter materials adaptable to 45-deg. idlers with short or long side rolls (Fig. 7-3*d* and *e*). Since the lighter materials do not require stiff belts for tensile strength, there is usually no problem with troughing.

Belt-conveyor idlers are available in a wide range of qualities. Figure 7-4 shows several designs of troughed-belt idlers. Figure 7-4*c* is a suspended-cable-type idler with molded-on rubber disks; only two bearings are required in this design and it is claimed to make belt training easier. Special idlers for absorbing shock at loading points are also shown (Fig. 7-4*b*), one being a zero-pressure pneumatic design, the other a solid rubber.

With the proper idlers selected for size and service

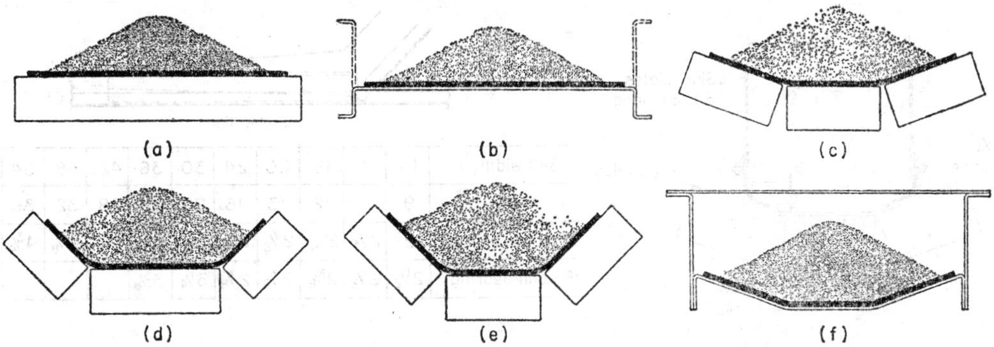

FIG. 7-3. Typical belt-conveyor idler and plate-support arrangements. (*a*) Flat belt on flat-belt idlers. (*b*) Flat belt on continuous plate. (*c*) Troughed belt on 20-deg. idlers. (*d*) Troughed belt on 45-deg. idlers with rolls of unequal length. (*e*) Troughed belt on 45-deg. idlers with rolls of equal length. (*f*) Troughed belt on continuous plate. (*Link-Belt Co.*)

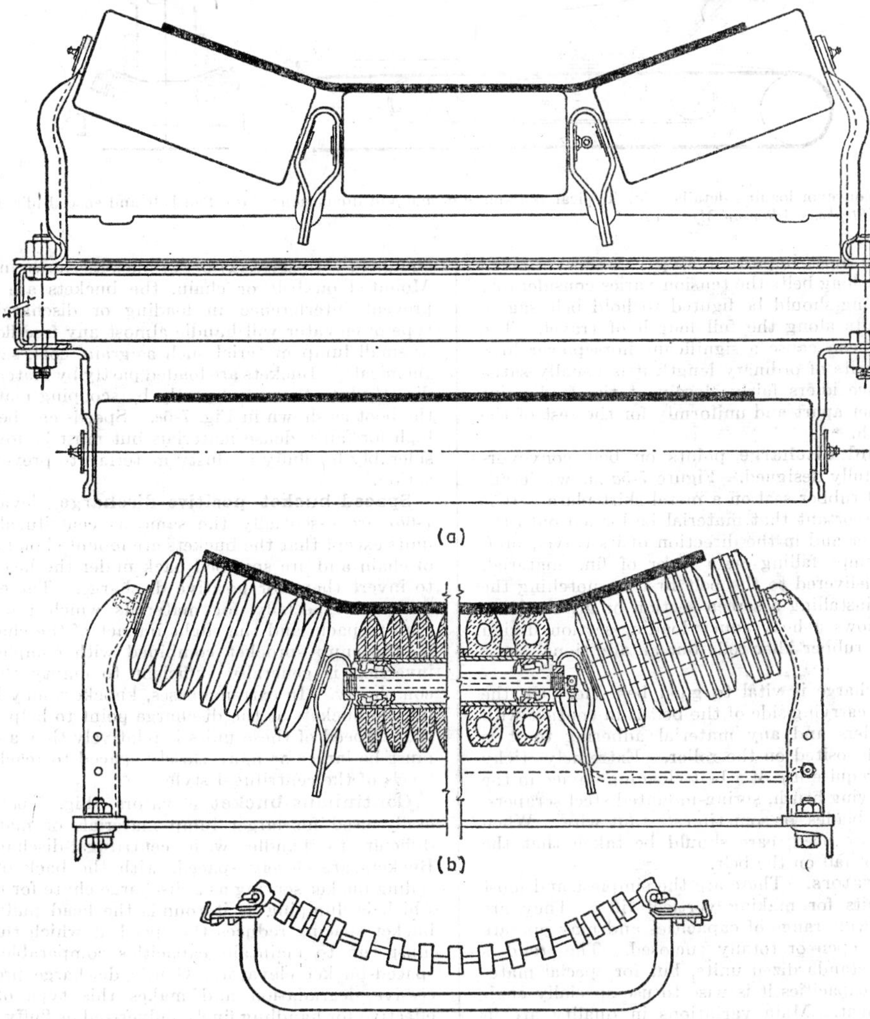

FIG. 7-4. Belt-conveyor idlers. (*a*) Antifriction idler and return roll. (*b*) Solid rubber and pneumatic impact idler. (*c*) Suspended-cable idler. (*Stephens-Adamson Mfg. Co., Joy Mfg. Co.*)

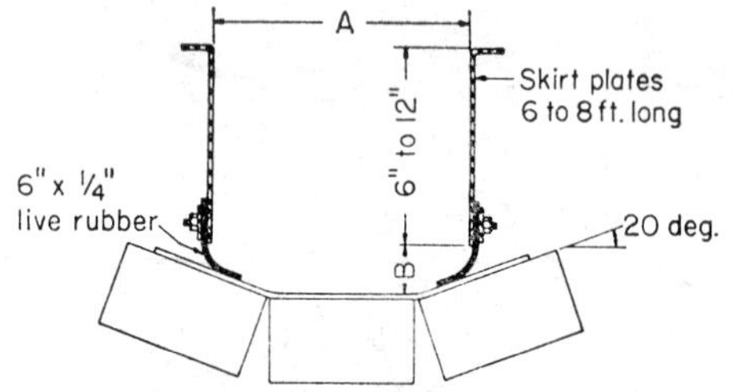

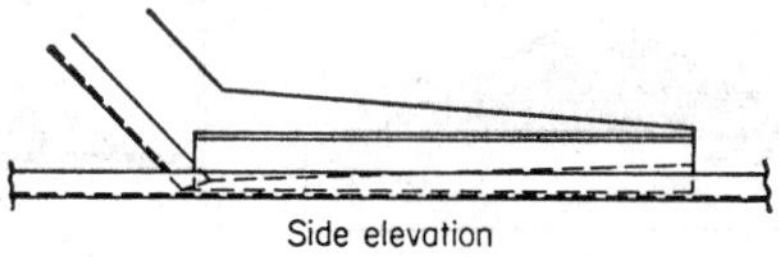

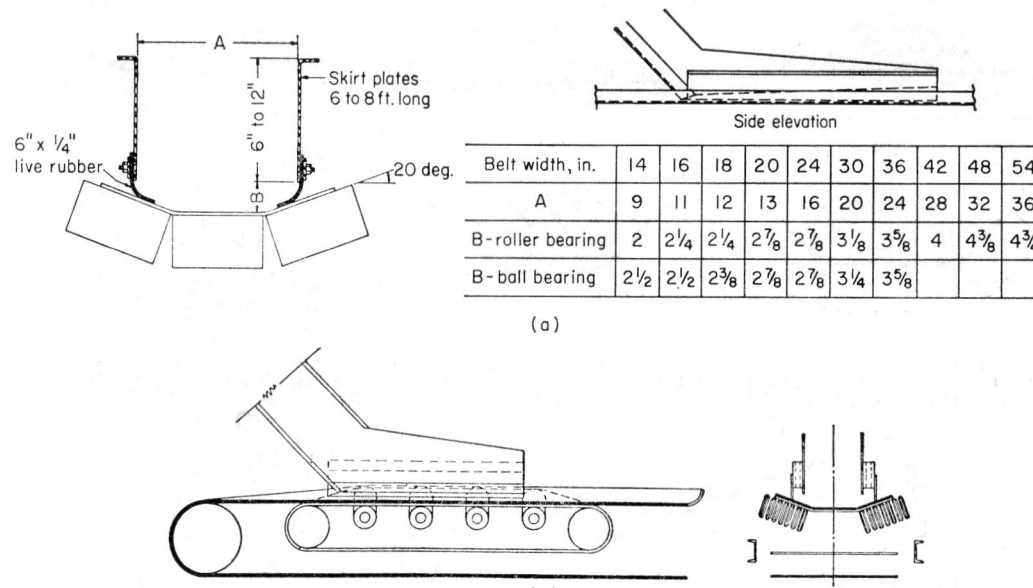

Belt width, in.	14	16	18	20	24	30	36	42	48	54	60
A	9	11	12	13	16	20	24	28	32	36	40
B-roller bearing	2	$2\frac{1}{4}$	$2\frac{1}{4}$	$2\frac{7}{8}$	$2\frac{7}{8}$	$3\frac{1}{8}$	$3\frac{5}{8}$	4	$4\frac{3}{8}$	$4\frac{3}{4}$	$5\frac{1}{4}$
B-ball bearing	$2\frac{1}{2}$	$2\frac{1}{2}$	$2\frac{3}{8}$	$2\frac{7}{8}$	$2\frac{7}{8}$	$3\frac{1}{4}$	$3\frac{5}{8}$				

(a)

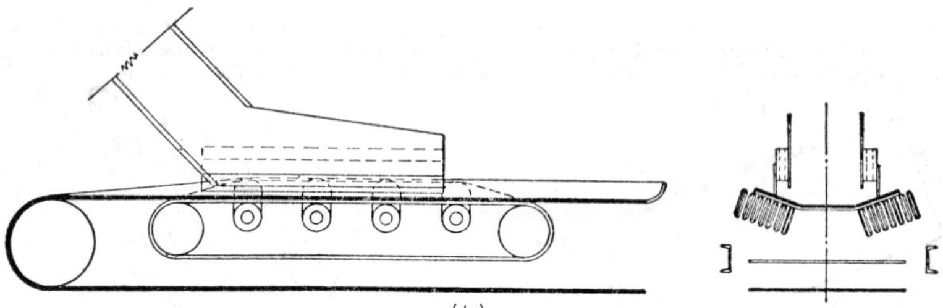

(b)

FIG. 7-5. Belt-conveyor loading details. (*a*) Typical skirt-plate design and dimensions. (*b*) Pad belt and special idlers for heavy-duty loading. (*Stephens-Adamson Mfg. Co.*)

conditions, the most important step is to locate them properly. For long belts the tension varies considerably and idler spacing should be figured to hold belt sag to reasonable limits along the full length of travel. Too much belt sag can cause a significant horsepower loss, but for most belts of ordinary length it is usually satisfactory to space idlers fairly closely at the feed point and then farther apart and uniformly for the rest of the conveyor length.

Loading and discharge points on belt conveyors should be carefully designed. Figure 7-5*a* shows details for one type of rubber seal on a metal skirt plate. It is particularly important that material be loaded onto the belt in its center and in the direction of its travel, preferably with lumps falling on a layer of fine material. Fines can be delivered to the belt first by notching the feed chute or installing a screen section or grizzly bars. Figure 7-5*b* shows a heavy-duty loading-section design using not only rubber idler rolls but an additional short pad belt.

A clean discharge is vital to good belt life. On the return run the carrying side of the belt is in contact with the return rollers and any material adhering to it is ground in or deposited on the roller. Extremely sticky material may require use of a belt-cleaning device in the form of a revolving brush, spring-mounted steel scrapers. rubber scraper blades, or sometimes a taut wire. When these devices are used, care should be taken that the dribble does not fall on the belt.

Bucket Elevators. These are the simplest and most dependable units for making vertical lifts. They are available in a wide range of capacities and may operate entirely in the open or totally enclosed. The trend is toward highly standardized units, but for special materials and high capacities it is wise to use specially engineered equipment. Main variations in quality are in casing thickness, bucket thickness, belt or chain quality, and drive equipment.

Spaced-bucket centrifugal-discharge elevators (Fig. 7-6*a*) are the most common. They are usually equipped with style (1) or (2) buckets shown in Fig. 7-6*h*. Mounted on belt or chain, the buckets are spaced to prevent interference in loading or discharging. This type of elevator will handle almost any free-flowing, fine or small lump material such as grain, coal, sand, or dry chemicals. Buckets are loaded partly by material flowing directly into them and partly by scooping material from the boot as shown in Fig. 7-6*e*. Speeds can be relatively high for fairly dense materials but must be lowered considerably for fluffy or dusty materials to prevent fanning action.

Spaced-bucket positive-discharge elevators (Fig. 7-6*b*) are essentially the same as centrifugal-discharge units except that the buckets are mounted on two strands of chain and are snubbed back under the head sprocket to invert them for positive discharge. These units are designed especially for materials which are sticky or tend to pack, and the slight impact of the chain seating on the snub sprocket combined with complete bucket inversion is generally sufficient to empty the buckets completely. In extreme cases, knockers may be used to hit the buckets at the discharge point to help free material. Speed of these units is relatively slow and buckets must be larger or more closely spaced to reach capacity levels of the centrifugal style.

Continuous-bucket elevators (Fig. 7-6*c*) are generally used for larger lump materials or materials too difficult to handle with centrifugal-discharge units. Buckets are closely spaced, with the back of the preceding bucket serving as a discharge chute for the bucket which is dumping as it rounds the head pulley. Close bucket spacing reduces the speed at which the elevator must run to maintain capacities comparable with the spaced-bucket elevator. Gentle discharge prevents excessive degradation and makes this type of elevator effective for handling finely pulverized or fluffy materials. Two boot styles and typical loading conditions are illustrated in Fig. 7-6*f* and *g*.

Supercapacity continuous-bucket elevators (Fig. 7-6*d*) are designed for high lifts and large-lump material.

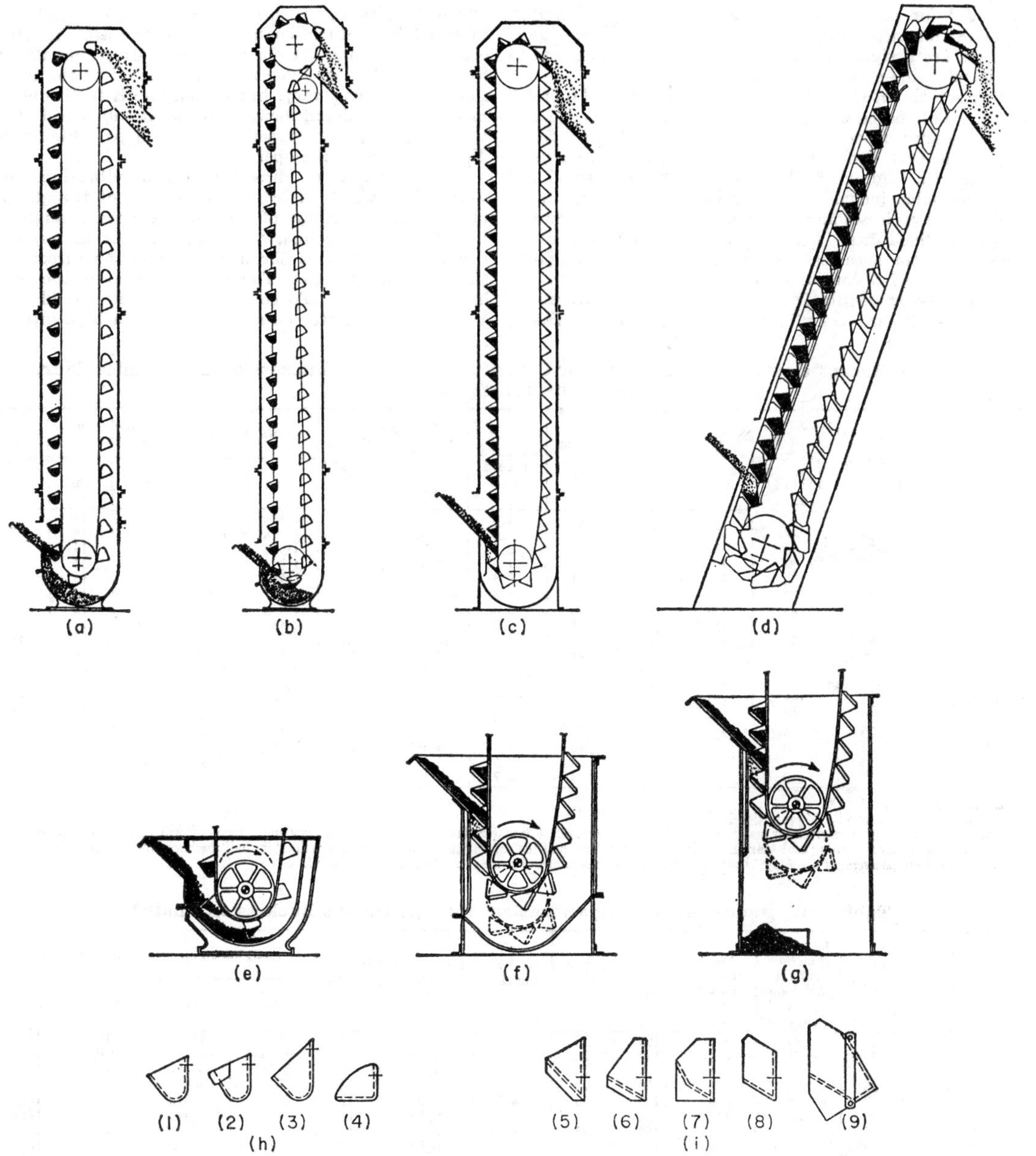

FIG. 7-6. Bucket-elevator types and bucket details. (*a*) Centrifugal discharge, spaced buckets. (*b*) Positive discharge, spaced buckets. (*c*) Continuous bucket. (*d*) Supercapacity continuous bucket. (*e*) Spaced buckets receive part of load direct and part by scooping from bottom. (*f*) Continuous: Buckets are filled as they pass through loading leg, with feed spout above tail wheel. (*g*) Continuous: Buckets in bottomless boot, with cleanout door. (*h*) Malleable-iron spaced buckets for centrifugal discharge. (*i*) Steel buckets for continuous-bucket elevators. (*Stephens-Adamson Mfg. Co.*)

They handle high tonnages and are usually operated at an incline to improve loading and discharge conditions. Operating speeds are low, and because of the heavy loads, the bucket-supporting chain is usually guided on the elevating and return runs.

Buckets for spaced-type elevators (Fig. 7-6*h*) are available in both malleable iron and steel, in a variety of styles. Style (1) is standard, with style (2) identical except for a reinforced lip. Styles (3) and (4) are low-front designs for wet, stringy, or sticky materials which are difficult to discharge.

Continuous-type buckets (Fig. 7-6*i*) are generally back-mounted to chain or belt at close intervals. They are usually fabricated of steel. Style (5) is standard for normal materials, with style (6) a low-front type for better discharge of difficult materials. Style (7) buckets are used for additional capacity or large lumps, and style (8) for inclined crusher-type elevators. Style (9) buckets are designed for extremely high capacities and are usually side-mounted and hinged together.

Bucket-elevator horsepower can be calculated quite easily. For spaced buckets and digging boots it is equal to the desired capacity in tons per hour multiplied by the lift in feet and divided by 500. For continuous buckets with loading leg, the divisor is increased to 550. Both formulas include normal drive losses as well as loading pickup losses and are applicable for vertical and slightly inclined lifts. For estimating purposes, general bucket-elevator specifications are given for centrifugal units in Table 7-8, continuous in Table 7-9.

Vibrating or Oscillating Conveyors. Most vibrating conveyors are essentially directional-throw units which consist of a spring-supported horizontal pan vibrated by a direct-connected eccentric arm, rotating eccentric weights, an electromagnet, or pneumatic or hydraulic cylinder. The motion imparted to the material particles may vary, but its purpose is to throw the material upward and forward so that it will travel along the conveyor path in a series of short hops. Figure 7-7 illustrates some basic operating principles.

The **capacity** of directional-throw vibrating conveyors is determined by the magnitude of trough displacement, frequency of this displacement, angle of throw, slope of trough, and ability of the material to receive and transmit through its mass the directional throw of the trough. The material itself is the most important factor. To convey properly it should have a high friction factor on steel as well as a high internal

Table 7-8. Bucket-elevator Specifications for Centrifugal-discharge Buckets on Belt, Malleable Iron or Steel Buckets*

Size† of bucket, in.	Elev. centers, ft.	Capacity, tons/hr. material weighing 100 lb.‡/cu. ft.	Size lumps handled, in.§	Bucket speed, ft./min.	R.p.m. head shaft	H.p.‡ required at head shaft	Additional hp.‡ per ft. for intermediate lengths	Bucket spacing, in.	Shaft diam., in.		Diam. of pulleys, in.		Belt width, in.
									Head	Tail	Head	Tail	
6 × 4 × 4¼	25	14	¾	225	43	1.0	0.02	12	1 15/16	1 11/16	20	14	7
	50	14	¾	225	43	1.6	0.02	12	1 15/16	1 11/16	20	14	7
	75	14	¾	225	43	2.1	0.02	12	1 15/16	1 11/16	20	14	7
8 × 5 × 5½	25	27	1	225	43	1.6	0.04	14	1 15/16	1 11/16	20	14	9
	50	30	1	260	41	3.5	0.05	14	1 15/16	1 11/16	24	14	9
	75	30	1	260	41	4.8	0.05	14	2 7/16	1 11/16	24	14	9
10 × 6 × 6¼	25	45	1¼	225	43	3.0	0.063	16	1 15/16	1 15/16	20	16	11
	50	52	1¼	260	41	5.2	0.07	16	2 7/16	1 15/16	24	16	11
	75	52	1¼	260	41	7.2	0.07	16	2 15/16	1 15/16	24	16	11
12 × 7 × 7¼	25	75	1½	260	41	4.7	0.1	18	2 7/16	1 15/16	24	18	13
	50	84	1½	300	38	8.9	0.115	18	2 15/16	1 15/16	30	18	13
	75	84	1½	300	38	11.7	0.115	18	3 7/16	2 7/16	30	18	13
14 × 7 × 7¼	25	100	1¾	300	38	7.3	0.14	18	2 15/16	2 7/16	30	18	15
	50	100	1¾	300	38	11.0	0.14	18	3 7/16	2 7/16	30	18	15
	75	100	1¾	300	38	14.3	0.14	18	3 7/16	2 7/16	30	18	15
16 × 8 × 8½	25	150	2	300	38	8.5	0.165	18	2 15/16	2 7/16	30	20	18
	50	150	2	300	38	12.6	0.165	18	3 7/16	2 7/16	30	20	18
	75	150	2	300	38	16.7	0.165	18	3 15/16	2 7/16	30	20	18

* Stephens-Adamson Mfg. Co.

† Size of buckets given: width × projection × depth.

‡ Capacities and horsepowers given for materials weighing 100 lb./cu. ft. For materials of other weights, capacity and horsepower will vary in direct proportion. For example, an elevator handling coal weighing 50 lb./cu. ft. will have half the capacity and will require approximately half the horsepower listed above.

§ If volume of lumps averages less than 15 per cent of total volume, lumps of twice size listed may be handled.

Table 7-9. Bucket-elevator Specifications for Continuous Buckets on Chain*

Size† of bucket, in.	Elev. centers, ft.	Capacity, tons/hr. material weighing 100 lb.‡/cu. ft.	Size lumps handled, in.§	Bucket speed, ft./min.	R.p.m. head shaft	Hp.‡ required at head shaft	Additional hp.‡ per ft. for intermediate lengths	Bucket spacing, in.	Shaft diam., in.		Sprocket diam., in.	
									Head	Tail	Head	Tail
8 × 5½ × 7¾	25	35	1	150	28	1.8	0.06	8	1 15/16	1 11/16	20½	14
	50	35	1	150	28	3.4	0.06	8	2 7/16	1 11/16	20½	14
	75	35	1	150	28	5.0	0.06	8	2 15/16	1 11/16	20½	14
10 × 7 × 11¾	25	60	1½	150	23	3.0	0.10	12	2 7/16	1 15/16	25	17½
	50	60	1½	150	23	5.5	0.10	12	2 7/16	1 15/16	25	17½
	75	60	1½	150	23	8.0	0.10	12	2 15/16	1 15/16	25	17½
12 × 7 × 11¾	25	70	1½	150	23	3.5	0.12	12	2 7/16	1 15/16	25	17½
	50	70	1½	150	23	6.5	0.12	12	2 15/16	1 15/16	25	17½
	75	70	1½	150	23	9.5	0.12	12	3 7/16	2 7/16	25	17½
14 × 7 × 11¾	25	80	1¾	150	23	4.0	0.14	12	2 7/16	2 7/16	25	17½
	50	80	1¾	150	20	7.5	0.14	12	2 15/16	2 7/16	29	17½
	75	80	1¾	150	20	11	0.14	12	3 7/16	2 7/16	29	17½
14 × 8 × 11¾	25	100	2	150	20	5.0	0.17	12	2 15/16	2 7/16	29	17½
	50	100	2	150	20	9.3	0.17	12	3 7/16	2 7/16	29	17½
	75	100	2	150	20	13.3	0.17	12	3 15/16	2 7/16	29	17½
16 × 8 × 11¾	25	115	2	150	20	6.0	0.20	12	2 15/16	2 7/16	29	17½
	50	115	2	150	20	11	0.20	12	3 15/16	2 7/16	29	17½
	75	115	2	150	20	16	0.20	12	4 7/16	2 7/16	29	17½
18 × 8 × 11¾	25	130	2	150	20	7	0.22	12	2 15/16	2 7/16	29	17½
	50	130	2	150	20	13	0.22	12	3 15/16	2 7/16	29	17½
	75	130	2	150	20	20	0.22	12	4 7/16	2 7/16	29	17½

* Stephens-Adamson Mfg. Co.

† Size of buckets given: width × projection × depth.

‡ Capacities and horsepowers given for materials weighing 100 lb./cu. ft. For materials of other weights, capacities and horsepower will vary in direct proportion. For example, an elevator handling coal weighing 50 lb. per cu. ft. will have half the capacity and will require approximately half the horsepower listed above.

§ If volume of lumps averages less than 15 per cent of total volume, lumps of twice size listed may be handled.

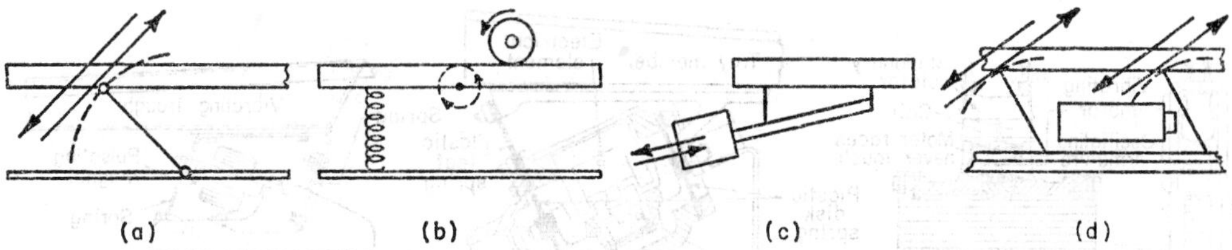

FIG. 7-7. Operating principles of vibrating conveyors. (*a*) Hinged rocker arm gives pan a reciprocating arc motion, almost straight line. (*b*) Coil-spring support allows pan to move in path dictated by eccentric weight or shaft. (*c*) Magnetic pulls at intervals impart straight-line motion to inclined support. (*d*) Magnetic pull on leaf spring creates arc motion similar to rocker arm. (*Modern Materials Handling.*)

friction factor so that conveying action is transmitted through its entire depth. Thus deep loads tend to move more slowly than thin ones. Material must also be dense enough to minimize the effect of air resistance on its trajectory, and it should not aerate. Tests have shown that granular materials handle better than pulverized, flat or irregular shapes better than spherical.

Classification of vibrating conveyors can probably best be based on drive characteristics as shown in Fig. 7-8. All these types transmit vibration to their supporting structures, but the direct or positive drive is the worst offender and should be mounted on a heavy supporting structure if it is not counterbalanced. Semipositive and non-positive drive types reduce vibration effects because thrust is transmitted over the entire support length rather than at a specific point. Regardless of drive type, care should be taken to mount the conveyor properly so that supporting structures will not be damaged. The frequency of vibration of the conveyor should in no case be at or near the natural frequency of the supporting structure.

Mechanical vibrating conveyors are designed to operate at specific frequencies and do not perform well at other frequencies without carefully designed alterations. Thus they are not adapted to frequent capacity changes except by varying the depth of material fed to the trough. Positive eccentric drives maintain their frequency and magnitude of stroke regardless of load, and serious drive damage can result from overloading. Rotating eccentric weights can also provide the motive force, and although they maintain a constant frequency, the magnitude of stroke is definitely affected by the load. Directional-throw mechanical vibrating conveyors are used primarily for conveying and do not usually perform well as feeders.

Electrical vibrating conveyors are characterized by the fact that there is no contact between the drive and the conveying medium. They operate on a pull-release cycle or a pull-push cycle, using direct current and pulsating electromagnets or alternating current combined with electro- and permanent magnets as shown in Fig. 7-9. While most electrical vibrating units are used as feeders, they also work well as conveyors. Most of them offer the advantage of capacity regulation through control of the electric-current magnitude via rheostats.

Pneumatic and hydraulic vibrating conveyors have as their greatest asset elimination of explosion hazards. Where pressurized air, water, or oil is available, they can be extremely practical since their drive design is relatively simple and pressure-control valves can be used to vary capacity, either manually or automatically.

Capacity of vibrating conveyors is extremely broad, ranging from thousands of tons down to ounces. Since there are so many variables affecting their ability to convey, there is no simple formula for figuring capacity and horsepower. Available data are generally the results of experiments and empirical equations, with most manufacturers providing selection charts for specific types of conveyors and materials. A typical leaf-spring unit is shown in Fig. 7-10, along with the graphical information required to select a standard unit. Conveyor lengths are limited to around 200 ft. with multiple drives

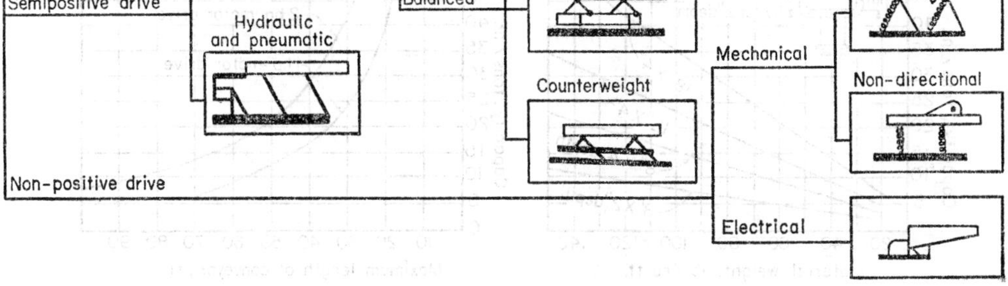

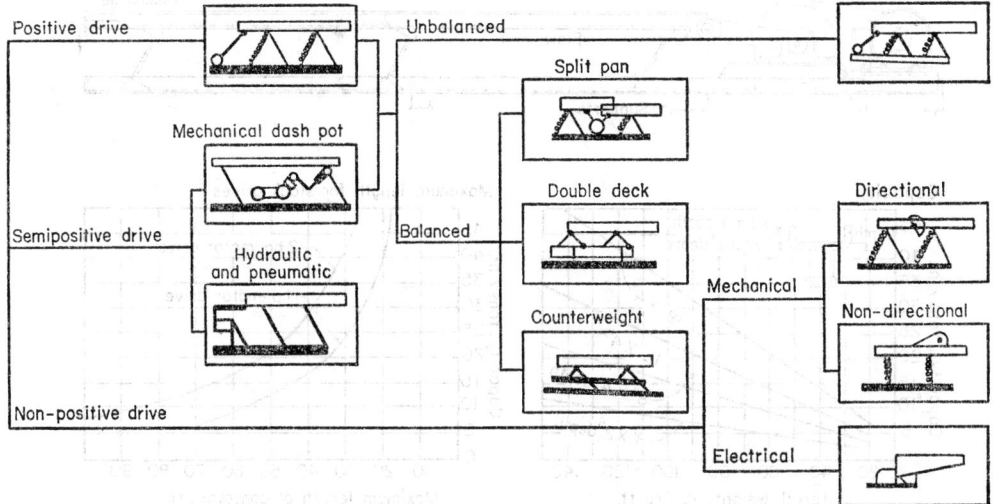

FIG. 7-8. Vibrating-conveyor classification. (*Modern Materials Handling.*)

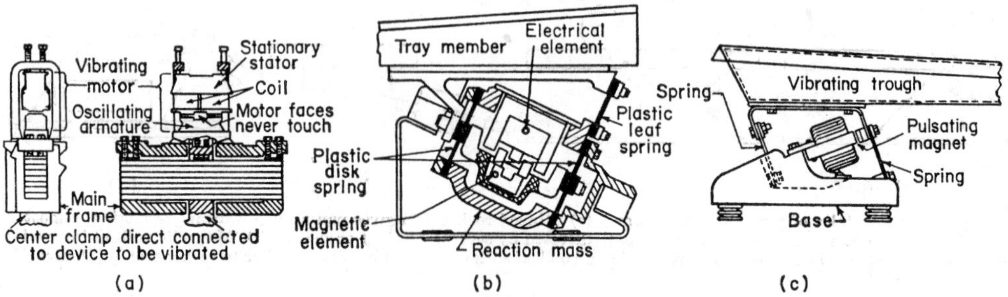

FIG. 7-9. Electric-vibrating-conveyor operating principles. (*a*) Pull-release type uses rigidly held bars activated by electromagnet. (*b*) Pull-push type uses electro- and permanent magnet to get positive action. (*c*) Pull-release type has electromagnet which activates leaf-type spring. (*Modern Materials Handling.*)

and around 100 ft. with a single drive. There are many exceptions to these general limitations, and they should not preclude study of a specific problem where vibrating conveyors seem desirable.

Processing operations of many types can be carried out in vibrating conveyors because their simple conveying troughs can be modified quite easily. While tube and flat-pan troughs are most common, troughs can be provided in a wide variety of shapes and materials. Although conveying action is usually so gentle that abrasion problems do not arise, such problems can be easily solved when they do occur by use of special materials or liners. Troughs are easily sealed to prevent contamination or for operation under positive or negative pressure. With screen or perforated deck plates, vibrating conveyors can dewater, rough screen, scalp, or dry. Heating and cooling can also be handled by the use of air streams blowing over or through the material, infrared panels, resistance-heating panels, or contact with air- or water-cooled or heated trough casings. Special vibrating-conveyor designs are available for elevating at relatively steep slopes or up a spiral trough. There is probably no other conveyor so readily adaptable to solution of processing problems.

Continuous-flow Conveyors. Principle of the continuous-flow conveyor is the fact that, when a surface is pulled transversely through a mass of granular, powdered, or small-lump material, it will pull a cross section of material along with it which is greater than the area of the surface itself. The conveying action of various designs of continuous-flow conveyors varies with the type of conveying flight but is theoretically not comparable with the action in a flight or drag conveyor. Flights vary from solid surfaces to skeleton designs, as shown in Fig. 7-11.

The continuous-flow conveyor is a totally enclosed unit which has a relatively high capacity per unit of cross-sectional area and can follow an irregular path in a single plane. These features make it extremely versatile. Figure 7-12 shows some typical arrangements and applications possible with these conveyors. Included is an example of the unit acting as a dewatering device (Fig. 7-12*c*).

These conveyors employ a chain-supported conveying element (some are cast integrally with the chain which is designed with easily detachable knuckle joints). Thus the connecting element runs along the outside of the casing so that head and tail sections do not become excessively large because of projecting conveying elements. This means that the material feeding into the conveyor must fall past the chain element and travel in a reverse direction before passing into the actual con-

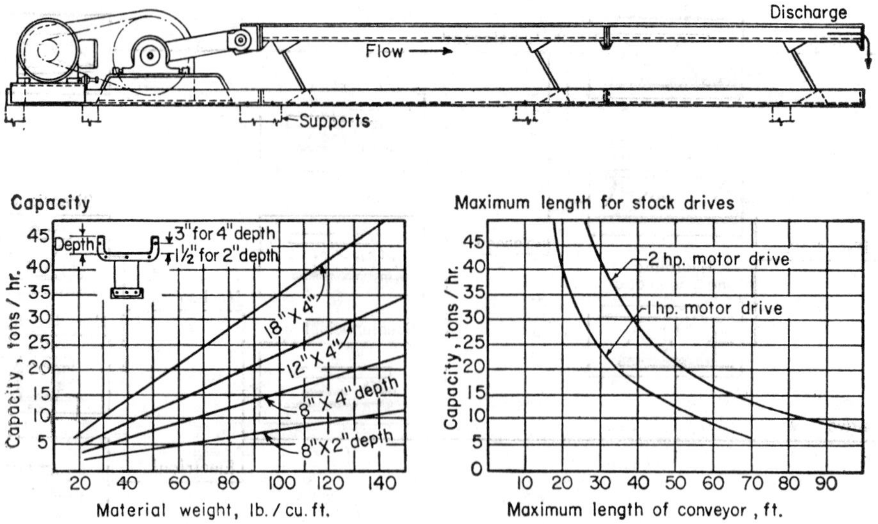

FIG. 7-10. Standardized leaf-spring mechanical oscillating conveyor with selection charts. (*Link-Belt Co.*)

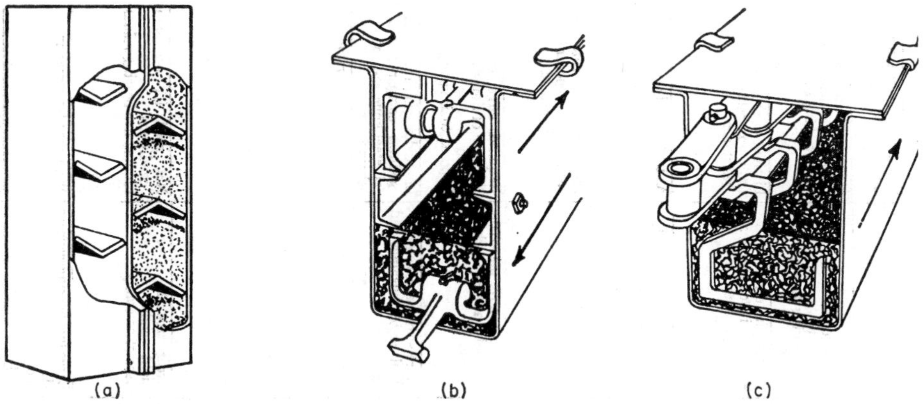

FIG. 7-11. Closed and open flights for continuous-flow conveyors. (*a*) and (*b*) Conveyor-elevator. (*c*) Horizontal conveyor with side-pull chain. (*Link-Belt Co., Stephens-Adamson Mfg. Co.*)

veying leg (see Fig. 7-12*a*). Since this affects the lump size the conveyor can conveniently handle, the loop design (Fig. 7-12*c*) is sometimes used for better feeding conditions, or separate carrying runs and return runs are provided with inclined loading chutes to the lower carrying run. In any event, lump size and abrasive characteristics of material are important considerations in the selection of continuous-flow conveyors.

The side-pull continuous-flow conveyor can follow a variety of paths in a horizontal plane, picking up and discharging material at many different points. Figure 7-11*c* is a detailed illustration of one type of conveying element and Fig. 7-12*d* shows a typical arrangement with 180-deg. turns. Triangular arrangements and rectangular layouts with 90-deg. corners are also available.

Capacity of the continuous-flow conveyor is dependent on the particular design being considered. Limiting speeds are subject to considerable controversy. It is advisable to follow manufacturer's recommendations closely for best conveyor service. Horsepower calculations are dependent on a number of experimentally determined constants which vary for different conveyor designs. One factor contributing to total power requirements is the power required on bend corners where flights assume a radial position and tend to compress material which was fed between them when they

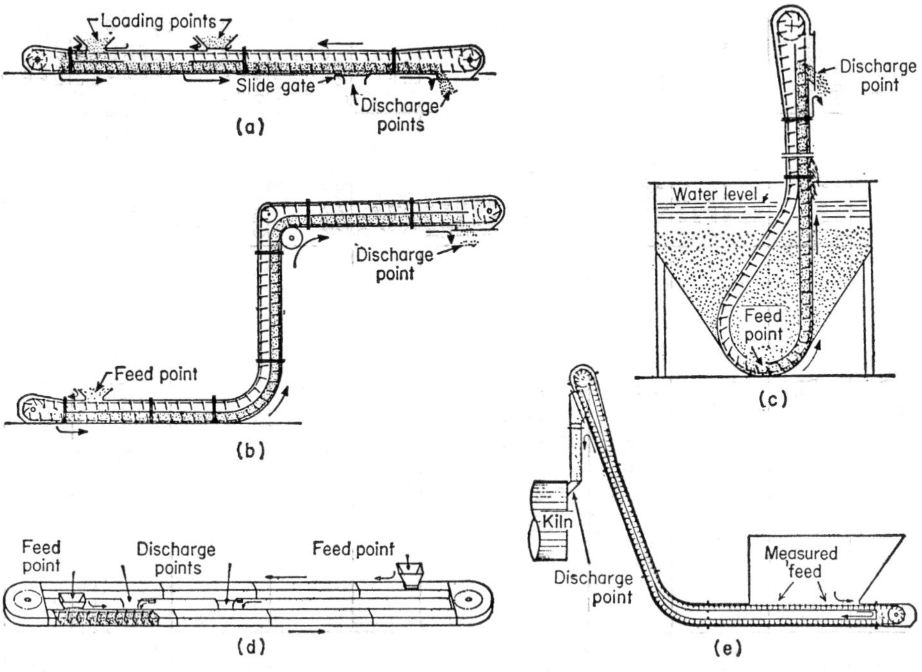

FIG. 7-12. Typical arrangements and applications for continuous-flow conveyors. (*a*) Horizontal conveyor. (*b*) Z-type conveyor-elevator. (*c*) Loop-feed elevator used for dewatering. (*d*) Side-pull horizontal recirculating conveyor. (*e*) Horizontal-inclined conveyor-elevator. (*Stephens-Adamson Mfg. Co.*)

Table 7-10. Conveyor-chain Selection Chart*

Type of chain	Sketch	Material handled	Typical use	Fabricated from	Max. r.p.m. for 12-tooth sprocket	Pitch range, in.	Average ultimate strength, lb.	Advantages	Limitations
Detachable		Non-abrasive	Drives Elevators†,‡ Conveyors†,‡	Malleable iron, steel	50–390	¾–4	700–17,000	Low cost Easily assembled	Low abrasion resistance Limited working strength
Pintle (light duty)		Moderately abrasive	Drives Elevators†,‡ Conveyors†,‡	Malleable iron, steel pins	90–260	1¼–4	3,600–22,000	Low cost Closed joint resists abrasion Pin locking lugs prevent rotation	Limited working strength Only moderately good fit and working strength
Pintle (heavy duty)		Moderately abrasive Sand and gravel Sewage sludge Coal Wood chips	Drives Elevators†,‡ Conveyors†,‡	Malleable iron, steel pins	35–45	4¾ and 6	22,000–30,000	As immediately above Available in longer pitches Better pin lock	Limited working strength Only moderate wear resistance
Pintle (H type)	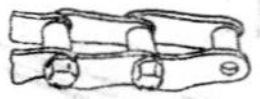	Moderately abrasive (Lumber and pulp and paper industry)	Drives Elevators†,‡ Conveyors†,‡	Malleable iron, steel pins	60–225	1¾–4	7,000–30,000	As for light-duty pintle Broad wearing surface for sliding Better pin lock	As immediately above
Drag		Ashes Wood chips Coal Wood refuse Unit items	Conveyors†,‡	Malleable iron, cast steel or both; steel pins	Slow speed	5, 6, 8, and 9	28,000–40,000	Broad wearing surface for sliding	Increased wear rate because of exposure to material handled
Transfer		Boxes Crates Lumber Sheet steel Bar stock	Conveyors‡	Malleable iron	Slow speed	2¾–6¼	15,000–25,000	Easy-to-remove materials at right angles to chain travel	Requires large sprockets because of limited articulation Exposed to dragging wear
Ley bushed		Cement Sand Crushed stone Ore	Drives Elevators†,‡ Conveyors†,‡	Malleable iron and steel	30–60	4 and 6	19,000–60,000	More abrasion-resistant Replaceable bushings and pins	Limited strength and ruggedness compared with all-steel knuckle-type chain
Cast roller		Non-abrasive Non-adhesive	Drives Elevators†,‡ Pan conveyors†,‡ Platform conveyors‡ Scraper conveyors†,‡	Malleable iron	35–90	3, 4, and 6	6,500–34,000	Low coefficient of friction	Limited working values
Combination		Cement Lumber Fertilizer Coal Sand and gravel Unit items	Drives Elevators†,‡ Conveyors†,‡	Malleable iron with steel connecting links	50–600	1¾–6	9,000–50,000	Large live bearing surface Increased strength and life Barrels can hold lube Economical	Limited strength and working values
Drop forged, rivetless		Unit items Non-abrasive bulk materials	Conveyors‡ Elevators‡ Assembly and overhead trolley conveyors Car hauls	Forged steel	18–90	3, 4, 6, and 9	18,000–220,000	Great strength Light weight Ease of assembly	Not good for corrosive conditions Limited live bearing values
Fabricated steel roller chain (short pitch)		....	Conveyors†,‡ Elevators†,‡ Drives	Steel	....	1½–8	8,000–125,000	Large live bearing surfaces High strength and rugged construction Replaceable parts	Weakened by corrosion
Fabricated steel roller chain (long pitch)	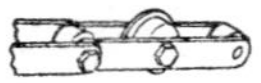	....	Elevating, conveying Bucket elevators Pivoted bucket carriers Gravity-discharge and apron conveyors	Steel with malleable-iron rollers	....	9, 12, 18, and 24	26,000–270,000	As above	Weakened by corrosion

Table 7-10. Conveyor-chain Selection Chart*—(*Continued*)

Type of chain	Sketch	Material handled	Typical use	Fabricated from	Max. r.p.m. for 12-tooth sprocket	Pitch range, in.	Average ultimate strength, lb.	Advantages	Limitations
Pocket sheave	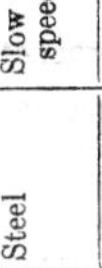	....	Chain hoists Gate-operating mechanisms	Steel	Slow speeds	¾–2	....	Simplicity Flexibility	Requires special connecting links
A.S.A. roller	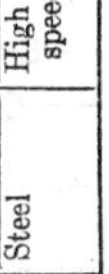	....	High-speed drives Precision conveyors	Steel	High speeds	8 mm.–3	....	Excellent live bearing surfaces	Must be protected from foreign material and corrosion

* *Modern Materials Handling.*
† Bulk materials.
‡ Package or unit items.

were running in a parallel position. Non-compressible materials may require special clearances and feed conditions. Thus, while conveyor components have been well standardized, many materials will not convey well unless special design alterations are made.

Because of the fabrication required for casings and the precision fitting of conveying elements within it, the continuous-flow conveyor is normally an expensive unit. However, it occupies little space, needs little support because the casing forms a rigid box girder, may travel in several directions with only a single drive, is self-feeding, and can feed and discharge at several points. These factors may often compensate for what sometimes appears as a rather high cost per foot. Because it is adaptable to many processing operations, the continuous-flow conveyor is widely used in the chemical industry where there is a great deal of rehandling or requirements for many feed and discharge points. The conveyors can be designed for self-cleaning to allow different materials to be handled in the same unit without contamination.

Closed-belt Conveyor. This device, with zipper-like teeth which mesh to form a closed tube, is particularly adaptable to the problem of handling fragile materials which cannot be subjected to degradation. Since the belt is wrapped snugly around the material, it moves with the belt and is not subject to any form of internal movement except at feed and discharge. In addition the belt can operate in many planes, with twists and turns to meet almost any layout condition within the fixed limit of curvature placed on the loaded belt. It can convey and elevate with only a single drive; multiple feed and discharge points are relatively easy to arrange.

The closed-belt conveyor is not readily adaptable to the handling of sticky materials, and special designs may be required for materials which are highly susceptible to aeration. Initial cost per foot is relatively high because of belting cost, but power requirements are low and with proper installation and maintenance belt life is good.

Since this type of conveyor is available in only one standard size, its capacity is determined by the belt speed and the fixed cross-sectional area. Tons per hour capacity is figured by multiplying the weight in pounds per cubic foot by the speed in feet per minute and a constant of 0.0021. Horsepower requirements are quite low and are figured in the same manner as those for conventional belt conveyors.

Figure 7-13 illustrates a typical closed-belt-conveyor arrangement, a detail of the opening or closing mechanism, and a cross section through a horizontal carrying and return run. Designs using two conventional conveyor belts have been developed to elevate material by pressing it between them, but their application is limited.

Chain Conveyors. These may consist simply of the chain itself, dragging material through a trough of metal, concrete, or wood. To eliminate the abrasion problem this creates at the chain joints, special attachment links may be added to hold flights for dragging the material through the trough, or pans or buckets may be attached to actually carry, rather than drag, the material. Whatever the chain-conveyor type, there is a wide variety of chain to choose from, and it is usually the chain which represents the greatest dollar investment. Chain selection and application are therefore of great importance. Table 7-10 lists the more common types of chain along with their physical properties and suggested areas of application, for both bulk and package or unit materials. Most chain problems arise because of misapplication and improper installation, although proper maintenance certainly cannot be ignored.

Apron conveyors are probably the most common chain conveyors. They are available in a wide variety

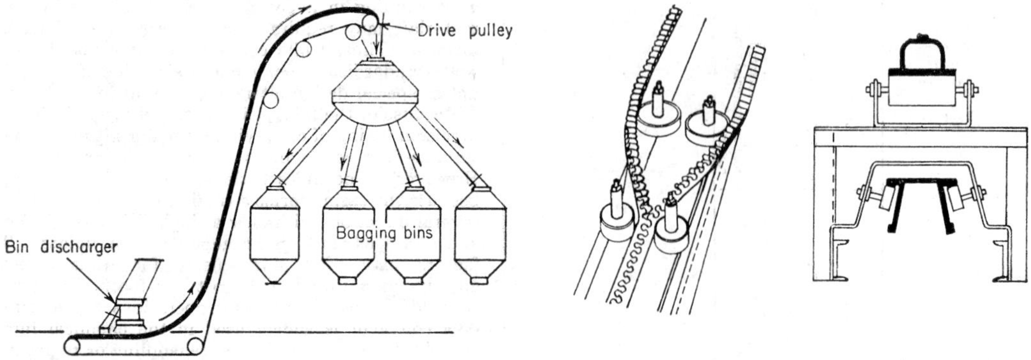

FIG. 7-13. Details and general arrangement for closed-belt conveyor. Opening and closing rollers mesh and unmesh teeth in same manner as conventional clothing fastener. (*Stephens-Adamson Mfg. Co.*)

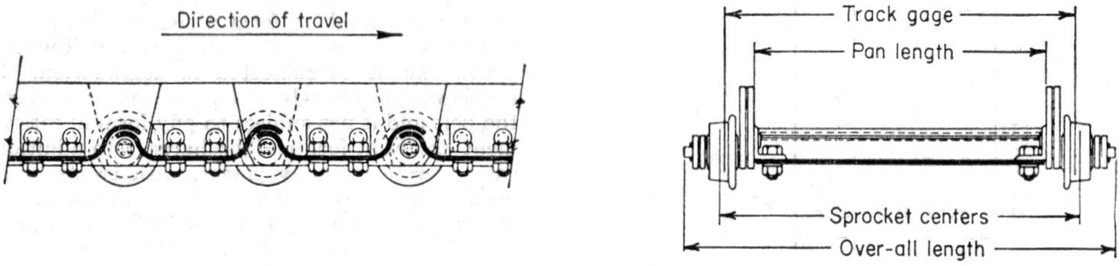

FIG. 7-14. Apron conveyor. (*Fairfield Engineering Co.*)

of designs for both horizontal and inclined travel. Their main application is the feeding of material at controlled rates, with lump sizes that are large enough to minimize dribble. The typical design is a series of pans mounted between two strands of roller chain, with pans overlapping to eliminate dribble, and often equipped with end plates for deeper loads. Pan design may vary according to material requirements. Figure 7-14 illustrates a typical apron-conveyor design, and Table 7-11 gives capacities for units with and without skirt plates. Apron-feeder applications range from fairly light-duty applications with light-gage steel pans up to extremely heavy-duty applications requiring reinforced manganese-steel pans with center supports.

Table 7-11. Apron-conveyor Capacities*

Capacities with No Skirts

Material depth of 4 in. on pans

Actual width of carrying surface, in.	50 ft./min.			100 ft./min.		
	Cu. ft./hr.	Tons/hr. 50 lb./cu. ft. material	Tons/hr. 100 lb./cu. ft. material	Cu. ft./hr.	Tons/hr. 50 lb./cu. ft. material	Tons/hr. 100 lb./cu. ft. material
18	1125	28	56	2250	56	112
24	1500	37.5	75	3000	75	150
30	1875	47	94	3750	94	188
36	2250	56.5	113	4500	113	226
42	2625	65.5	131	5250	131	262
48	3000	75	150	6000	150	300
54	3375	84.5	169	6750	169	338
60	3750	94	188	7500	188	376

Capacities with Skirts

50 lb./cu. ft. material at a speed of 10 ft./min.

Pan width, in.	Width between skirts, in.	Max. size lumps, in.		Capacities based on use of skirt boards, tons/hr. Depth of material on pans, in.									
		Sized	Unsized†	4	5	6	8	10	12	15	18	21	24
18	16	3	6	5.0	6.2	7.5	10.0	12.5	15.0	18.8	22.5	26.3	30.0
24	22	4	8	6.9	8.6	10.3	13.7	17.2	20.6	25.6	31.0	36.1	41.2
30	28	6	12	8.8	10.9	13.1	17.5	21.8	26.2	32.7	39.3	45.9	52.5
36	34	8	16	10.7	13.3	16.0	21.3	27.6	32.0	40.0	48.0	56.0	64.0
42	40	10	20	12.5	15.6	18.8	25.0	31.0	37.5	46.9	56.3	65.7	75.0
48	46	12	24	14.4	18.0	21.6	28.8	36.0	43.2	54.0	64.8	75.6	86.3

Above capacities are based on assumption that conveyor is loaded to 75 per cent of its maximum cross section.
For other widths of carrying surfaces, height of sides, speeds, and weights of material, capacities should be figured in direct proportion to the varying conditions.
Apron feeder speeds are usually 10 to 30 ft./min. and apron conveyors, 50 to 75 ft./min.
* Fairfield Engineering Co.
† Not to exceed 10 per cent of whole.

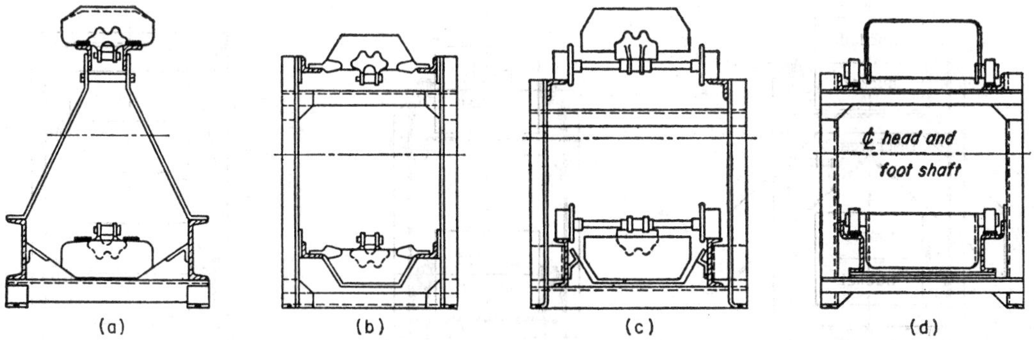

FIG. 7-15. Standard types of flight conveyors. (*a*) Scraper flight conveyor for small capacities and moderate lengths between centers. (*b*) Suspended flight conveyor for larger capacities, moderate lengths between centers, and for materials not containing large lumps. (*c*) and (*d*) Roller-flight and roller-chain conveyors for heavy duty. If the material contains large lumps, (*d*) is preferable as the chains do not restrict the feed to the conveyor.

Flight conveyors are available in an almost infinite variety, with four common types illustrated in Fig. 7-15. Most flight-conveyor applications are open designs for rough conveying operations, but some are built with totally enclosed casings. Table 7-12 gives typical design and capacity information.

V-bucket elevator-conveyors are still used for handling heavy materials, for coal and, in light-duty designs, for lightweight free-flowing materials. Typical cross sections and general arrangements are shown in Fig. 7-16; design details and capacities are shown in Table 7-13. Similar to the V-bucket, but with buckets swinging freely on supporting shafts mounted between two strands of roller chain, is the pivoted-bucket conveyor. This type can be equipped with a fixed or movable tripper to dump buckets by overturning them. While considerably more expensive than the V-bucket conveyor, it eliminates the abrasion created by dragging material along in a trough and operates more smoothly at lower horsepower per ton for heavy materials.

The most common chain conveyor is the bucket elevator already discussed, but there are a wide variety of special chain conveyors which are used so infrequently that they should be selected only on specific recommendation of a qualified materials-handling engineer.

Air Conveying. This field has probably made more rapid advances in recent years than any other field of materials handling. The list of materials which can be successfully handled by air is growing rapidly and the mechanical equipment to make these systems more versa tile and economical is rapidly being developed. While components are available for do-it-yourself assembly, such undertakings are not recommended without the advice of a competent engineer.

For a given length and capacity, the air conveyor usually requires more horsepower per ton than mechanical conveyors. However, a growing number of installations belie this rule, particularly as air systems grow longer and layouts become more complicated. Also, for aeratable materials, there are new fluidizing techniques which have greatly lowered horsepower requirements. Figure 7-17 indicates how fluidizing cuts air and power requirements when compared with traditional air conveying methods.

The **blow tank** was probably the earliest air conveying system. In its simplest form it consists of a pressure vessel with a feed opening which can be sealed off after material is allowed to flow in, a source of compressed air, and a quick-release discharge valve. The tank is filled, sealed, air pressure built up within it, and the

Table 7-12. Flight-conveyor Capacities*

Based on material weighing 50 lb./cu. ft.; speed 100 ft./min.

Single-strand Flight Conveyor

Using malleable-iron flights						Using steel flights with wearing shoes or rollers					
Flight size, length × depth, in.	Max. size lumps, in.		Capacity, tons/hr., horizontal†			Flight size, length × depth, in.	Max. size lumps, in.		Capacity, tons/hr., horizontal†		
			Flight spacing, in.						Flight spacing, in.		
	All lumps	10% lumps	18	24	36		All lumps	10% lumps	18	24	36
10 × 4	1½	3	32	25	16	12 × 5	1¾	3½	56	42	28
12 × 5	1¾	3½	46	35	23	15 × 7	2½	4½	78	58	39
15 × 5	2	4	66	50	33	18 × 8	3	5	124	93	62

Double-strand Flight Conveyor

Using steel flights on roller chain						Using steel flights on plain chain					
Flight size, length × depth, in.	Max. size lumps, in.		Capacity, tons/hr., horizontal†			Flight size, length × depth, in.	Max. size lumps, in.		Capacity, tons/hr., horizontal†		
			Flight spacing, in.						Flight spacing, in.		
	All lumps	10% lumps	18	24	36		All lumps	10% lumps	18	24	36
15 × 6	3½	7	87	67	44	12 × 5	2	4	56	42	28
16 × 8	4	8	110	82	55	15 × 6	3	5	76	57	38
18 × 8	5	9	124	93	62	18 × 7	4	8	96	72	48
20 × 10	6	10	...	141	94	24 × 8	8	12	...	124	83
24 × 10	8	12	...	176	116						
30 × 10	10	14	...	...	250						

* Fairfield Engineering Co.

† Capacities given are for horizontal conveyors. For inclined conveyors multiply capacities given by 80 per cent for 15-deg. slope, 55 per cent for 30-deg. slope, and 33 per cent for 45 deg. slope.

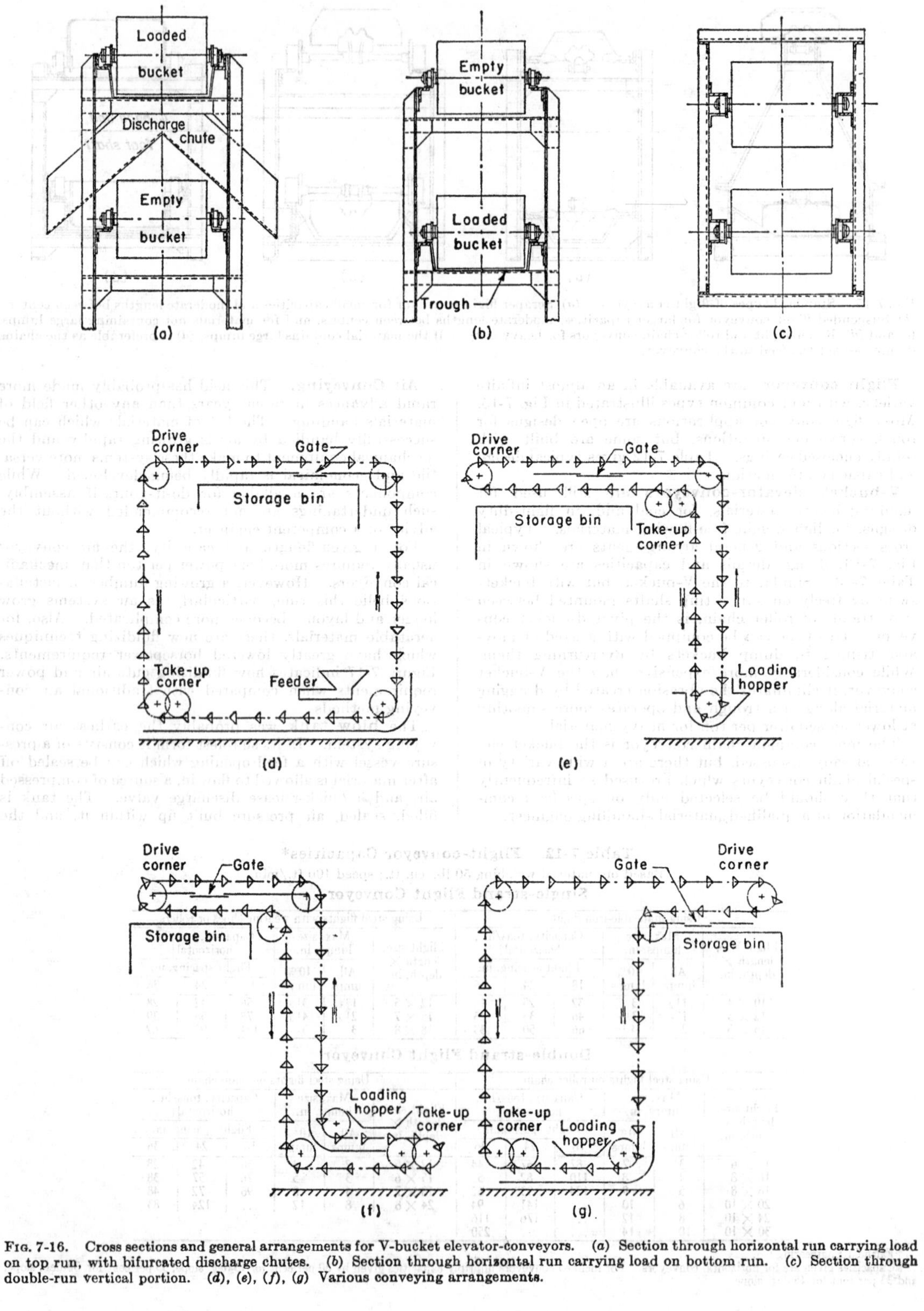

Fig. 7-16. Cross sections and general arrangements for V-bucket elevator-conveyors. *(a)* **Section through horizontal run carrying load on top run, with bifurcated discharge chutes.** *(b)* **Section through horizontal run carrying load on bottom run.** *(c)* **Section through double-run vertical portion.** *(d)*, *(e)*, *(f)*, *(g)* **Various conveying arrangements.**

Table 7-13. V-bucket Elevator-Conveyors*

Using steel V-buckets mounted on double-strand roller chain; based on material weighing 50 lb./cu. ft.; speed 100 ft./min.

Capacity, tons/hr.	Buckets			Max. size lumps, in.		Pitch of chain, in.	Horsepower†			Casing, inside, in.	
	Size, length × width, in.	Capacity, level full, cu. ft.	Spacing, in.	All lumps	10% lumps		Per 10 ft. vertical lift	Per 100 ft. horizontal, empty	Per 100 ft. horizontal, loaded	Double run	Single run
	12 × 12	0.292	18	3	6	6 or 9				20 × 48	20 × 18
20	16 × 12	0.388	24	3	6	6 or 12	0.30	1.50	3.15	24 × 48	24 × 18
	18 × 14	0.583	36	3½	7	6, 9 or 12				26 × 48	26 × 20
	14 × 12	0.341	18	3	6	6 or 9				22 × 48	22 × 18
25	14 × 14	0.455	24	3½	7	6 or 12	0.36	1.60	3.55	22 × 48	22 × 20
	16 × 16	0.686	36	4	8	6, 9 or 12				24 × 54	24 × 22
	18 × 12	0.438	18	3	6	6 or 9				26 × 48	26 × 18
30	18 × 14	0.583	24	3½	7	6 or 12	0.43	1.70	4.00	26 × 48	26 × 20
	20 × 16	0.857	36	4	8	6, 9 or 12				28 × 54	28 × 22
	16 × 14	0.519	18	3½	7	6 or 9				24 × 48	24 × 20
35	16 × 16	0.686	24	4	8	6 or 12	0.50	1.80	4.50	24 × 54	24 × 22
	18 × 18	0.960	36	4½	9	6, 9 or 12				26 × 54	26 × 24
	18 × 14	0.583	18	3½	7	6 or 9				26 × 48	26 × 20
40	18 × 16	0.771	24	4	8	6 or 12	0.58	1.90	5.00	26 × 54	26 × 22
	20 × 18	1.067	36	4½	9	6, 9 or 12				28 × 54	28 × 24
	16 × 16	0.686	18	4	8	9				24 × 54	24 × 22
50	18 × 18	0.960	24	4½	9	12	0.70	2.10	5.75	26 × 54	26 × 24
	20 × 20	1.301	36	5	10	9 or 12				28 × 60	28 × 26
	20 × 16	0.857	18	4	8	9				28 × 54	28 × 22
60	20 × 18	1.067	24	4½	9	12	0.82	2.25	6.90	28 × 54	28 × 24
	30 × 18	1.597	36	4½	9	9 or 12				40 × 54	40 × 24
	24 × 16	1.026	18	4	8	9				34 × 54	34 × 22
75	20 × 20	1.301	24	5	10	12	0.95	2.45	8.10	28 × 60	28 × 26
	30 × 20	1.952	36	5	10	9 or 12				40 × 60	40 × 26
	30 × 20	1.952	24	5	10	12				40 × 60	40 × 26
100	30 × 24	2.760	36	6	12	9 or 12	1.30	2.70	9.70	40 × 66	40 × 30

* Fairfield Engineering Co.
† Add 5 per cent to horsepower for each turn. Capacities based on buckets 75 per cent level full.

discharge valve opened suddenly to release material. The resulting conveying action goes through a number of stages which illustrate the several concepts currently used in modern air conveying systems.

The sudden release of the blow-tank discharge valve results in what is essentially a controlled explosion, with material forced along the conveying line like a bullet in a gun barrel. The initial velocity and friction between the material and the pipe wall determine the distance a material can be conveyed. This principle is still in use on conveying systems for handling heavy and sticky materials.

After the initial explosion, there is usually a certain amount of finer granular material which has entrained air in the pressurizing process. Since this causes the air-solids mixture to take on fluid properties, it flows through the conveyor line just like a liquid under pressure. This is, in simple terms, what is known as the fluidizing method which is currently in wide use on materials such as flour. Special mechanical equipment, particularly feeders, have been developed to help material entrain air and do it on a continuous basis. Thus a steady flow of material can be maintained with relatively low air and power requirements.

Another factor in blow-tank operation is the pressure drop between the surfaces of a solid particle as air passes through the orifices created between the individual particles. A number of conveyors based on this principle have been used for handling petroleum-processing catalysts, but the results of tests with different materials have been too erratic to make it practical for general use.

The last conveying action to occur in the old blow-tank design is dependent entirely on the velocity of the escaping air. At the final stage there is little material left in the tank and air can escape at high velocity. The friction drag of the air on the material is thus sufficient to drag some material with it. This is the conveying principle in most common use.

Conventional air conveying systems (those depending on air velocity) may operate as either pressure or vacuum systems. The latter is obviously the system best adapted to unloading railroad cars and trucks which have no bottom openings for gravity-flow unloading. *Low-pressure systems* usually operate at an air pressure of around 0.5 lb./sq. in. and depend on large fans for their air supply. They are suitable only for light materials (such as bran) and operate most commonly as a combination vacuum-pressure system by pulling material through the fan. Their primary application is in the grain-milling industry. They require a high volume of air for relatively small amounts of material; filters and/or cyclone separators are required to separate material from

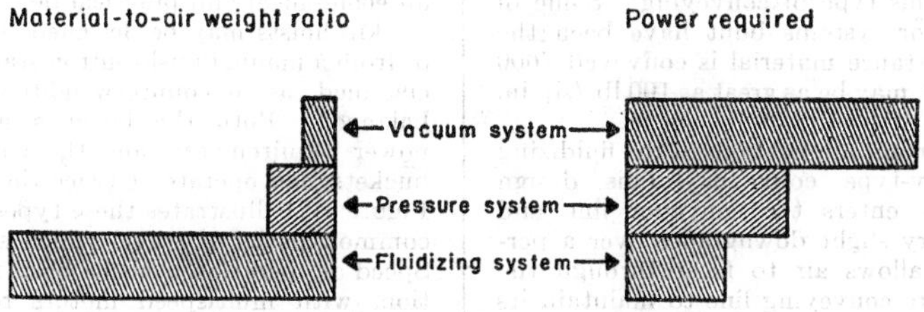

Fig. 7-17. Comparison of power requirements and material-to-air weight ratio for three air conveying systems handling a fluidizable material. Test values (indicated by relative bar lengths) are based on a conveying capacity of 20 tons/hr. of flour over approximately 80 ft. (*Modern Materials Handling.*)

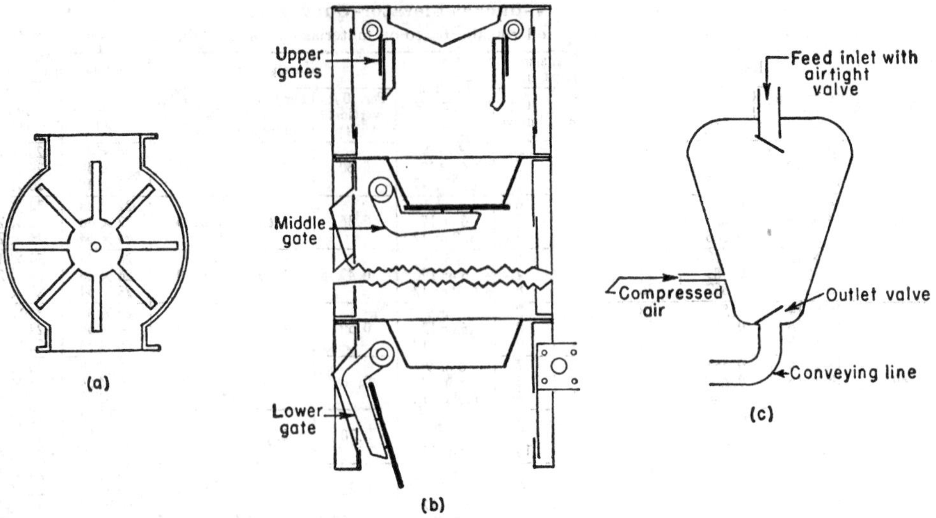

FIG. 7-18. Design details for air conveying systems. (*a*) Rotary-vane feeder has tight clearance between vanes and housing, minimizing air loss. Vanes may be equipped with replaceable wear strips. Feed is continuous. (*b*) System of interlocked gates gives semicontinuous feed without serious air loss; minimum abrasion. Upper compartment fills as lower gate opens for discharge; middle gate holds air pressure in conveyor line. (*c*) Blow-tank system uses large pressure tank for batch-type conveying. Each new load must be pressurized before discharge valve is opened.

the conveying air. *Medium-pressure systems* work at around 5 lb./sq. in. and may be either vacuum or pressure, or a combination of the two. Air is usually supplied by a centrifugal blower; filters and special air-lock feeders are required. Figure 7-18*a* illustrates the general design of a rotary-vane feeder with close tolerances providing the necessary air lock. The medium-pressure system may operate in closed circuit, making possible the introduction of an inert gas for conveying hazardous materials. Air requirements are from 3 to 30 cu. ft./lb. of material conveyed. *High-pressure systems* work at pressures up to 25 lb./sq. in. and a material-to-air weight ratio which may be as high as 30 to 1. Air is supplied from rotary positive-displacement blowers and the systems operate on pressure only. An air-lock feeder is required, and on the most efficient systems there is probably some fluidizing as a result of air entrainment by the material.

Fluidizing systems depend primarily for conveying action on the ability of the material to entrain air and assume fluid properties. They may be batch or continuous. A simplified version of a batch fluidizing vessel is shown in Fig. 7-18*c*. The continuous type operates with an air-lock feeder which is designed to admit air to the material for fluidizing as it is fed into the conveying line. Because of the close tolerances required in the feeder to prevent air loss, abrasive materials do not lend themselves readily to this type of conveying. Some of the longest air conveyor systems built have been the batch type. In one instance material is conveyed 7600 ft. Pressure in the tank may be as great as 100 lb./sq. in. but is normally limited to around 30 lb./sq. in.

One of the most important applications of the fluidizing principle is a gravity-type conveyor. This design fluidizes material as it enters the conveyor line and allows it to flow on very slight downgrades over a permeable surface which allows air to filter through the material along the entire conveying line to maintain its fluidized state. Developed specifically for the cement industry, the gravity fluidizing system has been widely used for other fine powdery and granular materials.

There is hardly any theoretical limit to the lump size which air conveyors can handle. To solve the feed problem with lumpy materials the semicontinuous feeder with a system of interlocking gates was developed (Fig. 7-18*b*). Metal parts of some 3 cu. in. volume are being handled by air. However, the size limitation is usually set by abrasive action in the conveying line because of extremely high velocity. For example, velocities of 6000 ft./min. are not uncommon. It is obvious that, for materials easily degraded, or very abrasive, such speeds are not practical.

In the past, one of the defects of the air conveyor was its inability to pick up and discharge materials at multiple points. To a great degree this has been eliminated by the design of diversion valves and other mechanical controls which, when combined with the proper control devices, have made air conveying amenable to a high degree of automation. In addition, air conveyors are being adapted to processing operations. For example, heating, cooling, and drying are now being successfully combined with the conveying operation through controlled air supplies. Figures 7-19 and 7-20 show typical systems using conventional and fluidizing concepts.

Skip Hoists. Because skip hoists operate on a batch, rather than continuous, principle, they are not so widely used as in the past. However, for high lifts and extremely lumpy or hot materials, the skip hoist is still an economical and practical device.

Skip hoists may be designed to operate automatically or from a manual push-button station. They are usually classified as uncounterweighted, counterweighted, or balanced. Both the latter systems reduce operating power requirements, and the balanced unit, using two buckets, can operate at twice the capacity of the others. Figure 7-21 illustrates these types as well as some of the common paths of travel which skip hoists may follow. Speed of operation is also a basis for skip-hoist classification, with multispeed motors required on high-speed operations to slow down bucket travel speed at loading and discharge points.

Table 7-14 gives typical horsepower and capacity

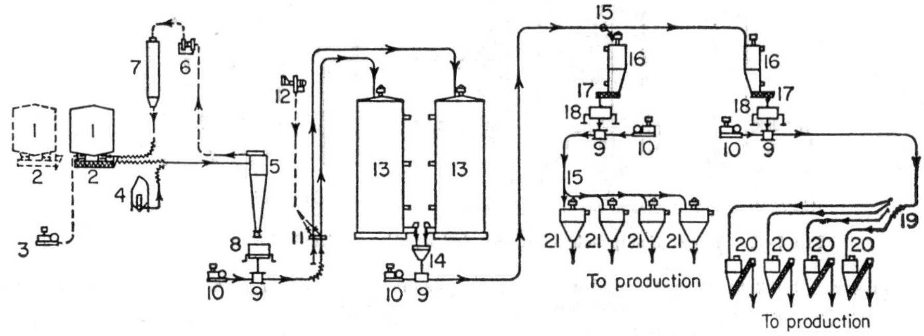

FIG. 7-19. Typical conventional pneumatic system shows use of vacuum system withdrawing from cars as well as pressure systems for plant distribution. Note how screw conveyors have been incorporated at various points in system.

1. Fluidized gravity-discharge car
2. Unloading screw
3. Blower
4. Portable dump hopper
5. Collector
6. Two-stage fan
7. Series filter
8. Sifter
9. Feeder
10. Blower
11. Shut-off valves
12. Air-circulating fan
13. Storage units
14. Surge bin
15. Four-way valve
16. Holding bins
17. Feeder screws
18. Sifters
19. Four-way valves
20. Sixth-floor bins
21. Fifth-floor bins

(*Modern Materials Handling.*)

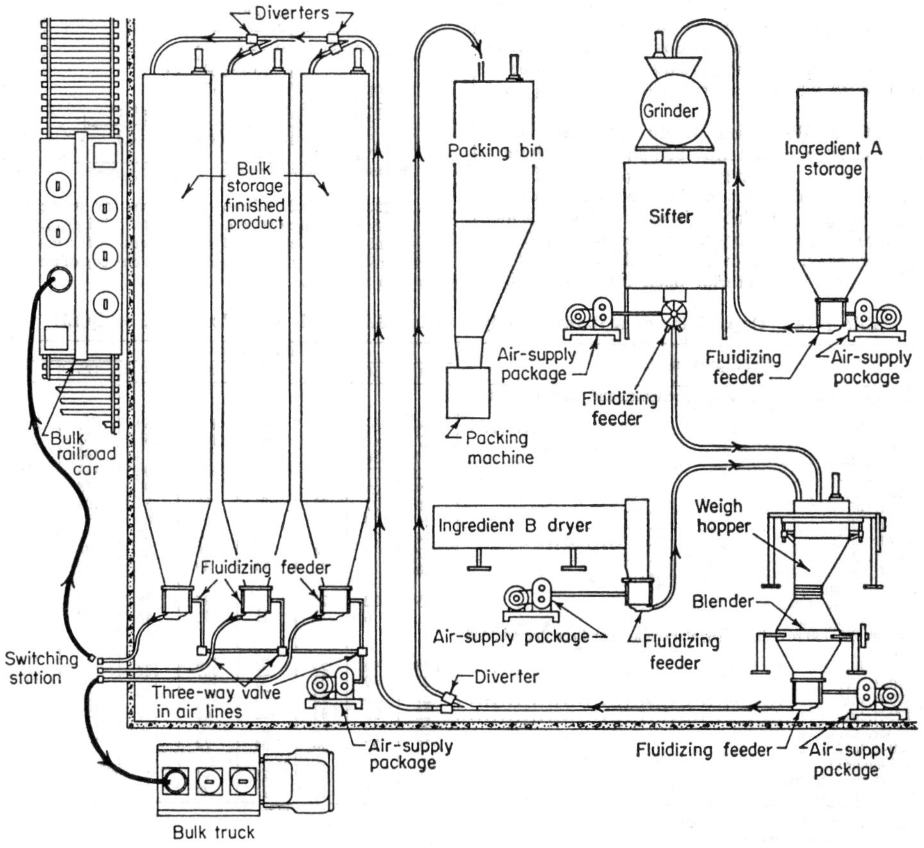

FIG. 7-20. Some typical uses of fluidizing systems are illustrated in this hypothetical plant diagram. Special railroad cars and trucks take advantage of gravity-flow fluidizing systems to speed unloading at user plants. (*Modern Materials Handling.*)

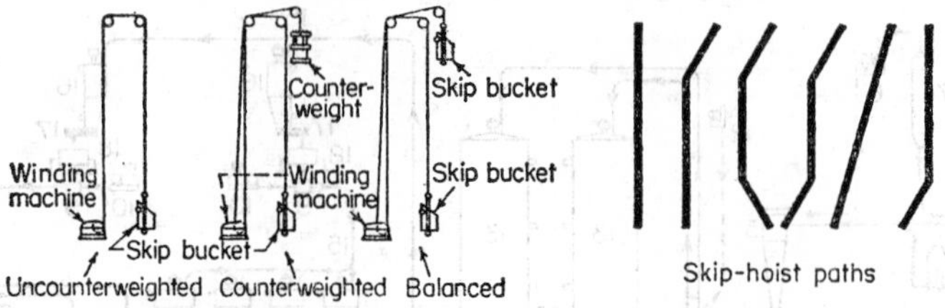

FIG. 7-21. Types of skip hoists and skip-hoist paths. *(Fairfield Engineering Co.)*

ratings for various-sized buckets on both medium- and high-speed skip hoists. Capacities are based on coal at 50 lb./cu. ft. and may be interpolated for other materials.

Auxiliary Equipment. Elevating conveyors must be equipped with some form of **holdback or brake** to prevent reversal of travel and subsequent jamming when power is unexpectedly cut off. Ratchet and wedge roller-type holdbacks are commonly used. Solenoid brakes and spring clutches may also be used.

Another problem with most conveyors is to cut out the driving force when a conveyor jams. Torque-limiting devices are often used, as are electrical controls which cut power to the drive motor. However, because of the high inertia of the motor rotor, it is sometimes desirable to eliminate the torque surge which may occur when the conveyor jams. The shear-pin hub is usually used in these cases, with power transmitted through a set of pins which are designed to shear at a fixed maximum torque. While equipment remains down until the pins can be replaced, there is an immediate disconnect between motor and conveyor which may prevent serious equipment damage.

Unless a material discharges freely, **cleaners** are required on belt conveyors and may be helpful on others. Common types use a rotating brush, powered from the conveyor head-pulley shaft or independently, or a spring-mounted blade. The latter is applicable only at some point where the belt conveyor lies reasonably flat. Whenever cleaners are used, provision should be made for catching and chuting the material back into the main discharge stream or to a collecting container which can be periodically emptied.

Shipping of Bulk Solids. Whether shipments are moved by rail, highway, or water, the most important

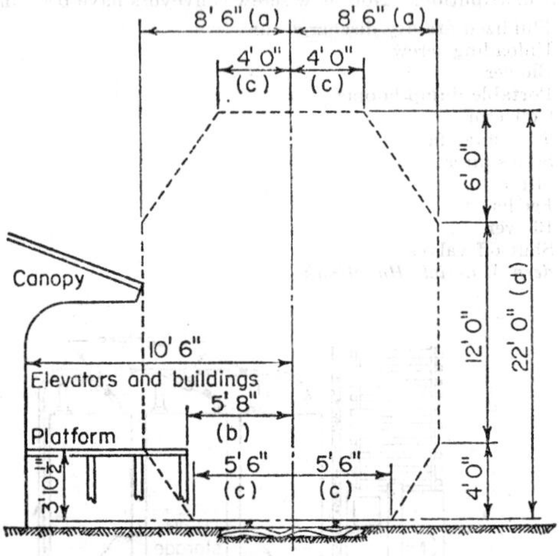

FIG. 7-22. Typical railroad clearances for straight track. *(a)* and *(b)* Some railroads require an 8-ft. minimum. *(c)* In some states, this clearance must be increased. *(d)* One Western railroad requires 24 ft. vertical clearance above top of ties. *(Stephens-Adamson Mfg. Co.)*

Table 7-14. Capacities of Automatically Loaded Skip Hoists in Tons/Hr. of Coal*

Hoist speed and lift	Bucket capacity, cu. ft.							
	20	30	40	60	80	100	125	150
Medium speed, 130 ft./min., uncounterweighted and counterweighted								
Tons/hr.								
40-ft. lift	34	51	68	102	136	160	211	255
50-ft. lift	27	41	54	82	108	135	167	203
60-ft. lift	24	36	48	72	96	118	149	180
70-ft. lift	22	33	43	66	86	108	133	161
80-ft. lift	19	29	38	58	76	95	118	143
90-ft. lift	18	27	35	54	70	88	109	131
100-ft. lift	16	24	32	48	64	80	99	120
120-ft. lift	14	20	27	40	54	68	84	101
140-ft. lift	12	18	24	36	48	60	74	90
160-ft. lift	10	16	21	32	42	53	65	79
Total motor hp.								
Uncounterweighted	15	22	28	36	47	58	73	88
Counterweighted	...	6	7	11	14	18	22	27
High speed, 260–130 ft./min., uncounterweighted and counterweighted								
Tons/hr.								
80-ft. lift	29	44	58	87	116	145	181	218
90-ft. lift	27	40	53	80	106	133	166	200
100-ft. lift	25	38	50	75	100	125	156	188
120-ft. lift	22	33	44	66	88	110	138	165
140-ft. lift	20	30	40	60	80	100	125	150
160-ft. lift	18	27	36	54	72	90	113	135
Total motor hp.								
Uncounterweighted	30	44	56	73	94			
Counterweighted	...	11	14	21	28	35	44	53

For balanced skip hoists multiply high-speed capacities by 2.
Weight of coal assumed at 50 lb./cu. ft.
Horsepowers are based on vertical lifts. For inclined runs less than 75 deg. with the horizontal, multiply horsepower by the following: 75 deg., 0.96; 65 deg., 0.91; 55 deg., 0.85.
* Fairfield Engineering Co.

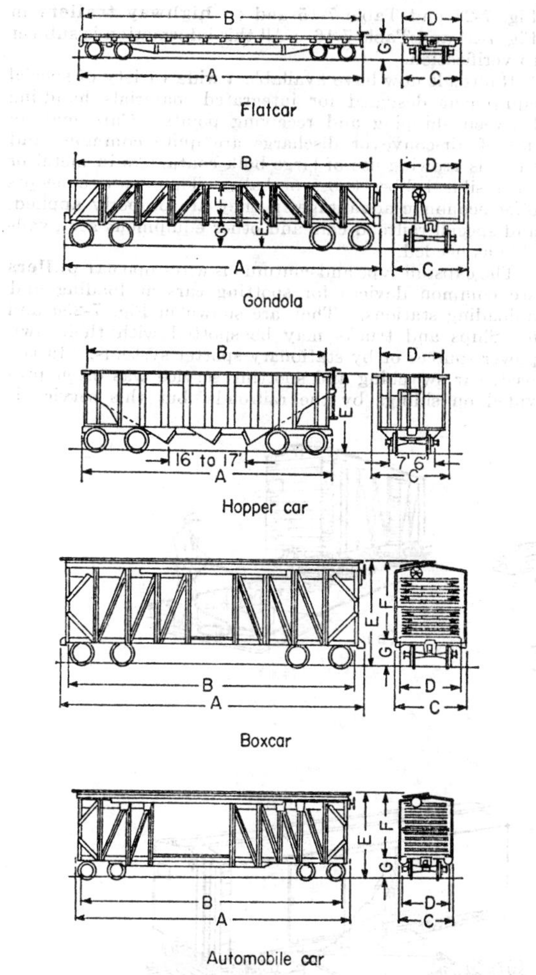

FIG. 7-23. Freight cars; see Table 7-15 for dimensions. (*Stephens-Adamson Mfg. Co.*)

problem in receiving or shipping is the proper design of loading or unloading stations.

Figure 7-22 gives some typical **railroad clearances,** but these figures must be carefully checked because railroad standards vary widely. Certain clearances between locomotives and cars and structures near tracks are required as a matter of safety precaution for both train crews and other individuals. Clearances given by Fig. 7-22 are averages for straight track and must not be taken as final—some railroad companies and states

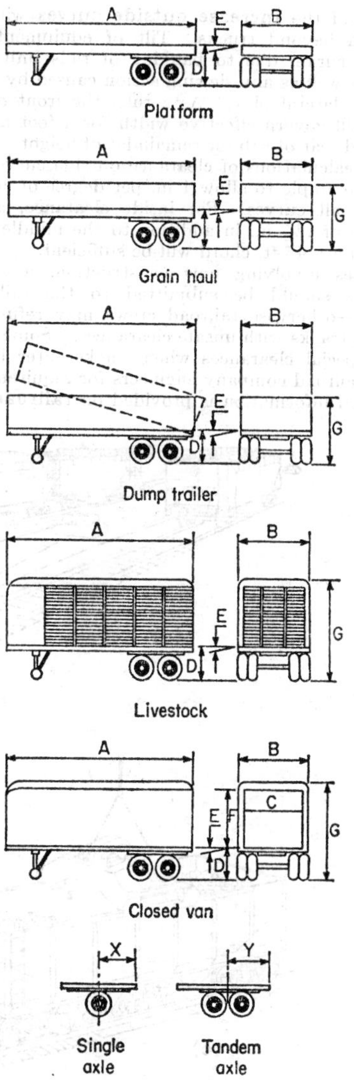

FIG. 7-24. Highway trailers; see Table 7-16 for dimensions. (*Stephens-Adamson Mfg. Co.*)

require more as noted. Dimensions are based on standard 4 ft. 8½ in. track gage.

Allowances must also be made on curves, due to the increase in effective width of equipment. The **increase inside curves** will depend on the distance between truck

Table 7-15. Average Dimensions, Weights, and Capacities of Railroad Cars*

Type of car	A Length over strikers	B Inside length	C Over-all width	D Inside width	E Over-all height	F Inside height	G Height of floor	Level full capacity, cu. ft.	Max. capacity, cu. ft.	Tare weight of cars, lb.
Flat car	53 ft. 0 in.	52 ft. 0 in.	10 ft. 3 in.	10 ft. 3 in.	....	....	3 ft. 10⅞ in.	....	....	48,700
Gondola	43 ft. 0½ in.	41 ft. 6 in.	10 ft. 3¾ in.	9 ft. 2 in.	8 ft. 7 3/16 in.	4 ft. 8 in.	3 ft. 11 3/16 in.	1775	2241	42,800
Hopper car	35 ft. 10 in.	34 ft. 10 in.	10 ft. 5 5/16 in.	10 ft. 2¾ in.	10 ft. 8 in.	....	....	2328	2605	30,000
Boxcar	41 ft. 9½ in.	40 ft. 6 in.	10 ft. 8⅜ in.†	9 ft. 2 in.	14 ft. 0 9/16 in.	9 ft. 4 in.	3 ft. 7 11/16 in.	3468	3468	48,200
Automobile car	52 ft. 2⅞ in.	50 ft. 6 in.	10 ft. 8 in.†	9 ft. 2 in.	15 ft. 0 15/16 in.	10 ft. 4⅜ in.	3 ft. 7 in.	4798	4860	53,300

The above dimensions give a general idea as to average sizes and capacities. Do not use for close clearances, as many roads operate cars both larger and smaller.
* Stephens-Adamson Mfg. Co.
† Maximum width over door fixtures.

centers and the **increase outside curves** will depend on length beyond trucks. Tilt of equipment toward inside of curve, due to banking of rails, must be included, as well as any slewing action caused by tire wear and other lateral play. As a rule, the front of a locomotive will govern effective width for a foot above top of rail and rear of cab for remainder of height. For preliminary calculations of clearance outside curves, it will usually be ample to allow 1 in. per degree of curve plus 2 in. for all curves. For inside clearance, a general allowance of $1\frac{1}{2}$ in. in addition to the middle ordinate distance for a 45-ft. chord will be sufficient.

In cases involving new construction, a sketch of clearances should be submitted to the railroad for approval—otherwise railroad crews may refuse to run cars onto tracks with unsafe clearances. Some railroads permit special clearances when tracks enter buildings; consult railroad company engineers for requirements.

Detailed information is provided on **railroad cars** in Fig. 7-23 and Table 7-15 and on **highway trailers** in Fig. 7-24 and Table 7-16. All this information is subject to verification.

Railroads now have available a wide variety of special equipment designed for integrated materials handling between shipping and receiving points. Cars making use of air-conveyor discharge are quite common, and there is growing use of large bulk containers in metal or collapsible rubber tubes or balls. These new concepts offer economic advantages if they are properly applied, and special railroad cars and other equipment are available as needed.

The capstan type and continuous wire-rope **car pullers** are common devices for spotting cars at loading and unloading stations. They are shown in Fig. 7-25*a* and *b*. Ships and trucks may be spotted with their own power sources or by stationary spotter systems. In the past, car switching and spotting service was often provided on sidings by the railroads, but this service is

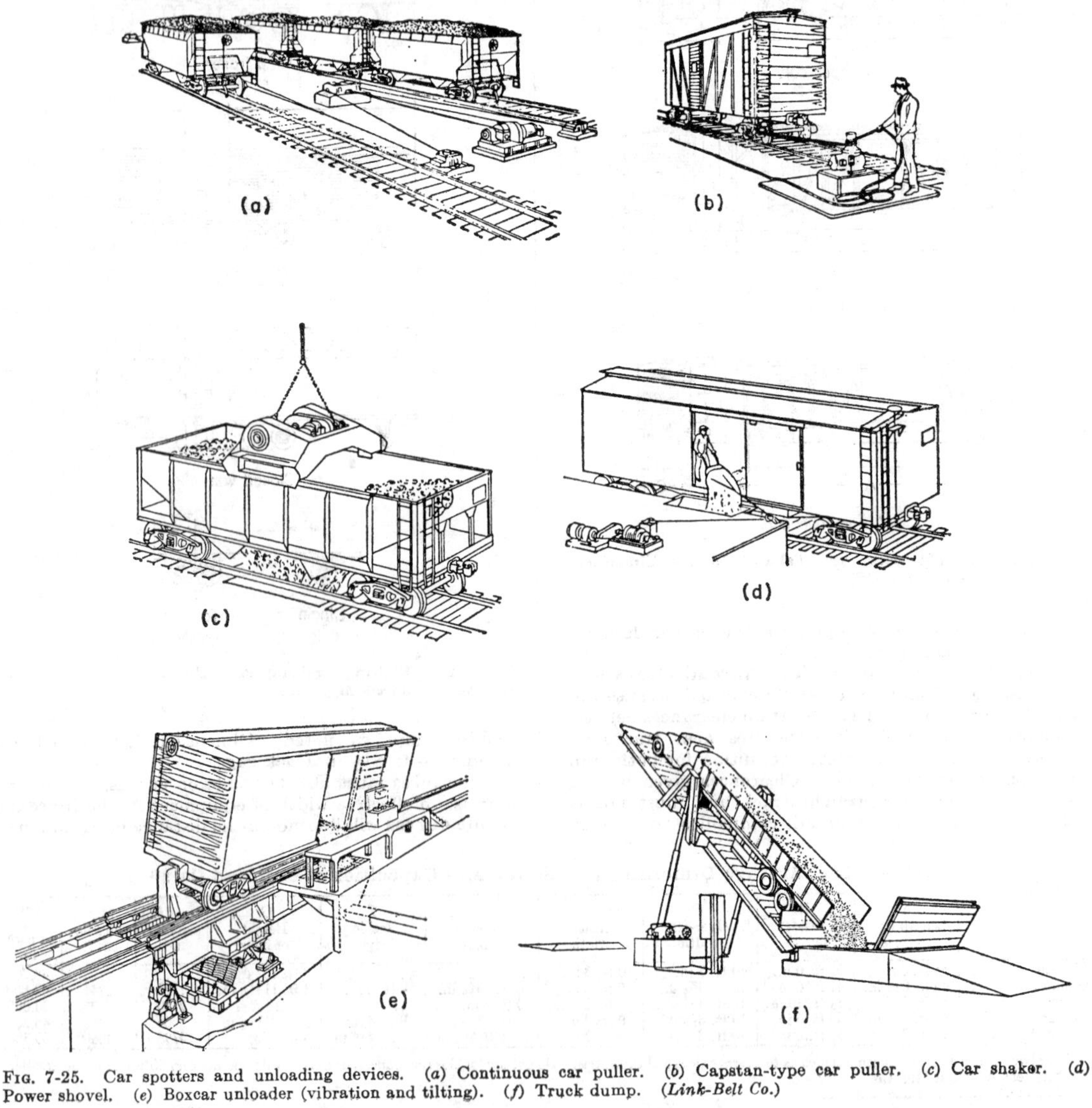

FIG. 7-25. Car spotters and unloading devices. (*a*) Continuous car puller. (*b*) Capstan-type car puller. (*c*) Car shaker. (*d*) Power shovel. (*e*) Boxcar unloader (vibration and tilting). (*f*) Truck dump. (*Link-Belt Co.*)

Table 7-16. Highway-trailer Dimensions*

Type of trailer	A Over-all length, ft.	B Over-all width	C Inside width	D Floor height from road	E Deflection under load	F Inside height	G Over-all height
Platform	24–32	7 ft. 6 in. to 8 ft. 0 in.	....			....	49 to 56¼ in.
Grain haul	24–32	to 8 ft. 0 in.	7 ft. 4 in. to 7 ft. 5 in.	49 to 56¼ in.	As much as 6 in.,	To 49½ in.	to 8 ft. 10 in.
Dump trailer	16–18	7 ft. 5 in. to 7 ft. 6 in.	6 ft. 8 in. to 6 ft. 10 in.	depending on	varies according	To 52 in.	9 ft. 0 in.
Livestock	24–34	to 8 ft. 0 in.	7 ft. 2 in. to 7 ft. 6 in.	size of tires	to load and	To 7 ft. 3 in.	Avg. 12 ft. 3 in.
Closed van	20–34	to 8 ft. 0 in.	to 7 ft. 5½ in.	used on trailer	position of load	To 7 ft. 3 in.	Avg. 12 ft. 6 in. Max. 12 ft. 8½ in.

Capacity: Varies in different states; 18,000 lb. gross load per axle general.
Single axle:
X = (on trailers 17 to 24 ft. long) 2 ft. 10¾ in.
X = (on trailers 25 to 32 ft. long) 3 ft. 10¾ in.
Tandem axle:
Y = (on trailers 23 to 30 ft. long) 7 ft. 1¼ in.
Y = (on trailers 31 to 34 ft. long) 8 ft. 7¾ in.
* Stephens-Adamson Mfg. Co.

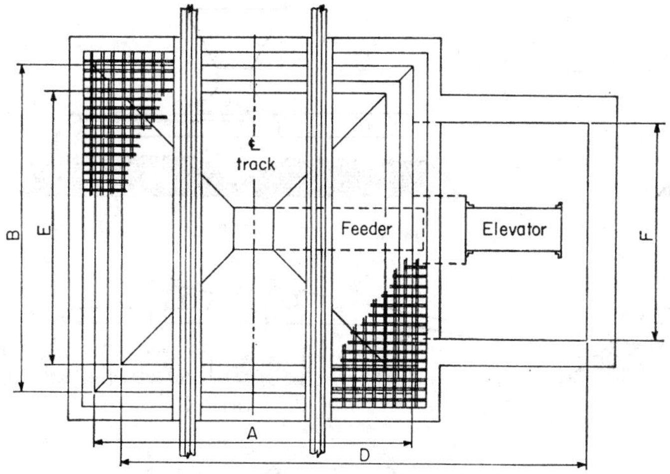

A x B	C	D	E	F
10' x 7'	9' 6"	16' 6"	5' 0"	7' 0"
10'x10'	11' 0"	16' 6"	8' 0"	8' 0"
12'x12'	12' 0"	17' 6"	10' 0"	8' 0"
14'x18'	15' 0"	19' 0"	15' 0"	10' 0"

FIG. 7-26. Single-track hoppers for elevators. C = Depth of pit for spaced bucket elevator. Must be increased for continuous-bucket design. (*Fairfield Engineering Co.*)

rapidly being discontinued. Many large plants now operate their own switch engines or other forms of mobile or stationary spotting equipment.

Bottom-dump cars are easily unloaded if material is free-flowing. However, where material does not flow well or becomes sticky because of moisture or freezing, **car shakers** may be required. There are many types available, including the overhead-mounted unit shown in Fig. 7-25*c*. Depending on required speed of unloading, or economic factors such as labor availability and efficiency, boxcars can be unloaded by power shovels or large vibratory tilting devices; these are shown in Fig. 7-25*d* and *e*. Vacuum air-conveyor systems, front-end loaders (power shovels), and portable machines with digging buckets may also be used.

Special truck trailers are available for a wide variety of bulk shipping. Many of these are similar in principle to the special railroad cars designed for air conveying or large bulk containers. Where self-dumping trucks are not used, large pneumatic or hydraulic truck-dumping platforms are available as shown in Fig. 7-25*f*.

For most boxcar and bottom-dump car shipments, **track hoppers** are required. Since boxcars discharge to one side, fairly light construction can be used for these hoppers to one side of the tracks. However, for bottom-dump cars the hoppers must be located on the center line of the tracks, requiring heavy track girders over a hopper and feeder conveyor pit. Figure 7-26 shows a single hopper designed for use with a bucket elevator. Typical dimensions are given, and hopper depth must be set to give sufficient angle for material to flow well. A belt or reciprocating-plate feeder is commonly used to carry material to the bucket elevator.

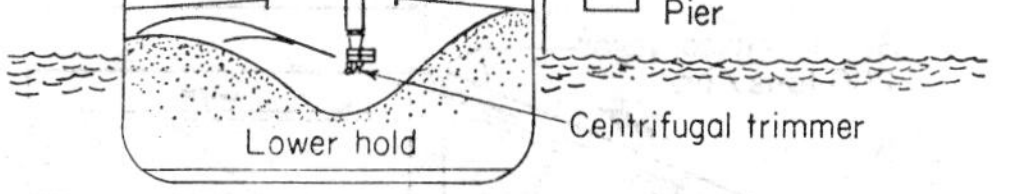

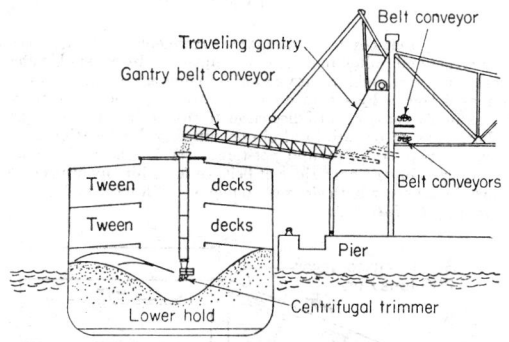

FIG. 7-27. Ship-loading system with trimmer and telescoping chute. (*Stephens-Adamson Mfg. Co.*)

Figure 7-27 shows a large dockside installation for **ship loading**. The centrifugal trimmer is also available in portable and fixed designs for use with boxcars and trucks.

STORAGE OF SOLIDS IN BULK

Storage Piles. Open-yard storage is probably best handled by belt conveyor when tonnages are large. Figure 7-28 shows some of the many discharge arrangements possible for single, multiple, or moving-tripper discharge from belt conveyors. Also shown is a tilting-plow arrangement for discharging flat belts. Most of these discharge methods are equally applicable for indoor storage. Large traveling stackers may also be used for outdoor storage. They may move along the length of a belt, forming a pile on one or both sides of the belt, or pivot about a fixed axis to form a circular pile.

Underground-tunnel belts fed by special gates (Fig. 7-29) are often used for reclaiming, as is mobile shovel equipment. Cable-drag scrapers are also used for large outside storage areas and sometimes on inside storage where large flat areas are used. A drag-scraper system may follow a single fixed cable line, or back posts may be provided to allow relocation of the cable line to cover almost any storage-space shape.

Bunkers and Silos. Inside storage in bunkers or silos may require special design to ensure full use of cubic content. Materials with rather steep angles of repose can waste a great deal of space unless conveyor discharge is designed to reach the full storage area. A common

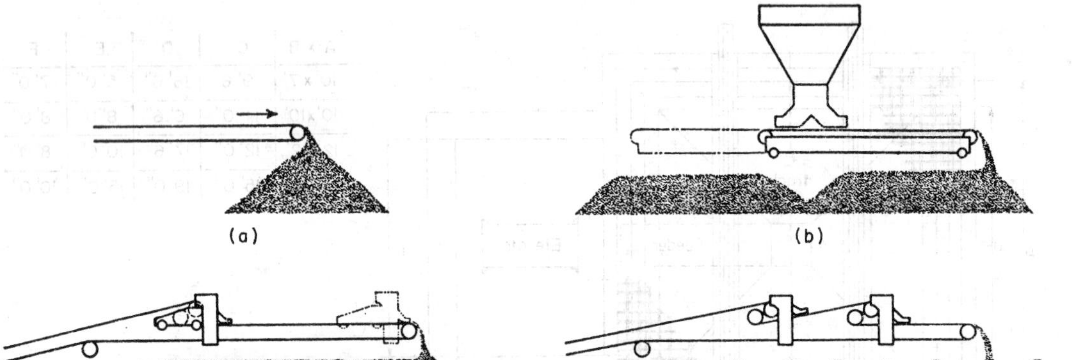

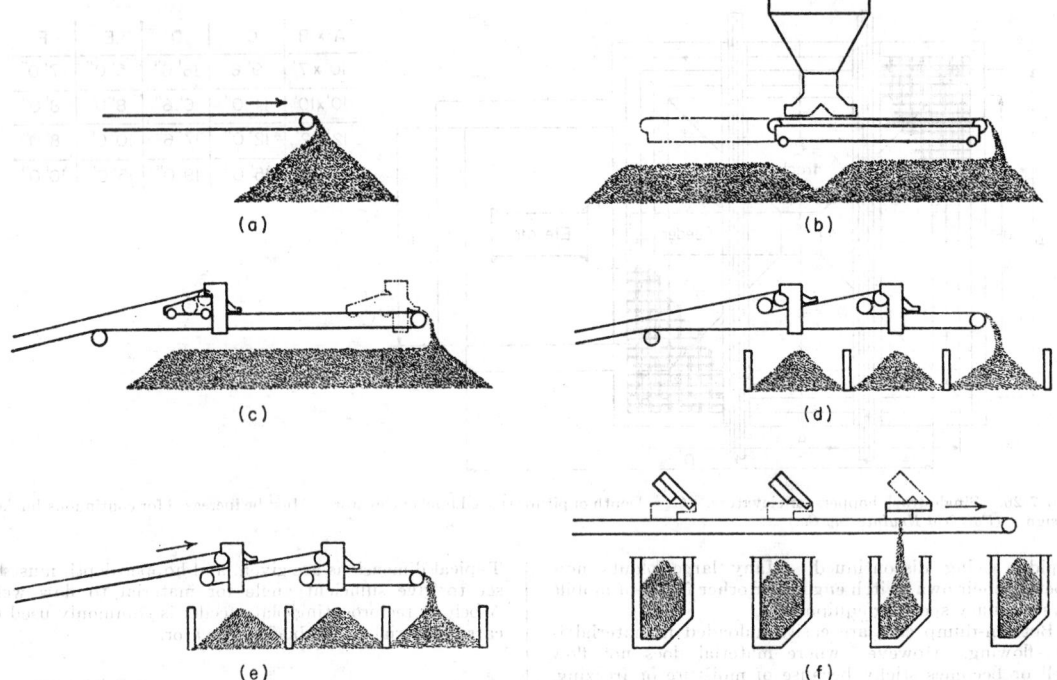

FIG. 7-28. Belt-conveyor discharge arrangements. (*a*) Discharge over end pulley forms conical pile at end of belt. (*b*) Discharge over either end pulley to distribute lengthwise by reversible shuttle conveyor. (*c*) Discharge through traveling tripper, with or without cross conveyor, to distribute material to one or both sides of conveyor for entire distance of tripper travel. Trippers can be propelled by conveyor belt or by separate motor. Motor-propelled trippers can also be automatically reversing to distribute material evenly or can be manually controlled to discharge at any desired point. (*d*) Discharge through fixed trippers, with or without cross conveyor to one or both sides of belt, to fixed bin openings or pile locations. Can also be done with multiple conveyors as shown in (*e*) or by stopping traveling trippers in desired position. (*e*) Discharge from multiple conveyors through fixed discharge chutes, with or without cross conveyor to one or both sides of belt, to fixed bin openings or pile locations. (*f*) Discharge by hinged plows to one or more fixed locations along one or both sides of conveyor. Plows may be adjusted to divide discharge into several places simultaneously in proportion desired. (*Link-Belt Co.*)

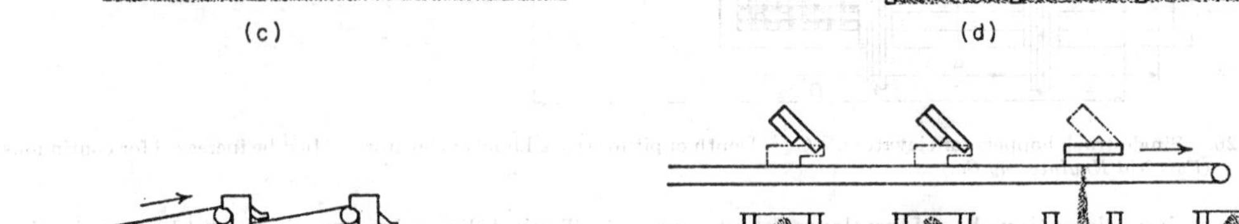

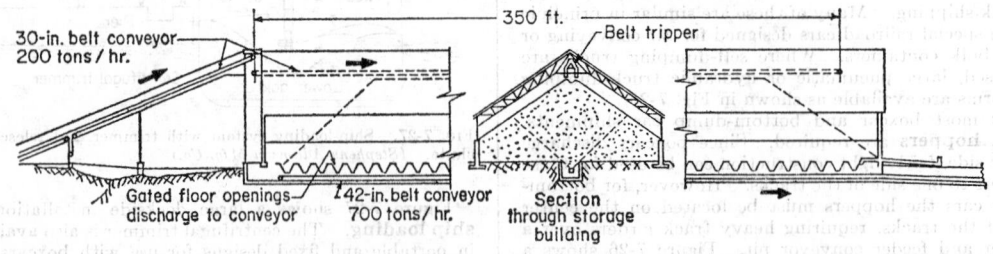

FIG. 7-29 Belt-conveyor storage and reclaiming in flat-floor building. (*Stephens-Adamson Mfg. Co.*)

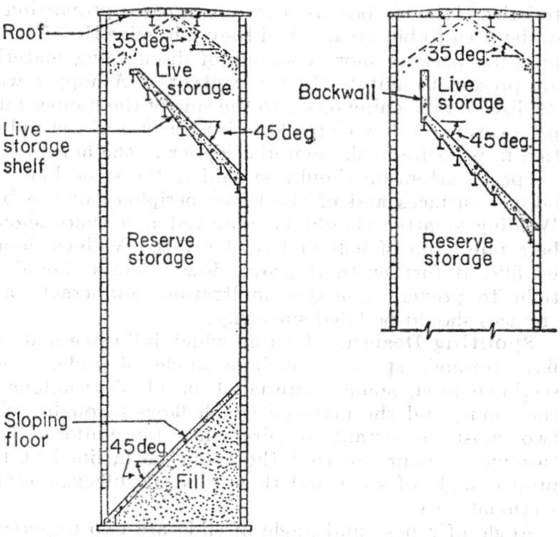

FIG. 7-30. Storage silo. (*Fairfield Engineering Co.*)

form of storage enclosure is the concrete, steel, or tile **silo.** Typical arrangements, dimensions, and capacities are shown in Fig. 7-30 and Table 7-17.

Information on the suspension **bunker**, often used in coal-burning steam stations, is shown in Fig. 7-31 and

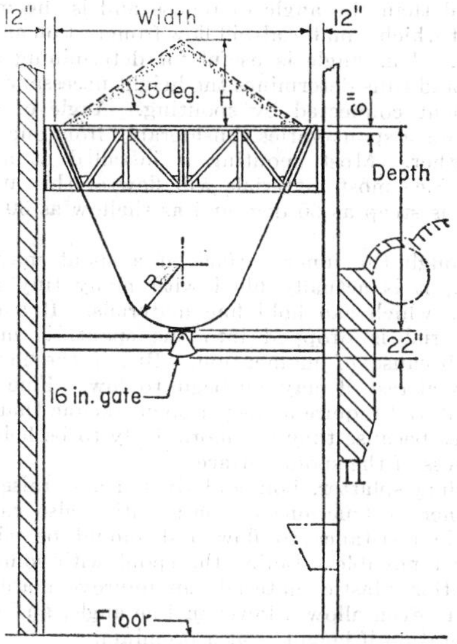

FIG. 7-31. Suspension coal bunker; for dimensions see Table 7-18. (*Fairfield Engineering Co.*)

Table 7-18. Cylindrical bunkers are covered in Fig. 7-32 and Table 7-19. While these designs apply to coal-storage conditions, they can be readily adapted to meet the demands of almost any other type of material.

Bin and Hopper Design. Bins may be built of wood, steel, concrete, tile, or other building materials. They may be either vertical or horizontal. Their cross section may be round, square, rectangular, oblong, hexagonal, or odd-shaped. Choice of bin design is affected somewhat by construction costs. Bins may feature different proportions of height to cross-sectional area. Bins usually increase in economy as their height

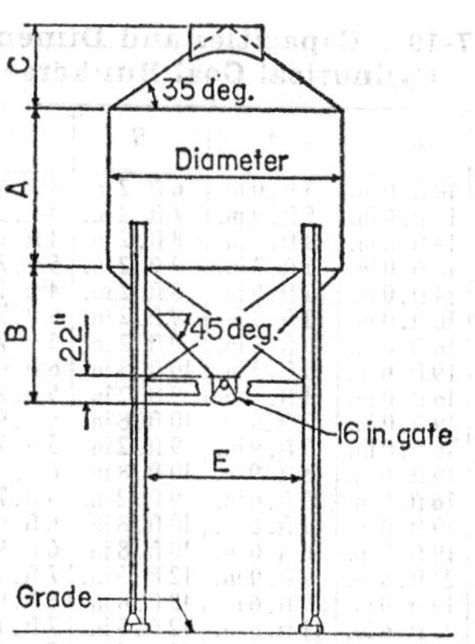

FIG. 7-32. Cylindrical coal bunker; for dimensions see Table 7-19. (*Fairfield Engineering Co.*)

and diameters increase. Best proportion for good flow of solids is obtained when bins are large in cross section and comparatively shallow. Materials are less apt to pack in such bins because of lower overhead material weight.

Square or rectangular bins possess an economic advantage over round bins in that they can be clustered together to share common walls. Square bins can utilize more space in a given area than round bins. However,

Table 7-17. Silo Capacities*

Inside diam., ft.	Normal live storage capacity, tons	Increase live storage per ft. if back wall used	Capacity of silo per ft. of height	Deduct from total for capacity lost in bottom fill, tons	Deduct from total for capacity lost in live-storage shelf, tons	Silo walls may be lowered if 35-deg. conical roof used, ft.
10	7	1.75	1.96	10	4	3.5
12	14	2.5	2.82	17	6	4.0
14	24	3.42	3.85	27	8	5.0
16	38	4.5	5.02	40	11	5.5
18	54	5.73	6.36	57	17	6.0
20	74	7.2	7.85	78	22	7.0
22	104	8.75	9.50	105	30	7.5
24	139	10.5	11.30	135	36	8.5
26	170	12.35	13.28	173	46	9.0

Based on bituminous coal weighing 50 lb./cu. ft. Capacities are approximate and depend upon character of the coal and operating conditions.

Tables are based on angle of repose of 35 deg. and shelf and floor slopes o f 45 deg.

* Fairfield Engineering Co.

Table 7-18. Capacities and Dimensions of Suspension Coal Bunkers*

Width, ft.	Capacity: Tons/ft., continuous loading	Capacity: Tons/ft., loaded every 8 ft.	Capacity: Tonnage lost in two ends	Depth	*R*	*H*
12	2.3	2.18	2.3	9 ft. 6 in.	3 ft. 0 in.	3 ft. 8 in.
13	2.65	2.53	2.75	10 ft. 3 in.	3 ft. 3 in.	4 ft. 0 in.
14	3.1	2.98	3.0	11 ft. 0 in.	3 ft. 6 in.	4 ft. 3 in.
15	3.5	3.38	3.25	11 ft. 9 in.	3 ft. 9 in.	4 ft. 7 in.
16	4.0	3.88	3.75	12 ft. 6 in.	4 ft. 0 in.	4 ft. 10 in.
17	4.5	4.38	4.4	13 ft. 3 in.	4 ft. 3 in.	5 ft. 2 in.
18	5.1	4.98	5.25	14 ft. 0 in.	4 ft. 6 in.	5 ft. 6 in.
19	5.65	5.53	6.25	14 ft. 9 in.	4 ft. 9 in.	5 ft. 10 in.
20	6.25	6.13	7.0	15 ft. 6 in.	5 ft. 0 in.	6 ft. 1 in.
21	6.95	6.83	8.4	16 ft. 3 in.	5 ft. 3 in.	6 ft. 5 in.
22	7.6	7.48	9.4	17 ft. 0 in.	5 ft. 6 in.	6 ft. 9 in.
23	8.3	8.18	10.5	17 ft. 9 in.	5 ft. 9 in.	7 ft. 0 in.
24	9.0	8.88	11.75	18 ft. 6 in.	6 ft. 0 in.	7 ft. 4 in.
25	9.8	9.68	13.0	19 ft. 3 in.	6 ft. 3 in.	7 ft. 8 in.

Capacity is based on 35-deg. slope for bituminous coal at 50 lb./cu. ft. Tonnage lost in ends is due to the fact that bunker cannot be fully surcharged its entire length.

* Fairfield Engineering Co.

Table 7-19. Capacities and Dimensions of Cylindrical Coal Bunkers*

Capacity		Diam.	*A*	*B*	*C*	*E*†
Tons	Cu. ft.					
15	600	10 ft. 0 in.	5 ft. 0 in.	6 ft. 2 in.	3 ft. 6 in.	6 ft. 9 in.
25	1,000	12 ft. 0 in.	5 ft. 9 in.	7 ft. 2 in.	4 ft. 2 in.	8 ft. 0 in.
50	2,000	14 ft. 0 in.	9 ft. 3 in.	8 ft. 2 in.	4 ft. 10 in.	9 ft. 6 in.
		16 ft. 0 in.	5 ft. 3 in.	9 ft. 2 in.	5 ft. 7 in.	10 ft. 10 in.
62½	2,500	14 ft. 0 in.	12 ft. 9 in.	8 ft. 2 in.	4 ft. 10 in.	9 ft. 6 in.
		16 ft. 0 in.	8 ft. 3 in.	9 ft. 2 in.	5 ft. 7 in.	10 ft. 10 in.
75	3,000	16 ft. 0 in.	10 ft. 6 in.	9 ft. 2 in.	5 ft. 7 in.	10 ft. 10 in.
		19 ft. 0 in.	5 ft. 3 in.	10 ft. 8 in.	6 ft. 9 in.	12 ft. 10 in.
87½	3,500	16 ft. 0 in.	13 ft. 3 in.	9 ft. 2 in.	5 ft. 7 in.	10 ft. 10 in.
		19 ft. 0 in.	7 ft. 0 in.	10 ft. 8 in.	6 ft. 9 in.	12 ft. 10 in.
100	4,000	16 ft. 0 in.	15 ft. 9 in.	9 ft. 2 in.	5 ft. 7 in.	10 ft. 10 in.
		19 ft. 0 in.	8 ft. 9 in.	10 ft. 8 in.	6 ft. 9 in.	12 ft. 10 in.
125	5,000	16 ft. 0 in.	20 ft. 6 in.	9 ft. 2 in.	5 ft. 7 in.	10 ft. 10 in.
		19 ft. 0 in.	12 ft. 6 in.	10 ft. 8 in.	6 ft. 9 in.	12 ft. 10 in.
150	6,000	19 ft. 0 in.	16 ft. 0 in.	10 ft. 8 in.	6 ft. 9 in.	12 ft. 10 in.
		22 ft. 6 in.	9 ft. 0 in.	12 ft. 5 in.	7 ft. 10 in.	15 ft. 3 in.
175	7,000	19 ft. 0 in.	19 ft. 6 in.	10 ft. 8 in.	6 ft. 9 in.	12 ft. 10 in.
		22 ft. 6 in.	11 ft. 6 in.	12 ft. 5 in.	7 ft. 10 in.	15 ft. 3 in.
200	8,000	22 ft. 6 in.	14 ft. 0 in.	12 ft. 5 in.	7 ft. 10 in.	15 ft. 3 in.
250	10,000	22 ft. 6 in.	19 ft. 0 in.	12 ft. 5 in.	7 ft. 10 in.	15 ft. 3 in.
300	12,000	24 ft. 0 in.	20 ft. 0 in.	13 ft. 2 in.	8 ft. 5 in.	16 ft. 0 in.
350	14,000	24 ft. 6 in.	24 ft. 6 in.	13 ft. 2 in.	8 ft. 5 in.	16 ft. 0 in.

Based on 35-deg. slope for bituminous coal at 50 lb./cu. ft.
* Fairfield Engineering Co.
† Dimension *E* may be increased to suit special conditions.

a round bin has greater wall strength for a given thickness than a square bin. And round bins are superior from a flow standpoint, because there are no corners in which materials can hold up.

Bin walls may taper inward or outward, although there is very little theoretical defense for either design.

Insurance rates on both wood construction and steel construction are higher than those for fireproof concrete. However, recent advances made in the prefabrication of steel have lowered steel construction costs to a position competitive with concrete. Concrete construction, of course, has a very long life.

Concrete walls should be allowed to cure completely before use. Since material arching occurs near the bottom of the bin, the lower circumference of concrete bins should be finished smooth and painted with plastic-type paint. Covering these lower surfaces with a plastic material will greatly decrease friction between the material and the wall. It is not always wise to finish the upper surfaces of a bin, because it is desirable that the walls support some of the weight of the material to prevent packing in the lower regions.

Condensation will occur whenever a temperature differential exists between the material in the bin and the bin walls. This moisture causes fine air-borne particles to stick to the walls. These particles may then decompose and fall off into the material, causing a contamination problem. Insulation should be provided to prevent this condition. Bin ventilation can help to reduce air temperatures in the bin, thus reducing condensation.

The **hopper** is the lowest part of the bin and is used to get complete discharge of the bin contents. No hopper is included in some bin designs; residual bin contents are removed manually. Hoppers actually create most bin-flow problems, and the ideal bin would not include a hopper.

Hoppers are commonly made of wood, steel, or concrete. Steel hoppers are usually preferred because most materials slide more easily on steel. Also, it is easy to provide probe holes in a steel hopper for convenience in prodding packed materials down into the hoppers. Vibrating devices can be attached to steel hoppers easily and to good effect. Hoppers may be of the same cross-sectional shapes as bins and may taper to discharge to any number of positions, either under the bin or offset to the side. A hopper may have multiple outlets.

Multiple outlets on a hopper improve the flow characteristics of the bin because they increase the proportion of outlet area to bin area. And they minimize the effect of packing, because more columns of discharging material are present to agitate the bin contents. A hopper with its discharge opening offset to the side of the hopper inlet possesses good flow characteristics because of the reduction in pressure in the material higher in the hopper.

Special attention should be paid to the smoothness of hopper surfaces and of the lower periphery of the bin. Welding splatter should be removed and there should be a minimum of bolt and rivet heads. Valleys should be filleted further to improve flow. Joints should be tight to prevent moisture infiltration, and cracks and crevices should be filled smoothly.

Spouting Design. Factors which influence material flow through spouting include angle of slide, cross-sectional area, spout material, type of obstructions in the spout, and the material which flows through. The two most important requirements for uniform flow through a spout are that the spout be inclined at the proper angle of slide and that it be of sufficient cross-sectional area.

Angle of repose and angle of slide are two important concepts which often cause confusion and which should be considered. **Angle of repose** is the angle at which a material will rest on a pile. It is useful for determining the capacity of a bin or a pile. The angle of the cone which develops at the top of the pile when a bin is being filled will be somewhat flatter than the angle of repose because of the effect of impact.

Angle of slide may be greater or less for a given material than the angle of repose and is the minimum angle at which a material will flow from rest on an inclined surface. This angle is useful for determining spouting angles and thus determines the height necessary between equipment connected by spouting. Angle of slide required for a spout varies considerably from one material to another. Most spouting is installed at a 45-deg. angle, since most materials will flow at this angle, but spouts as steep as 60 deg. and as shallow as 30 deg. are common.

Although the inner surface of a spout may appear smooth, it is actually filled with many tiny pits and crevices which can hold fine materials. If a quantity of material is dropped into the spout, it may slide easily because of momentum. But if the material is initially at rest, it may not begin to flow. Fine particles of a material require a steeper spout incline than coarser particles because they are more likely to be held by the roughness of the spout surface.

Welding splatter, bolt and rivet heads, raised joints, and other obstructions in the spouting also cause considerable resistance to flow and should be eliminated wherever possible. Lining the spout with some sort of antifriction plastic material can improve material flow and may even allow a lower incline angle, an important consideration if height is at a premium.

Several "right-wrong" **spouting installations** are illustrated in Fig. 7-33. It is better to locate a conveyor discharge such that the material will fall directly into the throat of the receiving hopper. It is unwise to restrict the size of the spout immediately after it leaves the hopper. When a spout is widened to fill an opening wider than the spout, it is essential that the angle of incline of the widened portion be sufficiently steep so that the material will spread the entire width. Vanes can be added to encourage the material to spread.

A spout which feeds a belt conveyor should be inclined in the direction of conveyor travel. Attaching a spout to the side of a screw conveyor can prevent overloading the conveyor.

When a spout feeds an enclosed space, the material

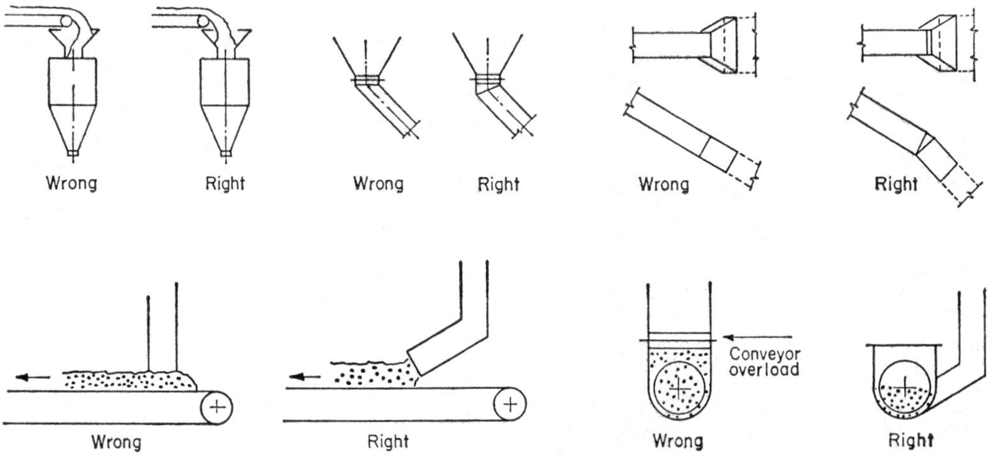

FIG. 7-33. Spouting installations.

entering this space displaces air. This air will attempt to counterflow through the spout, thus obstructing the material flow. This problem may be prevented by venting the enclosed area.

Warm materials flowing through a cold spout can cause condensation, which in turn can cause finely ground materials to stick to the spout. It is essential that this condition be corrected either by application of insulation or by increasing the temperature of the space through which the spout passes.

Specifying Bulk Materials for Best Flow. Many flow problems can be eliminated at the source by rigid, accurate, and sensible specification of the physical characteristics of the material.

Particle size is one of the most common and controllable factors which affect the flowability of a given material. In general, it may be assumed that the larger the particle size and the more free the material is from fines, the more easily the material will flow. Specifications can dictate the desired particle size and uniformity of particle size for purchased raw materials. Stage grinding in the plant can reduce waste and improve flowability by producing a ground material with a minimum of fines, but this involves extra operations which may not be economically defensible.

Handling ease is often enhanced by **pelleting** the raw materials. The large particle size, uniformity of particle size, and hard smooth surface of pellets all contribute to good flow.

Moisture content is another common and controllable flow factor. Most materials can safely absorb moisture up to a certain point; further addition of moisture can cause significant flow problems. Specifications can control the amount of moisture content present in purchased raw materials. Moisture content can be lowered in the plant by including a drying operation in the process line. The costs incurred in drying may be offset by more efficient flow, lower shipping cost, and control of deterioration losses.

Moisture control can also be effected by replacing the air in the material container or bin with a dry stable gas—nitrogen, for example. This technique is also used to protect the material from certain types of deterioration, such as vitamin loss from food materials.

High temperatures can cause serious flow problems in some materials which contain glutens, sugars, or other soluble or low-melting-point components. These materials become sticky at high temperatures, and it may be necessary to install cooling equipment. As with drying equipment, a study should be made to determine if the additional cost of cooling can be offset by the savings effected by improved flow. Other possible advantages, such as the keeping qualities of the product at lower temperatures, should of course be considered.

Age appears to improve the flowability of certain materials. This is probably the result of particle surface oxidation, more even moisture distribution, and the rounding of particle corners caused by handling.

Oil content does not materially decrease flowability. For example, the addition of oils and fats to animal-feed ingredients improves the quality of pellets made from these materials, making the pellet surfaces harder and enabling the pellets to resist attrition.

Bin Unloaders. It is sometimes necessary to provide auxiliary devices and techniques to attain smooth flow of solids through bins and hoppers. Ways to accomplish this were outlined in a series of articles by Berg (*Modern Materials Handling*, September, November, December, 1959).

Many flow problems may be solved entirely by the use of bin unloaders. It is certainly worthwhile to design the bin around the bin unloader to obtain optimum results. In some cases, the economy of bin design is improved by incorporating a bin unloader. Bin unloaders have two important advantages over simple gravity discharges. First, the bin unloader provides a uniform flow from the bin. Second, since the ideal bin discharge outlet size would be the size of the cross section of the bin itself, the bin unloader approaches this ideal by virtue of its large area.

Various examples of bin unloaders (Fig. 7-34) include the screw conveyor; the drag conveyor; the apron, pan, or belt conveyor; the sweep arm with chain cutter; the sweep arm with screw conveyor; the circular bin discharger; the feeder discharger; and the oscillating feeder.

Screw conveyors are most applicable to materials which arch only moderately. They may be used for materials which pack easily but which are not allowed to settle in the bin for long periods. It is very desirable that the screw conveyor under the bin be tapered or have variable-pitch flights so that it will accept material the entire length of the bin discharge.

A **drag conveyor** under a bin works well because it is not influenced by the weight of the bin contents. Like screw conveyors, most drag conveyors are applicable to materials which arch only moderately. One type uses

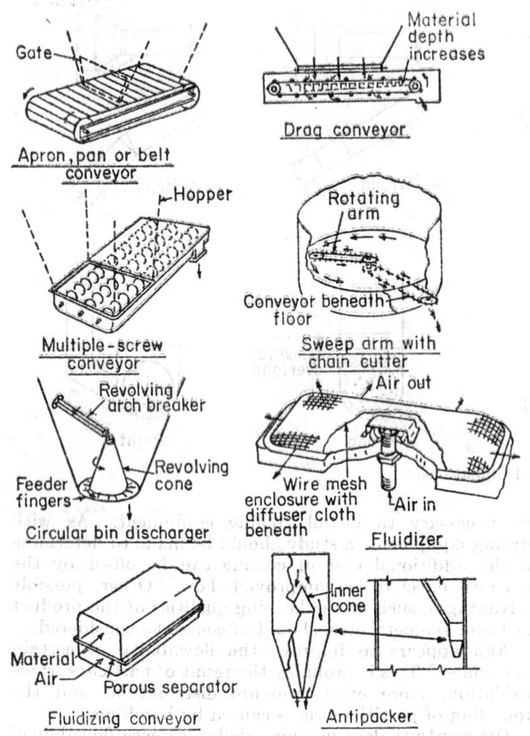

FIG. 7-34. Devices for promoting discharge from bins.

an upper chain to feed varying lengths of ports to the lower chain, which then carries the product to the discharge opening. This mechanism provides uniform flow from a large bin discharge area.

The **apron, pan, or belt conveyor** has been used for years to remove coal, ear corn, ore, and stringy, chunky, or irregularly shaped materials from bins.

The **sweep-arm bin unloader** has proved very successful under round bins. One type uses a chain on the revolving sweep arm. The chain cuts and pulls the material ahead of the arm and toward the center. The material then discharges into a second conveyor which removes the material to the outside of the bin. This bin unloader has successfully handled a wide range of materials, including those that arch very easily. It is effective for handling long stringy materials. Another sweep-arm type has a screw conveyor on the revolving arm.

The **circular bin discharger** may have an arch breaker which rotates on its own axis and rolls around the bin wall. The feeder-discharger type is a modification of the circular bin discharger. A feeder mechanism is added to provide a uniform volume delivery.

The **oscillating feeder** is a simply constructed bin unloader which is useful for chunky materials. Since the material is propelled by the oscillating action, it never comes into contact with moving mechanical parts.

Flow Aids. This term applies to devices which help keep stored materials in a fluid state. Various examples include the fluidizer, the distorter, the vibrator, the antipacker, and the agitator.

Fluidizing is most successful for handling finely ground materials and is effective for stringy materials with many voids. The fluidizing process effectively undermines the tall columns formed by materials which rathole easily. One fluidizing unit features a wire-mesh enclosure with an air-diffuser fabric which is fastened to the bin or hopper walls. Another consists of a perforated pipe probe covered with a flax-straw diffusing cloth. Still another has a blanket of polyurethane foam which covers the bottom of bins. Cast-in plenum chambers distribute air through this blanket. The fluidizing conveyor (see p. 7-22) has been used successfully for unloading bins.

Distorting the bin or hopper walls is an effective method of breaking down arched materials, but the effectiveness is dependent to some extent on the material. A spongy material may merely absorb the distortion. Rubber panels are a means of distorting the walls. They are inflated and deflated periodically at a predetermined rate to keep material in the bottom in a fluid state. Like the fluidizing process, distortion undermines the tall columns formed by materials which rathole easily.

Vibrators are useful for removing materials which cling and hang up in an emptied bin or hopper. Since vibrations cause packing, vibrators are ineffective for breaking down arched materials in a full bin. They are not satisfactory for low-density materials because vibrations do not carry well through these materials.

Antipacking devices help prevent packing, the root of all bulk-flow problems. The suspended-plate type consists of plates fastened to cables or rods which are suspended from the top of the bin. Each plate supports a portion of the material. Ledges and beams in the bin accomplish some antipacking. A double-cone device maintains material in an unpacked state. The column of material above the device is larger in diameter than that above a simple discharge opening, reducing the possibility for material to arch or cling to side walls.

Agitating devices usually consist of moving mechanical devices inside the bin which keep the material loose and moving downward. One type consists of a horizontal rotating shaft with paddles which is placed in the hopper immediately over the discharge. Vertical rotating shafts with chain flails are effective for opening a vertical section in the material. They continue to eat out the material as centrifugal force increases the flailing radius. Agitating devices are used mainly for those materials which arch easily near the bin discharge. It is impractical to install large agitating mechanisms.

Auxiliary Equipment. Feeders are vital to the proper operation of many solids-handling systems. For granular free-flowing materials a simple hand-operated slide gate may provide sufficient flow control; but for other materials, and particularly in processing operations requiring precise control, feeders are mandatory.

Heavy-duty apron feeders (Fig. 7-35*a*) are designed for high capacity and rugged service on applications such as railroad-car dumps and similar high-impact situations. They are usually fabricated from special steels, such as manganese alloys; pans are both side- and center-supported.

Apron feeders for normal operations (Fig. 7-35*b*) are usually equipped with overlapping pans to prevent leakage of material. Pans are mounted on roller chain and usually have side plates to increase the depth of load without spillage. Special pan shapes are available, those in the illustration being designed to minimize drop at the discharge point. Typical capacity and size ranges are shown in Table 7-20.

Belt feeders (Fig. 7-35*c*) are essentially short belt conveyors, with capacity and power requirements affected by full-length skirtboards which necessarily create a friction drag. They are usually designed with flat idlers, although troughed or spool-end idlers are not uncommon. Their chief advantage is the elimination of dribble which is difficult with apron-type feeders. Typical

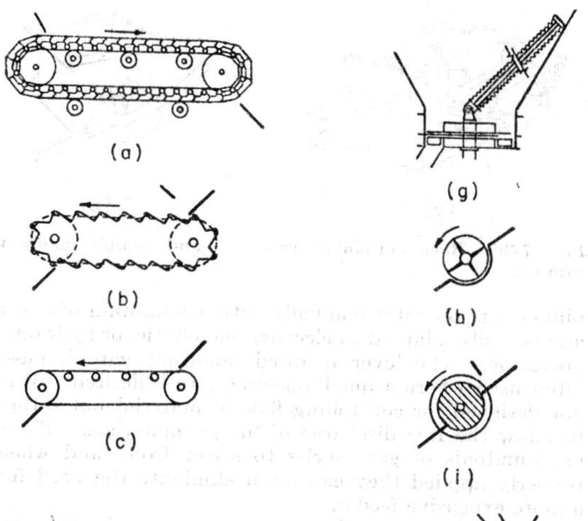

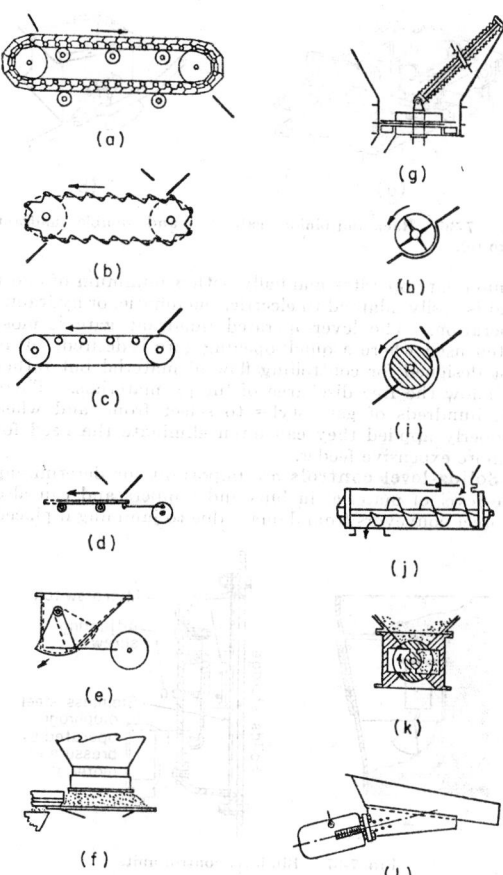

FIG. 7-35. Feeders for bulk materials. (*a*) Heavy-duty apron. (*b*) Apron with overlapping pans. (*c*) Belt (flat or troughed). (*d*) Reciprocating plate. (*e*) Swinging quadrant chop. (*f*) Rotary plate with plow. (*g*) Circular bin with rotating fingers. (*h*) Rotary vane. (*i*) Rotary drum. (*j*) Screw (single or multiple). (*k*) Rotary air lock. (*l*) Electrical vibrating.

Table 7-20. Apron-feeder Capacities
Based on coal weighing 50 lb./cu. ft.

Capacity, tons/hr.	Apron width, in.	Skirt boards		Speed, ft./min.	Max. size lumps, in.*
		Width between skirts, in.	Depth of skirts, in.		
10	15	13	8	20	6
15	18	16	8	20	6
20	18	16	10	20	6
25	18	16	12	20	6
30	18	16	14	21	6
35	24	22	12	21	8
40	24	22	14	20	8
50	24	22	16	22	8
60	30	28	16	20	12
75	36	34	16	21	16
100	42	40	18	21	20

Capacities are based on the feeder two-thirds full, and coal 2½ in. and under; capacities may be varied in proportion to depth of load and speed of travel.
Apron feeders usually run from 15 to 30 ft./min.
Maximum recommended inclination for apron feeders is 25 deg.
* 90 per cent to be less than size listed.

capacity, size, speed, and important dimensions are given in Table 7-21.

Reciprocating-plate feeders (Fig. 7-35*d*) are widely used for materials which are not seriously abrasive, and

Table 7-21. Belt-feeder Capacities
Based on coal weighing 50 lb./cu. ft.

Capacity, tons/hr.	Belt width, in.	Skirt boards		Speed, ft./min.	Max. size lumps, in.*
		Width between skirts, in.	Depth of skirts, in.		
10	18	12	8	25	4
15	18	12	8	30	4
20	18	12	10	30	4
25	18	12	12	30	4
30	18	12	14	30	4
35	24	18	12	30	6
40	24	18	14	30	6
50	24	18	16	30	6
60	30	24	14	30	8
75	30	24	16	30	8
100	36	30	16	30	10

Capacities are based on the feeder two-thirds full with other operating allowances and coal 2½ in. and under; capacities may be varied in proportion to the cross section of the load and speed of travel.
Belt feeders usually run from 20 to 60 ft./min.
Maximum recommended inclination for belt feeders is 15 deg.
* 90 per cent of coal to be less than size listed.

in particular for coal. Capacity is determined by depth of material, as well as frequency and length of stroke. Preliminary design information is given in Table 7-22.

Table 7-22. Reciprocating-feeder Capacities
Based on coal weighing 50 lb./cu. ft.

Capacity, tons/hr.	Max. lump, in.	Size feeder, width × depth, in.	Strokes per min.
10	6	16 × 12	15
15	6	16 × 12	23
20	6	16 × 12	30
25	10	18 × 15	27
30	10	18 × 15	32
35	10	18 × 18	31
40	12	20 × 18	32
50	15	24 × 20	30
60	15	24 × 20	36
75	18	30 × 24	30
100	18	36 × 24	33

Capacities are based on the feeder two-thirds full, and a travel of 6 in. capacities may be varied in proportion to length of travel and strokes per min. Reciprocating feeders usually run from 15 to 40 strokes per minute.

Flight feeders (Fig. 7-15) are also used, frequently in parallel rows forming live-bottomed bins to prevent arching of stored material. **Screw feeders** (Fig. 7-35*j*) are used in a similar fashion and also singly. They are usually equipped with a variable-pitch screw flight, sometimes to prevent packing and sometimes to pack material into a more dense mass. The **rotary-vane feeder** (Fig. 7-35*h*) is a measuring-type feeder and may be open as shown or completely enclosed. It can deliver relatively precise rates of flow. Size and capacity for standard units are shown in Table 7-23. **Rotary-**

Table 7-23. Rotary-vane-feeder Capacities
Based on sized coal weighing 50 lb./cu. ft.

Size, diam. × length, in.	Capacity, tons/hr. at 10 r.p.m.
12 × 12	7.65
12 × 14	8.95
15 × 14	14.3
15 × 16	16.3
18 × 16	23.6
18 × 18	26.6

Capacities are based on the feeder two-thirds full and coal 2½ in. and under; capacities may be varied in proportion with speed. Rotary-vane feeders usually operate at 10 to 30 r.p.m.

drum feeders (Fig. 7-35*i*) are relatively simple units with control through depth of material and speed of drum revolution. For extremely fine materials, a tightly sealed **rotary air-lock feeder** (Fig. 7-35*k*) may be desirable. It can prevent aeratable materials from fluidizing and flushing out of storage at high rates.

Mechanical and electrical **vibrating feeders** (Fig. 7-35*l*) are widely used as they are available in an extremely wide range of capacities. The electrical vibrating feeder is widely used where variable feed rate is desired, because simple rheostat controls can give extremely fine feed variations. Capacities and dimensions for one electrical unit are given in Table 7-24.

Table 7-24. Electrical Vibrating Feeder Capacities
Based on 100 lb./cu. ft. material

Size, width × depth, in.	Capacity, tons/hr.	Power consumption, watts	Current input, amp. at 220 volts, 60 cycles
18 × 6	50	750	9
24 × 7¼	100	1000	18
36 × 8¼	200	1500	25
48 × 12	500	2600	40

Chop-type feeders (Fig. 7-35*e*) give a semicontinuous feed by means of a quadrant gate driven back and forth by an eccentric. Varying the throw of the eccentric or the depth of cut gives some measure of feed control.

The **rotary-plate feeder** (Fig. 7-35*f*) gives good volume control with a simple plow arrangement for shearing material off to a discharge chute. The large diameter of the throat helps with materials that tend to arch in the bin. Another version of this feeder uses rotating fingers to draw material from the bin column and may be equipped with a secondary stage of solid-plate flights which prevent flushing. Either type of feeder can be equipped with a rotating-arch breaker arm which will break up arching action in the conical throat section of the bin. For heavy materials the rotating plate may be very small; for lighter materials such as wood chips it is usually very large. In general, the larger the base diameter, the less difficulty there is from material hanging up in the bin.

Gates (Fig. 7-36) are used to control flow from bins, hoppers, and processing equipment to feeders or directly to conveyors. They are available in a wide range of styles, from the simple hand slide gate (which can frequently be very difficult to operate by hand) to the precision rack-and-pinion design which is usually tightly sealed against dust and dribble. The rack-and-pinion gate operates manually with a minimum of effort and is easily adapted to electric, pneumatic, or hydraulic operation. The lever-operated quadrant gate is most often used where a quick-opening gate is desired. It is not designed for controlling flow of material but rather to allow the free discharge of lumpy materials. There are hundreds of gate styles to select from, and when properly applied they can often eliminate the need for a more expensive feeder.

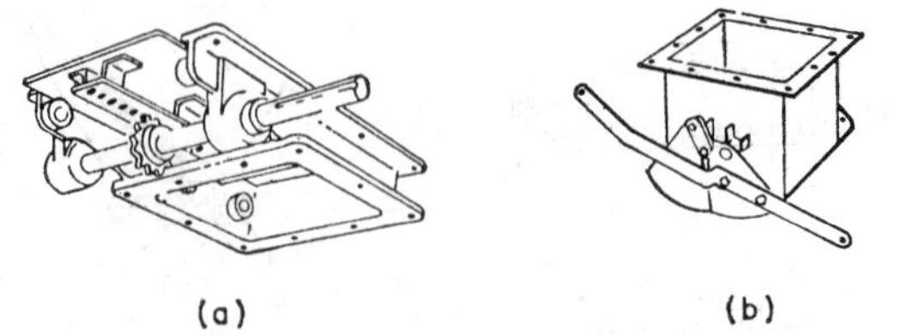

FIG. 7-36. Rack-and-pinion gate (*a*) and double-quadrant gate (*b*).

Solids-level controls are important for determining the level of material in bins and hoppers and can also protect conveyors from damage due to jamming if placed

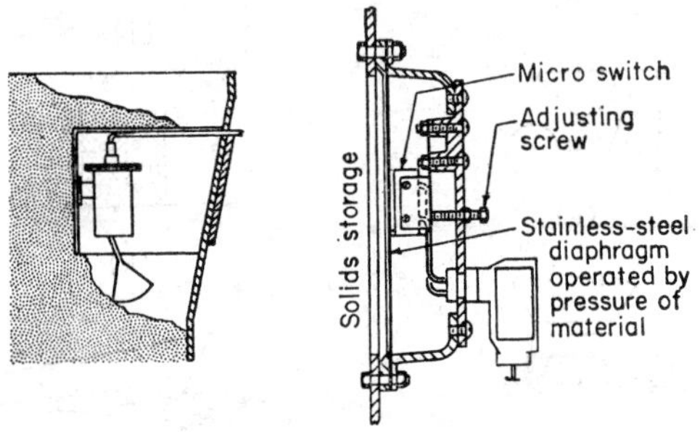

FIG. 7-37. Bin-level-control units.

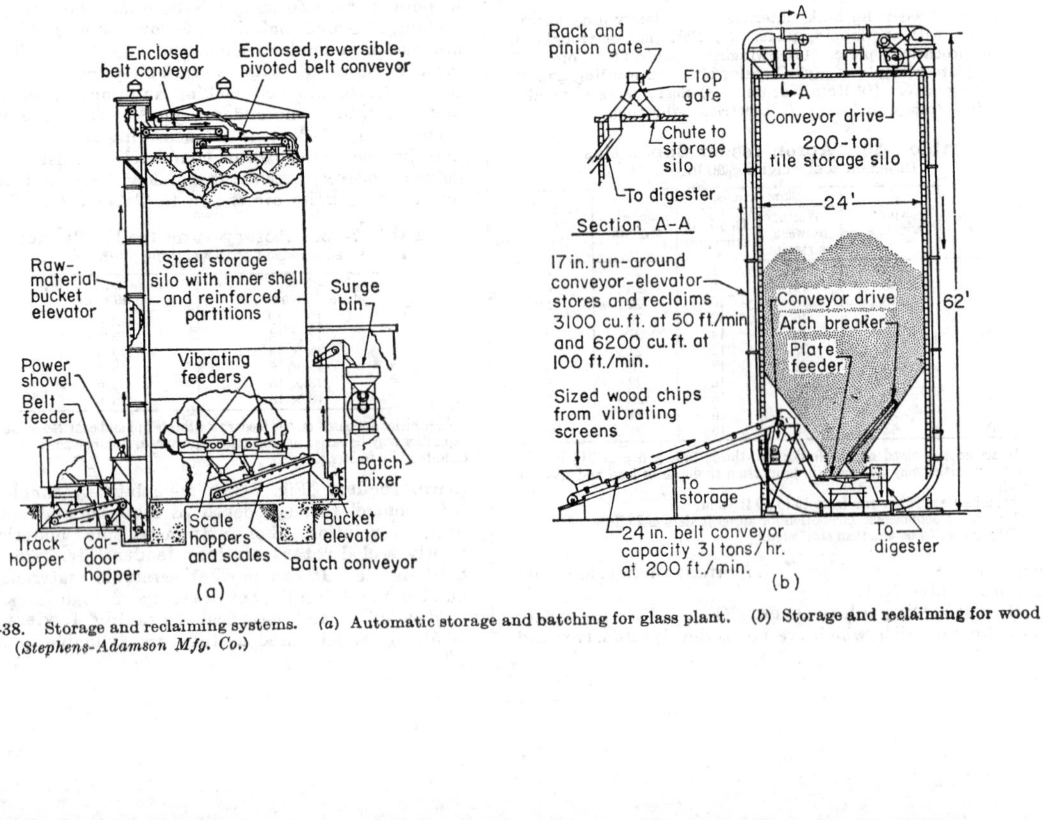

FIG. 7-38. Storage and reclaiming systems. (*a*) Automatic storage and batching for glass plant. (*b*) Storage and reclaiming for wood chips. (*Stephens-Adamson Mfg. Co.*)

in transfer and discharge chutes. They may simply activate an audio or visual warning signal or may be electrically tied into the conveying system to start or stop conveyors automatically. Many designs are available, ranging from expensive devices using radioactive isotopes down to simple paddles. The two designs shown in Fig. 7-37 both depend on limit switches, with activation from a pendant cone on one and from a stainless-steel diaphragm on the other. In either case, the presence of material resting against the cone or diaphragm opens or closes the switch, activating a warning signal in the latter case and turning off power to the conveyor in the former.

Figure 7-38 shows a variety of equipment in specific **storing and reclaiming** operations. The glass-plant batching operation (Fig. 7-38*a*) is highly automated, with all conveyors controlled from a central pushbutton panel. Batches of material are withdrawn from storage by placing a punched card in a reader which activates feeder conveyors in sequence as materials are weighed and conveyed to the batch mixer. Figure 7-38*b* illustrates a continuous-flow conveyor being used for both storage and reclaiming of wood chips, with a belt conveyor feeding material into it for storage and a circular bin discharger with arch-breaker arm feeding into it for delivery of chips to the digester.

TRANSPORT OF SOLIDS IN CONTAINERS

For materials shipped to a single customer in annual volumes of 10 million pounds or more, it is generally most economical for both shipper and receiver to work with bulk shipments. Thus the carrier itself, whether railroad car, truck, or ship, actually becomes the shipping container. Below 10 million pounds annual consumption there are many alternatives, with the basic choice between a returnable reusable container and a one-trip expendable container.

Figure 7-39 shows roughly the **economical range** of annual tonnages which can be served by returnable bulk

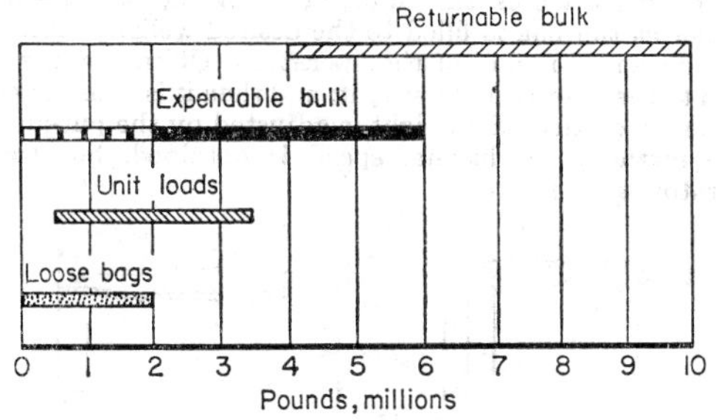

FIG. 7-39. Economical ranges of shipping containers.

containers, expendable bulk containers, unit loads (palletized and/or steel-strapped or taped loads), and loose bags.

Large Bulk Containers. These may be classified as returnable or expendable. Shown in Fig. 7-40 is a

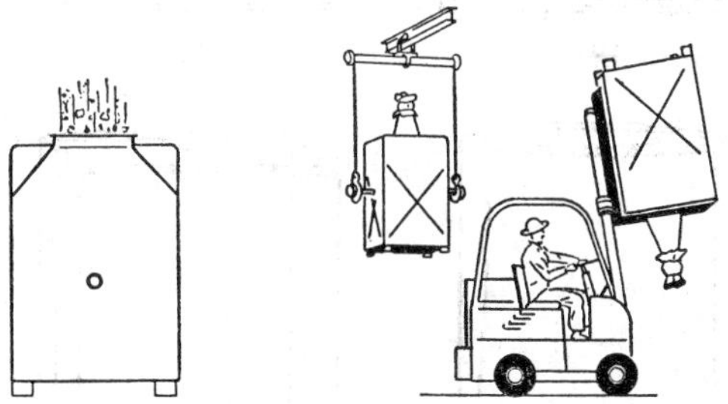

FIG. 7-40. Returnable metal bin.

steel bin which can be easily handled by fork truck, overhead crane, or even conveyors. It is sturdily constructed and can be shipped on open flat or gondola cars. It has the added advantage of allowing outside storage, since it is weathertight. There are many variations of this returnable bin, some fabricated of lightweight aluminum which can be disassembled into two nesting parts for economical return shipment.

Many types of pallet boxes are used for shipment of bulk materials. They can be fitted with bag or box-type liners which can be thrown away by the user, and the boxes themselves either folded or dismantled for return shipment. Fig. 7-41 illustrates a wire-mesh container

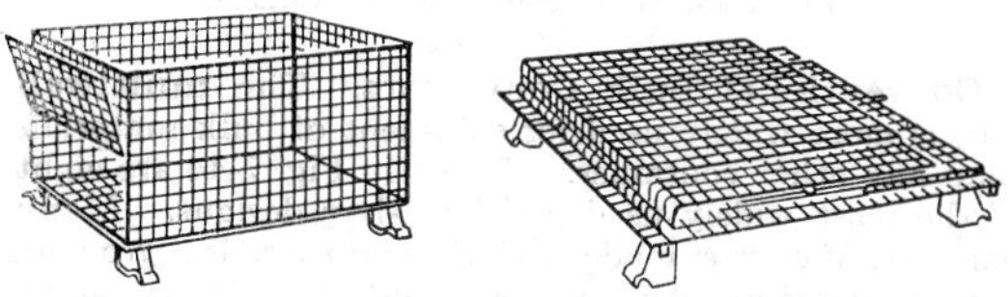

FIG. 7-41. Returnable wire-mesh container.

which, though primarily designed for small-parts handling, can be fitted with a paper or plastic liner for shipping bulk materials. It folds into a highly compact flat shape for economical return to the shipper. Also quite popular are large rubber containers (coated fabric) which can be collapsed and rolled up for return to the shipper. One type is shown in Fig. 7-42, and there are several

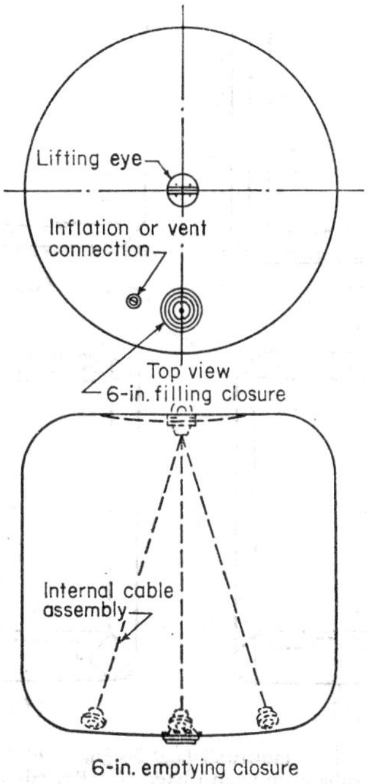

FIG. 7-42. Returnable rubber container.

others available. They have the advantage of being able to handle either solids or liquids and can be stored outdoors and shipped on open-deck carriers. For most efficient handling they may require special equipment.

Expendable large bulk shipping containers are available in a wide variety, most of them being constructed of fiberboard with pallet-type bases of wood or paper. Multiwall corrugated has also been used to make a sturdy container. Most of these are steel-strapped (flat or round) for tight closure, but they may also be stapled or glued. Figure 7-43 shows some typical expendable-container designs.

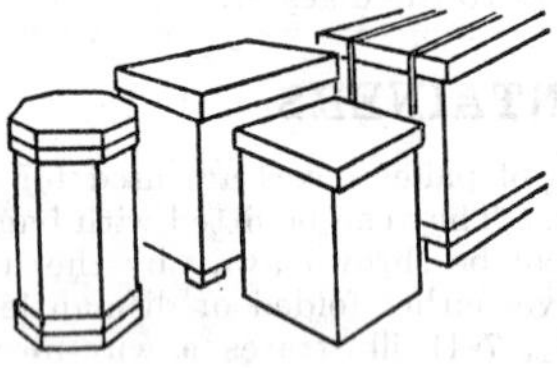

Fig. 7-43. Expendable bulk containers.

Conventional Bulk Containers. The **multiwall bag** is more widely used for shipment of bulk materials than any other container. Shown in Fig. 7-44 are eight of the most widely used multiwall-bag designs. Many bags are, of course, made of cloth, and there is a growing use by many shippers of bags made from heavy-duty polyethylene film. These bags can be readily heat-sealed to give a strong tight closure. For bags containing 50 to 100 lb. of material, typical dimensions vary from 24 to 36 in. long, 14 to 17 in. wide, and 6 to 10 in. thick.

Steel, aluminum, and fiber **drums** are used for the shipment of bulk materials, both solid and liquid. All are reusable, but the fiber drum has the disadvantage of not being able to withstand the water or steam cleaning commonly used with metal drums. Its initial cost, however, is lower.

Packaging Machinery. Machinery for the packaging of bulk materials includes (1) weighing and bagging equipment, and (2) filling and weighing equipment for packing dry materials into drums and barrels.

Automatic scales are used in conjunction with packing equipment. They automatically meter the flow according to preset weights. Such devices are best for volume production, can be arranged in batteries, and can handle most dry materials.

A typical automatic scale unit is mounted below a storage-bin hopper. It ordinarily consists of a top gate, a power feed (screw, belt, or spike), a feed chute (with or without a vibrator to settle the materials), a hopper, and a bottom gate. The whole unit is scale-mounted.

To fill a bag, the operator manually adjusts the bottom gate. This automatically starts the power feed and the vibrator. When the predetermined weight is delivered, the feed automatically cuts off and the vibrator stops. Frequently the filling speed is decreased (called dribble feed) as the correct weight is approached to obtain greater accuracy.

With **hand scales,** a bag is attached to the scale, and the operator closes the filling gate of the storage-bin hopper as the bag is filled to the desired weight. Accuracy depends on skill of the operator. Often the bag is filled to the approximate weight, and then it is transferred to the scale where the weight is adjusted by the put-and-take method. Additional speed is obtained, but two operators are required.

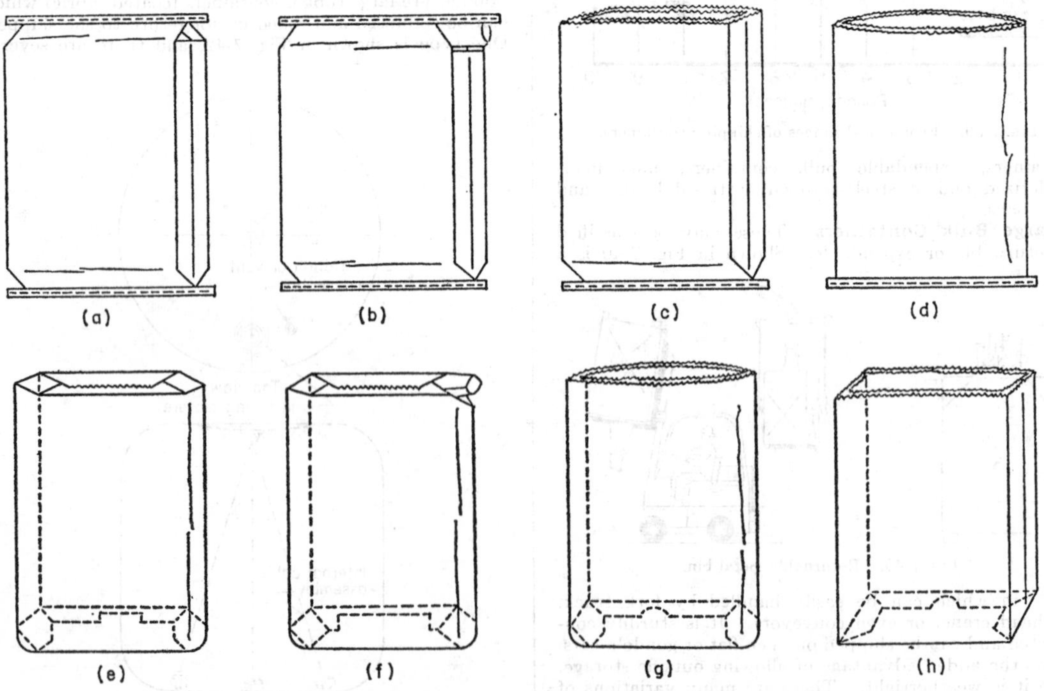

Fig. 7-44. Common multiwall bag designs. (*a*) Sewn-valve bag. (*b*) Sewn-valve tuck-in-sleeve bag. (*c*) Sewn open-mouth bag. (*d*) Flat sewn-tube open-mouth bag. (*e*) Pasted-valve bag. (*f*) Pasted-valve tuck-in-sleeve bag. (*g*) Pasted open-mouth satchel-bottom bag. (*h*) Pasted open-mouth automatic bag.

Auger packers are usually used in conjunction with automatic weighing. They are for materials which will not settle by vibration. These materials have to be forced into the container by an auger or screw which creates sufficient pressure to deaerate the material and compress it. The compacting sometimes takes place before the material is discharged into the container.

One common type of auger packer is fed from an overhead bin. After the bag has been slipped over the auger tube, a platform supporting the bag is released and raised by a counterweight. When it reaches the top position, a clutch is automatically engaged, causing the auger to force the materials into the bag. The platform is forced down against the resistance of a friction brake until the desired weight is in the bag. (Five adjustments can be made to the brake, permitting weight control to within a few ounces.) The clutch is then automatically disengaged. The brake is released by a foot pedal, and the platform drops to allow removal of the filled bag.

Machines used for the **filling of valve bags** are of the impeller, belt, and screw types and are equipped with either preweighing or gross-weighing scales.

Filling Open-mouthed Bags. Machines are available which can automatically weigh materials, introduce the charge into paper bags, and close the bags by stitching. There are variations. With one type, only one operator is required for a capacity of a thousand 100-lb. bags per hour. This type of machine has a revolving turret. Bags are carried on individual spouts located on the periphery. A charge is dropped into each spout from the hopper above. Mechanisms jog or settle the material in the bag. Automatic bag-gripping carrier chains divert the filled bag from the turret and guide it through a sewing unit and then through a taping mechanism.

Filling Drums and Barrels. Container economy often requires **agitation** of barrels and large drums during filling. This ordinarily prevents weighing until the approximate weight has been packed, when the container is removed from below the filling hopper to a platform scale. The correct weight is then adjusted by the put-and-take method. (A recently developed unit vibrates and weighs at essentially the same time, utilizing a strain gage. It requires a clamp to hold the bottom of the drum or barrel so it does not bounce off.)

Automatic scales are occasionally used for weighing and dumping into drums and barrels, but the speed of these devices often makes it difficult to pack, since insufficient time is allowed for settling. The best plan in using automatic scales for barrel filling is to divide the weight to be packed into two or more dumps of the scale and have the container agitated throughout the operation.

A **vacuum method** of packing can be used for filling drums and barrels that are not airtight if they are filled in an airtight shroud.

Vibrators are used during the packing of bags, barrels, and drums for quick settling of the contents. Most vibrators are adaptable for use with all three types of containers. One type of vibrator consists of a vibrating platform with the vibrator mounted under the cushioned top plate. Motion is accomplished by electronic control that changes alternating current to pulsating waves with a time interval between.

Hydraulic jolters compact light fluffy materials that cannot be settled by high-speed horizontal motion. These vibrators operate by water power to lift their deck plates a short distance and then drop them with a sharp jolt. One type of packer has both an oscillating and a vibrating motion to settle the contents of bags, drums, and barrels.

Unitized Loads. In 1959 the American Standards Association approved standard MH1.1-1955 for American Standard Pallet Sizes. This makes possible the maximum use of storage space and carrier cubic content with a more economical standard pallet. It is unfortunate that lack of standardization in containers and carriers still leaves the American Standard with 11 different pallet sizes as shown in Table 7-25. Figure 7-45 shows how these various pallet sizes utilize the shipping space in a standard A.A.R. boxcar.

Table 7-25. Standard Pallet Sizes

Size	Rectangular, in.	Size	Square, in.
R-1	24 × 32	S-1	36 × 36
R-2	32 × 40	S-2	42 × 42
R-3	36 × 42	S-3	48 × 48
R-4	32 × 48		
R-5	36 × 48		
R-6	40 × 48		
R-7	48 × 60		
R-8	48 × 72		

Unfortunately, although pallet sizes are now standardized, there are no standards for their materials or methods of construction, except for those of some of the manufacturer associations. Shown in Fig. 7-46 are a variety of pallets ranging from heavy skid types to expendable paper ones. Most common is the double-faced wood pallet, preferably of hard wood for durability. The con-

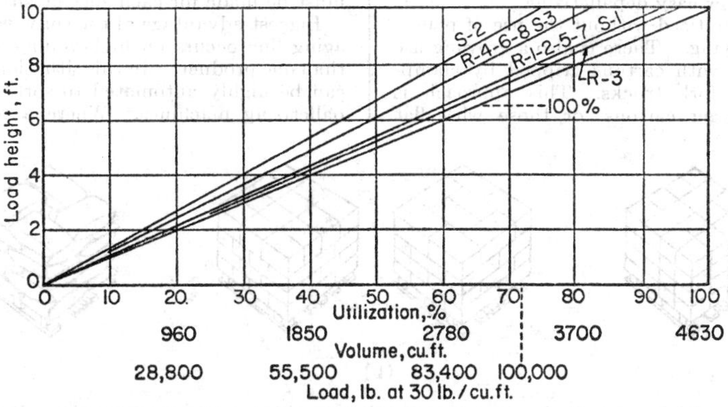

Fig. 7-45. Utilization of shipping space in standard boxcar when using various American Standard pallet sizes. Based on 1 in. clearance between pallets, 50-ton boxcar (50 ft. 6 in. by 9 ft. 2 in.). Chart shows that pallets R1, R2, R5, R7, and S1 are equally good for all heights of load, but pallet R3 is the most efficient.

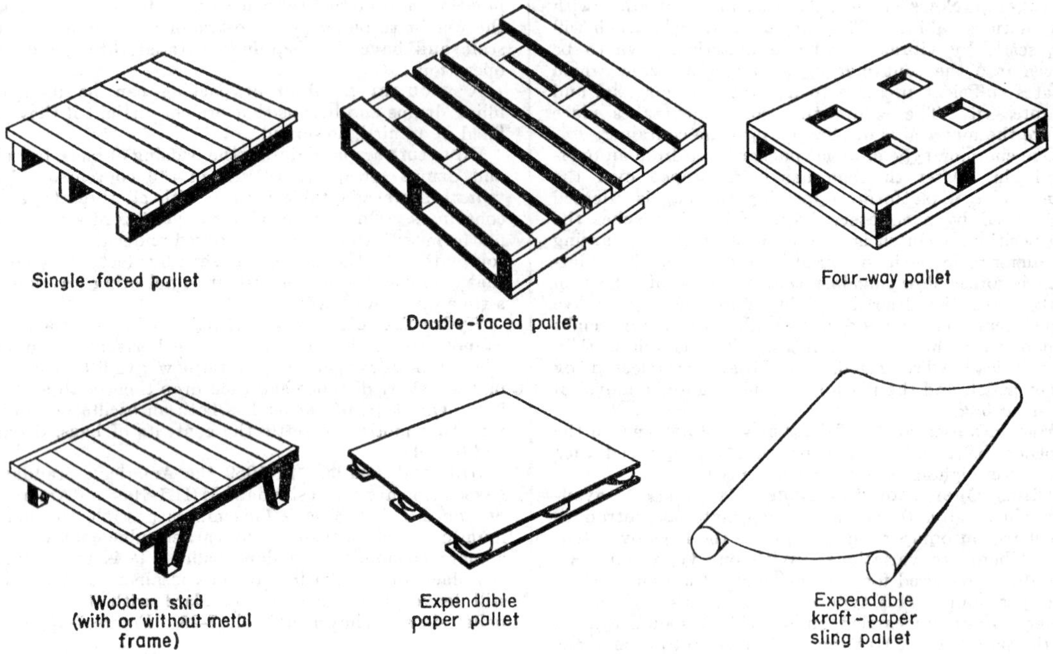

FIG. 7-46. Types of pallets.

struction of pallets which are intended for long-term use should be carefully studied if maintenance costs are to be minimized. This is of particular importance where pallets are to be handled by conveyor, since a damaged pallet can easily jam a conveyor system. Expendable pallets of wood can be obtained at fairly reasonable cost and can support relatively heavy loads. These are usually single-face types. Paper pallets of various types are being quite widely used.

Almost any type of container can be palletized, as shown in the sketches of typical pallet patterns in Fig. 7-47. In some cases a tie on the top tier of cartons, either cord, heavy-duty rubber band, or steel strap, will help to maintain stability of the load. It is also necessary or desirable on some loads to use multiple bands of steel strapping. Containers may also be treated with a mastic that is strong in shear and weak in tension to prevent sliding but allow easy depalletizing.

Loads may also be unitized without the use of pallets by steel strapping or tying. There is also a growing use of palletless handling, with cartons gripped by clamp-type attachments on fork trucks. This approach is most adaptable to larger cartons, or those with flat bottoms which are not readily deformed by the inside containers.

Container-handling Systems. Selection of a proper materials-handling system for containers involves numerous variables, in both the producer's and customer's plants. Economics of the handling system must take into consideration the customer's problems, because many chemical producers have lost markets to competitors because of the high cost of handling their products in the customers' plants. Since there is still wide use of hand trucks and other manual methods in small operations, this fact remains an important consideration in the design of a producing plant's handling system.

Mechanical handling can be achieved with either industrial powered trucks or conveyors, or a combination of both. There are no general rules which can establish the economics of these systems; so a careful cost study must be made for each specific situation.

Biggest advantage of the conveyor system in the packaging line occurs on high-volume operations with more than one product. In this situation, the conveyor system can be highly automated to sort, accumulate, and feed palletizing machines. Where a product is shipped as

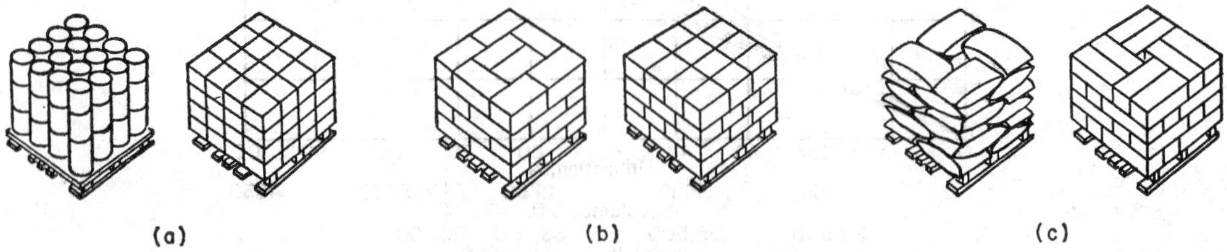

FIG. 7-47. Typical pallet patterns. (*a*) Block pattern is commonly used, although oftentimes unstable. It may be made more secure by encircling the top tier of containers with wire or strapping. (*b*) Brick pattern is most commonly used. Containers are interlocked to make a relatively stable load by placing alternate tiers at a 90-deg. position to each other. (*c*) Pinwheel pattern is used where the brick pattern is found unstable. Alternate tiers can be interlocked.

soon as packaged, without intermediate warehousing, the conveyor system may also prove advantageous. However, studies of fork-truck operations frequently give surprisingly economical results. Hence the decision as to which handling system to use must be based on careful research.

Industrial Trucks. There is an almost infinite variety of industrial trucks, with the simplest division between those which are powered and those which are not. There are few large material-handling systems built entirely around the use of hand trucks, but their use has continued to grow because of widespread effort to put manpower to more productive use than simple lifting and carrying, even in small plants. However, the operation of non-powered carrying and lifting equipment is highly dependent on good floor conditions and careful maintenance of equipment. Thus many manufacturers of non-powered equipment are making a compact power package available as optional equipment, to eliminate the need for manual effort.

The **low-lift skid** and **pallet hand truck** are probably the most widely used pieces of non-powered equipment. They are usually equipped with hydraulic-lift mechanisms which can be hand- or foot-operated. Mechanical-lift mechanisms are also available, and both types can be designed for single- or multiple-stroke lifts. Since the object is merely to get a pallet or skid clear of the floor so that a load can be pulled from one position to another, the lifts on these trucks are limited to a maximum of about 4 in. In addition to these two types of non-powered industrial trucks, there is a wide variety of special units for drum handling, high stacking, and other specialized applications.

Walkie trucks (Fig. 7-48) are the most popular industrial units in the low-cost powered truck field. While they are available in practically any capacity range, most standard models are limited to a lifting capacity of around 6000 lb. These battery-powered units are designed for control by a walking operator, hence are limited to speeds of around 2 to 3½ m.p.h. Table 7-26 compares the most common types of walkies—their areas of application, the way they handle loads, and their advantages and limitations.

Biggest advantage of walkie models is their **compact size** and resulting high degree of **maneuverability.**

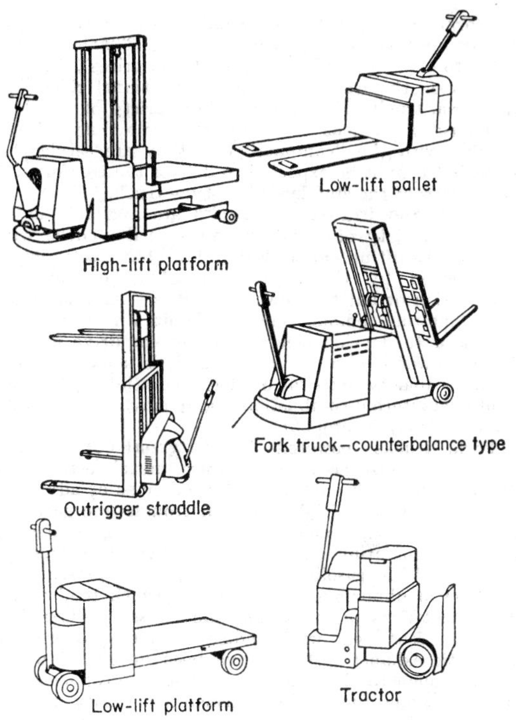

Fig. 7-48. Various types of walkie trucks.

They are also light in weight, with standard outrigger walkie lift trucks weighing only about 30 per cent of a standard rider fork truck. A typical walkie pallet truck which will handle a 6000-lb. load weighs less than 1500 lb., compared with the 6500-lb. (or more) weight of a standard fork truck. Thus the walkie is particularly desirable in older buildings or any other situation where floor loading is limited. Since it is relatively light, it follows that the walkie costs less. Low-lift

Table 7-26. Comparison of Various Types of Walkie Trucks*

Truck type	Low-lift pallet	Load carrier	Low-lift platform	High-lift platform	Outrigger straddle	Fork truck	Tractor
Application	Handles load on pallets	For load transfer	Handles loads on skids	Permits tiering loads on skids	For tiering loads on pallets or skids	For handling all types of loads, pallets, skids, etc.	For pulling loads on trailers
Handling method	Forks with wheels beneath forward end are inserted under load. Load is raised several inches off floor for moving	A simple non-elevating platform truck	Elevating platform is inserted beneath load. Load is raised several inches off floor for horizontal movement	Platform elevates on vertical uprights. Wheels beneath platform provide load support	Outriggers in front of truck equipped with wheels at forward end. Two types: one with forks nesting in top surface of outriggers; other with forks lowering in space between outriggers	Operates on counterbalanced principle, with load carried cantilever fashion in front of truck. Thin forks inserted under load. Truck designed for stacking	Many types for pulling trailers. Also with attachments for lifting end of semilive skids. Some permit moving trailers without use of couplings
Advantages and limitations	Designed for handling in confined areas or areas with limited floor capacity. For horizontal moves only. Will not permit stacking	Must be loaded by hand, with crane or another truck. Simple, low cost, and ideal for handling bulky or non-unitized loads	Requires 7 in. minimum underclearance beneath load for platform entry. For horizontal movement only. Will not stack. For confined areas and light-capacity floors	Requires 7 in. minimum underclearance when picking up load. Also floor clearance for front wheels when stacking. Ideal for stacking extra-long loads and bulky objects. High stacking stability due to forward support	Short turning radius for stacking in narrow aisles. Excellent stability. Nesting forks for single-faced pallets and skids. Forks between outriggers for wing or double-faced pallets. With either, space needed beneath or between stacked pallets for outrigger entry	Truck relatively heavy for load capacity. Most versatile of walkies. Can be equipped with variety of attachments for handling specialized loads. Provides most flexible method of tiering loads in storage	Provides most efficient means of moving volume of material over relatively long distances. Trailers can be loaded or unloaded with other types of trucks

* *Modern Materials Handling.*

platform- and pallet-type walkies cost only around \$1500, and walkie lift trucks around \$3000—for the 3000- to 4000-lb.-capacity models (1960 prices).

Between the walkie and the conventional rider-type industrial truck, there is a growing variety of stand-up and sit-down trucks for relatively light duty. Comparable with the "compact" car, they are serviceable units but cannot be expected to deliver the comfort and ruggedness of the standard rider-type truck.

Rider-type industrial trucks are available in an amazing variety of standard and special models, with almost any lifting capacity desired. Their selection is complicated by the availability of either internal-combustion or battery-powered models. Also available is an internal-combustion-engine unit which drives a generator to develop electric current for drive motors. Diesel power is also available, but it is usually limited to high-capacity units for outdoor operation. The conventional internal-combustion engine may be fueled with gasoline or liquid propane.

Fork trucks powered by **internal-combustion engines** have the advantage of lower initial cost. Most are available with automatic transmissions or advanced clutch designs which give smooth trouble-free acceleration. Lifting mechanisms are powered by hydraulic cylinders operating from a central hydraulic pressure system. With gasoline as a fuel, they present the problem of obnoxious exhaust odors which tend to increase as trucks age because of the excessive idling time usually associated with industrial truck operation. Catalytic exhaust systems have been developed which can do much to alleviate this problem. Proponents of liquid-propane fuel claim marked superiority in this respect, and there is evidence that engine life is increased with this fuel. However, regional prices of propane are quite variable, and it is impossible to generalize on relative fuel costs without making a specific study. It is also important to compare the relative cost of storage and fueling facilities for the two fuels.

Industrial trucks powered by lead-acid or nickel-iron-alkaline **batteries** have the disadvantage of higher initial cost when the price of the battery is included. For that reason, this type was selected in the past mainly where engine exhaust odors were considered seriously objectionable. It was also true that early batteries were often not capable of working a full 8-hr. shift at full-load capacity, and lift speeds on fork-lift models were often slow. However, recent improvements in battery capacity per unit of size, along with higher voltage and improved electrical systems, have largely eliminated the differences in performance between the electric and the engine power systems. In terms of numbers, the internal-combustion engine still leads, but the gap is narrowing noticeably when walkie units are included in the comparison.

Another advantage offered by the electric truck is the protection inherent in its acceleration system. Thus the unskilled operator has little opportunity to damage a truck by excessive acceleration or sudden reversals of travel direction. Of course, batteries must be kept charged, and it is important to consider the cost of battery charging and maintenance. Many trucks are equipped with built-in chargers which can be plugged into the nearest 110-volt outlet, but the central charging station may be either required or desirable.

The **engine-generator** type of truck claims the advantages of both systems. There is no connection between the engine and the electric motors which provide

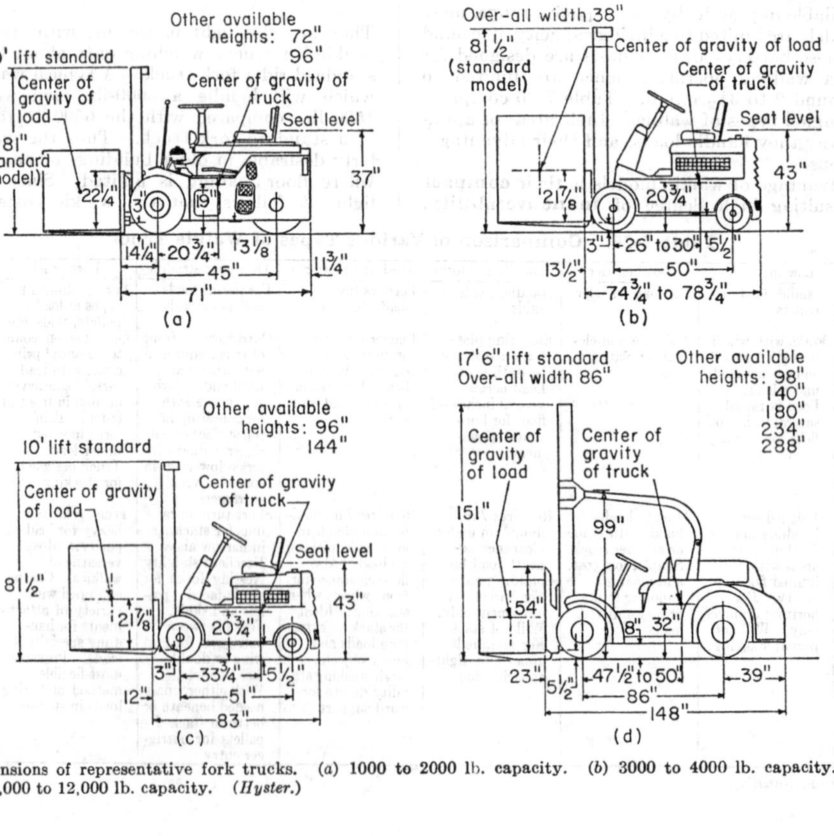

FIG. 7-49. Dimensions of representative fork trucks. (*a*) 1000 to 2000 lb. capacity. (*b*) 3000 to 4000 lb. capacity. (*c*) 5000 lb. capacity. (*d*) 10,000 to 12,000 lb. capacity. (*Hyster.*)

the operating power; hence smoother operation with less danger of shock-load damage is claimed. Also, electric current is generated as needed, with no resistance losses such as occur when battery-powered trucks are operated under loads from a constant voltage source.

Fork-truck specifications have been fairly well standardized. Load ratings are generally given for lift trucks in terms of the maximum load at a specific distance from the front-wheel center line—usually 24 in. Figure 7-49 shows typical important dimensional details for four representative trucks from one manufacturer's line. Where loads are to be stacked in areas of limited overhead, such as boxcars, particular attention should be paid to "free lift." This is the lift available before the mast begins to extend and thus raise the over-all height of the truck. Also, where heavy loads are to be handled at high speeds, truck stability may become important and should be thoroughly investigated to ensure safe operation.

While most industrial trucks are equipped with forks for the handling of palletized loads, they can be equipped with an almost limitless variety of **attachments** for handling a variety of containers, and even bulk material. Shown in Fig. 7-50 are some of the better-known attachments developed for single- or multipurpose use. For

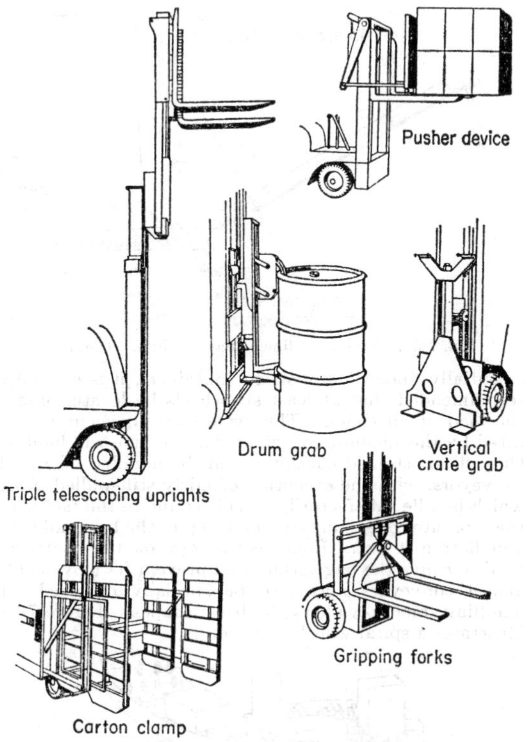

FIG. 7-50. Various types of fork-truck attachments.

example, the gripping-fork attachment may operate as a conventional set of forks for pallet handling. But it may also be used to grip a load for lifting and carrying without pallets. For example, stacks of cartons are frequently handled by gripping the bottom layer of a stack. The gripping fork is also readily adapted to handling ribbed drums.

The carton clamp, now available in a number of designs, is perhaps the most revolutionary advance in the industrial-truck field, for it eliminates the pallet. Relatively thin side-clamp members, usually lined inside with high-friction rubber, can grasp a large stack of cartons without exerting pressure sufficient to damage the contents. Thus loads can be carried with little danger of falling, and the expense of shipping and maintaining pallets is eliminated.

The **straddle truck,** designed for lifting bolsters with heavy loads or materials such as structural steel, is also finding application in handling van-type containers of packaged goods. For example, it can straddle a flat car, pick off a van container, and deposit it directly on a truck-trailer rig. It can also be used for loading railroad flatcars and even ocean-going vessels. It is just one of many special pieces of mobile equipment available for special handling problems.

Slide Conveyors. Simple gravity slides and spiral chutes, while not technically conveyors, are widely used with conveyor systems or as separate units for lowering materials from one floor to another. They are low in cost and require little floor space if slopes are held at fairly steep angles. However, they must be used only after a careful study of possible damage to containers, from bumping either together or against the sides of the chutes or slides.

Figure 7-51 shows an open-type single-blade **spiral chute.** Enclosed units are available for outside operation, and fire doors can be provided to meet requirements

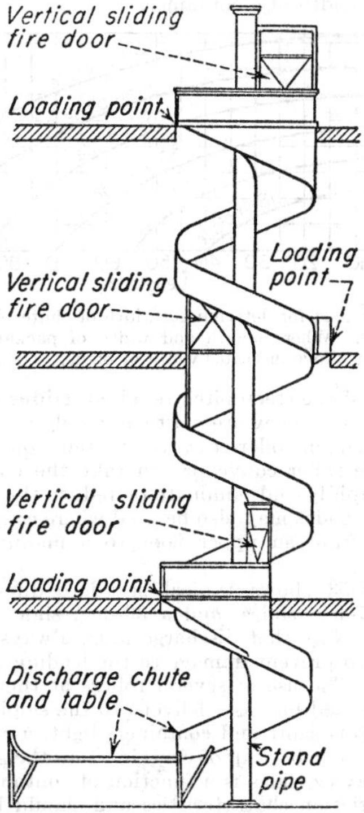

FIG. 7-51. Open-type single-blade spiral chute. Double-blade and enclosed types are available.

of local building codes. Multiple-blade chutes may be used for service to several floors, with separate inlet and outlet points. Blades may be lapped and riveted, to eliminate the possibility of containers hanging up on exposed edges. Flight sections may also be flanged and bolted together.

Speed of containers sliding down a spiral may be controlled by the pitch of the spiral or by banking the outer or inner edge of the blade. Banking tends to throw the container to one side of the blade, thus varying its total travel distance. While usually fabricated of steel, blades may be specified in different materials, as required by specific applications. Table 7-27 gives spiral chute

Table 7-27. Spiral-chute Specifications for Normal Conditions

Width of blade, in.	Gage of metal	Diam. of core, in.	Height of guard rail, in.	Outside diam. of chute
18	No. 16	10	9	3 ft. 10 in.
24	No. 16	12	12	5 ft. 0 in.
30	No. 16	15	15	6 ft. 3 in.
36	No. 14	18	15	7 ft. 6 in.
42	No. 14	21	18	8 ft. 9 in.
48	No. 12	24	18	10 ft. 0 in.

Width of blade, in.	Diam. floor opening, closed type	Pitch of spiral		Vertical door inlets, in.		Max. weight package, lb.
		Min.	Max.	High	Wide	
18	4 ft. 2 in.	4 ft. 0 in.	6 ft. 6 in.	18	14	150
24	5 ft. 4 in.	5 ft. 6 in.	8 ft. 6 in.	24	20	190
30	6 ft. 7 in.	7 ft. 0 in.	10 ft. 6 in.	30	24	230
36	7 ft. 10 in.	8 ft. 6 in.	12 ft. 6 in.	33	30	270
42	9 ft. 1 in.	10 ft. 0 in.	14 ft. 6 in.	36	36	310
48	10 ft. 4 in.	11 ft. 6 in.	16 ft. 6 in.	36	42	350

specifications for normal conditions. Figure 7-52 allows blade selection to be made on the basis of the known length and width of a container.

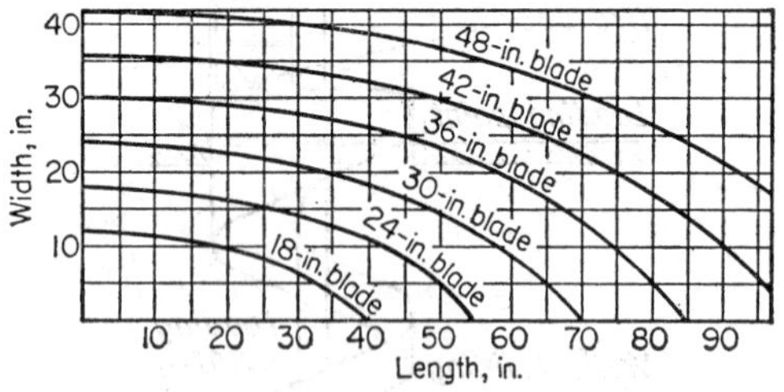

Fig. 7-52. Chart for determining width of chute blade for any size package. Where length and width of package intersect, curve nearest above indicates width of blade. (*Logan.*)

Because of the steep pitch required, **slides** are limited in application. They are most commonly used to bridge the gap between roller-conveyor systems on two floors, because the roller conveyor can take the container off the slide rapidly and eliminate or reduce the chance for collisions. Slides may also be used where containers can be chuted from an upper floor to a manually loaded carrier.

Figure 7-53 shows typical standard dimensions for 30- and 45-deg. slides, and a 30-deg. slide with roller clean-out. Note that discharge must always be on the horizontal to prevent damage to the leading edge of the container. The use of several rollers at the feed point is recommended for easy delivery to the sloping section. Where drop is short and containers light, a roller clean-out will prevent backup of containers on the slide. The slope of gravity slides is a function of container weight, size, and friction characteristics and should be selected with care to be sure that containers do not either move too swiftly or not at all. Slides usually use flat steel sheet, although wood, piping, or other surfaces are available.

Gravity Wheel Conveyors. These can be used as pusher units set horizontally, or inclined for gravity flow. They are highly standardized and are usually sold in 5- or 10-ft. sections; special lengths are available at extra charge. Since wheel conveyors give what is

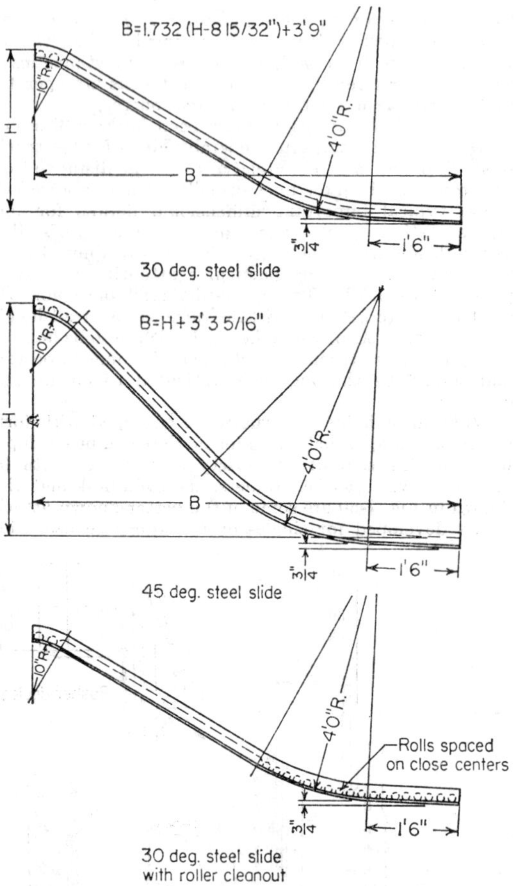

Fig. 7-53. Standard dimensions of slides. (*Logan.*)

essentially "point" support to containers, it is generally recommended that at least six wheels be located under the load at all times. Thus wheel arrangement is dictated by the smallest container that the line will handle. Only flat-bottomed containers can be handled on wheel conveyors, with the exception of fairly stiff-walled bags, which handle satisfactorily. This is due to the fact that the separate roller supports tend to pull the bag wall taut and flatten it out. Roller conveyors, on the contrary, tend to ripple the bag surface and prevent its movement. Wheel conveyors may also be specially designed for handling smooth-walled cylindrical shapes. Figure 7-54 illustrates a spiral wheel conveyor.

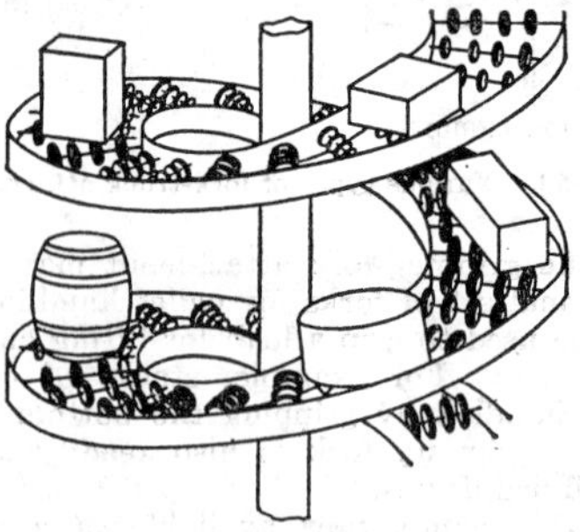

Fig. 7-54. Spiral wheel conveyor.

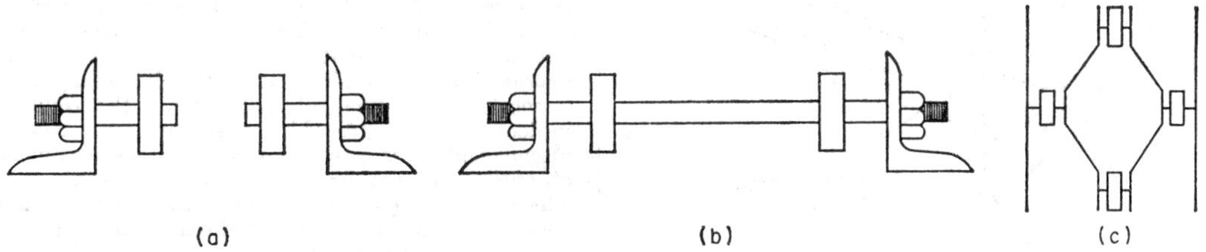

FIG. 7-55. Supports for conveyor wheels. (a) Bolt-mounted wheel. (b) Through-shaft-mounted wheel. (c) Short shafts supported by bent bar stock and side frame.

Wheels are available in a number of different designs, including variations in contour and material in contact with the container. Rubber or plastic tires are not uncommon. Through-shafts may be used, with several wheels mounted on each shaft; stub bolts with a single wheel may be mounted to the side frame, or short shafts supported by bent bars may also be used. Figure 7-55 illustrates these common wheel supports. Wheel conveyors are generally used on lighter loads, and although manufacturers may offer widths up to 36 in. or more, the smaller widths (up to about 18 in.) are generally standard. Load ratings are generally given as the total uniform load which a standard section will support.

Since wheel units are relatively light, they have relatively low inertia, and loads may be started and stopped quite easily. In addition, wheel bearings are designed with loose tolerance to reduce starting friction. Metal plates or projecting hardwood slats are commonly used as stops on conveyor lines. Special hinged sections for passage of personnel through the conveyor line are available, and standard supports from floor or ceiling are recommended. Wheel-conveyor units are widely used for live storage, and special telescoping units are available for extension and retraction to meet variable conditions. Wheel conveyors are sometimes powered by pressure belt or other method but are most widely used as pusher or gravity lines. They are adaptable only for end discharge or side discharge by lifting, since the individual rollers tend to grip the container and prevent its sliding off the line at right angles to direction of travel. Grades for wheel lines may be figured at about two-thirds of the values shown for roller lines in Table 7-28. Care should be taken not to overload the conveyor sections since they will assume a concave shape and prevent movement.

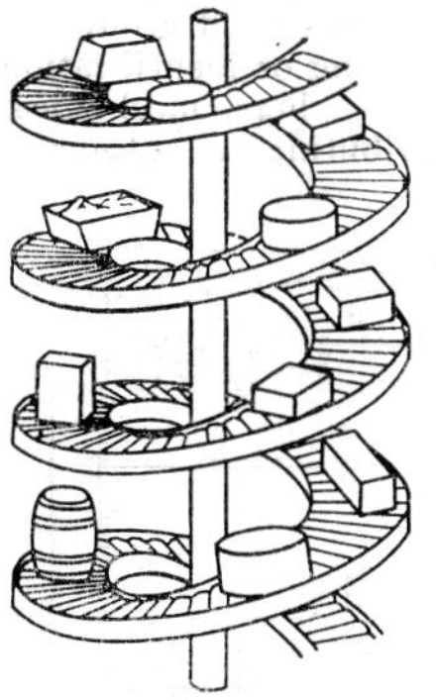

FIG. 7-56. Spiral roller conveyor.

Roller Conveyors. Gravity rollers are considerably heavier than the wheels on wheel conveyors, and the weight is concentrated at a greater distance from the shaft center line. Hence roller conveyors have a greater inertia; they are harder to start and harder to stop. In fact, they require more slope than wheel units and on long runs tend to speed up containers at an accelerating rate. Typical **roller-conveyor grades** are shown in Table 7-28.

Figure 7-56 shows a **spiral-roller unit,** usually equipped with tapered rollers to compensate for the difference in distance traveled by the inner and outer edges of the container. Tapered rollers are also used on curved sections of ordinary roller-conveyor lines.

Rollers are available in a wide variety of constructions, with tube ends either bored or formed to take the bearing insert. Bearings may be plain, with nylon rapidly becoming the most popular material for this type. Ball bearings are probably most common and are available with a variety of seals, or the bearing may be left unprotected. Lubrication fittings may be provided on a drilled shaft, or bearings may be prelubricated and sealed for life. Roller shafts are usually dead and may be cut from hexagonal stock to fit a similar opening in the side frame, or they may be round with ends milled flat to prevent turning. Rollers may be mounted in side frames in a variety of ways, above the side frames where containers are to be slid off the line, below where there is danger of the containers falling off.

Table 7-28. Grades for Roller Conveyor

Commodity	Plain or dust-protected rolls, in.		Grease-packed or pressure-lubricated, in.	
	10-ft. section	90-deg. curve	10-ft. section	90-deg. curve
Cartons:				
5–10 lb.	7½	6		
10–20 lb.	6	5		
20–50 lb.	5	4	7½	6
Crates:				
20–50 lb.	5	4	7½	6
50–100 lb.	4½	3	6½	5
100–250 lb.	4	3	5	4
Wood cases:				
20–50 lb.	5	4	7½	6
50–100 lb.	4½	3	6½	5
100–250 lb.	4	3	5	4
Barrels:				
Empty	6	5		
Full	5	4		
Baskets	5	4		
Drums, 150 lb. and up	4	3	6	5
Kegs	5	4	7½	6
Tote pans:				
50–100 lb.	4	3	6½	5
100–250 lb.	3½	3	5	4
250–500 lb.	3	2½	4½	3

Grades are in total number of inches drop required in each 10-ft. section or 90-deg. 2 ft. 6 in. inside radius curve.

Grades required for roller conveyor vary somewhat depending upon the size and spacing of rolls used. The grades suggested are for average conditions with rolls of a size and capacity to suit the material handled.

Steel strapping on crates or cases, also twine on packages or bundles, tend to slow up travel and may require a slight additional grade.

For level push lines, the average amount of push required to start the package from rest is about 3 per cent of its weight. With heavy loads, a pitch of about ⅛ in./ft. is recommended. This is not enough for the package to travel by gravity but will decrease the amount of push necessary.

For wheel conveyors, use grade of approximately two-thirds that shown.

Roller conveyors can handle containers with protruding edges, *i.e.*, oil drums, which is one of their advantages over wheel conveyors. However, they are not suitable for bags since the sides tend to sag between supports and prevent forward motion.

As with gravity wheel conveyors, roller units are highly standardized and auxiliary equipment is available for supporting the line from ceiling or floor. Many special rollers are available for retarding containers if speed becomes too great for safe handling. Switches, brakes, hinged sections, spurs, and frogs are also available.

Roller conveyors are quite frequently **powered,** the simplest method being use of a pressure belt in contact

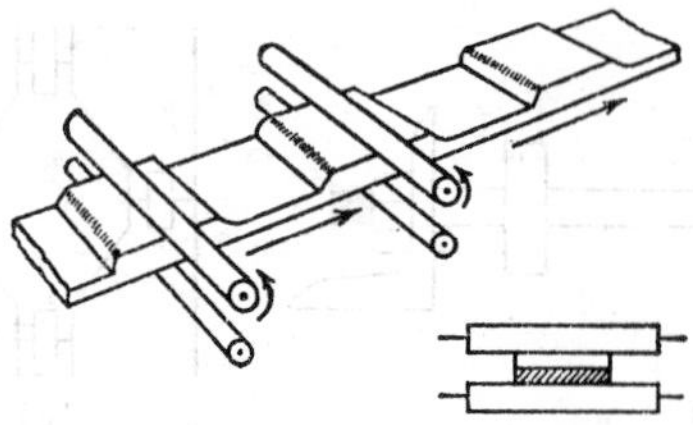

FIG. 7-57. Ripple belt for roller-conveyor drive.

with the lower surface of the rolls. Shown in Fig. 7-57 is a special ripple belt with raised pads which is capable of starting up the load but does not build up excessive blocked pressure if the line fills up. Other similar drives are available, with varying degrees of control over the applied power. Most expensive of the powered roller units are those in which each roll is equipped with V-belt or chain drives. Pusher bars suspended from overhead chain conveyors may also be used to move containers along a roller line.

One of the most important control devices on roller-conveyor lines is the escapement mechanism which allows containers to be released from a line individually. Powered escapement mechanisms are commonly available on highly mechanized systems. Their main function is to space out the containers so that they can be handled as discrete units.

Flat-belt Conveyors. These powered conveyors have the ability to lift containers up inclines. With the aid of special belt surfacing, grades can be quite steep. Belts also keep containers spaced out in exactly the way they are placed on the conveyor. However, because of the relatively high friction, containers cannot be slid off belts by pushing devices.

Belt-conveyor designs use both roller and slider bed supports for the flat belt. The variety of designs available allows proper selection of flat belts for heavy or light loads and for various applications such as carton filling or emptying.

Chain Conveyors. These devices for handling containers are available in either roller-chain designs or other, less costly types. Figure 7-58 illustrates a variety of **slat conveyors** using both single and double strands of roller chain, as well as a slider type using cheaper chain. In general, slat chain conveyors are used only on loads which are too heavy for economical handling by belt, roller, or wheel units, or which have odd shapes not suitable for roller or wheel units. They are particularly adaptable to pallet handling, as are simple open strands of chain with flat-surfaced attachments.

The most commonly used warehouse chain conveyor is the **tow chain.** Chain may be mounted overhead or in the floor, and trucks being towed can be designed for automatic detachment at a specific point. While the overhead chain is often used and is usually easy to support from structural members in the ceiling, the in-floor chain is probably most common. Automatic disengagement is possible should trucks encounter an obstruction or accidentally strike warehouse personnel. The tow-chain conveyor is, of course, most economical where large tonnages are moved over a fixed path.

Chain-type **elevators** such as the arm and tray units shown in Fig. 7-59 are commonly used for drums and

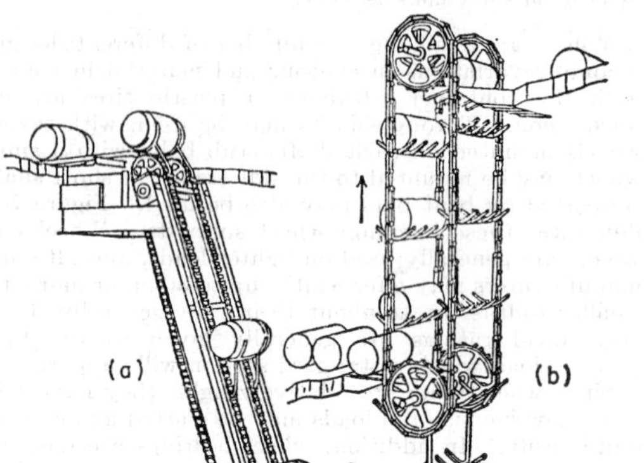

FIG. 7-59. (*a*) Arm elevator. (*b*) Tray elevator. (*Link-Belt.*)

barrels. Slight gravity runs at feed and discharge allow these units to roll on and off the conveyor easily, and without special equipment.

Elevators. Cable-type elevators are usually selected for heavy loads such as full pallets or large containers. They can be made fully automatic and are able to serve many floor levels. The use of properly designed elevator systems is often the only economical solution to multistory plant problems.

Conveyor Accessories. These may be divided into two groups, those which act on the container and those which are acted on by the container. In the first group are such items as deflectors, palletizers, pushers (powered by fluid, air, or mechanical linkage), upenders, sealers, staplers, and similar devices. In the second group are such items as electric eyes for counting or identification via printed or color codes, check-weighers, mechanical counters, and other devices contributing to automatic conveyor-line operation.

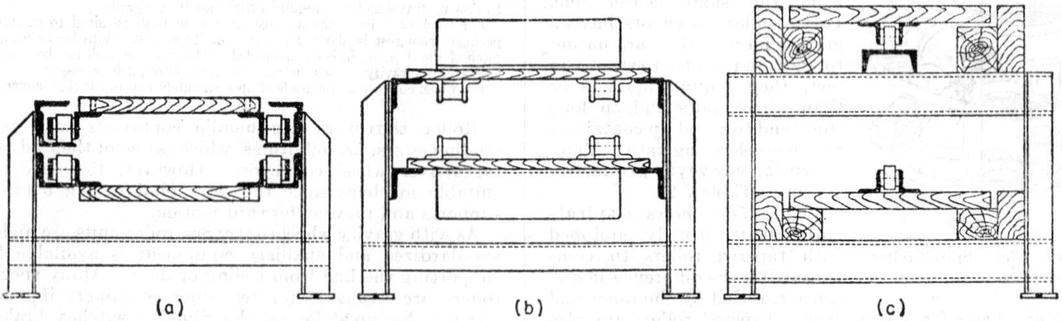

FIG. 7-58. Slat chain conveyors. (*a*) Conveyor with wooden slats operating on angle track, for handling packaged materials and similar articles. (*b*) Conveyor with wooden slats on angle track and cross angles, for carrying light packages up an inclined path. (*c*) Conveyor with wooden slats, center supporting roller, and single strand of chain, for carrying bags, boxes, etc. (*Link-Belt.*)

SECTION 8

SIZE REDUCTION AND SIZE ENLARGEMENT

BY

Lincoln T. Work, Ph.D., Consulting Engineer; Member, American Ceramic Society, American Chemical Society, American Institute of Chemical Engineers, American Institute of Chemists, American Institute of Mining, Metallurgical and Petroleum Engineers, American Society for Metals, American Society for Testing and Materials, Electrochemical Society, Institute of Metals, Society of Chemical Industry; Professional Engineer (New Jersey, New York). (Section Editor*)

Arthur L. Stern, B.Chem., Arthur L. Stern Co.; Member, American Association of Cost Engineers, American Chemical Society, American Institute of Chemical Engineers, Armed Forces Chemical Association, Franklin Institute; Professional Engineer (New Jersey). (Associate Editor, Size Reduction)

* Valuable advice in this revision has been received from C. E. Berry, editor of this section in the third edition; some of his material is still current and has been retained.

CONTENTS

PRINCIPLES OF SIZE REDUCTION

CRUSHING AND GRINDING EQUIPMENT

CRUSHING AND GRINDING PRACTICE

OTHER METHODS OF SIZE REDUCTION

SIZE ENLARGEMENT

PRINCIPLES OF SIZE REDUCTION

REFERENCES: *Particle-size Measurement:* Cadle, "Particle Size Determination," Interscience, New York, 1955. Chamot and Mason, "Handbook of Chemical Microscopy," vol. 1, 3d ed., Wiley, New York, 1958. Dalla Valle, "Micromeritics: The Technology of Fine Particles," 2d ed., Pitman, New York, 1948. Green, "Industrial Rheology and Rheological Structures," Wiley, New York, 1949. Herdan, "Small Particle Statistics," Elsevier, New York, 1953. Klug and Alexander, "X-ray Diffraction Procedures for Polycrystalline and Amorphous Materials," Wiley, New York, 1954. Orr and Dalla Valle, "Fine Particle Measurements," Macmillan, New York, 1959. Rose, "Measurement of Particle Size in Very Fine Powders," Constable, London, 1953. Stevens, "Microphotography," Wiley, New York, 1957. "Symposium on New Methods for Particle Size Determination in the Subsieve Range," American Society for Testing and Materials, Philadelphia, 1941. Symposium on Particle Size Measurement, *Special Tech. Publ.* 234, American Society for Testing and Materials, Philadelphia, 1959. Van de Hulst, "Light Scattering by Small Particles," Wiley, New York, 1957. Whitby and McFarlans, Bibliography of Particle Size Analysis," 1111 references, University of Minnesota, Minneapolis, 1959. Work and Whitby, Size Measurement of Particles," in Encyclopedia of Chemical Technology," vol. 12, pp. 472–496, Interscience, New York, 1954.

Size Reduction: "Chemical Engineering Catalog," 47th ed., Reinhold, New York, 1963. Cremer-Davies, "Chemical Engineering Practice," vol. 3, "Solid Systems," Butterworth, London, and Academic Press, New York, 1957. "Crushing and Grinding, a Bibliography," Chemical Publishing Co., New York, 1960. "Cyclone Dust Collectors," American Petroleum Institute, New York, 1956. Gaudin, "Principles of Mineral Dressing," McGraw-Hill, New York, 1939. Miller, "Crushers for Stone and Ore," Van Nostrand, Princeton, N.J., 1935. Richards and Locke, "Text Book of Ore Dressing," 3d ed., McGraw-Hill, New York, 1940. Rose and Sullivan, "Ball. Tube and Rod Mills," Chemical Publishing Co., New York, 1958. Stern, "Guide to Crushing and Grinding Practice," *Chem. Eng.*, **69** (25), 129 (1962). Symposium on Grinding, Institution of Chemical Engineers, London, 1956. Taggart, "Handbook of Mineral Dressing." Wiley, New York, 1945. Work, Size Reduction (annual reviews), *Ind. Eng. Chem.*, January issues, 1947–1954. March issues (Part II), 1955–1959, February, 1960, March, 1961, March, 1962, February, 1963. Work, "Size Reduction," in "Encyclopedia of Chemical Technology," vol. 12, pp 498–520, Interscience, New York, 1954.

Methods for Size Reduction. The terms "crushing" and "grinding" have become generic in common usage. Reduction of large pieces to intermediate or substantially smaller sizes is called breaking, crushing, or cutting. Reduction to fine sizes or powders goes under many names—grinding, comminution, pulverization, disintegration, or dispersion.

The two immediate **objectives** of crushing and grinding are to obtain products meeting maximum or minimum limiting size specifications, or both, and to produce materials to meet specific-surface requirements. As with most operations, size reduction ties in with economics, and the extent of reduction is ultimately determined by the cost of the operation (initial cost and operating cost) vs. enhancement of value and usefulness of the product thereof.

Sometimes certain lump-shape requirements have to be met in crushing operations. The ultimate objectives are numerous. The production of surface to obtain completeness and rapidity of chemical reaction often is a requirement. The production of the surface within maximum and minimum size limits may be important.

Methods of Size Enlargement. When solids are the subject of size enlargement, the ultimate structure desired may require a selected method or it may require a combination of methods. Crystal growth is a good technique where applicable. In some cases, it involves precipitation from solution by temperature or evaporation. In others, it may be done by calcination.

Granulation may be achieved by cementing fine particles together into irregular larger lumps. Pressing into tablets or briquettes with just enough interlocking of pieces or adhesiveness to retain shape is also used. In fluid systems, fine particles may be brought into coarser particulate form by agglomeration or flocculation.

Fine solid materials may be brought into a massive state with the use of heat, pressure, or both. Melting and casting is obvious, with variants in shotting and prilling. Pressure compaction with extrusion to coarser form than the feed is another method, employed with plastic materials. Heating to cause activity in grain growth also results in bonding. This is particularly true if reactions are also involved. With preformed or statically placed material, this is sintering; with tumbling or fluidized masses, it becomes nodulizing.

Properties of Solids. A single particle or lump has linear size, surface, hardness, and structure. The **linear size** may be the diameter in case of a sphere, an edge length for a cube, or some fictitious average linear dimension in case of an irregular-shaped lump. The **surface** is the exterior of most particles, although some have interstitial surface. The surface is readily calculated for cubes and spheres but in most cases must be estimated for irregular shapes. **Hardness** is indicated by the conventional scratch criterion and can be measured by indentation. **Structure** may be homogeneous or heterogeneous.

A mixture of particles such as those in a powder may be defined in terms of particle-size distribution, surface, specific surface, and limiting particle size. **Particle-size distribution** is the functional relation of the distribution with respect to size of individual particles in the powder. The **surface** is a summation of the individual grain surfaces, and **specific surface** is the surface of a unit of weight or volume. **Limiting particle size** is the size of the largest or smallest particles in the powder.

An important additional factor, **grindability,** is a measure of the grinding characteristics of a material. A number of grindability methods subject a sample of sized material to a miniature grinding operation with controlled energy input and a measured size reduction, in which one of these is fixed and the other is used as an index of grindability.

The ability of a material to withstand reduction depends upon its hardness, its structure, and the manner in which it is fractured [Gaudin, *Trans. Am. Inst. Mining Met. Engrs.*, **73**, 253 (1926)]. Other factors affecting the grinding characteristics of a material are water of combination, hygroscopicity, tendency to flocculate and agglomerate, combustibility, and sensitiveness to changes in temperature. Glauber's salt, for example, gives off water of crystallization at a comparatively low temperature, causing clogging of equipment; calcium chloride is so hygroscopic that it may actually dissolve in the moisture absorbed; resins and gums become soft and plastic beyond a critical temperature; other materials may burn or char; certain chemicals and dyestuffs are unstable and may ignite or explode if the temperature is excessive; and many mineral pigments such as ochres and siennas tend to change in color at elevated temperatures or under mechanical action.

Moisture in material being pulverized is a commonly encountered factor having a marked effect on the performance of equipment. The curves in Fig. 8-1 show

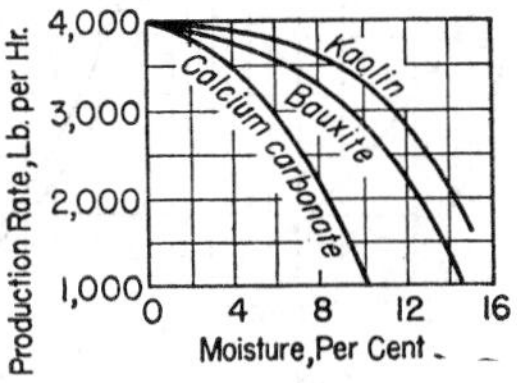

FIG. 8-1. Effect of moisture on production rate of a pulverizer. [*Work, Chem. & Met. Eng.*, **40**, 306 (1933).]

decreasing production rate with increasing moisture content. (Occasionally, a small amount of water may be beneficial over complete dryness.) All three materials were being ground to 99.9 per cent through a No. 200 sieve. The **fineness** to which a material is ground has a marked effect on its production rate, and it follows logically that, with a given horsepower expenditure, production rate decreases with increased fineness. Figure 8-2 shows the relation among capacity, power, and cost of pulverizing coal to different degrees of fineness.

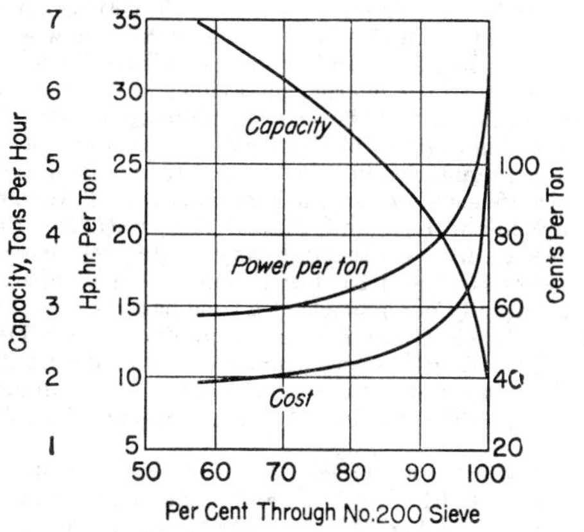

FIG. 8-2. Variation in capacity, power, and cost of grinding relative to fineness of product.

Specifications for Particulates. Feed and finished products from size-reduction operations are defined in terms of the particulate sizes involved. The products of size reduction involve a distribution of size which is best specified in some detail. It is also well to know if the ultimate individual particle is being measured; or, if any aggregation or agglomeration of particles exists, it is well to know if this has been created by the size-reduction operation.

The most complete description of a powder is given by its **particle-size distribution.** This can be plotted in terms of cumulative per cent oversize or undersize in relation to the diameters of particles, or it can be plotted as a distribution of the amounts present in each unit of diameter against the several diameters. It is common to employ a weight basis for percentage, but there are some data in the literature where frequency, or number of particles, is used. The basis of percentage, whether weight, frequency, or some less commonly used factor, should be specified, as also should be stated the diameter, its units, and preferably whether determined by sieve, settling velocity, or otherwise.

Figure 8-3 presents two sets of distributions—one cumulative and the other in unit intervals. The slopes of the cumulative curve, in 5-micron intervals, are converted

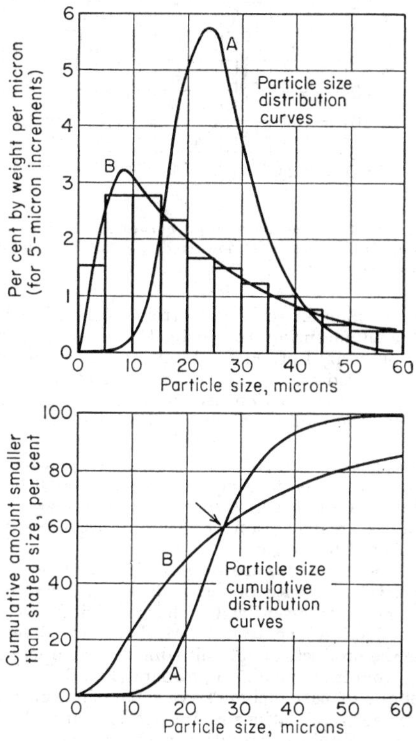

FIG. 8-3. Particle-size distribution curves for simple powders.

to per cent per micron and plotted as a block, or histogram, from which smooth curves are derived. Powder *A* has a narrower, or tighter, size range for the bulk of its weight than does *B*. Both materials have the same weights below and above the size marked by the arrow.

Simpler treatments of distribution are possible, as in table form showing the 10-50-90 per cent amounts or the quadrants of 25-50-75 per cent. Both have value but are not so definitive as the full distribution. In some cases, the significant value is the top size. Since the 100 per cent point is dubious, some amount, as 95 or 98 per cent, so specified, can be called top size. In other cases, the per cent on some sieve helps define coarseness. Merely stating that all, or all but a small percentage, passes a given sieve is inadequate to define the true fineness of a material. Complete particle-size analysis to show the distribution is essential for most comparisons and calculations.

Specific surface can be calculated from complete distribution data. The Gates diagram employs a plot of cumulative per cent by weight undersize vs. reciprocal diameter; the area beneath the curve represents surface. Likewise the area beneath the Roller diagram represents surface, this plot being per cent by weight per micron vs. logarithm of diameter (Work and Whitby, *op. cit.*, p. 477). Some of the methods of analysis determine surface directly.

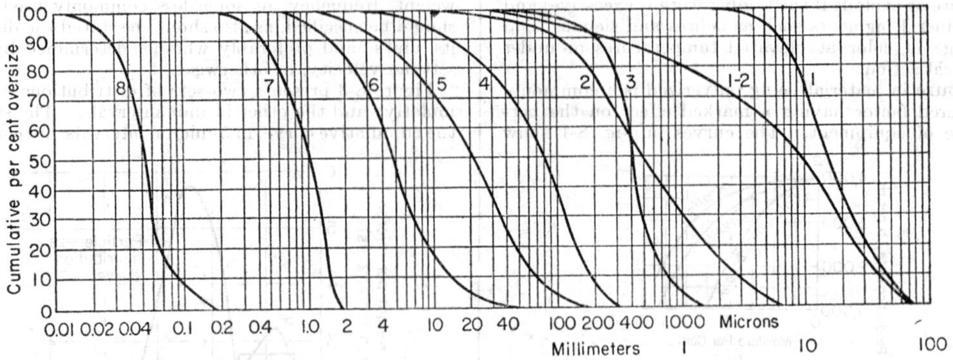

Fig. 8-4. Particle-size distribution curves for typical products. (1) Coarse aggregate; (1–2) a normal mixed aggregate; (2) fine aggregate; (3) filter sand; (4) powdered coal; (5) Portland cement; (6) mineral fillers; (7) pigments; (8) fine rubber fillers. (*Interscience Publishers, modified.*)

It is common in some industries, such as Portland-cement manufacturing, to specify the specific surface of the dry pulverized product. Limiting size specifications are not required but remain within close tolerances for a given surface specification because of the operating consistency of the equipment and uniformity of clinker in grinding.

Equipment manufacturers' performance data may be an average sieve mesh or may mean some small percentage retained on a sieve, setting a maximum size. Since such values are uncertain or meaningless, more precise figures should be sought.

Particle-size Measurement. Size distribution is a fundamental attribute of particulates, and methods of measurement are essential for characterizing the results of size-reduction operations. Methods are diversified, because the products are of quite different characteristics, ranging from large pieces to powders (Fig. 8-4).

Methods of test include sieve separation, microscope measurement, elutriation, sedimentation, and electronic counting to obtain distribution with or without separation into fractions. General over-all measurement of some property of fineness may be done with turbidimeter, sorption, permeability, or X-ray measurement. While these are the primary techniques, there are others, less frequently used, some of which measure application properties rather than true size characteristics.

Separation into size fractions by use of **sieves** is effective and economical where possible. Standard sieves made of wire, with essentially square apertures, range from 107.6 mm. (4.24 in.) down to 37 microns (No. 400 sieve) (p. 21-51). Sizes of 26 and 18 microns may become commercial. Electroplated mesh with square apertures is available from around 100 down to 10 microns (A.S.T.M. Standard E11 and *Special Tech. Publ.* 234 by Whitby, Daeschner, *et al.*). Round- and square-hole punched plate is available in sizes above 0.25 in. The use of testing sieves is described in W. S. Tyler Co. Catalogue 53. [See also Weber and Moran, *Ind. Eng. Chem., Anal. Ed.*, **10**, 180–184 (1938).]

For the coarse separations and quite often the fine ones, **dry sieving** is used. When the product contains very fine particles in large amounts, dry separation may be poor and the fine sieves become clogged. In such cases **wet sieving** is employed, using a fluid which does not dissolve or swell the sample. A combination of the two procedures is often effective: wet sieving to remove slimes or material easily passing the finest sieve, and dry sieving on a series of sieves the dry retained portion (Screen Testing of Ores, American Standards Association Method M5-32). Material smaller that the finest sieve (usually No. 325 or No. 400) is determined by difference, although these fines can be recovered and weighed. Standard procedures are given for sieve analysis of specific materials (A.S.T.M. Designation Standards, see *Special Tech. Publ.* 234, p. 302).

Observation and measurement in the **microscope** is revealing as to size, shape, and distribution. Projection methods and photography make observation and recording less tedious. There are problems in getting a representative slide, and this is particularly difficult when the important range is tenfold or more. Visible light is employed down to 0.2 micron, ultraviolet has been used to below 0.1 micron, and the electron microscope is definitive to below hundredths of a micron. Measurement with counting frequencies in selected size ranges is employed up to the finest sieve, but it is tedious (A.S.T.M. Designation E20 and Loveland, *Special Tech. Publ.* 234, 1959).

In **electronic counting,** a very dilute, well-dispersed suspension is caused to flow through a small aperture, with essentially one particle at a time passing a screening device. An electronic device recording each particle by size quickly develops an accurate count of distribution. The Coulter counter has recently come into prominence as one such device (Berg, A.S.T.M. *Special Tech. Publ.* 234).

The Flying Spot Particle Resolver (Instrument Corp. of America, Baltimore, Md.) affords an electronic means to count and analyze the size distribution of particulates as viewed in a microscope down to 0.6 micron.

Size fractions may be recovered through the difference in rates of settling of uniform-density particles as a function of size. A simple test is by **beaker sedimentation.** Two levels are marked on a beaker, and a suspension of dispersed particles is added to the upper level. The suspension is stirred and then allowed to stand for the time required for all of a given fine size to settle below the lower mark, at which time the upper layer is carefully siphoned off down to that mark. More fluid is added to the higher level; the mix is stirred and again settled for the same time and siphoned. Three or more such separations leave only oversize in the beaker. The oversize may be further separated into several fractions. Continuous techniques may be employed with liquid or gas dispersions. There is often difficulty with air elutriation of powders containing much fine material, around 1 micron or so.

In **elutriations,** cuts are made from about 5 microns up to sieve sizes (No. 200, normal maximum). This method may be exemplified by the **Roller analyzer**

(American Instrument Co.) (Roller, *U.S. Bur. Mines Tech. Publ.* 490, 1931). Materials are separated into closely sized fractions (<5, 5 to 10, 10 to 20, and 20 to 40, for example) by carrying upward in a controlled stream of air those particles too small to settle against the upward velocity and removing them from the air stream for weighing in a paper filter. A sample having a bulk volume of 10 cc. is required. The method is based on Stokes's law:

$$D = \sqrt{\frac{18\mu u \times 10^8}{(\rho_s - \rho_f)g}} \qquad (8\text{-}1)$$

where μ is viscosity, poises; u is velocity, cm./sec.; ρ_s is density of solid particle, g./cc.; ρ_f is density of fluid; D is diameter of a sphere, microns; and g is acceleration due to gravity, cm./sec.^{2}. For non-spherical particles, D is the equivalent diameter of a sphere rising at the same rate as the particle. Correction for deviation from Stokes's law may be necessary at the large end of the size range (see p. 5-62).

Methods utilizing the differences in **settling velocities** of different size particles without separation are extensive and varied. Liquid or gas suspensions may be employed. Gravity and centrifugal force are used. They are all based on the principle that a uniform, dilute dispersion settles differentially with respect to size. At some measured level below the top of the suspension, each size of particle will pass this level uniformly until the particles of such size at the top of the suspension have passed this plane, after which there will be only smaller sizes present. The time required for each size will depend upon its settling rate from the top. The concentration of solids and density of the suspension at that plane will diminish with time. Readings of a property of the solids content there at stated times will give a progressive measure of amounts with diminishing particle size, and a distribution curve can be constructed.

There are variations of this in the **suspended weighing pan** which collects the sediment and in the feeding of all the suspension at the top, so that the sediment will be of a size uncontaminated with fines. Commercial devices are the Sharples Micromerograph, which measures the settling of an air dispersion of material, preferably low in fine micron sizes [*Anal. Chem.*, **25**, 24A (August, 1953)] and the Mines Safety Appliances tester developed by Whitby for liquid settling under gravitational and centrifugal forces [Whitby, *Trans. Am. Soc. Heating Air Conditioning Engrs.*, **61**, 33–50, 449–462 (1955)].

Numerous **methods of recording** have been used with the more commonly employed gross settling technique. The **pipette method** is best known as the Andreasen modification [Andreasen, *Kolloid-Z.*, **49**, 253 (1929)]. The thoroughly dispersed material is allowed to settle, and definite small volumes of suspension are withdrawn from a fixed level at predetermined time intervals corresponding to the desired size limits (2.5, 5, 10, 20 microns, for example) as calculated from Stokes's law (Fig. 8-5). The weights of the dried residues in the samples, the immersion of the pipette tube, and the times of taking the samples are used to calculate particle-size distribution on a weight basis [Loomis, *J. Am. Ceram. Soc.*, **21**, 393 (1938)].

The **hydrometer method** is simpler in that the concentration of the suspension is read directly at predetermined settling times with a hydrometer [A.S.T.M. Designation D422; Klein, *Proc. Am. Soc. Testing Materials*, **41**, 953 (1941)]. A novel adaptation of the hydrometer method makes use of a series of small floats, or divers, of density between 1.001 and 1.01 (Berg, A.S.T.M. *Special Tech. Publ.* 234, 1959). Pressure differences based on density vs. time of a given column of suspension include

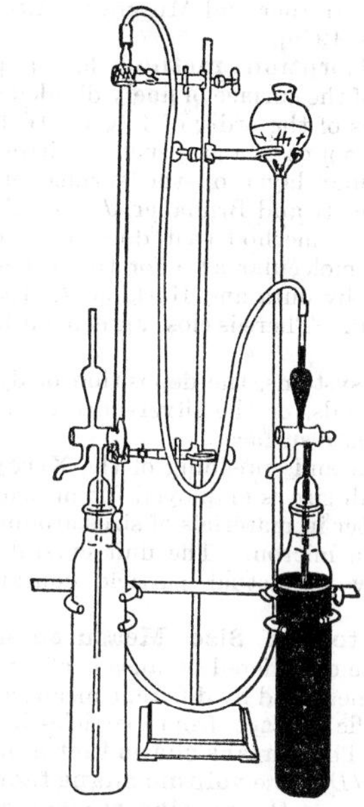

FIG. 8-5. Pipette apparatus for particle-size analysis by sedimentation.

the clear fluid capillary, or a pressure diaphragm with mirror and light-beam photography.

The use of **sedimentation turbidimetry** (A.S.T.M. Designation C115; Wagner Turbidimeter, Bowen Instrument Co.) is standard as noted in the reference and is also practiced on regular light-absorption devices. An interesting variant is the use of neutron bombardment of the suspension and measuring the radiation levels in a limited volume of settling material as a function of time [Abraham *et al.*, *Anal. Chem.*, **29**, 1058 (1957)].

These sedimentation methods are applicable from sieve limits, around 50 microns, down to a few microns and to tenths of a micron with careful procedures. The particle-size range can be extended to 0.01 micron by use of centrifugal fields and modifications of the hydrometer, pipette, and Odén methods [Norton and Speil, *J. Am. Ceram. Soc.*, **21**, 89 (1938). Dana, *J. Sediment. Petrol.*, **13**, 21 (1943). Jacobsen and Sullivan, *Ind. Eng. Chem.*, *Anal. Ed.*, **18**, 360 (1946)].

The **cascade impactor** is a device employing a jet stream to project the larger particles onto a plate while the finer ones are diverted with the flow of the air stream. It is often employed in stages and is applicable in the lower micron sizes [Brink, *Ind. Eng. Chem.*, **50**, 645 (1958)].

Single-property Measurements. A number of other testing methods are employed for measuring one property with a single reading. The **air-permeability method** gives only average particle size, not particle-size-distribution information, and is useful in the range from 50 to 0.1 microns. The method is based on the relation between specific surface of packed particles and their permeability [Carman, *J. Soc. Chem. Ind.* (*London*), **57**, 225 (1938)]. The Sub Sieve Sizer apparatus is available commercially (Fisher Scientific Co.) for taking advantage of the air-permeability method [Gooden and Smith, *Ind. Eng. Chem.*, *Anal. Ed.*, **12**, 479 (1940)]. It is good for comparative values on similar materials.

Turbidimetric methods are based on the property of suspensions of fine particles to affect the transmission of light through them [Stutz and Pfund, *Ind. Eng. Chem.*,

19, 51 (1927). Harner and Musgrave, A.S.T.M. *Special Tech. Publ.* 234, 1959].

The **gas-adsorption method** has application for measurement of the surface of finely divided solids having specific surfaces of the order of 1×10^4 to 100×10^4 sq. cm./g. The amount of a gas, such as nitrogen, adsorbed in a unimolecular layer on the surface of the solid is measured [Emmett and Brunauer, *J. Am. Chem. Soc.*, **59,** 1553 (1937)]. A method that does not require the assumption of a molecular area for the gas molecules has been described by Jura and Harkins [*J. Am. Chem. Soc.*, **66,** 1356 (1944)]. There is close agreement between these methods.

With liquid systems, the deposition of dyes, the reaction of fatty acids, or the silver-mirror test are related means to evaluate surface.

The diffusion and spreading of the **X-ray pattern** of crystals of small size is employed for measurement of an average diameter in materials of sizes around hundredths and tenths of a micron. The unit crystal is measured, not necessarily an actual particle containing several crystals.

Shape Factor in Size Measurement. Particle shape should be considered because it affects the relation between sizes measured by different means and the evaluation of specific surface from particle-size-distribution information. The **surface shape factor** K_a for spheres is 3.14 ($\pi = A/D^2$); the **volume shape factor** K_v is 0.52 ($\pi/6 = V/D^3$); and the **specific surface shape factor** K_s is 6 ($= AD/V = K_a/K_v$). Values for non-spherical particles such as crushed quartz are $K_a = 2.5$, $K_v = 0.27$, and $K_s = 9.3$ for a linear dimension which is the straight line dividing a particle lying on a microscope slide into two apparently equal parts [Martin, *Trans. Brit. Ceram. Soc.*, **27,** 285 (1928)].

Although volume shape factors for flaky materials such as mica are as small as 0.003, factors for many crushed materials lie between 0.2 and 0.4, based on mean projected diameters of the particles [Heywood, *Proc. Inst. Mech. Engrs. (London)*, **140,** 257 (1938)]; from these it can be shown from Heywood's data that the ratio of sedimentation size to sieve-aperture size should be 0.86 to 0.95, respectively. However, comparisons of No. 325 sieve analyses with sedimentation analyses show 53 microns to be the sedimentation size corresponding to the No. 325 sieve (44-micron aperture), a ratio of 1.2 [Schweyer, *Chem. Revs.*, **31,** 295 (1942)]. Perhaps the diagonal of sieve aperture controls.

Particle-size Representation. A number of equations have been proposed to correlate the quantity of a particulate material with its particle size to obtain a distribution relationship [Austin, *Ind. Eng. Chem., Anal. Ed.*, **11,** 334 (1939)], but it is unlikely that many practical powders comply with them throughout their complete size range. The relations do have value, however, within the limits of their application. The **logarithmic-probability relation** has general usefulness, and plotting paper designed by Hazen is available (Codex Book Co., Norwood, Mass., Logarithmic Probability Paper No. 3228). Many a cumulative particle-size distribution can be represented by a line that is approximately straight or by two straight lines on logarithmic-probability paper. The mathematical treatment of this relation to obtain the properties of particulate materials has been published [Hatch and Choate, *J. Franklin Inst.*, **207,** 369 (1929) Hatch, *J. Franklin Inst.*, **215,** 27 (1933)]. A comparison of a number of analytical relationships is shown in Fig. 8-6 for a hypothetical powder.

Other treatments have been combined to develop a **law of size distribution** in which the particle frequency per unit of diameter is a function of ae^{-bx} where x is diameter for that frequency. This is an exponential ex-

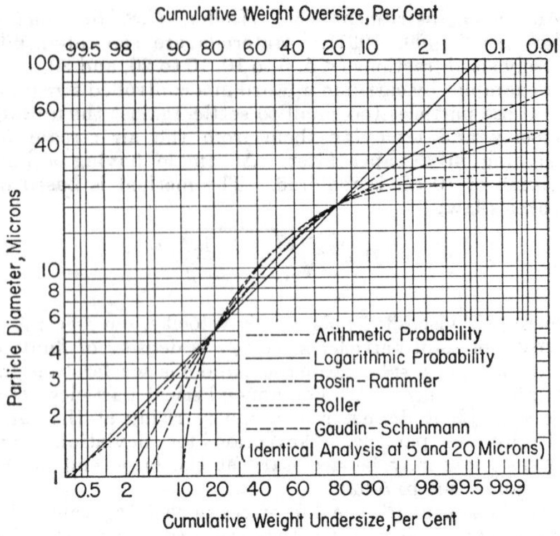

FIG. 8-6. Comparison of analytical particle-size distribution relationships. [*Lapple, Heating, Piping, Air Conditioning*, **18,** 108 (1946).]

pression for that initial fracture; but it requires an additional factor of secondary fracture or attrition to account for all the fine particles produced (Work, "Encyclopedia of Chemical Technology," vol. 12, pp. 499–501, 1954).

Average particle size of a powder may be obtained from its distribution relationship (Hatch, *loc. cit.*) and it can have a number of values depending on the property to be accented: weight or volume, surface, and specific surface (Hatch and Choate, *loc. cit.;* A.S.T.M. Designation E20). Volume and specific surface average sizes are expressed, respectively, as $\sqrt[3]{\Sigma\, \Delta W/\Sigma\, \Delta W\, D_m^{-3}}$ and $\Sigma\, \Delta W/\Sigma\, \Delta W\, D_m^{-1}$ on a weight basis; and as $\sqrt[3]{\Sigma\, \Delta n\, D_m^3/\Sigma\, \Delta n}$ and $\Sigma\, \Delta n\, D_m^3/\Sigma\, \Delta n\, D_m^2$ on a number basis; where ΔW and Δn are incremental weight and number of particles, respectively, and D_m is the mean size of the increment.

When determining size distribution, a powder should be divided into size increments bearing definite relation to each other. The accepted practice for testing sieves is that the ratio of the length of aperture of a sieve to that of the next finer sieve in the series is $\sqrt{2}$. This geometric progression can be extended indefinitely to molecular sizes. Ordinal numbers can be assigned to the size increments beginning with 1 for a mean aperture of $1 \times 10^{-4.07}$ and extending through 41 and 48, for example, for mean apertures of 89 and 1000 microns, respectively. The mean aperture of the No. 200 and No. 150 sieves is 89 microns, and it is 1000 for the No. 20 and No. 14 sieves [Weinig, *Quart. Colo. School Mines*, **28,** 3 (1933)]. The **weight-average size** of a material corresponds to the ordinal number obtained from a summation of the products of the incremental weights multiplied by the ordinal numbers of the increments and divided by the total weight of the material. This method is illustrated by Coghill [*Mining J.*, **126,** 934 (1928)]. A more closely nested series of sieves is based on $\sqrt[4]{2}$, and a less close cut may be made with a series based on 2. An international standard is under consideration using a root of 10. For practical purposes, the $\sqrt{2}$ nesting is most feasible for general use.

Reduction ratio is a ratio of the size of feed to the size of product from a mill operation. In its older use, its application was to lump- and mesh-size particles; as such, it expressed the degree of reduction capable in a mill. It was customary to use maximum diameters of feed and product. To be more informative, an average diameter, weight, or surface may be used. This would be more valuable for fine grinding, where energy considerations are important. In any event, the statement is necessary as to which is used: maximum-size reduction ratio, average-size reduction ratio, or surface-mean reduction ratio.

Specific surface can be expressed as surface per unit weight or volume. It can be obtained from the distribution relationship of a particulate material (Hatch, *loc. cit.*) or with the aid of ordinal numbers (Coghill, *loc. cit.*). In general, it can be expressed as $s = (K_s/\rho)(\Sigma\, \Delta W\, D_m^{-1}/\Sigma\, \Delta W)$ where s is specific surface, sq. cm./g.; K_s is specific surface shape factor (= 6 for spheres); ρ is density of the material, g./cc.; ΔW is incremental weight, g.; and D_m is mean size of the increment, cm.

Grindability. Chief purpose of a study of grindability is to evaluate the size and type of mill needed to produce a specified tonnage, and the power requirement for grinding. Of interest also is knowledge of the manner in which material breaks under slow pressure and under impact, abrasion, and other actions which occur in size reduction. Factors of hardness, elasticity, toughness and cleavage are important. Measurement of compressive strength, coefficient of elasticity, diamond-point hardness, and the like are helping to create a scientific basis for milling analysis; but the methods are more refined than is understanding, and rougher treatments still have value.

The **hardness** of a mineral as measured by the Moh scale is a criterion of its resistance to crushing [Fahrenwald, *Trans. Am. Inst. Mining. Met. Engrs.*, **112,** 88 (1934)]. It is a fairly good indication of the abrasive character of the mineral, a factor that determines the wear on the grinding media. Arranged in increasing order of hardness, the **Moh scale** is as follows: 1, talc; 2, gypsum; 3, calcite; 4, fluorite; 5, apatite; 6, feldspar; 7, quartz; 8, topaz; 9, corundum; 10, diamond.

For the purpose being considered, the tabulation may be expanded; materials of hardness 1 to 3, inclusive, may be classed as "soft," from 4 to 7, intermediate, and the others as "hard."

Soft Materials. (1) Talc, dried filter-press cakes, soapstone, waxes, aggregated salt crystals; (2) gypsum, rock salt, crystalline salts in general, soft coal; (3) calcite, marble, soft limestone, barytes, chalk, brimstone.

Intermediate Hardness. (4) Fluorite, soft phosphate, magnesite, limestone; (5) apatite, hard phosphate, hard limestone, chromite, bauxite; (6) feldspar, ilmenite, orthoclase, hornblendes.

Hard Materials. (7) Quartz, granite; (8) topaz; (9) corundum, sapphire, emery; (10) diamond.

A hardness classification of stone based on the **compressive strength** of 1-in. cubes is as follows, for loadings in lb./sq. in.: very soft, 10,000; soft, 15,000; medium, 20,000; hard, 25,000; very hard, 30,000.

In a basic study, Piret [*Chem. Eng. Progress*, **49,** 56 (1953)] has shown why there is not a close relation between hardness and grindability. Nonetheless, hardness is a basic property having some bearing on grinding and mill wear.

Grindability Methods. Two methods having particular application for **coal** are known as the ball-mill and Hardgrove methods. In the **ball-mill method,** the relative amounts of energy necessary to pulverize different coals are determined by placing a weighed sample of coal in a ball mill of a specified size and counting the number of revolutions required to grind the sample so that 80 per cent of it will pass through a No. 200 sieve. The grindability index in per cent is equal to the quotient of 50,000 divided by the average of the number of revolutions required by two tests (A.S.T.M. Designation D408).

In the **Hardgrove method** a prepared sample receives a definite amount of grinding energy in a miniature ball-ring pulverizer. The unknown sample is compared with a coal chosen as having 100 grindability. The Hardgrove grindability index = $13 + 6.93W$, where W is the weight of material passing the No. 200 sieve (see A.S.T.M. Designation D409). In both methods it has been assumed that the work expended per revolution of the pulverizer is constant. The grindability of coal has been determined with the Hardgrove machine and using the Lea-Nurse air-permeability method for measuring surface. The new specific surface per revolution of the machine is constant for a fixed quantity of material [see Romer, *Proc. Am. Soc. Testing Materials*, **41,** 1152 (1941)]. A comparison of the indexes is:

Hardgrove..........	20	30	40	50	60	70	80	90	100	110
Ball mill............	14	21	28	36	44	52	60	70	80	90

These methods have not come into general use for **materials other than coal** because of the diversity of grinding equipment that might be used and the dissimilar physical and chemical characteristics of materials to be pulverized. However, grindability values have been reported for many materials [Hardgrove, *Trans. Am. Inst. Chem. Engrs.*, **34,** 131 (1938)]. Standard ball-mill and rod-mill grindability tests have been made on many ores and minerals (Bond and Maxson, *Mining Tech., Tech. Publ.* 1579, 1943). Ball-mill tests are made at a simulated 250 per cent circulating load. Tests are conducted at the mesh size to which the material is to be ground in practice. The grindability of the sample is the number of **net grams of screen undersize** produced per revolution of the mill. In the case of grinding to No. 48 sieve fineness, values of 0.304 and 9.26 are reported as the grindabilities for petroleum coke and graphite, respectively. The standard rod-mill tests are made at a simulated 100 per cent circulating load, and the results are reported in a similar manner. Values of 9.26 and 59.5 are given for quartzite and barite, respectively, when grinding to No. 20 sieve fineness.

The **net work** in hp.-hr. required to grind 1 ton of a material to a maximum limiting size in a channel-roller pulverizer may be taken as its grindability. Many industrially important materials have been tested in this manner (Coe and Coghill, *U.S. Bur. Mines, Rept. Invest.* 3704, 1943); no correlation is shown among specific gravity, mineralogical hardness, and grinding resistance.

Equipment manufacturers maintain laboratories in which grindability tests are made to determine the suitability of their machines. When grindability comparisons are made on small equipment of the manufacturers' own class, there is a basis for scale-up to commercial equipment. This is better than relying on a grindability index obtained on a ball mill to esimate size and capacity of different types, such as hammer or jet mills.

Mill Wear. In general, hard materials, coarse particles, and fast motion are conducive to wear in mills. Wear may be resisted by using materials in the zones of mill wear which are harder than the material being ground. Causing particles to grind each other helps materially. Where mill movements are slow, resilient materials like rubber often withstand the wear of hard particles. For the hardest materials, the use of hard-surfacing techniques by welding and by inserts has contributed greatly to better maintenance and lower down time. Lutes and Reid [*Chem. Eng.*, **63** (6), 243 (1956)] have reviewed the subject with data on welding hard surfaces.

Mill wear or abrasion becomes critical on high-peripheral-speed equipment, particularly high-speed close-clearance hammer mills. There is an economic limit beyond which abrasion is so great that maintenance cannot be justified. Pulverizing Machinery Co. has developed a reasonably reliable **abrasion test** using a given weight (5 lb.) of feed to a Bantam (small-scale model) Mikro-Pulverizer using a standard rotor speed and drilled perforated screen (usually 0.027-in.-diameter holes) and forged hard-faced hammers. The drilled perforations are examined under a microscope as being clean cuts prior to testing and reexamined after test with blue paste for gaging on the far side of screen perforations. The depth of cutting is measured in microns on a calibrated eyepiece, and this figure is termed "abrasion index." Up to 20 microns is usually within economic limits and above 100 microns outside economic limits, unless there are unusual aspects to the case.

Work Required for Size Reduction. *Kick's Law.* On the basis of stress-analysis theory for plastic deformation within the elastic limit, the work required for crushing a given quantity of material is constant for the same **reduction ratio,** irrespective of the original size [Kick, "Das Gasetz der propertionalen Widerstande und seine Anwendung," Leipzig, 1885. See also Stadler, *Trans. Inst. Mining Met. (London),* **19,** 471, 509 (1910); **20,** 420 (1911)]. The law can be written

$$E = C \log \frac{D_1}{D_2} \tag{8-2}$$

where D_1/D_2 is the size-reduction ratio and E is the work done.

Rittinger's Law. Another theoretical analysis states that the work consumed for reduction of particle size is directly proportional to the new **surface produced** (Rittinger, "Lehrbuch der Aufbereitungskunde," Ernst and Korn, Berlin, 1867).

$$E = C'(s_2 - s_1) \tag{8-3}$$

where s_2 and s_1 are the specific surface values after and before size reduction, respectively; but $s = (K_s/\rho)(D^2/D^3)$, where K_s is the specific surface shape factor, so that

$$E = C''\left(\frac{1}{D_2} - \frac{1}{D_1}\right) \tag{8-4}$$

Generalized Relation. A differential equation for both cases (Walker, Lewis, McAdams, and Gilliland, "Principles of Chemical Engineering," 3d ed., McGraw-Hill, New York, 1937) is

$$dE = -\frac{C\,dD}{D^n} \tag{8-5}$$

Solutions of the equation for $n = 1$ and 2 result in the Kick and Rittinger laws, respectively. For $n > 1$ the solution is

$$E = \left(\frac{C}{n-1}\right)\left(\frac{1}{D_2^{n-1}} - \frac{1}{D_1^{n-1}}\right) \tag{8-6}$$

It has been commonly considered that Kick's law was related to crushing and perhaps to fine impact pulverizing, while Rittinger's law most closely fitted fine grinding and, in particular, ball milling. More recently Bond has proposed a **third law** intermediate between these [Bond, *Trans. Am. Inst. Mining Met. Engrs.,* **193,** 484 (1952)]. In this, he states that "the total work useful in breakage that has been applied to a stated weight of homogeneous broken materials is inversely proportional to the square root of the diameter of the product particles, directly proportional to the length of the crack tips formed, and directly proportional to the square root of the surface formed."

Application of Laws. When it is considered that anomalies exist in practical use of these laws, they may best be employed broadly and used to evaluate trends qualitatively rather than be rigidly applied. The general applicability of the Rittinger relation in a number of cases is supported by various investigators [Gross and Zimmerley, *Trans. Am. Inst. Mining Met. Engrs.,* **87,** 35 (1930). Bond and Maxson, *Trans. Am. Inst. Mining Met. Engrs.,* **134,** 296 (1939)]. Equations (8-2) and (8-4) contain constants that are reciprocal efficiency coefficients. The efficiency coefficient $(n - 1)/C$ is variable in Eq. (8-6) and may have greater usefulness over wide ranges of size.

In the use of the equations, the material will possess a distribution of sizes before and after grinding; and, for Eq. (8-4), $1/D = \Sigma(\Delta W/D_m)/\Sigma(\Delta W)$, where ΔW is the mass of a closely sized increment of the material and D_m is the average of the size limits of the increment. A sample of material can be divided into orderly sized increments by a number of particle-size measurement methods. In the case of testing sieves, a geometric series is used such that the edge length of the square openings of the sieve through which the increment of material passes is $\sqrt{2}$ or 1.4 times the edge length of the openings in the retaining sieve (see also p. 8-4). The chief difficulty en countered is the assignment of a value to D_m for the portion of material too fine to be subdivided and in which a major portion of the surface may be present.

If the equation of part of the size distribution is known and it is assumed to extend indefinitely into the small sizes, the specific surface can be calculated. This can be done for a number of representations of particle-size distribution [Gaudin, *Trans. Am. Inst. Mining Met. Engrs.,* **73,** 253 (1926). Hatch, *J. Franklin Inst.,* **215,** 27 (1933). Rosin and Rammler, *J. Inst. Fuel,* **7,** 29 (933)].

The specific surface (sq. cm./g.) and the size (cm.) of a particle having the same specific surface as the whole powder can be determined directly by use of the air-permeability method [Lea and Nurse, *J. Soc. Chem. Ind.,* **58,** 277 (1939). Gooden and Smith, *Ind. Eng. Chem., Anal. Ed.,* **12,** 479 (1940)]. The Lea-Nurse apparatus has been used to determine the surface of coal pulverized in the Hardgrove machine (see p. 8-7), which is shown to operate in accordance with Rittinger's law [Romer, *Proc. Am. Soc. Testing Materials,* **41,** 1152 (1941)]. Gas-adsorption methods may also be used for measuring the surface of pulverized materials (Gaudin and Hukki, *Mining Tech.,* **8,** *Tech. Publ.* 1779, 1944).

Grinding Efficiency

Theoretical. The energy efficiency of grinding operations is 0.06 to 1 per cent based on theoretical values of the surface energy of quartz [Martin, *Trans. Inst. Chem. Engrs. (London),* **4,** 42 (1926). Gaudin, *Trans. Am. Inst. Mining Met. Engrs.,* **73,** 253 (1926)].

Measured. Grinding efficiency ranges from 6 to 25 per cent, based on thermal measurements (Fahrenwald *et al., Mining Tech., Tech. Publ.* 416, 1931). Drop-weight devices have been used to obtain ratios of surface produced to work input under idealized conditions and the performance of commercial equipment compared with them; efficiencies of 25 to 60 per cent have been shown [Wilson, *Mining Tech., Tech. Publ.* 810, 1937; Bond and Maxson, *Trans. Am. Inst. Mining Met. Engrs.,* **134,** 296 (1939)].

Efficiency Coefficients. A practical requirement is that least power be consumed for the amount of crushing or grinding desired. For this purpose the input can be stated in ft.-lb./min. (or in horsepower) and the output in new surface as sq. ft./min., to obtain an efficiency coefficient of sq. ft./ft.-lb. which should be constant for a given material, for various reduction ratios, to satisfy Rittinger's law. Values in the range of 0.02 to 0.05 sq. ft./ft.-lb. have been reported for materials such as gold and copper ores, Portland-cement clinker, petroleum coke, and pyrite when using a twin-ball pendulum impact device for crushing. The values might be halved for commercial installations (Bond, *Mining Tech.*, **10**, *Tech. Publ.* 1895, 1946). A graphical method, based on the Rittinger law, compares crushing efficiencies [Gates, *Eng. & Mining J.*, **95**, 1039 (1913)]. If grinding to a limiting size is the criterion, the efficiency coefficient may be stated as the ratio of tons per hour output able to pass through a specified sieve to the input in horsepower. The ratio is then tons/hp.-hr. The value of this coefficient is between about 0.02 and 0.1 for wet ball-mill pulverizing hard to medium-hard minerals to No. 200 sieve size.

Dispersing Agents and Grinding Aids

Wet Grinding. The limiting product fineness in dry grinding operations is that being obtained when particles begin to cake on the grinding media and walls of the equipment. Wet grinding may be employed to disperse the particles so that further reduction in size can take place, but it is restricted in many instances because of flocculation of particles smaller than about 10 microns (see p. 8-59). In the production of finely divided solids, commonly used dispersing agents are silicates, phosphates, and alkyl aryl sulfonic acids (Daxad types). Less than 1 per cent of the agent is used on a solids basis. The function of dispersing agents in water is explained by the "double-layer" theory (Ward, "Colloids," p. 27, Interscience, New York, 1946).

The use of surface-active agents in "paint grinding" is common practice [Anon., *Paint, Oil & Chem. Rev.*, **102**, 70 (1940). Fischer and Jerome, *Ind. Eng. Chem.*, **35**, 336 (1943). Price, *Am. Ink Maker*, **22**, 21, 45 (1944)].

Dry Grinding. The practice of adding dispersing agents to wet-grinding circuits has its counterpart, which is known as the use of **grinding aids**, for dry pulverizing and disintegration. Such materials as RDA (aryl alkyl sulfonic acid) and TDA (a mixture of triethanolamine salts and soluble calcium salts of modified lignin sulfonic acids) are used for raw materials and finished cement pulverizing, respectively [Kennedy and Mardulier, *Rock Prods.*, **44**, 78 (1941). Kennedy, *Ind. Eng. Chem.*, **28**, 963 (1936)]. For equal fineness (specific surface) the production rate is 20 to 40 per cent greater when using 0.03 to 0.07 per cent of TDA (solids basis) in the form of a 10 to 15 per cent water solution added continuously to ball or tube mills (Fig. 8-7). Maximum-production-rate increases are obtained in mills that normally experience ball coating; lesser increases are obtained where no ball coating is experienced. Air-classifier efficiency is also improved with TDA. Application for RDA as a grinding aid has been found in the dry pulverizing of silica and graphite.

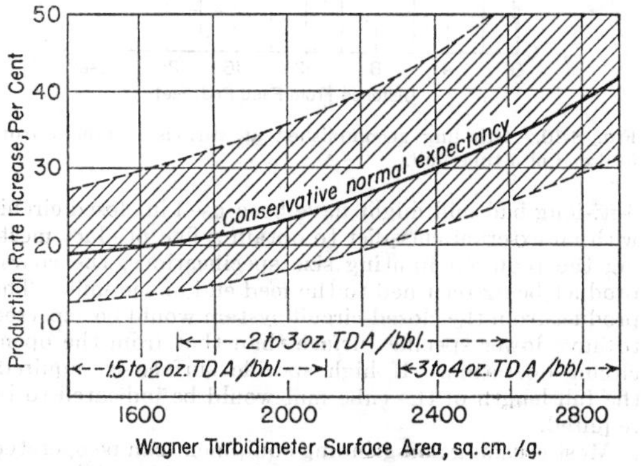

FIG. 8-7. Use of TDA grinding aid on cement clinker. *(Dewey and Almy Chemical Co.)*

Grinding aids also give a finer product for a fixed production rate as well as an increased production rate for a fixed fineness. Colloidal carbon is valuable for dry pulverizing [Sweitzer and Craig, *Ind. Eng. Chem.*, **32**, 751 (1940)]; the effect of increasing additions of carbon on fineness of product is shown in Fig. 8-8. Without the

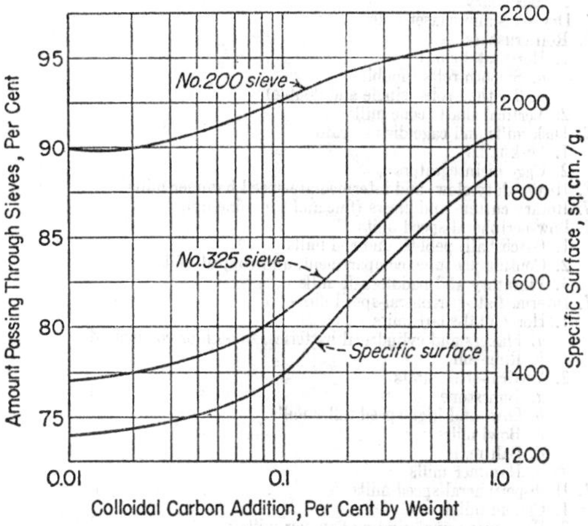

FIG. 8-8. Effect on cement fineness of colloidal carbon used as a grinding aid. [*Sweitzer and Craig, Ind. Eng. Chem.*, **32**, 751 (1940).]

use of carbon, the specific surface is 1270 sq. cm./g., and the No. 200 and No. 325 sieve finenesses are 90.0 and 77.3 per cent, respectively. Coal may be used as a grinding aid (Bond and Agthe, *Mining Tech.*, *Tech. Publ.* 1160, 1940). Carbon and coal, however, are not attractive for cement grinding because of their deleterious effect on durability. Small amounts of water added to ball mills grinding dry-process enamels serve to prevent packing of the powder on the mill walls and balls [Manson, *J. Am. Ceram. Soc.*, **21**, 316 (1938)].

A number of grinding aids have been developed. For wet grinding, these can be generalized as any suitable dispersing agent to prevent flocculation, which might inhibit grinding. For dry grinding, there are a number of specific ones. Vinsol resin, cod oil, beef tallow, and aluminum stearates are advantageous in grinding cement clinker [Dawley, *Pit and Quarry*, **36**, 57 (July, 1943)]. Patents have been issued over the years for many such agents: ammonium salts or urea for graphite; glycerol and wood resin for cement; oleic acid for zinc blende; stearates on bronze and aluminum powders; and polar and non-polar agents for fine white pigments

Classification and Selection of Equipment. A wide variety of size-reduction equipment is available, differing in details of design or having characteristic points of advantage. The chief reasons for lack of standardization are the variety of products to be ground and product qualities demanded as well as the limited amount of useful grinding theory. In addition to the properties of the materials (see p. 8-2), the economic balance between investment cost and operating cost is important in selecting equipment.

Units of equipment can be **classified** as (1) "crushers" and (2) "grinders" or "grinding mills," according to the commonly used nomenclature. Among grinders, pulverizers and disintegrators overlap so widely that it is impractical to distinguish between them. Hence "grinders" is the generic term for both. The classification does not imply that a grinding mill cannot be used for crushing, however. A classification of crushing and grinding equipment is given in Table 8-1.

Table 8-1. Types of Size-reduction Equipment

A. Jaw crushers
   1. Dodge
   2. Blake
B. Gyratory crushers
   1. Primary
   2. Secondary
C. Dry pans and chaser mills
D. Roll crushers
   1. Horizontal shaft
      a. Smooth rolls (double)
      b. Toothed rolls (single and double)
   2. Vertical shaft (cone mills)
E. Disk mills and cage disintegrators
   1. Disk mills
   2. Cage disintegrators
F. Heavy-duty slow- and intermediate-speed hammer mills
G. Rotary cutters and dicers (fine and superfine units)
H. Low-peripheral-speed units
   1. Batch ball, pebble, and rod mills
   2. Continuous tube, compartment, and conical mills
   3. Vibratory and paddle-ball mills
I. Intermediate-peripheral-speed units
   1. Horizontal-shaft units
      a. Flakers and cylindrical batteries, smooth or corrugated
      b. Ring roll
   2. Vertical-shaft units
      a. Buhrstone
      b. Low- and high-speed roller mills
      c. Bowl mills
      d. Ball mills
      e. Hammer mills
J. High-peripheral-speed mills
   1. Colloid mills
   2. High-speed fine-grinding hammer mills
   3. Superfine high-speed mechanical classifier mills
K. Fluid-energy superfine mills
L. Classifiers
   1. Screens
   2. Centrifugals

A guide to the **selection** of equipment may be based on feed **size** and **hardness** (p. 8-7) as shown in Table 8-2. It should be emphasized that Table 8-2 is merely a guide and that exceptions can be found in practice. An arbitrary distinction is made between crushing and grinding, in that feed materials from a lump size of 60 to ¼ in. require crushing, and feed materials of smaller size require pulverizing or disintegration. Primary and secondary crushing each have two stages, coarse and fine.

Table 8-2. Guide to Selection of Crushing and Grinding Equipment

Size-reduction operation	Hardness of material	Size*: Range of feeds, in.† Max.	Range of feeds, in.† Min.	Range of products, in.† Max.	Range of products, in.† Min.	Reduction ratio‡	Types of equipment
Crushing:							
Primary.....	Hard	60	12	20	4	3 to 1	*A* to *D*
		20	4	5	1	4 to 1	
Secondary....	Hard	5	1	1	0.2	5 to 1	*A* to *F*
		1.5	0.25	0.185 (4)	.033 (20)	7 to 1	
	Soft	20	4	2	0.4	10 to 1	*C* to *G*
Grinding:							
Pulverizing:							
Coarse.....	Hard	0.185 (4)	0.033 (20)	0.023 (28)	0.003 (200)	10 to 1	*C* to *I*
Fine.......	Hard	0.046 (14)	0.0058 (100)	0.003 (200)	0.00039 (1250)	15 to 1	*H* to *K*
Disintegration:							
Coarse......	Soft	0.5	0.065	0.023	0.003	20 to 1	*I* to *K*
Fine........	Soft	0.156 (5)	0.0195 (32)	0.003 (200)	0.00039 (1250)	50 to 1	*I* to *K*

* 85 per cent by weight smaller than the size given.
† Sieve number in parentheses.
‡ Higher reduction ratios for closed-circuit operations.

Pulverizing and disintegration differ chiefly in the homogeneity of the materials handled (see p. 8-2). There are two stages in each case. The reduction ratio increases as the size decreases for each operation, and a low reduction ratio is characteristic of crushing. The ratio is high for disintegration and pulverizing of soft materials [Anon., *Chem. & Met. Eng.*, **45**, 241 (1938)].

Size Reduction Combined with Size Classification. Grinding systems are batch or continuous in operation. Most operations are continuous; the outstanding exceptions are those using batch ball or pebble mills. Continuous operation is accomplished in open or closed circuit, as illustrated in Fig. 8-9.

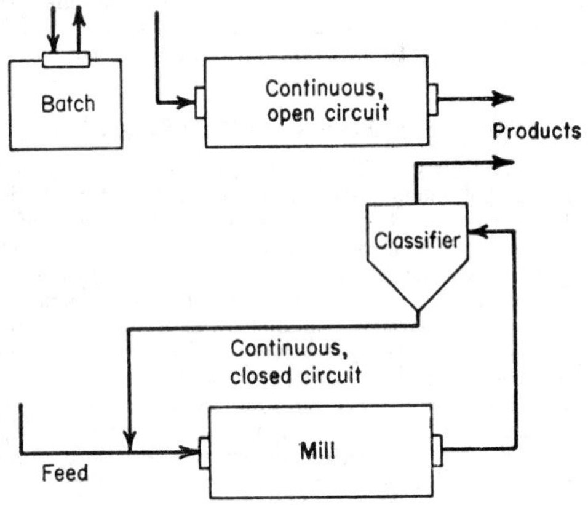

FIG. 8-9. Grinding systems.

In **continuous open-circuit operation,** as the raw material moves through a tube mill 6 ft. diameter by 26 ft. long, the greater portion is reduced to the required size in the first few feet, as illustrated in Fig. 8-10. A

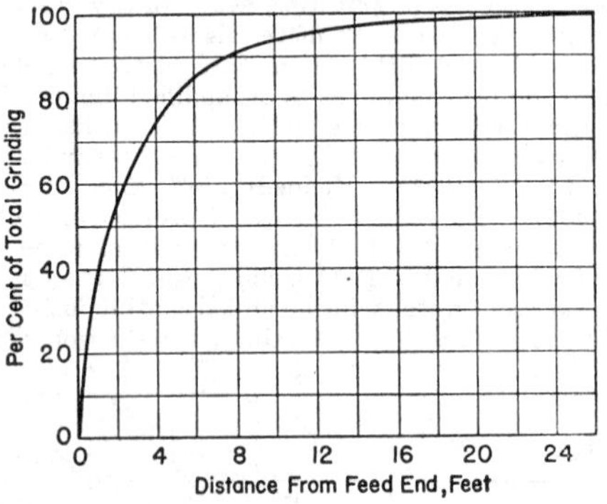

FIG. 8-10. Grinding accomplished at various distances from feed end of a tube mill.

6-ft.-long ball mill might have been used in closed circuit with an external classifier to obtain a fine product meeting the required limiting size specifications, the coarse product being returned to the feed end of the mill. The product from the closed-circuit system would be expected to have lower specific surface than that from the open-circuit operation. If high specific surface is required, the full length of the tube mill would be indicated to be required.

Most crushing and grinding equipment can be operated in **closed circuit** with size classifiers. Material from a size-reduction machine is conveyed to a classifier, in which large particles are removed and returned to the machine and particles of the desired size, and smaller, are discharged as product. By this procedure a product is obtained with **more uniform size distribution** than would be obtained by batch or continuous open-circuit operation to the same maximum limiting size. This is shown graphically in Fig. 8-11 [see also Work, *Bull. Am. Ceram. Soc.*, **17,** 1 (1938)]. Internal size classification

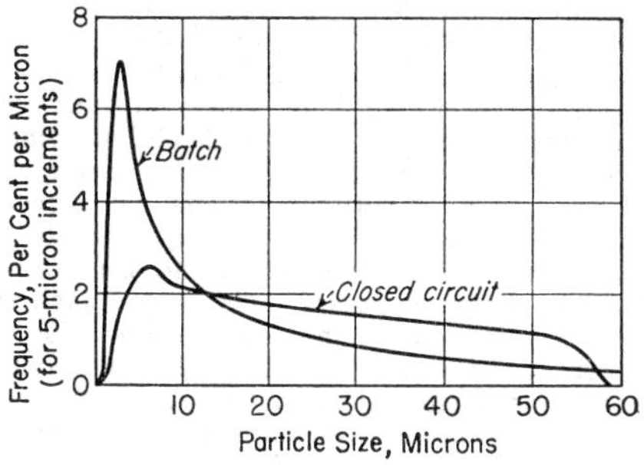

FIG. 8-11. Comparison of size distributions of products from batch and from continuous closed-circuit grinding systems.

plays an essential role in the functioning of machines for dry grinding in the fine size range; particles are retained in the grinding zone until they are as small as required in the finished product; then they are allowed to discharge.

Operating economy is the object of closed-circuit grinding to meet a limiting size specification. Production rate at a given limiting size is greater and product specific surface is less for closed-circuit than for batch or open-circuit operation. Coarse material returned to a mill by a classifier is known as the **circulating load;** its rate may be 100 to 1000 per cent of the production rate. Up to the limits of ability of a mill to grind material without choking, the production capacity increases with increase in circulating load, but at a diminishing rate until a constant value is reached. The per cent circulating load can be calculated from size analyses of the feed, fine product, and coarse product of the classifier in a closed-circuit grinding system [Bond, *Rock Prods.*, **41,** 64 (January, 1938)].

There are many possible **arrangements** for connecting classifiers in closed circuit with grinding equipment; the most suitable depends upon type and number of grinding units and nature of the finished product. A simple arrangement of a hammer mill with air classifier is shown in Fig. 8-12. A similar arrangement could be made with a tube mill and classifier. The product from a preliminary grinder, instead of going directly to the tube mill, may first be passed to a classifier, together with the tube-mill discharge, if the product of the preliminary grinder contains a substantial amount of material of final-product size. The classifier removes the fines from both streams, delivering the oversize to the tube mill. A similar arrangement can be made for a two-compartment mill, both compartments discharging to the classifier. A different arrangement may be used for a ball mill and a tube mill served by one classifier: the ball-mill discharge goes to the classifier, the coarse particles or tailings from which are returned to the feed end of the ball mill, while the fines go to the tube mill. In this case the ball mill operates in closed circuit with the classifier, while the tube mill functions as a finishing mill in open circuit. This arrangement may also be used for a two-compartment mill, the second compartment of which may serve as a finishing mill.

In an arrangement used for a three-compartment mill with single classifier, coarse tailings and fines from the

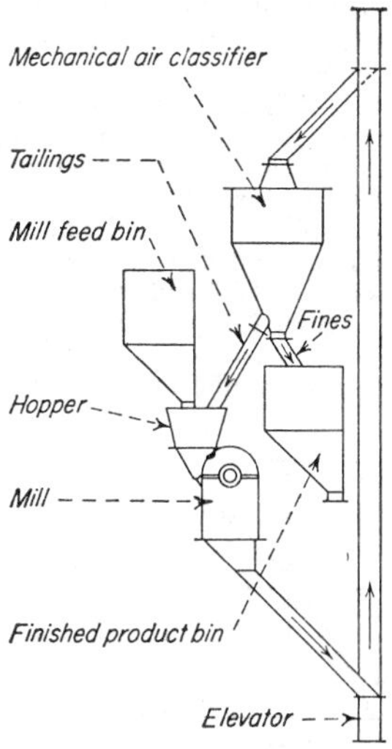

FIG. 8-12. Hammer mill in closed circuit with air classifier.

classifier may be returned to any compartment, depending upon the amount of fines required in the finished product. For a three-compartment mill with two classifiers, the following arrangement may be used: The first classifier receives the discharge from the first compartment and the second classifier the discharge from the second compartment and the fines from the first classifier; tailings from the two classifiers are the feed for the second compartment, while the fines from the second compartment go to the third compartment, which functions as a finishing mill. Many other flow sheets may be designed for compartmented mills as well as for separate units.

Dry vs. Wet Grinding. Ball mills have a large field of application for wet grinding in closed circuit with size classifiers. If the presence of liquid with the finished product is not objectionable or the feed is moist or wet, wet grinding generally is preferable to dry grinding. In the fine dry pulverizing or disintegration ranges, surface forces come into action to cause flocculation and "cushioning," with a less efficient use of energy. This condition limits the application of dry grinding and makes wet-grinding operations necessary in many instances. Other factors that influence the preference are availability of water, relative investment required, cost of drying, operating costs as influenced by local conditions, and effect on product properties.

Types of Size Classifiers. These can be divided into **gravity** and **centrifugal** types. Screens, sieves, and grizzlies are used for size classification with crushers. Sieves can be used in wet grinding, but the more commonly encountered unit is of hydraulic type such that particles are classified according to their size and density (see p. 21-46 on screening equipment and p. 21-52 on wet classifiers, as well as Chap. VII, Industrial Screening, and Chap. IX, Classification, in Gaudin, "Principles of Mineral Dressing," McGraw-Hill, New York, 1939). Centrifugal hydraulic size classifiers are employed to a limited extent; their use in wet-grinding systems for cement is an example.

Centrifugal air classifiers are used at fineness levels for which dry screens are impractical. (Some dry screening equipment becomes impractical at about No. 35 sieve; but vibratory types serve well to No. 100 sieve range and often finer, depending on the nature of the material and production rate that is required.) Centrifugal classifiers may be further subdivided into those where rotation is mechanically activated and those where it is created by momentum of the feed stream.

Use of Size Classifiers. Classifiers may be used **independently** of grinding equipment to classify a particulate material into two or more fractions more closely sized than the feed material (Fig. 8-31). The performance of a size classifier can be calculated for any size, between the size limits of the feed distribution, from particle-size analyses of the feed and fractions [Newton, *Rock Prods.*, **35**, 26 (August, 1932). See also p. 21-49.] If a graph of "efficiency" vs. particle size is prepared, as shown in Fig. 8-13, a maximum efficiency usually is obtained at

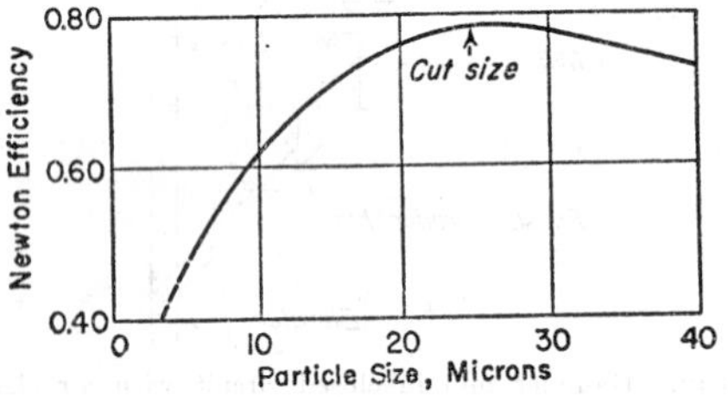

FIG. 8-13. Classifier efficiency and cut size.

the "cut size," which is defined as the size of feed particle having equal probability of entering either the fine or the coarse fraction. An efficient centrifugal classifier can scalp 80 to 85 per cent of available fines in its feed.

In a closed-circuit operation, the classifier may be placed **external** to the grinding mill, in which case material is conveyed to and away from it through lengths of elevator conduit (Fig. 8-12). If the grinding mill is air-swept, the discharge from it may be conveyed pneumatically to a cyclone collector and to the air-classifier unit, or directly to the latter (Fig. 8-32).

Many closed-circuit operations incorporate grinding and classification functions in a single housing or so closely integrated that the classifier is termed an **internal** type (Fig. 8-33). Internal classification has particular application for dry grinding; material remains in suspension and is conveyed pneumatically throughout its residence in the mill.

A distinction that can be made between internal and external classification is that the circulating load cannot be isolated or measured readily in the former case.

Size Reduction Combined with Other Operations. Batch ball mills with low ball charges can be used in **dry mixing** or standardizing of dyes, pigments, colors, and insecticides to incorporate wetting agents and inert extenders (see also Sec. 21). Rotation of the mill is favorable for many types of mixing, and presence of the balls tends to break up centrifuging of the charge and to promote lateral motion. **Mixing of liquids** is favored by use of a charge of small balls. Disk mills, hammer mills, and other high-speed disintegration equipment are useful for final intensive blending of insecticide compositions, earth colors, cosmetic powders, and a variety of other finely divided materials that tend to agglomerate in ribbon and conical blenders. The intensive action of a disk mill will break open these agglomerates of the components of a mixture and produce an intimate blend of ultimate particles.

Mills with air classification units may be equipped so that the **circulating air** can be **conditioned** by mixing with hot or cold air or gases introduced into the mill or by dehumidification to prepare the air for the grinding of hygroscopic materials. Liquid sprays, or gases, may be injected into the mill or air stream, for mixing with the material being pulverized, to effect chemical reaction or surface treatment.

Some materials are easier to disintegrate at elevated temperatures, even when thoroughly dry, because they disperse and flow more freely than at lower temperatures. Heat-sensitive materials with low softening temperatures are amenable to pulverizing if proper **temperature control** is exercised. Compositions containing fats and waxes are pulverized and blended readily, if refrigerated air is introduced into their grinding systems (U.S. Patents 1,739,761 and 2,098,798; see also p. 8-55).

Ball mills may have their shells and heads jacketed for the flow of hot or cold fluids, and good **heat transfer** to the material within the mill is obtained, provided that the material does not cake on the heat-transfer surfaces. In some cases, mills without jackets are placed over direct fire or erected inside a furnace with the cooled bearings external to it [Underwood, *Ind. Eng. Chem.*, **30**, 905 (1938)]. Other types of mills can be jacketed for heating or cooling, but many mills do not offer enough surface for effective heat transfer. There is danger of moisture condensation when cooling air-swept mills. It is wise to use temperature-controlled feed and to control air temperatures when air is employed.

Dehydration is the removal of combined water as well as free moisture, such as, for example, the removal of water of crystallization from copper sulfate, $CuSO_4.5H_2O$. This is done by introducing hot gases into a closed-circuit grinding system.

Many materials can be ground to better advantage when dry. Introduction of heated air into a system employing air conveying, or classification, serves to increase the productivity of the equipment (Fig. 8-1).

The **drying** of materials while they are being pulverized or disintegrated is known variously as "flash" or "dispersion" drying; a generic term is "pneumatic conveying" drying. A flash-drying system can be used for raw materials of moderate moisture content and also for precipitated products in the form of wet sludges or cakes coming from filters or centrifuges. The method of conditioning the air is the same whether the mill is of the ball, ring-roller, or hammer-mill type used for heating, cooling, dehydrating or drying. Data for the grinding and drying of bauxite in a ring-roller mill are given in Table 8-3.

Ball and pebble mills, batch or continuous, offer considerable opportunity for combining a number of **processing steps** that include grinding (Underwood, *loc. cit.*). Vacuum drying and pulverizing of heat-sensitive materials is possible; chemical and physical reactions

Table 8-3. Operating Data for Grinding and Drying of Bauxite in a Ring-roller Mill

Initial moisture, %	9.75
Final moisture, %	0.75
Feed, lb./hr	12,560
Product, lb./hr	11,420
Moisture evaporated, lb	1,140
Temperature of gases entering mill, °F	700
Temperature of gases leaving mill, °F	170
Temperature of feed, °F	70
Temperature of material leaving mill, °F	150
Oil consumed, gal	14.3
Heating value of oil, B.t.u./gal	142,000
Thermal efficiency, %	68.5
Total power for drying and pulverizing, hp	105
Power for drying, hp	10
Final product, % through No. 100 sieve	90

can be carried out; agitation, evaporation, chemical reaction, drying, and pulverizing can be accomplished in successive stages; and fibrous materials, for example, can be loosened by dry grinding, impregnated with hot liquid resin, vacuum-dried, chilled to increase friability, and pulverized and discharged as a fine dry molding powder.

Pulverizers equipped with air classification apparatus

for closed-circuit operation, or followed by air classifiers, can serve to **separate components of mixtures** because of differences in specific gravity and particle size. The removal of impurities by this means is known as **cleaning or concentrating.** Screens are used to separate coarse particles, not easily pulverized, from fine particles of the component that is pulverized readily. Throwout boxes are built into some mills for collection of grossly oversize foreign material. Magnetic separators frequently are employed to remove tramp magnetic solids from the feed to high-speed hammer and disk mills.

Sand may be removed from clay, and refractory impurities separated from hydrated lime. Phosphate rock may be freed from such impurities as clays and silt. The various oxides of lead, copper, and other metals often contain a certain amount of unoxidized material. When such materials are fed to a pulverizer and air-classification arrangement, the relatively soft oxide is reduced to fine powder and separated from the metal. To separate lead from dross, skimmings, and scrap battery plates, the material is first coarsely crushed in a high-speed hammer mill discharging to a screen. Oversize, almost all metallic lead, goes to the melting pot; undersize, a mixture of metal and oxide, goes to the pulverizer.

In the cleaning and concentrating of clays, chalks, and marls, water flotation is frequently used. The product is then dried and disintegrated in hammer mills. If further cleaning is desired, the washed product may be processed in a series of air classifiers, the tailings from one classifier being fed into the next. Tailings from the last classifier are either discarded or fed to the water-flotation system. Some clays give a sufficiently fine product by dry pulverization and air classification.

Lime, after hydration, usually contains all the impurities of the original lime, such as sand, gravel, coke, and clinker refractory material. For many uses, these impurities must be removed from the hydrate. This is most effectively accomplished by a special-purpose hammer mill with internal air separation and throwout devices. These units throw out essentially all impurities as oversize. Chemical hydrate is commonly produced 95 to 99 per cent minus 325 mesh, or even finer if desired. These units produce rather clean rejects.

In some cases the crude hydrated lime is fed first to a mechanical air separator. Here a good share of the available minus 325 mesh material is removed. The coarse fraction from the separator then goes to the special pulverizer mentioned above for final treatment. Typical results for this circuit are given in Table 8-4.

Table 8-4. Cleaning and Concentrating Hydrated Lime

Size of classifier, diam., ft	12
Power for classifier, hp	25
Power for pulverizer, hp	7.5
Power for pulverizer fan, hp	40
Feed to classifying system, tons/hr	8
Production of hydrated lime, tons/hr	7.2
Tailings, tons/hr	0.8

Chemical Analysis

	Feed	Finished product	Tailings
Calcium and magnesium hydrate, %	88.95	98.80	5.12
Silica, %	3.16	0.15	28.61
Iron and aluminum oxides, %	2.26	0.12	20.42
Calcium and magnesium carbonates, %	2.63	0.26	23.15
Calcium and magnesium oxides, %	3.00	0.67	22.70
Fineness, % through No. 200 sieve	90	99.5	4.5

Certain phosphate sands are cleaned and concentrated to remove sand and silt. Table 8-5 gives the results obtained in processing dry phosphatic sand in a Raymond automatic pulverizer with throwout.

Safety. Some metal powders present a hazard because of their **flammability.** Their combustion is favored during grinding operations in which ball, hammer, or ring roller mills are employed and during which a high grinding temperature may be reached. Isolation of the mills, use of non-sparking materials of construction, and magnetic separators to remove foreign magnetic material from the feed are useful precautions (Hartman, Nagy, and Brown, *U.S. Bur. Mines, Rept. Invest.* 3722, 1943). Stainless steel has less sparking tendency than ordinary steel or forgings. The use of inert atmosphere is frequently practiced for safety.

Table 8-5. Cleaning and Concentrating Phosphate Sand

Size of automatic pulverizer	No. 3
Feed, tons/hr	8.5
Capacity (of throwout), tons/hr	5.25
Fines, tons/hr	3.25
Power required by pulverizer, hp	15
Power required by fan, hp	40

Chemical Analysis

	Feed	Throwout product*	Fines
$Ca_3(PO_4)_2$ content, %	52	68	26
$Fe_2O_3 + Al_2O_3$ content, %	12.5	6	23

* Throwout product contains most of the valuable material and is the product required.

Many finely divided metal powders in suspension in air are potential **explosion hazards,** and causes for ignition of such dust clouds are numerous [Hartmann and Greenwald, *Mining Met.*, **26,** 331 (1945)]. Concentration of the dust in air and its particle size are important factors that determine explosibility. Below a lower limit of concentration, no explosion can result because the heat of combustion is insufficient to propagate it. Above a maximum limiting concentration, an explosion cannot be produced because insufficient oxygen is available. The finer the particles, the more easily is ignition accomplished and the more rapid is the rate of combustion. This is illustrated in Fig. 8-14.

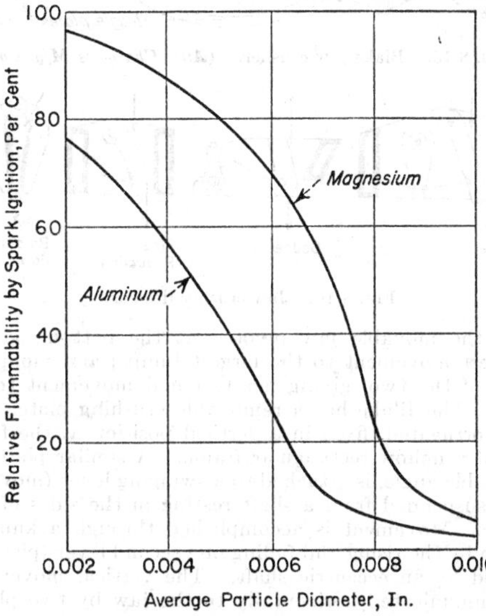

FIG. 8-14. Effect of fineness on the flammability of metal powders. (*Hartmann, Nagy, and Brown, U.S. Bur. Mines Rept. Invest.* 3722, 1943.)

Such non-metallic materials as sulfur, starch, wood flour, cereal dust, dextrin, coal, pitch, hard rubber, and plastics are potential hazards when in finely divided form. Explosions and fires may be initiated by discharges of static electricity, sparks from flames, hot surfaces, and spontaneous combustion. Reduction of the oxygen content of air present in grinding systems is a means for preventing dust explosions in the equipment (Brown, *U.S. Dept. Agr. Tech. Bull.* 74, 1928). Maintenance of oxygen content below 12 per cent should be safe for most materials, but 8 per cent is recommended for sulfur grinding.

Use of **inert gas** has particular adaptation to pulverizers equipped with air classification; flue gas can be used for this purpose, and it is mixed with the air normally present in a system (see p. 8-55 for sulfur grinding). Despite the protection afforded by use of inert gas, equipment should be provided with explosion vents, and structures should be designed with venting in mind [Brown and Hanson, *Chem. & Met. Eng.*, **40**, 116 (1933)].

Hard rubber presents a fire hazard when reduced on steam-heated rolls (see p. 8-55). Its dust is explosive [Twiss and McGowan, *India Rubber J.*, **107**, 292 (1944)]. Inert gas can be introduced at 110° to 130°F. into systems operating in closed circuit with sieves or air classifiers.

Many synthetic resins and plastics are hazardous in the finely divided state (Hartmann and Nagy, *U.S. Bur. Mines Rept. Invest.* 3751, 1944).

An annual publication, "National Fire Codes for the Prevention of Dust Explosions," is available from the National Fire Protection Association, Boston, and should be of interest to those handling hazardous powders.

CRUSHING AND GRINDING EQUIPMENT

Jaw Crushers. (Fig. 8-15.) *Design and Operation.* These may be divided into three main groups (Fig. 8-16): the *Blake,* with movable jaw pivoted at the top, giving greatest movement to the smallest lumps; the *Dodge,*

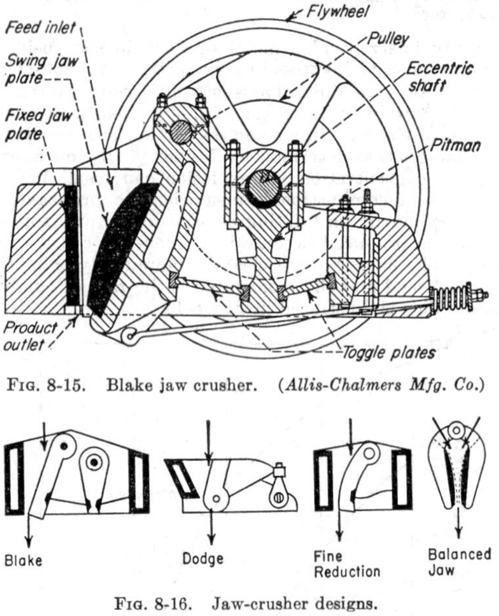

FIG. 8-15. Blake jaw crusher. (*Allis-Chalmers Mfg. Co.*)

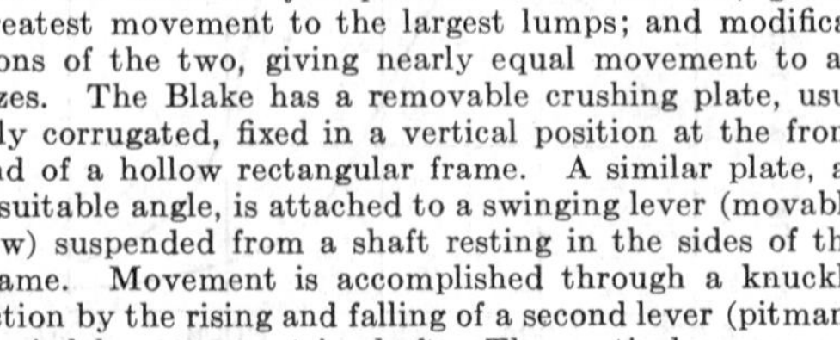

FIG. 8-16. Jaw-crusher designs.

with the movable jaw pivoted at the bottom, giving greatest movement to the largest lumps; and modifications of the two, giving nearly equal movement to all sizes. The Blake has a removable crushing plate, usually corrugated, fixed in a vertical position at the front end of a hollow rectangular frame. A similar plate, at a suitable angle, is attached to a swinging lever (movable jaw) suspended from a shaft resting in the sides of the frame. Movement is accomplished through a knuckle action by the rising and falling of a second lever (pitman) carried by an eccentric shaft. The vertical movement is communicated horizontally to the jaw by two plates (toggles).

The Dodge type has the advantage of a larger feed opening for the same cost as a Blake, and it is useful for low-production intermittent service to produce a uniform product in sizes having smaller than 11- by 15-in. feed opening.

The setting of a jaw crusher may be stated as being the close or the wide opening between the moving jaws at the outlet end. The reciprocating motion of the jaws causes the opening to vary between close and wide. Specifications usually are based on close settings. The setting is adjustable.

The *Fine Reduction* (*Allis-Chalmers*) and *Kue-Ken Balanced Jaw* (*Straub Manufacturing Co.*) principles (Fig. 8-16) fall into the third category. The crusher having the former principle is a single-toggle machine having its swing jaw mounted directly on the eccentric shaft so that it receives a downward as well as a forward motion. The lower end of the swing jaw is held in position against the toggle by a tension rod. The *Kue-Ken* balanced-jaw crusher has two opposed jaws, both swinging freely like two pendulums. Material is crushed without rubbing as the jaws move toward each other.

Performance. Jaw crushers are applied to primary crushing of hard materials, and are usually followed by other types of crushers. In smaller sizes they are used as single-stage machines. The Blake type is available with receiving opening as large as 66 by 86 in.

The *Type H* crusher (*Traylor*) is distinguished by a welded-plate construction, two-piece pitman, and curved jaw plates. It is available in 10 sizes from 8- by 12-in. to 30- by 42-in. openings with capacities varying from 4 to 275 tons/hr. when producing minus ⅞ to minus 5 in. stone. The maximum power requirements of the sizes are from 10 to 100 hp. The *Type HB* crusher is equipped with a rod-type *Bulldog Pitman* with safety device. It is available in five sizes from 36- by 42-in. to 56- by 72-in. openings with capacities varying from 120 to 640 tons/hr. when producing minus 2- to minus 9-in. stone. The maximum power requirements of the sizes are from 115 to 250 hp. The *Type S* crusher is designed to withstand the most severe crushing duty. It is available in seven sizes from 36- by 42-in. to 66- by 86-in. openings with capacities varying from 120 to 1100 tons/hr. when producing minus 2- to minus 11-in. stone. The maximum power requirements of these sizes are 115 to 300 hp.

The capacities and power consumption of a *Dodge* (*Allis-Chalmers*) type jaw crusher operating on a tough ore that offers considerable resistance to reduction are shown in Table 8-6.

Table 8-6. Performance Data of Dodge (Allis-Chalmers) Jaw Crusher

Size of opening, in.	Capacity, tons/hr. Size of product: ½ in.	¾ in.	1 in.	1½ in.	Approx. hp. required
4 × 6	¼	½	1	..	3
7 × 9	..	1	2	3	6
8 × 12	..	1½	3	4	10
11 × 15	..	2	4	6	15

The *Fine Reduction* jaw crusher is suitable for producing finished ball-mill feed in one pass. The character of material being crushed determines to a large extent the screen analysis of the crusher product. With a screened feed, approximately 90 per cent of the product will pass a round hole in a flat testing screen corresponding to the open setting and approximately 50 per cent corresponding to the closed setting. With a feed opening of 24 by 10 in., a 25-hp. drive, and ½-in. stroke, a capacity of 6 tons/hr. (1 ton = 20 cu. ft.) can be obtained with a close setting of ¼ in. Capacity increases directly with setting up to 1½ in.

The *Universal* jaw crusher (*Universal Engineering Corp.*) is a combination of the Dodge and Blake types. A high eccentric above the feed hopper and a radial toggle action at the bottom produce both horizontal and vertical actions of the movable jaw. The jaw moves forward and downward, tending to force the feed and force the discharge. The pitman that carries the moving jaw plate cannot drop directly away from the stationary jaw, and therefore large pieces of stone will not pass through until they are crushed. In this overhead-eccentric force-feed crusher, there are two crushing blows to each revolution of the shaft, a primary blow at the top where most needed and a secondary or finishing stroke at the bottom. Table 8-7 gives performance data for several

Table 8-7. Performance Data for Universal Jaw Crushers

No.	Jaw opening, in.	Capacity, tons/10 hr. Size of product				Power required, hp.
		3 in.	1½ in.	¾ in.		
1	24 × 36	800–1300	....	......	.....	70–100
2	20 × 36	750–1100	250–400	......	.....	60– 85
3	18 × 24	500– 750	190–270	......	.....	40– 55
4	12 × 20	330– 460	110–220	50– 90	.....	25– 40
		1½ in.	1 in.	¾ in.	¼ in. and finer	
5	10 × 24	190– 260	110–180	80–120	.....	25– 40
6	10 × 20	160– 220	90–140	70–100	.....	20– 30
7	10 × 16	120– 180	70–100	50– 70	.....	15– 20
8	9 × 16	70– 140	50– 90	30– 60	5–30	15– 20
9	9 × 12	50– 100	40– 60	20– 40	10–25	8– 15
10	9 × 8	20– 25	15– 20	10– 15	6–10	6– 10
11	5 × 6	10– 12	6– 8	5– 7	3– 5	3– 4

types and sizes of this crusher. Crushers 1 to 4 are used largely as prebreakers in rock quarries and mining industries where a large feed opening and a high ratio of reduction are required. Crushers 5 to 7 are well adapted for crushing to ¾ in. and finer and will produce a fine, uniform product for concrete construction and work of a similar nature. Crushers 8 to 11 are for producing small sizes of stone or ore in moderate capacities. Crushers 1 to 7 may be used advantageously in the production of a suitable feed size for a pulverizer.

The *Nertia* crusher (Southwestern Engineering Co.) is a jaw crusher in a spring mounting. The device is portable and needs no foundation to absorb shock. It is also reversible, and the jaws can be freed of material bound in them by reversing the motor.

Crusher Product Size Distribution. A number of equipment manufacturers have prepared charts for jaw, gyratory, and roll crushers based on the practice of setting the crusher so that 15 per cent of the product will be larger than the specified size. The charts show the approximate size distribution to be expected for the product. Figure 8-17 is an adaptation of these charts. For a crusher setting such that 85 per cent will pass through a 2-in. round opening, for example, it can be estimated that 47 per cent will pass a 1-in. round hole and 26 per cent through a 0.5-in. round hole.

Gyratory Crushers. (Fig. 8-18.) *Design.* The housing of a primary gyratory crusher has the shape of the frustums of two cones placed together with the narrow sections in the center. Crushing is done in the

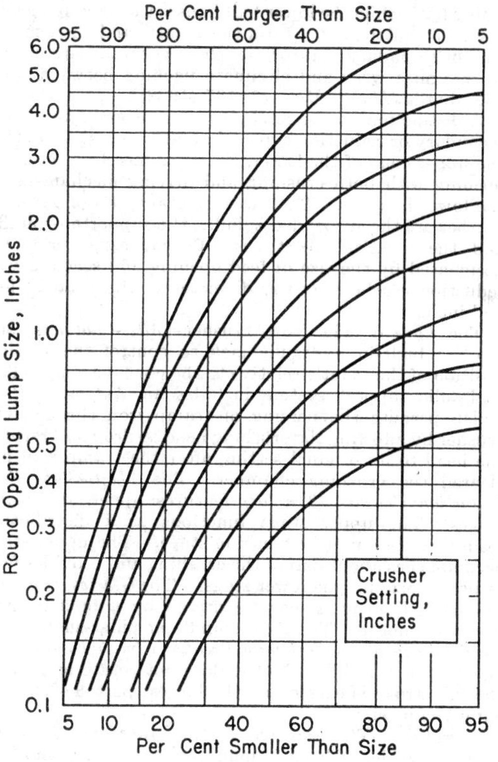

Fig. 8-17. Crusher-product size distribution.

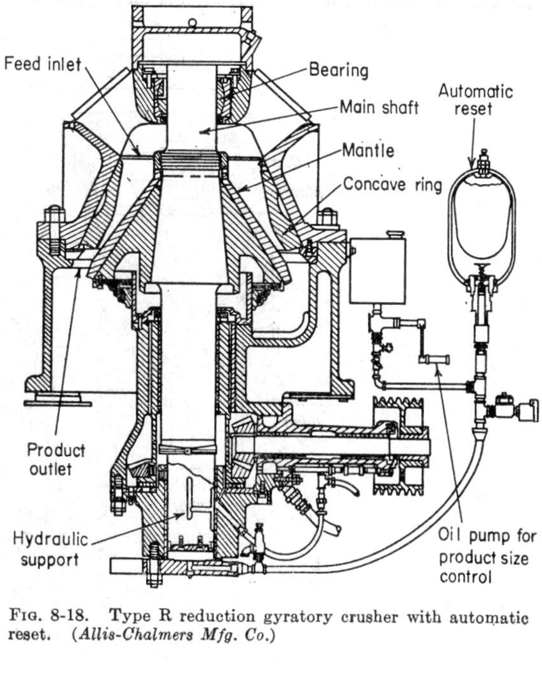

Fig. 8-18. Type R reduction gyratory crusher with automatic reset. (*Allis-Chalmers Mfg. Co.*)

upper half, while the lower half houses the driving mechanisms, eccentric, etc. Both the mantle and the concave ring of secondary gyratory crushers generally are curved to minimize wear and eliminate packing between them [Bernhard, *Mining Met.*, **13**, 107 (1932)].

A distinction can be made between primary types and secondary or reduction types of gyratory crushers in that the upper cone of the latter, if any, is merely a receiving opening with both crushing and driving mechanisms in the lower housing. The three general types of gyratory crusher are the suspended-spindle, the supported-spindle, and the fixed-spindle types. Primary gyratories are designated by the size of feed opening and secondary or reduction crushers by the diameter of the head in feet and inches.

The *Type R* (Fig. 8-18) crusher (*Allis-Chalmers*) employs a built-in hydraulic jack to control the vertical position of the mantle relative to the concave ring. This hydraulic support system includes an *Automatic Reset* which permits the passing of tramp iron through the crusher by allowing the crushing head to drop and returns the head to its original setting after the tramp iron has cleared the crushing chamber. The *Multi-Stage Fine Reduction Crusher* (*Traylor*) features upper and lower stages. The upper stage functions as a distributing feeder for the lower or finishing stage. The upper stage accomplishes about half of the crushing and provides feed of proper size for the lower stage. The *Gearless Gyratory* (*Kennedy-Van Saun*) can be driven by a built-in synchronous motor. The fixed-spindle or pillar-shaft gyratory, known as the *Telsmith Breaker* (*Smith Engineering Works*) has a rigid shaft that does not rotate or gyrate; the full stroke is exerted on the largest particles as they enter the bowl.

Operation. The eccentric at the lower end gives the shaft, on which a head is mounted, a gyratory motion; this causes the head and its mantle to approach or recede from the concave surfaces of the common gyratory, breaking the feed on its downward path. There is a close and a wide opening between the mantle and concave ring at the outlet end. The close opening is known as the close setting or the close-side setting and sometimes as the closed-side setting, while the wide opening is known as the wide-side or open-side setting. Specifications usually are based on close settings. The setting is adjustable.

Performance. The crushing rate of a gyratory generally is not dependent on the hardness of the material being crushed but will depend on the amount of product size material in the feed. Manufacturers give capacities estimated for average conditions based on full continuous feed of quarry- or mine-run material weighing 100 lb./cu. ft. after crushing. Gyratory crushers are used for high-capacity primary crushing, or to follow primary crushers of either the jaw or gyratory type.

The *Superior McCully* (*Allis-Chalmers*) crusher is made in 11 sizes; each size has two feed openings ranging from 8¾ by 35 in. to 59¾ by 196 in. Horsepower ranges from 15 to 500. Minimum settings range from ⅞ to 7 in. with capacity from 30 to 1070 tons/hr. Maximum settings range from 2⅜ to 10½ in. with capacity from 51 to 2120 tons/hr. The 18-in. *Fine Reduction Superior McCully* crusher's feed opening is 18 by 68 in. Settings range from 1½ to 4 in. with corresponding capacity of 245 to 734 tons/hr., and horsepower ranges from 150 to 200.

Type R crushers are made in four sizes. Each size can be equipped with either standard or fine-reduction con caves. With standard concaves, feed openings range from 3 to 8 in. with minimum close-side settings 3/16 to ⅜ in. and maximum close-side settings of 1¼ to 3¼ in. Capacity varies from 10 to 340 tons/hr. With the fine-reduction concaves, feed openings range from 2 to 5 in. with minimum close-side settings ⅛ to 3/16 in. and maximum close-side settings of ⅜ to ⅞ in. Capacity varies from 7 to 207 tons/hr. Horsepower ranges from 25 to 150.

Approximately 60 to 65 per cent of a *Type R* product will pass through a square opening of a testing sieve equal to the "close-side" opening of the crusher and 95 to 100 per cent of the "wide-side" opening.

The *Type T Bulldog* (*Traylor*) gyratory crusher is used for primary and secondary crushing. Fourteen standard sizes are available with receiving openings varying from

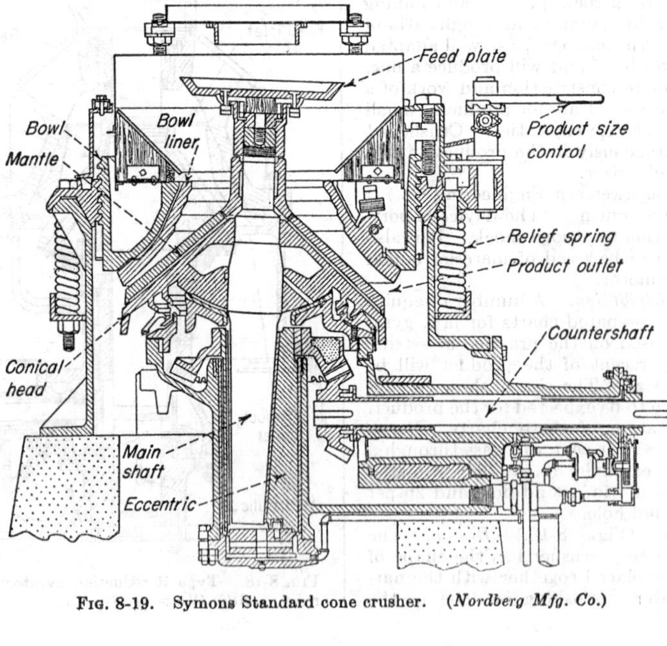

Fig. 8-19. Symons Standard cone crusher. (*Nordberg Mfg. Co.*)

2¼ by 14 in. to 60 by 210 in.; primary capacity varies from ¾ to 2400 tons/hr. for close-side discharge openings from ⅜ to 8¼ in. and from ½ to 1600 tons/hr. for openings from ¼ to 5¾ in.; secondary capacity varies from ¾ to 600 tons/hr. for close-side discharge openings from ⅜ to 6 in. and from ½ to 370 tons/hr. for openings from ¼ to 3½ in. The *Type TY Reduction Crusher* is made in six sizes with receiving openings varying from 3 by 15 in. to 22 by 66 in. Capacities range from 4 tons/hr. with the close side set to ⅛ in. in the smallest crusher up to 590 tons/hr. with the discharge opening set to 3½ in. in the largest crusher.

Gearless Gyratory crushers are available with feed-opening sizes from 3 by 8 in. to 66 by 235 in., crush to from ½ to 10 in. at ½ to 3600 tons/hr., and require from 1 to 250 hp. The fine crushers are built with feed openings from 1¾ to 14 in. wide.

Seven standard sizes of *Telsmith Breaker* are made, from 15 to 20 hp. to 100 to 125 hp., and receiving opening from 6¾ by 35 in. to 25 by 106 in. Capacities range from 17 to 18 tons/hr. for the smallest size to 300 to 350 tons/hr. for the largest, discharge opening from 1 to 4 in. The Telsmith reduction or secondary crusher has a large bowl, much wider at the bottom than at the top, allowing free escape of the material. Four standard sizes are made, 25 to 65 hp., 5- to 8-in. feed opening, ⅞- to 1⅝-in. discharge opening, with capacities ranging from 18 to 21 to 85 to 100 tons/hr.

Cone Crushers. (Fig. 8-19.) *Design and Operation.* The cone or conical head, gyrated by means of an eccentric driven through gears and a countershaft, is supported from the base. Heavy springs hold the upper frame fixed; when choked by overfeeding or tramp iron, the springs allow the upper frame to rise at the point of stress so that the material can be discharged. The conical head gyrates in much the same manner as for the gyratory crushers, but the cone travels a greater distance and gyrates faster. Material receives a series of rapid blows as it passes through the crushing cavity.

Performance. The cone crusher is a secondary or reduction crusher. The two common types are the *Symons* (*Nordberg Mfg. Co.*) and the *Telsmith* (*Smith Engineering Works*). Performance characteristics are given in Table 8-8. In addition to the *Standard* crusher (Fig. 8-19), *Symons Short Head Cone Crushers* are available for still greater reduction in size.

Pan Crushers. (Fig. 8-20.) *Design and Operation.* The pan crusher consists of one or more grinding wheels or mullers revolving in a pan; the pan may remain stationary and the mullers be driven, or the pan may be driven while the mullers revolve by friction. In some types the mullers are made of stone; in others they are of stone or of iron equipped with steel tires. Iron scrapers or plows at a proper angle feed the material under the mullers.

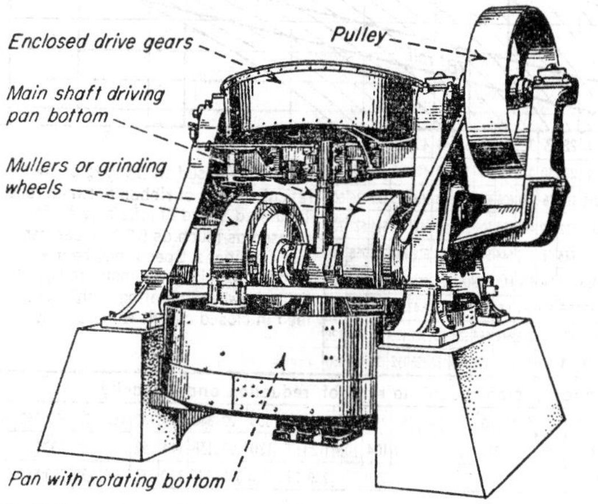

FIG. 8-20. Heavy-duty dry pan crusher. (*Bonnot Co.*)

In the *Bonnot Dry Pan* (Fig. 8-20), the clearance between the mullers and bottom of the pan can be regulated. The pan bottom rotates and has a central, solid crushing ring as well as an outer ring of screen plates with openings from $\frac{1}{16}$ to ½ in., as required.

Table 8-8. Operating Characteristics for Cone Crushers (Symons Standard)

Size of crusher, ft.	Width of feed opening, in.	Capacity, tons/hr. Discharge setting, in. ⅜	½	¾	1	1½	Hp.
2	2¼	20	25	35	...	...	25- 30
3	3⅞	35	40	70	...	...	50- 60
4	5	60	80	120	150	...	75-100
5½	7⅛	..	..	200	275	340	150-200
7	10	..	..	330	450	600	250-300

Performance. The dry pan is useful for crushing medium hard and soft materials such as clays, shales, cinders, and soft minerals such as barytes. Materials fed should normally be 3 in. or smaller, and a product can be delivered able to pass No. 4 to No. 16 sieves, depending on the hardness of the material. Finer products can be obtained by operating a pan in closed circuit with a vibrating screen. High reduction ratio with low power and maintenance are features of pan crushers.

The Bonnot dry pan is available from 5 to 10 ft. pan diameter with mullers ranging from 28 to 62 in. in diameter with 5- to 18-in. face and 1800 to 30,000 lb. weight per pair. Power ranges from 15 to 75 hp. or from 1 to 5 hp./ton of product. Production rate varies from 1 to 50 tons/hr. according to pan size and hardness of material as well as fineness of feed and product.

Smooth-roll Crushers. *Design and Operation.* Two rolls of the same diameter are revolved toward each other at the same speed. One of the shafts moves in fixed bearings, the other in movable bearings. The distance between the rolls is adjustable, and a nest of powerful springs holds the movable roll to the clearance that has been set.

The tension springs exert pressures on the rolls up to 6000 lb./lin. in. of roll face for light duty to as high as 40,000 lb./lin. in. for heavy duty. This is equivalent to crushing strengths of 18,000 to 120,000 lb./sq. in. based on effective face length equal to one-third of actual length. Automatic lateral adjusting mechanisms can be provided to move the fixed roll from side to side to minimize angular corrugation and flanging.

The angle of nip, the angle formed by the tangents to the roll faces at the point of contact with a particle to be crushed, is determined by $\cos(N/2) = (r + a)/(r + b)$, where r = radius of rolls, a = one-half distance between rolls, b = radius of particle, and N = angle of nip. The angle of nip varies for different operations, but seldom exceeds 30 deg. The required roll diameter is determined by the maximum size of feed that can be nipped without slippage: $b_{max} = 0.04r + a$; all dimensions usually are in inches.

The peripheral speed at which rolls normally operate is from 200 to 1200 ft./min., occasionally as high as 1500. The economical range of reduction usually is limited to a No. 12 to No. 16 sieve product. For crushing coarse material, the roll speed should be less than for fine material. For soft and brittle materials, higher speeds can be used. A reduction ratio of 4 should not be exceeded for hard materials. For large pieces of hard materials,

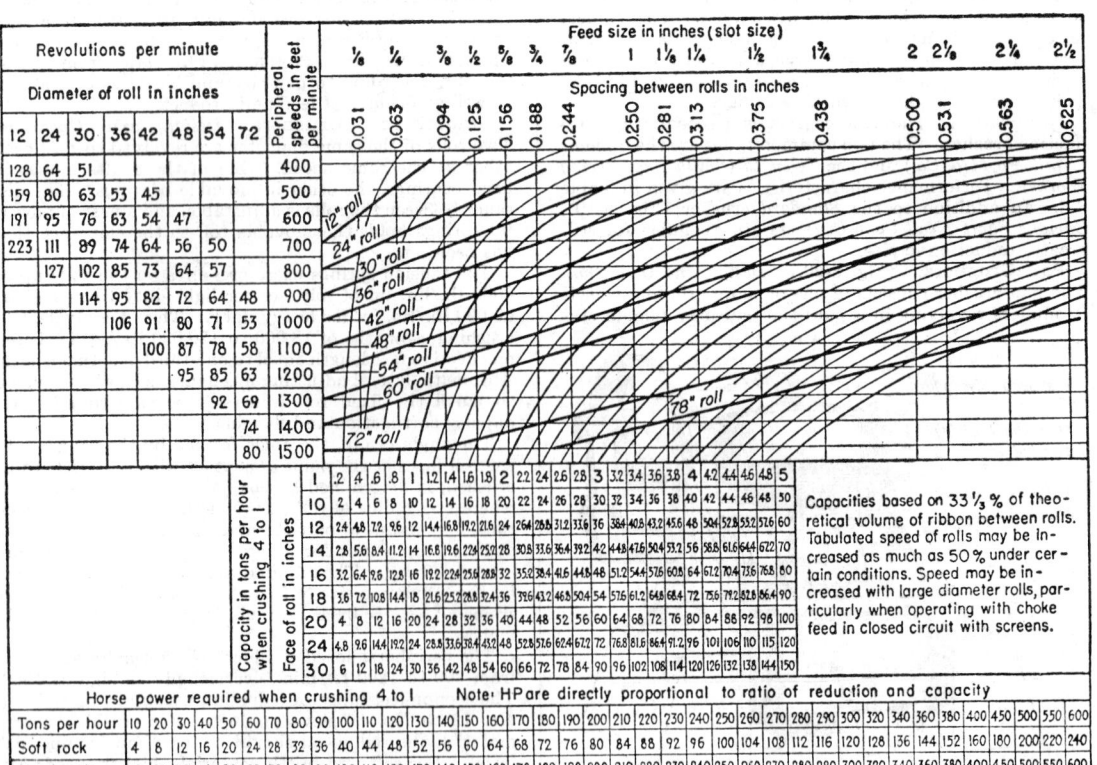

3 or 2.5 gives better results. For small feed material, however, about one-third or one-quarter of the size the rolls will nip, a reduction ratio of 8 may be made if a quantity of fines is not objectionable.

The capacity increases with the length and the diameter of the roll. When the rolls are kept full, the crushing is done not only by the action of the rolls but by the attrition between the particles themselves. This is called choke crushing. In free crushing the rolls are fed at such a rate that each particle is crushed and ejected before the next is nipped. Free crushing produces a larger proportion of coarser sizes and is generally more advantageous, whereas choke crushing is resorted to for the production of a fine product if other types of crushers are not found more suitable.

The following procedure may be used to determine operating characteristics of rolls, bearing in mind that capacity is influenced by the character of the feed, fineness of reduction, and the required manner of operation. Capacity is in direct ratio to width and peripheral speed and may be calculated by the following formula: $C = TWS/1728$, where C = capacity, cu. ft./min.; T = distance between rolls, in.; W = width of rolls, in.; and S = peripheral speed, in./min. This gives the theoretical capacity and is based on the rolls discharging a continuous, solid, uniform ribbon of material. Because of irregularity in the feed, the actual capacity may vary between 25 and 35 per cent of theoretical.

Performance. The chart shown in Fig. 8-21 can be used to find smooth-roll sizes, capacities, speeds, and power requirements for average conditions under which rolls operate. Although the chart has been prepared carefully and is based on many years of practical experience, the results obtained for a particular application must be considered approximate.

An example of the use of the chart can be based on the following conditions: hard-rock feed of minus 1 in. slot size, open circuit operation, ¼-in. roll spacing, 20 short tons/hr. average and 24 short tons/hr. maximum production rate, with rate controlled by feeder from bin.

1. Follow down vertical line from 1-in. feed size. First roll size diagonal intersect is 36-in. roll which means a 36-in. roll is the smallest which will nip 1-in. material. Use 42-in. roll for better nipping and longer roll-shell life.
2. Follow horizontal line from intersection of vertical line and 42-in. roll diagonal. A peripheral speed of 700 ft./min. or 64 r.p.m. is indicated.
3. Follow parabolic line from intersection of vertical line and 42-in. roll diagonal. A roll with a 16-in. face should crush 25.6 short tons/hr. with 33⅓ per cent of the theoretical ribbon. Always select standard-face rolls.
4. Horsepower can be determined by interpolation. In this case, a 25-hp. motor or two 15-hp. motors should be recommended.

Standard diameters for smooth-shell crushing rolls are 12, 18, 24, 30, 36, 42, 48, 54, 60, 64, 72, and 78 in. The length of the roll face is approximately one-half to one-fourth of the diameter. Standard roll lengths are 10, 12, 14, 16, 18, 20, 24, 30, and 36 in., but not all these lengths are available for all diameters.

Corrugated- and Toothed-roll Crushers. *Design and Operation.* These terms are used to describe a variety of machines consisting of one or more cylinders rotating in a horizontal plane; the rolls may be toothed or corrugated, the same or different sizes; and they may run at the same or differential speeds. Crushing rolls can be fitted with hardened shells of various designs, corru-

Revolutions per minute								
Diameter of roll in inches								Peripheral speeds in feet per minute
12	24	30	36	42	48	54	72	
128	64	51						400
159	80	63	53	45				500
191	95	76	63	54	47			600
223	111	89	74	64	56	50		700
	127	102	85	73	64	57		800
		114	95	82	72	64	48	900
			106	91	80	71	53	1000
				100	87	78	58	1100
					95	85	63	1200
						92	69	1300
							74	1400
							80	1500

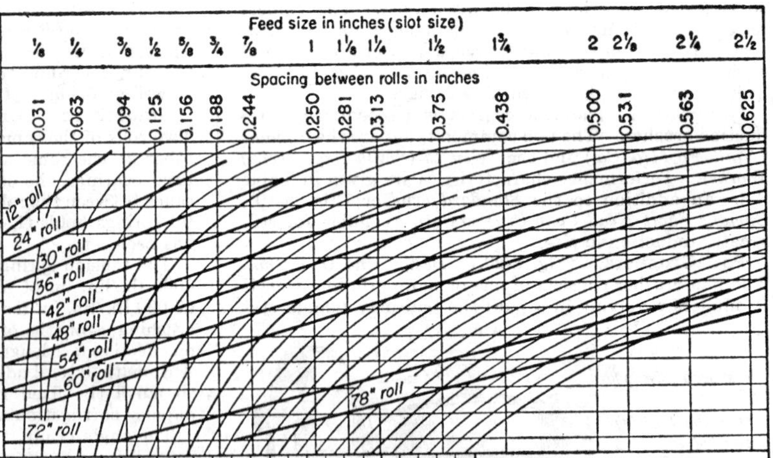

Capacity in tons per hour when crushing 4 to 1

Face of roll in inches																									
1	.2	.4	.6	.8	1	1.2	1.4	1.6	1.8	2	2.2	2.4	2.6	2.8	3	3.2	3.4	3.6	3.8	4	4.2	4.4	4.6	4.8	5
10	2	4	6	8	10	12	14	16	18	20	22	24	26	28	30	32	34	36	38	40	42	44	46	48	50
12	2.4	4.8	7.2	9.6	12	14.4	16.8	19.2	21.6	24	26.4	28.8	31.2	33.6	36	38.4	40.8	43.2	45.6	48	50.4	52.8	55.2	57.6	60
14	2.8	5.6	8.4	11.2	14	16.8	19.6	22.4	25.2	28	30.8	33.6	36.4	39.2	42	44.8	47.6	50.4	53.2	56	58.8	61.6	64.4	67.2	70
16	3.2	6.4	9.6	12.8	16	19.2	22.4	25.6	28.8	32	35.2	38.4	41.6	44.8	48	51.2	54.4	57.6	60.8	64	67.2	70.4	73.6	76.8	80
18	3.6	7.2	10.8	14.4	18	21.6	25.2	28.8	32.4	36	39.6	43.2	46.8	50.4	54	57.6	61.2	64.8	68.4	72	75.6	79.2	82.8	86.4	90
20	4	8	12	16	20	24	28	32	36	40	44	48	52	56	60	64	68	72	76	80	84	88	92	98	100
24	4.8	9.6	14.4	19.2	24	28.8	33.6	38.4	43.2	48	52.8	57.6	62.4	67.2	72	76.8	81.6	86.4	91.2	96	101	106	110	115	120
30	6	12	18	24	30	36	42	48	54	60	66	72	78	84	90	96	102	108	114	120	126	132	138	144	150

Capacities based on 33⅓ % of theoretical volume of ribbon between rolls. Tabulated speed of rolls may be increased as much as 50 % under certain conditions. Speed may be increased with large diameter rolls, particularly when operating with choke feed in closed circuit with screens.

Horse power required when crushing 4 to 1 Note: HP are directly proportional to ratio of reduction and capacity

Tons per hour	10	20	30	40	50	60	70	80	90	100	110	120	130	140	150	160	170	180	190	200	210	220	230	240	250	260	270	280	290	300	320	340	360	380	400	450	500	550	600
Soft rock	4	8	12	16	20	24	28	32	36	40	44	48	52	56	60	64	68	72	76	80	84	88	92	96	100	104	108	112	116	120	128	136	144	152	160	180	200	220	240
Hard rock	10	20	30	40	50	60	70	80	90	100	110	120	130	140	150	160	170	180	190	200	210	220	230	240	250	260	270	280	290	300	320	340	360	380	400	450	500	550	600

FIG. 8-21. Size, speed, capacity, and power required for smooth crushing rolls under average conditions. (*Allis-Chalmers Mfg. Co.*)

gated, grooved, or smooth. The size of feed to a two-roll smooth-shell crusher is smaller than to a corrugated- or toothed-roll crusher of the same roll diameter. The simplest type of toothed-roll crusher consists of a single roll operating against a breaker; generally it is used for coarse crushing.

The *Fairmount crusher* (Allis-Chalmers) contains a fixed element or curved anvil held in position in relation to the frame by heavy steel tie rods coacting against a powerful nest of springs, which are provided for taking up or equalizing excessive pressures (Fig. 8-22). The

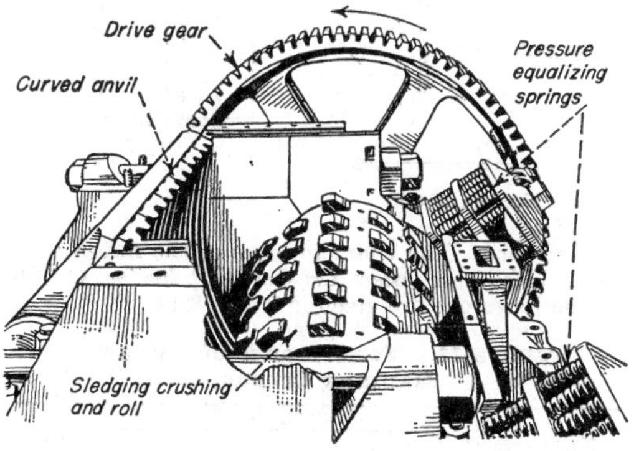

FIG. 8-22. Fairmount single-roll crusher. (*Allis-Chalmers Mfg. Co.*)

single roll is so located with relation to the anvil that preliminary fracturing of large pieces of rock is effected by the sledging action of the teeth on the roll. Secondary crushing is accomplished by direct nipping of the fragments between the roll projections and the anvil.

For many purposes the single-roll crusher is as satisfactory as the larger multiple-roll units. When crushing coal the *Bartlett and Snow single-roll unit* should be confined to conditions where a product $1\frac{1}{4}$ in. or larger is desired. If the capacity must be larger or the size of the product must be small, the two- or four-roll crushers give more uniform size of product.

The *Sawtooth Crusher* (*Sprout, Waldron & Co.*) has two shafts geared together at differential speeds normally in the ratio of $2\frac{1}{4}$ to 1. Each shaft carries sawtooth and spacer assemblies. The size of product can be controlled by the spacing of the saws and the peripheral speeds.

Performance. The *Fairmount single-roll crusher* is adapted to laminated stone deposits and to sedimentary formations in which the bedding planes produce shabby stone rather than cubical pieces when quarried. Soft materials such as limestones, dolomites, phosphate rock, cement rock of the Lehigh Valley district, shale, and similar deposits provide suitable feed for this toothed-roll crusher. The compressive strength of the rock should not exceed 15,000 lb./sq. in. Operating data are given in Table 8-9.

The *Jeffrey single-roll crusher* (*Jeffrey Mfg. Co.*) is available in sizes having openings from 18 by 18 in. to 36 by 54 in. with capacities from 25 to 700 tons/hr. on hard

Table 8-9. Operating Data for Standard Fairmount Crusher

Crusher size, in.	Approx. max. feed thickness, in.	Approx. cap., tons/hr. for discharge opening, in.					Hp.	Roll speed, r.p.m.
		2	3	4	5	6		
24 × 48	14	90	135	180	...	...	75–100	58
24 × 60	14	115	170	230	...	...	100–125	58
36 × 60	24	...	170	230	290	345	180–220	39

bituminous coal. The power requirements vary from 10 to 125 hp., depending on the size of the crusher.

Performance characteristics for toothed-roll crushers on bituminous coal are given in Table 8-10.

Table 8-10. Performance Characteristics for Bartlett and Snow Two-roll Crushers

Roll size, in.		Capacity, tons/hr. for various size products, in.				Hp. at given capacities for various sizes				Max. feed lump size, in.
Diam.	Width	1	$1\frac{1}{4}$	$1\frac{1}{2}$	2	1	$1\frac{1}{4}$	$1\frac{1}{2}$	2	Average hardness
26	24	50	65	75	100	20	22	24	27	14
26	36	75	95	110	150	30	33	35	40	14
30	36	85	115	140	180	35	40	45	50	16
37	36	100	140	160	210	40	48	50	60	18
37	48	130	190	210	280	50	60	65	75	18

The sawtooth crusher is available in a number of sizes. The action is largely tearing rather than compressing, leading to a minimum of heating, far fewer fines, and a somewhat lower power requirement than characterizes other types of preliminary breaking. Models are available for sheets up to 3 in. thickness and 60 in. width. Length is not a consideration and can be continuous.

Sawtooth crushers are also used for friable lump stocks up to 6-in. ring size. Applications include the processing of press cakes, phenolic plastics, alkali cellulose sheets, sheet glue, naphthalene, resins, sulfur, bark, lump pitch, calcium chloride, and asphalt floor tiling.

Prater Pulverizer Co. offers a double roll with heavy-duty teeth as a precrusher feeder. The *Mikro roll crusher* (Pulverizing Machinery Co.) serves as grinder or prebreaker and is of similar type. The *Rietz prebreaker* (see p. 8-56) differs somewhat from these.

Rotary Crushers. (Fig. 8-23.) *Design and Operation.* A shaft, usually vertical, carries a cone with large

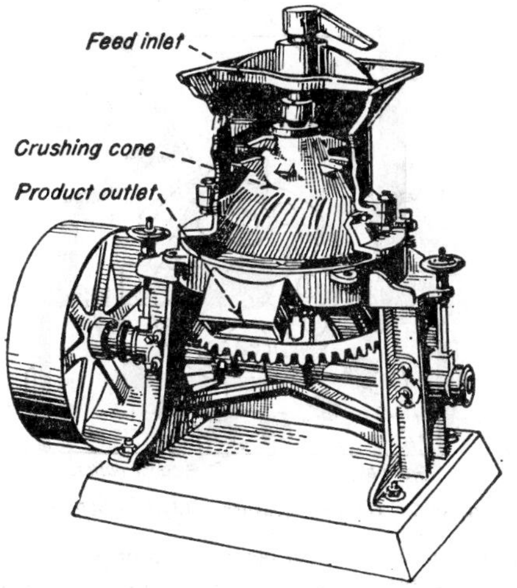

FIG. 8-23. Rotary crusher. (*Bartlett & Snow.*)

teeth at the top for initial crushing and small teeth or furrows at the bottom for finer crushing. The shell enclosing the cone has corresponding teeth. The clearance between cone and shell is adjustable by raising or lowering the cone. The *Horizontal Crusher* (*Sprout, Waldron & Co.*) has its cone supported on a horizontal shaft for preliminary crushing; final crushing takes place between close-fitting sections at the base of the cone (Fig. 8-24). Clearance is adjusted with a handwheel. The lower headroom required by the horizontal crusher is an advantage.

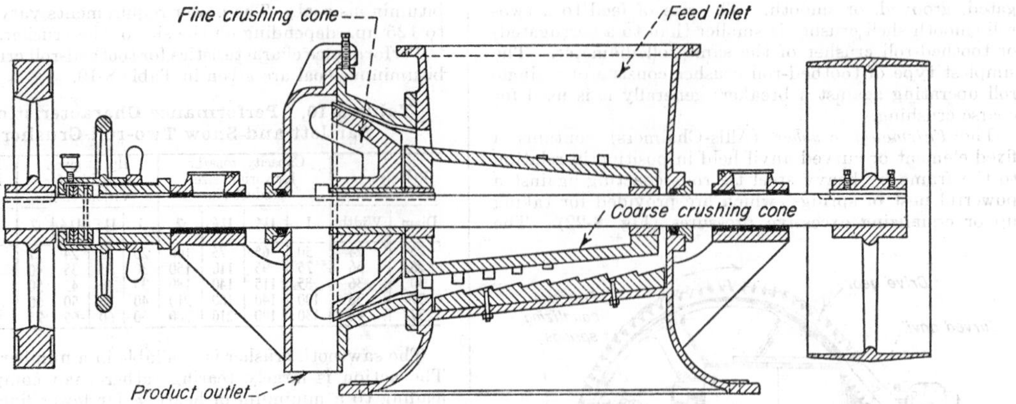

Fig. 8-24. Horizontal crusher. (*Sprout, Waldron & Co.*)

Performance. Rotary crushers are successfully applied to such materials as burned lime, gypsum, phosphate rock, clay, and filter-press cake. A *No. 4 Bartlett and Snow* crusher (Fig. 8-23) operating on burned lime or gypsum has a production rate of 3 to 5 tons/hr. between ½ and ¼ in.; it requires 8 to 10 hp. The horizontal crusher is used for friable material such as pitch, rosin, mica, coconut shells, and compacted inorganic salts. Its output ranges from 1 to 10 tons/hr. to a product that may all be able to pass through a No. 5 sieve and contain material finer than a No. 100 sieve depending on the feed quality. Power is less than 15 hp.

Hammer Crusher. (Fig. 8-25.) *Design and Operation.* Pivoted hammers are mounted on a horizontal

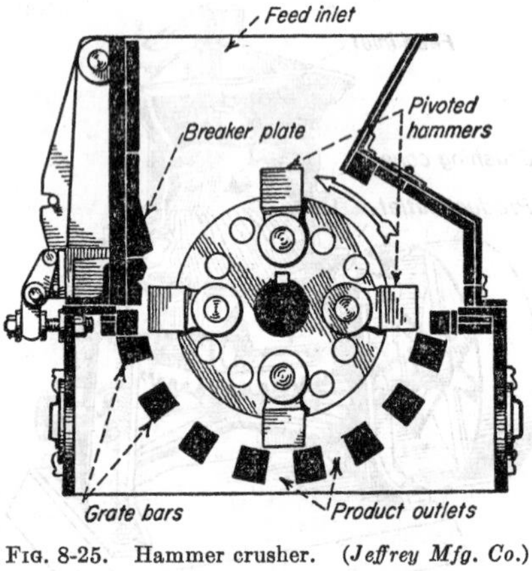

Fig. 8-25. Hammer crusher. (*Jeffrey Mfg. Co.*)

shaft, and crushing takes place by impact between the hammers and breaker plates. A cylindrical grating may be positioned beneath the rotor. It retains material until reduced to a size small enough to pass between the bars of the grating. A number of hammer crushers are symmetrically designed so that the direction of rotation can be reversed to distribute wear evenly on the hammers and breaker plates. The size of the product can be regulated by changing the spacing of the grate bars and also by lengthening or shortening the hammers. Speed varies from 500 to 1800 r.p.m., depending on size of the machine. The *Double Impeller Crusher* (*New Holland Machine Co.*) is a hammer mill with two rotors, each mounting three impeller bars. Crushing takes place by impact with the bars and breaker plates. High reduction ratio is claimed.

Performance. The characteristics of the *Super-Jumbo Crusher* (*Williams Patent Crusher & Pulverizer Co.*) for handling limestone are given in Table 8-11.

Table 8-11. Performance of Williams Hammer Crusher

Size No.	Throat opening, in.	Capacity, tons/hr. 2 in.	1¼ in.	¾ in.	Hp.
4	24 × 16	125	100	60	100
6	30 × 20	210	165	100	175
8	30 × 26	310	250	150	250
10	30 × 30	400	330	200	350

The *Jeffrey hammer crusher* (*Jeffrey Mfg. Co.*) is available in *Type A* for general purposes and *Type B* for fine-reduction severe duty. Performance is given in Table 8-12 for crushing limestone.

Table 8-12. Performance of Jeffrey Type B Hammer Crusher

Size of machine, in.	Production rate, tons/hr., for bar opening, in.		Sieve	% smaller than size* for bar opening, in.	
	⅛	1		⅛	1
20 × 12	2	5	½ in.	..	99
36 × 24	12	30	¼ in.	..	91
36 × 60	35	80	No. 10	96	54
42 × 66	55	150	No. 100	49	17

* 24-in. machine at 1600 r.p.m.

Feed should not exceed 6-in. lump size for 36-in. and smaller machines or 12-in. lump size for larger than 36-in. machines.

The *Impactor* (*Pennsylvania Crusher Co.*) is a reversible hammer crusher without a discharge grating or cage. It is used for size reduction of cement rock, limestone, and shale in large tonnages for cement mills and in limestone and gypsum operations. The *American Ring Crusher* (*American Pulverizer Co.*) features a rotor assembly with loose crushing rings, held outwardly by centrifugal force, which crush by impact. Performance on run-of-mine bituminous coal is given in Table 8-13. The rotor speed is 600 r.p.m. for 1½- and 1¼-in. product; 720 r.p.m. for

Table 8-13. Performance of American Ring Crusher

Number of mill	Capacity, tons/hr. 1½ in.	1¼ in.	1 in.	¾ in.	½ in.	Hp.
15 S	80	50–65	45–50	35–40	25–30	20–25
24 S	150	130–140	100–120	80–100	60–70	30–40
38 S	300	225–250	200–235	175–200	125–150	60–75
48 S	400	350–375	330–350	300–325	225–250	100–125
60 S	500	425–450	400–425	350–375	275–300	150–175

1-, ¾-, and ½-in. product. The maximum feed lump size is 10 to 28 in., depending on the size of machine.

The *Stedman Type B Heavy-Duty Crushers* (*Stedman's Foundry & Machine Works*) are designed for heavy-duty service, reducing run-of-mine coal, limestone, lump lime, cullet, clays, shale, barytes, and similar materials. These crushers will take a feed ranging from 8- to 24-in. cubes, depending upon size of machine, and reduce to 1½ to 1¼ in. and under in one stage. In the handling of many materials it is possible to crush to ¼ in. and even finer in one stage.

The *Joy-Hazemag impact crusher* (Joy Mfg. Co.) is a heavy-duty to high-speed fine crusher comprising a cylindrical rotor to the periphery of which are attached hard beater lugs. Lump feed passes over a built-in screen to by-pass undersize, then falls into the beater path to be projected onto hard breaker plates strategically located to produce fracture by impact. Maximum feed sizes for heavy-duty and standard machines are in the range of 5 to 40 in. and capacities are from a few to 500 tons/hr. Fine crushers, taking smaller feed, range from 5 to 50 tons/hr. Cement, lime, gypsum, coal, ores, salts, ceramic materials, glass, and slag have been ground in this machine.

Ball, Pebble, Rod, Tube, and Compartment Mills. These mills have a cylindrical or conical shell, rotating on a horizontal axis, and are charged with a grinding medium such as balls of steel, flint, or porcelain, or with steel rods. The **ball mill** differs from the tube mill by being short in length; its length, as a rule, does not exceed its diameter (Fig. 8-26). Conventional ball mills use large balls on a coarse feed to produce a comparatively coarse product. The **tube mill** is usually long in comparison with its diameter, uses smaller balls, and produces a finer product. The **compartment mill,** a combination of the above types, consists of a cylinder divided into two or more sections by perforated partitions; preliminary grinding takes place at one end and finish grinding at the discharge end. **Rod mills** deliver a more uniform and more granular product than other revolving mills, thus minimizing the percentage of fines, which are sometimes detrimental. The **pebble mill** is a tube mill with flint or ceramic pebbles as the grinding medium and may be lined with ceramic or other nonmetallic liners.

Tumbling mills is a generic term sometimes used in referring to ball, pebble, rod, tube, and compartment mills, because of the action of the grinding medium.

The ball mill and pebble mill are simple to operate and versatile in use. A steel or stone-lined cylindrical steel shell, containing a charge of steel balls or stone pebbles, is rotated horizontally about its axis so that size reduction or pulverizing is effected by the tumbling of the balls or pebbles on the material between them. The mills may be operated wet or dry, in either batch or open-circuit use or in closed circuit with size classifiers (see p. 8-27).

Design of Tumbling Mills. The conventional type of **batch mill** consists of a cylindrical steel shell with flat steel-flanged heads. Openings are provided through which the grinding medium and the process material can be loaded and discharged. Mill length is equal to or less than the diameter [Coghill, De Vaney, and O'Meara, *Trans. Am. Inst. Mining Met. Engrs.*, **112,** 79 (1934)]. The discharge opening is often opposite the loading manhole and for wet grinding usually is fitted with a valve. One or more vents are provided to release any pressure developed in the mill, to introduce inert gas, or to supply pressure to assist discharge of the mill. In dry grinding, the material is discharged into a hood through a grate over the manhole, while the mill rotates. Jackets can be provided for heating and cooling.

Continuous mills are more sturdily built than batch mills. Material is fed and discharged through hollow trunnions at opposite ends of the mill (Fig. 8-26). A grate or diaphragm just inside the discharge end may be employed to regulate the slurry level in wet grinding and thus control retention time. In the case of air-swept mills, provision is made for blowing air in at one end and removing the ground material in air suspension at the same or other end. The rod mill and compartment mill are variations of the tube mill.

The ball mill usually is equipped with horizontal **baffles,** if the lining is smooth, to key the charge to the

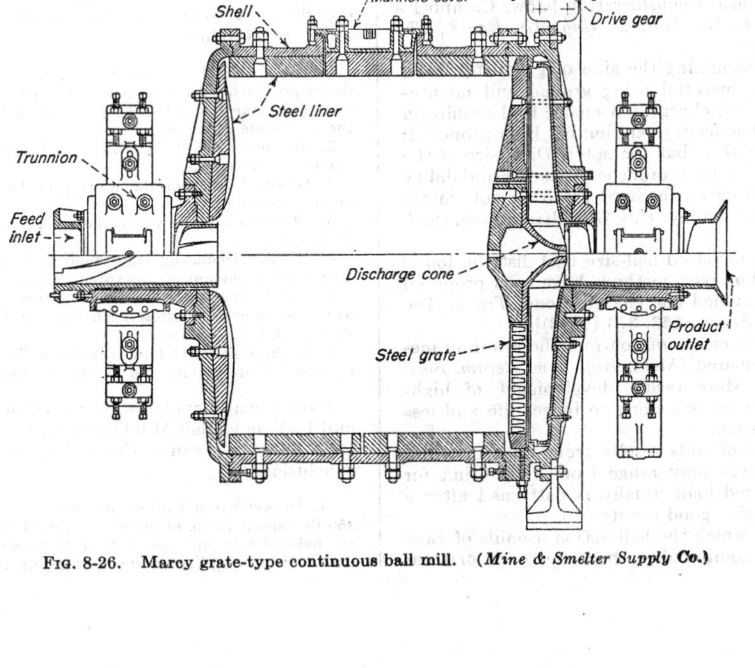

FIG. 8-26. Marcy grate-type continuous ball mill. (*Mine & Smelter Supply Co.*)

wall and prevent slippage. Ball mills usually have metallic **liners** which have a baffling action because of a wave shape or other irregular surface. A double-step liner is said to increase liner life and grinding efficiency (Howes, *Mining Tech., Tech. Publ.* 1577, 1943). Pebble mills generally are lined with non-metallic materials. Belgian silex (silica) block has been a common lining material, but quartzite and granite have been found to be satisfactory substitutes (Berry, *Mining Tech.*, **10,** *Tech. Publ.* 1948, March, 1946). Porcelain block linings are used to minimize color and metal contamination. Rubber linings have specialized application [Bennett, *Mining Met.*, **14,** 399 (1933)]. Smaller mills (up to about 50 gal. capacity) are made in one piece with a cover. U.S. Stoneware Co. makes these in wear-resistant Burundum-fortified ceramic and also makes larger three-piece units, in a metal protective case, up to 210 gal. capacity.

Design of a **conical mill** departs from the conventional all-cylindrical construction in that a section may be cylindrical while a conical shape is used for the ends. The Hardinge conical mill is an example (Figs. 8-27 and 8-32).

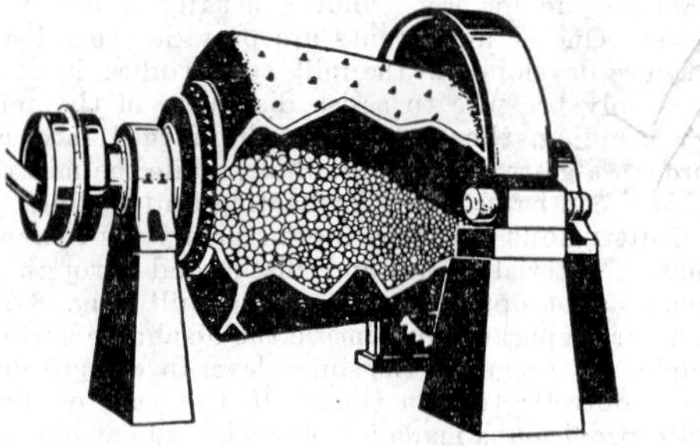

FIG. 8-27. Tri-Cone mill. (*Hardinge Co.*)

Operation of Tumbling Mills. Cascading and **cataracting** are the terms applied to the motion of the grinding media. The former applies to the rolling of balls or pebbles from top to bottom of the heap, and the latter refers to the throwing of the balls through the air to the toe of the heap. Ball action has been studied and given mathematical consideration [Gow, Campbell, and Coghill, *Trans. Am. Inst. Mining Met. Engrs.*, **87,** 51 (1930)].

Chief factors determining the **size of grinding balls** are fineness of the material being ground and maintenance cost for the ball charge. A coarse feed requires a larger ball than a fine feed; a relation has been proposed: $D_b^2 = KD_p$, where D_b is ball diameter, D_p is size of the coarser feed particles, both in inches; K is a grindability constant varying from 55 for hard to 35 for soft materials (Coghill and De Vaney, *U.S. Bur. Mines Tech. Publ.* 581, 1937).

The need for a calculated ball-size feed distribution is open to question; however, methods have been proposed for calculating a rationed ball charge [Bond, *Trans. Am. Inst. Mining Met. Engrs.*, **153,** 373 (1943)].

The lives and efficiencies of non-metallic grinding media have been compared [Metz, *Bull. Am. Ceram. Soc.*, **24,** 357 (1945)]. More recent development of high-density alumina media is leading to longer life and less product contamination.

A graded charge of rods results from wear in a rod mill. **Rod diameter** may range from 4 to 1 in., for example. A new rod load usually is patterned after a used one found to give good results.

The criterion by which the ball action in mills of various sizes may be compared is the concept of **critical speed.** It is the theoretical speed at which the centrifugal force on a ball in contact with the mill shell at the height of its path equals the force on it due to gravity: $N_c = 76.65/\sqrt{D}$, where N_c is critical speed in r.p.m. and D is diameter of the mill in feet for a ball diameter that is small with respect to the mill diameter.

Actual mill speeds vary from 65 to 80 per cent of critical. It might be generalized that 65 to 70 per cent is required for fine wet grinding in viscous suspension, 70 to 75 per cent for fine wet grinding in low-viscosity suspension and for dry grinding of large particles up to ½-in. size. The speeds might be increased 5 per cent of critical for unbaffled mills.

Material and Ball Charges. The load of a grinding medium can be expressed in terms of the percentage of the volume of the mill that it occupies, *i.e.*, a bulk volume of balls half filling a mill is a 50 per cent ball charge. The void space in a bulk volume of balls is approximately 38 per cent; it is 40 per cent for pebbles. Steel balls have a bulk density of approximately 300 lb./cu. ft.; stone pebbles of 100 lb./cu. ft.

As an aid in finding ball weights and cylindrical-ball mill volumes, the chart shown in Fig. 8-28 can be used. A mill with a volume of 98.5 cu. ft., for example, should contain 11,800 lb. of steel balls for a 40 per cent charge, and the void volume would be 15 cu. ft.

The amount of material in a mill can be expressed conveniently as the ratio of its volume to that of the voids in the ball charge. This is known as the material-to-void ratio. If the solid material and its suspending medium (water, air, etc.) just fills the ball voids, the M/V ratio is 1, for example. Grinding-medium charges vary from 20 to 50 per cent in practice and M/V ratios from 1 to 5.

The solids concentration in a pebble-mill slurry may be critical with respect to best grinding efficiency [Creyke and Webb, *Trans. Brit. Ceram. Soc.*, **40,** 55 (1941)].

Control of pulp level to obtain high circulating load is accomplished by use of grate-discharge mills. In one case an 18 per cent increase in capacity resulted from conversion of an overflow mill to a grate-discharge mill despite a loss of 10 per cent of the mill volume due to the change. The grates allowed passage of sufficient pulp to maintain the circulating load at 400 per cent (Duggan, *Mining Tech., Tech. Publ.* 1456, March, 1942).

General Considerations. The controlling factors conceded to govern the ore-grinding efficiency of cylindrical mills are as follows:

1. Speed of mill affects capacity, also liner and ball wear, in direct proportion up to 85 per cent of critical speed.
2. Ball charge equal to 50 per cent of the mill volume gives the maximum capacity.
3. Minimum-size balls capable of grinding the feed give maximum efficiency.
4. Grooved liners of the wave type have found much favor among operators.
5. Classifier efficiency becomes more important in multiple-stage grinding.
6. Higher circulating loads tend to increase production and decrease the amount of unwanted fine material.
7. Low-level or grate discharge has increased grinding capacity over the center or overflow discharge, but liner, grate, and charge wear is higher.
8. Ratio of solids to liquids in the mill must be considered on the basis of ore gravity and volumetric relation.

Experimental evidence presented in a paper by Coghill and DeVaney (Ball Mill Grinding, *U.S. Bur. Mines, Tech. Publ.* 581, 1937) causes the authors to draw the following conclusions:

1. In wet-batch ball milling with ore charges from 200 to 350 lb. (about 75 lb. of ore was required to fill the interstices of the balls at rest) and speeds from 30 to 80 per cent critical, the slow speed gave the same type of grinding as high speed. Heavy

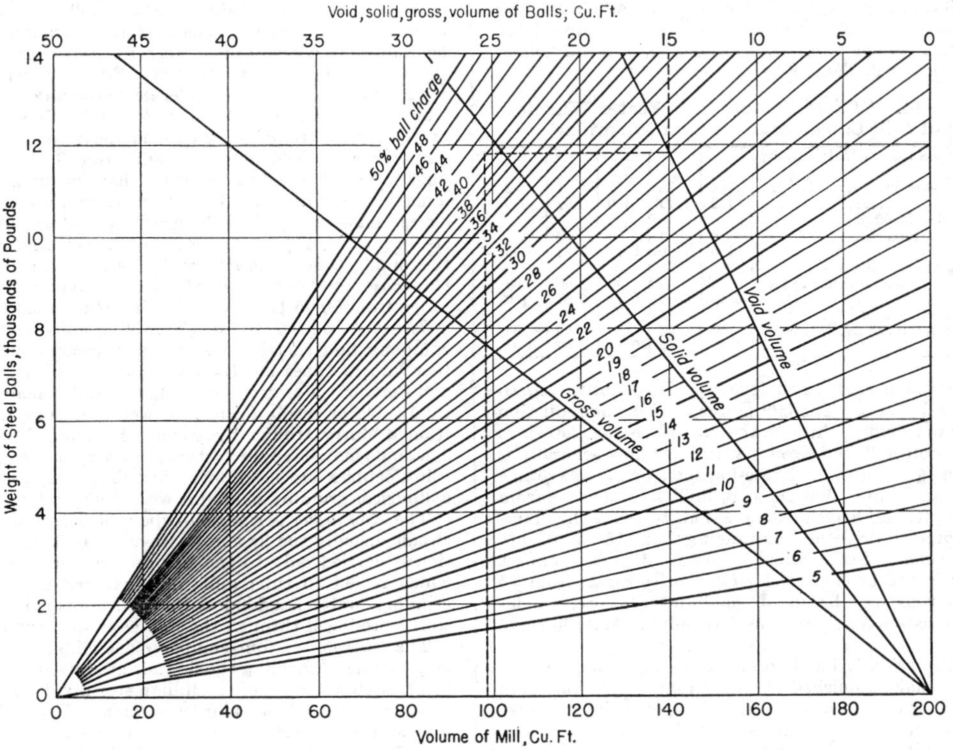

FIG. 8-28. Steel-ball charge relationships of ball mills.

ore charges yielded a little more selective grinding of the coarse particles than light charges. Best capacities were obtained with light charges, and slightly better efficiencies were obtained with heavy ore charges. To split hairs about efficiencies at various speeds the reader will have to study the table and be his own judge.

2. Some of the characteristics of dry-batch ball milling were unlike those of wet grinding. In the dry work, efficiency as well as capacity was best with the light ore charge. Power decreased with decrease in the amount of ore in the mill; in wet grinding it increased with a decrease in the amount of ore in the mill. In dry grinding high speed was more efficient than low speed.

3. In comparing wet and dry grinding the tests were paired so that all the set variables were the same, except pulp consistency (wet or dry). With an intermediate weight of ore charge, selective grinding was of the same degree; with a heavy ore charge, wet grinding was more selective, and with the light ore charge, dry grinding was more selective.

4. In comparing wet and dry open-circuit ball milling, wet grinding gave 39 per cent more capacity and 26 per cent more efficiency.

5. A small ball volume was not satisfactory in the overflow type of dry mill because too much ore built up in the mill. When building up of the ore was prevented by simulating the low-pulp-level mill, the small ball volume did good work.

6. With 60 per cent solids, pebbles the same size of balls did about the same type of work as balls when dolomite was ground, but they failed in selective grinding of chert. Pebbles gave about 35 per cent of the capacity and 81 per cent of the efficiency shown by the balls.

7. For hard and medium-hard ores, tetrahedrons were unsatisfactory for coarse grinding.

8. Very hard balls (Ni-hard) were better than ordinary balls; this was particularly so when the ore was very hard.

9. The efficiency of battered reject balls was about 11 per cent less than that of new spherical balls.

10. A ball mill as small as 19 by 36 in. duplicated the work of a plant-size mill. The tests led to the belief that, if each of a variety of mills, large or small, is run under the same conditions, and if each applies a unit of work to a unit of ore, the effect (comminution), as indicated by the products, will be the same; *i.e.*, the same relation between cause and effect will maintain.

Performance of Tumbling Mills. *Selection of Mill.* The selection of a ball- or rod-mill grinding unit is based on small-scale grindability tests (see p. 8-7). A procedure has been outlined by Michaelson (*Mining Tech.*, **9**, *Tech. Publ.* 1844, 1945). Laboratory ball-mill studies have shown capacity and power to be proportional to $D^{2.6}$, where D is mill diameter (see Gow, Campbell, and Coghill, *loc. cit.*). Capacity per unit of mill volume varies as $D^{0.6}$ [Fahrenwald, *Trans. Am. Inst. Mining Met. Engrs.*, **112**, 88 (1934)]. Capacity and power are directly proportional to mill length. These relationships also hold for commercial mills.

Capacity and Power Consumption. Theoretical considerations show the net power to drive a ball mill to be proportional to $D^{2.5}$, but this exponent may be used without modification in comparing two mills only when operating conditions are identical [Gow, Guggenheim, Campbell, and Coghill, *Trans. Am. Inst. Mining Met. Engrs.*, **112**, 24 (1934)]. The net power to drive a ball mill was found to be $P = [(0.5L - 1)K + 1][(0.5D)^{2.5}p]$, where L is the inside length of the mill, ft.; D is the mean inside diameter of the mill, ft.; p is the net power used by a 2- by 2-ft. laboratory mill under similar operating conditions; and K is 0.9 for mills less than 5 ft. long and 0.85 for mills over 5 ft. long.

An empirical relation for approximating the capacity of Foster Wheeler air-swept ball mills is $C = 0.008WNDsygz = 8000Ksygz$, where $K = WND \times 10^{-6}$ (private communication from Martin Frisch, Foster Wheeler Corp.). The horsepower required to drive these pulverizers for values of $K > 1$ is given approximately by $P = 49K^{0.9}$.

C is mill capacity, lb./hr.; W is weight of ball charge, lb.; N is mill speed, r.p.m.; D is average inside diameter to liner, ft.; P is net horsepower; and s, y, g, z are "effect factors" given in Table 8-14.

Table 8-14. "Effect Factors" for Foster Wheeler Ball Mill Capacity and Power Formulas

Feed size effect factor s, feed size, 100% through:					
Ring diameter, in.	1/16	1/8	3/4	1	2
s	1.2	1.13	1.0	0.97	0.9
Moisture effect factor y:					
Surface moisture, %	0	3	6	9	15
y	1.0	1.0	0.92	0.88	0.65
Grindability effect factor g:					
Grindability, Hardgrove index	30	40	60	80	100
g	0.43	0.55	0.73	0.83	1.0
Fineness effect factor z:					
Fineness % through No. 200 sieve	60	70	80	90	99
z	1.25	1.0	0.75	0.49	0.22

Performance of Proprietary Equipment. *Allis-Chalmers Mfg. Co.* The ball mill is used in the reduction of ores, wet or dry, through the No. 10 to No. 200 sieve range. Ball-mill feed size for very hard ores generally is less than 1/4 in.; with moderate-hardness ores, the average is less than 1/2 in. Ball mills are built in diameters from 3 to 10 1/2 ft. and length from one-half to twice the diameter, requiring drive motors ranging from 15 to 800 hp. Mills are charged with balls 1 1/2 to 5 in. diameter, of cast iron, or forged or cast steel. Capacities range from 16 to 1400 tons/day based on medium-hard ore, single-stage, closed-circuit, 1/2-in. feed to minus No. 100 sieve product.

The *Compeb mill* has two or more compartments, designed to make a finished product in one operation, as in the grinding of cement clinker. Compeb mills are operated in either open or closed circuit, being more efficient with classification. Their application lies in the preparation of products 90 per cent or more able to pass a No. 200 sieve. They are considered a combination of the ball and *Ball Peb* mills used for dry grinding. The Compeb mill is built in single diameters from 3 1/2 to 8 ft., with length up to five times the diameter. Two-diameter mills also are built. The primary compartment is charged with 2 1/2- to 5-in. forged-steel balls; the finishing compartments have 1–2-in. balls. Drive motors range from 125 to 1250 hp. Capacities based on grinding average-hardness cement clinker in closed circuit with air classifiers, from 1-in. feed (about 5 sq. cm./g.) to a product of 1800 sq. cm./g. specific surface (approximately 95 per cent through No. 325 sieve), range from 450 to 3000 bbl./day.

The *Ball Peb mill* is a dry-grinding finishing mill used on cement clinker. Ball Peb mill feed is prepared by a *Preliminator mill* to 95 per cent minus No. 20 sieve. The product from the Ball Peb is obtained from air classifiers which close-circuit the mill, and it averages 1800 sq. cm./g. specific surface (approximately 95 per cent minus No. 325 sieve), or finer. Capacities range from 850 to 4200 bbl./day. Ball Peb mills are built 3 to 8 ft. in diameter and in lengths four times the diameter. Longer mills are multicompartment, the charge in each compartment having a different size in order to grind the feed to that compartment more efficiently. The charge consists of forged-steel balls 3/4 to 1 1/2 in. in diameter. Drive motors range from 40 to 900 hp.

The *Allis-Chalmers rod mill* is a wet or dry grinder operating most efficiently in the size range from No. 10 to No. 35 sieve size. Less efficient operation results in the No. 35 to No. 65 sieve range, where operation overlaps the ball mill. Rod mills are best applied for primary grinding where the production of extremely small particles or sliming is undesirable. Large-diameter rod mills are used as intermediate stage of crushing and in instances have effectively displaced crushing rolls for preparing ball-mill feed. Such applications are warranted only for medium-hard and soft ores. It is a selective grinder, particularly on heterogeneous ores. Rod mills will receive 7/8-in. and larger feed of moderate-hardness ores; but extreme wear on feed-end mill liners and differential wear on rods result, requiring larger-diameter rods, which are less efficient. Rod mills are built from 3 to 9 1/2 ft. diameter, length equal to or greater than the diameter, with a maximum of about 16 ft. Overflow and peripheral discharge mills are used. The grinding medium consists of steel rods 2 to 4 1/2 in. diameter, a few inches shorter than the mill. Drive motors from 15 to 600 hp. are used. Capacities on medium-hard ores through No. 35 sieve range from 50 to 1600 tons/day in open circuit.

The F. L. Smidth & Co. Tumbling mills built by this company find their principal use in cement plants; the best known types are the *Kominuter*, *Unikom*, *Unidan*, and *Pyrator*. For dry operation, the mills usually are fed by a table or cradle feeder; for wet operation, feeding is from a slurry trough by means of an orifice or scoop. The mills may have silex (stone) or *dragpeb* (steel) linings. Flint pebbles are used with silex linings and *cylpebs* (a cylindrical grinding medium) with dragpeb lining.

The *Kominuter* is a screen-type mill operated in closed circuit, usually the first in a two-stage unit where reduction is carried only to the size of a rather coarse mesh, which is fed to tube mills for final grinding. In wet grinding, water is added at the feed hopper, passing the slurry produced through the mill as in dry grinding.

The *Unikom* is a four-compartment mill, a section with large diameter forming the first, or granulating, compartment, with a section of small diameter divided into three compartments. The enlarged section is fitted with liner plates and a special screening arrangement which bypasses fines to the first compartment in the second section and returns oversize to the granulating compartment for further reduction. The first chamber of the second section is equipped with grinding balls, the following compartments with cylpebs, graded downward in size.

The *Unidan* mill is a compartment mill, with three or more compartments, equally well suited for wet and dry grinding. Balls are used in the first compartment, which is also equipped with liners. The compartments for fine grinding are equipped with special rings and steel-alloy lining and with cylpebs graded downward in size toward the discharge end. An added feature of the mill is a special screen arrangement mounted within the mill body; the material does not leave the mill body until finally discharged at the outlet end.

The *Pyrator* mill is used for granulating, pulverizing, and drying damp material in a single unit; it consists of a two-compartment tube mill comprising a ball chamber with liners; a combined screening and ball-separating partition, and a fine-grinding chamber with special ring and alloy lining and cylpebs as the grinding medium. The steel balls are heated and have the double capacity of acting as grinding medium and supplying the heat required for drying. Hot air circulates around the mill body, which is provided with a jacket to retain the hot air in closed circuit, and the mill is provided with means for removing the balls, which are elevated, heated in a hot-air furnace, and returned to the feed end. When the material does not contain an excessive amount of moisture, this unit is very efficient, compact, and economical.

The Mine and Smelter Supply Co. The *Marcy* ball mill (Fig. 8-26), used extensively for wet and dry grinding of ores, will take feed as coarse as 2 in. and grind to No. 200 sieve size in closed circuit with a classifier. Discharge grates are used to give a rapid change of mill content with a high circulating load. Performance is given in Table 8-15. The *Open End rod mill* is designed for a

Table 8-15. Performance of Marcy Ball Mills

Size, ft.	Ball charge, tons	Hp. to run	Mill speed, r.p.m.	Capacity, tons/24 hr. (based on medium-hard ore)								
				No. 8 sieve*	No. 20 sieve	No. 35 sieve	No. 48 sieve	No. 65 sieve	No. 80 sieve	No. 100 sieve	No. 150 sieve	No. 200 sieve
				20% −200	35% −200	50% −200	60% −200	70% −200	80% −200	85% −200	93% −200	97% −200
3 × 2	0.85	5– 7	35	19	15	12	10	8	6½	5	4	3
4 × 3	2.73	20– 24	30	80	64	53	45	36	28	22	18	14
5 × 4	5.25	44– 50	27	180	145	120	102	82	63	51	41	32
6 × 4½	8.90	85– 95	24	375	300	250	210	170	135	105	85	66
7 × 5	13.10	135–150	22½	640	510	425	360	290	225	180	145	113
8 × 6	20.2	220–245	21	1100	885	735	625	500	390	310	250	195
9 × 7	30.0	345–380	20	1800	1450	1200	1020	815	635	505	410	315
10 × 10	56.50	700–750	18	3680	2960	2450	2100	1700	1325	1050	850	655
12 × 12	90.5	1260–1345	16.4	7125	5725	4750	4070	3290	2570	2035	1650	1275

* Sieve through which substantially all the material can pass.

heavy, revolving rod mass and a discharge pulp level below the rod mass, giving rapid passage through the mill. A specially designed discharge housing mounted independently of the mill and with a hinged door permits easy access for inspection, relining, and charging of rods. It takes a 1-in. feed, reducing it in one pass to No. 8 to No. 20 sieve size. The uniform discharge product results from the fact that the low-pulp-line mill does not make a displacement product, since the difference in elevation between feed and discharge ensures rapid removal of the finished product. For a finer product of No. 60 to 80 sieve size, the mill is closed-circuited with screens or classifiers. Performance on 1-in. medium-hard material is shown in Table 8-16.

Table 8-16. Performance of Marcy Rod Mills

Size, ft.	Rod charge, tons	Hp. to run	Mill speed, r.p.m.	Capacity, tons/24 hr.				
				No. 8 sieve	No. 20 sieve	No. 35 sieve	No. 48 sieve	No. 65 sieve
2 × 4	0.9	4– 6	38	20	15	12	10	7
3 × 6	3.6	18– 22	30	105	80	65	50	40
4 × 8	7.6	44– 48	25	240	180	145	120	90
5 × 10	14.5	85– 95	21	525	390	315	260	195
6 × 12	24.1	135–150	17½	855	640	510	425	320
7 × 15	42.1	225–250	15	1600	1200	965	800	600
8 × 12	43.4	230–250	13.2	1675	1250	1000	830	625
9 × 12	54.7	310–340	12.5	2240	1680	1350	1115	835

Hardinge Co. The Hardinge Conical mill, shown in Fig. 8-27, is used extensively for both wet and dry grinding in open and closed circuits. The conical mill is similar to the cylindrical mill in that it consists of a drum rotating about its horizontal axis and operating in much the same way, but unlike the cylindrical mill, it has conical ends instead of straight ends. Ball segregation takes place and roughly proportions the energy to the work performed, the large balls assembling in the cylinder at the feed end of the mill where the diameter is largest, while the smaller balls arrange themselves in decreasing sizes toward the discharge end of the mill.

Hardinge Ball Mills are lined with metallic liners of the wedge-bar type, or of the wave or ribbed type. The wearing bar of the wedge-bar type of lining serves the purpose of lifting the mass of balls and material as well as holding the liner plates in place. *Hardinge Pebble Mills* may be lined with adamant silica, silex, porcelain, or any other non-metallic lining required for the operation. Hardinge wet grinding mills are supplied with discharge arrangements for high, medium, or low pulp levels, the use of which depends on the particular problem under consideration. A suitable grate is used which will permit carrying a maximum ball charge and pulp load in a given-size mill and it also keeps the balls from spilling out of the mill and prevents an accumulation of tramp oversize at the discharge end of the mill. For dry grinding a vertical grate with low-pulp-level discharge vanes is used.

Mill feeders attached to the feed trunnion of the conical mill and used to pass the feed into the mill without backspill are of several types. A feed chute is generally used for dry grinding, this consisting of an inclined chute sealed at the outer edge of the trunnion, and down which the material slides to pass through the trunnion and into the mill. A screw feeder may also be used when dry grinding, consisting of a short section of screw conveyor which extends part way into the opening in the feed trunnion and conveys the material into the mill. For wet grinding, several different types of feeders are available; the scoop feeder attached to and rotating with the mill trunnion and which dips into a stationary box to pick up the material and pass it into the mill; a drum feeder attached to and rotating with the feed trunnion, having a central opening into which the material is fed, and an internal deflector or lifter to pass the material through the trunnion into the mill; or a combination drum and scoop feeder, where the new feed to the mill is fed through the central opening of the drum while the scoop picks up the oversize being returned from a classifier to a scoop box well below the center line of the mill. The mill feeder must be able to handle any quantity of material which the mill may be capable of grinding, and in addition, a circulating load which may be as high as 1000 per cent of the new feed rate. The dry-grinding performance of Hardinge mills on materials of average hardness is given in Table 8-17.

Table 8-17. Performance of Hardinge Ball and Pebble Mills

Size of mill*	Approx. weight, lb.			Speed, r.p.m.	Hp. to run	Capacity, tons per 24 hr.		
	Mill	Lining	Balls			1½ in. to 90%, through No. 100 sieve	Closed circuit with air classifier: ¾ in. to 90%, through No. 200 sieve	Closed circuit with air classifier: ½ in. to 98%, through No. 325 sieve
2′ × 8″	900	375	400	40	1	4	3	1½
4½′ × 24″	8,100	5,400	4,500	28	25	48	36	18
6′ × 48″	17,000	12,000	15,000	25	70	144	108	54
8′ × 48″	27,000	23,000	31,000	21	160	360	252	126
10′ × 66″	51,000	35,000	65,000	18	350	840	600	300
			Pebbles			Open circuit, ½-in. to No. 10 sieve size	Closed circuit, ½ in. to No. 48 sieve size	
2′ × 8″	900	400	175	42	½	2	1½	
4½′ × 24″	8,000	2,300	2,400	30	12	15	9	
6′ × 48″	12,000	5,000	8,500	27	30	54	36	
8′ × 48″	17,000	14,000	14,000	24	62	120	84	
10′ × 66″	32,000	20,000	28,000	18	160	336	216	

* Diameter by length of cylindrical section.

Regulating feeders are built in two basic designs, *i.e.*, constant-volume and constant-weight feeders. Typical of the constant-volume type is the *Hardinge Disc Feeder*, which consists of a circular hopper which is generally fastened to the bottom of the feed bin, the feed sliding from the hopper onto the center of a revolving disk, and then being scraped from the disk by one or two adjustable scrapers into the mill feeder. The quantity of material may be regulated by varying the speed of the feeder or by adjusting the scraper to vary the quantity of material being scraped from the disk. The disk feeder is suitable for damp materials or for a feed having large lumps. *The Hardinge Constant Weight Feeder*, or *Feedometer*, is a feeder of the constant-weight type which will aid the operator in securing maximum over-all mill efficiency and maintaining a record of the material fed to the mill. It controls the feed to the mill by a constant weight rather than a constant volume, regardless of bin segregation or changes in the physical characteristics of the material being fed. The Hardinge Constant Weight Feeder consists of an endless traveling belt, mounted on a structural-steel frame, the whole of which is suspended on pivots below a feeder hopper. A gate controlling the material at the front of the feeder hopper is also pivoted and connected to the frame through a linkage, and after the feeder is once set for the correct weight of the material on the feeder belt, any change in position of the feeder frame moves the gate to maintain a constant weight of the material on the belt. The quantity of material fed by this feeder is changed by means of a variable-speed drive. An improved design of this feeder is the Hardinge Feedometer, consisting of the same basic features but including instruments to indicate and record the quantity of material fed. Automatic control of feed in terms of sound aids in maintaining capacity and efficiency.

Foster Wheeler Corp. This ball mill is built for dry pulverizing fuels and other materials. The mill may be fitted with a single classifier at one end or with two classifiers, one at each end. Preheated air for drying the material while it is undergoing pulverization enters the mill through the trunnion at one end and, as it passes through the mill, picks up pulverized material and carries it through the trunnion at the other end into a spiral-flow classifier. The oversize particles rejected in the classifier mix with the feed that is introduced into the classifier, and the mixture is conveyed through the trunnion into the grinding zone by means of a ribbon conveyor direct-driven from the mill. The ratio of recirculating oversize to the feed may be as high as 6 and as low as 1.5. The hot oversize, which has lost most of its moisture, tends to coat the wet incoming feed particles and blot off the free surface moisture. The effect is to reduce the sensitivity of the pulverizing process to moisture. The feed is, and the product discharge and air temperature may be, controlled automatically, each factor independently of the others. The rate of feed is controlled by an automatic device actuated by the level of material within the mill. The variation of this level is held within close limits. The rate of product discharge is controlled by varying the air flow through the mill. Mill characteristics are given in Table 8-18.

Table 8-18. Characteristics of Foster Wheeler Ball Mills*

Size	1	3	5	7
Nominal inside diam., ft. (approx. = D)	5	7	8.5	10
Max. ball charge, lb., W	13,000	28,000	48,000	80,000
Max. $WND \times 10^{-6}$ (max. K)	1.9	4.4	8.5	15.0
Max. speed, r.p.m. (max. N)	28.5	23.4	21.2	19.3

* See capacity and power formulas on p. 8-23.

Autogenous Tumbling Mills. The principle of the ball mill has been employed in some cases where coarse lump feed will serve as the grinding medium while it is itself being ground. If the rate of primary reduction becomes too slow, such procedures become inefficient. The *Aerofall mill* was designed to ensure primary fracture and thus enhance the universality of this technique. Large-diameter drum and baffle devices were used. This dry crushing and grinding unit accepted quarry-size feed up to 12 or more inches in size to yield a fine-mesh product by air classification. Balls are occasionally used in limited amount for cascade impact action only.

Stirred Ball Mill. The *Attritor* (Union Process Co.) (Fig. 8-29) comprises a cylindrical tank with stirrer in

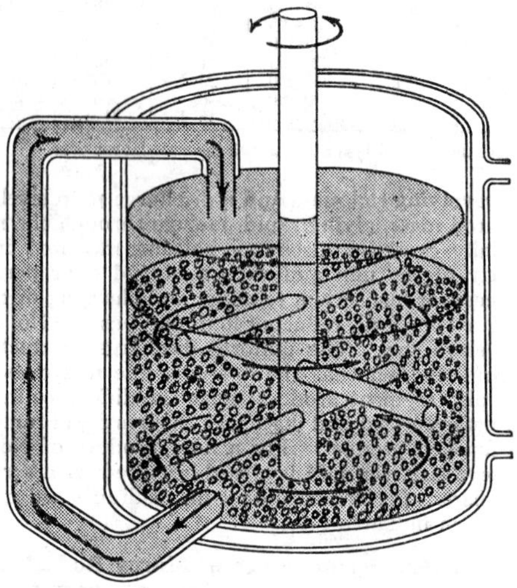

FIG. 8-29. The Attritor. (*Union Process Co.*)

which are media as pebbles, solid material to be ground, and liquid. There is a scheme of circulation to remove suspension from the bottom and discharge into the top of the chamber. Using low power consumption, it grinds and disperses. Model 100-S, with tank capacity of 128 gal., processes from 65 to 80 gal. with 4 kw. required.

Vibrating Mills. A German development has had considerable notice in the technical literature. Ball action in a cylindrical shell results from oscillating or vibrating the shell [Bachmann, *Chem. Tech.*, **15,** 195 (1942)]. There have been more recent developments bringing several mills of this class into the market [Rose and Sullivan, *Brit. Chem. Eng.*, **4,** 450 (1959)].

The *Vibratom* (Schutz-O'Neill Co.) comprises a cylindrical bottom chamber with cover. Through the center horizontally passes the activating shaft covered by a cylindrical shell. Balls in the chamber between the inner and outer casing are vibrated from the eccentric loading of the horizontal shaft. The mass of pebbles travels slowly in a rotary motion without cascading, while at the same time the short sharp impacts of vibrations effect the grinding. The mill is spring-mounted. One structure, a dual-chamber system, involves a chamber with large balls fed from above the charge. Passage of the particles through the grinding media is accomplished with some grinding, after which they are discharged through a screen to another grinding chamber containing finer media to complete the reduction.

The Allis-Chalmers *vibrating ball mill* also uses a horizontal eccentric-activated system in which a charge enters at the top of the cylinder through a flexible feed spout at one end of the cylinder and is discharged at the other end through screens to a flexible discharge spout. Media loading is on the order of 80 per cent of the volume of the grinding chamber. The eccentric drive mechanism passes through a shell in the mill. A new improved form uses two eccentric drive mechanisms located externally of the grinding shell and at each side. One example cited for the 15-in.-diameter vibrating mill shows a capacity of 1140 lb./hr. at 16 hp. when grinding limestone from minus ½ in. to 100 per cent through 100 mesh.

In the *Sweco Vibro-Energy mill* (Southwestern Engineering Co.), the same principle of vibrating through eccentric loading of a motor is applied to a vertical cylinder, with a central core to enhance the vibrations and to eliminate dead grinding space. The entire assembly is spring-mounted. The mill is a new development and has been employed chiefly for wet grinding, but it can also be used for dry grinding. The vibrating motion imparted causes the cylindrical media to pound and rub upon each other to effect grinding. The motion of the drive permits regulation of movement peripherally as well as an up and down circulation. It is used predominantly for fine sizes but may be adaptable to coarser grinding, such as is commonly done in the pebble mill. Horsepower for a given capacity is said to be one-half or less of comparable values on the pebble mill (Table 8-19).

Table 8-19. Performance Data for Sweco Vibro-energy Mill Grinding Zircon

Type of mill............ M80L
Media charge........... 14,000 lb. ½ in. diam., ½ in. long alumina cylinders
Material charge......... 1750 lb. zirconium silicate
Vehicle charge.......... 1168 lb. water
Size of feed material..... 117 mesh (125 microns)
Size of final product..... 2 microns average, 5 microns max.
Duration of test......... 39 hr.

Time, hr.	Particle size, microns			Surface area, sq. cm./g.	Energy input, kw.-hr./ton product
	Max.	Min.	Avg.		
Start			125		
5	170	1	70	2,668	57
10	75	1	25	9,844	132
15	30	1	12	16,008	212
20	20	1	10	19,136	292
25	17	1	8	22,080	374
30	12	1	5	23,276	456
33	8	1	3	24,932	508
36	7	1	3	25,944	558
39	5	1	2	27,140	608

Particle-size Classifiers Used with Grinding Mills. Ball mills or tube mills can be operated in closed circuit with external air classifiers with or without air sweeping being employed, as shown in Fig. 8-9. If air sweeping is employed, a cyclone separator may be placed between mill and classifier. (The principles of size reduction combined with size classification are discussed on pp. 8-10 to 8-12.) Likewise other types of grinding mill can be operated in closed circuit with external size classifiers (Fig. 8-12), as will be described at appropriate places on succeeding pages. However, many types of grinders are air-swept and are so closely coupled with their classifiers that the latter are termed internal classifiers.

Some equipment manufacturers refer to their air classifiers as "separators," but this is generic usage. For the sake of consistency and to conform with the generally accepted terminology for hydraulic and mechanical devices for the same purpose the term "air classifier," or simply "classifier," is used for a pneumatic device to separate a material into two or more fractions, each more closely sized than the feed material.

External Classifiers. The *Whizzer* (*Raymond Pulverizer Division, Combustion Engineering Co.*), *Spinner* (*Williams Patent Crusher & Pulverizer Co.*), *Gayco* (*Universal Road Machinery Co.*), and *Whirlwind* (*Sturtevant Mill Co.*) classifiers are examples. They may be used independently as well as externally, *i.e.*, in closed circuit with grinding mills. An external-classifier arrangement in which conveying is accomplished with an elevator is shown in Fig. 8-30. The *Reversal Current air classifiers* (*Hardinge Co.*) generally are not used independently. An external-classifier arrangement using the *Superfine type* is shown in Fig. 8-32. Conveying is done pneumatically.

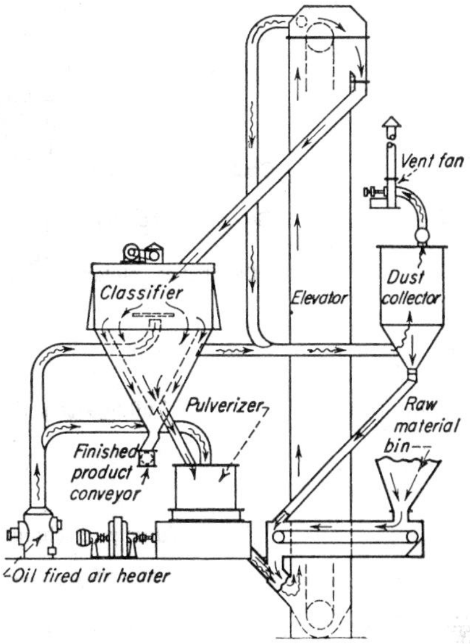

FIG. 8-30. Arrangement of B. & W. pulverizer in closed circuit with external air classifier. (*Babcock & Wilcox Co.*)

The *Whizzer classifier* is typical of those which may be used independently, or external to grinding equipment with which they are operated in closed circuit. It consists primarily of two cones with an annular space between them. A hollow vertical shaft extends through the top of the classifier, at the center, down into the inner cone. On the shaft, near the top, is mounted the main fan; below the fan is the whizzer, and below the whizzer the distributing plate. As this plate rotates at a high velocity, the centrifugal effect on the material throws it radially, in a uniform stream, in the space between the edge of the plate and the inner surface of the inner cone, into the path of an upblast of air. The dust-laden air passes up through the whizzer, where the coarser particles are eliminated, and discharges through the fan into the annular space between the cones. The rotating fan blades throw the material to the inner surface of the outer cone, and it is discharged through a valve in the bottom of the cone, while the air returns to the inside of the inner cone through the portholes formed by the deflector blades or vanes, placed radially around the inner cone. Material discarded by the whizzer drops to the bottom of the inner cone and is spouted from the classifier as tailings.

The whizzer type of air classifier often is built with two whizzers, one above the other. The purpose of the two whizzers is to obtain a finer product than is possible with the single-whizzer type. It is in fact a two-stage classifier. This is of particular advantage when classifying a material which is poor in fines, the first whizzer throwing out a high percentage of oversize, so that the upper whizzer receives a richer mixture on which to operate. The *Whizzer* classifier fineness characteristics are controlled mainly by changing the number and size of whizzer blades or by adjustment of the vertical slide dampers. In the *Whirlwind* classifier the fineness is controlled by adjustment of horizontal damper plates at the fan opening.

Centrifugal classifiers are capable of delivering fine products from 85 per cent able to pass through a No. 60 sieve to as fine as 99.9 per cent able to pass a No. 400 sieve. Sizes range from 3 to 18 ft. in diameter with power requirements from 2 to 200 hp.

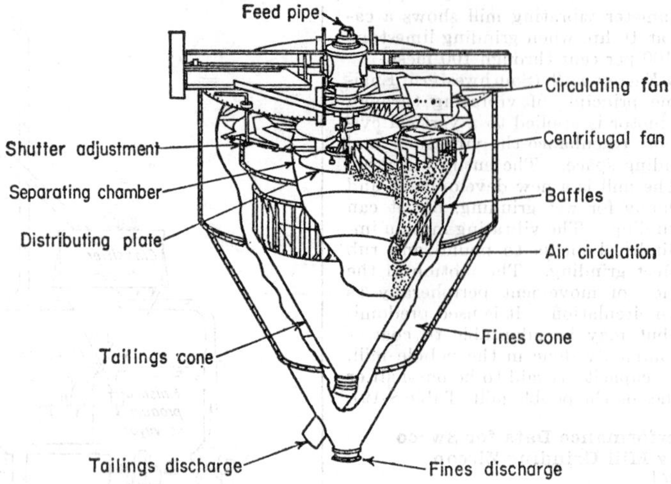

FIG. 8-31. Gayco centrifugal separator. (*Universal Road Machinery Co.*)

Reliance-Gayco centrifugal air separator (Universal Road Machinery Co.) as shown in Fig. 8-31 is an example of this class.

The Hardinge Air Classifier operates as a balanced air system, and the air in the classifying system, as well as in the mill, is under a slight negative pressure, which eliminates dust hazards and promotes clean plant operating conditions. The *Hardinge Superfine Air Classifier* is shown in Fig. 8-32. The only moving part of the classifying system is the fan, from which air is blown into the

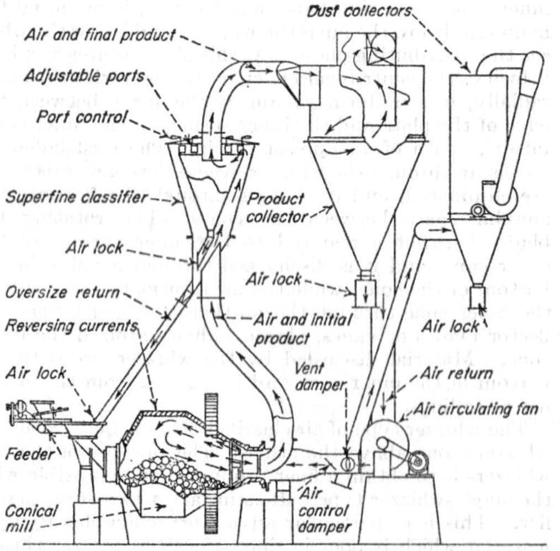

FIG. 8-32. Hardinge conical mill with reversed-current air classifier of the Superfine type.

mill, where the air reverses and picks up the semiground material and conveys it through the uptake pipe to the Superfine Classifier. A partial classification of the coarse and fine material is made between the outer and inner cones of the classifier by means of reduced velocity of the air. The remaining material and the air then pass through the ports into the inner cone of the classifier. The ports give a centrifugal action to the air and material and further classifying is made in the inner cone, the coarse material being thrown to the outside of the cone and sliding down and out through the bottom of the inner cone, where it joins the coarse material previously dropped between the two cones, and all is then returned to the feed end of the mill for further grinding. The fine material or final product is carried by the air out the top of the Superfine Classifier and into the product collector, where product and air are separated by centrifugal force. The product is discharged from the product collector at the bottom airlock, while the air from the top of the product collector is returned to the inlet side of the fan, thus completing the cycle. The discharge of the product collector may be placed any reasonable distance up to 100 ft. above the mill. In order to maintain a negative pressure in the air-classifying system and to prevent dusting, it is necessary to vent a sufficient amount of air to overcome air leakage into the system. This vent air may be discharged directly to the atmosphere or, if desired for economic, hazard, or nuisance reasons, it may be discharged into a bag-type dust collector and the dust in the vent air recovered. Hardinge Air Classifiers are of two types, the *Superfine Classifier* for products from No. 60 to No. 400 sieve size, and the *Loop Classifier* for products from No. 10 to No. 100 sieve size.

Internal Classifiers. A typical application of the *Whizzer classifier* to internal use is with the ring-roller mill. Its design and method of installation are shown in Fig. 8-33. The whizzer disks rotate in a horizontal plane. They may consist of one or two disks in number, each one fitted with multiwhizzer blades. The whizzer is driven through a variable drive, and the fineness of the finished product is regulated by the speed of the whizzer. The faster the whizzer rotates, the more particles are thrown out and the finer becomes the finished product. The raw material passes up from the grinding surfaces vertically and, before passing out of the machine at the top, is compelled to pass between the rotating-whizzer blades. The oversize is returned to the periphery and dropped back for further grinding while the desired fines pass up through the whizzer blades into the duct leading to the cyclone collector.

Vacuum Multi-vane air classifiers of the inverted double-cone type are employed with *Raymond ring-roller mills* where products of moderate fineness are being made. They occupy a position the same as shown for the *Whizzer classifier* in Fig. 8-33. The air containing the pulverized product travels upward between the two cones and enters

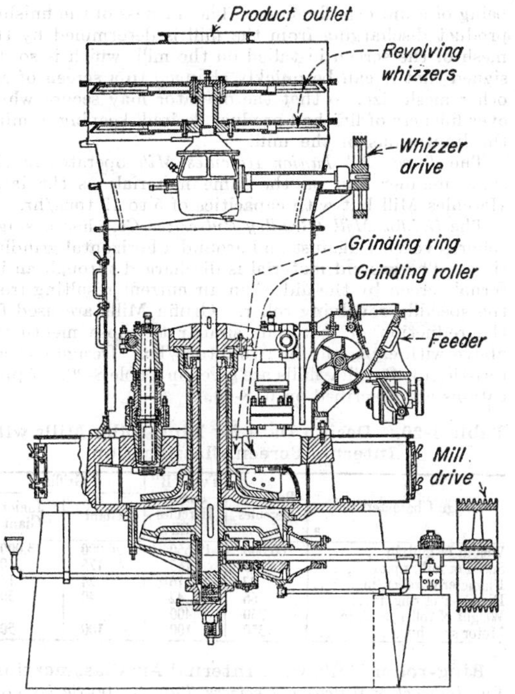

Fig. 8-33. Raymond high-side mill with internal Whizzer classifier.

the inner cone, guided by vertical and adjustable deflector vanes. The coarsest product is obtained with the vanes in a radial position and the finest with the vanes at the most extreme angle with the radial setting. The bottom of the inner cone is fitted with a flap valve for returning oversize material to the mill. Fine product is discharged through a suction sleeve centrally located in the top of the classifier.

Additional applications of internal size classification to various types of grinding mill will appear in the text.

Ring-roller Mills. (Fig. 8-34.) These are equipped with rollers that operate in conjunction with grinding rings. Grinding takes place between the surfaces of the grinding elements, *i.e.*, the ring and rollers. Pressure may be applied with heavy springs or by centrifugal force of the rollers against the ring. Either the ring or rollers may be stationary. The grinding ring may be in a vertical or horizontal position. Ring-roller mills also are referred to as ring-roll mills or roller mills. The ball and ring (Fig. 8-35) and bowl mills (Fig. 8-36) are types of ring-roller mill.

Ring-roller mills should be distinguished from roller mills. The latter are used for such operations as paint grinding and flour milling. Paint-grinding roller mills consist of two to five smooth rollers (sometimes called rolls) operating at differential speeds. A paste is fed between the first two or low-speed rollers and is discharged from the final or high-speed roller by a scraping blade. The paste passes from the surface of one roller to that of the next because of the differential speed, which also applies shear stress to the film of material passing between the rollers. A three-roller mill is illustrated in Fig. 8-48. Roller mills for producing flour from grain consist of one or more pairs of rollers. The rollers (or rolls) in each pair run toward each other at different speeds. Material is fed between the pairs of rollers in series, and reduction takes place on each pair. Grooved

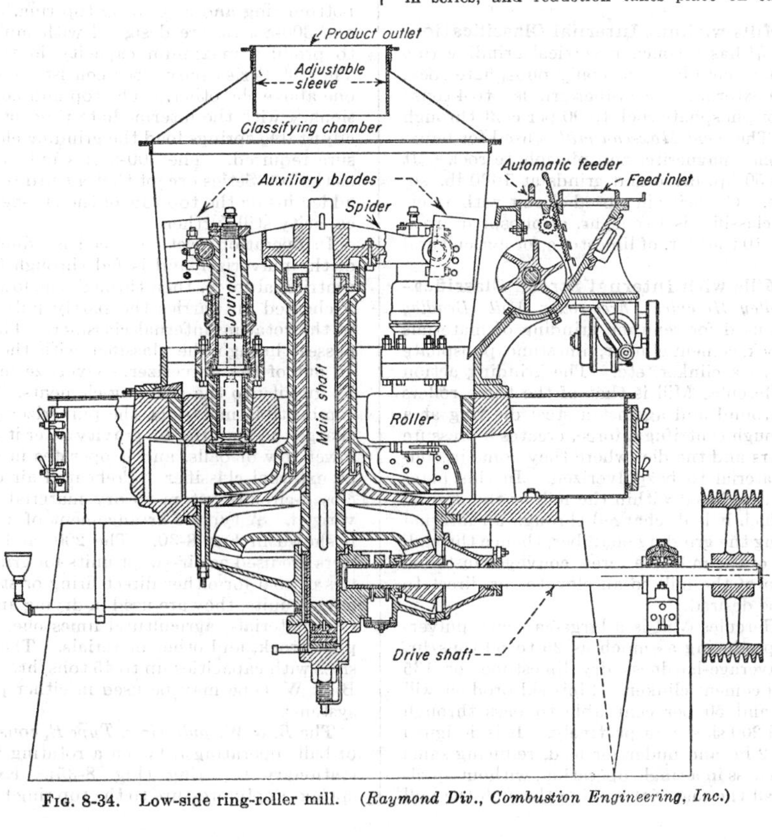

Fig. 8-34. Low-side ring-roller mill. *(Raymond Div., Combustion Engineering, Inc.)*

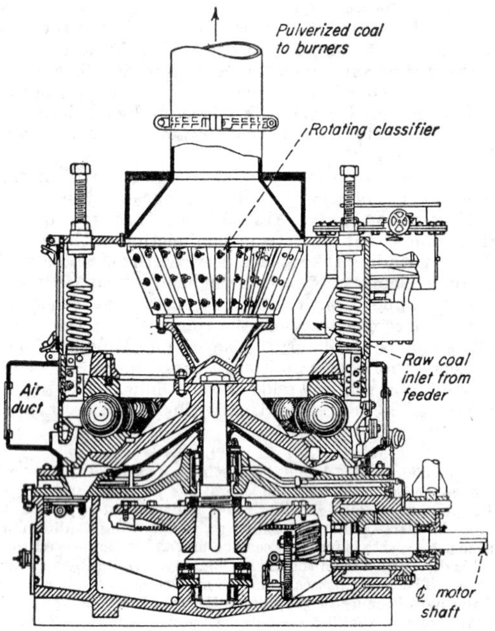

Fig. 8-35. B. & W. pulverizer, type E. (*Babcock & Wilcox Co.*)

rollers are used for crushing the grain and smooth rollers for final milling of flour.

Ring-roller Mills without Internal Classification. The *Sturtevant mill* has a concave vertical grinding ring and is used for non-metallics, especially phosphate rock. A No. 1 mill with external air classifier grinds 2 to 4 tons/hr. of limestone or phosphate rock to 90 per cent through a No. 80 sieve. The *Kent Maxecon mill* is used for bauxite, coke, limestone, magnesite, and phosphate rock. It requires a 25- to 50-hp. drive and grinds at 1000 lb./sq. in. roller pressure. Capacity in closed circuit with external screen or air classifier is 4 tons/hr. of phosphate rock for acidulation or 10 tons/hr. of limestone for agricultural use.

Ring-roller Mills with Internal Screen Classification. The *Bradley Hercules Three-roller Mill* (*Bradley Pulverizer Co.*) is used for semifine grinding of materials such as cement rock, cement clinker, limestone, phosphate rock, phosphate rock clinker, etc. The grinding action of the Bradley Hercules Mill is that of the three rollers being revolved around and against a steel die ring at a speed which, through centrifugal force, creates a pressure between the rollers and the die, where they come in contact with the material to be pulverized. In this manner the material is reduced within the mill to the desired fineness, after which it is discharged through an internal screen surrounding the grinding chamber, thence through ports in the base of the mill to a screw conveyor installed in the foundation of the mill to an elevator or direct to storage as may be desired.

The Bradley Hercules Mill is a large-capacity pulverizer, capable of producing as much as 25 to 50 tons/hr. when grinding average-hardness dry limestone, or 135 to 150 bbl./hr. of cement clinker. Finished product will average 90, 60, and 50 per cent able to pass through Nos. 20, 100, and 200 sieves, respectively. It is designed to take material 2 in. and under for feed, reducing same to the desired fineness in a single operation, without auxiliary machinery, all the material passing through the mill being of a uniform fineness. The fineness of the finished product discharging from the mill is determined by the mesh of the screen installed on the mill, which is so designed that it can be quickly changed to a screen of another mesh size, so that the operator may secure whatever fineness of finished product desired, keeping in mind the limitations of the mill.

The *Type "B" Junior Hercules Mill* operates in the same manner and on the same materials as the large Hercules Mill but with capacities of 5 to 12 tons/hr.

The *Griffin Mill* (*Bradley Pulverizer Co.*) has a single roller revolving against and around a horizontal grinding ring. The ground material is discharged through an internal screen by the aid of an air current resulting from the speedily revolving roller. Griffin Mills are used for the reduction of materials similar to those mentioned above with capacities of 1 to 6 tons/hr. Design characteristics for Bradley mills are given in Table 8-20. Applications are described on p. 8-49.

Table 8-20. Design Data for Ring-roller Mills with Internal Screen Classification

Design Characteristics	Bradley-Hercules	Type "B" Junior Hercules Mill	Griffin	
			Giant	Junior Giant
Weight of mill, lb.	60,000	19,650	26,000	13,000
Speed of mill, r.p.m.	130	165	175	210
Diameter of roller, in.	22	16½	24	18
Diameter of ring, in.	66	42	40	30
Weight of roller head, lb.	750	400		
Motor size, hp.	350	100	100	50

Ring-roller Mills with Internal Air Classification. The *Babcock & Wilcox pulverizers, Type B, 100-Series*, consist of a single row of balls operating between a stationary bottom ring and a rotating top ring. The *Type B, 200- and 300-Series*, are designed with multiple rows of balls to produce maximum capacity in the space occupied. The 200-Series pulverizer consists of two rows of balls, one above the other. The top and bottom rings are stationary with the intermediate ring rotating. Externally adjustable springs load the grinding elements to the pressure required. The 300-Series pulverizers are the same as the 200-Series except that a third row of balls has been added inside the top row of the 200-Series to increase the capacity still further.

In operation, wet raw feed is admitted to the center of the pulverizer and is fed through the upper balls by centrifugal force, then through the lower row by gravity. Preheated air carries the partly pulverized material up to the rotating internal classifier. The finished product passes through the classifier with the carrying air, and on out of the pulverizer. Oversize material is returned by gravity to the grinding elements. For grinding noncombustible materials, the pulverizer is arranged to discharge the material by gravity after it passes through the lower row of balls, and it operates in closed circuit with an external classifier. Preheated air can be used in the closed-circuit system to dry material as it is being pulverized. A typical arrangement of a closed-circuit unit is shown in Fig. 8-30. The 200- and 300-Series pulverizers are used as air-swept units for grinding large quantities of coal for either direct firing or storage. As closed-circuit units, they are used in drying and grinding cement raw materials, agricultural limestone, chrome ore, phosphate rock, and other materials. They are built in nine sizes with capacities up to 45 tons/hr. Pulverizers of the B. & W. type may be used in either pressure or suction systems.

The *B. & W. pulverizer, Type E*, consists of a single row of balls operating between a rotating bottom ring and a stationary top ring (Fig. 8-35). Externally adjusted springs apply pressure to the top ring to give the required

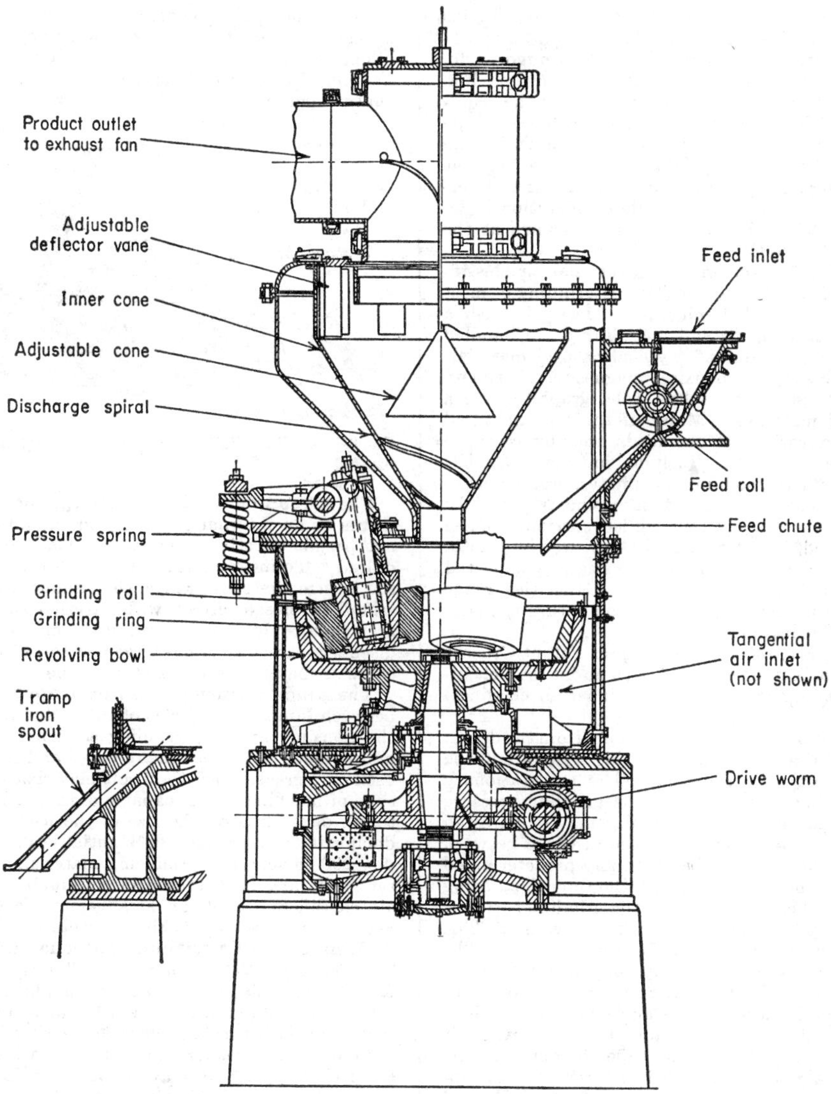

FIG. 8-36. Bowl mill. (*Raymond Div., Combustion Engineering, Inc.*)

loading for proper pulverizing. In operation wet raw coal is admitted inside the ball row and is fed through the grinding elements by centrifugal force. The partly pulverized coal is picked up outside the ball row by preheated air and carried to the rotating centrifugal classifier in the upper part of the pulverizer. Coal that is pulverized passes through the classifier with the air, and out of pulverizer, while the oversize coal is returned by gravity to the grinding elements. The classifier is designed with adjustable blades so that the fineness of pulverization can be varied by adjusting the classifier. The Type E pulverizer is particularly suited to the direct firing of rotary kilns and industrial furnaces where close temperature control is required and long periods of continuous operation are essential. It is built in 17 sizes with capacities up to 14 tons/hr.

B. & W. pulverizers operate successfully in circulating systems in which a single pulverizer fires two or more kilns or furnaces by distribution through a circulating loop, as shown in Fig. 8-30.

The *Raymond ring-roller mill* (Figs. 8-33 and 8-34) is of the internal air-classification type. The base of the mill carries the grinding ring, rigidly fixed in the base and lying in the horizontal plane. Underneath the grinding ring are tangential air ports through which the air enters the grinding chamber. A vertical shaft with a bevel gear near the bottom and resting on a thrust bearing is driven by a horizontal shaft through a pinion. Keyed rigidly to the shaft near the top is a spider which carries the roller journals. These journals have rollers on the bottom rotating on their own bearings while traveling around the ring. Two or more journals are pivotally suspended by trunnions fastened at the top of the journal housing and supported in the arms of the spider. They hang almost vertically, so that when the mill is at rest the rolls press only lightly against the grinding ring.

The method of classification used with Raymond mills depends on the fineness desired. If a medium-fine product is required (up to 85 or 90 per cent through a No. 100 sieve), a single-cone air classifier is used (see Fig. 8-34). This consists of a housing surrounding the grinding elements with an outlet on top through which the finished product is discharged. This is known as the low-side mill. For a finer product and where frequent changes in fineness are required, the vacuum- or whizzer-type classification is used. Its mode of operation is described on p. 8-27. This type of mill is known as the *high-side mill* (Fig. 8-33).

The Raymond ring roll mill with internal air classification is used for the large-capacity fine grinding of most of the softer non-metallic minerals. Materials with a Moh scale hardness up to and including 5 are handled economically on these units. Typical natural materials handled include barytes, bauxite, magnesite, phosphate rock, iron oxide pigments, sulfur, talc, graphite, and a host of similar materials. Many of the manufactured pigments and a variety of chemicals are pulverized to high fineness on such units. Included are such materials as calcium phosphates, sodium phosphates, organic insecticides, powdered cornstarch, and many similar materials.

These mills operate entirely under suction. When properly operated, they are entirely dust-free and automatic. They are available in six basic sizes. Connected horsepower ranges from 40 to 700. Capacities range from 0.5 to 40 tons/hr., depending upon nature of material and exact fineness of grind.

The *Williams ring-roller mill* (Williams Patent Crusher & Pulverizer Co.) can be supplied with an internal classifier of the rotating-blade type (the Spinner air classifier) or with a double-cone classifier

The Raymond **bowl mill** is a departure from the design of the standard ring-roller mill. In this style of mill the journals that carry the grinding rollers are stationary while the grinding ring rotates. The grinding pressure is produced by means of springs, which may be adjusted to give the required pressure, and the distance between the rollers and the ring may be set to any predetermined clearance. The rollers do not touch the ring, there being no metal-to-metal contact between the grinding surfaces. Figure 8-36 shows the construction of the bowl mill. The grinding ring is carried on the lip of the rotary bowl. The raw material from the feeder drops on the bowl where, owing to the centrifugal force of rotation, it is forced to the periphery and, owing to the angle of the ring, it is forced upward between the ring and the rollers, where it is pulverized. The action of the tapered rollers on the tapered ring causes the pulverized material to work upward and out of the grinding chamber into an upblast of air. The air with the pulverized material passes up into a classifier of the double-cone vacuum type (see p. 8-28). Here the required fines are removed and the oversize dropped back to the bowl, where it is mixed with the raw feed. This mill was especially developed to pulverize coal for direct boiler firing. It is equally popular for industrial furnace and kiln firing. Tramp iron and other extraneous hard materials are usually thrown out of the mill automatically through a spout.

Hammer Mills. (Figs. 8-25 and 8-37.) Hammer mills for pulverizing and disintegration are operated at high speeds. The rotor shaft may be vertical or horizontal, generally the latter. The shaft carries hammers, sometimes called beaters. The hammers may be T-shaped elements, stirrups, bars, or rings fixed or pivoted to the shaft or to disks fixed to the shaft. The rotor runs in a housing containing grinding plates or liners. The clearance maintained between the liners and rotor is important with respect to the fineness of product. A cylindrical screen or grating usually encloses all or part of the rotor. The fineness of product can be regulated by changing rotor speed, feed rate, or clearance between hammers and grinding plates, as well as by changing the number and type of hammers used and the size of discharge openings.

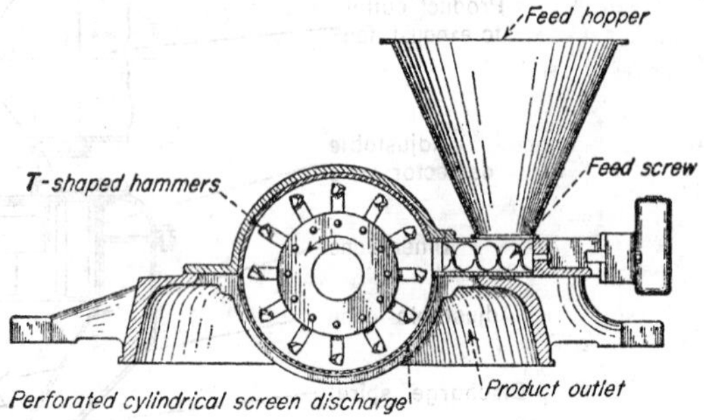

FIG. 8-37. Mikro-Pulverizer hammer mill. (*Pulverizing Machinery Co.*)

The **screen** or **grating discharge** for a hammer mill serves as an internal classifier, but its limited area does not permit effective usage when small apertures are required. To meet critical maximum-size specifications in the intermediate-size range, the hammer mill may be operated in closed circuit with external screens of larger area than could be employed in the mill itself. The mill discharge screen then has large apertures to retain grossly oversize material in the grinding zone.

The grinding action results from **impact** and **attrition** between lumps or particles of the material being ground, the housing, and the grinding elements. The hammer mill is made in a great many types and sizes and can be used on a greater variety of soft materials than any other type of machine. It is capable of taking ¾-in. feed material, depending on the size of the feed throat, and reducing it to a product substantially all able to pass a No. 200 sieve. For producing materials in the fine-size range, it may be operated in conjunction with external air classifiers. Such an arrangement is shown in Fig. 8-12. A number of machines have internal air classifiers.

Hammer Mills without Internal Air Classifiers. The *Williams Helix-Seal mill* (Williams Patent Crusher & Pulverizer Co.) is suitable for fine pulverizing, disintegration, and shredding. Twist hammers and chisel hammers may be used, the latter for tearing and shredding. A preliminary breaker can be provided for mounting on the feed hopper. It may be operated in closed circuit with a *Spinner air classifier*. Eight sizes are available requiring from 5 to 100 hp. Speed varies from 1800 to 5500 r.p.m. from largest to smallest mill. Clays, chemicals, pigments, drugs, and food products have been ground.

The *Stedman Type A Two-stage Swing Hammer Grinders* (*Stedman's Foundry and Machine Works*) are designed for the uniform reduction of many materials, whether friable, fibrous, tough, dry, or moist. They will grind greasy crackling cake to No. 10 sieve size or limestone and similar materials with equal facility. They grind friable materials to No. 20, 40, or 60 sieve size and finer. Rolling rings are furnished in place of hammers for abrasive materials. Type A machines are equipped with built-in metal trap and adjustable grinding plates. The *Stedman Disintegrator*, commonly referred to as a *cage mill*, is used for disintegrating clays, colors, press cake, asbestos, and packing-house by-products. This type of machine is desirable for handling tough, gummy, high-moisture-content or low-melting-point materials. Cages of two, three, four, six, and eight rows, with bars of special alloy steel, revolving in opposite directions, produce a powerful impact action that pulverizes many materials.

The *Jeffrey Type A Swing Hammer Pulverizer* (*Jeffrey Manufacturing Co.*) is a general-purpose machine. Product fineness attainable for a number of materials is given in Table 8-21 for a 24-in. mill with rotor speed of 1600 r.p.m. and a ⅛-in. grate bar opening.

Table 8-21. Sieve Analyses of Products from Jeffrey Swing Hammer Pulverizer

Material	% through sieve No.				
	10	20	35	65	100
Alum cake	90	72	43	23	14
Burned lime	98	92	80	71	65
Rock salt	97	88	62	35	22
Gypsum	97	87	69	53	42

The *Mikro-Pulverizer* (Pulverizing Machinery Co.) is a close-clearance, high-speed, controlled sealed feed hammer mill used for a wide range of non-abrasive materials. with the major applications being sugar, carbon black, chemicals, pharmaceuticals, plastics, dyestuffs, dry colors, and cosmetics. It is used not only for dry grinding but also for solid-liquid dispersions. Speeds, types of hammers, feed devices, housing variations, and perforations of screens are all varied to fit applications, with the result that finenesses and character of grind cover a wide range. Some of the grinds are as fine as 99.9 per cent through a 325-mesh screen, while others are a "close-mesh range," such as molding powders, with a maximum through a coarse screen such as 14 mesh and a minimum through an 80- or 100-mesh screen. Feed material should usually be down to 1½ in. or finer. If feed is larger, an auxiliary crusher may be required, preferably as a separate unit, because synchronization is difficult since the crusher has larger capacities than the pulverizer. Tie-in is possible with careful regulation of relative speeds of crusher and feed screw or screws.

Mikro-Pulverizers are made in five sizes as shown in Table 8-22. The smallest size is the Bantam, which is widely used in laboratories for development and pilot work. Results may be extrapolated and translated into what may be expected of full-scale production units.

Table 8-22. Mikro-Pulverizer Performance

Size	Rotor diam., in.	Max. r.p.m.	Hp.	Avg. capacities, lb./hr.		
				6X sugar	Clay-graphite water slurry	Pigments and colors (dry)
Bantam	5	16,000	¾–1	75–100	75–100	70–90
1	8	9,600	3–5	350–550	550	300–500
2	12	6,900	7½–15	800–1500	750–1600	800–2000
3	18	4,600	20–40	2000–4500	4800	2500–4500
4	24	3,450	40–100	4000–9000	7000	4500–7000

The *S.P.* (*Semi-Plastic*) *Mikro-Pulverizer* (Pulverizing Machinery Co.) (Fig. 8-38) is used to handle materials which normally clog and plaster up screen mills because the material is sticky, tacky, unctuous, or wet. It was originally developed to handle porcelain tile body mixtures of clay and feldspar containing 20 to 25 per cent moisture, and is unique because it uses no screen or perforated plate as do the screen hammer mills and, in fact, has a minimum of body or housing on which material may plaster or stick. Its use has been expanded to handle sticky materials, such as DDT, benzene hexachloride, and other similar insecticides which must otherwise be ground with artificial refrigerants, such as dry ice, in any screen mill, whereas with the S.P. Mikro-Pulverizer no dry ice is required. Capacities cover a wide range, from a few hundred pounds per hour to 4 to 5 tons/hr., using horsepowers from 3 to 10, and the fineness is usually in a granular free-flowing range of 6 to 20 mesh. Since the unit is frequently used with muller

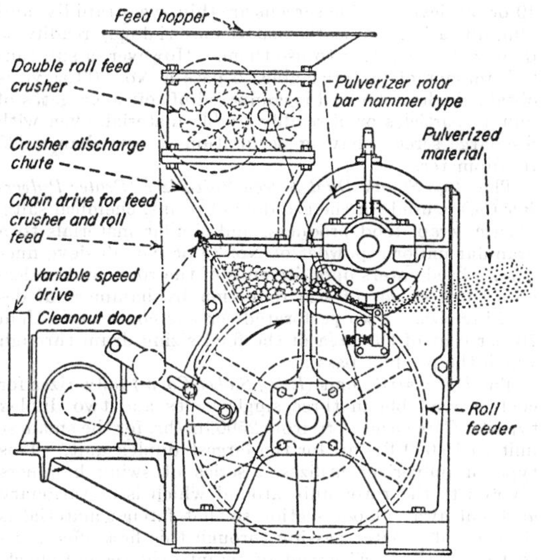

FIG. 8-38. No. 2 S.P. Mikro-Pulverizer. (*Pulverizing Machinery Co.*)

mixers which discharge lumpy masses of material, there is usually a two-roll crusher at the feed point which discharges downward to a slowly revolving drum or roll feeder with a swing hammer rotor just beyond the crest of the drum cycle and a scoop bar on the roll feed also close to the rotor lowest point. While the roll feed drum turns clockwise, the rotor turns counterclockwise, discharging material to either an inclined discharge belt conveyor or a bin (Fig. 8-38).

The *Raymond Screen Pulverizer* (*Raymond Pulverizer Division*) is adapted for filter-press products, chemicals, colors, and dyes. It is easily cleaned when changing from one color or chemical to another. A screw conveyor in the bottom of the hopper forces the feed into the grinding chamber uniformly against the tips of the hammers. This screw is designed to pack the material, making it act as a seal, thus aiding in dustless operation. Performance characteristics are given in Table 8-23. Larger sizes, in combination with air classifiers, are used for asbestos, mica, and similar fibrous and flaky materials. They cannot be cleaned so easily as the smaller sizes and are therefore used where changes of material are less frequent.

Although the screen mill is inexpensive, easy to operate, and efficient in its grinding range, it cannot be classed as a fine-grinding mill by present-day standards. The

Table 8-23. Performance of Raymond Screen Pulverizer

Material	Capacity, lb./hr.	Fineness	Hp.
Para red	800	97% through No. 200 sieve	5
Tartaric acid	600	99% through No. 60 sieve	5
Soap powder	2000	No. 30 sieve	7.5
Ultramarine blue	1500	98% through No. 200 sieve	7
Boric acid	1000	92% through No. 100 sieve	6.5
Malted milk	1500	No. 20 sieve	5
Bismarck brown	400	98% through No. 200 sieve	5
Sugar	650	90% through No. 200 sieve	5

finest round perforations in screen commercially available are 0.020 in. diameter. With any moderately tough material, a few hundredths per cent will be found in the finished product close to this screen size, which is approximately that of the No. 30 sieve. Even with readily pulverized materials, oversize will begin to show on the No.

40 or 50 sieves. Fine screens are thin, wear rapidly, and plug up easily. A heat-sensitive material may readily be damaged attempting to use them. However, a substantial amount of material able to pass a No. 200 sieve is obtained when the feed is composed of soft aggregates of minute particles or of readily friable material, even with discharge screens having perforations larger than 0.020 in. diameter.

The *Blue Streak Dual Screen Pulverizer* (*Prater Pulverizer Co.*) is used for the grinding of resins, chemical salts, plastic scrap, food products, and similar materials to a granular uniform powder of No. 30 or No. 40 sieve fineness. Feed enters opposite ends of the rotor and undergoes three stages of size reduction by hammers of decreasing size. Two perforated screens cover more than 70 per cent of the area of the final sizing drum through which the product passes.

The *Riley Atrita* unit (*Riley Stoker Corp.*) pulverizer for coal is available in three single types and two duplex types. Capacities vary from 2500 lb./hr. for the smallest unit to 15,000 lb./hr. for the largest duplex unit. This type of pulverizer utilizes a series of swing hammers pivoted to the rotor hub, around which is a stationary grid, cut away at one section so that foreign material is thrown out. After passing through this first effect, the coal is carried in a current of air into the second effect, which contains alternate rows of moving and stationary pegs, where most of the pulverizing is done. Leaving the second effect, the coal is passed through a rejector, a number of scooplike blades on the main shaft, where the heaviest particles are thrown back into the pulverizing compartment, permitting the passage of the finer particles only, which enter the fan inlet and are carried into the furnace. Hot air can be introduced into the machine for drying the coal. Air at 300°F. dries coal with 8 per cent moisture down to about 1 per cent.

The *Aero* (*Foster Wheeler Corp.*) unit pulverizer is used for coal, pitch, and coke, blowing the ground material directly into the furnace. The housing is divided into two or three short cylindrical pulverizing chambers. Primary air is admitted at the feed end and between the last chamber and fan. The horizontal shaft carries disks to which hammers are fixed, a set for each chamber. Coal is pulverized by impact and attrition. Annular baffles between the chambers of increasing diameter cause particles to be retained until properly reduced in size for discharge from the final chamber in suspension in the air stream. Hot gases can be introduced to dry the fuel being pulverized. Refractory material such as tramp iron is removed in the first pulverizing chamber and eliminated through a tramp-iron pocket.

Disintegrator. The Reitz machine (Fig. 8-39) combines the actions of attrition, cutting, impact, and screen mills in one tool. Its basic design consists of a rotor running inside a 360-deg. screen enclosure. The rotating shaft is usually vertical. The rotor includes a number of hammers designed to run at fairly close clearance relative to the inside of the cylindrical screen enclosing the disintegration chamber. The hammers sweep the inside surface of the sizing screen and keep the perforations open. The hammers are normally fixed rigidly to the shaft by keyways, pins, or welding, but swing hammers are used when indicated. The screen assembly can consist of as many as three perforated screens of different types to get desired action.

Feed enters the disintegration chamber parallel to the axis, as in disk attrition mills, rather than tangentially, as in hammer mills. Product is normally discharged radially out through a perforated sizing screen which completely surrounds the rotor. Materials processed in Rietz disintegrators are frequently "tough" and elastic rather than hard and crack-sensitive. Many applica-

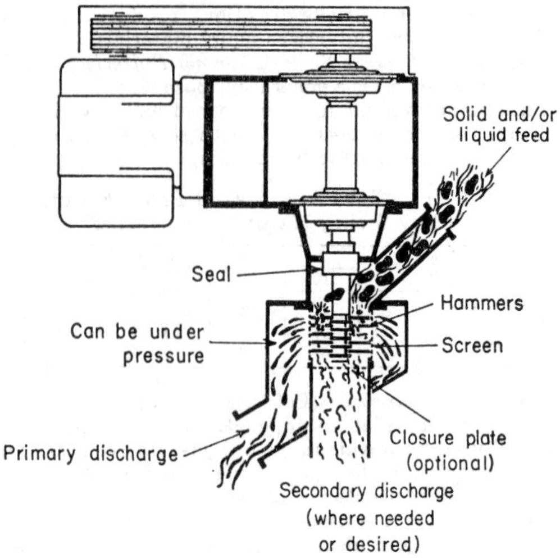

Fig. 8-39. Rietz disintegrator. (*Rietz Mfg. Co.*)

tions are on wet materials. Of these wet applications perhaps half are pumpable slurries or suspensions. Perhaps the greatest advantages of the disintegrator design are found in those applications where solids content is in the range of 40 to 80 per cent; it is here that sticky, gummy, flow-resistant materials are most frequently met. On these materials, which will often plug the screens of conventional hammer mills, the Rietz disintegrator keeps running because the close hammer clearance keeps the sizing screen open; this permits grinding to smaller and more uniform sizes than is normally possible in other equipment. On feeds running higher than 80 per cent in solids, impact frequently plays an important role in the Rietz disintegrator.

Solid feeds should be in the range of ⅛- to 2-in. pieces, such as would normally be discharged by a Rietz prebreaker. Product size is commonly from ½ in. to 40 mesh, with many applications aimed at minus 100-mesh products. A few applications, mostly of a deagglomerating nature, produce particles in the smaller than 325-mesh range. Developments are progressing toward the fine-grind field.

Many Rietz disintegrators offer separation simultaneously with grinding. This feature is termed "differential discharge" or "dual discharge." The product is normally that material reduced in size so as to pass through the sizing screen (the primary discharge), but since the feed enters along the axis of the cylindrical disintegration chamber, from one end only, it is possible to remove from the other end of the disintegration chamber a secondary discharge consisting of any material which has not passed through the sizing screen. This permits removal of junk material or often permits the separation of a tougher fraction of a mixed feed, such as the tough fibers from pith in bagasse fiber production. The secondary discharge feature is in many cases utilized as an overload control, with excess material being recycled to the feed end of the disintegrator until all material goes through the screen. This latter type of operation can sometimes eliminate external size-separation equipment.

Sometimes Rietz disintegrators are applied more for their intensive mixing and blending action than for pulverizing action. The fact that retention time can be controlled by partially blocking off the discharge area of the sizing screen with a blanking plate is of frequent advantage in this application.

Table 8-24. Performance of Rietz Disintegrators

Model	Rotor diam., in.	Max. r.p.m.	Hp. range	Screen perforation, in.	Typical applications	
					Material	Capacity
RA-1	4	16,000	½–5	1/32–¼	General lab use	1–10 lb./min.
RP-6	6	3,600	1–20	3/16	Horseradish	300 lb./hr.
RI-2	6 or 8	5,000	3–20	1/16	Detergent delumping	100 gal./min.
RD-8	8	8,400	3–20	⅛	Color coat	3600 lb./hr.
RA-2	8 or 12	8,400	3–20	1/32	Meat, cooked	3000–5000 lb./hr.
RP-8	8	3,600	10–60	¼	Blood declotting	20 gal./min.
RD-12	12	7,200	15–50	¼–¾	Polystyrene	3000–10,000 lb./hr.
RA-3	12 or 18	6,500	10–75	3/64	Corn, heated	350 lb./min.
RP-12	12	3,600	20–75	⅜	Asbestos-cement slurry	200 gal./min.
RD-18	18	3,600	30–150	⅜	Chemical-fertilizer delumping	15 tons/hr.
RP-18	18	3,600	25–100	¼	Animal fat (90°F.)	15,000 lb./hr.
RD-24	24	3,600	75–400	1	Wood-chip shredding	30 tons/hr.
RI-4	24	3,600	50–200	¼	Bagasse depithing	30 tons/hr. (dry)

Maximum horsepower depends upon maximum speed.
RA and RP models are normally supplied with stainless-steel contact parts.
Some disintegrators are available for operation under pressure.
Screens are available in various sizes and types of perforations down to 0.006 in.

Rietz disintegrators are normally supplied in rotor diameters from 4 to 24 in., with rotationals speeds to produce hammer tip speeds in range of 1000 to 22,000 ft./min. and horsepower ranges from ½ to 200 hp. Higher speeds and higher horsepowers are available. Models are available in various materials of construction and in highly sanitary, easy-cleaning models or heavy-duty industrial construction (Table 8-24).

The *Tornado mill* (F. J. Stokes Corp.) is a vertical-shaft type with full grinding ring beneath which is a 360-deg. circular screen.

Fitz mills (W. J. Fitzpatrick Co.) represent a wide variety of specialty types designed for individual needs.

Turbo-Pulverizers and *Turbo mills* (Pallmann Pulverizer Co.) combine the action of hammer and attrition mills, finding special application for grinding plastic materials that would be softened under high-energy warm mill conditions.

Hammer Mills with Internal Air Classifiers. A detailed description of two modern machines of this type, the *Mikro-Atomizer* and the *Raymond Vertical Mill*, has been published [see Berry, *Ind. Eng. Chem.*, **38**, 672 (1946)].

The *Imp Pulverizer* (*Raymond Div., Combustion Engineering Co.*) is an air-swept hammer mill, as illustrated in Fig. 8-40. This machine is made in many sizes from the smallest, having one row of hammers using 10 hp., to the largest size, with six rows of hammers and requiring 200 hp. to drive it. The machines are equipped with a hopper below which is the star feeder, actuated by a pawl-and-ratchet mechanism. A vent from the top of the return-air pipe passes through a tubular dust collector, which makes the system dustless.

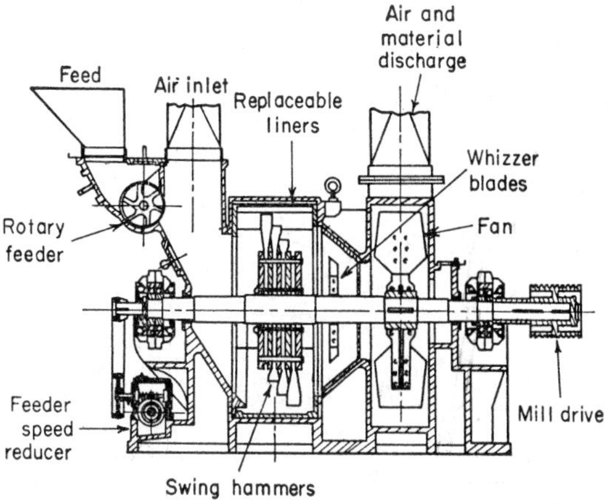

FIG. 8-40. Whizzer air classification applied to Raymond Imp mill.

A fan is placed on one end of the hammer shaft; between the fan and the hammers is the whizzer, consisting of two or more thin blades with tips tapered to conform to the housing. Distance between blades and housing is regulated by moving the whizzer along the shaft. As the whizzer is moved toward the hammers, a coarser product results. Action of the whizzer is that of a fan wheel opposing the action of the main fan. With minimum clearing between blades and housing, a maximum countercurrent is set up at the periphery in the direction indicated by the arrows. An air current accompanying the feed dropping into the pulverizing chamber carries the pulverized material through the clearing toward the fan intake. As the centrifugal force is greater on the coarser particles, their radial velocity will exceed the lateral; hence they are thrown to the periphery and deflected to the hammers by the countercurrent, while the finer particles discharge through the fan intake. The classified product passes through the fan and is blown to a cyclone collector, where it is discharged into bins or containers. The air goes back to the pulverizer, completing the cycle.

It is necessary to vent a small amount of surplus air to a final dust collector. If proper care is used in feed and product handling, the operation can be relatively dust-free.

These Imp units are excellent drying devices and are widely used for simultaneous drying, pulverizing, and classifying.

The *Automatic pulverizer* (Raymond Div.) is a hammer-type machine equipped with air classifier of the vacuum multivane type (see p. 8-28) or the double whizzer type. It has a horizontal shaft on which may be mounted one or more disks fitted with hammers. On the door of the pulverizing chamber is mounted an automatic throwout, the function of which is to remove resistant materials contained in the feed, such as sand and gravel from clay. A star feeder with pawl-and-ratchet mechanism receives the raw material from a stock bin and drops it into the pulverizing chamber, on top of which is mounted the air classifier. The air enters the pulverizing chamber at the rear and removes the pulverized material. Particles of proper fineness are blown to the cyclone, which discharges to bins or containers, while oversize is returned to the pulverizer through the bottom valve of the inner cone. Impurities in the oversize accumulate in the grinding chamber until they are picked up by the rapidly revolving hammers and thrown through the slot on the door into the throwout chamber, where they are finally rejected through the flap valve. The slide damper on top of the throwout may be adjusted to admit air from the atmosphere, which enters the pulverizer through the slot in the door. In its travel through the throwout the air cleans the rejects and blows fine particles back into the pulverizing chamber.

The automatic throwout is often used for concentrating valuable constituents in an aggregate, such as phosphatic granules, which are separated from silt and clay. In this case the product discharged through the throwout is the valuable material. The automatic pulverizer can be made to function as an external air classifier, receiving pulverized material from another machine. The hammers are run at comparatively low speed, doing no pulverizing but stirring the material and throwing it into an air current. The air carries the material into the classifier in the normal manner, the fines are removed, and the rejects are eliminated through the throwout.

This is the type of hammer mill with air separation referred to in the previous discussion of cleaning and concentrating (p. 8-13).

The Raymond **vertical mill** rotating components are carried on its vertical shaft. They are the grinding element, double whizzer classifier, and fan, as shown in Fig. 8-41. The grinding element at the bottom of the shaft carries bar-shaped hammers free to swing from the fixed end. Grinding of material takes place when it falls on the rotating grinding element and is accelerated to high speed in a upward spiral path as a result of the air entering at the bottom of the shaft. As the material rises to the double whizzer classifier, its rotational velocity is increased, and coarse particles are concentrated along the wall of the chamber because of the centrifugal force acting on them. Coarse particles are continually returned to the grinding elements, while fine particles pass between the radial blades of the whizzer classifier and are carried in the air stream through the fan and discharge port. The fine particles are separated from the air stream by a cyclone collector into a suitable container. The air discharged by the cyclone can be returned to the machine in any desired proportion or be vented to a cloth bag collector.

Machines are available with rotor diameters of 18 and 35 in., driven by 20- and 150-hp. motors, respectively. The larger mill is directly connected to a vertical motor. Normal rotor speed for the 18-in. Raymond vertical mill is 6500 r.p.m. and 3600 r.p.m. for the 35-in. machine. In general, relative production rates for the two machines are directly proportional to the power applied. Product fineness is controlled by the number of blades used in each bank of the whizzer classifier and by the size of the fan wheel. Materials of the smallest particle size generally are produced when the maximum number of whizzer blades and the smallest fan are used.

Field of application of the Raymond vertical mill is for producing materials that range in size from those having 99 per cent passing a No. 325 sieve to those having 99 per cent smaller than 5 to 10 microns, depending on the state of aggregation of the feed. A production rate of 500 lb./hr. is achieved with a chemical in an 18-in.

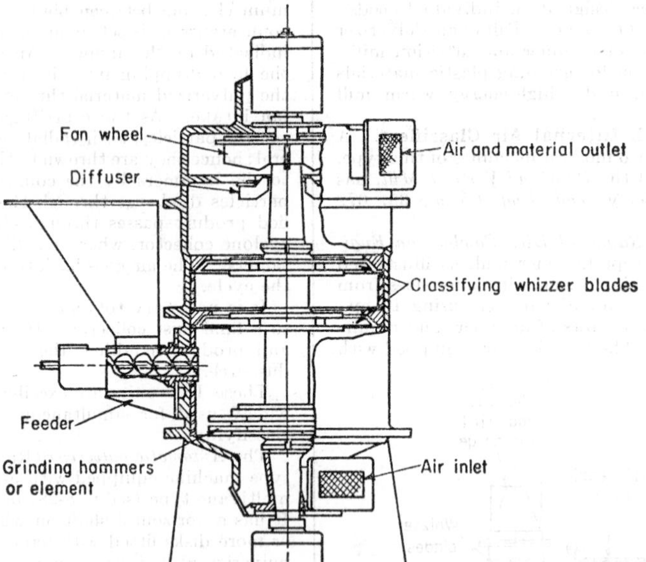

FIG. 8-41. Raymond vertical mill. (*Raymond Div., Combustion Engineering, Inc.*)

machine, consuming 18 hp. when the product is substantially smaller than 15 microns. In a talc operation on a 35-in. machine requiring 150 hp., a production rate of 700 lb./hr. is obtained when the product is 95 per cent smaller than 10 microns. At a production rate of 5000 lb./hr., a sample of the product leaves only a trace of talc on a No. 325 testing sieve.

The *Mikro-Atomizer* (Pulverizing Machinery Co.) is a built-in classifier unit as per Fig. 8-42 and has a horizontal rotor shaft carrying hammers, classifier wheels,

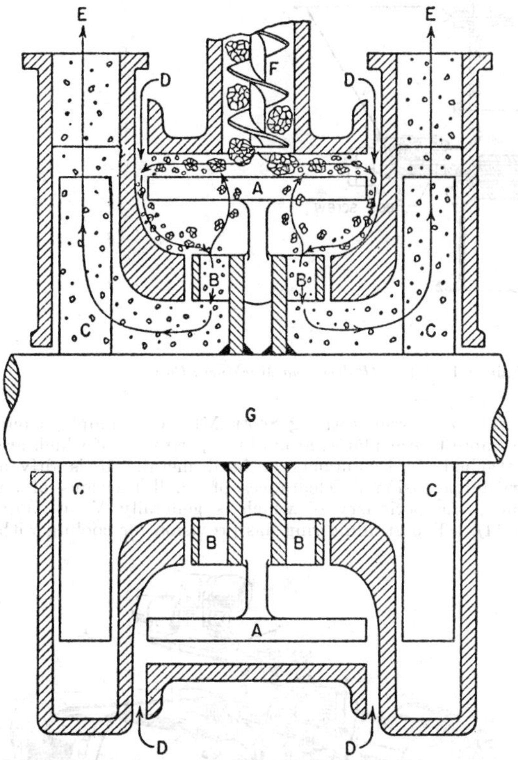

A Hammers or impact members
B Classifier wheels
C Fan wheels
D Annular air inlets
E Product outlets
F Feed screw
G Rotor shaft

Fig. 8-42. Mikro-Atomizer operating principle. [*Ind. Eng. Chem.*, **38**, 672 (1946).]

and fan wheels. Material is fed into the unit through a screw feed and comes in contact with the T-shaped hammers and divided into two streams with a spiral circular motion to either side of the hammers as grinding takes place between the high-speed hammers and a ridged main liner. Air entering the annular air inlets disperses the particles toward the classifier wheels, which carry closely spaced vanes at the periphery. Centrifugal force and aerodynamic drag are opposing forces on the particles between the vanes on the classifier wheels. When the centrifugal force on a particle exceeds the dynamic drag, it is returned to the grinding chamber zone, but when the aerodynamic drag exceeds the centrifugal force, then the particle passes through the vanes of the classifier wheel into the fans and out one of the product outlets, which usually converge into a single duct and thence either directly to a dust filter alone or to a cyclone or a combination of a cyclone and bag filter. Higher rotor classifier and fan speeds, larger vanes on the separator wheel, and smaller fan wheel diameter all contribute toward obtaining particles of the finest order, and various combinations of these factors are used to obtain variations in results.

Mikro-Atomizers are made in three sizes, with characteristics given in Table 8-25. Feed size is limited to 3/4 in. and smaller. Table 8-26 gives performance for the No. 6 Mikro-Atomizer on a series of products; similar finenesses are obtainable on the other sizes. The Mikro-Atomizer is also used to grind cocoa with cocoa-butter content varying from 12 to 23 per cent but requires refrigeration when producing a product which is 99.5 per cent through 100 mesh and 97.5 per cent through 200 mesh.

Table 8-25. Mikro-Atomizer Operating Characteristics

Machine No.	Rotor diam., in.	Max. rotor r.p.m.	Hp.	Relative capacity
5	8	14,000	5	1
6	12	7,000	20	4
8	24	3,450	75	18

Table 8-26. Performance of the No. 6 Mikro-Atomizer

Material	Particle size, microns		Production rate, lb./hr.
	Avg.	Max.	
Sugar	19	40	500
Polyvinyl chloride	10-12	20-30	125
Calcium carbonate	5	25	600
Nickel carbonate	2.5-5	10-20	300-650
Lead oxide	2	5	1250
Dry colors	4	15	500

The *Mikro-Bud Pulverizer* (Pulverizing Machinery Co.) is a vertical-shaft classifier unit with built-in classification, using an independently operated variable-speed classifier wheel as per Fig. 8-43. This unit is designed to produce intermediate finenesses between those of the Mikro-Atomizer and those of the Mikro-Pulverizer and is available in two sizes.

Unground material is fed to the unit through a feed screw and other controlled feed (pneumatic) close to the hammer tips when out at full-speed swing. The rotating hammers induce an upward flow of air through the hammer circle into a classifier area adjacent to the variable-speed separator wheel. Finer grinds are obtained at high separator wheel speeds, since coarser particles are rejected by the centrifugal action of the separator wheel and are returned to the grinding area. A baffle plate with secondary air inlet aids this recycle and regrinding action. Control of air flow through the unit is another factor influencing size of discharged particles, and discharge is to a bag filter which provides suitable negative pressure on the mill outlet. Finenesses obtained vary from "all through 40 mesh" to "all through 325 mesh," depending on the material being ground and the adjustments on the unit. The range of air flow per horsepower covers a wide range from 40 cu. ft./min./hp. and this large air flow alleviates the temperature rise produced by the work of grinding. Hence cocoa powder with 19 per cent cocoa-butter content can be ground to 99.9 per cent through 200 mesh but usually employs refrigeration. Similarly this same unit is being used to grind rubber accelerators, which are heat-sensitive. Since the finenesses are adjustable and clearances not so critical as those of either the Mikro-Pulverizer or the Mikro-Atomizer, this unit has found application handling certain materials normally considered too abrasive for either of the other units. Inert-gas atmosphere may be used on all the Mikro grinding units.

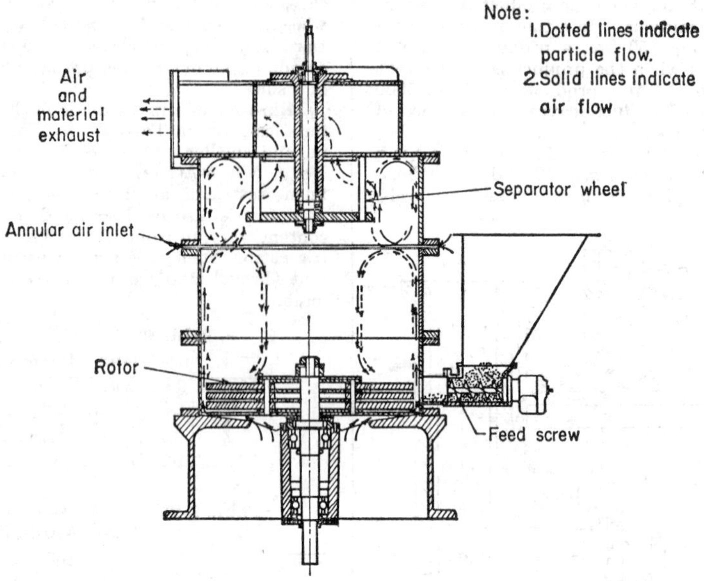

FIG. 8-43. Mikro-Bud pulverizer, showing paths of air and solids. (*Pulverizing Machinery Co.*)

The *Limited mill* (Schutz-O'Neill Co.) consists of two or more beater plates on which are mounted fixed hammers which pulverize the material against a shell, which usually is corrugated. Sometimes a perforated shell, similar to a grater, is used; this is of advantage in pulverizing tough fibrous material. Fineness of the finished product is regulated by a cone with attached blades or whizzers. The pulverized material travels longitudinally toward the cone and whizzer. When the cone plate is moved into the mill, a coarser product is obtained. With the plate in the extreme outer position, flush with the end of the mill, only the fines pass through, while the coarser particles are thrown into a tailings groove on top of the grinding chamber, at the end of which a rotary valve returns them to the feed end of the mill. For very fine grinding and for extremely hard materials, a perforated plate mounted on the shaft in front of the beater is employed. A row of holes in the plate, varying from ½ to ⅛ in. in diameter, provides an exit for the finely ground material and relieves the air pressure, thus permitting cooler operation. The mill is made in five sizes from 16 to 28 in. diameter, requiring 10 to 100 hp. for speeds from 3500 to 2600 r.p.m. Applications of the Limited mill are given in Table 8-27.

Table 8-27. Performance of Schutz-O'Neill Limited Mill

Material	Production, lb./hr.	Hp.
Pyrethrum flowers	35- 45	15-20
Quassia	25- 30	15-20
Senna leaves	100-125	20-25
Buchu	100-110	20-25
Stramonium	125-150	20-25
Bay leaves	125-150	20-25
Celery seed	125-150	15-20
Tragacanth gum	50- 60	15-20
China twigs	75- 80	20-25
Cassia	90-100	20-25
Ginger	90-100	20-25
Cloves	125-150	20-25
Pepper, white	200-225	20-25
Pepper, Singapore	225-250	20-25
Gelatin	60- 70	15-20
Cayenne pepper	100-125	20-25

The *Pulvocron* (Strong Scott Mfg. Co.) employs one or more beater plates, around the periphery of which are attached rigid hammers of hard metal. It is driven within a casing at clearances of small fractions of an inch, the periphery of which is generally V-cut (Fig. 8-44). The grinding ring has provision for cooling with

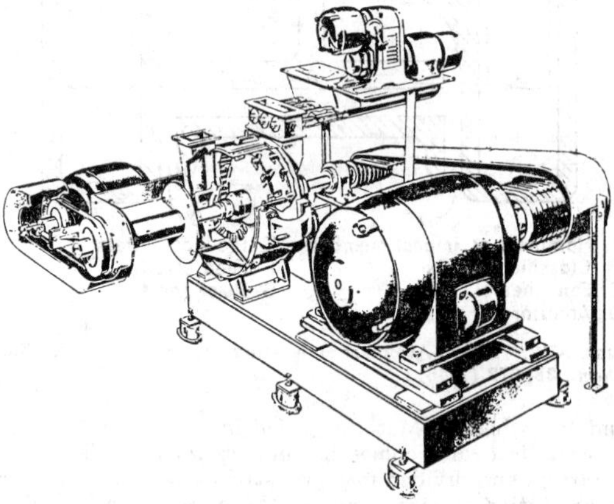

FIG. 8-44. The Pulvocron. (*Strong Scott Mfg. Co.*)

liquid in direct contact with its periphery. Feed enters around the driving shaft and is first broken by breaker plates on the first disk. It then travels circumferentially with an axial component to a classifying chamber, in which is a separately driven and controlled rotor with vanes. The volume of air carries the fine particles inward to an axial discharge opening, while the coarse particles are kept outward by centrifugal force. They discharge into a tailings return line, along with some of the air, and return to a low-pressure area near the axis of the inlet. Performance data of this mill are given in Table 8-28.

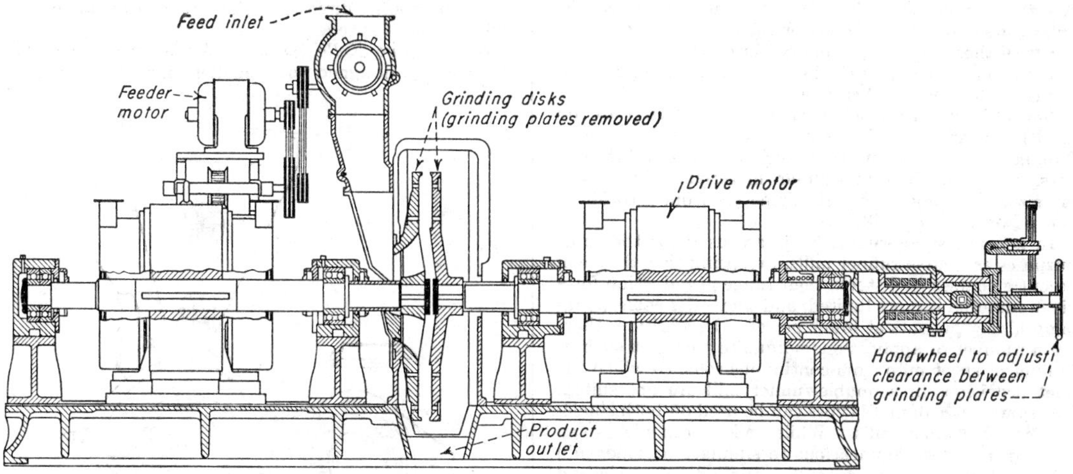

FIG. 8-45. Double-runner attrition mill. (*Sprout, Waldron & Co.*)

The Entoleter **impact mills** (Entoleter, Inc.) are a class of vertical-shaft devices in which feed at the shaft is caused to move rotationally and is thrown outward from the rotor to impact on an outer ring. Pin-type structures have been found effective; and, in these, the pins on the rotor do primary breakage, while the outer ring of pins gives further reduction. A wide range of speeds is employed, the higher ones for fine pulverizing. These mills grind a great variety of free-flowing or semi-free-flowing substances to controlled preset sizes. Among these are plastics, rubber, asbestos to fiber, grain and flour, coal, clay, slag, and salts. In some cases, external classification is required to remove oversize for return to the mill. Plastic materials are embrittled by liquid nitrogen or other suitable refrigerants to reduce their elasticity. For the highest speeds, the stator pins are mounted on a ring which is moving in reverse rotation to the central rotor. The mills are characterized by low horsepower, low heating, and high capacity.

Table 8-28. Performance of the 20-in. Pulvocron

Material	Particle analysis, by weight	Capacity, lb./hr.	Hp.
Sucrose	97.5% minus 325 mesh	1800	60
	100 % minus 5 microns		
Sodium chloride	99.4% minus 100 mesh	160	50
	99.95% minus 325 mesh	3600	45
Urea-formaldehyde and melamine molding compounds	99.2% minus 80 mesh	1600	45
Paraformaldehyde	99.7% minus 325 mesh	1300	40
Casein	99 % minus 80 mesh	650	50
Corn flour	88 % minus 200 mesh	800	35
Soy flakes	95 % minus 200 mesh	2000	60
Sterols	100 % minus 5 microns	700	60
Lactose	98.5% minus 200 mesh	1200	40
Alumina, hydrated	99 % minus 325 mesh	700	30
Cinnamon	99.7% minus 60 mesh	1000	50

Disk Attrition Mills. (Fig. 8-45.) The disk or attrition mill is a modern counterpart of the early buhrstone mill. Stones are replaced by steel disks mounting interchangeable metal or abrasive grinding plates rotating at higher speeds, thus permitting a much broader range of application. Grinding takes place between the plates, which may operate in a vertical or horizontal plane. One or both disks may be rotated; if both, then in opposite directions. The assembly, comprising a shaft, disk, and grinding plate, is called a runner. Feed material enters at *F* (Fig. 8-46), passes between the grinding plates *C* as indicated by arrow *D*, and is discharged at *E*. The grinding plates are bolted to disks *A* and *B*; the distance between them is adjustable.

The *Sprout-Waldron attrition mill* is available in single- and double-runner models with production sizes based on 16- to 36-in.-diameter disks and with power ranging up to 400 hp. By the use of a variety of plates and shell constructions these units are represented in such installations as coarse granulating, pulverizing, and shredding.

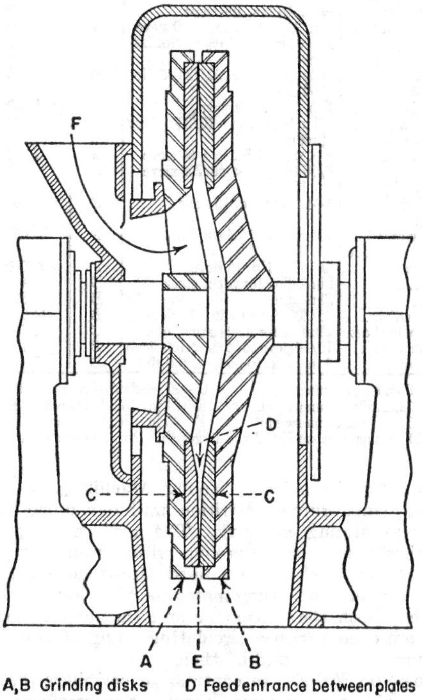

FIG. 8-46. Disk-mill principle. (*Bauer Bros. Co.*)

A single-runner model, having plates with concentric circular rows of projecting spikes on the rotating plate meshing with those on the stationary plate, acts much like a hammer mill, the spikes being the fixed hammers, and can serve for such applications.

Bauer Double Disk Mills (*The Bauer Bros. Co.*) are used for grinding of fibrous and non-fibrous substances, fluffing of fibrous materials, intensive mixing of fine powders, and hydration of cellular materials (Fig. 8-46). Six sizes are made with disk diameters from 8 to 36 in. and power from 5 to 400 hp.

In general, single-runner mills are used for the same purposes as double-runner mills, excepting that they will accept a coarser feed stock, their range of reduction for a given material is more limited, and they offer correspondingly higher outputs at lower power. In addition, there are a number of applications unique to this unit such as fluffing of sheet pulp from continuous rolls, to which the inlet provisions of a double-runner mill are not suited. The same range of plate types can be used on both single- and double-runner mills. While spike-tooth plates can be used in certain applications to simulate hammer-mill action, they are more generally applied to specialized tasks involving tearing, shredding, or controlled shattering, as in dehulling. The performance data presented in Table 8-29 typify the applications of the attrition mill.

Table 8-29. Performance of Attrition Mills

Material	Size-reduction details	Unit*	Capacity lb./hr.	Hp.
Alkali cellulose	Shredding for xanthation	B	4,860	5
Asbestos	Fluffing and shredding	C	1,500	50
Bagasse	Shredding	B	1,826	5
Bronze chips	⅛ in. to No. 100 sieve size	A	50	10
Carnauba wax	No. 4 sieve to 65% < No. 60 sieve	D	1,800	20
Cast-iron borings	¼ in. to No. 100 sieve	A	100	10
Cast-iron turnings	¼ in. to No. 100 sieve	E	500	50
Cocoanut shells	2 × 2 × ¼ in. to 5/100 sieve	B	1,560	17
	5/100 sieve to 43% < No. 200 sieve	D	337	20
Cork	2/20† sieve to 20/120 < No. 200 sieve	D	145	15
Corn cobs	1 in. to No. 10 sieve	F	1,500	150
Cotton seed oil and solvent	Oil release from 10/200 sieve product	B	2,400	30
Mica	4 × 4 × ¼ in. to 3/60 sieve	B	2,800	6
	8/60 to 75% < 60/200 sieve	D	510	7.5
Oil-seed cakes (hydraulic)	1-½ in. to No. 16 sieve	F	15,000	100
Oil-seed residue (screw press)	1 in. to No. 16 sieve size	F	25,000	100
Oil-seed residue (solvent)	¼ in. to No. 16 sieve	F	35,000	100
Rags	Shredding for paper stock	B	1,440	11
Ramie	Shredding	B	820	10
Sodium sulfate	35/200 sieve to 80/325 sieve	B	11,880	10
Sulfite pulp sheet	Fluffing for acetylation, etc.	C	1,500	50
Wood flour	10/50 sieve to 35% < 100 sieve	D	130	15
Wood rosin	4 in. max. to 45% < 100 sieve	B	7,200	15

* A—8 in. single-runner mill; B—24 in. single-runner mill; C—36 in. single-runner mill; D—20 in. double-runner mill; E—24 in. double-runner mill; F—36 in. double-runner mill

† 2/20, or smaller than No. 2 and larger than No. 20 sieve size.

The *Frigidisc grinder* (Young Machinery Co.) is a rugged, single-runner attrition mill developed for the rubber-reclaiming industry. The mill is suitable for materials that must be ground with a minimum rise in temperature, such as reclaimed tire-tread scrap, synthetic rubber, and other materials of a tough, resilient nature. Both the stationary and the moving grinding disks are cooled with a circulating liquid so that a high pressure can be exerted on them.

Pin-type Mills. In contrast to peripheral hammers of the rigid or swing types, there is a class of high-speed mills having pin breakers in the grinding circuit. These may be on a rotor with stator pins between circular rows of pins on the rotor disk, or they may be on rotors operating in opposite directions, thereby securing an increased differential of speed.

The *Alpine Kolloplex mill* (Alpine American Corp.) (Fig. 8-47), designed with smaller pins and operating at

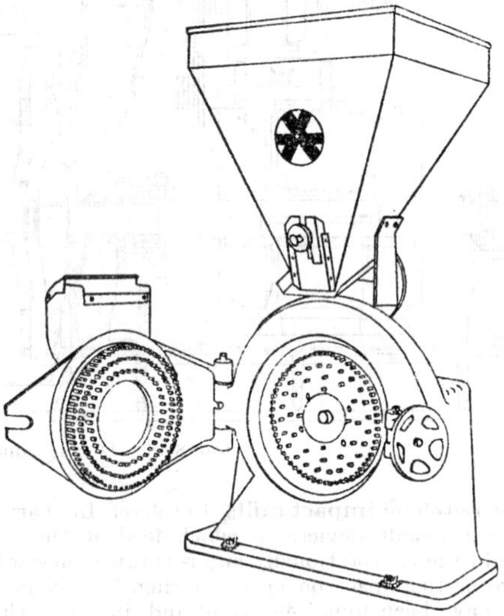

FIG. 8-47. Alpine-Kolloplex mill. (*Alpine American Corp.*)

high speeds, is used for finer sizes. This mill, as is customary with high-speed machines, is not used on hard feeds but is employed on medium-hard to soft ones. This mill and its double-rotor counterpart are of interest in flour milling.

Buhrstone mills are attrition mills with hard circular stones serving as grinding media, generally French, American, or Esopus buhrstones; rock emery or combination of French buhr and esopus or of pebble grit and emery rock are also used. Buhrstone mills are used extensively in the milling industry for grinding cereals and grains. Other uses include grinding of minerals, colors, spices, and mineral pigments; reduction of cork and sawdust; wet grinding of enamels, mica, starch, drop blocks, and polishing rouge. Feed enters the mill through a center hole in one of the stones. It is distributed between the stone faces and ground while working its way to the periphery. The buhrstone or stone mill for "paint grinding" is being replaced by the roller mill (Fig. 8-48).

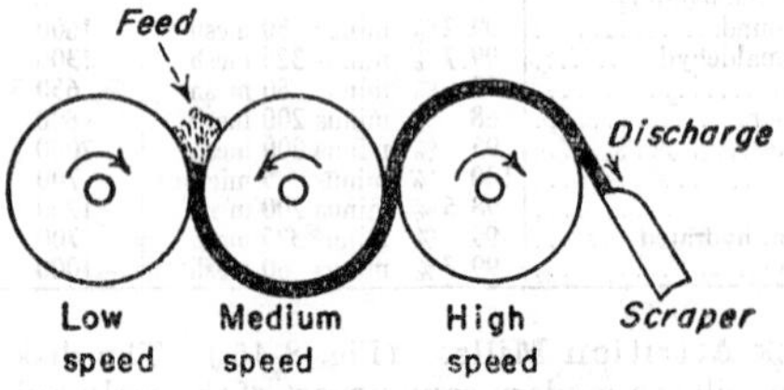

FIG. 8-48. Roller mill for paint grinding.

The *Sturtevant Rock-Emery Mill* (*Sturtevant Mill Co.*) is made in two types, a horizontal and a vertical; the former is made in one size and has 42-in. stones; it requires 15 to 20 hp. Four standard sizes are made of the vertical mill, with 24-, 30-, 36-, and 42-in. stones, requiring 12 to 15, 18 to 20, 30 to 35, and 45 to 80 hp., respectively. This mill is used for grinding coal and coke for foundry facing, shale, talc, siennas, ochers, and umbers. For very fine grinding it is operated in closed circuit with air classifiers.

Dispersion and Colloid Mills. Where there is to be very little breakdown of individual particles and where the problem is to disrupt lightly bonded clusters or agglomerates, a new aspect of fine grinding enters. This may be illustrated by the breakdown of pigments to incorporate them in liquid vehicles in the making of paints. Other comparatively weak structures are amenable to reduction in this way. Purees, food pastes, pulps, and the like are processed by this type of mill. Dispersion is also associated with the formation of emulsions which are basically two-fluid systems. Sirups, sauces, milk, ointments, creams, lotions, and asphalt and water-paint emulsions are in this category. There is a special class of mills employed for dispersion and colloidal operations. They operate on the principle of high-speed **fluid shear** with some impact. Although they are classed as grinders, they do not do much actual grinding. Their value lies in eliminating coarse particles, *i.e.*, a few microns and up, while ensuring a breakdown of agglomerates or, in the case of emulsions, the shearing of fluid phases to produce dispersed droplets of fine size, around 1 micron.

Energy requirements differ so much with materials involved that other devices are often used to obtain the same end. These include high-speed stirrers, turbine mixers, pebble mills, vibratory mills, as well as buhrstone, disk, hammer, and roll mills. In some cases, sonic devices are effective.

An interesting variant of the ball mill is the Du Pont **sand mill**, which is manufactured by the Chicago Boiler Works under license from E. I. du Pont de Nemours & Co. In this mill a rough mixture of vehicle and pigment is prepared and fed to a grinding chamber in which are a stirrer and a fine-grinding medium. Round grains of Ottawa sand serve as very small ball media and thereby have many more points of contact for carrying out dispersion. Since the problem of dispersion has to do with an exceedingly large number of particles which individually do not need the weight of heavy pebbles, the fine-grinding medium meets the requirements. The dispersed paint mix is screened away from the sand ready for packaging. Operating data are given in Table 8-30.

Table 8-30. Data on Du Pont Sand Mill*

Mill size, gal.	Avg. output, gal./hr. paste	Mill hp.	Premixers (2), gal. each	Total hp.
3	20–40	5.5	55	7.5
8	50–70	16.5	300	22.5
16	120–150	21.5	500	31.5
30	200–300	31.5	1000	51.5

* Chicago Boiler Co.

Colloid mills which are employed for dispersion or for emulsification fall into four main groups: the hammer or turbine, the smooth-surface disk, the rough-surface type, and valve or orifice devices. The principle of their action is to create a fluid stream of high velocity with very great shear forces existing within the fluid, which serve to disrupt the particles. Chemical aid in the form of dispersing agents very often is valuable. Some devices of this sort also include impacting wherein the high-velocity liquids strike a surface with further shattering effect. The concentration of energy in mills of this class is high, and there is a considerable amount of heating. This is materially reduced by use of a cooling-water jacket. In other cases, as where emulsions are made hot, the jacket is employed for heating.

The *Morehouse mill* (Morehouse-Cowles, Inc.) is a high-speed disk type of mill (Fig. 8-49). The undispersed phase is fed at the top and passes between converging

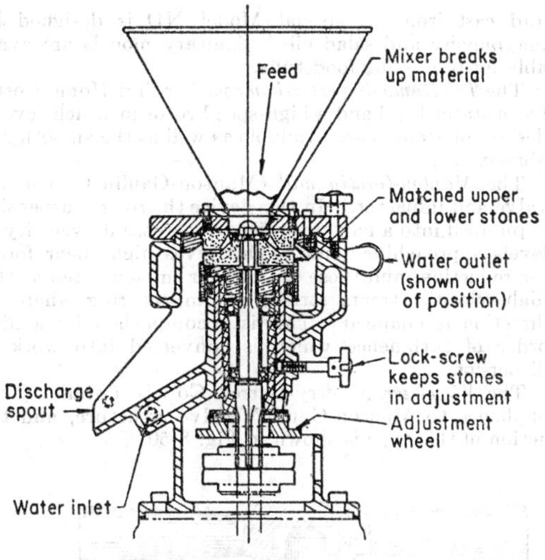

FIG. 8-49. Model M colloid mill. (*Morehouse-Cowles, Inc.*)

disks, being thrown outward at the periphery. As the larger particles are broken and dispersion becomes finer, the stream is subjected to still higher energy between the narrowest zone of disk spacing to complete the disintegration and to ensure essential freedom from coarser particles.

In the *Premier mill* (Premier Mill Corp.), the rotor is shaped like the frustum of a cone. Surfaces are smooth, and adjustment of the clearance can be made from 0.001 in. upward. The mill is jacketed for temperature control. Direct-connected liquid-type mills are available with 15- and 21-in. rotors. These mills operate at 3600 r.p.m. at capacities up to 3000 gal./hr. They are powered up to 100 hp. The direct-connected paste-type mills have 6- and 12-in. rotors operating at speeds of 1800 to 3600 r.p.m. The power requirement and capacity vary considerably, depending on the material processed. The range of power is 1½ to 50 hp. and of capacity is 5 to 1000 gal./hr. The geared-head high-speed paste-type mills have 6- and 10-in. rotors and operate at speeds up to 9000 r.p.m. with power of 3 to 30 hp. For pilot-plant operation, the *Premier Three-Purpose Laboratory Mill* is available with 3- and 4-in. rotors. These mills are belt-driven and operate at 7200 to 17,000 r.p.m. with capacities of 5 to 150 gal./hr. *Laboratory Mill No.* 200 has a 2-in. rotor and operates at 13,500 r.p.m. at a power of 1½ hp. and capacity of 2 to 25 gal./hr.

The *Charlotte mill* (Chemicolloid Corp.) also employs high speed of rotation with the fluid flowing between a grooved conical rotor and a corresponding grooved conical stator. Clearance between them is regulated by an external calibrated adjustment device.

The whirling currents set up within the grooves subject the product to both hydraulic shear and impact. All models operate at 3600 r.p.m. The following sizes are available:

Hp.	Capacity, Gal./Hr.
3	20– 50
7	50– 100
20	100–400
50	400–1000
75	1000–5000

Laboratory Model W-10 operates at 1 hp. with a capacity of 1 to 50 gal./hr. The mills are available in several materials, including stainless steel, nickel, monel, bronze, and cast iron. A special Model ND is designed for mayonnaise and salad oils. Sanitary models are available for processing foodstuffs.

The *Tri-Homo disperser-homogenizer* (Tri-Homo Corp.) has a stator head and a high-speed rotor in which several designs of grooves are available as well as the smooth and abrasive types.

The *Manton-Gaulin mill* (Manton-Gaulin Co.) uses a valve and impactor. In this device the rough suspension is pumped into a narrow orifice to increase its velocity to levels approaching sonic. This gives high shear forces for reduction, and these are further implemented as this high-velocity stream strikes an impact ring where its direction is changed. This is accomplished by a high order of turbulence which is converted into work of dispersion.

The *Viscolizer* (Cherry-Burrell Co.) is a similar type of device to Manton-Gaulin's valve structure, and the action of this type is shown in Fig. 8-50.

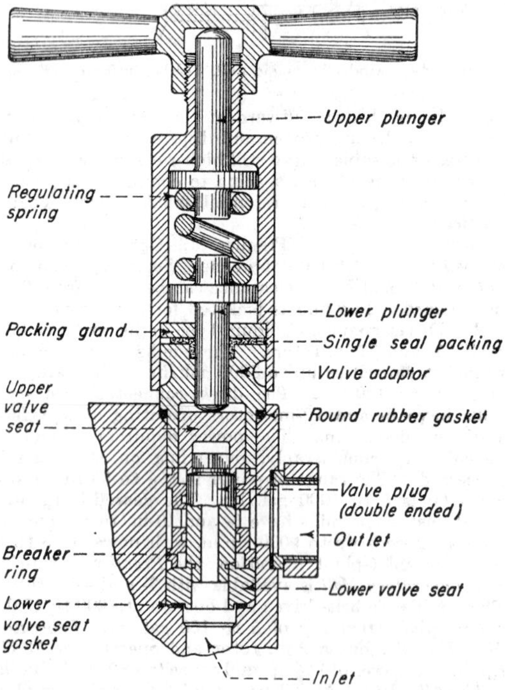

Fig. 8-50. Viscolizer assembled Split-Flo homogenizer valve.

Fluid-energy or Jet Mills. A detailed description of mills of this type, which includes the Micronizer, Reductionizer, and Eagle Mill, has been published [Berry, *Ind. Eng. Chem.*, **38**, 672 (1946)]. With recent developments fluid-energy mills may be classified in terms of the nature of the mill action. In one class of mills, the fluid energy is admitted in fine high-velocity streams at an angle around a portion or all of the periphery of a grinding and classifying chamber. In this class are the Micronizer, Jet Pulverizer, Reductionizer, Jet-O-Mizer, and others of somewhat similar structure. In the other class the fluid streams convey the particles at high velocity into a chamber where two streams impact upon each other. The Majac and other mills are in this class. Whether the particles are conveyed with the jet or are intercepted with angle jets as they travel around the periphery of the grinding-classifying chamber, there is a high energy release and a high order of turbulence which causes the particles to grind upon themselves and to be ruptured. Not all the particles are fully ground; so it is necessary to carry out a classifying operation and to return the oversize for further grinding. Most of these mills utilize the energy of the flowing fluid stream to effect a centrifugal classification. The Majac mill differs, using a mechanical device.

The *Micronizer* (Sturtevant Mill Corp.) consists of a shallow circular grinding chamber wherein the material to be pulverized is acted upon by a number of gaseous fluid jets issuing through orifices spaced around the periphery of the chamber, as shown in Fig. 8-51. The gas

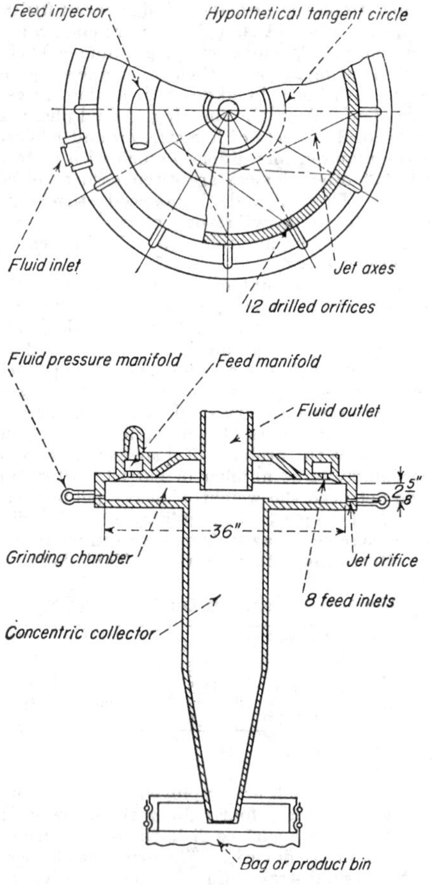

Fig. 8-51. Micronizer fluid-energy (jet) mill.

often is superheated steam supplied at pressures from 100 to 500 lb./sq. in. and at temperatures up to 800°F. superheat. Compressed air at 100 lb./sq. in. pressure, or higher, may be utilized instead of steam. The pulverizing chamber varies from 2 to 48 in. in diameter and from 1 to 2½ in. in axial height (Table 8-31).

Jet orifices are drilled through the peripheral wall of the grinding chamber and vary in number from 3 to 16, equally spaced around the chamber; the orifices vary in diameter up to ¼ in. They are generally placed in a tangential position so that entering steam or air will promote the rotation of the material to be pulverized in one direction. When a fluid of high energy content is introduced into a small pulverizing chamber, the fluid pressure is converted into velocity head by expansion to substantially atmospheric pressure. This causes a high-speed rotation of the contents of the grinding chamber. Centrifugal force of rotation causes the material to concentrate at the periphery where the jets are introduced. Since most of the energy of the fluid jets is dissipated near the point of entry, intense local velocity gradients and intense interactions are set up within the circulating material. A great deal of reduction of the material is thus caused by the impinging of the particles upon each other, which tends to reduce the wear on the pulverizer housing.

The gaseous fluid supplying the grinding energy is withdrawn at an inward point, tending to cause the dust-laden gas to travel spirally. The smaller particles are carried out with the gas, and the coarser particles thrown to the periphery are subjected to further reduction. Thus the grinding chamber also serves as an internal classifier.

The outlet from the grinding chamber leads directly into a concentric centrifugal collector. This collector receives the material as it is traveling in a high-velocity rotary motion which is conducive to the separation of the material from the fluid so that about 85 to 95 per cent of the product is collected in the concentric collector.

The feed size should be smaller than ¼ in. Production rate, fluid consumption, and fineness figures are shown in Table 8-31.

Table 8-31. Micronizer Performance*

Material	Product avg. size, μ	Feed		Fluid consumption, lb. fluid/lb. solid	
		Size, sieve No.	Rate, lb./hr.	Air	Steam
Ceylon graphite	2	3	200	...	8.5
Cryolite	3	60	900	...	4.0
Limestone	3.5	80	1000	...	4.0
Hard talc	3.5	20	1000	...	4.0
Silica gel	5.5	8	500	...	3.5
Soft talc	6.5	20	1800	...	2.5
Barytes	3.5	40	1800	...	2.2
Bituminous coal	2	10	1300	...	1.2
Copal resin	5	2	600	7.5	
Wolframite ore	5.5	10	800	5.6	
Sulfur	3.5	3	1300	3.5	

* Ind. Eng. Chem., **38**, 672 (1946).

The *Jet Pulverizer* (Jet Pulverizer Co.) is another mill of the shallow pan, angle jet, and radial inward classification type, like the Micronizer.

The *Jet-O-Mizer* (Fluid Energy Processing & Equipment Co.) is one of a group employing a hollow elongated torus which is placed vertically (Fig. 8-52). Feed is injected to the outer periphery of the base, where it is subjected to the high-velocity energy of jet streams introduced at the periphery. The fluid stream creates a rapidly circulating flow in the hollow doughnut-shaped mill casing. The upper turn of the casing is the classifying zone where the larger particles concentrate at the periphery while that amount of fluid which is being displaced by new fluid from jets passes to the outlet by a reversal of flow from the inner part of the ring. It carries with it the acceptable fines. Some fluid and the coarser particles pass down the stack for further grinding. The Jet-O-Mizer is also used for blending and mixing, coating, deodorizing, solvent removal, and for chemical changes including oxidation and reduction.

The *Majac Mill* (Majac Inc.) is an opposed-jet type with a mechanical classifier (Fig. 8-53). A screw feeder discharges the material to be pulverized directly into the impact zone of opposed jets. Fluid from the jets, partially pulverized feed, and pulverized oversize from the pulverizing zone pass into a duct leading to a mechanical classifier above. This classifier is of a whizzer type, but it has a positive external return zone. The oversize thrown out by the classifier drops into a small chamber on either side of the grinding chamber where it is picked up by the fluid jets and brought to substantial velocities for impacting in the grinding chamber. Fineness is controlled by varying the distance between jet nozzles, pressures, speed of the power-driven classifier, and amount of strip air. These pulverizers are available in capacities from 1000 to 30,000 lb./hr. (based on pounds of coal having more than 90 per cent passing a No. 200 sieve), using compressed air at 100 lb./sq. in. and at temperatures ranging up to 800°F. Standard air inputs range from 90 to 4,500 cu. ft./min. These capacity figures give an indication of a comparison of the jet-mill type with standard pulverizers. However, when such mills are used for grinding to low micron sizes, there is a sharp drop in capacity based more or less upon the substantial increase in the surface of such fine materials.

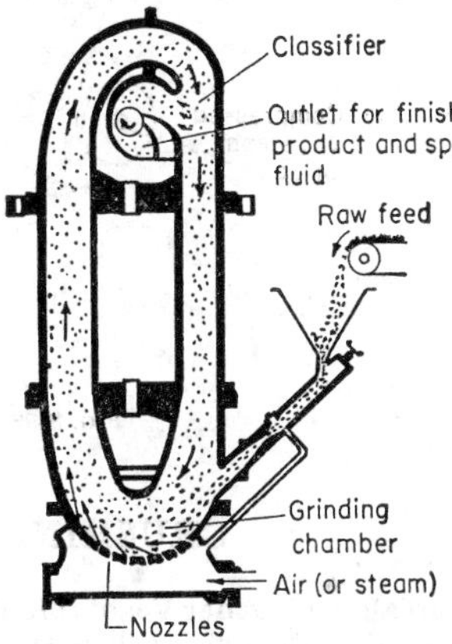

Fig. 8-52. The Jet-O-Mizer. *(Fluid Energy Processing & Equipment Co.)*

Flash Pulverization. A process called flash pulverization for drying and comminuting minerals was introduced in 1945 by the research staff of the Institute of Gas Technology [Yellott and Singh, *Power Plant Eng.*, **49**, 82 (December, 1945)]. It was found that a wide variety of friable materials, ranging from coal and coke breeze to oil shale, could be pulverized by introducing them into a stream of gas at moderate pressure and causing the streaming entrainment to pass through a nozzle or orifice into a zone of lower pressure. Originally conceived as a continuous explosion process, it was later demonstrated that the size reduction was actually accomplished by impact of the particles upon the nozzle walls, and by attrition among the particles as they passed at high velocity and in very turbulent flow through the nozzle. When superheated steam was used as the motive fluid, the product was dried to less than 1 per cent moisture content for an initial content of 7 per cent.

A number of nozzle pulverizers have been used abroad. Most important among these is the *Anger Mill*, which has been used widely in German power plants. A description of this and other types of nozzle pulverizer is given by Frisch ("Pulverized Fuel for the Gas Turbine," a paper presented on the panel Improved Application of Coal Burning Equipment, at the Annual Meeting, A.S.M.E., New York, Dec. 3, 1946).

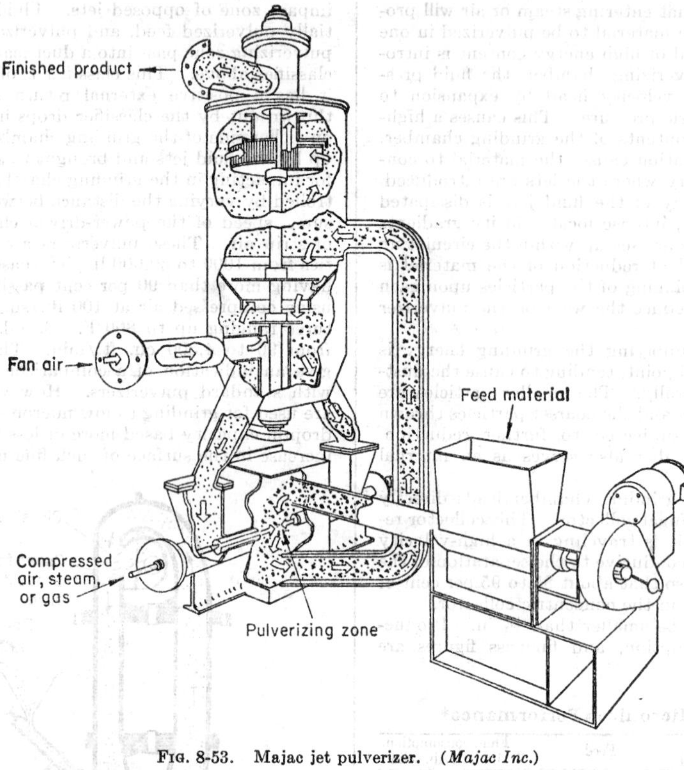

FIG. 8-53. Majac jet pulverizer. (*Majac Inc.*)

CRUSHING AND GRINDING PRACTICE

Milling of Cereals and Other Vegetable Products. *Flour and Feed Meal.* The roller mill is the one most widely used for grinding wheat and rye into high-grade flour. A typical mill used for this purpose is fitted with two pairs of rolls, capable of making two separate reductions. After each reduction the product is taken to a bolting machine to separate the fine flour, the coarse product being returned for further reduction. The rolls run toward each other at different speeds in order to produce a rubbing action. Grooved rolls are used for crushing the grain, cleaning up the bran, and for grinding corn. For grinding to a finished product, smooth rolls are employed. Feed is supplied at the top where a vibratory shaker spreads it out in a thin stream across the full width of the rolls. For best results the feed should be regular, continuous, and even from one end of the roll to the other.

Rolls are made with various types of corrugation, special corrugations being used where certain results are desired. Two standard types are most generally used: the dull and the sharp, the former mainly on wheat and rye, and the latter for corn and feed. Under ordinary conditions, a sharp roll is used against a sharp roll for very tough wheat; a sharp fast roll against a dull slow roll for moderately tough wheat; a dull fast roll against a sharp slow roll for slightly brittle wheat; and a dull roll against a dull roll for very brittle wheat. The speed ratio usually is 2½ to 1 for corrugated rolls and 1¼ to 1 for smooth rolls.

Milling of wheat is not only a question of grinding and sifting, but it also involves proper preparation of the wheat prior to grinding. As the grain arrives in the mill, it contains sticks, straw, string, sand, and other materials that must be removed. It is first passed through a receiving separator with three superimposed screens, where cleaning is aided by suction. When the grain is very dirty, a washer and dryer are used. A wheat steamer is often used advantageously. Uniform heating mellows the wheat berry and so conditions it that moisture can be added in whatever quantities desired in the milling. The grinding rolls become effective, and further granulation is secured; bolting is also made easier. A product can thus be maintained at a uniform standard, irrespective of season or the condition of the original wheat.

The cereal milling industry produces a great variety of products besides wheat flour: such as meal, corn flour, graham flour, barley, oats, rye, buckwheat, hominy grits, and whole-wheat flour. In addition to roller mills, buhrstone and attrition mills are used extensively, particularly when the whole grain is to be ground. Besides the double-roller mill used for flour, single-roller mills are used, principally for cracking corn and rolling oats. Two-pair high and three-pair high roller mills are used to a great extent in the feed industries, the former principally for coarse feed, such as screenings; the latter for all cereal grains for table use and also for various grains for feed. This mill can be used in combination, the top pair for cracking corn, the middle pair for finishing into coarse feed or corn meal, and the bottom pair exclusively for rolling oats. The various feedstuffs also are ground on hammer and pin mills. Performance of a single-runner attrition mill is given in Table 8-32.

Table 8-32. Operating Characteristics of a Single-runner Robinson Attrition Mill, Grinding Grain

	Size of mill							
	16 in.	18 in.	20 in.	24 in.	26 in.	30 in.	32 in.	36 in.
Speed, r.p.m.[1]	2500	2250	2200	1800	1600	1400	1300	1200
Speed, r.p.m.[2]	1000	950	900	800	750			
Capacity[3]	1200	1600	2000	3300	4000	5000	5300	6300
Capacity[4]	1200	1300	1500	1900	1900	2200		
Capacity[5]	65	80	100	150	200			
Hp[6]	9–12	10–15	12–18	20–30	22–32	25–35	28–38	30–50
Hp[7]	5– 8	6– 9	8–10	9–12	10–15	12–18		

[1] R.p.m. when grinding feed or corn meal.
[2] R.p.m. when cracking corn.
[3] Grinding feed, pounds per hour.
[4] Grinding corn meal, pounds per hour.
[5] Cracking corn, bushels per hour.
[6] Power when grinding feed or corn meal.
[7] Power for cracking corn.

Soybeans, Soybean Cake, and Other Pressed Cakes. Soybeans are ground in about the same manner as the various grains, depending on the nature of the product desired. Roller mills, driers, and bolting reels may be used. After granulation on rolls the granules are generally treated in presses to remove the oil. The product from the presses goes to attrition mills or flour rolls and then to bolters, depending upon whether the finished product is to be a feed meal or a flour. If the whole cake is to be pulverized without removal of fibrous particles, it may be ground in a hammer mill, with or without air classification. A 20-hp. hammer mill with air classifier, grinding pressed cake, had a capacity of 300 lb./hr., 90 per cent through No. 200 sieve; a 20-hp screen-hammer mill grinding to 1/16-in. screen produced 1000 lb./hr.

The method used for grinding pressed cakes depends upon the nature of the cake, its purity, residual oil, and moisture content. Many of these materials are treated in hammer mills, especially where no fine reduction is required. In many cases the hammer mill is used merely as a preliminary disintegrator, followed by an attrition mill. Typical performance of the attrition mill is given in Table 8-27. A finer product may be obtained in a hammer mill in closed circuit with an external screen or classifier. Table 8-33 gives the results obtained with hammer mills disintegrating linseed cake, cottonseed cake, and an expeller cake.

Table 8-33. Operating Results with Williams Hammer Mills, Disintegrating Various Seed Cakes

Material	Capacity, tons/hr.			Hp.
	Pea meal	Pea and finer	Extra fine	
Cottonseed cake	1	¾–1	½	8–12
Expeller cake	2½–3	2½–3	2	25–30
Linseed cake	6 –8	5 –6	4–5	50–60

Starch and Other Flours. Grinding of starch is not particularly difficult, but precautions must be taken against explosions; starches must not come in contact with hot surfaces, sparks, or flame when suspended in air. Where a product of medium fineness is required, a hammer mill of the screen type is employed. For finer products the air-classifying pulverizer of the hammer type, or a screen-hammer mill in closed circuit with an external air classifier, is used. Potato flour, tapioca, banana, and similar flours are handled in this manner. Table 8-34 gives the capacity of different types of pulverizers.

Metalliferous Ores. Grinding is one of the major problems in milling practice and one of the main items of expense. Mill manufacturers, operators, and engineers find it necessary to compare grinding practice in one plant with that of another, attempting to evaluate circuits and practices [The Staff, *Trans. Can. Inst. Mining Met.*, **43**, 299 (1940)]. Modern milling practice involves the closed-circuit principle, and this factor must be taken into account in such standardized test procedures as relate to the grindability of different ores (see p. 8-7).

Table 8-34. Pulverizer Capacity for Grinding Starch and Flour

	Cornstarch	Potato starch	Tapioca flour
	Screen mill	Screen mill	Hammer mill (with air classification)
Capacity, lb./hr.	3000	2000	2000
% through No. 200 sieve	75	92	98
Hp.	15	7.5	40
	Hammer mill (with air classifier)	Hammer mill (with air classifier)	Hammer mill (with air classifier)
Capacity, lb./hr.	4000	1000	1500
% through No. 200 sieve	95	98	90
Hp.	45	7.5	25
	Screen mill (external air classifier)		
Capacity, lb./hr.	3500		
% through No. 200 sieve	90		
Hp.	30		

Crushing rolls and rod and ball mills are used extensively. Most ores are heterogeneous; and, when they are ground in closed circuit in ball mills, the softer fraction tends to be reduced faster than the harder portion, causing the quantity of the latter in the circulating load to increase. The rod mill tends to grind a heterogeneous material differentially such that the soft portion is ground faster than the hard fraction. The rod mill on a homogeneous material gives a product like that from a crushing roll, lacking the fines ordinarily produced in ball mills. This characteristic reduces losses of mineral due to sliming and permits a higher recovery, particularly in the No. 10- to No. 48-sieve range.

A comparison of roll, rod-mill, and ball-mill products of a homogeneous ore is shown in Fig. 8-54. The curves show the narrower frequency distribution for the rod mill and roll crusher. The ore is ground to 11 per cent passing a No. 200 sieve in each case, but 10.2 per cent is retained on a No. 14 sieve in case of the ball mill in comparison

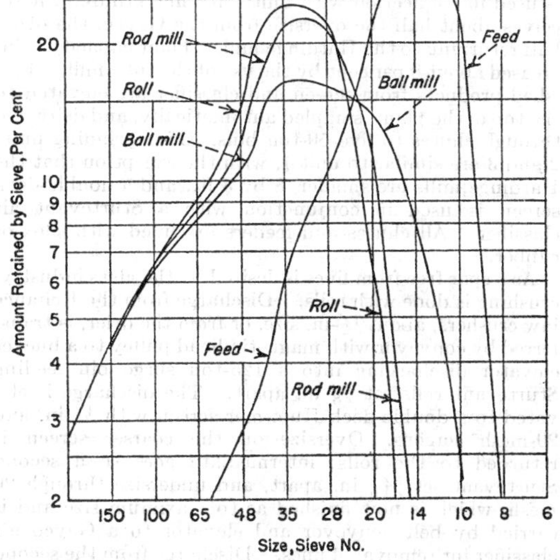

FIG. 8-54. Comparison of products from roll, rod, and ball mills. (*Allis-Chalmers Mfg. Co.*)

with 1.3 and 0.2 per cent for the rod mill and rolls. Reduction of the ball-mill product to pass a No. 14 sieve would cause the amount smaller than No. 200 to be increased.

Non-metallic Minerals. Dry grinding generally is used; wet grinding is resorted to where certain impurities have to be removed, such as iron oxide or fine grit, and where washing imparts certain desirable properties to the finished product. The system of wet grinding and classification chosen depends upon the nature of the material. Very hard materials are ground in ball mills with hydraulic classifiers, the finished product going to a filter and drier. After drying, the cake generally has to be broken up in some type of disintegrator or pulverizer.

It is often possible, particularly with a soft material like clay, to employ dry grinding with a series of air classifiers, at the same time eliminating impurities such as grit and sand. Nearly every type of pulverizer is used in the grinding of non-metallics in open or closed circuit. The objective may be to obtain many grades of the same material by tying air classifiers and screens into the grinding system to remove various-sized products. Choice of equipment generally depends on (1) hardness and (2) contaminations. Most of the refractory silicates are ground in ball mills and tube mills in continuous or batch operation. Silex or flint lining and balls of flint, porcelain, and similar materials are used where iron contamination must be avoided. Capacity of any system decreases rapidly with increasing fineness of the material; this applies particularly to non-metallics, where extreme fineness is usually required.

Silica and **feldspar** are ground in silex-lined mills with flint balls. Feldspar for ceramic and chemical industries is ground finer than for the glass industry. The following description of a feldspar mill is abstracted from *U.S. Bur. Mines Circ.* 6488. The fine-grinding department consists of three silex-lined Hardinge mill units with flint pebbles, 27 to 28 r.p.m., each fed from a 50-ton surge bin by James automatic belt feeders. Unit 1 has an 8- by 4-ft. Hardinge mill, discharging by an elevator to a Gayco air classifier or a James vibrating screen, according to the kind of product desired, a fine (No. 120 to 250 sieve) or a coarse (No. 20 sieve). An intermediate product (No. 40 to 100 sieve) is made by removing fines in the Gayco centrifugal classifier and screening the coarse. A tube mill is used in connection with unit 1 for fine grinding; it receives about half the oversize from the Gayco, the other half returning to the Hardinge mill. Plant capacity is increased about 8 per cent by the use of the tube mill. Finished products from screen and classifier are elevated to the top of the plant, sampled automatically, and delivered through chutes to five 50-ton bins. Fine-grinding units 2 and 3 are similar to unit 1, with the exception that the Hardinge mills are smaller, 8 by 3 ft., and a double-deck screen is used in conjunction with a Sturtevant air classifier. All chutes and feeders are lined with silex or rubber.

As a spar free from fines is desired by the glass industry, crushing is done with rolls. Discharge from the Reliance jaw crushers, about ½-in. size, or from the drier, is transferred by conveyor with magnetic-head pulley to a bucket elevator discharging into a 125-ton surge bin feeding Sturtevant rolls set ⅜ in. apart. The discharge is elevated to a double-deck Hum-mer screen with ¼-in. and 20-mesh screens. Oversize on the coarser screen is returned to the rolls; intermediate goes to a second Sturtevant set 3/16 in. apart, and undersize through 20 mesh, which is now finished as to maximum size and is carried by belt conveyor and elevator to a Gayco air classifier for removal of fines. Discharge from the second rolls is elevated to a second double-deck Hum-mer with 8- and 20-mesh screens; oversize from the coarser is returned to the rolls, intermediate to a third set of Sturtevant rolls set close, and the undersize through 20 mesh to the Gayco centrifugal classifier.

Discharge from the third set of rolls is elevated to a third double-deck Hum-mer with 10- and 20-mesh decks. Oversize on 10 mesh, principally mica, is removed as a by-product, the intermediate goes back to the rolls, and undersize through 20 mesh joins the similar products from the preceding screens on their way to the Gayco. A small amount of smaller than No. 140 sieve material in the undersize through 20 mesh is finally removed in the Gayco. The oversize from the Gayco is elevated to a Hum-mer and separated into two sizes, −20 +40 mesh, and −40 +140 mesh, which are held in 70-ton feed bins and run over two Johnson induction separators, one machine for each size.

Figure 8-55*A* and 8-55*B* gives the comparative sieve analysis of the two units as installed. The Hardinge mill,

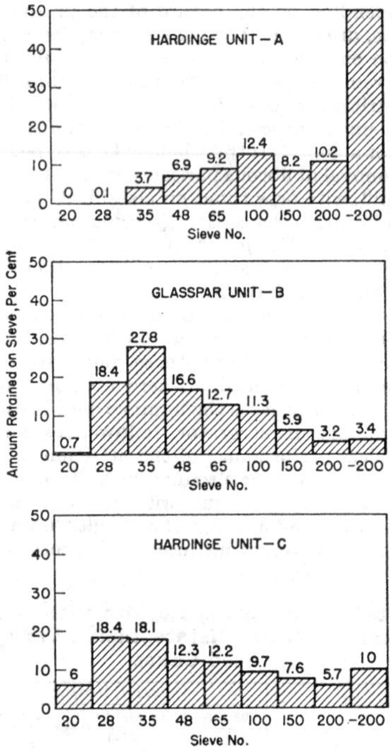

FIG. 8-55. Comparative sieve analyses of granular products from different types of installations.

just discussed, had not been designed for granulating. It was a very fine grinding mill arranged only for trunnion overflow. It was therefore not possible to pass the spar through the mill fast enough to prevent overgrinding. As a result the Hardinge product shows a much higher percentage of the undesirable material passing No. 200 sieve. Figure 8-55*C* gives the results of a Hardinge mill equipped with a vertical grate and discharge flights for granular grinding, which shows that the products from the two systems (*B* and *C*) are more nearly the same.

With slight modifications the systems may be used to produce a fine grade or granules from the following materials: quartz, slate, marble, corundum, Carborundum, tripoli, pumice, and volcanic ash. Practically all abrasive silicates are handled in ball and tube mills followed by air classifiers. Table 8-35 gives the results obtained with Hardinge pebble mills, grinding several siliceous refractory materials.

Table 8-35. Grinding Refractory Siliceous Materials in Pebble Mills

	Feldspar	Silica sand	Enamel frit	Grog
Size of mill	8′ × 60″	8′ × 48″	4½′ × 16″	5′ × 22″
Feed size	2″	20 mesh	⅛″	1½″
Size of product	99% through No. 200 sieve	98% through No. 325 sieve	97% through No. 100 sieve	95% through No. 10 sieve
Capacity, tons/hr.	1.75	1.25	0.225	5
Power for mill, hp.	68	58	8.5	28
Power for auxiliaries, hp	21	20		
Pebble load, lb.	10,000	12,000	2000	2800
Speed of mill, r.p.m.	22	18	30	30
Moisture, %	1	1	0	1
Type of classifier	Hardinge	Air	Trommel screen on mill	
Lining and grinding mediums	Flint blocks and flint pebbles			Steel

Talc and **soapstone** are generally easily pulverized, although certain fibrous and foliated talcs may offer great resistance to reduction to impalpable powder.

Ring-roll mills with internal air separation are widely used for the large-capacity fine grinding of the softer talcs. Pebble mills and mechanical air separators are usually used for the tough fibrous varieties. Fluid-energy mills also have application on these tough talcs. High-speed hammer mills with internal air separation are also an outstanding success on some of the softer high-purity talcs for very fine fineness. For a ring-roller mill receiving 1-in. feed, production rates range from 3000 to 6000 lb./hr. for 80 hp. grinding to 99 to 99.5 per cent able to pass a No. 200 sieve.

U.S. Bureau of Mines Bulletin 213 gives an excellent description of mining and processing talc and soapstone, which may be applied to many of the other non-metallics. Tube mills, 150 hp. each, lined with silex or porcelain, are set in two lines of four each in tandem. Each line has a capacity of 2 tons/hr. Closed-circuit grinding with air classifiers frequently is employed. Batch grinding is also used. Batch pebble mills are operated for a certain length of time up to 8 hr. for the finer grades, before dumping. In Talcville, N.Y., 6- to 8-ft. pebble mills are used, 30 to 35 hp., charged with 1 ton talc and 3 tons flint pebbles and rotated for 4 to 7 hr. at 22½ to 23 r.p.m.

Clays and Kaolins. A large percentage of clays and kaolins are washed and water-floated, after which they are filter-pressed, dried, and disintegrated in hammer mills, followed by air classifiers. This is of special advantage when the clay contains impurities such as fine mica flakes which are not removed by water flotation. Wet and dry pan crushers and swing hammer mills are used in most brick, tile, or pottery plants where comparatively coarse pulverizing is required.

Clays used in the chemical process industries as a constituent of paint and as a filler for paper and rubber are both wet-ground and dry-ground. When it is necessary to treat the clay chemically, it is generally wet-ground and treated as above. The tendency at present is to dry-grind most clays that do not require chemical treatment. The ring-roller mill with air classification is used nearly exclusively, particularly on southern clays. The raw material, after being crushed, passes through a rotary dryer, and the moisture content is reduced to about 8 or 10 per cent. Hot gases introduced to the mill complete the drying while the material is being pulverized to the necessary fineness. Even on washed clays there is a tendency to partial drying of the clay in an external dryer and to finishing the drying and pulverizing in an air-classification mill which may be of the ring-roller or hammer type. These mills are equipped with automatic throwout devices to eliminate impurities in the oversize form. A high percentage of an impurity such as silica sand can be eliminated. On an average grade of unwashed clay a No. 5057 Raymond ring-roller mill equipped with whizzer classification will grind from 3 to 3½ tons/hr. to a fineness of about 99.95 per cent through a No. 325 sieve, while on washed clay the capacity will be from 30 to 40 per cent higher. To grind 3½ tons/hr. of a raw clay, power consumption will be about 100 hp., and it takes about 1100 cu. ft. of natural gas (1000 B.t.u./cu. ft.) to dry the clay from 10 per cent moisture down to about 1 per cent.

Non-metallic Carbonates and Sulfates. Carbonates include limestone, calcite, marble, marls, chalk, dolomite, and magnesite; the most important sulfates are barite, celestite, anhydrite, and gypsum; these are used as fillers in paint, paper, and rubber. (Gypsum and anhydrite are discussed below as part of the cement, lime, and gypsum industries.)

Table 8-36 shows the performance of a Raymond 5057 ring-roller mill pulverizing limestone. A complete range of larger mill sizes is available.

Table 8-36. Performance of Raymond 5057 Ring-roller Mill Pulverizing Limestone

Fineness		Capacity, lb./hr.	Operating hp.
% through	Test sieve		
75	200	14,000	140
85	200	11,500	135
95	200	9,000	130
99	200	7,000	125
99	300	6,000	125
99	325	5,000	125
99.5	325	4,000	120

These results may be applied to practically the entire group. When a material is very soft, such as some high-grade barite, the capacities may be about 25 to 35 per cent higher. Of the carbonates, magnesite is generally the hardest to pulverize. This material is often calcined and pulverized in the same manner as lime. Dead-burned magnesite is treated as cement clinker.

A Raymond 5057 ring-roller mill pulverizing *fluorspar* produces 10,000 lb. of product per hour 95 per cent minus 200 mesh with 140 operating horsepower or 23.4 kw.-hr./ton. Fluorspar is also ground in continuous-tube mills with classification. Magnesite, generally the most difficult of the carbonates to pulverize, grinds similarly to fluorspar. When calcined it is ground in the same manner as quicklime. Table 8-37 gives the results obtained in a Hardinge mill, wet-grinding barytes and limestone to be used as a paint filler.

Table 8-37. Wet Grinding of Barytes and Limestone in Hardinge Mill

	Limestone	Barytes
Size of mill	8′ × 48″	7′ × 36″
Size of feed	1½″	1½″
Fineness of product, sieve No.	325	325
Capacity, tons/hr.	¾	2
Mill speed, r.p.m.	18	22
Power for mill, hp	40	25
Classifier system	Cone	Drag
Moisture in mill, %	30	28
Type of mill lining	Flint	Flint
Grinding mediums	Coarse limestone	Lump barytes

Asbestos and Mica. The choice of crusher for asbestos depends on whether a long or a short fiber is desired. Crushing is done in slow stages to preserve as much as possible of the fiber length. Primary crushers employed are usually of the jaw type with secondary crushers of the smaller jaw type. Small gyratories and corrugated rolls are also used. With some grades a third reduction may be required. After drying and crushing to about 2 in., the asbestos rock goes to the so-called fiberizing machines, which reduce the rock, liberate the fiber, and split it into fine and coarse fiber. There are different types of fiberizers, the swing hammer mill, the Jumbo, and the Laurie and Pharo cyclones. The *Jumbo* consists of a cylindrical shell surrounding a shaft with six pairs of arms placed at 6-in. intervals and disposed crosswise to each other. The arms are of heavy steel bars with chilled iron beaters, the faces of which are constructed on an angle. The *Laurie* cyclone consists of two beaters of the screw-propeller type, driven in opposite directions at 1700 to 2000 r.p.m., in a cast-iron chamber. The *Pharo* cyclone was designed to overcome the tearing effect on the fiber, one of the objections to the Laurie. It is of the same general type, but the hood above the discharging end is cut off immediately above the latter and the crushing blades, or beaters, of which the paddles are one right and the other left, rotate in the same direction.

As the material reaching the mill contains a large amount of freed asbestos, classification of the fiber begins immediately. It is first put through a screening trommel, the fines are discharged on a shaking screen, and the overflow—all above 1½ in.—falls into one of the fiberizing devices which discharges on the same screen. The latter is slightly inclined and is made from wire or perforated plates. It has an oscillating movement which, apart from the sizing of the rock and eliminating the sand, causes the fiberized asbestos to rise to the top. The liberated fiber is taken up by a fan, while the overflow falls into a second fiberizing machine, which discharges, like the first, on a screen, where the asbestos is again lifted by a fan, and so on until the rock is practically entirely pulverized. Tailings free from asbestos go to the dump.

Asbestos is often pulverized. This is the case when it is used for molded products. The pulverizing is usually accomplished by passing the material through a series of buhrstones or by using a high-speed screen mill with air-transport system. A mill with a 1/64-in. screen pulverized 400 lb./hr. with 13-hp. power consumption Certain impurities, such as sand, gravel, and hard fiber, may be removed by using an air-classification pulverizer with automatic throwout (see p. 8-35).

Asbestos floats for dry-wall joint cement are usually pulverized on a Raymond vertical mill. A 35-in. size with 150 hp. generally produces 2000 to 2500 lb./hr. of suitable product.

The micas, as a class, are difficult to grind to a fine powder; one exception is disintegrated schist, in which the mica occurs in minute flakes. The material pulverized is generally the waste from production of sheets and scrap from punching and trimming.

Mica is pulverized wet or dry; the wet-ground product is the more desirable, as it retains its luster to a high degree. When ground wet, it is first passed through revolving screens with a constant stream of water; it is then ground in wooden chaser mills at a slow rate and graded after drying, by passing through a series of bolting reels, the finest reel being about 200 mesh. A modification of this process is used in certain European countries, where the mica is ground in chaser mills and buhrstone mills. The water with the ground mica is passed over screens and thus graded. After pressing out the water, the solids are dried and disintegrated in a double-cage mill.

For dry grinding, hammer mills equipped with an air transport system are generally used. Maintenance is often high. The material, after dropping through a perforated screen into the intake of an exhauster, is collected in a cyclone followed by bolting reels.

The Fertilizer Industry. Many of the materials used in the fertilizer industry are pulverized, such as those serving as sources for calcium, phosphorus, potassium, and nitrogen. The most commonly used for their lime content are limestone, oyster shells, marls, lime, and, to a small extent, gypsum. Limestone is generally ground in hammer mills, ring-roller mills, and ball mills. Fineness required varies greatly from No. 10 sieve to 75 per cent through No. 100 sieve.

Oyster Shells and Lime Rock. Operating characteristics for hammer mills grinding oyster shells and burned lime for agricultural purposes are given in Table 8-38.

Table 8-38. Operating Data Grinding Oyster Shells and Burned Lime in Hammer Mills

Type of mill	Material	Size, in.	Capacity, tons/hr.	Hp.
Jeffrey	Oyster shells	15 × 8	0.5–0.75	8
		20 × 12	1 – 1.5	12
		24 × 18	2 – 3	20
		30 × 24	4 – 5	30
		36 × 24	8 – 10	40
Stedman	Burned lime	12 × 9	1.5	8
		20 × 12	4	20
		24 × 20	8	40
		30 × 30	12	60
		36 × 36	20	100

Phosphates. Phosphate rock is generally pulverized for one of two major purposes: for direct application to the soil, or for acidulation with sulfuric acid in the manufacture of acid- or superphosphate, phosphoric acid, and the various phosphates. Ring-roller and pebble mills are used for grinding phosphate rock. The most widely used fineness of grind is 90 per cent minus 100 mesh. In other plants it is common to grind 60 per cent minus 200 mesh for phosphoric acid manufacture and 75 per cent minus 200 mesh when acidulating with phosphoric acid to make concentrated superphosphate. Table 8-39 indicates the capacity of a modern 73-in. Raymond ring-roller mill with internal air separation when pulverizing phosphate rock. These results may be used for concentrates, pebble or for any mixture thereof. In general, phosphate rock from Tunis, Morocco, and the Pacific islands is easier to pulverize. Capacities will be 10 to 30 per cent greater than for Florida rock.

Table 8-39. Grinding Phosphate Materials

	Production rate, tons/hr.		Hp.	
	(a) 90–95% through No. 60 sieve; 50–55% through No. 200 sieve	(b) 90–95% through No. 200 sieve	a	b
Algiers	7.5	...	13	
Arkansas block rock	6.5	4	15	19
Belgium	8.5	...	12	
Bohemia (apatite)	6.5	...	17	
Canada (apatite)	6	3	18	26
Egypt	6.5	...	17	
Florida (pebble)	6.5	3.5	17	24
Florida (hard rock)	7	4	17	24
Florida (soft rock)	...	5.5	..	15
Idaho	7	4	14	19
Kentucky	7.5	5	12	17
Morocco	8	...	12	
Pacific and Indian oceans:				
Angaur Island	8.5	...	12	
Christmas Island	8	...	12	
Marshall Islands	8.5	...	12	
Makatea Island	7	...	13	
Nauru Island	7	...	13	
Ocean Island	7.5	...	13	
Russia (Podolian)	6.5	...	13	
Tennessee (blue rock)	7	4.5	14	18
Tennessee (brown rock)	7.5	5	12	17
Tennessee (gray rock)	8	5	12	17
Tennessee (phosphatic limestone)	7	4.5	14	18
South Carolina	6.5	3.5	17	24
Tunis	8	...	12	

The coarse material (a) is used for acidulation, and the fine material (b) for direct application to the soil.

Some average results obtained in grinding various organic and inorganic raw materials for fertilizers are given in Table 8-40.

Table 8-40. Results Obtained in Grinding Raw Materials for Fertilizers

Material	Hammer mill	Type or size	Bar opening, in.	Capacity, lb./hr.	Hp.
Acid phosphate...	Stedman	36 in.	...	12,000	40
Steamed bone.....	Jeffrey	A-30 × 24 in.	1/8	10,000	40
Dry kelp.........	Williams	Shredder 2	1/4	12,000	35
Guano (Peruvian).	Jeffrey	A-24 × 18 in.	1/8	7,000	40

Inorganic salts often do not require fine pulverizing, but they frequently become lumpy. In such cases, they are passed through a double-cage mill or some type of hammer mill with the screen or cage bars removed. In other cases, a coarse screen in the hammer mill gives better operation than no screen at all. This is done with ammonium sulfate from by-product ovens and sodium nitrate. When used as an ingredient of fertilizer the latter is generally mixed with other raw materials, and the mixture is later disintegrated. The various potassium salts used in fertilizers are generally shipped ready for use, but if they have become caked in transit they are broken in a disintegrator.

Basic slag is often used as a source of phosphorus. Its grinding resistance depends largely upon the way it has been cooled, slowly cooled slag generally being more easily pulverized. The most common method for grinding basic slag is in a ball mill, followed by a tube mill or a compartment mill. Both systems may be in closed circuit with an air classifier. A 7- by 5-ft. mill, requiring 125 hp., operating with a 14-ft. 30-hp. classifier, gave a capacity of 5 tons/hr. from the classifier, 95 per cent through a No. 200 sieve. Mill product was 68 per cent through a No. 200 sieve, and circulating load 100 per cent.

Cement, Lime, and Gypsum Industries. *Portland Cement.* This is manufactured by wet and dry processes. In the latter the material is dried in rotary dryers prior to grinding. It is then burned and the clinker pulverized. In the wet process the materials are mixed and ground; a certain amount of water is added, giving a mill discharge with up to 40 per cent water. The slurry is calcined in the usual manner and the clinker ground as in the dry process.

Crushing in the dry process is done in gyratories, jaw crushers, hammer mills, or ring-roller mills. Pulverizing the raw mix is done in mills of the ring-roller type with or without tube mills. Air classification is standard practice. Production for a 250-hp. Bradley-Hercules, operating on a 2-in. feed, was about 40 tons/hr., 51.8 per cent through No. 200 sieve, 60.2 per cent through No. 100 sieve, 69.9 through No. 50, 74.6 through No. 40, 81.4 through No. 30, and 90.1 per cent through No. 20 sieve. A 5- by 22-ft. Allis-Chalmers two-compartment Compeb mill, 200 hp., 26 r.p.m., operating on 1-in. feed, had an hourly capacity of 9 tons, 78 per cent through No. 200 sieve. An 8-ft. by 60-in., 345-hp. Hardinge conical mill, 18 r.p.m., operating on 3/8-in. feed with 2 per cent moisture, had an hourly capacity of 26 tons, 91 per cent through No. 200 sieve; type of air classifier, 12-ft. Superfine, with 145-hp. fan; lining and balls, steel. Performance of Griffin mills on cement and allied materials is given in Table 8-41.

Table 8-41. Performance of Griffin Mills on Cement and Allied Materials

Material	Output/hr.	Fineness of product	Screen on mill, mesh
Giant:			
Limestone...........	4.5-5 tons	83.2% through No. 200 sieve	30 and 35
Cement clinker preliminary to tube mill	26 bbl.	62%-64% through No. 200 sieve	6
White cement clinker.	35 bbl.	72% through No. 100 sieve; 54% through No. 200 sieve	6 and 8
Limestone...........	3-3.5 tons	96.5% through No. 100 sieve; 82.5 through No. 200 sieve	35
Cement clinker.......	12-14 bbl.	96.6% through No. 100 sieve; 82.8 through No. 200 sieve	35
Junior Giant:			
Coal................	1.5-2 tons	88%-90% through No. 100 sieve	30 and 35
Clinker.............	5.5-6 bbl.	80%-82% through No. 200 sieve	35
Coke................	0.5-0.75 tons	90% through No. 100 sieve	35
Limestone...........	2 tons	82%-85% through No. 100 sieve	16

A flow sheet for a 9½- by 8- by 40-ft. Compeb mill and two classifiers is shown in Fig. 8-56. Fifty tons of raw

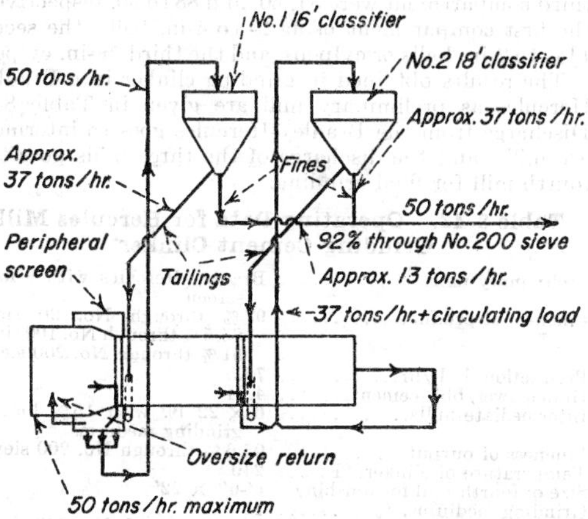

FIG. 8-56. Three-compartment Compeb mill (with peripheral screen on first compartment) in closed circuit with two air classifiers grinding and classifying raw mix in a cement plant.

material enter the mill. At the first compartment a peripheral screen removes the large oversize material and returns it to the front end of the mill. The final product from this compartment (38 per cent through No. 200 sieve) passes to an air classifier which divides the initial 50 tons into fines and tailings. Fines are considered to be about 13 tons testing 92 per cent through No. 200 sieve, tailings about 37 tons testing 18 per cent through No. 200 sieve. The tailings enter the second compartment of the mill; the product from this compartment enters the second classifier which removes the fines, the tailings entering the third compartment, the discharge from which is likewise fed to the second classifier.

Wet grinding of raw mix in an 8- by 4-ft., 150-hp. Hardinge mill, 17 r.p.m., with trommel screen, metal lining, and steel balls, grinding an 8-mesh feed, showed an hourly capacity of 32 tons, 100 per cent through No. 10 sieve; ball consumption 0.24 lb./ton. A 7- by 26-ft. Allis-Chalmers two-compartment Compeb mill, 500 hp., 20 r.p.m., with Dorr rake in closed circuit with the primary compartment and Dorr bowl in closed circuit with the secondary compartment, gave the operating characteristics shown in Table 8-42.

Clinker is ground by the same equipment in both processes; ball mills, tube mills, and compartment mills are used. Mills of the ring-roller type, such as the Bradley-Hercules, are sometimes used as preliminary to a tube mill. In recent years closed-circuit systems have been

Table 8-42. Operating Data for Mill with Hydraulic Classifier

	Open circuit	Closed circuit
Capacity, bbl./hr	70.1	167
Power consumption, kw.-hr./bbl	5.5	3.01
Loss of grinding medium, lb./bbl.		
In primary compartment	0.086	0.057
In secondary compartment	0.321	0.112
Fineness of product, % through No. 200 sieve	88	97
% through No. 100 sieve	95	
Charge in primary compartment	13 tons balls, 2¼–4 in.	
Charge in secondary compartment	39 tons balls, ¾–⅞ in.	

favored. A 7- by 24-ft. Allis-Chalmers mill with 185-kw. power consumption in open circuit gave a capacity of 46 bbl./hr. cement, 97.9 per cent through No. 200 sieve; clinker feed 115°F., discharge 174°F. An 8- by 7- by 40-ft. three-compartment mill, in open circuit, operating on 2½-in. clinker, produced 2000 bbl./24 hr. Percentages through No. 200 sieve at the end of first, second, and third compartment were 34, 60, and 88 to 90, respectively; the first compartment using 2- to 4-in. balls, the second 1¼- to 2-in. balls or cylpebs, and the third ⅝-in. cylpebs.

The results obtained in grinding clinker in a Bradley-Hercules as preliminary mill are given in Table 8-43. Discharge from the Bradley-Hercules goes to intermediate mills, and the discharge of the three mills goes to a fourth mill for final grinding.

Table 8-43. Operating Data for Hercules Mill, Grinding Cement Clinker

Preliminary mill	Bradley-Hercules with 9-mesh screen
Fineness of product	97% through No. 20 sieve, 65.5% through No. 100 sieve, 51% through No. 200 sieve
Production, bbl./hr	75.5
Horsepower/bbl. cement	4.64
Intermediate mills	6 × 22 ft. with 15% load of grinding mediums
Fineness of output	95.6% through No. 200 sieve
Temperature of clinker, °F	240
Size of fourth mill for finishing	6′-6″ × 22′
Grinding mediums, %	15
Fineness of finished product	97.6% through No. 200 sieve 96% through No. 300 sieve
Temperature of mill, °F	257
Horsepower/bbl. cement	3.97

Closed-circuit Grinding of Cement Clinker. Figure 8-57 shows a Compeb mill with two classifiers. Undersize

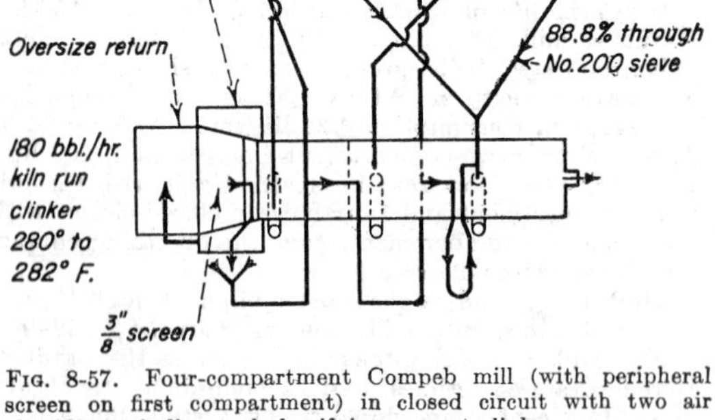

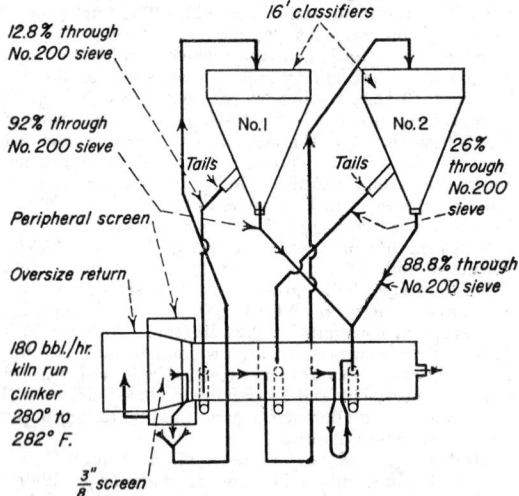

FIG. 8-57. Four-compartment Compeb mill (with peripheral screen on first compartment) in closed circuit with two air classifiers grinding and classifying cement clinker.

from the peripheral screen goes to the first classifier, which makes fines going to the fourth compartment and tailings going to the second compartment, the latter discharging to classifier No. 2. Here two products are made, fines for the fourth compartment, tailings for the third. Table 8-44 gives the results obtained when operating this system.

Table 8-44. Operating Data, Grinding Cement Clinker in Closed Circuit

Size of mill, ft		9.5 × 8 × 40
Size of mill motor, hp		1100
Capacity, kiln-run clinker fed to mill, bbl.*/hr		180
Temperature of kiln-run clinker, °F		280
Fineness of feed to the two classifiers:		
	Classifier 1, %	**Classifier 2, %**
No. 10 sieve	95.2	
No. 20 sieve	82.0	98.4
No. 28 sieve	73.2	97.6
No. 48 sieve	56.8	91.2
No. 100 sieve	42.4	68.4
No. 200 sieve	32.8	46.4
Fineness of finished product, through No. 200 sieve, %		90.2
Temperature of finished cement, °F		250

* The capacity at times was 250 bbl./hr., with a fineness of 88% through No. 200 sieve.

It has been found that time of setting and strength of many cements vary with the fineness to which the cement has been ground. A fineness between 94 and 98 per cent through a No. 325 sieve is often required to obtain a cement having the desired properties. An air classifier properly connected with the mills will often decrease the power required. Table 8-45 gives the results obtained when grinding cement to a fine state of subdivision in order to produce a superior product.

Table 8-45. Operating Data, Grinding Cement to a Very Fine Product

Type and size of mill, ft	Three-compartment, 7.5 × 43
Diam. classifier, ft	18
Hourly capacity, bbl	46
Feed to classifier, % through No. 200 sieve	98.7
Tailings from classifier, % through No. 200 sieve	83.2
Finished product, % through No. 200 sieve	99.8
through No. 325 sieve	97.9
-30μ	92.1
-25μ	83.8
-20μ	72.9
Total power required, hp	746
Horsepower/bbl. of product	12.1

When this cement was ground in open circuit to produce a comparable material, the power required was 19.7 hp./bbl. cement. A 10- by 6.5-ft. Hardinge mill with air classifier, grinding a ½-in. clinker to 82 per cent through No. 200 sieve, showed a power consumption of 4.95 hp./bbl. with an hourly capacity 102 bbl. (19.2 tons). Grinding to 88 per cent through No. 200 sieve, the consumption was 5.65 hp./bbl. and the capacity 88 bbl. (16.6 tons)/hr. Ball load in both cases was 60,000 lb. and mill speed 18 r.p.m.

The specific surface of cement is determined by a turbidimeter, generally of the Wagner type. A product having a high surface area indicates that it contains a higher percentage of impalpable powder than the same material when ground to a lower surface area. Use of the turbidimeter has become standard in the cement industry. Time of set and strength of cement vary with the surface area of the pulverized cement. High strength and early set are generally obtained by grinding and classifying the cement to a very fine state of division. Surface area of the ordinary cement may run 1700 to 2000 sq. cm./g., while surface area of the high early cement may run from 2700 to 3200 sq. cm./g.

Surface areas of products are being determined more and more in connection with the pulverizing of many other minerals. A product should, of course, not be ground to a surface much higher than is absolutely necessary, since the power for pulverizing and classifying increases rapidly as surface area increases. This is indicated in Table 8-46. For power at 1¢/kw.-hr., the total cost would be two or three times the power cost.

Table 8-46. Pulverizing Slate to Different Surface Areas

Surface area, sq. cm./g:	Production rate, tons/hr.	Power, kw.-hr./ton	Power ratio
1700	4.30	21.0	1.0
1850	3.40	25.0	1.2
2140	2.38	33.0	1.6
2275	2.00	38.0	1.8
2500	1.54	49.0	2.3
2800	1.10	68.0	3.2
2910	0.90	84.0	4.0
3100	.70	107.0	5.1
3300	.55	135.0	6.4
3500	.39	192.0	9.2
3660	.29	258.0	12.3
3910	.22	341.0	16.2
4060	.18	417.0	19.9

Lime for agricultural purposes generally is ground in hammer mills. Where a fine product is desired, as in the building trade and for chemical manufacture, ring-roller mills, ball mills, and certain types of hammer mills are used. Table 8-47 gives operating data for a Hardinge mill grinding quicklime. Fineness obtainable with a Jeffrey swing hammer pulverizer on burned lime is given in Table 8-21.

Table 8-47. Operating Data, Grinding Quicklime in Ball Mill

Size of mill, ft.	7 × 3
Type of classifier	Hardinge air classifier
Size of feed, % through No. 100 sieve	90
Capacity, tons/hr	12.5
Power required for mill, hp	100
Power required for auxiliaries, hp	35
Ball load, lb	20,000
Speed of mill, r.p.m	20

Ring-roller mills with air classification produce quicklime for the beet-sugar industry such that 99 to 99.9 per cent will pass through a No. 200 sieve. Power requirements vary between 20 and 30 hp.-hr./ton, depending on size of mill being used.

Lime coming from the hydrator is often pulverized without separating out the impurities by the use of ring-roller mills or ball mills. As a rule it is really not pulverized but is air classified to remove impurities such as sand, overburned, underburned, and core. The hydrate is passed through an automatic pulverizer with air classification and throwout. There is a tendency to handle this material with air classifiers in series, the tailings from the final classifier being discarded or sold for agricultural use. A modification of this system is to feed the tailings to an automatic pulverizer with throwout for final cleaning. Very clean tailings are thus obtained (see p. 8-35).

Gypsum is usually calcined in kettles. A very few rotary calciners are used. These of course use crushed and screened raw gypsum.

Gypsum is pulverized 85 to 95 per cent minus 100 mesh ahead of the calcining kettles. There is a growing trend toward requiring a Blaine surface area of 3000 or better. Ring-roller mills with internal classification are used exclusively for grinding raw gypsum ahead of the kettles. Table 8-48 indicates performance of a 6058 Raymond mill grinding raw gypsum rock from various sources; a complete range of other mill sizes is available. The majority of the new mills grinding gypsum are set up with heat so as to dry and grind in one operation.

Gypsum calcined in rotary kilns is pulverized after calcining. Tube mills are usually used. These impart plasticity and workability. Occasionally such calcined gypsum is passed through ring-roller mills ahead of the tube mills.

Table 8-48. Performance of Raymond 6058 Ring-roller Mill Grinding Raw Gypsum Rock from Various Sources, 90 Per Cent Minus 100 Mesh

Source	Tons/hr.	Kw. input	Kw.-hr./ton
Fort Dodge, Iowa	32	200	6.25
Jamaica	23	205	8.9
Shoals, Indiana	16	210	13.1
Nova Scotia (Dingwall)	10	230	23

Kettle-calcined plaster is sometimes passed through mechanical air separators. The coarse fraction is gaging plaster, and the fine is casting plaster.

In special cases, Raymond Imp pulverizers are used to grind and calcine in one operation. The result is a rapid-setting stucco. It is ideal for manufacture of wallboard and similar structural gypsum products A Raymond No. 50 Imp mill with 75 hp. will produce about 700 lb./hr. of stucco, 90 per cent minus 100 mesh, when starting with an average raw gypsum. Actual furnace heat input per ton of stucco is 1,200,000 B.t.u.

Coal, Coke, and Other Carbon Products. *Bituminous Coal.* The grinding characteristics of bituminous coal are affected by impurities contained, such as inherent ash, slate, gravel, sand, and sulfur balls. The grindability of coal is determined by grinding it in a standard laboratory mill and comparing the results with the results obtained under identical conditions on a coal selected as a standard. This standard coal is a low-volatile coal from Jerome Mines, Upper Kittaning bed, Somerset County, Pennsylvania, and is assumed to have a grindability of 100. Thus a coal with a grindability of 125 could be pulverized more easily than the standard, while a coal with a grindability of 70 would be more difficult to grind. (Grindability and grindability methods are discussed on p. 8-7.) The capacity obtained with a mill will be a function of grindability.

There are two general methods of burning pulverized coal: the unit system, in which the coal is blown directly into the furnace as it is pulverized; and the central grinding system, in which the coal is stored in a bin before it is used. Direct firing of boilers and rotary kilns is replacing the storage system. Mills of the ball, ring-roller, bowl, and ball-and-ring type are replacing hammer mills for direct firing of large installations because of the high maintenance cost of the latter.

A third method of burning pulverized coal is known as the direct-fired circulating system for which applications have been found in the iron and steel industry [Wilcoxson, *Iron Steel Engr.*, **21,** 74 (June, 1944)]. This method should be of interest to the chemical industry. The system is designed so that a pipe carries the pulverized coal and its primary air in a continuous loop arranged so that take-offs can be made to a number of furnaces or boilers. The advantages of a direct-fired system are obtained by heating a series of operations, no one of which could justify direct coal firing. A typical arrangement is shown in Fig. 8-58.

The Kennedy air-swept tube mill is of relatively short length. No screens are used either inside or out; the fine coal is mixed thoroughly with air and air-floated to the burners. The mill rotates slowly at a speed of 19 to 50 r.p.m., depending on the size. Hot air is used if drying is desired.

The Raymond bowl mill is used primarily for pulverizing coal and blowing it directly into industrial furnaces, boilers, or rotary kilns. Hot gases may be used for drying the coal while it is being pulverized. Table 8-49 gives pertinent data on operation of a bowl mill when grinding a typical grade of coal having a grindability of 55 to 60.

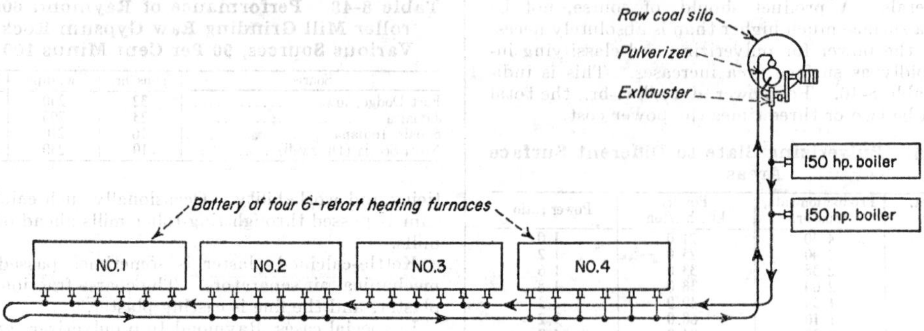

FIG. 8-58. Typical pulverized-coal direct-fired circulating system. (*Babcock & Wilcox Co.*)

Table 8-49. Performance of Bowl Mills Grinding Bituminous Coal

Mill size	Capacity, lb./hr.	Air, lb./min.	Power, kw.-hr./ton
271	2,520	130	18.4
312	2,980	150	18.0
352	3,740	170	17.5
372	5,200	200	17.0
412	6,720	250	15.9
452	8,125	310	15.9
492	11,150	400	15.4
493	14,100	450	14.9
532	17,100	550	14.2
533	20,000	600	13.3
593	23,700	700	12.7
613	27,500	820	12.7
673	34,900	960	12.7

The data are based on grinding coal to a fineness of approximately 80 per cent to pass a No. 200 sieve. Thermostatic control through a tempering device may be used to maintain a constant temperature in the mill irrespective of the moisture in the coal.

Ring-roller mills fill an important need as a bin-system pulverizer for coal. They are exceedingly economical in the larger sizes. They of course always incorporate internal air separation and usually simultaneous drying.

The B. & W. type E pulverizer is used for direct-firing industrial furnaces and has application in direct-fired circulating systems (Fig. 8-58).

Anthracite coal is harder to reduce than bituminous coal. It is pulverized for foundry facing mixtures, in ball mills or hammer mills followed by air classifiers. Only to a lesser extent is it used for fuel in powdered form.

A 10-ft. by 66-in. *Hardinge mill* with Superfine air classifier, grinding 4-mesh anthracite with 3.5 per cent moisture, produced 12 tons/hr., 82 per cent through No. 200 sieve. The power required for the mill was 370 hp., for auxiliaries, 70 hp.; speed of mill, 19 r.p.m.; ball load, 57,000 lb.; cost of ball consumption, 0.7 ¢/ton.

An 8- by 10-ft. tube mill, in closed circuit with a 14-ft. centrifugal air classifier, operating on a feed with 90 per cent through No. 40 sieve, pulverized 2 tons/hr., 99 per cent through No. 200 sieve, with 100 hp. for the mill and 30 hp. for the classifier.

Anthracite for use in the manufacture of electrodes is calcined, and the degree of calcination determines the grinding characteristics. Calcined anthracite is generally ground in ball and tube mills or ring-roller mills equipped with air classification. A *Raymond high-side ring-roller mill* grinding calcined anthracite for electrode manufacture has a capacity of 4600 lb./hr. for a product fineness of 76 per cent passing a No. 200 sieve and 70-hp. power requirement.

Coke. The grinding characteristics of coke vary widely. Petroleum coke is generally easier to grind than coke derived from bituminous coal. By-product coke is hard and abrasive, while certain foundry and retort coke is extremely hard to grind. For certain purposes it may be necessary to produce a uniform granule with minimum fines. This is best accomplished in rod or ball mills in closed circuit with screens. Hourly capacity of a 4- by 10-ft. rod mill with screens, operating on by-product-coke breeze, was 9 tons, 100 per cent through No. 10 sieve, and 73 per cent on No. 200 sieve; power requirement 40 hp.

Petroleum coke is generally pulverized for manufacture of electrodes: ring-roller mills with air classification and tube mills are generally used. A No. 5057 *Raymond ring-roller mill* gave an hourly output of 3.8 tons, 78.5 per cent through No. 200 sieve, with 90 hp.

Pitch may be pulverized as a fuel or for other commercial purposes; in the former case the unit system of burning is generally employed, and the same equipment is used as described for coal. The grinding characteristics vary with the melting point, which may be anywhere from 50° to 175°C.

Natural graphite may be divided into three grades in respect to grinding characteristics: flake, crystalline, and amorphous. Flake is generally most difficult to reduce to fine powder, and the crystalline variety is the most abrasive. Graphite is ground in ball mills, tube mills, ring-roller mills, and jet mills, with or without air classification. For large capacities, ball and tube mills are used, particularly on the flake and crystalline varieties. Performance of a tube mill with vacuum air classifier in closed circuit is given in Table 8-50.

Table 8-50. Performance of Tube Mill Grinding Graphite

	Ceylon	Madagascar	Korea
Size of mill, ft.	6 × 18	6 × 24	4 × 8
Feed, mesh	20	16	25
Discharge	40% through No. 250 sieve	60% through No. 220 sieve	50% through No. 100 sieve
Fineness of discharge from classifier	95% through No. 250 sieve	97% through No. 220 sieve	98% through No. 100 sieve
Capacity, lb./hr.	725	1500	800
Total horsepower	90	125	70

A *Raymond ring-roller mill*, grinding Mexican graphite, gave a capacity of 2500 lb./hr., 99.1 per cent through No. 200 sieve, with a power consumption of 75 hp.

Micronizer performance on natural graphite is given in Table 8-31. Graphite for pencils has 47, 83, 91, and 94 per cent by weight smaller than 4, 9, 18, and 31 microns, respectively.

Artificial graphite has been ground in ball mills in closed circuit with air classifiers. For lubricants the graphite is ground wet in a paste where water is eventually replaced by oil. The colloid mill is used for production of graphite paint.

Mineral black, a shale sometimes erroneously called "rotten stone," contains a large amount of carbon and is used as a filler for paints and other chemical operations. It is pulverized and classified with the same equipment as shale, limestone, and barytes.

Bone black is sometimes ground very fine, for paint, ink, or for chemical uses. A tube mill or a Griffin mill often is used, the mill discharging to a fan which blows the material to a series of cyclone collectors in tandem. The discharge from the first cyclone is usually returned to the mill for further grinding; the discharge from the last goes to an air filter where the finest grades are obtained. The number of cyclones used depends on the grades required.

Decolorizing carbons of vegetable origin should not be ground too fine. Standard fineness varies from 100 per cent through No. 30 sieve to 100 per cent through No. 50, with 50 to 70 per cent on No. 200 sieve as the upper limit. Ball mills, hammer mills, and rolls, followed by screens, are used. Where the material is used for filtering, a product of uniform size must be used.

Charcoal usually is ground in hammer mills with screen or air classification. For absorption of gases it is usually crushed and graded to about No. 16 sieve size. Care should be taken to prevent it from igniting during grinding.

Gilsonite sometimes is used in place of asphalt or pitch. It is easily pulverized and is generally reduced on hammer mills with screen or air classification. A hammer mill with vacuum air classification produced 950 lb./hr., 90 per cent through No. 200 sieve; 650 lb./hr., 95 per cent through No. 200 sieve; and 300 lb./hr., 99.5 per cent through No. 200 sieve; the pulverizer was driven by a 20-hp. motor.

Carbon mixtures (green mix) are generally made from flour of petroleum coke, graphite, and lampblack, mixed with a binder such as pitch; solvents such as benzol are incorporated in the mix. After cooling, the mixture is caked and therefore generally reground. Table 8-51 gives the results of several grinding mills used in the carbon brush industry for grinding such mixtures.

Table 8-51. Grinding Carbon Mixtures

	Hammer mill	Ring-roller mill
Material in mix	Graphite	Lampblack, pitch, coke
Capacity, lb./hr	700	1350
Fineness, % through No. 200 sieve	65	62.5
Power required, hp	20	30
Type of classification	Vacuum, air	Vacuum, air

Carbon blacks when manufactured are usually ver fine. The gas is passed through baffled chambers or ducts in which the various grades are precipitated; the coarser grades are often pulverized for the carbon brush industry. Grinding may be done in ball, hammer, ring-roller, or jet mills, with or without air classification. Where an extremely fine product is required, the same system as described for bone black may be used. A hammer mill equipped with air classification ground about 200 lb./hr. to a fineness of 95 per cent No. 200 sieve with a power consumption of 20 hp.

Pigments, Chemicals, and Insecticides. Most chemicals, dry colors, and dyes offer little resistance to disintegration. Many of them are loosely bonded agglomerates of fine particles, and the others are generally soft materials. The clusters of the former must be broken apart and the product handled in such a way as to prevent clustering or balling.

Dry colors and dyestuffs generally are pulverized in hammer mills (see Tables 8-22 and 8-26). The jar mill, or large pebble mill, is often used for small lots, since it is easily cleaned in changing from one color to another. It does, however, have a tendency to create agglomerates, when used dry, both decreasing efficiency and failing to eliminate grits. There is a special problem with some dyes which are coarsely crystalline. These are ground to the desired fineness with hammer or jet mills using air classification to limit the size.

Easily dispersible colors are not ordinarily ground fine, since they are subsequently processed in a liquid medium in pebble mills, rolls, or colloid mills. There is, however, a tendency to grind them wet with a dispersing agent, then drying and pulverizing, after which they are easily dispersed in the vehicle in which they are used.

White pigments are the basic commodities processed in large quantities. The problem of cleaning the mill between batches does not exist as with different colors. They are finish ground to sell as dry pigments using mills with air classification. For the denser, low-oil-absorption grades, roller and pebble mills are employed. For looser, fluffier products, hammer and jet mills are used. Often a combination of the two mill actions is used to set the finished quality. Operating data on ring-roller mills are given in Table 8-52. Jet-mill performance for

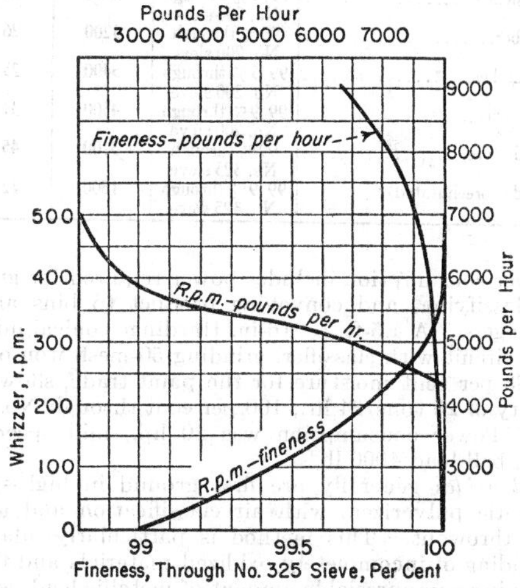

FIG. 8-59. Grinding characteristics of a ring-roller mill with Whizzer classifier when grinding a titanium pigment.

a number of extenders is given in Table 8-31. Figure 8-59 shows the grinding characteristics of a mill with whizzer classification when grinding a titanium pigment to different finenesses.

Table 8-52. Grinding Pigments in Ring-roller Mills

Pigment	Capacity, lb./hr.	Power, hp.-hr./ton	Fineness of product, % on No. 325 sieve
Barium sulfate	4500	28	
Zinc sulfide	5000	32	1
Barium carbonate	4600	29	0.9
Lithopone	5000	25	.1
Titanium with barium base	2000	63	.1
Titanium with calcium base	2200	57	.08
Titanium dioxide	1800	70	.05
Titanium with aluminum silicate	2800	45	.08
White lead	5500	23	.5

Mineral pigments, such as ochers, umbers, siennas, and red oxides of iron, were for years ground on buhrstone mills and bolted. When the materials were wet-ground and classified, they were filtered-pressed, dried, and disintegrated in a cage mill or a hammer mill with screen classification. This is still the process when the material is water-floated. When the oxides are ground dry, ring-roller and hammer mills with air classification have replaced a great many stone mills. Even when buhrstones are used, bolting has generally been replaced by air classification. Some of the red pigments are still ground on buhrstones, as the idea prevails in some quarters that the stones make a smoother and richer-colored material. A 36-in. buhrstone in closed circuit with an 8-ft. air classifier produced 300 lb./hr. of ground hematite, 99.2 per cent through No. 325 sieve, with 15 hp. on the stone. Table 8-53 gives operating characteristics of a Raymond No. 5057 high-side mill grinding various oxides of iron. Synthetic mineral pigments are usually fine agglomerates. They may be disintegrated with hammer or jet mills without elaborate pregrinding.

Table 8-53. Grinding Iron Oxides in a Ring-roller Mill

Material	Fineness	Capacity, lb./hr.	Total hp.-hr./ton
Raw sienna	99% through No. 200 sieve	5950	23.5
Burned sienna	99.5% through No. 200 sieve	5800	22.1
Raw umber	99% through No. 200 sieve	5200	26.9
Burned umber	99.5% through No. 200 sieve	5400	25.9
Natural ocher	99.9% through No. 200 sieve	4500	31.0
Iron oxide (ore)	99% through No. 325 sieve	3100	45.0
Iron oxide (precipitated)	99.9% through No. 325 sieve	1800	72.5

Power consumption includes power required for grinding, classifying, and conveying product to bins above the baggers. A 4.5-ft. by 16-in. Hardinge conical mill in closed circuit with classifier, grinding 50-mesh iron oxide with 33 per cent moisture for the paint trade, showed a capacity of 25 tons/24 hr., 100 per cent through No. 200 sieve. Power consumption was 20 hp., mill speed 30 r.p.m., ball load 4000 lb.

Lead oxides generally are first ground in high-speed automatic pulverizers with air classification and automatic throwout. This method is particularly adapted to grinding of incompletely oxidized materials and those containing an appreciable amount of metallic lead, which is eliminated through the throwout. The objective in the production of certain lead oxides is to obtain a product of lowest possible apparent density. Different types of mills produce oxides of varying densities, even though the sieve analyses may be quite similar. How the type of mill used and the grinding method applied affect the apparent density of the product may be seen from the following test: The lead oxide was first passed through a pulverizer with throwout, for removal of the metallic lead. It next went to a ring-roller mill equipped with air classification and was subjected to extremely fine grinding. Finally, the product from the ring-roller mill went to an Imp pulverizer equipped with whizzer classification. This pulverizer both changed the particle shape and reduced the apparent density of the material. The results are given in Table 8-54.

Table 8-54. Data Showing the Influence of the Type of Mill upon Apparent Density of Lead Oxide

Automatic Pulverizer	
Power (total) required by pulverizer system, hp	75
Production, lb./hr	4000
Apparent density, g./cu. in	38
Ring-roller Mill	
Power required by mill, hp	75
Capacity, lb./hr	4000
Apparent density, g./cu. in	27
Imp Pulverizer	
Power required by pulverizer, hp	75
Production, lb./hr	1900
Apparent density, g./cu. in	18

Raymond Imp mills are equally successful at producing low-apparent-density products even on leady litharge containing up to 30 per cent free lead. Many of these units are used for this purpose by manufacturers of storage batteries. In a typical case, a No. 51 Imp mill with 125 hp. produces 2500 and 3000 lb./hr. of product.

Chemicals. A high-speed pulverizer, with or without air classification and air conveying, gives a calcium arsenate product possessing proper physical properties. Table 8-55 gives the operating characteristics for a Raymond No. 00 automatic pulverizer, grinding calcium arsenate.

Table 8-55. Performance of Automatic Pulverizer Grinding Calcium Arsenate

Fineness, % through No. 200 sieve	Apparent density, cu. in./lb.	Production, lb./hr.	Hp.
90	81.5	1300	28
94	86.0	1100	28
96	90.6	950	27
98	94.2	750	27
99	98.7	625	25
99.5	104.8	550	24
99.9	110.0	475	22
99.99	124.8	400	20

The fineness obtainable with a hammer mill on rock salt and alum cake is given in Table 8-21.

Sometimes it is necessary to produce a granular product of definite size limits, such as a granulated monocalcium phosphate that will all pass through a No. 50 sieve and, within a few per cent, remain on a No. 200 sieve. This is not a simple problem of crushing and grinding but involves a complete process including the selection of a proper type of crusher or pulverizer, the best method of feeding, optimum number of stages, and the most suitable method of screening or air classification (see also p. 8-10). No pulverizer will produce such a material in one operation. For this purpose it is necessary to use a mill that will produce the largest percentage of particles between No. 50 and 200 sieve sizes. The pulverized material may be passed over a screen to remove particles above No. 50 sieve size, the undersize being bolted or air classified to remove all below No. 200 sieve size. Oversize is usually returned to the pulverizer.

Soft materials, such as fuller's earth, sodium bicarbonate, and monocalcium phosphate, are generally ground in flour mills to obtain a finely divided product. A ratio of reduction of 2.5 to 1 or even 1.5 to 1 is generally used; the material passes through a series of rolls with bolting reels. Sometimes air classifiers are used in the circuit for removal of fines. Table 8-56 gives the results obtained in granulating soft materials.

Table 8-56. Granulation of Soft Materials

	Fuller's earth	Sodium bicarbonate
Size of product required, sieve No.	−80 +150	−120 +200
Type of mill used	Two roller	Two roller
Number of mills in series	12	5
Size of rolls, in.	7 × 16	7 × 20
Capacity, lb./hr	3500	2500
Recovery from original feed, %	80	55
Horsepower required, total	80	30

D.D.T. Lump D.D.T. can be reduced in size in hammer mills. A granular product ranging from No. 8 to No. 18 sieve size is obtained with the *S.P. Mikro-Pulverizer* (see p. 8-33). Finer products require screen-discharge hammer mills, and cooling of the material is necessary to prevent fusion during grinding. A product having 60 to 70 per cent able to pass a No. 100 sieve is obtained with an *Imp pulverizer* at a rate of 20 lb./hp.-hr.

In many instances D.D.T. is ground with an inert extender to produce compositions having 10 to 75 per cent of the active ingredient. Grinding characteristics vary with the nature and quality of the D.D.T. as well as the nature and fineness of the extender. A *Raymond ring-roller mill* will handle most of these compositions. As an example, a fineness of 99 per cent smaller than 20 microns with a surface mean diameter of 4.8 microns is obtained at a rate of 30 lb./hp.-hr. Among hammer mills, the *Raymond vertical mill* and *Mikro-Pulverizer* have found application for fine grinding of D.D.T. compositions. Fluid-energy jet mills are used extensively for the higher concentrations.

Sulfur. The ring-roller mill can be used for the fine grinding of sulfur. Inert gases are supplied instead of hot air (see p. 8-13 for use of inert gas). Performance of a *Raymond No.* 5057 *ring-roller mill* is given in Table 8-57. If power cost is 2 ¢/kw.-hr., the total cost might be three to four times the power cost and include labor, inert gas, maintenance, and fixed charges.

Table 8-57. Grinding Sulfur

Fineness, % through	sieve No.	Capacity, tons/hr.	Power, kw.-hr./ton
60	200	13.50	6.6
70	200	11.50	7.7
80	200	9.00	9.8
90	200	6.50	13.0
90	325	4.50	17.0
95	325	3.75	19.2
97	325	3.50	20.6
99	325	3.00	24.0
99.5	325	2.25	32.5
99.7	325	1.75	39.0
99.9	325	1.50	45.5
99.95	325	1.25	55.0
99.99	325	1.00	67.0

Resins, Gums, Waxes, and Molding Powders. The grinding characteristics of the various resins, gums, waxes, hard rubbers, and molding powders depend greatly upon their softening temperatures. When a finely divided product is required, it is often necessary to use a water-jacketed mill or a pulverizer with air classifier in which cooled air is introduced into the system. Not all waxes can be ground, inasmuch as some of them are soft at the temperatures obtainable. However, a great many of them can be powdered if precautions are taken to prevent overheating. Hammer and cage mills are used for this purpose. Some low-softening-temperature resins can be ground by mixing with 15 to 50 per cent by weight of dry ice before grinding. Refrigerated air sometimes is introduced into the hammer mill to prevent softening and agglomeration [Dorris, *Chem. & Met. Eng.*, **51,** 114 (July, 1944). See also p. 8-12].

Most gums and resins, natural or artificial, when used in the paint, varnish, or plastic industries, are not ground very fine, and hammer or cage mills will produce a suitable product. Typical performance of the attrition mill is given in Table 8-29. Roll crushers will often give a sufficiently fine product. Certain resins used in the phenolic resin industries must be pulverized very fine; pebble mills, cooled with water or brine, in closed circuit with an air classifier, are used. In general, one may say that the grinding of the thermoplastic resins, or of the thermosetting resins after they have set, is difficult except in the very coarse range. In the case, however, of the thermosetting resins, before setting, a very high fineness may be obtained readily, although these materials, particularly when ground on a hammer mill, may cake up very rapidly after leaving the mill. Phenol-formaldehyde resins have been ground in the *Raymond Imp Mill* to about 80 per cent through No. 325 sieve at a rate of 30 lb./hp.-hr. This is about 99 per cent through No. 100 sieve.

The Raymond ring-roll mill with its internal air separation is widely used to pulverize *phenol-formaldehyde resins.* The usual fineness of grind is finer than 99 per cent minus 200 mesh. Air at 40°F. is usually introduced into the mill to limit temperature rise. A typical 3036 Raymond mill using 45 hp. will produce better than 2000 lb./hr. at 99 per cent minus 200 mesh.

Hard rubber is one of the few combustible materials which is generally ground on heavy steam-heated rollers. The raw material passes to a series of rolls in closed circuit with screens and air classifiers. Farrel-Birmingham rolls are used extensively for this work. There is a differential in the roll diameters, and the particular size best suited for the average hard rubber is one having rolls with 13 and 17 in. diameters and 20-in. face. The motor should be separated from the grinder by a fire wall. It is also desirable to run these machines at rather low speed and low differential between the rolls because it is very easy to overheat hard rubber in grinding, making it smolder, which necessitates the shutting down of the grinder until it cools off before clearing out the charred material. The performance of a series of rolls grinding hard rubber, producing a finished product through an air classifier is given in Table 8-58. A larger production could probably be attained, but operation at the lower rate is advisable to prevent generation of an excessive amount of heat.

Table 8-58. Grinding Hard Rubber

Number of roller mills	3
Size of each mill, in.	13 and 17 × 20
Motor on each mill, hp.	50
Size of vacuum air classifier, ft.	4.5
Size of motor on classifier fan, hp.	20
Fineness of feed to classifier, % through No. 100 sieve	32
Fineness of product from classifier, % through No. 100 sieve	95
Production, lb./hr.	250

Molding Powders. Specifications for molding powders vary widely, from a No. 8 to a No. 60 sieve product; generally the coarser products are No. 12, 14, or 20 sieve material. Specifications usually prescribe a minimum of fines (below No. 100 and No. 200 sieve). For most purposes the ideal molding powder would consist of particles testing smaller than No. 20 and larger than No. 100 sieve size. Molding powders are produced with hammer mills, either of the screen type or equipped with air classifiers.

Curves *A* and *B* of Fig. 8-60 give the screen analysis of a molding powder produced with screen pulverizers fitted with an 8-mesh screen. Curve *C* gives the data obtained

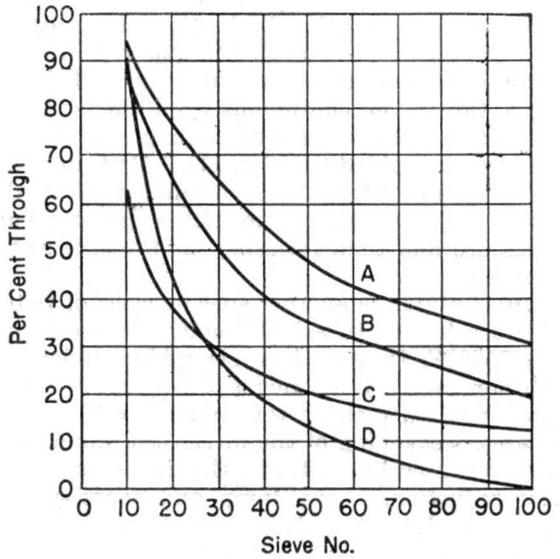

FIG. 8-60. Sieve analyses of molding powders produced by various installations.

with an air-classification pulverizer unit operated to give a minimum of No. 100 sieve material, which amounted to only 12 per cent. This material was passed over an 8-mesh screen to remove oversize, and the resulting product passed through an air classifier to remove the No. 100 sieve size particles. Curve *D* gives the screen analysis of the final granular product.

The following material may be ground at ordinary temperatures if only the regular commercial fineness is required: amber, arabac, tragacanth, rosin, olibanum, gum benzoin, myrrh, guaiacum, and montan wax. If a finer product is required, hammer mills or attrition mills in closed circuit, with screens or air classifiers, are used. Attrition-mill performance is given in Table 8-29.

Grinding of Soaps. Soaps in a finely divided form may be classified as soap powder, powdered soap, and chips or flakes. The term soap powder is applied to a granular product, No. 12 to No. 16 sieve size with a certain amount of fines, which is produced in hammer mills with perforated or slotted screens. A *No. 2 Mikro-Pulverizer* gives a production of 2750 lb./hr. analyzing a slight trace on No. 16 sieve and 19 per cent through a No. 80 sieve using 4 hp. for a moisture content of 19 per cent. The capacity drops to about 1000 lb./hr. at 25 per cent moisture content for the same fineness. Soaps of the type used for tooth powder show a production rate of 400 lb./hr., require 10 hp. and analyze about 98.5 per cent passing a No. 100 sieve. Lump soaps, which are mixtures of soap and caustic containing 20 per cent moisture, give a capacity of 1500 lb./hr. at 9 hp. for 98 per cent through a No. 100 sieve.

Powdered soap is a finely ground powder, with 99 per cent or more through No. 200 sieve. Grinding to this fineness, a Mikro-Pulverizer will handle 300 to 350 lb./hr. with 7½ hp. Cooling, generally by introduction of cold air in the air-classifying system, is sometimes required in grinding soap very fine. Grinding in closed circuit, with screens or air classification, often is advantageous, giving a granular product and preventing overheating.

Pulverizing of the metallic soaps, stearates, palmitates, resinates, laurates, and erucates is not difficult using modern equipment with provision for keeping the material cool and in rapid motion. Batch grinding is not practicable, as the material tends to cake, particularly if a fine product is needed. Oleates are usually most troublesome, as they tend to become plastic and creamy. Listed in order of their resistance to pulverization some of the metallic soaps are: lead, silver, zinc, copper, and nickel stearate; zinc, lead and copper palmitate; lead copper, and zinc laurate; silver, mercury, and lead erucate; and silver and lead oleate.

The oleates and erucates are best pulverized by multi-cage mills; laurates and palmitates in cage mills and also in hammer mills if particularly fine division is not required; stearates may generally be pulverized in multi cage mills, screen mills, and air-classification hammer mills. Table 8-59 gives the operating characteristics of hammer mills when grinding zinc stearate and aluminum stearate to a finely divided powder.

Table 8-59. Performance of Screen-type Hammer Mill Grinding Zinc and Aluminum Stearates

	Zinc stearate	Aluminum stearate
Capacity, lb./hr.	500	300
Fineness, % through No. 325 sieve	60	70
In closed circuit with air classifier:		
Capacity, lb./hr.	100	75
Fineness, % through No. 325 sieve	99.5	99.7
Horsepower required	25	20

OTHER METHODS OF SIZE REDUCTION

In addition to crushing and grinding, there are other size-reduction techniques of a specialized nature which are used to impart desirable product quality or to take advantage of unique properties of the solid material or the process of which it is a product.

Tough or fibrous materials can be reduced in size more readily by successive shear cuts than by impact or attrition. Granular materials of uniform size and shape can be prepared with precision shear cutters. Preparation of some of the metal powders by machining operations has advantages because of low cost, avoidance of surface oxidation, and the elimination of explosion hazards. Some materials that are prepared in the molten state are converted advantageously to flake form by cooling a thin layer continuously on the surface of a rotating drum. Thus massive cooling and subsequent pulverizing are avoided (see Sec. 11). Certain materials, particularly those of a fibrous nature, may be disintegrated by first saturating them with a gas or a vapor at high pressure and then releasing the pressure as rapidly as possible.

Thermal shock is another specific class of reduction. If solids are heated to a high enough temperature, say 1000° to 2500°F., they can be ruptured by sudden quenching. In some cases, the action is based on thermal-expansion changes under sharp temperature differential. In other cases, weakening of the interstitial bonds between particles is caused by heat, and the quenching completes the size reduction. Large-lump and coarse-mesh sizes are open to such treatment; it is rare to produce fine sizes by this technique.

Prebreakers. Aside from the normal problems of grinding, there are special procedures and equipment for breaking large masses of feed to smaller sizes. This is often necessary to ensure that the material is of uniform size for further grinding. There is the breaking or shredding of bales, as with rubber, cotton, or hay, where the compacted mass does not readily come apart. There also is often caking in bags of plastic or hygroscopic materials which were originally fine. Although crushers are sometimes used, the desired size-reduction ratio is often not obtainable. Furthermore, a lower capital investment may result through choosing a less rugged device which progressively attacks the large mass to remove only small amounts at a time.

Prebreakers are employed while also serving as feeders. In structure, they comprise a rotating shaft in a casing. On the shaft are attached radial breaker bars set at an angle to move the feed away from the large inlet as the material is broken. In some devices, the casing also has stator breaker bars further to implement the fracture. In another type of structure, the single-roll crusher is modified as to size of opening and discharge, having on the rotating roll a series of breaker bars or picks which continually dig out material from the feed mass and break it fine enough to pass between stator blades.

Such devices are of high capacity and generally low power requirements. They may, in fact, be regarded as preparation equipment. When difficulty in breaking is encountered, jaw crushers, gyratory crushers, or knobbed rolls are used.

Rietz prebreakers were developed as crusher-feeders for use ahead of Rietz disintegrators. The prebreaker often is used alone as a low-speed (5 to 300 r.p.m.), high-torque crushing or mixing device. Prebreakers have a horizontal shaft with pitched blades rotating between anvils which project inwardly from the shell surrounding the rotor. The pitched blades are most nearly described as part of a helical plane and vary in shape depending on use.

Feed entering the hopper is first cut or crushed by the rotating blades. The pieces of feed are carried along parallel to the axis by the screw action of the blades and crushed as they come into position between the edges of the rotating blades and anvils. The blade-to-anvil clearance is only 1⁄64 to 3⁄32 in. depending on service and size of prebreaker.

In cases where the random size resulting from the interaction of blades and anvils is not uniform or small enough, an orifice plate of suitable design is mounted at the discharge end further to control size. This permits breaking many materials down to minus ½ in. in particle size.

Rietz extructors and prebreakers are closely related. Prebreakers have bearings supporting the shaft at opposite ends of the working length. Extructors have the rotor or working length of the shaft overhung, thereby eliminating any contact between through-put and bearings.

The action in a prebreaker closely resembles the action of a pug mill, and for this reason some interesting mixing applications have been developed. The torque capacity of prebreakers and extructors permits kneading and mulling of very stiff doughs and relatively dry mixes. Organic powders with as little as 10 per cent liquid content are being mulled continuously and extruded in a spaghetti-like form.

Rotary cutters are used with tough or fibrous materials, where successive shear actions are more effective than pressure or impact. The feed stock should not exceed the cutter knife length, and the thickness is less than 1 in. The usual structure involves a rotor with knives spaced uniformly on the periphery so as to cut against stationary knives on the casing. Product is passed through screens; its maximum size is controlled by the screen aperture and by the design and operation of the mill. From the 20-mesh screen, in some cases down to 80 mesh, the collection system is pneumatic.

The data shown in Table 8-60 are for a unit operating at 920 r.p.m. with 10-in. rotor and knife length at 18 in. with five moving and five fixed knives.

Table 8-60. Performance of Rotary Knife Cutter

Material	Screen opening	Feed rate, lb./hr.	Hp.	Air	Remarks on product
Amosite asbestos pencils.	1½"	1000	11	Yes	Finer fiber bundles average length 2"
Cellophane bags..	1 1⁄32"	200	10	Yes	Finer than 5⁄16"
Cork............	3⁄16"	525	16	Yes	90% 4/24* sieve
Chemical cotton..	60 mesh	120	15	Yes	Flock; 35% under No. 100 sieve
Leather scrap....	¾"	600	20	Yes	Precutting before shredding
Fiberglas	3⁄16"	300	18	Yes	1" (approx.) lengths
Waste paper.....	5⁄16"	338	13	Yes	Through No. 4 sieve and finer
Sheet pulp.......	40 mesh	150	15	Yes	Flock; 85%, 40/100 sieve
Tenite scrap.....	5⁄16"	340	12	No	Granulated for reuse
Vinylite scrap....	7⁄32"	300	15	Yes	35%, 6/10 sieve; granular
⅛" Geon sheet...	5⁄16"	540	11	No	99%, 4/20 sieve; for molding granules
Cotton rags......	¾"	500	11	Yes	No linting
Buna scrap......	10 mesh	264	12	Yes	Granular
Neoprene scrap..	30 mesh	90	14	Yes	20°F. temperature rise
Soft-wood chips..	⅛"	960	12	Yes	90%, 10/50 sieve
Hard-wood chips.	1⁄16"	290	11	Yes	83%, 20/100 sieve

* 90 per cent 4/24 sieve, *i.e.*, 90 per cent is through No. 4 and on No. 24 sieve.

In general, rotary cutters are available in steel or stainless steel and may be specially supplied in other corrosion-resistant metals. Knives for shear cutting are also generally available, leading to reduction in shock loading. Laboratory units, using a few horsepower and having capacities up to a few hundred pounds per hour, are generally available, while production units of varying size use between 5 and 60 hp., are around 1 to 2 ft. diameter, have knife lengths from 12 to 30 in., and have capacities up to 1 or 2 tons/hr. Specifications by Paul O. Abbe (Table 8-61) and a description of the Sprout, Waldron heavy-duty rotary knife cutter illustrate details.

Table 8-61. Rotary Cutter Specifications

Machine No.	Floor space required, in.	Shipping weight, lb.	Speed, r.p.m.	Hp.	Screen size, in.
0	37 × 17¼	500	900–1200	2– 5	10 × 17
1	54 × 34	1,500	600– 900	5–15	20 × 24
2	68 × 42	4,000	600– 900	15–40	20 × 28
2½	96 × 39	6,000	500– 800	20–45	35 × 36
3	102 × 43	12,000	500– 750	30–60	51 × 30

Sprout, Waldron Heavy-Duty rotary knife cutters. This manufacturer offers two series of units as follows: (1) 10-in.-diameter, 920 r.p.m. rotor units with 18-, 24-, and 30-in. knife lengths mounted in a cast frame (iron, steel, stainless); and (2) 20-in.-diameter, 750 r.p.m. rotor units of 10- and 30-in. knife lengths with all-welded steel frame. A conventional arrangement of the largest of these units (Model F-11) is illustrated by Fig. 8-61.

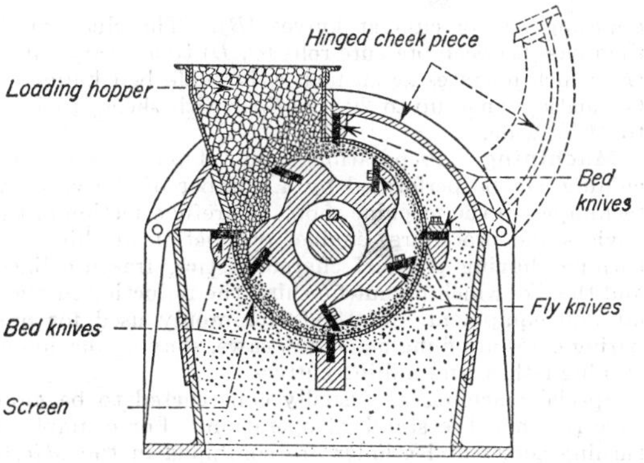

FIG. 8-61. Fabricated-steel rotary knife cutter. (*Sprout, Waldron & Co.*)

These basic units are varied considerably according to application. Entry of feed is by hopper, slot, or compression-feed rolls. Generally five rotor knives are specified, and these are set at a slight angle with the shaft to provide shear cuts with direction reversed on alternate knives to avoid conveying the charge against the end of the cutter. Two to seven stationary knives may be specified alternating with screen sections around the cage to provide maximum discharge area and to keep fines at a minimum. Variations in construction permit such widely different applications as sheet-plastic granulation, flocking, tobacco-leaf threshing, etc. Models are powered by 10- to 60-hp. motors through V-belts and employ shear-pin safety hubs.

Precision Cutters and Slitters. Many times it becomes desirable to reduce the size of a solid mass to regular smaller sizes. Examples that typify the range would be: punching or cutting metal plate; cutting or dicing of rubber or plastic masses, from an extruder, rolled sheet, or random pieces; and slicing of bread. With metal and other resistant solids, shearing action is generally employed wherein there is positive bearing area on the front edge of each cutting surface. A punch and die would serve as an example, as would also shearing rolls. With paper, rubber, plastics, and bread, a sharp-edged device is effective. In some cases, the direct pressure of a knife is employed, but generally some sliding or sawing action is helpful. For bread, direct pressure would be injurious to the structure, and the cutting knives, pinned to a rotating shaft, are curved for substantial sliding motion in the cut.

Precision knife cutters differ from random cutting mills in that a feeder is synchronized with the knives. This ensures the exact size, whether it be slit widths in a sheet, fiber length from a strand, or both width and length from a sheet, as in dicing. In the *Giant dicing cutter* (Fig. 8-62), the sheet stock (*A*) is first slit lengthwise with

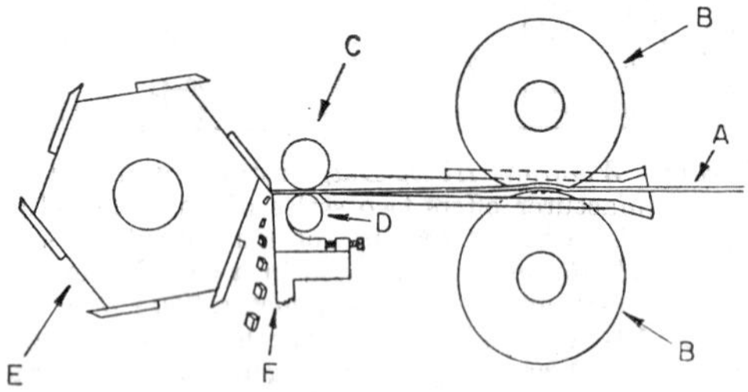

Fig. 8-62. "Giant" dicing cutter. (*Taylor, Stiles & Co.*)

opposing sets of circular knives (*B*). The slit strands then pass between pressure rolls (*C*, *D*) to a rotary cutter (*E*) which operates against an adjustable bed knife (*F*). Capacities range up to 20 tons/hr., with sheet stock up to 24 in. wide.

Machining. Preparation of metal powders by machining can be performed by a number of the classical techniques of the machine shop. Careful selection of the devices and procedures enables production of chips and turnings having physical characteristics, fracture lines, and the like which permit finishing the reduction in regular mill equipment. Methods commonly used for preparing chips are filing machines, saws, shaving machines, turning lathes, and milling cutters.

Special machines are usually constructed to be more effective than the standard operation. For example, a turning cutter and grinder are combined in the *Mikro-Chipper* (Fig. 8-63). It consists of a high-speed spindle

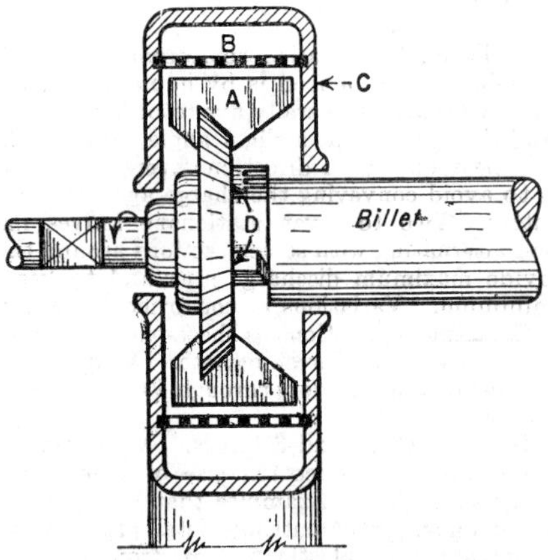

Fig. 8-63. The Mikro-Chipper. (*Pulverizing Machinery Co.*)

mounting a cutter face plate. The material, in billet form, to be chipped by the cutters *D* is mounted on a carriage which advances at a predetermined speed. The chipped material is broken by blades *A* on the periphery of the face plate and discharged through a screen *B* held in a volute casing *C*. Since the chips are thus broken, they are given a reduction equivalent to a primary grinding stage, producing a size distribution of which as high as 50 per cent is able to pass a No. 200 sieve.

It is desirable to use cutters of tungsten carbide or similar alloys that permit cutting speeds as high as 7500 ft./min. without resorting to the use of coolants or lubricants. Figure 8-64 illustrates three types of cutters that

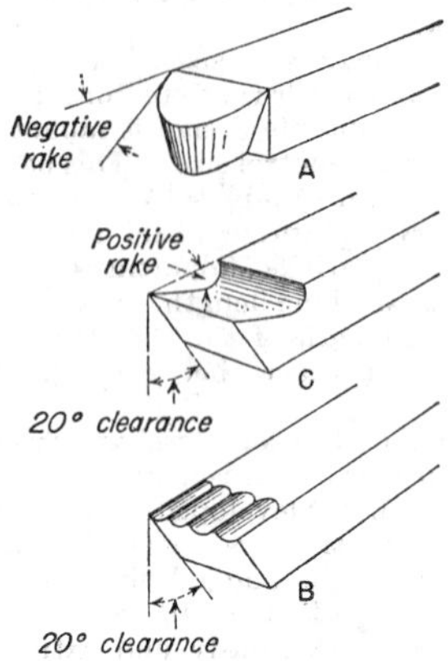

Fig. 8-64. Cutters for Mikro-Chipper.

have been used successfully in commercial operations. Cutter *A* has been particularly successful in chipping soft solder and materials of similar nature. Cutter *B* has given excellent results when chipping less ductile materials such as tin, zinc, antimony, magnesium, etc. Cutter *C* gives best results when chipping plastics. Care should be exercised that the clearance angle is sufficient to ensure that the cutter does not rub on the billet surface being cut.

Performance characteristics for the Mikro-Chipper are shown in Table 8-62.

Table 8-62. Mikro-Chipper Performance

Material	Feed rate, lb./hr.	Hp.	Product fineness	
			%	Through sieve No.
50:50 solder	400–600	5 –10	60	50
20:80 solder	400–600	5 –10	70	50
			50	100
Tin	500–700	7½–10	75	100
			25	200
Magnesium	100	10	90	20
Magnesium	30	10	90	50
Polystyrene	250	7½	90	12

Explosive Disintegration. When permeable materials contain gas or liquid under pressure, the sudden release of that pressure often results in explosive disintegration. The rupture of wood has been developed as the Masonite process (U.S. patent 1,578,609). Meigs describes a number of changes undergone by such materials [*Chem. & Met. Eng.*, **48**, 122 (1941)]. The U.S. Bureau of Mines has worked on the explosive shattering of minerals by what appears to be a combination of penetration and absorption techniques followed by sudden expansion (*U.S. Bur. Mines Rept. Invest.*, 3118, 1932; 3201, 1933).

Size Reduction via Liquid Phase. Massive solids may sometimes be reduced to small particles by converting the solid mass to a molten form, dispersing the liquid phase by a suitable means, then resolidifying the dispersed particles. Asphalt, waxes, resins, and the like, which are solids at ambient temperatures, may be emulsified with water at elevated temperatures where these materials are fluid. Quenching the emulsion fixes the dispersion as a solid-in-liquid system. Another approach is to dissolve the solid in sufficient solvent to fluidize it, emulsify, and steam-distill the solvent to leave solid particulates. This is the basis of the Olin ball powder process.

Fine metal powder may be prepared by spraying or by quenching vapor from an arc of the electrode metal. Metal is shotted by quenching droplets in a liquid medium. It is common to do this with lower-melting metals like lead, but it has been done as well with iron. Generally, where possible to do such quenching in a gaseous medium, liquid is not used.

Devices and techniques for producing liquid-liquid dispersions and emulsions are covered in Sec. 21. Shotting, prilling, spray drying, and other techniques for dispersing dissolved or molten materials in a continuous gas phase are covered in Sec. 20.

Flaking is a continuous process commonly used for converting certain molten materials into flake form by freezing the material in a layer on a revolving drum, cooling, and removing it as a solid flake. Where solidification results from evaporation, the operation is known as drum drying. This process is described in detail in Sec. 11 as an example of indirect heat transfer to and from the solid phase.

SIZE ENLARGEMENT

Objectives. The building up of solid masses or coarse particles from small particulates has long been used as a means of creating definite and useful shapes. The forming and molding of plastic powders, metal powders, and ceramic materials are well-established industrial operations. In this section, emphasis is placed on the building of size without special reference to form. The techniques used for forming to shape, as well as others, are applicable to this case.

There are numerous reasons for doing this:

1. To densify the material for more convenient storage or shipment
2. To reduce dust nuisance, particularly with irritating or obnoxious material
3. To prepare the material so that it will not cake or lump
4. To reduce dust losses, as in shipment or in operations like furnacing
5. To prepare the material for further processing, as in briquetting or tableting where high apparent density and freedom from dusting are important
6. To create uniform blends which can be handled without segregation

In some cases, the purpose is to bond the fine particulates permanently. Alternatively, it may be important to have the granules readily dispersible into the original fine particulates.

Size enlargement, whether for controlled or random shapes, may be illustrated by these applications and techniques:

Catalysts—Precipitation, calcination, grain growth, bonding, extrusion, pressing, pelleting

Ceramics—Forming as a paste, pressing, extrusion, slip casting

Cements and plasters—Forming as a paste, pressing, rolling, extrusion

Plastics and rubber—Pressure compaction, rolling, extrusion, spinning of filaments, solution and evaporation, melting and casting

Paper and board—Controlled filtration, slip casting, pressing and rolling, adhesive bonding

Ores—Sintering, nodulizing, briquetting

Metals—Extrusion, melting and casting, forging, welding, bonding with adhesive

Metal powders—Pressing, rolling, slip casting, extrusion, sintering

Cereals and baked goods—Wet bonding and drying, spray drying, briquetting, extrusion, pelleting, mixing, and baking

Feeds—Nodulizing, pelleting, extrusion

Chemicals (including fertilizers)—Rolls and reduction, sinter, melting and casting, prilling, spray drying, briquetting, pelleting, nodulizing, granulating

The operations involved to meet the needs of size enlargement are diverse; yet they are built from a few **basic steps:** normal contact of particulates with or without control of chemical environment; pressure for contact and usually for deformation as well; heat for enhancement of adhesive quality or even for evaporation and melting; chemical reaction; or a combination of these. They are usually associated with some inherent or added adhesive quality essential to strength in the bond. The products of bonding are often subjected to a normal size-reduction step, cautiously done to avoid dust formation, to eliminate undesirable oversize.

Flocculation. Fine particles in a fluid dispersion are often difficult to separate from the medium in which they are suspended. When the ultimate particles are in the low and fractional micron range of sizes, they settle too slowly for economic sedimentation and they are often difficult to filter. If the size of the ultimate particle is of no concern, process conditions might be arranged for coarser precipitation or for crystal growth to sizes which can be handled. However, many materials cannot be so treated, nor is it always desirable to do so. "Instant" foods, pigments, whitings, clays, carbon blacks, and mineral fillers are prepared to a fine ultimate size to fulfill their functions. The enlarged form is a temporary one. Other materials, *e.g.*, coal slurries, mineral slimes, and turbid waters, often difficult to handle in a fine state, may be permanently enlarged. Flocculation techniques must take these needs into account.

A comparison of flocculated and deflocculated systems is illustrated in Fig. 8-65. In the deflocculated system, the individual particles are dispersed in the fluid and they are separated and free to move independently of each other. Being small, they settle very slowly to a final dense sediment. When several particles are gathered together as flocculates, they settle much faster and the resulting sediment is less dense and is often mobile. They also filter more readily into a cake which is permeable and does not clog the filter.

Flocculation is basically a problem in **colloid chemistry.** If the conditions are right, flocculates will form. Gentle agitation often assists in bringing particles into contact for the action to take place. Some dispersions are unstable and chemically ready to flocculate. Others need to have the dispersing agent on their surfaces neutralized or precipitated. In still other cases, the particulates need to be flocculated with a precipitate, as in the lime-alum clarification of water. Once the chemical conditions are satisfied to permit flocculation, the action proceeds.

Little needs to be said here about equipment for flocculation. When chemicals need to be added to fix the environment, the solutions may be continuously added to a stream through an eductor to give complete and instant

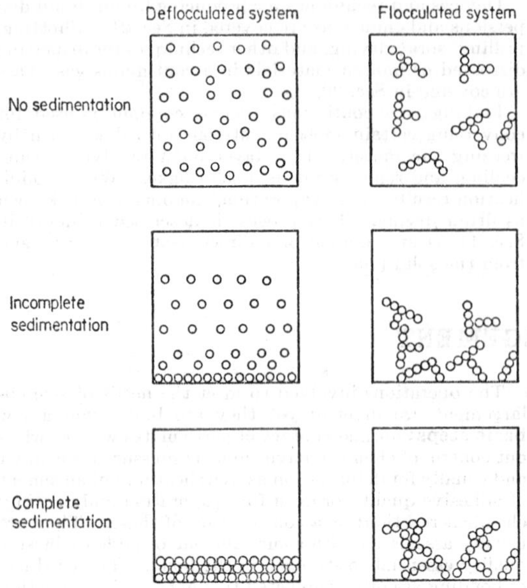

FIG. 8-65. Deflocculated and flocculated systems.

mixing on a continuous basis. They can also be added to a dispersion in a tank with mild stirring. There is a wide difference between dispersions and their flocculates, and often the flocculates are too large for best handling. Flocculate size can be regulated by controlled turbulence. This should be uniform and mild. Points of vigorous motion, as in pumps, partially closed valves, or sharp bends in pipe, tend to break agglomerates mechanically and should be avoided. Equipment for creating a critical degree of turbulence includes the *Dorr flocculator* and the *Permutit* (*Spaulding*) *precipitator*. For further dewatering of flocculated sediments, the *Dorr tray thickener* and the *Hardinge spiral clarifier* are used (see also Sedimentation in Sec. 19).

In addition to the liquid dispersions and flocculates of solid particulates, there are related cases with liquid particulates in liquids and with liquid or solid particulates in gases. With the former, the liquid dispersoid often flocculates to a liquid mass.

With the gas systems, flocculation is similar to that in liquids, where control of atmosphere, slow mixing, and also vapor condensation on particles are factors for agglomeration.

Agglomeration. While the term agglomeration is broadly generic for the gathering together of particulates, its most useful meaning pertains to the step where bodies of powdered materials are brought together in a loose state of bonding to form larger particulates. Such agglomerates are generally redispersible. The terms *granulation* and *nodulizing*, subsequently developed, are forms of agglomeration which refer to the end condition of the product.

While some materials have inherent qualities for agglomeration, it is usually necessary to add a **binder** or to create one by the use of heat or pressure. The surfaces of particulates may be conditioned by the use of binders to develop adhesive qualities. Moistening them with water, solvents, oils, and the like in small amounts enhances surface adhesion and causes them to gather into balls. In some cases, water alone will suffice, but this usually implies some soluble ingredient in the powder. In other cases, sugars, starches, glues, gums, salts, and gels are used. The droplet becomes the nucleus for agglomerate formation and the particle size may be controlled by droplet size. In other cases, a stream of fluid fed into a particulate mass that is being stirred gives agglomerates of adequately controlled size. Drying enhances the strength of the bond; but this complete treatment may be called granulation or nodulizing.

Equipment for agglomerating may comprise mixers (see Sec. 19) of the stirring or agitating types, rolls or roller mills, ball mills (see pp. 8-40 and 8-21), or tumbling barrels. For control of droplet size, nozzles may be chosen. The *Patterson-Kelley V-type blender* with a high-speed liquid feeder insert makes fine droplets. Fluid-energy mills are also employed for coating with binders. For fine to intermediate size agglomerates, the more vigorous agitation encountered in the *Strong Scott Turbulizer* tends to limit the maximum size of agglomerate.

When excess fluid is present, the agglomeration may be achieved during the process of **evaporation** of the fluid. Stirred kettles have been used with salts, such as fertilizers. Combined drying and moderate grinding do well. Extrusion, roll or belt drying, and spray drying are also employed. With clays and in some encapsulating techniques, the fluid mix is spray-dried. With clay, the hard filter cake is redispersed in its own water with a dispersing agent, and the sprayed droplet containing dispersible clay particulates becomes the agglomerate. In encapsulation, the emulsion and its coating are spray-dried into agglomerates of emulsion covered by dry coating.

The binder is often solid but can be **melted** to cause binding. This is the first action in cementing pressed mixes of copper, tin, and graphite used to make oil-less bearings. At higher temperatures, the tin and copper alloy to form bronze. Plastic molding powders are made from resin and filler. They are heated and the plastic is softened in friction rolls to create firmly bonded agglomerates which may be ground to a granular product when cooled. Effervescent salts are made homogeneous and dust-free by agglomeration through melting. The citric acid, in its mixture with bicarbonate, melts in its own water of crystallization and binds the material. Rapid cooling is needed to arrest the reaction, after which the agglomerates are ground, screened, and further dried. The latter cases are closely related to granulation.

Granulation. This term, though often employed in a broadly generic form, is here limited to the techniques of forming irregularly shaped clusters, in contrast to nodulizing, which creates essentially rounded ones. It is difficult to avoid conflict between the two terms, since coarse nodular products may be crushed to granular ones. In the restricted sense, granulation must be kept apart from crystallization, as in granulated sugar. Granulation thus becomes a procedure utilizing steps discussed elsewhere to create irregular forms of essentially dust-free particles. Where crushing and sieving are employed, the devices used produce less fines, as disks and rolls; and often the dust is sieved out and recycled. Granulation may be done by the common methods:

1. Briquette and crush
2. Press and crush
3. Roll-bond and crush
4. Extrude hot, cool, and crush
5. Extrude wet, dry, and crush
6. Solidify melt or dry a paste on belt and crush
7. Sinter bond and crush

There are other ways to accomplish granulation. In the process of **filtration,** a cake is formed which has a tendency to adhere through the resultant close physical contact. If there are binders or soluble ingredients in a filter cake, the dried cake is often a hard mass. Fibers, clays, metal powders, and filter aid cakes often possess a good degree of wet and dry strength. Each case is specific; but it is well to consider that filtration (Sec. 19) is a means for size enlargement. Crushed filter cake is a product of granulation.

Briquettes made from fine particles with a moist binder, or material which is not briquetted, may be fed to an **oscillating granulator** (Fig. 8-66). This consists of a

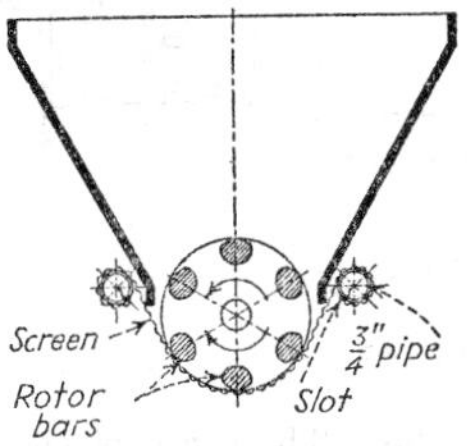

FIG. 8-66. Oscillating granulator, schematic section. (*F. J. Stokes Machine Co.*)

set of bars arranged in cylindrical form and oscillating over a screen of suitable mesh. The granules are coarse (20 mesh or over) and capacities are high, running up to 2000 lb./hr. using 6- and 4-mesh screens. Moisture control is critical.

A concentrated solution can be evaporated or a melt cooled while being stirred in a **graining kettle.** The resultant lumpy mass can be crushed to granular form. In lieu of stirring, vigorous shaking of the fluid mass as it solidifies achieves granulation.

Wet mixture of an antiacid tablet is first passed through a Tornado mill, tray dried, and finished by dry milling in a second Tornado mill [Bucholtz, *Drug & Cosmetic Ind.*, **86**, 478 (April, 1960)].

Nodulizing. Fine particulates may be gathered into larger ones of more or less spherical form by (1) working them together without additions, (2) coalescing them with binders, (3) drying fluid mixtures, (4) creating binding action through heat, or (5) chemical reaction.

Some particulates are susceptible to coalescence through **contact.** Pigments ground in a ball mill have a pebbly character. A process called Spheronizing has been developed for carbon black. The technique is one of subjecting particles to turbulent mechanical action in mixers with specially designed agitators. The charge is usually seeded with the finer agglomerates from a previous batch. It helps with some powders to subject them to ball milling before this finishing operation. Dyes, clays, silica gels, pigments, and the like are also amenable to this treatment. Early United States patents on spheronizing are: Reissue 19,750; 2,120,540; 2,316,043; 2,120,541.

The use of **binders** for agglomerating has been discussed. If the pebbles so formed are hardened by drying, nodular products result. This has been practiced for fertilizer blends to ensure uniform mixture and to reduce dusting and caking. In this, the term granulation has been used, but nodulizing is more appropriate (Fig. 8-67). The binding of taconite for pelleting or briquetting has been achieved with several ingredients. Bentonite and gelatinized starch have been effective. Caustic soda-peat binder has also given good pellets. Taconite of 69 to 76 per cent minus No. 325 sieve is blended with 12 lb. peat per ton, and with caustic; $\frac{3}{4}$-in. pellets made from this binder mix should crush green at 4 to 6 lb., after 100°C. drying at 10 lb., and there should be no decrepitation or breakdown after heating to 500°C. [Piret *et al.*, *Ind. Eng. Chem.*, **53**, 215 (1961)].

Agglomeration by **partial fusion** often results in the formation of nodules. In the making of cement clinker, partial fusion is accompanied by reaction to form the hydraulic compounds. The term **sintering** is applicable in the handling of ores where a combustible ingredient is mixed and reacted to create a firm bond. It is also applicable to heat bonding below the point of liquefaction, as in powder metallurgy.

Fusion methods may be static or dynamic. The latter produces nodules. A diagrammatic scheme for a nodules plant is illustrated in Fig. 8-68. Nodulizing and sintering are compared in Table 8-63.

Ceramic, metal, refractory, and radioactive particles

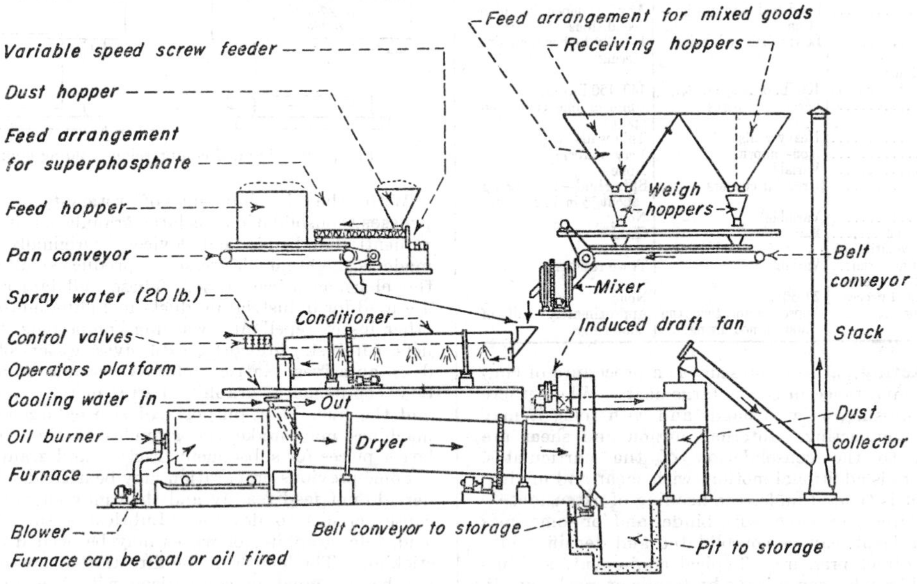

FIG. 8-67. Apparatus for granulation of fertilizers. [*Chem. & Met. Eng.*, **47**, 103 (1940).]

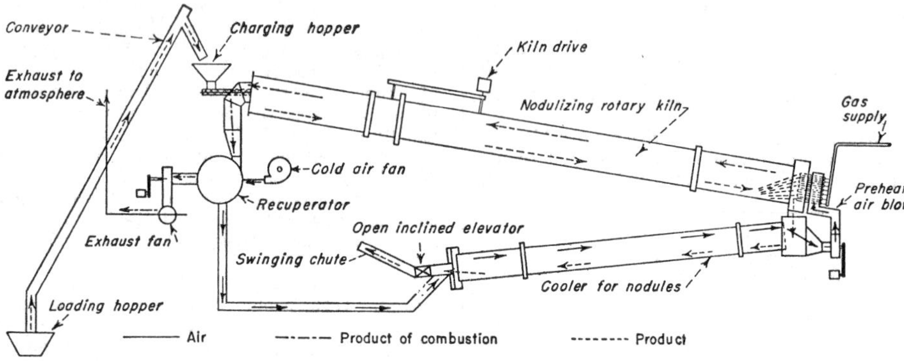

FIG. 8-68. Diagrammatic arrangement of nodules plant.

are gathered into spherical pellets by passing particulate gas suspensions through the plasma flame in a process devised by Thermal Dynamics Corp. [*Ind. Eng. Chem.*, **53**, Suppl. 95A (February, 1961)].

The freezing of molten droplets is well known in the making of lead **shot**. A melt discharged in a fine stream in a tower breaks up into droplets which assume a spherical shape as they fall and they solidify in that period of fall. Drop size, density, and tower height are design factors. Other metals, including steel, may be shotted, as may also salts and organic compounds.

Table 8-63. Comparison of Nodulizing and Sintering for Plants of the Same Capacity

Item	Sintering plant	Nodulizing plant
Capital costs	Higher than nodulizing	Less than sintering
Operating costs	Higher than nodulizing	Less than sintering
Maintenance	High	Very low
Engineering supervision	Constant	Intermittent
Operation	Semicontinuous	Continuous
Feed	Minimum variation—coarse with minimum of fines with controlled moisture and with solid fuel	All variations—any size, wet or dry, coarse or fine, with or without carbon
Fuel:		
Type	Solid fuel with gas ignition	Any fuel depending upon conditions
Cost	Lower than nodulizing	Usually higher than sintering
Finished product:		
Weight/cu. ft. (iron ore)	100 lb. or less/cu. ft.	140–150 lb./cu. ft.
Porosity	Large open pores	Uniform fine connected pores
Pore walls	Heavy walls	Thin walls
Uniformity	Non-uniform	Very uniform
Moisture	Variable	None
Shape	Irregular clusters	Spherical—averaging about ½ in. in diameter
Ignition loss	Variable	None
Rate of reduction	Fair	Good
Removal of volatile or combustion material	Variable	Trace residual
Finished product returned to beginning of process	20–30%	None
Required labor	Approximately twice the labor of nodulizing	Approximately half of sintering

Compacting. Use of pressure is a procedure of considerable importance in size enlargement Where there is direct pressure, as with molds and with rolls, it may be called compacting. Internal motion and shear are incidental to the consolidation of the particulates. Where there is additional motion, with shear and mixing, the subject is treated under the heading of extrusion.

Particulates, sometimes with binder and/or sometimes with a lubricant, can be consolidated and densified into cakes by direct pressure. Typical equipment, as illustrated in Fig. 8-69, comprises a hydraulic or mechanically operated **press** with platens containing a **mold** having a plunger and a die. These are often used for formed pieces; but such presses may be used for random shapes and sizes of material for easy handling and subsequent granulation. For example, the press cake from oil extraction is a consolidated residue in the form of flat blocks with irregular faces bearing the imprint of the bagging rather than mold which enclosed it. Because the cake is large and hence requires several steps in granulation and because labor is heavy, this is not often used for later granulation unless earlier processing steps call for the use of such a press.

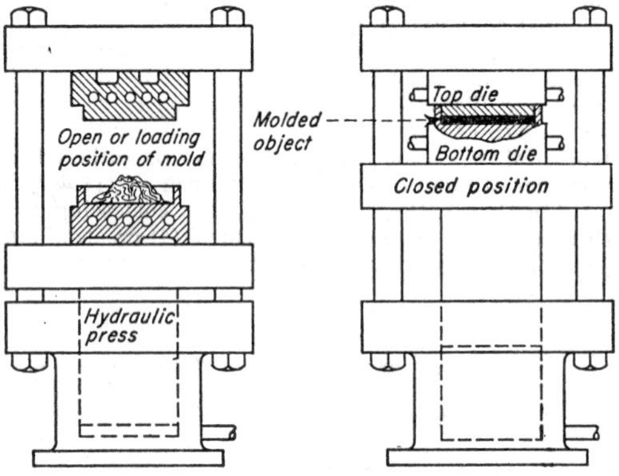

FIG. 8-69. Typical compression-molding equipment.

With the development of rotary-type **tableting presses,** consolidation for later granulation is more conveniently handled in such devices. Originally these were made as single-punch presses to produce small tablets for the pharmaceutical trade. These and larger machines are used for industrial products including moth balls and other insect repellants, washing compounds, food products, catalysts, fireworks, explosives, water-color paints, dyes, abrasives, plastic preforms, ceramic products, battery components, graphite parts, metal-powder forms, and the like. For purposes of size enlargement, these machines may make the granules or they may make larger pieces for subsequent fracture and granulation.

Some previous preparation may be needed. Fine powders do not feed readily and they may entrap air which causes cracks to develop. Lubricants such as stearic acid, talc, graphite, or waxes may be needed to prevent sticking. The length in the direction of pressing should not be too great in comparison with the diameter, as otherwise soft sections may develop in the pieces. The technique is applicable for catalysts, where many small pieces are needed, and production speeds up to 4000 or more per minute are obtained. Normally single-stroke machines operate up to 100 pieces per minute, while rotary and double-rotary types do up to 500 and 1000 pieces per minute. With larger pieces, the rate is substantially reduced as to number but the weight of output may be higher. The technique is used in powder metallurgy to prepare small shaped parts which are further hardened by sintering in a non-oxidizing atmosphere; it is also applicable to densify metal powders into small tablets to simplify the forming of larger pieces.

Many fine particulates are pregranulated before being fed to the tablet machine. The Stokes Force-Flo die feeder makes direct feeding possible. The feeder itself compacts and densifies the mixed powders and deaerates them for satisfactory functioning of the tablet machine [Kibbe, *Drug & Cosmetic Ind.*, **88** (2), 170 (1961)].

While the formation of tablets in the automatic tablet machine solves many **briquetting** problems, it is a relatively costly operation where large capacity is required and where lump shape and size and uniform density are not very important. Such would be the case with fuels, ores, fertilizers, and other bulk chemicals. Binders are usually required, such as pitch for coal, silicates, sugars, soluble salts, lignin products, and the like for other uses. A common device for such briquettes is a pair of large mated rolls, the surfaces of which are recessed in cavities in a waffle-iron effect (Fig. 8-70). Material fed into the

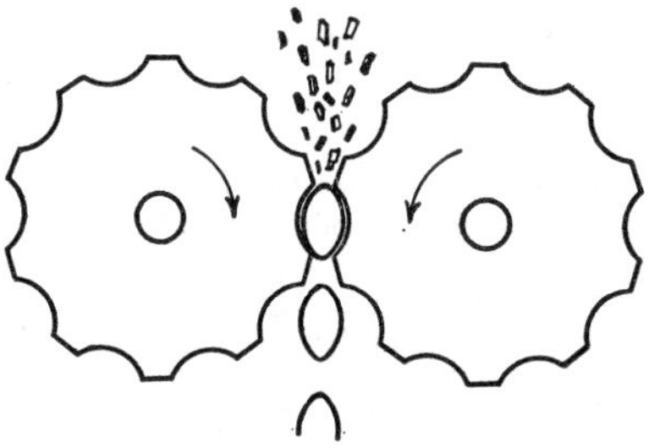

Fig. 8-70. Operating principle of briquetting rolls.

space between and above the rolls falls into successive cavities and is compacted as the rolls come together. The pieces then discharge as the rolls separate. The relation between the volume of material, loosely packed, as it is taken into the rolls and the cavity volume at the maximum compression places some requirements on size grading and the flow and volume relations with the binder present. Briquettes so formed are usually soft in their centers and hard on the surfaces and edges where there are greater pressure and particle rearrangements.

Paired rolls have been employed to compact powder masses. When operated at a speed differential, they produce friction and heat to soften, mix, and consolidate material. In general, pressures have not been high and soft materials, plastics, rubber, and the like have been so processed. Within recent years, there has been a more thorough study of roll action in compacting. Higher pressures have been used, and a resultant higher densification and strength have occurred. An art has developed in the forming of metal sheet from powder. The sheet is reasonably strong so that it can be moved to a sintering furnace to complete the bonding. It would be a good means to densify the metal powder by making a sheet, tearing it apart, and breaking it to granules.

Allis-Chalmers Mfg. Co. has developed the technique of high-pressure roll compaction for agglomerating to dense masses and granulating with fewer fines. Urea, calcium chloride, starch, potash, salt, and many others have been so processed (Fig. 8-71). The principles have been extensively developed [Kurtz and Barduhn, *Chem. Eng. Progress*, **56** (1), 67 (1960)]. There is the width at the bite point in the rolls, the void content there, and the roll clearance at its closest spacing between which the voids are reduced and the material compacted. There being little sliding friction, maintenance from wear is

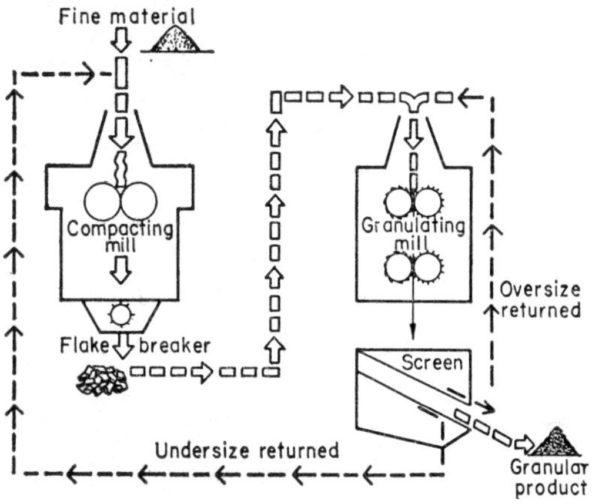

Fig. 8-71. Compacting-process flow diagram. (*Allis-Chalmers Mfg. Co.*)

generally low. However, high-pressure rolls are not inexpensive. Rolls of 24-in. face and 24 in. diameter down to 8-in. face and 18 in. diameter are used. Horsepower is up to 200, with roll surface speeds up to 190 ft./min. Capacities are high, at least with the larger sheet thicknesses of the range between 0.020 and 0.250 in.

Extrusion. This action is associated with the application of force in a manner which includes rubbing, shearing, and mixing. It is applied over a wide range of materials: metals and alloys; rubber and plastics; carbon and graphite; inorganic pastes; flour and starch pastes and doughs; feeds; coatings for wire (of plastic as insulation or mineral mixes as weld rods); and the like. It has many ramifications where shaped sections are concerned but is relatively simpler for random pieces.

The types of extrusion devices used in size enlargement are:

1. *Presses.* These may be hydraulic or mechanical in their operation, and they are used for difficult materials where high pressures and/or temperatures are needed. There are horizontal and vertical types. They are intermittent in operation, since the feed must be placed in a pressure chamber, as powder, granules, or preformed pellets or billets. The plunger then squeezes out the air and compacts the mass, after which the material is squeezed out through a die. If the die is small compared with the pressure cylinder, there is some flow and mixing of the feed. If it is large, the slug is pushed out with shearing. The design of presses requires strong tie bars to ensure alignment of the plunger and the press cylinder.

Vertical presses save space but are limited as to pressure, there being few over 12,000 tons total. Horizontal presses are generally used for heavier work, as in metal extrusion. They are also somewhat more convenient, with respect to feeding and flow direction (Fig. 8-72).

2. *Screws or Augers.* For more plastic or mobile masses where high pressures are not required, a screw extruder may be employed (Fig. 8-73). The design of the screw is quite important, since it must carry the stock from the feed point and create the pressure for extrusion.

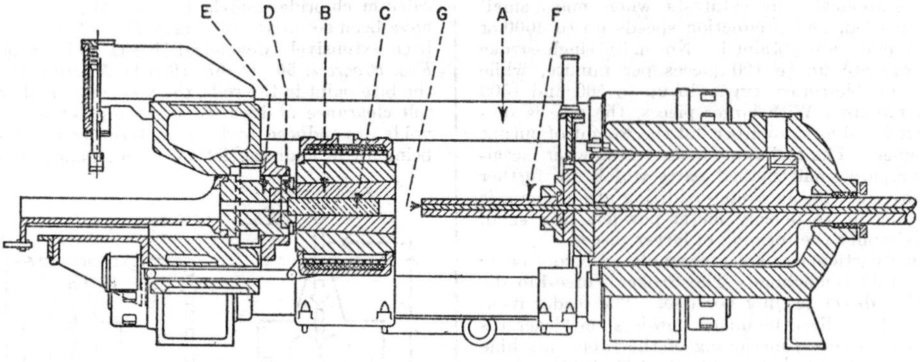

FIG. 8-72. Horizontal hydraulic extrusion press.

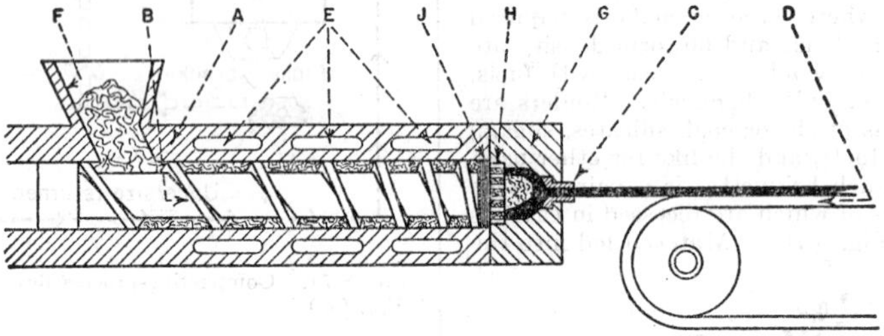

FIG. 8-73. Screw extruder for plastics.

It also serves to compress and compact the particulate or granular feed. There is also some mixing action in the screw. Temperature control is important, partly because of the value in enhancing properties of the extrudate and also to get the proper relation between slip in the screw compared with that at the wall.

3. *Roller and Die.* A roller or set of rollers operating within a perforated die ring forces the particulate, granular, or pasty feed into the holes and compacts it so that it is a continuous solid rod to be cut off by a knife at

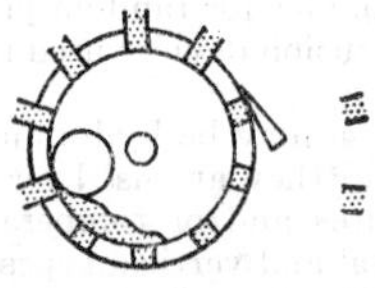

FIG. 8-74. Operating principle of pellet mill.

the periphery (Fig. 8-74). An improved form, the *Century pellet mill* (California Pellet Mill Co.), has the holes in the ring at an angle to the radius to achieve a direct thrust from the roller.

Presses are employed for the extrusion of metals, carbon and graphite, and some plastic and ceramic materials. Screw devices are used with plastics, clays, and other more flowable materials. The meat chopper, known in the home and the market, is a pelleting device of this type, and it has its counterpart in larger equipment in industry (Tables 8-64 and 8-65).

Dies and rolls as produced by Sprout, Waldon, California Pellet Mill, and a few others have found extensive use in pelleting grain, feed, and some food products The use has been extended to industrial operations.

Table 8-64. General Information on the Extrusion of Plastics

Plastic	Extrusion temp., °F.	Stability at extrusion temp.	Consistency at extrusion temp.	Extruded cross sections made
Cellulose acetate	340–500	Good	Semimelt	Sheets, rods, tubes, shapes
Cellulose acetate butyrate	340–500	Good	Semimelt	Sheets, rods, tubes, shapes
Ethyl cellulose	340–500	Good	Semimelt	Sheets, rods, tubes, shapes
Polyvinyl chloride	300–350	Fair	Dough	Sheets, rods, tubes, shapes
Polystyrene	375–500	Good	Rubbery	Sheets, rods, tubes, shapes
Acrylic resins	250–350	Good	Rubbery	Sheets, rods, tubes, shapes
Vinylidene chloride resins	300–350	Fair	Semimelt	Sheets, small cross sections, filaments
Polyethylene	300–500	Good	Dough	All shapes and filaments
Nylons	400–600	Fair	Semimelt	Sheets, small cross sections, filaments

Table 8-65. Average Productive Capacities of Screw Extrusion Machines for 0.25-in. Rod of Polyvinyl Chloride (Sp. Gr. 1.35)

Diameter of Screw, In.	Productive Capacity, Lb./Hr.
2	30– 50
2.5	40– 75
3.25	75–125
3.5	95–150
4.5	150–200
6	250–300

SECTION 9

HEAT GENERATION, TRANSPORT, AND STORAGE

BY

Charles E. Day, Jr., B.E.E., Senior Engineer, Engineering Department, E. I. du Pont de Nemours & Co.; Member, American Society of Mechanical Engineers. (Fuels)

Rowan P. Perkins, B.S.M.E., Senior Engineer, Engineering Department, E. I. du Pont de Nemours & Co.; Member, American Society of Mechanical Engineers. (Combustion)

Elmer S. Monroe, Jr., M.M.E., Consultant, Engineering Department, E. I. du Pont de Nemours & Co.; Member, American Society of Mechanical Engineers. (Combustion-equipment Design)

Frederick M. Brunn, B.S. M.E., Foster Wheeler Corporation. (Heat Transport)

A. C. Mueller, Ph.D., Principal Consultant, Engineering Department, E. I. du Pont de Nemours & Co.; Member, American Institute of Chemical Engineers, American Chemical Society, American Society of Mechanical Engineers, American Association for the Advancement of Science. (Heat Storage)

D. Barton Turkington, M.S.M.E., Professor and Chairman, School of Mechanical Engineering, University of Oklahoma; Member, American Society of Mechanical Engineers, American Society of Heating, Refrigerating and Air-Conditioning Engineers, American Society for Engineering Education. (Section Editor)

CONTENTS

FUELS

GENERAL REFERENCES: Skrotzki and Vopat, "Applied Energy Conversion," McGraw-Hill, New York, 1945.

THEORY OF COMBUSTION

The combustible matter in the various power-plant fuels is composed of carbon, hydrogen, and sulfur. Combustion is the chemical combination of the fuel elements with oxygen. The basic equations for combustion are as follows:

$$C + O_2 = CO_2$$
$$2C + O_2 = 2CO \text{ (partial combustion)}$$
$$2H_2 + O_2 = 2H_2O$$
$$S + O_2 = SO_2$$

The weight of oxygen chemically required for complete combustion is given by the following equation:

$$W_O = 2.67C + 8\left(H - \frac{O}{8}\right) + S \qquad (9\text{-}1)$$

where W_O = weight of oxygen, lb./lb. fuel

These values for C, O, H, and S are obtained from the ultimate analysis directly for solid and liquid fuels. For gaseous fuels a conversion from the volumetric analysis is required.

Since oxygen is rarely supplied in a pure state but is generally supplied as a constituent of air, it is necessary to include the nitrogen weight to obtain the total products of combustion. Equation (9-1) can be written for the weight of dry air required for complete combustion as follows:

$$W_a = 11.5C + 34.5\left(H - \frac{O}{8}\right) + 4.32S \qquad (9\text{-}2)$$

where W_a = weight of air, lb./lb.fuel

In operating furnaces, if the theoretical amount of air were supplied, the fuel would not burn completely. An amount greater than W_a or some excess air is required. If W_A is the amount of air actually supplied per pound of fuel, then

$$\text{Excess air percentage} = \frac{(W_A - W_a)(100)}{W_a} \qquad (9\text{-}3)$$

The volume of air corresponding to W_A or W_a for any air temperature and pressure is found by the gas equation

$$V = \frac{(W_A \text{ or } W_a)(53.3)(t_a + 460)}{144p_a} \qquad (9\text{-}4)$$

where V = air volume, cu. ft.
t_a = air temperature, °F.
p_a = air pressure, lb./sq. in. abs.

In the case of a gaseous fuel, the weight or volume of air is at times expressed in terms of 1 cu. ft. instead of 1 lb. of the fuel gas. The previous equations have been developed on the basis of 1 lb. of fuel (gas, liquid, or solid) for which the density of the fuel-gas mixture is needed. If not known, it can be obtained from the molal relations by

$$D_M = \frac{MW}{359(14.7/p_M)[(t_M + 460)/492]} \qquad (9\text{-}5)$$

where D_M = density of fuel-gas mixture, lb/cu. ft.
p_M = gas pressure, lb./sq. in. abs.
t_M = gas temperature, °F.
MW = molecular weight of gas mixture

SOLID FUELS

Coal

Coal is our most abundant fuel for power production. It is the principal fuel of the electric power industry and for industrial steam plants. Coal has virtually ceased to exist as a railroad fuel, a field which it once dominated, and is rapidly disappearing from the domestic heating market.

Coals are ranked according to their degree of progressive alteration from lignite to bituminous to anthracite. Table 9-1 shows the system of ranking most frequently used to group coals of similar characteristics. These classifications, however, have little meaning to the user who is actually most interested in cost, analysis, and performance. The analyses used for evaluating coal are the "proximate analysis" and the "ultimate analysis." The **ultimate analysis** gives the exact chemical composition of a fuel without describing the physical form. Such an analysis gives the data needed for combustion calculations.

The **proximate analysis** is useful in giving some idea of how a fuel will behave in a furnace. It includes:

1. Percentage of moisture
2. Percentage of ash
3. Percentage of volatile matter
4. Percentage of fixed carbon

These percentages add to 100.

The analytical procedures followed are purely arbitrary, and standard methods adopted by the A.S.T.M. and reported in Standards for Coal and Coke must therefore be followed carefully.

Moisture is determined by drying the coal under standard conditions for 1 hr. at 104° to 110°C. Values obtained in this way represent the sum of the surface moisture, from mine waters, rain, or preparation plant, and the bed or inherent moisture. The latter is characteristic of various coals and ranges from 2 to 4 per cent for anthracites and bituminous coals in Pennsylvania and West Virginia; from 7 to 15 per cent for the bituminous coals in Illinois, Indiana, and western Kentucky; and from 30 to 40 per cent for lignites. Additional moisture may be released by heating to higher temperatures, but such moisture is considered to be an integral part of the coal and is held by physical or chemical forces. Under comparable conditions of exposure, the amount of surface moisture progressively increases as the size of the coal particles is decreased.

The **volatile matter** is determined by heating a sample of coal in a covered crucible for 7 min. at 950°C. The loss in weight, minus the moisture, represents the amount of gaseous constituents produced by the decomposition of the coal substance. The **ash** is the inorganic residue resulting from the burning of the coal. It consists principally of silica, alumina, ferric oxide, and lime, together with smaller amounts of magnesia, titanium oxide, alkali compounds, and sulfur compounds. These

Table 9-1. Analyses of Selected Coals of Various Ranks
"As received" basis

Rank*	State	Seam	Proximate analysis, %				Ultimate analysis, %					Heating value, B.t.u./lb.
			Moisture	Volatile matter	Fixed carbon	Ash	Carbon	Hydrogen	Oxygen	Sulfur	Nitrogen	
Anthracitic:												
Meta-anthracite	Rhode Island	Uncorrelated	1.0	4.0	66.7	28.3	....	...	....	...	...	9,620
Anthracite	Pennsylvania	Mammoth	2.3	3.1	87.7	6.9	86.7	2.2	2.9	0.5	0.8	13,540
Anthracite	Pennsylvania	Big Lykens	2.1	7.5	80.3	10.1	80.9	3.3	4.2	0.5	1.0	13,480
Semianthracite	Virginia	Merrimac	2.2	12.4	67.4	18.0	72.4	3.6	4.7	0.5	0.8	12,270
Bituminous:												
Low-volatile	West Virginia	Pocahontas No. 3	3.5	18.2	74.4	3.9	84.0	4.8	5.6	0.6	1.1	14,550
Medium-volatile	West Virginia	Sewell	3.1	25.0	66.8	5.1	....	...	....	1.3	...	14,290
High-volatile A	Pennsylvania	Pittsburgh	2.6	30.0	58.3	9.1	76.6	5.2	6.2	1.3	1.6	13,610
High-volatile A	Kentucky	Elkhorn	3.1	35.0	58.9	3.0	79.2	5.7	10.0	0.6	1.5	14,290
High-volatile B	Ohio	Middle Kittanning	8.2	36.1	48.7	7.0	68.4	5.6	16.4	1.2	1.4	12,160
High-volatile B	Kentucky	No. 6	7.2	39.8	48.8	4.2	71.5	5.8	14.3	2.6	1.6	12,950
High-volatile C	Illinois	No. 2	12.1	40.2	39.1	8.6	62.8	5.9	17.4	4.3	1.0	11,480
High-volatile C	Indiana	No. 6	12.4	36.6	42.3	8.7	63.4	5.7	18.6	2.3	1.3	11,420
Subbituminous:												
Subbituminous A or high-volatile bituminous C	Wyoming	Uncorrelated	16.5	34.2	38.1	11.2	....	...	....	2.1	...	9,740
Subbituminous B	Wyoming	Monarch	23.2	33.3	39.7	3.8	54.6	6.4	33.8	0.4	1.0	9,420
Subbituminous C	Wyoming	Uncorrelated	24.6	27.7	39.9	7.8	....	...	....	1.1	...	8,610
Lignitic:												
Lignite	North Dakota	Beulah	34.8	28.2	30.8	6.2	42.4	6.7	43.3	0.7	1.7	7,210

* According to A.S.T.M. method of classification.

Table 9-2. Ash-softening Temperatures and Ash Composition of Selected Coals*

Sample	Softening temperature, °F.	Analysis of ash, %							
		SiO_2	Al_2O_3	Fe_2O_3	TiO_2	CaO	MgO	Na_2O+K_2O	SO_3
Montana subbituminous	2060	30.7	19.6	18.9	1.1	11.3	3.7	2.4	12.2
Illinois bituminous	2320	46.2	22.9	7.7	1.0	10.1	1.6	1.5	8.9
Pennsylvania bituminous	2500	49.7	26.8	11.4	1.2	4.2	0.8	2.9	2.5
West Virginia semibituminous	2730	51.0	30.9	10.7	1.9	2.1	0.9	1.4	0.6
Kentucky bituminous	+2900	58.5	30.6	4.2	1.8	2.0	0.4	1.6	0.9

* *U.S. Bur. Mines Bull.* 209.

compounds are derived largely from the clay, shale, slate, pyrite, and other mineral constituents in the coal. **Fixed carbon** is determined by subtracting from 100 the percentages of moisture, volatile matter, and ash. It represents the coke residue, minus the ash.

The percentages of sulfur, heating value, and ash-softening temperature are commonly reported with the proximate analysis but are separate determinations.

The proximate analysis is the most widely used procedure for evaluating coal, particularly when the general characteristics of other coals from the same district are known. It falls far short, however, of being a complete criterion for evaluation for utilization in specific equipment or for a specific process.

For the ultimate analysis, the percentages of carbon, hydrogen, nitrogen, and sulfur are determined by direct analytical methods. Ash is determined as in the proximate analysis. Since there is no satisfactory method for the direct determination of oxygen, it is found by subtracting the sum of the other five components from 100. The percentage of oxygen found in this way is subject to the errors incurred in the other determinations, and especially by the change in weight of the ash-forming mineral constituents upon ignition. Because the air-dried samples used for these determinations contain moisture, the oxygen and hydrogen in this moisture are included in the analysis. When the moisture content is known, the results may be calculated to the "dry" basis.

Table 9-1 lists the results of proximate and ultimate analyses of selected American coals of various ranks, as reported by the U.S. Bureau of Mines.

The **heating value** is obtained by the complete combustion of a unit quantity of coal in an oxygen-bomb calorimeter under carefully defined conditions. The "gross" or "high" heating value is obtained by this method, as the latent heat of moisture in the combustion products is recovered. The results may be expressed on the "as received" or "dry" or "dry and ash-free" basis.

The **ash-softening temperature** of coal ash is determined by a standard method adopted by the A.S.T.M. Ashes that fuse in the range 1900° to 2200°F. are considered **low fusing**; those in the range 2200° to 2600°F. **medium fusing**; and those above 2600°F. **high fusing.** In general, coal ashes having low softening temperatures are likely to form clinkers, but the chemical composition of the ash, combustion conditions, and other factors affects the clinker formation. Table 9-2 shows the composition and softening temperatures of the ashes from several selected coals.

Physical Properties. The A.S.T.M. has adopted standard procedures for determining the **true** and **apparent specific gravities** of coal and coke. It is necessary to distinguish between the apparent specific gravity of a lump of porous material, such as coke, and the true specific gravity of the substance forming the lump (see Table 9-3).

Coals differ considerably in **specific heats,** depending upon the kind of coal, its ash and moisture content, etc. The range is from about 0.25 to 0.37. For metallurgical coke of 5 per cent ash, the specific heats shown in Table 9-4 have been determined.

The **bulk density** is a measure of the weight per cubic

Table 9-3. Typical Specific Gravities

Fuel	Specific gravity		Pores, %
	True	Apparent	
Bituminous coal	1.25-1.45		
By-product coke	1.75-2.00	0.75-1.1	40-60
Low-temperature coke	1.50-1.75	0.5 -1.1*	30-70
Charcoal	1.4 -1.7	0.3 -0.6	65-80
Anthracite	1.45-1.7		
Wood	0.5 -1.1		

* By unusual procedures in preparing coal previous to carbonization, and control of carbonization conditions, an apparent specfic gravity as high as 1.4 may be obtained.

Table 9-4. Specific Heat of Coke

Temperature range, °C.	20-260	20-538	20-815	20-1093
Average specific heat	0.240	0.303	0.338	0.363

foot of broken coal, including the void space between particles. It is of interest in the storage of coal and in the preparation of coal to be charged in by-product coke ovens. Factors affecting the bulk density of coal are specific gravity, size consist, moisture content, degree of compaction, and use of oil in preparaing the coal. Typical values for the bulk density of coals are as follows: subbituminous and high-volatile bituminous, 42 to 56 lb./cu. ft.; low- and medium-volatile bituminous, 49 to 57 lb./cu. ft.; anthracite, 50 to 58 lb./cu. ft.

Size stability refers to the ability of coal to withstand breakage during handling and shipping. It is determined by twice dropping a 50-lb. sample of coal from a height of 6 ft. onto a steel plate. From the size distribution before and after the test, the size stability is reported as a percentage factor (A.S.T.M. D 440–37T). The friability test measures the tendency of a coal to break during handling. It is actually the complement of size stability and is determined by the standard tumbler test (A.S.T.M. D 441–37T). In general, the high-volatile bituminous coals are less friable than the low-volatile coals.

The **grindability index** is a term used to indicate the relative ease of pulverizing a coal. The A.S.T.M. has adopted both the Hardgrove-machine method and the ball-mill method as tentative standard procedures. The Hardgrove-machine method (A.S.T.M. D 409–37T), through use of a grinding machine of special design, furnishes a relative grindability index based on a coal that is assumed to have an index of 100. The ball-mill method (A.S.T.M. D 408–37T) determines the relative amounts of energy required to pulverize different coals by placing a sample of coal in a ball mill and finding the number of revolutions required to grind it so that 80 per cent of the sample passes a No. 200 sieve. Approximate conversions of ball-mill grindability indexes into Hardgrove grindability indexes may be made as follows:

Ball-mill grindability index, %	20	30	40	50	60	70	80	90	100
Hardgrove grindability index, %	39	43	56	68	80	90	100	110	118

Mineral Matter in Coal. The ash-forming mineral constituents in coal have originated from (1) original plant ash, (2) sedimentary deposition, (3) deposits from percolating ground waters, and (4) material from the roof or floor of the mine added during the mining process. The principal ingredients present are slate, clay, sandstone, shale, carbonates, pyrite, and gypsum. These and other minor constituents give rise to the ash residue following combustion of the coal. The ash ordinarily weighs less than the original mineral matter. During the combustion process, clay and shale lose their water of hydration; the carbonates are decomposed, freeing carbon dioxide; and pyrite is oxidized to ferric oxide, giving off sulfur dioxide. The relative amounts of mineral constituents present determine the characteristics of the ash and impose certain limitations on the utilization of the coal.

The **sulfur** in coal occurs in three forms: (1) pyritic sulfur in the form of pyrite or marcasite, (2) organic substance, and (3) sulfate sulfur, which appears as iron or calcium sulfate. There is no evidence that sulfur occurs in the coal in its free state. The relative proportions of the sulfur found in coal vary widely, although more than small amounts of the sulfate form are not present in most freshly mined coals. During combustion of a coal, from 70 to 90 per cent of the sulfur appears in the combustion products as sulfur dioxide. About half the sulfur in the coal carbonized in by-product ovens is retained in the coke.

Coke

Coke is the solid carbonaceous residue remaining after the high-temperature distillation of moisture and volatile matter from coal. Approximately 16 per cent of the bituminous coal mined in the United States is converted to coke. Coke is used principally in blast furnaces, also in foundries and to a limited degree in gas producers. Lump coke is generally desired for these purposes. Fine screenings from lump coke are called coke breeze. The coke breeze is treated as a by-product and is often sold for boiler fuel.

A typical range of analyses for coke and coke breeze is as follows:

	Coke	Coke breeze
Volatile, % by weight	0.5–2.0	4–6
Fixed, % by weight	88–95	76–80
Ash, % by weight	0.5–5.0	10–20
H_2O, % by weight	0.5–5.0	0.5–5.0

Carbonization of Coal. The carbonization of coal is accomplished by heating a suitable coal, or a blend of coals, in an oven or retort in the absence of air. The complex coal substance is broken down, with the evolution of combustible gases and condensible tars and oils, leaving a residue of coke. The ability to form a strong coke is found only in the bituminous class of coals, and relatively few of these are coking coals suitable for use in by-product ovens. The coal must form a strong coherent coke, should not expand in the oven during the heating process, and should not contain over 1.5 per cent sulfur or 9 per cent ash. For good yields of gas, the dry and ash-free volatile matter should be over 35 per cent. Coal charged into by-product ovens is usually a blend of high-volatile coal with 10 to 50 per cent low-volatile coal. Blending is done to improve the quality of the coke or to avoid damage to the oven caused by expansion of the charge.

Thermal Decomposition of Coal. When the temperature throughout a small mass of crushed bituminous coal is raised slowly, gases are evolved, slowly at first. They consist principally of carbon dioxide, carbon monoxide, and water vapor. As the temperature rises, the composition of the evolved gases changes continually. Traces of gaseous hydrocarbons, particularly methane, appear early in the process. Upon further heating, liquefiable hydrocarbons appear in the volatile products, but the rate of evolution of gases and vapors continues low until the **softening temperature** of the particular coal is reached. A coal does not fuse at a well-defined temperature, but for each coal there is a short temperature range within which enough liquid products form to cause the whole mass of coal particles to coalesce more or less completely. The degree of fusion varies widely for different coals.

The rate of evolution of volatile products formed by decomposition of the coal rapidly increases as the temperature rises above the softening point. If the coal is one that fuses sufficiently to become plastic, the evolved gases form bubbles that work their way out of the plastic mass, causing it to become spongy. As decomposition of the coal substance progresses, with continued evolution of volatile products, the plasticity of the coking mass becomes less and less, until finally the bubbles are trapped and the mass takes on a fairly rigid cellular structure. Further evolution of gas can then occur only by diffusion through the cell walls or through cracks in the structure.

As the temperature is carried still higher, several processes occur simultaneously. Volatile products continue to be evolved, and the coke pieces shrink in volume, these two processes being opposite in their effect so far as the apparent specific gravity is concerned. Depending upon the nature of the original coal, either may predominate; *i.e.*, the apparent specific gravity may either increase or decrease. The true specific gravity of the coke substance, however, always increases, going from about 1.5 at 500°C. to 1.9 or higher at 1000°C. The reactivity of the coke decreases steadily during the devolatilization process, and for most cokes the hardness and strength of the coke increase with devolatilization.

The Process of Carbonization in By-product Ovens. Modern by-product coke ovens are commonly about 40 ft. long, 12 to 14 ft. high, and 12 to 18 in. in average width, with an outward taper of about 1.5 to 4 in. from pushing to discharge end. The ovens are separated by heating flues and are arranged side to side in "batteries" of as many as 80 ovens. The heating flues are usually vertical, and coal gas or producer gas is used as a fuel. Coal is charged from the top; and. at the end of the coking period, doors at each end of the oven are opened, and the coke is pushed from the oven onto a wharf or into special quenching cars. The volatile products evolved are collected in mains; and tars, light oils, fuel gas, and other primary by-products are recovered.

When the coal is charged into a hot oven, the layer of coal adjacent to the heated walls is quickly decomposed. A plastic layer is formed, which moves slowly toward the center of the oven as carbonization proceeds. The gases and primary tar vapors, evolved by decomposition of the coal substance in the plastic zone and the semicoke residue, travel outward toward the wall of the oven and upward through the coke and semicoke. Because of the resistance of the plastic layer to the passage of gases, the travel is outward rather than inward. Coal is an extremely poor conductor of heat, and the center of the charge remains at a low temperature for several hours after being discharged. The plastic zone is about 0.5 in. thick, and the drop in temperature from the heated side to the inner side may be from 700° to 900°F. The two plastic layers finally meet in the center at the end of the coking process. The average coking rate is about 1 in./hr., and the final carbonizing temperature is from 900° to 1000°C.

Products of Coal Carbonization. In addition to about 1400 lb. of coke, the complex volatile constituents yield the following by-products per ton of coal charged:

1. About 11,000 cu. ft. of fuel gas of approximately 550 B.t.u./cu. ft.
2. Two to four gallons of **crude light oil** removed from the fuel gas by scrubbing with oil.
3. An **aqueous liquor** containing ammonia, ammonium salts, and various other water-soluble compounds. This liquor is usually heated with a slurry lime to remove all ammonia and is then discarded.
4. **Ammonia**, recovered as indicated above and also scrubbed out of the fuel gas. In most coke plants, all the ammonia is converted to ammonium sulfate. About 20 lb. are recovered.
5. **Tar**, amounting to about 10 gal., is collected from various points in the by-product recovery system. The tar is composed of a large number of liquids and of crystalline compounds, such as naphthalene, anthracene, and others, dissolved in the complex liquid mixture.

In the ordinary coke oven and gas retort, the volatile products liberated from the coal are subjected to subsequent **cracking** by the hot coke and hot walls, and the volatile products listed above are therefore not those initially liberated products, and the gaseous and liquid products finally collected are therefore different both in character and in relative amounts.

Typical yields for a low-temperature carbonization process operating on a high-rank coking coal having 35 per cent volatile matter are:

Semicoke (12% volatile matter)	1500 lb.
Tar	30 gal.
Ammonia	2 lb.
Gas, 950 B.t.u./cu. ft.	3000 cu. ft.

Miscellaneous Solid Fuels

Char. Char is the carbonaceous solid product derived from the low-temperature carbonization of coal.

Low-temperature carbonization is a coal-distillation process at some temperature substantially lower than 2000°F. and generally refers to a process controlled between 900 and 1200°F. In this temperature range, the products consist of (1) semicoke or "char," (2) complex, partly oxygenated liquid hydrocarbons or tar, (3) fixed gases, and (4) water.

The "char" which constitutes about 60 to 80 per cent of the original coal has characteristics making it, in certain respects, superior to the original coal for use as boiler fuel. Because it has been dried, the "char" may actually be higher in B.t.u. content than the original coal, particularly if wet, lower-rank coals are used. The "char" will generally be lower in B.t.u. than the original coal if the dryer high-rank coals are used. Unlike coke, "char" is soft and easy to pulverize. "Char" from relatively hard bituminous coal (50 to 60 grindability) will have a grindability index of near 100. This softening, therefore, may permit uprating of plants where capacity is limited by the pulverizing equipment. Also, unlike coke, "char" has remaining an appreciable volatile content (15 to 20 per cent) and may be burned directly in pulverized-fuel furnaces or as a blend with coal.

Petroleum Cokes. Refineries designed to obtain the greatest yield of gasoline may have an end residue product of coke rather than residual oil. The two principal such products are known as delayed coke and fluid coke. These cokes are produced in a fine granular form. They are similar to coke breeze except that, like residual oil, they contain the impurities from the crude oil and are therefore usually high in sulfur and may also be high in vanadium. Typical analyses of delayed coke and fluid coke are shown in Table 9-5.

Table 9-5. Analysis of Petroleum Cokes

	Delayed-process coke, range	Fluid-process coke, range
Volatile, % by weight	8–18	3.7–7.0
Ash, % by weight	0.05–1.6	0.1–2.8
Bulk density, lb./cu. ft.		55–65
True density, g./ml	1.28–1.42	1.5–1.6
B.t.u. as received		13,900–14,400
Hydrogen, % by weight		1.6–2.1
Carbon, % by weight		88–95
Sulfur, % by weight		1.5–10.0
Ash-softening temp		2200–2800
Grindability	40–60	20–30

Wood. The fuel values of different woods (except resinous woods) are nearly proportional to their weights

Table 9-6. Approximate Weights and Heating Values per Cord of Fuel Woods*

Variety of wood	Weight per cord, lb.		Available heat units per cord, million B.t.u.		Equivalent in heat value to tons of coal†	
	Green	Air dry	Green	Air dry	Green	Air dry
Ash, white	4300	3800	19.9	20.5	0.77	0.79
Beech	5000	3900	19.7	20.9	.76	.80
Birch, yellow	5100	4000	19.4	20.9	.75	.80
Chestnut	4900	2700	12.9	15.6	.50	.60
Cottonwood	4200	2500	12.7	15.0	.49	.58
Elm, white	4400	3100	15.8	17.7	.61	.68
Hickory	5700	4600	23.1	24.8	.89	.95
Maple, sugar	5000	3900	20.4	21.8	.78	.84
Maple, red	4700	3200	17.6	19.1	.68	.73
Oak, red	5800	3900	19.6	21.7	.75	.83
Oak, white	5600	4300	22.4	23.9	.86	.92
Pine, yellow	....	....	21.1	22.0	.81	.85
Pine, white	....	....	12.9	14.2	.50	.55
Walnut, black	....	....	18.6	20.8	.72	.80
Willow	4600	2300	10.9	13.5	.42	.52

* The Use of Wood for Fuel, *U.S. Dept. Agr. Bull.* 753.
† Short ton (2000 lb.) of coal having a heating value of 13,000 B.t.u./lb.

Table 9-7. Detailed Requirements for Fuel Oils—A.S.T.M. D 396 48T (1959)*

Grade of fuel oil†	Flash point, deg. F.	Pour point, deg. F.	Water and sediment, % by volume	Carbon residue on 10% bottoms, %	Ash, % by weight	Distillation temperature, deg. F. 10% point	10% point	End point	Saybolt viscosity, sec. Universal at 100°F.		Furol at 122°F.		Kinematic viscosity, centistokes At 100°F.		At 122°F.		Gravity, deg. A.P.I.	Corrosion, copper strip, 3 hr. at 122°F.§
	Min.	Max.	Max.	Max.	Max.	Max.	Max.	Max.	Max.	Min.	Max.	Min.	Max.	Min.	Max.	Min.	Min.	
No. 1. A distillate oil intended for vaporizing pot-type burners and other burners requiring this grade of fuel	100 or legal	0	trace	0.15	....	420	...	625	...	...	...	..	2.2	1.4	.....	...	35	pass
No. 2. A distillate oil for general-purpose domestic heating in burners not requiring No. 1 fuel oil	100 or legal	20‡	0.10	0.35	....	‖	675	...	40	...	...	..	(4.3)	......	.....	...	26	
No. 4. An oil for burner installations not equipped with preheating facilities	130 or legal	20	0.50	....	0.10	...	...	...	125	45	...	..	(26.4)	(5.8)				
No. 5. A residual-type oil for burner installations equipped with preheating facilities	130 or legal	....	1.00	....	0.10	...	...	...	...	150	40	..	......	(32.1)	(81)			
No. 6. An oil for use in burners equipped with preheaters permitting a high-viscosity fuel....	150	....	2.00¶	....	....	...	...	...	...	...	300	45	......	......	(638)	(92)		

* Recognizing the necessity for low-sulfur fuel oils used in connection with heat-treatment, non-ferrous metal, glass, and ceramic furnaces, and other special uses, a sulfur requirement may be specified in accordance with the following table:

Grade of Fuel Oil	Sulfur, Max., Per Cent
No. 1	0.5
No. 2	1.0
No. 4	no limit
No. 5	no limit
No. 6	no limit

Other sulfur limits may be specified only by mutual agreement between the purchaser and the seller.

† It is the intent of these classifications that failure to meet any requirement of a given grade does not automatically place an oil in the next lower grade unless in fact it meets all requirements of the lower grade.

‡ Lower or higher pour points may be specified whenever required by conditions of storage or use. However, these specifications shall not require a pour point lower than 0°F. under any conditions.

§ The exposed copper strip shall show no gray or black deposit.

‖ The 10 per cent point may be specified at 440°F. maximum for use in other than atomizing burners.

¶ The amount of water by distillation plus the sediment by extraction shall not exceed 2.00 per cent. The amount of sediment by extraction shall not exceed 0.50 per cent. A deduction in quantity shall be made for all water and sediment in excess of 3.0 per cent.

on a dry basis. The resinous woods possess higher heating values than the non-resinous ones. Table 9-6 gives pertinent data for various woods.

Charcoal. Charcoal is the residue remaining after the destructive distillation of wood. It absorbs moisture readily, often containing as much as 10 to 15 per cent water. In addition it usually contains about 2 to 3 per cent ash and 0.5 to 1.0 per cent hydrogen. The heating value of charcoal is about 12,000 to 13,000 B.t.u./lb.

Tanbark. Tanbark is the residue remaining after the bark has been used in tanning operations. It usually contains from 60 to 70 per cent water and has a heating value of 2500 to 3000 B.t.u./lb. In the use of tanbark as a fuel, a very large combustion space is required.

Bagasse. Bagasse is the solid residue remaining after sugar cane has been crushed by pressure rolls. It usually contains from 40 to 50 per cent water. The dry bagasse has a heating value of 8000 to 9000 B.t.u./lb.

LIQUID FUELS

Petroleum

The principal industrial liquid fuels are the by-products of natural petroleum. These fuel oils are marketed in two principal divisions, distillates and residuals. Table 9-7 gives the A.S.T.M. Detailed Requirements for fuel oils. On the West Coast a somewhat different specification for fuel oils known as "Pacific Specification" is generally used. Table 9-8 gives the Pacific Specification for fuel oils. A general classification of fuel oils is given in Table 9-9.

Residual Oil

The principal industrial boiler fuel is residual oil, known variously as No. 6, Bunker C, or PS 400. The residual oil, as the name implies, is left over after the more valuable products are distilled off. As an industrial fuel it competes with coal and its price is generally

Table 9-8. Pacific Specification for Fuel Oils

PS No.	Flash point, °F. Max.	Flash point, °F. Min.	Water and sediment, % max.	Viscosity, sec. Max.	Viscosity, sec. Min.	Distillation temp. 10% point Max.	10% point Min.	90% point Max.	90% point Min.
PS-100	165	110*	0.25	...	...	420	350	550	450
PS-200	...	150	0.50	55†	35†	...	425	...	600
PS-300	...	150	1.00	40‡	25‡				
PS-400	...	150	2.00	...	60‡				

* Or legal.
† Seconds Saybolt Universal at 100°F.
‡ Seconds Saybolt Furol at 122°F.

Table 9-9. General Classification of Fuel Oils*

Trade No.	Principal use	Present specifications, CS12-48 Gravity, °A.P.I.	Lb./gal.	B.t.u./gal.
1	A distillate oil intended for vaporizing pot-type burners and other uses requiring a volatile fuel	35–40	6.879–7.085	135,800–138,800
2	A distillate oil for general-purpose domestic heating for use in burners not requirng No. 1. Moderately volatile	26–34	7.128–7.490	139,400–144,300
3	Formerly, a distillate oil for use in burners requiring a low-viscosity fuel. Now incorporated as part of new No. 2 oil			
4	An oil for burner installations not equipped with preheating facilities	24–25	7.538–7.587	145,000–145,600
5	A residual-type oil for burners equipped with preheating facilities. Sold as Bunker B. Preheat suggested 170°–220°F.	18–22	7.686–7.891	146,800–149,400
6	An oil for use in burners equipped with preheaters permitting a high-viscosity fuel. Bunker C. Preheat suggested 220°–260°F.	14–16	7.998–8.108	150,700–152,000

* As gravities are not included in commercial standards (excepting minimum gravities of 35 for No. 1 oil and 26 for No. 2 oil) this table is unofficial, based on trade practices under code CS12-40.

governed by this competition to a fairly large degree. It is a heavy oil requiring heating to lower the viscosity for pumping and for atomizing. It contains various undesirable impurities including sulfur, vanadium, and sodium, which under certain conditions may cause serious metal corrosion.

A blend of residual oil with lighter oil is marketed as No. 5 oil for installations lacking facilities for heating the oil tanks. The No. 5 can be pumped without preheating but heating before combustion is recommended to obtain satisfactory atomization.

Purchase of Fuel Oils

Units of Sale. Fuel oil is sold in the United States in multiples of the 42-gal. barrel, the contents being measured at 60°F. Measurements made at other temperatures must be corrected to the standard, using expansion coefficients or the tables cited below under Quality of Fuel Oils.

Though fuel oil is purchased for its available heat, this factor is never specified nor is it usually determined. As a matter of fact, the heat of combustion per unit weight varies only to a small extent. However, since fuel oil is invariably purchased by volume, the differences in weight, hence in heating value, should be allowed for in considering price.

Checking Receipts and Testing Quality of Fuel Oils

In drawing contracts and in making acceptance tests, it is advisable to refer to Petroleum Products and Lubricants, *Am. Soc. Testing Materials Rept. Comm.* D2. This report is issued annually and contains standard methods for determination of any physical property. The descriptions of tests given below are intended only to indicate the nature of the tests. Actual determinations of these empirical factors should be carried out precisely as described in the above publication.

Sampling the Oil and Determining Receipts. On receipt in consumers' tanks, the volume of oil should be measured and its average temperature (°F.) obtained immediately. Any recognized method of sampling for laboratory inspection may be used under conditions dictated by the fact that heavy fuel oil, especially, may not be homogeneous but may contain considerable water and salts in suspension or at the bottom of tanks.

Specific Gravity. This determination complements that of temperature of shipments in checking the volume of receipts. Determination can be made by a hydrometer graduated in terms of specific gravity, but it is preferably made with a hydrometer carrying an arbitrary scale termed degrees A.P.I. The latter is defined by

$$\text{Degrees A.P.I.} = \frac{141.5}{\text{specific gravity } 60°\text{F.}/60°\text{F.}} - 131.5 \qquad (9\text{-}6)$$

If the measured temperature of the oil is 60 ±30°F., the true volume at 60°F. can be determined with sufficient accuracy for most cases from the following coefficients of cubical expansion:

Up to 35°A.P.I. = 0.004 per degree
35 to 50°A.P.I. = 0.005 per degree

Abridged volume-correction tables of greater actual and recognized legal accuracy will be found in the publication named above, the same being based upon a complete table in *Nat. Bur. Standards Circ.* 154.

Specifications for Fuel Oils. The specifications described in Table 9-7 are those promulgated as Tentative Specifications for Fuel Oils by the A.S.T.M., as revised for 1959.

Water and Sediment. (For Grades 1 to 5, Inclusive.) Standard Method of Test for Water and Sediment in Petroleum Products by Means of Centrifuge, A.S.T.M. Designation D 96.

Water by Distillation. (For Grade 6.) Standard Method of Test for Water in Petroleum Products and Other Bituminous Materials, A.S.T.M. Designation D 95.

Sediment by Extraction. (For Grade 6.) Sediment in Fuel Oil by Extraction, A.S.T.M. Designation D 473.

Pour Point. Standard Method of Test for Cloud and Pour Points, A.S.T.M. Designation D 97.

Carbon Residue. Standard Method of Test for Carbon Residue of Petroleum Products (Ramsbottom Carbon Residue), A.S.T.M. Designation D 524.

Ash. Procedure for Determination of Ash as Described in the Standard Methods of Analysis of Oils, A.S.T.M. Designation D 482. Sample shall be thoroughly mixed to ensure that the portion for ash determination is representative of the sample.

Distillation. Distillation of Grade 1 oil shall be made in accordance with the Standard Method of Test for Distillation of Gasoline, Naphtha, Kerosene, and Similar Petroleum Products, A.S.T.M. Designation D 86, and of Grade 2 in accordance with the Standard Methods of Testing Gas Oils, A.S.T.M. Designation D 158.

Viscosity. The standard test method designated as D 88-44 calls for the use of a Saybolt Furol or Saybolt Universal viscosimeter. The reading obtained is the time, in seconds, required for 60 cc. of oil at constant temperature to flow through the Furol or Universal orifice under its own (continually decreasing) head. On the other hand, if only relative values of viscosity are required, the expensive Saybolt instrument may be dispensed with and a pipette-type viscosimeter such as described by Ferris [*Ind. Eng. Chem.*, **20**, 974 (1928)] may be used.

The Saybolt Furol orifice is to be used for viscous oils only and at a single standard temperature of 122°F. If the oil shows less than 25 sec. efflux time at this temperature, its viscosity is to be measured at 100°F. with the Saybolt Universal orifice.

Viscosity of Grade 1 shall be determined in accordance with the Tentative Method of Test for Kinematic Viscosity (A.S.T.M. Designation D 445) and of Grades 2, 4, 5, and 6 in accordance with the Standard Method for Viscosity by Means of the Saybolt Viscosimeter (A.S.T.M. Designation D 88).

Flash Point. Special equipment is required for determining the flash point of fuel oil, according to the American standard method D 93 using the A.S.T.M. Pensky-Martens tester. The flash point has scarcely any connection with the manner in which an oil behaves in an oil burner. However, it does bear some relation to safety in storage even though it is obscure. In general, the lower the flash point, the greater the possibility of fire in storage tanks due to a spark or flame. The small consumer will not find it necessary to check the flash point of his fuel oils, but its value should be obtained from the refiner and provision made to keep storage tanks well below this temperature.

Miscellaneous Liquid Fuels

A discussion of liquid fuels can hardly ignore certain fuels other than fuel oil. Gasoline and kerosene are used to a considerable extent for stoves in isolated localities, and gasoline is commonly used as the fuel for plumbers' torches and similar devices. Alcohol and benzol are also used to a limited extent, usually in small

Table 9-10. Combustion Data for Various Alcohol and Benzol Fuels

Fuel	O_2 required for combustion, lb./lb.	Air required for combustion, lb./lb.	Products of combustion, lb./lb.			Approximate higher heating value, B.t.u./lb.
			CO_2	H_2O	N_2	
Ethyl alcohol (C_2H_6O)	2.08	9.04	1.91	1.17	6.95	12,780
Methyl alcohol (CH_4O)	1.5	6.50	1.38	1.12	5.0	9,550
Benzol (C_6H_6)........	3.1	13.32	3.39	0.69	0.24	18,000
Denatured alcohol.....	1.81	7.83	1.66	1.15	6.02	11,600
50% mixture of alcohol and benzol..........	2.45	10.60	2.53	0.92	8.16	14,200

and highly specialized devices. The devices that use any one of these higher-priced fuels are usually made as a unit by the manufacturer, who supplies detailed instructions as to quality of fuel suitable and method for using most satisfactorily.

Industrial use of such liquid fuels as shale oils, coal tar, tar oil, and distillates or residues from low-temperature carbonization of coal is sometimes justified. Suitable methods for using such materials are to be learned only by trial, and little in the way of generalization can be offered.

Coal Tar. Coal tar is a by-product of the manufacture of coke and of coal gas. This tar is a viscous mixture consisting, for the most part, of aromatic compounds. Its heating value varies from 15,000 to 16,500 B.t.u./lb. In order to burn coal tar in regular fuel-oil burners, the tar must be filtered and preheated to such a temperature that its viscosity is reduced to that of the oils for which the particular burner is designed.

Tar Oil. Tar oil is obtained by the distillation of coal tar and consists of so-called "creosote oil," "anthracene oil," and other materials. Its heating value is about the same as that of coal tar.

Gasoline. The composition of an average gasoline is carbon, 83.5 to 85 per cent; hydrogen, 15.0 to 15.8 per cent; nitrogen plus sulfur plus oxygen, 0 to 1 per cent. The heating value is about 20,000 B.t.u./lb. Gasoline containing tetraethyl lead should not be used for heating equipment.

Kerosene. The average composition of kerosene is carbon 85 per cent, hydrogen 16 per cent. Sulfur should not exceed 0.125 per cent (United States government specification). The heating value varies from 20,000 to 21,000 B.t.u./lb. The government specifications require a distillation end point of 625°F. maximum and a flash point of 115°F. minimum.

Alcohol and Benzol. Table 9-10 gives pertinent combustion data for various alcohol and benzol fuels.

GASEOUS FUELS

Description of Various Gaseous Fuels

Natural Gas. Gaseous fuels consist of natural gas and various manufactured or by-product gases. Only natural gas has a substantial market for steam generation as the other gases are too high in cost except for those plants obtaining them as their own by-products.

Typical natural-gas analyses are given in Table 9-11.

It will be noted that natural gas generally contains a high percentage of methane (CH_4) with varying amounts of ethane (C_2H_6) and inerts (CO_2, nitrogen, and helium). Most natural gas delivered by utilities will have under 10 per cent of inerts. The heating value will generally range between 1000 and 1100 B.t.u./cu. ft. for standard conditions of 62°F. and 30 in. Hg.

Natural-gas pipe lines are rapidly being extended into all the principal industrial areas of the United States. Natural gas generally is available for industrial process use but for boilers may be available only on an "interruptible" basis. That is, in winter, domestic home heating takes priority over boiler use, and gas for boiler fuel will be discontinued while the demands for home requirements are met. This requires industrial consumers with "interruptible" contracts to maintain a second fuel, oil or coal, for winter use.

Liquefied Petroleum Gases. These distillation products come from both natural gas and the oil refineries. These gases, particularly propane, are much used for domestic service. They are supplied either in tanks or by pipe lines. They are clean fuels, suitable for almost any service where they are priced competitively. Table 9-12 gives the properties of these fuels. Table 9-13 gives their combustion data.

Acetylene. The use of acetylene as a fuel and illuminant is generally limited to cutting and welding operations requiring high flame temperature, to small isolated lighting plants, and to single "carbide" lights. It is made from calcium carbide and water. To avoid a dangerous rise in temperature, sufficient water (about ½ gal./lb. carbide) should be present in the generator. The crude gas contains as impurities ammonia, hydrogen sulfide, and phosphine, which must be removed before the gas can be used for indoor illumination. Acetylene forms explosive acetylides, particularly with copper, has wide explosive limits when mixed with air, and is explosive per se at pressures of 5.9 lb./sq. in. gage or greater and at 15 lb./sq. in. requires only 540°C. to set it off. It ignites at 635°C. at atmospheric pressure. Its use as a liquid is therefore prohibited, and it is ordinarily dis

Table 9-11. Analyses of Fuel Gases*

Gas	Constituents of gas, % by volume							Illuminants		Sp. gr. air = 1.000	Cu. ft. of air required for combustion of 1 cu. ft. gas	B.t.u./cu. ft. gross	B.t.u./cu. ft. net	Products of combustion, cu. ft./cu. ft. gas				Ultimate CO_2, %	Net B.t.u./cu. ft. of the products of combustion	Flame temperature corrected for dissociation
	CO	CO_2	H_2	N_2	O_2	CH_4	C_2H_6	C_2H_4	C_6H_6					CO_2	H_2O	N_2	Total (dry)			
Natural gas, Texarkana..........	....	0.80	....	3.20	...	96.00	.....	...	...	0.57	9.17	967	873	0.97	1.92	7.29	8.26	11.7	80.2	3580
Natural gas, Cleveland..........	....	....	....	1.30	...	80.50	18.20	...	...	.65	10.70	1131	1025	1.17	2.16	8.50	9.67	12.1	81.1	3600
Natural gas, Oil City, Pa..........	....	....	....	1.10	...	67.60	31.30	...	...	.71	11.70	1232	1120	1.30	2.29	9.26	10.56	12.3	81.7	3620
Retort coal gas (horizontal).......	8.6	1.5	52.5	3.5	0.3	31.4	.....	1.1	1.1	.42	5.00	575	510	0.50	1.21	3.99	4.49	11.2	83.5	3665
Coke-oven gas..................	6.3	1.8	53.0	3.4	.2	31.6	.....	2.7	1.0	.42	5.19	588	521	.51	1.25	4.13	4.64	11.0	82.7	3660
Coke-oven gas, Koppers ovens.....	6.8	2.2	47.3	6.0	.3	33.9	.....	2.6	0.9	.44	5.23	591	525	.54	1.23	4.19	4.73	11.4	82.3	3650
Carbureted water gas..........	33.4	3.9	34.6	7.9	.9	10.4	.....	6.7	2.2	.65	4.37	536	496	.74	0.75	3.54	4.28	17.2	88.5	3815
Blue water gas..................	42.8	3.0	49.9	3.3	.5	0.5	.....	...	...	.53	2.26	308	281	.46	.51	1.82	2.28	22.3	89.7	3800
Theoretical water gas..........	50.0	....	50.0	....	...	....	.....	...	...	.52	2.39	325	298	.50	.50	1.89	2.39	20.9	90.3	3830
Anthracite producer gas..........	24.0	7.5	16.5	50.2	.6	1.2	.....	...	...	.85	1.05	134	124	.33	.19	1.36	1.69	19.5	65.6	3000
Bituminous producer gas..........	27.0	4.5	14.0	50.9	.6	3.0	.....	...	...	.86	1.24	150	140	.35	.19	1.49	1.84	19.0	69.2	3160
Blast-furnace gas..............	27.5	10.0	3.0	58.0	1.0	0.5	.....	...	...	1.00	0.78	102	100	.38	.04	1.21	1.59	23.9	61.0	2800
Oil gas (Protero 1920)..........	6.8	1.0	59.2	2.7	0.1	25.4	.....	3.8	1.0	0.35	4.91	575	510	.47	1.21	3.91	4.38	10.7	84.2	3725

* From "Combustion," 2d ed., Table 20, p. 34, American Gas Association, 1926. Reproduced by permission.

Table 9-12. Physical Properties of Light Hydrocarbons*
Exclusive of combustion data

	Methane	Ethane	Propane	Isobutane	Butane	Pentane
Molecular volume of gas, cu. ft.†	378.7	375.8	372.7	366.7	365.4	
Molecular weight of gas	16.04	30.07	44.09	58.12	58.12	72.15
Gal./lb.-mole at 60°F	6.4‡	9.64	10.41	12.38	11.94	13.71
Weight:						
% carbon	74.88	79.88	81.72	82.66		
% hydrogen	25.12	20.12	18.28	17.34	17.34	
Specific gravity:						
Of liquid (water = 1)	0.248	0.377	0.508	0.563	0.584	0.631
Of liquid, °A.P.I.	340†	247	147	120	111	93
Of gas (air = 1)	0.555	1.048	1.550	2.077	2.084	2.490
Weights and volumes:						
Lb./gal. liquid	2.5†	3.145	4.235	4.694	4.873	5.250
Cu. ft. gas/gal. liquid	59.0†	39.69	36.28	30.65	31.46	27.67
Cu. ft. gas/lb. liquid	24.8	12.50	8.55	6.50		
Ratio, gas volume to liquid volume§	443†	293.4	272.7	229.3	237.8	207.0
Initial boiling point (atmospheric pressure)	−259	−128.2	−43.7	10.9	31.1	97
Heat value (gross):						
B.t.u./cu. ft. gas	1,012	1,786	2,522	3,163	3,261	4,023
B.t.u./lb. liquid	23,885	22,323	21,560	20,732	21,180	21,110
B.t.u./gal. liquid		70,210	91,500	103,750	102,600	110,800
Vapor pressure, lb./sq. in. abs						
At −44°F		88	0	−9	−12	−14
At 0°F		206	38	12	−7	−13
At 33°F		343	54	17	0	−11
At 70°F		563	124	45	31	−6
At 90°F		710	165	62	44	
At 100°F			189	72	52	4
At 130°F			275	110	81	11
At 150°F			346	138	87	21
Latent heat of vaporization at boiling point:						
B.t.u./lb	221	211	185	158	167	153
B.t.u./gal	553	664	785	742	808	802
Specific heat:						
Of liquid, at C_p and 60°F., B.t.u./(lb.)(°F.)		0.780	0.588	0.560	0.549	
Of gas, at C_p and 60°F., B.t.u./(lb.)(°F.)	0.526	0.413	0.390	0.406	0.396	0.402
Of gas, at C_v and 60°F., B.t.u./(lb.)(°F.)	0.402	0.347	0.346	0.373	0.363	0.376

* Johnson and Auth (Eds.), "Fuels and Combustion Handbook," p. 285, McGraw-Hill, New York, 1951.
† Ideal gas = 379.5 cu. ft.
‡ Apparent values for dissolved methane at 60°F.
§ Based on "perfect gas."

solved in acetone under pressure. (Fulweiler, chapter on Industrial Gases, in Rogers, "Manual of Industrial Chemistry," 5th ed., Van Nostrand, Princeton, N.J., 1931. Vogel, "Das Acetylen," Spamer, Leipzig, 1923. Leeds and Butterfield, "Acetylene. The Principles of Its Generation and Use," Griffin, London, 1910. Nieuwland and Vogt, "The Chemistry of Acetylene," Reinhold, New York. *Cf.* also Jones *et al.*, *U.S. Bur. Mines Rept. Investigations*, 3567, 3755, 3809, 3826.)

Blast-furnace gas is a by-product from the smelting of iron ore with coke and preheated air in the blast furnace. About one-third of the exit gases from the top of the furnace is used for heating the blast stoves, and the remainder may be burned.

The gas is carefully cleaned and washed before use. The low B.t.u. value requires regenerative preheating, as with producer gas. [Camp and Francis, chapter on Blast Furnace Gas, in Bacon and Hamor, "American Fuels," McGraw-Hill, New York, 1922. Wagner, "The Cleaning of Blast Furnace Gases," McGraw-Hill, New York, 1914. *Blast Furnace and Steel Plant*, **17**, 1048–1052 (1929).]

Table 9-13. Combustion Data of Light Hydrocarbons*

	Methane	Ethane	Propane	Isobutane	Butane	Pentane
Ultimate CO_2 in flue products, %	11.7	13.1	13.7	....	14.0	14.2
Required for complete combustion:						
Cu. ft. O_2/cu. ft. gas	2.0	3.5	5.0	6.5	6.5	8.0
Cu. ft. air/cu. ft. gas	9.55	16.70	23.86	31.02	31.02	38.19
Lb. O_2/lb. gas	3.98	3.73	3.63	3.58	3.58	3.54
Lb. air/lb. gas	17.24	16.13	15.71	15.49	15.49	15.35
Products of combustion:						
Cu. ft. CO_2/cu. ft. gas burned	1.0	2.0	3.0	4.0	4.0	5.0
Cu. ft. water vapor/cu. ft. gas burned	2.0	3.0	4.0	5.0	5.0	6.0
Cu. ft. nitrogen/cu. ft. gas burned	7.55	13.20	18.86	24.52	24.52	30.19
Lb. CO_2/lb. gas burned	2.74	2.92	2.99	3.03	3.03	3.05
Lb. water vapor/lb. gas burned	2.24	1.79	1.63	1.55	1.55	1.50
Lb. nitrogen/lb. gas burned	13.26	12.40	12.08	11.91	11.91	11.80
Maximum flame temp. in air:						
Observed temp., °F	3416	3443	3497	3452	3443	
% gas for max. temp.:						
Min	9.45	5.70	4.05	3.15	3.15	
Max	10.10	5.95	4.30	3.25	3.40	
Ignition temp. in air, °F	1202	986	932	950	896	
Flash temp., °F. (calculated)	−306	−211	−156	−117	−101	
Max. flame propagation:						
In./sec	26	34	33.4	33	34.3	
% of gas in mixture	9.5–10	5.7–6	4–4.3	3.6–3.8	3.6–3.8	
Limits of inflammability in air:						
Lower limit (% gas in mixture)	5.0	3.2	2.4	1.8	1.9	
Higher limit (% gas in mixture)	15.0	12.5	9.5	8.4	8.4	

* Johnson and Auth (Eds.), "Fuels and Combustion Handbook," p. 286, McGraw-Hill, New York, 1951.

Blue water gas is the product obtained by the interaction of steam and a highly heated solid carbonaceous fuel. The fuel is brought to a high temperature by blasting with air, after which the air supply is cut off and steam is injected. The blast of air is again admitted to restore the temperature, after which another steam run is made. [Fulweiler, chapter on City Gas, *op. cit.* Meade, "Modern Gas Works Practice," *op. cit.* Travers, *Trans. Inst. Chem. Engrs. (London)*, **2**, 65 (1924). Morgan, "American Gas Practice" (privately printed), vol. 1, Chap. 15, 1931. Fulweiler, *Proc. 1st Intern. Conf. Bituminous Coal*, p. 472; *U.S. Bur. Mines Bull.* 203; *Tech. Papers* 246, 274, 284, 335; *Rept. Investigations* 2183. Pettyjohn, *Am. Gas Assoc. Proc.*, 1930, p. 1535. Lowry *et al.*, "Chemistry of Coal Utilization," Chap. 37, Wiley, New York, 1945.]

Carbureted Water Gas. As the thermal content of blue water gas is too low to meet present public requirements, the gas is carbureted with oil gas which is formed by the thermal decomposition of the oil, usually in supplementary shells connected in series to the generator shell of the water-gas machine.

Coal gas (retort) is obtained by the destructive distillation of bituminous coal of suitable characteristics, usually designated as a gas coal, in a closed, highly heated retort of fire clay or silica. (Fulweiler, chapter on City Gas, in Rogers, "Manual of Industrial Chemistry," 5th ed., Van Nostrand, Princeton, N.J., 1931. Meade, *loc. cit.* Morgan, *loc. cit.* Also publications of the American Gas Institute and the American Gas Association, particularly the Carbonization Committee of the latter. See also references under Coke-oven Gas.)

Coke-oven gas is a coal gas derived from the distillation of a bituminous coal generally known as a "coking coal," which is somewhat lower in volatile content than the usual gas coal. The carbonizing chamber is very much larger than the coal-gas retort and is built up from silica forms. (Sperr, chapter on the Technology of Coke, in Bacon and Hamor, "American Fuels," McGraw-Hill, New York, 1922. See references under Coal Gas; also Haslam and Russell, "Fuels and Their Combustion," chapter on the Carbonization of Coal, with bibliography, McGraw-Hill, New York, 1925. Gluud, American ed. by Jacobson. *Cf.* also Lowry *et al.*, *loc. cit.*)

Hydrogen. The use of hydrogen as a fuel is limited to certain special industrial purposes, such as certain welding and cutting operations. One of the methods of production at present favored involves the catalytic oxidation of the carbon monoxide in blue water gas to carbon dioxide with steam. Electrolysis and the low-temperature fractionation of coal gas are also used. (Taylor, "Industrial Hydrogen" Reinhold, New York, 1921. Greenwood, "Industrial Gases," Sec. VI, Bailliere, Tindall and Cox, 1920. Pincass, "Die Industrielle Herstellung von Wasserstoff," Steinkopf, Dresden, 1933. See also "Fixed Nitrogen," Reinhold, New York, 1932.)

Oil Gas. The oil gas manufactured for public-utility distribution on the Pacific Coast is made by the gasification of oil with steam in a chamber containing hot checker brick. The heat is obtained by burning oil in the same chamber, and the process is a cyclic one, as in the water gas process. [Pike and West, *Ind. Eng. Chem.*, **21**, 104–109 (1929). Morgan, *op. cit.*]

There are a number of other oil-gas processes, none of which are, however, widely used in the United States. The gases from oil refineries, particularly from the operation of various cracking processes for the production of gasoline from higher-boiling oils, are utilized to some extent, and this utilization for a time tended to increase. Recent developments in the production of synthetic rubber have provided other outlets. The recent widespread supplanting of manufactured gas by natural gas from long-distance transmission mains has stimulated great interest in stand-by substitute high-B.t.u. oil-gas processes, and development of such processes continues.

Producer gas is generated by blasting a deep hot bed of coal or coke continuously with a mixture of air and steam. Because of the large percentage of nitrogen in the gas thus obtained, its heating value is low. Solid fuels of widely different characteristics, including wood waste, may be employed in the process, and the variations in the thermal value of the resulting gas with the various volatile contents of the solid fuels are correspondingly large. Gas having as much as 180 B.t.u./cu. ft. is made with high-volatile coals, while low-volatile coke with poor operations may give 110 B.t.u./cu. ft. or lower. (Rambush, "Modern Gas Producers," Benn, London, 1923. *U.S. Bur. Mines Bull.* 7 and 13. Haslam and Russell, chapter on Producer Gas with bibliography in "Fuels and Their Combustion," McGraw-Hill, New York, 1925. Reports, Carbonization Comm. and Subcomm. on Producer Gas, *Am. Gas. Assoc. Proc.*, 1927, 1928, 1929, 1930.)

Re-formed Gas. Although applicable to any gas transformed by suitable treatment, the term "re-formed gas" is ordinarily applied to lower-thermal-value gases obtained by the pyrolysis and steam decomposition of high-thermal-value gases, such as natural gas or oil-refinery gas. The steam minimizes carbon loss and possesses other advantages. Catalytic re-forming to meet peak loads is now important. (*Cf.* Odell, *U.S. Bur. Mines Bull.* 301; *Tech. Paper* 483; *Rept. Investigations* 2973 and 2991. Also Schlegel, *Am. Gas Assoc. Proc.*, 1930, p. 1466. Morgan, *op. cit.*, Chap. 19. Milbourne, Catalytic Cracking Plants for Relieving Gas Utility Peak Loads, Paper 68-A-101, A.S.M.E., Fuel Division, Annual Meeting, Nov. 28–Dec. 3, 1948.)

Sulfur Impurities and By-products

The chief sulfur impurity in gaseous fuels is hydrogen sulfide. Certain natural and petroleum gases are found free from this undesirable impurity, but its presence may otherwise be expected rather universally in raw fuel gases in amounts which may range from approximately 100 grains/100 cu. ft. in blue and carbureted water gas to several hundred grains per 100 cu. ft. in coal and coke-oven gases. In refinery gases from sulfur crudes and natural gases from sulfur-bearing regions the concentration may be several thousand grains per 100 cu. ft.

Another important sulfur impurity is carbon disulfide, which may contribute as much as 80 per cent of the organic sulfur present in manufactured fuel gases. In such gases, however, the total organic sulfur is relatively small, usually much less than the 30 grains/100 cu. ft. of gas limit permitted by most states.

Other sulfur compounds, which may be present in small amounts, are the thiophenes, carbon oxysulfide, mercaptans, thioesters, and organic sulfide.

Compressibility of Natural Gas at High Pressures

Deviations from the simple gas laws may be important in many engineering operations involving fuel gases. (Burrell and Robertson, *U.S. Bur. Mines Tech. Papers* 131, 158. Johnson and Berwald, *U.S. Bur. Mines Tech. Paper* 539, U.S. Bur. Mines Monograph 6. American Gas Assoc., Gas Measurement Committee, Report 1, Natural Gas Dept.) As natural gas is more compressible under usual high pressures at ordinary temperatures than is called for by the simple gas laws, gas purchased at an elevated pressure gives a greater volume when the pressure is reduced than it would if the gas were ideal. Burrell and Robertson (*op. cit.*, *Tech. Paper* 158) give the following formula for calculating the compressibility of

Table 9-14. Cost of Fuel in Electric-power Generation*

Cents per million B.t.u.

Region	Coal	Oil	Gas	Coal	Oil	Gas	Coal	Oil	Gas
	1959			1958			1957		
New England	37.7	35.8	34.5	40.1	40.7	37.8	41.0	46.9	40.7
Middle Atlantic	30.8	35.5	33.0	32.3	38.5	32.0	31.9	45.9	32.1
East North Central	25.6	73.2	24.5†	25.8	68.5	24.6	25.8	68.2	23.1
West North Central	27.5	46.7	22.4	28.1	51.3	22.0	28.2	47.6	22.2
South Atlantic	27.2	35.5	29.7‡	28.6	39.7	27.6	29.0	46.2	25.8
East South Central	19.1	47.1	23.4	19.4	37.6	21.6	19.4	46.1	21.6
West South Central	15.8	43.2	15.0	15.6	41.8	12.9	14.9	41.7	12.9
Mountain	21.3	24.3	25.7	21.9	25.2	22.2	22.0	25.1	22.2
Pacific		34.8	32.0		42.0	26.5		41.5	26.5
Average, United States	26.5	35.2	22.3	27.4	39.6	19.5	27.5	44.4	19.5
	1956			1955			1954		
New England	38.8	41.4	37.9	35.4	36.6	36.0	35.3	34.7	33.6
Middle Atlantic	30.0	40.2	31.9	28.4	35.7	30.8	28.6	33.9	29.4
East North Central	24.6	74.3	21.7	23.9	69.1	22.2	24.9	57.5	22.4
West North Central	26.9	43.4	22.1	26.5	31.0	22.6	27.2	31.6	22.0
South Atlantic	28.1	39.5	25.2	25.9	36.0	25.3	26.6	33.8	23.1
East South Central	18.7	42.4	19.8	18.3	43.8	18.3	19.2	44.2	17.1
West South Central	15.2	40.4	12.4	20.5	40.0	11.4	11.6	39.1	10.5
Mountain	22.0	26.0	22.0	21.7	24.9	21.6	22.5	24.0	20.0
Pacific		33.0	25.0		27.8	23.8		28.5	22.8
Average, United States	26.2	37.9	18.5	25.2	33.2	18.0	26.1	32.8	17.3

* Federal Power Commission S-123, 11th Ann. Supp. 1959.
† Excludes blast-furnace gas, which would lower cost slightly.
‡ Includes plants using natural gas.

natural gas:

$$D = aP_1 + bP_2 + cP_3 + dP_4 + \quad \text{etc.} \qquad (9\text{-}7)$$

where D expresses the percentage deviation from Boyle's law; P_1, P_2, P_3, P_4, etc., represent the partial pressures of the respective constituents expressed in atmospheres under the conditions in question; and a, b, c, d, e, and f are characteristic factors for constituents of natural gas having the following values:

Methane	a	0.228
Ethane	b	0.90
Propane	c	1.9
Carbon dioxide	d	0.67
Nitrogen	e	0.01
Air	f	0.05

The work of Johnson and Berwald (*loc. cit.*) extends the study and gives deviation curves for characteristic natural gases. Contrary to the assumption implicit in the work of Burrell and Roberston, Johnson and Berwald found that the deviation curves were not always straight lines. For details, their work should be consulted.

FUEL COSTS

Fuel costs are extremely variable including, as they do, not only the cost of the fuel itself, but also the cost of various modes of transportation. Perhaps the most reliable source of fuel costs is the Federal Power Commission report of utility costs. These costs are given in Table 9-14 for coal, oil, and gas and broken down by regions. While these costs will not apply to specific locations, they do give valuable assistance in determining fuel-cost trends. Utility-gas costs, in particular, may appear to be low as many of the utilities are gas distributors and burn cheap "dump" gas. Oil costs are particularly low for utilities in coastal areas where oil is received in tanker or large loads.

COMBUSTION

GENERAL

Combustion is the rapid combining of oxygen with carbon, hydrogen, and sulfur; however, very little of each fuel is burned in the pure state. All commercial fuels are composed of hydrocarbons, some with sizable quantities of free carbon and all with some impurities. Complex reactions from existing fuel to simple elements for combustion appear at several different temperature levels. In all furnaces these reactions proceed simultaneously; so combustion is concerned with controlled chemical reactions in flowing streams.

Slightly **different combustion processes** take place, depending upon whether the mixing of fuel and oxygen occurs as part of fuel preparation (premix) or immediately prior to combustion (burner mix). Most general heat applications use the burner mix, while those applications requiring precise or stoichiometric conditions use the premix type. The different combustion processes are best illustrated by comparing the fishtail gas burner with a bunsen burner. In the fishtail burner, gas is emitted from a slot in the blunt end of the tube. Air mixes with the outer fringes of the gas, and the resultant combustion heats the gas which has not been exposed to air; this thermally decomposes or **cracks** the gas to carbon and hydrogen. Hydrogen burns with no visible flame, but the carbon particles become incandescent and produce a yellow luminescence. In a bunsen burner, air is inspirated by gas, and they are mixed in the bunsen tube. The fuel and oxygen heat together, and the result is a small blue flame with little or no luminescence. This combustion process is **hydroxylation** and is identified by the mixing of oxygen and hydrocarbons before ignition to form hydroxylated compounds. With the addition of more heat and oxygen, these compounds break down to form CO_2, H_2O, CO, and H_2. If combustion is incomplete, soot and carbon black are formed from the cracking process (fishtail burner), while hydroxylation produces some aldehydes which may not be completely decomposed and can be identified by their faint acrid odor.

The **elements of practical combustion** are normally referred to as the three T's of combustion—*time, temperature,* and *turbulence.* Every combustion process

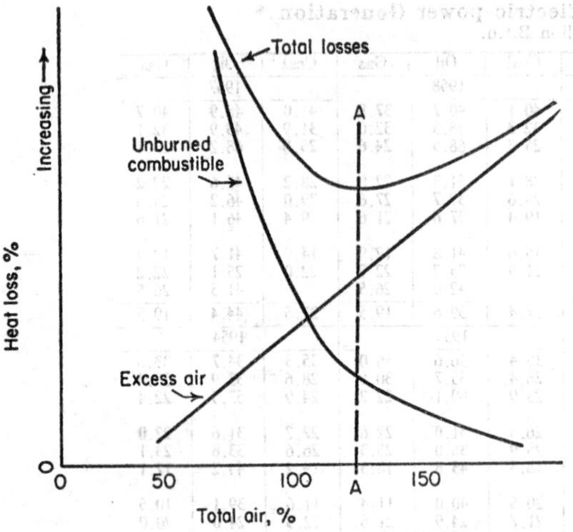

FIG. 9-1. Relationship of air and unburned combustible to total heat losses.

must have (1) sufficient time for complete chemical reactions, (2) sufficient temperature to heat the fuel through its various decomposition stages and to ignite the carbon and hydrogen, and (3) sufficient turbulence to mix the oxygen and fuel elements completely for the proper commercialization of the heat from the combustion reaction. Combustion is complete when all the chemical fuel has been oxidized (burned). Economical combustion is achieved when sufficient air (oxygen) has been supplied to oxidize only the economically available fuel. This point of efficient combustion has been passed when heat loss of the dry gases from the additional air exceeds the heat gained from the combustion of any additional fuel. The point A is shown in Fig. 9-1 and will vary with the fuel and firing equipment. As gas is easily mixed with air, it is the easiest fuel with which to obtain complete combustion. Commercial burners are available which can operate with 0 to 10 per cent excess air, still obtaining complete combustion. Liquid fuels are less easily mixed with air, so require from 0 to 18 per cent excess air. Solid fuels require from 12 to 50 per cent excess air for economical combustion and still leave some unburned carbon in the ash residue.

The amount of **excess air** supplied is determined by an Orsat apparatus or a combustible and oxygen analyzer. An Orsat apparatus exposes a measured sample of flue gases to reagents which absorb carbon dioxide, oxygen, and carbon monoxide; nitrogen is calculated by difference. Oxygen and combustible analyzers determine the amount of oxygen remaining in the flue gases and the per cent combustible, though the actual chemistry of the combustible must be known before the weight of the combustible is known. From an Orsat analysis, the weight of dry gas can be calculated by the formula

$$W_{dg} = \frac{11CO_2 + 8O_2 + 7(N_2 + CO)}{3(CO_2 + CO)} C_b + \frac{S}{1.833} \qquad (9\text{-}8)$$

where C_b is the amount of carbon burned per pound of dry fuel. The heat loss can be determined from this equation as can the weight of air supplied. Where weight of air supplied equals

$$W_A = W_{dg} + 8\left(H - \frac{O_{fuel}}{8}\right) + (C - C_b) - (C + N + S) \qquad (9\text{-}9)$$

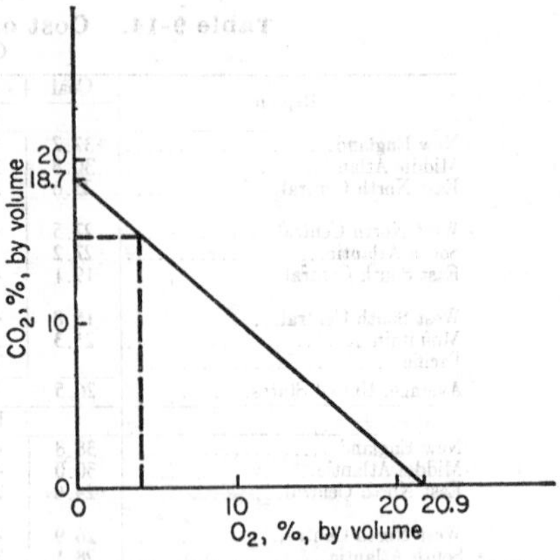

FIG. 9-2. Ostwald diagram showing relationship of CO_2 and O_2 for a low-volatile bituminous coal.

Excess air is calculated from Eq. (9-3) as

$$\text{Excess air} = \frac{(W_A - W_a)}{W_a}(100) \qquad (9\text{-}3)$$

Table 9-15. Maximum CO_2 and Air Required for Combustion*

Fuel	Combustion conditions at zero excess air			
	Atmospheric air required (lb./10,000 B.t.u.)		Max. CO_2 %	
	Range	Avg.	Range	Avg.
Anthracite:				
New Mexico	....	7.83	....	19.5
Colorado	....	7.85	....	19.3
Pennsylvania	7.81–7.93	6.87	20.0–20.0	20.0
Semianthracite	7.68–7.82	7.74	19.1–19.2	19.1
Bituminous coal:				
Low-volatile	7.62–7.76	7.69	18.5–18.9	18.7
Medium-volatile	....	7.77	....	18.5
High-volatile A	7.51–7.73	7.63	17.7–18.7	18.4
High-volatile B	7.56–7.73	7.66	18.0–18.7	18.4
High-volatile C	7.54–7.67	7.60	18.0–18.5	18.2
Subbituminous coal	7.56–7.57	7.56	19.1–19.2	19.1
Lignite:				
North Dakota	....	7.47	....	19.5
Texas	....	7.52	....	19.2
Coke:				
High-temperature	....	7.96	....	20.7
Low-temperature	....	7.63	....	19.3
Beehive	....	8.05	....	20.5
By-product	....	8.01	....	20.5
Gasworks coke	8.02–8.10	8.06	20.4–20.6	20.6
Petroleum coke	....	7.73	....	19.5
Pitch coke	....	8.13	....	20.7
Wood:				
Softwoods	7.02–7.22	7.11	18.7–20.4	19.8
Hardwoods	7.09–7.28	7.15	19.5–20.5	20.0
Bagasse	6.25–6.99	6.59	19.4–20.5	20.3
Petroleum oils:				
Gasoline (60°A.P.I.)	....	7.46	....	14.9
Kerosene (45°-A.P.I.)	....	7.42	....	15.1
Gas oil (30°A.P.I.)	....	7.45	....	15.5
Fuel oil (15°A.P.I.)	....	7.58	....	15.9
Gaseous fuels:				
Natural gas	7.32–7.41	7.37	6.9–15.2	12.2
Refinery and oil gas	6.52–7.38	7.44	10.7–13.6	12.8
Blast-furnace gas	5.73–6.27	5.82	20.0–26.9	24.7
Coke-oven gas	6.66–7.02	6.80	9.5–12.7	11.1
Carbureted water gas	....	....	....	17.2
Producer gas:				
Anthracite	....	....	....	19.4
Bituminous coal	....	....	....	18.9
Coke	....	....	....	20.5
Retort coal gas	....	....	....	11.9
Water gas, coke	....	....	....	20.1
Water gas, bituminous	....	....	....	18.0
Propane	....	7.24	....	13.7
Butane	....	7.26	....	14.0
Methane	....	7.20	....	11.7

* From Johnson and Auth, "Fuels and Combustion Handbook," p. 355, McGraw-Hill, New York, 1951.

An easier method of determining excess air by Orsat method is to use the Orsat analysis in the following formula:

$$\text{Total air} = \frac{\text{per cent } N_2(100)}{\text{per cent } N_2 - 3.78(\text{per cent } O_2)} \qquad (9\text{-}10)$$

A simple **Ostwald diagram** for the particular fuel being used is always helpful to check the Orsat readings. As shown in Fig. 9-2, an Ostwald diagram is constructed by graphing O_2 and CO_2; the O_2 in air (20.9 per cent by volume) is connected to the maximum CO_2 in the flue gases possible with a particular fuel (18.7 per cent for low-volatile eastern bituminous coal). The O_2 and CO_2 readings should fall along this line; Table 9-15 indicates the air required for combustion and the maximum CO_2 possible for the more popular fuels.

Oxygen and combustibles are determined by new instruments which accurately measure the amount of oxygen in a flue-gas stream using the electromagnetic properties of oxygen. More accurate combustion control is possible because of the precise measurement of a minor flue-gas constituent (O_2) which is directly related to the quantity of air supplied. Figure 9-3 is a graph showing the relationship of excess air and oxygen for various fuels. The following formula indicates the ease with which excess air can be calculated using precise oxygen measurements (assuming no combustibles).

$$\text{Excess air, per cent} = \frac{100\ O_2}{21 - O_2} K \qquad (9\text{-}11)$$

where K = 0.96 for bituminous coal, 0.95 for oil, and 0.90 for natural gas.

Combustion calculations are involved in determining performance of any fuel. Normal chemical equations and relationships are used to determine the volume and weight of air required, dry flue gas, and air supplied. These quantities are used in determining combustion efficiency. Table 9-16 gives values of combustion constants for the popular fuels.

SOLID FUELS

Combustion

The combustion of solid fuels takes place in three zones: distillation, incandescence, and flame. In the **distillation zone** the fuel is exposed to heat, and the volatiles are distilled out ot the solid material. In the **incandescent zone** the non-volatile fixed carbon is above ignition temperature and burns in live incandescent coals. In the **flame zone** the voltaile matter is burning after being ignited by the incandescent zone. The identification of these zones can vary widely from well-defined areas, as in an underfeed stoker, to the atmosphere surrounding each of millions of small particles of coal, as in pulverized-coal firing. The earlier part of this section discussed the various solid fuels from anthracite coal through bagasse. Each type of fuel requires a special consideration in the construction of equipment to burn it efficiently.

Solid fuels are burned in a fuel bed, in suspension, or a combination of the two. The selection of firing equipment must be based upon the type of fuel, the type of load for which heat is to be furnished, the amount of heat to be generated, and the comparative cost of equipment. Table 9-17 indicates the capacity range of solid-fuel-burning equipment, the normal burning rates in pounds of fuel per square foot of grate area per hour, and the heat liberated per cubic foot of furnace volume.

Coal

Coal is the most widely used fuel, and the firing methods and equipment are discussed as related to coal. The firing of other solid fuels on similar equipment is discussed at the end of this section.

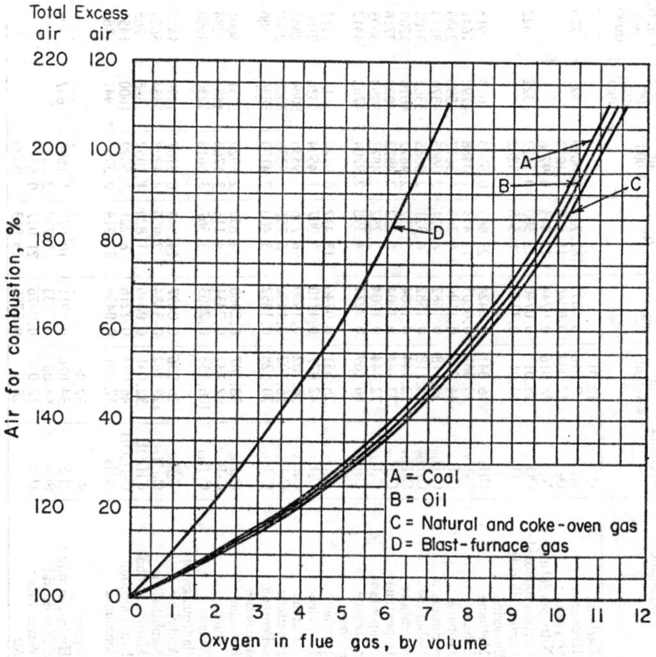

FIG. 9-3. Relationship of O_2 in the flue gas to excess air for various fuels. (*Bailey Meter Co.*)

Table 9-16. Combustion Constants *,†

No.	Substance	Formula	Molecular weight	Lb./cu. ft.	Cu. ft./lb.	Sp. gr. air 1.000	Heat of combustion: B.t.u. per gross (high)	Cu. ft. net (low)	B.t.u./lb. Gross (high)	B.t.u./lb. Net (low)	For 100% total air, moles/mole combustible or cu. ft./cu. ft combustible — Required for combustion: O_2	N_2	Air	Flue products: CO_2	H_2O	N_2	For 100 % total air. lb./lb. combustible — Required for combustion: O_2	N_2	Air	Flue products: CO_2	H_2O	N_2
1	Carbon‡	C	12.01	......	....	......	....	....	14.093	14.093	1.0	3.76	4.76	1.0	...	3.76	2.66	8.86	11.53	3.66	....	8.86
2	Hydrogen	H_2	2.016	0.0053	187.723	0.0696	325	275	61.100	51.623	0.5	1.88	2.38	....	1.0	1.88	7.94	26.41	34.34	....	8.94	26.41
3	Oxygen	O_2	32.000	0.0846	11.819	1.1053																
4	Nitrogen (atm.)	N_2	28.016	0.0744	13.443	0.9718																
5	Carbon monoxide	CO	28.01	0.0740	13.506	0.9672	322	322	4.347	4.347	0.5	1.88	2.38	1.0	...	1.88	0.57	1.90	2.47	1.57	....	1.90
6	Carbon dioxide	CO_2	44.01	0.1170	8.548	1.5282																
Paraffin series																						
7	Methane	CH_4	16.041	0.0424	23.565	0.5543	1013	913	23.879	21.520	2.0	7.53	9.53	1.0	2.0	7.53	3.99	13.28	17.27	2.74	2.25	13.28
8	Ethane	C_2H_6	30.067	0.0803	12.455	1.0488	1792	1641	22.320	20.432	3.5	13.18	16.68	2.0	3.0	13.18	3.73	12.39	16.12	2.93	1.80	12.39
9	Propane	C_3H_8	44.092	0.1196	8.365	1.5617	2590	2385	21.661	19.944	5.0	18.82	23.82	3.0	4.0	18.82	3.63	12.07	15.70	2.99	1.63	12.07
10	*n*-Butane	C_4H_{10}	58.118	0.1582	6.321	2.0665	3370	3113	21.308	19.680	6.5	24.47	30.97	4.0	5.0	24.47	3.58	11.91	15.49	3.03	1.55	11.91
11	Isobutane	C_4H_{10}	58.118	0.1582	6.321	2.0665	3363	3105	21.257	19.629	6.5	24.47	30.97	4.0	5.0	24.47	3.58	11.91	15.49	3.03	1.55	11.91
12	*n*-Pentane	C_5H_{12}	72.144	0.1904	5.252	2.4872	4016	3709	21.091	19.517	8.0	30.11	38.11	5.0	6.0	30.11	3.55	11.81	15.35	3.05	1.50	11.81
13	Isopentane	C_5H_{12}	72.144	0.1904	5.252	2.4872	4008	3716	21.052	19.478	8.0	30.11	38.11	5.0	6.0	30.11	3.55	11.81	15.35	3.05	1.50	11.81
14	Neopentane	C_5H_{12}	72.144	0.1904	5.252	2.4872	3993	3693	20.970	19.396	8.0	30.11	38.11	5.0	6.0	30.11	3.55	11.81	15.35	3.05	1.50	11.81
15	*n*-Hexane	C_6H_{14}	86.169	0.2274	4.398	2.9704	4762	4412	20.940	19.403	9.5	35.76	45.26	6.0	7.0	35.76	3.53	11.74	15.27	3.06	1.46	11.74
Olefin series																						
16	Ethylene	C_2H_4	28.051	0.0746	13.412	0.9740	1614	1513	21.644	20.295	3.0	11.29	14.29	2.0	2.0	11.29	3.42	11.39	14.81	3.14	1.29	11.39
17	Propylene	C_3H_6	42.077	0.1110	9.007	1.4504	2336	2186	21.041	19.691	4.5	16.94	21.44	3.0	3.0	16.94	3.42	11.39	14.81	3.14	1.29	11.39
18	*n*-Butene	C_4H_8	56.102	0.1480	6.756	1.9336	3084	2885	20.840	19.496	6.0	22.59	28.59	4.0	4.0	22.59	3.42	11.39	14.81	3.14	1.29	11.39
19	Isobutene	C_4H_8	56.102	0.1480	6.756	1.9336	3068	2869	20.730	19.382	6.0	22.59	28.59	4.0	4.0	22.59	3.42	11.39	14.81	3.14	1.29	11.39
20	*n*-Pentene	C_5H_{10}	70.128	0.1852	5.400	2.4190	3836	3686	20.712	19.363	7.5	28.23	35.73	5.0	6.0	28.23	3.42	11.39	14.81	3.14	1.29	11.39
Aromatic series																						
21	Benzene	C_6H_6	78.107	0.2060	4.852	2.6920	3751	3601	18.210	17.480	7.5	28.23	35.73	6.0	3.0	28.23	3.07	10.22	13.30	3.38	0.69	10.22
22	Toluene	C_7H_8	92.132	0.2431	4.113	3.1760	4484	4284	18.440	17.620	9.0	33.88	42.88	7.0	4.0	33.88	3.13	10.40	13.53	3.34	0.78	10.40
23	Xylene	C_8H_{10}	106.158	0.2803	3.567	3.6618	5230	4980	18.650	17.760	10.5	39.52	50.02	8.0	5.0	39.52	3.17	10.53	13.70	3.32	0.85	10.53
Miscellaneous gases																						
24	Acetylene	C_2H_6	26.036	0.0697	14.344	0.9107	1499	1448	21.500	20.776	2.5	9.41	11.91	2.0	1.0	9.41	3.07	10.22	13.30	3.38	0.69	10.22
25	Naphthalene	$C_{10}H_8$	128.162	0.3384	2.955	4.4208	5854	5654	17.298	16.708	12.0	45.17	57.17	10.0	4.0	45.17	3.00	9.97	12.96	3.43	0.56	9.97
26	Methyl alcohol	CH_3OH	32.041	0.0846	11.820	1.1052	868	768	10.259	9.078	1.5	5.65	7.15	1.0	2.0	5.65	1.50	4.98	6.48	1.37	1.13	4.98
27	Ethyl alcohol	C_2H_5OH	46.067	0.1216	8.221	1.5890	1600	1451	13.161	11.929	3.0	11.29	14.29	2.0	3.0	11.29	2.08	6.93	9.02	1.92	1.17	6.93
28	Ammonia	NH_3	17.031	0.0456	21.914	0.5961	441	365	9.668	8.001	0.75	2.82	3.57	....	1.5	3.32	1.41	4.69	6.10	....	1.59	5.51
29	Sulfur‡	S	32.06	......	....	......	....	....	3.983	3.983	1.0	3.76	4.76	SO 1.0	...	3.76	1.00	3.29	4.29	SO 2.00	....	3.29
30	Hydrogen sulfide	H_2S	34.076	0.0911	10.979	1.1898	647	596	7.100	6.545	1.5	5.65	7.15	1.0	1.0	5.65	1.41	4.69	6.10	1.88	0.53	4.69
31	Sulfur dioxide	SO_2	64.06	0.1733	5.770	2.264																
32	Water vapor	H_2O	18.016	0.0476	21.017	0.6215																
33	Air	....	28.9	0.0766	13.063	1.0000																

* From American Gas Association.
† All gas volumes corrected to 60°F. and 30 in. Hg dry.
‡ Carbon and sulfur are considered as gases for molal calculations only.

Table 9-17. Capacity Range of Solid-fuel-burning Equipment

Fuel	Equipment	Capacity range, lb. fuel/hr	Burning rate: Grate, lb./(sq. ft.)(hr.)	Burning rate: Furnace, B.t.u./cu. ft.
Anthracite coal	Retort	up to 1000	20	
	Traveling grate	100–30,000	40	
	Pulverizer	5000 up	......	15,000
Bituminous coal	Retort	300–15,000	25–45	30,000–50,000
	Traveling grate	1500–20,000	40	30,000
	Spreader stoker	700–30,000	40–60*	30,000–35,000
	Pulverizer	3500 up	......	10,000–25,000
Lignite†	Traveling grate	1750–30,000	50	30,000–35,000
	Spreader stoker	1750–30,000	50	30,000–35,000
	Pulverizer	4500–60,000	......	35,000
Coke breeze	Traveling grate	750–10,000	30–40	35,000–40,000
Fluid coke†	Pulverizer	1000–50,000	......	20,000
Wood and bagasse†	Spreader stoker	750–300,000	50–75	20,000

* Value depends on type of grate used; highest value is for continuous-discharge grates.
† Supplemental fuel often required because of moisture in lignite and wood and low volatile of coke.

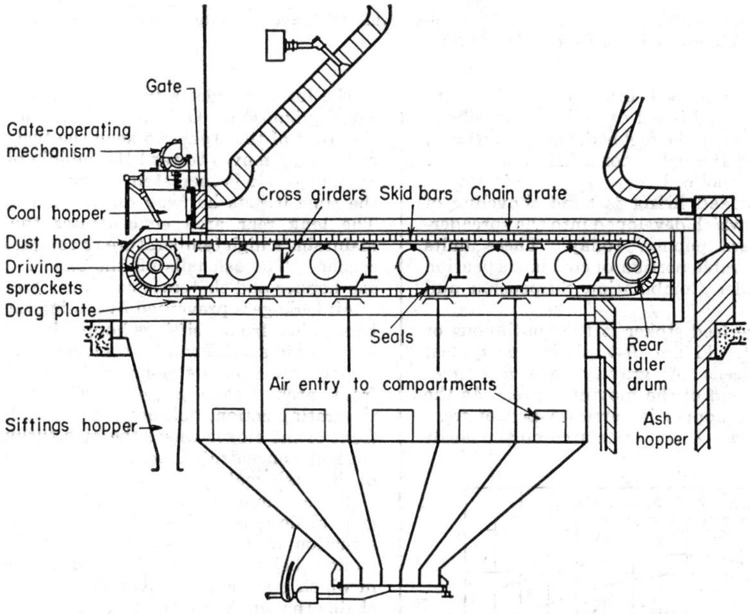

Fig. 9-4. Arrangement of a chain-grate stoker. (*Babcock & Wilcox Co.*)

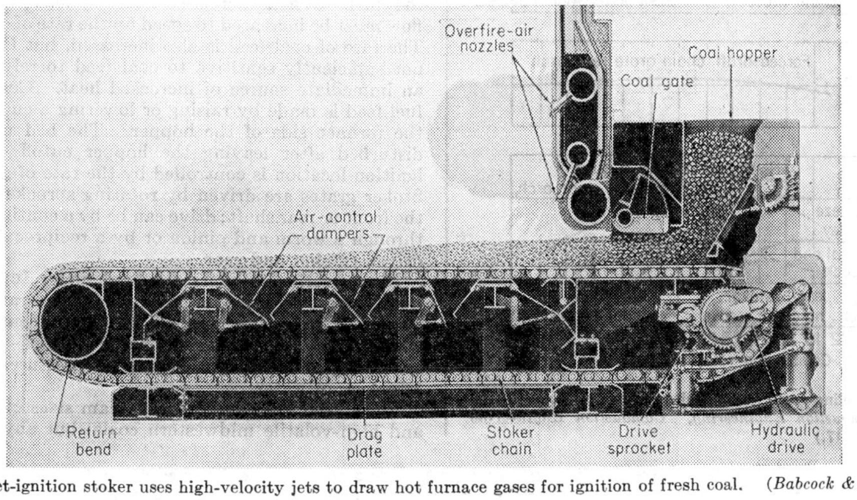

Fig. 9-5. Jet-ignition stoker uses high-velocity jets to draw hot furnace gases for ignition of fresh coal. (*Babcock & Wilcox Co.*)

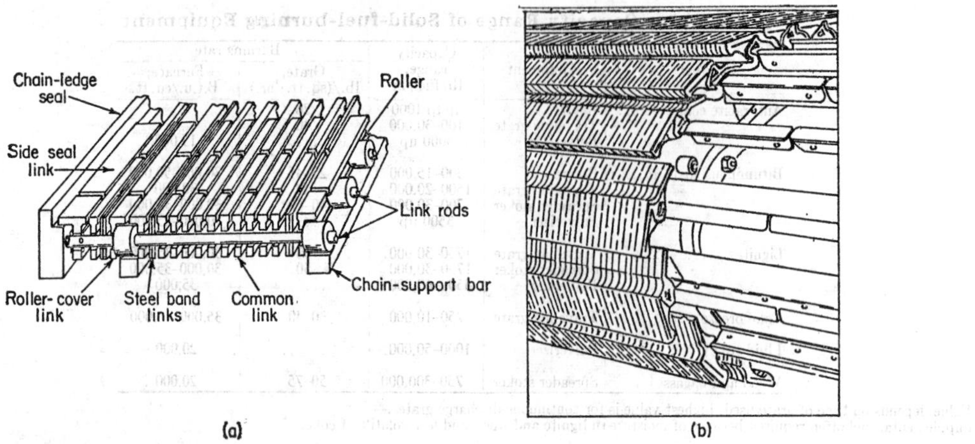

FIG. 9-6. A chain-grate stoker uses the grates as links in the chain while the traveling grate supports its grate clips from bars carried on the chains. (*Babcock & Wilcox Co. and Riley Stoker Corp.*)

Fuel-bed Firing. Fuel-bed firing is divided into **overfeed,** in which the coal is fed onto the grates above the point of air admission to the fuel bed, and **underfeed,** where coal is admitted through retorts below the point of air admission to the fuel bed.

An example of **overfeed firing** is hand shoveling of coal onto the fuel bed, which developed into the spreader-stoker units which are popular today. These units actually burn a considerable portion of coal in suspension and are discussed under Combination Suspension and Fuel, p. 9-22.

Another type of overfeed stoker is the continuous or **traveling-grate** unit. Figure 9-4 shows a typical arrangement. Coal feeds by gravity into a hopper located on top of one end of the moving grate. As the grate passes under the hopper it carries a bed of fresh coal toward the furnace. A moderate arch on the inside of the furnace reflects furnace heat onto the fresh coal, causing ignition. Only a small amount of air is fed at the front of the stoker to keep the fuel mixture rich, but as the coal moves toward the middle of the furnace, the amount of air is increased, burning most of the coal by the time it gets halfway down the length of the grate. The long rear arch concentrates the lean gases and maintains a high temperature to complete burn-out of the carbon. The ash falls off the end of the grate into the ash hopper and the grate continues around for reuse.

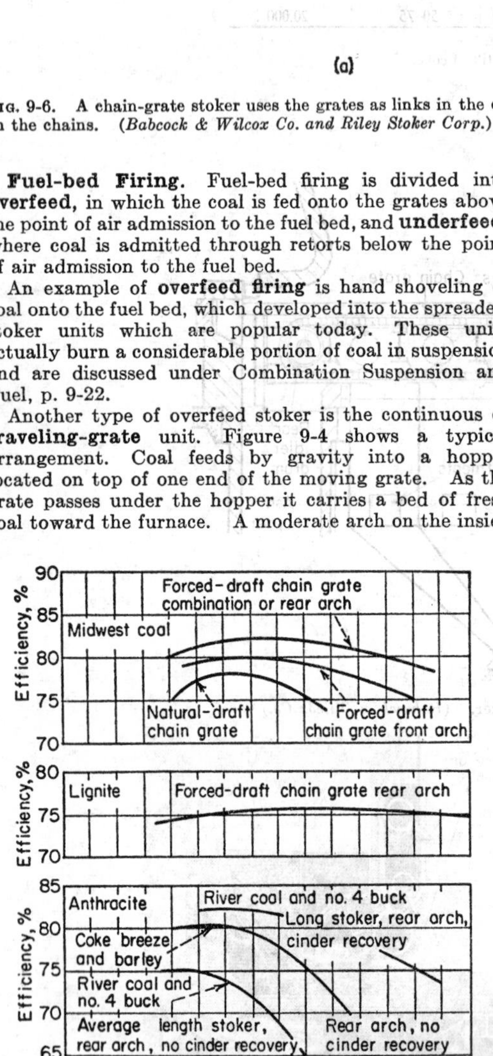

FIG. 9-7. Traveling-grate efficiencies with various fuels. (*deLorenzi, "Combustion Engineering," Combustion Engineering Co., New York,* 1947.)

Air leakage is prevented by sealing the grates. Air can be supplied from a siftings hopper located under both the grates or in special windboxes located between the grates.

One stoker uses the principle of **jets** to replace the front arch (see Fig. 9-5). The jets, through their inspirating action, pull hot gases from the furnace to the front of the stoker where the high turbulence produces a zone of concentrated heat which ensures good ignition of the fresh coal.

The continuous cleaning **grates** are constructed in two general designs. Figure 9-6*a* shows a chain-grate construction in which the grate clips themselves are the endless belt; Fig. 9-6*b* shows an alternate construction in which grate clips fit over T-bars which are attached to chains that make up the endless belt.

Fuel-bed depth varies from 4 to 8 in., depending on the fuel. When increased heat is demanded, the air flow must be increased to speed up the rate of combustion. The rate of coal feed is also increased, but the units are not sufficiently sensitive to coal feed to rely on this as an immediate source of increased heat. Control of the fuel feed is made by raising or lowering a cutoff plate on the furnace side of the hopper. The bed must not be disturbed after leaving the hopper cutoff plate. The ignition location is controlled by the rate of grate travel. Stoker grates are driven by rotating sprockets on either the front or rear shaft; drive can be by a continuous motor through a worm and pinion or by a reciprocating piston-driven ratchet and gear.

Most overfeed stokers are fired under **forced draft,** but a few are designed for natural draft. Grates designed for forced draft have only 7 to 10 per cent air space, which permits use of much smaller coal, ¾- to 1-in. top size being satisfactory. Forced air pressures vary from 1 to 4 in. of water.

Fuels used are coke breeze, steam sizes of anthracite, and high-volatile midwestern coals; but any clinkering,

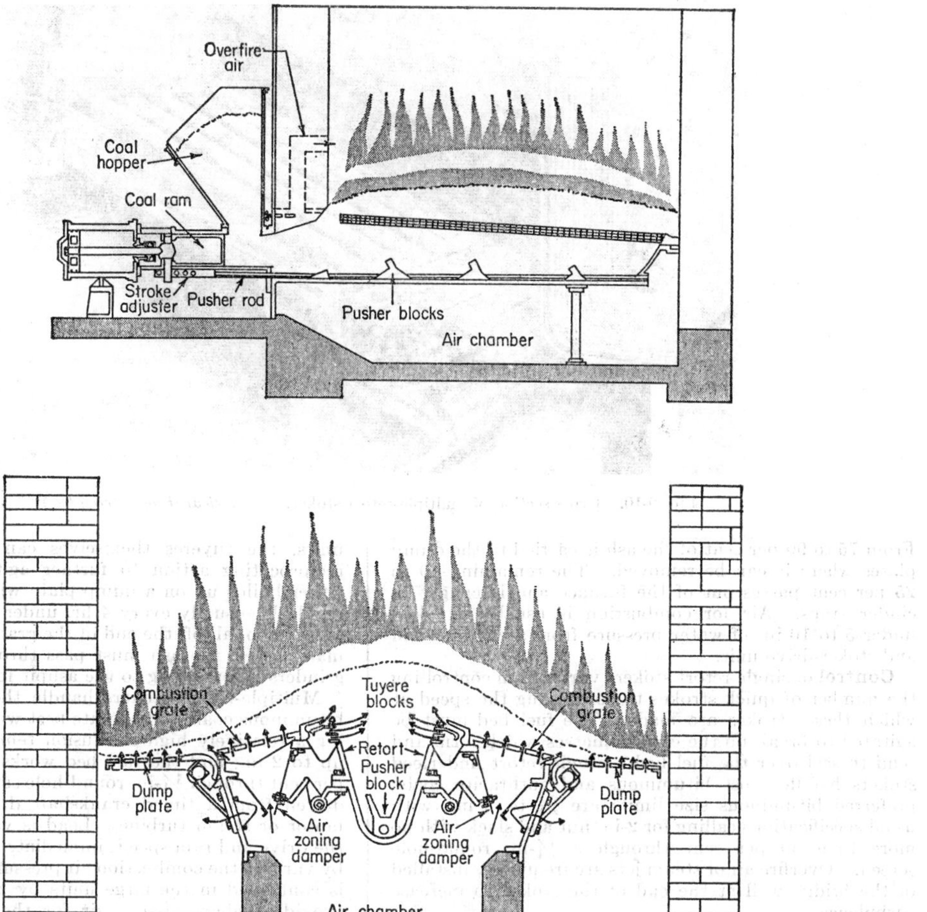

FIG. 9-8. Cross sections of a single-retort side-dump stoker with stationary grates. (*Riley Stoker Corp.*)

non-coking fuel may be used. The depth of fuel bed will vary with the coal being used, but at least 4 to 8 in. of ash should be maintained leaving the grate for adequate grate protection. Depending upon the coal size, from 25 to 35 per cent of the ash will pass out of the furnace and 65 to 70 per cent will come out through the ash hopper.

Traveling grates have varying **efficiencies**, depending on the fuel used. Figure 9-7 gives average efficiencies for the more common fuels.

Underfeed firing is accomplished by pushing or ramming the coal in such a manner that it comes up from beneath the grate. Figure 9-8 shows a **single-retort** side-dump stoker with stationary grates; the ram pushes coal into the retort. As the ram and pusher blocks move in, they push the coal toward the end of the stoker and upward toward the tuyere blocks where air is admitted to the bed. The heat in this area drives off the volatiles, and air mixes with the volatiles, carrying them upward through the glowing incandescent zone in which the fixed carbon is burning. The hot gases burn in the flame zone, and the heat passes upward through the furnace.

The **capacity** of this equipment can be increased by adding another retort and providing a reciprocating motion to the combustion grates. Coal for this stoker should have between 3 and 10 per cent ash in order to keep the grates adequately covered with ash but yet not so much as to become a hindrance to proper combustion.

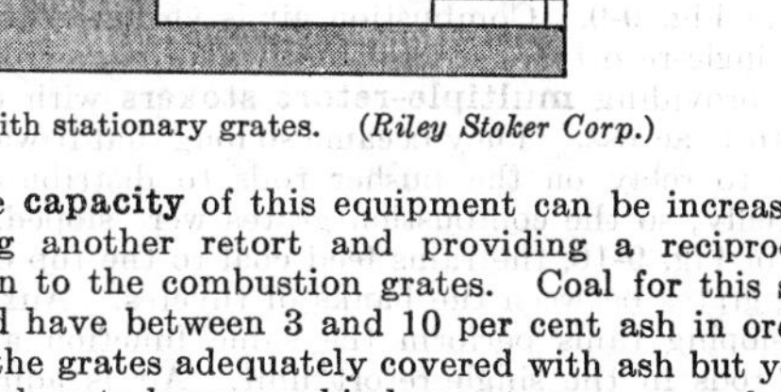

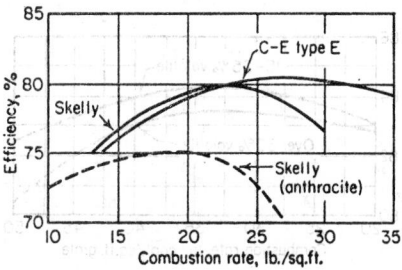

FIG. 9-9. Typical efficiency curves of single-retort stokers. (*Johnson and Auth, "Fuels and Combustion Handbook," p. 779, McGraw-Hill, New York,* 1951.)

FIG. 9-10. Cross section of multiple-retort stoker. (*American Engineering Co.*)

From 75 to 90 per cent of the ash is carried to the dump plates where it can be removed. The remaining 10 to 25 per cent passes out of the furnace and is caught in cinder traps. Air for combustion is usually supplied under 5 to 10 in. of water pressure from a common fan and stoker-drive unit.

Control of single-retort stokers varies from controlling the number of quick strokes to controlling the speed at which these strokes are made. The fuel bed must be agitated to break up the clinker masses which form and tend to seal over the fuel bed. Single-retort underfeed stokers handle most bituminous and anthracite coals; preferred bituminous size limits are ¾ to 2 in., with usual specifications calling for 2-in. nut and slack with no more than 50 per cent through a ¼-in. round-hole screen. Overfire air or steam jets are frequently installed in the bridge wall at the end of the stoker to increase turbulence.

Typical **efficiency curves** of single-retort stokers are shown in Fig. 9-9. Combustion air is never preheated.

The single-retort stoker was modified for higher capacities by providing **multiple-retort stokers** with up to nine retorts across. They became so long that it was not feasible to relay on the pusher rods to distribute the coal evenly; so the combustion grates were sloped. As shown in Fig. 9-10, the rams feed coal to the top of the sloping grates between the banks of tuyeres. Auxiliary small sloping rams perform the same function as the pusher rods in the single-retort unit. Air is admitted along the top of the banks of tuyeres, and on the largest

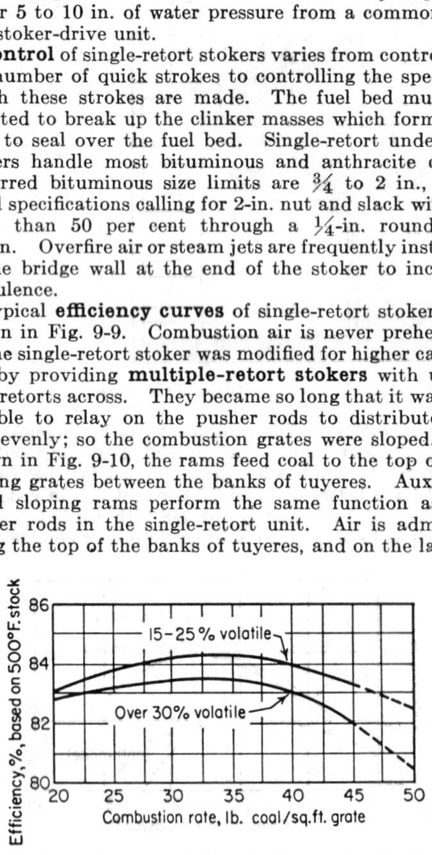

FIG. 9-11. Typical efficiency curves of multiple-retort stokers. (*deLorenzi, "Combustion Engineering," Combustion Engineering Co., New York*, 1947.)

units, the tuyeres themselves can be given a slight reciprocating action to further agitate the bed. Ash either builds up on a dump plate which can be dumped regularly, usually every 4 hr. under full load, or can be allowed to fall off the end of the grate continuously. In many cases, the ash must pass through a set of clinker grinders before going to the ashpit for disposal.

Multiple-retort stokers handle the various grades of bituminous coals and operate best with caking coals having a relatively high ash-fusion temperature. Sizing is up to 2 in., and the fuel bed works best with 30 to 50 per cent through ¼-in. round-hole screen. The rams are driven from a timed crankshaft driven by an electric motor or steam turbine. Load is varied by controlling the drive and ram speed; immediate response is obtained by varying the combustion air pressure. Air distribution is controlled in the large units by zoning the stoker to provide higher-pressure air for the tuyeres under the greatest fuel-bed depth.

Typical **efficiency curves** for multiple-retort stokers are shown in Fig. 9-11. Occasionally combustion air may be preheated to 250°F. to increase efficiency if the ash-fusion temperature is high.

Suspension Firing. The suspension firing of coal requires elaborate fuel preparation as coal must be reduced to minute particles whose combustion can be completed before reaching a cooler surface or the ash hopper. When a coal particle is first exposed to heat, the volatile matter distills off and ignites, encasing the particle in a reducing atmosphere. Turbulence and a velocity differential between the coal particle and the secondary air mass sweep the particle clear so that fresh oxygen can combine with the remaining carbon. The time required for combustion of a particle varies inversely with the ratio of surface area to particle weight. For efficiency, the particle must be consumed before it leaves the furnace.

The common methods of firing are vertical, horizontal, tangential, cyclonic, and opposed inclined, as indicated in Fig. 9-12.

Safety in the design of suspension systems is urged by the adoption of standards set forth by Code 60 of the National Bureau of Fire Underwriters.

Most installations use a **direct system** in which coal is burned immediately after pulverizing; occasionally pulverized coal is stored in bins after preparation. The **bin system** incorporates the danger of storage of a high

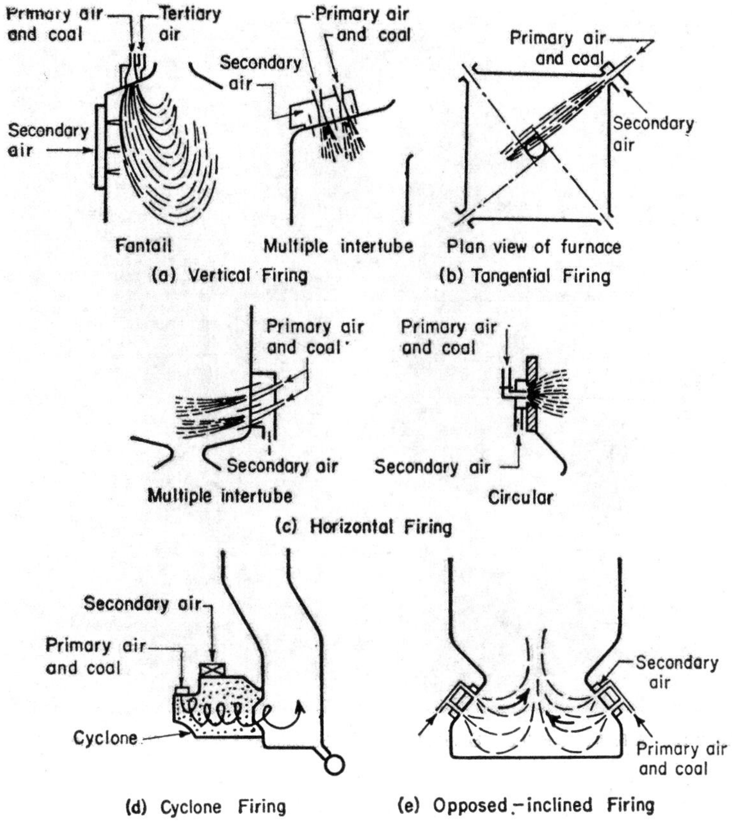

FIG. 9-12. Pulverized coal can be fired in various types of furnaces.

explosive but provides the advantage that fuel can be ground at an average rate rather than a peak-demand rate. All but 1 to 1½ per cent of the moisture in the fuel is dissipated during the pulverizing process and does not become a combustion loss. In designing such a system, careful attention should be paid the notes on bin firing in Sections 2214 and 223 of N.B.F.U. Code 60.

The heart of any solid-fuel suspension-firing system is the **pulverizer.** Air is used to dry the coal, transport it through the pulverizer, classify it, and transport the acceptable fines to the burner where the transport air provides sufficient oxygen for initial combustion. The pulverizers themselves are classified as pressure or suction; that is, whether the pulverizer itself operates under pressure or suction. Both types grind coal equally well, the only difference being in the sealing required for the pulverizer.

Pulverization takes place by impact, attrition, or crushing. Figure 9-13 shows a ball-race mill which grinds by crushing. The lower race is turned by a motor, causing the balls to rotate. Coal enters the center of the mill and is thrown out against the moving balls which crush it against the races. The fine coal spills over the lower race where it is picked up by air and carried around the upper ring to the centrifugal classifier section. Fine particles are carried with the air stream to the burner and the coarse particles returned for additional pulverization. The capacity of a pulverizer is affected by the grindability of the coal and the fineness desired, as indicated by Fig. 9-14. Pulverizer capacity is also affected by excessive moisture in the coal. Capacity can be restored by using transport air at a temperature sufficient for drying. Figure 9-15 indicates air temperatures required.

The degree of pulverization required for bituminous coals varies from 65 per cent through U.S. Sieve No. 200 (74 micron) with high-volatile coals to 75 to 80 per cent through for the low-volatile coals. Rittinger's law states that "the work required to produce material of a given size from a larger size is proportional to the new surface produced"; this law comes closest to predicting the effect of desired fineness on the capacity of various pulverizers. The **degree of fineness** should be held to the least possible which will still maintain satisfactory furnace and combustible loss conditions. Efficient classification is important to restrict passage of particles larger than U.S. Sieve No. 50 to less than 1 per cent of the coal fired as these particles will not be fully burned, thus increasing the loss due to combustible in the refuse. In addition, coarse particles tend to increase adherence of molten ash or slag and may increase erosion of transport piping, burners, and hot gas passages.

The pulverized coal is fed into a **burner** (using air as a transport medium) where it is ignited and mixes with the main combustion air. The transport air is called primary air and constitutes from 5 to 20 per cent of the total air for combustion. The main combustion air is supplied as secondary air through the burners. The velocity of the primary air must be such that it will keep

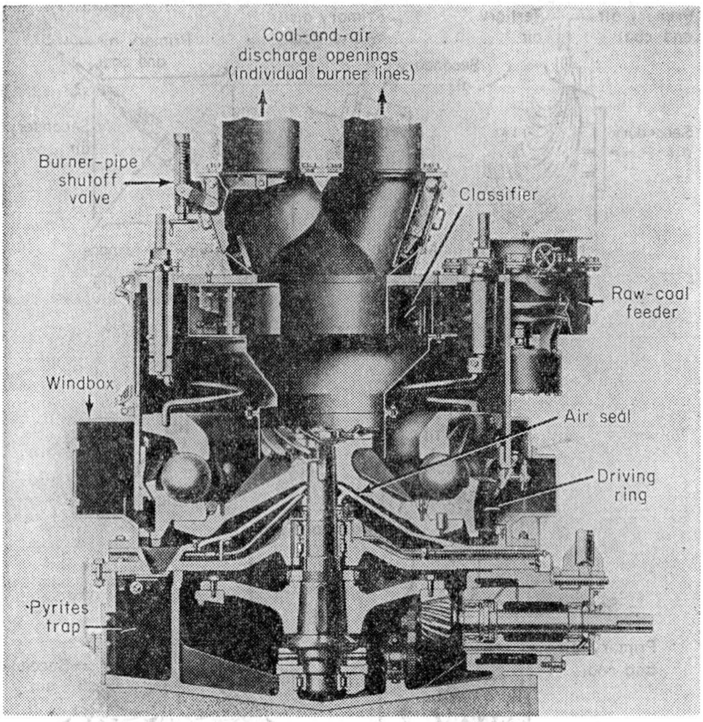

FIG. 9-13. A ball-race mill crushes coal between the balls and races. (*Babcock & Wilcox Co.*)

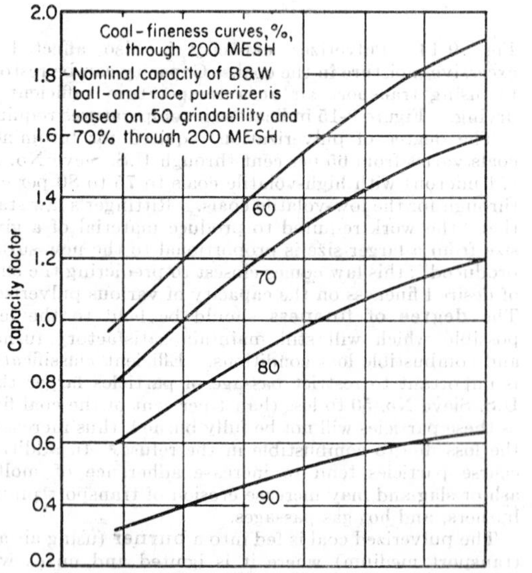

FIG. 9-14. Capacity of a pulverizer varies with (*a*) the grindability of the coal and (*b*) the fineness to which the coal is ground. (*Babcock & Wilcox Co.*)

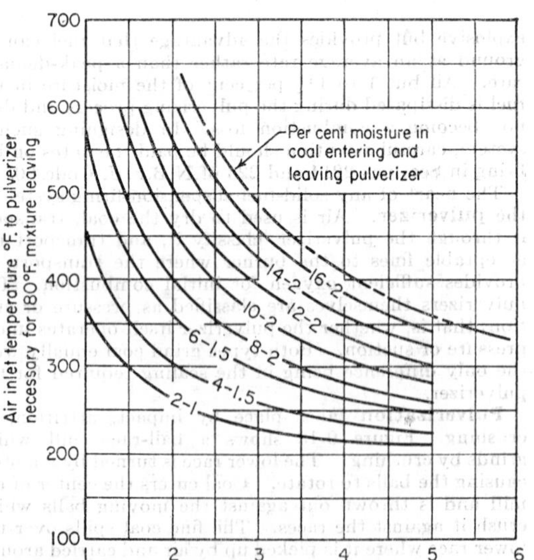

FIG. 9-15. Excessive moisture in coal limits pulverizer capacity; sufficient drying can be accomplished to restore capacity if air temperatures are high enough. (*deLorenzi, "Combustion Engineering," Combustion Engineering Co., New York,* 1947.)

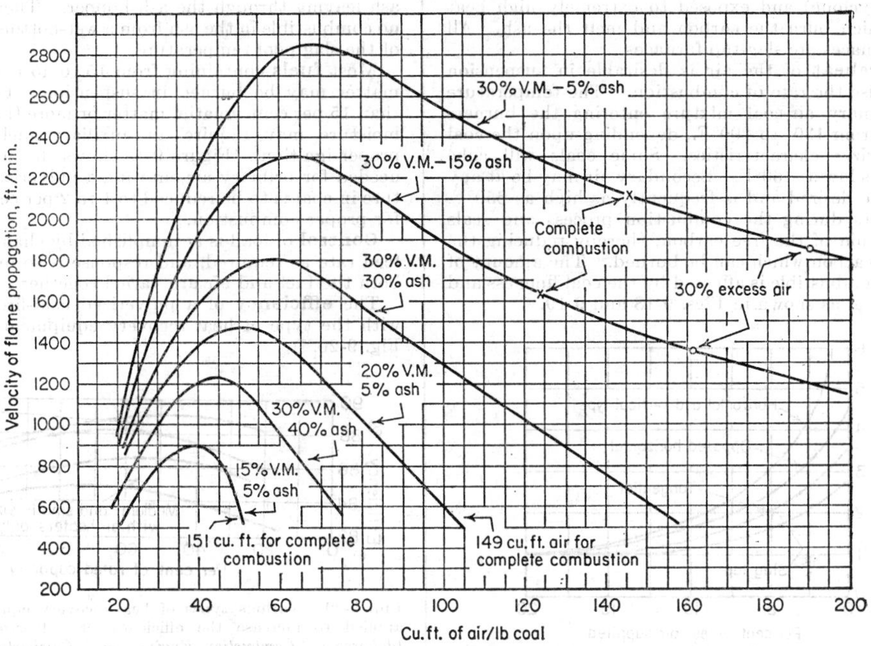

FIG. 9-16. Primary air-fuel velocity must be above the rate of flame propagation to prevent flarebacks into the pulverizer.

the fuel suspended in transport from the preparation device to the burner, and it must be above the rate of flame propagation to prevent flash back along the primary air-coal piping. Figure 9-16 shows the rate of flame travel for mixtures of air and pulverized coal of various analyses. A cross section of a pulverized-coal burner shows the way in which the coal and primary air mix with the secondary air (see Fig. 9-17). Ignition is maintained by the radiant heat from the burner tile. Pulverized-coal burners lend themselves to firing of multiple fuels, oil and gas being the most common adjuncts.

In **cyclone** firing the coal does not need to be ground so fine because the coal-air mixture is swirled in a very tight

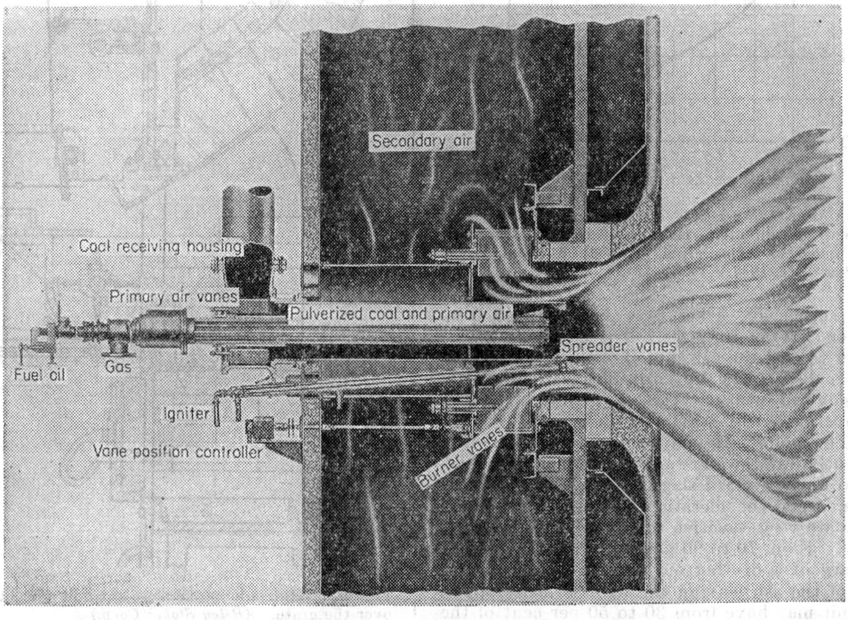

FIG. 9-17. A pulverized coal burner must maintain ignition under varying load conditions. (*Riley Stoker Corp.*)

ring (the cyclone) and exposed to extremely high heat releases which burn the carbon and melt the ash. All cyclone furnaces are slag-tap furnaces.

Some **preheat** of the air is desirable in suspension firing to raise the rate of combustion. The temperature of the primary air-coal mixture entering the burners may vary from 130° to 200°F., depending upon the coal and pulverizer characteristics. Some coals will coke readily at as low as 160°F. Secondary air may be at any temperature desired and is frequently as high as 650°F.

Ash melts during the combustion process and seals over a portion of the free carbon, thereby reducing the amount of carbon which can be burned. The amount of unburned combustible is affected by the coal fineness and type of firing, as shown in Figs. 9-18 and 9-19.

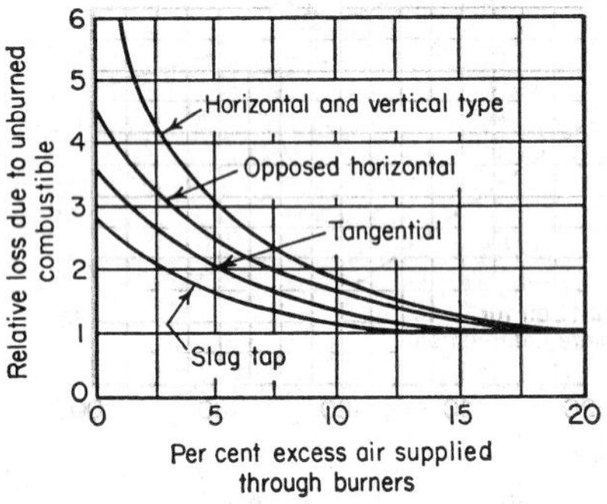

Fig. 9-18. The loss due to unburned combustibles varies with excess air and the type of mixing methods. (*deLorenzi, "Combustion Engineering," p.* 8.8, *Combustion Engineering Co., New York*, 1947.)

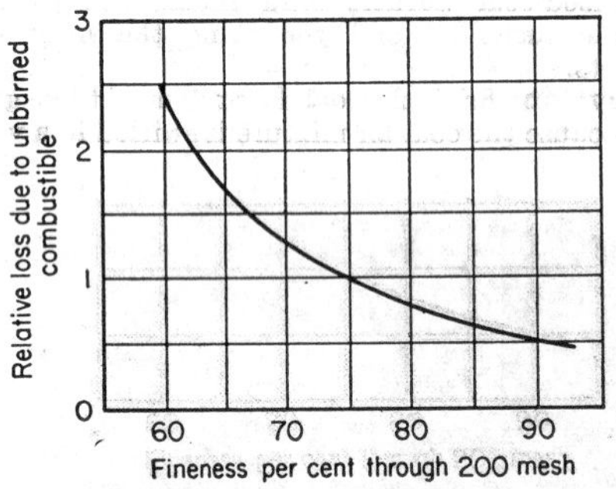

Fig. 9-19. Unburned-combustible loss for any firing method (except cyclone) is directly related to the fuel fineness. (*deLorenzi, "Combustion Engineering," p.* 8.4, *Combustion Engineering Co., New York*, 1947.)

Units for suspension firing may be equipped with dry-bottom or slag-tap furnaces. The ash hopper may contain water to cool the ash, but if the ash itself is not molten, it is called a **dry bottom** furnace. In a **wet bottom** or slag-tap furnace the ash is maintained above the fluid temperature so it leaves the furnace in a molten condition. The molten slag may be tapped continuously or intermittently into a water tank where it is quenched, breaking into finely divided slag droplets. Wet-bottom units require special considerations in the purchasing of coals as they are very sensitive to ash fluid temperature and viscosity. From 70 to 90 per cent of the ash is lost up the furnace of a dry-bottom unit, with only 10 to 30 per cent of the ash leaving through the ash hopper. A slag-tap unit may have from 30 to 50 per cent of the ash leaving through the ash hopper. There is normally no combustible in the ash from a wet-bottom unit because of the slag pool temperature.

Most **fuels** containing from 15 to 45 per cent volatile matter may be burned in suspension. Fuels with less than 15 per cent volatile matter or more than 25 per cent moisture may require an auxiliary fuel to maintain proper ignition. Figure 9-15 shows the air temperature needed for primary air entering a pulverizer if the moisture in coal is to be reduced to 1 to 2 per cent as required for proper combustion.

Control of load is accomplished by changes in the fuel feed rate as required, and response is so immediate that both the fuel and air are varied together.

The **efficiency** of a pulverized coal-fired unit varies with the type of heat-recovery equipment, as shown in Fig. 9-20.

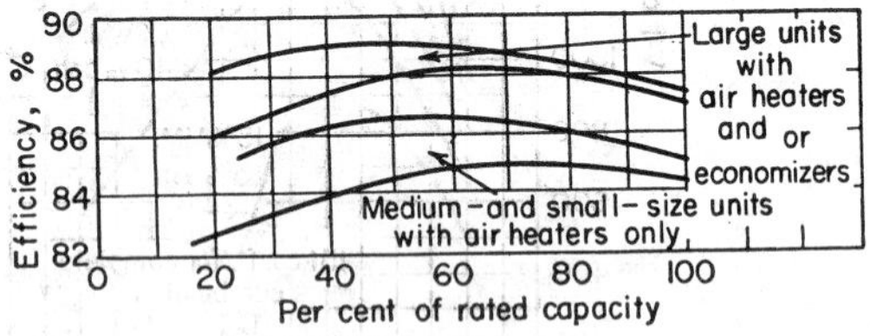

Fig. 9-20. Various types of heat-recovery equipment can be applied to increase the efficiency of pulverized coal firing. (*deLorenzi, "Combustion Engineering," Combustion Engineering Co., New York*, 1947.)

Combination Suspension and Fuel Bed. **Spreader stokers** burn coal by propelling it on a grate. A portion of the coal burns in suspension (the percentage depending on the coal fineness) while the rest burns on a grate. In most units coal is pushed off of a plate under the storage hopper (see Fig. 9-21) onto revolving paddles

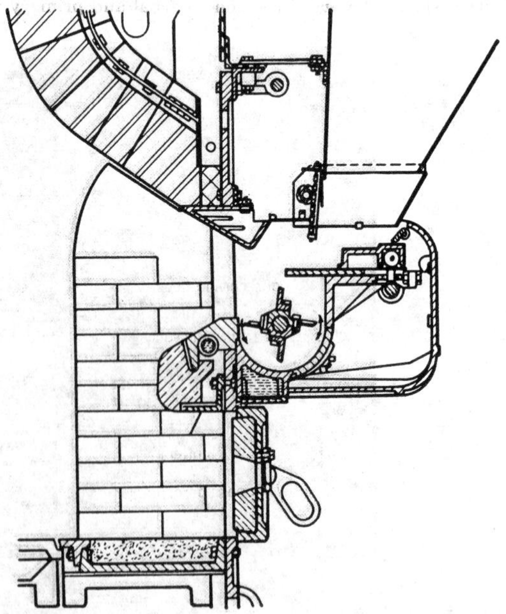

Fig. 9-21. Spreader stokers use a paddle wheel to distribute coal over the grate. (*Riley Stoker Corp.*)

(either overthrow or underthrow) which distribute the coal on the grate. The angle and speed of the paddles control coal distribution. The largest coal particles travel the farthest while the smallest ones become partially consumed during their trajectory and fall on the forward half of the grate.

A few spreaders use air to transport the coal to the furnace and distribute it, while others use mechanical means to transport the coal to a series of pneumatic jets. Figure 9-24 illustrates a pneumatic distributor.

The **performance** of spreader stokers is affected by changes in coal sizing, the main problem being the size consist of the fuel fired. The equipment can distribute a wide range of fuel sizes, but it distributes each particle based upon the size and weight of the particle. For proper distribution, then, a normal distribution of sizes must be supplied. Normal size specifications call for $\frac{3}{4}$-in. nut and slack with not more than 30 per cent less than $\frac{1}{4}$ in.

Approximately 30 to 50 per cent of the coal is burned in suspension. If excessive fines are present, more coal will be burned in suspension, more coal particles will be carried out of the furnace, and very little ash will be available to provide a protective cover for the grate surface. If sufficient fines are not present, the capacity of the unit will be reduced because the grate is not designed to burn the entire capacity on the grate, usually resulting in excessive live coals being dumped to the ash hopper.

The **grates** used with spreader stokers are of several types, as shown in Fig. 9-22. **Stationary grates** are the cheapest to install, but they must be divided up into zones for cleaning and ash removal. In the **dumping-grate stoker** the grates themselves can be dumped, thereby eliminating the hoeing of ashes. This provides some reduction in the time necessary for cleaning the grates. **Continuous-cleaning grates** do not need to be zoned for ash removal; the higher grate heat releases possible make such grates economical. Small units can be equipped with grates installed at a slight slope and using a vibrating or oscillating motion to propel the ash to the end of the grate. The stoker is in motion only a small portion of the time, and the fuel bed moves forward as one mass so there is no serious intermixing of ash and burning coals. These units are restricted by the size of grate, weight of fuel bed, and the physical size of the driving apparatus. Large spreader stokers are normally equipped with traveling grates.

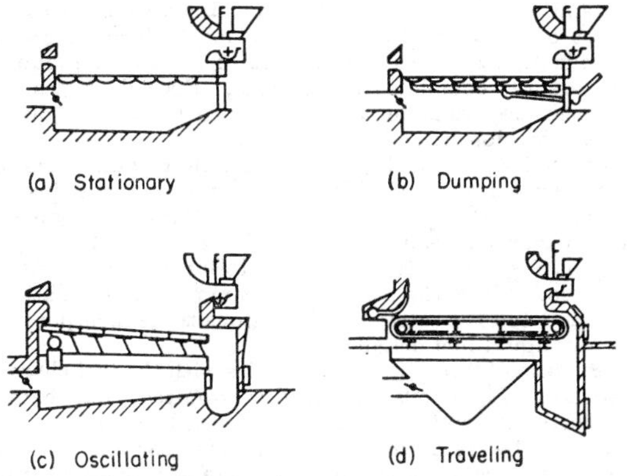

FIG. 9-22. Spreader stokers are used to fire many types of grates.

Grate **heat-release** rates used in sizing spreader stokers are listed in Table 9-18. The figures given in the table are for normal designs and will vary for a particular installation, depending upon the coal used and the load factor of the particular unit. Furnace heights vary from 12 ft. for eastern coals to 14 ft. for subbituminous coals, lignite, and refuse firing.

Table 9-18. Grate Heat Releases in Spreader Stokers

Grate type	Grate heat release KB.t.u./(hr.)(sq. ft.)	
	Without dust collector	With dust collector
For bituminous coals		
Stationary	350	400
Maximum continuous load, 2-hr. peak	400	450
Dumping:		
Maximum continuous load	375	475
2-hr peak	450	525
Oscillating:		
Maximum continuous load	...	555
2-hr. peak	...	625
Traveling, continuous boiler capacity:		
Klb./hr	...	100 200 300
Maximum continuous load	...	650 700 725
2-hr. peak load	...	725 775 800
For Iowa coal, subbituminous coal, lignite, wood, and bagasse		
Stationary:		
Maximum continuous load	450	600
2-hr. peak load	550	750
Dumping:		
Maximum continuous load	500	650
2-hr. peak load	600	750
Oscillating:		
Maximum continuous load	...	650 Refractory with clinker chill
Maximum continuous load	...	700 Water-cooled furnace
2-hr. peak load	...	800 All furnaces
Traveling:		
Klb./hr. continuous boiler capacity	...	100 200 300
Maximum continuous load	...	750 850 850
2-hr. peak load	...	850 900 1000

Excess air is usually 30 to 40 per cent for stationary and dumping grates, while continuous-cleaning grates are operated from 22 to 30 per cent excess air. Preheat air can be supplied for all types of grates, but the temperature is usually limited to 250° to 300°F. to prevent any excessive slagging of the fuel bed.

Overfire air nozzles are located in the front wall underneath the spreaders and in the rear wall from 12 to 36 in. above the grate level. These nozzles use air directly from a fan or inspirate air with steam to provide a **turbulence** above the grate for most effective mixing of fuel and air. They supply about 15 per cent of the total combustion air. A few nozzles are installed in the front wall under the spreaders to induce hot gases toward the front wall for ignition purposes; the majority of overfire air is supplied in the rear wall and is admitted through several small openings rather than a few large ones.

The **size** range of spreader stokers extends into that for which multiple-fuel firing is generally considered necessary. It is usually easy to increase the height of the furnace and install oil or gas burners in the upper portions of the furnace. During firing of this auxiliary fuel the grate must be protected from overheating by a very deep bed of ash or a firebrick cover, both with slight air leakages.

The carbon content of the ash passing out of the furnace varies from 30 to 50 per cent. Over-all efficiency of a spreader stoker can be increased from 2 to 5 per cent by **reburning** this **fly ash**, as shown in Fig. 9-23. It is returned to the stoker grate by a gravity or pneumatic feed system. The reinjected ash must be retained on the fuel bed to keep the fly-ash loading in the boiler passes at reasonable values.

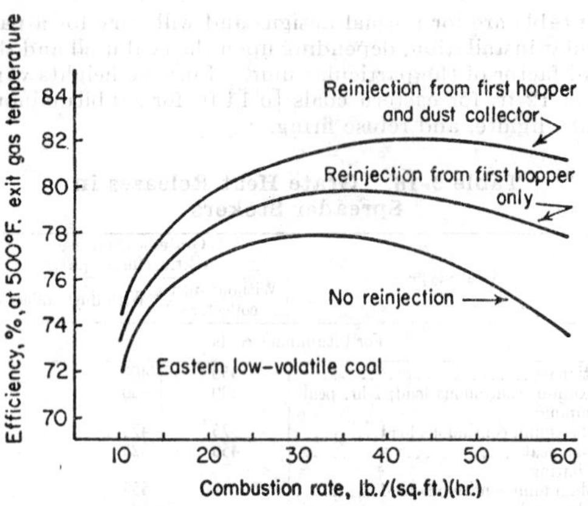

FIG. 9-23. Reinjection of ashes from the first hopper is common; additional efficiency can be obtained if dust-collector ashes are reinjected.

Control of spreader-stoker firing is normally accomplished by varying the feed rate of the coal and air simultaneously. Sufficient fuel burns in suspension to meet the changing needs of most processes.

Other Fuels

Other solid fuels are fired on equipment similar to that described for coal but modified for the characteristics of the particular fuel.

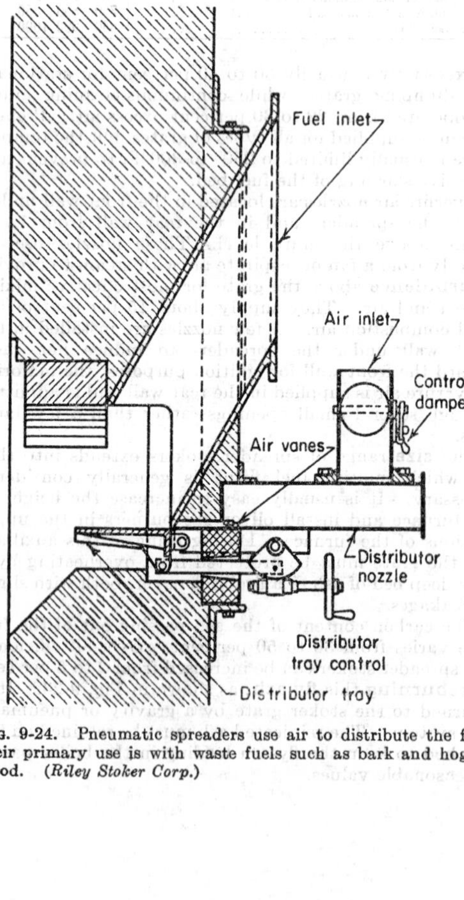

FIG. 9-24. Pneumatic spreaders use air to distribute the fuel; their primary use is with waste fuels such as bark and hogged wood. (*Riley Stoker Corp.*)

Wood refuse in the forms of **hogged waste, bark, tanning bark,** or **sawdust** is burned by itself in spreader-stoker units or on top of a coal bed on single- and multiple-retort stokers. It is burned in a dutch-oven furnace if moisture is excessively high or if burned in conjunction with a suspension fuel. It is usually distributed by air as shown in Fig. 9-24 rather than by a mechanical spreader.

Bagasse is normally burned on spreader stokers but can be burned on top of a coal bed on single- or multiple-retort stokers. The spreader in Fig. 9-24 is normally used for distribution. Occasionally it is pulverized and burned in suspension with fuel oil.

Lignite may be burned by itself but is usually aided by a supplementary fuel. It can be fired on top of a coal bed on single- or multiple-retort stokers or by itself on spreader stokers, traveling-grate stokers, and through pulverizers.

Coke and **coke breeze** are fired on traveling-grate stokers. **Char** is burned on traveling-grate stokers or is pulverized. **Petroleum coke** is pulverized.

LIQUID FUELS

General

Liquid fuels cannot be retained on a grate nor can they be burned efficiently in a pool. The liquid must be reduced to small droplets to present a larger surface area for combining with oxygen. These small droplets are easily vaporized when exposed to furnace heat. Actual combustion takes place as a gas.

Liquid dispersion or **atomization** is accomplished by several different means, with results varying from a sheet of oil to an extremely fine mist. The degree of atomization controls the amount of excess air required to assure complete combustion. Special types of burners are available which can burn the lighter distillates stoichiometrically.

Installation of liquid-fuel handling and burning equipment appears simple, but because improper installations present safety hazards, the National Board of Fire Underwriters has established a code entitled Regulations for the Installation of Oil Burning Equipment. This code forms the basis for most municipal regulations which detail the safety considerations to be incorporated in any liquid-fuel installation.

Preparation of liquid fuels varies with the fuel characteristics. Light oils are easily atomized, but heavy residual oils and tars must be heated to reduce the viscosity before atomization. Rotary gear and reciprocating pumps are used to pump the fuel; shell-and-tube heat exchangers raise the fuel temperature to obtain the desired viscosity. Small electric oil heaters are used to heat small amounts of oil for start-up. Figure 9-25 shows the viscosity range of the popular fuel oils.

Two general classes of liquid-fuel **burners** are (1) burners that vaporize the liquid within the burner and (2) burners that atomize the liquid so vaporization will occur in the combustion space. The vaporizing burners are limited to the most volatile liquids but have the advantage of burning such liquids at stoichiometric conditions, and one such burner is shown in Fig. 9-26. Vaporization of the oil is accomplished by recirculation of the combustion gases within the burner, producing more combustion by hydroxylation than "cracking." The flame emitted from the burner front is short, blue, and non-luminous. Atomizing burners use a mechanical force to atomize the liquid and are the most common type. They are categorized by the means employed to atomize the fuel: rotary type, auxiliary fluid (steam or air), and mechanical atomizers (straight pressure or straight pressure with return flow).

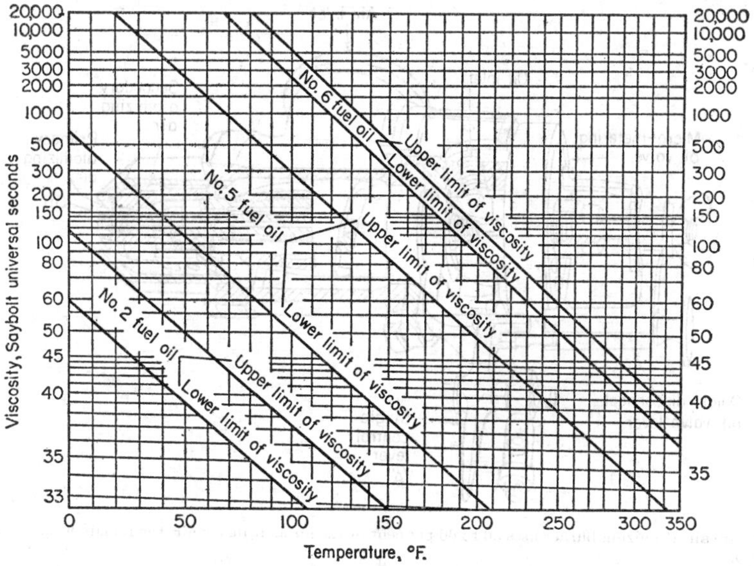

FIG. 9-25. Temperature-viscosity curves for Nos. 2, 5, and 6 fuel oils. (*From Chart A, A.S.T.M. Standard Charts D341-43.*)

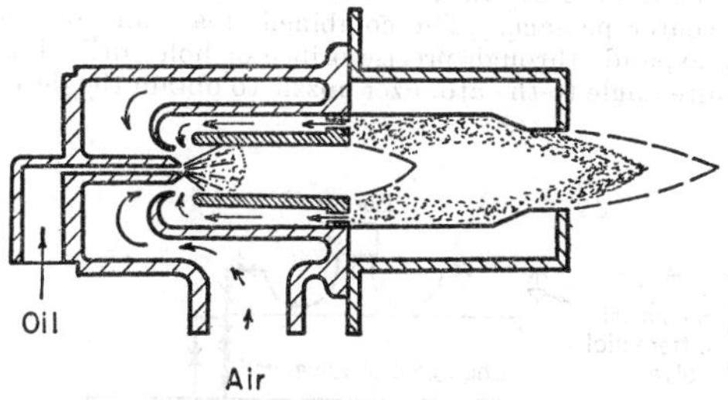

FIG. 9-26. The high-velocity burner produces combustion results similar to hydroxylation because of the high heat release. (*Thermal Research and Engineering Co.*)

Atomizing Burner

Rotary-cup Atomizer. Rotary-cup atomizers (Fig. 9-27) are used in small installations because of their simplicity. Oil under pressure is forced out of the nozzle against a conical cup rotating at about 3500 r.p.m. As centrifugal force drives the oil off the outlet of the cup, primary air from the integral fan unit is admitted in a rotation counter to the direction of the cup. This provides considerable turbulence for mixing the sheet or droplets of oil with air.

Load range is about 16 to 1, which is adequate for most industrial installations. Viscosities up to 300 S.U.S. can be atomized, but better atomization is obtained with lower viscosities. Oil temperatures must be kept moderate to prevent gasification which would destroy the rotary-cup action.

The maximum **capacity** of the largest rotary-cup unit is 1400 lb. of oil per hour. The furnace heat release usually varies from 30,000 to 80,000 B.t.u./cu ft.

Auxiliary-fluid Atomizer. Steam or air is used to atomize the fuel oil. The fluid is introduced to the oil either within the tip body or at the end of the burner tip. The fluid breaks up the oil stream and the expansion of the fluid under furnace temperatures assists in atomization.

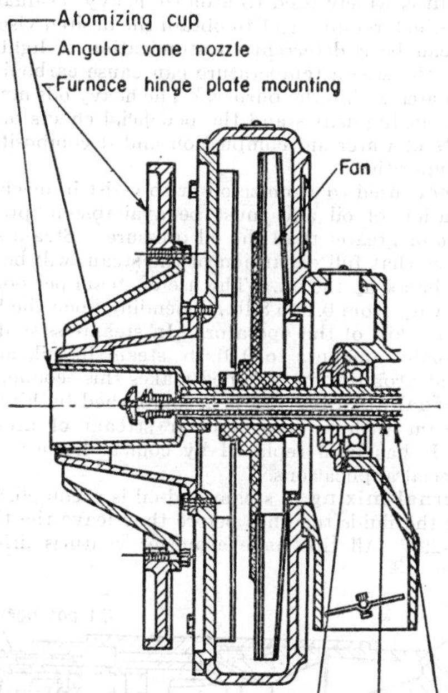

FIG. 9-27. The rotary-cup burner uses centrifugal force to spray oil from the atomizing cup. (*Ray Oil Burner Co.*)

High-pressure compressed **air** is not economical for fuel atomization; however, blowers can supply air up to 3 lb./sq. in. for low-pressure **air-atomizing** burners (see Fig. 9-28).

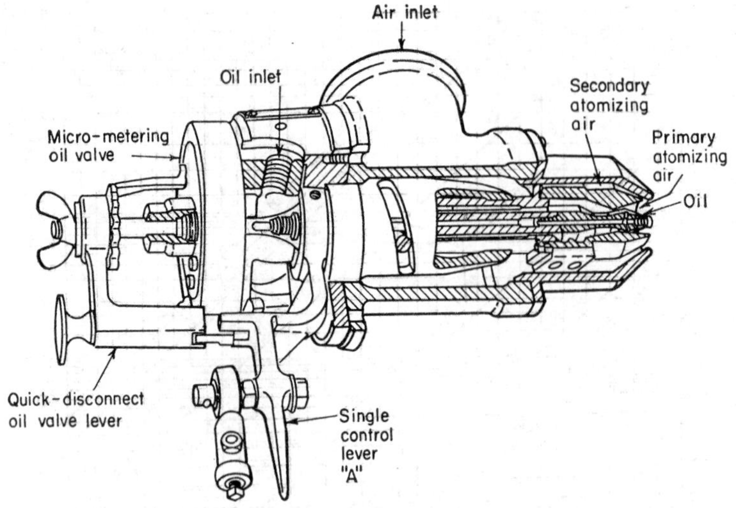

FIG. 9-28. A low-pressure air-atomizing burner uses 30 to 60 per cent of the air as primary air, the remainder being supplied by natural draft. (*Hauck Mfg. Co.*)

Steam is widely used to atomize heavy residual fuels or tars which require heat to obtain the desired viscosity; steam can be a deterrent to atomization of light fuels because the steam temperature can cause carbonization of distillates within the burner. The heavy oils normally are high in impurities and the beneficial effects of small amounts of water aid combustion and decomposition of these impurities.

Steam is used to atomize oil or to assist in mechanical atomization of oil and must be available in pressures equal to or greater than the oil pressure. Steam should be dry so that full expansion of the steam will be available to break up the oil. The use of steam per pound of oil will vary from 0.1 to 8 lb., depending upon the burner type and skill of the operator. In steam-assisted units this usually amounts to 0.01 lb. steam/lb. oil, and the excellent atomization obtained makes this economical.

External atomization is accomplished by hitting an oil stream with a perpendicular stream of atomizing fluid. It has been replaced by conical burners for all but special applications.

Internal mixing of steam and oil is accomplished by mixing the fluids together before they leave the tip (see Fig. 9-29). All tips have atomizer venturis drilled to

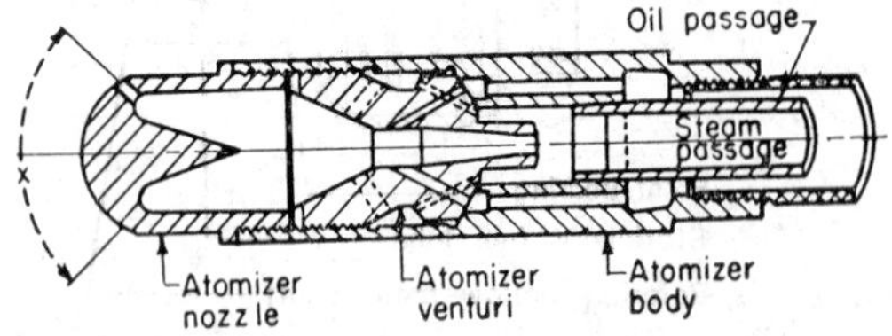

FIG. 9-29. Steam and oil are usually mixed within the tip; atomization occurs when the mixture is expanded through one or more orifices. (*The Engineer Co.*)

supply the steam or oil in small high-velocity jets to impart a high degree of rotational turbulence, although the manufacturers differ on which fluid is supplied in the center passage. The combined steam and oil mixture expands through precise orifice or holes drilled at a definite angle to the atomizer nozzle to obtain the desired

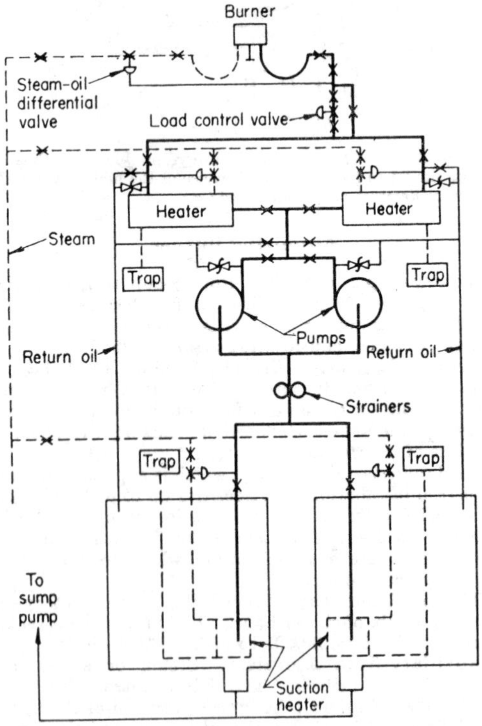

FIG. 9-30. A typical arrangement for firing heavy residual fuel oil with steam-atomizing burners.

conical flame shape. The angle of the conical oil mixture can be changed only by changing the atomizer orifice or tip. In designing an installation it is important that the burner manufacturer be acquainted with the furnace design so tips can be furnished to provide a flame pattern matching the general furnace dimensions.

Control of steam-atomizing burners is achieved by varying the amount of oil supplied to the burner. Control of the fuel-oil temperature is important, but the steam-atomizing feature will produce good results over a wide range. As shown in Fig. 9-30, a steam-oil pressure ratio control valve is installed to assure that steam pressure is held from 10 to 25 lb./sq. in. above the fuel-oil pressure. Connections are provided to introduce steam to the oil side of the burner to clean the burner gun when it is removed from service. Steam-atomizing units require very little maintenance and the tips seldom need cleaning.

Mechanical Atomizing. The straight **pressure atomizer** is the simplest mechanical atomizer. Oil under pressure is forced through tangential slots in a sprayer plate to impart a rotating motion to the oil. The oil leaves the sprayer plate through a precise orifice which controls the conical angle of the oil mist. Control of this type of burner is by pressure only, the pressure being increased as more heat is desired. Atomization is a function of pressure so that a narrow range of 3 to 1 is all that is obtainable.

Wide-range **mechanical atomizing guns** require oil under high pressure but allow some to return to the fuel-oil tank. Figure 9-31 shows this arrangement and indi-

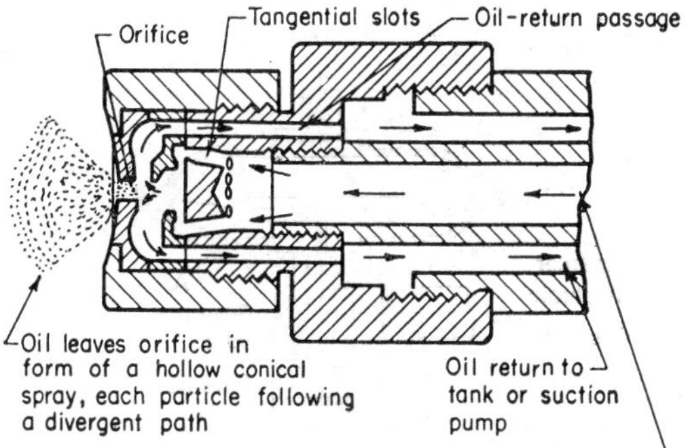

FIG. 9-31. Mechanical atomization is achieved by imparting a swirling motion to fuel oil before expanding it through an orifice. Control of fuel fired is usually achieved by regulation of oil returned to the tank. (*Todd Shipyards Corp.*)

cates that the pressure available for atomizing the oil is more than the return-oil pressure. The nozzle body incorporates tangential slots to provide a whirling motion so oil leaving the orifice will flare out in a hollow conical shape. Oil is supplied at a constant pressure and quantity, the amount of oil fired being the difference between the oil supplied and the oil returned from the burner. Load-control valves are placed in the return-oil piping.

Mechanical atomization depends upon the fuel-oil pressure, which must be high enough to provide a slight oil expansion after leaving the orifice. The pressure required will vary with the oil being fired but should be in the range of 250 lb./sq. in. for light distillates and from 600 to 1000 lb./sq. in. for heavy residuals. Unless these pressures are used, atomization will be imperfect and combustion will be slow, even to the point of having liquid oil impinge on the furnace surfaces. This is particularly serious with heavy residual oils because of the impurities they contain; the constituents are extremely corrosive at both high and low temperatures.

Frequent cleaning of tips is required even with the best orifice; eddy currents of oil are set up which return and impinge on the burner tip. Return-flow mechanical atomizing tips can operate in ranges of approximately 6 to 1 turn-down ratio although ratios as high as 10 to 1 may be possible under certain conditions.

Air Registers

Air is supplied to oil burners by natural or forced draft. The majority of units are equipped with forced-draft firing, although natural-draft registers are still used in small installations. Figure 9-32 shows a steam-

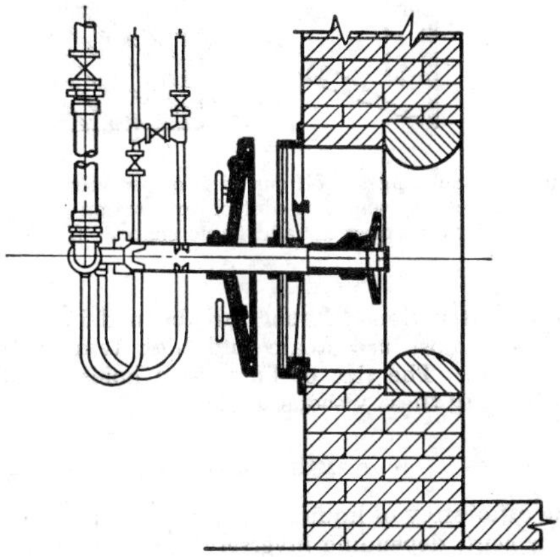

FIG. 9-32. This steam-atomizing oil burner uses natural draft to draw in the air for combustion.

atomizing oil gun installed in a **natural-draft** register; the oil must be atomized into extremely fine particles as natural draft provides a very low velocity for turbulence.

A **forced-draft** register with a steam-atomizing burner is shown in Fig. 9-33. A damper controls the amount of air supplied to the register while peripheral burner vanes control the angle at which the air enters the burner. This angle controls the shape of the flame by varying the degree of rotation imparted to the air; a tight rotation provides a short bushy flame, while a wide-open vane setting imparts little rotation and produces a long flame.

The best **performance** is obtained when the oil cone closely approaches the burner throat tile, with ignition taking place no later than this closest approach, restricting all air to passage through the oil flame itself.

Diffuser plates are installed on mechanical atomizing burners to prevent high-velocity air from quenching ignition of the oil cone. The plate provides a small amount of low-velocity air to help promote early combustion in a rich fuel mixture.

Other Fuels

Gasoline, kerosene, benzol, and **alcohol** are burned in special limited applications. **Shale oil, coal tar,**

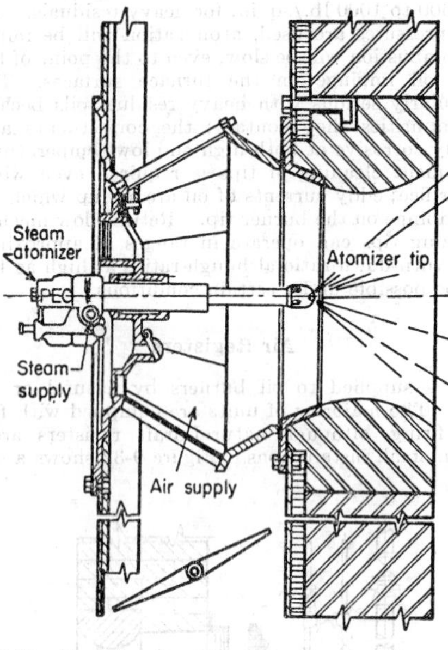

Fig. 9-33. Enclosing the oil gun in a pressuretight casing and installing directional vanes to control air rotation provide maximum control over excess air and flame shape. (*Peabody Engineering Co.*)

tar oil, and various "**heels**" are burned in several installations; most use steam and high temperature for atomization. The size of burner-tip holes is increased when burning these viscous fluids.

Efficiency

The **efficiency** of liquid-fuel burners varies from 85 to 100 per cent, depending inversely upon the hydrogen in the gas and directly on the mixing of the gas and air (see Fig. 9-34).

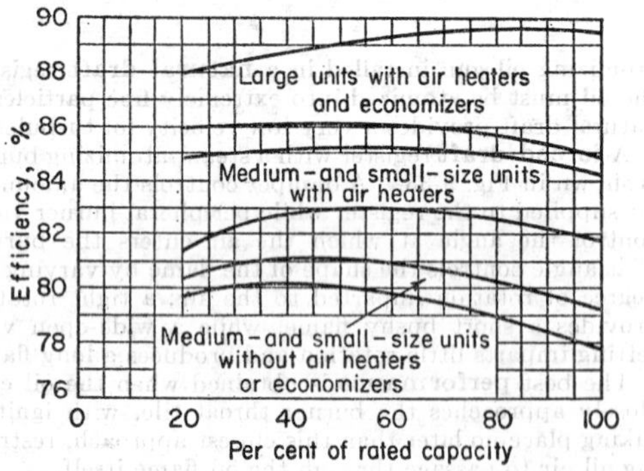

Fig. 9-34. Various types of heat recovery equipment can be applied to raise the efficiency of liquid-fuel firing. (*deLorenzi, "Combustion Engineering," Combustion Engineering Co., New York,* 1947.)

GASEOUS FUELS

General

Because gaseous fuels are easily dispersed in air no fuel preparation is necessary. Combustion time is short once ignition temperature is reached and proper turbulence is provided. The combustion of gas takes place in two ways, depending upon when gas and air are mixed. When gas and air are mixed prior to ignition, as in a bunsen burner, burning proceeds by hydroxylation.

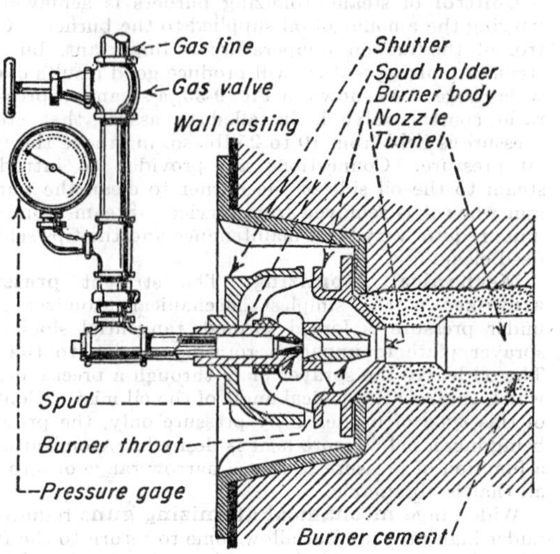

Fig. 9-35. Atmospheric industrial gas-burner installation with individual air control to each burner.

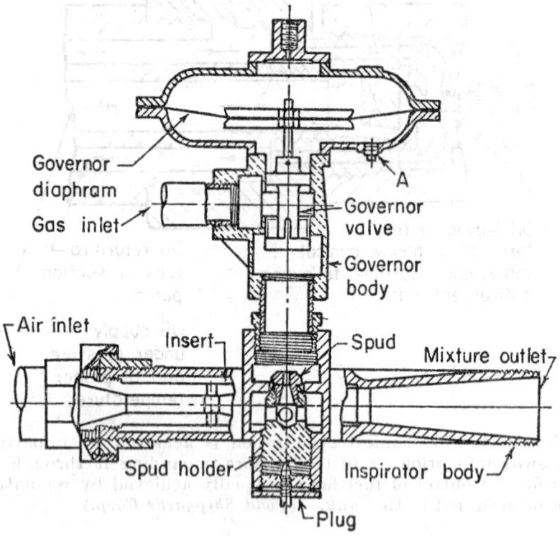

Fig. 9-36. This proportional mixer uses air velocity to draw in a measured amount of gas. (*Surface Combustion Division, Midland-Ross Corp.*)

The hydrocarbons and oxygen form hydroxylated compounds which become aldehydes; the addition of heat and additional oxygen breaks down the aldehydes to H_2, CO, CO_2, and H_2O. As carbon is converted to aldehydes in the initial stages of mixing, no soot can be developed even if the flame is quenched.

"Cracking" occurs when oxygen is added to hydrocarbons after they have been heated, decomposing the hydrocarbons into carbon and hydrogen which, when combined with sufficient oxygen, form CO_2 and H_2O. Soot and carbon black are formed if insufficient oxygen is present or if the combustion process is arrested before completion.

Each locale has a **code** for installation of gas-burning equipment. Most of these codes are patterned after that adopted by the National Bureau of Fire Underwriters.

Burners

Premix Burners. Premix burners burn by hydroxylation and are used for many natural-draft applications and for forced-draft applications when accurate furnace conditions must be maintained. Figure 9-35 indicates a

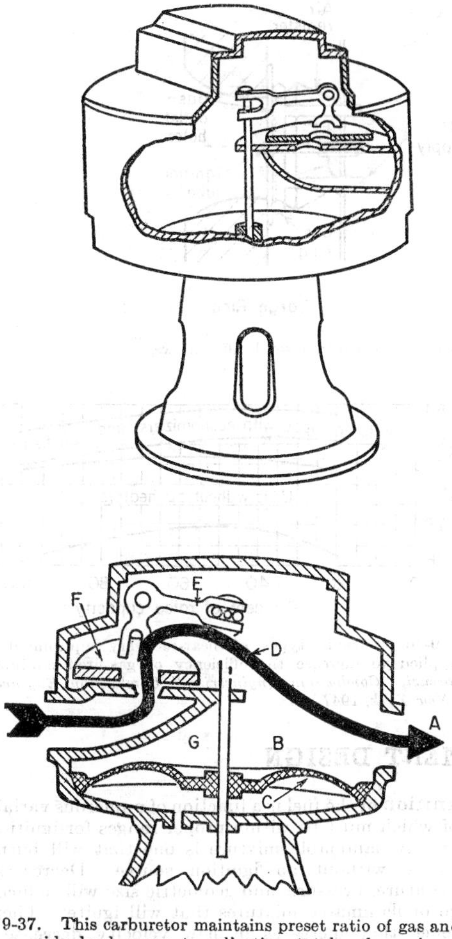

Fig. 9-37. This carburetor maintains preset ratio of gas and air over a wide load range to adjusting total volume handled. (*C. M. Kemp. Mfg. Co.*)

common natural-draft industrial-type burner with air being aspirated at the spud and burner throat. Figure 9-36 shows another type of premix burner where high-pressure air is used to aspirate the gas. The governor diaphragm controls the amount of gas admitted to the aspirator.

Burners used for close air control, such as for generating inert gas, must exercise close control over both the fuel and air admitted to the burners. Figure 9-37 shows a typical carburetor arrangement used for this control. The high-velocity burner shown in Fig. 9-26 can be adapted for use with various gaseous fuels. Although not strictly a premix burner, its temperatures and mixing produce results similar to premix burners.

Rate of **flame propagation** must be **exceeded** in premix burners to assure that ignition cannot travel back into the burner. Figure 9-38 indicates the rate of flame propagation at various air-gas ratios for several gases.

Nozzle-mix Burners. Nozzle-mix burners mix air and gas at the burner tile. As shown in Fig. 9-39 these burners can take four arrangements. The burner may

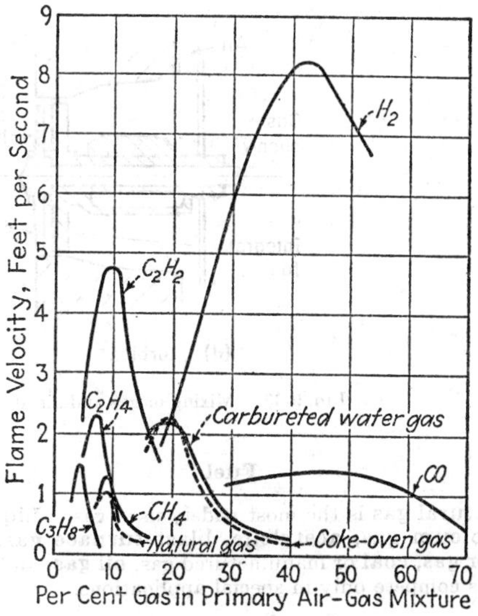

Fig. 9-38. Flame velocities of various gas-air mixtures. Data on individual gases from *Bur. Standards J. Research*, **17**, 7–43 (1936). Data on natural gas, coke-oven gas, and carbureted water gas from "Combustion," Am. Gas Assoc., 1932 (as compiled by Elliott and Denues of U.S. Bureau of Mines for Marks, "Mechanical Engineers' Handbook," McGraw-Hill, New York, 1941).

be a standard forced-draft register with the gas emitted from holes drilled in the end of a supply pipe. This method is easy to build but large holes are used and gas mixing becomes a problem; these burners frequently produce a luminous gas flame. Small-diameter pipe can be inserted at the center of the burner or large-diameter rings can extend to the outside of the burner tile. These rings use very small holes and give better dispersion of gas in the air, though they can plug up easily. One burner has a spider located in the burner inlet and through which gas is emitted in all the several radial arms. The spider is drilled to emit gas from the sides of the bars to provide a reaction from emission of high-pressure gas, causing the spider to turn. The spider can be attached to a fan so that forced draft is provided by the movement of the spider. The spider arrangement provides high turbulence for close regulation of excess air.

Control of gas burners is accomplished by regulating only the flow of gas in aspirating burners or by regulating both gas and air flows where controlled separately.

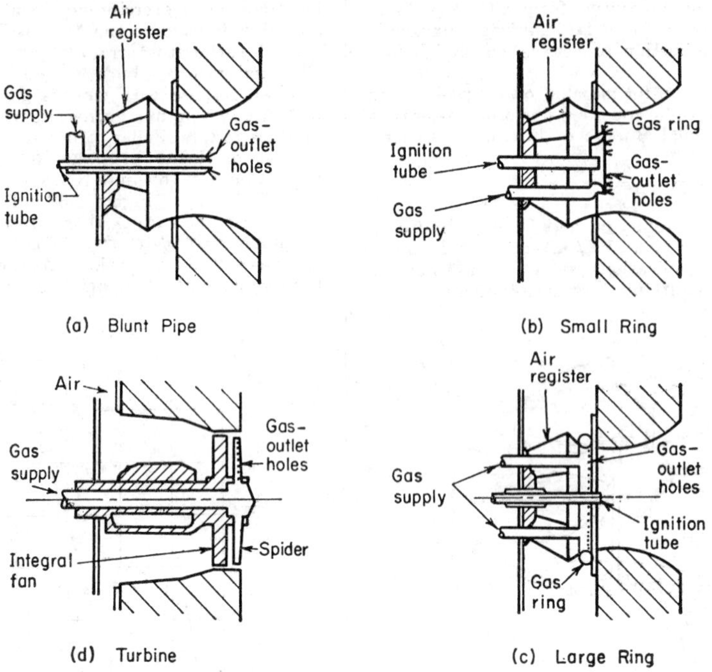

FIG. 9-39. Mixing of gas and air at the burner can be accomplished in several different ways.

Fuel

Natural gas is the most widely used gas. **Liquefied petroleum gas, acetylene, blast-furnace gas, blue water gas, coal** or manufactured gas, **oil gas,** and many others compete only in special applications.

Efficiency

The **efficiency** of a gas burner is inversely related to the hydrogen content of the gas and directly related to the mixing accomplished. The combustion efficiency depends on the type of heat-recovery equipment installed as shown in Fig. 9-40.

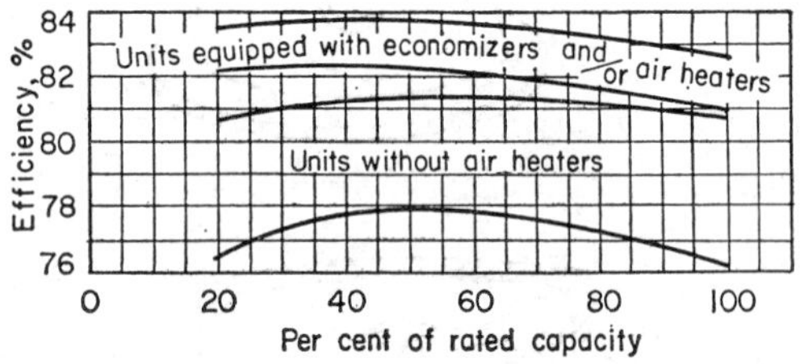

FIG. 9-40. Various types of heat-recovery equipment can be applied to increase the efficiency of gas-fired equipment. (*deLorenzi, "Combustion Engineering," Combustion Engineering Co., New York,* 1947.)

COMBUSTION-EQUIPMENT DESIGN

INTRODUCTION

Definitions

A **burner** is a device which produces a flame. It must mix the fuel and an oxidizing agent in proportions that are within the limits of flammability for ignition as well as for steady combustion. It must supply the fuel and its oxidizer at rates that will allow complete combustion without any burning back into the fuel-supply system or carrying of the flame into a low-temperature region where it will be quenched. Some burners include part of the fuel-preparation system in their construction. Most oil burners are in this category since the division of the oil into fine particles is accomplished at the burner. Two basic types of burners are premix and direct. In the premix burner the fuel and oxidizer are mixed prior to ignition. In the direct burner the fuel and oxidizer are mixed at the point of ignition.

Ignition of the fuel is a function of numerous variables, all of which must be within proper ranges for ignition to occur. A flammable mixture is one that will burn indefinitely without an ignition source. Decreases in temperature, pressure, and geometric size will reduce the range of flammable mixtures that will ignite. There is evidence that increases in flow velocity decrease the flammability limits. Vitiated or polluted atmospheres will also decrease the range.

Table 9-19 gives the flammability limits of some fuels at atmospheric pressure and temperature. To ignite the mixture, many methods may be used, such as electric sparks, hot surfaces, other flames, or shock waves. These raise the mixture to its ignition temperature, which is defined as the lowest temperature at which the heat loss from the combustible mixture is exceeded by the heat produced in the chemical reaction. Figure 9-41 shows the variation of ignition temperature with the fuel-to-air

Table 9-19. Basic Considerations in the Combustion of Hydrocarbon Fuels with Air, Physical and Combustion Properties of Fuels*

Fuel	Molecular weight	H_v B.t.u./lb.	H_B gas-gas, B.t.u./lb.	Stoichiometric mixture, % by volume	Flammability limit, % stoichiometric		Spontaneous ignition temp., °F.	Max. flame speed ft./sec. U_F	Adiabatic temp. °F., at U_F
					Lean	Rich			
Acetaldehyde	44.1	245	......	7.72					
Acetone	58.1	224	......	4.97	59	233	1042	1.5	3820
Acetylene	26.0	...	20,734	7.72	31	....	581	4.6	
Acrolein	56.1	...	......	5.64	48	752	532	1.8	
Acrylonitrile	53.1	...	......	5.28	87	....	898	1.4	4430
Allene (propadiene)	40.1	...	19,921	4.97	...	....	......	2.4	4430
Ammonia	17.0	590	......	21.81	...	....	1204		
Aniline	93.1	187	......	2.63	...	....	1100—		
Benzene	78.1	169	17,446	2.71	43	336	1097—	1.3	4150
n-Butyl-	134.2	...	17,984	1.53	...	....	821	1.1	4185
sec-Butyl-	134.2	...	......	1.53	...	....	836		
tert-Butyl-	134.2	...	......	1.53	...	....	891	1.1	4175
1,2-Diethyl-	134.2	...	......	1.53	...	....	759		
1,3-Diethyl-	134.2	...	......	1.53	...	....	851		
1,4-Diethyl-	134.2	...	......	1.53	...	....	844		
1,2-Dimethyl- (*o*-xylene)	106.2	149	17,723	1.95	...	....	934—	1.0	4205
1,3-Dimethyl- (*m*-xylene)	106.2	147	17,716	1.95	45	307	1045		
1,4-Dimethyl- (*p*-xylene)	106.2	146	17,719	1.95	...	....	1048		
Ethyl-	106.2	146	17,767	1.95	50	....	860		
Isobutyl-	134.2	...	......	1.53	...	....	853		
Isopropyl- (cumene)	120.2	134	17,873	1.71	52	352	873		
1-Methyl-2-ethyl-	120.2	139	17,864	1.71	...	....	836		
1-Methyl-3-ethyl-	120.2	138	17,853	1.71	...	....	905		
1-Methyl-4-ethyl-	120.2	137	17,848	1.71	...	....	902		
1-Methyl-3,5-diethyl-	148.2	...	......	1.38	...	....	861		
Nitro-	123.1	142	......	3.24	...	....	900		
Tropyl-	120.2	137	17,887	1.71	...	....	853		
1,2,3-Trimethyl- (hemimellitene)	120.2	143	17,825	1.71	...	....	895		
1,2,4-Trimethyl- (pseudocumene)	120.2	140	17,809	1.71	...	....	970	1.1	4180
1,3,5-Trimethyl- (mesitylene)	120.2	140	17,802	1.71	...	....	1039		
Vinyl- (styrene)	104.1	...	17,598	2.05	...	....	914		
Benzyl alcohol	108.1	...	......	2.40	...	....	802		
Biphenyl	154.2	...	......	1.41	...	....	1071		
2-Butyl-	210.3	...	......	1.01	...	....	811		
2-Ethyl-	182.3	...	......	1.18	...	....	840		
2-Methyl-	168.2	...	......	1.29	...	....	936		
2-Propyl-	196.3	...	......	1.09	...	....	845		
1,2-Butadiene (methylallene)	54.1	...	19,567	3.66	...	....	......	1.9	4355
1,3-Butadiene (divinyl, vinylethylene)	54.1	...	19,153	3.66	53	340	784	1.8	4275
2,3-Dimethyl-	82.1	...	......	2.40	...	....	......	1.4	4170
2-Methyl- (isoprene)	68.1	...	19,003	2.90	...	....	824	1.5	4220
n-Butane	58.1	166	19,655	3.12	54	330	807—	1.2	4060
2-Gyclopropyl-	98.2	...	......	1.95	...	....	......	1.3	
2,2-Dimethyl-	86.2	131	19,299	2.16	55	351	824	1.2	4055
2,3-Dimethyl-	86.2	136	19,338	2.16	55	372	790	1.2	4055
1,1-Diphenyl-	210.3	...	......	1.01	...	....	863		
2-Methyl- (isopentane)	72.1	146	19,451	2.55	50	359	800—	1.2	4055
2,2,3-Trimethyl-	100.2	124	19,241	1.87	58	358	849	1.2	4035
Butanone (methylethyl ketone)	72.1	191	......	3.66	...	....	......	1.2	
1-Butene	56.1	168	19,475	3.37	53	353	830	1.4	4175
2-Gyclopropyl-	96.2	...	......	2.05	...	....	......	1.4	4215
2,3-Dimethyl-	84.2	...	19,159	2.27	...	....	697	1.3	3970
2-Ethyl-	84.2	...	19,198	2.27	...	....	615	1.3	4110
2-Methyl-	70.1	...	19,252	2.71	...	....	......	1.3	4135
3-Methyl- (a-isoamylene)	70.1	...	19,297	2.71	...	....	706	1.4	4150
2,3,3-Trimethyl-	98.2	...	19,092	1.95	...	....	721		
trans-2-Butene	56.1	174	19,389	3.37	52	307			
2,3-Dimethyl-2-butene	84.2	...	19,135	2.27	...	....	764	1.2	4115
2-Methyl-2-butene	70.1	...	19,214	2.71					
3-Buten-1-yne (vinylacetylene)	52.1	...	......	4.02	...	....	......	2.5	4520
n-Butyl chloride	92.6	...	......	3.24					
1-Butyne	54.1	...	19,590	3.66	...	....	......	1.9	4345
3,3-Dimethyl-	82.1	...	......	2.40	...	....	......	1.6	4210
2-Butyne	54.1	...	19,440	3.66	...	....	......	1.7	4320
d-Camphor	152.2	...	......	1.53	...	....	871		
Carbon disulfide	76.1	151	......	6.52	18	1120	248	1.6	
Carbon monoxide	28.0	91	......	29.50	34	676	1128	1.3	
Cyanogen	52.0	186	......	9.47	...	....	1562		
Cyclobutane	56.1	...	......	3.37	...	....	......	1.9	4155
Ethyl-	84.2	...	......	2.27	55	376	......	1.5	4125
Isopropyl-	98.2	...	......	1.95	...	....	......	1.3	3900
Methyl-	70.1	...	......	2.71	...	....	......	1.5	
Methylene-	68.1	...	......	2.90	...	....	......	1.7	
Cyclohexane	84.2	154	18,846	2.27	48	401	518	1.3	4050
Ethyl-	112.2	133	18,816	1.71	55	420	507		
Methyl-	98.2	139	18,797	1.95	45	359	509	1.2	3935
1-Methyl-2-tert-butyl-	154.3	...	......	1.25	...	....	597		
Cyclohexane	82.1	...	......	2.40	...	....	......	1.3	
Cyclopentadiene	66.1	...	......	3.12	...	....	......	1.3	
Cyclopentane	70.1	167	19,001	2.71	...	....	725	1.2	4075
Methyl-	84.2	148	18,930	2.27	43	368	614	1.2	4010
n-Propyl-	112.2	...	18,907	1.71	...	....	545		
Cyclopentene	68.1	...	......	2.90	...	....	......	1.3	
Cyclopropane	42.1	...	......	4.44	58	276	928	1.6	4190
cis-1,2-Dimethyl-	70.1	...	......	2.71	...	....	......	1.5	4170
Trans-1,2-Dimethyl-	70.1	...	......	2.71	...	....	......	1.5	4160
Ethyl-	70.1	...	......	2.71	...	....	......	1.6	4125

Table 9-19. Basic Considerations in the Combustion of Hydrocarbon Fuels with Air, Physical and Combustion Properties of Fuels*—(*Continued*)

Fuel	Molecular weight	H_v B.t.u./lb.	H_B gas-gas, B.t.u./lb.	Stoichiometric mixture, % by volume	Flammability limit, % stoichiometric		Spontaneous ignition temp., °F.	Max. flame speed ft./sec. U_F	Adiabatic temp. °F, at U_F
					Lean	Rich			
Methyl-	56.1	...	......	3.37	...	....	......	1.6	4170
1,1,2-Trimethyl-	84.2	...	......	2.27	...	....	......	1.4	4155
trans-Decalin (decahydronaphthalene)	138.2	...	......	1.42	...	....	521—	1.0	4000
n-Decane	142.3	119	19,175	1.33	45	356	449	1.2	4115
1-Decene	140.3	...	19,094	1.38	36	392	471	1.2	4135
Diethyl ether	74.1	151	......	3.37	55	2640	366	1.3	4055
Dihydropyran	84.1	...	......	3.12					
Diisopropyl ether	102.2	...	......	2.27					
Dimethoxymethane	76.1	...	......	4.97					
Dimethyl ether	46.1	...	......	6.52	50	330	662	1.5	4010
Dimethyl sulfide	62.1	...	......	4.44					
Di-tert-butyl peroxide	146.2	...	......	1.79					
Divinyl ether	70.1	...	......	4.02	...	....	680		
Ethane	30.1	210	20,416	5.64	50	272	882	1.3	4040
1,1-Diphenyl-	182.3	...	......	1.18	...	....	909		
Ethene	28.1	208	20,276	6.52	41	610	914	2.2	4275
Ethyl acetate	88.1	...	......	4.02	61	236	907	1.1	
Ethyl alcohol	46.1	368	......	6.52	...	....	738		
Ethylamine	45.1	263	......	5.28					
Ethylene oxide	44.1	250	......	7.72	...	....	804	3.0	4340
Ethylenimine	43.1	...	......	6.05	...	....	......	1.3	
Furan	68.1	172	......	4.44					
Tetrahydro-	72.1	...	......	3.66					
Thio- (thiophene)	84.1	...	......	3.37					
n-Heptane	100.2	136	19,314	1.87	53	450	477—	1.3	3985
3,3-Dimethyl-	128.3	118	......	1.47	...	....	626		
1-Heptene	98.2	...	19,202	1.95	...	....	505		
1-Heptyne	96.2	...	19,262	2.05					
Hexadecane	226.4	98	19,052	0.85	...	....	446	1.2	4115
1-Hexadecene	224.4	...	19,000	0.86	...	....	464		
1,5-Hexadiene	82.1	...	......	2.40	...	....	......	1.4	
n-Hexane	86.2	144	19,391	2.16	51	400	501—	1.3	4030
2,3-Dimethyl-	114.2	126	19,236	1.65	...	....	820		
1-Hexene	84.2	...	19,262	2.27	52	393	521	1.4	4115
1-Hexyne	82.1	...	19,334	2.40	...	....	......	1.6	4200
3-Hexyne	82.1	...	......	2.40	...	....	......	1.5	4150
Hydrogen	2.0	194	51,571	29.50	...	....	1060—	8.7	
Hydrogen sulfide	34.1	237	......	12.24	...	....	554		
Isoprophy chloride	78.5	...	......	4.22					
Isoprophy mercaptan	76.2	...	......	3.37					
Isopropyl alcohol	60.1	286	......	4.44	...	....	852	1.1	
Isopropylamine	59.1	...	......	3.83	...	....	......	.9	4030
di-Limonene	136.2	125	......	1.47	...	....	505		
Methane	16.0	219	21,502	9.47	46	164	1170—	1.1	4025
Diphenyl-	168.2	...	......	1.29	...	....	962	1.0	4280
Methyl alcohol	32.0	473	......	12.24	48	408	878	1.6	
Methyl formate	60.1	203	......	9.47					
Naphthalene, 1-ethyl-	156.2	...	......	1.38	...	....	898		
1-Methyl	142.2	...	......	1.53	...	....	1017		
n-Nonane	128.3	124	19,211	1.47	47	434	453		
2-Methyl-	142.3	...	......	1.33	...	....	418		
n-Octane	114.2	129	19,256	1.65	51	425	464—		
2,3-Dimethyl-	142.3	...	......	1.33	...	....	447		
4-Ethyl-	142.3	...	......	1.33	...	....	458		
2-Methyl-	128.3	123	......	1.47	...	....	440		
3-Methyl-	128.3	123	......	1.47	...	....	442		
4-Methyl-	128.3	123	......	1.47	...	....	450		
1-Octene	112.2	...	19,157	1.71	46	384	493		
1,2 Pentadiene (ethylallene)	68.1	...	19,444	2.90	...	....	......	1.7	4285
cis-1,3-Pentadiene	68.1	...	19,018	2.90	...	....	......	1.5	4205
trans-1,3-Pentadiene (piperylene)	68.1	...	19,016	2.90	...	....	......	1.5	4230
2-Nethyl-(cis or trans)	82.1	...	......	2.40	...	....	......	1.3	4220
1,4-Pentadiene	68.1	...	19,190	2.90	...	....	......	1.5	4270
2,3-Pentadiene	68.1	...	19,399	2.90	...	....	......	1.7	4280
n-Pentane	72.1	154	19,499	2.55	54	359	544	1.3	4050
2,2-Dimethyl-	100.2	125	19,235	.....	...	....	......	1.1	4040
2,3-Dimethyl-	100.2	130	19,265	1.87	69	437	640	1.2	3995
2,4-Dimethyl-	100.2	127	19,253	1.87	...	....	......	1.2	4025
n-Pentane, 2,4-dimethyl-3-ethyl-	128.3	119	......	1.47	...	....	734		
3,3-Dimethyl-	100.2	127	19,255	1.87					
2-Methyl-	86.2	139	19,356	2.16	60	372	585	1.2	4050
3-Methyl-	86.2	140	19,369	2.16	...	....	580	1.2	4040
2,2,3,3-Tetramethyl-	128.3	118	......	1.47	54	344	845		
2,3,3,4-Tetramethyl-	128.3	117	......	1.47	...	....	818		
2,2,3-Trimethyl-	114.2	121	19,212	1.65	...	....	816		
2,2,4-Trimethyl- (isooctane)	114.2	117	19,197	1.65	48	360	837—	1.1	4020
2,3,3-Trimethyl-	114.2	123	19,226	1.65	...	....	806		
1-Pentene	70.1	...	19,346	2.71	47	370	569—	1.4	4165
2-Methyl-	84.2	...	19,185	2.27	...	....	582	1.3	4025
4-Methyl-	84.2	...	19,225	2.27	...	....	580	1.3	4130
2,3,4-Trimethyl-	112.2	...	......	1.71	...	....	495		
2,4,4-Trimethyl- (diisobutylene)	112.2	...	......	1.71	...	....	788		
cis-2-Pentene	70.1	...	19,308	2.71	49	345	......	1.4	4035
2,4,4-Trimethyl-	112.2	...	......	1.71	...	....	587		
3,4,4-Trimethyl-(cis or trans)	112.2	...	......	1.71	...	....	626		
trans-2-Pentene	70.1	...	19,280	2.71					

Table 9-19. Basic Considerations in the Combustion of Hydrocarbon Fuels with Air, Physical and Combustion Properties of Fuels*—(*Continued*)

Fuel	Molecular weight	H_v B.t.u./lb.	H_B gas-gas, B.t.u./lb.	Stoichiometric mixture, % by volume	Flammability limit, % stoichiometric		Spontaneous ignition temp., °F.	Max. flame speed ft./sec. U_F	Adiabatic temp. °F, at U_F
					Lean	Rich			
1-Pentyne	68.1	...	19,436	2.90	...	....	......	1.7	4265
4-Methyl-	82.1	...	......	2.40	...	....	......	1.5	4220
2-Pentyne	68.1	...	19,338	2.90	...	....	......	1.7	4280
4-Methyl-	82.1	...	......	2.40	...	....	......	1.5	4160
a-Pinene	136.2	...	......	1.47	...	....	......	506	
Propadiene (see Allene)									
Propane	44.1	183	19,929	4.02	51	283	940–	1.3	4050
2-Cyclopropyl-	84.2	...	......	2.27	...	....	......	1.4	
1-Deutero-	45.1	...	......	4.02	...	....	......	1.1	
1-Deutero-2-methyl-	59.1	...	......	3.12	...	....	......	1.1	
2-Deutero-2-methyl-	59.1	...	......	3.12	...	....	......	1.1	
2,2-Dimethyl- (neopentane)	72.1	136	......	2.55	54	283	853	1.1	4060
1,1-Diphenyl-	196.3	...	......	1.09	...	....	870		
2-Methyl- (isobutane)	58.1	158	19,593	3.12	60	321	890–	1.2	4065
Propene	42.1	188	19,683	4.44	48	272	1036–	1.4	4210
2-Cyclopropyl-	82.1	...	......	2.40	...	....	......	1.5	
2-Methyl-	56.1	169	19,346	3.37	...	....	......	1.2	
Propionaldehyde	58.1	...	......	4.97	...	....	......	1.6	3855
n-Propyl alcohol	60.1	295	......	4.44	...	....	812		
n-Propyl chloride	78.5	...	......	4.22					
Propylene oxide (1,2-epoxypropane)	58.1	...	......	4.97	47	....	......	2.3	4170
1-Propyne	40.1	...	19,849	4.97	...	....	......	2.3	4450
Spiropentane	68.1	...	......	2.90	...	....	......	2.0	
1-Tetradecene	196.4	...	19,022	0.99	...	....	463		
Tetrahydropyran	86.1	...	......	2.90	...	....	......	1.3	
Tetralin (tetrahydronaphthalene)	132.2	...	......	1.58	...	....	794	1.1	4175
Toluene (methylbenzene)	92.1	156	17,601	2.27	43	322	1054–	1.2	4220
Triethylamine	101.2	...	......	2.10					
Turpentine (mainly a-pinene)		...	......	.....	...	....	486		
Vinyl acetate	86.1	...	......	4.44					
Gasoline, 73-octane	.....	...	......	.....	...	....	570		
Gasoline, 100-octane		...	......	.....	...	....	800–950	1.1	
Jet fuel, grade JP-1	150	...	18,500	1.3	...	....	480	1.1	
Jet fuel, grade JP-3	112	...	18,700	1.7					
Jet fuel, grade JP-4	126	...	18,700	1.5	...	....	502	1.1	
Jet fuel, grade JP-5	170	...	18,500	1.1	...	....	468		

* Adapted from Table XXXII, NACA Report 1300, 1959.

ratio. In general, ignition is easier with the richer fuel-to-oxidizer mixtures. Some burners employ a choke to enrich the mixture for ignition purposes.

Even when conditions are favorable for ignition a time will exist known as ignition lag between the introduction of the igniter and the first indication of ignition. Increases in pressure and temperature decrease the ignition lag. Figure 9-42 gives examples of the ignition lag for methane. Richer mixtures will also have smaller ignition lag times as shown in Fig. 9-43. The effects of

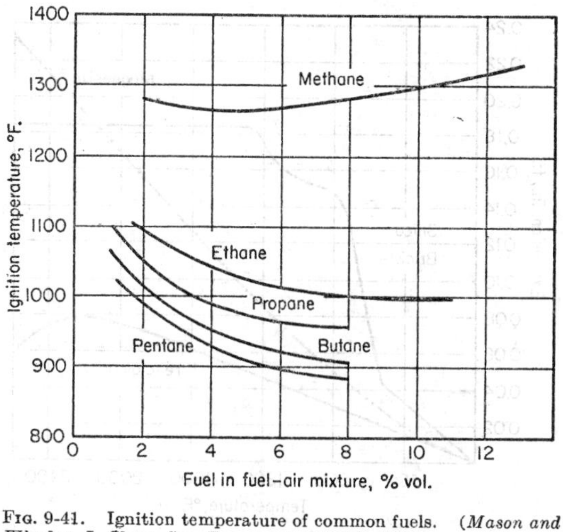

FIG. 9-41. Ignition temperature of common fuels. (*Mason and Wheeler, J. Chem. Soc. Trans., vol.* CXXV, 1924.)

pilot size in igniting a methane-air mixture are shown in Fig. 9-44.

Flame stability must be maintained after ignition is accomplished in a burner. If not maintained the combustion may be extinguished or result in severe furnace pulsations which damage the equipment. In extreme cases explosions may occur with disastrous effects. To maintain flame stability at a point the velocity of the fuel and its oxidizing agent must be less than the flame-propagation speed to prevent blowout of the flame. This may be accomplished by use of direct burners which maintain all factors for flammability within the required limits. For premix burners where the velocity of the fuel-oxidizer mixture must exceed the flame-propagation speed prior to the point of combustion, some type of flame holder must be utilized. Diffusion into larger spaces or eddy-producing devices are common. Table 9-19 lists some flame velocities for hydrocarbons. Figure 9-45 shows the effect of oxygen-enriched atmospheres upon flame velocity. Great care must be exercised in

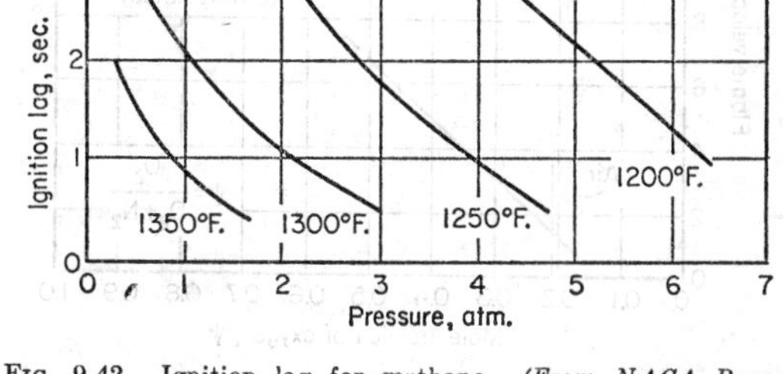

FIG. 9-42. Ignition lag for methane. (*From NACA Report* 1300, 1959.)

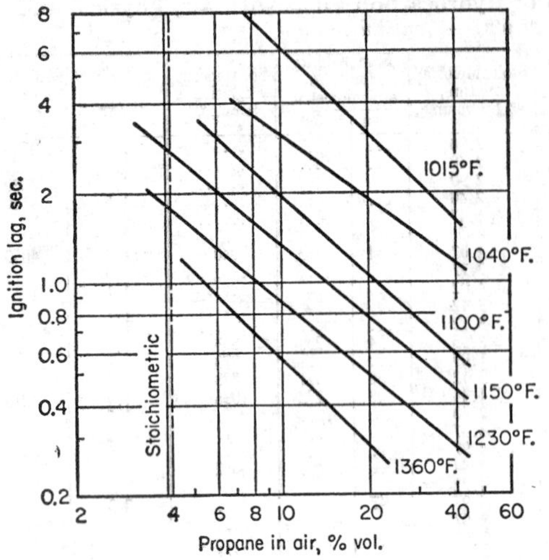

FIG. 9-43. Ignition lag for propane in air. (*From NACA RME54B19*, 1954.)

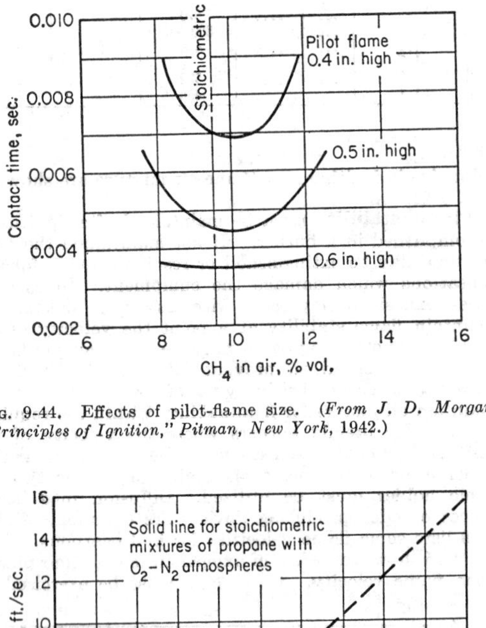

FIG. 9-44. Effects of pilot-flame size. (*From J. D. Morgan, "Principles of Ignition," Pitman, New York*, 1942.)

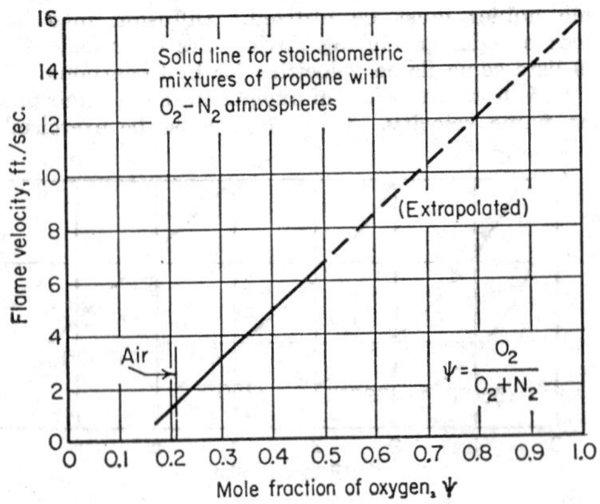

FIG. 9-45. Flame velocity of propane. (*From NACA RME52J24*, 1952.)

applying published values of flame velocity since they are affected by many variables including geometry. Frequently problems in flame stability may be traced to the fuel-transport system or to the air-supply system where unsuspected transient variations in the fuel-air ratio may originate even if average conditions are favorable. In extreme cases constant pilots may be utilized, such as oil torches in pulverized-anthracite furnaces or refractory heat storage for chemical processes and incinerators where fuel interruptions may occur.

A **furnace** may be defined as an enclosed space in which heat is produced from the chemical oxidation of a fuel.

The requirements of a furnace are that it shall complement the burner(s) firing into it to obtain the desired combustion reaction(s). The best possible burner cannot function efficiently in a furnace where cold surfaces and excessive air dilution reduce the temperature below that required to maintain ignition. It is essential that a furnace and burner combination be considered together to provide the four elements of good combustion, which are (1) intimate mixing of the fuel and the oxidizer, (2) admission of sufficient oxidizer to burn the fuel completely, (3) sufficient temperature to ignite and complete combustion, and (4) the required time for combustion to be completed.

To these main fundamental ones may be added many special requirements, depending upon the application. For example, if the fuel has appreciable ash content, the flue gases must be cooled sufficiently before leaving the furnace to prevent any molten particles of ash from solidifying on cold surfaces and stopping the flow of gases (slagging).

The **geometry** of the furnace is also dependent upon the type of burners and service which are utilized within a given furnace. Direct flame impingement is to be avoided. Fuel-air ratios, within the limits of flammability, and suitable ignition temperatures must be maintained at a point of relative stability. If unburned solid products are obtained, provision must be made to remove them from the furnace either continuously or periodically.

The design of the furnace must provide a suitable container for the **combustion reaction.** If made of refractory suitable insulation and metal casing seals are often added. Care must be taken to allow for expansion of the unit (Fig. 9-46). Air- or liquid-cooled surfaces

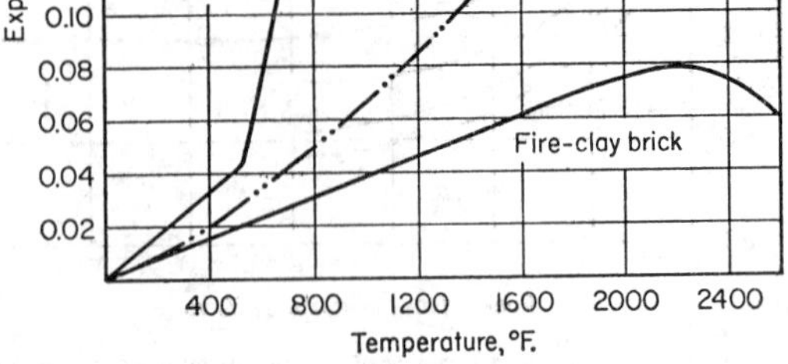

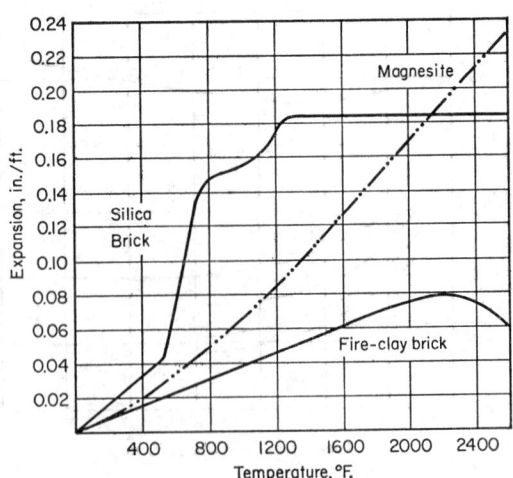

FIG. 9-46. Expansion of refractories.

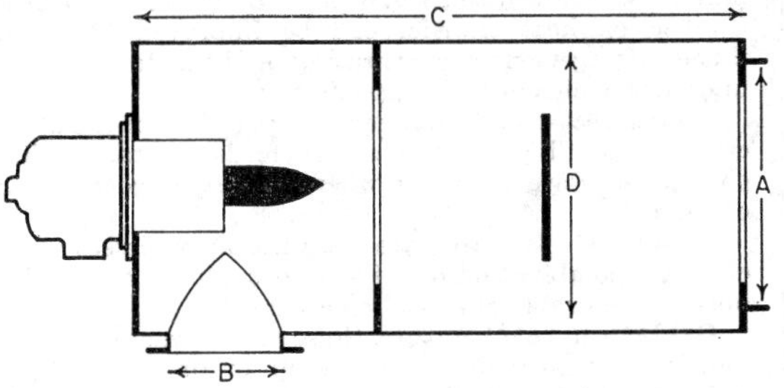

Air-heated SCFM	Inlet temp., °F.	Outlet temp., °F.	Burner output btu/hr.	Heater construction	A, in.	B, in.	C, in.	D, in.
600	60	850	520,000	Stainless steel	10	6	48	12
3200	60	300	850,000	Mild steel	20	14	60	24
14500	400	500	1,600,000	Mild steel	48	42	84	54
3900	60	1000	4,000,000	Stainless steel	30	27	72	30
7100	60	1050	7,900,000	Stainless steel	40	24	84	46

FIG. 9-47. Thermal direct-fired heater.

are used frequently to eliminate or reduce the amount of refractory.

Various other requirements are imposed by the processes to which the furnace applies. These will be discussed subsequently.

Classifications

Direct-fired combustion equipment is that in which the flame and/or products of combustion are used to achieve the desired result by direct contact with another material. Common examples are kilns, open-hearth furnaces, submerged combustion evaporators, and so forth.

Indirect-fired combustion equipment is that in which the flame and products of combustion are separated from any contact with the principal material in the process by means of metallic or refractory walls. Examples are vaporizers, heat exchangers, melting pots, and so forth.

Some **other types** of combustion equipment do not fall into either direct- or indirect-fired classifications as given above. Examples are (1) a **pebble heater** discussed later in this section where alumina pebbles are direct-fired while process gas is heated through indirect firing and (2) an **inert-gas** generator where fuel is burned stoichiometrically to produce an inert gas.

FIRED PROCESS EQUIPMENT

Direct-fired

Heaters. *Gaseous* direct-fired heaters are often utilized in many cases where the products of combustion do not seriously affect the process stream. Their low first cost and lower operating cost make them ideal in such cases. Where high temperatures are required and thin metal walls cannot serve as a heat-transfer medium to the process stream, they may be utilized to obtain otherwise unattainable temperatures despite some process-gas contamination. For such applications, preheating and care in selecting the combustion fuel may reduce the effects of contamination. Ash- and/or sulfur-free fuels, fuels with favorable hydrogen-carbon ratios, and substitution of oxygen for combustion air may be economically justified when process yields and quality are considered.

Operating temperatures of 1500°C. are available with commercial equipment, although oxygen for combustion may be required to attain such temperatures without

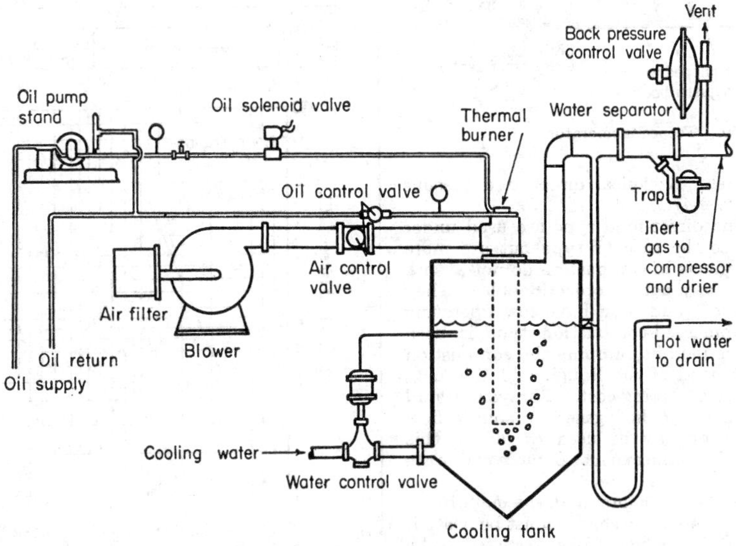

FIG. 9-48. Submerged combustion-liquid heater.

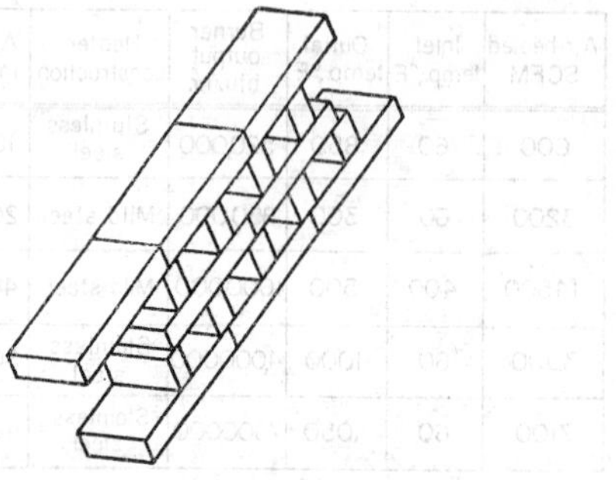

FIG. 9-49. Typical filter-baffle construction.

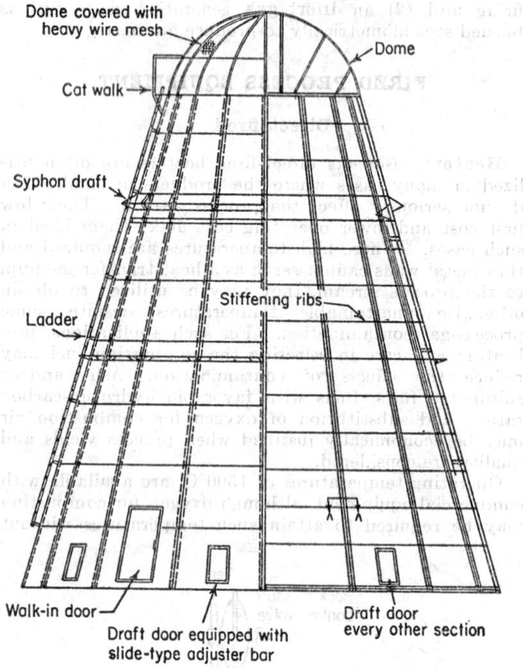

FIG. 9-50. Teepee incinerator.

requiring excessive fuel. A typical direct-fired gaseous heater is shown in Fig. 9-47.

Liquid heaters of the direct-fired type are used under the same conditions as the gaseous type but are more common since the products of combustion do not absorb to a large extent and may not be objectionable. They also are low in first cost and may have low operating cost. Where the submerged-combustion type is used (Fig. 9-48) a penalty is paid in pumping the combustion air against the static head of the liquid, and this may often result in excessive operating cost. Sprays of liquid may be passed through the hot gases or counterflow packed-column scrubbers may be used to reduce this pumping loss but usually at the expense of more elaborate and costly designs.

Direct-fired *solid* heaters are common in the metallurgical and other fields. Where large shapes must be heated, emphasis must be placed on efficient heat transfer to the solids. Radiant-heat transfer is often used effectively by either porous-wall refractory burners or multiple-wall burners which heat refractory cups to high temperatures. Convection heat transfer can be improved by direct flame impingement if overheating of the solid surface or undesirable chemical changes do not occur.

Some direct-fired heaters are *combinations* of the above cases where liquid or gaseous feeds contain solids, changes of state occur, or where multiple processes are combined.

Reactors. Reactors are combustion processes where chemical combination of a fuel and oxidizers are used to obtain a desirable chemical compound.

Oxidation reactors are those units where stoichiometric or greater quantities of air or oxygen are provided to obtain complete combustion of the fuel. The Leonard-Monsanto sulfuric acid process, for example, combines sulfur as a fuel with oxygen from the combustion air to produce sulfur dioxide as a first step. The production of nitric acid by the ammonia oxidation

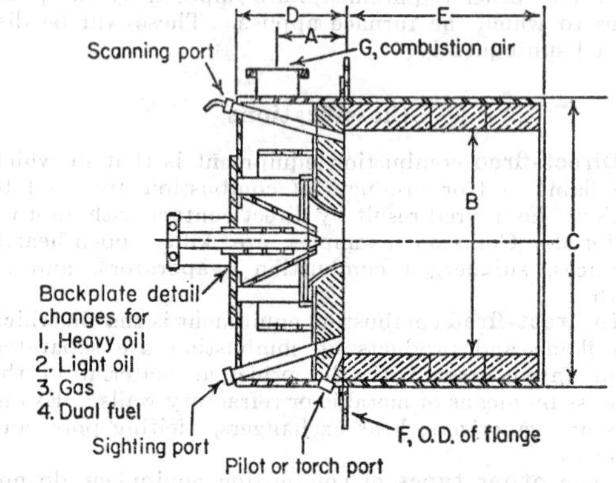

Model	Millions of B.t.u./hr.	A	B	C	D	E	F	G
LV3	3	7	15	24	10½	18	28	4
LV7	7	9	21	30	13½	22½	34	8
LV10	10	10½	26	35	15½	27	39	10
LV18	18	12	32	41	18½	31½	44	12
LV30	30	13½	42	51	21½	40½	56	18
LV48	48	15	54	63	25½	49½	69	20

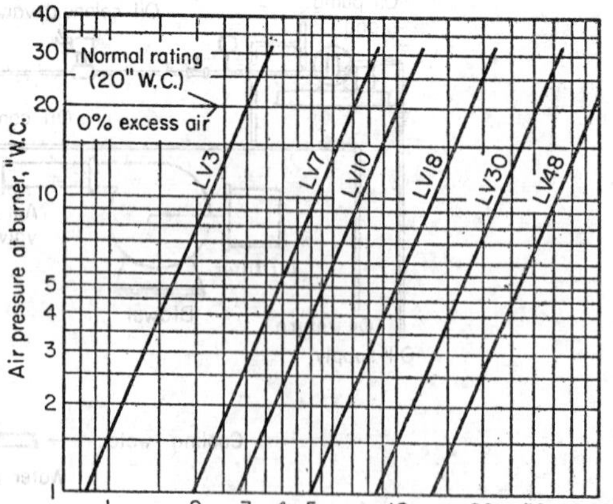

FIG. 9-51. Vortex burner.

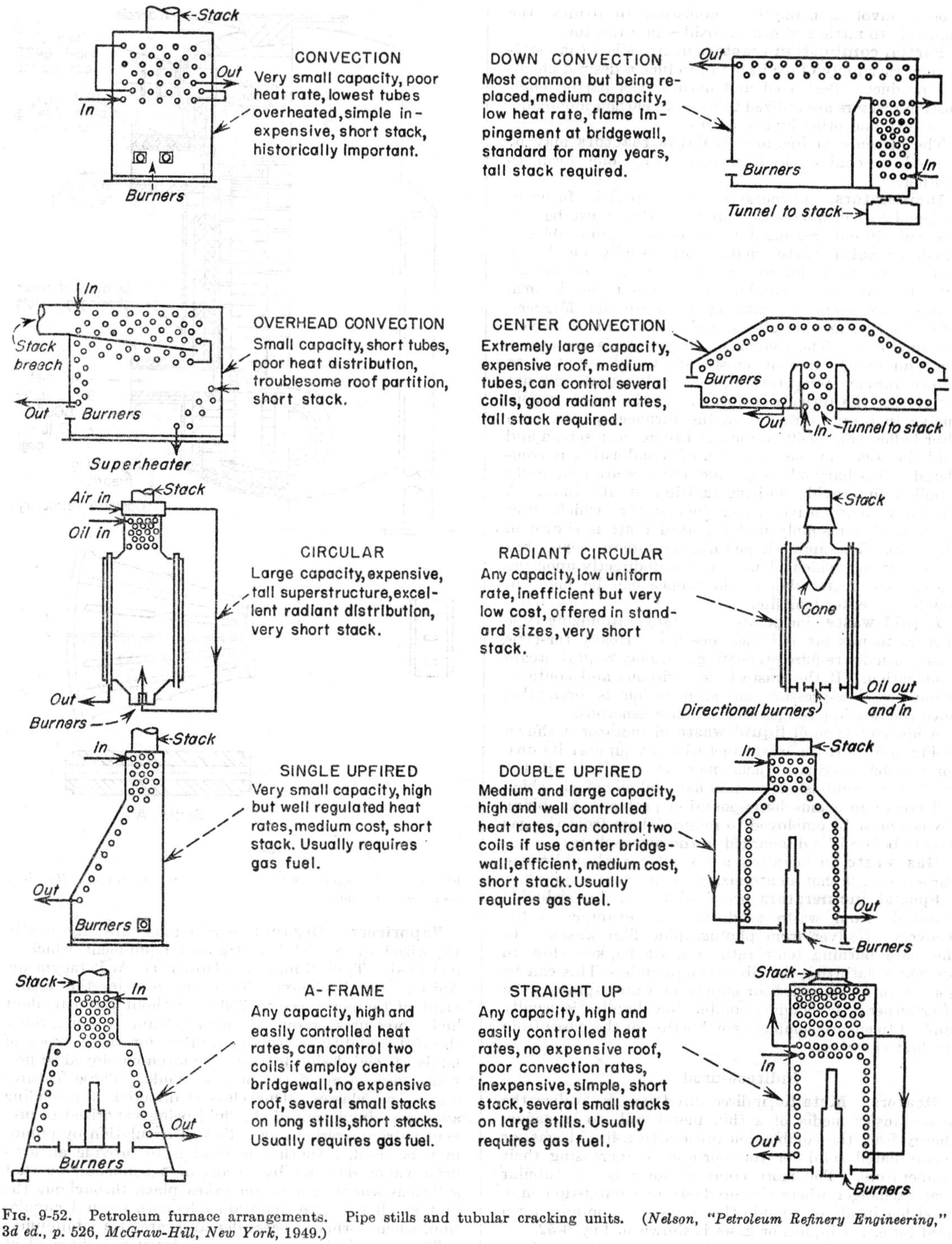
Stack
In
Out
Burners
CONVECTION
Very small capacity, poor heat rate, lowest tubes overheated, simple inexpensive, short stack, historically important.
DOWN CONVECTION
Most common but being replaced, medium capacity, low heat rate, flame impingement at bridgewall, standard for many years, tall stack required.
Out
Burners
In
Tunnel to stack
In
Stack breech
Out
Burners
Superheater
OVERHEAD CONVECTION
Small capacity, short tubes, poor heat distribution, troublesome roof partition, short stack.
CENTER CONVECTION
Extremely large capacity, expensive roof, medium tubes, can control several coils, good radiant rates, tall stack required.
Burners
Out
In
Tunnel to stack
Air in
Stack
Oil in
Out
Burners
CIRCULAR
Large capacity, expensive, tall superstructure, excellent radiant distribution, very short stack.
RADIANT CIRCULAR
Any capacity, low uniform rate, inefficient but very low cost, offered in standard sizes, very short stack.
Stack
Cone
Oil out and in
Directional burners
Stack
In
Out
Burners
SINGLE UPFIRED
Very small capacity, high but well regulated heat rates, medium cost, short stack. Usually requires gas fuel.
DOUBLE UPFIRED
Medium and large capacity, high and well controlled heat rates, can control two coils if use center bridgewall, efficient, medium cost, short stack. Usually requires gas fuel.
In
Stack
Out
Burners
Stack
In
Out
Burners
A-FRAME
Any capacity, high and easily controlled heat rates, can control two coils if employ center bridgewall, no expensive roof, several small stacks on long stills, short stacks. Usually requires gas fuel.
STRAIGHT UP
Any capacity, high and easily controlled heat rates, no expensive roof, poor convection rates, inexpensive, simple, short stack, several small stacks on large stills. Usually requires gas fuel.
Stack
In
Out
Burners

FIG. 9-52. Petroleum furnace arrangements. Pipe stills and tubular cracking units. (*Nelson, "Petroleum Refinery Engineering," 3d ed., p. 526, McGraw-Hill, New York,* 1949.)

process involves catalytic combustion to oxidize the ammonia to nitric and nitrous oxides in a reactor.

Partial combustion reactors utilize a less than stoichiometric supply of oxidizer to produce a desired chemical product. Both coal and natural gas partial combustion reactors are utilized to produce carbon monoxide, hydrogen, and other hydrocarbons.

The presence of free ions in **flame reactors** may be utilized to convert hydrocarbons from one form to another.

Incinerators. Incinerators are special furnaces designed to consume waste products that must be disposed of without creating dumping or pollution problems. Trash or **solid-waste** incinerators usually employ a grate or rotating kiln to accomplish mixing of the air with the waste for combustion. Various mechanical feeding arrangements ranging from special hoppers, screw feeders, moving grates, and rams to hand shovels are employed. The control of air supply is important since an excess amount must usually be supplied to reduce furnace temperatures to a value that will not deteriorate the furnace enclosure. If the waste is conducive to being carried from the furnace (paper, etc.) filter baffles (Fig. 9-49) are utilized to act as a screen and hold the waste in the furnace until combustion is completed. Auxiliary oil- or gas-fuel burners are frequently supplied to provide positive ignition at all times. A relatively inexpensive trash incinerator which uses forced-draft air supply under a fixed grate is shown in Fig. 9-50. This unit, shaped like an Indian teepee, has a door through which a truck can dump directly upon the grate. The metal skin of the teepee can be made of stainless steel for long life.

Liquid-waste incinerators employ atomizing-type burners to mix air and fuel together. Heavy tar-type wastes usually require preheating and may require steam atomization. If the waste is less viscous and contains impurities, low-pressure air atomization is preferable since the nozzle passages will be more generous.

A low-cost type of **liquid waste** incinerator is shown in Fig. 9-51. If the waste fuel will not support its own combustion, auxiliary fuels may be supplied. If the products of combustion contain harmful chemicals which will create an atmospheric-pollution problem, scrubbing devices must be employed to remove them from the gas stream before it is discharged to the atmosphere.

Gas waste incinerators are similar to liquid-waste burners except that an atomizing agent is not required.

Special incinerators are used to salvage valuable materials from waste products. An example is the recovery of silver from photographic film wastes. In this case burning temperatures must be kept low to prevent volatilizing the silver compounds. This can be done with an excessive air supply or water sprays. An afterburner in a secondary combustion chamber is usually applied to ensure complete combustion of the gases from the first chamber.

Indirect-fired

Heaters. Metallic indirect-fired heaters utilize the heat-transfer media of a thin metal wall to transport energy from the combustion process to a liquid, gas, or encapsulated solid for the purpose of increasing their temperature. The more common form is the tubular heat exchanger where the products of combustion may be either inside or outside the tubes. A common form used for either liquids or gases is shown in Fig. 9-52.

Non-metallic indirect-fired heaters utilize refractories or silica glass as a heat-transfer media. Silicon has a relatively high thermal conductivity and a design of high-temperature-gas heat exchanger utilizing silicon blocks with preformed gas passages as shown in Fig. 9-53.

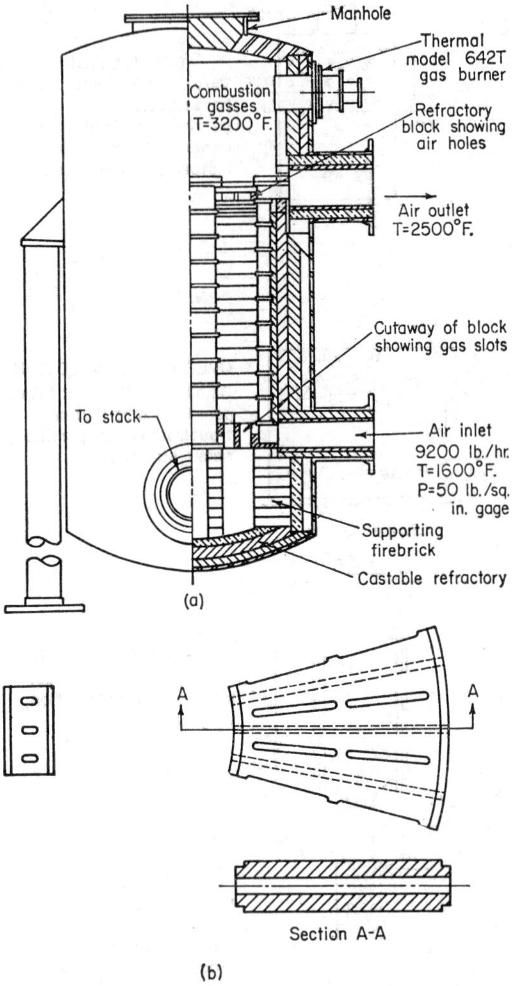

FIG. 9-53. Silicon block heater. (*a*) Heat exchanger. (*b*) Heat exchanger element.

Vaporizers. Organic compounds are frequently vaporized in special heat-transfer equipment which is fuel-fired. Typical fluids are Dowtherm A, Paracymene, Anisole, and Diphenyl. They are used for the attainment of temperatures to 750°F. without the attendant high pressures required with steam vapor. Since thermal stability is usually limited for these types of fluids, special design features are often employed to prevent overheating of the organic fluids. These features are of two classes. One class is directed at providing adequate circulation of the fluid being vaporized to prevent it from overheating. Forced circulation by pumps may be used. Another method is to provide an artificial vapor demand by means of a condenser so that sufficient vapor generation takes place throughout the unit at all times to maintain adequate natural circulation, when normal process demands are at a minimum.

The second class of protective feature is directed at preventing the contact of the hottest gases against the heat-transfer surfaces of the vaporizer. These may include the design of special burners and combustion chambers to prevent flame impingement, low flame tem-

FIG. 9-54. Fire-tube boiler.

peratures through the admission of excess secondary air, or the recirculation of exhaust gases back into the furnace. Since most organics are highly combustible special precautions must be taken to prevent leakage wherever mechanical joints and seals are used. Rupture disks are permitted by many codes beneath safety valves if properly installed, and seal welding of access openings is common.

Other compounds and elements such as mercury are sometimes vaporized in fuel-fired equipment, and each such application must be carefully analyzed for potential operating hazards occasioned by the particular fluid used in the application. Mercury has the advantage of being suitable for very high temperatures at modest pressures. Its cost limits its widespread use.

Steam Generators. Steam generators are the most common vaporizers. They fall into two general categories, namely, (1) industrial and (2) power-utility steam boilers.

Industrial steam-boiler types include fire-tube boilers and water-tube boilers. **Fire-tube boilers** (or steam generators) are characterized by the containment of the products of combustion within the tubes of the boiler. The water being vaporized surrounds the tubes and is contained by a larger shell with front and rear tube sheets. Prior to 1940, these were built in many different types, but almost all fire-tube boilers built today are of the modified Scotch marine type. This design (Fig. 9-54) utilizes a central cylindrical combustion chamber with return of the gases through smaller tubes. Baffles are frequently provided to return the gases through more tubes for a third or fourth pass. These units are usually completed as a shop-erected package boiler with all combustion equipment and controls installed and ready to

FIG. 9-55. Water-tube boiler.

operate after electrical and piping connections are made at the place of utilization. Fire-tube boilers are rated for capacity in terms of boiler horsepower. One boiler horsepower is defined as the ability to evaporate 34.5 lb. water from and at 212°F. Such units are available in sizes from 5 to 600 hp. (about 20,000 lb./hr. steam) and in pressures to 250 lb./sq. in. For this size and pressure range they are very competitive in price and installation costs. They do not lend themselves readily to the installation of superheaters and are thus limited to the generation of saturated steam only. They are applicable to oil- and gas-fuel firing only.

Water-tube boilers are characterized by the containment of the vaporizing water within the tubes while the products of combustion are on the outer surfaces. The furnace chamber may consist of containment by either refractory walls or special configurations of the water tubes. For economic reasons, sizes of 10,000 to 120,000 lb./hr. are generally of "package" shop-erected construction. These are currently available only for oil- and gas-fuel firing, with active work underway to develop similar coal-fired units. A few coal-fired units have been built but full acceptance and utilization have yet to develop. Larger-capacity oil and gas-fired units and almost all coal-fired units are generally "field-erected," or constructed in place. Since the water tubes are of small diameter compared with the shells of fire-tube boilers, there is no similar limitation on their operating pressures. Figure 9-55 shows a typical package unit.

Many older water-tube boilers are of the straight-water-tube construction, but modern units are almost universally of bent water-tube design. The use of bent tubes allows extreme flexibility in design. The shaping of the tubes to enclose the combustion space has sharply reduced the amount of refractory used and has permitted higher rates of burning within the combustion space. Superheaters may be readily fitted to such units. Industrial units in excess of 250,000 lb./hr. capacity are rare

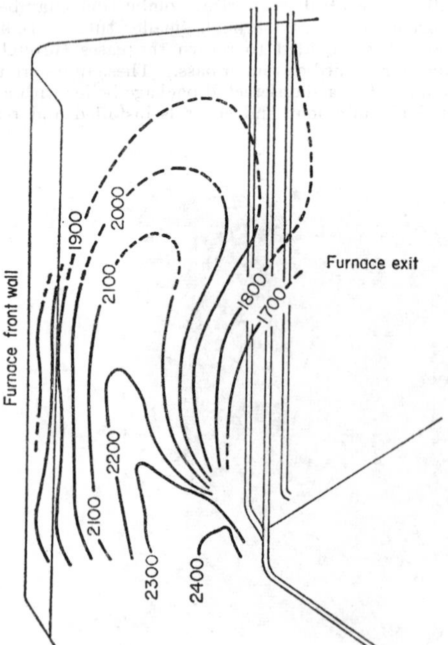

FIG. 9-56. Temperature isotherms in a large furnace.

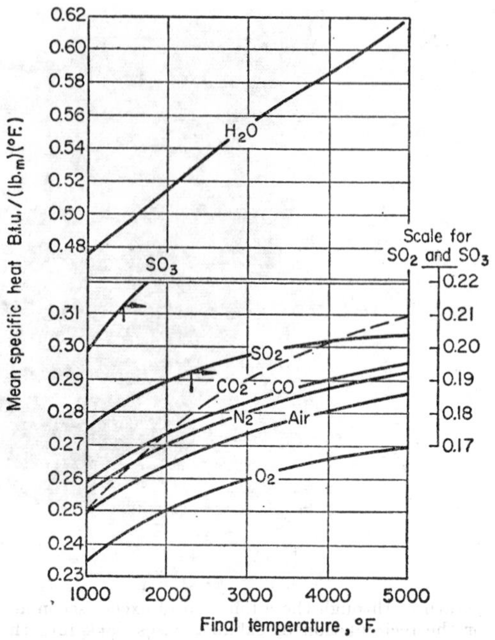

FIG. 9-57. Mean specific heats of gases above 60°F.

Table of Equilibrium Constants

Reaction	$H_2 + \frac{1}{2}O_2 \rightleftharpoons H_2O$	$CO + \frac{1}{2}O_2 \rightleftharpoons CO_2$
Abs. temp., °R.	$K_p = \frac{pH_2O}{pH_2\sqrt{pO_2}}$	$K_p = \frac{pCO_2}{pCO\sqrt{pO_2}}$
2500	$2.77(10)^6$	$1.26(10)^6$
3000	$7.24(10)^4$	$2.11(10)^4$
3500	$5.13(10)^3$	$1.12(10)^3$
4000	708	126
4500	159	24.8
5000	50.5	7.08
5500	17.8	2.32

(p = atm.)

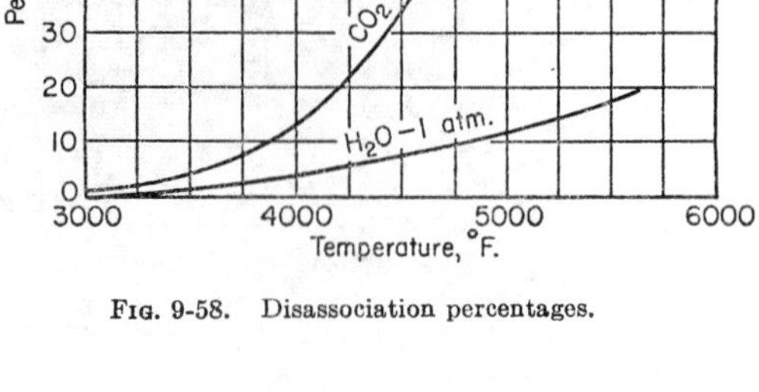

FIG. 9-58. Disassociation percentages.

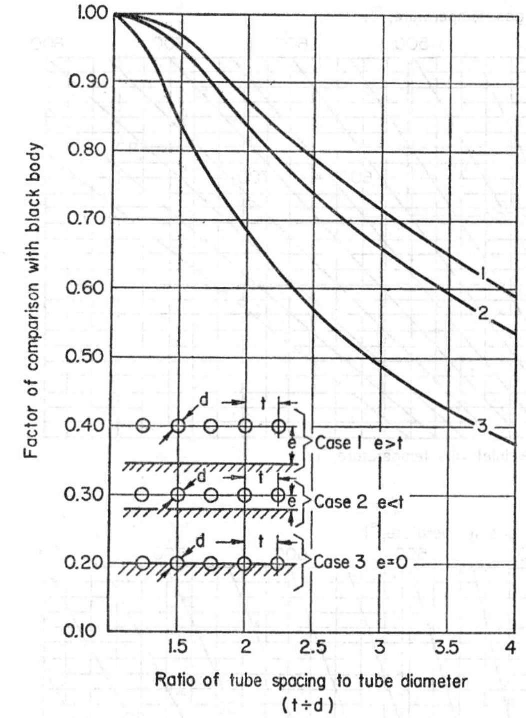

FIG. 9-59. Factor of comparison with black bodies. (*Courtesy of Bigelow-Liptak Corporation.*)

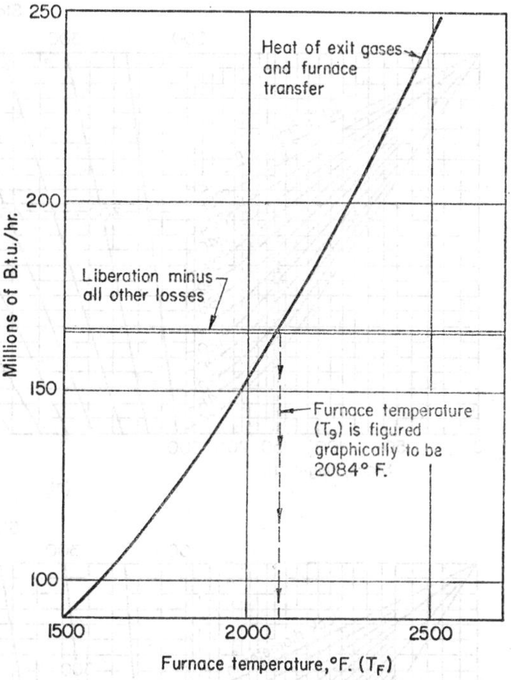

FIG. 9-60. Solution to furnace temperatures. (*Courtesy of Bigelow-Liptak Corporation.*)

and operating pressures in excess of 600 lb./sq. in. are also seldom encountered. Higher-pressure units are sometimes installed where electric power is generated within the plant, but the economic trend had been away from power generation with a few notable exceptions.

Utility boilers include conventional boilers and unconventional boilers. **Conventional boilers** used in power utility plants are those units operating below the critical pressure of the steam with widely accepted modes of operation. They may include features that yesterday were unconventional such as forced circulation, reheat, divided furnaces, once-through flow, and pressurized furnaces. They are usually custom-designed and built, with the trend to larger units in the multimillion pounds per hour capacity. Their superheated output is taken directly to a single turbine generator in recent designs for the production of electricity. They are universally of water-tube design, and all fuels are fired, with coal being the most common.

Unconventional boilers are those which are experimental or extremely rare in their application. Currently, mercury binary, combination gas turbine, supercritical, and nuclear boilers are in this category. Supercritical units are conventionally fired once-through forced-fluid-flow designs where the entire system is pressurized over the critical vapor pressure. Units of over 5000 lb./sq. in. operating pressure have been constructed and are in operation. Mercury-binary-system boilers impose a mercury-vapor topping system on a conventional steam cycle. The mercury is vaporized at a high saturated vapor temperature by conventional fuel firing. After electricity is produced in a mercury-vapor turbine generator the latent heat of the mercury is transferred to steam in a condenser-boiler. A number of such plants have been built and are in operation. Combination gas-turbine and steam-turbine plants have been built for many years (Velox boilers). New designs are currently being built which incorporate a more active part by the gas turbine. These designs include those where the exhaust gases of large gas turbines are reheated by supplemental fuel firing to serve as the combustion gases of conventional steam boilers. Nuclear units have been built for power utility steam boilers both in the United States and abroad. It does not appear that they will compete economically with fossil-fuel plants until fundamental problems in fuel preparation and waste disposal are solved.

DESIGN PROCEDURES

Furnace Temperatures

Finding an exact temperature in a furnace is a difficult and tedious problem. Figure 9-56 shows the variations of temperature measured by high-velocity thermocouple probes in the upper section of a large furnace. A great deal of experience and knowledge of surface conditions, radiating characteristics of the particular flame, convection effects, etc., are required to predict such results on a rational basis. One can, however, predict a maximum theoretical temperature and an approximate furnace exit temperature with relative ease. These can be used with sufficient confidence in most industrial processes to select refractories and to determine operating conditions.

Adiabatic Flame Temperature. The maximum or adiabatic flame temperature may be calculated by assuming that the enthalpy of the products of combustion is equal to the enthalpy of the reactants. Thus:

$$(H^\circ - H^\circ_0 + \Delta H^0{}_{f0})\ \text{products} = (H^\circ - H^\circ_0 + \Delta H^\circ{}_{f0})\ \text{reactants} \quad (9\text{-}12)$$

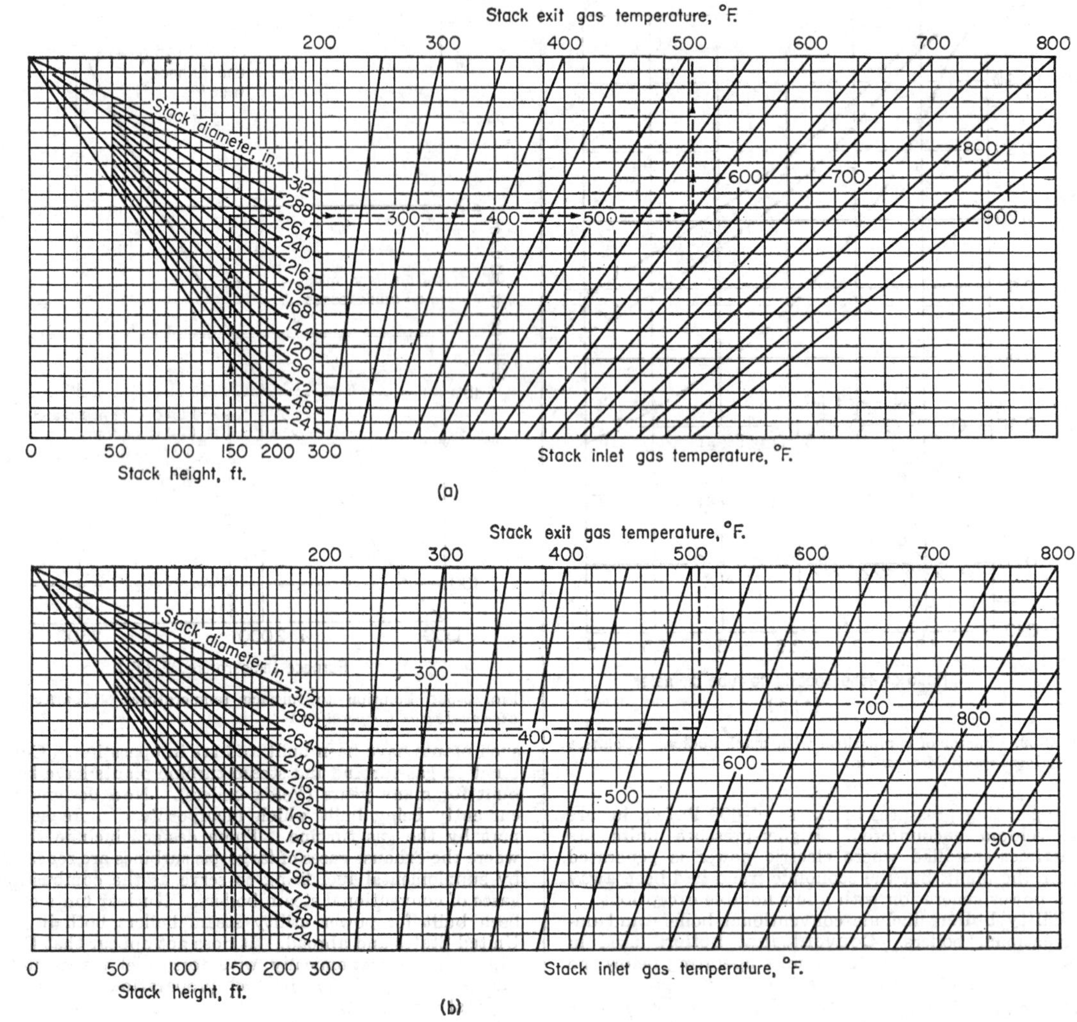

FIG. 9-61. Exit-gas temperatures from stacks. (*a*) Concrete, brick, and unlined steel stacks. (*b*) Lined steel stacks.

As an approximation, the lower heating value may be divided by the summation of the product of the specific heats of the reactants and their weights. Thus:

$$\text{Temperature of the flame (maximum)} = \frac{\text{lower heating value (B.t.u./lb.)}}{\Sigma \text{ product weights (lb.) [mean specific heats (B.t.u./(lb.) °F.)]}} \quad (9\text{-}13)$$

Values of mean specific heat for common products of combustion are given in Fig. 9-57 for various temperatures. A trial-and-error solution is necessary to equate the two sides of the equation.

If carbohydrate fuels are burned to give flame temperatures above 3000°F., disassociation becomes appreciable and must be considered in the calculations. Some common values are given in Fig. 9-58.

Exit Temperature. The approximate temperature of the furnace gases can be calculated by performing a heat balance at the furnace exit. A solution is obtained by equating (1) the furnace heat input minus the radiation loss, moisture loss, hydrogen loss, unburned-fuel loss, and the furnace heat transfer to the (2) heat transported by the gases out of the furnace exit. There is disagreement as to the extent of convective heat transfer in furnaces. Most designers have in the past used coefficients in the radiation heat-transfer equation that allow for the convective effects, and the method presented does this:

$$Q = 0.172 A\sigma \left[\left(\frac{T_g + 460}{100} \right)^4 - \left(\frac{T_F + 460}{100} \right)^4 \right] \quad (9\text{-}14)$$

Where Q = furnace heat transfer, B.t.u./hr.
0.172 = Stefan-Boltzmann constant
σ = emmissivity; use 0.64 for gas, 0.75 for oil, and 0.81 for coal
A = effective area for absorbing heat as calculated below, sq. ft.
T_g = furnace exit temperature, °F.
T_F = absorbing-surface temperature, °F.

For tangent tubes or boiler banks, the projected area is used for the effective area for absorbing heat A. Where tubes are spaced on centers greater than their diameters, Fig. 9-59 must be applied to obtain a factor of comparison. This factor multiplied by the projected area will give the effective absorbing surface.

The equating of the two sides of the equation is again a trial-and-error solution which can be easily solved graphically, usually with only two points. Transposing the furnace heat-transfer term will allow one side of the equation to remain constant. A typical solution is shown in Fig. 9-60, where the equation form was

(Fuel, lb./hr.)(higher heating value, B.t.u./lb.)
− moisture and hydrogen, B.t.u./hr.
− radiation loss, B.t.u./hr.
− carbon loss, B.t.u./hr.
= furnace heat absorption, B.t.u./hr.
+ Σ (specific heats times weights of gas products, B.t.u./hr. °F)(temperature rise above ambient, °F.) (9-15)

Stacks and Chimneys

Theoretical Draft. The theoretical draft is that which is produced by the difference in static head of equal columns of atmospheric air and flue gas when at rest. The theoretical draft of a smokestack or a chimney can be readily calculated from the formula:

$$\text{Stack draft (in. } H_2O) = 0.256HP\left(\frac{1}{T} - \frac{1}{T_1}\right) \quad (9\text{-}16)$$

where H = stack height above breeching, ft.
P = barometric pressure, in. Hg
T = ambient temperature, °R.
T_1 = average stack temperature, °R.

Figure 9-61 may be used to estimate the exit-gas temperature required to obtain the average stack temperature for masonry or steel stacks. Figure 9-62 gives solutions to the equations for sea level and 80°F.

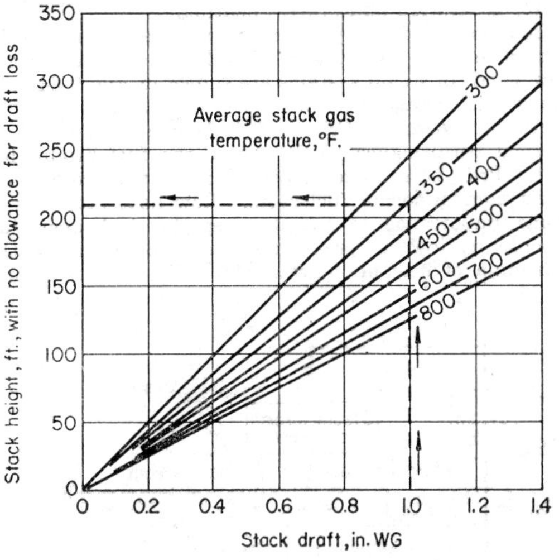

Fig. 9-62. Theoretical stack drafts.

Actual Draft. To obtain the actual draft for a chimney or stack, the losses that occur with flow must be deducted from the theoretical draft. These losses are both frictional and of exit velocity in nature. They may be evaluated by the following equation:

Stack flow loss (in. H_2O)

$$= 0.0942\left(\frac{T_1}{D^4}\right)\left(\frac{W}{100{,}000}\right)^2\left(1 + \frac{fH}{D}\right) \quad (9\text{-}17)$$

where T_1 = average stack temperature, °R.
D = stack diameter, ft.
W = gas flow, lb./hr.
f = friction factor from Fig. 9-63
H = stack height above breeching, ft.

To apply Fig. 9-63, the Reynolds number may be calculated by the equation

$$N_{Re} = \frac{27{,}600W}{T_1D} \quad (9\text{-}18)$$

The available draft may be obtained by subtracting the frictional losses from the theoretical draft. This

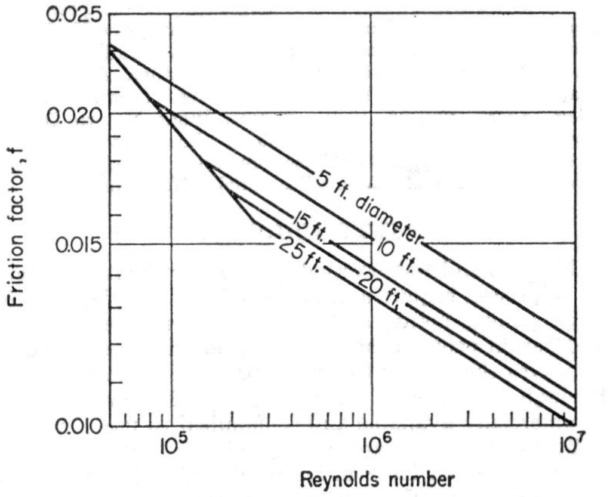

Fig. 9-63. Friction factors for stacks.

quantity is known as the natural draft of the chimney since it is produced without mechanical means. Where it is insufficient to overcome the flow resistance of the system, fans must be added. If the fans supply air at pressures above atmospheric to the burners and combustion space, they are called forced-draft fans. If the fans handle the products of combustion they usually operate at pressures below atmospheric and are called induced-draft fans.

Special Problems. Frequently stacks are required to handle gases of **highly corrosive** nature. Even the gases of conventional fuels often contain sufficient amounts of acid to attack steel and concrete rapidly. Where corrosive conditions warrant the extra expense, chimneys and stacks are frequently lined with glass, acid-resisting brick, or acid-resisting cement. Steel stacks may be purchased lined with bonded glass for erection as a unit, or they may be lined in place with brick after erection. Masonry stacks are erected in place of either brick or reinforced-concrete design. Either steel or masonry stacks may be lined after erection with special coatings applied by hand or by pressure spraying (gunniting). It is advisable to inspect stacks for internal corrosion at periodic intervals. Water washing after cooling is advisable to expose the surface for inspection if it is heavily coated with soot.

Masonry stacks are subject to damage from **extreme cold** when out of service because of the freezing of trapped water in small cracks which gradually enlarge. Damage of this sort can usually be avoided by keeping the stack in service. Visual inspection with binoculars is adequate to check for this condition and repairs are generally made by the installation of steel bands and the application of waterproofing.

All stacks should be grounded against **lightning** strikes. Masonry stacks should have cast-iron or aluminum caps with lightning rods. Two or more grounding wires should be used.

Stacks and chimneys that are not in recognized built-up areas or that are adjacent to air fields are required by Federal regulations to display visual **warning lights** (CAA Standard Order N 18).

HEAT TRANSPORT

REFERENCES: Kent, "Mechanical Engineers' Handbook," 12th ed., Power, Wiley, New York, 1950. Marks, "Mechanical Engineers' Handbook," 6th ed., McGraw-Hill, New York, 1958. Gaffert, "Steam Power Stations," 4th ed., McGraw-Hill, New York, 1952. Betz and Betz, "Handbook of Industrial Water Conditioning," 4th ed., Betz Laboratories, Philadelphia, 1953. Keenan and Keyes, "Thermodynamic Properties of Steam," Wiley, New York, 1956. McAdams, "Heat Transmission," 3d ed., McGraw-Hill, New York, 1954. Faires, "Applied Thermodynamics," Macmillan, New York, 1949. American Society of Mechanical Engineers, Boiler Construction Code, 1959. American Society of Mechanical Engineers, Power Test Codes. Kern, "Process Heat Transfer," McGraw-Hill, New York, 1950. Dow Chemical Company, "The Dowtherm Handbook," Midland, Mich., 1960. Kirst, Nagle, and Castner, A New Heat Transfer Medium for High Temperatures, *Trans. Am. Inst. Chem. Engrs.*, vol. 36, 1940. Badger, What Not to Do with Dowtherm, *Chem. Eng.*, vol. 62, No. 5. Loss Prevention Bulletins of Factory Mutual Insurance Company. Geiringer, "Handbook of Heat Transfer Media," Reinhold, New York, 1960.

INTRODUCTION

Liquids and **vapors** used to transport heat and give it up to process require a unique combination of properties. High boiling points and low pressures reduce hazards and permit economical designs, while high heat capacity improves the ability to carry heat and spread it evenly through the process system. The fluids must also be commercially available and economical to use.

Solid materials are also used for heat transport. These materials have never reached the importance of liquids and vapors, primarily because of the difficulty of transporting the solid particles through small pipes and bent tubes. Pebbles, sand, and iron balls can be heated to higher temperatures than liquids and have found application in air and gas heaters for high-temperature equipment.

The commonly used heat-transport fluids are:

Fluid	Temp., °F.	Pressure, lb./sq. in. gage
Steam	200–1100	0–4500
Water	300–400	90–230
Dowtherm A	450–750	0–145
Dowtherm E	300–500	0–72
Oil	30–600	0
Molten salts	290–1100	0
Mercury	600–1000	0–180
Flue gas or air	30–2000	0–100

Historically, the **open flame** is the oldest source of heat known to man. Basic simplicity and low equipment cost have enabled it to survive in many industrial processes. The open flame as a heat source for industrial product heating has several limitations, however. These include low fuel efficiency, minimum control over uniformity of heat absorption, and correspondingly poor control over local temperatures in the product material. The burners, fuel supply, and controls must be at the operating point, making the units unwieldy and not suitable to locations of advantage to the manufacturing operations. As a result of these limitations, fluids adaptable to much closer control long ago supplanted flame for process work.

STEAM SYSTEMS

Performance

Steam is the most widely used heat-transport fluid, being a non-toxic substance whose only hazards are in its basic limitations, its high vapor pressure and its low critical point. Steam pressures required to give a saturation temperature of 400°F. are frequently not available in an industrial plant, and latent heat ceases to exist at 703°F. Steam excels all others in availability, stability, low cost, high heat-transport capacity, and safety. Industry has numerous demands not only for electric power but for heat at various temperature levels. If the desired temperature lies within the range of 200° to 500°F., steam is the ideal working fluid. No other material is so adaptable to a dual function of electric power generation and process heating.

Commercial steam systems start with raw energy in the form of heat of combustion of fuels. Basic elementary flow sheets of steam systems are shown in Fig. 9-64. In the steam plant fuel constitutes the largest item of operating expense. Prices of fuels can be applied to thermal performance to determine the fuel production cost. Price bases of cents per million B.t.u. are best for direct comparison of fuel costs. Low heat rates are of prime importance in maintaining the fuel operating expense as low as practicable, and for utilizing the maximum of heat of the raw fuel. The **heat rate** of a

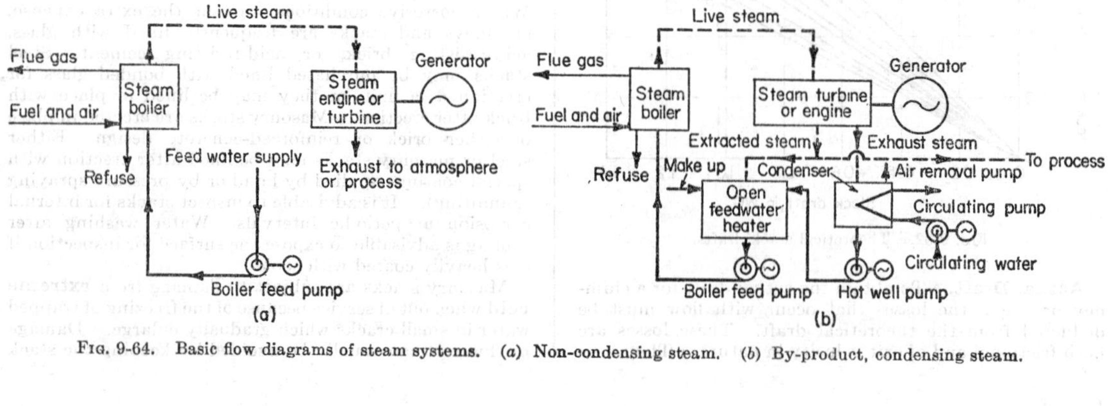

FIG. 9-64. Basic flow diagrams of steam systems. (*a*) Non-condensing steam. (*b*) By-product, condensing steam.

power plant is defined as

$$\text{Heat rate, B.t.u./kw.-hr.} = \frac{\text{heat supplied in fuel, B.t.u.}}{\text{energy generated, kw.-hr.}} \tag{9-19}$$

and thus

$$\text{Fuel production cost, cents/kw.-hr.} = \frac{\text{(heat rate, B.t.u./kw.-hr.)}\ \text{(fuel price, cents/million B.t.u.)}}{10^6} \tag{9-20}$$

Heat rates of several representative power plants are given in Table 9-20. The best and most efficient utility steam plant heat rate of 8500 B.t.u./kw.-hr. obtains only

Table 9-20. Typical Heat Rates of Representative Power Plants

Type of heat	Plant heat rate, B.t.u./kw.-hr.	Plant thermal efficiency
All stationary steam plants, average	25,000	0.14
Central-station steam plants, average	11,500	0.30
Best large central-station steam plant	8,500	0.40
Small non-condensing industrial steam plant	35,000	0.10
Small condensing industrial steam plant	20,000	0.17
"By-product" steam power plant	4,500–5,000	0.70–0.75
Diesel plant	11,500	0.30
Natural-gas-engine plant	14,000	0.24
Gasoline-engine plant	16,000	0.21
Producer-gas-engine plant	18,000	0.19

with the largest units (about 300,000 kw.) using high pressures and high temperatures (4500 lb./sq. in. 1100°F.). Process industries often find it difficult to justify small industrial steam plant heat rates with the cost of generating their own power, when confronted with low rates from reliable, efficient public utilities. Installation of a generating plant can to a large degree be linked with availability of by-product fuel or with the opportunity to utilize process steam for both the main industrial process and plant services of electricity, space heating, air compression, cleaning, and general services. Industries can make use of such **by-product fuels** as bark, black liquor, bagasse, sawdust, blast-furnace and coke-oven gas, and fluid coke, either as the main fuel or in combination with standard fuels such as coal, natural gas, or oil. Details on fuels can be found earlier in this section. Industrial multipurpose steam plants with mutual by-products of electric power and process heating allow all exhaust heat in the steam to be charged to process. This results in the absolute minimum of heat rates: 4500 to 5000 B.t.u./kw.-hr. This value is calculated from the mechanical equivalent of heat (3413 B.t.u./kw.-hr.) divided by electric generator efficiency (0.95+), the boiler efficiency (0.88+), auxiliary power allowance (0.9+), and the realization ratio, which accounts for plant losses such as soot blowing, blowdown, makeup heat losses, and gland leakage (0.9+).

Loads and Load Curves

Power must be generated at the instant of its use, because there is no practical way of storing, in appreciable amounts, mechanical energy, electrical energy, steam, heat, or compressed air. Proper design and proper operation can be effected only if loads and their fluctuations, as to nature and magnitude, are accurately known. Graphical presentation of load data on the daily, monthly, seasonal, or annual basis prevails. Integrated readings over a period of 15 min., 30 min., or 1 hr. are employed rather than instantaneous readings. Flywheel and storage effects must handle momentary fluctuations. Some representative load curves are given in Figs. 9-65 and 9-66. Figures 9-65*b* and 9-66*b* show the load duration curves as calculated from Figs. 9-65*a* and 9-66*a* by integration of the area under the load curve. These curves, together with energy-time and energy-utilization curves, are all useful in studies involving plant loading, operation, and design. Many factors are variously employed briefly to define the character of the load. Among them are

$$\text{Load factor} = \frac{\text{average load for period}}{\text{peak load for period}} \tag{9-21}$$

and

$$\text{Capacity factor} = \frac{\text{output for period}}{\text{(rated capacity)(hr. in period)}} \tag{9-22}$$

Factors may be daily, weekly, monthly, or annual. Load factor may be larger or smaller than capacity factor. Each can be applied to any service offered by, or any equipment included in, a power plant.

In the design of an industrial plant typically to deliver electric power and process steam, the load curves for each of the services must be considered separately and in combination. If the power is to be generated as a by-product of the process steam, using an arrangement in which the boiler delivers steam at high pressure to a turbine or engine, with exhaust delivered to the process header, the demand for one service will limit the availability of the other. Consider, as in Fig. 9-67*a*, the electric-demand, and Fig. 9-67*b*, the process-steam-demand curves. If all the power is to be generated as a by-product of the process steam, the available electric generation will be as shown in curve *c*. A comparison of this curve with the kilowatt-demand curve *a* discloses

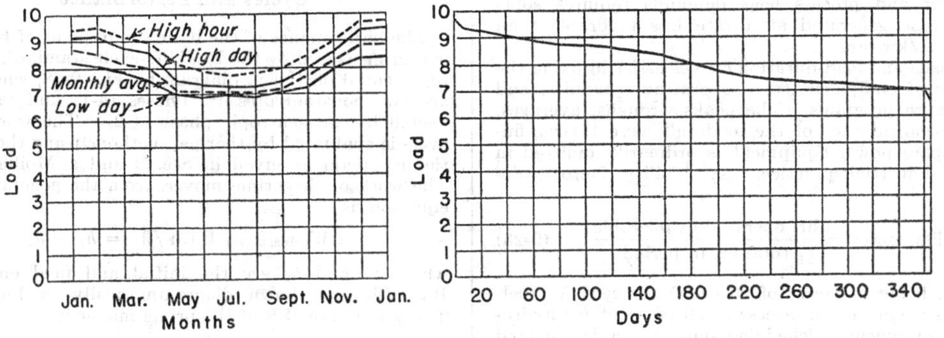

FIG. 9-65. Industrial-plant load curves (high load factor). (*a*) Annual load curves. (*b*) Load duration curve.

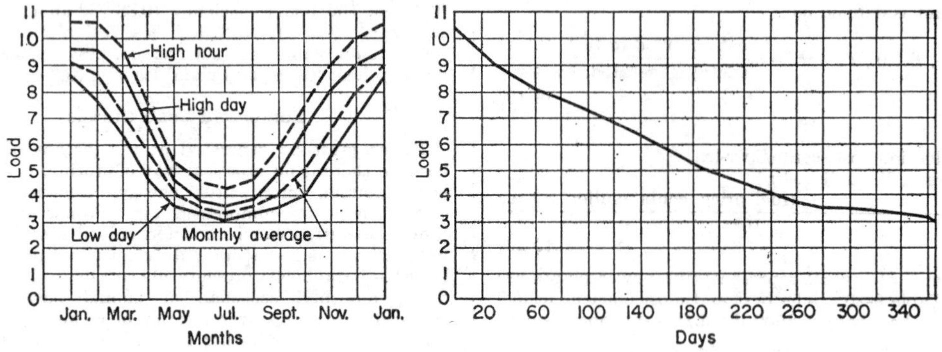

(a) (b)

FIG. 9-66. Industrial-plant load curves (low load factor). (a) Annual load curves. (b) Load duration curve.

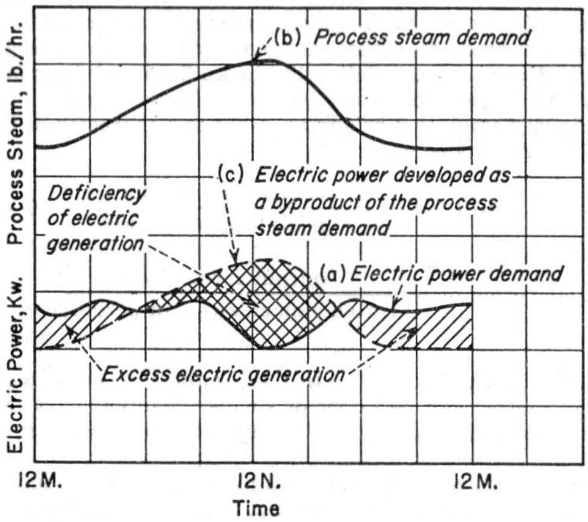

FIG. 9-67. Daily load curves to demonstrate non-coincidence of process steam and electric-power load demands.

periods when there is a deficiency of electric energy and others when there is an excess. Deficiencies can be met only by purchase of electric power or by use of condensing steam equipment or hydroelectric or internal-combustion engines. Excess electric generation entails some disposal to some user or the installation of a reducing valve to by-pass the prime mover. The simple, thermodynamically desirable, by-product power plant thus becomes a complicated reality. The non-coincidence of the power and process heat demands requires some power to be generated at a rate less favorable than 4500 B.t.u./kw.-hr.

The loads and load-duration curves assist in fixing the propriety of equipment sizes, operating schedules, and maintenance programs. The peaks, troughs, averages, and non-coincidences of the loads all have their influence. Spare power equipment is ordinarily omitted in modern industrial practice. Availability factors, defined as

$$\text{Availability factor} = \frac{\text{hr. operated or operable}}{\text{total hr. in period}} \tag{9-23}$$

are high, being in excess of 90 or 95 per cent for fuel-burning systems and in excess of 99 per cent for hydroelectric equipment. Scheduled outage can be effected during lower load periods if equipment sizes are correct. The severity of forced, or breakdown, outages can likewise be minimized. Larger sizes favor lower unit investment and labor costs. The fuel economy of steam equipment improves with larger size. Internal-combustion and hydroelectric plant efficiencies, however, are not much affected by size. Thus, considering all factors, the best sizes for boilers, turbines, and auxiliaries would not be the same for two different load types, illustrated by Figs. 9-65 and 9-66, even though the peaks and troughs might be equal. One of the most practical and economical ways of meeting loads with wide variations is to use a multiplicity of smaller units rather than to have wide range governing at sustained efficiency on a larger unit.

Production and fixed costs for a typical steam boiler plant are given in Table 9-21.

Table 9-21. Production and Fixed Costs in Steam Boiler Plant

Size of plant, lb./hr	100,000
Capacity factor, %	60
Load factor, %	65
Steam output, lb./year	525(10⁶)
Heat added to steam, B.t.u./lb	1,100
Boiler efficiency, %	82
Heat in fuel, B.t.u./year	705(10⁹)
Fuel price, ¢/million B.t.u	20
Investment, $/lb./hr. capacity	5
Fixed charges:	
Annual, %	12
¢/thousand lb. steam	11.4
Production cost:	
Fuel, ¢/thousand lb. steam	26.9
Labor and supervision, ¢/thousand lb. steam	3.8
Maintenance m and l, ¢/thousand lb. steam	1.1
Supplies and expense, ¢/thousand lb. steam	0.2
Total production cost, ¢/thousand lb. steam	32.0
Total cost of steam, ¢/thousand lb. steam	43.4

Cycles and Performance

The performance of the basic steam plant of Fig. 9-64*a* is best measured by the Rankine-cycle standard, which is represented on the *pv* diagram by Fig. 9-68, where there are two constant-pressure phases (4-1) and (2-3) connected by an isentropic phase (1-2). The work of the cycle is evaluated by thermal methods using the properties of steam as given in Sec. 3 and a Mollier chart. The work of the prime mover, from the general energy equation, is

$$\Delta W_{\text{prime mover}} \text{ B.t.u./lb.} = h_1 - h_2 \tag{9-24}$$

where h_1 and h_2 are the initial and final enthalpies, B.t.u./lb., as shown diagrammatically in Fig. 9-68*b*. The water rate *WR* of the prime mover is

$$WR, \text{ lb./kw.-hr.} = \frac{3412.75}{\Delta W_{\text{prime mover}}} \tag{9-25}$$

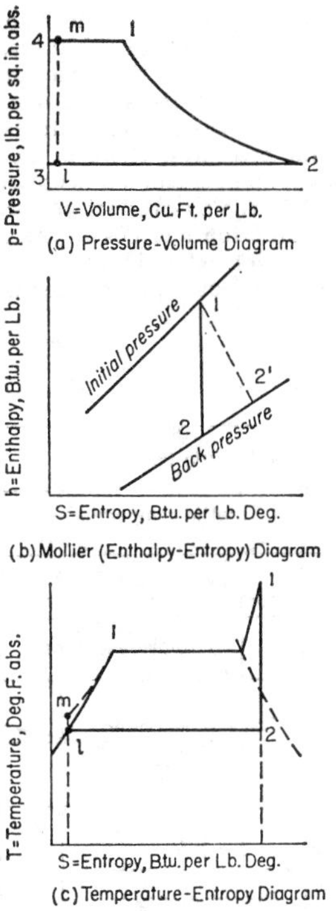

FIG. 9-68. Rankine cycle diagrams.

The work of the cycle is the work of the prime mover less the work of the feed pump (area 31m4, Fig. 9-68*a*), or

$$\Delta W_{\text{cycle}},\ \text{B.t.u./lb.} = h_1 - h_2 - \Delta W_{\text{pump}} \quad (9\text{-}26)$$

The thermal efficiency of the cycle is

$$\text{Thermal efficiency} = \frac{\text{work of cycle}}{\text{heat added}} = \frac{\Delta W_{\text{cycle}}}{\Delta Q_{\text{added}}}$$
$$= \frac{h_1 - h_2 - \Delta W_{\text{pump}}}{h_1 - h_{\text{liq}} - \Delta W_{\text{pump}}} \quad (9\text{-}27)$$

where h_{liq} is the enthalpy of the saturated liquid at the back pressure 2. The pump work can ordinarily be neglected in these equations, because it is small except with the highest steam pressures (more than 900 lb./sq. in.).

The heat consumption or heat rate of the cycle is

$$HR,\ \text{B.t.u./kw.-hr.} = \frac{3412.75}{\text{thermal efficiency}}$$
$$= WR(h_1 - h_{\text{liq}} - \Delta W_{\text{pump}}) \quad (9\text{-}28)$$

Some of the effects of variation in steam pressure, steam temperature, and back pressure on the Rankine cycle performance are demonstrated by the data of Fig. 9-69.

Industrial practice generally uses pressures of less than 600 lb./sq. in. and central stations favor pressures in excess of 900 lb./sq. in. Steam temperatures are limited to 450°F. with cast-iron parts; 750°F. with carbon steel parts; and 900 to 1050°F. with alloy steel (Cr, Mo, etc.) parts. Vacuum operation is in the region of 1 to 3 in. Hg abs. pressure. The initial steam temperature is fixed by maintenance of not more than 10 to 15 per cent moisture in the turbine exhaust under vacuum operation.

These basic data and calculations are modified to give performance of real steam plants by including inefficiencies and losses. The engine efficiency of a prime mover is

$$\text{Engine efficiency} = \frac{\text{actual work}}{\text{ideal work}} = \frac{h_1 - h_2'}{h_1 - h_2} \quad (9\text{-}29)$$

where h_2' is the actual exhaust enthalpy as illustrated in Fig. 9-68*b*. If allowances for generator efficiency, boiler efficiency, auxiliary power, and realization ratio are included, the over-all plant performance will result:

Over-all plant heat rate, B.t.u./kw.-hr. net output

$$= \frac{\text{gross turbine room heat rate}}{(\text{generator efficiency})(\text{boiler efficiency})(1 - \text{auxiliary power fraction})(\text{realization ratio})} \quad (9\text{-}30)$$

Values of engine efficiency, generator efficiency, and boiler efficiency can be estimated from the data given below. Auxiliary power will range from 3 to 12 per cent of the gross output, being higher for non-condensing plants, and increasing with steam pressure. Realization ratios will variously range from 0.9 to 1.0 and will depend upon the reduction of unaccounted for losses. Inclusion of this allowance therefore makes the computed heat rate of Eq. (9-30) equal to the actual observed heat rate of Eq. (9-19).

The gross turbine room heat rate of Eq. (9-30) is

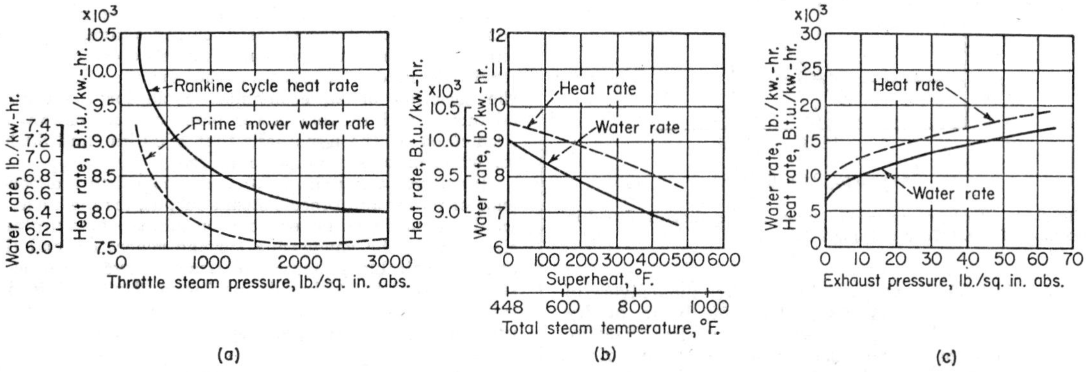

FIG. 9-69. Rankine cycle performance. (*a*) Effect of throttle pressure. Throttle temperature = 900°F., exhaust pressure = 2 in. Hg abs. (*b*) Effect of superheat. Throttle pressure = 400 lb./sq. in., exhaust pressure = 2 in. Hg abs. (*c*) Effect of exhaust pressure. Throttle conditions = 400 lb./sq. in., 800°F., 1415.8 B.t.u./lb.

usually not the value of the Rankine cycle but is the value as modified by regenerative feed heating, resuperheating, or binary vapor. Theoretical and cyclic details of these factors are to be found in textbooks on thermodynamics. The treatment that follows is for the actual cycles of real power plants.

A typical heat balance and its calculations are shown in Figs. 9-70 and 9-71 and Table 9-22. This is the cycle

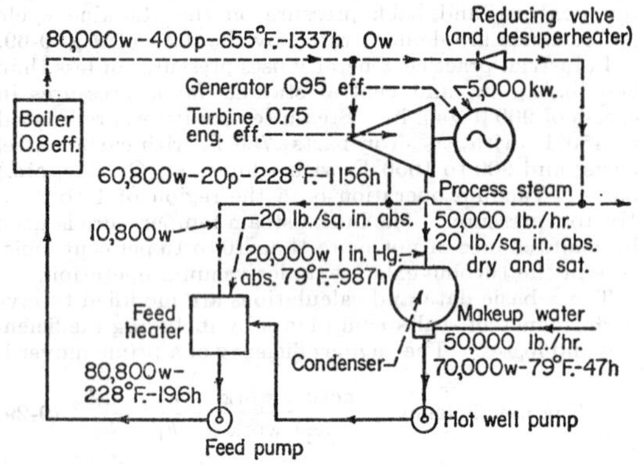

FIG. 9-70. Steam-plant cycle diagram showing by-product generation of electric power and process steam. Heat supplied in steam = 92 (10^6) B.t.u./hr. Heat supplied in fuel = 115 (10^6) B.t.u./hr. Net plant electric send-out = 4700 kw.

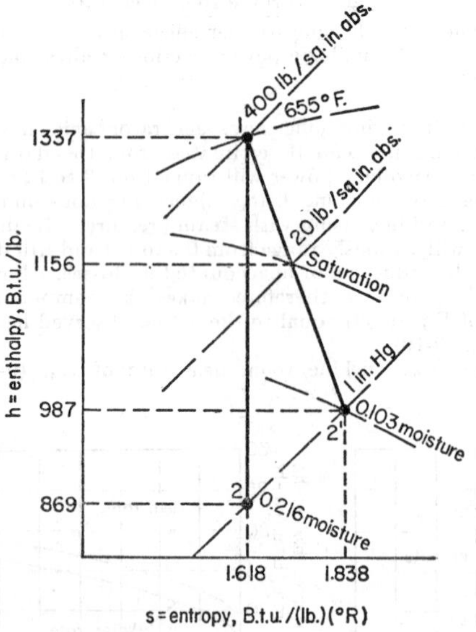

FIG. 9-71. Turbine expansion line on Mollier diagram (used in example of Fig. 9-70 and Table 9-22).

of an industrial power plant that requires the delivery of 5000 kw. of electric energy and 50,000 lb./hr. of dry saturated process steam at 20 lb./sq. in. abs. Because all power cannot here be generated as a by-product of the process steam flow, a condensing element is added to the turbine and operated at 1 in. Hg abs. pressure. The steps in the calculation can be followed in Table 9-22.

Figure 9-72 shows the results of several similar heat balance calculations for different throttle pressures and temperatures. The same load (5000 kw.) is imposed on the generator terminals, and the same process steam output (50,000 lb./hr. at 20 lb./sq. in. abs., dry and saturated) prevails in all cases. The curves show that, for increasing steam pressures, there is an increase in the necessary throttle temperature, a decrease in the throttle flow, an increase in the by-product power, and a decrease in the fuel consumption and cost. Such analyses serve to guide the selection of optimum steam pressures and temperatures even though many other factors must also be taken into account.

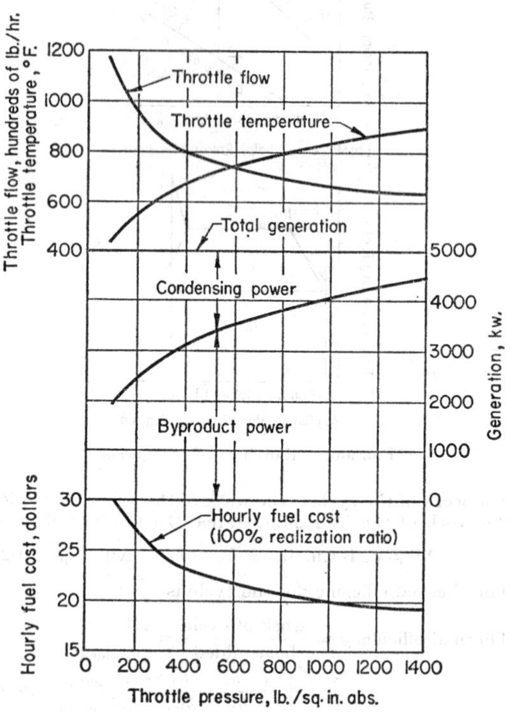

FIG. 9-72. Performance of by-product power cycle as affected by throttle pressure (see Fig. 9-70 and Table 9-22).

The heat balance of Fig. 9-70 is for one set of load conditions. Load curves, as discussed above, show not only variations but also non-coincidence of the several service demands. The steps in the reasoning that lead to the selection of an economical cycle for a suitable, adequate, and reliable power plant are as follows, all predicated on the hypothesis that 5000 kw. and 50,000 lb./hr. of process steam are required.

Arrangement A (Fig. 9-73). For complete independence of power and process steam output, arrangement *A* would require two boilers, one of suitable pressure and size serving the condensing turbine generator, and the other of suitable pressure and size to serve the process steam demand. Although maximum flexibility is obtained by this arrangement, the space requirements, investment, fuel, labor, and maintenance would all be a maximum.

Arrangement B (Fig. 9-73) combines the two boilers of arrangement *A* and adds a reducing valve and desuperheater. The complete independence of the power and process steam supplies is maintained. No by-product power is generated, since all process steam passes through the reducing valve. The investment is still high, and the pump work and operating costs are a maximum.

Arrangement C (Fig. 9-73) substitutes a non-condensing turbine generator for the reducing valve of arrangement *B*. By-product power (4500 to 5000 B.t.u./kw.-hr. heat rate) can be generated in the amount dictated by the process steam flow. Additional generation is supplied by the condensing unit at a higher heat rate (15,000 B.t.u./kw.-hr.). Boiler size is reduced, thus lowering investment at the same time that fuel costs are reduced. Complete independence of the power and process steam demands is lost. All by-product power, which is delivered by the back-pressure unit, must be accepted.

Table 9-22. Heat Balance Calculations, By-product Power Cycle*

Requirements: 5000 kw. and 50,000 lb./hr. process steam at 20 lb./sq. in. abs., dry and saturated; throttle conditions, 400 lb./sq. in. abs., 655°F.; exhaust conditions: 1 in. Hg abs.

Item	Performance
Condenser:	
Steam flow, lb./hr	20,000
Pressure, in. Hg abs	1
Hot-well temperature, °F	79
Hot-well enthalpy, B.t.u./lb	47
Make-up water flow, lb./hr	50,000
Water flow out, lb./hr	70,000
Feed heater:	
Heater pressure, lb./sq. in. abs	20
Heater saturation temperature, °F	230
Enthalpy, water in, B.t.u./lb	47
Enthalpy, water out, B.t.u./lb	196
Heat added to water, B.t.u./lb	149
Heat added to water, 10^6 B.t.u./hr	10.4
Bleed enthalpy, B.t.u./lb	1,156
Heat available from bleed, B.t.u./lb	960
Extraction required, lb./hr	10,800
Boiler feed, lb./hr	80,800
Turbine generator:	
Enthalpy at throttle, B.t.u./lb	1,337
Enthalpy at bleed point, B.t.u./lb	1,156
Enthalpy drop to bleed point, B.t.u./lb	181
Extraction, lb./hr	60,800
Internal generation by extracted steam, kw	3,220
Enthalpy at exhaust, B.t.u./lb	987
Enthalpy drop to exhaust, B.t.u./lb	350
Condenser flow, lb./hr	20,000
Internal generation by condenser flow, kw	2,050
Total internal generation, kw	5,270
Generator efficiency	0.95
Generator electrical and mechanical losses, kw	270
Gross load, generator terminals, kw	5,000
Throttle water rate, lb./kw.-hr	16.2
Condenser water rate, lb./kw.-hr	4.0
Boiler:	
Enthalpy at superheater outlet, B.t.u./lb	1,337
Enthalpy at feed, B.t.u./lb	196
Heat added to steam, B.t.u./hr	1,141
Heat added to steam, 10^6 B.t.u./hr	92
Boiler efficiency	0.8
Heat supplied in fuel, 10^6 B.t.u./hr	115
Plant performance:	
Auxiliary power	0.06
Auxiliary power, kw	300
Net plant electric sendout, kw	4,700
Plant realization ratio	0.95
Net plant heat supplied, 10^6 B.t.u./hr	121
Fuel price, ¢/million B.t.u	20
Fuel cost/hr	$24.20
Allocation of heat charges:	
To process:	
Steam flow, lb./hr	50,000
Enthalpy of steam, B.t.u./lb	1,156
Enthalpy of make-up, B.t.u./lb	47
Heat to process, B.t.u./lb	1,109
Heat to process, 10^6 B.t.u./hr	55.4
To power (balance), 10^6 B.t.u./hr	36.6
Fraction chargeable to process	0.60
Fraction chargeable to power	0.40
Fuel cost, process steam, per hr	$14.50
Fuel cost, power, per hr	$9.70
Fuel cost, process steam, ¢/thousand lb	29
Fuel cost, power, net, mills/kw.-hr	2.06
Net plant heat rate, chargeable to power, B.t.u./kw.-hr	10,300

* *Cf.* Figs. 9-70, 9-71, and 9-72.

The non-condensing unit must be operated on base load, and all power-load swings must be carried on the condensing turbine.

Arrangement D (Fig. 9-73) is essentially the same as arrangement *C* except that a single constant-pressure extraction turbine generator is substituted for the two units. This lowers the investment but does not avoid the dependence of power generation on process steam demand.

If, in arrangements *C* or *D*, the process steam demand were to drop to zero but the power demand were to remain at 5000 kw., then in *C* a condensing turbine generator of 5000 kw. capacity would be required and in *D* more turbine would have to be bought even though the generator would remain unchanged. Conversely, if the power demand dropped to zero and the process steam demand remained at 50,000 lb./hr., the opposite extreme would be reached, which could only be handled in *C* or *D* by the use of a reducing valve between the live steam and the process steam headers. A suitable arrangement (with a feed heater added) is shown in Fig. 9-70 even though the flow through the reducing valve is zero for the data given.

By such arrangements it is possible to utilize the full thermodynamic advantages of by-product (4500 to 5000 B.t.u./kw.-hr.) power in a practical way. The overturbining, the condensing capacity, and the reducing valve are all necessary components of the real plant which add to the basic investment cost. The fundamental thermodynamic operating gain is consequently compromised. The alternative would be to operate during some periods on a straight non-condensing power cycle with its prohibitive heat rates of 25,000 to 50,000 B.t.u./kw.-hr.

The many possible combinations of expected power and process steam loads cannot usually be predicted, nor can the burden of their detailed analysis be borne by the design. A reasonable practical compromise is to design for the usual expected load coincidences but to be prepared, as above, to meet the maximum power peak and the minimum process steam demand simultaneously, and vice versa. The whole problem may be restated in rate schedule terms; *i.e.*, "capacity cannot be traded for energy, and energy cannot be traded for capacity." Alternate solutions to the problem might of course include consideration of the use of purchased power, internal-combustion engines, hydroelectric power, gas turbines, and heat pumps simultaneously to meet the variety of demands imposed on the industrial power plant.

The thermodynamic advantages of regenerative feed heating, as typified by the cycle of Fig. 9-70, are analogous to those of by-product power. If steam can be used for feed heating instead of being exhausted to atmosphere or to a condenser, the energy generated, by expansion from throttle pressure to heater pressure, is at the low heat rate of mechanical equivalence of by-product power. The aggregate heat savings on all the power generated are a function of the final feed temperature and the number of stages of heating, as shown by the data of Fig. 9-74. Any source of low-pressure steam may be used, but the greatest gain requires maximum generation of work by the steam prior to its use in a feed heater. High engine efficiency is desired, and main unit bleed is consequently preferred to auxiliary exhaust. Final feed temperatures are determined from data like Fig. 9-74 plus considerations of pump types and locations in cycle, feed heater designs, deaerator location, economizers, air heater, flue gas temperatures, and furnace characteristics. Central stations use four to eight stages of heating with final temperatures between 350 and 475°F. Industrial plants seldom exceed three stages of heating, or 300 to 350°F., unless plants are of exceptional size.

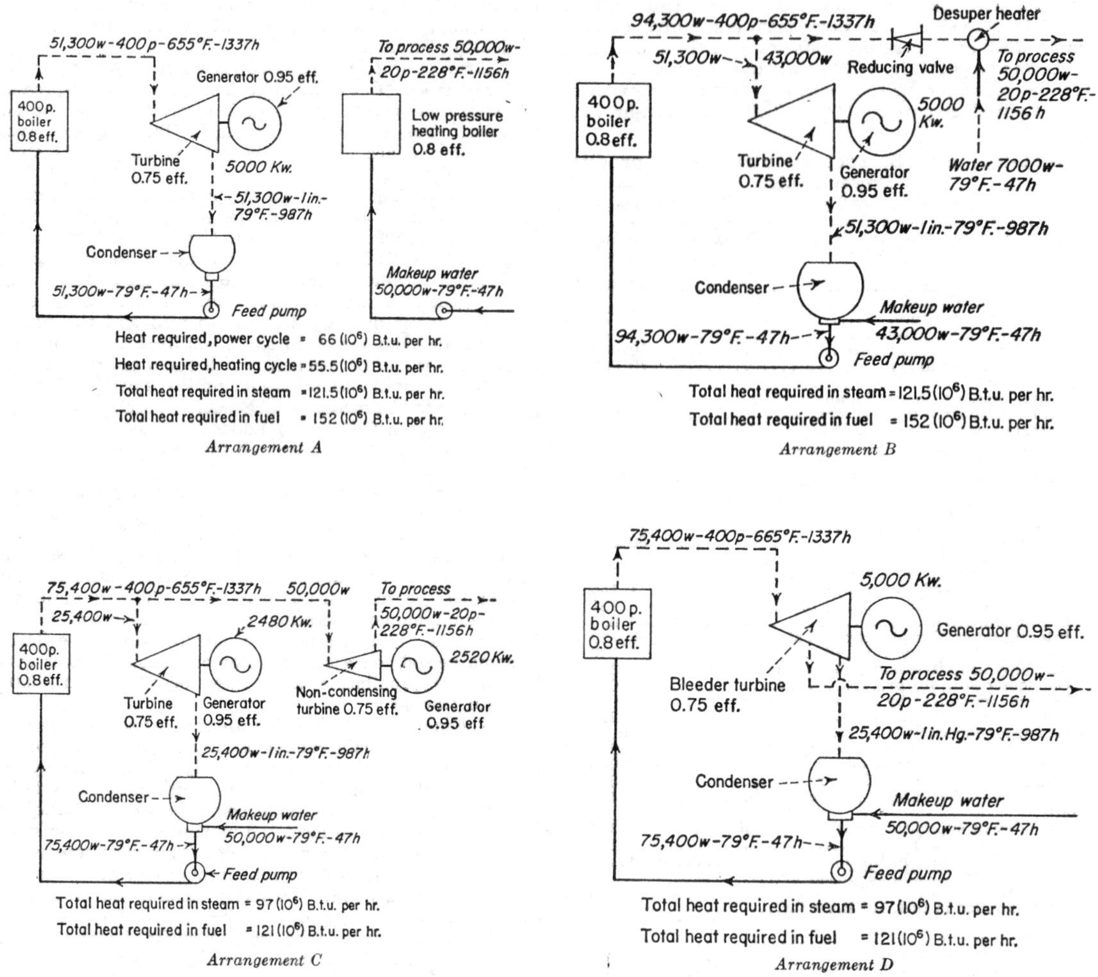

FIG. 9-73. By-product power cycles.

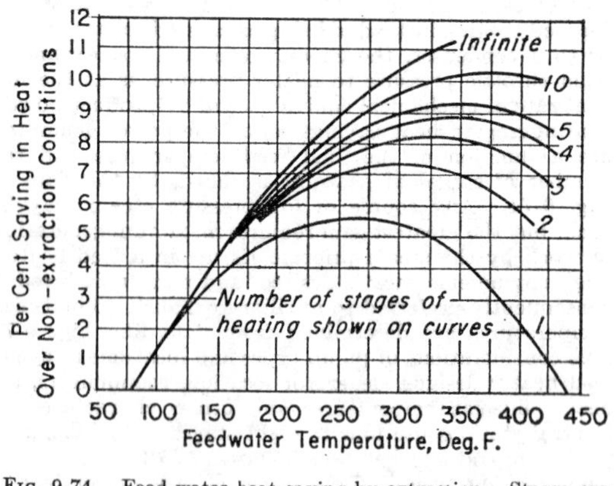

FIG. 9-74. Feed-water heat saving by extraction. Steam conditions, 400 lb./sq. in., 700°F. to 1 in. abs. back pressure.

Water Constituents

Water, as the working fluid of steam systems, is one of the most widely dispersed of natural substances but is never found in a pure state, suitable for direct feed to a boiler. Water in its natural state is usually turbid with solid matter in fine suspension. Even when clear, natural water contains solutions of salts and acids that will quickly damage steel or copper-bearing metals in steam systems. **Recycling** of steam condensate from process heating is desirable to take advantage of the relatively pure condensate. Because of atmospheric dissipation and contamination from process equipment some raw makeup is constantly required.

Various **constituents** in waters may be classed in accordance with the troubles that may result from their presence:

1. Corrosive substances
2. Scale-forming substances
3. Foam-producing substances

Corrosive substances are usually in the form of acid solutions, or as dissolved gases such as carbon dioxide, oxygen, hydrogen sulfide, or ammonia. Oxygen and carbon dioxide are dissolved in the feed water by aeration and unavoidable contact with the atmosphere. Since the solubility of oxygen decreases with an increase in water temperature, the most common method of removal is the deaeration of water, in which the water is heated to the boiling point by direct contact with steam, and the heated water is allowed to cascade over trays. The trays increase the exposed surface and permit easier dissipation of the oxygen. Deaeration is also effective in removing other dissolved gases, and all modern steam systems use any of several types of deaerators. In addition to deaeration use is made of chemicals, such as sodium sulfite, which combines with oxygen and is introduced into the boiler with a chemical feed pump. At higher boiler pressures sodium sulfite is less desirable, because of an increase in the dissolved solids produced by the end-product sodium sulfate, and a decomposition into sulfur dioxide and hydrogen sulfide which contribute to corrosion. Hydrazine removes dissolved oxygen without increasing dissolved solids at high pressures with the following reaction:

$$N_2H_4 + O_2 \rightarrow 2H_2O + N_2$$

High residuals of hydrazine in the water must be avoided to prevent the decomposition-product ammonia from attacking copper-bearing alloys in the system.

Reused water that is high in acidity must be treated to maintain a proper alkaline environment, where the pH is between 10.5 and 11.0. Bicarbonate alkalinity in the boiler can hydrolyze under the action of heat, and liberate carbon dioxide, which will be carried along with the steam to form a corrosive carbonic acid product with the condensate in process heat exchangers or condensate piping. Present-day practice calls for water treatment to prevent corrosion in the recycling system by means of neutralizing or filming amines. Neutralizing amines combine with CO_2 and neutralize its acidity. Filming amines do not combine chemically, but act by forming an impervious, non-wettable film on metal surfaces which acts as a barrier between metal and condensate, preventing both oxygen and carbon dioxide attack.

Steam systems in which the bulk of condensate is unrecoverable are more often subject to difficulties caused by **scale-forming** substances. The makeup water invariably has constituents which will be scale-forming when present in the water in concentrations in excess of their solubility. Some materials exhibit a decrease in solubility with an increase in temperature, and the scales commonly deposited in boilers belong to this class. Chemical treatment in the preboiler system is successful in reducing most scale-forming substances to a soft sludge, which is removed before entering the boiler, while sludges formed by internal treatment may be collected in quiescent zones of the boiler and removed through blowdown pipes.

Water recovered from process heating causes **foaming** within the boiler from the presence of organic, inorganic, or insoluble materials, when they are present in sufficiently large quantities. Oil and the products of decomposition of sewage and humic matter are the chief causes of foaming, and these products should be strictly excluded from condensate returns. The foaming effect of these materials is especially true in the presence of high alkalinities, and the alkaline concentration of boiler water shuld be limited for this reason. See Table 9-23 for recommended limits of boiler-water constituents. Continuous or intermittent blowdown of the boiler water to keep concentrations below recommended limits is the most effective way of preventing foaming. When the blowdown results in large quantities of heat being lost to the system, much of this heat may be recovered by passing the blowdown through heat exchangers used to heat feed water or air, which returns the heat to the unit.

Table 9-23. Recommended Limits for Boiler-water Constituents, Parts per Million

Pressure, lb./sq. in.	Total dissolved solids	Alkalinity	Hardness	Silica	Turbidity	Oil	Phosphate residual
0–300	3500	700	0	100–60	175	7	140
301–450	3000	600	0	60–45	150	7	120
451–600	2500	500	0	45–35	125	7	100
601–750	2000	400	0	35–25	100	7	80
751–900	1500	300	0	25–15	75	7	60
901–1000	1250	250	0	15–12	63	7	50
1001–1500	1000	200	0	12–2	50	7	40

THERMAL-LIQUID SYSTEMS

Liquids and Their Properties

Thermal liquids used in the field of process heating and cooling may be in the form of liquids, vapors, or a combination of both. With the exception of steam, thermal liquids include hot water, mercury, diphenyl-diphenyloxide (Dowtherm A), *o*-dichlorobenzene (Dowtherm E), molten salt mixtures, and mineral oils. Physical properties of these materials are given in Table 9-24.

Table 9-24. Physical Properties of Thermal Fluids

	Water	Dowtherm A*	Dowtherm E*	Fused salt Hi Tec†	Mercury	Oil Mobiltherm 600‡	Oil Mobiltherm light‡
Chemical formula	H_2O	$(C_6H_5)_2O$ $(C_6H_5)_2$	$C_6H_4Cl_2$	$NaNO_2$ $NaNO_3$ KNO_3	Hg		
Molecular weight	18	165	147	92	200		
Specific gravity at 212°F	0.958	0.997	1.181	1.98(300°F.)	13.35	0.90	0.930
Melting point, °F	32	53.6	−6.7	288	−38.2	20 (pour point)	−20 (pour point)
Boiling point, °F. (atm. pressure)	212	495.8	352	....	674.6	>600	>400
Flash point, COC, °F	....	255	155	....	....	360	250
Specific heat of liquid, B.t.u./(lb.)(°F.)	1.005(212°F.)	0.526(496°F.)	0.412(352°F.)	0.373(300°F.)	0.033(212°F.)	0.580(500°F.)	0.53(300°F.)
Heat of vaporization, B.t.u./lb	970.2	125.0	119.0	....	117.0		
Heat of fusion, B.t.u./lb	143.3	64	38	35	5.1		
Cubical expansion coefficient	0.0024	0.00043	....	0.00020	0.000101	0.00035	0.00035
Absolute viscosity of liquid, centipoise	0.284(212°F.)	0.30(600°F.)	0.30(400°F.)	1.7(800°F)	1.23(200°F.)	0.595(500°F.)	0.873(300°F.)
Surface tension (contact with air), dynes/cm	72.8	43	37	....	487		
Thermal conductivity liquid, B.t.u./(ft.)(hr.)(sq. ft.)(°F.)	0.393	0.076	0.064	0.35	4.85	0.067	0.0652

* The Dow Chemical Company.
† E. I. du Pont de Nemours & Co., Explosives Department, Wilmington, Del.
‡ Socony Mobil Oil Company.

Dowtherm A (The Dow Chemical Company) presently dominates the 400° to 750°F. field of indirect process heating. This fluid is an organic compound of high heat stability, a eutectic mixture containing 73.5 per cent diphenyloxide and 26.5 per cent diphenyl by weight. At its freezing point of 54°F. Dowtherm A contracts slightly, thereby removing the possibility of damage to process equipment when shut down under cold-weather conditions. At room temperatures it is a clear, almost colorless liquid, which darkens rapidly in use without change in physical characteristics, and has a characteristic rose-geranium odor. It does not react chemically with metals commonly used in heat-transport systems and is not toxic to humans, presenting no appreciable hazard to health in heat-transfer use and requiring no special precautions.

Dowtherm A is quite stable at high temperatures. Many vaporizers and accessories have operated for years at Dowtherm temperatures of 650°F. with no decomposition. At higher temperatures decomposition may occur in two ways. Above about 750°F. two molecules of diphenyl may react to yield one molecule of *p*-diphenyl benzene and one of benzene. The *p*-diphenyl benzene dissolves in Dowtherm A, but the benzene, being a non-condensing vapor in practical Dowtherm heating installations, escapes into vent pipes. There is a similar reaction in the case of diphenyloxide.

The second form of decomposition is more troublesome. When Dowtherm A is severely overheated, such as by flame impingement on the tubes of a vaporizer, or forcing the heater beyond its rated capacity, complete decomposition into carbon and hydrogen may take place. The formation of carbon occurs when inadequate circulation caused by the accumulation of materials holds the Dowtherm in a stagnant condition. The lighter fractions then distill off, leaving behind the higher-boiling-point fractions, which carbonize. When this begins the carbon forms a skin on the heating surface of the vaporizer, and this increases the thermal resistance, so that decomposition is greatly accelerated. In this manner, a Dowtherm vaporizer may be filled completely full of carbon in a few hours.

To prevent overheating and decomposition, Dowtherm vaporizers are of liquid-tube or fire-tube natural-circulation design or liquid-tube forced-circulation design. Small laboratory vaporizers are frequently heated by electricity. A natural-circulation vaporizer as in Fig. 9-75 is arranged with few bends or restrictions to allow fast recirculation of the Dowtherm liquid, and is designed with ample furnace capacity. Good flame-shape control prevents hot spots from forming along the vaporizer tubes.

Dowtherm E, a specially processed *o*-dichlorobenzene which boils at 350°F. and has a freezing point below zero, is commonly used between 350 and 500°F. No trace of decomposition of Dowtherm E has been noted in tests conducted at temperatures and heat loads considerably higher than those recommended for commercial installations. There is some evidence that aluminum can catalyze the decomposition of Dowtherm E to form hydrochloric acid. This acid is likely to corrode severely the polished surfaces of precision tools, machines, and sheet or formed metals. Aluminum should not be used with Dowtherm E.

High-temperature hot water is a favorable system for process temperatures of 300° to 400°F. but requires pump pressures greater than the saturation pressure of 250 lb./sq. in. to maintain the water in liquid form. Hot-water systems are stable, with simple equipment, and easy to control. Corrosion is at a minimum when air is excluded from the system. Deleterious solids in the water do not build up to high concentrations in the

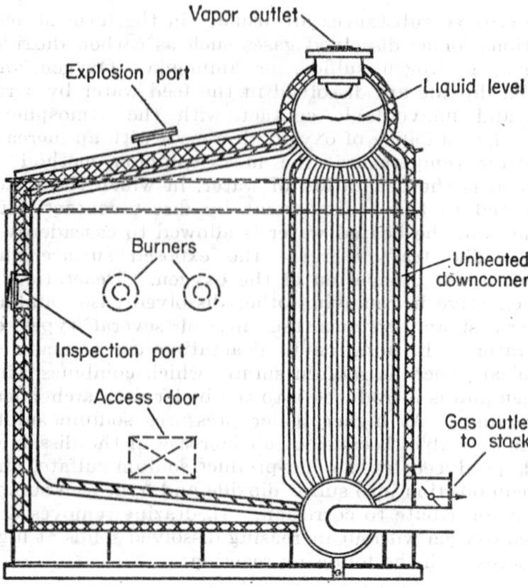

FIG. 9-75. Dowtherm vaporizer. (*Foster-Wheeler Corp.*)

absence of evaporation, and scale formation and foaming are at a minimum.

Mercury is a basic element that is useful in thermal liquid systems. Its stability as an element makes it suitable for high temperatures, in the range of 600° to 1000°F. Experimental work shows that it has no corrosive effect on metals commonly used in practice. Mercury is toxic to humans, and mercury systems must include elaborate precautions to prevent the escape of mercury vapor to the surrounding atmosphere. The low latent heat of vaporization of mercury makes it unattractive to use as a vapor at low temperatures during which heat must be given up during condensation. The high cost of mercury, in comparison with other thermal liquids commercially available, precludes its use at temperatures below 600°F.

Inorganic Salts. Molten mixtures of **inorganic salts,** one of which is a eutectic consisting of 40 per cent $NaNO_2$, 7 per cent $NaNO_3$, and 53 per cent KNO_3, are widely used in salt baths and petroleum refining where high temperatures are maintained and where the system is kept in continuous operation. A melting point of 288°F. precludes its use in low-temperature systems and requires that the circulating fluid be kept hot and molten throughout its flow path. The salt mixture need not be pressurized higher than required to overcome the pressure drop of the system.

Inorganic salt mixtures are non-toxic and chemically stable up to 800° to 850°F., in the absence of contaminants. Between 850 and 1100°F., which is the maximum operating temperature, the salt undergoes a slow thermal decomposition, which is largely a thermal breakdown of the nitrite to nitrate, alkali metal oxide, and nitrogen:

$$5\,NaNO_2 \rightarrow 3\,NaNO_3 + Na_2O + N_2$$

This reaction is evidenced by the slow evolution of nitrogen gas, and it is accompanied by a gradual rise in the freezing point of the mixture [Alexander and Hindin, *Ind. Eng. Chem.*, **39,** 1044 (1947)].

The nitrite is also subject to slow oxidation by atmospheric oxygen above 850°F. with formation of sodium nitrate. This reaction is eliminated by excluding air or blanketing the salt with an atmosphere of inert gas such as nitrogen.

Table 9-25. Corrosion with Inorganic Salt Mixture*

Metals	Corrosion rate, in. penetration/month						
	612°F.	785°F.	850°F.	1000°F.	1058°F.		1100°F.
					1st period	2d period	
Steel—open hearth (A.S.M.E. S-17)	....	....	0.0003	0.001–0.002	....	....	0.01–0.05
Alloy steels:							
15–16% chromium iron	....	....	......	0.0000			
Alcrosil 3	....	....	0.0002	0.001	....	....	0.002–0.006
Alcrosil 5	....	....	0.0002	0.0005	....	....	0.001–0.002
Stainless steels:							
Type 304	....	....	......	0.0007			
Type 304L	....	....	......	0.0006			
Type 309 (annealed)	0.00002	0.00001	0.0000	....	0.00110	0.00064	
Type 309 Cb	....	....	......	....	0.00156	0.00094	
Type 310	....	....	......	....	0.00117	0.00077	
Type 316	....	....	......	0.0000			
Type 321	....	....	......	....	0.00111	0.00056	
Type 347	....	....	......	0.0004	0.00109	0.00068	
Type 446	....	....	......	....	0.00146	0.00072	
Inconel	....	....	......	0.0000	0.00153	0.00151	
Carpenter 20	....	....	......	....	0.00097	0.00059	
Hastelloy B	0.00011	0.000003					
Monel	....	....		0.0001			
Bronze	0.00006	0.00008	0.0001				
Phosphorized admiralty	0.00006	0.00005	0.0001				
Copper	....	....	......	0.03			
Nickel	....	....	......	....	....	....	0.00025

* Courtesy of E. I. du Pont de Nemours and Co., Explosives Department, Wilmington, Del.

Other reactions will gradually alter the composition of the salt: (1) absorption of carbon dioxide to form carbonates which may settle out in the system; (2) absorption of water vapor to form alkali metal hydroxides. These reactions do not interfere with process operation but if allowed to continue will ultimately affect utility of the system. They may be eliminated by blanketing the molten salt with nitrogen.

Ordinary carbon steel may be used successfully in molten-salt equipment up to 850°F. Above this temperature more resistant alloys are recommended. Copper equipment has been used satisfactorily at moderate temperatures (about 600°F.), but cast iron is not recommended because of a reaction between the molten salt and the iron which results in embrittlement or fissuring. Table 9-25 shows corrosion rates with fused salts.

Conventional **mineral oils** are of low cost and readily available for process use and are valuable in systems operating from 30° to 600°F. They need not be pressurized in this range. The paraffinic-type cylinder oils are often employed in open systems to about 450°F., such as are used in tempering metal. At higher temperatures the conventional mineral oils are used in closed systems, up to 600°F., in which temperature region the oils become susceptible to thermal cracking. This decomposition, similar to the controlled cracking process used to produce gasoline from heavy oils, is not nearly so severe as the cracking that occurs in petroleum refining but will produce volatile materials that reduce the flash point of the oil. At the same time, the decomposition yields heavier products, which after long periods of operation flow less readily, leading to formation of coke deposits.

Mineral Oil. Mobiltherm 600 and Mobiltherm Light (Socony Mobil Oil Company) are **aromatic mineral oils** of lower viscosity than conventional mineral oils and can operate between 30 and 600°F. for the former, and at −15°F. but not above 400°F. for the latter. They will not be broken down by temperature when used in the recommended range. Their flash points thus remain unchanged after many hours of service life. When the aromatic oils are subjected to excessive temperatures thermal cracking will occur in a form similar to the decomposition of conventional mineral oils. Sludge and coke deposits do not readily occur with such aromatic mineral oils, as they have a powerful solvent action, and some installations have operated for years without an oil change or cleaning of the system.

Neither aromatic mineral oil is suitable for operation in an open system, in direct contact with air. Oxidation results in deterioration of the oil, a chemical breakdown that is accelerated when the oil is at an elevated temperature. All process systems must include a "cold-oil" expansion tank, in which the temperature of the oil will not exceed 130°F. The expansion tank prevents the hot oil of the process system from coming into contact with air. The aromatic oils should not be used with copper or copper-bearing-alloy parts, since these metals are powerful catalysts which promote oxidation and sludging. Iron and carbon are preferred for the entire system. Other oils, whether lubricating or mineral oils, should not come into contact with aromatic oils, as this causes the

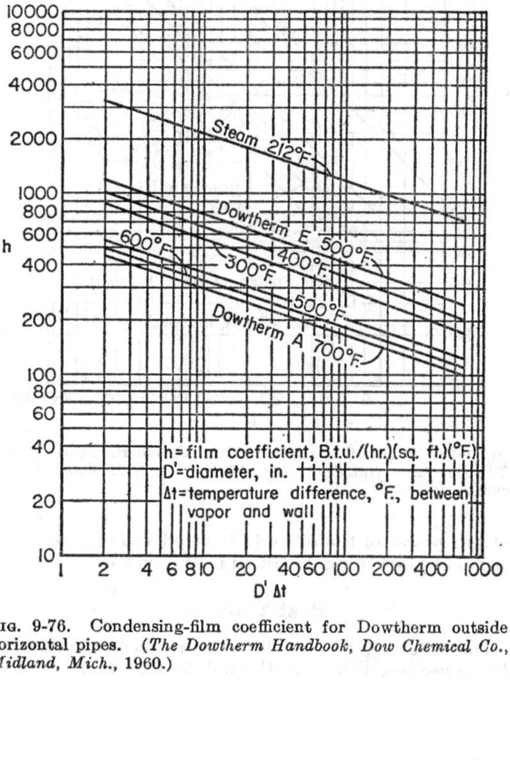

Fig. 9-76. Condensing-film coefficient for Dowtherm outside horizontal pipes. (*The Dowtherm Handbook, Dow Chemical Co., Midland, Mich.*, 1960.)

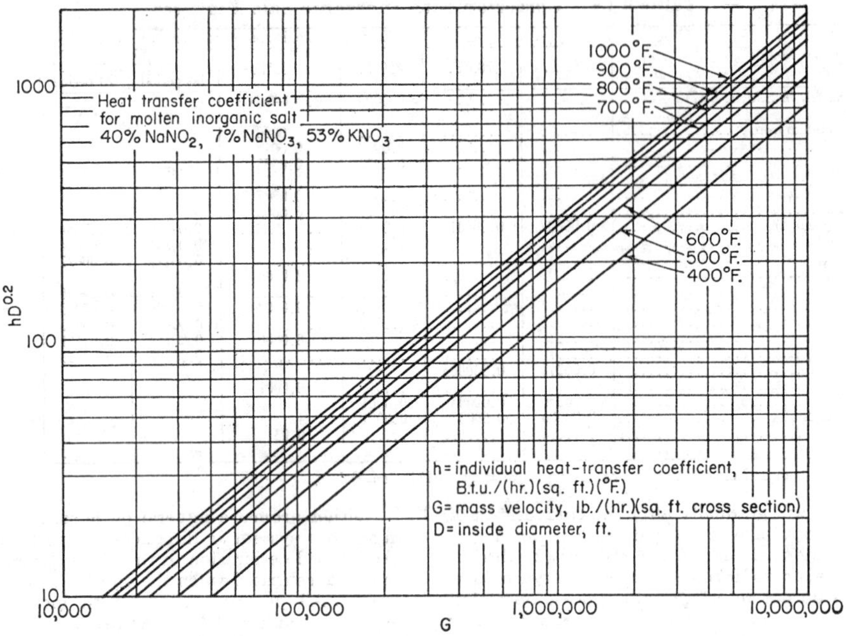

FIG. 9-77. Heat-transfer coefficient for fused salt. (*Hoffman and Cohen, "Fused Salt Heat Transfer—Part* III," *ORNL* 2433 [*unclassified*].)

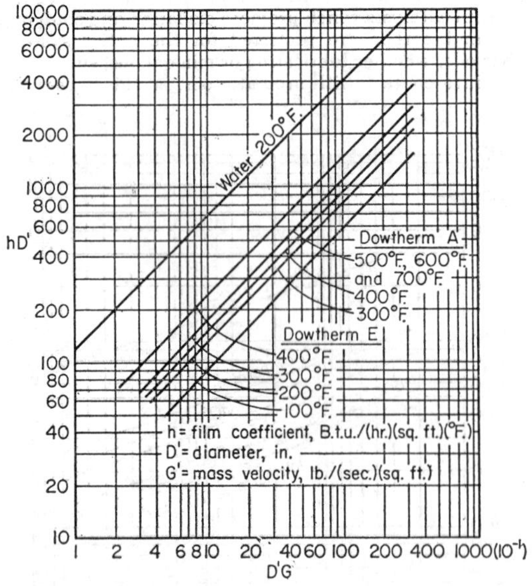

FIG. 9-78. Liquid-film coefficient for Dowtherm inside pipes. (*The Dowtherm Handbook, Dow Chemical Co., Midland, Mich.*, 1960.)

solvent power of the oil to be lowered and may result in harmful sludge being deposited in the system.

Heat Transfer

The following film coefficients are recommended for design use (see Figs. 9-76 through 9-80). Estimation of over-all heat-transfer coefficients depends on experience with similar equipment and products. In almost all cases, the product side resistance will control the over-all heat-transfer coefficient (see Sec. 10).

Process Systems

Dowtherm. Dowtherm process systems are either gravity return or pumped return. The most desirable system is the gravity system, in which the vapor rises from the vaporizer to the heated vessels, condenses, and flows back to the vaporizer by gravity. No moving parts are required. It is essential that the gravity-return system piping be suitably proportioned to the limitations of the headroom available between the bottom of the heated vessel and the liquid level in the vaporizer. This involves the frictional loss in the vapor piping, the user, and the condensate return. Figure 9-81 is a gravity-return system, and Fig. 9-82 shows the pumped-return system. Pumps should generally be of cast-steel construction with a deep water-cooled stuffing box designed for metallic-foil packing.

Transport of heat at **two different temperatures** may be accomplished with Dowtherm in a single vaporizer by supplying the higher-temperature process with vapor and the lower-temperature process with Dowtherm liquid. Close control of the vapor temperature is achieved by maintaining the pressure in the vaporizer, while the liquid temperature is controlled by circulating only part of the process returns through the heating unit. In such an installation, illustrated in Fig. 9-83, the Dowtherm vaporizer provides vapor at the desired temperature for two high-temperature users. A liquid-Dowtherm circulating system heats the low-temperature users. In this system, the hot liquid is withdrawn from the vaporizer and returned to it after passing through the heating elements of the users. A three-way valve, which divides the return liquid flow, provides automatic control of the liquid circuit. Part of this flow returns to

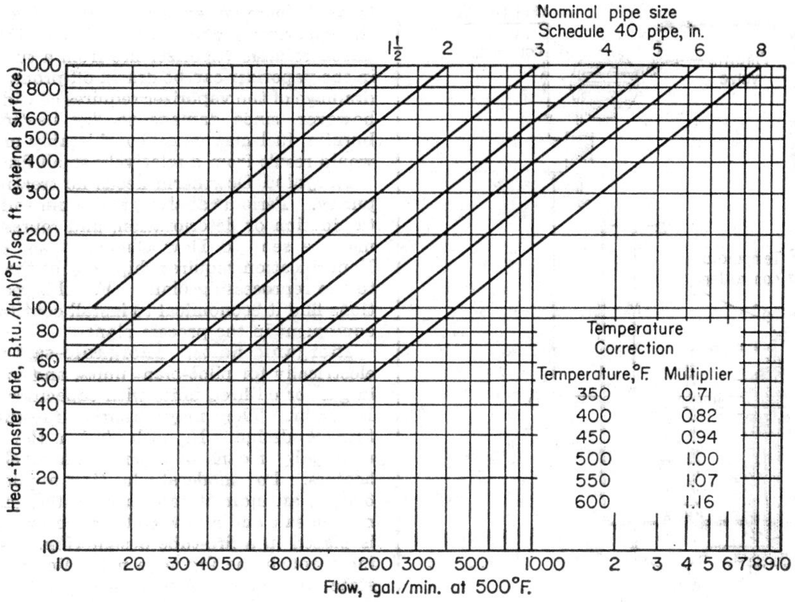

FIG. 9-79. Heat-transfer coefficient for Mobiltherm 600. (*Struther-Wells Corp.*)

the vaporizer to be reheated, while the remainder bypasses the vaporizer and flows directly to the circulating pump section. The amount of heat put into the liquid system is controlled by varying that part of the flow returning to the vaporizer.

As Dowtherms have extremely low surface tension and viscosity at high temperature, more than ordinary care is necessary in the fabrication and erection of equipment to **prevent leakage**. There is ordinarily more or less evidence of leakage at pump stuffing boxes, relief-valve outlets, etc. Welded construction in accordance with A.S.M.E. specifications is advisable whenever possible. The wide range of temperature requires adequate provision for expansion of piping. The high temperature renders ordinary relief-valve springs unsafe, and only special tungsten-steel-alloy relief-valve springs are suitable. Other relief-valve parts and other fittings should be steel rather than brass or bronze.

The condensate line of a gravity-return system should include the so-called **Hartford loop**. This consists of a line connecting the lower vaporizer drum and the vapor space above the upper drum. The condensate return

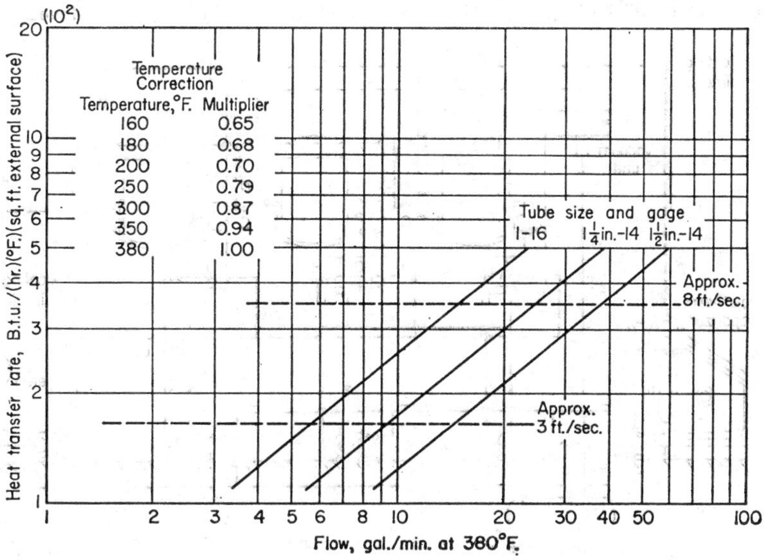

FIG. 9-80. Heat-transfer coefficient for Mobiltherm Light. (*Struther-Wells Corp.*)

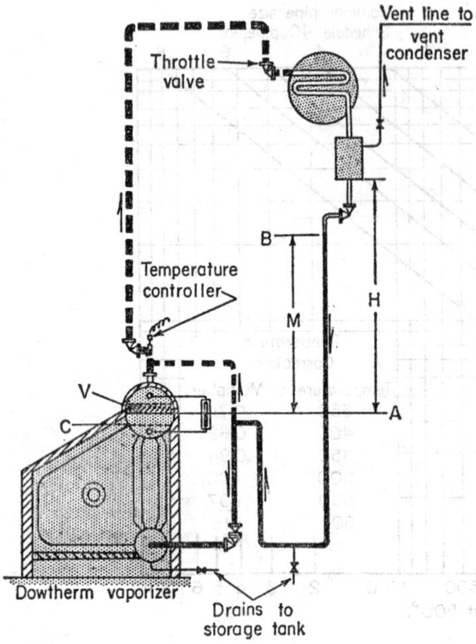

Fig. 9-81. Dowtherm gravity-return system. (*Foster-Wheeler Corp.*)

is brought into this line at a point just above the top of the tubes in the vaporizer. With this loop it is impossible to draw liquid out of the vaporizer up through the condensate line after the liquid level in the vaporizer falls below the point where the condensate line enters this connection. If the liquid level is drawn lower than this point, vapor will be drawn back into the condensate line, and the resulting "water-hammer" effect will give warning that the liquid level is too low.

Other recommended **safety features** include installation of a storage tank of sufficient capacity to contain the entire system charge. It should be buried or otherwise located where not exposed to fire. The drain valve from the vaporizer should be accessible so that in event of an uncontrollable vaporizer fire from a tube leak, the liquid in the vaporizer can be drawn off promptly. Emergency drainage of the vaporizer requires considerable judgment, however, since damage to dry heating surfaces from burning fuel may cause considerably more damage than would result from a relatively small fire or tube leak.

Recycled Dowtherm needs no treatment to maintain purity. Periodic analysis is recommended to detect contamination or deterioration, and representative samples may be sent to Dow Chemical Co. for this purpose. Repurification requires shipment of the complete charge to the reprocessing plant. For this reason remote locations find it economical to install continuous reclamation equipment in the process plant.

Inorganic Salts. Inorganic-salt mixes are heated electrically for pilot-plant units, and for larger processes in gas- or oil-fired units with capacities up to 15,000,000 B.t.u./hr. They may be either fire-tube or circulating furnace design. In each design the initial charge is melted by means of steam coils or electric immersion heaters. For moderate heating applications, to about 600°F., an indirect salt-bath heater, including both the molten salt and a flow coil for the product to be heated, is placed in a fire-tube design (Fig. 9-84). Gases passing through the fire tube maintain the salt in a molten state with precise control over the temperature of the product passing through the flow coil. Advantages for this indirect heater are its safety of operation, even heat distribution to the flow coil, high efficiency, and elimination of flow-coil failure because of flame impingement or localized overheating. Maximum size of these heaters of 8,000,000 B.t.u./hr. can be supplemented by installing several in battery fashion.

Heating and cooling is accomplished in one unit, shown in Fig. 9-85, for processes where reactions taking place at high temperature level require removal of exothermic heat. Once the salt initiates the exothermic-process reaction, it maintains the reaction temperature by switching the flow of molten salt from the heating unit to the steam generator that is mounted integrally with the heating unit. By means of a three-way valve, all or a portion of the salt flow can go to the cooler. Controls on the system maintain temperature levels by forestalling pump

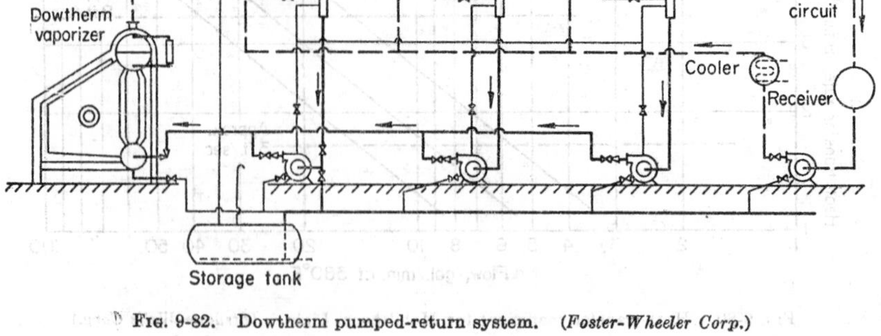

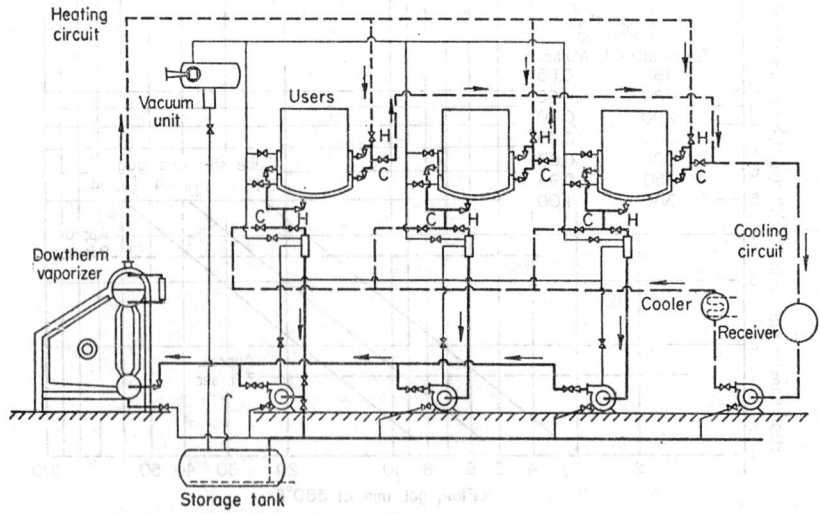

Fig. 9-82. Dowtherm pumped-return system. (*Foster-Wheeler Corp.*)

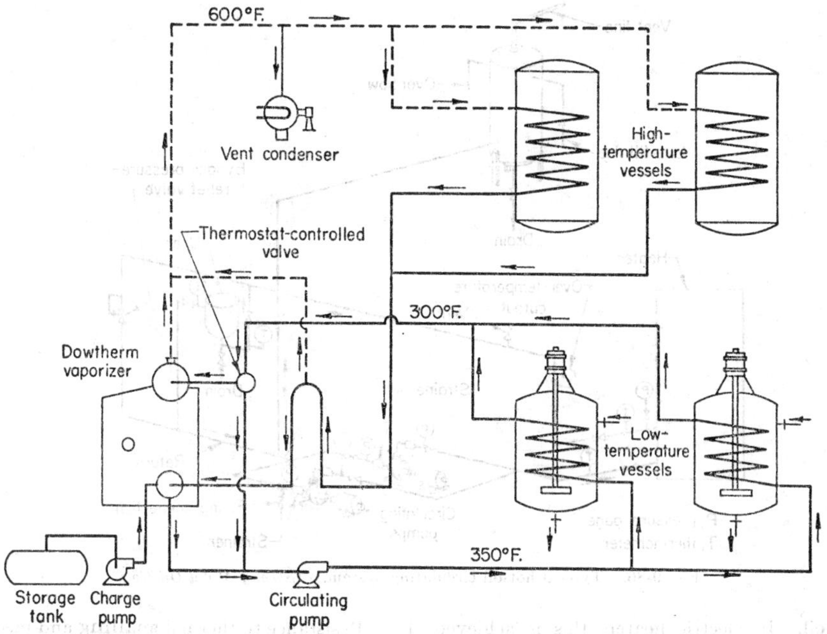

FIG. 9-83. Combination vapor and liquid heating with Dowtherm. (*Foster-Wheeler Corp.*)

operation when the salt temperature falls below the desired level and sounds an alarm if the salt temperature exceeds a safe limit of the process.

Because of the high melting point of the inorganic-salt mix, salt lines and valves must be traced or steam-jacketed to prevent **freezing** by solidified salt, especially for intermittent operation. Submerged centrifugal pumps are used to circulate the salt and are of a type which permits no contact of the salt with the packing gland.

Remelting of salt, or fusing of the initial charge, is done with electric immersion heaters or steam coils that pass below the surface of the bath. Heating a solid bath of salt from the bottom alone can develop sufficient pressure to rupture equipment or expel the molten salt through the solid surface.

Combustible solids, such as wood, coke, paper, plastics, cyanides, chlorates, and ammonium salts, and active metals, such as aluminum and magnesium, are potential **hazards**. Magnesium, except as an alloying agent in low concentration, must not come in contact with the salt mix. The salt itself is not flammable but will support combustion. Water from spray sprinklers or low-velocity fog nozzles is recommended as fire protection.

Mineral Oils. Conventional **mineral oils** are not affected by contact with air at temperatures about 450°F., but aromatic mineral oils must always be used in a closed system with a cold-oil expansion tank to prevent the hot oil from contact with air. Figure 9-86 is a layout for indirect heating with hot-oil recirculation.

The **heater** may be direct-fired with combustion gases passing over the tubes through which the heated oil circulates, or electrically heated with the oil flowing through narrow channels over the heating source. Other heater designs utilize high-temperature steam passing through heating coils with the circulating oil outside. The heat source must be such that excessive temperatures are avoided. Large heating-surface areas and moderate temperature differences between the oil and the heat source are preferred to minimize thermal breakdown of

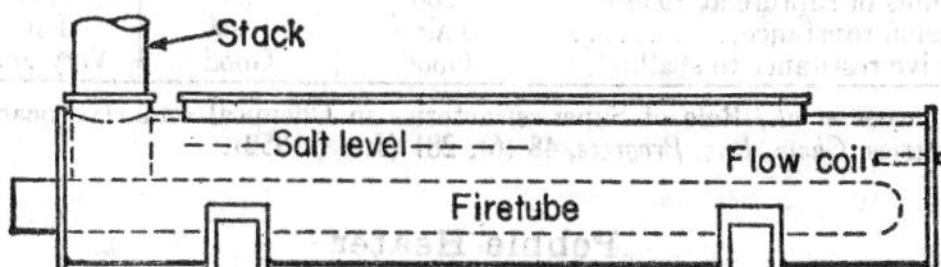

FIG. 9-84. Fire-tube salt-bath heater. (*Explosives Dept., E. I. du Pont de Nemours and Co.*)

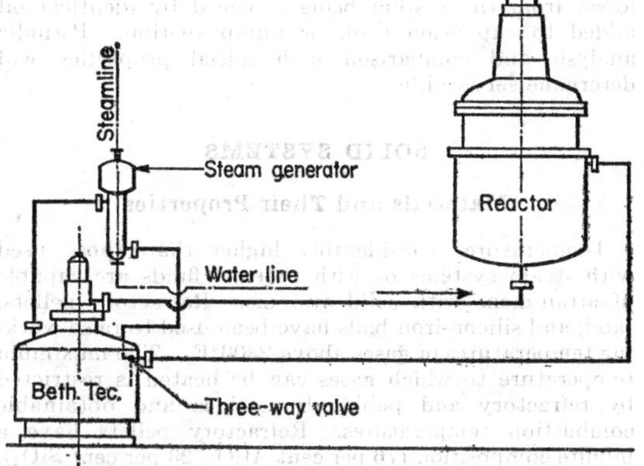

FIG. 9-85. Circulating salt system for heating and cooling operation. (*Bethlehem Foundry and Machine Co.*)

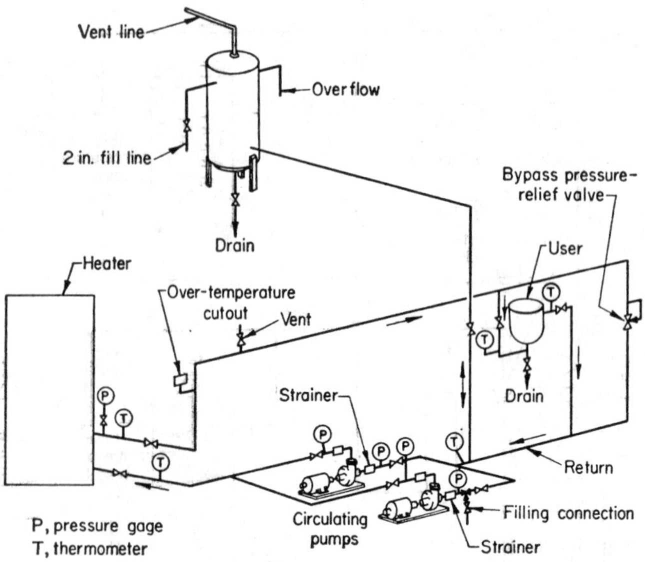

FIG. 9-86. Typical hot-oil circulating system. (*Socony Mobil Oil Co.*)

the aromatic oil. In electric heaters this is achieved with a power input of not more than 12 watts/sq. in. of heating surface; for oil- or gas-fired radiant heaters the input should not exceed 40,000 to 50,000 B.t.u./(hr.)(sq. ft.) of coil surface.

All hot-oil systems use **forced circulation** because of absence of gravity-head differences between heated and cooled oil. Centrifugal pumps are usually supplied with exterior lubrication of the shaft bearings to prevent lubricating oil from entering the system. The pump should have sufficient capacity to provide a velocity through the heater of not less than 4 ft./sec. for oil temperatures up to 400°F., and about 10 ft./sec. for 600°F.

A thermostat maintains the desired temperature in the process vessel and acts to cut out burners or electric current in the heaters when oil temperatures rise too high. To prevent constant on-off switching of the heaters a relief valve is supplied to act as a by-pass and maintain a constant flow of oil through the pump and heater when the thermostat reduces the flow of hot oil to the processing vessel.

Reuse of aromatic mineral oils is continuous, with losses from the system being replaced by identical oil added to expansion tank or pump suction. Periodic analysis and comparison with initial properties will determine service life.

SOLID SYSTEMS

Materials and Their Properties

Temperatures considerably higher than those used with steam systems or with thermal fluids are capable of attainment with solid systems. Refractory pellets, sand, and silicon-iron balls have been used to raise working temperatures of gases above 2300°F. The maximum temperature to which gases can be heated is restricted by refractory and pebble limitations and obtainable combustion temperatures. Refractory pellets have a mullite composition (76 per cent Al_2O_3, 23 per cent SiO_2). Other suitable compositions are kaolin, an 81 per cent Al_2O_3 mix, and fused alumina, 99 per cent Al_2O_3.

Resistance to thermal **spalling** and mechanical impact are necessary for all pebble-heater materials. Heating and cooling cycles are rapid and frequent. Wear occurs against both metallic and refractory surfaces. High bearing loads are present depending on the size of the vessels and the material from which the balls are made. The pebbles must be inert to chemical reactions and must withstand oxidizing, reducing, and corrosive atmospheres. Turner *et al* have reported on refractory conditions [*Chem. Eng. Progress*, **48**, 281 (June, 1952)]. Their data on analyses and **physical properties** of refractory pellets are shown in Table 9-26.

Table 9-26. Analysis and Physical Properties of Refractory Pebbles*

	Made from electric-furnace products		
	Fused alumina	Lightweight fused alumina	Electric furnace mullite
Chemical analysis:			
Al_2O_3	98.99	81.02	75.57
SiO_2	0.50	16.80	23.47
Fe_2O_3	0.13	0.09	0.27
CaO	Nil	Trace	0.10
MgO	Trace	0.10	0.10
Na_2O	0.37	1.59	0.40
TiO_2	0.01	0.40	0.09
Physical properties			
Pyrometric cone equivalent	39–40	38–39	38–39
Avg. bulk density, c.g.s	2.90	1.30	2.50
Porosity, %	21.9	66.6	22.7
Mean specific heat, 0°–1400°C	....	0.320	0.230
Mean coefficient expansion per °C., 25°–1400°C	7.4 (10^{-6})	8.6 (10^{-6})	5.9 (10^{-6})
Thermal conductivity at 2200°C. in British units	24	7	15
Modulus of rupture at 1350°C	200	63	433
Abrasion resistance	Fair	Poor	Fair
Relative resistance to spalling	Good	Good	Very good

* Turner *et al.*, Role of Super-refractories in Chemical and Hydrocarbon Industries, *Chem. Eng. Progress*, **48** (6), 281 (June, 1952).

Pebble Heater

The pebble heater was developed in the early 1940's by the Babcock & Wilcox Co. for the purpose of heating steam to temperatures higher than could be obtained in metallic units. It can be used for heating air, hydrogen, methane, steam, etc., for use in various industrial operations. Also it can be used for recovering the heat from hot gases discharged from another process. Furthermore, the lower section of the heater can be used as a reactor for vapor-phase operations at high temperature. It is a special form of shaft furnace.

Its construction and operation have been described by Norton [*Chem. & Met. Eng.*, **53** (7), 116 (1946)]. Figure 9-87 shows its general arrangement, (*a*) vertical cross

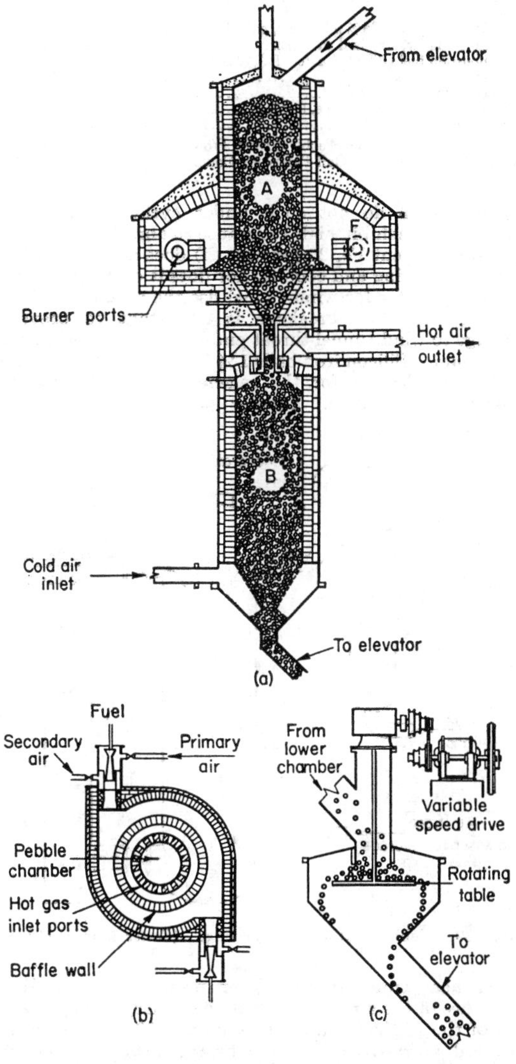

FIG. 9-87. Pebble heater. (*a*) Vertical section; *A*, pebble heating chamber; *B*, heat-transfer chamber. (*b*) Horizontal section, combustion chamber. (*c*) Variable feeder. [*Norton, Chem. & Met. Eng.*, **53**, 117 (1946).]

section of a unit for heating air, (*b*) horizontal section through the combustion chamber, and (*c*) variable feeder which regulates the flow of the pebbles through the system. A bucket elevator (not shown) lifts the cold pebbles from the bottom and charges them in at the top to complete their recycle. The pebbles are heated in the upper chamber by direct contact with combustion gases and then are passed through a throat to the lower chamber where their heat is transmitted to air, steam, or other gases. The throat increases the resistance to flow of gases between the two chambers. In operation, the two chambers are kept at the same pressure so that there is no flow. A damper in the stack from the upper chamber may be used to cause a small gas flow in either direction through this throat. An average cycle on the pebbles is 30 to 50 min. Typical operating data are shown in Table 9-27.

Table 9-27. Pebble Heater Typical Operating Data*

	Unit 1	Unit 2
Gas being heated	Air	Steam
Exit gas temperature, °F.	2180	1800
Inlet gas temperature, °F.	100	230
Weight of gas heated, lb./hr.	1800	4400
Fuel heat, B.t.u./hr.	1,760,000	5,550,000
Weight of flue gas, lb./hr.	2240	8000
Pebble circulation, lb./hr.	2150	9500†
Flue gas exit temperature, °F.	750	805
Lower bed diameter, in.	19	27

* Norton, *Chem. & Met. Eng.*, **53** (7), 117 (1946).
† Computed.

The large surface of these pebbles available for transmitting heat is a major advantage of this unit. The pebble surface per cubic foot in the furnace is compared with other types of surface in Table 9-28.

Table 9-28. Heat-transfer Surface per Cubic Foot of Volume*

	Sq. Ft.
Pebbles, 5/16 in. diameter	135.5
Pebbles, 1/2 in. diameter	86.5
Steel tubes, 2 1/2 in. o.d. (3 1/4 by 3 1/4 in. on centers)	9.0
Regenerator checkerbrick	3.0–8.0

* Norton, *J. Am. Ceram. Soc.*, **29** (7), 189 (1946).

The limiting factor which governs the capacity of the heater is the gas velocity through the bed, which will cause pebble lifting or stoppage of pebble flow through the throat. Table 9-29 shows the maximum allowable flow of various gases per square foot of bed cross-sectional area with different sizes of pebbles when the gas is being heated to 1900°F. This table shows also the pressure drop per foot of bed height at these maximum flow rates.

The equation shown below covers the transfer of heat in this unit.

$$Q = UA\,\Delta t_m \tag{9-31}$$

where Q = heat transferred, B.t.u./hr.
U = transfer coefficient, B.t.u./(hr)(sq. ft.)(°F.)
A = surface area of transfer medium, sq. ft.
Δt_m = mean temperature difference, °F., between hot and cold substances

The coefficient U has been determined experimentally. Values are shown in Table 9-29 for a unit heating gases from 100° to 1900°F. for the gas-flow rates shown in this same table.

Table 9-29. Pebble Heater Performance Data*

Gas being heated (to 1900°F.)	Maximum allowable flow, lb./(hr.)(sq. ft. of bed)		Pressure drop, in. H_2O/ft. bed height		Values of U, B.t.u./(hr.)(sq. ft.)(°F.)	
	Pebble size, in.					
	5/16	1/2	5/16	1/2	5/16	1/2
Air	938	1180	7.7	6.9	4.3	4.5
Steam	740	933	7.7	6.9	5.0	5.3
Methane	698	880	7.7	6.9	8.2	8.7
Hydrogen	248	312	10.5	8.0	20.	22.

* Norton, *Chem. & Met. Eng.*, **53** (7), 119 (1946).

An average bed height would range from 3 to 5 ft. The temperature difference between the pebbles and the gas will average about 200°F. for usual operating conditions. The specific heat of the pebbles varies from 0.25 to 0.30 depending on their composition and on the temperature range.

A process for **light-hydrocarbon cracking** or for high-temperature superheating utilizing a pebble heater is described by Kilpatrick *et al.* [*Petrol. Refiner*, **33** (4) (April, 1954)]. Superheating temperatures as high as 2500°F. are practical. The described unit, shown in Fig. 9-88, was designed for thermal cracking of *n*-butane

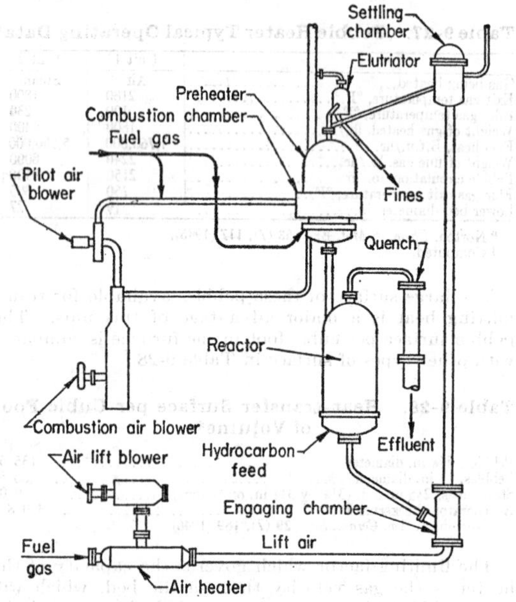

FIG. 9-88. Pebble heater for *n*-butane cracking. [*Kilpatrick et al., New Pebble Heater Process, Petrol. Refiner*, **33** (4), 171–174 (1954). *Copyright Gulf Publishing Co.*]

with a rated size of 30,000,000 B.t.u./hr. Refractory pebbles were the heat-transfer medium, being approximately ⅜-in. spheres of material developed specifically for this use.

A bed of contiguous pebbles extends from the top of the preheater down through the reactor and into the engaging chamber. In the engaging chamber the pebbles fall into a stream of preheated air and are elevated pneumatically through the lift line and into the settling chamber. As the pebble bed moves downward through the preheater at a rate set by a flow-control device in the engaging chamber, the pebbles are heated by upward flow of hot gases which are generated under pressure in the circumferential combustion chamber. Natural gas is burned in multiple burners to provide a uniform combustion temperature completely around the pebble bed. In the reactor, the downward-moving hot pebbles are contacted directly by the upward-flowing gaseous charge for heating or cracking.

Continuous elutriation is provided to prevent build-up in the circulating pebble bed of the small quantity of pebble fines and chips produced by thermal and mechanical shock and abrasion. The fines thus removed from the main pebble stream are separated from the gas and returned to the ground. Table 9-30 indicates typical operating data for this pebble heater when used for *n*-butane cracking.

Table 9-30. Typical Pebble Heater Operating Data for n-Butane Cracking*

Pressure, lb./sq. in. gage:	
Combustion chamber	3.4
Reactor feed inlet	5.2
Reactor outlet	3.3
Temperatures, °F.:	
Combustion chamber	2300
Reactor effluent	1625
Pebbles to reactor	1730
Pebbles from reactor	950
Air to airlift	950
Quantities:	
Hydrocarbon feed (95% *n*-butane), gal./day	34,600
Combustion air, standard cu. ft./hr	560,000
Combustion fuel (1000 B.t.u./cu. ft.), standard cu. ft./hr	30,000
Cooling water, B.t.u./hr	19,000,000
Electric power, kw.-hr./day	530
Steam at 250 lb./sq. in. gage, lb./day	440,000
Pebble makeup, lb./day	150

* Kilpatrick *et al.*, New Pebble Heater Process, *Petrol. Refiner*, **33**, (4), (April, 1954). Copyright Gulf Publishing Company.

Iron balls do not spall under cyclic heating and cooling, and exhibit high resistance to abrasion. Silicon iron (80 per cent Fe, 20 per cent Si) does not break after repeated heating and cooling, nor does it corrode or rust. In an air heater for wind-tunnel use the absence of rust, spalling, and ball breakage is important to prevent damage to wind-tunnel throat and models installed in the air stream. Silicon iron balls 1¼ in. in diameter were an optimum selection for the regenerative pebble heater shown in Fig. 9-89. Smaller pellets would provide

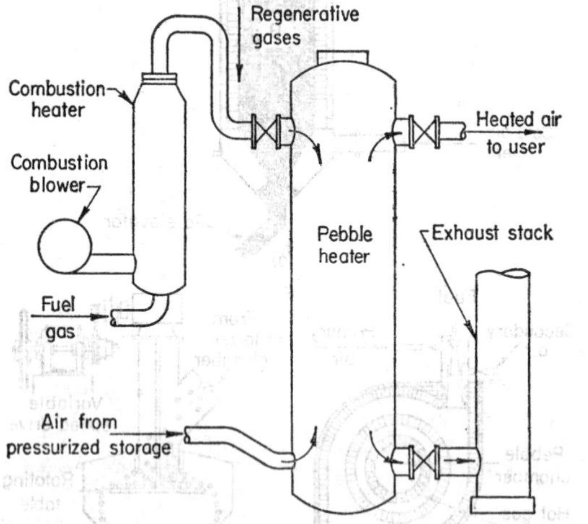

FIG. 9-89. Pebble heater for air heating. (*Foster-Wheeler Corp.*)

faster heat transfer but higher pressure drop. High velocities of the air stream would also carry smaller balls out of the pebble bed. Air at up to 2200 lb./sq. in. is directed upward through the heated mass of approximately 57 tons of balls which retain for a considerable time the 1000°F. temperature regenerated in the heater by a propane-gas-fired combustion chamber located adjacent to the heater assembly. The combustion-chamber capacity is sufficient to regenerate the pebble bed from 500° to 1000°F. in 2 hr. Air from the pebble bed at temperatures up to 1000°F. is sent to the wind tunnel, or alternatively through an electric heater where 1500°F. may be reached.

HEAT STORAGE

GENERAL

Storage of heat is a temporary operation since perfect thermal insulators are unknown; thus heat is temporarily absorbed in solids or liquids as sensible or latent heat to be released later at designated times and conditions. Examples of collecting and releasing heat on a batch or continuous basis are the check-work **regenerator** for blast furnaces as a batch operation or the Ljungstrom type as a continuous operation. **Recuperators** continuously transfer heat through a wall separating the two streams. They come in a wide variety of designs such as shell-and-tube, plate, and extended exchangers and are covered in the discussion on heat-transfer equipment.

REGENERATORS

Checkerbrick Regenerators

Preheating combustion air in open-hearth furnaces, ingot-soaking pits, glass-melting tanks, by-product coke ovens, heat-treating furnaces, and the like have been universally carried out in **regenerators** constructed of fireclay, chrome, or silica brick shapes. Although many geometric arrangements have been used in practice, the so-called basket-weave design shown in Fig. 9-90*a* and *b* has been adopted in many applications and is typical enough of current checkerbrick design.

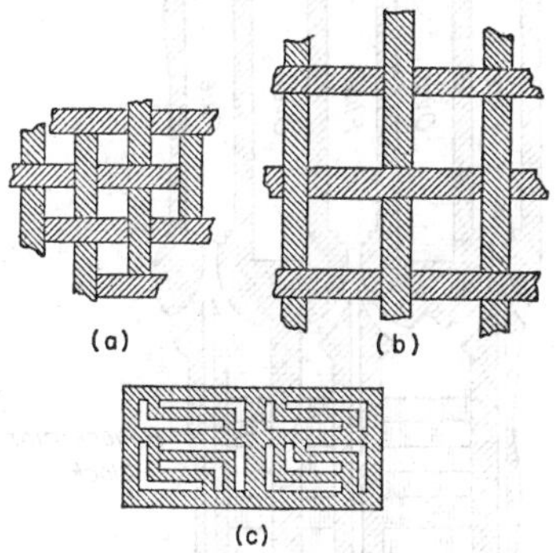

FIG. 9-90. Checkerwork designs.

In **blast-furnace** stove construction, standard 9- by 4.5- by 2.5-in. firebrick, assembled in basket-weave design, form square flues 3.25 by 3.25 in. (Fig. 9-90*a*). In **open-hearth regenerators,** 18- by 6- by 3-in. tiles form flues 7.5 by 7.5 in. (Fig. 9-90*b*). Special shapes have been devised for more complicated, if frequently less rugged, heat-absorbing elements, *e.g.*, coke-oven tiles (Fig. 9-90*c*). Standard firebrick are cheaper than special shapes, and this fact has tended to confine regenerator design to the readily available and less expensive standard refractories.

Blast-furnace Stoves

A modern blast furnace, producing 1650 tons pig iron/day, will be blown with 100,000 standard cu. ft./min. of atmospheric air, preheated to temperatures ranging in normal practice from 900° to 1200°F., with 1000°F. close to an average. To preheat this blast volume, a set of four stoves is usually provided. A vertical and horizontal section of one such stove is shown in Fig. 9-91. Each stove consists of a vertical steel cylinder 24 ft. in diameter, 110 ft. high, topped with a spherical dome. A side combustion chamber is separated by a bridge wall with a lens-shaped horizontal cross section. The remaining volume is filled with heat-absorbing checkerwork.

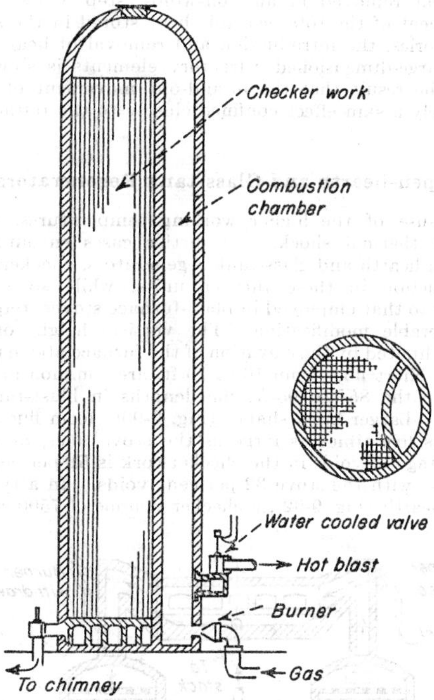

FIG. 9-91. Blast-furnace stove.

The **heat-exchanging surface** in each stove is just under 3 acres (124,000 sq. ft.), indicating 4.7 sq. ft./cu. ft. of checker volume. In operation, each stove is carried through a two-step 4-hr. cycle. In one 3-hr. "on-gas" step, the checkers are heated by the combustion of blast-furnace gas. In the alternating "on-wind" 1-hr. step, the checkers are cooled by the passage of cold air through the stove. At any given time, three stoves are simultaneously on gas, while a single stove is on wind.

After 3 hr. of "on gas," an "on-wind" step is initiated. At the start, about one-half the air, entering at 200°F. (blower discharge temperature at 15 lb./sq. in. gage) passes through the checkers, the other half being by-passed around the stove through the cold-blast mixer valve. The gas passing through the stove exhausts initially at 2000°F. Mixing this with the unheated air produces a blast temperature of 1000°F. The temperature of the heated air from the stove falls rapidly, minute by minute, throughout the "on-wind" step. The fraction of total air volume by-passed through the mixer valve is continually decreased by progressive closing of this valve, its operation being automatically regulated under control of a thermocouple and potentiometer. At the end of 60 min. of "on-wind" operation, in usual practice, the cold-blast mixer valve is practically closed, the entire blast then passing through the checkers.

Satisfactory approach to uniform blast temperature can readily be realized by this automatic control of the mixer valve, provided that the uniform blast temperature does not greatly exceed one-half of the combustion temperature in the preceding on-gas step. The rapid decrease in temperature exhibited by the air discharging from the checkers is a characteristic feature of classical checkerwork heat transfer. The thickness of the refractory flue walls retards the flow of heat by thermal diffusion into the central portions of the brick. Although the heat removed in an "on-wind" step is less than 5 per cent of the total sensible heat stored in the stove refractories, the introduction and removal of heat from such large-dimensioned refractory elements is sluggish, with the result that the in-and-out movement of heat is largely a skin effect confined closely to the refractory surface.

Open-hearth and Glass-tank Regenerators

Because of the higher working temperatures, more drastic thermal shock, and dirtier gases encountered in open-hearth and glass-tank regenerators, checkerwork construction in these furnace units, while somewhat similar to that employed in blast-furnace stoves, requires considerable modification. The vertical height of the flues is limited by the elevation of the furnace above plant level. Short flues from 10 to 16 ft. are common in contrast to the 85- to 95-ft. flue lengths in blast-furnace stoves. Larger brick shapes (Fig. 9-90*b*) form flue cross sections five times as large as the stove flues, and the percentage of voids in the checkerwork is 51 per cent in contrast with the stove 32 per cent voids. In a typical open hearth (Fig. 9-92), a checker volume of 7500 cu. ft.

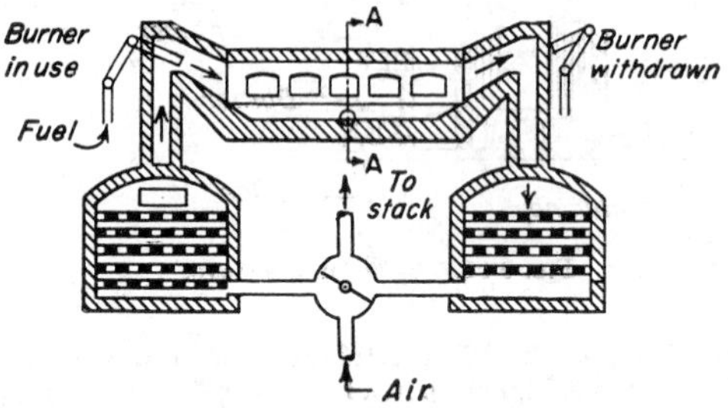

FIG. 9-92. Cross section of open-hearth steel furnace.

contains 810 flues having a heat-transfer area of 3.4 sq. ft./cu. ft., for a total of 25,000 sq. ft. for each of the two regenerators. The total flue length in the two regenerators is 3.7 miles, only 4.2 per cent of the flue length in the blast-furnace stoves, although the gas to be heated and cooled is 12.5 per cent of the air heated in its blast-furnace counterpart.

As a result of the larger dimensions of flue and the restricted surface per unit gas passed, regenerators employed with this type of reverberatory furnace exhibit much **lower efficiency** than would be realized with smaller flue dimensions. In view, however, of the large amount of iron oxide contained in the open-hearth exhaust gas and the alkali fume present in glass-tank stack gases, resort to smaller checker dimensions has appeared impractical.

Coke-oven Regenerators

In the by-product coke oven, waste-heat recovery is effected in the standard Siemens manner, although, as seen in Fig. 9-93, the dimensions of the upstream and downstream regenerators show little outward resemblance either to the blast-furnace stove or to the reverberatory-furnace regenerators. From structural necessity, the coke-oven regenerator is located under the oven itself and must assume the dimensions of an extremely narrow parallelepiped. Fortunately, the design problem is simplified because of the absence of fume and dust in the flue system. Special regenerator blocks are commonly employed, a typical design being shown in Fig. 9-90*c*. An oven 40 ft. by 12 ft. by 16 in. carbonizing 24 tons/day coal to produce 17 tons/day coke will be provided with a pair of regenerators having a horizontal cross section of 70 sq. ft. containing 210 flues ("slots") and an over-all volume of 300 cu. ft. Because fuels used in underfiring are either cleaned coke-oven gas, clean blast-furnace gas, or mixtures of the two, difficulty with dirt and fume accumulation in the flues is not encountered, and because of the lower working temperatures in coking, this intricate type of flue has been found satisfactory. Attempts to duplicate coke-oven regenerator construction in other Siemens units have not been successful.

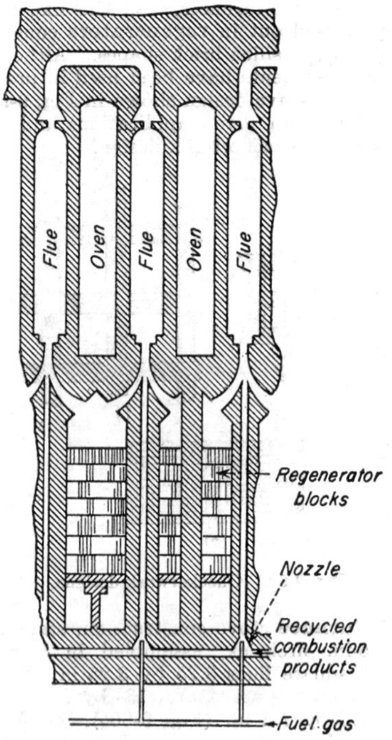

FIG. 9-93. Cross section of open-hearth steel furnace, including regenerators.

Pebble Stove

Although considerable ingenuity has been applied to the design of the Cowper checkerwork, involving variations in bricklaying patterns and special ceramic shapes, the checkerbrick regenerators still exhibit five engineering defects: (1) high initial cost of construction; (2) unsatisfactory thermal efficiency with clean heat-exchanging surfaces; (3) tendency to lose efficiency with dust- and fume-coated surfaces inevitable with dirty gas; (4) inaccessibility of surface causing lost time and high labor cost in any cleaning operation; and (5) danger

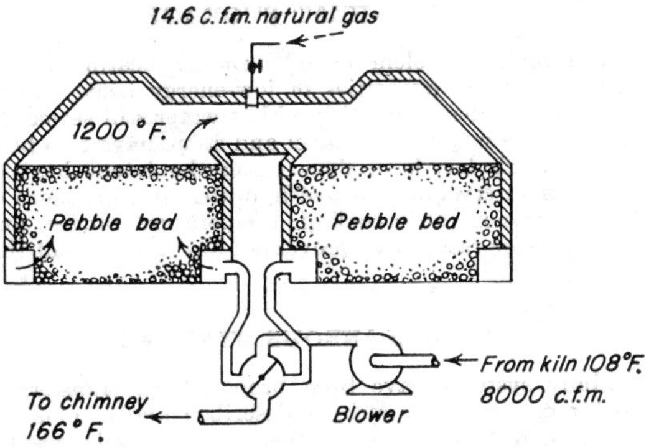

FIG. 9-94. By-product coke oven and regenerators.

of fusion, slagging, and spalling when subjected to high maximum temperatures and rapid temperature changes. It is possible that one or even all of these difficulties are inherent in the Cowper checkerbrick system, as such. No serious attempt, however, to alter 1832 construction appears to have been made prior to 1929, when the Department of Agriculture undertook to substitute the so-called "**pebble bed**" heat-exchanging structure for the classical checkerwork in order to provide higher air preheat in the blast-furnace smelting of phosphate rock.

In this departure from regenerator precedent, a mass of small refractory particles, enclosed in a brick-lined steel shell, was substituted as a functional equivalent of standard checkerwork (see Fig. 9-94). In the operation of an experimental phosphate blast furnace, blast temperatures as high as 2000°F. were readily obtained. In later operation of a 25 ton/day blast furnace producing pig iron, ferromanganese, ferrochromium, and ferrosilicon, air preheat temperatures of 2800°F. were attained and maintained. In connection with the process of converting air into NO [Daniels and Gilbert, *Ind. Eng. Chem.*, **40**, 1719 (1948)] air was preheated to 3600°F. in magnesia refractory pebble stoves.

Aside from the engineering value of the elevated temperatures attained with pebble-stove regenerators, extremely **high thermal efficiencies** are observed to be an inherent characteristic of this type of heat interchanger and indicate its importance in processes where gases are subjected to a specified and restricted time-temperature history.

LJUNGSTROM HEATER

The continuous-regenerative type of air heater or recuperator is familiarly known as the **Ljungstrom heater** (Fig. 9-95). The heater assembly consists of a slow-moving rotor packed with closely spaced metal plates or wires. At each end of the rotor is a housing divided by partitions to confine the hot gas to one side and the cold gas to the other. Radial and circumferential seals sliding on the rotor limit the leakage between streams. The rotor is divided into sectors and each sector packed with a filling to promote high heat transfer at low pressure drop. The packing may be divided into

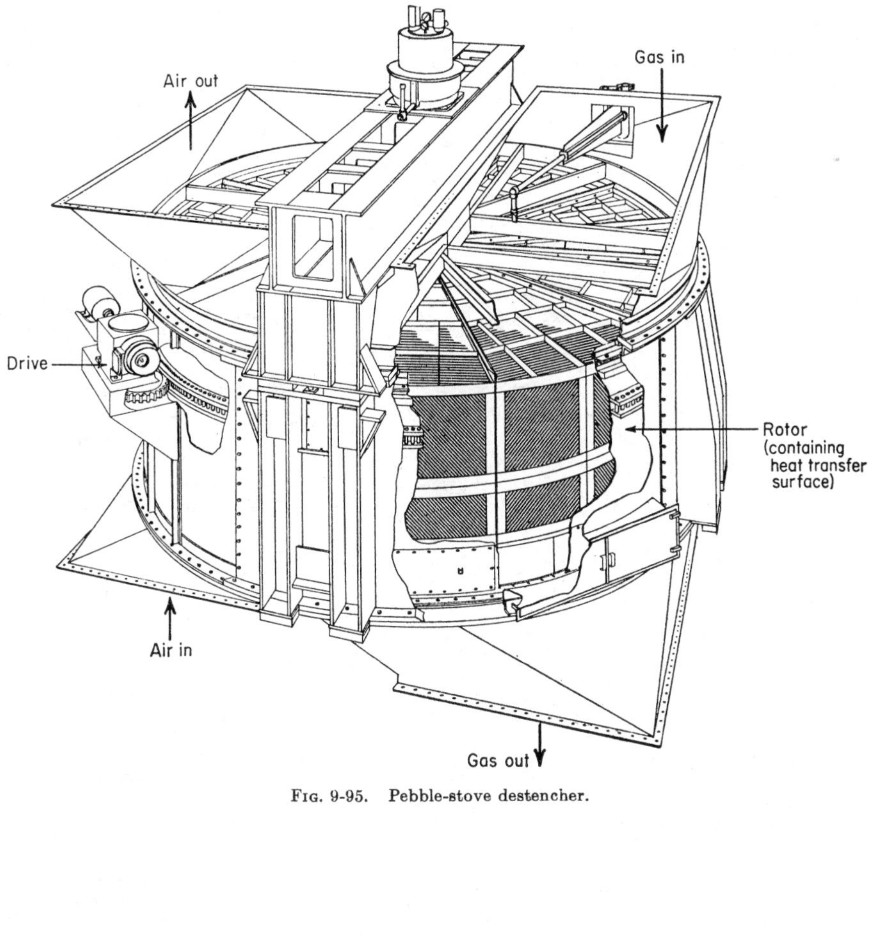

FIG. 9-95. Pebble-stove destencher.

layers of different materials to suit the temperature and corrosion conditions.

Leakage between streams comes from (1) entrainment in the rotor passages (this can be reduced by providing for a blow-out section between the hot and cold zones), (2) leakage around circumference of rotor through the annular space between rotor shell and housing, (3) leakage of radial seals.

These heaters are available in many standard sizes with rotors up to 10 ft. diameter and larger sizes are custom-designed. Gas temperatures up to 1500°F. can be handled (higher temperature of 1800°F. with special alloys) and gas face velocities are usually around 500 ft./min. Thickness of rotor depends on service, efficiency, and operating conditions but usually ranges from 8 to 36 in. Rotors are driven by small motors with rotor speed up to 10 to 20 r.p.m. Effectiveness of these heaters can be as high as 85 to 90 per cent.

Ljunstrom-type heaters are widely used in powerplant boilers and use in process industries is increasing for air conditioning and building heating by transferring heat between the fresh and exhaust air streams, and for process heat recovery.

SOLAR-HEAT STORAGE

The major problem in solar-energy heating is the storing of large quantities of low-energy heat. Many systems have been investigated but water still seems the best storage medium. Gravel and stone have also been used. Work has been done using the latent heat of fusion or of crystallization of hydrates, but problems of cost, corrosion, supercooling, temperature ranges, and heat-transfer rates have prevented any wide use of this method.

MISCELLANEOUS SYSTEMS

Many systems have been proposed for transferring heat regeneratively, such as described above, plus the use of high-temperature liquids and fluidized beds for direct contact with gases, but other problems are encountered which limit industrial application. These systems are covered by methods described in Sec. 11.

The **latent-heat** effect of storing energy is most widely practiced in manufacture and distribution of ice; see Sec. 12, Refrigeration.

SECTION 10

HEAT TRANSMISSION

BY

Charles H. Gilmour, M.S., Senior Engineering Consultant, Union Carbide Chemical Company; Member, American Institute of Chemical Engineers, American Chemical Society; Fellow, American Institute of Chemists. (Heat Transmission by Conduction and Convection)

Hoyt C. Hottel, S.M., Professor of Fuel Engineering and Director, Fuels Research Laboratory, Massachusetts Institute of Technology; Member, American Institute of Chemical Engineers, American Chemical Society, American Society of Mechanical Engineers, and American Academy of Arts and Sciences. (Radiant-heat Transmission)

Eric Weger, D.Eng., Associate Professor, Washington University; Member, American Institute of Chemical Engineers, American Chemical Society, American Society for Engineering Education, American Association for the Advancement of Science. (Radiation Bibliography)

CONTENTS

HEAT TRANSMISSION BY CONDUCTION AND CONVECTION

RADIANT-HEAT TRANSMISSION

HEAT TRANSMISSION BY CONDUCTION AND CONVECTION

REFERENCES: Brown and Marco, "Introduction to Heat Transfer," 3d ed., McGraw-Hill, New York, 1958. Drew and Hoopes, "Advances in Chemical Engineering," Academic Press, Inc., New York, vol. 1, 1956; vol. 2, 1958. Eckert and Drake, "Heat and Mass Transfer," 2d ed., McGraw-Hill, New York, 1959. Hutchinson, "Industrial Heat Transfer," The Industrial Press, New York, 1952. Ingersoll, Zobel, and Ingersoll, "Heat Conduction," University of Wisconsin Press, Madison, Wis., 1954. Jakob, "Heat Transfer," Wiley, New York, vol. 1, 1949; vol. 2, 1957. Jakob and Hawkins, "Elements of Heat Transfer," 3d ed., Wiley, New York, 1957. Kays and London, "Compact Heat Exchangers," McGraw-Hill, New York, 1958. Kern, "Process Heat Transfer," McGraw-Hill, New York, 1950. Knudsen and Katz, "Fluid Dynamics and Heat Transfer," McGraw-Hill, New York, 1958. McAdams, "Heat Transmission," 3d ed., McGraw-Hill, New York, 1954. Schack, "Industrial Heat Transfer," translated by Goldschmidt and Partridge, Wiley, New York, 1933. Stoever, "Applied Heat Transmission," McGraw-Hill, New York, 1941.

MODES OF HEAT TRANSFER

There are three fundamental types of heat transfer: conduction, convection, and radiation. All three types of heat transfer may occur at the same time, and it is advisable to consider the heat transfer by each type in any particular case.

Conduction is the transfer of heat from one part of a body to another part of the same body, or from one body to another in physical contact with it, without appreciable displacement of the particles of the body.

Convection is the transfer of heat from one point to another within a fluid, gas, or liquid, by the mixing of one portion of the fluid with another. In natural convection, the motion of the fluid is entirely the result of differences in density resulting from temperature differences; in forced convection, the motion is produced by mechanical means. When the forced velocity is relatively low, it should be realized that "free-convection" factors, such as density and temperature difference, may have an important influence.

Radiation is the transfer of heat from one body to another, not in contact with it, by means of wave motion through space.

Nomenclature and Units

(The units are based on feet, pounds, hours, degrees Fahrenheit, and B.t.u. Any other consistent set may be used in the dimensionless relations given, but for the dimensional equations the units of this table must be used.)

a = dimensionless proportionality coefficient in Eq. (10-28); dimensionless proportionality coefficient in Eqs. (10-41) to (10-43); dimensionless proportionality coefficient in Eq. (10-84); dimensional proportionality coefficient ni Eq. (10-90), (hr.)(ft.)^2 (°F.)/B.t.u.

a_2 = dimensionless proportionality coefficient in Eq. (10-69).

a_x = cross-sectional area of a fin, sq. ft., Eq. (10-80).

A = area of heat-transfer surface, sq. ft.; A_i for inside; A_o for outside; A_m for mean; A_{avg} for average; A_1, A_2, and A_3 for points 1, 2, and 3, respectively; A_B for bare surface of finned tube; A_f for finned surface; A_{uf} for unfinned area of finned tube; A_{of} for external area of finned tube before fins are attached, equals A_o; A_T for total external area of finned tube; A_d dimensionless proportionality coefficient in Eq. (10-51).

b = height of fin, ft.; dimensional constant in Eq. (10-90) representing all the constant and variable factors, other than velocity, that influence heat transfer for turbulent flow inside tubes, B.t.u./(hr.)$^{0.2}$ (ft.)$^{2.8}$ (°F.).

c, C_p = specific heat at constant pressure, B.t.u./(lb.)(°F.).

c, C = specific heat at constant pressure of cold fluid and hot fluid, respectively, in Figs. 10-16 and 10-16a, B.t.u./(lb.)(°F.).

C = thermal conductance, B.t.u./(hr.)(°F.), equals kA/x, hA, or UA.; C_1, C_2, C_3, C_n, thermal conductance of sections 1, 2, 3, and n, respectively, of a composite body.

C_r = a correlating constant in Eq. (10-54), dimensionless.

D = diameter, ft.; D_o for outside; D_i for inside.

D' = diameter, in.; D_o' for outside; D_i' for inside; D_s' for inside diameter of shell of heat exchanger.

D_c = diameter of a coil or helix, ft.

D_e = equivalent diameter of a cross section, usually 4 times free area divided by wetted perimeter, ft.

D_j = diameter of a jacketed cylindrical vessel, ft.

D_p = diameter of packing in a packed tube, ft.

D_1, D_2 = diameter at points 1 and 2, respectively, ft.

f = friction factor, dimensionless.

F = temperature-difference correction factor, no units.

F_t = dimensionless factor, ratio of the temperature difference across tube side film to the over-all mean temperature difference.

F_s = dimensionless factor, ratio of the temperature difference across shell side film to the over-all mean temperature difference.

F_w = dimensionless factor, ratio of the temperature difference across retaining wall to the over-all mean temperature difference between bulk fluids in a heat exchanger.

F_D = dimensionless factor, ratio of the temperature difference across combined dirt or scale films to the over-all mean temperature difference between bulk fluids in a heat exchanger.

g, g_L = acceleration due to gravity, 4.18 × 10^8 ft./hr.^{2}.

g_c = conversion factor, 4.18 × 10^8 (lb. mass)(ft.)/(lb. force)(hr.)^2.

G = mass velocity, lb./(hr.)(sq. ft.), equals $V\rho$ or W/S.

G' = mass velocity, lb./(sec.)(sq. ft.), equals $V'\rho$.

G_{max} = mass velocity through minimum free area between rows of tubes normal to the fluid stream, lb./(hr.)(sq. ft.); G'_{max} maximum mass velocity, lb./(sec.)(sq. ft.).

G_e = effective mass velocity of fluid flow on shell side of baffled heat exchanger, equals $(G_cG_b)^{1/2}$, lb./(hr.)(sq. ft.).

G_c = mass velocity for cross flow (normal to

tube bank) on baffled shell side of heat exchanger, lb./(hr.)(sq. ft.).

G_b = mass velocity for parallel flow through baffle window on shell side of heat exchanger, lb./(hr.)(sq. ft.).

h = local individual coefficient of heat transfer, equals $dq/(dA)(\Delta T)$, B.t.u./(hr.)(sq. ft.)(°F.).

$h_{a.m.}$ = film coefficient based on arithmetic mean temperature difference, B.t.u./(hr.)(sq. ft.)(°F.).

h_b = film coefficient delivered at base of fin, B.t.u./(hr.)(sq. ft.)(°F.).

h_c = convection heat-transfer coefficient, B.t.u./(hr.)(sq. ft.)(°F.); convection coefficient for condensate film in Eqs. (10-66) and (10-68), B.t.u./(hr.)(sq. ft.)(°F.).

h_{cg} = effective combined coefficient for simultaneous gas-vapor cooling and vapor condensation, B.t.u./(hr.)(sq. ft.)(°F.).

h_{co} = convection coefficient for film boiling in Eq. (10-70), B.t.u./(hr.)(sq. ft.)(°F.).

$h_c + h_r$ = combined coefficient for conduction, convection, and radiation between surface and surroundings, B.t.u./(hr.)(sq. ft.)(°F.).

h_{do}, h_{di} = film coefficient for dirt or scale on outside or inside, respectively, of a surface, B.t.u./(hr.)(sq. ft.)(°F.).

h_f = film coefficient for air film of air-cooled finned-tube exchangers based on total external surface, Eq. (10-76), B.t.u./(hr.)(sq. ft.)(°F.).

h_{fi} = effective outside film coefficient of a finned tube based on inside area, B.t.u./(hr.)(sq. ft.)(°F.).

h_{fo} = film coefficient for air film of an air-cooled finned-tube exchanger based on external bare surface, Eq. (10-75), B.t.u./(hr.)(sq. ft.)(°F.).

h_F, h_s = effective film coefficient for dirt or scale on heat-transfer surface, B.t.u./(hr.)(sq. ft.)(°F.).

h_g = heat-transfer coefficient for gas film, Eqs. (10-66) and (10-68); B.t.u./(hr.)(sq. ft.)(°F.).

h_i, h_o = film coefficient for heat transfer for inside and outside surface, respectively, B.t.u./(hr.)(sq. ft.)(°F.).

h_m = mean film coefficient for falling film, Eq. (10-70) based on log mean temperature difference, B.t.u./(hr.)(sq. ft.)(°F.).

h_r = heat-transfer coefficient for radiation, B.t.u./(hr.)(sq. ft.)(°F.).

h_T = coefficient of total heat transfer by conduction, convection, and radiation between the surrounding and the surface of a body subject to unsteady-state heat transfer, Eq. (10-15), B.t.u./(hr.)(sq. ft.)(°F.).

h_w = equivalent coefficient of retaining wall, equals k/x, B.t.u./(hr.)(sq. ft.)(°F.).

j = dimensionless ordinate, Colburn j-factor, equals $f/2$, equals products of dimensionless groups, *e.g.*, $(h/cG)\ (c\mu/k)^{2/3}$ in Eq. (10-24).

J = mechanical equivalent of heat, 778 ft.-lb./B.t.u.

k = thermal conductivity, B.t.u./(hr.)(sq. ft.)(unit temperature gradient, °F./ft.); also indicated as B.t.u./(hr.)(ft.)(°F.); k_1, k_2, k_3, thermal conductivities of bodies 1, 2, and 3.

k_v = thermal conductivity of vapor, (B.t.u.)(ft.)/(hr.)(sq. ft.)(°F.).

k_f = thermal conductivity of fluid at film temperature, (B.t.u.)(ft.)/(hr.)(sq. ft.)(°F.).

k_m = mean thermal conductivity, (B.t.u.)(ft.)/(hr.)(sq. ft.)(°F.).

k_w = thermal conductivity of the material of the retaining wall, (B.t.u.)(ft.)/(hr.)(sq. ft.)(°F.).

L = length of heat-transfer surface, ft.; total length of n tubes in parallel, Eq. (10-91).

L_u = undisturbed length of path of fluid flow, ft.

L_F = thickness of dirt or scale on tube wall, ft.

L_p = diameter of agitator blade, ft.; Eq. (10-84).

m = dimensionless ratio, Eq. (10-15); a variable exponent on dimensionless groups in Eqs. (10-28) and (10-43).

m = dimensional term in Eqs. (10-79) and (10-80), defined by Eq. (10-80), ft^{-1}.

M = molecular weight, lb./mole.

n = dimensionless position ratio, Eq. (10-15); number of tubes in parallel in a heat exchanger, no units; number of rows in a vertical plane, no units.

n' = flow behavior index for non-Newtonian fluids.

n_c = number of tubes across center line of a tube bundle, D_s'/p' approx.

N = speed of agitator, revolutions per hour, Eq. (10-84).

N_{Pe} = Peclet number, DGc/k.

N_{Nu} = Nusselt number, hD/k.

N_{Re} = Reynolds number, DG/μ.

N_{Pr} = Prandtl number, $c\mu/k$.

N_{PT} = number of passes on tube side of heat exchanger, an integer, no units.

p = pressure, lb. force/(in.)^2 abs.

p = perimeter of a fin, ft., Eq. (10-80).

p' = center-to-center spacing of tubes in tube bundle (tube pitch), in.

Δp = pressure of the vapor in a bubble minus saturation pressure of a flat liquid surface, lb. force/(ft.)^2 abs., Eq. (10-55).

P = absolute pressure, lb. force/(ft.)^2; P_c for critical pressure.

P' = spacing between adjacent baffles on shell side of a heat exchanger (baffle pitch), in.

q = rate of heat flow, B.t.u./hr., equals Q/θ.

Q = quantity of heat, B.t.u.

$(Q/\theta)_g$ = heat load for gas and vapor cooling, B.t.u./hr.

$(Q/\theta)_T$ = heat load, total, for gas-vapor cooling and condensation, B.t.u./hr.

r = radius, ft.; distance from midplane to a point in a body, ft.; r_m for distance from midplane or center of a body to the exterior surface of the body, ft.

R = thermal resistance, (hr.)(°F.)/B.t.u., equals x/kA, $1/UA$, $1/hA$; R_1, R_2, R_3, R_n for thermal resistance of sections 1, 2, 3, and n of a composite body; R_T for sum of individual resistances of several resistances in series or parallel.

S = cross-sectional area, sq. ft.; S_{min} for minimum cross-sectional area between rows of tubes, flow normal to tubes.

s = specific gravity of fluid referred to liquid water.

t = bulk temperature, °F.; temperature at a given point in a body at time θ, °F.

t_1, t_2, t_3, t_4, t_5, t_6, t_7 = temperature at points 1, 2, 3, 4, 5, 6, and 7 in a system through which heat is being transferred, °F.

t' = temperature of surroundings, °F.

t_1', t_2' = inlet and outlet temperature, respectively, of hotter fluid, °F.

t_2'', t_1'' = inlet and outlet temperature, respectively, of colder fluid, °F.

t_b = initial uniform bulk temperature of a body, °F.

t_H, t_L = high and low temperature, respectively, on tube side of a heat exchanger, °F.

T_H, T_L = high and low temperature, respectively, on shell side of a heat exchanger, °F.

T = temperature, °F. abs., equals $(t + 460)$.

ΔT, Δt = temperature difference, °F.; Δt_1, Δt_2, and Δt_3 temperature difference across bodies 1, 2, and 3; ΔT_o, Δt_o for over-all temperature difference; $\Delta t_{o,l.m.}$ for log mean temperature difference.

$\Delta t_{a.m.}$, $\Delta t_{l.m.}$ = arithmetic and logarithmic means, respectively, of terminal temperature differences, °F.
Δt_{om} = mean effective over-all temperature difference, °F.
Δt_1, Δt_2 = temperature difference at points 1 and 2, respectively, °F.
ΔT_H, Δt_H = the greater terminal temperature difference, °F.
ΔT_L, Δt_L = the lesser terminal temperature difference, °F.
ΔT_m, Δt_m = mean temperature difference, °F.
U = over-all coefficient of heat transfer, B.t.u./(hr.)(sq. ft.)(°F.); U_o for outside surface basis.
U_1, U_2 = over-all coefficient of heat transfer at points 1 and 2, respectively, in a heat exchanger, B.t.u./(hr.)(sq. ft.)(°F.).
U_m = mean over-all coefficient of heat transfer, B.t.u./(hr.)(sq. ft.)(°F.).
V = velocity, ft./hr.
V', V_s = velocity, ft./sec.
V_F = face velocity of a fluid approaching a bank of finned tubes, ft./min., Eq. (10-75).
V'_{max} = maximum velocity through minimum free area between rows of tubes normal to the fluid stream, ft./sec.
w = weight rate of flow tube, lb./(hr.)(tube); total weight rate of flow of cold fluid, lb./hr., in Figs. 10-16 and 10-16a.
W = total weight of flow of hot fluid, lb./hr., in Figs. 10-16 and 10-16a; total mass rate of flow, lb./hr.; mass rate of vapor generated, lb./hr., in Eqs. (10-53) to (10-57).
W_1, W_o = total mass rate of flow on tube side and shell side, respectively, of a heat exchanger, lb./hr.
x = length of conduction path, ft.; x_s for thickness of scale; x_1, x_2, and x_3 in a body through which heat is being transferred.
X = dimensionless time factor in Eq. (10-14); dimensionless temperature efficiency factor in Fig. 10-7, equals $t_2'' - t_1''/t_1' - t_1''$.
$[X]$ = product of Grashof modulus and Prandtl number, Eq. (10-28).
Y = dimensionless temperature-difference factor in Eq. (10-14); temperature-difference correction factor in Eq. (10-23a) and Fig. 10-7.
z = viscosity at bulk temperature, centipoises; z_w for viscosity at wall temperature.
z_p = distance (perimeter) traveled by fluid across fin, ft., Eq. (10-77).
Z = dimensionless temperature-range ratio in Fig. 10-7, equals $t_1' - t_2'/t_2'' - t_1''$ or wc/WC.
α = thermal diffusivity, (ft.)^2/hr., equals $k/\rho c$.
β = volumetric coefficient of thermal expansion, (°F.)$^{-1}$.
β' = contact angle of a bubble, degrees, Eq. (10-54a).
γ = fluid consistency, lb. mass/(ft.)(sec.$^{2-n'}$), Eq. (10-88).
Γ = mass rate of flow of a falling film from a tube or surface per unit perimeter, lb./(hr.)(ft.); equals $w/\pi D$ for vertical tube, $w/2L$ for horizontal tube.
δ = correction factor, ratio of non-Newtonian to Newtonian shear rates, Eq. (10-88).
θ = time, hr.
λ = latent heat (enthalpy) of vaporization (condensation), B.t.u./lb.
μ = viscosity, lb./(hr.)(ft.); μ_w for viscosity at wall temperature; μ_b for viscosity at bulk temperature; μ_f for viscosity at film temperature; μ_G, μ_v for viscosity of gas or vapor; μ_L for viscosity of liquid.
ρ = density, lb. mass/cu. ft.; ρ_L for density of liquid; ρ_G, ρ_v for density of gas or vapor.
Σ = term indicating summation of variables.
σ = surface tension between a liquid and its vapor, lb. force/ft.; σ' surface tension, dynes/cm.
ϕ = numerical correlating factor in Eq. (10-52).
Ψ = ratio of eddy diffusivity of heat to eddy diffusivity of momentum, dimensionless; assumed unity in Eq. (10-87a).
Ω = fin efficiency, dimensionless, equals h_b/h_f, defined by Eqs. (10-79) and (10-80), expressed as a decimal fraction.

CONDUCTION

Steady Conduction

Fourier's Law. Fourier's law is the fundamental differential equation for heat transfer by conduction:

$$\frac{dQ}{d\theta} = -kA\frac{dt}{dx} \tag{10-1}$$

where $dQ/d\theta$ (quantity per unit time) is the rate of flow of heat, A is the area at right angles to the direction in which the heat flows, and $-dt/dx$ is the rate of change of temperature with the distance in the direction of the flow of heat, *i.e.*, the temperature gradient. The factor k is called the thermal conductivity and is dependent upon the material through which the heat is flowing and upon temperature.

Thermal Conductivity. Thermal conductivity varies with temperature but not always in the same direction. The thermal conductivity for many materials, as a function of temperature, may be found in Sec. 3. Additional and more comprehensive information may be obtained from the various fabricators of the materials. Impurities, especially in metals, are responsible for from 50 to 75 per cent variation in thermal conductivity. In using thermal conductivities it should be remembered that conduction is not the sole method of transferring heat and that, particularly with liquids and gases, radiation and convection may be much more important. The thermal conductivity at a given temperature is a function of the apparent or bulk density. Thus, at 32°F., k for asbestos wool is 0.052 when the bulk density is 24.9 lb./cu. ft. and is 0.111 for a density of 43.6 lb./cu. ft. In determining the apparent thermal conductivity of granular solids, such as granulated cork or charcoal grains, Griffiths [*Spec. Rept.* 5, Food Investigation Board (1921), H.M. Stationery Office] finds that air circulates within the mass of granular solid. Under a certain set of conditions, the apparent thermal conductivity of a charcoal was 9 per cent greater when the test section was vertical than when horizontal. When the apparent conductivity of a mixture of cellular or porous nonhomogeneous solid is determined, the observed temperature coefficient may be much larger than for the homogeneous solid alone, because heat is transferred not only by the mechanism of conduction but also by convection in the gas pockets and by radiation from surface to surface of the individual particles. If internal radiation is an important factor, a plot of the apparent conductivity as ordinates vs. temperature should show a curve concave upward, since radiation increases with the fourth power of the absolute temperature. Griffiths notes that cork, slag wood, charcoal, and wood fibers, when of good quality and dry, have thermal conductivities of about 2.2 times that of still air, whereas a highly cellular form of rubber, 7 lb./cu. ft., had a thermal conductivity only 1.6 times that of still air. In measuring the apparent thermal conductivity of diathermanous substances, such as quartz (especially when exposed to radiation emitted at high temperatures), it should be remembered that a part of the heat is transmitted by radiation.

Bridgman [*Proc. Am. Acad. Arts Sci.*, **59,** 141 (1923)] has shown that the thermal conductivity of liquids is increased only a few per cent under a pressure of 1000 atm. The thermal conductivity of some liquids varies with temperature through a maximum. It will often be necessary for one to estimate thermal conductivities; methods are indicated in Sec. 3.

For the steady flow of heat, the term $dQ/d\theta$ in Eq. (10-1) is constant and may be replaced by Q/θ or q. If k and A are independent of t and x, the equation may be expressed:

$$q = kA \frac{(t_1 - t_2)}{(x_2 - x_1)} = kA \frac{\Delta t}{x} \qquad (10\text{-}2)$$

wherein Δt represents the difference in temperatures. Usually, the thermal conductivity k is not constant but is a function of the temperature. In most cases, over the ranges of values used, the relation is linear. Integration of Eq. (10-1), with k linear in t, gives

$$q = k_{\text{avg}} A \frac{\Delta t}{x} \qquad (10\text{-}3)$$

where k_{avg} is the arithmetic average thermal conductivity between the temperatures t_1 and t_2. This average probably gives results which are correct within the precision of the data in the majority of cases, though a special integration can be made whenever k is known to be greatly different from linear in temperature.

In case the cross-sectional area A varies with the distance x, A may be expressed in terms of x, in order to integrate Eq. (10-1). This may, however, lead to complicated expressions, and it is customary to use Eq. (10-3) substituting the proper average value of A, as listed below.

1. A flat wall of constant area:

$$A_{\text{avg}} = A_1 = A_2 \qquad (10\text{-}4)$$

2. Area is proportional to first power of distance, as for insulated pipes, L ft. long:

$$A_{\text{avg}} = \frac{(A_2 - A_1)}{2.3 \log_{10} (A_2/A_1)} \qquad (10\text{-}5)$$

where A_2 and A_1 are the larger and smaller areas, respectively. Whence,

$$q = \frac{2.73Lk(\Delta t)}{\log_{10} (D_2/D_1)} \qquad (10\text{-}6)$$

3. Area is proportional to square of distance:

$$A_{\text{avg}} = \sqrt{A_2 A_1} \qquad (10\text{-}7)$$

Conduction through Several Bodies in Series. Figure 10-1 illustrates diagrammatically the temperature gradients accompanying the steady conduction of heat in series through three solids.

Since the heat flow through each of the three walls must be the same

$$q = \frac{k_1 A_1 \Delta t_1}{x_1} = \frac{k_2 A_2 \Delta t_2}{x_2} = \frac{k_3 A_3 \Delta t_3}{x_3} \qquad (10\text{-}8)$$

Since, by definition,

$$R = \frac{x}{kA} = \text{individual thermal resistance} \qquad (10\text{-}9)$$

$$\Delta t_1 = qR_1, \qquad \Delta t_2 = qR_2, \qquad \Delta t_3 = qR_3 \qquad (10\text{-}10)$$

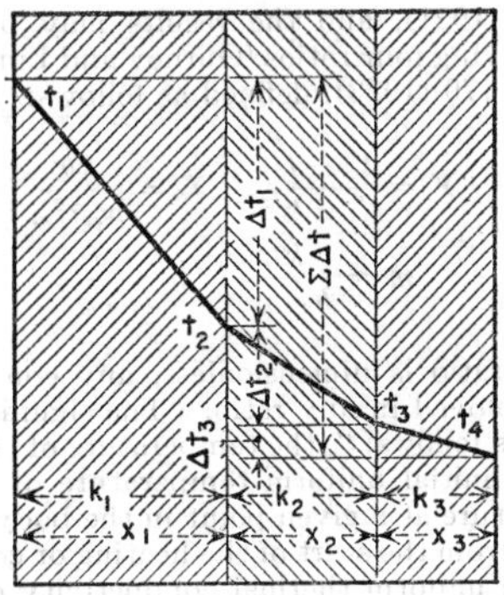

FIG. 10-1. Temperature gradients for steady heat conduction in series through three solids.

Adding the individual temperature drops, noting that q is uniform,

$$q(R_1 + R_2 + R_3) = \Delta t_1 + \Delta t_2 + \Delta t_3 = \Sigma\, \Delta t \qquad (10\text{-}11)$$

or

$$q = \frac{\Sigma\, \Delta t}{R_T} = \frac{t_1 - t_4}{R_T} \qquad (10\text{-}12)$$

where R_T is the over-all resistance and is the sum of the individual resistances in series, then

$$R_T = R_1 + R_2 + \cdots + R_n \qquad (10\text{-}12a)$$

When a wall is constructed of several layers of solids, the joints between adjacent layers may not perfectly exclude air spaces, and these additional resistances should not be overlooked.

Conduction through Several Bodies in Parallel. For n resistances in parallel, the rates of heat flow are additive:

$$q = \frac{\Delta t}{R_1} + \frac{\Delta t}{R_2} + \cdots + \frac{\Delta t}{R_n} \qquad (10\text{-}13)$$

$$q = \left(\frac{1}{R_1} + \frac{1}{R_2} + \cdots + \frac{1}{R_n}\right) \Delta t \qquad (10\text{-}13a)$$

$$q = (C_1 + C_2 + \cdots + C_n)\, \Delta t = \Sigma C\, \Delta t \qquad (10\text{-}13b)$$

where R_1 to R_n are the individual resistances and C_1 to C_n are the individual conductances; $C = kA/x$.

Complex Problems in Steady Conduction. Two-dimensional heat conduction can be predicted by the graphical method of Awbery and Schofield [*Proc. Intern. Congr. Refrig.*, 5th Congr., **3,** 591 (1929)], or by the relaxation procedure of Southwell, "Relaxation Method of Theory of Physics," Oxford Univ. Press, New York, 1946. These and other methods are to be found in the reference books listed in this section.

Unsteady-state Conduction

In problems involving conduction of heat in the transient state, as in the warming or cooling of solid bodies, the temperature of the body varies with both time and the position of points in the body, and the mathematical relations are complicated. The advent and availability of electronic computers have reduced the time required for solving problems of this kind. However, the basic differential equations for conduction have been integrated for various shapes and boundary conditions (see Ingersoll *et al.*, "Heat Conduction," McGraw-Hill, New York, 1948; Byerly, "Elementary Treatise on Fourier Series," Ginn, Boston, 1928; Carslaw, "Mathematical Theory of Heat," Macmillan,

New York, 1921), and the results may be plotted as curves involving four ratios [Gurney and Lurie, *Ind. Eng. Chem.*, **15**, 1170 (1923)] defined as follows:

$$Y = \frac{t' - t}{t' - t_b} \qquad X = \frac{k\theta}{\rho c_p r^2_m} \tag{10-14}$$

$$m = \frac{k}{h_T r_m} \qquad n = \frac{r}{r_m} \tag{10-15}$$

Since each ratio is dimensionless, any consistent units may be employed in any ratio. The significance of the symbols is as follows: t', the temperature of the surroundings; t_b, the initial uniform temperature of the body; t, the temperature at a given point in the body at the time θ measured from the start of the heating or cooling operations; k, the uniform thermal conductivity of the body; ρ, the uniform density of the body; c_p, the specific heat of the body; h_T, the coefficient of total heat transfer between the surroundings and the surface of the body expressed as heat transferred per unit time per unit area of the surface per unit difference in temperature between surroundings and surface; r, the distance, in the direction of heat conduction, from the mid-point or mid-plane of the body to the point under consideration; r_m, the radius of a sphere or cylinder, one-half the thickness of a slab heated from both faces, the total thickness of a slab heated from one face and insulated perfectly at the other; x, the distance, in the direction of heat conduction, from the surface of a semi-infinite body (such as the surface of the earth) to the point under consideration. In making the integrations which lead to the curves shown, the following factors were assumed constant: c_p, h_T, k, r, r_m, t', x, and ρ.

The working curves are shown in Figs. 10-2 to 10-5 for cylinders of infinite length, spheres, slabs of infinite faces, and semi-infinite solids, respectively, with Y plotted as ordinates on a logarithmic scale vs. X as abscissas to an arithmetic scale, for various values of the ratios m and n. To facilitate calculations involving instantaneous rates of cooling or heating of the semi-infinite body, Fig. 10-5 shows also a curve of dY/dX vs. X. Similar plots to a larger scale are given in McAdams, Brown and Marco, and Schack (see references, p. 10-2).

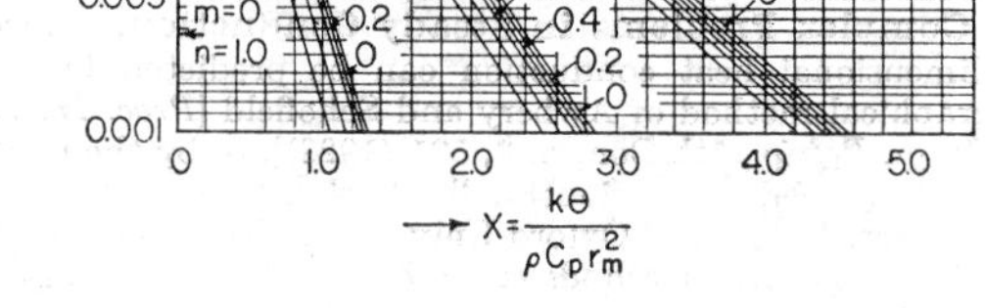

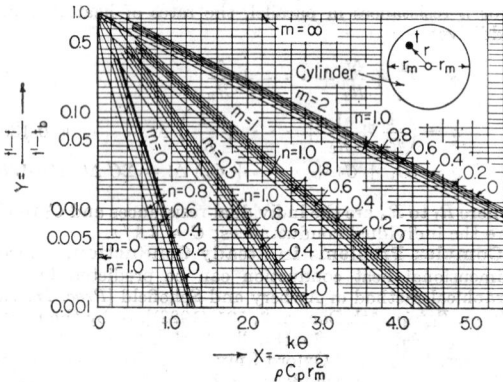

FIG. 10-2. Heating and cooling of a solid cylinder having infinite ratio of length to diameter.

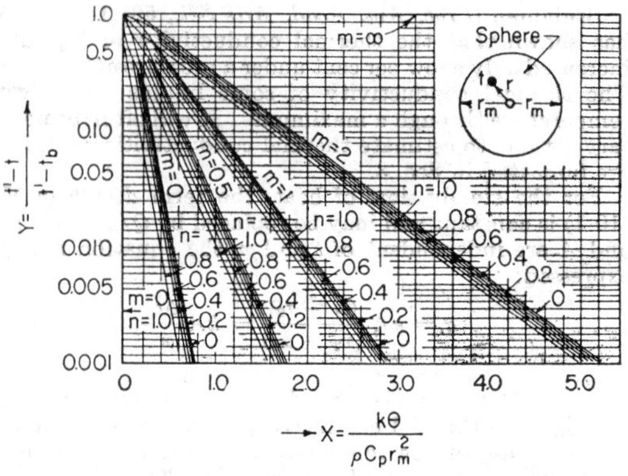

FIG. 10-3. Heating and cooling of a solid sphere.

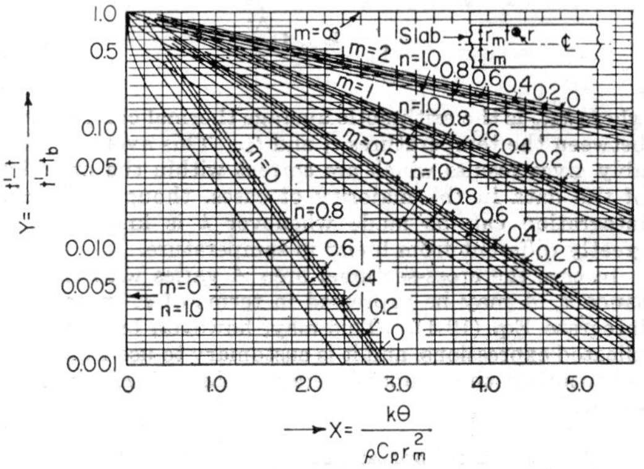

FIG. 10-4. Heating and cooling of a solid slab having a large face area relative to that of the edges.

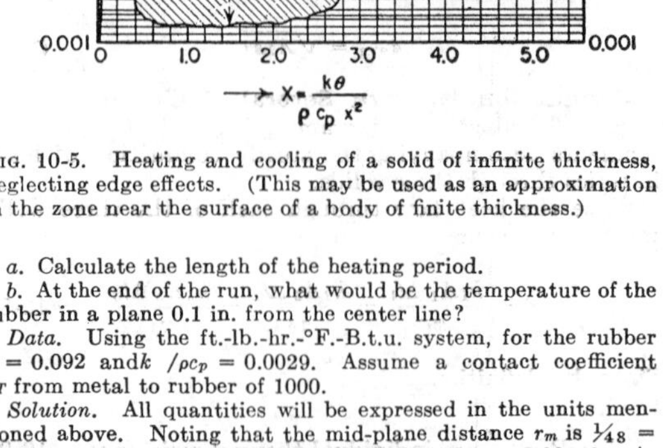

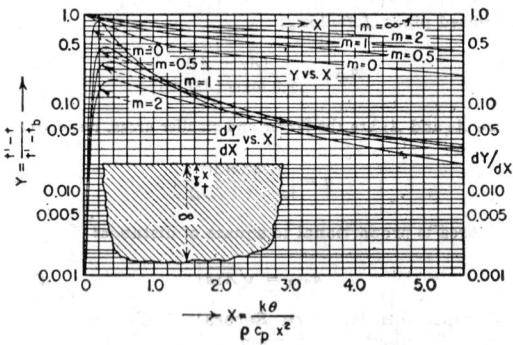

FIG. 10-5. Heating and cooling of a solid of infinite thickness, neglecting edge effects. (This may be used as an approximation in the zone near the surface of a body of finite thickness.)

Example. A flat slab of rubber, ½ in. thick, initially at 80°F., is to be placed between two electrically heated steel plates maintained at 287°F. The heating is to be discontinued when the temperature at the center line of the rubber slab reaches 270°F.

a. Calculate the length of the heating period.

b. At the end of the run, what would be the temperature of the rubber in a plane 0.1 in. from the center line?

Data. Using the ft.-lb.-hr.-°F.-B.t.u. system, for the rubber $k = 0.092$ and $k/\rho c_p = 0.0029$. Assume a contact coefficient h_T from metal to rubber of 1000.

Solution. All quantities will be expressed in the units mentioned above. Noting that the mid-plane distance r_m is $1/48 = 0.0208$ ft., $m = k/h_T r_m = 0.092/(1000)(0.0208) = 0.00442$. At the end of θ hr. of heating, $Y = (287 - 270)/(287 - 80) = 0.0821$. At the center line of the rubber slab, $n = r/r_m = 0$.

From Fig. 10-4, for $Y = 0.0821$, $n = 0$, by interpolation to $m = 0.0044$, $X = 1.13 = k\theta/\rho c_p r_m^2 = 0.0029\theta/(0.0208)^2$, whence $\theta = 0.169$ hr., giving the answer to part (*a*). At this same time, $X = 1.13$, for the point 0.1 in. from the center line, $n = 0.1/0.25 = 0.4$, and, as before, $m = 0.0044$; from Fig. 10-4, $Y = 0.065 = (287 - t)/(287 - 80)$, whence $t = 273.5$°F., the answer to part (*b*). By similar procedure, temperatures at various positions and times may be predicted, thus making it possible to construct curves of t vs. θ for various positions, n.

With the infinite slab, in the early stages of the operation where Fig. 10-4 gives insufficient precision, Fig. 10-5 may be used for points near the surface. For a brick-shaped solid having the dimensions $2r_{m1}$, $2r_{m2}$, and $2r_{m3}$, the value of Y at a given time and position may be evaluated by the method of Newman [*Trans. Am. Inst. Chem. Engrs.*, **27**, 310 (1931)] as follows: Y equals the product $Y_1Y_2Y_3$, where Y_1 is evaluated from Fig. 10-4 at $X_1 = k\theta/\rho c_p r_{m1}^2$, $n_1 = r_1/r_{m1}$, and $m_1 = k/h_T r_{m1}$; similarly Y_2 and Y_3 are read for the same θ at X_2, n_2, and m_2, and at X_3, n_3, and m_3, corresponding to r_{m2} and r_{m3}.

When assumptions made for the analytical treatment need broadening (h_T varies with surface temperature, t_b is non-uniform, etc.), close approximation for one-dimensional problems can be made by the ingenious graphical method of E. Schmidt ("Foppls Festschrift" Springer, Berlin), given in Sherwood and Reed ("Applied Mathematics in Chemical Engineering," p. 241, McGraw-Hill, New York, 1939), and the method of Dusinberre [*Trans. Am. Soc. Mech. Engrs.*, **67**, 703 (1945)]. For two- or three-dimensional cases the ingenious method of Southwell is applicable; see Emmons [*Trans. Am. Soc. Mech. Engrs.*, **65**, 607 (1943)] or Fowder [*Quart. Appl. Math.*, **3**, 361 (1946)].

CONVECTION

Introduction to Convection. In many cases of heat transfer, involving either a liquid or a gas, convection is an important factor. In the majority of heat-transfer cases met in industrial practice, heat is being transferred from one fluid through a solid wall to another fluid. Assume a hot fluid, at a temperature t_1, flowing past one side of a metal wall, and a cold fluid, at t_7, flowing past the other side, to which a scale of thickness x_s adheres. In such a case, the conditions obtaining at a given section are illustrated diagrammatically in Fig. 10-6. In case of

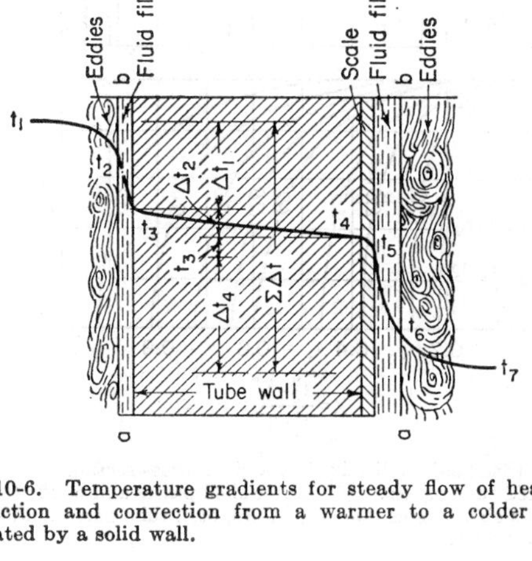

Fig. 10-6. Temperature gradients for steady flow of heat by conduction and convection from a warmer to a colder fluid separated by a solid wall.

turbulent flow of a fluid past a solid, it has long been known that, in the immediate neighborhood of the surface, there exists a relatively quiet zone of fluid, commonly called the "film," and that a considerable fraction of the total drop in temperature, between the main body of the fluid and the surface of the solid, occurs in the film. In more recent years it has been recognized that, for **isothermal** turbulent flow, the motion in the film is laminar (streamline) in character, and the outer boundary *ab* of the film is now commonly defined as characterized by some critical value of the Reynolds dimensionless group, DG/μ. For convenience in visualization, it has often been assumed that the temperature gradient is wholly confined to the film flowing in laminar motion, although because of lack of perfect mixing in the main body of the fluid this assumption may be substantially in error.

Heat-transfer Coefficients

Individual Coefficient of Heat Transfer. Since it is not convenient to measure the thickness of the fluid film or the temperature at the interface between the film and the main body of the fluid, and since both conduction and convection are involved, the differential rate of heat flow between fluid and solid is calculated from the equations

$$dq = h_i\, dA_i\, (t_1 - t_3) \qquad (10\text{-}16)$$
$$dq = h_o\, dA_o\, (t_5 - t_7) \qquad (10\text{-}17)$$

and the observed value of h is called the individual coefficient, "film coefficient," or surface coefficient, and includes the thermal resistances of the laminar film, "buffer" layer between film and core, and turbulent core. The coefficient h is determined by dividing the known rate of heat flow per unit surface of the wall by the difference between the temperatures of the fluid and surface. In single-tube experimental work, it is possible to make these temperature-difference measurements but for tests on or design of industrial exchangers these measurements are not usually possible. In connection with the equations given herein one should employ the bulk temperature of the fluid, *i.e.*, the temperature obtained on mixing, in evaluating both q and the temperature difference.

It is to be noted that the definition of film coefficient is k/x and that it may be convenient also to represent the conductance of solids, such as the tube wall or scale, in the same manner. The reciprocal of h is called the resistance.

Over-all Coefficient of Heat Transfer. In testing commercial heat-transfer equipment, it is not convenient to measure tube temperatures (t_3 or t_4 in Fig. 10-6), and hence the over-all performance is expressed as an over-all coefficient of heat transfer U based on a convenient area dA which may be dA_i, dA_o, or an average of dA_i and dA_o; whence, by definition,

$$dq = U\, dA\, (t_1 - t_7) \qquad (10\text{-}18)$$

U is called the "over-all coefficient of heat transfer," or merely "over-all coefficient." The rate of conduction through the tube wall and scale deposit is given by

$$dq = \frac{k\, dA_{\text{avg}}\, (t_3 - t_4)}{x} = h_d\, dA\, (t_4 - t_5) \qquad (10\text{-}19)$$

Upon eliminating t_3, t_4, and t_5 from Eqs. (10-16), (10-17), (10-18), and (10-19), the complete expression for the steady rate of heat flow from one fluid through the wall

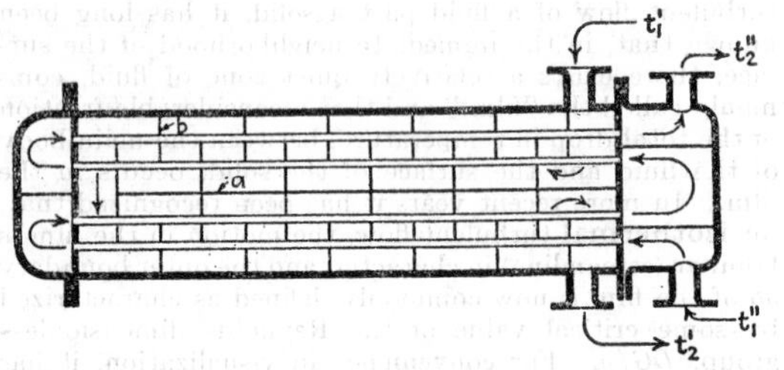

FIG. 10-7a. Diagram of "2-4 exchanger" (two well-baffled shell passes and four tube passes).

and scale to a second fluid, as illustrated in Fig. 10-6, is

$$dq = \frac{t_1 - t_7}{\dfrac{1}{h_i\, dA_1} + \dfrac{x}{k\, dA_{\text{avg}}} + \dfrac{1}{h_d\, dA} + \dfrac{1}{h_o\, dA_o}} = U\, dA\, (t_1 - t_7) \qquad (10\text{-}20)$$

Mean Temperature Difference. In a continuously operated heat exchanger the temperature difference between warmer and colder fluids varies, in general, throughout the length of the exchanger. To allow for this condition it is necessary to integrate the basic relation $dq = U\, dA\, \Delta t_o$, wherein Δt_o denotes the over-all temperature difference between hot and cold fluids. The assumptions usually made are constant U, constant mass rates of flow, no changes in phase, constant specific heats, and negligible heat losses. For parallel or counterflow of fluids, the resulting equation is

$$q = UA\, \Delta t_{o,lm} = UA \frac{\Delta t_H - \Delta t_L}{\ln (\Delta t_H/\Delta t_L)} \qquad (10\text{-}21)$$

in which the term $\Delta t_{o,lm}$ is the logarithmic mean of the terminal temperature differences Δt_H and Δt_L. The value of UA is obtained from the resistance concept

$$\frac{1}{UA} = \frac{1}{h_i A_i} + \frac{1}{h_{di} A_i} + \frac{x}{k A_{\text{avg}}} + \frac{1}{h_{do} A_o} + \frac{1}{h_o A_o} \qquad (10\text{-}22)$$

If U varies considerably with temperature, the apparatus should be visualized as divided into stages, in each of which variation of U with temperature or temperature difference is linear. Then for parallel or counterflow operation the following equation [Colburn, *Ind. Eng. Chem.*, **25**, 873 (1933)] may be applied to obtain the surface required in each stage. Subscripts 1 and 2 refer to inlet and outlet ends, respectively, (or vice versa) of exchanger.

$$q = A \frac{U_2 \Delta t_1 - U_1 \Delta t_2}{\ln (U_2 \Delta t_1 / U_1 \Delta t_2)} \qquad (10\text{-}23)$$

Example. In a proposed design of a liquid-to-liquid cooler, Δt_1 is 60° and Δt_2 is 5°; the values of U_1 and U_2 are 305 and 141, respectively. Compare the values of q/A based on (*a*) the correct method, Eq. (10-23); (*b*) the arbitrarily chosen product of

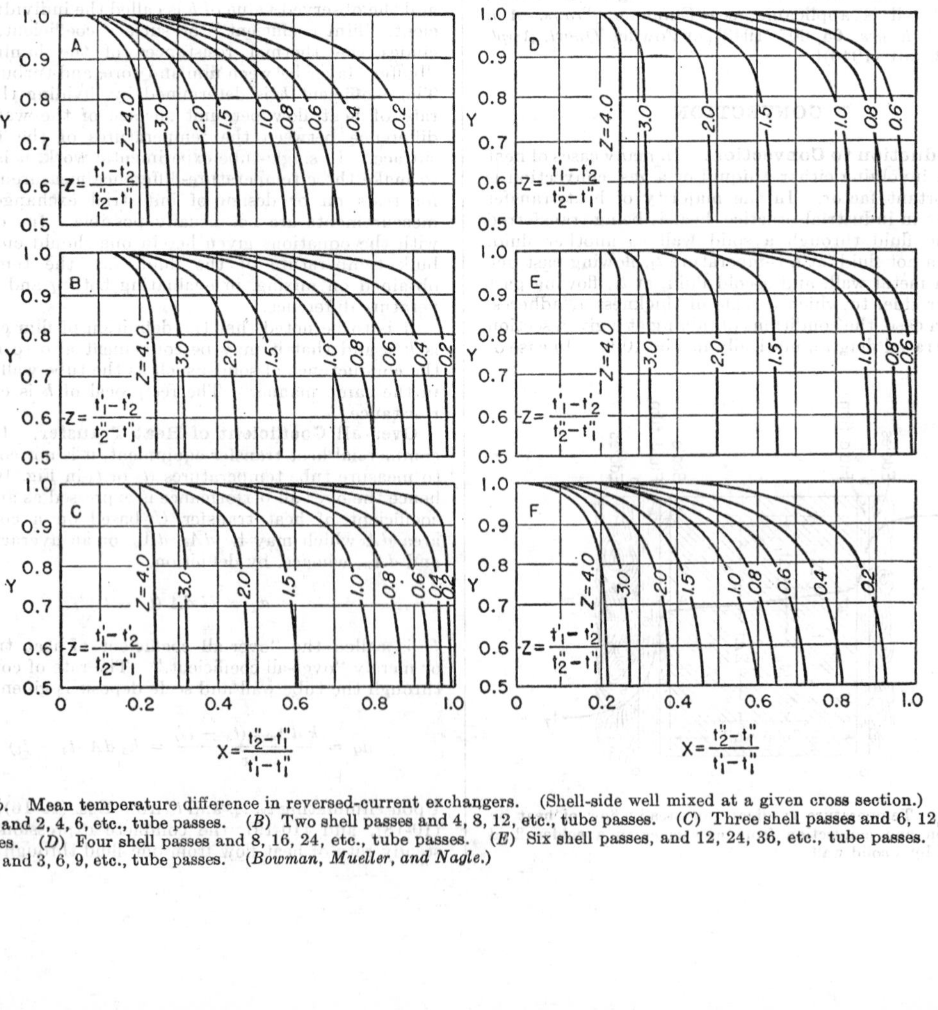

FIG. 10-7b. Mean temperature difference in reversed-current exchangers. (Shell-side well mixed at a given cross section.) (*A*) One shell pass and 2, 4, 6, etc., tube passes. (*B*) Two shell passes and 4, 8, 12, etc., tube passes. (*C*) Three shell passes and 6, 12, 18, etc., tube passes. (*D*) Four shell passes and 8, 16, 24, etc., tube passes. (*E*) Six shell passes, and 12, 24, 36, etc., tube passes. (*F*) One shell pass and 3, 6, 9, etc., tube passes. (*Bowman, Mueller, and Nagle.*)

$(U_1 + U_2)/2$ and Eq. (10-21), and (c) the arbitrarily chosen product of $(U_1 + U_2)/2$ and $\Delta t_m = (\Delta t_1 + \Delta t_2)/2$.

a. By Eq. (10-23)

$$\frac{q}{A} = \frac{(141 \times 60) - (305 \times 5)}{2.3 \log_{10} (141 \times 60/365 \times 5)} = 4050 \text{ B.t.u./(hr.)(sq. ft.)}$$

$$b.\ \frac{q}{A} = \frac{U_1 + U_2}{2} \frac{\Delta t_1 - \Delta t_2}{2.3 \log (\Delta t_1/\Delta t_2)} = (223)(22.2)$$

$$= 4950 \text{ B.t.u./(hr.)(sq. ft.)}$$

$$c.\ \frac{q}{A} = \frac{U_1 + U_2}{2} \frac{\Delta t_1 + \Delta t_2}{2} = \frac{305 + 141}{2} \frac{60 + 5}{2}$$

$$= 7250 \text{ B.t.u./(hr.)(sq. ft.)}$$

Multipass and Cross-flow Exchangers. In these exchangers, where the flow is neither parallel nor countercurrent, the logarithmic mean temperature difference does not apply when the temperatures of both fluids change. Figure 10-7a shows an exchanger with two well-baffled passes in the shell and four passes in the tubes.

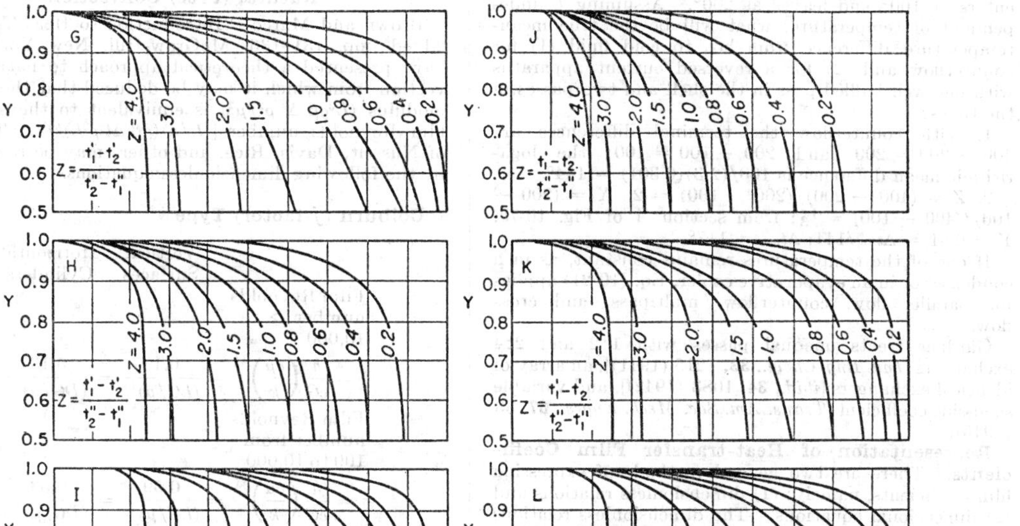

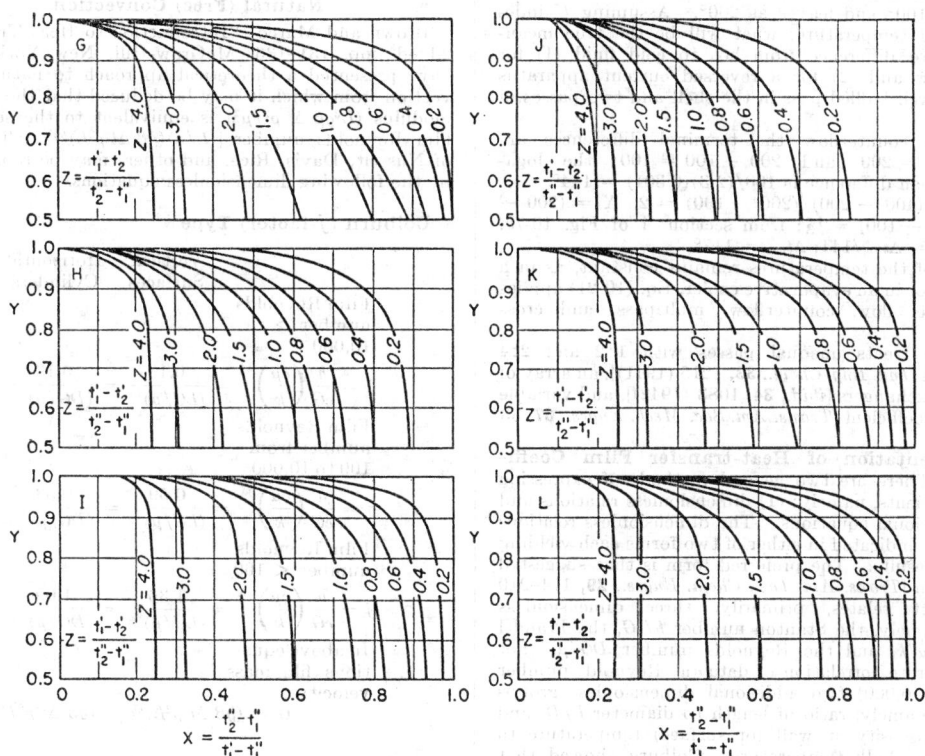

Fig. 10-7c. Mean temperature difference in cross-flow exchangers. (G) Cross flow, both fluids unmixed, 1 tube pass. (H) Cross flow, shell fluid mixed, 1 tube pass. (I) Cross flow, shell fluid mixed, 2 tube passes, shell fluid flows across second and first passes in series. (J) Cross flow, shell fluid mixed, 2 tube passes, shell fluid flows over first and second passes in series. (K) Cross flow (drip type), 2 horizontal passes with U-bend connections (trombone type). (L) Cross flow (drip type), helical coils with 2 turns. (*Bowman, Mueller, and Nagle.*)

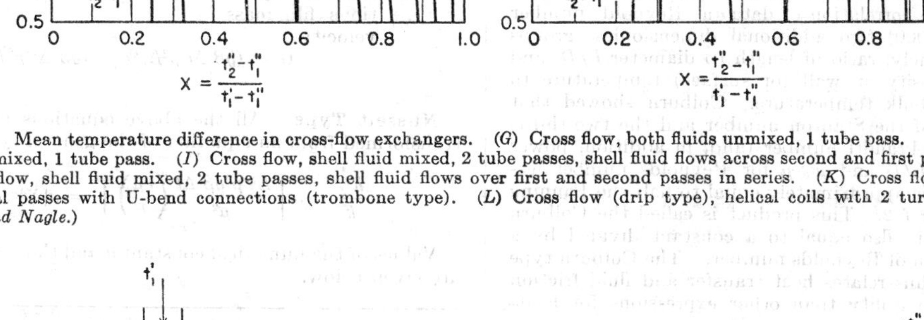

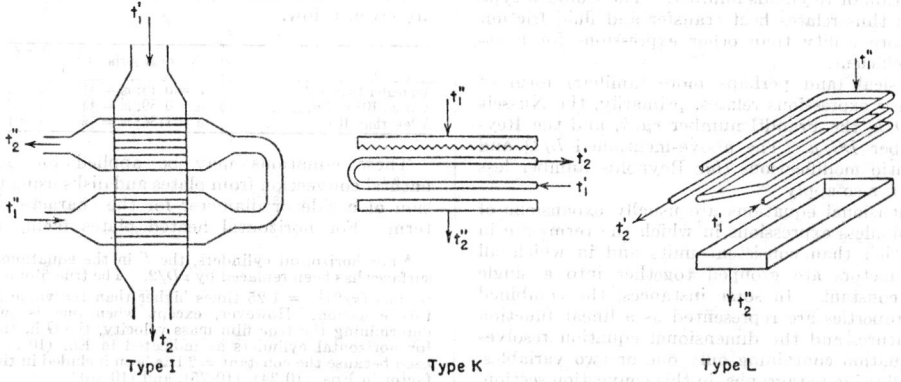

Fig. 10-7d. Pictorial representation of types *I*, *K*, and *L*.

Making the same assumptions which led to Eq. (10-21), plus the assumption that the shell-side fluid is well mixed by suitable baffles, one employs the relation

$$q = U_m A\, \Delta t_{om} = U_m AY\, \Delta t_{o,lm} \qquad (10\text{-}23a)$$

evaluating Y from Fig. 10-7*b* or 10-7*c*. Figure 10-7*d* pictorially represents types *I*, *K*, and *L* of Fig. 10-7*c*. [Bowman, Mueller, and Nagle, *Trans. Am. Soc. Mech. Engrs.*, **62**, 283 (1940).]

For example, assume an exchanger in which the hot fluid enters at 400° and leaves at 200°; the cold fluid enters at 100° and leaves at 200°. Assuming U independent of temperature, what will be the true mean-temperature difference from hot to cold fluid (1) for counterflow and (2) for a reversed current apparatus with one well-baffled pass in the shell and two passes in the tubes?

1. With counterflow the terminal differences are $400 - 200 = 200$, and $200 - 100 = 100$; the logarithmic mean difference is $100/(2.3)(0.301) = 144°$.

2. $Z = (400 - 200)/(200 - 100) = 2$, $X = (200 - 100)/(400 - 100) = \frac{1}{3}$; from section *A* of Fig. 10-7*b*, $Y = 0.81 = \Delta t_{om}/144$; $\Delta t_{om} = 117°$.

If one of the temperatures remains constant, as in a condenser or in an evaporative cooler, Eq. (10-21) applies for parallel flow, counterflow, multipass, and cross flow.

Gardner treats unequal passes with 1:2 and 2:4 exchangers [*Ind. Eng. Chem.*, **33**, 1215 (1941)], an array of identical exchangers [*ibid.*, **34**, 1083 (1942)], and variable shell-side coefficient [*Trans. Am. Soc. Mech. Engrs.*, **67**, 33 (1945)].

Representation of Heat-transfer Film Coefficients. There are two general methods of expressing film coefficients, namely: (1) dimensionless relations and (2) dimensional equations. The dimensionless relations are usually indicated in either of two forms each yielding identical results. The preferred form is that suggested by Colburn [*Trans. Am. Inst. Chem. Engrs.*, **29**, 174–210 (1933)]. It relates, primarily, three dimensionless groups, namely, the Stanton number h/cG, the Prandtl number $c\mu/k$, and the Reynolds number DG/μ. For more accurate correlation of data (at Reynolds number less than 10,000) two additional dimensionless groups are used, namely, ratio of length to diameter L/D, and ratio of viscosity at wall (or surface) temperature to viscosity at bulk temperature. Colburn showed that the product of the Stanton number and the two-thirds power of the Prandtl number (and, in addition, power functions of L/D and μ_w/μ for Reynolds number less than 10,000) is approximately equal to half the Fanning friction factor $f/2$. This product is called the Colburn j factor. It is also equal to a constant divided by a power function of Reynolds number. The Colburn type of equation thus relates heat transfer and fluid friction and has more utility than other expressions for heat-transfer coefficient.

The classical (and perhaps more familiar) form of dimensionless expressions relates, primarily, the Nusselt number hD/k, the Prandtl number $c\mu/k$, and the Reynolds number DG/μ. The above-mentioned L/D and viscosity-ratio modifications (for Reynolds number less than 10,000) also apply.

The dimensional equations are usually expansions of the dimensionless expressions in which the terms are in familiar rather than consistent units and in which all numerical factors are grouped together into a single numerical constant. In some instances, the combined physical properties are represented as a linear function of temperature, and the dimensional equation resolves into an equation containing only one or two variables.

In the following paragraphs, in this convection section, expressions for film heat-transfer coefficients will be given in the following order: (1) dimensionless equations of the Colburn type, (2) dimensionless equations of the Nusselt type, and (3) dimensional equations of various types. The order of presentation will be: (1) natural (free) convection; (2) forced convection (no change in phase), (*a*) viscous (laminar) flow, (*b*) transition region, (*c*) fully turbulent region; (3) forced convection, with change in phase (condensing and boiling); and (4) miscellaneous classifications.

Natural (Free) Convection

Brown and Marco ("Introduction to Heat Transfer," 2d ed., pp. 131–136, McGraw-Hill, New York, 1951) have presented a theoretical approach to natural convection from which it may be deduced that the Grashof modulus $(L^3 g\beta\, \Delta t\, \rho^2/\mu^2)$ is equivalent to the square of film Reynolds number $[(L/\mu)(g\beta\, \Delta t\, \rho^2 L)^{1/2}]^2$. The data of Nusselt, Davis, Rice, and others may be represented by the following dimensionless equations.

Colburn (j-factor) Type

Vertical Surfaces / Horizontal Cylinders

Film Reynolds number > 10,000

$$j = \frac{h}{cG}\left(\frac{c\mu}{k}\right)^{2/3} = \frac{0.13}{(LG/\mu)^{1/3}} = \frac{0.13}{(DG/\mu)^{1/3}} \qquad (10\text{-}24)$$

Film Reynolds number from 100 to 10,000

$$j = \frac{h}{cG}\left(\frac{c\mu}{k}\right)^{3/4} = \frac{0.59}{(LG/\mu)^{1/2}} = \frac{0.53}{(DG/\mu)^{1/2}} \qquad (10\text{-}25)$$

Film Reynolds number < 100

$$j = \frac{h}{cG}\left(\frac{c\mu}{k}\right)^{5/6} = \frac{1.36}{(LG/\mu)^{2/3}} = \frac{1.09}{(DG/\mu)^{2/3}} \qquad (10\text{-}26)$$

In above equations (film mass velocity),

$$G = (g\beta\, \Delta t\, \rho^2 L)^{1/2} = (g\beta\, \Delta t\, \rho^2 D)^{1/2}* \qquad (10\text{-}27)$$

Nusselt Type. All the above equations have been transformed from an equation of the general type

$$\frac{hL}{k} = a\left[\frac{L^3\, \rho^2 g\beta\, \Delta t}{\mu^2}\left(\frac{c\mu}{k}\right)\right]^m = a[X]^m \qquad (10\text{-}28)$$

Values of the numerical constant a and the exponent m are given below.

	Vertical surfaces	Horizontal cylinders (replace L with D)
X greater than 10^9	$a = 0.13$; $m = \frac{1}{3}$	$a = 0.13$; $m = \frac{1}{3}$
X from 10^4 to 10^9	$a = 0.59$; $m = \frac{1}{4}$	$a = 0.53$; $m = \frac{1}{4}$
X less than 10^4	$a = 1.36$; $m = \frac{1}{6}$	$a = 1.09$; $m = \frac{1}{6}$

These equations may be applied for determining natural convection from plates and disks using the dimension of a side or diameter for the characteristic length term. For horizontal heated plates facing downward

* For horizontal cylinders, the L in the equations of vertical surfaces has been replaced by $\pi D/2$. The true film mass velocity is thus $(\pi/2)^{1/2} = 1.25$ times higher than the value indicated in this equation. However, except when one is interested in determining the true film mass velocity, the G in the equations for horizontal cylinders as indicated in Eq. (10-27) should be used because the constant $\pi/2$ has been included in the numerical factor in Eqs. (10-24), (10-25), and (10-26).

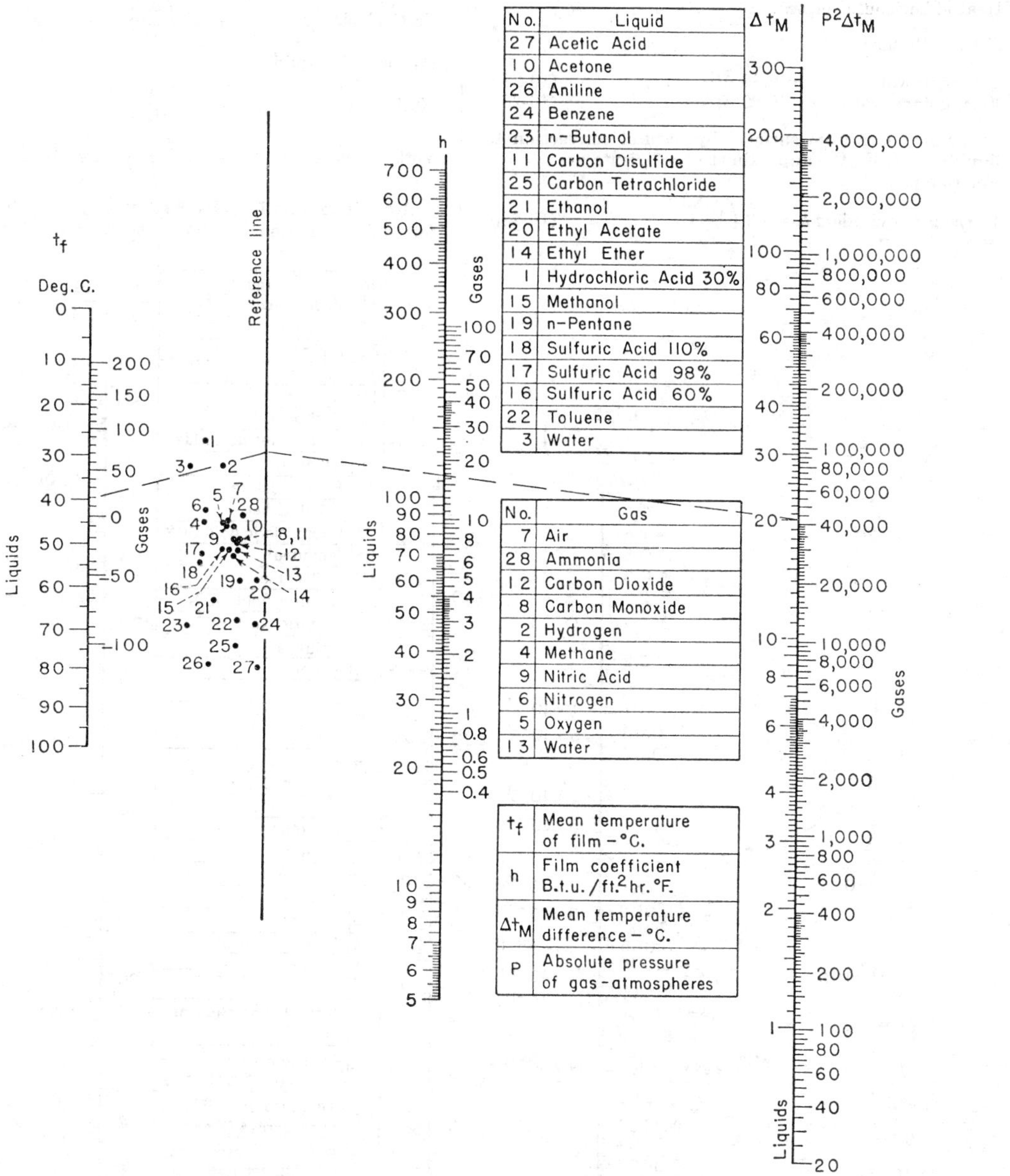

Fig. 10-8. Chart for gases and liquids flowing upward at low velocities inside vertical tubes, or for natural convection from vertical surfaces, $X > 109$. Based on Eq. (10-28).

or cooled plates facing upward, McAdams suggests that coefficients will be one-half the values obtained from the above equations.

The above equations are based on data for vertical surfaces less than 3 ft. high and horizontal cylinders less than 8 in. in diameter.

Dimensional Type. Figure 10-8 may be used for estimating natural convection from vertical tubes or plates for values of X [Eq. (10-28)] $> 10^9$. Figure 10-9 may be used for estimating natural convection from outside horizontal cylinders for values of X [Eq. (10-28)] between 10^4 and 10^9.

For heat loss from surfaces by natural convection to air at atmospheric pressure and at ordinary temperatures the coefficients are given by the dimensional equations:

$X > 10^9$ $$h = 0.18\,\Delta t^{1/3} \tag{10-28a}$$

X from 10^3 to 10^9:

Horizontal cylinder $$h = 0.27\left(\frac{\Delta t}{D_o}\right)^{1/4} \tag{10-28b}$$

Horizontal cylinder $$h = 0.50\left(\frac{\Delta t}{D_o'}\right)^{1/4} \tag{10-28c}$$

Vertical plates $$h = 0.28\left(\frac{\Delta t}{L}\right)^{1/4} \tag{10-28d}$$

Heated horizontal plates:

X from 10^5 to 10^7

Facing upward $h = 0.38\ \Delta t^{1/4}$ (10-28e)

Facing downward $h = 0.20\ \Delta t^{1/4}$ (10-28f)

For heat loss from surfaces by natural convection to liquids at 70°F., the approximate coefficients are

For water:

Horizontal cylinders $h = 43\left(\frac{\Delta t}{D'}\right)^{1/4}$ (10-28g)

Vertical plates $h = 26\left(\frac{\Delta t}{L}\right)^{1/4}$ (10-28h)

For organic liquids:

Horizontal cylinders $h = 20\left(\frac{\Delta t}{D'}\right)^{1/4}$ (10-28i)

Vertical plates $h = 12\left(\frac{\Delta t}{L}\right)^{1/4}$ (10-28j)

Simultaneous Loss by Radiation. The heat transferred by radiation is often of significant magnitude in

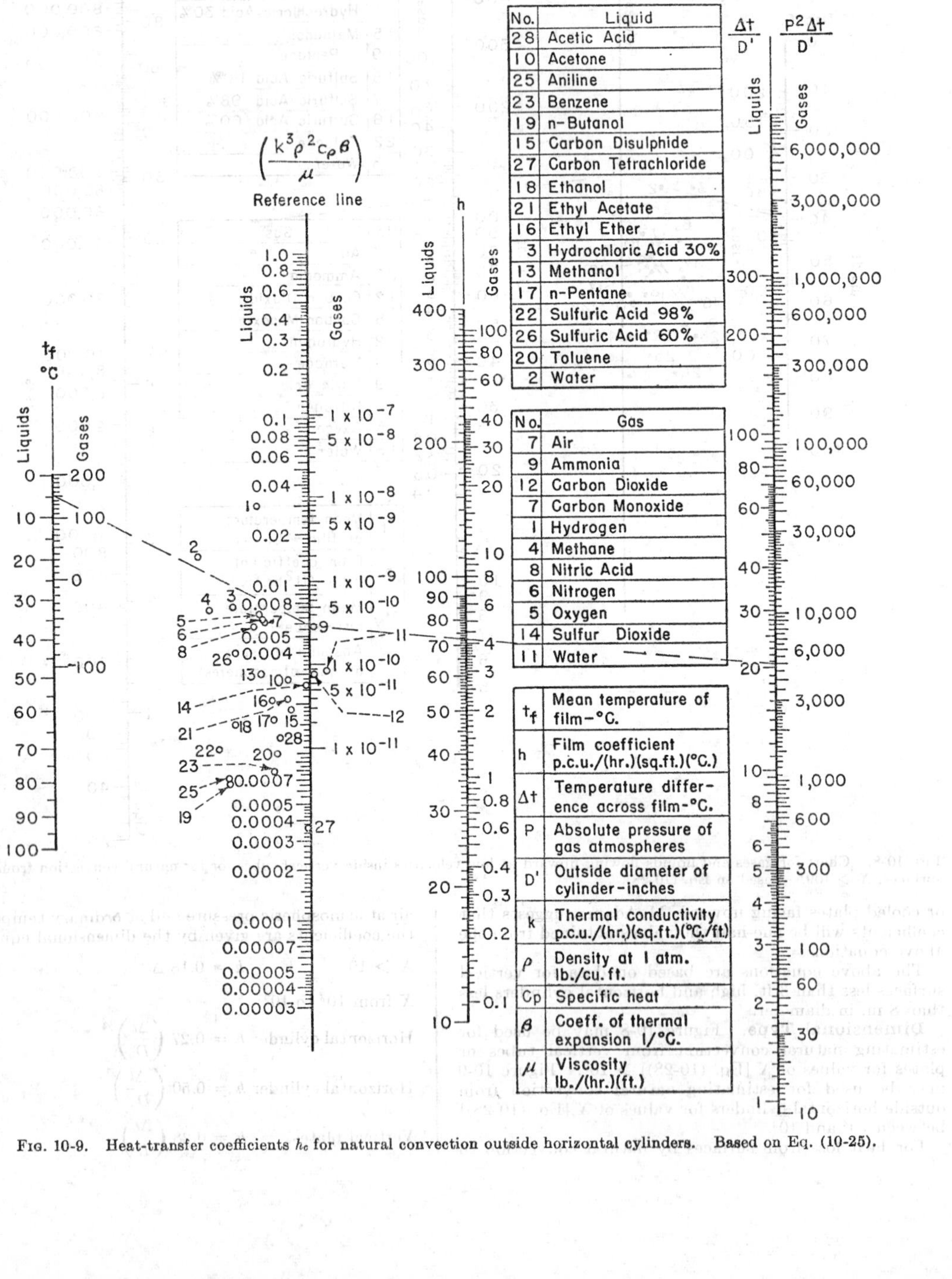

FIG. 10-9. Heat-transfer coefficients h_c for natural convection outside horizontal cylinders. Based on Eq. (10-25).

Table 10-1. Values of $(h_c + h_r)$
B.t.u./(hr.)(sq. ft.) (°F. from pipe to room)
For horizontal bare standard steel pipe of various sizes in a room at 80°F.

Nominal pipe diam., in.	Temperature difference, °F.														
	30	50	100	150	200	250	300	350	400	450	500	550	600	650	700
1	2.16	2.26	2.50	2.73	3.00	3.29	3.60	3.95	4.34	4.73	5.16	5.60	6.05	6.51	6.98
3	1.97	2.05	2.25	2.47	2.73	3.00	3.31	3.69	4.03	4.43	4.85	5.26	5.71	6.19	6.66
5	. . .	1.95	2.15	2.36	2.61	2.90	3.20	3.54	3.90						
10	1.80	1.87	2.07	2.29	2.54	2.82	3.12	3.47	3.84						

Bailey and Lyell [*Engineering*, **147**, 60 (1939)] give values for $h_c + h_r$ up to Δt_s of 1000°F.

the loss of heat from surfaces to the surroundings because of the diathermanous nature of atmospheric gases (air). It is convenient to represent radiant-heat transfer, for this case, as a radiation film coefficient which is added to the film coefficient for convection giving the combined coefficient for convection and radiation $(h_c + h_r)$. In Fig. 10-10 values of the film coefficient for radiation h_r are plotted against the two surface temperatures for emissivity = 1.0.

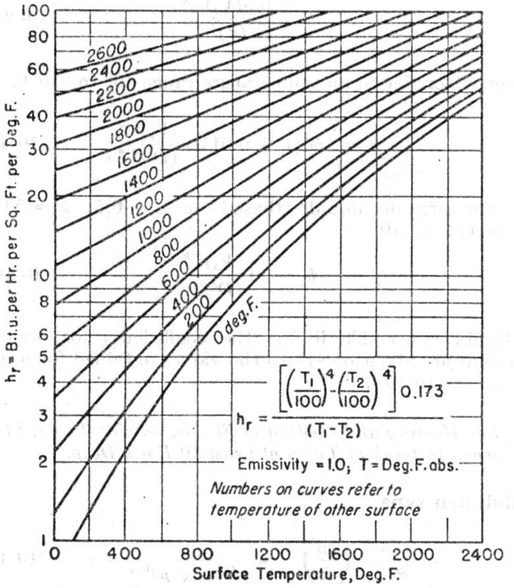

FIG. 10-10. Radiation coefficients of heat transfer h_r.

Table 10-1 based on data of Heilman and of McMillan shows values of $(h_c + h_r)$ from single horizontal oxidized pipe surfaces.

Forced Convection (No Change in Phase)

Viscous (Laminar) Flow (Reynolds Number < 2100). *For Heating or Cooling inside or outside Tubes Flow Parallel with Tubes.* In the laminar region fluid and heat flow are variable and somewhat unpredictable. Authorities agree that the most practical expression for prediction of heat transfer in this region is the correlation of Sieder and Tate [*Ind. Eng. Chem.*, **28**, 1429–1436 (1936)]. For reasonable values of tube diameter (less than 3 in.) and temperature difference (less than 100°F.) the **Colburn-type** equation is

$$\frac{h_{a.m.}}{cG}\left(\frac{c\mu}{k}\right)^{2/3}\left(\frac{L_u}{D}\right)^{1/3}\left(\frac{\mu_w}{\mu}\right)^{0.14} = \frac{1.86}{(DG/\mu)^{2/3}} = j \qquad (10\text{-}29)$$

The corresponding **Nusselt-type** equation is

$$\frac{h_{a.m.}D}{k}\left(\frac{\mu_w}{\mu}\right)^{0.14} = 1.86\left(\frac{DG}{\mu}\frac{c\mu}{k}\frac{D}{L_u}\right)^{1/3} \qquad (10\text{-}30)$$

In these equations, for flow outside tubes, substitute D_e for D. $D_e = 4 \times$ free cross-sectional area ÷ perimeter.

Either of these equations reduces to the **dimensional form** (flow inside tubes only)

$$h_{a.m.} = 24.2c^{1/3}k^{2/3}(\mu/\mu_w)^{0.14}\frac{w^{1/3}}{D_i{}'L_u{}^{1/3}} \qquad (10\text{-}31)$$

Satisfactory results may be obtained from these equations if the significance of the variables is judiciously considered. The following suggestions are offered.

1. *The Length-to-diameter Ratio L_u/D.* The length term L_u is the length of path (in the direction of flow) in which the fluid is undisturbed. In both single and multipass exchangers it is thus the length of one pass. The ratio L_u/D may be substantially reduced (and the coefficient significantly increased) by installing turbulence promoters inside the tubes, but it is of questionable advisability to use values of L_u/D less than unity. The coefficient is not infinite at the entrance to the tube, a condition which might be deduced from Eq. (10-31) if the term L_u were not explicitly defined as undisturbed length.

2. *The Viscosity Ratio μ_w/μ.* When the bulk viscosity varies considerably over the range of heating or cooling, it is advisable to determine the coefficient for incremental lengths (each pass separately) because it would be difficult to select arbitrarily the correct average bulk viscosity.

3. *The Temperature Difference.* The subscripts (a.m.) on the symbol for heat-transfer coefficient indicate that with these equations the arithmetic-mean temperature difference is to be used. However, McAdams states ("Heat Transmission," 3d ed., p. 232, McGraw-Hill, New York, 1954) that there is only a small error, at values of wc/kL_u above 24, if logarithmic-mean temperature difference is used. Therefore, for most of the range of application, one may use the more convenient temperature difference.

4. *Limitations* (Flow inside Tubes Only). The theoretical basis for Eq. (10-29) dictates a limit of application. For values of wc/kL_u less than 10, the coefficient cannot exceed the value given by

$$h_{max} = \frac{2k}{\pi D}\frac{wc}{kL_u} \qquad (10\text{-}32)$$

equivalent to

$$h_{max} = \frac{DGc}{2L_u} = \frac{2}{\pi}\frac{wc}{DL_u} \qquad (10\text{-}32a)$$

The accuracy of Eq. (10-29) is reportedly low, possibly because of simultaneous natural convection effects. However, for design purposes, the equation should give conservative results. At high values of Δt, natural convection may be significant. The net heat-transfer coefficient may be approximated by adding the coefficients of natural convection (10-24) and laminar forced convection (10-29).

Transition Region (Reynolds Number 2100 to 10,000). *For Heating or Cooling inside or outside Tubes*

Flow Parallel with Tubes. There is a considerable scatter of experimental data in the region of Reynolds number between 2100 and 10,000. It is customary to represent the probable magnitude of coefficients in this region by hand-drawn curves. Equation (10-29) is plotted as a series of curves (j factor vs. Reynolds number with L_u/D as parameters) terminating at Reynolds number = 2100. Continuous curves for various values of L_u/D are then hand-drawn from these terminal points to coincide tangentially with the curve for forced-convection, fully turbulent flow [Eq. (10-41)]. See Fig. 10-11.

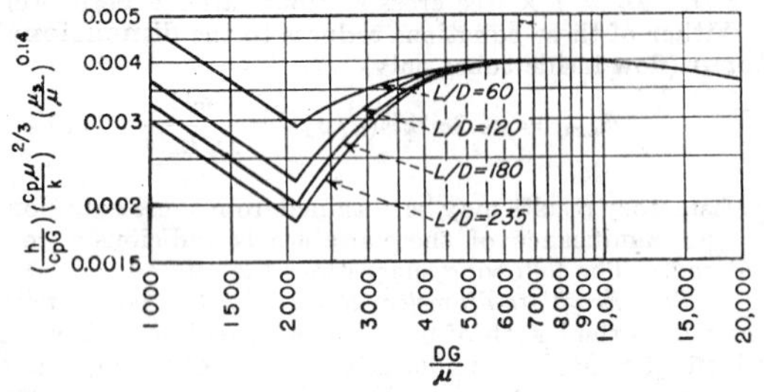

FIG. 10-11. Graphical representation of the Colburn j factor for heating and cooling of fluids inside tubes. The curves for Re below 2100 are based on Eq. (10-29). L is length of each pass in feet. The curves for Re between 2100 and 10,000 are represented by Eq. (10-33). The curve for Re above 10,000 is represented by Eq. (10-36).

Hausen [*Z. Ver. deut. Ingr., Beih. Verfahrenstech.* (4), 91–98 (1943)] has suggested an applicable **Colburn-type** equation for these curves in the transition region

$$\frac{(h/cG)(c\mu/k)^{2/3}(\mu_w/\mu)^{0.14}}{1 + (D/L)^{2/3}} = \frac{0.116[(DG/\mu)^{2/3} - 125]}{DG/\mu} = j \tag{10-33}$$

The equivalent **Nusselt-type** equation is

$$\frac{hD}{k} = 0.116\left[\left(\frac{DG}{\mu}\right)^{2/3} - 125\right]\left(\frac{c\mu}{k}\right)^{1/3}\left(\frac{\mu}{\mu_w}\right)^{0.14}\left[1 + \left(\frac{D}{L_u}\right)^{2/3}\right] \tag{10-34}$$

The **Dimensional Equation** *(for Flow inside Tubes Only).*

$$h = 1.87\left[\left(\frac{6.3w}{D'z}\right)^{2/3} - 125\right] c^{1/3}z^{1/3}k^{2/3}\left(\frac{z}{z_w}\right)^{0.14}\frac{1}{D'}\left[1 + \left(\frac{D'}{12L_u}\right)^{2/3}\right] \tag{10-35}$$

Fully Turbulent Region (Reynolds Number > 10,000). *For Heating or Cooling, inside or outside Tubes, Flow Parallel with Tubes.*

Colburn-type equation

$$\frac{h}{cG}\left(\frac{c\mu}{k}\right)^{2/3} = \frac{0.023}{(DG/\mu)^{0.2}} = j \tag{10-36}$$

Nusselt-type equation

$$\frac{hD}{k} = 0.023\left(\frac{DG}{\mu}\right)^{0.8}\left(\frac{c\mu}{k}\right)^{1/3} \tag{10-37}$$

For flow outside and parallel with tubes, substitute D_e for D. ($D_e = 4 \times$ free area $\div$ perimeter.)

A general **dimensional equation,** for flow inside tubes only, is

$$h = 1.62\frac{c^{1/3}k^{2/3}}{z^{0.467}}\frac{w^{0.8}}{(D')^{1.8}} \tag{10-38}$$

Dimensional Equations for Various Conditions *(for Flow inside Tubes Only).* For gases at ordinary pressures and temperatures [based on $c\mu/k = 0.78$ and $\mu = 0.0426$ lb./(hr.)(ft.)]

$$h = 0.0144c\frac{G^{0.8}}{D^{0.2}} = 16.6c\frac{(G')^{0.8}}{(D')^{0.2}} \tag{10-39}$$

$$h = 16.6c\,\rho^{0.8}\frac{(V_s)^{0.8}}{(D')^{0.2}} \tag{10-39a}$$

For air at atmospheric pressure

$$h = \frac{0.5(V_s)^{0.8}}{(D')^{0.2}} \tag{10-39b}$$

For water (based on temperature range 40° to 220°F.)

$$h = 150(1 + 0.011t)\frac{(V_s)^{0.8}}{(D')^{0.2}} \tag{10-40}$$

For organic liquids (based on $c = 0.5$; $k = 0.08$; $z = 1$; $\rho = 50$).

$$h = 60\frac{(V_s)^{0.8}}{(D')^{0.2}} \tag{10-40a}$$

Within reasonable limits, the coefficients for organic liquids are about one-third the values obtained for water [*cf.* Eq. (10-40)].

For Heating and Cooling of Fluids, outside Tubes, Flow Normal to Bank of Tubes at Least 10 *Rows Deep.*

Colburn type

$$\frac{h}{cG_{max}}\left(\frac{c\mu}{k}\right)^{2/3} = \frac{a}{(DG_{max}/\mu)^{0.4}} = j \tag{10-41}$$

Nusselt type

$$\frac{hD}{k} = a\left(\frac{DG_{max}}{\mu}\right)^{0.6}\left(\frac{c\mu}{k}\right)^{1/3} \tag{10-42}$$

The dimensionless constant a in these equations varies depending upon conditions.

Conditions, Reynolds Number > 3000	Value of a
Flow normal to apex of diamond, staggered arrangement:	
No leakage	0.330
Normal leakage in baffled exchanger	0.198
Flow normal to flat side of diamond, not staggered (in-line) arrangement:	
No leakage	0.260
Normal leakage in baffled exchanger	0.156

For Reynolds number less than 3000, Eq. (10-41) would give conservative results, but more accuracy (if desired) may be obtained by using the following equation.

$$\frac{h}{cG_{max}}\left(\frac{c\mu}{k}\right)^{2/3} = \frac{a}{(D_oG_{max}/\mu)^{m}} = j \tag{10-43}$$

in which the constant a and exponent m are as follows:

Reynolds number	m	Tube pitch	Leakage	a
100–300	0.492	Staggered	None	0.695
			Normal	0.416
		In-line	None	0.548
			Normal	0.329
1–100	0.590	Staggered	None	1.086
			Normal	0.650
		In-line	None	0.855
			Normal	0.513

The following **dimensional equations** (10-44 to 10-44*e*) are based on flow normal to a bank of staggered tubes without leakage. Multiply the values obtained for h by 0.6 for normal leakage and, in addition, by 0.79 for in-line (not staggered) tube arrangement.

$$h = 0.26 \frac{c^{1/3} k^{2/3}}{z^{0.267}} \frac{(G_{\max})^{0.6}}{(D_o)^{0.4}} = 96 \frac{c^{1/3} k^{2/3}}{z^{0.267}} \frac{(G'_{\max})^{0.6}}{(D_o')^{0.4}} \qquad (10\text{-}44)$$

$$h = 96 \frac{c^{1/3} k^{2/3} \rho^{0.6}}{z^{0.267}} \frac{(V'_{\max})^{0.6}}{(D_o')^{0.4}} \qquad (10\text{-}44a)$$

For gases at ordinary pressures and temperatures [based on $c\mu/k = 0.78$; $\mu = 0.0426$ lb./(hr.)(ft.)]

$$h = 0.11c \frac{(G_{\max})^{0.6}}{(D_o)^{0.4}} = 40c \frac{(G'_{\max})^{0.6}}{(D_o')^{0.4}} \qquad (10\text{-}44b)$$

For air at atmospheric pressure

$$h = 2 \frac{(V'_{\max})^{0.6}}{(D_o')^{0.4}} \qquad (10\text{-}44c)$$

For water (based on temperature range 40° to 220°F.)

$$h = 370(1 + 0.0067t) \frac{(V_{\max})^{0.6}}{(D_o')^{0.4}} \qquad (10\text{-}44d)$$

For organic liquids (based on $c = 0.53$; $k = 0.08$; $z = 1$; $\rho = 50$)

$$h = 150 \frac{(V_{\max})^{0.6}}{(D_o')^{0.4}} \qquad (10\text{-}44e)$$

Forced Convection (Change in Phase)

Condensation of Pure Saturated Vapors. Condensation occurs when a saturated vapor comes in contact with a surface whose temperature is below the saturation temperature. Normally, a film of condensate is formed on the surface and the thickness of this film, per unit of breadth, increases with increase in extent of the surface. This is called film-type condensation.

Another type of condensation, called dropwise, occurs when the wall is not uniformly wetted by the condensate with the result that the condensate appears in many small droplets at various points on the surface. There is a growth of individual droplets, a coalescence of adjacent droplets, and finally a formation of a rivulet. Adhesional force is overcome by gravitational force and the rivulet flows quickly to the bottom of the surface capturing and absorbing all droplets in its path and leaving dry surface in its wake.

Film-type condensation is more common and more dependable. Dropwise condensation normally needs to be promoted by introducing an impurity into the vapor stream. Substantially higher (six to eighteen times) coefficients are obtained for dropwise condensation of steam, but design methods are not available. Therefore, the development of equations for condensation will be for the film type only.

The physical properties of the liquid, rather than those of the vapor, are used for determining the film coefficient for condensation. Nusselt [*Z. Ver. deut. Ingr.*, **60**, 541, 569 (1916)] derived theoretical relationships for predicting the film coefficient of heat transfer for condensation of a pure saturated vapor. A number of simplifying assumptions were used in the derivation. Before recording the various forms of the Nusselt equation it will be of interest to define some terms.

The weight rate of flow (loading rate) of condensate per unit perimeter, lb./(hr.)(ft.), is designated by the Greek letter gamma (Γ).

The Reynolds number of the condensate film (falling film) is $4\Gamma/\mu$.

The thickness of the condensate film for Reynolds number less than 2100 is $(3\mu\Gamma/\rho^2 g)^{1/3}$.

Vertical Tubes; Reynolds Number < 2100.

$$\Gamma = \frac{w}{\pi D}$$

The Nusselt equation for heat-transfer coefficient for condensate films may be written in the following ways. (Use liquid physical properties)

Colburn type

$$\frac{h}{cG} \frac{c\mu}{k} = \frac{5.35}{4\Gamma/\mu} \qquad (10\text{-}45)$$

$$G = \frac{\Gamma}{(3\mu\Gamma/\rho^2 g)^{1/3}} = \text{lb./(hr.)(sq. ft.)} = \left(\frac{w^2\rho^2 g}{29.6D^2\mu}\right)^{1/3}$$

Nusselt type

$$\frac{hL}{k} = 0.943 \left(\frac{L^3\rho^2 g\lambda}{k\mu\,\Delta t}\right)^{1/4} = 0.925 \left(\frac{L^3\rho^2 g}{\mu\Gamma}\right)^{1/3} \qquad (10\text{-}46)$$

Dimensional

$$h = 330 \left(\frac{k^3\rho^2 D'}{zw}\right)^{1/3} \qquad (10\text{-}47)$$

For steam at atmospheric pressure ($k = 0.394$; $\rho = 60$; $z = 0.28$)

$$h = 3050 \left(\frac{D'}{w}\right)^{1/3} \qquad (10\text{-}47a)$$

For organic vapors at normal boiling point ($k = 0.08$; $\rho = 45$; $z = 0.35$)

$$h = 472 \left(\frac{D'}{w}\right)^{1/3} \qquad (10\text{-}47b)$$

Horizontal Tubes; Reynolds Number < 2100.

$$\Gamma = \frac{w}{2L}.$$

Colburn type

$$\frac{h}{cG} \frac{c\mu}{k} = \frac{4.4}{4\Gamma/\mu} \qquad (10\text{-}48)$$

$$G = \frac{\Gamma}{(3\mu\Gamma/\rho^2 g)^{1/3}} = \text{lb./(hr.)(ft.)} = \left(\frac{w^2\rho^2 g}{12L^2\mu}\right)^{1/3}$$

Nusselt type

$$\frac{hD}{k} = 0.73 \left(\frac{D^3\rho^2 g\lambda}{k\mu\,\Delta t}\right)^{1/4} = 0.76 \left(\frac{D^3\rho^2 g}{\mu\Gamma}\right)^{1/3} \qquad (10\text{-}49)$$

Dimensional.

$$h = 534\left(\frac{k^3\rho^2 L}{zw}\right)^{1/3} \qquad (10\text{-}50)$$

For steam at atmospheric pressure

$$h = 4920\left(\frac{L}{w}\right)^{1/3} \qquad (10\text{-}50a)$$

For organic vapors at normal boiling point

$$h = 766\left(\frac{L}{w}\right)^{1/3} \qquad (10\text{-}50b)$$

Figure 10-12 is a nomograph for determining coefficients of heat transfer for condensation of pure vapors.

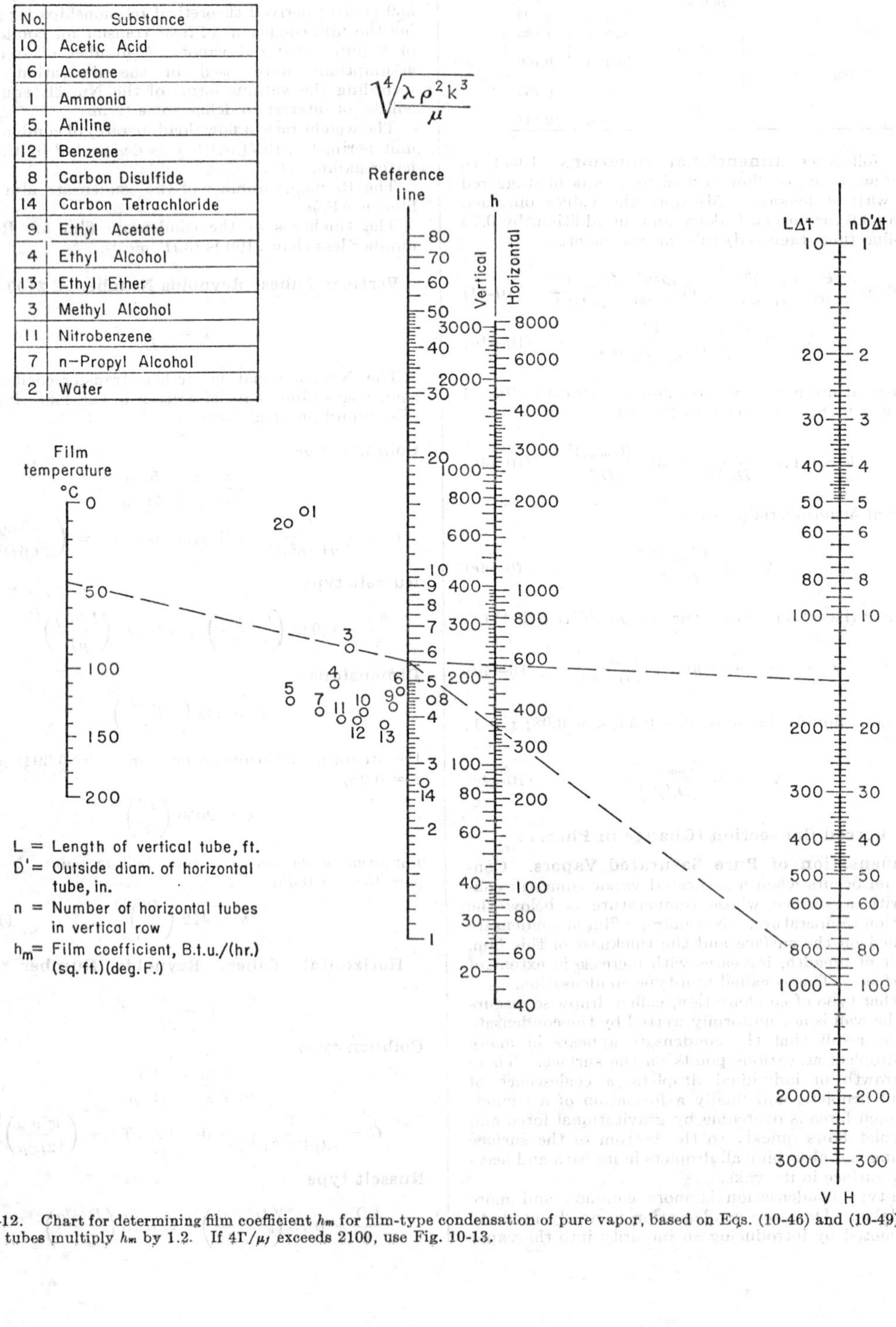

FIG. 10-12. Chart for determining film coefficient h_m for film-type condensation of pure vapor, based on Eqs. (10-46) and (10-49). For vertical tubes multiply h_m by 1.2. If $4\Gamma/\mu_f$ exceeds 2100, use Fig. 10-13.

The preceding expressions for condensation are based on the classical Nusselt theory. It is generally known and conceded that the film coefficients, for steam and organic vapors, calculated by the Nusselt theory are conservatively low. Dukler [*Chem. Eng. Progress*, **55**, 62 (1959)] has developed equations for velocity and temperature distribution in thin films on vertical walls based on expressions of Deissler (*N.A.C.A. Tech. Notes* 2129, 1950; 2138, 1952; 3145, 1959) for the eddy viscosity and thermal conductivity near the solid boundary. According to the Dukler theory, three fixed factors must be known to establish the value of the average film coefficient. These are the terminal Reynolds number, the Prandtl number of the condensed phase, and a dimensionless group designated by the letter A_d and defined as follows:

$$A_d = \frac{0.250\mu_L{}^{1.173}\mu_G{}^{0.16}}{g^{2/3}D^2\rho_L{}^{0.553}\rho_G{}^{0.78}} \qquad (10\text{-}51)$$

Graphical relationships of these variables are available in Document 6058, A.D.I. Auxiliary Publications Project, Library of Congress, Washington 25, D.C. If rigorous values for condensing-film coefficients are desired, especially if the value of A_d in Eq. (10-51) exceeds 1×10^{-5}, it is suggested that these graphs be used. For the case in which interfacial shear is zero, Fig. 10-13

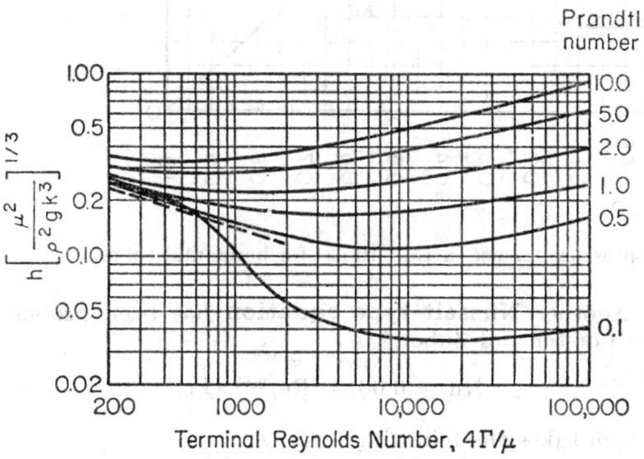

FIG. 10-13. Dukler plot showing average condensing film coefficient as a function of physical properties of the condensate film and the terminal Reynolds number. (Dotted line indicates Nusselt theory for Reynolds number < 2100.) [*Reproduced, by permission, from Chem. Eng. Progress*, **55**, 64 (1959).]

may be used. It is interesting to note that, according to the Dukler development, there is no definite transition Reynolds number; deviation from Nusselt theory is less at low Reynolds numbers; and when the Prandtl number of a fluid is less than 0.4 (at Reynolds number above 1000), the predicted values for film coefficient are lower than those predicted by the Nusselt theory.

The Dukler theory is applicable for condensate films on horizontal tubes and also for falling films, in general, *i.e.*, those not associated with condensation or vaporization processes.

Forced-convection (Change-in-phase) Vaporization (Boiling) of Liquids

Vaporization of liquids may result from various mechanisms of heat transfer, or combinations thereof. For example, vaporization may occur as a result of heat absorbed, by radiation and convection, at the surface of a pool of liquid; or as a result of heat absorbed by natural convection from a hot wall beneath the disengaging surface, in which case the vaporization takes place when the superheated liquid reaches the pool surface. Vaporization also occurs from falling films (the reverse of condensation) or from the flashing of liquids superheated by forced convection under pressure. These mechanisms are described elsewhere in this section.

Heat transfer by *nucleate boiling* is an important mechanism in the vaporization of liquids. It is the type of heat transfer which occurs in the vaporization of liquids in kettle-type and natural-circulation reboilers commonly used in the process industries. High rates of heat transfer per unit of area (heat flux) are obtained as a result of bubble formation at the liquid-solid interface rather than from mechanical devices external to the heat exchanger. The mechanism has not yet been clearly established, but, as a result of considerable activity in the field of nucleate boiling, there are available several expressions from which reasonable values of the film coefficients may be obtained. These expressions do not yield exactly the same numerical results even though the correlations were based upon much of the same data. There is thus neither a prominent nor a unique equation for nucleate boiling. Either convenience or familiarity will govern the user's selection of one of the following equations.

Colburn Type. A Colburn-type equation for the film coefficient for nucleate boiling has been developed by Gilmour [*Chem. Eng. Progress*, **54**, 77 (1958)] which includes a term to take care of variation of coefficient with pressure. A special Reynolds number is also defined

$$\frac{h}{cG}\left(\frac{c\mu}{k}\right)^{0.6}\left(\frac{\rho_L\sigma}{P^2}\frac{g}{g_c}\right)^{0.425} = \frac{\Phi}{(D_oG/\mu)^{0.3}} \qquad (10\text{-}52)$$

$$G = \left(\frac{W}{A}\frac{\rho_L}{\rho_V}\right) \qquad (10\text{-}53)$$

(Note that A is the surface area, not a cross-sectional area.) Φ, which is a numerical correlating factor, varies with the nature (material of construction) of the surface. Recommended values are:

1×10^{-3} for commercial copper and steel surfaces

5.9×10^{-4} for stainless steel or chromium and nickel alloys

4.0×10^{-4} for polished surfaces

Surface conditions have a profound effect on boiling phenomena. The above numerical factors have been obtained from plots of existing data. Extreme accuracy cannot be claimed for these values because of the variable condition of the surfaces in these tests.

Limitations. There is both an upper and lower limit of applicability of Eq. (10-52). At the upper limit, nucleation is diminished because of the insulating effects of a vapor film; at the lower limit, nucleation is inhibited because of natural convection effects.

For horizontal tubes, the criterion for determining the upper limit of applicability of Eq. (10-52) is the maximum allowable value of the factor $W/A\rho_v$ which is, by definition, vapor velocity. This factor, when multiplied by $\rho_v\lambda$, is the heat flux. A plot of $(W/A\rho_v)_{max}$ as a function of reduced pressure (P/P_c) is shown in Fig. 10-14. The technique of relating the maximum criteria and reduced pressure is due to Cichelli and Bonilla [*Trans. Am. Inst. Chem. Engrs.*, **41**, 755 (1945)]. The data for Fig. 10-14 were obtained from a smoothed curve based on various data reported in the literature on nucleate boiling. The maximum values in Fig. 10-14 are lower than the absolute maximum values indicated in the literature sources, because the latter values appear at the apex of a line of considerable curvature. Equation (10-52) is a straight line with a positive slope. The maximum values for disks, facing upward, will be π times those for horizontal tubes.

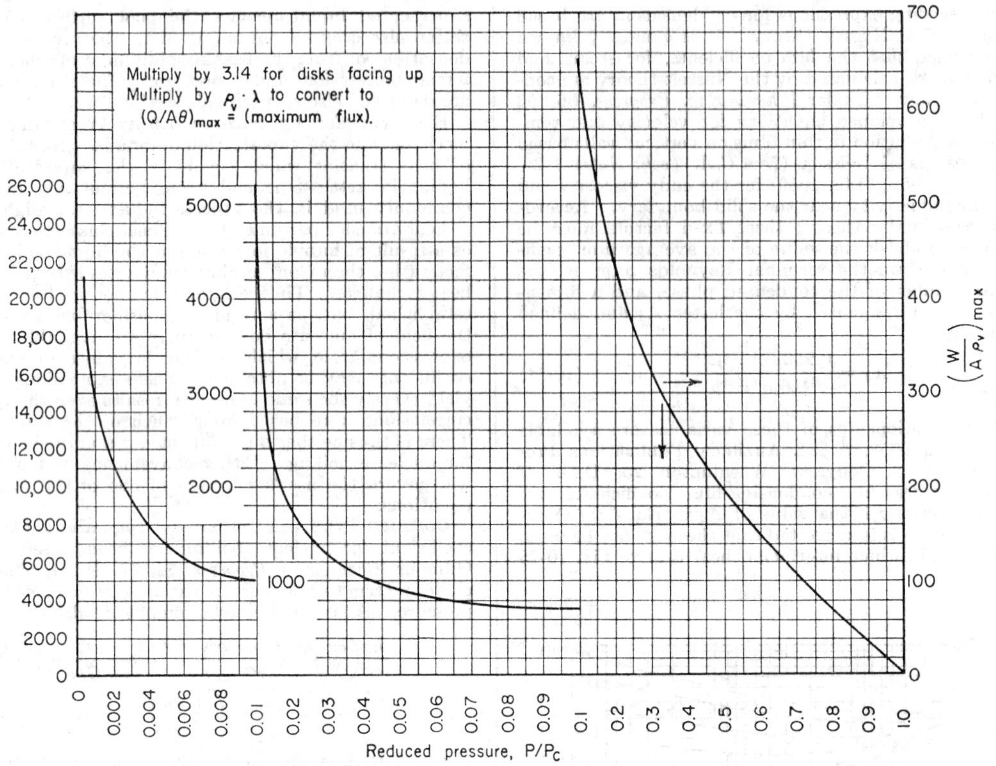

FIG. 10-14. Value of $(W/A\rho_v)_{max}$ as a function of reduced pressure for use in Eq. (10-52) for horizontal tubes.

The lower limit of applicability of Eq. (10-52) is from one-tenth to one-fifth of the maximum limit and depends upon the magnitude of natural convection heat transfer for the liquid. The best method of determining the lower limit is to plot two curves: one of h vs. ΔT for natural convection, the other of h vs. ΔT for nucleate boiling. The intersection of these two curves may be considered the lower limit of applicability of Eq. (10-52).

Nusselt-type Equation—*Rohsenow Equation.* An equation of the Nusselt type has been suggested by Rohsenow [*Trans. Am. Soc. Mech. Engrs.*, **74**, 969 (1952)].

$$\frac{hD}{k} = C_r \left(\frac{DG}{\mu}\right)^{2/3} \left(\frac{c\mu}{k}\right)^{-0.7} \tag{10-54}$$

in which the variables assume the following form:

$$\frac{h\beta'}{k}\left[\frac{g_c\sigma}{g(\rho_L - \rho_v)}\right]^{1/2} = C_r \left\{\frac{\beta'}{\mu}\left(\frac{g_c\sigma}{g(\rho_L - \rho_v)}\right)^{1/2} \frac{W}{A}\right\}^{2/3} \left(\frac{c\mu}{k}\right)^{-0.7} \tag{10-54a}$$

The constant C_r is not truly constant but varies from 0.006 to 0.015.* A deviation of the same amount is indicated for the correlating constant of Eq. (10-52). It is possible that the nature of the surface is partly responsible for the variation in the constant. The only factor in Eq. (10-54a) not readily available is the value of the contact angle β'.

* Reported by J. W. Westwater in Drew and Hoopes, "Advances in Chemical Engineering," vol. I, p. 15, Academic Press, Inc., New York, 1956.

Another **Nusselt-type equation** has been proposed by Forster and Zuber.*

$$Nu = 0.0015\ (Re)^{0.62}\ (Pr)^{1/3}$$

which takes the following form

$$\frac{c\rho_L \sqrt{\pi\alpha}}{k\rho_v}\frac{W}{A}\left(\frac{2\sigma}{\Delta p}\right)^{1/2}\left(\frac{\rho_L}{\Delta p\, g}\right)^{1/4} = 0.0015\left[\frac{\rho_L}{\mu}\left(\frac{c\rho_L\,\Delta T\,\sqrt{\pi\alpha}}{\lambda\rho_v}\right)^2\right]^{0.62}\left(\frac{c\mu}{k}\right)^{1/2} \tag{10-55}$$

where $\alpha = k/\rho c$ (all liquid properties)
Δp = pressure of the vapor in a bubble minus saturation pressure of a flat liquid surface

Equations (10-54) and (10-55) have been arranged in dimensional form by Westwater.

Dimensional Equations. For single horizontal copper or steel tubes Eq. (10-52) may be written

$$h = \frac{3c^{0.4}k^{0.6}\rho_L{}^{0.275}p^{0.85}}{z^{0.3}(\sigma')^{0.425}(D_o)^{0.3}}\left(\frac{W}{A\rho_V}\right)^{0.7} \tag{10-56}$$

or also

$$h = \frac{16c^{0.4}k^{0.6}\rho_L{}^{0.275}p^{0.85}}{z^{0.3}(\sigma')^{0.425}\rho_v{}^{0.7}D_o'}\frac{W^{0.7}}{L^{0.7}} \tag{10-57}$$

* Forster, *J. Appl. Phys.*, **25**, 1067 (1954). Forster and Zuber, *J. Appl. Phys.*, **25**, 474 (1954). Forster and Zuber, Conference on Nuclear Engineering, University of California, Los Angeles, 1955. Excellent treatise on boiling of liquids by J. W. Westwater, in Drew and Hoopes, "Advances in Chemical Engineering," vol. I, Academic Press, Inc., New York, 1956.

For stainless-steel tubes multiply results from above equations by 0.6.

For boiling from horizontal copper disks, multiply result from Eq. (10-56) by 0.57 and substitute diameter of disk D_d for D_o, making additional corrections for materials of construction.

These equations will give conservative results because they are based on a considerable amount of data from various sources. The numerical constant may be adjusted to suit any particular set of data if one desires to use a certain criterion. However, surface conditions vary so greatly that deviations may be as large as ±25 per cent from results obtained from Eqs. (10-56) and (10-57).

APPLICATIONS TO DESIGN

To apply the foregoing equations, one needs to know the physical properties of the fluids and the mechanism of heat transfer. Physical properties usually have to be estimated and the mechanism of heat transfer often has to be assumed. Deviations between design and performance are more often due to lack of accuracy in the assumptions than to lack of accuracy of the equations.

Physical Properties

Physical properties for a few pure compounds and aqueous mixtures within a limited temperature range are available in tabular form (see Sec. 3). Methods for estimating physical properties of pure compounds or mixtures are outlined in Sec. 3. Because estimates usually have to be made, there is no point in attempting to determine true film temperatures; average bulk fluid temperatures are suitable for design purposes.

Shell-and-tube Heat Exchangers (Sensible Heat Transfer)

Tube Side. Determine the Reynolds number; use applicable equation for flow parallel with tubes; assume uniform distribution of bulk flow in each tube of each pass. (Note: Uniform distribution is not always attained; corrective measures consist of installation of perforated plates or straightening vanes within the heads or channels.) Convert inside coefficient to outside area basis by multiplying h by ratio of inside tube diameter to outside tube diameter.

Shell Side. Fluid flow on the shell side of multitube heat exchangers is considered to be *normal* to the tubes located between the segmental baffle cuts and *parallel* with the tubes located in the segmental areas beyond the baffle cuts. Equation (10-41) ($a = 0.198$) may be used for the shell side of a heat exchanger in which all the tubes are located between baffle cuts (no tubes in segments). In the usual case (in which tubes are located in the segmental areas), one may use Eq. (10-41) ($a = 0.198$) for the tubes located between the baffle cuts and the applicable equation [(10-29), (10-33), or (10-36)] for the tubes located in the segmental area beyond the baffle cuts. In the latter instance D_e is substituted for D where D_e = 4 times net free area divided by wetted perimeter.

It is both convenient and conservative to use the minimum area at the center line of the shell of a heat exchanger for calculating the maximum mass velocity for cross flow G_{max}. This leads to the following equation for minimum area:

$$S_{min} = \left(D_s' - \frac{D_s'D_o'}{p'}\right)\frac{P'}{144} \qquad (10\text{-}58)$$

For the usual case in which $p' = 1.25D_o'$, this reduces to

$$S_{min} = \frac{D_s'P'}{720} \qquad (10\text{-}59)$$

and

$$G_{max} = \frac{720W}{D_s'P'} \qquad (10\text{-}60)$$

Donohue [*Ind. Eng. Chem.*, **41**, 2499 (1949)] has suggested a single equation for use in determining the film coefficient for the fluid on the outside of baffled shell-and-tube exchangers in which a weighted mean mass velocity of the shell fluid is used. The equation (for unbored shells) follows:

$$\frac{hD}{k} = 0.2\left(\frac{DG_e}{\mu}\right)^{0.6}\left(\frac{c\mu}{k}\right)^{0.33}\left(\frac{\mu}{\mu_w}\right)^{0.14} \qquad (10\text{-}61)$$

G_e is defined as $(G_cG_b)^{0.5}$.

G_c is mass velocity for cross flow (flow normal to tube bank).

G_b is mass velocity for parallel flow (in baffle window).

Sometimes flow rates on the shell side are so high that cross flow cannot be tolerated (high pressure drop). In these cases, circular baffles containing several segmental openings are used for tube support. The flow through the shell side of the exchanger is essentially parallel with the tubes. Equations (10-29), (10-33), or (10-36) apply; D_e is substituted for D. Because of the turbulence caused by the baffles, multiply the result by 1.30.

The equation for flow normal to a bank of tubes yields rather high values for film coefficient. These coefficients can be realized only if great care is exercised in assuring close clearance between baffle and shell, close baffle spacing, small percentage baffle cut (100 × height of segment ÷ shell diameter), and means for reducing by-passing of shell-side fluid in the plane of the baffle between the outermost tubes of the bundle and the inside diameter of shell. Deviations between design and performance are often attributed to fouling of the surface whereas, in reality, the deviation is due to excessive leakages of the shell-side fluid resulting in reduced flow across the tubes and reduced effective value of the film coefficient. Practical values for clearances between the tubes and tube holes in baffles and between the baffle and the shell are given in TEMA (4th ed., Pars. C-4.2 and C-4.3, p. 39). (The abbreviation TEMA indicates the publication entitled "Standards of Tubular Exchanger Manufacturers Association, Inc.," 53 Park Place, New York 7, N.Y.)

The effect of leakage around the tube bundle in the direction of fluid flow is indicated in a paper by Bergelin, Bell, and Leighton, "Heat Transfer and Fluid Friction during Flow across Banks of Tubes—VII. Fluid By-passing between Tube Bundle and Shell." This was presented at the Second National Heat Transfer Conference, A.I.Ch.E.-A.S.M.E., Chicago, Ill., August, 1958.

Tube Wall. It is convenient to represent the thermal resistance of the tube wall as its reciprocal, a coefficient. The thermal conductivity of materials, from which tubular products are made, is usually known. The coefficient for the tube wall is thus

$$h_w = \frac{2k}{D_o - D_i}\,\frac{D_o - D_i}{\ln D_o/D_i}\,\frac{1}{D_o} = \frac{2k}{D_o \ln D_o/D_i} = \frac{24k}{D_o' \ln D_o'/D_i'} \qquad (10\text{-}62)$$

based on outside area.

Fouling. Unless one possesses actual data on fouling, the use of fouling factors must be considered to be arbitrary. Information on the effect of fouling, fouling resistances for uniform deposits of various materials, and suggested fouling resistances for use in the design of industrial heat exchangers is indicated on pp. 58 to 63, inclusive, of TEMA. It is convenient to represent fouling as the reciprocal of the resistance, a coefficient. If the thermal conductivity and thickness of the fouling material are known, the fouling coefficient is obtained from the following expression:

$$h_F = \frac{k}{L_F} \tag{10-63}$$

If the fouling is on the inside of the tube, the coefficient is converted to outside by multiplying by the ratio of inside to outside diameter.

There are certain statements that may be made to mitigate the vagueness of the subject of fouling in heat exchangers: (1) Many fluids do not foul heat exchange surfaces at all. (2) Fouling rates decrease with increase in fluid velocity. (Fouling is often reduced to negligible proportions if fluid velocities above 10 ft./sec. are maintained.) (3) Fouling is more prevalent in vaporizers because non-volatile substances remain on the tube as the volatile liquid is vaporized. (4) Reasonable values for fouling resistance for various services are: clean dry gas—none; liquids or condensing vapors—0.001; reboilers or vaporizers—0.002. See also Table 10-2.

Table 10-2. Heat-transfer Coefficients for Deposits*

Water

Temperature of heating medium	Up to 240°F.		240°–400°F.	
Temperature of water	125°F. or less		Above 125°F.	
Water velocity, ft./sec.	3 and less	Over 3	3 and less	Over 3
Distilled	2000	2000	2000	2000
Sea water	2000	2000	1000	1000
Treated boiler feed water	1000	2000	1000	1000
Treated makeup for cooling tower	1000	1000	500	500
City, well, Great Lakes	1000	1000	500	500
Brackish, clean river water	500	1000	330	500
River water, muddy, silty	330	500	250	330
Hard (over 15 g./gal.)	330	330	200	200
Chicago Sanitary Canal	125	170	100	125

Chemicals

Inorganic:	
Gases (oil-bearing or dirty)	500
Liquids (heating or vaporization)	500
Refrigerant brines	1000
Organic:	
Gases	
Process	1000
Utility (oil-bearing, refrigerant, etc.)	500
Condensing vapors (condensers)	1000
Liquids	
Process	1000
Vaporizing liquids (reboilers)	500
Heat-transfer media	1000
Refrigerant liquids	1000
Polymer-forming liquids	200
Oils (vegetable and heavy gas oil)	330
Asphalt and residuum	100

* Rearranged and reproduced, by permission, from Standards of Tubular Manufacturers Association, New York 7, N.Y., 1959.

Over-all Coefficient. After determining the two fluid film coefficients and the coefficients for the tube wall and fouling scale, all based on outside area, the over-all coefficient U for design is obtained from Eq. (10-64).

$$\frac{1}{U_o} = \frac{1}{h_i} + \frac{1}{h_o} + \frac{1}{h_w} + \frac{1}{h_F} \tag{10-64}$$

After design has been accomplished, it is a foolhardy procedure to add additional area as a safety factor. If this is done without altering fluid velocities, no harm results except that one buys more surface than necessary and engenders an abiding lack of confidence in design expressions. It is sound practice, however, to use standard-diameter shells (standard tube counts) and standard tube lengths rather than to use non-standard dimensions.

Condensers. *Vertical Tubes.* For condensing on the inside of vertical tubes or on the outside of vertical tubes, in exchangers *without* tube supports or baffles, the application of Eq. (10-46) needs no clarification. For condensing on the outside of vertical tubes, in exchangers *with* tube supports or baffles, Eq. (10-46) yields conservative results because some of the condensate is stripped off the tubes by the baffles, resulting in a lower average value of the term Γ. Since it is practically impossible to determine the true average tube loading in this case, one ignores the probable advantage and uses the result based upon uniform tube loading. The loading factor for vertical tubes is thus $\Gamma = W/n\,\pi D$.

Horizontal Tubes. For condensing on the *outside* of horizontal tube bundles it is assumed that the total quantity of liquid is uniformly distributed over the tubes in two adjacent rows at the center line of the heat exchanger. The loading factor in Eq. (10-49) is thus $\Gamma = W/2n_c2L$ or $\Gamma = W/4n_cL$ where n_c is the number of tubes across the center line of the bundle. The value of n_c is approximately D_s'/p' or $D_s'/1.25D_o'$ for the usual case in which tube spacing (pitch) is 1.25 times tube diameter; or

$$\Gamma = \frac{WD_o'}{3.2LD_s'} \tag{10-65}$$

For condensing on the inside of horizontal tubes the theoretical tube loading factor is $\Gamma = W/n\,2L$. However, one must realize, for this case, that the condensate remains within the tube. The condensate flows in a segmentally shaped stream at the bottom of the tube. The surface area wetted by the condensate stream is not available for condensation, and therefore there is a variable reduction of heat-transfer area as the vapor and condensate proceed along the length of the tube. The practice of condensing inside horizontal tubes is very common (kettle coils) but there is no rigorous method for determining the blanketing effect of the condensate. The larger the tube diameter and the shorter the tube length the less the blanketing effect.

Condensation of Vapors Containing Non-condensable Gases. When a mixture of a condensable vapor and a non-condensable gas is exposed to a surface colder than the dew point of the mixture, some condensation occurs. In the absence of dropwise condensation, a layer of condensate forms on the cooling surfaces and a film of a mixture of non-condensable gas and vapor collects next to the condensate layer, the concentration of vapor in the gas film being lower than in the main body of the mixture. As pointed out by Lewis [*Chem. & Met. Eng.*, **34**, 735 (1927)], owing to the differences in partial pressure of the vapor between the main body of the mixture and that at the interface between films, the vapor diffuses from the main body through the gas film to liquefy at the interface. Thus both the latent heat of condensation and the sensible heat lost by the vapor are conducted through the condensate layer. However, the latent heat is not transferred through the gas film, unless under special conditions with a very cold surface the dew point might be reached somewhere in the gas film. As the main body of the mixture flows past the cooling surface, it is cooled and the sensible heat so removed is conducted through the gas film, later to pass through the condensate layer by conduction. The rate of condensation is thus governed by the laws of diffusion of the vapor through a film of non-condensable gas, whereas the sensible heat transmitted is governed by the usual laws of heat transfer.

A general procedure (for a simple mixture of gas and condensable vapor) is given by Colburn and Hougen [*Ind. Eng. Chem.*, **26**, 1178–1187 (1934)]; but this method is somewhat complicated for application to industrial gas-vapor mixtures and involves step-by-step calculations or graphical integration procedures.

The mechanism described in the first paragraph suggests a simpler (but less rigorous) method which appears to yield good results for cases in which the condensate and cooling vapor-gas mixture are in substantial equilibrium, such as in vertical vapor-in-tube or horizontal one-pass cross-flow condenser-coolers. In accordance with the above mechanism, one may write the following equations:

$$\frac{(Q/\theta)_g}{h_g} + \frac{(Q/\theta)_T}{h_c} = A\,\Delta T_0 \qquad (10\text{-}66)$$

$$\frac{(Q/\theta)_T}{A\,\Delta T_0} = h_{cg} \qquad (10\text{-}67)$$

Whence by substitution of (10-66) in (10-67)

$$h_{cg} = \frac{1}{\dfrac{(Q/\theta)_g}{(Q/\theta)_T}\dfrac{1}{h_g} + \dfrac{1}{h_c}} \qquad (10\text{-}68)$$

The following procedure is used for estimating the net film coefficient for the gas-vapor side of the condenser.

1. The sensible heat $(Q/\theta)_g$ for cooling the uncondensed gas is calculated. [Note that some of the fluid leaving the condenser in the vent stream is not condensed even though it is a condensable vapor. Note also that the vapor that does condense is cooled to some extent in the gas phase and this heat must be included in $(Q/\theta)_g$.]

2. The total heat $(Q/\theta)_T$ includes the gas-phase sensible heat $(Q/\theta)_g$ (1, above) plus the latent heat of condensation of the vapor that condenses plus the sensible heat of liquid-phase subcooling.

3. The gas film coefficient, h_g, is calculated using a mean mass velocity based on the entering and exit gas-vapor rates.

4. The condensate film coefficient h_c is calculated for the loading rate represented by the condensate film.

5. The net effective coefficient is then calculated from Eq. (10-68). If the gas and condensate are inside a vertical tube, the net effective coefficient must be multiplied by the ratio of inside to outside tube diameter.

The following generalizations may be deduced from Eq. (10-68): (1) The value of the net effective coefficient will lie between the values for the gas and condensate film coefficients. (2) The greater the ratio of sensible heat to total heat, the more closely the net effective coefficient approaches the gas film coefficient. (3) The gas film coefficient is usually controlling and therefore the higher the gas velocity, the higher the net effective coefficient. It is thus possible to obtain widely different values of net effective coefficient from mixtures of identical composition operating between identical temperature limits but in exchangers of widely different design from the standpoint of number, size, and length of tubes. This probably accounts for the lack of published data on this type of heat transfer.

Example. A process gas containing several non-condensable constituents plus steam is to be cooled from 156° to 103°F. with cooling water rising from 84° to 99°F. Calulate the area required based on the following data.

Vertical vapor-in-tube condenser.

Inlet stream: 29,500 lb./hr. gas; 6125 lb./hr. vapor.

Vent stream: 29,500 lb./hr. gas; 1290 lb./hr. vapor.

Condensate: 4835 lb./hr. liquid.

Sensible heat (gas phase) $(Q/\theta)_g$: 460,000 B.t.u./hr.

Latent heat: 4,984,000 B.t.u./hr.

Sensible heat (liquid phase): 116,000 B.t.u./hr.

Total heat $(Q/\theta)_T$: 5,560,000 B.t.u./hr.

Gas film coefficient (based on inside area): 15 B.t.u./(hr.)(sq. ft.)(°F.). Equation (10-39).

Condensate film coefficient (based on inside area): 985 B.t.u./(hr.)(sq. ft.)(°F.). Equation (10-46).

Water film coefficient (based on outside area): 670 B.t.u./(hr).(sq. ft.)(°F.). Equation (10-41).

Wall coefficient (based on outside area): 4040 B.t.u./(hr.)(sq. ft.)(°F.). Equation (10-62).

Fouling coefficient (based on outside area): 1000 B.t.u./(hr.)(sq. ft.)(°F.).

Log mean temperature difference based on terminal temperatures 34.6°F.

Tube diameter: 1.25 in. outside, 0.875 in. inside.

$$h_{cg} = \frac{1}{\dfrac{460}{5560}\dfrac{1}{15} + \dfrac{1}{985}} \times \frac{0.875}{1.250} = 107$$

$$\frac{1}{U} = \frac{1}{h_{cg}} + \frac{1}{h_o} + \frac{1}{h_w} + \frac{1}{h_F}$$

$$= \frac{1}{107} + \frac{1}{670} + \frac{1}{4040} + \frac{1}{1000} = \frac{1}{83}$$

$U = 83$ B.t.u./(hr.)(sq. ft.)(°F.)(net effective over-all coefficient)

$$\text{Area required} = \frac{5,560,000}{83 \times 34.6} = 1940 \text{ sq. ft.}$$

NOTE: Coefficients of the above order of magnitude would apply for a condenser containing 439 tubes in parallel in a shell 37 in. in diameter containing 16 equally spaced 25 per cent cut baffles.

Condensation of Superheated Vapors. If the temperature of the wall is above the saturation temperature at the prevailing pressure, there will be no condensation and the case should be treated as cooling a gas.

If the temperature of the wall is well below the saturation temperature, condensation at the wall will occur even though the bulk of the vapor is not yet at saturation temperature (desuperheated). A process of simultaneous condensation and vapor desuperheating occurs. The sensible heat travels across the gas film; the total heat (sensible plus latent) travels across the condensate film. For superheated vapor (within limits at constant heat load), the condensate loading is lower and therefore the condensing coefficient is slightly higher. Desuperheating occurs at the expense of the available temperature difference between the superheat temperature and the saturation temperature. Normal procedure for estimating the condensing coefficient consists of neglecting the superheated temperature of the steam, calculating the coefficient as for a saturated vapor, and using the saturated temperature when calculating temperature difference.

The above procedure, although satisfactory, is an oversimplification of the mechanism. In condensation of superheated steam in industrial apparatus, little attention is paid to heat balances, heat losses, steam blow-through during trap discharge intervals, etc. Condensate film resistances rarely control. Excess pressure is usually available to compensate for error in design. Therefore, little attention is given to the mechanism of heat transfer. In the condensation of superheated *process* vapors, the pressure is usually fixed and it is not practical to blow down heat exchangers to relieve vapor binding or to make adjustments in process conditions in case an exchanger is underdesigned because of the presence of a large amount of superheat. Vapors in the superheated state behave like non-condensable gases and Eq. (10-68) may be applied to give a result which conforms to the probable mechanism.

Example. A heater is designed to heat a water stream from 100° to 200°F. using saturated steam at 100 lb./sq. in. abs. (327.8°F.). The same heater works equally well when supplied with superheated steam at 100 lb./sq. in. abs. and 550°F. Explain.

Data: Enthalpy: Superheated vapor, 1304; saturated vapor, 1187; liquid, 298; desuperheat, 117; condensation, 889.

Temperature differences: ΔT_H (superheated) = 550 − 200 = 350; ΔT_H (saturated) = 328 − 200 = 128; ΔT_L = 328 − 100 = 228; ΔT_M (superheated) 287°F.; ΔT_M (saturated) 173°F. Film coefficients: cooling water, 1000; tube wall, 4800; condensing film, 1105; gas film (desuperheat) 83.

Solution (a): Based on saturated steam:

$$U = \frac{1}{\dfrac{1}{1105} + \dfrac{1}{1000} + \dfrac{1}{4800}} = 474$$

$$Q/A\theta = 474 \times 173 = 82{,}000 \text{ (B.t.u.)(hr.)(sq. ft.)}$$

Solution (b): Based on superheated steam but using saturated steam temperature. The total steam usage will be less than that used in solution (*a*) by the ratio of enthalpies 889/(117 + 889) = 0.884.

According to Eq. (10-46) or (10-49), the film coefficient for condensing is inversely proportional to the cube root of the weight rate of flow. Therefore, the film coefficient for the superheated steam will be 1105 × (1/0.884)⅓ = 1155. The over-all coefficient becomes 482 and the calculated heat transferred will be 482 × 173 = 83,400 (B.t.u.)(hr.)(sq. ft.) which is less than 2 per cent greater than the heat rate obtained in solution (*a*), much less than experimental error and therefore a safe design procedure.

Solution (c): Based on superheated steam, superheated temperatures, and Eq. (10-68):

$$h_{eq} = \frac{1}{\dfrac{117}{1006}\left(\dfrac{1}{83}\right) + \dfrac{1}{1155}} = 440$$

$$U = \frac{1}{\dfrac{1}{440} + \dfrac{1}{1000} + \dfrac{1}{4800}} = 288$$

$$Q/A\theta = 288 \times 287 = 82{,}500 \text{ B.t.u./(hr.)(sq. ft.)}$$

The value of the gas film coefficient (chosen to give exactly the same heat flux) is reasonable for the high velocities on the steam side of exchangers operating at high loads. However, if a sizable error is made in estimating the gas film coefficient, either the pressure of the steam will rise yielding higher temperature difference or the condensate will subcool yielding more total heat from the condensed phase even though complete desuperheating has not taken place. Neither of these conditions would be noticeable from readings on industrial instruments. The use of Eq. (10-68) is recommended for condensation of superheated vapors when conservative design is necessary. When condensing superheated vapors on the shell side of heat exchangers there is a considerable amount of splashing of condensate as it is alternately stripped off the tubes and blown back on the tubes at the edges of the baffles or tube supports. This direct-contact heat transfer to an unknown and indeterminate amount of liquid-surface area is equivalent to an increase in gas film coefficient based on tube area. The condensate coefficient is also increased as condensate is stripped off the tubes. The difficulty of discerning the true mechanism and the reasons for equal performance of superheated or saturated steam are apparent. Similar but less extensive conditions occur in the case of condensing inside tubes.

Reboilers and Vaporizers

Liquids Boiling outside Submerged Horizontal Tubes. In natural convection evaporators the heat may be supplied by submerged tubes, usually heated internally by condensing steam. At very small temperature differences the coefficients are of the order of those found when warming liquids, but, as the temperature difference is increased, the coefficient increases more rapidly owing to better agitation caused by boiling. (This is called the range of nucleate boiling.) When the critical temperature difference is reached, the heat flux ($q/A = h\,\Delta t$) reaches a maximum, and with further moderate increase in Δt the flux decreases sharply owing to a vapor film of low thermal conductivity which forms on the surface. At very high temperature differences (not encountered in steam-heated evaporators) the flux rises because of the effect of radiation. For a given liquid and boiling pressure, the nature of the surface may substantially influence the results (see Table 10-3) [taken from Sauer, Cooper, Akin, and McAdams, *Mech. Eng.*, **60**, 669 (1938); Akin and McAdams, *Trans. Am. Inst. Chem. Engrs.*, **35**, 137 (1939)]. These data, obtained for single tubes, may be used as a rough approximation for a bank of submerged clean tubes.

Table 10-3. Maximum Flux [B.t.u./(Hr.)(Sq. Ft.)] and Corresponding Critical Over-all Temperature Difference (°F.) for Liquids Boiled at 1 Atm. with a Submerged Clean Horizontal Tube

Liquid	Surface							
	Aluminum		Copper		Chromium plate copper		Steel	
	$\frac{q/A}{1000}$	$(\Delta t)_0$	$\frac{q/A}{1000}$	$(\Delta t)_0$	$\frac{q/A}{1000}$	$(\Delta t)_0$	$\frac{q/A}{1000}$	$(\Delta t)_0$
Ethyl acetate	41	70	61	55	77	55		
Benzene	51	80	58	70	73	100	82	100
Ethanol	55	80	85	65	124	65		
Methanol	..	..	100	95	110	110	155	110
Distilled water	..	..	230	85	350	75	410	150

Cichelli and Bonilla [*Trans. Am. Inst. Chem. Engrs.*, **41**, 755–788 (1945)] boiled a number of organic liquids at pressures ranging from atmospheric to a reduced pressure 0.95, using an electrically heated horizontal chrome-plated surface, and found that the ratio of the estimated maximum flux to the critical pressure was a unique function of reduced pressure, reaching a maximum at a reduced pressure of 0.35 and Δt of 32°F.; Δt decreased with increase in reduced pressure. At constant q/A less then the maximum, h increased with increase in pressure.

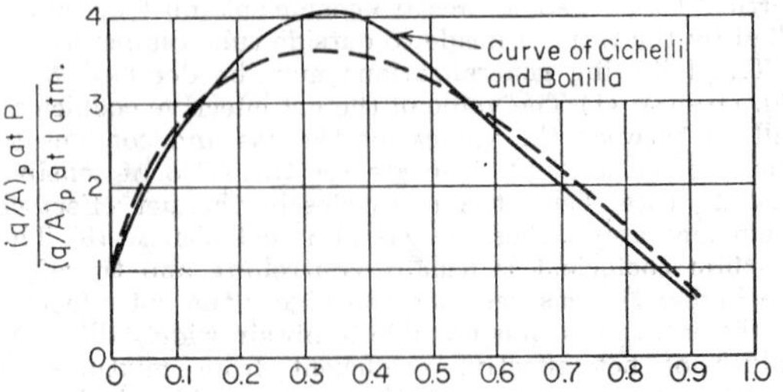

Fig. 10-15. Data of Kazakova for water boiling on a horizontal platinum wire (0.059 in.) compared with the prediction of Cichelli and Bonilla for organic liquids.

At film temperature differences of less than 10°F. Eqs. (10-24), (10-25), and (10-26) apply. At film temperature differences between 10° and 50°F. (or up to the critical ΔT), Eqs. (10-52), (10-53), or (10-54) apply

For film temperature differences above 50°F. (or above the critical) the following dimensional equation derived by Bromley applies [*Chem. Eng. Progress*, **46,** 221–227 (1950)]:

$$h_{co} = a_2 \left[\frac{k_v{}^3 \rho_v (\rho_L - \rho_V) g \lambda}{D \mu_v \, \Delta T} \right]^{1/4} \qquad (10\text{-}69)$$

The value of the numerical coefficient a_2 was shown to vary from 0.512 for stagnant-liquid conditions to 0.724 for cases in which the liquid rises freely with the vapor. For use in design or evaluation of industrial exchangers the use of 0.7 should yield sufficient accuracy. At extremely high temperature differences, radiation across the stagnant vapor film becomes of importance and McAdams ("Heat Transmission," 3d ed., p. 387, Eq. 14-4, McGraw-Hill, New York, 1954) suggests a value for the combined film coefficient for convection h_{co} and radiation h_r as follows:

$$h = h_{co} \left(\frac{h_{co}}{h} \right)^{1/3} + h_r \qquad (10\text{-}70)$$

Because of the geometry of the tube bundle in industrial kettle-type reboilers, heat may be transferred by natural convection from the lower tubes in a tier and by nucleate boiling from the upper tubes.

In horizontal reboilers, into which a cold stream is fed, the cold liquid is assumed to be heated to the boiling point by direct contact with vapor bubbles so that the heat-transfer mechanism from wall to fluid is considered to be nucleate boiling. The heat load is based on the total heat, sensible plus latent, and not on the heat in the vapors leaving the vessel.

Liquids Boiling inside Vertical Tubes (Natural-circulation Reboilers or Vaporizers). The advantages of natural-circulation vaporizers are: (1) low hold-up of process fluid, (2) ease of cleaning, (3) low installation cost, (4) reasonably high heat-transfer rates, and (5) low susceptibility to fouling. The circulation in this type of vaporizer is due to the difference in density between a heated column of liquid in the exchanger and an unheated column of liquid outside the exchanger. The amount of vapor generated is a function of the heat-transfer rate but the ratio of liquid to vapor leaving the vaporizer is a function of the hydraulic characteristics associated with the exchanger, piping, and separation chamber. There are two distinct heat-transfer mechanisms: (1) sensible heat transfer to the entering liquid stream as its temperature is raised to a boiling point (higher than either the inlet or outlet temperatures), and (2) nucleate boiling to the liquid in the zone between the point at which boiling commences and the outlet of the tubes. Descriptions of the mechanism, too lengthy for inclusion here, are given by Fair [*Petrol. Refiner*, **39,** 105 (1960)] and Kern ["Process Heat Transfer," pp. 486–491, McGraw-Hill, New York, 1950].

Values of maximum heat flux and over-all temperature difference for several liquids vaporizing in a thermosiphon reboiler containing seven tubes, 0.834 in. diameter by 10 ft. long, are shown in Table 10-4. The maximum fluxes are somewhat less than those shown in Table 10-3 for the horizontal tubes. The submergence for the horizontal tubes was about 1 in., whereas the head on the bottom of the vertical tubes was at least 10 ft. For design, it is suggested, by the authors, that values of maximum flux should not exceed 0.6 of the experimental values.

Experimental values (obtained from a single-tube thermosiphon reboiler) of flux and boiling-side film temperature differences are also shown in this table for several liquids. The geometry of the system, the material of construction of the tubes, the presence of impurities, the extent of fouling, all have an influence on the magnitude of the coefficient. Therefore, the tabulated values should be used with discretion, and mainly for a comparative check with design values.

Table 10-4. Flux, B.t.u./(Hr.)(Sq. Ft.), and Corresponding Temperature Difference for Liquids Boiled in Vertical Tubes, Natural Circulation

Liquid	7-tube thermosiphon reboiler tubes, admiralty* 0.834 in. i.d. × 10 ft. (0.834 in. i.d. × 5 ft.)†			Single-tube thermosiphon reboiler tubes, brass‡ 0.75 in. × 6 ft. 1.00 in. × 6.5 ft.		
	$\frac{Q/A\theta}{1000}$	Pressure, lb./sq. in. abs.	ΔT_o, °F.	$\frac{Q/A\theta}{1000}$	Pressure, lb./sq. in. abs.	ΔTf
Acetone	37.0	58.0	37			
Benzene	22.0	14.7	41	20.3	14.7	24.2
n-Butane	20.7	14.5	14.5			
Cyclohexane	....	......	....	17.0	14.7	21.8
Ethyl toluene	25.0	14.7	41			
Heptane	....	......	....	14.2	14.7	17.7
Methanol	....	......	....	28.1	14.7	23.9
Pentane	....	......	....	15.0	14.7	17.0
n-Propanol	30.0	14.7	38			
Propylene glycol	35.6	7.28	70			
Water	54.8	14.7	45			
Water†	93.0	14.7	64			
Water	78.0	127	31			

* These data are from Lee, Dorsey, Moore, and Mayfield, *Chem. Eng. Progress*, **52,** 160 (1956).

† The tube length was 5 ft. for this test.

‡ These data are from Guerrieri and Talty, *Am. Inst. Chem. Engrs. Symp. Ser.*, **52** (18), (1956), Heat Transfer.

In natural-circulation reboilers, as the length of tubes is increased, the pressure drop in the system and the net hydrostatic head are increased and part of the advantages of this type of vaporizer are lost. It is, therefore, customary to use tube lengths of 3 or 4 ft. for vertical natural-circulation reboilers built inside evaporator bodies and lengths from 6 to 12 ft. for exchangers external to the flash chamber.

The *long-tube* vertical evaporator is usually used for once-through operation. That is, all the liquid entering the tube, usually from the discharge of a pump, is eventually vaporized. Long tubes (20 ft.) small in diameter are used. Liquid velocities and sensible heat coefficients are high; near the top of the tube nucleate boiling occurs. If there is no provision for return of entrained liquid, extra length must be provided to assure that splashed or entrained liquid is vaporized. The vapor, therefore, usually is slightly superheated as it leaves the top of the vaporizer.

MISCELLANEOUS APPLICATIONS

Annular Spaces. Most of the heat-transfer data for annular spaces, space between concentric tubes, has been correlated using one of two equivalent diameters defined as four times the free area divided by (1) the *wetted* perimeter or (2) the *heated* perimeter. If the physical characteristics of a proposed design are the same as those existing in the experimental work, one is justified in using the proposed equation (usually an equation for flow inside tubes) and the suggested equivalent diameter and numerical constant. The subject of equivalent diameter for fluid flow in annular spaces has been reported by Walker and Rothfus [*Am. Inst. Chem. Engrs. J.*, **5,** 51 (1959)] and by Lohrenz and Kurata [*Ind. Eng. Chem.*, **52,** 703 (1960)]. Based on the information in these articles and the Reynolds analogy, it is clear that neither of the equivalent diameters formerly used is entirely correct. The alternatives are to use these equivalent diameters and accept error in design or refer to the above publications and use suggested equivalent diameters together with correction factors based on ratios of D_o to D_1.

McKee [M.S. Thesis, in Chemical Engineering, W. Va. University, (1961)] derived an expression for equivalent diameter for annuli which eliminates certain anomalies exhibited by the equivalent diameters as defined in the previous paragraph. The McKee equivalent diameter is defined as the square root of the difference in the squares of the diameters of the two concentric cylinders or $D_e = (D_2^2 - D_1^2)^{1/2}$ where D_2 is the inside diameter of the outer pipe and D_1 is the outside diameter of the inner pipe. Although the basis of the derivation was, for the most part, fluid friction data, there is reason to expect it to be valid (with modifications) for heat transfer.

Over-all coefficients are given by Foust and Christian [*Trans. Am. Inst. Chem. Engrs.*, **36**, 541 (1940)], Foust and Thompson [*ibid.*, **36**, 555 (1940)]; and McMillen and Larson [*ibid.*, **40**, 177 (1944)]; film coefficients were deduced by use of Wilson plots. Directly measured film coefficients are reported by Monrad and Pelton [*Trans. Am. Inst. Chem. Engrs.*, **38**, 593 (1942)]. Data of the various observers have been compared in various papers including Davis [*Trans. Am. Soc. Mech. Engrs.*, **65**, 755 (1943)] and Wiegand [*Trans. Am. Inst. Chem. Engrs.*, **41**, 147 (1945)]. Results of various observers are not in agreement for heating and cooling with turbulent flow in annuli or rectangular sections, and it is recommended that equations for flow inside tubes be used, with D taken as equal to four times the ratio of free cross section to total wetted perimeter.

Mueller [*Trans. Am. Inst. Chem. Engrs.*, **38**, 613 (1942)] reports film coefficients for flow of air parallel to wires ranging from 0.0007 to 0.0030 in., for air velocities ranging from 7 to 50 ft./sec., and he obtained values of h ranging from 50 to 220 B.t.u./(hr.)(sq. ft.)(°F.).

Coils. For flow *inside* helical coils, Reynolds number above 10,000, multiply the value of the film coefficient obtained from the applicable equation for straight tubes by the term $(1 + 3.5\, D_i/D_c)$.

For flow *inside* helical coils, Reynolds number less than 10,000, substitute the term $(D_c/D_1)^{1/2}$ for (L_u/D_1) where the latter appears in the applicable equation for straight tubes.

For flat spiral (pancake) coils, in which the ratio D_c/D_i varies for each turn, a different value of coefficient will be obtained for each turn; a weighted average based on length per turn is used.

For flow *outside* helical coils use the equation for flow normal to a bank of tubes, in-line flow.

Double-pipe Exchangers. See Annular Spaces.

Falling Films. When a liquid is distributed uniformly around the periphery at the top of a vertical tube (either inside or outside) and allowed to fall down the tube wall by the influence of gravity, the fluid does not fill the tube but rather flows as a thin layer. Similarly, when a liquid is applied uniformly to the outside and top of a horizontal tube, it flows in layer form around the periphery and falls off the bottom. In both these cases the mechanism is called gravity flow of liquid layers or falling films.

For the turbulent flow of water in layer form down the walls of vertical tubes the dimensional equation of McAdams, Drew, and Bays [*Trans. Am. Soc. Mech. Engrs.*, **62**, 627 (1940)] is recommended:

$$h_m = 120\Gamma^{1/3} \tag{10-71}$$

and is based on values of $\Gamma = w/\pi D$ ranging from 600 to 15,000 lb./(hr.)(ft.) of wetted perimeter. This type of water flow is used in vertical vapor-in-shell ammonia condensers, acid coolers, cycle water coolers, and other process fluid coolers.

The following dimensional equations may be used for any liquid flowing in layer form down vertical surfaces:

$$\text{For } \frac{4\Gamma}{\mu} > 2100 \quad h_m = 7.5\left[\left(\frac{k^2\rho^2c}{\mu}\right)\left(\frac{4\Gamma}{\mu}\right)\right]^{1/3} \tag{10-72}$$

$$\text{For } \frac{4\Gamma}{\mu} < 2100 \quad h_{a.m.} = 55\left(\frac{k^2\rho^{4/3}c}{L\mu^{1/3}}\right)^{1/3}\left(\frac{\mu}{\mu_w}\right)^{1/4}\left(\frac{4\Gamma}{\mu}\right)^{1/9} \tag{10-73}$$

Equation (10-73) is based on the work of Bays and McAdams [*Ind. Eng. Chem.*, **29**, 1240 (1937)]. The significance of the term L is not clear. When $L = 0$, the coefficient is definitely not infinite. When L is large, and the fluid temperature has not yet closely approached the wall temperature, it does not appear that the coefficient should necessarily decrease. Within the finite limits of 0.4 to 6 ft., this equation should give results of the proper order of magnitude.

For falling films applied to the outside of horizontal tubes, the Reynolds number rarely exceeds 2100. Equations may be used for falling films on the outside of horizontal tubes by substituting $\pi D/2$ for L.

For water flowing over a horizontal tube, data for several sizes of pipe are roughly correlated by the dimensional equation of McAdams, Drew, and Bays [*Trans. Am. Soc. Mech. Engrs.*, **62**, 627 (1940)].

$$h_{a.m.} = 150\left(\frac{\Gamma}{D_o'}\right)^{1/3} \tag{10-74}$$

for Γ ranging from 100 to 1000 lb. water/hr./ft. of pipe.

Falling films are also used for evaporation in which the film is both entirely or partially evaporated (juice concentration). This principle is also used in crystallization (freezing).

The advantage of high coefficient in falling-film exchangers is partially offset by the difficulties involved in distribution of the film, maintaining complete wettability of the tube, and the pumping costs required to lift the liquid to the top of the exchanger.

Finned Tubes (Extended Surface). When the film coefficient on the outside of a metal tube is much lower than that on the inside, as when steam condensing in a pipe is being used to heat air, externally finned (or extended) heating surfaces are of value in increasing substantially the rate of heat transfer per unit length of tube. The data on extended heating surfaces, for the case of air flowing outside and at right angles to the axes of a bank of finned pipes, can be represented approximately by the dimensional equation derived from Eq. (10-44*c*):

$$h_f = 0.17\,\frac{(V_F)^{0.6}}{(D_o')^{0.4}}\left(\frac{p'}{p' - D_o'}\right)^{0.6} \tag{10-75}$$

in which h_f is the film coefficient of heat transfer on the air side; V_F is the face velocity, ft./min., of the air; p' is the center-to-center spacing, in., of the tubes in a row; and D_o' is the outside diameter, in., of the bare tube (diameter at the root of the fins).

In atmospheric air-cooled finned-tube exchangers, the air-film coefficient from Eq. (10-75) is sometimes converted to a value based on outside bare surface as follows:

$$h_{f_o} = h_f\,\frac{A_f + A_{uf}}{A_{of}} = h_f\,\frac{A_T}{A_o} \tag{10-76}$$

in which h_{fo} is the air-film coefficient based on external bare surface; h_f is air-film coefficient based on total external surface; A_T is total external surface, and A_o is external bare surface of the unfinned tube; A_f is the area of the fins; A_{uf} is the external area of the unfinned portion of the tube; A_{of} is area of tube before fins are attached.

Fin efficiency is defined as the ratio of the mean temperature difference from surface to fluid divided by the temperature difference from fin to fluid at the base or root of the fin. Graphs of fin efficiency for extended surfaces of various types are given by Gardner [*Trans. Am. Soc. Mech. Engrs.*, **67**, 621 (1945)].

Heat-transfer coefficients for finned tubes of various types are given in a series of papers [*Trans. Am. Soc. Mech. Engrs.*, **67**, 601 (1945)].

For flow of air normal to fins in the form of short strips or pins, Norris and Spofford [*Trans. Am. Soc. Mech. Engrs.*, **64**, 489 (1942)] correlate their results for air by the dimensionless equation of Pohlhausen:

$$\frac{h_m}{c_pG_{\max}}\left(\frac{c_p\mu}{k}\right)^{2/3} = 1.0\left(\frac{z_pG_{\max}}{\mu}\right)^{-0.5} \qquad (10\text{-}77)$$

for values of $z_p/G_{\max}\ \mu$ ranging from 2700 to 10,000.

For the general case, the treatment suggested by Kern ("Process Heat Transfer," p. 512, McGraw-Hill, New York, 1950) is recommended. Because of the wide variations in fin-tube construction, it is convenient to convert all film coefficients to values based on the inside bare surface of the tube. Thus to convert the film coefficient based on outside area (finned side) to a value based on inside area Kern gives the following relationship:

$$h_{f_i} = (\Omega A_f + A_o)\frac{h_f}{A_i} \qquad (10\text{-}78)$$

in which h_{f_i} is the effective outside film coefficient based on inside area, h_f is the outside film coefficient calculated from the applicable equation for bare tubes, A_f is the surface area of the fins, A_o is the surface area on the outside of the tube which is not finned, A_i is the inside area of the tube, and Ω is the fin efficiency defined as

$$\Omega = \frac{\tanh mb}{mb} \qquad (10\text{-}79)$$

in which

$$m = \left(\frac{h_fp}{ka_x}\right)^{1/2} \qquad (10\text{-}80)$$

and b = height of fin, ft. The other symbols are defined as follows: p is the perimeter of the fin, ft.; a_x is the cross-sectional area of the fin, sq. ft.; k is the thermal conductivity of the material from which the fin is made, B.t.u./(hr.)(ft.)(°F.).

Fin efficiencies and fin dimensions are available from manufacturers. Ratios of finned to inside surface are usually available so that the terms A_f, A_o, and A_i may be obtained from these ratios rather than from the total surface areas of the heat exchangers.

Gases Flowing at Right Angles to Single Tubes. Such data are valuable in calculating the true temperature of a gas based on the apparent temperature indicated by a thermocouple. Sometimes the thermocouple is placed directly in the gas stream and at other times it is protected by a pyrometer well; hence it is desirable to know the effect of diameter upon the convection coefficients between gas and a single cylinder for a large range of diameters. Data are available only for air at room temperature flowing at right angles to the axes of single cylinders ranging in diameter from 0.001 to 3.75 in.; the temperature of the cylinder ranged up to 1800°F. for the wires but extended only to 212°F. for the tubes. These data are correlated by the dimensionless equations:

For D_oG/μ_f from 0.1 to 1000

$$\frac{h_mD_o/k_f}{(c_p\mu_f/k_f)^{0.3}} = 0.35 + 0.47\left(\frac{D_oG}{\mu_f}\right)^{0.52} \qquad (10\text{-}81)$$

For D_oG/μ_f from 1000 to 50,000

$$\frac{h_mD_o/k_f}{(c_p\mu_f/k_f)^{0.3}} = 0.26\left(\frac{D_oG}{\mu_f}\right)^{0.6} \qquad (10\text{-}82)$$

For gases at moderate temperatures, with DG/μ_f ranging from 1000 to 50,000, a simplified dimensional equation is

$$h = \frac{0.3c_pG^{0.6}}{(D_o')^{0.4}} \qquad (10\text{-}83)$$

JACKETS AND COILS OF CYLINDRICAL VESSELS WITH AGITATORS

Film coefficients for the inner walls of cylindrical vessels in which the contained fluid is agitated may be estimated by an equation suggested by Chilton, Drew, and Jebens [*Ind. Eng. Chem.*, **36**, 510 (1944)].

$$\frac{hD_j}{k} = a\left(\frac{L_p{}^2N\rho}{\mu}\right)^{2/3}\left(\frac{c\mu}{k}\right)^{1/3}\left(\frac{\mu_B}{\mu_w}\right)^{0.14} \qquad (10\text{-}84)$$

In a summarization of results obtained by several investigators, Ackley [*Chem. Eng.*, **67**, 133 (1960)] has shown that this type of equation may be used to estimate film coefficients for both the inner wall of the vessel and the outer wall of tubular surfaces contained within the vessel. Average values of the correlating numerical coefficient a for various conditions are as follows:

Agitator	Surface	a
Turbine	Jacket	0.62
Turbine	Coil	1.50
Paddle	Jacket	0.36
Paddle	Coil	0.87
Anchor	Jacket	0.46
Propeller	Jacket	0.54
Propeller	Coil	0.83

The term $(L_p{}^2N\rho/\mu)$ is referred to as the Reynolds number for agitated fluids in which L_p is the diameter and N the speed of the agitator; ρ and μ are, respectively, the density and viscosity of the fluid. Consistent units must be employed.

LIQUID METALS

The following theoretical expression for liquid metals heat transfer was proposed by Lyon [*Chem. Eng. Progress*, **47**, 75 (1951)] for values of Peclet number above 100 (flow inside tubes):

$$\frac{hD}{k} = 7 + 0.025\left(\frac{DGc}{k}\right)^{0.8} \qquad (10\text{-}85)$$

Data reported from various sources indicated values much lower than those obtained by this equation. Among possible reasons given for the deviation were (1) variation in wettability, (2) variation in surface conditions, (3) resistance of gas film between liquid metal and surface, and (4) impurities in the liquid metals. The data of Johnson, Hartnett, and Clabaugh [reported (together with data of others) in *Trans. Am. Soc. Mech. Engrs.*, **76**, 509 (1954)] may be represented (N_{Pe} 200 to 10,000) by a formula similar to that of Lyon as follows:

$$\frac{hD}{k} = 5 + 0.016\left(\frac{DGc}{k}\right)^{0.8} \qquad (10\text{-}86)$$

The data of other investigators appear to fall within ±20 per cent of this curve.

In the laminar or transient range (N_{Pe} 20 to 200), the data of Johnson fall much below theoretical predictions ($N_{Nu} = 4.36$). A curve which fits the data of Johnson *et al.* within ±20 per cent may be expressed by the following formula:

$$\frac{hD}{k} = 1.7\left(\frac{DGc}{k}\right)^{1/3} - 3.9 \qquad (10\text{-}87)$$

For *flow outside* and parallel with a bundle of tubes, tube diameter D' and pitch or spacing p', the following equation has been proposed by Friedland and Bonilla [*Am. Inst. Chem. Engrs. J.*, **7**, 107 (1961)]:

$$\frac{hD_e}{k} = 7.0 + 0.027\left(\frac{D_eGc}{k}\right)^{0.8}\left(\frac{p'}{D'}\right)^{0.27} + 3.8\left(\frac{p'}{D'}\right)^{1.52} \qquad (10\text{-}87a)$$

This equation correlates data within 10 per cent in the ranges Peclet number 10^1 to 10^5; p'/D' 1.375 to 10.

NON-NEWTONIAN FLUIDS

For film coefficients for laminar flow of non-Newtonian fluids, Metzner, Vaughn, and Houghton [*Am. Inst. Chem. Engrs. J.*, **3**, 92 (1957)] suggest the following equation:

$$\frac{h_aD}{k} = 1.75\delta^{1/3}\left(\frac{wc}{kL}\right)^{1/3}\left(\frac{\gamma}{\gamma_w}\right)^{0.14} \qquad (10\text{-}88)$$

This equation, similar to the expression for Newtonian fluids, contains a correction factor δ defined as $(3n' + 1)/4n'$ or the ratio of non-Newtonian to Newtonian shear rates. The term n' is called the flow-behavior index. The term γ is called the fluid consistency. For detailed definition of terms the above reference and bibliography should be consulted.

Based on a few data points, Metzner suggests a method for obtaining film heat-transfer coefficients for non-Newtonian fluids in the fully turbulent range (Re above 10,000) by use of generalized dimensionless groups bearing names similar to those used for Newtonian fluids. Refer to Fig. 10 in the above reference.

PACKED TUBES

Apparent coefficients of heat transfer for gases flowing through externally heated tubes filled with granular materials, based on the inside surface of the tube, were experimentally determined by Colburn [*Ind. Eng. Chem.*, **23**, 910 (1931)]. He passed air at velocities from 0.25 to 4.0 lb./(sec.)(sq. ft.) of cross section of the tube through both 1¼- and 3-in. tubes which were steam-jacketed and filled with granular materials ranging from ⅛- to 1-in. particle size. The ratio of the observed apparent coefficient for the packed tube to that for a 1-in. inside diameter empty tube, both having the same mass velocity based on the gross cross section, depends on the ratio of the diameter of the packing to the inside diameter of the tube:

D_p/D_i	0.05	0.10	0.2	0.3
Apparent h for packed/h for 1-in. empty	5.5	7.0	7.5	6.6

Coefficients of heat transfer between air and shallow beds of small cylindrical pellets are given by Wilkie and Hougen [*Trans. Am. Inst. Chem. Engrs.*, **41**, 445 (1945)] and by Hurt [*Ind. Eng. Chem.*, **35**, 522 (1943)]. Refer to Sec. 4 for additional material under heterogeneously catalyzed reactors.

TECHNIQUES IN APPLIED HEAT TRANSMISSION

For the successful application of heat-transfer theory one resorts to certain techniques such as (1) the simplifying assumption, (2) discernment of the mechanism, (3) trial-and-error solutions, (4) analogies, and (5) experiment and experience. Among the many available techniques, the following are quite generally used.

Ten Broeck Charts for Thermal Efficiency. When it is desired to evaluate an existing exchanger for a service other than that for which it was designed, it is convenient to use charts relating three dimensionless groups. One of these groups is called the thermal efficiency defined as the ratio of the actual temperature range of the tube-side fluid to the maximum possible temperature range ($t_2'' - t_1''/t_1' - t_1''$). The second group is the ratio of the actual temperature range of the tube-side fluid to the effective mean temperature difference ($t_2'' - t_1''/F\Delta T_m$) but more conveniently expressed in the known and equal ratio (UA/wc). The third group is the ratio of the actual temperature ranges of the shell-side and tube-side fluids ($t_1' - t_2'/t_2'' - t_1''$) but more conveniently expressed as the known and equal ratio (wc/WC). The plots, developed by Ten Broeck [*Ind. Eng. Chem.*, **30**, 1041 (1938)], show thermal efficiency plotted as ordinate on an arithmetic scale from zero to unity; UA/wc plotted as abscissa on a logarithmic scale; and $Z = wc/WC$ plotted as a parameter. Two plots are shown in Figs. 10-16 and 10-16*a*, respectively, for

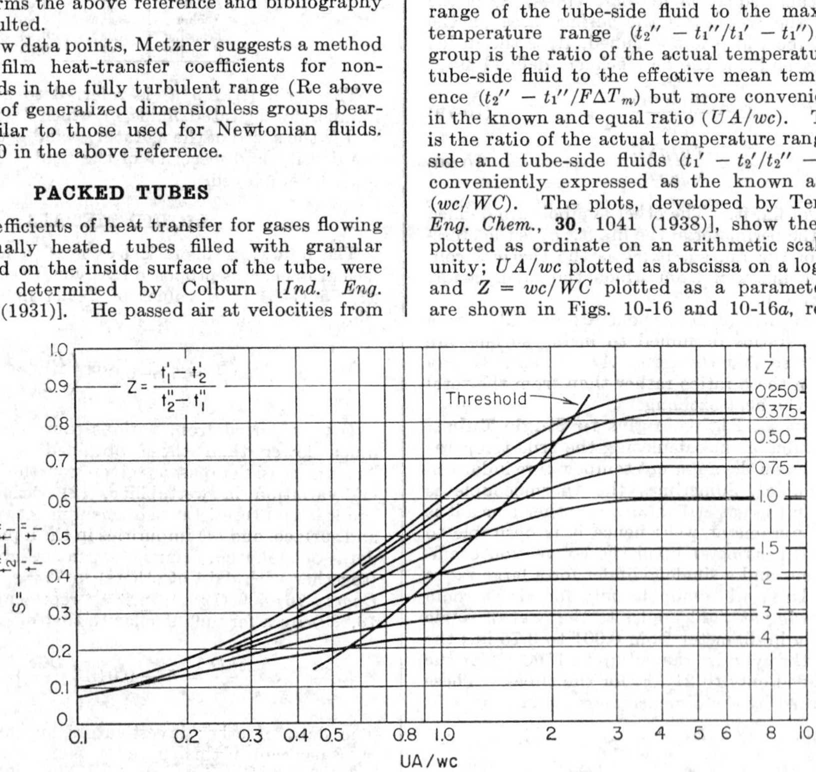

FIG. 10-16. Ten Broeck chart for determining t_2'' when t_1' and t_1'' are known in a 1-2 exchanger. (*Ind. Eng. Chem.*)

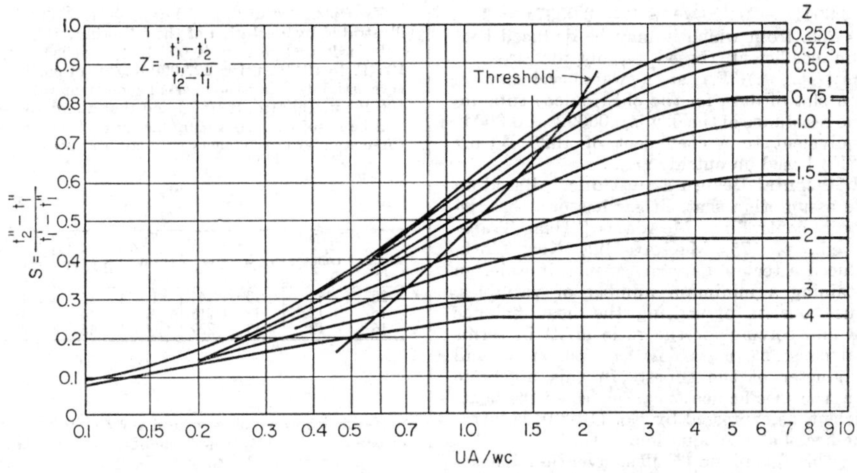

FIG. 10-16*a*. Ten Broeck chart for determining t_2'' in a 2-4 exchanger. (*Ind. Eng. Chem.*)

1-2 and 2-4 exchangers. A similar plot for counter-current flow appears in TEMA (4th ed., p. 65, 1959). In using these charts, the unknown outlet temperature of the tube-side fluid t_2'' is readily calculated; and from this, and the known ratio Z (heat balance), the outlet temperature of the shell-side fluid t_2' may also be calculated.

Graphical Method of Interpreting Over-all Coefficients of Heat Transfer. *Wilson Plot.* Wilson [*Trans. Am. Soc. Mech. Engrs.*, **37,** 47 (1915)] proposed a useful graphical method of interpreting heat transfer in surface condensers. This method may be applied to many exchanger problems. The relationship between over-all and film coefficients of heat transfer is

$$\frac{1}{U_o} = \frac{1}{h_i} + \frac{1}{h_w} + \frac{1}{h_s} + \frac{1}{h_o} \qquad (10\text{-}89)$$

If, in a series (three or more) of tests run on an exchanger, the fluid rate is varied on one side only, the variation in over-all coefficient is a function of the variation in that film coefficient. For example, the over-all coefficient of heat transfer is obtained from three tests in which the tube-side velocities are 2, 4, and 8 ft./sec., respectively; the shell-side fluid rate is maintained constant. It is known from heat-transfer theory that $h_i = bV_s^{0.8}$ in which the constant b represents the non-varying factors in the expression for film coefficient. Since h_w, h_s, and h_o are essentially constant for these tests, the sum of the reciprocals may be designated as a constant a. Equation (10-89) may then be written as follows:

$$\frac{1}{U_o} = a + \frac{1}{bV_s^{0.8}} \qquad (10\text{-}90)$$

A straight line drawn through the points representing the observed values of $1/U_o$, plotted on cartesian coordinates, against $1/V_s^{0.8}$ (0.575, 0.330, and 0.189) will have a slope of $1/b$ and an intercept on the Y-axis of a. If the tube were clean ($1/h_s = 0$), the shell-side resistance could be obtained by subtracting out the known resistance of the tube wall from the value of the intercept a. The procedure is identical when the shell-side fluid is varied and tube-side fluid held constant except that one must correctly assume the relationship between shell-side film coefficient and velocity. In condensers, supplied by a constant quantity of vapor, the film coefficients for both the condensing side and the coolant side may be estimated quickly from observed over-all coefficients obtained from tests in which the coolant rate is varied. This method is extremely useful for determining coefficients for cases in which the geometry on one side of an exchanger is complicated. The technique is applicable to practically all mechanisms of heat transfer. However, it must be realized that, as the velocity of fluid on one side is varied, there may be a significant variation in temperatures (and therefore physical properties) of fluids on both sides, thus introducing a slight error in the results obtained.

An example of a Wilson plot is shown in Fig. 10-17 taken from McAdams, Sherwood, and Turner [*Trans.*

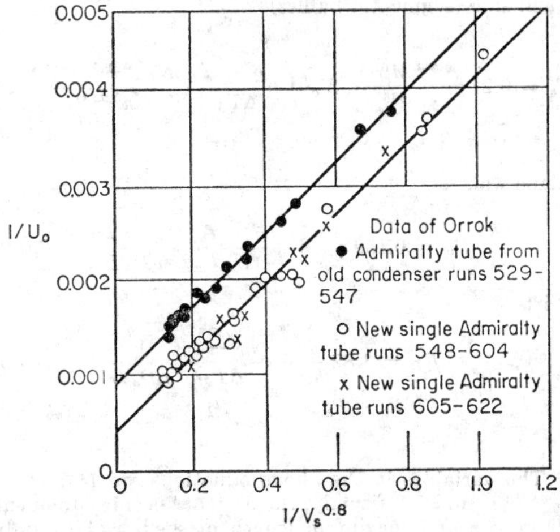

FIG. 10-17. Graphical analysis of over-all thermal resistances in surface condenser for steam.

Am. Soc. Mech. Engrs., **48,** 1233 (1926)]. This plot shows that for a clean tube the combined resistance of the tube wall and condensate film is 0.0004 (intercept when V_s = infinity). The resistance of the wall based on outside area is 0.000068, and therefore the steam film resistance is 0.0004 minus 0.000068 = 0.000332 or the steam film coefficient is (reciprocal) 3010. The slope of the line is 0.00411 − 0.0004/1 − 0 = 0.00371 = $1/b$; therefore, b = 268, from which it may be deduced that the water film coefficient (based on outside area) is 268 B.t.u./(hr.)(sq. ft.)(°F.) at a water velocity of 1 ft./sec. The plot of data for the old (fouled) tube indicates that the resistance of the dirt is 0.00092 − 0.00040 = 0.00052 equivalent to a coefficient of 1920 B.t.u./(hr.)(sq. ft.)(°F.) based on outside area.

Simplified Thermal Design Equations. Based on the reasonable assumption that, in gas heaters, the gas-side resistance is controlling, McAdams ["Heat Transmission," 2d ed., p. 175, McGraw-Hill, New York, (1942)] introduced a technique which results in a design equation containing a minimum number of variables. This technique consists of writing the heat balance $hA\ \Delta t = wc\ dt$ and solving for the ratio $dt/\Delta t$ in terms of a numerical constant, mass flow rate per tube, and length and diameter of the tubes. In this algebraic transformation, the specific heat c cancels when the heat-transfer coefficient, as expressed by Eq. (10-39), is introduced into the heat-balance equation.

By applying this technique to all conventional heat-exchanger mechanisms, Gilmour [*Chem. Eng.*, **61**, 144 (1952)] showed that shell-and-tube heat exchangers may be designed by solving five unique equations containing a minimum number of variables involving the tube-side, shell-side, tube-wall, and dirt resistances. Thus, for the thermal design of liquid-liquid heat exchangers containing segmental (cross-flow) baffles on the shell side, one solves the following five equations.

Tube side (Reynolds number above 10,000)

$$F_t = 2.62 \frac{z^{0.466} M^{0.222}}{s^{0.888}} W_1^{0.2} \frac{t_H - t_L}{\Delta T_M} \frac{(D_i')^{0.8}}{n^{0.2} L} \qquad (10\text{-}91)$$

Shell side (segmental baffles)

$$F_s = 0.27 \frac{z^{0.266} M^{0.222}}{s^{0.888}} W_o^{0.4} \frac{T_H - T_L}{\Delta T_M} \frac{N_{PT}^{0.282} (P')^{0.6}}{n^{0.718} L} \qquad (10\text{-}92)$$

Tube wall

$$F_w = 0.159 \frac{c}{k_w} W_1 \frac{t_H - t_L}{\Delta T_M} \frac{D_o' - D_i'}{n D_o' L} \qquad (10\text{-}93)$$

Dirt

$$F_D = 3.82 \frac{c}{h_s} W_1 \frac{t_H - t_L}{\Delta T_M} \frac{1}{n D_o' L} \qquad (10\text{-}94)$$

$$F_t + F_s + F_w + F_D = 1 \qquad (10\text{-}95)$$

The variables in the above equations are D_o', D_i', n, L, N_{PT}, and P'. Usually, the designer decides upon tube diameters and maximum length of shell. The number of independent variables is thereby reduced to two, namely, n and L. In this or any other method of heat-exchanger design, the final design is a function of the allowable pressure drops. Pressure drop is not considered in this section; so the above equations illustrate a technique for thermal design only. Many manufacturers list standard lines of heat exchangers. Since all factors would be known, Eqs. (10-91) through (10-95) may be used to evaluate the applicability of these standard exchangers for specified thermal duties.

Example. The utility of Eqs. (10-91) through (10-95) may be illustrated by a solution of the following problem.

It is desired to cool 40,000 lb./hr. of isopropyl alcohol from 196°F. to 104°F. using 207,000 lb./hr. of cooling water at 86°F. It is estimated that the over-all coefficient will be approximately 160 B.t.u./(hr.)(sq. ft.)(°F.) and that about 450 sq. ft. of surface will be required. In a manufacturer's catalogue it is noted that three standard exchangers with copper tubes are available.

Shell			Tubes			Passes		
Diam., in.	Length, ft.	Baffles	No.	Diam., in.	B.W.G.	Tube	Shell	Area, sq. ft.
20	12	13	144	1	16	4	1	454
18	12	13	216	¾	16	4	1	510
16	12	13	220	⅝	16	4	1	433

If the isopropanol is placed on the tube side and the dirt resistance is 0.0005, which one of these standard coolers will be satisfactory? Tables may be prepared to record the value of variables. The quantities marked with an asterisk (*) are terms in Eqs. (10-91) through (10-94).

Table of the Performance Characteristics

	Tube	Shell	Wall	Dirt
Equation	10-91	10-92	10-93	10-94
Numerical term	2.62*	0.27*	0.159*	3.82*
$(z)\ z^{0.466}$ (0.74)	0.869*			
$(z)\ z^{0.266}$	(0.7)	0.909*		
$(M)\ M^{0.222}$ (60)	2.48* (18)	1.90*		
$(S)\ S^{0.888}$ (0.75)	0.755* (1)	1.00*		
(C)	....	......	0.79*	0.79*
(k_w)	....	......	226*	
$(hs) = 1/0.0005$	....	......	....	2000*
$(w_i)\ w_i^{0.2}$ (40,000)	8.33*	......	(40,000)*	(40,000)*
$(w_o)\ w_o^{0.4}$	(207,000)	134*		
$t_H - t_L$ (196-104)	92*	......	92*	92*
$T_H - T_L$ (100-86)	....	14*		
ΔT_M	40*	40*	40*	40*

Table of Mechanical Design Features of the Standard Heat Exchangers

D_o'	1.00*	0.75*	0.625*
D_i'	0.87	0.62	0.495
$D_o' - D_i'$	0.13*	0.13*	0.13*
$(D_i')^{0.8}$	0.895*	0.682*	0.570*
n	36*	54*	55*
$n^{0.2}$	2.05*	2.22*	2.23*
$n^{0.718}$	13.1*	17.6*	17.8*
L	48*	48*	48*
$(N_{PT})\ N_{PT}^{0.282}$ (4)	1.478*	1.478*	1.478*
$(P')\ (P')^{0.6}$ (10-¼)	4.05*	4.05*	4.05*
$nD_o'L$	1726*	1940*	1650*
$(D_i')^{0.8}/n^{0.2}L$	0.00910*	0.00640*	0.00533*
$\frac{N_{PT}^{0.282}(P')^{0.6}}{n^{0.718}L}$	0.00950*	0.00708*	0.00700*
$\frac{D_o' - D_i'}{nD_o'L}$	$\frac{0.13}{1726}$*	$\frac{0.13}{1940}$*	$\frac{0.13}{1650}$*
$\frac{1}{nD_o'L}$	$\frac{1}{1726}$*	$\frac{1}{1940}$*	$\frac{1}{1650}$*
F_t (10-91)	1.270	0.890	0.743
F_s (10-92)	0.208	0.155	0.153
F_w (10-93)	0.003	0.003	0.004
F_D (10-94)	0.080	0.071	0.084
Eq. (10-95)	1.561	1.119	0.984

Since the sum of the four items in Eq. (10-95) is less than 1, it may be concluded that the exchanger with ⅝-in.-O.D. tubes will be satisfactory. Neither of the other larger exchangers, with larger tubes, will meet the specified conditions because the solution of (10-95) for these exchangers yields a sum exceeding 1.

NOMOGRAPHS FOR FILM COEFFICIENTS OF HEAT TRANSFER (STOEVER)

A series of tables (Tables 10-5 to 10-14) and nomographs for quickly determining film coefficients for several fluids have been prepared by Stoever [*Chem. & Met. Eng.*, **51**, 5 (1944)].

The numbers in the body of the tables are the values of film coefficients uncorrected for the variables which appear in the associated nomographs. In sensible heat transfer, the correction factor takes care of deviation from unity of values of velocity and tube diameter. In other cases temperature difference Δt, pressure, and condensate loading are related to the correction factor.

To obtain the desired film coefficient the base factor is taken from the proper table and multiplied by a correction factor read from the nomograph accompanying that table. The following assumptions apply in each case: (1) the system is in equilibrium, that is, there is no change in temperature gradient with time; (2) radiation is negligible or has been taken into account by other calculations; (3) film temperature is defined as the arithmetic average of the temperatures of the retaining wall and the main body of the liquid. Wall temperature, generally not known, can be estimated or calculated by trial and error. Values of base factors in italics are extrapolated from physical properties.

Table 10-5. Base Factors for Gases Heated Outside Single Horizontal Tubes, Natural Convection

Units: B.t.u./(hr.)(sq. ft.)(°F.)

Avg. film temp., °F.	−100	0	100	200	300	400	500
Acetone	....	....	0.94	1.06	1.19	1.32	*1.45*
Acetylene	0.83	0.90	0.96	1.02	*1.07*	*1.13*	*1.18*
Air	0.91	0.89	0.88	0.87	0.85	0.84	*0.83*
Ammonia	0.82	0.88	0.94	0.99	*1.04*	*1.08*	*1.12*
Benzene	....	....	1.00	1.17	1.36	1.58	*1.80*
Butane	....	1.25	1.36	1.47	*1.58*	*1.68*	*1.78*
Carbon dioxide	0.71	0.76	0.80	0.82	0.84	0.86	0.87
Carbon monoxide	0.86	0.86	0.86	0.85	*0.84*	*0.83*	*0.82*
Chlorine	....	0.56	0.55	0.55	*0.55*	*0.54*	*0.53*
Chloroform	....	....	0.72	0.77	0.82	0.86	*0.91*
Ethane	0.85	0.95	1.06	1.16	*1.26*	*1.36*	*1.45*
Ethyl acetate	....	....	1.12	1.29	1.45	1.60	*1.76*
Ethyl alcohol	....	....	1.17	1.16	*1.13*	*1.12*	*1.10*
Ethyl chloride	....	....	0.84	0.89	0.94	*0.98*	*1.02*
Ethylene	*0.79*	0.86	0.95	1.04	*1.11*	*1.19*	*1.26*
Ethyl ether	....	....	1.42	1.57	1.72	*1.88*	*2.02*
Helium	2.02	1.94	1.88	*1.84*	*1.82*		
Hydrogen	2.44	2.39	2.34	2.30	*2.25*	*2.21*	*2.16*
Hydrogen sulfide	....	0.66	0.67	0.68	*0.68*		
Methane	1.04	1.15	1.21	*1.27*	*1.33*	*1.39*	*1.44*
Methyl chloride	....	0.61	0.71	0.79	0.87	*0.95*	*1.03*
Nitric oxide	0.86	0.86	0.85	0.84	*0.82*	*0.81*	*0.79*
Nitrogen	0.92	0.91	0.89	0.87	*0.85*	*0.84*	*0.81*
Nitrous oxide	0.86	0.79	0.75	*0.71*	*0.68*	*0.65*	
Oxygen	0.92	0.91	0.90	0.89	*0.87*	*0.85*	*0.84*
Pentane, iso	....	1.26	1.40	1.56	*1.74*	*1.42*	*2.14*
Steam	....	....	0.80	0.81	0.83	0.85	0.86
Sulfur dioxide	....	....	0.59	0.60	0.61	0.61	0.61

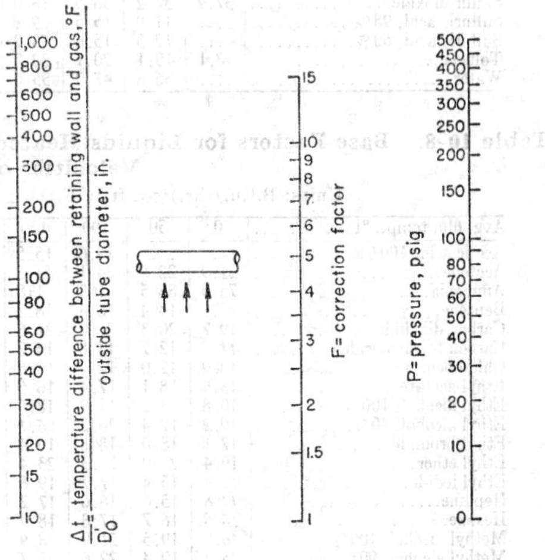

Table 10-6. Base Factors for Gases Heated Inside or Outside Vertical Tubes or on Vertical Plates, Natural Convection

Units: B.t.u./(hr.)(sq. ft.)(°F.)

Avg. film temp., °F.	−100	0	100	200	300	400	500
Acetone	....	....	0.65	0.69	0.73	0.78	*0.83*
Acetylene	0.56	0.55	0.54	0.53	*0.53*	*0.53*	*0.52*
Air	0.53	0.49	0.46	0.43	0.41	0.39	*0.38*
Ammonia	0.50	0.50	0.50	0.49	*0.49*	*0.48*	*0.48*
Benzene	....	....	0.72	0.79	0.88	0.97	*1.06*
Butane	....	0.83	0.93	0.94	*0.96*	*0.97*	*0.98*
Carbon dioxide	0.49	0.48	0.47	0.46	0.45	0.44	0.43
Carbon monoxide	0.51	0.48	0.45	0.42	*0.40*	*0.38*	*0.36*
Chlorine	....	0.38	0.36	0.34	*0.32*	*0.31*	*0.30*
Chloroform	....	....	0.53	0.53	0.54	0.55	*0.56*
Ethane	0.57	0.59	0.61	0.63	*0.65*	*0.67*	*0.69*
Ethyl acetate	....	....	0.83	0.89	0.95	1.02	*1.06*
Ethyl alcohol	....	....	0.76	0.71	*0.67*	*0.62*	*0.58*
Ethyl chloride	....	....	0.56	0.55	0.54	*0.54*	*0.53*
Ethylene	*0.52*	0.54	0.55	0.56	*0.58*	*0.59*	*0.60*
Ethyl ether	....	....	1.03	1.05	1.11	*1.17*	*1.24*
Helium	0.83	0.74	0.69	*0.65*	*0.62*		
Hydrogen	1.04	0.95	0.88	0.82	*0.77*	*0.72*	*0.68*
Hydrogen sulfide	....	0.41	0.39	0.37	*0.35*		
Methane	0.46	0.45	0.44	*0.43*	*0.42*	*0.41*	*0.40*
Methyl chloride	....	0.41	0.45	0.48	0.51	*0.54*	*0.55*
Nitric oxide	0.52	0.48	0.45	0.42	*0.40*	*0.37*	*0.35*
Nitrogen	0.54	0.49	0.46	0.43	*0.40*	*0.38*	*0.36*
Nitrous oxide	0.55	0.49	0.44	*0.40*	*0.37*	*0.34*	
Oxygen	0.54	0.50	0.47	0.44	*0.41*	*0.39*	*0.37*
Pentane, iso	....	0.99	1.01	1.05	*1.12*	*1.20*	*1.30*
Steam	....	....	0.44	0.42	0.41	0.40	0.39
Sulfur dioxide	....	....	0.38	0.36	0.35	0.34	0.33

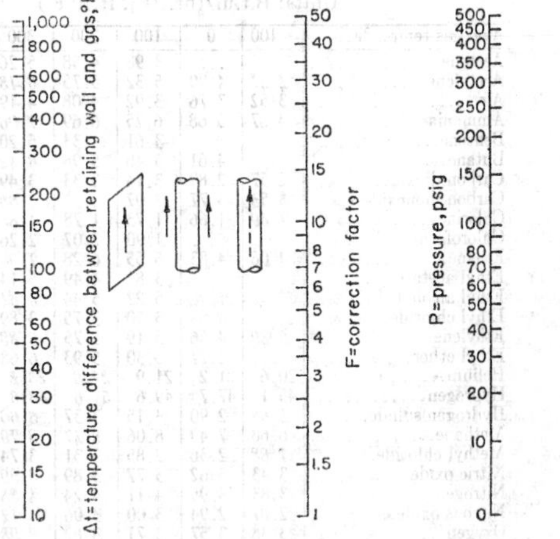

Table 10-7. Base Factors for Liquids Heated Outside Single Horizontal Tubes, Natural Convection

Units: B.t.u./(hr.)(sq. ft.)(°F.)

Avg. film temp., °F	0	50	100	150	200	250
Acetic acid, 100%	....	....	19.8	18.8	17.8	17.2
Acetone	....	27.1	28.0	28.2	28.5	28.8
Ammonia	85.5	96.3	108	120	132	144
Benzene	....	18.4	20.3	21.9	23.5	25.0
Carbon disulfide	23.9	24.1	24.6	24.8	25.1	25.3
Carbon tetrachloride	....	15.7	16.6	16.5	16.3	15.9
Chlorobenzene	16.4	15.5	14.8	14.0	13.4	13.0
Ethyl acetate	23.5	21.7	20.1	18.5	17.1	15.6
Ethyl alcohol, 100%	15.6	18.1	20.6	23.1	25.3	27.4
Ethyl alcohol, 40%	17.9	26.6	36.5	47.2	57.8	
Ethyl bromide	20.1	20.7	21.1	21.5	21.7	21.9
Ethyl ether	22.3	23.9	24.8	25.6	26.4	26.9
Ethyl iodide	15.9	17.9	19.8	21.4	23.0	23.6
Heptane	19.4	20.0	20.4	21.0	21.5	21.9
Hexane	18.7	19.9	21.0	21.8	22.5	22.9
Methyl alcohol, 100%	22.5	25.2	27.1	28.7	29.8	30.9
Methyl alcohol, 90%	21.5	25.9	29.1	31.8	34.1	36.4
n-Octane	17.0	18.1	18.5	19.2	20.0	20.5
n-Pentane	21.9	22.3	22.8	23.3	24.0	24.4
Sulfur dioxide	37.9	37.2	36.5	36.0	35.6	35.2
Sulfuric acid, 98%	....	11.8	15.5	19.2	22.9	
Sulfuric acid, 60%	....	12.5	15.6	18.2	20.3	21.7
Toluene	18.1	19.1	20.1	20.9	21.5	21.7
Water	....	36.8	47.9	55.0	60.2	65.0

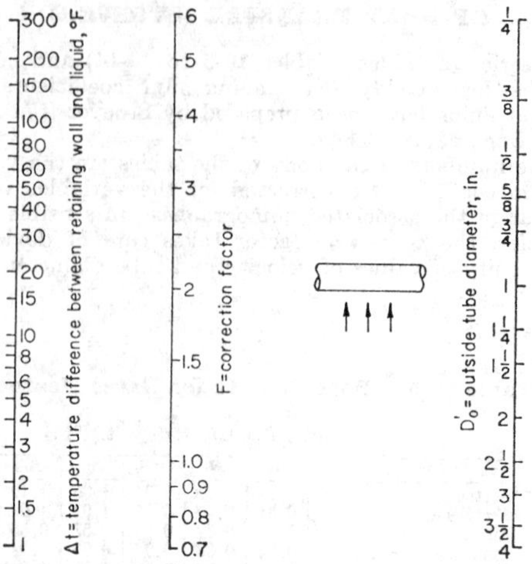

Table 10-8. Base Factors for Liquids Heated Inside or Outside Vertical Tubes or on Vertical Plates, Low Velocities or Natural Convection Only

Units: B.t.u./(hr.)(sq. ft.)(°F.)

Avg. film temp., °F	0	50	100	150	200	250
Acetic acid, 100%	....	....	15.6	15.5	15.5	15.5
Acetone	21.0	22.6	24.1	24.8	25.3	25.8
Ammonia	75.0	88.5	103	118	136	155
Benzene	....	14.4	16.4	18.2	20.0	21.7
Carbon disulfide	19.7	20.3	21.0	21.6	22.2	22.8
Carbon tetrachloride	11.4	12.7	13.8	14.2	14.4	14.8
Chlorobenzene	12.0	12.0	12.0	11.8	11.8	11.7
Ethyl acetate	18.6	18.1	17.4	16.6	15.9	15.0
Ethyl alcohol, 100%	10.8	13.2	15.9	18.6	21.2	23.9
Ethyl alcohol, 40%	10.2	17.4	26.2	25.1	45.4	
Ethyl bromide	17.1	18.0	18.8	19.4	19.8	20.2
Ethyl ether	19.4	21.0	22.3	23.4	24.1	24.6
Ethyl iodide	12.6	15.4	17.7	19.8	21.8	24.0
Heptane	14.8	15.6	16.6	17.2	18.5	19.5
Hexane	15.6	16.7	17.8	18.9	19.4	19.9
Methyl alcohol, 100%	16.7	19.5	21.9	23.9	25.9	27.4
Methyl alcohol, 90%	15.1	19.4	22.6	25.4	27.8	30.3
n-Octane	12.7	13.9	14.8	15.8	16.7	17.7
n-Pentane	18.3	19.3	20.1	20.7	21.1	21.5
Sulfur dioxide	33.6	33.6	33.6	33.6	33.6	33.6
Sulfuric acid, 98%	....	7.2	9.4	11.6	13.8	15.9
Sulfuric acid, 60%	....	8.5	11.2	13.3	14.7	15.3
Toluene	13.7	14.9	16.1	17.3	18.5	19.6
Water	....	23.3	31.9	38.0	42.4	47.9

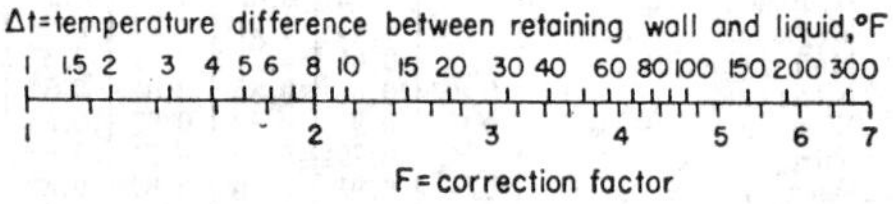

Table 10-9. Base Factors for Gases Heated or Cooled Inside Horizontal or Vertical Tubes, Turbulent Flow

Units: B.t.u./(hr.)(sq. ft.)(°F.)

Avg. gas temp., °F	−100	0	100	200	300	400	500
Acetone	.....	.....	3.98	4.58	5.26	6.33	7.36
Acetylene	4.47	4.90	5.32	5.75	6.13	6.55	
Air	3.52	3.76	3.92	4.08	4.19	4.27	4.39
Ammonia	4.87	5.68	6.25	6.69	7.06	7.36	7.64
Benzene	.....	.....	3.61	4.33	5.20	6.10	7.00
Butane	.....	4.61	5.48	5.98	6.42	6.74	7.03
Carbon dioxide	2.57	2.89	3.14	3.33	3.49	3.64	3.83
Carbon monoxide	3.53	3.77	3.97	4.17	4.33	4.49	4.65
Chlorine	1.59	1.66	1.73	1.78	1.83	1.88	1.92
Chloroform	.....	.....	1.90	2.07	2.26	2.45	2.64
Ethane	4.06	4.83	5.55	6.28	7.00	7.72	8.45
Ethyl acetate	.....	.....	3.81	4.49	5.14	5.75	6.32
Ethyl alcohol	.....	.....	5.22	5.44	5.64	5.85	6.06
Ethyl chloride	.....	3.08	3.50	3.75	3.89	4.03	4.13
Ethylene	3.89	4.56	5.19	5.75	6.33	6.90	7.46
Ethyl ether	.....	4.71	5.30	5.93	6.68	7.47	8.78
Helium	20.6	21.2	21.9	22.6	23.2	23.9	24.6
Hydrogen	45.1	47.7	49.6	51.6	53.6	55.6	57.5
Hydrogen sulfide	2.68	2.90	3.15	3.37	3.60	3.79	3.98
Methane	6.68	7.49	8.06	8.47	8.79	9.11	9.35
Methyl chloride	1.88	2.36	2.85	3.31	3.74	4.16	4.56
Nitric oxide	3.43	3.62	3.77	3.89	3.99	4.07	4.15
Nitrogen	3.83	3.95	4.11	4.24	4.33	4.41	4.49
Nitrous oxide	2.87	2.94	3.00	3.06	3.12	3.18	3.24
Oxygen	3.38	3.57	3.71	3.82	3.93	4.01	4.09
Pentane, iso	.....	4.73	5.37	6.13	7.00	8.02	
Steam	.....	.....	5.82	6.00	6.18	6.41	6.64
Sulfur dioxide	.....	1.88	2.00	2.10	2.20	2.28	2.36

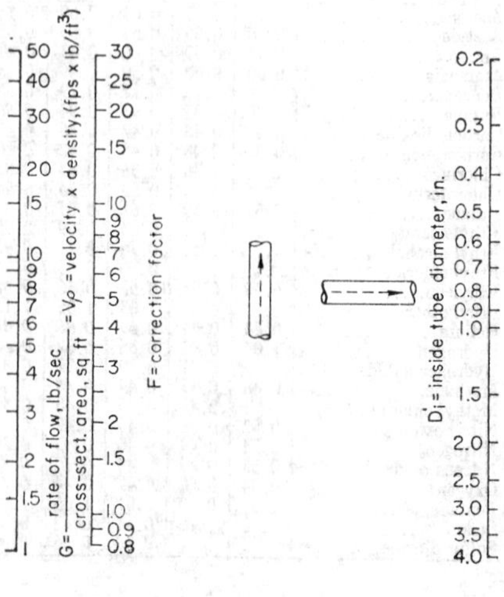

Table 10-10. Base Factors for Gases Heated or Cooled Outside Single Tubes, Direction of Flow Normal to Tube, Turbulent Flow

Units: B.t.u./(hr.)(sq. ft.)(°F.)

Avg. film temp., °F.	−100	0	100	200	300	400	500
Acetone	.....	.....	6.69	8.09	9.63	11.4	13.1
Acetylene	7.15	8.54	9.92	11.2	12.4	13.6	
Air	6.97	7.71	8.38	8.96	9.46	9.88	10.2
Ammonia	8.34	10.4	12.1	13.4	14.6	15.7	16.8
Benzene	.....	.....	6.16	7.70	9.55	11.5	
Butane	.....	8.05	9.47	10.0	12.4	13.9	15.4
Carbon dioxide	4.62	5.57	6.32	6.95	7.59	8.15	8.73
Carbon monoxide	6.91	7.68	8.42	9.10	9.79	10.4	11.0
Chlorine	2.85	3.12	3.39	3.63	3.86	4.06	4.27
Chloroform	.....	....	3.46	3.94	4.46	5.02	5.53
Ethane	6.82	8.46	10.2	12.3	14.4		
Ethyl acetate	.....	.....	6.42	7.85	9.38	10.0	12.6
Ethyl alcohol	.....	.....	9.10	9.75	10.5	11.1	11.7
Ethyl chloride	.....	4.80	5.59	6.30	6.98	7.15	8.37
Ethylene	6.40	8.02	9.54	11.0	12.5	13.9	15.4
Ethyl ether	....	7.78	8.95	10.3	12.0	14.1	16.1
Helium	41.8	45.2	48.1	50.9	53.3	56.3	58.6
Hydrogen	75.5	82.4	88.8	94.2	97.7	101	105
Hydrogen sulfide	4.94	5.55	6.10	6.59	7.02	7.38	7.75
Methane	7.61	8.32	8.95	9.57	10.1	10.7	11.3
Nitric oxide	6.64	7.36	8.00	8.56	9.04	9.44	9.84
Nitrogen	7.38	8.06	8.67	9.18	9.53	9.87	10.2
Nitrous oxide	5.49	5.72	5.90	6.01	6.32	6.49	6.66
Oxygen	6.83	7.54	8.12	8.60	9.09	9.50	9.89
Steam	.....	.....	9.97	11.1	12.1	13.1	14.0
Sulfur dioxide	...	3.42	3.83	4.21	4.52	4.79	5.10

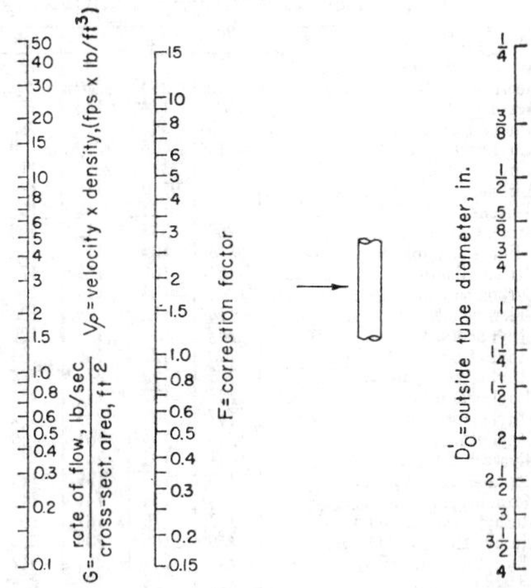

Table 10-11. Base Factors for Liquids Heated Inside Horizontal or Vertical Tubes, Turbulent Flow

Units: B.t.u./(hr.)(sq. ft.)(°F.)

Avg. liquid temp., °F	0	50	100	150	200	250
Acetic acid, 100%	....	....	97.2	101	105	109
Acetic acid, 50%	....	117	156	180	203	228
Acetone	104	122	134	137	139	142
Ammonia	350	425	507	599	690	790
Amyl acetate	65.0	66.2	67.7	71.8	78.5	86.0
Amyl alcohol, iso	21.6	35.8	52.7	73.3	96.0	118
Aniline	....	43.8	58.4	76.5	99.2	123
Benzene	....	75.6	94.5	108	121	134
Brine, $CaCl_2$, 25%	139	190	257	332	420	517
n-Butyl alcohol	31.2	45.5	62.4	83.0	107	133
Carbon disulfide	114	119	125	129	132	133
Carbon tetrachloride	57.4	69.2	78.6	82.6	85.8	88.2
Chlorobenzene	64.6	73.3	78.8	80.5	82.0	82.8
Ethyl acetate	126	126	125	123	122	121
Ethyl alcohol, 100%	58.0	73.6	92.3	112	132	151
Ethyl bromide	97.8	104	110	114	119	122
Ethylene glycol	71.4	105	158	222	299	380
Ethyl ether	100	115	123	130	137	144
Glycerol, 50%	59.0	90.5	131	182	242	302
Heptane	81.4	87.0	94.7	102	112	122
Hexane	85.8	93.8	102	109	114	117
Methyl alcohol, 100%	83.0	110	126	138	149	160
n-Octane	72.0	79.0	85.9	92.0	97.0	102
n-Pentane	103	105	110	115	118	121
Propyl alcohol, iso	25.7	49.3	71.5	94.5	117	139
Sulfur dioxide	167	171	175	180	182	194
Sulfuric acid, 60%	....	65.9	79.4	94.5	110	129
Toluene	77.3	86.9	96.6	104	112	119
Water	....	225	322	408	392	508

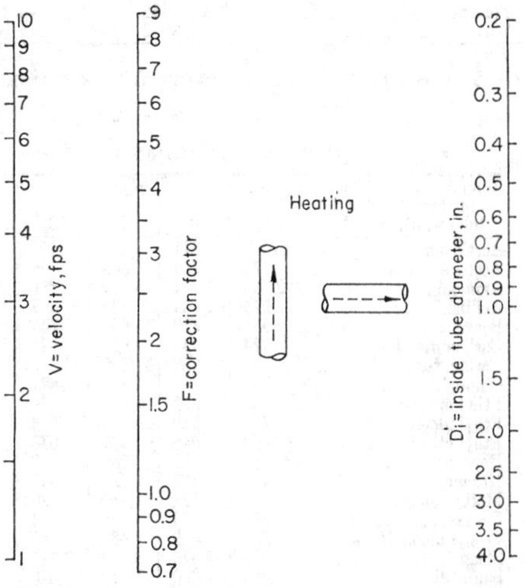

Table 10-12. Base Factors for Liquids Cooled Inside Horizontal or Vertical Tubes, Turbulent Flow

Units: B.t.u./(hr.)(sq. ft.)(°F.)

Avg. liquid temp., °F	0	50	100	150	200	250
Acetic acid, 100%	....	....	72.2	75.0	78.7	81.6
Acetic acid, 50%	....	85.2	122	153	179	201
Acetone	88.4	105	118	121	124	126
Ammonia	314	380	507	650	797	938
Amyl acetate	48.1	50.7	52.3	53.3	54.4	55.5
Amyl alcohol, iso	....	22.7	36.0	53.0	72.3	91.8
Aniline	....	31.6	45.2	63.3	86.9	110
Benzene	....	61.7	79.1	93.5	107	120
Brine, $CaCl_2$, 25%	106	152	217	312	397	510
n-Butyl alcohol	19.2	31.4	45.6	64.0	84.9	107
Carbon disulfide	103	110	116	121	126	128
Carbon tetrachloride	40.4	55.8	67.3	72.0	76.0	78.7
Chlorobenzene	54.5	57.5	60.7	63.8	65.0	65.6
Ethyl acetate	83.3	84.1	84.1	84.1	83.3	82.4
Ethyl alcohol, 100%	41.2	54.8	71.1	89.0	108	128
Ethyl bromide	84.9	92.9	99.9	106	112	116
Ethylene glycol, 50%	44.2	71.7	120	183	261	
Ethyl ether	86.0	99.0	109	118	126	135
Glycerol, 50%	34.9	59.5	94.5	134	179	222
Heptane	66.8	74.2	81.5	88.8	97.0	104
Hexane	70.7	78.5	87.2	95.2	102	108
Methyl alcohol, 100%	65.4	88.5	105	118	132	146
n-Octane	56.0	63.8	70.9	77.2	82.2	88.0
n-Pentane	82.8	89.6	96.4	101	106	110
Propyl alcohol, iso	....	32.4	51.5	71.7	92.7	116
Sulfur dioxide	150	155	161	166	174	178
Sulfuric acid, 60%	....	35.3	54.4	66.9	74.0	77.7
Toluene	61.8	71.5	81.4	90.3	97.6	103
Water	....	153	273	355	427	483

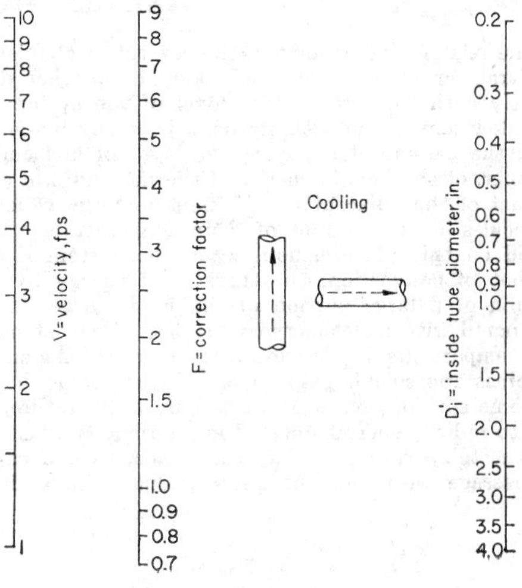

Table 10-13. Base Factors for Liquids Heated or Cooled Outside Single Tubes, Direction of Flow Normal to Tube

Units: B.t.u./(hr.)(sq. ft.)(°F.)

Avg. film temp., °F	0	50	100	150	200	250
Acetic acid, 100%	....	....	142	136	*131*	*125*
Acetic acid, 50%	....	214	260	292	310	*321*
Acetone	*165*	174	184	186	*187*	*189*
Ammonia	486	548	616	*685*	*758*	*827*
Amyl acetate	114	106	97.9	91.0	*84.3*	*76.5*
Amyl alcohol, iso	*54.0*	73.0	94.9	118	140	*163*
Aniline	....	97.0	116	139	164	*194*
Benzene	....	124	140	152	163	*174*
Brine, $CaCl_2$, 25%	264	335	419	508	617	*734*
n-Butyl alcohol	*93.5*	100	112	136	*167*	*206*
Carbon disulfide	164	166	169	171	*173*	*173*
Carbon tetrachloride	....	105	114	116	*117*	*118*
Chlorobenzene	*115*	112	109	106	103	*102*
Ethyl acetate	*154*	145	137	129	*119*	*111*
Ethyl alcohol, 100%	*108*	127	146	165	183	*199*
Ethyl alcohol, 40%	*130*	199	277	*355*	*430*	*508*
Ethyl bromide	*131*	137	142	144	*146*	*147*
Ethylene glycol, 50%	*147*	209	283	362	447	*545*
Ethyl ether	*146*	154	161	169	*175*	*182*
Glycerol, 50%	*147*	192	249	*331*	*431*	
Heptane	*126*	133	139	143	*147*	*151*
Hexane	*128*	134	141	147	151	*155*
Methyl alcohol, 100%	*147*	170	187	*198*	*206*	*212*
Methyl alcohol, 90%	*159*	186	209	*226*	*238*	*251*
Methyl alcohol, 40%	*132*	201	264	317	*359*	*397*
n-Octane	*117*	124	129	*135*	*140*	*146*
n-Pentane	139	144	148	*151*	*152*	*154*
Propyl alcohol, iso	*62.5*	91.0	118	143	163	*180*
Sulfur dioxide	230	225	223	*221*	*221*	*218*
Sulfuric acid, 60%	....	*110*	137	150	164	*176*
Toluene	128	135	142	148	152	*155*
Water	....	382	497	525	645	*700*

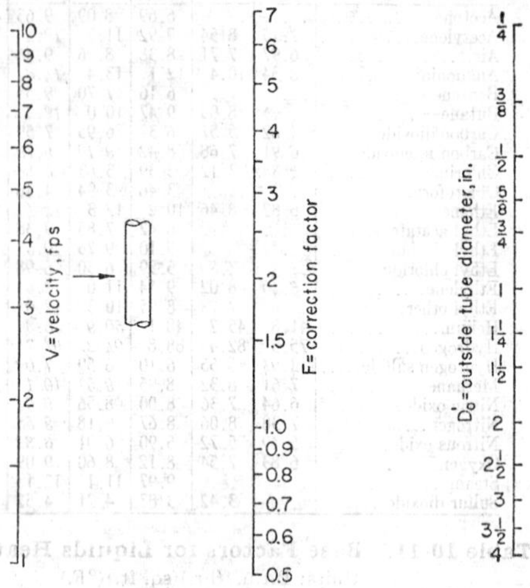

Table 10-14. Base Factors for Condensation of Pure Saturated Vapors on Horizontal Tubes

Units: B.t.u./(hr.)(sq. ft.)(°F.)

Temp. of condensate film (assume equal to tube wall), °F	50	100	150	200	250	300
Acetic acid	.....	511	495	470	424	373
Acetone	772	789	805	805	795	780
Ammonia	2,768	3,145	3,459	3,711	*3,875*	*3,965*
Aniline	*275*	405	544	685	830	977
Benzene	554	609	658	706	755	798
Carbon disulfide	924	933	933	924	905	868
Carbon tetrachloride	551	580	569	*482*		
Chloroform	735	791	847	*895*	*950*	*997*
Ethyl acetate	*702*	772	835	889	936	990
Ethyl alcohol	*495*	556	618	678	745	807
Ethyl ether	620	646	665	678	691	705
Heptane	*488*	537	580	607	628	645
Hexane	*525*	552	576	592	608	614
Methyl alcohol	695	772	850	920	972	103
Octane	*482*	513	538	554	575	585
Propyl alcohol, iso	*284*	400	488	548	*596*	*632*
Steam	1,830	2,440	3,020	3,590	4,120	4,660
Sulfur dioxide	1,260	1,200	1,115	1,010	*900*	780

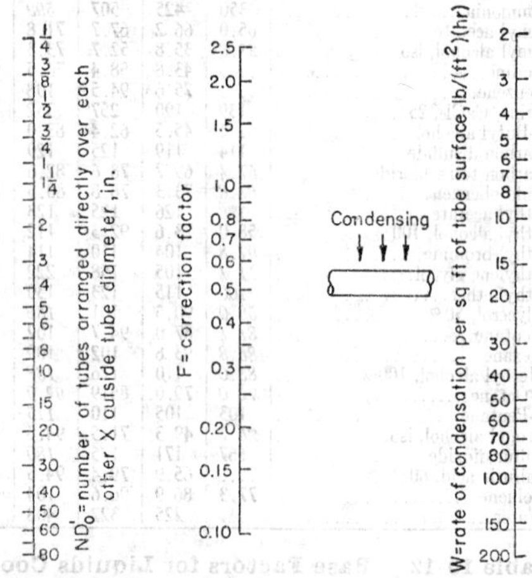

RADIANT-HEAT TRANSMISSION

The relative importance of the several mechanisms of the transfer of heat from one body to another differs greatly with the temperature level of the system. At very low temperatures the transfer is chiefly by conduction, the passing along, from one layer of molecules to another, of the kinetic energy of the molecules in excess of that of the adjacent layer—kinetic energy which the molecules have by virtue of their temperature. Superposed on this phenomenon, when the system is fluid, is that of convection, the transfer of energy by mass motion of a large portion of the fluid—large, that is, compared with molecular magnitudes. Even at moderate temperature levels, however, another phenomenon becomes appreciable. The molecules or atoms, because of some sort of excitation caused by temperature, give rise to radiant energy, emitted in an amount determined by the temperature level of the molecules and capable of passage with more or less absorption to a distant receiver of the radiation. If the phenomena of conduction and convection on the one hand are contrasted with thermal radiation on the other, it is found that the former are affected by temperature difference, and very little by temperature level, whereas the later increases rapidly with increase in temperature level. It follows that, at very low temperatures, conduction and convection are the major contributors to the total heat transfer; at very high temperatures, radiation is the controlling factor. The temperature at which radiation accounts for roughly one-half of the total heat transmission depends on such factors as the emissivity of the surface or the magnitude of the convection coefficient. For large pipes losing heat by free convection, this is room temperature; for fine wires of low emissivity, it is above a red heat.

Subject matter will be divided into (1) the nature of thermal radiation, (2) radiant-heat interchange between the surfaces of solids separated by a non-absorbing medium, (3) radiation from non-luminous gases, (4) radiation from clouds of particles, and (5) the combined effect of all these mechanisms in the combustion chamber of a furnace. Nomenclature is summarized below.

Nomenclature

A = areas of surface, sq. ft. A_c for cold body (sink); A_R, A_S, A_T for refractory zones; $A_1, A_2, \ldots$ for source-sink type surfaces.
C_c = dimensionless factor to allow for effect of total pressure on CO_2 radiation.
C_w = dimensionless factor to allow for effects of total pressure and partial pressure on H_2O radiation.
$(C_p)_m$ = mean specific heat of combustion gas, B.t.u./(lb.)(°F.).
c_1, c_2 = dimensional constants in Planck's law [Eq. (10-97)].
F = dimensionless geometrical factor to allow for *direct* interchange between two surfaces, F_{12} from surface 1 to 2, based on A_1; F_{21} from surfaces 2 to 1, based on A_2.
$\bar{F}$ = dimensionless geometrical factor to allow for net radiation between *black* surfaces, including the effect of refractory surfaces.
$\mathfrak{F}$ = dimensionless factor to allow for interchange between gray surfaces, defined by Eq. (10-110) and evaluated by Eq. (10-111). $\mathfrak{F}_{12}$ is based on A_1.
h = coefficient of heat transfer by convection, B.t.u./(hr.)(sq. ft.)(°F.).
I = radiation intensity, B.t.u./(hr.)(sq. ft.)
i = enthalpy of entering fuel, air, and any recirculated flue gas, above a base temperature T_0 (water as vapor), B.t.u./hr.
KL = dimensionless factor, absorption strength (Fig. 10-26).
x_w/k = wall thickness/thermal conductivity, following Eq. (10-121) only.
L = beam length for gas radiation, ft. (see Table 10-30).
M = molecular weight.
N_B = intensity of radiation from a black surface, B.t.u./(sq. ft.)(hr.) per unit solid angle in direction normal to surface.
P = gas pressure, atm., P_c, P_w = partial pressure of CO_2, H_2O; P_T = total pressure.
q = rate of heat transfer, B.t.u./hr.; q_F, from flame; q_C to cold surface (sink); q_L, lost to surroundings.
r_{af} = weight ratio of air to fuel.
S = sulfur dioxide radiation, B.t.u./(sq. ft.)(hr.)
T = absolute temperature; Rankine, Fahrenheit absolute (460 + °F.); T_c, cold body (sink); T_F, flame; T_G, gas; T_g, T_r, green, red brightness temperature T_S, surface; T_0, base temperature. In Figs. 10-26 and 10-27, T is in degrees Kelvin (273 + °C.).
t = thermometric temperature, °F.
U_R = over-all coefficient of heat transfer through refractory, B.t.u./(hr.)(sq. ft.)(°F.).
W = total emissive power, B.t.u./(sq. ft.)(hr.); W_B for black body; $W_{B\lambda}$ for monochromatic emissive power, B.t.u./(hr.)(sq. ft.)(cm.).
v_{IA} = firing rate, defined after Eq. (10-125).
w_G = combustion-gas rate, lb./hr.
x, y, z = distances, ft., defined in Fig. 10-20.
Y, Z = dimension ratios, defined in Fig. 10-20.
α = absorptivity, dimensionless.
Δ = $T_g - T_r$ (see Fig. 10-26).
ϵ = emissivity, dimensionless.
ϵ' = "effective" emissivity.
θ = angle.
η = efficiency, dimensionless.
λ = wave length, cm.
σ = Stefan-Boltzmann constant.

Selected Bibliography of Recent Literature on Radiant-heat Transfer

A. General References

1. Jakob, "Heat Transfer," Wiley, New York (Vol. I, 1949; Vol. II, 1957) Chaps. 4, 7, 31, and 32.
2. Chandrasekhar, "Radiative Transfer," Oxford, New York, 1950.
3. Kourganoff, "Basic Methods in Transfer Problems," Oxford, London, 1952.
4. Planck, "Theory of Heat," Vol. V of "Introduction to Theoretical Physics," Macmillan, New York, 1957.
5. Rutgers, "Temperature Radiation of Solids," Vol. XXVI of "Handbuch der Physik," S. Flügge (ed.), Springer Verlag, Berlin, Vienna, 1958.

B. Emissivities of Solid Materials

1. Sieber, *Z. Tech. Physik*, **22**, 130 (1941).
2. Forsythe and Adams, *J. Opt. Soc. Am.*, **35**, 108 (1945).
3. Benford, Lloyd, and Schwartz, *J. Opt. Soc. Am.*, **38**, 445 (1948).
4. Nottingham and Mutter, *Phys. Rev.*, **74**, 1261 (1948).
5. Euler, *Elektrotech. Z.*, **70**, 427 (1949).
6. Müller, *Elektrotech. Z.*, **71**, 11, 287 (1950).
7. McMahon, *J. Am. Ceram. Soc.*, **34**, 91 (1951).
8. Middleton and Sander, *J. Opt. Soc. Am.*, **41**, 419 (1951).
9. Gier, Dunkle, and Bevans, *J. Opt. Soc. Am.*, **44**, 558 (1954).
10. de Corso and Coit *Mech. Eng.*, **76**, 682 (1954).
11. DeVos, *Physica*, **20**, 669, 690 (1954).
12. Tellex and Wadion, *J. Opt. Soc. Am.*, **45**, 19 (1955).
13. Larrabee, The Spectral and Optical Properties of Tungsten, *Mass. Inst. of Technol. Res. Lab. Electron., Tech. Rept.* 328 (May, 1957).
14. Wade, *NACA TN* 4206 (March, 1958).
15. Richmond and Stewart, *NASA Memo.* 4-4-59W (April, 1959).
16. Wade and Casey, *NASA Memo.* 5-13-59L (June, 1959).
17. Dunkle, Ehrenburg, and Gier, *J. Heat Transfer*, **C82**, 64 (1960).
18. Allen *et al.*, *J. Appl. Phys.*, **31**, 1382 (1960).
19. Brandt, Irvine, and Eckert, *Proc. of 1960 Heat Transfer and Fluid Mech. Inst.*, 220 (1960).
20. Bennet and Porteus, *J. Opt. Soc. Am.*, **51**, 123 (1961).

C. Radiation in Liquids

1. Curico and Petty, *J. Opt. Soc. Am.*, **41**, 302 (1951).
2. Bocharov and Krutikov, *Izv. Akad. Nauk USSR*, 1957 Geophysical Series: translation of Am. Geophysical Union, No. 7, 528 (1958).

D. Radiation in Gases

1. Plass and Fivel, *Quart. J. Roy. Meterol. Soc., London*, **81**, 48 (1955).
2. Howard, Air Force Cambridge Research Center, *Geophys. Res. Paper* 40 (1955).
3. Howard, Burch, and Williams, *J. Opt. Soc. Am.*, **46**, 237, 242 (1956).
4. Goulard and Goulard, *Heat Transfer and Fluid Mech. Inst.*, 126 (1959).
5. Plass, *J. Opt. Soc. Am.*, **49**, 821 (1959).
6. Penner, "Quantitative Molecular Spectroscopy and Gas Emissivities," Addison-Wesley, Reading, Mass., 1959.

E. Radiation from Flames

1. Wolfhard and Parker, *Proc. Phys. Soc. (London)*, **B62**, 523 (1949).
2. Sherman, *Trans. ASME*, **79**, 1727 (1957).

F. Radiation in Dispersions

1. Chu and Churchill, *J. Phys. Chem.*, **59**, 855 (1955).
2. Sleicher and Churchill, *Ind. Eng. Chem.*, **48**, 1819 (1956).
3. Chu, Clark, and Churchill, *J. Phys. Chem.*, **61**, 1303 (1957).
4. Scott and Churchill, *J. Phys. Chem.*, **62**, 1300 (1958).
5. Stull and Plass, *J. Opt. Soc. Am.*, **50**, 121 (1960).

G. Radiant-heat Exchange between Solid Bodies

1. Mackey, Wright, Clark, and Gay, *Cornell Univ. Exp. Sta. Bull.* 32, Ithaca (August, 1943).
2. Jensen, Kgl. Danske Videnskabernes Selskal. *Matematisk-Fysiske Meddelser*, **24**, No. (1948).
3. Konakov, *Izv. Akad. Nauk SSSR, Otd. Tekh. Nauk* **3** (1951).
4. Shorin, *Izv. Akad. Nauk SSSR, Otd. Tekh. Nauk* **3** (1951).
5. Kellett, *J. Opt. Soc. Am.*, **42**, 339 (1952).
6. Filippov, *Izv. Akad. Nauk SSSR, Otd. Tekh. Nauk*, **1**, 155 (1955).
7. Oppenheim, *Trans. ASME*, **78**, 725 (1956).
8. Konakov, Filimonov, and Khrustalev, *Soviet Phys.-Tech. Phys.*, **2**, No. 5 (May 1957).

9. Adianov and Shorin, *Izv. Akad. Nauk SSSR, Otd. Tekh. Nauk* No. 5, 46 (1958).
10. Hottel and Cohen, *A.I.Ch.E. J.*, **4,** 3 (1958).
11. Kazakevich, et al., *Teploenerge.*, **6,** 34 (1959).
12. Gebhart, *Trans. ASHRAE*, **65,** 321 (1959).
13. Bevans and Dunkle, *J. Heat Transfer*, **C82,** 1 (1960).
14. Oppenheim and Bevans, *J. Heat Transfer*, **C82,** 360 (1960).
15. Usiskin and Siegel, *J. Heat Transfer*, **C82,** 369 (1960).
16. Sparrow, *J. Heat Transfer*, **C82,** 375 (1960).
17. Sparrow, Gregg, Szel, and Manos, *ASME Paper* No. 60-HT-4 (1960).
18. Usiskin and Sparrow, *Intern. J. Heat Mass Transfer*, **1,** 28 (1960).
19. Goulard and Goulard, *Intern. J. Heat Mass Transfer*, **1,** 81 (1960).
20. Eckert, Irvine, and Sparrow, *J. Amer. Rocket Soc.*, **30,** 644 (1960).
21. Krishman and Sundaram, *Nature (London)*, **188,** 483 (1960).
22. Detkov, *Zh. Tekhn. Fiz.*, **30,** 96 (1960).
23. Sparrow, Usiskin, and Hubbard, *J. Heat Transfer*, **C83,** 199 (1961).
24. Sparrow, Gregg, Szel, and Manos, *J. Heat Transfer*, **C83,** 207 (1961).
25. Bevans, *J. Heat Transfer*, **C83,** 226 (1961).
26. Sparrow and Gregg, *J. Heat Transfer*, **C83,** 494 (1961).
27. Eckert and Sparrow, *Intern. J. Heat Mass Transfer*, **3,** 42 (1961).
28. Parkes, *Intern. J. Heat Mass Transfer*, **2,** 155 (1961).
29. Branstetter, *NASA TN* D-1088 (August, 1961).
30. Edwards, *J. Heat Transfer*, **C84,** 1 (1962).
31. Sparrow and E. R. G. Eckert, *J. Heat Transfer*, **C84,** 12 (1962).
32. Sparrow, Albers, and Eckert, *J. Heat Transfer*, **C84,** 73 (1962).

H. Simultaneous Radiation, Convection, and Conduction

1. Hamaker, *Philips Res. Repts.*, **2,** 55, 103 (1947).
2. Grigull, *Brennstoff-Waerme-Kraft*, **3,** 253 (1951).
3. Van Der Held, *Appl. Sci. Res.*, **A3,** 237 (1952); also **A4,** 77 (1953).
4. Genzel, *Z. Physik*, **135,** 177 (1953).
5. Labuntsov, *Dokl. Akad. Nauk SSSR* (N.S.) **118,** 1118 (1958).
6. Zaeschmar, *Allgem. Waermetech.*, **9,** 33 (1958/59).
7. Larkin and Churchill, *A.I.Ch.E. J.*, **5,** 467 (1959).
8. Hill and Wilhelm, *A.I.Ch.E. J.*, **5,** 486 (1959).
9. Vishanta and Grosh, *J. Heat Transfer*, **C84,** 63 (1962).

THE NATURE OF THERMAL RADIATION

If two small bodies of areas A_1 and A_2 are placed in a large evacuated enclosure perfectly insulated externally, then, when the system has come to thermal equilibrium, the bodies will emit radiation at the rates A_1W_1 and A_2W_2, respectively, where W is the total emissive power,* energy per unit time per unit area of the surface [B.t.u./(sq. ft.)(hr.)] emitted throughout the hemisphere above each element of surface. Let the energy impinging on unit area of any small body in the enclosure, due to radiation from the walls of the latter, be I. If the bodies have *absorptivities* (fraction of incident radiation which is absorbed) of α_1 and α_2, then energy balances on the bodies will have the form

$$IA_1\alpha_1 = A_1W_1 \quad \text{and} \quad IA_2\alpha_2 = A_2W_2$$

from which $W_1/\alpha_1 = W_2/\alpha_2 (= W_x/\alpha_x$, where x is *any* body). This generalization, that at thermal equilibrium the ratio of the emissive power of a surface to its absorptivity is the same for all bodies, is known as *Kirchhoff's law*. Since α cannot exceed unity, Kirchhoff's law places an upper limit on W, called W_B; and any surface having this upper limiting emissive power is called a *perfect radiator*. Since such a surface must have an absorptivity of unity and therefore a reflectivity of zero, the perfect radiator is more commonly referred to as a *black body*. The ratio of the emissive power of an actual surface to that of a black body is called the *emissivity* ϵ of the surface. Kirchhoff's law restated is as follows: At thermal equilibrium the emissivity and absorptivity of a body are the same.

* Sometimes called *emittance, total hemispherical intensity,* or *radiant flux density.*

The emissive power of a black body depends on its temperature only, and the second law of thermodynamics may be used to prove a proportionality between emissive power and the fourth power of the absolute temperature. The relation

$$W_B = \sigma T^4 \tag{10-96}$$

is known as the *Stefan-Boltzmann law;* and the proportionality constant σ is known as the Stefan-Boltzmann constant [0.173×10^{-8} B.t.u./(sq. ft.)(hr.)(°R.)^4; 5.71×10^{-5} ergs/(sq. cm.)(sec.)(°K.)^4; 4.92×10^{-8} kg.-cal./(sq. m.)(hr.)(°K.)^4].

Other properties of black-body radiation of interest in heat transmission are related to the nature of its distribution in the spectrum and the shift of that distribution with temperature. If $W_{B,\lambda}$ is the *monochromatic emissive power* at wave length λ such that $W_{B,\lambda} \cdot d\lambda$ is the energy emitted from a surface per unit area per unit time in the wave-length interval λ to $\lambda + d\lambda$, the relation among $W_{B,\lambda}$, λ, and T is given by *Planck's law*

$$W_{B,\lambda} = \frac{c_1\lambda^{-5}}{e^{\frac{c_2}{\lambda T}} - 1} \tag{10-97}$$

$c_1 = 1.176 \times 10^{-8}$ [B.t.u./(sq. ft.)(hr.)] (cm.)^4 or 0.885×10^{-12} (cal.)(sq. cm.)/(sec.); $c_2 = 2.58$ (cm.) (°R.) or 1.433 cm. °K. According to Planck's law the monochromatic emissive power at any temperature varies from 0 at $\lambda = 0$ through a maximum and back to 0 at $\lambda = \infty$; at any wave length it increases with temperature, but values at shorter wave lengths increase faster so that the maximum value shifts to shorter wave lengths as the temperature rises. The position of the maximum is inversely proportional to the absolute temperature (*Wien's displacement law*), derivable from Eq. (10-97). The relation is: $\lambda_{max}T = 0.5193$ cm. °R. or 0.2885 cm. °K.

The emissivity ϵ of a surface (more properly the total hemispherical emissivity, to differentiate it from monochromatic emissivity ϵ_λ, the ratio of radiating powers at the wave length λ, and from directional emissivity ϵ_θ, the ratio of radiating powers in a direction making the angle θ with the normal to the surface) varies with its temperature, its degree of roughness, and, if a metal, its degree of oxidation. Table 10-15 gives the emissivities of various surfaces and emphasizes the large variation possible in a single material. Although the values in the table apply strictly to normal radiation from the surface (with few exceptions), they may be used with negligible error for hemispherical emissivity except in the case of well-polished metal surfaces, for which the hemispherical emissivity is 15 to 20 per cent higher than the normal value.

A few generalizations may be made concerning the emissivity of surfaces: (1) The emissivities of metallic conductors have been shown to be very low and proportional to the absolute temperature; and the proportionality constant for different metals varies as the square root of the electrical resistance at a standard base temperature. Unless extraordinary pains are taken to prevent any possibility of oxidation or imperfection of polish, however, a specimen may exhibit several times this theoretical minimum emissivity. (2) The emissivities of non-conductors are much higher and, in contrast to metals, generally decrease with increase in temperature.

Table 10-15. The Normal Total Emissivity of Various Surfaces

A. Metals and Their Oxides

Surface	t, °F.*	Emissivity*	Reference
Aluminum			
Highly polished plate, 98.3% pure	440–1070	0.039–0.057	*SF*
Polished plate	73	0.040	*ES*
Rough plate	78	0.055	*ES*
Oxidized at 1110°F	390–1110	0.11–0.19	*RO*
Al-surfaced roofing	100	0.216	*RH*
Calorized surfaces, heated at 1110°F.			
Copper	390–1110	0.18–0.19	*RO*
Steel	390–1110	0.52–0.57	*RO*
Brass			
Highly polished:			
73.2% Cu, 26.7% Zn	476–674	0.028–0.031	*SF*
62.4% Cu, 36.8% Zn, 0.4% Pb, 0.3% Al	494–710	0.033–0.037	*SF*
82.9% Cu, 17.0% Zn	530	0.030	*SF*
Hard rolled, polished, but direction of polishing visible	70	0.038	*ES*
but somewhat attacked	73	0.043	*ES*
but traces of stearin from polish left on	75	0.053	*ES*
Polished	100–600	0.096	*RH*
Rolled plate, natural surface	72	0.06	*ES*
rubbed with coarse emery	72	0.20	*ES*
Dull plate	120–660	0.22	*Wam*
Oxidized by heating at 1110°F	390–1110	0.61–0.59	*RO*
Chromium; see Nickel Alloys for Ni-Cr steels	100–1000	0.08–0.26	
Copper			
Carefully polished electrolytic copper	176	0.018	*KH*
Comm'l, emeried, polished, but pits remaining	66	0.030	*ES*
Comm'l, scraped shiny but not mirror-like	72	0.072	*ES*
Polished	242	0.023	*WW*
Plate, heated long time, covered with thick oxide layer	77	0.78	*ES*
Plate heated at 1110°F	390–1110	0.57	*RO*
Cuprous oxide	1470–2010	0.66–0.54	*B*
Molten copper	1970–2330	0.16–0.13	*B*
Gold			
Pure, highly polished	440–1160	0.018–0.035	*SF*
Iron and steel			
Metallic surfaces (or very thin oxide layer):			
Electrolytic iron, highly polished	350–440	0.052–0.064	*SF*
Polished iron	800–1880	0.144–0.377	*VS*
Iron freshly emeried	68	0.242	*ES*
Cast iron, polished	392	0.21	*RO*
Wrought iron, highly polished	100–480	0.28	*Wam*
Cast iron, newly turned	72	0.435	*ES*
Polished steel casting	1420–1900	0.52–0.56	*P*
Ground sheet steel	1720–2010	0.55–0.61	*P*
Smooth sheet iron	1650–1900	0.55–0.60	*P*
Cast iron, turned on lathe	1620–1810	0.60–0.70	*P*
Oxidized surfaces:			
Iron plate, pickled, then rusted red	68	0.612	*ES*
completely rusted	67	0.685	*ES*
Rolled sheet steel	70	0.657	*ES*
Oxidized iron	212	0.736	*HN*
Cast iron, oxidized at 1100°F	390–1110	0.64–0.78	*RO*
Steel, oxidized at 1100°F	390–1110	0.79	*RO*
Smooth oxidized electrolytic iron	260–980	0.78–0.82	*SF*
Iron and Steel—(*Continued*)			
Oxidized surfaces—(*Continued*)			
Iron oxide	930–2190	0.85–0.89	*BF2*
Rough ingot iron	1700–2040	0.87–0.95	*P*
Sheet steel, strong rough oxide layer	75	0.80	*ES*
dense shiny oxide layer	75	0.82	*ES*
Cast plate, smooth	73	0.80	*ES*
rough	73	0.82	*ES*
Cast iron, rough, strongly oxidized	100–480	0.95	*Wam*
Wrought iron, dull oxidized	70–680	0.94	*Wam*
Steel plate, rough	100–700	0.94–0.97	*RH*
High temp. alloy steels (see Nickel Alloys).			
Molten metal			
cast iron	2370–2550	0.29	*T*
mild steel	2910–3270	0.28	*T*
Lead			
Pure (99.96%), unoxidized	260–440	0.057–0.075	*SF*
Gray oxidized	75	0.281	*ES*
Oxidized at 390°F	390	0.63	*RO*
Mercury	32–212	0.09–0.12	*C*
Molybdenum filament	1340–4700	0.096–0.292	*AW*
Monel metal, oxidized at 1110°F	390–1110	0.41–0.46	*RO*
Nickel			
Electroplated on polished iron, then polished	74	0.045	*ES*
Technically pure (98.9% Ni, + Mn), polished	440–710	0.07–0.087	*SF*
Electropolated on pickled iron, not polished	68	0.11	*ES*
Wire	368–1844	0.096–0.186	*VS*
Plate, oxidized by heating at 1110°F	390–1110	0.37–0.48	*RO*
Nickel oxide	1200–2290	0.59–0.86	*BF-1*
Nickel alloys			
Chromnickel	125–1894	0.64–0.76	*VS*
Nickelin (18–32 Ni; 55–68 Cu; 20 Zn), gray oxidized	70	0.262	*ES*
KA-2S alloy steel (8% Ni; 18% Cr), light silvery, rough, brown, after heating	420–914	0.44–0.36	*R*
after 42 hr. heating at 980°F	420–980	0.62–0.73	*R*
NCT-3 alloy (20% Ni; 25% Cr.). Brown, splotched, oxidized from service	420–980	0.90–0.97	*R*
NCT-6 alloy (60% Ni; 12% Cr). Smooth, black, firm adhesive oxide coat from service	520–1045	0.89–0.82	*R*
Platinum			
Pure, polished plate	440–1160	0.054–0.104	*SF*
Strip	1700–2960	0.12–0.17	*F*
Filament	80–2240	0.036–0.192	*DW*
Wire	440–2510	0.073–0.182	*G*
Silver			
Polished, pure	440–1160	0.0198–0.0324	*SF*
Polished	100–700	0.0221–0.0312	*RH*
Steel, see Iron.			
Tantalum filament	2420–5430	0.194–0.31	*AW*
Tin—Bright tinned iron sheet	76	0.043 and 0.064	*ES*
Tungsten			
Filament, aged	80–6000	0.032–0.35	*FW*
Filament	6000	0.39	*Z*
Zinc			
Comm'l, 99.1% pure, polished	440–620	0.045–0.053	*SF*
Oxidized by heating at 750°F	750	0.11	*RO*
Galvanized sheet iron, fairly bright	82	0.228	*ES*
Galvanized sheet iron, gray oxidized	75	0.276	*ES*

B. Refractories, Building Materials, Paints, and Miscellaneous

Surface	t, °F.*	Emissivity*	Reference
Asbestos			
Board	74	0.96	*ES*
Paper	100–700	0.93–0.945	*RH*
Brick			
Red, rough, but no gross irregularities	70	0.93	*ES*
Silica, unglazed, rough	1832	0.80	*P*
Silica, glazed, rough	2012	0.85	*P*
Grog brick, glazed	2012	0.75	*P*
See Refractory Materials below.			
Carbon			
T-carbon (Gebr. Siemens) 0.9% ash	260–1160	0.81–0.79	*SF*
This started with emissivity at 260°F. of 0.72, but on heating changed to values given			
Carbon filament	1900–2560	0.526	*L*
Candle soot	206–520	0.952	*WW*
Lampblack-waterglass coating	209–362	0.959–0.947	*KH*
Carbon—(*Continued*)			
Same	260–440	0.957–0.952	*SF*
thin layer on iron plate	69	0.927	*ES*
thick coat	68	0.967	*ES*
Lampblack, 0.003 in. or thicker	100–700	0.945	*RH*
Enamel, white fused, on iron	66	0.897	*ES*
Glass, smooth	72	0.937	*ES*
Gypsum, 0.02 in. thick on smooth or blackened plate	70	0.903	*ES*
Marble, light gray, polished	72	0.931	*ES*
Oak, planed	70	0.895	*ES*
Oil layers on polished nickel (lub. oil)	68	....	*ES*
Polished surface, alone	....	0.045	
+0.001-in. oil	....	0.27	
+0.002-in. oil	....	0.46	
+0.005-in. oil	....	0.72	
∞ thick oil layer	....	0.82	

* When two temperatures and two emissivities are given, they correspond, first to first and second to second, and linear interpolation is permissible.

Table 10-15. The Normal Total Emissivity of Various Surfaces—(*Concluded*)

Surface	t, °F.*	Emissivity*	Reference
Oil layers on aluminum foil (linseed oil)	....	....	*HN*
Al foil	212	0.087†	
+1 coat oil	212	0.561	
+2 coats oil	212	0.574	
Paints, lacquers, varnishes			
Snowhite enamel varnish or rough iron plate	73	0.906	*ES*
Black shiny lacquer, sprayed on iron	76	0.875	*ES*
Black shiny shellac on tinned iron sheet	70	0.821	*ES*
Black matte shellac	170–295	0.91	*WW*
Black lacquer	100–200	0.80–0.95	*RH*
Flat black lacquer	100–200	0.96–0.98	*RH*
White lacquer	100–200	0.80–0.95	*RH*
Oil paints, sixteen different, all colors	212	0.92–0.96	*HN*
Aluminum paints and lacquers			
10% Al, 22% lacquer body, on rough or smooth surface	212	0.52	*HN*
26% Al, 27% lacquer body, on rough or smooth surface	212	0.3	*HN*
Other Al paints, varying age and Al-content	212	0.27–0.67	*HN*

Surface	t, °F.*	Emissivity*	Reference
Paint, lacquers, varnishes—(*Continued*)			
Al lacquer, varnish binder, on rough plate	70	0.39	*ES*
Al paint, after heating to 620°F	300–600	0.35	*SF*
Paper, thin			
Pasted on tinned iron plate	66	0.924	*ES*
rough iron plate	66	0.929	*ES*
black lacquered plate	66	0.944	*ES*
Plaster, rough lime	50–190	0.91	*Wam*
Porcelain, glazed	72	0.924	*ES*
Quartz, rough, fused	70	0.932	*ES*
Refractory materials, 40 different	1110–1830	....	*KW*
poor radiators	....	[0.65 } –0.75	
	....	0.70 }	
good radiators	....	0.80 } – { 0.85	
	....	0.85 } – { 0.90]	
Roofing paper	69	0.91	*ES*
Rubber			
Hard, glossy plate	74	0.945	*ES*
Soft, gray, rough (reclaimed)	76	0.859	*ES*
Serpentine, polished	74	0.900	*ES*
Water	32–212	0.95–0.963	*H*

* When two temperatures and two emissivities are given, they correspond, first to first and second to second, and linear interpolation is permissible.

† Although this value is probably high, it is given for comparison with the data, by the same investigator, to show the effect of oil layers. See "Aluminum," part A of this table.

NOTE. The results of many investigators have been omitted because of obvious defects in experimental method. A comprehensive bibliography is given in reference *SF*, following this table.

C. REFERENCES IN TABLE OF EMISSIVITIES

Year	Author and source	Key
1907	K. Siegel, *Sitzungsber. Akad. Wien.*, **116**, 2A, 1203	*S*
1908	C. B. Thwing, *Phys. Rev.*, **26**, 190	*T*
1909	G. K. Burgess, *Bur. Standards Bull.* 6, *Sci. Paper* 121, p. 111	*B*
1911	F. Wamsler, *Z. Ver. deut. Ing.*, **55**, 599; *Forschungsarb. Ver. deut. Ing.*, **98**	*Wam*
1912	W. Westphal, *Verh. physik. Ges.* (2), **14**, 987; **15**, 897	*WW*
1913	Randolph and Overholzer, *Phys. Rev.*, **2**, 144	*RO*
1913	O. Lummer, *Electrotech. Z.*, **34**, 1428	*L*
1914	Burgess and Foote, *Bur. Standards Bull.* 11, *Sci. Paper* 224, pp. 41–64	*BF1*
1914	P. D. Foote, *Bur. Standards Bull.* 11, *Sci. Paper* 243, p. 607; *J. Wash. Acad.*, **5**, 1 (1915)	*F*
1915	Burgess and Foote, *Bur. Standards Bull.* 12, *Sci. Paper* 249 pp. 83–89	*BF2*
1915	V. A. Suydam, *Phys. Rev.*, (2), **5**, 497	*VS*
1923	K. Hoffmann, *Z. Physik.*, **14**, 310	*KH*
1924	Davison and Weeks, *J. Optical Soc. Am.*, **8**, 581	*DW*
1925	Forsythe and Worthing, *Astrophys. J.*, **61**, 146	*FW*
1925	W. Geiss, *Physica*, **5**, 203	*G*
1925	"Hütte," 25th ed., vol. 1, W. Ernst u. Sohn.	*Hü*
1925	C. Zwikker, *Arch. Néerb.*, IIIA, **9**, 207	*Z*
1926	A. G. Worthing, *Phys. Rev.* (2), **28**, 190	*AW*
1927	V. Polak, *Z. tech. Physik*, **8**, 307	*P*
1927	E. Schmidt, *Beih. Gesundh.-Ing.*, Beiheft 22, Reihe 1, p. 1.	*ES*
1927	M. Wenzl and F. Morawe, *Stahl und Eisen*, **47**, 867–871	*WM*
1927	K. Wetzler, Dissertation, Darmstadt	*KW*
1928	H. Schmidt and E. Furthmann, *Mitt. K.W.-Inst. Eisenforsch., Abhandl.*, **109**, 225	*SF*
1928	Private communication from Standard Oil Development Co.	*HN*
1929	R. H. Heilman, *Trans. Am. Soc. Mech. Engrs.* F. St. Power Sec., Surface Heat Transmission	*RH*
1931	H. S. Rice, M.I.T. thesis in Fuel and Gas Engineering	*R*
1932	Calculated from formula of Foote	*C*
1932	Calculated from spectral data	*H*

(3) The low temperature emissivity of most non-metals is above 0.8. (4) Iron and steel vary widely with the degree of oxidation and roughness, clean metallic surfaces having an emissivity of 0.05 to 0.45 at low temperatures to 0.4 to 0.7 at high temperatures; oxidized and/or rough surfaces, 0.6 to 0.95 at low temperatures to 0.9 to 0.95 at high temperatures.

The absorptivity α of a surface depends on the factors affecting emissivity and in addition on the quality of the incident radiation, measured by its distribution in the spectrum. One may assign two subscripts to α, the first to indicate the temperature of the receiver and the second that of the incident radiation. It has already been seen that, according to Kirchhoff's law, the emissivity of a surface at temperature T_1 is equal to the absorptivity $\alpha_{1,1}$ which the surface exhibits for black radiation from a source at the same temperature; *i.e.*, a surface of low radiating power is also a poor absorber (or good reflector or transmitter) of radiation from a source at its own temperature. If the monochromatic absorptivity α_λ varies considerably with wave length and much less with temperature (which is generally the case). it follows that the total absorptivity $\alpha_{1,2}$ will vary more with T_2 than with T_1. Data on $\alpha_{1,2}$ at $t_1 = 70$°F. for a large group of non-metals indicate a decrease with T_2 from 0.8–0.95 at 500°R. to 0.1–0.9 at 5000°R. The value of $\alpha_{1,2}$ for a metal is approximately its emissivity evaluated at $T = \sqrt{T_1 \cdot T_2}$.

If α_λ is a constant independent of λ, the surface is called *gray*, and its total absorptivity α will be independent of the spectral-energy distribution of the incident radiation; then $\alpha_{1,2} = \alpha_{1,1} \equiv \epsilon_1$, *i.e.*, emissivity ϵ may be used in substitution for α even though the temperatures of the incident radiation and the receiver are not the same.

Radiation between the Surfaces of Solids Separated by a Non-absorbing Medium

The net loss of energy by radiation from a body at temperature T_1 in *black* surroundings at T_2 is given by

$$q_{1,\text{net}} = 0.173 A_1 \left[\epsilon_1 \left(\frac{T_1}{100}\right)^4 - \alpha_{1,2} \left(\frac{T_2}{100}\right)^4 \right] \quad \text{B.t.u./hr.} \qquad (10\text{-}98)$$

when A_1 is square feet and T is degrees Rankine.

When $\alpha_{1,2} = \epsilon_1$, *i.e.*, when the body is gray (see above), this simplifies to

$$q_{1,\text{net}} = 0.173 A_1 \epsilon_1 \left[\left(\frac{T_1}{100}\right)^4 - \left(\frac{T_2}{100}\right)^4 \right] \qquad (10\text{-}99)$$

The more complicated but important case of radiation interchange in a system of several surfaces at different temperatures and emissivities involves the concept of a geometrical factor F. F_{12} is defined as the fraction of the radiation leaving surface A_1 in all directions which is intercepted by surface A_2. Evaluation of this factor is as follows: Visualize, on black surface A_1 of total emissive power W_{B1}, a small surface element dA_1 radiat-

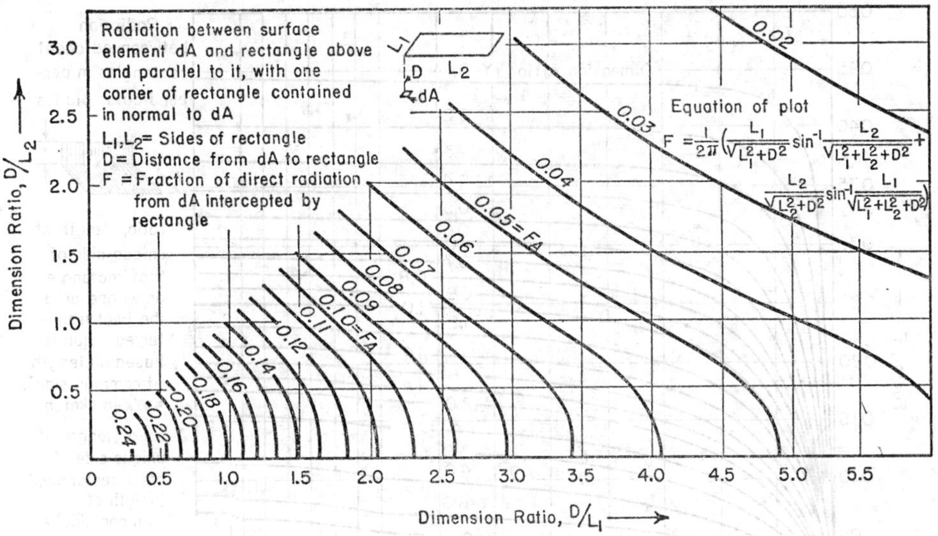

FIG. 10-18. Radiation from a plane element to a rectangle above it.

ing in all directions from one side, and on black surface A_2 a small surface element dA_2 intercepting some of the radiation from dA_1. Let the straight line connecting dA_1 and dA_2 have length r, and let r make angles θ_1 and θ_2 with the normals to dA_1 and dA_2, respectively. The rate of radiation from dA_1 to dA_2, called $dq_{1\rightarrow 2}$, will be proportional to $dA_1 \cos \theta_1$, the apparent area of dA_1 viewed from dA_2; to $dA_2 \cos \theta_2$, the apparent area of dA_2 viewed from dA_1; and inversely proportional to the square of the distance separating the elements. Calling the proportionality constant N_{B1}, one may write

$$dq_{1\rightarrow 2} = N_{B1} \frac{dA_1 \cos \theta_1 \, dA_2 \cos \theta_2}{r^2} \qquad (10\text{-}100)$$

This equation defines N_B, the *intensity* of radiation from a black surface.

By integration of Eq. (10-100) over a receiving surface filling the field of view of dA_1, one obtains $W_{B1}\,dA_1$, the total rate of emission from dA_1 throughout the hemisphere. The integration gives $\pi N_{B1}\,dA_1$, from which one concludes that the emissive power W_B of a black surface is π times its intensity of radiation N_B. By integration of Eq. (10-100) over finite areas A_1 and A_2 to obtain the rate of radiation from one to the other and dividing the result by $A_1 \cdot W_{B1}$, one obtains F_{12}, the desired fraction of the radiation leaving surface A_1 in all directions which is intercepted by surface A_2. Although the discussion has been restricted to black surfaces, it is apparent that for a non-black surface A_1 the emissivity of which is independent of angle of emission F_{12} calculated by the method above will continue to represent the fractional radiation from A_1 intercepted by A_2 (though not necessarily absorbed unless A_2 is black).

Values of F have been calculated for various surface arrangements on the assumption that emissivity ϵ_θ is constant, independent of θ (exact for black surfaces, quite good for most non-metallic or tarnished or rough metal surfaces). These values of F for a surface element dA and a rectangle in a parallel plane appear in Fig. 10-18; for opposed parallel rectangles and disks of equal size as lines 1 to 4 of Fig. 10-19; for adjacent rectangles in perpendicular planes in Fig. 10-20; for an infinite plane parallel to a system of parallel tubes as lines 1 and 3 of Fig. 10-21. Other cases are treated in the literature [Hottel, *Mech. Eng.*, **52**, 699 (1932)]. Important and useful concepts in evaluating F's are that

$$A_1F_{12} = A_2F_{21} \qquad (10\text{-}101)$$

(since otherwise there would be a net heat flux between A_1 and A_2 when at the same temperature); that

$$F_{11} + F_{12} + F_{13} + \cdot \cdot \cdot = 1 \qquad (10\text{-}102)$$

that, of course, $F_{11} = 0$ when A_1 can "see" no part of itself.

The rate of radiation from a black surface A_1 to black surface A_2 is now $A_1F_{12}\sigma T_1^4$; from A_2 to A_1, it is $A_2F_{21}\sigma T_2^4$; the net interchange is their difference, which may be written as either $A_1F_{12}\sigma(T_1^4 - T_2^4)$ or $A_2F_{21}\sigma(T_1^4 - T_2^4)$. One thus reaches the important conclusion that interchange may be obtained by evaluating the one-way radiation from either surface to the other, whichever is more convenient, and then replacing the emissive power by the difference of emissive powers of the two surfaces.

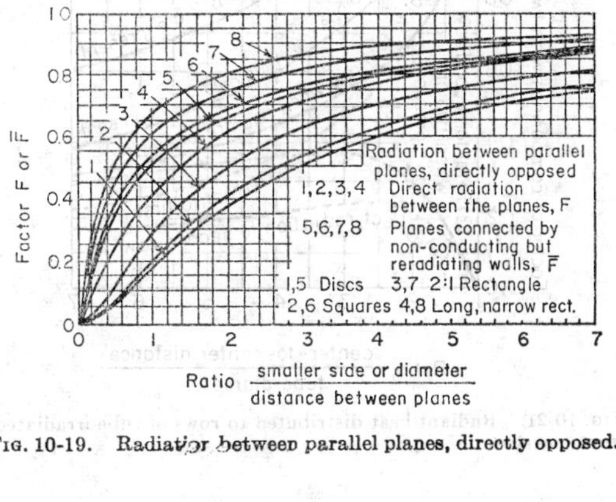

FIG. 10-19. Radiation between parallel planes, directly opposed.

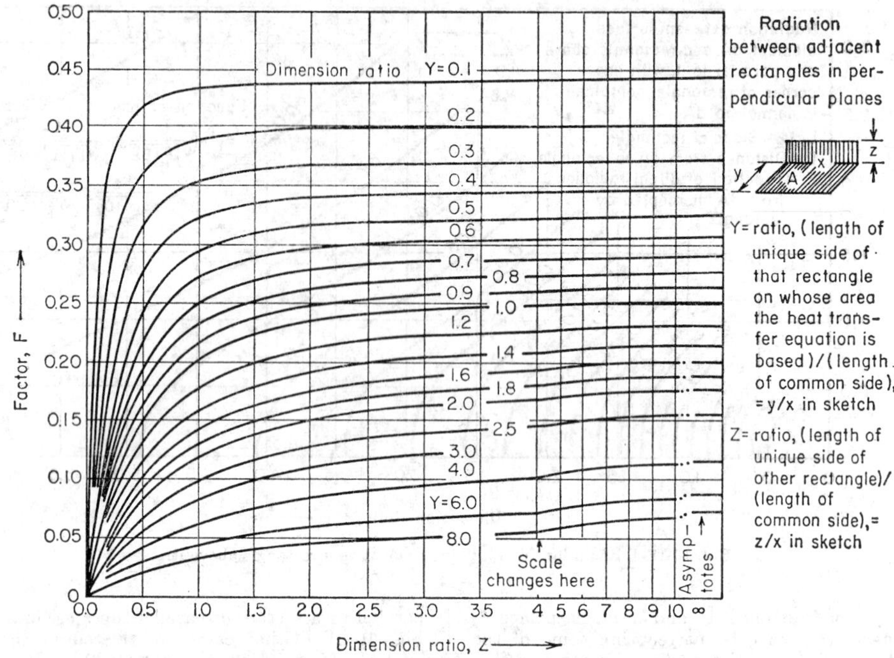

FIG. 10-20. Radiation between adjacent rectangles in perpendicular planes.

In an *enclosure of black surfaces* the net heat flux from A_1 is then given by

$$
\begin{aligned}
q_{1,\text{net}} &= (A_1F_{12}\sigma T_1^4 - A_2F_{21}\sigma T_2^4) \\
&\qquad + (A_1F_{13}\sigma T_1^4 - A_3F_{31}\sigma T_3^4) + \cdots \\
&\equiv A_1F_{12}\sigma(T_1^4 - T_2^4) + A_1F_{13}\sigma(T_1^4 - T_3^4) + \cdots \\
&\equiv A_1\sigma T_1^4 - (A_1F_{11}\sigma T_1^4 \\
&\qquad + A_2F_{21}\sigma T_2^4 + A_3F_{31}\sigma T_3^4 + \cdots)
\end{aligned} \tag{10-103}
$$

Allowance for Refractory Surfaces. The Factor $\bar{F}$. One of the commonest problems of radiant-heat transfer in industrial-furnace design is that in which a portion of the enclosure constitutes a heat source or heat sources (such as a fuel bed, a carborundum muffle, a row of electric resistors), another portion a heat sink or heat sinks (such as the surface of a row of billets, the tubes of a tube still or boiler furnace, etc.), and another portion an intermediate refractory connecting-wall system which is a heat sink only to the extent that it loses heat by conduction through its walls to the furnace exterior. If the convection from gases on the inside of such refractory walls is approximately equal to the loss by conduction through the walls, then the net radiant-heat interchange of the inside surface of the walls with the rest of the furnace interior is zero; and, since the radiation incident on the refractory walls is generally so enormous compared with the difference between gas convection and wall conduction, the assumption that the *net radiant*-heat transfer at the wall surface is zero is an excellent one. It enormously simplifies the treatment of the problem of the transfer of heat from sources to sinks, and the effect of the refractory surfaces thereon.

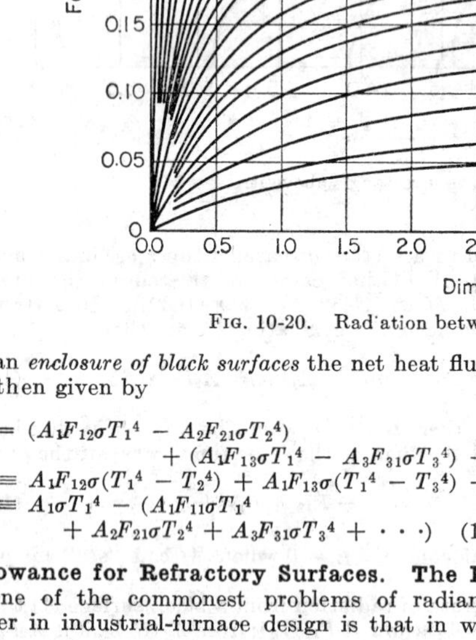

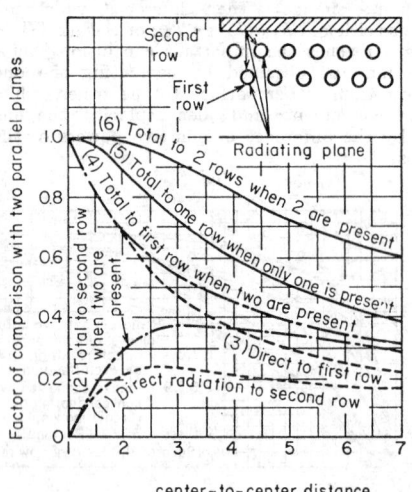

FIG. 10-21. Radiant heat distributed to rows of tube irradiated from one side.

Let the problem be restricted temporarily to source- or sink-type surfaces which are black, of areas A_1, A_2, etc., and to refractory surfaces A_R, A_S, A_T, etc., at which there is no net radiant flux. Since all the radiation A_1W_1 initially emitted by zone A_1 must ultimately either reach and be absorbed by A_2 or A_3 or A_4, etc., or be returned to A_1 for absorption (none of it disappearing at the refractory surfaces unless an equal quantity is emitted), it becomes desirable to define a new kind of factor $\bar{F}$, $\bar{F}_{12}$ being the fraction of the beam A_1W_1, streaming away from A_1, which reaches A_2 directly *and* by the assistance of the refractory surfaces. Then, just as the *direct* radiant transfer from A_1 to A_2 due to initial radiation from A_1 was $A_1W_1F_{12}$, so the *direct plus refractory-reradiated* energy transfer is $A_1W_1\bar{F}_{12}$. Similarly, the transmission from A_2 to A_1, due to initial radiation from A_2, is $A_2W_2\bar{F}_{21}$.

By the same argument applicable to the factor AF [see Eq. (10-101)], namely, the necessary equality of

$A_1W_1\bar{F}_{21}$ and $A_2W_2\bar{F}_{21}$ when $T_1 = T_2(W_1 = W_2)$, it is concluded that $A_1\bar{F}_{12} = A_2\bar{F}_{21}$ and that, since this relation contains only geometrical factors, it is true regardless of temperature equality or inequality of A_1 and A_2. Finally, then, the net radiant-heat interchange between zones A_1 and A_2, due to direct-plus-refractory action, is given by

$$q_{1\rightleftharpoons 2} = A_1\bar{F}_{12}\sigma(T_1^4 - T_2^4) \equiv A_2\bar{F}_{21}\sigma(T_1^4 - T_2^4) \qquad (10\text{-}104)$$

It is to be noted [Eq. (10-102) with new nomenclature] that the direct factors F by definition obey relations of the type

$$F_{11} + F_{12} + F_{13} + \cdots + F_{1R} + F_{1S} + F_{1T} + \cdots = 1 \qquad (10\text{-}102a)$$

whereas the direct-plus-reradiation factors $\bar{F}$ obey relations of the type

$$\bar{F}_{11} + \bar{F}_{12} + \bar{F}_{13} + \cdots = 1 \qquad (10\text{-}105)$$

The factor $\bar{F}$ has been determined exactly for a few geometrically simple cases [Hottel and Keller, *Trans. Am. Soc. Mech. Engrs., Iron and Steel*, **55**, 39 (1933)] and may be approximated for others. If A_1 and A_2 are equal parallel disks, squares, or rectangles connected by non-conducting but reradiating refractory walls, then $\bar{F}$ is given by Fig. 10-19, lines 5 to 8. If A_2 represents an infinite plane and A_1 is one or two rows of infinite parallel tubes in a parallel plane and if the only other surface is a refractory surface behind the tubes, $\bar{F}_{21}$ is given by line 5 or 6 of Fig. 10-21. If an enclosure may be divided into several radiant-heat sources or sinks A_1, A_2, etc., and the rest of the enclosure (reradiating refractory surface) may be lumped together as A_R at a uniform temperature T_R, then the factor $\bar{F}_{12}$ is given in terms of the direct geometrical factors F by the expression

$$\bar{F}_{12} = F_{12} + \frac{F_{1R}F_{R2}}{1 - F_{RR}} \qquad (10\text{-}106)$$

If there are but two source-sink-type surfaces, A_1 and A_2, the above expression reduces, by application of the principles expressed in Eqs. (10-101) and (10-102), to the more readily used

$$\bar{F}_{12} = F_{12} + \frac{1}{\dfrac{1}{F_{1R}} + \dfrac{A_1}{A_2}\cdot\dfrac{1}{F_{2R}}} \qquad (10\text{-}107)$$

If this case is further simplified by considering that neither A_1 nor A_2 can "see" itself (*i.e.*, has no negative curvature), the above expression reduces to

$$\bar{F}_{12} = \frac{A_2 - A_1F_{12}^2}{A_1 + A_2 - 2A_1F_{12}} \qquad (10\text{-}108)$$

which necessitates the evaluation of but one geometrical factor F. This case covers a major fraction of problems of radiant-heat interchange between source and sink in a furnace enclosure and is in error only to the extent to which the assumption of uniform refractory temperature is not permissible. More complicated expressions are available, permitting approach to the exact answer to any desired degree of accuracy depending on the number of zones into which the refractory is divided.

It is sometimes desirable to find the equilibrium value of refractory surface temperature. For the conditions for which Eq. (10-108) is valid, the refractory surface temperature is given by

$$T_R = \sqrt[4]{\frac{(A_1 - A_1F_{12})T_1^4 + (A_2 - A_1F_{12})T_2^4}{(A_1 - A_1F_{12}) + (A_2 - A_1F_{12})}} \qquad (10\text{-}109)$$

Allowance for Non-black Surfaces. The Factor $\mathfrak{F}$. Exact allowance for the departure of surfaces from black or ideal radiating characteristics is in general too complicated for engineering use. However, if the assumption that *all surfaces are gray* is permitted, a simple and adequate treatment is possible. If nomenclature is as for $\bar{F}$ except that A_1, A_2, etc., are now surfaces having emissivities (and absorptivities) ϵ_1, ϵ_2, etc., it is found that the net radiant interchange between A_1 and A_2 (due now to the combined mechanisms of direct radiation, reradiation from refractory surfaces, and multiple reflection inside the enclosure) may be expressed in the form

$$q_{1\rightleftharpoons 2} = A_1\mathfrak{F}_{12}\sigma(T_1^4 - T_2^4) \equiv A_2\mathfrak{F}_{21}\sigma(T_1^4 - T_2^4) \qquad (10\text{-}110)$$

Just as the factor $\bar{F}$ could be evaluated from F, so the factor $\mathfrak{F}$ may be evaluated from $\bar{F}$. For the case of two non-refractory surfaces A_1 and A_2 and however many refractory zones,

$$\mathfrak{F}_{12} = \frac{1}{\dfrac{1}{\bar{F}_{12}} + \left(\dfrac{1}{\epsilon_1} - 1\right) + \dfrac{A_1}{A_2}\left(\dfrac{1}{\epsilon_2} - 1\right)} \qquad (10\text{-}111)$$

It is to be noted that the emissivity of the refractory surfaces forming the system is not a factor, *i.e.*, that whether a refractory surface maintains its equilibrium by complete absorption and black-body reradiation or by complete diffuse reflection and no radiation is immaterial.

The limitation of Eq. (10-111) to conditions for which the division of source- and sink-type surfaces into but two zones A_1 and A_2 must be remembered; it is valid only when all elements of surfaces on A_1 (or A_2) "see" substantially the same picture, *i.e.*, when $F_{dA_1\to A_2}/F_{dA_1\to A_R}$ is about the same for all points on A_1.

As in the case of $\bar{F}$, $\mathfrak{F}$ may be evaluated to any desired degree of accuracy by dividing the system into a sufficient number of zones; but most furnace problems do not justify going beyond the expression given above.

Recommended Procedure. The use of the preceding principles is best illustrated by some examples.

Example 1. What is the heat transfer by radiation between an oxidized nickel tube 4 in. outside diameter, at a temperature of 800°F., and an enclosing chamber of silica brick at 1800°F., the brick chamber being (*a*) very large relative to the tube diameter, and (*b*) 8 in. square inside?

a. If A_1 is the enclosed surface, $\bar{F}_{12} = F_{12} = 1$. Then, according to Eq. (10-111)

$$\mathfrak{F}_{12} = \frac{1}{\dfrac{1}{\bar{F}_{12}} + \left(\dfrac{1}{\epsilon_1} - 1\right)} = \epsilon_1$$

i.e., the interchange factor is independent of emissivity of surroundings when the latter are of great extent, and Eq. (10-98) applies. The emissivity of oxidized nickel at 800°F. is, by interpolation from Table 10-15, about 0.43; its absorptivity for radiation from a source at 1800° is approximately its emissivity at 1800°F., which by extrapolation is about 0.58. The tube area per foot length is $\pi 4/12 = 1.05$ sq. ft./ft. Then

$$q \text{ (per ft. length)} = 0.173 \times 1.05\left[0.43\left(\frac{800 + 460}{100}\right)^4 - 0.58\left(\frac{1800 + 460}{100}\right)^4\right]$$
$$= 23{,}540 \text{ B.t.u./hr./ft. of tube}$$

The more usual procedure of using a single value for α and ϵ [Eq. (10-99)] would give, for $\epsilon = 0.58$, q per ft. $= 24{,}840$.

b. As before, $\bar{F}_{12} = 1$. When $\epsilon_1 = 0.58$ and $\epsilon_2 = 0.8$, Eq. (10-111) gives

$$\mathfrak{F}_{12} = \frac{1}{1 + \left(\frac{1}{0.58} - 1\right) + \frac{1.05}{2.67}\left(\frac{1}{0.8} - 1\right)} = 0.549$$

Therefore, $q = 24{,}840 \times 0.549/0.58 = 23{,}500$.

If one wished to allow for the difference between ϵ and α, an approximation for this case would be to use

$$q_{\text{net}} = A_1\mathfrak{F}_{12}\sigma T_1^4 - A_1\mathfrak{F}_{12}\sigma T_2^4$$

and to evaluate $\mathfrak{F}_{12}$ in the first term using ϵ_1 and ϵ_2 at $T_1(\mathfrak{F}_{12} = 0.412)$ and in the second term using ϵ_1 and ϵ_2 at $T_2(\mathfrak{F}_{12} = 0.549)$.

$$q_{\text{net}} = 0.173 \times 1.05(0.412 \times 12.6^4 - 0.549 \times 22.6^4) = 24{,}140$$

Example 2. A muffle-type furnace in which the carborundum muffle forms a continuous floor of dimensions 15 by 20 ft. has its ultimate-heat-receiving surface in the form of a row of 4-in. tubes on 9-in. centers above and parallel to the muffle and backed by a well-insulated refractory roof; the distance from the muffle top to the row of tubes is 10 ft. The tubes fill the furnace top, of area equal to that of the carborundum floor. The average muffle-surface temperature is 2100°F.; the tubes are at 600°F. The side walls of the chamber are assumed substantially nonconducting but reradiating and are at some equilibrium temperature between 600° and 2100°F., such that they radiate just as much heat as they receive. The tubes are oxidized steel of emissivity 0.8; the carborundum has an emissivity of 0.7. Find the radiant-heat transmission between the carborundum floor and the tubes above, taking into account the reradiation from the side walls.

Call the area of the roof tubes A_1, that of the carborundum floor A_3, that of the refractory side walls of the furnace A_R. The problem must be broken up into two parts, first considering the roof with its refractory-backed tubes. To an imaginary plane A_2 of area 15 × 20 ft. located just below the tubes, the tubes emit radiation $A_1\mathfrak{F}_{12}T_1^4$, equal to $A_2\mathfrak{F}_{12}T_1^4$. To obtain $\mathfrak{F}_{21}$, one must first evaluate $\bar{F}_{21}$, which comes from Fig. 10-21, line 5, from which $\bar{F}_{21} = 0.84$. From Eq. (10-111)

$$\mathfrak{F}_{21} = \frac{1}{\frac{1}{0.84} + \left(\frac{1}{1} - 1\right) + \frac{9}{4\pi}\left(\frac{1}{0.8} - 1\right)} = 0.73^*$$

This amounts to saying that the system of refractory-backed tubes is equal in radiating power to a continuous plane A_2 replacing the tubes and refractory above them, having a temperature equal to the tubes and an equivalent or effective emissivity of 0.73.

The new simplified furnace now consists of an enclosure formed by a 15 × 20 ft. rectangle A_3 of emissivity 0.7, above and parallel to it a 15 × 20 ft. rectangle A_2 of temperature T_1 and emissivity 0.73, and refractory walls A_R to complete the enclosure. The desired heat transfer is $q_{2\rightleftharpoons 3}$.

$$q_{2\rightleftharpoons 3} = \sigma(T_1^4 - T_3^4)A_2\mathfrak{F}_{23}.$$

Normally to evaluate $\mathfrak{F}_{23}$, one would find F_{23} first, then evaluate $\bar{F}_{23}$ by Eq. (10-107), an approximation to the extent that it assumes a constant side-wall temperature. For the present case, however, Fig. 10-19, line 6, presents an exact allowance for the continuous variation in side-wall temperature from top to bottom. The interchange factor between parallel 15 × 20 ft. rectangles separated by 10 ft. may be taken as the geometric mean of the factors for 15-ft. squares separated by 10 ft. and 20-ft. squares separated by 10 ft. Then, from Fig. 10-19, line 6, $\bar{F}_{23} = \sqrt{0.63 \times 0.69} = 0.66$. From Eq. (10-111)

$$\mathfrak{F}_{23} = \frac{1}{\frac{1}{0.66} + \left(\frac{1}{0.73} - 1\right) + 1 \cdot \left(\frac{1}{0.7} - 1\right)} = 0.433 = \mathfrak{F}_{32}$$

i.e., the floor and tubes interchange 43.3 per cent as much radiation as parallel black planes close together, each of area equal to the floor. The net interchange is

$$q_{\text{net}} = 0.173 \times (15 \times 20)(25.6^4 - 10.6^4)0.433 = 9{,}380{,}000 \text{ B.t.u./hr.}$$

Example 3. The distribution of radiant heat to the different rows of tubes in a tube nest irradiated from one side is desired, when the tubes are 4.0 in. outside diameter on 8-in. triangular centers. Let the area of the continuous plane below the tube nest be A_2 and the area of the tubes A_1. According to Fig. 10-21, curve 3, the first row of tubes will intercept directly 0.66 of the total. According to curve 1, the second row will intercept 0.21 of the total, leaving 1 − 0.66 − 0.21 = 0.13 to be intercepted by the remaining rows.

Suppose the tube nest replaced by a single row of tubes A_1 with refractory back wall A_R. Equation (10-106) gives $\bar{F}_{21}$. For the present case $F_{RR} = 0$ and $F_{2R} = 1 - F_{21}$ and $F_{R1} = F_{21}$; so Eq. (10-106) becomes

$$\bar{F}_{21} = F_{21} + (1 - F_{21})F_{21} = 0.66 + 0.34(0.66) = 0.88$$

a value which could have been read from Fig. 10-21, curve 5. A single tube and back wall will therefore be 88 per cent as effective a heat receiver as an infinite number of rows, so far as radiant-heat transmission is concerned.

Suppose the tube nest had been replaced by two rows of tubes with refractory back wall, instead of by a single row. According to Fig. 10-21, curves 4 and 2, the total radiation to the first row is 0.69, to the second 0.29, to both 0.69 + 0.29, or 0.98 as much as to an infinite number of rows (or to a continuous plane).

From Fig. 10-21, it is seen that only when the tubes are of small diameter relative to their distance apart is there any considerable quantity of radiant-heat penetration beyond the second row. The solution of a three- or four-row problem may be made readily by a graphical method [Hottel, *Trans. Am. Soc. Mech. Engrs., Fuel Steam Power*, **53**, 265 (1931)].

Radiation from Non-luminous Gases

If black-body radiation passes through a gas mass containing, *e.g.*, carbon dioxide, absorption occurs in certain regions of the infrared spectrum. Conversely, if the gas mass is heated it radiates in those same wavelength regions. This infrared spectrum of gases has its origin in simultaneous quantum changes in the energy levels of rotation and of interatomic vibration of the molecules; and, at the temperature levels reached in

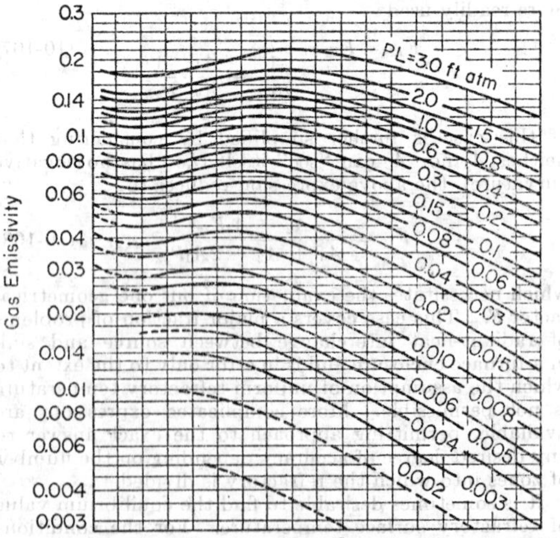

Fig. 10-22. Emissivity of carbon dioxide.

* The use of Eq. (10-111) was hardly justifiable here, since the "views" from spots on the top and the bottom of the tubes comprising the area A_1 are so different; but, when A_1 is divided into two zones, the value of $\mathfrak{F}_{21}$ is raised only to 0.74.

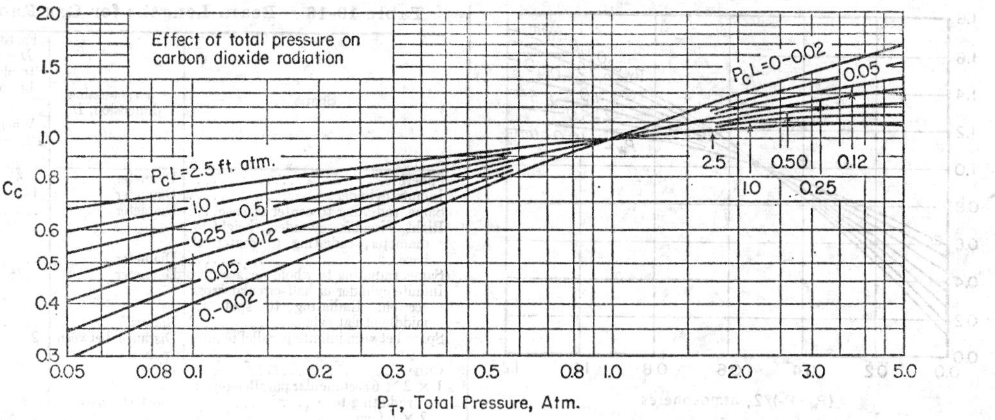

FIG. 10-22*a*. Correction factor C_c for converting emissivity of carbon dioxide at 1 atm. total pressure to emissivity at P_T atm.

industrial furnaces, is of importance only in the case of the heteropolar gases. *Of the gases encountered in heat-transfer equipment, carbon monoxide, the hydrocarbons, water vapor, carbon dioxide, sulfur dioxide, ammonia, and hydrogen chloride are among those with emission bands of sufficient magnitude to merit consideration.* The gases with symmetrical molecules, hydrogen, oxygen, nitrogen, etc., have been found not to show absorption bands in those wave-length regions of importance in radiant-heat transmission at temperatures met in industrial practice.

Consider a hemispherical gas mass of radius L containing carbon dioxide of partial pressure P_c, and let the problem be the evaluation of radiant-heat interchange between the gas at temperature T_G and a small element of surface at temperature T_s, located on the base of the hemisphere at its center. Per unit of surface the emission of the gas to the surface is $\sigma T_G^4 \cdot \epsilon_G$, where ϵ_G denotes gas emissivity. For carbon dioxide ϵ_G depends on T_G, the product term P_cL, and the total pressure P_T. Its value for $P_T = 1$ atm. is given in Fig. 10-22; an approximate correction factor C_c for a total pressure differing from 1 atm. is given in Fig. 10-22*a*. The absorption, by the gas, of radiation from the surface is $\sigma T_s^4 \cdot \alpha_G$, where α_G is the absorptivity of the gas for black-body radiation from the surface. Approximately α_G is obtained from the gas emissivity chart at the same value of P_cL as before but at the temperature T_s instead of T_G. Such an approximation is adequate if the gas is hotter than the surface and the absorption term consequently of secondary importance. If the reverse is the case, an accurate value of α_G may be obtained if one reads an emissivity from Fig. 10-22 at T_s as before, but at $P_cL(T_s/T_G)$ instead of P_cL, and then multiplies the result by $(T_G/T_s)^{0.65}$. The same correction factor C_c applies to absorptivity if the total pressure is not 1 atm.

The net radiant-heat interchange per unit of black bounding surface is then

$$q/A = (\sigma T_G^4 \epsilon_G - \sigma T_s^4 \alpha_G) C_c \qquad (10\text{-}112)$$

In the case of water-vapor radiation the gas emissivity ϵ_G depends on T_G and P_wL, as before, and in addition somewhat on the partial pressure of water vapor P_w and the total pressure P_T. Correlation of the data of various experimenters is found possible by reducing all measured emissivities to values corresponding to an idealized case where $P_w = 0$ and $P_T = 1$, by the use of a factor depending on $(P_w + P_T)$ and on P_wL. The smoothed curves through the resulting corrected data appear in Fig. 10-23 as a plot of ϵ_G vs. T_G for the various values of P_wL, for the "ideal" system at zero partial pressure of water vapor and a total pressure of 1 atm. Allowance for departure from this "ideal" state is then made by multiplying ϵ_G as read from Fig. 10-23 by a factor C_w read from Fig. 10-23*a* as a function of $(P_w + P_T)$ and P_wL.

The absorptivity of water vapor for black-body radiation may be obtained like that of CO_2. Approximately, α_G is ϵ_G read at P_wL and T_s instead of T_G; more accurately, it is obtained by reading emissivity from Fig. 10-23 at T_S but at $P_wL(T_S/T_G)$ instead of P_wL, and then multiplying the result by $(T_G/T_S)^{0.45}$. The correction factor C_w still applies.

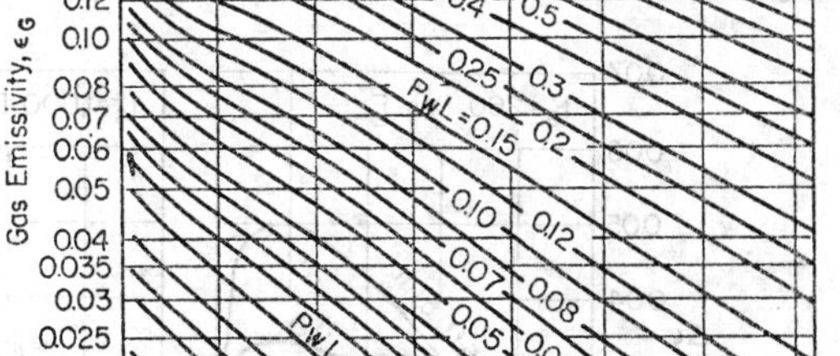

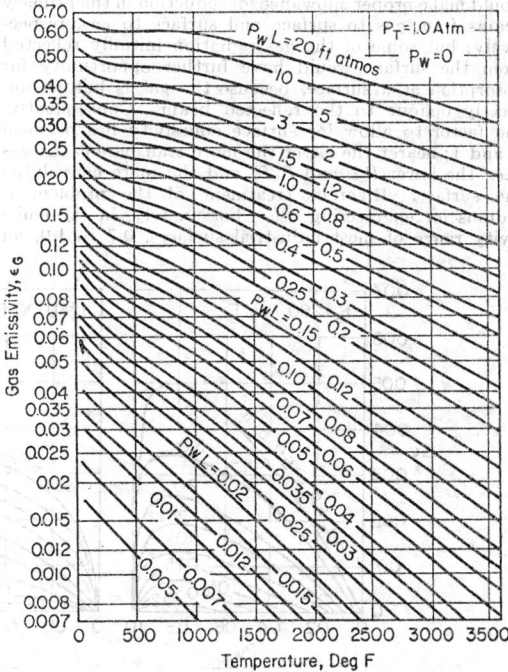

FIG. 10-23. Emissivity of water vapor at zero partial pressure in system with total pressure = 1 atm.

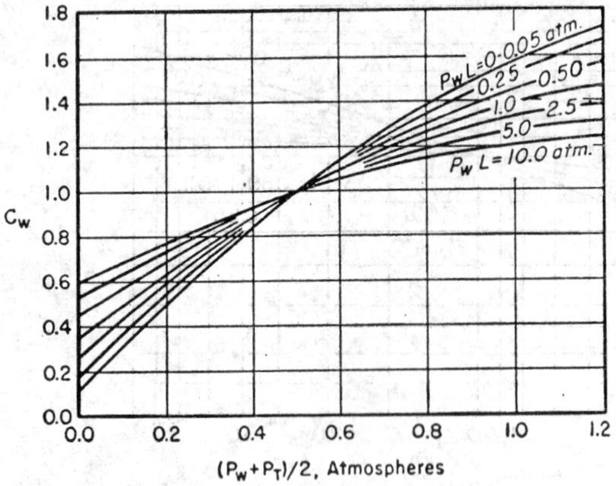

FIG. 10-23*a*. Correction of factor C_w for converting emissivity of water to values of P_w and P_T other than 0 and 1 atm., respectively.

When carbon dioxide and water vapor are present together, the total radiation due to both is somewhat less than the sum of the separately calculated effects, because each gas is somewhat opaque to radiation from the other. A correction for this effect may be read from Fig. 10-24, which gives the amount $\Delta\epsilon$ by which to reduce the sum of ϵ_G for CO_2 and ϵ_G for H_2O (each evaluated as if the other gas were absent) to obtain the ϵ_G due to the two together. The same type of correction applies in calculating α_G.

Discussion has so far been restricted to interchange between a gas and its bounding surface when the latter is black. If the surface is gray, with an emissivity (and absorptivity) equal to ϵ_s, multiplication by ϵ_s would make proper allowance for reduction in the primary beams from gas to surface and surface to gas, respectively; but some of the gas radiation initially reflected from the surface would have further opportunity for absorption at a surface, because the gas is but incompletely opaque to the reflected beam. Consequently, the factor to allow for surface emissivity lies between ϵ_s and 1; nearer the latter the more transparent the gas (*i.e.*, the lower P_cL and P_wL) and the more convoluted the surface. Rigorous treatment of the problem is tedious for engineering use. Fortunately, in the emissivity range of most industrial surfaces, 0.7 to 1.0, an

Table 10-16. Beam Lengths for Gas Radiation

Shape	Characterizing dimension, D	Factor by which D is multiplied to obtain mean beam length, L: When $PL = 0$	Factor: For average values of PL
Sphere	Diameter	⅔	0.60
Infinite cylinder	Diameter	1	0.90
Same, radiating to center of base	Diameter	......	0.90
Right circular cylinder, height = diameter, radiating to center of base	Diameter	......	0.77
Same, radiating to whole surface	Diameter	⅔	0.60
Infinite cylinder of half-circular cross section. Radiating to spot on middle of flat side	Radius	......	1.26
Space between infinite parallel planes	Distance between planes	2	1.8
Cube	Edge	⅔	0.60
1 × 2 × 6 rectangular parallelepiped, radiating to	Shortest edge		
2 × 6 face	....	1.18	1.06
1 × 6 face	....	1.24	1.06
1 × 2 face	....	1.18	1.06
All faces	....	1.20	1.06
Space outside infinite bank of tubes with centers on equilateral triangles; tube diameter = clearance	Clearance	3.4	2.8
Same as preceding, except tube diameter = one-half clearance	Clearance	4.45	3.8
Same, except tube centers on squares; diameter = clearance	Clearance	4.1	3.5

adequate approximation consists in multiplying by an effective emissivity ϵ_s' lying halfway between the actual value of ϵ_s and unity.

The final formulation of radiant interchange between a gas and its bounding surface when the gas contains CO_2 and H_2O is now

$$\frac{q}{A} = \sigma\epsilon_s'(\epsilon_G T_G^4 - \alpha_G T_s^4)$$

$$\equiv 0.173\epsilon_s'\left[\epsilon_G\left(\frac{T_G}{100}\right)^4 - \alpha_G\left(\frac{T_s}{100}\right)^4\right] \qquad (10\text{-}113)$$

To keep straight on nomenclature, a series of subscripts will be appended to the value of ϵ read from Fig. 10-22 or 10-23, the first representing the gas (whether CO_2 or H_2O), the second the temperature on the plot (whether T_G or T_s), the third the values of P_L at which ϵ is read.

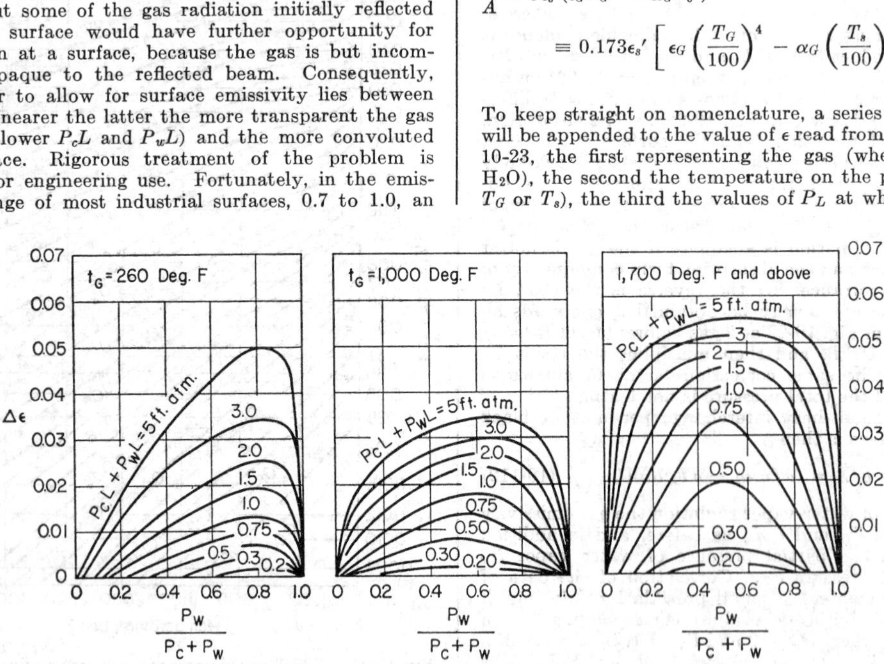

FIG. 10-24. Correction for superimposed radiation from carbon dioxide and water vapor.

In this nomenclature, terms in Eq. (10-113) are defined as follows:

$$\epsilon_G = (\epsilon_{CO_2,T_G,P_cL})C_c + (\epsilon_{H_2O,T_G,P_wL})C_w - \Delta\epsilon_{T_G}$$
$$\alpha_G = \alpha_{CO_2} + \alpha_{H_2O} - \Delta\alpha$$
$$\alpha_{CO_2} = (\epsilon_{CO_2,T_s,P_cLT_s/T_G})\left(\frac{T_G}{T_s}\right)^{0.65} \cdot C_c$$
$$= \epsilon_{CO_2,T_s,P_cL} \cdot C_c \text{ approx.}$$
$$\alpha_{H_2O} = (\epsilon_{H_2O,T_s,P_wLT_s/T_G})\left(\frac{T_G}{T_s}\right)^{0.45} \cdot C_w$$
$$= \epsilon_{H_2O,T_s,P_wL} \cdot C_w \text{ approx.}$$

As previously pointed out the error in q/A is negligible where α is evaluated as ϵ at T_s and P_cL or P_wL, if $T_s \ll T_G$. The maximum error so introduced is about 10 per cent when $T_s = 0.8T_G$.

The above expression was formulated for the case of interchange between a gas hemisphere and a spot on its base, *i.e.*, for the case in which the length of path L of the radiant beam is the same in all directions. For gas shapes of industrial importance it is found that any shape is approximately representable by an "equivalent" hemisphere of proper radius or that there is a mean beam length which can be used in evaluating gas emissivities and absorptivities from Figs. 10-22 and 10-23. As PL approaches zero, the mean beam length approaches as a limit the value, 4 × (ratio of gas volume to bounding area). For the range of PL encountered in practice, L is always less; 85 per cent of the limiting value is generally a satisfactory approximation (Port, Sc.D. Thesis, M.I.T., 1939). Table 10-16 summarizes the results of tedious graphical or analytical treatment of various shapes.

If gas radiation occurs in equipment in which there is a continuous change in temperature of the gas and the surface from one end to the other of the interchanger, exact allowance therefor can be made by conventional graphical integration. To a generally adequate degree of approximation, however, one may use a mean surface temperature equal to the arithmetic mean, and a mean gas temperature equal to the mean surface temperature plus the logarithmic mean of the temperature difference, gas to surface, at the two ends.

$$t_{S_{avg}} = \frac{(t_{S_1} + t_{S_2})}{2} \qquad (10\text{-}114)$$

$$t_{G_{avg}} = t_{S_{avg}} + \frac{(t_{G_1} - t_{S_1}) - (t_{G_2} - t_{S_2})}{2.3 \log \dfrac{(t_{G_1} - t_{S_1})}{(t_{G_2} - t_{S_2})}} \qquad (10\text{-}115)$$

Effect of Presence of Two Surfaces at Different Temperatures. When a radiating gas fills a chamber the walls of which consist of the ultimate heat-receiving surface and of an intermediate heat receiver and reradiator such as a refractory surface, the question arises as to how to evaluate the total heat interchange between gas and ultimate heat receiver by the combined mechanisms of direct radiation from the gas to the ultimate receiver, and radiation from the gas to the refractory surface, and thence to the ultimate receiver. This problem, in its general form involving heat balances, external heat losses from the furnace, and convection heat transfer inside the chamber, is treated in detail in the last part of the present section. As an approximation, however, the total heat transfer to the ultimate receiver may be estimated by assuming that its effective area is that of itself plus a certain fraction x of that of the refractory, and that the only temperatures involved are those of the gas and the ultimate receiving surface. The fraction x, the effectiveness of the refractory surface, varies from zero when the ratio of refractory surface to ultimate receiving surface is very high, to unity when the ratio is very low and the value of ϵ_G is low. When the refractory-surface area and ultimate heat-receiving surface area are of the same order of magnitude, a value of 0.7 may be used for x, although for more exact calculations the method of the last section of this chapter should be used.

Radiation from Sulfur Dioxide. In the design of sulfur burners and of sulfur dioxide coolers the radiation from the gas may be a major factor in the evaluation of the total heat transferred. The data of Coblentz ("Investigations of Infra-red Spectra," Carnegie Institute, 1905) on the infrared absorption spectrum of sulfur dioxide, while hardly adequate as a basis for quantitative calculations, have been used for want of something better. The results are presented in Fig. 10-25, by S. A. Guerrieri, in a form similar to the water-vapor and carbon dioxide plots. The equation of radiant-heat transfer is

$$\frac{q}{A} = \epsilon_s'(S_g - S_s) \qquad (10\text{-}116)$$

in which q/A is B.t.u./sq. ft. bounding surface per hr.; ϵ_s', the effective emissivity of the surface; S_g, the sulfur dioxide radiation, as read from Fig. 10-25 corresponding

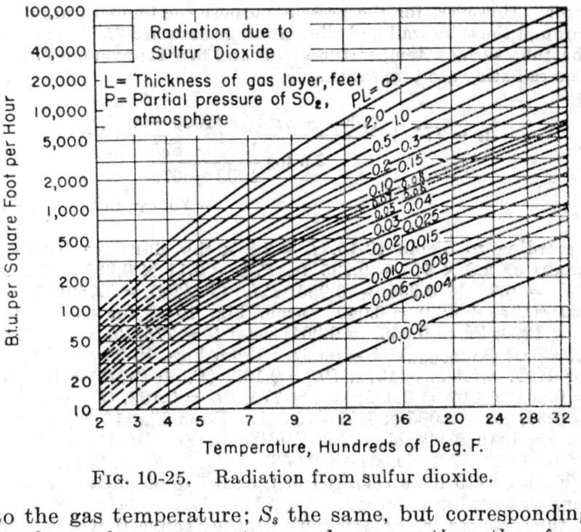

FIG. 10-25. Radiation from sulfur dioxide.

to the gas temperature; S_s the same, but corresponding to the surface temperature and representing, therefore, the amount of radiation from the surface which is absorbed by the gas.

Radiation from Other Gases. Measurements of total radiation from carbon monoxide have been made by Ullrich (Sc.D. Thesis, M.I.T., 1935) who found that the gas emissivity is a maximum at around 1600°F., that at $PL = 2$ its emission is about half that of carbon dioxide at all temperatures from 600° to 2500°F., and that at $PL = 0.01$ its emission varies from 40 to 90 per cent of that of carbon dioxide as the temperature varies from 600° to 2500°F.

Measurements of total radiation from ammonia have been made by Port (Sc.D. Thesis, M.I.T., 1939) who found that the gas emissivity is very high compared with carbon dioxide or water vapor, that it decreases continuously from room temperature up, that at $PL = 2$ it varies from one to two times that of water vapor, and that at $PL = 0.01$ it varies from 1.5 to 4 times that of water vapor over the range, room temperature to 2000°F.

For other gases of interest one must rely on evaluations similar to those on SO_2 above, based on the infrared absorption spectra of the gases in question. For the method of such calculation and for a more complete story on gas radiation see Schack [*Z. tech. Physik*, **5**, 266 (1924)], Hottel [*Ind. Eng. Chem.*, **19**, 888 (1927)], Schmidt [*Forsch. Gebiete Ingenieurw*, **3**, 57 (1932)], Hottel and Mangelsdorf [*Trans. Am. Inst. Chem. Engrs.*, **31**, 517 (1935)], Eckert [*V. deut. Ing. Forschungsheft*, 387 (1937)], Hottel and Egbert, [*Trans. Am. Soc. Mech. Engrs.*, **63** (1941); *Trans. Am. Inst. Chem. Engrs.*, **38**, 531 (1942)].

Example 4. Flue gas containing 6 per cent carbon dioxide and 11 per cent water vapor by volume (wet basis) flows through the convection bank of an oil tube still consisting of rows of 4-in. tubes on 8-in. centers, nine 25-ft. tubes in a row, the rows staggered to put the tubes on equilateral triangular centers. The flue gas enters at 1600° and leaves at 1000°F. The oil flows countercurrent to the gas and rises from 600° to 800°F. Tube surface emissivity is 0.8. What is the average heat input rate, due to gas radiation alone, per square foot of external tube area?

With each row of tubes there is associated $8/12 \times \sqrt{3}/2$ or 0.577 ft. of wall height, of area $(8/12 \times 9 \times 2 + 25 \times 2) \times 0.577 = 35.8$ sq. ft. One row of tubes has an area of $\pi \times 4/12 \times 25 \times 9 = 235$ sq. ft. If the recommended factor of 0.7 on the refractory area is used, the effective area of the tubes is $\dfrac{235 + 0.7 \times 35.8}{235} = 1.11$ sq. ft./sq. ft. of actual area. The exact evaluation of outside tube temperature from the known oil temperature would involve a knowledge of oil-film coefficient, tube-wall resistance, and rate of heat flow into the tube, the evaluation usually involving trial and error. However, for the present purpose the temperature drop through the tube wall and oil film will be assumed 75°F., making the tube surface temperatures 675° and 875°F.; average 775°F. The radiating gas temperature is

$$t_g = 775 + \frac{(1600 - 875) - (1000 - 675)}{2.3 \log \dfrac{1600 - 875}{1000 - 675}}$$

$$= 755 + 499 = 1274°\text{F}$$

According to Table 10-16, $L = 2.8 \times$ the clearance between tubes, or $2.8 \times 4/12 = 0.935$ ft. $P_wL = 0.11 \times 0.935 = 0.102$; $P_cL = 0.06 \times 0.935 = 0.056$; $P_cL \cdot (T_S/T_G) = 0.056(775 + 460)/(1274 + 460) = 0.040$. From Fig. 10-22 for CO_2, ϵ_G(at $t_G = 1274$, $PL = 0.056$) = 0.064; α_G(at $t_s = 775, PL = 0.040$) = $0.0535 \times (1734/1235)^{0.65} = 0.067$. From Figs. 10-23 and 10-23*a* for H_2O, ϵ_G(at $t_G = 1274$, $PL = 0.102$, $(P_w + P_T)/2 = 1.11/2$) $= 0.064 \times 1.07 = 0.068$; at $t_s = 775$, $PL = 0.102$, $(P_w + P_T)/2 = 0.56$, $\alpha_G = 0.085 \times 1.07 = 0.091$. From Fig. 10-24, $\Delta\epsilon$ and $\Delta\alpha$ are both negligible. Substituting in Eq. (10-113), $q/A = 0.9[0.173 \times 17.34^4(0.064 + 0.068) - 0.173 \times 12.35^4(0.067 + 0.091)] = 1275$ B.t.u./(sq. ft.)(hr.), exclusive of effect of refractory surfaces, or approximately $1275 \times 1.11 = 1415$ B.t.u./sq. ft. tube area per hr. This is equivalent to a convection coefficient of $1415/499$ or 2.8, which is the order of magnitude expected of the convection coefficient itself.

Luminous Flames. There are two methods of attacking the problem of developing a suitable method for predicting the radiation to be expected from a luminous flame. The first is to collect data on actual flames under varying conditions of aeration, fuel-gas composition, flame volume, etc., and to use the data as a basis for calculations. Unfortunately the published data of this sort are woefully inadequate, usually consisting of a measurement of total radiation from small laboratory flames, with no basis for determining the opacity of the flame or, consequently, the radiation from a larger flame of similar type. The changes in soot concentration attending changes in burner design, shape of combustion chamber, degree of primary and secondary aeration, fuel-gas composition, and draft regulation, all make the estimation of the luminous-flame radiation to be expected in a proposed installation exceedingly uncertain.

It is possible to show, however, how data may be obtained from a furnace with known conditions of combustion, and applied to a different size or shape of furnace in which the conditions of combustion are roughly the same. From a quantitative investigation of the variation, with wave length, of the monochromatic absorptivity of luminous flames it has been shown [Hottel and Broughton, The Determination of True Temperature and Total Radiation from Luminous Gas Flames, *Ind. Eng. Chem.*, anal. ed., **4**, 166 (1932)] that the absorptivity (and emissivity) decreases with increase in wave length and that the total emissivity is less than the emissivity in the visible spectrum. This makes direct visual estimation of luminous-flame emissivity very misleading. However, by the use of an optical pyrometer containing color screens of different wave lengths (red and green), it is shown that two apparent temperatures, the red-brightness temperature T_r and the green-brightness temperature T_g, may be obtained, which permit a calculation of both true flame temperature and total flame emissivity. Figure 10-26 is a working plot (in °K.) from

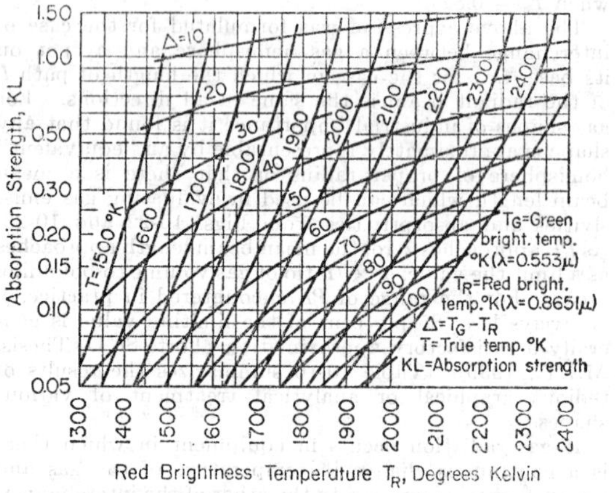

FIG. 10-26. "Absorption strength" of luminous flames.

which the true temperature may be obtained, given T_r and $\Delta = (T_g - T_r)$. On the same plot one obtains the value of the absorption strength *KL*, in which *K* is a term measuring the soot concentration of the flame, and *L* is the thickness of flame through which the pyrometer is sighted. With absorption strength known, Fig. 10-27 may be used to determine the effective emissivity of the flame envelope. The transfer of heat from the flame envelope of area *A* and true flame temperature T_F to the confining walls of temperature T_s is given by

$$q = 0.173A\left[\left(\frac{T_F}{100}\right)^4 - \left(\frac{T_s}{100}\right)^4\right] \cdot \epsilon_F \cdot \epsilon_s' \qquad (10\text{-}117)$$

in which ϵ_F is the emissivity of the flame envelope as determined by Fig. 10-27, and ϵ_s' is the effective emissivity of the surroundings.

If an optical pyrometer with both red and green screens is not available, Fig. 10-26 may still be used to determine absorption strength: (*a*) if the red-brightness temperature T_r is determined with an ordinary optical pyrometer and the true temperature T_F with a high-velocity thermocouple; or (*b*) if a mirror is held behind the flame in the line of sight of the optical pyrometer. The first method is open to the serious objection that the absorption strength *KL* changes rapidly with a change in the usually small quantity $T_F - T_r$ representing the difference between the temperature readings of two entirely different kinds of instruments.

In using the two-color principle for determining the true temperature and total emissivity of a flame, it should be borne in mind that the pyrometer must not "see" anything but the flame itself; *i.e.*, the background of the flame should be an open peephole in the back wall

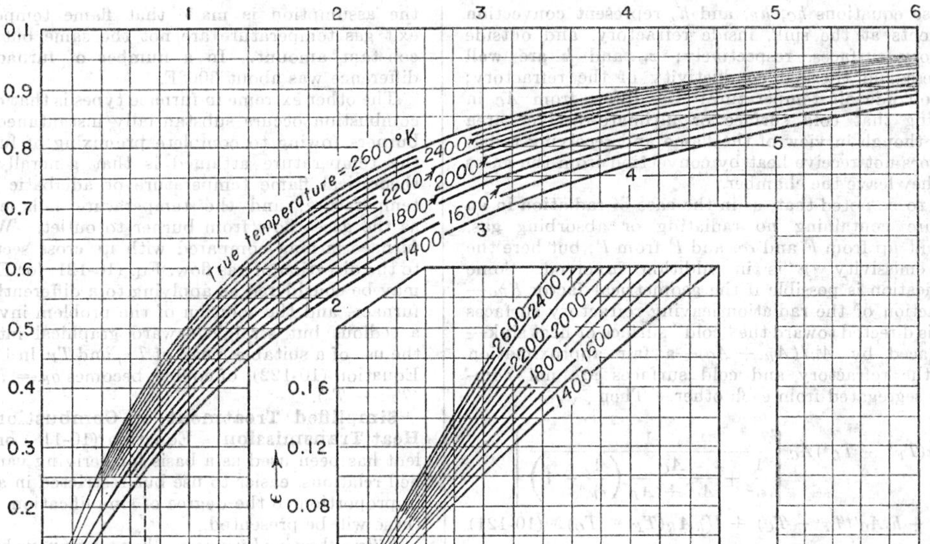

FIG. 10-27. Emissivity of luminous flames.

of the furnace or a cold non-reflecting surface, never a hot refractory surface. When temperature measurements have been made on an industrial flame of one size to determine its absorption strength KL, for the purpose of estimating the emissivity ϵ_F of a similar but larger flame, the absorption strength KL_1 determined from Fig. 10-26 should be multiplied by the dimension ratio L_2/L_1 before Fig. 10-27 is used. In addition, the value of KL should correspond to the particular shape of flame under consideration, in accordance with the principles discussed in connection with the use of Table 10-16. An example will be found at the end of this article.

The data available on luminous flames in industrial furnaces indicate that radiation from the soot is frequently of a greater order of magnitude than non-luminous gas radiation. Lent [*Wärme*, **49**, 145 (1926)] has made a blast-furnace gas flame practically black by addition of benzene to form soot. Haslam and Boyer [*Ind. Eng. Chem.*, **19**, 4 (1927)] found that a luminous acetylene flame radiated roughly four times as much heat as when non-luminous, and the size of their experimental flame was such as to indicate that maximum blackness had not been obtained. Sherman [*Trans. Am. Soc. Mech. Engrs.*, **56**, 177 (1934)] has measured emissivities of luminous gas flames in an experimental furnace.

The General Problem of Heat Transfer in a Combustion Chamber

One of the most complex problems of heat transmission is the evaluation of the performance of a combustion chamber of a furnace, in which heat is being transmitted simultaneously by all or most of the mechanisms so far discussed. Two methods of treatment of this problem are possible: either (1) the theoretical one in which the attempt is made to consider the various individual factors, each acting in accordance with the principles discussed previously, and to combine them; or (2) the empirical one in which furnace test data are analyzed in the attempt to detect the effect of factors suspected of being of importance. These methods will be considered in order.

Allowance is to be made for the combined actions of direct radiation from the flame to the stock or heat sink; radiation from flame to refractory surfaces thence back through the flame (with partial absorption therein) to the sink; convection; and external losses. A solution of the problem is possible if the following assumptions are accepted: (1) external losses from refractory walls equal convection from flame to refractory; (2) the flame is gray and has an emissivity ϵ_F; (3) all refractory surfaces have a common average (but unknown) temperature; (4) a mean temperature T_F is assignable to the flame and combustion products in the chamber; (5) the heat sink or ultimate receiver has a uniform surface temperature T_C and is gray, with emissivity ϵ_C and area A_C. The solution of the problem, giving the net rate of heat transfer q_F from the flame by all mechanisms, is

$$q_F = \underbrace{\sigma(T_F^4 - T_C^4)A_C\mathfrak{F}_{CF}}_{\text{Radiation to sink}} + \underbrace{h_C A_C'(T_F - T_C)}_{\text{Convection to sink}} + \underbrace{U_R A_R(T_F - T_O)}_{\text{External loss (= convection to refractory)}} \qquad (10\text{-}118)$$

in which

$$\mathfrak{F}_{CF} = \frac{1}{\dfrac{1}{\bar{F}_{CF}} + \dfrac{1}{\epsilon_C} - 1} \qquad (10\text{-}119)$$

$$\bar{F}_{CF} = \epsilon_F\left(1 + \frac{A_R/A_C}{1 + \dfrac{\epsilon_F}{1 - \epsilon_F}\,\dfrac{1}{F_{RC}}}\right) \qquad (10\text{-}120)$$

$$U_R = \frac{1}{\dfrac{1}{h_R} + \dfrac{x_w}{k} + \dfrac{1}{h_o}}$$

In these equations h_C, h_R, and h_o represent convection coefficients at the sink, inside refractory, and outside refractory surfaces, respectively; x_w and k are wall thickness and thermal conductivity of the refractory; T_O is outside air temperature; A_C' differs from A_C in excluding that cold surface or ultimate-receiver area which, though in view of the flame and receiving radiation, does not receive heat by convection from the gases until they leave the chamber.

It is to be noted that, as in the case of radiation in an enclosure containing no radiating or absorbing gas, $\mathfrak{F}$ is built up from $\bar{F}$ and ϵ_C, and $\bar{F}$ from F; but here the flame emissivity ϵ_F is in addition involved. Some simplification is possible if the geometrical factor F_{RC}—the fraction of the radiation leaving refractory surfaces which is directed toward the "cold" surface or heat sink—is replaced by $A_C/(A_R + A_C)$—a fair approximation when the refractory and cold surfaces are not completely segregated from each other. Then

$$q_F = \sigma(T_F^4 - T_C^4)A_C\left[\frac{1}{\dfrac{1}{\epsilon_C} + \dfrac{A_C}{A_C + A_R}\left(\dfrac{1}{\epsilon_F} - 1\right)}\right] + h_cA_C'(T_F - T_C) + U_RA_R(T_F - T_O) \quad (10\text{-}121)$$

From this simplified form much more readily than from the more general Eq. (10-118) it is to be noted that increasing the flame emissivity increases the heat transmission, but not proportionately; that decreasing surface emissivity (and absorptivity) from unity when the flame is very transparent produces almost no effect on the heat transmission; but that decreasing ϵ_C from unity when the flame is substantially opaque ($\epsilon_F = 1$) produces a proportional decrease in heat transmission.

The derivation of Eq. (10-118) [or Eq. (10-121)] was based on the assumption that A_C was composed of plane areas. Suppose instead that A_C is a row of tubes mounted in front of a refractory wall. A little consideration will show that the value of A_C to use in the radiation term of the above equations is the continuous plane A_p in which the tubes are located, multiplied by the proper factor $\bar{F}$ for tubes with a refractory background (see Fig. 10-21), and that the refractory surface A_R should be increased by the amount $(1 - \bar{F})A_p$.

Equation (10-118) [or Eq. (10-121)] expresses a relation between two unknowns T_F and q_F, and a second relation is necessary if a solution is to be obtained. The other relation is an energy balance. If one assumes turbulence to be so great that the mean flame temperature T_F used for calculation of radiation is the same as the temperature T_G of the gas leaving the chamber, then

$$q_F = i - w_G(C_p)_m(T_F - T_0) \quad (10\text{-}122)$$

where i represents the hourly enthalpy or heat content of the entering fuel, air, and recirculated flue gas, if any, above a base temperature T_0 (water as vapor); and $(C_p)_m$ represents the mean heat capacity (evaluated between T_F and T_0) of the gas leaving the chamber, at hourly mass rate w_G. Equations (10-118) [or (10-121)] and (10-122) may be solved by trial and error or by graphical methods involving superimposed plots.

The pair of equations just discussed apply strictly to one of two limiting furnace types—that one in which the assignment of a mean flame temperature equal to the temperature of the gases leaving is justifiable. For this to be the case, combustion must be relatively slow, delayed by retarded mixing of secondary air with the flame and progressing uniformly at all points in the chamber. Better agreement between predicted and experimental results is obtained on some furnaces when the assumption is made that flame temperature and exit gas temperature are not the same but differ by a constant amount. In a number of furnace tests the difference was about 300°F.

The other extreme in furnace types is that one in which combustion occurs substantially instantaneously at the burners (owing to complete premixing of fuel and air); the temperature attained is that generally known as theoretical flame temperature or adiabatic combustion temperature; and the temperature falls continuously as the gases flow from burner to outlet. When such a furnace is long compared with its cross section normal to the direction of gas flow, Eq. (10-121) [or Eq. (10-118)] may be considered as applying to a differential length of furnace, and the solution of the problem involves either a tedious but straightforward graphical integration or the use of a suitable mean of T_{F_1} and T_{F_2} in Eq. (10-121). Equation (10-122), of course, becomes $q_F = i - w_G(C_p)_m(T_{F_2} - T_0)$.

Simplified Treatment of Combustion-chamber Heat Transmission. Equation (10-118) or its equivalent has been used as a basis for deriving various simplified relations, easier to use but restricted in applicability in proportion to the degree of simplification. Several of these will be presented.

Billet-reheating Furnaces. For continuous billet-reheating furnaces, Eq. (10-118) has been modified as follows: (1) q is heat transferred to the stock, not from the flame; (2) convection terms have been omitted; (3) to compensate therefor and to allow for steadiness of furnace operation, $\mathfrak{F}_{CF}$ is evaluated using $1.2r_f \cdot \epsilon_F$ instead of ϵ_F, where r_f is the ratio of average billet-pushing rate over a period of several hours to pushing rate during periods of steady operation; (4) ϵ_F is flame emissivity due to CO_2 and H_2O only, as calculated in the previous example on gas radiation; (5) $F_{RC} = A_CF_{CR}/A_R = A_C/A_R$; (6) an average value of $(T_F^4 - T_C^4)$ is used, equal to the geometric mean of its value at the two ends of the furnace, and at the hot end T_F is taken as the calculated "theoretical" flame temperature, or adiabatic combustion temperature. The equation has been tested on reheating furnaces of various types and found satisfactory [Eberhardt and Hottel, *Trans. Am. Soc. Mech. Engrs.*, **58**, 185 (1936); *Heat Treatment Forging*, **22**, 144–149, 193–198, (1936)].

Petroleum Heaters. For cracking-coil and tube-still furnaces Eq. (10-118) has been modified as follows: (1) by omitting the last term, q becomes heat transferred to oil instead of heat lost by flame; (2) h_CA_C' has for simplification been assigned an average value equal to $7A_C\mathfrak{F}_{CF}$ (the term is unimportant relative to the radiation term). The relation is then

$$q_C = [\sigma(T_F^4 - T_C^4) + 7(T_F - T_C)]A_C\mathfrak{F}_{CF} \quad (10\text{-}123)$$

Previous comments concerning the proper values of A_C and A_R for the case of tubes mounted on a wall apply. In evaluating $\mathfrak{F}_{CF}$, ϵ_F is calculated allowing for gas radiation only; $\epsilon_C = 0.9$. In applying Eq. (10-123) to data on 19 furnaces, Lobo and Evans [*Trans. Am. Inst. Chem. Engrs.*, **35**, 743 (1939)] found that F_{RC} was represented adequately by $A_C/(A_C + A_R)$ for values of A_R/A_C from 0 to 1, by A_C/A_R for values of A_R/A_C from 3 to 6.5. Since Eq. (10-123) involves heat received by oil rather than heat lost by the flame, when it is combined with the energy balance represented by Eq. (10-122) the latter must be modified. i is replaced by $i - q_L$, where q_L is the external heat loss from the combustion chamber. A simplified graphical treatment of the solution of Eqs. (10-123) and (10-122) is available in the reference given, together with a comparison on results with 85 tests on 19 furnaces of widely different types and excess air, burning fuel oil or refinery gas; the average deviation was 5.3 per cent; excluding tests almost certainly bad, the average deviation was less than 4 per cent (q_{exp} vs. q_{calc}).

A relation for petroleum heaters, somewhat simpler and quicker to use than Eq. (10-123) but not so safe, is obtainable by assuming certain terms in Eq. (10-118) constant, combining with Eq. (10-122) to eliminate T_F, and finding an expression different in form but numerically similar over the range of interest. The relation is

$$\eta = \frac{1}{1 + \dfrac{\sqrt{i/A_C\mathfrak{F}_{CF}}}{1.4\left[\dfrac{i/w_G(C_p)_m}{100}\right]^{1.6}}} \qquad (10\text{-}124)$$

where η is the ratio of heat transferred to oil to the enthalpy of the entering air and fuel (net value). Other equations applicable in this field are available (Wilson, Lobo, and Hottel, *Ind. Eng. Chem.*, **24**, 486 (1932); Mekler, *Nat. Petroleum News*, July 27, 1938).

Steam Boiler Furnaces. For calculating heat transmission in the radiant sections of steam boiler furnace settings, many empirical relations are available. One of the simplest is the Orrok-Hudson equation

$$\eta = \frac{1}{1 + \dfrac{r_{af}\sqrt{w_A}}{27}} \qquad (10\text{-}125)$$

in which r_{af} is the weight ratio of air to fuel; w_A is the firing rate expressed as pounds of equivalent good bituminous coal per hour per square foot of exposed tube area (complete circumference if not buried in wall).

Mullikin [*Trans. Am. Soc. Mech. Engrs.*, **57**, 517 (1935)] assumes that the flame emissivity ϵ_F is unity for large pulverized coal-, oil-, or gas-fired furnaces and that compensation for this somewhat too high value comes from use of the same value for gas temperature in Eqs. (10-118) and (10-122). When ϵ_F is unity, the term $A_C\mathfrak{F}_{CF}$ of Eq. (10-118) becomes simply $A_C\epsilon_C$ (though the remarks of p. 10-46 concerning proper evaluation of A_C apply). Mullikin introduces additional multiplying factors on A_C to allow for resistance of overlying slag or refractory facing on metal-block walls. These are 0.7 for bare-faced metal blocks on tubes and 0.35 for refractory-faced metal blocks on tubes. The simplification suggested is unsafe to use on small furnaces where ϵ_F is certainly not unity.

Wohlenberg [*Trans. Am. Soc. Mech. Engrs.*, **47**, 127 (1925); **57**, 531 (1935)] uses a relation intrinsically similar to Eq. (10-121) together with a heat balance involving the assumption of equality of flame and exit gas temperatures; he presents the relation for η in the form of the product of a number of quantities each making separate allowance for one of the variables under control.

Example 5. Natural gas is being burned for steam generation in a combustion chamber of which the back wall and floor are water-cooled. The gas passes through a tube nest directly above and covering the top of the combustion chamber. The chamber is 16 ft. wide by 16 ft. long by 20 ft. high. The gas, fired at the rate of 130,000 cu. ft./hr. (measured and fired at 60°F., 30 in. Hg, saturated) with 15 per cent excess air (saturated), has the equivalent composition $C_{1.25}H_{4.5}$ and a net heating value of 1070 B.t.u./cu. ft. The "cold" surfaces of the chamber have an average temperature of 350°F. What is the rate of heat input to the water-cooled walls, floor, and tubes above, exclusive of any convection to the roof tubes as the gas passes up through them? What percentage of the enthalpy of the entering fuel does this represent?

Derived Data. By stoichiometry, the products of combustion contain 8.60 per cent CO_2, 16.36 per cent H_2O, 2.44 per cent O_2, and 72.60 per cent N_2, wet basis; their total is 4911 lb.-moles. From specific heat charts the average molal heat capacity of the products between 2000° and 60°F. is 8.25; between 2500° and 60°F. it is 8.45.

Assumptions. The external loss from the refractory walls will be assumed equal to the convection to them on the inside. Convection coefficients inside the chamber = 2.0. Refractory wall conductance k_w/x_w = 0.9. The flame completely fills the chamber. To the emissivity of the flame due to non-luminous gases will be added 0.1 to allow for the luminosity due to cracked hydrocarbons in the flame (this varies enormously with burner type). The emissivity of the "cold" surfaces = 0.8, and absorptivity equals emissivity. The mean flame temperature is 100°F. above the exit-gas temperature (these approach one another as firing rate increases).

Solution. Equations (10-118) and (10-122) are to be solved for g_F and T_F. $A_C = 16 \times 20 + 16 \times 16 \times 2 = 832$ sq. ft. (The effective area of the tube test, for radiation reception, is that of a plane replacing the tubes.) $A_R = 16 \times 20 \times 3 = 960$ sq. ft. $A_C' = 16 \times 20 + 16 \times 6 = 576$ (plane of tube nest is excluded here). Evaluation of $\mathfrak{F}$ involves F_{RC} (or F_{CR}) and ϵ_F. In this problem F_{RC} and F_{CR} are equally tedious to evaluate; we shall choose the first. Since the three refractory rectangles do not all "see" the same arrangement of surfaces above them, it is necessary to determine the product A_RF_{RC} for each and to add them, then to divide by the total A_R. Consider first the front wall, 16 × 20 ft., which "sees" three cold faces, one directly opposite, one above, and one below. The fraction of its radiation intercepted by the wall opposite comes from Fig. 10-19, line 2. By the method of Example 2 of this section, $F = \sqrt{0.196 \times 0.26} = 0.225$, the fraction of the radiation from the front refractory wall intercepted by the rear water-cooled wall. To find the fraction intercepted by the water-cooled floor, reference is made to Fig. 10-20. From that figure, when $Y = {}^{20}\!/_{16}$ and $Z = {}^{16}\!/_{16}$, $F = 0.17$. Since the imaginary top plane replacing the tubes intercepts the same fraction as the water-cooled floor, the total fraction intercepted by cold surfaces is $0.17 \times 2 + 0.225 = 0.565$; and A_RF_{RC} for the front refractory wall is $16 \times 20 \times 0.565 = 181$ sq. ft. A similar procedure leads to the value $(0.17 \times 2 + 0.213)$ or 0.553 as the fraction of the radiation from either refractory side wall which is intercepted by the three cold faces. Then the final value of F_{RC} is

$$F_{RC} = \frac{(16)(20)(0.565) + (16)(20)(0.553)(2)}{(16)(20) + (16)(20)(2)} = 0.56$$

Flame emissivity ϵ_F is next to be evaluated. The equivalent gray-body emissivity of a flame at T_G in interchange with cold surfaces at T_S is defined in the relation

$$\begin{aligned} q/A &= \sigma(\epsilon_G T_G^4 - \alpha_G T_S^4) \\ &= \epsilon_F\sigma(T_G^4 - T_S^4) \end{aligned}$$

from which

$$\epsilon_F = \frac{\epsilon_G - \alpha_G(T_S/T_G^4)}{1 - (T_S/T_G)^4}$$

One must first make a provisional guess as to the value of t_G and adjust later if necessary. Temporarily assume 2500°F. The effective beam length for gas radiation would be 0.6 times one side if the chamber were cubical (see Table 10-30); 0.6 times an average side of 18 ft., or 10.8 ft., may be used (a considerable error in this assumption will not materially affect the result). Then $P_CL = (0.086)(10.8) = 0.93$, and $P_WL = (0.1636)(10.8) = 1.77$. Because t_S is so low compared with t_G the approximate method of determining α_G for CO_2 and H_2O will be used (see p. 10-43). At t_G = 2500°F. and t_S = 350°, using Figs. 10-22, 10-22*a*, 10-23, 10-23*a*, and 10-24 and substituting into the above expression for ϵ_F, one obtains

$$\epsilon_F = \frac{(0.11 + 0.193 \times 1.08 - 0.05) - ({}^{810}\!/_{2960})^4(0.12 + 0.35 \times 1.08 - 0.028)}{1 - ({}^{810}\!/_{2960})^4}$$

due to gas radiation. (In this particular example ϵ_F could have been taken as the sum of the ϵ_G's with no allowance for the absorption terms.) Adding on an allowance for soot luminosity,

$_F = 0.37$. From Eq. (10-120),

$$\bar{F}_{CF} = 0.37\left(1 + \frac{960/832}{1 + \frac{0.37}{0.63}\cdot\frac{1}{0.56}}\right) = 0.578$$

In using Eq. (10-119) to allow for the effect of receiver-surface emissivity, one should note that the radiation-receiving surfaces are of two kinds, phase surfaces in floor and back wall and a nest of tubes in the roof. The former will have an emissivity (or absorptivity) of 0.8. The tube nest will exhibit an effective absorptivity much higher because any beams penetrating up between tubes will have many chances for absorption after reflection. In the present example a mean value of 0.9 will be used on the whole of A_C. Then, by Eq. (10-119),

$$\mathfrak{F}_{CF} = \frac{1}{\frac{1}{0.578} + \frac{1}{0.9} - 1} = 0.544$$

This amounts to saying that the flame-wall system interchanges 54 per cent as much heat as a system of parallel black planes close together, having an area A_C and temperatures T_F and T_C. The over-all refractory-wall coefficient $= U = 1(\frac{1}{2} + 1/0.9 + \frac{1}{2}) = 0.47$. Substitution into Eq. (10-118) now gives

$$q_F = 0.173\left[\left(\frac{T_F}{100}\right)^4 - 8.1^4\right](832)(0.544) + (2)(576)(T_F - 810) + (0.47)(960)(T_F - 520)$$

An energy balance, Eq. (10-122) (with the gas-exit temperature assumed 100°F. below T_F), gives

$$q_F = (130{,}000)(1070) - (4911)(8.45)(T_F - 100 - 520)$$

Solution by trial and error of these two simultaneous equations gives $T_F = 2780$(2320°F.) and $q_F = 50{,}400{,}000$ B.t.u./hr. If the flame emissivity and heat capacity are adjusted to 2300° instead of 2500° and the solution of equations repeated, one obtains $t_F = 2290°$ and $q_F = 51{,}600{,}000$ B.t.u./hr., indicating that the final result is insensitive to the temperature at which ϵ_F and MC_p are evaluated. Not all the heat q_F goes to the water-cooled surfaces; the third term in the heat-transfer equation represents loss through refractory walls. This is (0.47)(960)(2190) or 1,000,000 B.t.u./hr. Then, finally, the heat received by the water-cooled surfaces, exclusive of convection to the first tube row, is 51,600,000 − 1,000,000 = 50,600,000 B.t.u./hr., or 50,600,000/(130,000)(1070) = 36.4 per cent of the enthalpy of the entering fuel.

SECTION 11

HEAT-TRANSFER EQUIPMENT

BY

Frank L. Rubin, B.A., B.Ch.E., P.E., Product Engineer, Downingtown Iron Works, Division, Pressed Steel Tank Co.; Member, American Institute of Chemical Engineers, American Society of Mechanical Engineers. Section Editor. (Unfired Heat-transfer Equipment for Liquids and Gases)

WITH

David Stuhlbarg, Ch.E., Heat Transfer Specialist, The Procter & Gamble Co. (Coils and Jacketed Vessels)

F. C. Standiford, M.S., P.E., President, W. L. Badger Associates, Inc.; Member, American Institute of Chemical Engineers, American Chemical Society. (Evaporation)

Arthur D. Holt, P.E., Chief, Vibratory and Heat-processing Equipment Research, The Jeffrey Manufacturing Co.; Member, American Institute of Chemical Engineers, American Society of Mechanical Engineers, National Society of Professional Engineers. (Indirect Heat-transfer Equipment for Solids)

CONTENTS

UNFIRED HEAT-TRANSFER EQUIPMENT FOR LIQUIDS AND GASES

HEAT-TRANSFER EQUIPMENT

The investment in chemical plant equipment indicates that heat exchangers are generally the most important items in such plants. Individual exchangers may be small but the over-all cost of the heat-transfer equipment is such that careful attention should be paid to design, specification, and performance.

SHELL-AND-TUBE-TYPE EXCHANGERS

Shell-and-tube-type exchangers constitute the bulk of the unfired heat-transfer equipment, although increasing emphasis has been developing in other designs. Features of the principal shell-and-tube-type exchangers are summarized in Table 11-1.

Table 11-1. Features of Principal Shell-and-tube-type Exchangers*

Type of design	Fixed tube sheet	U-tube	Packed lantern-ring floating head	Internal floating head (split backing ring)	Outside-packed floating head	Pull-through floating head
T.E.M.A. rear-head type	L or M or N	U	W	S	P	T
Relative cost increases from A (least expensive) through E (most expensive)	B	A	C	E	D	E
Provision for differential expansion	Expansion joint in shell	Individual tubes free to expand	Floating head	Floating head	Floating head	Floating head
Removable bundle	No	Yes	Yes	Yes	Yes	Yes
Replacement bundle possible	No	Yes	Yes	Yes	Yes	Yes
Individual tubes replaceable	Yes	Only those in outside row†	Yes	Yes	Yes	Yes
Tube cleaning by chemicals inside and outside	Yes	Yes	Yes	Yes	Yes	Yes
Interior tube cleaning mechanically	Yes	Special tools required	Yes	Yes	Yes	Yes
Exterior tube cleaning mechanically:						
Triangular pitch	No	No‡	No§	No§	No§	No§
Square pitch	No	Yes	Yes	Yes	Yes	Yes
Hydraulic-jet cleaning:						
Tube interior	Yes	Special tools required	Yes	Yes	Yes	Yes
Tube exterior	No	Yes	Yes	Yes	Yes	Yes
Double tubes sheet feasible	Yes	Yes	No	No	Yes	No
Number of tube passes	No practical limitations	Any practical number possible	Limited to one or two passes	No practical limitations§	No practical limitations	No practical limitations§
Internal gaskets eliminated	Yes	Yes	Yes	No	Yes	No

NOTE: Relative costs A and B are not significantly different and interchange for long lengths of tubing.

* Modified from page a-8 of the Patterson-Kelley Co. Manual No. 700A, Heat Exchangers.

† U-tube bundles have been built with tube supports which permit the U-bends to be spread apart and tubes inside of the bundle replaced.

‡ Normal triangular pitch does not permit mechanical cleaning. With a wide triangular pitch, which is equal to 2 (tube diameter plus cleaning lane)/$\sqrt{3}$ mechanical cleaning is possible on removable bundles. This wide spacing is infrequently used.

§ For odd number of tube side passes, floating head requires packed joint or expansion joint.

CONSTRUCTION CODES

"Rules for Construction of Unfired Pressure Vessels" published by the American Society of Mechanical Engineers serve as a construction code for engineers by providing minimum standards. The current edition was published in 1962 and new editions usually are issued every three years. Interim revisions are made semiannually in the form of addenda. Compliance with A.S.M.E. Code requirements is mandatory in most of the United States and Canada. These rules were not prepared for heat exchangers, and no references to tube sheets, tube rolling, tube welding, baffle spacing, etc., appear.

"Standards of Tubular Exchanger Manufacturers Association," fourth edition, 1959 (commonly referred to as the "T.E.M.A. Standards"), serve to supplement and define the A.S.M.E. Code for all shell-and-tube-type heat-exchanger applications (other than double-pipe construction). T.E.M.A. Class R design is "for the generally severe requirements of petroleum and chemical processing applications. Equipment fabricated in accordance with these standards is designed for safety and durability under the rigorous service and maintenance conditions of such applications." T.E.M.A. Class C design is "for the generally moderate requirements of commercial and general process applications. Equipment fabricated in accordance with these standards is designed for the maximum economy and overall compactness consistent with safety and service requirements in such applications."

Among the topics of the T.E.M.A. Standards are nomenclature, fabrication tolerances, inspection, guarantees, tubes, shells, baffles and support plates, floating heads, gaskets, tube sheets, channels, nozzles, end flanges and bolting, material specifications, and fouling resistances. An analysis of the T.E.M.A. Standards with a comparison of Class R and Class C requirements as well as differences between the third and fourth editions has been made by F. L. Rubin [*Petrol. Refiner*, **40**, 147–154 (June, 1961)]. Many companies in the chemical and petroleum processing fields have their own standards, which serve to supplement both A.S.M.E. and T.E.M.A. requirements.

Design pressures and temperatures for exchangers usually are specified with a margin of safety beyond the conditions expected in service. Design pressure is generally about 25 lb./sq. in. greater than the maximum expected during operation or at pump shutoff. Design temperature is commonly 25°F. greater than the maximum temperature in service.

Performance testing of heat exchangers is described in the American Institute of Chemical Engineers "Stand-

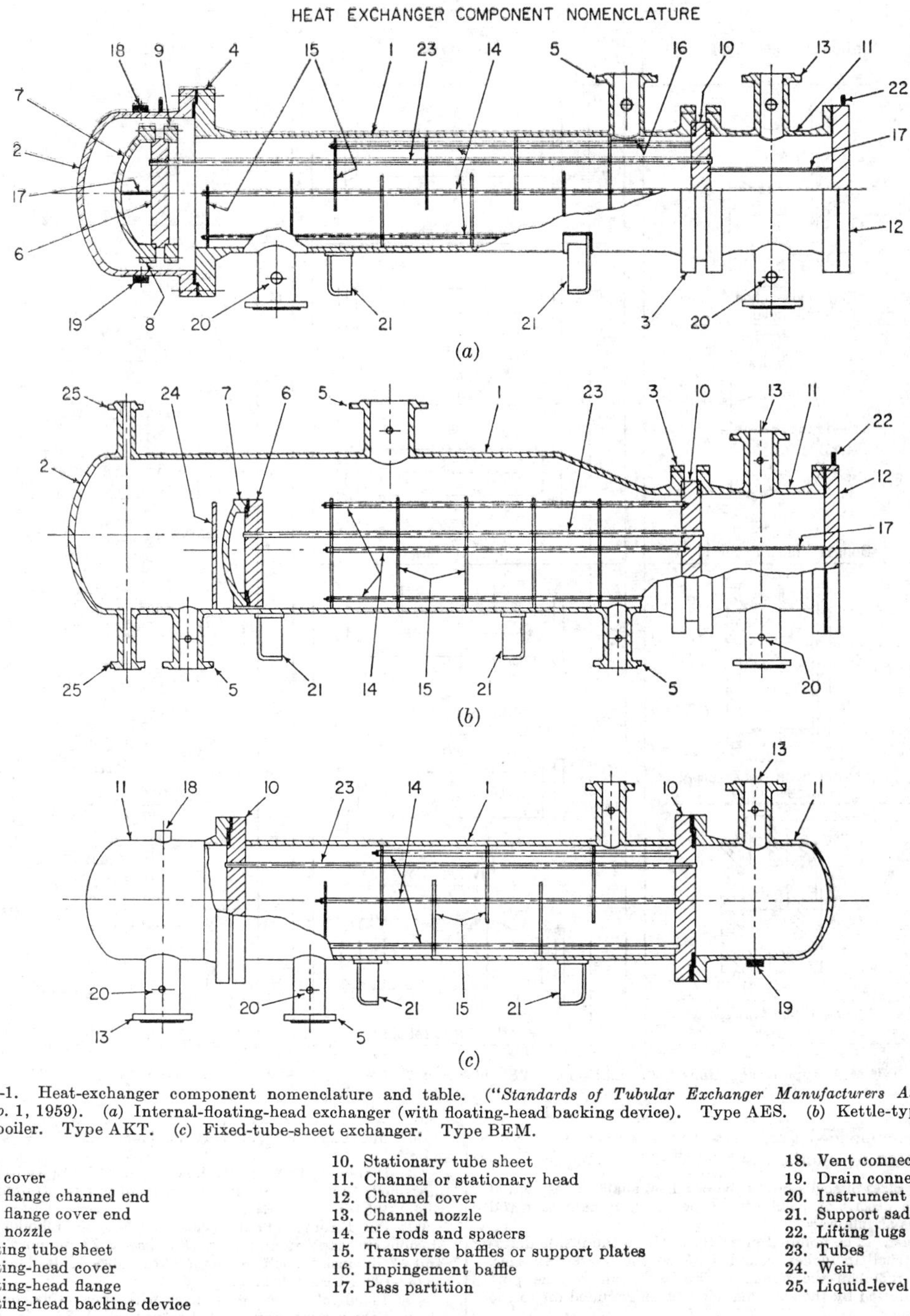

Fig. 11-1. Heat-exchanger component nomenclature and table. ("*Standards of Tubular Exchanger Manufacturers Association,*" *4th ed. p.* 1, 1959). (*a*) Internal-floating-head exchanger (with floating-head backing device). Type AES. (*b*) Kettle-type floating-head reboiler. Type AKT. (*c*) Fixed-tube-sheet exchanger. Type BEM.

1. Shell
2. Shell cover
3. Shell flange channel end
4. Shell flange cover end
5. Shell nozzle
6. Floating tube sheet
7. Floating-head cover
8. Floating-head flange
9. Floating-head backing device
10. Stationary tube sheet
11. Channel or stationary head
12. Channel cover
13. Channel nozzle
14. Tie rods and spacers
15. Transverse baffles or support plates
16. Impingement baffle
17. Pass partition
18. Vent connection
19. Drain connection
20. Instrument connection
21. Support saddles
22. Lifting lugs
23. Tubes
24. Weir
25. Liquid-level connection

ard Testing Procedure for Heat Exchangers," Section 1, Sensible Heat Transfer in Shell and Tube-type Equipment.

NOMENCLATURE

Nomenclature of components is presented in the table accompanying Fig. 11-1.

Size Numbering and Type Designation. Recommended practice for the designation of conventional shell-and-tube heat exchangers by numbers and letters has been established by the Tubular Exchanger Manufacturers Association. This information from the fourth edition of the T.E.M.A. Standards is reproduced below and in Fig. 11-2.

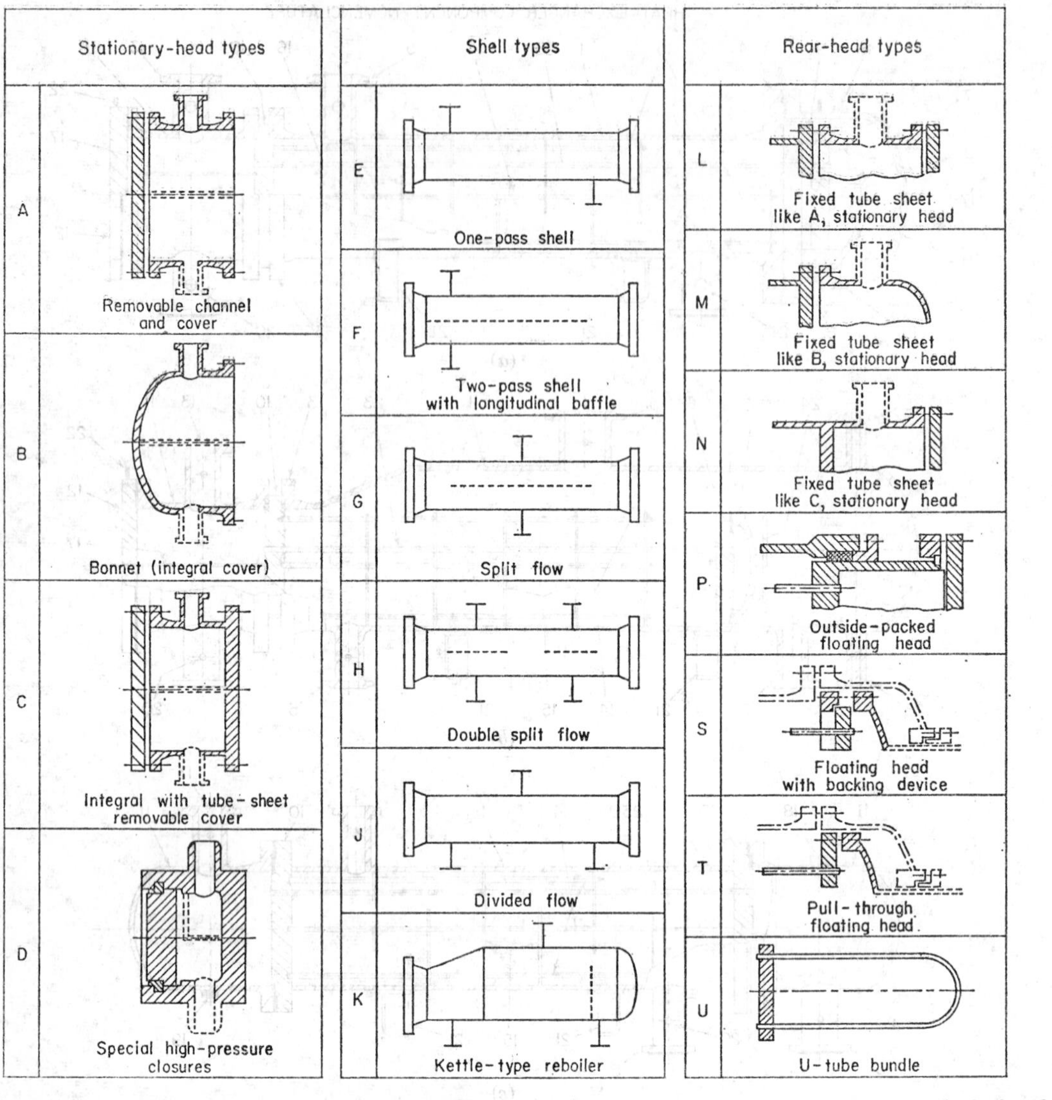

FIG. 11-2. T.E.M.A. type designations for exchangers. (*"Standards of Tubular Exchanger Manufacturers Association," 4th ed. p. 2,* 1959.)

It is recommended that heat-exchanger size and type be designated by numbers and letters.

1. *Size.* Sizes of shells (and tube bundles) shall be designated by numbers describing shell (and tube-bundle) diameters and tube lengths as follows:

2. *Diameter.* The nominal diameter shall be the inside diameter of the shell in inches, rounded off to the nearest integer. For kettle reboilers the nominal diameter shall be the port diameter followed by the shell diameter, each rounded off to the nearest integer.

3. *Length.* The nominal length shall be the tube length in inches. Tube length for straight tubes shall be taken as the actual over-all length. For U-tubes the length shall be taken as the straight length from end of tube to bend tangent.

4. *Type.* Type designation shall be by letters describing stationary head, shell (omitted for bundles only), and rear head, in that order, as indicated in Fig. 11-2.

Typical Examples. (*A*) Split-ring floating-head exchanger with removable channel and cover, single-pass shell, 23¼ in. inside diameter with tubes 16 ft. long. SIZE 23-192 TYPE AES.

(*B*) U-tube exchanger with bonnet-type stationary head, split-flow shell, 19 in. inside diameter with tubes 7 ft. straight length. SIZE 19-84 TYPE BGU.

(*C*) Pull-through floating-head-kettle-type reboiler having stationary head integral with tube sheet, 23 in. port diameter and 37 in. inside shell diameter with tubes 10 ft. long. SIZE 23/37-192 TYPE CKT.

(*D*) Fixed-tube sheet exchanger with removable channel and cover, bonnet-type rear head, two-pass shell, 33⅛ in. diameter with tubes 8 ft. long. SIZE 33-96 TYPE AFM.

(*E*) Fixed-tube sheet exchanger having stationary and rear heads integral with tube sheets, single-pass shell, 17 in. inside diameter with tubes 16 ft. long. SIZE 17-192 TYPE CEN.

Special designs are not covered and may be described as best suits the manufacturer.

Functional Definitions. Heat-transfer equipment can be designated by type (*e.g.*, fixed tube sheet, outside packed head, etc.) or by function (chiller, condenser, cooler, etc.). Almost any type of unit can be used to perform any or all of the above functions.

Many of these terms were defined by Donahue [*Petrol. Processing*, March, 1956, p. 103.]

Equipment	Function
Chiller	Cools a fluid to a temperature below that obtainable if water only were used as a coolant. It uses a refrigerant such as ammonia or Freon
Condenser	Condenses a vapor or mixture of vapors, either alone or in the presence of a non-condensable gas
Partial condenser	Condenses vapors at a point high enough to provide a temperature difference sufficient to preheat a cold stream of process fluid. This saves heat and eliminates the need for providing a separate preheater (using flame or steam)
Final condenser	Condenses the vapors to a final storage temperature of approximately 100°F. It uses water cooling, which means the transferred heat is lost to the process
Cooler	Cools liquids or gases by means of water
Exchanger	Performs a double function: (1) heats a cold fluid by (2) using a hot fluid which it cools. None of the transferred heat is lost
Heater	Imparts sensible heat to a liquid or a gas by means of condensing steam or Dowtherm
Reboiler	Connected to the bottom of a fractionating tower, it provides the reboil heat necessary for distillation. The heating medium may be either steam or a hot process fluid
Thermosiphon reboiler	Natural circulation of the boiling medium is obtained by maintaining sufficient liquid head to provide for circulation
Forced-circulation reboiler	A pump is used to force liquid through the reboiler
Steam generator	Generates steam for use elsewhere in the plant by using the available high-level heat in tar or a heavy oil
Superheater	Heats a vapor above the saturation temperature
Vaporizer	A heater which vaporizes part of the liquid
Waste-heat boiler	Produces steam; similar to steam generator, except that the heating medium is a hot gas or liquid produced in a chemical reaction

GENERAL DESIGN CONSIDERATIONS

In selecting the flow path for two fluids through an exchanger several general approaches are used. The tube-side fluid is more corrosive or dirtier or at a higher pressure. The shell-side fluid is a liquid of high viscosity or a gas.

When alloy construction for one of the two fluids is required, a carbon-steel shell combined with alloy tube-side parts is less expensive than alloy in contact with the shell-side fluid combined with carbon-steel headers.

Cleaning of the inside of tubes is more readily done than cleaning of exterior surfaces.

For pressures in excess of 300 lb./sq. in. for one of the fluids, the less expensive construction has the high-pressure fluid in the tubes.

For a given pressure drop higher heat-transfer coefficients are obtained on the shell side than on the tube side.

Shutdowns. Heat-exchanger shutdowns are most often caused by fouling, corrosion, and erosion (*Chem. Processing*, July, 1959, p. 125).

Testing. Upon completion of shop fabrication and also during maintenance operations it is desirable hydrostatically to test on the shell side of tubular exchangers so that visual examination of tube ends can be made. Leaking tubes can be readily located and serviced. When leaks are determined without access to the tube ends it is necessary to reroll or reweld all the tube-to-tube-sheet joints with possible damage to the satisfactory joints.

Testing for leaks in heat exchangers was discussed by F. L. Rubin [*Chem. Eng.*, **68,** 160–166 (July 24, 1961)].

FIXED-TUBE-SHEET HEAT EXCHANGER
(Fig. 11-1*c*)

Fixed-tube-sheet exchangers are used more often than any other type. The tube sheets are welded to the shell. Usually these extend beyond the shell and serve as flanges to which the tube-side headers are bolted. This construction requires that the shell and tube-sheet materials must be weldable to each other.

When such welding is not possible a "blind" gasket type of construction is utilized. The "blind" gasket is not accessible for maintenance or replacement once the unit has been constructed. This construction is used for low-pressure and low-temperature services (up to 150 lb./sq. in. and 300°F).

There is no limitation on the number of tube-side passes. Shell-side passes can be one or more, although shells with more than two shell-side passes are rarely used.

Tubes can completely fill the heat-exchanger shell. Clearance between the outermost tubes and the shell is only the minimum necessary for fabrication. Between the inside of the shell and the baffles some clearance must be provided so that baffles can slide into the shell. Fabrication tolerances then require some additional clearance between the outside of the baffles and the outermost tubes. The edge distance between the outer tube limit (O.T.L.) and the baffle diameter must be sufficient to prevent vibration of the tubes from breaking through the baffle holes. The outermost tube must be contained within the O.T.L. Clearances between the inside shell diameter and O.T.L. are ½ in. for 25 in. inside diameter shells and up, 7/16 in. for 10- through 24-in. pipe shells, and slightly less for smaller-diameter pipe shells.

Maintenance. Tubes can be replaced. Tube-side headers, channel covers, gaskets, etc., are accessible for maintenance and replacement. Neither the shell-side baffle structure nor the "blind" gasket referred to above is accessible. During tube removal, a tube may break within the shell. When this occurs it is most difficult to remove or to replace the tube. The usual procedure is to plug the appropriate holes in the tube sheets.

Differential expansion between the shell and the tubes can develop because of differences in length caused by thermal expansion. Various types of expansion joints are used to eliminate excessive stresses caused by expansion.

The Expansion Joint in Fixed-tube-sheet Exchangers

Expansion joints are often provided when differential expansion between the shell and tubes is expected during either startup, shutdown, cleaning, or normal operation. The need for an expansion joint is a function of both the amount of differential expansion and the cycling conditions to be expected during operation.

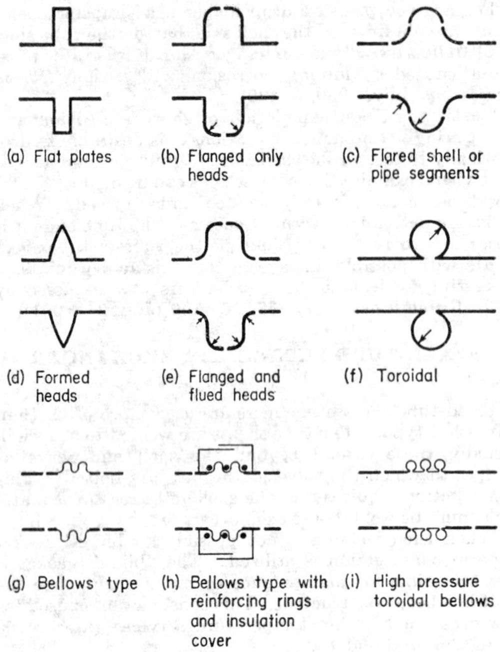

FIG. 11-3. Expansion joints

Types of Expansion Joints (Fig. 11-3). (*a*) *Flat Plates.* Two concentric flat plates with a bar at the outer edges. The flat plates can flex to make some allowance for differential expansion. This design is generally used for vacuum service and pressures below 15 lb./sq. in. gage pressure. All welds are subject to severe stress during differential expansion.

(*b*) *Flanged-only Heads.* The flat plates are flanged (or curved). The diameter of these heads is generally 8 or more inches greater than the shell diameter. The welded joint at the shell is subject to the stress referred to above, but the joint connecting the heads is subjected to less stress during expansion because of the curved shape.

(*c*) *Flared Shell or Pipe Segments.* The shell may be flared to connect with a pipe section or a pipe may be halved and quartered to provide a ring.

(*d*) *Formed Heads.* A pair of dished-only or elliptical or flanged and dished heads can be used. These are welded together or connected by a ring. This type of joint is similar to the flanged-only-head type but apparently is subject to less stress.

(*e*) *Flanged and Flued Heads.* A pair of flanged-only heads is provided with concentric, reverse flue holes. These heads are relatively expensive because of the cost of the fluing operation. The curved shape of the heads reduces the amount of stress at the welds to the shell and also connecting the heads.

(*f*) *Toroidal.* The toroidal joint has a mathematically predictable smooth stress pattern of low magnitude, with maximum stresses at side walls of the corrugation and minimum stresses at top and bottom.

The above designs are discussed as ring expansion joints by S. Kopp and M. F. Sayre, "Expansion Joints for Heat Exchangers" (A.S.M.E. Misc. Paper, vol. 6, No. 211). All are statically indeterminate but are subjected to analysis by introducing various simplifying assumptions. Some joints in current industrial use are of lighter wall construction than is indicated by the method of this paper.

(*g*) *Bellows.* Thin-wall bellows joints are produced by various manufacturers. These are designed for differential expansion and are tested for axial and transverse movement as well as for cyclical life. Bellows may be of stainless steel, nickel alloys, or copper. (Aluminum, monel, phosphor bronze, and titanium bellows have been manufactured.) Welding nipples of the same composition as the heat-exchanger shell are generally furnished. The bellows may be hydraulically formed from a single piece of metal or may consist of welded pieces. External insulation covers of carbon steel are often provided to protect the light-gage bellows from damage. The cover also prevents insulation from interfering with movement of the bellows.

(*i*) *Toroidal Bellows.* For high-pressure service the bellows type of joint has been modified so that movement is taken up by thin-wall small-diameter bellows of a toroidal shape. Thickness of parts under high pressure is reduced considerably [see (*f*) above].

Improper handling during manufacture, transit, installation, or maintenance of the heat exchanger equipped with the thin-wall-bellows type or toroidal type of expansion joint can damage the joint. In larger units these light-wall joints are particularly susceptible to damage, and some designers prefer the use of the heavier walls of formed heads.

Chemical plant exchangers requiring expansion joints most commonly have used the flanged-and-flued-head type. There is a trend toward the more common use of the light-wall-bellows type.

U-TUBE HEAT EXCHANGER (Fig. 11-2*U*)

The tube bundle consists of a stationary tube sheet, U-tubes (or hairpin tubes), baffles or support plates, and appropriate tie rods and spacers. The tube bundle can be removed from the heat-exchanger shell. A tube-side header (stationary head) and a shell with integral shell cover, which is welded to the shell, are provided. Each tube is free to expand or contract without any limitation being placed upon it by the other tubes.

The U-tube bundle has the advantage of providing the minimum clearance between the outer tube limit and the inside of the shell for any of the removable-tube-bundle constructions. Clearances are of the same magnitude as for fixed-tube-sheet heat exchangers.

The number of tube holes in a given shell is less than that for a fixed-tube-sheet exchanger because of limitations on bending tubes of a very short radius.

The U-tube design offers the advantage of reducing the number of joints. In high-pressure construction this feature becomes of considerable importance in reducing both initial and maintenance costs.

Mechanical cleaning of the inside of the tubes is described by A. John [*Chem. Eng.*, **66**, 187–192 (Dec. 14, 1959)]. Rods and conventional mechanical tube cleaners cannot pass from one end of the U-tube to the other. Power-driven tube cleaners, which can clean both the straight legs of the tubes and the bends, are available.

Hydraulic jetting with water forced through spray nozzles at high pressure for cleaning tube interiors and exteriors of removal bundles is reported in B. L. Canaday's "Hydraulic Jetting Tools for Cleaning Heat Exchangers" (A.S.M.E. Paper 58-A-217, 8 pp.; an unpublished paper). Hydraulic jetting can also be used to clean the inside of U-tubes.

The tank suction heater, as illustrated in Fig. 11-4,

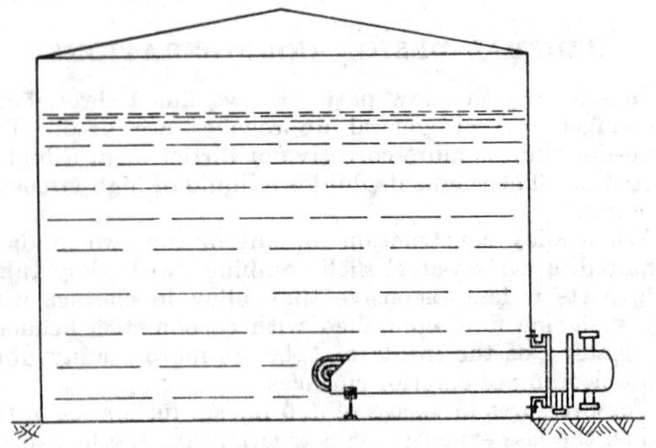

FIG. 11-4. Tank suction heater.

contains a U-tube bundle. This design is often used with outdoor storage tanks for heavy fuel oils, tar, molasses, and similar fluids whose viscosity must be lowered to permit easy pumping. Usually the tube-side heating medium is steam. One end of the heater shell is open and the liquid being heated passes across the outside of the tubes. Pumping costs can be reduced without heating the entire contents of the tank. Bare tube and integral low-fin tubes are provided with baffles. Longitudinal fin-tube heaters are not baffled.

Kettle-type reboilers, evaporators, etc., are often U-tube exchangers with enlarged shell sections for vapor-liquid separation. The U-tube bundle replaces the floating-head bundle of Fig. 11-1*b*.

PACKED-LANTERN-RING EXCHANGER (Fig. 11-5)

This removable bundle exchanger is to be designated as T.E.M.A. type W. (As of this writing, public announcement of the designation has not been made.) The shell- and tube-side fluids are each contained by separate rings of packing separated by a lantern ring and are installed at the floating tube sheet. The lantern ring is provided with weep holes. Any leakage passing the packing goes through the weep holes and then drips to the floor. Leakage at the packing will not result in mixing within the exchanger of the two fluids.

The width of the floating tube sheet must be great enough to allow for the packings, the lantern ring, and differential expansion. Sometimes a small skirt is attached to a thin tube sheet to provide the required bearing surface for packings and lantern ring.

The clearance between the outer tube limit and the inside of the shell is slightly larger than that for fixed-tube-sheet and U-tube exchangers. The use of a floating-tube-sheet skirt increases this clearance. Without the skirt the clearance must make allowance for tube-hole distortion during tube rolling near the outside edge of the tube sheet or for tube-end welding at the floating tube sheet.

The packed-lantern-ring construction is generally limited to 150 lb./sq. in. at temperatures of 500°F. or less and is not used for volatile or flammable fluids.

OUTSIDE-PACKED FLOATING-HEAD EXCHANGER (Fig. 11-2*P*)

The shell-side fluid is contained by rings of packing, which are compressed within a stuffing box by a packing follower ring. This removable-bundle construction accommodates differential expansion between shell and tubes and is used for shell-side service up to 600 lb./sq. in. at 600°F. There are no limitations upon the number of tube-side passes or upon the tube-side design pressure and temperature. The outside-packed floating-head exchanger is the most commonly used type of removable-bundle construction in chemical-plant service. A typical condenser with vapor-liquid separating head is illustrated in Fig. 11-6.

The floating-tube-sheet skirt, where in contact with the rings of packing, has a fine machine finish. A split shear ring is inserted into a groove in the floating-tube-sheet skirt. A slip-on backing flange, which in service is held in place by the shear ring, bolts to the external floating-head cover.

The floating-head cover is usually a circular disk as shown in Fig. 11-2*P*. With an odd number of tube-side passes an axial nozzle can be installed in such a floating-head cover. If a side nozzle is required, the circular disk is replaced by either a dished head (with or without the vapor-liquid separating cone of Fig. 11-6) or a channel barrel (similar to Fig. 11-2*L*) bolted between floating-head cover and floating-tube-sheet skirt.

The outer tube limit approaches the inside of the skirt but is farther removed from the inside of the shell than for any of the previously discussed constructions. Clearances between shell diameter and bundle O.T.L. are 7/8 in. for small-diameter pipe shells, 1 3/4 in. for large-diameter pipe shells, and 2 1/16 in. for moderate-diameter plate shells.

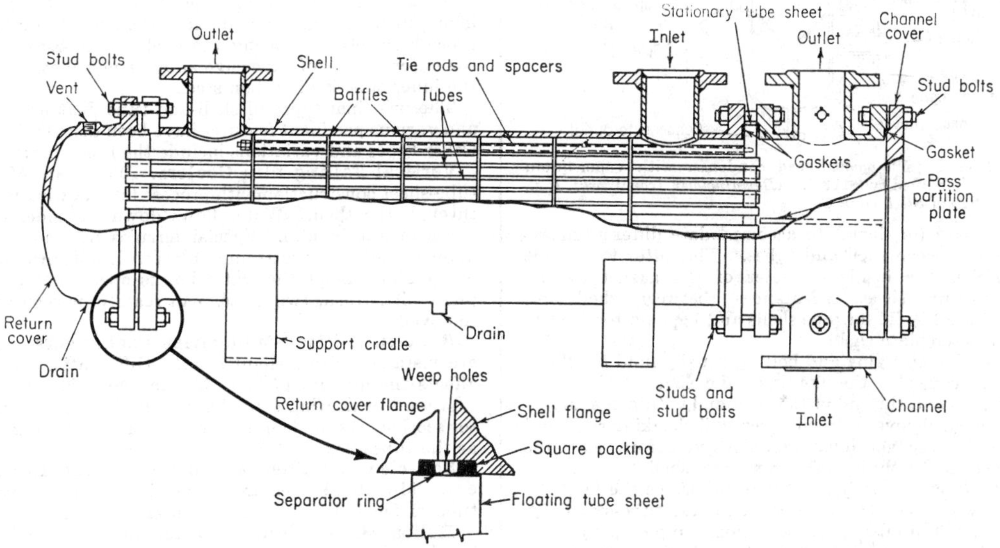

Fig. 11-5. Packed-lantern-ring exchanger. Type AEW.

INTERNAL FLOATING-HEAD EXCHANGER (Fig. 11-1*a*)

The internal floating-head design is used extensively in petroleum refinery service.

The tube bundle is removable and the floating tube

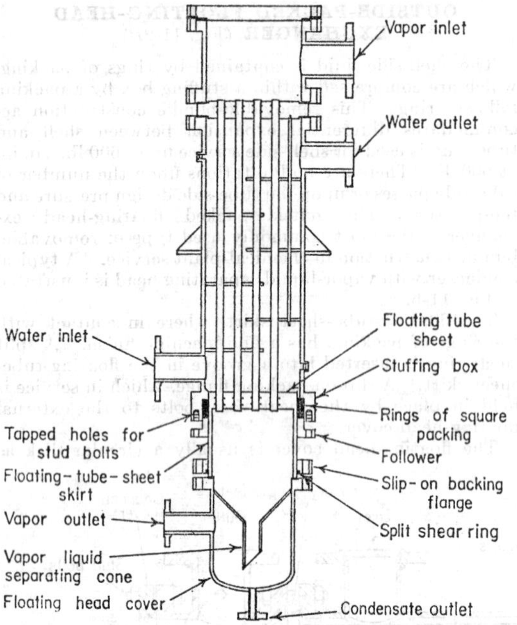

FIG. 11-6. Outside-packed-head condenser with vapor-liquid separator; modified type AEP. (*Downingtown Iron Works, Inc., Div. of Pressed Steel Tank Co.*)

sheet moves (or floats) to accommodate differential expansion between shell and tubes. The outer tube limit approaches the inside diameter of the gasket at the floating tube sheet. Clearances (between shell and O.T.L.) are 1⅛ in. for pipe shells and 1 7/16 in. for moderate-diameter plate shells.

A split backing ring and bolting usually hold the floating-head cover at the floating tube sheet. These are located beyond the end of the shell and within the larger-diameter shell cover. Shell cover, split backing ring, and floating-head cover must be removed before the tube bundle can pass through the exchanger shell.

With an even number of tube-side passes the floating-head cover serves as return cover for the tube-side fluid. With an odd number of passes a nozzle pipe must extend from the floating-head cover through the shell cover. Provision for both differential expansion and tube-bundle removal must be made.

PULL-THROUGH FLOATING-HEAD EXCHANGER (Fig. 11-2*T*)

Construction is similar to that of the internal-floating-head split-backing-ring exchanger except that the floating-head cover bolts directly to the floating tube sheet. The tube bundle can be withdrawn from the shell without removing either shell cover or floating-head cover. This feature reduces maintenance time during inspection and repair.

The large clearance between the tubes and the shell must provide for both the gasket and the bolting at the floating-head cover. This clearance is about 2 to 2½ times that required by the split-ring design. Sealing strips or dummy tubes are often installed to reduce by-passing of the tube bundle.

BAYONET-TUBE EXCHANGER (Fig. 11-7)

The bayonet-type heat exchanger is useful, when there is an extreme temperature difference between shell- and tube-side fluids, since all parts subject to differential expansion are free to move independently of each other. Costs are relatively high since only the outer bundle tubes transfer heat to the shell-side fluid. The inner tubes are unsupported. The outer tubes are supported by conventional baffles or support plates.

A bayonet-tube *element* consists of an outer and an inner tube. These elements are inserted into tanks and process vessels for heating and cooling purposes. Often the outer tube is of expensive alloy or non-metallic while the inner tube is of carbon steel.

The principal types of shell-and-tube heat exchangers and various pertinent features have been discussed above. Other types and variations include the following:

Vertical Falling-film Coolers. These are of fixed-tube-sheet construction with process fluid flowing upward through the shell. Water flows down the sides of the tubes in a thin film. Special ferrules in 2 in. outside diameter tubes or protruding tubes with slots produce the water film. Since the water box is open to the atmosphere dirt, trash, twigs, etc., can readily be seen and be removed.

Bent-tube Fixed-tube-sheet Exchangers. Tubes are installed with a slight bend. Differential expansion affects the amount of bend but the need for an expansion joint or floating tube sheet is eliminated. Evaporator sections are made in this manner and descaling occurs as the tubes flex.

Self-cleaning Shell-and-bayonet-tube Exchangers. Movable baffles are installed to keep the exterior tube surfaces clean (Davis Engineering Corp.).

Helical-fin sections in rectangular frames for gas heating, **helical-fin-tube packed-head exchangers,** and **helical-fin-tube exchanger sections** for fuel-oil heaters, gas heaters, gas cooling, and residium exchangers are available and have been discussed by F. L. Rubin [*Chem. Eng.*, **60**, 232 (September, 1953)].

Double-pipe exchangers have only one tube per shell. **Scraped-surface exchangers** are generally a variation of the double-pipe design. Spiral-tube units also have a

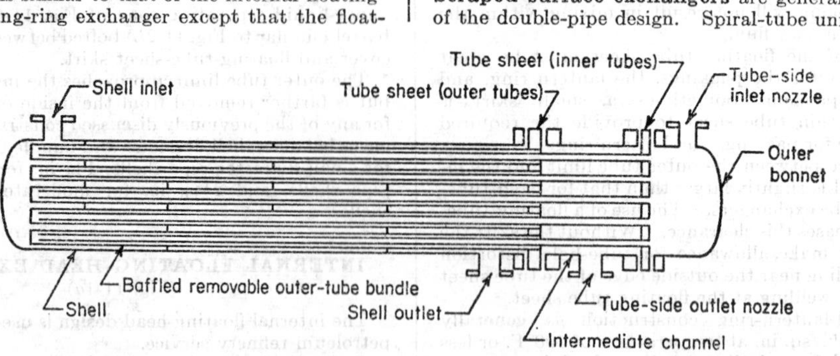

FIG. 11-7. Bayonet-tube exchanger. (*Downingtown Iron Works, Div. of Pressed Steel Tank Co.*)

shell and a tubular section. These types are discussed below.

DOUBLE-PIPE EXCHANGERS

Double-pipe heat exchangers have been used for many years primarily for low flow rates and high temperature ranges. These double-pipe sections are well adapted to high-temperature high-pressure applications because of their relatively small diameters, which allow the use of small flanges and thin wall sections as compared with conventional shell-and-tube equipment.

Commercially available double-pipe sections range from 2 through 4 in. pipe size shells with inner tubes varying from ¾ to 2½ in. pipe size. About 12 per cent of the double-pipe sections use bare tube and the balance have longitudinal fins on the outside of the inner tube.

Double-pipe exchangers can be made by inserting one pipe within another and then welding the outer jacket to the inner pipe. A packed stuffing box (which is similar to that used for the outside-packed heat exchanger, Fig. 11-6) may be employed to permit differential movement and removal of the inner pipe for cleaning or maintenance purposes. Double-pipe (Vilter Manufacturing Co.) fittings for 2- by 1¼-in. and 3- by 2-in. double-pipe sections are available. These are most commonly used in refrigeration service and may be either factory- or field-assembled.

Several manufacturers now offer standard double-pipe sections with removable tubes and provision for differential expansion between the shell and tube. A typical design is illustrated in Fig. 11-8.

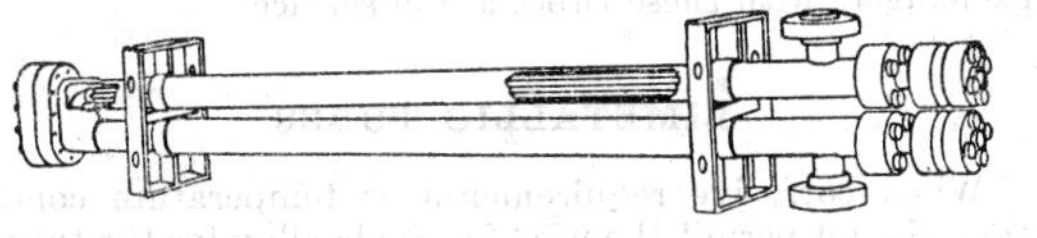

Fig. 11-8. Double-pipe exchanger section with longitudinal fins. (*Brown Fintube Co.*)

Double-pipe sections have been designed for up to 2000 lb./sq. in. on the shell side and up to 20,000 lb./sq. in. on the tube side. Ring joints and metallic seals are used at lower pressures and lens ring joints at extremely high pressures.

Double-pipe sections permit true countercurrent flow, which is of particular advantage when very close temperature approaches are required. The number of sections and the series-parallel arrangement can be varied to meet conditions. Double-pipe extended-surface sections are particularly useful when one fluid has a relatively low heat-transfer coefficient and can be placed on the outside of the fins.

Recently a multitube double-pipe section with seven longitudinally finned tubes within a 4-in. outer pipe section has been made available. The tubes are rolled into a tube sheet at one end and have individual U-bend connectors at the other. General appearance is much like that of the illustrated conventional double-pipe section.

SCRAPED-SURFACE EXCHANGERS

Scraped-surface exchangers have a rotating element with spring-loaded scraper blades to wipe the inside surface. Generally the blades are mounted inside 6-in. pipe. Double-pipe construction with an 8-in. pipe jacket and several sections connected in series is most common. Seven 6-in. pipes can be installed within a single 27-in. shell. In direct contact with the scraped surface is the process fluid, which may crystallize or be extremely fouling or of very high viscosity.

Motors, chain drives, appropriate guards, etc., are required for the rotating element.

Scraped-surface units are in use in paraffin-wax plants and for evaporating viscous or heat-sensitive materials under high vacuum.

SPIRAL-TUBE EXCHANGERS

Spiral-tube exchangers consist of a group of concentric spirally wound coils, which are generally connected by manifolds. Features include countercurrent flow, elimination of differential-expansion difficulties, constant velocity, and compactness.

For general-process exchanger applications sizes available range from 2 to 327 sq. ft. of surface. The largest of these equipped with bare tubing requires a space of 37¼ by 48 by 31½ in. Tubing used is ¼ in. outside diameter for the 2.56 sq. ft. exchangers, ⅜ in. outside diameter for 4.4 sq. ft. exchanger, and ½ in. outside diameter for larger sizes. Tubes of ⅝ and ¾ in. outside diameter are used in the largest sizes. Standard constructions of Graham Manufacturing Co. include cast-iron shell side with tube side of copper, steel, stainless 304, or stainless 316. Stainless 304 and 316 are available on both shell and tube sides.

Some *cryogenic exchanger applications* require thermodynamic reversibility with small temperature differences, and the spiral-type unit is used in these services. Air-separation-plant exchangers have the high-pressure gas inside the tubes and the low-pressure gas outside the tubes in a combination of counterflow and cross flow. It is important to make the tube spacing quite uniform to prevent channeling of the low-pressure gas stream and consequent reduction of efficiency. In a typical air-separation plant the temperature change in the gas being warmed is 400°F. and the temperature difference at the hot end may be as low as 3° or 5°F.

The coils are usually fabricated from drawn copper tubing, although other materials can be used. Typical tubing dimensions range from $\frac{3}{16}$ in. outside diameter by 20 ft. through ¼ in. outside diameter by 100 ft., to ⅜ in. outside diameter by 150 ft. long. Helically finned tubes have been used to increase the relative amount of heat-transfer surface on the low-pressure side.

SHELL-SIDE ARRANGEMENTS

One-pass Shell (Fig. 11-2*E*). This is the most commonly used arrangement. Condensers for single-component vapors often have the nozzles moved to the center of the shell for vacuum and steam services.

Two-pass Shell (Fig. 11-2*F*). A solid longitudinal baffle is provided. It may be insulated to improve thermal efficiency. A two-pass shell can improve thermal effectiveness at a cost lower than for two shells in series.

Split Flow (Fig. 11-2*G*). The longitudinal baffle may be solid or perforated. The latter feature is used with condensing vapors, when subcooling of condensate is required.

Double Split Flow (Fig. 11-2*H*). The longitudinal baffles may be solid or perforated.

Divided Flow (Fig. 11-2*J*). Mechanically this design is like the one-pass shell except for the addition of a nozzle. Divided flow is used to meet low-pressure-drop requirements.

Kettle-type Reboiler (Fig. 11-2*K*). When vaporization occurs on the shell side, this common design provides adequate dome space for separation of vapor and liquid above the tube bundle and surge capacity beyond the weir near the shell cover.

THE TUBE-SIDE HEADER

The tube-side header (or stationary head) contains one or more flow nozzles.

Bonnet. The bonnet (Fig. 11-2*B*) bolts to the shell. It is necessary to remove the bonnet in order to examine the tube ends. The fixed-tube-sheet exchanger of Fig. 11-1*c* has bonnets at both ends of the shell.

Channel. The channel (Fig. 11-2*A*) has a removable channel cover. The tube ends can be examined by removing this cover without disturbing the piping connections to the channel nozzles. The channel can bolt to the shell as shown in Fig. 11-1*a* and *b*. The type *C* channel of Fig. 11-2 is welded to the tube sheet. The latter design is comparable in cost with the bonnet but has the advantages of permitting access to the tubes without disturbing the piping connections and of eliminating a gasketed joint.

Special high-pressure closures (Fig. 11-2*D*). The channel barrel and the tube sheet are forged integrally. The removable channel cover is seated in place by hydrostatic pressure while a shear ring subjected to shearing stress absorbs the end force. For pressures above 900 lb./sq. in. these designs are generally more economical than bolted constructions, which require larger flanges and bolting as pressure increases and contain the end force with bolts in tension. Relatively light gage internal pass partitions are provided to direct the flow of tube-side fluids but are designed only for the differential pressure across the tube bundle.

Most exchangers have an even number of tube-side passes. The fixed-tube-sheet exchanger (which has no shell cover) usually has a return cover without any flow nozzles as shown in Fig. 11-2*N*; types *L* and *N* are also used. All removable-bundle designs (except for the U-tube) have a floating-head cover directing the flow of tube-side fluid at the floating tube sheet.

TUBES

Standard heat exchanger tubing is ¼, ⅜, ½, ⅝, ¾, 1, 1¼, and 1½ in. outside diameter. Wall thickness is measured in Birmingham wire gage (B.W.G.) units. (Tubing characteristics appear in Table 11-2.) The most commonly used tubes in chemical plants and petroleum refineries are ¾ and 1 in. outside diameter. Standard tube lengths are 8, 10, 12, 16, and 20 ft. with 16 ft. as the most common.

Manufacturing tolerances for steel, stainless-steel, and nickel-alloy tubes are such that the tubing is produced to either average or minimum wall thickness. Seamless carbon-steel tube of minimum wall thickness may vary from zero to 22 per cent above the nominal wall thickness. Average-wall seamless tubing has an allowable variation of plus or minus 10 per cent. Welded carbon-steel tube is produced to closer tolerances (0 to plus 18 per cent on minimum wall; plus or minus 8 per cent on average wall). Tubing of aluminum, copper, and their alloys can be drawn easily and is made to minimum wall specifications.

Common practice is to specify exchanger surface in terms of total external square feet of tubing. The effective outside heat-transfer surface is based on the length of tubes measured between the inner faces of tube sheets. In most heat exchangers there is little difference between the total and effective surface. Significant differences are usually found in high-pressure and double-tube-sheet designs.

Integrally finned tube, which is available in a variety of alloys and sizes, is being used in shell-and-tube heat exchangers. The fins are radially extruded from thick-walled tube to a height of 1⁄16 in. External surface is approximately 2½ times the outside surface of a bare tube with the same outside diameter. Bare ends of nominal tube diameter are provided, while the fin height is slightly less than this diameter. The tube can be inserted into a conventional tube bundle and rolled or welded to the tube sheet by the same means used for bare tubes. An integrally finned tube rolled into a tube sheet with double serrations and flared at the inlet is shown in Fig. 11-9.

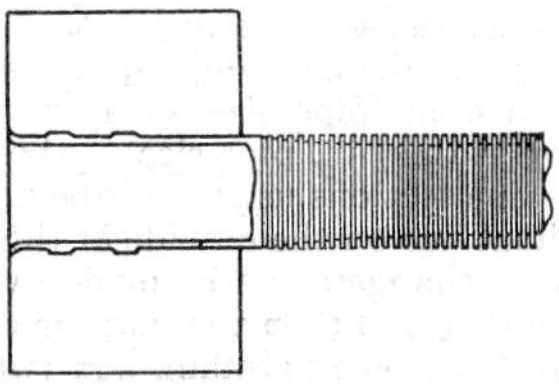

FIG. 11-9. Integrally finned tube rolled into tube sheet with double serrations and flared inlet. (*Wolverine Tube, Division of Calument & Hecla, Inc.*)

Longitudinal fins are commonly used in double-pipe exchangers upon the outside of the inner tube. U-tube and conventional removable tube bundles are also made from such tubing. The ratio of external to internal surface generally is about 10 or 15 to 1.

Transverse fins upon tubes are used in low-pressure gas services. The primary application is in air-cooled heat exchangers (as discussed on p. 11-15) but shell and tube exchangers with these tubes are in service.

BIMETALLIC TUBES

When corrosive requirements or temperature conditions do not permit the use of a single alloy for the tubes, bimetallic (or duplex) tubes may be used. These can be made from almost any possible combination of metals. Tube sizes and gages can be varied. For thin gages the wall thickness is generally divided equally between the two components. In heavier gages the more expensive component may comprise from a fifth to a third of the total thickness.

The component materials comply with applicable A.S.T.M. specifications, but after manufacture the outer component may increase in hardness beyond specification limits and special care is required during the tube-rolling operation. When the harder material is on the outside precautions must be exercised to expand the tube properly. When the inner material is considerably softer, rolling may not be practical unless ferrules of the soft material are used.

In order to eliminate galvanic action the outer tube material may be stripped from the tube ends and replaced with ferrules of the inner tube material. When the end of a tube with a ferrule is expanded or welded to a tube sheet, the tube-side fluid can contact only the inner tube material, while the outer material is exposed to the shell-side fluid.

ROLLED TUBE JOINTS

Expanded tube-to-tube-sheet joints are standard. Properly rolled joints have uniform tightness to minimize tube fractures, stress corrosion, tube-sheet ligament push-over and enlargement, and dishing of the tube sheet. Tubes are expanded into the tube sheet for a length of 2 tube diameters, or 2 in., or tube-sheet thickness minus ⅛ in. Generally tubes are rolled for the last of these

Table 11-2. Tubing Characteristics*

o.d. of tubing	B.W.G. gage	Thickness, in.	Internal area, sq. in.	Sq. ft. external surface per ft. length	Sq. ft. internal surface per ft. length	Weight per ft. length steel, lb.†	i.d. tubing, in.	Moment of inertia, in.⁴	Section modulus, in.³	Radius of gyration, in.	Constant C‡	o.d./i.d.	Metal area (transverse metal area), sq. in.
1/4	22	0.028	0.0295	0.0655	0.0508	0.066	0.194	0.00012	0.00098	0.0792	46	1.289	0.0195
1/4	24	.022	.0333	.0655	.0539	.054	.206	.00011	.00083	.0810	52	1.214	.0159
1/4	26	.018	.0360	.0655	.0560	.045	.214	.00009	.00071	.0824	56	1.168	.0131
3/8	18	.049	.0603	.0982	.0725	.171	.277	.00068	.0036	.1164	94	1.354	.0502
3/8	20	.035	.0731	.0982	.0798	.127	.305	.00055	.0029	.1213	114	1.233	.0374
3/8	22	.028	.0799	.0982	.0835	.104	.319	.00046	.0025	.1227	125	1.176	.0305
3/8	24	.022	.0860	.0982	.0867	.083	.331	.00038	.0020	.1248	134	1.133	.0244
1/2	16	.065	.1075	.1309	.0969	.302	.370	.0022	.0086	.1556	168	1.351	.0888
1/2	18	.049	.1269	.1309	.1052	.236	.402	.0018	.0072	.1606	198	1.244	.0694
1/2	20	.035	.1452	.1309	.1126	.174	.430	.0014	.0056	.1649	227	1.163	.0511
1/2	22	.028	.1548	.1309	.1162	.141	.444	.0012	.0046	.1671	241	1.126	.0415
5/8	12	.109	.1301	.1636	.1066	.602	.407	.0061	.0197	.1864	203	1.536	.177
5/8	13	.095	.1486	.1636	.1139	.537	.435	.0057	.0183	.1903	232	1.437	.158
5/8	14	.083	.1655	.1636	.1202	.479	.459	.0053	.0170	.1938	258	1.362	.141
5/8	15	.072	.1817	.1636	.1259	.425	.481	.0049	.0156	.1971	283	1.299	.125
5/8	16	.065	.1924	.1636	.1296	.388	.495	.0045	.0145	.1993	300	1.263	.114
5/8	17	.058	.2035	.1636	.1333	.350	.509	.0042	.0134	.2016	317	1.228	.103
5/8	18	.049	.2181	.1636	.1380	.303	.527	.0037	.0118	.2043	340	1.186	.089
5/8	19	.042	.2298	.1636	.1416	.262	.541	.0033	.0105	.2068	358	1.155	.077
5/8	20	.035	.2419	.1636	.1453	.221	.555	.0028	.0091	.2089	377	1.126	.065
3/4	10	.134	.1825	.1963	.1262	.884	.482	.0129	.0344	.2229	285	1.556	.260
3/4	11	.120	.2043	.1963	.1335	.809	.510	.0122	.0326	.2267	319	1.471	.238
3/4	12	.109	.2223	.1963	.1393	.748	.532	.0116	.0309	.2299	347	1.410	.220
3/4	13	.095	.2463	.1963	.1466	.666	.560	.0107	.0285	.2340	384	1.339	.196
3/4	14	.083	.2679	.1963	.1529	.592	.584	.0098	.0262	.2376	418	1.284	.174
3/4	15	.072	.2884	.1963	.1587	.520	.606	.0089	.0238	.2410	450	1.238	.153
3/4	16	.065	.3019	.1963	.1623	.476	.620	.0083	.0221	.2433	471	1.210	.140
3/4	17	.058	.3157	.1963	.1660	.428	.634	.0076	.0203	.2455	492	1.183	.126
3/4	18	049	.3339	.1963	.1707	.367	.652	.0067	.0178	.2484	521	1.150	.108
3/4	20	.035	.3632	.1963	.1780	.269	.680	.0050	.0134	.2532	567	1.103	.079
7/8	10	.134	.2892	.2291	.1589	1.061	.607	.0221	.0505	.2662	451	1.441	.312
7/8	11	.120	.3166	.2291	.1662	.969	.635	.0208	.0475	.2703	494	1.378	.285
7/8	12	.109	.3390	.2291	.1720	.891	.657	.0196	.0449	.2736	529	1.332	.262
7/8	13	.095	.3685	.2291	.1793	.792	.685	.0180	.0411	.2778	575	1.277	.233
7/8	14	.083	.3948	.2291	.1856	.704	.709	.0164	.0374	.2815	616	1.234	.207
7/8	16	.065	.4359	.2291	.1950	.561	.745	.0137	.0312	.2873	680	1.174	.165
7/8	18	.049	.4742	.2291	.2034	.432	.777	.0109	.0249	.2925	740	1.126	.127
7/8	20	.035	.5090	.2291	.2107	.313	.805	.0082	.0187	.2972	794	1.087	.092
1	8	.165	.3526	.2618	.1754	1.462	.670	.0392	.0784	.3009	550	1.493	.430
1	10	.134	.4208	.2618	.1916	1.237	.732	.0350	.0700	.3098	656	1.366	.364
1	11	.120	.4536	.2618	.1990	1.129	.760	.0327	.0654	.3140	708	1.316	.332
1	12	.109	.4803	.2618	.2047	1.037	.782	.0307	.0615	.3174	749	1.279	.305
1	13	.095	.5153	.2618	.2121	.918	.810	.0280	.0559	.3217	804	1.235	.270
1	14	.083	.5463	.2618	.2183	.813	.834	.0253	.0507	.3255	852	1.199	.239
1	15	.072	.5755	.2818	.2241	.714	.856	.0227	.0455	.3291	898	1.167	.210
1	16	.065	.5945	.2618	.2278	.649	.870	.0210	.0419	.3314	927	1.149	.191
1	18	.049	.6390	.2618	.2361	.496	.902	.0166	.0332	.3366	997	1.109	.146
1	20	.035	.6793	.2618	.2435	.360	.930	.0124	.0247	.3414	1060	1.075	.106
1 1/4	7	.180	.6221	.3272	.2330	2.057	.890	.0890	.1425	.3836	970	1.404	.605
1 1/4	8	.165	.6648	.3272	.2409	1.921	.920	.0847	.1355	.3880	1037	1.359	.565
1 1/4	10	.134	.7574	.3272	.2571	1.598	.982	.0741	.1186	.3974	1182	1.273	.470
1 1/4	11	.120	.8012	.3272	.2644	1.448	1.010	.0688	.1100	.4018	1250	1.238	.426
1 1/4	12	.109	.8365	.3272	.2702	1.329	1.032	.0642	.1027	.4052	1305	1.211	.391
1 1/4	13	.095	.8825	.3272	.2775	1.173	1.060	.0579	.0926	.4097	1377	1.179	.345
1 1/4	14	.083	.9229	.3272	.2838	1.033	1.084	.0521	.0833	.4136	1440	1.153	.304
1 1/4	16	.065	.9852	.3272	.2932	.823	1.120	.0426	.0682	.4196	1537	1.116	.242
1 1/4	18	.049	1.042	.3272	.3016	.629	1.152	.0334	.0534	.4250	1626	1.085	.185
1 1/4	20	.035	1.094	.3272	.3089	.456	1.180	.0247	.0395	.4297	1707	1.059	.134
1 1/2	10	.134	1.192	.3927	.3225	1.955	1.232	.1354	.1806	.4853	1860	1.218	.575
1 1/2	12	.109	1.291	.3927	.3356	1.618	1.282	.1159	.1546	.4933	2014	1.170	.476
1 1/2	14	.083	1.398	.3927	.3492	1.258	1.334	.0931	.1241	.5018	2181	1.124	.370
1 1/2	16	.065	1.474	.3927	.3587	.996	1.370	.0756	.1008	.5079	2299	1.095	.293
2	11	.120	2.433	.5236	.4608	2.410	1.760	.3144	.3144	.6660	3795	1.136	.709
2	13	.095	2.573	.5236	.4739	1.934	1.810	.2586	.2586	.6744	4014	1.105	.569
2 1/2	9	.148	3.815	.6540	.5770	3.719	2.204	.7592	.6074	.8332	5951	1.134	1.094

* Standards of Tubular Exchanger Manufacturers Association, 4th ed., 1960.

† Weights are based on low-carbon steel with a density of 0.2833 lb./cu. in. For other metals multiply by the following factors:

Aluminum	0.35	Nickel-chrome-iron	1.07
A.I.S.I. 400 series stainless steels	0.99	Admiralty	1.09
A.I.S.I. 300 series stainless steels	1.02	Nickel and nickel-copper	1.13
Aluminum bronze	1.04	Copper and cupronickels	1.14
Aluminum brass	1.06		

‡ Liquid velocity $= \dfrac{\text{lb. per tube per hr.}}{C \times \text{sp. gr. of liquid}}$ in ft/sec. (sp. gr. of water at 60°F. = 1.0).

alternates. The expanded portion should never extend beyond the shell-side face of the tube sheet since removing such a tube is extremely difficult. Methods and tools for tube removal and tube rolling are discussed by A. John [*Chem. Eng.*, **66**, 77–80 (Dec. 28, 1959)], and rolling techniques by H. A. Bach [*Petrol. Refiner*, **39**, 8, 104 (1960)].

Tube ends may be projecting, flush, flared, or beaded (listing in order of usage). The flare or bellmouth tube end is usually restricted to water service in condensers and serves to reduce erosion near the tube inlet.

For moderate general process requirements at less than 300 lb./sq. in. and less than 350°F tube-sheet holes without grooves are standard. For all other services with expanded tubes at least two grooves (each 1/8 in. wide by 1/64 in. deep) in each tube hole are common. The number of grooves is sometimes changed to one or three in proportion to tube-sheet thickness.

Expanding the tube into the grooved tube holes provides a stronger joint but results in greater difficulties during tube removal.

WELDED TUBE JOINTS

When suitable materials of construction are used the tube ends may be welded to the tube sheets. Welded joints may be seal-welded "for additional tightness beyond that of tube rolling" or may be strength-welded. Strength-welded joints have been found satisfactory in very severe services. Welded joints may or may not be rolled before or after welding.

BAFFLES AND TUBE BUNDLES

The tube bundle is the most important part of a tubular heat exchanger. The tubes generally constitute the most expensive component of the exchanger and are the one most likely to corrode. Tube sheets, baffles or support plates, tie rods, and usually spacers complete the bundle.

Minimum baffle spacing is generally one-fifth of the shell diameter and not less than 2 in. Maximum baffle spacing is limited by the requirement to provide adequate support for the tubes. The maximum unsupported tube span is generally about 75 tube diameters but is reduced to about 60 diameters for aluminum, copper, and alloys of either of these.

Baffles are provided for heat-transfer purposes. When shell-side baffles are not required for heat-transfer purposes, as may be the case in condensers or reboilers, tube supports are installed.

Segmental Baffles. Segmental or cross-flow baffles are standard. Baffle cuts are expressed as the ratio of segment opening height to shell inside diameter. Cross-flow baffles with horizontal cut are shown in Fig. 11-1*a* and *c*. This arrangement is not satisfactory for horizontal condensers, since the condensate can be trapped between baffles, or for dirty fluids where the dirt might settle out. Vertical-cut baffles are used for side-to-side flow in horizontal exchangers with condensing fluids or dirty fluids. Baffles are notched to assume complete drainage when the units are taken out of service. (These notches do permit some by-passing of the tube bundle during normal operation.)

Tubes are most commonly arranged on an equilateral triangular pitch. Experimental heat-transfer results have almost invariably been based upon shell-side flow into the apex of the 60-deg. angle (which is at right angles to the base of the triangle). In exchangers designed from such correlations the segmental baffle cut should provide for the same type of flow. Tubes are arranged on a square pitch primarily for mechanical cleaning purposes in removable-bundle exchangers.

Maximum baffle cut is limited to 50 per cent so that every pair of baffles will support each tube. Tube bundles are generally provided with baffles cut so that at least one row of tubes passes through all the baffles or support plates. These tubes hold the entire bundle together. In pipe-shell exchangers with a horizontal baffle cut and a horizontal pass rib for directing tube-side flow in the channel the maximum baffle cut, which permits a minimum of one row of tubes to pass through all baffles, is approximately 33 per cent in small shells and 40 per cent in larger pipe shells.

Maximum shell-side heat-transfer rates in forced convection are apparently obtained by cross flow of the fluid at right angles to the tubes. In order to maximize this type of flow some heat exchangers are built with segmental-cut baffles and with no tubes in the baffle cutout. Cross-flow clearances for exchangers were published by Rubin [*Chem. Eng.*, **64**, 257 (February, 1957)].

Orifice Baffles. Orifice baffles which cover the full cross section of the shell are provided with oversize tube holes and flow is parallel to the tubes. At the baffles the openings produce an increase in heat-transfer coefficient and a pressure drop as the fluid passes through the orifice. This design is limited to clean fluids and is no longer in common use.

Disk and Doughnut Baffles. Disk and doughnut baffles are infrequently used. The doughnut baffle is a full support from which a concentric circular hole has been cut. The disk baffle is circular and has a diameter equal to or slightly larger than the opening in the doughnut. The shell-side fluid passes through the doughnut baffle and then moves radially across the tube bundle and around the disk baffle.

Window-cut Baffles. Window-cut baffles are generally made in groups of three. Theoretical opening is two-thirds of the net free shell-side area. Every tube is supported by at least every third baffle. This design is used to reduce shell-side pressure drop. Baffle spacing should, of course, maintain adequate tube support.

Tie Rods and Spacers. Tie rods are used to hold the baffles in place with spacers, which are pieces of tubing or pipe placed on the rods to locate the baffles. Occasionally baffles are welded to the tie rods and spacers are eliminated. Properly located tie rods and spacers serve both to hold the bundle together and to reduce by-passing of the tubes.

In very large units, where concentricity of shells decreases, baffles are occasionally welded to the shell to eliminate by-passing between the baffle and the shell.

Metal baffles are standard. Occasionally plastic baffles are used either to reduce corrosion or in vibratory service, where metal baffles may cut the tubes.

Spacers are replaced by some manufacturers with seal strip baffles. These serve both as spacers and to prevent by-passing of the tube nest.

Impingement Baffle. The tube bundle is customarily protected against impingement by the incoming fluid at the shell inlet nozzle, when the shell-side fluid is condensing or contains abrasive matter or is entering at a high velocity. Minimum entrance area about the nozzle is equal to the inlet nozzle area. A full bundle without any provision for shell inlet nozzle area can increase the velocity of the inlet fluid by as much as 300 per cent with a consequent loss in pressure.

Impingement baffles are flat or curved, solid or perforated. (Some designers object to perforated impingement plates.) In order to maintain a maximum tube count the impingement plate is often placed in a conical nozzle opening or in a dome cap above the shell.

Vapor Distribution. Relatively large shell inlet nozzles, which may be used in condensers under low pressure or vacuum, require provision for uniform vapor distribution.

TUBE-BUNDLE BY-PASSING

Shell-side heat-transfer rates are maximized when by-passing of the tube bundle is at a minimum. Under ideal conditions the tubes are arranged on a continuous pitch from side to side of the shell. Some laboratory tests have been made with bundles of this type although such construction is not practical in industrial usage.

By-pass area is reduced as the clearance between the inside of the shell and the outermost tubes is lessened.

Arrangements to reduce tube-bundle by-passing include:

Dummy Tubes. These tubes do not pass through the tube sheets and can be located close to the inside of the shell.

Tie Rods with Spacers. These hold the baffles in place but can be located to prevent by-passing.

Sealing Strips. These longitudinal strips either extend from baffle to baffle or may be inserted in slots cut into the baffles.

Tie Rods with Seal-strip Baffles. The tie rods are located close to the shell and the by-passing fluid is forced back into the tube nest by the seal-strip baffles, which also serve as spacers.

LONGITUDINAL BAFFLES

In fixed-tube-sheet construction with multipass shells the baffle is usually welded to the shell and positive assurance against by-passing results. Removable tube bundles have a sealing device between the shell and the longitudinal baffle. Flexible light-gage sealing strips and various packing devices have been used.

In split-flow shells the longitudinal baffles may be installed without a positive seal at the edges if design conditions are not seriously affected by a limited amount of by-passing.

Fouling in petroleum-refinery service has necessitated rough treatment of tube bundles during cleaning operations. Many refineries avoid the use of longitudinal baffles, since the sealing devices are subject to damage during cleaning and maintenance operations, when adequate care is not provided.

DOUBLE-TUBE-SHEET CONSTRUCTION

This design prevents the passage of either fluid into the other because of leakage at the tube-to-tube-sheet joints, which are generally the weakest points in heat exchangers. Any leakage at these joints admits the fluid to the gap between the tube sheets. Mechanical design, fabrication, and maintenance of double-tube-sheet designs require special consideration.

CLAD TUBE SHEETS

Usually tube sheets and other exchanger parts are of a solid metal. Clad or bimetallic tube sheets are used to reduce costs or because no single metal is satisfactory for the corrosive conditions. The alloy material (e.g., stainless steel, monel) is generally bonded or clad to a carbon-steel backing material. In fixed-tube-sheet construction a copper-alloy-clad tube sheet can be welded to a steel shell, while most copper-alloy tube sheets cannot be welded to steel in a manner acceptable to A.S.M.E. Code authorities.

Clad tube sheets in service with carbon-steel backer material include stainless-steel types 304, 304L, 316, 316L, 317, monel, inconel, nickel, naval rolled brass, copper, admiralty, silicon bronze, and titanium. Naval rolled brass and monel clad on stainless steel are also in service.

Clad materials are prepared by bonding techniques, which involve rolling, heat-treatment, etc. When properly manufactured the two metals do not separate because of thermal-expansion differences encountered in service. Clad materials can be prepared by brazing techniques and by weld overlay of the alloy. Applied tube-sheet facings prepared by tack welding at the outer edges of alloy and base metal or bolting together of the two metals are in limited use.

PLATE-TYPE EXCHANGERS

Plate-type exchangers are available in several distinctively different forms: spiral, plate (and frame), brazed-plate fin, and plate fin-and-tube types.

Spiral-plate Exchanger. The spiral-plate exchanger is made from a pair of plates rolled to provide two relatively long rectangular passages for fluids in countercurrent flow. The continuous path eliminates flow reversals (and accompanying pressure drop), by-passing, and differential-expansion problems. Solids can be maintained in suspension. Turbulence occurs at a lower Reynolds number than in straight tubes.

Spiral design is compact. One thousand square feet of heat-transfer surface can be provided in a unit of 42 in. diameter and 60 in. length with a 100-ft-long length of path.

Each path of the exchanger is accessible by removing the respective cover. Spirals can be designed for pressure as high as 150 lb./sq. in. Materials of construction include carbon steel, stainless-steel types 304, 316, and 430F, alloy 20, inconel, monel, nickel, Hastelloy B and C, Everdur, and cupronickel (American Heat Reclaiming Corp.).

Plate-type Heat Exchanger. Plate exchangers consist of standard plates, which serve as heat-transfer surfaces, and a frame to support them and were described by F. J. Lawry [*Chem. Eng.*, **66**, 89–94 (June 29, 1959)]. The design principle is much like that of the plate-and-frame filter press. Pressure drop is low and interleakage of fluids is impossible.

Standard heat-transfer plates (normally of stainless-steel types 304 and 316, but titanium, Hastelloy C, and cupronickel are also available) pressed in a single piece from 0.05- to 0.125-in. material are provided with grooves for rubber gaskets or packing. Corrugated plate design imparts rigidity to the plate, induces turbulence in the fluids, and assures complete flow distribution. The frame and supporting members are available in clad stainless steel or enamel-coated mild steel. Plates are easily cleaned and replaced. The area can be readily adjusted by adding or subtracting plates.

Plate heat exchangers can be used for multiple duty; several different fluids can flow through different parts of the exchanger. Viscous fluids also yield relatively high transfer rates since many plate-type heat exchangers secure turbulent flow at a Reynolds number as low as 180.

Design limitations include 150 lb./sq. in. maximum pressure, 300°F. maximum temperature; condensation of large volumes of vapor are impractical, not satisfactory for true gases; and with solid-liquid suspensions the largest particle should be 0.02 in. less than the distance between plates.

Figure 11-10 presents a four-plate exchanger in which one stream is either heated or cooled by the two other streams. A connecting plate (sometimes called a terminal plate) at the center serves as the header for both these streams. The primary fluid enters at the right and leaves at the left. At the stationary end of the unit a

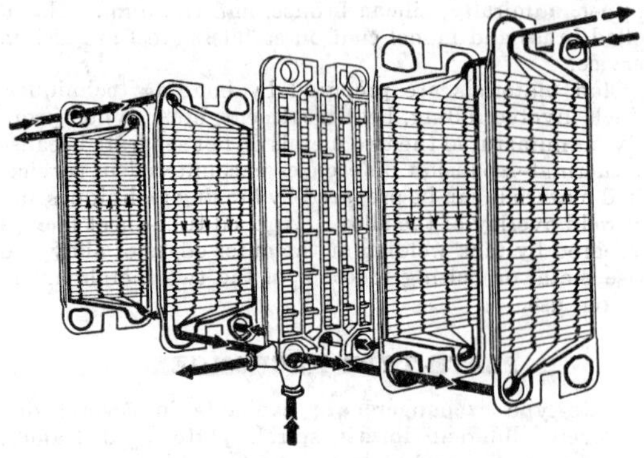

Fig. 11-10. Plate (and frame) type exchanger. (*Chem. Eng., June* 29, 1959, *p.* 89.)

"frame" plate is provided. At the movable end a "pressure" plate serves to compress the various plates.

When multiple-service or stainless-steel tube-side construction is specified, the plate type competes with the tubular design. If all-stainless-steel construction is required, the plate type will be less expensive than the tubular units.

The upper limit of a standard plate exchanger is reported as 1600 sq. ft. of heat-transfer surface occupying 180-in. by 33-in. by 73-in. high.

Brazed-plate-fin Heat Exchanger. Brazed-aluminum-plate-fin heat exchangers were first manufactured for aircraft applications during World War II. In 1950, the first tonnage air-separation plant with these compact, lightweight reversing heat exchangers began producing oxygen for a steel mill. Aluminum-plate-fin exchangers are used in the process industries, particularly for services below −50°F., and in gas-separation processes operating between 400 and −450°F.

Plate-fin heat-transfer surface is made up of a stack of layers, with each layer consisting of a corrugated fin between flat metal sheets sealed off on two sides by channels or bars to form one passage for the flow of fluid. An exploded view of a typical layer is shown in Fig. 11-11.

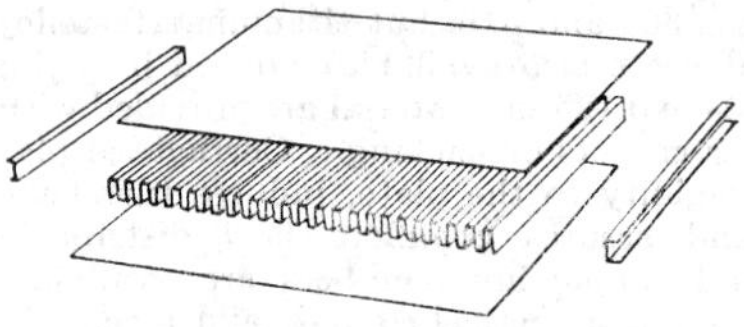

Fig. 11-11. Exploded view, typical plate-fin arrangement. (*The Trane Co.*)

The simple straight corrugation shown here may be replaced by a wavy or herringbone pattern or a serrated or strip fin when higher performance is required.

Maximum design condition has been 600 lb./sq. in. at 100°F. Typical design is for lower pressures at subzero temperatures.

The most widely used plate-fin heat-exchanger core is the 17 by 21 by 106½ in. reversing unit with approximately 7000 sq. ft. of total heat-transfer surface. Larger cores are being developed and a range of core sizes and densities are available with up to 450 sq. ft. of total heat-transfer surface per cubic foot of heat-exchanger volume. The surface may be arranged for countercurrent or parallel flow or both with several different process streams. Exchangers handling as many as five different streams have been built.

These heat exchangers are used with gases, liquids, and liquid-vapor mixtures for sensible heat-transfer, evaporation, and condensation.

The cost of aluminum-plate-fin process heat exchangers varies considerably with core size, quantity, and design complexity. The range is from $0.75 to $2.75 per square foot of total heat-transfer surface, with two-stream low-pressure cores in large quantities priced at the low side and multiple-stream high-pressure cores in small quantities at the higher figure. These exchangers are economical when surface requirements exceed 4000 sq. ft. and are marginal for services with less than 2000 sq. ft.

The brazed-plate-fin exchanger and also the type described below are discussed by W. F. Stahlheber in "Extended Surface Process Heat Exchangers" (A.S.M.E. Paper 59-SA-37, unpublished).

Plate Fin-and-tube Surface. Rectangular fins are pierced, formed, belled, and stacked before tubes are inserted into the fin collars and expanded to produce the plate fin-and-tube surface. No solder or brazing metal is used. Tube diameters range from ⅜ to 1½ in. outside diameter; fin spacing varies from 8 to 156 fins per foot; and the external to internal surface ratio extends up to 40 to 1.

MISCELLANEOUS TYPES OF EXCHANGERS

Miscellaneous heat-exchanger designs include the cascade coolers, submerged sections, a variety of designs available only in non-metallics, and the plate coils (which are discussed elsewhere in this section).

Cascade Coolers. Cascade coolers consist of a series of tubes mounted horizontally, one above the other. These are sometimes referred to as trombone coolers, trickle coolers, or serpentine coolers. Cooling water from a distributing trough drips over each tube and then flows to a drain. The hot fluid flows generally in countercurrent flow from bottom to top of the bank of tubes. Cascade coolers of glass, impervious graphite, cast iron, and other materials are available.

Non-metallic Construction. Glass heat exchangers are available in the following forms: shell-and-tube units, cascade coolers, double-pipe exchangers, bayonet type, and coil type. Design pressures range from 50 lb./sq. in. in the smallest sizes to 15 lb./sq. in. in the largest.

Shell-and-tube exchangers provide 13.5 or 60 sq. ft. of surface with ¾ in. outside diameter by 0.030-in. wall by 118¼-in.-long tubes. Shells can be of steel pipe or glass. Each tube is free to expand since a Teflon sealer sheet is used at the tube-to-tube-sheet joint.

Cascade coolers use 1½-, 2-, and 3-in. glass pipe elements with 10-ft.-long tubes.

Double-pipe exchangers have 1-, 1½-, 2-, 3-, and 4-in. glass pipe 10 ft. long mounted inside standard iron pipe.

Bayonet-type elements with 2- or 3-in. glass pipe (with lengths to 108 in.) in contact with the external fluid and with an inner tube of metal are available.

Standard glass *coils* with 2, 3.5, 5, 15, 25, and 60 sq. ft. of heat-transfer surface are available.

Impervious graphite heat-exchanger equipment is made in a variety of forms: outside-packed-heat exchangers, double-pipe, bayonet-type elements, cascade coolers, cubic, block, and immersion-plate type.

Outside-packed-head and *double-pipe exchangers* are fabricated with impervious graphite tubes and tube-side headers and metallic shells.

Cubic exchangers of impervious graphite consist of solid cubes perforated by rows of parallel holes which are at right angles to those above and below. Headers bolted to the opposite sides of the vertical faces of the cube provide for flow of process fluid through the block. Appropriate headers on the remaining vertical faces direct the heating or cooling medium through the exchangers.

A *block-type exchanger*, which consists of a series of cylindrical impervious graphite blocks, with radial and axial passages, is also available (The Carbone Corp.).

Plate-type units for insertion into tanks as heating or cooling elements are also available.

CORROSION IN HEAT EXCHANGERS

Some of the special considerations in regard to heat-exchanger corrosion are discussed below. A more extended presentation in Sec. 23 covers corrosion and its various forms as well as materials of construction.

MATERIALS OF CONSTRUCTION

The most common material of construction for heat exchangers is carbon steel. Stainless-steel construction throughout is sometimes used in chemical plant service and on rare occasions in petroleum refining. Many exchangers are constructed from dissimilar metals. Such combinations are functioning satisfactorily in certain services. Extreme care in their selection is required since electrolytic attack can develop.

Carbon steel and alloy combinations appear in Table 11-3. "Alloys" in chemical- and petrochemical-plant service in approximate order of use are stainless steel series 300, nickel, monel, copper alloy, aluminum, inconel, stainless steel series 400, and other alloys. In petroleum-refinery service the frequency order shifts, with copper alloy (for water-cooled units) in first place and low-alloy steel in second place. In some segments of the petroleum industry copper alloy, stainless series 400, low-alloy steel, and aluminum are becoming the most commonly used alloys.

Table 11-3. Dissimilar Materials in Heat-exchanger Construction

Part	Relative use	1	2	3	4	5	6
	Relative cost	A	B	C	D	C	E
Tubes		●	●	●	●	●	●
Tube sheets			●	●	●	●	●
Tube-side headers				●	●		
Baffles					●	●	●
Shell							●

Carbon steel replaced by an alloy when ● appears.
Relative use: from 1 (most popular) through 6 (least popular) combinations.
Relative cost: from A (least expensive) to E (most expensive).

Copper-alloy tubing, particularly inhibited admiralty, is generally used with cooling water. The use of bimetallic tubing with a copper alloy on the water side and carbon steel or stainless steel on the process side is expanding. Copper-alloy tube sheets and baffles are generally of naval brass.

Aluminum alloy (and in particular alclad aluminum) tubing is being used more frequently in water service. The alclad alloy has a sacrificial aluminum-alloy layer metallurgically bonded to a core alloy.

Tube-side headers for water service are made in a wide variety of materials: carbon steel, copper alloy, cast iron, lead-lined or plastic-lined or specially painted carbon steel.

Clad tube-sheet materials are used in corrosive service and are discussed elsewhere in this section of the handbook.

Fabrication. Expanding of the tube into the tube sheet reduces the tube wall thickness and work-hardens the metal. The induced stresses can lead to stress corrosion. Differential expansion between tubes and shell in fixed-tube-sheet exchangers can develop stresses, which lead to stress corrosion.

When austenitic stainless-steel tubes are used for corrosion resistance a close fit between the tube and tube hole is recommended in order to minimize work hardening and the resulting loss of corrosion resistance.

In order to facilitate removal and replacement of tubes it is customary to roller expand the tubes to within ⅛ in. of the shell-side face of the tube sheet. A ⅛-in.-long gap is thus created between the tube and the tube hole at this tube-sheet face. In some services this gap has been found to be a focal point for corrosion.

It is standard practice to provide a chamfer at the inside edges of tube holes in tube sheets to prevent cutting of the tubes and to remove burrs produced by drilling or reaming the tube sheet. In the lower tube sheet of vertical units this chamfer serves as a pocket to collect material, dirt, etc., and to serve as a corrosion center.

Adequate venting of exchangers is required both for proper operation and to reduce corrosion. Improper venting of the water side of exchangers can cause alternate wetting and drying and accompanying chloride concentration which is particularly destructive to the series 300 stainless steels.

Certain corrosive conditions require that special consideration be given to complete drainage when the unit is taken out of service. Particular consideration is required for the upper surfaces of tube sheets in vertical heat exchangers, for sagging tubes, and for shell-side baffles in horizontal units.

AIR-COOLED HEAT EXCHANGERS

Atmospheric air has been used for many years to cool process fluids in areas of water scarcity. The 1958 annual meeting of the American Institute of Chemical Engineers presented a series of papers which first brought widespread American attention to the use of this equipment in areas with unlimited supplies of available cooling water.

Kern, D. Q., and R. E. Seaton, *Chem. Eng. Progress*, vol. 55, p. 69, July, 1959.
Mathews, R. T., *Chem. Eng. Progress*, vol. 55, p. 68, May, 1959.
Nakayama, E. U., *Petrol. Refiner*, vol. 38, p. 109, April, 1959.
Perkins, R. G., *Petrol. Refiner*, vol. 38, p. 99, April, 1959.
Segal, K. D., *Petrol. Refiner*, vol. 38, p. 106, April, 1959.
Thomas, J. W., *Petrol. Refiner*, vol. 38, p. 103, April, 1959.
Todd, J. F., *Chem. Eng. Progress*, vol. 55, p. 74, June, 1959.
Young, E. H., and M. L. Katz, *Chem. Eng. Progress*, vol. 55, p. 45, April, 1959.
Additional papers of recent interest include:
Worsham, H. N., "Factors Governing the Design and Use of Air Fin Coolers," A.S.M.E. Paper 59-PET-27 (unpublished), presented at 1959 Petroleum Mechanical Engineering Conference, Houston, Tex.
Smith, E. C., *Chem. Eng.*, vol. 65, p. 145, 1958.
Anon., *Chem. Eng.*, vol. 66, p. 145, May 4, 1959.
Collins, G. F., and R. T. Mathews, *Chem. Eng.*, vol. 67, p. 137, May 16, 1960.
Rubin, F. L., *Chem. Eng.*, vol. 67, p. 91, Oct. 31, 1960.

General Description

Ambient air is forced or induced by a fan to flow across a bank of externally finned tubes. A typical air cooler has a horizontal section containing finned tubes, a steel supporting structure with plenum chambers and fan ring, axial-flow fan, drive assembly, and miscellaneous accessories such as louvers, fan guards, fencing, and hail screens.

Finned Tube Element

The 1 in. outside diameter tube is most commonly used. Fin heights vary from 0.5 to 0.625 in., fin spacing from 7 to 11 per linear inch, and tube triangular pitch from 2.0 to 2.5 in. Ratio of extended surface to bare-tube outside surface varies from about 7 to 20. The 1½-in. tube has

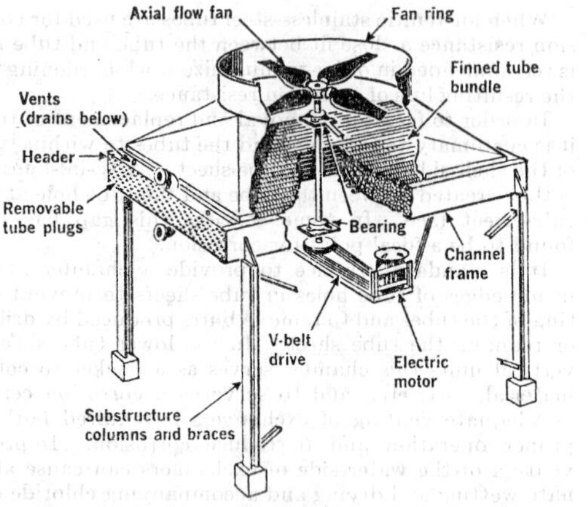

FIG. 11-12. Air-cooled heat exchanger. Process fluid inlet nozzle is on top of the header, with process fluid outlet nozzle below. (*Chem. Eng., Oct.* 31, 1960, *p.* 91.)

been used for flue-gas and viscous-oil service. Tube size, fin heights, and fin spacing can be further varied.

The standard tube lengths are 8, 10, 12, 20, 24, and 30 ft. Common bundle widths are 4 and 8 ft. Bundle depth may vary from 3 to 30 rows of tubes. Bundles may be stacked. Individual bundle depth may be limited by services with high fluid-temperature differences per pass.

Aluminum is the most economical fin material up to 750°F. on the process side, which limits fin temperature to about 450°F. Steel finned tubes operate well at higher temperatures. (Bare steel tubes have been used for bottoms coolers operating at low heat-transfer rates.)

The least expensive finned tubing has the aluminum fins mechanically wrapped under tension to the knurled outside surface of the tubes. For low-temperature services (250°F. or less) where vibration can be minimized, this tubing is adequate.

Bimetallic tubing, which is often used, consists of an inner tube of material required by the process corrosive conditions and an aluminum outer tube from which most of the metal has been cold-extruded into high fins and in which process a complete mechanical bond is formed between the two tubes (the inner liner and the outer finned tube). Design temperature is limited to about 550°F. on process side.

Another type of tube has the aluminum fin mechanically wrapped under tension and inserted into a groove about 0.008 in. deep in the tube wall. This type is adequate for services up to 750°F.

Tube ends are left bare to permit insertion of the tubes into appropriate holes in the headers. Tube ends are usually roller expanded into these tube holes.

The **tube bundle** consists of headers, finned tubes, structural-steel side channels, and supports.

Tube bundles are generally designed to be rigid and self-contained and are mounted so that they expand independently of the supporting structure.

The face area of the tube bundle is its length times width. The net free area for air flow through each tube is about 50 per cent of the face area of the bundle.

The standard air face velocity (F.V.) is the velocity in feet per minute of standard air passing through the tube bundle and generally ranges from 300 to 700 ft./min.

Fans

Axial-flow fans are large-volume low-pressure devices. Fan diameters are selected to give velocity pressures of approximately 0.1 in. of water. Total fan efficiency is about 65 per cent, and fan drives usually have a minimum of 95 per cent mechanical efficiency.

Usually fans are provided with four or six blades. Fan diameter is generally equal to or slightly less than the bundle width.

At the fan tip speeds required for economical performance, a large amount of noise is produced. The noise level is directly related to the tip speed. Location of the air cooler should be considered in setting the maximum speed.

The axial-flow fan is inherently a device for moving a consistent volume of air, when blade setting and speed of rotation are constant. Variation in the amount of air flow can be obtained by adjusting the blade angle of the fan and the speed of rotation. The blade angle can be either (1) permanently fixed, (2) hand adjustable, or (3) automatically adjusted. Air delivery and horsepower are a direct function of blade pitch angle.

Fan mounting should provide a minimum of one-half to three-fourths diameter between fan and ground on a forced-draft heat exchanger and one-half diameter between tubes and fan on an induced-draft cooler.

Fan blades can be made of aluminum, molded plastic, laminated plastic, carbon steel, stainless steel, and monel.

Fan Drivers

Steam turbines or electric motors are most commonly used. These connect with gears or V-belts. Gas engines connected through gears and hydraulic motors either direct-connected or connected through gears are in use. Fans may be driven by a prime mover such as a compressor with a V-belt take-off from the flywheel to a jack shaft and then through a gear or V-belt to the fan. Direct motor drive is generally limited to small-diameter fans.

V-belt drive assemblies are generally used with fans 10 ft. and less in diameter and motors of 20 hp. and less.

Right-angle gear drive is preferred for fans over 10 ft. in diameter, for electric motors 25 hp. and up, and with steam-turbine drives.

Fan Ring and Plenum Chambers

The air must be distributed from the circular fan to the rectangular face of the tube bundle. The air velocity at the fan is between 1000 and 2000 ft./min. The plenum chamber depth (from fan to tube bundle) is generally one-half fan diameter or more (fan manufacturers prefer one diameter).

The fan ring must be made to commercial tolerances for the relatively large diameter fan. These tolerances are greater than those upon closely machined fan rings used for small-diameter laboratory performance testing. Fan performance is directly affected by this increased clearance between the blade tip and the ring and adequate provision in design must be made for the reduction in air flow.

The depth of the fan ring is critical. Worsham reports an increase in flow varying from 5 to 15 per cent with the same power consumption when the depth of a fan ring was doubled. The percentage increase was proportional to the volume of air and static pressure against which the fan was operating.

When making a selection, the stall-out condition, which develops when the fan cannot produce any more air regardless of power input, should be considered.

Forced and Induced Draft

The forced-draft unit pushes air across the finned tube surface. The fan is located below the tube nest. The induced-draft design has the fan above the bundle and the air is pulled across the finned tube surface.

In theory, a primary advantage of the forced-draft unit is that less horsepower is required. Actually, the smaller-diameter fan that is required by the mechanical design takes more power, which cancels the theoretical saving. The induced-draft unit gives better air distribution and less air recirculation.

The forced-draft unit requires less horsepower because it moves air at the lowest available temperature (or highest density). Structural costs are less.

Induced-draft design provides more even distribution of air across the bundle since air velocity approaching the bundle is relatively low.

Induced-draft units are less likely to recirculate the hot exhaust air, since the exit air velocity is several times that of the forced-draft unit.

Induced-draft design more readily permits the installation of the air-cooled equipment above other mechanical equipment such as pipe racks or shell-and-tube exchangers.

In a service where sudden temperature change would cause upset and loss of product the induced-draft unit gives more protection in that only a fraction of the surface (as compared with the forced-draft unit) is exposed to rainfall, sleet, or snow.

Design Considerations

1. *Design Air Temperature.* Maximum ambient temperatures will be 10° to 20°F. higher than the maximum dry-bulb design temperature selected on an economic basis.

2. *Air Recirculation.* Spacing of adjacent air coolers and location of other equipment are factors which influence the amount of hot-air recirculation.

3. *Wintertime Operations.* Freezing of the process fluid, use of excess air, heavy rain, strong winds, freezing of moisture upon the fins, etc., should be considered.

4. *Noise.* The noise level for several identical fans operating in parallel is only slightly greater than the noise of one fan operating at the same tip speed.

5. *Ground Area and Space Requirements.* Comparisons of the over-all space requirements for plants using air cooling vs. water cooling are not consistent.

Some air-cooled units are installed above other equipment—pipe racks, shell-and-tube exchangers, etc. Some plants avoid this location of space because of safety considerations, as discussed below.

6. *Safety.* Leaks in air-cooled units are directly to the atmosphere and can cause fire hazards or toxic-fume hazards. However, the large air flow through an air-cooled exchanger greatly reduces any concentration of toxic fluids. Segal reports that air-fin coolers "are not located over pumps, compressors, electrical switch gear, control houses and in general, the amount of equipment such as drums and shell and tube exchangers located beneath them are minimized."

7. *Atmospheric Corrosion.* Air coolers should not be located where corrosive vapors and fumes from vent stacks will pass through them.

8. *Air-side Fouling.* Air-side fouling is generally negligible.

9. *Process-side Cleaning.* Either chemical or mechanical cleaning on the inside of the tubes can readily be accomplished.

10. *Process-side Design Pressure.* The high-pressure process fluid is always in the tubes. Tube-side headers are relatively small as compared with water-cooled units, and design for high pressure is relatively simple.

11. *Bond Resistance.* Vibration and thermal cycling affect the bond resistance of the various types of tubes in different manners and thus affect the amount of heat transfer through the fin tube.

12. *Mean Temperature Difference.* For a zero-degree approach (when the outlet temperature of both fluids is the same) the M.T.D. correction factor for shell-and-tube exchangers (single-pass shell and two or more tube passes) is approximately 0.8. For a single-pass air cooler this factor is 0.91. For multiple "over-and-under passes" the factor is 0.96.

13. *Air Distribution.* Air distribution across the tube bundle rarely is uniform. Mechanical design may make provision for distributing baffles to equalize air flow.

14. *Maintenance Cost.* Maintenance for air-cooled equipment as compared with shell-and-tube coolers (complete with cooling-tower costs) indicates that the air-cooling maintenance costs are approximately 0.3 to 0.5 those for water-cooled equipment.

15. *Operating Costs.* Power requirements for air coolers can vary throughout the year if the amount of air moved is varied.

Trim Coolers

When ambient air temperatures cannot readily cool the process fluid a combination of air cooler and water-cooled trim cooler is used. When approach temperatures of less

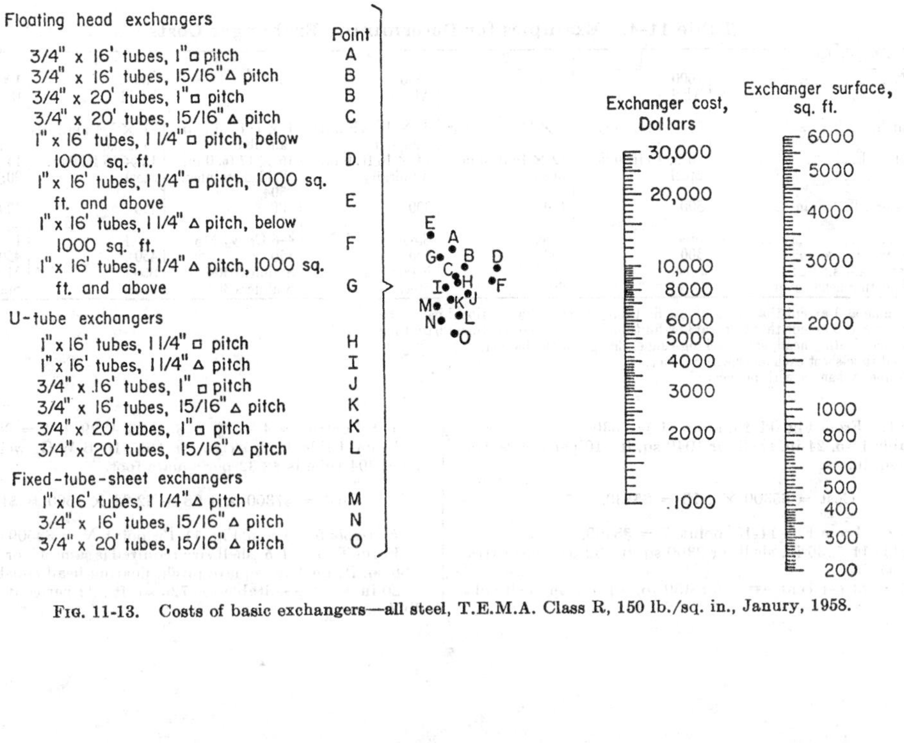

Fig. 11-13. Costs of basic exchangers—all steel, T.E.M.A. Class R, 150 lb./sq. in., Janury, 1958.

than 40°F. are required, a combination of air-fin coolers and conventional shell-and-tube water coolers is often used.

Comparison of Capital and Operating Costs

Smith published a study on three air-cooled exchangers designed for the same service showing that operating horsepower requirements can be considerably reduced as the initial cost increases.

Fan hp. ratio	1.0	0.45	0.33
Initial cost ratio	1.0	1.11	1.38

Evaporative Cooling

Water sprayed into the incoming air stream of induced-draft units can effectively precool the air. A relatively small amount of untreated water is required. When outlet process temperatures are so low that air cooling alone is not economical, the evaporative air cooler may be of use.

HEAT-EXCHANGER COSTS

Basic costs of custom-built heat exchangers as published by DeLamater for January, 1958, by R. H. Densmore [*Petrol. Refiner*, **38**, 9, 289 (1959)] for mid-1959, and by Sieder and Elliott for January, 1960, are in close agreement, even though published industrial cost indices show continuous increases. Densmore states, "the user of heat exchanger equipment must finally come to the manufacturer for a price which will reflect the many variables in design details and present market conditions." (These are *not* closely related to published cost indices.)

Costs of exchangers can be estimated from Fig. 11-13, Table 11-5, and Table 11-6, which in part are based upon the sources named above. This procedure applies when large quantities of material are required for custom-built exchangers of typical petroleum refineries and chemical plants. In the event that the total amount of tubing is small, the quantity extras applied by the tube mills will affect prices. Additional costs for reduced quantities of ¾ in. outside diameter 14 B.W.G. tubing are given in Table 11-7.

Sample calculations of exchanger costs appear below, and the examples are in Table 11-4. Reduced quantity costs are shown only for Example 6.

From Table 11-6, extra for 1-in. 12 B.W.G. steel tube is $0.07 per square foot.

$$\text{Cost} = \$8400 \times 1.23 + \$0.07 \times 2000 = \$10{,}500.$$

Example 3. From Fig. 11-13, point B = $11,600.

Factor for additional surface in a given shell for $1\frac{5}{16}$ triangular pitch is $(^{16}/_{15})^2 \times 1.15 = 1.31$ [$(^{16}/_{15})^2$ for change in spacing from 1 in., 15 per cent increase for triangular pitch in place of square pitch.]

Shell size required is same as for (3500/1.31) = 2670 sq. ft. on 1 in. square pitch.

From Table 11-5, 36-in. shell for 2740 sq. ft. 44 per cent extra for 600 lb./sq. in., 13 per cent extra for 300 lb./sq. in.

44 per cent × 0.7 = 31 per cent extra for 600 lb./sq. in. shell side.

13 per cent × 0.3 = 4 per cent extra for 300 lb./sq. in. channel and floating-head cover.

From Table 11-5, 24 per cent extra for naval-brass tube sheets and baffles.

Combined alloy-pressure extra for tube sheets is 24 × 0.44 × 0.9 = 10.

Total extras = 31 + 4 + 24 + 10 = 69.

From Table 11-6, extra for ¾-in. 14 B.W.G. admiralty tube is $1.20 per square foot.

$$\text{Cost} = 11{,}600 \times 1.69 + \$1.20 \times 3000 = \$23{,}800.$$

Example 4. The shell diameter for 1500 sq. ft. with 12 ft. 0 in. tubes is the same as for (1500 × $^{16}/_{12}$ =) 2000 sq. ft. with 16 ft. 0 in. tubes.

From Fig. 11-13, point G = $7800 for 2000 sq. ft.

Length variations of steel heat exchangers affect costs by approximately $1 *per square foot.*

Reducing tube length by 4 ft. decreases surface by 500 sq. ft. and cost by $500.

Revised base cost is $7800 − $500 = $7300.

Shell size required is same as for (2000/1.15 =) 1740 sq. ft. on 1¼ square pitch.

From Table 11-5, 33-in. shell for 1860 sq. ft. (which is close enough for estimating purposes) 12 per cent extra for 300 lb./sq. in. Mixed pressure extra is 12 × 0.3 = 4 per cent.

Stainless steel 304 tube sheet and baffle extra, 30 per cent.

Combined alloy-pressure extra for tube sheets is 30 × 0.12 × 0.9 = 3.

4–6 chrome, ½ moly shell and shell cover extra is 28 per cent.

Stainless steel 304 channel and floating-head cover, 29 per cent.

Combined alloy-pressure extra for channel and channel cover is 29 × 0.12 = 4 per cent.

Table 11-4. Examples for Determining Exchanger Costs

Example	1	2	3	4	5	6
Surface, sq. ft.	1000	2000	3500	1500	900	1900
Type	AES	AES	AES	AES	BEM	BEU
Tube:						
O.d. and pitch	¾ × 1 in., square	1 × 1¼ in., square	¾ × 1⁵⁄₁₆ in., triangular	1 × 1¼ in., triangular	¾ × 1⁵⁄₁₆ in., triangular	¾ × 1⁵⁄₁₆ in., triangular
B.W.G. × length	16 × 16 ft. 0 in.	12 × 16 ft. 0 in.	14 × 16 ft. 0 in.	16 × 12 ft. 0 in.	12 × 16 ft. 0 in.	14 × 20 ft. 0 in.
Material	Steel	Steel	Admiralty	Welded stainless 304	Steel	90: 10 Cu: Ni
Design pressure, lb./sq. in.	300	150	300	300	450	300
Shell:						
Material	Steel	Steel	Steel	4–6 Cr, ½ Mo	Steel	1¼; Cr; ½ Mo
Design pressure, lb./sq. in.	300	450	600	150	450	450
Tube sheets and baffles	Steel	Steel	Naval brass	Stainless 304	Steel	Monel
Channel and floating-head cover	Steel	Steel	Steel	Stainless 304	Steel	Stainless 304

Example 7 same as 1 except that integral low-fin tubing replaces conventional bare tube.
Example 8 same as 3 except that integral low-fin tubing replaces conventional bare tube.
AES = internal-floating-head, split-backing-ring exchanger with channel.
BEM = fixed-tube-sheet exchanger with bonnet.
BEU = U-tube exchanger with bonnet.

Example 1. From Fig. 11-13, point A = $5300.

From Table 11-5, 24-in. shell for 1040 sq. ft., 10 per cent extra for 300 lb./sq. in.

$$\text{Cost} = \$5300 \times 1.10 = \$5830.$$

Example 2. From Fig. 11-13, point E = $8400.

From Table 11-5, 36-in. shell for 2360 sq. ft., 32 per cent extra for 450 lb./sq. in.

32 × 0.7 = 23 per cent extra for 450 lb./sq. in. on shell side only.

Total extras = 4 + 30 + 3 + 28 + 29 + 4 = 98.

From Table 11-6, extra for 1-in. 16 B.W.G. welded stainless steel 304 tube is $2.32 per square foot.

$$\text{Cost} = \$7300 \times 1.98 + \$2.32 \times 1500 = \$17{,}900.$$

Example 5. From Fig. 11-13, point N = $3500.

From Table 11-5, shell size required is same as for (900/1.31 =) 686 sq. ft. on 1-in.-square pitch, floating-head construction.

20-in. shell is suitable for 726 sq. ft., 22 per cent extra for 450 lb./sq. in.

Table 11-5. Extras for Pressure and Alloy Construction and Surface and Weights*

Per cent of steel base price, 150 lb./sq. in. working pressure

		Shell diameters												
		12	14	16	18	20	22	24	27	30	33	36	39	42
Pressure†	300 lb./sq. in.	7	7	8	8	9	9	10	11	11	12	13	14	15
	450 lb./sq. in.	18	19	20	21	22	23	24	27	29	31	32	33	35
	600 lb./sq. in.	28	29	31	33	35	37	39	40	41	32	44	45	50
Alloy	All-steel heat exchanger	100	100	100	100	100	100	100	100	100	100	100	100	100
	Tube sheets and baffles:													
	Naval rolled brass	14	17	19	21	22	22	22	22	22	23	24	24	25
	Monel	24	31	35	37	39	39	40	40	41	41	41	41	42
	1¼ Cr, ½ Mo	6	7	7	7	8	8	8	8	9	10	10	10	11
	4–6 Cr, ½ Mo	19	22	24	25	26	26	26	25	25	25	26	26	26
	11–13 Cr (stainless 410)	21	24	26	27	27	27	27	27	27	27	27	27	28
	Stainless 304	22	27	29	30	31	31	31	31	30	30	30	31	31
	Shell and shell cover:													
	Monel	45	48	51	52	53	53	52	51	49	47	45	44	44
	1¼ Cr, ½ Mo	20	22	24	25	25	25	24	22	20	19	18	17	17
	4–6 Cr ½ Mo	28	31	33	35	35	35	34	32	30	28	27	26	26
	11–13 Cr (stainless 410)	29	33	35	36	36	36	25	34	32	30	29	27	27
	Stainless 304	32	34	36	37	38	37	37	35	33	31	30	29	28
	Channel and floating-head cover:													
	Monel	40	42	42	43	42	41	40	37	34	32	31	30	30
	1¼ Cr, ½ Mo	23	24	24	25	24	24	23	22	21	21	21	20	20
	4–6 Cr, ½ Mo	36	37	38	38	37	36	34	31	29	27	26	25	24
	11–13 Cr (stainless 410)	37	38	39	39	38	37	35	32	30	28	27	26	25
	Stainless 304	37	39	39	39	38	37	36	33	31	29	28	26	26
Surface	Surface, sq. ft., internal floating head: ¾ in. o.d. by 1 in. square pitch 16 ft. 0 in., tube‡	251	302	438	565	726	890	1040	1470	1820	2270	2740	3220	3700
	1 in. o.d. by 1¼ in. square pitch, 16 ft. 0 in. tube§	218	252	352	470	620	755	876	1260	1560	1860	2360	2770	3200
	Weight, lb., internal floating head, 1 in. o.d., 14 B.W.G. tube	2750	3150	4200	5300	6600	7800	9400	11,500	14,300	17,600	20,500	24,000	29,000

* Modified from E. N. Sieder and G. H. Elliot, *Petrol. Refiner*, **39**, 5,223 (1960).

† Total extra is 0.7 × pressure extra on shell side plus 0.3 × pressure extra on tube side.

‡ Fixed-tube-sheet construction with ¾ in. outside diameter tube on $^{15}/_{16}$-in. triangular pitch provides 36 per cent more surface.

§ Fixed-tube-sheet construction with 1 in. outside diameter tube on 1¼-in. triangular pitch provides 18 per cent more surface.

For an all-steel heat exchanger with mixed design pressures the total extra for pressure is 0.7 × pressure extra on shell side plus 0.3 × pressure extra tube side.

For an exchanger with alloy parts and a design pressure of 150 lb./sq. in., the alloy extras are added. For shell and shell cover the combined alloy-pressure extra is the alloy extra times the shell-side pressure extra/100. For channel and floating-head cover the combined alloy-pressure extra is the alloy extra times the tube side pressure extra/100. For tube sheets and baffles the combined alloy-pressure extra is the alloy extra times the higher pressure extra times 0.9/100. (The 0.9 factor is included since baffle thickness does not increase because of pressure.)

From Table 11-6 extra for ¾-in. 12 B.W.G. steel tube is \$0.06 per square foot.

$$\text{Cost} = \$3500 \times 1.22 + \$0.06 \times 900 = \$4320.$$

Example 6. From Fig. 11-13, point L = \$5800.

Shell diameters for a given surface are approximately equal for U-tube and floating-head construction. Shell size required is same as for [1900/1.31($^{20}/_{16}$) =] 1160 sq. ft. on 1 in. square pitch internal-floating-head design (31 per cent increase for triangular pitch as in Example 3: $^{20}/_{16}$ is tube-length ratio).

From Table 11-5, 27-in. shell for 1470 sq. ft. on 1 in. square pitch, 27 per cent extra for 450 lb./sq. in., 11 per cent extra for 300 lb./sq. in.

Mixed design pressure extra is 0.7 × 27 + 0.3 × 11 = 22 per cent.

Monel tube sheet and baffle, extra 40 per cent.

(Assume saving on single tube sheet for U-tube construction is balanced by length extra and bending costs of tubing.)

Combined alloy-pressure extra for tube sheet is 40 × 0.27 × 0.9 = 10 per cent.

1¼ chrome, ½ moly shell and shell cover extra is 22 per cent. Since the shell and shell cover are welded together in U-tube construction, the bolting flanges are eliminated, and the 22 per cent extra may be multiplied by a factor of 0.67 to become 15 per cent.

Combined alloy-pressure extra for shell and shell cover is

$$15 \times 0.27 = 4 \text{ per cent.}$$

Stainless steel 304 channel and floating-head cover extra, 33 per cent. Since there is no floating-head cover in U-tube construction, apply a 0.67 factor to reduce the extra to 22 per cent.

Combined alloy-pressure extra for the channel is 22 × 0.11 = 2 per cent.

Total extras = 22 + 40 + 10 + 15 + 4 + 22 + 2 = 115.

From Table 11-6, extra for ¾-in. 14 B.W.G. 90-10 cupronickel tubing is \$1.89 per square foot.

$$\text{Cost} = \$5800 \times 2.15 + \$1.89 \times 1900 = \$16,100.$$

Since 90-10 cupronickel tubing is not normally stocked by exchanger manufacturers, *quantity extras* will be applicable to this 900 sq. ft. exchanger unless the total amount of cupronickel tube required for the various exchangers on the project weighs 10,000 lb. or more. From Table 11-8 the extra for 1000 sq. ft. is \$0.11 per square foot and only \$0.02 for 5000 sq. ft. The 1800 sq. ft. extra can be approximated at \$0.09 per square foot.

As an isolated item the exchanger cost is \$16,100 + \$0.09 × 1900 = \$16,270.

Example 7. Shell size is same as for (1000/2.5 =) 400 sq. ft. of bare tubing.

(*Low fin tube provides* 2.5 *times more surface per linear foot than bare tubing.*)

From Fig. 11-13, point A for 400 sq. ft. = \$3300.

From Table 11-5, 16-in.-shell for 438 sq. ft., 8 per cent extra for 300 lb./sq. in.

From Table 11-6, extra for ¾-in. 16 B.W.G. low fin tube is \$0.22 per square foot.

$$\text{Cost} = \$3300 \times 1.08 + \$0.22 \times 1000 = \$3780.$$

Example 8 (see Example 3). Shell size for (3500/2.5 =) 1400 sq. ft. of bare tubing is required.

From Fig. 11-13, point B for 1400 sq. ft. = \$6100.

Shell size required is for (1400/1.31 =) 1070 sq. ft., bare tube on 1-in. pitch.

From Table 11-5, 24-in. shell for 1040 sq. ft. 39 per cent extra for 600 lb./sq. in., 10 per cent extra for 300 lb./sq. in.

39 × 0.7 = 27 per cent extra for 600 lb./sq. in. shell side.

10 × 0.3 = 3 per cent extra for 300 lb./sq. in. channel and floating-head cover.

From Table 11-5, 22 per cent extra for naval-brass tube sheets and baffles.

Combined alloy-pressure extra for tube sheets is 22 × 0.39 × 0.9 = 8.

Total extras = 27 + 3 + 22 + 8 = 60.

From Table 11-6, extra for ¾-in. 14 B.W.G. integral-fin admiralty tubing is \$0.75 per square foot.

$$\text{Cost} = \$6100 \times 1.60 + \$0.75 \times 3000 = \$12,000.$$

Table 11-6. Base Quantity Extra Cost for Tube Gage and Alloy

Dollars per square foot

	¾ in. o.d. tubes			1 in. o.d. tubes		
	16 B.W.G.	14 B.W.G.	12 B.W.G.	16 B.W.G.	14 B.W.G.	12 B.W.G.
Carbon steel	0	0.02	0.06	0	0.01	0.07
Admiralty	0.78	1.20	1.81	0.94	1.39	2.03
(T-11) 1¼ Cr, ½ Mo	1.01	1.04	1.11	0.79	0.82	0.95
(T-5) 4–6 Cr	1.61	1.65	1.74	1.28	1.32	1.48
Stainless 410 welded	2.62	3.16	4.12	2.40	2.89	3.96
Stainless 410 seamless	3.10	3.58	4.63	2.84	3.31	4.47
Stainless 304 welded	2.50	3.05	3.99	2.32	2.83	3.88
Stainless 304 seamless	3.86	4.43	5.69	3.53	4.08	5.46
Stainless 316 welded	3.40	4.17	5.41	3.25	3.99	5.36
Stainless 316 seamless	7.02	7.95	10.01	6.37	7.27	9.53
90:10 cupronickel	1.33	1.89	2.67	1.50	2.09	2.90
Monel	4.25	5.22	6.68	4.01	4.97	6.47
Low fin:						
Carbon steel	0.22	0.23	.....	0.18	0.19	
Admiralty	0.58	0.75	.....	0.70	0.87	
90:10 cupronickel	0.72	0.96	.....	0.86	1.06	

Table 11-7. Small Quantity Extra for ¾ in. by 14 B.W.G. Tubes

Dollars per square foot

Tube material	Surface, sq. ft.				
	100	250	500	1000	5000
Steel	0.95	0.73	0.50	0.34	0.11
Admiralty	0.54	0.34	0.24	0.10	0.02
Stainless 304 welded	1.24	0.62	0.31	0.10	0
Stainless 304 seamless	1.69	1.08	0.77	0.61	0.14
Stainless 316 welded	1.58	0.79	0.40	0.13	0
Stainless 316 seamless	2.77	1.77	1.27	1.01	0.23
90:10 Cu:Ni	0.58	0.35	0.25	0.11	0.02
Monel	0.63	0.44	0.25	0.19	0
Steel low fin	0.83	0.56	0.43	0.30	0.13
Admiralty low fin	....	0.71	0.40	0.40	0.07
90:10 Cu:Ni low fin	....	0.83	0.47	0.47	0.08

Standard heat exchangers (which are in some instances "off-the-shelf" items) are available in sizes ranging from 20 to 400 sq. ft. at costs lower than for custom-built units. Steel costs are approximately one-half, admiralty tube-side costs are two-thirds, and stainless costs are three-fourths those for equivalent custom-built exchangers.

Costs for double-pipe hairpin sections (as illustrated in Fig. 11-8) with both bare tubes and longitudinally finned tubes are shown in Fig. 11-14 and Table 11-9).

Kettle-type reboiler costs are 15 to 25 per cent greater than for equivalent internal-floating-head or U-tube exchangers. The higher extra is applicable with relatively large kettle-to-port-diameter ratios and with increased internals (*e.g.*, vapor-liquid separators, foam breakers, sight glasses).

Costs of standard heat exchangers (and of some custom-built units) were published by De Lamater in *Chemical Engineering* (U-tube Exchangers, Oct. 6, 1958; Finned Tube Floating Head Exchangers, Nov. 17, 1958; Split Ring Floating Head Exchangers, Dec. 1, 1958; Fixed Tube Sheet and Kettle Reboilers, Dec. 15, 1958). Installation costs were published by D. F. Brosnan [*Chem. Eng.*, **67**, p. 152 (Aug. 8, 1960)].

Air-cooled heat-exchanger costs appear in Table 11-8.

Table 11-8. Air-cooled Heat-exchanger Costs

Surface (bare tube), sq ft	500	1000	2000	3000	5000
Cost for 12-row-deep bundle, dollars/square foot	9.0	7.6	6.8	5.7	5.3
Factor for bundle depth:					
6 rows	1.07	1.07	1.07	1.12	1.12
4 rows	1.2	1.2	1.2	1.3	1.3
3 rows	1.25	1.25	1.25	1.5	1.5

Base: Bare-tube external surface 1 in. o.d. by 12 B.W.G. by 24 ft 0 in. steel tube with 8 aluminum fins per inch ⅝-in. high. Steel headers. 150 lb./sq. in. design pressure. V-belt drive and explosion-proof motor. Bare-tube surface 0.262 sq. ft./ft. Fin-tube surface/bare-tube surface ratio is 16.9.

Factors:	20 ft. tube length	1.05
	30 ft. tube length	0.95
	18 B.W.G. admiralty tube	1.04
	16 B.W.G. admiralty tube	1.12

HEAT-TRANSFER COEFFICIENTS

Over-all heat-transfer coefficients for preliminary estimating purposes are shown in Tables 11-10 to 11-13.

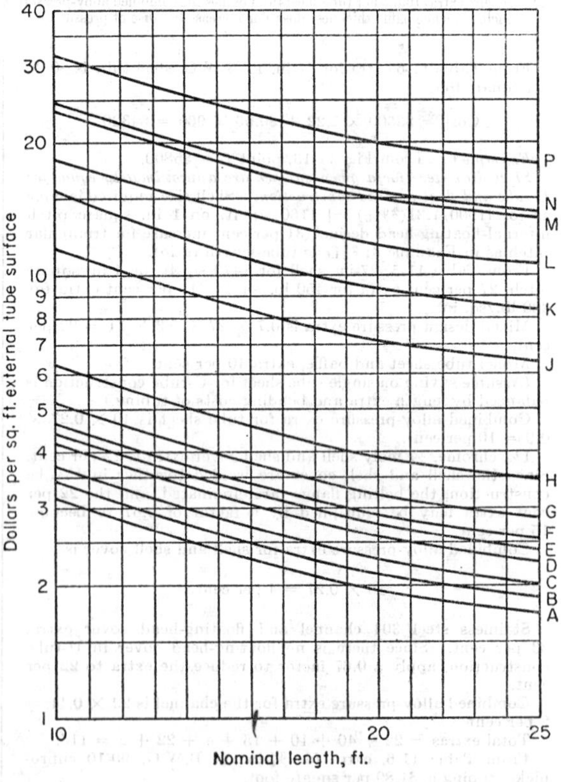

Fig. 11-14. Costs of double-pipe section (refer to Table 11-9 for double-pipe descriptive data). (*Brown Fintube Co.*)

Table 11-9. Double-pipe Hairpin-section Data (for costs shown in Fig. 11-14)

Curve	Outer pipe, in.	Inner pipe o.d., in.	Inner pipe material	Inner pipe thickness, in.	No. of fins on inner tube	Surface, sq. ft. Nominal tube length, ft. 10	20	25
P	4	1.900	Admiralty	0.109	None	10.9	20.9	25.9
N	3	1.900	Admiralty	0.109	None	10.9	20.9	25.9
M	4	1.900	Steel	0.145	None	10.9	20.9	25.9
L	3	1.900	Steel	0.145	None	10.9	20.9	25.9
K	4	1.000	Admiralty	0.065	None	37.6	74.3	92.6
J	4	1.000	Steel	0.134	None	37.6	74.3	92.6
H	3	1.900	Admiralty	0.109	24	50.9	100.9	125.9
G	4	1.900	Admiralty	0.109	24	90.9	180.9	225.9
F	4	0.875	Admiralty	0.065	24	150.7	300.3	375.2
E	3	1.900	Steel	0.145	24	50.9	100.9	125.9
D	4	2.875	Steel	0.203	36	76	151.1	188.7
C	4	0.875	Steel	0.083	20	131.1	261.1	326.2
B	4	2.875	Steel	0.203	48	96	191.1	238.6
A	4	1.900	Steel	0.145	24	90.9	180.9	225.9

Outer pipe is schedule 40 carbon steel, iron pipe size.
Admiralty inner tube has longitudinal yellow-brass fins. Steel tube has longitudinal steel fins.

Table 11-10. Coils Immersed in Liquids. Over-all Coefficients

U expressed as B.t.u./(hr.)(sq. ft.)(°F.)

Substance inside coil	Substance outside coil	Coil material	Agitation	*U*
Steam	Water	Lead	Agitated	70
Steam	Sugar and molasses solutions	Copper	None	50–240
Steam	Boiling aqueous solution	....	....	600
Cold water	Dilute organic dye intermediate	Lead	Turboagitator at 95 r.p.m.	300
Cold water	Warm water	Wrought iron	Ar bubbled into water surrounding coil	150–300
Cold water	Hot water	Lead	0.40 r.p.m. paddle stirre	90–360
Brine	Amino acids	....	30 r.p.m.	100
Cold water	25% oleum at 60°C.	Wrought iron	Agitated	20
Water	Aqueous solution	Lead	500 r.p.m. sleeve propeller	250
Water	8% NaOH	....	22 r.p.m.	155
Steam	Fatty acid	Copper (pancake)	None	96–100
Milk	Water	....	Agitation	300
Cold water	Hot water	Copper	None	105–180
60°F. water	50% aqueous sugar solution	Lead	Mild	50–60
Steam and hydrogen at 1500 lb./sq. in.	60°F. water	Steel	....	100–165
Steam 110–146 lb./sq. in. gage	Vegetable oil	Steel	None	23–29
Steam	Vegetable oil	Steel	Various	39–72
Cold water	Vegetable oil	Steel	Various	29–72

NOTES: Chilton, Drew, and Jebens [*Ind. Eng. Chem.*, **36**, 510 (1944)] give film coefficients for heating and cooling agitated fluids using a coil in a jacketed vessel.

Because of the many factors affecting heat transfer, such as viscosity, temperature difference, and coil size, the values in this table should be used primarily for preliminary design estimates and checking calculated coefficients.

TANK COILS

Pipe tank coils are made in a wide variety of configurations, depending upon the application and shape of the vessel. *Helical* and *spiral* coils are most commonly shop-fabricated while the *hairpin* pattern is generally field-fabricated. The helical coils are used principally in process tanks and pressure vessels where large areas for rapid heating or cooling are required. In general, heating coils are placed low in the tank and cooling coils are placed high or distributed uniformly through the vertical height.

Stocks which tend to solidify on cooling require uniform coverage of the bottom or agitation. A maximum spacing of 2 ft. between turns of 2-in. and larger pipe and a close approach to the tank wall are recommended. For smaller pipe, or for low-temperature heating media, closer spacing should be used. In the case of the common hairpin coils in vertical cylindrical tanks, this means adding an encircling ring within 6 in. of the tank wall (see Fig. 11-16 for this and other typical coil layouts). The coils should be set directly on the bottom, or raised not more than 2 to 6 in., depending upon the difficulty of remelting the solids, in order to permit free movement of product within the vessel. The coil inlet should be above the liquid level (or an internal melt-out riser installed) to provide a molten path for liquid expansion or venting of vapors.

Coils may be sloped to facilitate drainage. When it is impossible to do so and remain close enough to the bottom to get proper remelting, the coils should be blown out after usage in cold weather to avoid damage by freezing.

Most coils are firmly clamped (but not welded) to supports. Supports should allow expansion but be rigid enough to prevent uncontrolled motion (see Fig. 11-15).

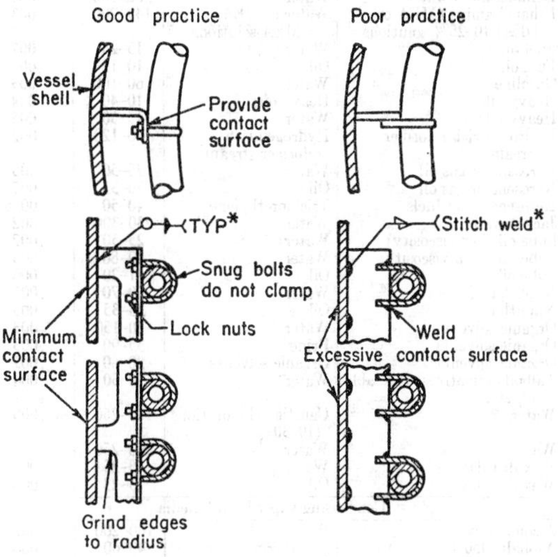

FIG. 11-15. Right and wrong way to support coils. (*Chem. Eng., May* 16, 1960, *p.* 172.)

Table 11-11. Over-all Coefficients for Air-cooled Exchangers on Bare-tube Basis

B.t.u./(°F)(sq. ft.)(hr.)

Condensing	Coefficient	Liquid cooling	Coefficient
Ammonia..............	110	Engine-jacket water.....	125
Freon-12..............	70	Fuel oil................	25
Gasoline..............	80	Light gas oil...........	65
Light hydrocarbons......	90	Light hydrocarbons......	85
Light naphtha...........	75	Light naphtha..........	70
Heavy naphtha...........	65	Reformer liquid streams.	70
Reformer reactor effluent.	70	Residuum...............	15
Low-pressure steam......	135	Tar....................	7
Overhead vapors.........	65		

Gas cooling	Operating pressure, lb./sq. in. gage	Pressure drop, lb./sq. in.	Coefficient
Air or flue gas...........	50	0.1 to 0.5	10
	100	2	20
	100	5	30
Hydrocarbon gas..........	35	1	35
	125	3	55
	1000	5	80
Ammonia reactor stream...			85

Bare-tube external surface is 0.262 sq. ft./lineal ft.
Fin-tube surface/bare-tube surface ratio is 16.9.

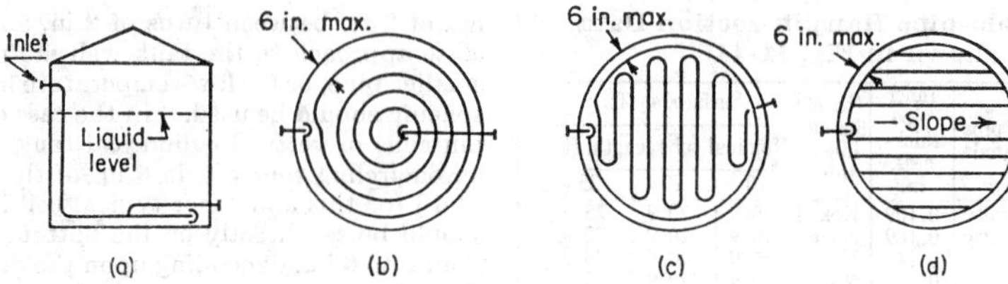

FIG. 11-16. Typical coil designs for good bottom coverage. (*a*) Elevated inlet on spiral coil. (*b*) Spiral with encircling ring. (*c*) Hairpin with encircling ring. (*d*) Ring header type.

Table 11-12. Typical Over-all Heat-transfer Coefficients in Tubular Heat Exchangers

U = B.T.U./(°F)(sq. ft.)(hr.)

Shell side	Tube side	Design U	Includes total dirt
Liquid-liquid media			
Aroclor 1248	Jet fuels	100–150	0.0015
Cutback asphalt	Water	10–20	.01
Demineralized water	Water	300–500	.001
Ethanol amine (MEA or DEA) 10–25% solutions	Water or DEA, or MEA solutions	140–200	.003
Fuel oil	Water	15–25	.007
Fuel oil	Oil	10–15	.008
Gasoline	Water	60–100	.003
Heavy oils	Heavy oils	10–40	.004
Heavy oils	Water	15–50	.005
Hydrogen-rich reformer stream	Hydrogen-rich reformer stream	90–120	.002
Kerosene or gas oil	Water	25–50	.005
Kerosene or gas oil	Oil	20–35	.005
Kerosene or jet fuels	Trichlorethylene	40–50	.0015
Jacket water	Water	230–300	.002
Lube oil (low viscosity)	Water	25–50	.002
Lube oil (high viscosity)	Water	40–80	.003
Lube oil	Oil	11–20	.006
Naphtha	Water	50–70	.005
Naphtha	Oil	25–35	.005
Organic solvents	Water	50–150	.003
Organic solvents	Brine	35–90	.003
Organic solvents	Organic solvents	20–60	.002
Tall oil derivatives, vegetable oil, etc.	Water	20–50	.004
Water	Caustic soda solutions (10–30%)	100–250	.003
Water	Water	200–250	.003
Wax distillate	Water	15–25	.005
Wax distillate	Oil	13–23	.005
Condensing vapor-liquid media			
Alcohol vapor	Water	100–200	.002
Asphalt (450°F.)	Dowtherm vapor	40–60	.006
Dowtherm vapor	Tall oil and derivatives	60–80	.004

Shell side	Tube side	Design U	Includes total dirt
Dowtherm vapor	Dowtherm liquid	80–120	.0015
Gas-plant tar	Steam	40–50	.0055
High-boiling hydrocarbons V	Water	20–50	.003
Low-boiling hydrocarbons A	Water	80–200	.003
Hydrocarbon vapors (partial condenser)	Oil	25–40	.004
Organic solvents A	Water	100–200	.003
Organic solvents high NC, A	Water or brine	20–60	.003
Organic solvents low NC, V	Water or brine	50–120	.003
Kerosene	Water	30–65	.004
Kerosene	Oil	20–30	.005
Naphtha	Water	50–75	.005
Naphtha	Oil	20–30	.005
Stabilizer reflux vapors	Water	80–120	.003
Steam	Feed water	400–1000	.0005
Steam	No. 6 fuel oil	15–25	.0055
Steam	No. 22 fuel oil	60–90	.0025
Sulfur dioxide	Water	150–200	.003
Tall-oil derivatives, vegetable oils (vapor)	Water	20–50	.004
Water	Aromatic vapor-steam azeotrope	40–80	.005
Gas-liquid media			
Air, N_2, etc. (compressed)	Water or brine	40–80	.005
Air, N_2, etc., A	Water or brine	10–50	.005
Water or brine	Air, N_2 (compressed)	20–40	.005
Water or brine	Air, N_2, etc., A	5–20	.005
Water	Hydrogen containing natural-gas mixtures	80–125	.003
Vaporizers			
Anhydrous ammonia	Steam condensing	150–300	.0015
Chlorine	Steam condensing	150–300	.0015
Chlorine	Light heat transfer oil-heating medium	40–60	.0015
Propane, butane, etc.	Steam condensing	200–300	.0015
Water	Steam condensing	250–400	.0015

NC = non-condensable gas present.
V = vacuum.
A = atmospheric pressure.
Dirt (or fouling factor) units are (hr.)(sq. ft.)(°F)/B.t.u.

Table 11-13. Refinery Transfer Rates

B.t.u./(°F)(sq. ft.)(hr.)

	Fluid	API	Fouling factor (one stream)	Reboiler steam, heated	Condenser water,* cooled	Exchangers, liquid to liquid (tube-side fluid designation appears below)			Reboilers liquid heating (designation appears below)			Condenser liquid cooling (designation appears below)			
						C	G	H	C	G†	K	D	F	G	J
A	Propane	...	0.001	160	95	85	85	80	110	95	35				
B	Butane	...	.001	155	90	80	75	75	105	90	35	80	55	40	30
C	400° EP gasoline	50	.001	120	80	70	65	60	65	50	30				
D	Virgin light naphtha	70	.001	140	85	70	55	55	75	60	35	75			
E	Virgin heavy naphtha	45	.001	95	75	65	55	50	55	45	30	70	50	35	30
F	Kerosene	40	.001	85	60	60	55	50	...	45	25	...	50	35	30
G	Light gas oil	30	.002	70	50	60	50	50	...	40	25	70	45	30	30
H	Heavy gas oil	22	.003	60	45	55	50	45	50	40	20	70	40	30	20
J	Reduced crude	17	.005	...	...	55	45	40							
K	Heavy fuel oil (tar)	10	.005	...	...	50	40	35							

Fouling factor, water side 0.002.
Heating or cooling streams are shown at top of columns as C, D, F, G, etc.
* Cooler, water-cooled, rates are about 5 per cent lower.
† With heavy gas oil (H) as heating medium rates are about 5 per cent lower.

Nuts and bolts should be securely fastened. Reinforcement of the inlet and outlet connections through the tank wall is recommended since bending stresses due to thermal expansion are usually high at such points.

In general, 2- and 2½-in. coils are the most economical for shop fabrication and 1½- and 2-in. for field fabrication. The tube-side heat-transfer coefficient, high pressure, or layout problems may lead to the use of smaller-size pipe.

The wall thickness selected varies with the service and material. Carbon-steel coils are often made from schedule 80 or heavier pipe to allow for corrosion. When stainless-steel or other high-alloy coils are not subject to corrosion or excessive pressure, they may be of schedule 5 or 10 pipe to keep costs at a minimum although high-quality welding is required for these thin walls to assure trouble-free service.

Methods for calculating heat loss from tanks and the sizing of tank coils have been published by Stuhlbarg [*Petrol. Refiner*, **38**, 143 (April, 1959)].

Fin-tube coils are used for fluids which have poor heat-transfer characteristics to provide more surface for the same configuration at reduced cost. Fin tubing is not generally used where bottom coverage is important. **Fin-tube tank heaters** are compact prefabricated bundles which can be brought into tanks through manholes. These are normally installed vertically with longitudinal fins to produce good convection currents. To keep the heaters low in the tank, they can be installed horizontally with helical fins or with perforated longitudinal fins to prevent entrapment. Fin tubing is often used for heat-sensitive material because of the lower surface temperature for the same heating medium.

Plate or panel coils made from two metal sheets with one or both embossed to form passages for a heating or cooling medium can be used in lieu of pipe coils. Panel coils are relatively light in weight, easy to install, and easily removed for cleaning. They are available in a range of standard sizes and in both flat and curved patterns. Process tanks have been built using panel coils for the sides or bottom. A serpentine construction is generally utilized when liquid flows through the unit. Header-type construction is used with steam.

Table 11-14. Panel Coils Immersed in Liquid. Over-all Average Heat-transfer Coefficients*

U expressed in B.t.u./(hr.)(sq. ft.)(°F.)

Hot side	Cold side	Clean-surface coefficients		Design coefficients, considering usual fouling in this service	
		Natural convection	Forced convection	Natural convection	Forced convection
Heating applications:					
Steam	Watery solution	250–500	300–550	100–200	150–275
Steam	Light oils	50–70	110–140	40–45	60–110
Steam	Medium lube oil	40–60	100–130	35–40	50–100
Steam	Bunker C or No. 6 fuel oil	20–40	70–90	15–30	60–80
Steam	Tar or asphalt	15–35	50–70	15–25	40–60
Steam	Molten sulfur	35–45	45–55	20–35	35–45
Steam	Molten paraffin	35–45	45–55	25–35	40–50
Steam	Air or gases	2–4	5–10	1–3	4–8
Steam	Molasses or corn sirup	20–40	70–90	15–30	60–80
High temperature hot water	Watery solutions	115–140	200–250	70–100	110–160
High temperature heat-transfer oil	Tar or asphalt	12–30	45–65	10–20	30–50
Dowtherm or Aroclor	Tar or asphalt	15–30	50–60	12–20	30–50
Cooling applications:					
Water	Watery solution	110–135	195–245	65–95	105–155
Water	Quench oil	10–15	25–45	7–10	15–25
Water	Medium lube oil	8–12	20–30	5–8	10–20
Water	Molasses or corn sirup	7–10	18–26	4–7	8–15
Water	Air or gases	2–4	5–10	1–3	4–8
Freon or ammonia	Watery solution	35–45	60–90	20–35	40–60
Calcium or sodium brine	Watery solution	100–120	175–200	50–75	80–125

* Tranter Manufacturing, Inc.

EXTERNAL COILS AND PIPE-LINE TRACERS

Tanks, vessels, and pipe lines can be equipped for heating or cooling purposes with external coils. These are generally ⅜ to ¾ in. so as to provide good distribution over the surface and are often of soft copper or aluminum, which can be bent by hand to the contour of the tank or line. When necessary to avoid "hot spots" the tracer is so mounted that it does not touch the tank.

External coils spaced away from the tank wall exhibit a coefficient of around 1 B.t.u./(hr.)(sq. ft. of coil-surface)(°F.). Direct contact with the tank wall produces higher coefficients, but these are difficult to predict since they are strongly dependent upon the degree of contact. The use of heat-transfer cements does improve performance. These puttylike materials of high thermal conductivity are troweled or calked into the space between the coil and the tank or pipe surface. Typical coefficients for external

Table 11-15. Jacketed Vessels. Over-all Coefficients

U expressed in B.t.u./(hr.)(sq. ft.)(°F.)

Fluid inside jacket	Fluid in vessel	Wall material	Agitation	*U*
Steam	Water	Enameled C. I.*	0–400 r.p.m.	96–120
Steam	Milk	Enameled C. I.	None	200
Steam	Milk	Enameled C. I.	Stirring	300
Steam	Milk boiling	Enameled C. I.	None	500
Steam	Milk	Enameled C. I.	200 r.p.m.	86
Steam	Fruit slurry	Enameled C. I.	None	33–90
Steam	Fruit slurry	Enameled C. I.	Stirring	154
Steam	Water	C. I. and loose lead lining	Agitated	4–9
Steam	Water	C. I. and loose lead lining	None	3
Steam	Boiling SO_2	Steel	None	60
Steam	Boiling water	Steel	None	187
Hot water	Warm water	Enameled C. I.	None	70
Cold water	Cold water	Enameled C. I.	None	43
Ice water	Cold water	Stoneware	Agitated	7
Ice water	Cold water	Stoneware	None	5
Brine, low velocity	Nitration slurry	....	35–58 r.p.m.	32–60
Water	Sodium alcoholate solution	"Frederking" (cast-in-coil)	Agitated, baffled	80
Steam	Evaporating water	Copper	....	381
Steam	Evaporating water	Enamelware	....	36.7
Steam	Water	Copper	None	148
Steam	Water	Copper	Simple stirring	244
Steam	Boiling water	Copper	None	250
Steam	Paraffin wax	Copper	None	27.4
Steam	Paraffin wax	Cast iron	Scraper	107
Water	Paraffin wax	Copper	None	24.4
Water	Paraffin wax	Cast iron	Scraper	72.3
Steam	Solution	Cast iron	Double scrapers	175–210
Steam	Slurry	Cast iron	Double scrapers	160–175
Steam	Paste	Cast iron	Double scrapers	125–150
Steam	Lumpy mass	Cast iron	Double scrapers	75–96
Steam	Powder (5% moisture)	Cast iron	Double scrapers	41–51

* C. I. = cast iron.

Table 11-16. External Coils. Typical Over-all Coefficients*

U expressed in B.t.u./(hr.)(sq. ft.†)(°F.)

Type of coil	Coil spacing, in.	Fluid in coil	Fluid in vessel	Temp. range, °F.	*U*‡ without cement	*U* with heat-transfer cement
⅜ in. o.d. copper tubing attached with bands at 24-in. spacing	2	5 to 50 lb./sq. in. gage steam	Water under light agitation	158–210	1–5	42–46
	3⅛			158–210	1–5	50–53
	6¼			158–210	1–5	60–64
	12½ or greater			158–210	1–5	69–72
⅜ in. o.d. copper tubing attached with bands at 24-in. spacing	2	50 lb./sq. in. gage steam	No. 6 fuel oil under light agitation	158–258	1–5	20–30
	3⅛			158–258	1–5	25–38
	6¼			158–240	1–5	30–40
	12½ or greater			158–238	1–5	35–46
Panel coils		50 lb./sq. in. gage steam	Boiling water	212	29	48–54
		Water	Water	158–212	8–30	19–48
		Water	No. 6 fuel oil	228–278	6–15	24–56
			Water	130–150	7	15
			No. 6 fuel oil	130–150	4	9–19

* Data courtesy of Thermon Manufacturing Co.
† External surface of tubing or side of panel coil facing tank.
‡ For tubing, the coefficients are more dependent upon tightness of the coil against the tank than upon either fluid. The low end of the range is recommended.

coils with and without the cement are given in Table 11-16.

Costs of the cements (in 1960) varied from 37 to 63 cents per pound, with requirements running from about 0.27 lb./ft. of ⅜ in. outside diameter tubing to 1.48 lb./ft. of 1-in. pipe. Panel coils require ½ to 1 lb./sq. ft. A rule of thumb for preliminary estimating is that the per foot installed cost of tracer with cement is about double that of the tracer alone.

JACKETED VESSELS

Jacketing is often used for vessels needing frequent cleaning and for glass-lined vessels which are difficult to equip with internal coils. The jacket eliminates the need for the coil yet gives a better over-all coefficient than external coils. However, only a limited heat-transfer area is available.

Wall thicknesses are often high unless reinforcement rings are installed.

Spiral baffles, which are sometimes installed for liquid services to improve heat transfer and prevent channeling, can be designed and installed to serve as reinforcements. A spiral-wound channel welded to the vessel wall is a recently developed alternate to the spiral baffle which is more predictable in performance, since cross-baffle leakage is eliminated, and is reportedly lower in cost [C. A. Feichtinger, *Chem. Eng.*, 67, 197 (Sept. 5, 1960)].

Nozzles which set up a swirling motion in the jacket have also proved effective for improvement of heat transfer.

Typical jacketed-vessel coefficients are given in Table 11-15.

EVAPORATION

REFERENCES: Badger and Banchero, "Introduction to Chemical Engineering," McGraw-Hill, New York, 1955. Badger and Lindsay, "Evaporation" in Annual Unit Operations Review, *Ind. Eng. Chem.*, January, 1946 through 1954, March, 1955–1958. Lindsay, same, March, 1959. "Testing Procedure for Evaporators," American Institute of Chemical Engineers, 1961.

Evaporation is the removal of solvent as vapor from a solution or a slurry. The vapor may or may not be recovered, depending on its value. The end product may be a solid, but the transfer of heat in the evaporator must be to a solution or a suspension of the solid in liquid if the apparatus is not to be classed as a dryer. Evaporators are similar to stills or reboilers of distillation columns except that no attempt is made to separate components of the vapor.

There are three principal elements involved in evaporator design—heat transfer, vapor-liquid separation, and energy utilization. The units in which heat transfer takes place are called *heating elements* or *calandrias.* Calandria is also used to describe a particular type of evaporator. The vapor-liquid separators are variously called **bodies, vapor heads,** or **flash chambers.** The term **body** is also used to denote the minimum building block of an evaporator, comprising one heating element and one vapor head. An **effect** is one or more bodies boiling at the same pressure. A **multiple-effect evaporator** is one in which the vapor from one effect is used as the heating medium for another effect boiling at a lower pressure. The term **evaporator** denotes the entire assemblage of effects and not necessarily one effect or one body.

PRIMARY DESIGN PROBLEMS

Heat transfer is the most important single factor in evaporator design since the heating surface represents the largest part of evaporator cost. Equipment costs are usually correlated as functions only of heating-surface area, materials of construction, and evaporator type. Other things being equal, the type of evaporator selected is the one having the highest heat-transfer "coefficient" under desired operating conditions in terms of B.t.u. per hour per degree Fahrenheit per dollar of installed cost. When power is required to induce circulation past the heating surface, the "coefficient" must be even higher to offset the cost of power for circulation.

Vapor-liquid separation may be important for a number of reasons. Most important is usually prevention of entrainment because of value of product lost, pollution, contamination of the condensed vapor, or fouling or corrosion of the surfaces on which the vapor is condensed. Vapor-liquid separation in the vapor head may also be important when spray forms deposits on the walls, when vortices increase head requirements of circulating pumps, and when short circuiting allows vapor or unflashed liquid to be carried back to the circulating pump and heating element.

The thermodynamic efficiency of **energy utilization** in an evaporator is very low since the minimum energy requirement is only equal to the heat that would be liberated if the feed were reconstituted by mixing product and **liquid** solvent. This is very much smaller than the heat required to **vaporize** the solvent as is done in an evaporator. Consequently, evaporator performance is rated on the basis of **steam economy**—pounds of solvent evaporated per pound of steam used. Heat is required (1) to raise the feed from its initial temperature to the boiling temperature, (2) to provide the minimum thermodynamic energy to separate liquid solvent from the feed, and (3) to vaporize the solvent. The first of these can be changed appreciably by reducing the boiling temperature or by heat interchange between the feed and the residual product and/or condensate. The greatest increase in steam economy is achieved by reusing the vaporized solvent. This is done in a multiple-effect evaporator by using the vapor from one effect as the heating medium for another effect in which boiling takes place at a lower temperature and pressure. Another method of increasing the utilization of energy is to employ a *thermocompression* evaporator, in which the vapor is compressed so that it will condense at a temperature high enough to permit its use as the heating medium in the same evaporator.

Selection Problems. Aside from heat-transfer considerations, the selection of type of evaporator best suited for a particular service is governed by the characteristics of the feed and product. Points that must be considered are crystallization, salting and scaling, product quality, corrosion, and foaming. In the case of a **crystallizing evaporator,** the desirability of producing crystals of a definite uniform size usually limits the choice to evaporators having a positive means of circulation. **Salting,** which is the growth on body and heating-surface walls of a material having a solubility that increases with increase in temperature, is frequently encountered in crystallizing evaporators. It can be reduced or eliminated by keeping the evaporating liquid in close or frequent contact with a large surface area of crystallized solid. *Scaling* is the deposition and growth on body walls, and especially on heating surfaces, of a material undergoing an irreversible chemical reaction in the evaporator or having a solubility that decreases with an increase in temperature. Scaling can be reduced or eliminated in the same general manner as salting. Both salting and scaling liquids are usually best handled in evaporators that do not depend on boiling to induce circulation. *Fouling* is the formation of deposits other than salt or scale and may be due to corrosion, solid matter entering with the feed, or deposits formed by the condensing vapor.

Product quality considerations may require low hold-up time and low-temperature operation to avoid thermal degradation. The low hold-up time eliminates some types of evaporators, and some types are also eliminated because of poor heat-transfer characteristics at low temperature. Product quality may also dictate special materials of construction to avoid metallic contamination or a catalytic effect on decomposition of the product. **Corrosion** may also influence evaporator selection since the advantages of evaporators having high heat-transfer coefficients are more apparent when expensive materials of construction are indicated. Corrosion and erosion are frequently more severe in evaporators than in other types of equipment because of the high liquid and vapor velocities used, the frequent presence of solids in suspension, and the necessary concentration differences.

EVAPORATOR TYPES AND APPLICATIONS

Evaporators may be classified as follows:

1. Heating medium separated from evaporating liquid by tubular heating surfaces.
2. Heating medium confined by coils, jackets, double walls, flat plates, etc.
3. Heating medium brought into direct contact with evaporating liquid.
4. Heating by solar radiation.

By far the largest number of industrial evaporators employ tubular heating surfaces. Circulation of liquid past the heating surface may be induced by boiling or by mechanical means. In the latter case, boiling may or may not occur at the heating surface.

Forced-circulation Evaporators (Fig. 11-17*a*, *b*, *c*). Although it may not be the most economical for many

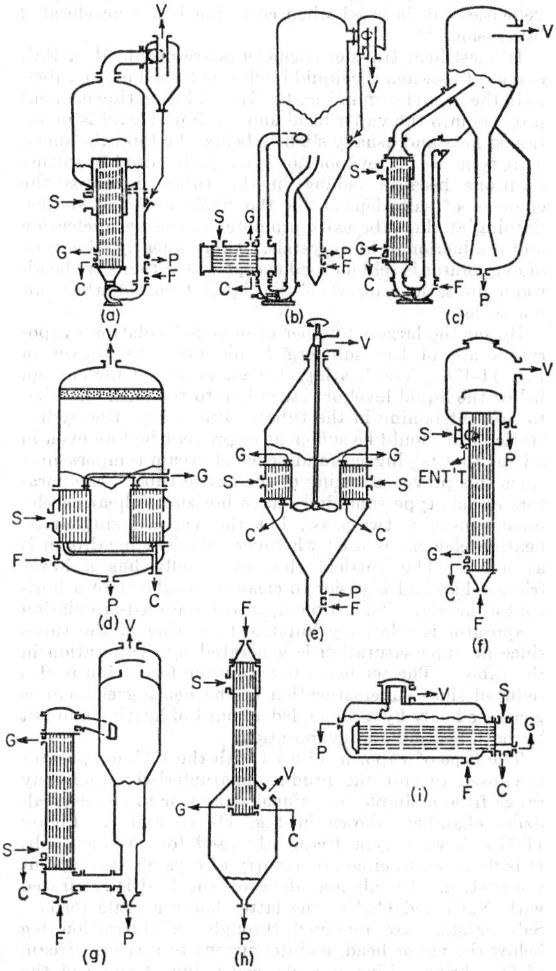

FIG. 11-17. Evaporator types. (*a*) Forced circulation, (*b*) submerged-tube forced circulation, (*c*) Oslo-type crystallizer, (*d*) short-tube vertical, (*e*) propeller calandria, (*f*) long-tube vertical (ENT'T—separated entrainment outlet), (*g*) recirculating long-tube vertical, (*h*) falling film, (*i*) horizontal-tube evaporator. *C*, condensate; *F*, feed; *G*, vent; *P*, product; *S*, steam; *V*, vapor.

uses, the forced-circulation (F.C.) evaporator is suitable for the widest variety of evaporator applications. The use of a pump to ensure circulation past the heating surface makes possible separating the functions of heat transfer, vapor-liquid separation, and crystallization. The pump withdraws liquor from the flash chamber and forces it through the heating element back to the flash chamber. Circulation is maintained regardless of the evaporation rate; so this type of evaporator is well suited to crystallizing operation where solids must be maintained in suspension at all times. The liquid velocity past the heating surface is limited only by the pumping power needed or available and by accelerated corrosion and erosion at the higher velocities. Tube velocities normally range from a minimum of about 4 ft./sec. in salt evaporators with copper or brass tubes and liquid containing 5 per cent or more solids, up to about 10 ft./sec. in caustic evaporators having nickel tubes and liquid containing only a small amount of solids. Even higher velocities can be used when corrosion is not accelerated by erosion.

Highest heat-transfer coefficients are obtained in F.C. evaporators when the liquid is allowed to boil in the tubes, as in the type shown in Fig. 11-17*a*. The heating element projects into the vapor head and the liquid level is maintained near and usually slightly below the top tube sheet. This type of F.C. evaporator is not well suited to salting solutions because boiling in the tubes increases the chances of salt deposit on the walls and the sudden flashing at the tube exits promotes excessive nucleation and production of fine crystals. Consequently, this type of evaporator is seldom used except where there are headroom limitations or when the liquid forms neither salt nor scale.

By far the largest number of forced-circulation evaporators are of the submerged-tube type, as shown in Fig. 11-17*b*. The heating element is placed far enough below the liquid level or return line to the flash chamber to prevent boiling in the tubes. Preferably, the hydrostatic head should be sufficient to prevent boiling even in a tube that is plugged (and hence at steam temperature) since this prevents salting of the entire tube. Evaporators of this type sometimes have horizontal heating elements (usually two-pass), but the vertical single-pass heating element is used wherever sufficient headroom is available. The vertical element usually has a lower friction loss and is easier to clean or retube than a horizontal heater. The submerged-tube forced-circulation evaporator is relatively immune to salting in the tubes since no supersaturation is generated by evaporation in the tubes. The tendency toward scale formation is also reduced since supersaturation in the heating element is generated only by a controlled amount of heating and not by both heating and evaporation.

The type of vapor head used with the F.C. evaporator is chosen to suit the product characteristics and may range from a simple centrifugal separator to the crystallizing chambers shown in Fig. 11-17*b* and *c*. Figure 11-17*b* shows a type frequently used for common salt. It is designed to circulate a slurry of crystals throughout the system. In salt manufacture, the feed is saturated with NaCl and $CaSO_4$, the latter being a scale former. Salt crystals are removed through an elutriation leg below the vapor head, countercurrent to a rising stream of feed brine. Fine crystals, consisting of some of the salt and most of the $CaSO_4$, are washed back into the body so that the salt can grow to reasonable size and the $CaSO_4$ can serve as seeds on which the dissolved $CaSO_4$ can deposit. Figure 11-7*c* shows a submerged-tube F.C. evaporator in which heating, flashing, and crystallization are completely separated. The crystallizing solids are maintained as a fluidized bed in the chamber below the vapor head and little or no solids circulate through the heater and flash chamber. This type is well adapted to growing coarse crystals, but the crystals usually approach a spherical shape and careful design is required to avoid production of fines in the flash chamber.

In a submerged-tube F.C. evaporator, all heat is imparted as sensible heat, resulting in a temperature rise of the circulating liquor that reduces the over-all temperature difference available for heat transfer. Temperature rise, tube proportions, tube velocity, and head requirements on the circulating pump all influence the selection of circulation rate. Head requirements are frequently difficult to estimate since they consist not only of the usual friction, entrance and contraction, and elevation losses when the return to the flash chamber is above the liquid level, but also of increased friction losses due to flashing in the return line and vortex losses in the flash chamber. Circulation is sometimes limited by vapor in the pump suction line. This may be drawn in as a result of inadequate vapor-liquid separation or may come from vortices near the pump suction connection to the body or may be formed in the line itself by short circuiting from heater outlet to pump inlet of liquor that has not flashed completely to equilibrium at the pressure in the vapor head.

Advantages of Forced-circulation Evaporators

1. High heat-transfer coefficients
2. Positive circulation
3. Relative freedom from salting, scaling, and fouling

Disadvantages of Forced-circulation Evaporators

1. High cost
2. Power required for circulating pump
3. Relatively high hold-up or residence time

Best Applications of Forced-circulation Evaporators

1. Crystalline product
2. Corrosive solutions
3. Viscous solutions

Frequent Difficulties with Forced-circulation Evaporators

1. Plugging of tube inlets by salt deposits detached from walls of equipment
2. Poor circulation due to higher than expected head losses
3. Salting due to boiling in tubes
4. Corrosion—erosion

Short-tube Vertical Evaporators (Fig. 11-17*d*). Also called the Roberts, calandria, or standard evaporator, this is one of the earliest types still in widespread commercial use. Its principal use at present is in the evaporation of cane-sugar juice. Circulation past the heating surface is induced by boiling in the tubes, which are usually 2 to 3 in. in diameter by 4 to 6 ft. long. The body is a vertical cylinder, usually of cast iron, and the tubes are expanded into horizontal tube sheets that span the body diameter. The circulation rate through the tubes is many times the feed rate; so there must be a return passage from above the top tube sheet to below the bottom tube sheet. Most commonly used is a central well or *downtake* as shown in Fig. 11-17*d*. In order that friction losses through the downtake do not appreciably impede circulation up through the tubes, the area of the downtake should be of the same order of magnitude as the combined cross-sectional area of the tubes. This results in a downtake almost half the diameter of the tube sheet.

Circulation and heat transfer in this type of evaporator are strongly affected by the liquid "level." Highest heat-transfer coefficients are achieved when the level, as indicated by an external gage glass, is only about halfway up the tubes. Slight reductions in level below the optimum result in incomplete wetting of the tube walls with a consequent increased tendency to foul and a rapid reduction in capacity. When this type of evaporator is used with a liquid that can deposit salt or scale, it is customary to operate with the liquid level appreciably higher than the optimum and usually appreciably above the top tube sheet.

Circulation in the standard short-tube vertical evaporator is dependent entirely on boiling, and when boiling stops any solids present settle out of suspension. Consequently, this type is seldom used as a crystallizing evaporator. By installing a propeller in the downtake, this objection can be overcome. Such an evaporator, usually called a **propeller calandria,** is illustrated in Fig. 11-17*e*. The propeller is usually placed as low as possible to reduce cavitation and is shrouded by an extension of the downtake well. The use of the propeller can sometimes double the capacity of a short-tube vertical evaporator. The evaporator shown in Fig. 11-17*e* includes an elutriation leg for salt manufacture similar to that used on the F.C. evaporator of Fig. 11-17*b*. The shape of the bottom will, of course, depend on the particular application and on whether the propeller is driven from above or below. To avoid salting when used for crystallizing solutions, the liquid level must be kept appreciably above the top tube sheet.

Advantages of Short-tube Vertical Evaporators

1. High heat-transfer coefficients at high temperature differences
2. Low headroom
3. Easy mechanical descaling
4. Relatively inexpensive

Disadvantages of Short-tube Vertical Evaporator

1. Poor heat transfer at low temperature differences and low temperature
2. High floor space and weight
3. Relatively high hold-up
4. Poor heat transfer with viscous liquids

Best Applications of Short-tube Vertical Evaporators

1. Clear liquids
2. Crystalline product, if propeller used
3. Relatively non-corrosive liquids, since body is large and expensive if built of materials other than mild steel or cast iron
4. Mild scaling solutions requiring mechanical cleaning, since tubes are short and large in diameter

Long-tube Vertical Evaporators (Fig. 11-17*f, g, h*). More total evaporation is accomplished in this type than in all others combined, because it is normally the cheapest per unit of capacity. The long-tube vertical (L.T.V.) evaporator consists of a simple one-pass vertical shell-and-tube heat exchanger discharging into a relatively small vapor head. Normally, no liquid level is maintained in the vapor head and the residence time of liquor is only a few seconds. The tubes are usually about 2 in. in diameter but may be smaller than 1 in. Tube length may vary from less than 20 to more than 35 ft. The evaporator is usually operated single-pass, concentrating from the feed to discharge density in just the time it takes the liquid and evolved vapor to pass through a tube. An extreme case is the caustic high concentrator, producing a substantially anhydrous product at 700°F. from an inlet feed of 50 per cent NaOH at 300°F. in one pass up ⅞ in. outside diameter nickel tubes, 20 ft. long. The largest use of L.T.V. evaporators is for concentrating black liquor in the pulp and paper industry. Because of the long tubes and relatively high heat-transfer coefficients, it is possible to achieve higher single-unit capacities in this type of evaporator than in any other.

The L.T.V. evaporator shown in Fig. 11-17*f* is typical of those commonly used, especially for black liquor. Feed enters at the bottom of the tube, starts to boil part way up the tube, and the mixture of liquid and vapor leaving at the top at high velocity impinges against a deflector placed above the tube sheet. This deflector is effective both as a primary separator and as a foam breaker.

In many cases, as when the ratio of feed to evaporation or the ratio of feed to heating surface is low, it is desirable to provide for recirculation of product through the evaporator. This can be done in the type shown in Fig. 11-17*f* by adding a pipe connection between the product line and the feed line. Higher recirculation rates can be achieved in the type shown in Fig. 11-17*g*, which is used widely for condensed milk. By extending the enlarged portion of the vapor head still lower to provide storage space for liquor, this type can be used as a batch evaporator.

Liquid temperatures in the tubes of an L.T.V. evaporator are far from uniform and are difficult to predict. At the lower end, the liquid is usually not boiling and the liquor picks up heat as sensible heat. Since entering liquid velocities are usually very low, true heat-transfer coefficients are low in this non-boiling zone. At some point up the tube, the liquid starts to boil and from that point on the liquid temperature decreases because of the reduction in static, friction, and acceleration heads, until the vapor-liquid mixture reaches the top of the tubes at substantially vapor-head temperature. Thus the true temperature difference in the boiling zone is always less than the total temperature difference as measured from steam and vapor-head temperatures.

Although the true heat-transfer coefficients in the boiling zone are quite high, they are partially offset by the reduced temperature difference. The point in the tubes at which boiling starts and at which the maximum temperature is reached is sensitive to operating conditions, such as feed properties, feed temperature, feed rate, and heat flux. Figure 11-18 shows, typical variations in liquid temperature in tubes of an L.T.V. evaporator operating at constant terminal temperature difference.

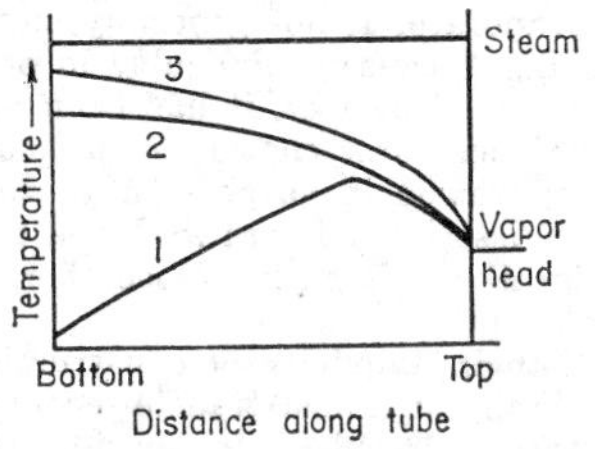

Fig. 11-18. Temperature variations in an L.T.V. evaporator.

Curve 1 shows the normal case where the feed is not boiling at the tube inlet. Curve 2 gives an indication of the temperature difference lost when the feed enters at the boiling point. Curve 3 is for exactly the same conditions as curve 2 except that the feed contained 0.01 per cent Teepol to reduce surface tension [Coulson and Mehta, *Trans. Inst. Chem. Engrs.*, **31**, 208 (1953)]. The surface-active agent yields a more intimate mixture of vapor and liquid, with the result that liquid is accelerated to a velocity more nearly approaching the vapor velocity, thereby increasing the pressure drop in the tube. Although the surface-active agent caused an increase of more than 100 per cent in the true heat-transfer coefficient, this was more than offset by the reduced temperature difference so that the net result was a reduction in evaporator capacity. This sensitivity of the L.T.V. evaporator to changes in operating conditions is less pronounced at high than at low temperature differences and temperature levels.

The falling-film version of the L.T.V. evaporator (Fig. 11-17*h*) eliminates these problems of hydrostatic head. Liquid is fed to the tops of the tubes and flows down the walls as a film. Vapor-liquid separation usually takes place at the bottom, although some evaporators of this type are arranged for vapor to rise through the tube countercurrent to the liquid. The pressure drop through the tubes is usually very small, and the boiling-liquid temperature is substantially the same as the vapor-head temperature. The falling-film evaporator is widely used for concentrating heat-sensitive materials, such as fruit juices, because the hold-up time is very small, the liquid is not overheated during passage through the evaporator, and heat-transfer coefficients are high even at low boiling temperatures.

The principal problem with the falling-film L.T.V. evaporator is that of feed distribution to the tubes. It is essential that all tube surfaces be wetted continually. This usually requires recirculation of the liquid unless the ratio of feed to evaporation is quite high. An alternative to the simple recirculation system of Fig. 11-17*h* is sometimes used when the feed undergoes an appreciable concentration change and the product is viscous. The feed chamber and vapor head are divided into a number of liquor compartments and separate pumps are used to pass the liquor through the various banks of tubes in series, all in parallel as to steam and vapor pressures. The actual distribution of feed to the individual tubes of a falling-film evaporator may be accomplished by orifices at the inlet to each tube, by a number of perforated plates above the tube sheet, or by one or more spray nozzles.

Both rising-film and falling-film L.T.V. evaporators are generally unsuited to salting or severely scaling liquids. However, the rising-film evaporator is widely used for black liquor, which presents a mild scaling problem, and also is used to carry solutions beyond saturation with respect to a crystallizing salt. In the latter case, deposits can usually be removed quickly by increasing the feed rate or reducing the steam rate in order to make the product unsaturated for a short time. The falling-film evaporator is not generally suited to liquids containing solids because of difficulty in plugging of the feed distributors. However, it has been applied to the evaporation of sea water containing a small amount of magnesium hydroxide in suspension (1 to 5 per cent) (W. L. Badger Associates, Inc., U.S. Department Interior, *Office of Saline Water Rept.* 26, December, 1959, O.T.S. Publ. PB 161290).

Because of their simplicity of construction, compactness, and generally high heat-transfer coefficients, L.T.V. evaporators are well suited to service with corrosive liquids. An example is the reconcentration of rayon spin-bath liquor, which is highly acid. These evaporators employ Karbate tubes, lead, rubber-covered or Karbate tube sheets, and rubber-lined vapor heads. Polished stainless-steel L.T.V. evaporators are widely used for food products. The latter evaporators are usually similar to that shown in Fig. 11-17*g*, where the heating element is at one side of the vapor head to permit easy access to the tubes for cleaning.

Advantages of Long-tube Vertical Evaporators

1. Low cost
2. Large heating surface in one body
3. Low hold-up
4. Small floor space
5. Good heat-transfer coefficients at reasonable temperature differences (rising film)
6. Good heat-transfer coefficients at all temperature differences (falling film)

Disadvantages of Long-tube Vertical Evaporators

1. High headroom
2. Generally unsuitable for salting and severely scaling liquids
3. Poor heat-transfer coefficients of rising-film version at low temperature differences
4. Recirculation usually required for falling-film version

Best Applications of Long-tube Vertical Evaporators

1. Clear liquids
2. Foaming liquids
3. Corrosive solutions
4. Large evaporation loads
5. High temperature differences—rising film, low temperature differences—falling film
6. Low-temperature operation—falling film

Frequent Difficulties with Long-tube Vertical Evaporators

1. Sensitivity of rising-film units to changes in operating conditions
2. Poor feed distribution to falling-film units

Horizontal-tube Evaporators (Fig. 11-17*i*). This type is seldom used except for the preparation of boiler feed water and, in a special construction, for severely scaling liquids. In this type, the steam is inside and the liquid outside the tubes. The earliest design, called the Wellner-Jelinek, had a rectangular body with a hemicylindrical top. The evaporator was made of flat or slightly curved cast-iron sections which made for compact shipment. This type is still sometimes used where there are severe headroom limitations. A later version for chemical service used a vertical cylindrical body with the tubes extending between two flat vertical tube sheets tangent to the cylinder near the bottom. Most boiler makeup evaporators employ horizontal cylindrical shells as shown in Fig. 11-17*i*, since these have the largest ratio of vapor-liquid disengaging surface to shell diameter. Low entrainment loss is the primary aim in these evaporators, and small shell diameters are desirable because the evaporators frequently operate at high steam and vapor pressures.

The original forms of horizontal-tube evaporators could not be used for salting or scaling liquids because it was almost impossible to remove the deposits from the outside of tubes. However, evaporators of the type shown in Fig. 11-17*i* are used for the extreme scaling found in the evaporation of hard waters. In this design, tube spacing is larger than normal and the tubes are deformed to crack off the scale. The deformation is accomplished by draining the shell and spraying cold water on the tubes while still subjected to steam pressure. The tubes are made susceptible to deformation by flattening or crimping or by installation between tube sheets restrained so that the tubes bend on being shocked.

Advantages of Horizontal-tube Evaporators

1. Very low headroom
2. Large vapor-liquid disengaging area
3. Relatively low cost in small-capacity straight-tube type
4. Good heat-transfer coefficients
5. Easy semiautomatic descaling—bent-tube type

Disadvantages of Horizontal-tube Evaporators

1. Unsuitable for salting liquids
2. Unsuitable for scaling liquids—straight-tube type
3. High cost—bent-tube type

Best Applications of Horizontal-tube Evaporators

1. Limited headroom
2. Small capacity
3. Non-scaling non-salting liquids—straight-tube type
4. Severely scaling liquids—bent-tube type

Miscellaneous Forms of Heating Surface. Special evaporator designs are sometimes indicated when the heat loads are small, special product characteristics are desired, or the product is especially difficult to handle. Jacketed kettles, frequently with agitators, are used when the product is very viscous, the batches are small, intimate mixing is required, and/or ease of cleaning is an important factor. Evaporators with steam in coiled tubes may be used for small capacities with scaling liquids in designs that permit "cold shocking" or complete withdrawal of the coil from the shell for manual scale removal. Other designs for scaling liquids employ flat-plate heat exchangers, since in general, a scale deposit can be removed more easily from a flat plate than from a curved surface. One such design, the channel-switching evaporator, alternates the duty of either side of the heating surface periodically from boiling liquid to condensing vapor so that scale formed when in contact with boiling liquid is dissolved when the surface is next in contact with condensing vapor.

Agitated-film evaporators are finding increasing favor for use with very viscous liquids. These evaporators employ a heating surface consisting of one relatively large diameter tube that may be either straight or tapered. Liquid is spread on the tube wall by a rotating assembly of wipers which either maintain a close clearance with the wall or actually ride on the film of liquid on the wall. The wiper assembly also serves to break down foam and throw entrainment out of the cental vapor passage. Because of the small surface that can be provided by only one tube (up to about 200 sq. ft.) and the expensive construction, agitated-film evaporator applications are limited to small evaporation rates from materials that cannot be handled in conventional evaporators.

The **grainer** is a type of evaporator confined to use in the salt industry. The brine is contained in a shallow pan about 20 by 150 ft. by 2 ft. deep. The temperature is maintained somewhat below the atmospheric boiling point by circulation through external heaters or by steam tubes running the length of the grainer below the brine surface, or by both. Evaporation takes place at the quiescent air-water interface, forming crystals that develop a hopper shape as they grow on the surface. The peculiar crystal shape is the sole justification for the grainer. The predecessor to the grainer was the direct-fired flat-bottom pan, which was in use in medieval times and is still occasionally used today.

Evaporators without Heating Surfaces. The **submerged-combustion** evaporator makes use of combustion gases bubbling through the liquid as the means of heat transfer. It consists simply of a tank to hold the liquid, a burner and gas distributor that can be lowered into the liquid, and a combustion-control system. Since there are no heating surfaces on which scale can deposit, this evaporator is well suited to use with severely scaling liquids. The ease of constructing the tank and burner of special alloys or non-metallic materials makes practical the handling of highly corrosive solutions. However, since the vapor is mixed with large quantities of non-condensable gases, it is impossible to reuse the heat in this vapor and installations are usually limited to areas of low fuel cost. One difficulty frequently encountered in the use of submerged-combustion evaporators is a high entrainment loss. Also, these evaporators cannot be used when control of crystal size is important.

Disk or **cascade evaporators** are used in the pulp and paper industry to recover heat and entrained chemicals from boiler stack gases and to effect a final concentration of the black liquor before it is burned in the boiler. These evaporators consist of a horizontal shaft on which are mounted disks perpendicular to the shaft or bars parallel to the shaft. The assembly is partially immersed in the thick black liquor so that films of liquor are carried into the hot-gas stream as the shaft rotates.

Some forms of **flash evaporators** require no heating surface. An example is a recrystallizing process for separating salts having normal solubility curves from salts having inverse solubility curves, as separating sodium chloride from calcium sulfate [Richards, *Chem. Eng.*, **59** (3), 140 (1952)]. A suspension of raw solid feed in a recirculating brine stream is heated by direct steam injection. The increased temperature and dilution by the steam dissolves the salt having the normal solubility curve. The other salt remains undissolved and is separated from the hot solution before it is flashed to a lower temperature. The cooling and loss of water on flashing cause recrystallization of the salt having the normal solubility curve, which is separated from the brine before the brine is mixed with more solid feed for recycle to the heater. This system can be operated as a multiple effect by flashing down to the lower temperature in stages and using flash vapor from all but the last stage to heat the recycle brine by direct injection. In this process no net evaporation occurs from the total system and the process cannot be used to concentrate solutions unless heating surfaces are added.

HEAT TRANSFER IN EVAPORATORS

General. While the rate of heat transfer in evaporators is expressed most conveniently in terms of the usual equation, $q = UA\,\Delta T$, the *heat-transfer coefficient* U in most types of evaporators is a strong function of *temperature difference* ΔT. Unless otherwise specified, the *area* A used in reporting evaporator sizes or heat-transfer coefficients is the surface through which heat transfer takes place, measured on the liquid side of the surface.

The *temperature difference* used in computing heat transfer in evaporators is frequently an arbitrary figure since it is quite difficult to determine the temperature of the liquid at all parts of the heating surface of most types of evaporators. The condensing temperature of steam, the most common heating medium, can usually be determined simply and accurately from a measurement of pressure in the steam side of the heating element, together with use of the "Steam Tables." No allowances are made for superheat in the steam or subcooling of the condensate when calculating steam temperature. In a similar manner, a pressure measurement in the vapor space above the boiling liquid will give the saturated vapor temperature which, assuming a negligible boiling-point rise, would be substantially the same as the boiling-liquid temperature. Temperature differences calculated on the basis of this assumption are called **apparent temperature differences** and heat-transfer coefficients are called **apparent coefficients.**

Boiling-point rise (B.P.R.) is the difference between the boiling point of a solution and the boiling point of water at the same pressure. Data on B.P.R. of a number of commonly encountered materials can be estimated from Fig. 11-19. When the boiling-point rise is deducted from the apparent temperature difference, or when the boiling-liquid temperature in the evaporator is actually measured, the terms **temperature difference corrected for boiling-point rise** and **heat-transfer coefficient corrected for boiling-point rise** are used. This is the most common basis of reporting evaporator heat-transfer data and is the basis understood in the absence of any qualifying statement.

The submerged-tube forced-circulation evaporator is one of the few cases where it is possible to obtain true temperature differences. The liquid temperatures at the inlet and outlet of the heater can be measured if precautions are taken that the thermometer in the outlet fluid is not situated so far above the heater that flashing has started. Alternately, the temperature rise through the heater can be calculated from known heat input and known circulation rate and the inlet temperature can be either measured directly or calculated from vapor pressure and boiling-point rise.

Heat-transfer Coefficients in Forced-circulation Evaporators. In F.C. evaporators where no boiling occurs, heat-transfer coefficients can be calculated in the same manner as for a shell-and-tube exchanger. The steam-film coefficient can be calculated from Eqs. (10-46) and (10-49) for the known or assumed arrangement of heating surface, temperature, and condensation rate. The liquid-film coefficient can be calculated

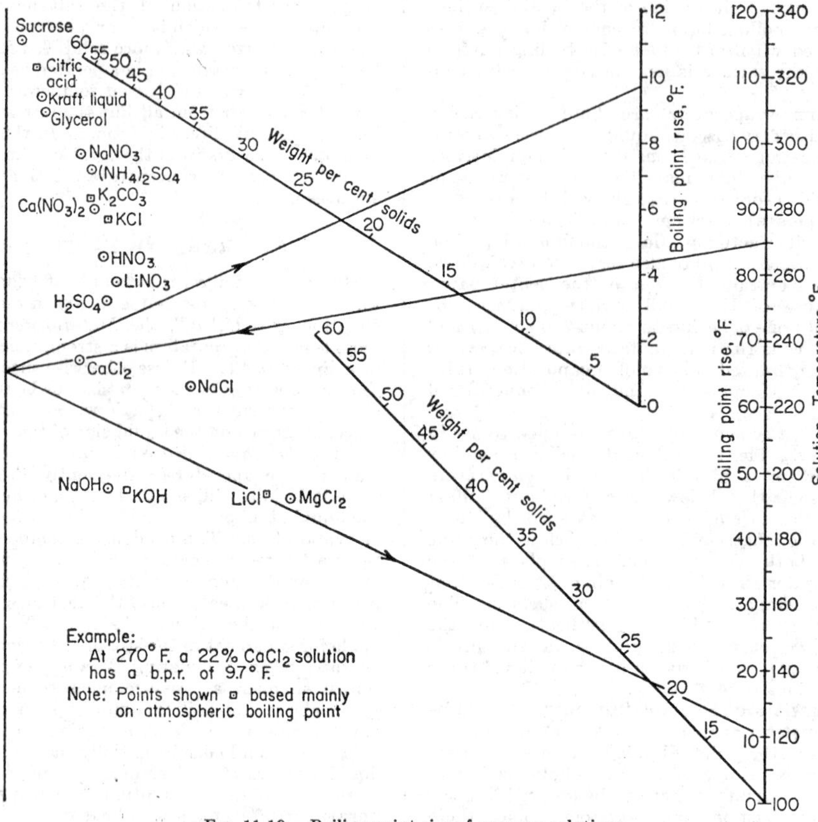

Fig. 11-19. Boiling-point rise of aqueous solutions.

from the Nusselt, Reynolds, and Prandtl numbers using a constant α of 0.0225:

$$hD/k = \alpha(Du\rho/\mu)^{0.8}(c\mu/k)^{0.4} \tag{11-1}$$

where h = film coefficient, B.t.u./(hr.)(sq. ft.)(°F.)
D = diameter, ft.
k = thermal conductivity, B.t.u./(hr.)(sq. ft.)(°F./ft.)
u = velocity, ft./hr.
μ = viscosity, lb./hr.-ft.
c = specific heat, B.t.u./(lb.)(°F.)

Typical over-all heat-transfer coefficients for an evaporator for sodium chloride brine at a velocity of 4.5 ft./sec. in 1¼ in. outside diameter 14 gage vertical copper tubes 20 ft. long and a condensation rate of 10 lb./hr./sq. ft. are shown in Fig. 11-20.

In a forced-circulation evaporator where boiling in the tubes is not completely suppressed, the liquid-film heat-transfer coefficient is appreciably improved. In cases where only the film next to the tube wall is above the boiling point, Boarts, Badger, and Meisenburg [*Ind. Eng. Chem.*, **29**, 912 (1937)] found that results could be correlated by the Dittus-Boelter equation with a constant α of 0.0278. In such cases, the course of the liquid temperature can still be calculated from known circulation rate and heat input.

In forced-circulation evaporators where the bulk of the liquid is boiling in part of the tube length, the constant α is even higher. However, the liquid temperature starts dropping as soon as full boiling develops and it is quite difficult to estimate the course of the temperature curve. It is certainly safe to estimate the heat-transfer coefficient on the basis that no bulk boiling occurs. Fragen and Badger [*Ind. Eng. Chem.*, **28**, 534 (1936)] obtained an empirical correlation of over-all heat-transfer coefficients [B.t.u./(hr.)(sq. ft.)(°F.)] in this type of

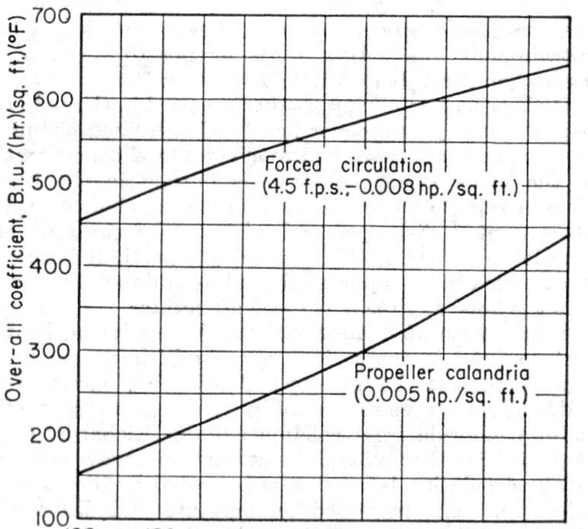

Fig. 11-20. Heat-transfer coefficients in salt evaporators.

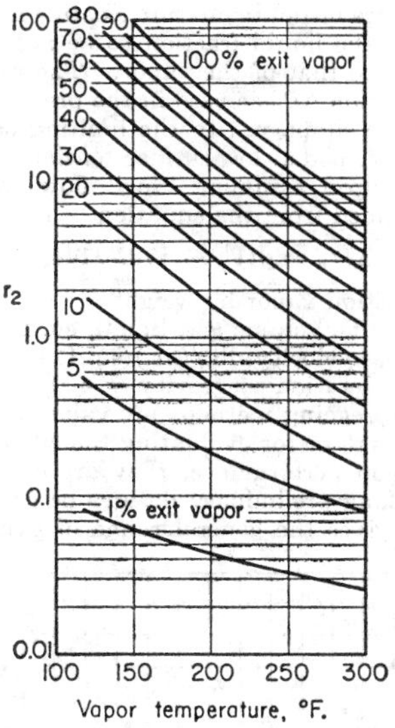

FIG. 11-21. Acceleration losses in boiling flow.

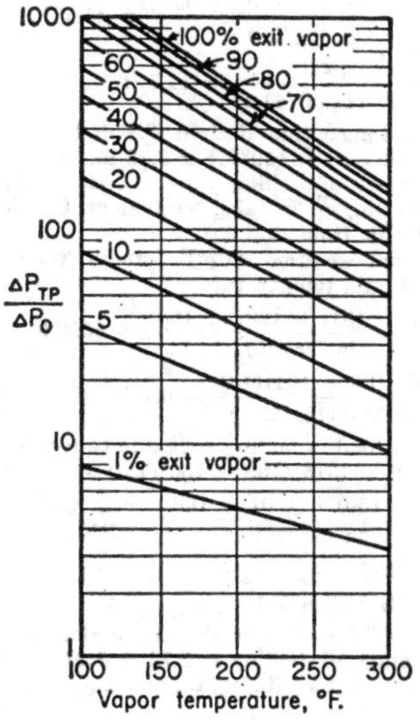

FIG. 11-22. Friction pressure drop in boiling flow.

evaporator based on the temperature difference ΔT(°F.) between steam and liquid at the heater inlet:

$$U = 490D^{0.57}v^{3.6/L}/\mu^{0.25}\Delta T^{0.1} \qquad (11\text{-}2)$$

where D = mean tube diameter, in.; v = inlet velocity, ft./sec.; L = tube length, ft.; μ = liquid viscosity, lb./hr.-ft. This equation is based primarily on experiments with copper tubes ⅞ in. outside diameter, 16 gage, 8 ft. long, but includes some work with ½-in. tubes 8 ft. long and 1-in. tubes 12 ft. long.

Heat-transfer Coefficients in Long-tube Vertical Evaporators. In the rising-film version of this type of evaporator, there is usually a non-boiling zone in the bottom section and a boiling zone in the top section. The length of the non-boiling zone depends on heat-transfer characteristics in the two zones and on pressure drop during two-phase flow in the boiling zone. The work of Martinelli and coworkers [Lockhart and Martinelli, *Chem. Eng. Progress*, **45**, 39–48 (January, 1949), Martinelli and Nelson, *Trans. Am. Soc. Mech. Engrs.*, **70**, 695–702 (August, 1948)] permits a prediction of pressure drop, and a number of correlations are available for estimating film coefficients of heat transfer in the two zones. In estimating pressure drop, integrated curves similar to those presented by Martinelli and Nelson are the easiest to use. The curves for pure water are shown in Figs. 11-21 and 11-22, based on the assumption that the flow of both vapor and liquid would be turbulent if each were flowing alone in the tube. Similar curves can be prepared if one or both flows are viscous or if the properties of the liquid differ appreciably from the properties of pure water. The application of these curves can best be illustrated by example.

Assume a non-recirculating L.T.V. evaporator effect with 1.25 in. outside diameter by 1.12 in. inside diameter by 18 ft. 6 in. long copper tubes fed with 315 lb. of water/hr./tube at 131°F. Evaporation rate is to be 200 lb./hr./tube at a vapor-head saturation temperature of 150°F. The primary unknowns are steam temperature required, length of the boiling section, and maximum liquid temperature (reached at the beginning of the boiling section).

1. Determine friction drop for liquid flowing alone (assume average liquid temperature of 155°F.):

u = 0.210 ft./sec.; G = 12.8 lb./(sec.)(sq. ft.); Re = 4300; $(\Delta P/\Delta L)_{L_0}$ = 0.000121 lb./sq. in./ft. (friction factor from Sec. 5).

2. Determine acceleration head ΔP_a:

Exit fraction vapor $y = \frac{200}{315} = 0.635$:

From Fig. 11-21, r_2 = 36 at 150°F.

$\Delta P_a = r_2G^2/144g$ = (36)(12.8)²/(144)(32.2) = 1.27 lb./sq. in.

3. Determine boiling-zone friction loss $(\Delta P/\Delta L)_B$:

From Fig. 11-22, $\Delta P_{TP}/\Delta P_0$ = 510.

$(\Delta P/\Delta L)_B$ = (510)(0.000121) = 0.0617 lb./sq. in./ft.

4. Determine log mean static head in boiling zone ΔP_H:

Vapor V_g = 97.1 ft.³/lb. Liquid V_l = 0.0163 ft.³/lb.

Outlet V = (97.1)(0.635) + (0.0163)(1 − 0.635) = 61.6 ft.³/lb.

V_m = (61.6 − 0.0163)/ln (61.6/0.0163) = 7.48 ft.³/lb.

ΔP_H = 1/(7.48)(144) = 0.000928 lb./sq. in./ft.

Total pressure drop in boiling zone (lb./sq. in.) = 1.27 + 0.0626L_B.

5. Determine steam-film coefficient in boiling zone:

q = (200)(1008) = 201,600 B.t.u./hr. (neglecting evaporation by flashing).

Assuming 205° steam; condensate = q/974.8 = 207 lb./hr.

$$\frac{4\Gamma}{\mu_F} = \frac{(4)(207)(12)}{(\pi)(1.25)(2.42)(0.30)} = 3480.$$

$h_m = (0.0077)(4\Gamma/\mu)^{0.4}(k^3\rho^2g/\mu^2)^{1/3}$ = 1135.

6. Steam-film coefficient at bottom is about 75 per cent of average, or about 850.

7. Non-boiling coefficient: Eq. (11-1) with α = 0.0278

h_{NB} = (0.0278)(4300)$^{0.8}$ (2.7)$^{0.4}$(0.38)(12)/(1.12) = 135.

$$U_{NB} = \frac{1}{(1/850)(1.12/1.25) + (0.065)/(12)(218) + 1/135} = 118.$$

8. Boiling coefficient (assuming proportional to $u^{0.8}$ and based on log mean velocity):

$Re_m = Re_l(V_m/V_l)$ = (4300)(7.48/0.0163) = 1,970,000.

h_B = (0.0225)(1,970,000)$^{0.8}$(2.7)$^{0.4}$(0.38)(12)/(1.12) = 14,800.

$$U_B = \frac{1}{(1/1135)(1.12/1.25) + (0.065)/(12)(218) + 1/14{,}800} = 1135.$$

9*a*. Assume 205° steam temperature and 175° maximum liquid temperature:

$$\Delta T_{NB} = \frac{(205 - 131) - (205 - 175)}{\ln (74/30)} = 48.6°\text{F.}$$

$$L_{NB} = \frac{(315)(175 - 131)(1.0)}{(0.2932 \text{ ft.}^2/\text{ft.})(118)(48.6)} = 8.2 \text{ ft.}$$

$$\Delta T_B = \frac{(205 - 150) - (205 - 175)}{\ln (55/30)} = 41.1°\text{F.}$$

$$L_B = \frac{201{,}600}{(0.2932)(1135)(41.1)} = 14.7 \text{ ft.}$$

Total length is longer than desired (8.2 + 14.7 = 22.9 ft.).
Pressure at tube outlet (150°F.) = 3.72 lb./sq. in. abs.
Pressure at start of boiling zone = 3.72 + 1.27 + (0.0626)(14.7 ft.) = 5.91 lb./sq. in. abs. equivalent to 168°F. (0.0626 from step 4; 14.7 ft. from step 9*a*).

9*b*. Second trial—assume 207°F. steam temperature and 168° maximum liquid temperature:

$$\Delta T_{NB} = \frac{(207 - 131) - (207 - 168)}{\ln (76/39)} = 55.4°\text{F.}$$

$$L_{NB} = \frac{(315)(168 - 131)(1.0)}{(0.2932)(118)(55.4)} = 6.1 \text{ ft.}$$

Corrected heat load in boiling zone due to feed flash
= 201,600 − (315)(168 − 150)(1.0) = 195,900 B.t.u./hr.

$$\Delta T_B = \frac{(207 - 150) - (207 - 168)}{\ln (57/39)} = 47.4°\text{F.}$$

$$L_B = \frac{195{,}900}{(0.2932)(1135)(47.4)} = 12.4 \text{ ft.}$$

Total length = 6.1 + 12.4 = 18.5 ft. vs. desired 18.5 ft.
Pressure at start of boiling = 3.72 + 1.27 + (0.0626)(12.4) = 5.77 lb./sq. in. abs. equivalent to 167.4°F.

If the steam pressure had been fixed, this method could be used to determine the tube length required, or more frequently, the duty per tube could be adjusted to suit any desired tube length.

This method of calculation can be refined by using the differential methods of analysis of pressure drop and heat transfer developed by Jacob *et al.*; Johnson; Guerrieri and Talty; and Dengler and Addoms [*Chem. Eng. Progress* (1956), *Symp. Ser.* 18, **52,** 29, 37, 69, and 95, respectively)]. These methods require point-to-point calculation and then an integration of the results. Film coefficients for boiling of liquids other than water have been investigated. Coulson and McNeely [*Trans. Inst. Chem. Engrs.*, **34,** 247 (1956)] derived the following relation, which also correlated the data of Badger and coworkers on water:

$$\text{Nu} = (1.3 + 39D)(\text{Pr}_l)^{0.9}(\text{Re}_l)^{0.23}(\text{Re}_g)^{0.34}(\rho_l/\rho_g)^{0.25}(\mu_g/\mu_l) \quad (11\text{-}3)$$

where Nu = Nusselt number based on liquid thermal conductivity, D = tube diameter, ft., and the remaining terms are dimensionless groupings of liquid Prandtl number, liquid Reynolds number, vapor Reynolds number, and ratios of densities and viscosities. The Reynolds numbers are calculated on the basis of each fluid flowing by itself in the tube.

Additional corrections must be applied when the fraction of vapor is so high that the remaining liquid does not wet the tube wall or when the velocity of the mixture at the tube exits approaches sonic velocity. McAdams, Woods, and Bryan (*Trans. Am. Soc. Mech. Engrs.*, 1940); Dengler and Addoms [*loc. cit.*]; and Stroebe, Baker, and Badger [*Ind. Eng. Chem.*, **31,** 200 (1939)] encountered dry-wall conditions and reduced coefficients when the weight fraction of vapor exceeded about 80 per cent. Schweppe and Foust [*Chem. Eng. Progress, Symp. Ser.* 5, **49,** 77 (1953)] and Harvey and Foust (*ibid.*, p. 91) found that "sonic choking" occurred at surprisingly low flow rates.

The simplified method of calculation outlined above includes no allowance for the effect of surface tension. Stroebe, Baker, and Badger (*loc. cit.*) found by adding a small amount of surface-active agent that the boiling-film coefficient varied inversely as the square of the surface tension. Coulson and Mehta [*Trans. Inst. Chem. Engrs.*, **31,** 208 (1953)] found the exponent to be −1.4. The higher coefficients at low surface tension are offset to some extent by a higher pressure drop, probably because the more intimate mixture existing at low surface tension causes the liquid fraction to be accelerated to a velocity closer to that of the vapor. The pressure drop due to acceleration ΔP_a as used in the preceding example allows for some slippage. In the limiting case, such as might be approached at low surface tension, the acceleration pressure drop assuming "fog" flow (no slippage) can be determined from the equation

$$\Delta P'_a = y(V_g - V_l)G^2/144g \quad (11\text{-}4)$$

where y = fraction vapor by weight
V_g, V_l = specific volume gas, liquid, cu. ft./lb.
G = mass velocity, lb./(hr.)(sq. ft.)
g = acceleration by gravity = 4.18 × 10^8 ft./hr.^{2}

While the foregoing methods are valuable for detailed evaporator design or for evaluating the effect of changes in conditions on performance, they are cumbersome to use when making preliminary designs or cost estimates. Figure 11-23 gives the general range of over-all L.T.V.

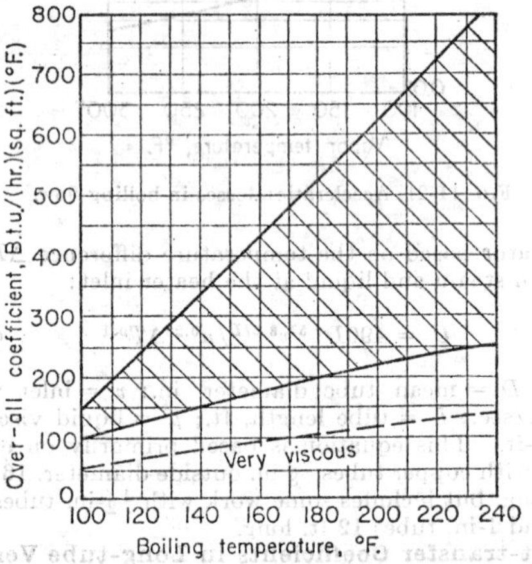

FIG. 11-23. General range of L.T.V. coefficients.

evaporator heat-transfer coefficients usually encountered in commercial practice. The higher coefficients are encountered when evaporating dilute solutions and the lower range when evaporating viscous liquids. The dashed curve represents the approximate lower limit, for liquids with viscosities of about 100 centipoises. The L.T.V. evaporator does not work well at low temperature differences, as indicated by the results shown in Fig. 11-24 for sea water in 2-in. 12-gage brass tubes

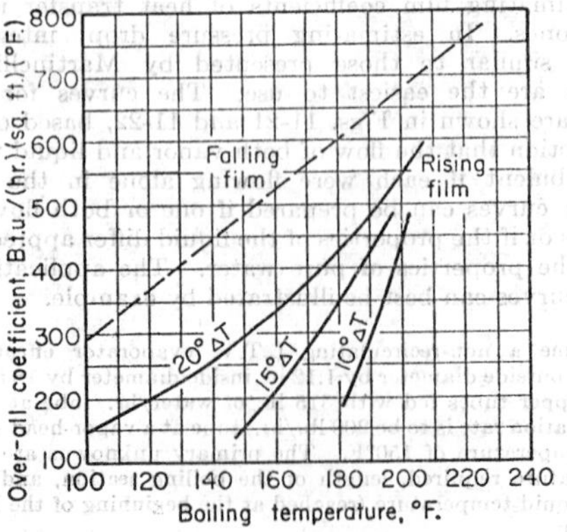

FIG. 11-24. Heat-transfer coefficients in L.T.V. sea-water evaporators.

24 ft. 0 in. long (W. L. Badger Associates, Inc., U.S. Department Interior, *Office of Saline Water Rept.* 26, December, 1959, O.T.S. Publ. PB 161290). The feed was at its boiling point at the vapor-head pressure, and feed rates varied from 200 to 400 lb./hr./tube at the higher temperature to 300 to 1000 lb./hr./tube at the lowest temperature.

Falling-film evaporators exhibit approximately the same performance as falling-film heat exchanges for non-boiling liquids (*q.v.*). The liquid generally flows down the tube as a film and is not mixed with, or accelerated by, the vapor core. The boiling point in the tubes is higher than in the vapor head because frictional pressure drop of the vapor and the superheat required to form vapor bubbles in the film (Sinek, Ph.D. thesis, University of Michigan, 1961). Both these factors can be predicted. They tend to make over-all coefficients lower than those for non-boiling conditions. Figure 11-24 shows over-all heat-transfer coefficients determined in a falling-film sea-water evaporator using the same tubes and flow rates as for the rising-film tests (W. L. Badger Associates, Inc., *loc. cit.*).

Heat-transfer Coefficients in Short-tube Vertical Evaporators. These coefficients can be estimated by the same detailed method as described previously for recirculating L.T.V. evaporators. Performance is primarily a function of temperature level, temperature difference, and viscosity. While liquid level can also have an important influence, this is usually encountered only at levels lower than considered safe in commercial operation. Over-all heat-transfer coefficients are shown in Fig. 11-25 for a basket-type evaporator (one with an

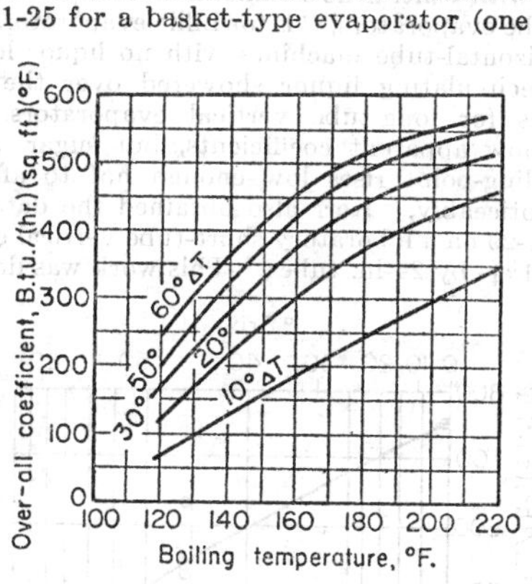

FIG. 11-25. Heat-transfer coefficients for water in short tube.

annular downtake) when boiling water with 2 in. outside diameter 12-gage 4-ft.-long steel tubes [Badger and Shepard, *Chem. & Met. Eng.*, **23**, 281 (1920)]. Liquid level was maintained at the top tube sheet. Foust, Baker, and Badger [*Ind. Eng. Chem.*, **31**, 206 (1939)] measured recirculating velocities and heat-transfer coefficients in the same evaporator except with 2.5-in. 10-gage 4-ft.-long tubes and temperature differences from 12° to 46°F. In the normal range of liquid levels, their results can be expressed as

$$U_c = \frac{375(\Delta T_c)^{0.22}(\mathrm{Pr})^{0.4}}{(V_g - V_l)^{0.37}} \qquad (11\text{-}5)$$

where the subscript c refers to true liquid temperature, which under these conditions was about 1°F. above the vapor-head temperature. This work was done with water.

No detailed tests have been reported for performance of propeller calandrias. Not enough is known regarding the performance of the propellers themselves under the cavitating conditions usually encountered to permit predicting circulation rates. Figure 11-20 shows an average of plant test data on evaporators for sodium chloride brine with 2½- to 3-in. copper tubes 4 ft. 6 in. to 5 ft. long [Hester and Diamond, *Ind. Eng. Chem.*, **47**, 672 (1955); Badger and Standiford, *Chem. Eng.*, **62** (3), 173 (1955)]. Power consumption by the propellers was about 0.005 hp./sq. ft. of heating surface. Data on only one commercial installation indicate that the heat-transfer coefficient varies as the 0.8 power of the power consumption, at least up to 0.0075 hp./sq. ft.

Heat Transfer in Miscellaneous Evaporator Types. Horizontal-tube evaporators behave in much the same way as short-tube verticals and heat-transfer coefficients are of the same order of magnitude. Some test results for water were published by Badger [*Trans. Am. Inst. Chem. Engrs.*, **13**, 139 (1921)].

Heat-transfer coefficients in clean coiled-tube evaporators for sea water are shown in Fig. 11-26 [Hillier, *Proc.*

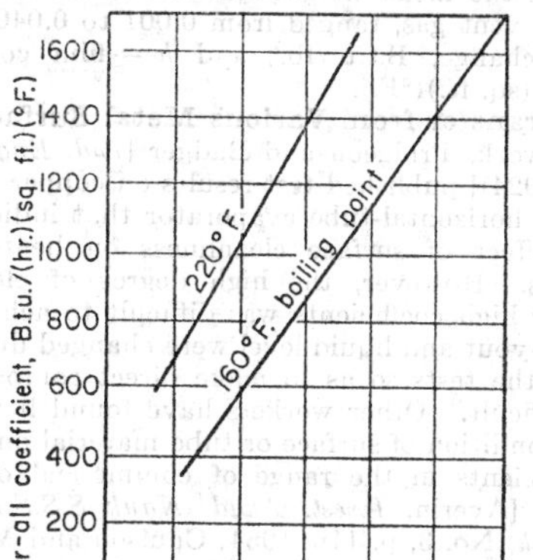

FIG. 11-26. Heat-transfer coefficients for sea water in coil-tube evaporators.

Inst. Mech. Engrs. (*London*), **1B** (7), 295 (1953)]. The tubes were of copper.

Heat-transfer coefficients in agitated-film evaporators depend primarily on liquid viscosity. This type is usually justifiable only for very viscous materials. Figure 11-27 shows general ranges of over-all coefficients

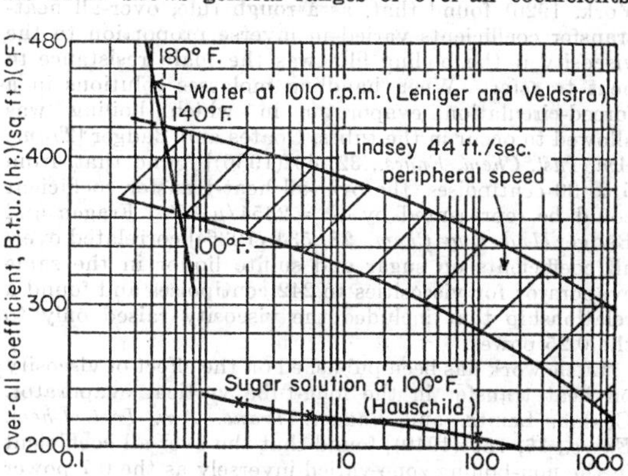

FIG. 11-27. Over-all heat-transfer coefficients in agitated-film evaporators.

[Hauschild, *Chem. Ing. Tech.*, **25**, 573 (1953); Lindsey, *Chem. Eng.*, **60** (4), 227 (1953); Leniger and Veldstra, *Chem. Ing. Tech.*, **31**, 493 (1959)]. When used with non-viscous fluids, a wiped-film evaporator having fluted external surfaces can exhibit very high coefficients (Lustenader *et al.*, *Trans. Am. Soc. Mech. Engrs.*, Paper 59-SA-30, 1959) although at a probably unwarranted first cost.

Heat Transfer in Presence of Non-condensable Gases. When the heating medium for an evaporator effect is vapor from a preceding effect, some non-condensable gases will usually be present. These gases can reduce the condensing-steam-film coefficient quite appreciably. Meisenberg, Boarts, and Badger [*Trans. Am. Inst. Chem. Engrs.*, **31**, 622 (1936)] have determined steam-film coefficients in the presence of air:

$$h_s = 0.670 \left(\frac{k^3\rho^2 g\, \Delta H}{L\mu\, \Delta T}\right)^{0.25} \left(\frac{1}{C}\right)^{0.11} \qquad (11\text{-}6)$$

where C is the mean weight fraction of air in entering steam and vent gas, ranged from 0.001 to 0.040; ΔH = enthalpy change, B.t.u./lb.; and h = film coefficient, B.t.u./hr. (sq. ft.)(°F.).

Heat Transfer from Various Metal Surfaces. In an early work, Pridgeon and Badger [*Ind. Eng. Chem.*, **16**, 474 (1924)] published test results on copper and iron tubes in a horizontal-tube evaporator that indicated an extreme effect of surface cleanliness on heat-transfer coefficients. However, the high degree of cleanliness needed for high coefficients was difficult to achieve and the tube layout and liquid level were changed during the course of the tests so as to make direct comparison of results difficult. Other workers have found little or no effect of condition of surface or tube material on boiling-film coefficients in the range of commercial operating conditions [Averin, *Izvest. Akad. Nauk S.S.S.R. Otdel. Tekh. Nauk*, No. 3, p. 116, 1954; Coulson and McNeely, *Trans. Inst. Chem. Engrs.*, **34**, 247 (1956)].

Effect of Fluid Properties on Heat Transfer. Most of the heat-transfer data reported above were obtained with water or with dilute solutions having properties close to those of water. Heat transfer with other materials will depend on the type of evaporator used. For forced-circulation evaporators, methods have been presented to calculate the effect of changes in fluid properties. For natural-circulation evaporators, viscosity is the most important variable as far as aqueous solutions are concerned. Badger ("Heat Transfer and Evaporation," pp. 133–134, Chemical Catalog, New York, 1926) found that, as a rough rule, over-all heat-transfer coefficients varied in inverse proportion to the viscosity if the boiling film was the main resistance to heat transfer. When handling molasses solutions in a forced-circulation evaporator in which boiling was allowed to occur in the tubes, Coates and Badger [*Trans. Am. Inst. Chem. Engrs.*, **32**, 49 (1936)] found that, from 5 to 30 centipoises, the over-all heat-transfer coefficient could be represented by $U = 2354/\mu_f^{1.24}$. Fragen and Badger [*Ind. Eng. Chem.*, **28**, 534 (1936)] correlated over-all coefficients on sugar and sulfite liquor in the same evaporator for viscosities to 242 centipoises and found a relationship that included the viscosity raised only to the 0.25 power.

Little work has been published on the effect of viscosity on heat transfer in the long-tube vertical evaporator. Cessna, Leintz, and Badger [*Trans. Am. Inst. Chem. Engrs.*, **36**, 759 (1940)] found that the over-all coefficient in the non-boiling zone varied inversely as the 0.7 power of viscosity (with sugar solutions). Coulson and Mehta [*Trans. Inst. Chem. Engrs.*, **31**, 208 (1953)] found the exponent to be −0.44, and Stroebe, Baker, and Badger (*loc. cit.*) arrived at an exponent of −0.3 for the effect of viscosity on the film coefficient in the boiling zone.

Kerr (*Louisiana Agr. Expt. Sta. Bull.* 149) obtained plant data shown in Fig. 11-28 on various types of full-sized evaporators for cane sugar. These are invariably forward-feed evaporators concentrating to about 50°Brix, corresponding to a viscosity on the order of 5 centipoises in the last effect. In Fig. 11-28, curve A is for short-tube

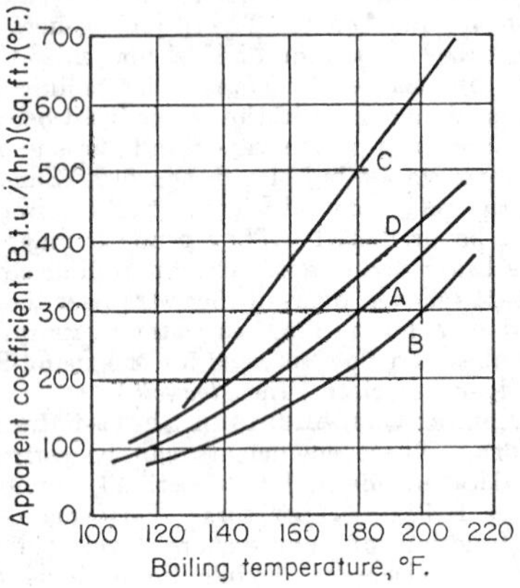

FIG. 11-28. Kerr's tests with full-sized sugar evaporators.

verticals with central downtake, B is for standard horizontal-tube evaporators, C is for Lillie evaporators (which were horizontal-tube machines with no liquor level but having recirculating liquor showered over the tubes), and D is for long-tube vertical evaporators. These curves show apparent coefficients, but sugar solutions have boiling-point rises low enough not to affect the results noticeably. Kerr also obtained the data shown in Fig. 11-29 on a laboratory short-tube vertical evaporator with 1¾- by 24-in. tubes. This work was done with

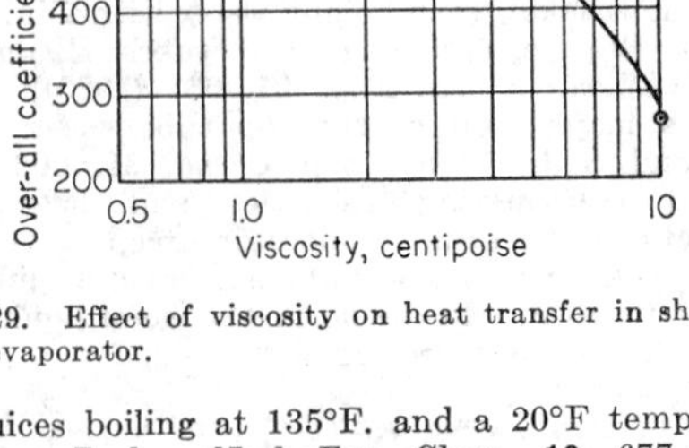

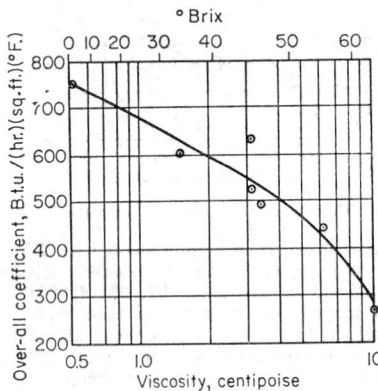

FIG. 11-29. Effect of viscosity on heat transfer in short-tube vertical evaporator.

sugar juices boiling at 135°F. and a 20°F temperature difference. Badger [*Ind. Eng. Chem.*, **19**, 677 (1927)] obtained the test data on sulfite black liquor shown in Fig. 11-30. This work was done in a forced-circulation boiling machine, under the conditions shown in Table 11-17, to simulate conditions that would be encountered in a forward-feed evaporator. The concentrated liquor was also tested at first-effect boiling point, represented by the upper curve at high concentrations.

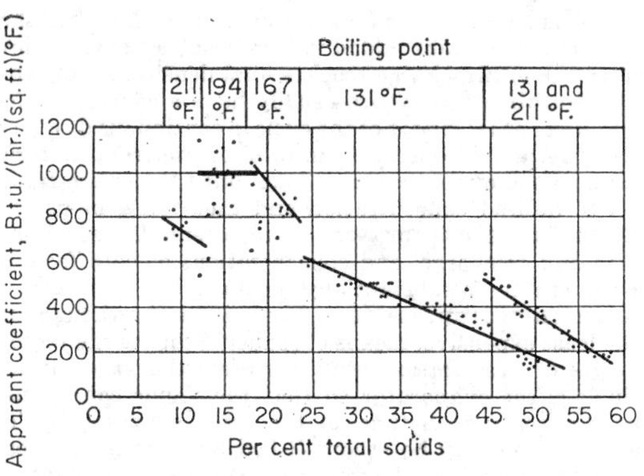

FIG. 11-30. Heat-transfer coefficients in evaporating sulfite liquor.

Table 11-17. Operating Data for the Evaporation of Sulfite-pulp Liquor

⅞ in. o.d., ¾ in. i.d. nickel tubes 8 ft. 0 in. long

	First effect		Second effect	Third effect	Fourth effect
Liquor temperature, °F.	211	211	194	167	131
Temperature drop, °F.	20	36	20	25	45
% total solids	8–12	45–59	13–17	18–23	24–52
Approx. viscosity, centipoise	0.4–0.5	6–30	0.5	1–1.2	1.6–80
Avg. inlet velocity, ft./sec.	11.5	7.6	7.9	7.1	9.4
Avg. pressure drop, ft. H_2O	14.8	24.0	15.2	19.1	22.6

VAPOR-LIQUID SEPARATION

Product losses in evaporator vapor may result from foaming, splashing, or entrainment. By definition of an evaporator, losses of solute by actual evaporation of the solute are of no concern to evaporator design. Because the value of product may vary from less than a cent to several dollars a pound or the product may be injurious if allowed to escape, no uniform standards of product loss with the vapor are possible.

Foaming losses usually result from the presence in the evaporating liquid of colloids or of surface-tension depressants and finely divided solids. Antifoam agents such as vegetable oils, fatty acids, and sulfonated castor oil are sometimes effective and silicone preparations are often very effective. Other means of combating foam include the use of steam jets impinging on the foam surface, the removal of product at the surface layer where the foaming agents seem to concentrate, and operation at very low liquid level so that hot surfaces can break the foam. Impingement at high velocity against a baffle tends to break the foam mechanically, and this is the reason that the long-tube vertical, forced-circulation, and agitated-film evaporators are particularly effective with foaming liquids. A frequent cause of foaming is the presence of air or dissolved gases in the liquid. An air leak below the liquid level can result in foaming of a liquid that would not ordinarily give difficulty.

Splashing losses are usually insignificant if a reasonable height has been provided between the liquid level and the top of the vapor head. The height required depends on the violence of boiling. Heights of 8 to 12 ft. or more are provided in short-tube vertical evaporators where the liquid and vapor leaving the tubes are projected upward. Less height is required in forced-circulation evaporators where the liquid is given a centrifugal motion or is projected downward as by a baffle. The same is true of long-tube vertical evaporators where the rising vapor-liquid mixture is projected against a baffle.

Entrainment losses result from the presence of droplets in the vapor that cannot settle against the moving vapor current. The extent of losses will depend on the size distribution of droplets and the vapor velocity. The limiting velocity for a given size of droplet can be inferred from Stokes's law, which may be written

$$G = C' \sqrt{\rho_g(\rho_l - \rho_g)} \tag{11-7}$$

where G = mass vapor velocity, lb./(hr.)(sq. ft.), and ρ_l and ρ_g = liquid and vapor densities, lb./cu. ft. The constant C' is a measure of the droplet size that will be carried over by the vapor. Little is known regarding the size distribution of droplets from an evaporator or the effect of evaporator type on droplet size. However, it can be inferred that operation under conditions such that C' has a certain value will result in carry-over of all droplets below a certain size and will thus be a measure of entrainment losses. Available data [Cessna and Badger, *Ind. Eng. Chem.*, **26**, 485 (1934); Manowitz, Bretton, and Horrigan, *Chem. Eng. Progress*, **51**, 313 (1955); Carpenter and Othmer, *Am. Inst. Chem. Engrs. Journal*, **1**, 549 (1955)] are plotted in Fig. 11-31 as decontamination factor (pounds vapor per pound of liquid at

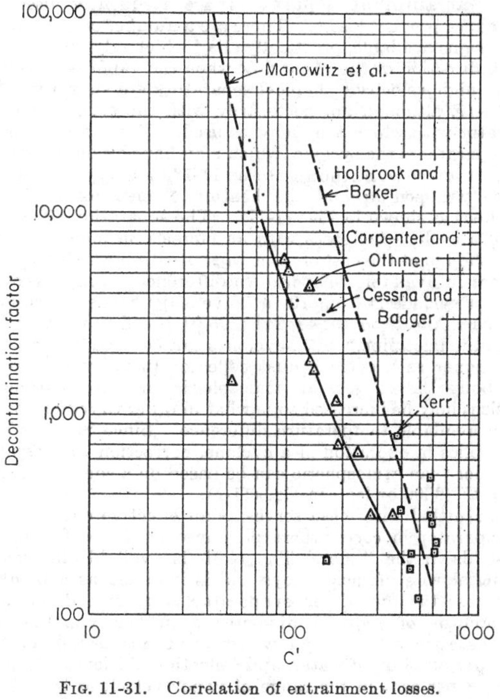

FIG. 11-31. Correlation of entrainment losses.

the composition in the evaporator) vs. the constant C'. The lower curve is based primarily on data for short-tube vertical evaporators. The data of Cessna and Badger are for a forced-circulation evaporator of the type shown in Fig. 11-17*a* in which the vapor-liquid mixture impinges against an umbrella-shaped baffle. In all cases, the mass velocity is computed on the basis of the largest horizontal cross-sectional area for vapor flow. The upper curve [Holbrook and Baker, *Ind. Eng. Chem.*, **26**, 1063 (1934)] was determined with steam and brine in a bubble-cap column and is an extrapolation to tray spacings over 3 ft. Since there was no vaporization in this case, droplet sizes were probably larger than is usually the case in evaporators and the entrainment losses were lower. At very low vapor-flow rates, equivalent to low values of C', there may be an increase in entrainment with a decrease in vapor velocity. Apparently, with very gentle boiling, the vapor bubbles have more time to collapse, the film around the bubbles is thinner, and the droplets are smaller. This phenomenon is apparent at decontamination factors somewhere above 10,000 [Manowitz, Bretton, and Horrigan, *loc. cit.;* O'Connell and Pettyjohn, *Trans. Am. Inst. Chem. Engrs.*, **42**, 795 (1946)].

Entrainment losses by flashing are frequently encountered in an evaporator. If the feed is above the boiling point and is introduced above or only a short distance below the liquid level, entrainment losses may be excessive. This can occur in a short-tube-type evaporator if the feed is introduced at only one point below the lower tube sheet [Kerr, *Louisiana Agr. Expt. Sta. Bull.* 149, 1915]. The same difficulty may be encountered in forced-circulation evaporators having too high a temperature rise through the heating element and thus too wide a flashing range as the circulating liquid enters the body. Poor vacuum control, especially during startup, can cause generation of far more vapor than the evaporator was designed to handle, with a consequent increase in entrainment.

Entrainment separators are frequently used to reduce product losses. There are a number of specialized designs available, practically all of which rely on a change in direction of the vapor flow when the vapor is traveling at high velocity. Typical separators are shown in Fig. 11-17, although not necessarily with the type of evaporator with which they may be used. The most common separator is the cyclone, which may have either a top or a bottom outlet as shown in Fig. 11-17*a* and *b*, or may even be wrapped around the heating element of the next effect as shown in Fig. 11-17*f*. The separation efficiency of a cyclone increases with an increase in inlet velocity, although at the cost of some pressure drop which means a loss in available temperature difference. Pressure drop in a cyclone is from 10 to 16 velocity heads [Lawrence, *Chem. Eng. Progress*, **48**, 241 (1952)], based on the velocity in the inlet pipe. Such cyclones can be sized in the same manner as a cyclone dust collector (using velocities of about 100 ft./sec. at atmospheric pressure) although sizes may be increased somewhat in order to reduce losses in available temperature difference. Since Stokes's law applies in operation of a cyclone, correction to pressures other than atmospheric can be based on a constant value of C' (9000 or less) in Eq. (11-7).

Knitted wire mesh serves as an effective entrainment separator in cases where it cannot easily be fouled by solids in the liquor. The mesh is available in woven metal wire of most alloys and is installed as a blanket across the top of the evaporator (Fig. 11-17*d*) or in a monitor of reduced diameter atop the vapor head. These separators have low pressure drops, usually on the order of ½ in. of water, and collection efficiency is above 99.8 per cent in the range of vapor velocities from 8 to 20 ft./sec. [Carpenter and Othmer, *J. Am. Inst. Chem. Engrs.*, **1**, 549 (1955)].

EVAPORATOR ARRANGEMENT

Single-effect Evaporators. Single-effect evaporators are used where the required capacity is small, steam is cheap, the material is so corrosive that very expensive materials of construction are required, or the vapor is so contaminated that it cannot be reused. Single-effect evaporators may be operated batch, semibatch, continuous-batch, or continuously. Strictly speaking, **batch evaporators** are ones in which filling, evaporating, and emptying are consecutive steps. This method of operation is rarely used since it requires that the body be large enough to hold the entire charge of feed and the heating element be placed low enough so as not to be uncovered when the volume is reduced to that of the product. The more usual method of operation is **semibatch,** where feed is continually added to maintain a constant level until the entire charge reaches final density. **Continuous-batch evaporators** usually have a continuous feed and, over at least part of the cycle, a continuous discharge. One method of operation is to circulate from a storage tank to the evaporator and back until the entire tank is up to desired concentration and then finish in batches. **Continuous evaporators** have essentially continuous feed and discharge, and concentrations of both feed and product remain substantially constant.

Thermocompression. The simplest, though not the least expensive, means of reducing the energy requirements of evaporation is to compress the vapor from a single-effect evaporator so that the vapor can be used as the heating medium in the same evaporator. The compression may be accomplished by mechanical means or by a steam jet. In order to keep the compressor cost and power requirements within reason, the evaporator must work with a fairly narrow temperature difference, usually from about 10° to 20°F. This means that a large evaporator heating surface is needed, partially offsetting the advantages of thermocompression. Such evaporators are widely used in Europe, primarily because cheap hydroelectric power is available and fuel for steam generation is expensive. Only two uses of thermocompression evaporators have developed in the United States. One is for the concentration of fruit juices, which must be carried out at such a low temperature that multiple-effect operation is impractical. The other is for production of fresh water from sea water or brackish water utilizing an engine-driven compressor. The power unit, compressor, evaporator, and auxiliaries can be assembled on a skid compact enough for easy shipment and can be put into operation in a very short time. These evaporators are widely used by the military for remote bases since they require far less shipping space for fuel than would have been required for water.

Mechanical thermocompression may employ reciprocating, rotary positive-displacement, centrifugal, or axial-flow compressors. Positive-displacement compressors are impractical for all but the smallest capacities, such as the portable sea-water evaporators. Axial-flow compressors can be built for capacities of more than 1 million cu. ft./min. Centrifugal compressors are usually cheapest for the intermediate capacity ranges that are normally encountered. In all cases, great care must be taken to keep entrainment at a minimum since the vapor becomes superheated on compression and any liquid present will evaporate, leaving the dissolved solids behind. In some cases a vapor scrubbing tower may be installed to protect the compressor. A mechanical recompression evaporator usually requires more heat than is available from the compressed vapor. Some of this extra heat can be obtained by preheating the feed with the condensate and, if possible, with the product. Rather extensive heat-exchange systems with close approach temperatures are usually justified, especially if the evaporator is operated at high temperature to reduce the volume of vapor to be compressed. When the product is a solid, an elutriation leg such as that shown in Fig. 11-17*b* is advantageous, since it cools the product almost to feed temperature. The remaining heat needed to maintain the evaporator in operation must be obtained from outside sources. If an electric drive is used, makeup steam may be furnished from an electrically heated boiler, which adds appreciably to the power requirements. When a diesel drive is employed, makeup heat can be obtained from the exhaust gases or by operating the entire jacket-cooling system at a temperature high enough to produce steam.

While the theoretical compressor power requirements are reduced slightly by going to lower evaporating temperatures, the volume of vapor to be compressed and hence the compressor size and cost increase so rapidly that low-temperature operation is more expensive than high-temperature operation. The requirement of low temperature for fruit-juice concentration has led to the development of an evaporator employing a **secondary fluid,** usually Freon or ammonia. In this evaporator, the vapor is condensed in an exchanger cooled by boiling Freon. The Freon, at much higher vapor density than the water vapor, is then compressed to serve as the heating medium for the evaporator. This system requires that the latent heat be transferred through two surfaces instead of one, but the savings in compressor size and cost are enough to justify the extra cost of heating surface or the cost of compressing through a wider temperature range.

Steam-jet thermocompression is advantageous when steam is available at a pressure appreciably higher than can be used in the evaporator. The steam jet then serves as a reducing valve while doing some useful work. The efficiency of a steam jet is quite low and falls off rapidly when the jet is not used at the vapor-flow rate and terminal pressure conditions for which it was designed. Consequently multiple jets are used when wide variations in evaporation rate are expected. Because of the low first cost and the ability to handle large volumes of vapor, steam-jet thermocompressors are used to increase the economy of evaporators that must operate at low temperatures and hence cannot be operated in multiple effect. The steam-jet thermocompression evaporator has a heat input larger than needed to balance the system, and some heat must be rejected. This is usually done by venting some of the vapor at the suction of the compressor. This vapor may be wasted to a condenser or may be used as the heating medium in another evaporator body. The same is true with a steam-turbine-driven mechanical compressor. If the thermocompression evaporator is operated at a high enough temperature, the extra vapors can be used as heating medium for a multiple-effect evaporator.

Multiple-effect Evaporation. Multiple-effect evaporation is the principal means in use for economizing on energy consumption. Most such evaporators operate on a continuous basis, although for a few difficult materials a continuous-batch cycle may be employed. In a multiple-effect evaporator, steam from an outside source is condensed in the heating element of the first effect. If the feed to the effect is at a temperature near the boiling point in the first effect, 1 lb. of steam will evaporate almost 1 lb. of water. The first effect operates at (but is not controlled at) a boiling temperature high enough so that the evaporated water can serve as the heating medium of the second effect. Here almost another pound of water is evaporated, which may go to a condenser if the evaporator is a double effect or may be used as the heating medium of the third effect. This may be repeated for any number of effects. Large evaporators having six and seven effects are common in the pulp and paper industry and evaporators having 10 or more effects have been built. As a first approximation, the *steam economy* of a multiple-effect evaporator will increase in proportion to the number of effects and usually will be somewhat less numerically than the number of effects.

The increased steam economy of a multiple-effect evaporator is gained at the expense of evaporator first cost. Consider a single-effect evaporator operating between a fixed steam temperature of 250°F and a fixed final vacuum corresponding to a boiling point of 125°F. If the feed is at 125°F. and heats of solution are negligible, the evaporator will require about 1 million B.t.u./hr. to evaporate 1000 lb. of water/hr. If the over-all heat-transfer coefficient is 200, a heating surface of 40 sq. ft. is required. If this evaporator is replaced with a double effect, the heat load in each effect will be halved. However, the total available temperature difference of 125°F. will also have to be divided between the two effects. If heat-transfer coefficients do not change, each effect will have the same heating surface as the single effect. Thus the total heat-transfer surface will increase substantially in proportion to the number of effects in the evaporator. This is only an approximation since going from one to two effects means that about half the heat transfer is at a higher temperature level where heat-transfer coefficients are generally higher. On the other hand, operating at lower temperature differences reduces the heat-transfer coefficient for many types of evaporator. If the material has an appreciable boiling-point elevation, this will also lower the available temperature difference. The only accurate means of predicting the changes in steam economy and surface requirements with changes in the number of effects is by detailed heat and material balances together with an analysis of the effect of changes in operating conditions on heat-transfer performance.

The approximate **temperature distribution** in a multiple-effect evaporator is under the control of the designer, but once built, the evaporator establishes its own equilibrium. Basically, the effects are a number of series resistances to heat transfer, each resistance being approximately proportional to $1/U_nA_n$. The total available temperature drop is divided between the effects in proportion to their resistances. If one effect has a higher coefficient or larger area, it will have a lower temperature drop than the others. If one effect starts to scale, its temperature drop will increase at the expense of the temperature drops across the other effects. This provides a convenient means of detecting a drop in heat-transfer coefficient in an effect of an operating evaporator. If the steam pressure and final vacuum do not change, the temperature in the effect that is scaling will decrease and the temperature in the preceding effect will increase. Any attempts at control of the temperatures in individual effects of an evaporator would involve throttling the vapor, which would result in a pressure drop and therefore a loss in available total temperature difference and a loss in capacity.

The feed to a multiple-effect evaporator is usually transferred from one effect to another in series so that the ultimate product concentration is reached only in one effect of the evaporator. In **backward-feed** operation, the raw feed enters the last (coldest) effect, the discharge from this effect becomes the feed to the next to the last effect, and so on until product is discharged from the first effect. This method of operation is advantageous when the feed is cold, since much less liquid must be heated to the higher temperature existing in the early effects. It is also used when the product is so viscous that high temperatures are needed to keep the viscosity low enough to give reasonable heat-transfer coefficients. When product viscosity is high but a hot product is not needed, the liquid from the first effect is sometimes flashed to a lower temperature in one or more stages and the flash vapor added to the vapor from one or more later effects of the evaporator.

In **forward-feed** operation, raw feed is introduced in the first effect and passed from effect to effect parallel to the steam flow. Product is withdrawn from the last effect. This method of operation is advantageous when the feed is hot or when the concentrated product would be damaged or would deposit scale at high temperature. Forward feed simplifies operation when liquor can be transferred by pressure difference alone, thus eliminating all intermediate liquor pumps. When the feed is cold, forward feed gives a low steam economy since an appreciable part of the prime steam is needed to heat the feed to the boiling point and thus accomplishes no evaporation. If forward feed is necessary and feed is cold, steam economy can be improved markedly by preheating the feed in stages with vapor bled from intermediate effects of the evaporator. This usually represents little increase in total heating surface or cost since the feed must be heated in any event and shell-and-tube heat exchangers are generally less expensive per square foot than evaporator heating surface.

Mixed-feed operation is used only for special applications, as when liquor at an intermediate concentration and a certain temperature is desired for additional processing.

Parallel feed involves the introduction of raw feed and the withdrawal of product at each effect of the evaporator. It is used primarily when the feed is substantially saturated and the product is a solid. An example is the evaporation of brine to make common salt. Evaporators of the types shown in Fig. 11-17*b* or *e* are used and the product is withdrawn as a slurry. In this case, parallel feed is desirable because the feed washes impurities from the salt leaving the body.

Heat-recovery systems are frequently incorporated in an evaporator to increase the steam economy. Ideally, product and evaporator condensate should leave the system at a temperature as low as possible. Also, heat should be recovered from these streams by exchange with feed or evaporating liquid at the highest possible temperature. This would normally require separate liquid-liquid heat exchangers, which add greatly to the complexity of the evaporator and are justifiable only in large plants. Normally, the loss in thermodynamic availability due to flashing is tolerated since the flash vapor can then be used directly in the evaporator effects. The most commonly used is a **condensate flash** system in which the condensate from each effect but the first (which normally must be returned to the boiler) is flashed in successive stages to the pressure in the heating element of each succeeding effect of the evaporator. Product flash tanks may also be used in a backward- or mixed-feed evaporator. In a forward-feed evaporator, the principal means of heat recovery may be by use of **feed preheaters** heated by vapor bled from each effect of the evaporator. In this case, condensate may be either flashed as before or used in a separate set of exchangers to accomplish some of the feed preheating. A feed preheated by last-effect vapor may also materially reduce condenser water requirements.

Flash Evaporators. As the feed-to-evaporation ratio is increased in a forward-feed evaporator having the feed heated by vapor bled from each effect, a point is reached where all the vapor is needed to preheat the feed and none is available to heat the succeeding effect. Then all the heating surface is in the feed heaters and the evaporators themselves become merely flash chambers. This limiting case is called a flash evaporator. It was originated as the Alberger process for salt manufacture and is currently most widely used for the manufacture of fresh water from sea water. In this application, sea water is heated in stages by vapor at successively higher temperatures, the last stage being heated by steam from an outside source. The hot sea water is then flashed to the pressure required to provide heat to the next to last preheater, and from there it is flashed successively to the pressure of the remaining preheaters. The vapor condensed in the various preheaters is flashed in turn to the remaining preheaters and the combined condensate from the last preheater is the product of the plant. By suitable baffling, a number of flash and preheating stages can be combined in one vessel with the result that a large number of stages are practical. Such plants have an advantage in simplicity since pumps are required only to supply the raw feed and remove the final concentrate and condensate. However, they require more heating surface than an evaporator of the same steam economy and have a high power consumption because of the large volume of feed and concentrate that must be pumped in relation to the condensate output.

EVAPORATOR CALCULATIONS

Single-effect Evaporators. The **heat requirements** of a single-effect continuous evaporator can be calculated by the usual methods of stoichiometry. If enthalpy data or specific heat and heat of solution data are not available, the heat requirement can be estimated as the sum of the heat needed to raise the feed from feed to product temperature and the heat required to evaporate the water. The latent heat of water is taken at the vapor-head pressure instead of at the product temperature in order to compensate partially for any heat of solution. If sufficient vapor-pressure data are available for the solution, methods are available to calculate the true latent heat from the slope of the Dühring line [Othmer, *Ind. Eng. Chem.*, **32**, 841 (1940)].

The heat requirements in batch evaporation are the same as those in continuous evaporation except that the temperature (and sometimes pressure) of the vapor changes during the course of the cycle. Since the enthalpy of water vapor changes but little relative to latent heat, the difference between continuous and batch heat requirements is almost always negligible. More important usually is the effect of variation of fluid properties, such as viscosity and boiling-point rise, during the cycle. These can only be estimated by a step-by-step calculation.

In selecting the **boiling temperature,** consideration must be given to the effect of temperature on heat-transfer characteristics of the type of evaporator to be used. Some evaporators show a marked drop in coefficient at low temperature—more than enough to offset any gain in available temperature difference. The condenser **cooling-water** temperature and cost must also be considered.

Thermocompression Evaporators. Thermocompression evaporator calculations [Pridgeon, *Chem. & Met. Eng.*, **28,** 1109 (1923); Peter, *Chimia (Switz.)*, **3,** 114 (1949); Petzold, *Chem. Ing. Tech.*, **22,** 147 (1950)] are much the same as single-effect calculations with the added complication that the heat supplied to the evaporator from compressed vapor and other sources must exactly balance the heat requirements. Some knowledge of compressor efficiency is also required. Large axial-flow machines on the order of 500,000 cu. ft./min. capacity may have efficiencies of 80 to 85 per cent. Efficiency drops to about 75 per cent for a 30,000 cu. ft./min. centrifugal compressor. Steam-jet compressors have thermodynamic efficiencies on the order of only 25 to 30 per cent.

Flash Evaporators. The calculation of a heat and material balance on a flash evaporator is relatively easy once it is understood that the temperature rise in each heater and temperature drop in each flasher must all be substantially equal. This equality is almost exact if the condensate from each heater is flashed to the following heater. The steam economy (E/S) may be approximated from

$$\frac{E}{S} = \frac{1.1\Delta T}{A + R + \Delta T/N} \tag{11-8}$$

where ΔT is the total temperature difference, °F., between feed to the first flasher and discharge from the last flasher, N is the number of flash stages, A is the approach between vapor temperature from the first flasher and liquid leaving the heater in which this vapor is condensed (the approach is usually substantially constant for all stages), and R is the boiling-point rise in the first flasher. The temperature differences across each heater are A at the liquid outlet and $(A + \Delta T/N)$ at the liquid inlet to the heater.

Multiple-effect Evaporators. A number of approximate methods have been published for estimating performance and heating-surface requirements of a multiple-effect evaporator [Coates and Pressburg, *Chem. Eng.*, **67** (6), 157 (1960); Coates, *Chem. Eng. Progress*, **45**, 25 (1949); Ray and Carnahan, *Trans. Am. Inst. Chem. Engrs.*, **41**, 253 (1945)]. However, because of the wide variety of methods of feeding and the added complication of feed heaters and condensate flash systems, the only certain way of determining performance is by detailed heat and material balances. Algebraic solutions may be used, but if more than a few effects are involved, trial-and-error methods are usually quicker. These frequently involve trial-and-error within trial-and-error solutions. Usually, if condensate flash systems or feed heaters are involved, it is best to start at the first effect. The basic steps in the calculation are then as follows:

1. Estimate temperature distribution in the evaporator, taking into account boiling-point elevations. If all heating surfaces are to be equal, the temperature drop across each effect will be approximately inversely proportional to the heat-transfer coefficient in that effect.
2. Determine total evaporation required and estimate steam consumption for the number of effects chosen.
3. From assumed feed temperature (forward feed) or feed flow (backward feed) to the first effect and assumed steam flow, calculate evaporation in the first effect. Repeat for each succeeding effect, checking intermediate assumptions as the calculation proceeds. Heat input from condensate flash can be incorporated easily since the condensate flow from the preceding effects will have already been determined.
4. The result of the calculation will be a feed to or a product discharge from the last effect that may not agree with actual requirements. The calculation must then be repeated with a new assumption of steam flow to the first effect.
5. These calculations should yield liquor concentrations in each effect that make possible a revised estimate of boiling-point rises. They also give the quantity of heat that must be transferred in each effect. From the heat loads, assumed temperature differences, and heat-transfer coefficients, heating-surface requirements can be determined. If the distribution of heating surface is not as desired, the entire calculation may need to be repeated with revised estimates of the temperature in each effect.
6. If sufficient data are available, heat-transfer coefficients under the proposed operating conditions can be calculated in more detail and surface requirements readjusted.

Such calculations require considerable judgment to avoid repetitive trials but are usually well worth the effort. Sample calculations are given in the American Institute of Chemical Engineers "Testing Procedure for Evaporators" and by Badger and Banchero ("Introduction to Chemical Engineering," McGraw-Hill, New York, 1955).

Optimization. The primary purpose of evaporator design is to enable production of the necessary amount of satisfactory product at the lowest total cost. This requires economic balance calculations that may include a great number of variables. Among the possible variables are the following:

1. Initial steam pressure vs. cost or availability
2. Final vacuum vs. water temperature, water cost, heat-transfer performance, and product quality
3. Number of effects vs. steam, water, and pump power cost
4. Distribution of heating surface between effects vs. evaporator cost
5. Type of evaporator vs. cost and continuity of operation
6. Materials of construction vs. product quality, tube life, evaporator life, and evaporator cost
7. Corrosion, erosion, and power consumption vs. tube velocity
8. Down time for retubing and repairs
9. Operating labor and maintenance requirements
10. Method of feeding and use of heat-recovery systems
11. Size of recovery heat exchangers
12. Possible withdrawal of steam from an intermediate effect for use elsewhere
13. Entrainment separation requirements

The type of evaporator to be used and the materials of construction are generally selected on the basis of past experience with the material to be concentrated. The method of feeding can usually be decided on the basis of known feed temperature and the properties of feed and product. However, few of the variables listed above are completely independent. For instance, if a large number of effects is to be used, with a consequent low temperature drop per effect, it is impractical to use a natural-circulation evaporator. If expensive materials of construction are desirable, it may be found that the forced-circulation evaporator is the cheapest and that only a few effects are justifiable.

The variable having the greatest influence on total cost is the number of effects in the evaporator. An economic balance can establish the optimum number where the number is not limited by such factors as viscosity, corrosiveness, freezing point, boiling-point rise, or thermal sensitivity. Under present United States conditions, savings in steam and water costs justify the extra capital, maintenance, and power costs of about seven effects in large commercial installations where the properties of the fluid are favorable, as in black-liquor evaporation. Under governmental financing conditions, as for plants to supply fresh water from sea water, evaporators containing over 12 effects can be justified.

As a general rule, the optimum number of effects increases with an increase in steam cost or plant size. Larger plants favor more effects, partly because they make it easier to install heat-recovery systems that increase the steam economy attainable with a given number of effects. Such recovery systems usually do not increase the total surface needed but do require that the heating surface be distributed between more pieces of equipment.

A simplified method is available for estimating the optimum number of effects for simple systems [Reinhold and Connelly, *Chem. Eng. Progress*, **55** (12), 45 (1959)]. However, this can lead to erroneous conclusions when a large number of effects are involved since it neglects such factors as the effects of methods of feeding and heat-recovery systems on steam economy. The preferred method of optimizing the number of effects is on the basis of detailed estimates of plant performance and cost. In this way, it is also possible to investigate the effect of minor variables on plant cost. Thus, the most common evaporator design is based on the use of the same heating surface in each effect. This is by no means essential since few evaporators are "standard" or involve the use of the same patterns. In fact there is no reason why all effects in an evaporator must be of the same type. Figure 11-20, for instance, indicates that the cheapest salt evaporator might use propeller calandrias for the early effects and forced-circulation effects at the low-temperature end where their higher cost per square foot is more than offset by higher heat-transfer coefficients.

Bonilla [*Trans. Am. Inst. Chem. Engrs.*, **41**, 529 (1945)] has developed a simplified method for distributing the heating surface in a multiple-effect evaporator to achieve minimum cost. If the cost of the evaporator per square foot of heating surface is constant throughout, then minimum cost and area will be achieved if the ratio of area to temperature difference $A/\Delta T$ is the same for all effects. If the cost per square foot z varies, as when different tube materials or evaporator types are used, then $zA/\Delta T$ should be the same for all effects.

EVAPORATOR ACCESSORIES

Condensers. The vapor from the last effect of an evaporator is usually removed by a condenser. **Surface condensers** are employed where mixing of condensate with condenser cooling water is not desired. They are for the most part shell-and-tube condensers with vapor on the shell side and multipass flow of cooling water on the tube side. Heat loads, temperature differences, sizes, and costs are usually of the same order of magnitude as for another effect of the evaporator. Surface condensers use more cooling water and are so much more expensive that they are never used where a direct-contact condenser is suitable.

The most common type of direct-contact condenser is the countercurrent **barometric condenser,** in which vapor is condensed by rising against a rain of cooling water. The condenser is set high enough so that water can discharge by gravity from the vacuum in the condenser. Such condensers are inexpensive and are economical on water consumption. They can usually be relied on to maintain a vacuum corresponding to a saturated vapor temperature within 5°F. of the water temperature leaving the condenser [How, *Chem. Eng.*, **63** (2), 174 (1956)]. The ratio of water consumption to vapor condensed can be determined from the following equation:

$$\frac{\text{Water flow}}{\text{Vapor flow}} = \frac{H_v - (T_2 - 32)}{T_2 - T_1} \qquad (11\text{-}9)$$

where H_v = vapor enthalpy (B.t.u./lb.) and T_1 and T_2 = water temperatures entering and leaving the condenser, °F. Another type of direct-contact condenser is the **jet** or **wet condenser,** which makes use of high-velocity jets of water to both condense the vapor and force the non-condensable gases out the tailpipe. This type of condenser is frequently placed below barometric height and requires a pump to remove the mixture of water and gases. Jet condensers usually require more water than the more common barometric-type condensers and cannot be throttled easily to conserve water when operating at low evaporation rates.

Vent Systems. Non-condensable gases may be present in the evaporator vapor as a result of leakage, air dissolved in the feed, or decomposition reactions in the feed. When the vapor is condensed in the succeeding effect, the non-condensables increase in concentration and impede heat transfer. This is partially because of the reduced partial pressure of vapor in the mixture but mainly because the vapor flow toward the heating surface creates a film of poorly conducting gas at the interface. The section on Heat Transfer in Evaporators provides means of estimating the effect of non-condensable gases on the steam-film coefficient. The concentration at which the over-all coefficient is affected is quite low and is lowest in evaporators having high over-all coefficients and in evaporators having poorly defined steam-flow paths.

In any event, non-condensable gases should be vented well before their concentration reaches 10 per cent. Since gas concentrations are difficult to measure, the usual practice is to overvent. This means that an appreciable amount of vapor can be lost.

To help reduce losses in steam economy, the venting is usually done from the steam chest of one effect to the steam chest of the next. In this way, excess vapor in the vents does useful evaporation at a steam economy only about one less than the over-all steam economy. Only where there are large amounts of non-condensable gases present, as in beet-sugar evaporation, is it desirable to pass the vents directly to the condenser to avoid serious losses in heat-transfer rates. In such cases, it can be worthwhile to recover heat from the vents in separate heat exchangers, which preheat the entering feed.

The non-condensable gases eventually reach the condenser (unless vented from an effect above atmospheric pressure to the atmosphere or to auxiliary vent condensers). These gases will be supplemented by air dissolved in the condenser water and by carbon dioxide given off on decomposition of bicarbonates in the water if a barometric condenser is used. These gases may be removed by the use of a water-jet-type condenser but are usually removed by a separate vacuum pump.

The vacuum pump is usually of the steam-jet type if high-pressure steam is available. These are usually two-stage units for absolute pressures below about 4 in. of mercury. A separate large single-stage (hogging) ejector is frequently provided to assist in rapid evacuation of the system on startup. Where high-pressure steam is not available, more expensive mechanical pumps may be used. These may be either a water-ring (Hytor) type or a reciprocating pump. Reciprocating vacuum pumps usually have large-diameter cylinders and special precautions must be taken to avoid carry-over of water with the gases. They may be provided with hot-water jackets to avoid condensation in the cylinders. Reciprocating vacuum pumps usually will show the lowest total operating cost because of their high efficiency, but can be a source of heavy maintenance.

Little data are available for determining the capacity required of vacuum pumps. Leakage tests on small sea-water evaporators (The Griscom Russell Co., Office of Saline Water, *Res. & Dev. Rept.* 18, 1958) gave rates on the order of 0.2 lb. of air/hr. per 1000 lin. in. of joint (flanges, screwed fittings, pump shafts and casing joints, valve stem and bonnet joints, etc.). These tests were made with a vacuum below half atmospheric pressure; so flow rates should have been independent of vacuum. Power-plant standards for air leakage range from 10 lb./hr., for systems in which the vapor flow from the turbine to the condenser is less than 5000 lb./hr., up to 20 lb./hr. at vapor flows of 50,000 to 75,000 lb./hr. These figures are doubled when the prime movers are steam engines instead of turbines.

The primary source of non-condensable gases usually is air dissolved in the condenser water. Figure 11-32

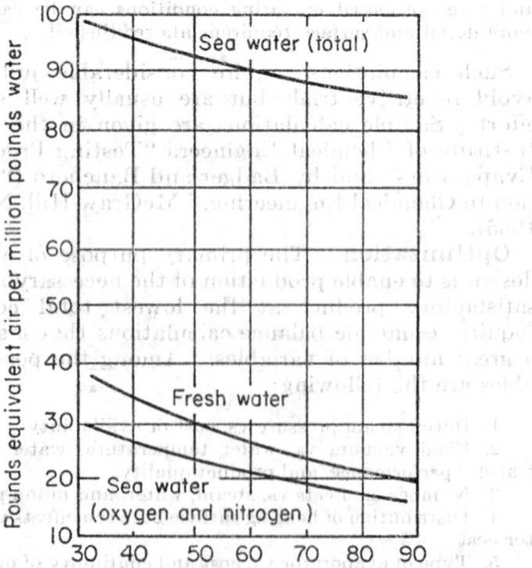

FIG. 11-32. Gas content of water saturated at atmospheric pressure.

shows dissolved gas content of fresh water and sea water, calculated as equivalent air. The lower curve for sea water includes only dissolved oxygen and nitrogen. The upper curve includes carbon dioxide that can be evolved by complete breakdown of bicarbonate in sea water. Breakdown of bicarbonates is usually not appreciable in a condenser but may go almost to completion in a sea-water evaporator. The large increase in gas volume as a result of possible bicarbonate breakdown is illustrative of the uncertainties involved in sizing vacuum systems.

By far the largest load on the vacuum pump is water vapor carried with the non-condensable gases. Standard power-plant practice assumes that the mixture leaving a surface condenser will have been cooled 7.5°F. below the saturation temperature of the vapor. This usually corresponds to about 2.5 lb. of water vapor/lb. of air. One advantage of the countercurrent barometric condenser is that it can cool the gases almost to the temperature of the incoming water and thus reduce the amount of water vapor carried with the air.

Salt Removal. When an evaporator is used to make a crystalline product, a number of means are available for concentrating and removing the salt from the system. The simplest is to provide settling space in the evaporator itself. This is done in the types shown in Fig. 11-17*b*, *c*, and *e* by providing a relatively quiescent zone in which the salt can settle. Sufficiently high slurry densities can usually be achieved in this manner to reach the limit of pumpability. The evaporators are usually placed above barometric height so that the slurry can be discharged intermittently on a short time cycle. This permits the use of high velocities in large lines that have little tendency to plug.

If the amount of salts crystallized is on the order of a ton an hour or less, a salt trap may be used. This is simply a receiver that is connected to the bottom of the evaporator and is closed off from the evaporator periodically for emptying. The salt receiver may contain a screen bottom to permit draining residual liquor and a side door through which the solids may be raked. Alternatively, the entire contents of solids and liquid may be dumped through a bottom valve after venting the receiver to the atmosphere. Such traps are useful when insufficient headroom is available for gravity removal of the solids. However, traps require a great deal of labor, give frequent trouble with the shutoff valves, and also can upset evaporator operation completely if a trap is reconnected to the evaporator without first displacing all air with feed liquor.

EVAPORATOR COSTS

Capital Cost. Approximate **selling prices** of various types of evaporators are shown in Fig. 11-33 [Zimmerman and Lavine, "Chemical Engineering Costs," Industrial Research Service, Dover, N.H., 1950; Gushin, *Chem. Eng.*, **65** (12), 187 (1958); and private communication]. These prices include all auxiliary equipment that a manufacturer would normally supply, such as vapor piping, barometric condenser, steam jets, condensate flash tanks, and in some cases, liquor piping and pumps. Costs are correlated against total heating surface in all effects of the evaporator. This permits inclusion of such equipment as a vacuum system. Appreciable errors can result if the evaporator under consideration does not contain roughly the same number of effects as the ones on which the curves of Fig. 11-33 are based. These range from single effects for curves 4, 5, and 12 through six and seven effects for curves 1 and 2.

Estimated **installed costs** of a number of types of evaporators are shown in Fig. 11-34 [Chilton, *Chem. Eng.*, **56** (6), 97 (1949); and private communication]. These costs include foundation, steelwork, evaporator

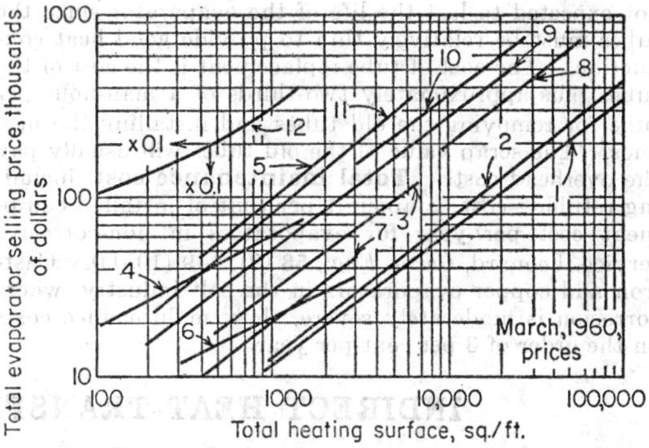

FIG. 11-33. Approximate evaporator selling prices. (1) Long-tube-vertical, steel body, steel tubes (12 gage). (2) Long-tube-vertical, steel body, aluminum brass tubes (16 gage). (3) Long-tube-vertical, cast-iron body, copper tubes. (4) Long-tube-vertical, rubber-lined body, Karbate tubes. (5) Long-tube-vertical, all nickel, 700°F., 300 lb/sq. in. (6) Horizontal or short-tube vertical, cast-iron body, copper tubes. (7) Horizontal tube-steel shell, admiralty tubes (100 lb./sq. in. shell). (8) Propeller calandria, cast-iron body, copper tubes. (9) Forced-circulation, cast-iron body, copper tubes. (10) Forced-circulation, all-monel body, 90/10 Cu-Ni tubes. (11) Forced-circulation, nickel–cast-iron body, nickel tubes. (12) Agitated film, type 316 stainless steel.

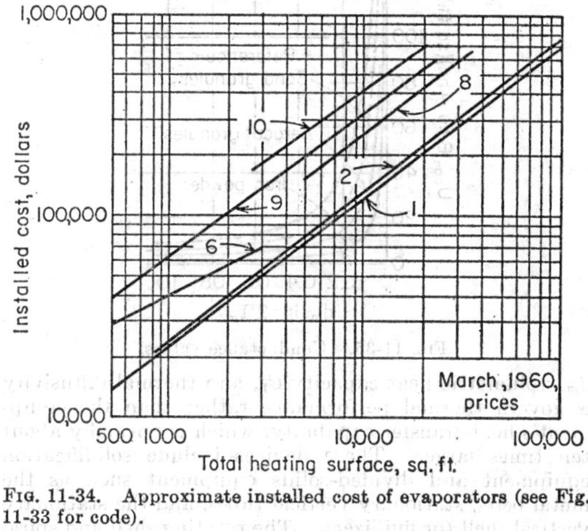

FIG. 11-34. Approximate installed cost of evaporators (see Fig. 11-33 for code).

assembly, pumps, piping, insulation, painting, and a moderate degree of instrumentation. When costs of evaporators constructed of other materials are desired, the incremental cost will be approximately equal to the change in tube cost if only the tubes are changed. It is usually impossible to estimate the effect of a change in body material—in some cases, welded alloy bodies are cheaper than cast-iron bodies.

Operating Cost. Operating labor requirements depend mainly on the proximity of the evaporator to other process units where occasional assistance and maintenance help can be obtained. Normally, one man can easily control an evaporator of any number of effects —several such evaporators if a moderate number of control instruments are used [Bergstrom and Lientz, *Paper Trade J.*, **124** (1), 6 (1947)]. Occasional maintenance labor is required for the repacking of pumps and valves and the repair of piping. The main maintenance requirement is for mechanical cleaning and for tube replacement. The tubes in an evaporator are normally not expected to last the life of the evaporator since the tubes must be relatively thin to provide good heat conduction. The cost of tube replacement is the cost of the tubes plus approximately two-thirds of a man-hour per tube for removing the old tubes and installing the new ones. The scrap value of the old tubes will usually pay the overhead costs. **Total maintenance cost,** including retubing cost, is about 1 per cent of installed equipment cost per year for evaporators in non-corrosive service [Leonard, *Chem. Eng.*, **58** (9), 149 (1951)]. Cast-iron and copper evaporators in the salt industry, where corrosion is moderately severe, show maintenance costs on the order of 3 per cent per year.

EVAPORATOR OPERATION

Control of an evaporator requires more than proper instrumentation. Operator logs should reflect changes in basic characteristics, as by use of *pseudo heat-transfer coefficients,* which can detect obstructions to heat flow, hence to capacity. These are merely the ratio of any convenient measure of heat flow to the temperature drop across each effect. *Dilution* by wash and seal water should be monitored since it absorbs evaporative capacity. Detailed tests, routine measurements, and operating problems are covered more fully in "Testing Procedure for Evaporator" (*loc. cit.*) and by Standiford [*Chem. Eng. Progress,* **58** (1962)].

INDIRECT HEAT-TRANSFER EQUIPMENT FOR SOLIDS

The equipment available for **heat-processing solids**[1] bears little resemblance to its counterparts for heat transfer to liquid and gases. Indirect heat transfer for solids is by *conduction.* Performance of devices that handle the solids burden in a static or laminar flowing bed can be determined from the heat-conductance rate (U_{co}) charts exemplified by Fig. 11-35. The burden's layer thickness

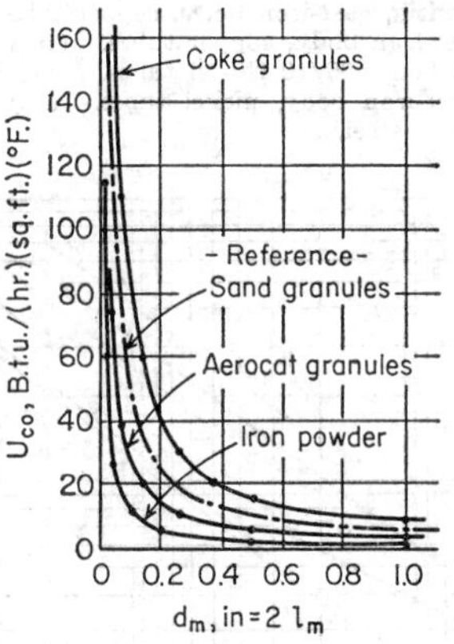

FIG. 11-35. Conductance values.

d_m, volumetric heat capacity C_p, and thermal diffusivity α govern thermal performance rather than the equipment's heat-transfer capability, which is normally about ten times larger. These devices include solidification equipment and divided-solids equipment such as the metal belts, stationary vertical tubes, and the stationary vertical shell (or fluidizer). The rotating shell and spiral conveyor devices can be considered *continuously agitated kettles.* These and the fusion *batch* tank and kettle equipment (see Fig. 11-38*a* and *b*) have their heat-transfer performance influenced in accordance with an adaptation from the basic liquid-phase kettle equations (Auckley, *Chem. Eng.,* August, 1960, p. 133) which state

$$U_{co} \propto (a)(C_p)(D)^x(N)^y(\cos\phi)(\text{per cent fill})^z \qquad (11\text{-}10)$$

where a is a constant; C_p = volumetric heat capacity, B.t.u./cu. ft.; D = vessel diameter, ft.; N = turning speed, rpm; ϕ = angle of repose for the divided-solids mass. This has the D, N, and ϕ terms in common with kiln and spiral travel-time equations vital for material-handling aspects. Present thinking lumps the D, N, and $\cos\phi$ factors together into an effective-diffusivity term to yield

$$U_{co} \propto (a)(C_p)(\alpha_e)^v(\text{per cent fill})^z \qquad (11\text{-}11)$$

[1] A more thorough treatment of terminology and mathematical concepts for heat-transfer equipment for processing solids material was made by A. D. Holt [*Chem. Eng.,* **69,** 107 (Jan. 8, 1962)].

which is analogous to the static condition where

$$U_{co} \propto (b)(C_p)(\alpha)(d_m)^{-1} \qquad (11\text{-}12)$$

Vibratory devices, although constantly agitating the solids bed, maintain a quite constant U_{co} value throughout the layer depth within their working range so

$$U_{co} \propto (c)\ (C_p)\ (\alpha) \qquad (11\text{-}13)$$

INDIRECT HEAT-TRANSFER EQUIPMENT FOR SOLIDIFICATION

General. A frequent operation in the chemical field is the removal of heat from a material in a liquid state to effect its *solidification* to the solid state. When the operation is carried on batchwise, it is termed "casting," but when done continuously, it is termed "flaking." The heat-transfer rate q_{co} is expressed in terms of B.t.u./hr./sq. ft. Because of the substantial q_{co} values and temperature variations, jacketed types are limited to an initial temperature of 450°F. Higher temperatures (to 600°F.) require extreme care in jacket design and cooling-liquid flow pattern. Best performance and greatest capacity are obtained by (1) holding precooling to the minimum and (2) optimizing the cake thickness (see Fig. 11-35), which cannot always be done from the heat-transfer standpoint as size specifications for the end product may dictate thickness.

Table Type. This is a simple flat metal sheet with slightly upturned edges and jacketed on the underside for coolant flow. This was the mainstay of food processors. The table types are still widely used where production is in small batches, where considerable variation hatch to hatch occurs, for pilot investigation, and when the cost of continuous devices is unjustifiable Slab thicknesses are usually in the ½- to 1-in. range. These units are "home-made" with no standards available. Initial cost is low but operating labor is high.

Vibratory Type. This type (Fig. 11-36) takes advantage of the burden's special needs and the *characteristic* of *vibratory actuation.* A flammable burden requires the use of an inert atmosphere over it and a suitable nonhazardous fluid in the jacket. The vibratory action permits construction of rigid self-cleaning chambers with simple flexible connections. When solidification has been completed and vibrators started the intense vibratory motion of the whole deck structure (as a rigid unit) breaks the friable cake (up to 3 in.) free, shatters it into lumps, and conveys it up over the dam to discharge. Heat-transfer performance is good with U_{co} at about 12, the q_{co} values in the order of 3700. Application of timing-cycle controls and a surge hopper for the discharge solids makes operation of the caster automatic and operation and subsequent equipment continuous.

Belt Types. The patented *metal-belt* type (Fig. 11-37*a*), termed the "water-bed" conveyor, features a

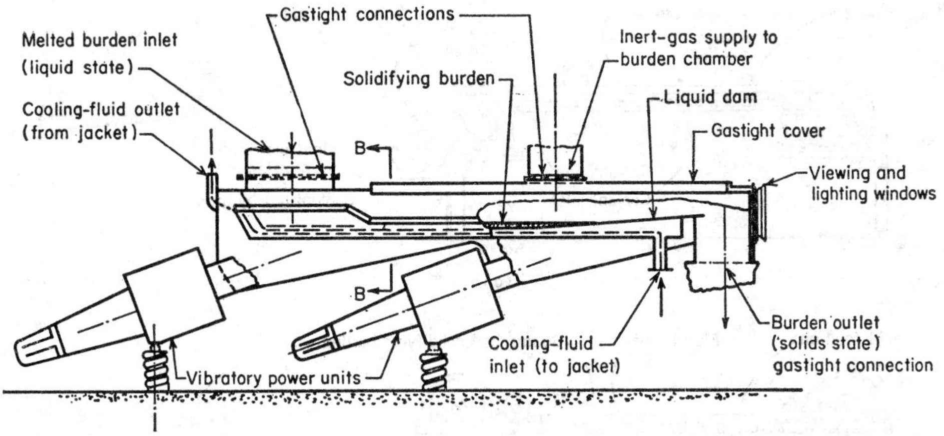

Fig. 11-36. Heat-transfer equipment for batch solidification. Vibrating-conveyor type. (*Courtesy of The Jeffrey Manufacturing Co.*)

thin wall, a well-agitated fluid side for a thin water film (no rigid welded jackets to fail), stainless-steel or Swedish-iron belt "floated" on the water with aid of guides, no removal knife, and cleanability. It is mostly used for medium ⅛- to ⅝-in. cake at speeds ranging to 50 ft./min. with 150-ft. pulley centers common. For 1- to 1¼-in. cake another belt on top to give two-sided cooling is frequently used. Applications are in food operations for cooling to harden candies, cheeses, gelatins, margarines, gums, etc.; in chemical operations for solidification of sulfur, greases, resins, soaps, waxes, chloride salts, and some insecticides. Heat transfer is good with a sulfur solidification showing values of q_{co} 1850 and U_{co} 17 for a $\frac{5}{16}$-in. cake.

The *submerged metal belt* (Fig. 11-37*b*) is a special version of the metal belt to meet the peculiar handling properties of pitch in its solidification process. Although adhesive to a dry metal wall, pitch will not stick to the submerged wetted belt or rubber edge strips. Submergence helps to offset the very poor thermal conductivity through two-sided heat transfer.

Rotating-drum Type. This type (Fig. 11-37*c* and *d*) is not an adaptation of a material-handling device (though volumetric material throughput is a first consideration) but is designed for heat-transfer service. It is well engineered, established, and widely used. Improvements and a new version (Fig. 11-37*d*) have been effected recently. This new drum type is best suited to thin ($\frac{1}{64}$- to ¼-in.) cake production. For temperatures to 300°F. the coolant water is piped in and siphoned out. Spray application of coolant water to the inside is employed for high-temperature work permitting feed temperatures to at least 1000°F. which are double those for jacketed equipment. Vaporizing refrigerants are readily applicable for very low temperature work. The burden must have a definite solidification temperature to assure proper pick-up from the feed pan. This limitation is now overcome by side feeding through an auxiliary rotating spreader roll. Application limits are further extended by special feed devices for burdens having oxidation-sensitive and/or supercooling characteristics. The standard double-drum model turns down with adjustable roll spacing to control sheet thickness. The newer twin-drum model (Fig. 11-37*d*) turns up, and though subject to variable cake thickness, it handles viscous and indefinite solidification-temperature-point burden materials well. Drums have been successfully applied to a wide range of chemical products, both inorganic and organic, related pharmaceutical compounds, waxes, soaps, insecticides, food products to a limited extent (including lard cooling), and even flake-ice production. Heat-transfer performance, in terms of q_{co} reported, is: for an 80°C. melting-point wax, 2500; for an 80°C. melting point hydrated salt, 5400; for a 130°C. melting point organic chemical, 6500; and for high 318°C. melting point caustic soda (water sprayed in drum), 30,000 to 40,000 with a 60 to 80 U_{co} value. Similar rotating-drum indirect heat-transfer equipment is also extensively used for drying duty on liquids and thick slurries of solids.

Rotating-shelf Type. The patented *Roto-shelf* type (Fig. 11-37*e*) developed in 1958 features: (1) a large heat-transfer surface provided over a small floor space and in a small building volume, (2) easy floor cleaning, (3) nonhazardous machinery, (4) stainless-steel surfaces, (5) good control range, and (6) substantial capacity by providing as needed 1 to 10 shelves operated in parallel. It is best suited for thick-cake production and burden materials having an indefinite solidification temperature. Solidification of liquid sulfur into ½- to ¾-in.-thick lumps is a successful application. Heat transfer, by liquid-coolant circulation through jackets, limits feed temperatures to 400° to 450°F. Heat-transfer rate, controlled by the thick cake rather than construction, should be equivalent to the belt type. Thermal performance is aided by applying water sprayed directly to the burden top to obtain two-side cooling.

INDIRECT HEAT-TRANSFER EQUIPMENT FOR SOLIDS MELTING OR FUSION

General. The thermal operation here is the *reversal* of the previous solidification operation. The indirect heat-transfer equipment suitable for one operation is not suitable for the other because of the material handling rather than thermal aspects. A definite and ranging temperature on transformation is of little import in the equipment selection. The burden is much agitated (see p. 11-42) but the beds are deep. Only fair U_{co} values may be expected although q_{co} values are good.

Horizontal-tank Type. This type (Fig. 11-38*a*) is used to transfer heat for melting or cooking dry powdered solids, rendering lard from meat-scrap solids, and drying divided solids. U_{co} values are 3 to 15 for drying and 5 to 25 for vacuum and/or solvent recovery.

Vertical Agitated-kettle Type. Shown in Fig. 11-38*b*, this type is used to cook, melt to the liquid state, and provide or remove reaction heat for solids that vary greatly in "body" during the process so that material

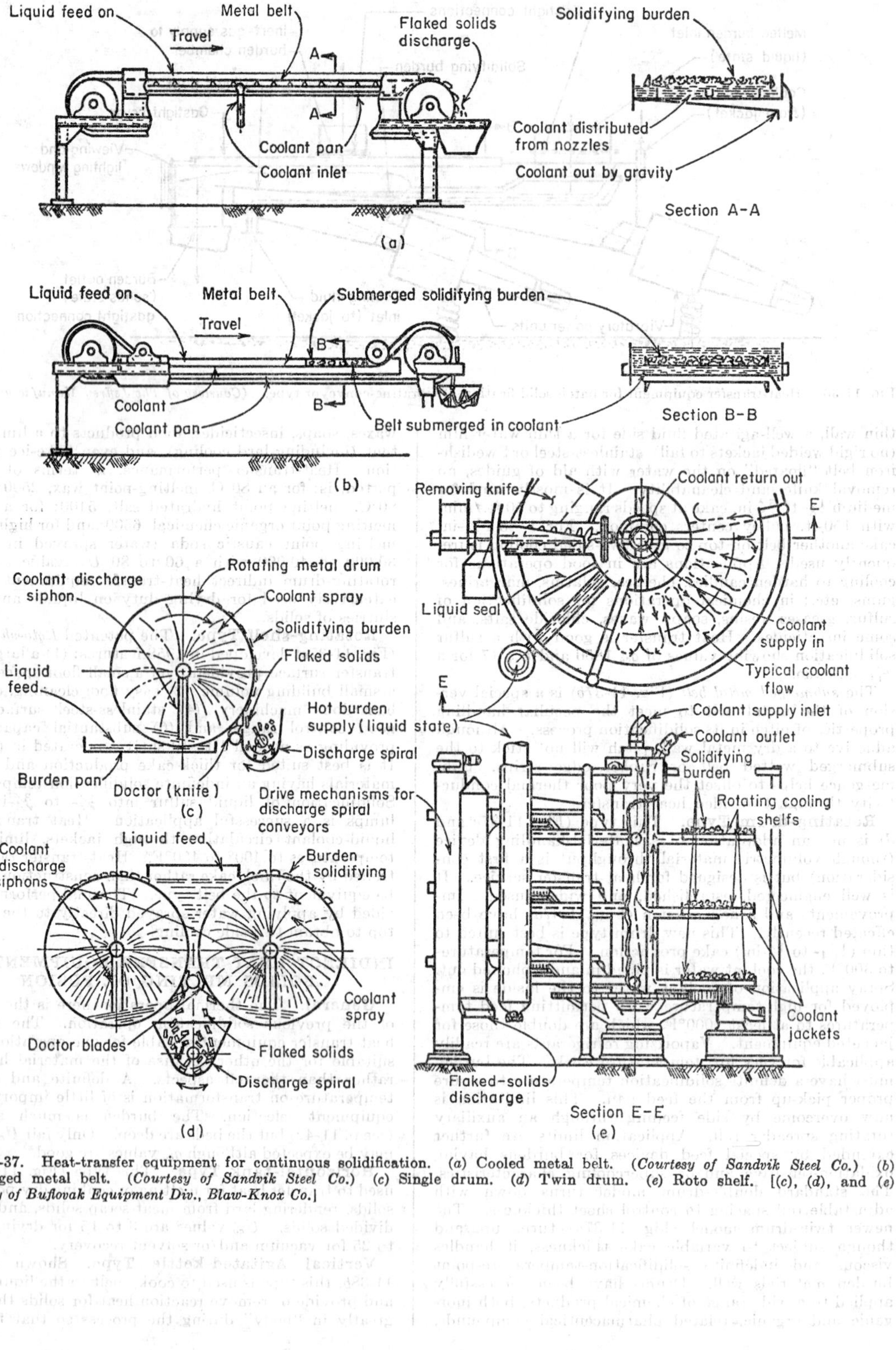

Fig. 11-37. Heat-transfer equipment for continuous solidification. (*a*) Cooled metal belt. (*Courtesy of Sandvik Steel Co.*) (*b*) Submerged metal belt. (*Courtesy of Sandvik Steel Co.*) (*c*) Single drum. (*d*) Twin drum. (*e*) Roto shelf. [(*c*), (*d*), and (*e*) *Courtesy of Buflovak Equipment Div., Blaw-Knox Co.*]

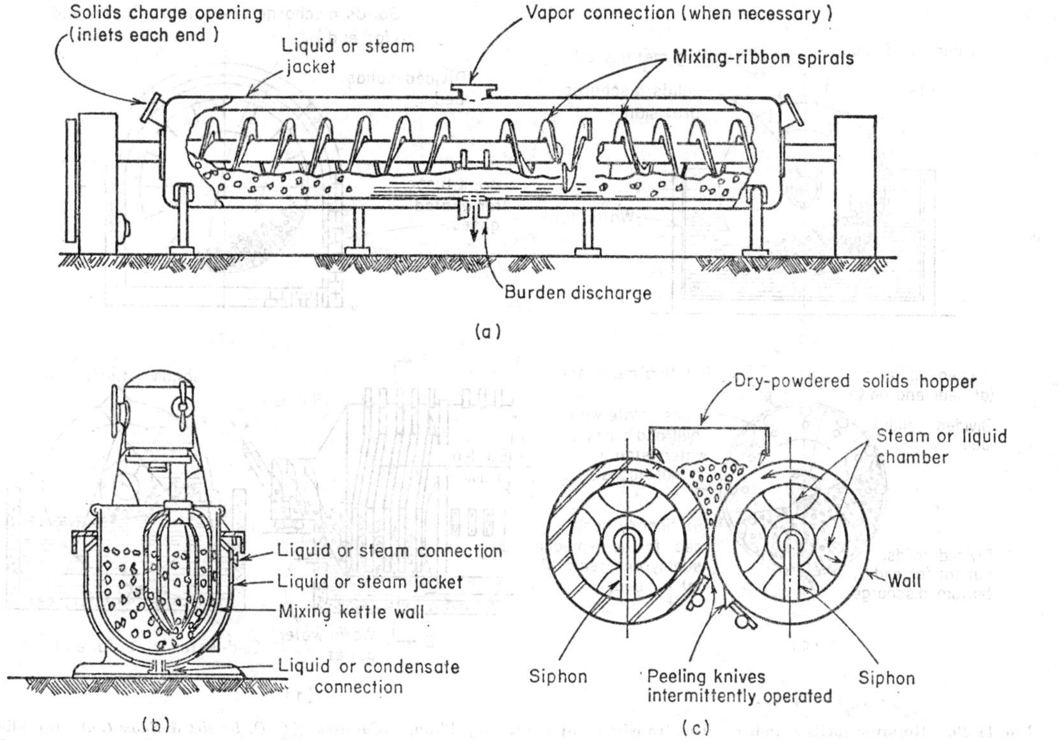

FIG. 11-38. Heat-transfer equipment for melting or fusion of solids. (*a*) Horizontal-tank type. (*Courtesy of Struthers-Wells Co.*) (*b*) Agitated kettle. (*Courtesy of Read-Standard Div., Capital Products Co.*) (*c*) Double-drum mill. (*Courtesy of Farrel-Birmingham Co.*)

handling is a real problem. The virtues are simplicity and 100 per cent cleanability. Either often outweighs the poor heat-transfer aspect. They exist from the small jacketed type illustrated to huge cast-iron direct underfired bowls for calcining gypsum. Temperature limits vary with construction; the simpler jackets allow temperature to 600° to 700°F. (as with Dowtherm), which is not true of all jacketed equipment.

Mill Type. Figure 11-38*c* shows one model of a roll construction used. Note the ruggedness as it is a *power device,* as well as one *for indirect* heat transfer, employed to knead and heat a mixture of dry powdered-solid ingredients with the objective of reacting and reforming via fusion to a one-piece solid. In this compounding operation frictional heat generated by the kneading may require heat-flow reversal (by cooling). Heat-flow control and temperature-level considerations often predominate over heat-transfer performance. Power and mixing considerations, rather than heat transfer, similarly govern. The two-roll mill shown is employed in compounding the raw plastic, rubber, and rubberlike elastometer stocks. Multiple-roll mills less knives (termed calenders) are used for continuous sheet or film production in widths up to 92 in. Similar equipment is employed in the chemical compounding of inks, dyes, paint pigments, and the like.

INDIRECT HEAT-TRANSFER EQUIPMENT FOR DIVIDED SOLIDS

General. Most equipment for this service is some *adaptation* of a *material-handling* device whether or not the transport ability is desired. The old vertical tube and relatively new vertical shell (fluidizer) are exceptions. Material-handling considerations, plant transport needs, power, and maintenance are prime considerations in equipment selection, frequently overshadowing pure heat-transfer and capital-cost considerations. Material handling is generally the most important aspect. Material-handling characteristics of the divided solids vary during the heat processing. The body changes are usually important in drying, occasionally significant for heating, and on occasion important for cooling. The ability to minimize effects of changes is a major consideration in equipment selection. Dehydration operations, often miscalled drying, are better performed on contactive apparatus (see Sec. 20) that provides air to carry off water vapor on its release—before a semiliquid form occurs.

Some of the equipment is convertible from heat removal to heat supply by simply changing the temperature level of the fluid or air. Others require an auxiliary change. Still others require constructional changes varying from minor to completely new equipment. Temperature limits for the equipment generally vary with the thermal operation. The *kind* of *thermal operation* has a *major effect* on heat-transfer values. For drying, U_{co} values are substantially higher in the presence of moisture of the constant-rate period than in finishing. However, a stiff "body" occurrence due to moisture can prevent a normal "mixing" with an adverse effect on U_{co}.

Stationary-shell Type. Known as the cylindrical fluidizer, this operates with a bed of fluidized solids. It is a "newcomer" to this field as an indirect heat-transfer version of the contactive type in Sec. 20. An application disadvantage is the need for batch operations unless

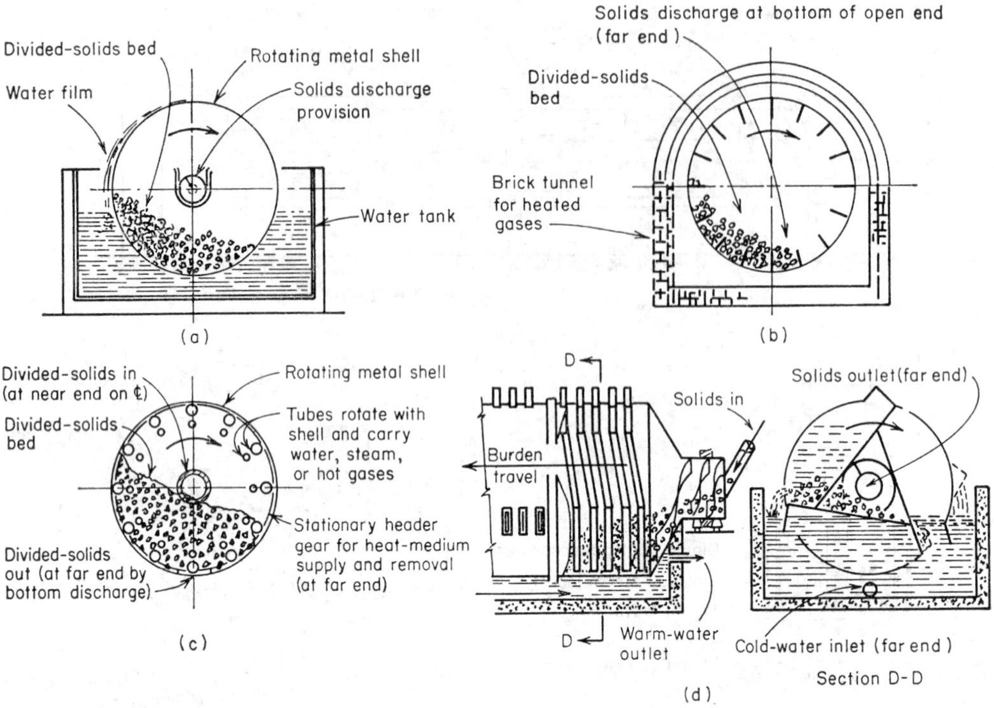

Fig. 11-39. Rotating shells as indirect heat-transfer equipment. (*a*) Plain. (*Courtesy of C. O. Bartlet & Snow Co.*) (*b*) Flighted. (*Courtesy of C. O. Bartlet & Snow Co.*) (*c*) Tubed. For notations and side view, see Fig. 11-35. (*Courtesy of General American Transportation Corp.*) (*d*) Deep-finned type. (*Courtesy of Link-Belt Co.*).

some short circuiting can be tolerated. Solids-cooling applications are few as they can be more effectively accomplished by the fluidizing gas via the contactive mechanism cited in Sec. 10. Heating applications are many and varied. These are subject to one shortcoming, which is the dissipation of the heat input by carry-off in the fluidizing gas. Heat-transfer performance, for the indirect mode to solids, has been phenomenal with U_{co} values in the 100 to 150 range. This device with its thin film does for solids what the falling-film and other thin-film techniques do for fluids, as shown by Holt ("Continuous Heat-processing of Granular and/or Powdered Solids—in Dry State Fluidization," 4th National Heat-transfer Conference, Paper 11, August, 1960).

Stationary-tube Type. This is a single-pass tube bundle in a vertical shell with the divided solids flowing by gravity in the tubes. It is little used for solids. A major difficulty in divided-solids applications is the problem of charging and discharging with uniformity. A second is poor heat-transfer rates, values of which can be read from charts of Fig. 11-35 using $d_m = 2\,(0.233 \times \text{tube diameter})$ for speeds up to 10 ft./min. Higher speeds show some improvement but soon pass the realm of practical material handling.

Rotating-shell Devices. These (see Fig. 11-39) are installed horizontally whereas the stationary-shell installations are vertical. Material-handling aspects are of prime importance to thermal performance (see p. 11-42). Thermal results are customarily given in terms of U_{co} on the *basis* of the *total area* provided, which varies greatly with the design type. The *effective use*, chiefly per cent fill factor, varies widely to reduce the worth of stated U_{co} values. The fill factor and other variables make any typical U_{co} values nearly "meaningless." For detail refer to Friedman and Marshall [*Chem. Eng. Progress*, **45**, 482, 573 (1949)]. These devices are used on any of the three operations of cooling, heating, or drying and are the workhorses for heat-processing divided solids in the large-capacity range. Different modifications are requisite for each of the three operations.

The *plain* type (Fig. 11-39*a*) features simplicity and yet versatility through end-construction modifications enabling wide and varied application. As a heat-transfer device this plain type provides a 3.14 A/D ratio with a nominal 0.3 use for an effective A/D ratio of 1.0. Thermal performance is strongly affected by the "body" characteristics because of its dependency for material handling on frictional contact. Hence performance ranges from well-agitated beds with good thin-film conductance rates to slightly agitated beds with poor thick-film conductance rates. Temperature limits in application are: (1) low-range cooling with shell dipped in water—750°F. and less; (2) intermediate cooling with forced circulation of tank water—to 1400°F.; (3) primary cooling—above 1400°F.—water copiously sprayed and loading kept light; (4) low-range heating, below steam temperature, hot-water dip; and (5) high-range heating by tempered combustion gases or ribbon radiant-gas burners.

The *flighted* type (Fig. 11-39*b*) is a first-step modification of the plain type. The simple flight addition improves heat-transfer performance. The A/D rating is the same. This type is most effective on semifluid burdens which slide readily. Flighted models are restricted from applications where soft-cake sticking occurs, breakage must be minimized, and abrasion is severe. A special flighting is one having the cross section

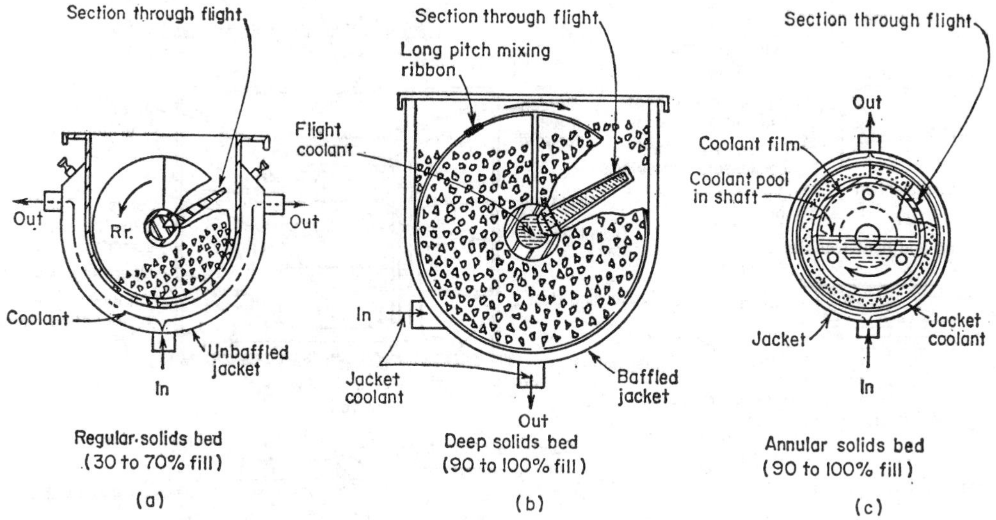

FIG. 11-40. Spiral-conveyor adaptations as heat-transfer equipment. (*a*) Standard jacketed solid flight. (*Courtesy of The Jeffrey Mfg. Co.*) (*b*) Large spiral, hollow flight. (*Courtesy of Reitz Mfg. Co.*) (*c*) Small spiral, large shaft. (*Courtesy of Fuller Co.*)

comparted into four lesser areas with ducts between. Hot gases are drawn through the ducts en route from the outer oven to the stack to provide about 75 per cent more heating surface, improving efficiency and capacity with a modest cost increase. Another similar unit has the flights made in a triangular-duct cross section and hot gases drawn through them.

The *tubed* type (Fig. 11-39*c*) features a high effective (1.5 to 2.25) A/D ratio provision and good mixing with the objective of increased heat-transfer performance. Tube-side fluid may be water, steam, or combustion gas. Bottom discharge slots in the shell are used to allow heat medium supply and removal through the ends; these restrict wide-range loading and make the tubed type inapplicable for floody materials. These units are seldom applicable for sticky soft-caking, scaling, heat-sensitive burdens. They are not recommended for abrasive materials. This type has high thermal efficiency because heat loss is minimized. Heat-transfer performances expressed as average U_{co} values are: water 6, steam 6 with q_{co} reliably constant at 1200 B.t.u./(hr.)(sq. ft.), and gas 3 with a high Δt.

The patented *deep-finned* type in Fig. 11-39*d* is a 1959 design, named the "Roto-fin cooler." It features provision of a high A/D ratio (12.7 with a 0.35 use in a 6 ft. 4 in. diameter size), loading with a small layer thickness, excellent mixing to give a good effective diffusivity value, and a thin fluid-side film. Unlike other rotating-shell types, it is installed horizontally, and the burden is moved positively by the fins acting as an Archimedes spiral. Rotational speed and spiral pitch determine travel time rather than the general rotating-shell equations. For cooling it is applicable to both secondary- and intermediate-cooling-range duties. Applications include solids in the small lump (¾ in.) and granular (¼ to 0 in.) range size with no larger pieces to plug the fins, solids that have a free-flowing body characteristic with no sticking or caking tendencies, and drying of solids that have a low moisture and powder content unless special modifications are made for substantial vapor and dust handling. Thermal performance is very good with U_{co} values to 20 with 10 to 11 nominal for cooling based on the total area provided (nearly double those reported for other indirect rotaries).

Conveyor-belt Devices. The *metal-belt* type (Fig. 11-37*a*) is the only device in this classification of material-handling equipment that has had serious adaptative effort expended on it for *indirect heat-transfer* service with divided solids. It features a lightweight construction of a large area with a thin metal wall. Indirect-cooling applications have been made with poor thermal performance, as could be expected with a static layer. Mixing plowlike auxiliary devices, which are considered an absolute necessity to secure any worthwhile results for this service, restrict applications.

Spiral-conveyor Devices, General. Figure 11-40 illustrates the major adaptations of this widely used class of material-handling equipment to indirect heat-transfer purposes. These conveyors can be considered for heat-transfer purposes as *continuously agitated kettles* (see p. 11-42). The adaptation of Fig. 11-40*b* offers a batch-operated version for evaporation duty. For this service all are package-priced, package-shipped items requiring few, if any, auxiliaries.

The *standard jacketed solid-flight* type (Fig. 11-40*a*) is the standard low-cost (parts-basis priced) material-handling device, with a simple jacket added and employed for secondary-range heat transfer of an incidental nature. The effective A/D ratio is 1.25 and U_{co} values are low as 2 to 6 on sensible heat transfer and 2 to 12 on drying because of substantial static solids-side film.

The *large spiral hollow flight* type (Fig. 11-40*b*) is an adaptation (with external bearings, full fill, and salient construction points as shown) that is highly versatile in application and intended for secondary-range heat transfer. It has an effective A/D of 7.5 with good U_{co} values at 6 to 10 for poor, 8 to 15 for fair, and 10 to 20 for wet conductors.

The *small-spiral–large-shaft* type (Fig. 11-40*c*) is an adaptation design to be inserted in a solids product line as pipe banks are in a fluid line, solely as a heat-transfer device of secondary range. It features a thin burden ring carried at a high rotative speed and subjected to two-sided conductance to yield an effective A/D ratio of 5.75 with estimated U_{co} values of 50—thereby ranking thermally next to the shell-fluidizer type. This device for powdered solids is comparable with the Votator of the fluid field.

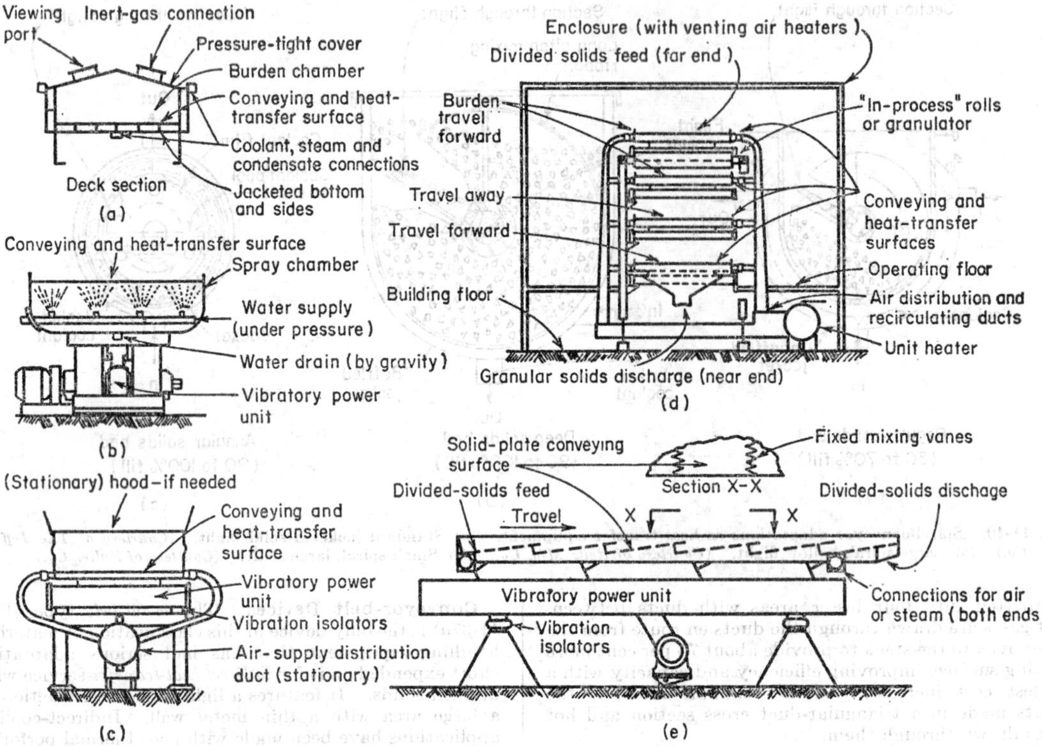

FIG. 11-41. Vibratory-conveyor adaptations as indirect heat-transfer equipment. (*a*) Heaty-duty jacketed for liquid coolant or high-pressure steam. (*b*) Jacketed for coolant spraying. (*c*) Light-duty jacketed construction. (*d*) Jacketed for air or steam in tiered arrangement. (*e*) Jacketed for air or steam with "Mix-R-Step" surface. (*Courtesy of The Jeffrey Mfg. Co.*)

Vibratory-conveyor Devices, General. Figure 11-41 shows the various adaptations of vibratory material-handling equipment for *indirect* heat-transfer service on divided solids which has been developed in a coordinated line within the past 20 years under benefit of patents. These indirect heat-transfer adaptations feature simplicity, non-hazardous construction, non-degradation, non-dusting, no wear, ready conveying-rate variation (5 to 15 ft./min.), and use of all the heat-transfer surface by an A/D ratio of 1.0 at a good U_{co} value of 20 for sand which is steady through depths 0 to 0.5-in. (see p. 11-42). They usually require feed rate and distribution auxiliaries. They are suited for secondary-range thermal operations on divided solids in the powdered, granular, or moist forms but not sticky, liquefying, or floody ones. Terminal-temperature differences less than 20° on cooling and 30° on heating or drying operations are seldom practical. These devices are for medium and light capacities.

The *heavy-duty jacketed* type (Fig. 11-41*a*), is a special custom-built adaptation of a heavy-duty vibratory conveyor shown in Fig. 11-36. Its application is to cool, in continuous operation, the crushed material (from about 350°F.) produced by the vibratory-type "caster" of Fig. 11-36. It does not have the liquid dam and is made in longer lengths that employ L, switch-back, and S arrangements on one floor. The capacity rate is 30 to 35 tons/hr. with a U_{co} value in the order of 25 to 30. For heating or drying applications, it employs steam to 60 lb/sq. in.

The *jacketed or coolant-spraying* type (Fig. 11-41*b*) is designed to assure a very thin, highly agitated liquid-side film, and the same initial coolant temperature over the entire length. It is frequently employed for transport purposes of substantial capacities in the *primary* temperature range with cooling as an incidental consideration. For heating or drying applications hot water or steam at 1 lb./sq. in. gage may be employed. It is widely used because of its versatility, simplicity, cleanability, and good thermal performance.

The *light-duty jacketed* type (Fig. 11-41*c*), is designed for use of air as a heat carrier. The flow through the jacket is highly turbulent and is usually counterflow. On long installations the air flow is parallel to every two sections for more heat-carrying capacity and a fairly uniform surface temperature. The outstanding feature is that a wide range of temperature control is obtained by merely changing the heat-carrier temperature level from as low as atmospheric moisture condensation will allow to 400°. On heating operations a very good thermal efficiency, is obtained by insulating and recycling air. Cooler application is limited to the secondary range. While U_{co} rating is good, the q_{co} rating is less than for the type in Fig. 11-41*b* as the heat-removal capacity is limited. Cooler units are often used in series with like units operated as dryers, or where the water supply is foul, unavailable, or unwanted. Drying applications are for heat-sensitive (120° to 270°F.) products; where temperatures, higher than steam can provide, are wanted but heavy-duty equipment is too costly; where the jacket corrosion hazard of steam is unwanted; where headroom space is at a premium; and for highly abrasive burden materials as fritted or crushed glasses and porcelains.

The *tiered arrangement* (Fig. 11-41*d*) employs the units

of Fig. 11-41*c* with either air or 1 lb./sq. in. steam as a heat medium. They are custom-designed and built to provide a large amount of heat-transfer surface in a small space with the minimum of transport and to provide a complete processing system. These receive a damp material, resize while in process by granulators or rolls, finish dry, cool, and deliver to packaging or tabulating. The applications are primarily in the fine chemical, food, and pharmaceutic manufacturing fields. This arrangement replaces costly batch multiple-unit operations, and manual-handling practices (delivering a non-dusty, better-sized, and better-colored product) with a continuous, temperature-variable (but automatic-controlled) operation requiring part of one man's time plus a helper at clean-up. Though custom-built at high cost, amortizations within 2 years have been reported.

The patented *Mix-R-Step* type in Fig. 11-41*e* is an adaptation of a vibratory-conveyor. It features better heat-transfer rates, *practically doubling* the U_{co} values of the standard flat surface and *trebling* q_{co} values as the layer depth can be increased from the normal ½ to 1 and 1¼ in. It may be provided on decks jacketed for air, steam, or water spray.

Elevator Devices. The *Elevating-spiral*-type (Fig. 11-42) adaptation is the only serious attempt to employ divided-solids-elevating material-handling equipment for heat-transfer service. It features a large heat-transfer area over a small floor space and employs a reciprocating shaker motion to effect transport. Thermal performance is as given above for the vibratory-conveyor adaptations. Applications, layer depth, and capacities are restricted as burdens must be of such "body" character as to

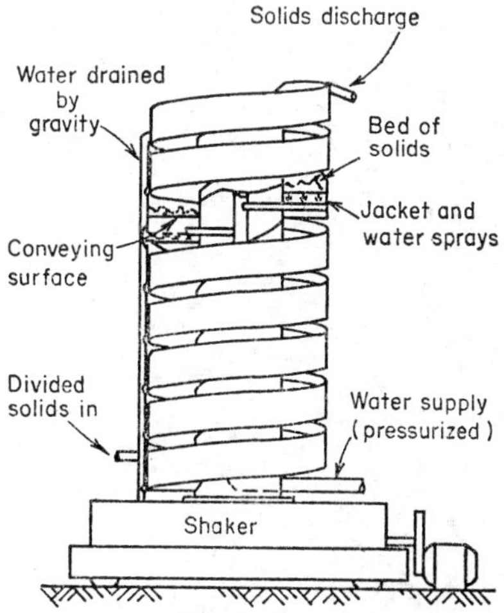

Fig. 11-42. Elevator type as heat-transfer equipment. (*Courtesy of Carrier Conveyor Corp.*)

convey uphill by the microhopping-transport principle. Though it lacks self-emptying ability, complete wash-down and cleaning is a feature not inherent in any other elevating device. A typical application is the cooling of a low-density plastic powder at the rate of 1200 lb./hr. For heating or drying, hot water or low-pressure steam would be applicable.

SECTION 12

REFRIGERATION

BY

Carl F. Kayan, M.E., Professor, Columbia University; Member, American Society of Mechanical Engineers, International Institute of Refrigeration, American Society of Heating, Refrigerating and Air-Conditioning Engineers, Instrument Society of America, American Society for Engineering Education, American Association for the Advancement of Science. (Normal Refrigeration)

Victor J. Johnson, B.S., Chief, Cryogenic Technical Services, National Bureau of Standards, Boulder Colorado Laboratories; Member, American Society of Mechanical Engineers, American Rocket Society, American Society of Heating, Refrigerating and Air-Conditioning Engineers. (Cryogenic Processes)

CONTENTS

NORMAL REFRIGERATION

CRYOGENIC PROCESSES

NORMAL REFRIGERATION

REFERENCES: MacIntire, "Handbook of Mechanical Refrigeration," Wiley, New York, 1928. Morrison, "Power's Practical Refrigeration," McGraw-Hill, New York, 1928. Moyer and Fittz, "Refrigeration," McGraw-Hill, New York, 1932. Dodge, "Chemical Engineering Thermodynamics," Chap. X, Refrigeration, McGraw-Hill, New York, 1944. Plank, "Amerikanische Kältetechnik," V.D.I. Verlag, Berlin, 1929. Siebel, "Compendium of Mechanical Refrigeration," Nickerson and Collins, Chicago, 1918. Instructions for Operation, Care and Repair of Refrigerating Plants, Navy Dept., Bur. Eng., Government Printing Office, Washington, 1918. Crocker, "Piping Handbook," Chap. XVI, McGraw-Hill, New York, 1945. Quinn and Jones, "Carbon Dioxide," Reinhold, New York, 1936. Jordan and Priester, "Refrigeration and Air Conditioning," Prentice-Hall, Englewood Cliffs, N.J., 1956. Jennings and Lewis, "Air Conditioning and Refrigeration," International Textbook, Scranton, Pa., 1958. Sparks and Dillio, "Mechanical Refrigeration," 2d ed., McGraw-Hill, New York, 1959. Periodicals: *A.S.H.R.A.E. Journal*, *Industrial Refrigeration*.

INTRODUCTION

Refrigeration as considered in the following may be broadly defined as the art of producing cold, referring particularly to cooling below atmospheric temperature. The means most commonly employed for such cooling is to induce a change of phase in a heat-abstracting body such as is involved in the vaporization of liquid ammonia or the melting of ice. In the production of liquid air, however, cooling is brought by expanding the gas through a nozzle (Joule-Thomson effect) or by causing it to do work against a brake (Claude system). Other physical changes, such as the contraction of stretched rubber or the extension of a steel spring, the passage of an electric current through a bimetallic junction, and, in fact, any reversible physical change involving the expenditure of work, are capable of producing cold. Radiation of heat from the surface of the earth to interstellar space may be used in certain localities for freezing water, and cool ground waters have from time immemorial been used for preserving foodstuffs.

In recent years, many new applications of refrigeration have developed. Witness the great expansion in the air-conditioning field. Among the new uses may be mentioned the concentration of penicillin and blood plasma, which involves the evaporation of water at very low temperature (−20°C.). The dehydration of food at low temperature also has proved commercially successful, because taste may be preserved. In the fabrication of aluminum parts, chilling is employed to control age-hardening, and in electric welding, refrigerated electrodes have been found to give longer service because less molten metal adheres to the tips. In established applications, the great expansion in the use of frozen foods may be mentioned, with corresponding developments in storage and shipment, notably in marine transportation. In purely chemical industries, such as synthetic rubber manufacture, a great deal of refrigeration is used. The use of dry air in blast-furnace operation, although an old process, has been stimulated by increased demands for steel. Production of pure oxygen for various operations has been extensively developed in Russia and is being followed closely in other countries. The present discussion will not consider details of these numerous applications and will be limited to the general principles of how heat is transferred from a lower to a higher temperature, which is the distinguishing characteristic of refrigeration.

Definitions. A **refrigerant** in its broadest sense may be defined as any material which is used for abstracting heat. In a narrower, but more commonly used, sense the term refers only to those materials which are used in **mechanical refrigeration.**

Mechanical refrigeration includes those processes in which the refrigerant is recovered and recirculated, as distinguished from those in which the spent refrigerant is wasted (ice refrigeration, ice-cream freezing by salt-ice mixtures, cold ground waters in spring houses). Mechanical refrigeration falls into two general groupings, depending on the state of the refrigerant during the cold-producing process, *i.e.*, involving either latent heat of a liquid-vapor fluid, or sensible heat of a gaseous fluid. In the latent-heat group the refrigerant vapor may be moved with a suction effect created either by a compression machine or by an absorption effect created by a liquid or solid absorber substance. Thus these arrangements are identified as vapor-compression or absorption system, respectively.

In the **vapor-compression** system a compression machine is used which may have either a positive-displacement mechanism (reciprocating or rotary compressor) or an impeller (centrifugal compressor). A third form of vapor compressor is the jet, deriving its compressive power from a high-pressure expanding vapor whose discharge jet entrains low-pressure refrigerant vapor. Although the thermodynamic cycle is the same for these types of compression, the kinematic considerations, particularly with regard to the refrigerant used, are markedly different.

The **absorption system** differs essentially from the compression system in requiring no positive work input to produce cold though generally requiring some accessory power. Circulation is effected by absorption of the refrigerant in appropriate liquids or solids which are regenerated by heat in another part of the refrigerating system. Absorption machines are classified as **continuous** or **intermittent,** the latter corresponding quite closely to batch processes. All continuous machines use liquid absorbents because of the great practical difficulties in moving a solid absorbent about from the absorption side to the generator. When continuous refrigeration is required with intermittent units, two or more machines must be installed.

This classification is neither absolute nor all-inclusive. Combinations of absorption and compression systems have been developed (Westinghouse-Leblanc). The processes for manufacturing liquid air or solid carbon dioxide do not fall into the above scheme since they employ compression but do not recirculate the refrigerant. The distinctions are useful, however, in considering the operations involved.

Practically, mechanical refrigeration is the most important branch of the art, and developments have centered extensively about the vapor-compression machine.

Absorption machines still find considerable industrial application where large quantities of waste heat are available. Interest has also been revived in absorption systems tied in with heating arrangements for year-round air conditioning, involving summer cooling and winter heating. The main investigations have been in the direction of developing refrigerant-solvent combinations which can produce refrigeration with a minimum heat expenditure.

The **gaseous** system conventionally uses air (often "dense," to cut down size) and operates on the Brayton cycle. In practice, the efficiency is low because of the large volumes of air which must be handled for a relatively small effect. The safety of air as regards toxicity, flammability, and odor was an important factor in its favor some years ago, but in recent years refrigerants have been developed which are practically as safe and more efficient.

Energy Transfer. The basic principle involved in a refrigerating system is that of transporting heat from an environment at low temperature to one at a higher temperature. The heat absorption at the low temperature, as noted above, may involve a refrigerant with sensible-heat effect (gaseous system) or latent-heat effect (vapor-compression system). The latter energy-transfer system is by far the more prevalent; it uses a volatile liquid (the refrigerant) to absorb heat at the low temperature by vaporization in an evaporator at low pressure, and then to dissipate this heat at higher temperature and higher pressure by condensation heat transfer to some coolant as water in the condenser. In one approach the pressure difference may be maintained by a compressor, hence the term "vapor-compression" system. Figure 12-1 shows illustratively the temperature relations for such a system, involving refrigeration to maintain a space at reduced temperature.

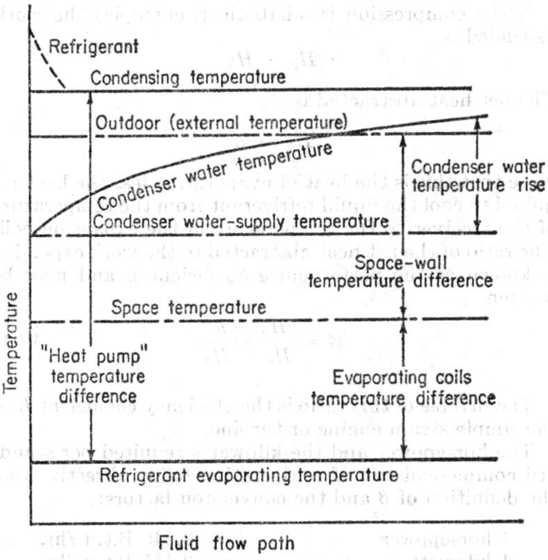

FIG. 12-1. Temperature levels for refrigeration systems.

Properties of Refrigerants Used in Vapor-compression and Assorption Systems. The choice of a refrigerant is always determined by the specific conditions of refrigeration to be met. A refrigerant cannot be used in a compression machine if the temperature of the available cooling water lies above the critical temperature of the refrigerant. The temperature of cooling waters in America is usually too high to use carbon dioxide with any great advantage. For absorption machines, it is necessary that the absorbent be capable of taking up large quantities of the refrigerant. In centrifugal compression machines it is necessary that the vapor pressures be as low as possible so as to reduce the number of stages and that the molecular weight be as high as possible so as to reduce the peripheral speed of the rotor.

In vapor-compression machines of the reciprocating type, refrigerants of high vapor pressure are desired since these give low piston displacement and smaller friction losses. A comparison of the vapor pressures of various materials is shown in Fig. 12-2, where the logarithm of

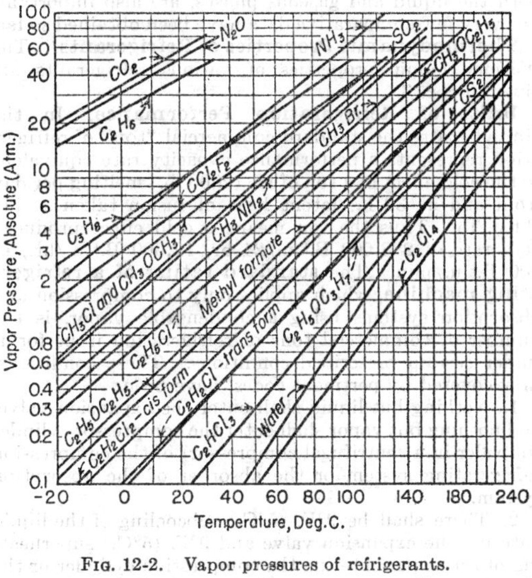

FIG. 12-2. Vapor pressures of refrigerants.

the vapor pressure is plotted against centigrade temperature. The slopes of all the lines are very nearly parallel (Trouton's law), water being the notable exception, and the compression ratios for any given temperature interval are very nearly equal. Additional vapor pressures may be found in Sec. 3.

Other properties of importance are: chemical stability, inertness to metals (corrosion), ease of detection in case of leaks, and behavior with lubricants. Cheapness of the refrigerant is a very important item in larger units since it is not practicable to prevent leakage altogether.

Ammonia is the most important refrigerant used in industrial work, but the irritating and toxic character of the vapor excludes it from certain applications, such as marine refrigeration or air conditioning, where carbon dioxide and dichlorodifluoromethane (F-12)* have been preferred. Although the thermodynamic efficiency of ammonia is not very different from other refrigerants, its low gas density is a distinct practical advantage in reducing power losses in refrigerant piping. In certain chemical processes, notably those in which free chlorine may be present, ammonia is also undesirable. Propane having nearly the same pressures may be substituted in machines designed for ammonia. Carbon dioxide is now rarely used, and is of interest primarily historically. The rapidly evolving low-pressure, high-molecular-weight refrigerants—methylene chloride and the more complex fluoro-chloro-methanes—are used in centrifugal compressors for air-conditioning work.

Small admixtures of warning or detecting agents are sometimes added. Thus peppermint may be added to carbon dioxide, acrolein to methyl chloride (both of which have characteristic odors), or ethyl nitrite for the detection of pinholes by discoloration of starch-potassium

* Since 1960 the A.S.A. has identified this compound as "Refrigerant 12," and similar designations are used for other refrigerants.

iodide paper. With ammonia, a sulfur candle, a piece of litmus paper, or a glass rod dipped in acid serves as means of detection. Refrigerants containing chlorine can usually be detected by lighting a taper which gives a bluish-green flame in the escaping vapors, but this procedure is to be used with care in the case of methyl chloride, which may form an explosive mixture with air.

The heat-transfer characteristics of refrigerants, in both the liquid and gaseous phases, are also important, but very few comparative data have been obtained so far.

Thermodynamic Properties of Refrigerants. The thermodynamic properties of various refrigerants are given in Sec. 3.

Units of Refrigeration Performance. In the United States the standard commercial "ton" of refrigeration represents a performance capacity rate equivalent to the cold effect of a ton of ice (2000 lb.) melting per day from and at 32°F., latent heat of fusion taken at 144 B.t.u./lb. Thus the ton means a cold effect produced at a rate of 288,000 B.t.u./24 hr, 12,000 B.t.u./hr., or 200 B.t.u./min. The **standard rating of a refrigerating machine,** which applies only to compression and absorption systems using a condensable vapor, is the number of commercial tons of refrigeration it performs under certain prescribed conditions. These conditions, now covered by pertinent codes, have been:

1. Nothing but liquid shall enter the expansion valve, and nothing but vapor shall enter the compressor cylinder (impeller in a centrifugal compressor) of the compression refrigerating system or the absorber of the absorption system.

2. There shall be 9°F. (5°C.) subcooling of the liquid entering the expansion valve and 9°F. (5°C.) superheating of the vapor entering the compression cylinder or the absorber. The points at which subcooling and superheating are determined must be within 10 ft. of the cylinder or absorber.

3. The inlet pressure is that which corresponds to a saturation temperature of 5°F. (−15°C.).

4. The outlet pressure from the compressor cylinder or generator is that which corresponds to a saturation temperature of 86°F. (30°C.).

The American Society of Refrigerating Engineers* has for a number of years been sponsoring a compilation of standard methods for rating refrigeration equipment such as compressors, condensers, evaporators, and brine coolers. Various circulars dealing with these subjects are being issued from time to time as completed.

The **British unit of refrigeration** is based on a rate of cooling of 1 kg.-cal./sec. or 237.6 B.t.u./min., with inlet pressures corresponding to a saturation temperature of 23°F. (−5°C.) and outlet pressures corresponding to a saturation temperature of 59°F. (15°C.).

Vapor Cycles vs. Gas Cycles. Vapor cycles (of either the vapor-compression or absorption type) employ both an evaporator (expansion coil) and a condenser. The apparatus used for transferring the refrigerant from the low- to the high-pressure side is technically the "refrigerating machine," but the term is not always used in strict conformity with this definition. In the vapor-compression system the machine is actuated by a prime mover, and in the absorption machine by heat. Economy requires that a given amount of refrigeration be produced with a minimum expenditure of work or heat.

In the gaseous system of refrigeration, the components are essentially a gas compressor (creating a gas pressure differential), a gas cooler (rejecting heat to an atmospheric-level coolant), an expander machine whose output is low-temperature gas and some power, and finally the cold-side heat exchanger in which the cold gas absorbs heat on a sensible-heat basis. The difference in power between the requirement of the compressor and the output of the expander (displacement machine or turbine) is made up from an outside motive-power source. This represents the investment of energy to produce a given refrigerating effect. The cycle involving isentropic compression and expansion (ideally), with constant-pressure heat-transfer effects, is known as the Brayton cycle and is closely allied to the gas-turbine power-producing cycle.

* Now American Society of Heating, Refrigerating and Air-Conditioning Engineers.

VAPOR REFRIGERATION CYCLES

Single-stage Compression. A diagrammatic representation of a simple compression system of refrigeration is shown in Fig. 12-3. Refrigerant vapor is drawn from the expansion coil A at the pressure p_1 by the compressor B; forced into the condenser C at a pressure p_2, dependent on the temperature of the cooling water, where the vapor liquefies; and collected in the receiver D from which it returns through the expansion valve E, under the pressure difference $p_2 - p_1$, into the expansion coil.

In this process the following heat quantities (enthalpies) are involved, which may be taken from the tables of thermodynamic properties (Sec. 3):

H_b = heat content of vapor leaving evaporator (expansion coil).
H_c = heat content of vapor leaving compressor.
h_e = heat content of liquid entering evaporator (expansion coil).

If the compression is adiabatic (isentropic) the work expended is

$$H_c - H_b$$

The net heat abstracted is

$$H_b - h_e$$

Note that this is the heat of evaporation less the heat required to cool the liquid refrigerant from the temperature of the receiver to the temperature of the expansion coil. The ratio of the net heat abstracted to the work expended is known as the performance coefficient β and may be written

$$\beta = \frac{H_b - h_e}{H_c - H_b} \tag{12-1}$$

The inverse of this ratio is the efficiency coefficient E of the simple steam engine or turbine.

The horsepower and the kilowatts required per standard commercial ton of refrigeration follow directly from the definition of β and the conversion factors:

1 horsepower	= 2,546 B.t.u./hr.
1 kilowatt	= 3,415 B.t.u./hr.
1 standard commercial ton	= 12,000 B.t.u./hr.

This gives

$$\text{Horsepower per ton} = \frac{12,000}{2,546\beta} = \frac{4.713}{\beta} \tag{12-2a}$$

$$\text{Kilowatt per ton} = \frac{12,000}{3,415\beta} = \frac{3.514}{\beta} \tag{12-2b}$$

which represent the **theoretical horsepower** or **kilowatts** per standard commercial ton of refrigeration.

The theoretical horsepower can be realized only in a frictionless machine with a weightless piston. In general it will be very nearly equal to the **indicated horsepower** shown by the actual card of an indicator, which reveals the imperfections in the operation of the valves

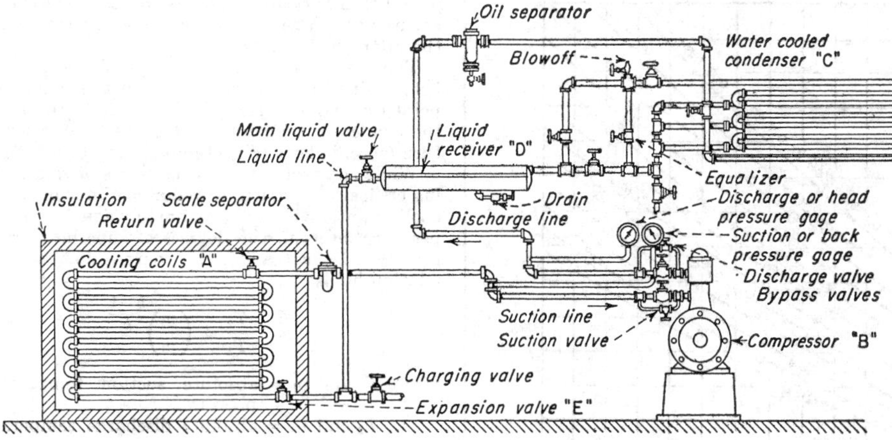

FIG. 12-3. Simple vapor-compression machine.

and the departure from strictly adiabatic compression. The **brake horsepower** is the indicated horsepower plus the power necessary to overcome the friction at the cylinder walls and bearings and the inertia of the piston. The brake horsepower will be 10 to 20 per cent more than the theoretical horsepower. The difference between brake horsepower and indicated horsepower is sometimes designated as **friction horsepower.** The friction horsepower is relatively larger in small than in large machines.

Since refrigeration involves a conversion of work into heat it might appear that the performance coefficient is dependent only on the temperature difference and independent of the refrigerant used. This is only approximately true, as shown by Table 12-1, carbon dioxide being a marked exception. The temperature difference is, however, important; and, consequently, a machine tested according to the standard American temperature interval will show much better performance when tested on the British standard.

Sample Calculation of Performance Coefficient. Assume that the refrigerant is ammonia; the absolute evaporator pressure (p_1) 35 lb./sq. in. corresponding to 5.89°F., and the absolute condenser pressure (p_2) 160 lb./sq. in. corresponding to 82.64°F.

The heat content (H_b) of the saturated vapor in the evaporator is 613.6 B.t.u./lb., and the entropy (S) is 1.3236 B.t.u./lb./°F.

Table 12-1. Comparison of Refrigerants*

One-ton refrigeration, 5 to 86°F.

Cycle	Weight, lb./min.	Volume, cu. ft./min.	Ratio of compression	Coefficient of performance	Horsepower per ton	Relative efficiencies, %
Ideal	.....	.....	.....	5.74	0.8214	100
Ammonia	0.4214	3.44	4.93	4.85	0.973	84.5
Propane	1.396	3.35	3.64	4.88	0.9668	85
Carbon dioxide	3.74	0.999	3.11	2.56	1.843	44.6
Sulfur dioxide	1.388	9.24	5.63	4.735	0.995	82.5
Ethyl ether	1.555	60.8	7.12	4.86	0.971	84.6
Dichloroethylene	1.768	108.4	8.23	5.14	0.918	89.4
Trichloroethylene	2.137	513	10.84	5.085	0.928	88.5
Water	0.1996	1972	21.9	4.1	1.15	71.5

* Carrier and Waterfill, *Refrig. Eng.*, **10**, 415 (1923).

To determine the heat content (H_c) of the vapor in the condenser, find the heat content of the superheated vapor corresponding to 160 lb./sq. in. and entropy 1.3236. This is 707.5. The temperature of the superheated vapor is 199.5°F.

The work of compression per pound of vapor is therefore

$$H_c - H_b = 707.5 - 613.6 = 93.9 \text{ B.t.u.}$$

The heat content of the liquid (h_e) entering the evaporator at 82.64°F. is 135.0 B.t.u. Hence the net heat extracted is

$$H_b - h_e = 613.6 - 135.0 = 478.6 \text{ B.t.u.}$$

The performance coefficient is

$$\beta = \frac{478.6}{93.9} = 5.097$$

and

$$\text{Horsepower per ton refrigeration} = \frac{4.713}{5.097} = 0.925$$

Table 12-1 gives the comparative theoretical performance coefficient and other significant values for various

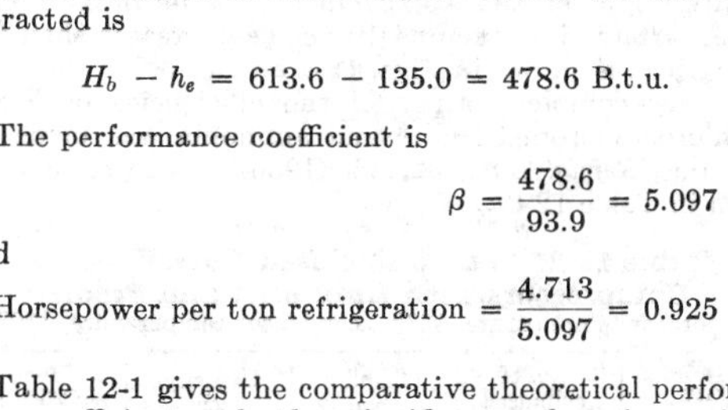

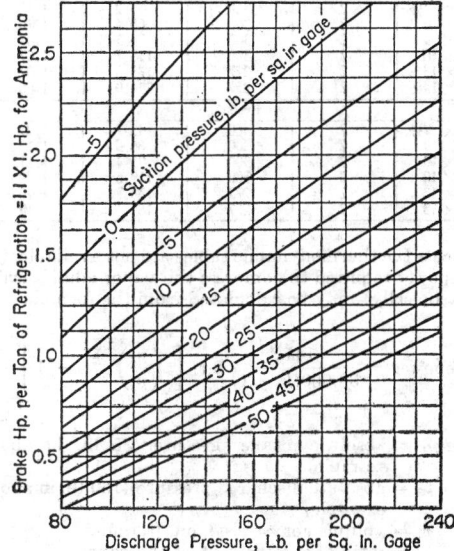

FIG. 12-4. Brake horsepower per ton of refrigeration for ammonia.

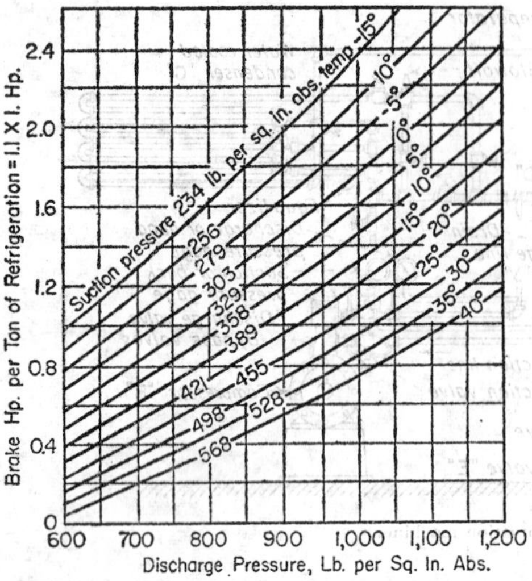

FIG. 12-5. Brake horsepower per ton of refrigeration for carbon.

refrigerants including ammonia, which will be found to hold approximately for all other refrigerants except those boiling much below ammonia. Carbon dioxide will require a greater power expenditure. The brake horsepower, arbitrarily taken as 10 per cent greater than the theoretical, is shown in Figs. 12-4 and 12-5.

A very complete study of the efficiencies of Freon (dichlorodifluoromethane)* and ammonia was made by Williams [*Refrig. Eng.*, **31**, 36, (1936)]. The results are given in Table 12-2.

Table 12-2. Large Enclosed York V. S. A. Compressors with Ammonia and Freon

Evaporator temperature, 35°F., condenser temperature, 110°F.

Size	No. of cylinders	Speed, r.p.m.	Capacity, tons	Brake horsepower per ton
		Ammonia		
7½ × 7½	2	360	55.2	1.10
8 × 8	2	360	68.4	1.10
9 × 9	2	300	84.3	1.07
10 × 10	2	300	118.7	1.07
11 × 13	2	277	173.0	1.07
12½ × 14½	2	257	234.0	1.06
		Freon		
9 × 7½	2	360	43.7	1.27
11 × 9	2	300	66.5	1.23
12½ × 10	2	300	95.4	1.215
14 × 10	2	300	119.6	1.20
13½ × 13	2	277	133.7	1.20
15 × 13	2	277	165.1	1.19

In case the thermodynamic tables are not available, the horsepower required to compress the vapor adiabatically (isentropically) may be calculated from the formula

$$\text{Horsepower} = \frac{144k}{33{,}000(k-1)} p_1 v_1 \left[\left(\frac{p_2}{p_1}\right)^{\frac{k-1}{k}} - 1 \right] \tag{12-3}$$

where p_1 = absolute intake pressure (35 lb. in above example).
p_2 = absolute discharge pressure (160 lb. in above example).
v_1 = volume compressed, cu. ft./min.
k = ratio of specific heat of the vapor, c_p/c_v.

* F-12 now designated as R-12 by A.S.A.

The volume v_1 may usually be found with sufficient accuracy from the general gas law equation expressed in the appropriate units.

The net heat extracted is similarly the difference between the heat of evaporation at the evaporating temperature and the sensible heat of the liquid between the condenser temperature and the evaporator temperature (specific heat times temperature difference).

While the performance coefficients of refrigerants having critical temperatures well above that of the available cooling water will be approximately equal for a given temperature interval, the degrees of superheating will vary greatly. In an adiabatic compression the following relation holds:

$$\frac{T_2}{T_1} = \left(\frac{p_2}{p_1}\right)^{\frac{k-1}{k}} \tag{12-4}$$

where T_1 and p_1 = absolute suction temperature and pressure.
T_2 and p_2 = absolute discharge temperature and pressure.
k = ratio of specific heats.

The compression ratio p_2/p_1, which is determined by the molal latent heats, will be nearly the same for all refrigerants (Trouton's law) while the specific heat ratio will be lowest for those refrigerants having high molal heat capacities. The refrigerants having complex molecules will therefore have a much smaller temperature rise in adiabatic compression than those having simple molecules. In the case of ethyl ether ($C_4H_{10}O$) there is actually no superheating but supercooling and liquefaction, while ammonia (NH_3) and sulfur dioxide (SO_2) give the greatest superheating on compression.

Dual Compression. When two refrigerating temperatures are required, the **dual-compression** system may be employed. The general principle of this design is to draw in the vapor from the low-pressure (low-temperature) expansion coils, and, at or near the end of the stroke, vapor from the higher pressure coils will be admitted. The whole mixture will then be compressed to the saturation pressure corresponding to the temperature of the condenser water. The advantages of this system are the use of one condenser for the two cooling systems and a markedly higher capacity, since the low-pressure cooling unit requires much larger piston displacement than the higher-pressure unit. The chief disadvantage is the difficulty of securing continuous adjustment between the loads on the two systems.

Wet Compression. In wet compression liquid refrigerant is admitted with the refrigerant vapor from the expansion coils. This liquid evaporates during adiabatic compression and thereby makes the compression approach more nearly to the isothermal line. The vapor leaves the compressor with a much smaller degree of superheat, which also lessens the load on the condenser. Although the scheme is sound in theory, it is difficult in practice to adjust the amount of liquid added, and the capacity is very much reduced owing to the increased cylinder volume required by the liquid after vaporization. The scheme can naturally not be used with a refrigerant like ethyl ether, which liquefies on adiabatic compression, and it would not be particularly advantageous for those refrigerants which superheat slightly.

Multistage Compression. The most promising developments toward diminishing the power requirements of refrigeration are along the lines of multistage compression. This principle has long been used in air compression, but in refrigeration the problem is more complicated. In general it will prove economical with ammonia only where suction pressures lower than 5 lb./sq. in. (gage) are encountered. As in the case of wet compression, it can be applied with best advantage to those refrigerants which superheat markedly on adiabatic compression (ammonia, sulfur dioxide, and carbon dioxide but not ethyl ether, dichlorodifluoromethane, propane, and butane). Multistage compression is frequently used with the latter type of refrigerant, but intercoolers are of much less importance than with ammonia, and the power savings are less marked.

Several possibilities in multiple compression are presented. First, the vapor from the first stage may be cooled by water in a heat exchanger before going to the

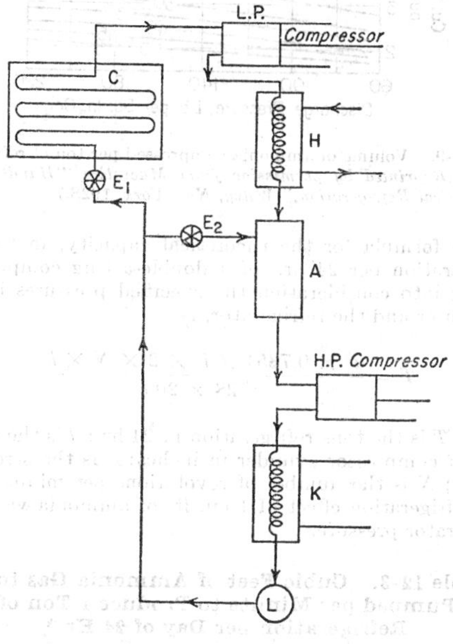

Fig. 12-6a. Multiple-stage (two-stage) compression. (*Macintire, "Handbook of Mechanical Refrigeration," Wiley, New York, 1928.*)

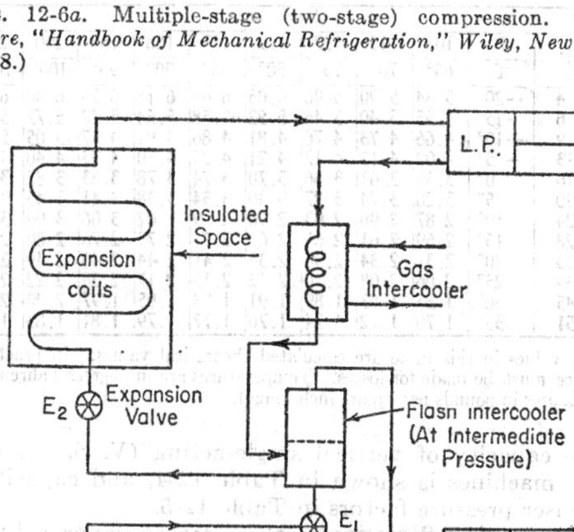

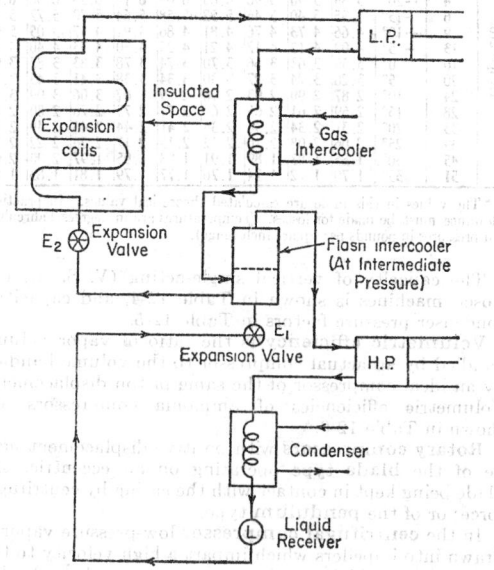

Fig. 12-6b. Two-stage arrangement with flash intercooler.

second stage. Second, the vapor may be cooled by the liquid refrigerant, injected into the vapors from the first stage, to the temperature corresponding to the vapor pressure of the refrigerant equal to the pressure at the beginning of the second stage. Third, a combination of both may be used. Fourth, a flash intercooler with series-expansion valves may be used. The intermediate-pressure gas, after being cooled in an intercooler heat exchanger, is put through a flash intercooler. From here it ultimately goes to the high-pressure stage. A diagrammatic sketch of the third scheme is shown in Fig. 12-6*a*, and of the fourth scheme in Fig. 12-6*b*.

In Fig. 12-6*a* vapor is pumped from the expansion coils *C* by the low-pressure compressor *LP* into the heat exchanger *H* where it is cooled by water. From *H* it passes into the accumulator *A* where it meets liquid refrigerant from the liquid receiver *L* which cools the vapor further. The high-pressure compressor then compresses the vapor to the saturation pressure of the condenser *K* in which it liquefies and is collected by the liquid receiver *L*. The liquid refrigerant then returns to the expansion coils through the valve E_1 and to the accumulator through the valve E_2.

When ammonia is used for low-temperature cooling, a booster compressor is generally used to raise the low-pressure vapor to some intermediate pressure. The vapors are cooled before going to the high-pressure compressor, partly to save power, partly to take out the superheat which would continue to build up in the second compressor. A further advantage is the saving in cylinder volume.

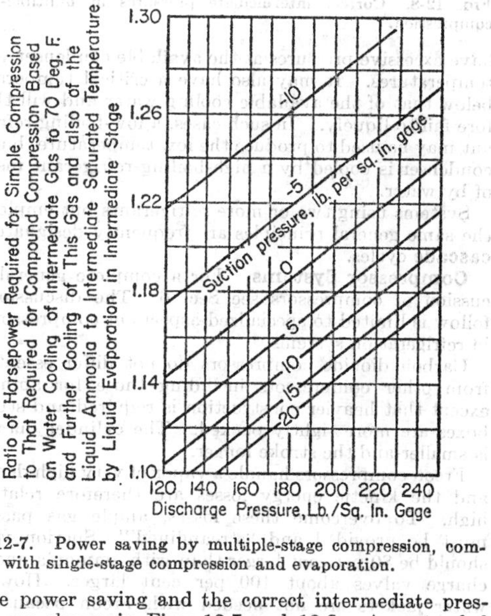

Fig. 12-7. Power saving by multiple-stage compression, compared with single-stage compression and evaporation.

The power saving and the correct intermediate pressures are shown in Figs. 12-7 and 12-8. An extended analysis of the power savings in obtaining low temperatures by multistage compression has been made by Sloan [*Refrig. Eng.*, **45**, 419 (1943)].

Split-stage Compression or Binary Cycles (Two or More Refrigerants). When very low temperatures are required, it is sometimes advantageous to employ two or more refrigerants in order to maintain pressures within reasonable limits. Thus a refrigerant of relatively high boiling point will have such a low vapor pressure at low temperatures that excessive cylinder volume will be needed, whereas a refrigerant of low boiling point will

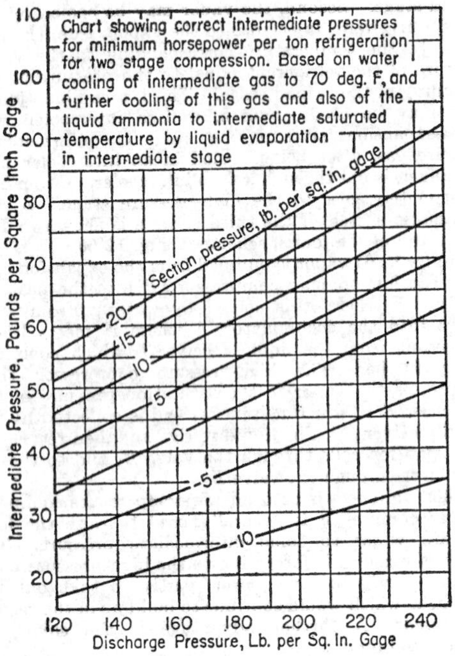

Fig. 12-8. Correct intermediate pressures in multiple-stage compression.

have excessive pressures at the available condenser water temperatures. It may also have a critical temperature below that of the available cooling water and will therefore fail to liquefy. In such cases, a low-boiling refrigerant may be used to produce the low temperature, but the condenser is cooled by a high-boiling refrigerant instead of by water.

Systems using two or more refrigerants but employing the same general principles are frequently designated as **cascade** cycles.

Compressor Systems. For a complete general discussion of compressors see Sec. 6. The discussion to follow is limited to specialized aspects of compressor use in refrigeration systems.

Carbon dioxide compressors do not differ essentially from other compressors including those for ammonia except that heavier construction is required and stuffing boxes are more tightly packed. The cylinder diameter is smaller and the stroke longer.

Freon compressors handle a vapor of very high density, and the kinetic energy losses are therefore relatively high. To overcome these losses, ample gas passages must be provided and "streamlined." Suction valves should be 80 per cent larger than with ammonia and discharge valves about 100 per cent larger. However, water jackets are not needed with Freon because the gas superheats very little on compression. An extensive discussion of Freon compressor design is given by Williams [*Refrig. Eng.*, **31**, 36 (1936)].

Reciprocating-machine Capacity. The weight of dry saturated gas that must be handled by the compressor per minute to produce 1 ton of refrigeration per 24 hr. is given by the formula: $W = 200/(H_b - h_e)$, where W is the weight of gas compressed per minute, H_b is the total heat in 1 lb. of vapor at the evaporator pressure, h_e is the heat of the liquid at the receiver pressure, and 200 is the number of B.t.u. removed per minute to equal 1 ton of refrigeration per 24 hr. (Table 12-3 and Fig. 12-9).

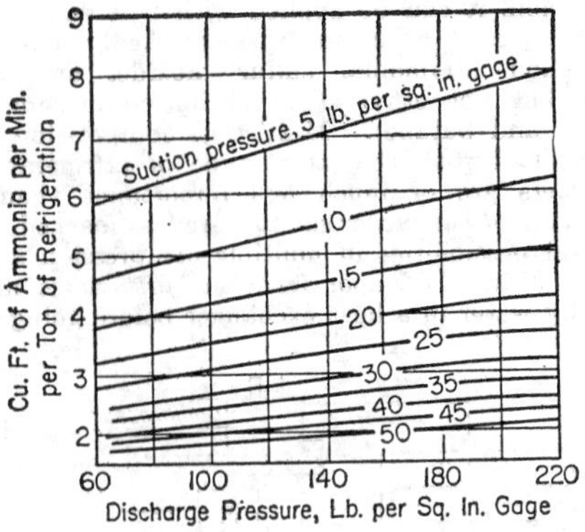

Fig. 12-9. Volume of ammonia compressed per ton of refrigeration. (*Reprinted by permission from Macintire, "Handbook of Mechanical Refrigeration," Wiley, New York,* 1928.)

The formula for the theoretical capacity, in tons of refrigeration per 24 hr., of a double-acting compressor, taking into consideration the specified pressures in the condenser and the refrigerator, is

$$T = \frac{d^2 \times 0.7854 \times L \times 2 \times N \times h}{1728 \times 200} \tag{12-5}$$

where T is the tons refrigeration in 24 hr.; d is the diameter of compressor cylinder in inches; L is the stroke in inches; N is the number of revolutions per minute; h is the refrigeration effect of 1 cu. ft. of ammonia vapor at evaporator pressure.

Table 12-3. Cubic Feet of Ammonia Gas to Be Pumped per Minute to Produce 1 Ton of Refrigeration per Day of 24 Hr.*

Evaporator P	Condenser P →	103	115	127	139	153	168	185	200	218
	T	65°	70°	75°	80°	85°	90°	95°	100°	105°
4	−20°	5.84	5.90	5.96	6.03	6.09	6.16	6.23	6.30	6.43
6	−15°	5.35	5.40	5.46	5.52	5.58	5.64	5.70	5.77	5.83
9	−10°	4.66	4.73	4.76	4.81	4.86	4.91	4.97	5.05	5.08
13	− 5°	4.09	4.12	4.17	4.21	4.25	4.30	4.35	4.40	4.44
16	0°	3.59	3.63	3.66	3.70	3.74	3.78	3.83	3.87	3.91
20	5°	3.20	3.24	3.27	3.30	3.34	3.38	3.41	3.45	3.49
24	10°	2.87	2.90	2.93	2.96	2.99	3.02	3.06	3.09	3.12
28	15°	2.59	2.61	2.65	2.68	2.71	2.73	2.76	2.80	2.82
33	20°	2.31	2.34	2.36	2.38	2.41	2.44	2.46	2.49	2.51
39	25°	2.06	2.08	2.10	2.12	2.15	2.17	2.20	2.22	2.24
45	30°	1.85	1.87	1.89	1.91	1.93	1.95	1.97	2.00	2.01
51	35°	1.70	1.72	1.74	1.76	1.77	1.79	1.81	1.83	1.85

* The values in this table are calculated theoretical values. In practice, allowance must be made for losses. Temperatures are in degrees Fahrenheit and pressures in pounds per square inch (gage).

The capacity of vertical single-acting (V. S. A.) enclosed machines is shown in Table 12-4, and capacity–condenser pressure factors in Table 12-5.

Volumetric efficiency is the ratio of vapor volume handled by an actual compressor to the volume handled by an ideal compressor of the same piston displacement. Volumetric efficiencies of ammonia compressors are shown in Table 12-6.

Rotary compressors with positive displacement may be of the **blade** type operating on an eccentric, the blade being kept in contact with the casing by centrifugal force; or of the **pendulum** type.

In the **centrifugal compressor** low-pressure vapor is drawn into impellers which impart a high velocity to the vapors. The high-speed vapors emerge through discharge vanes, and their kinetic energy is then converted

Table 12-4. Capacities of V. S. A. Enclosed-type Machines

Cylinder			Piston speed per min.		Displacement per min.		Capacity in tons/24 hr., 185 lb./sq. in. condensing pressure								
Number	Bore	Stroke	R.p.m.	Ft.	Cu. in.	Cu. ft.	6 lb. −15°F., refg.	9 lb. −10°F., refg.	12 lb. −5°F., refg.	16 lb., 0°F. Ice	16 lb., 0°F. Refg.	19 lb. 5°F., refg.	24 lb. 10°F., refg.	28 lb. 15°F., refg.	33 lb. 20°F., refg.
1	3	3	300	150	6,362	3.68	0.47	0.51	0.65	0.47	0.75	0.85	1.96	1.07	1.24
1	4	4	275	183	13,828	7.99	0.98	1.12	1.35	1.0	1.6	1.78	2.0	2.2	2.6
2	4	4	275	183	27,646	15.98	1.96	2.24	2.7	2.0	3.2	3.5	4.0	4.4	5.2
2	5	5	240	200	47,124	27.3	3.34	3.84	4.6	3.3	5.3	5.97	6.8	7.7	8.85
2	6	6	220	220	74,644	43.2	5.5	6.6	7.6	5.5	8.8	10.0	11.4	12.6	14.5
2	7	7	210	245	113,146	65.6	8.5	10.2	11.9	8.5	13.6	15.5	17.4	19.6	22.4
2	8	8	200	266	160,848	93.08	12.2	14.6	16.9	12.1	19.5	22.1	24.9	28.0	32.1
2	9	9	190	285	217,570	125.8	16.6	19.2	22.9	16.6	26.4	29.8	33.8	37.9	43.5
2	10	10	180	300	282,744	163.62	22.1	26.1	30.4	21.9	35.0	38.8	44.9	50.4	57.8
2	12	12	170	340	461,448	267.04	35.1	41.9	48.6	35.0	56.0	63.4	71.6	80.3	92.4

Multiply above capacities by factors in Table 12-5 to obtain capacities at different condenser pressures.

nto pressure energy. The speed is usually 3000 to 6000 r.p.m. Several stages are necessary to raise the vapor to the discharge velocity (see Fig. 12-10). Since the kinetic energy is a function of mass, refrigerants of high gas density are preferred. Slippage losses are less with low-pressure refrigerants than with high-pressure refrigerants; and, since only high-molecular-weight refrigerants can give high densities at low pressures, a special class of such refrigerants has been developed for these machines. In general, centrifugal compressors cannot be used advantageously below certain load limits characteristic of each refrigerant. Zwicke [*Refrig. Eng.*, **45**, 179 (1943)] gives the following lower limits in tons refrigeration: ammonia, 1400; methyl chloride, 780; Freon 12, 810; sulfur dioxide, 561; Freon 114, 260; Freon 21, 260; Freon 11, 150; methylene chloride, 83; and Freon 113, 62.

Table 12-5. Factors for Capacities at Different Condenser Pressures

Condenser pressure, lb./sq. in. gage	Ammonia suction pressure							
	6 lb.	9 lb.	12 lb.	16 lb.	19 lb.	24 lb.	28 lb.	33 lb.
200	0.975	0.969	0.975	0.977	0.978	0.977	0.976	0.977
168	1.029	1.028	1.028	1.02	1.027	1.026	1.022	
153	1.046	1.049	1.05	1.05	1.043	1.05	1.042	1.042

Table 12-6. Volumetric Efficiency of Ammonia Compressors

Condenser pressure, lb./sq. in. gage		Suction pressure, lb./sq. in., gage				
		0	10	20	30	40
120	*A*	0.77	0.83	0.87	0.89	0.91
	B	.60	.70	.77	.81	.84
	C	.52	.65	.72	.77	.80
160	*A*	.74	.80	.83	.86	.88
	B	.54	.65	.72	.76	.80
	C	.44	.58	.66	.72	.75
200	*A*	.71	.77	.81	.84	.86
	B	.49	.61	.68	.72	.75
	C	.37	.52	.62	.67	.71

A, no clearance.
B, 4 per cent clearance.
C, 6 per cent clearance.

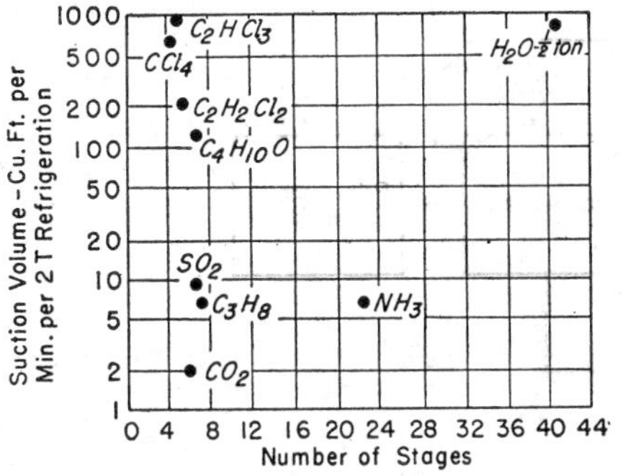

FIG. 12-10. Relative size and number of stages required for various refrigerants (5° to 86°F.). [*Carrier and Waterfill, Refrig. Eng.*, **10**, 423 (1924).]

Steam Jets. Low-pressure water vapor may be compressed by high-pressure steam in a steam jet, the operation involving conversion of kinetic energy into pressure-volume energy. In this way a vacuum can be created over water with resultant evaporation and cooling. This method is frequently very useful where moderate cooling is needed, such as in chilling water for air conditioning or other uses. Temperatures from 35°F. up can generally be attained.

Steam jets have been greatly improved in recent years, and various operating details have appeared in the literature. Steam requirements are given in Table 12-7. Figure 12-11 shows a representative arrangement for chilled water.

Table 12-7. Steam and Water Requirements for Steam Jet Vacuum Cooling Units*

Lb. steam/hr./ton refrigeration
Gal./min./ton refrigeration

Booster condenser pressure, in. Hg abs.	Chilled water temp., °F				
	40	45	50	55	60
1.5	23.4	20.7	17.6	16.1	12.9
2.0	31.4	27.0	22.5	20.8	16.5
2.5	41.2	32.8	27.5	23.6	20.6
Condensing water (75°F.):					
1.5	6.51	6.05	5.44	5.16	4.51
2.0	4.45	3.98	3.52	3.34	2.90
Condensing water (85°F.):					
2.0	8.45	7.56	6.67	6.34	5.50
2.5	6.16	5.80	4.57	4.10	3.75

* Stinson, *Refrig. Eng.*, **46**, 316 (1943).

Condensers used with steam jets may be of three kinds: (1) Surface condensers with steam condensed on the outside of the tubes, in which condensed vapor and motive steam from the booster are pumped from the high vacuum with recovery of motive steam condensate; (2) low-level jet condensers in which steam and vapor are mixed directly with the cooling water; and (3) barometric condensers, in which steam and vapor are also mixed directly with the cooling water but are removed by gravity without an auxiliary pump.

For variable load, several jets are required with provision for cutting out as the load varies. Steam at 2 lb. gage pressure is said to be suitable for steam jet refrigeration [Stevens, *Refrig. Eng.*, **40**, 146 (1940)]. As the motive steam pressure decreases a point is reached at which the compressor "breaks back" or suddenly drops all the load.

A full discussion of cycles, standards, thermodynamic diagrams, and test codes for steam jets may be found in

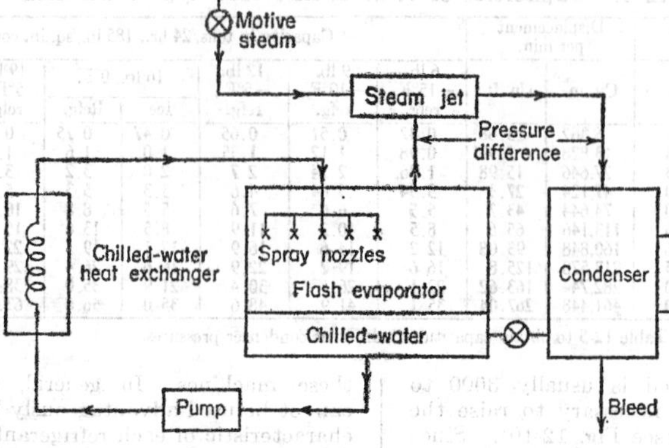

Fig. 12-11. Representative chilled-water steam-jet arrangement.

"Steam Jet Ejector and Vacuum Cooling Systems," Heat Exchange Institute, New York, 1956.

Lubricants. The oil used for a refrigeration system should have a sufficiently low pour point so that it does not congeal on the coldest parts of the system. Most of the oil companies prepare such a grade of mineral oil, the usual specification being a pour point of −20 to −30°F. Such oils may be used for ammonia, carbon dioxide, and sulfur dioxide. Propane dissolves to a very appreciable extent, and the oil when removed from the oil separator foams extensively. Liquid sulfur dioxide has some lubricating effect and has a higher specific gravity than oil. The oil used for SO_2 machines must be highly anhydrous.

Light mineral oils can be used for methyl chloride and ethyl chloride machines; but, since they are soluble in oil, glycerin is often used as lubricant with these refrigerants. When propane or butane is used in household machines, the best results are obtained with glycerin or glycol mixed with deflocculated graphite. Household machines in general require extreme precautions against infiltration of moisture.

GAS-CYCLE SYSTEMS

Whereas in principle for refrigeration, with the closed gas circuit, any permanent gas could be used, the prevailing gas utilized is air. With a closed circuit connecting the compressor, rejection-heat exchanger, expander, and the refrigeration-effect heat exchanger back to the compressor, the gas-pressure levels may be upped, so that the physical size of the equipment may be reduced and certain aspects of control also introduced through adjustment of the pressure levels. However, one of the advantages when using air as the refrigerant is that it is cheap and safe, and under these circumstances the expander may discharge directly into the refrigerated space and the compressor draw directly out of this space.

With open cycles using air, humidity problems are introduced. Freeze-up of valves may take place because of the circulated water vapor of a humid system. This, as well as the air-borne dirt problem, is remedied in the closed cycle. Thermodynamically, as previously pointed out, the process cycle (in the United States) is known as the Brayton and is similar to that involved in gas-turbine operations. A typical arrangement is shown in Fig. 12-12, for the closed cycle. To reiterate, in the gas cycle the heat-exchange effects all involve sensible heat of gas.

ABSORPTION SYSTEMS

In the continuous absorption system, conventionally (Fig. 12-13) the refrigerant, usually ammonia, is drawn from the expansion coils F at a given pressure p_1 and dis-

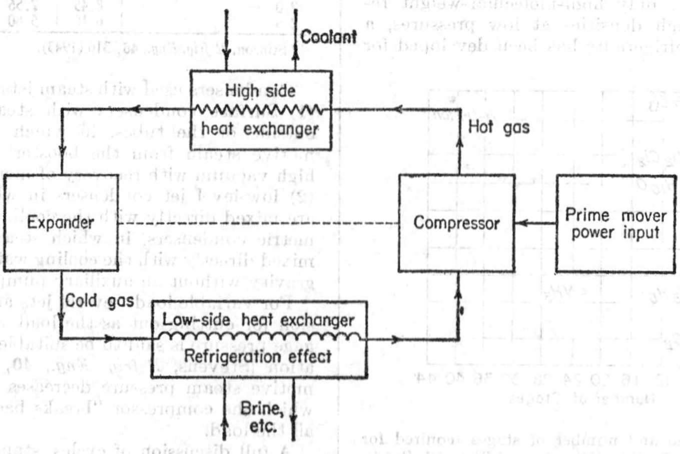

Fig. 12-12. Typical arrangement for closed-circuit gas-cycle system.

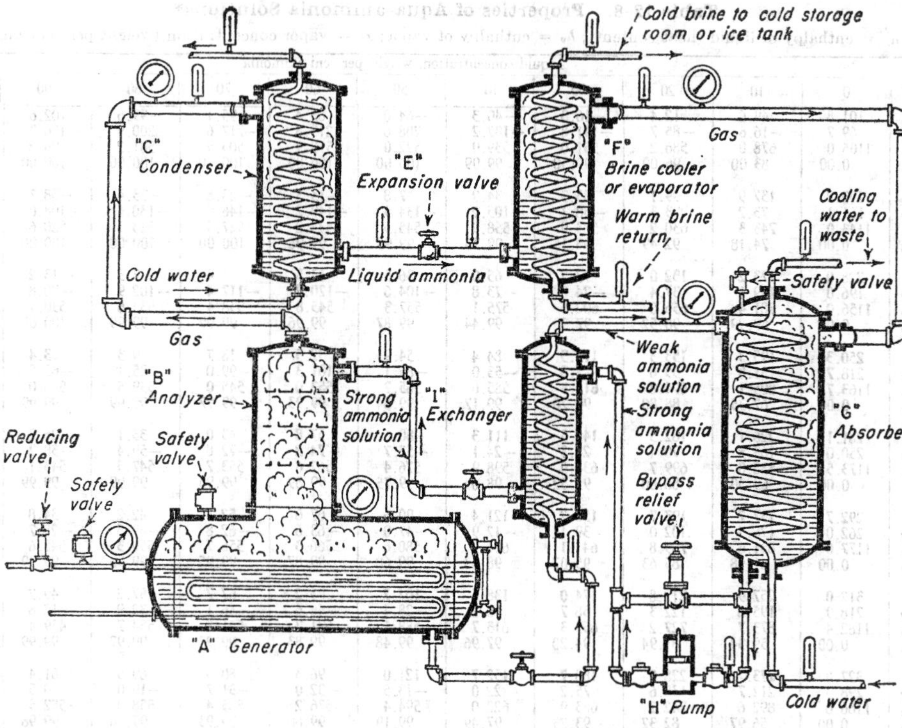

FIG. 12-13. Continuous absorption system.

solved in the absorber G where the combined pressure of solvent and refrigerant must be less than p_1. The refrigerant is recovered by applying heat to the generator A; separated from entrained water by the analyzer or rectifier B; liquefied in the condenser C; collected in a liquid receiver D (not shown); and returned to the expansion coils F through the expansion valve E. Since the absorber is at lower pressure than the generator, it is necessary to insert between them a pump H to transfer the ammonia solution usually known as strong aqua. The generator does not remove all the ammonia from the water, and this weak aqua solution is returned to the absorber through the heat exchanger I. Considerable heat is evolved in the absorption of ammonia vapor, and cooling water must be supplied to keep down the temperature and pressure. In the absorption system two complete cycles are in operation: (1) the refrigerant cycle, and (2) the absorbent cycle. Just as the absorbent contains some ammonia, so the refrigerant contains a small quantity of water.

The heat requirements of an absorption system may be approximately calculated by the following method (Glazebrook, "Dictionary of Applied Physics," Article on Refrigeration, Macmillan, London, 1921). Assume that a quantity of heat Q_2 is available at an absolute temperature T_2, and is transferred to the generator at a lower temperature T_1. The work W available from this heat in a Carnot cycle is given by the relation

$$W = Q_2 \frac{(T_2 - T_1)}{T_2} \tag{12-6}$$

Next assume that a quantity of heat Q_1 is to be transferred from the evaporator at a temperature T_4 to the condenser at the temperature T_3. The work required to effect this transfer is

$$W = Q_1 \frac{(T_3 - T_4)}{T_3} \tag{12-7}$$

The work available may now be set equal to the work required, from which it follows that

$$\frac{Q_2}{Q_1} = \frac{T_2}{T_3}\left(\frac{T_3 - T_4}{T_2 - T_1}\right) \tag{12-8}$$

If Q_1 is regarded as refrigeration, the heat requirement per unit of refrigeration is given by the ratio Q_2/Q_1. The value of this ratio calculated by the above method is necessarily a minimum, since there are various losses and irreversible effects that will add to the heat requirements.

Calculation of pressures, temperatures, and heat effects is facilitated by the use of an enthalpy concentration table for water-ammonia solution of which an abbreviated form is given in Table 12-8.

Results of various performances under practical operating conditions are given in Table 12-9.

Absorption units in large sizes are still being installed in custom-built units. Bubble cap rectifying towers are used to separate ammonia so that it reaches the evaporator in very high purity. Shell and tube exchangers with interval baffles are used to recover heat. Installations are bulky; but, where waste heat is available, economies over mechanical refrigeration may be obtained.

Absorption Systems with Other Refrigerants. Interest in the employment of absorption systems for air conditioning has been revived [Zellhoefer, *Refrig. Eng.*, May, 1937; Hainsworth, *ibid.*, **48,** 97 (1944)]. Because of its odor, ammonia cannot be used in this application, and considerable research has been devoted toward

Table 12-8. Properties of Aqua-ammonia Solutions*

t = °F.; h_f = enthalpy of liquid (heat content); h_v = enthalpy of vapor; x_v = vapor concentration (weight per cent ammonia)

Presure, lb./sq. in. (absolute)		Liquid concentration, weight per ceni ammonia										
		0	10	20	30	40	50	60	70	80	90	100
1	t	101.8	49.6	12.4	−16.3	−40.3	−64.0	−83.4	−95.1	−99.6	−102.6	−105.0
	h_f	69.7	−16.6	−85.7	−141.8	−182.2	−208.6	−219.8	−217.6	−200.9	−176.7	−146.0
	h_v	1105.0	678.0	586.2	551.0	539.0	522.0	510.9	505.5	501.2	496.2	490.7
	x_v	0.00	83.00	96.00	99.50	99.99	100.00	100.00	100.00	100.00	100.00	100.00
10	t	193.2	137.9	99.1	65.3	34.9	7.8	−13.3	−25.8	−33.4	−38.7	−41.3
	h_f	161.1	73.2	3.3	−58.1	−105.2	−134.5	−149.2	−146.0	−130.6	−108.0	−79.3
	h_v	1143.0	743.3	630.2	583.9	558.9	545.5	534.2	527.5	523.5	520.6	519.2
	x_v	0.00	74.18	92.49	98.15	99.75	99.90	99.98	100.00	100.00	100.00	100.00
20	t	228.0	173.2	132.0	97.2	65.0	36.5	14.5	1.4	−7.3	−13.2	−16.6
	h_f	196.0	109.1	37.4	−24.8	−73.8	−104.6	−120.2	−117.4	−102.9	−80.8	−52.9
	h_v	1156.0	781.4	656.0	602.5	575.1	557.3	545.8	538.4	533.6	530.9	528.3
	x_v	0.00	69.99	90.52	97.39	99.44	99.87	99.96	99.99	99.99	100.00	100.00
30	t	250.3	195.3	153.3	117.3	84.4	54.9	32.5	18.7	9.3	3.4	−0.6
	h_f	218.7	131.8	59.6	−3.3	−53.0	−85.1	−101.3	−99.0	−85.1	−62.8	−35.6
	h_v	1163.7	805.1	674.8	615.3	585.0	565.7	553.0	545.0	539.5	536.0	533.7
	x_v	0.00	67.35	88.80	96.70	99.17	99.84	99.93	99.97	99.99	99.99	100.00
50	t	281.1	226.1	182.5	145.5	111.3	80.6	57.8	43.0	33.1	26.2	21.7
	h_f	250.0	163.5	90.4	27.3	−24.1	−57.7	−74.2	−72.8	−59.4	−38.2	−11.4
	h_v	1173.5	838.8	699.7	634.0	598.9	576.4	562.6	553.7	547.5	543.1	540.3
	x_v	0.00	63.50	86.60	95.52	98.69	99.75	99.89	99.95	99.99	99.99	100.00
60	t	292.7	237.7	193.7	156.2	121.4	90.6	67.6	52.3	42.2	34.8	30.2
	h_f	262.0	175.5	102.0	39.1	−12.9	−47.0	−63.6	−62.8	−49.5	−28.7	−2.0
	h_v	1177.0	851.6	709.8	641.1	604.2	580.6	566.3	556.7	550.3	545.6	542.6
	x_v	0.00	61.98	85.63	95.07	98.43	99.68	99.87	99.95	99.98	99.99	100.00
80	t	312.0	257.9	212.8	174.0	138.6	107.7	83.2	67.7	57.2	49.2	44.4
	h_f	218.9	195.8	122.3	58.7	6.2	−28.4	−46.6	−46.1	−32.9	−12.8	13.8
	h_v	1182.4	873.7	727.2	653.3	613.7	588.1	571.7	561.8	554.7	459.4	546.1
	x_v	0.00	59.34	83.94	94.20	97.96	99.48	99.83	99.93	99.97	99.99	100.00
100	t	327.8	273.7	228.0	188.7	152.7	121.0	96.3	80.5	69.5	61.4	56.0
	h_f	298.3	212.7	138.6	75.2	22.0	−13.5	−32.0	−31.7	−19.0	0.5	26.8
	h_v	1186.6	892.6	742.2	663.9	622.0	594.4	576.2	565.4	558.0	552.5	548.6
	x_v	0.00	56.97	82.37	93.23	97.49	99.19	99.80	99.93	99.96	99.98	100.00
120	t	341.3	287.5	241.5	201.4	164.9	132.5	107.6	91.4	80.0	71.6	66.0
	h_f	312.4	227.1	153.1	89.6	36.0	−0.6	−19.2	−19.5	−7.2	11.6	38.1
	h_v	1189.8	908.9	754.4	673.4	628.8	599.7	580.5	568.6	560.8	554.7	550.5
	x_v	0.00	54.91	81.11	92.44	97.08	98.93	99.70	99.89	99.94	99.98	100.00
140	t	353.0	299.5	253.4	212.4	175.8	142.7	117.4	101.2	89.4	80.8	74.8
	h_f	324.7	240.0	166.1	102.2	48.6	10.9	−8.0	−8.6	3.5	22.3	48.1
	h_v	1192.4	921.5	765.9	682.4	635.4	604.5	584.2	572.0	563.1	556.7	552.0
	x_v	0.00	53.18	79.92	91.78	96.66	98.72	99.54	99.79	99.89	99.96	100.00
160	t	363.6	310.2	264.0	222.5	185.4	151.8	126.2	109.8	97.9	89.0	82.6
	h_f	335.9	251.2	177.5	113.7	59.8	21.2	2.0	1.3	13.3	31.9	57.1
	h_v	1194.5	933.0	776.0	690.1	641.2	608.6	587.5	574.6	565.2	558.3	553.2
	x_v	0.00	51.70	78.85	91.12	96.26	98.51	99.40	99.71	99.87	99.95	100.00
180	t	373.0	319.9	273.2	231.6	193.8	160.2	134.4	117.7	105.5	96.5	89.8
	h_f	346.0	261.6	187.5	124.0	69.9	31.0	11.3	10.5	22.2	40.4	65.4
	h_v	1196.3	943.0	785.2	696.9	646.6	612.6	590.5	576.8	566.9	559.6	554.1
	x_v	0.00	50.41	77.83	90.49	95.87	98.30	99.28	99.66	99.86	99.94	100.00
200	t	381.8	328.8	281.7	239.8	202.0	167.7	142.2	124.9	112.6	103.2	96.3
	h_f	355.3	271.4	196.8	133.5	79.7	39.8	20.3	18.8	30.4	48.2	73.0
	h_v	1197.8	952.0	793.7	703.7	651.5	616.0	593.1	578.8	568.4	560.6	554.8
	x_v	0.00	49.25	76.86	89.88	95.52	98.09	99.20	99.63	99.84	99.94	100.00
250	t	401.0	348.2	300.8	257.7	219.2	184.5	158.4	140.8	127.6	118.2	110.8
	h_f	376.0	293.0	217.5	155.2	100.7	59.5	39.6	37.5	48.2	65.8	90.1
	h_v	1200.5	970.1	812.9	717.5	661.8	623.4	598.4	582.4	570.9	562.5	555.9
	x_v	0.00	46.94	74.70	88.64	94.75	97.67	99.02	99.58	99.81	99.93	100.00
300	t	417.3	365.3	316.9	273.2	234.6	198.9	172.4	154.4	141.6	130.1	123.2
	h_f	393.9	311.7	235.3	172.4	119.8	77.1	56.1	53.4	64.6	81.0	104.1
	h_v	1202.4	984.5	829.3	730.3	671.2	629.6	602.9	585.8	573.6	536.6	556.1
	x_v	0.00	45.17	72.70	87.44	94.00	97.43	98.84	99.52	99.78	99.92	100.00

* Jennings and Shannon, Lehigh University Studies, Science and Technology Series 1, 1938. Data obtained through courtesy of Prof. Jennings. Original paper contains much more complete data.

finding other combinations of refrigerants and solvents that will be as efficient as the ammonia-water system. The prime requirement is that the refrigerant shall be highly soluble to minimize the heat waste in warming the solvent. Various cycles that may be used with such units are discussed by Taylor [*Refrig. Eng.*, **49, 188** (1945)].

Systems involving lithium bromide are now extensively used in air-conditioning applications.

Platen-Munters Continuous Absorption System. In the Platen-Munters system (**Electrolux Household Refrigerator**), circulation of refrigerant and absorbent is effected by the operation of hydrostatic forces developed within the system itself, and consequently there are no mechanical moving parts. In order to produce these hydrostatic forces, it is necessary to add a third component, which must differ in density (molecular

Table 12-9. Performance of Absorption Machine with Different Condenser and Suction Pressures*

	Condenser pressure, lb./sq. in. abs.								
	155			185			215		
	Suction pressure, lb./sq. in. abs.								
	15	30	45	15	30	45	15	30	45
S.L., %	24.0	35.0	42.0	22.0	32.0	38.0	18.0	28.0	36.0
W.L., %	13.1	25.8	33.7	10.9	22.3	29.2	6.3	17.7	26.9
S.G., lb.	30.1	27.9	22.9	41.3	30.9	26.2	48.7	34.1	27.9
S.P., lb.	31.8	29.5	24.3	43.4	32.8	28.0	51.1	36.4	30.1
Relative capacities:									
Absorption	0.97	1.03	1.09	0.94	1.00	1.05	0.91	0.97	1.03
Compression	0.46	1.05	1.62	0.43	1.00	1.56	0.41	0.95	1.49

S.L. is strong liquor.
W.L. is weak liquor.
S.G. is the steam consumption of the generator.
S.P. is the steam consumption of the pump.
* Voorhees, "Refrigerating Machines."

weight) from the refrigerant and be capable of separation from the refrigerant. The usual combination is ammonia, water, and hydrogen.

The essential features are shown in Fig. 12-14. Strong ammonia solution is heated in the lower portion of the

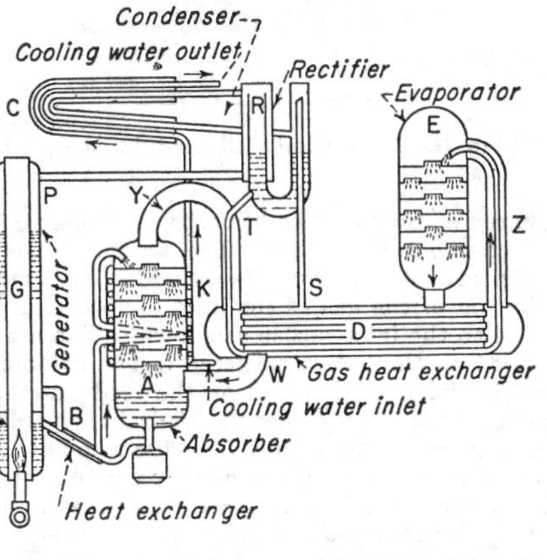

Fig. 12-14. Electrolux gas-heated refrigerating unit.

generator *G*, the weak liquor flowing back to the absorber *A*, while the ammonia-water vapors are separated in the rectifier *R* and the ammonia vapors liquefied in the condenser *C*. The liquid ammonia passes through a heat exchanger *D* into the evaporator *E*. In the evaporator it flows into an atmosphere of hydrogen and is vaporized, though the process is more analogous to humidification. The ammonia-hydrogen mixture then moves back to the absorber *A* through the heat exchanger, and the ammonia is dissolved leaving substantially pure hydrogen. Circulation is produced because the column of hydrogen in the absorber is opposed by a heavier column of hydrogen-ammonia vapors in the evaporator, although the total gas pressure throughout the unit is equal. A difference in hydrostatic pressure, obtained partly by heat, partly by change in liquid density, also prevails between the generator and absorber.

The Platen-Munters system employs hydrogen, ammonia, and water and is therefore known as a **three-fluid cycle** as distinguished from a **two-fluid** as in large absorption units. The third fluid is necessary to obtain circulation without a pump.

Intermittent Absorption Machine. In the intermittent absorption machine the absorber and generator, and the condenser and the evaporator, are combined. During the cooling period the refrigerant is taken up by the absorbent, which may be water, silica gel, activated charcoal, or chlorides of the alkaline earth metals. When the absorbent has become saturated it is regenerated by heating and the vapors condensed in the evaporator which is cooled by running water. These machines have not proved very successful for two reasons: (1) the general desirability of maintaining continuous refrigeration and (2) the great explosion hazard in overheating during regeneration.

HIGH-SIDE HEAT EXCHANGE

Condensers. For a complete discussion of condenser sizing see Sec. 10; for a complete discussion of condenser fabrication methods see Sec. 11. The following discussion is limited to aspects specialized for refrigeration systems.

The primary function of the condenser is to transfer to the environment (usually water or air) the heat extracted at the lower temperature. If c is the specific heat of water (or air), W the weight of water sent through the condenser per minute, Δt the temperature rise in degrees Fahrenheit, and n the number of tons refrigeration produced, then

$$W = \frac{200n}{c\Delta t} \qquad (12\text{-}9)$$

Usually Δt will not be more than 30°F., from which it follows that W is approximately 7 lb./min./ton refrigeration or about 1100 to 1200 gal./day/ton refrigeration.

In considering any refrigeration installation it is always important to determine whether the condensing water requirements can be met from the available sources. In large metropolitan centers this may often be a serious problem [Gardner, *Refrig. Eng.*, **41,** 17 (1941)]. The question of cooling-water economy was discussed by Sherwood (*Refrig. Eng.*, February, 1927) and Waterfill (*op. cit.*, September, 1927).

Types of Condensers. Condensers may be divided into the following types: (1) submerged coil; (2) atmospheric; (3) atmospheric counterflow; (4) double pipe; (5) multicoil; (6) flooded; (7) vertical shell and tube; (8) horizontal shell and tube. These types have been characteristically developed for ammonia.

Submerged-coil Condensers. The early condensers consisted of pipe coils placed in a tank. Ammonia flowed downward through the coil while water was introduced at the lower part of the tank and overflowed through a connection near the tank top. This was a cheap condenser to build, but the maximum heat transfer rate was only 30 B.t.u./sq. ft./°F./hr. because of stagnant water along the coil.

Atmospheric Condensers. Atmospheric condensers are made of a vertical row of horizontal pipe lengths, from 8 to 20 in number, with the ends connected by return bends forming a continuous pipe through which the ammonia passes. Ammonia enters at the top from a header connecting two or more of the rows of pipes and flows downward, losing its heat to the water. Liquid ammonia settles in the bottom coils and passes off to the receiver or storage tank. Water is fed into a trough placed over the top pipe and, overflowing, drops into the top pipe and thence successively flows over each pipe into a basin beneath the coil. This type is illustrated in Fig. 12-15.

Bottom-inlet Atmospheric Condensers. In bottom-inlet condensers the flow is made countercurrent by feeding the vapor at the bottom and by taking liquid off at the top, but, unless bleeder connections are taken off every few coils, the liquid tends to flow back toward the bottom. The condition prevails in those condensers where, after passing upward through the two lower pipes, the ammonia vapor is conveyed by an outside connection

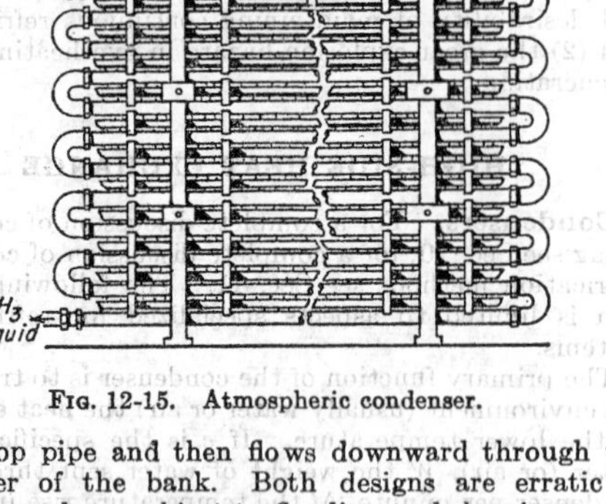

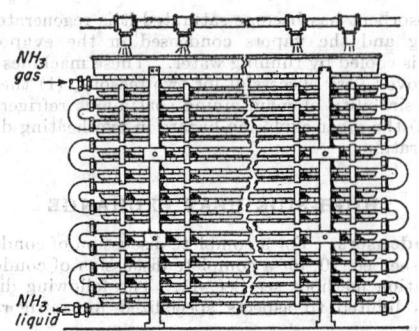

FIG. 12-15. Atmospheric condenser.

to the top pipe and then flows downward through the remainder of the bank. Both designs are erratic in operation and are subject to flooding and slugging.

Countercurrent Atmospheric Condensers. As stated above, the coldest water in the ordinary atmospheric condenser is at the top in contact with the hottest gases, while the hottest water at the bottom is in contact with the coldest ammonia. To reduce the ammonia temperature on leaving the condenser, condensers are designed with the gas inlet at the bottom where it meets the hottest water and the liquid discharge higher where the water is cooler. In its passage upward through the coils the condensing ammonia will have a tendency to trickle downward against the entering vapor. To prevent the bottom coils from filling up with liquid, trap drains are provided at several points.

Double-pipe Condensers. The desirability of having a condenser suitable for locations where the splashing of water by an atmospheric condenser could not be permitted led to the use of the double-pipe condenser (Fig. 12-16). In this design, two pipes are placed one within

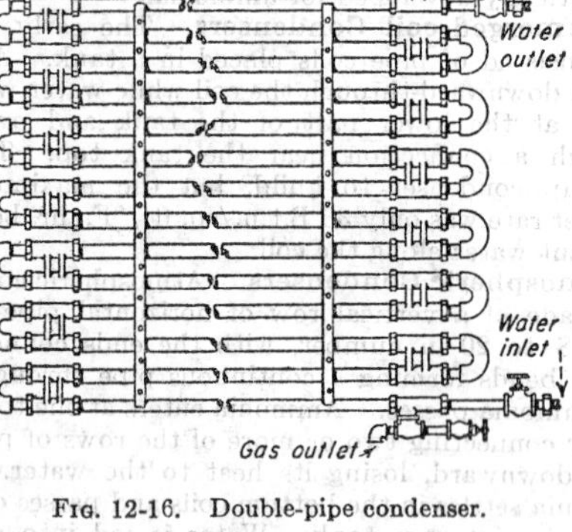

FIG. 12-16. Double-pipe condenser.

the other. The inner one is usually 1¼ in. in diameter and is filled with cooling water. The outer pipe is 2 in. in diameter, and the ammonia gas flows between the inner and outer pipes. Suitable connections permit the water to flow from one inner pipe to the next upper one, while at the same time the ammonia gas can pass in the opposite direction. The inner pipe extends through the fitting and through two stuffing boxes which seal the connection against leakage.

Shell-and-tube Condensers. A type of construction of the vertical single-pass multitube condenser is illustrated in Fig. 12-17. This consists of a welded shell

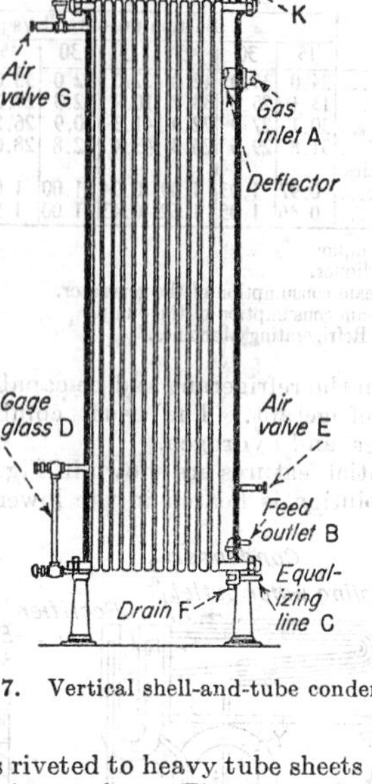

FIG. 12-17. Vertical shell-and-tube condenser.

with flared ends riveted to heavy tube sheets and a number of charcoal-iron tubes. The ammonia gas inlet is at the point *A*. In order to provide for a more even distribution of the gas at the inlet, a special deflector is attached to the inlet nozzle as shown. The ammonia is condensed on the tubes, collected in the bottom part of the shell, and is drained off at the feed outlet *B*. An equalizing line is provided at *C*. A drain is installed at *F*, while purge connections may be made at points *E* and *F*. A circular water box *H* is attached to the top sheet, and a special water baffle *I*, having serrated edges *K*, is placed within the water box as shown. Water-distributing devices *J* are placed on the top end of each tube. These distributors are made of cast iron and are hollow and with spiral grooves, and cause the water to flow in a corkscrew motion down the tube. A certain amount of air is drawn in through the hollow cores of the device. The vertical shell-and-tube condenser has the advantage that a greater amount of cooling surface can be obtained for a given floor space than with any other type.

Heat Transfer in Ammonia Condensers (See Sec. 10). Exhaustive investigations on heat transfer in ammonia condensers were carried on by the University of Illinois; the results appear in the University of Illinois Bulletin 25. In these investigations tests were run on shell-and-tube, atmospheric-bleeder, and double-pipe condensers, and both the unit condenser tonnage and the total condenser tonnage have been broadly studied comparatively in terms of the unit water rate for initial water temperature of 68°F. When the total tonnage developed is taken into consideration the shell-and-tube condenser shows the greatest capacity. The total area of the bleeder condenser exposed to saturated ammonia is 105 sq. ft., while that of the double-pipe condenser is 92 sq. ft. and in the case of the shell-and-tube condenser is 251 sq. ft.

As reported by the University of Illinois Bulletin 186, the heat removed by a 16-ft. vertical shell-and-tube condenser having thirty 2-in. tubes is found to vary with the water flow. Water requirements are shown in Table 12-10. The variations in heat transfer with varying water flows and tonnages are shown in Fig. 12-18.

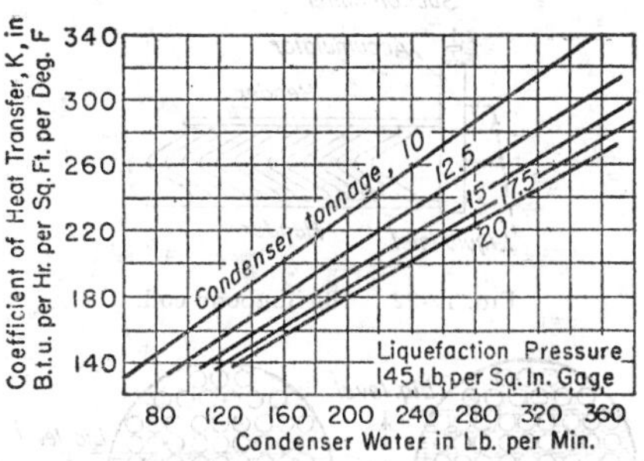

FIG. 12-18. Variation of heat transfer with water rate for shell-and-tube condensers.

The conclusions reached in these tests were as follows:

1. The thickness of the layer of liquid ammonia adhering to the tubes of the vertical shell-and-tube condenser materially affects the rate of heat transfer per unit of surface.

2. At a constant water rate the coefficient of heat transfer decreases with increasing values of the mean temperature difference between the ammonia and the water in the vertical shell-and-tube condenser.

3. Irrespective of the proportions of the vertical shell-and-tube condenser no appreciable subcooling of the liquid occurs.

4. The condenser tonnage developed per square foot of surface in the shell-and-tube condenser is independent of the size or proportions of the condenser and is a function only of the initial temperature of the water and the amount circulated per square foot of surface per unit of time.

5. The condenser tonnage developed per square foot of surface in the condensers when the effective surface is altered by raising the liquid level or by plugging pumps, as was done in the investigation, is approximately independent of the proportions or arrangement of surface if a given amount of water at a given initial temperature is circulated per square foot of surface in a given time.

6. One square foot of surface is approximately eight times as effective in transferring heat from saturated ammonia vapor to water as it is in transferring heat from superheated ammonia gas to water.*

7. For conditions of viscous flow on the water side, the coefficient of heat transfer in a superheat remover is a linear function of the water velocity.*

Table 12-10. Gallons Condenser Water per Ton Refrigeration

Condenser pressure, lb./sq. in. gage	Corresponding temp., °F.	60°F. water				70°F. water				80°F. water			
		Range °F.	Water per ton of refrigeration, gal./min. Suction pressure, lb. gage			Range °F.	Water per ton of refrigeration, gal./min. Suction pressure, lb. gage			Range °F.	Water per ton of refrigeration, gal./min. Suction pressure, lb. gage		
			15	20	25		15	20	25		15	20	25
126.4	75	10	2.90	2.85	2.80								
131.4	77	12	2.40	2.35	2.30								
136.6	79	14	2.05	2.00	1.95								
141.8	81	16	1.85	1.80	1.75	6	4.87	4.80	4.70				
147.2	83	18	1.65	1.60	1.55	8	3.67	3.60	3.55				
152.7	85	20	1.47	1.45	1.41	10	2.95	2.90	2.85				
158.3	87	22	1.35	1.32	1.30	12	2.45	2.40	2.35				
164.1	89	24	1.25	1.22	1.20	14	2.10	2.05	2.00				
170.1	91	26	1.15	1.13	1.10	16	1.90	1.85	1.80	6	5.00	4.90	4.80
176.2	93	28	1.08	1.05	1.03	18	1.68	1.63	1.60	8	3.75	3.70	3.65
182.6	95	30	1.00	0.99	0.97	20	1.50	1.48	1.45	10	3.00	2.95	2.90
189.1	97	32	0.95	0.93	0.90	22	1.38	1.35	1.32	12	2.52	2.48	2.43
195.7	99	...	...	...	...	24	1.28	1.25	1.22	14	2.13	2.10	2.06
202.5	101	...	...	...	...	26	1.17	1.15	1.13	16	1.92	1.85	1.83
209.5	103	...	...	...	...	28	1.10	1.07	1.05	18	1.70	1.67	1.63
216.5	105	...	...	...	...	30	1.02	1.00	0.98	20	1.53	1.50	1.48
223.7	107	...	...	...	...	32	0.95	0.93	0.92	22	1.40	1.37	1.35
231.1	109	...	...	...	...	...	...	...	...	24	1.30	1.28	1.25
238.7	111	...	...	...	...	...	...	...	...	26	1.20	1.16	1.15
246.5	113	...	...	...	...	...	...	...	...	28	1.12	1.08	1.06
254.5	115	...	...	...	...	...	...	...	...	30	1.05	1.02	1.00
262.7	117	...	...	...	...	...	...	...	...	32	1.00	0.98	0.95

Air Cooling. Because of water problems (supply, purity, etc.) the use of air-cooled condensers, particularly for air-conditioning purposes, is growing rapidly. Condensers are available up to 50 tons and more for air-conditioning use, usually with Freon compounds.

LOW-SIDE HEAT EXCHANGE

Cooling Systems. The term **cooling system** refers to that portion of a refrigeration unit in which cold is applied. Two types of cooling system are in use: (1) **direct-expansion** and (2) **indirect-brine** systems.

With the **direct-expansion** system, where ammonia is allowed to boil in the cold-storage rooms, there is danger from ammonia leakage at all times. The pipe lines may become corroded or may split because of imperfect welding, or fittings may be broken accidentally with resulting damage to life or commodities. In a large system with long supply and return pipes, or extensive refrigerating piping, the amount of the initial charge has to be very large, and constant care to maintain the piping tight at all times is required.

In the **brine system of indirect refrigeration,** the high-pressure side is the same as in the direct-expansion system. The low-pressure side consists of a brine cooler, usually of the shell-and-tube type, similar in construction to a steam condenser. The brine is a non-freezing solution of sodium chloride or calcium chloride, of such concentration as will not freeze at the temperature carried in the cooling system. The brine system then is really an additional unit, in which the brine is kept cool by boiling ammonia and the cold-storage rooms or other refrigerating applications are kept cold by the brine. Appreciable amounts of refrigeration may be stored up in the brine to take up peak loads or provide reserve refrigeration for closing down periods.

In the direct-expansion system one less heat transfer is necessary, and consequently the expansion coils can be maintained at a higher temperature and pressure so that the compression work is less. Moreover, the refrigerant extracts heat by evaporation (latent heat) so it can be distributed at room temperatures, whereas brine extracts heat only by being colder than the surroundings (sensible heat) and must be distributed cold in well-insulated piping. The direct-expansion system is therefore much more efficient in theory, and the only obstacle to its general adoption is the difficulty of constructing leakproof systems.

Evaporation or Expansion Coils.† Just as the function of the condenser is to dissipate heat, so the function of the evaporating coil is to collect heat at the lower temperature of the refrigerating system.

It is quite possible to inject the liquid refrigerant into the material to be cooled and then cause it to evaporate, but this is in general undesirable for two reasons: first, the refrigerant will have a deleterious effect on the substance cooled, and, second, its vapor pressure will be lower because of dilution and the power expenditure in compression will be greater. However, in case the refrigerant can also be used as a solvent, this system may prove very satisfactory, and one notable application is found in the

* If the superheated vapor is condensing, the rate of heat transfer is probably as good as for saturated vapor. The above conclusions apply to the case in which superheated vapor goes to a lower degree of superheat.

† For a more general discussion see Consley, Heat Transfer in Ammonia Shell-and-tube Brine Coolers as Affected by Operating Conditions, *Refrig. Eng.*, **35**, 409 (1938).

dewaxing of petroleum oils by liquid propane [Beiter, *Refrig. Eng.*, **40**, 293 (1940)] and in the Edeleanu process for extracting asphaltic materials from mineral oils by sulfur dioxide.

The simplest method of cooling brine is to thrust a pipe coil into the brine tank with one end connected to the liquid refrigerant supply and the other to the compressor. An older form of construction with a series of continuous coils attached to headers is shown in Fig. 12-19. Liquid

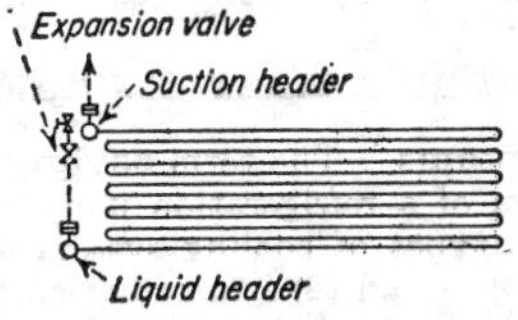

Fig. 12-19. Continuous-coil evaporator.

ammonia is fed into the bottom and drawn off on top. Under these conditions liquid ammonia is present on the inside surface of the coils, and if this is accidentally drawn into the compressor it may fill up the clearance space in the cylinder and blow off the head on the compression stroke. This difficulty is overcome by placing an accumulator (shown by dotted lines in Fig. 12-20) between

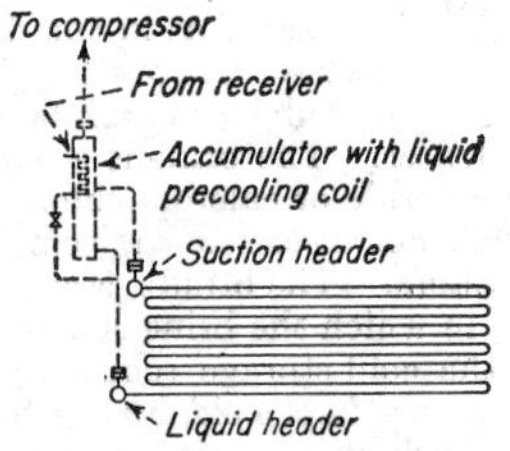

Fig. 12-20. Evaporator coil with accumulator.

the expansion coil and the compressor. The accumulator may serve the further purpose of precooling the liquid ammonia returning to the expansion coil. This arrangement of coils with accumulator is known as the **flooded system.** In order to facilitate transfer of heat, brine tanks may be built with partitions and bulkheads so arranged that the brine may be agitated and swirled around and through the coils.

One type of short evaporator coil is shown in Fig. 12-21. This is sometimes made with three sets of pipes between

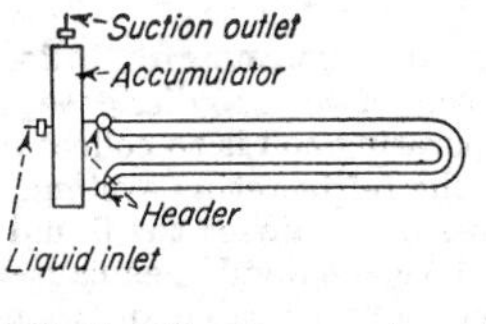

Fig. 12-21. Short evaporator coil.

the upper and lower headers and placed in a covered brine compartment. The herringbone coil shown in Fig. 12-22 can be placed in a trough through which the brine is circulated at high velocity.

Besides the *submerged* types of coils, which are used chiefly in ice making, shell-and-tube brine coolers, and double-pipe brine coolers with brine flowing through the inner tube are also used. Shell-and-tube coolers are largely displacing other types in more recent installations (Fig. 12-23). Brine flows through the tubes, and a sur-

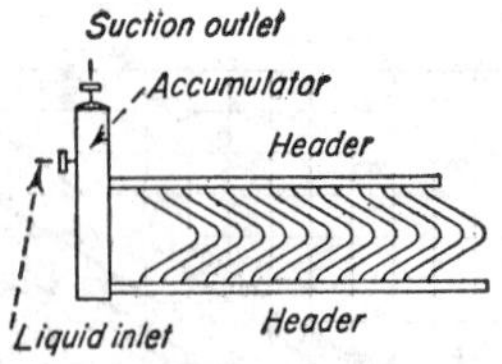

Fig. 12-22. Herringbone coil.

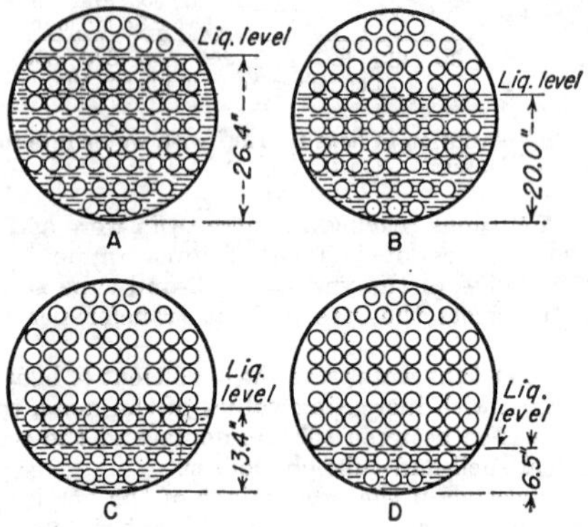

Fig. 12-23. Liquid levels used in shell-and-tube coolers. Shell diameter about 32.9 in.

face of 8 to 15 sq. ft. is usually allowed per ton of refrigeration. They may be placed either upright or horizontal and require small floor space. A float valve can be placed in the liquid receiver to regulate the amount of ammonia fed to the expansion coils.

Heat Transfer in Evaporators. (See Sec. 11.) The York Ice Machinery Corp. conducted a series of tests on heat transfer in various evaporators. For shell-and-tube evaporators with tube arrangements and liquid levels shown in Fig. 12-23 the results were as given in Table 12-11.

Table 12-11. Results of Tests on Shell-and-tube Cooler*

	17.9° brine in				34° brine in			
	A	B	C	D	A	B	C	D
Brine temp., °F	17.6	17.9	17.9	17.8	34.3	34.0	33.9	33.6
Suction pressure at cooler, lb. gage	14.9	13.9	10.6	6.3	24.6	22.7	18.0	10.5
Superheat at cooler, °F	3.4	7.3	13.3	23.0	3.5	7.8	14.5	28.7
Tons of refrigeration	61.4	59.0	51.3	41.0	79.2	75.5	66.2	49.8
Tube surface below liquid level, %	87.5	62.5	37.5	12.5	87.5	62.5	37.5	12.5
Height of ammonia, in.	26.4	20.0	13.4	6.5	26.4	20.0	13.4	6.5
Mean temp. difference	15.5	17.3	22.7	30.6	19.3	21.3	27.5	38.9
B.t.u. transfer/sq. ft./hr./deg. mean temp. difference	62.5	54.5	36.4	21.5	68.4	56.8	38.6	20.5
Brine velocity, ft./min.	129	131	134	133	133	133	135	133

* The York Ice Machinery Corporation, by permission.

For short flooded coils, the results obtained are shown in Table 12-12.

Table 12-12. Results with Short Flooded Coils*

	A	B	C	D
1¼-in. pipe, ft.	500	500	500	500
Suction pressure, lb. gage	19.6	21.2	18.9	21.5
Brine temperature, °F	14.0	14.0	14.0	14.0
Brine velocity, ft./min.	133	133	133	133
Tons refrigeration	7.3	9.0	12.0	15.7
B.t.u. transfer	43	68	66	120

* The York Ice Machinery Corp., by permission.

Refrigerant Liquid Controls. To prevent evaporating coils from overflowing with liquid refrigerant, some form of automatic control valve is usually employed. These may be classified into four groups (see Sec. 22):

1. The diaphragm-operated pressure-reducing valves controlling the refrigerant feed to the evaporator according to the pressure in the evaporator.
2. Diaphragm-operated pressure-reducing valves controlling the refrigerant feed to the evaporator by means of the temperature of the refrigerant gas leaving the evaporator.
3. Thermostatically controlled shutoff valves actuated by change of temperature in room or tank and used in series with hand-adjusted expansion valves or valves under group 1 or 2.
4. Float-controlled valves which function according to the change in liquid refrigerant level in the evaporators, or used as liquid traps to pass the refrigerant from the high side to the evaporator as it is condensed.

In low-temperature refrigeration, where the liquid control must operate under small pressure differences, special thermostatic valves have been developed [Carter, *Refrig. Eng.*, **47**, 96 (1944); **50**, 39 (1945)].

BRINES

Types. A *brine* may be defined as a liquid of low freezing point used in the transmission of refrigeration without change of state (see Sec. 3). The brines commonly employed in refrigeration are calcium and sodium chlorides. The latter is cheaper but cannot be used below its eutectic point of −6.03°F. Calcium chloride of commercial grade does not operate very satisfactorily below −40°F. The specific gravity, freezing point, composition by weight, and heat content per pound of solution have been compiled by Jessup [*Refrig. Eng.*, **22**, 168–169 (1931)].

Although these brines have the great advantage of low cost, they have the disadvantage of being extremely corrosive, and the calcium brines have the disadvantage of throwing down insoluble precipitates with untreated waters. Corrosion in closed systems can be largely overcome by the addition of sodium dichromate, $Na_2Cr_2O_7.2H_2O$, 100 lb. and 200 lb. being required per 1000 cu. ft. of calcium and sodium brines, respectively. Enough caustic is added to make the brines slightly alkaline. In open systems using sodium brines, disodium phosphate, $Na_2HPO_4.12H_2O$, may be used at the rate of 100 lb./1000 cu. ft., but the solutions should be colorless to phenolphthalein. Open calcium-brine systems may be protected by adding zinc dust at the rate of 60 lb./1000 cu. ft., a little at a time.

Magnesium chloride brines are used to some extent, but their eutectic temperature is not low enough to give them much advantage over sodium chloride.

Other materials that may be used are methanol, denatured alcohol, ethylene glycol, and glycerin. These have been much used for protection of automobile radiators and are no more corrosive than water. Their main disadvantage is cost, but they have been used in place of brines for household refrigerators. Methanol and denatured alcohol solutions are not inflammable at refrigeration temperatures, but at higher temperatures they may give off inflammable vapors. A comparison of freezing points is shown in Fig. 12-24. The eutectic for the alcohols lies well below that of calcium chloride. The alcohols will give no difficulty from crystallization; but, if the concentrations of the sodium and calcium brines are greater than 23 or 33 per cent, respectively, solid salt may deposit out. When solutions begin to freeze, their fluidity persists until some lower temperature is reached. The temperature at which the slush of ice crystals and liquid ceases to flow through a ¼-in. pipe has arbitrarily been defined as the **flow point** [Olsen, Brunjes, and Olsen, *Ind. Eng. Chem.*, **22**, 1316 (1930)].

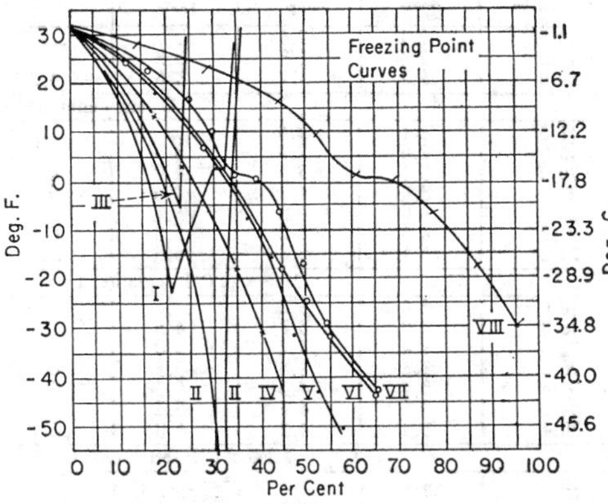

FIG. 12-24. Compositions and freezing points of solutions.
I. MgCl2, per cent by weight
II. CaCl2, per cent by weight
III. NaCl, per cent by weight
IV. Methanol, per cent by volume
V. Ethylene glycol, per cent by volume
VI. Denatured alcohol, per cent by volume
VII. Glycerol U.S.P. 96.5 per cent, per cent by volume
VIII. Glycerol U.S.P. 60 per cent, per cent by volume

Nessler's Solution. To determine ammonia leakage into the brine Nessler's solution is used, which is prepared as follows: Dissolve 17 g. mercuric chloride in about 300 cc. distilled water; dissolve 35 g. potassium iodide in 100 cc. water. Add the former solution to the latter, with constant stirring, until a slight permanent red precipitate is formed. Next dissolve 120 g. potassium hydrate in about 200 cc. water; allow the solution to cool and then add to the previous solution and make up with water to 1 l. Add mercuric chloride solution until a permanent precipitate again forms. Allow to stand till settled and decant off the clear solution for use. Store in glass-stoppered blue bottles in a dark place.

In calcium chloride brine, Nessler's solution will form a yellow precipitate, but if no ammonia is present the precipitate will be almost white. In water or brine the precipitate will be yellow if there is but a trace of ammonia present, and a reddish brown if there is considerable ammonia in the sample.

Pressure Drop and Power Required in Brine Circulation. The pressure drop in brine pipes is determined by the rate of flow, the internal diameter and length of the pipe, and the viscosity of the brine. The method for finding the pressure drop with water has already been discussed in Sec. 5. The pressure drop for brines may be found by multiplying the values for water by the ratio of the kinematic viscosities of brine and water. This factor f is given by the formula

$$f = \frac{\text{viscosity of brine}}{\text{viscosity of water}} \times \frac{\text{density of water}}{\text{density of brine}} \qquad (12\text{-}10)$$

The viscosities of most solutions have not been experimentally determined at low temperatures. However, the curve obtained by plotting the logarithm of the absolute viscosity against the logarithm of the absolute temperature gives a straight line [Genereaux, *Ind. Eng. Chem.*, **22**, 1382 (1930)]. Extrapolation of this plot has given the viscosities in Table 12-13. Thermal conductivities of brines are given in Table 12-14.

Table 12-13. Viscosities (Extrapolated) of Refrigerating Solutions (Centipoises)

Weight, %	0°C. 32°F.	−5°C. 23°F.	−10°C. 14°F.	−15°C. 5°F.	−20°C. −4°F.	−25°C. −13°F.	−30°C. −22°F.	−35°C. −31°F.	−40°C. −40°F.	Freezing point
Sodium chloride [Jessup, *Refrig. Eng.*, 12, 171 (1925)]										
10.5	2.1	2.4	....	....	....	....	....	....	....	+20°F.
16.8	2.4	2.8	3.2	....	....	....	....	....	....	+10°F.
21.0	2.7	3.1	3.6	4.2	....	....	....	....	....	0°F.
Calcium chloride [Jessup, *Refrig. Eng.*, 12, 171 (1925)]										
11.0	2.1	2.4	....	....	....	....	....	....	....	+20°F.
16.0	2.6	2.9	3.3	....	....	....	....	....	....	+10°F.
20.0	3.1	3.5	4.0	4.5	....	....	....	....	....	0°F.
22.8	3.6	4.1	4.6	5.2	5.9	....	....	....	....	−10°F.
25.2	4.0	4.6	5.1	5.8	6.6	7.4	....	....	....	−20°F.
27.2	4.6	5.2	5.8	6.6	7.5	8.4	9.6	....	....	−30°F.
29.0	5.1	5.8	6.6	7.4	8.4	9.5	10.8	12.3	14.1	−40°F.
Methanol ("International Critical Tables" and Landolt-Börnstein Tables, 5th ed.)										
10.0	2.6	3.2	....	....	....	....	....	....	....	+20°F.
16.8	3.0	3.7	4.5	....	....	....	....	....	....	+10°F.
22.0	3.4	4.2	5.0	6.1	....	....	....	....	....	0°F.
26.2	3.6	4.4	5.3	6.5	7.9	....	....	....	....	−10°F.
30.4	3.7	4.5	5.5	6.8	8.3	10.3	....	....	....	−20°F.
34.2	3.6	4.4	5.3	6.5	7.9	9.7	12.0	....	....	−30°F.
38.4	3.4	4.2	5.0	6.1	7.3	8.9	11.0	13.3	16.5	−40°F.
Ethanol ("International Critical Tables" and Landolt-Börnstein Tables, 5th ed.)										
15.0	4.1	5.2	....	....	....	....	....	....	....	+20°F.
22.8	5.7	7.4	9.5	....	....	....	....	....	....	+10°F.
29.0	6.9	9.0	11.8	15.5	....	....	....	....	....	0°F.
35.0	7.2	9.5	12.4	16.4	22.0	....	....	....	....	−10°F.
41.2	7.0	8.9	11.6	15.0	19.7	26.0	....	....	....	−20°F.
48.8	6.7	8.4	10.8	13.8	17.7	23.0	30.0	....	....	−30°F.
56.8	6.1	7.6	9.5	12.1	15.4	19.8	25.5	32.5	42.5	−40°F.
Glycerol [Green and Parke, *J. Soc. Chem. Ind.*, 58, 319 (1939)]										
30	....	6.5	....	....	....	....	....	....	....	+15°F.
40	....	10.3	14.4	....	....	....	....	....	....	+ 4.3°F.
50	....	18.8	24.4	....	48.1	....	....	....	....	− 9.4°F.
60	....	41.6	59.1	....	108.0	....	244.0	....	....	−30.5°F.

Brine Piping. Brine is seldom allowed to warm more than 20°F. in performing refrigeration, and the heat absorbed per pound is much smaller than that absorbed by the evaporation of an equal weight of refrigerant. Consequently brine piping is larger than refrigerant piping. Standard-weight piping is sufficient for all ordinary purposes.

Table 12-14. Thermal Conductivities of Refrigerating Brines

Brines	Weight, %	Temp., °C.	Conductivity,‡ cal./cm./sec./°C.
*NaCl	12.5	32	0.001403
	25.0	32	.001141
*$CaCl_2$	15.0	32	.001383
	30.0	32	.001315
*$MgCl_2$	11.0	32	.001376
	14.5	32	.001329
	22.0	32	.001290
	29.0	32	.001238
†CH_3OH	0	19	.00141
	25	19	.00107
	50	19	.00078
	75	19	.00061
	100	19	.00050
†C_2H_5OH	0	10	.00149
	25	10	.00104
	50	11	.00079
	75	12	.00059
	100	10	.00047
†Glycerin	0	20	.00140
	25	20	.00119
	50	20	.00101
	75	20	.00081
	100	20	.00070
*Ethylene glycol	100	0	.00064

* Landolt-Börnstein Tables, 5th ed.
† Lees, *Phil. Trans. Roy. Soc.*, (A) 191, 399 (1898).
‡ For conversion factors see 1-25.

The same rule for threads applies as in any threaded pipe work.

Copper Piping. Copper piping is extensively used for handling refrigerants in direct-expansion systems. Joints can be sweated together, and the piping can readily be bent around obstructions. However, ammonia attacks copper, and such tubing can therefore not be used except with the Freon type of refrigerants or methyl and ethyl chlorides. Small commercial installations of 1 to 5 tons capacity are tending to go over to copper piping with these refrigerants because of the ease of installation.

INSULATION

It is customary, in system design, to assume an average maximum temperature during the period of peak refrigerating loads. The average temperatures in the United States may be obtained from government reports. The average temperature experienced during a 24-hr. period for conditions that are likely to prevail for a week's time should be used in making estimates. The actual choice of the thickness of insulation for any particular case will be decided by the relative costs of the insulation itself and the book value of a ton of refrigeration.

The standard insulation of the American Warehouse Association has been: For walls, ceilings, floors, partitions, etc., of cold-storage buildings, the insulation consists of corkboard of good quality and of medium density with both outer surfaces sealed by either dipping or coating with an asphaltic mastic, or by applying a waterproof Portland cement plaster as a finish. An additional ½ in. of waterproof Portland cement is used between the layers of the cork to seal the voids between the cork granules against atmospheric or other moisture. The standard thickness for temperatures down to 32°F. is two layers of 2-in. corkboard; to this is added 1 in. for each 15°F. below 32°F. Piping, fittings, etc., should be covered with molded cork covering, which should have its outer and inner surfaces sealed with a rubber or asphaltic mastic. Standard brine-pipe covering for temperatures down to 0°F. varies from 2 to 3 in. thickness with the diameter of the pipe.

Table 12-15. Piping for General Storage

Cu. ft. of space cooled per linear foot of 1¼-in. and of 2-in. pipe. 15.67 lb. suction pressure. Temperature of ammonia expansion, 0°F. Mean temperature of brine, 10°F.

Size of room, cu. ft.	Room temp., 40°F.					Room temp., 36°F.					Room temp., 32°F.					Room temp., 28°F.				
	Tons refriger.	Direct expansion, in.		Brine, in.		Tons refriger.	Direct expansion, in.		Brine, in.		Tons refriger.	Direct expansion, in.		Brine, in.		Tons refriger.	Direct expansion, in.		Brine, in.	
		1¼	2	1¼	2		1¼	2	1¼	2		1¼	2	1¼	2		1¼	2	1¼	2
1,000	0.7	8	12	6	9	0.75	7	10	4.5	6	0.8	6	8	4	5	1.1	4	5	2	3
2,000	1.1	10	15	7	11	1.3	8	12	7	7	1.4	7	9	5	6	1.9	4.5	6	2.5	3.5
3,000	1.5	11	16	8	12	1.6	9	14	6	8	1.7	8	12	5.5	7	2.3	5	7	3	4
4,000	1.8	12	18	9	13	2.0	10	15	6.5	10	2.2	8.5	12.5	6	8	3.0	5.5	7.5	3.5	4.5
5,000	2.2	13	19	10	14	2.4	11	16	7	11	2.6	9	14	6.5	9	3.5	6	8	4	5
7,000	2.8	14	20	11	15	3.0	12	17	8	13	3.2	10	16	7	11	4.3	6.5	9	4.5	5.5
10,000	3.6	16	23	12	17	3.9	13	19	9	14	4.2	11	18	7.5	12	5.7	7	10	5	6
15,000	4.8	18	26	13	19	5.2	15	21	10	15	5.6	12	19	8	13	7.5	8	11	5.5	7
20,000	6.0	20	28	15	21	6.5	16	25	11	16	7.0	13	23	9	15	9.5	9	12	6	8
30,000	7.5	23	32	17	24	8.0	19	28	13	20	8.7	15	25	10	17	11.7	10	15	6.5	9
40,000	9.3	25	35	19	26	10.0	21	30	15	21	10.8	17	26	11	17.5	14.6	11	16	7	10
60,000	12.8	27	37	20	28	13.8	22	32	15.5	22	15.0	18	27	12	18	20.2	12	17	7.5	10.5
80,000	16.6	28	39	21	29	17.9	23	33	16	23	19.4	18.5	27.5	12.5	18.5	26.2	12.5	17.5	8	11
100,000	20.3	29	40	22	30	22.0	24	34	17	24	23.8	19	28	13	19	32.1	13	18	8.5	11.5

For other ammonia and brine temperatures multiply the number of feet of pipe found from the above table by the constants in the following table.

Suction pressure abs.	Ammonia temp., °F.	Brine temp., °F.	Room temp., °F.							
			Direct expansion				Brine			
			40	36	32	28	40	36	32	28
19.46	5	15	1.2	1.2	1.2	1.2	1.2	1.2	1.3	1.4
23.64	10	20	1.3	1.4	1.5	1.6	1.5	1.6	1.8	2.3
28.24	15	25	1.6	1.7	1.9	2.2	2.0	2.4	3.0	
32.25	20	30	2.0	2.3	2.7	3.5	3.0	4.3		

Table 12-15 (taken from Marks, "Mechanical Engineers' Handbook," 4th ed., p. 2170, McGraw-Hill, New York, 1941) shows the cubic feet of space cooled per linear foot of pipe in general storage.

PRIMARY REFRIGERATION PROCESSES (NON-RECIRCULATING SYSTEMS)

These processes, as distinguished from mechanical refrigeration processes, are those in which the heat flow follows its normal course from a higher to a lower temperature. They may also be distinguished from the conventional mechanical or absorption systems in that the refrigerant is not recovered. The most important natural refrigerant is ice, but within recent years solid CO_2 has become very popular and has replaced ice in several instances. As far back as 1910, the evaporation of liquid ammonia was used for cooling refrigerator cars on the Russian railways, the vapors being absorbed in water for recovery by redistillation at convenient points. Liquid butane and propane have recently been applied to truck refrigeration in the same way, the vapors being used as fuel in the motor [Schlumbohm, *Refrig. Eng.*, **42**, 14 (1941)]. Chemical refrigeration methods in which a solid is dissolved in a liquid or two solids melt and go into solution are other examples.

Solid Refrigerants. **Manufactured ice** is made by two methods: (1) the **plate** system and (2) the **can** system. In the **plate system** a plate at 0°F. or lower is immersed in a tank of water. In a week's time a plate of ice about 1 ft. thick is formed which is removed from the plate by permitting hot gas from the compressor to run through the hollow part of the plate. Although the ice is of excellent quality, it is non-uniform in thickness and has not found much favor in the retail trade.

In the **can system**, a can containing 300 or 400 lb. water is immersed in brine at such a temperature that the water will freeze in about 44 hr. time. If distilled water is used the freezing is straightforward; but, if raw hard water saturated with air is used, two effects must be overcome. Unless the water is agitated, air bubbles will be set free and freeze into the ice giving it a marblelike appearance and poor strength. Agitation with low- or high-pressure air is the usual method of overcoming this difficulty. The dissolved salts in the water will also precipitate on freezing and deposit on the ice surface to cause discoloration. Air agitation will also prevent this effect by keeping the particles in suspension, but at the end of the freezing period a core of turbid water remains. This is removed by a **core sucker** and replaced with fresh water. The air used for agitation must be dehumidified at a temperature below 32°F. to avoid freezing of the pipes. Air agitation is a rather expensive operation but is preferable to the use of distilled water such as was used in the older installations. The brine used for freezing is vigorously stirred to promote heat transfer. At the completion of freezing the cans are immersed in water at room temperature or above to loosen the cake, which is then removed from the can by dumping. In recent years much of the commercially made ice is reduced to small cubes to be supplied for domestic table use.

Ice for refrigerator cars is manufactured in plants at strategic points along the railroad lines, with icing platforms sufficiently long to handle a whole train of cars at once. Many attempts have been made to refrigerate cars by mechanical means, but until recently they have not been successful in this country though they are used to some extent abroad. The program of development using electric refrigerating units with diesel-electric generators is now developing rapidly.

Flakice. For numerous applications ice cakes have to be cracked up before they can be used. Field has developed a machine for freezing water directly in small chips or flakes [*Refrig. Eng.*, **31**, 95 (1936)]. The machine consists of a flexible cylinder with several metal panels separated by rubber strips. This cylinder is cooled internally while revolving partly submerged in water. A thin layer of ice freezes upon the metal panels, which is discharged from the panels as the freezing edge emerges from the water. This is a rapid ice-making process.

The method of discharge is unique. The freezing cylinder is slightly flexible. Inside the cylinder at the point of discharge is a deflecting roller which distorts the circular form. The ice sheet, being rigid, leaves the cylinder at a tangent and rolls onto a chute where it cracks up and drops into a bin. The relation of thickness to time of freezing is shown in Fig. 12-25.

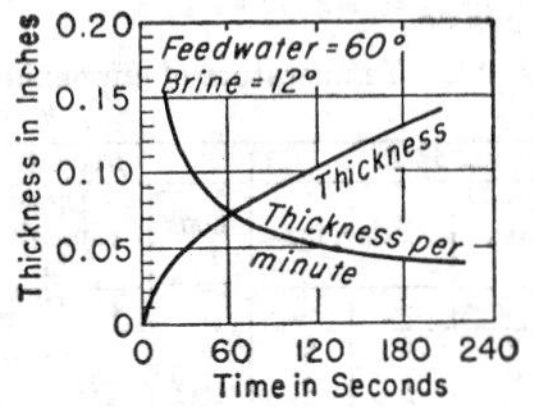

FIG. 12-25. Freezing curve showing the rates of thickness to time of freezing.

The operation of the machine is indicated by Fig. 12-26.

The width of the strips depends on the width of the panels, since no ice forms on the rubber separators because of their low thermal conductivity. The thickness is about ⅛ in. and the length not over 2 ft. In storage, about 20 to 30 per cent of the space is void. The chips are usually frozen to a temperature 10 to 12° below 32°F. and are therefore crisp and dry. Because of their large exposed surface, the chips cool water about six times as rapidly as does crushed ice.

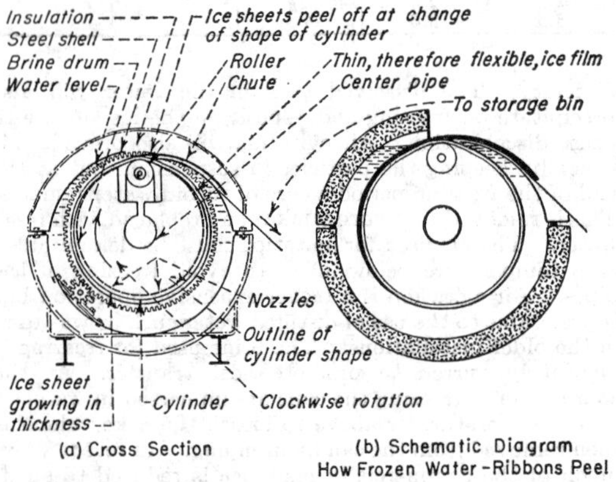

FIG. 12-26. Flakice machine.

Eutectic Salt-ice Mixtures. Where temperatures lower than the freezing point of ice are desired, it is possible to freeze a salt solution to the eutectic temperature −6°F. Such mixtures have been used in sealed cans and carried about for the servicing of ice-cream cabinets in isolated localities. When the brine melts, the can is returned for freezing. Flakice machines can be used for freezing such mixtures. "Ice-cream bullets," another form of eutectic salt-ice mixture, have been manufactured by one of the larger metropolitan ice producers as a substitute for salt and cracked ice in making homemade ice cream.

The latent heat of fusion of 1 lb. of eutectic mixture is 101 B.t.u. Hence its reserve capacity for storing cold, although less than that of ice, 144 B.t.u., is considerably better than that of a cold liquid brine.

Manufacture of Solid Carbon Dioxide. Solid carbon dioxide has become a very important source of cold, especially in the handling and transportation of foods. An exhaustive discussion of production and uses is given by Quinn and Jones ("Carbon Dioxide," Chaps. VI to VIII, Reinhold, New York, 1936). Successful manufacture is dependent on a cheap supply of pure clean gas, as the product must be free from color, odor, taste, or any material injurious to health. The supply should be close to the market because there is considerable wastage in transportation.

The most important source of supply appears to be by-product gas from fermentation [Jones, *Ind. Eng. Chem.*, **23**, 519, 798, 848 (1931)]. Other sources are flue gases from combustion and waste gases from lime burning. Certain natural gas wells also supply large quantities of gas at favorable pressures [Martin, *Ind. Eng. Chem.*, **23**, 256 (1931)] but are too far away from the market. The same may be said of other industrial sources, such as the production of CO_2 as a by-product of the manufacture of hydrogen by the water-gas reaction.

Recovery of carbon dioxide is generally accomplished by absorption in cold sodium or potassium carbonate solutions. On heating, the resulting bicarbonate liberates CO_2 and reverts to the carbonate. The equilibrium concentrations for a 2N K_2CO_3 solution (12 per cent) for a gas mixture containing 15 per cent CO_2 are given by Quinn and Jones (Table 12-16).

Table 12-16. Percentages of Carbonate and Bicarbonate at Varying Temperatures in a 2N K_2CO_3 Solution with 15 Per Cent CO_2 at Atmospheric Pressure

Temp., °C.	% K as K_2CO_3	% K as $KHCO_3$
20	9.5	90.5
40	14.2	85.8
60	22.2	77.8
80	34.0	66.0
100	47.9	52.1

Absorption is usually effected in coke towers and desorption in steam-heated lye boilers. Water vapor carried out with the gas is removed by condensers.

The CO_2 gas is next purified by chemical reagents such as permanganate or dichromate, or by adsorption on activated charcoal, silica, or aluminum gel. Traces of water vapor are removed by calcium chloride, by refrigeration, or by adsorption.

Following purification, the gas is compressed in three- or four-stage compressors and is condensed. Oil fiters or separators are necessary to prevent oil contamination. The liquid carbon dioxide is the starting point for manufacture of the solid; but, if there is a demand for the liquid itself, it may be filled into cylinders.

Liquid carbon dioxide is transformed into solid carbon dioxide by the cooling effect of its own evaporation. At a temperature of 84°F. and 70 atm., the yield of solid on expansion to atmospheric pressure is 0.23 lb./lb. of liquid, and 0.77 lb. of evaporated gas must be recompressed in a three- or four-stage compressor. Several cycles have been devised for carrying out this recompression most economically. These are: (*a*) *the simple cycle* in which the expanded gas is simply recompressed after expansion; (*b*) *the precooling cycle* in which the expanded gas is allowed to cool the liquid before it is expanded; (*c*) *the bleeder cycle* in which the liquid is expanded in three stages corresponding to the three stages of the compressor, the gas flashing in the first expansion being sucked into the third stage of the compressor, that from the second expansion into the second stage, and that from the last expansion into the first stage; (*d*) *the bleeder precooling cycle*, which is a combination of (*b*) and (*c*); (*e*) the *pressure snow-making* cycle in which the ice is frozen at the triple point rather than at atmospheric pressure; and finally (*f*) *the binary cycle* in which the liquid is cooled to some low temperature by an auxiliary ammonia refrigeration system.

The simple cycle obviously requires less capital investment than the more complicated cycles and may therefore be most satisfactory for small plants. The pressure snow-making cycle is used by most large plants. For further comparison see Rabe and Duevel, *Refrig. Eng.*, **22**, 18, 90, 260, 388 (1931).

The snow formed by any of the above cycles is in a light fluffy condition and is squeezed into solid blocks (10 by 10 by 10 in.) in a hydraulic press at 2000 lb. pressure. The transfer from the snow-making equipment to the press is effected by rabble arms.

Numerous other processes have been developed. Mention may be made of the Carba process in which the solid block is frozen directly without auxiliary pressure. Capital expenditures are low, but the regulation is delicate. Somewhat similar in principle are the Linde-Sürth and Agefko processes. The Maiuri process (*Cold Storage and Produce Rev.*, Sept. 21, 1931) uses an ammonia absorption system to produce temperatures of −76 to −94°F., which are used to cool an alcohol water bath surrounding freezing cans containing liquid carbon dioxide under 80 to 100 lb. pressure.

Table 12-17. Physical Properties of Ice and Solid CO_2

Physical property	Solid CO_2	Water ice
Specific gravity	1.53	0.90
Melting point, °F	−109.6	32
Latent heat of fusion, B.t.u./lb	82.0	144
Latent heat of sublimation, B.t.u./lb	240.6	
Sensible heat of gas to 32°F., B.t.u./lb	34.4	
Net refrigerating effect, B.t.u./lb	275	144

Solid carbon dioxide in 50-lb. blocks wrapped in paper is shipped in specially built refrigerator cars or trucks. When removed from the truck, it will not evaporate completely in 24 hours' time on exposure to the atmosphere, which is a decided advantage in handling as compared with water ice. Comparison of water ice and solid carbon dioxide is shown in Table 12-17.

In many applications solid carbon dioxide may be used directly, but in some applications the vapors are detrimental, and the condensation of moisture may produce excessive dryness in the refrigerated space. The usual method of avoiding these effects is to use the solid indirectly through an intermediate low-freezing liquid, such as aqueous solutions of alcohol or methanol, the flow of which is regulated automatically to meet the refrigerating requirements. Calcium chloride brines cannot be used as their minimum freezing point is −60°F. (eutectic temperature), but 75 per cent solutions of ethanol on methanol in water have eutectic temperatures of −200°F. and are never in danger of freezing up by solid CO_2. Systems employing auxiliary circulating liquids are used quite extensively in truck refrigeration.

THE HEAT-PUMP PRINCIPLE

In a mechanical refrigeration system, heat is abstracted in one part of the cycle at a low temperature and transferred in another part of the cycle to a higher temperature. Although mechanical refrigeration is primarily designed to produce a temperature lower than that of the environment, it can also be used to produce a higher temperature. The first proposal of this sort was made by Lord Kelvin, who showed that a more efficient utilization of heat for warming could be obtained if it were applied to a steam engine operating between steam temperature and outside atmospheric temperature, driving a refrigerating machine operating between outside atmospheric temperature and inside room temperature. This proposal has acquired considerable interest in the last few years.

A further application of the heat-pump principle is found in the vapor recompression systems of evaporation. (See Sec. 11.)

CRYOGENIC PROCESSES*

Introduction. The development and use of low-temperature processes has been tremendously expanded during the past decade. The use of liquid oxygen and liquid nitrogen in missile and rocket development has caused a manifold increase in air liquefaction and separation capacity. The space age has put a tenfold increase in the need for helium which has spurred the construction of more and better helium separation plants and the initiation of large-scale helium liquefaction and transport facilities. Liquid hydrogen production has risen from laboratory quantities to a hundred thousand gallon a day level, first initiated for nuclear weapons development and later for rocket propulsion. The liquefaction of natural gas (methane) for large-scale ship and rail transport has been greatly expanded.

The increased activity and interest in cryogenic processes have resulted in many startling developments in equipment design and thermal insulations. Many new materials have been developed and low-temperature properties measurement work is being greatly accelerated in laboratories throughout the world. The information that follows will deal mostly with fundamental systems for the liquefaction and separation of gases, a description of high-efficiency thermal insulations and their applications, and a tabulation of properties of materials most pertinent for cryogenic processes.

Fundamental Methods of Producing Refrigeration at Low Temperatures. A process for gas separation by low-temperature (defined here as any temperature below −200°F) methods involves two main steps, *liquefaction*, and *distillation* or *rectification* of the liquid. The first step is essentially one of refrigeration or heat pumping at low temperature levels and the general principles of methods for accomplishing this are treated next. Only three methods have come into practical use. They are (1) vaporization of a liquid, (2) the Joule-Thomson effect in gases, and (3) expansion of a gas in an engine doing external work. These methods may be used separately or in combination. Method 1 can be used to reach liquid air temperatures by employing a series of liquids, the one of lowest boiling point absorbing heat from the system to be refrigerated and delivering this heat to the next higher boiling fluid in a condenser-boiler combination. Finally the fluid of highest boiling point is condensed by air or water cooling and thus discharges the heat to the atmosphere. Such a process is called a cascade, and it has been applied to the liquefaction of air and of natural gas and to the separation of air into its components. The lowest temperature that can be produced by this method is 63°K., the triple point of nitrogen, since there is no more volatile fluid that will condense at this temperature.

Although the self-cooling produced on expanding a gas such as air from a high pressure to 1 atm. through a throttle is relatively small, by using an efficient heat exchanger to make it accumulative (see Fig. 12-27) temperatures within a few degrees of absolute zero can be reached. The refrigerating effect in such a scheme is the isothermal enthalpy difference between streams 1 and 3. The fraction of a gas that can be liquefied on passage through an

* This section makes liberal use of material from the previous edition written by Barnett F. Dodge.

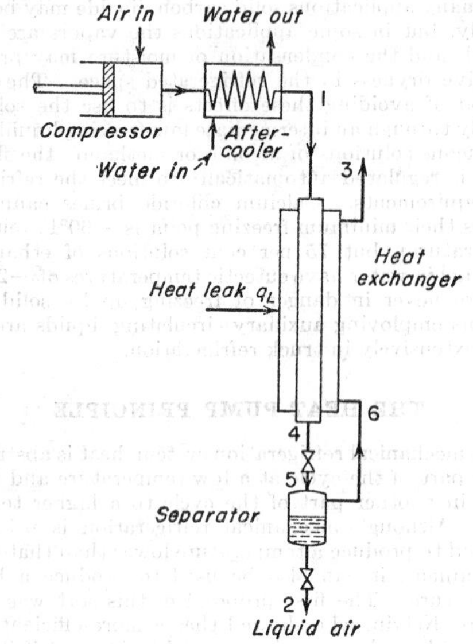

FIG. 12-27. Simple air liquefaction process.

apparatus using this process is readily obtained from an enthalpy balance, which leads to the equation

$$x = \frac{H_3 - H_1 - q_L}{H_3 - H_2} \qquad (12\text{-}11)$$

where x = fraction liquefied, H_1, H_2, and H_3 are the enthalpies of unit mass of fluid at the points designated by the numbers, and q_L = heat leaking in from the surroundings per unit of entering gas. The maximum possible degree of liquefaction occurs when $q_L = 0$ and H_3 and H_1 refer to the same temperature.

Method 3 is probably the most important of the three methods, since it offers the best possibility for an economical process on a large scale. It utilizes expansion with external work (isentropic expansion at the limit) instead of isenthalpic expansion, and the amount of cooling for a given pressure difference is much greater. This is illustrated diagrammatically in Fig. 12-28, where $T_A - T_B$ is the isentropic cooling and $T_A - T_C$ the isenthalpic cooling for adiabatic expansions between the same pressure limits.

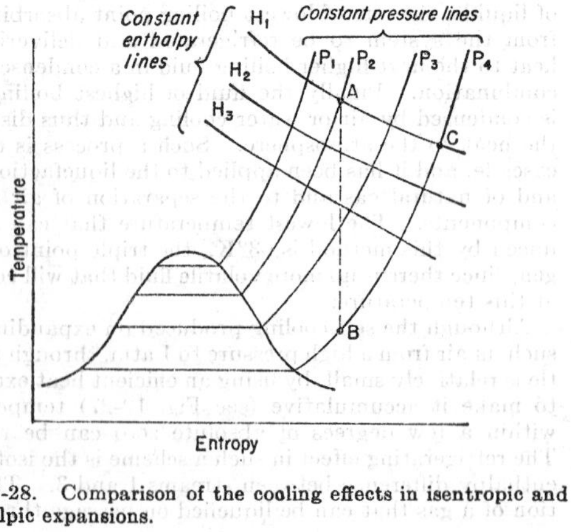

FIG. 12-28. Comparison of the cooling effects in isentropic and isenthalpic expansions.

Although expansion in an engine can theoretically be made to approach complete reversibility and hence should be more efficient than a Joule-Thomson expansion, nevertheless it is possible to devise a low-temperature, air-separation process using the latter type expansion which has substantially the same power requirement as a process using an engine for refrigeration. The reason for this lies in two facts: (1) the refrigerating effect from a Joule-Thomson effect is considerably increased by increasing the pressure and precooling the gas by an auxiliary liquid-vapor refrigeration cycle, and (2) only a relatively small fraction of the power input to the compressor of an air-separation system is needed to supply the refrigeration, the major portion being necessary to carry out the separation of the gases. For details on this point reference may be made to the paper by Bliss and Dodge [Oxygen Manufacture, Thermodynamic Analyses of Processes Depending on Low Temperature Distillation of Air, *Chem. Eng. Progress*, **45**, 51, 129, (1949)].

The great problem in the practical realization of expan sion with external work has been the development of a suitable engine. This was originally solved by the French engineer Georges Claude who developed a reciprocating engine that, though not very efficient, was at least better than a throttle. Recently both reciprocating and turbine engines of high efficiency (80 per cent and over) have been developed, and the development of compact efficient turboexpanders makes possible the separation of air on a very large scale in a low-pressure (and consequently low-power) compact system.

Work of Gas Liquefaction and Separation. Cost of power is an important consideration in any large-scale gas liquefaction and separation process, and hence it becomes important to know the thermodynamic efficiency of any proposal process. This is defined as the ratio of the minimum reversible work for the given process to the actual work. This is the product of two other efficiencies defined below:

$$\text{Cycle efficiency} = \frac{\text{reversible work for the process}}{\text{theoretical work for ideal operation of the cycle}} \qquad (12\text{-}12)$$

$$\text{Practial efficiency} = \frac{\text{theoretical work for ideal operation of the cycle}}{\text{actual work for the cycle}} \qquad (12\text{-}13)$$

The reversible work is the least possible amount of work to effect the change in question and is calculated from the expression

$$-W = \Delta H - T_0 \Delta S \qquad (12\text{-}14)$$

where T_0 is the lowest temperature on the absolute scale at which large amounts of heat may be rejected. The reversible work clearly depends only on the initial and final state of the system and is entirely independent of the cycle or the mechanisms used. On the other hand, certain cycles may have inherent irreversible effect such as throttle expansions or unavoidable temperature differences but can, in imagination, be operated in a frictionless or ideal manner, and the calculated work is used to give the cycle efficiency. This furnishes a measure of how good the cycle is without regard to the imperfections of the equipment used to realize the cycle. The practical efficiency is a measure of the approach to perfection of the equipment as distinct from that of the process.

The minimum or reversible work is readily calculated from Eq. (12-14) and a table or diagram of thermodynamic properties. Some figures for a few processes are given herewith, based on $T_0 = 300°K.$ (80°F.).

Process	Reversible Work, Kw.-hr.	
1. Liquefaction of oxygen starting with O_2 gas at 80°F. and 1 atm. and producing liquid at the normal boiling point	2.56	(per lb.-mole of air)
2. Complete separation of air at 80°F. and 1 atm. into oxygen and nitrogen (including argon) gases at the same pressure and temperature	0.1615	(per lb.-mole of air)
	0.767	(per lb.-mole of O_2)
	1.95	(per 1000 cu. ft. of O_2)
3. Separation of air at 80°F. and 1 atm. into gaseous nitrogen (plus argon, etc.) at 80°F. and 1 atm. and liquid O_2 at the normal boiling point	0.700	(per lb.-mole of air)
	3.33	(per lb.-mole of O_2)
4. Separation of air (assumed a binary system) into gaseous oxygen and nitrogen		

Oxygen purity % O_2 in the oxygen product	Nitrogen purity % O_2 in the nitrogen product	Hp. hr./lb. mole of pure O_2 in the oxygen product
100	0	1.033
95	0	.950
95	0.01	.910
70	0	.663
50	0	.447
30	0	.174
70	0.01	.615

Even the best low-temperature processes have a relatively low thermodynamic efficiency (15 to 20 per cent) because of the multiplication of a number of factors each resulting from a given irreversible effect, such as friction in engines, fluid friction in pipes and through equipment, heat leak, throttling, temperature differences across heat exchangers, and mass transfer in rectifying columns between fluids not in phase equilibrium. The last named effect is generally overlooked, but it is probably the greatest single contributor to loss in efficiency. An ideally operated adiabatic rectifying column has an efficiency of 67 per cent, and under practical operating conditions its efficiency is of the order of 35 to 40 per cent.

Analysis to Determine Power Requirement and Distribution of Losses. The first and second laws of thermodynamics are the fundamental tools for low-temperature-process analysis. Neglecting kinetic energy and potential energy due to position in the gravitational field, the first law may be written

$$\Delta H = Q - W_{sh} \qquad (12\text{-}15)$$

where ΔH is the summation of the enthalpy differences for all fluids entering and leaving the section in question, Q designates the algebraic summation of all heat exchanges between the section and its surroundings including auxiliary cycles, and W_{sh} is the shaft work. There will, in general, be as many first-law equations as there are units of equipment such as heat exchangers, expanders, columns, or points of mixing of streams. If the first law is applied to the whole, which is customary, one of these equations is dependent. There will, of course, be considerably more unknowns; so it will be necessary to hold some of them as parameters. While the choice of these parameters is arbitrary, convenience in the solution of the system of simultaneous equations will in most cases serve as a suitable guide. Solution will yield all the necessary quantities, compositions, enthalpies, and temperatures. Obviously different solutions will result from different choices of variables to be fixed. Solutions obtained may be unworkable, however, because of hidden second-law violations, which will be discussed presently.

If one is to obtain a practical, in contrast to a theoretical, figure for the power requirement from such an analysis, it is clear that one must make due allowance for the inevitable irreversible effects that always accompany the operation of any equipment in actual practice. This means that reasonable estimates, based on practice, must be made for such things as heat leak, compressor and expander efficiencies, temperature differences in heat exchangers, pressure drop due to fluid flow, and excess reflux above the minimum for rectification.

Second Law. The part played by the second law in these analyses is not so straightforward. It leads to no particular set of orderly equations, but only to the observation that all driving forces must be positive. For example, applied to heat transfer, it means that the fluid giving up heat must be higher in temperature than the fluid receiving heat at all points in the exchanger. This seems so obvious as not to require discussion, but the difficulty arises from the fact that fixing the terminal temperature differences of exchangers does not ensure absence of negative Δt's at intermediate points. Such virtual second-law violations are likely to occur when one of the fluids undergoes a phase change or even in the absence of phase changes, when one of the fluids is near its critical state. The place where a virtual second-law violation is most likely to occur is in a liquefier. This is illustrated in Fig. 12-29, which shows the temperature-

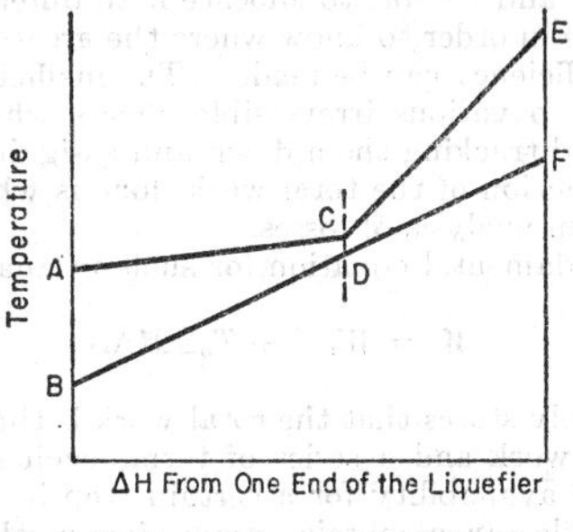

FIG. 12-29. Examination of liquefier in light of the second law.

enthalpy relation of two streams in an exchanger when liquefaction occurs in one of the fluids. At the point of incipient liquefaction C, the Δt may be much less than at the two terminals. It is easy to see that reduction in the terminal Δt's could readily lead to an impossible case of zero or negative Δt at the "pinch."

Reversibility and Irreversibility. The measure of the general quality of a process is its reversibility. A process will approach the minimum power requirement as it approaches the reversible one. On the other hand, any item of equipment will approach minimum size as it departs from reversibility—most easily seen with heat exchangers.

The temperature difference is a measure of reversibility in heat exchangers; *i.e.*, when it is small, reversibility is approached, and vice versa. The absolute temperature at which temperature differences occur is also important. Thus a 5°C. temperature difference at ambient levels is not badly irreversible, but the same at 77°K. is considerably more so. The entropy increase in a heat exchanger, of course, weighs both these effects, and the smaller such increase is, the closer the approach to reversibility. A good guide to heat exchangers in process planning is always to exchange sensible heat with sensible heat and latent with latent. If latent and sensible heats are exchanged it is impossible to avoid excessive temperature differences. Processes have been proposed in which gaseous helium was to be used as a cooling medium for reflux with a compound-type column. Such a provision leads to great temperature difference at the lowest temperature of the process and hence to considerable irreversibility.

In general, the entropy increase is the best guide to the degree of irreversibility of any process. According to the second law of thermodynamics, the entropy of an isolated system must either increase or remain constant.

If one imagines a *virtual* change in such a system and finds $\Delta S < 0$ for the entire system, then one can say at once that the change is not possible. If all changes occur reversibly, $\Delta S = 0$, and if there is any irreversible effect of any kind occurring in the system, $\Delta S > 0$. One must be careful to avoid making the erroneous assumption that entropy always increases in any irreversible process. The statement that $\Delta S \gtreqless 0$ applies to an *isolated* system, *i.e.*, the particular system plus its surroundings. One must likewise avoid assuming that any virtual process is possible if it involves an increase in entropy of the isolated system. For example, it is easily possible to imagine a heat exchanger in which the net $\Delta S > 0$ but the assumed conditions would be impossible because of negative temperature differences.

Analysis of Losses. Values of the thermodynamic efficiency for low-temperature-liquefaction and gas-separation processes generally fall in the range of 3 to 30 per cent. From the standpoint of process improvement it is important to account for the 97 to 70 per cent of the work done and be able to allocate it to different steps of the process in order to know where the greatest improvement in efficiency can be made. The inefficiency is due, of course, to various irreversible effects which are well known, and tracking them down and assigning to each a definite fraction of the total work done is what is meant by the term analysis of losses.

The fundamental equation for such an analysis is:

$$W = W_{\text{rev}} + T_o \Sigma M \Delta S \tag{12-16}$$

which simply states that the total work is the sum of the reversible work and a series of terms each representing the loss in availability for a certain step in the process. For example, an algebraic summation of the entropies of the fluids entering and leaving a heat exchanger, each multiplied by the corresponding mass of the fluid, gives $\Sigma M \Delta S$ for the exchanger; and when this is multiplied by the absolute ambient temperature, one obtains the work that was required as a result of the irreversibilities in this exchanger.

In the application of this method to actual processes there are several details that require further elucidation which can best be done by numerical examples. Consider the simple air-liquefaction process sketched in Fig. 12-27. Conditions for the process are indicated in Table 12-18. For a heat leak of 2.0 B.t.u./lb. of entering

Table 12-18. States and Values of Properties for Process of Fig. 12-27*

Properties based on Kellogg Temperature-Entropy diagram

Point	Pressure, atm.	Temperature, °F.	Mass, lb.	*H*, B.t.u./lb.	*S*, B.t.u./(lb.)(°R.)
1	100	80	41	121.0	0.583
2	1	−318	1	−53.0	0
3	1	70	40	127.4	0.911
4	100	−165	41	32.0	.355
5	1	−318	41	32.0	.583
6	1	−318	40	35.0	.598

* Lobo, Technical Data Pertaining to Air; Its Liquefaction and Distillation, P.B. 8900 (1945).

air, the fraction of air liquefied is 0.0244, as calculated by Eq. (12-11). The total work requirement for the process assuming three-stage adiabatic compression and 75 per cent compression efficiency is 11,650 B.t.u./lb. of liquid air. The reversible work is 312 and the problem is to account for the difference. Using the data in the table, the following calculations are made:

For the exchanger,

$$T_o \Sigma M \Delta S = 540[40(0.911 - 0.598) - 41(0.583 - 0.355)] = 1720 \text{ B.t.u.}$$

Similarly for the throttle valve,

$$T_o \Sigma M \Delta S = 5040$$

The compression of the air is irreversible not only because of frictional losses but also because adiabatic compression followed by constant pressure cooling is inherently irreversible. Determination of the loss could be made from ΔS values, just as was done for the low-temperature parts of the process, but since the work of compression was obtained algebraically, it was more convenient to calculate the work of reversible isothermal compression and take the difference. The isothermal work is 6980 B.t.u. and hence the loss in the compression itself is 11,650 − 6980 = 4670 B.t.u.

One may now set up a balance sheet of work requirements and/or losses as follows:

	B.t.u.	Per cent
1. Reversible work	312	2.7
2. Loss in compression	4,670	39.8
3. Loss in exchanger	1,720	14.6
4. Loss due to throttling	5,040	42.9
Total	11,742	100.0

The discrepancy of about 1 per cent in the total work is well within the error of the calculation.

This analysis shows at once where the greatest gains in efficiency can be made. There is, however, one irreversible effect, namely, heat leak, whose effect does not appear directly in such an analysis because it is distributed over all the steps of the process. An insight into the effect of heat leak can, however, be readily obtained by making a first-law or enthalpy balance for zero heat leak and recalculating the work per pound of liquid produced. The total work obtained in this way is 8020 B.t.u. Therefore, we may conclude that heat leak alone increased the work by 3630 B.t.u., or 31 per cent of the work is attributable directly to this cause.

As a second illustration an air-separation process will be chosen, as this introduces some new problems. In order not to complicate the calculation and obscure the principles the very simple process shown in Fig. 12-30 has been chosen.

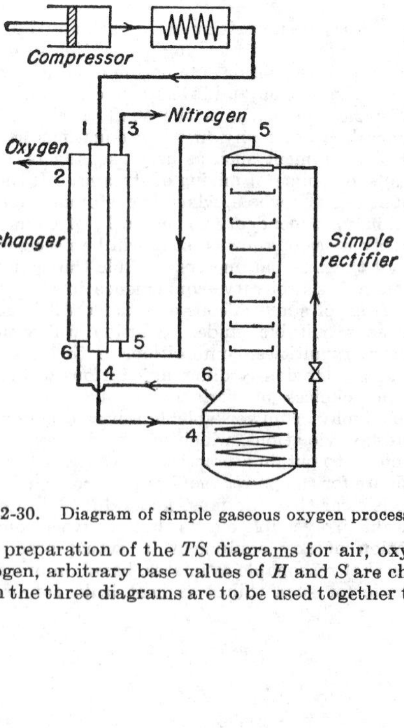

FIG. 12-30. Diagram of simple gaseous oxygen process.

In the preparation of the *TS* diagrams for air, oxygen, and nitrogen, arbitrary base values of *H* and *S* are chosen and when the three diagrams are to be used together there are certain relations between the H and S of a mixture and those of the pure components which must be taken into account. If we assume that the various gases and mixtures are ideal at low pressure (1 atm., *e.g.*) the following relations apply:

$$H_{\text{mix}} = \Sigma x_i H_i \qquad (12\text{-}17)$$
$$S_{\text{mix}} = \Sigma x_i S_i - R\Sigma x_i \ln x_i \qquad (12\text{-}18)$$

the H's and S's for the individual gases being taken at the same temperature and total pressure. Using these equations at the state $p = 1$ atm. and $t = 80°$F., one can readily derive the following relations for placing values for air read from the Kellogg *TS* diagram on the basis of the Millar and Sullivan diagrams [*U.S. Bur. Mines Tech. Paper* 424 (1928)]:

$$\frac{H_K \times 29}{1.8} + 872 = H_{M \text{ and } S}$$
$$S_K \times 29 + 1.518 = S_{M \text{ and } S}$$

To obtain H and S for any other mixture than air Eqs. (12-17) and (12-18) are used directly, but it is to be noted that a difficulty arises in the case of a saturated vapor as at point 5 in Fig. 12-30. Oxygen does not exist as a vapor at the temperature and total pressure of the mixture. This situation can be handled in various ways and the very simple one has been chosen of extrapolating into the unstable region. This is a very slight extrapolation and cannot introduce serious error.

Conditions chosen for the process are indicated in Table 12-19 along with the various properties calculated

Table 12-19. States and Values of Properties for Process of Fig. 12-30*

Basis: 1-lb.-mole of entering air

Point	P, atm.	t, °F.	T, °K.	Composition	State	H, p.c.u./lb.-mole	S, p.c.u./(lb.-mole)(°K.)
1	54.5	80	300	air	Superheated	2877	19.82
2	1.0	71	295	O_2	Superheated	3215	28.30
3	1.0	71	295	8.52% O_2	Superheated	2884	27.31
4	54.5	−196	147	air	Superheated	1397	12.44
5	1.0	.....	79.3	8.52% O_2	Sat. vapor	1379	18.11
6	1.0	.....	90.2	O_2	Sat. vapor	1788	19.99

* Properties on basis of Millar and Sullivan, *U.S. Bur. Mines Tech. Paper* 424 (1928).

by the methods previously outlined or illustrated. In addition it is to be noted that a heat leak of 50 p.c.u./lb.-mole of air was assumed and it was distributed 70 per cent to the column and 30 per cent to the exchanger. It was further assumed that the column would yield 65 per cent of the oxygen in the air as pure oxygen.

Proceeding as in the previous example, losses may be distributed:

	p.c.u./lb.-mole air	Per cent
Reversible work	150	3.8
Loss in compression	1480	37.7
Loss in rectifying column	1790	45.5
Loss in heat exchanger	510	13.0
Total	3930	100.0

It is of interest to note that the greatest loss is in the column and next greatest in the compression. Again, of course, the effect of heat leak does not appear directly but can be calculated. Presumably the column losses could be further localized to show the losses in the throttle valve, boiler, etc., if desirable.

It is believed that the method for analysis of the losses has been sufficiently demonstrated by means of simple examples so that it can readily be applied to any process for liquefaction or separation at low temperatures and such an analysis should prove valuable as a starting point for process improvement.

Results of Thermodynamic Analyses. Bliss and Dodge (*loc. cit.*) present results of the analysis of 17 liquid oxygen and 12 gaseous oxygen processes. Some of the conclusions from this study are summarized below. In order to follow the results conveniently a classification of processes on the basis of the method used for producing refrigeration is first presented as follows:

1. Joule-Thompson effect only
2. Joule-Thompson effect plus auxiliary refrigeration with an ordinary liquid-vapor cycle at moderate or high-temperature levels, *i.e.*, relative to liquid-air temperature
3. Joule-Thomson effect plus approximately reversible expansion of the air or products in an expander
4. Refrigeration essentially due only to approximately reversible expansions of auxiliary fluid or fluids such as helium through expanders, *i.e.*, processes in which the fluid remains entirely in the gas phase
5. Refrigeration essentially due only to auxiliary fluid or fluids operating in liquid-vapor cycles, *i.e.*, the cascade process
6. Refrigeration essentially due only to approximately reversible expansion of air or products in an expander, *i.e.*, low-pressure processes
7. Processes using an auxiliary nitrogen-liquefaction cycle

It was very difficult, if not impossible, to put all processes on a strictly comparable basis. Many assumptions have to be made in the course of such calculations and it was not possible to be entirely consistent in making them. The chief factors about which assumptions had to be made were: heat leak, temperature differences in exchangers, efficiencies of compressors and expanders, state of initial air, excess (over the theoretical) reflux in the column, purity of gases, pressure drop due to fluid flow, number of stages of compression, fraction of expander work recovered, and state of expander exhaust.

In view of this fact, it is easy to see that differences in power requirement of 10 to 20 per cent can readily be due to differences in assumed variables and are not significant from the standpoint of comparing one process with another.

It appears entirely possible and practical to produce substantially pure gaseous oxygen in large plants with a minimum energy consumption of 0.15 hp.-hr./lb. (224 kw.-hr./ton or 10.0 kw.-hr./1000 cu. ft. at 32°F. and 1 atm. abs.). This requires, however, a favorable combination of circumstances and a more practical figure for a large plant would seem to be about 0.20 hp.-hr./lb. Clark [Large Scale Production of Oxygen and Atmospheric Gases, BIOS Final Report 591, P.B. 41229 (1946)] states that the actual energy requirement in Linde-Frankl plants varied from 0.272 to 0.462 hp.-hr./lb., though the Linde Co. claimed an energy consumption of only 0.194 hp.-hr./lb. A medium-sized plant operating on the cascade process in this country yielded a figure of 0.22 hp.-hr./lb. It seems equally possible and practicable to produce essentially pure liquid oxygen with a minimum energy consumption of 0.5 hp.-hr./lb., although 0.6 would probably represent a more practical figure.

Processes of various types including ones classified as 2, 3, 5, and 6 are comparable from the standpoint of energy requirements and the choice between them must be based on other considerations. Processes 1 and 4 are definitely inferior from this standpoint; process 1 because it utilizes only the Joule-Thomson effect in air for refrigeration and process 4 because of the large inherent Δt in the reflux condenser of the column. So little work has been done with process 7 that no general conclusion can be drawn about it, but on the basis of the one type analyzed for gaseous oxygen, it would appear to require somewhat more work than the four processes first mentioned. This is believed to be reasonable because the separate nitrogen cycle has its own irreversible effects and the total gas handled in the air and nitrogen circuits is considerably greater than in a process such as 6 where the air is its own refrigerant.

On the other hand, process 7 has certain advantages which may offset the somewhat greater power requirement. Among these may be mentioned: (1) the fact that the expander always operates on highly purified gas (2) since the air to be separated is at substantially atmospheric pressure, its temperature as it leaves the exchanger will be considerably lower than air at 4 to 5 atm. and hence it will carry less impurities into the column, and (3) the compound column is simpler to control and requires fewer plates than a double column. However, these advantages are partly balanced by certain disadvantages such as the fact that the heat-exchange and purification system is probably bulkier than in process 6, due to the low pressure of the air and the added N_2 system. Furthermore the moisture content of the air is so much greater that external removal must be used.

It has been claimed that the cascade process for gas liquefaction is much more efficient than the other well-known methods and this, by implication, leads one to expect that this process for air separation should have the least energy requirement. This is not borne out by the calculations. Furthermore it should be noted that the cascade process is more complex than the others and since it has no power advantage, it is not likely to be considered for the production of oxygen on a tonnage scale. However, it should be noted that it involves no cold moving parts.

It may be noted that the higher yield attainable in double columns is very beneficial in reducing the energy requirement of gaseous oxygen processes, but it is much less so in the case of liquid oxygen. The predominant portion of the work is required for the liquefaction, and when the yield is increased, the liquefaction work is increased proportionately.

There is an important point in regard to internal purification (discussed later) which warrants discussion here since it has a bearing on the thermodynamics of the process. In the simplest example of processes of class 6, where the air is compressed to 4 to 6 atm. abs., cooled in regenerators or reversing exchangers by separated gases, and a portion expanded for refrigeration, the separated gases returning from the column will cool the entering air down to the saturation point. Thus, (1) the turbine will operate in the wet region, which probably lowers its efficiency, and (2) the cold-end Δt of the exchangers is too large to permit complete removal of carbon dioxide and deriming must be more frequent.

A general study by means of over-all balances only was made on processes of type 6 with the object of investigating the effect on power requirement of (1) heat leak, (2) expander efficiency, (3) warm-end Δt, and (4) material leak. These effects under comparable conditions were as follows:

1. A heat leak of 100 B.t.u./lb.-mole of air increased the energy requirement about 20 per cent over that for no heat leak.

2. An expander efficiency of 40 per cent increased the energy requirement about 20 per cent over that with 100 per cent efficiency.

3. A warm-end temperature difference of 20°F. increased the energy requirement about 40 per cent over that with zero difference.

4. A material leak of 5 per cent of the cold air at the expander inlet increased the energy requirement by about 25 per cent.

The energy or thermodynamic efficiency of the gaseous oxygen processes analyzed varied from 9 to 23 per cent and the liquid oxygen ones from 6 to 29 per cent. At first thought this would seem to allow considerable leeway for marked improvement. However, this is probably not the case as an analysis of the losses will show. In general, the irreversible effects are of two kinds, (1) those inherent in the particular process such as a Joule-Thomson expansion or an adiabatic column, and (2) those which can be reduced to zero at the limit. Those of class (1) may be avoided by modifying the process but usually this means greater complexity of equipment. Any attempt to reduce the irreversible effects of class (2) will inevitably lead to smaller driving forces and larger equipment. From a consideration of the economic balance between power cost and fixed charges on the investment in equipment, it appears very doubtful if significant increases in over-all efficiency over the maxima cited above will be achieved in the near future.

Gas Liquefaction. Low-temperature gas-liquefaction processes may be based either on the Joule-Thomson expansion or engine expansion. Processes based on the first are usually called Linde processes after the German engineer who pioneered in the field. Processes based on the use of engine expansion are commonly given the name Claude after the French engineer who did much of the original development work. It might be noted that an engine-expansion process also generally uses a Joule-Thomson expansion for the final refrigeration in order to avoid formation of liquid in the engine. Equation (12-11) may be used to calculate the percentage liquefaction in a simple Linde process such as that shown in Fig. 12-27. It should be noted that this percentage is determined by conditions at the warm end of the heat exchanger which is just ahead of the expansion valve. Under certain conditions, notably with hydrogen and helium at room temperature, $H_1 > H_3$ and no liquefaction could be obtained. Assuming H_3 to be fixed at the lowest possible pressure and the highest possible temperature (when $t_3 = t_1$), the maximum degree of liquefaction occurs when H_1 is a minimum. The criterion for this is

$$\left(\frac{\partial H}{\partial p_1}\right)_{T_1} = T_1\left(\frac{\partial V_1}{\partial T_1}\right)_{p_1} - V_1 = 0 \qquad (12\text{-}19)$$

or

$$T_1\left(\frac{\partial V_1}{\partial T_1}\right)_{p_1} = V_1 \qquad (12\text{-}20)$$

This is the equation of the Joule-Thomson inversion and hence it is concluded that maximum liquefaction occurs when the initial pressure for a given temperature of gas entering the exchanger is the inversion temperature. Referring to Fig. 12-31, which shows a generalized Joule-

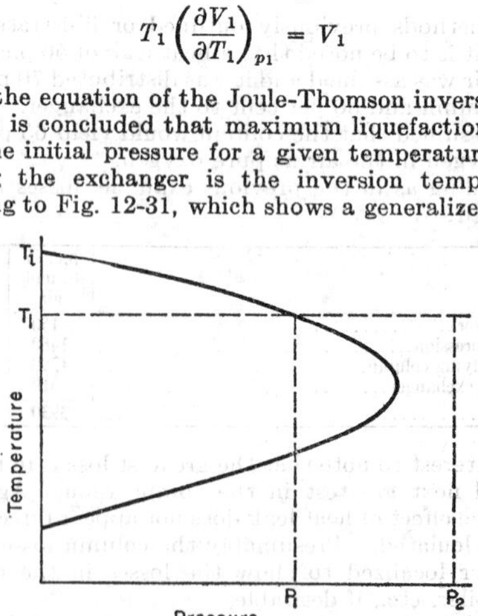

Fig. 12-31. Relation of degree of liquefaction to the Joule-Thomson inversion.

Thomson inversion curve, no liquefaction could be obtained at any pressure if the entering temperature were above T_i, which is known as the Joule-Thomson inversion temperature. For air this temperature is about 325°C., for hydrogen about 200°K., and for helium about 24°K. In general, as the temperature of the gas entering the main heat exchanger is lowered, the value of $H_3 - H_1$ increases and the degree of liquefaction increases. For example, if air at 200 atm. is precooled to −100°F. by a Freon refrigeration cycle, the yield of liquid air is about 2.2 times as great as for water cooling to 80°F. Referring to Fig. 12-31 again, if the entering temperature were T_1, Eq. (12-20) shows that the maximum degree of liquefaction would occur when the pressure is p_1. Higher pressures, such as p_2, would actually give less liquid.

Figure 12-32 shows a diagram of a process for liquefying hydrogen using precooling with liquid air.

One of the problems in liquefying a gas such as hydrogen or helium is the presence of impurities such as oxygen and nitrogen which are solids at the low temperatures involved. Oxygen can be removed by chemical means but nitrogen is particularly difficult to remove. The Kapitza scheme shown in Fig. 12-32 solves this in an

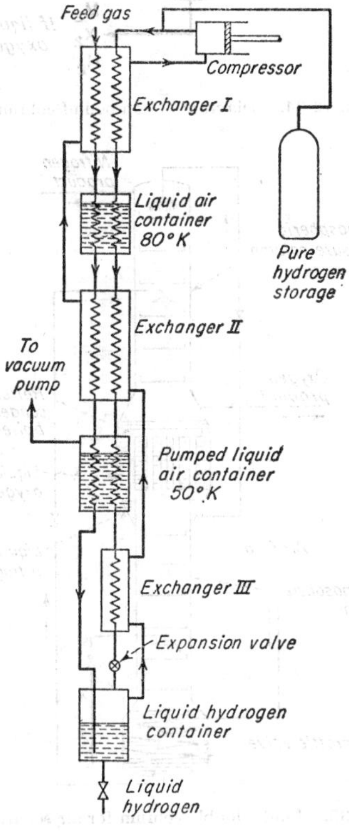

FIG. 12-32. Simplified diagram of the Kapitza scheme for hydrogen liquefaction.

ingenious manner. Ordinary cylinder hydrogen throttled to low pressure is the feed gas. After precooling in exchangers I and II by exchange of heat with return gas and in the two liquid-air (or nitrogen) containers, it passes directly to the liquid-hydrogen container, where it condenses by evaporating an equivalent amount of hydrogen. At the same time the impurities are condensed as solids and drawn off with the liquid product. The gaseous hydrogen, now completely purified, returns through the exchangers and is then compressed to about 150 atm. and is sent down through the various exchangers and liquid-air containers to the expansion valve, where it liquefies by the Joule-Thomson effect. This system must be started the first time with an independent source of purified hydrogen, but once started the supply of pure hydrogen in the storage system can be replenished from the hydrogen circulating in the closed system. Further details on plants using this scheme are given by Blanchard and Bittner [*Rev. Sci. Instruments,* **13,** 394 (1942)] and Huffman [*Chem. Rev.,* **40,** 1 (1947)].

To liquefy helium by the Joule-Thomson process requires precooling with liquid hydrogen, since the inversion temperature is well below the temperature of liquid air. Both hydrogen and helium can be liquefied by an expansion-engine process without the necessity of using any precooling by other fluids. Figure 12-33 shows a

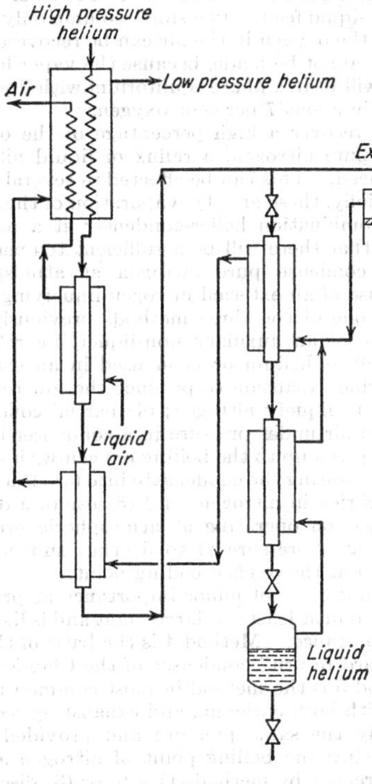

FIG. 12-33. Helium liquefaction process using an expansion engine.

diagram of the process used at the Physics Laboratory of Yale University for the liquefaction of helium. This is the expansion-engine process developed by Kapitza with the addition of precooling by means of liquid air. Arthur D. Little, Inc., produces a helium liquefier and cryostat, developed by Dr. S. C. Collins, which uses two reciprocating expanders and no auxiliary cooling system. The helium is continuously recycled in a system especially designed to avoid contamination of the gas.

For the calculation of per cent liquefaction by an expansion-engine process see Dodge, "Chemical Engineering Thermodynamics," McGraw-Hill, New York, 1944. Further information on the liquefaction of hydrogen and helium is available in the following papers: Helium—Lane, *Rev. Sci. Instruments,* **12,** 326 (1941); Hydrogen—Starr, *Rev. Sci. Instruments,* **12,** 193 (1941); Keyes, Gerry, and Hicks, *J. Am. Chem. Soc.,* **59,** 1426 (1937); Johnston, Begman, and Hood, P.B. 31880 (1946).

Rectification at Low Temperatures. A low-temperature gas-separation process is essentially a liquefaction cycle plus a rectification column. The latter does not differ in principle or materially in construction from those used above room temperature, but some conditions peculiar to low-temperature columns are worth mentioning. In the following discussion, attention will be focused on columns for rectification of liquid air.

Just as at ordinary temperatures, low-temperature columns must have boilers and condensers and may consist of a single or exhausting column or may have both exhasuting and enriching sections as in double columns or in compound columns. It is important to note that the heat that is to be added in the boiler must always be obtained by removing it from some other cold part of the system and never from any outside source. Thus, in the single column or in the lower section of a double column, the heat for boiling is obtained by condensation of the air to produce the liquid feed. In a single column only about 70 per cent of the oxygen in the air can be recovered and pure nitrogen cannot be made, because the vapor leaving the top plate will be in a phase equilibrium with liquid air and will contain about 7 per cent oxygen.

In order to recover a high percentage of the oxygen and/or make pure nitrogen, a reflux of liquid nitrogen must be produced. This can be effected in several possible ways. Briefly, these are (1) evaporation of the liquid oxygen in a combination boiler-condenser at a reduced pressure such that there will be a sufficient temperature difference to condense pure nitrogen at atmospheric pressure; (2) use of an external nitrogen liquefying cycle based on any one of the three methods previously discussed; (3) use of an auxiliary non-liquefying refrigerating fluid such as helium or neon used in an external cycle with engine expansion to produce the low temperature required to liquefy nitrogen; (4) partial condensation of the feed air under pressure in a condenser-boiler, the heat being given up to the boiling oxygen with means provided for separating the condensate into two fractions, one of which is rich in nitrogen; and (5) use of a double column, one section operating at atmospheric pressure and the other at a pressure (4 to 5 atm.) sufficient to liquefy nitrogen at the oxygen boiling point.

Methods 1 and 3 are of minor importance at present. Method 2 is used in at least one large plant and is likely to increase in importance. Method 4 is the basis of the so-called "backward return" condenser of the Claude process, and method 5 is the method in most common use.

A column with both enriching and exhausting sections at substantially the same pressure and provided with refrigeration below the boiling point of nitrogen at the column pressure, say by method (1), (2), or (3) discussed above, will be known as a compound column and is illustrated in Fig. 12-34. Another form of compound column uses a nitrogen-liquefaction cycle in which nitrogen is condensed under pressure by the boiling oxygen and then throttled into the top of the column as the reflux.

Figure 12-35 shows a Linde double column, which consists of a column operating at elevated pressure surmounted by an atmospheric-pressure column. The boiler of the upper column is at the same time the reflux condenser for both columns. Gaseous air plus enough liquid to take care of heat leak into the column (more liquid, of course, if liquid-oxygen product is withdrawn) enters the exchanger at the base of the lower column and condenses, giving up heat to the boiling liquid and thus supplying the vapor flow for this column. The liquid air enters an intermediate point in this column, as shown. The vapors rising in this column are partially condensed to form the reflux, and the uncondensed vapor passes to an outer row of tubes and is totally condensed, the liquid nitrogen collecting in an annulus, as shown. If this

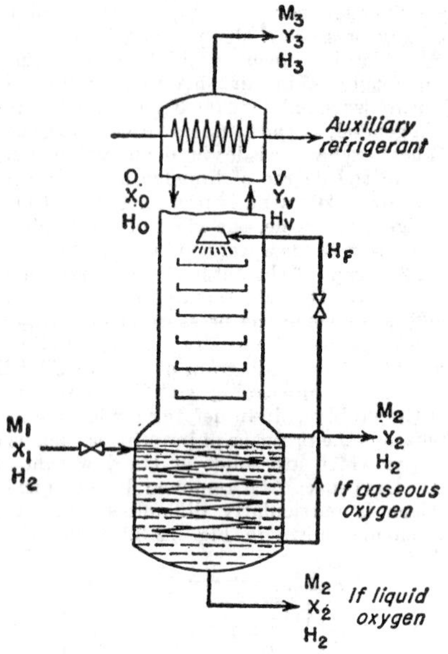

FIG. 12-34. Diagram of compound column.

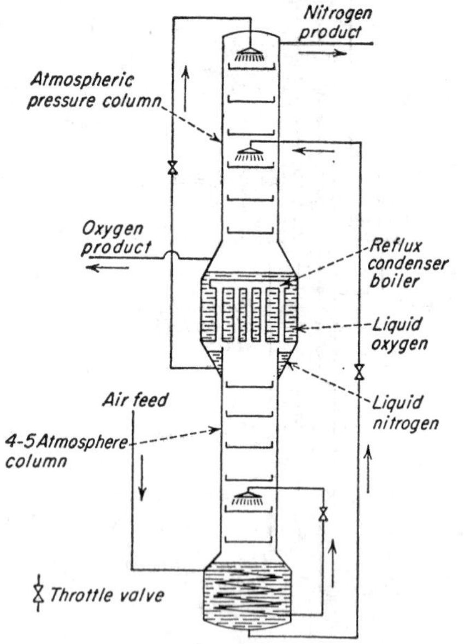

FIG. 12-35. Linde double column for air separation.

column is operated at 4 to 5 atm. the liquid oxygen boiling at 1 atm. is cold enough to condense pure nitrogen. The liquid that collects in the bottom of the lower column contains about 45 per cent O_2 and forms the feed for the upper column. Such a double column can produce a very pure oxygen with high oxygen recovery or a very pure nitrogen with oxygen of moderate purity. It cannot produce both products simultaneously in a high state of purity, owing primarily to the fact that air is really a ternary mixture and the argon must be taken off with one of the products.

The determination of number of plates is made by the usual procedure for rectifying columns; but it is particularly to be noted that it is not satisfactory to treat air as a binary solution of oxygen and nitrogen when a pure oxygen (99 per cent or better) is to be made, because most of the plates are required to separate the oxygen-argon binary. This is a much more difficult separation than the oxygen-nitrogen binary; and, if the argon is not separated, only 95 per cent oxygen would be produced.

In analyzing a low-temperature, gas-separation process, the rectifying column must be examined for possible second-law violations. In other words, one must check to find out if there is sufficient reflux available to permit the attainment of the desired degree of separation. Details of methods for doing this for all three types of columns are given in the paper by Bliss and Dodge (*loc. cit.*). They are based on the use of enthalpy-concentration diagrams. Such an analysis also reveals the fact that there is appreciably more than the minimum amount of reflux necessary for separating the liquid feed, available in the upper section of a double column separating air into gaseous products. This makes possible either one of two procedures:

1. Some of the nitrogen may be withdrawn from the condenser-boiler as a vapor instead of being condensed and used as reflux and this nitrogen under pressure may be expanded in a turbine to produce some refrigeration. This is used in the Linde-Fränkl process.
2. Extra air can be added to the upper column as a saturated vapor. Since this air requires very little compression, the net result is a greater yield of oxygen with no increase in power requirement. This scheme is usually called the Lachmann procedure. It poses a problem of purification of the extra air and of course reduces the driving force in the column and hence requires more plates. Further details on this procedure are given in the Bliss and Dodge paper.

Various Low-temperature Processes. There are many possible cycles for gas liquefaction and separation. Two are illustrated by flow sheets in Figs. 12-36 and 12-37 (see also *Chem. Eng.*, March, 1947, p. 134). Figure 12-36 shows a Linde cycle for air liquefaction using two methods for obtaining the refrigeration, namely, precooling with a refrigerant such as ammonia or one of the Freons and the Joule-Thomson effect. The air is compressed to 100 to 200 atm., this high a pressure being necessary to obtain sufficient refrigeration by the Joule-Thomson effect. The precooling would generally lower the temperature of the compressed air to about −40°F., though lower temperatures could be used to advantage. Such a process is used for small liquid air, nitrogen, or oxygen plants.

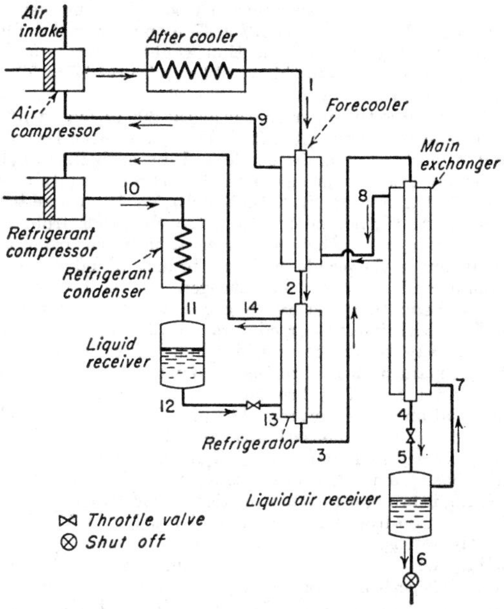

FIG. 12-36. Liquid air cycle using Joule-Thomson effect supplemented by an auxiliary refrigerator.

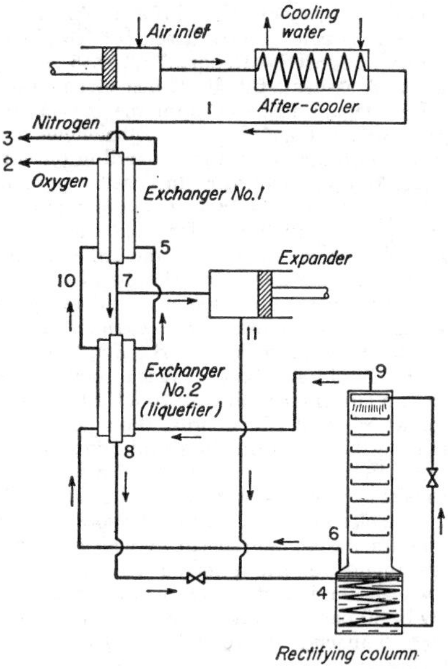

FIG. 12-37. Air-separation cycle using expansion engine for refrigeration.

Figure 12-37 shows an expansion-engine or Claude cycle for producing pure gaseous oxygen and an impure gaseous nitrogen. It will be noted that only a portion of the air is expanded in the engine, the remainder going to exchanger No. 2, commonly called a liquefier. In this exchanger enough of the air is liquefied to compensate for heat leak into the column. For a liquid oxygen product, the portion to the liquefier would, of course, have to be greater. There are many possible variations of this cycle, but the one shown has been in common use in medium-sized plants for the production of both gaseous and liquid oxygen. With reciprocating expanders the cycle producing gaseous oxygen has operated with an air pressure of about 250 lb./sq. in., but this of course depends on the expander efficiency and size of the plant. Recently plants using a somewhat similar cycle but with efficient turboexpanders have operated at pressures as low as 70 lb./sq. in. gage.

Expanders. Two types have been used: (1) reciprocating piston and (2) turbine. Machines of type 1 of relatively low efficiency and small size have been used for many years in the air-separation industry. Little information has been published about them, but it is believed that most of them have been single-acting engines using a specially treated leather packing for the piston.

Kapitza [*Proc. Roy. Soc.*, **A147**, 189 (1934)] describes a small expander that he developed for use in a helium liquefaction cycle. One of the novel features of it is a piston without packing or rings. The piston is a very close lapped fit in the cylinder and has circumferential grooves around it to equalize the pressure and keep it centered. Lane [*Rev. Sci. Instruments*, **12**, 326 (1941)] describes an expander of the Kapitza type which is in successful use for helium liquefaction in the laboratory. Efficiencies of the order of 80 per cent are claimed for these expanders. An expander of the same general type but considerably different in detail has been constructed by Clark Bros. Co., Inc., Olean, N.Y., based on the design of Dr. S. C. Collins of the Massachusetts Institute of Technology. This was used in small, portable oxygen plants. Considerable information about it is given in some of the reports listed in "Bibliography of Scientific and Industrial Reports" (Apr. 5, Apr. 19, and Apr. 26, 1946, issues), by the Office of the Publication Board, U.S. Department of Commerce, especially reports P.B. 9415, 9381, 8600, and 8606. Efficiencies of 60 to 75 per cent were obtained with it depending on conditions.

For large oxygen plants, reciprocating expanders are out of the question, and turboexpanders must be used because of their much smaller size and cost. Such expanders have been used for some time in the Linde-Fränkl plants in Germany, but details about them have only recently been published. Considerable publicity has been given to a small turboexpander developed in Russia by Kapitza [*J. Physics* (*U.S.S.R.*), **1**, 7 (1939)] and used in small liquid-air plants. It is a single-stage radial-flow reaction turbine running at about 40,000 r.p.m., has an 8-cm. wheel, and can handle about 1250 lb. air/hr. Kapitza describes the principles underlying its design in some detail in his paper. A single-stage turbine of the same general type has been built by the Elliott Company and the Sharples Corporation in collaboration, and some details on its design and performance are available in the government reports referred to above. It has a 6⅞-in. wheel running at 22,000 r.p.m., is capable of an efficiency of 80 per cent with an expansion ratio of 5 to 1, and has a capacity of 7000 lb. air/hr. at operating temperature.

Some further details on the Elliott-Sharples expander are given in a paper by Swearingen [*Trans. Am. Inst. Chem. Engrs.*, **43**, 85 (1947)]. This paper gives the basis for the design and illustrates many of the mechanical details. It also gives some mechanical details and performance data on the German turboexpanders used in Linde plants as early as 1936. Several manufacturers have since built larger expanders for tonnage oxygen plants.

Compressors. In small air-separation plants the compressor has always been of the reciprocating type but in very large plants this type of compressor becomes so bulky and expensive that it is being replaced by the turbocompressor. This type is characterized by high speed, large capacity for a given bulk, and relatively low pressure ratio per stage. There is no theoretical limit to the pressure that may be obtained, however, if one uses enough stages or wheels in series. There is a limit to the pressure ratio in any one stage set by the velocity of sound in the gas. It is generally considered not to be good practice to approach too closely to the sonic velocity. Allowing a maximum velocity, say about 70 per cent of the sonic for the particular conditions, one can calculate at least approximately the pressure rise obtainable from a wheel by conversion of the kinetic energy to the energy associated with static pressure. To reach pressures of the order of 100 lb./sq. in., which are required for the tonnage oxygen processes, the compressor would probably be in at least two sections of about 4 or 5 stages each with intercooling between them.

Turbocompressors are of two general types, *axial flow*, and *radial flow* or *centrifugal*. Both are capable of handling very large volumes with high adiabatic efficiency. Efficiencies up to 88 per cent are claimed for the axial-flow type and somewhat lower for the centrifugal. In general the centrifugal machine is used for the higher pressures and it is also somewhat more flexible in handling varying capacities. Because of its high speed the best drive for the turbocompressor is a steam turbine. Centrifugal compressors have been built for pressure as high as 900 lb./sq. in. Pressures considerably higher than this are used in some low-temperature processes, and in those cases reciprocating compressors would still be used, as well as in all small plants where the volume does not lend itself to use of the turbocompressor. A series of papers by Karassik [*Chem. Eng.*, Oct., 110, Nov., 132, Dec., 126 (1947); Jan., 118, Feb., 134 (1948)] gives useful information on centrifugal compressors from the viewpoint of the process engineer. Also, see Sec. 6 of this handbook.

Helium Separation from Natural Gas. For some years the U.S. Bureau of Mines has operated plants for the extraction of helium from natural gas and during the last war the production was greatly expanded. The history of the development up to 1937 is reviewed by Seibel [*Trans. Am. Soc. Mech. Engrs.*, **59**, 55 (1937)]. The helium content of the natural gases processed in the various plants varies from 1 to 8 per cent, the nitrogen content from 12 to 80 per cent, with the balance chiefly methane but with small amounts of higher hydrocarbons also present.

Figure 12-38 shows a flow diagram of the Bureau of Mines helium-separation process. Refrigeration is obtained from two sources: (1) Joule-Thomson expansion of the gas from about 600 lb./sq. in. gage, and (2) an auxiliary nitrogen refrigeration cycle involving engine expansion from 600 to 15 lb./sq. in. abs. No rectification is used since the difference between the boiling points of nitrogen and helium is so great that a single partial condensation step will effect a considerable enrichment to yield a crude helium of 60 per cent content and a second partial condensation at higher pressure yields a helium of 98.5 per cent. A further purification to 99.7 per cent or higher can be achieved by adsorption on activated carbon at about −275°F. Rectification would require liquefaction of the helium and this would require refrigeration to much lower temperatures.

Referring to the diagram, the gas at 600 lb./sq. in. after treatment to remove CO_2, H_2S, and water vapor is cooled and almost completely condensed in exchanger 1 by returning low-pressure gas and then throttled into separator 2 at a pressure of 200 to 300 lb./sq. in., where both phases are further cooled by nitrogen vapor from the auxiliary cycle. The gas phase withdrawn from the separator is the crude helium product of 60 per cent helium and 40 per cent nitrogen. It is brought to atmospheric temperature in exchanger 9 by exchange of heat with itself after compression to 2700 lb./sq. in. on its way to further purification. The liquid phase from separator 2 is throttled and passed back through exchanger 1 and is brought to atmospheric temperature and finally recompressed to pipe-line pressure. The second partial condensation is carried out at 2700 lb./sq. in. in vessel 5 surrounded by liquid nitrogen in 3. The gas phase from this condensation, which is 98.5 per cent helium, is brought to atmospheric temperature in 9. The liquid phase from the partial condensation in 5 which is mostly nitrogen is throttled to 4 to flash off dissolved helium which joins the crude helium stream in 2. The liquid phase from 4 passes to vessel 3 where it serves as the cooling agent for the helium purification step. The rest of the diagram shows the nitrogen liquefaction cycle for supplying the liquid which maintains the bath in 3

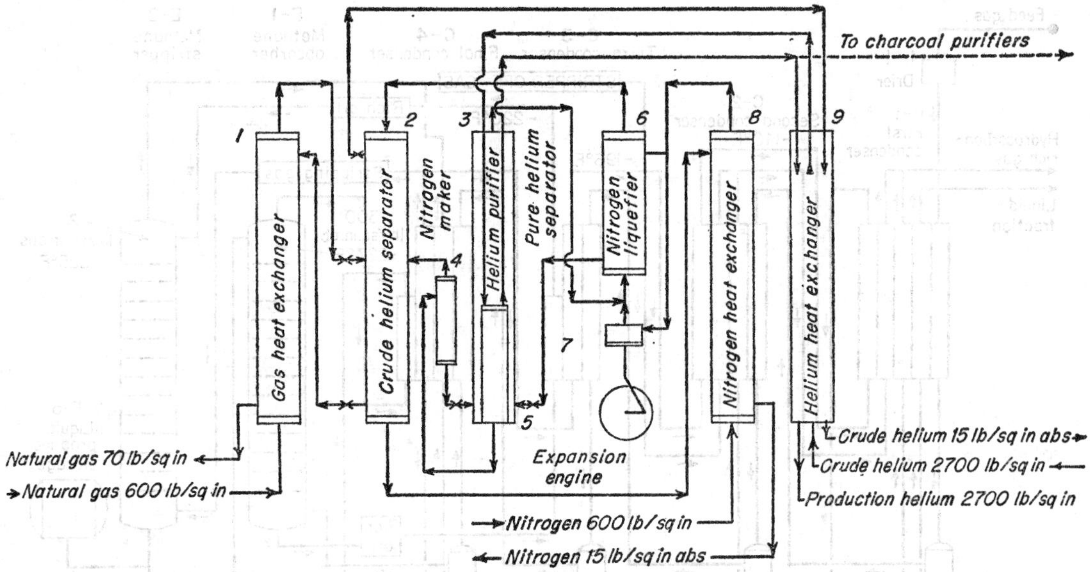

FIG. 12-38. Simplified diagram of Bureau of Mines helium-separation process. [*Chem. Eng. Progress*, **44**, 567 (1948).]

around the partial condenser 5. For further details on the process and on the plant equipment reference is made to a paper by Mullins [*Chem. Eng. Progress*, **44**, 567 (1948)] from which the diagram in Fig. 12-38 was taken. This paper also gives some enthalpy data and phase equilibrium data for the natural gas processed at the Otis, Kansas, plant of the Bureau of Mines.

Nitrogen Removal from Natural Gas. Removal of nitrogen from natural gases of high nitrogen content by low-temperature rectification is a process of potential importance. There are large quantities of gas that have nitrogen contents ranging from 1 to 34 per cent and appreciable amounts with a much higher nitrogen content. Removal of the inert nitrogen would have obvious economic advantages due to the increase in heating value of the gas. This is discussed in some detail in a paper by Mullins and Wilson, Prospective Benefits from Removing Excess Nitrogen from Natural Gas, published by the American Gas Association (1948). This paper also contains an extensive bibliography on gas separation. Processes for nitrogen removal are treated in considerable detail in a paper by Deschner and Bodle [*Oil Gas J.*, Apr. 15 and 29 (1948)]. Flow diagrams, material balances, heat balances, and power requirements are given for three processes.

Distillation of Light Hydrocarbons. The separation of light hydrocarbons in a more or less pure state from mixtures such as petroleum refinery gases and cracked natural gases is an important operation at the present time, conducted primarily to recover the olefins for use in chemical syntheses. A typical process for producing 95 per cent ethylene is described by Pratt and Foskett [*Trans. Am. Inst. Chem. Engrs.*, **42**, 149 (1946)] as follows:

The olefin-bearing gas from the cracking furnace or other source is compressed in three or four stages to a pressure of 600 lb./sq. in. gage. The gas is cooled between stages and small quantities of condensate and water removed in interstage separators. The gas leaving the last stage of compression is cooled to an economical approach to the cooling water temperature, then subcooled to approximately 70°F. by high-level refrigeration. The cracked gas, after removal of water and hydrocarbon condensate, flows to the dehydrators. These units remove the remaining moisture from the gas by adsorption on activated bauxite or alumina. The dried gas is then cooled to 0°F. and introduced to the demethanizer tower. Hydrogen and methane are taken overhead in this tower and released to the plant fuel system. Reflux is produced by a runback-type condenser refrigerated by the evaporation of liquid ethylene at 5 lb./sq. in. gage. The reflux temperature is approximately −130°F. A small quantity of ethylene is lost in the overhead product in order to satisfy the dew point requirements at the top of the tower of −130°F. and 575 lb./sq. in. gage. The bottoms from the methane tower, essentially free of hydrogen and methane, flow to the ethylene tower, where ethylene is removed as an overhead product. Reflux is produced by a condenser refrigerated by propane or ammonia evaporating at −15°F.

The subsequent processing of the ethane and heavier components which comprise the ethylene tower bottoms depends on the number and the purity of the products desired. An ethane tower and propylene tower are required if a propylene-propane product is required. On the other hand, if ethylene is the only primary product, the ethane and C_3's may be recycled to the cracking furnace; in which case, a single tower would suffice to separate the recycle stream from the C_4's and heavier components.

Table 12-20 shows the compositions of the gas streams at various points. Low-level refrigeration is obtained from a vapor-compression refrigeration system using ethylene which is evaporated at −150°F. and condensed by propane or ammonia, which in turn discharges the heat to cooling water. The paper referred to gives further details on operating conditions, gas compression,

Table 12-20. Stream Compositions Mole Per Cent

Constituent	Feed	Methane tower		Ethylene tower		Ethane tower		Propylene tower	
		Net overhead	Bottoms	Net overhead	Bottoms	Net-overhead	Bottoms	Net overhead	Bottoms
Hydrogen	11.5	40.0							
Methane	16.5	56.0	0.5	2.0					
Ethylene	19.4	4.0	25.6	95.0	0.9	2.8			
Ethane	17.7		24.9	3.0	32.6	95.0	1.4	1.5	
Propylene	8.9		12.5		17.0	2.2	24.3	25.7	
Propane	24.0		33.7		45.7		68.6	72.2	5.0
C_4's	1.5		2.1		2.9		4.3	0.6	69.0
C_5's	0.5		0.7		0.9		1.4		26.0
Total	100.0	100.0	100.0	100.0	100.0	100.0	100.0	100.0	100.0
Moles/100 moles of feed	100	28.8	71.2	18.7	52.5	17.5	35.0	33.1	1.9

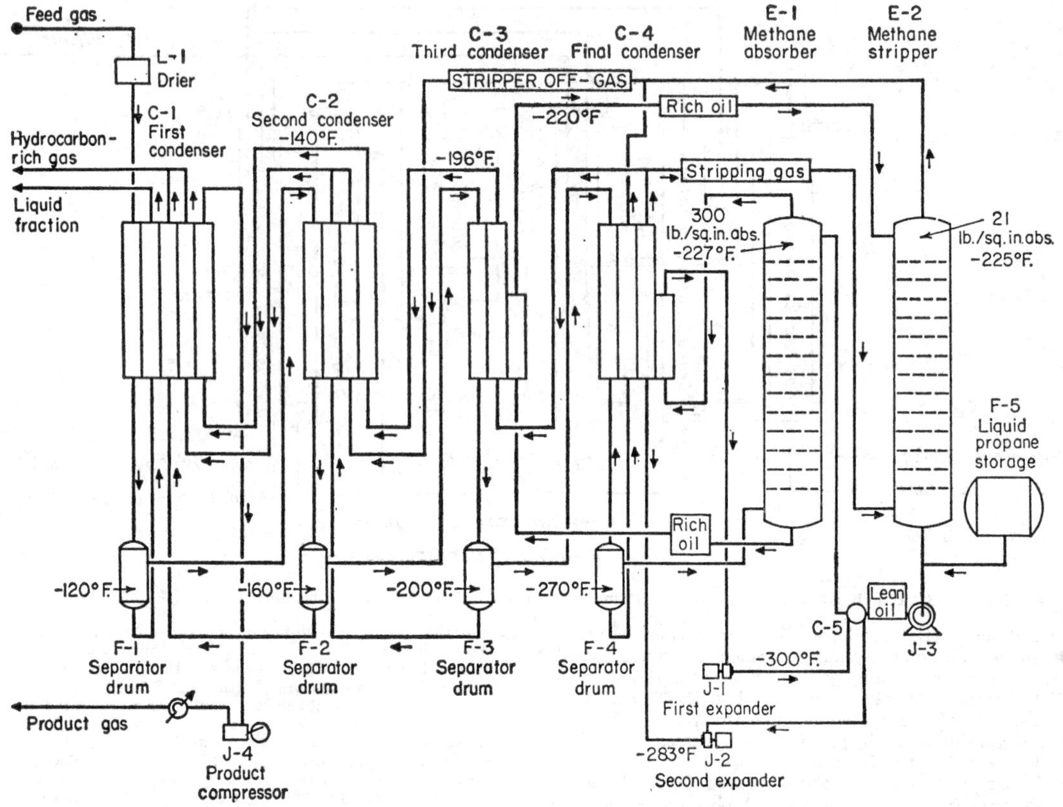

FIG. 12-39. Low-temperature hydrogen-purification plant.

power requirement, purification of the feed gas, materials of construction, and instrumentation.

Recovery of Hydrogen from Refinery Gases. Nearly a billion cubic feet of hydrogen gas a day is becoming available from refinery reformer operations. This by-product hydrogen is from 60 to 95 per cent pure with most of the impurities being light hydrocarbons such as methane, ethane, ethylene, propane, and butane. Because of the expanding need for hydrogen by the ammonia industry and as a liquid rocket fuel and because of the relatively cheap price of by-product hydrogen there have been a number of interesting developments of purification processes, most of them employing low temperatures. [See Gifford and Fuller, Liquid Hydrogen from Refinery Waste Gases, Paper D-1, "Advances in Cryogenic Engineering," Plenum Press, New York, 1961. Cryogenic Route to Pure Hydrogen, *Chem. Eng.*, **66**, 69–72 (July 13, 1959). Palazzo, Schreiner, and Skaperdas, Low Temperature Recovery of Hydrogen from Refinery Gases, *Ind. Eng. Chem.*, **49**, 685–688 (April, 1957).]

The purification process described by Palazzo, Schreiner, and Skaperdas is illustrated in Fig. 12-39. The process is adaptable to refinery gases containing as little as 65 per cent hydrogen as well as the more pure sources. Also a fairly wide range of feed pressures can be handled. A typical process is illustrated.

Feed-gas conditions are as follows: temperature 100°F.; pressure 320 lb./sq. in. abs.; moisture content, saturated; flow rate 7831.5 lb./hr.; composition, mole per cent, dry basis, hydrogen 85.2, methane 8.5, ethane 4.4, propane 1.8, butanes 0.1.

The feed gas is first passed through an alumina drying unit (L-1) where the water dew point is reduced to approximately −100°F. The gas then flows through the first bank of multistream extended surface exchangers and is cooled to −120°F. The point at which the cut is made may be dictated by specifications on the recovery of a given group of hydrocarbons or simply by a convenient process arrangement, if no requirements are to be satisfied. In the present general case the cut point was set arbitrarily to obtain a fraction rich in propane-butane. From the fraction sufficient propane can be recovered, if desired, to supply the makeup required in the absorber-stripper.

After the first separation in drum F-1, the gas is cooled in progressive steps to −160°, −200°, and −270°F., while a vapor-liquid separation is made at each of these points.

The gas leaving the last separator, F-4, flows to the methane absorber tower, E-1, where the residual hydrocarbon impurities are removed by countercurrent washing with liquid propane. The rich propane (rich oil) is then depressured, heated in exchanger C-3, and stripped of the hydrocarbon impurities by a portion of the product gas in tower E-2.

The product gas, containing less than 0.05 per cent methane by volume, leaves the top of the absorber and flows to exchanger C-4, where it is warmed to −259°F. and is then expanded in a turboexpander, J-1. The cold gas, now at −300°F., exchanges heat with the lean propane, which it cools to operating temperature, and is then expanded through a second machine. The discharged gas, now at a temperature of −283°F., is returned to exchanger C-4, where it is heated to −220°F. Upon leaving the exchanger it is divided into a product stream and a stripping-gas stream. The latter goes directly to stripper E-2, while the product flows through exchangers C-3, C-2, and C-1 in that order.

The liquefied hydrocarbon fraction from drum F-4 is flashed to approximately 23 lb./sq. in. abs. and returned through exchanger C-4. This fraction is then joined with the stripper tail gas and sent through exchangers C-2 and C-1. The liquid hydrocarbon fractions from drums F-2 and F-3 are similarly flashed to low pressures and evaporated to supply part of the refrigeration in C-1 and C-2. The hydrocarbons separated out in F-1 are recovered as a liquid which is returned to exchanger C-1 under pressure. As this stream is assumed to be further processed, a hydrogen-product stream, a waste-gas stream, and a liquid-hydrocarbon stream leave the plant. The condition of the product streams leaving the process is summarized as in Table 12-21.

Table 12-21. Analysis of Product Streams (Mole Per Cent) Leaving Hydrogen-purification Plant

	Product hydrogen	Waste gas	Liquid hydro-carbon
Pressure, lb./sq. in. abs.	320	18	308
Temperature, °F.	100	67	67
Flow rate, lb./hr.	2227.3	4316.4	1287.8
Hydrogen, %	99.95	48.0	1.0
Methane, %	0.05	34.8	4.1
Ethane, %	....	14.8	37.3
Propane, %	....	2.4	53.4
Butane, %	....	......	4.2

The hydrogen gas of 99.95 per cent purity is about as pure as the best electrolytic hydrogen available and can be produced at a small fraction of the cost of electrolytic gas.

Low-temperature Insulation. Many of the developments in the cryogenic field in the past few years would not have been possible without the development of high-efficiency insulations that are ten to ten thousand times better than ordinary refrigeration insulations. For instance, a foot-thick slab of cork perfectly applied has a heat conductivity of roughly 0.02 B.t.u./(hr.)(sq. ft.)(°F.) whereas 1 in. thickness of the new multiple-layer superinsulation with 100 lamination of foil in high vacuum has of the order of 1×10^{-4} B.t.u./(hr.)(sq. ft.)(°F.) average conductivity between 36°R. and room temperature.

There are four general types of insulation being used for cryogenic applications. These are (1) high vacuum, (2) multiple layer, (3) powder, and (4) rigid foam. Pertinent information concerning each type follows:

1. High-vacuum Insulation. The first successful means of insulating containers for holding cryogenic liquids (accomplished by Sir James Dewar at the end of the last century) was by the use of high vacuum in doubled-walled vessels with reflective surfaces. Such vessels are still referred to as Dewars. The heat leak into Dewar-type containers is principally by radiation, gas conduction, and direct thermal conduction through supports and other connections to the inner shell.

Radiation. The following adaptation of the Stefan-Boltzmann equation for r adiant-heat transfer is generally used for calculating heat transfer into a Dewar vessel where the surfaces are parallel or at a constant distance apart as in concentric spheres or coaxial cylinders and where the emissivities of the facing surfaces are known:

$$\frac{Q}{A} = \sigma \frac{1}{(1/\epsilon_1) + (A_1/A_2)[(1/\epsilon_2) - 1]} (T_2^4 - T_1^4) \quad \text{watts/sq. ft.} \qquad (12\text{-}21)$$

where Q = total reduced heat flow, watts
A_1 = inside (cold) surface area, sq. ft.
A_2 = outside (warm) surface area, sq. ft.
σ = Stefan-Boltzmann constant; 5.076×10^{-10} watts/sq. ft.
ϵ_1 and ϵ_2 = inner and outer surface emissivities
T_1 and T_2 = inner and outer surface temperature, °R.

Table 12-22. Total Emissivities

Surface	Temp., °R.			
	7	37	140	540
Copper	0.0050	.....	0.008	0.018
Gold	......	.....	.01	.02
Silver	.0044	.....	.008	.02
Aluminum	.011	.....	.018	.03
Magnesium	......	.....	.....	.07
Chromium	......	.....	.08	.08
Nickel	......	.....	.022	.04
Rhodium	......	.....	.078	
Lead	.012	.....	.036	.05
Tin	.012	.....	.013	.05
Zinc	......	.....	.026	.05
Brass	.018	.....	.....	.035
18-8 stainless steel	......	.....	.048	.08
50 lead 50 tin solder	......	.....	.032	
Silver plate on copper	......	0.013	.017	
Nickel plate on copper	......	.027	.033	

Table 12-22 gives the minimum total emissivities that can be expected for various reflective materials. Figures 12-40 and 12-41 are plots of calculated heat flow in watts per square foot for various values of emissivity and area ratios.

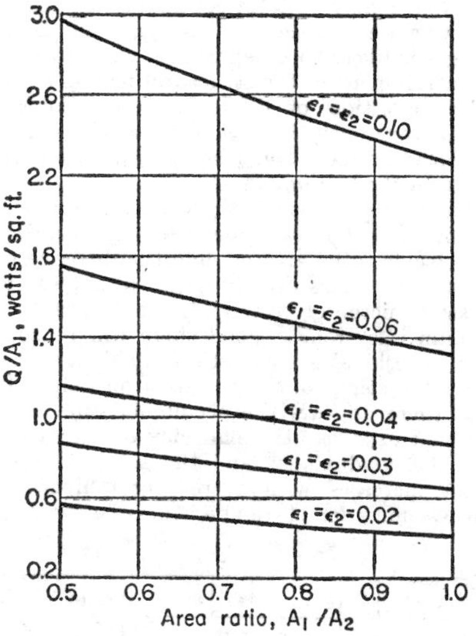

FIG. 12-40. Radiation heat transfer between 540 and 138°R.

Good-reflecting surfaces are achieved in practice by such means as application of aluminum foil, chemical deposition of silver, or electrodeposition of silver or gold. In Dewars built of copper or aluminum, only a cleaning or polishing of the structural metal is required. Whatever the materials used to obtain low emissivities, it will be important to remove surface contaminants such as oxides or films of oil or grease. There will be some advantage in using cleaning procedures that avoid work hardening of the metal, *e.g.*, solvent cleaning and electropolishing.

In Dewar vessels for the lowest-boiling liquids, helium (7°R.) and hydrogen (37°R.), it is customary to intercept the radiation from the warm boundary by a shield cooled

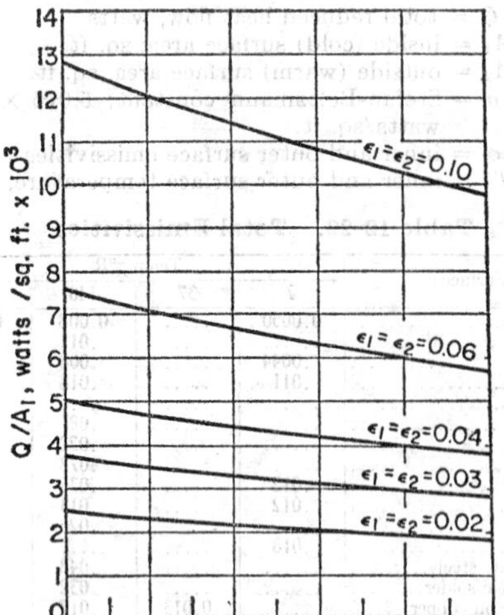

FIG. 12-41. Radiation heat transfer between 138 and 36°R.

with liquid nitrogen (140°R.). In such vessels a significant portion of the heat exchange between shield and inner container may be from conduction by residual gas in the evacuated space. In a hydrogen Dewar the residual gas is likely to be hydrogen, released from solution or entrainment in the structural metals or resulting from decomposition of diffusion pump fluids. In a helium Dewar, such hydrogen is condensed on the helium-cooled surface, and residual gas can result only from leaks in the helium vessel.

Gas Conduction. Insulating vacuums for cryogenic applications must be high enough for the mean free path of the molecule to be greater than the distance between facing surfaces. This usually requires that the vacuum be at least 1 micron or better ($<10^{-3}$ mm. Hg). Unless the vacuum is extremely good there will be some heat leak due to residual gas condition. This may be calculated by adaptations of the Knudsen formula. In these formulas there appears the accommodation coefficient, a factor that expresses the efficiency of energy exchange between the residual gas and the solid surface. This coefficient increases with decreasing temperature and approaches unity for all temperatures below the critical

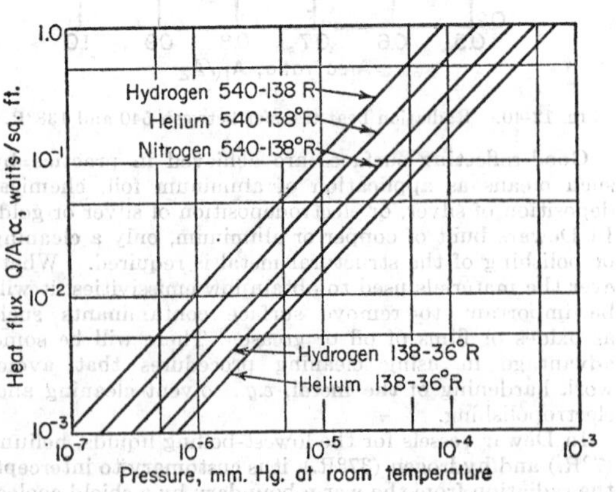

FIG. 12-42. Gaseous heat conduction.

temperature of the gas. Of the common gases only hydrogen and helium will have accommodation coefficients appreciably less than unity at cryogenic temperatures (see Table 12-23). Figure 12-42 gives the gaseous heat conduction calculated from the following formulas for some typical gases:

$$\frac{Q}{A_1\alpha} = 7.2\,\frac{\gamma + 1}{\gamma - 1}\,\frac{P_{mm}}{\sqrt{M}}\,(T_2 - T_1) \qquad (12\text{-}22)$$

$$\alpha = \frac{\alpha_1\alpha_2}{\alpha_2 + (A_1/A_2)(1 - \alpha_2)\alpha_1} \qquad (12\text{-}23)$$

where A_1 = inner area, sq. ft.
A_2 = outer area, sq. ft.
α_1 and α_2 = accommodation coefficients at the two boundaries
γ = specific heat ratio of the gas
M = molecular weight of the gas
T_1 and T_2 = boundary temperatures, °R.
P_{mm} = gas pressure, mm. Hg, as indicated by a gage at room temperature

It should be noted that the formula for α above applies to parallel plates, coaxial cylinders, or concentric spheres.

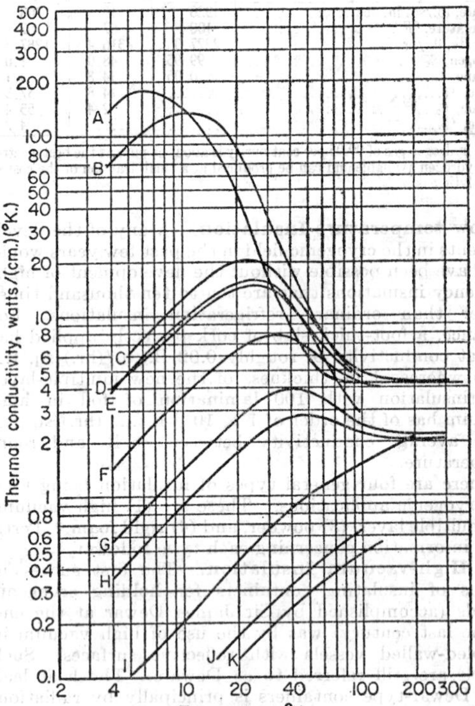

FIG. 12-43. Thermal conductivity of some good conductors.

A. Silver 99.999 per cent pure
B. High-purity copper
C. Coalesced copper
D. Copper, electrolytic tough pitch
E. Aluminum, single crystal
F. Free-machining tellurium copper
G. Aluminum, 1100-F
H. Aluminum, 6063-T5
I. Copper, phosphorus deoxidized
J. Aluminum, 2024-T4
K. Free-machining loaded brass

1 watt/(cm.)(°K.) = 57.79 B.t.u./(hr.)(ft.)(°R.)

Table 12-23. Accommodation Coefficients

Temp., °R.	Helium	Hydrogen	Air
540	0.3	0.3	0.8-0.9
140	0.4	0.5	1
37	0.6	1	1
7	1	1	1

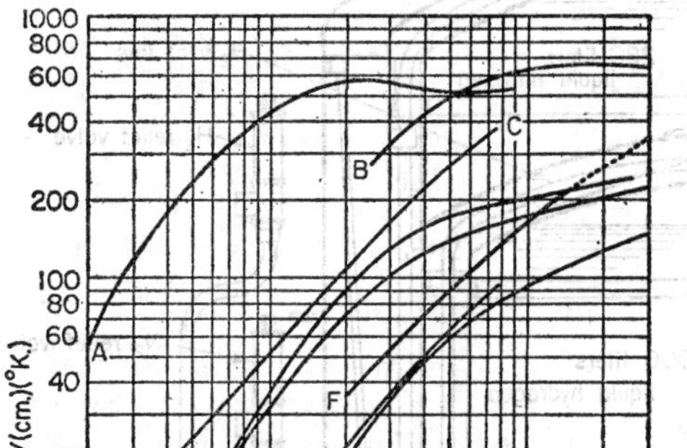

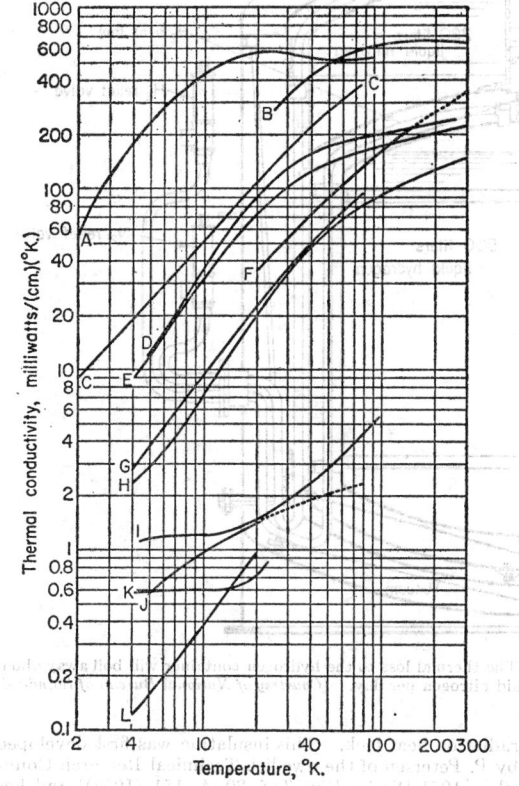

FIG. 12-44. Thermal conductivity of some poor conductors.

A. 50-50 lead-tin solder
B. Steel S.A.E. 1020
C. Beryllium copper
D. Constantan
E. Monel
F. Silicon bronze
G. Inconel
H. Type 347 stainless steel
I. Fused quartz
J. Polytetrafluoroethylene (Teflon)
K. Polymethylmethacrylate (Perspex)
L. Nylon

1 mw/(cm)(°K) = 57.79×10^{-3} B.t.u./(hr.)(ft.)(°R.)

Conductivity of Supports. The heat conduction through supports and other connections between the warm and cold shells can become an appreciable percentage of the total if careful consideration is not given to their design and a good choice of material made. To minimize heat flow a material of high strength and low thermal conductivity is desired. Many other factors, of course, must also be considered, such as a tendency to outgas and brittleness, in making a final choice. Table 12-24 lists a number of materials suitable for use at low temperatures. A comparison of the net relative heat conduction can be made by dividing the yield strength by the average thermal-conductivity value given. Figures 12-43 and 12-44 show the variation of thermal conductivity with temperatures for a number of materials.

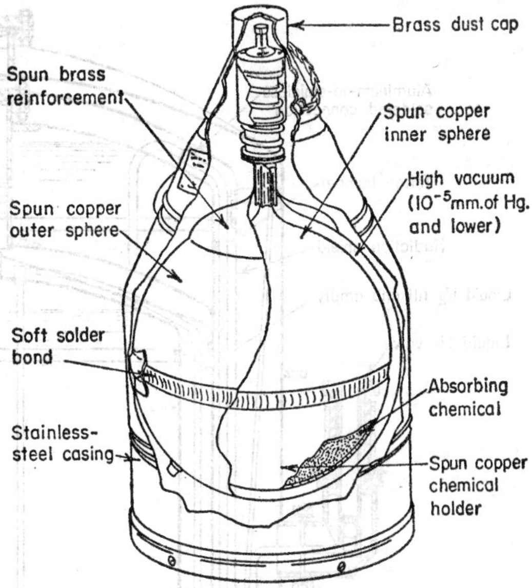

FIG. 12-45. Typical liquid-nitrogen or oxygen Dewar of 10- to 100-liter class. The 50-liter size loses about 2 liters/day because of heat leak. (*Courtesy of Hofman Laboratories, Inc.*)

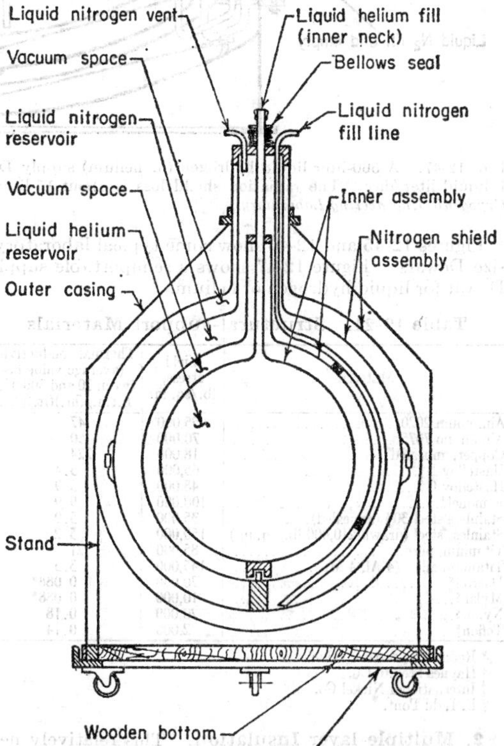

FIG. 12-46. Typical design of portable liquid-helium (or hydrogen) Dewar—10- to 100-liter class. A good 50-liter container of this type will lose ½ to 1 liter/day of liquid helium (less than ¼ liter/day for hydrogen). About 4 liters/day of liquid nitrogen used in cold shielding boils away. (*Courtesy of Superior Air Products.*)

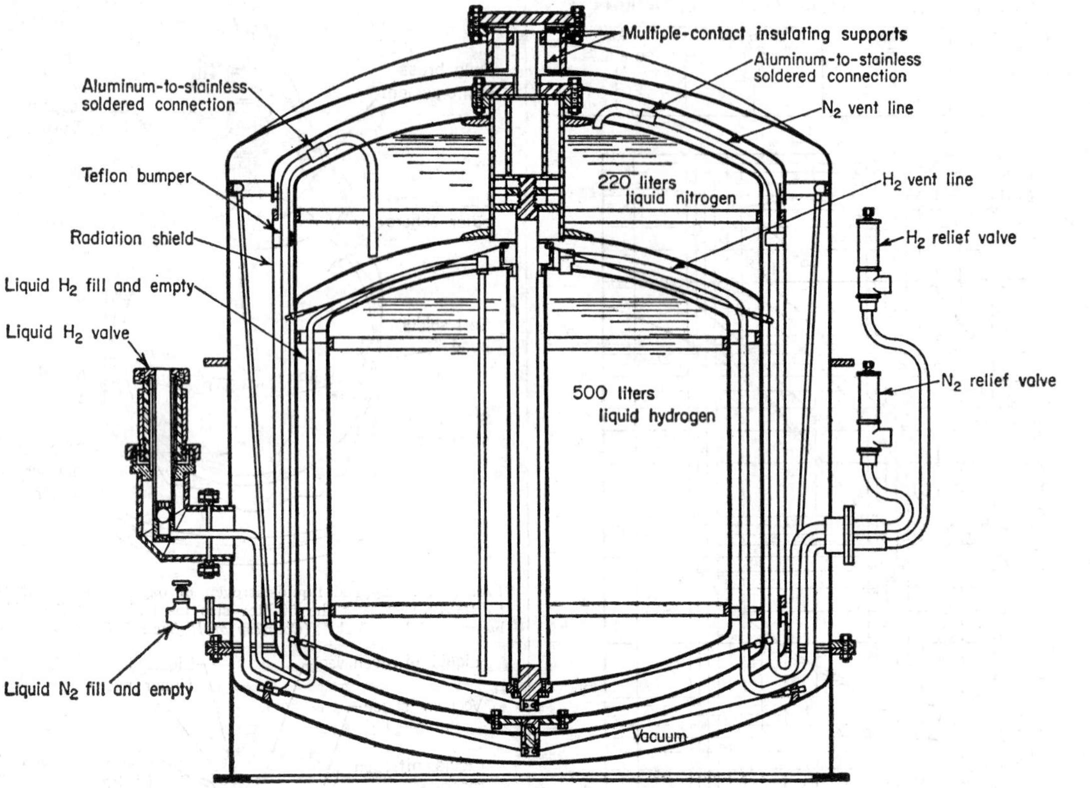

FIG. 12-47. A 500-liter liquid hydrogen (or helium) supply Dewar. The thermal loss to the hydrogen container will boil away about 1 liquid liter/day. The radiation shield loss is about 15 liters of liquid nitrogen per day. (*Courtesy of National Bureau of Standards Cryogenic Engineering Laboratory.*)

Figures 12-45 and 12-46 show some typical laboratory-size Dewars. Figure 12-47 shows a semiportable supply Dewar for liquid hydrogen or helium.

Table 12-24. Structural-support Materials

Material	Yield stress, lb./sq. in.	Thermal conductivity (average value between 20 and 300°K.), B.t.u./(hr.)(ft.)(°R.)
Aluminum 2020	55,000	47
Aluminum 7075	70,000	50
Copper, annealed	18,000	224
Hastelloy B†	65,000	5.4
Hastelloy C†	48,000	5.9
K monel‡	100,000	9.9
Stainless steel 304 (annealed)	35,000	5.9
Stainless steel (drawn 210,000 lb./sq. in.)	150,000	5.2
Titanium, pure	85,000	21
Titanium alloy (4 Al, 4 Mn)	145,000	3.5
Dacron§	20,000	0.088*
Mylar§	10,000	0.088*
Nylon§	20,000	0.18
Teflon§	2,000	0.14

* Room-temperature value.
† Haynes Stellite Co.
‡ International Nickel Co.
§ E. I. du Pont.

2. Multiple-layer Insulation. This relatively new type of insulation for cryogenic applications has yielded the lowest over-all heat conduction into Dewar-type vessels and is often referred to as superinsulation. It is the application of many floating radiation shields closely spaced but thermally separated by a poor-conducting fiber in the evacuated space for great reduction in the radiation heat lack. This insulation was first developed by P. Petersen of the Swedish Technical Research Council in 1951 [*Sartryck ur Tuf,* 29, **4,** 151 (1958)] and has

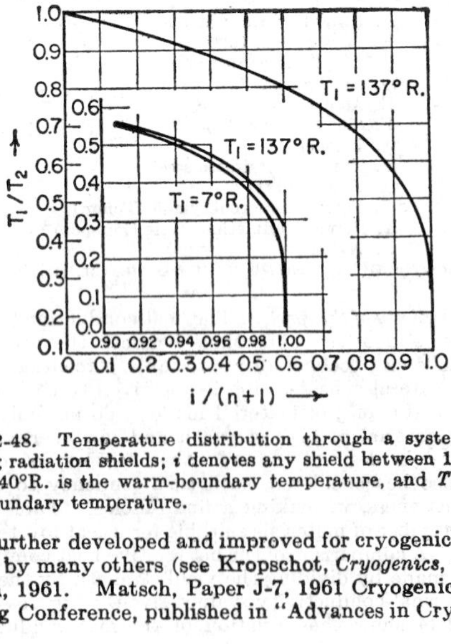

FIG. 12-48. Temperature distribution through a system of n floating radiation shields; i denotes any shield between 1 and n, T_2 = 540°R. is the warm-boundary temperature, and T_1 is the cold-boundary temperature.

been further developed and improved for cryogenic application by many others (see Kropschot, *Cryogenics,* vol. 4, March, 1961. Matsch, Paper J-7, 1961 Cryogenic Engineering Conference, published in "Advances in Cryogenic

Engineering," vol. 7, Plenum Press, New York, 1962). When properly applied this insulation has an apparent mean thermal conductivity between 540 and 36°R. of 2 to 4 × 10^{-5} B.t.u./(hr.)(ft.)(°R.).

For a theoretical evaluation of the effectiveness of multiple radiation shields the following equation may be used:

$$Q = \frac{E\sigma A}{n+1}(T_2^4 - T_1^4) \qquad (12\text{-}24)$$

where A = area
σ = Stefan-Boltzmann constant
E = effective emissivity
n = number of floating radiation shields
T_1 and T_2 = temperatures of the hot and cold boundaries

Figure 12-48 shows the theoretical temperature distribution for radiation shields separated by a vacuum between parallel walls at 540 and 137°R. and parallel walls of 540 and 7°R. The curves were obtained from the relation

$$T_i = \left[T_2^4 - \frac{i}{n+1}(T_2^4 - T_1^4)\right]^{\frac{1}{4}} \qquad (12\text{-}25)$$

where T_i = temperature of the ith shield
i = number of the ith shield counting from the hot wall
n = total number of shields in the system

To arrive at an apparent mean thermal conductivity k for multilayer insulations, however, the well-known Fourier equation is used:

$$Q_T = \frac{kA(T_2 - T_1)}{t} \qquad (12\text{-}26)$$

where t = thickness of the insulation.

There are a number of choices of reflective foils and fiber mats but the lowest thermal-conductivity values have been achieved with aluminum foil separated by glass-fiber paper. Table 12-25 gives a number of values of k reported by Kropschot for a number of material combinations and conditions.

Table 12-25. The Approach Mean Thermal Conductivity k of Some Selected Multiple-layer Insulations

Insulator (see code below)	Reflector	Inches t	No. of shields per inch	Density, lb./cu. ft.	Cold wall, °R.	k, B.t.u./(hr.)(ft.)(°R.)
A	2	1.3	55	7.5	137	0.32×10^{-4}
					36	0.23×10^{-4}
B	1	1.5	50	7.0	137	0.30×10^{-4}
					36	0.24×10^{-4}
B	1	1.0	50	7.0	137	0.41×10^{-4}
					36	0.35×10^{-4}
A	1	1.2	52	...	137	0.75×10^{-4}
A	3	1.5	...	3.8	137	1.85×10^{-4}
					36	1.39×10^{-4}
A	1	1.4	37	6.9	137	0.43×10^{-4}
					36	0.30×10^{-4}
A	1	1.5	23	6.9	137	0.49×10^{-4}
C	1	1.2	29	6.9	137	0.41×10^{-4}
					36	0.29×10^{-4}
A	2	2.0	48	7.5	137	0.64×10^{-4}
D	1	1.2	52	...	137	1.33×10^{-4}
A	2	1.5	52	5.9	137	0.87×10^{-4}

Code	Description
A	Fiber-glass paper, 0.008 in. thick, 90 per cent B fiber; Dexter Paper Company
B	Fiber-glass paper, 0.0048 in. thick, 90 per cent B fiber; Dexter Paper Company
C	Fiberglas mat, styrene-bonded, 0.008 in. thick, average fiber diameter 0.0007 in., Owens-Corning Fiberglas Corporation
D	Nylon net, 0.006 in., 90% void
1	Aluminum foil, 0.0005 in. thick; Alcoa Aluminum Corporation
2	Aluminum foil, 0.00023 in. thick; Alcoa Aluminum Corporation
3	Mylar, aluminized both sides, 1.5 to 2.0 ohms/sq. ft.; Dobeckmun Company

Gaps between adjacent shields at corners or joints can add significantly to the total heat transport. Therefore, design considerations and techniques of application are of utmost importance. For this reason, a cylindrical shape is to be preferred over a spherical shape. In addition, since an interstitial gas pressure lower than 10^{-4} mm. of Hg is required to attain low conductivities, the insulation must be installed clean and dry. (See Fig. 12-49 for a typical small superinsulated Dewar arrangement.)

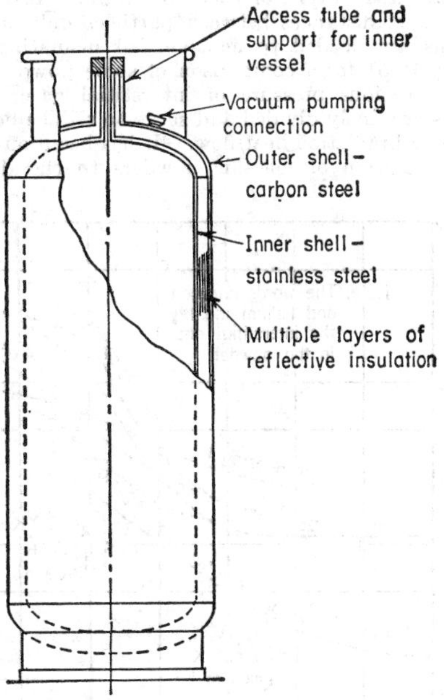

FIG. 12-49. Typical laminar insulated Dewar. 175-liter size loses ½ per cent LN_2 or 1½ per cent LH_2 per day. (*Courtesy of Cryogenic Engineering Co.*)

Very significant advances in the use of multiple-layer insulation have been reported by the Linde Company. They have insulated several thousand vessels ranging in size from 8 to 28,000 gal. Figure 12-50 shows a 5000-gal. transport container being insulated.

FIG. 12-50. A 5000-gal. hydrogen/helium container being insulated with multiple-layer insulation. (*Photograph courtesy of The Linde Company.*)

3. Powder Insulation. (For a rather thorough discussion of this type of cryogenic insulation, see Fulk, Evacuated Powder Insulation for Low Temperatures, in "Progress in Cryogenics," vol. 1, pp. 63–84, Heywood and Co., London, 1959; and Kropschot, Cryogenic Insulation, *A.S.H.R.A.E. Journal*, **1**, 48–54.) Evacuated powder insulation has become one of the most commonly used types of cryogenic insulation. It has the advantage over high vacuum alone or multiple-layer insulation in high vacuum in that it retains a reasonable resistance to heat flow in the event of vacuum failure. Also because of the short distances between particles only moderate vacuums are needed to achieve full insulating value. See Fig. 12-51 for a comparison of some powder insulations at various pressure of interstitial gases. These powders are finely divided and serve to reduce both convection and radiation heat flow. It has been found that, by the addition of metallic powders to the dielectric

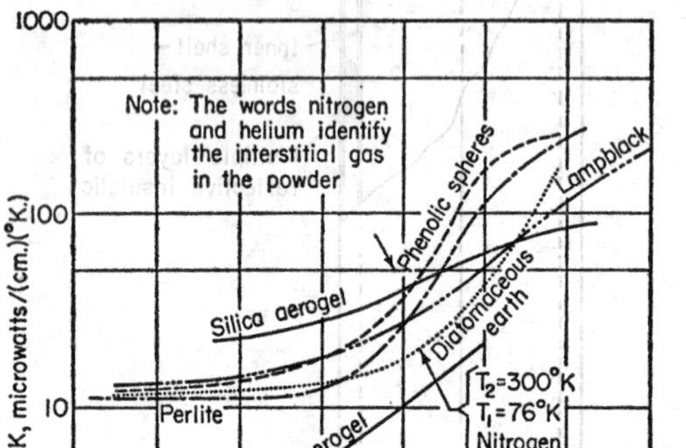

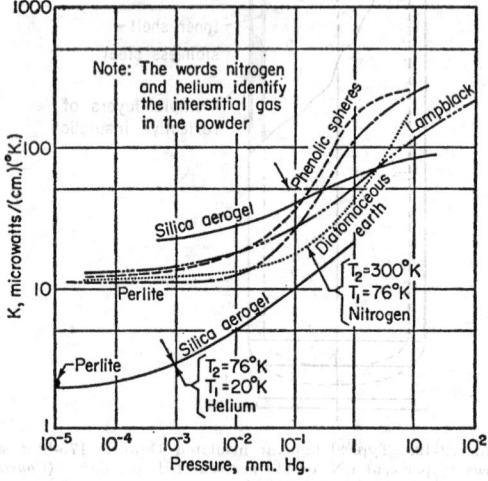

FIG. 12-51. Apparent mean thermal conductivities of several powders as a function of interstitial gas pressure.

1 mw./(cm.)(°K.) = 57.79 × 10^{-6} B.t.u./(hr.)(ft.)(°R.)

powders such as Santocel, perlite, or Cab-O-Sil, a further reduction in radiation heat transfer can be achieved. Figure 12-52 illustrates the effect of adding various percentages of aluminum powder. Table 12-26 lists the apparent mean thermal conductivity of several evacu-

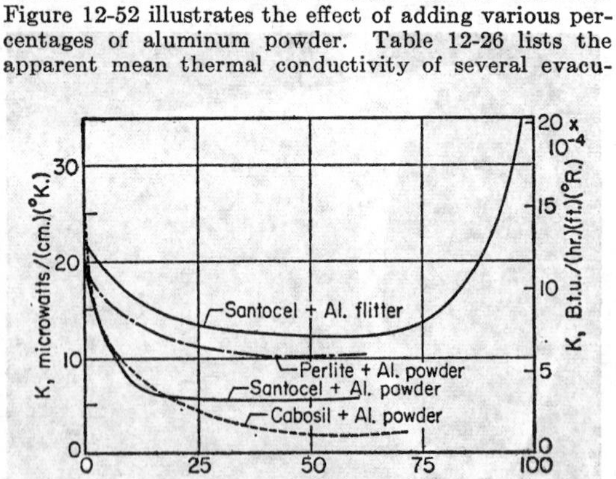

FIG. 12-52. The apparent mean thermal conductivity between 540 and 137°R. of some evacuated powders with added aluminum.

ated powders at various conditions. Figure 12-53 shows a typical arrangement of a powder insulated vessel.

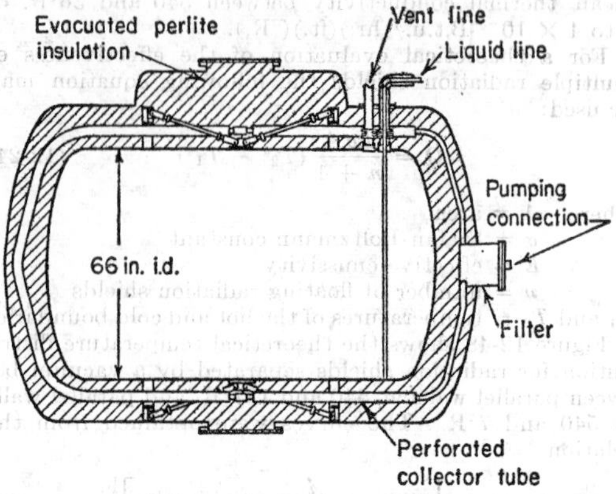

FIG. 12-53. Typical vessel for liquid hydrogen with evacuated powder insulation. 1500-gal. semitrailer transport size loses 1½ per cent per day or less. (*Courtesy of Beech Aircraft Corp.*)

Most powders are highly adsorbent so must be thoroughly dry for attainment of required vacuum. Once a good vacuum is achieved their adsorbing quality helps to keep it. Precaution must be taken in vacuum pumping of powders. Fine-mesh filters are used to protect vacuum pumps from abrasion. Dry fine metallic powders are quite combustible and must be kept reasonably cool or isolated from air to avoid danger of ignition.

4. Rigid-foam Insulation. This class of insulation is not so thermally efficient as the others but has the advantage of not requiring an evacuated atmosphere, thus permitting single-shell construction of vessels and pipe lines. Successful application is often difficult, however, particularly for operating temperatures below the liquefaction temperature of the surrounding atmosphere. Foams having closed cells containing a condensable gas greatly improve in performance at lower temperatures. Table 12-27 lists the apparent mean thermal conductivity of some selected foams.

Properties of Materials at Low Temperatures. The properties of most concern to designers and fabricators of equipment for low-temperature application are (1) specific heat, (2) thermal expansion, (3) thermal conductivity, (4) mechanical properties, and (5) thermophysical properties of fluids. [See Corruccini, *Chem. Eng. Progress*, **53**, 262–267, 342 (1957). National Bureau of Standards Monograph 21 (1960) and Monograph 29 (1961). Scott, "Cryogenic Engineering," Van Nostrand, Princeton, N.J., 1959.]

Specific Heat. Specific heats of solids rise rapidly from absolute zero, then usually increase less and less rapidly as the temperature rises toward ambient. Table 12-28 gives data on selected substances. A compilation by Kelley covering elements and inorganic compounds is the most comprehensive source of specific-heat data. Low-temperature data on commercial alloys is scarce but can be approximated by combining the specific heats of the component elements in proportion to their concentrations in the alloy.

Thermal Expansion. For crystalline substances, including most metals, the coefficient of thermal expansion is approximately proportional to the specific heat. Correspondingly, length or volume changes between any two temperatures are approximately proportional to the enthalpy difference between the same two temperatures. Table 12-29 presents selected data on structural materials including an epoxy resin (Araldite 501) representative

Table 12-26. Apparent Mean Thermal Conductivity of Several Powders
(1-in. sample thickness, boundary temperatures of 540 and 137°R., and wall emissivities greater then 0.8)[a]

Powder	Remarks	Density, lb./cu. ft.	Gas pressure, mm. Hg	Interstitial gas	Conductivity, B.t.u./(hr.)(ft.)(°R.)
Silica aerogel	Chemically prepared	6.2	10^{-4}	....	12×10^{-4}[c]
	250A	6.2	628[a]	Nitrogen	113×10^{-4}
		6.2	628	Helium	358×10^{-4}
		6.2	628	Hydrogen	462×10^{-4}
	+10% free silicon dust by weight	7	10^{-4}	....	10.5×10^{-4}
Silica	Flame prepared	3.7	10^{-4}	....	12×10^{-4}
	150–200A	3.7	630	Nitrogen	107×10^{-4}
Perlite, expanded	+30 mesh	3.7	10^{-4}	....	12×10^{-4}
	+30 mesh	6.2	10^{-4}	....	10.5×10^{-4}
	+30 mesh	6.2	628	Nitrogen	192×10^{-4}
	+30 mesh	6.2	628	Helium	735×10^{-4}
	+30 mesh	6.2	628	Hydrogen	845×10^{-4}
	−30 + 80 mesh	8.1	10^{-4}	....	7×10^{-4}
	−30 + 80 mesh	8.1	628	Nitrogen	188×10^{-4}
	−30 + 80 mesh	8.1	628	Helium	728×10^{-4}
	−30 + 80 mesh	8.1	628	Hydrogen	838×10^{-4}
	−80 mesh	8.7	10^{-4}	....	5.8×10^{-4}
	−80 mesh	8.7	628	Nitrogen	202×10^{-4}
	−80 mesh	8.7	628	Helium	780×10^{-4}
	−80 mesh	8.7	628	Hydrogen	840×10^{-4}
	−30 mesh	8.7	10^{-4}	....	5.8×10^{-4}[d,e,f]
Diatomaceous earth	1–100 microns	15.0	10^{-4}	....	9×10^{-4}
		15.6	10^{-4}	....	8×10^{-4}
		18.0	10^{-4}	....	5.8×10^{-4}
Alumina, fused	−50 + 100 mesh	125	10^{-4}	....	10.5×10^{-4}
Alumina, laminar	0.1–10 microns	4.4	10^{-4}	....	13.3×10^{-4}
Mica, expanded	−20 + 30 mesh 30%	9.4	10^{-4}	....	10.5×10^{-4}
	−30 + 15 mesh 70%	9.4	628	Nitrogen	290×10^{-4}
	−30 + 15 mesh 70%	9.4	628	Helium	867×10^{-4}
Lampblack	....	12.5	10^{-4}	....	7.2×10^{-4}
Charcoal peach pits	20–30 mesh	30	10^{-4}	....	10.5×10^{-4}
Carbon + 7% ash[b]	30% 44 microns	12.5	10^{-4}	....	3.5×10^{-4}
Calcium silicate (synthetic)	0.02 micron	10.6	10^{-5}	....	4.3×10^{-4}
	0.02–0.07 micron	22.5	10^{-5}	....	3.2×10^{-4}
	0.02–0.07 micron	22.5	628	Nitrogen	263×10^{-4}

[a] Barometric pressure at Boulder, Colo.
[b] Mostly SiO_2 and Al_2O_3.
[c] 1.2×10^{-4} B.t.u./(hr.)(ft.)(°R.) for boundary temperatures of 137 and 36°R.
[d] 3.8×10^{-4} B.t.u./(hr.)(ft.)(°R.) for boundary temperatures of 540 and 36°R.
[e] 1.2×10^{-4} B.t.u./(hr.)(ft.)(°R.) for boundary temperatures of 137 and 36°R.
[f] 0.46×10^{-4} B.t.u./(hr.)(ft.)(°R.) for boundary temperatures of 137 and 7.6°R.

Table 12-27. Apparent Mean Thermal Conductivity of Some Selected Foams

Foam type	Density, lb./cu. ft.	Boundary temp., °R.	Test-space pressure	k, B.t.u./(hr.)(ft.)(°R.)	Supplier and trade name
Polystyrene	2.4	540–137	1 atm.	1.9×10^{-2}	Dow Chemical Co., Styrofoam
	2.9	540–137	1 atm.	1.5×10^{-2}	
	2.9	137–36	10^{-5} mm. Hg	0.47×10^{-2}	
Epoxy resin	5.0	540–137	1 atm.	1.9×10^{-2}	Debell & Richardson, Du Ra Foam
	5.0	540–137	10^{-2} mm. Hg	0.97×10^{-2}	
	5.0	540–137	4×10^{-3} mm. Hg	0.75×10^{-2}	
Polyurethane (isocyanate)	5.0–8.5	540–137	1 atm.	1.9×10^{-2}	Nopco Chemical Co., Lock Foam
		540–137	10^{-3} mm. Hg	0.7×10^{-2}	
Rubber	5.0	540–137	1 atm.	2.1×10^{-2}	U.S. Rubber
Silica	10	540–137	1 atm.	3.2×10^{-2}	Pittsburgh Corning, Foam Sil
Glass	9	540–137	1 atm.	2.0×10^{-2}	Pittsburgh Corning, Foam Glass

Table 12-28. Specific Heats

Temp., °R.	Specific heat, B.t.u./(lb.)(°R.)								
	Al	Mg	Cu	Ni	Fe	18-8 stainless*	Monel*	Pyrex*	Teflon
37 (b.p. H_2)	0.0024	0.0040	0.0019	0.0012	0.0011	0.0011	0.0014	0.0055	0.0183
100	.0431	.0713	.0290	.0224	.0170	.0207	.0244	.031	.0545
139 (b.p. N_2)	.0815	.119	.0471	.0392	.0343	.038	.0417	.047	.0739
162 (b.p. O_2)	.102	.141	.0554	.0488	.0441	.050	.0509	.575	.0851
200	.130	.169	.0659	.0621	.0587	.0651	.0632	.073	.102
300	.175	.210	.0808	.0844	.0835	.0910	.0833	.111	.144
400	.200	.226	.0891	.097	.098	.103	.0946	.145	.181
500	.213	.233	.0917	.104	.105	.112	.1003	.173	.242

* Estimated.

Table 12-29. Mean Linear Thermal Expansion (Parts per Hundred Thousand)

Temp., °R.	Cu	Ni	Al	Mg	Zn	1020 low-carbon steel	304 stainless	Monel	Inconel	Free-machining yellow brass	Pyrex	Araldite 501	Teflon
0	0	0	0	0	0	0	0	0	0	0	0	0	0
50	0	0	0	2	4	0	−1	0	0	1	−1	20	50
100	8	3	8	11	24	3	+2	5	4	12	−2	68	140
150	28	14	28	34	63	12	17	17	14	38	+1	135	260
200	57	31	60	73	115	27	41	38	32	73	7	215	390
250	91	54	102	122	174	46	72	63	55	113	13	307	530
300	129	81	150	178	236	69	106	92	81	157	19	412	710
350	169	110	202	240	300	95	143	123	110	204	26	530	940
400	212	142	259	308	368	123	183	157	142	253	34	662	1240
450	256	176	319	378	439	153	225	193	175	304	42	810	1560
500	302	211	381	448	513	185	269	231	210	356	50	970	1880
550	349	247	444	517	588	217	313	269	246	408	59	1150	2540*

* The length changes rapidly at a first-order transition at about 530°R.

of a class of materials used as cryogenic adhesives and sealants.

Thermal Conductivity. The thermal conductivity of nearly pure metals rises to a maximum at low temperatures that may be many times the room-temperature value. The height of the maximum is reduced by impurities and cold work. Consequently, where it is critically important to achieve high conductivity, a metal of high purity should be selected and it should be

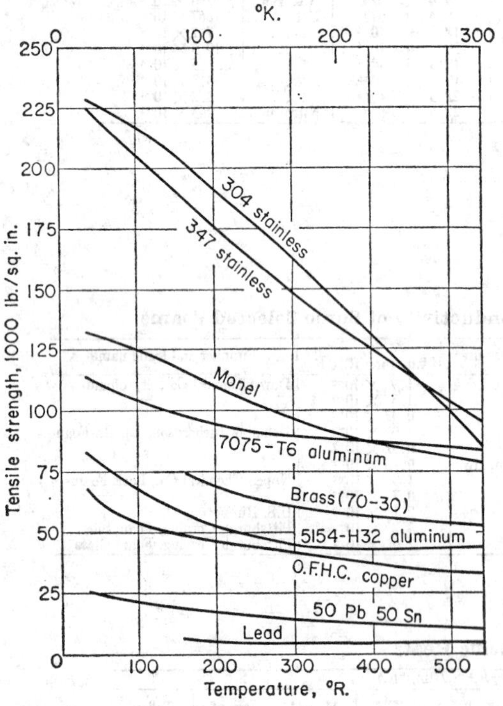

Fig. 12-54. Tensile strengths of selected materials (all in annealed condition except the two aluminum alloys).

annealed if possible. Addition of alloying constituents can eliminate the conductivity maximum and result in the conductivity's rising continuously with temperature. Table 12-24 and Figs. 12-43 and 12-44 show the thermal-conductivity values of a number of good and poor conducting materials.

Mechanical Properties. Carbon steels and martensitic steels (400 series) have low strength in impact at low temperatures and are avoided in applications where shock and multidirectional loading are expected. Materials which are both strong and ductile at the lowest temperatures involved in engineering applications are copper, aluminum, nickel, most solid-solution alloys of these metals, and the austenitic stainless steels (300 series). Tensile and yield strengths, modulus of elasticity, and fatigue strength of the desirable cryogenic materials in most cases increase with decreasing temperature. Certain intermediate steels such as the 3½ and

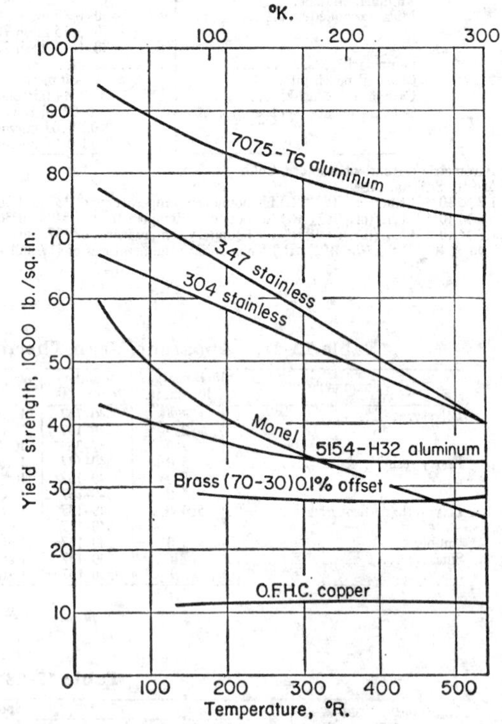

Fig. 12-55. Yield strengths of selected materials (all in annealed condition except the two aluminum alloys—0.2 per cent offset except as noted).

8 per cent nickel steels may be used for reasons of economy at the higher cryogenic temperatures or under loading conditions of moderate severity. Extended heating of unstabilized 300 series steels in the range 750° to 1650°F. may result in considerable loss of impact strength because of formation of the sorbite or sigma phase. By proper techniques welded and brazed joints can be made with little or no loss of strength in the heated zone. Table 12-24 and Figs. 12-54 and 12-55 give strengths of selected metals and alloys.

With the exception of Teflon, plastics are embrittled at low temperatures. However, fiber-reinforced plastics can show good properties. Among the film-forming plastics, Mylar retains good flexibility even at 40°R. (see Table 12-30).

Thermophysical Properties of Fluids. Thermal properties and physical constants of a number of fluids used in low-temperature processes or required for cryogenic applications are listed in Table 12-31. Other data may be found in Sec. 3.

Additional Sources of Information on Cryogenic Processes. Timmerhaus (Ed.) ("Advances in Cryogenic Engineering," vols. 1–7, Plenum Press, New York, 1954–1961) contains papers presented at National Annual Cryogenic Engineering Conferences. Mendelssohn (Ed.) ("Progress in Cryogenics," vols. 1–3, Academic Press, New York, 1959–1961). International Institute of Refrigeration, 177 Boulevard Malesherbes, Paris 17, publishes a bimonthly Bulletin of abstracts of current literature. National Bureau of Standards, Cryogenic Engineering Laboratory, Boulder, Colo., maintains a mechanized bibliography file of cryogenic literature.

Table 12-30. Mechanical Properties of Plastic

	Temp., °R.	Tensile strength, lb./sq. in. $\times 10^{-3}$	Compressive yield strength, lb./sq. in. $\times 10^{-3}$	Young's modulus, lb./sq. in. $\times 10^{-6}$
Teflon	530	2.0	....	0.06
	350	5.5	....	0.26
	275	8.0	9.0	0.54
	140	15.0	18.5	0.74
	37	....	25.0	
	7	....	27.0	1.0
Kel-F	530	6.3	....	0.26
	360	14.0	....	0.62
	140	16.2	....	0.84
	7	....	44.0	
Poly ethylene	540	1.3	....	0.02
	7	....	25.0	
Polyvinyl-chloride	530	7.7	....	0.52
	360	17.4	....	0.55
	140	19.7	....	1.11
Nylon	530	9.5	....	0.43
	360	20.1	....	0.56
	275	24.3	....	0.75
	140	27.9	....	1.10
Mylar	540	21.0	....	1.01
	350	27.0	....	1.16
	140	31.0	....	1.85

Table 12-31. Property Values of Some Cryogenic Fluids at Selected Conditions

Property/Fluid	He^4	H_2 (normal)	H_2 (para)	Ne	Air	A	N_2	O_2	CO	CH_4
Molecular weight	4.0026	2.0159	2.0159	20.183	28.97	39.948	28.013	31.9988	28.0106	16.043
Triple-point values:										
Temperature, °F	−455.76[a]	−434.56	−434.81	−415.48	....	−308.87	−346.02	−361.82	−337.11	−296.48
Pressure, lb./sq. in. abs	0.743[a]	1.04	1.023	6.26	....	9.97	1.864	0.022	2.23	1.69
Density, lb./ft.³:										
Solid	12.5[a]	5.41	....	90.15	....	101.32	64.08[b]	85.64	58.0[c]	30.6
Liquid	9.152	4.82	4.81	77.91	....	87.96	54.3	....	53.06	28.0
Vapor	....	0.00785	.00784	0.29	....	0.25	0.44	....	0.50	....
Normal boiling values:										
Temperature (T_b):										
°K	4.215	20.39	20.268	27.07	78.8/81.8	87.27	77.35	90.190	81.63	111.73
°F	−452.09	−422.97	−423.187	−410.94	−317.83	−302.59	−320.44	−297.33	−312.74	−258.56
Density, lb./ft.³:										
Liquid	7.803	4.43	4.42	75.35	54.56	87.4	50.4	71.24	50.0	26.48
Vapor	1.061	0.0832	0.0837	0.58	0.28	0.36	0.28	0.296	0.27	0.115
Critical values:										
Temperature, °F	−450.31	−399.95	−400.30	−379.66	−221.31[d]	−188.37	−232.40	−181.08	−220.41	−116.4
Pressure, lb./sq. in. abs	33.21	190.75	187.67	395.3	547.4[d]	709.8	492.3	736.3	507.4	673
Density, lb./ft.³	4.326	1.880	1.921	30.21	20.5[d]	33.46	19.42	26.84	19.04	10.11
1 gal liquid (NBT) equivalents:										
Weight, lb	1.043	0.5922	0.5909	10.07	7.29	11.68	6.74	9.52	6.68	3.54
Cubic feet of gas:										
NBT	0.983	7.12	7.06	17.4	26.1	32.1	24.1	32.2	24.7	30.8
NTP	100.3	113.3	113.0	192.5	97.0	112.8	92.7	114.8	91.9	84.9
Equivalent volumes of gas per volume of liquid:										
NBT	7.35	53.3	52.8	130	195	243	180	241	185	230
NTP	750	847	845	1440	726	843	694	858	688	635
Heat of fusion, B.t.u./lb	2.25[e]	25.00	25.03	7.15	....	12.65	11.0	5.97	12.83	25.24
Heat of vaporization, B.t.u./lb	8.8	193	192	37.1	88.22	70.19	85.86	91.5	92.77	219.2

T_b or NBT = normal boiling temperature; NTP = normal temperature and pressure (68°F., 14.7 lb./sq. in. abs.; 273.15°K. = 0°C. = 32°F. = 491.67°R.

[a] Lambda-phase transition point (about 40 atm. pressure required to solidify He^4 at lambda-point temperature; about 25 atm. at 1°K.).

[b] At 20.7°K. (−422.41°F.).

[c] At 65°K. (−343°F.).

[d] Plait point.

[e] At 3.5°K. and 100 atm.

SECTION 13

DISTILLATION

BY

J. A. Gerster, Ph.D., Professor of Chemical Engineering, University of Delaware; Member, American Institute of Chemical Engineers, American Chemical Society, American Society for Engineering Education.

CONTENTS

DISTILLATION

General References: Robinson and Gilliland, "Elements of Fractional Distillation," 4th ed., McGraw-Hill, New York, 1950. Treybal, "Mass-transfer Operations," McGraw-Hill, New York, 1955. Brown, "Unit Operations," Wiley, New York, 1950. Cremer and Davies, "Chemical Engineering Practice," vol. 5, Academic Press, New York, 1958. Leva, "Tower Packings and Packed Tower Design," U.S. Stoneware Co., Akron, Ohio, 1953. Badger and Banchero, "Introduction to Chemical Engineering," McGraw-Hill, New York, 1955. McCabe and Smith, "Unit Operations of Chemical Engineering," McGraw-Hill, New York, 1956. Foust, Wenzel, Clump, Maus, and Andersen, "Principles of Unit Operations," Wiley, New York, 1960. Kirschbaum, "Distillation and Rectification," Chemical Publishing, New York, 1948. Coulson and Richardson, "Chemical Engineering," vol. 2, Permagon Press, London, 1955. Rose and Rose, "Distillation Literature, Index, and Abstracts," vols. 1, 2, Applied Science Laboratories, State College, Pa., 1953. Nielsen, "Distillation in Practice," Reinhold, New York, 1956. Nelson, "Petroleum Refinery Engineering," 4th ed., McGraw-Hill, New York, 1958. Hengstebeck, "Petroleum Processing," McGraw-Hill, New York, 1959. Carney, "Laboratory Fractional Distillation," Macmillan, New York, 1949. Coulson and Herington, "Laboratory Distillation Practice," Interscience, New York, 1958. Gerster, *Ind. Eng. Chem.*, **52,** 645 (1960); **47,** 253 (1955). Geddes, *Chem. Eng. Progress, Symp. Ser.* 25, **55,** 87 (1959). Walsh, *Ind. Eng. Chem.*, **52,** 277 (1960); **51,** 370 (1959); **50,** 453 (1958); **49,** 503 (1957); **48,** 492 (1956).

Distillation is the separation of the constituents of a liquid mixture by partial vaporization of the mixture and separate recovery of vapor and residue. The more volatile constituents of the original mixture are obtained in increased concentration in the vapor, the less volatile in greater concentration in the liquid residue. Completeness of separation depends upon certain properties of the components involved and upon arrangement of the distillation process.

In general, *distillation* applies to vaporization processes in which the vapor evolved is recovered, usually by condensation. *Evaporation* commonly refers to removal of water from aqueous solutions of non-volatile substances by vaporization. The vapor evolved, *i.e.*, the water, is discarded.

Rectification is a distillation in which a vapor is continuously and countercurrently contacted with a condensed portion of the vapor. This process secures a greater enrichment of the vapor in the more volatile components than could be secured with a single distillation operation using the same amount of heat. The condensate returned to accomplish this object is termed **reflux.**

Fractional distillation or **fractionation** is synonymous with rectification; this term is commonly used in the petroleum industry.

The generally used devices in which vapors from a still on their way to a condenser can flow countercurrently to a portion of the condensate returned as reflux are called *rectifying columns* or *towers.* Rectifying columns are most commonly fed at or near the center of the column, in which case the section above the feed is known as the *rectifying section,* while the part below the feed is the *stripping section.* If a liquid feed is added at the top of a column, it is known as a *stripping column;* such a column does not require a portion of the overhead vapors to be condensed and returned as reflux.

VAPOR-LIQUID EQUILIBRIUM RELATIONSHIPS

Ideal Gas and Liquid Phases. If the liquid phase is ideal, Raoult's law applies. This law states that the partial pressure p_1 of any component in the vapor is equal to its mole fraction in the liquid x_1 times the vapor pressure P_1 of the pure component at the same temperature. Thus, for any number of components,

$$p_1 = P_1x_1 \qquad p_2 = P_2x_2 \qquad \text{etc.} \tag{13-1}$$

If the gas phase is ideal, Dalton's law is followed. This law states that the partial pressure p_1 of any component in the vapor is equal to its mole fraction in the vapor y_1 times the total pressure of the system P. Again, for any number of components,

$$p_1 = Py_1 \qquad p_2 = Py_2 \qquad \text{etc.} \tag{13-2}$$

Combination of Eqs. (13-1) and (13-2) leads to

$$\alpha_{12} = \frac{y_1/x_1}{y_2/x_2} = \frac{P_1}{P_2} \tag{13-3}$$

where α_{12} is the **relative volatility** of components 1 and 2. Inasmuch as the ratios of vapor pressures are often nearly constant over moderate temperature ranges for ideal mixtures, relative volatility values for such mixtures are usually also constant.

For **binary mixtures,** pressure and one composition will fix the temperature and vapor composition, or pressure and temperature will fix both compositions. At a given total pressure it is possible to choose a series of temperatures between the equilibrium temperatures of the two pure components and solve for the corresponding compositions as

$$x_1 = \frac{P - P_2}{P_1 - P_2} \tag{13-4}$$

Values of y_1 can then be found by use of Eqs. (13-1) and (13-2).

A calculation of this type for the benzene-toluene system at $P = 760$ mm. Hg total pressure is given in Table 13-1. The temperatures in column 1 are chosen

Table 13-1. Equilibrium Vapor-Liquid Compositions, Benzene and Toluene Mixtures

Temp., °C.	P_1 (benzene), mm. Hg	P_2 (toluene), mm. Hg	x_1 by Eq. (13-4)	$y_1 = P_1x_1/P$
80.0	760	300	1.000	1.000
84.0	852	333	0.823	0.922
88.0	957	380	0.659	0.830
92.0	1078	432	0.508	0.720
96.0	1204	493	0.376	0.596
100.0	1344	559	0.256	0.453
104.0	1495	626	0.155	0.304
108.0	1659	741	0.058	0.128
110.4	1748	760	0.000	0.000

at reasonable increments between the boiling points of pure benzene (80.0°C.) and pure toluene (110.4°C.). Columns 2 and 3 give the vapor pressures of pure benzene and pure toluene corresponding to the temperatures of column 1.

Under conditions where P_1/P_2 and α_{12} are constant, it may be more convenient to compute values of y and x from the relations

$$y_1 = \frac{\alpha_{12}x_1}{1 + (\alpha_{12} - 1)x_1} \qquad (13\text{-}5)$$

or

$$x_1 = \frac{y_1}{\alpha_{12} - (\alpha_{12} - 1)y_1} \qquad (13\text{-}6)$$

The above equations were obtained from Eq. (13-3) noting that for binary mixtures $y_1 = 1 - y_2$ and $x_1 = 1 - x_2$.

A compilation of typical data for ideal binary mixtures is given by Table 13-2.

Table 13-2. Relative Volatilities of Ideal Mixtures
Values of P_1/P_2 (approximately equal to α) are given at the boiling points of components 1 and 2, respectively

Mixture 1 and 2	B.p. of 1, °C.	P_1/P_2	B.p. of 2, °C.	P_1/P_2
Benzene–ethylene dichloride	80.1	1.113	83.48	1.109
Benzene-toluene	80.1	2.61	110.7	2.315
n-Butyl chloride-n-butyl bromide	77.5	2.08	101.6	1.87
Chloroform–carbon tetrachloride	61.1	1.71	76.6	1.60
Ethanol-isopropanol	78.3	1.18	82.3	1.17
Ethanol-propanol	78.3	2.18	97.2	2.03
Ethyl chloride–ethyl bromide	12.5	3.23	38.4	2.79
Ethyl ether–benzene	34.6	5.16	80.2	3.95
Ethylene dibromide–propylene dibromide	131.7	1.30	141.5	1.30
Ethylene dichloride–trichloroethane	83.5	2.52	113.7	2.33
n-Heptane–methylcyclohexane	98.4	1.058	100.3	1.056
n-Hexane-n-heptane	69.0	2.613	98.4	2.33
Methanol-ethanol	64.7	1.73	78.1	1.64
Methanol-isobutanol	64.6	6.1	107.5	4.4
Methanol-propanol	64.6	3.89	97.2	3.15
Methyl acetone–ethyl acetate	56.8	2.036	77.1	1.923
Phenol-o-cresol	181.2	1.30	190.6	1.275
Phenol-m-cresol	181.2	1.768	201.5	1.699
Phenol-p-cresol	181.2	1.793	202.2	1.728
Toluene–benzyl chloride	110.7	7.75	178.0	4.45
Toluene-chlorotoluene	110.7	4.76	162.0	3.65
Water–ethylene glycol	100.0	49.8	197.0	13.2
Water–ethylene glycol*	60.1	98	150.2	21
Water-glycerol†	38.1	76,400	202.0	244

* Pressure = 150 mm. Hg.
† Pressure = 50 mm. Hg.

Non-ideal Gas and Liquid Phases. Although methods are given later for correlating, extending, and in some cases predicting the vapor-liquid behavior of non-ideal mixtures, it is always highly desirable to base a distillation-column design upon experimental vapor-liquid data. A listing of all literature sources of vapor-liquid data is far beyond the scope of this section, but data for a number of the more common binary systems are given in Tables 13-3 and 13-4.

One of the best **compilations of experimental vapor-liquid equilibrium data** is by Hala, Pick, Fried, and Vilim ("Vapour-Liquid Equilibrium," 2d ed., translated into English by G. Standart, Permagon Press, London, 1958), which contains more than 1000 original sources covering the literature up to February, 1957. Also valuable are the works of Timmermans ("The Physico-chemical Constants of Binary Systems," vols. 1, 2, Interscience, New York, 1959) and Chu ("Vapor-Liquid Equilibrium Data," Edwards, Ann Arbor, Mich., 1956; "Distillation Equilibrium Data," Reinhold, New York, 1950). Pierotti, Deal, and Derr reported valuable new data for 275 binary systems [*Ind. Eng. Chem.*, **51**, 95 (1959)]. Other literature articles on vapor-liquid equilibrium are summarized in the reviews of "Thermodynamics" and "High-temperature Distillation" which appear annually in *Industrial and Engineering Chemistry*.

Binary Mixtures Non-ideal in Liquid Phase. The treatment here assumes that the vapors follow the ideal-gas law. For cases having appreciable deviation from ideal-gas behavior, appropriate methods are given on p. 13-13.

Deviations from ideality in the liquid state are conveniently treated as multiplying factors. These have the thermodynamic significance of **activity coefficients,** defined by the relations

$$Py_1 = \gamma_1 P_1 x_1 \qquad Py_2 = \gamma_2 P_2 x_2 \qquad (13\text{-}7)$$

also

$$\alpha_{12} = \frac{y_1/x_1}{y_2/x_2} = \frac{\gamma_1 P_1}{\gamma_2 P_2} \qquad (13\text{-}8)$$

The activity coefficients γ_1 and γ_2 vary widely with concentration, and to some degree with temperature. The typical variation with composition is shown by Figs. 13-1 and 13-2. In Fig. 13-1 the "deviations are

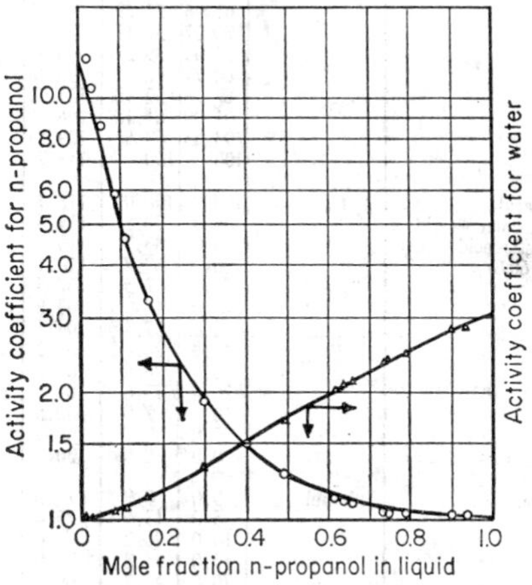

FIG. 13-1. Typical variation of liquid-phase activity coefficient with composition. System *n*-propanol–water at 1 atm. Points are observed data of Gadwa (M.I.T. Thesis, 1936); curves are calculated from van Laar equations [Eqs. (13-14) and (13-15)] with $A_{12} = 1.13$ and $A_{21} = 0.49$.

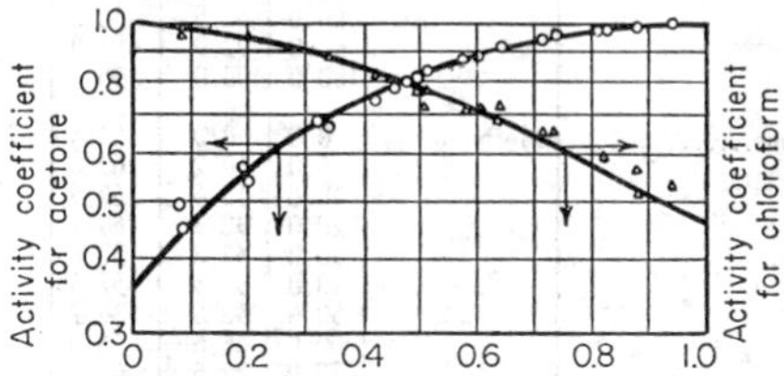

FIG. 13-2. Typical variation of liquid-phase activity coefficient with composition. System acetone-chloroform. Points are observed data of Zawidski [*Z. physik. Chem.*, **35,** 129 (1900)] at 35°C. Curves calculated by van Laar equations [Eqs. (13-14) and (13-15)] with $A_{12} = -0.44$ and $A_{21} = -0.34$.

positive," *i.e.*, the activity coefficients are greater than unity and their logarithms are positive; in Fig. 13-2 the activity coefficients are fractional, and the logarithms are negative. In both cases the γ values approach unity as the concentration of the component considered approaches unity. This is necessarily true in all cases. The γ values nearly always have a maximum value as the component concentration approaches zero.

Activity Coefficient as Function of Composition. The fundamental thermodynamic equation relating activity coefficients and composition is the **Gibbs-Duhem** relation

$$x_1\left(\frac{\partial \log \gamma_1}{\partial x_1}\right)_{T,P} + x_2\left(\frac{\partial \log \gamma_2}{\partial x_1}\right)_{T,P} = 0 \qquad (13\text{-}9)$$

Table 13-3. Constant-pressure Liquid-Vapor Equilibrium Data for Binary Mixtures*

Component A	Component B	Mole % A in Liquid	Mole % A in Vapor	Temp., °C.	Total pressure, mm.	Ref.
Acetaldehyde	Water	0	0	100	760	15
		0.5	25	93.5		
		1	50	82.0		
		4	75	63.0		
		10	89	43.0		
		20	93	33.0		
		30	....	29.0		
		50	....	25.3		
		60	....	24.6		
		75	....	23.8		
Acetic acid	Benzene	0	0	80.2	760	14
		35.49	14.96	84.72		
		54.61	22.48	88.96		
		61.96	25.79	90.85		
		70.07	31.41	93.99		
		75.03	35.57	96.23		
		80.77	42.24	99.44		
		87.28	52.18	103.71		
		91.09	61.18	106.82		
		93.53	68.51	109.51		
		100	100	118.7		
Acetic acid (Molecular weight of acetic acid taken as 60.0)	Water	100.0	100.0	118.1	760	2, 1, 8
		95.0	90.8	115.4		
		90.0	83.3	113.8		
		80.0	69.8	110.1		
		70.0	57.5	107.5		
		60.0	47.0	105.8		
		50.0	37.4	104.4		
		40.0	28.4	103.2		
		30.0	20.5	102.1		
		20.0	13.6	101.3		
		10.0	7.0	100.6		
		5.0	3.7	100.3		
		0.0	0.0	100.0		
Acetone	Ethanol	0.0	0.0	78.3	760	4
		5.0	15.5	75.4		
		10.0	26.2	73.0		
		15.0	34.8	71.0		
		20.0	41.7	69.0		
		25.0	47.8	67.3		
		30.0	52.4	65.9		
		35.0	56.6	64.7		
		40.0	60.5	63.6		
		50.0	67.4	61.8		
		60.0	73.9	60.4		
		70.0	80.2	59.1		
		80.0	86.5	58.0		
		90.0	92.9	57.0		
		100.0	100.0	56.1		
Acetone	Methanol	0.0	0.0	64.5	760	1
		5.0	10.2	63.6		
		10.0	18.6	62.5		
		20.0	32.2	60.2		
		30.0	42.8	58.65		
		40.0	51.3	57.55		
		50.0	58.6	56.7		
		60.0	65.6	56.0		
		70.0	72.5	55.3		
		80.0	80.0	55.05		
		100.0	100.0	56.1		
Benzene	Ethanol	0	0	78.1	750	15
		6	20	74.4		
		11	30	72.4		
		20	40	70.1		
		39	50	68.3		
		57	56	67.8		
		72	60	68.3		
		89	70	70.8		
		96	85	75.2		
		100	100	79.7		
Benzene	Ethylene dichloride	0.0	0.0	83.48	760	10
		5.0	5.5	83.32		
		10.0	11.0	83.14		
		20.0	21.7	82.79		
		30.0	32.2	82.45		
		40.0	42.6	82.10		
		50.0	52.6	81.77		
		60.0	62.5	81.43		
		70.0	72.2	81.09		
		80.0	81.6	80.76		
		90.0	90.9	80.42		
		95.0	95.5	80.27		
		100.0	100.0	80.09		
Butanol (n-)	Water	0.1	1.9	99.4	760	19
		0.2	4.9	98.4		
		0.3	7.1	98.3		
		0.6	11.6	96.8		
		0.8	15.7	95.4		
		1.2	19.2	93.7		
		1.4	21.6	93.4		
		1.5	22.5	93.4		
		1.8	24.2	92.8		
		2.0	24.4	93.0		
		2.5	24.8	92.7		
		42.3	25.0	92.8		
		42.9	25.2	92.9		
		43.6	24.8	92.9		
		44.8	25.0	92.9		
		49.4	26.0	93.4		
		50.4	26.4	93.5		
		69.5	33.8	96.3		
		70.8	34.5	96.7		
		72.5	35.9	97.2		
		74.3	37.1	97.9		
		93.0	64.8	108.8		
		94.5	67.7	109.6		
		95.3	70.1	110.6		
		96.1	73.3	111.5		
Butanol (i-)	Water	0.2	4.3	98.9	760	19
		0.3	6.9	98.1		
		0.4	10.1	97.1		
		0.5	14.7	95.9		
		0.7	16.3	95.1		
		0.9	21.8	93.4		
		1.2	27.0	91.9		
		1.4	28.6	91.5		
		2.0	32.2	89.9		
		2.2	32.7	90.1		
		2.5	32.8	89.5		
		3.2	32.6	89.5		
		4.1	33.0	89.5		
		4.6	33.2	89.5		
		33.1	33.4	89.2		
		33.0	33.1	89.2		
		36.2	32.9	89.4		
		36.5	33.1	89.4		
		39.5	33.3	89.4		
		40.1	33.3	89.5		
		42.4	33.9	89.5		
		43.1	33.9	89.5		
		43.6	34.0	89.5		
		58.7	36.5	90.2		
		60.3	37.4	90.3		
		82.8	55.4	96.0		
		85.0	58.0	97.1		
		86.5	59.9	97.7		
Carbon tetrachloride	Benzene	0	0	80.0	760	15
		13.64	15.82	79.3		
		21.57	24.15	78.8		
		25.73	28.80	78.6		
		29.44	32.15	78.5		
		36.34	39.15	78.2		
		40.57	43.50	78.0		
		52.69	54.80	77.6		
		62.02	63.80	77.4		
		72.23	73.30	77.1		
Carbon tetrachloride	Ethyl acetate	0.0	0.0	74.1	685	9
		5.0	7.0	73.6		
		10.0	13.3	73.1		
		20.0	24.5	72.5		
		30.0	34.2	72.1		
		40.0	43.3	71.8		
		50.0	51.8	71.6		
		58.2	58.2	71.56		
		60.0	59.7	71.6		
		70.0	68.1	71.8		
		80.0	77.3	72.1		
		90.0	88.1	72.6		
		95.0	94.0	72.9		
		100.0	100.0	73.4		
Carbon tetrachloride	Toluene	0	0	110.4	762	20
		5.75	12.65			
		16.25	31.05			
		28.85	49.35			
		42.60	64.25			
		56.05	75.50			
		64.25	81.22			
		78.20	89.95			
		94.55	97.35	75.9		

* Arranged by H. C. Carlson and J. A. Lane, E. I. duPont de Nemours & Co., Wilmington, Del.

Table 13-3. Constant-pressure Liquid-Vapor Equilibrium Data for Binary Mixtures—(*Continued*)

Component A	Component B	Mole % A in Liquid	Mole % A in Vapor	Temp., °C.	Total pressure, mm.	Ref.
Carbon disulfide	Carbon tetrachloride	0	0	76.7	760	14
		2.96	8.23	74.9		
		6.15	15.55	73.1		
		11.06	26.60	70.3		
		14.35	33.25	68.6		
		25.85	49.50	63.8		
		39.08	63.40	59.3		
		53.18	74.70	55.3		
		66.30	82.90	52.3		
		75.74	87.80	50.4		
		86.04	93.20	48.5		
		100.0	100.0	46.3		
Carbon disulfide	Acetone	0	0	56.2	760	14
		1.90	8.32	54.0		
		4.76	18.50	51.4		
		13.40	35.10	46.6		
		18.58	44.30	44.0		
		29.12	52.75	41.4		
		37.98	57.40	40.3		
		44.77	59.80	39.8		
		53.60	62.70	39.3		
		65.30	66.10	39.1		
		78.94	70.50	39.3		
		80.23	72.30	39.6		
		87.99	76.00	40.5		
		96.83	88.60	43.5		
		100.0	100.0	46.3		
Chloroform	Acetone	0	0	56.2	760	14
		8.55	4.78	57.5		
		14.10	8.35	58.3		
		20.45	13.12	59.4		
		26.12	17.65	60.4		
		33.67	24.95	61.6		
		42.50	35.20	62.8		
		52.29	48.30	63.9		
		73.40	76.30	64.4		
		78.92	82.40	63.8		
		86.25	90.00	63.1		
		88.92	93.50	62.8		
		100.0	100.0	61.3		
Chloroform	Benzene	0	0	80.6	760	15
		8	10	79.8		
		15	20	79.0		
		22	30	78.2		
		29	40	77.3		
		36	50	76.4		
		44	60	75.3		
		54	70	74.0		
		66	80	71.9		
		79	90	68.9		
		100	100	61.4		
Chloroform	Methanol	0	0	64.9	757	15
		3.6	10.0	63.7		
		10.0	23.4	60.8		
		13.7	30.0	59.5		
		20.0	39.8	57.7		
		30.4	50.0	55.6		
		40.0	54.4	54.4		
		50.0	58.4	53.7		
		63.0	58.0	53.4		
		.....	68.0	53.6		
		71.0	....	53.7		
		100.0	100.0	61.4		
Ethanol	Water	0	0	100	760	16, 18
		1.90	17.00	95.5		
		7.21	38.91	89.0		
		9.66	43.75	86.7		
		12.38	47.04	85.3		
		16.61	50.89	84.1		
		23.37	54.45	82.7		
		26.08	55.80	82.3		
		32.73	58.26	81.5		
		39.65	61.22	80.7		
		50.79	65.64	79.8		
		51.98	65.99	79.7		
		57.32	68.41	79.3		
		67.63	73.85	78.74		
		74.72	78.15	78.41		
		89.43	89.43	78.15		
Ethyl acetate	Ethanol	0.0	0.0	78.3	760	5, 11
		5.0	10.2	76.6		
		10.0	18.7	75.5		
		20.0	30.5	73.9		
Ethyl acetate (*con't.*)	Ethanol	30.0	38.9	72.8		
		40.0	45.7	72.1		
		50.0	51.6	71.8		
		54.0	54.0	71.8		
		60.0	57.6	71.9		
		70.0	64.4	72.2		
		80.0	72.6	73.0		
		90.0	83.7	74.7		
		95.0	91.4	76.0		
		100.0	100.0	77.1		
Ethylene glycol	Water	100.0	100.0	160.6	228	12
		99.0	69.0	152.4		
		98.0	55.2	148.3		
		97.0	46.5	145.1		
		96.0	40.0	142.1		
		95.0	35.0	139.5		
		92.0	25.5	132.0		
		90.0	21.4	127.5		
		80.0	10.0	111.2		
		70.0	5.0	100.5		
		60.0	2.8	93.1		
		50.0	1.8	87.7		
		40.0	1.1	82.9		
		30.0	0.7	78.8		
		20.0	0.4	75.6		
		10.0	0.2	72.8		
		0.0	0.0	69.5		
Furfural	Water	0	0	100	760	15
		1	5.5	98.56		
		2	8.0	98.07		
		4	9.2	97.90		
		9.2	9.2	97.90		
		50	9.2	97.90		
		70	9.5	98.7		
		80	11	100.6		
		90	19	109.5		
		92	32	122.5		
		94	64	146.0		
		96	81	154.8		
		98	90	158.8		
		100	100	161.7		
Methanol	Water	0.0	0.0	100.0	760	2, 13, 3
		2.0	13.4	96.4		
		4.0	23.0	93.5		
		6.0	30.4	91.2		
		8.0	36.5	89.3		
		10.0	41.8	87.7		
		15.0	51.7	84.4		
		20.0	57.9	81.7		
		30.0	66.5	78.0		
		40.0	72.9	75.3		
		50.0	77.9	73.1		
		60.0	82.5	71.2		
		70.0	87.0	69.3		
		80.0	91.5	67.6		
		90.0	95.8	66.0		
		95.0	97.9	65.0		
		100.0	100.0	64.5		
Nitric acid	Water	8.36	0.627	106.5	760	15
		12.3	1.76	112.0		
		22.1	6.60	118.5		
		30.8	16.6	121.6		
		38.3	38.3	121.9		
		40.2	60.2	121.0		
		46.5	75.9	118.0		
		53.0	89.1	112.0		
		61.5	92.1	99.0		
Nitrogen	Oxygen	3.85	13.97	.....	760	17
		8.02	26.10			
		12.40	36.60			
		17.05	46.00			
		22.20	54.20			
		27.73	61.60			
		33.8	67.95			
		40.47	73.74			
		47.83	78.95			
		56.62	84.35			
		66.65	88.95			
		78.40	93.50			
		91.90	97.70			
Nitrogen	Oxygen	4	9.0	.....	3800	17
		12	27.0			
		22	42.0			
		33	56.0			

Table 13-3. Constant-pressure Liquid-Vapor Equilibrium Data for Binary Mixtures—(*Concluded*)

Component		Mole % *A* in		Temp., °C.	Total pressure, mm.	Ref.
A	B	Liquid	Vapor			
Nitrogen (*cont.*).......	Oxygen	46	69.0			
		61	80.5			
		69	85.5			
		79	91.0			
		90	96.0			
Isopropyl ether.......	Isopropanol	0.0	0.0	82.3	760	7
		5.0	18.7	77.8		
		10.0	30.6	75.4		
		15.0	39.6	73.5		
		20.0	46.6	71.8		
		25.0	51.9	70.6		
		30.0	55.6	69.6		
		35.0	58.7	68.9		
		40.0	61.5	68.3		
		50.0	66.2	67.3		
		60.0	70.2	66.6		
		70.0	74.3	66.3		
		78.2	78.2	66.2		
		80.0	79.1	66.2		
		85.0	81.9	66.3		
		90.0	85.3	66.6		
		95.0	90.2	67.0		
		100.0	100.0	68.5		
Isopropanol..........	Water	0	0	100	760	15
		1	19	95.0		
		2	34	90.0		
Isopropanol (*cont.*)...	Water	3	43	86.7		
		6	50.5	83.5		
		15	56	81.5		
		30	58	81.0		
		50	63	80.7		
		70	70	80.5		
		80	77	81.0		
		90	83	82.3		
n-Propanol..........	Water	0.0	0.0	100.0	760	6, 3
		1.0	11.0	95.0		
		2.0	21.6	92.0		
		4.0	32.0	90.5		
		6.0	35.1	89.3		
		10.0	37.2	88.5		
		20.0	39.2	88.1		
		30.0	40.4	87.9		
		40.0	42.4	87.8		
		43.2	43.2	87.8		
		50.0	45.2	87.9		
		60.0	49.2	88.3		
		70.0	55.1	89.0		
		80.0	64.1	90.5		
		85.0	70.4	91.5		
		90.0	77.8	92.8		
		96.0	90.0	95.0		
		100.0	100.0	97.3		

[1] Bergstrom, data from "Principles and Practice of Industrial Distillation" by Hausbrand, trans. by E. H. Tripp, Wiley, New York, 1926 (compositions below 26 mole per cent water and boiling points).
[2] Cornell and Montonna, *Ind. Eng. Chem.*, **25**, 1331 (1933) (compositions of acetic acid–water above 26 mole per cent water; compositions of methanol-water, which agree with Uchida and Kato's).
[3] Doroszewsky and Polansky, *Z. physik. Chem.*, **73**, 192 (1910) (boiling points of aqueous mixtures).
[4] Duffey, private communication, 1935.
[5] Furnas and Leighton, *Ind. Eng. Chem.*, **29**, 709 (1937).
[6] Gadwa, Sc. D. Thesis in Chemical Engineering, Mass. Inst. Tech., 1936 (compositions of *n*-propyl alcohol–water).
[7] Miller and Bliss, *Ind. Eng. Chem.*, **32**, 123 (1940).
[8] Povarnina and Markova, *J. Russ. Phys.-Chem. Soc.*, **55**, 381 (1924) (boiling points of mixtures).
[9] Schutz, *J. Am. Chem. Soc.*, **61**, 2691 (1939).
[10] Smith and Matheson, *Bur. Standards J. Research*, **20**, 641 (1938) (data calculated from their vapor pressures using Raoult's law).
[11] Stockhardt, private communication, 1931.
[12] Trimble and Potts, *Ind. Eng. Chem.*, **27**, 66 (1935).
[13] Uchida and Kato, *J. Soc. Chem. Ind., Japan*, **37**, 525 (1934) (compositions of mixtures).
[14] Rosanoff and Easley, *J. Am. Chem. Soc.*, **31**, 979 (1914).
[15] "International Critical Tables," McGraw-Hill, New York.
[16] Carey and Lewis, *Ind. Eng. Chem.*, **24**, 882 (1932).
[17] Dodge and Dunbar, *J. Am. Chem. Soc.*, **44**, 608 (1927).
[18] Noyes and Warfle, *J. Am. Chem. Soc.*, **23**, 463 (1901).
[19] Stockhardt and Hull, *Ind. Eng. Chem.*, **23**, 1438 (1931).
[20] Carey, Sc. D. Thesis, Mass. Inst. Tech., 1930.

This equation relates the slopes of the curves in Figs. 13-1 and 13-2 and provides a means of testing experimental data. It is much more convenient, however, to utilize integrated forms of these relations. A large number of different solutions to the basic Gibbs-Duhem equation are available, each of which gives a different functional relationship between $\log \gamma$ and x. However, most binary systems can be characterized by either the three- or four-suffix equations of Margules or by the two-suffix van Laar equations, given below in the manner of Wohl [*Trans. Am. Inst. Chem. Engrs.*, **42**, 215 (1946); *Chem. Eng. Progress*, **49**, 218 (1953)]. The three-suffix **Margules** binary equations are

$$\log \gamma_1 = x_2^2[A_{12} + 2x_1(A_{21} - A_{12})] \qquad (13\text{-}10)$$
$$\log \gamma_2 = x_1^2[A_{21} + 2x_2(A_{12} - A_{21})] \qquad (13\text{-}11)$$

Constants A_{12} and A_{21} are the limiting values of $\log \gamma$ as the composition of the component considered approaches zero; for example, in Eq. (13-10), $A_{12} = \log \gamma_1$ where $x_1 = 0$.

The four-suffix Margules binary equations are

$$\log \gamma_1 = x_2^2[A_{12} + 2x_1(A_{21} - A_{12} - D) + 3Dx_1^2] \qquad (13\text{-}12)$$
$$\log \gamma_2 = x_1^2[A_{21} + 2x_2(A_{12} - A_{21} - D) + 3Dx_2^2] \qquad (13\text{-}13)$$

A_{12} and A_{21} have the same significance as before; D is a third constant. Equations (13-12) and (13-13) are more complex than Eqs. (13-10) and (13-11), but because they contain an additional constant D, they are more flexible. Note that, when D becomes zero in Eqs. (13-12) and (13-13), they become identical with the three-suffix equations.

The two-suffix **van Laar** binary equations are

$$\log \gamma_1 = \frac{A_{12}}{[1 + (A_{12}x_1/A_{21}x_2)]^2} \qquad (13\text{-}14)$$
$$\log \gamma_2 = \frac{A_{21}}{[1 + (A_{21}x_2/A_{12}x_1)]^2} \qquad (13\text{-}15)$$

These equations become identical with the Margules equations when $A_{12} = A_{21}$, and the functional form of these two types of equations is not greatly different unless the A constants differ by more than about 50 per cent.

The Margules and van Laar equations apply only at *constant temperature and pressure*, as they were derived from Eq. (13-9), which also contains this restriction. The effect of pressure upon γ values and A constants is usually negligible, especially at pressures far removed from the critical. The effect of temperature is considered in the next section.

Other equation forms suitable for describing activity coefficient–composition behavior are those of Redlich and Kister [*Ind. Eng. Chem.*, **40**, 345 (1948)] and Black [*Ind. Eng. Chem.*, **51**, 211 (1959); **50**, 391, 403 (1958)].

Table 13-4. Binary Constants for Equations for Activity Coefficients

NOTE. These constants were obtained for the Van Laar equations but can be utilized in the Margules equations where the ratio of A_{1-2} to A_{2-1} is within the range of about 0.75 to 1.3.

Where the data cover a rather wide range of temperature, the equations can be considered only approximate. The temperature and pressure ranges are indicated with the first and last numbers referring to the pure components; if there is a constant boiling mixture, its temperature is given between the other two.

The mixtures are given with the lower boiling component stated first, and the temperatures and constants apply in the same order. Pressure is 760 mm. Hg except where noted.

Mixture	Temp., °C.	A_{1-2}	A_{2-1}	Ref.
Acetaldehyde-ethanol	19.8–78.2	−0.10	−0.20	28
Acetaldehyde-water	19.8–100	.69	.78	6, 36, 41
Acetone-benzene	56.1–80.1	.176	.176	49, 51
Acetone-methanol	56.1–55.5–64.6	.243	.243	3, 18, 39
Acetone-water	56.1–100	.89	.65	3, 8, 18, 57
Acetone-water*	25	.82	.72	2, 52
Benzene-isopropanol	80.1–71.9–82.3	.591	.845	38
n-Butane-furfural†	37.8	1.10	1.26	34
	51.7	1.05	1.17	
	66.6	1.00	1.11	
	93.3	0.91	0.98	
Butanol-butyl acetate	117.7–116.6–126.1	.22	.24	5
Butene-1-furfural†	37.8	.84	1.03	34
	51.7	.80	0.99	
	66.6	.76	.95	
	93.3	.70	.90	
Carbon disulfide–acetone	46.3–39.5–56.1	.556	.778	19, 43, 59
Carbon disulfide–carbon tetrachloride	46.3–76.7	.10	.07	40, 42, 43
Carbon tetrachloride–benzene	76.4–80.2	.052	.046	45
Carbon tetrachloride–ethylene dichloride	76.4–74.5–83.5	.334	.258	25, 58
Ethanol-benzene	78.3–67.0–80.1	.845	.699	15, 29, 53
Ethanol-cyclohexane	78.3–66.3–80.8	.913	.751	37, 54
Ethanol-toluene	78.3–76.4–110.7	.763	.763	56
Ethanol-trichloroethylene	78.3–70.0–87.5	.845	.653	15
Ethanol-water‡	25	.67	.42	11, 48
Ethyl acetate–benzene	77.2–71.1–80.2	.50	.40	46
Ethyl acetate–ethanol	77.2–71.7–78.3	.389	.389	16, 24
Ethyl acetate–toluene	77.2–110.7	.04	.25	30
Ethyl ether–acetone	34.6–56.1	.322	.322	9, 18, 44
Ethyl ether–ethanol	34.6–78.3	.42	.55	10, 24, 31
n-Hexane–ethanol	68.9–59.3–78.3	.68	1.12	22
Isobutane-furfural†	37.8	1.14	1.31	34
	51.7	1.09	1.23	
	66.6	1.04	1.16	
	93.3	0.96	1.03	
Isopropanol-water	82.3–100	1.042	0.492	26
Isopropyl ether–isopropanol	68.5–66.1–82.3	0.42	.60	35
Methanol-benzene	56.1–55.5–64.6	.243	.243	14, 15, 27
Methanol–ethyl acetate	64.6–62.1–77.1	.505	.505	4
Methanol-trichloroethylene	64.6–59.8–87.5	.845	.845	15
Methanol-water	64.6–100	.36	.22	
Methanol-water§	25	.25	.20	7
Methyl acetate–methanol	57.2–53.7–64.6	.462	.462	3, 4
Methyl acetate–water	57.0–100	1.30	.82	32, 33
Methyl ethyl ketone–water	79.6–73.6–100	1.50	.75	33
Propanol-water	97.3–88.0–100	1.10	.492	7, 17, 55
Water-Cellosolve	100–134.5	0.26	.88	1, 12
Water-p-dioxane	100–87.7–101.3	.66	.87	20, 21, 50
Water-phenol	100–181	.36	1.40	47, 49
Water-pyridine	100–115.5	.38	0.62	13

* Pressure = 23.8 to 229.6 mm. Hg.
† Pressure = 5.9 to 13,260 mm. Hg.
‡ Pressure = 23.8 to 59 mm. Hg.
§ Pressure = 23.8 to 123.5 mm. Hg.

References:

1 Baker, Hubbard, Huguet, and Michalowski, *Ind. Eng. Chem.*, **31**, 1260 (1939).
2 Beare, McVicar, and Ferguson, *J. Phys. Chem.*, **34**, 1310 (1930).
3 Bergstrom, from Hausbrand, "Principles and Practice of Industrial Distillation," Wiley, New York, 1926.
4 Bredig and Bayer, *Z. physik. Chem.*, **130** (1927).
5 Brunjes and Furnas, *Ind. Eng. Chem.*, **27**, 396 (1935).
6 Bushmakin and Kuchinskaya, *Trudy Gosudarst. Opyt. Zavoda Sintet. Kauchuka*, Litera B. IV (1935).
7 Butler, Thomson, and Maclennan, *J. Chem. Soc.*, **1933**, p. 674.
8 Carveth, *J. Phys. Chem.*, **3**, 193 (1899).
9 Cunaeus, *Z. physik. Chem.*, **36**, 2321 (1901).
10 Desmaroux, *Mém. poudres*, **23**, 198 (1928).
11 Dobson, *J. Chem. Soc.*, **127**, 2866 (1925).
12 Dominik and Wojciechowska, *Przemysl Chem.*, **23**, 61 (1939).
13 Ewert, *Bull. soc. chim.*, **45**, 493 (1936).
14 Fink, Mass. Inst. Tech. Thesis, 1933.
15 Fritzweiler and Dietrich, *Angew. Chem.*, **46**, 241 (1933).
16 Furnas and Leighton, *Ind. Eng. Chem.*, **29**, 709 (1937).

Activity Coefficient as Function of Temperature. The exact relationship which applies at any particular composition is

$$\frac{\partial \log \gamma_1}{\partial(1/T)} = \frac{L_1}{2.3R} \qquad (13\text{-}16)$$

where T is the absolute temperature, L_1 is the partial heat of solution of component 1, and R is the gas-law constant, usually taken as 1.99 B.t.u./(lb.-mole)(°R.). When heat is evolved upon mixing of two liquids, L is negative and the activity coefficient rises with temperature. This is the case for most electrolytes, *i.e.*, substances with negative deviations, and for many polar organic solvents mixed with water. Most mixtures of organic liquids take up heat when mixing occurs, L is positive, and γ values decrease with increasing temperature.

If values of L_1 are constant over the range of interest, or if L_1 values are linear functions of $1/T$, Eq. (13-16) may be expressed as

$$(\log \gamma_1)_{T_f} - (\log \gamma_1)_{T_i} = \frac{(L_1)_{\text{avg}}}{2.3R}\left(\frac{1}{T_f} - \frac{1}{T_i}\right) \qquad (13\text{-}17)$$

where T_i and T_f are the initial and final temperatures and $(L_1)_{\text{avg}}$ is the average partial molal heat of solution of component 1. For example, data are plotted in Fig. 13-3 for values of $L/2.3R$ for various alcohol-water binary mixtures. Suppose $\log \gamma_1$ for methanol (component 1) is 0.36 at 80°C. when it is present in trace amounts with water, and one wishes to know $\log \gamma_1$ at the same composition but at 25°C. The value of $(L_1)_{\text{avg}}/2.3R$ from Fig. 13-3 over the 25° to 80°C. temperature range is −265. By Eq. (13-17),

$$(\log \gamma_1)_{25} = 0.36 + (-265)(1/_{298} - 1/_{353}) = 0.22$$

17 Gadwa, Mass. Inst. Tech. Thesis, 1936.
18 Haywood, *J. Phys. Chem.*, **3**, 317 (1899).
19 Hirschberg, *Bull. soc. chim. Belg.*, **41**, 163 (1932).
20 Hovorka, Schaefer, and Dreisbach, *J. Am. Chem. Soc.*, **58** 2264 (1936).
21 Hovorka, Schaefer, and Dreisbach, *J. Am. Chem. Soc.*, **59**, 2753 (1937).
22 Isii, *J. Soc. Chem. Ind. Japan*, **38**, 661 (1935).
23 Kireev, Klinov, and Grigorovich., *J. Chem. Ind. (U.S.S.R.)*, **12**, 936 (1935).
24 Kireev and Popov, *J. Applied Chem. (U.S.S.R.)*, **7**, 489 (1934).
25 Kireev and Skavortsova, *J. Phys. Chem. (U.S.S.R.)*, **7**, 63 (1936).
26 Lebo, *J. Am. Chem. Soc.*, **43**, 1005 (1921).
27 Lee, *J. Phys. Chem.*, **35**, 3558 (1931).
28 Leeuw, *Z. physik. Chem.*, **77**, 284 (1911).
29 Lehfeldt, *Phil. Mag.*, **46**, 42 (1898).
30 Litkenhous, Van Arsdale, and Hutchison, *J. Phys. Chem.*, **44**, 377 (1940).
31 Louder, Briggs, and Brown, *Ind. Eng. Chem.*, **16**, 932 (1924).
32 McKeown and Stowell, *J. Chem. Soc.*, **1927**, p. 97.
33 Marshall, *J. Chem. Soc.*, **89**, 1350 (1906).
34 Mertes and Colburn, *Ind. Eng. Chem.*, **39**, 787 (1947).
35 Miller and Bliss, *Ind. Eng. Chem.*, **32**, 123 (1940).
36 Morozov, Kagan, and Grossblyat, *J. Gen. Chem. (U.S.S.R.)*, **4**, 1322 (1934).
37 Nagai and Ishii, *Proc. Imp. Acad. (Tokyo)* **11**, 23 (1935).
38 Olsen and Eastburn, *J. Phys. Chem.*, **41**, 457 (1937).
39 Othmer, *Ind. Eng. Chem.*, **20**, 743 (1928).
40 Pahlavouni, *Bull. soc. chim. Belg.*, **36**, 533 (1927).
41 Pascal, Dupuy, Ero, and Garnier, *Bull. soc. chim.*, **29**, 9 (1921). Given also in International Critical Tables.
42 Rosanoff, Bacon, and White, *J. Am. Chem. Soc.*, **36**, 1803 (1914).
43 Rosanoff and Easley, *J. Am. Chem. Soc.*, **31**, 953 (1909).
44 Sameshima, *J. Am. Chem. Soc.*, **40**, 1482 (1918).
45 Scatchard, Wood, and Moehel, *J. Am. Chem. Soc.*, **62**, 712 (1940).
46 Schmidt, *Z. physik. Chem.*, **121**, 221 (1926).
47 Schreinemakers, *Z. physik. Chem.*, **35**, 459 (1900).
48 Shaw and Butler, *Proc. Roy. Soc. (London)*, **A129**, 519 (1930).
49 Sims, Mass. Inst. Tech. Thesis, 1933.
50 Smith and Wojciechowski, *Roczniki Chem.*, **17**, 125 (1937).
51 Soday and Bennett, *J. Chem. Education*, **7**, 1336 (1930).
52 Taylor, *J. Phys. Chem.*, **4**, 355 (1900).
53 Thayer, *J. Phys. Chem.*, **2**, 382 (1898).
54 Washburn and Handorf, *J. Am. Chem. Soc.*, **57**, 441 (1935).
55 Wrewsky, *Z. physik. Chem.*, **81**, 1 (1912).
56 Wright, *J. Phys. Chem.*, **37**, 233 (1933).
57 York and Holmes, *Ind. Eng. Chem.*, **34**, 345 (1942).
58 Young and Nelson, *Ind. Eng. Chem.*, anal. ed., **4**, 67 (1932).
59 Zawidski, *Z. physik. Chem.*, **35**, 129 (1900).

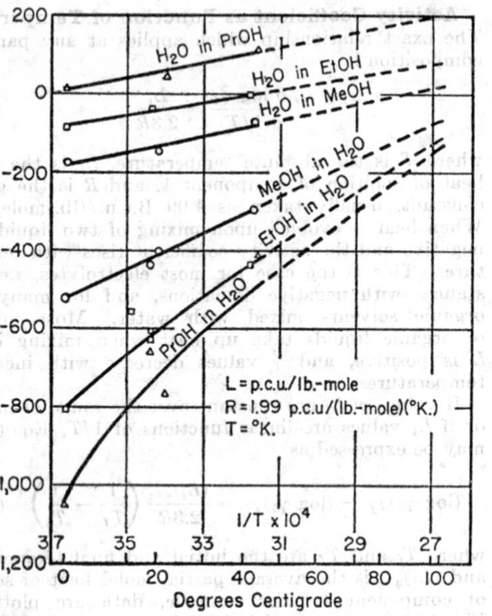

FIG. 13-3. Heats of solution at infinite dilution of alcohols and water.

In the absence of specific data on heats of solution, an approximate rule sometimes used for the effect of temperature upon activity coefficients is given by $T \log \gamma_1 =$ const. This rule does not apply to the methanol-water example worked out above and is not valid for many organic solvent–water mixtures; it does hold, however, for many organic mixtures.

Application of Activity-coefficient Principles. No rigorous procedures are available for predicting whether the van Laar or the Margules three- or four-suffix equations will best define the activity coefficient–composition relationship for a given binary system, nor is it possible to relate the magnitude of the A constants to any combination of the physical properties of the pure components. Thus it is necessary to have ready access to compilations of experimental binary data.

Some progress in the prediction of A constants has been shown by Pierotti, Deal, and Derr (*loc. cit.*), who developed a series of empirical equations for this purpose. Their equations cover a large number of binary systems containing water, paraffins, or organic compounds containing a single functional group. These equations involve constants which vary with the nature of the functional group and the number of carbon chains in the molecule for each component, and a relatively few interaction constants. This leads to the possibility of using data available for related binary systems to predict the behavior of an unknown binary. This reference includes valuable data for 275 binary systems. A few typical values of A constants are given in Table 13-4.

Although it is difficult to predict non-ideal vapor-liquid equilibrium data for any given binary system, activity-coefficient principles are valuable because (1) they provide a means for testing whether experimental data are thermodynamically consistent; (2) they permit data available at a given total pressure and temperature to be converted to other conditions; (3) they explain the behavior of systems which form homogeneous or heterogeneous azeotropes; (4) they explain immiscibility in liquid solutions; (5) they are useful in extending a limited amount of experimental data; and (6) they provide the basis for predicting multicomponent equilibrium data for systems which are non-ideal in the liquid phase.

Testing Binary Data. If a given set of experimental data can be defined by one of the Margules or van Laar equation forms, such data are thermodynamically consistent. If the data will not fit one of these equation forms, they may still be consistent inasmuch as a more complicated equation form may apply. In such an instance one may test for consistency by checking the slopes of the experimental activity coefficient–composition plots; in every instance the slopes must be related according to Eq. (13-9).

Alternatively, one may plot values of $\log \gamma_1/\gamma_2$ vs. x_1. As shown by Redlich and Kister (*loc. cit.*) the area under such a curve, which consists of both positive and negative portions, must be zero if the data are thermodynamically consistent. If one of the binary components is above its critical temperature, the thermodynamic-consistency tests of Adler *et al.* [*Am. Inst. Chem. Engrs. J.*, **6**, 104 (1960)] or of Prausnitz [*Am. Inst. Chem. Engrs. J.*, **6**, 78 (1960)] may be employed.

Conversion of Equilibrium Data to New Conditions of Pressure and Temperature. For systems which are non-ideal in the liquid phase, activity-coefficient principles permit vapor-liquid data to be converted to new conditions of pressure and temperature. Consider the data of Bachman and Simons [*Ind. Eng. Chem.*, **44**, 202 (1952)] for the binary system, acetone–carbon tetrachloride. At 760 mm. Hg total pressure, a liquid containing 37.4 mole per cent acetone boiled at 59.8°C. and the equilibrium vapor contained 56.55 mole per cent acetone. With pure-component vapor pressures at this temperature taken as 865 mm. for acetone and 437 mm. for carbon tetrachloride, Eq. (13-7) predicts γ_1 (for acetone) to be 1.33 and γ_2 (for CCl_4) to be 1.20 when gas-law deviations are neglected. Now predict the boiling temperature and vapor composition if liquid of the same composition is boiled at 300 mm. pressure.

First assume a temperature, say 34.3°C. Then estimate the variation of the γ values with temperature by the approximate rule that $T \log \gamma =$ constant. The resulting values are $\gamma_1 = 1.36$ and $\gamma_2 = 1.22$. At the temperature chosen, the pure-component vapor pressures are 331 mm. Hg for acetone and 170 mm. for CCl_4; now compute the equilibrium partial pressures of the two components p_1 and p_2 by Eq. (13-7). For acetone, $p_1 = \gamma_1 P_1 x_1 = (1.36)(331)(0.374) = 168$ mm.; $p_2 = \gamma_2 P_2 x_2 = (1.22)(170)(0.626) = 130$ mm. The solution at 34.3°C. will then boil at a total pressure of $p_1 + p_2$ or 298 mm., which is close to the desired value.

The equilibrium vapor composition y_1 is $^{168}/_{298}$, or 56.5 mole per cent acetone, a value identical with that found at 760 mm. total pressure. Negligible variation of y-x values for this system in the 760- to 300-mm. total pressure range was found experimentally by Bachman and Simons (*loc. cit.*). The reason for this behavior is made clear by reference to Eq. (13-8); as the activity-coefficient ratio was found to increase slightly, and the pure-component vapor pressure ratio decreased slightly, the relative volatility remained constant. In most cases where these two ratios change by different amounts when the total pressure (and temperature) change, α_{12} may either increase or decrease (except near the critical as discussed below).

Binary Azeotropes. Although in most binary systems one of the components is more volatile than the other over the entire composition range, some systems exist where one component is the more volatile over only a part of the composition range. Two systems of this type are shown in Fig. 13-4: ethyl acetate–ethanol and chloroform-acetone. In the latter case, for example, chloroform is less volatile than acetone up to a con-

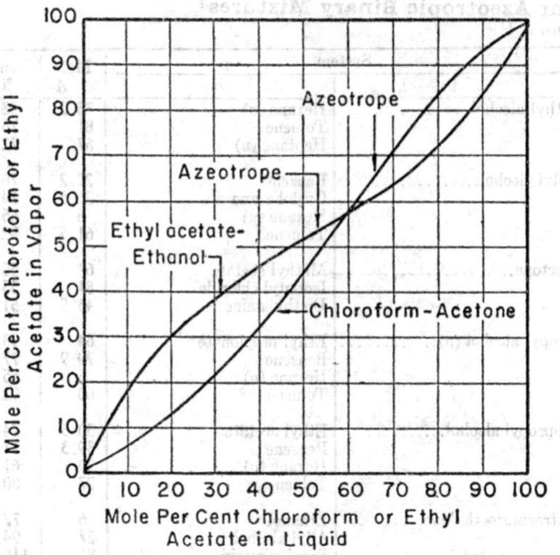

FIG. 13-4. Vapor-liquid equilibrium data at 760 mm. for chloroform-acetone and ethyl acetate–ethanol systems.

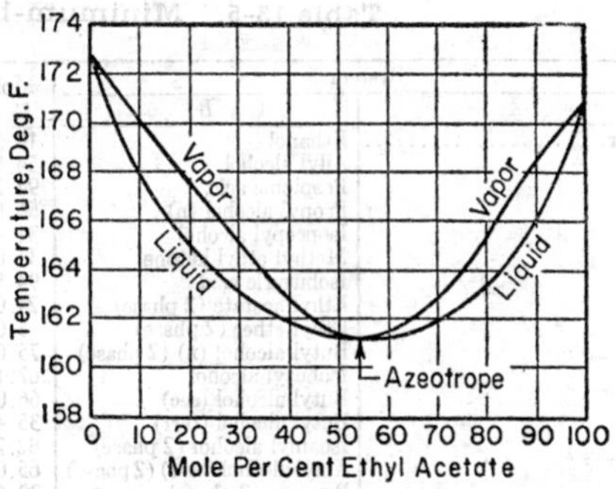

FIG. 13-5. Liquid boiling points and vapor condensation temperatures for mixtures of ethyl acetate and ethanol at 760 mm. total pressure.

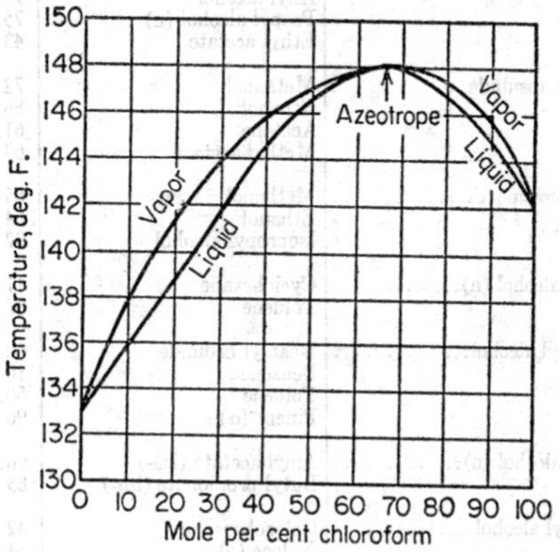

FIG. 13-6. Liquid boiling points and vapor condensation temperatures for mixtures of chloroform and acetone at 760 mm. total pressure.

centration of 66 mole per cent chloroform; beyond this concentration, chloroform is the more volatile component. At the 66 per cent concentration point, both components have the same volatility; *i.e.*, the vapor and liquid compositions are identical.

Mixtures in which it is possible for the volatility to be reversed are known as **azeotropic mixtures,** and the composition at which the reversal takes place, which is the composition at which the vapor and liquid compositions are equal, is the *azeotropic composition* or simply the *azeotrope.* The azeotropic liquid may consist of either a single phase or two immiscible phases. In the former case the azeotrope is **homogeneous,** while in the latter it is **heterogeneous.** The two azeotropes shown in Fig. 13-4 are both homogeneous; heterogeneous azeotropes are discussed later. The presence of an azeotrope often prevents a binary mixture from being separated by ordinary distillation methods into two essentially pure products.

At the azeotropic composition, α_{12} equals unity. For an ideal binary mixture, where γ_1 and γ_2 are unity, Eq. (13-8) shows that an azeotrope can form if the ratio P_1/P_2 is unity. The vapor-pressure curves for two components often do cross at some temperature, especially if the vapor-pressure relationships are nearly the same.

For non-ideal miscible mixtures, α_{12} may be unity if, as shown by Eq. (13-8), the ratio γ_1/γ_2 equals the ratio P_2/P_1. Thus for a system where P_2/P_1 is, say, around 3, an azeotrope cannot form unless the system is sufficiently non-ideal that the γ values are as large as 3. Highly non-ideal mixtures are thus more likely to form azeotropes, as their γ_1/γ_2 ratios vary so widely with composition that some composition can often be found where $\gamma_1/\gamma_2 = P_2/P_1$.

Homogeneous azeotropes are either **minimum-boiling** or **maximum-boiling** at a given total pressure; *i.e.*, their boiling points are either less than or greater than the boiling points of the pure components. This is illustrated in Figs. 13-5 and 13-6 for the same two systems shown in Fig. 13-4. The variation of boiling point with composition may be predicted by use of Eq. (13-7) written as $P = \gamma_1 P_1 x_1 + \gamma_2 P_2 x_2$. At any composition and total pressure P, the temperature at which the vapor-pressure values satisfy this equation is the correct one. For systems which form homogeneous azeotropes but whose vapor-pressure curves do not cross, the azeotrope will be minimum-boiling if the activity coefficients are greater than unity, and the azeotrope will be maximum-boiling if the activity coefficients are less than unity.

Activity-coefficient principles may be used to predict the variation of azeotropic composition with pressure and temperature. Consider the homogeneous system propanol-water for which activity-coefficient data at 1 atm. total pressure are available in Fig. 13-1; determine the azeotropic composition at 2 atm. total pressure. A temperature is assumed; P_2/P_1 is evaluated; and in the first trial γ values are not corrected for temperature variation. A composition is found in Fig. 13-1 where $\gamma_1/\gamma_2 = P_2/P_1$, and the total pressure P is then computed as $P = p_1 + p_2 = (\gamma_1 P_1 x_1) + (\gamma_2 P_2 x_2)$. New temperatures are assumed until the desired total pressure is obtained; refinements as to variation of γ with T may then be made, if desired. (Prediction of heterogeneous azeotropes is considered later when immiscible systems are discussed.)

Experimental data for several homogeneous and heterogeneous azeotropes are given in Tables 13-5, 13-6, and 13-7. An extensive listing of hydrocarbon azeotropes is given by Ewell, Harrison, and Berg [*Petrol. Engr.*, **16** (1), 255 (October, 1944); **16** (2), 263 (November, 1944); **16** (3), 219 (December, 1944)]. Information on over 14,000 binary and over 400 ternary systems is given by Horsley ("Azeotropic Data," Advances in Chemistry Series 6, American Chemical Society, Washington, 1952), and another useful reference is Lecat

Table 13-5. Minimum-boiling-point Azeotropic Binary Mixtures*

Pressure 760 mm. Hg

System A	System B	Mole % A	Temp., °C.
Water	Ethanol	10.57	78.15
	Allyl alcohol	54.50	88.20
	Propionic acid	94.70	99.98
	Propyl alcohol (n)	56.83	87.72
	Isopropyl alcohol	31.46	80.37
	Methyl ethyl ketone	33.00	73.45
	Isobutyric acid	94.50	99.30
	Ethyl acetate (2 phase)	24.00	70.40
	Ethyl ether (2 phase)	5.00	34.15
	Butyl alcohol (n) (2 phase)	75.0	92.25
	Isobutyl alcohol	67.14	89.92
	Butyl alcohol (sec)	66.00	88.50
	Butyl alcohol (tert)	35.41	79.91
	Isoamyl alcohol (2 phase)	82.79	95.15
	Amyl alcohol (tert) (2 phase)	65.00	87.00
	Benzene (2 phase)	29.60	69.25
	Toluene (2 phase)	55.6	84.10
Carbon tetrachloride	Methanol	44.5	55.70
	Ethanol	61.3	64.95
	Allyl alcohol	73.0	72.32
	Propyl alcohol (n)	75.0	72.80
	Ethyl acetate	43.0	74.75
Carbon disulfide	Methanol	72.0	37.65
	Ethanol	86.0	42.40
	Acetone	61.0	39.25
	Methyl acetate	69.5	40.15
Chloroform	Methanol	65	53.5
	Ethanol	84	59.3
	Isopropyl alcohol	92	60.8
Butyl alcohol (n)	Cyclohexane	11	79.8
	Toluene	37	105.5
Isobutyl alcohol	Isoamyl bromide	60.0	103.80
	Benzene	10.0	79.84
	Toluene	50.0	101.15
	Pinene (α)	96.5	107.90
Amyl alcohol (n)	Amyl acetate (iso-)	96.4	131.3
	Butyl propionate (iso-)	85	130.5
Isoamyl alcohol	Chlorobenzene	42	124.3
	Xylene (o)	64	128
	Xylene (m)	58	127
	Xylene (p)	56	126.8
Nitrobenzene	Benzyl alcohol	39	204.3
	Borneol	60	207.75
	Menthol	60	207.9
Phenol	Bromotoluene (p)	58	176.2
	Carvene	49.5	169.0
	Pinene (α)	25	152.75
Aniline	Carvene	48	171.35
Benzyl alcohol	Guaiacol	38	204.4
	Naphthalene	64	204.3
Acetic acid	Chlorobenzene	72.5	114.65
	Benzene	2.5	80.05
	Toluene	62.7	105.4
	Xylene (m)	40	115.38
Ethyl alcohol	Methyl ethyl ketone	45	74.8
	Ethyl acetate	46	71.8
	Methyl propionate	67.5	73.2
	Propyl formate (n)	72	73.5
	Benzene	44.8	68.24
	Cyclohexane	44.5	64.9
Ethyl alcohol	Hexane (n)	33.2	58.68
	Toluene	81	76.65
	Heptane (n)	67	72
Allyl alcohol	Benzene	22.2	76.75
	Cyclohexane	26.6	74
	Hexane (n)	6.5	65.5
	Toluene	61.5	92.4
Acetone	Methyl acetate	61	56.1
	Isobutyl chloride	81	55.8
	Diethylamine	43.5	51.5
Propyl alcohol (n)	Ethyl propionate	64	93.4
	Benzene	20.9	77.12
	Hexane (n)	6	65.65
	Toluene	60	92.6
Isopropyl alcohol	Ethyl acetate	30.5	74.8
	Benzene	39.3	71.92
	Hexane (n)	29	61
	Toluene	77	80.6
Tetrachloroethylene	Ethanol	6	77.95
	Allyl alcohol	27	94.0
	Propionic acid	81	118.95
	Propyl alcohol (n)	24	94
	Isopropyl alcohol	8	81.7
	Butyl alcohol (n)	47	110
	Isobutyl alcohol	40	103.05
Trichloroethylene	Allyl alcohol	70	80.95
	Propyl alcohol (n)	69	81.75
	Isopropyl alcohol	54	74
	Isobutyl alcohol	86	85.4
	Butyl alcohol (tert)	74	75
	Amyl alcohol (tert)	83	84
Dichloroethylene	Allyl alcohol	76	79.6
		77	80
Chloral hydrate	Cyclohexane	13	76
Ethylene bromide	Acetic acid	20.7	114.35
	Propionic acid	65	127.75
	Isobutyl alcohol	22	106.2
	Isoamyl alcohol	52	123.2
	Ethyl benzene	83.5	131.1
Methanol	Trichloroethylene	70	60.2
	Acetonitrile	84.5	63.45
	Ethylene dichloride	62	59.5
	1, 1-Dichlorethane	28.5	49.05
	Ethyl bromide	14	34.95
	Chloromethyl methyl ether	57.5	56
	Ethyl iodide	52.5	54.7
	Acetone	20	55.7
	Ethyl formate	30.5	50.95
	Methyl acetate	35	54.0
	Propyl bromide (n)	49	54.1
	Propyl iodide (n)	88	63.5
	Methylal	34.5	41.82
	Trimethyl borate	87	59
	Ethyl acetate	91.7	62.3
	Pentane (n)	13	31
	Pentane (iso-)	9	24.5
	Benzene	61.4	53.84
	Cyclohexene	63.0	55.9
	Cyclohexane	61.0	54.2
	Hexane (n)	51	50.6
	Heptane (n)	83	60.5
	Pinene (d)	98.5	64.5

* Abstracted from "International Critical Tables," McGraw-Hill.

("Tables azeotropiques," 10th ed., published by the author, Brussels, 1949).

Immiscible Systems. If a boiling system at equilibrium consists of two immiscible liquid phases and a gas phase, then

$$Py_1 = \gamma_1 P_1 x_1 = \bar{\gamma}_1 P_1 \bar{x}_1 \qquad Py_2 = \gamma_2 P_2 x_2 = \bar{\gamma}_2 P_2 \bar{x}_2 \tag{13-18}$$

where x_1 and x_2 are the compositions of one liquid phase and $\bar{x}_1$ and $\bar{x}_2$ are the compositions of the other phase. If values of γ, P, and x are known for either phase, the equilibrium vapor composition may be computed. If only the two coexisting liquid phases are considered, the above equation simplifies to

$$\gamma_1 x_1 = \bar{\gamma}_1 \bar{x}_1 \qquad \gamma_2 x_2 = \bar{\gamma}_2 \bar{x}_2 \tag{13-19}$$

Obviously only non-ideal liquid systems can be immiscible, because for ideal systems where all γ values are unity, the above equations predict both layers to have the same composition (50 per cent); *i.e.*, no im-

Table 13-6. Maximum-boiling-point Azeotropic Binary Mixtures*

A	B	Mole % A	Temp., °C.	Pressure, mm.
Water	Hydrofluoric acid	65.4	120	760
	Hydrochloric acid	88.9	110	
	Perchloric acid	32.0	203	
	Hydrobromic acid	83.1	126	
	Hydriodic acid	84.3	127	
	Nitric acid	62.2	120.5	735
	Formic acid	43.3	107.1	760
Chloroform	Acetone	65.5	64.5	760
Formic acid	Diethyl ketone	48	105.4	
	Methyl propyl ketone	47	105.3	
Phenol	Cyclohexanol	90	182.45	
	Benzaldehyde	54	185.6	
	Benzyl alcohol	8	206.0	
Cresol (o)	Acetophenone	24	203.7	
	Phenyl acetate	42.5	198.6	
	Methyl hexyl ketone	97	191.5	
	Isoamyl butyrate	80	192.0	
Cresol (m)	Acetophenone	54	209.0	
	Isoamyl lactate	60	207.6	
Cresol (p)	Benzyl alcohol	38	207.0	
	Acetophenone	52	208.45	
	Camphor	38	213.15	

* From "International Critical Tables," McGraw-Hill.

Table 13-7. Ternary Azeotropic Mixtures*
Pressure 760 mm. Hg

Component A Mole % A = 100 − (B + C)	Components B and C	Mole % B and C	Temp., °C.
Water	Carbon tetrachloride	57.6	61.8
	Ethanol	23.0	2 phase
	Trichloroethylene	38.4	67.25
	Ethanol	41.2	2 phase
	Trichloroethylene	49.2	71.4
	Allyl alcohol	17.3	2 phase
	Trichloroethylene	51.1	71.55
	Propyl alcohol (n)	16.6	2 phase
	Ethanol	12.4	70.3
	Ethyl acetate	60.1	
	Ethanol	22.8	64.86
	Benzene	53.9	
	Allyl alcohol	9.5	68.3
	Benzene	62.2	
	Propyl alcohol (n)	8.9	68.48
	Benzene	62.8	
Carbon disulfide	Methanol	24.1	33.92
	Ethyl bromide	35.4	
Methyl formate	Ethyl bromide	23.8	16.95
	Isopentane	31.0	
	Ethyl ether	7.2	20.4
	Pentane (n)	48.2	
Propyl lactate (n)	Phenetol	35.2	163.0
	Menthene	34.1	

* From "International Critical Tables," McGraw-Hill.

miscibility exists. For systems which are highly immiscible, for example, where x_1 might be 0.001 and $\bar{x}_1$ (the composition of the same component in the other layer) might be 0.998, $\bar{\gamma}_1$ would be nearly unity and γ_1 would be closely approximated by Eq. (13-19) as 0/0.001 or 1000.

A test can readily be made to determine if immiscibility occurs, provided van Laar constants A_{12} and A_{21} are available for the system of interest. In Fig. 13-7 the dashed curve represents the locus of **critical solution points.** Thus, using one constant, say A_{12}, a value of x_1 can be read from the dashed curve. Subtracting this

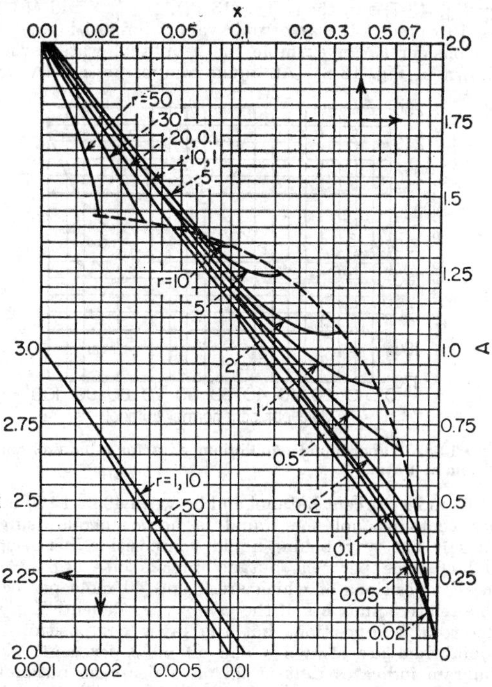

FIG. 13-7. Relationship between compositions of two immiscible liquid layers and van Laar constants for binary system. If $x = x_1$, $r = \bar{x}_2/x_1$ and $A = A_{12}$. If $x = \bar{x}_2$, $r = x_1/\bar{x}_2$ and $A = A_{21}$.

from unity gives the composition of the other component (at the critical solution point). From the second composition and the dashed curve, the corresponding value of A_{21} is read. If this value of A_{21} is less than the true value of A_{21}, immiscibility occurs; if it is greater than the true value, the liquids are miscible in all proportions.

The composition of each liquid layer can also be determined from Fig. 13-7. At an assumed value of $x = x_1$ and for the known value of $A = A_{12}$, read from the graph a value of r and solve for $\bar{x}_2$ as rx_1. Now with $x = \bar{x}_2$ and with r taken this time as $x_1/\bar{x}_2$, read from the graph the value of A which will be A_{21}. If this value of A_{21} checks with the known value, the assumed value of x_1 is correct; if it does not check, the trials are repeated until the answer is obtained. For the special case where $A_{12} = A_{21}$, the values of x_1 and $\bar{x}_2$ are equal and are related to the A constants as follows:

Van Laar Constants, $A_{12} = A_{21}$	Solubility Limits, Mole Fraction
0.87	0.5
0.92	0.3
1.00	0.2
1.20	0.1
1.43	0.05
1.77	0.02
2.03	0.01

Heterogeneous Azeotropes. All two-phase liquids at the boiling point form a heterogeneous azeotrope. If experimental vapor-liquid data are available for the homogeneous range of composition, values of A_{12} and A_{21} can be computed, and the miscibility limits evaluated from the methods described above; the heterogeneous azeotropic vapor composition may then be computed from Eq. (13-18). Alternatively, if only the miscibility limits are known, the A constants may be evaluated by Fig. 13-7, and then Eqs. (13-18), (13-14), and (13-15) used to predict the azeotropic vapor composition.

Consider as an example the *n*-butanol–water system shown in Fig. 13-8. At liquid compositions between 0

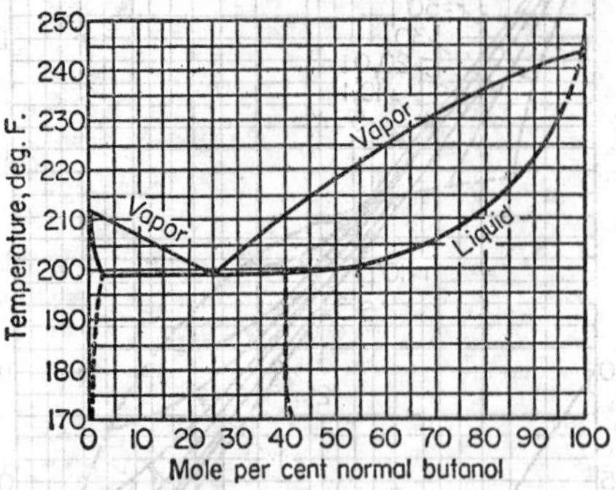

FIG. 13-8. Vapor-liquid equilibrium data for *n*-butanol–water system at 1 atm.

and 3 mole per cent butanol and between 40 and 100 mole per cent butanol the liquid is homogeneous (single-phase); but any boiling-liquid composition between 3 and 40 mole per cent butanol breaks into two layers, the compositions of which are 3 and 40 mole per cent. The relative amounts of the layers vary depending upon the total composition, but the layer compositions at equilibrium are always 3 and 40 mole per cent. The diagram indicates that at 25 mole per cent butanol a heterogeneous azeotrope forms; that is, a condition exists where the vapor and liquid compositions are equal. Actually, of course, although the liquid phase may have a total composition of 25 mole per cent butanol, it consists of two separate layers of 3 and 40 mole per cent composition. And, regardless of the relative amounts of the two liquid layers present, the equilibrium vapor composition is always 25 per cent butanol.

For the case of highly immiscible binary systems, Eq. (13-18) may be rearranged to give $P = \gamma_1 P_1 x_1 + \bar{\gamma}_2 P_2 \bar{x}_2$; if one layer is essentially pure component 1, both x_1 and γ_1 become unity, and if the other layer is essentially pure component 2, both $\bar{x}_2$ and $\bar{\gamma}_2$ also are unity, giving the relationships $P = P_1 + P_2$ and $y_1 = P_1/P$.

Methods for Extending Limited Experimental Data. If experimental vapor-liquid data are available for only a single composition or for a limited composition range, activity coefficients can be computed from Eq. (13-7) and the constants A_{12} and A_{21} evaluated for either the three-suffix Margules equations [Eqs. (13-10) and (13-11)] or the two-suffix van Laar equations [Eqs. (13-14) and (13-15)] which can be rearranged as follows: For the Margules three-suffix,

$$A_{12} = \frac{\log \gamma_1}{x_2^2} + 2x_1\left(\frac{\log \gamma_2}{x_1^2} - \frac{\log \gamma_1}{x_2^2}\right) \qquad (13\text{-}20)$$

$$A_{21} = \frac{\log \gamma_2}{x_1^2} + 2x_2\left(\frac{\log \gamma_1}{x_2^2} - \frac{\log \gamma_2}{x_1^2}\right) \qquad (13\text{-}21)$$

For the van Laar,

$$A_{12} = \log \gamma_1 \left(1 + \frac{x_2 \log \gamma_2}{x_1 \log \gamma_1}\right)^2 \qquad (13\text{-}22)$$

$$A_{21} = \log \gamma_2 \left(1 + \frac{x_1 \log \gamma_1}{x_2 \log \gamma_2}\right)^2 \qquad (13\text{-}23)$$

Once the *A* constants are known, the γ values and the *y-x* behavior can be predicted over the entire composition range. The only difficulty with this procedure is lack of assurance that either equation type will apply to the binary system in question, although they will apply in more than two-thirds of the cases. The method gives useful approximations when only azeotropic data, Henry's-law constants, or absorption equilibria are available. For details, see Carlson and Colburn (*loc. cit.*).

As shown in this same reference, if experimental values of solubility limits are available for a given binary system, one can solve for the van Laar constants. In this regard Fig. 13-7 may be used to predict the values of A_{12} and A_{21}, or the following equations may be used:

$$\frac{A_{12}}{A_{21}} = \frac{\left(\frac{x_1}{x_2} + \frac{\bar{x}_1}{\bar{x}_2}\right)\left(\frac{\log \bar{x}_1/x_1}{\log x_2/\bar{x}_2}\right) - 2}{\frac{x_1}{x_2} + \frac{\bar{x}_1}{\bar{x}_2} - \frac{2x_1\bar{x}_1 \log \bar{x}_1/x_1}{x_2\bar{x}_2 \log x_2/\bar{x}_2}} \qquad (13\text{-}24)$$

$$A_{12} = \frac{\log \bar{x}_1/x_1}{\frac{1}{\left(1 + \frac{A_{12}x_1}{A_{21}x_2}\right)^2} - \frac{1}{\left(1 + \frac{A_{12}\bar{x}_1}{A_{21}\bar{x}_2}\right)^2}} \qquad (13\text{-}25)$$

Multicomponent Mixtures Non-ideal in Liquid Phase. Equations (13-7) and (13-8) apply to multicomponent as well as to binary mixtures which are non-ideal in the liquid phase. The γ values in these equations are functions of the multicomponent liquid composition and temperature. For example, the γ value for acetone when mixed with chloroform is different from the γ value for acetone when mixed with both chloroform and methanol; in the second case the γ value varies not only with acetone liquid composition but also with the relative amounts of chloroform and methanol in the liquid.

At any temperature, multicomponent γ values may be correlated in terms of the *A* constants of the binary mixtures which make up the multicomponent mixture, the liquid compositions, and higher-order interaction terms. Fortunately, the higher-order interaction terms are often of minor importance, in which case multicomponent γ values can be predicted from knowledge of the non-ideal behavior of the binary mixtures involved.

Wohl [*Trans. Am. Inst. Chem. Engrs.*, **42**, 215 (1946); *Chem. Eng. Progress*, **49**, 218 (1953)] presents both Margules and van Laar equations for ternary mixtures. The van Laar two-suffix ternary equations are of limited usefulness, as they require that the *A* constants for the three binary pairs comprising the ternary mixtures be related as

$$\frac{A_{32}}{A_{23}} = \frac{A_{31}}{A_{13}}\frac{A_{12}}{A_{21}} \qquad (13\text{-}26)$$

The Margules three-suffix equations have no such restriction and have been found to be suitable for many ternary systems; the equation for $\log \gamma_1$ as given by Wohl is

$$\begin{aligned}\log \gamma_1 = {} & x_2^2[A_{12} + 2x_1(A_{21} - A_{12})] \\ & + x_3^2[A_{13} + 2x_1(A_{31} - A_{13})] \\ & + x_2x_3[\tfrac{1}{2}(A_{21} + A_{12} + A_{31} + A_{13} - A_{23} - A_{32}) \\ & + x_1(A_{21} - A_{12} + A_{31} - A_{13}) \\ & \quad + (x_2 - x_3)(A_{23} - A_{32}) - (1 - 2x_1)C^*] \end{aligned} \qquad (13\text{-}27)$$

Similar equations for $\log \gamma_2$ and $\log \gamma_3$ may be obtained by changing subscripts from 1 to 2, from 2 to 3, and from 3 to 1; if the subscripts are changed once, the equation for $\log \gamma_2$ is obtained, and if they are changed twice, the equation for $\log \gamma_3$ is obtained. In most cases the ternary interaction term C^* may be taken as zero; this has been demonstrated by Severns *et al.* [*Am. Inst. Chem. Engrs. J.*, **1**, 401 (1955)].

Under conditions where ternary data are to be expressed in terms of relative volatilities, Eq. (13-8) applies, and γ_1/γ_2 may be predicted by combining Eq. (13-27) written first for γ_1 and then for γ_2. This leads to

$$\log \frac{\gamma_1}{\gamma_2} = x_2^2 A_{12} - x_1^2 A_{21} + 2x_1x_2(A_{21} - A_{12}) + x_3^2\{2x_1A_{31} - 2x_2A_{32} + x_3(A_{13} - A_{23}) + (x_2 - x_1)[\tfrac{1}{2}(A_{12} + A_{21} + A_{13} + A_{31} + A_{23} + A_{32}) - C^*]\} \quad (13\text{-}28)$$

Values of log (γ_2/γ_3) and log (γ_3/γ_1) follow by rotation of subscripts as described above.

For unusual situations where one or more of the binary systems must be fitted with the more complex four-suffix Margules binary equation, then the four-suffix Margules ternary equations must be used to predict ternary γ values. These equations are given by Wohl (*loc. cit.*). Under conditions where four components are present, the four-component Margules three-suffix equations may be used [Jordan *et al.*, *Chem. Eng. Progress*, **46**, 601 (1950)]. If more than four components are present but only three different chemical types of components are represented (such as ketones, paraffins, and alcohols) the approximations used by Gerster *et al.* [*Am. Inst. Chem. Engrs. J.*, **1**, 536 (1955)] are helpful.

Other equations for predicting multicomponent γ values are those of Redlich and Kister [*Ind. Eng. Chem.*, **40**, 345 (1948)] and Black [*Ind. Eng. Chem.*, **50**, 391, 403 (1958); **51**, 211 (1959)]. The latter equations are modified van Laar equations in which the binary systems are characterized in terms of three constants instead of the two constants found in the ordinary two-suffix van Laar equations. The multicomponent form of Black's equations includes only coefficients derived from binary data.

Testing of experimental multicomponent γ values for thermodynamic consistency may be carried out using the methods of Prausnitz and Snider [*Am. Inst. Chem. Engrs. J.*, **5**, 7-S (1959)].

Correction Term for Moderate Pressures. At elevated pressures, **gas-law deviations** affect vapor-liquid behavior in a marked manner, whether the system is ideal in the liquid state or not. Even at atmospheric pressure there may be a slight effect which needs to be considered in precise work.

Where the total or vapor pressure is not higher than 200 lb./sq. in., Eq. (13-7) may be modified as follows to take into account gas-law deviations:

$$\log \frac{y_1}{x_1} = \log \frac{\gamma_1 P_1}{P} - \frac{(V_1 - B_1)(P_1 - P)}{2.3RT} \quad (13\text{-}29)$$

where V_1 is molar liquid volume. B_1 is the second virial coefficient for component 1 defined as

$$B = V - \frac{RT}{P} = (Z - 1)\frac{RT}{P} \quad (13\text{-}30)$$

where V is the true molar volume of the gas and Z is the compressibility factor ($= PV/RT$). Values of Z may be obtained from experimental data or from the generalized relationships given in Fig. 3-52 (p. 3-217). Equation (13-29) assumes no volume change on mixing the pure liquids or vapors, and that the virial coefficients for each pure component are the same as those for each corresponding component as it exists in the mixture. Systems exhibiting deviations from these assumptions even at low pressures have been described by Prausnitz and Benson [*Am. Inst. Chem. Engrs. J.*, **5**, 301 (1959)] and recommended procedures to follow in such instances are given in this reference and again by Prausnitz [*Am. Inst. Chem. Engrs. J.*, **6**, 78 (1960)].

Recommendations for High Pressures Where Simple-mixture Rules Apply. At low pressures the simple-mixture rule applied to the gas phase is $p_1 = Py_1$, while the simple-mixture rule for the liquid phase is $p_1 = P_1x_1$. For mixtures such as light hydrocarbons for which the simple-mixture rules apply at low pressures, the same rules apply at moderately high pressures, provided *fugacities*, instead of pressures, are used in the basic equations. This leads to the expression

$$\frac{y_1}{x_1} = \frac{f_{L_1}}{f_{V_1}} = K \quad (13\text{-}31)$$

where f_{L_1} is the fugacity of pure component 1 corresponding to its vapor pressure, and f_{V_1} is the fugacity of pure component 1 corresponding to the total pressure of the system. K is defined as the **equilibrium vaporization ratio** y_1/x_1, usually called **K factor.** Pure-component fugacities may be evaluated from experimental compressibility-factor data by Eq. (4-282), or from the generalized fugacity chart in Fig. 4-37 (see Sec. 4).

Even for simple-mixture-rule systems, Eq. (13-31) will be in error if the operating pressure exceeds 40 per cent of the "convergence pressure" for the system, *i.e.*, the pressure at which K factors for all components approach unity. (Corrections for this effect are presented later.) A second possible source of error in using Eq. (13-31) is due to lack of a correction for the effect of total pressure upon the fugacity corresponding to the pure-component vapor pressure. The value of f_{L_1} obtained from compressibility data or from Fig. 4-37 applies at a total pressure of P_1, whereas the proper value of f_{L_1} to use in Eq. (13-31) is that corresponding to total pressure P. The appropriate correction is given by the relation

$$\log \frac{f_{L1(\text{at } P)}}{f_{L1(\text{at } P_1)}} = \frac{V_1(P - P_1)}{2.3RT} \quad (13\text{-}32)$$

where, as before, V_1 is the molar liquid specific volume. The magnitude of this correction is often small.

As an example of the application of these methods, consider the prediction of K for benzene in a mixture with toluene at 392°F. and 131 lb./sq. in. abs. Other data: $P_1 = 206$ lb./sq. in. abs., $P_c = 704$, $T_c = 1011$°R. Then $P_R = P/P_c = 131/704 = 0.186$; $T_R = T/T_c = 852/1011 = 0.843$. From Fig. 4-37, $f_{V_1}/P = 0.88$, whence $f_{V_1} = (0.88)(131) = 115$. Now $P_1/P_c = 206/704 = 0.292$; again from Fig. 4-37, $f_{L_1}/P_1 = 0.825$, and f_{L_1} (at P_1) = (0.825)(206) = 170. Applying Eq. (13-32), V_1 is 1.90 cu. ft./lb.-mole, R is 10.7, and $V_1(P - P_1)/2.3RT = (1.90)(131\text{–}206)/(2.3)(10.7)(852) = -0.0068$, the antilog of which is 0.985. Thus f_{L_1} (at P) = (0.985)(170) = 167. Finally, by Eq. (13-31), $K = y/x = f_{L_1}/f_{V_1} = 167/115 = 1.45$. The experimental value of y/x obtained by Griswold, Andres, and Klein [*Trans. Am. Inst. Chem. Engrs.*, **39**, 223 (1943)] was 1.44, which agrees closely with the value of 1.45 predicted by fugacities and the simple-mixture rules; if the ideal-gas law had been assumed to apply, y/x would have been computed as $P_1/P = 206/131 = 1.57$, in error from the experimental value by 9 per cent.

Vapor-Liquid Behavior in Critical Regions. The phase behavior of a typical binary mixture at pressures and temperatures up to and above the critical is illustrated in Fig. 13-9. Curve AB is the vapor pressure–temperature relationship for one of the components, terminating at point B, the critical pressure and temperature for the component. Similarly, curve GH is the vapor pressure–temperature relationship for the second component. For a given mixture of these two

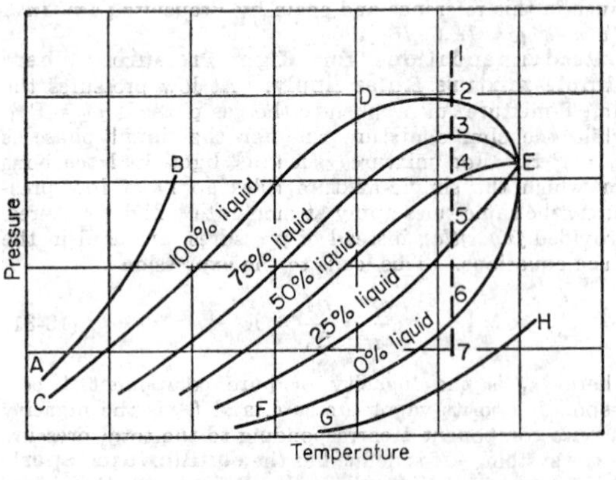

FIG. 13-9. Phase behavior of typical binary mixture in critical region.

components contained in a closed vessel or bomb, say a mixture containing one mole of each component, the phase relationships are given by the loop *CDEF*. Point *E* defines the critical temperature and pressure for this mixture. Curve *CDE* is the **bubble-point** curve for this mixture; for all conditions above this curve, the mixture is a liquid below its boiling point. However, as the pressure is lowered, say from point 1 to point 2, the liquid begins to boil (the first bubble of vapor forms). As the pressure is lowered further, at constant temperature, definite quantities of vapor form in the bomb; for example, at point 5, 25 per cent of the material in the bomb remains liquid while 75 per cent has been vaporized. Curve *FE* is the **dew point** for this particular mixture; for all conditions to the right of this curve, the mixture

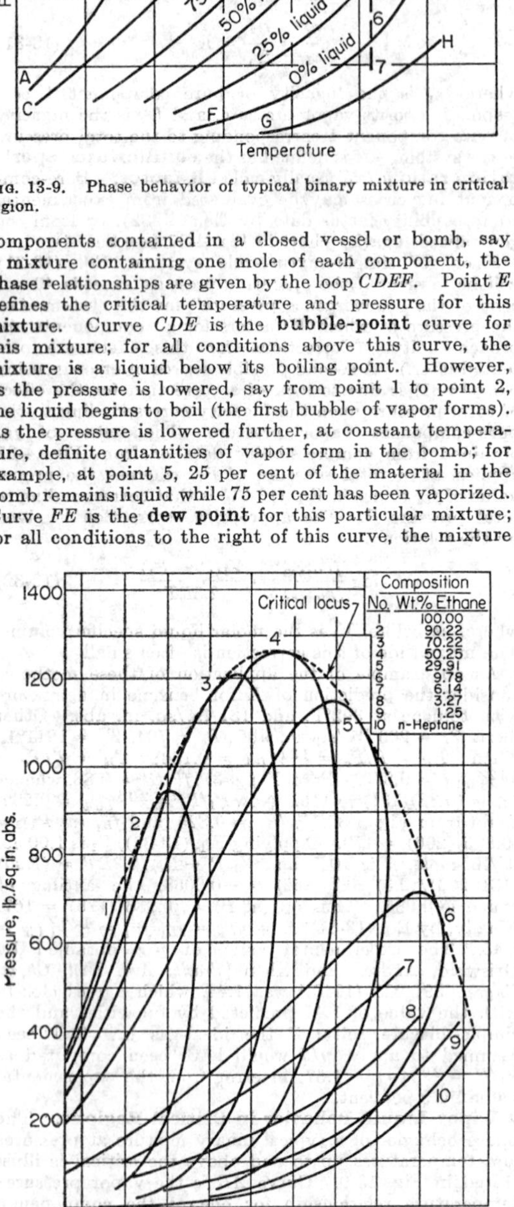

FIG. 13-10. Experimental phase boundaries for ethane–*n*-heptane system. [*Kay, Ind. Eng. Chem.*, **30**, 459 (1938).]

is a superheated vapor. As the pressure is raised from point 7 to 6, the vapor loses its superheat and reaches saturation as the first drop of "dew" or condensation forms. Point *E* is the critical point for the mixture because only at this point can one move from a saturated liquid to a saturated vapor with only a differential change in pressure and temperature.

As the loop *CDEF* applies only for a particular total composition, there are obviously an infinite number of such loops for all possible binary compositions. Experimental phase boundaries or loops determined by Kay [*Ind. Eng. Chem.*, **30**, 459 (1938)] for the system ethane–*n*-heptane are shown in Fig. 13-10 for a number of total compositions. The critical points of each loop have been joined by a dashed line known as the **critical locus line.** Kay also showed that, at the critical point for each of the loops, the densities of the saturated vapor and liquid phases became equal.

Critical loci for the methane-propane-pentane system are given in Fig. 13-11. This chart taken from Hadden

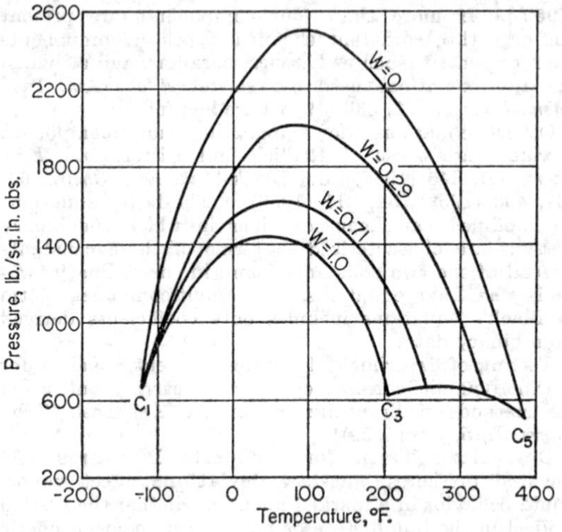

FIG. 13-11. Critical loci for methane-propane-pentane system according to Hadden [*Chem. Eng. Progress, Symp. Ser.* **7**, **49**, 58 (1953)]. Parameter *W* is weight fraction propane on a methane-free basis.

[*Chem. Eng. Progress, Symp. Ser.* 7, **49**, 53 (1953)] shows critical loci for the binary systems C_1-C_3, C_3-C_5, and C_1-C_5, terminating in each case at the critical points for the pure components. The critical loci for the ternary mixture were shown to vary linearly, at constant temperature, with the weight per cent propane on a methane-free basis; in both binary and ternary systems the critical loci are independent of the concentration of the lightest component in the mixture.

The *K*-factor behavior of the ethane–*n*-heptane system in the critical region was determined by Kay (*loc. cit.*). Figure 13-12 shows that the *K* factors for both components converge to unity at the pressure on the critical locus line corresponding to the temperature at which the data were determined. The pressure at which constant-temperature *K* factors converge to unity is known as the **convergence pressure** for the system.

The importance of composition upon *K* factors for *n*-pentane at 220°F. is illustrated by Fig. 13-13. As the variation in the mixture composition causes the convergence pressure to vary, it also causes a variation in the *K* factors at pressures below the convergence pressure. The mixture composition effect becomes less

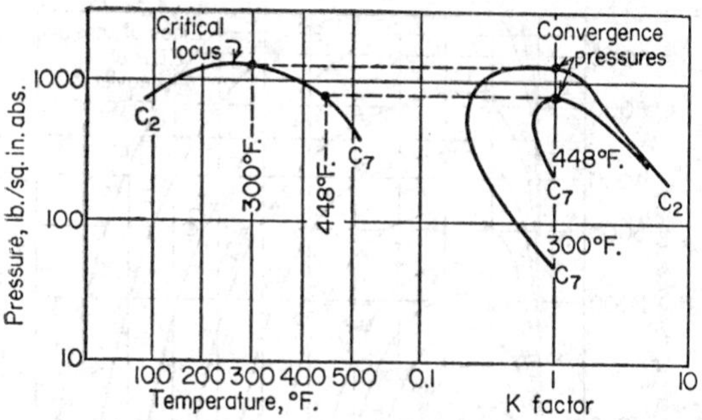

FIG. 13-12. Relationship between convergence pressure and critical locus for ethane–*n*-heptane system. Data of Kay [*Ind. Eng. Chem.*, **30,** 459 (1938)].

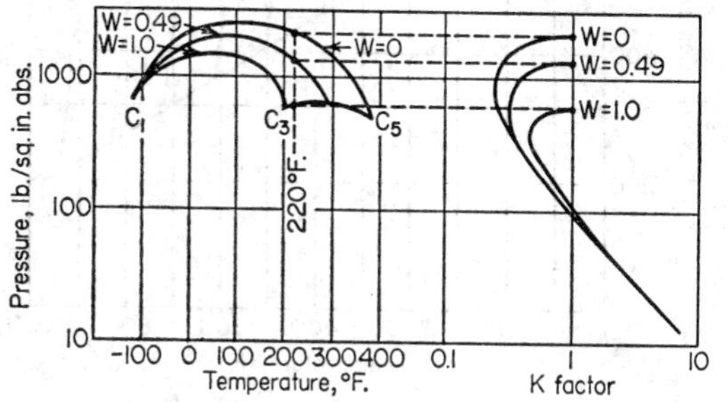

FIG. 13-13. Effect of mixture composition upon *K* factor for *n*-pentane at 220°F. *K* factors are shown for various values of *W*, weight fraction propane on a methane-free basis for the methane-propane-pentane system [*Hadden, Chem. Eng. Progress, Symp. Ser.* 7, **49,** 58 (1953)].

important, however, as the total pressure is reduced, as indicated in the figure.

The phase behavior of a typical complex mixture is illustrated by Fig. 13-14. This chart is applicable only for a single mixture composition.

K Factors for Light Hydrocarbons. As described in the previous paragraphs, *K* factors at high or even moderate pressures vary with the convergence pressure for the system, which is in turn a function of the system composition. A useful correlation of *K* factors for light hydrocarbons which includes composition as a variable is that of Myers and Lenoir [*Petrol. Refiner*, **36** (2), 167 (1957)], based upon a procedure developed by Lenoir and White [*Petrol. Refiner*, **32** (10), 121 (1953); **32** (12), 115 (1953)]. A slightly improved version of their nomograph is given by Cajander, Hipkin, and Lenoir [*J. Chem. Eng. Data*, **5,** 251 (1960)].

Other commonly used aids for predicting *K* factors for light hydrocarbons from knowledge of temperature, pressure, and convergence pressure are charts of the Natural Gasoline Association ("NGAA Equilibrium-ratio Data Book," Tulsa, 1955); the tables of Rzasa, Glass, and Opfel [*Chem. Eng. Progress, Symp. Ser.* 2, **48,** 28 (1952)]; the nomograms of Winn [*Chem. Eng. Progress, Symp. Ser.* 2, **48,** 121 (1952)] or of Neyrey [*Petrol. Refiner*, **39** (12), 129 (1960)].

Perhaps a more fundamental procedure for characterizing the effect of mixture composition upon *K* factors is by application of the **Benedict equation of state** [*Chem. Eng. Progress*, **47,** 419, 449, 571, 609 (1951)]. To express mixture composition in terms of an easily correlated function, the molal average normal boiling point of each phase is used. The resulting **Kellogg charts** are available from the M. W. Kellogg Co., New York. DePriester later found a way of expressing the more than 300 Kellogg charts into 24 charts with but little loss of accuracy [*Chem. Eng. Progress, Symp. Ser.* 7, **49,** 1 (1953)], as did Edmister and Ruby [*Chem. Eng. Progress*, **51** (2), 95-F (1955)]. The latter have been expressed in equation form suitable for use on a digital computer by Gordon *et al.* [*Chem. Eng. Progress, Symp. Ser.* 21, **55,** 1 (1959)]. Later experimental data by Price *et al.* [*Chem. Eng. Progress, Symp. Ser.* 21, **55,** 13 (1959)] for the methane-ethane-propane system at temperatures down to −200°F. should be used as a source of *K* factors for these components in the low-temperature range, as few data of this type were available when the earlier correlations were developed.

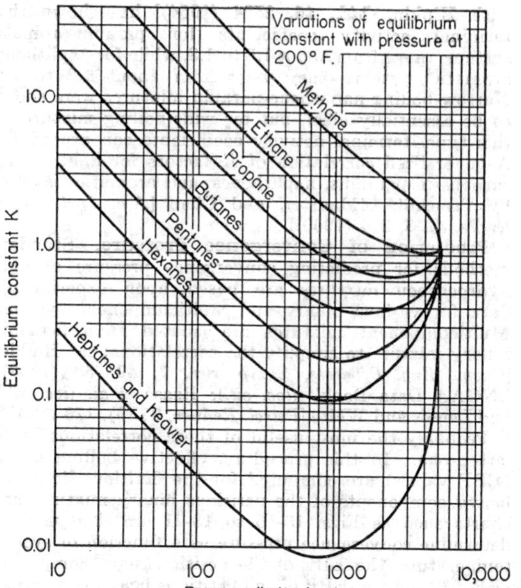

FIG. 13-14. Typical variation of *K* factors with total pressure at constant temperature for complex mixture. Light hydrocarbons in admixture with crude oil. [*Katz and Hachmuth, Ind. Eng. Chem.*, **29,** 1072 (1937).]

A more promising yet more tedious method for applying the Benedict equation (*loc. cit.*) for prediction of *K* factors is to combine each set of eight empirical constants needed to characterize the behavior of each component into a set of eight constants suitable for characterizing the behavior of the mixture of interest. Rules are given by Benedict (*loc. cit.*) for "weighting" each set of pure-component constants as a function of the mixture composition in order to achieve this purpose, but application of these rules by Price *et al.* (*loc. cit.*) showed deviations of 13.5 per cent between their experimental propane *K* factors and those predicted by the Benedict equation. Progress in the development of more sophisticated rules for combining the pure-component Benedict constants to predict mixture behavior has been reported by Pings and Sage [*J. Chem. Eng. Data,* **1,** 56 (1956)] and by Hsieh and Zimmerman [*J. Chem. Eng. Data,* **3,** 194 (1958)].

All correlations in this section hold only for *paraffin* and *olefin* light hydrocarbons, and when naphthenes and/or aromatics are introduced, additional nonidealities become evident because of differences in chemical types present. Myers [*Petrol. Refiner*, **36** (3), 175 (1957); *Ind. Eng. Chem.*, **47,** 2215 (1955); **48,** 1104 (1956);

with Hipkin, *ibid.*, **46**, 2524 (1954)] has shown that terminal activity coefficients for paraffin-aromatic systems range from about 1.3 to 1.8, while for naphthene-aromatic systems, they vary from about 1.2 to 1.4. Narrow-boiling naphthene-paraffin mixtures were shown to be essentially ideal, but for wide-boiling mixtures of this type, terminal activity coefficients can exceed 1.1. A generalized correlation of K factors for light hydrocarbons in paraffins, naphthenes, and aromatics is given by Prausnitz, Edmister, and Chao [*Am. Inst. Chem. Engrs. J.*, **6**, 214 (1960)].

Prediction of Convergence Pressure. Standard methods for predicting convergence pressure of light hydrocarbon mixtures are based upon experimental data for various binary and multicomponent systems. Multicomponent mixtures are treated as a fictitious binary mixture to simplify the correlations; see Hadden [*Chem. Eng. Progress, Symp. Ser.* 7, **49**, 53 (1953)]; "NGAA Data Book" (*loc. cit.*); Rzasa *et al.* (*loc. cit.*); and Lenoir and White [*Petrol. Refiner*, **37** (3), 173 (1958)].

Probably the most useful of these correlations is the latter one. In this procedure, effective boiling points (EBP values) are computed for the fictitious light and heavy components of the fictitious binary mixture, and charts such as Figs. 13-15 to 13-21 are then used to determine convergence pressure as a function of system temperature, the EBP of the fictitious light component $(EBP)_L$, and the EBP of the fictitious heavy component $(EBP)_H$. Figures 13-22 and 13-23 and Table 13-8 are used to compute values of $(EBP)_L$ and $(EBP)_H$, as illustrated below.

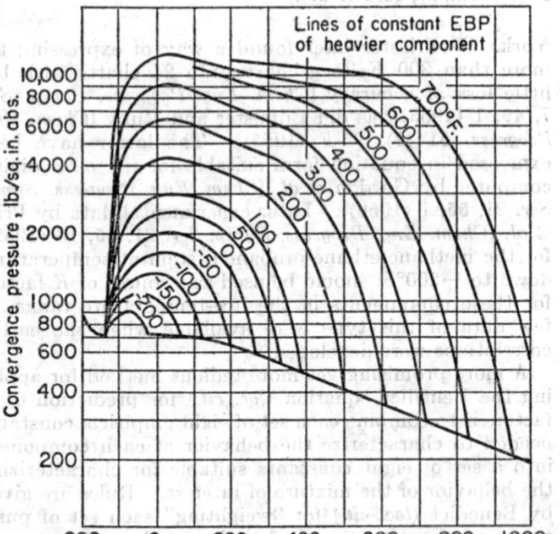

FIG. 13-15. Convergence pressures for hydrocarbon mixtures in which light component has effective boiling point $(EBP)_L$ of −280°F. Parameter is EBP of heavier component. [*Lenoir and White, Petrol. Refiner*, **37** (3), 173 (1958).]

Consider prediction of the convergence pressure for a ternary mixture at 100°F. and 500 lb./sq. in. abs. Liquid-phase compositions (x values), in mole fraction units, are 0.069 for methane, 0.279 for ethylene, and 0.652 for isobutane. To calculate $(EBP)_L$, ignore all components having effective boiling points equal to or higher than $(EBP)_H$. In the present instance, as a first trial, ignore isobutane but include methane and ethylene. Next, list values of effective boiling point

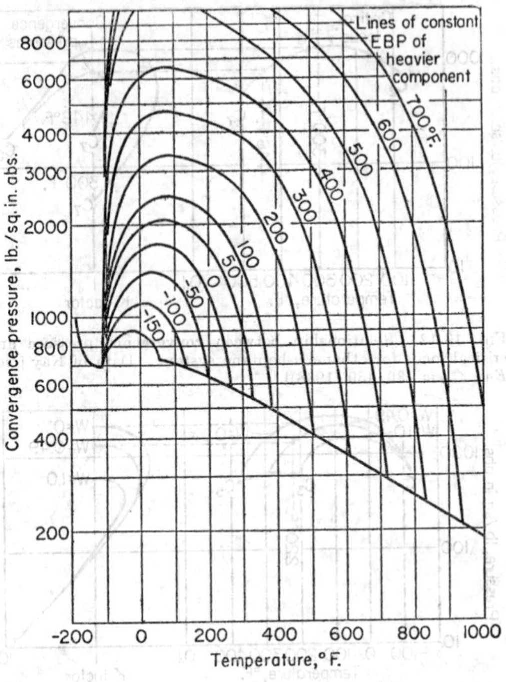

FIG. 13-16. Convergence pressures when light component has effective boiling point $(EBP)_L$ of −259°F. [*Lenoir and White, Petrol. Refiner*, **37** (3), 173 (1958).]

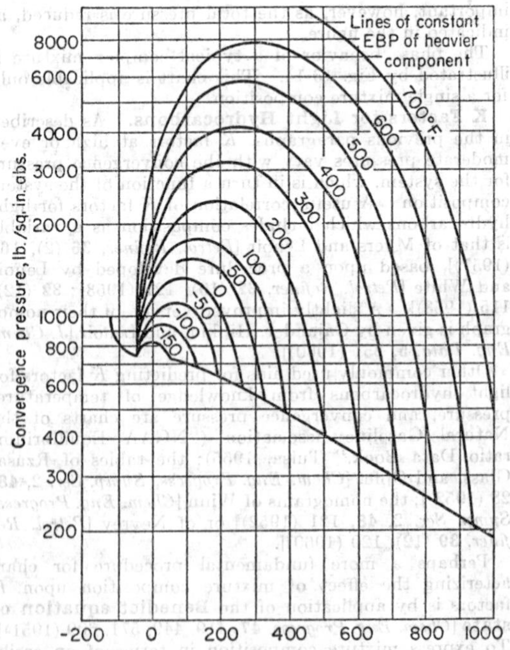

FIG. 13-17. Convergence pressures when $(EBP)_L$ = −220°F. [*Lenoir and White, Petrol. Refiner*, **37** (3), 173 (1958).]

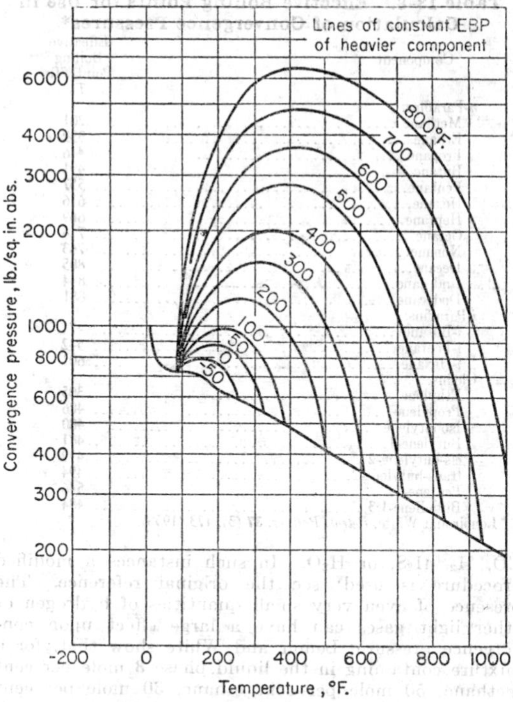

FIG. 13-18. Convergence pressures when $(EBP)_L = -128$°F. [*Lenoir and White, Petrol. Refiner*, **37** (3), 173 (1958).]

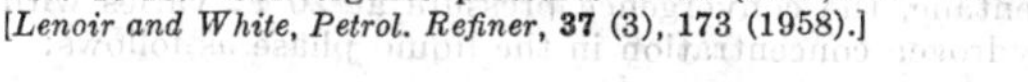

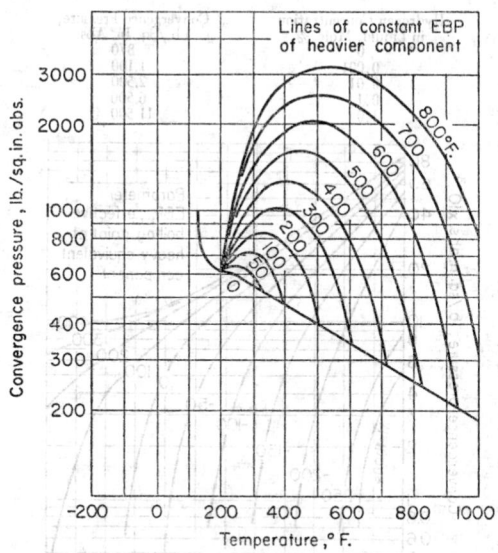

FIG. 13-19. Convergence pressures when $(EBP)_L = -44$°F. [*Lenoir and White, Petrol. Refiner*, **37** (3), 173 (1958).]

T_b for methane and ethylene from Table 13-8, and compute values of the ratio T_L/T_b for these two components (T_L is the effective boiling point of the lightest component). Then from Fig. 13-22 tabulate values of F_e, and compute values of F_ex and F_exT_b. Divide the sum of the values of F_exT_b by the sum of the values of F_ex to get $(EBP)_L$:

Component	x	T_b	T_L/T_b	F_e	F_ex	F_exT_b
Methane........	0.069	201	1.000	1.000	0.069	13.9
Ethylene........	0.279	305	0.659	0.092	0.0257	7.84
					0.0947	21.74

$$(EBP)_L = 21.74/0.0947 = 229°R.$$

To compute $(EBP)_H$, ignore all components having effective boiling points equal to or lower than $(EBP)_L$. In this case, as $(EBP)_L$ is 229°R., methane is ignored. Next list values of T_b for ethylene and isobutane from Table 13-8, and compute values of the ratio T_b/T_H for these two components (T_H is the effective boiling point of the heaviest component). Then from Fig. 13-23

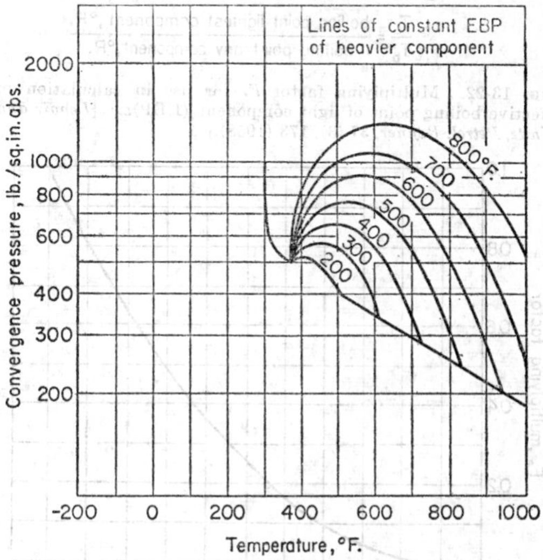

FIG. 13-20. Convergence pressures when $(EBP)_L = 80$°F. [*Lenoir and White, Petrol. Refiner*, **37** (3), 173 (1958).]

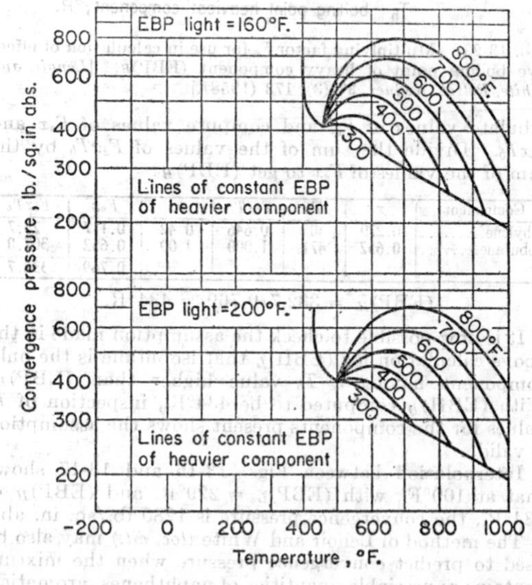

FIG. 13-21. Convergence pressures when $(EBP)_L = 160$°F. and 200°F. [*Lenoir and White, Petrol. Refiner*, **37** (3), 173 (1958).]

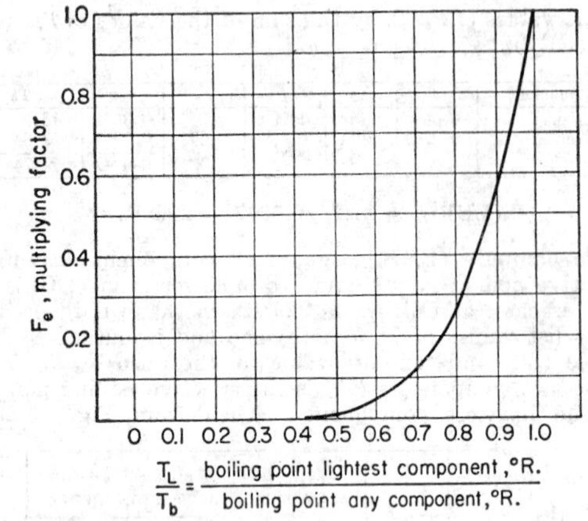

FIG. 13-22. Multiplying factor F_e for use in calculation of effective boiling point of light component $(EBP)_L$. [*Lenoir and White, Petrol. Refiner*, **37** (3), 173 (1958).]

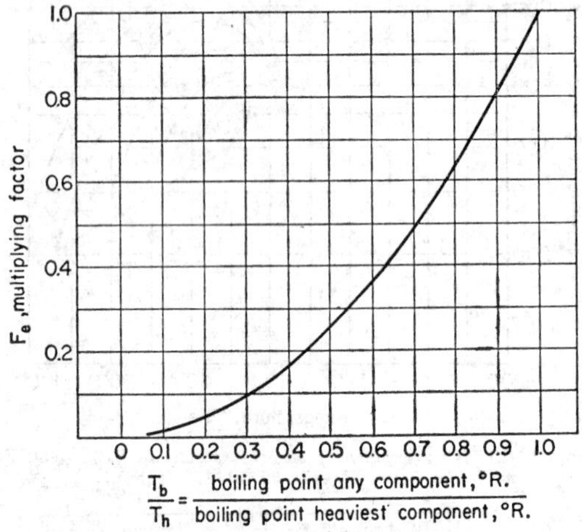

FIG. 13-23. Multiplying factor F_e for use in calculation of effective boiling point of heavy component $(EBP)_H$. [*Lenoir and White, Petrol. Refiner*, **37** (3), 173 (1958).]

tabulate values of F_e, and compute values of F_ex and F_exT_b. Divide the sum of the values of F_exT_b by the sum of the values of F_ex to get $(EBP)_H$:

Component	x	T_b	T_b/T_H	F_e	F_ex	F_exT_b
Ethylene........	0.279	305	0.646	0.42	0.117	25.7
Isobutane........	0.652	471	1.000	1.00	0.652	307.0
					0.769	332.7

$$(EBP)_H = 332.7/0.769 = 434°R.$$

It is now possible to check the assumption made in the above calculation for $(EBH)_L$ that isobutane is the only component having a T_b value higher than $(EBP)_H$. With $(EBH)_H$ computed to be 434°R., inspection of T_b values for the components present shows the assumption is valid.

Interpolation between Figs. 13-16 and 13-17 shows that at 100°F., with $(EBP)_L$ = 229°R. and $(EBP)_H$ = 434°R., the convergence pressure is 1280 lb./sq. in. abs.

The method of Lenoir and White (*loc. cit.*) may also be used to predict convergence pressure when the mixture contains appreciable quantities of naphthenes, aromatics, acetylenes, or non-hydrocarbon gases such as air, CO_2,

Table 13-8. Effective Boiling Points for Use in Calculation of Convergence Pressures*

Component	Effective Boiling Point, °R. T_b
n-Paraffins:	
Methane	201
Ethane..	332
Propane..	416
Butane..	491
Pentane..	557
Hexane..	616
Heptane..	669
Octane..	718
Nonane..	763
Decane..	805
Undecane..	844
Dodecane..	881
i-Paraffins:	
i-Butane..	471
i-Pentane..	542
i-Hexane..	601
Olefins:	
Ethylene..	305
Propylene..	406
Isobutylene..	480
Butylene-1..	481
cis-butylene-2..	499
trans-butylene-2..	494
Pentene-1..	546
Butadiene-1,3..	484

* Lenoir and White, *Petrol. Refiner*, **37** (3), 173 (1958).

CO, H_2, H_2S, or H_2O. In such instances a modified procedure is used; see the original reference. The presence of even very small quantities of hydrogen or other light gases can have a large effect upon convergence pressure; Lenoir and White show that, for a mixture containing in the liquid phase 3 mole per cent methane, 50 mole per cent ethane, 30 mole per cent propane, 12 mole per cent butane, and 5 mole per cent pentane, the convergence pressure at 20°F. varies with hydrogen concentration in the liquid phase as follows:

Hydrogen Concentration in Liquid, Mole %	Convergence Pressure, Lb./Sq. In. Abs.
0	870
0.001	1,100
0.01	2,500
0.1	6,500
1.0	11,500

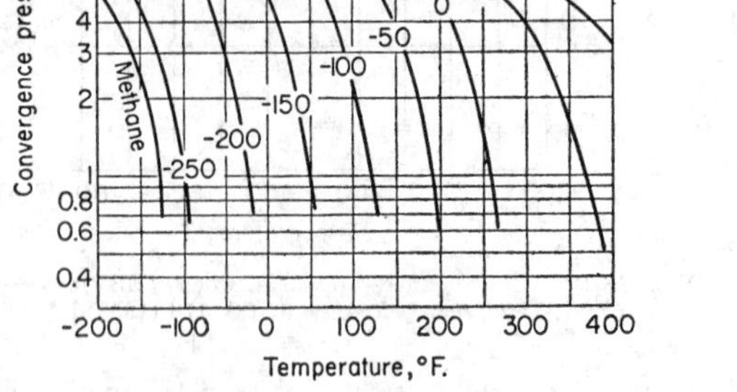

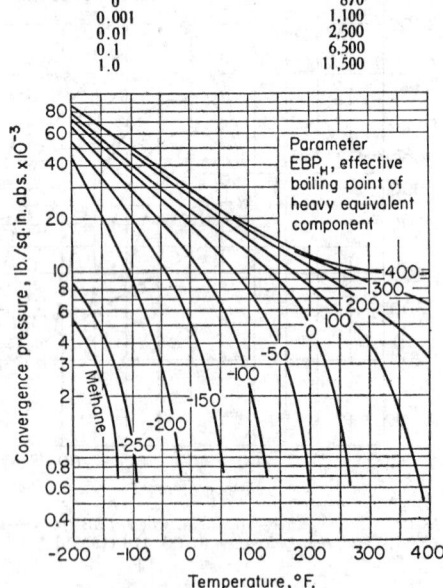

FIG. 13-24. Convergence pressures for hydrogen-paraffin mixtures. Effective boiling point of heavy component $(EBP)_H$ is computed by methods given on p. 13-17. [*Lenoir and Hipkin, Am. Inst. Chem. Engrs.*, **3**, 318 (1957).]

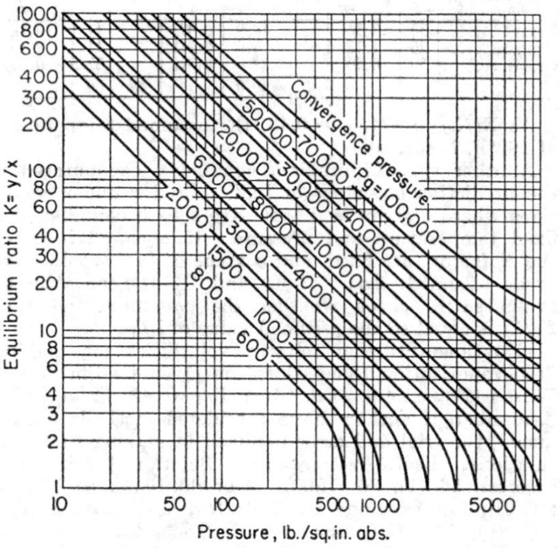

FIG. 13-25. *K* factors for hydrogen in hydrogen-paraffin mixtures. [*Lenoir and Hipkin, Am. Inst. Chem. Engrs. J.*, **3**, 318 (1957).]

However, if the operating pressure is less than 60 per cent of the convergence pressure, the magnitude of the convergence pressure does not affect the magnitude of the *K* factor significantly, and an estimate of convergence pressure is usually sufficient.

The **phase behavior of hydrogen-paraffin mixtures** is not only important, it is unusual in that, unlike all light hydrocarbons, *K* factors for hydrogen *decrease* with increasing temperature.

Lenoir and Hipkin [*Am. Inst. Chem. Engrs. J.*, **3**, 318 (1957)] contend that because hydrogen is usually present at temperatures well above its critical temperature, *K* factors for hydrogen are independent of temperature; the increase in *K* factors for hydrogen with decreasing temperature is said to be caused not by a temperature effect, but by an increase in convergence pressure. These authors correlated convergence pressure for hydrogen-paraffin mixtures as a function of system temperature and effective boiling point of the non-hydrogen components of the mixture as shown in Fig. 13-24; using this figure, the authors then correlated hydrogen *K* factors for all mixtures, all temperatures, and all pressures on one plot as a function of only two variables—system pressure and convergence pressure. The latter correlation is shown as Fig. 13-25. The average deviation between predicted and experimental *K* factors for hydrogen using Figs. 13-24 and 13-25 is said by Lenoir and Hipkin to be 11.3 per cent for 375 comparisons made with hydrogen-paraffin, hydrogen-olefin, and hydrogen-olefin-paraffin mixtures.

Sources of experimental data for hydrogen–light hydrocarbon systems are conveniently summarized by Benham, Katz, and Williams [*Am. Inst. Chem. Engrs. J.*, **3**, 236 (1957)]; additional data are given by Nichols *et al.* [*ibid.*, **3**, 262 (1957)], by Cosway and Katz [*ibid.*, **5**, 46 (1959)], and by Prausnitz and Duffin [*Petrol. Refiner*, **39** (5), 213 (1960)].

DISTILLATION PROCESSES

Simple Batch Distillation. In this case a batch of material is charged to a still pot, boiling is initiated, and the vapors are then continuously removed, condensed, and collected until their average composition has reached a desired value. If at any particular time during the distillation the total moles of liquid in the still pot (boiler) is S, the mole fraction of the more volatile component in the liquid is x, and the mole fraction of this same component in the vapor is y, then a material balance shows

$$y(-dS) = -d(Sx) = -S\,dx - x\,dS \qquad (13\text{-}33)$$

Rearranging and integrating gives

$$\ln \frac{S_1}{S_2} = \int_{x_2}^{x_1} \frac{dx}{y - x} \qquad (13\text{-}34)$$

If equilibrium may be assumed between the liquid and vapor of the still pot, the right-hand side of Eq. (13-34) may be evaluated by plotting $1/(y - x)$ vs. x and measuring the area under the curve between the limits x_1 and x_2. If the relative volatility α is constant, or reasonably so, and if the mixture being distilled consists of only two components, substitution of Eq. (13-5) into Eq. (13-34) permits a direct integration to be made:

$$\ln \frac{S_1}{S_2} = \frac{1}{\alpha - 1}\left(\ln \frac{x_1}{x_2} + \alpha \ln \frac{1 - x_2}{1 - x_1}\right) \qquad (13\text{-}35)$$

For a multicomponent mixture having constant α values, $-dS_A/-dS_B = y_A/y_B = \alpha(x_A/x_B)$ which, when integrated, gives

$$\ln \frac{S_{A(1)}}{S_{A(2)}} = \alpha \ln \frac{S_{B(1)}}{S_{B(2)}} \qquad (13\text{-}36)$$

where $S_{A(1)}$ and $S_{A(2)}$ are the moles of component A present in the still pot before and after the batch distillation, and $S_{B(1)}$ and $S_{B(2)}$ are the moles of component B in the pot before and after the distillation.

Consider as an application of simple batch distillation the removal of water from a furfural-water mixture. Assume an initial charge of 100 moles, containing 70 moles of furfural and 30 moles of water, which is to be distilled at 1 atm. total pressure until the material remaining in the still pot contains 96 mole per cent furfural. Compute the moles to be distilled and the loss of furfural with the overhead vapors. Equilibrium data for this system are available from Table 13-3; these data show the system to be miscible at liquid concentrations of 70 mole per cent furfural and greater. Values of y, x, and $1/(y - x)$ in the units of mole fraction water taken from Table 13-3 are as follows:

x	y	$y - x$	$1/(y - x)$
0.30	0.905	0.605	1.65
0.20	0.89	0.69	1.45
0.10	0.81	0.71	1.41
0.08	0.68	0.60	1.67
0.06	0.36	0.30	3.33
0.04	0.19	0.15	6.67

After values of $1/(y - x)$ are plotted along the ordinate vs. x, the area under the curve between $x_1 = 0.30$ and $x_2 = 0.04$ is found to be 0.46; the antilog of 0.46 is 1.58, so that by Eq. (13-34) the value of S_2, moles remaining in the still pot at the end of the distillation, is $S_1/1.58 = 100/1.58$ or 63.3 moles. The liquid remaining consists of (63.3)(0.96) = 60.8 moles of furfural and 2.5 moles of water, and by material balance with the charge, the distillate must consist of 70 − 60.8 or 9.2 moles of furfural and 30 − 2.5 or 27.5 moles of water; total moles distilled is thus 36.7 moles and the distillate composition 27.5/36.7 or 0.750 mole fraction water. However, at 100°F. the solubility of furfural in water is only 1.8 mole per cent, while the solubility of water in furfural is 26.4 mole per cent [*Chem. & Met. Eng.*, **26**, 779 (1922)]. Thus if the distillate is at this temperature it will consist of two layers, distributed as follows:

	Water-rich layer	Furfural-rich layer
Moles of water.......	24.4	3.1
Moles of furfural.....	0.44	8.8
	24.8	11.9

If the water layer is discarded but the furfural layer is added to the next batch to be distilled, the furfural loss will be only 0.44/70 or 0.63 per cent of the original furfural charged to the still pot.

Simple Continuous Distillation. In this process a feed stream is partly vaporized and the vapor and liquid portions are continuously withdrawn. The operation may be carried out in a still pot or boiler to which the feed is continuously supplied; vapor is continuously removed and liquid is withdrawn from the pot at a rate such as to keep the level constant. Alternatively, a "pipe still" may be used, where the feed is pumped through a long pipe externally heated, usually by direct firing. The vapor-liquid mixture from the pipe still may then go to a "flash chamber" where the vapor and liquid portions are continuously removed. These operations are also known as **continuous equilibrium vaporization** or **equilibrium flash vaporization.** The latter terms imply that equilibrium exists between the vapor and liquid streams leaving the apparatus.

Calculations for this process are most conveniently made by combining material balances and equilibrium relationships in the following manner. Let F = moles of feed per unit time to the still pot or flash chamber, and let V and L be the moles of vapor and liquid, respectively, per unit time issuing from the still pot or flash chamber; let the corresponding compositions expressed in mole fraction units be z_F, y, and x. Then

$$F = V + L \tag{13-37}$$

and for any component

$$Fz_F = (V + L)z_F = Vy + Lx \tag{13-38}$$

Using K factors (see p. 13-13) to express the equilibrium relationship between y and x, substitution of y/K for x in Eq. (13-38) gives

$$y = \frac{(1 + L/V)z_F}{1 + (L/KV)} \tag{13-39}$$

Defining f, v, and l as moles of a component per unit time in the feed, vapor, and liquid, respectively, the term v/V may be substituted for y in the above equation to give

$$v = \frac{(V + L)z_F}{1 + (L/KV)} = \frac{f}{1 + (L/KV)} \tag{13-40}$$

By a similar treatment,

$$l = \frac{f}{1 + (KV/L)} \tag{13-41}$$

Consider 100 moles/hr. of a feed stream containing 30 mole per cent hexane, 20 mole per cent heptane, and 50 mole per cent octane subjected to simple continuous distillation at 10 lb./sq. in. abs. The amount of the feed which is continuously vaporized is 40 per cent; compute the composition of vapor and liquid product streams and their temperature, assuming they leave the still pot or flash chamber under equilibrium conditions. To solve this problem, assume a temperature; find the K factors from a suitable literature reference; compute values of v and l from Eqs. (13-40) and (13-41); and check the assumed temperature by determining whether $V/F = \Sigma v/\Sigma f = 0.40$:

Component	z	$K_{192°F.}$	v	y	l	x
Hexane........	30	2.56	18.9	0.473	11.1	0.185
Heptane.......	20	1.12	8.6	0.215	11.4	0.190
Octane........	50	0.50	12.5	0.312	37.5	0.625
			$\Sigma v = 40.0$		$\Sigma l = 60.0$	

As $\Sigma v/\Sigma f = 40/100 = 0.40$, the assumed temperature of 192°F. is correct.

Another type of problem commonly encountered is the prediction of values of L/V, y, and x under conditions where a given feed is sent to a flash chamber at a fixed temperature and pressure. In such an instance the K factors are fixed, and a value of L/V would have to be assumed; Eqs. (13-40) and (13-41) can then be evaluated to check whether the computed value of $\Sigma v/\Sigma l$ is equal to the assumed value of L/V.

Equations utilizing relative volatilities for making flash-vaporization calculations are given by Smith and Wilson [*Trans. Am. Inst. Chem. Engrs.*, **42**, 927 (1946)]. A number of authors have considered methods for reducing the trial and error involved in making flash calculations. Useful references are Bejarano [*Chem. Eng. Progress*, **56** (1), 86 (1960)]; Albright [*ibid.*, **55** (8), 78 (1959)]; Edmister and Okamoto [*Petrol. Refiner*, **38** (8), 117; (9), 271; (10), 163 (1959)]; Holland and Davison [*Petrol. Refiner*, **36** (3), 183; (4), 203 (1957)]; Bachelor [*Petrol. Refiner*, **36** (10), 113 (1957)]; Salmon [*Petrol. Refiner*, **36** (12), 133 (1957)].

The principles illustrated above are useful in **calculations involving light hydrocarbons.** However, when dealing with higher-boiling fractions or entire crudes, the calculations become impractical because of the large number of compounds present with only slightly differing boiling points. For this reason, empirical correlations have been widely used for predicting equilibrium-flash-vaporization curves from one of the two commonly employed types of standard laboratory distillations used in characterizing petroleum fractions, the A.S.T.M. distillation or the "true-boiling-point" distillation (see p. 13-45). The A.S.T.M. method (Tests D86-46 and D158-41, Book of A.S.T.M. Standards, American Society for Testing Materials, Philadelphia, Pa.) is essentially a batch distillation carried out at a uniform rate with no reflux and with no plates or packing, whereas the true-boiling-point distillation employs a batch distillation but with a high reflux ratio and an efficient fractionating column [Beiswenger and Child, *Ind. Eng. Chem., Anal. Ed.*, **2**, 284 (1930)]. A recommended correlation of this type is that of Edmister and Okamoto [*Petrol. Refiner*, **38** (8), 117; (9), 271; (10), 163; (12), 125 (1959); **39** (1), 161 (1960)].

Steam distillation is a simple distillation where vaporization of the charge is achieved by blowing live steam directly through it. The practice has special value where it is desired to separate substances at a temperature lower than their normal boiling points because of heat sensitivity or other reasons.

If the steam is superheated and remains so during its travel through the liquid, then

$$\frac{p_S}{P} = \frac{L_S}{L_T} \tag{13-42}$$

where p_S is the partial pressure of the steam, P is the system total pressure, L_S is the moles of steam issuing from the liquid, and L_T is the total moles of vapor generated from the liquid. In this instance both L_S and L_T may be independently varied by varying the rate of steam supplied, its degree of superheat, and in some cases by supplying heat from an external source. Thus in effect both the temperature and the pressure of the distillation can be chosen at any desired value (except under a condition where liquid water forms in the still pot). Obviously a lowering of the partial pressure of the volatile constituents could also be obtained by use of any chemically inert gas besides steam; in many cases, however, such use introduces added problems in condensation and in recovery of both the distillate and the gas.

If the components to be separated are essentially immiscible with water, and if the steam supplied is such that liquid water is present in the still pot, Eq. (13-42) applies, but the temperature of the distillation is fixed at any chosen value of total pressure. This is true because Eq. (13-18) must be satisfied, and this equation is satisfied at only a single value of temperature.

Steam consumption is often an important factor in steam distillation; it can be reduced by increasing the temperature of the distillation to as high a value as can be tolerated. This is accomplished at a given total pressure by indirect heating of the still-pot liquid, which eliminates the liquid-water phase, raises the vapor pressure of the components being distilled, and lowers the partial pressure (and flow rate) of the steam. Alternatively, the total pressure of the system can be reduced.

Partial Condensation. If a saturated vapor is cooled until only a part of it is condensed, and if equilibrium is achieved between the vapor and liquid streams moving through the unit in cocurrent flow, a continuous separation process results. Such a process is termed equilibrium partial condensation. It is treated mathematically in a manner similar to that developed above for simple continuous distillation. Such a process is not commonly employed for separation purposes because of the small degree of separation obtained and because at high heat-transfer rates equilibrium is usually not achieved [Colburn and Drew, *Trans. Am. Inst. Chem. Engrs.*, **33**, 197 (1937)]. Partial condensers are employed on distillation columns, however, where hard-to-condense components present in the overhead product are not condensed, but some liquefaction is produced to provide a liquid-reflux stream to the column.

A high degree of separation can be obtained in a countercurrent partial condenser. This consists of a vertical, in-tube condenser supplied with vapor at the bottom; the uncondensed vapor product leaves at the top, while the condensate runs vertically downward inside the tube countercurrently to the rising vapor. A careful study of this operation has been reported by Kent and Pigford [*Am. Inst. Chem. Engrs. J.*, **2**, 363 (1956)].

Batch Rectification. Unless the feed components to a distillation process have a large relative volatility, a single vaporization and condensation step will not yield products having a composition appreciably different from that of the feed. To produce a high degree of separation by distillation, it is usually necessary to provide a plurality of successive vaporization and condensation operations. This can be accomplished by causing a boiling liquid and a saturated vapor to **contact** each other **countercurrently** in some type of distillation column.

In **batch-column distillation** or **batch rectification,** the mass of material to be distilled is heated to the boiling point in a still pot, the vapors are passed upward through a column or tower, and then condensed; part of the condensate is returned to the top of the tower as the source of liquid for countercurrent contacting of the vapor, while the remainder is withdrawn as the overhead product. The returned liquid stream is known as the **reflux**; it need not be at its boiling point when returned to the column, as it will soon be raised to the boiling point within the column by the hot vapor stream. The distillation is carried out until the desired recovery of the "lighter" (low-boiling, more volatile) component or components has been achieved in the overhead product at the desired purity. If the liquid remaining in the still pot contains more than the desired amount of lighter material, distillation is continued until the required purity of the bottoms product is achieved; the overhead product during this step of the operation, known as an intermediate cut, is collected separately and usually reworked in a subsequent batch.

In **continuous column distillation** or **continuous rectification,** startup of the unit is carried out as for batch column distillation, except that no overhead product is withdrawn. This stage is known as *total reflux operation*. After uniform conditions throughout the column have been reached, the feed is continuously added at an intermediate point in the column, part of the reflux stream is diverted as overhead product, and a bottoms product is withdrawn continuously from the still pot or reboiler. The portion of the column above the feed point is known as the **rectifying** or **enriching** section, while that below the feed point is the **stripping** or **exhausting** section.

Countercurrent contacting of the gas and liquid streams within a distillation tower is achieved by causing either (1) the gas to be dispersed within the liquid; or (2) the liquid to be dispersed within a continuous gas phase.

In the first case the liquid flows downward after passing successively across each of several horizontal **plates** or **trays** contained within the column; in industrial operations, the plates are spaced anywhere from a few inches to several feet apart. The vapor bubbles upward through the liquid flowing across each tray, and is dispersed into the liquid from holes or slots in the tray, or from bubble caps fastened to the tray. After the liquid flows across a tray, it drops to the tray below through closed *downpipes;* in *grid trays*, however, the tray openings are large enough to permit the liquid to pass downward through the same openings provided for upward flow of vapor. Section 18, Liquid-Gas Systems, provides design details of the trays most commonly used in industrial practice. It also presents design equations for computing tower diameter, tray spacing, and tray and downpipe dimensions which give efficient and uniform gas-liquid contacting at minimum cost.

When the liquid is to be dispersed within a continuous gas phase, **packed columns** are usually employed, although it is possible to use shower trays, disk-and-doughnut trays, or wetted-wall columns. Packed columns are often preferable to plate (tray) columns when corrosion-resistant materials are needed; they also have a low gas pressure drop and a low liquid hold-up. They are especially useful where through-puts are small but a large number of plates or transfer units must be obtained in relatively low height. However, they are not usually favored for large-diameter columns because of high cost and the difficulty of maintaining good liquid distribution. Mechanical and hydraulic design of packed columns is discussed also in Sec. 18.

CONTINUOUS BINARY DISTILLATION

Material-balance Equations. Consider a continuous column operating as shown in Fig. 13-26 with F moles/hr. of feed, and producing D moles/hr. of overhead product or distillate and W moles/hr. of bottoms product or waste. Under steady-state conditions, equating input to output,

$$F = D + W \tag{13-43}$$

If the compositions of these three streams are z_F, x_D, and x_W mole fraction of the more volatile component, an

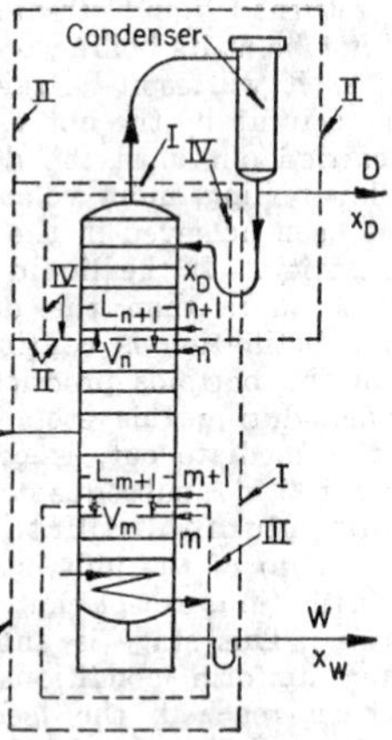

Fig. 13-26. Material-balance relationships in continuous distillation column.

over-all component balance is

$$Fz_F = Dx_D + Wx_W \qquad (13\text{-}44)$$

Inspection of Eqs. (13-43) and (13-44) shows that, in the usual case where F and z_F are fixed from process considerations, and x_D and x_W represent desired product purities, flow rates D and W are then fixed.

Consider now a section of the apparatus bounded by dotted line II which includes the portion of the tower above the nth plate. If there are V_n moles/hr. of vapor rising from the nth plate, and L_{n+1} moles/hr. of liquid coming down from the plate above (plate $n + 1$), a material balance gives

$$V_n = L_{n+1} + D \qquad (13\text{-}45)$$

If the compositions of the vapor and liquid streams between plates n and $n + 1$ are y_n and x_{n+1}, respectively, the corresponding component balance is

$$V_n y_n = L_{n+1} x_{n+1} + Dx_D \qquad (13\text{-}46)$$

or

$$y_n = \frac{L_{n+1}}{V_n} x_{n+1} + \frac{D}{V_n} x_D \qquad (13\text{-}47)$$

Similarly, for the section bounded by the dotted line III, Fig. 13-26,

$$L_{m+1} = V_m + W \qquad (13\text{-}48)$$

and

$$y_m = \frac{L_{m+1}}{V_m} x_{m+1} - \frac{W}{V_m} x_W \qquad (13\text{-}49)$$

where L_{m+1} and V_m are the flows in moles/hr. of the liquid and vapor streams between plates m and $m + 1$, and y_m and x_{m+1} are the compositions of the vapor and liquid streams between the same two plates.

If both D and x_D are fixed by considerations just discussed above, Eqs. (13-45) and (13-47) are not sufficient to compute values of V_n, L_{n+1}, and y_n at a position in the rectifying section where the liquid composition is x_{n+1}. As shown later, the additional equation required for such a calculation is an **enthalpy balance** written for area II of Fig. 13-26. By similar reasoning, an enthalpy balance for III of Fig. 13-26 is needed to compute values of V_m, L_{m+1}, and y_m at a position in the stripping section where the liquid composition is x_{m+1}.

In many cases, however, values of V_n and L_{n+1} are nearly constant for all trays in the rectifying section, and values of V_m and L_{m+1} are nearly constant in the stripping section, so that enthalpy balances are not needed. Constancy of flow rates, or **equal molal overflow,** will be achieved if

1. Molar latent heats of vaporization of the two components are equal.
2. Sensible-heat changes are negligible in comparison with latent heats.
3. Heats of solution in both phases are absent.
4. Heat losses from the tower are absent.

Under conditions of equal molal overflow, the relationship between the flow rates above and below the feed tray depends upon the thermal condition of the feed. If the feed is a liquid at its boiling point,

$$L_{m+1} = L_{n+1} + F \quad \text{and} \quad V_m = V_n \qquad (13\text{-}50)$$

while if the feed is a saturated vapor,

$$L_{m+1} = L_{n+1} \quad \text{and} \quad V_m = V_n - F \qquad (13\text{-}51)$$

Thus under conditions where external flows F, D, and W and the thermal condition of the feed are fixed by process requirements, only one internal flow rate can be independently chosen. If this chosen value is the reflux flow L_{n+1}, then V_n is fixed by Eq. (13-45) and L_{m+1} and V_m are fixed by either Eq. (13-50) or Eq. (13-51).

The **McCabe-Thiele graphical method** [*Ind. Eng. Chem.*, **17**, 605 (1925)] can be used for determining the number of theoretical plates or contacting stages required for a given binary distillation operation. By assuming equal molal overflow, the material-balance equations (13-47) and (13-49) are readily plotted on a graph as straight lines; values of y are plotted along the ordinate and values of x along the abscissa (Fig. 13-27).

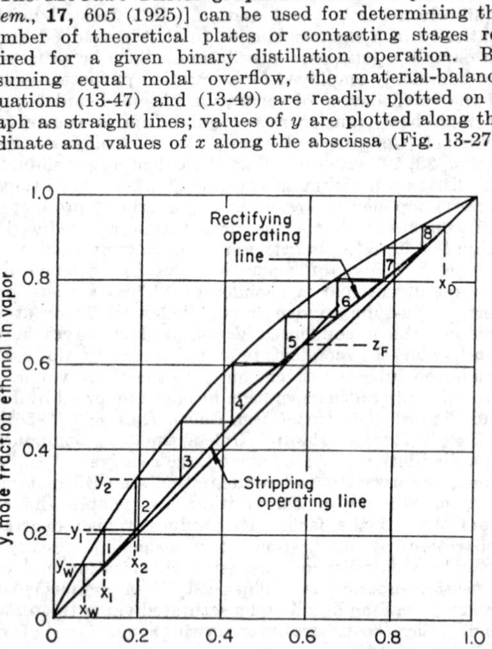

Fig. 13-27. Solution to example by McCabe-Thiele graphical method.

Plots of these two equations are known as **operating lines,** and their slopes equal the ratios of the liquid and vapor molar flow rates. Also plotted on the same graph is the vapor-liquid equilibrium relationship for the particular binary mixture of interest at the chosen operating pressure. The stepwise procedure for determining the number of "perfect" plates or trays is illustrated by the following example.

Consider the separation of 100 moles/hr. of an ethanol-propanol mixture containing 65 mole per cent ethanol. The separation is to be carried out in a continuous plate column operating at 1 atm. total pressure. The desired terminal compositions, in units of mole fraction ethanol, are $x_D = 0.92$ and $x_W = 0.07$; the feed is a saturated vapor and a total condenser is employed. When the reflux flow rate L_{n+1} is chosen as $4D$, find the number of plates required.

First step in solving this problem is to solve for W and D. Combining Eqs. (13-43) and (13-44) and substituting known values gives

$$Fz_F = Dx_D + (F - D)x_W$$
$$(100)(0.65) = D(0.92) + (100 - D)(0.07)$$

Solving, $D = 68.2$ moles/hr. By Eq. (13-43), $W = F - D = 100 - 68.2$ or 31.8 moles/hr. The internal flows are now readily computed. By Eq. (13-45), $V_n = L_{n+1} + D = 4D + D = 272.8 + 68.2 = 341.0$. By Eq. (13-51), $L_{m+1} = L_{n+1} = 272.8$; $V_m = V_n - F = 341.0 - 100 = 241.0$. Substituting known values into Eqs. (13-47) and (13-49) gives the operating-line equations. For the rectifying section,

$$y_n = (272.8/341.0)x_{n+1} + (68.2/341.0)(0.92)$$
$$y_n = 0.800x_{n+1} + 0.184$$

For the stripping section,

$$y_{m+1} = (272.8/241.0)x_{m+1} - (31.8/241.0)(0.07)$$
$$y_{m+1} = 1.132x_{m+1} - 0.0092$$

The two operating-line equations are plotted on a y-x diagram as shown in Fig. 13-27. Inherent in this plot is the fact that the rectifying operating line crosses the diagonal at $x = x_D$, whereas the stripping operating line crosses the diagonal at $x = x_W$.

Vapor-liquid equilibrium relationships for this system are available from Table 13-2. Using Eq. (13-5), equilibrium values of y and x are also plotted onto Fig. 13-27. The number of plates required is one less than the number of "steps" drawn in the manner shown on the figure between the operating lines and the equilibrium curve between the limits of x_W and x_D. The proof of this is as follows:

Suppose the stepwise procedure is started at the reboiler where $x = x_W$. By proceeding vertically upward from x_w to the equilibrium curve, a value is found for y_w, the composition of the vapor generated by the reboiler. Now by proceeding horizontally from y_w to the stripping operating line, a value may be determined for x_1, the composition of the liquid leaving the bottom tray of the column, tray 1. It is assumed that the liquid on each tray is perfectly mixed so that the composition of the liquid on the tray is the same as the liquid leaving the tray. It is now possible to move vertically upward from x_1 to the equilibrium curve to find y_1, the composition of the vapor generated by the boiling liquid on tray 1 (assumed to have a composition x_1). The next step is to move horizontally from y_1 to the operating line to find x_2, then to move upward from x_2 to the equilibrium curve to find y_2 (the vapor generated from the boiling liquid on tray 2). It is obvious that the first "step" in the graphical construction corresponds to the reboiler, and that each subsequent step represents a tray in the column. The stepwise procedure is continued as shown in Fig. 13-27 until the desired overhead product composition x_D is reached; in the present case, eight trays and the reboiler are required for the proposed separation.

In addition to the assumptions of equal molar overflow and perfect mixing of the liquid on each tray, the McCabe-Thiele method assumes that the vapor from the reboiler and from each tray is in true equilibrium with the liquid from which it is generated. The method thus predicts the number of **theoretical trays.** As shown later (p. 13-51), an efficiency factor must be employed to account for deviations from the assumed perfect gas-liquid contacting and perfect liquid mixing.

Effect of Thermal Condition of Feed and Reflux Streams. Introduction of the feed stream affects the flow rates of vapor and liquid above and below the feed tray. If the feed is a saturated liquid or a saturated vapor and equal molal overflow applies, the flows above and below the feed are simply related by Eqs. (13-50) and (13-51).

In the general case, the feed may vary from a subcooled liquid to a superheated vapor; this requires use of material and enthalpy balances for calculation of the relationship between the flows above and below the feed point. Let q be defined as the heat required to bring one mole of feed to the feed-plate temperature and to vaporize it, divided by the molal latent heat of vaporization of the feed. Then if equal molal overflow applies, the liquid flow below and above the feed is related by

$$q = \frac{L_{m+1} - L_{n+1}}{F} \qquad (13\text{-}52)$$

As an example, consider a liquid feed which is 40°F. below the feed-tray temperature. If the heat capacity of the liquid feed is 30 B.t.u./(lb.-mole)(°F.), and the latent heat of vaporization of the feed is 9000 B.t.u./lb.-mole, the value of $q = [(30)(40) + 9000]/9000 = 1.13$. If the feed rate is 100 lb.-moles/hr., the liquid-flow rate in the column below the feed tray L_{m+1} is $(1.13)(100) = 113$ moles/hr. greater than the corresponding flow above the feed; thus 13 moles/hr. of the vapor entering the feed tray condense in the liquid so that its latent heat of condensation will raise the 100 moles/hr. of cold feed to the boiling point. The liquid in passing down through the feed tray then picks up not only the 100 moles/hr. of feed but the 13 moles/hr. of condensed vapor, and the vapor flow above the feed is 13 moles/hr. less than that below the feed. In a second example, consider a vapor feed which is 50°F. above the feed-tray temperature. Let the heat capacity of the vapor feed be 14 B.t.u./(lb.-mole)(°F.) and the latent heat of vaporization be 9000 B.t.u./lb.-mole. In this instance

$$q = \frac{[(14)(-50)]}{9000} = -0.078$$

and with $F = 100$ the value of $L_{m+1} - L_{n+1} = -7.8$; *i.e.*, the liquid flow above the feed is 7.8 moles/hr. greater than that below the feed. The physical interpretation is that in order to cool the superheated vapor by 50°F. it is necessary to evaporate 7.8 moles/hr. of the liquid entering the feed tray from the tray above; the vapor flow above the feed is then 107.8 moles/hr. greater than the vapor flow below the feed.

If the reflux stream enters the top tray of the column below the top-tray temperature, some of the vapor reaching the top tray condenses in the liquid to supply the sensible heat needed to raise the reflux to the boiling point. The required calculations are similar to those made for the case of cold feed.

In using the McCabe-Thiele procedure for determining the number of theoretical plates, it is convenient to relate the point where the upper and lower operating lines intersect to the composition and thermal condition of the feed. If the two operating lines intersect at x_i, y_i, then by Eqs. (13-46) and (13-49),

$$V_n y_i = L_{n+1}x_i + Dx_D$$
$$V_m y_i = L_{m+1}x_i - Wx_W$$

Subtracting the first equation from the second, substituting $Fz_F = Wx_W + Dx_D$, and rearranging gives

$$\frac{(V_m - V_n)y_i}{F} = \frac{(L_{m+1} - L_{n+1})x_i}{F} - z_F$$

However, $(L_{m+1} - L_{n+1})/F = q$, and $(V_m - V_n)/F = q - 1$; making the substitutions and rearranging gives

$$y_i = \frac{q}{q-1} x_i - \frac{z_F}{q-1} \qquad (13\text{-}53)$$

Equation (13-53) is the locus of all possible intersection points of the rectifying and stripping operating lines; it is a straight line passing through the point $y = x = z_F$ with slope $q/(q - 1)$.

Figure 13-28 shows the effects of various thermal conditions of the feed upon the intersections of the operating lines. A constant L/V ratio is employed in the rectifying section represented by the operating line $AC_1C_2C_3C_4C_5$. The lines MC_1, MC_2, MC_3, MC_4, and MC_5 are plots of Eq. (13-53) for several different values of q:

MC_1: Feed is a liquid below the boiling point, $q > 1$, $q/(q - 1) > 1$.

MC_2: Feed is a liquid at the boiling point, $q = 1$, $q/(q - 1) = \infty$.

MC_3: Feed is partly vaporized, q is between 0 and 1, $q/(q - 1)$ is negative.

Mc_4: Feed is a saturated vapor, $q = 0$, $q/(q - 1) = 0$.

Mc_5: Feed is a superheated vapor, q is negative, $q/(q - 1)$ is between 0 and 1.

Figure 13-28 shows that for the chosen L/V ratio in the rectifying section, the L/V ratio in the stripping section decreases the colder the feed. For a given separation this reduces the tray requirements but increases the steam consumption in the reboiler.

Minimum Reflux Ratio. Suppose a **reflux ratio** L/D is chosen such that the rectifying operating line in Fig. 13-28 is AC_3. If the bottoms composition is x_W,

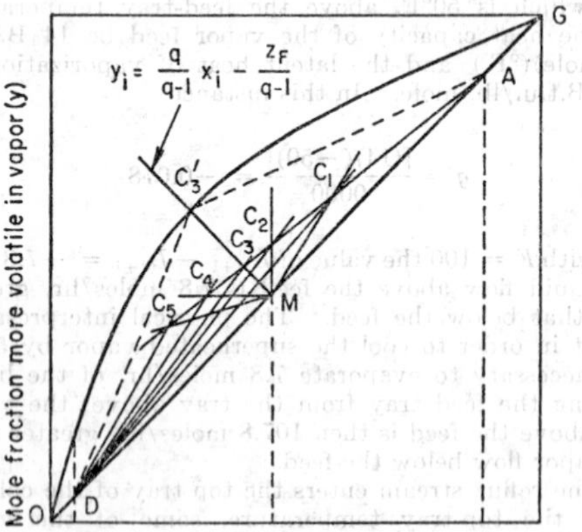

FIG. 13-28. Effect of thermal condition of the feed upon intersections of the operating lines and upon minimum reflux ratio.

the stripping operating line will then be C_3D. The number of theoretical plates required can then be stepped off as described previously. Actually, reflux ratios smaller than that just chosen would permit the same separation to be made; the point x_i, y_i would move toward C_3' as the reflux ratio is decreased. This procedure causes the number of theoretical plates to increase and when x_i, y_i reaches C_3' the number of theoretical plates becomes infinite. As a further reduction in reflux ratio will not permit the desired values of x_D and x_W to be achieved, the operating line AC_3' describes the condition of **minimum reflux.** In the general case, a straight line from x_D to the point where the "locus line" or "q line" [*i.e.*, Eq. (13-53)] intersects the equilibrium curve is the operating line corresponding to minimum reflux conditions. The slope of the operating line L/V may be read from the graph from which L/D is computed as $(L/V)/[1 - (L/V)]$, or it may be computed directly by the equation

$$(L/D)_{\min} = \frac{x_D - y_c}{y_c - x_c} \qquad (13\text{-}54)$$

where the point x_c, y_c is the point of intersection between the q line and the equilibrium curve. If the equilibrium relationships are such that as the reflux ratio is decreased the operating line becomes tangent to the equilibrium curve before it reaches the point x_c, y_c, then the tangent operating line represents the limit of column operability and its slope is $(L/V)_{\min}$.

Total Reflux. As the intersection point of the two operating lines moves from point C_3 in Fig. 13-28 along the q line toward point M, the L/V ratio approaches unity and L/D approaches infinity. This total-reflux condition is achieved if the amounts of feed, distillate, and bottoms are reduced to zero; or it can be approached if the amount of reflux is extremely large compared with the amounts of feed, distillate, and bottoms. At total reflux, the *number of theoretical plates is a minimum* and $L = V$ for all plates in the column.

Selection of Reflux Ratio and Degree of Feed Preheat. At reflux ratios approaching the minimum, the number of plates is extremely large, meaning a tall and costly column. At reflux ratios close to total reflux, the number of plates is near the minimum but vapor and liquid flows within the column are extremely large per mole of distillate; at this extreme condition the costs of reboiler, condenser, steam, and cooling water are large and the column diameter must be large to handle the large vapor flow. Sound design practice thus requires choice of a reflux ratio between the extremes of minimum reflux ratio and total reflux, at an intermediate value where the total fixed investment costs and operating costs reach a minimum. As thermal condition of the feed affects column flow rates and steam requirements, this variable must be included in the economic analysis. **Optimum reflux ratio** for a wide variety of cases is shown by Happel to be seldom more than 1.3 times $(L/D)_{\min}$ [*Chem. Eng.*, **65** (14), 144 (1958)]; values of L/D much less than $1.3(L/D)_{\min}$ are not commonly employed because product compositions change greatly with small but unforeseen changes in reflux flow in a column operating close to the minimum reflux point.

Optimum Feed-tray Location. When steps are drawn between the operating lines and equilibrium curve to determine the number of theoretical plates on a McCabe-Thiele diagram, the last step on the stripping operating line locates the liquid composition on the feed tray. The feed tray is the tray to which liquid feed is added or above which vapor feed is added. Three possible feed-tray locations are shown in Figs. 13-29, 13-30, and 13-31, but the optimum location, that which gives the fewest number of theoretical trays, is that shown in Fig. 13-30. Thus the feed tray should always be chosen by the designer as that step which straddles the intersection point of the two operating lines y_i, x_i. Column performance will be less than optimum when the feed is introduced onto a non-optimum feed tray, as in Fig. 13-29 or 13-31; if possibilities exist for changing the feed point to the optimum location, this should be done in

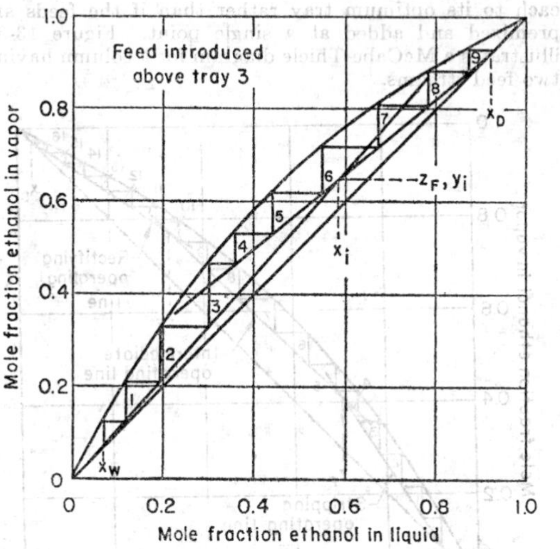

FIG. 13-29. Solution to example when feed is introduced above tray 3; nine theoretical trays required.

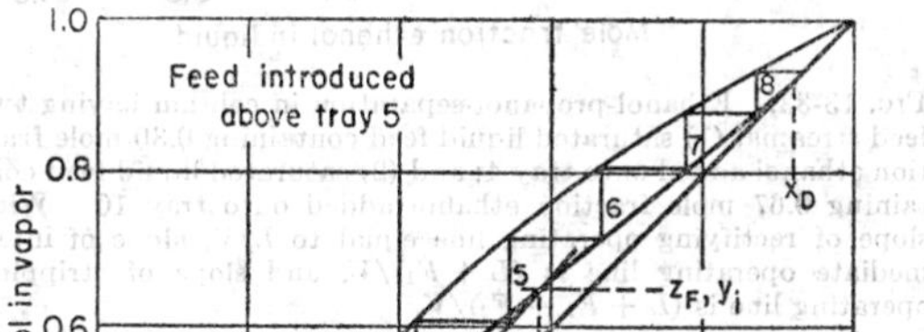

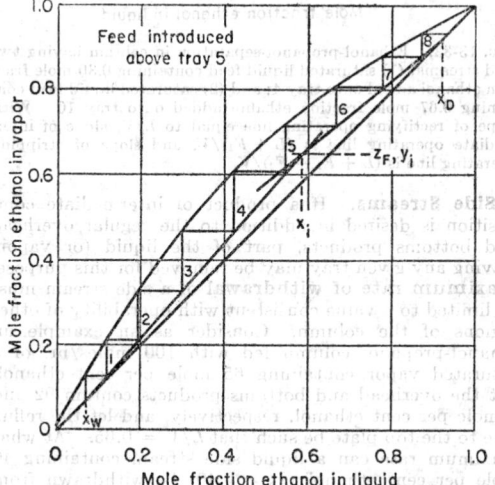

FIG. 13-30. Solution to example when feed is introduced above tray 5 (optimum feed-tray location); eight theoretical trays required.

order to achieve the maximum possible separation with the number of trays available.

Summary of McCabe-Thiele Design Procedure. Assume that a binary plate column is to be designed for which the McCabe-Thiele assumptions listed on p. 13-22 are known to apply. Design conditions usually specified in advance are feed rate, feed composition, thermal condition of feed, and desired composition of overhead and bottoms products. The usual steps in the design procedure are as follows:

1. Choose the operating pressure. Usually this is chosen so that the overhead vapors can be condensed by ordinary cooling water. Vacuum operation may be required if the substances are heat-sensitive or if reboiler temperatures are too high for the available heating medium.
2. Compute D and W by Eqs. (13-43) and (13-44).
3. Plot equilibrium relationships on y-x diagram.
4. Plot q line as given by Eq. (13-53) on y-x diagram.
5. Determine minimum reflux ratio by Eq. (13-54); use an operating reflux ratio of about $1.3(L/D)_{\min}$.
6. Draw rectifying operating line [Eq. (13-47)] at chosen reflux ratio on y-x diagram; then connect the point x_i, y_i with the point where x_w intersects the diagonal line to obtain the stripping operating line [Eq. (13-49)].
7. Determine number of theoretical plates by drawing in steps as illustrated in Fig. 13-27.

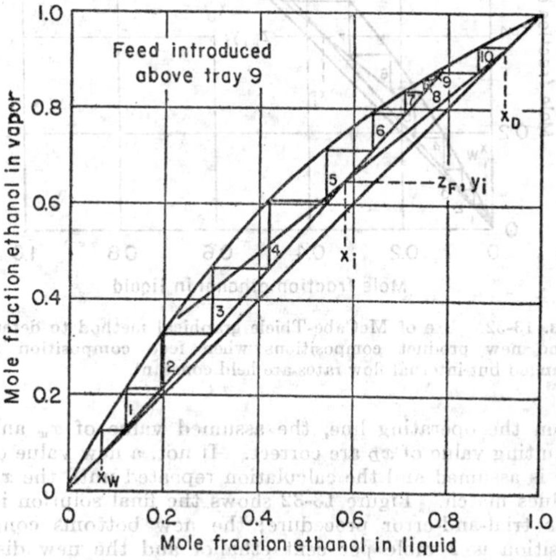

FIG. 13-31. Solution to example when feed is introduced above tray 9; 10 theoretical trays required.

Use of McCabe-Thiele Diagram in Column Operations. The procedures described can also be used to predict the effect of changes in feed and in operating conditions upon the compositions of the products from an existing column; and they can be used to compute the changes in vapor boil-up and in reflux rate which are required to maintain optimum product compositions when feed conditions vary.

Consider, for example, the ethanol-propanol separation described on p. 13-22; feed is a saturated vapor containing 65 mole per cent ethanol, and products of 7 and 92 per cent purity are obtained in an atmospheric-pressure column containing five theoretical plates below and $2\frac{1}{2}$ theoretical plates above the feed with $L/D = 4/1$. Suppose this column has been operating as designed, but composition of the saturated-vapor feed will be changed to 40 mole per cent ethanol. Compute for the new case the composition of the products from the column if the amount of vapor from the reboiler and the amount of reflux returned to the column are unchanged; compute also the changes which should be made in the flows of these two streams to maintain the original separation.

In the instance where the flow rates are unchanged, there are no changes in the slopes of the stripping operating line, which is $L_{m+1}/V_m = 1.132$, or the rectifying operating line, which is $L_{n+1}/V_n = 0.800$. Therefore, on a McCabe-Thiele diagram as shown in Fig. 13-32, first locate the new q line, then plot the stripping operating line at an assumed value for x_W. The rectifying operating line is now drawn from point x_i, y_i with a slope of 0.800; intersection of this operating line with the diagonal gives a trial value for x_D. Next, 6 stripping steps and $2\frac{1}{2}$ rectifying steps are drawn starting at the assumed value for x_w. If the composition x_D arrived at by this procedure matches the trial value obtained

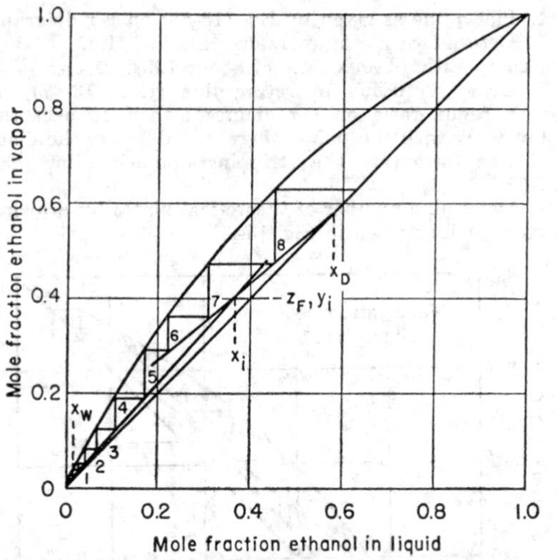

FIG. 13-32. Use of McCabe-Thiele graphical method to determine new product compositions when feed composition is changed but internal flow rates are held constant.

from the operating line, the assumed value of x_w and resulting value of x_D are correct. If not, a new value of x_W is assumed and the calculation repeated until the x_D values match. Figure 13-32 shows the final solution in this trial-and-error procedure; the new bottoms composition is 2 mole per cent ethanol and the new distillate composition is 58 per cent.

To compute the operating changes required to bring the product compositions back to $x_D = 0.92$ and $x_W = 0.07$ via the McCabe-Thiele diagram, draw a stripping operating line with an assumed slope from a point on the diagonal where $x_W = 0.07$; connect point x_i, y_i with the point on the diagonal where $x_D = 0.92$ to obtain the rectifying operating line. Draw in the fixed number of steps and check to determine if x_D obtained this way equals the desired value; if not, continue assuming values for L_{m+1}/V_m until a match is obtained. The solution for L/V in the stripping section is 1.18, while the corresponding value for the rectifying section is 0.913. At these new conditions the moles of vapor generated by the reboiler must be increased, and the moles of reflux must also be increased. As the new flow rates are the only ones which will maintain the same product compositions at the new feed condition, it is obvious that any automatic control scheme for the column must include provisions for changing both the reflux and boil-up flows.

Open Steam. Computations on binary columns with unusual design features are readily handled when McCabe-Thiele procedures apply. When the bottoms product of a column is water containing a small amount of the overhead component, the source of vapor for the column may be steam taken directly from the steam supply line. The reboiler is eliminated, and the liquid from the bottom plate is the bottoms product. Such a column is said to operate with open steam. The usual stripping operating line [Eq. (13-49)] applies as before, but the coordinates of the starting point for the stepwise calculation are $x = x_w$ and $y = 0$. Use of open steam eliminates investment cost for the reboiler but requires about one additional theoretical tray in the column.

Multiple Feeds. When feed streams of different compositions are to be processed in a single binary column, best separation results if the feeds are added each to its optimum tray rather than if the feeds are premixed and added at a single point. Figure 13-33 illustrates a McCabe-Thiele diagram for a column having two feed streams.

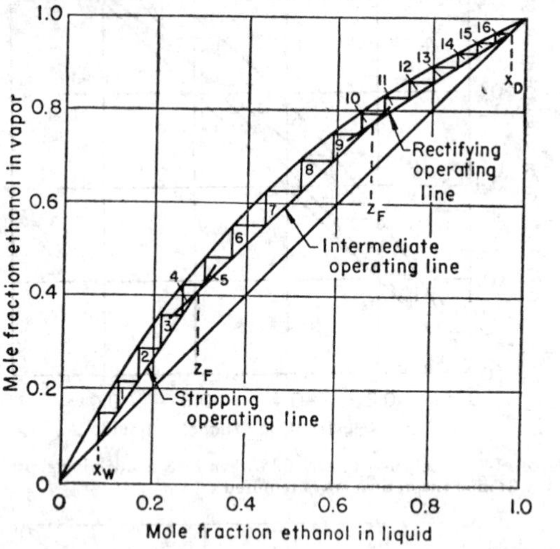

FIG. 13-33. Ethanol-propanol separation in column having two feed streams: (1) saturated liquid feed containing 0.30 mole fraction ethanol added onto tray 4; and (2) saturated liquid feed containing 0.67 mole fraction ethanol added onto tray 10. With slope of rectifying operating line equal to L/V, slope of intermediate operating line is $(L + F_1)/V$, and slope of stripping operating line is $(L + F_1 + F_2)/V$.

Side Streams. If a product of intermediate composition is desired in addition to the regular overhead and bottoms products, part of the liquid (or vapor) leaving any given tray may be removed for this purpose. **Maximum rate of withdrawal** of a side stream must be limited to a value consistent with operability of other regions of the column. Consider as an example an ethanol-propanol column fed with 100 moles/hr. of a saturated vapor containing 65 mole per cent ethanol. Let the overhead and bottoms products contain 92 and 7 mole per cent ethanol, respectively, and let the reflux rate to the top plate be such that $L/V = 0.65$. At what maximum rate can a liquid side stream containing 40 mole per cent ethanol ($x_S = 0.40$) be withdrawn from this column?

Solution is shown in Fig. 13-34. The operating lines for the column sections above and below the side stream have slopes equal to L/V and intersect on the vertical line $x_S = 0.40$. As the vapor rate in these two sections is constant, withdrawal rate is at a maximum when L/V above the side stream has a maximum value and L/V below the side stream has a minimum value. The dashed lines in Fig. 13-34 show that the maximum operating-line slope above the side stream is 2.4 whereas the minimum slope below the side stream is 1.0, a condition yielding zero moles of bottoms. Under this limiting condition the over-all material balance is

$$F = D + S$$

where S = moles/hr. of side stream, and the over-all component balance is

$$Fz_F = Dx_D + Sx_S$$

These equations show 52 moles/hr. of side stream and 48 moles/hr. of overhead. Obviously to have a finite amount of bottoms, the side-stream withdrawal rate must be less than the maximum value of 52 moles/hr. The minimum rate of side-stream withdrawal is zero, as indicated by the dotted operating line in Fig. 13-34.

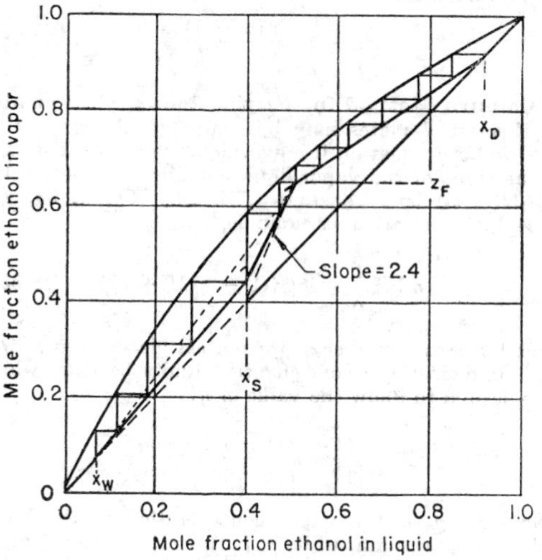

FIG. 13-34. Solution to problem containing side stream.

Operating lines for an intermediate case where the side-stream withdrawal rate is 42 moles/hr. are shown in the same figure as solid lines. In this instance the material and component balances are

$$F = W + D + S$$
$$Fz_F = Wx_W + Dx_D + Sx_S$$

which give, when solved simultaneously, $W = 6$ and $D = 52$. With L/V at the top of the column fixed at 0.65, fixing the side-stream withdrawal rate fixes the location of the two lower operating lines: L and V above the feed are 96.6 and 148.6 moles/hr., respectively; with 100 moles/hr. of vapor feed, L and V below the feed are 96.6 and 48.6 moles/hr., respectively; and with 42 moles/hr. of side stream, L and V below the withdrawal point are 54.6 and 48.6 moles/hr., respectively. Values other than 0.65 may be chosen for L/V at the top of the column and the same side-stream withdrawal rate of 42 moles/hr. may still be obtained; in such an instance the two lower operating lines will have different slopes which are readily computed as above.

Unequal Molal Overflow in Binary Columns. Many industrial distillations lack the necessary conditions for achieving equal molal overflow. As discussed previously (p. 13-22), **enthalpy-balance equations** are required in addition to material-balance relationships to describe completely the composition changes in such separations.

Consider the continuous column operating as shown in Fig. 13-26. Let h_F be the enthalpy of the feed, h_D the enthalpy of the distillate, and h_W the enthalpy of the bottoms product, all expressed as B.t.u./(lb.-mole). If Q_C is the heat removed by the condenser per hour, and Q_S is the heat added by the reboiler per hour, and if there are no heat losses from the system, an over-all enthalpy balance gives

$$Fh_F = Dh_D + Wh_W + Q_c - Q_S \qquad (13\text{-}55)$$

Again neglecting heat losses, the corresponding equations for the sections bounded by dotted lines II and III in Fig. 13-26 are as follows:

$$V_nH_n = L_{n+1}h_{n+1} + Dh_D + Q_c \qquad (13\text{-}56)$$
$$L_{m+1}h_{m+1} = V_mH_m + Wh_W - Q_s \qquad (13\text{-}57)$$

where H_n and H_m are saturated vapor enthalpies, B.t.u./(lb.-mole), and h_{n+1} and h_{m+1} are saturated liquid enthalpies, B.t.u./(lb.-mole). Defining Q' as $h_D + Q_c/D$ and combining Eqs. (13-45), (13-46), and (13-56), the operating-line relationship for the rectifying section is

$$y_n = \frac{Q' - H_n}{Q' - h_{n+1}} x_{n+1} + \frac{H_n - h_{n+1}}{Q' - h_{n+1}} x_D \qquad (13\text{-}58)$$

while combination of Eqs. (13-48), (13-49), and (13-57) along with the definition of Q'' as $h_w - Q_s/W$ gives the corresponding operating-line equation for the stripping section:

$$y_m = \frac{Q'' - H_m}{Q'' - h_{m+1}} x_{m+1} + \frac{H_m - h_{m+1}}{Q'' - h_{m+1}} x_w \qquad (13\text{-}59)$$

In the usual design or operating situation, all terms in Eq. (13-55) are known except Q_c and Q_s; Q_c (and Q') are readily computed, however, from knowledge of the reflux and distillate rates and the enthalpies of the reflux, distillate, and vapor to the condenser. Equation (13-55) thus permits ready calculation of Q_S (and Q'').

The operating-line equations (13-58) and (13-59) may be plotted on a y-x (McCabe-Thiele) diagram as follows: Assume several values of x_{n+1} and x_{m+1} at which it is desired to know the corresponding values of y_n and y_m. From the chosen values of x_{n+1} and x_{m+1} it is possible to evaluate the corresponding values of h_{n+1} and h_{m+1}. Working first with Eq. (13-58), two unknowns remain: y_n and H_n. It is necessary to assume a value for y_n, evaluate the corresponding vapor enthalpy H_n, and then determine if the assumed values satisfy Eq. (13-58). After a correct value of y_n is found for each chosen value of x_{n+1}, a similar procedure is followed to determine the correct values of y_m using Eq. (13-59). Operating-line points are then plotted on the y-x diagram and connected with smooth curves, and plates are stepped off in the usual manner.

A direct solution is obtained for the corresponding values of y and x between plates of a column if Eqs. (13-58) and (13-59) are solved graphically on an enthalpy-concentration diagram. The procedure was first developed by **Ponchon and Savarit** and is given in good detail by Robinson and Gilliland (*op. cit.*). This type of diagram is also useful in determining minimum reflux for columns having unequal molal overflow.

In some cases unequal molal overflow is due only to a difference in the latent heats of vaporization of the two components. If the latent heat of each component is fairly independent of temperature so that the ratio of the latent heats for the two components may be approximated as a constant, a **simple modification** permits the conventional McCabe-Thiele procedures to be employed. The modification consists of using a fictitious molecular weight for one of the components to force the molar latent heats of vaporization to be equal. When molar flows and compositions are recomputed on this new basis, the equal-molal-overflow calculation procedures may be employed without loss of precision.

Analytical Equations. The use of analytical equations rather than graphical procedures for computing tray requirements is somewhat limited because of the difficulties involved in expressing non-ideal vapor-liquid equilibrium relationships with simple enough equations. Operating-line relationships are also difficult to express mathematically when unequal molal overflow is present. However, tray requirements may be computed analytically over small concentration ranges of non-ideal columns where the operating line is reasonably straight and where the equilibrium curve can be approximated by a straight line or by a constant relative volatility. These procedures are especially useful for determining tray requirements in high-purity regions of a column where graphical methods require considerable enlargement of the y-x diagram. Analytical equations for binary mixtures are available for cases of (1) total reflux and constant relative volatility α; (2) partial reflux, constant α, and equal molal overflow; and (3) partial reflux, linear vapor-liquid equilibrium relationship, and equal molal overflow.

Total Reflux. When a plate column is operated under total reflux conditions, and relative volatility α is constant, the number of theoretical plates n which are required to change the composition ratio of two components on a lower plate $(x_1/x_2)_o$ to a value on an upper plate of $(x_1/x_2)_p$ is given by

$$n \log \alpha = \log \left[\frac{(x_1/x_2)_p}{(x_1/x_2)_o}\right] \tag{13-60}$$

In this expression component 1 is the more volatile of the two components. Equation (13-60) is known as the **Fenske-Underwood equation** [for derivation see *Ind. Eng. Chem.*, **24**, 482 (1932)]. If α varies over the column, Eq. (13-60) may be successively applied to small sections of the column over which α is reasonably constant.

Underwood Method for Partial Reflux. If a binary separation is being carried out at partial reflux under conditions where α is constant and equal molal overflow applies, the equations of Underwood may be used to compute tray requirements [*J. Inst. Petrol.*, **29**, 147 (1943); **30**, 225 (1944)]. The equations are applied first to one section of the column and then to the other.

First step is to solve for the two points of intersection between a given operating line, $y = (L/V)x + b$, and the equilibrium curve by means of the relation

$$\left[\frac{L}{V}(\alpha - 1)\right]k^2 + \left[\frac{L}{V} + b(\alpha - 1) - \alpha\right]k + b = 0 \tag{13-61}$$

Equation (13-61) is a quadratic equation having two roots which are designated as k_1, the lower intersection point, and k_2, the upper. For the rectifying operating line, k_1 will lie between 0 and 1, while k_2 will be greater than unity; for the stripping operating line, k_1 will be negative while k_2 will lie between 0 and 1.

The number of theoretical plates n between any two points x_o and x_p on a given operating line is computed by the following equation:

$$n \log \frac{\alpha/(L/V)}{[1 + (\alpha - 1)k_1]^2} = \log \frac{(x_p - k_1)(k_2 - x_o)}{(x_o - k_1)(k_2 - x_p)} \tag{13-62}$$

where x_o is the liquid composition on a lower plate while x_p is the liquid composition on an upper plate. When Eq. (13-62) is applied to the rectifying section, x_o will usually be taken as x_i, the intersection point of the two operating lines, and x_p will usually be taken as x_D; when Eq. (13-62) is applied to the stripping section, x_o will usually be taken as x_W and x_p will be taken as x_i.

If the distillate is of extremely high purity, then values of x_D (which is x_p) and k_2 (which is the upper intersection point) are very nearly the same and the exact magnitude of the term $(k_2 - x_p)$ in Eq. (13-62) will be difficult to determine accurately. In such an instance the expression

$$k_2 - x_p = \frac{(\alpha - 1)\delta}{(L/V)(\alpha) - 1} \tag{13-63}$$

should be used with δ taken as $1 - x_D$. Similar difficulty is experienced when x_W (which is x_o) is nearly zero because k_1 (the lower intersection point) is only slightly below zero. In this instance the term $(x_o - k_1)$ should be evaluated by

$$x_o - k_1 = \frac{(\alpha - 1)x_W}{\alpha - (L/V)} \tag{13-64}$$

Colburn Method for Partial Reflux. The number of theoretical plates may be computed analytically by the Colburn equation if equal molal overflow exists and if the slope of the vapor-liquid equilibrium relationship $dy/dx(= m)$ is a constant [*Ind. Eng. Chem.*, **33**, 459 (1941)]. For enriching columns,

$$n \log \frac{1}{\lambda} = \log [(1 - \lambda)M + \lambda] \tag{13-65a}$$

where n is the number of theoretical plates, $\lambda = mV/L$, and M defines the concentration limits between which it is desired to know the value of n:

$$M = \frac{(1 - y_o) - m(1 - x_p)}{(1 - y_p) - m(1 - x_p)}$$

The term y_o is the vapor concentration at the lower point in the column, while y_p is the vapor concentration at the upper point in the column; x_p is the operating-line point corresponding to y_p. If the upper point is chosen as the top of the column and if a total condenser is used, $y_p = x_p = x_D$.

For stripping columns,

$$n \log \lambda = \log\left(M - \frac{M - 1}{\lambda}\right) \tag{13-65b}$$

When Eq. (13-65b) is used for stripping columns employing an ordinary reboiler,

$$M = \frac{x_p - x_o/m}{x_o - x_o/m}$$

where x_o is the liquid concentration at the lower point in the column (usually taken as x_W) and x_p is the liquid concentration at the upper point in the column. For stripping columns employing open steam,

$$M = \frac{x_p}{x_o}$$

Continuous Binary Distillation in Packed Columns. The initial calculation procedures for determining design, performance, and operational characteristics of packed columns are the same as those described in previous pages for plate columns; *i.e.*, the equilibrium curve and operating-line relationships are first established. In the case of a packed column, the operating line describes the relationship between y and x, the actual vapor and liquid compositions at any elevation in the column, but the equations are identical to those used to describe the relationship between values of y and x between any pair of adjacent plates in a plate column.

Because vapor and liquid compositions change differentially in a packed column, rather than in a stepwise fashion as in a plate column, the difficulty of the separation to be accomplished is characterized in terms of **transfer units** rather than theoretical plates. The significance and derivation of the transfer-unit concept is given in Sec. 14, p. 14-19. The number of transfer units N_{OG} can be obtained by graphically integrating the following equation:

$$N_{OG} = \int_{y_o}^{y_p} \frac{dy}{y^* - y} \qquad (13\text{-}66)$$

The procedure involves plotting values of $1/(y^* - y)$ vs. assumed values of y chosen at reasonable intervals between y_o and y_p, the lower and upper concentrations in the column between which it is desired to know N_{OG}. Each value of y^* is the equilibrium vapor composition corresponding to the same value of x as each chosen value of y.

Alternatively, transfer units may be evaluated by a modified stepwise procedure as described in Sec. 14, p. 14-29. For cases of total reflux and mixtures of constant relative volatility α, a convenient analytical solution was given by Chilton and Colburn [*Ind. Eng. Chem.*, **27**, 205 (1935)] as follows:

$$N_{OG} = \frac{2.3}{\alpha - 1} \log \frac{y_p(1 - y_o)}{y_o(1 - y_p)} + 2.3 \log \frac{(1 - y_o)}{(1 - y_p)} \qquad (13\text{-}67)$$

This equation is particularly useful in interpreting data on column testing with an ideal mixture.

Although use of transfer units is often more exact than use of theoretical plates for packed-column design, a given packed column can be said to be equivalent to a column having a certain number of theoretical plates. Indeed, if the term mV/L (ratio of slope of equilibrium curve to slope of operating line) is unity, a transfer unit and a theoretical plate become identical (see Sec. 14, p. 14-19); if mV/L lies between 0.9 and 1.1, the difference between a transfer unit and a theoretical plate is insignificant. Thus for tall packed columns where the separations are difficult and the operating lines are nearly parallel to the equilibrium curve, theoretical plates may be used to characterize the separation obtained.

In distillation work, the number of transfer units is usually calculated as N_{OG}; *i.e.*, it is based upon gas-composition changes, even though considerable transfer resistance lies in the liquid phase. Additional discussion and examples of the transfer-unit concept in packed-column distillation are given by Chilton and Colburn [*Ind. Eng. Chem.*, **27**, 255 (1935)] and Colburn [*Trans. Am. Inst. Chem. Engrs.*, **35**, 211, 587 (1939); *Ind. Eng. Chem.*, **33**, 459 (1941)].

Required height of packing for a given design is obtained by multiplying the number of transfer units or theoretical plates by the height of packing equivalent to a transfer unit or theoretical plate. Values of **H.T.U.** (height of a transfer unit) or **H.E.T.P.** (height equivalent to a theoretical plate) are given in Sec. 18. Because experimental data often have to be extended, it is helpful to list the effects of the controlling variables. Increasing liquid rate causes values of H.T.U. to decrease, but the effect of gas rate is minor. Increased temperature causes H.T.U. values to decrease, but the effect of pressure is small or negligible, except for its effect upon the boiling temperature. The smaller the particle size of packing the greater the surface area; thus one would expect lower values of H.T.U. In general such is the case, although the effect is not direct. The through-put capacity for very small packings is too low to make them very useful for large-scale operations.

There is considerable uncertainty regarding the **effect of column diameter.** It is generally believed that, owing to poorer liquid distribution, values of H.T.U. become less favorable for a given packing the larger the diameter of the column. In general, values of H.T.U. are found to become slightly less favorable for greater heights of packing, possibly because of progressive maldistribution effects. It is usually considered good practice to install liquid redistributors every 10 ft. of packed height.

BATCH BINARY DISTILLATION

In **batch rectification,** the equipment is the same as that used in continuous rectification: a reboiler, a column (usually packed or plate), and a condenser. However, operating procedures differ. In batch rectification, a batch of liquid is charged to the reboiler and the system is first brought to steady state under total reflux, after which an overhead product is continuously withdrawn. The entire column thus operates as an enriching section. Obviously as time proceeds the composition of the material being distilled becomes less rich in the more volatile component, and the distillation must be stopped after a certain time to attain a desired average composition and yield of the more volatile component in the overhead product.

Batch rectifications are commonly employed when the amount of material to be processed is small or when the batch components and compositions vary. Batch-rectification equipment usually does not employ so elaborate controls as continuous equipment but labor cost per unit of product may be greater.

Batch rectifications may be carried out in two ways:

1. *Constant Overhead Product Composition, Variable Reflux Ratio.* If it is desired to maintain a constant overhead product composition, the amount of reflux returned to the column must be constantly increased throughout the run. As time proceeds, the reboiler is gradually depleted of the lighter component, and the increased difference in composition between the bottom and top of the column makes the required separation constantly more difficult to attain. Finally the point is reached at or near total reflux where the desired product

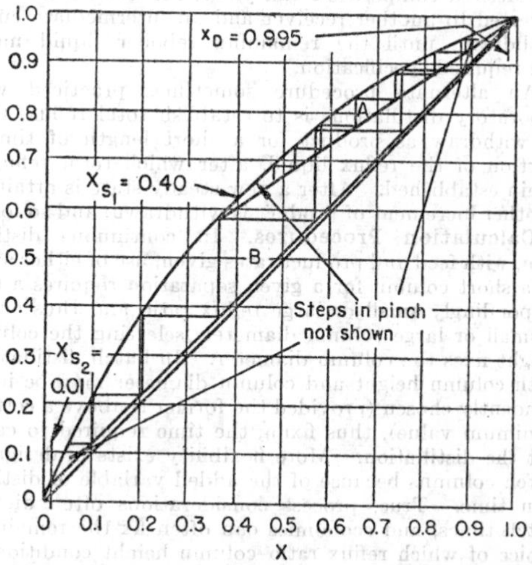

FIG. 13-35. Solution to problem on separation of benzene-toluene by batch distillation with constant overhead product composition.

composition can no longer be made; the overhead product, now the *intermediate cut*, is collected in a separate receiver. The distillation is terminated when the composition of more volatile component remaining in the reboiler has been reduced to the desired value. The intermediate cut, which will have an average composition similar to that of the original charge, is usually added to the next batch for further processing.

2. *Variable Overhead Product Composition, Constant Reflux Ratio.* This simpler type of operation is perhaps more common, as no changes in operation are required during the course of the run. In this case product compositions vary as shown in Fig. 13-36, the shapes of

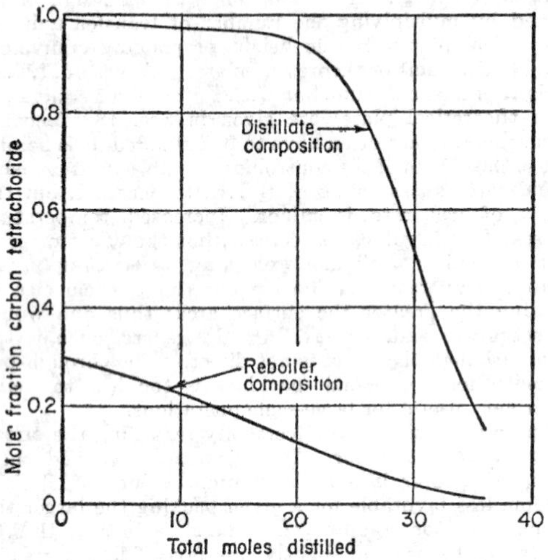

FIG. 13-36. Typical variation in distillate and reboiler compositions with amount distilled in batch distillation at constant reflux ratio (see example).

the curves being functions of relative volatility, reflux ratio, and number of plates. The distillation proceeds until the average composition of the distillate represents the desired composition and yield; the overhead is then diverted to another receiver and an intermediate cut is withdrawn until the remaining reboiler liquid meets the required specification.

An alternate procedure sometimes practiced with laboratory distillations is to establish total reflux, then to withdraw as product for a short length of time a portion of the reflux liquid, after which total reflux is again established. After a new steady state is attained, another increment of product is withdrawn, and so forth.

Calculation Procedures. In continuous distillation, with feed and product rates given, use of either a tall or a short column for a given separation requires a correspondingly small or large reflux ratio and thus either a small or large column diameter; selecting the column height fixes the column diameter. In batch distillation, both column height and column diameter may be independently chosen (provided the former is above a certain minimum value), thus fixing the time required to carry out the distillation. More flexibility exists in design of batch columns because of the added variable of distillation time. True, process considerations often dictate batch times, and economics can often fix the remaining choice of which reflux ratio–column height condition to employ. But in many instances, an all-purpose batch-distillation unit of given height and diameter is available and the problem is to compute the time required to achieve the desired separation. Calculation procedures are given below for these various cases.

Because compositions within batch units are constantly changing with time, an added variable in the calculation procedures is the amount of **liquid hold-up** in the system. Since this variable complicates the calculations considerably, procedures are given first in which the effect of hold-up is neglected; in a later section more exact relationships are presented, along with conclusions as to the probable errors involved in neglecting hold-up.

Time Required for Batch Rectification with Constant Overhead Product Composition. Bogart [*Trans. Am. Inst. Chem. Engrs.*, **33,** 139 (1937)] developed the following equation for this situation assuming column hold-up to be negligible:

$$\theta_T = \frac{S_1(x_D - x_{S_1})}{V} \int_{x_{S_2}}^{x_{S_1}} \frac{dx}{(1 - L/V)(x_D - x)^2} \tag{13-68}$$

where θ_T = time of batch cycle, hr.; S_1 = initial batch charge, moles; S_2 = residue in reboiler at end of cycle, moles; x_D = fixed product composition, mole fraction; x_{S_1} = initial reboiler liquid composition, mole fraction; x_{S_2} = final reboiler liquid composition, mole fraction; x = instantaneous value of reboiler liquid composition, mole fraction; L = liquid downflow, moles/hr.; V = vapor flow, moles/hr.

Process and economic considerations usually fix S_1, x_{S_1}, x_D, and the yield (defined as the moles of more volatile component recovered in the overhead product); from this information, a material balance gives a value for S_2 and x_{S_2}. Equation (13-68) will then predict, for a column containing a fixed number of plates, either (1) the cycle time θ_T for a given vapor-flow rate; or (2) the required vapor-flow rate for a fixed cycle time.

As an example, consider a charge containing 40 moles of benzene and 60 moles of toluene which is to be rectified into an overhead product containing 99.5 mole per cent benzene with a 98.5 per cent benzene yield in the overhead product. If 18 theoretical plates are available in a column having a diameter of 3 ft., what is the cycle time?

From the conditions of the problem, the moles of benzene in overhead product are (40)(0.985) = 39.4 and the total moles of overhead product are 39.4/0.995 = 39.6. The composition of the reboiler liquid at the end of the distillation is x_{S_2} = (40 − 39.4)/(100 − 39.6) = 0.010 mole fraction benzene. Figure 13-35 shows the y-x diagram for benzene-toluene upon which a number of enriching-section operating lines are drawn from x_D = 0.995. By stepping off 18 theoretical plates, plus one added step for the reboiler, on each of these lines, successive values of the reboiler composition are obtained as the batch operation proceeds. (In Fig. 13-35, because of size limitations, only the initial and final lines designated as *A* and *B*, respectively, are shown.) By such graphical constructions it is possible to compile the following table:

L/V	x	$\frac{1}{(1 - L/V)(x_D - x)^2}$
0.636 (*A*)	0.400	7.75
0.713	0.270	6.62
0.782	0.180	6.93
0.840	0.120	8.20
0.915	0.050	13.2
0.969 (*B*)	0.010	33.4

By plotting values in the third column vs. x, it is possible to find the area under the curve graphically between limits of x_{S_2} = 0.01 and x_{S_1} = 0.40 as 3.41, which is the value of the integral in Eq. (13-68). It is next necessary to evaluate V; if the allowable vapor rate through the tower according to procedures outlined in Sec. 18 is 28.7 lb.-moles/(hr.)(sq. ft. of tower cross section), then $V = (28.7)(\pi)(3^2)/4 = 203$ moles/hr.

From Eq. (13-68), θ_T is found to be

$$\frac{(100)(0.995 - 0.400)(3.41)}{203} = 1 \text{ hr.}$$

[If the same separation is carried out in a continuous manner with the feed a liquid at the boiling point and a reflux ratio equal to 1.5 $(L/D)_{min}$, the required reboiler vapor would be 142 moles/100 moles of feed. Continuous operation is thus more economical, even overlooking the time required for charging, heating, pump-out, and cleaning in the batch case.]

Equation (13-68) shows that as the term $(1 - L/V)$ approaches zero the value of θ_T increases rapidly. As L/V is largest at the end of the run, the number of plates should be chosen so that, even at the end of the run, L/V is not too close to unity. The minimum number of plates should also be evaluated with an operating line under the worst condition, *i.e.*, at the end of the run.

Equation (13-68) may be directly integrated if the column is assumed to have infinite plates and if the relative volatility α is constant. The result, given below, often permits a useful approximation to be made, especially when the number of plates is large:

$$\theta_T = \frac{S_1(x_D - x_{S_1})}{V(\alpha - 1)} \left[\frac{2.3}{x_D} \log \frac{x_{S_1}(x_D - x_{S_2})}{x_{S_2}(x_D - x_{S_1})} + \frac{2.3}{1 - x_D} \log \frac{(1 - x_{S_1})(x_D - x_{S_2})}{(1 - x_{S_2})(x_D - x_{S_1})} \right] \quad (13\text{-}69)$$

Substitution of appropriate values from the above example (with $\alpha = 2.58$) gives a value of $\theta_T = 0.78$ hr.

Batch Rectification at Constant Reflux Ratio. Smoker and Rose [*Trans. Am. Inst. Chem. Engrs.*, **36,** 285 (1940)] have shown that the following equation applies for this case when column hold-up is negligible:

$$\ln \frac{S_1}{S_2} = \int_{x_{S_2}}^{x_{S_1}} \frac{dx_S}{x_D - x_S} \quad (13\text{-}70)$$

To illustrate use of this equation, consider a mixture of 100 moles of carbon tetrachloride and toluene containing 30 mole per cent CCl_4, the more volatile component, which is to be distilled at 1 atm. with a constant reflux ratio of $L/D = 9/1$ in a column containing six theoretical plates. (The reboiler acts as an additional perfect plate.) Desired average composition of the distillate is 97.4 mole per cent CCl_4 and desired average composition of the material in the reboiler at the end of the distillation is 1.0 mole per cent CCl_4. How many moles of each of these products will be obtained, and what will be the amount and composition of the intermediate fraction?

Using the vapor-liquid equilibrium data for this system from Table 13-3, plot a y-x diagram. Next, by trial, locate a rectifying operating line on this diagram which has a slope $= L/V = 9/10$ and which contains exactly seven theoretical steps between the known reboiler composition $x_{S_1} = 0.300$ and the distillate. The distillate composition x_D is thus found to be 0.990. Repeat the procedure with the reboiler composition taken as $x_{S_2} = 0.010$, at which condition x_D is found to be 0.150. The distillate composition will thus vary between 0.990 and 0.150 as the operation proceeds. Now choose intermediate values of x_D between these limiting values, and from knowledge of L/V and the number of steps available, determine from the y-x diagram the corresponding values of x_S. Now compute values of S_2 for each value of x_D via Eq. (13-70) as per the following table:

x_D	x_S	$\frac{1}{x_D - x_S}$	$\ln \frac{S_1}{S_2}$	S_2
0.990	0.300	1.450	.....	100.0
0.980	0.255	1.380	0.0637	93.8
0.970	0.182	1.269	0.159	85.1
0.960	0.162	1.251	0.184	83.0
0.950	0.137	1.232	0.216	80.6
0.900	0.104	1.255	0.257	77.5
0.750	0.065	1.460	0.308	73.5
0.550	0.040	1.960	0.349	70.5
0.400	0.028	2.69	0.377	68.5
0.250	0.016	4.27	0.416	65.9
0.150	0.010	7.15	0.448	64.0

Values of ln (S_1/S_2) are obtained by integrating Eq. (13-70) graphically between limits of each assumed value of x_S and $x_{S_1} = 0.300$; for example, when the distillation has proceeded to the point where $x_S = 0.104$, the area under the curve of $1/(x_D - x_S)$ vs. x_S between the limits of 0.104 and 0.300 is 0.257, which by Eq. (13-70) equals ln (S_1/S_2). A total material balance and a component material balance now permits the amount and composition of the two distillate fractions to be computed:

S_2	Total moles distilled $(100 - S_2)$	Moles CCl_4 in reboiler $Sc = (S_2)(x_S)$	Moles CCl_4 distilled $(30 - Sc)$	Avg. comp. of distillate $\frac{(30 - Sc)}{(100 - S_2)}$
100.0	0	30.0	0	
93.8	6.2	23.9	6.1	0.985
85.1	14.9	15.49	14.51	0.977
83.0	17.0	13.45	16.55	0.974

This table shows that, when 17.0 total moles have been distilled, the average composition of the distillate has the desired value of 97.4 mole per cent CCl_4. Thus at this point the distillate is diverted to another receiver and an intermediate fraction is collected until the reboiler composition is lowered to 1 mole per cent CCl_4; the previous table showed that this point is reached when a total of (100 − 64.0) or 36.0 moles has been distilled, so that the amount of the intermediate fraction is 36.0 − 17.0 or 19.0 moles. The moles of CCl_4 in the reboiler at the end of the distillation is (64)(0.01) or 0.64 moles; so the total moles of CCl_4 distilled is (30.0 − 0.64) or 29.36 moles and the moles of CCl_4 in the intermediate fraction is 29.36 − 16.55 or 12.81. The composition of the intermediate fraction is then 12.81/19.0 or 0.675 mole fraction CCl_4. The yield of CCl_4 in the first cut is 16.55/30 or 0.551, and the fraction of original CCl_4 in the intermediate cut which must be reworked is 12.81/30 or 0.427. Figure 13-36 is a plot of instantaneous values of distillate and reboiler liquid compositions vs. total moles distilled.

Effect of Column Hold-up. When the hold-up of liquid within the column itself is not negligible compared with the hold-up in the reboiler, the distillate composition at constant reflux ratio changes with time at a different rate than when column hold-up is negligible. There are two separate effects which cause the rate to vary. First, with appreciable column hold-up the composition of the charge to the reboiler will be higher in the light component than the reboiler liquid composition at the start of the distillation; the reason for this is that, before product take-off begins, column hold-up must be supplied, and its average composition is higher than that of the charge liquid from which it is supplied. Thus when overhead take-off begins, the reboiler composition is lower than it would be if there were no column hold-up, and the separation is more difficult. The second effect of column hold-up is to slow down the rate of exchange of the components; the hold-up exerts an inertia effect which prevents the compositions from changing as rapidly as they would otherwise, and the degree of separation is usually improved. As both these effects occur at the same time and change in importance during the course of the distillation, it is difficult to predict whether the over-all effect of hold-up will be favorable or detrimental; it is equally difficult to estimate the magnitude of the hold-up effect.

A more detailed discussion of hold-up effects is given by Pigford, Tepe, and Garrahan [*Ind. Eng. Chem.*, **43**, 2592 (1951)]. These authors predicted the effect of column hold-up on the **sharpness of separation** by means of computer solutions of the pertinent differential equations. Rose and associates [*Ind. Eng. Chem.*, **32**, 668, 673 (1940); **33**, 594 (1941); **42**, 1876, 2145 (1950); **43**, 2459, 2608 (1951); **44**, 1480 (1952); *Chem. Eng. Progress*, **48**, 549 (1952); **49**, 15 (1953)] have contributed much to the theory on this subject and have also investigated hold-up effects experimentally.

The approaches of Pigford and of Rose permit a distillation curve (such as Fig. 13-36) to be predicted for any given set of conditions by computer solution of the fairly complex differential equations involved. However, an equation developed by Zuiderweg [*Chem. Ing. Tech.*, **25**, 297 (1953)] permits direct calculation to be made of the reflux ratio necessary to obtain a certain sharpness of separation for given values of column hold-up and number of plates; Zuiderweg's relationships are also given in an article by Houtman and Husain [*Chem. Eng. Sci.*, **5**, 178 (1956)]. A typical result taken from the latter reference is shown as Fig. 13-37. The effect of column hold-up upon sharpness of the separation is seen first to have a beneficial then a detrimental result. Houtman and Husain noted that a certain optimum hold-up existed at any particular reflux ratio and extended Zuiderweg's relationships to permit calculation of the most useful number of plates, the necessary reflux ratio, and the optimum column hold-up for the batch separation of a particular charge into products of specified purity and with a specified size of the intermediate fraction; they also indicated procedures for selecting the best column from those available for a specific separation, and for adjusting the amount of the charge in case only one column is available.

Husain [*Brit. Chem. Eng.*, **3**, 668 (1958)] has suggested an approximate method for taking hold-up into account when making batch-distillation calculations. The method is based upon experimental observations in small-diameter packed and empty (Vigreux) columns. Calculations are made by assuming that the part of the distillation curve representing the first cut or desired fraction is a horizontal line with an ordinate equal to the average composition of the fraction; the remainder of the curve is computed by Eq. (13-70) by procedures described above assuming no hold-up, but with values of the amount of the first cut (A) suitably altered to take the hold-up into account. If the hold-up is less than 3 per cent of the charge, the value of A to be used in the no-hold-up calculations should be $9/10$ of the desired value of A; in the range of from 3 to 5 per cent hold-up, no correction is required; while for hold-ups of 5 per cent or greater, the value of A to be used in the calculations should be $10/9$ of the desired value of A. For the case of close-boiling mixtures in high-hold-up columns, the corrections may be even greater. The

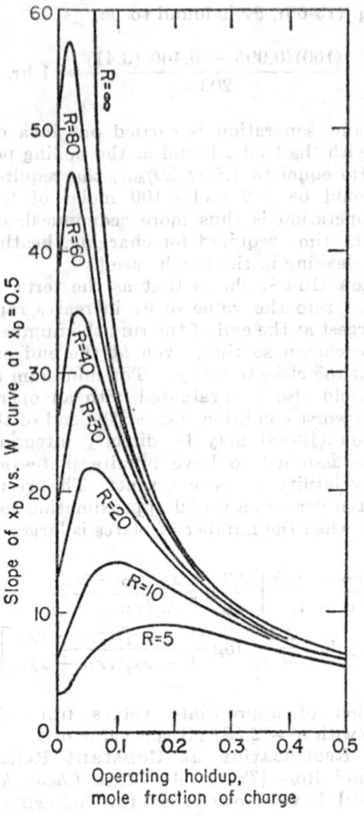

FIG. 13-37. Sharpness of batch separation as function of operating hold-up and reflux ratio (L/D) for cyclohexane–n-heptane equimolar mixture in 25 theoretical-plate column. [*Houtman and Husain, Chem. Eng. Sci.*, **5**, 180 (1956).]

method gave predicted values of yield for the more volatile component in the desired fraction which were within 10 per cent of the actual values determined experimentally for systems having α values varying from 1.1 to 2.8, for hold-up-to-charge ratios of from 3 to 17 mole per cent, and for L/D values of from 5 to 20.

Rate of Approach to Steady State. Equations of the type used to characterize batch-column behavior when hold-up is present may also be used to compute the time required for a continuous column to approach steady-state conditions. The calculation is of greatest interest when the separation is very difficult or the total column hold-up is very large, in which case the startup time may be considerable. Recommended procedure to follow is that of Jackson and Pigford [*Ind. Eng. Chem.*, **48**, 1020 (1956)]; the works of Davidson [*Trans. Inst. Chem. Engrs.*, **34**, 44 (1956)] and Cohen ("Theory of Isotope Separation as Applied to Large-scale Production of U^{235}," McGraw-Hill, New York, 1951) are also useful.

MULTICOMPONENT DISTILLATION

Most multicomponent columns separate a single feed stream containing three or more components into a single overhead product and a single bottoms product in equipment similar to that employed in binary distillations. In such an instance, a total of $n - 1$ columns is required to separate n feed components into n essentially pure products. Consider, for example, a mixture of ethanol, n-propanol, and n-butanol. If this mixture enters a multicomponent column, it is possible to obtain the lightest component, ethanol, as an essentially pure overhead product, in which case the bottoms product is a mixture of propanol and butanol. The latter mixture is then fed to a second column to recover essentially pure propanol and butanol as final products. An alternate processing scheme is equally workable: an ethanol-propanol mixture is taken overhead in the first column while the heaviest component, butanol, is the bottoms product, and in this instance the second column separates the ethanol-propanol mixture.

Application of the phase rule to multicomponent columns shows that in the usual design situation the overhead and bottoms compositions of only two of the feed components may be fixed in advance. Fixing of these two sets of compositions then fixes the theoretical tray requirements at a chosen reflux ratio which in turn fixes the overhead and bottoms compositions of all other components. Returning to the ethanol-propanol-butanol example, suppose the input moles and desired output moles are as follows:

Component	Moles/hr. of component in		
	Feed	Overhead	Bottoms
Ethanol	100	85	15
Propanol	100	12	88
Butanol	100	?	?

The distribution of butanol between overhead and bottoms cannot be chosen in advance but rather must be computed by methods developed later. In the case shown above, because butanol is heavier than the propanol, its presence in the overhead would be less than that of propanol, although it would be present in some finite amount.

It is helpful in multicomponent distillation to designate two of the feed components as **key components.** The key components are the two components whose recoveries in the overhead and bottoms are specified in advance; in the above table, ethanol is the **light key component** and propanol is the **heavy key component.** The key components may also be thought of as the components between which the "split" or "cut" is made; that is, all components lighter than the light key appear mostly in the overhead product, while all components heavier than the heavy key appear mostly in the bottoms product.

In many non-ideal systems where liquid composition has a strong effect upon relative volatility, a given non-key component may be more volatile than the keys in one region of the column whereas it may be less volatile in another. Discussion of such cases is treated later; the first design procedures to be considered are those wherein each of the components has a volatility which remains greater or less than that of the other components throughout the column.

Basic Tray-to-Tray Procedure for Computing Tray Requirements. In the usual design problem, the composition, rate, and thermal condition of the feed are specified, the pressure of the column is fixed by ability to condense at least part of the overhead vapors as reflux, and the desired recovery of the two key components is chosen. First step is to estimate the **distribution of non-key components** in the overhead and bottoms, after which the minimum reflux ratio is computed; procedures for these two steps are given later. As in binary distillation, an operating reflux ratio of about $1.3(L/D)_{\min}$ is customarily employed unless economic-balance calculations are used to determine the optimum operating reflux ratio more exactly. "Tray-to-tray" calculations are now made from one end of the column to the other to determine the number of trays required to obtain the desired recovery of the keys. A product distribution of the non-key components is also obtained; if this does not match the assumed distribution, new values are assumed and the calculations repeated until the computed product compositions match the trial values.

"Tray-to-tray" calculations which start at the reboiler first employ a multicomponent vapor-liquid calculation to determine the temperature and composition of the vapor to the bottom tray of the column; material and enthalpy balances between this vapor stream, the bottoms product, and the liquid leaving the bottom tray permit a calculation to be made of the flow rate, composition, and temperature of the liquid leaving the bottom tray. If it is assumed that each tray has a 100 per cent tray efficiency and discharges a perfectly mixed liquid, vapor-liquid equilibrium calculations now permit the composition of vapor leaving the bottom tray to be obtained. The material-enthalpy balance calculations and the vapor-liquid equilibrium calculations are then applied alternately to each tray in turn until the feed plate is reached; the material-enthalpy balance calculations are modified to include the addition of the feed, and the tray-to-tray calculations are continued upward until the specified recovery of the keys is obtained.

Tray-to-tray calculations may also be made by starting at the top of the column and proceeding downward, or the calculations may start at both ends of the column and work to the feed tray; in the latter case the assumed distribution of non-key components is correct if the compositions of all components match at the feed tray. To reduce the number of trials, tray-to-tray calculations are usually started at the point where non-key compositions are most readily estimated; this matter is described in more detail later. Tray-to-tray calculations are seldom started at the feed tray because no simple relationship exists between feed composition and feed-tray composition.

These tray-to-tray procedures are quite tedious, and prior to the ready availability of electronic computers, it was common practice to make various simplifying assumptions to cut down the number of trial calculations. "Short-cut" methods were also used extensively. Although the simpler procedures (given later) are useful for estimating purposes, exact tray-to-tray methods are recommended for most cases.

Design Example Using Tray-to-Tray Method. To illustrate the basic design procedure, an example problem is worked out here. This example assumes that equal molal overflow applies and that the relative volatility α of each component is independent of temperature and composition. The feed is a liquid at its boiling point as follows:

Component	Feed rate, moles/hr.	Relative volatility
A	25	5.0
B	25	2.5
C	25	1.0
D	25	0.2
	100	

Suppose the key components are *B* and *C*, and the allowable contamination of *C* in the overhead product is 1 mole/hr. and the allowable contamination of *B* in the bottoms product is also 1 mole/hr. If 4 moles of saturated liquid are returned as reflux to the top tray of the column per mole of overhead product, how many theoretical trays are required?

First step is to estimate the distribution of non-key components in the products. In the present instance as *B* appears in the bottoms to only a small extent, and as *A* is considerably more volatile than *B*, it is reasonable to assume that *A* is essentially absent in the bottoms; by similar reasoning, *D* is assumed to be essentially absent in the overhead. The probable distribution of components in the two product streams is then as follows:

Component	Distillate rate, moles/hr.	Distillate composition, mole fraction	Bottoms rate, moles/hr.	Bottoms composition, mole fraction
A	25	0.50	Trace	0.00
B	24	0.48	1	0.02
C	1	0.02	24	0.48
D	Trace	0.00	25	0.50
	50	1.00	50	1.00

Flows within the column are readily computed. With a reflux ratio L/D of 4/1, the liquid downflow in the rectifying section is 200 moles/hr. and the liquid downflow in the stripping section is 200 moles/hr. plus the liquid feed, or 300 moles/hr. The vapor flow in both sections of the column is 250 moles/hr. As the overhead product contains a large amount of A, which is difficult to condense because of its high volatility, assume that a partial condenser is used, *i.e.*, the only liquid condensed in the condenser is that sufficient to provide the reflux, and the overhead product is withdrawn as a vapor.

Considerable trial-and-error calculations are required to obtain a complete and accurate solution to this problem by conventional tray-to-tray methods. The exact procedure involves assuming a value for either the trace quantity of D in the distillate or the trace quantity of A in the bottoms, and then making tray-to-tray calculations to the other end of the column; when the calculation is started at the bottom, if the distillate composition arrived at by the tray-to-tray procedure matches that required by the over-all material balance (*i.e.*, the distillate composition given in the above table), then the assumed quantity is correct and the calculation is completed. Unfortunately, the calculation is very sensitive to the magnitude of the assumed trace quantity; although the value may be very small, it must be known fairly precisely to obtain a good match in composition at the other end of the column.

To illustrate the tray-to-tray procedure, assume the composition of A in the bottoms to be 2.33×10^{-4} mole fraction. Now compute the composition of the equilibrium vapor from the reboiler. When equilibrium data are available in terms of α, the equilibrium values of vapor and liquid composition for any component y and x are related to α as follows:

$$y = \frac{\alpha x}{\Sigma(\alpha x)} \qquad x = \frac{y/\alpha}{\Sigma(y/\alpha)} \tag{13-71}$$

The summation terms refer to the sum of individual αx or y/α terms for each component. Use of the first of these equations is illustrated below:

Component	Bottoms composition x_w	α	αx	Vapor from reboiler y_w
A	0.000233	5.0	0.001165	0.001845
B	0.020	2.5	0.050	0.0792
C	0.480	1.0	0.480	0.7604
D	0.500	0.2	0.100	0.1584
			$\Sigma(\alpha x) = 0.6312$	

The value of y_w for component A is computed as

$$\frac{(\alpha x)}{(\Sigma \alpha x)} = \frac{0.001165}{0.6312} = 0.001845$$

To continue the stepwise calculation upward, it is now necessary to compute values of x_1, the liquid leaving the bottom tray (tray 1). This is done by means of a material balance with the bottoms. As there are $300/50 =$ 6 moles of liquid downflow per mole of bottoms and $250/50 = 5$ moles of vapor upflow per mole of bottoms in the stripping section, the material-balance relation, for any component, is $6x_1 = 5y_w + x_w$. Use of this relationship gives values of $6x_1$ for each component, from which the values of $5y_1$ are readily computed as $(5)(6\alpha x_1)/(\Sigma 6\alpha x_1)$. Continuing the illustration,

$5y_w$	$6x_1$	α	$6\alpha x_1$	$5y_1$	$6x_2$
0.00923	0.00946	5.0	0.0473	0.0421	0.0423
0.396	0.416	2.5	1.040	0.925	0.945
3.802	4.282	1.0	4.282	3.807	4.287
0.792	1.292	0.2	0.258	0.230	0.730
			5.627		

$6\alpha x_2$	$5y_2$	$6x_3$	$6\alpha x_3$	$5y_3$	$6x_4$
0.212	0.151	0.151	0.755	0.435	0.435
2.362	1.685	1.705	4.264	2.456	2.476
4.287	3.059	3.539	3.539	2.039	2.519
0.146	0.104	0.604	0.121	0.070	0.570
7.007			8.679		

Note that values of $6x_2$ are computed as the sum of the corresponding values of $5y_1$ and x_w, after which equilibrium and material-balance calculations are carried out alternatively up to the fourth tray from the bottom. On the fourth tray, the composition of the keys (components B and C) in the liquid is very nearly the same, and as B and C are equal in the feed liquid itself, the feed is added onto the fourth tray. (The reason for this choice of feed-tray location is given in a later section where the problem is discussed generally for multicomponent columns.)

Adding the feed to tray 4 does not alter the validity of the material-balance calculation by which values of $6x_4$ were obtained, and values of y_4 are readily obtained from values of x_4 by the usual vapor-liquid relationship. However, in applying a material balance to obtain values of x_5, the composition of the liquid leaving the fifth tray from the bottom, the material balance is more conveniently applied using the overhead product stream. With $200/50 = 4$ moles of liquid downflow per mole of overhead and $250/50 = 5$ moles of vapor upflow per mole of overhead in the rectifying section, the proper material balance is $4x_5 = 5y_4 - y_D$, where y_D is the composition of the overhead vapor product. Continuing the same stepwise procedure upward, then, gives

$6x_4$	$6\alpha x_4$	$5y_4$	$4x_5$	$4\alpha x_5$	$5y_5$
0.435	2.175	0.990	0.490	2.450	1.300
2.476	6.190	2.813	2.333	5.833	3.097
2.519	2.519	1.145	1.125	1.125	0.597
0.570	0.114	0.0518	0.0518	0.0104	0.00550
	10.998			9.418	

$4x_6$	$4\alpha x_6$	$5y_6$	$4x_R$	$4\alpha x_R$	y_D
0.800	4.000	1.799	1.299	6.495	0.504
2.617	6.542	2.941	2.461	6.153	0.477
0.577	0.577	0.259	0.239	0.239	0.0186
0.00550	0.00110	0.000494	0.000494	0.0000988	0.00000767
	11.120			12.887	

The above tabulation shows that the stepwise calculations are continued until the desired key-component compositions in the vapor are obtained. (The exact values are never achieved because of the finite composition change experienced in passing through each tray.) The column required for the desired separation must contain a total of six theoretical trays, with the feed being added on the fourth tray from the bottom. Because the value for y_D obtained for component A by the stepwise calculations closely matches the 0.500 value demanded by an over-all material balance for component A, the assumed value of x_w for A, which is 2.33×10^{-4}, is essentially correct. Also, the value of y_D for component D, originally assumed equal to zero, must be very close to the calculated value of 7.67×10^{-6}.

The many trials required for the above calculation are not difficult to carry out on a computer, but with hand calculation, the labor is considerable. The difficulty lies with proper choice for an assumed value of the composition of A in the bottoms. For example, if this value is taken as either 2.0×10^{-4} or 3.0×10^{-4}, the values for y_D by the same stepwise calculation employing the same feed-tray location and the same number of theoretical trays compares with the correct solution as follows:

Component	Values of y_D when x_w for component A is chosen as		
	2.0×10^{-4}	2.33×10^{-4}	3.0×10^{-4}
A	0.346	0.504	0.677
B	0.630	0.477	0.310
C	0.0237	0.0186	0.0129
D	0.00000963	0.00000767	0.00000552

If all the non-key components are appreciably lighter than the light key, these components will be essentially absent in the bottoms; in such an instance the overhead product composition is precisely defined, and the stepwise calculations can be made without any trials being involved by starting at the top of the column. Similarly, if all the non-key components are appreciably heavier than the heavy key, the bottoms product composition is defined and a single stepwise calculation starting at the bottom will give the desired answer.

In the general case where non-key components are both lighter and heavier than the keys and have α values not widely different from the keys, initial assumptions must be made for the distribution of the non-key components in the overhead and bottoms products, and the assumptions must then be proved or corrected according to the results of some type of stepwise calculation.

A useful **approximate procedure** often employed in this instance to determine tray requirements is based upon the observation that components much heavier than the heavy key disappear quickly in proceeding upward from the feed tray, whereas components much lighter than the light key disappear quickly in proceeding downward from the feed tray. Stepwise calculations can be made up from the bottom to the feed tray neglecting components lighter than the light key, followed by stepwise calculations made down from the top of the column to the feed tray neglecting components heavier than the heavy key. The required number of trays is then the sum of those obtained for the upper and lower sections of the column. The procedure is readily illustrated by the same example just worked out above. Starting at the bottom first, and ignoring component A, the stepwise calculations are as follows:

Component	x_w	α	αx	$5y_w$	$6x_1$	$6\alpha x_1$
B	0.020	2.5	0.050	0.397	0.417	1.043
C	0.480	1.0	0.480	3.81	4.29	4.29
D	0.500	0.2	0.100	0.794	1.294	0.259
			0.630			5.59

$5y_1$	$6x_2$	$6\alpha x_2$	$5y_2$	$6x_3$	$6\alpha x_3$	$5y_3$	$6x_4$	x_4
0.935	0.955	2.388	1.749	1.769	4.423	2.71	2.73	0.455
3.83	4.31	4.31	3.15	3.63	3.63	2.22	2.70	0.450
0.232	0.732	0.146	0.107	0.607	0.121	0.0742	0.574	0.095
		6.84			8.17			

The corresponding calculations made from the top down, this time neglecting component D, are:

Component	y_D	α	y/α	$4x_R$	$5y_T$	$5y_T/\alpha$
A	0.500	5.0	0.100	1.280	1.780	0.356
B	0.480	2.5	0.192	2.46	2.94	1.176
C	0.020	1.0	0.020	0.256	0.276	0.276
			0.312			1.808

$4x_T$	$5y_{T-1}$	$5y_{T-1}/\alpha$	$4x_{T-1}$	$5y_{T-2}$	$5y_{T-2}/\alpha$	x_{T-2}
0.788	1.288	0.258	0.486	0.986	0.197	0.078
2.60	3.08	1.232	2.324	2.804	1.122	0.444
0.611	0.631	0.631	1.190	1.210	1.210	0.478
		2.121			2.529	

The value of $4x_R$ for component A is computed above as $4(y/\alpha)/\Sigma(y/\alpha) = (4)(0.100)/0.312 = 1.280$, and $5y_T$ (where subscript T refers to the top tray) is computed as $4x_R + y_D$. The above calculation shows that after working up four trays from the bottom the key liquid compositions become equal, whereas it takes three trays from the top down to cause the key liquid compositions to become equal. As trays 4 and $T - 2$ are the same tray—the feed tray—the total number of trays required is six.

The approximate procedure gives very nearly the same answer as the more exact method, although the composition change of the keys from either end of the column to the feed tray is slightly greater in the approximate method where in each instance one of the non-keys was ignored. Obviously the results obtained by the approximate method will give errors greater than those found in the present example if the non-key components do not disappear as quickly as postulated; the non-keys will be slow to disappear if their α values are closer to those for the keys than in the example.

The approximate method also does not give directly a value for the feed-tray composition which includes all components. However, this can be estimated if the two feed-tray compositions (x_4 and x_{T-2} in the above example) are combined in a way such that the ratios of non-key- to key-component compositions are maintained constant. Following this suggestion in the present example gives an estimated feed-tray composition which compares quite closely with that obtained by the exact method:

Component	Feed-tray composition obtained by	
	Approximate method	Exact method
A	0.071	0.073
B	0.420	0.412
C	0.420	0.420
D	0.088	0.095

In the approximate method it was necessary to assume that the key compositions were equal in x_4 and in x_{T-2} before the two sets of compositions could be combined in the manner specified.

The approximate method neglects any small effect which the presence of the lighter-than-light key components below the feed tray might have on the tray requirements. To investigate this, the usual procedure is to add trace quantities of these components a number of trays below the feed, and then to repeat the stepwise calculation up to the feed point; several trials are required, as the addition of each trace quantity must be made onto the proper tray, *i.e.*, onto the tray chosen such that the subsequent calculations up to the feed point yield a feed-tray composition for each added component which matches that arrived at by the stepwise calculation from the top down. A similar procedure is employed for the heavier-than-heavy components above the feed. The method is illustrated by Robinson and Gilliland (*op. cit.*, pp. 261–270).

Variation of Composition with Tray Location; Pinch Composition. To understand better the manner in which compositions change with position from one end of a multicomponent column to the other, it is useful to plot tray-composition diagrams such as Figs. 13-38 and 13-39. The two cases illustrated show the manner in which the volatilities of the non-keys affect the composition–tray number behavior of the keys.

Figure 13-38 describes the composition changes which occur for a column performing the following separation:

Component	Relative volatility	Composition, mole fraction, of		
		Feed	Distillate	Bottoms
A	5.0	0.25	0.50	Trace
B	1.6	0.25	0.49	0.01
C	1.0	0.25	0.01	0.49
D	0.2	0.25	Trace	0.50

As in the previous example described on p. 13-33, the reflux ratio L/D is $\frac{4}{1}$, the feed is a saturated liquid, and equal molal overflow applies. A total condenser is used. Because recovery of the keys is somewhat better in this instance—their contamination is 0.01 mole fraction in

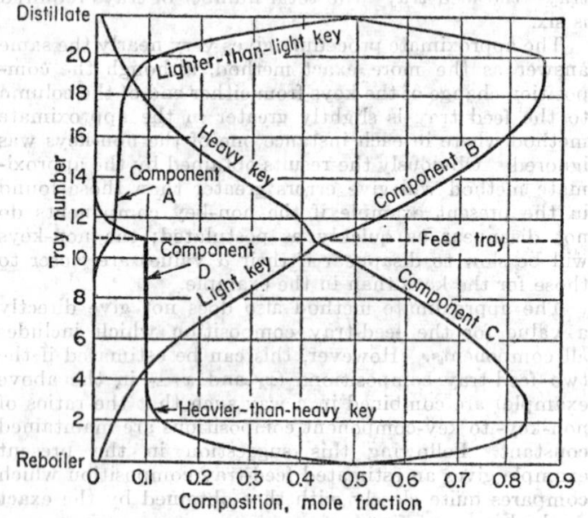

Fig. 13-38. Typical variation of tray composition with position in tower for multicomponent separation (see example, p. 13-35).

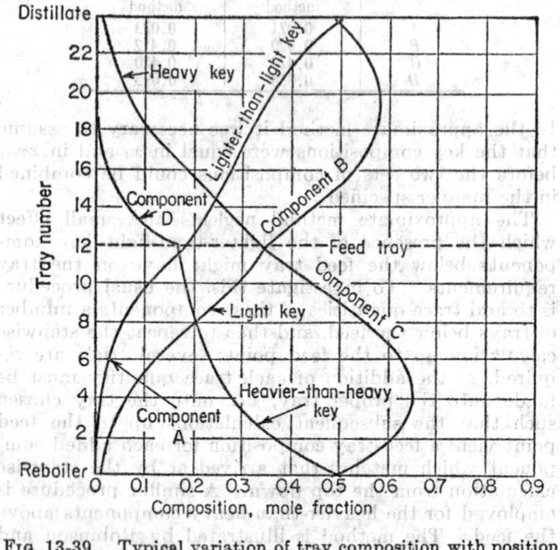

Fig. 13-39. Typical variation of tray composition with position in tower for multicomponent separation (see example, p. 13-37).

the products instead of 0.02—the separation is said to be more *sharp*. The other major difference between this example and that on p. 13-33 is the smaller value of α for the keys. These differences cause the theoretical tray requirements to increase from 6 in the previous case to 22 in the present.

Figure 13-38 shows that the concentration of the lighter-than-light key component A falls off rapidly in proceeding from the top downward but reaches a constant value after about four trays. Similarly, concentration of the heavier-than-heavy key component D falls off rapidly in proceeding upward from the bottom, but after about three trays this composition also reaches a constant value. This behavior is typical of that for non-keys whose volatilities are appreciably different from that of the keys; the constant compositions are commonly known as **pinch compositions.** Actually, any component will reach a pinch composition if a stepwise calculation from the top or bottom is continued for a sufficiently long time, but only lighter-than-light keys of high volatility or heavier-than-heavy keys of low volatility reach pinch compositions in a small number of trays.

Pinch compositions are readily computed without resorting to stepwise calculations by solving simultaneously the equilibrium and operating-line relationships for a component; for light components in the rectifying section, the pinch composition of any component x_n is

$$x_n = \frac{x_D}{(\alpha - 1)(L/D) + \alpha x_{hD}/x_{hn}} \tag{13-72}$$

where x_D is the distillate composition of the component and α is its volatility relative to the heavy key; L/D is the reflux ratio, x_{hD} is the composition of heavy key in the distillate, and x_{hn} is the pinch composition of the heavy key. As this equation assumes that heavier-than-heavy keys are absent at the pinch point, x_{hn} may be obtained by difference once values of x_n are obtained for the light key and all lighter-than-light keys by this equation; obviously a trial value of x_{hn} must be employed in the initial calculations for obtaining x_n values.

The corresponding equation for the pinch composition of any heavy component in the stripping section x_m is

$$x_m = \frac{\alpha_l x_w}{(\alpha_l - \alpha)(L/W) + \alpha x_{lw}/x_{lm}} \tag{13-73}$$

where α is the relative volatility of component m and α is the relative volatility of the light key; both α values are relative to the heavy key. The term L/W is the ratio of stripping-column liquid flow to bottoms flow, x_w is the bottoms composition for component m, x_{lw} is the bottoms composition for the light key, and x_{lm} is the light-key composition at the pinch point.

Application of Eq. (13-72) to the present example shows that the rectifying pinch composition is $x_A = 0.0311$, $x_B = 0.202$, and $x_C = 0.767$; Eq. (13-73) shows the stripping pinch composition to be $x_B = 0.688$, $x_C = 0.217$, and $x_D = 0.0953$. Only the non-keys are seen to approach their pinch compositions in Fig. 13-38; but if the stepwise calculations had continued from the top downward for an additional 20 or 30 trays without introducing the feed, the keys would approach the computed rectifying pinch compositions in magnitude. Also, the stripping pinch compositions would be approached if the stepwise procedure had been continued upward without introducing the feed.

A fuller explanation of the behavior shown by Fig. 13-38 is now possible. Component A, being very volatile, changes rapidly in concentration in working down from the top; but once its pinch composition is approached, its concentration changes hardly at all with added trays. Component D, being least volatile, drops off rapidly in concentration in working up from the bottom; but once its pinch composition is approached, it likewise changes very little with added trays.

The behavior of the heavy key in working up from the bottom is interesting. Although in the absence of a heavier-than-heavy key component the heavy key itself would normally decrease in working up from the bottom, in the present instance the rapidly decreasing concentration of component D requires the corresponding increase in concentration of another component; as components A and B are both present in small amounts on the lower trays, the only component which can increase sufficiently is component C. However, as soon as the light key B

builds up to a reasonably important magnitude, the heavy key reverses its previous trend and diminishes in concentration throughout the remainder of the trays. The initial trend of composition change for the light key in working down the first few trays of the rectifying section is also reversed from its normal trend, for similar reasons.

Importance of the volatility of the non-keys upon the composition behavior of the keys is further illustrated by Fig. 13-39. In this instance the same conditions which apply for the case shown on Fig. 13-38 are retained except that the relative volatility of component A is changed to 1.9 and that of component D is changed to 0.7:

Component	Relative volatility	Composition, mole fraction, of		
		Feed	Distillate	Bottoms
A	1.9	0.25	0.50	Trace
B	1.6	0.25	0.49	0.01
C	1.0	0.25	0.01	0.49
D	0.7	0.25	Trace	0.50

These changed relative volatilities cause an increased contamination of the non-keys in the products; component A is present in the bottoms to the extent of 6.0×10^{-4} mole fraction, and component D is present in the overhead to the extent of 1.1×10^{-4}. Although these concentrations are much larger than found in the previous example, they are still so small that the concentrations of the other components in the products are unchanged.

Figure 13-39 shows that the non-keys do not reach pinch compositions; the volatilities of the non-keys is too close to those of the keys themselves for this to occur. The pattern described by the keys is similar to that found in the previous case except that the maximum composition value reached by the heavy key in the stripping section is smaller in magnitude; also the maximum point occurs farther up the column. The reason for this is simply that the heavier-than-heavy key does not diminish in value as fast in the present case as it did in the previous case. The light key in the rectifying section also shows a smaller maximum value occurring at a lower tray because of the slower composition change per plate for the lighter-than-light key.

Comparison of Figs. 13-38 and 13-39 shows that two additional theoretical trays are required for the case where the α values of the non-keys are closer to the α values of the keys, even though the product compositions of the keys are the same in the two cases.

Tray-to-Tray Calculations When α Varies. The previous examples assumed that the relative volatility for any component was constant over the entire column. However, in most cases, α values vary with temperature, and in some cases they are also functions of vapor and liquid compositions as well. In making tray-to-tray calculations upward, the liquid composition is obtained by material balance with the vapor from the tray below and with the bottoms, but the liquid temperature and the equilibrium vapor composition must be assumed in the first trial in order to determine the α values. Equilibrium vapor composition is then computed by Eq. (13-71); the temperature is checked by computing the vapor pressure of any component from the basic vapor-liquid equilibrium relation of Eq. (13-7) as $(Py)/(\gamma x)$; if the vapor pressure as computed from the compositions x and y is the same as that corresponding to the assumed temperature, the assumed temperature is correct. Several trials may be required before the proper α value is determined. When the tray-to-tray calculations are made down the column, vapor compositions are determined by material balance, and assumptions must be made for vapor temperature and equilibrium liquid compositions. The procedure for checking these assumptions is the same as that just described.

Under conditions where α varies markedly with composition, it is usually quite difficult to estimate in advance even the approximate composition of the overhead and bottoms products. In such an instance the tray-to-tray calculations for the entire column often need to be repeated over and over again before the desired result is obtained. Use of automatic computers, as mentioned later, is helpful.

Unequal Molal Overflow. The previous examples assumed also that equal molal overflow prevailed within the rectifying and stripping sections of the multicomponent column; *i.e.*, they assumed the liquid- and vapor-flow rates to be constant in each section. This assumption will not hold if the latent heats of vaporization change with temperature and/or with the nature of the component, if heats of solution are present, or if heat losses are appreciable.

To compute the variation of vapor- and liquid-flow rates from one tray to the next, it is necessary to employ enthalpy-balance calculations. The same over-all enthalpy-balance relationships developed for binary mixtures, Eqs. (13-55), (13-56), and (13-57), apply also to multicomponent mixtures. These equations are most conveniently applied, however, when combined with the material-balance equations [Eqs. (13-45) and (13-48)] and with the component-balance equations [Eqs. (13-47) and (13-49)]; for the rectifying section, the result is

$$\frac{L_{n+1}}{D} = \frac{(\Sigma x_D \bar{h}_D + Q_c/D) - (\Sigma x_D \bar{H}_n)}{(\Sigma x_{n+1} \bar{H}_n - \Sigma x_{n+1} \bar{h}_{n+1})} \qquad (13\text{-}74)$$

while for the stripping section the relationship is

$$\frac{V_m}{W} = \frac{Q_s/W - \Sigma x_w \bar{h}_w + \Sigma x_w \bar{h}_{m+1}}{(\Sigma y_m \bar{H}_m - \Sigma y_m \bar{h}_{m+1})} \qquad (13\text{-}75)$$

where $\bar{h}_D$ is the partial enthalpy of each component in the distillate, B.t.u./(lb.-mole), while $\bar{h}_w$, $\bar{h}_{m+1}$, and $\bar{h}_{n+1}$ are partial enthalpies for each component in the bottoms, in the liquid leaving tray $m + 1$, and in the liquid leaving tray $n + 1$, respectively. Similarly, $\bar{H}_n$ and $\bar{H}_m$ are partial enthalpies of each component in the vapor leaving tray n and tray m, respectively.

Application of Eq. (13-74) is usually made in a tray-to-tray calculation working down from the top of a column. In such a calculation, values of D, x_D, $\bar{h}_D$, and Q_c would all be known. Also, the temperature and composition of the liquid on (and leaving) the top tray are readily computed from a vapor-liquid equilibrium calculation, so that values of x_{n+1} and $\bar{h}_{n+1}$ are also known. The only remaining unknowns in Eq. (13-74) are L_{n+1} and the $\bar{H}_n$ values for each component; values of the latter are assumed (often this requires only the assumption of a temperature) and a trial value of L_{n+1} is then computed. From this trial value, V_n is computed from Eq. (13-45) and values of y_n are computed from Eq. (13-47). The saturation temperature of the just-computed vapor composition—and the vapor composition itself—are then sufficient to check whether the assumed values of $\bar{H}_n$ are the correct ones. Application of Eq. (13-75) to tray-to-tray calculations proceeding upward in the stripping section requires an assumption for values of $\bar{h}_{m+1}$ which are subsequently checked after trial values of V_m, L_{m+1}, x_{m+1}, and the temperature of the liquid on tray $m + 1$ are computed.

For ideal solutions at low pressures, partial enthalpies are the same numerically as pure-component enthalpies and are a function of temperature only. For solutions which are non-ideal in the liquid phase, heats of solution can often be large enough to make partial enthalpies considerably different from pure-component enthalpies. At moderate and high pressures, partial enthalpies are likely to differ from pure-component enthalpies and to depend upon the mixture composition; see Canjar and Edmister [*Chem. Eng. Progress, Symp. Ser.* 7, **49,** 73–84, 85–91 (1953)] and Papadopoulos, Pigford, and Friend [*Chem. Eng. Progress, Symp. Ser.* 7, **49,** 119 (1953)] for partial enthalpies of the light hydrocarbons as a function of temperature and composition.

For the special case where enthalpies are essentially independent of composition and temperature but vary with the nature of the component (because latent heats of vaporization vary with the nature of the component), Robinson and Gilliland (*op. cit.*, pp. 158–160, 276–283) describe a useful procedure employing pseudo mole fractions and pseudo flow quantities.

The **minimum reflux ratio** for a multicomponent column is the smallest reflux ratio which can be employed to give the desired separation of the keys. Because minimum reflux implies an infinite number of trays, all lighter-than-light keys (which have α values greater by a finite amount than the α value of the light key) are absent in the bottoms product, and all heavier-than-heavy keys are absent in the overhead.

Thus when stepwise calculations are made from the top downward for a multicomponent column operating at minimum reflux, only the heavy key and the light components are involved, and proceeding downward for an infinite number of trays causes each component to reach its pinch composition. Likewise in working from the bottom upward, the light key and the heavy components eventually reach their pinch compositions. The two pinch compositions arrived at by these procedures are not identical, however, because in the first instance the heavier-than-heavy keys are absent and in the second instance the lighter-than-lights are absent. In fact, the rectifying-column pinch lies well above the feed tray, and the stripping-column pinch lies well below the feed tray. The truth of this becomes evident when stepwise calculations from the feed tray are considered. All components are present in finite amounts on the feed tray, but a stepwise calculation from the feed tray downward, when continued for an infinite number of trays, causes all lighter-than-light key components to disappear; after they have disappeared, the stripping-column pinch point has been reached. Similarly, stepwise calculations from the feed tray upward will reach the rectifying pinch point after the heavier-than-heavy key components have disappeared. If the multicomponent column contains no lighter-than-light key components in the feed, the stripping-column pinch occurs at the feed tray, but the rectifying-column pinch point remains well above the feed tray; only in the binary case are both pinch points coincident at the feed tray.

The **exact method** for determining minimum reflux ratio is as follows: (1) assume a value for minimum reflux ratio; (2) from the known overhead and bottoms compositions, make stepwise calculations from both ends of the column toward the center until pinch compositions (essentially no change in composition per plate) result; or, under conditions of constant α and equal molal overflow, use Eqs. (13-72) and (13-73) to obtain the pinch compositions; (3) add trace amounts of the lighter-than-light key components at the stripping-column pinch point and make stepwise calculations upward, adding the feed at the proper point; then continue upward beyond the feed until the heavier-than-heavy key components essentially disappear, which gives a trial value for the rectifying-column pinch point; (4) compare the rectifying pinch composition obtained from (3) with that obtained from (2); and (5) if a match in composition is obtained, the assumed value for minimum reflux is correct; if not, assume a new value and repeat the calculation.

The exact method just described is tedious to use. Sometimes only an approximate answer is needed. **Colburn** [*Trans. Am. Inst. Chem. Engrs.*, **37,** 805 (1941)] developed a **simplification** of the exact procedure by correlating the ratio of the light key composition to the heavy key composition at the rectifying pinch r_n divided by the corresponding ratio at the stripping pinch r_m. His empirical relationship is

$$\frac{r_m}{r_n} = \frac{1}{(1 - \Sigma C_m \alpha x_m)(1 - \Sigma C_n x_n)} \qquad (13\text{-}76)$$

In the above expression, values of $C_m \alpha x_m$ are computed for each heavier-than-heavy key component, and the summation taken. The proper values of C_m are taken from Fig. 13-40; x_m is the stripping pinch composition. Values of $C_n x_n$ are computed for each lighter-than-light key component; C_n values are taken from Fig. 13-41; x_n is the rectifying pinch composition.

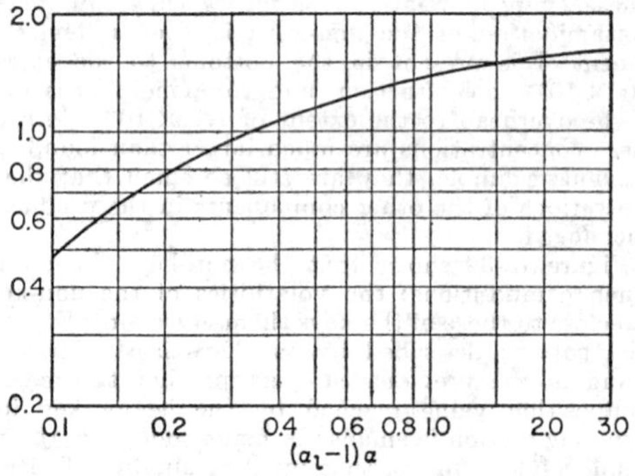

FIG. 13-40. Correction factor C_m for use in Eq. (13-76).

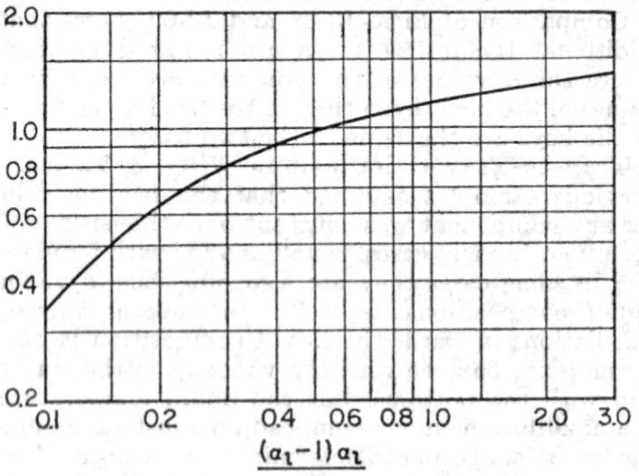

FIG. 13-41. Correction factor C_n for use in Eq. (13-76).

Colburn's minimum reflux method may then be summarized as follows: (1) assume a value for minimum reflux ratio; (2) from Eqs. (13-72) and (13-73) compute the pinch compositions from which a value of r_m/r_n is obtained; (3) compute a value of r_m/r_n from Eq. (13-76); and (4) compare values of r_m/r_n from (2) and (3); if they agree, the assumed minimum reflux ratio is correct; if not, repeat the calculation. Colburn's method assumes that equal molal overflow applies; the proper α values to use are those which apply at the pinch points.

Calculation of minimum reflux may be made more simply for cases where α values are constant and where equal molal overflow applies by the **Underwood method** [*J. Inst. Petrol.*, **32**, 614 (1946)]. Minimum reflux ratio is found by solving the equation

$$\left(\frac{L}{D}\right)_{\min} + 1 = \frac{\alpha_a x_{Da}}{\alpha_a - \theta} + \frac{\alpha_b x_{Db}}{\alpha_b - \theta} + \frac{\alpha_c x_{Dc}}{\alpha_c - \theta} + \cdots + \frac{\alpha_z x_{Dz}}{\alpha_z - \theta} \qquad (13\text{-}77)$$

The value of θ to use in the above expression is obtained by solving the following equation for the value of θ which lies between the α values of the key components:

$$\frac{\alpha_a z_{Fa}}{\alpha_a - \theta} + \frac{\alpha_b z_{Fb}}{\alpha_b - \theta} + \frac{\alpha_c z_{Fc}}{\alpha_c - \theta} + \cdots + \frac{\alpha_z z_{Fz}}{\alpha_z - \theta} = 1 - q \qquad (13\text{-}78)$$

In these equations the subscripts a, b, c, . . . , z refer to the individual components in order of decreasing volatility, the subscripts D and F refer to overhead product and feed, respectively, and q is related to the thermal condition of the feed as defined by Eq. (13-52). The terms z_{Fa}, z_{Fb}, . . . , z_{Fz} denote the mole fractions of components a, b, . . . , z in the total feed.

If the feed contains a component whose α value lies intermediate between the α values of the keys (a so-called *distributed component*), Eq. (13-78) is solved for the *two* values of θ which lie between the α values of the keys. As the value of x_D for the distributed component is unknown as well as the value of $(L/D)_{\min}$, it is necessary to write Eq. (13-77) twice, once using the first value of θ, and once using the second value. The two equations thus obtained may be solved for the two unknowns $(L/D)_{\min}$ and the recovery of the distributed component in the overhead [see Underwood, *Chem. Eng. Progress*, **44**, 612 (1948)].

Consider as an example of the methods for computing minimum reflux the separation described on p. 13-35. Substituting appropriate values into Eq. (13-78) gives

$$\frac{(5)(0.25)}{5 - \theta} + \frac{(1.6)(0.25)}{1.6 - \theta} + \frac{(1.0)(0.25)}{1.0 - \theta} + \frac{(0.2)(0.25)}{0.2 - \theta} = 1 - 1 = 0$$

By trial and error, it is found that the value of θ between 1.6 and 1.0 which satisfies the above expression is 1.197. Now substituting into Eq. (13-77) gives

$$\left(\frac{L}{D}\right)_{\min} + 1 = \frac{(5)(0.50)}{(5 - 1.197)} + \frac{(1.6)(0.49)}{(1.6 - 1.197)} + \frac{(1.0)(0.01)}{(1.0 - 1.197)}$$

Solving, $(L/D)_{\min} = 1.55$.

This same example may also be worked by the Colburn method. Assume $(L/D)_{\min} = 1.55$. Then by Eq. (13-72), with $L/D = 1.55$, the upper pinch composition is $x_A = 0.079$, $x_B = 0.505$, and $x_C = 0.416$. By Eq. (13-73), with $L/W = 3.55$, the lower pinch composition is found to be $x_B = 0.474$, $x_C = 0.365$, and $x_D = 0.161$. Then $r_m/r_n = (0.474/0.365)/(0.505/0.416) = 1.073$. Now it is necessary to check the r_m/r_n ratio by Eq. (13-76). From Fig. 13-40, $C_m = 0.55$ for the heavier-than-heavy key component, and from Fig. 13-41, $C_n =$ 0.62 for the lighter-than-light key component. Substituting into Eq. (13-76),

$$\frac{r_m}{r_n} = \frac{1}{[1 - (0.55)(0.2)(0.161)][1 - (0.62)(0.079)]}$$

Solving, $r_m/r_n = 1.07$; as this checks the value computed by Eqs. (13-72) and (13-73), the assumed value of minimum reflux is correct.

For columns where relative volatility values and internal flow rates vary with tray number, minimum reflux may be computed by the method of Bachelor [*Petrol. Refiner*, **36** (6), 161 (1957)]. This procedure employs a relaxation technique to converge in successive steps upon the true minimum reflux with any degree of accuracy.

Minimum Theoretical Plates (Total Reflux). The Fenske-Underwood equation [Eq. (13-60)] applies to any two components of a multicomponent column as well as to binary columns; its only limitation is the requirement of constant relative volatility. If α values vary over the height of the column, stepwise calculations should be employed. When Eq. (13-60) is applied to the key components of the separation described on p. 13-35, the number of theoretical plates at total reflux n is equal to log [(0.49/0.01)/(0.01/0.49)]/(log 1.6) = 16.5, compared with the 22 plates required at a reflux ratio of 4/1 (2.58 times the minimum reflux ratio).

Location of Optimum Feed Tray. As in binary distillation, the feed must be added onto the proper tray if a fixed total number of trays is to give maximum separation of the keys. Gilliland [*Ind. Eng. Chem.*, **32**, 918 (1940)] has shown that, if the feed is a saturated liquid, it is proper to introduce the feed onto the tray where the ratio of the key components in the tray liquid is the same as the key ratio in the feed; or, if the compositions cannot be made to match exactly, it should be added to the tray where the light-key-to-heavy-key ratio is slightly lower (rather than slightly higher) than the same ratio in the feed.

When the thermal condition of the feed is other than a saturated liquid, Gilliland (*loc. cit.*) showed that the optimum feed-tray location is a function of the ratio of the key-component compositions at the intersection of the operating lines. This latter ratio $(x_l/x_h)_i$ is given by

$$\left(\frac{x_l}{x_h}\right)_i = \frac{Fz_{Fl} + (V_n/V_m - 1)Wx_{wl}}{Fz_{Fh} + (V_n/V_m - 1)Wx_{wh}} \qquad (13\text{-}79)$$

where z_{Fl} and z_{Fh} are the compositions of the light key and the heavy key, respectively, in the total feed. The optimum feed-tray location is then as follows:

Case 1. Either the feed is all liquid, or, if partly vaporized, the vapor portion is introduced in such a manner that it comes into intimate contact with the feed-plate liquid. For this condition, it is very nearly true that

$$\left(\frac{x_l}{x_h}\right)_f \leqq \left(\frac{x_l}{x_h}\right)_i \leqq \left(\frac{x_l}{x_h}\right)_{(f+1)} \qquad (13\text{-}80)$$

where subscript f refers to the feed plate, subscript $f + 1$ refers to the plate above the feed, and subscript i refers to the point of intersection of the operating lines.

Case 2. The feed is partly vaporized, the liquid and vapor portions of the feed are in equilibrium, the liquid portion mixes with the feed-plate liquid, and the vapor portion mixes with the feed-plate vapor. For this case, it is very nearly true that

$$\left(\frac{x_l}{x_h}\right)_f \leqq \left(\frac{x_l}{x_h}\right)_F \leqq \left(\frac{x_l}{x_h}\right)_{(f+1)} \qquad (13\text{-}81)$$

where subscript F refers to the liquid portion of the feed.

Case 3. The feed is a superheated vapor that mixes with the vapor from the feed plate but does not come in contact with the feed-plate liquid. For this case, it is very nearly true that

$$\left(\frac{x_l}{x_h}\right)_{(f+1)} \leqq \left(\frac{x_l}{x_h}\right)_i \leqq \left(\frac{x_l}{x_h}\right)_{(f+2)} \qquad (13\text{-}82)$$

The reason the above relationships are not exactly true is that the effect of the changing compositions of the non-key components has been neglected. For exact determination of the optimum feed-tray location, trial calculations in the neighborhood of the feed are useful. Starting several trays below the approximate feed tray, make tray-to-tray calculations upward, testing on each tray whether the enrichment of the keys is greater by continuing in the stripping section or by changing over to the rectifying section. By such a procedure the optimum feed-tray location is definitely and accurately determined.

Summary of Exact Procedures for Designing New Columns or Determining Separating Ability of Existing Columns. If a multicomponent column is to be designed, usually the feed conditions and product distribution of the keys are fixed, and it is desired to compute the number of theoretical trays, the operating reflux ratio, and the feed-tray location.

The exact procedure to follow is first to compute the minimum reflux ratio and then, by economic considerations, decide upon an operating reflux ratio; an operating reflux ratio L/D of about $1.3(L/D)_{\min}$ is often acceptable. Next it is necessary to estimate the distribution of non-key components in the overhead and bottoms products, which is followed by tray-to-tray calculations down from the top and up from the bottom toward the feed tray. The variation of α values and vapor- and liquid-flow rates on each tray should be taken into account in these calculations if necessary. The feed tray is reached when the key ratio reaches the value prescribed by Eq. (13-80), (13-81), or (13-82). In the first trial, the non-key component compositions will not match at the feed tray, and adjustment of the non-key compositions in the overhead and bottoms products must then be made and the calculations repeated until the match is reasonably close. This procedure is commonly known as the **Lewis and Matheson method** [*Ind. Eng. Chem.*, **24**, 494 (1932)].

One of the important difficulties of this procedure is the inability to predict in advance the distribution in the products of the non-key components. As mentioned on p. 13-35, if the non-keys have α values appreciably different from the keys, it can often be assumed that the lighter-than-light keys will be absent in the stripping column and the heavier-than-heavy keys will be absent in the rectifying column, and the number of trays can then be computed based upon this assumption. If this assumption cannot be made, it is often helpful to use the **approximation of Hengstebeck** [*Trans. Am. Inst. Chem. Engrs.*, **42**, 309 (1946)] to estimate the distribution of the non-keys. He suggests that values of log (Dx_D/Wx_w) for the two keys be plotted vs. α and that the resulting two points be connected by a straight line. The product distribution of the non-keys can then be obtained by reading from an extension of this straight line the value of log (Dx_D/Wx_W) for any non-key component from knowledge of its α value.

If the separating ability of an existing column is to be computed, usually the number of trays, feed-tray location, feed conditions, and reflux ratio are specified, and it is desired to predict the product distribution to be obtained. In such an instance a useful tool is the **Thiele and Geddes method** [*Ind. Eng. Chem.*, **25**, 289 (1933)]. According to this method the overhead and bottoms compositions remain as unknowns, and the ratio of the tray composition of interest to the appropriate terminal concentration is successively computed for each tray by a modified tray-to-tray calculation. For example, in the stripping section, the vapor-liquid relationship is given by

$$\frac{y_m}{x_w} = K_m \frac{x_m}{x_w} \qquad (13\text{-}83)$$

where K_m is the K factor for tray m as defined by Eq. (13-31); for the rectifying section, the vapor-liquid relationship is

$$\frac{x_n}{x_D} = \frac{y_n/x_D}{K_n} \qquad (13\text{-}84)$$

(It is readily apparent that α values are not suitable for this type of calculation.)

Operating-line relationships are obtained by dividing both sides of the regular operating-line equation for the rectifying section [Eq. (13-47)] by x_D, and by dividing both sides of the stripping operating line [Eq. (13-49)] by x_W; this gives

$$\frac{y_n}{x_D} = \frac{L_{n+1}}{V_n}\left(\frac{x_{n+1}}{x_D} - 1\right) + 1 \qquad (13\text{-}85)$$

$$\frac{x_{m+1}}{x_W} = \frac{V_m}{L_{m+1}}\left(\frac{y_m}{x_W} - 1\right) + 1 \qquad (13\text{-}86)$$

As an example of the use of these equations, consider a tray-to-tray calculation starting at the reboiler where three components are involved and where $V_m/L_{m+1} = 0.8$. Assume the reboiler temperature to be t_w, at which temperature the K factors are as given below. The liquid composition on the bottom tray (tray 1) in terms of x_1/x_w is then computed as follows:

Component	Bottoms composition	K_w	(y_w/x_w) by Eq. (13-83)	(x_1/x_w) by Eq. (13-86)
A	$x_w/x_w = 1$	2.0	2.0	1.80
B	$x_w/x_w = 1$	1.2	1.2	1.16
C	$x_w/x_w = 1$	0.5	0.5	0.60

After assuming a new temperature for tray 1, the calculations are continued another step upward as follows:

Component	(x_1/x_w)	K_1	(y_1/x_w) by Eq. (13-83)	(x_2/x_w) by Eq. (13-86)
A	1.80	1.8	3.24	2.79
B	1.16	1.0	1.16	1.13
C	0.60	0.33	0.20	0.36

It should be obvious that calculations of this type can be continued upward to the feed tray, and also from the top of the column downward to the feed tray, provided a temperature profile is assumed for the trays of the existing column, and provided an L/V ratio is assumed for the rectifying section.

The vapor leaving the feed tray has the same composition regardless of whether it was computed from calculations made from the top down or from the bottom up; so that the ratio $(y_f/x_w)/(y_f/x_D)$ when next computed for each component is also equal to x_D/x_W. These x_D/x_W ratios can then be used to compute the total moles of distillate D by the equation

$$\frac{z_A}{(D/F)[1 - (x_{AW}/x_{AD})] + (x_{AW}/x_{AD})} + \frac{z_B}{(D/F)[1 - (x_{BW}/x_{BD})] + (x_{BW}/x_{BD})} + \cdots = 1 \qquad (13\text{-}87)$$

where z_A is the mole fraction of component A in the total feed, F is the total moles of feed, and x_{AW}/x_{AD} is the x_W/x_D ratio for component A. Once a value is found for D, W is readily obtained as $F - D$, and individual values of x_D may be obtained by writing Eq. (13-44) as $Fz_F = Dx_D + W(x_W/x_D)x_D$. Individual tray liquid compositions may now be computed, and if these values for each tray do not add up to unity, the assumed temperature profile is in error and the calculation must be repeated with new temperature values.

A systematic procedure for estimating column temperature profiles has been given by Hummel [*Trans. Am. Inst. Chem. Engrs.*, **40**, 445 (1944)], and other modifications of the Thiele-Geddes method have been proposed by Rea and Hanson [*Petrol. Refiner*, **31** (11), 139 (1952)] and by Opler and Heitz [*Ind. Eng. Chem.*, **43**, 2465 (1951)]. In the latter reference a Thiele-Geddes calculation is used to obtain a first approximation of the distribution of components in the overhead and bottoms products, after which a Lewis-Matheson calculation is made, based upon the just-computed products distribution, to determine a more exact temperature profile. This is used in turn to obtain a more exact products distribution by a second Thiele-Geddes calculation, and the process is repeated until an exact solution results.

The use of absorption and stripping factors for design of multicomponent columns was developed by Brown and Souders [*Trans. Am. Inst. Chem. Engrs.*, **30**, 438 (1934)]. Later information on this approach to multicomponent calculations is given by Edmister [*Am. Inst. Chem. Engrs. J.*, **3**, 165 (1957)].

Use of Automatic Computers. The considerable trial and error involved in the exact design procedures described above points to the profitable use of automatic computers for the design of multicomponent distillation columns. Ready availability of such computers in many organizations has favored the present-day use of the exact but tedious design methods over the short-cut methods used so extensively in previous years. The development of computer programs for multicomponent column design has proceeded along two main lines of endeavor: (1) development of computer solutions for handling existing design procedures; and (2) development of new exact procedures which were, before the advent of computers, too complex to be practical.

Computer Programs Using Existing Design Methods. Programs of this type use either the Lewis-Matheson method (*loc. cit.*), the Thiele-Geddes method (*loc. cit.*), or modifications thereof.

The only difficulties encountered with the various computer solutions of the Lewis-Matheson method are (1) development of a foolproof procedure for adjusting the trial values of products distribution so that successive trials converge rapidly upon the true solution; and (2) availability of a sound basis for choosing the initial trial values required.

Bonner made a number of recommendations in this regard [*Petrol. Processing*, **11** (6), 64 (1956); *Chem. Eng. Progress, Symp. Ser.* 21, **55**, 87 (1959)]. He suggests it should be assumed initially that no light components appear in the bottoms, no heavy components appear in the distillate, and then the resulting zero concentrations are replaced with 10^{-40} moles/hr.; that a linear temperature profile be assumed, with limits taken as values which lie well outside the expected temperature range; and that vapor rates be assumed constant regardless of feed condition. The computer then bases its first plate-to-plate calculation on these assumptions, and in succeeding trials, each of these three factors is recalculated on the assumption that the other two remain constant. Bonner states that "in spite of the apparent coarseness of the technique, convergence to a solution is extremely rapid." After each trial Bonner adjusts the distillate and bottoms rate of each component by a factor related to the degree of "mismatch" of that component at the feed tray. A computer procedure recommended by Shelton and McIntire [*Chem. Eng. Progress, Symp. Ser.* 21, **55**, 69 (1959)] is quite similar in its basic methods to that of Bonner.

Rose *et al.* pointed out that difficulties are sometimes encountered in the computer procedures just discussed in the choice of successive trial values [*Ind. Eng. Chem.*, **50**, 737 (1958)].

An intensive study by Lyster *et al.* [*Petrol. Refiner*, **38** (6), 221 (1959); **38** (7), 151 (1959); **38** (10), 139 (1959); **39** (8), 121 (1960)] resulted in a recommended computer procedure which converges rapidly upon the true solution. These authors use a Thiele-Geddes procedure to compute trial values of bottoms-to-distillate withdrawal-rate ratios (b/d values) for each component, and these values are then corrected so that the required total distillate rate and all over-all balances are satisfied. The correction is made by use of a multiplier θ, which is the same for all components, by the relation $(b/d)_{\text{corrected}} = \theta(b/d)_{\text{trial}}$. Choice of the proper value of θ to be employed uses a short computer sub-routine in which Newton's method is applied. Lyster *et al.* also recommend the use of two "forcing procedures" which increase the rate at which the computer converges on the correct answer. The first is an improved procedure for adjusting the temperature profile, and the second is to compensate for deviations in calculated values of distillate rate which result in the third trial when enthalpy balances are introduced for the first time. Application of all these modifications is straightforward, and rapidly converging solutions were obtained by the authors for more than fifty different examples. The extensive experience and good results underlying the Lyster method make it quite attractive for widespread application to most hydrocarbon distillations. Details are available on programming the Lyster method for an IBM 705 computer [*Chem. Eng. Progress*, **55** (7), 90 (1959)].

A multicomponent distillation program designed especially for the IBM 704 computer has been described by Greenstadt, Bard, and Morse [*Ind. Eng. Chem.*, **50**, 1644 (1958)]. This program employs assumed "starting" values of appropriate variables at the top and bottom of the column and performs tray-to-tray calculations to obtain values of all other variables in the column. Discrepancies in material and heat balances at the feed tray are used to supply new estimates of the starting values using an "appropriately framed" form of Newton's method. The authors state that at times the Newton method fails to converge, in which case corrections are made to the trial values in a way such that an improvement toward convergence is achieved. The article gives no specific example, and only four or five types of problems appear to have been evaluated. However, solution time for the problems considered on this large computer was apparently 12 min. or less.

Mills [*Chem. Eng. Progress*, **55** (7), 93 (1959)] described a program for handling up to ten components in a mixture where liquid-phase activity coefficients differed considerably from unity. He stated that manual intervention may be required to ensure convergence.

Edison (M.S. Thesis in Chemical Engineering, University of Delaware, 1961) has found a number of different procedures which are useful in forcing a computer program to converge steadily to the final answer under conditions where the relative volatility varies widely with composition. No one procedure was found, however, which could be used unassisted in all cases. Rose *et al.* have given the results of their experience in computing tray requirements for a methanol-ethanol-water separation [*Chem. Eng. Progress, Symp. Ser.* 21, **55**, 79 (1959)]. O'Brien and Franks demonstrated the feasibility of using an analog computer for making plate-to-plate calculations for a column separating acetylene from ethylene by extractive distillation [*Chem. Eng. Progress, Symp. Ser.* 21, **55**, 25 (1959)].

Example of Computer Solution. Details of a computer solution to a typical multicomponent design problem have been given by Edison (*loc. cit.*). In this instance a medium-speed computer, the Bendix G-15D, was used, along with a Bendix standard computer program for multicomponent distillation (Applications Section Project 94, Bendix Computer Div., Bendix Aviation Corp., Los Angeles, July 24, 1959). This program was originally written by Dow Chemical Co. and later adapted to the Intercom 1000 interpretive system.

The Bendix program calculates overhead and bottoms compositions from knowledge of the feed composition and thermal condition, reflux ratio, number of theoretical plates above and below the feed, per cent recovery for one of the components in the distillate, and relative volatilities of the components. It is assumed in the program that relative volatilities are constant and that equal molal overflow prevails in the rectifying and stripping sections, although modifications may be introduced to account for variations in these quantities. As many as ten components can be accommodated.

The computer solution proceeds in the following manner: Initial arbitrary assumptions are made for the moles of each non-specified component in the overhead and in the bottoms. Tray-to-tray calculations are then made from the bottom up and from the top down to the feed tray. The degree of unbalance in the feed-tray compositions is used to obtain a new set of estimates for the moles in the overhead and bottoms, and the process is repeated until a match in composition is obtained at the feed tray.

Consider the following case as an example. The feed condition is

Component	Relative volatility	Moles/hr. in feed
A	1.9	25
B	1.6	25
C	1.0	25
D	0.7	25

The feed is a saturated liquid, reflux ratio L/D is $4/1$, and there are 12 theoretical plates in both the rectifying and stripping sections. A closed reboiler and total condenser are used, and equal molal overflow and constant relative volatilities are assumed. It is desired to compute overhead and bottoms compositions when 98 per cent recovery of component *B* in the overhead is specified. (These conditions are essentially the same as those considered in the example on p. 13-37.)

The computer first calculates the distribution of *B* in the overhead and bottoms, and then arbitrarily assumes a distribution for the other components as follows:

Component	Moles/hr. in	
	Overhead	Bottoms
A	25.0	0.00001
B	24.5	0.5
C	0.00001	25.0
D	0.00001	25.0

After tray-to-tray calculations are completed from each end of the column to the feed tray in the first trial, the correction term Δ_i is computed as follows for each component i:

$$\Delta_i = 1.5 \frac{x_{FW} - x_{FD}}{(x_{FW}/w_i) - (x_{FD}/d_i)}$$

where x_{FW} is the feed-tray composition for component i as computed by the tray-to-tray calculation from the bottom upward; x_{FD} is the feed-tray composition for the same component as computed from the top down; w_i and d_i are the moles/hr. of component i in the bottoms and distillate, respectively.

After values of Δ_i are computed for each component, adjustment of the w_i and d_i values is made as follows:

Case 1. If d_i is greater than w_i for the trial just completed, subtract Δ_i from w_i. If this sum is positive, use it as the value for w_i in the next trial; compute d_i for the next trial as $f_i - w_i$, where f_i is the moles of component i in the feed. If the value of $w_i - \Delta_i$ was negative, the new assumption for w_i is taken instead to be one-half the value of w_i from the trial just completed.

Case 2. If d_i is less than w_i for the trial just completed, subtract Δ_i from d_i. If this sum is positive, use it as the value for d_i in the next trial; compute w_i for the next trial as $f_i - d_i$. If $d_i - \Delta_i$ was negative, the new value for d_i is one-half the previous value for d_i.

The effectiveness of the proposed scheme for adjusting the overhead and bottoms flows may now be considered. Note that, in Case 1 where d_i is large, the term x_{FD}/d_i in the definition of Δ_i becomes unimportant, and Δ_i becomes approximately $1.5(\Delta x_F/x_{FW})w_i$, where Δx_F is the degree of mismatch at the feed tray. Thus Δ_i, which is the correction to w_i in Case 1 provided it is not larger than w_i, causes w_i to change approximately by a factor of $[1 - 1.5(\Delta x_F/x_{FW})]$, a most reasonable premise. It should be noted that, if x_{FD} is greater than x_{FW}, then Δx_F is negative and w_i is increased to promote convergence. The factor 1.5 in the definition of Δ_i was found necessary by experience to promote convergence at a reasonably fast rate.

In the example considered, ten trials or iterations were required to cause the ratio x_{FW}/x_{FD} to lie within the range 0.998 to 1.002, a condition considered in the program to be close enough to the true solution to eliminate the need for further trials. Computer time for the entire solution was 55 min., including type-out of the result of each iteration. A plot of the iterative results is shown in Fig. 13-42. The final distribution of components after the tenth iteration was found to be the following:

Component	Moles/hr. in		Composition, mole fraction, in	
	Overhead	Bottoms	Overhead	Bottoms
A	24.9680	0.0324	0.5010	0.0006
B	24.5000	0.5000	0.4916	0.0099
C	0.3626	24.6370	0.0072	0.4911
D	0.0023	24.9980	0.00004	0.4982
	49.8330	50.1680		

These results are similar to those obtained on p. 13-37.

New Computer Procedures for Multicomponent Design. An interesting procedure for making exact multicomponent design calculations has been developed by Acrivos and Amundson [*Ind. Eng. Chem.*, **47**, 1533 (1955)] and has been adapted for a Remington Rand Univac Model 1103 computer by Amundson and Pontinen [*Ind. Eng. Chem.*, **50**, 740 (1958); *Am. Inst. Chem. Engrs. J.*, **5**, 295 (1959)].

These authors express in matrix form the set of heat- and mass-balance equations which apply to each tray of the column. The equations for the whole column are then solved simultaneously, component by component, based upon an assumed temperature gradient; a **matrix-inversion technique** is used. If the assumed temperature gradient is not correct, the liquid compositions x on any tray will not add up to unity, nor will the summation of Kx values for all components on any tray add up to unity (where K is the equilibrium vaporization ratio). In such a case the compositions are normalized, and a

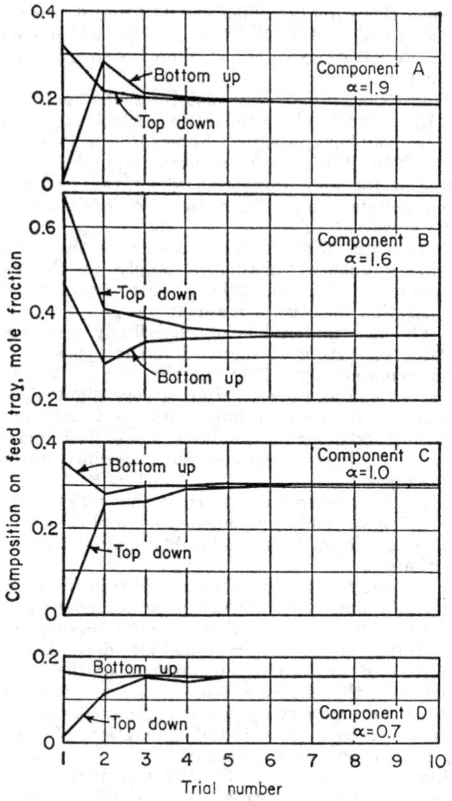

FIG. 13-42. Feed-tray compositions obtained by stepwise calculations from top down and from bottom upward; convergence of these compositions by successive trials on automatic computer is indicated (see example).

new set of temperatures is computed such that the summation of Kx values (where the individual x values are the normalized values) for all trays equals unity. Complete solutions are usually obtained in four or five iterations, but of course the techniques for solving a large number of linear simultaneous algebraic equations require the services of a large, fast computer.

A second new design procedure for making multicomponent calculations is the **relaxation method** suggested by Rose, Sweeny, and Schrodt [*Ind. Eng. Chem.*, **50**, 737 (1958)]. In this method calculations are made for the gradual change in all the plate and product compositions which occur in a column from initial startup until steady state is achieved; batch-distillation equations for the case of appreciable liquid hold-up on the trays are used. The steady-state results obtained are independent of the starting compositions and hold-up quantities used in the calculations, and the method has special value for complicated design problems where multiple columns, non-ideal equilibrium behavior, or multiple draw-offs are encountered. The relaxation method does require repeated trials for cases where the number of trays or feed-tray location is unknown; but each trial does give an exact answer for the chosen conditions. The rate of approach toward steady-state compositions is rapid at first but extremely slow toward the end; thus an approximate solution can be obtained quickly, but an exact solution takes longer unless one is willing to calculate only the first portion of the composition-time curve and extrapolate this to steady state.

Baer, Seader, and Crozier have adapted the Bachelor minimum-reflux method to a Datatron 205 computer [*Chem. Eng. Progress*, **55** (12), 88 (1959)].

Approximate Design Methods. Such methods are of value in many cases, as, for example, when rough cost estimates are to be made, or when various process alternatives are being considered.

Simplest of the various approximate methods is the **Gilliland correlation** [*Ind. Eng. Chem.*, **32**, 1220 (1940)] of reflux ratio and number of plates as functions of minimum reflux and minimum plates. To use Gilliland's correlation, presented graphically in Fig. 13-43, a value

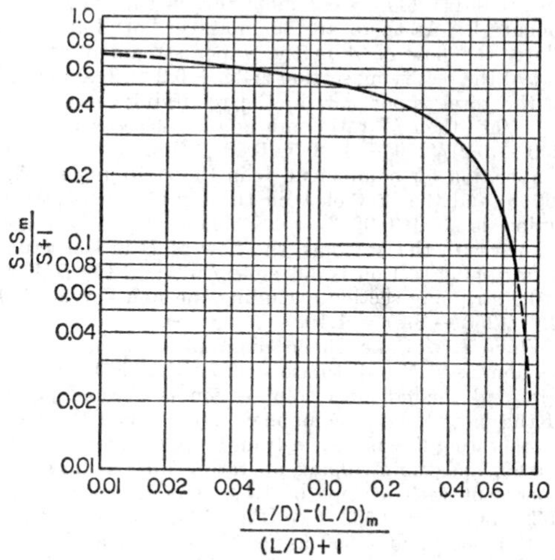

FIG. 13-43. Gilliland's correlation of number of theoretical plates as a function of reflux ratio.

for minimum reflux $(L/D)_m$ is first computed by any of the methods outlined on pp. 13-38 to 13-39, and minimum plates S_m is determined by Eq. (13-60). An operating reflux ratio is chosen, say $L/D = 1.3(L/D)_m$, and from Fig. 13-43 the number of theoretical stages S is determined. For a tower employing a total condenser, $S = N + 1$, where N is the number of theoretical plates in the tower. If a partial condenser is used and the overhead product is removed as a vapor, then $S = N + 2$.

Another widely used design procedure is the **Hengstebeck method** [*Trans. Am. Inst. Chem. Engrs.*, **42**, 309 (1946)]. This method is applicable when the non-key components have α values sufficiently different from those of the keys that the non-keys reach pinch compositions in one section of the column and are essentially absent in the other section. (The tray number–composition diagram for this type of separation is typified in Fig. 13-38.) The method also assumes the applicability of equal molal overflow.

To use the method, a products distribution is assumed, a reflux ratio chosen, and a few tray-to-tray calculations are made from each end of the column until the appropriate non-key components nearly reach their pinch compositions. Exact values for the pinch compositions of the non-keys are then computed by Eqs. (13-72) and (13-73). From the known pinch compositions of the non-keys and the total vapor- and liquid-flow rates in the section of the column considered, it is possible to compute the vapor- and liquid-flow rates of only the non-keys, and by difference to compute the flow rates of only the keys. With this information, a modified McCabe-Thiele diagram is prepared, with compositions computed on a non-key-free basis; the operating lines are drawn from the non-key-free products compositions with slopes equal to L/V computed as the ratio of the key flow rate in the liquid divided by the key flow rate in the vapor. Steps are drawn as on a binary diagram, and the optimum feed tray is located as the step which straddles the intersection point of the operating lines.

As an example of the use of the Hengstebeck method, consider the same problem given on p. 13-35 for which the tray number–composition diagram is Fig. 13-38. In the rectifying section, the lighter-than-light key, component A, approaches its pinch composition of 0.0311 mole fraction. With 100 moles/hr. of feed, the total liquid flow in the rectifying section is 200 moles/hr.; of this, $(0.0311)(200) = 6.2$ moles/hr. is the flow of component A. As there are 25 moles/hr. of A in the distillate, the flow of A in the vapor stream of the main part of the rectifying section is $25 + 6.2$ or 31.2 moles/hr. As the total vapor flow in the rectifying section is 250 moles/hr., the L/V ratio on a non-key-free basis becomes $(200 - 6.2)/(250 - 31.2) = 0.89$. Similarly, the pinch composition for component D in the stripping section is 0.0953, and the flow of D in the liquid of the stripping section is $(300)(0.0953) = 28.6$ moles/hr. By material balance with the bottoms, the flow of D in the vapor of the stripping section is 3.6 moles/hr., and the L/V ratio in the stripping section excluding the non-key is $(300 - 28.6)/(250 - 3.6) = 1.10$.

When a McCabe-Thiele diagram is drawn omitting the non-keys, the distillate composition is 98 mole per cent, and the bottoms composition is 2 mole per cent (of the more volatile component B). When the rectifying operating line is drawn from 98 per cent with a slope of 0.89, and the stripping operating line is drawn from 2 per cent with a slope of 1.10, they intersect at $x_i = 0.532$ and $y_i = 0.583$ (see Fig. 13-44). Note that x_i does not occur at 0.500 as for the case of a binary distillation where the saturated liquid feed has a composition of 0.500. The y-x equilibrium curve is drawn using an α value of 1.6, which is that of the light key relative to the heavy key. Before steps are drawn on the modified McCabe-Thiele diagram, four tray-to-tray calculations are made from the top down to reach the approximate lighter-than-light key pinch composition, and three tray-to-tray calculations are made from the bottom up to reach the heavier-than-heavy key pinch. The number of steps on the McCabe-Thiele diagram

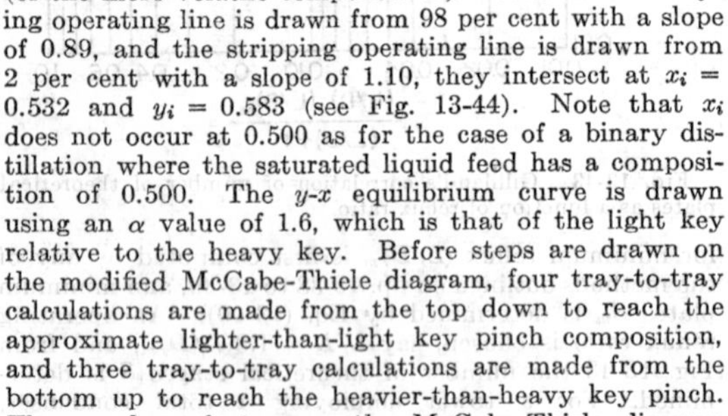

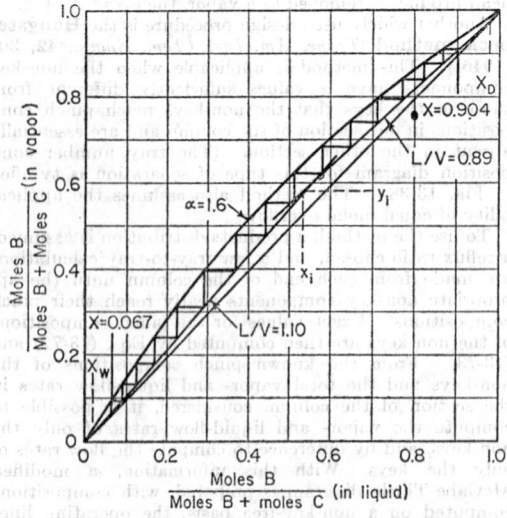

FIG. 13-44. Solution to problem by Hengstebeck method.

between these limits, which are 90.4 and 6.7 per cent B on an A-free and D-free basis, is 15, which compares favorably with the 15 steps found by an exact tray-to-tray calculation.

Hengstebeck (*loc. cit.*) also presents recommended procedures for handling separations which are not sharp; in a later publication with Schubert [*Chem. Eng. Progress*, **53** (5), 243 (1957)], a more exact graphical method is presented for handling cases where the feed contains large amounts of materials with volatilities close to those of the keys.

Petroleum Distillation. Although the principles of multicomponent distillation apply to the case of petroleum distillation, this subject warrants special consideration for several reasons:

1. The raw material is of exceedingly complex composition, consisting of many different types of hydrocarbon compounds. The number of such compounds in a given boiling range exhibiting very slight differences in volatility multiplies rapidly with rise in boiling point.
2. Most commercial products made from petroleum are in themselves complex mixtures specified by boiling-point ranges.
3. The character and yields of the various fractions vary widely depending upon the source of the crude, and even crudes from the same locality may exhibit marked variations.
4. The scale of distillation operations in the petroleum industry is much greater than in any other industry.

Crude Distillation. The optimum manner in which to separate a crude oil in each instance depends upon the properties of the crude, the markets of the individual refiner, and the characteristics of the refinery (such as whether the refinery includes equipment for making lubricating oils). The initial separation of crude oil into its various cuts is accomplished by atmospheric distillation in a **pipe-still distillation unit.** As shown by Hengstebeck ("Petroleum Processing," McGraw-Hill, New York, 1959), this unit is mainly a rectifying column from which a number of side-stream products are withdrawn as well as overhead and bottoms: an overhead gas product and light gasoline liquid overhead product at about 240°F.; a heavy gasoline side stream at about 335°F.; a kerosene side stream at about 420°F.; a gas-oil side stream at about 500°F.; a light wax-distillate side stream at about 600°F.; and a bottoms product at about 800°F. (see Fig. 13-45). Separate steam strippers are often used with each side stream to

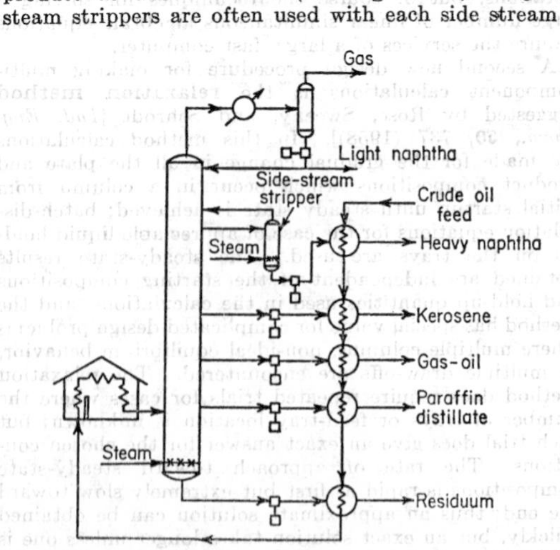

FIG. 13-45 Pipe-still crude-distillation unit. (*Hengstebeck, "Petroleum Processing," McGraw-Hill, New York,* 1959.)

eliminate "light ends," which are returned to the main column.

Vacuum Distillation. The bottoms from the initial atmospheric-pressure distillation of the crude may next be subjected to a vacuum distillation operation to make an overhead product suitable for further refining into lubricating oils or for use as a charge stock for catalytic cracking; the bottoms product may be used for asphalt. Pressures usually range between 30 and 80 mm. mercury absolute, and steam is also used to reduce further the hydrocarbon partial pressure. Additional information on petroleum distillations is contained in Nelson ("Petroleum Refinery Engineering," 4th ed., McGraw-Hill, New York, 1958).

Characterizing Petroleum Products by Laboratory Distillations. Because it is difficult to identify the various chemical entities present in a given petroleum fraction, three types of laboratory distillations are commonly used to characterize such fractions. These are the true boiling point (TBP) distillation, the American Society for Testing Materials (A.S.T.M.) distillation, and the equilibrium-flash vaporization (EFV) distillation.

In the **TBP distillation,** a sample of the petroleum fraction to be characterized is batch-distilled in a column containing as many as 100 equilibrium stages and with a reflux ratio as high as 100 to 1. If the sample contains compounds which have moderate differences in boiling point such as in a light gasoline containing *i*-butane, *n*-butane, *i*-pentane, etc., a plot of overhead vapor temperature vs. per cent distilled would appear as in Fig. 13-46. However, if the sample has a higher average boiling range where the number of close-boiling isomers increases, the steps are no longer distinct and a curve such as that in Fig. 13-47 results.

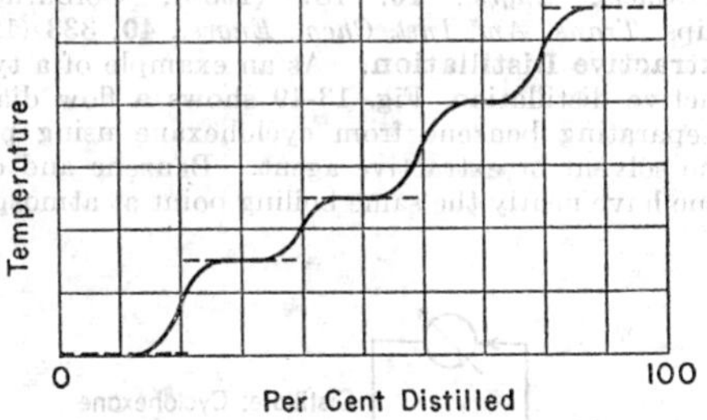

FIG. 13-46. Variation of boiling temperature with per cent distilled in true-boiling-point distillation of light hydrocarbons.

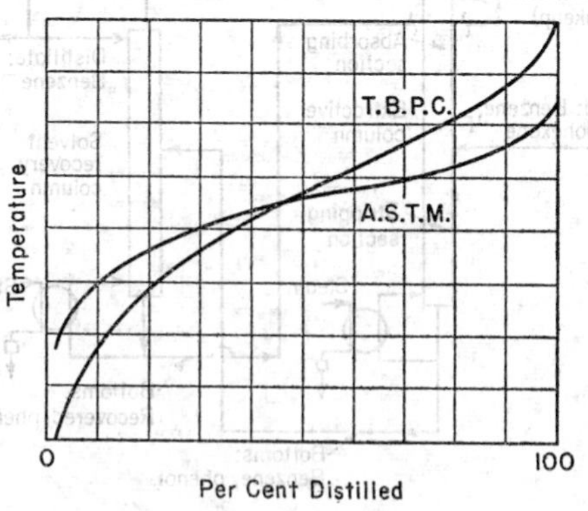

FIG. 13-47. True boiling-point curve (TBPC) compared with A.S.T.M. distillation curve.

An **A.S.T.M. distillation** is a simple distillation using equipment and procedure which are rigorously specified in the A.S.T.M. Book of Standards (American Society for Testing Materials, Philadelphia, 1960). The apparatus is shown in Fig. 13-48. The procedure involves charging

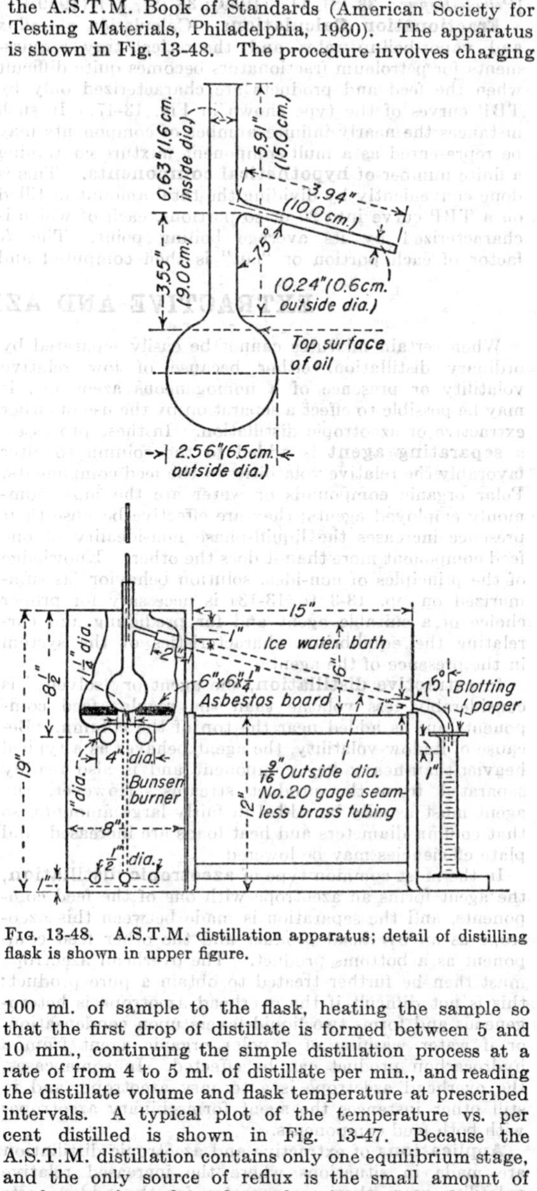

FIG. 13-48. A.S.T.M. distillation apparatus; detail of distilling flask is shown in upper figure.

100 ml. of sample to the flask, heating the sample so that the first drop of distillate is formed between 5 and 10 min., continuing the simple distillation process at a rate of from 4 to 5 ml. of distillate per min., and reading the distillate volume and flask temperature at prescribed intervals. A typical plot of the temperature vs. per cent distilled is shown in Fig. 13-47. Because the A.S.T.M. distillation contains only one equilibrium stage, and the only source of reflux is the small amount of condensate formed on the cool surfaces of the flask, the degree of separation is not so high as with the TBP distillation. Thus the initial boiling point is lower and the end-point temperature is higher when a given sample is distilled with the TBP method as compared with the A.S.T.M. method.

In the **equilibrium-flash vaporization** (EFV) **distillation,** vapor and liquid are brought together at a given temperature until equilibrium is established, and the amount vaporized is recorded. The process is repeated at various temperatures. The separation is poorer than with the A.S.T.M. procedure.

If either the TBP, A.S.T.M., or EFV curves are available, the other two may be predicted using empirical methods presented by Edmister and Pollock [*Chem. Eng. Progress*, **44**, 905 (1948)] and Edmister and Okamoto [*Petrol. Refiner*, **38** (8), 117 (1959); **38** (9), 271 (1959)].

Fractionation Calculations. Calculation of reflux and vapor-boilup rates and theoretical tray requirements for petroleum fractionators becomes quite difficult when the feed and products are characterized only by TBP curves of the type shown in Fig. 13-47. In such instances the nearly infinite number of components may be represented as a multicomponent mixture containing a finite number of **hypothetical components.** This is done conveniently by dividing the total amount distilled on a TBP curve into 20 or so portions, each of which is characterized by its average boiling point. The K factor of each portion or "cut" is then computed and fractionation design calculations made in the usual way. For irregularly shaped TBP curves the hypothetical-component boiling points may be taken at irregular intervals, or narrow cuts of equal boiling point width but of varying amount may be used.

Obviously the accuracy of such calculations increases as the number of hypothetical components is increased, and methods are available whereby a petroleum fraction may be considered as a continuum mixture containing an infinite number of components. The procedures are illustrated by Bowman and Edmister [*Ind. Eng. Chem.*, **43,** 2625 (1951); *Chem. Eng. Progress, Symp. Ser.* 2, **48,** 112 (1952); *Chem. Eng. Progress, Symp. Ser.* 3, **48,** 46 (1952)] and by Edmister [*Petrol. Refiner*, **38** (10), 163 (1959); **39** (4), 193 (1960)].

EXTRACTIVE AND AZEOTROPIC DISTILLATION

When certain mixtures cannot be easily separated by ordinary distillation, either because of low relative volatility or presence of a homogeneous azeotrope, it may be possible to effect a separation by the use of either extractive or azeotropic distillation. In these processes, a **separating agent** is added to the column to alter favorably the relative volatilities of the feed components. Polar organic compounds or water are the most commonly employed agents; they are effective because their presence increases the liquid-phase non-ideality of one feed component more than it does the other. Knowledge of the principles of non-ideal solution behavior (as summarized on pp. 13-3 to 13-13) is necessary for proper choice of a suitable agent and for predicting and correlating the equilibrium characteristics of the system in the presence of the agent.

In **extractive distillation,** the agent or "solvent" is considerably less volatile than the regular feed components and is added near the top of the column. Because of its low volatility, the agent behaves as a typical heavier-than-heavy key component and is also readily separated from the product streams. However, the agent must usually be added in fairly large amounts, so that column diameters and heat loads are increased, and plate efficiencies may be lowered.

In the most common type of **azeotropic distillation,** the agent forms an azeotrope with one of the feed components, and the separation is made between this azeotrope as an overhead product and the other feed component as a bottoms product. The overhead azeotrope must then be further treated to obtain a pure product; this is not difficult if the overhead azeotrope is heterogeneous and forms two liquid layers upon condensation, or if water washing of a polar organic agent from a hydrocarbon product can be effected. In some cases, the overhead azeotrope is a ternary azeotrope, and in still other instances the agent forms binary azeotropes with both feed components.

Applications of extractive and azeotropic distillation are made in situations where the increased relative volatility more than compensates for the added costs incurred by purchasing the agents and providing for their recycle through the process. The number of process applications in this area is not large, but several are quite important. The use of extractive distillation as a method for separating butanes from butylenes and butylenes from butadiene was introduced during World War II. At that time Phillips developed its furfural-water process [Buell and Boatright, *Ind. Eng. Chem.*, **39,** 695 (1947). Happel, *Trans. Am. Inst. Chem. Engrs.*, **42,** 189 (1946)] and Shell developed its acetone-water process [Brack and Beychock, *Petrol. Refiner*, **36** (6), 143 (1957)]. Shell has found it profitable to use acetonitrile in place of acetone as the extractive solvent for n-butane–1-butene separations in one of its plants [Chilton, *Chem. Eng.*, **64** (2), 146 (1957)], although much interest remains in the use of acetone for this separation [Ewanchyna and Ambridge, *Can. J. Chem. Eng.*, **36**, 19 (1958)].

Carlson, Smith, and Morrell [*Ind. Eng. Chem.*, **46,** 350 (1954)] reported that water is an effective extractive distillation agent for separating the products from a Fischer-Tropsch synthesis plant. Water has also been suitable for separating some of the various products derived from the partial oxidation of hydrocarbons, according to Hopkins and Fritsch [*Chem. Eng. Progress*, **51,** 361 (1955)], although azeotropic distillation with either water or a pure hydrocarbon as the agent is also used to advantage for other separations required in this process. Dehydration of alcohols is readily accomplished by azeotropic distillation when the agent is either an aromatic hydrocarbon, a paraffin hydrocarbon, or a chlorinated hydrocarbon [Guinot and Clark, *Trans. Inst. Chem. Engrs.*, **16,** 187 (1938). Colburn and Phillips, *Trans. Am. Inst. Chem. Engrs.*, **40,** 333 (1944)].

Extractive Distillation. As an example of a typical extractive distillation, Fig. 13-49 shows a flow diagram for separating benzene from cyclohexane using phenol as the solvent or extractive agent. Benzene and cyclohexane have nearly the same boiling point at atmospheric

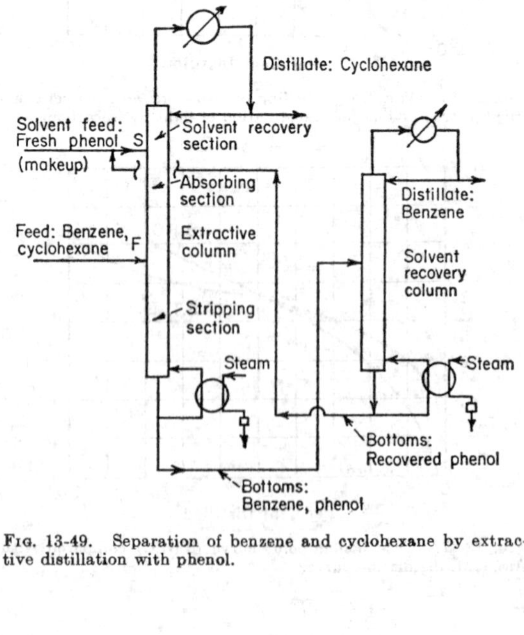

FIG. 13-49. Separation of benzene and cyclohexane by extractive distillation with phenol.

pressure and form a homogeneous azeotrope containing about 45 weight per cent cyclohexane. However, if phenol is present in the liquid phase in fairly large amounts, the volatility of cyclohexane is nearly twice that of benzene over all cyclohexane-to-benzene concentration ratios [Dunn, Millar, Pierotti, Shiras, and Souders, *Trans. Am. Inst. Chem. Engrs.*, **41**, 631 (1945)]. Presence of the relatively polar phenol causes the activity coefficients for cyclohexane to be nearly twice as large as those for benzene.

In Fig. 13-49 the benzene-cyclohexane feed is introduced continuously at point F while phenol is fed continuously at point S, several trays from the top of the column. Phenol is considerably less volatile than either benzene or cyclohexane and flows down the column and out the bottom. The few trays above point S remove small amounts of phenol from the vapor stream. The overhead vapor is essentially pure cyclohexane; after condensation, part of the cyclohexane is returned to the top tray as reflux. The bottom-tray liquid is partly reboiled, but most of it, consisting of benzene-phenol with a trace of cyclohexane, is sent to a second column where phenol is separated from the benzene by ordinary distillation. The phenol is then recycled to the extractive column.

Choice of Separating Agent. The solvent chosen for an extractive distillation should be non-corrosive to the equipment, non-reactive with the feed components, thermally stable, readily available, inexpensive, and non-toxic. It should have a boiling point sufficiently higher than the feed components so that separation of the solvent and the bottoms product is easily accomplished, but preferably not so high that the sensible heat requirement of the solvent cycle becomes a large fraction of the total heat input. Of most importance, however, are the selectivity and capacity of the separating agent. **Selectivity** may be defined as the relative volatility of the feed components in the presence of the agent divided by the relative volatility of the feed components in the absence of the agent. **Capacity** is the liquid concentration of the feed components in the agent at which the selectivity is measured; the capacity is often limited by miscibility considerations. For example, water as an agent for separating paraffins from olefins gives good selectivity but its capacity is severely limited.

If the two feed components are designated as 1 and 2, and if, in the absence of the agent, $\gamma_1 = \gamma_2 = 1$, application of Eq. (13-8) shows that the selectivity is γ_1/γ_2. Gerster, Gorton, and Eklund [*J. Chem. Eng. Data*, **5**, 423 (1960)] have shown that, for the case where the feed components are infinitely dilute, the γ_1/γ_2 ratio for pentane-pentene in various extractive agents increases as γ_1 increases. Their data for 25°C., shown in Fig. 13-50, indicate that selectivity is greatest when the non-ideality of the pentane-agent binary is greatest. An upper limit is usually set on the degree of non-ideality which can be tolerated, however, by miscibility considerations; as shown on p. 13-10, if the maximum solubility or capacity of the feed components in the solvent is desired to exceed, say, 10 mole per cent, the activity coefficients must not exceed about 10. From Fig. 13-50, maximum selectivity obtainable at this chosen capacity is then about 1.85. Figure 13-50 also shows clearly the selectivity advantage presented by non-hydrogen-bonding solvents at any chosen capacity.

Although Fig. 13-50 indicates that for a given temperature and concentration the only factor affecting paraffin-olefin selectivity is the capacity, it is not known whether such a conclusion is completely general.

Final choice of an extractive agent for a new application is usually based upon laboratory measurements of the selectivity and capacity of several promising agents. The work of Hess, Naragon, and Coghlan [*Chem. Eng. Progress, Symp. Series* 2, **48**, 72 (1952)] is typical of this approach; solvents of nearly every chemical type were evaluated for a n-butane–2-butene separation. Such a procedure is time-consuming; selectivity is affected by temperature, solvent concentration, and the relative amount of the feed components in the liquid. On the other hand, the number of experiments can be minimized by eliminating solvents not producing the proper activity-coefficient range and by utilizing the principles of non-ideal, multicomponent solution behavior presented in

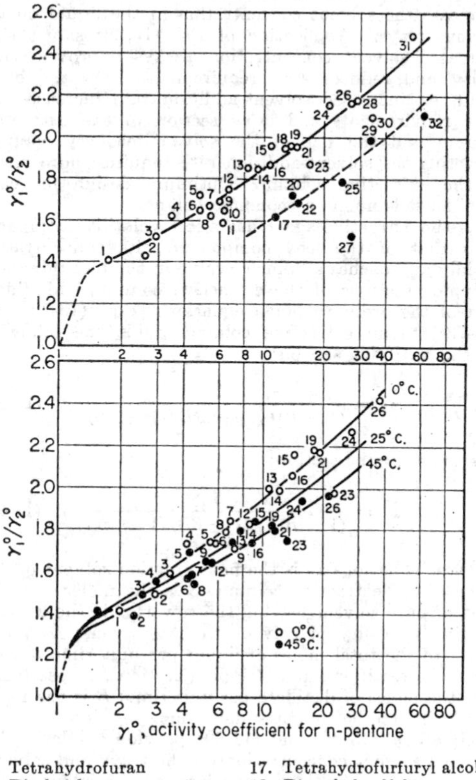

1. Tetrahydrofuran
2. Diethyl ketone
3. Diethyl carbonate
4. Methyl ethyl ketone
5. Pentanedione
6. Cyclopentanone
7. Acetone
8. Butyronitrile
9. Acetyl piperidine
10. Acetophenone
11. Pyridine
12. Diethyl oxalate
13. Propionitrile
14. Dimethyl acetamide
15. n-Methyl pyrrolidone
16. Acetonyl acetone
17. Tetrahydrofurfuryl alcohol
18. Dimethyl sulfolane
19. Dimethyl cyanamide
20. Methyl Carbitol
21. Dimethyl formamide
22. Methyl Cellosolve
23. Furfural
24. Acetonitrile
25. Ethylene chlorhydrin
26. γ-Butyrolactone
27. Methanol
28. β-Chloropropionitrile
29. Pyrrolidone
30. Propylene carbonate
31. Nitromethane
32. Ethylene diamine

Fig. 13-50. Effect of activity coefficient for n-pentane at infinite dilution in extractive agent γ_1^0 upon selectivity of agent for n-pentane–1-pentene separation by extractive distillation (γ_1^0/γ_2^0). Upper graph shows results at 25°C. for various agents listed by number below; solid points and dashed line are for hydrogen-bonding agents, open points and solid line are for non-hydrogen-bonding agents. Lower graph shows results for 0° and 45°C. for non-hydrogen-bonding agents; solid line from upper graph, representing results at 25°C., is reproduced without points in lower graph. [*Gerster, Gorton, and Eklund, J. Chem. Eng. Data*, **5**, 423 (1960).]

pp. 13-12 to 13-13 to correlate and extend the experimental results.

An alternate approach for reducing the amount of experimental work involved is to use a gas chromatography apparatus in place of a vapor-liquid still. Use of such an apparatus to determine the selectivity of various agents has been described by Warren, Warren, and Yarborough [*Ind. Eng. Chem.*, **51**, 1475 (1959)] and by Porter, Deal, and Stross [*J. Am. Chem. Soc.*, **78**, 2999 (1956)].

Optimum Solvent-addition Rate. Under fixed operating conditions an increase in solvent-addition rate increases the solvent concentration in the liquid on the various trays. Application of Eq. (13-28) shows that increased solvent concentration always improves selectivity and reduces tray requirements. On the other hand, an increased solvent-addition rate increases the heat requirements and cross section of the extractive column and the size of the solvent-recovery column. Lowering the solvent-addition rate requires more plates in the extractive column. Optimum design for each case depends upon an economic balance.

As the extractive agent has a low volatility compared with that of the feed components, its concentration rapidly approaches a "pinch" value in the rectifying and stripping sections of the extractive column. Modification of the ordinary pinch equations [Eqs. (13-72) and (13-73)] to an extractive column yields the following for the rectifying section:

$$x_S = \frac{S}{(1-\beta)L_{n+1} - \beta D/(1-x_S)} \tag{13-88}$$

For the stripping section:

$$x_S = \frac{S}{(1-\beta)L_{m+1} + \beta B/(1-x_S)} \tag{13-89}$$

In these equations x_S is the mole fraction solvent on the trays of the extractive column; S is the moles per unit time of pure solvent leaving the tower; β is the average relative volatility of solvent to non-solvent; L_{n+1} and L_{m+1} are the total moles of liquid per unit time flowing down the rectifying and stripping sections, respectively; D is the moles of distillate per unit time; B is the moles of solvent-free bottoms per unit time.

Equations (13-88) and (13-89) provide a relationship between solvent concentration on the trays and solvent-addition rate. As these equations are based upon the assumption of equal molal overflow, a condition which does not generally apply in extractive columns, they must be considered as approximate. Comparison of Eqs. (13-88) and (13-89) shows that x_S is identical above and below the feed point provided $L_{n+1} = L_{m+1}$ and provided $B = D$.

Design of Extractive Columns. First step in design is to decide upon a solvent-addition rate based upon economic and miscibility considerations. Minimum reflux ratio and tray requirements at operating reflux ratio are then determined by procedures described earlier (pp. 13-33 to 13-39) for multicomponent columns having unequal molal overflow; the only unusual features of the design are that two separate feed streams are present and non-ideal equilibrium relationships apply. Application of an analog computer for design of a column separating acetylene and carbon dioxide from ethylene by extractive distillation with dimethyl formamide has been described by O'Brien and Franks [*Chem. Eng. Progress, Symp. Ser.* 21, **55**, 25 (1959)]. A graphical procedure applicable to design of three-component extractive columns has been developed by Chambers [*Chem. Eng. Progress*, **47**, 555 (1951)].

Gerster, Mizushina, Marks, and Catanach [*Am. Inst. Chem. Engrs. J.*, **1**, 536 (1955)] have detailed the calculations required to compute the performance of a commercial furfural extractive distillation column separating iso- and n-butane from 1- and 2-butene. As an example, calculations are outlined here for design of this column.

The feed consists of the following, in mole per cent: isobutane, 35.6 per cent; n-butane, 15.1 per cent; 1-butene, 29.6 per cent; 2-butenes, 9.6 per cent; isobutylene, 2.7 per cent; butadiene, 1.2 per cent; propanes, 6.2 per cent. In the presence of the furfural-water solvent, n-butane is the light key and 1-butene is the heavy key; isobutane and propanes are lighter-than-light keys and the 2-butenes, isobutylene, and butadiene are heavier-than-heavy keys. Complete vapor-liquid equilibrium data for this system are given by Jordan, Gerster, Colburn, and Wohl [*Chem. Eng. Progress*, **46**, 601 (1950)] and Welty, Gerster, and Colburn [*Ind. Eng. Chem.*, **43**, 162 (1951)]. Feed rate is 1010 lb.-moles/hr. and vapor at 166°F. It is desired to recover 82 per cent of the n-butane in the overhead and 96 per cent of the 1-butene in the bottoms when the reflux ratio L/D is 1.49 and the solvent-addition rate is 17.0 moles per mole of C_4 hydrocarbon feed. Compute the theoretical tray requirements and heat loads. The solvent is fed to the column below the top tray to eliminate solvent losses in the overhead.

After assuming a product distribution for the non-key components, the first step of the design calculation is to fix the tower pressure. Assuming that the overhead vapor can be readily condensed at 112°F., the corresponding pressure is 86 lb./sq. in. gage. The bottoms composition is next calculated, and its boiling point found to be 292°F. A temperature of 98°F. is chosen for the C_4 hydrocarbon reflux to the tower, and a temperature of 131°F. is chosen for the solvent feed to the tower. From knowledge of these external temperatures and flow rates, it is now possible to compute enthalpies of the external streams, and by difference to compute the reboiler duty. The results of these calculations, with enthalpies based upon the pure liquids at 32°F. and 1 atm. and expressed as B.t.u. $\times 10^{-6}$/hr., are as follows:

Input enthalpies:	
Solvent feed	53.5
Reboiler	107.5
C_4 hydrocarbon feed	11.9
C_4 hydrocarbon reflux	1.8
	174.7
Output enthalpies:	
Vapor to condenser	15.2
Bottoms product	159.5
	174.7

The above table shows that nearly all the reboiler duty is required to raise the solvent from its inlet temperature of 131°F. to its outlet temperature of 292°F. (the bottoms product contains 97.5 per cent furfural-water solvent). This means that the large enthalpy brought to the tower by the entering solvent is an important factor controlling internal vapor rate; thus the solvent entry temperature must be carefully chosen.

Heat-of-solution data of C_4 hydrocarbons in wet furfural given by Jordan *et al.* (*loc. cit.*) and Welty *et al.* (*loc. cit.*) are utilized in the enthalpy calculations. These heats of solution are 35 to 40 per cent as large as the latent heats of vaporization of the C_4 hydrocarbons; so in a careful design calculation they cannot be ignored.

With external flows and enthalpies computed, it is now possible to make tray-to-tray calculations upward from the reboiler, continuing through the feed and the solvent entry tray to the top of the column. Both material and enthalpy balances are required; the necessary equations which apply to extractive columns were originally given by Colburn [*Can. Chem. Process. Inds.*, **34**, 286 (1950)] and are also given, with examples, by Gerster, Mizushina, *et al.* (*loc. cit.*). The usual considerations for optimum feed-tray location of multicomponent columns (*cf.* pp. 13-39 to 13-40) apply in the present instance for the C_4 hydrocarbon feed, and the solvent entry tray is reached when the heavy key concentration has been reduced to the value desired in the overhead. Stepwise calculations are then continued upward until the solvent concentration in the vapor has been reduced to an optimum value. In the present example, the desired product concentrations are reached in 25 theoretical trays, the contamination of the 2-butenes, isobutylene, and butadiene in the overhead is essentially zero, the contamination of isobutane in the bottoms is only 0.5 per cent (solvent-free basis).

The tray-to-tray calculations show that local conditions change within the tower as follows:

	Theoretical tray number from bottom of tower						
	Bottoms	1	6	12*	19	24†	Overhead
Temp., °F........	292	158	151	145	135	133	112
C_3-C_4 hydrocarbon concentration in liquid, mole %...	2.5	22.9	20.6	18.1	12.7	11.4	100
C_3-C_4 hydrocarbon liquid rate, moles/mole feed	0.45	3.51	3.02	2.58	1.70	1.52	

* Tray below vapor feed.
† Solvent entry tray.

The above table shows the rapid drop in concentration of the solvent in proceeding from the reboiler to the bottom tray; the temperature also drops accordingly. The solvent thus behaves as a heavier-than-heavy key component having a very small relative volatility. It is also apparent that equal molal overflow is not approached in this example, and as a corollary, the solvent concentration varies from 100 − 22.9 or 77.1 per cent on the bottom tray to 100 − 11.4 or 88.6 per cent on the solvent entry tray. The furfural-water solvent is essentially non-volatile at tower conditions; so that local vapor rates are readily obtained from the local liquid rates by material balance with an external stream.

Approximate Design Methods. In cases where equal molal overflow is more nearly approached than in the previous example, the solvent concentration more nearly approaches a true pinch composition and the method of Hengstebeck (*loc. cit.*) can be applied to the design of an extractive column. A McCabe-Thiele diagram on a solvent-free basis is utilized to determine tray requirements as demonstrated by Grohse *et al.* [*Chem. Eng. Progress*, **45**, 725 (1949)] and by Happel (*loc. cit.*). A diagram of this type is particularly useful in estimating minimum reflux; the solvent does not undergo any rapid composition changes in the vicinity of the feed and the binary-type diagram gives minimum reflux values which are exact if equal molal overflow applies and if the feed is a saturated vapor.

Azeotropic Distillation. This process is usually defined as a separation made possible by the formation of one or more azeotropes between the feed components and a deliberately added separating agent (*cf.* p. 13-46). However, it is often possible to obtain a separation between two components which form a heterogeneous azeotrope without the use of an agent by the two-column scheme shown in Fig. 13-51.

This figure is a flowsheet for separating a feed containing 35 mole per cent *n*-butanol and 65 mole per cent water into butanol and water of any desired purities. The vapor-liquid equilibrium relationships for this system were presented in Fig. 13-8.

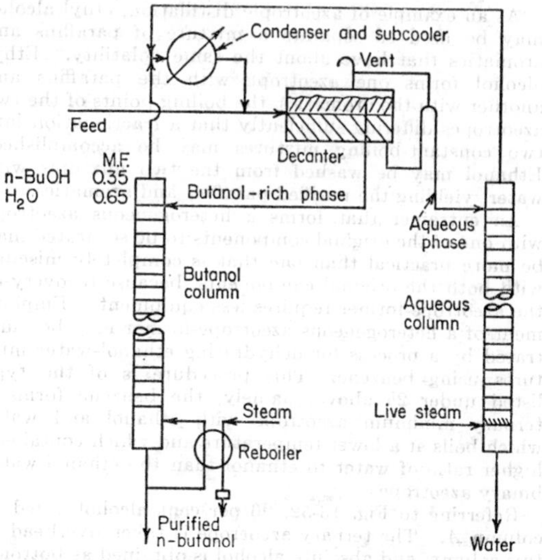

Fig. 13-51. Separation of *n*-butanol and water by two-column scheme.

As the fresh feed exists in two immiscible liquid phases, it is first sent to a gravity decanter where the *n*-butanol phase disengages from the aqueous phase and rises to the top. The butanol-rich phase is fed to the top of the butanol column from which nearly pure butanol is removed from the bottom. Overhead from this column approaches the heterogeneous azeotrope in composition which, after condensing and subcooling, is sent to the common decanter. The aqueous phase from the decanter is fed to the aqueous column where nearly pure water is removed as waste; as before, the overhead approaches the azeotropic composition and is again sent to the decanter. If the feed composition does not lie between 3 and 40 mole per cent butanol, where two liquid layers form, it should not be fed to the decanter but rather onto a tray of one of the columns according to the procedures set forth on pp. 13-39 to 13-40.

Methods of Using Azeotropic Formers. In the usual type of azeotropic distillation where a separating agent ("entrainer," "azeotrope-former," or "solvent") is employed, the following alternative methods may be used [Ewell, Harrison, and Berg, *Ind. Eng. Chem.*, **36**, 871 (1944)]:

1. To separate a closely boiling pair or a maximum azeotrope:
   a. The entrainer forms a binary minimum azeotrope with only one component.
   b. The entrainer forms binary minimum azeotropes with each component, but one minimum is sufficiently lower than the other.
   c. The entrainer forms a ternary minimum azeotrope that is sufficiently lower than any binary azeotropes. The ratio of the original components in the ternary must be different from their ratio before the entrainer was added.
2. To separate a minimum azeotrope:
   a. The entrainer forms a binary minimum azeotrope with one component that is sufficiently lower than the original minimum azeotrope.
   b. The entrainer forms a ternary minimum azeotrope that is sufficiently lower than any binary minimum azeotrope and in which the ratio of the original components is different from their ratio in the binary minimum azeotrope.

As an example of azeotropic distillation, ethyl alcohol may be used to separate a mixture of paraffins and aromatics that have about the same volatility. Ethyl alcohol forms one azeotrope with the paraffins and another with the aromatics, the boiling points of the two azeotropes differing sufficiently that a fractionation into two constant-boiling mixtures may be accomplished. Ethanol may be washed from the two mixtures with water, yielding the purified paraffins and aromatics.

An entrainer that forms a heterogeneous azeotrope with one of the original components to be separated may be more practical than one that is completely miscible with both the original components, because recovery of the azeotrope-former requires less equipment. Employment of a heterogeneous azeotrope-former may be illustrated by a process for dehydrating ethanol-water mixtures using benzene. This procedure is of the type listed under 2*b* above; namely, the benzene forms a ternary minimum azeotrope with ethanol and water which boils at a lower temperature and which contains a higher ratio of water to ethanol than the ethanol-water binary azeotrope.

Referring to Fig. 13-52, 96 per cent alcohol is fed to column *A*. The ternary azeotrope is taken overhead in this column, and absolute alcohol is obtained as bottoms product. The overhead vapors are condensed and passed to decanter *B*, in which two liquid layers form. The upper layer, rich in benzene, is returned to column *A* as reflux, and the lower layer is fed to column *C*, which produces the ternary azeotrope as the overhead product and benzene-free aqueous alcohol as the bottoms product. This latter product is fed to column *D* which produces by ordinary distillation an overhead product which is 96 per cent alcohol and a bottoms product which is nearly pure water. The overhead from column *D* is recycled to column *A* for removal of the water. The benzene is recycled continuously in this system.

Choice of Separating Agent. Suitability of any proposed separating agent is readily evaluated if complete vapor-liquid equilibrium data are available for the non-ideal multicomponent system involved. Experimental data of this type are rarely available, but fairly reliable methods for predicting such data are presented in pp. 13-12 to 13-13.

It is difficult to make generalizations for ternary or multicomponent systems containing binary or ternary azeotropes which are homogeneous; study of the behavior of four such systems as presented by Severns, Sesonske, Perry, and Pigford [*Am. Inst. Chem. Engrs. J.*, **1**, 401 (1955)] is helpful.

A few generalizations are possible when the entrainer is a hydrocarbon added to remove water from a polar organic compound. In this instance the azeotrope is heterogeneous, although it may be either a binary or a ternary azeotrope. [Reference to a tabulation of azeotropes (see p. 13-11) will often show whether a ternary azeotrope will form or not.] Choice of the agent is made solely on the basis of its vapor pressure, as any substance such as trichloroethylene, toluene, cyclohexane, or pentane will form an azeotrope with water so long as it is essentially immiscible with the water. Vapor pressure of the hydrocarbon agent should be high enough so that it will be essentially absent in the bottoms, but not so high that its composition in the overhead azeotrope is excessively large. This latter condition is to be avoided so that the moles of agent required to carry overhead one mole of water are not so large that steam costs and column diameters become excessive.

Hydrocarbons are also effective in azeotroping overhead highly polar organic compounds, and water is effective in azeotroping overhead certain hydrocarbons with which it is immiscible. Examples of such applications are given by Hopkins and Fritsch [*Chem. Eng. Progress*, **51**, 361 (1955)].

In addition to providing desirable vapor-liquid equilibrium characteristics, an ideal azeotrope-former should be non-corrosive, non-reactive with the feed, thermally stable, readily obtainable, inexpensive, and non-toxic, and should have a low molar latent heat of vaporization.

Design of Azeotropic Columns. Once the highly non-ideal equilibrium characteristics of the system are known, tray-to-tray calculations are employed to determine tray requirements. Minimum reflux may be determined by the exact method (*cf.* p. 13-38), but it is tedious to apply. Useful approximations have been suggested by Hands and Norman [*Trans. Inst. Chem. Engrs.*, **23**, 76 (1945)] and by Robinson and Gilliland ("Elements of Fractional Distillation," 4th ed., p. 321, McGraw-Hill, New York, 1950). Benedict and Rubin [*Trans. Am. Inst. Chem. Engrs.*, **41**, 353 (1945)] analyze the effect of introducing the separating agent in a continuous azeotropic column (1) at the bottom of the column, (2) with the principal feed, and (3) at the top. They conclude that the optimum point for solvent addition will usually be at the top of the column.

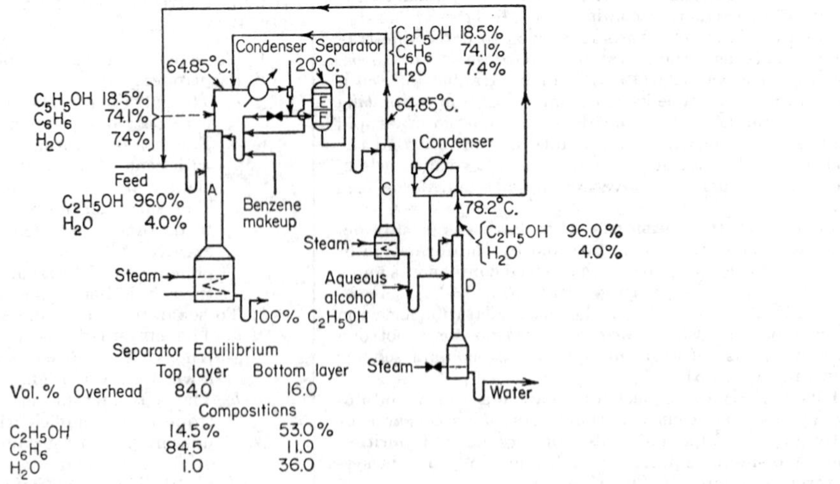

Fig. 13-52. Dehydration of 96 per cent ethanol to absolute alcohol by azeotropic distillation with benzene at 1 atm.

As an example of the composition behavior of a homogeneous azeotropic column, consider the separation of paraffin from toluene using methanol as the azeotropic agent. Benedict, Johnson, Solomon, and Rubin [*Trans. Am. Inst. Chem. Engrs.*, **41**, 371 (1945)] have shown that this system contains three minimum-boiling binary azeotropes: methanol-toluene, methanol-paraffin, and paraffin-toluene (the paraffin component was assumed to have the same vapor pressure as toluene). No ternary azeotrope is present.

The separation of paraffin from toluene is accomplished in a column where the bottoms product is essentially pure toluene. In working up the column, the trace quantity of methanol in the bottoms increases very rapidly because the activity coefficients for methanol out of toluene are very large. Several trays up from the bottom the methanol reaches such a large composition in the liquid that it now becomes effective as a separating agent; it increases the relative volatility of paraffin to toluene to about 1.7, permitting the paraffin to increase from a trace amount and the toluene to decrease; this situation continues until the overhead product contains only methanol and paraffin. Water washing of the product permits recovery and recycle of the methanol to the top of the column. Benedict *et al.* (*loc. cit.*) show that, if the amount of methanol sent to the azeotropic column is too great, the bottoms product will not be methanol-free but rather will approach the methanol-toluene azeotrope in composition.

Use of methyl ethyl ketone to aid in separating toluene from paraffins has been described by Lake [*Trans. Am. Inst. Chem. Engrs.*, **41**, 327 (1945)]; in this case pure toluene is the bottoms product from the azeotropic column and a paraffin–methyl ethyl ketone homogeneous azeotrope is the overhead product. Poffenberger *et al.* [*Trans. Am. Inst. Chem. Engrs.*, **42**, 815 (1946)] describe the use of ammonia to separate 1-butene from 1,3-butadiene by taking the butene-ammonia azeotrope overhead in an azeotropic column; pure butadiene is the bottoms product.

Behavior of azeotropic columns where heterogeneous azeotropes are formed is similar to that described earlier (p. 13-50) for the dehydration of ethanol. A complete example for this separation is given by Robinson and Gilliland (*op. cit.*, p. 313). Colburn and Phillips [*Trans. Am. Inst. Chem. Engrs.*, **40**, 333 (1944)] describe the dehydration of ethanol by azeotropic distillation with trichloroethylene as the agent, while Hands and Norman (*loc. cit.*) show that allyl alcohol can be successfully dehydrated by azeotropic distillation with the same agent.

Comparison of Extractive and Azeotropic Distillations. In extractive distillation the volatility of the solvent must not match the volatility of the feed components, whereas for azeotropic distillation the solvent, in order to be effective, must boil within about 10° to 40° of some of the feed components so that an azeotrope can form. Consequently, a larger number of suitable **separating agents** can usually be found in the case of extractive distillation.

For a given separation by extractive distillation, a wide variety of **towers** may be designed because the solvent concentration in the tower may be controlled by heat and material inflow. Design of an azeotropic column, on the other hand, is controlled by the composition of the azeotrope formed with the solvent.

Heat requirements in azeotropic distillation are usually greater than those in extractive distillation, since most of the solvent is vaporized and taken overhead. Thus many of the azeotropic processes described above are not in actual commercial use. However, if the overhead component is a small fraction of the feed, azeotropic distillation becomes competitive with extractive distillation in terms of heat economy. Azeotropic distillation is also more easily adapted to batch distillations than is extractive distillation.

DESIGN FACTORS IN DISTILLATION

Plate efficiencies are reported either as **Murphree efficiencies** or as **over-all column efficiencies.** The former gives the efficiency of a single tray; when expressed in vapor concentrations, it is the ratio of the actual change in vapor composition experienced by the vapor in passing through a tray to the composition change which the vapor would attain if it discharged from the tray in vapor-liquid equilibrium with the tray liquid. Over-all efficiency is defined as the ratio of the number of theoretical trays required for a specified separation to the number of actual trays required. Over-all efficiencies are easier to use in design calculations because of the relative ease of estimating theoretical plates. But Murphree efficiencies have more fundamental significance, as shown later.

Murphree efficiencies may apply either to the entire tray or to a point on the tray. In terms of vapor compositions, the Murphree efficiency of the **entire tray** for tray $n + 1$ is designated as E_{MV} and is defined as

$$E_{MV} = \frac{y_{n+1} - y_n}{y^*_{n+1} - y_n} \tag{13-90}$$

where y_n and y_{n+1} are the vapor compositions to and from the tray, and y^*_{n+1} is the composition of the vapor in equilibrium with the liquid leaving the tray x_{n+1}. The **point Murphree efficiency,** in vapor compositions, is designated as E_{OV} and is defined as

$$E_{OV} = \frac{\bar{y}_{n+1} - \bar{y}_n}{\bar{y}^*_{n+1} - \bar{y}_n} \tag{13-91}$$

where $\bar{y}_n$ and $\bar{y}_{n+1}$ are the vapor compositions to and from the tray at the point considered, and $\bar{y}^*_{n+1}$ is the composition of the vapor in equilibrium with the liquid on the tray at the point considered, $\bar{x}_{n+1}$. If the liquid on the tray is completely mixed and thus has the same composition as the liquid leaving the tray, the point efficiency is numerically the same as the entire tray efficiency. In most commercial columns the liquid is not fully mixed as it flows across the tray and each vapor stream issuing from various tray locations has a different composition; usually, however, the vapor is completely mixed by the time it reaches the tray above.

Murphree efficiencies may be expressed in terms of either vapor of liquid compositions, whichever is more convenient. In terms of liquid compositions, the entire tray efficiency E_{ML} for tray n is

$$E_{ML} = \frac{x_{n+1} - x_n}{x_{n+1} - x_n^*} \tag{13-92}$$

where x_{n+1} and x_n are the liquid compositions to and from the tray and x_n^* is the composition the liquid leaving tray n would have if it discharged from the tray in equilibrium with the vapor leaving the tray y_n. A Murphree liquid point efficiency may also be defined, but it is not very useful.

The relationship between Murphree efficiency E_{MV} and over-all column efficiency E_O is as follows:

$$E_O = \frac{\ln [1 + E_{MV}(\lambda - 1)]}{\ln \lambda} \tag{13-93}$$

where $\lambda = m/(L/V) = mV/L$, the ratio of the slope of the equilibrium curve to the slope of the operating line. If λ is unity, $E_O = E_{MV}$. As λ is seldom a constant and E_{MV} itself is a function of λ, an approximation is involved when E_O is taken to be constant for a given tower.

Values of Murphree tray efficiency may be converted from a gas to a liquid composition basis and vice versa by the following equations:

$$E_{MV} = \frac{E_{ML}}{E_{ML} + \lambda(1 - E_{ML})} \tag{13-94}$$

$$E_{ML} = \frac{E_{MV}\lambda}{1 + E_{MV}(\lambda - 1)} \tag{13-95}$$

The above equations show that, when $\lambda = 1$, $E_{MV} = E_{ML}$. When λ is large, values of E_{MV} are much smaller than the corresponding values of E_{ML}; when λ is small, the reverse is true.

Relationships between E_{MV} and E_{OV} are complex functions of the degree of liquid mixing on the tray. These relationships are given in Sec. 18, p. 18-19.

The Murphree efficiency of an entire tray is commonly known simply as the "Murphree efficiency" or the "Murphree tray efficiency," while the Murphree point efficiency is commonly known as the "point efficiency." Unless otherwise designated, it is common practice to express the concentrations appearing in the definition of efficiency in the units of mole fraction of the more volatile component in the vapor phase. Efficiencies are commonly expressed in percentages in much of the literature, but in Eqs. (13-90) to (13-95) and later equations the efficiencies are fractions.

Relationship between Efficiency and Mass-transfer Factors. Transfer of material between phases on a bubble plate takes place according to the laws of mass transfer. The efficiency obtained in a given situation is a function of the mass-transfer resistance between the vapor phase and the interface, and of that between the interface and the liquid phase. These factors have been shown ("Tray Efficiencies in Distillation Columns, Final Report from University of Delaware to A.I.Ch.E. Research Committee," American Institute of Chemical Engineers, New York, 1958) to affect point efficiency E_{OV} as follows:

$$\frac{1}{-2.3 \log (1 - E_{OV})} = \frac{1}{N_V} + \frac{\lambda}{N_L} \tag{13-96}$$

where $1/N_V$ is the vapor-phase mass-transfer resistance and λ/N_L is the liquid-phase mass-transfer resistance.

The term N_V in Eq. (13-96) is the **number of vapor-phase (or gas-phase) transfer units** and is related to the vapor-phase transfer coefficient k_V as follows for an ideal-gas-law vapor:

$$N_V = -2.3 \log (1 - E_V) = k_V a R T t_V \tag{13-97}$$

where E_V = point efficiency when liquid-phase mass-transfer resistance is absent; k_V = mass-transfer coefficient, lb.-moles transferred/(sec.)(sq. ft. interfacial area)(unit driving force, atm.); a = interfacial area on bubble tray, sq. ft./(cu. ft. of gas hold-up on tray); R = gas-law constant, (atm.)(cu. ft.)/(lb.-moles)(°R.); T = temperature, °R.; t_V = average time of contact of gas with liquid, sec. The value of t_V is computed by dividing the total gas hold-up on the bubble tray, cu. ft., by the gas rate, cu. ft./sec. Equation (13-97) was derived assuming plug flow of vapor upward through a pool of liquid which is well mixed vertically.

The term N_L in Eq. (13-96) is the number of **liquid-phase transfer units,** and λ is mV/L, the ratio of the slope of the equilibrium curve m to the slope of the operating line L/V. N_L is related to the liquid-phase mass-transfer coefficient k_L as follows:

$$N_L = k_L \bar{a} t_L \tag{13-98}$$

where k_L = mass-transfer coefficient, lb.-moles transferred/(sec.)(sq. ft. interfacial area)(unit concentration driving force, lb.-moles/cu. ft.); $\bar{a}$ = interfacial area, sq. ft./(cu. ft. liquid hold-up on tray); t_L = average time of contact of liquid with gas on tray, sec. The value of t_L is computed by dividing the total liquid hold-up on the bubble tray, cu. ft., by the liquid rate, cu. ft./sec. If the liquid flows across the tray in plug flow, that is, without mixing, the relationship between N_L and E_L, which is the point efficiency expressed in liquid concentration units when gas-phase mass-transfer resistance is absent, is

$$N_L = -2.3 \log (1 - E_L) \tag{13-99}$$

If, on the other hand, the liquid on the bubble tray is completely mixed,

$$N_L = \frac{E_L}{1 - E_L} \tag{13-100}$$

Performance Data and Predictive Correlations. For plate-efficiency data from actual distillation columns, as well as methods for predicting plate efficiencies, see Sec. 18.

Basic Design Principles. Previous parts of this section have presented methods for computing the number of theoretical trays or transfer units and the vapor- and liquid-flow rates which are required to effect a given binary or multicomponent separation in a distillation column. Although these calculations are usually the most important and most extensive of the required design calculations needed for a particular installation, there are a number of other factors to be considered by the designer. These include the following: (1) relationship of the column to the remainder of the plant with regard to maximum capacity and flexibility; (2) choice of optimum pressure level for the column; (3) choice of type of column (packed or plate), type of plate or type of packing, material of construction, and type of reboiler and condenser; (4) choice of thermal condition of feed; and (5) choice of column diameter and (if a plate column) selection of tray spacing and downpipe size. Each of these factors is considered below.

Capacity and Flexibility. Choice of design capacity for a given distillation column is usually governed by the relationship of the column to the rest of the plant. It is usually uneconomical to design a column for a capacity or through-put greater than that of the other major pieces of equipment in the process. Flexibility of the column, *i.e.*, the range of through-put conditions over which the column will give products of satisfactory purity, should also be fixed before the design is started.

Choice of Optimum Pressure Level. Because most columns operate satisfactorily at various pressure levels an attempt should be made to determine the optimum value. Increased pressure means increased temperatures within the column, so that thermal stability of the materials being distilled can be a major consideration. Equipment costs increase as pressure is raised or lowered from atmospheric, and although use of moderate pressures (up to 150 lb./sq. in.) does not involve excessive costs, vacuum operation is usually expensive because of the need for vacuum-producing equipment and (in some cases) the need for refrigerated condensers. In general, tower pressures should be high enough to permit reflux to be condensed without resort to refrigeration, but the pressures should not be so excessive that the bottoms liquid cannot be reboiled with the available heat-transfer medium.

Use of higher pressures and temperatures usually reduces the relative volatilities. However, at higher pressures the same vapor through-put can be handled in a column of smaller diameter, and tray efficiencies may also be affected favorably by increased temperatures.

Clay, Huston, and Kleiss [*Chem. Eng. Progress*, **50**, 10 (1954)] measured the change in capacity of a debutanizer vs. pressure. Pressure for maximum capacity changed with the desired separation, varying from 70 to 140 lb./sq. in. abs. Within 20 lb./sq. in. of the optimum pressure, the effect of pressure on capacity was small; because of this, and because reflux requirements increase with pressure, the optimum design pressure should be lower than the pressure for maximum capacity. Atkins and Wilson [*Petrol. Refiner*, **33** (5), 144 (1954)] recommend choice of the lowest operating pressure which will permit satisfactory condensation of the distillate and reflux at normal cooling-water temperatures.

Choice of Equipment Type. Packed columns have low pressure drop and low first cost in columns of small diameter and are easily made from corrosion-resistant materials. However, they are rarely used for distillation where column diameter is greater than about 3 ft. because of difficulty in maintaining uniform liquid distribution over the packing when the column diameter is large. For tall packed columns this requires the use of liquid redistributors every 6 to 20 ft. of height. Special design is also desirable at the base of the packing to prevent flooding at this point. A recent advance in this area is the availability of plastic tower packings which have lower weight, lower cost, and minimum handling loss but are limited to operating temperatures of about 250°F. Another new type of packing, Pall rings, tends to maintain uniform liquid distribution; this packing is especially useful in towers of large diameter.

Plate (tray) towers are most commonly employed in industrial applications. A wide variety of tray types is used, including bubble-cap, sieve, Flexitray, ballast, Kaskade, float-valve, Uniflux, Turbogrid, and ripple trays. Choice of proper tray for a particular application depends upon whether there will be suspended solids or sludges or products of corrosion, whether low pressure drop, low liquid hold-up, or unusual materials of construction are required, and whether the tray must deliver a high efficiency over a wide range of operating conditions. A comparison of the various tray types made by Fryback and Hufnagel [*Ind. Eng. Chem.*, **52**, 654 (1960)] is shown in Table 13-9. Tray efficiencies and through-put characteristics are given in Sec. 18.

Most distillation columns employ total **condensers** which also subcool the condensate for ease in pumping and metering. Partial condensers are employed if the overhead vapors contain some components which are difficult or impossible to liquefy, but they are not commonly used merely for the purpose of effecting additional enrichment through dephlegmation (see p. 13-21).

Distillation-column **reboilers** may be of the kettle, forced-circulation, thermosiphon or direct-fired type. Forced-circulation reboilers may be used where space is limited or where viscous liquids are present. Direct-fired reboilers are used where bottoms temperatures are higher than that of the available heat-transfer medium. Kettle-type reboilers are most suitable where pressure drop must be kept to an absolute minimum and where flexible operation is desired. Vertical and horizontal thermosiphon reboilers permit the liquid to pass over the heat-transfer surfaces at high velocity, giving high heat-transfer coefficients and lower-cost units. A discussion of factors to be considered in choice of reboiler and condenser is given by Fryback and Hufnagel (*loc. cit.*). Methods for the design of reboilers have been given by Fair [*Petrol. Refiner*, **39** (2), 105 (1960)]; see also Sec. 11, p. 11-3.

Choice of Thermal Condition of Feed. A feed which is highly superheated or highly subcooled can result in unnecessarily high condenser or reboiler duties. It is usually desirable to adjust the thermal condition of the feed by external heat exchange to ensure that tray requirements are not excessive because of unbalanced flows of vapor and liquid above and below the feed tray.

Choice of Column Diameter, Tray Spacing, Downpipe Size. These must each be sufficiently large so that anticipated vapor and liquid through-puts can be handled without flooding of the unit. Procedures for choosing these particular dimensions of a column based upon knowledge of the flow rates and physical properties of the vapor and liquid streams are given on pp. 18-5 to 18-16 of Sec. 18. Hydraulic considerations alone should not govern final design, however, but rather the effect of column diameter and tray spacing upon tray efficiency should also be taken into account; accessibility of a column for inspection is another factor to be considered in choosing tray spacing.

Laboratory Columns. Design of small laboratory columns often presents a number of problems not encountered in the design of larger units. Enthalpy losses from a small-diameter column can represent appreciable percentages of the enthalpy in the vapor stream to the column. In such instances vapor and liquid rates are sharply reduced in proceeding up the column. Good practice requires prevention of such heat losses by the use of electric windings or vacuum jackets.

Splitting of the overhead condensate into reflux and product streams is difficult to achieve with accuracy when flows are small. Intermittent splitters which direct the condensate first to the reflux line for a few seconds and then to the product line for another time interval have found widespread use. Much attention has been paid to the development of efficient packings for small columns; however, if a primary objective is to obtain performance data for scale-up at a later date, it is desirable to use a sieve-tray laboratory column. Detailed information on the design of laboratory columns is available from Coulson and Herington ("Laboratory Distillation Practice," Interscience, New York, 1958).

Table 13-9. Comparison of Several Types of Trays with the Bubble Tray*

Type	Vapor capacity relative to bubble tray	Efficiency: Range of high efficiency	Efficiency: Relative to bubble tray	Dirty-service performance	Tray ΔP relative to bubble tray	Cost relative to bubble tray
No liquid downcomers: Turbogrid, ripple tray	20–40% greater	Relatively narrow, poor at low vapor load	Approx. same at 60–80% of flood or above, less at lower vapor rates	Good	Low, for Turbogrid about ⅓ at 60–100% of flooding	½
Valve type: Flexitray, ballast	20–50% greater	Wide (20–85% of flooding)	5–10% higher at optimum	Good	Slightly lower at high vapor rates	⅔
Uniflux	10–20% greater	Relatively wide, good above 50% of flooding	10% higher at optimum	Questionable	Low	½
Sieve trays, $\frac{1}{16}$- to ¼-in. holes	20–40% greater	Relatively wide	Approx. 10% higher	Poor	Low	⅔

* Fryback and Hufnagel, *Ind. Eng. Chem.*, **52**, 654 (1960).

Automatic Control of Distillation Columns. Section 22 of this handbook includes a presentation of the principles of automatic control, description of available control instruments, sensing devices, final control elements, and examples of the application of automatic control in the chemical process industries. A discussion of the problems peculiar to control of distillation columns follows.

In most instances it is desired to provide automatic control of a distillation column for the purpose of **maintaining specified purity** in the top or bottoms product, or both, in the face of possible fluctuations in steam supply to the reboiler, in water supply to the condenser, in ambient temperature, and in composition, rate, and thermal condition of the feed. The usual way of accomplishing this objective is to measure changes in the product compositions with sensing elements and to deliver this information to automatic controllers which take the necessary corrective actions. The required **corrective action,** for a column containing a fixed number of trays and a fixed feed location, is to change either the vapor boil-up rate or the reflux return rate or both. For columns where both the overhead and bottoms product compositions are to be maintained at specified values, changes in both the vapor boil-up and reflux rates are mandatory. The use of McCabe-Thiele diagrams to determine the degree of control attainable with a given distillation system is shown by Bauer and Orr [*Chem. Eng. Progress,* **50,** 312 (1954)] and by Uitti [*Petrol. Refiner,* **29** (3), 130 (1950)].

Automatic controls are also useful in **maintaining proper pressure or vacuum** within the column and in providing for liquid-level control in the reboiler and reflux drum. Automatic controls can guard against flooding of a column by continuous measurement of the gas pressure drop across the column and taking the necessary corrective action before a critical pressure drop is reached; controls can also prevent a critical-temperature-drop condition from being reached in the reboiler.

Composition-sensing Devices. Temperature has been used extensively as an indication of composition. However, in order for temperature to be a true indication of composition, the column should contain only two components and the total pressure should be constant. To eliminate difficulties due to pressure fluctuations, it is sometimes possible to use the temperature difference between two positions in the tower as a measure of the average composition in this region. Also, to obtain sensitivity to changes in composition, a temperature-sensing point should not be located in a region of the column where the composition change per tray is small, *i.e.,* in "pinch" regions, which are likely to occur near the ends of the column or adjacent to the feed tray. Temperature is of limited usefulness for sensing composition when the difference in boiling points of the feed components is small. Direct measurement of composition within a column by means of vapor-phase chromatographs, infrared analyzers, or refractometers offers a more positive means of control.

Vacuum and Pressure Control. The simplest control over the **vacuum** for a given column is to provide for a slightly greater vacuum than required from the steam jet, pump, or barometric leg to be used, and to control the rate of an air bleed into the line to the vacuum source so as to maintain a constant vacuum within the column.

O'Connor (Nielsen, "Distillation in Practice," p. 100, Reinhold, New York, 1956) suggests three methods for **pressure** control: (1) use of a control valve in the vapor line to the condenser; (2) control of the rate of coolant flow in the condenser; or (3) flooding of a varying portion of the condensing surface by controlling the outlet flow rate from the condenser. If inert gases are present in the overhead product, a control valve in the vapor-product line provides suitable pressure control.

Rate of Corrective Action. The most difficult part of control of distillation columns is predicting the rate at which corrective action should be taken to bring the product purities back to their desired values in the shortest length of time after an upset has occurred. Even more desirable is the development of a plan for corrective action which, from knowledge of changes in feed conditions to a tower, anticipates the need for corrective action and carries it out in a manner such that the product purities remain constant.

If the **process dynamics** of any given distillation system may be predicted in advance from design information, proper controller settings may be determined by application of automatic-control theory [Ceaglske, "Automatic Process Control for Chemical Engineers," Wiley, New York, 1956. Campbell, "Process Dynamics," Wiley, New York, 1958. Williams, series of articles in *Petrol. Refiner,* **35** (4), 211 (1956), through **39** (12), 153 (1960)]. Although progress has been made along these lines, optimum control is best developed by analyzing the transient behavior of a given column and its auxiliaries after it has been installed in the plant. For example, Woods [*Control Eng.,* **5,** 91 (1958)] imposed a step change in the reflux ratio of a plant column separating monoethylene glycol from water; from the transient-response curve obtained, the frequency response of the column installation including its instruments was obtained. From this information, optimum controller settings for the plant column were found, and response times of the unit to various load changes were computed.

Endtz *et al.* ("Proceedings of Conference on Plant and Process Dynamic Characteristics," p. 170, Butterworth, London, 1957) describe a portable process-dynamics analyzer used for determining response characteristics of plant columns. The analyzer consists of a disturbance generator, detecting elements, and recording equipment. The disturbance is injected into the process in the form of a pneumatic signal superimposed upon the regular signal from a controller to its control valve; the disturbance may be adjustable sine waves or step changes. The responses of various column temperatures, pressures, levels, and compositions are then recorded. Rademaker (International Symposium on Distillation, p. 140, May, 1960, Institution of Chemical Engineers, London) describes the use of such a process-dynamics analyzer for determination of transient behavior of a 91-tray ethane-ethylene splitter containing Turbogrid trays.

Plant-scale experimentation of the type just mentioned has not, however, led to generalized correlations of the transient behavior of columns. One reason for this is that the desired information cannot usually be obtained over a wide range of operating conditions or with variable liquid hold-ups on the trays. Another is the difficulty in separating the reboiler and condenser dynamics from those of the column itself.

Another approach to the problem of developing generalized correlations for column transient behavior is a strictly mathematical one. However, although basic differential equations may be developed to predict transient behavior, exact solutions to these equations are quite difficult to obtain even with the use of computers. Theoretical studies of process dynamics of distillation columns have been made by Davidson [*Trans. Inst. Chem. Engrs.,* **34,** 44 (1956)]; Gerardin ("Proc. 1st Congress, IFAC, Moscow," p. 917, Butterworth, London, 1960); Rademaker and Rijnsdorp (Fifth World Petroleum Congress, New York, 1959); Rijnsdorp and Maarleveld (Symposium on Instrumentation, Institution of Chemical Engineers, London, 1959); Rose, Johnson, and Williams [*Ind. Eng. Chem.,* **43,** 2459 (1951); **42,** 2145 (1950); **48,**

1173 (1956); **47,** 2284 (1955)]; Rosenbrock [*Trans. Inst. Chem. Engrs.*, **35,** 347, 361 (1957); "Proc. 1st Congress, IFAC, Moscow," p. 1277, Butterworth, London, 1960]; Voetter ("Proceedings Conference on Plant and Process Dynamic Characteristics," p. 73, Butterworth, London, 1957); Williams and Harnett [*Chem. Eng. Progress*, **53,** 220 (1957); *Ind. Eng. Chem.*, **48,** 1008 (1956)].

One of the difficulties preventing ready solution of the basic differential equations describing column transient behavior lies in the non-linearity of the vapor-liquid equilibrium curve. The use of linear vapor-liquid relationships and other simplifying assumptions reduces many of the difficulties in applying the basic equations, but in only a few cases has the validity of these various assumptions been supported by experimental data. The recommendations of Williams for optimum control of distillation columns [*Ind. Eng. Chem.*, **50,** 1214 (1958)] were arrived at by analog-computer simulation and were verified by experimental studies reported by others in the literature. Also, the transient equations of Rosenbrock (*loc. cit.*) were confirmed by experimental transient-response studies carried out by Armstrong and Wilkinson in a 4-in.-diameter bubble-cap column [*Trans. Inst. Chem. Engrs.*, **35,** 352 (1957)]. See also Wilkinson and Armstrong [*Chem. Eng. Sci.*, **7,** 1 (1957)]; Wood and Armstrong [*Chem. Eng. Sci.*, **12,** 272 (1960)]; Armstrong and Wood [*Trans. Inst. Chem. Engrs.*, **39,** 65 (1961)].

Baber, Edwards, Harper, Witte, and Gerster (A.I.Ch.E. meeting, Washington, December, 1960) reported on the experimental transient response of a 2-ft.-diameter bubble-cap column operating under various conditions up to the flooding point with the acetone-benzene system at variable total pressure. They measured tray composition behavior as a function of time after introduction of a step change in reflux rate, reflux composition, or vapor rate to the column. Their composition-time curves for different trays in the column could be predicted from knowledge of the liquid hold-ups on the trays and in the downpipes, the relative volatility, the operating-line slope, and the tray efficiency using perturbation-type equations developed by Lamb and Pigford (A.I.Ch.E. meeting, San Francisco, December, 1959). These equations show promise of great usefulness in characterizing the transient behavior of distillation columns as their predictions are accurate, yet their solution on an analog computer is manageable.

Rippin and Lamb (A.I.Ch.E. meeting, Washington, December, 1960) suggested that the equations of Lamb and Pigford (*loc. cit.*) be used in conjunction with an analog computer to effect a "feed-forward" type of control for a distillation column. In their proposal, changes in feed conditions are continuously sensed and passed on to an analog computer, which uses the equations of Lamb and Pigford to compute and execute the proper rate of corrective action so that product compositions were undisturbed. Rippin and Lamb simulated such a column using analog components and applied their control method to it; product compositions were demonstrated to vary only slightly in the face of appreciable and rapid changes in feed condition.

Use of **analog computers** for distillation-column control has also been suggested by Pink [*Petrol. Refiner*, **38** (3), 215 (1959)]. In this instance the computer receives information on feed analysis, feed rate, and column temperatures, and computes the top and bottom temperatures necessary to produce specification products as a function of feed composition. The appropriate control settings to produce these temperatures at the required times are then calculated and transmitted to the controllers.

Analog computers are being used to manipulate operating capacity in fractionation towers (Webber, Martin, Pink, and Hargett, Refining Division, A.P.I. meeting, May, 1959). One such instrument computes actual vapor rate from measured product and reflux rates, vapor capacity as a function of measured pressure, and per cent of vapor capacity actually utilized. The latter value can be used to control the tower to any desired percentage of capacity.

Analog computers are available for control of internal reflux in fractionating columns [Lupfer and Berger, *ISA Journal*, **6,** 34 (June, 1959)]. The computer receives information on the external reflux flow rate and the temperature difference between the top tray and the pumped reflux stream, from which the internal reflux flow rate is computed and used as a signal for control purposes.

Haines [*Ind. Eng. Chem.*, **52,** 662 (1960)] reviewed the advantages to be gained by the use of up-to-date control procedures.

SECTION 14

GAS ABSORPTION AND SOLVENT EXTRACTION

BY

R. E. Emmert, Ph.D., Research Supervisor, Engineering Research Laboratory, E. I. du Pont de Nemours Co.; Member, American Institute of Chemical Engineers, American Chemical Society.

R. L. Pigford, Ph.D., Colburn Professor of Chemical Engineering, University of Delaware; Member, American Institute of Chemical Engineers, American Chemical Society.

CONTENTS

GAS ABSORPTION

SOLVENT EXTRACTION

GAS ABSORPTION

REFERENCES: Sherwood and Pigford, "Absorption and Extraction," McGraw-Hill, New York, 1952. Leva, "Tower Packings and Packed Tower Design," U.S. Stoneware Co., Akron, Ohio, 1953. Treybal, "Mass-transfer Operations," McGraw-Hill, New York, 1955. Morris and Jackson, "Absorption Towers," Butterworth, London, 1953. Brown, "Unit Operations," Wiley, New York, 1950. Cremer and Davies, "Chemical Engineering Practice," vol. 6, Academic Press, New York, 1958. Walker, Lewis, McAdams, and Gilliland, "Principles of Chemical Engineering," 3d ed., McGraw-Hill, New York, 1937. McCabe and Smith, "Unit Operations of Chemical Engineering," McGraw-Hill, New York, 1956. Colburn, *Trans. Am. Inst. Chem. Engrs.*, **35**, 211 (1939). Colburn, *Ind. Eng. Chem.*, **33**, 459 (1941). Unit Operations Reviews, *Ind. Eng. Chem.*, **42**, 17 (1950); **34**, 41 (1951); **44**, 25 (1952); **45**, 957 (1953); **46**, 61, 937 (1954); **47**, 505, 658 (1955); **48**, 468, 669 (1956); **49**, 457, 577 (1957); **50**, 421, 555 (1958); **51**, 337, 466 (1959). Kohl and Riesenfeld, *Chem. Eng.*, **66** (12), 127 (1959).

INTRODUCTION

Gas absorption is a unit operation in which a soluble component of a gas mixture is dissolved in a liquid. The inverse operation, called **stripping** or **desorption,** is employed when it is desired to transfer a volatile component from a liquid mixture into a gas. The following section is concerned principally with the design of commercial equipment for carrying out either of these operations continuously. Many gaseous materials are amenable to gas-absorption processes. Table 14-1 lists some gas-absorption systems of commercial importance.

The **apparatus** used for contacting a liquid and a gas stream continuously may be a tower filled with irregular solid packing material, an empty tower into which the liquid is sprayed, or a tower containing a number of bubble-cap or sieve plates. Ordinarily, the gas and liquid streams flow countercurrently through the equipment in order to obtain the greatest rate of absorption. Occasionally, gas-absorption operations are carried out in spray columns, wetted-wall columns, stirred vessels, or mechanically aided devices.

There are three main **steps in design** of an absorption or stripping tower:

1. Data on the vapor-liquid equilibrium relations for the system are used to determine (*a*) the quantity of liquid needed to absorb the required amount of the soluble component from the gas or (*b*) the quantity of gas needed to strip the required amount of the volatile component from the liquid.

2. Data on the liquid- and vapor-handling capacity of equipment of the type being considered are used to determine the required cross-sectional area of the channels through which the liquid and vapor streams will flow. (Economic factors may dictate use of fluid velocities well below the maximum values that can be employed.)

3. Equilibrium data and material balances are used to determine the number of equilibrium stages (theoretical plates or transfer units) required for the separation desired. Difficulty of the separation depends on the degree of recovery that is economically most desirable. Required time of contact between the flowing streams, or required height of the tower, can be calculated if data are available for the specific rate of transfer of material between the gas and liquid phases, expressed in terms of the plate efficiency or the height of one transfer unit (H.T.U.).

EQUILIBRIUM DATA

Solubility of Various Gases in Water. In order to define the solubility factor of a gas in a liquid, it is generally necessary to state the temperature, the equilibrium partial pressure of the solute gas in the gas phase, and the concentration of the solute gas in the liquid phase.

Table 14-1. Gas-absorption Systems of Commercial Importance*

Solute	Solvent	Reagent	Degree of commercial importance		
			High	Moderate	Low
CO_2, H_2S	Water	....	x		
CO_2, H_2S	Water	Monoethanolamine	x		
CO_2, H_2S	Water	Diethanolamine	x		
CO_2, H_2S	Water	Triethanolamine	...	...	x
CO_2, H_2S	Water	Diaminoisopropanol	...	...	x
CO_2, H_2S	Water	Methyl diethanolamine	...	...	x
CO_2, H_2S	Water	K_2CO_3, Na_2CO_3	x		
CO_2, H_2S	Water	NH_3	...	x	
CO_2, H_2S	Water	NaOH, KOH	...	x	
CO_2, H_2S	Water	K_3PO_4	...	x	
CO_2	Propylene carbonate	....	...	x	
CO_2	Glycerol triacetate	....	...	x	
CO_2	Butoxy diethylene glycol acetate	....	...	x	
CO_2	Methoxy triethylene glycol acetate	....	...	x	
HCl, HF	Water	....	x		
HCl, HF	Water	NaOH	x		
Cl_2	Water	....	x		
SO_2	Water	....			
SO_2	Water	NH_3	...	x	
SO_2	Water	Xylidine	...	x	
SO_2	Water	Dimethyl aniline	...	x	
SO_2	Water	$Ca(OH)_2$, oxygen	...	...	x
SO_2	Water	Aluminum hydroxide-sulfate	...	x	
NH_3	Water	....	x		
NO_2	Water	....	x		
HCN	Water	NaOH	x		
CO	Water	Copper ammonium salts	x		

* Kohl and Riesenfeld, *Chem. Eng.*, **66** (12), 127 (1959); Sherwood and Pigford, "Absorption and Extraction," McGraw-Hill, New York, 1952.

(Strictly speaking the total pressure on the system as well as the partial pressure of the solute gas should be stated, but where the total pressure is not more than a few, perhaps 5, atmospheres, the solubility for a particular partial pressure of solute gas may be safely considered independent of total pressure.) The solubility of NH_3 (Table 14-4) at a temperature of 30°C. for a partial pressure of NH_3 of 260 mm. is given as 20 weights of NH_3 per 100 weights of H_2O. This method of stating temperature, partial pressure of solute gas in the gas phase, and concentration of solute in the liquid phase will be employed for systems where Henry's law does not hold.

If **Henry's law** holds, solubility is defined by giving the Henry's law constant H and the temperature where $H = p_A/x_A$ = atm./mole fraction of solute in solution. For quite a number of gases, Henry's law holds very well where the partial pressure of the solute gas does not exceed 1 atm. For partial pressures of solute gas greater than 1 atm., H is seldom independent of the partial pressure of the solute gas, and a given value of H can be used over only a narrow range of partial pressures. In defining gas solubility at these higher pressures, the partial pressure of the solute gas as well as the temperature and the value of H must be specified. In the following tables, if the partial pressure of the solute gas is not specified, the values of H may be safely used only for partial pressures of solute gas not greater than 1 atm. Where the partial pressure of the solute gas is specified, the given values of H may be used for partial pressures not more than perhaps an atmosphere higher or lower than the stated partial pressure. The use of Henry's law constants is illustrated by the examples given below.

Example 1. It is desired to find out how much hydrogen can be dissolved in 100 weights of water from a gas mixture when the total pressure is 760 mm. Hg, the partial pressure of H_2 is 200 mm., and the temperature is 20°C.

For partial pressures of H_2 up to 1 atm., the value of H is 6.83×10^4 at 20°C. (see Table 14-19).

$$x_A = \frac{p_A}{H} \qquad (14\text{-}1)$$

$$p_A = \frac{200}{760} = 0.263 \text{ atm.}$$

$$x_A = \frac{0.263}{68{,}300} = 0.00000385$$

where x_A is the mole fraction of H_2 in the liquid phase. (Mole fraction is the ratio of the number of moles of a particular constituent contained in a given weight of the solution to the total moles of all constituents contained.) To calculate the units of weight of H_2 per 100 weights of H_2O, the following formula may be used:

$$\left(\frac{x_A}{1 - x_A}\right)\frac{M_A}{M_S}100 = \left(\frac{0.00000385}{1 - 0.00000385}\right)\frac{2.02}{18.02}100 = 0.0000431$$

Thus, 0.0000431 weight of H_2 may be dissolved in 100 weights of H_2O at 20°C. from a gas mixture where the partial pressure of H_2 is 200 mm.

Example 2. Oxygen is dissolved in water to the extent of 0.03 weight of O_2 per 100 weights of H_2O. What equilibrium partial pressure of O_2 would this solution exert at 25°C.?

Take as a basis 100 weights of H_2O.

$$x_A = \frac{0.03/32}{0.03/32 + 100/18} = 0.0001688$$

$$p_A = Hx_A$$

If p_A is greater than 1 atm., the value of p_A should be known before the proper value of H can be selected. A trial-and-error solution is indicated. As a first approximation, assume that p_A will not exceed 1 atm. and select the value of H corresponding to 25°C. from Table 14-27.

$$H = 4.38 \times 10^4$$
$$p_A = 43{,}800 \times 0.0001688 = 7.39 \text{ atm.}$$

Select another value of H for a partial pressure of 7.39 atm. (5620 mm.) from Table 14-28, interpolating to obtain a value for 25°C.

$$H = 4.89 \times 10^4$$
$$p_A = 48{,}900 \times 0.0001688 = 8.25 \text{ atm.} = 6280 \text{ mm.}$$

A third approximation, using Table 14-28, assuming p_A = 8.35 atm., gives a value of p_A which is as accurate as the available values of H will permit.

$$H = 4.95 \times 10^4$$
$$p_A = 49{,}500 \times 0.0001688 = 8.35 \text{ atm.} = 6350 \text{ mm.}$$

Thus, 0.03 weight of O_2 dissolved in 100 weights of H_2O would exert a partial pressure of 6350 mm. at 25°C.

There may also be a sufficiently close, though less accurate, proportionality between the concentrations of the gas in the liquid and the gas phases when compositions are expressed in other units, particularly when comparatively dilute solutions are involved. Henry's law, though quite useful if it can be applied, must be checked experimentally in each instance to determine the accuracy with which it can be used. The following tables and charts give data on the solubility of some of the more **common gases in water.**

The solubility tables have been taken from the "International Critical Tables" and other reliable sources. In many instances, the tables here presented represent only a part of the solubility data given in the original. Where the data given are not sufficient for a particular problem, reference to the original is recommended. Markham and Kobe [*Chem. Rev.*, **28**, 519 (1941)] have summarized and critically reviewed the gas-solubility data that were available prior to 1941. Reference may also be made to Seidell and Linke, "Solubilities of Inorganic and Metal Compounds," Van Nostrand, Princeton, N.J., 1952.

Table 14-2.[1] **Acetylene** (C_2H_2)

t, °C.	0	5	10	15	20	25	30
$10^{-3} \times H$*	0.72	0.84	0.96	1.08	1.21	1.33	1.46

"International Critical Tables," vol. 3, p. 260, McGraw-Hill, 1928.

[1] Superior numbers refer to table footnote references on p. 14-7.

* The H in these solubility tables is the proportionality constant for the expression of Henry's law, $p = Hx$, where x = mole fraction of the solute in the liquid phase; p = partial pressure of the solute in the gas phase, expressed in atmospheres; H = a proportionality constant and is in units of atmospheres of solute pressure in the gas phase per unit concentration of the solute in the liquid phase. (The unit of concentration of the solute in the liquid phase is moles solute per mole solution.)

Table 14-3.[2] **Air**

t, °C.	0	5	10	15	20	25	30	35
$10^{-4} \times H$*	4.32	4.88	5.49	6.07	6.64	7.20	7.71	8.23
t, °C.	40	45	50	60	70	80	90	100
$10^{-4} \times H$*	8.70	9.11	9.46	10.1	10.5	10.7	10.8	10.7

"International Critical Tables," vol. 3, p. 257.

* H is calculated from the absorption coefficients of O_2 and N_2, taking into consideration the correction for constant argon content.

According to Whitney and Vivian [*Ind. Eng. Chem.*, **33**, 741 (1941)], the solubility of chlorine in water, in lb.-moles Cl_2/cu. ft., follows the equation

$$C = H'p + (K_eH'p)^{1/3} \qquad (14\text{-}2)$$

obtained by assuming that the solubility of molecular chlorine follows Henry's law and that the equilibrium in the hydration reaction

$$Cl_2 + H_2O = HOCl + H^+ + Cl^-$$

is represented by an equilibrium constant K_e. The observed values of H' and K_e are given in Table 14-12.

Solubility of Gases in Non-aqueous Pure Liquids. The solubility of a gas in a non-aqueous pure liquid is

Table 14-4.[3,4] **Ammonia** (NH_3)

Weight NH_3 per 100 weights H_2O	Partial pressure of NH_3, mm. Hg							
	0°C.	10°C.	20°C.	25°C.	30°C.	40°C.	50°C.	60°C.
100	947							
90	785							
80	636	987	1450	....	.....	3300		
70	500	780	1170	....	.....	2760		
60	380	600	945	....	.....	2130		
50	275	439	686	....	.....	1520		
40	190	301	470	....	719	1065		
30	119	190	298	....	454	692		
25	89.5	144	227	....	352	534	825	
20	64	103.5	166	....	260	395	596	834
15	42.7	70.1	114	....	179	273	405	583
10	25.1	41.8	69.6	....	110	167	247	361
7.5	17.7	29.9	50.0	....	79.7	120	179	261
5	11.2	19.1	31.7	....	51.0	76.5	115	165
4	.....	16.1	24.9	....	40.1	60.8	91.1	129.2
3	.....	11.3	18.2	23.5	29.6	45	67.1	94.3
2.5	.....	.....	15.0	19.4	24.4	(37.6)*	(55.7)	77.0
2	.....	.....	12.0	15.3	19.3	(30.0)	(44.5)	61.0
1.6	.....	.....	......	12.0	15.3	(24.1)	(35.5)	48.7
1.2	.....	.....	......	9.1	11.5	(18.3)	(26.7)	36.3
1.0	.....	.....	......	7.4	.....	(15.4)	(22.2)	30.2
0.5	.....	.....	......	3.4				

* Extrapolated values.

Table 14-5. **Ammonia** (NH_3)

Weight NH_3 per 100 weights H_2O.........	0.105	0.244	0.32	0.38	0.576	0.751	1.02
Partial pressure NH_3, mm. Hg, at 25°C........	0.791	1.83	2.41	2.89	4.41	5.80	7.96
Weight NH_3 per 100 weights H_2O.........	1.31	1.53	1.71	1.98	2.11	2.58	2.75
Partial pressure NH_3, mm. Hg, at 25°C.......	10.31	11.91	13.46	15.75	16.94	20.86	22.38

"Landolt-Börnstein Physikalische-chemische Tabellen," Eg. I, p. 303, 1927. Phase-equilibrium data for the binary system NH_3-H_2O are given by Clifford and Hunter, *J. Phys. Chem.*, **37**, 101 (1933).

Table 14-6.[5,6] **Bromine** (Br_2)

t, °C..................	0	5	10	15	20	25
$10^{-2} \times H$..................	0.213	0.275	0.366	0.466	0.593	0.737
t, °C..................	30	40	50	60	70	80
$10^{-2} \times H$..................	0.905	1.33	1.91	2.51	3.21	4.04

"International Critical Tables," vol. 3, p. 255.

Table 14-7.[7,8] **Carbon Dioxide** (CO_2)

t, °C......	0	5	10	15	20	25	30	35	40	45	50	60
$10^{-3} \times H$..	0.728	0.876	1.04	1.22	1.42	1.64	1.86	2.09	2.33	2.57	2.83	3.41

"International Critical Tables," vol. 3, p. 260.

Table 14-8.[21] **Carbon Dioxide** (CO_2)

Total pressure, atm.	Weight of CO_2 per 100 weights of H_2O*								
	12°C.	18°C.	25°C.	31.04°C.	35°C.	40°C.	50°C.	75°C.	100°C.
25	....	3.86	....	2.80	2.56	2.30	1.92	1.35	1.06
50	7.03	6.33	5.38	4.77	4.39	4.02	3.41	2.49	2.01
75	7.18	6.69	6.17	5.80	5.51	5.10	4.45	3.37	2.82
100	7.27	6.72	6.28	5.97	5.76	5.50	5.07	4.07	3.49
150	7.59	7.07	....	6.25	6.03	5.81	5.47	4.86	4.49
200	....	....	....	6.48	6.29	6.28	5.76	5.27	5.08
300	7.86	7.35	....	....	....	....	6.20	5.83	5.84
400	8.12	7.77	7.54	7.27	7.06	6.89	6.58	6.30	6.40
500	....	....	....	7.65	7.51	7.26	....	....	....
700	....	....	....	....	....	....	7.58	7.43	7.61

* In the original, concentration is expressed in cubic centimeters of CO_2 (reduced to 0°C. and 1 atm.) dissolved in 1 g. of water.

frequently of great interest to the chemical engineer. The possible combinations of solutes and solvents that come under the above classification are very numerous. Solubility tables in the "International Critical Tables," "Landolt-Börnstein Physikalisch-chemische Tabellen," and Seidell and Linke ("Solubilities of Inorganic and Organic Compounds," Van Nostrand, Princeton, N.J., 1952) present most of the available data. The list of solutes and solvent in Table 14-34 will give some idea of the type of systems for which solubility data are available. The list, which has been made up from tables appearing in the "International Critical Tables," vol. 3, pp. 261–270, does not include, by any means, all the solutes and solvents considered in the "International Critical Tables," but only some of those most commonly encountered.

Solubility data for hydrocarbons in oil are usually expressed in the form of an equilibrium constant $K = y^*/x$, where y^* = mole fraction of the solute in the gas phase, and x = mole fraction of the solute in the liquid phase. The value of K varies with temperature, pressure, and composition (see p. 13-13). Values of K are given by Katz and Hachmuth [*Ind. Eng. Chem.*, **29**, 1072 (1937)]. See also Sherwood and Pigford ("Absorption and Extraction," McGraw-Hill, New York, 1952) and an extensive series of articles by Sage *et al.* [*Ind. Eng. Chem.*, 1934 to date]. The available data are discussed in Sec. 13.

Solubilities of Gases in Aqueous Solutions. These data may be found in Seidell, Landolt-Börnstein, and the "International Critical Tables," vol. 3, pp. 271–281. The solutes considered in the "International Critical Tables" include, in general, the same gases as listed in Table 14-34. The solvents are aqueous solutions containing various concentrations of both inorganic and

Table 14-9.[2,9] **Carbon Monoxide** (CO)

t, °C..........	0	5	10	15	20	25	30	35
$10^{-4} \times H$......	3.52	3.96	4.42	4.89	5.36	5.80	6.20	6.59
t, °C..........	40	45	50	60	70	80	90	100
$10^{-4} \times H$......	6.96	7.29	7.61	8.21	8.45	8.45	8.46	8.46

"International Critical Tables," vol. 3, p. 260.

Table 14-10.[10] **Carbon Monoxide** (CO)

Partial pressure of CO, mm. Hg	$10^{-4} \times H$	
	17.7°C.	19.0°C.
900	4.77	4.88
2000	4.77	4.91
3000	4.77	4.93
4000	4.78	4.95
5000	4.80	4.97
6000	4.82	4.98
7000	4.86	5.02
8000	4.88	5.08

"International Critical Tables," vol. 3, p. 260.

Table 14-11. **Carbonyl Sulfide** (COS)

t, °C..................	0	5	10	15	20	25	30
$10^{-3} \times H$..............	0.92	1.17	1.48	1.82	2.19	2.59	3.04

"International Critical Tables," vol. 3, p. 261.

Table 14-12. **Chlorine** (Cl_2)

Temp., °C.	Henry's law coefficient H', lb.-moles Cl_2/(cu. ft.)(atm.)	Equilibrium constant K_e, (lb.-moles/cu. ft.)^2
10	0.00707	7.10
15	.00584	8.55
20	.00469	10.7
25	.00390	12.8

Whitney and Vivian, *Ind. Eng. Chem.*, **33**, 741 (1941).

Table 14-13.[22] **Chlorine** (Cl_2)

Partial pressure of Cl_2, mm. Hg	Solubility, g. of Cl_2 per liter					
	0°C.	10°C.	20°C.	30°C.	40°C.	50°C.
5	0.488	0.451	0.438	0.424	0.412	0.398
10	.679	.603	.575	.553	.532	.512
30	1.221	1.024	.937	.873	.821	.781
50	1.717	1.354	1.210	1.106	1.025	.962
100	2.79	2.08	1.773	1.573	1.424	1.313
150	3.81	2.73	2.27	1.966	1.754	1.599
200	4.78	3.35	2.74	2.34	2.05	1.856
250	5.71	3.95	3.19	2.69	2.34	2.09
300	.....	4.54	3.63	3.03	2.61	2.31
350	.....	5.13	4.06	3.35	2.86	2.53
400	.....	5.71	4.48	3.69	3.11	2.74
450	.....	6.26	4.88	3.98	3.36	2.94
500	.....	6.85	5.29	4.30	3.61	3.14
550	.....	7.39	5.71	4.60	3.84	3.33
600	.....	7.97	6.12	4.91	4.08	3.52
650	.....	8.52	6.52	5.21	4.32	3.71
700	.....	9.09	6.90	5.50	4.54	3.89
750	.....	9.65	7.29	5.80	4.77	4.07
800	.....	10.21	7.69	6.08	4.99	4.27
900	.....	......	8.46	6.68	5.44	4.62
1000	.....	......	9.27	7.27	5.89	4.97
1200	$Cl_2.8H_2O$ separates		10.84	8.42	6.81	5.67
1500	.....	......	13.23	10.14	8.05	6.70
2000	.....	......	17.07	13.02	10.22	8.38
2500	.....	......	21.0	15.84	12.32	10.03
3000	.....	......	......	18.73	14.47	11.70
3500	.....	......	......	21.7	16.62	13.38
4000	.....	......	......	24.7	18.84	15.04
4500	.....	......	......	27.7	20.7	16.75
5000	.....	......	......	30.8	23.3	18.46

Partial pressure of Cl_2, mm. Hg	Solubility, g. of Cl_2 per liter					
	60°C.	70°C.	80°C.	90°C.	100°C.	110°C.
5	0.383	0.369	0.351	0.339	0.326	0.316
10	.492	.470	.447	.431	.415	.402
30	.743	.704	.671	.642	.627	.598
50	.912	.863	.815	.781	.747	.722
100	1.228	1.149	1.085	1.034	.987	.950
150	1.482	1.382	1.294	1.227	1.174	1.137
200	1.706	1.580	1.479	1.396	1.333	1.276
250	1.914	1.764	1.642	1.553	1.480	1.413
300	2.10	1.932	1.793	1.700	1.610	1.542
350	2.28	2.10	1.940	1.831	1.736	1.661
400	2.47	2.25	2.08	1.965	1.854	1.773
450	2.64	2.41	2.22	2.09	1.972	1.880
500	2.80	2.55	2.35	2.21	2.08	1.986
550	2.97	2.69	2.47	2.32	2.19	2.09
600	3.13	2.83	2.59	2.43	2.29	2.19
650	3.29	2.97	2.72	2.55	2.41	2.28
700	3.44	3.10	2.84	2.66	2.50	2.37
750	3.59	3.23	2.96	2.76	2.60	2.47
800	3.75	3.37	3.08	2.87	2.69	2.56
900	4.04	3.63	3.30	3.08	2.89	2.74
1000	4.36	3.88	3.53	3.28	3.07	2.91
1200	4.92	4.37	3.95	3.67	3.43	3.25
1500	5.76	5.09	4.58	4.23	3.95	3.74
2000	7.14	6.26	5.63	5.17	4.78	4.49
2500	8.48	7.40	6.61	6.05	5.59	5.25
3000	9.83	8.52	7.54	6.92	6.38	5.97
3500	11.22	9.65	8.53	7.79	7.16	6.72
4000	12.54	10.76	9.52	8.65	7.94	7.42
4500	13.88	11.91	10.46	9.49	8.72	8.13
5000	15.26	13.01	11.42	10.35	9.48	8.84

organic compounds. Among the inorganic compounds are included many common acids, bases, and salts. Some of the organic compounds considered are: methyl alcohol, ethyl alcohol, glycerol, glucose, sucrose, chloral hydrate, and urea.

Solubilities of gases, particularly carbon dioxide, hydrogen, and nitrous oxide, in certain **colloidal solutions** in water may be found in the "International Critical Tables," vol. 3, p. 281. Typical colloids considered are gelatin, starch, dextrin, egg albumen, serum albumen, glycogen, peptone, hemoglobin, arsenic trisulfide, ferric hydroxide, and silicic acid.

Data on solubility under pressures up to 200 atm. for N_2, H_2, O_2, CH_4, C_2H_4, C_3H_8, C_3H_6, and H_2S in water and a number of organic solvents are given by Frolich, Tauch, Hogan, and Peer [*Ind. Eng. Chem.*, **23**, 548 (1931)]. Goodman and Krase [*Ind. Eng. Chem.*, **23**, 401 (1931)] present experimental data on the solubility of N_2 in water at pressures from 100 to 300 atm. and temperatures from 0° to 170°C. Wiebe and Gaddy [*J. Am. Chem. Soc.*, **61**, 315 (1939)] give data up to 700 atm. and from 50° to 100°C.

Ether Vapor in Various Solvents. The recovery of ether vapor is frequently accomplished by absorption in a liquid absorbent such as sulfuric acid or meta-cresol.

Table 14-14. Chlorine Dioxide (ClO_2)

Vol. % of ClO_2 in gas phase	Weight of ClO_2, grams per liter of solution						
	0°C.	5°C.	10°C.	15°C.	20°C.	30°C.	40°C.
1	2.00	1.50	1.25	1.00	0.90	0.60	0.46
3	6.00	4.7	3.85	3.20	2.70	1.95	1.30
5	10.0	7.8	6.30	5.25	4.30	3.20	2.25
7	14.0	10.9	8.95	7.35	6.15	4.40	3.20
10	20.0	15.5	12.8	10.5	8.80	6.30	4.50
11	.....	17.0	14.0	11.7	9.70	7.00	5.00
12	.....	18.6	15.3	12.8	10.55	7.50	5.45
13	.....	20.3	16.6	13.8	11.5	8.20	5.85
14	.....	.....	18.0	14.9	12.3	8.80	6.35
15	.....	.....	19.2	16.0	13.2	9.50	6.80
16	.....	.....	20.3	17.0	14.2	10.1	7.20

Ishi, *Chem. Eng.* (*Japan*), **22**, 153 (1958).

Table 14-15.[2] **Ethane** (C_2H_6)

t, °C.	0	5	10	15	20	25	30	35
$10^{-4} \times H$	1.26	1.55	1.89	2.26	2.63	3.02	3.42	3.83

t, °C.	40	45	50	60	70	80	90	100
$10^{-4} \times H$	4.23	4.63	5.00	5.65	6.23	6.61	6.87	6.92

"International Critical Tables," vol. 3, p. 261.

Table 14-16.[1] **Ethylene** (C_2H_4)

t, °C.	0	5	10	15	20	25	30
$10^{-3} \times H$	5.52	6.53	7.68	8.95	10.2	11.4	12.7

"International Critical Tables," vol. 3, p. 260.

Table 14-17. Helium (He)

t, °C.	0	10	20	30	40	50
$10^{-4} \times H$	12.9	12.6	12.5	12.4	12.1	11.5

See also Pray, Schweickert, and Minnich, *Ind. Eng. Chem.*, **44**, 1146 (1952)

Table 14-18.[9,12,13] **Hydrogen** (H_2)

t, °C.	0	5	10	15	20	25	30	35
$10^{-4} \times H$	5.79	6.08	6.36	6.61	6.83	7.07	7.29	7.42

t, °C.	40	45	50	60	70	80	90	100
$10^{-4} \times H$	7.51	7.60	7.65	7.65	7.61	7.55	7.51	7.45

"International Critical Tables," vol. 3, p. 256.
See also Pray, Schweickert, and Minnich, *Ind. Eng. Chem.*, **44**, 1146 (1952)

Table 14-19.[10] **Hydrogen** (H_2)

Partial pressure H_2, mm. Hg	$10^{-4} \times H$	
	19.5°C.	23°C.
900	7.42	....
1100	....	7.75
2000	7.42	7.76
3000	7.43	7.77
4000	7.47	7.81
5000	7.56	7.89
6000	7.70	8.00
7000	7.87	8.16
8200	....	8.41
8250	8.17	....

"International Critical Tables," vol. 3, p. 256.

Table 14-20.[14] **Hydrogen Chloride** (HCl)

Weights of HCl per 100 weights of H_2O	Partial pressure of HCl, mm. Hg			
	0°C.	10°C.	20°C.	30°C.
78.6	510	840		
66.7	130	233	399	627
56.3	29.0	56.4	105.5	188
47.0	5.7	11.8	23.5	44.5
38.9	1.0	2.27	4.90	9.90
31.6	0.175	0.43	1.00	2.17
25.0	.0316	.084	0.205	0.48
19.05	.0056	.016	.0428	.106
13.64	.00099	.00305	.0088	.0234
8.70	.000118	.000583	.00178	.00515
4.17	.000018	.000069	.00024	.00077
2.04	....	.0000117	.000044	.000151

Weights of HCl per 100 weights of H_2O	Partial pressure of HCl, mm. Hg		
	50°C.	80°C.	110°C.
78.6			
66.7			
56.3	535		
47.0	141	623	
38.9	35.7	188	760
31.6	8.9	54.5	253
25.0	2.21	15.6	83
19.05	0.55	4.66	28
13.64	.136	1.34	9.3
8.70	.0344	0.39	3.10
4.17	.0064	.095	0.93
2.04	.00140	.0245	.280

Enthalpy and phase-equilibrium data for the binary system HCl-H_2O are given by Van Nuys, *Trans. Am. Inst. Chem. Engrs.*, **39**, 663 (1943).

Table 14-21.[11] **Hydrogen Sulfide** (H_2S)

t, °C.	0	5	10	15	20	25	30	35
$10^{-2} \times H$	2.68	3.15	3.67	4.23	4.83	5.45	6.09	6.76
t, °C.	40	45	50	60	70	80	90	100
$10^{-2} \times H$	7.45	8.14	8.84	10.3	11.9	13.5	14.4	14.8

"International Critical Tables," vol. 3, p. 259.

Table 14-22.[2] **Methane** (CH_4)

t, °C.	0	5	10	15	20	25	30	35
$10^{-4} \times H$	2.24	2.59	2.97	3.37	3.76	4.13	4.49	4.86
t, °C.	40	45	50	60	70	80	90	100
$10^{-4} \times H$	5.20	5.51	5.77	6.26	6.66	6.82	6.92	7.01

"International Critical Tables," vol. 3, p. 260.

Table 14-23.[2,9] **Nitric Oxide** (NO)

t, °C.	0	5	10	15	20	25	30	35
$10^{-4} \times H$	1.69	1.93	2.18	2.42	2.64	2.87	3.10	3.31
t, °C.	40	45	50	60	70	80	90	100
$10^{-4} \times H$	3.52	3.72	3.90	4.18	4.38	4.48	4.52	4.54

"International Critical Tables," vol. 3, p. 259.

Table 14-24.[9,13,15] **Nitrogen** (N_2)*

t, °C.	0	5	10	15	20	25	30	35
$10^{-4} \times H$	5.29	5.97	6.68	7.38	8.04	8.65	9.24	9.85
t, °C.	40	45	50	60	70	80	90	100
$10^{-4} \times H$	10.4	10.9	11.3	12.0	12.5	12.6	12.6	12.6

"International Critical Tables," vol. 3, p. 256. See also Pray, Schweickert, and Minnich, *Ind. Eng. Chem.*, **44**, 1146 (1952).
* Atmospheric nitrogen = 98.815 vol. % N_2 + 1.185 vol. % A.

Table 14-25.[10] **Nitrogen** (N_2)

Partial pressure of N_2, mm. Hg	$10^{-4} \times H$	
	19.4°C.	24.9°C.
900	8.24	9.08
2000	8.32	9.15
3000	8.41	9.25
4000	8.49	9.38
5000	8.59	9.49
6000	8.74	9.62
7000	8.86	9.75
8100	9.04	
8200	....	9.91

See also Goodman and Krase [*Ind. Eng. Chem.*, **23**, 401(1931)] for values up to 169°C. and 300 atm.

Table 14-26.[16,17] **Nitrous Oxide** (N_2O)

t, °C.	5	10	15	20	25	30	35
$10^{-3} \times H$	1.17	1.41	1.66	1.98	2.25	2.59	3.02

"International Critical Tables," vol. 3, p. 259.

Table 14-27.[9,13,15,18,19] **Oxygen** (O_2)

t, °C.	0	5	10	15	20	25	30	35
$10^{-4} \times H$	2.55	2.91	3.27	3.64	4.01	4.38	4.75	5.07
t, °C.	40	45	50	60	70	80	90	100
$10^{-4} \times H$	5.35	5.63	5.88	6.29	6.63	6.87	6.99	7.01

"International Critical Tables," vol. 3, p. 257. Pray, Schweickert, and Minnich [*Ind. Eng. Chem.*, **44**, 1146 (1952)] give $H = 4.46 \times 10^{-4}$ at 25°C. and other values up to 343°C.

Table 14-28.[10] **Oxygen** (O_2)

Partial pressure of O_2, mm. Hg	$10^{-4} \times H$	
	23°C.	25.9°C.
800	....	4.79
900	4.58	
2000	4.59	4.80
3000	4.60	4.83
4000	4.68	4.88
5000	4.73	4.92
6000	4.80	4.98
7000	4.88	5.05
8150	4.98	
8200	....	5.16

"International Critical Tables," vol. 3, p. 257. See also *Trans. Am. Soc. Mech. Engrs.*, **76**, 69 (1954) for solubility of O_2 for 100°F. $< T <$ 650°F., 300 $< P <$ 2000 lb./sq. in.

Table 14-29. Ozone (O_3)

t, °C.	0	5	10	15	20	25	30	35	40	50
$10^{-3} \times H$	1.94	2.18	2.48	2.88	3.76	4.57	5.98	8.18	12.0	27.4

"International Critical Tables," vol. 3, p. 257.

Table 14-30.[20] **Propylene** (C_3H_6)

t, °C.	2	6	10	14	18
$10^{-3} \times H$	3.04	3.84	4.46	5.06	5.69

"International Critical Tables," vol. 3, p. 260.

Table 14-31.[3] **Sulfur Dioxide** (SO_2)

Weight of SO_2 per 100 weights of H_2O	Partial pressure of SO_2, mm. Hg							
	0°C.	7°C.	10°C.	15°C.	20°C.	30°C.	40°C.	50°C.
20	646	657						
15	474	637	726					
10	308	417	474	567	698			
7.5	228	307	349	419	517	688		
5.0	148	198	226	270	336	452	665	
2.5	69	92	105	127	161	216	322	458
1.5	38	51	59	71	92	125	186	266
1.0	23.3	31	37	44	59	79	121	172
0.7	15.2	20.6	23.6	28.0	39.0	52	87	116
.5	9.9	13.5	15.6	19.3	26.0	36	57	82.0
.3	5.1	6.9	7.9	10.0	14.1	19.7		
.2	2.8	3.7	4.6	5.7	8.5	11.8	.....	31.0
.15	1.9	2.6	3.1	3.8	5.8	8.1	12.9	20.0
.10	1.2	1.5	1.75	2.2	3.2	4.7	7.5	12.0
.05	0.6	0.7	0.75	0.8	1.2	1.7	2.8	4.7
.02	.25	.3	.3	.3	0.5	0.6	0.8	1.3

Table 14-32. Sulfur Dioxide (SO_2)

Weight of SO_2 per 100 weights of H_2O	Partial pressure of SO_2, mm. Hg						
	0°C.	10°C.	20°C.	25°C.	30°C.	40°C.	50°C.
15	500	735					
10	310	470	...	840			
8	240	370	580	670	780		
6	175	270	430	505	580	770	
4	110	170	270	320	380	510	700
2	50	75	110	150	170	250	340
1	20	35	30	60	70	110	160

Seidell and Linke, "Solubilities of Inorganic and Organic Compounds," p. 519, Van Nostrand, Princeton, N.J., 1952.

Table 14-33. Sulfur Dioxide (SO_2)

Weight of SO_2 per 100 weights of H_2O	Partial pressure, mm. Hg				
	30°C.	50°C.	70°C.	90°C.	110°C.
7.45	750	1243			
4.36	420	778	1272		
1.04	82.5	149	301	465	
0.51	.....	76.0	146	239	348

See Pearson, Lundberg, West, and McCarthey [*Chem. Eng. Progress*, **47**, 257 (1951)] for a review of all available solubility data for SO_2 in H_2O.

References for Tables 14-2 to 14-33

1 Winkler, "Landolt-Börnstein Physikalisch-chemische Tabellen."
2 Winkler, *Ber.*, **34**, 1408 (1901).
3 Sherwood, *Ind. Eng. Chem.*, **17**, 745 (1925).
4 Breitenbach, *Bull. Univ. Wis. Eng. Exp. Sta., Ser.* 68.
5 Winkler, *Magyar Chemiai Folyóirat*, **4**, 33 (1898).
6 Winkler, *Chem.-Ztg.*, **23**, 687 (1899).
7 Bohr, *Ann. Physik*, **68**, 500 (1899).
8 Sander, *Z. physik. Chem.*, **78**, 513 (1912).
9 Winkler, *Z. physik. Chem.*, **9**, 171 (1892).
10 Cassuto, *Physik. Z.*, **5**, 233 (1904).
11 Winkler, *Mathematikai ès Természettudomanyi Ertesito*, Budapest, **25**, 86 (1907).
12 Winkler, *Ber.*, **24**, 89 (1891).
13 Winkler, *Math. naturw. Ber. Ungarn.* **9**, 195 (1892).
14 Zeisberg, *Chem. & Met. Eng.*, **32**, 326 (1925).
15 Winkler, *Ber.*, **24**, 3602 (1891).
16 Geffcken, *Z. physik. Chem.*, **49**, 257 (1904).
17 Kunerth, *Phys. Rev.*, **19**, 512 (1922).
18 Winkler, *Z. physik. Chem.*, **55**, 344 (1906).
19 Winkler, *Ber.*, **22**, 1764 (1889).
20 Than, *Liebigs Ann. Chem.*, **123**, 187 (1862).
21 Wiebe and Gaddy, *J. Am. Chem. Soc.*, **61**, 315 (1939); **62**, 815 (1940).
22 Adams and Edmonds, *Ind. Eng. Chem.*, **29**, 447 (1937).

Table 14-34. Non-aqueous Solvents for Gas Absorption

Solutes:

Acetylene, C_2H_2	Hydrogen, H_2
Air	Hydrogen chloride, HCl
Ammonia, NH_3	Hydrogen sulfide, H_2S
Bromine, Br_2	Methane, CH_4
Carbon dioxide, CO_2	Methyl chloride, CH_3Cl
Carbon monoxide, CO	Nitric oxide, NO
Chlorine, Cl_2	Nitrogen, N_2
Ethane, C_2H_6	Nitrous oxide, N_2O
Ethylene, C_2H_4	Oxygen, O_2
	Sulfur dioxide, SO_2
	Etc.

Solvents:

Acetic acid (glacial), $C_2H_4O_2$	Ethyl acetate, $C_4H_8O_2$
Acetic anhydride, $C_4H_6O_3$	Ethyl alcohol, C_2H_6O
Acetone, C_3H_6O	Ethylene chloride, C_2H_4Cl
Amyl alcohol, $C_5H_{12}O$	Ethyl ether, $C_4H_{10}O$
Aniline, C_6H_7N	Methyl acetate, $C_3H_6O_2$
Benzene, C_6H_6	Methyl alcohol, CH_4O
Bromobenzene, C_6H_5Br	Nitrobenzene, $C_6H_5NO_2$
Carbon disulfide, CS_2	Propyl alcohol, C_3H_8O
Carbon tetrachloride, CCl_4	Propylene, C_3H_6
Chlorobenzene, C_6H_5Cl	Toluene, C_7H_8
Chloroform, $CHCl_3$	Etc.

Figures 14-1 and 14-2 give the solubility of ether in various solvents. All the solubility curves given with the exception of that for butyl alcohol are for 20°C. The butyl alcohol curve is for 15°C. (Robinson, "Recovery of Volatile Solvents," pp. 154–156, Reinhold, New York, 1922.)

Carbon Dioxide and Hydrogen Sulfide in Aqueous Ammonia. When carbon dioxide dissolves in an aqueous ammonia solution the following ionic equilibria are established:

$$NH_3 + CO_2 + H_2O \rightleftharpoons NH_4^+ + HCO_3^- \qquad (a)$$
$$NH_3 + HCO_3^- \rightleftharpoons NH_2COO^- + H_2O \qquad (b)$$
$$NH_3 + HCO_3^- \rightleftharpoons NH_4^+ + CO_3^+ \qquad (c)$$

Van Krevelen, Hoftijzer, and Huntjens [*Rec. trav. chim.*, **68**, 193 (1949)] have shown how mass-action expressions and nitrogen, carbon, and ion balances can be employed to represent the composition of the solution and the equilibrium partial pressures of NH_3 and CO_2. The mass-action constants vary with temperature and ionic strength. Figures 14-3 and 14-4 give typical calculated results. Figure 14-3 shows the variation of

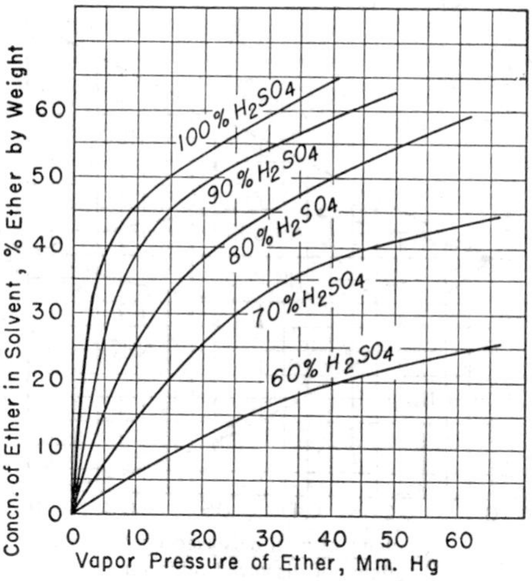

FIG. 14-1. Vapor pressure of ether at 20°C. from H_2SO_4 solutions of several concentrations of H_2SO_4 and H_2O.

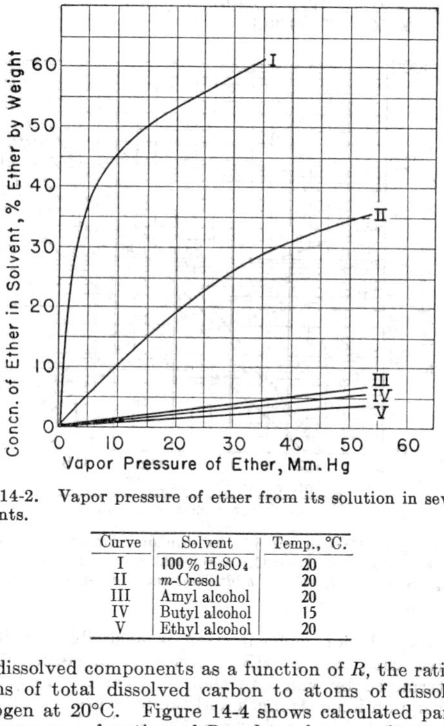

FIG. 14-2. Vapor pressure of ether from its solution in several solvents.

Curve	Solvent	Temp., °C.
I	100% H_2SO_4	20
II	*m*-Cresol	20
III	Amyl alcohol	20
IV	Butyl alcohol	15
V	Ethyl alcohol	20

the dissolved components as a function of R, the ratio of atoms of total dissolved carbon to atoms of dissolved nitrogen at 20°C. Figure 14-4 shows calculated partial pressures as a function of R and total ammonia concentration n at the same temperature. The calculated results agree closely with the experimental data of van Krevelen *et al.*, as well as with data of Preston and Badger [*J. Soc. Chem. Ind.*, **57**, 106 (1938)], Badger and Silver [*J. Soc. Chem. Ind.*, **57**, 110 (1938)], Badger [*J. Soc. Chem. Ind.*, **57**, 112 (1938)], Badger and Wilson [*J. Soc. Chem. Ind.*, **66**, 54 (1947)], and Dryden [*J. Soc. Chem. Ind.*, **66**, 59 (1947)].

Solution of hydrogen sulfide in aqueous ammonia involves the ionic reaction

$$NH_3 + H_2S \rightleftharpoons NH_4^+ + HS^- \qquad (d)$$

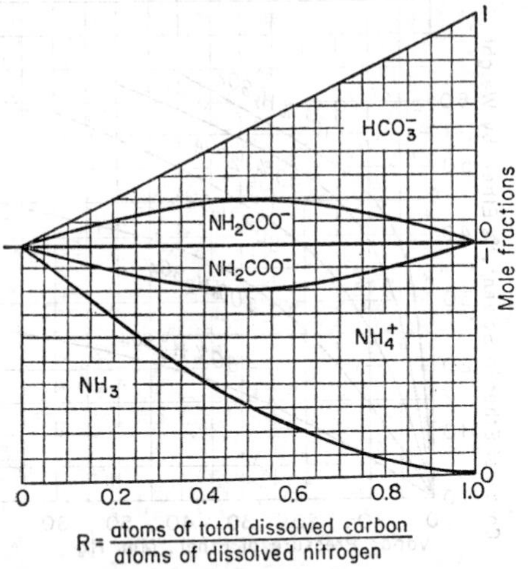

Fig. 14-3. Carbon dioxide in aqueous ammonia; variation of dissolved components at 20°C.; n = total ammonia concentration = 2.0*N*. [*Van Krevelen, Hoftijzer, and Huntjens, Rec. trav. chim.*, **68**, 193 (1949).]

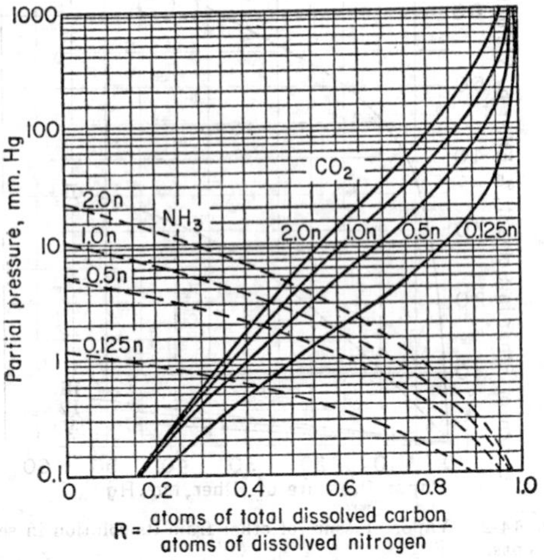

Fig. 14-4. Carbon dioxide in aqueous ammonia; calculated partial pressures at 20°C.; n = total ammonia concentration. [*Van Krevelen, Hoftijzer, and Huntjens, Rec. trav. chim.*, **68**, 193 (1949).]

The sulfide ion concentration is negligibly small compared with that of HS^-. Mass-action constants were determined by van Krevelen *et al.* and were found to depend on ionic strength and temperature. Using these values and those applying to CO_2 and NH_3, equilibrium partial pressures of H_2S could be calculated. Typical results are given in Table 14-35. The carbon dioxide

Table 14-35. Typical Partial Pressures of H_2S at Equilibrium with Aqueous Solutions of NH_3 and CO_2*

Composition of solution, g.-moles/liter			Partial pressure of H_2S, mm. Hg	
Total NH_3	Total CO_2	Total H_2S	Observed	Calculated
1.17	0.41	0.184	11.7	11.5
1.13	0.21	0.290	12.1	12.3
2.16	0.94	0.360	38.4	34.4
2.16	0.40	0.60	27.0	25.5

* Temperature = 40°C. From van Krevelen *et al.*, *Rec. trav. chim.*, **68**, 193 (1949).

Table 14-36A. Equilibrium Data for Monoethanolamine Solutions

Temp., °C.	Normality of amine	Partial pressure of CO_2, mm. Hg	Liquid concentration, moles CO_2 per mole amine
0.0	0.5	745.8	1.110
.0	.5	256.3	0.990
.0	.5	45.3	.817
.0	.5	10.6	.675
25.0	.5	735.7	1.004
25.0	.5	251.8	0.886
25.0	.5	99.6	.795
25.0	.5	44.2	.720
25.0	.5	10.8	.607
50.0	.5	661.3	.880
50.0	.5	228.3	.757
50.0	.5	40.1	.596
75.0	.5	475.8	.685
75.0	.5	130.3	.584
75.0	.5	50.0	.476
0.0	2.0	754.4	.900
.0	2.0	206.1	.776
.0	2.0	79.4	.718
.0	2.0	11.4	.601
25.0	2.0	736.4	.795
25.0	2.0	252.2	.697
25.0	2.0	98.6	.623
25.0	2.0	44.2	.589
25.0	2.0	10.6	.527
50.0	2.0	668.2	.698
50.0	2.0	183.1	.607
50.0	2.0	70.9	.556
50.0	2.0	10.1	.489
75.0	2.0	477.0	.560
75.0	2.0	130.6	.474
75.0	2.0	51.1	.430
0.0	5.0	751.5	.761
.0	5.0	272.2	.679
.0	5.0	206.2	.649
.0	5.0	80.1	.600
.0	5.0	11.5	.600
25.0	5.0	742.9	0.657
25.0	5.0	254.9	.601
25.0	5.0	98.7	.563
25.0	5.0	44.6	.539
25.0	5.0	10.6	.507
50.0	5.0	677.0	.574
50.0	5.0	245.3	.527
50.0	5.0	71.5	.505
50.0	5.0	10.4	.453
75.0	5.0	518.1	.493
75.0	5.0	142.6	.460
75.0	5.0	54.8	.418
0.0	9.5	752.4	.622
.0	9.5	272.2	.592
.0	9.5	79.2	.568
.0	9.5	11.4	.538
25.0	9.5	735.9	.588
25.0	9.5	252.2	.554
25.0	9.5	99.0	.532
25.0	9.5	44.8	.519
25.0	9.5	11.1	.495
50.0	9.5	701.3	.538
50.0	9.5	255.3	.522
50.0	9.5	74.3	.492
50.0	9.5	10.8	.443
75.0	9.5	559.7	.468
75.0	9.5	153.1	.458
75.0	9.5	56.7	.424
25.0	12.5	749.1	.548
25.0	12.5	256.3	.518
25.0	12.5	45.4	.521
50.0	12.5	716.2	.525
50.0	12.5	259.5	.501
50.0	12.5	196.0	.495
50.0	12.5	75.6	.483
50.0	12.5	10.9	.467
75.0	12.5	629.9	.479
75.0	12.5	168.1	.453
75.0	12.5	64.2	.395

Table 14-36B. Equilibrium Data for Diethanolamine Solutions

Temp., °C.	Normality of amine	Partial pressure of CO_2, mm. Hg	Liquid concentration, moles CO_2/mole of amine
0.0	0.5	750.7	1.119
.0	.5	272.7	1.044
.0	.5	271.6	1.035
.0	.5	79.1	0.883
.0	.5	11.0	.741
25.0	.5	732.3	.987
25.0	.5	249.6	.912
25.0	.5	97.9	.797
25.0	.5	44.3	.714
25.0	.5	11.0	.551
50.0	.5	666.4	.883
50.0	.5	241.2	.778
50.0	.5	70.8	.588
50.0	.5	10.1	.336
75.0	.5	474.5	.630
75.0	.5	129.8	.456
75.0	.5	50.0	.355
0.0	2.0	751.0	.936
.0	2.0	272.1	.837
.0	2.0	80.1	.752
.0	2.0	11.5	.604
25.0	2.0	735.5	.753
25.0	2.0	729.0	.813
25.0	2.0	249.9	.717
25.0	2.0	99.3	.633
25.0	2.0	44.3	.553
25.0	2.0	10.5	.451
50.0	2.0	668.4	.680
50.0	2.0	242.3	.562
50.0	2.0	183.8	.548
50.0	2.0	71.0	.489
50.0	2.0	10.2	.302
75.0	2.0	488.6	.464
75.0	2.0	133.3	.356
75.0	2.0	51.1	.263
0.0	5.0	755.1	.762
.0	5.0	206.3	.683
.0	5.0	79.4	.638
.0	5.0	11.4	.526
25.0	5.0	741.1	.661
25.0	5.0	253.6	.589
25.0	5.0	44.8	.506
50.0	5.0	682.4	.562
50.0	5.0	246.1	.491
50.0	5.0	71.8	.414
50.0	5.0	10.4	.254
75.0	5.0	520.0	.403
75.0	5.0	142.6	.327
75.0	5.0	54.9	.242
25.0	8.0	744.0	0.582
25.0	8.0	268.4	.553
25.0	8.0	78.4	.480
50.0	8.0	703.5	.515
50.0	8.0	193.0	.458
50.0	8.0	74.5	.387
50.0	8.0	10.6	.250
75.0	8.0	574.0	.368
75.0	8.0	155.9	.302
75.0	8.0	58.9	.215

Table 14-36C. Equilibrium Data for Triethanolamine Solutions

Temp., °C.	Normality of amine	Partial pressure of CO_2, mm. Hg	Liquid concentration, moles CO_2/mole of amine
0.0	0.5	756.4	1.100
.0	.5	258.9	0.943
.0	.5	100.3	.805
.0	.5	45.6	.645
.0	.5	10.7	.378
25.0	.5	739.3	.921
25.0	.5	253.6	.715
25.0	.5	99.3	.512
25.0	.5	44.5	.375
25.0	.5	10.5	.191
50.0	.5	658.7	.623
50.0	.5	229.1	.408
50.0	.5	88.2	.262
50.0	.5	40.3	.162
50.0	.5	8.3	.0812
75.0	.5	474.7	.327
75.0	.5	129.9	.177
75.0	.5	50.1	.116
25.0	1.0	723.0	.805
25.0	1.0	259.0	.612
25.0	1.0	96.7	.424
25.0	1.0	43.4	.294
25.0	1.0	10.8	.161
25.0	1.0	1.4	.0587
0.0	2.0	752.0	.954
.0	2.0	259.3	.818
.0	2.0	100.4	.662
.0	2.0	45.8	.484
.0	2.0	10.7	.263
25.0	2.0	734.0	0.715
25.0	2.0	99.5	.316
25.0	2.0	45.4	.209
25.0	2.0	11.0	.0930
25.0	2.0	1.4	.0332
50.0	2.0	662.8	.382
50.0	2.0	230.3	.216
50.0	2.0	88.7	.130
50.0	2.0	40.4	.0791
50.0	2.0	9.4	.0346
75.0	2.0	485.9	.158
75.0	2.0	132.6	.0771
75.0	2.0	51.2	.0518
25.0	3.5	731.0	.595
25.0	3.5	420.0	.484
25.0	3.5	183.0	.312
25.0	3.5	46.6	.143
25.0	3.5	31.6	.114
25.0	3.5	10.0	.0620
25.0	5.0	738.6	.453
25.0	5.0	266.4	.258
25.0	5.0	98.7	.115
25.0	5.0	77.8	.108
25.0	5.0	44.5	.0729
25.0	5.0	10.6	.0292
50.0	5.0	678.8	.142
50.0	5.0	234.2	.0682
50.0	5.0	41.2	.0248
75.0	5.0	534.7	.0669
75.0	5.0	146.6	.0302
75.0	5.0	56.1	.0133

and ammonia partial pressures above solutions also containing H_2S are approximately the same as in a sulfur-free solution containing a quantity of ammonia equal to the moles of NH_3 less the moles of H_2S in the actual solution. Pressures of NH_3 and CO_2 over solutions containing all three gases can therefore be found from data in sulfur-free solutions.

Acid Gases in Alkanolamines. The absorption process for purifying carbon dioxide and hydrogen sulfide involves the absorption of carbon dioxide in an alkaline solution. This absorption is of a special type where the dissolved gas reacts with the absorbent to form a loose chemical compound. Organic bases such as monoethanolamine, diethanolamine, and triethanolamine are used for absorption of carbon dioxide and hydrogen sulfide.

The vapor pressures of CO_2 from ethanolamine solutions of various concentrations at temperatures of 0° to 75°C. are given in Table 14-36 [Mason and Dodge, *Trans. Am. Inst. Chem. Engrs.*, **32**, 27 (1936)]. Jones, Froning, and Clayton [*J. Chem. Eng. Data*, **4**, 85 (1959)] have more recently published data on solubilities in aqueous monoethanolamine solutions of CO_2, H_2S, and mixtures of the two. Their smoothed data are given in Table 14-37. The solutions contained 15.3 per cent by weight amine, equivalent to 2.5N. Reference may also be made to the work of Reed and Wood [*Trans. Am. Inst. Chem. Engrs.*, **37**, 363 (1941)], Reed (U.S. Patent 2,399,142), Lyud-

Table 14-37A. Smoothed Values for Solubility of Carbon Dioxide in 15.3 Weight Per Cent Monoethanolamine

Partial pressure CO_2, mm. Hg	Moles carbon dioxide per mole amine					
	40°C.	60°C.	80°C.	100°C.	120°C.	140°C.
1	0.383	.....	.....	0.096		
5	.438	.....	.....	.152		
10	.471	0.412	.....	.194		
30	.518	.459	0.379	.265		
50	.542	.482	.405	.299		
70	.558	.498	.422	.322	0.200	
100	.576	.516	.442	.347	.227	0.109
200	.614	.552	.481	.393	.281	.162
300	.639	.574	.505	.423	.314	.194
400	.657	.591	.523	.442	.336	.219
500	.672	.605	.538	.458	.355	.237
600	.686	.615	.550	.472	.370	.254
760	.705	.631	.566	.489	.390	.275
1000	.727	.650	.584	.509	.413	.300
2000	.....	.702	.637	.562	.476	.366
3000	.....	.....	.669	.596	.513	.408
5000	.....	.....	.712	.641	.562	.464
7000	.....	.....	.742	.672	.597	.500

Table 14-37B. Smoothed Values for Solubility of Hydrogen Sulfide in 15.3 Weight Per Cent Monoethanolamine

Partial pressure H_2S, mm. Hg	Moles hydrogen sulfide per mole amine					
	40°C.	60°C.	80°C.	100°C.	120°C.	140°C.
1	0.128	.....	.....	0.029		
3	.212	0.137	.....	.050	0.025	0.016
5	.271	.171	.....	.065	.036	.025
10	.374	.240	0.141	.091	.056	.040
30	.579	.386	.243	.160	.101	.072
50	.683	.472	.314	.203	.139	.091
70	.750	.534	.364	.238	.153	.106
100	.802	.600	.422	.279	.182	.124
200	.890	.722	.545	.374	.256	.167
300	.931	.790	.617	.439	.312	.200
400	.949	.836	.666	.490	.357	.226
500	.959	.871	.706	.536	.393	
600	.970	.900	.738	.575	.426	
700	.980	.921	.....	.607	.453	
800	.....	.942	.....	.636		

kovskaya and Liebush [*J. Appl. Chem.* (*U.S.S.R.*), **23,** 145 (1949)], and Muhlbauer and Monaghan [*Oil Gas J.*, **55,** 139 (1957)] for additional data on CO_2 solubilities in monoethanolamine solutions. Riegger, Tartar, and Lingafelter [*J. Am. Chem. Soc.*, **66,** 2024 (1944)], Liebush and Sneerson [*J. Appl. Chem.* (*U.S.S.R.*), **23,** 145 (1950)], Reed (*loc. cit.*), Muhlbauer and Monaghan (*loc. cit.*), Atwood, Arnold, and Kindrick [*Ind. Eng. Chem.*, **49,** 1439 (1957)], and Bottoms [*Ind. Eng. Chem.*, **23,** 501 (1931)] have also published data on H_2S solubilities.

Carbon Dioxide in Carbonate Solution. When carbon dioxide is dissolved in an aqueous solution of sodium (or potassium) carbonate the following reversible reaction occurs:

$$Na_2CO_3 + CO_2 + H_2O \rightleftarrows 2NaHCO_3$$

The solubility of CO_2 in such a solution depends on the ratio of carbonate to bicarbonate, the total amount of salt in the solution, the temperature, and the partial pressure of the carbon dioxide in the gas.

The relation between these variables was first worked out and formulated by McCoy [*J. Am. Chem. Soc.*, **29,** 437 (1903)]. Harte, Baker, and Purcell [*Ind. Eng. Chem.*, **25,** 528 (1933)] obtained more data and expressed the relation in an empirical formula, which reduces to

$$p_{CO_2} = \frac{137f^2N^{1.29}}{S(1-f)(365-t)} \tag{14-3}$$

where p_{CO_2} = partial pressure of CO_2, mm. Hg; f = fraction of total base present as bicarbonate; N = sodium normality; S = solubility of CO_2 in water under a pressure of 1 atm. of CO_2, g.-moles per liter (see Table 14-38); t = temperature, °F.

Equation (14-3) has been tested only over the temperature range of 65° to 150°F. and sodium normalities from 0.5 to 2.0.

Sherwood and Pigford ("Absorption and Extraction," p. 358, McGraw-Hill, New York, 1952) report that the

Table 14-37C. Hydrogen Sulfide Partial Pressure over Monoethanolamine Solutions Containing Carbon Dioxide and Hydrogen Sulfide

Temp., °C.	Partial pressure H_2S, mm. Hg	Moles H_2S per mole amine					
		R_L = 0.01*	R_L = 0.05	R_L = 0.10	R_L = 0.50	R_L = 1.0	$R_L = \infty$
40	1	0.0047	0.0190	0.0327	0.0863	0.1140	0.128
	3	.0055	.0225	.0395	.1160	.1630	.212
	10	.0066	.0263	.0468	.1510	.2220	.374
	30	.0077	.0301	.0540	.1820	.2720	.579
	100	.0092	.0351	.0619	.2120	.3260	.802
	300	......	.0399	.0710	.2450	.3720	.931
	1000	......	.0464	.0830	.2700	.4250	1.00
60	1	.0037	.0145	.0237	.0650	.0775	0.085
	3	.0046	.0184	.0304	.0845	.1130	.137
	10	.0059	.0234	.0396	.1125	.1600	.240
	30	.0074	.0288	.0492	.1450	.2120	.386
	100	.0092	.0355	.0605	.1840	.2750	.600
	300	......	.0431	.0730	.2190	.3230	.790
	1000	......	......	.0910	.2620	.3840	.970
100	1	.0024	.0067	.0103	.0220	.0247	.029
	3	.0036	.0101	.0155	.0340	.0407	.050
	10	.0056	.0155	.0239	.0540	.0675	.091
	30	.0082	.0228	.0349	.0810	.1040	.160
	100	......	.0343	.0524	.1250	.1650	.279
	300	......	.0503	.0762	.1800	.2430	.439
	1000	......	......	......	.2480	.3340	.680
120	1	.0016	.0031	.0040	.0072	.0088	.012
	3	.0030	.0059	.0078	.0146	.0184	.025
	10	.0059	.0120	.0163	.0312	.0393	.056
	30	.0110	.0228	.0308	.0590	.0750	.101
	100	......	.0424	.0558	.1075	.1400	.182
	300	......	......	.0935	.1800	.2325	.312
	1000	......	......	......	.3120	.4050	.520

* $R_L = \dfrac{\text{moles } H_2S\text{/mole amine}}{\text{moles } CO_2\text{/mole amine}}$.

Table 14-37D. Hydrogen Sulfide and Carbon Dioxide Partial Pressures over Monoethanolamine Solutions Containing Hydrogen Sulfide and Carbon Dioxide

Temp., °C.	Partial pressure H_2S, mm. Hg	Moles H_2S per mole amine						
		$R_V = 0.01$*	$R_V = 0.05$	$R_V = 0.10$	$R_V = 0.50$	$R_V = 1.0$	$R_V = 10$	$R_V = \infty$
40	1	0.0013	0.0035	0.0050	0.0120	0.0178	0.0500	0.128
	3	.0022	.0057	.0084	.0208	.0300	.0825	.212
	10	.0039	.0100	.0149	.0380	.0540	.1450	.374
	30	.0064	.0166	.0250	.0630	.0910	.2400	.579
	100	.0107	.0279	.0415	.1050	.1510	.3900	.802
	300	.0167	.0430	.0638	.1550	.2200	.5500	.931
	1000	......	.0625	.0920	.2170	.3050	.7300	1.00
60	1	.0019	.0049	.0070	.0172	.0239	.0643	0.085
	3	.0029	.0074	.0108	.0260	.0363	.0940	.137
	10	.0044	.0115	.0172	.0414	.0565	.1420	.240
	30	.0066	.0175	.0260	.0621	.0850	.2080	.386
	100	.0102	.0272	.0405	.0980	.1360	.3140	.600
	300	......	.0410	.0610	.1480	.2040	.4320	.790
	1000	......	......	.0940	.2170	.2900	.5500	.970
100	1	.0017	.0034	.0046	.0095	.0118	.0224	.029
	3	.0030	.0061	.0082	.0163	.0207	.0390	.050
	10	.0056	.0114	.0155	.0301	.0381	.0720	.091
	30	.0098	.0200	.0270	.0525	.0665	.1260	.160
	100	.0176	.0360	.0483	.0945	.1200	.2250	.279
	300	......	.0585	.0780	.1510	.1910	.3700	.439
	1000	......	......	......	.2250	.2880	.5820	.680
120	1	.0013	.0024	.0031	.0058	.0078	.0115	.012
	3	.0026	.0050	.0065	.0122	.0160	.0245	.025
	10	.0056	.0107	.0140	.0265	.0352	.0520	.056
	30	.0110	.0210	.0278	.0535	.0705	.0980	.101
	100	......	.0429	.0573	.1110	.1380	.1800	.182
	300	......	......	.1010	.1850	.2250	.3020	.312
	1000	......	......	......	.3000	.3630	.5000	.520

* $R_V = \frac{\text{partial pressure } H_2S}{\text{partial pressure } CO_2}$.

data of Sieverts and Fritzsche [*Z. anorg. allgem. Chem.*, **133,** 1 (1924)] on the *potassium* system may be approximated by the equation

$$p_{CO_2} = \frac{45f^2N^{1.29}}{S(1 - f)(302 - t)} \tag{14-4}$$

for temperatures from 30° to 100°F., and *potassium* normalities from 1.0 to 2.0.

Table 14-38. Values of *S* for Eqs. (14-3) and (14-4)

Temp., °F.	S = g.-moles CO_2 per liter at 1 atm. CO_2
59	0.0455
77	.0336
95	.0262
113	.0215
131	.0175
145.4	.0151
167	.0120
185	.0090
212	.0065

Sulfur Dioxide in Alkaline Solutions. Johnstone [*Ind. Eng. Chem.*, **27,** 587 (1935); **30,** 101 (1938)] determined solubilities of sulfur dioxide in aqueous solutions of ammonia, of sodium sulfite–bisulfite, and of methyl amine. The vapor pressure of SO_2 in mm. Hg is given by the equation

$$p_{SO_2} = F_1(T)\,\frac{(2S - C)^2}{C - S} \tag{14-5}$$

where S = total concentration of dissolved SO_2, moles/100 moles H_2O; C = total concentration of base, moles/100 moles H_2O; and

$$\log_{10} F_1 = 4.519 - \left(\frac{1987}{T}\right) \quad \text{for sodium solutions} \tag{14-6}$$

$$\log_{10} F_1 = 5.390 - \left(\frac{2308}{T}\right) \quad \text{for methyl amine solutions} \tag{14-7}$$

$$\log_{10} F_1 = 5.865 - \left(\frac{2368}{T}\right) \quad \text{for ammonia solutions} \tag{14-8}$$

The range of temperatures studied corresponds to $308° < T < 363°K$. The vapor pressure of water over these solutions may be calculated from Raoult's law. The vapor pressure of ammonia in mm. Hg over solutions containing SO_2 follows the equation

$$p_{NH_3} = F_2(T)\,\frac{C(C - S)}{2S - C} \tag{14-9}$$

where

$$\log_{10} F_2 = 13.680 - \left(\frac{4987}{T}\right) \tag{14-10}$$

The solutions investigated contained sodium and ammonium ions and methyl amine in the following concentration ranges: sodium, 4.0 to 7.8 g.-atoms/100 g.-moles H_2O; ammonia, 5.8 to 22.4 g.-moles/100 g.-moles H_2O; methyl amine, 7.3 to 22.0 g.-moles/100 g.-moles H_2O.

Olefins in Cuprous Salt Solutions. Gilliland and Seebold [*Ind. Eng. Chem.*, **33,** 1143 (1941)] determined the solubility of ethylene and propylene in aqueous solutions of cuprous chloride. The results are expressed by the following equations. For ethylene in a solution containing 1.90 g.-moles CuCl/liter, 3.0 g.-moles NH_4Cl/liter, and 2.52 g.-moles HCl/liter,

$$\log_{10}\left[\frac{X}{(1 - X)f}\right] = \frac{2060}{T} - 8.20 \tag{14-11}$$

in the range $288 < T < 330°K$. For propylene in a solution containing 1.89 g.-moles CuCl/liter, 3.0 g.-moles NH_4Cl/liter, and 2.27 g.-moles HCl/liter,

$$\log_{10}\left[\frac{X}{(1 - X)f}\right] = \frac{1520}{T} - 6.86 \tag{14-12}$$

Table 14-39. Natural Gas (94 Per Cent Methane) in Diethylene Glycol–Water Solution (95 Per Cent by Weight Glycol) at 100°F.*

P, lb./sq. in. gage	200	700	1000	1500	2000
$(1/H')$, atm./(lb.-mole/cu. ft.)	4.1×10^3	5.2×10^3	4.9×10^3	5.4×10^3	5.8×10^3

* Russell, Reid, and Huntington, *Trans. Am. Inst. Chem. Engrs.*, **41**, 315 (1945).

in the range $270 < T < 310°K$. In Eqs. (14-11) and (14-12), f = fugacity of hydrocarbon, atm., and X = concentration of olefin in the liquid phase, g.-moles olefin/g.-atom copper.

The data of Morrell *et al.* [*Trans. Am. Inst. Chem. Engrs.*, **42**, 473 (1946)] on the solubility of unsaturated C_4 hydrocarbons in ammoniacal cuprous acetate solution containing 1.5 g.-moles/liter of Cu_2H ion are expressed by the equations

1-butene:

$$\log_{10} \frac{(U.Cu_2H)}{[1.5 - (U.Cu_2H)](p_U)} = \frac{1860}{T} - 7.840 \qquad (14\text{-}13)$$

1,3-butadiene:

$$\log_{10} \frac{(U.Cu_2H)}{[1.5 - (U.Cu_2H)](p_U)} = \frac{3053}{T} - 10.845 \qquad (14\text{-}14)$$

1,2-butadiene:

$$\log_{10} \frac{(U.Cu_2H)}{[1.5 - (U.Cu_2H)](p_U)} = \frac{3157}{T} - 10.573 \qquad (14\text{-}15)$$

trans-2-butene:

$$\log_{10} \frac{[(2U).Cu_2H]}{\{1.5 - [(2U).Cu_2H]\}(p_U)^2} = \frac{2600}{T} - 11.013 \qquad (14\text{-}16)$$

where $(U.Cu_2H)$ and $[(2U).Cu_2H]$ represent the concentrations of dissolved unsaturated hydrocarbon complex, g.-moles/liter; and p_U is the partial pressure of hydrocarbon over the solution, atm. Equations (14-14) and (14-15) may be used in the temperature range $0 < t < 40°C$. and Eqs. (14-13) and (14-16) within the range $0 < t < 10°C$.

MASS-TRANSFER FUNDAMENTALS

Homogeneous Diffusion. When a homogeneous material—either gas, liquid, or solid—contains two or more components whose concentrations vary from point to point, there is a tendency for transfer of mass to take place in such a way as to cause the concentrations to become uniform. This phenomenon is associated with the thermal agitation of molecules; in a region where molecules of one kind are concentrated, there is a greater tendency for molecules of this kind to escape than to enter the region. The net rate of diffusion N_A of material A at a point in a stationary fluid is found from experiment as well as from theory to be proportional to the concentration gradient at the point:

$$N_A = -D_v \frac{\partial c}{\partial s} \qquad (14\text{-}17)$$

where c = concentration, s = distance, and D_v = diffusivity. If c is expressed in g.-moles/cu. cm., s in cm., and D_v in sq. cm./sec., then the units of N_A are g.-moles/(sec.)(sq. cm.). The rate of diffusion is rapid in gases and much slower in liquids.

In the application of the theory of diffusion, it is often desirable to employ integrated forms of the diffusion equation, rather than Eq. (14-17), which is applicable only at a single point. Treatments of the use of Eq. (14-17) for steady-state diffusion are given by Treybal ("Mass-transfer Operations," McGraw-Hill, New York, 1955) and by Sherwood and Pigford ("Absorption and Extraction," McGraw-Hill, New York, 1952).

Several **integrated forms** of Eq. (14-17) are presented below, along with integrated expressions for the analogous equation for unsteady-state diffusion [Eq. (14-21)]. All these relationships are based on the assumption that diffusivity is not dependent on concentration. This assumption is good for gaseous systems (except at high pressure) and for dilute liquid solutions but may not be true for concentrated solutions. Dependence on concentration is the result of (1) change of mobility of the solute with concentration because of a change in average molecule size of the medium, and (2) deviations of the mixture from ideal behavior [see Eq. (14-61)].

Steady-state Equimolal Counterdiffusion. This case is typified by the mixing of two gases in a confined space and by counterdiffusion of two components in distillation. For this case, assuming D_v constant, Eq. (14-17) integrates to

$$N_A = \frac{D_v}{B_F}(c - c_i) = \frac{D_v}{RTB_F}(p - p_i) = \frac{D_vP}{RTB_F}(y - y_i) = k_G(y - y_i) \qquad (14\text{-}18)$$

where concentration c can be expressed alternatively in terms of partial pressure p or mole fraction y. In c.g.s. units, N_A = g.-moles/(sec.)(sq. cm.); D_v = sq. cm./sec.; c = g.-moles/cc.; p = atm.; B_F = layer thickness, cm.; R = universal gas constant, 82.06 (cc.)(atm.)/(g.-mole)(°K.); T = temperature, °K.; P = absolute pressure, atm.; k_G = gas-phase mass-transfer coefficient, g.-moles/(sec.)(sq. cm.)(mole fraction). Subscript i refers to the interface. Other consistent sets of units may be used, with suitable adjustments in the numerical value of R.

Steady-state Diffusion of One Component through a Second Stagnant Component. Examples are absorption of a soluble gas from a second insoluble gas and absorption of a slightly soluble gas into a non-volatile liquid. The integrated equation is

$$N_A = \frac{D_vP}{RTB_F}\frac{y - y_i}{(1 - y)_{lm}} = k_G'(y - y_i) \qquad (14\text{-}19)$$

Table 14-40. Vapor Pressure of Water and Diethylene Glycol over Glycol-Water Solution (95 Per Cent by Weight Glycol) at 100°F.*

P, lb./sq. in. gage	0	200	500	800	1000	1500	2000
K_{glycol} $(= y^*/x)$	93×10^{-6}	....	4.6×10^{-6}	....	3.8×10^{-6}	3.4×10^{-6}	4.2×10^{-6}
γ_{glycol}†	1.2	....	2.0	....	3.3	4.4	7.2
K_{water} $(= y^*/x)$	5.4×10^{-2}	4.3×10^{-3}	1.9×10^{-3}	1.2×10^{-3}	1.1×10^{-3}	9.1×10^{-4}	1.2×10^{-3}
γ_{water}	0.84	0.98	1.00	1.00	1.1	1.4	2.5

* Russell, Reid, and Huntington, *Trans. Am. Inst. Chem. Engrs.*, **41**, 315 (1945).
† Based on vapor pressure of pure diethylene glycol = 0.06 mm. Hg at 100°F.

where k_G' = gas-phase mass-transfer coefficient corrected for inert gas concentration = $k_G(p_{BM}/P)$; p_{BM} = partial pressure of inert gas; lm = logarithmic mean; other symbols as defined above.

Steady-state Diffusion of One Component through a Stagnant Multicomponent Mixture. According to Wilke [*Chem. Eng. Progress*, **46**, 95 (1950)], Eq. (14-19) may be applied to this case provided an effective diffusivity of the diffusing species A is defined as

$$D_{vA}' = \frac{1 - y_A}{(y_B/D_{vAB}) + (y_C/D_{vAC}) + (y_D/D_{vAD}) + \cdots} \tag{14-20}$$

Unsteady-state Diffusion. Diffusion does not lead to conditions of constant concentration gradient unless a steady state is established. It is therefore often necessary to consider the change of concentration c with time t caused by diffusion as represented by the differential equation

$$\frac{\partial c}{\partial t} = D_v \frac{\partial^2 c}{\partial s^2} \tag{14-21}$$

where s = distance and D_v = diffusivity.

Solutions of this equation for a diversity of physical situations are given by Crank ("Mathematics of Diffusion," Oxford, New York, 1956) and by Jost ("Diffusion," Academic Press, New York, 1952). Figure 14-5

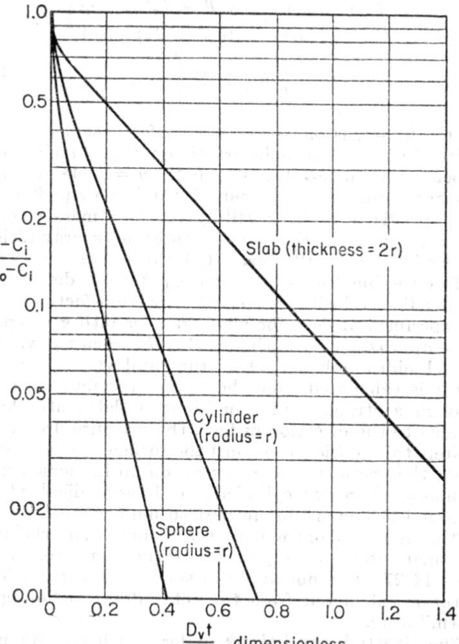

FIG. 14-5. Unsteady-state diffusion; c_0 = uniform initial concentration, c_i = constant surface concentration, $\bar{c}$ = average concentration. (*Crank, "Mathematics of Diffusion," Oxford, Clarendon*, 1956.)

shows the change in average concentration $\bar{c}$ of a component in a slab, cylinder, or sphere as a function of time t when a constant surface concentration c_i is provided to permit that component to diffuse (*i.e.*, where the relative resistance to diffusion in the surrounding medium is negligible). The solution is analogous to that for the conduction of heat under the influence of a temperature gradient. Figure 14-5 is applicable only when the phase in question is not internally mixed and retains its shape during the period of time involved. This is not the case in packed or plate-column gas absorbers but may be so in some spray, descending-liquid-sheet, or falling-jet devices if the fluid is stagnant or in laminar flow.

Diffusion with Flow. If fluid motion is **laminar,** transfer of mass between adjacent layers of fluid takes place purely by **molecular diffusion.** If the velocity pattern of the flow is known, it is sometimes possible to calculate the over-all rate of mass transfer into the moving fluid by the use of the basic equations of molecular diffusion. If the flow is turbulent, however, such calculations are generally impossible, since the laws that govern the transport of matter by turbulent mixing of small volumes of fluid are not well enough understood. Prediction of mass-transfer rates under such conditions is frequently based on empirical methods.

Laminar Flow, Uniform Velocity. If the velocity of a flowing stream is uniform over a very deep region (thickness $B_F \gg \sqrt{D_v t}$) in which diffusion is taking place, Eq. (14-21) is applicable. It has been integrated by Higbie [*Trans. Am. Inst. Chem. Engrs.*, **31**, 365 (1935)] to give

$$k_L = \frac{2}{\sqrt{\pi}} \sqrt{\frac{D}{t}} \tag{14-22}$$

where k_L = liquid-phase mass-transfer coefficient, g.-moles/(sec.) (sq. cm.)(g.-moles/cc.); D = diffusivity, sq. cm./sec.; t = time, sec.

This equation closely represents gas-absorption data taken with falling laminar jets of liquid [Cullen and Davidson, *Trans. Faraday Soc.*, **53**, 113 (1957). Nijsing and Kramers, *Chem. Eng. Sci.*, **10**, 88 (1959). Scriven and Pigford, *Am. Inst. Chem. Engrs. J.*, **4**, 439 (1958)] and with liquid layers descending in short wetted-wall columns when rippling is absent [Vivian and Peaceman, *Am. Inst. Chem. Engrs. J.*, **2**, 437 (1956)]. In the latter case, Eq. (14-22) predicts rates up to 15 per cent higher than those observed, possibly because of end effects [Lynn, Straatemeier, and Kramers, *Chem. Eng. Sci.*, **4**, 49, 58, 63 (1955)]. Equation (14-22) is applicable only when the diffusing molecules have not completely penetrated the fluid layer in question. It thus must be restricted to short contact times (less than about 1 sec. for freely descending water layers).

Laminar Flow, Parabolic Velocity Distribution. Gas absorption or desorption is frequently accomplished into or from liquid layers flowing down a solid surface, as in a wetted-wall column or over packing. The liquid layer in this case moves with maximum velocity at its free surface and zero velocity at the solid surface. The fully established velocity profile appears to be nearly parabolic between these limits as long as ripples are absent, according to the investigation of Grimley [*Trans. Inst. Chem. Engrs. (London)*, **23**, 228 (1945)].

Pigford (Ph.D. Thesis, University of Illinois, 1941) solved the differential equation for this case with the result shown in Fig. 14-6. The dashed line on Fig. 14-6 represents Eq. (14-22) for a uniform velocity profile. Figure 14-6 has been shown to represent wetted-wall column data, as long as rippling is absent, by Emmert and Pigford [*Chem. Eng. Progress*, **50**, 87 (1954)] and Lynn, Straatemeier, and Kramers (*loc. cit.*). Both investigations avoided rippling by using wetting agents in the liquid or by employing short wetted-wall columns (less than 4 in.).

Ripples are normally present on the surface when the

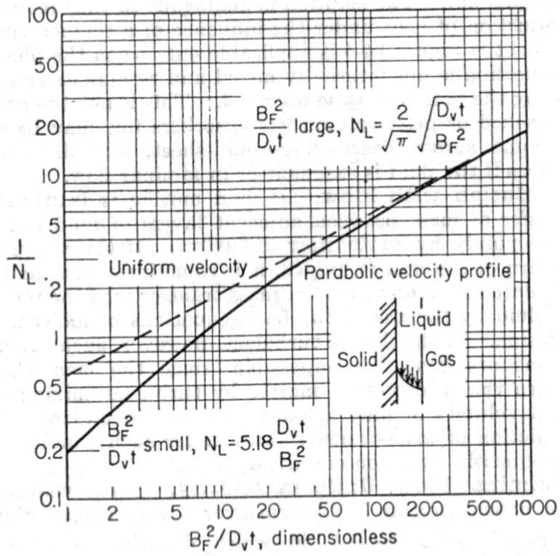

FIG. 14-6. Absorption or desorption to descending liquid; t = time of surface exposure; N_L = number of liquid-phase transfer units. [*Emmert and Pigford, Chem. Eng. Progress*, **50**, 87 (1954).]

Reynolds number for the liquid exceeds a critical value $(N_{Re})_c$ given by the relation (Grimley, *loc. cit.*)

$$\frac{\gamma^3 \rho}{\mu^4 g} = 0.3(N_{Re})_c{}^8 \tag{14-23}$$

where γ = surface tension; ρ = density; μ = viscosity; g = gravitational constant; all in consistent units. For water, the **critical Reynolds number** is about 25. Turbulence within the liquid layer begins at a Reynolds number of about 1200 [Thomas and Portalski, *Ind. Eng. Chem.*, **50**, 108 (1958)]. Up to the Reynolds number at which actual turbulence sets in, surface rippling can be avoided by adding certain wetting agents or by employing such a short distance of flow that surface instability does not develop.

Two auxiliary relations are needed for using Fig. 14-6. **Film thickness** B_F can be calculated using the Nusselt equation

$$B_F = \left(\frac{3\mu\Gamma}{g\rho^2}\right)^{1/3} \tag{14-24}$$

which has been confirmed experimentally by Fallah, Hunter, and Nash [*J. Soc. Chem. Ind. (London)*, **53**, 368 (1934)] and others, even when rippling occurs. In Eq. (14-24), Γ = flow rate per unit of peripheral distance. **Contact time** t between gas and liquid is fixed by the velocity u of the free liquid interface, which is related to the average film velocity by the relation

$$u = \tfrac{3}{2}u_{avg} \tag{14-25}$$

Turbulent Flow. When a fluid phase through which mass transfer is occurring is in turbulent motion, transfer takes place by the relatively fast process of **eddy diffusion.** Experimental measurements of eddy diffusivities at very high Reynolds numbers in ducts have revealed values in gases as high as 100 times the molecular diffusivities [Sherwood and Woertz, *Trans. Am. Inst. Chem. Engrs.*, **35**, 1034 (1939)] and in liquids as high as 100,000 times the molecular diffusivities [Kalinske and Pien, *Ind. Eng. Chem.*, **36**, 220 (1944)]. The following approximate equation can be fitted to the data of Sherwood and Woertz for gases in turbulent flow through ducts:

$$E\rho = 6.6 \times 10^{-5} N_{Re} + 0.2 \tag{14-26}$$

where eddy diffusivity E is expressed in sq. ft./hr., and density of the medium ρ is in lb./cu. ft.

When a fluid moves over either a liquid or a solid surface, the eddy motion that causes mass transfer also causes heat transfer and fluid friction owing to transfer of heat and momentum, respectively. The close similarity among the transfer of mass, heat, and momentum is brought out by the **Reynolds analogy,** which states that, when heat, mass, and momentum are supplied to the fluid in corresponding ways, the following ratios are equal:

$$\frac{\text{Rate at which mass is transferred from the solid surface}}{\text{Total rate at which the component, in excess of the interfacial concentration, flows past the surface}}$$

$$= \frac{\text{rate of heat transfer from the solid surface}}{\text{total rate at which heat, measured above the surface temperature, flows past the surface}}$$

$$= \frac{\text{rate of momentum loss due to friction}}{\text{total momentum of stream which flows past the surface}}$$

In terms of mathematical symbols, these statements may be written as

$$\frac{k_G(y - y_i)}{G_M(y - y_i)} = \frac{h(T - T_i)}{c_p G(T - T_i)} = \frac{g_c \tau_0}{\rho V^2} \tag{14-27}$$

or

$$\frac{k_G}{G_M} = \frac{h}{c_p G} = \frac{f}{2} \tag{14-28}$$

where k_G = gas-phase mass-transfer coefficient, lb.-moles/(hr.)(sq. ft.)(mole fraction); G_M = molar mass velocity, lb.-moles/(hr.)(sq. ft.); y = mole fraction; h = heat-transfer coefficient, B.t.u./(hr.)(sq. ft.)(°F.); c_p = specific heat, B.t.u./(lb.)(°F.); G = mass velocity, lb./(hr.)(sq. ft.); T = temperature; g_c = gravitational conversion factor, (lb. mass)(ft.)/(lb. force)(sec.²); τ_0 = surface frictional stress, lb. force/sq. ft.; ρ = density, lb./cu. ft.; V = velocity, ft./sec.; f = friction factor.

Experimental data for mass transfer into gas streams agree approximately with Eq. (14-27) when the value of the Schmidt number $\mu/\rho D_v$ is near 1 and when the friction factor is calculated from the "skin" friction. For flow through a straight tube, or along a flat plate that is parallel to the direction of flow, the pressure drop is due entirely to skin friction against the surface. On the other hand, the frictional force exerted on an immersed body, such as a sphere or a cylinder placed perpendicular to the direction of flow, is due in part to fluid pressure exerted on the front face of the body that is not counterbalanced by equal and opposite pressure on the rear face. Equation (14-27) does not apply in such cases if the friction factor is calculated from the total drag, including the "form" drag.

The **limited conditions** under which the Reynolds analogy can be expected to hold may be seen from the equations that govern the rate of transfer through a turbulent fluid [von Karman, *Trans. Am. Soc. Mech. Engrs.*, **61**, 705 (1939)]. For mass transfer it is assumed that

$$N_A = N_m + N_t = -(D_v + E)\left(\frac{dc}{ds}\right) \tag{14-29}$$

and for friction

$$\tau = \tau_m + \tau_t = -\left(\frac{\mu + \rho E_v}{g_c}\right)\left(\frac{du}{ds}\right) \tag{14-30}$$

where N_m = rate of mass transfer due to molecular diffusion and N_t = rate of mass transfer due to turbulent mixing, lb.-mole/(hr.)(sq. ft.); D_v = molecular diffusivity and E = eddy diffusivity for mass transfer, sq. ft./hr.; c = concentration, lb.-moles/cu. ft.; s = distance, ft.; τ_m = shear stress due to molecular motion and τ_t = shear stress due to turbulent mixing, lb. force/sq. ft.; μ = viscosity, lb./(ft.)(hr.); ρ = density, lb./cu. ft.; E_v = eddy kinematic viscosity, sq. ft./hr.; g_c = gravitational conversion factor, (lb. mass)(ft.)/(lb. force)(hr.^{2}); u = velocity, ft./hr.

In Eqs. (14-29) and (14-30) the first term in the parentheses gives the rate of transfer of mass or of momentum due to molecular diffusion, and the second term gives the rate due to turbulent mixing. The Reynolds analogy follows from these equations if it is assumed that (1) either $\mu/\rho D_v = 1$ or both D_v and μ/ρ are much smaller than E and E_v, (2) $E = E_v$, and (3) N_A/τ is independent of position s. Under these conditions the concentration and velocity fields are similar and, just as Reynolds assumed, mass and momentum are transferred in the same way.

The Reynolds analogy thus fails to account for the mass-transfer resistance of the region of fluid near the solid (or liquid) boundary, in which transfer occurs principally by molecular motion. Colburn [*Trans. Am. Inst. Chem. Engrs.*, **29**, 174 (1933)] and Chilton and Colburn [*Ind. Eng. Chem.*, **26**, 1183 (1934)] showed empirically that the resistance of this laminar sublayer can be expressed by the following modification to the Reynolds analogy:

$$\frac{k_G}{G_M}\left(\frac{\mu}{\rho D_v}\right)^{2/3} = j_M = \frac{h}{c_pG}\left(\frac{c_p\mu}{k}\right)^{2/3} = j_H = \frac{f}{2} \qquad (14\text{-}31)$$

for turbulent flow through straight tubes and across plane surfaces, and

$$j_M = j_H \leq \frac{f}{2} \qquad (14\text{-}32)$$

for turbulent flow around cylinders, where j_M = mass-transfer factor; j_H = heat-transfer factor; k = thermal conductivity, B.t.u./(hr.)(ft.)(°F.); other symbols as defined immediately above. Experimental data show Eqs. (14-31) and (14-32) to be approximately valid for values of $(\mu/\rho D_v)$ between 0.5 and 2, whereas the Reynolds analogy is substantially in error at these extremes.

Flow over Packings. Higbie [*Trans. Am. Inst. Chem. Engrs.*, **31**, 365 (1935)] advanced the theory that, in a packed absorption tower, the liquid flows across each packing piece in laminar flow and is mixed with other liquid meeting it at the points of discontinuity between packing elements. Danckwerts [*Ind. Eng. Chem.*, **43**, 1460 (1951)] proposed a modification of this theory. It allows for eddy motion in the liquid that continually brings masses of fresh liquid from the interior to the surface, where they are exposed to the gas for a finite length of time before being replaced. Danckwerts assumed that any element has an equal chance of being replaced regardless of its age. The Higbie model leads to Eq. (14-22), where t is the time for flow across a single packing piece. The Danckwerts model gives

$$k_L = \sqrt{Ds_r} \qquad (14\text{-}33)$$

where s_r is the fractional rate of surface renewal.

Note that both models predict a dependence on $\sqrt{D}$. Few data exist to confirm the validity of this effect of diffusivity. Sherwood and Holloway [*Trans. Am. Inst. Chem. Engrs.*, **36**, 39 (1940)] have compared absorption rates in a packed tower for CO_2, O_2, and H_2 and found them to vary nearly as $\sqrt{D}$. Danckwerts [*Am. Inst. Chem. Engrs. J.*, **1**, 456 (1955)] gives a more thorough treatment of the merits of these models as well as others. No theoretical model has yet proved adequate to predict absorption rates in packed columns, and empirical correlations (see pp. 14-34*ff.*) are recommended.

Diffusion with Reaction. Gas absorptions are often conducted using a solvent which is reactive with the gas or which contains a solute that is reactive. When a chemical reaction takes place in the liquid with the absorbed molecules as they are diffusing, the concentration profiles are altered; hence, the rate of absorption is affected. For a liquid that is stagnant or undergoing rodlike laminar flow, unsteady-state diffusion equations akin to Eq. (14-21) can be written to represent diffusion with reaction of various types. Certain of these differential equations have been solved representing the following cases:

1. Absorption accompanied by first-order reaction [for irreversible reaction, see Danckwerts, *Trans. Faraday Soc.*, **46**, 300 (1950); for reversible case, see Sherwood and Pigford, "Absorption and Extraction," McGraw-Hill, New York, 1952]

$$A \rightleftharpoons C$$

2. Absorption accompanied by very fast second-order reaction (Danckwerts, *loc. cit.;* Sherwood and Pigford, *op. cit.*)

$$A + B \rightarrow 2C$$

3. Absorption accompanied by finite-rate reversible second-order reaction [Perry and Pigford, *Ind. Eng. Chem.*, **45**, 1247 (1953); **49**, 1400 (1957)]

$$A + B \rightleftharpoons 2C$$

4. Simultaneous absorption of two or more gases which react rapidly with a component in the liquid [Roper, Hatch, and Pigford, *Ind. Eng. Chem., Fund. Quarterly*, **1**, 144 (1962)]

$$A + R \rightarrow \qquad B + R \rightarrow \qquad \text{etc.}$$

5. Two gases which dissolve in an inert medium, then react with one another (Roper, Hatch, and Pigford, *loc. cit.*).

Absorption with First-order Reaction. Figure 14-7 shows the relation predicted for first-order reaction. The ordinate k_L/k_L^0 is the ratio of mass-transfer coefficients with and without reaction and thus represents the enhancement due to reaction. Both coefficients are averaged over time period t. The first-order reaction rate constant is k_I sec.$^{-1}$, and K is the equilibrium constant. Approximate experimental confirmation of the upper line of Fig. 14-7 has been obtained for absorption of CO_2 into alkaline buffer solutions by Danckwerts and

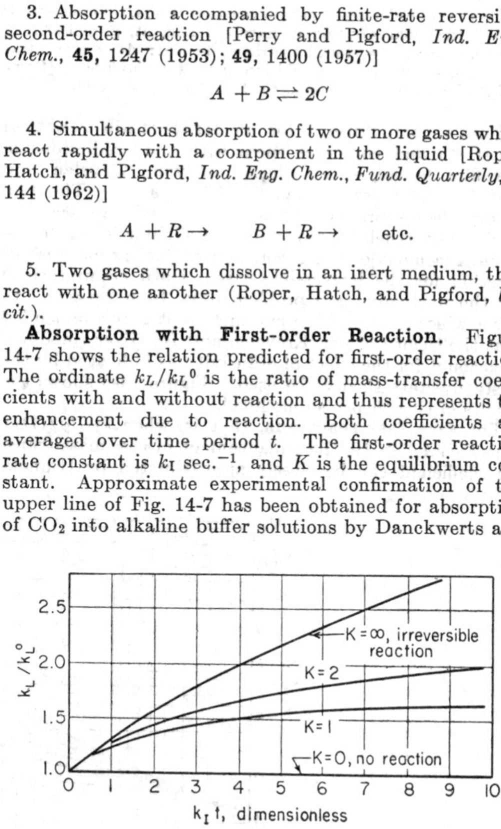

Fig. 14-7. Absorption with first-order reaction. (*Sherwood and Pigford, "Absorption and Extraction," McGraw-Hill, New York, 1952.*)

Kennedy [*Trans. Inst. Chem. Engrs. (London), Supplement*, **32**, S49, S53 (1954)] using a rotating-drum apparatus, and by Nijsing and Kramers ("Chemical Reaction Engineering," pp. 81–89, Pergamon Press, London, 1958) using a short wetted-wall column. No adequate data are available to test the allowance the theory makes for effect of the reverse reaction.

Absorption with Second-order Reaction. Although the computational methods needed to provide a similar treatment for second-order reaction have been described by Perry and Pigford (*loc. cit.*), solutions have been obtained only for a limited range of the variables of interest. Figure 14-8 shows the results of Perry and

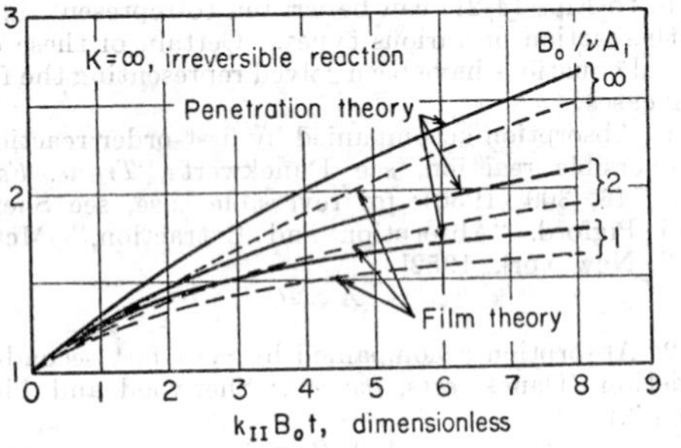

FIG. 14-8. Absorption with second-order irreversible reaction; k_{II} = second-order reaction-rate constant, liters/(g.-mole)(sec.); B_0 = initial concentration of dissolved reagent, g.-moles/liter; t = time, sec.; ν = stoichiometric coefficient; A_i = concentration of dissolving gas at liquid interface, g.-moles/liter. [*Perry and Pigford, Ind. Eng. Chem.*, **45**, 1247 (1953); **49**, 1400 (1957).]

Pigford's computations for an **irreversible reaction** ($K = \infty$) and compares these with the predictions of the film (steady-state) theory of van Krevelen and Hoftijzer [*Rec. trav. chim.*, **67**, 563 (1948)]. The film theory, less representative of the actual physical behavior, nevertheless predicts only a slightly lesser degree of enhancement of the absorption coefficient because of reaction for the irreversible case. Until computations for the unsteady-state problem have been extended to cover wider ranges of the parameters, it is recommended that the theory of van Krevelen and Hoftijzer (modified to account for the effect of diffusivity as indicated by the unsteady-state theory) be used. Figure 14-9 shows the results of this theory so modified.

For **very fast reactions**, that is, when $k_{II}B_0t/(D_B/D_A)(B_0/\nu A_i) > 10$, the enhancement of the mass-transfer coefficient can be closely approximated by [Danckwerts, *Trans. Faraday Soc.*, **46**, 300 (1950)]

$$\frac{k_L}{k_L^0} = \frac{1 + (D_B/D_A)(B_0/\nu A_i)}{(D_B/D_A)^{0.5}} \qquad (14\text{-}34)$$

where k_L/k_L^0 is the ratio of mass-transfer coefficients with and without reaction; k_{II} = second-order reaction-rate constant, liters/(g.-mole)(sec.); B_0 = initial concentration of dissolved reagent, g.-moles/liter; A_i = concentration of dissolving gas at liquid interface, g.-moles/liter; ν = stoichiometric coefficient relating the number of moles of B reacting with 1 mole of A; D_A = diffusivity of dissolving gas A, sq. cm./sec.; D_B = diffusivity of dissolved reagent, sq. cm./sec.

When **several soluble gases** ($A, B, C, \ldots$) dissolve simultaneously and diffuse to a moving reaction boundary in the liquid, where they all react very quickly with a single reagent R by the simultaneous reactions

$$A + \nu_A R \rightarrow \qquad B + \nu_B R \rightarrow \qquad \text{etc.}$$

Eq. (14-34) should be replaced by (Roper, Hatch, and Pigford, *loc. cit.*)

$$\frac{k_L a}{k_L^0 a} = \sqrt{\frac{D_A}{D_R}} \left[1 + \frac{1}{(\nu_A A_i/R_0)\left(\frac{D_A}{D_R}\right) + \left(\frac{\nu_B B_i}{R_0}\right)\left(\frac{D_B}{D_R}\right) + \cdots} \right] \qquad (14\text{-}35)$$

Symbols are analogous with those of Eq. (14-34). When $D_A > 2D_R$, a more exact solution is to be preferred, and reference to the original paper is recommended.

Both Eq. (14-34) and Fig. 14-9 apply only to irreversible reactions ($K = \infty$). The effect of **reversibility** can be accounted for by using Fig. 14-10, which, like

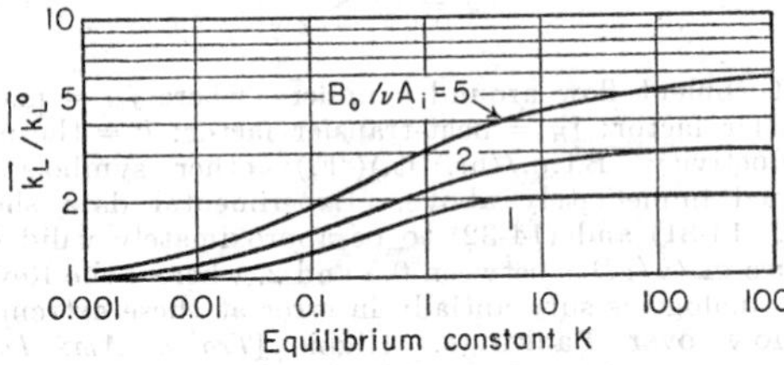

FIG. 14-10. Effect of reversibility on absorption with second-order reaction. (*Pigford, Am. Inst. Chem. Engrs. meeting, Philadelphia, June 24, 1958.*)

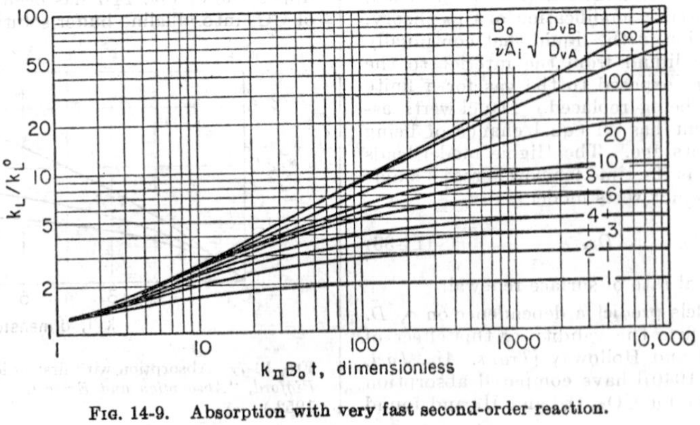

FIG. 14-9. Absorption with very fast second-order reaction.

Eq. (14-34), was derived for very fast reactions but which may also be used as an approximation for slower reactions. Equation (14-34) has been approximately confirmed by Emmert (Ph.D. Thesis, University of Delaware, 1954), who studied absorption of CO_2 in aqueous monoethanolamine in a short wetted-wall column, and more closely by Nijsing and Kramers (Dissertation, Delft, 1957), who studied the absorption of CO_2 in NaOH and KOH solutions in a wetted-wall column.

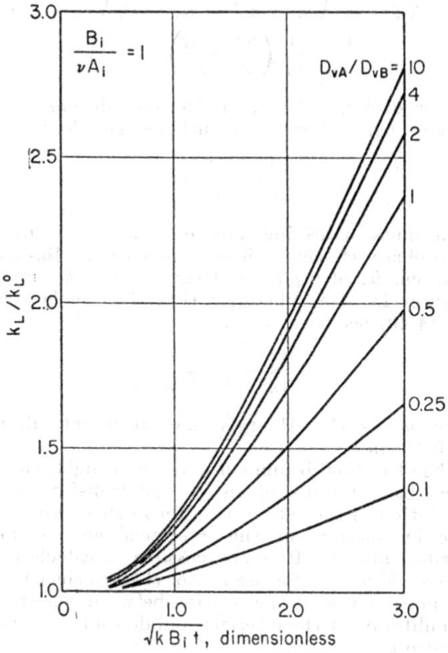

A

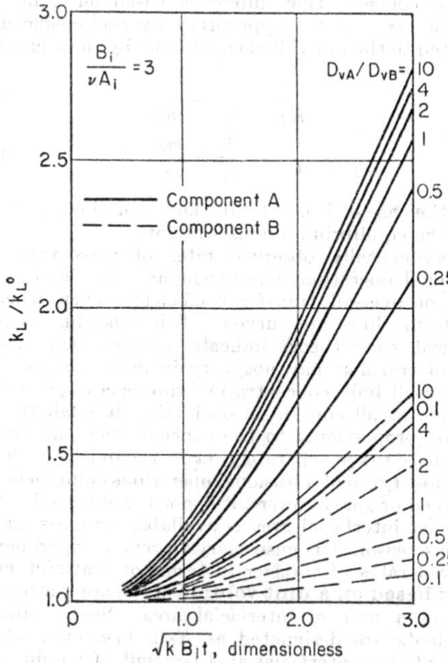

B

Absorption of Two Reacting Gases. Roper, Hatch, and Pigford (*loc. cit.*) have obtained a theoretical solution for the case where two absorbing gases react with one another. Their results are given in Fig. 14-11*A*, *B*, *C*. Figure 14-11*C* represents the case of a pseudo first-order reaction ($B_0/\nu A_i = \infty$), where the interfacial concentration of component *B* far exceeds that of component *A*. In Fig. 14-11*A* the value of k_L/k_L^0 applies to both components *A* and *B*. In Fig. 14-11*B*, separate curves are given for each component. In Fig. 14-11*C*, k_L/k_L^0 for component $B = 1$ for all values of time and diffusivity ratio.

Hatch and Pigford [*Ind. Eng. Chem., Fund. Quarterly*, **1**, 209 (1962)] describe an experimental study in which CO_2 and NH_3 simultaneously dissolve in water and react with one another. Their results confirm the aforementioned theory for the pseudo first-order case.

Mass Transfer between Phases. When material is transferred from one phase to another across an interface that separates the two, the resistance to mass transfer in each phase causes a **concentration gradient** in each, as shown in Fig. 14-12. The concentrations of the diffusing material in the two phases immediately adjacent to the interface are generally unequal, even if expressed in the same units, but are usually assumed to be related to each other by the laws of thermodynamic equilibrium, as discussed previously.

Rate of transfer varies with time and may be expressed, at least for the laminar sublayer, by the Higbie or Danckwerts equations [Eqs. (14-22) and (14-33)] which predict that the rate of transfer is proportional to the difference between the bulk concentration and the concentration at the interface. Thus

$$N_A = k_L(x - x_i) = k_G(y_i - y) \qquad (14\text{-}36)$$

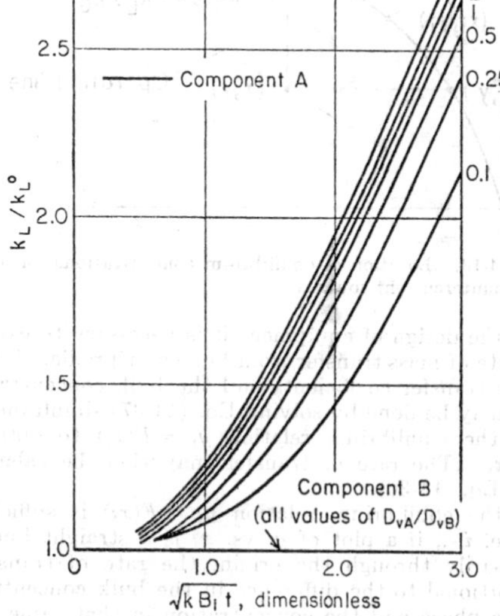

C

Fig. 14-11. Absorption of two reacting gases; k_L/k_L^0 applies to either *A* or *B*. [*Roper, Hatch, and Pigford, Ind. Eng. Chem., Fund. Quarterly*, **1**, 144 (1962).]

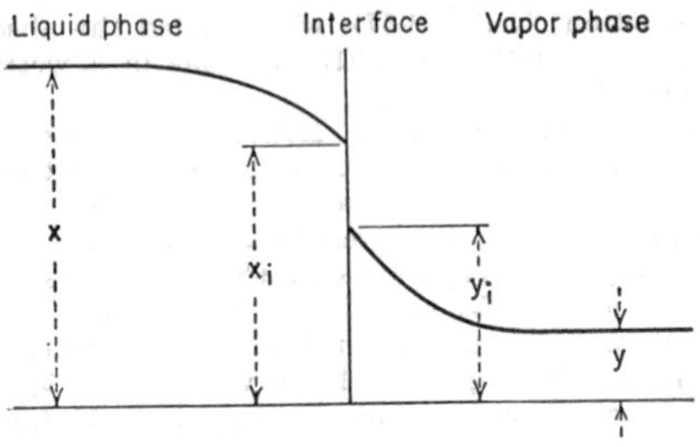

FIG. 14-12. Distribution of concentrations near an interface.

where N_A = mass-transfer rate, lb.-moles/(hr.)(sq. ft.); k_L = liquid-phase mass-transfer coefficient and k_G = gas-phase mass-transfer coefficient, lb.-mole/(hr.)(sq. ft.)(mole fraction); x = mole fraction in bulk liquid phase; x_i = mole fraction in liquid at interface; y = mole fraction in bulk gas phase; y_i = mole fraction in gas at interface.

This equation may be used to find the **interfacial concentrations** corresponding to any set of values of x and y, provided that the ratio of the individual coefficients is known. Thus

$$\frac{y_i - y}{x - x_i} = \frac{k_L}{k_G} = \frac{L_M H_G}{G_M H_L} \tag{14-37}$$

where L_M = molar liquid mass velocity, lb.-moles/(hr.)(sq. ft.); G_M = molar gas mass velocity, lb.-moles/(hr.)(sq. ft.); H_L = height of a transfer unit based on liquid-phase resistance, ft.; H_G = height of a transfer unit based on gas-phase resistance, ft.

Equation (14-37) may be solved graphically if a plot is made of the equilibrium vapor and liquid compositions, and a point is located representing the bulk concentrations x and y on this same diagram. A construction of this type is shown in Fig. 14-13.

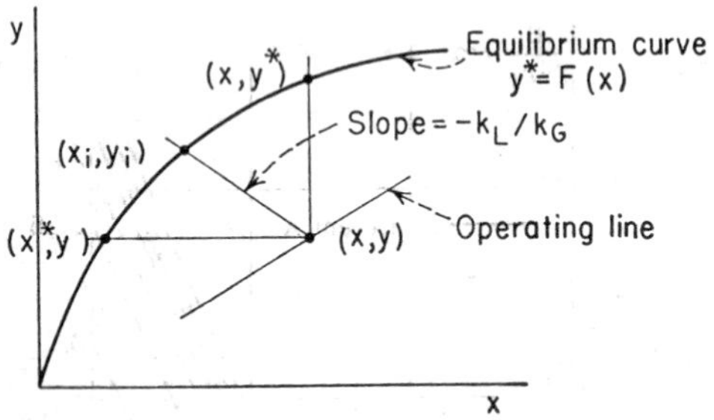

FIG. 14-13. Location of equilibrium concentrations for a point in a countercurrent tower.

In the design of equipment it is necessary to estimate the rate of mass transfer from known or predicted values of the transfer coefficients and the bulk concentrations. This may be done by solving Eq. (14-37) simultaneously with the equilibrium relation $y_i = F(x_i)$ to obtain y_i and x_i. The rate of transfer may then be calculated from Eq. (14-36).

If the equilibrium relation $y_i = F(x_i)$ is sufficiently simple, *i.e.*, if a plot of y_i vs. x_i is a straight line, not necessarily through the origin, the rate of transfer is proportional to the difference in the bulk concentration in one phase and the concentration in that same phase which would be in equilibrium with the bulk concentration in the other phase. One such difference is $y^* - y$, and another $x - x^*$. In this case there is no need to solve for the interfacial compositions, as may be seen from the following derivation: Since

$$N_A = k_G(y_i - y) = k_L(x - x_i) = K_G(y^* - y) \tag{14-38}$$

where K_G = **over-all** gas-phase **mass-transfer coefficient** and y^* = vapor composition in equilibrium with x,

$$\frac{1}{K_G} = \frac{1}{k_G}\left(\frac{y^* - y}{y_i - y}\right) = \frac{1}{k_G} + \frac{1}{k_G}\left(\frac{y^* - y_i}{y_i - y}\right)$$
$$= \frac{1}{k_G} + \frac{1}{k_L}\left(\frac{y^* - y_i}{x - x_i}\right) \tag{14-39}$$

in view of Eq. (14-37). If the equilibrium curve is a straight line, the term in parentheses is its slope m. Thus

$$\frac{1}{K_G} = \frac{1}{k_G} + \frac{m}{k_L} \tag{14-40}$$

If the units of driving force on which k_L is based are liquid-phase concentrations expressed in lb.-moles of solute/cu. ft. of liquid, and the units of k_G are partial pressures in atmospheres, rather than mole fractions, Eq. (14-40) becomes

$$\frac{1}{K_G} = \frac{1}{k_G} + \frac{1}{m_c k_L} \tag{14-41}$$

where m_c is the Henry's law coefficient, lb.-moles/(cu. ft.)(atm.).

When the equilibrium curve is not straight, there is no logical basis for use of an over-all transfer coefficient. Calculation of the rate of transfer in such cases must be made by solving for the interfacial compositions, as described above. It is not possible to calculate a true average value of m for use in Eq. (14-40), since the value used must represent the relation between concentrations in equilibrium at the interface and depends, therefore, on the ratio k_L/k_G.

If it is desired to calculate the rate of transfer from the over-all concentration difference based on liquid compositions $x^* - x$, the appropriate over-all coefficient K_L is related to the individual coefficients by the equations

$$\frac{1}{K_L} = \frac{1}{k_L} + \frac{1}{m k_G} \tag{14-42}$$

or

$$\frac{1}{K_L} = \frac{1}{k_L} + \frac{m_c}{k_G} \tag{14-43}$$

As in the case of Eq. (14-40), these equations apply only when the equilibrium line is straight.

Experimentally observed rates of mass transfer in diffusional operations equipment are often expressed in terms of over-all transfer coefficients, even when the equilibrium lines are curved. This procedure is purely empirical, since theory indicates that in such cases the rates of transfer may not vary in direct proportion to the over-all bulk concentration differences $(y^* - y)$ and $(x - x^*)$ at all concentration levels, although the rates may be proportional to the concentration difference in each phase taken separately, $(x - x_1)$ and $(y_1 - y)$.

In most types of diffusional operations equipment, such as packed or spray towers, it is not possible to determine just what interfacial area is available for mass transfer. For this reason it is customary to report experimentally observed rates of transfer in terms of **transfer coefficients based on a unit volume** of the apparatus rather than on a unit of interfacial area. Such volumetric coefficients are designated as K_Ga, k_La, etc., where a represents the interfacial area per unit of volume of the apparatus. Experimentally observed variations in the values of volumetric coefficients due to variations in flow rates, type of packing, etc., may be due as much to changes in the value of a as to changes in k. Calculation of the over-all coefficient from the individual coefficients is made by means of the equations

$$\frac{1}{K_G a} = \frac{1}{k_G a} + \frac{m}{k_L a} \tag{14-44}$$

$$\frac{1}{K_G a} = \frac{1}{k_G a} + \frac{1}{m_c k_L a} \tag{14-45}$$

$$\frac{1}{K_L a} = \frac{1}{k_L a} + \frac{1}{m k_G a} \tag{14-46}$$

$$\frac{1}{K_L a} = \frac{1}{k_L a} + \frac{m_c}{k_G a} \tag{14-47}$$

Because of the wide variation in the solubilities of gases in liquids, the variation in the value of m from one system to another sometimes has an important effect on the type of equipment that should be used for contacting. If, for example, it is desired to dissolve an insoluble gas, such as oxygen, in water, the large value of m for this system would cause the liquid-phase part of the over-all resistance to be extremely large in a spray tower, where the poor fluid mixing obtained in the liquid phase might result in a small value of k_L. On the other hand, this line of reasoning must be applied with caution, since gases with different solubilities are ordinarily absorbed under different conditions of operation; and the effect on the over-all resistance of changes in the solubility is therefore partly counterbalanced by changes in the specific resistance as the flow rates are changed.

Height Equivalent to a Transfer Unit (H.T.U.). Frequently the values of individual coefficients of mass transfer vary so rapidly with flow rates that the quantity obtained by dividing each coefficient by the flow rate of the phase to which it applies is more nearly constant than the coefficient itself. The quantity obtained by this division is called [Chilton and Colburn, *Ind. Eng. Chem.*, **27**, 255 (1935)] the height of one transfer unit, since it expresses in terms of a single length dimension the height of apparatus required to accomplish a separation of standard difficulty.

The number of over-all gas-phase transfer units N_{OG} required for changing the composition of the vapor stream from y_1 to y_2 is

$$N_{OG} = \int_{y_2}^{y_1} \frac{dy}{y^* - y} \tag{14-48}$$

for equimolal diffusion, and

$$N_{OG} = \int_{y_2}^{y_1} \frac{(1 - y)_f \, dy}{(1 - y)(y^* - y)} \tag{14-49}$$

for diffusion in one direction only, where y = mole fraction in gas and y^* = mole fraction in gas in equilibrium with liquid. Convenient solutions of these equations are given later.

The number of transfer units required for a given separation is closely related to the number of theoretical plates or stages required to carry out the same separation in plate-type or stagewise apparatus. In terms of H.T.U.'s the equations that express the addition of resistances become [Colburn, *Trans. Am. Inst. Chem. Engrs.*, **35**, 211 (1939)]

$$H_{OG} = H_G + H_L \left(\frac{mG_M}{L_M}\right) \frac{(1 - x)_f}{(1 - y)_f} \tag{14-50}$$

and

$$H_{OL} = H_L + H_G \left(\frac{L_M}{mG_M}\right) \frac{(1 - y)_f}{(1 - x)_f} \tag{14-51}$$

where H_{OG}, H_{OL}, H_G, and H_L = heights of transfer units, ft., based on, respectively, over-all gas-phase resistance, over-all liquid-phase resistance, gas-phase resistance, and liquid-phase resistance; $(1 - y)_f$ = logarithmic mean of $1 - y$ and $1 - y^*$; $(1 - x)_f$ = logarithmic mean of $1 - x$ and $1 - x^*$; x = mole fraction in liquid; x^* = mole fraction in liquid in equilibrium with gas; y, y^*, m, G_M, and L_M as defined earlier.

The following relations between the transfer coefficient and the values of H.T.U. apply, where the prime indicates that the coefficient is corrected for inert gas concentration by the factor p_{BM}/P (p_{BM} = partial pressure of inert gas, P = total absolute pressure):

$$H_{OG} = \frac{G_M}{K_G' a(1 - y)_f} \tag{14-52}$$

$$H_G = \frac{G_M}{k_G' a(1 - y)_f} \tag{14-53}$$

$$H_{OL} = \frac{L_M}{K_L a(1 - x)_f} \tag{14-54}$$

$$H_L = \frac{L_M}{k_L a(1 - x)_f} \tag{14-55}$$

Presence of the factor $(1 - y)_f$ is due to the fact that, in the diffusion of one gas through a second stationary layer of insoluble gas, the resistance to diffusion varies with the concentration of the stationary gas, approaching zero as the concentration of this gas approaches zero. The factor $(1 - x)_f$ cannot be justified on the basis of kinetic theory for the liquid phase but is included in the equations on the assumption that diffusion through liquids is similar to that through gases. (In binary distillation, where both components diffuse simultaneously, both these factors should be omitted.)

H.E.T.P. (height equivalent to one theoretical plate) is another quantity that is used occasionally to express the efficiency of a packing material for carrying out a separation. Experimental data should be reported as H.T.U.'s rather than H.E.T.P.'s, since the former quantity is theoretically correct for equipment, such as packed columns, in which mass is transferred by a differential rather than a stepwise action. If equilibrium and operating lines are parallel, *i.e.*, $mG_M/L_M = 1$, H.E.T.P.'s and H.T.U.'s are equal. If the equilibrium and operating lines are straight, but not parallel,

$$\frac{H_{OG}}{\text{H.E.T.P.}} = \frac{(mG_M/L_M) - 1}{\ln (mG_M/L_M)} \tag{14-56}$$

DIFFUSION COEFFICIENTS

Diffusivities in Gases. The study of diffusion, along with viscosity and thermal conduction in gases, is a part of the well-developed kinetic theory of gases. One of the most modern accounts of this theory is that of Hirschfelder, Curtiss, and Bird ("Molecular Theory of Gases and Liquids," Wiley, New York, 1954), who give equations based on various assumptions regarding the nature of the interaction between molecules at collision, from which values of the diffusion coefficient for a binary mixture may be calculated. The most advanced treatment predicts that the diffusion coefficient should vary only slightly with composition, and this is confirmed by experiment. Table 14-41 shows the experimentally observed variation of the diffusion coefficient with composition in the case of mixtures of hydrogen and carbon dioxide. This variation is greatest when the ratio of the masses of

Table 14-41. Diffusivity in Hydrogen–Carbon Dioxide Mixtures, Variation with Composition

% H_2	D_v, sq. cm./sec.*
25	0.594
50	.605
75	.633

* Based on experiments at 15°C. and 1 atm. by Lonius, *Ann. Physik*, **29** (4), 664 (1909).

the molecules is large, but in no case has the maximum variation been found to exceed 13 per cent.

When experimentally determined diffusivities are not available, several **prediction methods** based on the kinetic theory are available to provide estimates. When **accurate estimates** are desired, the Wilke and Lee modification [*Ind. Eng. Chem.*, **47**, 1253 (1955)] of the equation by Hirschfelder, Bird, and Spotz [*Trans. Am. Soc. Mech. Engrs.*, **71**, 921 (1949)] is recommended.

$$D_G = \frac{BT^{3/2}\sqrt{(1/M_1) + (1/M_2)}}{Pr_{12}^2 I_D} \tag{14-57}$$

where D_G = gas diffusivity, sq. cm./sec.

$$B = (10.7 - 2.46\sqrt{1/M_1 + 1/M_2}) \times 10^{-4} \tag{14-57a}$$

T = absolute temperature, °K.

M_1, M_2 = molecular weights of components 1 and 2

P = absolute pressure, atm.

r_{12} = collision diameter, angstroms

$$= \frac{(r_0)_1 + (r_0)_2}{2} \tag{14-57b}$$

$$r_0 = 1.18\, V_0^{1/3} \text{ (see Table 14-44)} \tag{14-57c}$$

V_0 = molal volume of liquid at normal boiling point, cc./g.-mole (see Tables 14-42 and 14-43)

I_D = collision integral for diffusion, function of kT/ϵ_{12} (see Table 14-45)

$$\frac{\epsilon_{12}}{k} = \sqrt{\left(\frac{\epsilon_1}{k}\right)\left(\frac{\epsilon_2}{k}\right)} \text{ (see Table 14-44)} \tag{14-57d}$$

k = Boltzmann constant = 1.38×10^{-16} erg/°K.

ϵ_{12} = energy of molecular interaction, ergs

Table 14-42. Atomic Volumes*

For use in calculating molal volume V_0 at the normal boiling point, expressed in cc./g.-mole, as used in Eq. (14-57c)

Element	Atomic Volume, cc./g.-atom
Arsenic	30.5
Bismuth	48.0
Bromine	27.0
Carbon	14.8
Chlorine, terminal, as in R-Cl	21.6
Medial, as in R-CHCl-R′	24.6
Chromium	27.4
Fluorine	8.7
Germanium	34.5
Hydrogen	3.7
In hydrogen molecule	7.15
Iodine	37.0
Lead	46.5–50.1
Mercury	19.0
Nitrogen	15.6
In primary amines	10.5
In secondary amines	12.0
Oxygen	12.8
Doubly bound, as carbonyl oxygen	7.4
Coupled to two other elements:	
In aldehydes and ketones	7.4
In methyl esters	9.1
In methyl ethers	9.9
In higher ethers and esters	11.0
In acids	12.0
In union with S, P, N	8.3
Phosphorus	27.0
Silicon	32.0
Sulfur	25.6
Tin	42.3
Titanium	35.7
Vanadium	32.0
Water	18.8
Zinc	20.4
For three-membered ring, as in ethylene oxide, deduct	6
For four-membered ring, as in cyclobutane, deduct	8.5
For five-membered ring, as in furan, thiophene, deduct	11.5
For six-membered ring, as in benzene, cyclohexane, pyridine, deduct	15
For naphthalene ring, deduct	30
For anthracene ring, deduct	47.5

* LeBas, "The Molecular Volumes of Liquid Chemical Compounds," Longmans, London, 1915.

Molal volume V_0 may be calculated from the molecular weight and the density at the normal boiling point if the latter figure is known. Otherwise, V_0 may be estimated by summing the atomic volumes given in Table 14-42. Table 14-43 lists molecular volumes for some common gases. These values may be used directly in Eq. (14-57c)

Table 14-43. Molecular Volumes of Common Gases*

Gas	Molecular Volume V_0, cc./g.-mole
Air	29.9
Br_2	53.2
Cl_2	48.4
CO	30.7
CO_2	34.0
COS	51.5
H_2	14.3
H_2O	18.9
H_2S	32.9
I_2	71.5
N_2	31.2
NH_3	25.8
NO	23.6
N_2O	36.4
O_2	25.6
SO_2	44.8

* Treybal, "Mass-transfer Operations," McGraw-Hill, New York, 1955.

Table 14-44. Force Constants and Collision Diameters*

For use in Eqs. (14-57b) and (14-57d)

Gas	ϵ/k, °K. (from viscosity)	r_0, angstroms (from viscosity)
Air	97.0	3.617
Ammonia	315	2.624
Argon	124.0	3.418
Benzene	440	5.270
CO_2	190	3.996
CO	110.3	3.590
CCl_4	327	5.881
Diphenyl	600	6.223
Ethane	230	4.418
Ethanol	391	4.455
Ethyl ether	350	5.424
Ethylene	205	4.232
Fluorocarbon F-12	288	5.110
Helium	6.03	2.70
n-Heptadecane	800	7.923
Hydrogen	33.3	2.968
HCl	360	3.305
Iodine	550	4.982
Methane	136.5	3.882
Neon	35.7	2.80
Nitrobenzene	539	4.931
NO	119	3.47
Nitrogen	91.5	3.681
N_2O	220	3.879
n-Octadecane	820	7.963
n-Octane	320	7.451
Oxygen	113.2	3.433
Propane	254	5.061
SO_2	252	4.290
Water	363	2.655

* Wilke and Lee, *Ind. Eng. Chem.*, **47**, 1253 (1955).

to estimate r_0 if desired, but better values of r_0 as well as the force constant ϵ/k are given in Table 14-44 for some systems. Use of Table 14-44 is recommended for obtaining both ϵ/k and r_0 when possible. When ϵ/k is not known, Hirschfelder, Bird, and Spotz (*loc. cit.*) recommend the following empirical equations:

$$\frac{\epsilon}{k} = 0.77\, T_c \tag{14-58a}$$

$$\frac{\epsilon}{k} = 1.15\, T_b \tag{14-58b}$$

$$\frac{\epsilon}{k} = 1.92\, T_m \tag{14-58c}$$

where T_c, T_b, and T_m are the critical temperature, the normal boiling point, and the melting point, respectively. Collision integral I_D may be taken from Table 14-45.

Table 14-45. Values of Collision Integral*
As a function of kT/ϵ_{12}, for use in Eq. (14-57)

kT/ϵ_{12}	I_D	kT/ϵ_{12}	I_D
0.3	1.331	4.2	0.4370
.4	1.159	4.4	.4326
.5	1.033	4.6	.4284
.6	0.9383	4.8	.4246
.7	.8644	5.0	.4211
.8	.8058		
.9	.7585	6	.4062
1.0	.7197	7	.3948
		8	.3856
1.1	.6873	9	.3778
1.2	.6601	10	.3712
1.3	.6367		
1.4	.6166	20	.3320
1.5	.5991	30	.3116
1.6	.5837	40	.2980
1.7	.5701	50	.2878
1.8	.5580	60	.2798
1.9	.5471	70	.2732
2.0	.5373	80	.2676
		90	.2628
2.2	.5203	100	.2585
2.4	.5061		
2.6	.4939	200	.2322
2.8	.4836		
3.0	.4745	300	.2180
		400	.2085
3.2	.4664		
3.4	.4593		
3.6	.4529		
3.8	.4471		
4.0	.4418		

* From Hirschfelder, Bird, and Spotz, *Trans. Am. Soc. Mech. Engrs.*, **71**, 921 (1949).

For **multicomponent systems**, the diffusivity may be a strong function of composition and is different for each component. Equation (14-20) may be employed in this instance.

For **crude calculations**, the faster method of Gilliland [*Ind. Eng. Chem.*, **26**, 681 (1934)] may be employed in place of Eq. (14-57). According to Gilliland

$$D_G = 0.0043 \frac{T^{3/2}}{P(V_1^{1/3} + V_2^{1/3})^2} \sqrt{\frac{1}{M_1} + \frac{1}{M_2}} \qquad (14\text{-}59)$$

where definitions are the same as for Eq. (14-57). Gilliland's equation was developed for hard, spherical molecules with no interactions, while Eq. (14-57) accounts for attractive or repulsive effects.

Accuracy of predictions from Eq. (14-57) should be within ± 5 per cent for non-polar–non-polar pairs or for polar–non-polar pairs. For pairs of the following molecules, however, errors up to 20 per cent should be expected: (1) polar molecules—H_2O, NH_3, HBr, HCN, HI, mercury halides; (2) metal vapors and valence-unsaturated molecules—Hg, Cd, Zn; (3) cigar-shaped molecules—*n*-heptane and higher straight-chain hydrocarbons; (4) others—F_2, CS_2, CCl_4, $SnBr_4$, $SnCl_4$, CH_3Cl. Table 14-46 gives a comparison of the relative accuracy to be expected from the various prediction equations. Arnold's method [*Ind. Eng. Chem.*, **22**, 1091 (1930)] gives predictions nearly as good as Eq. (14-57).

Table 14-46. Approximate Error for Gas-diffusivity Prediction Methods*

Basic equation	Source of ϵ/k	Source of r_0	Avg. deviation, %	Max. deviation, %
Eq. (14-57)	Table 14-44	Table 14-44	4	16
Eq. (14-57)	Table 14-44	Eq. (14-57*c*)	7	22
Eq. (14-57)	Eq. (14-58*a*)	Table 14-44	5	26
Eq. (14-57)	Eq. (14-58*b*)	Table 14-44	5	20
Eq. (14-57)	Eq. (14-58*c*)	Eq. (14-57*e*)	8	24
Eq. (14-59)			20	47

* Wilke and Lee, *Ind. Eng. Chem.*, **47**, 1253 (1955).

Experimental data are given in Table 14-47. Values are reported in sq. cm./sec., which may be converted to sq. ft./hr. by multiplying by 3.88. Values of the dimensionless Schmidt group $\mu/\rho D_v$ are also given in some instances. Both theory and experiment indicate that $\mu/\rho D_v$ is independent of pressure and varies only slightly with temperature, at least over moderate ranges. In some instances, studies have been made over wide temperature or pressure ranges, and the original references should be consulted if this is noted.

Diffusivities in Liquids. The theory of diffusion in liquids is less well developed than for gases. Diffusion coefficients in liquids are typically about four orders of magnitude smaller than in gases and are therefore more difficult to measure accurately. There are few measurements of liquid diffusivities outside the temperature range 0° to 40°C. The recommended relation for **estimation of diffusivities of non-electrolytes** in liquids at low concentrations of the diffusing component is [Wilke and Chang, *Am. Inst. Chem. Engrs. J.*, **1**, 264 (1955)]

$$\frac{D_L\mu}{T} = 7.4 \times 10^{-8} \frac{(XM)^{0.5}}{V_0^{0.6}} \qquad (14\text{-}60)$$

where D_L = diffusivity of solute at infinite dilution, sq. cm./sec.; μ = solution viscosity, centipoise; T = absolute temperature, °K.; X = association parameter (see Table 14-48); M = *solvent* molecular weight; V_0 = molal volume of *solute* at normal boiling point (see Tables 14-42 and 14-43).

Association parameter X refers to the solvent and is 1.0 for non-associated liquids. Table 14-48 gives values of X for some liquids. For liquids not listed, the use of 1.0 is recommended [except for electrolytes, for which Eq. (14-62) should be used]. Use of Eq. (14-60) for temperatures below 0°C. and above 100°C. must be considered suspect, since the effect of temperature is based on the theoretical Stokes-Einstein relation and does not agree with the recent data of Reamer and Sage [*Am. Inst. Chem. Engrs. J.*, **3**, 449 (1957)], who studied a wider range of temperature than the data on which Eq. (14-60) was based.

In thermodynamically non-ideal solutions the **effect of concentration** on D_L may be estimated by [Wilke, *Chem. Eng. Progress*, **45**, 218 (1949)]

$$\left(\frac{D_L\mu}{T}\right)_1 = \frac{d \ln a_1}{d \ln x_1}\left[x_1\left(\frac{D_L\mu}{T}\right)_2^0 + (1 - x_1)\left(\frac{D_L\mu}{T}\right)_1^0\right] \qquad (14\text{-}61)$$

where $\left(\frac{D_L\mu}{T}\right)_1$ = Stokes-Einstein group for diffusion of component 1 in 2 at concentration x_1

$\left(\frac{D_L\mu}{T}\right)_1^0$ = Stokes-Einstein group for diffusion of component 1 in 2 at infinite dilution of 1

$\left(\frac{D_L\mu}{T}\right)_2^0$ = Stokes-Einstein group for diffusion of component 2 in 1 at infinite dilution of 2

x_1 = mole fraction of 1

a_1 = activity of 1

The term $d \ln a_1/d \ln x_1$ may be determined from vapor-liquid equilibrium data and is 1.0 for ideal solutions. For non-ideal solutions, the term approaches 1.0 as x_1 approaches 1.

Diffusion coefficients of **electrolytes** can be predicted very accurately at **infinite dilution** using the equation

Table 14-47. Diffusivities of Pairs of Gases and Vapors (1 atm.)

D_v in sq. cm./sec.

Substance	Temp., °C.	Air	A	H_2	O_2	N_2	CO_2	N_2O	CH_4	C_2H_6	C_2H_4	n-C_4H_{10}	i-C_4H_{10}	Ref.
Acetic acid	0	0.1064		0.416			0.0716							8
Acetone	0	.109		.361										6, 16
n-Amyl alcohol	0	.0589		.235			.0422							8
sec-Amyl alcohol	30	.072												5
Amyl butyrate	0	.040												8
Amyl formate	0	.0543												8
i-Amyl formate	0	.058												8
Amyl isobutyrate	0	.0419		.171										8
Amyl propionate	0	.046		.1914			.0347							8
Aniline	0	.0610												8
	30	.075												5
Anthracene	0	.0421												8
Argon	20					0.194								18
Benzene	0	.077		.306	0.0797		.0528							8, 15
Benzidine	0	.0298												8
Benzyl chloride	0	.066												8
n-Butyl acetate	0	.058												8
i-Butyl acetate	0	.0612		.2364			.0425							8
n-Butyl alcohol	0	.0703		.2716			.0476							8
	30	.088												5
i-Butyl alcohol	0	.0727		.2771			.0483							8
Butyl amine	0	.0821												8
i-Butyl amine	0	.0853												8
i-Butyl butyrate	0	.0468		.185			.0327							8
i-Butyl formate	0	.0705												8
i-Butyl isobutyrate	0	.0457		.191			.0364							8
i-Butyl proprionate	0	.0529		.203			.0366							8
i-Butyl valerate	0	.0424		.173			.0308							8
Butyric acid	0	.067		.264			.0476							8
i-Butyric acid	0	.0679		.271			.0471							8
Cadmium	0					.17								13
Caproic acid	0	.050												8
i-Caproic acid	0	.0513												8
Carbon dioxide	0	.138		.550	.139			0.096	0.153					8
	20					.163								19
	25							.0996*	.00215†					1, 9
	500‡				.9									18
Carbon disulfide	0	.0892		.369			.063							8
Carbon monoxide	0			.651	.185		.137				0.116			8
	450‡				1.0									18
Carbon tetrachloride	0			.293	0.0636									16, 17
Chlorobenzene	30	.075												5
Chloroform	0	.091												6
Chloropicrin	25	.088												10
m-Chlorotoluene	0	.054												8
o-Chlorotoluene	0	.059												8
p-Chlorotoluene	0	.051												8
Cyanogen chloride	0	.111												10
Cyclohexane	15		0.0719	.319	.0744	.0760								3
	45	.086												6
n-Decane	90			.306		.0841								3
Diethylamine	0	.0884												8
2,3-Dimethyl butane	15		.0657	.301	.0753	.0751								3
Diphenyl	0	.0610												8
n-Dodecane	126			.308		.0813								3
Ethane	0			.459										8
Ethanol	0			.377			.0686							20
Ether (diethyl)	0	.0778		.298			.0546							7, 8
Ethyl acetate	0	.0715		.273			.0487							8
	30	.089												5
Ethyl alcohol	0	.102		.375			.0685							8
Ethyl benzene	0	.0658												8
Ethyl *n*-butyrate	0	.0579		.224			.0407							8
Ethyl *i*-butyrate	0	.0591		.229			.0413							8
Ethylene	0			.486										8
Ethyl formate	0	.0840		.337			.0573							8
Ethyl propionate	0	.068		.236			.0450							4, 8
Ethyl valerate	0	.0512		.205			.0367							8
Eugenol	0	.0377												8
Formic acid	0	.1308		.510			.0874							8
Helium	0		.641											8
	20					.705								19
n-Heptane	38								.066§					
n-Hexane	15		.0663	.290	.0753	.0757								3
Hexyl alcohol	0	.0499		.200			.0351							8
Hydrogen	0	.611			.697	.674	.550	.535	.625	0.459	0.486	0.272	0.277	8
	25						.646			.537	.726			2
	500				4.2									18
Hydrogen cyanide	0	.173												10
Hydrogen peroxide	60	.188												11
Iodine	0	.07				.070								8, 12, 14
Mercury	0	.112		.53		.13								8, 12, 13
Mesitylene	0	.056												8
Methane	500				1.1									18
Methyl acetate	0	.084		.333			.0567							8
Methyl alcohol	0	.132		.506			.0879							8
Methyl butyrate	0	.0633		.242			.0446							8
Methyl *i*-butyrate	0	.0639		.257			.0451							8
Methyl cyclopentane	15		.0731	.318	0.0742	.0758								3
Methyl formate	0	.0872												8
Methyl propionate	0	.0735		.295			.0528							8

Table 14-47. Diffusivities of Pairs of Gases and Vapors (1 atm.)—(*Continued*)

D_v in sq. cm./sec.

Substance	Temp., °C.	Air	A	H_2	O_2	N_2	CO_2	N_2O	CH_4	C_2H_6	C_2H_4	n-C_4H_{10}	i-C_4H_{10}	Ref.
Methyl valerate	0	0.0569												8
Naphthalene	0	.0513												8
Nitrogen	0				0.181									8
	25						0.165			0.148	0.163	0.0960	0.0908	2
Nitrous oxide	0			0.535			.096							8
n-Octane	0	.0505												8
	30		0.0642	.271	.0705	0.0710								3
Oxygen	0	.178		.697		.181	.139							8
Phosgene	0	.095												10
Propionic acid	0	.0829		.330			.0588							8
Propyl acetate	0	.067												8
n-Propyl alcohol	0	.085		.315			.0577							8
i-Propyl alcohol	0	.0818												8
	30	.101												5
n-Propyl benzene	0	.0481												8
i-Propyl benzene	0	.0489												8
n-Propyl bromide	0	.085												8
i-Propyl bromide	0	.0902												8
Propyl butyrate	0	.0530		.206			.0364							8
Propyl formate	0	.0712		.281			.0490							8
n-Propyl iodide	0	.079												8
i-Propyl iodide	0	.0802												8
n-Propyl isobutyrate	0	.0549		.212			.0388							8
i-Propyl isobutyrate	0	.059												8
Propyl propionate	0	.057		.212			.0395							8
Propyl valerate	0	.0466		.189			.0341							8
Safrol	0	.0434												8
i-Safrol	0	.0455												8
Sulfur hexafluoride	25			.418										2
Toluene	0	.076	.071											4, 8
	30	.088												5
Trimethyl carbinol	0	.087												8
2,2,4-Trimethyl pentane	30		.0618	.288	.0688	.0705								3
2,2,3-Trimethyl heptane	90			.270		.0684								3
n-Valeric acid	0	.050												8
i-Valeric acid	0	.0544		.212			.0376							8
Water	0	.220		.75			.138							8, 20
	450				1.3									18

* 320 mm. Hg.
† 40 atm.
‡ Also at other temperatures.
§ Strong function of concentration.

References for Table 14-47
[1] Amdur, Irvine, Mason, and Ross, *J. Chem. Phys.*, **20,** 436 (1952).
[2] Boyd, Stein, Steingrimsson, and Rumpel, *J. Chem. Phys.*, **19,** 548 (1951).
[3] Cummings and Ubbelohde, *J. Chem. Soc. (London)*, 1953, p. 3751.
[4] Fairbanks and Wilke, *Ind. Eng. Chem.*, **42,** 471 (1950).
[5] Gilliland, *Ind. Eng. Chem.*, **26,** 681 (1934).
[6] Gorynnova and Kuvskinskii, *Zhur. Tekh. Fiz.*, **18,** 1421 (1948).
[7] Hansen, Dissertation, Jena, 1907.
[8] "International Critical Tables," vol. 5, p. 62.
[9] Jeffries and Drickamer, *J. Chem. Phys.*, **22,** 436 (1954).
[10] Klotz and Miller, *J. Am. Chem. Soc.*, **69,** 2557 (1947).
[11] McMurtrie and Keyes, *J. Am. Chem. Soc.*, **70,** 3755 (1948).
[12] Mullaly and Jacques, *Phil. Mag.*, **48** (6), 1105 (1924).
[13] Spier, *Physica*, **6,** 453 (1939); **7,** 381 (1940).
[14] Topley and Whytlaw-Gray, *Phil. Mag.*, **4,** 873 (1927).
[15] Trautz and Ludwig, *Ann. Physik*, **5** (5), 887 (1930).
[16] Trautz and Muller, *Ann. Physik*, **22,** 353 (1935).
[17] Trautz and Ries, *Ann. Physik*, **8,** 163 (1931).
[18] Walker and Westenberg, *J. Chem. Phys.*, **32,** 436 (1960).
[19] Westenberg and Walker, *J. Chem. Phys.*, **26,** 1753 (1957).
[20] Winkelmann, *Wied. Ann.*, **22,** 1, 152 (1884); **23,** 203 (1884); **26,** 105 (1885); **33,** 445 (1888); **36,** 92 (1889).

[Nernst, *Z. physik. Chem.*, **2,** 613 (1888)]

$$D_0 = 8.931 \times 10^{-10} T \left(\frac{l_+^0 l_-^0}{\Lambda^0}\right)\left(\frac{z_+ + z_-}{z_+ z_-}\right) \qquad (14\text{-}62)$$

where D_0 = diffusivity of molecule, sq. cm./sec.; l_+^0 = cationic conductance at infinite dilution, mhos/equivalent; l_-^0 = anionic conductance at infinite dilution, mhos/equivalent; $\Lambda^0 = l_+^0 + l_-^0$ = electrolyte conductance at infinite dilution, mhos/equivalent; T = absolute temperature, °K.; z_+ = valence of cation (absolute, *i.e.*, no sign); z_- = valence on anion (absolute, *i.e.*, no sign).

Table 14-49 lists limiting ionic conductances in water at 25°C. (Robinson and Stokes, "Electrolyte Solutions," p. 452, Butterworth, London, 1955). Table 14-50 provides means of correcting for the effect of temperature for some of the more common ions (Harned and Owen, "Physical Chemistry of Electrolytes," pp. 589–591, Reinhold, New York, 1950).

Table 14-48. Association Numbers for Solvents*

Solvent	X
Water	2.6
Methanol	1.9
Ethanol	1.5
Benzene	1.0
Ether	1.0
Heptane	1.0

* From Wilke and Chang, *Am. Inst. Chem. Engrs. J.*, **1,** 264 (1955).

For determination of diffusivities at **other than infinite dilution,** the following relation of Gordon [*J. Chem. Phys.*, **5,** 522 (1937)] is recommended:

$$D_L = D_0\left(1 + \frac{m\,\partial \ln \gamma_\pm}{\partial m}\right)\frac{1}{c_B \bar{V}_B}\left(\frac{\mu_B}{\mu}\right) \qquad (14\text{-}63)$$

where m = molality; $\gamma_\pm$ = mean ionic activity coefficient based on molality (see Glasstone, "Thermodynamics for Chemists," p. 402, Van Nostrand, Princeton, N.J., 1947); c_B = g.-moles water/cc. of solution; $\bar{V}_B$ = partial molal volume of water, cc./g.-mole; μ_B = viscosity of water; μ = viscosity of solution.

Table 14-51 gives **experimental data** for diffusion coefficients of non-electrolytes in liquids. Values are reported in sq. cm./sec. and may be converted to sq. ft./hr. by multiplying by 3.88. Data have been corrected from the temperature of the study to 25°C. using the relation

$$\frac{D_L \mu}{T} = \text{const.} \qquad (14\text{-}64)$$

where necessary. This equation may be used to adjust data to other temperatures but must be employed with caution in cases where the viscosity is high. At high

Table 14-49. Ionic Conductances at Infinite Dilution in Water (25°C.)

For use with Eq. (14-62)

Cation	l_+^0	Anion	l_-^0
Monovalent			
Ag^+	61.90	Acetate	40.9
$CH_3NH_3^+$	58.7	Benzoate	32.4
$(CH_3)_2NH_2^+$	51.9	Butyrate	32.6
$(CH_3)_3NH^+$	47.2	Br^-	78.4
Cs^+	77.3	BrO_3^-	55.7
H^+	349.8	Cl^-	76.35
K^+	73.50	ClO_3^-	64.6
Li^+	38.7	ClO_4^-	67.4
Na^+	50.10	Cyanoacetate	41.8
NH_4^+	73.6	F^-	55.4
NMe_4^+	44.9	Formate	54.6
		HCO_3^-	44.5
NEt_4^+	32.7	I^-	76.8
NPr_4^+	23.4	IO_4^-	54.6
NBu_4^+	19.5	N_3^-	69
NAm_4^+	17.5	NO_3^-	71.46
Rb^+	77.8	OH^-	198.6
Tl^+	74.7	Picrate	30.39
		Propionate	35.8
		ReO_4	55.0
Bivalent			
Ba^{++}	63.6	CO_3^{--}	69.3
Be^{++}	45	$C_2O_4^{--}$	74.2
Ca^{++}	59.50	SO_4^{--}	80.0
Co^{++}	55		
Cu^{++}	56.6		
Mg^{++}	53.0		
Sr^{++}	59.4		
Zn^{++}	52.8		
Trivalent			
Ce^{3+}	69.8	$Fe(CN)_6^{3-}$	100.9
$CO(NH_3)_6^{3+}$	101.9		
Dy^{3+}	65.6	P_3O_9	83.6
Er^{3+}	65.9		
Eu^{3+}	67.8		
Gd^{3+}	67.3		
HO^{3+}	66.3		
La^{3+}	69.7		
Nd^{3+}	69.4		
Pr^{3+}	69.6		
Sm^{3+}	68.5		
Tm^{3+}	65.4		
Yb^{3+}	65.6		
Other			
		$Fe(CN)_6^{4-}$	110
		$P_4O_{12}^{4-}$	94
		$P_2O_7^{4-}$	96
		$P_3O_{10}^{5-}$	109

Table 14-50. Effect of Temperature on Limiting Ionic Conductance

$$l^0 = l^0_{25°} + a(t-25) + b(t-25)^2 + c(t-25)^3$$

Ion	a	$b \times 10^2$	$c \times 10^4$
H^+	4.816	−1.031	−0.767
Li^+	0.890	0.441	−0.204
Na^+	1.092	0.472	−0.115
K^+	1.433	0.406	−0.318
Cl^-	1.540	0.465	−0.128
Br^-	1.544	0.447	−0.230
I^-	1.509	0.438	−0.217

viscosities, the diffusivity is diminished less by increases in viscosity than predicted by the equation. Where values reported by several investigators are nearly the same, they have been averaged. Otherwise, individual values are reported.

DESIGN CALCULATIONS

Outline of General Design Procedure. The problem presented to the designer of an absorption plant usually specifies the following quantities: (1) gas flow rate; (2) gas composition, at least with respect to the component to be absorbed; (3) operating pressure and pressure drop permissible across the absorber; (4) minimum degree of recovery of one or more solutes; and, possibly, (5) solvent to be employed. Items (3), (4), and (5) may be subject to economic considerations and therefore are sometimes left up to the designer. Recovery of the solvent, sometimes by chemical means but more often by distillation, is almost always required, and the recovery apparatus usually has to be considered along with the absorber; the more effective the solvent regeneration the less costly will be the absorber, owing to a smaller concentration of residual dissolved solute in the regenerated solvent.

The designer is ordinarily required to determine (1) the best solvent; (2) the best gas velocity through the absorber, *i.e.*, the vessel diameter; (3) the height of the vessel and its internal members, *e.g.*, the depth and type of packing or the number of trays; (4) the optimum rate of liquid circulation through the absorber and regenerator; (5) the temperatures of streams entering and leaving the absorber and the quantity of heat to be removed to account for heat of solution and other heat effects, if necessary; (6) possibly the pressures at which the absorber and stripper operate; and (7) the mechanical design of the absorption and stripping towers, including flow distributors, etc. This section is concerned with all these choices except the last, which is discussed in Sec. 18.

Selection of Solvent. Where choice is possible, preference is given to liquids with high solubilities for the solute; a high solubility reduces the amount of solvent to be circulated. Sometimes a reversible chemical reaction will result in very high solubility and a minimum solvent rate. Data on the actual systems are desirable in the latter cases, and those available are given on pp. 14-3 to 14-12. Furthermore, the solvent should be relatively non-volatile, cheap, non-corrosive, stable, non-viscous, non-foaming, and preferably non-flammable. Since the exit gas usually is saturated with solvent, solvent loss may be costly; low-cost solvents may therefore supplant more expensive ones of higher solubility or lower volatility. Water is generally used for gases fairly soluble in water, oils for light hydrocarbons, and special chemical solvents for acid gases such as H_2S, CO_2, and SO_2.

Selection of Vapor-Liquid Equilibrium or Solubility Data. Solubility values determine the liquid rate necessary for complete or economic solute recovery. They may be obtained in one of the following ways:

1. From collection of data and references in this section, beginning p. 14-3.

2. For ideal liquid solutions (similar chemical compounds, *e.g.*, families of hydrocarbons), by methods based on Raoult's law. To correct for high pressure, see p. 13-13.

3. For chemically dissimilar compounds not covered under item 1, by methods of extending and predicting data given on p. 13-12.

4. For mixtures for which no data are found or no predictions are possible under the preceding paragraphs, by reference to *Chemical Abstracts;* in the absence of the necessary data, actual experimental determinations may need to be performed.

Calculation of Liquid-Gas Ratio. The minimum possible liquid rate is readily calculated from the entering-gas composition and solubility in the exit liquor, assuming saturation. It may be necessary to estimate the effect of the heat of solution of the gas on the exit-liquor temperature. Values of latent and specific heats and values of heat of solution (at infinite dilution) are given in Sec. 3.

The actual liquid-gas ratio is greater than the minimum by from 25 to 100 per cent and may be arrived at on the basis of economics, as shown by the example, p. 14-32, and discussed on p. 14-31.

In some packed-tower applications involving very soluble gases or vacuum operation, the minimum quantity of solvent needed to dissolve the solute may be

Table 14-51. Diffusivities in Liquids (25°C.)

(Dilute solutions and 1 atm. unless otherwise noted; use $D_L\mu/T$ = constant to estimate effect of temperature; * indicates that reference gives effect of concentration)

Solute	Solvent	$D_L \times 10^5$, sq. cm./sec.	Estimated possible, error, ± %	Ref.
Acetal*	Ethanol	1.25	5	11
Acetamide*	Ethanol	0.68	5	11
Acetamide*	Water	1.19	3	11
Acetic acid	Acetone	3.31	...	4
Acetic acid	Benzene	2.11	...	1, 4
Acetic acid	Carbon tetrachloride	1.49	...	4
Acetic acid	Ethylene glycol	0.13	...	4
Acetic acid	Toluene	2.26	...	4
Acetic acid*	Water	1.24	3	11
Acetonitrile	Water	1.66	5	11
Acetylene	Water	1.78, 2.11	...	1, 24
Allyl alcohol*	Ethanol	1.06	5	11
Allyl alcohol	Water	1.19	6	11
Ammonia*	Water	1.7, 2.0, 2.3	...	1, 11
i-Amyl alcohol*	Ethanol	0.87	5	11
i-Amyl alcohol	Water	1.0	8	11, 25
Benzene	Carbon tetrachloride	1.53	...	7
Benzene (50 mole %)	*n*-Decane	1.72	...	26
Benzene (50 mole %)	2,4-Dimethyl pentane	2.49	...	26
Benzene (50 mole %)	*n*-Dodecane	1.40	...	26
Benzene (50 mole %)	*n*-Heptane	2.47	...	26
Benzene (50 mole %)	*n*-Hexadecane	0.96	...	26
Benzene (50 mole %)	*n*-Octadecane	0.86	...	26
Benzoic acid	Acetone	2.62	...	4
Benzoic acid	Benzene	1.38	...	4
Benzoic acid	Carbon tetrachloride	0.91	...	4
Benzoic acid	Ethylene glycol	0.043	...	4
Benzoic acid	Toluene	1.49	...	4
Bromine	Benzene	2.7	...	11
Bromine	Carbon disulfide	4.1	...	11
Bromine	Water	1.3	...	11
Bromobenzene	Benzene	2.30	...	25
Bromoform*	Acetone	2.90	...	11
Bromoform	*i*-Amyl alcohol	0.53	...	11
Bromoform	Ethanol	1.08	5	11
Bromoform*	Ethyl ether	3.62	...	11
Bromoform	Methanol	2.20	...	23
Bromoform	*n*-Propanol	0.94	...	11
n-Butanol	Water	0.96	5	1, 11, 18, 25
Caffeine	Water	0.63	6	11
Carbon dioxide	Ethanol	4.0	6	11
Carbon dioxide	Water	1.96	1	1, 3, 5, 20, 24, 28
Carbon disulfide (50 mole %, 200 atm.)	*n*-Butanol	3.57	...	14
Carbon disulfide (50 mole %, 200 atm.)	*i*-Butanol	2.42	...	14
Carbon disulfide (50 mole %, 218 atm.)	Chlorobenzene	3.00	...	14
Carbon disulfide (50 mole %, 200 atm.)	2,4-Dimethyl pentane	3.63	...	14
Carbon disulfide (50 mole %, 100 atm.)	*n*-Heptane	3.0	...	14
Carbon disulfide (50 mole %, 50 atm.)	Methyl cyclohexane	3.5	...	14
Carbon disulfide (50 mole %, 200 atm.)	*n*-Octane	3.10	...	14
Carbon disulfide (50 mole %)	Toluene	2.06	...	14
Carbon tetrachloride	Benzene	2.04	3	7, 9
Carbon tetrachloride*	Cyclohexane	1.49	2	9, 10*
Carbon tetrachloride	Decalin	0.776	2	9
Carbon tetrachloride	Dioxane	1.02	2	9
Carbon tetrachloride*	Ethanol	1.50	2	9, 10*
Carbon tetrachloride	*n*-Heptane	3.17	2	9
Carbon tetrachloride	Kerosene	0.961	2	9
Carbon tetrachloride	Methanol	2.30	2	9
Carbon tetrachloride	*i*-Octane	2.57	2	9
Carbon tetrachloride	Tetralin	0.735	2	9
Chloral*	Ethanol	0.68	5	11
Chloral hydrate	Water	0.77	7	11
Chlorine	Water	1.44	4	1, 28
Chlorobenzene	Benzene	2.66	...	25
Chloroform	Benzene	2.50	6	1, 25
Chloroform	Ethanol	1.38	3	11
Cinnamic acid	Acetone	2.41	...	4
Cinnamic acid	Benzene	1.12	...	4
Cinnamic acid	Carbon tetrachloride	0.76	...	4
Cinnamic acid	Toluene	2.41	...	4
1,1′-Dichloropropanol	Water	1.0	6	11
Dicyanodiamide*	Water	1.18	4	11
Diethyl ether	Benzene	2.73	...	25
Diethyl ether	Water	0.85	...	2
2,4-Dimethyl pentane (50 mole %)	*n*-Dodecane	1.44	...	26
2,4-Dimethyl pentane (50 mole %)	*n*-Hexadecane	0.88	...	26
Ethanol*	Water	1.28	4	1, 7, 9,* 11,* 22
Ethyl acetate	Ethyl benzoate	0.94	...	6
Ethylene dichloride	Benzene	2.8	...	1, 25
Formic acid	Acetone	3.77	...	4
Formic acid	Benzene	2.28	...	4
Formic acid	Carbon tetrachloride	1.89	...	4
Formic acid	Ethylene glycol	0.094	...	4
Formic acid	Toluene	2.65	...	
Formic acid	Water	1.37	10	11
Glucose	Water	0.69	6	11
Glycerol	*i*-Amyl alcohol	0.12	...	11

Table 14-51. Diffusivities in Liquids (25°C.)—(*Continued*)

Solute	Solvent	$D_L \times 10^5$, sq. cm./sec.	Estimated possible error, ± %	Ref.
Glycerol	Ethanol	0.56	...	11
Glycerol*	Water	0.94	6	1, 11*
n-Heptane (50 mole %)	*n*-Dodecane	1.58	...	26
n-Heptane (50 mole %)	*n*-Hexadecane	1.00	...	26
n-Heptane (50 mole %)	*n*-Octadecane	0.92	...	26
n-Heptane (50 mole %)	*n*-Tetradecane	1.29	...	26
Hexamethylene tetramine	Water	0.67	...	11
Hydrogen chloride*	Water	3.10	3	4, 11,* 12*
Hydrogen	Water	5.85 (4.4?)	...	1, 11, 24(?)
Hydrogen sulfide	Water	1.61	...	1
Hydroquinone*	Ethanol	0.53	5	11
Hydroquinone*	Water	0.88, 1.12	...	2, 11*
Iodine	Acetic acid	1.13	...	11
Iodine	Anisole	1.25	...	11
Iodine	Benzene	1.98	...	9, 19, 23
Iodine	Bromobenzene	1.25	10	4, 11, 19
Iodine	Carbon disulfide	3.2	...	11, 19, 23
Iodine	Carbon tetrachloride	1.45	8	9, 11, 19
Iodine	Chloroform	2.30	3	11, 23
Iodine	Cyclohexane	1.80	...	4
Iodine	Dioxane	1.07	...	9
Iodine*	Ethanol	1.30	...	4, 11*
Iodine	Ethyl acetate	2.2	...	11, 19
Iodine	Ethyl ether	3.61	...	11
Iodine	Ethylene bromide	0.93	...	11
Iodine	*n*-Heptane	3.4, 2.5	...	9, 11, 19
Iodine	*n*-Hexane	4.15	...	4, 9
Iodine	Mesitylene	1.49	...	9
Iodine	Methanol	1.74	...	19
Iodine	Methyl cyclohexane	2.1	...	4
Iodine	*n*-Octane	2.76	...	4
Iodine	Tetrabromoethane	2.0	...	11
Iodine	*n*-Tetradecane	0.96	...	4
Iodine	Toluene	2.1	...	11
Iodine	*m*-Xylene	1.82	...	9, 11
Iodobenzene	Ethanol	1.09	3	11
Lactose*	Water	0.49	5	11
Maltose*	Water	0.48	5	11
Mannitol*	Water	0.65	5	11
Methanol	Water	1.6	...	1, 7, 11
Micotine*	Water	0.60	8	11
Nitric acid*	Water	2.98	2	11
Nitrobenzene	Carbon tetrachloride	1.00	...	7
Nitrogen	Water	1.9	...	1, 24
Nitrous oxide	Water	1.8	...	1, 11
Oxalic acid*	Water	1.61	2	11
Oxygen	Glycerol*-water (106 poise)	0.24	...	13
Oxygen	Sucrose*-water (125 poise)	0.25	...	13
Oxygen	Water	2.5	20	1, 3, 15, 21, 24
Pentaerythritol*	Water	0.77	4	11
Phenol	*i*-Amyl alcohol	0.2	...	11
Phenol	Benzene	1.68	...	1
Phenol	Carbon disulfide	3.7	...	11
Phenol	Chloroform	2.0	...	11
Phenol	Ethanol	0.89	...	11
Phenol	Ethyl ether	3.9	...	11
n-Propanol	Water	1.1	...	1, 7, 11
Pyridine*	Ethanol	1.24	3	11
Pyridine	Water	0.76	7	11
Pyrogallol	Water	0.74	7	11
Raffinose*	Water	0.41	4	11
Resorcinol*	Ethanol	0.46	5	11
Resorcinol*	Water	0.87	4	11
Saccharose*	Water	0.49	4	11
Stearic acid*	Ethanol	0.65	5	11
Succinic acid*	Water	0.94	...	11
Sucrose	Water	0.56	6	2, 27
Sulfur dioxide	Water	1.7	...	15, 17
Sulfuric acid*	Water	1.97	3	11
Tartaric acid*	Water	0.80	10	11
1,1,2,2-Tetrabromoethane	1,1,2,2-Tetrachloroethane	0.61	4	11
Toluene	*n*-Decane	2.09	...	4
Toluene	*n*-Dodecane	1.38	...	4
Toluene	*n*-Heptane	3.72	...	4
Toluene	*n*-Hexane	4.21	...	4
Toluene	*n*-Tetradecane	1.02	...	4
Urea	Ethanol	0.73	...	11
Urea	Water	1.37	2	8, 11
Urethane	Water	1.06	...	11, 25
Water	Glycerol	0.021	...	16

References for Table 14–51
[1] Arnold, *J. Am. Chem. Soc.*, **52**, 3937 (1930).
[2] Calvet, *J. chim. phys.*, **44**, 47 (1947).
[3] Carlson, *J. Am. Chem. Soc.*, **33**, 1027 (1911).
[4] Chang and Wilke, *J. Phys. Chem.*, **59**, 592 (1955).
[5] Davidson and Cullen, *Trans. Inst. Chem. Engrs.*, **35**, 51 (1957).
[6] Dummer, *Z. anorg. Chem.*, **109**, 31 (1949).
[7] Gerlach, *Ann. Phys. (Leipzig)*, **10**, 437 (1931).
[8] Gosting and Akeley, *J. Am. Chem. Soc.*, **74**, 2058 (1952).
[9] Hammond and Stokes, *Trans. Faraday Soc.*, **49**, 890 (1953); **49**, 886 (1953).
[10] Hammond and Stokes, *Trans. Faraday Soc.*, **52**, 781 (1956).
[11] "International Critical Tables," vol. 5, p. 63.
[12] James, Hollingshead, and Gordon, *J. Chem. Phys.*, **7**, 89 (1939); **7**, 936 (1939).
[13] Jordon, Ackermann, and Berger, *J. Am. Chem. Soc.*, **78**, 2979 (1956).
[14] Koeller and Drickamer, *J. Chem. Phys.*, **21**, 575 (1953).
[15] Kolthoff and Miller, *J. Am. Chem. Soc.*, **63**, 1013 (1941).

Table 14-51. Diffusivities in Liquids (25°C.)—(*Continued*)

[16] Lamm and Sjosteldt, *Trans. Faraday Soc.*, **34,** 1158 (1938).
[17] Lynn, Straatemeier, and Kramers, *Chem. Eng. Sci.*, **4,** 49 (1955).
[18] Lyons and Sandquist, *J. Am. Chem. Soc.*, **75,** 3896 (1953).
[19] Miller, *Proc. Roy. Soc. (London)*, **A106,** 724 (1924).
[20] Ringbom, *Z. anorg. allgem. chem.*, **238,** 94 (1938).
[21] Semerano, Riccoboni, and Foffani, *Gazz. chim. ital.*, **79,** 395 (1949).
[22] Smith and Storrow, *J. Appl. Chem. (London)*, **2,** 225 (1952).
[23] Steran, Irish, and Eyring, *J. Phys. Chem.*, **44,** 981 (1940).
[24] Tammann and Jessen, *Z. anorg. allgem. Chem.*, **179,** 125 (1929).
[25] Thovert, *Ann. Phys. (Leipzig)*, **2,** 369 (1914).
[26] Trevoy and Drickamer, *J. Chem. Phys.*, **17,** 1117 (1949).
[27] Tsvetkov, *Zhur. Eksptl. i Teoret. Fiz.*, **21,** 701 (1951).
[28] Vivian and Peacemen, *Am. Inst. Chem. Engrs. J.*, **2,** 437 (1956).

insufficient to keep the packing surface thoroughly wet, leading to poor distribution of the liquid stream. Although there is no single flow rate at which a packing material becomes thoroughly wet and below which flow conditions are poor, it is desirable to operate at or above a **minimum wetting rate.** Morris and Jackson ("Absorption Towers," Butterworth, London, 1953) recommend that minimum wetting rate (M.W.R.) be taken as 0.85 cu. ft./(hr.)(ft.) except for ring packings larger than 3 in. and grids of pitch greater than 2 in., and as 1.3 cu. ft./(hr.)(ft.) for other packings. M.W.R. is computed as V_L/a, where V_L = volumetric liquid flow, cu. ft./(hr.)(sq. ft. of tower cross section) and a = packing surface area, sq. ft./cu. ft. For 1-in. Raschig rings, $a = 30$ (approx.). For such packings, therefore, the liquid rate should be at least 5 gal./(min.)(sq. ft.) (see further in Sec. 18, p. 18-34). When the net flow to the packed column is smaller it may be desirable to recirculate liquid over the packing, at the expense of a reduced mean driving force.

Selection of Equipment. Usually packed columns are chosen for corrosive materials, for low pressure drop, for pilot-plant or small-scale operations (say less than 2 ft. diameter), and for liquids that foam badly. Plate columns are preferred for large-scale operations (they are cheaper), for low liquor rates (where packing would be inadequately wetted), and where internal cooling is desired.

In packed towers the type of packing is chosen for its mechanical strength, resistance to corrosion, cost, capacity, and efficiency, as discussed on pp. 14-30 and 14-31. Packings found to be most economical and generally useful are 1- to 2-in. ceramic or carbon rings (½-in. size for columns under 4 in. diameter), 1-in. saddles, 3-in. spiral or partition rings, drip-point tile, and wood grids. Descriptions and cost data on packings are given in Sec. 18.

Calculation of Column Diameter. Allowable vapor velocities in plate columns are sometimes chosen to limit **entrainment** to less than 10 per cent and at other times are calculated from established factors. Such information is given in Sec. 18. For very high liquid-gas ratios, say over 5, liquid-flow capacity across the plate may determine the diameter.

For packed columns, **flooding** determines the minimum possible diameter, and usual design is for 50 to 75 per cent of the flooding velocity, data for which are given for common packings on p. 18-26 in Sec. 18. These safe operating velocities are normally rather close to the calculated economic velocities discussed on p. 14-32.

Pressure Drop. For plate columns, methods of estimating pressure drop are given on p. 18-8. For packed columns, data on typical packings are given on p. 18-26. Pressure drop at flooding for packings commonly used is around 2 in. of water per foot of packing height. For operation at about 50 per cent of flooding the pressure drop is roughly ½ in. of water per foot of height. This value is a convenient one to keep in mind for operating control.

Height of Column. Height is dependent on the degree of removal of solute from the gases. This is usually an economic matter, as treated on p. 14-32 (for valuable solutes, optimum recovery usually runs nearly complete, say 99+ per cent). To compute the economic recovery as well as the eventual height, it is necessary to have values of plate efficiency (plate column) or height of a transfer unit (packed column). Data on plate efficiencies are given in Secs. 13 and 18. In case of packed columns, over-all values of H.T.U. given on pp. 14-34 to 14-36 are used if available for the conditions of the problem; otherwise, separate gas and liquid values of H.T.U., respectively, are estimated from data for the separate resistances, p. 18-35, and combined by Eqs. (14-50) and (14-51).

Final calculation of height of a plate column requires finding the number of theoretical plates for the separation, as described below. For a packed column, the number of transfer units is determined as indicated in the following discussion.

Computation of Tower Height. Methods for estimating the height of the active section of an absorber needed to effect a given separation are based on the use of rate expressions for representing mass transfer at a point on the interface, and on material balances (when required) to represent the changes in bulk composition in the two phases that flow past each other. The rate expressions are grounded in the diffusion theory outlined previously in this section. Combination of such expressions leads to an integral expression for the number of transfer units, or to very closely related equations for numbers of theoretical plates. The paragraphs immediately below set forth convenient methods for using such equations, first in a general case and later in simpler ways, depending on certain approximations.

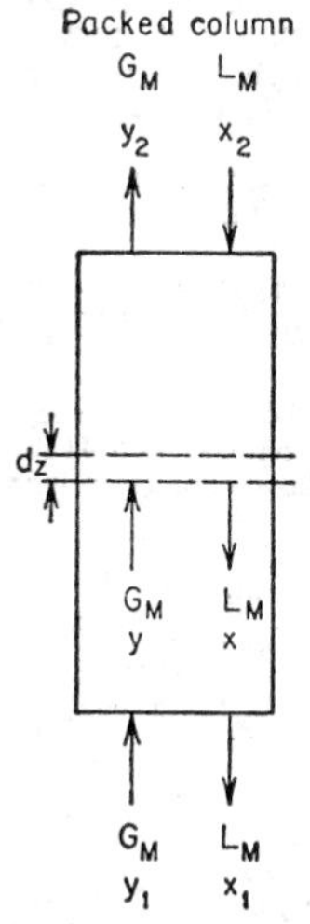

FIG. 14-14. Material balance, operating, and equilibrium lines.

Use of Mass-transfer Rate Expression for Packed Columns. Consider the change in the gas mole fraction of solute y in the differential section of packing dz indicated in Fig. 14-14. Equating the rate at which solute is lost from the gas to the rate at which it is transferred through the gas phase to the interface,

$$-d(G_My) = -G_M' \frac{dy}{(1-y)^2} = k_GaP \frac{y - y_i}{(1-y)_{lm}} dz \tag{14-65}$$

where G_M = molar mass velocity of the gas stream; G_M' = molar superficial mass velocity of the inert gas; k_G = gas-phase mass-transfer coefficient; a = interfacial area per unit of packed volume (smaller than the packing surface S); P = absolute pressure; y_i = mole fraction solute in the gas at the interface; $(1 - y)_{lm}$ = logarithmic mean of the mole fraction inert gas in the bulk stream $1 - y$ and that at the interface $1 - y_i$. The height of packing Z needed for a specified change in gas composition from y_1 entering to y_2 emerging is given formally by the integral

$$Z = G_M' \int_{y_2}^{y_1} \frac{(1-y)_{lm}\, dy}{k_GaP(1-y)^2(y-y_i)} \tag{14-66}$$

This expression is more complex than is usually required, but it applies in the most **general cases** and must be used when the mass-transfer coefficient varies from point to point, as it may if the gas velocity varies as gas dissolves or when the gas is not dilute. Values of y_i depend on the liquid composition x_i and on the temperature. The dependence is best represented by operating and equilibrium lines (see below).

The following example illustrates the use of Eq. (14-66) for computing the packed height of an absorber for scrubbing chlorine from air with aqueous caustic solution. The interfacial partial pressure of chlorine over aqueous caustic solution is zero, owing to the rapid and complete reaction of chlorine after it dissolves.

Example 3. Find the packed height needed to reduce the chlorine content of 396 lb./(hr.)(sq. ft.) of a chlorine-air mixture containing 0.503 mole fraction chlorine to 0.0403 mole fraction. Based on test data (Sherwood and Pigford, "Gas Absorption," p. 121, McGraw-Hill, New York, 1952) the value of k_GaP may be taken equal to 26.4 lb.-moles/(hr.)(cu. ft.) (mole fraction), at a gas velocity equal to that at the bottom of the packing. Back pressure y_i is zero.

Solution. Assuming that the mass-transfer coefficient varies as the 0.8 power of the local mass gas velocity, we have

$$k_GaP = 26.4 \left[\frac{71y + 29(1-y)}{71y_1 + 29(1-y_1)} \left(\frac{1-y_1}{1-y} \right) \right]^{0.8}$$

where 71 and 29 are the molecular weights of chlorine and air, respectively. Noting that G_M' = 3.94 lb.-moles air/(hr.)(sq. ft.) and introducing the above expression into the integral gives

$$Z = \frac{3.94}{26.4} \int_{0.0403}^{0.503} \left[\frac{71 \dfrac{0.503}{1-0.503} + 29}{71 \dfrac{y}{1-y} + 29} \right]^{0.8} \frac{dy}{(1-y)^2 \ln\left(\dfrac{1}{1-y}\right)}$$

$$= 1 \text{ ft.}$$

Frequently it is not possible to assume that $y_i = 0$ as in Example 3, owing to the diffusional resistance of the liquid phase or to the accumulation of solute in the liquid stream. When there is appreciable back pressure it is necessary to supplement the rate equations with a material balance leading to an operating line. Frequently, too, the changes in gas flow and in the mole fraction of inert gas are so small that inclusion of terms such as $(1 - y)$ and $(1 - y)_{lm}$ is not important, or at least can be included in an approximate way. The following sections illustrate the less general and somewhat simplified procedure.

Use of Material Balance to Obtain Driving Force. Considering the countercurrent flows into and from the differential section of packing shown in Fig. 14-14 a steady-state material balance leads to

$$d(G_My) = d(L_Mx) \tag{14-67}$$

or to

$$G_M' \frac{dy}{(1-y)^2} = L_M' \frac{dx}{(1-x)^2} \tag{14-68}$$

where L_M = molar mass velocity of the liquid stream; L_M' = molar mass velocity of the inert liquid component; x = mole fraction in liquid; other symbols as for Eq. (14-65).

This is the differential equation of the operating line. Its integral around the upper portion of the packing is the equation for the operating line,

$$G_M' \left(\frac{y}{1-y} - \frac{y_2}{1-y_2} \right) = L_M' \left(\frac{x}{1-x} - \frac{x_2}{1-x_2} \right) \tag{14-69}$$

When mole fractions y and x are sufficiently small (dilute solutions), the molar total flows G_M and L_M will be very nearly constant, and the **operating line equation** becomes

$$G_M(y - y_2) = L_M(x - x_2) \tag{14-70}$$

This equation gives the relation between the bulk compositions of the gas and liquid streams at each level in the apparatus. A plot of the equation in a typical example involving solvent recovery is illustrated in Fig. 14-15, which also shows the equilibrium relationship

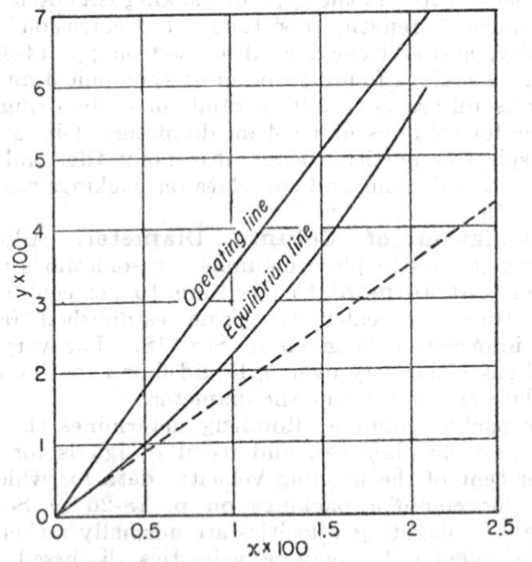

FIG. 14-15. Example of absorption of acetone, with a curved equilibrium line owing to heat of absorption. Dashed line is a tangent to the equilibrium curve at the origin.

between the interfacial compositions y_i and x_i. Once y is known as a function of x along the operating line, y_i can be found at corresponding points on the equilibrium line by Eq. (14-37). Thence, the integral in Eq. (14-66) can be evaluated.

Calculation of Transfer Units. When the local mass-transfer coefficient k_GaP in Eq. (14-66) is nearly proportional to the first power of the local gas mass velocity G_M, it is possible to take $G_M'/k_GaP(1 - y)$ as a constant in the equation. The constant has the units of length; it is called the **height of a transfer unit for**

the gas phase and is symbolized by H_G. Furthermore, the driving force $y - y_i$ across the gas phase can be computed from the over-all driving force $y - y^*$ under certain assumptions as shown on p. 14-18. Since $(y - y_i)/(y - y^*) = H_G/H_{OG}$, the equation for packed height can be written in either of the two alternate forms:

$$Z = H_G \int_{y_2}^{y_1} \frac{(1 - y)_{lm}\, dy}{(1 - y)(y - y_i)} = H_G N_G \quad (14\text{-}71)$$

where N_G = number of transfer units based on gas-phase resistance, and

$$Z = H_{OG} \int_{y_2}^{y_1} \frac{(1 - y)_{lm}\, dy}{(1 - y)(y - y^*)} = H_{OG} N_{OG} \quad (14\text{-}72)$$

where H_{OG} = height of a transfer unit and N_{OG} = number of transfer units, based on over-all gas-phase resistance. Equation (14-72) is the more useful practically; it requires either empirical knowledge of or computation of H_{OG} by adding estimated values of H_G and H_L with Eq. (14-50).

A further convenient simplification of Eqs. (14-71) and (14-72) was suggested by Wiegand [*Trans. Am. Inst. Chem. Engrs.*, **35**, 679 (1939)], who pointed out that the logarithmic mean mole fraction of inert gas $(1 - y)_{lm}$ is often very nearly equal to the arithmetic mean. With this substitution the quotient of the first factors in the numerator and denominator of these equations becomes

$$\frac{(1 - y)_{lm}}{1 - y} \approx \frac{(1 - y^*) + (1 - y)}{2(1 - y)} = \frac{y - y^*}{2(1 - y)} + 1 \quad (14\text{-}73)$$

so the equations may be simplified to

$$N_G = \frac{1}{2} \ln \frac{1 - y_2}{1 - y_1} + \int_{y_2}^{y_1} \frac{dy}{y - y_i} \quad (14\text{-}74)$$

$$N_{OG} = \frac{1}{2} \ln \frac{1 - y_2}{1 - y_1} + \int_{y_2}^{y_1} \frac{dy}{y - y^*} \quad (14\text{-}75)$$

The second terms represent the numbers of transfer units for an **infinitely dilute gas.** The first terms, usually amounting to only small corrections, give the effect of the **finite level of gas concentration.**

The remainder of the discussion concerns the evaluation of the integrals in Eqs. (14-74) and (14-75). It is assumed that after these have been evaluated by means of charts or formulas, as indicated below, the corrections corresponding to the first terms in these equations will be added.

An especially simple case occurs when both **operating and equilibrium lines are straight,** owing to dilute solutions, validity of Henry's law ($y^*/x = y_i/x_i = m$), and absence of heat effects. Then it is possible to evaluate the integral in Eq. (14-75) explicitly, obtaining the equation [approximate, in that the first-term correction in Eq. (14-75) is omitted]

$$N_{OG} = \frac{1}{1 - (mG_M/L_M)} \ln \left[\left(1 - \frac{mG_M}{L_M}\right)\left(\frac{y_1 - mx_2}{y_2 - mx_2}\right) + \frac{mG_M}{L_M} \right] \quad (14\text{-}76)$$

Even when there are concentrated solutions or heat effects, it is possible to obtain an **approximate result** from the above equation if, as in many practical examples involving nearly complete clean-up of the gas, the driving forces in the upper part of the tower are very much smaller than those at the bottom. Then the value of mG_M/L_M used in the equation should be the ratio of slopes of equilibrium line m and operating line G_M/L_M

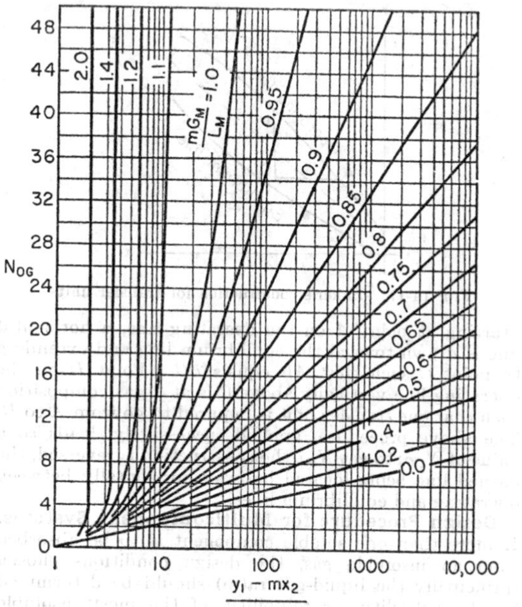

Fig. 14-16. Number of transfer units in an absorption column. Condition of constant mG_M/L_M, a plot of Eq. (14-76).

in the low-concentration range. Figure 14-16 is a plot of Eq. (14-76) from which the value of N_{OG} can be read directly as a function of the ratio of slopes and the ratio of concentrations. This plot and Eq. (14-76) are equivalent to the use of a logarithmic mean of terminal driving forces but are more convenient because they avoid computation of the exit-liquid concentration x_1.

Analytical evaluation of the integral in Eq. (14-75) when either equilibrium line, operating line, or both are curved has been given by Othmer and Scheibel [*Trans. Am. Inst. Chem. Engrs.*, **38**, 339 (1942)] and by Colburn [*Ind. Eng. Chem.*, **33**, 459 (1941)]. Colburn's formulation is particularly convenient because Fig. 14-16 can be used, as indicated below where heat effects are discussed.

When the change in the concentration of the liquid stream is of principal concern rather than that of the gas, as in stripping or desorption, it is more convenient to formulate the rate equation analogous to Eq. (14-65) in terms of liquid composition x. This leads to equations defining numbers of **transfer units** and heights of transfer units based on **liquid-phase** resistance:

$$Z = H_L \int_{x_2}^{x_1} \frac{(1 - x)_{lm}\, dx}{(1 - x)(x_i - x)} = H_L N_L \quad (14\text{-}77)$$

$$Z = H_{OL} \int_{x_2}^{x_1} \frac{(1 - x)_{lm}\, dx}{(1 - x)(x^* - x)} = H_{OL} N_{OL} \quad (14\text{-}78)$$

When the assumptions of straight operating and equilibrium lines are made, an equation analogous to Eq. (14-76) is obtained.

Graphical Estimation of Transfer Units. A graphical construction involving the operating and equilibrium lines on the x-y diagram, similar to the construction of theoretical stages, is possible by either the method of White [*Trans. Am. Inst. Chem. Engrs.*, **36**, 359 (1940)] or that of Baker [*Ind. Eng. Chem.*, **27**, 977 (1935)]. Baker's method is the simpler. It involves the location of a line vertically halfway between the operating and equilibrium lines, as shown on Fig. 14-17.

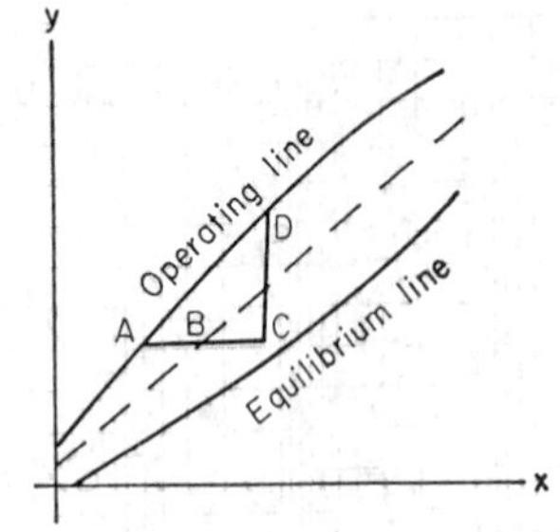

Fig. 14-17. Baker's construction for transfer units.

Starting at point A on the operating line, a horizontal line is drawn toward the equilibrium line and extending to point C such that AB equals BC. Point D on the operating line vertically above C is at a gas composition such that one transfer unit is required to go from A to D. The above procedure, applied successively, leads to a value of N_{OG}; to get N_{OL} the construction is reversed, the dashed line being located halfway horizontally between operating and equilibrium lines.

Design Procedure for Multicomponent Systems. If more than one soluble component is to be absorbed from an insoluble gas, the design conditions chosen (principally the liquid-gas ratio) should be determined by the volatility, or solubility, of the most insoluble constituent that it is economical to recover completely. Less volatile components will also be recovered completely; absorption of more volatile components will be incomplete, even though the effluent liquid becomes saturated with respect to these components. When the latter condition exists, even an infinite number of transfer units or plates gives only a limited, finite value of y_1/y_2, as shown by the vertical asymptotes in Fig. 14-16 for $mG_M/L_M > 1$. If there is no solute in the fresh liquid fed to the absorption column the limiting value of y_1/y_2 is equal to $\lambda/(\lambda - 1)$, where $\lambda = mG_M/L_M > 1$.

Figure 14-18 (Sherwood and Pigford, "Absorption and Extraction," p. 197, McGraw-Hill, New York, 1952) illustrates the significance of these considerations for a column used to absorb hydrocarbons in an oil. For this case, the liquid-gas ratio is chosen such that complete recovery of pentane and heavier components is obtained. Six theoretical plates are sufficient to give 77 per cent recovery of butane, but even an infinite number of plates would give only limited recovery of the lighter constituents.

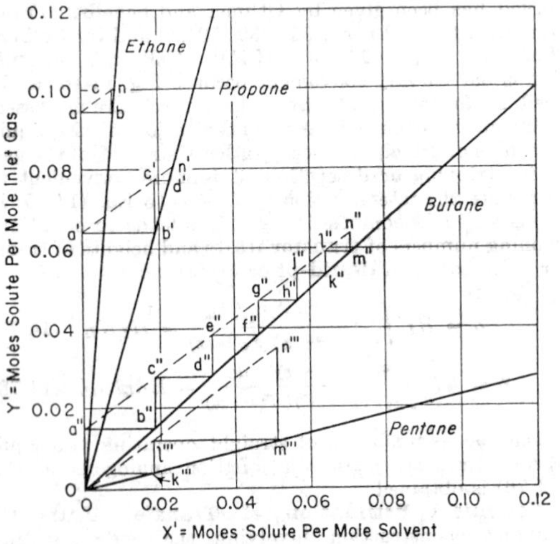

Fig. 14-18. Graphical computation of theoretical plates for multicomponent isothermal absorption. Points a, c, e, etc., show compositions of gas and liquid streams. Points marked a correspond to the bottom of the tower, points marked n to the top. Pentane is lightest component being recovered nearly completely. (*After Sherwood and Pigford, "Absorption and Extraction," McGraw-Hill, New York, 1952.*)

When the gas stream is dilute, absorption of each constituent can be considered separately as though the other soluble components were absent. In concentrated gases, however, the change in gas and liquid flow rates within the column and the heat effects accompanying absorption of all components must be considered. Usually a trial-and-error calculation is involved from one theoretical stage to the next if accurate results are to be obtained. Degree of recovery of the light components is not known until mole fractions of the various components in the effluent liquid and the temperature of this liquid are known; these properties depend in turn on the degree of recovery. Examples involving concentrated gases are discussed by Sherwood and Pigford (*op. cit.*, pp. 179–211) and by Sherwood and Jackson [*Trans. Am. Inst. Chem. Engrs.*, **37**, 959 (1941)]. Edmister (see Sherwood and Pigford, *op. cit.*) has shown how approximations can be introduced in plate-tower calculations to allow for variable fluid temperatures and flow rates.

Example 4. Air entering a tower contains 1 per cent acetaldehyde and 2 per cent acetone. The optimum liquid flow, permitting nearly complete recovery of acetone, is $L_M/G_M = 3.1$ moles/mole when the fresh solvent temperature is 31.5°C. What will be the percentage recovery of acetaldehyde if the tower recovers the optimum amount of acetone?

Solution. The value of y^*/x for acetaldehyde is measured as 50 at the boiling point of a dilute solution, 93.5°C. Neglecting the heat of solution, y^*/x at 31.5°C. is equal to 50 $(^{120}/_{730}) = 8.2$, where the factor in parentheses is the ratio of pure acetaldehyde vapor pressures at 31.5 and 93.5°C., respectively. Since $L_M/G_M = 3.1$, mG_M/L_M for the aldehyde is $8.2/3.1 = 2.64 = \lambda$, and y_1/y_2 for the aldehyde equals $\lambda/(\lambda - 1) = 2.64/1.64 = 1.61$, corresponding to only $0.61/1.61 = 38$ per cent recovery.

Economic Design of Absorption Systems

Although equations and experimental data for transfer coefficients or units are useful in calculating absorption problems once the various conditions involved are known, it is even more important to have a rational basis for choice of the operating variables. These variables include the type of equipment to be used, its internals, the liquid-gas ratio, the diameter (or gas velocity), and the height (or exit-gas strength). All these factors involve economic balances, as shown by Colburn ("Absorption of Gases by Liquids," Collected Papers on the Teaching of Chemical Engineering, p. 269, American Institute of Chemical Engineers, New York, 1940); also see Sherwood and Pigford ("Absorption and Extraction," pp. 451–454, McGraw-Hill, New York, 1952).

Packed Towers vs. Plate Towers. The relative advantages and disadvantages of packed and plate towers may be summarized as follows:

1. Packed towers may be advantageous for vacuum operations because the pressure drop through a packed tower can be less than for a plate tower.
2. Packed towers may be preferred in the case of liquids that foam.
3. Liquid hold-up is generally less in a packed tower.
4. Plate towers may be preferred when there are deposits of solid material that must be removed periodically. A plate tower can be fitted with manholes, and the plates may be spaced far enough apart to facilitate cleaning.

5. Total weight of a plate tower is usually less than for a packed tower designed for the same duty. The limited crushing strength of packing materials may make it impossible for one packing-support plate to bear the weight of a tall column of packing.

6. Plate towers may be more suitable when the operation is carried out intermittently at temperatures either higher or lower than atmospheric temperature. Alternate expansion and contraction of the shell under such circumstances may crush a packing.

7. Cooling coils are installed readily on plates, making plate towers more desirable when heat of solution requires internal cooling.

8. Plate columns may be preferable for operations that require a large number of transfer units or theoretical plates, because packed towers are subject to channeling of the vapor or liquid streams and are thus limited in the amount of material that can be transferred.

9. Higher liquid rates usually can be handled in plate towers, provided that the distance the liquid must travel to cross each plate is not greater than a few feet.

10. Construction of packed towers is usually simpler and cheaper when corrosive substances must be handled.

11. Other things being equal, economic considerations usually show that packed columns are favored over plate columns for absorption when the column diameter is less than about 2 ft.

Column and Packing. Consideration is first made of factors such as corrosion and fouling, available apparatus, and life of the process. Then selection is made by comparison of costs of various types under the most favorable design conditions for each. Among packing materials, ½- and 1-in. ceramic rings, 1-in. saddles, 3-in. spiral or partition rings, drip-point tile, and wood grids appear favorable from a cost viewpoint for absorption of soluble gases.

An interesting point in the selection of packed columns is that cost of the shell varies approximately as the square of the diameter. This cost can therefore be expressed in terms of dollars per cubic foot of tower volume. This value can then be added to the cost per cubic foot of packing. It is readily apparent, then, that there is little advantage in searching for packings having a unit cost much less than that of the shell. For example, gravel costs only a fraction of a dollar per cubic foot compared with, say, \$5 per cubic foot for 1-in. rings, but a shell of so much larger diameter is required when gravel is used that it is an uneconomic packing. Cost data are summarized on p. 18-52.

Liquid-Gas Ratio. The design factor of first importance is the value mG_M/L_M. This factor is needed to determine the height of a transfer unit and the number of transfer units. The liquid-gas ratio also affects the column diameter. If the solute gas is dilute so that the term mG_M/L_M is apt to be nearly constant through the column, the problem is simplified.

Magnitude of mG_M/L_M is often based on economic factors. The greater mG_M/L_M, the more concentrated will be the exit liquor and therefore the cheaper will be the operation of concentrating the solute in cases of solute recovery. This is ordinarily accomplished by stripping in a second column, as indicated in Fig. 14-19. On the other hand, the greater the value of mG_M/L_M, the higher and therefore more expensive the absorption column will be and also the more solute will be lost in the exit gases. A typical calculation of the economic optimum liquid-gas ratio in the absorption of acetone by water resulted in a value of $mG_M/L_M = 0.7$. For less valuable solutes a lower value of this ratio is employed, *e.g.*, in the absorption of petroleum refinery gases. **In the design of stripping columns, the value of L_M/mG_M usually should be in the range 0.5 to 0.8.**

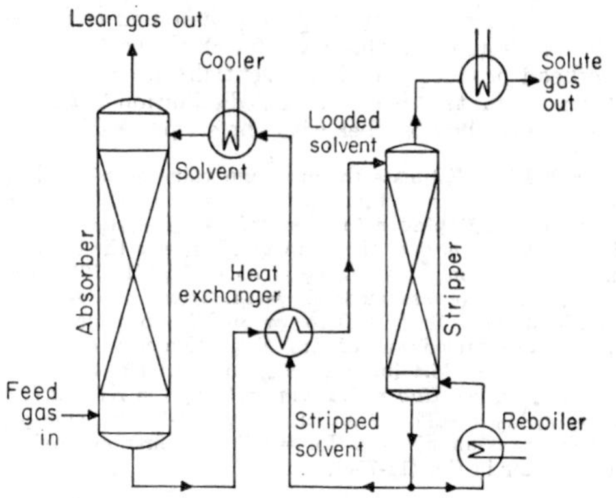

FIG. 14-19. Typical flow sheet for absorber-stripper combination.

Where the solute is not very dilute (*i.e.*, more than a few mole per cent in the exit liquor), heat of solution will cause a temperature rise, and the value of m at the bottom of the column will be greater than at the top. Where, for this reason or for others, mG_M/L_M is not constant, choice of the liquid-gas ratio is more difficult; however, the conditions at the dilute end are usually more important since, in case of nearly complete absorption, most of the transfer units are required in the dilute region.

The following equation represents a **balance of the costs of absorption and of subsequent stripping** to recover the solute:

$$\left(\frac{L_M}{m_2G_M} - 1\right)^2 = \frac{BC_3H_{OG}(K_D - 1)}{C_5\theta rG_Mm_2} \qquad (14\text{-}79)$$

where
$$B = \left[1 + n\left(\frac{L_M}{m_2G_M} - 1\right)\right] 2.3 \log_{10}\left[\left(\frac{y_1}{y_2}\right)\frac{(1 - m_2G_M/L_M)^2}{(1 - K_1G_M/L_M)}\right] - \frac{(1 - m_2G_M/L_M) - 2(K_1/m_2 - 1)}{1 - K_1G_M/L_M} \qquad (14\text{-}79a)$$

K_D = y^*/x, at its boiling point, of the feed to the stripping column
m_2 = slope of equilibrium curve y^*/x at the temperature of the inlet liquid to the absorption column
K_1 = y^*/x at the temperature of the rich absorption liquor as it leaves the absorption column
C_3 = annual cost of apparatus and power for the absorption column, \$/(cu. ft.)(year) = $C_1[(G_{opt}/G) + 0.5(G/G_{opt})^2]$ (the latter terms are defined below)
C_5 = total cost of stripping operation, expressed as \$/lb.-mole of vapor supplied to the stripper; includes fixed charges, cost of cooling water, and cost of steam
y_1/y_2 = optimum ratio of solute mole fractions in gas stream flowing through absorber; cf. Column Height (Exit-gas Strength), p. 14-32
θ = hr. operation/year
G_M = molal gas velocity through absorber, lb.-moles/(hr.)(sq. ft.)
r = (actual reflux ratio in distillation column) ÷ (minimum reflux ratio, defined as ratio of reflux to product)
n = exponent in the relation $H_{OG} \sim (G/L)^n$

In deriving this equation, it is assumed that the distillation column produces essentially pure solute as an overhead product and that essentially no solute is withdrawn from the base of the distillation column and returned to the absorber with the stripped solvent.

Example 5. Estimate the optimum value of mG_M/L_M for an absorber to recover acetone vapor from air by water absorption followed by stripping with open steam. In order to simplify the calculation, neglect the temperature rise of the liquid in the absorption column, making $m_2 = K_1$ in Eq. (14-79). The following data are assumed: C_3 = \$4.35/(cu. ft.)(year); C_5 = \$0.0108/lb.-mole (30¢/1000 lb. or \$0.0054/lb.-mole for steam, times 2, an assumed ratio of total distillation cost to steam cost); $r = 1.25$; G_M = 25.4 lb.-moles air/(hr.)(sq. ft.); θ = 8400 hr./year of operation; H_{OG} = 2.5 ft.; $n = 0.5$; $m_2 = K_1 = 2.7$; $K_D = 23$; $(y_1/y_2)_{\text{opt}} = 435$. Solution of Eq. (14-79) is made by trial and error, assuming $mG_M/L_M = 0.7$ as a first approximation. Substituting in Eq. (14-79*a*),

$$B = [1 + (0.5)(1.43 - 1)]2.3 \log_{10}\left[435\frac{(1-0.7)^2}{1-0.7}\right] - \frac{(1-0.7) - 2(1-1)}{1-0.7}$$

$$= 4.91$$

$$\left(\frac{L_M}{mG_M} - 1\right)^2 = \frac{(4.91)(4.35)(2.5)(23-1)}{(0.0108)(8400)(1.25)(25.4)(2.7)} = 0.151$$

$$\frac{mG_M}{L_M} = 0.720$$

A second trial, using $mG_M/L_M = 0.72$ in the right-hand side of Eq. (14-79), gives $mG_M/L_M = 0.724$.

Column Diameter (or Gas Velocity). Gas velocity is selected by considering first the safe operating velocity with respect to flooding, and second the optimum velocity calculated by an economic balance between column cost and power cost. Data on flooding velocities are given on p. 18-26. Design is usually for not greater than 60 per cent of flooding; this allows for temporary fluctuations and for a possible future increase in the load on the unit. Furthermore, since flooding of a column is serious and might lead to a shutdown of operations, a liberal margin of safety is desirable.

After checking on a safe velocity with respect to flooding, it is desirable to run an **economic balance of column cost vs. power cost.** Inasmuch as column cross-sectional area varies inversely as the velocity whereas power cost for moving gas through the packing varies approximately as the cube of the velocity, there is a reasonably sharp optimum point.

Pressure drop through the column at constant liquid-gas ratio can be expressed as

$$\Delta P = \frac{b'G^s}{\rho} \tag{14-80}$$

where ΔP = pressure drop per unit cross section and unit height, G = mass velocity, and ρ = gas density. The annual cost of power becomes, per unit weight of gas through-put and per unit height, $C_2'\theta b'G^s/\rho^2$, where C_2' = cost of delivered energy, \$/ft.-lb., and θ = hr./year operation. The annual cost of column per unit gas through-put and per unit height is C_1/G, where C_1 = annual cost of packing and shell, \$/(year)(cu. ft.). Adding these values and solving for the velocity giving a minimum cost gives

$$G_{\text{opt}} = \left(\frac{C_1\rho^2}{sC_2'\theta b'}\right)^{1/(s+1)} \tag{14-81}$$

Often slope s is close to 2, under which conditions

$$G_{\text{opt}} = \left(\frac{C_1\rho^2}{2C_2'\theta b'}\right)^{1/3} \tag{14-82}$$

A more convenient expression of this equation is

$$G_{\text{opt}} = 2680\phi^{2/3}\left(\frac{C_1}{C_2\theta b}\right)^{1/3} \tag{14-83}$$

where $\phi = (\rho/0.075)^{1/2}$; C_2 = cost of delivered energy, \$/kw.-hr.; and b = pressure drop, in. H_2O/ft. height at G/ϕ = 1000 lb./(hr.)(sq. ft.). Note that b may be an extrapolated value. Pressure-drop data are summarized on p. 18-26.

If the column operates at the economic gas velocity, the total annual cost per transfer unit and per hourly pound of gas through-put is

$$\text{Cost}/(\text{T.U.})(\text{lb./hr.}) = \frac{1.5H_{OG}C_1^{2/3}(C_2\theta b)^{1/3}}{2680\phi^{2/3}} \tag{14-84}$$

which shows that the cost of a given operation varies directly as the value of H_{OG}, is slightly less sensitive to the unit investment charge, and varies only slightly as the annual cost of energy is varied.

Note that flooding velocity and optimum velocity are both related to the pressure drop. It is therefore appropriate that, for many packings, the two velocities are of the same order.

At the economic velocity according to Eq. (14-82) or (14-83), the annual cost of energy per cubic foot turns out to be approximately ½ of C_1, so that the total annual cost of column and energy C_3 in dollars per cubic foot becomes equal to 1.5 C_1.

Example 6. Assume a column will be packed with 1-in. Raschig rings, for which b = 1.0 in. H_2O/ft. at G/ϕ = 1000 lb./(hr.)(sq. ft.). [This quantity depends somewhat on the liquid rate, so that a cut-and-try computation is needed. The figure given applies at $L \approx 2000$ lb./(hr.)(sq. ft.).] Taking C_1 = \$2.90/(cu. ft.) (year), C_2 = \$0.017/kw.-hr., θ = 8400 hr./year, and $\phi = 1$ (corresponding to a gas stream principally air at atmospheric pressure), Eq. (14-83) gives G_{opt} = 736 lb./(hr.)(sq. ft.). Since $mG_M/L_M \approx 0.7$, $L \approx (18)(736)(2.7/0.7)(29)$ = 1760 lb./(hr.)(sq. ft.), in close enough agreement with the initial assumption leading to b. (The value of $m = 2.7$ is that for acetone in water at room temperature.) The annual cost of fixed charges plus power to overcome pressure drop is C_3 = (1.5)(2.90) = \$4.35/(cu. ft.)(year) if the gas velocity chosen is G = 736. Since the flooding velocity is about 1250 (lb./(hr.)(sq. ft.), operation at the economic optimum velocity is satisfactory.

Column Height (Exit-gas Strength). At a given value of mG_M/L_M, the required column height is dependent upon the value chosen for the exit-gas strength. The latter quantity may be determined by an **economic balance between the cost of lost solute and the cost of additional column height.**

The annual cost of solute loss per unit cross-sectional area of column can be represented as $C_4\theta G_M y_2$, and the annual cost of column and pressure drop as $C_3H_{OG}N_{OG}$. Substituting for N_{OG} in terms of mG_M/L_M, y_1, and y_2 and solving for the value of exit-gas strength y_2 at which the sum of the costs is a minimum, there results, approximately,

$$y_2 - mx_2 = \frac{C_3H_{OG}}{C_4\theta G_M(1 - mG_M/L_M)} \tag{14-85}$$

for packed towers, where C_3 = annual cost of apparatus and energy for pressure drop, \$/(year)(cu. ft.); C_4 = value of solute at its concentration in the exit liquor, \$/lb.-mole of solute; θ = hr./year operation.

A similar result for plate columns is

$$y_2 - mx_2 = \frac{C_6}{C_4\theta G_M E(2.3 \log L_M/mG_M)} \tag{14-86}$$

where C_6 = annual cost of column and pressure drop, \$/(year)(plate)(sq. ft.), and E = over-all plate efficiency, fractional. Tiller [*Trans. Am. Inst. Chem. Engrs.*, **40**, 331 (1944)] gives an equivalent equation for the optimum number of plates in an absorber.

Optimum exit-liquor strength for a stripping column depends on a balance between the cost of lost solute in the exit liquor and the cost of additional tower height required for more stripping. Equations analogous to those for exit-gas strength in absorption are

$$\left(x_2 - \frac{y_2}{m}\right)_{\text{opt}} = \frac{C_3 H_{OL}}{C_4 L_M \theta (1 - L_M/mG_M)} \qquad (14\text{-}87)$$

for a packed column, and

$$\left(x_2 - \frac{y_2}{m}\right)_{\text{opt}} = \frac{C_6}{C_4 L_M \theta E \ln (mG_M/L_M)} \qquad (14\text{-}88)$$

for a plate column. In these equations, C_3 = annual cost of apparatus (amortization and depreciation of column and packing) and power, \$/(cu. ft.)(year); C_6 = annual cost of apparatus and power, \$/(year)(plate)(sq. ft. of cross section); C_4 = value of solute at concentration of exist gas, \$/lb.-mole of pure solute; E = over-all plate efficiency, fractional; H_{OL} = over-all H.T.U. based on liquid-phase driving force, ft.; θ = hr./year of operation; L_M and G_M = molar velocities, lb.-moles/(hr.)(sq. ft.); m = slope of equilibrium curve y^*/x at dilute end of stripper.

Example 7. Assume a column of 1-in. Raschig rings will be used to remove acetone from air. H.T.U. is estimated to be 2.3 ft., the value of recovered acetone at its low concentration in the stripper feed is \$3.70/lb.-mole, and other quantities will be as in the previous examples. For these conditions $(y_2)_{\text{opt.}}$ = (4.35)(2.3)/(3.70)(8400)(25.4)(1 − 0.724) = 0.000046 mole fraction, assuming that the fresh liquid feed to the absorber is completely stripped (x_2 = 0).

Column Pressure. In some applications the gas is compressed before it is fed to the absorber, thus increasing its solubility and increasing the allowable gas mass velocity through the unit. These gains are of course obtained at the expense of the cost of compression. Frequently the absorber pressure will be set by requirements of other steps in the process, when the optimum pressure can be found only by considering alternate detailed designs.

Absorber Liquid-feed Temperature. Continuous operation of an absorber-stripper combination such as that shown in Fig. 14-19 requires that a heat exchanger be used to recover heat from the stripper effluent before it is returned to the absorber. This stream is frequently cooled still further either by a second exchanger before it enters the absorber or by intercoolers through which it is diverted after it has passed part way down the absorber and consequently has been warmed by the heat of solution of the solute. Cooling the liquid increases the solubility of the solute (decreases m) and thereby decreases the liquid rate required. The economic balance is between the saving in stripper cost at the lower liquid flows and the cost of the additional heat-exchange equipment. Optimum conditions are best found by comparing alternate complete designs.

Optimum Conditions for Multicomponent Systems. The simplified equations presented above can be only rough guides to optimum design conditions when several solutes are being recovered or when the recovery of an important component of the gas is not nearly complete. In such cases detailed computations have to be made for alternate designs. However, optimum gas velocity will be nearly that given by Eq. (14-83) and optimum ratio of gas flow to liquid flow will be such that the operating line is nearly parallel to the equilibrium line for the most volatile component that it is desired to recover nearly completely.

Non-isothermal Absorption

Computation of tower dimensions and required flows is straightforward when heat effects can be neglected, as indicated above. However, when temperature of the liquid stream varies from point to point in the absorber, owing to heat of solution of the solutes, heat of vaporization of the solvent, or to sensible heat exchange between gas and liquid phases, the problem is more difficult. Computations have to be made differentially from point to point through the absorber if they are to be precise, because solubility of the solute depends on the temperature and the driving force cannot be found until the temperature profile is known. If the temperature changes are not large, however, approximate procedures may suffice.

Mild Heat Effects. Principal object of considering heat effects is to fix the equilibrium line, which depends on liquid temperatures. Mild effects can be allowed for on the basis of estimated liquid temperatures at the top and bottom of the absorber. The former is fixed by external considerations (available cooling capacity applied to the liquid-feed circuit, for example), and the latter can be estimated from an energy balance around the whole absorber. These temperatures fix the gas solubilities at the ends of the absorber. Thus they determine the slope of the equilibrium curve at the inlet-liquid composition and a point on the curve at the proposed exit-liquid composition. If an approximate equilibrium line can be drawn through the end points without very much curvature it may reasonably be assumed that driving forces are correct.

Example 8. Consider the absorption of acetone from air at atmospheric pressure in pure water fed to a packed absorber at 25°C. Inlet gas at 35°C. contains 2 per cent by volume acetone and is 70 per cent saturated with water vapor (4 per cent H_2O by volume). Mole fraction acetone in the exit gas is to be reduced to 1/400 the inlet value. Per 100 lb.-moles of feed-gas mixture, how many pound-moles of fresh water should be fed to provide a positive driving force throughout the packing? How many transfer units will be needed?

Differential heat of solution of acetone vapor in pure water = 2500 p.c.u./lb.-mole acetone, where p.c.u. = pound-centigrade unit = 1.8 B.t.u. Latent heats at 25°C. are 7220 p.c.u./lb.-mole for acetone and 10,490 for water. Specific heat of air = 7.0 p.c.u./(lb.-mole)(°C.). Solubilities are given as a function of temperature by the following table:

t, °C.	25	30	35	40
γ_1, activity coefficient for acetone	6.7	7.1	7.5	7.8
P_1, vapor pressure of pure acetone, mm. Hg	229	283	346	421
$m = \frac{y^*}{x} = \gamma_1 \frac{P_1}{P}$	2.02	2.64	3.41	4.33

Solution. Relative to dry gas and liquid water at 25°C., the following enthalpies are computed for the inlet- and exit-gas streams (basis = 100 lb.-moles gas entering).

Entering gas:

Acetone, 2(2500 + 7220) = 19,440 p.c.u.
Water vapor, (4)(10,490) = 41,960
Sensible heat, (100)(7.0)(35 − 25) = 7,000
68,400 p.c.u.

Exit gas (assumed saturated with water at 25°C.):

Acetone, (2/400)(98/100)(2500) = 12 p.c.u.

$$\text{Water vapor, } 94\left(\frac{23.7}{760 - 23.7}\right)(10{,}490) = 31{,}600$$

31,600 p.c.u.

Enthalpy change of liquid = 68,400 − 31,600 = 36,800 p.c.u.

Δ = temperature rise of liquid = $36{,}800/18L_M$

$$L_M = \frac{36{,}800}{18\Delta}$$

Δ, °C.	Δ_1, °C.	L_M	$m_1 = y_1^*/x_1$	m_1G_M/L_M	m_2G_M/L_M
0	25	....	2.02	0	0
2	27	1022	2.26	0.221	0.198
3	28	681	2.39	0.351	0.297
4	29	511	2.51	0.492	0.398
5	30	409	2.64	0.645	0.494
6	31	341	2.78	0.815	0.592
7	32	292	2.93	1.002	0.692

Evidently Δ = 6°C. will give an operable absorber, *i.e.*, one having a positive driving force from gas to liquid at all points. Δ = 7°C. is a barely inoperable condition because the equilibrium line touches the operating line. Figure 14-20 shows

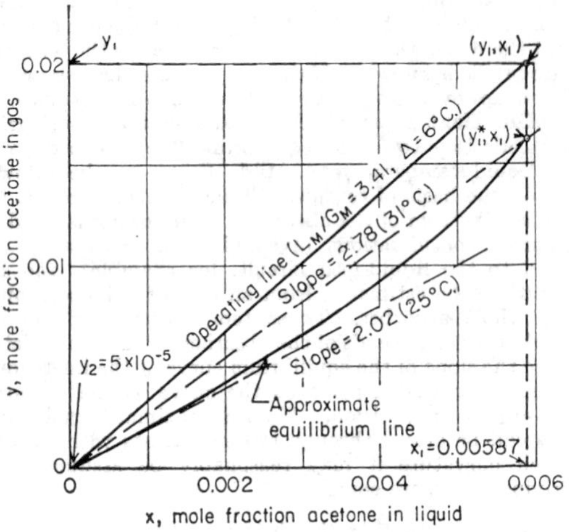

FIG. 14-20. Operating and equilibrium lines in adiabatic acetone absorber, Example 8.

operating and equilibrium lines for L_M = 341 lb.-mole, the latter being drawn with a French curve so that it has the right slope at the origin and passes through a point corresponding to $x_1 = 0.02(^{100}/_{341}) = 0.00587$ mole fraction and $y_1 = 0.02$.

The number of transfer units can be computed from the integral formula, but a quicker method is to use a formula derived by Colburn [*Trans. Am. Inst. Chem. Engrs.*, **35**, 211 (1939)] on the assumption that the equilibrium line is a parabolic arc having a slope m_2 at the bottom end and passing through the point (x_1, m_1x_1) at the upper end:

$$N_{OG} = \frac{1}{1 - (m_2G_M/L_M)} \ln \left\{ \frac{[1 - (m_2G_M/L_M)]^2}{1 - (m_1G_M/L_M)} \frac{y_1 - m_2x_2}{y_2 - m_2x_2} + \frac{m_2G_M}{L_M} \right\} \quad (14\text{-}89)$$

In the present instance

$$N_{OG} = \frac{1}{1 - 0.592} \ln \left[\frac{(1 - 0.592)^2}{1 - 0.815} (400) + 0.592 \right] = 14.4$$

Note that Eq. (14-89) allows for curvature of the equilibrium line in the middle range of x. Erroneous use of the logarithmic mean of the terminal values of $y - y^*$, equal to 0.000843 mole fraction units, gives $N_{OG} = (y_1 - y_2)/\Delta y_{lm} = 23.8$ and leads to an overestimate of the packed height needed.

Large Heat Effects. When the solute has a large heat of solution and when it is sometimes desired to treat feed gases containing high percentages of the solute, as in the absorption of hydrogen chloride in water, the effects of heat release during absorption may be pronounced. In such situations the **requirement of heat-transfer surface to remove the heat** of absorption of the solute may be as important as the requirement of providing enough interface for the mass-transfer process. Although it is possible to operate such absorbers under adiabatic conditions, it is frequently preferable to employ a shell-and-tube heat exchanger as a cooled, wetted-wall-column absorber, removing the exothermic heat of absorption as it is released into the thin film of acidic liquid on the inside surface of the tubes.

Oldershaw, Simenson, Brown, and Radcliff [*Chem. Eng. Progress*, **43**, 371 (1947)] reported test data from the operation of both adiabatic and cooled absorbers used to remove HCl from inert gases. The heat of absorption in the **adiabatic tower** caused the liquid effluent to be much warmer than the feed water. In some of the runs it was also warmer than the inlet gas. Furthermore, the exit gas was also at a substantially higher temperature than the feed water. In other words, the temperature differences between gas and liquid streams were in opposite directions at the top and the bottom of the column. As the gas flows into such an absorber it begins to warm as it flows upward in contact with the warmer liquid. Before it leaves, however, its temperature starts to fall because it is in contact with cooler liquid. Consequently, the gas temperature goes through a maximum inside the column. Furthermore, at the point where the gas is at its maximum temperature the liquid must be at the same temperature, for with any temperature difference at all the gas temperature could not remain constant. These are the conditions of a **hot spot** in the absorber, a situation that can be avoided only by removing heat within the absorber itself.

Quantitative Allowance for Heat Effects. The true calculation of the depth of packing needed for an absorber handling HCl gas requires a knowledge of the internal liquid temperatures in order to locate the equilibrium line correctly. These temperatures depend on the rates of absorption of HCl, the rates of evaporation of H_2O, and the rate of sensible heat transfer. Although these rates can be calculated, an **approximate empirical equation** developed by Gaylord and Miranda [*Chem. Eng. Progress*, **53**, 139 (1957)] may be employed if the absorber is of the wetted-wall heat-exchanger type.

Object of calculations of heat effects in the design of absorbers is to locate the equilibrium and operating lines. Once these are determined, computation of the number of transfer units required is straightforward. The equilibrium line cannot be located precisely until the temperature is known at each value of liquid composition, although when the heat effects are slight it can be placed approximately with only a knowledge of inlet- and exit-liquid temperatures, as indicated on p. 14-33.

Precise quantitative computation of large heat effects on liquid temperatures is beyond the scope of this handbook (see Sherwood and Pigford, "Absorption and Extraction," pp. 158–172, McGraw-Hill, New York, 1952).

GAS-ABSORPTION RATES

Packed Towers. If reliable data on H_{OG} or H_{OL} are available for the system involved under the desired conditions of operation, these should be applied to the problem at hand. Table 14-52 lists experimental studies on a diversity of absorption systems as recorded in the literature. Use of **experimental values** is particularly important in the case of absorption or desorption occurring simultaneously with chemical reaction, since prediction methods are not well developed for these cases. Table 14-53 lists some experimental studies on simultaneous absorption (or desorption) and reaction systems. Particular attention must be given for reaction systems to using the same driving-force definition as was employed in obtaining experimental H.T.U.'s.

Table 14-52. Data on Mass-transfer Rates in Packed Absorbers

Solute	Solvent	Packing type	Tower diam., in.	Ref.
Acetone	Water	Raschig rings	9⅞	39
Acetone	Water	Raschig rings	6	58
Acetone	Water	Raschig rings	6, 10	26
Acetone	Water	Raschig rings	12	25
Acetone	Water	Raschig rings	4	44
Acetone	Water	Berl saddles	12	58
Acetone	Water	Stedman triangles	6	53
Ammonia	Water	Raschig rings	10	46
Ammonia	Water	Raschig rings	18	17
Ammonia	Water	Raschig rings	12	12, 25
Ammonia	Water	Carbon Raschig rings	...	7, 14
Ammonia	Water	Berl saddles	18	17
Ammonia	Water	Spiral rings	16	33
Ammonia	Water	Spheres	3,6, 11	7
Ammonia	Water	Drip-point grid	12	41
Ammonia	Water	Glass fibers	6	56
Benzene	Kerosene	Berl saddles	12	22
Carbon dioxide	Water	Raschig rings	5	18
Carbon dioxide	Water	Raschig rings	4.5	57
Carbon dioxide	Methanol	Raschig rings	4.5	57
Carbon dioxide	Water	Raschig rings	6, 8	30
Carbon dioxide	Water	Raschig rings	9.7	48
Carbon dioxide	Water	Raschig rings	6	13
Carbon dioxide	Water	Steel Raschig rings	30 (square)	11
Carbon dioxide	Water	Raschig rings	20	47
Carbon dioxide	Water	Berl saddles	4.5	57
Carbon dioxide	Methanol	Berl saddles	4.5	57
Carbon dioxide	Water	Berl saddles	5	18
Carbon dioxide	Water	Berl saddles	20	47
Carbon dioxide	Water	Spheres	4.5	57
Carbon dioxide	Methanol	Spheres	4.5	57
Carbon dioxide	Water	Spiral tile	20	47
Chlorine	Water	Coke	6	2
Chloroform	Kerosene	Berl saddles	12	22
Ethanol	Water	Raschig rings	15 (square)	36
Ethanol	Water	Raschig rings	12	25
Ethanol	Water	Berl saddles	15 (square)	36
Ethanol	Water	Drip-point grid	15 (square)	36
Ethylene oxide	Acetone	Raschig rings	1.1	6
Ethylene oxide	Benzene	Raschig rings	1.1	6
Ethylene oxide	Ethanol	Raschig rings	1.1	6
Ethylene oxide	Ethyl acetoacetate	Raschig rings	1.1	6
Hydrogen chloride	Water	Raschig rings	10	38
Hydrogen chloride	Water	Raschig rings	16	38
Hydrogen chloride	Water	Shell-and-tube absorber	....	24
Hydrogen	Water	Raschig rings	20	47
Hydrogen	Water	Berl saddles	20	47
Hydrogen	Water	Spiral tile	20	47
Methanol	Water	Raschig rings	6	58
Methanol	Water	Berl saddles	12	58
Methanol	Water	Raschig rings	12	25
Methyl ethyl ketone	Water	Raschig rings	4	44
Methyl *i*-butyl ketone	Water	Raschig rings	4	44
Methyl *n*-amyl ketone	Water	Raschig rings	4	44
Oxygen	Water	Raschig rings	20	47
Oxygen	Water	Raschig rings	6	13
Oxygen	Water	Raschig rings	4, 14	52
Oxygen	Water	Raschig rings	8	55
Oxygen	Water	Raschig rings	15 (square)	35
Oxygen	Water	Berl saddles	20	47
Oxygen	Water	Berl saddles	15 (square)	35
Oxygen	Water	Spiral tile	20	47
Oxygen	Water	Single spiral tile	15 (square)	35
Oxygen	Water	Triple spiral tile	15 (square)	35
Oxygen	Water	Partition tile	15 (square)	35
Oxygen	Water	Stedman triangles	6	29
Phosphoric acid (mist)	Water	Coke	21	3
Sulfur dioxide	Water	Raschig rings	12	42
Sulfur dioxide	Water	Raschig rings	4	42
Sulfur dioxide	Water	Raschig rings	6	27
Sulfur dioxide	Water	Spiral rings	18	1
Sulfur dioxide	Water	Spiral rings	8	23
Sulfur dioxide	Water	Coke	8	23
Sulfur dioxide	Water	....	8	40
Trichloroethylene	Kerosene	Berl saddles	12	22

When no over-all H.T.U. data are available, values of the individual resistances H_G and H_L may be estimated, based on the **general correlations** given in Sec. 18 (pp. 18-35 to 18-39). These resistances may then be combined by use of Eqs. (14-50) and (14-51). In these equations, the factors $(1 - x)_f$ and $(1 - y)_f$ account for the diffusion of one liquid or gas through a second stagnant liquid or gas. They are unimportant for the case of a dilute gas stream, since the mean partial pressure of inerts and the mean concentration of solvent do not change significantly.

In general, resistance in the gas phase is found to be of primary importance for highly soluble gases; and resistance in the liquid phase, for slightly soluble gases. Table 14-54 indicates the **source of the primary resistance** for some common systems. Under certain circumstances, these systems may fall into categories other than those indicated. For example, H_2S-alkali can be gas-phase-controlled if the H_2S is dilute. Also, some gas-phase influence may exist for CO_2-alkali if the CO_2 is very dilute, or even for CO_2-H_2O if, as in commercial practice, the liquid-to-gas ratio is high.

When Chemical Reaction Accompanies Absorption. When a rapid, irreversible chemical reaction occurs in the liquid phase, the rate of absorption may be governed only by the **resistance of the gas phase** to mass transfer. In such an instance, the mass-transfer rate may be estimated using the methods for obtaining H_G. Such a situation would exist, for instance, for the case of NH_3 absorption in acid solution, SO_2 absorption in alkali solution, and H_2S absorption from a dilute gas stream into strong alkali solution, as long as there is adequate reagent in the liquid to consume rapidly all the dissolved gas. Moreover, calculation of the tower height becomes relatively simple, since the equilibrium back pressure of the gas over the solvent is zero. Even if the reaction is sufficiently reversible to allow a small back pressure, the absorption may be gas-phase-controlled, and the value of H_G that would apply to a physical absorption process governs the rate.

Frequently, however, even though reaction consumes the solute as it is dissolving, enhancing both the mass-transfer coefficient and the driving force for absorption, the reaction rate is slow enough that liquid-phase resistance may be of some importance. This may be due either to an insufficient supply of reagent or to an inherently slow reaction. In fact, in some of the most important industrial systems (CO_2 absorption in alkaline solutions), **liquid-phase diffusion is controlling.** Table 14-55 compares absorption coefficients for the absorption of CO_2 in different liquids, showing that only for the most concentrated caustic solutions is the influence of the gas-phase resistance even noticeable. Unfortunately, generalized prediction methods for H_L are unsuitable when chemical reaction occurs in the liquid phase, and reliance must be placed on **operating data for the system** in question. In reaction systems, mass-transfer rates are dependent not only on the usual operating variables but strongly on such factors as reagent concentration and temperature as well. Presentation of available data on a comprehensive basis is thus not possible. Specific data in Sec. 18 (pp. 18-40 to 18-49) and references listed in Table 14-53, dealing with some systems of commercial importance, should be consulted.

Where liquid-phase resistance is important, particular care should be taken in employing any specific set of data that the equilibrium data used conform with those used by the author to calculate transfer coefficients (or H.T.U.'s). Furthermore, extrapolation to widely different concentration ranges should be made with caution, since the mass-transfer coefficient may vary in an unexpected fashion. This phenomenon arises from the fact that the coefficient itself can be strongly altered by a reaction which changes the concentration gradients near the interface (see p. 14-15). In some cases (such as CO_2-monoethanolamine), the reaction which alters the coefficient may be a fast one, while the ultimate equilib-

Table 14-53. Data on Mass-transfer Rates with Chemical Reaction in Packed Absorbers

Solute	Solvent	Reagent	Packing type	Tower diam., in.	Ref.
Acetylenes........	Water	Copper ammonium acetate	Raschig rings	6, 8	37
Ammonia..........	Water	Acetic acid	Wood grids	....	28
Carbon dioxide......	Water	Potassium hydroxide	Raschig rings	2.8, 4	5
Carbon dioxide......	Water	Sodium hydroxide	Raschig rings	8	20, 34
Carbon dioxide......	Water	Sodium hydroxide	Raschig rings	2.8, 4	5
Carbon dioxide......	Water	Sodium hydroxide	Raschig rings	6	51
Carbon dioxide......	Water	Sodium hydroxide	....		49
Carbon dioxide......	Water	Sodium hydroxide	Berl saddles	8	34
Carbon dioxide......	Water	Sodium hydroxide	Intalox saddles	8	34
Carbon dioxide......	Water	Sodium hydroxide	Pall rings	30	16
Carbon dioxide......	Water	Sodium hydroxide	Lessing rings	8	20
Carbon dioxide......	Water	Hot potassium carbonate	Raschig rings	6, 8	4
Carbon dioxide......	Water	Hot potassium carbonate	....	Commercial plant	8
Carbon dioxide......	Water	Potassium carbonate	Raschig rings	3	10
Carbon dioxide......	Water	Sodium carbonate	Raschig rings	2.8, 4	5
Carbon dioxide......	Water	Sodium carbonate	Raschig rings and Berl saddles	12	19
Carbon dioxide......	Water	Sodium carbonate	Raschig rings	3	10
Carbon dioxide......	Water	Monoethanolamine	....	....	31
Carbon dioxide......	Water	Monoethanolamine	....	2, 4	32
Carbon dioxide......	Water	Monoethanolamine	Raschig rings	12	21
Carbon dioxide......	Water	Monoethanolamine	Steel Raschig rings	8	50
Carbon dioxide......	Water	Monoethanolamine	Berl saddles	8	50
Carbon dioxide......	Water	Monoethanolamine	Tellerettes	8	50
Carbon dioxide......	Water	Diethanolamine	Raschig rings	8	12
Carbon dioxide......	Water	Diamino *i*-propanol	Raschig rings	12	21
Chlorine	Water	Ferrous sulfate	Raschig rings	6	43
Sulfur dioxide......	Water	Sodium hydroxide	Spiral rings	....	28
Sulfur dioxide......	Water	Sodium hydroxide	Wood grids	....	28
Sulfur dioxide......	Water	Sodium hydroxide	Raschig rings	....	28
Sulfur dioxide......	Water	Sodium carbonate	Raschig rings	4	54
Diolefins.........	Water	Copper ammonium acetate	Raschig rings	6, 8	37
Ethylene.........	Water	Cuprous chloride (acidic)	Raschig rings	3	45
Olefins...........	Water	Copper ammonium acetate	Raschig rings	6, 8	37

References for Tables 14-52 and 14-53
1 Adams, *Ind. Eng. Chem.*, **25**, 424 (1933).
2 Adams and Edmonds, *Ind. Eng. Chem.*, **29**, 447 (1937).
3 Baskewill, *Trans. Am. Inst. Chem. Engrs.*, **37**, 79 (1941).
4 Benson, Field, and Haynes, *Chem. Eng. Progress*, **52**, 433 (1956).
5 Blum, Stutzman, and Dodds, *Ind. Eng. Chem.*, **44**, 2969 (1952).
6 Bonilla and Baron, *Am. Inst. Chem. Engrs. J.*, **1**, 49 (1955).
7 Bordon and Squires, *cf.* Sherwood and Holloway (Ref. 46).
8 Buck and Leitch, *Petrol. Refiner*, **37**, 241 (November, 1958).
9 Chilton, Duffey, and Vernon, *Ind. Eng. Chem.*, **29**, 298 (1937).
10 Comstock and Dodge, *Ind. Eng. Chem.*, **29**, 520 (1937).
11 Cooper, Christl, and Perry, *Trans. Am. Inst. Chem. Engrs.*, **37**, 979 (1941).
12 Cryder and Maloney, *Trans. Am. Inst. Chem. Engrs.*, **37**, 827 (1941).
13 Deed, Schutz, and Drew, *Ind. Eng. Chem.*, **39**, 766 (1947).
14 Dougherty and Johnson, *cf.* Sherwood and Holloway (Ref. 46).
15 Dwyer and Dodge, *Ind. Eng. Chem.*, **33**, 485 (1941).
16 Eckert, Foote, and Huntington, *Chem. Eng. Progress*, **54**, 70 (1958).
17 Fellinger, Sc.D. Thesis in Chemical Engineering, M.I.T., 1941.
18 Fujita and Hayakawa, *Chem. Eng. (Japan)*, **20**, 113 (1956).
19 Furnas and Bellinger, *Trans. Am. Inst. Chem. Engrs.*, **34**, 251 (1938).
20 Greenwood and Pearce, *Trans. Am. Inst. Chem. Engrs.*, **31**, 201 (1953).
21 Gregory and Scharmann, *Ind. Eng. Chem.*, **29**, 514 (1937).
22 Gross and Simmons, *Trans. Am. Inst. Chem. Engrs.*, **40**, 121 (1940).
23 Haslam, Ryan, and Weber, *Trans. Am. Inst. Chem. Engrs.*, **15**, 177 (1923).
24 Hatfield and Ford, *Trans. Am. Inst. Chem. Engrs.*, **42**, 121 (1946).
25 Houston and Walker, *Ind. Eng. Chem.*, **42**, 1105 (1950).
26 Hutchings, Stutzman, and Koch, *Chem. Eng. Progress*, **45**, 253 (1949).
27 Jennes and Caulfield, *Paper Trade J.*, **109** (26), 37 (1939).
28 Johnstone and Singh, *Ind. Eng. Chem.*, **29**, 286 (1937).
29 Knoedler and Bonilla, *Chem. Eng. Progress*, **50**, 125 (1954).
30 Koch, Stutzman, Blum, and Hutchings, *Chem. Eng. Progress*, **45**, 677 (1949).
31 Kohl, *Am. Inst. Chem. Engrs. J.*, **2**, 264 (1956).
32 Kondo and Fukuba, *Chem. Eng. (Japan)*, **22**, 610 (1958).
33 Kowalke, Hougen, and Watson, *Univ. Wis. Eng. Expt. Sta. Bull.* 68, June, 1925.
34 Leva, *Am. Inst. Chem. Engrs. J.*, **1**, 224 (1955).
35 Molstad, Abbey, Thompson, and McKinney, *Trans. Am. Inst. Chem. Engrs.*, **38**, 410 (1942).
36 Molstad and Parsley, *Chem. Eng. Progress*, **46**, 20 (1950).
37 Morris *et al.*, *Trans. Am. Inst. Chem. Engrs.*, **42**, 473 (1946).
38 Oldershaw, Simenson, Brown, and Radcliffe, *Chem. Eng. Progress*, **43**, 371 (1947).
39 Othmer and Scheibel, *Trans. Am. Inst. Chem. Engrs.*, **37**, 211 (1941).
40 Parkison, *Tappi*, **39**, 522 (1956).
41 Parsley, Molstad, Cress, and Bauer, *Chem. Eng. Progress*, **46**, 17 (1950).
42 Pearson, Lundberg, West, and McCarthy, *Chem. Eng. Progress*, **47**, 257 (1951).
43 Riggle and Tepe, *Ind. Eng. Chem.*, **42**, 1036 (1950).
44 Scheibel and Othmer, *Trans. Am. Inst. Chem. Engrs.*, **40**, 611 (1944).
45 Seebold and Gilliland, *Ind. Eng. Chem.*, **33**, 1143 (1941).
46 Sherwood and Holloway, *Trans. Am. Inst. Chem. Engrs.*, **36**, 21 (1940).
47 Sherwood and Holloway, *Trans. Am. Inst. Chem. Engrs.*, **36**, 39 (1940).
48 Shulman and DeGouff, *Ind. Eng. Chem.*, **44**, 1915 (1952).
49 Spector and Dodge, *Trans. Am. Inst. Chem. Engrs.*, **42**, 827 (1946).
50 Teller and Ford, *Ind. Eng. Chem.*, **50**, 1201 (1958).
51 Tepe and Dodge, *Trans. Am. Inst. Chem. Engrs.*, **39**, 255 (1943).
52 Vivian and Whitney, *Chem. Eng. Progress*, **43**, 691 (1947).
53 White and Othmer, *Trans. Am. Inst. Chem. Engrs.*, **38**, 1067 (1942).
54 Whitney, Han, and Davis, *Tappi*, **36**, 172 (1953).
55 Whitney and Vivian, *Chem. Eng. Progress*, **45**, 323 (1949).
56 Williams, Akell, and Talbott, *Chem. Eng. Progress*, **43**, 558 (1947).
57 Yoshida and Koyanagi, *Ind. Eng. Chem.*, **50**, 365 (1958).
58 Zabban and Dodge, *Chem. Eng. Progress, Symp. Ser.*, **50** (10), 61 (1954).

rium may be fixed by a slower subsequent reaction. Thus the proper driving force to be employed is that based on the concentration of dissolved, but unreacted, solute, and the coefficient to be used with that driving force is the physical coefficient suitably enhanced by the effect of the initial rapid reaction (see Figs. 14-7 through 14-11). Extrapolation to other concentrations would then be feasible with such a coefficient. It is customary, however, to report coefficients based on the concentration of total dissolved gas (part of which is reacted). Prediction of coefficients at concentrations other than those at which they have been measured is less certain.

A better understanding of the effect of chemical reaction on liquid-phase mass-transfer coefficients in packed towers is possible through the efforts of Danckwerts and Kennedy [*Trans. Inst. Chem. Engrs. (London), Supplement*, **32**, S49, S53 (1954)], who assessed carefully conducted experiments on the basis of unsteady-state reaction-absorption theory (p. 14-15). Their assessment tests the applicability of the penetration theory

Table 14-54. Source of Major Resistance to Mass Transfer for Some Common Systems

Liquid phase	Both phases	Gas phase
O_2-H_2O	SO_2-H_2O	NH_3-H_2O
H_2-H_2O	NO_2-H_2SO_4	NH_3-acid
CO_2-H_2O	Acetone-H_2O	SO_2-H_2O
Cl_2-H_2O	H_2S-alkali	SO_2-alkali
CO_2-NaOH		HCl-H_2O
CO_2-amines		H_2O-acid
		H_2O-$CaCl_2$ brine
		Evaporation
		Condensation

Table 14-55. Approximate Absorption Coefficients for CO_2 in Various Solutions

Basis: L = 2500 lb./(hr.)(sq. ft.); G = 300 lb./(hr.)(sq. ft.); T = 25°C. (liquid temperature)

Liquid	K_Ga, lb.-moles/(hr.)(cu. ft.) (unit Δy)	Ref.
Water	0.05	1
1N sodium carbonate, 20% of sodium as bicarbonate	.03	2
3N diethanolamine, 50% conversion to carbonate	.4	3
2N sodium hydroxide, 20% of sodium as carbonate	3.2	4
2N potassium hydroxide, 15% of potassium as carbonate	4.3	5
Approximate maximum value (gas-film coefficient)	24	6

References:
[1] Sherwood and Holloway, *Trans. Am. Inst. Chem. Engrs.*, **36**, 39 (1940).
[2] Furnas and Bellinger, *Trans. Am. Inst. Chem. Engrs.*, **34**, 251 (1938).
[3] Cryder and Maloney, *Trans. Am. Inst. Chem. Engrs.*, **37**, 827 (1941).
[4] Tepe and Dodge, *Trans. Am. Inst. Chem. Engrs.*, **39**, 255 (1943).
[5] Spector and Dodge, *Trans. Am. Inst. Chem. Engrs.*, **42**, 827 (1946).
[6] Sherwood and Holloway, *Trans. Am. Inst. Chem. Engrs.*, **36**, 21 (1940).

(either in terms of the Higbie assumption about liquid residence time or in terms of the Danckwerts surface-replacement assumptions). Danckwerts and Kennedy measured absorption rates of CO_2 into NaOH solutions in a 4-in.-diameter tower packed with 0.5-in. porcelain Raschig rings. In addition, they measured the mass-transfer coefficient without reaction $k_L{}^0a$ by using a non-reactive solution containing enough dissolved salt to give it the same physical properties as the NaOH liquor. It was assumed that the wetted area of the packing was the same in the reaction experiments and in the physical absorption experiments. The ratios of coefficients found by Danckwerts are compared in Fig. 14-21

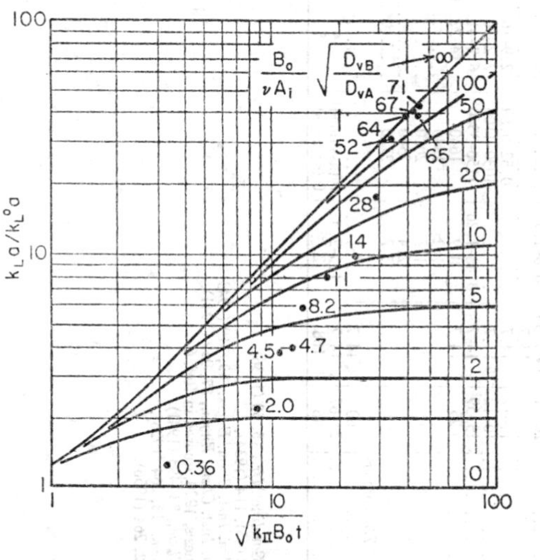

Fig. 14-21. Enhancement of mass-transfer coefficients for absorption of CO_2 in a packed column by employing NaOH. [*Data from Danckwerts and Kennedy, Trans. Inst. Chem. Engrs. (London)*, **32**, 549, 553 (1954).]

with the theory for absorption with second-order irreversible reaction (see Fig. 14-9). The experimental data are seen to be in approximate agreement with the theory. Note that the enhancement of k_La is significant (up to a factor of 40).

Plate Towers. General methods for prediction of plate efficiencies in bubble-cap and sieve-plate towers given in Secs. 13 and 18 may be applied also for gas-absorption or desorption operations. Table 14-56 lists experimental values for some common gas-absorption systems for **bubble-cap trays.**

Sieve trays have found significant use only in recent years, and operating data are not available for many absorption systems. For the case of CO_2 and H_2S absorption and regeneration in hot K_2CO_3 solutions, a substantial quantity of performance data have been presented by Palo and Armstrong [*Petrol. Refiner*, **37** (12), 123 (1958)] and by Buck and Leitch [*Petrol. Refiner*, **37** (11), 241 (1958)]. For this system, sieve trays are reported to be more economical than packed absorbers.

Plate towers are frequently employed for the **absorption of nitrogen oxides** to produce nitric acid, nitrites, or nitrates. These towers function as both reactors and absorbers with the principal reactions being

$$2\,NO_2 \rightleftharpoons N_2O_4 \qquad (a)$$
$$N_2O_4 + H_2O \rightleftharpoons HNO_3 + HNO_2 \qquad (b)$$
$$3\,HNO_2 \rightleftharpoons HNO_3 + 2\,NO + H_2O \qquad (c)$$
$$2\,NO + O_2 \rightleftharpoons 2\,NO_2 \qquad (d)$$

Oxidation of NO (by air or O_2) takes place in the gas space between trays. Reaction (b) is the rate-determining step in the liquid phase [Wendel and Pigford, *Am. Inst. Chem. Engrs. J.*, **4**, 249 (1958)]. Information on plate efficiencies for this important system is not available and, to an extent, would be of limited utility without information on the concentration of N_2O_4 entering each tray. The N_2O_4 concentration depends on reactions (a) and (d) in the vapor phase, as well as on reactions (b) and (c) in the liquid phase. For further information on this system, see Chilton ("The Manufacture of Nitric Acid," American Institute of Chemical Engineers Monograph 3-M, 1960) and Sherwood and Pigford ("Absorption and Extraction," pp. 368–383, McGraw-Hill, New York, 1952).

Spray Towers. The simplest spray absorber consists of an empty tower into which liquid is sprayed at the top and gas is introduced at the bottom. Such a unit has the advantages of very low pressure drop and inexpensive construction. Because of mixing of the gas within the chamber (promoted by entrainment of gas by the sprays) and entrainment of fine spray droplets, spray absorbers are unsuitable where true countercurrent action is needed to obtain a large number of transfer units. Table 14-57 shows a comparison of a spray chamber with a duplicate chamber filled with 2-in. Raschig rings. Although not so effective, a spray chamber closely approaches the performance of a packed tower for very short heights (both for liquid- and gas-phase-controlled systems). Thus where only a few transfer units are needed, spray absorbers may be more economical, particularly when low pressure drop is important.

Calculation procedures for spray towers have not reached the stage where they can be predicted from fundamentals, though certain generalizations have been suggested (see p. 18-53). Table 14-58 lists various studies of simple spray absorbers for further reference.

Cyclone Scrubbers. High gas rates cannot be obtained in simple spray absorbers owing to entrainment. This can be markedly reduced by resorting to cyclone spray devices in which the droplets are thrown to the wall by centrifugal force (owing to their tangential entry) before they are swept out the top of the chamber by the gas stream. Such devices give a cross-flow type of contact, however, so are limited to operations requiring no more than one theoretical stage. For further information see p. 18-54.

Stirred Absorbers. Rates of absorption in stirred vessels are most commonly needed for application to

Table 14-56. Plate Efficiencies for Bubble-tray Absorbers

System	Avg. temp., °C.	Abs. pressure, lb./sq. in.	Avg. liquid, viscosity, cp.	$m = y^*/x$	L_M/G_M	Col. diam., in.	No. plates	Plate spacing, in.	No. caps per plate	Size of caps, in.	Slot area, % of tower cross section	Static seal depth, in.	Range of F factor, (ft./sec.)(lb./cu. ft.)$^{1/2}$	Plate efficiency, % Over-all	Plate efficiency, % Murphree	Ref.
C_1-C_5 in 220 M.W.† oil	38	78	0.81	0.68–0.93 for C_4	1.0	72	21	20	50	6.5	9.8	2	....	18	....	1
C_1-C_6 in 161 M.W. oil	34	485	.42	0.27 for C_4	0.185	...	24	...	...	....	.....	.....	....	49 for n-C_4	....	2
	38	60	.42	....	....	...	10	...	...	....	.....	.....	....	50		
H_2S, C_1-C_5 in 185 M.W. oil	15	92	1.9	0.83–0.94 for C_3	1.16–1.24	108	19	30	92	6.31	8.04	0.75	0.18	26–27 for C_3	....	4
C_1-C_6 in 206 M.W. oil	52	255	0.40	....	0.05	48	24	18	...	....	.....	.....	1.04	42	....	3
C_1-C_6 in 157 M.W. oil	53	260	.41	....	0.25	60	16	30	...	....	.....	.....	1.05	39	....	3
C_1-C_6 in 164 M.W. oil	51	265	.50	....	0.25	60	16	30	...	....	.....	.....	1.24	38	....	3
C_1-C_6 in 201 M.W. oil	49	260	.48	....	0.08	48	24	18	...	....	.....	.....	0.76	36	....	3
C_1-C_6 in 135 M.W. oil	59	267	.22	....	0.4–0.5	60	16	30	...	....	.....	.....	.46	56	....	3
C_1-C_5 in 135 M.W. oil	55	254	.31	....	0.3–0.4	48	24	18	...	....	.....	.....	.49	50	....	3
C_1-C_6 in 250 M.W. oil	47	94	.41	....	0.5	48	24	18	...	....	.....	.....	.88	10	....	3
i-C_4H_8 in heavy naphtha	26	66	.97	0.61	0.45	2	1	...	1	2	10	.75	.6	....	36	6
i-C_4H_8 in gas oil	25–37	66	3.9–5.4	0.65–0.95	0.45	2	1	...	1	2	10	.75	.6	....	17	6
i-C_4H_8 in gas oil + lube oil	24	66	20.6	0.50	0.45	2	1	...	1	2	10	.75	.6	....	9–10	6
C_3H_6 in heavy naphtha	18–43	46–66	0.74–1.10	1.95–3.29	0.47–0.73	2	1	...	1	2	10	.75	.6	....	22–24	6
C_3H_6 in gas oil	24–48	66	2.8–5.8	2.34–3.67	0.52	2	1	...	1	2	10	.75	.6	....	11–13	6
C_3H_6 in gas oil + lube oil	23–41	66	10.5–21.5	1.92–2.70	0.34	2	1	...	1	2	10	.75	.6	....	5–11	6
H_2O evaporation into air	20–31	14.7–55	0.8–1.0	....	....	2	1	...	1	2	10	.75	0.2–0.8	....	85–92	6
NH_3 in water	.....	14.7	....	....	....	...	1	...	5	3	.....	.....	....	....	65–85	5
NH_3 in water	11–17	14.7	....	0.52–0.69	2.9–16	18	1	...	7	4	10.6	.375	0.08–0.46	....	69	6
CO_2 in water	10–12	14.7	....	1030–1100	2.2–16	18	1	...	7	4	10.6	.375	0.08–0.46	....	1.8–2.6	6
CO_2 in water	13–59	14.7	0.48–1.20	1150–3330	6.3–41	5	4	11	1	3.5	15.2	1.5	0.2–1.5	....	1.5–3.5	6
CO_2 in glycerol solution	25	14.7	0.9	1640	14–22	5	4	11	1	3.5	15.2	1.5	0.33	....	2.0	6
			1.2	1840	....	...	...	...	...	....	.....	.....	....	....	1.6	6
			1.7	2080	....	...	...	...	...	....	.....	.....	....	....	0.96	6
			2.4	2340	....	...	...	...	...	....	.....	.....	....	....	0.96	6
			3.7	2720	....	...	...	...	...	....	.....	.....	....	....	0.65	6
CO_2 in Na_2CO_3-HCO_3 solution; Na = 1.7N; conversion to HCO_3 = 35%	60	14.7	....	....	....	...	15	...	1	....	.....	.....	....	....	7	7
CO_2 in MEA (1.5–3.6 moles/liter)	25–67	14.7	1.5–2.0	0 (assumed)	14	48	16	24	15	Rectangular	.....	3	0.2–0.8	....	8–22	8
CO_2 in MEA (2.3 moles/liter)	46	188	2	0 (assumed)	5	48	16	24	15	Rectangular	.....	3	0.5	....	16	8

† M.W. = molecular weight.

References:
[1] Atkins and Franklin, *Refiner Nat. Gasoline Mfr.*, **15**, 30 (1936).
[2] Brown and Souders, *Oil Gas J.*, **32** (45), 114 (1934).
[3] Drickamer and Bradford, *Trans. Am. Inst. Chem. Engrs.*, **39**, 319 (1943).
[4] Sherwood and Jackson, *Trans. Am. Inst. Chem. Engrs.*, **37**, 959 (1941).
[5] Reynolds and Saunders, M.I.T. Thesis, 1920, quoted in Ref. 6.
[6] Walter and Sherwood, *Ind. Eng. Chem.*, **33**, 493 (1941).
[7] Whitman and Davis, *Ind. Eng. Chem.*, **18**, 264 (1926).
[8] Kohl, *Am. Inst. Chem. Engrs. J.*, **2**, 264 (1956).

Table 14-57. Comparison of Spray Chambers and Packed Columns*

G	L	Spray tower	Packed tower, 2-in. rings
52-in. depth of packing		N_L for O_2-H_2O at 30°C.	
450	900	3.6	5.0
450	650	2.7	5.3
450	350	1.5	5.7
26-in. depth of packing			
450	900	2.7	2.5
450	600	2.0	2.7
450	300	1.2	2.9
52-in. depth of packing		N_{OG} for NH_3-H_2O	
500	500	0.7	1.3
800	500	0.6	1.1
500	1000	1.6	2.1
800	1000	1.1	1.7
26-in. depth of packing			
500	500	0.6	0.7
800	500	0.5	0.6
500	1000	1.2	1.0
800	1000	0.9	0.9

* From Sherwood and Pigford, "Absorption and Extraction," McGraw-Hill, New York, 1952.

chemical reactors in which a gas is first absorbed and then reacts with a component in the solution. The feature of long liquid residence time cannot be so easily provided in tower-type absorbers. In general, an agitated absorber also has a slight advantage in size and power consumption over a packed tower, but it is limited to low gas through-puts (under 10 ft./min.).

Available data on absorption rates are for **liquid-phase-controlled systems** only but, fortunately, such systems are most commonly encountered in stirred absorbers. Notable studies include those of Bernard (American Institute of Chemical Engineers meeting, Chicago, 1957); Cooper, Fernstrom, and Miller [*Ind. Eng. Chem.*, **36**, 504 (1944)]; Friedman and Lightfoot [*Ind. Eng. Chem.*, **49**, 1227 (1957)]; and Calderbank [*Trans. Inst. Chem. Engrs.*, **36**, 443 (1958); **37**, 173 (1959)]. Probably the most broadly useful correlation, since it accounts for the effect of vessel size, is that of Bernard, who used a multicurvilinear regression to correlate liquid-phase mass-transfer coefficient k_La for absorption of oxygen in water in a vessel with a **flat-bladed paddle:**

$$\log k_La = 0.0425 - 0.0939 \log l + 0.5690 \log P - 0.0457 (\log P)^2 + 0.4190 \log V_s - 0.1699 (\log V_s)^2 \quad (14\text{-}90)$$

where k_La = min.$^{-1}$; l = impeller length, in. (tested over range of 2 to 12 in.); P = power, hp./1000 gal. (tested over range of 0.05 to 46); V_s = superficial gas velocity, ft./min. (tested over range of 0.015 to 0.98 ft./min.). The correlation coefficient for Bernard's data was 0.995.

Table 14-59. Dimensional Ratios in Agitated Absorber Studied by Bernard*

See Eq. (14-90) for correlation of mass-transfer data

Dimension	Magnitude
Paddle length	l
Paddle width	0.125 l
Paddle thickness	0.0313 l
Vessel inside diameter	1.90 l
Baffle width (four)	0.250 l
Baffle thickness	0.0625 l
Height of gas nozzle above vessel bottom	0.750 l
Inside diameter of gas nozzle	0.0195 l
Height of bottom of paddle above vessel bottom	1.08 l
Height of liquid above vessel bottom	3.00 l

* A.I.Ch.E. meeting, Chicago, 1957.

Table 14-59 indicates the dimensional ratios in the vessels Bernard studied; these approximate the geometry of oft-used commercial equipment. Change in vessel geometry undoubtedly has some effect on mass-transfer coefficient, as does the use of other types of dispersers. Adequate data are not available to permit broad comparison of impeller types and vessel geometries.

Additional data on stirred absorbers have been obtained by Ayerst and Herbert [*Trans. Inst. Chem. Engrs.*, **32**, 68 (1954)] on the system CO_2-NH_4OH; by Bedekar [*J. Appl. Chem.*, **3**, 524 (1953)] on the system CO-Na_2CO_3; and by Phillips and Johnson [*Ind. Eng. Chem.*, **51**, 83 (1959)] on the system O_2-Na_2SO_3 (see also pp. 18-78 to 18-82).

Wetted-wall Columns. These devices have been tested by many investigators because of their utility in studying mass-transfer mechanisms. In addition, wetted-wall columns sometimes find use in commercial absorption operations, particularly when heat release is high and heat-transfer surface must be provided adjacent to the liquid. Primary example of this application is the HCl cooler-absorber, usually consisting of multiple impervious graphite tubes arranged in a bundle. For this important system, mass-transfer rates are not predictable by the usual correlation for gas-phase systems (p. 18-56).

For **gas-phase-controlled absorptions** not complicated by the strong heat effects described for the HCl-water system, mass-transfer coefficients can be predicted by the equation of Gilliland [Eq. (18-98), p. 18-57] when flow is **turbulent** and is not subject to unusual entrance disturbances.

For **liquid-phase-controlled absorptions**, mass-transfer rates depend on the character of the liquid flow.

Table 14-58. Sources of Simple Spray-absorber Data

Gas	Liquid	Tower		Nozzle	Range of N.T.U.	Ref
		Diam., in.	Height, in.			
Air	Water (evaporation)	31.5	52	Six Sprayco 5B on 12-in. circle	0.2–2.0	8
Air	Water (evaporation)	36	38-60	Buffalo hollow-cone (1/16, 3/32, 1/8)	2	1
Air	Water (evaporation)	24 × 36	69	Four Binks hollow-cone (0.156 in.)	0.2–1.0	7
Ammonia	Water	31.5	25, 52	Six Sprayco 5B on 12-in. circle	0.3–2.4	8
Ammonia	Water	18	48	Five Vermorel sprays on 8-in. circle	1.5–2.9	6
Ammonia	Water	3	19–54	Thirty-seven 0.028-in. holes in 3/16-in. plate	....	4
Benzene	Oil	3	19–54	Thirty-seven 0.028-in. holes in 3/16-in. plate	....	4
Carbon dioxide	Ammonium hydroxide	4	48	Several nozzles	....	9
Carbon dioxide	Sugar-lime	12	6–96	Eighty-five 1/16-in. holes	....	2
Sulfur dioxide	Water	3	19–54	Thirty-seven 0.028-in. holes in 3/16-in. plate	....	4
Sulfur dioxide	Water	8	30		....	3
Sulfur dioxide	Ammonium sulfite	42	104	Ten Sprayco 2B hollow-cone on 21-in. circle	....	5

References for Tables 14-58
[1] Bonilla, Mottes, and Wolf, *Ind. Eng. Chem.*, **42**, 2521 (1950).
[2] Bosworth, *Australian Chem. Inst. J. & Proc.*, **13**, 53 (1946).
[3] Haslam, Ryan, and Weber, *Trans. Am. Inst. Chem. Engrs.*, **15**, 177 (1923).
[4] Hixson and Scott, *Ind. Eng. Chem.*, **27**, 307 (1935).
[5] Johnstone and Williams, *Ind. Eng. Chem.*, **31**, 993 (1939).
[6] Kowalke, Hougen, and Watson, *Univ. Wisconsin Eng. Expt. Sta. Bull.*, Ser. 68, June, 1925.
[7] Niederman *et al.*, *Heating, Piping, Air Conditioning*, **13**, 591 (1941).
[8] Pigford and Pyle, *Ind. Eng. Chem.*, **43**, 1649 (1951).
[9] Rumford *et al.*, *Trans. Am. Inst. Chem. Engrs.*, **32**, 181 (1954).

When the liquid is in **laminar flow** ($N_{Re} < 1200$), and if there is no surface rippling as for very short columns (less than 4 in.) or when an appropriate wetting agent has been added, rates can be predicted using Fig. 14-6. Further discussion of rates in the absence of rippling is presented on pp. 14-13 to 14-14. Under other circumstances, ripples do exist on the liquid surface even though the main body of liquid is in laminar flow, and the result is an enhancement of the mass-transfer coefficient by up to 250 per cent. Data of various investigators on absorption with rippling conditions scatter widely, and a general correlation cannot be presented with confidence. Rates usually exceed those of Fig. 14-6 by factors of 1.5 to 2.5 (see also pp. 18-56 to 18-59).

SOLVENT EXTRACTION

REFERENCES: Treybal, "Liquid Extraction," McGraw-Hill, New York, 1951; "Mass-transfer Operations," McGraw-Hill, New York, 1955. Alders, "Liquid-Liquid Extraction," Elsevier, New York, 1955. Sherwood and Pigford, "Absorption and Extraction," McGraw-Hill, New York, 1952. Bird, Stewart, and Lightfoot, "Transport Phenomena," Wiley, New York, 1960. Coulson and Richardson, "Chemical Engineering," vol. II, Pergamon, London, 1955. Jantzen, "Fractional Distillation and Extraction," Dechema Monograph, vol. 5, No. 48, Verlag Chemie, Berlin, 1932. Kalichevsky, "Modern Methods of Refining Lubricating Oils," Reinhold, New York, 1938. Brown *et al.*, "Unit Operations," Wiley, New York, 1950. McCabe and Smith, "Unit Operations of Chemical Engineering," McGraw-Hill, New York, 1956. Foust, Wenzel, Clump, Maus, and Andersen, "Principles of Unit Operations," Wiley, New York, 1960. Walker, Lewis, McAdams, and Gilliland, "Principles of Chemical Engineering," 3d ed., McGraw-Hill, New York, 1937. Larian, "Fundamentals of Chemical Engineering Operations," Prentice-Hall, Englewood Cliffs, N.J., 1958. Colburn, *Trans. Am. Inst. Chem. Engrs.*, **35**, 211 (1939); *Ind. Eng. Chem.*, **33**, 459 (1941). Elgin, *Chem. & Met. Eng.*, **49**, 110 (1942). Scheibel and Othmer, *Trans. Am. Inst. Chem. Engrs.*, **38**, 339, 383 (1942). Randall and Longtin, *Ind. Eng. Chem.*, **30**, 1063, 1188, 1311 (1938).

Much of what follows is based on material by J. C. Elgin in the previous edition; liberal use has also been made of material by R. E. Treybal.

INTRODUCTION

Separation processes in which two immiscible or partially soluble liquid phases are brought into contact for the transfer of one or more components are referred to as **liquid-liquid extraction** or, more loosely, as solvent extraction. The processes taking place are primarily physical, since the solutes being transferred are ordinarily recovered without chemical change. On the other hand, the physical equilibrium relationships on which such operations are based depend mainly on the chemical characteristics of the solutes and solvents. Thus, use of a solvent that chemically resembles one component of a mixture more than the other components will lead to concentration of that component in the solvent phase, with the exclusion from that phase of the dissimilar components.

Solvent extraction may be carried out in various ways. In the simplest case the solvent is added to a liquid mixture, causing a second liquid phase to form. Sometimes it is desirable to add two liquids, insoluble in each other, permitting the components of the solution being treated to distribute between the two liquid phases. It may be desirable to add a salt to an aqueous phase to enhance the activity of a component, causing it to transfer into a non-aqueous phase in which the salt is insoluble. It may be desirable to adjust the pH of an aqueous phase containing organic acidic or basic solutes to depress the ionization of some, causing them to concentrate in the non-aqueous solvent phase. It is often helpful to change the temperature of the phases in contact to give the most favorable equilibrium at each step of the extraction.

Simple **leaching** of a soluble component away from an inert solid may be regarded as a special case of liquid-liquid extraction. In fact many of the methods of computation derived for liquid-liquid systems apply (see pp. 17-2 to 17-7).

In every case the successful **operation of extraction equipment** requires that the solvent phase and the phase being treated be brought into intimate contact so that mass transfer can occur. Then, after equilibrium has been approached, the two phases have to be separated mechanically. After one contact-and-separation sequence, it may be desirable to treat each phase further, *e.g.*, in countercurrent fashion. Finally, the solvent-laden phases have to be freed of solvent in order to release the enriched components and to recover the solvent for reuse. This final step is usually accomplished by distillation, so that the cost of a solvent-extraction process must allow for the cost of the auxiliary distillation operation in addition to the liquid-liquid extraction operation itself. Figure 14-22 shows how an extractor is combined

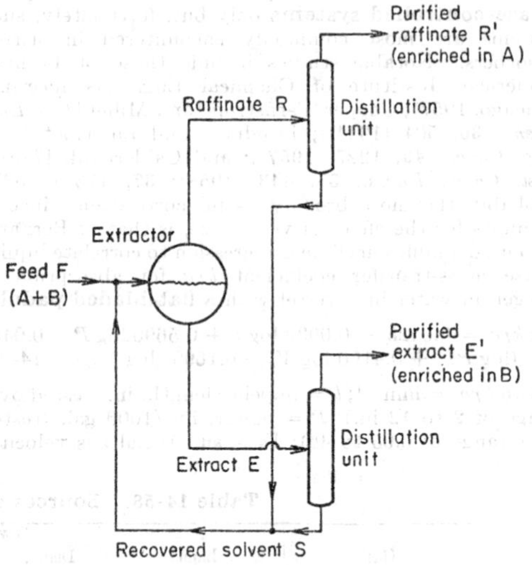

FIG. 14-22. Simplified flow sheet of liquid-liquid extraction process with solvent recovery.

with two distillation units to provide for a continuous operation yielding essentially pure streams of two volatile components A and B. Referring to the two streams leaving the extractor, the phase composed principally of solvent is referred to conventionally as the **extract** phase and the corresponding product stream as the purified extract; the other phase, having been treated by the solvent, is called the **raffinate** phase. Either raffinate or extract may be the lighter phase.

A typical **triangular phase diagram** corresponding to the operation illustrated in Fig. 14-22 is shown by Fig. 14-23*a*. This diagram is of type I, in which the region of immiscibility touches only one side of the triangle. Solvent S is so similar chemically to component

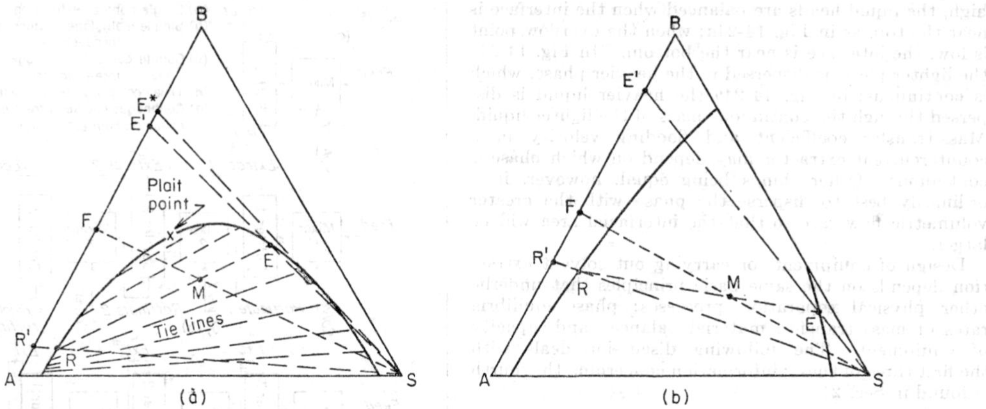

FIG. 14-23. Triangular phase diagrams. (*a*) Type I, more common. (*b*) Type II, less common; complete separation of *A* from *B* is possible.

B that binary mixtures of *B* and *S* are completely miscible. The solvent is chemically unlike component *A*, however, and binary mixtures of *A* and *S* split into two liquid phases. Addition of *B* to such mixtures tends to make *A* become more soluble in *S* and vice versa. At the **plait point** the two phases become one. Compositions of extract layers lie to the right of the plait point; raffinates are on the left. *RE* is a **tie line** which connects the compositions of raffinate and extract phases in thermodynamic equilibrium. The physical mixture *M* of feed and solvent splits into phases *R* and *E*. Upon removal of solvent from these phases, *R'* and *E'* are obtained. This kind of operation frequently involves countercurrent multiple mixing and phase separation, rather than the single contact and separation illustrated on the diagram.

It is seen in Fig. 14-23*a* that the concentration of component *B* in the purified extract is limited because of the closure of the two-phase region at the plait point. The most concentrated extract that can be produced lies at *E**. In the less common type II systems, illustrated by Fig. 14-23*b*, complete separation of *A* and *B* is possible.

A good solvent produces contrasting thermodynamic properties of the solute molecules in the extract and the raffinate phases. An appreciable difference in densities of the phases and a large interfacial tension are also desired in order that phase separation will be easy.

Either phase may be dispersed in the other, as indicated in Fig. 14-24. The extractor is, in effect, one arm of a two-fluid manometer operated so that the interface between the main bodies of the phases may be either at the top or at the bottom of the chamber provided for phase contact. With the right-hand overflow point

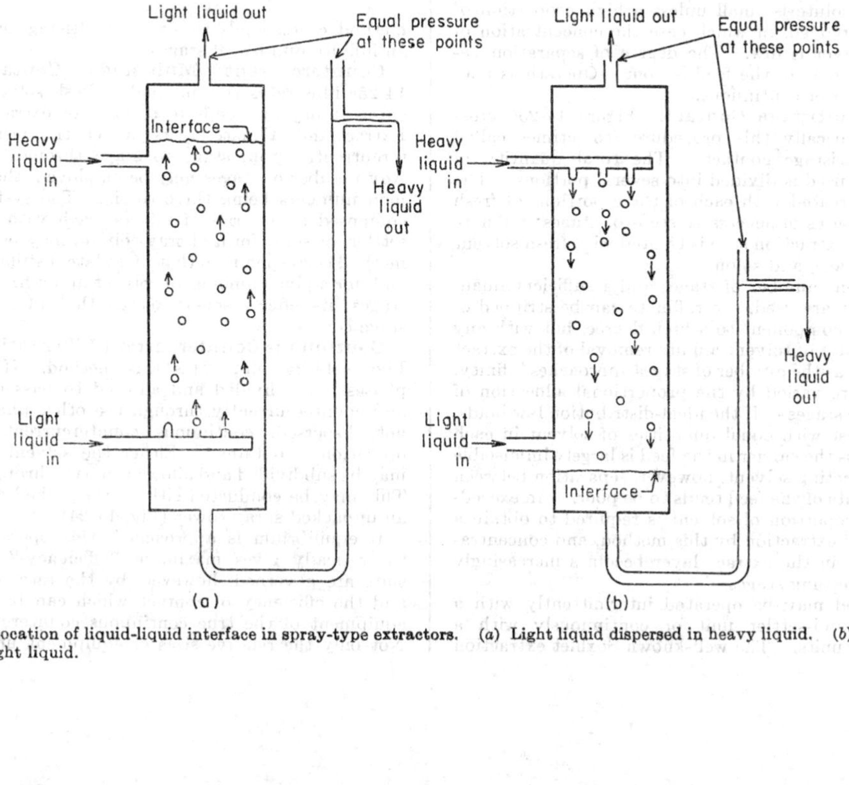

FIG. 14-24. Location of liquid-liquid interface in spray-type extractors. (*a*) Light liquid dispersed in heavy liquid. (*b*) Heavy liquid dispersed in light liquid.

high, the liquid heads are balanced when the interface is near the top, as in Fig. 14-24*a*; when the overflow point is low, the interface is near the bottom. In Fig. 14-24*a* the lighter phase is dispersed in the heavier phase, which is continuous; in Fig. 14-24*b* the heavier liquid is dispersed through the continuous mass of the lighter liquid. Mass-transfer coefficient and flooding velocity in a countercurrent extractor may depend on which phase is continuous. Other things being equal, however, it is ordinarily best to disperse the phase with the greater volumetric flow rate so that the interfacial area will be larger.

Design of equipment for carrying out solvent extraction depends on the same basic principles that underlie other physical separation processes: phase equilibria rates of mass transfer, material balances, and capacity of equipment. The following discussion deals with the first three of these; information concerning the fourth is found in Sec. 21.

EXTRACTION SYSTEMS

Any of the operating methods by which interphase mass-transfer processes can be conducted may conceivably be used in the conduct of solvent extraction. Industrial processes most commonly employ continuous countercurrent multistage contact in a series of mixers and settlers or a tray-type tower, or countercurrent differential contact in a continuous tower of the packed or spray type. In laboratory practice, cocurrent batch operation by single or simple multistage contact is common.

Single Contact. The simplest method and that most common on the laboratory scale is to bring the entire quantities of solvent and feed together in one contact and then recover the product and solvent without further extraction (see Fig. 14-25*a*). This method is the least effective and is rarely feasible on an industrial scale. As usually practiced, equilibrium is closely approached; hence the amount of solute extracted is fixed solely by equilibrium relations and the quantity of solvent used. Recovery of solute is small unless a high proportion of solvent is employed, in which case the concentration of the extract layer is low. The degree of separation between components of the feed is poor. Operations may be either batch or continuous.

Simple Multistage Contact. Figure 14-25*b* illustrates schematically this procedure (sometimes called *cocurrent* multistage contact). The total quantity of solvent to be used is divided into several portions. The feed is then treated with each of these portions of fresh solvent in a series of successive steps or stages; raffinate from the first extraction step is treated with fresh solvent in a second stage, and so on.

If a sufficient number of stages and a sufficient quantity of solvent are used, the raffinate can be stripped of the extracted component to a high degree, but with any specified amount of solvent a finite removal of the extract is approached as the number of stages approaches infinity. The results are varied by the proportional allocation of solvent to the stages. If the ideal-distribution law holds, results are best with equal quantities of solvent in each stage. Unless the carrier in the feed is largely immiscible with the extracting solvent, however, separation between the components of the feed tends to be poor. An exceedingly large proportion of solvent is required to obtain a high degree of extraction by this method, and concentration of solute in the extract layer becomes increasingly dilute in succeeding stages.

The method may be operated intermittently with a single mixer-and-settler unit or continuously with a series of such units. The well-known Soxhlet extraction

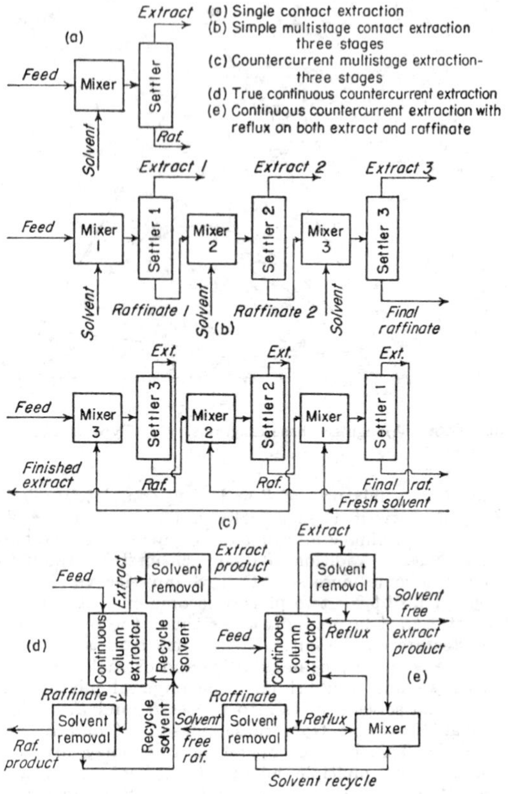

FIG. 14-25. Schematic flow diagrams illustrating various methods of operating extraction processes.

method corresponds to simple multistage contact with an infinite number of stages.

Countercurrent Multistage Contact. Figure 14-25*c* illustrates this method. Fresh solvent and feed enter at opposite ends of a series of extraction stages. Extract and raffinate layers pass continuously and countercurrently from stage to stage through the system. Any number of stages may be employed, the more common numbers being three to six. The system may be composed of a series of mixers, each with its separate settler, or some form of tray column may be used. The method corresponds to that of a plate distillation column and, for a given amount of solvent and a fixed number of stages, its effectiveness exceeds that of simple multistage contact.

Continuous Countercurrent Differential Contact. Figure 14-25*d* illustrates this method. If one of the phases is subdivided and allowed to pass continuously and countercurrently through the other phase, which is not dispersed, continuous countercurrent differential operation is obtained. Either the solvent or the feed may be subdivided and allowed to pass through the other. This may be conducted either in a packed column or in an unpacked spray tower (Fig. 14-24).

If equilibrium is approached, this operating system theoretically gives maximum "efficiency." Actual results are governed, however, by the rate of extraction and the efficiency of contact which can be obtained in equipment of the true continuous countercurrent type. Not only the relative sizes of equipment units but also their first costs and operating costs must be considered in judging the effectiveness of this method.

Countercurrent Extraction with Reflux. The flow scheme is illustrated in Fig. 14-25*e*. Unless one component of the feed is immiscible with the extracting solvent, countercurrent extraction cannot, in general, completely separate the components of the feed into the extract and raffinate products. A theoretical limiting value of the extract product composition is attained which with infinite number of stages or infinite tower height tends to approach equilibrium with the incoming feed.*

Reflux may be supplied to either or both ends of the extraction system in order to increase the degree of separation between the components of the feed.† Extract reflux is supplied by returning a portion of the extract layer from which the solvent has been wholly or partly removed (usually to just the point where the extract is saturated with the solvent). Similarly, for raffinate reflux a part of the raffinate layer is mixed with the incoming solvent (usually just to the point of saturation with the solvent). In general, with weaker feeds, extract reflux raises the concentration of the solute in the extract layer above that corresponding to equilibrium with the feed. If the extract or both streams are refluxed, the feed enters an intermediate point in the system or tower; if only the raffinate end is refluxed, the feed enters the opposite end of the unit.

The underlying **principle of reflux** in extraction is analogous to that in distillation, namely, that the outgoing extract layer is given an opportunity to be in equilibrium with a richer raffinate (*i.e.*, the extract reduced in solvent content). It is, however, subject to certain limitations not met in distillation. Reflux return must not result in a completely miscible system at either end, *i.e.*, over-all composition must still fall in the two-layer region. Reflux density must be different from that of the extract (or raffinate) layer. Even with reflux, the extract and raffinate products theoretically cannot both consist of the two pure components of the feed, respectively, unless the extracting solvent is only partly miscible with both (Fig. 14-23*b*). If it is completely miscible with the pure extract component (Fig. 14-23*a*), the raffinate (carrier) component can theoretically be obtained in 100 per cent purity, while the extract must always be a mixture of both components.

Use of reflux to obtain sharper separation of the feed into extract and raffinate products means the use of larger quantities of solvent or, what is equivalent, larger heat consumption.

Availability of reflux makes it possible to obtain high degrees of separation even with poorly selective solvents. By using reflux on the raffinate, it is possible to strip the latter of the extract component even though the solvent is selective for the raffinate component. If the feed is an aqueous solution, with a water-selective solvent, the solute can be stripped from it, leaving water as waste, by employing the solvent saturated initially with water (the extract is of course weaker, in this case, than the feed). This corresponds to the use of raffinate reflux. If the raffinate is water which is waste, fresh water may replace a portion of the raffinate as reflux. Possibilities in the use of reflux must be determined in relation to the specific extraction system and its phase equilibria.

* If types of phase equilibrium for specific cases are examined, it will be seen that the highest concentration of the desired component in the extract does not always correspond to its highest concentration in the raffinate layer; in certain cases enhanced concentration in one layer accompanies diminishing concentration in the other.

† The usefulness of raffinate reflux has been questioned by Wehner [*Am. Inst. Chem. Engrs. J.*, **5**, 406 (1959)] and by Skelland [*Ind. Eng. Chem.*, **53**, 799 (1961)].

Separation of One Component from a Mixture. Solvent extraction can be employed to isolate a single component from a mixture of several in solution. This is accomplished by extracting the desired component plus either the more or less soluble materials in the solvent, followed by treating the extract or raffinate (whichever contains the desired product) to separate the desired component from the other materials. Figure 14-26

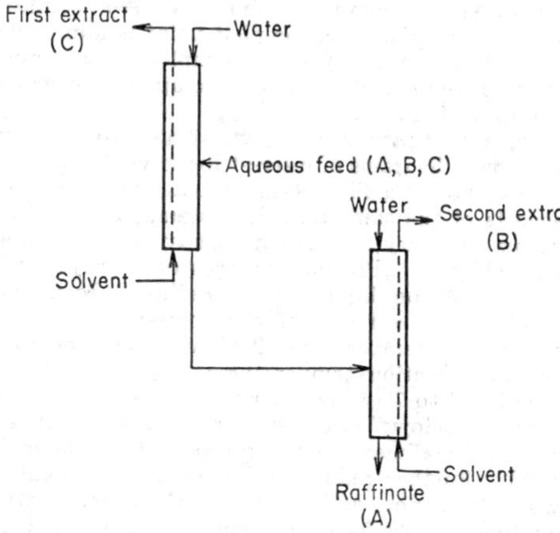

FIG. 14-26. Double cascade for isolation of a single solute.

illustrates a scheme for doing this where the aqueous feed contains components *A*, *B*, and *C*, and the solvent is immiscible with the aqueous solutions. The most soluble of these components in the solvent is *C*, and the least soluble is *A*. Different solvents may be employed in the two cascades if desired.

Batch (Pseudo) Countercurrent Multistage Extraction. In order to simulate in the laboratory a continuous multistage extraction, an operating scheme such as that illustrated in Fig. 14-27 can be used.

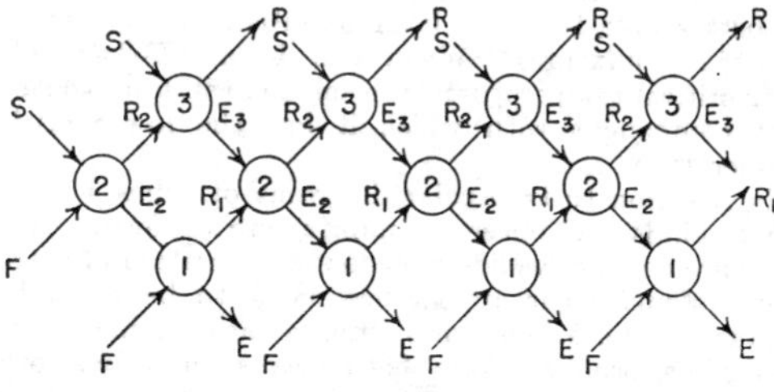

FIG. 14-27. Schematic flow diagram for a three-stage batch countercurrent multistage extraction. S = fresh solvent, F = feed to be extracted, R = raffinate, E = extract.

PHASE EQUILIBRIA

Accurate knowledge of phase-equilibrium relationships is vital for quantitative consideration of extraction processes. The required quantities of solvent (and reflux, if used) are set by these data. Also, the driving forces determining rates of mass transfer are governed by these thermodynamic considerations. Since formation of two stable liquid phases in contact with each other is an essential requirement, at least one phase is almost certain to be one in which solute components behave thermodynamically in a strongly non-ideal way. In fact, a solvent having high selectivity for one component of the feed must be a material in which the other components have large activity coefficients and from which these other components are consequently excluded when phase equilibrium has been achieved. The quantitative expression of liquid-liquid phase-equilibrium relationships therefore unavoidably involves the use of methods for representing thermodynamic properties of **non-ideal solutions.** In the simplest case these solutions are composed of three components; only if the solvent and component A are completely immiscible—a condition that cannot be satisfied as the plait point is approached by adding B to the mixture—can simple relations applicable to two-component mixtures be employed, except as a rough approximation.

Triangular Phase Diagrams. The two principal types of phase diagrams of interest for solvent-extraction operations, shown in Fig. 14-23, actually may represent two aspects of the same ternary system. Figure 14-28 shows how a ternary system may behave as the temperature is changed. (Pressure changes ordinarily have a negligible effect on liquid-liquid equilibria because of the small partial volumes of the components.) At a sufficiently high temperature all binary pairs are above their critical solution temperatures. As the temperature is reduced to T_{AS} the binary pair AS begins to form two phases. Below T_{AS} the isothermal (horizontal) section of the three-dimensional figure shows phase behavior of type I. Further reduction in temperature enlarges the two-phase region, and when T_{BS}, the binary critical solution temperature for components B and S, is reached the two-phase ternary region touches line BS. Upon further reduction in temperature the system exhibits type II characteristics.

Figure 14-28 shows why the experimental observation of **binary critical solution temperatures** of mixtures of pure components with prospective solvents is a good guide to solvent selection. As brought out by Treybal ("Liquid Extraction," McGraw-Hill, New York, 1951) and as employed by Francis [*Ind. Eng. Chem.*, **36**, 764, 1096 (1944)] for aniline and by Drew and Hixson [*Trans. Am. Inst. Chem. Engrs.*, **40**, 675 (1944)] and Hixson and Bockelmann [*Trans. Am. Inst. Chem. Engrs.*, **38**, 891 (1942)] for propane as solvents, the solvent S having the lower critical solution temperature with solute B will be better able to select it preferentially during extraction of A-B mixtures. When both A-S and B-S are below their critical temperatures, the solvent will tend to select that component with which it has the lower critical temperature.

In addition to triangular diagrams of types I and II other kinds of phase equilibria are known. While these are not always desirable for the operation of extraction systems, their appearance needs to be recognized because they are sometimes obtained at extreme temperatures in a ternary system that behaves normally at other temperatures. Figure 14-29 shows several ways in which a hypothetical three-component mixture can change progressively as the temperature is reduced. In Fig. 14-29c all three binary pairs are below their critical

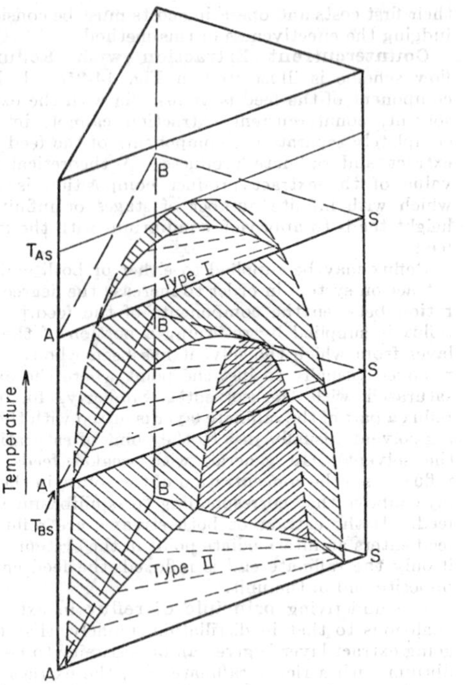

Fig. 14-28. Effect of temperature on ternary liquid-liquid equilibrium.

solution temperatures, and a three-phase region forms in the center of the diagram. In Fig. 14-29e the binary pair A-C becomes completely miscible as the temperature is raised, but a two-phase region persists inside the triangular region.

Thermodynamic Basis of Liquid-Liquid Equilibria. Equilibrium distribution of a component B between two liquid phases denoted $'$ and $''$, respectively, occurs when the activities a are equal:

$$a_{B}' = a_{B}'' \tag{14-91}$$

Or, when the activity coefficient γ is introduced,

$$K = \frac{x_{B}'}{x_{B}''} = \frac{\gamma_{B}''}{\gamma_{B}'} \tag{14-92}$$

where K = distribution coefficient and x = mole fraction. Equation (14-92) applies to each of the three components of a ternary system. For the present, however, consider the distribution of B between immiscible liquids such that the $'$ phase is nearly pure S and the $''$ phase is nearly pure A. Then γ_{B}' is the activity coefficient of B in the binary system AS; γ_{B}'' is the value for

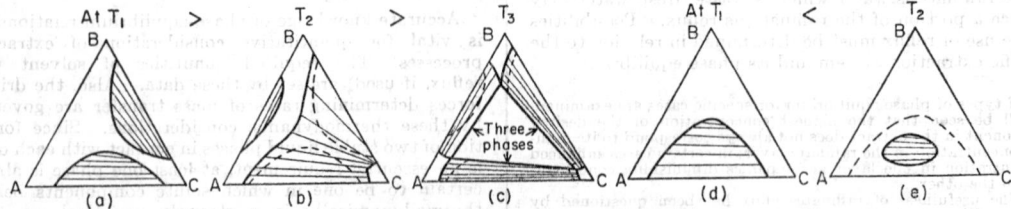

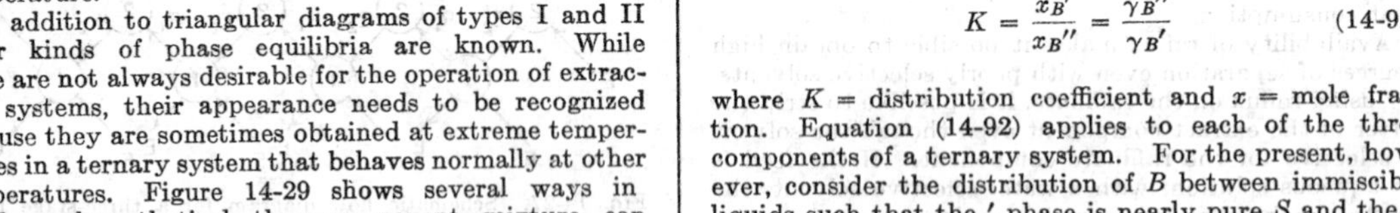

Fig. 14-29. Unusual phase behavior in ternary systems as affected by temperature.

Table 14-60. Selected Distribution Coefficients for Aqueous Systems

Solute B distributed between nearly immiscible components A and C; component C is water

Components		Temp., °C.	Distribution coefficient K*
Solute B	A		
Chlorine	Carbon tetrachloride	0	5.0
Bromine	Carbon tetrachloride	0	20
		25	27
		40	30
Iodine	Carbon tetrachloride	25	55
Ammonia	Carbon tetrachloride	25	0.0042
Chlorine dioxide	Carbon tetrachloride	0	0.85
		25	0.63
Ammonia	Chloroform	25	0.040
Sulfur dioxide	Chloroform	0	0.71
		20	0.71
Nitric acid	Ethyl ether	25	0.012
Ethanol	Benzene	25	1.1
Isopropanol	Benzene	25	0.50
Isopropanol	Toluene	25	0.21
Phenol	Carbon tetrachloride	25	0.36
Phenol	Chloroform	25	2.8
Phenol	Benzene	25	2.3
Phenol	Xylene	25	1.4
Acetone	Carbon tetrachloride	25	0.44
Acetone	Chloroform	25	5.5
Acetone	Toluene	0	0.48
		20	0.49
		30	0.51
Acetic acid	Carbon tetrachloride	25	0.059
Acetic acid	Bromoform	25	0.083
Acetic acid	Chloroform	20	0.028
Acetic acid	Ethyl ether	0	0.56
		15	0.48
		25	0.45
Acetic acid	Benzene	15	0.012
		25	0.023
Acetic acid	o-Xylene	25	0.042
Benzoic acid	Chloroform	10	4.2
		25	2.4
		40	3.2
Benzoic acid	Benzene	6	4.0
		20	4.3
		25	1.8
Diethylamine	Chloroform	25	2.2
Diethylamine	Benzene	25	0.63
Diethylamine	Toluene	18	0.48
		25	0.63
		32	0.90
Diethylamine	Xylene	25	0.20
Aniline	Toluene	25	7.7
Aniline	Xylene	25	3.0

* $K = C_{B(A)}/C_{B(C)}$; C_B = g.-formula weight of B per liter of solution; values of K are extrapolated to zero concentration of B.

Reference: "International Critical Tables," vol. III, pp. 418*ff.*, 1928.

B in the AB binary system. If the quantity of B is very small in each phase, as in Table 14-60, distribution coefficient K is simply related to the Margules or van Laar constants A for the two binary systems by

$$\log_{10} K = A_{BA} - A_{BS} \tag{14-93}$$

Values of such constants are given elsewhere (Kux, in "Zahlenwerte und Functionen," Landolt-Börnstein, vol. II, Part 2a, Springer, Berlin, 1960; binary systems, pp. 336–711; ternary systems, pp. 712–767); they are useful for estimating phase equilibria for systems for which observed distribution coefficients are not available.

Example 9. Estimate the distribution coefficient for acetone between liquid phases composed of water and chloroform. The end values of activity coefficients are available from measurements of vapor-liquid equilibria as follows:

System	Margules constant	Reference
Acetone (B), water (A)	$A_{BA} = +0.79$	Beare, McVicar, and Ferguson, *J. Phys. Chem.*, **34**, 1310 (1930)
Acetone (B), chloroform (S)	$A_{BS} = -0.57$	Mueller and Kearns, *J. Phys. Chem.*, **62**, 1441 (1958)

Introducing these values into Eq. (14-93),

$$K_B = 10^{(0.79+0.57)} = 22.9$$

In order to express this quantity in terms of molar concentrations instead of mole fractions, for comparison with Table 14-60, introduce the molecular weights and liquid densities of water and chloroform, obtaining

$$K = 22.9 \left(\frac{18}{1}\right)\left(\frac{1.5}{119.5}\right)$$

$$= 5.2 \frac{\text{g.-mole/liter in chloroform phase}}{\text{g.-mole/liter in water phase}}$$

The corresponding value given in the table is 5.5.

When the mutual solubility of components A and S is to be taken into account so as to calculate a complete binodal curve on a triangular phase diagram, the condition of equality of activities has to be satisfied for each of the three components. In principle this is possible, though the computations are tedious, if expressions are available for the activity coefficients of the components in the three-component solutions. This requires not only that numerical values of the six binary constants be known but also that ternary constants be known or estimated. The computations are made by successive approximations, the six mole fractions in two phases satisfying the three equations for activities plus two equations summing the mole fractions to unity.

A simpler, more limited computation that nevertheless has practical value permits the **location of tie lines** connecting the sides of the binodal curve, the compositions along the curve having been found experimentally. Thus, if x_A, x_B, and x_S are known along the whole binodal curve but the corresponding points (x_A', x_B', x_S' and x_A'', x_B'', x_S'') at the ends of tie lines are not known, a simple computation can be carried out as shown by Treybal ("Liquid Extraction," p. 64, McGraw-Hill, New York, 1951). For this purpose the important information required of an equilibrium computation is the distribution ratio β:

$$\beta_{BA} = \frac{x_{BS}\,x_{AA}}{x_{AS}\,x_{BA}} = \frac{AS\,BA}{BS\,AA} \tag{14-94}$$

The larger β is, the more selective is the solvent between B and A. In Eq. (14-94) x_{BS} and x_{BA} are the mole fractions of B in the solvent-rich phase and in the B-rich, or raffinate, phase, respectively; x_{AS} and x_{AA} are the mole fractions of A in the same phases.

Example 10. Estimate the distribution ratios β for the system ethanol-water with ethyl acetate as a solvent, and compare the estimates with the data of Beech and Gladstone (*J. Chem. Soc.*, 1938, p. 67) for the same system at 20°C. The data available include the following information for the three binary systems: (*a*) for the system ethyl acetate–ethanol, Furnas and Leighton [*Ind. Eng. Chem.*, **29**, 709 (1937)] determined vapor-liquid equilibrium compositions at 1 atm. pressure, the end values of activity coefficient corresponding to $A_{BS} = 0.34$ and $A_{SB} = 0.36$; (*b*) for the system ethanol-water, vapor-liquid equilibrium data at 20°C. give end values of log γ corresponding to $A_{BA} = 0.63$ and $A_{AB} = 0.38$; for the binary pair water–ethyl acetate, the A's have not been determined but mutual solubility data are available from "International Critical Tables," vol. III. At 20°C. the two phases contain, respectively, 7.94 and 96.99 per cent ethyl acetate by weight.

Treybal (*op. cit.*, pp. 66*ff.*) has solved this problem using the two-suffix van Laar equations for the ternary system. The following computations are carried out instead with the three-suffix Margules equations for the sake of comparison. It will be seen that substantially equal values of the distribution ratio are obtained in both methods.

Solution. First it is necessary to determine the Margules constants for the water–ethyl acetate (AS) binary system. From the binary Margules equations an equation can be found relating the compositions in the coexisting phases by equating the activities in the phases. Upon solving this equation for the

Margules constants A the following simultaneous equations are obtained:

$$A_{AS} = \frac{\log (x_{AS}/x_{AA})}{(2A_{SA}/A_{AS} - 1)M - 2(A_{SA}/A_{AS} - 1)N} \quad (14\text{-}95)$$

$$\frac{A_{AS}}{A_{SA}} = \frac{2(M - N)\log (x_{SS}/x_{SA}) + (W - 2Z)\log (x_{AS}/x_{AA})}{2(W - Z)\log (x_{AS}/x_{AA}) + (M - 2N)\log (x_{SS}/x_{SA})} \quad (14\text{-}96)$$

where
$$M = x_{SA}^2 - x_{SS}^2$$
$$N = x_{SA}^3 - x_{SS}^3$$
$$W = x_{AA}^2 - x_{AS}^2$$
$$Z = x_{AA}^3 - x_{AS}^3$$

Introducing $x_{AS} = 0.1321$, $x_{SS} = 0.8679$, $x_{SA} = 0.01738$, $x_{AA} = 0.9826$, based on the reported weight fractions, the following numerical values are obtained from the simultaneous equations (note that the first subscript used with the mole fractions refers to the component in question; the second subscript refers to the component of which the phase is principally composed):

$$\frac{A_{AS}}{A_{SA}} = 0.6323 \qquad A_{AS} = 1.00 \qquad A_{SA} = 1.60$$

(Use of the van Laar equations for the same binary pair gave 0.565, 1.03, and 1.79, respectively, for the same quantities, according to Treybal.)

Next, the six binary constants are used in the ternary Margules equation of Wohl [*Trans. Am. Inst. Chem. Engrs.*, **42**, 215 (1946); *Chem. Eng. Progress*, **49**, 218 (1953)] to estimate the activity coefficients of components A and B in the two liquid phases at compositions along the experimentally observed binodal curve. The equations are

$$\begin{aligned}\log_{10}\gamma_B = {} & x_A^2[A_{BA} + 2x_B(A_{AB} - A_{BA})] \\ & + x_S^2[A_{BS} + 2x_B(A_{SB} - A_{BS})] \\ & + x_Ax_S[\tfrac{1}{2}(A_{AB} + A_{BA} + A_{BS} + A_{SB} - A_{AS} - A_{SA}) \\ & + x_B(A_{AB} - A_{BA} + A_{SB} - A_{BS}) \\ & + (x_A - x_S)(A_{AS} - A_{SA}) - (1 - 2x_B)C^*] \quad (14\text{-}97)\end{aligned}$$

$$\begin{aligned}\log_{10}\gamma_A = {} & x_S^2[A_{AS} + 2x_A(A_{SA} - A_{AS})] \\ & + x_B^2[A_{AB} + 2x_A(A_{BA} - A_{AB})] \\ & + x_Sx_B[\tfrac{1}{2}(A_{AS} + A_{SA} + A_{AB} + A_{BA} - A_{SB} - A_{BS}) \\ & + x_A(A_{SA} - A_{AS} + A_{BA} - A_{AB}) \\ & + (x_S - x_B)(A_{SB} - A_{BS}) - (1 - 2x_A)C^*] \quad (14\text{-}98)\end{aligned}$$

Ternary constant C^* is not available from experiment but will be set equal to zero based on the suggestion of Colburn [*cf.* Severns, Sesonske, Perry, and Pigford, *Am. Inst. Chem. Engrs. J.*, **1**, 401 (1955)]. Table 14-61 shows the experimentally observed

Table 14-61. Calculation of Activities in Example 10

Coordinates of binodal curve			Calculated results	
x_A (water)	x_S (ethyl acetate)	x_B (ethanol)	γ_B	a_B
Water-rich layers				
0.983	0.01738	0	3.91	0
.966	.01772	0.01718	3.66	0.0628
.947	.0194	.0335	3.40	.1140
.932	.0219	.0473	3.21	.1517
.909	.0263	.0645	2.97	.1914
.886	.0335	.0812	2.71	.220
.847	.0496	.1034	2.36	.244
Ethyl acetate-rich layers				
0.1321	0.8679	0	1.915	0
.1520	.815	0.0330	1.775	0.0586
.2055	.711	.0837	1.543	.1291
.2545	.634	.1110	1.405	.1560
.294	.569	.1368	1.312	.1795
.396	.437	.1678	1.196	.2007
.522	.303	.1754	1.196	.2098

values of the three mole fractions along the binodal curve, the computed values of activity coefficient for component B, and the resulting activities. Compositions at the ends of tie lines are found from a plot of the activity of B in the A-rich and in the

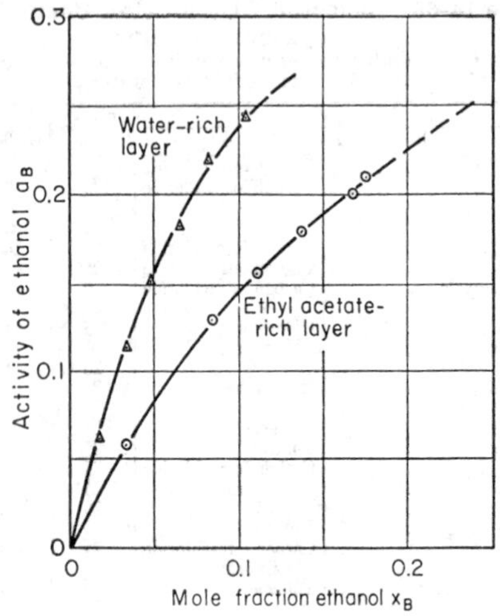

FIG. 14-30. Calculated activities of ethanol in system ethanol-water-ethyl acetate, Example 10.

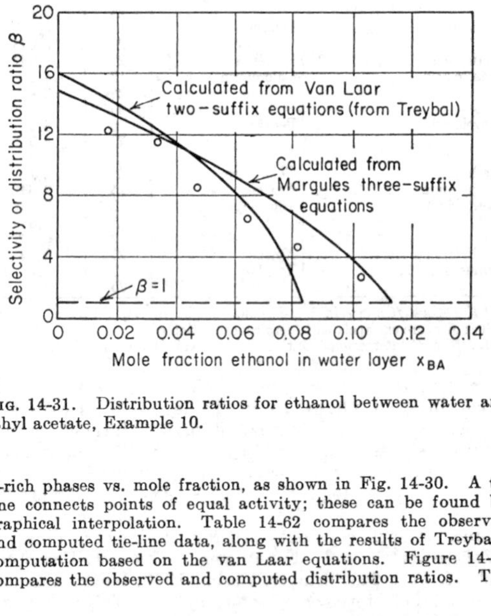

FIG. 14-31. Distribution ratios for ethanol between water and ethyl acetate, Example 10.

S-rich phases vs. mole fraction, as shown in Fig. 14-30. A tie line connects points of equal activity; these can be found by graphical interpolation. Table 14-62 compares the observed and computed tie-line data, along with the results of Treybal's computation based on the van Laar equations. Figure 14-31 compares the observed and computed distribution ratios. The

Table 14-62. Comparison of Observed and Calculated Tie-line Compositions, Example 10

System: Water (A)–ethanol (B)–ethyl acetate (S)
Temperature: 20°C.
Data of Beech and Gladstone (*J. Chem. Soc.*, 1938, p. 67)

Water-rich layer	Ethyl acetate-rich layer		
		x_{BS} (calculated)	
x_{BA} (observed)	x_{BS} (observed)	van Laar equations	Margules equations
0	0	0	0
0.01718	0.0330	0.038	0.036
.0335	.0837	.076	.072
.0473	.1110	.110	.106
.0645	.1368	.156	.145
.0812	.1678	.183	.186
.1034	.1754	.....	.226

latter are found from

$$\beta_{BA} = \frac{x_{BS}/x_{AS}}{x_{BA}/x_{AA}} = \frac{\gamma_{AS}\,\gamma_{AB}}{\gamma_{BS}\,\gamma_{AA}} \tag{14-99}$$

The thermodynamic treatment of **four-component liquid-liquid equilibria** is sometimes helpful in the analysis of extraction processes, particularly those in which the solvent is itself a mixture of two substances or those in which two solvents (components 3 and 4) partially soluble in each other are used to effect the distribution of two or more feed components (1 and 2) between the 3-rich and 4-rich phases. Equating the activities of 1 and 2, respectively, between phases and substituting the activity coefficients, the distribution ratio is found to be

$$\beta_{12} = \frac{x_{13}/x_{23}}{x_{14}/x_{24}} = \frac{(\gamma_1/\gamma_2)_4}{(\gamma_1/\gamma_2)_3} \tag{14-100}$$

In this equation x_{13}, for example, is the mole fraction of component 1 in the phase that is principally solvent, component 3; $(\gamma_1/\gamma_2)_3$ means the ratio of activity coefficients of components 1 and 2 in the 3-rich phase. If the mutual solubility of the solvents is slight each phase is a ternary solution, the representation of activity coefficients for which is given above. If mutual solubility has to be allowed for, four-component equations for activity coefficients are required.

Jordan, Gerster, Colburn, and Wohl [*Chem. Eng. Progress*, **46**, 601 (1950)] discussed the use of Margules-type equations for quarternary systems. A three-suffix equation for the activity coefficient of component 1, equivalent to that given by Jordan *et al.* but arranged in a form permitting ready generalization for any number of components, is

$$\begin{aligned}
\log_{10}\gamma_1 &= x_2^2A_{12} + 2x_1x_2[(1-x_1)A_{21} - x_2A_{12}] \\
&\quad + x_3^2A_{13} + 2x_1x_3[(1-x_1)A_{31} - x_3A_{13}] \\
&\quad + x_4^2A_{14} + 2x_1x_4[(1-x_1)A_{41} - x_4A_{14}] \qquad (a)\\
&\quad - 2x_2x_3(x_2A_{32} + x_3A_{23}) - 2x_3x_4(x_3A_{43} + x_4A_{34}) \\
&\quad - 2x_2x_4(x_2A_{42} + x_4A_{24}) \qquad (b)\\
&\quad + x_2x_3(1-2x_1)\left(\frac{1}{2}\sum_{123} - C^*_{123}\right) \\
&\quad + x_3x_4(1-2x_1)\left(\frac{1}{2}\sum_{134} - C^*_{134}\right) \\
&\quad + x_2x_4(1-2x_1)\left(\frac{1}{2}\sum_{124} - C^*_{124}\right) \qquad (c)\\
&\quad - 2x_2x_3x_4\left(\frac{1}{2}\sum_{234} - C^*_{234}\right) \qquad (d)
\end{aligned} \tag{14-101}$$

where $\sum_{ijk} = A_{ij} + A_{ji} + A_{jk} + A_{kj} + A_{ik} + A_{ki}$

Equation (14-101) is arranged in parts (*a*) to (*d*), each of which can be extended to provide for additional components if desired without changing the terms already present. The first group of terms (*a*) arises from binary terms in the excess free-energy expression containing x_1 as a factor; the second group (*b*) comes from binary terms not containing x_1; the third group (*c*) comes from ternary terms containing x_1 as a factor; finally, the fourth group (*d*) comes from ternary terms not containing x_1. It is likely that $C^* = 0$ will be an acceptable estimate, except in mixtures for which negative deviations occur.

Equation (14-101) is simplified somewhat when the logarithm of the ratio of activities, required for the distribution coefficient, is used:

$$\begin{aligned}
\log_{10}\frac{\gamma_1}{\gamma_2} &= x_2^2A_{12} - x_1^2A_{21} - 2x_1x_2(A_{12} - A_{21}) \\
&\quad + x_3[x_3(A_{13} - A_{23}) + 2x_1A_{31} - 2x_2A_{32}] \\
&\quad + x_4[x_4(A_{14} - A_{24}) + 2x_1A_{41} - 2x_2A_{42}] \\
&\quad + (x_2 - x_1)\left[x_3\left(\frac{1}{2}\sum_{123} - C^*_{123}\right) + x_4\left(\frac{1}{2}\sum_{124} - C^*_{214}\right)\right] \\
&\quad + x_3x_4\left(\frac{1}{2}\sum_{134} - C^*_{134} - \frac{1}{2}\sum_{234} + C^*_{234}\right)
\end{aligned} \tag{14-102}$$

Note that constants which do not involve either component 1 or 2 have disappeared.

Equation (14-102) can be used to estimate from binary data the effect on a ternary system of adding a fourth component. It can also be applied to three-component systems by setting $x_4 = 0$.

Empirical Representation of Liquid-Liquid Equilibria by Selectivity Plots. One of the most important attributes of a good solvent S is the ability to extract component A from a mixture of A and B preferentially, such that the ratio of quantities of A and B in the extract after removal of the solvent exceeds the ratio of these same components in the solvent-free raffinate phase. The selectivity ratio or distribution ratio β, as used in Example 10, is similar to the relative volatility used in distillation:

$$\beta_{BA} = \frac{x_{BS}/x_{AS}}{x_{BA}/x_{AA}} \tag{14-99}$$

Significance of this quantity is seen on the triangular diagram for the system ABS (Fig. 14-32). PR is a tie

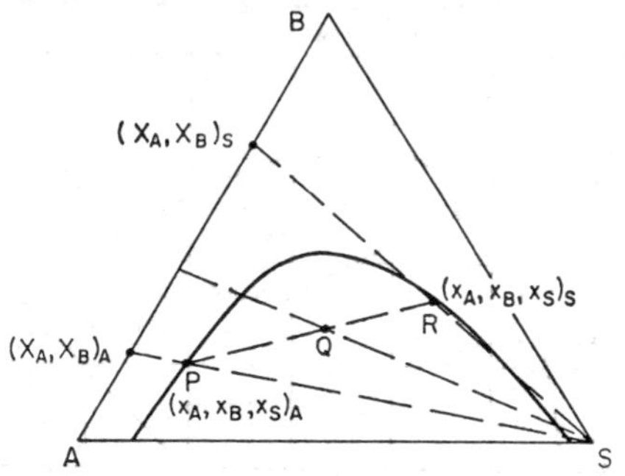

FIG. 14-32. Determination of solvent-free compositions for type I systems.

line joining points P and R, representing the compositions of A-rich and solvent-rich phases in equilibrium, respectively. Q represents the two-phase mixture formed in the single-stage contact under consideration. At the conclusion of the single-stage operation the solvent-free compositions of the two phases provide the best indication of the enrichment that has been accomplished. These compositions, X_{AA}, X_{AS}, X_{BA}, and X_{BS}, can be found by projecting lines from the solvent vertex through points P and R to the line AB. A simple calculation shows that the selectivity ratio β has the same numerical value, whether expressed in solvent-free compositions X or in mole fractions x in the coexisting phases.

$$\beta_{BA} = \frac{x_{BS}/x_{AS}}{x_{BA}/x_{AA}} = \frac{X_{BS}/X_{AS}}{X_{BA}/X_{AA}} = \frac{C_{BS}/C_{AS}}{C_{BA}/C_{AA}} \tag{14-103}$$

In fact, the value of β_{BA} is also the same when expressed in terms of the volumetric concentrations C in the phases.

Selection of the solvent in the ternary system ABS is based on the obvious fact that the binary mixture for which a separation has to be accomplished is the pair AB, substance S having been selected as the third (solvent) component to accomplish the separation. The same ternary equilibrium data apply, however, to another process situation in which B and S are the components of the binary system that has to be separated and A is the solvent selected to accomplish the job, as indicated

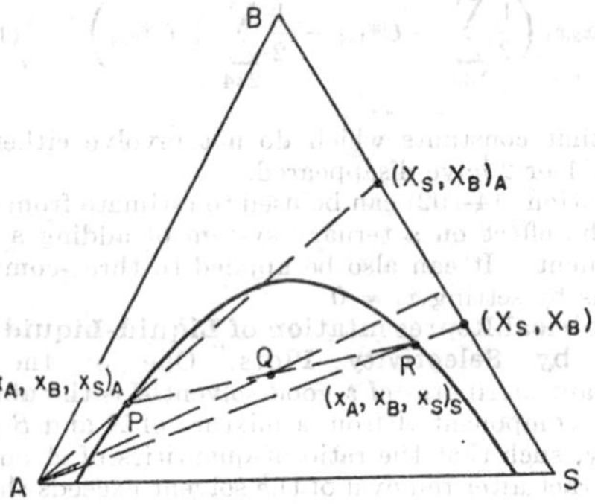

Fig. 14-33. Determination of solvent-free compositions for type I system; alternate designation of solvent.

in Fig. 14-33. Thus other values of the selectivity ratio β_{BS} can be found from the same ternary data:

$$\beta_{BS} = \frac{x_{BA}/x_{SA}}{x_{BS}/x_{SS}} = \frac{X_{BA}/X_{SA}}{X_{BS}/X_{SS}} \tag{14-104}$$

Use of one definition or the other depends on the process situation for which solvent extraction is being considered.

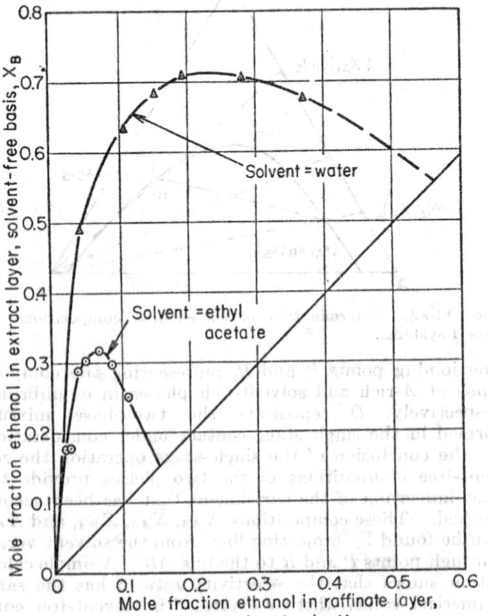

Fig. 14-34. Selectivity diagram for type I system: water (*A*), ethanol (*B*), ethyl acetate (*S*) at 20°C. (*Data of Beech and Glasstone, J. Chem. Soc.*, 1938, *p.* 67.)

Figures 14-34 and 14-35 show the variation of the solvent-free composition of substance B in the binary pairs being treated. Figure 14-34 shows mole fractions X_B; Fig. 14-35 gives the equivalent mass fractions W_B

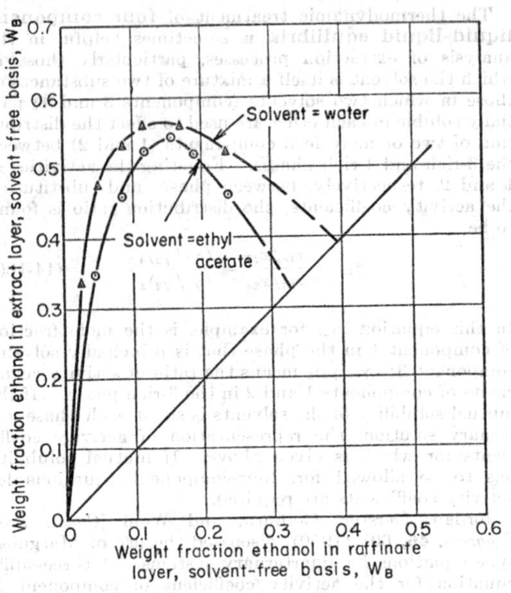

Fig. 14-35. Selectivity diagram for type I system: water (*A*), ethanol (*B*), ethyl acetate (*S*) at 20°C. (*Data of Beech and Glasstone, J. Chem. Soc.*, 1938, *p.* 67.)

in the same system, ethanol–water–ethyl acetate. For one curve the solvent is water; for the other it is ethyl acetate. In the first case water is added to a binary mixture of alcohol and ester to extract more alcohol than ester; in the second, the binary system being treated is alcohol-water, the ester solvent removing more alcohol than ester from the feed layer. Although the values of W_B along the two mass-fraction curves agree approximately in Fig. 14-35 for this system, this is not true of X_B in Fig. 14-34. Depending on the slopes of the tie lines, one of the components (A or S) is more selective toward component B than the other.

Systems of type II, in which the two-phase region extends from one side of the triangular diagram to the other, do not have plait points. (Solvent-free compositions for such a system are illustrated in Fig. 14-36.) As a result, their selectivity diagrams extend from 0 to 1

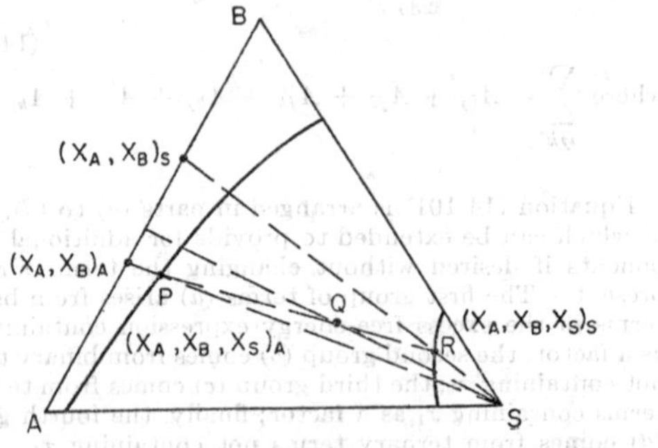

Fig. 14-36. Determination of solvent-free compositions for type II system.

across the horizontal coordinate, as indicated in Fig. 14-37 for the ternary system *n*-heptane–methyl cyclohexane–aniline, for which the selectivity ratio β is 1.90 (weight-fraction basis) and is constant. In such systems only one designation of the solvent component is possible, there being miscibility gaps on two sides of the triangular diagram.

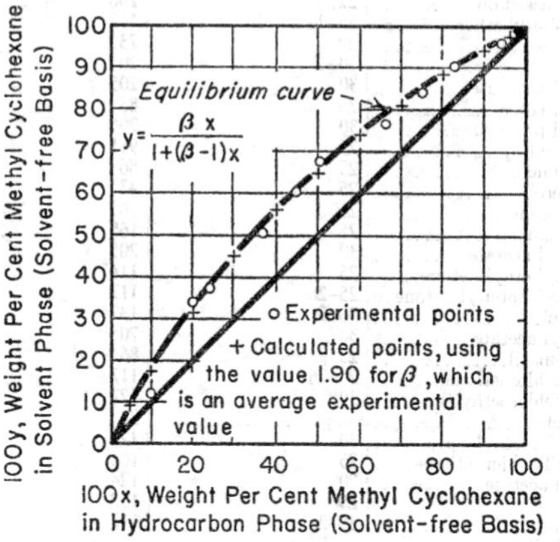

FIG. 14-37. Selectivity diagram for the system methyl cyclohexane, aniline, *n*-heptane at 25°C. and 1 atm. with aniline as solvent (aniline-free basis). Equation of curve is $y = \beta x/[1 + (\beta - 1)x]$ where $\beta = 1.90$.

Tie-line Correlations. Interpolation of experimentally observed tie-line compositions is difficult on a triangular diagram, yet closely spaced tie lines are needed for design computations of stagewise extractors. Several methods of extrapolating and interpolating data have been proposed by Brancker, Hunter, and Nash [*Ind. Eng. Chem., Anal. Ed.*, **12,** 35 (1940)], Bachman [*Ind. Eng. Chem., Anal. Ed.*, **12,** 38 (1940)], Hand [*J. Phys. Chem.*, **34,** 1961 (1930)], Othmer and Tobias [*Ind. Eng. Chem.*, **34,** 693 (1942)], Treybal [*Ind. Eng. Chem.*, **36,** 875 (1944)], and Campbell [*Ind. Eng. Chem.*, **36,** 1158 (1944)]. Of all these the procedures of Treybal and of Othmer and Tobias are probably most useful. They depend on the observation that certain tie-line compositions give straight lines on log-log coordinates. The methods are more reliable when the concentrations of the distributed component are small and when the solvent and nonsolvent phases are slightly miscible.

Othmer and Tobias (*loc. cit.*) found tie-line data for a large number of systems to give straight lines when $(1 - a)/a$ is plotted against $(1 - b)/b$, where a is the weight fraction solvent in the solvent-rich phase and b is the weight fraction of the carrier or diluent component (component A in Figs. 14-32 and 14-36) in the equilibrium raffinate phase. Figure 14-38 is a plot of the Othmer and Tobias coordinates for the system water (A)–ethanol (B)–ethyl acetate(S) at 20°C. Such a plot aids in interpolation or extrapolation of fragmentary data.

Experimental Equilibrium Data. A large number of ternary systems containing at least two liquid phases, for which experimental data have been reported, are listed in Tables 14-63 and 14-64. The literature references should be consulted for the actual data. Convenient collections of data and references have been prepared by Francis (in "Solubilities of Inorganic and Organic Compounds," Seidell and Linke, eds., Supplement to 3d ed., pp. 823–1122, Van Nostrand, Princeton, N.J., 1952); Himmelblau, Brady, and McKetta (*Special Pub.* 30, Bureau of Engineering Research, University of

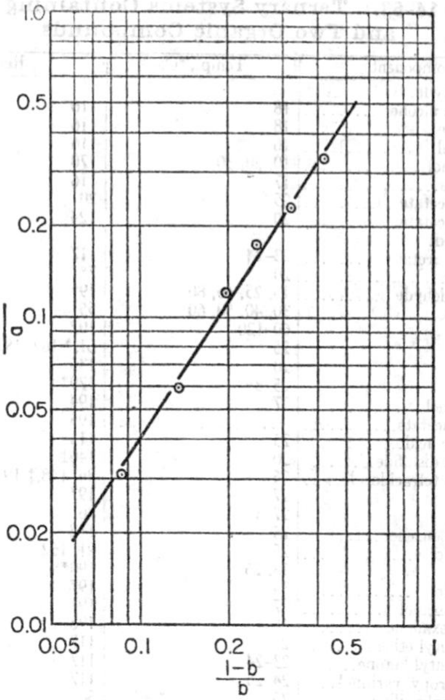

FIG. 14-38. Othmer-Tobias plot of tie-line data for system water (A), ethanol (B), ethyl acetate (S). a = weight fraction solvent S in S-rich layer; b = weight fraction carrier A in A-rich layer. (*Data of Beech and Glasstone, J. Chem. Soc.*, 1938, *p.* 67.)

Texas, Austin, Tex. 1959); Irving, Williams, and coworkers (*J. Chem. Soc.*, **1955**, pp. 1906–1966); Gladel and Durandet [*Rev. inst. franç. pétrole*, **10,** 258 (1955); **11,** 488 (1956)]. The annual reviews of solvent-extraction developments prepared by Elgin [*Ind. Eng. Chem.*, **38,** 23 (1946); **39,** 23 (1947); **40,** 53 (1948); **41,** 35 (1949); **42,** 47 (1950)] and Treybal [*Ind. Eng. Chem.*, **43,** 79 (1951); **44,** 53 (1952); **45,** 58 (1953); **46,** 91 (1954); **47,** 536 (1955); **48,** 511 (1956); **49,** 514 (1957); **50,** 463 (1958); **51,** 378 (1959); **52,** 262 (1960)] contain numerous references to sources of original data.

In addition to the systems listed in Tables 14-63 and 14-64, **mutual-solubility isotherms** without tie lines have been determined for a number of systems. The missing tie-line data for these can sometimes be computed with the van Laar or Margules equations, as indicated above.

Methods for the experimental investigation of coexisting phase equilibria are discussed by Alders ("Liquid-Liquid Extraction," Elsevier, New York, 1955); Smith and Braun [*Ind. Eng. Chem.*, **37,** 1047 (1945)]; Othmer, Truger, and White [*Ind. Eng. Chem.*, **33,** 1240 (1941)].

Experimental data for four-component systems are not included in Tables 14-63 and 14-64. References to sources of data may be found in the series of review articles by Elgin and by Treybal (*loc. cit.*). Graphical representation of quaternary data is discussed by Treybal ("Liquid Extraction," Chap. VII, McGraw-Hill, New York, 1951).

Many-component Systems. When more than four components are involved, as in the solvent refining of hydrocarbon oils or vegetable oils, the representation of phase equilibria in terms of individual components is frequently impractical. Extraction processes used in these cases usually have as their aim a separation into fractions differing in some important **physical property,** such as density, viscosity, viscosity index, or iodine number. Laboratory extractions can be carried out and the

Table 14-63. Ternary Systems Containing Water and Two Organic Compounds

Components	Temp., °C.	Ref.
Acetaldehyde:		
n-Amyl alcohol	18	116
Benzene	18	116
Furfural	16	116
Methanol	10, 20, 30	170
Toluene	17	116
Vinyl acetate	25	20
Vinyl acetate	20	124
Acetic acid:		
i-Amyl acetate	23–24	117
Aniline	20	7*
Benzaldehyde	15, 25, 40, 80	191
Benzene	30, 40, 50, 60	55
	60–120	192
	25	61,* 162, 193
	20	136
	25, 35	179*,†
1-Butanol	27	194
Butyl acetate	...	195
Caproic acid	25	115
Carbon disulfide	20	140‡
Carbon tetrachloride	25	86, 148,‡ 193
	27	197
	27.5	86
Chlorobenzene	25	112
Chloroform	25	21, 162
	18, 25	190*
Creosote	34	197
Cyclohexanol	27	194
Cyclohexanone	18	198
Di-*n*-butyl ether	25	117
Di-isobutyl ketone	23–24	117
Di-isopropyl carbinol	24–25	117
Dimethyl aniline	25	56
Epichlorohydrin	10	92†
Ethyl acetate	20	198
	25	28, 60
	30	158
Ethyl benzoate	...	199
2-Ethyl butyric acid	25	115
Ethyl ether	25	97
	19	200
2-Ethyl hexoic acid	25	115
Ethylidene diacetate	25	152
Ethyl propionate	28	201
Fenchone	23–24	116
Furfural	20, 25, 30	120
	27	194
Gasoline (straight-run)	25	49
Heptadecanol	25, 50	171
3-Heptanol	25	202
Hexalin acetate	23–24	117
Hexane	31	203
Isophorone	24	117
Methyl acetate	...	195
Methyl cyclohexanone	23–24	117
	18	198
Methyl isobutyl carbinol	30	204
Methylene chloride	19	200
Methyl ethyl ketone	27	194
Methyl iosbutyl ketone	15	28, 145
	22	117
Nitrobenzene	25	175‡
Nitromethane	27	194
Octyl acetate	23	117
Propyl acetate	...	195
Propylene	25	49
i-Propyl acetate	20	198
i-Propyl ether	20	8
	23–24	117
Toluene	25, 40, 55, 65, 75	131
	25	188*,†
m-Toluidine	20	6
Trichloroethylene	27	197
	30	86
	25	86
Vinyl acetate	28	151
Acetone:		
Aniline	30	27*
Amyl acetate	30	205
n-Amyl alcohol	25	73‡
Benzene	15, 30, 45	22
Bromobenzene	0	18*,†
i-Butanol	25	52‡
Butyl acetate	20, 25	206
	...	195
	30	205
Carbon disulfide	21	140‡
Carbon tetrachloride	21	140‡

Table 14-63. Ternary Systems Containing Water and Two Organic Compounds—(*Continued*)

Components	Temp., °C.	Ref.
Acetone:		
Carbon tetrachloride	30	207
Chlorobenzene	25–26	117
Chloroform	25	10, 21, 61,* 162
	0	18*,†
	25, 60	130
Cottonseed oil	22, 45	208
Di-*n*-butyl ether	25–26	117
Ethyl acetate	29	73‡
	30	205
Ethyl butyrate	30	205
Ethyl ether	25	86
Ethyl propionate	30	205
Furfural	25	93*
Gasoline	25	86
Glycerol	25	43
n-Heptane	25	165
n-Hexane	25	165
Methyl acetate	30	205
Methyl ethyl ketone	25	114
Methyl isobutyl ketone	25–26	117
Phenol	56.5	137†
Propyl acetate	30	205
Solvent oil	25	86
Tetrachloroethane	25–26	117
Tetrachloroethylene	30	127
Toluene	...	73
Trichloroethylene	30	127
1,1,2-Trichloroethane	25	166
Vinyl acetate	20	124
	25	152
Xylene	25–26	117
Acetonitrile:		
Trichloroethylene	20 and b.p.	123
Allyl alcohol:		
Carbon tetrachloride	25 and b.p.	63
Diallyl ether	22	210
Trichloroethylene	25 and b.p.	63
i-Amyl alcohol:		
Ethanol	0	18*
	15.5, 28	47†
Lactic acid	25	211
Methanol	28	47†
n-Propyl alcohol	25	34*
Aniline:		
Acetic acid	20	7*
Acetone	30	27*
Aniline hydrochloride	25	147
Benzene	25, 50	58
Butyric acid	20	5
Ethanol	0, 25	160
Formic acid	15	122*
Glycerol	25, 75	43
n-Heptane	25, 50	58
Lactic acid	20	2
Methyl cyclohexane	25, 50	58
Nitrobenzene	25	155
Phenol	8.6, 25.4, 48, 66.3, 96.7	26
Propionic acid	30	4
Toluene	25	154
Antipyrine:		
Chloral hydrate	Various	212
Pyrocatechol	Various	212
Resorcinol	Various	212
Benzene:		
Acetaldehyde	18	116
Acetic acid	30, 40, 50, 60	55
	25	61,* 162
	20	136
	25, 35	179*,†
Acetone	15, 30, 45	22
Aniline	25, 50	58
i-Butyl alcohol	25	1
n-Butyl alcohol	25, 35	186
tert-Butyl alcohol	25	149
Diethylene glycol	25	77
Dimethyl formamide	20–50	213
Dioxane	25	16
Ethanol	25	10, 106, 164, 172, 184
	25, 60	11*,†
	25, 50	103
	20, 25	162
	0, 20, 40	163
Ethyl isovalerate	25	106
Methanol	25	12*
Methyl ethyl ketone	25, 50	144
Monochlorobenzene dichloroacetic acid	25	217

Table 14-63. Ternary Systems Containing Water and Two Organic Compounds—(*Continued*)

Components	Temp., °C.	Ref.
Benzene:		
Morpholine	20–100	214
Phenol	25	215
	15, 30	216
2-Picoline	20	29
Propionic acid	25	140‡
i-Propyl alcohol	25	112*
n-Propyl alcohol	20	38
Pyridine	25	148,‡ 153, 178, 189†
	15–60	156
Trimethylamine	25, 70	78
i-Butyl alcohol:		
Acetone	25	52
Benzene	25	1
Ethanol	0	18*,†
Ethyl acetate	0, 20	13
Ethyl ether	....	52
1,1,2,2-Tetrachloroethane	25	52
n-Butyl alcohol:		
Benzene	25, 35	186
	....	220
n-Butyl acetate	25	125
2,3-Butylene glycol	26, 50	113
Dibutyl ether	15	90
Diethylene glycol	20, 40	100
Ethanol	20	42*
Ethyl acetate	0, 20	13
Ethylene glycol	20, 40	218
Glycerol	25	43
	20, 40	219
Methanol	0, 15, 30, 45, 60, 75, 90	108
Methyl butyl ketone	37.8	79
Toluene	30	53
	20	143‡
Trichloroethylene	....	220
Triethylene glycol	20, 40	100
3,5,5-Trimethyl hexyl sodium sulfate	25	23‡
tert-Butyl alcohol:		
Benzene	25	149
Butyl hypochlorite	0, 20, 40	221
Ethyl acetate	0, 20	13
Butylamine:		
Monochlorobenzene	25	217
2,3-Butylene glycol:		
n-Butyl acetate	26, 50	113
n-Butyl alcohol	26, 50	113
2,3-Butylene glycol diacetate	26, 75	113
Methyl vinyl carbinol acetate	26, 50, 75	113
1-Butyraldehyde:		
Ethanol	25	57
Ethyl acetate	37.8	79
Butyric acid:		
Ethyl benzoate	....	199
Methyl iosbutyl carbinol	30	204
Carbon disulfide:		
Acetic acid	20	140‡
Acetic anhydride	0, 18	222
Acetone	21	140‡
Ethanol	17–21	140‡
Methanol	20	140‡
Propionic acid	20	140‡
i-Propyl alcohol	20	140‡
n-Propyl alcohol	20	140‡
Carbon tetrachloride:		
Acetic acid	25	86, 148‡
Acetone	20	62‡
	21	140‡
Allyl alcohol	25 and b.p.	63
Ethanol	0	18*,†
Formic acid	25	140‡
Methanol	0	18*,†
Propionic acid	25	38‡
i-Propyl alcohol	25	76
	15, 30	219
n-Propyl alcohol	0	18*,†
	20	38
Chlorobenzene:		
Acetic acid	25	111
Acetone	25–26	117
n-Butylamine	25	111
Dichloroacetic acid	25	111
Methanol	25	148‡
Methyl ethyl ketone	25	109
Pyridine	25	111
Chloroform:		
Acetic acid	25	21, 162
	18, 25	190*

Table 14-63. Ternary Systems Containing Water and Two Organic Compounds—(*Continued*)

Components	Temp., °C.	Ref.
Chloroform:		
Acetone	25	10, 21, 61,* 162
	0	18*,†
	25, 60	130
Ethanol	0	18*,†
	25	102
Methanol	0	18*,†
i-Propyl alcohol	25	76
	20	140‡
n-Propyl alcohol	0	18*,†
p-Cresol:		
Methyl naphthalene	35	225
Cyclohexane:		
Ethanol	25	161,* 177*
Methanol	25	185*
Methyl ethyl ketone	30	203
i-Propyl alcohol	25	182
n-Propyl alcohol	25, 35	182
Cyclohexene:		
Ethanol	25	183
Methanol	25	183
i-Propyl alcohol	15, 25, 35	183
Diacetone alcohol:		
Ethyl benzene	25	36
Styrene	25	36
Ethanol:		
i-Amyl alcohol	0	18*
	15.5, 28	47†
n-Amyl alcohol	25–26	117
i-Amyl bromide	0	18*,†
i-Amyl ether	0	18*,†
Aniline	0, 25	160
Benzaldehyde	0	18*,†
Benzene	25	10, 106, 164,† 174, 184*
	35, 64	226
	25, 60	11*,†
	25, 50	103
	20, 25	162
	0, 20, 40	163*
Benzyl acetate	0	18*,†
Benzyl alcohol	0	18*,†
Benzyl ethyl ether	0	18*,†
Bromobenzene	0	18*,†
Bromotoluene	0	18*,†
i-Butyl alcohol	0	18*,†
n-Butyl alcohol	20	42*
i-Butyl bromide	0	18*,†
Butyraldehyde	25	57
Carbon dioxide	10–50	227
Carbon disulfide	17–21	140‡
Carbon tetrachloride	0	18*,†
	15, 30	219
Chloroform	0	18*,†
	25	102†
Cottonseed oil	30	64
Cyclohexane	25	161,* 177*
Cyclohexene	25	183
Di-*n*-butyl ether	25–26	117
Di-*n*-propyl ketone	25–26	117
1,2-Dichloroethane	30, 40, 50, 60	228
Ethyl acetate	0, 20	13*
	0	18*,†
	25	102†
	70	229
Ethyl bromide	0	18†
Ethyl butyrate	0	18*,†
Ethylene chloride	0	18*,†
Ethyl ether	0	18*,† 33†
	25	69,† 84,† 102†
	−15	89*
	15	98
Ethyl isovalerate	25	106
Ethyl vinyl ether	25	148†
Ethylidene chloride	0	18*,†
Ethyl propionate	0	18*,†
Furfural	25	40
Heptadecanol	25, 30	171
3-Heptanol	25	202
n-Heptane	30	139
n-Hexane	0	18*,†
	25	161
n-Hexanol	28	230
Mesitylene	0	18*,†
Methyl aniline	0	18*,†
Nitrobenzene	15	18*,†
p-Nitrotoluene	0	18*,†
n-Octene	0, 25	110
sec-Octyl alcohol	28	230
Phenetol	0	18*,†
Pinene	0	18*,†

Table 14-63. Ternary Systems Containing Water and Two Organic Compounds—(*Continued*)

Components	Temp., °C.	Ref.
Ethanol:		
Propyl bromide	0	18*,†
Salicylic acid	25	87
Toluene	0, 20, 40	156*
	25	181*
Trichloroethylene	25	30
	20, 67	130
Triethylamine	30	101
2,2,4-Trimethyl pentane	0, 25	110
Vinylidene chloride	20	146
m-Xylene	0, 19	68†
	0, 50	103
o-Xylene	0	18*,†
p-Xylene	15	18*,†
Ethyl acetate:		
Acetic acid	25	28, 60
	30	158
Acetone	29	73‡
i-Butyl alcohol	0, 20	13
n-Butyl alcohol	0, 20	13
sec-Butyl alcohol	0, 20	13
tert-Butyl alcohol	0, 20	13
Ethanol	0, 20	13*
	0	18†
Furfural	25	93,* 167
Methanol	0, 20	13*
i-Propyl alcohol	0, 20	13
n-Propyl alcohol	0, 20	13
3,5,5-Trimethyl hexyl sodium sulfate	25	23‡
Sodium benzene sulfonate	25, 60	19‡
Ethyl cellulose:		
Ethyl benzene	20	231
Styrene	20	231
Ethyl ether:		
Acetic acid	25	97
Acetone	25	86
Ethanol	0	18,*,† 33†
	25	69,† 84,† 102†
	−15	89*
	15	98
Malonic acid	15	81*,†
i-Propyl alcohol	25	125
Succinic acid	15, 20, 25	48†
Triethylamine	0, 12.4, 30.5	101†
Ethylene glycol:		
n-Amyl alcohol	20	89
Butanol	20, 40	218
	27	203
Furfural	25	31
n-Hexyl alcohol	20	89
Methyl ethyl ketone	30	203
Formic acid:		
Ethyl benzoate	....	199
Methyl isobutyl carbinol	30	204
Propyl formate	25, 40	232
Furfural:		
Acetaldehyde	16	116
Acetic acid	20, 25, 30	120
Acetone	25	93*
i-Amyl acetate	25	93*
i-Butane	37.8, 51.8, 66, 79.8	233
n-Butane	38, 52, 66, 80, 93	59
	37.8, 66, 93	233
1-Butene	37.8, 66	233
i-Butene	37.8	233
Ethanol	25	40
Ethyl acetate	25	93,* 167
Ethylene glycol	25	31
Methyl isobutyl ketone	25	32
Propane	23.9, 37.8	233
Propylene	23.9, 37.8	233
Toluene	25	82
Glycerol:		
Acetone	25	43
tert-Amyl alcohol	7.6, 25, 48.6	43
Aniline	25, 75	43
Benzyl alcohol	25, 75	43
n-Butyl alcohol	25	43
	20, 40	219
Cyclohexanol	60	43
Methyl ethyl ketone	25	43
Sucrose	25	46
Hexane:		
2-Butanone	38	234
n-Propanol	38	235
Lactic acid:		
n-Butanol	22	236
n-Butyl ether	22	236
Dichloroisopropyl ether	22	236

Table 14-63. Ternary Systems Containing Water and Two Organic Compounds—(*Continued*)

Components	Temp., °C.	Ref.
Lactic acid:		
Hexone	22	236
Toluene	22	236
Methanol:		
Acetaldehyde	10, 20, 30	170
i-Amyl alcohol	28	47†
Benzene	25	12*
Bromobenzene	0	18*,†
Butyl acetate	30	237
n-Butyl alcohol	0, 15, 30, 45, 60, 75, 90	108*
Carbon disulfide	20	140‡
Carbon tetrachloride	0	18*,†
Chlorobenzene	25	148‡
Chloroform	0	18*,†
p-Cresol	35	225
Cyclohexane	25	184*
Cyclohexene	25	183
Ethyl acetate	0, 20	13*
Ethyl bromide	0	18*,†
Ethyl butyrate	30	237
Ethyl propionate	30	237
n-Heptane	2–60	83
n-Hexane	2–60	83
Hexanol	28	238
Methyl acetate	25	35
Methyl methacrylate	25	85
Methyl naphthalene	25, 35	225
Naphtha (solvent)	25, 60	80
n-Nonane	2–60	83
n-Octane	2–60	83
sec-Octanol	28	238
Pentyl acetate	30	237
Phenol	25	225
Styrene	15	169
Toluene	25	99*
Trichloroethylene	25	86
	27.5	196
	20–50	213
Xylene	20, 30, 40	65
Methyl ethyl ketone:		
Acetone	25	114
Acetic acid	27	194
Aconitic acid	25	239
Benzene	25, 50	144
Butyl cellosolve	25	109
Chlorobenzene	25	109
Cyclohexane	30	203
Gasoline (aviation)	25	107
Glycerol	25	165
n-Heptane	25	165
n-Hexane	25	165
	37.8	241
2-Methyl furane	25	240
Naphtha	27	14
Phenol	20, 45, 75	242
1,1,2-Trichloroethane	25	109
Trichloroethylene	25	109
2,2,4-Trimethyl pentane	25	107
Methyl isobutyl ketone:		
Aconitic acid	25	239
Benzoic acid	27	243
Nitric acid	25	244
Propionic acid	27, 29	243
Nicotine:		
Carbon tetrachloride	25	246
Kerosene	64, 67, 70	245
Sulfuric acid	25	247
Nitrobenzene:		
Acetic acid	56.5	175‡
Aniline	25	155
Ethanol	15	18*,†
Phenol:		
Acetone	56.5	137†
Aniline	8.6, 25.4, 48, 66.3, 96.7	26
Benzene	25	70,* 215
	15, 30	216
Butyl acetate	20, 40, 60	248
	44.4	249
α-Methyl styrene	45, 70	25
	....	250
Pentenes	25	49
Triethylamine	−2.7, 10, 57, 75	101†
	15, 35	251
m-Phenylenediamine:		
Resorcinol	Various	212
2-Picoline:		
Benzene	20	29
Di-isobutylene	20	29
n-Heptane	20	29
Methyl cyclohexane	20	29

Table 14-63. Ternary Systems Containing Water and Two Organic Compounds—(*Continued*)

Components	Temp., °C.	Ref.
i-Propyl alcohol:		
Benzene	25	112*
Butyl acetate	25	125
Carbon disulfide	20	140‡
Carbon tetrachloride	25	76
Chloroform	25	76
	20	140‡
Cottonseed oil	30	64
Cyclohexane	25	182
Cyclohexene	15, 25, 35	183
Di-isopropyl ether	25	51
	20, 60	88
Ethyl acetate	0, 20	13
Ethyl chloride	25	76
Ethyl ether	25	125
n-Hexane	25	49
Propylene	25	49
Tetrachloroethylene	25	15
Toluene	25	180
n-Propyl alcohol:		
i-Amyl alcohol	25	34*
Benzene	20	38
	38	235
Bromobenzene	0	18*
Bromotoluene	0	18*,†
n-Butanol	38	235
Butyl acetate	....	125
Carbon disulfide	20	140‡
Carbon tetrachloride	0	18*,†
	20	38
Chloroform	0	18*
Cyclohexane	25, 35	182
Ethyl acetate	0, 20	13
Ethyl ether	....	125
Heptane	38	235
Hexane	38	235
n-Propyl acetate	20, 35	157
Toluene	20	140‡
	25	253
	....	220
Xylene	20	140‡
	....	220
Propionic acid:		
Aniline	30	4
Benzene	25	140‡
	30	254
	31	255
Carbon disulfide	20	140‡
Carbon tetrachloride	25	38‡
Chlorobenzene	30	254
Cyclohexane	31	255
Cyclohexene	31	255
Ethyl acetate	30	201
Ethyl benzoate	....	199
Ethyl butyrate	30	201
Ethyl propionate	30	201
Hexane	31	255
Methyl isobutyl carbinol	30	204
n-Octane	25	256
Tetrachloroethylene	31	255
Toluene	25	140‡
m-Toluidine	20	6
o-Toluidine	20	4
Trichloroethylene	30	254
Xylene	20	140‡
Propylene glycol:		
Sucrose	25	46
Pyridine:		
Benzene	25	148,‡ 153, 178, 189†
	15–60	156
Carbon tetrachloride	15, 30	219
Chloral hydrate	Various	212
Chlorobenzene	25	111
Toluene	25	178
Xylene	25	178
Salicylic acid:		
Aminopyrine	Various	258
Gasoline	Various	259
Toluene:		
Acetaldehyde	17	116
Acetic acid	25, 40, 55, 65, 75	131
Aniline	25	154, 188*,†
Bromobenzene	0	73
n-Butyl alcohol	30	53
	20	143‡
Diethylamine	25	187
Dimethylamine	24.4	44
Ethanol	0, 20, 40	163*
	25	181*
Furfural	25	82

Table 14-63. Ternary Systems Containing Water and Two Organic Compounds—(*Continued*)

Components	Temp., °C.	Ref.
Toluene:		
Methanol	25	99*
Propionic acid	25	140‡
i-Propyl alcohol	25	180
n-Propyl alcohol	20	140‡
Pyridine	25	178
m-Toluidine:		
Acetic acid	20	6
Butyric acid	20	6
Propionic acid	20	6
o-Toluidine:		
Butyric acid	20	5
Lactic acid	30	3
Propionic acid	20	4
Tetrachloroethane:		
Acetone	25–26	117
i-Butyl alcohol	25	52
Trichloroethane:		
Acetone	25	166
Methyl ethyl ketone	25	109
Trichloroethylene:		
Acetic acid	25	86
Acetonitrile	20 and b.p.	123
Allyl alcohol	25 and b.p.	63
Ethanol	25	30
	20, 67	130
Methanol	25	86
Methyl ethyl ketone	25	109
Nicotine	17	129‡

* Data given by Seidell.
† Data given by "International Critical Tables."
‡ Data given by Seidell, Supplement.

pertinent property of the layers measured. Such data can be used to locate tie lines on a plot such as Fig. 14-39, which represents the phase equilibria for the system hydrocarbon oil–nitrobenzene. As shown on the diagram, the oils can be separated into fractions having viscosity-gravity constants ranging between 0.800 and 0.995 by treatment with nitrobenzene. Other solvents may produce other changes in the property, and the complex oil mixture may contain individual components having still higher or still lower values of the index. If it can be established by experiment, however, that the property is additive on mixing, the diagram of Fig. 14-39 can be employed for design work.

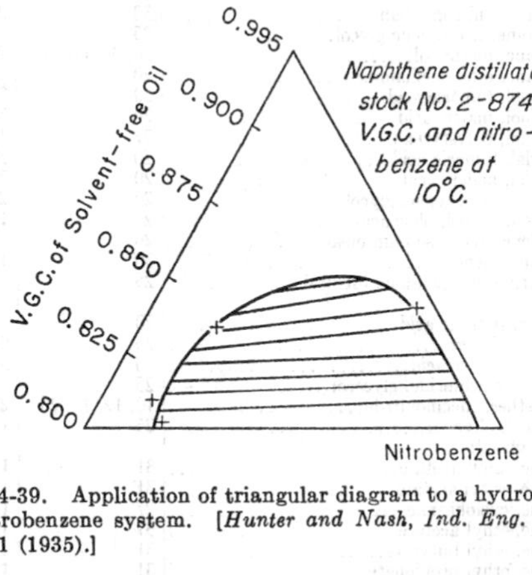

FIG. 14-39. Application of triangular diagram to a hydrocarbon oil–nitrobenzene system. [*Hunter and Nash, Ind. Eng. Chem.*, **27**, 841 (1935).]

Other diagrams of this kind for hydrocarbon-oil systems are given by Hunter and Nash [*Proc. World Petrol. Congr., London,* **2,** 340 (1933)]; Hill and Coats [*Ind. Eng. Chem.*, **20,** 641 (1928)]; Thompson (Dunstan, "Science of Petroleum," vol. 3, p. 1829, Oxford, New York, 1938); and by Ruthruff and Wilcock [*Trans. Am. Inst. Chem. Engrs.*, **37,** 649 (1941)] for the soybean oil–furfural system.

Table 14-64. Non-aqueous Ternary Systems

Components	Temp., °C.	Ref.
Acetic acid:		
Decane, 2,6-lutidine	25	261
Toluene, *n*-heptane	23	116
Acetone, ethylene glycol:		
Amyl acetate	31	126
Benzene	27	168*
Bromobenzene	25	168*
Chlorobenzene	23	168*
Cyclohexane	27	126
Ethyl acetate	31	126
Ethyl butyrate	31	126
Ethyl propionate	31	126
Nitrobenzene	22	168*
Toluene	27	168*
Xylene	25	168*
Acetylene:		
Ethane, ethylene	4.4, 15.6	94†
Aniline:		
Cetane, benzene	25	71, 72
Cetane, cyclohexane	25	71, 72
Cetane, *n*-heptane	25	71, 72
Cyclohexane, *n*-heptane	25	71, 72
Cyclopentane, neohexane	15, 25	142
Heptane, 1,2,-dichloroethylene	20, 40, 60	263
Heptane, toluene	0, 13, 20, 40	262
N,*N*-Dimethyl aniline, ethylene glycol	20	264
N-Methyl aniline, ethylene glycol	20	264
Methanol, methyl cyclohexane	14.1	50
Methyl cyclohexane, *n*-heptane	25	173
Methyl cyclopentane, *n*-hexane	25, 34.5, 45	37
Benzene:		
Acetone, ethylene glycol	27	168*
Acetone, formamide	25	265
Acetone, fumaric acid	20	39†
Acetone, maleic acid	20	39†
Aniline, cetane	25	71, 72
Cyclohexane, methanol	20, 30, 60	91
Cyclohexane, nitromethane	25	266
Dioxane, fumaric acid	20	39†
Dioxane, maleic acid	20	39†
Diethylene glycol, *n*-heptane	25	77
Ethanol, fumaric acid	20	39†
Ethanol, glycerol	25	95*
Ethanol, maleic acid	20	39†
Ethylene dichloride, tetraethyl ammonium iodide	25	176
Formamide, acetone	25	265
Formamide, diethyl formamide	25	24
Formic acid, bromoform	25, 50, 75	260
n-Heptane, dipropylene glycol	25	267
n-Heptane, methanol	20, 40, 60	91
n-Heptane, methyl sulfate	25	49
	17	119
n-Heptane, nitromethane	30	269
n-Heptane, triethylene glycol	25	268
n-Hexane, methanol	20, 30, 60	91
n-Hexane, ethylenediamine	20	17
Methanol, fumaric acid	20	39†
Methanol, maleic acid	20	39†
Methanol, polystyrene	27	141
Methylal, fumaric acid	20	39†
Methylal, maleic acid	20	39†
2-Picoline, triethylene glycol	20	29
Propylene glycol, oleic acid	25	135
Propylene glycol, sodium oleate	20	118
Toluene, xylene	30	128
2,2,4-Trimethyl pentane, furfural	25	270
Ethanol:		
Benzene, fumaric acid	20	39†
Benzene, glycerol	25	95*
Benzene, maleic acid	20	39†
Carbon tetrachloride, glycerol	25	96
Ethyl ether, succinonitrile	10, 12, 15, 20	271
Oleic acid, olive oil	25	132, 133
Ethylene glycol:		
Acetone, amyl acetate	31	126
Acetone, butyl acetate	31	126
Acetone, cyclohexane	27	126
Acetone, ethyl acetate	31	126
Acetone, ethyl butyrate	31	126
Acetone, ethyl propionate	31	126
Aniline, *N*,*N*-dimethyl aniline	20	264
Aniline, *N*-methyl aniline	20	264
Heptane, toluene	25	211
Glycerol:		
Methanol, ethanol, propanol with CCl_3F, CCl_2F_2, $CHCl_2F$, $CHClF_2$, $CClF_3$, all ternary combinations	10, 30	273
Phenol, aromatic hydrocarbons	20, 40, 60	134
Fumaric acid:		
Acetone, benzene	20	39†
Acetone, ethyl ether	20	39†
Dioxane, benzene	20	39†
Dioxane, ethyl ether	20	39†
Ethanol, benzene	20	39†
Ethanol, ethyl ether	20	39†
Methanol, benzene	20	39†
Methanol, ethyl ether	20	39†
Methylal, benzene	20	39†
Methylal, ethyl ether	20	39†
Furfural:		
i-Butene-butadiene	0.65	150
Cyclohexane, *n*-heptane	30	274
Cyclohexane, oleic acid	25	135
Docosane, diphenyl hexane	45, 80, 115	22
n-Heptane, toluene	20	54
n-Heptane, iso-octane	30	274
Naphtha, butadiene	−6.7	150
Naphtha, isobutene	−6.7	150
n-Pentane, oleic acid	25	135
Toluene, methyl cyclohexane	20	54
n-Heptane:		
Acetic acid, toluene	23	116
Aniline, toluene	0, 13, 20, 40	262
Benzene, methyl sulfate	25	49
Benzene, β,β'-thiodipropionitrile	25	9
Cetane, aniline	25	71, 72
Cyclohexane, aniline	25	71, 72
Cyclohexane, benzyl alcohol	0, 15	276
Cyclohexane, diethyl formamide	0	275
Diethylene glycol, benzene	25	77
Ethyl benzene, β,β'-oxydipropionitrile	25	9
Ethyl benzene, β,β'-thiodipropionitrile	25	9
Ethyl benzene, triethylene glycol	25	268
Methanol, benzene	20, 30, 60	91
Methanol, nitrobenzene	14.1	50
Methyl cyclohexane, aniline	25	173
Methyl ethyl ketone, toluene	88–108	159
Octene, ammonia	20	74
2-Picoline, triethylene glycol	20	29
Toluene, ammonia	−7.5, −15	75
Toluene, benzyl alcohol	0	276
Toluene, diethyl formamide	0, 20	275
Toluene, ethylene glycol	25	211
Toluene, furfural	20	121
Toluene, β,β'-thiodipropionitrile	25	289
p-Xylene, β,β'-thiodipropionitrile	25	289
n-Hexane:		
Aniline, methyl cyclopentane	25, 34.5, 45	37
Benzene, methanol	20, 30, 60	91
Cyclohexane, ammonia	20	74
Maleic acid:		
Acetone, benzene	20	39†
Acetone, ethyl ether	20	39†
Dioxane, benzene	20	39†
Dioxane, ethyl ether	20	39†
Ethanol, benzene	20	39†
Ethanol, ethyl ether	20	39†
Methanol, benzene	20	39†
Methanol, ethyl ether	20	39†
Methylal, benzene	20	39†
Methylal, ethyl ether	20	39†
Methanol:		
Aniline, methyl cyclohexane	14.1	50
Benzene, cyclohexane	20, 30, 60	91
Benzene, fumaric acid	20	39†
Benzene, *n*-heptane	20, 30, 60	91
Benzene, *n*-hexane	20, 30, 60	91
Benzene, maleic acid	20	39†
Benzene, polystyrene	27	141
Butyraldehyde, polystyrene	57	146
Dilaurin, trilaurin	60	272
Fumaric acid, ethyl ether	20	39†
Oleic acid, cyclohexane	25	135
Oleic acid, olive oil	25	132, 133
Oleic acid, triolein	20	252
Nitrobenzene, *n*-heptane	14.1	50
Nitrobenzene, iso-octane	0–42.6	224
Nitrobenzene, *n*-pentane	14.1	50
Nitrobenzene, 2,2,4-trimethyl pentane	14.1	50
Palm oil, fatty acids	50	105
Nicotine:		
Carbon tetrachloride, sulfuric acid	25	247
Nitroethane:		
Perfluorotributyl amine, 2,2,4-trimethyl pentane	21–51.3	223
Oleic acid:		
Acetone, palmitic acid	0, −10, −20	209
Ethanol, cottonseed oil	25	133
Ethanol, olive oil	25	133

Table 14-64. Non-aqueous Ternary Systems—(*Continued*)

Components	Temp., °C.	Ref.
Oleic acid:		
Furfural, cyclohexane	25	135
Furfural, *n*-pentane	25	135
Furfuryl alcohol, cyclohexane	25	135
Hexane, palmitic acid	−30, −40	209
Methanol, cyclohexane	25	135
Methanol, olive oil	25	133
Propylene glycol, benzene	25	133
Propylene glycol, carbon tetrachloride	25	133
Propylene glycol, *p*-chlorotoluene	25	133
Propylene glycol, cyclohexane	25	133
Propylene glycol, *o*-dichlorobenzene	25	133
Propylene glycol, ethylene dichloride	25	133
Propylene glycol, *n*-pentane	25	133
Propylene glycol, tetrachloroethylene	25	133
Propylene glycol, toluene	25	133
Propylene glycol, trichloroethylene	25	133
Propylene glycol, xylene	25	133
Phenol:		
Glycerol, aromatic hydrocarbons	20, 40, 60	134
Triethylene glycol, aromatic hydrocarbons	20, 40, 60	134
2-Picoline:		
Benzene, triethylene glycol	20	29
Di-isobutylene, triethylene glycol	20	196
n-Heptane, triethylene glycol	20	29
Methyl cyclohexane, triethylene glycol	20	196
Polystyrene:		
Butyraldehyde, methanol	57	146
Carbon tetrachloride, cyclohexane	57	146
Ethyl cyclohexane, cyclohexanol	57	146
Methanol, benzene	27	138
i-Propyl acetate:		
Petroleum ether, sulfuric acid	25	49
Styrene:		
Ethyl benzene, diethylene glycol	25	104
Toluene:		
Acetic acid, *n*-heptane	23	116
Acetone, ethylene glycol	27	168*
Aniline, heptane	0, 13, 20, 40	262
Benzene, xylene	30	128
Furfural, *n*-heptane	20	54
Heptane, ammonia	−7.5, −15	54
Heptane, benzyl alcohol	0	276
Heptane, diethyl formamide	0	275
Heptane, dipropylene glycol	25	267
Heptane, ethylene glycol	25	211
Heptane, methyl sulfate	17	119
Heptane, nitromethane	30	269
Heptane, oxydipropionitrile	25	45
Heptane, thiodipropionitrile	25	45
Heptane, triethylene glycol	25	268
Methyl cyclohexane, furfural	20	54
Oleic acid, propylene glycol	25	133

* Data given by Seidell.
† Data given by Seidell, Supplement.

References for Tables 14-63 and 14-64
1 Alberty and Washburn, *J. Phys. Chem.*, **49**, 4 (1945).
2 Angelescu, *Bul. soc. chim. România*, **7**, 72 (1925).
3 Angelescu, *Bul. soc. chim. România*, **9**, 19 (1927).
4 Angelescu, *Bul. soc. chim. România*, **10**, 160, 183 (1929).
5 Angelescu and Cristodulo, *Bul. chim. Soc. chim. românia*, [**2**]2, 114, 123 (1940).
6 Angelescu and Cristodulo, *Bul. chim. Soc. chim. românia*, [**2**]**3**, A32 (1941–1942).
7 Angelescu and Motzoc, *Bul. soc. chim. România*, **7**, 11 (1925).
8 Anon., *Trans. Am. Inst. Chem. Engrs.*, **36**, 594 (1940).
9 Skinner, *Ind. Eng. Chem.*, **47**, 222 (1955).
10 Bancroft and Hubard, *J. Am. Chem. Soc.*, **64**, 347 (1942).
11 Barbaudy, *Compt. rend.*, **182**, 1279 (1926).
12 Barbaudy, *Rec. trav. chim.*, **45**, 207 (1926).
13 Beech and Glasstone, *J. Chem. Soc.* (*London*), 1938, p. 67.
14 Berg, Manders, and Switzer, *Chem. Eng. Progress*, **47**, 11 (1951).
15 Bergelin, Lockhart, and Brown, *Trans. Am. Inst. Chem. Engrs.*, **39**, 173 (1943).
16 Berndt and Lynch, *J. Am. Chem. Soc.*, **66**, 282 (1944).
17 Cumming and Morton, *J. Appl. Chem.*, **3**, 358 (1953).
18 Bonner, *J. Phys. Chem.*, **14**, 738 (1910).
19 Booth and Everson, *Ind. Eng. Chem.*, **41**, 2627 (1949).
20 Brancker, *Ind. Chemist*, **27**, 243 (1951).
21 Brancker, Hunter, and Nash, *J. Phys. Chem.*, **44**, 683 (1940).
22 Briggs and Comings, *Ind. Eng. Chem.*, **35**, 411 (1943).
23 Bruner, *Ind. Eng. Chem.*, **41**, 2860 (1949).
24 Przhevlotskaya and Vasenko, *Ukrain. Khim. Zhur.*, **20**, 631 (1954).
25 Byk, Stroiteleve, and Aerov, *Zhur. Priklad. Khim.*, **29**, 1880 (1956).
26 Campbell, *J. Am. Chem. Soc.*, **67**, 981 (1945).
27 Campbell and Brown, *Trans. Faraday Soc.*, **29**, 835 (1933).
28 Chantry, Von Berg, and Wiegandt, *Ind. Eng. Chem.*, **47**, 1153 (1955).
29 Charles and Morton, *J. Appl. Chem.* (*London*), **7**, 39 (1957).
30 Colburn and Phillips, *Trans. Am. Inst. Chem. Engrs.*, **40**, 333 (1944).
31 Conway and Norton, *Ind. Eng. Chem.*, **43**, 1433 (1951).
32 Conway and Philip, *Ind. Eng. Chem.*, **45**, 1083 (1953).
33 Corliss, *J. Phys. Chem.*, **18**, 681 (1914).
34 Coull and Hope, *J. Phys. Chem.*, **39**, 967 (1935).
35 Crawford, Edwards, and Lindsay, *J. Chem. Soc.* (*London*), 1949, p. 1054.
36 Crooke and Van Winkle, *Ind. Eng. Chem.*, **46**, 1474 (1954).
37 Darwent and Winkler, *J. Phys. Chem.*, **47**, 442 (1943).
38 Densler, *J. Phys. Chem.*, **49**, 358 (1945).
39 Descamps, *Bull. soc. chim. Belges*, **49**, 91 (1940).
40 Domansky, *Chem. listy*, **46**, 765 (1952).
41 Drew and Hixson, *Trans. Am. Inst. Chem. Engrs.*, **40**, 675 (1944).
42 Drouillon, *J. Chim. Phys.*, **22**, 149 (1925).
43 Elgin, U.S. Patent 2,479,041, Aug. 16, 1949.
44 Wehn and Franke, *Ind. Eng. Chem.* **41**, 2853 (1949).
45 Durandet, *Rev. inst. franç. pétrole et Ann. combustibles liquides*, **12**, 1161 (1957).
46 Fey, Weil, and Segur, *Ind. Eng. Chem.*, **43**, 1435 (1951).
47 Fontein, *Z. physik. Chem.*, **73**, 212 (1910).
48 Forbes and Coolidge, *J. Am. Chem. Soc.*, **41**, 150 (1919).
49 Francis, "Physical Chemistry of Hydrocarbons," ed. by A. Farkas, Chap. VII, Academic Press, New York, 1959.
50 Francis, *J. Am. Chem. Soc.*, **76**, 393 (1954).
51 Frere, *Ind. Eng. Chem.*, **41**, 2365 (1949).
52 Fritzche and Stockton, *Ind. Eng. Chem.*, **38**, 737 (1946).
53 Fuoss, *J. Am. Chem. Soc.*, **65**, 78 (1943).
54 Garner, *J. Inst. Petrol.*, **41**, 1 (1955).
55 Garner, Ellis, and Roy, *Chem. Eng. Sci.*, **2**, 14 (1953).
56 Garwin and Haddad, *Anal. Chem.*, **25**, 435 (1935).
57 Gathman and Egberts, U.S. Patent 2,487,124, Nov. 8, 1949.
58 Griswold, Chew, and Klecka, *Ind. Eng. Chem.*, **42**, 1246 (1950).
59 Griswold, Klecka, and West, *Chem. Eng. Progress*, **44**, 839 (1948).
60 Guinot and Chassaing, U.S. Patent 2,437,519, Mar. 9, 1948.
61 Hand, *J. Phys. Chem.*, **34**, 1961 (1930).
62 Hands and Norman, *Ind. Chemist*, **21**, 307 (1945).
63 Hands and Norman, *Trans. Inst. Chem. Engrs.* (*London*), **23**, 76 (1945).
64 Harris, Bishop, Lyman, and Helpert, *J. Am. Oil Chem. Soc.*, **23**, 370 (1947).
65 Hartley, *J. Soc. Chem. Ind.* (*London*), **69**, 60 (1950).
66 Hixson and Bockelmann, *Trans. Am. Inst. Chem. Engrs.*, **38**, 891 (1942).
67 Hixson and Hixson, *Trans. Am. Inst. Chem. Engrs.*, **37**, 927 (1941).
68 Holt and Bell, *J. Chem. Soc.* (*London*), **105**, 633 (1914).
69 Horiba, *Mem. Coll. Eng. Kyoto Imp. Univ.*, **3**, 63 (1941).
70 Horiba, *Mem. Coll. Sci. Eng. Kyoto*, (*N.S.*), **1**, 49 (1914).
71 Hunter and Brown, *Ind. Eng. Chem.*, **39**, 1343 (1947).
72 Hunter and Brown, *J. Inst. Petrol.*, **35**, 73 (1949).
73 "International Critical Tables," vol. III, p. 398; vol. IV, pp. 400–413, 424, 1928.
74 Ishida, *J. Chem. Soc. Japan, Ind. Chem. Sect.*, **57**, 479 (1954).
75 Ishida, *Bull. Chem. Soc. Japan*, **29**, 956 (1956).
76 Ismailov and Franke, *Zhur. Fiz. Khim.*, **29**, 120 (1955).
77 Johnson, *Ind. Eng. Chem.*, **46**, 1662 (1954).
78 Jones and Grigsby, *Ind. Eng. Chem.*, **44**, 378 (1952).
79 Jones and McCants, *Ind. Eng. Chem.*, **46**, 1956 (1954).
80 Kiyama, Kozaki, and Kido, *Coal Tar* (*Japan*), **5**, 283 (1953).
81 Klobbie, *Z. Physik. Chem.*, **24**, 623 (1897).
82 Knight, *Trans. Am. Inst. Chem. Engrs.*, **39**, 439 (1943).
83 Kogan, Deizenrot, Kul'dyaeva, and Fridman, *Zhur. Priklad. Khim.*, **29**, 1387 (1956).
84 Kono, *J. Chem. Soc. Japan*, **44**, 406 (1923).
85 Kooi, *Rec. trav. chim.*, **68**, 34 (1949).
86 Krishnamurty, Murti, and Rao, *J. Sci. Ind. Research* (*India*), **12B**, 583 (1953).
87 Krupatkin, *Sbornik Statei Obshchei Khim. Akad. Nauk S.S.S.R.*, **1**, 151 (1953).
88 Krupatkin and Bodin, *J. Gen. Chem. U.S.S.R.*, **17**, 1993 (1947).
89 Laddha and Smith, *Ind. Eng. Chem.*, **40**, 494 (1948).
90 Lazzari, *Ann. chim. appl.*, **38**, 287 (1948).
91 Leibnitz, Konnecke, and Lippert, *J. Prakt. Chem.*, **3**, 311 (1956).
92 Leone and Benelli, *Gazz. chim. ital.*, **52**, II, 75 (1922).
93 Lloyd, Thompson, and Ferguson, *Can. J. Research*, **15B**, 98 (1937).
94 McCurdy and Katz, *Ind. Eng. Chem.*, **36**, 674 (1944).
95 McDonald, *J. Am. Chem. Soc.*, **62**, 3183 (1940).
96 McDonald, Kluender, and Lane, *J. Phys. Chem.*, **46**, 946 (1942).
97 Major and Swenson, *Ind. Eng. Chem.*, **38**, 834 (1946).
98 Marqueyrol and Goutal, *Mem. poudres*, **19**, 368 (1922).
99 Mason and Washburn, *J. Am. Chem. Soc.*, **59**, 2076 (1937).
100 Matsumoto and Sone, *J. Pharm. Soc. Japan*, **76**, 478 (1956).
101 Meerburg, *Z. physik. Chem.*, **40**, 641 (1902).
102 Miller and McPherson, *J. Phys. Chem.*, **12**, 706 (1908).
103 Mochalov, *Bull. inst. recherches biol. et sta. biol. univ. Perm*, **11**, 25 (1937).
104 Boobar *et al.*, *Ind. Eng. Chem.*, **43**, 2922 (1951).
105 Moreno and Paniagua, *Bull. soc. chim. France*, 1949, p. 388.
106 Moulton and Yi-Chang, *Ind. Eng. Chem.*, **45**, 2350 (1953).
107 Moulton and Walkey, *Trans. Am. Inst. Chem. Engrs.*, **40**, 695 (1944).
108 Mueller, Pugsley, and Ferguson, *J. Phys. Chem.*, **35**, 1314 (1931).
109 Newman, Hayworth, and Treybal, *Ind. Eng. Chem.*, **41**, 2039 (1949).
110 Nowakowska, Kretschmer, and Wiebe, *Ind. Eng. Chem.*, *Data Series*, **1** (1), 42 (1956).
111 Oeake and Thompson, *Ind. Eng. Chem.*, **44**, 2439 (1952).
112 Olsen and Washburn, *J. Am. Chem. Soc.*, **57**, 303 (1935).
113 Othmer, Bergen, Shlechter, and Bruins, *Ind. Eng. Chem.*, **37**, 890 (1945).
114 Othmer, Chudgar, and Levy, *Ind. Eng. Chem.*, **44**, 1872 (1952)
115 Othmer and Serrano, *Ind. Eng. Chem.*, **41**, 1030 (1949).
116 Othmer and Tobias, *Ind. Eng. Chem.*, **34**, 690 (1942).
117 Othmer, White, and Truegar, *Ind. Eng. Chem.*, **33**, 1240 (1941).

[118] Palit and McBain, *Ind. Eng. Chem.*, **38**, 741 (1946).
[119] Pascal and Quinet, *Ann. chim. anal.*, **23**, 5 (1941).
[120] Pegoraro and Guglielmi, *Chim. e ind. (Milan)*, **36**, 1035 (1955).
[121] Penneman and Audrieth, *J. Am. Chem. Soc.*, **71**, 1644 (1949).
[122] Pound and Wilson, *J. Phys. Chem.*, **39**, 709 (1935).
[123] Pratt, *Ind. Chemist*, **23**, 658 (1947).
[124] Pratt and Glover, *Trans. Inst. Chem. Engrs. (London)*, **24**, 54 (1946).
[125] Rao, Krishnamurty, and Rao, *Trans. Indian Inst. Chem. Engrs.*, **8**, 46 (1955–1956).
[126] Rao and Rao, *J. Sci. Ind. Research (India)*, **14B**, 204 (1955).
[127] Rao and Rao, *Trans. Indian Inst. Chem. Engrs.*, **7**, 78 (1954–1955).
[128] Ratliff and Strobel, *Oil Gas J.*, **53** (4), 87 (1954).
[129] Reilly, Kelly, and O'Conner, *J. Chem. Soc. (London)*, 1941, p. 245.
[130] Reinders and Minjer, *Rec. trav. chim.*, **66**, 552 (1947).
[131] Rius and Gandara, *Anales real. soc. españ. fis. y quím. (Madrid)*, **48B**, 569 (1952).
[132] Rius and Moreno, *Anales fis. y quím. (Madrid)*, **42**, 123 (1947).
[133] Rius and Moreno, *Chem. Prod.*, **11**, 63 (1948).
[134] Cummings and Morton, *J. Appl. Chem.*, **2**, 314 (1952).
[135] Sample, Bennett, and Holcomb, *Ind. Eng. Chem., Data Series*, **1** (1), 17 (1956).
[136] Sasaki, *Bull. Chem. Soc. Japan*, **14**, 3 (1939).
[137] Schreinemakers, *Z. physik. Chem.*, **39**, 485 (1902).
[138] Schulz and Jirgensons, *Z. physik. Chem.*, **B46**, 105 (1940).
[139] Schweppe and Lorah, *Ind. Eng. Chem.*, **46**, 2391 (1954).
[140] Seidell, "Solubilities of Inorganic and Organic Compounds," Supplement to 3d ed., Van Nostrand, Princeton, N.J., 1952.
[141] Selikson and Ricci, *J. Am. Chem. Soc.*, **64**, 2474 (1942).
[142] Serijan, Spurr, and Gibbons, *J. Am. Chem. Soc.*, **68**, 1763 (1946).
[143] Shanahan, *Analyst*, **73**, 502 (1948).
[144] Shell Chemical Co., "Methyl Ethyl Ketone," p. 33, San Francisco, 1938.
[145] Sherwood, Evans, and Longcor, *Ind. Eng. Chem.*, **31**, 1144 (1939); *Trans. Am. Inst. Chem. Engrs.*, **35**, 597 (1939).
[146] Shultz and Flory, *J. Am. Chem. Soc.*, **75**, 5681 (1953).
[147] Sidgwick, Pickford, and Wilsdon, *J. Chem. Soc. (London)*, **99**, 1122 (1911).
[148] Siggia and Hanna, *Ind. Eng. Chem.*, **41**, 1086 (1949).
[149] Simonsen and Washburn, *J. Am. Chem. Soc.*, **68**, 235 (1946).
[150] Smith and Braun, *Ind. Eng. Chem.*, **37**, 1047 (1945).
[151] Smith, *J. Phys. Chem.*, **45**, 1301 (1941).
[152] Smith, *J. Phys. Chem.*, **46**, 229 (1942).
[153] Smith, *J. Phys. Chem.*, **46**, 376 (1942).
[154] Smith and Drexel, *Ind. Eng. Chem.*, **37**, 601 (1945).
[155] Smith, Foecking, and Barber, *Ind. Eng. Chem.*, **41**, 2289 (1949).
[156] Smith, Stibolt, and Day, *Ind. Eng. Chem.*, **43**, 190 (1951).
[157] Smith and Bonner, *Ind. Eng. Chem.*, **42**, 896 (1950).
[158] Sohoni and Warhadpande, *Ind. Eng. Chem.*, **44**, 1428 (1952).
[159] Steinhauser and White, *Ind. Eng. Chem.*, **41**, 2912 (1949).
[160] Tarasenkov and Avenarius, *J. Gen. Chem. (U.S.S.R.)*, **16**, 1577 (1956).
[161] Tarasenkov and Paulsen, *J. Gen. Chem. (U.S.S.R.)*, **7**, 2143 (1937).
[162] Tarasenkov and Paulsen, *J. Gen. Chem. (U.S.S.R.)*, **8**, 76 (1938).
[163] Tarasenkov and Polozhintzeva, *J. Gen. Chem. (U.S.S.R.)*, **2**, 84 (1932).
[164] Taylor, *J. Phys. Chem.*, **1**, 461 (1896–1897).
[165] Treybal and Vondrak, *Ind. Eng. Chem.*, **41**, 1761 (1949).
[166] Treybal, Weber, and Daley, *Ind. Eng. Chem.*, **38**, 817 (1946).
[167] Trimble and Dunlop, *Ind. Eng. Chem., Anal. Ed.*, **12**, 721 (1940).
[168] Trimble and Frazer, *Ind. Eng. Chem.*, **21**, 1063 (1929).
[169] Troyan, *Rubber Age*, **63**, 585 (1948).
[170] Tsiklis and Korman, *Zhur. Fiz. Khim.*, **31**, 100 (1957).
[171] Upchurch and Van Winkle, *Ind. Eng. Chem.*, **44**, 618 (1952).
[172] Varteressian and Fenske, *Ind. Eng. Chem.*, **28**, 928 (1936).
[173] Varteressian and Fenske, *Ind. Eng. Chem.*, **29**, 270 (1937).
[174] Vener and Thompson, *Ind. Eng. Chem.*, **42**, 171 (1950).
[175] Vernon and Brown, *J. Chem. Educ.*, **14**, 143 (1937).
[176] Vernon and Sheard, *J. Am. Chem. Soc.*, **70**, 2035 (1948).
[177] Vold and Washburn, *J. Am. Chem. Soc.*, **54**, 4217 (1932).
[178] Vriens and Medcalf, *Ind. Eng. Chem.*, **45**, 1098 (1953).
[179] Waddell, *J. Phys. Chem.*, **2**, 236 (1898).
[180] Washburn and Beguin, *J. Am. Chem. Soc.*, **62**, 579 (1940).
[181] Washburn, Beguin, and Beckford, *J. Am. Chem. Soc.*, **61**, 1694 (1939).
[182] Washburn, Brockway, Graham, and Deming, *J. Am. Chem. Soc.*, **64** 1886 (1942).
[183] Washburn, Graham, Arnold, and Transue, *J. Am. Chem. Soc.*, **62**, 1454 (1940).
[184] Washburn, Hnizda, and Vold, *J. Am. Chem. Soc.*, **53**, 3237 (1931).
[185] Washburn and Spencer, *J. Am. Chem. Soc.*, **56**, 361 (1934).
[186] Washburn and Strandskov, *J. Phys. Chem.*, **48**, 241 (1944).
[187] Wehn and Franke, *Ind. Eng. Chem.*, **41**, 2853 (1949).
[188] Woodman, *J. Phys. Chem.*, **30**, 1283 (1926).
[189] Woodman and Corbet, *J. Chem. Soc. (London)*, **127**, 2461 (1925).
[190] Wright, Thompson, and Leon, *Proc. Roy. Soc. (London)*, **49**, 174 (1891); 50, 375 (1892).
[191] Amell and Teates, *J. Phys. Chem.*, **59**, 285 (1955).
[192] Tagliavini, Arich, and Biancani, *Ann. chim. (Rome)*, **45**, 292 (1955).
[193] Prince and Hunter, *Chem. Eng. Sci.*, **6**, 245 (1957).
[194] Skrzec and Murphy, *Chem. Eng. Sci.*, **46**, 2245 (1954).
[195] Murti, Venkataratnam, and Rao, *J. Sci. Ind. Research*, **13B**, 77 (1954).
[196] Charles and Morton, *J. Appl. Chem.*, **7**, 39 (1957).
[197] Saletore, Mene, and Warhadpande, *Trans. Indian Inst. Chem. Engrs.*, **2**, 16 (1948–1949).
[198] Eaglesfield, Kelly, and Short, *Ind. Chemist*, **29**, 147, 243 (1953).
[199] Rao and Rao, *J. Sci. Ind. Research (India)*, **16B**, 102 (1957).
[200] Casarico, *Ann. chim. (Rome)*, **41**, 199 (1951).
[201] Rao and Rao, *J. Sci. Ind. Research (India)*, **14B**, 444 (1955).
[202] Oualline and Van Winkle, *Ind. Eng. Chem.*, **44**, 1668 (1952).
[203] Rao and Rao, *J. Appl. Chem. (London)*, **7**, 659 (1957).
[204] Rao, Ramamurty, and Rao, *Chem. Eng. Sci.*, **8**, 265 (1958).
[205] Venkataratnam, Rao, and Rao, *Chem. Eng. Sci.*, **7**, 102 (1957).
[206] Thornton and Pratt, *Trans. Inst. Chem. Engrs.*, **81**, 289 (1953).
[207] Buchanan, *Ind. Eng. Chem.*, **44**, 2449 (1952).
[208] Rigamonti and Botto, *Oléagineux*, **13**, 199 (1958).
[209] Singleton, *J. Am. Oil Chem. Soc.*, **26**, 332 (1949).
[210] Fairburn, Cheney, and Cherniavsky, *Chem. Eng. Progress*, **43**, 280 (1947).
[211] Weiser and Geankoplis, *Ind. Eng. Chem.*, **47**, 858 (1955).
[212] Zhuravlev, *Uchenye Zapiski Molotov Gosudarst. Univ. im. A.M. Gorkogo*, **8** (3), *Mat. Fiz. Khim.*, 3 (1954).
[213] Rothlin, Grutzen, and Schultze, *Chem. Ing. Tech.*, **29**, 211 (1957).
[214] Tagliavini, Arch, and Biancani, *Chim. e ind. (São Paulo)*, **37**, 882 (1955).
[215] Hirata and Fujita, *Kagaku Kikai*, **21**, 201 (1957).
[216] Nagata and Eguchi, *Mem. Fac. Eng. Kyoto Univ.*, **19**, 102 (1957).
[217] Peake and Thompson, *Ind. Eng. Chem.*, **44**, 2439 (1952).
[218] Matsumoto and Sone, *J. Pharm. Soc. Japan*, **76**, 457 (1956).
[219] Matsumoto and Sone, *Yakugaku Zasshi*, **77**, 1151 (1957).
[220] Krishnamurty and Rao, *Trans. Indian Inst. Chem. Engrs.*, **8**, 52, (1955–1956).
[221] Ishiguro, Kakuma, and Okumura, *J. Pharm. Soc. Japan*, **74**, 1391 (1954
[222] Mochalov, *J. Gen. Chem. (U.S.S.R.)*, **8**, 529 (1938).
[223] Vreeland and Dunlap, *J. Phys. Chem.*, **61**, 329 (1957).
[224] Francis, *J. Am. Chem. Soc.*, **76**, 393 (1954).
[225] Prutton, Walsh, and Desai, *Ind. Eng. Chem.*, **42**, 1210 (1950).
[226] Morachevskii and Belousov, *Vestnik Leningrad Univ.*, **13**(4), *Ser. Fiz Khim.*, No. 1, 117 (1958).
[227] Baker and Anderson, *J. Am. Chem. Soc.*, **79**, 2071 (1957).
[228] Udovenko and Fatkulina, *Zhur. Fiz. Khim.*, **26**, 892 (1952).
[229] Griswold *et al.*, *Ind. Eng. Chem.*, **41**, 2352 (1949).
[230] Krishnamurty and Rao, *Trans. Indian Inst. Chem. Engrs.*, **6**, 153 (1954).
[231] Kuchynka, Boublik, and Fried, *Chem. listy*, **50**, 1848 (1956).
[232] Rius and Alfonso, *Anales real. soc. españ. fís. y quím.*, **51B**, 649, (1955).
[233] Griswold, West, and McMillin, *Chem. Eng. Progress, Symp. Ser.*, **2**, 62 (1952).
[234] Jones and McCants, *Ind. Eng. Chem.*, **46**, 1956 (1954).
[235] McCants, Jones, and Hopson, *Ind. Eng. Chem.*, **45**, 454 (1953).
[236] Congleton, Princeton University Chemical Engineering Thesis, 1942.
[237] Rao and Rao, *J. Appl. Chem.*, **7**, 435 (1957).
[238] Krishnamurty and Rao, *J. Sci. Ind. Research (India)*, **14B**, 614 (1955).
[239] Regna and Bruins, *Ind. Eng. Chem.*, **48**, 1268 (1956).
[240] Smith and LaBonte, *Ind. Eng. Chem.*, **44**, 2740 (1952).
[241] Jones and McCants, *Ind. Eng. Chem.*, **46**, 1956 (1954).
[242] Byk, Shcherback, and Stroiteleva, *Zhur. Fiz. Khim.*, **30**, 305, (1956).
[243] Johnson and Bliss, *Trans. Am. Inst. Chem. Engrs.*, **42**, 331 (1946).
[244] Powell and Newton, *U.S. Atomic Energy Comm.* TID-5212 144, 1955.
[245] Badgett, *Ind. Eng. Chem.*, **43**, 2370 (1951).
[246] Fowler and Noble, *J. Appl. Chem.*, **4**, 546 (1954).
[247] Fowler and Noble, *J. Appl. Chem.*, **7**, 97 (1957).
[248] Rock and Rothe, *Z. physik. Chem. (Frankfurt)*, **12**, 47 (1957).
[249] Schuberth and Leibnitz, *J. prakt. Chem.*, **6**, 31 (1958).
[250] Shcherbak, Byk, and Aerov, *Zhur. Priklad. Khim.*, **29**, 353 (1956); *J. Appl. Chem. U.S.S.R.*, **29**, 391 (1956).
[251] Markuzin and Storoukin, *Vestnik Leningrad Univ.*, **12**(10), *Ser. Fiz. Khim.*, **2**, 123 (1957).
[252] Rigamonti, Vaccarino, and Duzzi, *Chim. ind. (Milan)*, **33**, 619 (1951).
[253] Baker, *J. Phys. Chem.*, **59**, 1182 (1955).
[254] Krishnamurty, Rao, and Rao, *Trans. Indian Inst. Chem. Engrs.*, **6**, 161 (1954).
[255] Rao and Rao, *J. Appl. Chem.*, **6**, 269 (1956).
[256] Johnson, Furter, and Barry, *Can. J. Technol.*, **32**, 179 (1954).
[257] Matsumoto and Sone, *Yakugaku Zasshi*, **77**, 1149 (1957).
[258] Krupatkin, *Zhur. Obschei Khim.*, **26**, 1050 (1956); *J. Gen. Chem. U.S.S.R*, **26**, 1197 (1956).
[259] Krupatkin, *Zhur. Obscheĭ Khim.*, **26**, 3240 (1956).
[260] Avenarius and Tarasenkov, *J. Gen. Chem. (U.S.S.R.)*, **16**, 1777 (1946).
[261] Zieborak and Brzostowski, *Bull. acad. polon. sci. Classe*, **III** (5), 309 (1957).
[262] Durandet and Gladel, *Rev. inst. franc. pétrole*, **9**, 296 (1954).
[263] Arich, Tagliavini, and Biancani, *Chim. ind. (Milan)*, **38**, 937 (1956).
[264] Crutzen, Jost, and Sieg, *Z. Elektrochem.*, **61**, 229 (1957).
[265] Vasenko and Blank, *Ukrain. Khim. Zhur.*, **21**, 327 (1955).
[266] Weck and Hunt, *Ind. Eng. Chem.*, **46**, 2521 (1954).
[267] Rifai, *Riv. combustibili*, **11**, 811 (1957).
[268] Rifai, *Riv. combustibili*, **11**, 829 (1957).
[269] Kimura, Kashiwaya, and Asahara, *Kôgyô Kagaku Zasshi*, **59**, 1126 (1956).
[270] Kenny, *Chem. Eng. Sci.*, **6**, 116 (1957).
[271] Mertslin and Vasev, *Zhur. Obscheĭ Khim.*, **21**, 417 (1951).
[272] Monick and Treybal, *J. Am. Oil Chem. Soc.*, **33**, 193 (1956).
[273] Kageyama and Toteyama, *Nippon Kagaku Zasshi*, **78**, 517 (1957).
[274] Pennington and Marwill, *Ind. Eng. Chem.*, **45**, 1371 (1953).
[275] Durandet, Gladel, and Graziani, *Rev. inst. franç. pétrole*, **11**, 811 (1956).
[276] Durandet, Gladel, and Graziani, *Rev. inst. franç. pétrole*, **10**, 585 (1955).

CALCULATION AND DESIGN METHODS

Multistage Liquid-Liquid Extraction Systems. Calculation of multistage extraction systems is simplified by introducing the concept of the **theoretical, ideal,** or **equilibrium stage.** The equipment itself may consist of interconnected mixers and settlers or it may be a tower. The number of theoretical stages required to effect a desired composition change is computed first; the number of actual stages or the actual height of the contacting device is then determined by use of a tray efficiency or height equivalent to a theoretical plate (H.E.T.P.). Reference is made to data on these expressions of rate phenomena below (p. 14-67).

In principle, computation of stagewise extraction systems is similar to the computation of plate-type gas absorbers or distillation towers. Extraction systems, however, always involve at least three components and, in most practical cases, the phases are composed of three components owing to mutual solubility of the phases. Consequently, the familiar simplifying assumptions, such as constant molar flow rates of the streams or straight operating and equilibrium lines, are less often permissible in extraction computations. Nevertheless, stage-by-stage computations can be made graphically in a straightforward manner without adverse effect from faulty simplifications.

The general **algebraic material balance–equilibrium relationships** for extraction systems have been developed by Varteressian and Fenske [*Ind. Eng. Chem.*, **28,** 1353 (1936)]; Hunter and Nash [*J. Soc. Chem. Ind.*, **51,** 285T (1932)]; and Underwood [*Ind. Chemist,* **10,** 129 (1934)]. These relationships are also discussed in standard texts, such as Treybal ("Liquid Extraction," McGraw-Hill, New York, 1951); Alders ("Liquid-Liquid Extraction," Elsevier, New York, 1955); Coulson and Richardson ("Chemical Engineering," vol. 2, Pergamon, London, 1955); and Sherwood and Pigford ("Absorption and Extraction," McGraw-Hill, New York, 1952). **Graphical computation** can be based on the triangular diagram [see Hunter and Nash, *loc. cit.;* Saal and van Dyck, *Proc. World Petrol. Congr., London,* **2,** 352 (1933); Varteressian and Fenske, *loc. cit.;* and Schiebel, *Chem. Eng. Progress,* **44,** 681 (1948), for example] or on the rectangular or Ponchon-type diagram using coordinates introduced by Janecke (*cf.* Treybal, "Liquid Extraction," p. 128, McGraw-Hill, New York, 1951). In the latter connection see Maloney and Schubert [*Trans. Am. Inst. Chem. Engrs.*, **36,** 741 (1940)]; Randall and Longtin [*Ind. Eng. Chem.*, **30,** 1063, 1188, 1311 (1938)]; and Thiele [*Ind. Eng. Chem.*, **27,** 392 (1935)].

The two methods are algebraically equivalent in every respect, and the choice between them is largely a matter of preference. For the sake of brevity we refer here to the second procedure, using the **Janecke coordinates** to plot the solvent content of the equilibrium phases and the **Thiele coordinates** to plot the solvent-free compositions of the two substances being separated, referred to as A and B in the preceding. Equilibrium and operating lines established on the solvent-free coordinates can be employed either for stagewise computations, as shown first by Maloney and Schubert (*loc. cit.*), or for calculations of transfer units applicable to continuously distributed interface.

Figure 14-40 shows typical phase-equilibrium data for a ternary system. The upper part uses Janecke coordinates, in which the ordinate is either S, units of solvent per unit of $A + B$ in the extract phase, or s, ratio of solvent to $A + B$ in the raffinate phase. S is plotted vs. Y, the fraction of B in the $A + B$ mixture on a solvent-free basis in the extract phase; s is plotted vs. X, the fraction of B in the raffinate phase. The extract and raffinate curves meet at the plait point.

The lower portion of Fig. 14-40 is a plot of the solvent-free compositions, Y vs. X. A tie line on the upper graph can be drawn through any point on either the upper or the lower curve by referring to the lower graph. (The horizontal scales of the two graphs are common.) Starting with a value of X, for example, to find the equilibrium value of Y at the other end of a tie line on the upper graph it is necessary only to locate Y on the vertical scale of the

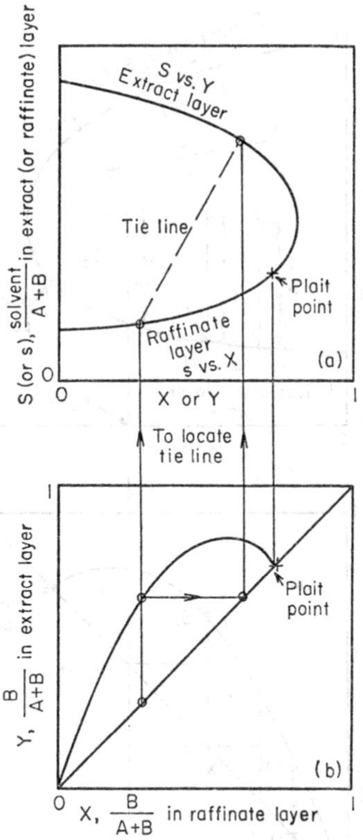

FIG. 14-40. Graphical representation of ternary phase-equilibrium data for material-balance calculations. (*a*) Janecke coordinates, solvent content on solvent-free basis. (*b*) Thiele coordinates, equilibrium compositions on solvent-free basis.

lower figure, draw a horizontal line to the 45-deg. diagonal, then draw a vertical line to its point of intersection with the upper, extract-layer curve on the Janecke coordinates. In this way a tie line can be drawn whenever it is needed, and approximate interpolation between tie lines is not required.

The solvent-content diagram and the solvent-free mole-fraction diagram can be constructed on either a mass or a mole basis, or on the basis of any other constant unit quantity of each substance. The material balance and equilibrium principles apply in any case, and the results of calculations made on one basis must be the same as those obtained from other bases; of course, the curves will not be identical when different bases are used.

Use of the solvent-content and solvent-free compositions in material-balance computations is formally equivalent to the use of enthalpy-concentration coordinates on the Ponchon-Savarit diagram in distillation, as discussed in Sec. 13. In ternary liquid-liquid extraction the solvent plays the same role as does heat in binary distillation.

Simple Multistage (Cross-flow) Extraction. This method is illustrated by Fig. 14-41. It is desired to calculate the number of theoretical stages needed to recover component A from a feed mixture F containing both A and B by treating successively with pure solvent S. The triangular diagram is of type I, in which binary systems AB and BS are fully miscible while AS is partially miscible. The total quantity Q of solvent is to be subdivided into parts Q_0, Q_1, . . . , Q_{n-1}, which are known

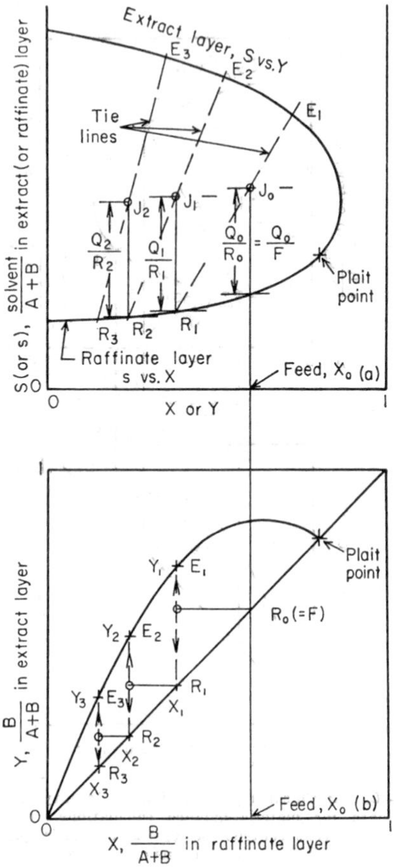

FIG. 14-41. Graphical calculation of multistage cross-flow extraction. (*a*) Solvent-content–concentration diagram, Janecke coordinates. (*b*) Solvent-free concentrations of key components, Thiele coordinates.

in advance, and the allowable concentration in the raffinate from the last stage of the extraction cascade is specified.

Figure 14-41 shows the information from the phase diagram, the tie lines being located on the upper graph at required points by projection from the lower graph. Material balances around stage n of the cascade may be made for solvent, for the sum of components $A + B$, and for B alone. For $A + B$:

$$R_{n-1} = R_n + E_n \qquad (14\text{-}105)$$

where R = mass flow rate of raffinate phase and E = mass flow rate of extract phase. For solvent:

$$R_{n-1}s_{n-1} + Q_{n-1} = R_n s_n + E_n S_n \qquad (14\text{-}106)$$

from which, upon introducing Eq. (14-105),

$$J_{n-1} = s_{n-1} + \frac{Q_{n-1}}{R_{n-1}} = \frac{R_n}{R_{n-1}} s_n + \frac{E_n}{R_{n-1}} S_n \qquad (14\text{-}107)$$

Note that the symbol J is introduced for the expression between the equal signs; it represents the ratio of total solvent introduced into stage n to the quantity of solvent-free raffinate flowing into the same stage. With this definition of J_{n-1} it also follows that

$$S_n - J_{n-1} = \frac{R_n}{R_{n-1}}(S_n - s_n) \qquad (14\text{-}108)$$

For substance B alone:

$$R_{n-1}X_{n-1} = R_n X_n + E_n Y_n \qquad (14\text{-}109)$$

which, upon introduction of Eq. (14-105), becomes

$$Y_n - X_{n-1} = \frac{R_n}{R_{n-1}}(Y_n - X_n) \qquad (14\text{-}110)$$

Combination of Eqs. (14-108) and (14-110) leads to

$$\frac{S_n - J_{n-1}}{Y_n - X_{n-1}} = \frac{S_n - s_n}{Y_n - X_n} \qquad (14\text{-}111)$$

This is the equation of a straight line on the upper coordinates of Fig. 14-40, indicating that the three points (S_n, Y_n), (J_{n-1}, X_{n-1}), and (s_n, X_n) are connected by a straight line. Furthermore, according to its definition by Eq. (14-107), J_{n-1} lies at a distance Q_{n-1}/R_{n-1} above point (s_{n-1}, X_{n-1}).

Figure 14-41 shows the indicated straight-line construction corresponding to successive extraction with fresh solvent in three equilibrium stages. The raffinate layers become successively weaker in B and stronger in A as this phase is passed from one stage to the next. Comparison of the vertical segments between the equilibrium curve and the 45-deg. line for each stage shows the proportions into which the feed to a stage are divided when two layers are formed upon addition of solvent in that stage.

When quantities of solvent Q_n are fixed, the tie lines on the upper figure have to be located by a cut-and-try method so that they will pass through points J, but this is facilitated by using the lower figure. The optimum distribution of a fixed total quantity of solvent into fractions depends on the phase-equilibrium characteristics of the system being treated. The methods of dynamic programming can be applied to compute optimum distributions in such problems [*cf.* Aris, Bellman, and Kalaba, *Chem. Eng. Progress, Symp. Ser.*, **56,** 95 (1960)].

If the ideal distribution law can be assumed, according to which the concentrations (mole or mass fractions, volume fractions, or moles or mass per unit volume) in the two phases are proportional to each other ($y_n = Kx_n$, where y = extract concentration and x = raffinate concentration) and the solvent is insoluble in the non-solvent (raffinate) phase, the mass balances are greatly simplified. For a single equilibrium stage

$$x_n = \frac{H}{H + KS} x_{n-1} \qquad (14\text{-}112)$$

where H = mass of component A in the raffinate feed (and in the effluent) and S = mass of solvent in the feed (and in the extract effluent). For equal quantities of fresh solvent containing no solute initially, the concentration of the unextracted component B in the raffinate phase after N equilibrium contacts of the multistage, cross-flow type is

$$x_N = \left(1 + \frac{KS}{H}\right)^{-N} x_0 \qquad (14\text{-}113)$$

For a fixed total quantity NS of solvent, x_N will be least when the total is divided equally, as assumed in Eq. (14-113).

Underwood [*Ind. Chemist*, **10,** 129 (1934)] has given a

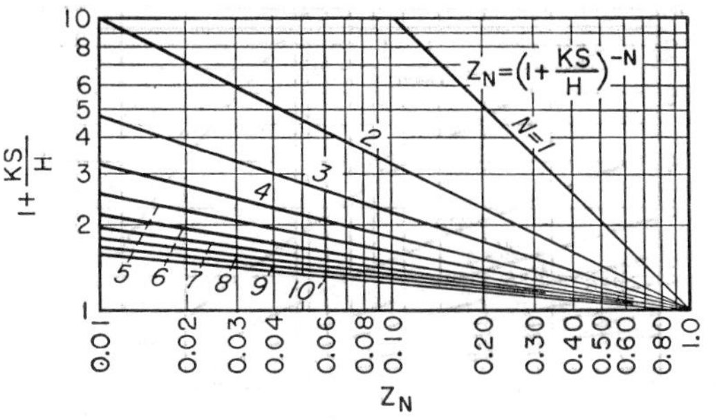

FIG. 14-42. Underwood's chart for graphical solution of Eq. (14-113). [*Underwood, Ind. Chemist*, **10**, 128 (1934).]

graphical solution of this equation in terms of $Z_N(= x_N/x_0)$ vs. the stripping factor, KS/H (see Fig. 14-42). If the total quantity of solvent is fixed the same figure and equation may be used with the quantity $K(NS)/NH$ replacing KS/H.

Countercurrent Multistage Extraction. The general flow sheet for this continuous extraction process is shown in Fig. 14-25*e*. In the following we consider first the stripping of component B from an A-B feed mixture, using solvent S; next we consider the enrichment of an extract phase, using an enriching column with reflux; finally we put two such cascades together to form a multistage, countercurrent extractor with reflux at each end. The computations are made graphically on the Janecke-Thiele or Maloney-Schubert coordinates.

Stripping Column. Figure 14-43 shows the countercurrent flow of raffinate stream downward and extract

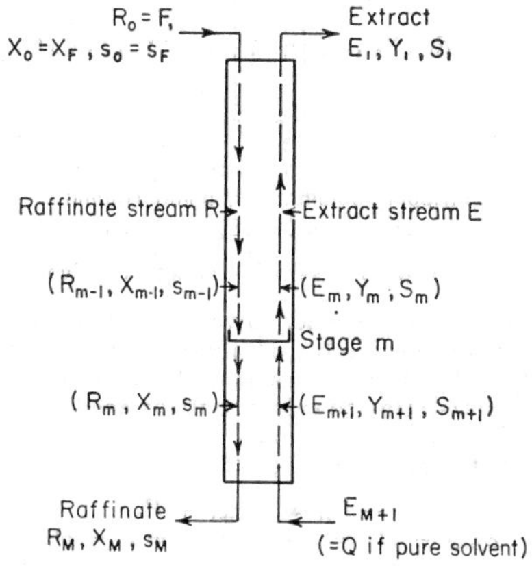

FIG. 14-43. Diagram of solvent-extraction stripping tower.

upward—the directions depend on the relative densities of the phases—in a stripping column. **Material balances** around the bottom of the cascade needed to establish the operating line relationship are, for $A + B$:

$$R_{m-1} + E_{M+1} = R_M + E_m \tag{14-114}$$

where E_{M+1} = mass flow rate of fresh solvent = Q if the fresh solvent does not contain either A or B; R_M = mass flow rate of stripped raffinate phase; E_m = extract leaving stage m; R_{m-1} = raffinate entering stage m from stage $(m-1)$. Equation (14-114) is equivalent to

$$R_{m-1} - E_m = R_M - E_{M+1} = K \tag{14-115}$$

where K, the net downward flow of $A + B$, is the same for every stage m. Material balance for the solvent:

$$R_{m-1}s_{m-1} + E_{M+1}S_{M+1} = R_M s_M + E_m S_m \tag{14-116}$$

or
$$R_{m-1}s_{m-1} - E_m S_m = R_M s_M - E_{M+1}S_{M+1} = Ks_K \tag{14-117}$$

where S and s are defined as per Fig. 14-40. The right-hand side represents the net downward flow of solvent through any stage, a negative quantity. If the fresh solvent feed to the bottom stage M is pure, $s_K = s_M - (Q/R_M)$. In general,

$$s_K = \frac{R_M s_M - E_{M+1}S_{M+1}}{R_M - E_{M+1}} \tag{14-118}$$

For component B:

$$R_{m-1}X_{m-1} + E_{M+1}Y_{M+1} = R_M X_M + E_m Y_m \tag{14-119}$$

or
$$R_{m-1}X_{m-1} - E_m Y_m = R_M X_M - E_{M+1}Y_{M+1} = KX_K \tag{14-120}$$

where X and Y are defined as per Fig. 14-40. The right side represents the net downward flow of component B through any stage. If the fresh solvent fed to the bottom stage is pure, $X_K = X_M$. In general,

$$X_K = \frac{R_M X_M - E_{M+1}Y_{M+1}}{R_M - E_{M+1}} \tag{14-121}$$

Equations (14-117) and (14-120) are first-order difference equations representing the stage-by-stage changes in composition of the countercurrent streams. They are to be solved graphically.

Solving Eq. (14-117) and (14-120) for R_{m-1}/E_m with the aid of Eq. (14-115), we get

$$\frac{R_{m-1}}{E_m} = \frac{Y_m - X_K}{X_{m-1} - X_K} = \frac{S_m - s_K}{s_{m-1} - s_K} \tag{14-122}$$

which indicates that three points on the Janecke coordinates lie on a straight line: (s_K, X_K), (s_{m-1}, X_{m-1}), and (S_m, Y_m). The latter two apply at one level in the cascade, *i.e.*, between stages $m-1$ and m; the first point applies to all the stages.

Construction of the operating line now proceeds as indicated in Fig. 14-44: (*a*) Locate point K. This is done very simply when the fresh solvent is pure by finding a point below the point (s_M, X_M) on the lower branch of the upper figure at a distance downward equal to Q/R_M or to $Q/(R_0 - E_1)$, where R_0 is the solvent-free feed rate, R_M is the solvent-free raffinate rate, and E_1 is the solvent-free extract rate. (*b*) Draw a number of straight lines in arbitrary directions through K across both lower and upper branches of the upper figure, thereby locating possible pairs of values of X_{m-1} and Y_m. (*c*) Transfer these to the lower part of the figure, thereby locating the operating line. (*d*) Finally, step off theoretical stages between equilibrium and operating lines on the lower figure, extending from the specified compositions of the raffinate to that of the feed.

If the ideal distribution law can be assumed, *i.e.*, if $y_m = Kx_m$, the computations can be made with a simple formula. This will be possible only when components A and S are mutually insoluble and, ordinarily, only when small amounts of B are distributed between A-rich and solvent-rich phases. In this case operating and equilibrium lines are straight, and solution of the difference equations expressing material balances and equilibrium

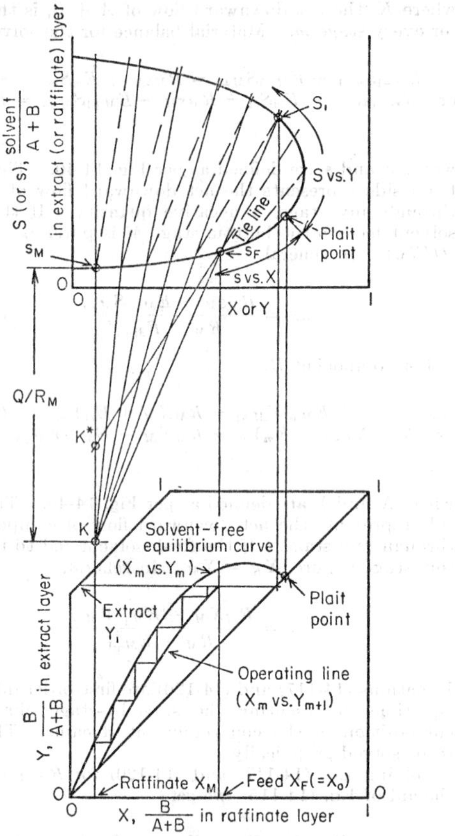

FIG. 14-44. Graphical construction of operating line, stripping column.

can be expressed by the **Kremser formula** [*cf.* Underwood, *Ind. Chemist*, **10**, 129 (1934); Hunter and Nash, *J. Soc. Chem. Ind.*, **51**, 285T (1932)]:

$$Z_M = \frac{x_0 - (y_1/K)}{x_M - (y_1/K)} = \frac{U-1}{U^{M+1}-1} \qquad (14\text{-}123)$$

where $U = SK/H$; x_0 = concentration of component B in raffinate feed to stripping column; y_1 = concentration of B in extract product stream; x_M = concentration of B in stripped raffinate product from the Mth stage; S = solvent rate to column; H = feed rate of A in the A-rich phase. S and K must be expressed in the same units that are used for expressing concentrations x and y in the distribution law. Figure 14-45 is a plot of Eq. (14-123), as given by Underwood. An alternate form of Eq. (14-123) which has been solved for number of stages required M is [Colburn, *Trans. Am. Inst. Chem. Engrs.*, **35**, 211 (1939)]

$$M = \frac{\log\{[(1-U)/UZ] + (1/U)\}}{-\log(1/U)} \qquad (14\text{-}124)$$

Ordinarily U is greater than unity for a stripping column.

Enriching Column. It is obvious that, depending on the shape of the binodal curve for the ternary system, it may be possible to effect a further purification of the extract stream coming from the stripping column of the previous section by countercurrent contact with a raffinate stream. This is especially true when the system is

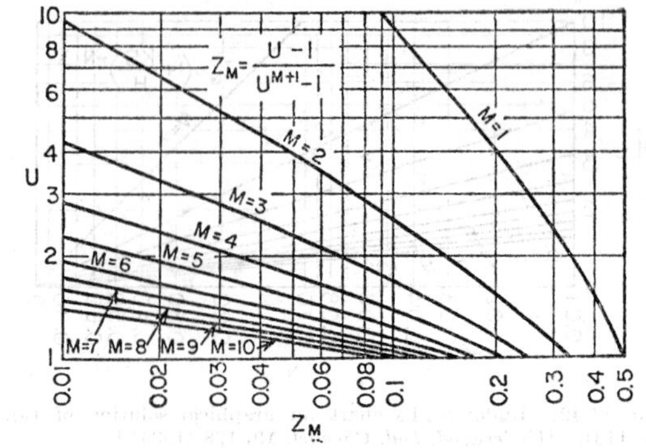

FIG. 14-45. Underwood's chart for graphical solution of Eq. (14-123). [*Underwood, Ind. Chemist*, **10**, 129 (1934).]

of type II and the two-phase region therefore extends all the way across the solvent-free composition scale. Figure 14-46 shows the flow sheet of such an operation.

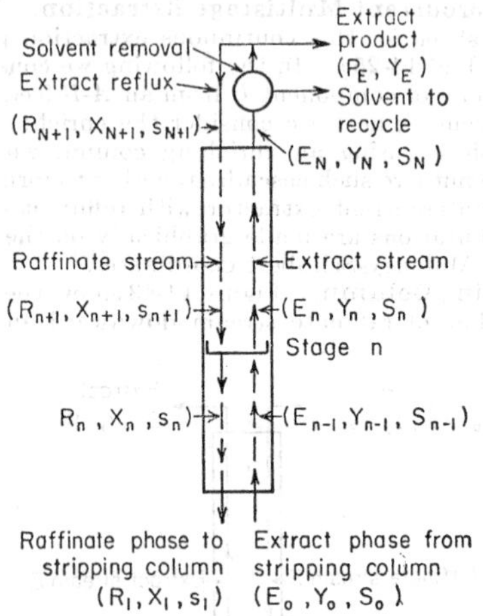

FIG. 14-46. Diagram of solvent-extraction enriching tower.

At the top of the cascade, solvent is removed from the extract product—*e.g.*, by distillation—and part of the solvent-free stream becomes available as raffinate reflux. The **material-balance relationships** needed to find the operating line for this section are similar to those for the stripping column. For $A + B$:

$$R_n + E_N = R_{N+1} + E_{n-1} \qquad (14\text{-}125)$$

$$E_{n-1} - R_n = E_N - R_{N+1} = J = P_E \qquad (14\text{-}126)$$

where P_E = net upward flow of $A + B$. For solvent:

$$R_n s_n + E_N S_N = R_{N+1} s_{N+1} + E_{n-1} S_{n-1} \qquad (14\text{-}127)$$

$$E_{n-1} S_{n-1} - R_n s_n = E_N S_N - R_{N+1} s_{N+1} = J S_J \qquad (14\text{-}128)$$

$$S = \frac{E_N S_N - R_{N+1} s_{N+1}}{E_N - R_{N+1}} = \frac{E_N}{P_E} S_N \qquad (14\text{-}129)$$

Equation (14-129) applies only if the solvent separator removes all the solvent from the extract product stream. For component B:

$$R_n X_n + E_N Y_N = R_{N+1} X_{N+1} + E_{n-1} Y_{n-1} \qquad (14\text{-}130)$$

$$E_{n-1} Y_{n-1} - R_n X_n = E_N Y_N - R_{N+1} X_{N+1} = J Y_J \qquad (14\text{-}131)$$

$$Y_J = \frac{E_N Y_N - R_{N+1} X_{N+1}}{E_N - R_{N+1}} = X_{N+1} = Y_N \qquad (14\text{-}132)$$

The last two equations apply only if the solvent removed from the extract effluent in the solvent separator does not contain either A or B. These first-order difference equations are used graphically to find the functional relationship between Y_n and X_{n+1} along the operating line.

Solving Eqs. (14-128) and (14-131) for R_n/E_{n-1} with the aid of Eq. (14-125), we get

$$\frac{R_n}{E_{n-1}} = \frac{X_J - Y_{n-1}}{X_J - X_n} = \frac{S_J - S_{n-1}}{S_J - s_n} \qquad (14\text{-}133)$$

which indicates that the three points (S_J, X_J), (S_{n-1}, Y_{n-1}), and (s_n, X_n) lie on the same straight line.

Construction of the operating line for the enriching column now proceeds as follows in Fig. 14-47: (*a*)

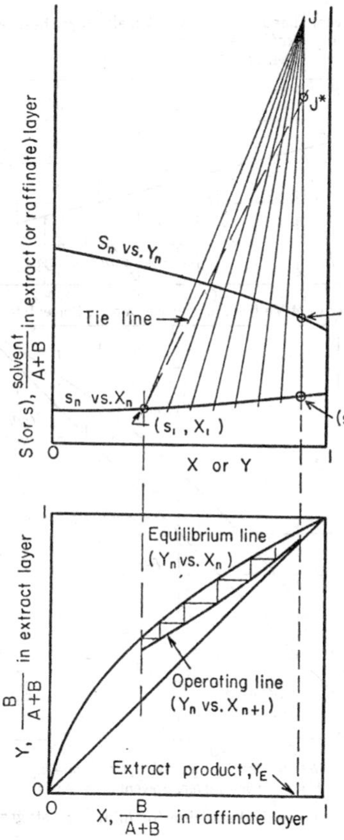

FIG. 14-47. Graphical construction of operating line, enriching column.

Locate point J. When the solvent separator is perfectly effective, J lies above the solvent-free composition of top product Y_N, the distance being $(R_{N+1}/P_E)S_N$, where the first factor is the external reflux ratio. (*b*) Draw a number of straight lines in random directions through J toward the phase-boundary curves on the upper diagram. These intersect the upper and lower curves of the figure at values of Y_{n-1} and X_n, respectively, that will satisfy the solvent and component material balances. (*c*) Transfer these solvent-free compositions to the lower graph, determining the operating line. (*d*) Finally, step off theoretical stages between equilibrium and operating lines on the lower graph, extending from the specified compositions of purified extract and raffinate.

It is clear that the **minimum reflux rate** in the enriching column is found by locating point J^* such that one of the lines radiating from J^* will coincide with a tie line. Usually the critical tie line is the one at the left, corresponding to the lower end of the operating line.

Double Column with Reflux at each End.* Figure 14-48 shows the flow sheet for this process, which

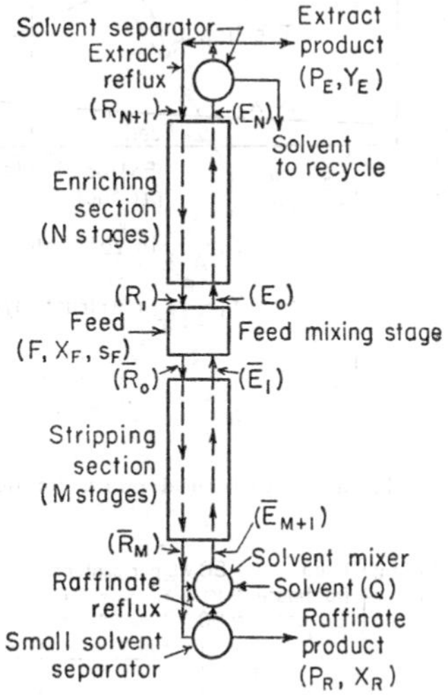

FIG. 14-48. Diagram of double solvent-extraction column with two reflux streams.

consists of stripping and enriching columns plus a feed stage. Total number of theoretical stages is $N + M + 1$. The material-balance relationships just derived apply in the upper and lower sections. The equations are coupled, however, by the material balances on the feed section. (In the following, a bar above a symbol means that it applies in the stripping section.) For $A + B$:

$$F + R_1 + \bar{E}_1 = E_0 + \bar{R}_0 \qquad (14\text{-}134)$$

$$F = (E_0 - R_1) + (\bar{R}_0 - \bar{E}_1) = J + K \qquad (14\text{-}135)$$

where F = feed flow rate, solvent-free basis. For solvent:

$$Fs_F + R_1s_1 + \bar{E}_1\bar{S}_1 = \bar{R}_0\bar{s}_0 + E_0S_0 \qquad (14\text{-}136)$$

$$Fs_F = (E_0S_0 - R_1s_1) + (\bar{R}_0\bar{s}_0 - \bar{E}_1\bar{S}_1) = JS_J + K\bar{s}_K = (J + K)s_F \qquad (14\text{-}137)$$

For component B:

$$FX_F + R_1X_1 + \bar{E}_1\bar{Y}_1 = \bar{R}_0X_0 + \bar{E}_0\bar{Y}_0 \qquad (14\text{-}138)$$

$$FX_F = (\bar{R}_0\bar{X}_0 - \bar{E}_1\bar{Y}_1) + (E_0Y_0 - R_1X_1) = KX_K + JY_J = (J + K)X_F \qquad (14\text{-}139)$$

Solving Eq. (14-137) and (14-139) for J/K we get

$$\frac{J}{K} = \frac{s_F - \bar{s}_K}{S_J - s_F} = \frac{X_F - \bar{X}_K}{Y_J - X_F} \qquad (14\text{-}140)$$

* Wehner [*Am. Inst. Chem. Engrs. J.*, **5**, 406 (1959)] and Skelland [*Ind. Eng. Chem.*, **53**, 799 (1961)] have called attention to the "futility of raffinate reflux in liquid extraction."

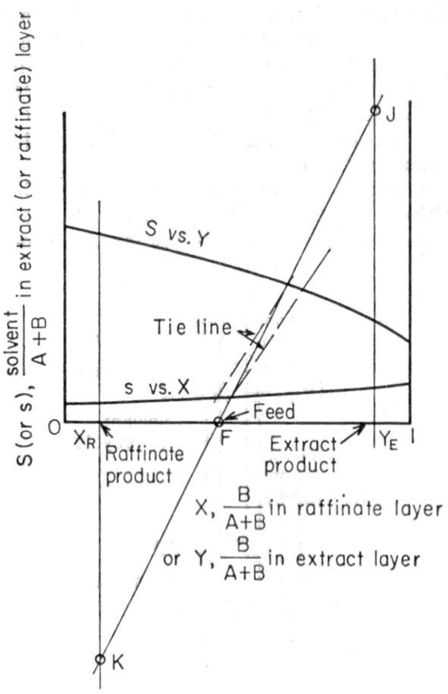

FIG. 14-49. Relation between focal points for double column with two reflux streams.

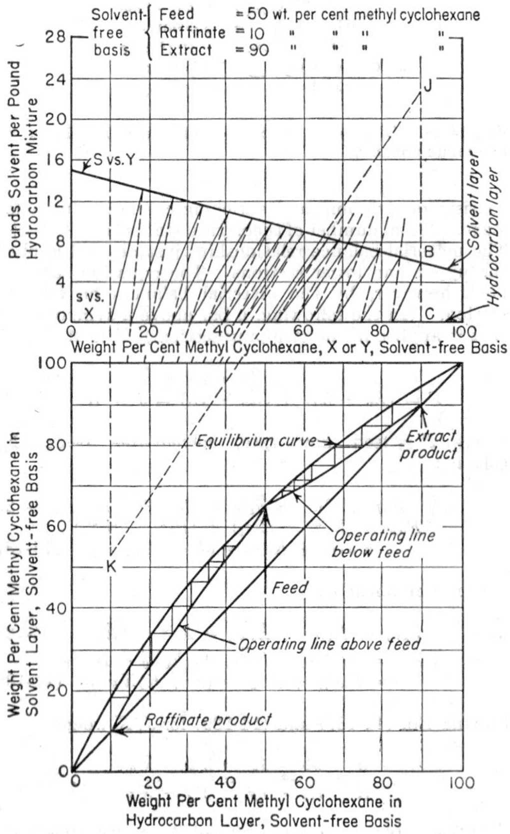

FIG. 14-50. Graphical solution of illustrative problem, minimum reflux condition.

which indicates that the following three points lie on a single straight line: $(\bar{s}_K, \bar{X}_K)$, (s_F, X_F), and (S_J, Y_J). Figure 14-49 shows this relationship graphically and indicates that any two of points K, F, and J are sufficient to determine the other. For example, having fixed the solvent-free compositions of feed and the raffinate and extract products and having selected the external reflux ratio at the extract product end of the cascade, the three points are determined and the operating lines in both columns are set. The minimum quantity of reflux is set, as before, by locating a point below J from which a radiating line coincides with a tie line. For an operable column the slope of the line KJ must be greater than that of the tie line passing through the feed point.

Figures 14-50, 14-51, and 14-52 taken from the paper of Maloney and Schubert [*Trans. Am. Inst. Chem. Engrs.*, **36**, 741 (1940)] illustrate these constructions for countercurrent extraction of a mixture of n-heptane and methyl cyclohexane with aniline as a solvent, corresponding to the minimum-reflux condition, to minimum stages, and to an operable condition, respectively.

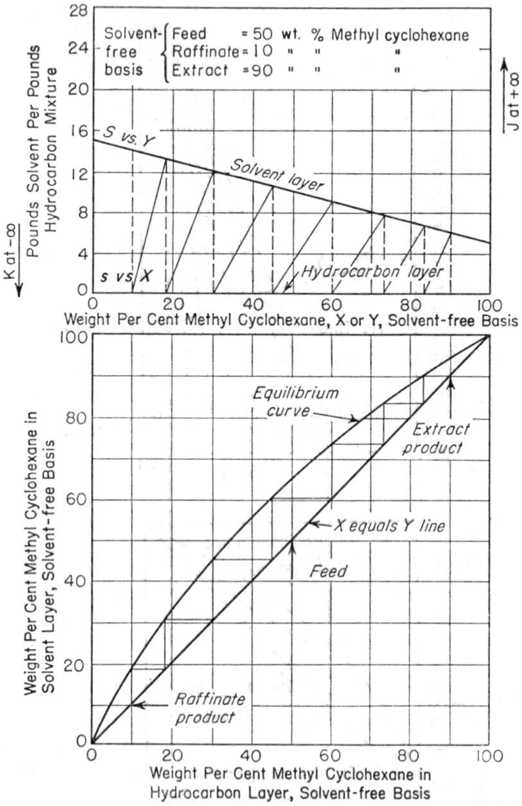

FIG. 14-51. Graphical solution for minimum stages.

Differential Countercurrent Extraction. Calculation of differential extraction operations, such as may occur in packed extraction columns, is formally similar to the calculations done in gas absorption or in distillation, as shown by Colburn [*Trans. Am. Inst. Chem. Engrs.*, **35**, 211 (1939)]. The simplest procedure involves computation of the **number of transfer units** N_{tOR}, given by the integral

$$N_{tOR} = \int_{x_N}^{x_0} \frac{dx}{x - x^*} \tag{14-141}$$

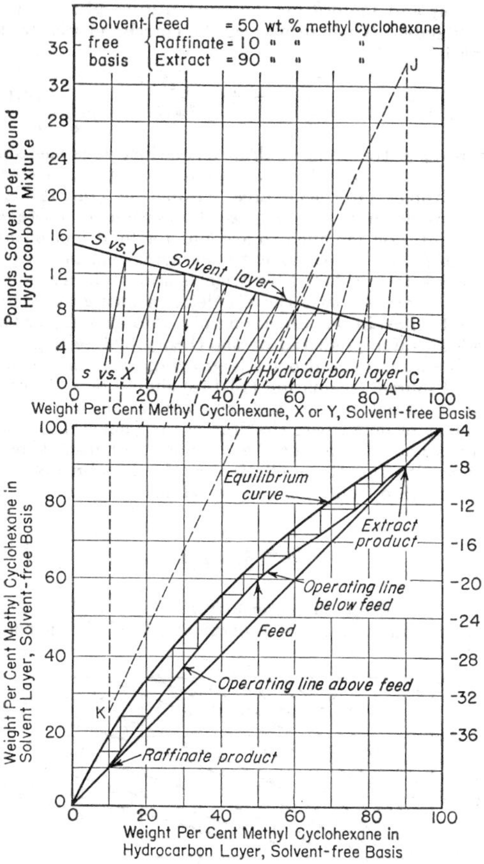

FIG. 14-52. Graphical solution for reflux ratio $L_e/E = 5$.

where x = fraction of component B in the bulk of the raffinate phase and x^* = fraction of B in a raffinate phase that would be at phase equilibrium with the extract phase containing bulk fraction y of substance B. The fractions may be either mole fractions or weight fractions but must be consistent. N_{tOR} is based on raffinate-phase concentrations, as indicated; number of transfer units on the basis of extract-phase concentrations would be defined as

$$N_{tOE} = \int_{y_N}^{y_0} \frac{dy}{y^* - y} \qquad (14\text{-}142)$$

Each of these is related to the required height of packing through the corresponding **over-all height of a transfer unit,** H_{OR} or H_{OE}. Evaluation of the N's can be done graphically, once operating and equilibrium lines are determined. This can be accomplished as indicated in the previous sections on stagewise countercurrent operations. In certain simplified cases the integral can be evaluated from a formula, as shown in Example 11.

Example 11. It is desired to extract a 25 weight per cent solution of acetic acid in water with isopropyl ether at 20°C. The exit-water phase is to contain 0.01 weight per cent acid, and 3.8 lb. of acid-free ether solvent will be used per pound of aqueous acid solution fed to the extractor-stripper. How many over-all transfer units, based on raffinate-phase concentrations, will be required?

Solution. Equilibrium data for this system are given by Nichols *et al.* [*Trans. Am. Inst. Chem. Engrs.*, **36,** 601, 609 (1940)].

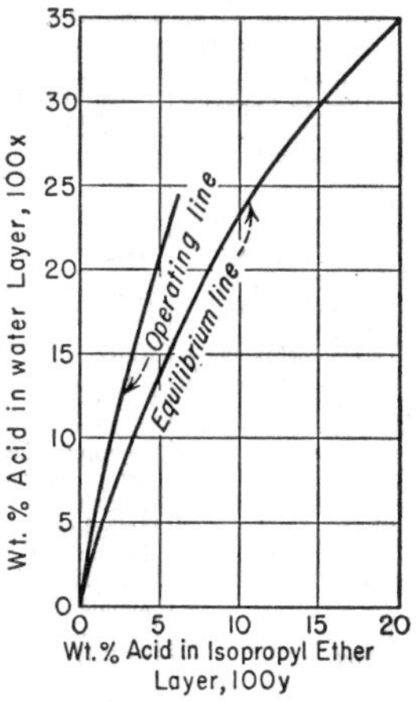

FIG. 14-53. Graphical solution of Example 11.

Using the graphical method for carrying out three-component material balances in order to locate the operating line, as illustrated by Fig. 14-44, the plot of bulk mole fractions in raffinate and extract phases shown in Fig. 14-53 was obtained. The value of the integral in Eq. (14-141) will be found by means of an approximate formula, as suggested by Colburn [*Ind. Eng. Chem.*, **33,** 459 (1941)]:

$$N_{tOR} = \frac{1}{1 - (mL_R/L_E)} \ln \left[\left(1 - \frac{mL_R}{L_E}\right) \frac{x_1 - my_2}{x_2 - my_2} \frac{1 - (mL_R/L_E)}{1 - (x_1^*/x_1)} + \frac{mL_R}{L_E} \right] \qquad (14\text{-}143)$$

where m = slope of the equilibrium line dx^*/dy at the lower left corner of Fig. 14-53; L_R = total flow rate of raffinate phase at point where it leaves column; L_E = total flow rate of extract phase at point where it enters column, *i.e.*, the flow rate of entering solvent; subscripts 1 and 2 indicate the raffinate-feed end and the solvent-feed end of the extractor, respectively.

Figure 14-53 shows that $L_E/L_R = 6.0$ at the dilute end and $m = 4.2$, using weight-fraction units. Furthermore, $x_1 = 0.25$ weight fraction, $x_2 = 0.0001$, $x_1^* = 0.16$, and $y_2 = 0$. These values give $mL_R/L_E = 0.70$ and

$$N_{tOR} = \frac{1}{1 - 0.7} \ln \left[(1 - 0.7) \frac{0.25}{0.0001} \frac{1 - 0.7}{1 - (0.16/0.25)} + 0.7 \right]$$
$$= 21$$

EXTRACTION RATES

Because of the large number of variables which influence mass-transfer rates in extraction equipment, development of generalized correlations has proved difficult. Approximate design procedures are given in this section for common extractor types, but these have not been tested broadly enough to justify their unrestricted use. For this reason, summaries of representative experimental results are also given for each type of extractor as an additional design guide. Empirical correlations are included which represent the results of these experimental studies.

Mass Transfer to Droplets. Studies of extraction with **single drops** have been used to elicit information regarding the mechanism of mass transfer under conditions of known interfacial area and time of contact. Table 14-65 lists some of these studies in which over-all mass-transfer coefficients were determined.

In order to measure individual phase coefficients, a technique first employed by Colburn and Welsh [*Trans. Am. Inst. Chem. Engrs.*, **38,** 179 (1942)] has also been used by Johnson and Hamielec [*Am. Inst. Chem. Engrs. J.*, **6,**

Table 14-65. Sources of Extraction-rate Data for Single Droplets

Solute	Dispersed phase	Continuous phase	Approx. m*	Ref.
Acetic acid........	Nitrobenzene	Water	0.016	3
Acetic acid........	Benzene	Water	0.03	7
Acetic acid........	Benzene	Water	0.03	8
Acetic acid........	Benzene	Water	0.03	4
Acetic acid........	Methyl isobutyl ketone	Water	0.5	7
Acetic acid........	Methyl isobutyl ketone	Water	0.5	4
Acetic acid........	Perchloroethylene	Water	....	6
Acetic acid........	Carbon tetrachloride	Water	....	6
Acetic acid........	Ondina 17 oil	Water	0.001	4
Acetic acid........	Ondina-kerosene	Water	0.0015	4
Acetic acid........	Water	Isopropyl ether	....	5
Acetic acid........	Water	Methyl isobutyl ketone	2	5
Acetic acid........	Water	Methyl isobutyl ketone	2	6
Acetic acid........	Water	Methyl isobutyl ketone	2	4
Acetic acid........	Water	Ethyl acetate	....	5
Acetic acid........	Water	Benzene	33	4
Acetone...........	Benzene	Water	0.94	4
Benzoic acid.......	Toluene	Water	10	1
Benzoic acid.......	Benzene	Water	6	4
Benzoic acid.......	Benzene	Water	6	2
Benzoic acid.......	Water	Benzene	0.1	4
Diethylamine.	Water	Toluene	....	3
Phenol............	Benzene	Water	2.7	4
Phenol............	Water	Benzene	0.37	4
Propionic acid.....	Benzene	Water	....	2
Salicylic acid......	Benzene	Water	2	4

* $m = c_D/c_C$, where c_D = concentration of solute in dispersed phase in equilibrium with continuous phase having concentration c_C.

References:

[1] Appel and Elgin, *Ind. Eng. Chem.*, **29**, 451 (1937).
[2] Coulson and Skinner, *Chem. Eng. Sci.*, **1**, 197 (1952).
[3] Garner and Skelland, *Ind. Eng. Chem.*, **46**, 1255 (1954).
[4] Handlos and Baron, *Am. Inst. Chem. Engrs. J.*, **3**, 127 (1957).
[5] Licht and Conway, *Ind. Eng. Chem.*, **42**, 1151 (1950).
[6] Licht and Pansing, *Ind. Eng. Chem.*, **45**, 1885 (1953).
[7] Sherwood, Evans, and Longcor, *Trans. Am. Inst. Chem. Engrs.*, **35**, 597 (1939).
[8] West *et al.*, *Ind. Eng. Chem.*, **43**, 234 (1951); **44**, 621 (1952).

145 (1960)]; Heertjes, Holve, and Talsma [*Chem. Eng. Sci.*, **3**, 122 (1954)]; and Laddha and Smith [*Chem. Eng. Progress*, **46**, 195 (1950)]. This involves contacting two slightly soluble liquids without a third solute present and observing the rate at which saturation of one or the other takes place. These various studies have led to information which permits estimating mass-transfer coefficients and interfacial areas for single drops. Coulson and Skinner have shown that extraction rates measured for single droplets can be employed to predict rates in spray and perforated-plate towers. Estimating methods for these types of commercial extractors thus rely on fundamental information on single droplets.

The total amount of extraction that occurs during the contact of a dispersed and continuous phase can be separated into three parts—that occurring during drop formation, that during rise or fall, and that upon coalescence. The rates during each of these stages will be treated separately.

Extraction During Drop Formation. Mass-transfer rates during drop formation have been considered by several workers, including Licht and coworkers; Sherwood, Evans, and Longcor; West and coworkers; Coulson and Skinner; Heertjes *et al.*; Johnson and Hamielec; Garner and Skelland; and Michels and Pigford. Licht and Conway, and West and coworkers have shown that as much as 20 per cent approach to equilibrium can occur during drop formation. Agreement among various workers on over-all mass-transfer coefficients during drop formation is poor, which is due in part to difficulty in finding suitable experimental techniques and in part to the effects of such extraneous variables as wettability of the nozzle tip and shape of the nozzle or orifice.

Probably the most reliable result is that obtained by Michels and Pigford for the **continuous-phase coefficient** only. Their results can be correlated well by the equation

$$(k_d)_C = 4.6\sqrt{\frac{D}{\pi t_d}} \qquad (14\text{-}144)$$

where t_d is the time of drop formation, D is the diffusivity, and $(k_d)_C$ is the average coefficient based on the final droplet interfacial area. Equation (14-144) is of the same form as the theoretical equation for unsteady-state diffusion modified to account for fluid motion near the interface. The constant 4.6 is somewhat higher than the 3.8 value predicted by Michels and Pigford's theory, which recognizes that the droplet is growing away from a fixed orifice in one direction only, and also higher than the 3.43 value predicted by the theory of Heertjes *et al.*, which assumes the droplet is growing uniformly around a fixed source. Equation (14-144) should be suitable for droplet formation from a sharp-edged orifice or from any capillary or hole where the droplet does not wet the face. It does not account for the promotion of mass transfer that results from the oscillations as the drop breaks away. Time of drop formation can be calculated from

$$t_d = \frac{2d^3}{3U_D D_c^2} \qquad (14\text{-}145)$$

where d = drop diameter (from Fig. 14-54); D_c = column diameter; U_D = superficial velocity of dispersed

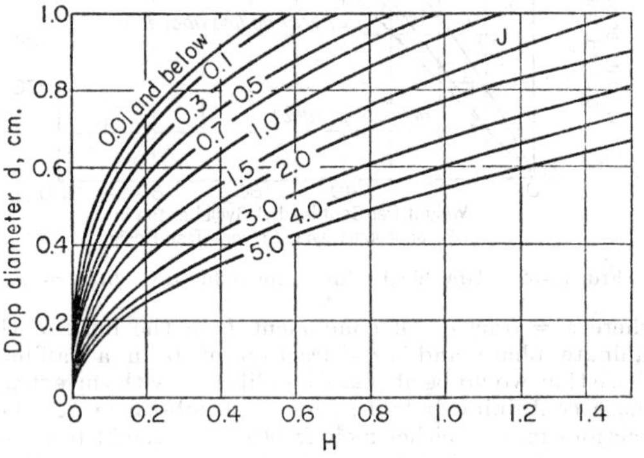

FIG. 14-54. Diameter of liquid droplets discharged from a simple nozzle into an immiscible liquid. [*Hayworth and Treybal, Ind. Eng. Chem.*, **42**, 1180 (1950).]

U_N = nozzle velocity, cm./sec.
D_N = nozzle diameter, cm.
ρ_D = density of dispersed phase, g./cc.
$\Delta\rho$ = density difference between phases, g./cc.
γ = interfacial tension, dynes/cm.
μ_c = viscosity of continuous phase, poise
$J = 0.00411\rho_D U_N^2/\Delta\rho$
$H = 0.0021\gamma D_N/\Delta\rho + 0.01069(D_N^{0.747}U_N^{0.365}\mu_c^{0.186}/\Delta\rho)^{3/2}$

phase (based on empty column). For individual droplets, the surface area to be employed in conjunction with $(k_d)_C$ of Eq. (14-144) can, of course, be calculated from drop diameter d.

Equation (14-144) applies outside the drop only. In many instances, this will be nearly equal to the **over-all coefficient** K_d, since internal circulation in the droplet during formation creates a high mass-transfer coefficient there. But if the equilibrium strongly favors the presence of solute in the continuous phase, the resistance to mass transfer within the droplet may not be negligible. It is noteworthy, however, that with an m value as low as 0.03

($m = c_D/c_C$) for the extraction of acetic acid from nitrobenzene drops forming in water, Garner and Skelland obtained data which could be correlated by the expression $K_d = 0.017\ t_d^{-0.58}$; this is in substantial agreement with Eq. (14-144) for a diffusion coefficient of 1.4×10^{-5} sq. cm./sec., despite the low equilibrium constant. Garner and Skelland did observe a slight increase of the over-all coefficient upon decreasing the internal diameter of their capillary for a given outside diameter. This suggests that internal circulation enhanced the coefficient within the drop, which exerted a small influence on the over-all coefficient. Unfortunately, for those systems for which the m value is appreciably lower than 0.03, the internal resistance will be significant, and no good methods for estimating it exist. A lower limit can be obtained for the droplet interior by employing the treatment of Heertjes *et al.*, which assumes that the droplet is growing uniformly around a point source. The result is

$$(k_d)_D = \frac{24}{7}\sqrt{\frac{D}{\pi t_d}} \qquad (14\text{-}146)$$

This result has been confirmed very approximately by Johnson and Hamielec. Heertjes *et al.*, however, found Eq. (14-146) gave lower results by a factor of 2 to 4 than their experimental values.

Extraction During Rise or Fall. As in the case of extraction during drop formation, agreement is poor among various workers studying different systems, largely because only over-all coefficients are reported. These coefficients are useful only for application with the system in question operated at approximately the same conditions (see Table 14-65 for specific sources of data). Handlos and Baron [*Am. Inst. Chem. Engrs. J.*, **3**, 127 (1957)] have tried to resolve this problem by employing theoretical models developed for each phase separately [see Kronig and Brink, *Appl. Sci. Research*, **A2**, 1942 (1950); also Licht and Pansing, *Ind. Eng. Chem.*, **45**, 1885 (1953)]. The resulting equations have been compared with a substantial quantity of mass-transfer (and heat-transfer) data with moderate success. The root-mean-square deviation of the observed transfer coefficients from the measured coefficients was 30 per cent when activities were employed as driving forces and somewhat poorer using concentrations. The equation for the **fluid surrounding the drop** is

$$k_0 = 2\sqrt{\frac{DV}{\pi d}} \qquad (14\text{-}147)$$

where V = relative velocity of rise or fall, cm./sec.; d = drop diameter, cm.; D = diffusivity, sq. cm./sec. Equation (14-147) is simply the Higbie equation, given earlier as Eq. (14-22). Use of this equation requires knowledge of drop diameter, which can be estimated using Fig. 14-54. Drop velocity also must be known. This may be estimated by one of two equations, depending on whether the drop diameter is greater than or less than a critical value [Klee and Treybal, *Am. Inst. Chem. Engrs. J.*, **2**, 444 (1956)]. The critical drop diameter d_c is

$$d_c = 0.33\rho_C^{-0.14}\Delta\rho^{-0.43}\mu_C^{0.30}\gamma^{0.24} \qquad (14\text{-}148)$$

where ρ_C = density of continuous phase, g./cc.; $\Delta\rho$ = density difference, g./cc.; μ_C = viscosity of continuous phase, poises; γ = interfacial tension, dynes/cm. For $d < d_c$,

$$V_I = 38.3\rho_C^{-0.45}\Delta\rho^{0.58}\mu_C^{-0.11}d^{0.70} \qquad (14\text{-}149a)$$

For $d > d_c$,

$$V_{II} = 17.6\rho_C^{-0.55}\Delta\rho^{0.28}\mu_C^{0.10}\gamma^{0.18} \qquad (14\text{-}149b)$$

where V is in cm./sec. Equations (14-149) differ from the equations based on solid spheres in that they account for oscillations and eccentricities of the drops.

For the **fluid within the drop** (Handlos and Baron, *loc. cit.*),

$$k_i = 0.00375\frac{V}{1 + (\mu_D/\mu_C)} \qquad (14\text{-}150)$$

Equation (14-150) is based on a model that accounts for surface replacement caused by internal circulation. The effect of interfacial tension in influencing internal circulation is not accounted for by these equations, and this is probably the most serious shortcoming of the model. It is noteworthy that observed coefficients and those predicted from Eq. (14-150) are at least an order of magnitude higher than would be expected for simple molecular diffusion into a rigid sphere of liquid during rise or fall. Equations (14-147) and (14-150) are probably best applicable for large drops, where interfacial tension forces are negligible, and for low velocities, where drop deformation is not significant.

Extraction During Coalescence. This rate process has been least well defined of those associated with droplets. Licht and Conway, studying three different systems, found that from 6 to 13 per cent approach to equilibrium was achieved during coalescence. In those instances, this amount was roughly equivalent to that extracted during drop formation. Johnson and Hamielec presented a theoretical model applicable to the situation where the major resistance to mass transfer upon coalescence is in the dispersed phase. They assumed that, as each drop settles, it spreads instantaneously as a layer of uniform initial concentration across the entire coalescence surface. Thus, the Higbie equation

$$(k_c)_D = \frac{2}{\sqrt{\pi}}\sqrt{\frac{D}{t_d}} \qquad (14\text{-}151)$$

can be applied in conjunction with the area of the entire coalescence surface. Johnson and Hamielec found this equation to be approximately correct when applied to their experiment in which they measured dispersed-phase coefficients only for the water-cyclohexanol system. Equation (14-151) should be used judiciously in this application, since it does not account for resistance in the continuous phase which may be controlling in many instances. In fact, if the layer of continuous-phase liquid adjacent to the coalescence interface is not well mixed, it is probable that the continuous-phase resistance will control (except for low values of $m = c_D/c_C$).

Spray Towers. The equations given above for mass transfer to droplets can be used to estimate transfer rates in spray towers if drop size and dispersed-phase hold-up are known. It should be noted that all these methods are based on idealized models which are not always met in practice. Droplet oscillations, departure of drops from spherical shape, effects of surface contaminants, effects of mass transfer on the character of the interface, and many other factors cause deviations of transfer rates from those predicted by these simple models. In order to understand more fully the actual mechanisms, many investigators have studied droplet behavior and interface character. References to a few such studies are: Klee and Treybal [*Am. Inst. Chem. Engrs. J.*, **2**, 444 (1956)]; Shevyaknova and Smirnov [*J. Appl. Chem. (U.S.S.R.)*, **29**, 207 (1956)]; Christiansen and Hixson [*Ind. Eng. Chem.*, **49**, 1017 (1957)]; Siemes and Kauffmann [*Chem. Ing. Tech.*, **29**, 32 (1957)]; Vermeulen, Williams, and Langlois [*Chem. Eng. Progress*, **51**, 85 (1955)]; Spells [*Proc. Roy. Soc. (London)*, **B65**, 541 (1952)];

Table 14-66. Extraction Rates in Spray Columns
H.T.U.'s in ft., Ka's in ft./hr., Z is height in ft.

Solute	Dispersed phase	Continuous phase	Direction of extraction	U_C, ft./hr.	U_D, ft./hr.	Tower Diam., in.	Tower Height, in.	Distributor	Rate ($K = BU_C^R U_D^S$), units in ft. and hr. B	R	S	K	Ref.
Acetic acid	Water	Isopropyl ether	$D \to C$	44–103	71–102	2.03	48.8	⅛-in. nozzle	5.4	−0.54	0.54	H.T.U.$_{OD}$	3
Acetic acid	Water	Isopropyl ether	$C \to D$	31–112	99–103	2.03	48.8	⅛-in. nozzle	5.9	−0.74	0.74	H.T.U.$_{OD}$	3
Acetic acid	Water	Methyl isobutyl ketone	$D \to C$	16–45	15–46	1.82	46	9 0.10-in. holes	3.6	0.60	−0.60	H.T.U.$_{OC}$	8
Acetic acid	Water	Methyl isobutyl ketone	$C \to D$	16–45	15–45	1.82	46	9 0.10-in. holes	2.8	0.60	−0.60	H.T.U.$_{OC}$	8
Acetic acid	Water	Methyl isobutyl ketone	$C \to D$	16–46	44–191	1.82	46	36 0.10-in. holes	2.0	0.60	−0.60	H.T.U.$_{OC}$	8
Acetic acid	Water	Benzene	$D \to C$	45	44–175	1.82	46	36 0.10-in. holes	0.16	0	1.0	K_{Ca}	8
Acetic acid	Ethylene dichloride	Water	$D \to C$	103–246	49–306	4.0	96	3-in. nozzle	40	−1	1	H.T.U.$_{OD}$	9
Acetic acid	Isopropyl ether	Water	$D \to C$	37–496	58–178	2.03	48.8	⅛-in. nozzle	10.8	0.9	−0.9	H.T.U.$_{OC}$	3
Acetic acid	Isopropyl ether	Water	$C \to D$	99–168	35–95	2.03	48.8	⅛-in. nozzle	5.9	0.8	−0.8	H.T.U.$_{OC}$	3
Acetic acid	Methyl isobutyl ketone	Water	$D \to C$ $C \to D$	16–45	13–45	1.82	46	9 0.10-in. holes	2.6	−0.3	0.3	H.T.U.$_{OD}$	8
Acetic acid	Methyl isobutyl ketone	Water	$C \to D$	44–197	44–237	1.82	46	36 0.10-in. holes	1.5	−0.2	0.2	H.T.U.$_{OD}$	8
Acetic acid	Methyl isobutyl ketone	Water	$C \to D$	40–90	40	3.55	66	6 0.12-in. holes	2.6	−1.4	1.4	H.T.U.$_{OD}$	14
Acetic acid	Methyl isobutyl ketone	Water	$D \to C$ $C \to D$	45–195	45–290	2	29.5	21 and 56 0.10-in. holes	Not correlated by this expression				4
Acetic acid	Benzene	Water	$C \to D$	16–45	45–120	1.82	46	36 0.10-in. holes	0.16	0	1.0	K_{Da}	8
Acetic acid	Benzene	Water	$C \to D$	10–60	30	3.55	66	6 0.12-in. holes	3.5	−0.13	0.13	H.T.U.$_{OD}$	14
Acetic acid	Toluene	Water	$D \to C$	50–60	18–67	3.75	72	2.94-in. nozzle	Not correlated by this expression				6
Adipic acid	Diethyl ether	Water	$C \to D$	11–80	20–55	6	60	113 ³⁄₃₂-in. holes	0.5	0	1	K_{Da}	7
Benzoic acid	Water	Methyl isobutyl ketone	$C \to D$	46	44–175	1.82	46	36 0.10-in. holes	0.0067	0	1.0	K_{Ca}	8
Benzoic acid	Toluene	Water	$D \to C$	11–38	12–62	8.75	69	³⁄₃₂-in. holes	16	1.0	1.0	H.T.U.$_{OC}$	13
Benzoic acid	Toluene	Water	$D \to C$	12–37	12–63	8.75	69	⅛-in. holes	16	1.0	−1.0	H.T.U.$_{OC}$	13
Benzoic acid	Toluene	Water	$D \to C$	11–179	11–63	8.75	69	¹⁄₁₆-in. holes	9.3	0.9	−0.9	H.T.U.$_{OC}$	13
Benzoic acid	Toluene	Water	$D \to C$	44–133	13–58	2.03	60	R-Filtros nozzle	1.85	0.9	−0.9	H.T.U.$_{OC}$	1
Benzoic acid	Toluene	Water	$D \to C$	50–166	21–63	2.03	60	H-Filtros nozzle	1.10	0.5	−0.5	H.T.U.$_{OC}$	1
Benzoic acid	Toluene	Water	$D \to C$	44–133	13–44	2.03	60	Sprayco 5B nozzle	9.3	0.9	−0.9	H.T.U.$_{OC}$	1
$CoCl_2$	Capryl alcohol	Water-HCl	$C \to D$	22–49	45–150	1.25	68	10 0.10-in. tubes	Not correlated by this expression				11
$CoCl_2$-$NiCl_2$	Capryl alcohol	Water-HCl	$C \to D$	23–51	42–170	1.25	68	10 0.10-in. tubes	Not correlated by this expression				11
$FeCl_3$	Isopropyl ether	Water-HCl	$C \to D$	56–59	10–58	1.45	31	1.12-in. nozzle	Depends on $FeCl_3$ concentration				5
Formic acid	Methyl isobutyl ketone	Water	$C \to D$	....	....	Several columns		Several nozzles	Not correlated by this expression				15
HCl	Mixed pentanols	Water	$C \to D$	....	....	1.45	31	1.12-in. nozzle	Depends on HCl concentration				2
Propionic acid	Methyl isobutyl ketone	Water	$C \to D$	45	49–132	1.82	46	36 0.10-in. holes	0.281	0	1.0	K_{Da}	8
Propionic acid	Methyl isobutyl ketone	Water	$C \to D$	38–40	20–49	1.4	30, 42, 54	4 0.159-in. holes	2.34	0.87	−0.87	H.T.U.$_{OC}$ × $1.59^{1/Z}$	10
Propionic acid	Methyl isobutyl ketone	Water	$C \to D$	28–50	20–40	Several columns		Several nozzles	Not correlated by this expression				15
Propionic acid	Ethylene dichloride	Water	$D \to C$	103–246	45–350	4.0	96	3-in. nozzle	10	−1	1	H.T.U.$_{OD}$	9
Propionic acid	Water	Methyl isobutyl ketone	$C \to D$	45	16–132	1.82	46	36 0.10-in. holes	0.267	0	1.0	K_{Ca}	8
Water	Methyl ethyl ketone	$CaCl_2$-H_2O	$D \to C$	16–36	27–66	3.55	66	6 0.12-in. holes	0.4	0	1.0	K_{Da}	12

[1] Appel and Elgin, *Ind. Eng. Chem.*, **29**, 451 (1937).
[2] Crittendon and Hixson, *Ind. Eng. Chem.*, **46**, 265 (1954).
[3] Elgin and Browning, *Trans. Am. Inst. Chem. Engrs.*, **31**, 639 (1935); **32**, 105 (1936).
[4] Fleming and Johnson, *Chem. Eng. Progress*, **49**, 497 (1953).
[5] Geankoplis and Hixson, *Ind. Eng. Chem.*, **42**, 1141 (1950).
[6] Geankoplis, Wells, and Hawk, *Ind. Eng. Chem.*, **43**, 1848 (1951).
[7] Gier and Hougen, *Ind. Eng. Chem.*, **45**, 1362 (1953).
[8] Johnson and Bliss, *Trans. Am. Inst. Chem. Engrs.*, **42**, 331 (1946).
[9] Johnson, Minard, Huang, Hansuld, and McNamara, *Am. Inst. Chem. Engrs. J.*, **3**, 101 (1957).
[10] Kreager and Geankoplis, *Ind. Eng. Chem.*, **45**, 2155 (1953).
[11] Kylander and Garwin, *Chem. Eng. Progress*, **47**, 186 (1951).
[12] Meissner, Stokes, Hunter, and Morrow, *Ind. Eng. Chem.*, **36**, 917 (1944).
[13] Row, Koffolt, and Withrow, *Trans. Am. Inst. Chem. Engrs.*, **37**, 559 (1941).
[14] Sherwood, Evans, and Longcor, *Ind. Eng. Chem.*, **31**, 1144 (1939); *Trans. Am. Inst. Chem. Engrs.*, **35**, 597 (1939).
[15] Vogt and Geankoplis, *Ind. Eng. Chem.*, **46**, 1763 (1954).

Table 14-67. Extraction-rate Data for Sieve-plate Columns
H.E.T.S.'s and H.T.U.'s in ft., U_C and U_D in ft./hr.

Solute	Dispersed phase	Continuous phase	Tower diam., in.	Free area, %	Plate spacing, in.	Equation	Ref.
Acetic acid	Ether	Water	8.6	3.3	4.6	$H_{OD} = 1.75U_C/U_D$	6
Acetic acid	Ethyl acetate	Water	2.0	....	8, 16, 24	E_{OD} = 25 to 100%	4
Adipic acid	Methyl isobutyl ketone	Water	4.0	6.0	6.0	H_{OD} = 1.8 to 8.4	3
Adipic acid	Water	Methyl isobutyl ketone	4.0	6.0	6.0	H_{OC} = 1.4 to 11.5	3
Benzoic acid	Kerosene	Water	3.6	13.6	4.7	$H_{OC} = 5.4(U_C/U_D)^{0.94}$	1
Benzoic acid	Toluene	Water	3.6	13.6	4.8	$H_{OC} = 5.4(U_C/U_D)^{0.94}$	1
Benzoic acid	Toluene	Water	3.6	4.7	3	$H_{OC} = 4.3(U_C/U_D)^{0.91}$	8
Benzoic acid	Toluene	Water	3.6	4.7	6	$H_{OC} = 7.2(U_C/U_D)^{0.91}$	8
Benzoic acid	Toluene	Water	3.6	4.7	9	$H_{OC} = 8.1(U_C/U_D)^{0.91}$	8
Benzoic acid	Toluene	Water	8.8	9.5	6	$H_{OC} = 4.9(U_C/U_D)^{1.03}$	7
Benzoic acid	Toluene	Water	8.8	5.4	6	$H_{OC} = 4.3(U_C/U_D)^{1.32}$	7
Benzoic acid	Toluene	Water	2.0	....	8, 16, 24	E_{OD} = 3 to 16%	4
Diethylamine	Toluene	Water	4.0	6.0	6.0	H_{OC} = 2 to 50	2
Diethylamine	Toluene	Water	4.0	6.0	6.0	H_{OC} = 3 to 33	3
Methyl ethyl ketone	Gasoline	Water	3.8	3.0	3	$H_{OC} = 1.45(U_C/U_D)^{0.71}$	5
Methyl ethyl ketone	Gasoline	Water	3.8	3.0	6	$H_{OC} = 1.95(U_C/U_D)^{0.72}$	5

References for Table 14-67
[1] Allerton, Strom, and Treybal, *Trans. Am. Inst. Chem. Engrs.*, **39**, 361 (1943).
[2] Garner, Ellis, and Hill, *Am. Inst. Chem. Engrs. J.*, **1**, 185 (1955).
[3] Garner, Ellis, and Hill, *Trans. Inst. Chem. Engrs.*, **34**, 223 (1956).
[4] Mayfield and Church, *Ind. Eng. Chem.*, **44**, 2253 (1952).
[5] Moulton and Walkey, *Trans. Am. Inst. Chem. Engrs.*, **40**, 695 (1944).
[6] Pyle, Colburn, and Duffey, *Ind. Eng. Chem.*, **42**, 1042 (1950).
[7] Row, Koffolt, and Withrow, *Trans. Am. Inst. Chem. Engrs.*, **37**, 559 (1941).
[8] Treybal and Dumoulin, *Ind. Eng. Chem.*, **34**, 709 (1942).

Buchanan [*Australian J. Appl. Sci.*, **3**, 233 (1952)]; Garner and Skelland [*Trans. Inst. Chem. Engrs.*, **29**, 315 (1951)]; Hughes and Gilliland [*Chem. Eng. Progress*, **48**, 497 (1952)]; and Hayworth and Treybal [*Ind. Eng. Chem.*, **42**, 1174 (1950)].

Generalized procedures for predicting extraction rate coefficients in spray towers are given in Sec. 21 (pp. 21-24 to 21-25). Because of the uncertainties in the application of such generalized procedures, a list of **representative spray-column data** is included (Table 14-66) as a design guide. Transfer coefficients are reported as presented by the authors with no attempt to ascertain whether consistent driving forces were employed. Inspection of the table shows that the nature of the spray distributor can have a large effect. In some instances, direction of extraction is important. Results of many of the investigations are expressed by the relation $K = BU_C^R U_D^S$, and the values of the constants are tabulated. In some cases, this correlating expression represents the data less well than the correlation of the original investigator, and reference to the original work may be desirable. In other cases, correlation in this form is not feasible. Most of the data were taken at room temperature; if more precise information is needed, the original references should be consulted.

Plate Towers. In the **sieve-plate column,** one of the phases is dispersed at intervals by perforated plates spaced throughout the column, and therefore behaves as a series of short spray columns with a continuous phase between each phase which is nearly completely mixed. Coulson and Skinner [*Chem. Eng. Sci.*, **1**, 197 (1952)] have shown that data on single droplets can be used to predict performance of sieve-plate columns. See Sec. 21 (p. 21-27) for design procedures.

Generalized design methods are best fortified by experimental data on individual coefficients or areas or even over-all coefficients where possible, since factors not accounted for by these methods can often be important. Table 14-67 summarizes some experimental results for various systems. Morello and Poffenberger [*Ind. Eng. Chem.*, **42**, 1021 (1950)] report results of operation of commercial perforated-plate columns for lubricating-oil extractions with phenol.

Bubble-cap towers are not normally effective as liquid-liquid contacting devices and find little service in extraction. Perforated-plate towers, however, are often constructed with holes in vertical risers after the fashion of bubble caps (at some loss in effective height for extraction) to minimize tendencies of holes in horizontal plates to plug. Bubble caps as such, though, with vertical slots, are inefficient in producing small drops and are not commonly used.

Packed Towers. The presence of packing increases mass-transfer coefficients over those obtained in a spray tower by increasing interfacial area and turbulence. The same variables are important, but their influence may be somewhat different. Distributor design is less critical, since the packing regulates dispersed-phase hold-up and interfacial area. Interchange of the phase being dispersed can have a large effect, since this may result in a complete change of flow pattern. In some cases, the dispersed phase wets the packing and flows along it in rivulets. In other cases, the dispersed phase passes through as droplets whose progress is hindered by the presence of the packing.

The diverse types of behavior make it very difficult to obtain a satisfactory general design method (see pp. 21-25 to 21-27). Table 14-68 gives representative experimental extraction data on packed columns. Approximate correlating equations are given where feasible and ranges of transfer coefficients are given in other cases. For more precise results, the original references should be consulted.

Transfer coefficients for individual films have also been obtained by several workers by the method described by Colburn and Welsh [*Trans. Am. Inst. Chem. Engrs.*, **38**, 179 (1942)]. Table 14-69 lists results of some of these studies.

Pulse Columns. The application of a pulsing action to the continuous phase in an extraction column can increase mass-transfer rates significantly. Under conditions where unpulsed columns give poor extraction efficiency, up to fifteenfold improvement has been observed by resorting to pulsation. Even under conditions which are optimum for unpulsed extraction, as much as threefold improvement can be obtained. Pulsation gives the least improvement near the flooding point of the column. For systems that form stable emulsions, pulsing is not advantageous and may even be detrimental. Pulse techniques have been applied most commonly to sieve-plate and packed towers but have also been used for spray towers.

Table 14-68. Extraction Rates in Packed Columns

H.T.U.'s and H.E.T.S.'s in ft., *Ka*'s in ft./hr.

Solute	Dispersed phase	Continuous phase	Direction of extraction	Phase wetting packing	U_C, ft./hr.	U_D, ft./hr.	Tower diam., in.	Packing	Equation	Ref.
Acetaldehyde	Vinyl acetate	Water	$D \to C$	*C*	11–28	8–25	1.8	10-mm. rings	H.T.U.$_{OD}$ = $5.1(U_D/U_C)^{0.35}$	14
Acetic acid	Benzene	Water	$C \to D$	*C*	3–40	10–30	3.6	½-in. rings	K_{Da} = 2.6 to 13.8	16
Acetic acid	Ethyl acetate	Water	$C \to D$	...	......	......	1.0	6-mm. saddles	K_{Ca} = 3.8 to 3.9	7
Acetic acid	Methyl cyclohexane	Water	$C \to D$	...	......	......	1.0	6-mm. saddles	K_{Ca} = 2.0	7
Acetic acid	Methyl isobutyl ketone	Water	$C \to D$	*C*	10–80	30–70	3.6	½-in. rings	H.T.U.$_{OD}$ = $0.77(U_D/U_C)^{0.65}$	16
Acetic acid	Methyl isobutyl ketone	Water	$C \to D$	*C*	10–60	10	3.6	½-in. rings	$K_{Da} = 7.8 + 0.17U_C$	16
Acetic acid	Methyl isobutyl ketone	Water	$C \to D$	*C*	10–40	40	3.6	½-in. saddles	$K_{Da} = 2.13U_C$	16
Acetic acid	Methyl isobutyl ketone	Water	$C \to D$	*C*	10–40	40	3.6	1-in. rings	$K_{Da} = 15 + 0.64U_C$	16
Acetic acid	*i*-Propyl acetate	Water	$C \to D$	...	......	......	1.0	6-mm. saddles	K_{Ca} = 2.9 to 4.9	7
Acetic acid	Water	Benzene	$D \to C$	*D*	5–60	7–17	1.9, 5.9, 7.5	½- and 1-in. saddles; ½-, ¾-, and 1-in. rings	$K_{Ca} = 1.4U_D^{0.5}U_C^{0.2}$	6
Acetic acid	Water	Benzene	$D \to C$	*D*	10–40	30	3.6	½-in. rings	$K_{Ca} = 1.3 + 0.153U_C$	16
Acetic acid	Water	Cyclohexane	$D \to C$	...	......	......	1.0	6-mm. saddles	H_{Da} = 1.5 to 4.3	7
Acetic acid	Water	Ethyl acetate	$D \to C$	...	......	......	1.0	6-mm. saddles	K_{Da} = 4.7 to 6.5	7
Acetic acid	Water	Methyl cyclohexane	$D \to C$	...	......	......	1.0	6-mm. saddles	K_{Da} = 2.1 to 2.9	7
Acetic acid	Water	*i*-Propyl acetate	$D \to C$	...	......	......	1.0	6-mm. saddles	K_{Da} = 4.1 to 5.3	7
Acetone	Vinyl acetate	Water	$D \to C$	*C*	10–31	5–25	1.8	10-mm. rings	H.T.U.$_{OD}$ = $5.1(U_D/U_C)^{0.35}$	14
Acetone	Water	Vinyl acetate	$C \to D$	*D*	8–22	8–26	1.8	10-mm. rings	H.T.U.$_{OC}$ = $5.6(U_C/U_D)^{0.82}$	14
Ammonia	Butylene	Water	$D \to C$	...	19	4	12	1-in. rings	H.E.T.S. = 7.5	13
Benzoic acid	Benzene	Water	$D \to C$	*C*	5–31	24	1.9	½-in. saddles	H.T.U.$_{OC}$ = 5.2 to 8.0	6
Benzoic acid	Kerosene	Water	$D \to C$	*C*	26–99	34–106	3.6	½-in. rings	H.T.U.$_{OC}$ = $10.4(U_C/U_D)^{0.53}$	1
Benzoic acid	Toluene	Water	$D \to C$	*C*	12–86	12–47	8.8	½-in. rings	H.T.U.$_{OC}$ = $3.7(U_C/U_D)^{0.78}$	15
Benzoic acid	Toluene	Water	$D \to C$	*C*	10–102	12–57	8.8	½-in. saddles	H.T.U.$_{OC}$ = $4(U_C/U_D)^{0.77}$	15
Benzoic acid	Toluene	Water	$D \to C$	*C*	12–84	13–44	2.0	½-in. saddles	H.T.U.$_{OC}$ = $2.1(U_C/U_D)^{1.13}$	2
Benzoic acid	Toluene	Water	$D \to C$	*C*	10–178	12–64	8.8	Knit copper cloth (hung)	H.T.U.$_{OC}$ = $10(U_C/U_D)^{0.84}$	15
Benzoic acid	Toluene	Water	$D \to C$	*C*	10–102	12–39	8.8	Knit copper cloth (dumped)	H.T.U.$_{OC}$ = $10(U_C/U_D)^{0.84}$	15
Benzoic acid	Toluene	Water	$D \to C$	*C*	11	8–12	8.8	Knit copper cloth (rolled)	H.T.U.$_{OC}$ = $2.6(U_C/U_D)^{1.05}$	15
Benzoic acid	Water	Benzene	$C \to D$	*D*	7–96	19–78	5.9	½-in. saddles	K_{Da} = 4.4 to 12.7	6
Benzoic acid	Water	Benzene	$C \to D$	*D*	......	......	2	¼-in. rings	....	3
Benzoic acid	Water	Toluene	$C \to D$	*D*	22	13–44	2.0	½-in. saddles	$K_{Da} = 6 + 0.18U_D$	2
Benzoic acid	Water	Toluene	$C \to D$	*D*	44	13–44	2.0	½-in. saddles	$K_{Da} = 7.5 + 0.18U_D$	2
Diethylamine	Toluene	Water	$C \to D$	...	1–9	0.2–5	1.3	4-mm. beads	H.T.U.$_{OC}$ = $1.3(U_C/U_D)$	12
Diethylamine	Toluene	Water	$C \to D$	...	6–24	3–19	3, 4, 6	¼-, ⅜-, ½-, ⅝-, ¾-, and 1-in. rings	Depends on column size and packing	10
Ethylene cyanohydrin	Methyl ethyl ketone	NaCl brine	$C \to D$	...	15	17	20	¾-in. rings	H.E.T.S. = 5.8	13
Furfural	Toluene	Water	$C \to D$	...	15–58	8–28	4.0	½-in. saddles	H.T.U.$_{OC}$ = $3.3(U_C/U_D)^{0.95}$	9
Lactic acid	Amyl alcohol	Fermented wash	$C \to D$	...	......	......	1, 4, 6	½-, 1-in. rings; ¼-, ⅜-in. saddles	....	17
Lactic acid	Butanol	Fermented wash	$C \to D$	...	......	......	1, 4, 6	½-, 1-in. rings; ¼-, ⅜-in. saddles	....	17
Lactic acid	Fermented wash	Butanol	$D \to C$	...	......	......	1, 4, 6	½-, 1-in. rings; ¼-, ⅜-in. saddles	....	17
Lactic acid	Fermented wash	Amyl alcohol	$D \to C$	...	......	......	1, 4, 6	½-, 1-in. rings; ¼-, ⅜-in. saddles	....	17
Lubricating-oil fraction	Furfural	Lubricating oil	$C \to D$	...	4–15	5–38	2.0	¼-in. rings	H.E.T.S. = 4.1	8
Nicotine	Kerosene	Water	$C \to D$	*C*	6–66	8–44	1.88	⅜-, ½-in. rings; ¼-, ½-in. saddles	H.T.U.$_{OC}$ = 1 to 7	4
Phenol	Benzene	Water	$C \to D$	...	21	12	80	⅝-in. rings	H.E.T.S. = 7.6	13
Phenol	Benzene	15% HCl in water	$C \to D$	...	13	8	16	1-in. rings	H.E.T.S. = 15 to 22	13
Thiodiacetic acid	Water	2-Butanone	$D \to C$	...	13–24	10–29	4	½-in. rings	H.T.U.$_{OD}$ = 4 to 5	5
Thiodiacetic acid	Aqueous solution	Methyl ethyl ketone	$D \to C$	...	......	......	4	½-in. rings	H.E.T.S. = 4 to 6	13
Water	Methyl ethyl ketone	$CaCl_2$-water	$D \to C$	*C*	16–34	26–70	3.6	½-in. saddles and rings	$K_{Da} = 0.74U_D$	11
Water	$CaCl_2$-water	Methyl ethyl ketone	$C \to D$	*D*	28–66	17	3.6	½-in. saddles	$K_{Ca} = 3.8U_C^{0.42}$	11

References for Table 14-68
1 Allerton, Strom, and Treybal, *Trans. Am. Inst. Chem. Engrs.*, **39**, 361 (1943).
2 Appel and Elgin, *Ind. Eng. Chem.*, **29**, 451 (1937).
3 Chu, Taylor, and Levy, *Ind. Eng. Chem.*, **42**, 1157 (1950).
4 Claffey, Badgett, Skalamera, and Phillips, *Ind. Eng. Chem.*, **42**, 166 (1950); **49**, 274 (1952).
5 Clegg and Bearse, *Ind. Eng. Chem.*, **42**, 1222 (1950).
6 Comings and Briggs, *Trans. Am. Inst. Chem. Engrs.*, **38**, 143 (1942).
7 Eaglesfield, Kelly, and Short, *Ind. Chemist*, **29**, 243 (1953).
8 Garwin and Barber, *Petrol. Refiner*, **32** (1), 144 (1953).
9 Knight, *Trans. Am. Inst. Chem. Engrs.*, **39**, 439 (1943).
10 Leibson and Beckmann, *Chem. Eng. Progress*, **49**, 405 (1953).
11 Meissner, Stokes, Hunter, and Morrow, *Ind. Eng. Chem.*, **36**, 917 (1944).
12 Morello and Beckmann, *Ind. Eng. Chem.*, **42**, 1078 (1950).
13 Morello and Poffenberger, *Ind. Eng. Chem.*, **42**, 1028 (1950).
14 Pratt and Glover, *Trans. Inst. Chem. Engrs.* (*London*), **24**, 54 (1946).
15 Row, Koffolt, and Withrow, *Trans. Am. Inst. Chem. Engrs.*, **37**, 559 (1941).
16 Sherwood, Evans, and Longcor, *Ind. Eng. Chem.*, **31**, 1144 (1939); *Trans. Am. Inst. Chem. Engrs.*, **35**, 597 (1939).
17 Short and Eaglesfield, *Trans. Inst. Chem. Engrs.*, **30**, 109 (1952).

Table 14-69. Individual-phase Mass-transfer Rates for Packed Columns

$H_D = C_1$ in ft.; $H_C = C_2 (U_C/U_D)^n$ in ft.

Dispersed phase	Continuous phase	U_C, ft./hr.	U_D, ft./hr.	Packing	C_1	C_2	n	Ref.
i-Butanol	Water	5–29	5–42	½-in. rings	1.04	1.3	0.80	1
i-Butyraldehyde	Water	7–19	11–34	¼-in. rings	....	2.2	0.58	3
i-Butyraldehyde	Water	7–19	11–34	⅜-in. rings	....	2.6	0.58	3
Ethyl acetate	Water	10–100	10–70	½-in. rings	0.81	1.70	0.54	2
Methyl ethyl ketone	Water	......	.....	½-in. rings	1.1	0.82	0.63	4
Methyl isobutyl carbinol	Water	12–53	3–33	½-in. rings	1.44	0.90	0.78	4
3-Pentanol	Water	26–42	7–16	⅜-in. rings	0.75	0.63	0.94	3
3-Pentanol	Water	26–42	7–16	¼-in. rings	0.75	0.61	0.98	3
Water	*i*-Butanol	......	.....	½-in. rings	0.64	2.2	0.61	1
Water	*i*-Butyraldehyde	12–40	11–38	⅜-in. rings	2.5	....	....	3
Water	*i*-Butyraldehyde	12–40	11–38	¼-in. rings	2.5	....	....	3
Water	3-Pentanol	8–26	6–40	¼-in. rings	0.80	1.4	0.87	3
Water	3-Pentanol	8–26	6–40	⅜-in. rings	0.80	1.6	0.87	3

References for Table 14-69
[1] Colburn and Welsh, *Trans. Am. Inst. Chem. Engrs.*, **38**, 179 (1942).
[2] Gaylor and Pratt, *Trans. Inst. Chem. Engrs.*, **31**, 78 (1953).
[3] Laddha and Smith, *Chem. Eng. Progress*, **46**, 195 (1950).
[4] Smith and Beckmann, *Am. Inst. Chem. Engrs. J.*, **4**, 181 (1958).

Design and performance of pulsed columns are treated in Sec. 21 (p. 21-32). Data on specific extraction systems can be found in the references cited in Table 14-70.

Other Types of Columns. In the ordinary pulse column, a pulsation is imparted to the continuous phase by means of a valveless pump or an air bellows. An alternative, however, is to reciprocate the trays themselves. Chief advantage claimed for the **reciprocating plate column** is a substantially higher through-put.

Baffle-plate columns are generally either of the disk-and-doughnut type or of the alternate-segment type.

Table 14-70. Mass-transfer Data in Pulsed Sieve-plate Columns

System	Ref.
Acetic acid, methyl isobutyl ketone, water	1, 2
Acetone, butyl acetate, water	7, 11
Acetone, toluene, water	7, 11
Benzoic acid, toluene, water	6
Cobalt chloride, nickel chloride, methyl isobutyl ketone, ammonium thiocyanate, water	4
Phenol, kerosene, water	10
Uranyl nitrate, cyclohexanone, water	8
Uranyl nitrate, pentaether, water	5, 8
Uranyl nitrate, tributyl phosphate, carbon tetrachloride, nitric acid, water	9
Uranyl nitrate, tributyl phosphate, kerosene, water	3

References for Table 14-70
[1] Belaga and Bigelow, *U.S. A.E.C. Rept.* KT-133, 1952.
[2] Chantry, Von Berg, and Wiegandt, *Ind. Eng. Chem.*, **47**, 1153 (1955).
[3] Ellison, *U.S. A.E.C. Rept.* ORNL-912, 1956.
[4] Griffith, Jasny, and Tupper, *U.S. A.E.C. Rept.* KT-114, 1952.
[5] Lane, *U.S. A.E.C. Rept.* UCRL-2983, 1955.
[6] Li and Newton, *Am. Inst. Chem. Engrs. J.*, **3**, 56 (1957).
[7] Logsdail and Thornton, *Trans. Inst. Chem. Engrs. (London)*, **35**, 331 (1957).
[8] Rubin and Lehman, *U.S. A.E.C. Rept.* UCRL-718, 1950.
[9] Sege and Woodfield, *Chem. Eng. Progress*, **50**, 396 (1954).
[10] Swisher, *Dissertation Abstr.*, **16**, 1421 (1956).
[11] Thornton, *Trans. Inst. Chem. Engrs. (London)*, **35**, 316 (1957).

Estimation methods for determining mass-transfer efficiencies are not yet available.

A diversity of devices have been employed to enhance extraction by mechanical means, such as **multistage mixer columns, rotation-disk contactors,** and **rotating-core columns.** For design factors on these and other devices, see Sec. 21.

Wetted-wall towers have been used on an experimental scale because they offer an opportunity for control over interfacial area. They are little used commercially because of their low contacting efficiency and their narrow range of allowable operating conditions.

Other Extraction Devices. For systems in which the density difference between phases is small, or when low hold-up time is desirable because of sensitivity of the materials to decomposition, it may be desirable to employ centrifugal force to enhance separation efficiency. This is the principle of the **Podbielniak extractor,** which operates at high rotational speeds (3000 to 5000 r.p.m.).

Mixer-settlers are especially useful where long contact times are needed. Various styles have been devised, and design correlations have not been generalized to all types.

Murphy, Lastovica, and Skrzec [*Am. Inst. Chem. Engrs. J.*, **2**, 451 (1956)] have studied extraction rates of five systems in countercurrent flow in a **horizontal pipeline contactor** and have obtained a correlating expression for each of the phases. Additional extraction data in horizontal tubes have been presented by Bergelin, Lockhart, and Brown [*Trans. Am. Inst. Chem. Engrs.*, **39**, 173 (1943)].

Design procedures and performance data for these and other extraction devices will be found in Sec. 21.

SECTION 15
HUMIDIFICATION AND DRYING

BY

Eno Bagnoli, M.S., Senior Research Engineer, E. I. du Pont de Nemours & Co.; Member, American Institute of Chemical Engineers. (Psychrometry, Drying of Solids)

Frank H. Fuller, M.S., Consulting Engineer, E. I. du Pont de Nemours & Co.; Member, American Society of Heating, Refrigerating and Air-Conditioning Engineers; Professional Engineer (Delaware). (Air Conditioning)

Robert W. Norris, B.S., Consulting Engineer, E. I. du Pont de Nemours & Co.; Member, American Society of Heating, Refrigerating and Air-Conditioning Engineers; Professional Engineer (Delaware). (Evaporative Cooling)

CONTENTS

PSYCHROMETRY

REFERENCES: Brown *et al.*, "Unit Operations," Wiley, New York, 1950. Coulson and Richardson, "Chemical Engineering," vol. I, McGraw-Hill, New York, 1955. Penman, "Humidity," Institute of Physics Monographs, London, 1955. Sherwood and Pigford, "Absorption and Extraction," 2d ed., McGraw-Hill, New York, 1952. Treybal, "Mass-transfer Operations," McGraw-Hill, New York, 1955. Walker, Lewis, McAdams, and Gilliland, "Principles of Chemical Engineering," 3d ed., McGraw-Hill, New York, 1937. Wexler and Bombacher, *N.B.S. Circ.* 512, September, 1951. Zimmerman and Lavine, "Psychrometric Charts and Tables," Industrial Research Service, Dover, N.H., 1945.

Psychrometry is concerned with determination of the properties of gas-vapor mixtures. The air–water vapor system is by far the one most commonly encountered.

Principles involved in determining the properties of other systems are the same as with air–water vapor, with one major exception. Whereas the psychrometric ratio (ratio of heat-transfer coefficient to product of mass-transfer coefficient and humid heat, terms defined below) for the air–water vapor system can be taken as 1, the ratio for other systems, in general, does not equal 1. This has the effect of making the adiabatic-saturation temperature different from the wet-bulb temperature. Thus, for systems other than air–water vapor, calculation of psychrometric and drying problems is complicated by the necessity for point-to-point calculation of the temperature of the evaporating surface. For example, for the air-water system, the temperature of the evaporating surface will be constant during the constant-rate drying period, even though temperature and humidity of the gas stream change. For other systems, the temperature of the evaporating surface would change.

Terminology and relationships pertinent to psychrometry are:

Absolute humidity H equals the pounds of water vapor carried by one pound of dry air. If ideal gas behavior is assumed, $H = M_w p/[M_a(P - p)]$, where M_w = molecular weight of water; M_a = molecular weight of air; p = partial pressure of water vapor, atm.; P = total pressure, atm.

When the partial pressure p of water vapor in the air at a given temperature equals the vapor pressure of water p_s at the same temperature, the air is saturated and the absolute humidity is designated the **saturation humidity** H_s.

Percentage absolute humidity (percentage saturation) is defined as the ratio of absolute humidity to saturation humidity and is given by $100\ H/H_s = 100p(P - p_s)/[p_s(P - p)]$.

Percentage relative humidity is defined as the partial pressure of water vapor in air divided by the vapor pressure of water at the given temperature. Thus R.H. $= 100p/p_s$.

Dew point or **saturation temperature** is the temperature at which a given mixture of water vapor and air is saturated, *i.e.*, the temperature at which water exerts a vapor pressure equal to the partial pressure of water vapor in the given mixture.

Humid heat c_s is the heat capacity of 1 lb. of dry air and the moisture it contains. For most engineering calculations, $c_s = 0.24 + 0.45H$, where 0.24 and 0.45 are the heat capacities of dry air and water vapor, respectively, and both are assumed constant.

Humid volume is the volume in cubic feet of 1 lb. of dry air and the water vapor it contains.

Saturated volume is the humid volume when the air is saturated.

Wet-bulb temperature is the dynamic equilibrium temperature attained by a water surface when the rate of heat transfer to the surface by convection equals the rate of mass transfer away from the surface. At equilibrium, assuming negligible change in the dry-bulb temperature, a heat balance on the surface is

$$k_g\lambda(p_s - p) = h_c(t - t_w) \qquad (15\text{-}1)$$

where k_g = mass-transfer coefficient, lb./(hr.)(sq. ft.)(atm.); λ = latent heat of vaporization, B.t.u./lb.; p_s = vapor pressure of water at wet-bulb temperature, atm.; p = partial pressure of water vapor in the environment, atm.; h_c = heat-transfer coefficient, B.t.u./(hr.)(sq. ft.)(°F.); t = temperature of air–water vapor mixture (dry-bulb temperature), °F.; t_w = wet-bulb temperature, °F. Under ordinary conditions the partial pressure and vapor pressure are small relative to the total pressure, and the wet-bulb equation can be written in terms of humidity differences as

$$H_s - H = \frac{h_c}{\lambda k'}(t - t_w) \qquad (15\text{-}1a)$$

where k' = lb./(hr.)(sq. ft.) (unit humidity difference) = $(M_a/M_w)k_g = 1.6k_g$.

Adiabatic-saturation Temperature or **Constant-enthalpy Lines.** If a stream of air is intimately mixed with a quantity of water at a temperature t_s in an adiabatic system, the temperature of the air will drop and its humidity will increase. If t_s is such that the air leaving the system is in equilibrium with the water, t_s will be the adiabatic-saturation temperature, and the line relating the temperature and humidity of the air is the adiabatic-saturation line. The equation for the adiabatic-saturation line is

$$H_s - H = \frac{c_s}{\lambda}(t - t_s) \qquad (15\text{-}2)$$

Relation between Wet-bulb and Adiabatic-saturation Temperature. Experimentally it has been shown that for air-water systems the value of $h_c/k'c_s$, **the psychrometric ratio,** is approximately equal to 1. Under these conditions the wet-bulb temperatures and adiabatic-saturation temperatures are substantially equal and can be used interchangeably. The difference between the adiabatic-saturation temperature and wet-bulb temperature increases with increasing humidity, but this effect is unimportant for most engineering calculations.

For systems other than air–water vapor, the value of $h_c/k'c_s$ may differ appreciably from unity, and the wet-bulb and adiabatic-saturation temperatures are no longer equal. For these systems the psychrometric ratio may be obtained by determining h_c/k' from heat- and mass-transfer analogies such as the Chilton-Colburn analogy [*Ind. Eng. Chem.*, **26**, 1183 (1934)]. For low humidities this analogy gives

$$\frac{h_c}{k'} = c_s\left[\frac{\mu/\rho D_v}{c_s\mu/k}\right]^{2/3} \qquad (15\text{-}3)$$

where c_s = humid heat, B.t.u./(lb.)(°F.); μ = viscosity, lb./(ft.)(hr.); ρ = density, lb./cu. ft.; D_v = diffusivity, sq. ft./hr.; k = thermal conductivity, B.t.u./(hr.)(sq. ft.)(°F./ft.). All properties should be evaluated for the gas mixture.

For the case of **flow past cylinders**, such as a wet-bulb thermometer, Bedingfield and Drew [*Ind. Eng. Chem.*, **42**, 1164 (1950)] obtained a correlation for their data on sublimation of cylinders into air and for the data of others on wet-bulb thermometers. For wet-bulb thermometers in air they give

$$\frac{h_c}{k'} = 0.294\left(\frac{\mu}{\rho D_v}\right)^{0.56} \tag{15-4}$$

where the nomenclature is identical to that in Eq. (15-3). For evaporation into gases other than air, Eq. (15-3) with an exponent of 0.56 would apply.

Application of these equations is illustrated in the following example.

Example 1. For the air-water system at atmospheric pressure, the measured values of dry-bulb and wet-bulb temperatures are 85°F. and 72°F., respectively. Determine the absolute humidity and compare the wet-bulb temperature and adiabatic-saturation temperature. Assume that h_c/k' is given by Eq. (15-4).

Solution. For relatively dry air the Schmidt number $\mu/\rho D_v$ is 0.60, and from Eq. (15-4), $h_c/k' = 0.294(0.60)^{0.56} = 0.221$. At 72°F. the vapor pressure of water is 20.07 mm. Hg and the latent heat of vaporization is 1051.6 B.t.u./lb. From Eq. (15-1a), $[20.07/(760 - 20.07)](^{18}\!/_{29}) - H = (0.221/1051.6)(85 - 72)$ or $H = 0.0140$ lb. water/lb. dry air. The humid heat is calculated as $c_s = 0.24 + 0.45(0.0140) = 0.246$. The adiabatic-saturation temperature is obtained from Eq. (15-2) as

$$H_s - 0.0140 = \frac{0.246}{1051.6}(85 - t_s)$$

Values of H_s and t_s are given by the saturation curve of the humidity chart, such as Fig. 15-2. By trial and error, t_s = 72.1°F., or the adiabatic-saturation temperature is 0.1°F. higher than the wet-bulb temperature.

Three **charts for the air-water vapor system** are given as Figs. 15-1, 15-2, and 15-3 for low-, medium-, and high-temperature ranges. Figure 15-4 shows a modified Grosvenor chart, which is more familiar to the chemical engineer. These charts are for an absolute pressure of 1 atm. The corrections required at pressures different from atmospheric are given in Table 15-2. Figure 15-5 shows a psychrometric chart for combustion products in air. The thermodynamic properties of moist air and of water are given in Tables 15-1 and 15-3, respectively.

Examples Illustrating Use of Psychrometric Charts. In these examples the following nomenclature is used:

t = dry-bulb temperature, °F.
t_w = wet-bulb temperature, °F.
t_d = dew-point temperature, °F.
H = moisture content, lb. water/lb. dry air.
ΔH = moisture added to or rejected from the air stream, lb. water/lb. dry air.
h' = enthalpy at saturation, B.t.u./lb. dry air.
D = enthalpy deviation, B.t.u./lb. dry air.
$h = h' + D$ = true enthalpy, B.t.u./lb. dry air.
h_w = enthalpy of water added to or rejected from the system, B.t.u./lb. dry air.
q_a = heat added to the system, B.t.u./lb. dry air.
q_r = heat removed from system, B.t.u./lb. dry air.

Subscripts 1, 2, 3, etc., indicate entering and subsequent states.

Example 2. Find the properties of moist air when dry-bulb temperature is 80°F. and wet-bulb temperature is 67°F.

Solution. Read directly from Fig. 15-2 (Fig. 15-6 shows the solution diagrammatically).

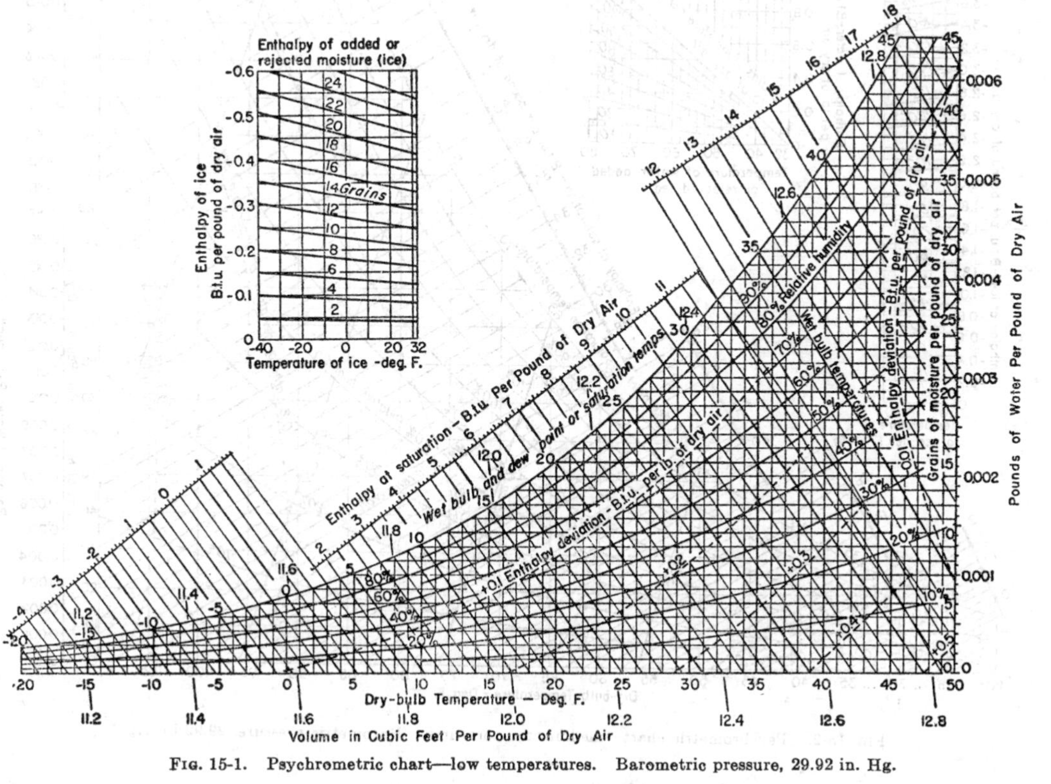

FIG. 15-1. Psychrometric chart—low temperatures. Barometric pressure, 29.92 in. Hg.

Moisture content H = 78 grains/lb. dry air = 0.011 lb. water/lb. dry air
Enthalpy at saturation h' = 31.6 B.t.u./lb. dry air
Enthalpy deviation D = −0.1 B.t.u./lb. dry air
True enthalpy h = 31.5 B.t.u./lb. dry air
Specific volume v = 13.8 cu. ft./lb. dry air
Relative humidity = 51 per cent
Dew point t_d = 60.3°F.

Example 3. Air is heated by a steam coil from 30°F. dry-bulb temperature and 80 per cent relative humidity to 75°F. dry-bulb temperature. Find the relative humidity, wet-bulb temperature, and dew point of the heated air. Determine the quantity of heat added per pound of dry air.

Solution. Reading directly from the psychrometric chart (Fig. 15-2),

Relative humidity = 15 per cent
Wet-bulb temperature = 51.5°F.
Dew point = 25.2°F.

The enthalpy of the inlet air is obtained from Fig. 15-2 as $h_1 = h_1' + D_1 = 10.1 + 0.06 = 10.16$ B.t.u./lb. dry air; at the exit, $h_2 = h_2' + D_2 = 21.1 - 0.1 = 21$ B.t.u./lb. dry air. The heat added equals the enthalpy difference, or

$$q_a = \Delta h = h_2 - h_1 = 21 - 10.16 = 10.84 \text{ B.t.u./lb. dry air}$$

If the enthalpy deviation is ignored, the heat added q_a is $\Delta h = 21.1 - 10.1 = 11$ B.t.u./lb. dry air, or the result is 1.5 per cent high. Figure 15-7 shows the heating path on the psychrometric chart.

Example 4. Air at 95°F. dry-bulb temperature and 70°F. wet-bulb temperature contacts a water spray where its relative humidity is increased to 90 per cent. The spray water is recirculated; makeup water enters at 70°F. Determine exit dry-bulb temperature, wet-bulb temperature, change in enthalpy of the air, and quantity of moisture added per pound of dry air.

Solution. Figure 15-8 shows the path on a psychrometric chart. The leaving dry-bulb temperature is obtained directly from Fig. 15-2 as 72.2°F. Since the spray water enters at the wet-bulb temperature of 70°F. and there is no heat added to or removed from it, this is by definition an adiabatic process and there will be no change in wet-bulb temperature. The only change in enthalpy is that from the heat content of the makeup water. This can be demonstrated as follows:

Inlet moisture H_1 = 70 grains/lb. dry air
Exit moisture H_2 = 107 grains/lb. dry air
ΔH = 37 grains/lb. dry air
Inlet enthalpy $h_1 = h_1' + D_1 = 34.1 - 0.22$
= 33.88 B.t.u./lb. dry air
Exit enthalpy $h_2 = h_2' + D_2 = 34.1 - 0.02$
= 34.08 B.t.u./lb. dry air
Enthalpy of added water h_w = 0.2 B.t.u./lb. dry air (from small diagram, 37 grains at 70°F.)

Then $q_a = h_2 - h_1 + h_w$
$= 34.08 - 33.88 + 0.2 = 0$

Example 5. Find the cooling load per pound of dry air resulting from infiltration of room air at 80°F. dry-bulb temperature and 67°F. wet-bulb temperature into a cooler maintained at 30°F. dry-bulb and 28°F. wet-bulb temperature, where moisture freezes on the coil, which is maintained at 20°F.

Solution. The path followed on a psychrometric chart is shown in Fig. 15-9.

Inlet enthalpy $h_1 = h_1' + D_1 = 31.62 - 0.1$
= 31.52 B.t.u./lb. dry air
Exit enthalpy $h_2 = h_2' + D_2 = 10.1 + 0.06$
= 10.16 B.t.u./lb. dry air
Inlet moisture H_1 = 78 grains/lb. dry air
Exit moisture H_2 = 19 grains/lb. dry air
Moisture rejected ΔH = 59 grains/lb. dry air
Enthalpy of rejected moisture = −1.26 B.t.u./lb. dry air (from small diagram of Fig. 15-2)
Cooling load $q_r = 31.52 - 10.16 + 1.26$
= 22.62 B.t.u./lb. dry air

Note that if the enthalpy deviations are ignored the calculated cooling load would be about 5 per cent low.

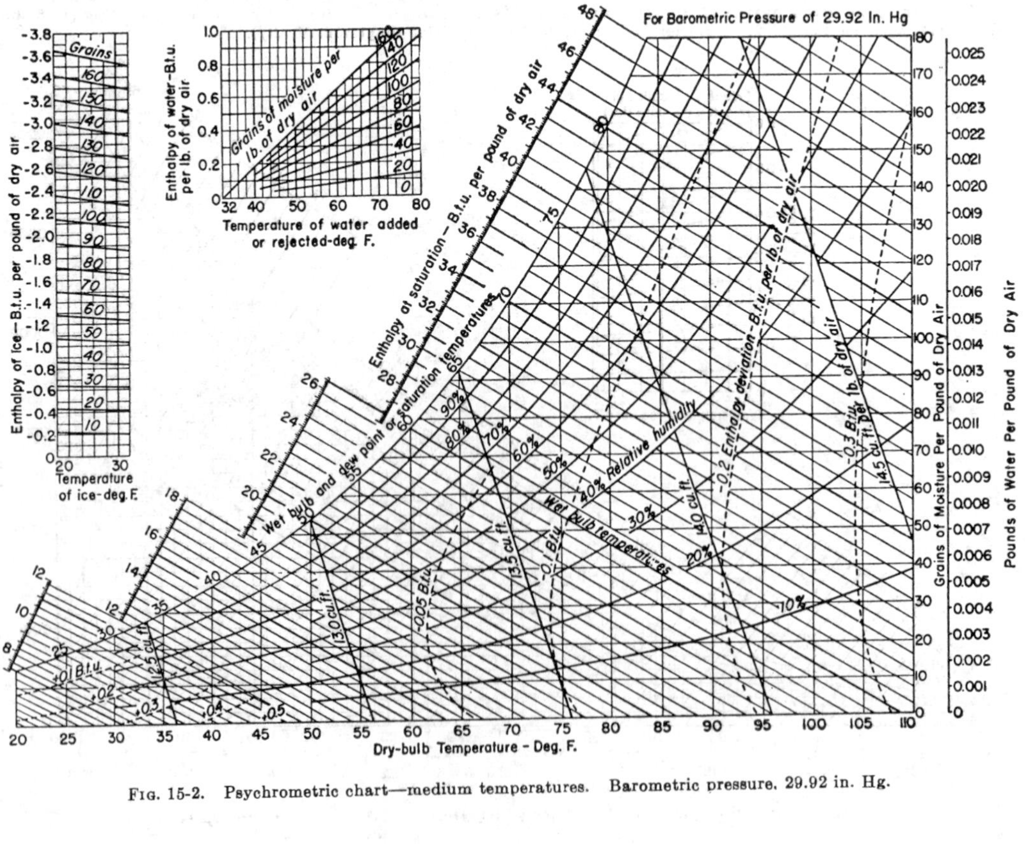

FIG. 15-2. Psychrometric chart—medium temperatures. Barometric pressure, 29.92 in. Hg.

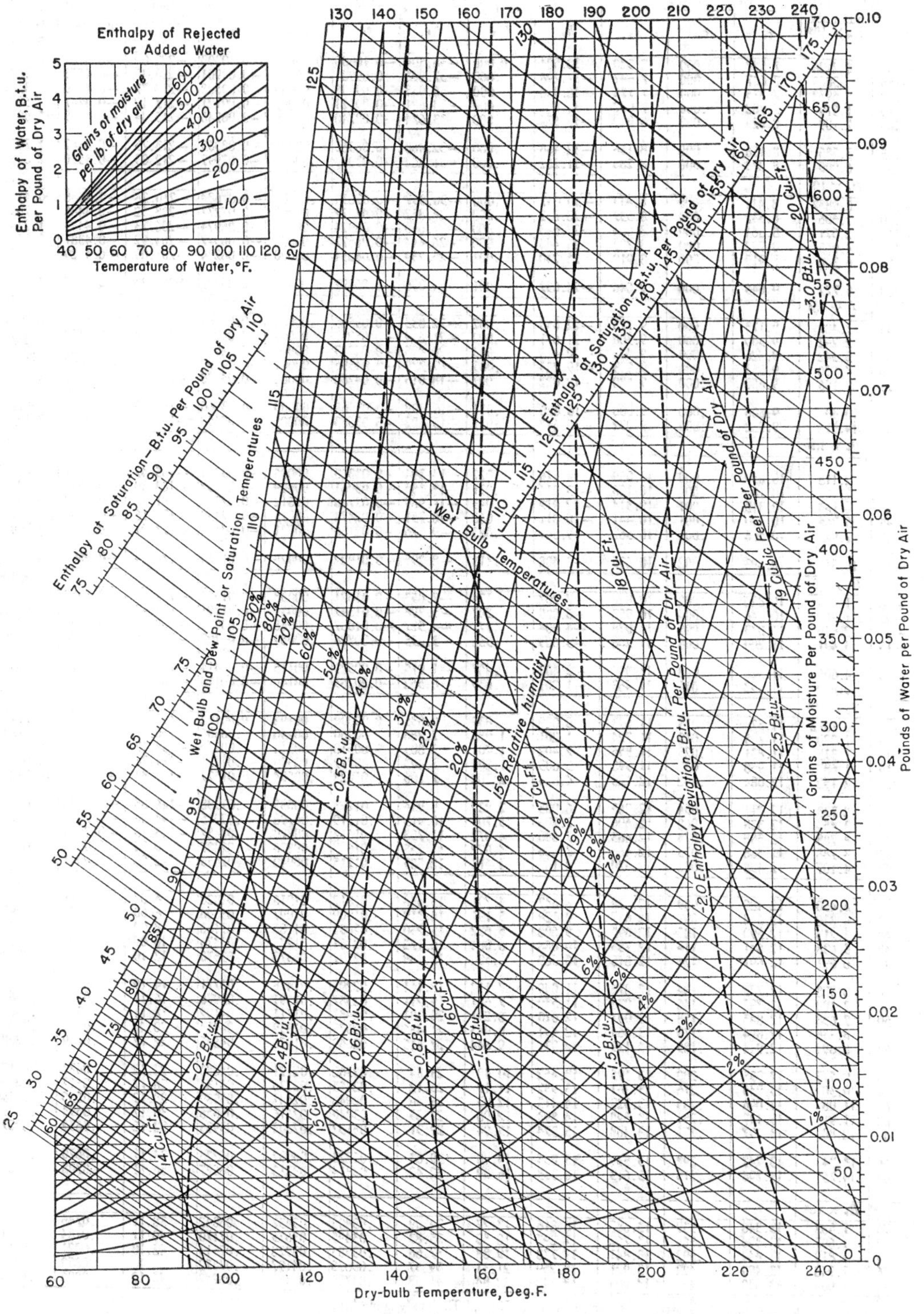

FIG. 15-3. Psychrometric chart—high temperatures. Barometric pressure, 29.92 in. Hg.

Table 15-1. Thermodynamic Properties of Moist Air (Standard Atmospheric Pressure, 29.921 in. Hg)

Temp. t, °F.	Saturation humidity $H_s \times 10^8$	Volume, cu. ft./lb. dry air v_a	v_{as}	v_s	Enthalpy, B.t.u./lb. dry air h_a	h_{as}	h_s	Entropy, B.t.u./(°F.)(lb. dry air) s_a	s_{as}	s_s	Condensed water: Enthalpy, B.t.u./lb. h_w	Entropy, B.t.u./(lb.)(°F.) s_w	Vapor press., in. Hg $p_s \times 10^8$	Temp. t, °F.
−160	0.2120	7.520	0.000	7.520	−38.504	0.000	−38.504	−0.10300	0.00000	−0.10300	−222.00	−0.4907	0.1009	−160
−155	.3869	7.647	.000	7.647	−37.296	.000	−37.296	−0.09901	.00000	−0.09901	−220.40	−0.4853	.1842	−155
−150	.6932	7.775	.000	7.775	−36.088	.000	−36.088	−0.09508	.00000	−0.09508	−218.77	−0.4800	.3301	−150
−145	1.219	7.902	.000	7.902	−34.881	.000	−34.881	−0.09121	.00000	−0.09121	−217.12	−0.4747	.5807	−145
−140	2.109	8.029	.000	8.029	−33.674	.000	−33.674	−0.08740	.00000	−0.08740	−215.44	−0.4695	1.004	−140
−135	3.586	8.156	.000	8.156	−32.468	.000	−32.468	−0.08365	.00000	−0.08365	−213.75	−0.4642	1.707	−135
−130	6.000	8.283	.000	8.283	−31.262	.000	−31.262	−0.07997	.00000	−0.07997	−212.03	−0.4590	2.858	−130
	$H_s \times 10^7$												$p_s \times 10^5$	
−125	0.9887	8.411	.000	8.411	−30.057	.000	−30.057	−0.07634	.00000	−0.07634	−210.28	−0.4538	0.4710	−125
−120	1.606	8.537	.000	8.537	−28.852	.000	−28.852	−0.07277	.00000	−0.07277	−208.52	−0.4485	.7653	−120
−115	2.571	8.664	.000	8.664	−27.648	.000	−27.648	−0.06924	.00000	−0.06924	−206.73	−0.4433	1.226	−115
−110	4.063	8.792	.000	8.792	−26.444	.000	−26.444	−0.06577	.00000	−0.06577	−204.92	−0.4381	1.939	−110
−105	6.340	8.919	.000	8.919	−25.240	.001	−25.239	−0.06234	.00000	−0.06234	−203.09	−0.4329	3.026	−105
−100	9.772	9.046	.000	9.046	−24.037	.001	−24.036	−0.05897	.00000	−0.05897	−201.23	−0.4277	4.666	−100
	$H_s \times 10^6$												$p_s \times 10^4$	
−95	1.489	9.173	.000	9.173	−22.835	.002	−22.833	−0.05565	.00000	−0.05565	−199.35	−0.4225	0.7111	−95
−90	2.242	9.300	.000	9.300	−21.631	.002	−21.629	−0.05237	.00001	−0.05236	−197.44	−0.4173	1.071	−90
−85	3.342	9.426	.000	9.426	−20.428	.003	−20.425	−0.04913	.00001	−0.04912	−195.51	−0.4121	1.597	−85
−80	4.930	9.553	.000	9.553	−19.225	.005	−19.220	−0.04595	.00001	−0.04594	−193.55	−0.4069	2.356	−80
−75	7.196	9.680	.000	9.680	−18.022	.007	−18.015	−0.04280	.00002	−0.04278	−191.57	−0.4017	3.441	−75
−70	10.40	9.806	.000	9.806	−16.820	.011	−16.809	−0.03969	.00003	−0.03966	−189.56	−0.3965	4.976	−70
−65	14.91	9.932	.000	9.932	−15.617	.015	−15.602	−0.03663	.00005	−0.03658	−187.53	−0.3913	7.130	−65
	$H_s \times 10^5$												$p_s \times 10^3$	
−60	2.118	10.059	.000	10.059	−14.416	.022	−14.394	−0.03360	.00006	−0.03354	−185.47	−0.3861	1.0127	−60
−55	2.982	10.186	.000	10.186	−13.214	.031	−13.183	−0.03061	.00009	−0.03052	−183.39	−0.3810	1.4258	−55
−50	4.163	10.313	.001	10.314	−12.012	.043	−11.969	−0.02766	.00012	−0.02754	−181.29	−0.3758	1.9910	−50
−45	5.766	10.440	.001	10.441	−10.811	.060	−10.751	−0.02474	.00015	−0.02459	−179.16	−0.3707	2.7578	−45
−40	7.925	10.566	.001	10.567	−9.609	.083	−9.526	−0.02186	.00021	−0.02165	−177.01	−0.3655	3.7906	−40
−35	10.81	10.693	.002	10.695	−8.408	.113	−8.295	−0.01902	.00028	−0.01874	−174.84	−0.3604	5.1713	−35
	$H_s \times 10^4$												$p_s \times 10^2$	
−30	1.464	10.820	.002	10.822	−7.207	.154	−7.053	−0.01621	.00038	−0.01583	−172.64	−0.3552	0.70046	−30
−25	1.969	10.946	.004	10.950	−6.005	.207	−5.798	−0.01342	.00051	−0.01291	−170.42	−0.3500	.94212	−25
−20	2.630	11.073	.005	11.078	−4.804	.277	−4.527	−0.01067	.00068	−0.00999	−168.17	−0.3449	1.2587	−20
−15	3.491	11.200	.006	11.206	−3.603	.368	−3.235	−0.00796	.00089	−0.00707	−165.90	−0.3398	1.6706	−15
−10	4.606	11.326	.008	11.334	−2.402	.487	−1.915	−0.00529	.00115	−0.00414	−163.60	−0.3346	2.2035	−10
−5	6.040	11.452	.011	11.463	−1.201	.639	−0.562	−0.00263	.00149	−0.00114	−161.28	−0.3295	2.8886	−5
	$H_s \times 10^3$													
0	0.7872	11.578	.015	11.593	0.000	.835	0.835	0.00000	.00192	0.00192	−158.93	−0.3244	3.7645	0
5	1.020	11.705	.019	11.724	1.201	1.085	2.286	.00260	.00246	.00506	−156.57	−0.3193	4.8779	5
10	1.315	11.831	.025	11.856	2.402	1.401	3.803	.00518	.00314	.00832	−154.17	−0.3141	6.2858	10
15	1.687	11.958	.032	11.990	3.603	1.800	5.403	.00772	.00399	.01171	−151.76	−0.3090	8.0565	15
20	2.152	12.084	.042	12.126	4.804	2.302	7.106	.01023	.00504	.01527	−149.31	−0.3039	10.272	20
25	2.733	12.211	.054	12.265	6.005	2.929	8.934	.01273	.00635	.01908	−146.85	−0.2988	13.032	25
30	3.454	12.338	.068	12.406	7.206	3.709	10.915	.01519	.00796	.02315	−144.36	−0.2936	16.452	30
32	3.788	12.388	.075	12.463	7.686	4.072	11.758	.01617	.00870	.02487	−143.36	−0.2916	18.035	32
32*	3.788	12.388	.075	12.463	7.686	4.072	11.758	.01617	.00870	.02487	0.04	0.0000	18.037	32*
34	4.107	12.438	.082	12.520	8.167	4.418	12.585	.01715	.00940	.02655	2.06	.0041	19.546	34
													p_s	
36	4.450	12.489	.089	12.578	8.647	4.791	13.438	.01812	.01016	.02828	4.07	.0081	0.21166	36
38	4.818	12.540	.097	12.637	9.128	5.191	14.319	.01909	.01097	.03006	6.08	.0122	.22904	38
40	5.213	12.590	.105	12.695	9.608	5.622	15.230	.02005	.01183	.03188	8.09	.0162	.24767	40
42	5.638	12.641	.114	12.755	10.088	6.084	16.172	.02101	.01275	.03376	10.09	.0202	.26763	42
44	6.091	12.691	.124	12.815	10.569	6.580	17.149	.02197	.01373	.03570	12.10	.0242	.28899	44
46	6.578	12.742	.134	12.876	11.049	7.112	18.161	.02293	.01478	.03771	14.10	.0282	.31185	46
48	7.100	12.792	.146	12.938	11.530	7.681	19.211	.02387	.01591	.03978	16.11	.0321	.33629	48
50	7.658	12.843	.158	13.001	12.010	8.291	20.301	.02481	.01711	.04192	18.11	.0361	.36240	50
52	8.256	12.894	.170	13.064	12.491	8.945	21.436	.02575	.01839	.04414	20.11	.0400	.39028	52
54	8.894	12.944	.185	13.129	12.971	9.644	22.615	.02669	.01976	.04645	22.12	.0439	.42004	54
56	9.575	12.995	.200	13.195	13.452	10.39	23.84	.02762	.02121	.04883	24.12	.0478	.45176	56
58	10.30	13.045	.216	13.261	13.932	11.19	25.12	.02855	.02276	.05131	26.12	.0517	.48558	58
60	11.08	13.096	.233	13.329	14.413	12.05	26.46	.02948	.02441	.05389	28.12	.0555	.52159	60
62	11.91	13.147	.251	13.398	14.893	12.96	27.85	.03040	.02616	.05656	30.12	.0594	.55994	62
64	12.80	13.197	.271	13 468	15.374	13.94	29.31	.03132	.02803	.05935	32.12	.0632	.60073	64
66	13.74	13.247	.292	13.539	15.855	14.98	30.83	.03223	.03002	.06225	34.11	.0670	.64411	66
68	14.75	13.298	.315	13.613	16.335	16.09	32.42	.03314	.03213	.06527	36.11	.0708	.69019	68
	$H_s \times 10^2$													
70	1.582	13.348	.339	13.687	16.816	17.27	34.09	.03405	.03437	.06842	38.11	.0746	.73915	70
72	1.697	13.398	.364	13.762	17.297	18.53	35.83	.03495	.03675	.07170	40.11	.0784	.79112	72
74	1.819	13.449	.392	13.841	17.778	19.88	37.66	.03585	.03928	.07513	42.10	.0821	.84624	74
76	1.948	13.499	.422	13.921	18.259	21.31	39.57	.03675	.04197	.07872	44.10	.0859	.90470	76
78	2.086	13.550	.453	14.003	18.740	22.84	41.58	.03765	.04482	.08247	46.10	.0896	.96665	78

Compiled by John A. Goff and S. Gratch. See also Keenan and Kaye, "Thermodynamic Properties of Air," Wiley, New York, 1945.
Enthalpy of dry air taken as zero at 0°F. Enthalpy of liquid water taken as zero at 32°F.
* Extrapolated to represent metastable equilibrium with undercooled liquid.

Table 15-1. Thermodynamic Properties of Moist Air (Standard Atmospheric Pressure, 29.921 in. Hg)— *(Continued)*

Temp. t, °F.	Saturation humidity $H_s \times 10^2$	Volume, cu. ft./lb. dry air v_a	v_{as}	v_s	Enthalpy, B.t.u./lb. dry air h_a	h_{as}	h_s	Entropy, B.t.u./(°F.)(lb. dry air) s_a	s_{as}	s_s	Condensed water: Enthalpy B.t.u./lb. h_w	Entropy, B.t.u./(lb.)(°F.) s_w	Vapor press., in. Hg p_s	Temp. t, °F.
80	2.233	13.601	0.486	14.087	19.221	24.47	43.69	0.03854	0.04784	0.08638	48.10	0.0933	1.0323	80
82	2.389	13.651	.523	14.174	19.702	26.20	45.90	.03943	.05105	.09048	50.09	.0970	1.1017	82
84	2.555	13.702	.560	14.262	20.183	28.04	48.22	.04031	.05446	.09477	52.09	.1007	1.1752	84
86	2.731	13.752	.602	14.354	20.663	30.00	50.66	.04119	.05807	.09926	54.08	.1043	1.2529	86
88	2.919	13.803	.645	14.448	21.144	32.09	53.23	.04207	.06189	.10396	56.08	.1080	1.3351	88
90	3.118	13.853	.692	14.545	21.625	34.31	55.93	.04295	.06596	.10890	58.08	.1116	1.4219	90
92	3.330	13.904	.741	14.645	22.106	36.67	58.78	.04382	.07025	.11407	60.07	.1153	1.5135	92
94	3.556	13.954	.795	14.749	22.587	39.18	61.77	.04469	.07480	.11949	62.07	.1188	1.6102	94
96	3.795	14.005	.851	14.856	23.068	41.85	64.92	.04556	.07963	.12519	64.06	.1224	1.7123	96
98	4.049	14.056	.911	14.967	23.548	44.68	68.23	.04643	.08474	.13117	66.06	.1260	1.8199	98
100	4.319	14.106	.975	15.081	24.029	47.70	71.73	.04729	.09016	.13745	68.06	.1296	1.9333	100
102	4.606	14.157	1.043	15.200	24.510	50.91	75.42	.04815	.09591	.14406	70.05	.1332	2.0528	102
104	4.911	14.207	1.117	15.324	24.991	54.32	79.31	.04900	.1020	.1510	72.05	.1367	2.1786	104
	$H_s \times 10$													
106	0.5234	14.258	1.194	15.452	25.472	57.95	83.42	.04985	.1085	.1584	74.04	.1403	2.3109	106
108	.5578	14.308	1.278	15.586	25.953	61.80	87.76	.05070	.1153	.1660	76.04	.1438	2.4502	108
110	.5944	14.359	1.365	15.724	26.434	65.91	92.34	.05155	.1226	.1742	78.03	.1472	2.5966	110
112	.6333	14.409	1.460	15.869	26.915	70.27	97.18	.05239	.1302	.1826	80.03	.1508	2.7505	112
114	.6746	14.460	1.560	16.020	27.397	74.91	102.31	.05323	.1384	.1916	82.03	.1543	2.9123	114
116	.7185	14.510	1.668	16.178	27.878	79.85	107.73	.05407	.1470	.2011	84.02	.1577	3.0821	116
118	.7652	14.561	1.782	16.343	28.359	85.10	113.46	.05490	.1562	.2111	86.02	.1612	3.2603	118
120	.8149	14.611	1.905	16.516	28.841	90.70	119.54	.05573	.1659	.2216	88.01	.1646	3.4474	120
122	.8678	14.662	2.034	16.696	29.322	96.66	125.98	.05656	.1763	.2329	90.01	.1681	3.6436	122
124	.9242	14.712	2.174	16.886	29.804	103.0	132.8	.05739	.1872	.2446	92.01	.1715	3.8493	124
126	.9841	14.763	2.323	17.086	30.285	109.8	140.1	.05821	.1989	.2571	94.01	.1749	4.0649	126
128	1.048	14.813	2.482	17.295	30.766	117.0	147.8	.05903	.2113	.2703	96.00	.1783	4.2907	128
130	1.116	14.864	2.652	17.516	31.248	124.7	155.9	.05985	.2245	.2844	98.00	.1817	4.5272	130
132	1.189	14.915	2.834	17.749	31.729	133.0	164.7	.06067	.2386	.2993	100.00	.1851	4.7747	132
134	1.267	14.965	3.029	17.994	32.211	141.8	174.0	.06148	.2536	.3151	102.00	.1885	5.0337	134
136	1.350	15.016	3.237	18.253	32.692	151.2	183.9	.06229	.2695	.3318	104.00	.1918	5.3046	136
138	1.439	15.066	3.462	18.528	33.174	161.2	194.4	.06310	.2865	.3496	106.00	.1952	5.5878	138
	H_s													
140	0.1534	15.117	3.702	18.819	33.655	172.0	205.7	.06390	.3047	.3686	107.99	.1985	5.8838	140
142	.1636	15.167	3.961	19.128	34.136	183.6	217.7	.06470	.3241	.3888	109.99	.2018	6.1930	142
144	.1745	15.218	4.239	19.457	34.618	196.0	230.6	.06549	.3449	.4104	111.99	.2051	6.5160	144
146	.1862	15.268	4.539	19.807	35.099	209.3	244.4	.06629	.3672	.4335	113.99	.2084	6.8532	146
148	.1989	15.319	4.862	20.181	35.581	223.7	259.3	.06708	.3912	.4583	115.99	.2117	7.2051	148
150	.2125	15.369	5.211	20.580	36.063	239.2	275.3	.06787	.4169	.4848	117.99	.2150	7.5722	150
152	.2271	15.420	5.587	21.007	36.545	255.9	292.4	.06866	.4445	.5132	119.99	.2183	7.9550	152
154	.2430	15.470	5.996	21.466	37.026	273.9	310.9	.06945	.4743	.5438	121.99	.2216	8.3541	154
156	.2602	15.521	6.439	21.960	37.508	293.5	331.0	.07023	.5066	.5768	123.99	.2248	8.7701	156
158	.2788	15.571	6.922	22.493	37.990	314.7	352.7	.07101	.5415	.6125	125.99	.2281	9.2036	158
160	.2990	15.622	7.446	23.068	38.472	337.8	376.3	.07179	.5793	.6511	128.00	.2313	9.6556	160
162	.3211	15.672	8.020	23.692	38.954	363.0	402.0	.07257	.6204	.6930	130.00	.2345	10.125	162
164	.3452	15.723	8.648	24.371	39.436	390.5	429.9	.07334	.6652	.7385	132.00	.2377	10.614	164
166	.3716	15.773	9.339	25.112	39.918	420.8	460.7	.07411	.7142	.7883	134.00	.2409	11.123	166
168	.4007	15.824	10.098	25.922	40.400	454.0	494.4	.07488	.7680	.8429	136.01	.2441	11.652	168
170	.4327	15.874	10.938	26.812	40.882	490.6	531.5	.07565	.8273	.9030	138.01	.2473	12.203	170
172	.4682	15.925	11.870	27.795	41.364	531.3	572.7	.07641	.8927	.9691	140.01	.2505	12.775	172
174	.5078	15.975	12.911	28.886	41.846	576.5	618.3	.07718	.9654	1.0426	142.02	.2537	13.369	174
176	.5519	16.026	14.074	30.100	42.328	627.1	669.4	.07794	1.047	1.125	144.02	.2568	13.987	176
178	.6016	16.076	15.386	31.462	42.810	684.1	726.9	.07870	1.137	1.216	146.03	.2600	14.628	178
180	.6578	16.127	16.870	32.997	43.292	748.5	791.8	.07946	1.240	1.319	148.03	.2631	15.294	180
182	.7218	16.177	18.565	34.742	43.775	821.9	865.7	.08021	1.357	1.437	150.04	.2662	15.985	182
184	.7953	16.228	20.513	36.741	44.257	906.2	950.5	.08096	1.490	1.571	152.04	.2693	16.702	184
186	.8805	16.278	22.775	39.053	44.740	1004	1049	.08171	1.645	1.727	154.05	.2724	17.446	186
188	.9802	16.329	25.427	41.756	45.222	1119	1164	.08245	1.825	1.907	156.06	.2755	18.217	188
190	1.099	16.379	28.580	44.959	45.704	1255	1301	.08320	2.039	2.122	158.07	.2786	19.017	190
192	1.241	16.430	32.375	48.805	46.187	1418	1464	.08394	2.296	2.380	160.07	.2817	19.845	192
194	1.416	16.480	37.036	53.516	46.670	1619	1666	.08468	2.609	2.694	162.08	.2848	20.704	194
196	1.635	16.531	42.885	59.416	47.153	1871	1918	.08542	3.002	3.087	164.09	.2879	21.594	196
198	1.917	16.581	50.426	67.007	47.636	2195	2243	.08616	3.507	3.593	166.10	.2910	22.514	198
200	2.295	16.632	60.510	77.142	48.119	2629	2677	.08689	4.179	4.266	168.11	.2940	23.468	200

Table 15-2. Additive Corrections for H, h, and v When Barometric Pressure Differs from Standard Barometer

Approximate altitude in feet

Wet-bulb temp. t_w	Sat. vapor press., in. Hg	−900		900		1800		2700		3700		4800		5900	
		$\Delta p = +1$		$\Delta p = -1$		$\Delta p = -2$		$\Delta p = -3$		$\Delta p = -4$		$\Delta p = -5$		$\Delta p = -6$	
		ΔH_s	Δh	ΔH_s	Δh	ΔH_s	Δh	ΔH_s	Δh	ΔH_s	Δh	ΔH_s	Δh	ΔH_s	Δh
−10	0.022	−0.10	−0.02	0.11	0.02	0.23	0.03	0.36	0.05	0.50	0.07	0.64	0.10	0.81	0.12
−8	.025	−0.12	−0.02	.12	.02	.26	.04	.40	.06	.55	.08	.72	.11	.90	.13
−6	.027	−0.13	−0.02	.14	.02	.29	.04	.44	.07	.62	.09	.80	.12	1.00	.15
−4	.030	−0.14	0.02	.15	.02	.32	.05	.50	.07	.69	.10	.89	.13	1.12	.17
−2	.034	−0.16	−0.02	.17	.02	.35	.05	.55	.08	.76	.11	.99	.15	1.24	.19
0	.038	−0.18	−0.03	.19	.03	.39	.06	.61	.09	.85	.13	1.10	.17	1.38	.21
2	.042	−0.20	−0.03	.21	.03	.44	.07	.68	.10	.94	.14	1.22	.19	1.53	.23
4	.046	−0.22	−0.03	.23	.03	.48	.07	.75	.11	1.05	.16	1.36	.21	1.70	.26
6	.051	−0.24	−0.04	.26	.04	.54	.08	.83	.13	1.16	.18	1.51	.23	1.89	.29
8	.057	−0.27	−0.04	.29	.04	.59	.09	.93	.14	1.28	.19	1.67	.25	2.09	.32
10	.063	−0.30	−0.04	.32	.05	.66	.10	1.03	.16	1.42	.22	1.85	.28	2.31	.35
12	.069	−0.33	−0.05	.35	.05	.73	.11	1.13	.17	1.57	.24	2.04	.31	2.56	.39
14	.077	−0.36	−0.05	.39	.06	.81	.12	1.25	.19	1.74	.26	2.26	.34	2.82	.43
16	.085	−0.40	−0.06	.43	.06	.89	.14	1.38	.21	1.92	.29	2.49	.38	3.12	.48
18	.093	−0.44	−0.07	.47	.07	.98	.15	1.53	.23	2.12	.32	2.75	.42	3.44	.53
20	.103	−0.49	−0.08	.52	.08	1.08	.17	1.68	.26	2.33	.36	3.03	.46	3.79	.58
22	.113	−0.5	−0.08	.6	.09	1.2	.18	1.9	.29	2.6	.40	3.4	.52	4.2	.64
24	.124	−0.6	−0.09	.6	.10	1.3	.20	2.1	.32	2.8	.43	3.7	.57	4.6	.71
26	.137	−0.7	−0.10	.7	.11	1.4	.22	2.3	.35	3.1	.48	4.1	.63	5.1	.78
28	.150	−0.7	−0.11	.8	.12	1.6	.24	2.5	.38	3.4	.52	4.5	.69	5.6	.86
30	.165	−0.8	−0.12	.8	.13	1.7	.27	2.7	.42	3.8	.58	4.9	.75	6.1	.92
32	.180	−0.9	−0.13	.9	.14	1.9	.29	3.0	.45	4.1	.63	5.3	.82	6.6	1.01
34	.197	−0.9	−0.14	1.0	.15	2.1	.32	3.2	.49	4.4	.68	5.7	.88	7.2	1.11
36	.212	−1.0	−0.15	1.1	.17	2.2	.35	3.5	.53	4.8	.74	6.2	.96	7.8	1.20
38	.229	−1.1	−0.17	1.2	.18	2.4	.37	3.8	.58	5.2	.80	6.8	1.05	8.4	1.30
40	.248	−1.2	−0.18	1.3	.20	2.6	.41	4.1	.63	5 7	.88	7.4	1.14	9.2	1.42
42	.268	−1.3	−0.20	1.4	.21	2.8	.44	4.4	.69	6.1	.94	8.0	1.23	10.0	1.54
44	.289	−1.4	−0.22	1.5	.23	3.1	.47	4.8	.74	6.7	1.04	8.7	1.34	10.8	1.67
46	.312	−1.5	−0.23	1.6	.25	3.3	.51	5.2	.80	7.2	1.11	9.4	1.45	11.7	1.81
48	.336	−1.6	−0.25	1.8	.27	3.6	.56	5.6	.87	7.8	1.21	10.2	1.58	12.6	1.95
50	.3624	−1.7	−0.27	1.9	.29	3.9	.60	6.1	.94	8.4	1.30	10.9	1.69	13.6	2.11
52	.3903	−1.9	−0.29	2.0	.32	4.2	.65	6.5	1.01	9.0	1.40	11.8	1.83	14.7	2.28
54	.4200	−2.0	−0.31	2.2	.34	4.5	.70	7.0	1.09	9.7	1.50	12.7	1.97	15.8	2.45
56	.4518	−2.2	−0.34	2.4	.37	4.9	.76	7.6	1.18	10.5	1.63	13.7	2.13	17.1	2.66
58	.4856	−2.3	−0.37	2.5	.39	5.3	.82	8.2	1.27	11.3	1.76	14.7	2.28	18.4	2.86
60	.522	−2.5	−0.40	2.7	.42	5.7	.88	8.8	1.37	12.2	1.90	15.9	2.47	19.9	3.09
62	.560	−2.7	−0.43	2.9	.46	6.1	.95	9.5	1.48	13.2	2.05	17.1	2.66	21.4	3.33
64	.601	−2.9	−0.46	3.2	.49	6.5	1.02	10.2	1.59	14.2	2.21	18.4	2.87	23.1	3.60
66	.644	−3.2	−0.50	3.4	.53	7.1	1.10	11.0	1.72	15.3	2.38	19.8	3.09	24.8	3.87
68	.690	−3.4	−0.53	3.7	.57	7.6	1.18	11.8	1.84	16.4	2.56	21.3	3.32	26.7	4.16
70	.739	−3.7	−0.57	3.9	.61	8.1	1.27	12.7	1.98	17.6	2.75	22.9	3.58	28.7	4.48
72	.791	−3.9	−0.61	4.2	.66	8.7	1.36	13.6	2.13	18.8	2.94	24.6	3.84	30.9	4.82
74	.846	−4.2	−0.66	4.6	.71	9.4	1.46	14.6	2.28	20.2	3.16	26.4	4.14	33.1	5.18
76	.905	−4.5	−0.71	4.9	.77	10.0	1.57	15.7	2.46	21.7	3.39	28.3	4.42	35.5	5.56
78	.967	−4.9	−0.76	5.2	.82	10.8	1.69	16.9	2.65	23.3	3.65	30.5	4.77	38.2	5.98
80	1.032	−5.2	−0.82	5.6	.88	11.6	1.82	18.1	2.84	25.1	3.93	32.7	5.13	41.0	6.43
82	1.102	−5.6	−0.88	6.0	.94	12.5	1.96	19.5	3.06	27.0	4.24	35.1	5.51	44.0	6.90
84	1.175	−6.0	−0.94	6.4	1.00	13.3	2.10	20.9	3.28	28.9	4.54	37.7	5.92	47.2	7.41
86	1.253	−6.4	−1.00	6.9	1.08	14.3	2.24	22.3	3.50	30.9	4.85	40.4	6.34	50.6	7.94
88	1.335	−6.9	−1.08	7.4	1.16	15.3	2.40	23.9	3.75	33.1	5.20	43.2	6.79	54.2	8.51
90	1.422	−7.4	−1.16	7.9	1.24	16.5	2.59	25.7	4.04	35.6	5.60	46.4	7.29	58.2	9.15
92	1.514	−7.9	−1.24	8.5	1.34	17.6	2.77	27.5	4.33	38.2	6.01	49.8	7.83	62.5	9.83
94	1.610	−8.5	−1.34	9.1	1.43	18.9	2.98	29.5	4.64	41.0	6.46	53.4	8.41	67.0	10.55
96	1.712	−9.1	−1.43	9.8	1.54	20.2	3.18	31.5	4.96	43.8	6.90	57.2	9.01	71.7	11.30
98	1.820	−9.7	−1.53	10.4	1.64	21.7	3.42	33.8	5.33	47.0	7.41	61.3	9.67	76.8	12.11
100	1.933	−10.4	−1.64	11.2	1.77	23.2	3.66	36.3	5.73	50.4	7.95	65.7	10.37	82.5	13.02
102	2.053	−11.1	−1.75	12.0	1.90	24.8	3.92	38.9	6.14	54.1	8.54	70.5	11.13	88.5	13.98
104	2.179	−11.9	−1.88	12.8	2.02	26.6	4.20	41.6	6.58	57.9	9.15	75.5	11.93	94.8	14.98
106	2.311	−12.8	−2.02	13.7	2.17	28.6	4.52	44.6	7.06	62.1	9.82	81.1	12.83	101.7	16.09
108	2.450	−13.7	−2.17	14.7	2.33	30.6	4.84	47.7	7.55	66.5	10.53	87.0	13.77	109.1	17.27
110	2.597	−14.7	−2.33	15.8	2.50	32.8	5.20	51.3	8.13	71.3	11.30	93.1	14.75	117.0	18.54
112	2.751	−15.7	−2.49	16.9	2.68	35.2	5.58	55.0	8.72	76.4	12.11	99.9	15.84	125.9	19.96
114	2.913	−16.9	−2.68	18.1	2.87	37.7	5.98	58.9	9.50	82.0	13.01	107.3	17.03	135.0	21.42
116	3.082	−18.0	−2.86	19.4	3.08	40.4	6.42	63.2	10.03	88.0	13.97	115.1	18.28	144.7	22.98
118	3.260	−19.3	−3.07	20.8	3.31	43.3	6.88	67.8	10.77	94.4	15.00	123.5	19.63	155.4	24.73
120	3.448	−20.7	−3.29	22.4	3.56	46.6	7.41	72.8	11.58	101.4	16.13	132.7	21.10	167.1	26.58
122	3.644	−22.2	−3.53	24.0	3.82	50.0	7.96	78.2	12.45	109.0	17.35	142.6	22.70	179.6	28.58
124	3.850	−23.8	−3.79	25.8	4.11	53.7	8.55	84.0	13.38	117.1	18.65	153.3	24.42	193.2	30.77
126	4.065	−25.6	−4.08	27.6	4.40	57.7	9.20	90.3	14.39	125.9	20.07	165.0	26.30	208.0	33.15
128	4.291	−27.5	−4.39	29.7	4.74	62.0	9.89	97.1	15.49	135.5	21.61	177.6	28.33	224.0	35.73
130	4.527	−29.5	−4.71	32.0	5.11	66.7	10.64	104.5	16.68	145.9	23.29	191.4	30.55	241.5	38.55
132	4.775	−31.8	−5.08	34.4	5.50	71.8	11.47	112.6	17.99	157.2	25.11	206.3	32.96	260.6	41.63
134	5.034	−34.2	−5.47	37.1	5.93	77.4	12.37	121.4	19.41	169.6	27.12	222.7	35.60	281.4	44.99
136	5.305	−36.8	−5.89	40.0	6.40	83.4	13.34	130.9	20.94	183.1	29.30	240.5	38.48	304.2	48.67
138	5.588	−39.7	−6.36	43.2	6.92	90.0	14.41	141.4	22.64	197.8	31.67	260.1	41.65	329.3	52.73
140	5.884	−42.8	−6.86	46.5	8.45	97.3	15.59	152.8	24.48	214.0	34.29	281.6	45.12	356.8	57.17

Table 15-2. Additive Corrections for H, h, and v When Barometeric Pressure Differs from Standard Barometer—(*Continued*)

t = dry-bulb temperature, °F.
t_w = wet-bulb temperature, °F.
p = barometric pressure, in. Hg
Δp = pressure difference from standard barometer (in. Hg)
H = moisture content of air, grains/lb. dry air
H_s = moisture content of air saturated at wet-bulb temperature t_w, grains/lb. dry air
ΔH = moisture-content correction of air when barometric pressure differs from standard barometer, grains/lb. dry air
ΔH_s = moisture-content correction of air saturated at wet-bulb temperature when barometric pressure differs from standard barometer, grains/lb. dry air

NOTE: To obtain ΔH reduce value of ΔH_s by 1 per cent where $t - t_w$ = 24°F. and correct proportionally when $t - t_w$ is not 24°F.

h = enthalpy of moist air, B.t.u./lb. dry air
Δh = enthalpy correction when barometer pressure differs from standard barometer, for saturated or unsaturated air, B.t.u./lb. dry air

v = volume of moist air, cu. ft./lb. dry air

$$= \frac{0.754(t + 459.8)}{p}\left(1 + \frac{H}{4360}\right)$$

Example. At a barometric pressure of 25.92 with 220°F. dry-bulb and 100°F. wet-bulb, determine H, h, and v. $\Delta p = -4$ and from table ΔH_s = 50.4. From note above,

$$\Delta H = \Delta H_s - \left(\frac{120}{24} \times 0.01 \times 50.4\right) = 50.4 - 2.5 = 47.9$$

Therefore H = 102 (from chart) + 47.9 = 149.9 grains/lb. dry air. From table Δh = 7.95. Therefore, h = saturation enthalpy from chart + deviation + 7.95 = 71.7 − 2.0 + 7.95 = 77.65 B.t.u./lb. dry air. From equation above

$$v = \frac{0.754(220 + 459.7)}{25.92}\left(1 + \frac{149.9}{4360}\right) = 20.43 \text{ cu. ft./lb. dry air}$$

Table 15-3. Thermodynamic Properties of Water at Saturation

Temp. t, °F.	Absolute press. $p_s \times 10^7$ Lb./sq. in.	In. Hg	Specific volume, cu. ft./lb. Sat. solid v_i	Evap. $v_{ig} \times 10^{-8}$	Sat. vapor $v_g \times 10^{-8}$	Enthalpy, B.t.u./lb. Sat. solid h_i	Evap. h_{ig}	Sat. vapor h_g	Entropy, B.t.u./(lb.)(°F.) Sat. solid s_i	Evap. s_{ig}	Sat. vapor s_g	Temp. t, °F.
−160	0.4949	1.008	0.01722	36.07	36.07	−222.05	1212.43	990.38	−0.4907	4.0456	3.5549	−160
−155	.9040	1.840	.01723	20.08	20.08	−220.44	1213.02	992.58	−0.4854	3.9812	3.4958	−155
−150	1.620	3.298	.01723	11.39	11.39	−218.82	1213.62	994.80	−0.4801	3.9188	3.4387	−150
−145	2.850	5.803	.01724	6.577	6.577	−217.17	1214.17	997.00	−0.4748	3.8583	3.3835	−145
−140	4.928	10.03	.01724	3.864	3.864	−215.49	1214.70	999.21	−0.4695	3.7996	3.3301	−140
−135	8.380	17.06	.01725	2.308	2.308	−213.80	1215.22	1001.42	−0.4643	3.7428	3.2785	−135
−130	14.03	28.56	.01725	1.400	1.400	−212.08	1215.71	1003.63	−0.4590	3.6874	3.2284	−130
	$p_s \times 10^6$			$v_{ig} \times 10^{-7}$	$v_g \times 10^{-7}$							
−125	2.312	4.708	.01726	8.622	8.622	−210.34	1216.18	1005.84	−0.4538	3.6338	3.1800	−125
−120	3.757	7.649	.01726	5.386	5.386	−208.58	1216.63	1008.05	−0.4485	3.5815	3.1330	−120
−115	6.019	12.26	.01727	3.411	3.411	−206.79	1217.05	1010.26	−0.4433	3.5308	3.0875	−115
−110	9.517	19.38	.01728	2.189	2.189	−204.98	1217.45	1012.47	−0.4381	3.4815	3.0434	−110
−105	14.86	30.25	.01728	1.422	1.422	−203.14	1217.82	1014.68	−0.4329	3.4335	3.0006	−105
−100	22.91	46.64	.01729	0.9352	0.9352	−201.28	1218.17	1016.89	−0.4277	3.3868	2.9591	−100
	$p_s \times 10^5$			$v_{ig} \times 10^{-6}$	$v_g \times 10^{-6}$							
−95	3.491	7.108	.01729	6.223	6.223	−199.40	1218.50	1019.10	−0.4225	3.3412	2.9187	−95
−90	5.260	10.71	.01730	4.186	4.186	−197.49	1218.80	1021.31	−0.4173	3.2969	2.8796	−90
−85	7.841	15.96	.01730	2.846	2.846	−195.56	1219.03	1023.52	−0.4121	3.2536	2.8415	−85
−80	11.57	23.55	.01731	1.955	1.955	−193.60	1219.33	1025.73	−0.4069	3.2114	2.8045	−80
−75	16.89	34.39	.01732	1.356	1.356	−191.62	1219.56	1027.94	−0.4017	3.1702	2.7685	−75
−70	24.43	49.74	.07132	0.9501	0.9501	−189.61	1219.76	1030.15	−0.3965	3.1301	2.7336	−70
−65	35.01	71.28	.01733	.6715	.6715	−187.58	1219.94	1032.36	−0.3914	3.0910	2.6996	−65
	$p_s \times 10^3$			$v_{ig} \times 10^{-5}$	$v_g \times 10^{-5}$							
−60	0.4972	1.012	.01734	4.788	4.788	−185.52	1220.10	1034.58	−0.3862	3.0526	2.6664	−60
−55	.7001	1.426	.01734	3.443	3.443	−183.44	1220.23	1036.79	−0.3810	3.0152	2.6342	−55
−50	.9776	1.990	.01735	2.496	2.496	−181.34	1220.34	1039.00	−0.3758	2.9786	2.6028	−50
−45	1.354	2.757	.01736	1.824	1.824	−179.21	1220.42	1041.21	−0.3707	2.9430	2.5723	−45
−40	1.861	3.790	.01737	1.343	1.343	−177.06	1220.48	1043.42	−0.3655	2.9080	2.5425	−40
−35	2.540	5.170	.01737	0.9961	0.9961	−174.88	1220.51	1045.63	−0.3604	2.8739	2.5135	−35
	$p_s \times 10^2$			$v_{ig} \times 10^{-4}$	$v_g \times 10^{-4}$							
−30	0.3440	0.7003	.01738	7.441	7.441	−172.68	1220.52	1047.84	−0.3552	2.8405	2.4853	−30
−25	.4627	.9420	.01739	5.596	5.596	−170.46	1220.51	1050.05	−0.3501	2.8078	2.4577	−25
−20	.6181	1.259	.01739	4.237	4.237	−168.21	1220.47	1052.26	−0.3449	2.7757	2.4308	−20
−15	.8204	1.670	.01740	3.228	3.228	−165.94	1220.41	1054.47	−0.3398	2.7444	2.4046	−15
−10	1.082	2.203	.01741	2.475	2.475	−163.65	1220.32	1056.67	−0.3347	2.7138	2.3791	−10
−5	1.419	2.888	.01741	1.909	1.909	−161.33	1220.21	1058.88	−0.3295	2.6836	2.3541	−5
	p_s			$v_{ig} \times 10^{-3}$	$v_g \times 10^{-3}$							
0	0.01849	0.03764	.01742	14.81	14.81	−158.98	1220.07	1061.09	−0.3244	2.6541	2.3297	0
5	.02396	.04878	.01743	11.55	11.55	−156.61	1219.90	1063.29	−0.3193	2.6252	2.3059	5
10	.03087	.06286	.01744	9.060	9.060	−154.22	1219.72	1065.50	−0.3142	2.5969	2.2827	10
15	.03957	.08056	.01744	7.144	7.144	−151.80	1219.50	1067.70	−0.3090	2.5690	2.2600	15
20	.05045	.1027	.01745	5.662	5.662	−149.36	1219.26	1069.90	−0.3039	2.5417	2.2378	20
25	.06400	.1303	.01746	4.509	4.509	−146.89	1218.98	1072.09	−0.2988	2.5150	2.2162	25
30	.08080	.1645	.01747	3.608	3.608	−144.40	1218.69	1074.29	−0.2937	2.4887	2.1950	30
32	.08858	.1803	.01747	3.305	3.305	−143.40	1218.56	1075.16	−0.2916	2.4783	2.1867	32
			Sat. liquid v_i	v_{ig}	v_g	Sat. liquid h_i			Sat. liquid s_i			
32*	.088586	.18036	.01602	3304.6	3304.6	0.00	1075.16	1075.16	0.00000	2.1867	2.1867	32*
34	.095999	.19546	.01602	3061.7	3061.7	2.01	1074.03	1076.04	.00409	2.1755	2.1796	34
36	.10396	.21166	.01602	2838.7	2838.7	4.02	1072.90	1076.92	.00815	2.1644	2.1726	36
38	.11249	.22904	.01602	2633.8	2633.8	6.03	1071.77	1077.80	.01220	2.1535	2.1657	38
40	.12164	.24767	.01602	2445.4	2445.4	8.04	1070.64	1078.68	.01623	2.1426	2.1588	40
42	.13145	.26763	.01602	2272.0	2272.0	10.05	1069.50	1079.55	.02024	2.1318	2.1520	42
44	.14194	.28899	.01602	2112.3	2112.3	12.06	1068.37	1080.43	.02423	2.1211	2.1453	44
46	.15317	.31185	.01602	1965.2	1965.2	14.06	1067.24	1081.30	.02820	2.1005	2.1387	46
48	.16517	.33629	.01602	1829.5	1829.5	16.07	1066.11	1082.18	.03216	2.0999	2.1321	48
50	.17799	.36240	.01602	1704.3	1704.3	18.07	1064.99	1083.06	.03610	2.0895	2.1256	50
52	.19169	.39028	.01602	1588.7	1588.7	20.07	1063.86	1083.93	.04002	2.0791	2.1191	52
54	.20630	.42003	.01603	1481.9	1481.9	22.08	1062.72	1084.80	.04392	2.0688	2.1127	54
56	.22188	.45176	.01603	1383.1	1383.1	24.08	1061.60	1085.68	.04781	2.0586	2.1064	56
58	.23849	.48558	.01603	1291.7	1291.7	26.08	1060.47	1086.55	.05168	2.0485	2.1002	58
60	.25618	5.2160	.01603	1207.1	1207.1	28.08	1059.34	1087.42	.05553	2.0385	2.0940	60

* Extrapolated to represent metastable equilibrium with undercooled liquid.

Table 15-3. Thermodynamic Properties of Water at Saturation—(*Continued*)

Temp. t, °F.	Absolute press. p_s Lb./sq. in.	Absolute press. p_s In. Hg	Specific volume, cu. ft./lb. Sat. liquid v_l	Specific volume Evap. v_{lg}	Specific volume Sat. vapor v_g	Enthalpy, B.t.u./lb. Sat. liquid h_l	Enthalpy Evap. h_{lg}	Enthalpy Sat. vapor h_g	Entropy, B.t.u./(lb.)(°F.) Sat. liquid s_l	Entropy Evap. s_{lg}	Entropy Sat. vapor s_g	Temp. t, °F.
62	0.27502	0.55994	0.01604	1128.7	1128.7	30.08	1058.22	1088.30	0.05937	2.0824	2.0878	62
64	.29505	.60073	.01604	1056.1	1056.1	32.08	1057.09	1089.17	.06320	2.0186	2.0818	64
66	.31636	.64411	.01604	988.63	988.65	34.07	1055.97	1090.04	.06700	2.0087	2.0757	66
68	.33900	.69021	.01605	926.06	926.08	36.07	1054.84	1090.91	.07080	1.9990	2.0698	68
70	.36304	.73916	.01605	867.95	867.97	38.07	1053.71	1091.78	.07458	1.9893	2.0639	70
72	.38856	.79113	.01606	813.95	813.97	40.07	1052.58	1092.65	.07834	1.9797	2.0580	72
74	.41564	.84626	.01606	763.73	763.75	42.06	1051.46	1093.52	.08209	1.9701	2.0522	74
76	.44435	.90472	.01606	717.01	717.03	44.06	1050.32	1094.38	.08582	1.9607	2.0465	76
78	.47478	.96666	.01607	673.52	673.54	46.06	1049.19	1095.25	.08954	1.9513	2.0408	78
80	.50701	1.0323	.01607	633.01	633.03	48.05	1048.07	1096.12	.09325	1.9419	2.0352	80
82	.54112	1.1017	.01608	595.25	595.27	50.05	1046.93	1096.98	.09694	1.9328	2.0297	82
84	.57722	1.1752	.01608	560.04	560.06	52.05	1045.80	1097.85	.10062	1.9236	2.0242	84
86	.61540	1.2530	.01609	527.19	527.21	54.04	1044.67	1098.71	.10429	1.9144	2.0187	86
88	.65575	1.3351	.01610	496.52	496.54	56.04	1043.54	1099.58	.10794	1.9054	2.0133	88
90	.69838	1.4219	.01610	467.88	467.90	58.04	1042.40	1100.44	.11158	1.8963	2.0079	90
92	.74340	1.5136	.01611	441.10	441.12	60.03	1041.27	1101.30	.11520	1.8874	2.0026	92
94	.79091	1.6103	.01611	416.07	416.09	62.03	1040.13	1102.16	.11881	1.8786	1.9974	94
96	.84103	1.7124	.01612	392.65	392.67	64.02	1039.00	1103.02	.12241	1.8698	1.9922	96
98	.89388	1.8200	.01612	370.73	370.75	66.02	1037.86	1103.88	.12600	1.8610	1.9870	98
100	.94959	1.9334	.01613	350.20	350.22	68.02	1036.72	1104.74	.12957	1.8523	1.9819	100
102	1.0083	2.0529	.01614	330.96	330.98	70.01	1035.58	1105.59	.13313	1.8437	1.9768	102
104	1.0700	2.1786	.01614	312.93	312.95	72.01	1034.44	1106.45	.13667	1.8351	1.9718	104
106	1.1351	2.3110	.01615	296.02	296.04	74.01	1033.29	1107.30	.14021	1.8266	1.9668	106
108	1.2035	2.4503	.01616	280.14	280.16	76.00	1032.16	1108.16	.14373	1.8182	1.9619	108
110	1.2754	2.5968	.01617	265.24	265.26	78.00	1031.01	1109.01	.14724	1.8098	1.9570	110
112	1.3510	2.7507	.01617	251.25	251.27	80.00	1029.86	1109.86	.15074	1.8015	1.9522	112
114	1.4305	2.9125	.01618	238.10	238.12	81.99	1028.72	1110.71	.15423	1.7932	1.9474	114
116	1.5139	3.0823	.01619	225.73	225.75	83.99	1027.57	1111.56	.15770	1.7849	1.9426	116
118	1.6014	3.2606	.01620	214.10	214.12	85.99	1026.42	1112.41	.16116	1.7767	1.9379	118
120	1.6933	3.4477	.01620	203.16	203.18	87.98	1025.28	1113.26	.16461	1.7687	1.9333	120
122	1.7897	3.6439	.01621	192.85	192.87	89.98	1024.12	1114.10	.16805	1.7606	1.9286	122
124	1.8907	3.8496	.01622	183.15	183.17	91.98	1022.96	1114.94	.17148	1.7526	1.9241	124
126	1.9966	4.0651	.01623	174.00	174.02	93.98	1021.81	1115.79	.17490	1.7446	1.9195	126
128	2.1075	4.2910	.01624	165.38	165.40	95.97	1020.66	1116.63	.17830	1.7367	1.9150	128
130	2.2237	4.5274	.01625	157.25	157.27	97.97	1019.50	1117.47	.18170	1.7289	1.9106	130
132	2.3452	4.7750	.01626	149.58	149.60	99.97	1018.34	1118.31	.18508	1.7211	1.9062	132
134	2.4725	5.0340	.01626	142.34	142.36	101.97	1017.18	1119.15	.18845	1.7134	1.9018	134
136	2.6055	5.3049	.01627	135.50	135.52	103.97	1016.01	1119.98	.19181	1.7056	1.8974	136
138	2.7446	5.5881	.01628	129.04	129.06	105.97	1014.85	1120.82	.19516	1.6979	1.8931	138
140	2.8900	5.8842	.01629	122.94	122.96	107.96	1013.69	1121.65	.19850	1.6903	1.8888	140
142	3.0419	6.1934	.01630	117.16	117.18	109.96	1012.52	1122.48	.20182	1.6828	1.8846	142
144	3.2006	6.5164	.01631	111.70	111.72	111.96	1011.35	1123.31	.20514	1.6753	1.8804	144
146	3.3662	6.8536	.01632	106.54	106.56	113.96	1010.18	1124.14	.20845	1.6678	1.8763	146
148	3.5390	7.2056	.01633	101.65	101.67	115.96	1009.01	1124.97	.21174	1.6604	1.8721	148
150	3.7194	7.5727	.01634	97.022	97.038	117.96	1007.83	1125.79	.21503	1.6530	1.8680	150
152	3.9074	7.9556	.01635	92.635	92.651	119.96	1006.66	1126.62	.21830	1.6457	1.8640	152
154	4.1035	8.3548	.01636	86.477	88.493	121.97	1005.47	1127.44	.22157	1.6384	1.8600	154
156	4.3078	8.7708	.01637	84.536	84.552	123.97	1004.29	1128.26	.22482	1.6312	1.8560	156
158	4.5207	9.2042	.01638	80.798	80.814	125.97	1003.11	1129.08	.22807	1.6239	1.8520	158
160	4.7424	9.6556	.01639	77.251	77.267	127.97	1001.92	1129.89	.23130	1.6168	1.8481	160
162	4.9732	10.126	.01640	73.885	73.901	129.97	1000.74	1130.71	.23453	1.6097	1.8442	162
164	5.2134	10.615	.01642	70.690	70.706	131.98	999.54	1131.52	.23774	1.6027	1.8404	164
166	5.4634	11.124	.01643	67.654	67.670	133.98	998.35	1132.33	.24095	1.5956	1.8365	166
168	5.7233	11.653	.01644	64.770	64.786	135.98	997.16	1133.14	.24414	1.5887	1.8328	168
170	5.9936	12.203	.01645	62.029	62.045	137.99	995.95	1133.94	.24733	1.5817	1.8290	170
172	6.2746	12.775	.01646	59.423	59.439	139.99	994.76	1134.75	.25051	1.5748	1.8253	172
174	6.5666	13.370	.06147	56.944	56.960	142.00	993.55	1135.55	.25367	1.5679	1.8216	174
176	6.8699	13.987	.01648	54.586	54.602	144.00	992.35	1136.35	.25683	1.5611	1.8179	176
178	7.1849	14.629	.01650	52.341	52.357	146.01	991.14	1137.15	.25998	1.5543	1.8143	178
180	7.5119	15.295	.01651	50.203	50.220	148.01	989.93	1137.94	.26312	1.5475	1.8106	180
182	7.8514	15.986	.01652	48.168	48.185	150.02	988.72	1138.74	.26625	1.5408	1.8071	182
184	8.2035	16.703	.01653	46.229	46.246	152.03	987.50	1139.53	.26937	1.5341	1.8035	184
186	8.5688	17.446	.01654	44.381	44.398	154.04	986.28	1140.32	.27248	1.5275	1.8000	186
188	8.9476	18.218	.01656	42.619	42.636	156.04	985.07	1141.11	.27559	1.5209	1.7965	188
190	9.3403	19.017	.01657	40.939	40.956	158.05	983.84	1141.89	.27868	1.5143	1.7930	190
192	9.7473	19.846	.01658	39.337	39.354	160.06	982.61	1142.67	.28176	1.5078	1.7896	192
194	10.169	20.704	.01659	37.807	37.824	162.07	981.38	1143.45	.28484	1.5013	1.7861	194
196	10.606	21.594	.01661	36.348	36.365	164.08	980.15	1144.23	.28791	1.4949	1.7828	196
198	11.058	22.515	.01662	34.954	34.971	166.09	978.91	1145.00	.29097	1.4884	1.7794	198
200	11.526	23.468	.01663	33.623	33.640	168.10	977.68	1145.78	.29402	1.4820	1.7760	200
202	12.011	24.455	.01665	32.351	32.368	170.11	976.43	1146.54	.29706	1.4756	1.7727	202
204	12.513	25.476	.01666	31.136	31.153	172.12	975.19	1147.31	.30010	1.4693	1.7694	204
206	13.031	26.532	.01667	29.974	29.991	174.14	973.94	1148.08	.30312	1.4631	1.7662	206
208	13.568	27.625	.01669	28.863	28.880	176.15	972.69	1148.84	.30614	1.4568	1.7629	208
210	14.123	28.754	.01670	27.801	27.818	178.17	971.43	1149.60	.30915	1.4506	1.7597	210
212	14.696	29.921	.01671	26.784	26.801	180.18	970.17	1150.35	.31215	1.4444	1.7565	212

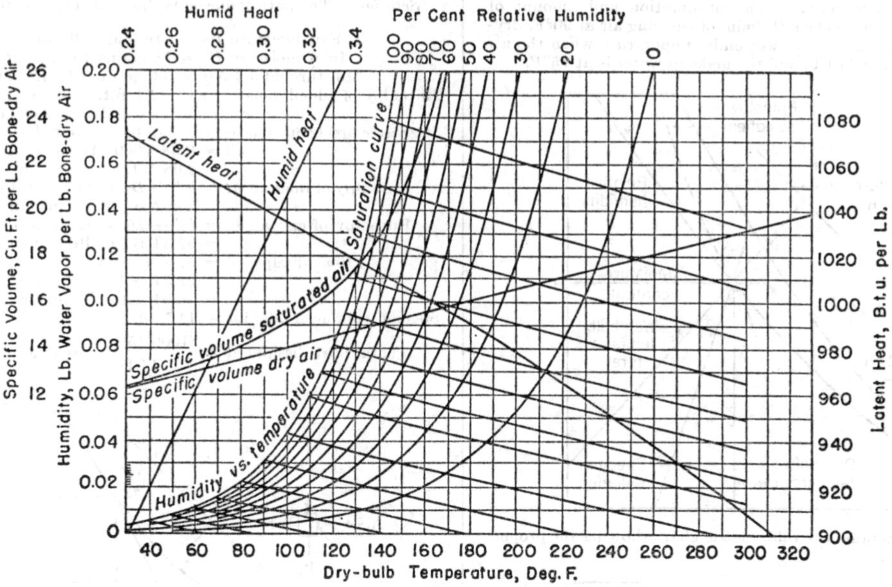

FIG. 15-4. Humidity chart for air–water vapor mixtures.

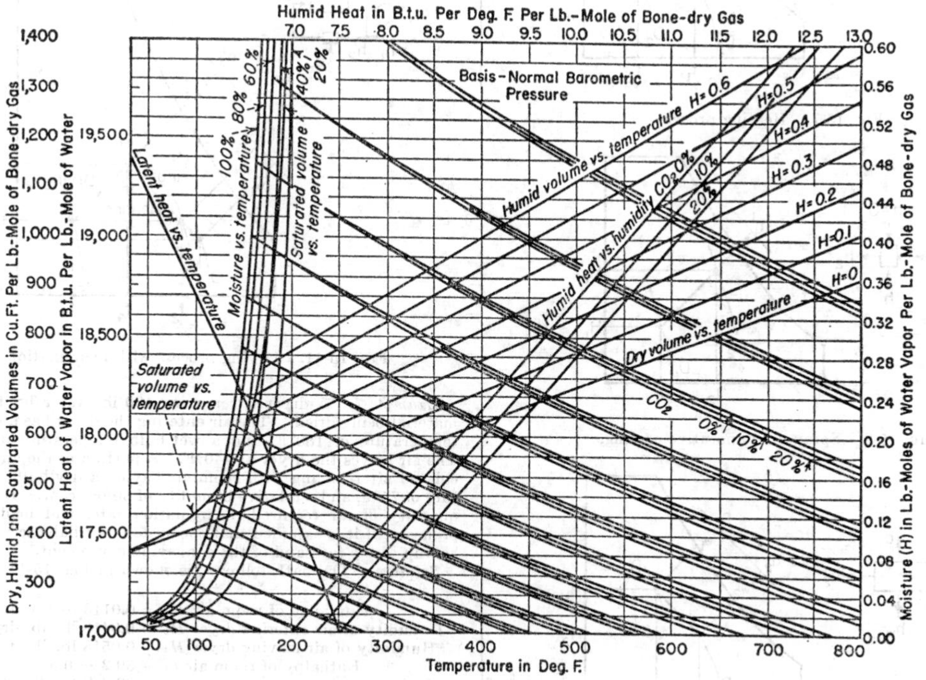

FIG. 15-5. Revised form of high-temperature psychrometric chart for air and combustion products, based on pound-moles of water vapor and dry gases. [*Hatta, Chem. Met. Eng.*, **37**, 164 (1930).]

Example 6. Determine water consumption and amount of heat dissipated per 1000 cu. ft./min. of entering air at 90°F. dry-bulb temperature and 70°F. wet-bulb temperature when the air leaves saturated at 110°F. and the makeup water is at 75°F.

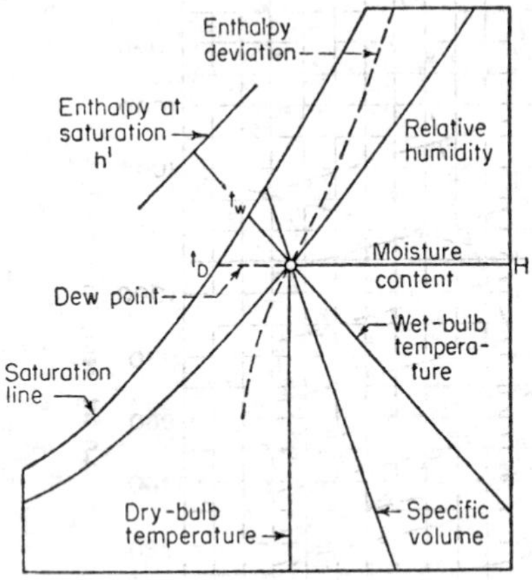

FIG. 15-6. Diagram of psychrometric chart showing the properties of moist air.

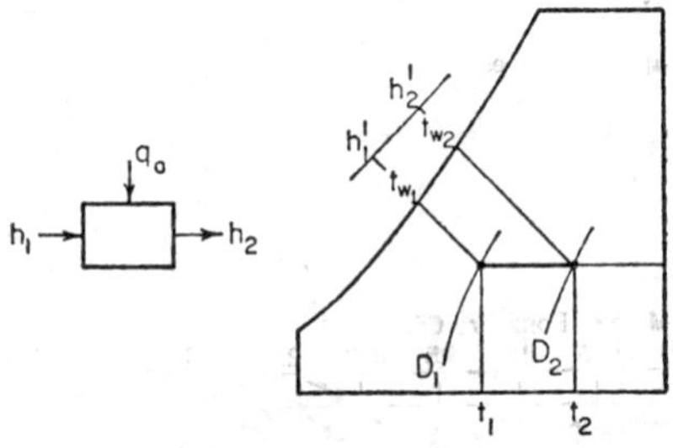

FIG. 15-7. Heating process.

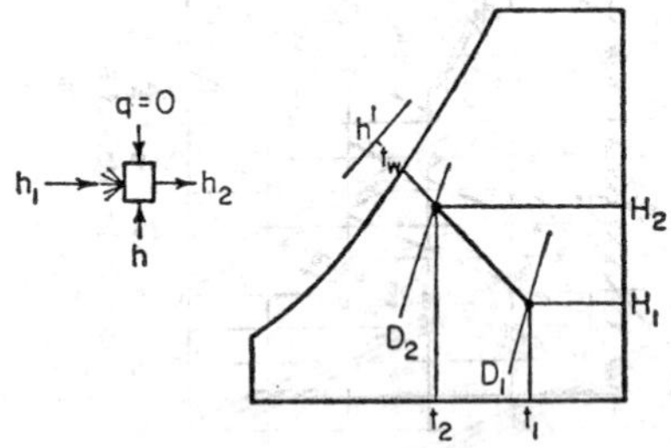

FIG. 15-8. Spray or evaporative cooling.

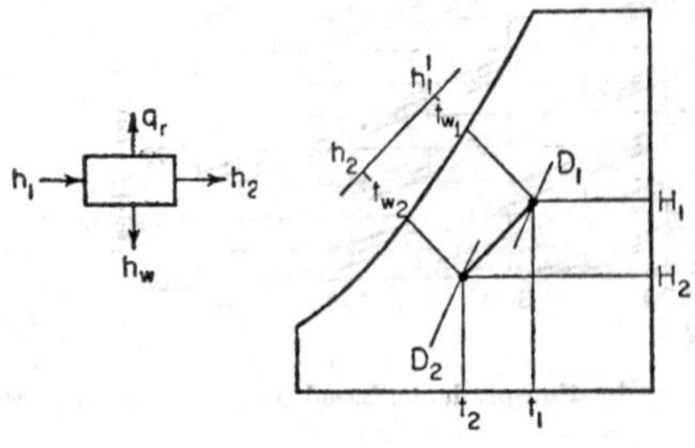

FIG. 15-9. Cooling and dehumidifying process.

Solution. The path followed is shown in Fig. 15-10.

Exit moisture H_2 = 416 grains/lb. dry air
Inlet moisture H_1 = 78 grains/lb. dry air
Moisture added ΔH = 338 grains/lb. dry air
Enthalpy of added moisture h_w = 2.1 B.t.u./lb. dry air (from small diagram of Fig. 15-3)

If greater precision is desired h_w can be calculated as

$$h_w = (338/7000)(1)(75 - 32) = 2.08 \text{ B.t.u./lb. dry air}$$

Enthalpy of inlet air $h_1 = h_1' + D_1 = 34.1 - 0.18 = 33.92$ B.t.u./lb. dry air

Enthalpy of exit air $h_2 = h_2' + D_2 = 92.34 + 0 = 92.34$ B.t.u./lb. dry air

Heat dissipated $= h_2 - h_1 - h_w = 92.34 - 33.92 - 2.08 = 56.34$ B.t.u./lb. dry air

Specific volume of inlet air = 14.1 cu. ft./lb. dry air

$$\text{Total heat dissipated} = \frac{(1000)(56.34)}{14.1} = 3990 \text{ B.t.u./min.}$$

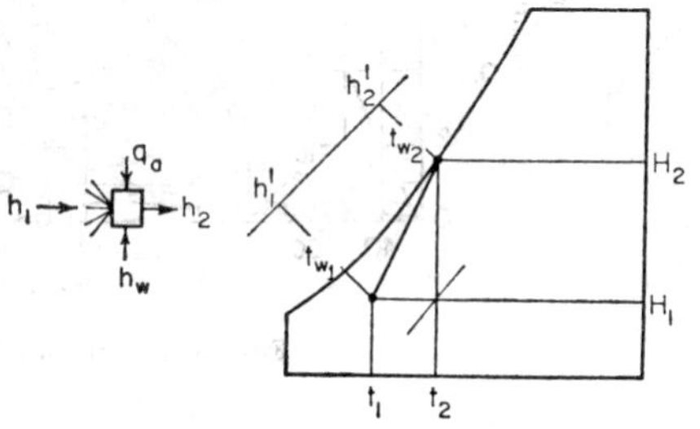

FIG. 15-10. Cooling tower.

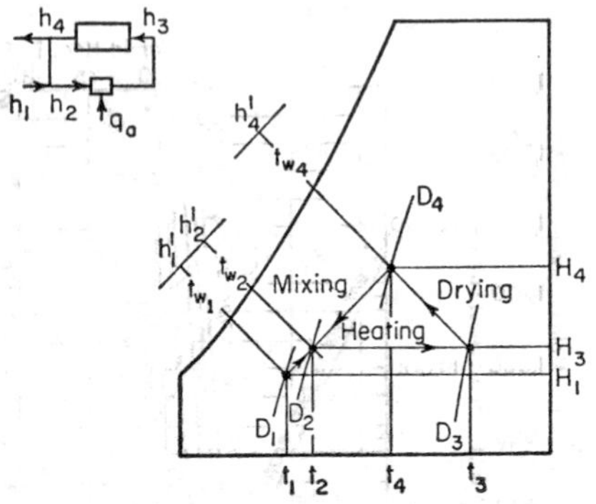

FIG. 15-11. Drying process with recirculation.

Example 7. A dryer is removing 100 lb. water/hr. from the material being dried. The air entering the dryer has a dry-bulb temperature of 180°F. and a wet-bulb temperature of 110°F. The air leaves the dryer at 140°F. A portion of the air is recirculated after mixing with room air having a dry-bulb temperature of 75°F. and a relative humidity of 60 per cent. Determine quantity of air required, recirculation rate, and load on the preheater if it is assumed that the system is adiabatic. Neglect heatup of the feed and of the conveying equipment.

Solution. The path followed is shown in Fig. 15-11.

Humidity of room air H_1 = 0.0113 lb./lb. dry air
Humidity of air entering dryer H_3 = 0.0418 lb./lb. dry air
Humidity of air leaving dryer H_4 = 0.0518 lb./lb. dry air
Enthalpy of room air $h_1 = 30.2 - 0.3 = 29.9$ B.t.u./lb. dry air
Enthalpy of entering air $h_3 = 92.5 - 1.3 = 91.2$ B.t.u./lb. dry air
Enthalpy of leaving air $h_4 = 92.5 - 0.55 = 91.95$ B.t.u./lb. dry air

Quantity of air required is 100/(0.0518 − 0.0418) = 10,000 lb. dry air/hr.

At the dryer inlet the specific volume is 17.1 cu. ft./lb. dry air.

Air volume is (10,000)(17.1)/60 = 2850 cu. ft./min.

Fraction exhausted is

$$\frac{X}{W_a} = \frac{0.0518 - 0.0418}{0.0518 - 0.0113} = 0.247$$

where X = quantity of fresh air and W_a = total air flow. Thus 75.3 per cent of the air is recirculated. Load on the preheater is obtained from an enthalpy balance

$$q_a = 10{,}000(91.2) - 2470(29.9) - 7530(91.95) = 146{,}000 \text{ B.t.u./hr.}$$

Use of Psychrometric Charts at Pressures Other than Atmospheric. The psychrometric charts shown as Figs. 15-1 through 15-4 and the data of Table 15-1 are based on a system pressure of 1 atm. (29.92 in. Hg). For other system pressures, these data must be corrected for the effect of pressure. Additive corrections to be applied to the atmospheric values of absolute humidity and enthalpy are given in Table 15-2.

The **specific volume** of moist air in cu. ft./lb. dry air can be determined for other pressures, assuming ideal gas behavior, by the following equation:

$$v = \frac{0.754(t + 460)}{P}\left(1 + \frac{HM_a}{M_w}\right) \qquad (15\text{-}5)$$

where v = specific volume, cu. ft./lb. dry air; t = dry-bulb temperature, °F.; P = pressure, in. Hg; H = absolute humidity, lb. water/lb. dry air; M_a = molecular weight of air, lb./lb.-mole; M_w = molecular weight of water vapor, lb./lb.-mole.

Relative humidity and **dew point** can be determined for other than atmospheric pressure from the partial pressure of water in the mixture and from the vapor presure of water vapor. The partial pressure of water is calculated, assuming ideal gas behavior, as

$$p = \frac{HP}{(M_w/M_a) + H} \qquad (15\text{-}6)$$

where p = partial pressure of water vapor, in. Hg; P = total pressure, in. Hg; H = absolute humidity, lb. water/lb. dry air, corrected to the actual pressure; M_a = molecular weight of air, lb./lb.-mole; M_w = molecular weight of water vapor, lb./lb.-mole. The dew point of the mixture is then read directly from a table of vapor pressures as the temperature corresponding to the calculated partial pressure.

The relative humidity is obtained by dividing the calculated partial pressure by the vapor pressure of water at the dry-bulb temperature. Thus:

$$\text{Relative humidity} = \frac{100p}{p_s} \qquad (15\text{-}7)$$

where p = calculated partial pressure, in. Hg; p_s = vapor pressure at dry-bulb temperature, in. Hg.

The preceding equations, which have assumed that both the air and water vapor behave as ideal gases, are sufficiently accurate for most engineering calculations. Where it is desired to remove the restriction that water vapor behaves as an ideal gas, the actual density ratio should be used in place of the molecular-weight ratio in Eqs. (15-5) and (15-6).

Since the Schmidt number, Prandtl number, latent heat of vaporization, and humid heat are all essentially independent of pressure, the adiabatic-saturation temperature and wet-bulb temperature line will be substantially equal at pressures different from atmospheric.

Example 8. For a barometric pressure of 25.92 in. Hg ($\Delta p = -4$), a dry-bulb temperature of 90°F., and a wet-bulb temperature of 70°F. determine the following: absolute humidity, enthalpy, dew point, relative humidity, and specific volume.

Solution. From Fig. 15-2, the moisture content is 78 grains/lb. dry air = 0.0114 lb./lb. dry air. From Table 15-2 at t_w = 70°F. and $\Delta p = -4$ read ΔH_s = 17.6 grains/lb. dry air (additive correction for air saturated at the wet-bulb temperature).

$\Delta H = 17.6[1 - (20/24)\ (0.01)] = 17.4$, or actual humidity is 78 + 17.4 = 95.4 grains/lb. dry air or 0.01362 lb./lb. dry air. (See footnotes for Table 15-2.)

The enthalpy is obtained from Fig. 15-2 as $h = h' + D$ = 34.1 − 0.18 = 33.92. To this must be added the correction of 2.75 read from Table 15-2 for $\Delta p = -4$ and t_w = 70°F., giving the true enthalpy as 33.92 + 2.75 = 36.67 B.t.u./lb. dry air.

The partial pressure of water vapor is calculated from Eq. (15-6) as

$$p = \frac{HP}{(M_w/M_a) + H} = \frac{0.01362 \times 25.92}{0.622 + 0.01362} = 0.556 \text{ in. Hg}$$

From a table of vapor pressures, this corresponds to a dew point of 61.8°F.

Relative humidity is obtained from Eq. (15-7) as $100\ p/p_s$ = (100 × 0.556)/1.422 = 39.1 per cent.

The specific volume in cu. ft./lb. dry air is obtained from Eq. (15-5):

$$v = \frac{0.754(t + 460)}{25.92}\left(1 + \frac{HM_a}{M_w}\right) = \frac{0.754(90 + 460)}{25.92}\left(1 + \frac{0.01362}{0.622}\right) = 16.35 \text{ cu. ft./lb. dry air}$$

MEASUREMENT OF HUMIDITY

Dew-point Method. The dew point of wet air is measured directly by observing the temperature at which moisture begins to form on an artificially cooled polished surface. The polished surface is usually cooled by evaporation of a low-boiling solvent such as ether, by vaporization of a condensed permanent gas such as carbon dioxide or liquid air, or by a temperature-regulated stream of water.

Although the dew-point method may be considered a fundamental technique for determining humidity, several uncertainties occur in its use. It is not always possible to measure precisely the temperature of the polished surface or to eliminate gradients across the surface. It is also difficult to detect the appearance or disappearance of fog; usual practice is to take the dew point as the average of the temperatures when fog first appears on cooling and disappears on heating.

Wet-bulb Method. Probably the most commonly used method for determining the humidity of a gas stream is the measurement of wet- and dry-bulb temperatures. The wet-bulb temperature is measured by contacting the air with a thermometer whose bulb is covered by a wick saturated with water. If the process is adiabatic, the thermometer bulb attains the wet-bulb temperature. When the wet- and dry-bulb temperatures are known, the humidity is readily obtained from charts such as Figs. 15-1 through 15-4. In order to obtain reliable information, care must be exercised to ensure that the wet-bulb thermometer remains wet and that radiation to the bulb is minimized. The latter is accomplished by making the relative velocity between wick and gas stream high (a velocity of 15 ft./sec. is usually adequate for commonly used thermometers) or by the use of radiation shielding. Making sure that the wick remains wet is a mechanical problem, and the method used depends to a large extent on the particular arrangement. Again, as with the dew-point method, errors associated with the measurement of temperature can cause difficulty.

For measurement of atmospheric humidities the **sling psychrometer** is widely used. This is composed of a wet- and dry-bulb thermometer mounted in a sling which is whirled manually to give the desired gas velocity across the bulb. In the **Assmann psychrometer** the air is drawn past the bulbs by a motor-driven fan.

In addition to the mercury-in-glass thermometer, other temperature-sensing elements may be used for psychrometers. These include resistance thermometers, thermocouples, bimetal thermometers, and thermistors.

Mechanical Hygrometers. Materials such as human hair, wood fiber, and plastics have been used to measure humidity. These methods rely on a change in dimension with humidity.

Electric hygrometers measure the electrical resistance of a film of moisture-absorbing materials exposed to the gas. A wide variety of sensing elements have been used. See Wexler (*N.B.S. Circ.* 586, Sept. 3, 1957) for a discussion of these hygrometers.

The **gravimetric method** is accepted as the most accurate humidity-measuring technique. In this method a known quantity of gas is passed over a moisture-absorbing chemical, such as phosphorus pentoxide, and the increase in weight is determined.

EVAPORATIVE COOLING

REFERENCES: "Heating, Ventilating, Air Conditioning Guide," 38th ed., American Society of Heating, Refrigerating and Air-Conditioning Engineers, New York, 1960. "Refrigerating Data Book," Design vol., 10th ed., American Society of Refrigerating Engineers, New York, 1957–1958. Kelley and Swenson, *Chem. Eng. Progress*, **52**, 263 (1956). Lewis, *Trans. Am. Soc. Mech. Engrs.*, **44**, 329 (1922). Lichtenstein, *Trans. Am. Soc. Mech. Engrs.*, **65**, 779 (1943). London, Mason, and Boelter, *Trans. Am. Soc. Mech. Engrs.*, **62**, 41 (1940). McAdams, "Heat Transmission," 3d ed., pp. 356–365, McGraw-Hill, New York, 1954. Merkel, *Ver. Deut. Ing. Forschungsarb.*, No. 275, Berlin, 1925. Woods and Betts, *Engineer*, **189** (4912), 337; (4913), 349 (1950). Zivi and Brand, *Refrig. Eng.*, **64**, 8, 31–34, 90 (1956). *Tech. Bulls.* R-54-P-5, R-58-P-5, Marley Co., Kansas City, Mo., 1957. "Counterflow Cooling Tower Performance," J. F. Pritchard Co., Kansas City, Mo., 1957.

Principles. The processes of cooling water are among the oldest and simplest known to man. All that is required to cool water is to expose its surface to air. Some of these cooling processes are slow, such as cooling of water on the surface of a pond; others are comparatively fast, such as spraying of water into air. These processes all involve the exposure of water surface to air in varying degrees.

The heat-transfer process involves (1) latent heat transfer owing to vaporization of a small portion of the water and (2) sensible heat transfer owing to the difference in temperature of water and air. Approximately 80 per cent of this heat transfer is due to latent heat and 20 per cent from sensible heat.

Theoretical possible heat removal per pound of air circulated in a cooling tower depends on the temperature and moisture content of air. An indication of the moisture content of the air is its wet-bulb temperature. Ideally, then, the wet-bulb temperature is the lowest theoretical temperature to which the water can be cooled. Practically, the cold-water temperature approaches but does not equal the air wet-bulb temperature in a cooling tower; this is because it is impossible to contact all the water with fresh air as the water drops through the wetted fill surface to the basin. The magnitude of approach to the wet-bulb temperature is dependent on tower design. Important factors are air-to-water contact time, amount of fill surface, and break-up of water into droplets. In actual practice, cooling towers are seldom designed for approaches closer than 5°F.

Cooling-tower Theory. The most generally accepted theory of the cooling-tower heat-transfer process is that developed by Merkel (*op. cit.*). This analysis is based upon **enthalpy potential difference** as the driving force.

Each particle of water is assumed to be surrounded by a film of air, and the enthalpy difference between the film and surrounding air provides the driving force for the cooling process. In the integrated form the Merkel equation is

$$\frac{KaV}{L} = \int_{T_2}^{T_1} \frac{dT}{h' - h} \qquad (15\text{-}8)$$

where K = mass-transfer coefficient, lb. water/(hr.)(sq. ft.); a = contact area, sq. ft./cu. ft. tower volume; V = active cooling volume, cu. ft./sq. ft. of plan area; L = water rate, lb./hr.; h' = enthalpy of saturated air at water temperature, B.t.u./lb.; h = enthalpy of air stream, B.t.u./lb.; T_1 and T_2 = entering and leaving water temperatures, °F. The right-hand side of Eq. (15-8) is entirely in terms of air and water properties and is independent of tower dimensions.

Figure 15-12 illustrates water and air relationships and the driving potential which exist in a counterflow tower, where air flows parallel but opposite in direction to water flow. An understanding of this diagram is important in visualizing the tower cooling process.

The water operating line is shown by line AB and is fixed by the inlet and outlet tower water temperatures. The air operating line begins at C, vertically below B and at a point having an enthalpy corresponding to that of the entering wet-bulb. Line BC represents the initial driving force $(h' - h)$. In cooling water 1°F., the enthalpy per pound of air is increased 1 B.t.u. multiplied by the ratio of pounds of water per pound of air. The liquid/gas ratio L/G is the slope of the operating line. The air leaving the tower is represented by point D. The cooling range is the projected length of line CD on the temperature scale. The cooling-tower approach is shown on the diagram as the difference between the cold-water temperature leaving the tower and the ambient wet-bulb.

The coordinates refer directly to the temperature and enthalpy of any point on the water operating line but refer directly only to the enthalpy of a point on the air operating line. The corresponding wet-bulb temperature of any point on CD is found by projecting the point horizontally to the saturation curve, then vertically to the temperature coordinate. The integral [Eq. (15-8)] is represented by the area $ABCD$ in the diagram. This value is known as the **tower characteristic,** varying with the L/G ratio.

For example, an increase in entering wet-bulb temperature moves the origin C upward, and the line CD shifts to the right to maintain a constant KaV/L. If the cooling range increases, line CD lengthens. At a constant wet-bulb temperature, equilibrium is established by moving the line to the right to maintain a constant KaV/L. On the other hand, a change in L/G ratio changes the slope of CD, and the tower comes to equilibrium with a new KaV/L.

In order to predict tower performance it is necessary to know the required tower characteristics for fixed ambient and water conditions. This would require a rather tedious integration, which is overcome by use of a nomograph (Fig. 15-13) prepared by Woods and Betts (*loc. cit.*). Mechanical-draft cooling towers normally are designed for L/G ratios ranging from 0.75 to 1.50; accordingly, the values of KaV/L vary from 0.50 to 2.50. With these ranges in mind, an example of the use of the nomograph will readily explain the effect of changing variables.

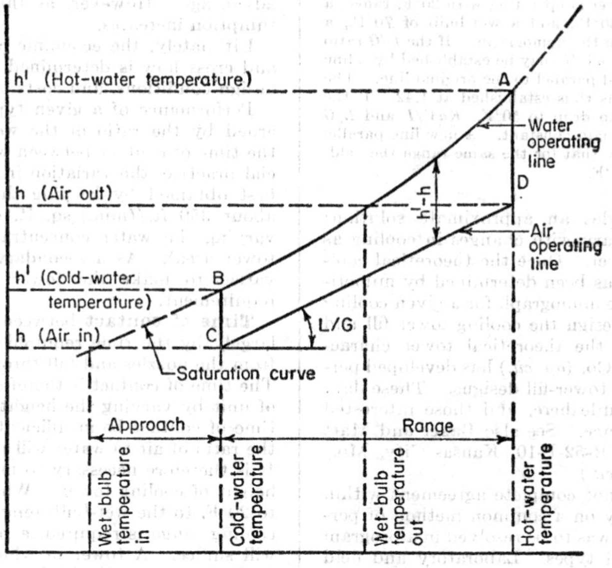

Fig. 15-12. Cooling-tower process heat balance. *(Marley Co.)*

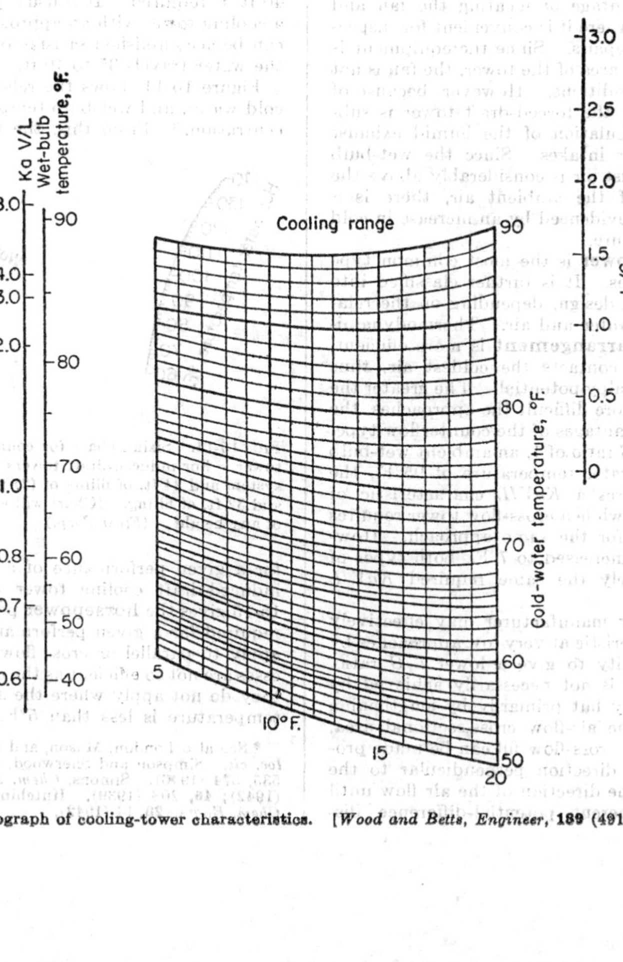

Fig. 15-13. Nomograph of cooling-tower characteristics. *[Wood and Betts, Engineer,* **189** *(4912), 337 (1950).]*

Example 9. If a given tower is operating with 20°F. range, a cold-water temperature of 80°F., and a wet-bulb of 70°F., a straight line may be drawn on the nomograph. If the L/G ratio is calculated to be 1.0, then KaV/L may be established by a line drawn through $L/G = 1.0$ and parallel to the original line. The tower characteristic KaV/L is thus established at 1.42. If the wet-bulb temperature were to drop to 50°F., KaV/L and L/G ratios may be assumed to remain constant. A new line parallel to the original will then show that for the same range the cold-water temperature will be 70°F.

The nomograph provides an approximate solution; degree of accuracy will vary with changes in cooling as well as from tower to tower. Once the theoretical cooling-tower characteristic has been determined by numerical integration or from the nomograph for a given cooling duty, it is necessary to design the cooling-tower fill and air distribution to meet the theoretical tower characteristic. J. F. Pritchard Co. (*op. cit.*) has developed performance data on various tower-fill designs. These data are too extensive to include here, and those interested should consult this reference. See also Baker and Mart (Marley Co., *Tech. Bull.* R-52-P-10, Kansas City, Mo.) and Zivi and Brand (*loc. cit.*).

As of 1961, there was not complete agreement within the cooling-tower industry on a common method of performance analysis. This was to be resolved in a program involving industries of all types. Laboratory and field tests are normally used to verify performance ratings.

Mechanical-draft Towers. Two types of mechanical-draft towers are in use today—the forced draft and the induced draft. In the **forced-draft tower** the fan is mounted at the base and air is forced in at the bottom and discharged at low velocity through the top. This arrangement has the advantage of locating the fan and drive outside the tower, where it is convenient for inspection, maintenance, and repairs. Since the equipment is out of the hot, humid top area of the tower, the fan is not subjected to corrosive conditions. However, because of the low exit air velocity, the forced-draft tower is subjected to excessive recirculation of the humid exhaust vapors back into the air intakes. Since the wet-bulb temperature of the exhaust air is considerably above the wet-bulb temperature of the ambient air, there is a decrease in performance evidenced by an increase in cold (leaving) water temperature.

The **induced-draft tower** is the most common type used in the United States. It is further classified into counterflow or cross-flow design, depending on the relative flow directions of water and air. Thermodynamically, the **counterflow arrangement** is more efficient, since the coldest water contacts the coldest air, thus obtaining maximum enthalpy potential. The greater the cooling ranges and the more difficult the approaches, the more distinct are the advantages of the counterflow type. For example, with an L/G ratio of 1, an ambient wet-bulb of 78°F., and an inlet water temperature of 95°F., the counterflow tower requires a KaV/L characteristic of 1.75 for a 5°F. approach, while a cross-flow tower requires a characteristic of 2.25 for the same approach. However, if the approach is increased to 7°F., both types of tower have approximately the same required KaV/L (within 1 per cent).

The **cross-flow tower** manufacturer may effectively reduce the tower characteristic at very low approaches by increasing the air quantity to give a lower L/G ratio. The increase in air flow is not necessarily achieved by increasing the air velocity but primarily by lengthening the tower to increase the air-flow cross-sectional area. It appears then that the cross-flow fill can be made progressively longer in the direction perpendicular to the air flow and shorter in the direction of the air flow until it almost loses its inherent potential-difference disadvantage. However, as this is done, fan power consumption increases.

Ultimately, the economic choice between counterflow and cross flow is determined by effectiveness of the fill, design conditions, and costs of tower manufacture.

Performance of a given type of cooling tower is governed by the ratio of the weights of air to water and the time of contact between water and air. In commercial practice, the variation in the ratio of air to water is first obtained by keeping the air velocity constant at about 350 ft./(min.)(sq. ft. of active tower area) and varying the water concentration, gal./(min.)(sq. ft. of tower area). As a secondary operation, air velocity is varied to make the tower accommodate the cooling requirement.

Time of contact between water and air is governed largely by the time required for the water to discharge from the nozzles and fall through the tower to the basin. The time of contact is therefore obtained in a given type of unit by varying the height of the tower. Should the time of contact be insufficient, no amount of increase in the ratio of air to water will produce the desired cooling. It is therefore necessary to maintain a certain minimum height of cooling tower. Where a wide approach of 15° to 20°F. to the wet-bulb temperature and a 25° to 35°F. cooling range is required, a relatively low cooling tower will suffice. A tower in which the water travels 15 to 20 ft. from the distributing system to the basin is sufficient. Where a moderate approach of 8° to 15°F. and a cooling range of 25° to 35°F. is required, a tower in which the water travels 25 to 30 ft. is adequate. Where a close approach of 4° to 8°F. with a 25° to 35°F. cooling range is required, a tower in which the water travels from 35 to 40 ft. is required. It is usually not economical to design a cooling tower with an approach of less than 5°F., but it can be accomplished satisfactorily with a tower in which the water travels 35 to 40 ft.

Figure 15-14 shows the relationship of the hot water, cold water, and wet-bulb temperatures to the water concentration.* From this, the **minimum area** required for a given performance of a well-designed counterflow induced-draft cooling tower can be obtained. Figure 15-15 gives the **horsepower** per square foot of tower area required for a given performance. These curves do not apply to parallel or cross-flow cooling, since these processes are not so efficient as the counterflow process. Also, they do not apply where the approach to the cold-water temperature is less than 5°F. These charts should be

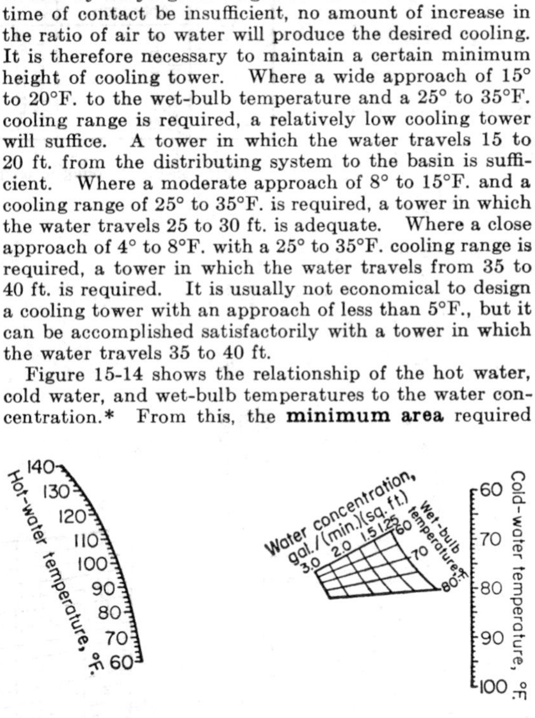

FIG. 15-14. Sizing chart for counterflow induced-draft cooling tower. For induced-draft towers with (1) upspray distributing system and 24 ft. of filling of (2) flume-type distributing system and 32 ft. of filling. (Chart will give approximations for towers of any height. (*Fluor Corp.*)

* See also London, Mason, and Boelter, *loc. cit.* Lichtenstein, *loc. cit.* Simpson and Sherwood, *J. Am. Soc. Refrig. Engrs.*, **52**, 535, 574 (1946). Simons, *Chem. Met. Eng.*, **49** (5), 138; (6), 83 (1942); **46**, 208 (1939). Hutchinson and Spivey, *Trans. Inst. Chem. Engrs.*, **20**, 14 (1942).

considered approximate and for preliminary estimates only. Since many factors not shown in the graphs must be included in the computation, the manufacturer should be consulted for final design recommendations.

The cooling performance of any tower containing a given depth of filling varies with the **water concentration**. It has been found that maximum contact and performance are obtained with a tower having a water concentration of 2 to 3 gal./(min.)(sq. ft. of ground area). Thus the problem of calculating the size of a cooling

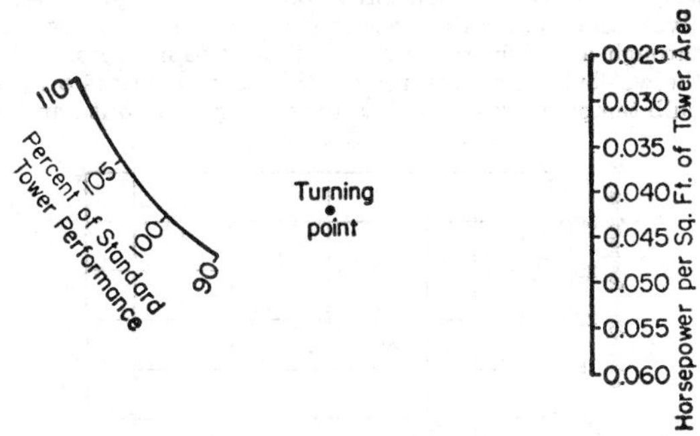

FIG. 15-15. Horsepower chart for counterflow induced-draft cooling tower. (*Fluor Corp.*)

tower becomes one of determining the proper concentration of water required to obtain the desired results. Once the necessary water concentration is established, tower area can be calculated by dividing the gal./min. circulated by the water concentration in gal./(min.) (sq. ft.). The required tower size then is a function of the following:

1. Cooling range (hot-water temperature minus cold-water temperature)
2. Approach to wet-bulb temperature (cold-water temperature minus wet-bulb temperature)
3. Quantity of water to be cooled
4. Wet-bulb temperature
5. Air velocity through the cell
6. Tower height

Example 10. To illustrate use of the charts, assume the following conditions:

Hot-water temperature T_1, °F.	= 102
Cold-water temperature T_2, °F.	= 78
Wet-bulb temperature t_w, °F.	= 70
Water rate, gal./min.	= 2000

A straight line on Fig. 15-14, connecting the points representing the design water and wet-bulb temperatures, shows that a water concentration of 2 gal./(min.)(sq. ft.) is required. The area of the tower is calculated as 1000 sq. ft. (quantity of water circulated divided by water concentration).

Fan horsepower is obtained from Fig. 15-15. Connecting the point representing 100 per cent of standard tower performance with the turning point, and extending this straight line to the horsepower scale, shows that it will require 0.041 hp./sq. ft. of actual effective tower area. For a tower area of 1000 sq. ft., 41.0 fan hp. is required to perform the necessary cooling.

Suppose that the actual commercial tower size has an area of only 910 sq. ft. Within reasonable limits, the shortage of actual area can be compensated for by an increase in air velocity through the tower. However, this requires boosting fan horsepower to achieve 110 per cent of standard tower performance. From Fig. 15-15, the fan horsepower is found to be 0.057 hp./sq. ft. of actual tower area, or $0.057 \times 910 = 51.9$ hp.

On the other hand, if the actual commercial tower area is 1110 sq. ft., the cooling equivalent to 1000 sq. ft. of standard tower area can be accomplished with less air and less fan horsepower. From Fig. 15-15, the fan horsepower for a tower operating at 90 per cent of standard performance is 0.031 hp./sq. ft. of actual tower area, or 34.5 hp.

This example illustrates the sensitivity of fan horsepower to small changes in tower area. The importance of designing a tower that is slightly oversize in ground area and of providing plenty of fan capacity becomes immediately apparent.

Example 11. Assume the same cooling range and approach as used in Example 10, except that the wet-bulb temperature is lower. Design conditions would then be

Water rate, gal./min.	= 2000
Temperature range ($T_1 - T_2$), °F.	= 24
Temperature approach ($T_2 - t_w$), °F.	= 8
Hot-water temperature T_1, °F.	= 92
Cold-water temperature T_2, °F.	= 68
Wet-bulb temperature t_w, °F.	= 60

From Fig. 15-14, the water concentration required to perform the cooling is 1.75 gal./(min.)(sq. ft.), giving a tower area of 1145 sq. ft. vs. 1000 sq. ft. for a 70°F. wet-bulb temperature. This shows that the lower the wet-bulb temperature for the same cooling range and approach, the larger is the area of the tower required, and therefore the more difficult is the cooling job.

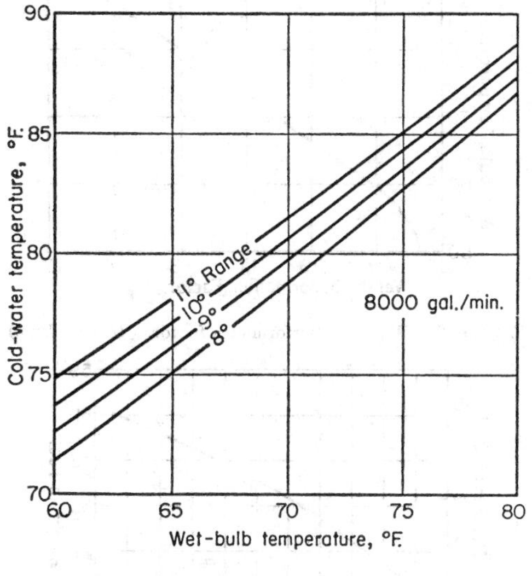

FIG. 15-16. Typical cooling-tower performance curve.

Figure 15-16 illustrates the type of **performance curve** furnished by the cooling-tower manufacturer. This shows the variation in performance with changes in wet-bulb and hot-water temperatures while the water quantity is maintained constant.

Atmospheric Cooling Towers. An atmospheric cooling tower is one in which water cooling is obtained primarily by natural wind movement through the structure. Data for estimating size and performance of an atmospheric tower are shown in Figs. 15-17 through 15-21. The cooling capacity of any tower, with a given wet-bulb temperature and wind velocity, varies with the water concentration. Thus the problem of calculating tower size becomes one of obtaining the correct water concentration for one of chosen height, which will operate under a certain wind velocity and wet-bulb temperature. Once this water concentration factor is obtained, the area of a tower of given height can easily be calculated by dividing the circulating load by the concentration factor.

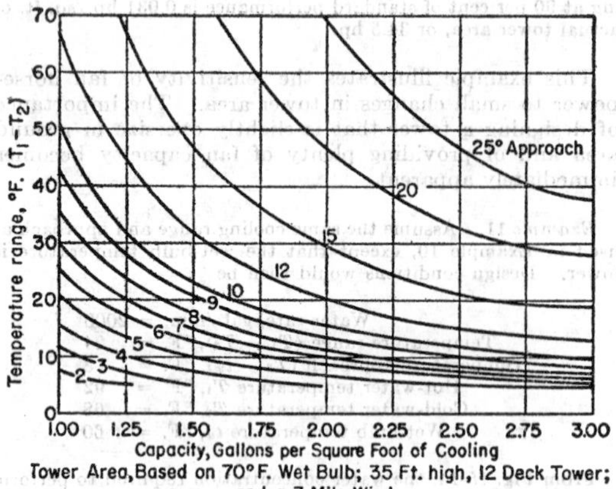

FIG. 15-17. Capacity curves—approach to wet-bulb temperature. (*Fluor Corp.*)

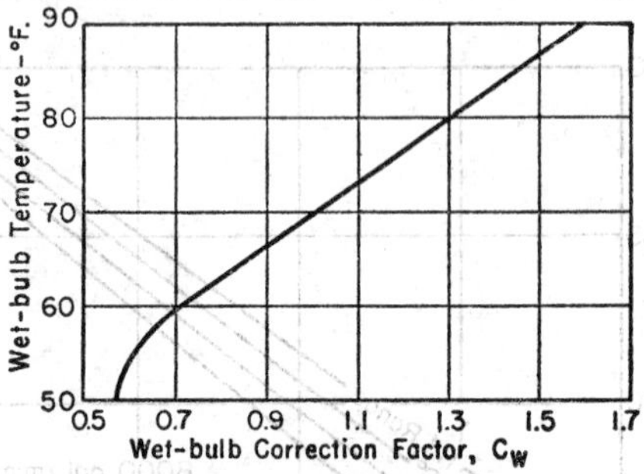

FIG. 15-18. Wet-bulb performance factor. (*Fluor Corp.*)

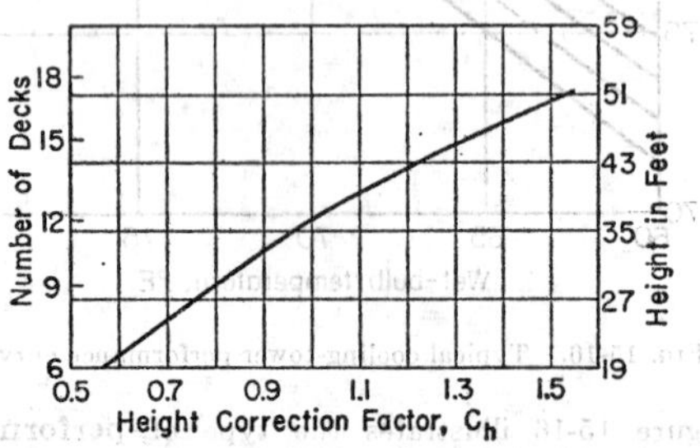

FIG. 15-19. Tower-height performance factor. (*Fluor Corp.*)

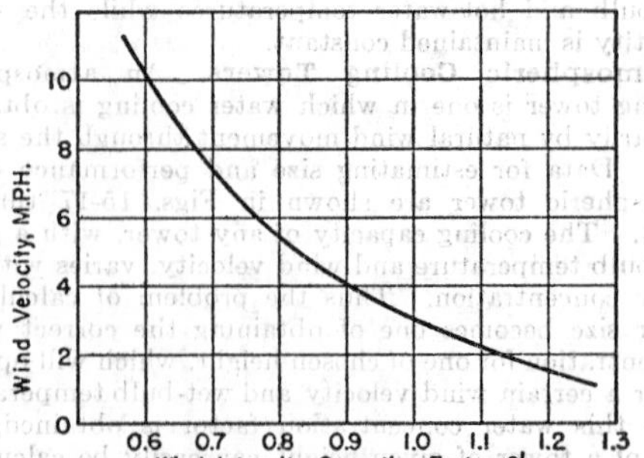

FIG. 15-20. Wind-intensity performance factor. (*Fluor Corp.*)

The concentration required to produce desired cooling depends primarily on the following factors:

1. Temperature range $(T_1 - T_2)$
2. Approach to wet-bulb temperature $(T_2 - t_w)$
3. Tower height
4. Wind velocity
5. Wet-bulb temperature t_w

Because of the infinite number of possible combinations of these values, it is impractical to have one curve representing the correct concentration factor. Figure 15-17 gives the required concentration for cooling water through a certain range and with a certain approach to the wet-bulb temperature; but this curve assumes a wet-bulb temperature of 70°F., a tower height of 35 ft., and a

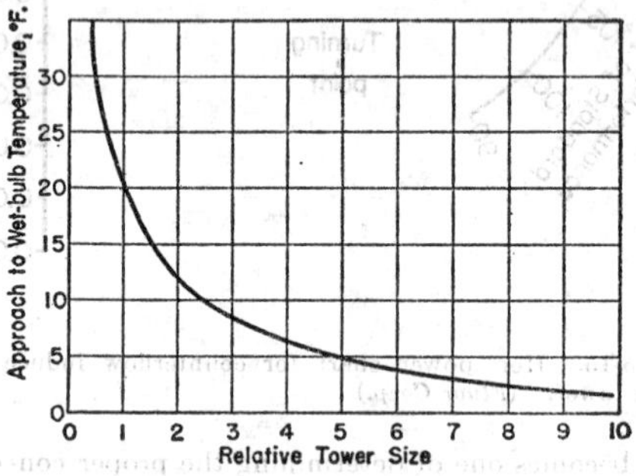

FIG. 15-21. Variation of tower size with approach to wet-bulb temperature. (*Fluor Corp.*)

wind velocity of 3 m.p.h. For different values of any of these variables, the concentration must be corrected by the use of one or more of the factors shown in Figs. 15-18 to 15-20 [see also Hutchinson and Spivey, *Trans. Inst. Chem. Engrs.*, **20**, 14 (1942)].

To calculate the size of an atmospheric cooling tower with effective width of 12 ft., the following general formula may be used:

$$Z_t = \frac{L_w(C_w')}{12C(C_w)(C_h)} \tag{15-9}$$

where Z_t = length of tower, ft.
L_w = quantity of water, gal./min.
C_w' = wind correction factor
C = concentration of water, gal./sq. ft. of tower area
C_w = wet-bulb correction factor
C_h = tower-height correction factor
T_1 = inlet temperature, °F.
T_2 = outlet temperature, °F.
$(T_1 - T_2)$ = temperature range, °F.
t_w = wet-bulb temperature, °F.
$(T_2 - t_w)$ = approach to wet-bulb temperature, °F.

Example 12. Determine the length of a 35-ft.-high tower required to cool 1500 gal./min. from 90° to 75°F. with a 70°F. wet-bulb temperature and a 3 m.p.h. wind. For these conditions the approach $(T_2 - t_w)$ = 5°F. and the range $(T_1 - T_2)$ = 15°F. From Fig. 15-19, a concentration C = 1.17 is required for these conditions. Correction factors C_h, C_w, and C_w' will each equal 1, as shown on their respective correction-factor curves (Fig. 15-17 is based upon the same conditions as those given in the example). From Eq. (15-9) the required tower length is 107 ft.

Example 13. For conditions of Example 12 determine the effect of increasing the wind velocity to 5 m.p.h. From Fig. 15-20, at a wind velocity of 5 m.p.h., C_w' = 0.83. Substitution of this value for C_w' in Eq. (15-9) shows that an 89-ft.-long tower is required.

Example 14. Again assume the same conditions of Example 12 except that, because of space considerations, it is necessary to have a 51-ft.-high tower. From Fig. 15-19, when tower height is 51 ft., $C_h = 1.53$. With this value of C_h the tower length required is 70 ft.

Example 15. Assuming conditions identical to those of Example 12, except that water is to be cooled from 85° to 70°F. and the wet-bulb temperature is 65°F., determine the tower length. From Fig. 15-18 for a wet-bulb temperature of 65°F., $C_w = 0.86$. Substituting this factor in Eq. (15-9) gives a tower length of 124 ft.

Example 16. Once a tower is installed, it is necessary to determine the expected cold-water temperature under operating conditions differing from those for which the tower was designed. For the tower calculated in Example 12, what cold-water temperature T_2 can be expected when the wet-bulb temperature is 60°F., wind velocity 4 m.p.h., cooling range 15°F., and water circulation 2000 gal./min.?

The wet-bulb temperature correction factor C_w from Fig. 15-18 is 0.71. The wind-velocity correction factor C_w' from Fig. 15-20 is 0.90. By substituting these values in Eq. (15-9) and solving for water concentration, we find

$$C = \frac{(2000)(0.90)}{(107)(12)(0.71)(1)} = 1.97 \text{ gal./sq. ft.}$$

From Fig. 15-17, when the cooling range is 15°F. and the water concentration is 1.97, the approach to the wet-bulb temperature is 10°F. Thus the cold-water temperature will be 60°F. + 10°F. = 70°F.

The above examples illustrate the effects of the more important factors affecting the design of atmospheric cooling towers. For firm designs, consideration must be given to the effects of excessive or insufficient concentration, higher relative humidity, change in wind direction, and other factors which influence tower operation. As a result, the cooling-tower sizes calculated in the above examples are only approximate.

Natural-draft Towers. Natural-draft or hyperbolic-type towers have been in use since about 1916 in Europe and have become standard practice for water-cooling requirements of British power stations. They are primarily suited to very large cooling-water quantities, and the reinforced-concrete structures used are as large as diameters of 265 ft. and heights of 340 ft.

The design convenience obtained from the steady air flow of mechanical-draft towers is not realized in natural-draft-tower design. Air flow through a natural-draft tower is due largely to the difference in density between the cool inlet air and the warm exit air. The air leaving the stack is lighter than the ambient air and a draft is created by chimney effect, thus eliminating the need for mechanical fans. McKelvey and Brooke ("The Industrial Cooling Tower," p. 108, Elsevier, New York, 1959) note that natural-draft towers commonly operate at air-pressure differences in the region of 0.2 in. water gage when under full load. The mean velocity of the air above the tower packing is generally about 4 to 6 ft./sec.

The performance of the natural-draft tower differs from that of the mechanical-draft tower in that the cooling is dependent upon the relative humidity as well as the wet-bulb temperature. The draft will increase through the tower at high humidity conditions because of the increase in available static pressure difference to promote air flow against internal resistances. Thus the higher the humidity at a given wet-bulb, the colder the outlet water will be for a given set of conditions. This fundamental relationship has been used to advantage in Great Britain, where relative humidities are commonly 75 to 80 per cent. Therefore, it is important in the design stages to determine correctly and specify the density of the entering and effluent air in addition to the usual tower-design conditions of range, approach, and water quantity. The performance relationship to humidity conditions makes exact control of outlet water temperature difficult to achieve with the natural-draft tower.

Data for determining the size of natural-draft towers have been presented by Chilton [*Proc. Inst. Elec. Engrs.*, **99,** 440 (1952)] and Rish and Steel (A.S.C.E. Symposium on Thermal Power Plants, October, 1958). Chilton showed that the duty coefficient D_t of a tower is approximately constant over its normal range of operation and is related to tower size by an efficiency factor or performance coefficient C_t as follows:

$$D_t = \frac{A\sqrt{Z_t}}{C_t\sqrt{C_t}} \qquad (15\text{-}10)$$

where A = base area of tower, sq. ft., measured at pond sill level, and Z_t = height of tower, ft., measured above sill level. The duty coefficient may be determined from the formula

$$\frac{W_L}{D_t} = 90.59\frac{\Delta h}{\Delta T}\sqrt{\Delta t + 0.3124\,\Delta h} \qquad (15\text{-}11)$$

where Δh = change in total heat of the air passing through the tower, B.t.u./lb.; ΔT = change of water temperature passing through tower, °F.; Δt = difference between air temperature leaving the packing and inlet dry-bulb temperature, °F.; W_L = water load in the tower, lb./hr. The air leaving the packing inside the tower is assumed to be saturated at a temperature halfway between the inlet and outlet water temperatures. A divergence between theory and practice of a few degrees in this latter assumption does not significantly affect the results, as the draft component depends on the ratio of the change of density to change of total heat and not on change of temperature alone.

Example 17. Determine the duty coefficient for a hyperbolic tower operating with:

Temperature of water to tower, °F.	= 82
Leaving (recooled) water temperature, °F.	= 70
Temperature range ΔT, °F.	= 12
Dry-bulb air temperature t_2	= 57
Aspirated (ambient) wet-bulb air temperature t_{w2}, °F.	= 51.7
Water loading to tower W_L, lb./hr.	= 38,200,000

$t_1 = (82° + 70°)/2 = 76°$ $\quad h_1 = 39.8$ (from Fig. 15-2)
$t_2 = 57°$ $\quad h_2 = 21.3$
$\Delta t = 19°$ $\quad \Delta h = 18.5$

$$\frac{W_L}{D_t} = 90.59\left(\frac{18.5}{12}\right)\sqrt{19 + 0.3124(18.5)} = 696$$

$$D_t = \frac{38{,}200{,}000}{696} = 55{,}000$$

The performance coefficients usually attained have been about 5.2 for water loadings in excess of 750 lb./(hr.)(sq. ft.), though new types of packing are improving (lowering) it. Taking a C_t value of 5.0 and a tower height of 320 ft., the base area of the tower will be $(55{,}000)(5\sqrt{5})/\sqrt{320}$ = 34,600 sq. ft., or the internal base diameter at sill level will be 210 ft. A ratio of height to base diameter of 3 to 2 is normally employed.

To determine how a natural-draft tower of any given duty coefficient will perform under varying conditions, Rish and Steel have plotted the nomograph in Fig. 15-22. The straight line shown on the nomograph illustrates the conditions of the above example.

Spray Ponds. Spray ponds provide an arrangement for lowering the temperature of water by evaporative cooling and, in so doing, greatly reduce the cooling area required in comparison with a cooling pond. A spray pond uses a number of nozzles which spray water into contact with the surrounding air. A well-designed spray nozzle should provide fine water drops but should not produce a mist which would be carried off as excessive drift loss.

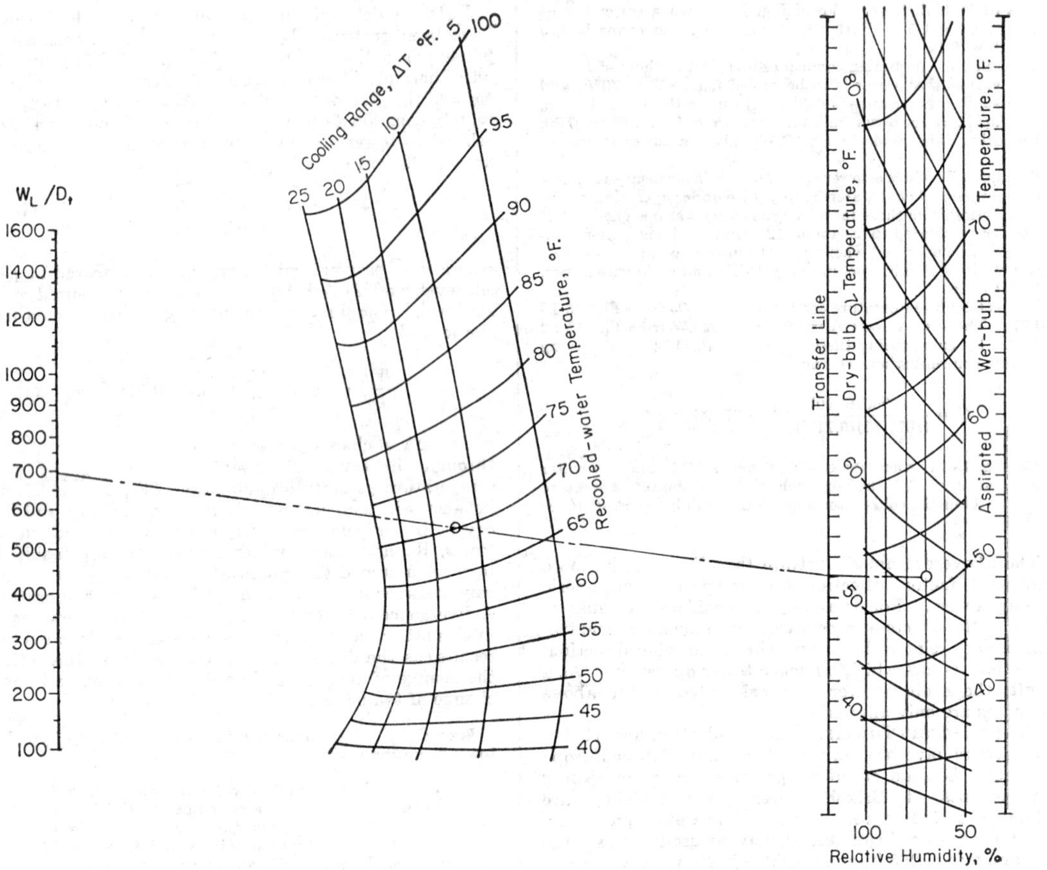

FIG. 15-22. Universal performance chart for natural-draft cooling towers. (*Rish and Steel, A.S.C.E. Symposium on Thermal Power Plants, October*, 1958.)

Table 15-4 provides design data which will assist in layout of a spray pond. The pond should be placed with its long axis at right angles to the prevailing summer wind. A long narrow pond is more effective than a square one, so that decreasing pond width and increasing pond length will improve performance. Performance can also be increased by decreasing the amount of water sprayed per unit of pond area, increasing height and fineness of spray drops, and increasing nozzle height above the basin sides.

Sufficient distance should be provided from the outer nozzles to keep spray from being carried over the sides of the basin. If it is not possible to provide 25 to 35 ft. of space, the pond should be enclosed with a louver fence, equal in height to the maximum height of the spray, to minimize drift loss. Also, during cold-weather periods, fogging can occur from the spray pond, so that consideration should be given to possible hazards to roadways or buildings in the immediate vicinity.

Table 15-4. Spray-pond Engineering Data and Design*

Recommendations	Usual	Minimum	Maximum
Nozzle capacity, gal./min. each	35–50	10	60
Nozzles per 12-ft. length of pipe	5–6	4	8
Height of nozzles above sides of basin, ft.	7–8	2	10
Nozzle pressure, lb./sq. in.	5–7	4	10
Size of nozzles and nozzle arms, in.	2	1¼	2½
Distance between spray lateral piping, ft.	25	13	38
Distance of nozzles from side of pond, unfenced, ft.	25–35	20	50
Distance of nozzles from side of pond, fenced, ft.	12–18	10	25
Height of louver fence, ft.	12	6	18
Depth of pond basin, ft.	4–5	2	7
Friction loss per 100 ft. pipe, in. of water	1–3	....	6
Design wind velocity, m.p.h.	5	3	10

* From *Spray Pond Bull.* No. SP-51, p. 3, Marley Co.

The physical designs and operating conditions of spray-pond installations vary greatly, and it is difficult to develop exact rating data that can be used for determining cooling performance in all cases. However, Fig. 15-23 shows performance that can be obtained with a well-designed spray pond, based on a 70°F. wet-bulb and 5 m.p.h. wind. This curve shows that a 6°F. approach to the wet-bulb is possible at a 4°F. range, but at higher ranges the obtainable approach increases. If it is necessary to cool water through a large temperature range to a reasonably close approach, the spray pond could be staged. With this method, the water is initially sprayed, collected, and then resprayed in another part of a sectionalized pond basin.

Figure 15-24 shows performance curves for a spray pond used in steam-condensing service at varying wet-bulb and range conditions. Spray-pond performance can be calculated within reasonable accuracy based on the leaving wet-bulb temperature of the air passing through the spray-filled volume. The air temperature leaving cannot exceed the warm water to the pond, and the

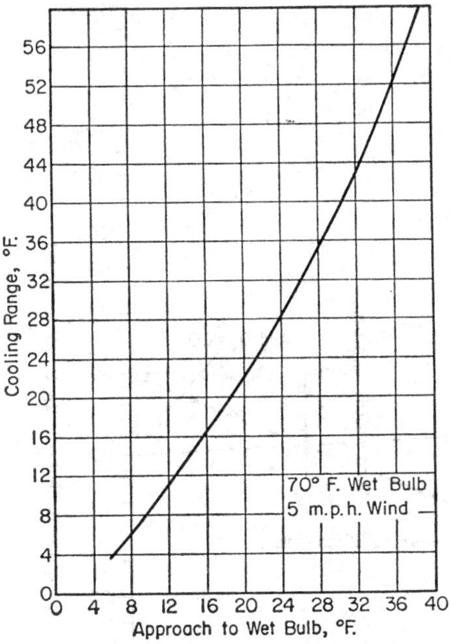

FIG. 15-23. Spray-pond performance curve.

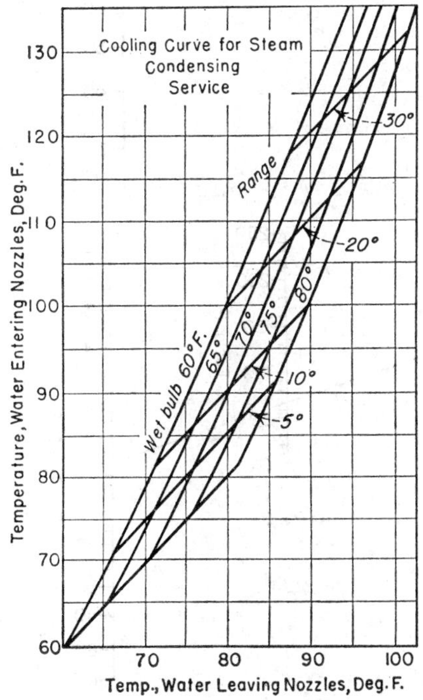

FIG. 15-24. Spray ponds—cooling curves for steam-condensing service.

closeness of approach will be dependent on the pond layout. In calculating the cooling obtained, the spray-filled volume is figured from the height equal to the elevation of the nozzles above the pond surface plus 1 ft. for each lb./sq. in. nozzle pressure and a plan area extending 10 ft. beyond the outer nozzles. The air area involved is the projected area of a vertical plane through the filled volume and broadside to the direction of air movement. The horizontal distance that the air moves through the filled volume is considered the length of air travel.

Example 18. Determine the cooling capacity of a spray pond operating at the following conditions:

Water flow, gal./min. 46,000
Spray nozzle pressure, lb./sq. in. 7
Water flow per nozzle, gal./min. 42.5
Effective area, length × width, sq. ft. . . . . 434 × 100
Effective height, ft. . . . . 7 + 7 spray height
Wind velocity, ft./min. 440
Prevailing wind. . . . . broadside to pond
Ambient wet-bulb temperature, °F. 78
Water temperature in, °F. 102

Effective air area = (434)(14) = 6080 sq. ft.

Air flow = (440)(6080) = 2,680,000 cu. ft./min.
L = (46,000)(8.33) = 384,000 lb. water/min.
G = 2,680,000/14.3 = 187,500 lb. air/min.

$$L/G = \frac{384,000}{187,500} = 2.05$$

h' at 78°F. wet-bulb temperature = 41.58 B.t.u./lb. (from Fig. 15-2)

Assume water temperature out = 92°F.

$$L/G = \frac{(h_2')\text{ air out} - (h_1')\text{ air in}}{\text{water temp. in} - \text{water temp. out}} = 2.05 = \frac{h_2' - 41.58}{10}$$

h_2' = 61.63 B.t.u./lb.

Corresponding wet-bulb temperature = 94°F. air leaving pond.
Approach possible to air leaving, from Table 15-5, = −2°F.
Water temperature leaving spray pond = 94° − 2°F. = 92°F.

Since leaving water temperature checks assumption, spray pond is capable of cooling 46,000 gal./min. from 102° to 92°F. with 78°F. wet-bulb and 5 m.p.h. wind. Total of 1080 spray nozzles required at 42.5 gal./min. each, nozzles at 7 lb./sq. in. pressure.

Table 15-5. Degree Adjustment to Be Applied to Leaving-air Wet-bulb Temperature to Find Cooled-water Temperature of Spray Ponds*

Cooling range, °F.	Entering wet-bulb temp.,† °F.	Adjustment, °F. Length of air travel, ft.‡ 100	50	25
10	80	−3	+2	+4
	70	−2	+3	+5
	60	−1.5	+3.5	+5.5
15	80	−5.0	+1	+5
	70	−4.0	+2	+5.5
	60	−3.5	+2.5	+6
20	80	−7	0	+6
	70	−6	+1	+7
	60	−5.5	+1.5	+7.5

Cooled-water temperature = wet-bulb temperature of leaving air plus values shown.

* From "Heating, Ventilating, Air Conditioning Guide," 38th ed., p. 598, American Society of Heating, Refrigerating and Air-Conditioning Engineers, 1960.

† Wet-bulb temperature of air entering spray-filled volume.

‡ Length of air travel through spray-filled volume.

Cooling Ponds. Where large ground areas are available, cooling ponds offer a satisfactory method of removing heat from water. A pond may be constructed at a relatively small investment by pushing up an earth dike 6 to 10 ft. high. For a successful pond installation, the soil must be reasonably impervious, and location in a flat area is desirable. Four principal heat-transfer processes are involved in obtaining cooling from an open pond. Heat is lost through evaporation, convection, and radiation and is gained through solar radiation. The required pond area depends on the number of degrees of cooling required and the net heat loss from each square foot of pond surface.

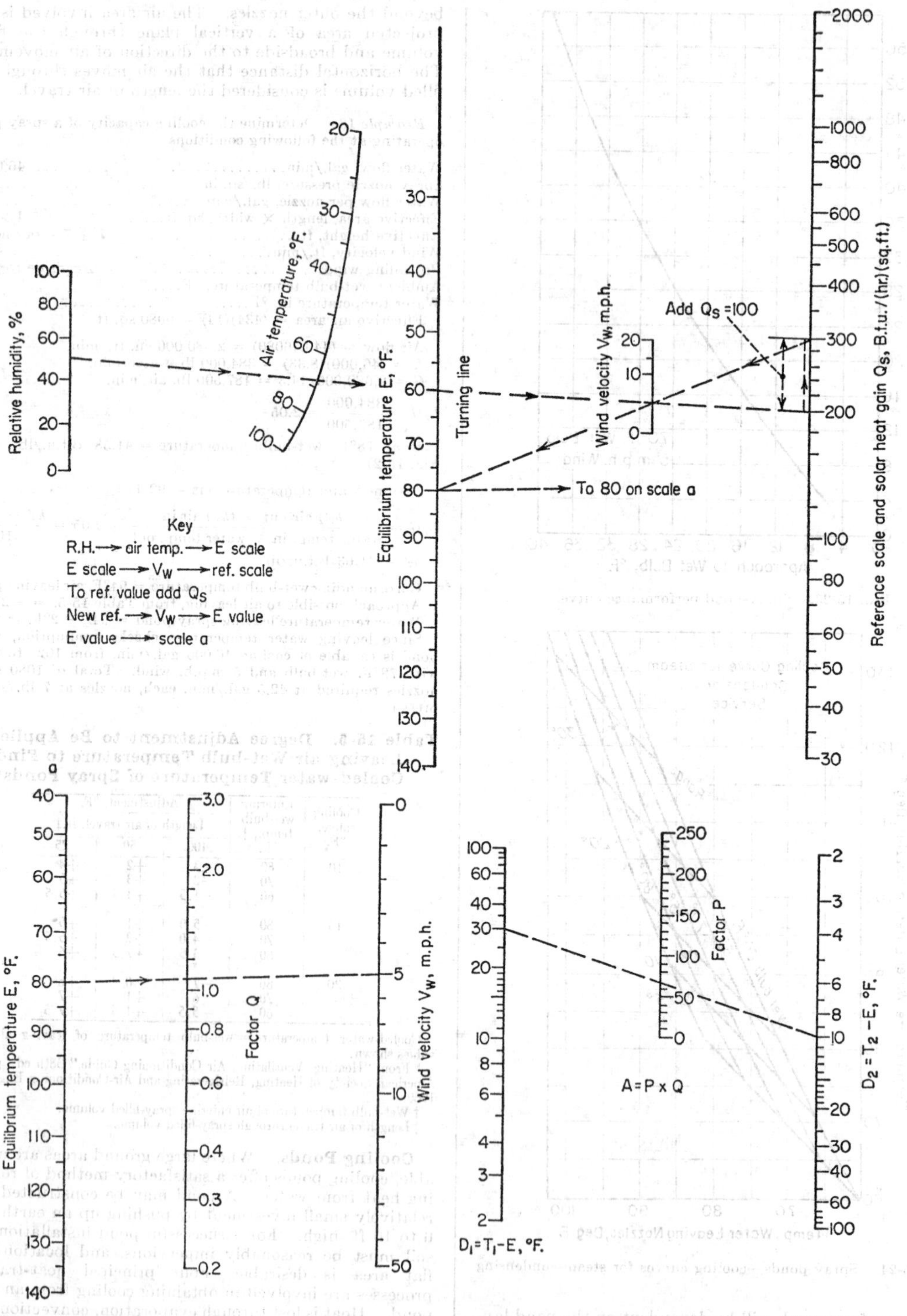

Fig. 15-25. Nomograph for determining cooling-pond performance and size. [*Langhaar, Chem. Eng.*, **60** (8), 194 (1953).]

Langhaar [*Chem. Eng.*, **60** (8), 194 (1953)] states that under given atmospheric conditions a body of water would eventually come to a temperature at which heat loss would equal heat gain. This temperature is referred to as the equilibrium temperature and is designated as E on Fig. 15-25, a nomograph of cooling-pond performance. The equilibrium temperature is greatly affected by the amount of solar radiation, which is usually not known very accurately and which varies throughout the day. If a pond has at least a 24-hr. hold-up, then daily average weather conditions may be used. For practical purposes, it is recommended that the equilibrium temperature should be taken as equal to normal river-water or lake temperature for the specified weather conditions.

In order to cool to the equilibrium temperature, a pond of infinite size would be required for warm water. An approach of 3° to 4°F. is the lowest practicable in a pond of reasonable size. For a pond having more than a 24-hr. hold-up, the leaving-water temperature will vary from the average by plus or minus 2°F. for a 5-ft. depth and 3°F. variation for a 3-ft. depth.

The area of pond required for a given cooling load is almost independent of pond depth. A depth of at least 3 ft. appears advisable to prevent excessive channeling of flow with ponds having irregular bottoms and to avoid large day-to-night changes in outlet temperature.

Factors considered to affect pond performance are air temperature, relative humidity, wind speed, and solar radiation. Items appearing to have only a minor effect include heat transfer between the earth and the pond, changing temperature and humidity of the air as it traverses the water, and rain.

Figure 15-25 provides a rapid method of determining the pond-area requirements for a given cooling duty. D_1 and D_2 are the approaches to equilibrium for the entering and leaving water, °F.; V_w is the wind velocity, m.p.h.; product PQ represents the area of the pond surface, sq. ft./(gal./min.) of flow to the pond. The P factor assumes a pond with uniform flow, without turbulence, and with the water warmer than the air.

Example 19. Determine the required size of a cooling pond operating at the following conditions:

Relative humidity, per cent =	50
Wind velocity, m.p.h. =	5
Dry-bulb air temperature, °F. =	68
Solar heat gain, B.t.u./(hr.)(sq. ft.) =	100
Water quantity, gal./min. =	10,000
Water inlet, °F. =	110
Water outlet, °F. =	90

From nomograph, $P = 68$ and $Q = 1.07$, giving an area required of 73 sq. ft./(gal./min.). Area for 10,000 gal./min. is thus 730,000 sq. ft., or 17 acres.

With a depth of 5 ft., total volume of the pond would amount to 45.5 hr. hold-up, which is more than the 24-hr. hold-up required to maintain a fairly constant discharge temperature throughout the day.

Table 15-6 presents typical values of solar radiation on a horizontal surface, B.t.u./(hr.)(sq. ft.), based on analysis of Weather Bureau records for a number of stations throughout the United States. These are clear-day values, rarely exceeded even in the high arid regions. The normal or actual average monthly values are only 50 to 60 per cent of the tabulated figures for most of the Eastern United States and 80 to 90 per cent in the arid Southwest. Also the solar radiation should be multiplied by the absorption coefficient for the pond, which appears to exceed 95 per cent.

Table 15-6. Maximum Expected Solar Radiation at Various North Latitudes*
B.t.u./(hr.)(sq. ft.)

	24-hr. avg. at north latitude				Noon value at north latitude			
	30°	35°	40°	45°	30°	35°	40°	45°
Jan. 1	65	50	40	30	240	205	170	135
Feb. 1	75	65	55	45	270	240	210	175
Mar. 1	90	80	75	65	305	285	255	230
Apr. 1	110	105	95	90	340	320	300	280
May 1	120	120	120	115	360	350	335	320
June 1	130	130	130	130	365	360	345	335
July 1	130	130	130	130	365	360	350	340
Aug. 1	125	125	125	120	360	350	340	325
Sept. 1	115	110	105	100	350	335	315	300
Oct. 1	100	90	80	75	315	295	270	245
Nov. 1	80	70	60	50	270	245	215	185
Dec. 1	65	55	45	35	240	210	175	140

* Langhaar, *Chem. Eng.*, **60** (8), 194 (1953).

AIR CONDITIONING

REFERENCES: "A.R.I. Standard 530, Application Standard for Air Conditioning," Air Conditioning & Refrigeration Institute, Washington, D.C., 1956. "A.S.R.E. Data Book—Refrigeration Applications," vol. 1, American Society of Refrigerating Engineers, New York, 1959. "Heating, Ventilating, Air Conditioning Guide," 38th ed., American Society of Heating, Refrigerating and Air-Conditioning Engineers, New York, 1960. Carrier, Cherne, Grant, and Roberts, "Modern Air Conditioning, Heating, and Ventilating," 3d ed., Pitman, New York, 1959. Jordan and Priester, "Refrigeration and Air Conditioning," Prentice-Hall, Englewood Cliffs, N.J., 1948. Miner and Seastone, "Handbook of Engineering Materials," Wiley, New York, 1955. Raber and Hutchinson, "Refrigeration and Air Conditioning Engineering," Wiley, New York, 1945. Strock, "Handbook of Air Conditioning, Heating and Ventilating," The Industrial Press, New York, 1959. "Fan Engineering," 5th ed., Buffalo Forge Co., Buffalo, 1949. "Air Conditioning Manual," Trane Co., La Crosse, Wis., 1953.

Air conditioning is the process of treating air so as to control simultaneously its temperature, humidity, cleanliness, and distribution to meet the requirements of the conditioned space. Applications of air conditioning include the promotion of human comfort and the maintenance of proper conditions for the manufacture, processing, and preserving of material and equipment. Also, in industrial environments where, for economic or other reasons, conditions cannot be made entirely comfortable, air conditioning may be used for maintaining the efficiency, health, and safety of workers at safe tolerance limits.

Comfort Air Conditioning. Comfort is influenced not only by temperature and humidity but also by air velocity, radiant heat, clothing, work intensity, and differences between individuals. Thus it is impossible for a given temperature and humidity to satisfy everyone. For the average person, however, the **effective temperature (E.T.)** concept, derived from work done by the American Society of Heating, Refrigerating and Air-Conditioning Engineers, relates the variables of dry-bulb, wet-bulb, and air velocity to comfort for light work and normal indoor clothing.

Effective temperature, an empirically determined index combining in a single value the effects of temperature, humidity, and air movement, cannot be measured directly. For still air (15 to 25 ft./min.), Fig. 15-26 shows effective temperature for various combinations of dry- and wet-bulb temperatures. (Refer to A.S.H.R.A.E. Guide for chart showing effects of air velocity on E.T.) Note that no provision is made for the effects of radiant heat. However, Bedford ("Environmental Warmth and Its Measurement," p. 24, Her Majesty's Stationery Office, London, 1946) has suggested use of globe instead of dry-bulb temperature to allow for radiant-heat effects (globe temperature is measured by an ordinary glass thermometer with its bulb in the center of a 6- to 8-in. hollow copper sphere painted black).

Any combination of wet- and dry-bulb temperatures which follows along the same E.T. line is said to give the same sensation of comfort. For example, one has the same feeling of comfort at 80°F. dry-bulb and 55°F. wet-bulb as at 70°F. dry-bulb and 70° wet-bulb.

At high dry-bulb temperatures the body loses less heat by radiation and convection than at lower temperatures. Therefore, at the higher ambient temperatures, the body must lose more heat by evaporation than at the lower temperatures if body temperature is to be maintained. Since lower humidities are more conducive to evaporation than high humidities, combinations of higher temperatures and lower humidities give the same feeling of comfort as do lower temperatures and higher humidities. The general zone in which the majority of people are comfortable is commonly referred to as the **comfort zone.** For sedentary activity, the optimum condition (where the greatest number of people are comfortable) is 67.5°F. E.T. for winter and 71°F. E.T. for summer, as shown by Fig. 15-26. This difference between winter and summer conditions is caused by the human body's becoming more acclimated to higher temperatures in summertime and also by differences in clothing.

For normal comfort applications, room conditions for summer are usually designed for 80°F. dry-bulb and 50 per cent relative humidity, equivalent to 74°F. E.T. In the United States, the trend is toward lower temperatures, however, with dry-bulb temperatures of 76° to 78°F. and relative humidities of 45 to 50 per cent in common use. For winter, indoor dry-bulb temperatures usually specified are 65° to 68°F. for stores, 68° to 72°F. for public buildings, and 60° to 65°F. for factories. When no provision is made for humidity control, the optimum dry-bulb temperature for comfort will be slightly higher than the above values.

Control of Industrial Environment. Much work has been done at various physiological research laboratories on the physiological effects of hot atmospheres on workers and on means for reducing the associated stress and hazards.

Mosher [*Heating, Piping, Air Conditioning,* **17,** 385 (1945)] has developed a curve of maximum permissible level of effective temperatures for varying degrees of activity, based on data developed by Fleisher, Stacey, Houghten, and Ferderber [*Trans. Am. Soc. Heating*

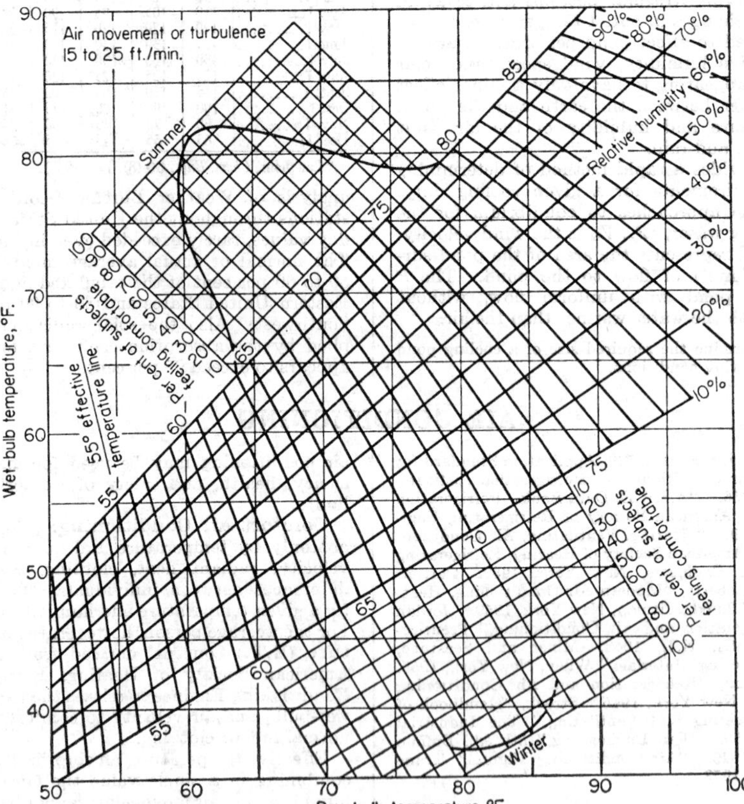

FIG. 15-26. Effective temperature chart showing comfort zone for still air. (*From "Heating, Ventilating, Air Conditioning Guide," American Society of Heating, Refrigerating and Air-Conditioning Engineers,* 1960.)

NOTES: (*a*) Both summer and winter comfort lines apply to inhabitants of the United States only. Application of winter comfort line is further limited to rooms heated by central systems of the convection type; the line does not apply to rooms heated by radiant methods. Application of summer comfort line is limited to homes, offices, and the like, where the occupants become fully adapted to the artificial air conditions; the line does not apply to theaters, department stores, and the like, where the exposure is less than 3 hr. The summer comfort line shown pertains to Pittsburgh and to other cities in the northern portion of the United States and southern Canada, and at elevations not in excess of 1000 ft. above sea level. An increase of 1° E.T. should be made approximately per 5° reduction in north latitude. (*b*) Dotted portion of winter comfort line is extrapolated beyond test data.

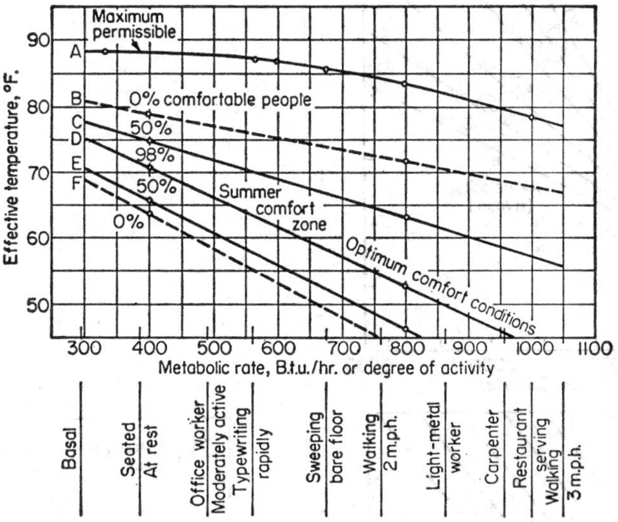

FIG. 15-27. Effective temperatures required at various degrees of activity. [*Mosher, Heating, Piping, Air Conditioning,* **17,** 385 (1945).]

Ventilating Engrs., **45,** 59 (1939)]. This curve (Fig. 15-27) is based on a maximum permissible rise in body temperature of 1.5°F. after exposure of the subject 3 hr. at the given E.T. The curve should be used as a guide only, since further testing is required at the higher workload levels. As seen on the chart, the maximum permissible E.T.'s are somewhat above the comfort zone. While these temperatures are not comfortable, they are not unhealthful.

Another index used for assessing the effects of industrial environments is the **heat-stress index (H.S.I.).** The H.S.I. relates the amount of evaporation or perspiration required for a particular job and for particular environmental temperature conditions to the maximum evaporative capacity of an average person. Table 15-7 is an evaluation of heat stress in terms of heat-stress index. The charts of Fig. 15-28 are used for determining the heat-stress index. The method of solution is illustrated by a representative example. However, data by Belding, Hertig, and Riedesel [*Am. Hyg. Assoc. J.*, **21** (1), 25 (1960)] indicate that the heat stress predicted from Fig. 15-28 is higher than that determined in laboratory experiments. This was attributed to the reduction in radiation received by the body when it is protected by clothing. In using Fig. 15-28, it is tentatively recommended that the values for both radiation and convection be multiplied by 0.60 when workers are covered with light clothing, except at very high air velocities.

Table 15-7. Heat-stress-index Evaluation*

Index of Heat Stress	Physiological and Hygienic Implications of 8-hr. Exposures to Various Heat Stresses
−20 −10	Mild cold strain. This condition frequently exists in areas where men recover from exposure to heat
0	No thermal strain
+10 20 30	Mild to moderate heat strain. Where a job involves higher intellectual functions, dexterity, or alertness, subtle to substantial decrements in performance may be expected. In performance of heavy physical work, little decrement expected unless ability of individuals to perform such work under no thermal stress is marginal
40 50 60	Severe heat strain, involving a threat to health unless men are physically fit. Break-in period required for men not previously acclimatized. Some decrement in performance of physical work is to be expected. Medical selection of personnel desirable because these conditions are unsuitable for those with cardiovascular or respiratory impairment or with chronic dermatitis. These working conditions are also unsuitable for activities requiring sustained mental effort
70 80 90	Very severe heat strain. Only a small percentage of the population may be expected to qualify for this work. Personnel should be selected (1) by medical examination and (2) by trial on the job (after acclimatization). Special measures are needed to assure adequate water and salt intake. Amelioration of working conditions by any feasible means is highly desirable and may be expected to decrease the health hazard while increasing efficiency on the job. Slight "indisposition" which in most jobs would be insufficient to affect performance may render workers unfit for this exposure
100	Maximum strain tolerated daily by fit, acclimatized young men

* From "Heating, Ventilating, Air Conditioning Guide," American Society of Heating, Refrigerating and Air-Conditioning Engineers, 1960.

Process and Product Air Conditioning. Process air conditioning includes the following: (1) control of moisture of hygroscopic materials; (2) control of chemical reaction rates, crystallization, biochemical reaction rates, and corrosion of metals; (3) elimination of static electricity; (4) control of temperature for close-tolerance machining; and (5) control of conditions in materials-testing laboratories. Approximate design temperatures and humidities applicable to air conditioning of various industrial operations are given in Table 15-8.

Table 15-9 shows the equilibrium moisture content at various relative humidities for natural textile fibers, rayons, paper, and other materials. Figure 15-29 shows the equilibrium moisture content for several synthetic fibers.

In handling explosive materials, it is important from a safety standpoint to control relative humidity of the ambient air to a minimum of 55 per cent. Also, where light materials having poor electrical conductivity are handled, a minimum 55 per cent relative humidity level is recommended to avoid static electricity, which causes difficulty in handling due to the attraction between adjacent particles or sheets.

Ventilation. In the design of comfort air-conditioning systems, odors arising from occupants, cooking, or other sources must be controlled. This is accomplished by introducing fresh air or purified recirculated air in sufficient quantities to reduce odor concentrations to an acceptable level by dilution. Recommended fresh-air requirements for general offices are 15 cu. ft./min. per person; for private offices, 25 cu. ft./min. per person; for factories, 10 cu. ft./min. per person. Minimum requirement for factories is 0.10 cu. ft./min. per sq. ft. of floor area or as governed by local codes.

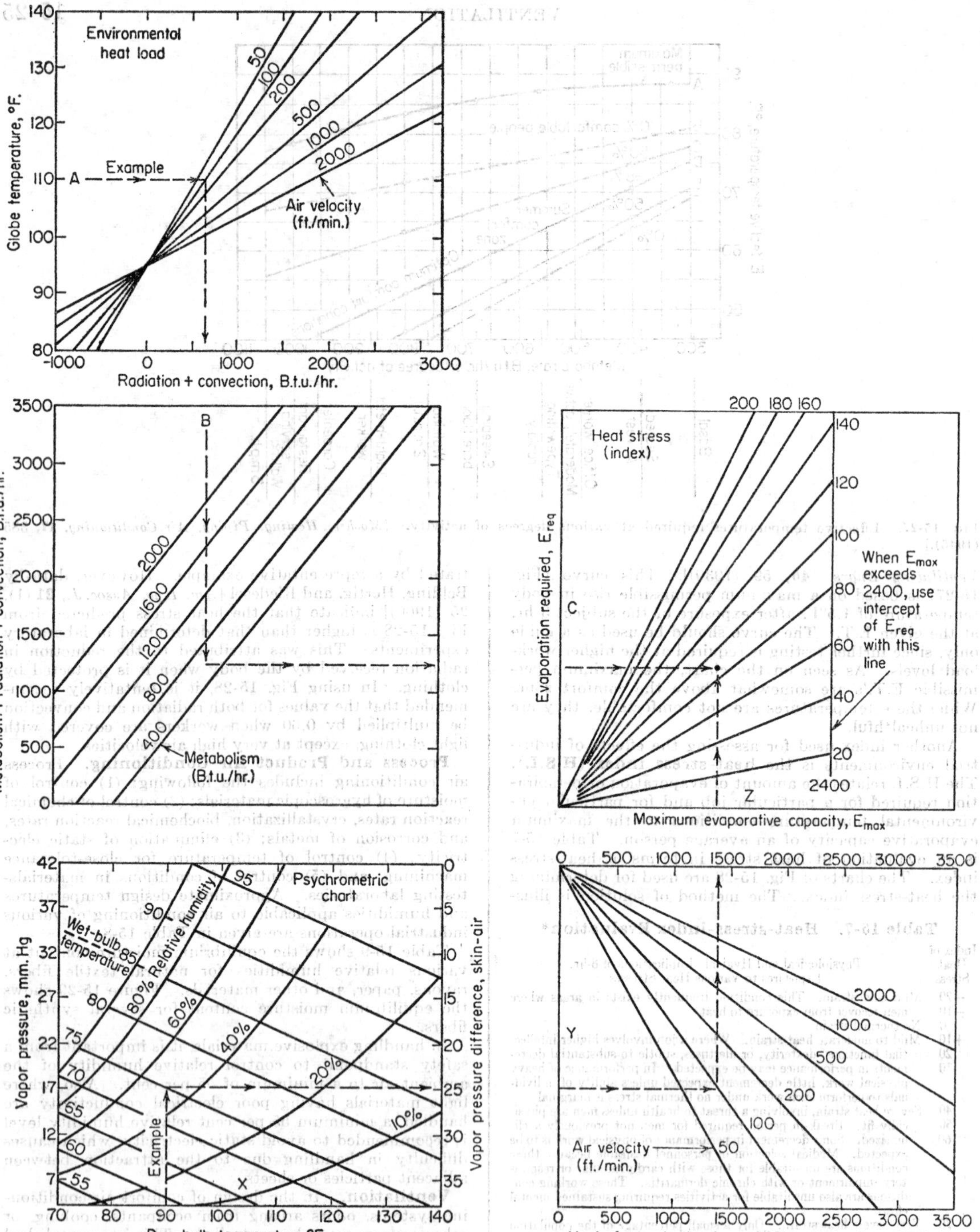

Fig. 15-28. Charts for determining heat-stress index. *(From "Heating, Ventilating, Air Conditioning Guide," American Society of Heating, Refrigerating and Air-Conditioning Engineers,* 1960.)

Example. Determine heat-stress index for worker doing light arm work while standing at a bench.

Metabolism....................................	600 B.t.u./hr.
Environmental conditions:	
Globe-thermometer temperature............	110°F.
Dry-bulb temperature......................	90°F.
Wet-bulb temperature......................	75°F.
Air velocity..................................	100 ft./min.

Solution. Follow the broken lines from the globe-thermometer temperature and from dry-bulb temperature to their intersection on above diagram *C* to read a heat-stress index of 90.

In industrial air-conditioning systems, harmful environmental gases, vapors, dusts, and fumes are often encountered. These contaminants can be controlled by exhaust systems at the source, by dilution ventilation, or by a combination of the two methods. When exhaust systems are used, it is necessary to introduce sufficient fresh air into the air-conditioned area to make up for that exhausted. Generally, local exhaust systems are used where the contaminant sources are concentrated. Where the contamination comes from widely dispersed points, however, dilution ventilation is usually employed. Combinations of the two systems sometimes provide the least expensive installation. In the design of dilution systems for gases and vapors the quantity of air to be circulated to obtain an acceptable concentration of contaminants can be calculated by the equation

Table 15-8. Temperatures and Humidities Applicable to Industrial Air Conditioning*

Application	Summer		Winter	
	Dry-bulb, °F.	% relative humidity	Dry-bulb, °F.	% relative humidity
Bakery:				
Bread mixing	75–80	45–55	75	45–55
Bread fermentation	80	70–80	80	70–80
Bread proof boxes	90–95	80–95	90–95	80–95
Bread cooling	70	70–80	70	70–80
Bread wrapping	65–75	50–65	65	50–65
Flour storage	70–80	50–60	70	50–60
Sugar storage	70–80	35	70	35
Cake mixing	70–75	65	70	65
Cake icing	70–80	45–50	70	45–50
Cellophane:				
Manufacture	75–80	65	70–75	65
Folding, printing	75–80	55–65	70–75	55–65
Ceramics:				
Molding room	80	60	80	60
Clay storage	80	35–65	60–75	35–65
Decorating room	75–80	45–50	75–80	45–50
Distilling:				
Grain storage	60	35–40	60	35–40
General manufacture	60–75	45–65	60–75	45–65
Aging	65–72	50–60	65–72	50–60
Food products:				
Bicarbonate of soda	80	50	60–70	40–50
Butter making	60	60	60	60
Cereals	60–80	38–50	60–80	35–50
Coffee substitutes	75–80	40–45	75	40
Flour milling	E.C.	60	70	60
Macaroni	70–80	38	70–80	38
Malted milk	80	35–40	80	35–40
Mayonnaise	75	40–50	75	40
Mushroom houses	55–80	75	55–80	75
Laboratory:				
Animal assay rooms	75–80	40	75	40
General analytical (A.S.T.M. standard conditions)	73.4	50	73.4	50
Leather drying:				
Hides	90	....	90	....
Vegetable tanned	70	75	70	75
Chrome tanned	120	45	120	45
Matches, manufacturing	72–80	45–50	72	45–50
Pharmaceutical:				
Ampoule manufacturing	80	35	80	35
Bottle-cap drying	135	40–50	135	40–50
Capsule filling	75–80	35–40	75	35–40
Colloids	70	30–50	70	30–50
Deliquescent salts	75	30–35	75	30–35
Drying granulations	130–160	20	130–160	20
Effervescent salts	80–90	15–40	80–90	15–40
Gelatin capsules	78	40–50	78	40–50
Glandular products	70–80	5–20	70–80	5–20
Powder manufacturing	75–80	15–35	75–80	15–35
Microanalysis	75–80	45–50	75–80	45–50
Tablet compressing	70–80	35–40	70–80	35–40
Tablet coating	75–80	35–40	75–80	35–40
Serums	74–78	45–50	74–78	45–50
Photographic material:				
Cutting	72–75	60–65	72–75	60–65
Developing	70–75	60	70–75	60
Printing	73–75	65–70	73–75	65–70
Finished storage	60–80	45–50	60–80	45–50
Plastics, thermosetting molding	80	25–30	80	25–30
Plywood:				
Fabrication	E.C.	55–60	70	55–60
Gluing	E.C.	55–60	70	55–60
Rubber:				
Cementing room	80	25–30	80	25–30
Dipping room	75–80	25–30	75–80	25–30
Manufacturing	90	....	90	....
Textile, rayon (viscose):				
Aging	64	....	64	....
Grading and sorting	80	55	80	55
Ripening	72	....	72	....
Spinning	70–75	85	70–75	85
Throwing	70	60	70	60
Warping and quilling	80	55	80	55
Weaving	75–80	60–75	75	60
Xanthating	78	....	78	....

These conditions are typical of what has been used and may vary appreciably from application to application.

E. C. = evaporative cooling.

* Carrier, Cherne, Grant, and Roberts, "Modern Air Conditioning, Heating, and Ventilating," 3d ed., pp. 396–399, Pitman, New York, 1959.

$$Q_a = \frac{10^6 Q_c}{(\text{M.A.C.}) - (\text{S.A.C.})} \tag{15-12}$$

where Q_a = air circulation, cu. ft./min.; Q_c = contaminant generation rate, cu. ft./min.; M.A.C. = maximum allowable concentration of contaminant, p.p.m. by volume; S.A.C. = concentration of contaminant in supply air, p.p.m. by volume.

The generation rate Q_c of a vapor for use in the above equation can be determined from the following equation:

$$Q_c = \frac{W}{M_w}(359)\left(\frac{t + 460}{492}\right) \tag{15-13}$$

where W = generation rate of liquid contaminant, lb./min.; M_w = molecular weight of contaminant, lb./lb.-mole; t = air temperature, °F.

Example 20. Determine the air-circulation rate required to reduce the carbon disulfide concentration in a process area to the maximum allowable concentration (20 p.p.m.). The process liberates 1 lb./min. of carbon disulfide. Air temperature is 95°F. and 100 per cent fresh air will be used (S.A.C. = 0).

Solution. Vapor-generation rate obtained from Eq. (15-13) is

$$Q_c = \frac{1}{76.14}(359)\left(\frac{555}{492}\right) = 5.33 \text{ cu. ft./min.}$$

Air-circulation rate calculated from Eq. (15-12) is

$$Q_a = \frac{5.33 \times 10^6}{20} = 266{,}000 \text{ cu. ft./min.}$$

If the source of contaminant generation were localized, an exhaust hood could be used, thereby reducing the fresh air requirement.

Air-conditioning Equipment. Basically, an air-conditioning system consists of a fan unit which forces a mixture of fresh outdoor air and room air through a series of devices which act upon the air to clean it, to increase or decrease its temperature, and to increase or decrease its water-vapor content or humidity. Modern air-conditioning equipment generally falls into three classes: (1) self-contained air conditioners, (2) unit-type air conditioners, and (3) central air-conditioning systems.

Self-contained equipment, also called **unitary** or **packaged equipment**, may be further classified as **room air conditioners**, **residential units**, and **commercial** or **industrial units**. These units contain a complete cooling system in one package, consisting of a compressor, condenser, evaporator, fan, filter, and controls. A heating coil may also be included and a humidifier may be added to provide winter humidification. Self-contained units may have either air-cooled or water-cooled refrigerant condensers. If water-cooled, cooling water piping to and from the condenser is required. Cooling water may be either once-through or recirculated; in the latter case a cooling tower or spray pond is used to remove heat from the water. Evaporative condensers may be used in place of the condenser–cooling-tower

Table 15-9. Equilibrium Moisture Content for Various Materials*

Moisture content expressed in per cent of dry weight of the substance at various relative humidities—temperature, 75°F.

Classification	Material	Description	Relative humidity, %								
			10	20	30	40	50	60	70	80	90
Natural textile fibers	Cotton	Sea island—roving	2.5	3.7	4.6	5.5	6.6	7.9	9.5	11.5	14.1
	Cotton	American—cloth	2.6	3.7	4.4	5.2	5.9	6.8	8.1	10.0	14.3
	Cotton	Absorbent	4.8	9.0	12.5	15.7	18.5	20.8	22.8	24.3	25.8
	Wool	Australian merino—skein	4.7	7.0	8.9	10.8	12.8	14.9	17.2	19.9	23.4
	Silk	Raw chevennes—skein	3.2	5.5	6.9	8.0	8.9	10.2	11.9	14.3	18.3
	Linen	Table cloth	1.9	2.9	3.6	4.3	5.1	6.1	7.0	8.4	10.2
	Linen	Dry spun—yarn	3.6	5.4	6.5	7.3	8.1	8.9	9.8	11.2	13.8
	Jute	Average of several grades	3.1	5.2	6.9	8.5	10.2	12.2	14.4	17.1	20.2
	Hemp	Manila and sisal—rope	2.7	4.7	6.0	7.2	8.5	9.9	11.6	13.6	15.7
Rayons	Viscose	Average skein	4.0	5.7	6.8	7.9	9.2	10.8	12.4	14.2	16.0
	Cellulose acetate	....	0.8	1.1	1.4	1.9	2.4	3.0	3.6	4.3	5.3
Paper	M. F. newsprint	Wood pulp—24% ash	2.1	3.2	4.0	4.7	5.3	6.1	7.2	8.7	10.6
	H. M. F. writing	Wood pulp—3% ash	3.0	4.2	5.2	6.2	7.2	8.3	9.9	11.9	14.2
	White bond	Rag—1% ash	2.4	3.7	4.7	5.5	6.5	7.5	8.8	10.8	13.2
	Com. ledger	75% rag—1% ash	3.2	4.2	5.0	5.6	6.2	6.9	8.1	10.3	13.9
	Kraft wrapping	Coniferous	3.2	4.6	5.7	6.6	7.6	8.9	10.5	12.6	14.9
Misc. organic materials	Leather	Sole oak—tanned	5.0	8.5	11.2	13.6	16.0	18.3	20.6	24.0	29.2
	Glue	Hide	3.4	4.8	5.8	6.6	7.6	9.0	10.7	11.8	12.5
	Rubber	Solid tires	0.11	0.21	0.32	0.44	0.54	0.66	0.76	0.88	0.99
	Wood	Timber (average)	3.0	4.4	5.9	7.6	9.3	11.3	14.0	17.5	22.0
	Soap	White	1.9	3.8	5.7	7.6	10.0	12.9	16.1	19.8	23.8
	Tobacco	Cigarette	5.4	8.6	11.0	13.3	16.0	19.5	25.0	33.5	50.0
Foodstuffs	White bread	....	0.5	1.7	3.1	4.5	6.2	8.5	11.1	14.5	19.0
	Crackers	....	2.1	2.8	3.3	3.9	5.0	6.5	8.3	10.9	14.9
	Macaroni	....	5.1	7.4	8.8	10.2	11.7	13.7	16.2	19.0	22.1
	Flour	....	2.6	4.1	5.3	6.5	8.0	9.9	12.4	15.4	19.1
	Starch	....	2.2	3.8	5.2	6.4	7.4	8.3	9.2	10.6	12.7
	Gelatin	....	0.7	1.6	2.8	3.8	4.9	6.1	7.6	9.3	11.4
Misc. inorganic materials	Asbestos fiber	Finely divided	0.16	0.24	0.26	0.32	0.41	0.51	0.62	0.73	0.84
	Silica gel	....	5.7	9.8	12.7	15.2	17.2	18.8	20.2	21.5	22.6
	Domestic coke	....	0.20	0.40	0.61	0.81	1.03	1.24	1.46	1.67	1.89
	Activated charcoal	Steam activated	7.1	14.3	22.8	26.2	28.3	29.2	30.0	31.1	32.7

* From "Heating, Ventilating, Air Conditioning Guide," American Society of Heating, Refrigerating and Air-Conditioning Engineers, 1960.

system. Room units with capacities of from 0.5 to 2 tons are usually air-cooled. Types include window sill, through-the-wall, and floor-mounted consoles. Residential units range in size up to 10 tons. Combination units for cooling and heating are available for either oil- or gas-heat installations.

Commercial or **industrial units** are built in sizes of 2 to 75 tons or more and may employ moderate runs of ductwork. Steam, hot water, or electric heating can be used. The unit-type air conditioners are designed for one room only and require a remotely connected refrigeration machine or other means of cooling, and a remotely connected source of heat. These units consist of one or more motor-driven centrifugal fans, a cleanable or disposable air filter, a water or direct-expansion coil, outside air damper, and controls. Capacities of ½ to 2 tons are available.

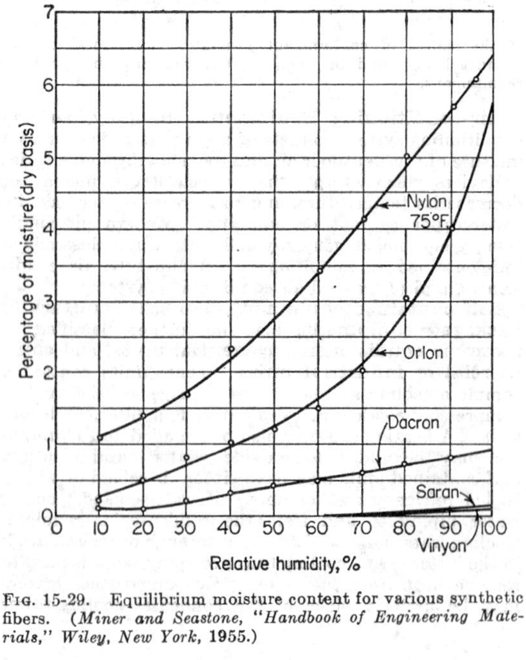

FIG. 15-29. Equilibrium moisture content for various synthetic fibers. (*Miner and Seastone, "Handbook of Engineering Materials," Wiley, New York,* 1955.)

Central-station systems may serve one or several areas with conditioned air being supplied to the various areas through ductwork. A typical built-up central air-conditioning system is shown in Fig. 15-30. Either water or direct-expansion refrigerant coils or air washers may be used for cooling. Steam or hot-water coils are available for heating, and humidification may be provided by target-type water nozzles, pan humidifiers, steam humidifiers, air washers, or sprayed coils. Air cleaning is usually provided by cleanable or throwaway filters. Central-station air-conditioning units in capacities up to about 50,000 cu. ft./min. are available in prefabricated units.

A detailed analysis of the proposed installation is usually necessary to select the air-conditioning equipment which is best in over-all performance. Each type of air conditioner has its own particular advantages and disadvantages. Important factors to be considered in the selection of air-conditioning equipment are degree of temperature and humidity control required, investment, owning and operating costs, and space requirements. Another important factor is the building itself, that is, whether it is new or existing construction. For example, for existing buildings where it may be inadvisable to install air-supply ducts, the self-contained or unit-type air conditioner may offer the greatest advantages in reduced installation costs. For large industrial processes where close temperature and humidity control are required, a central-station system is usually employed.

Load Calculations. First step in the solution of an air-conditioning problem is to determine the proper design temperature conditions. Since both outdoor and indoor temperatures greatly influence the size of the equipment, the designer must exercise good judgment in selecting the proper conditions for his particular case. Table 15-10 lists winter and summer outdoor temperature

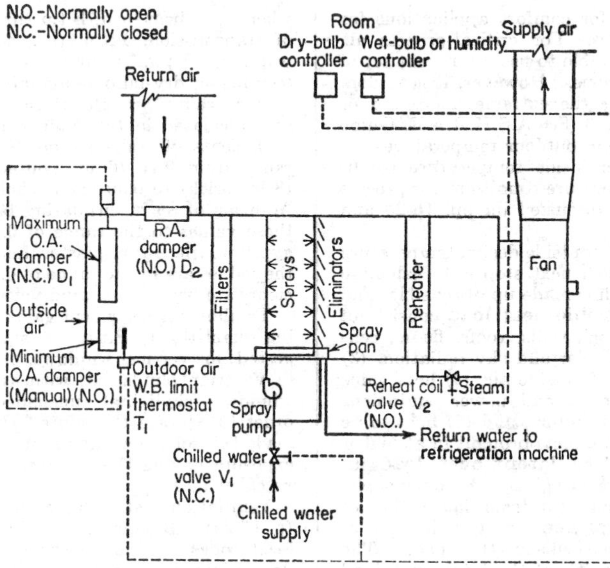

FIG. 15-30. Typical central-station air-conditioning unit and control system. On a rising room wet-bulb temperature, the wet-bulb branch-line air pressure increases through the reverse-acting outdoor-air wet-bulb temperature-limit thermostat T_1 to open gradually the maximum outdoor-air damper D_1 and simultaneously close return-air damper D_2, then gradually open chilled-water valve V_1. On a rising room dry-bulb temperature, the dry-bulb branch-line air pressure gradually increases to close reheat steam valve V_2. When outdoor wet-bulb temperature exceeds the set point of the outdoor-air wet-bulb-limit thermostat T_1, which is set at the return-air wet-bulb temperature, this thermostat decreases branch-line pressure to close gradually maximum outdoor damper D_1 and simultaneously open return-air damper D_2. The reverse sequences are followed during the heating season.

Table 15-10. Outdoor Design Temperatures*

City—state	Winter	Summer	
	Dry-bulb, °F.	Dry-bulb, °F.	Wet-bulb, °F.
Akron, Ohio	−5	95	75
Albany, N.Y	−10	93	75
Albuquerque, N.M	0	95	70
Atlanta, Ga	10	95	76
Baltimore, Md	0	95	78
Billings, Mont	−25	90	66
Birmingham, Ala	10	95	78
Bloomfield, N.J	0	95	75
Boise, Idaho	−10	95	65
Boston, Mass	0	92	75
Bridgeport, Conn	0	95	75
Buffalo, N.Y	−5	93	73
Charleston, S.C	15	95	78
Chattanooga, Tenn	10	95	76
Chicago, Ill	−10	95	75
Cincinnati, Ohio	0	95	78
Cleveland, Ohio	0	95	75
Columbus, Ohio	−10	95	76
Dallas, Tex	0	100	78
Dayton, Ohio	0	95	78
Denver, Colo	−10	95	64
Des Moines, Iowa	−15	95	78
Detroit, Mich	−10	95	75
Duluth, Minn	−25	93	73
East Orange, N.J	0	95	75
El Paso, Tex	10	100	69
Erie, Pa	−5	93	75
Fitchburg, Mass	−10	93	75
Flint, Mich	−10	95	75
Fort Wayne, Ind	−10	95	75
Fort Worth, Tex	10	100	78
Grand Rapids, Mich	−10	95	75
Hartford, Conn	0	93	75
Houston, Tex	20	95	80
Indianapolis, Ind	−10	95	76
Jacksonville, Fla	25	95	78
Jersey City, N.J	0	95	75
Kansas City, Mo	−10	100	76
Lincoln, Nebr	−10	95	78
Little Rock, Ark	5	95	78
Long Beach, Calif	35	90	70
Los Angeles, Calif	35	90	70
Louisville, Ky	0	95	78
Memphis, Tenn	0	95	78
Miami, Fla	35	91	79
Milwaukee, Wis	−15	95	75
Minneapolis, Minn	−20	95	75
Nashville, Tenn	0	95	78
New Haven, Conn	0	95	75
New Orleans, La	20	95	80
New York, N.Y	0	95	75
Newark, N.J	0	95	75
Norfolk, Va	15	95	78
Oakland, Calif	30	85	65
Oklahoma City, Okla	0	101	77
Omaha, Nebr	−10	95	78
Peoria, Ill	−10	96	76
Philadelphia, Pa	0	95	78
Phoenix, Ariz	0	105	76
Pittsburgh, Pa	−5	95	75
Portland, Me	−5	90	73
Portland, Ore	10	90	68
Providence, R.I	0	93	75
Reno, Nev	−5	95	65
Richmond, Va	15	95	78
Roanoke, Va	0	95	76
Rochester, N.Y	−5	95	75
St. Louis, Mo	0	95	78
St. Paul, Minn	−20	95	75
Salt Lake City, Utah	−10	95	65
San Antonio, Tex	20	100	78
San Francisco, Calif	35	85	65
Schenectady, N.Y	−10	93	75
Scranton, Pa	−5	95	75
Seattle, Wash	15	85	65
Shreveport, La	20	100	78
Sioux City, Iowa	−20	95	78
Spokane, Wash	−15	93	65
Springfield, Mass	−10	93	75
Syracuse, N.Y	−10	93	75
Tampa, Fla	30	95	78
Toledo, Ohio	−10	95	75
Tucson, Ariz	25	105	72
Tulsa, Okla	0	101	77
Washington, D.C	0	95	78
Wichita, Kans	−10	100	75
Wilmington, Del	0	95	78
Worcester, Mass	0	93	75
Youngstown, Ohio	−5	95	75

* Carrier, Cherne, Grant, and Roberts, "Modern Air Conditioning, Heating, and Ventilating," 3d ed., p. 531, Pitman, New York, 1959.

conditions in common use for comfort applications for various United States cities. For critical-process air conditioning, it may be desirable to use a different set of outdoor-temperature conditions. However, it is seldom good practice to design for the extreme maximum or minimum outside conditions. (See A.S.H.R.A.E. Guide for more extensive coverage of outdoor temperatures.)

Both winter and summer inside temperature conditions for comfort and temperature conditions for process air conditioning have been discussed on pp. 15-23 and 15-25, respectively.

After the proper inside and outside design temperature conditions have been selected, next step is to calculate the space-cooling load, which is made up of sensible- and latent-heat loads. The **sensible-heat load** consists of (1) transmission gains through walls, roofs, floors, ceilings, and window glass, (2) solar and sky radiation, (3) heat gains from infiltration of outside air, (4) heat gains from people, lights, appliances, and power equipment (including the supply-air fan motor), and (5) heat to be removed from materials or products brought in at higher than room temperature. The **latent-heat load** includes loads due to moisture (1) given off from people, appliances, and products, and (2) from infiltration of outside air. The space **total heat load** is the sum of the sensible- and latent-heat loads of the space. The total **refrigeration load** consists of the total space load plus the sensible and latent heat removed from the outside air introduced at the conditioning unit.

It is usual practice to take into account equivalent **by-pass factor** F_b in calculating space-cooling load. Air in passing across a finned-tube coil does not all contact the coil or fin surface unless the coil is several rows deep in the direction of air flow. The equivalent by-pass factor is defined as $(t_2 - t_m)/(t_1 - t_m)$, where t_1 and t_2 are the inlet and exit dry-bulb temperatures of the air, respectively, and t_m is the mean coil temperature. The value of the by-pass factor (1 minus the efficiency) is a function of coil design and face velocity. Typical values for cooling surfaces are:

No. of rows deep	Face velocity 500 ft./min.	Face velocity 600 ft./min.
	By-pass factors	
2	0.42	0.43
4	0.18	0.20
8	0.03	0.04

Therefore, when outside air for ventilation is taken through the conditioning equipment, the portion equal to the by-pass factor becomes an addition to the space load. This in turn causes an increase in the quantity of conditioned supply air. The balance, or 1 minus the by-pass factor, imposes a load on the refrigeration equipment but does not affect the supply-air requirement.

In well-designed spray-type dehumidifiers having sufficient length of spray chamber and spray density, the by-pass factor is sufficiently low to be neglected. A typical value for a two-bank washer is 0.025 for 500 ft./min. air velocity and 35 lb./sq. in. spray nozzle pressure.

Heat conduction or transmission through building walls is a complex phenomenon. However, except where extreme accuracy is desired, approximations can be made which give results adequate for most engineering calculations. For shaded outside walls and roofs, heat gains are calculated using the difference between the inside and outside design dry-bulb temperatures. For sunlit walls and roofs, equivalent outside temperatures of 120°F. and 140°F., respectively, are used in the United States. Transmission gains are calculated from

$$q_1 = UA(t_o - t_i) \qquad (15\text{-}14)$$

where q_1 = heat load, B.t.u./hr.; U = over-all coefficient of transmission, B.t.u./(hr.)(sq. ft.)(°F.); A = area of wall, sq. ft.; t_o = outside dry-bulb temperature, °F.; t_i = inside dry-bulb temperature, °F.

Heat gains through interior walls, floors, and ceilings are calculated in the same manner. Typical values of coefficients of transmission U for plain masonry walls range from 0.79 (6 in. poured concrete) through 0.50 (8 in. brick) to 0.30 (12 in. hollow tile, stucco exterior). Addition of ½ in. insulating board with furring reduces these values to the range of 0.17 to 0.27. With furred gypsum lath, ½ in. plaster, and 1 in. blanket insulation, the values are in the range of 0.12 to 0.16. These coefficients are based on a wind velocity of 15 m.p.h.

To allow for solar heat gains through glass, the following quantities in B.t.u./hr./sq. ft. of sash area are suggested: for vertical windows, unshaded, 100; with shades or venetian blinds, 60; with awnings, 25; for horizontal windows (skylights), unshaded, 160; shaded, 80. In order to average the sun effect in figuring total cooling load, the solar-heat gains only on the roof and on the exposure having the greatest radiant-heat load need to be calculated.

Ventilation rates have been discussed previously (p. 15-25). Reference should also be made to applicable local codes or ordinances on ventilation requirements. As explained previously, the by-passed portion of the outside-air ventilation load should be included in the space load when a coil of high by-pass factor is used but may be neglected when a well-designed spray dehumidifier is used. If included, the load is determined from

$$q_2 = 1.08Q_vF_b(t_o - t_i) \qquad (15\text{-}15)$$

where q_2 = sensible heat load due to by-passed portion of the ventilation air, B.t.u./hr.; Q_v = outside air for ventilation, cu. ft./min.; $(t_o - t_i)$ = design dry-bulb temperature difference between inside and outside, °F.; F_b = coil by-pass factor.

The corresponding space latent-heat load is obtained from

$$q_3 = 4840Q_vF_b(H_o - H_i) \qquad (15\text{-}16)$$

where $(H_o - H_i)$ = humidity difference between inside and outside, lb. water/lb. dry air.

Infiltration load must be included whenever the fresh air introduced at the air-conditioning unit is not sufficient to maintain a positive pressure in the area. If infiltration load is included, the sensible load is equal to

$$q_4 = 1.08Q_i(t_o - t_i) \qquad (15\text{-}17)$$

where q_4 = infiltration load, B.t.u./hr.; Q_i = volume of air infiltration from Table 15-11, cu. ft./min.; $(t_o - t_i)$ = design dry-bulb temperature difference between inside and outside, °F.

The space latent load due to infiltration of outside air is equal to

$$q_5 = 4840Q(H_o - H_i) \qquad (15\text{-}18)$$

where $(H_o - H_i)$ = humidity difference between indoor and outdoor, lb. water/lb. dry air.

Table 15-12 gives sensible- and latent-heat loads produced by people engaged in various activities.

The **sensible-heat factor (S.H.F.)**, which is the ratio of space sensible to space total heat, is determined next. The **apparatus dew point (A.D.P.)** is then obtained from tables, a sample of which is shown in Table 15-13. Apparatus dew point is the temperature of the saturated air which will enable removal of sensible and latent heat at the exact rates gained when air is supplied in the proper quantity. It is the effective surface temperature of a coil or spray of water over or through which air is passed in processes involving condensation. Normally, for a given space temperature condition and a given space sensible-heat factor, there is only one apparatus dew point which will be satisfactory.

Next step is to determine the supply-air-temperature condition to balance the sensible- and latent-heat gains in the space. With commercial apparatus, complete saturation of the air is seldom obtained. However, for practical purposes when using a coil of eight or more rows or a spray dehumidifier, it is sufficiently accurate

Table 15-11. Infiltration*

Kind of room or building	Air changes per hour			
	Summer		Winter	
	Ordinary	Weather-stripping or storm sash	Ordinary	Weather-stripping or storm sash
No windows or outside doors....	0.30	0.15	0.50	0.25
Entrance halls..............	1.20-1.80	0.60-0.90	2.00-3.00	1.00-1.50
Reception halls..............	1.20	0.60	2.00	1.00
Bathrooms..............	1.20	0.60	2.00	1.00
Infiltration through windows:				
Rooms, 1 side exposed........	0.60	0.30	1.00	0.50
Rooms, 2 sides exposed.......	0.90	0.45	1.50	0.75
Rooms, 3 sides exposed.......	1.20	0.60	2.00	1.00
Rooms, 4 sides exposed.......	1.20	0.60	2.00	1.00

NOTE: The total simultaneous infiltration for an entire building will be approximately 50 per cent of the sum of the infiltration allowances of individual rooms.

Infiltration through doors: For each person passing through a door leading to the outside or to an unconditioned space, add the following door infiltration to the summer infiltration through windows:

Usage	Cu. ft./min.
Infrequent..................	60
Average..................	50
Heavy..................	40
36-in. swinging door..........	100

These figures are based on the assumption that there is no wind pressure and that swinging doors are in use in one wall only. Any swinging doors in other walls should be kept closed to ensure air conditioning in accordance with these recommended standards.

* Air Conditioning and Refrigerating Institute Standard 530-56, p. 12.

Table 15-12. Heat Gain from Occupants*

Degree of activity	Total heat, adult male, B.t.u./hr.	Total heat adjusted,† B.t.u./hr.	Sensible heat, B.t.u./hr.	Latent heat, B.t.u./hr.
Seated at rest..............	390	330	180	150
Seated, very light work.......	450	400	195	205
Moderately active office work..	475	450	200	250
Standing, light work; walking slowly..............	550	450	200	250
Walking; seated..............	550	500	200	300
Sedentary work..............	490	550	220	330
Light bench work..............	800	750	220	530
Moderately heavy work.......	1000	1000	300	700
Heavy work..............	1500	1450	465	985

NOTE: The above values are based on 80°F. room dry-bulb temperature. For 78°F. room dry-bulb temperature, the total heat gain remains the same, but the sensible-heat values should be increased by approximately 10 per cent and the latent-heat values decreased accordingly.

* Air Conditioning and Refrigerating Institute Standard 530-56, p. 9.

† *Adjusted total heat gain* is based on normal percentage of men, women, and children for the usual applications and is based on the gain from an adult female being 85 per cent of the value for an adult male and the gain from a child being 75 per cent of the value for an adult male.

to assume 100 per cent saturation, and the apparatus dew point becomes the supply-air temperature. For coils of fewer than eight rows, the supply-air-temperature conditions should be determined using the by-pass factor as illustrated below.

Example 21. Determine the wet- and dry-bulb temperatures of the air leaving a coil having a by-pass factor of 0.20. The entering air has a dry-bulb temperature of 85°F. and a wet-bulb temperature of 69°F. The apparatus dew point is 55°F.

Solution. By-pass factor $0.20 = (t_2 - 55)/(85 - 55)$. Therefore, t_2, the leaving-air dry-bulb temperature, is 61°F. On the psychrometric chart, connect the point 85°F. dry-bulb, 69°F. wet-bulb, with the apparatus dew point, 55°F. Now locate 61°F. dry-bulb on this line and pick off the leaving wet-bulb temperature of 58°F.

The required space supply-air flow may now be determined from

$$Q_s = \frac{q_s}{1.08(t_1 - t_2)} \tag{15-19}$$

where Q_s = supply-air volume, cu. ft./min.; q_s = space sensible-heat load, B.t.u./hr.; t_1 = space design dry-bulb

Table 15-13. Sensible-heat Factor and Apparatus Dew Point*

Room conditions: Relative humidity, %	Room conditions: Wet bulb, °F.	Sensible-heat factor and apparatus dew point								
72°F., dry bulb										
35	55.9	S.H.F.	1.00	0.98	0.93					
		A.D.P.	42.8	42	40					
40	57.3	S.H.F.	1.00	0.95	0.92	0.87	0.84			
		A.D.P.	46.3	45	44	42	40			
45	58.7	S.H.F.	1.00	0.94	0.87	0.82	0.79	0.76		
		A.D.P.	49.5	48	46	44	42	40		
50	60.1	S.H.F.	1.00	0.92	0.88	0.81	0.77	0.73	0.70	
		A.D.P.	52.4	51	50	48	46	43	40	
55	61.4	S.H.F.	1.00	0.93	0.83	0.77	0.72	0.68	0.66	
		A.D.P.	54.9	54	52	50	48	45	42	
60	62.7	S.H.F.	1.00	0.89	0.79	0.72	0.68	0.65	0.63	0.61
		A.D.P.	57.3	56	54	52	50	48	46	42
76°F., dry bulb										
35	58.9	S.H.F.	1.00	0.96	0.91	.87				
		A.D.P.	46.3	45	43	41				
40	60.4	S.H.F.	1.00	0.96	0.89	0.84	0.81	0.78		
		A.D.P.	49.9	49	47	45	43	41		
45	61.9	S.H.F.	1.00	0.94	0.86	0.81	0.77	0.74	0.71	
		A.D.P.	53.2	52	50	48	46	44	40	
50	63.4	S.H.F.	1.00	0.93	0.83	0.77	0.73	0.69	0.67	0.65
		A.D.P.	56.2	55	53	51	49	46	43	40
55	64.9	S.H.F.	1.00	0.94	0.82	0.75	0.70	0.67	0.65	0.62
		A.D.P.	58.7	58	56	54	52	50	48	44
60	66.2	S.H.F.	1.00	0.90	0.77	0.70	0.66	0.62	0.60	0.58
		A.D.P.	61.1	60	58	56	54	52	49	46
78°F., dry bulb										
35	60.3	S.H.F.	1.00	0.96	0.91	0.87	0.83			
		A.D.P.	48.2	47	45	43	41			
40	61.9	S.H.F.	1.00	0.93	0.87	0.82	0.79	0.77		
		A.D.P.	51.7	50	48	46	44	42		
45	63.5	S.H.F.	1.00	0.95	0.86	0.81	0.76	0.74	0.70	
		A.D.P.	55.0	54	52	50	48	46	42	
50	65.0	S.H.F.	1.00	0.94	0.83	0.76	0.73	0.70	0.67	0.64
		A.D.P.	57.9	57	55	53	51	49	47	42
55	66.6	S.H.F.	1.00	0.96	0.83	0.75	0.70	0.65	0.62	0.60
		A.D.P.	60.5	60	58	56	54	51	48	44
60	67.9	S.H.F.	1.00	0.90	0.82	0.76	0.69	0.64	0.60	0.57
		A.D.P.	63.0	62	61	60	58	56	53	49
80°F., dry bulb										
35	61.8	S.H.F.	1.00	0.94	0.88	0.85	0.82	0.79		
		A.D.P.	49.8	48	46	44	42	40		
40	63.5	S.H.F.	1.00	0.94	0.90	0.84	0.80	0.76	0.73	
		A.D.P.	53.5	52	51	49	47	44	41	
45	65.1	S.H.F.	1.00	0.96	0.87	0.81	0.76	0.73	0.70	0.67
		A.D.P.	56.8	56	54	52	50	48	45	41
50	66.7	S.H.F.	1.00	0.89	0.80	0.74	0.70	0.66	0.64	0.62
		A.D.P.	59.7	58	56	54	52	49	46	42
55	68.2	S.H.F.	1.00	0.89	0.82	0.74	0.69	0.65	0.61	0.59
		A.D.P.	62.3	61	60	58	56	54	50	47
60	69.6	S.H.F.	1.00	0.91	0.83	0.72	0.66	0.62	0.59	0.57
		A.D.P.	64.8	64	63	61	59	57	55	53
82°F., dry bulb										
35	63.3	S.H.F.	1.00	0.92	0.88	0.84	0.80			
		A.D.P.	51.6	49	48	46	43			
40	65.0	S.H.F.	1.00	0.90	0.87	0.82	0.78	0.74	0.71	
		A.D.P.	55.2	53	52	50	48	45	41	
45	66.7	S.H.F.	1.00	0.91	0.87	0.80	0.75	0.72	0.68	0.65
		A.D.P.	58.5	57	56	54	52	50	46	41
50	68.3	S.H.F.	1.00	0.90	0.80	0.74	0.70	0.64	0.62	0.60
		A.D.P.	61.5	60	58	56	54	50	47	42
55	69.8	S.H.F.	1.00	0.90	0.83	0.74	0.68	0.64	0.61	0.58
		A.D.P.	64.2	63	62	60	58	56	54	50

* Carrier, Cherne, Grant, and Roberts, "Modern Air Conditioning, Heating, and Ventilating," 3d ed., p. 545, Pitman, New York, 1959.

temperature, °F.; t_2 = supply-air dry-bulb temperature, °F.

Next step after determining the space supply-air flow and the space total heat load is to calculate the total refrigeration load in order to size the cooling and dehumidifying equipment. Total load is obtained by adding the sensible- and latent-heat loads due to the introduction of outside air for ventilation purposes.

Winter-heating load depends on many of the same factors as the summer-cooling load; however, winter heat losses may be partially or totally offset by the heat gains from lights, electrical equipment, solar transmission, people, and other heat sources. Often these heat gains are excluded when determining heating-coil and steam-valve sizes for peak-heating requirements.

Example 22. Process Air-conditioning Calculation. A building 200 ft. long, 100 ft. wide, and 20 ft. high is to be conditioned to 80°F. dry-bulb and 50 per cent relative humidity the year around. All walls are exposed except one 100-ft. wall which adjoins an air-conditioned area at 80°F. dry-bulb temperature. The walls are of face and common brick having a total thickness of 12 in. The flat roof is 4 in. concrete covered with built-up roofing and 2 in. insulation. Over-all heat-transfer coefficient for the roof is 0.14 B.t.u./(hr.)(sq. ft.)(°F.), while that for the walls is 0.35 B.t.u./(hr.)(sq. ft.)(°F.). The building has no windows. There are 75 people engaged in light work. Illumination is 3 watts/sq. ft. The measured motor load is 500 kw.

Determine supply air, refrigeration, and heating requirements, if an air washer is used. Assume that the air leaving the washer is saturated. For determining winter reheat requirements, assume that all the lights are burning and 75 per cent of motors are in operation. In selecting the reheat coils and steam valve, however, it may be desirable to ignore the motor-heat load. Figure 15-30 shows a schematic of the proposed installation and an explanation of the control system. A preheat coil will not be required in this installation since the outside and return air are mixed in the required proportions to provide the proper dew point leaving the washer, the mixture conditions being above the freezing point of water. Where the minimum outside-air requirements are such that there is a possibility of introduction of air below 32°F. to the washer, a preheat coil is necessary.

1. Design conditions

	Outside	Inside
Summer		
Dry-bulb, °F	95	80
Wet-bulb, °F	78	66.7
E.T.	84	74
Relative humidity, per cent	47.5	50
Dew point, °F	71.7	59.5
Humidity, lb./lb. dry air	0.0168	0.011
Enthalpy, B.t.u./lb. dry air	41.4	31.3
Winter		
Dry-bulb, °F	10	80
Wet-bulb, °F	9	66.7
E.T.	—	74
Relative humidity, %	80	50
Dew point, °F	6	59.5
Humidity, lb./lb. dry air	0.0014	0.011
Enthalpy, B.t.u./lb. dry air	3.5	31.3

Walls	Area, sq. ft.	Coeff. heat transfer, B.t.u./(hr.)(sq. ft.)(°F.)	Temp. diff., °F. [Summer / Winter]
N (shaded)	4000	0.35	[95–80 / 80–10]
E (interior)	2000	0.35	0
W (shaded)	2000	0.35	[95–80 / 80–10]
S (sunlit)	4000	0.35	[120–80 / 80–10]
Glass—no windows	—	—	
Roof	20,000	0.14	[140–80 / 80–10]
Floor (on ground)	20,000		

	Summer load, B.t.u./hr.	Winter load, B.t.u./hr.
2. Transmission		
Walls		
N (shaded)	21,000	98,000
E (interior)	—	—
W (shaded)	10,500	49,000
S (sunlit)	56,000	98,000
Roof	168,000	196,000
Floor	Neglect	
Subtotals	(gain) 255,500	(loss)441,000

	Summer cooling, B.t.u./hr.	Winter cooling, B.t.u./hr.
3. Internal heat (sensible)		
People, 75 × 220 B.t.u./(hr.)(person)	16,500	
Lights, 200 ft. × 100 ft. × 3 watts/sq. ft. × 3.4 B.t.u./(hr.)(watt)	205,000	205,000
Motors, 500 kw. × 3413 B.t.u./(hr.)(kw.)	1,700,000	1,275,000 (75 per cent)
4. Room sensible-heat subtotal	2,177,000	1,039,000
Fan hp. (5 per cent) + safety factor 5 per cent	218,000	Neglect
Room sensible heat, B.t.u./hr	2,395,000	1,039,000

5. Internal heat (latent)

People, 75 × 530	39,700 B.t.u./hr.
Safety factor 5 per cent	2,000 B.t.u./hr.
6. Room latent heat	41,700 B.t.u./hr.
7. Room total heat	2,436,700 B.t.u./hr.

8. Sensible-heat factor and apparatus dew point

$$\text{S.H.F.} = \frac{2,395,000}{2,436,000} = 0.986$$

A.D.P. = 59.5°F. (from Table 15-14)

9. Room supply air

$$\frac{2,395,000}{1.08\,(80 - 59.5)} = 108,500 \text{ cu. ft./min.}$$

10. Outside-air heat

Outside air (*a*) 75 people × 10 cu. ft./(min.)(person) = 750 cu. ft./min. or (*b*) 200 × 100 × 0.1 cu. ft./(min.)(sq. ft.) = 2000 cu. ft./min.

For practical purposes use 5000 cu. ft./min. (or approximately 5 per cent) as 2000 cu. ft./min. is probably insufficient to prevent infiltration of outside air through doors.

Sensible load, 5000 × (95 − 80) × 1.08 = 81,000 B.t.u./hr.

Latent load,

5000 × (0.0168 − 0.011) × 4840 = 140,000 B.t.u./hr.

Subtotal = 221,000 B.t.u./hr.

11. Spray pump brake horsepower (3 per cent). 80,000 B.t.u./hr.

Dehumidifier and piping loss (2 per cent). . 53,000 B.t.u./hr.

12. Grand total heat (summer) . . . 2,790,000 B.t.u./hr.

Tons refrigeration (1 ton = 12,000 B.t.u./hr.) . . . 232

13. Winter peak reheat = room sensible cooling load (summer) − room sensible cooling load (winter) (see item 4)

Reheat = 2,395,000 − 1,039,000
= 1,356,000 B.t.u./hr.

14. Mixture temperature conditions of minimum outdoor air on winter design day and recirculated room air

$$\text{Dry-bulb temperature} = \frac{103,500(80) + 5000(10)}{108,500} = 76.8\text{°F.}$$

$$\text{Enthalpy} = \frac{103,500(31.3) + 5000(3.8)}{108,500}$$

$$= 30.1 \text{ B.t.u./lb. dry air}$$

From psychrometric chart, the corresponding wet-bulb is 65°F. Therefore, the outside-air dampers will open to provide a 59.5°F. wet-bulb condition entering the washer. The washer will saturate the air adiabatically, thus giving the required entering dew-point temperature of 59.5°F. Neither preheat nor washer spray-water heating is required.

DRYING OF SOLIDS

REFERENCES: Brown *et al.*, "Unit Operations, Wiley, New York, 1950. Coulson and Richardson, "Chemical Engineering," vol. II, McGraw-Hill, New York, 1955. Hirsch, "Die Trockentechnik," Springer, Berlin, 1932. Krischer, "Die wissenschaftenlichen Grundlagen der Trocknungstechnik," Springer, Berlin, 1956. Lapple and Clark, *Chem. Eng.*, **62** (10), 191 (1955). Lapple, Clark, and Dybdal, *Chem. Eng.*, **62** (11), 177 (1955). Symposium on Drying, *Ind. Eng. Chem.*, **30**, 384–397, 506–514, 993–1010, 1115–1138 (1938). Treybal, "Mass-transfer Operations," McGraw-Hill, New York, 1955. Walker, Lewis, McAdams, and Gilliland, "Principles of Chemical Engineering," 3d ed., McGraw-Hill, New York, 1937. Zimmerman and

Lavine, "Psychrometric Charts and Tables," Industrial Research Service, Dover, N.H., 1945.

Drying generally refers to the removal of a liquid from a solid by **evaporation,** the necessary heat of vaporization being provided by conduction from a solid surface, convection from a hot gas, or radiation. Mechanical methods for separating a liquid from a solid are not generally considered drying, although they often precede a drying operation, since it is less expensive and frequently easier to use mechanical methods than thermal methods.

This section presents the theory and fundamental concepts of the drying of solids. Equipment descriptions, dryer performance, and recommended design procedures can be found in Sec. 11 (indirect heat transfer) and Sec. 20 (direct-contact heat transfer). For drying of gases, see Sec. 16.

Terminology. The generally accepted definitions, peculiar to drying, are given alphabetically below (see also under Psychrometry, p. 15-2).

Bound moisture in a solid is that liquid which exerts a vapor pressure less than that of the pure liquid at the given temperature. Liquid may become bound by retention in small capillaries, by solution in cell or fiber walls, by homogeneous solution throughout the solid, and by chemical or physical adsorption on solid surfaces. Bound moisture can be removed from a solid only under specific conditions of humidity in the external surroundings.

Capillary flow is the flow of liquid through the interstices and over the surface of a solid, caused by liquid-solid molecular attraction.

Commercial dry basis expresses moisture content leaving the dryer as pounds of water per pound of product.

Constant-rate period is that drying period during which the rate of water removal per unit of drying surface is constant.

Critical moisture content is the average moisture content when the constant-rate period ends.

Dry-weight basis expresses the moisture content of wet solid as pounds of water per pound of bone-dry solid. The advantage of using this basis is that the moisture loss is obtained by subtraction of the moisture contents before and after drying (see Wet-weight basis).

Dryer efficiency is the ratio of heat used to evaporate water to the total heat supplied by the fuel. "Over-all efficiency" is sometimes used to distinguish "total system efficiency" from "efficiency of the drying space."

Equilibrium moisture content is the limiting moisture to which a given material can be dried under specific conditions of air temperature and humidity (see further discussion, p. 15-41).

Falling-rate period is that drying period during which the instantaneous drying rate continually decreases (p. 15-38).

Fiber-saturation point is the moisture content of cellular materials (*e.g.*, wood) at which the cell walls are completely saturated while the cavities are liquid-free. It may be defined as the equilibrium moisture content as the humidity of the surrounding atmosphere approaches saturation.

Free-moisture content is that liquid which is removable at a given temperature and humidity. It may include bound and unbound moisture.

Funicular state is that condition in drying a porous body when capillary suction results in air being sucked into the pores.

Hygroscopic material is one that may contain bound moisture.

Initial moisture distribution refers to the moisture distribution throughout a solid at the start of drying.

Internal diffusion may be defined as the movement of liquid or vapor through a solid as the result of a concentration difference.

Moisture content of a solid is usually expressed as moisture quantity per unit weight or volume of the dry or wet solid. A weight basis is preferred.

Moisture gradient refers to the distribution of water in a solid at a given moment in the drying process, the nature of which depends on the characteristics and history of the solid involved.

Non-hygroscopic material is one that can contain no bound moisture.

Pendular state is that state of a liquid in a porous solid when a continuous film of liquid no longer exists around and between discrete particles so that flow by capillarity cannot occur. This state succeeds the funicular state.

Unaccomplished moisture change is the ratio of the free moisture present at any time to that initially present.

Unbound moisture in a hygroscopic material is that moisture in excess of the equilibrium moisture content corresponding to saturation humidity. All water in a non-hygroscopic material is unbound water.

Wet-weight basis expresses the moisture in a material as a percentage of the weight of the wet solid. Use of a dry-weight basis is recommended since the percentage change of moisture is constant for all moisture levels. When the wet-weight basis is used to express moisture content, a 2 or 3 per cent change at high moisture contents (above 70 per cent) actually represents a 15 to 20 per cent change in evaporative load. This might tax the capacity of a dryer. See Fig. 15-31 for the relationship between the dry- and wet-weight bases.

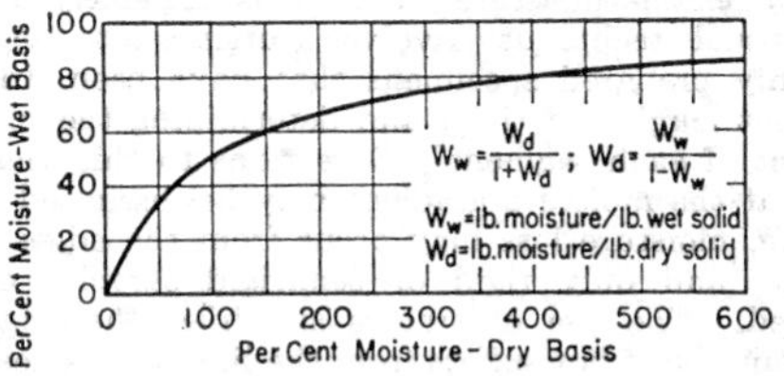

Fig. 15-31. Relationship between wet-weight and dry-weight bases.

THEORY AND FUNDAMENTAL CONCEPTS

When a solid dries, two fundamental and simultaneous processes occur: (1) **heat** is transferred to evaporate liquid; (2) **mass** is transferred as a liquid or vapor within the solid and as a vapor from the surface. The factors governing the rates of these processes determine the drying rate.

Commercial drying operations may utilize heat transfer by convection, conduction, radiation, or a combination of these. Industrial dryers differ fundamentally by the methods of heat transfer employed (see Classification of Dryers, p. 15-45). However, irrespective of the mode of heat transfer, heat must flow to the outer surface and then into the interior of the solid. The single exception is dielectric drying, in which high-frequency electricity generates heat internally and produces a higher temperature within the material than on its surface. In this case, heat flows from the interior to the external surfaces.

Mass is transferred in drying as a liquid or vapor within the solid and as vapor from the exposed surfaces. Movement within the solid results from a concentration gradient which is dependent on the characteristics of the solid.

Internal vs. External Conditions

A study of how a solid dries may be based on the **internal mechanism** of liquid flow or on the effect of the **external conditions** of temperature, humidity, air flow, state of subdivision, etc., on the drying rate of the solid. The former procedure generally requires a fundamental study of the internal conditions. The latter procedure, although less fundamental, is more generally used because the results have greater immediate applicability in equipment design and evaluation.

Internal Mechanism of Liquid Flow. Internal liquid flow may occur by several mechanisms, depending on the structure of the solid. Some of the possible mechanisms are (1) **diffusion** in continuous homogeneous solids, (2) **capillary flow** in granular and porous solids, (3) flow caused by **shrinkage** and **pressure** gradients, (4) flow caused by **gravity,** and (5) flow caused by a **vaporization-condensation** sequence.

In general, one mechanism predominates at any given time in a solid during drying, but it is not uncommon to find different mechanisms predominating at different times during the drying cycle.

The particular mechanism that controls during the drying of a solid can be determined by a study of **internal moisture gradients.** The experimental determination of reliable moisture gradients is extremely difficult. The usual technique involves cutting into segments specially prepared specimens that have been dried for different lengths of time, and determining the moisture content of each segment. Objections to this technique are that the moisture gradient may be disrupted during cutting, moisture loss may occur from the edges of the sample, and only rigid or semirigid samples can be handled. The use of tracers simplifies the analytical determinations but suffers from the limitations described above.

Experimental moisture-gradient curves have been measured by numerous investigators. Among these are McCready and McCabe [*Trans. Am. Inst. Chem. Engrs.*, **29,** 131 (1933)] and Dreshfield [*Chem. Eng. Progress*, **53,** 174 (1957)] for paper drying; Ceaglske and Hougen [*Trans. Am. Inst. Chem. Engrs.*, **33,** 283 (1937)] for sand; Oliver and Newitt [*Trans. Inst. Chem. Engrs.*, **27,** 9 (1949)] for beds of glass beads and silica flour; Bateman, Hohf, and Stamm [*Ind. Eng. Chem.*, **31,** 1150 (1939)] and Stamm (*U.S. Dept. Agr. Tech. Bull.* 929, 1946) for wood; and Perry [*Trans. Am. Soc. Mech. Engrs.*, **66,** 447 (1944)] for drying prunes.

Hougen, McCauley, and Marshall [*Trans. Am. Inst. Chem. Engrs.*, **36,** 183 (1940)] discussed the conditions under which capillary and diffusional flow may be expected in a drying solid, and analyzed the published experimental moisture-gradient data for the two cases. Their curves indicate that capillary flow is typified by a moisture gradient involving a double curvature and point of inflection (Fig. 15-32*a*) while diffusional flow is a smooth curve, concave downward (Fig. 15-32*b*), as would be predicted from the diffusion equations. They also showed that the liquid-diffusion coefficient is usually a function of moisture content which decreases with decreasing moisture. The effect of variable diffusivity is illustrated in Fig. 15-32*b*, where the dashed line is calculated for constant diffusivity and the solid line is experimental for the case where the diffusion coefficient is moisture-dependent. Thus, the integrated diffusion equations assuming constant diffusivity only approximate the actual behavior.

These authors classified solids on the basis of capillary and diffusional flow:

Capillary Flow. Moisture which is held in the interstices of solids, as liquid on the surface, or as free moisture in cell cavities, moves by gravity and capillarity, provided that passageways for continuous flow are present. In drying, liquid flow resulting from capillarity applies to liquids not held in solution and to all moisture above the fiber-saturation point, as in textiles, paper, and leather, and to all moisture above the equilibrium moisture content at atmospheric saturation, as in fine powders and granular solids, such as paint pigments, minerals, clays, soil, and sand.

Vapor Diffusion. Moisture may move by vapor diffusion through the solid, provided that a temperature gradient is established by heating, thus creating a vapor-pressure gradient. Vaporization and vapor diffusion may occur in any solid where heating takes place at one surface and drying from the other, and where liquid is isolated between granules of solid.

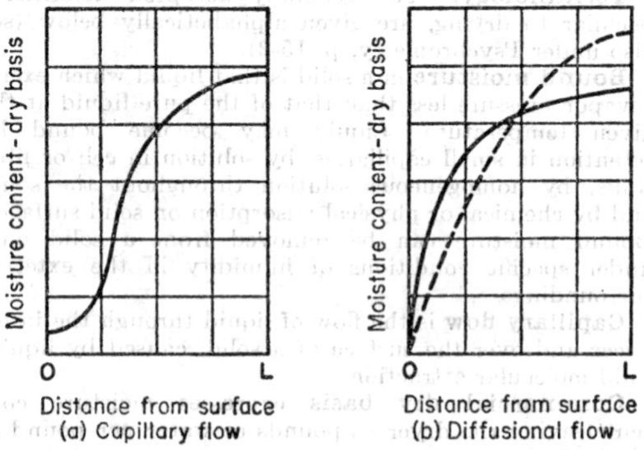

FIG. 15-32. Two types of internal moisture gradients obtained in drying solids.

Liquid Diffusion. The movement of liquids by diffusion in solids is restricted to the equilibrium moisture content below the point of atmospheric saturation, and to systems in which moisture and solid are mutually soluble. The first class applies to the last stages in the drying of clays, starches, flour, textiles, paper, and wood; the second class includes the drying of soaps, glues, gelatins, and pastes.

External Variables. A study of drying based on the effects of the external variables is the most common method used to investigate the drying characteristics of solids. This is because the results so obtained are usually directly applicable to the design and operation of dryers.

The principal external variables involved in any drying study are temperature, humidity, air flow, state of subdivision of the solid, agitation of the solid, method of supporting the solid, and the contact between hot surfaces and wet solid. All these variables will not necessarily occur in one problem.

Periods of Drying

When a solid is dried experimentally, data are usually obtained relating moisture content to time. These data are then plotted as moisture content (dry basis) W vs. time θ, as shown in Fig. 15-33*a*. This curve represents the general case when a wet solid loses moisture first by evaporation from a saturated surface on the solid, followed in turn by a period of evaporation from a saturated surface of gradually decreasing area, and finally when the water evaporates in the interior of the solid.

Although Fig. 15-33*a* indicates that the drying rate is subject to variation with time or moisture content, this variation can be better illustrated by graphically or numerically differentiating the curve and plotting $dW/d\theta$

vs. W, as shown in Fig. 15-33*b*, or as $dW/d\theta$ vs. θ, as shown in Fig. 15-33*c*. These **rate curves** show that the drying process is not a smooth, continuous one in which a single mechanism controls throughout. Figure 15-33*c* has the advantage of showing how long each drying period lasts.

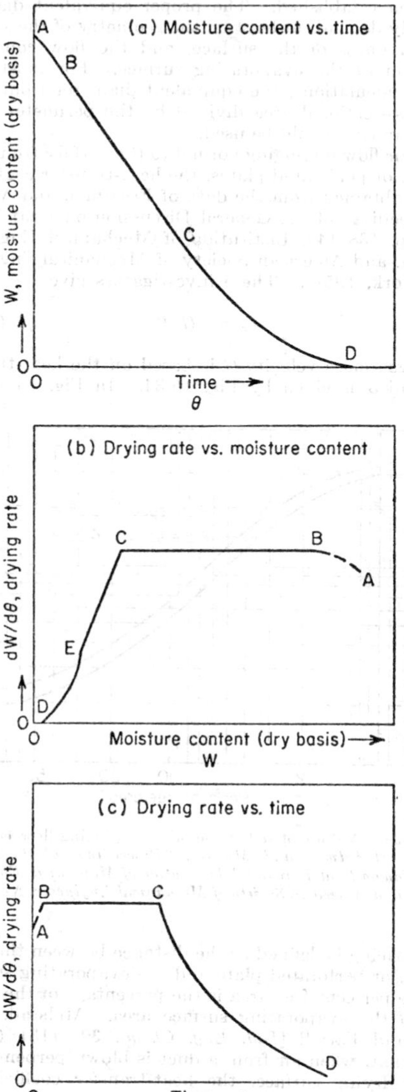

FIG. 15-33. The periods of drying.

Section BC on each curve represents the **constant-rate period.** In Fig. 15-33*a*, it is shown by a straight line of constant slope $dW/d\theta$, which becomes a horizontal line on the rate curves in Fig. 15-33*b* and *c*.

The curved portion CD of Fig. 15-33*a* is termed the **falling-rate period** and, as shown in Fig. 15-33*b* and *c*, is typified by a continuously changing rate throughout the remainder of the drying cycle. Point E (Fig. 15-33*b*) represents the point at which all the exposed surface becomes completely unsaturated and marks the start of that portion of the drying cycle during which the rate of internal moisture movement controls the drying rate. Point C, where the constant rate ends and the drying rate begins to fall, is termed the **critical moisture content.** The portion designated by AB represents a warming-up period, which may or may not be significant in the total process.

CONSTANT-RATE PERIOD

In the **constant-rate period,** drying proceeds by diffusion of vapor from the saturated surface of the material across a stagnant-air film into the environment. Moisture movement within the solid is rapid enough to maintain a saturated condition at the surface, and the rate of drying is controlled by the rate of heat transfer to the evaporating surface. The rate of mass transfer balances the rate of heat transfer, and the temperature of the saturated surface remains constant. The mechanism of moisture removal is equivalent to evaporation from a body of water* and is essentially independent of the nature of the solids.

Although temperature of the saturated surface remains constant, its level depends on the mode of heat transfer. If heat is transferred solely by **convection,** and in the absence of other heat effects, the surface temperature approaches the wet-bulb temperature. However, when heat is transferred by radiation, conduction, or a combination of these and convection, the temperature of the saturated surface is between the wet-bulb temperature and the boiling point of water. Under these conditions, the rate of heat transfer is increased and a higher drying rate results.

When heat is transferred to a wet solid by **conduction** through hot surfaces, and heat transfer by convection is negligible, the solids approach the boiling-point temperature rather than the wet-bulb temperature. In such cases, the drying rate will be appreciably higher than by convection drying with air at the same temperature as the heating surfaces. This method of heat transfer is utilized in indirect dryers (see Classification of Dryers, p. 15-45) in which the material is made to contact hot surfaces, frequently with vigorous agitation.

Radiation is also effective in increasing the constant rate by augmenting the convection heat transfer and raising the surface temperature above the wet-bulb temperature. In most drying operations, the effect of radiation is minor, although in some cases it is the primary mechanism, as in infrared drying.

When the heat for evaporation in the constant-rate period is supplied by a hot gas, a dynamic equilibrium is established between the rate of heat transfer to the material and the rate of vapor removal from the surface (see p. 15-2). This equilibrium between heat- and mass-transfer rates can be expressed as

$$\frac{dw}{d\theta} = \frac{h_t A\,\Delta t}{\lambda} = k_g A\,\Delta p \qquad (15\text{-}20)$$

where $dw/d\theta$ = drying rate, lb. water/hr.; h_t = total heat-transfer coefficient, B.t.u./(hr.)(sq. ft.)(°F.); A = area for heat transfer and evaporation, sq. ft.; λ = latent heat of evaporation at t_s', B.t.u./lb.; k_g = mass-transfer coefficient, lb./(hr.)(sq. ft.)(atm.); $\Delta t = t - t_s'$, where t = gas (dry-bulb) temperature, °F., and t_s' = temperature of surface of evaporation, °F.; $\Delta p = p_s - p$, where p_s = vapor pressure of water at surface temperature t_s', atm.; p = partial pressure of water vapor in the gas, atm.

When h_t is the coefficient of heat transfer by convec-

* The term water is used for convenience; the discussion applies equally well to other liquids.

tion only, then t_s' under equilibrium conditions is the wet-bulb temperature of the air, and p_s is the vapor pressure at this temperature. If heat is also supplied by radiation, then h_t is the sum $h_c + h_r$, where h_r is the radiation coefficient and h_c is the convection coefficient, and t_s' becomes higher than the wet-bulb temperature. A similar result, which is covered below, occurs when heat reaches the surface of evaporation by convection and conduction.

It is evident from Eq. (15-20) that the magnitude of the constant rate depends upon three factors: (1) the heat- or mass-transfer coefficient, (2) the area exposed to the drying medium, and (3) the difference in temperature or humidity between the gas stream and the wet surface of the solid. All these factors are the external variables, as noted above. The internal mechanism of liquid flow does not affect the constant rate.

Prediction of Heat- and Mass-transfer Coefficients

In convection phenomena, the heat-transfer coefficients depend on the geometry of the system, the gas velocity past the evaporating surface, and the physical properties of the drying gas. In estimating drying rates, the use of heat-transfer coefficients is preferred because they are usually more reliable than mass-transfer coefficients. In calculating mass-transfer coefficients from drying experiments, the partial pressure at the surface is usually inferred from the measured or calculated temperature of the evaporating surface. Small errors in temperature have negligible effect on the heat-transfer coefficient but introduce relatively large errors in the partial pressure and hence in the mass-transfer coefficient [for example, see Shepherd, Brewer, and Hadlock, *Ind. Eng. Chem.*, **30**, 388 (1938)].

For many cases in drying, the heat-transfer coefficient can be expressed as

$$h_c = \frac{\alpha G^n}{D_c^m} \tag{15-21}$$

where h_c = heat-transfer coefficient, B.t.u./(hr.)(sq. ft.)(°F.); G = mass velocity of drying gas, lb./(hr.)(sq. ft.); D_c = characteristic dimension of the system, ft.; α, n, and m are empirical constants. When radiation and conduction effects are negligible the constant rate of drying from a surface is thus given by the following heat-transfer expression derived from Eqs. (15-20) and (15-21):

$$\frac{dw}{d\theta} = \frac{\alpha G^n A}{\lambda D_c^m}(t - t_s') \tag{15-22}$$

When the liquid is water and the drying gas air, t_s' is the wet-bulb temperature.

In order to estimate drying rate from Eq. (15-22), values of the empirical constants are required for the particular geometry under consideration. For flow parallel to plane plates, exponent n has been reported to range from 0.35 to 0.8 [Chu, Lane, and Conklin, *Ind. Eng. Chem.*, **45**, 1586 (1953). Wenzel and White, *Ind. Eng. Chem.*, **43**, 1829 (1951). Chu *et al.*, *Ind. Eng. Chem.*, **51**, 275 (1958)]. The differences in exponent have been attributed to differences in flow pattern in the space above the evaporating surface. In the absence of applicable specific data, the heat-transfer coefficient for the parallel-flow case can be taken, for estimating purposes, as

$$h_c = \frac{0.01G^{0.8}}{D_c^{0.2}} \tag{15-23}$$

where the experimental data have been weighted in favor of an exponent of 0.8 in conformity with the usual Colburn j factor, and average values of the properties of air at 200°F. have been incorporated.

Experimental data for drying from flat surfaces have been correlated using the equivalent diameter of the flow channel or the length of the evaporating surface as the characteristic length dimension in the Reynolds number. However, the validity of one vs. the other has not been established. The proper equivalent diameter probably depends at least on the geometry of the system, the roughness of the surface, and the flow conditions upstream of the evaporating surface. For most tray-drying calculations, the equivalent diameter (four times the cross-sectional area divided by the perimeter of the flow channel) should be used.

For air flow impinging normal to the surface from slots, nozzles, or perforated plates, the heat-transfer coefficient can be obtained from the data of Friedman and Mueller ("Proceedings of the General Discussion on Heat Transfer," pp. 138–142, Institution of Mechanical Engineers, London, and American Society of Mechanical Engineers, New York, 1951). These investigators give

$$h_c = \alpha G^{0.78} \tag{15-24}$$

where gas mass velocity G is based on the heat-transfer area and α is given by Fig. 15-34. In Fig. 15-34, the

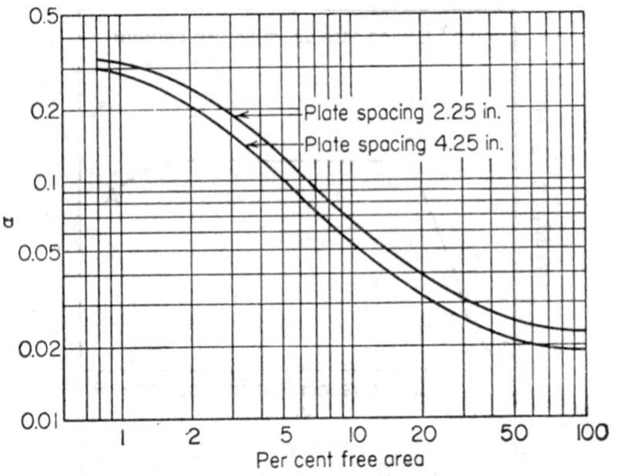

FIG. 15-34. Values of α for use with impinging-flow equation (15-24). *(Friedman and Mueller, "Proceedings of the General Discussion on Heat Transfer," Institution of Mechanical Engineers, London, and American Society of Mechanical Engineers, New York, 1951.)*

plate spacing is defined as the distance between the slots, nozzles, or perforated plate and the evaporating surface, and the per cent free area is the percentage of the air-jet area to the evaporating surface area. Molstad, Farevaag, and Farrell [*Ind. Eng. Chem.*, **30**, 1131 (1938)] found that, when air from a duct is blown perpendicular to the drying surface, the heat-transfer coefficient is given by

$$h_c = 0.37G^{0.37} \tag{15-25}$$

Equations (15-24) and (15-25) are strictly applicable only to the geometries studied, and care must be exercised if the geometry of interest differs greatly from those upon which the equations are based.

For through-circulation drying where the drying gases flow either upward or downward through a permeable bed of wet granular solids, the results obtained by Gamson, Thodos, and Hougen [*Trans. Am. Inst. Chem. Engrs.*, **39**, 1 (1943)] and Wilke and Hougen [*ibid.*, **41**, 441 (1945)] for the rates of adiabatic evaporation of water from packed beds of porous solids are applicable. These are

$$\frac{h_c}{c_pG}\left(\frac{c_p\mu}{k}\right)^{2/3} = 1.064\left(\frac{D_pG}{\mu}\right)^{-0.41} \quad \text{for } \frac{D_pG}{\mu} > 350 \tag{15-26}$$

$$\frac{h_c}{c_pG}\left(\frac{c_p\mu}{k}\right)^{2/3} = 1.95\left(\frac{D_pG}{\mu}\right)^{-0.51} \quad \text{for } \frac{D_pG}{\mu} < 350 \tag{15-27}$$

where c_p = heat capacity of air, B.t.u./(lb.)(°F.); μ = gas viscosity, lb./(ft.)(hr.); k = gas thermal conductivity, B.t.u./(hr.)(sq. ft.)(°F./ft.); D_p = diameter of sphere having the same surface area as particle, ft.; other symbols have the same meanings as in Eq. (15-21). Substituting average additive properties of the drying gas leads to

$$h_c = 0.11\frac{G^{0.59}}{D_p^{0.41}} \quad \text{for } \frac{D_pG}{\mu} > 350 \tag{15-26a}$$

and

$$h_c = 0.15\frac{G^{0.49}}{D_p^{0.51}} \quad \text{for } \frac{D_pG}{\mu} < 350 \tag{15-27a}$$

Determination of Temperature of Evaporating Surface

When radiation and conduction are negligible the temperature of the evaporating surface approaches the wet-bulb temperature and is readily obtained from the humidity and dry-bulb temperature. Frequently, however, radiation and conduction cause the temperature of the evaporating surface to exceed the wet-bulb temperature. When this occurs the true surface temperature must be estimated in order to estimate the constant drying rate.

Under steady-state conditions the temperature of the evaporating surface increases until the rate of sensible heat transfer to the surface equals the rate of heat removed by evaporation from the surface. To calculate this temperature, it is convenient to modify Eq. (15-20) in terms of humidity rather than partial-pressure difference, as follows:

$$k_g(p_s - p) = k'(H_s - H) \tag{15-28}$$

where k' = mass-transfer coefficient, lb./(hr.)(sq. ft.)(unit humidity difference), and $k' = Pk_g(M_a/M_w)$ is a suitable approximation at low humidities; k_g = mass-transfer coefficient, lb./(hr.)(sq. ft.)(atm.); M_a = molecular weight of air; M_w = molecular weight of the diffusing vapor; p_s = vapor pressure of the liquid at the temperature of the evaporating surface, atm.; p = partial pressure of vapor in air, atm.; H_s = saturation humidity of the air at the temperature of the drying surface, lb./lb. dry air; H = humidity of the drying air, lb./lb. dry air; P = total pressure, atm. For air-water mixtures k' is approximately $1.6k_g$ at atmospheric pressure.

A rate balance between evaporation and heat transfer when radiation occurs may be written as follows:

$$\lambda k'A(H_s - H) = h_cA(t - t_s') + h_r\epsilon A(t_r - t_s') \tag{15-29}$$

where λ = latent heat of evaporation, B.t.u./lb. at t_s'; A = area for both heat and mass transfer, sq. ft.; h_c = convection heat-transfer coefficient, B.t.u./(hr.)(sq. ft.)(°F.); h_r = radiation heat-transfer coefficient, B.t.u./(hr.)(sq. ft.)(°F.), as defined in Fig. 10-10; t = temperature of drying gases, °F.; t_s' = temperature of the wet surface, °F.; t_r = temperature of source radiating heat to the wet surface, °F.; ϵ = emissivity of surface receiving radiation.

Equation (15-29) may be modified by means of the psychrometric ratio for air–water vapor mixtures, $h_c/k' = c_s$, where c_s = heat capacity of humid air, B.t.u./(lb. dry air)(°F.), as defined on p. 15-2. Thus, Eq. (15-29) becomes

$$\frac{\lambda}{c_s}(H_s - H) = (t - t_s') + \frac{h_r\epsilon}{h_c}(t_r - t_s') \tag{15-29a}$$

Equation (15-29a) may be solved by trial and error or graphically as indicated in Example 23 to estimate the true values of H_s and t_s' and, hence, the actual drying rate. The values of λ and h_r depend on the value of t_s' but can generally be considered constant over the range of temperatures usually encountered in air drying.

Example 23. A wet material is drying in a tray, exposed to air at 300°F. and a humidity of 0.02 lb. water/lb. dry air. Air velocity is 450 ft./min., and the equivalent diameter of the flow channel is 1 ft. Determine the true surface temperature (1) when the effect of radiation is neglected and (2) when radiation is included.

Solution. If radiation is neglected, the wet-surface temperature is obtained from Fig. 15-4 as 114°F. with a corresponding value of H_s = 0.0673 lb. water/lb. air. If a metal tray directly above the wet material attains the air temperature of 300°F., t_s will be above 114°F. For this example, let ϵ = 0.9 and from Eq. (15-23) h_c = 3.3. From Fig. 10-10, h_r is estimated to be 1.5. The heat of vaporization λ will be about 1020 and c_s = 0.25. Substituting in Eq. (15-29a),

$$\frac{1020}{0.25}(H_s - 0.02) = \left[1 + \frac{(0.9)(1.5)}{3.3}\right](300 - t_s')$$

$$H_s - 0.02 = 0.000345(300 - t_s')$$

The values of t_s and H_s may be obtained by solving the above by trial and error to give H_s = 0.082 and t_s' = 120.4°F. Alternatively, they may be obtained by drawing a line on a humidity chart through the point H = 0.02, t = 300 with slope = 0.000345 and reading at the intersection with the saturated-humidity curve (*cf.* Fig. 15-35) the values H_s = 0.08 and t_s' = 120°F., which check the trial-and-error solution. The effect of radiation is to increase the driving force for mass transfer by (0.082 − 0.02)/(0.0673 − 0.02), or 1.31, an increase of 31 per cent.

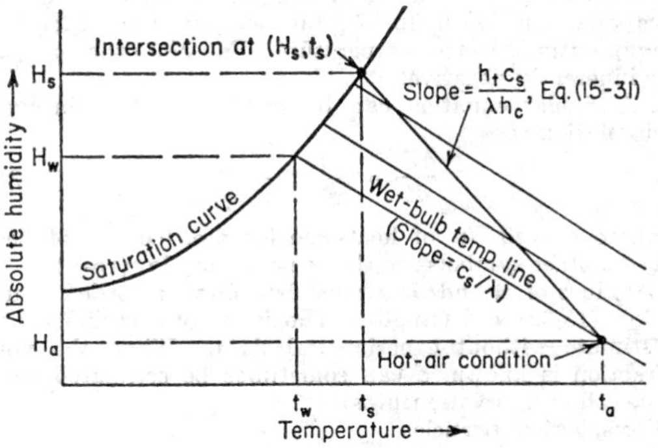

FIG. 15-35. Graphical estimation of surface temperature during constant-rate period.

Frequently, particularly in tray drying, heat arrives at the evaporating surface from the tray walls by conduction through the wet material. For this case where both radiation and conduction are significant, the total heat-transfer coefficient is given by Shepherd, Brewer, and Hadlock [*Ind. Eng. Chem.*, **30**, 388 (1938)] as

$$h_t = (h_c + h_r)\left[1 + \frac{A_u}{1 + d(h_c + h_r)/k}\right] \tag{15-30}$$

where h_t = total heat-transfer coefficient, B.t.u./(hr.)(sq. ft.)(°F.); A_u = ratio of outside unwetted surface to evaporating-surface area; d = depth of material in tray, ft.; k = thermal conductivity of the wet material,

B.t.u./(hr.)(sq. ft.)(°F./ft.). Note that h_r must be corrected for emissivity of the surface. For insulated trays, the arithmetic average of inside and outside unwetted area should be used.

Equation (15-30) assumes that all heat sources are at the same temperature and the convection coefficients to the evaporating surface and to the unwetted portions of the tray are equal. When radiation occurs from a source at a different temperature, the radiation coefficient can be corrected to the same basis by multiplying by the ratio $(t - t_s')/(t_r - t_s')$, where t, t_s', t_r are the drying gas, evaporating surface, and radiator temperatures, respectively.

A relationship for estimating the surface temperature t_s', based on the use of Eq. (15-30) to determine h_t, is as follows:

$$(H_s - H) = \frac{h_t c_s}{\lambda h_c}(t - t_s') \qquad (15\text{-}31)$$

Equation (15-31) can be solved numerically or graphically. Figure 15-35 indicates how H_s and t_s' may be determined graphically on a humidity chart by the point of intersection on the saturation-humidity curve of a straight line of slope $h_t c_s/\lambda h_c$ passing through point (H, t).

Estimation of Constant Rate

For drying calculations it is convenient to express Eq. (15-20) in terms of the decrease in moisture content rather than quantity of water evaporated. For evaporation from a tray of wet material, assuming no change in volume during drying, Eq. (15-20) becomes

$$\frac{dW}{d\theta} = \frac{h_t}{\rho_s d\lambda}(t - t_s') \qquad (15\text{-}32)$$

where $dW/d\theta$ = drying rate, lb. water/(hr.)(lb. dry solids); h_t = total heat-transfer coefficient, B.t.u./(hr.)(sq. ft.)(°F.); ρ_s = bulk density dry material, lb./cu. ft.; d = thickness of bed, ft.; λ = latent heat of vaporization, B.t.u./lb.; t = air temperature, °F.; t_s' = evaporating-surface temperature, °F. Note that $dW/d\theta$ is inherently negative.

A similar equation can be written for the through-circulation case:

$$\frac{dW}{d\theta} = \frac{h_t a}{\rho_s \lambda}(t - t_s') \qquad (15\text{-}33)$$

where a = sq. ft. of heat-transfer area/cu. ft. of bed, 1/ft.; other symbols are the same as for Eq. (15-32).

Values of ρ_s and/or a must be known in order to use Eqs. (15-32) and (15-33). The value of a is difficult to estimate without experimental data. When the void fraction is known, a can sometimes be estimated from the following relationships:

For spherical particles,

$$a = \frac{6(1 - F)}{(D_p)_m} \qquad (15\text{-}34)$$

For uniform cylindrical particles,

$$a = \frac{4(0.5D_o + Z)(1 - F)}{D_o Z} \qquad (15\text{-}35)$$

where F = void fraction; $(D_p)_m$ = harmonic mean diameter of spherical particles, ft.; D_o = diameter of cylinder, ft.; z = height of cylinder, ft. For cylindrical particles that are long relative to their diameter the term $0.5D_o$ in Eq. (15-35) can be neglected.

Application of the previous equations is illustrated below.

Example 24. An inorganic pigment having a bulk density of 40 lb./cu. ft. is being dried in a tray dryer which consists of two tiers of 44 stainless-steel trays, 1.25 in. deep and spaced 1.5 in. apart. The trays are 26 in. square and the equivalent diameter of the flow channel is 0.237 ft. Inlet air velocity is 300 ft./min. corresponding to a mass velocity of 1000 lb./(hr.)(sq. ft.). Inlet air temperature is 250°F. and its humidity is 0.072 lb./lb. corresponding to a wet-bulb temperature of 128°F. Calculate the initial and average drying rates in the constant-rate period.

Solution. The convection coefficient is calculated from Eq. (15-23) as

$$h_c = \frac{(0.01)(1000)^{0.8}}{(0.237)^{0.2}} = 3.3$$

This value must be corrected for radiation and conduction according to Eq. (15-30). For the trays of the dimensions specified, A_u = 1.2 and d = 0.104 ft.; h_r will be taken as 1.5 (once t_s' is calculated this value can be checked and the calculation repreated if necessary). The value of k is usually difficult to determine. For this example, let k = 0.8. Then

$$h_t = (3.3 + 1.5)\left[1 + \frac{1.2}{1 + (0.104)(3.3 + 1.5)/0.8}\right] = 8.4$$

Temperature of the evaporating surface is now calculated from Eq. (15-31):

$$(H_s - 0.072) = \frac{(8.4)(0.27)}{(1015)(3.3)}(250 - t_s')$$

By trial and error t_s' = 138°F. and H_s = 0.147 lb./lb. The initial drying rate is obtained from Eq. (15-32) as

$$\frac{dW}{d\theta} = \frac{8.4(250 - 138)}{(40)(0.104)(1015)} = 0.223 \frac{\text{lb.}}{\text{(hr.)(lb. dry solids)}}$$

In flowing across the trays the air temperature drops. If heat losses are negligible the air temperature leaving the tray is obtained by integrating the differential heat balance over the tray length to give

$$t_2 = t_s' + (t_1 - t_s')\exp.\frac{-h_t L_t}{Gbc_s} \qquad (15\text{-}36)$$

where t_1, t_2, t_s' are inlet air, leaving air, and evaporating-surface temperatures, respectively, °F.; L_t = length of tray, ft.; b = tray spacing, ft. Then

$$t_2 = 138 + (250 - 138)\exp.\frac{-(8.4)(2.17)}{(1000)(0.125)(0.27)} = 203°\text{F.}$$

The logarithmic mean temperature difference is 86.8°F. and the average drying rate as calculated from Eq. (15-32) is 0.173 lb. water/(hr.)(lb. dry solids).

FALLING-RATE PERIOD

The drying process consists of a period in which the rate of evaporation is constant and one or more periods during which the rate is continuously decreasing (see p. 15-34). The latter periods are designated the **falling-rate periods** and begin when the constant-rate period ends, at the critical moisture content. If the final moisture content is above the critical moisture content (for the specified drying conditions), the whole drying process will occur under constant-rate conditions. If, on the other hand, the initial moisture content is below the critical moisture content, the entire drying process will occur in the falling-rate period. This period is usually divided into two zones: (1) the zone of **unsaturated surface drying** and (2) the zone where **internal moisture movement controls.**

In the first zone, the entire evaporating surface can no longer be maintained saturated by moisture movement within the solid. The drying rate decreases for the unsaturated portion, and hence the rate for the total surface decreases. In some cases the drying rate is a linear function of the water content of the solid as shown by line *CE* in Fig. 15-33*b*. Generally, however, the drying rate depends on factors affecting the diffusion of moisture away from the evaporating surface and those affecting the rate of internal moisture movement.

As drying proceeds, the point is reached where the evaporating surface is unsaturated. The plane of evaporation moves into the solid, and the drying process enters the second falling-rate period. The drying rate is now governed by the rate of internal moisture movement; the influence of external variables diminishes. In drying to low moisture contents, this period usually predominates in determining the over-all drying time.

Studies of internal moisture movement indicate the possibility of several controlling mechanisms, the more significant ones being postulated as diffusion, capillarity, and pressure gradients caused by shrinkage. Internal moisture movement by diffusion has been studied extensively; capillary flow and flow caused by shrinkage and pressure gradients have received preliminary consideration.

Liquid Diffusion

When liquid diffusion controls in the falling-rate period the Fourier heat-conduction equation may be used to describe the rate of moisture movement. Sherwood [*Ind. Eng. Chem.*, **21**, 12 (1929)] solved the diffusion equation for the falling-rate period in a slab assuming that the surface is dry or at its equilibrium moisture content and that the initial moisture distribution is uniform. For these conditions the following equation is obtained:

$$\frac{W - W_e}{W_c - W_e} = \frac{8}{\pi^2}\left[e^{-D_l\theta(\pi/2d)^2} + \frac{1}{9}e^{-9D_l\theta(\pi/2d)^2} + \frac{1}{25}e^{-25D_l\theta(\pi/2d)^2} + \cdots\right] \quad (15\text{-}37)$$

where W, W_c, W_e = average moisture content (dry basis) at any time θ, at the start of the falling-rate period, and in equilibrium with the environment, respectively, lb./lb.; D_l = liquid diffusivity, sq. ft./hr.; θ = time from start of falling-rate period, hr.; d = one-half the thickness of the solid layer through which diffusion occurs, ft. Equation (15-37) was derived for evaporation from both faces of the slab. When evaporation occurs from only one face, d = total thickness, ft.

Equation (15-37) assumes D_l constant. As noted earlier, D_l is rarely constant but varies with moisture content, temperature, and humidity [Hougen, McCauley, and Marshall, *Trans. Am. Inst. Chem. Engrs.*, **36**, 183 (1950). Bateman, Hohf, and Stamm, *Ind. Eng. Chem.*, **31**, 1150 (1939)]. A graphical method for taking into account the variation of D_l with moisture content in drying hydrophilic solids to low final moistures has been developed by Van Arsdel [*Trans. Am. Inst. Chem. Engrs.*, **43**, 13 (1947)].

For long drying times, Eq. (15-37) simplifies to a limiting form of the diffusion equation as follows:

$$\frac{W - W_e}{W_c - W_e} = \frac{8}{\pi^2}e^{-D_l\theta(\pi/2d)^2} \quad (15\text{-}38)$$

Equation (15-38) may be differentiated to give the drying rate as

$$\frac{dW}{d\theta} = \frac{-\pi^2 D_l}{4d^2}(W - W_e) \quad (15\text{-}39)$$

where $dW/d\theta$ = drying rate, lb./(hr.)(lb. dry solid). Equation (15-39) states that, when internal diffusion controls for long times, the rate of drying is directly proportional to the free-water content ($W - W_e$) and the liquid diffusivity D_l, and that drying time varies as the square of the material thickness. When Eq. (15-37) is plotted on semilogarithmic graph paper, a straight line is obtained for values of $(W - W_e)/(W_c - W_e) < 0.6$. It is in the straight-line portion that the approximate form [Eq. (15-39)] applies.

Equations (15-37), (15-38), and (15-39) hold only for a slab-shaped solid whose thickness is small relative to the other two dimensions. For other shapes, reference should be made to Newman [*Trans. Am. Inst. Chem. Engrs.*, **27**, 310 (1931)] or to Crank ("The Mathematics of Diffusion," Oxford, London, 1956).

Capillary Theory

The above discussion assumed that moisture movement was the result of a concentration gradient and that capillary and gravitational forces were negligible. If the pore size of a granular material is suitable, moisture may move from a region of high to one of low concentration as the result of capillary action rather than by diffusion. Ceaglske and Hougen [*Trans. Am. Inst. Chem. Engrs.*, **33**, 283 (1937)] suggested the capillary theory to explain this method of moisture movement in a bed of granular particles during surface drying. This theory has been extended by Newitt *et al.* [*Trans. Inst. Chem. Engrs.*, **27**, 1 (1949); *ibid.*, **33**, 52 (1955)] and that analysis is outlined briefly.

The capillary theory assumes that a bed of non-porous spheres is composed of particles surrounding a space called a pore. These pores are connected by passages of various sizes, the smallest portions of which are called waists. As water is progressively removed from the bed, the curvature of the water surface in the interstices of the top layer of spheres increases and a suction pressure, resulting from curvature, is set up. As the removal of water continues, the suction pressure attains a value at which air is drawn into the pore spaces between successive layers of spheres.

This entry suction or **suction potential** is a measure of the resultant forces tending to draw water from the interior of the bed to the surface. For a pore formed by regularly packed non-porous spheres, the suction potential is given by

$$P_s = \frac{X\sigma}{r\rho g} \quad (15\text{-}40)$$

where P_s = suction potential, cm. of water; σ = surface tension, dynes/cm.; ρ = density of water, g./cu. cm.; g = 980 cm./sec.^{2}; r = sphere radius, cm.; X is a packing factor equal to 12.9 for rhombohedral and 4.8 for cubical packing. As drying proceeds, the surface moisture evaporates, causing retreat of the surface menisci until the suction potential reaches a value given by Eq. (15-40). At this point, the pores at the surface will open, air will enter, and the moisture will redistribute itself with a slight lowering of the suction potential. As evaporation proceeds, the suction potential again increases until a slightly higher entry value is reached when a further redistribution occurs.

The drying-rate curve (Fig. 15-33*b*) can be analyzed in terms of capillary theory. In region BC, there is a loss in moisture with a gradual increase in the suction and emptying of the bulk of the larger pores in the solid. In region CE, there is an increase in suction as the moisture content decreases and finer pores are opened. Section ED represents a condition in which moisture is being removed by vapor diffusion from the interior of the body, although there is still sufficient water in the bed to give rise to capillary forces.

If it is assumed that all the liquid movement occurs in the fine pores of the bed and the bed consists of uniform, spherical, non-porous particles, a modified form of the Poiseuille equation for laminar flow can be used to determine the head of fluid required to overcome friction. This equation takes the form

$$H_p = \frac{K_2 \mu V_f \rho_t^2 S^2 (1 - F)^2 d}{g\rho F^3} \quad (15\text{-}41)$$

where H_p = pressure head, cm.; K_2 = Kozeny constant (5 for spherical particles); ρ = density of water, g./cu. cm.; V_f = flow velocity, cm./sec.; μ = viscosity of water, poise; S = specific surface of particles, sq. cm.; ρ_t = density of particles, g./cu. cm.; F = porosity of bed, dimensionless; d = depth of bed, cm.; g = 980 cm./sec.^{2}. If flow to the surface of a drying solid is to be maintained,

$P_1 = P_2 + d_2 + H_p$, where P_1 and P_2 are the suction potentials at the surface and at a depth d_2 cm., respectively, and H_p is a measure of the frictional resistance of the bed over distance d.

Substituting in Eq. (15-41) for rhombohedral packing of spheres the values $(1 - F)^2/F^3 = 3.15$ and $\rho_t^2 S^2 = 9/r^2$ where r = radius of spheres, cm., we obtain

$$\frac{P_1 - P_2 - d}{d} = 141.7 \frac{\mu V_f}{g\rho r^2} \qquad (15\text{-}42)$$

For other packings and particle shapes, appropriate values of the above constants should be used. Drying rate $dw/d\theta$ and liquid velocity are related by

$$V_f = \frac{1}{y}\frac{dw}{d\theta}$$

where $dw/d\theta$ = drying rate, g./(sq. cm.)(sec.), and y = fraction of fine pores at the surface. Finally, we obtain

$$\frac{dw}{d\theta} = \frac{yr^2}{3.25 \times 10^{-5}\, d}(P_1 - P_2 - d) \qquad (15\text{-}43)$$

Thus, if P_1, P_2, and y are known the drying rate may be calculated. For beds of silica flour and glass spheres, Newitt has found good agreement between drying rates calculated from suction-potential measurements and measured values. Subsequently, Newitt has interpreted the drying-rate curves for porous granules in terms of the capillary theory.

Approximate Equations for Falling-rate Period

The falling rate frequently can be expressed with fair accuracy over the required range of moisture contents by an equation similar to Eq. (15-39); thus

$$\left(\frac{dW}{d\theta}\right)_f = -K_1(W - W_e) \qquad (15\text{-}44)$$

K_1 is a function of the constant rate as follows:

$$K_1 = -\frac{(dW/d\theta)_c}{(W_c - W_e)} \qquad (15\text{-}45)$$

where $(dW/d\theta)_c$ = constant drying rate, lb./(hr.)(lb. dry solid); W_c = critical moisture content, lb./lb. dry solid. Substituting the expression for $(dW/d\theta)_c$ as given by Eq. (15-32) the value of K_1 becomes

$$K_1 = \frac{-h_t(t - t_s')}{\rho_s \lambda d(W_c - W_e)} \qquad (15\text{-}46)$$

Hence the falling rate for this case is given by

$$\left(\frac{dW}{d\theta}\right)_f = -\frac{h_t(t - t_s')(W - W_e)}{\rho_s \lambda d(W_c - W_e)} \qquad (15\text{-}47)$$

For materials obeying Eq. (15-47), drying time varies inversely as the thickness. When the surface temperature in the constant-rate period is at the wet-bulb temperature, t_w can be substituted for t_s' and the value of h_t can be obtained from the appropriate form of Eq. (15-21). For the through-circulation case, identical equations obtain with the term $1/d$ replaced by the quantity a in Eq. (15-47).

Drying time for each case of the falling-rate period may be obtained by integration of Eqs. (15-39) and (15-47), to give

1. For materials in which moisture movement is controlled by diffusion,

$$\theta_f = \frac{4d^2}{D_l \pi^2} \ln \frac{W_c - W_e}{W - W_e} \qquad (15\text{-}48)$$

2. For materials in which moisture movement is controlled by capillary flow,

$$\theta_f = \frac{\rho_s\, d\lambda(W_c - W_e)}{h_t(t - t_s')} \ln \frac{W_c - W_e}{W - W_e} \qquad (15\text{-}49)$$

Table 15-14 gives an approximate classification of materials that obey Eqs. (15-48) and (15-49).

Table 15-14. Materials Obeying Eqs. (15-48) and (15-49)

Materials Obeying Eq. (15-48)	Materials Obeying Eq. (15-49)
1. Single-phase solid systems, such as soap, gelatin, glue	1. Coarse granular solids, such as sand, paint pigments, minerals
2. Wood and similar solids below the fiber-saturation point	2. Materials in which moisture flow occurs at concentrations above the equilibrium moisture content at atmospheric saturation, or above the fiber-saturation point
3. Last stages of drying starches, textiles, paper, clay, hydrophilic solids, and other materials when bound water is being removed	

Critical Moisture Content

To use the above equations for estimating drying times in the falling-rate period, it is necessary to know values of critical moisture content W_c. Such values are difficult to obtain without making actual drying tests, which in themselves would give the required drying time and thereby obviate the necessity of solving the equations. However, in those cases where drying tests are not feasible, some estimate of critical moisture content must be made. Broughton [*Ind. Eng. Chem.*, **37**, 1184 (1945)] correlated critical moisture contents for the drying of kaolin and china clay by cross circulation. His correlation, however, applies only to those solids in which liquid diffusion is the internal mechanism of moisture flow.

Values of critical moisture contents for some representative materials are given in Table 15-15 for drying by cross circulation and in Table 20-5 for drying by through

Table 15-15. Approximate Critical Moisture Contents Obtained on the Air Drying of Various Materials, Expressed as Percentage Water on the Dry Basis

Material	Thickness, in.	Critical moisture, % water, dry basis
Barium nitrate crystals, on trays	1.0	7
Beaverboard	0.17	Above 120
Brick clay	.62	14
Carbon pigment	1	40
Celotex	0.44	160
Chrome leather	.04	125
Copper carbonate (on trays)	1–1.5	60
English china clay	1	16
Flint clay refractory brick mix	2.0	13
Gelatin, initially 400% water	0.1–0.2 (wet)	300
Iron blue pigment (on trays)	0.25–0.75	110
Kaolin	....	14
Lithol red	1	50
Lithopone press cake (in trays)	0.25	6.4
	.50	8.0
	.75	12.0
	1.0	16.0
Niter cake fines, on trays	....	Above 16
Paper, white eggshell	0.0075	41
Fine book	.005	33
Coated	.004	34
Newsprint	....	60–70
Plastic clay brick mix	2.0	19
Poplar wood	0.165	120
Prussian blue	....	40
Pulp lead, initially 140% water	....	Below 15
Rock salt (in trays)	1.0	7
Sand, 50–150 mesh	2.0	5
Sand, 200–325 mesh	2.0	10
Sand, through 325 mesh	2.0	21
Sea sand (on trays)	0.25	3
	.5	4.7
	.75	5.5
	1.0	5.9
	2.0	6.0
Silica brick mix	2.0	8
Sole leather	0.25	Above 90
Stannic tetrachloride sludge	1	180
Subsoil, clay fraction 55.4%	....	21
Subsoil, much higher clay content	....	35
Sulfite pulp	0.25–0.75	60–80
Sulfite pulp (pulp lap)	0.039	110
White lead	....	11
Whiting	0.25–1.5	6.9
Wool fabric, worsted	....	31
Wool, undyed serge	....	8

circulation. The tabulated values are only approximate, since critical moisture content is dependent on the drying history. It appears that the constant-rate period ends when the moisture content at the surface reaches a specific value. Since the critical moisture content is the average moisture through the material, its value depends on the rate of drying, the thickness of the material, and the factors influencing moisture movement and resulting gradients within the solid. As a result the critical moisture content increases with increased drying rate and with increased thickness of the mass of material being dried.

Equilibrium Moisture Content

In drying of solids it is important to distinguish between hygroscopic and non-hygroscopic materials. If a hygroscopic material is maintained in contact with air at constant temperature and humidity until equilibrium is reached, the material will attain a definite moisture content. This moisture is termed the equilibrium moisture content for the specified conditions. Equilibrium moisture may be adsorbed as a surface film or condensed in the fine capillaries of the solid at reduced pressure, and its concentration will vary with the temperature and humidity of the surrounding air. However, at low temperatures, *e.g.*, 60° to 120°F., a plot of equilibrium moisture content vs. humidity is essentially independent of temperature. Typical data for a number of common materials are shown in Table 15-9 and Fig. 15-29.

Equilibrium moisture content at a given humidity is not strictly independent of temperature, however. As temperature increases for a given relative humidity, equilibrium moisture content decreases. At zero humidity the equilibrium moisture content of all materials is zero.

Equilibrium moisture content depends greatly on the nature of the solid. For non-porous, *i.e.*, non-hygroscopic, materials, the equilibrium moisture content is essentially zero at all temperatures and humidities. For organic materials such as wood, paper and soap, equilibrium moisture contents vary regularly over wide ranges as temperature and humidity change. In the special case of the dehydration of hydrated inorganic salts, such as copper sulfate, sodium sulfate, or barium chloride, temperature and humidity control is very important in obtaining the desired degree of moisture removal, and the proper conditions must be determined from data on the water of hydration or crystallization as a function of air temperature and humidity.

Equilibrium moisture content of a solid is particularly important in drying because it represents the limiting moisture content for given conditions of humidity and temperature. If the material is dried to a moisture content less than it normally possesses in equilibrium with atmospheric air, it will return to its equilibrium value on storage unless special precautions are taken. Thus, a portion of the drying operation may be wasted.

Determination of Equilibrium Moisture

Equilibrium moisture content of a hygroscopic material may be determined in a number of ways, the only requirement being a source of constant-temperature and constant-humidity air. Determination may be made under static or dynamic conditions, although the latter case is preferred if the data are to be used for drying calculations. A simple static procedure is to place a number of samples in ordinary laboratory desiccators containing sulfuric acid solutions of known concentrations which produce atmospheres of known relative humidity. The sample in each desiccator is weighed periodically until a constant weight is obtained. Moisture content at this final weight represents the equilibrium moisture content for the particular conditions.

The value of equilibrium moisture content, for many materials, depends on the direction in which equilibrium is approached. A different value is reached when a wet material loses moisture by desorption, as in drying, from that obtained when a dry material gains it by adsorption. For drying calculations the desorption values are preferred. In the general case, the equilibrium moisture content reached by losing moisture is higher than that reached by adsorbing it.

Table 15-16. Maintenance of Constant Humidity

The following systems, rearranged in the order of increasing humidities, are taken from "International Critical Tables," vol. 1, pp. 67–68. A saturated aqueous solution of a salt in contact with an excess of a definite solid phase and at a definite temperature will maintain a constant humidity within an enclosed space.

Solid phase	Max. temp., °C.	% humidity
$H_3PO_4.\frac{1}{2}H_2O$	24.5	9
$ZnCl_2.\frac{1}{2}H_2O$	20	10
$KC_2H_3O_2$	168	13
$LiCl.H_2O$	20	15
$KC_2H_3O_2$	20	20
KF	100	22.9
NaBr	100	22.9
$CaCl_2.6H_2O$	24.5	31
$CaCl_2.6H_2O$	20	32.3
$CaCl_2.6H_2O$	18.5	35
CrO_3	20	35
$CaCl_2.6H_2O$	10	38
$CaCl_2.6H_2O$	5	39.8
$K_2CO_3.2H_2O$	24.5	43
$K_2CO_3.2H_2O$	18.5	44
$Ca(NO_3)_2.4H_2O$	24.5	51
$NaHSO_4.H_2O$	20	52
$Mg(NO_3)_2.6H_2O$	24.5	52
$NaClO_3$	100	54
$Ca(NO_3)_2.4H_2O$	18.5	56
$Mg(NO_3)_2.6H_2O$	18.5	56
$NaBr.2H_2O$	20	58
$Mg(C_2H_3O_2).4H_2O$	20	65
$NaNO_2$	20	66
$(NH_4)_2SO_4$	108.2	75
$(NH_4)_2SO_4$	20	81
$NaC_2H_3O_2.3H_2O$	20	76
$Na_2S_2O_3.5H_2O$	20	78
NH_4Cl	20	79.2
NH_4Cl	25	79.3
NH_4Cl	30	79.5
KBr	20	84
Tl_2SO_4	104.7	84.8
$KHSO_4$	20	86
$Na_2CO_3.10H_2O$	24.5	87
K_2CrO_4	20	88
$NaBrO_3$	20	92
$Na_2CO_3.10H_2O$	18.5	92
$Na_2SO_4.10H_2O$	20	93
$Na_2HPO_4.12H_2O$	20	95
NaF	100	96.6
$Pb(NO_3)_2$	20	98
$TlNO_3$	100.3	98.7
TlCl	100.1	99.7

For a more complete list of salts, and for references to the literature see "International Critical Tables," vol. 1, p. 68.

Equilibrium moisture content can be measured dynamically by placing the sample in a U-tube through which is drawn a continuous flow of controlled-humidity air. Again the sample is weighed periodically until a constant weight is reached. Properly humidified air for such a procedure can be obtained by bubbling dry air through a large volume of a saturated salt solution which produces a definite degree of saturation of the air. Care must be taken to ensure that the air and salt solution reach equilibrium. Values of the humidity over various salt solutions may be found in Table 15-16.

APPROXIMATE EQUATIONS FOR TOTAL DRYING TIME

In order to estimate total drying time for a given drying operation, estimates of both the falling-rate and constant-rate drying times are required. An approximate equation for over-all drying time can be obtained for materials in which moisture movement is controlled by capillary flow:

$$\theta_t = \theta_c + \theta_f = \frac{(W_o - W_c)\rho_s\lambda d}{h_t(t - t_s')_m} + \frac{(W_c - W_e)\rho_s\lambda d}{h_t(t - t_s')_m} \ln \frac{W_c - W_e}{W_t - W_e} \qquad (15\text{-}50)$$

$$\theta_t = B\left(\frac{W_o - W_c}{W_c - W_e} + \ln \frac{W_c - W_e}{W_t - W_e}\right) \qquad (15\text{-}51)$$

where $$B = \frac{(W_c - W_e)\rho_s\lambda d}{h_t(t - t_s')_m} = \frac{1}{K_1}$$

and θ_t = total drying time, hr.; θ_c = drying time for constant-rate period, hr.; θ_f = drying time for falling-rate period, hr.; W_o = initial moisture content, lb. water/lb. dry solid; W_c = average critical moisture content, lb. water/lb. dry solid; W_e = average equilibrium moisture content, lb. water/lb. dry solid; W_t = average moisture content at time θ_t, lb. water/lb. dry solid; h_t = total heat-transfer coefficient given by Eq. (15-30), B.t.u./(hr.)(sq. ft.)(°F.); $(t - t_s')_m$ = logarithmic mean temperature difference, $[(t_1 - t_s') - (t_2 - t_s')]/\ln[(t_1 - t_s')/(t_2 - t_s')]$; t_1, t_2, and t_s' are inlet-air, exit-air, and solids temperature, respectively, °F.; d = depth of material on tray, ft.; λ = latent heat of vaporization at t_s', B.t.u./lb.; ρ_s = bulk density of dry solid, lb./cu. ft.

For an adiabatic system, the temperature of the leaving gas, obtained by integrating the differential heat balance over the tray length, is given by $t_2 - t_s' + (t_1 - t_s')\,[\exp.\,(-h_tL_t/Gbc_s)]$ where L_t = length of tray, ft.; G = air-mass velocity, lb./(hr.)(sq.ft.); b = tray spacing, ft.; c_s = humid heat, B.t.u./(lb.)(°F.). Under these conditions, the mean temperature driving force can be expressed in terms of the initial temperature difference and quantity B in Eq. (15-51) becomes

$$B = \frac{(W_c - W_e)\rho_s\lambda dL_t}{Gc_sb(t_1 - t_s')[1 - \exp.\,(-h_tL_t/Gbc_s)]} \qquad (15\text{-}51a)$$

Equation (15-51) applies to cross-circulation drying. It applies also for through-circulation drying, except that B is

$$B = \frac{(W_c - W_e)\rho_s\lambda}{h_ta(t - t_s')_m} \qquad (15\text{-}51b)$$

where h_t is obtained from Eqs. (15-26a), (15-27a), and (15-30) and a = sq. ft. of heat-transfer area per cu. ft. of bed volume. In terms of the initial temperature difference for an adiabatic system,

$$B = \frac{(W_c - W_e)\rho_s\lambda d}{Gc_s(t_1 - t_s')[1 - \exp.\,(-h_tad/Gc_s)]} \qquad (15\text{-}51c)$$

where d = depth of bed, ft.

Equation (15-51) applies to those materials satisfying the proportional-to-thickness law when they are not dried to very low moisture contents. As noted previously, estimates of the critical moisture content are not readily made. This inability detracts from the usefulness of Eq. (15-51).

Example 25. An extruded paste is to be dried in a conveying-screen dryer from a moisture content of 1 lb. water/lb. dry solid to a moisture of 0.1 lb./lb. The extrusions are cylinders 0.25 in. diameter by 4 in. long and the screens will be loaded to a depth of 2 in. Bulk density of the dry solid is 40 lb./cu. ft. and its true density is 100 lb./cu. ft. Inlet-air temperature is 250°F. and its moisture is 0.04 lb. water/lb. dry air. A superficial gas velocity of 150 ft./min. will be used. Assuming that Eq. (15-51) applies, that the critical moisture content is 0.5 lb. water/lb. dry solid, and that the equilibrium moisture is 0.01 lb./lb., estimate the total drying time required.

Solution. Heat-transfer area is estimated from Eq. (15-35) as

$$a = 4\,\frac{[(0.5)(0.25)/12 + 4/12][1 - (100 - 40)/100]}{(0.25/12)(4/12)} = 79.4 \text{ sq. ft./cu. ft.}$$

For the conditions specified, the Reynolds number exceeds 350 and the heat-transfer coefficient is obtained from Eq. (15-26a) as

$$h_c = \frac{0.11[150(60)/19]^{0.59}}{(0.0839)^{0.41}} = 11.6$$

where 0.0839 is the diameter in feet of a sphere having the same surface area as the extrusion. If radiation and conduction heat transfer are neglected, the solids temperature will be at the wet-bulb temperature. From Fig. 15-4, this is found to be 117°F. The value B is calculated from Eq. (15-51c) as

$$B = \frac{(0.5 - 0.01)(40)(1027)(2/12)}{(473)(0.26)(250 - 117)\left[1 - \exp.\,\frac{-(11.6)(79.4)(2)}{(473)(0.26)(12)}\right]} = 0.288$$

The total drying time is

$$0.288\left(\frac{1.0 - 0.5}{0.5 - 0.01} + \ln \frac{0.5 - 0.01}{0.1 - 0.01}\right) = 0.78 \text{ hr.}$$

ANALYSIS OF DRYING DATA

Drying experiments may be carried out for one or more of the following reasons: (1) to select a suitable dryer, (2) to obtain design data, (3) to study the efficiency or capacity potential of existing dryers, (4) to study the effect of operating variables on product form and quality, or (5) to study the mechanism of drying.

When experiments are carried out to select a suitable dryer design and to obtain design data, the effect of

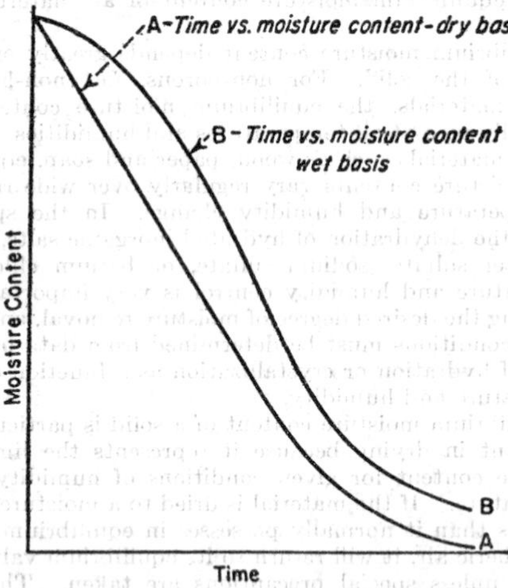

FIG. 15-36. Drying-time curves.

changes in various external variables is studied. These experiments should be conducted in an experimental unit that simulates the large-scale dryer from both the thermal and material-handling aspects, and only material which is truly representative of the final production should be used.

Data expressing moisture content in terms of elapsed time should be obtained and the results plotted as shown in Fig. 15-36. Curve A is typical of the case where moisture content is on a dry basis, while curve B shows similar data when moisture content is on a wet basis. As discussed previously, the former method of expression is preferred; subsequent discussion will employ the dry basis. For purposes of analysis, the moisture-time curve must be differentiated graphically or numerically and the drying rates so obtained plotted to determine the nature and extent of the drying periods in the cycle. It is customary to plot drying rate vs. moisture content as in Fig. 15-33*b*. Although instructive, this type of plot gives no information on duration of the drying periods. These are better shown by plots similar to Fig. 15-33*c*, where drying rate is plotted as a function of time on either arithmetic or logarithmic coordinates. Logarithmic plots permit easy reading at low moisture contents or long times.

In order to determine whether a simple relationship exists in the falling-rate period, the unaccomplished moisture change, defined as ratio of free moisture in the

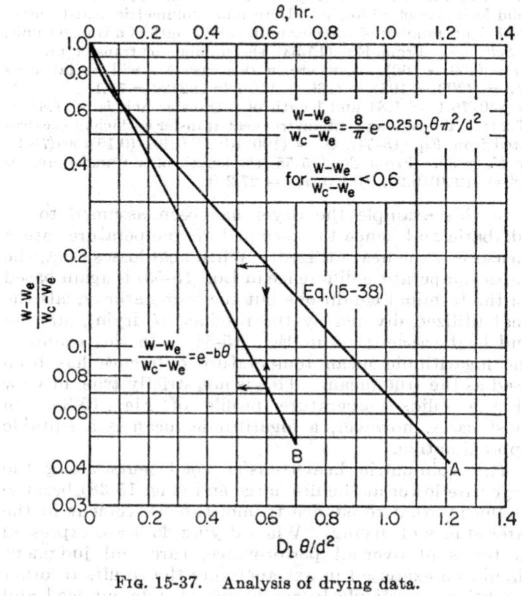

FIG. 15-37. Analysis of drying data.

solid at time θ to total free moisture present at start of the falling-rate period $(W - W_e)/(W_c - W_e)$, is plotted as a function of time on semilogarithmic paper. If a straight line is obtained such as curve *B* of Fig. 15-37 using the upper scale of abscissa, either Eq. (15-48), for materials in which the moisture moves by diffusion, or Eq. (15-44), for materials in which the moisture movement is by capillary flow, may be applicable. If Eq. (15-44) applies, K_1, the slope of the falling-rate drying curve, is related to the constant drying rate. The latter is calculated from Eq. (15-45) and can be compared with the measured value. If the slopes agree, the moisture movement is by capillary flow. If the slopes do not agree, the moisture movement is by diffusion and the slope of the line should equal $\pi^2 D_l/4d^2$.

The dependency of drying rate on material thickness must be established experimentally. With the effect of material thickness established, liquid diffusivity can be calculated as indicated below. For this calculation, the theoretical values for an infinite slab are required. These are:

$\frac{D_l\theta}{d}$	0.02	0.05	0.10	0.15	0.20	0.30	0.50	1.0
$\frac{W - W_e}{W_c - W_e}$	0.84	0.75	0.642	0.563	0.496	0.387	0.236	0.069

A plot of these values is shown as curve *A* in Fig. 15-37.

If a straight line such as curve *B* of Fig. 15-37 represents the experimental data, and if it has been established that the drying time varies inversely as the square of the thickness, the average liquid diffusivity can be obtained as follows: At a given value of $(W - W_e)/(W_c - W_e)$, read the corresponding value of $D_l\theta/d^2$ from curve *A*, Eq. (15-38), Fig. 15-37. At the same value of $(W - W_e)/(W_c - W_e)$, read the corresponding experimental value of θ from curve *B* (upper scale). Then

$$D_{l_{avg}} = \frac{(D_l\theta/d^2)\text{ theo.}}{(\theta/d^2)\text{ exp.}} \qquad (15\text{-}52)$$

where $D_{l_{avg}}$ = average experimental value of liquid diffusivity, sq. ft./hr. The value of diffusivity calculated from Eq. (15-52) must be recognized as an average value over the entire range of moisture change from $(W - W_e)/(W_c - W_e) = 1$ to the value $(W - W_e)/(W_c - W_e)$ at which θ/d^2 was evaluated. Further, Eq. (15-52) assumes that the theoretical curve is a straight line for all values of time. This is not true for values of $(W - W_e)/(W_c - W_e)$ less than 0.6.

A more accurate value of $D_{l_{avg}}$ can be obtained by taking a ratio of slopes of the curves of Fig. 15-37. Thus the ratio of the slope of the experimental curve of unaccomplished moisture change vs. drying time on a semilogarithmic plot [Eq. (15-38)] to the slope of the theoretical curve at the same unaccomplished moisture change, again on a semilogarithmic plot, equals the quantity D_l/d^2. If d is known, D_l can be evaluated.

Example 26. Assume that a material dries to give the unaccomplished moisture change vs. time relationship shown by curve *B* in Fig. 15-37. Assume, further, that this material is 0.2 ft. in thickness and is drying from both sides. Determine the diffusivity at values of the unaccomplished moisture changes of 0.8, 0.2, and 0.07, from Eq. (15-52) and from the ratio of slopes.

Solution. The average diffusivities are calculated by Eq. (15-52), using $d = 0.2/2 = 0.1$ ft. At unaccomplished moisture changes of 0.8, 0.2, and 0.07, the values of $(D_l\theta/d^2)$ theoretical are 0.03, 0.57, and 0.99, respectively, from curve *A* of Fig. 15-37. At these same values of unaccomplished moisture changes the values of drying time θ are 0.055, 0.36, and 0.61, respectively, from curve *B*, Fig. 15-37. Then at an unaccomplished moisture change of 0.8, $D_{l_{avg}} = (0.03)(0.1)^2/0.055 = 0.0055$ sq. ft./hr. At an unaccomplished moisture change of 0.3, $D_{l_{avg}} = (0.57)(0.1)^2/0.36 = 0.016$ sq. ft./hr. Finally at an unaccomplished moisture change of 0.07, $D_{l_{avg}} = (0.99)(0.2)^2/0.61 = 0.016$ sq. ft./hr. The value of $D_l = 0.0055$ is in error because the unaccomplished moisture change exceeded 0.6 and the straight-line portion of Eq. (15-38) is no longer valid.

More precise values of diffusivity are obtained by the method of slopes. At unaccomplished moisture changes of 0.8, 0.2, 0.07, the slope of curve *A*, Fig. 15-37, is −1.74, −1.07, and −1.07, respectively, and the slope of curve *B* is −1.90 for all three values. Then $D_l = -1.90(0.1)^2/(-1.74) = 0.0109$ sq. ft./hr. at an unaccomplished moisture change of 0.8 and $D_l = (-1.90)(0.1)^2/(-1.07) = 0.017$ sq. ft./hr. for unaccomplished moisture changes of 0.2 and 0.07. As would be expected, the value of diffusivity for values of the unaccomplished moisture change less than 0.6 is constant. The value of $D_l = 0.0109$ is incorrect because of curvature of the theoretical line. In principle, a diffusion mechanism is inconsistent with an experimental curve which does not show curvature at the higher values of unaccomplished moisture change.

Tests on Plant Dryers

Tests on plant-scale dryers are usually carried out to obtain design data for a specific material, to select a suitable dryer type, or to check present performance of an existing dryer with the objective of determining its capacity potential. In these tests over-all performance data are obtained and the results used to make heat and material balances and to estimate over-all drying rates or heat-transfer coefficients.

Generally, the minimum data to be taken in order to calculate the performance of a dryer are:

1. Inlet and outlet moisture contents
2. Inlet and outlet gas temperatures
3. Inlet and outlet material temperatures
4. Feed rate
5. Gas rate
6. Inlet and outlet humidities
7. Retention time or time of passage through the dryer
8. Fuel consumption

Wherever possible, moisture contents and temperatures should be measured at various points within the dryer.

Typical experimental and calculated results of a drying test for a continuous, adiabatic, convection dryer are shown in Fig. 15-38. Test data as complete as those shown are not usually justified economically except where basic studies, aimed at clarifying the effect of operating

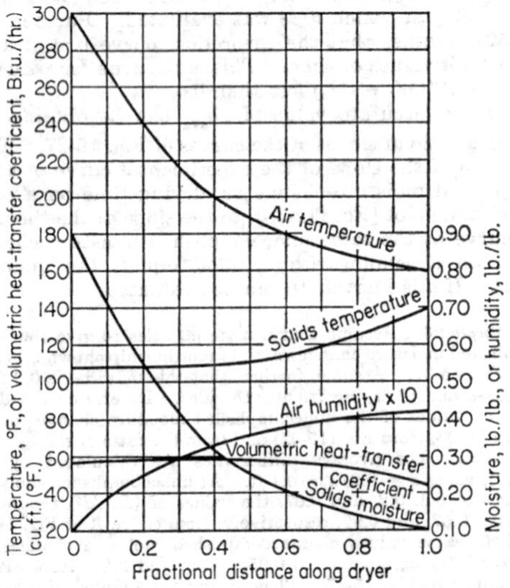

FIG. 15-38. Typical results of dryer-performance tests.

variables, are being carried out in order to arrive at a reliable design procedure. The completeness of the information which is sought in any given test depends on the ultimate use of the data. In any case data for at least two sets of operating conditions are needed if a good analysis of dryer performance is to be made.

Results of drying tests can be correlated empirically in terms of **over-all heat-transfer coefficient** or **length of a transfer unit** as a function of operating variables. The former is generally applicable to all types of dryers, while the latter applies only in the case of continuous dryers. The relationship between these quantities is as follows.

The number of transfer units in any direct dryer is given by

$$N_t = \frac{t_1 - t_2}{\Delta t_m} \tag{15-53}$$

where N_t = number of transfer units; t_1 = inlet gas temperature, °F.; t_2 = exit gas temperature for an equivalent adiabatic dryer, °F.; Δt_m = mean temperature difference between gas and solids through the dryer, °F.

The volumetric heat-transfer coefficient is given by

$$U_v = \frac{q_d}{V_d\,\Delta t_m} = \frac{wc_s(t_2 - t_1)}{A_d L_d\,\Delta t_m} \tag{15-54}$$

where U_v = volumetric heat-transfer coefficient, B.t.u./(hr.)(cu. ft.)(°F.); q_d = heat used for drying, B.t.u./hr.; V_d = dryer volume, cu. ft.; w = drying air rate, lb./hr.; c_s = heat capacity of air, B.t.u./(lb.)(°F.); A_d = cross-sectional area of dryer, sq. ft.; L_d = dryer length, ft. Substituting Eq. (15-53) into Eq. (15-54) leads to a relationship between volumetric heat-transfer coefficient and length of a transfer unit:

$$\frac{L_d}{N_t} = L_d' = \frac{Gc_s}{U_v} \tag{15-55}$$

where L_d' = length of a transfer unit, ft.; G = air mass velocity, lb./(hr.)(sq. ft.).

Example 27. Drying tests on a pneumatic conveying dryer 50 ft. long and 0.15 sq. ft. cross-sectional area gave the profiles shown in Fig. 15-38 for a drying air rate of 1000 lb./hr. and a solid-feed rate of 40 lb./hr. Determine volumetric heat-transfer coefficient, number of transfer units, and length of a transfer unit.

Solution. From Eq. (15-53) the number of transfer units is $N_t = (300 - 160)/\Delta t_m$ where in this case Δt_m will be taken as $\Delta t_m = [(300 - 108) - (160 - 140)]/\ln 192/20 = 76.1$. Thus $N_t = 140/76.1 = 1.84$ and length of a transfer unit is $50/1.84 = 27.2$ ft. The average volumetric heat-transfer coefficient is calculated from Eq. (15-54), $U_v = (1000)(0.24)(140)/(0.15)(50)(76.1)$, or $U_v = 59$. From Eq. (15-55) the length of a transfer unit is $L_d' = (1000)(0.24)/(0.15)(59) = 27.2$ ft.

In this example the dryer has been assumed to be adiabatic and hence the terminal air temperatures are a measure of the heat utilized. When heat losses exist, the mean temperature difference in Eq. (15-53) is again based on the terminal conditions but the numerator equals the heat utilized divided by the product of drying air rate and heat capacity as in Eq. (15-54). In this example, the logarithmic mean temperature difference has been used as the true mean. This is not strictly true, in view of the solids-temperature profile of Fig. 15-38. In most cases, however, a logarithmic mean is a suitable approximation.

The volumetric heat-transfer coefficients along the dryer are lower at the discharge end (Fig. 15-38) because of the internal resistance to moisture movement in the later stages of drying. When drying data are expressed in terms of over-all performance, care and judgment should be exercised in extrapolating the results to other conditions, particularly conditions of different feed and product moisture. If, for example, the over-all heat-transfer coefficients, from the data of Fig. 15-38, were used to predict a dryer design for reducing the product moisture below 10 per cent, the design would be in error. Obviously, this problem can be circumvented by making sure that the final moisture in the experiments is below that desired in the product.

In any capacity test to determine the potential of a plant dryer, the effects of the following variables should be studied:

1. Effect of increased temperature. This is often the simplest way to achieve increased capacity. Frequently, plant dryers can be operated at temperatures higher than design values.

2. Effect of increased final moisture. This, too, can be the source of increased capacity if overdrying occurs. Generally, it is uneconomical to dry a material below its equilibrium moisture in atmosphereic air. Because of the marked increase in drying time required to dry to low moisture contents, the permissible maximum final moisture should always be established.

3. Effect of increasing air velocity should be determined. Frequently, higher air rates are necessary to provide the required additional heat at higher capacities.

4. Uniformity of air flow should be established. Air-flow maldistribution can seriously reduce dryer capacity and efficiency.

5. Possible benefits from **air recirculation** should be considered.

CLASSIFICATION OF DRYERS

Drying equipment may be classified in several ways. The two most useful classifications are based on (1) the method of transferring heat to the wet solids or (2) the handling characteristics and physical properties of the wet material. The first method of classification reveals differences in dryer design and operation, while the second method is most useful in the selection of a group of dryers for preliminary consideration in a given drying problem.

A classification chart of drying equipment on the basis of heat transfer is shown in Fig. 15-39 [Marshall, *Heating, Piping, Air Conditioning,* **18,** 71 (1946)]. This chart classifies dryers as direct or indirect, with subclasses of continuous or batchwise operation. In direct dryers, hot gases in direct contact with the wet solid are used to supply heat and carry away the vaporized moisture, and the principal mode of heat transfer, except at high temperatures, is by convection. The heat required to accomplish drying in indirect dryers is transferred from the heating fluid into the wet solid through a retaining wall. Conduction is the principal mode of heat transfer and the vaporized moisture is removed, independently of the heating fluid, by means of a sweep gas stream or by discharge into a vacuum space.

Direct Dryers. The general operating characteristics of direct dryers are these:

1. Drying depends on heat transfer to the wet solid from a hot gas, the latter removing the vaporized liquid.
2. The hot gases may be steam-heated air, combustion products, an inert gas, or a superheated vapor.
3. Drying temperatures may range up to 1400°F., the limiting temperature for most common structural metals. At the higher temperatures, radiation becomes an important heat-transfer mechanism.
4. At gas temperatures below the boiling point, the vapor content of gas influences the rate of drying and the final moisture content of the solid. With gas temperatures above the boiling point throughout, the vapor content of the gas has only a slight retarding effect on the drying rate and final moisture content. Thus, superheated vapors of the liquid being removed can be used for drying.
5. For low-temperature drying, dehumidification of the drying air may be required when atmospheric humidities are excessively high.
6. A direct dryer consumes more fuel per pound of water evaporated, the lower the final moisture content. Likewise, the investment cost increases markedly.
7. Efficiency increases with an increase in the inlet-gas temperature for a constant exhaust temperature.

Direct continuous dryers usually handle in the range of 50 to 1000 lb./hr. of dry product, depending to a large extent on the initial moisture content.

Over-all thermal efficiency of direct continuous dryers in which air is not reheated between inlet and outlet is

$$\eta = \frac{100q_d}{q_s} = \frac{100(t_1 - t_2)}{t_1 - t_a} \qquad (15\text{-}56)$$

where η = per cent over-all thermal efficiency; q_d = heat actually used for drying, B.t.u./hr.; q_s = heat supplied to the dryer, B.t.u./hr.; t_1 = inlet-gas temperature, °F.; t_2 = exit temperature for an equivalent adiabatic dryer, °F.; t_a = inlet temperature to air heaters.

Evaporating efficiency in a direct continuous dryer with no reheating is

$$\eta_e = \frac{100(t_1 - t_2)}{t_1 - t_s} \qquad (15\text{-}57)$$

where η_e = evaporative efficiency and t_s = adiabatic-saturation temperature of entering gas. This equation compares the evaporation actually obtained to that which is theoretically possible.

Equations (15-56) and (15-57) apply to direct rotary dryers, tunnel dryers, spray dryers, penumatic conveying dryers, direct continuous-sheeting dryers, and other direct continuous types in which air passes through without being reheated. In these equations, the small change in humid heat has been neglected.

The efficiency equations indicate the following:

1. Increasing t_1 with t_2 constant increases efficiency and reduces air requirements.
2. Increasing t_a or t_s by recirculation of exhaust gases, for example, increases efficiency. The increased efficiency must be balanced against the larger dryer size required.

Over-all operating costs for continuous direct dryers expressed as cost per pound of product are usually lower than for batch direct dryers because of lower labor and fuel costs and higher production rates. They may range from $0.0005 to $0.025 per pound of dry product for labor, power, fuel, and maintenance.

Direct batch dryers are used for low production rates and for special handling of high-cost product. They are characterized by long drying times (6 to 40 hr.), and unsteady-state operation with air temperature, humidity, material temperature, and moisture content changing continually with time at a given position in the dryer. Direct batch dryers do not dry uniformly unless carefully designed from the standpoint of tray spacing and uniformity of air flow.

High fuel and labor costs for these dryers result in high over-all operating costs per pound of product. Fuel consumption in some cases may run as high as 6 to 8 lb. steam/lb. water evaporated. This ratio is seldom less than 2.5 and increases as the final moisture content is decreased.

Indirect dryers differ from direct dryers with respect to heat transfer and vapor removal. Their general operating characteristics follow.

1. Heat is transferred to the wet material by conduction through a solid retaining wall, usually metallic. The source of heat may be condensing steam, hot water, combustion gases, molten heat-transfer salts, hot oil, electricity, etc.
2. Surface temperatures may range from below freezing in the case of freeze dryers to above 1000°F. in the case of indirect dryers heated by combustion products.
3. Indirect dryers are suited to drying under reduced pressures and inert atmospheres to permit the recovery of solvents and to prevent the occurrence of explosive mixtures or the oxidation of easily decomposed materials.
4. Indirect dryers using condensing fluids as the heating medium are generally economical from the standpoint of heat consumption, since they furnish heat only in accordance with the demand made by the material being dried. However, their efficiency decreases as the final moisture content increases.
5. Dust recovery and dusty materials can be handled more satisfactorily in indirect dryers than in direct dryers.
6. Indirect dryers may utilize some method of agitation to eliminate moisture gradients in the solid and to increase the drying rate.
7. Indirect continuous dryers are usually more economical to operate than direct dryers.

Indirect continuous dryers can sometimes be operated at pressures below atmospheric. With good seals at the charging and discharging points, negative pressures of 27 to 28 in. Hg can be maintained during continuous operation. This is particularly useful for

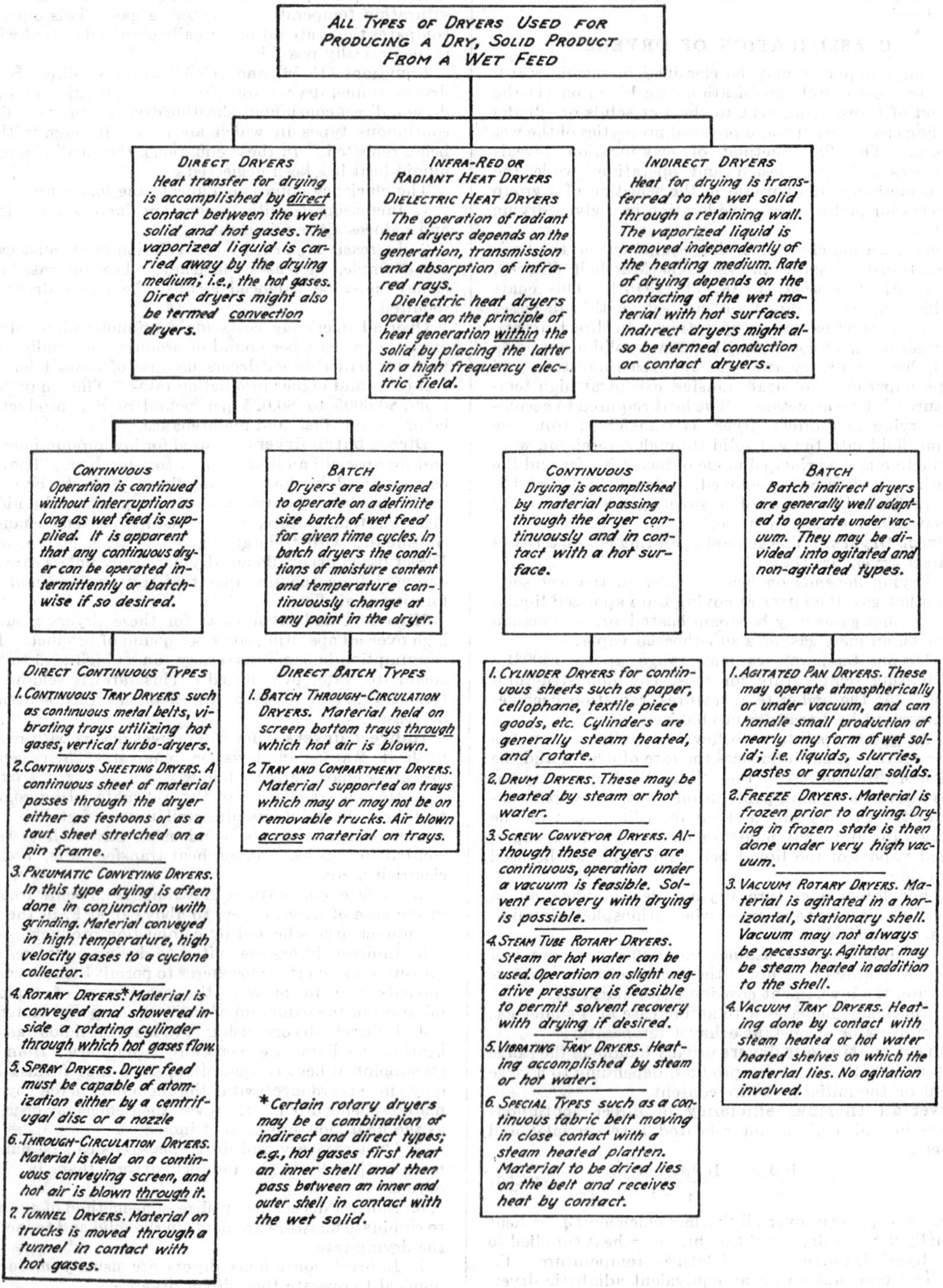

Fig. 15-39. Classification of dryers, based on methods of heat transfer. [*Marshall, Heating, Piping, Air Conditioning*, **18**, 71 (1946).]

heat-sensitive materials or where solvent recovery is important.

Indirect batch dryers are suited for evaporating and drying solutions or slurries, for drying pastes and granular solids, and for drying under high vacuum. They may be divided into two groups in which (1) the solids remain stationary throughout the cycle, and (2) the solids are agitated during the drying cycle. The former is typified by the vacuum shelf dryer, the latter by the agitated-pan dryer, which may or may not operate under vacuum.

Major operating cost of batch indirect dryers is labor for charging and discharging the dryers and for clean-up. Fuel requirements lie in the range of 1.5 to 3.0 lb. steam/lb. water evaporated, depending on the desired degree of dryness. Power costs depend on degree of agitation required, nature of the material, and if vacuum is used, degree of evacuation.

Miscellaneous Dryers. **Infrared dryers** depend on the transfer of radiant energy to evaporate moisture. The radiant energy is supplied electrically by infrared lamps, by electric resistance elements, or by incandescent refractories heated by gas. The latter method has the added advantage of convection heating. Infrared heating is not widely used in the chemical industries for the removal of moisture. Its principal use is in baking or drying paint films and in heating thin layers of materials. The power costs for infrared drying will be two to four times the fuel cost for the dryers described above.

Dielectric dryers have not, as yet, found a wide field of application. Their fundamental characteristic of generating heat within the solid indicates potentialities for drying massive geometrical objects such as wood, sponge-rubber shapes, and ceramics. Power costs may range to ten times the fuel costs of conventional methods.

SELECTION OF DRYING EQUIPMENT

Careful consideration of many factors is necessary in the final selection of the most suitable type of dryer for a given application. Such a selection is complicated by the large number of different types of dryers available on the market. Commercial dryers are not usually flexible enough to compensate for design inaccuracies or for problems in the physical handling of the material that have not been previously considered. For this reason, it is particularly important that all pertinent facts be considered and that experimental tests be made before a dryer is finally selected for a given problem.

The following procedure is recommended for selecting the best dryer to perform a given operation most economically:

1. Initial Selection of Dryers. Select those dryers which appear best suited to handling the wet material and dry product, which fit into the continuity of the process as a whole, and which will produce a product of the desired physical properties. This preliminary selection can be made with the aid of Table 15-17, which classifies the various types of dryers on the basis of the materials handled.

2. Initial Comparison of Dryers. The dryers so selected should be evaluated, approximately, from available cost and performance data. From this evaluation, those dryers which appear to be uneconomical or unsuitable from the standpoint of performance should be eliminated from further consideration.

3. Drying Tests. Drying tests should be conducted in those dryers still under consideration. These tests will determine the optimum operating conditions and the product characteristics and will form the basis for firm quotations from equipment vendors.

4. Final Selection of Dryer. From the results of the drying tests and quotations, the final selection of the most suitable dryer can be made.

Preliminary Dryer Selection

The important factors to consider in the preliminary selection of a dryer are the following:

1. Properties of the material being handled
   a. Physical characteristics when wet
   b. Physical characteristics when dry
   c. Corrosiveness
   d. Toxicity
   e. Flammability
   f. Particle size
   g. Abrasiveness
2. Drying characteristics of the material
   a. Type of moisture (bound, unbound, or both)
   b. Initial moisture content
   c. Final moisture content (maximum)
   d. Permissible drying temperature
   e. Probable drying time for different dryers
3. Flow of material to and from the dryer
   a. Quantity to be handled per hour
   b. Continuous or batch operation
   c. Process prior to drying
   d. Process subsequent to drying
4. Product qualities
   a. Shrinkage
   b. Contamination
   c. Uniformity of final moisture content
   d. Decomposition of product
   e. Overdrying
   f. State of subdivision
   g. Product temperature
   h. Bulk density
5. Recovery problems
   a. Dust recovery
   b. Solvent recovery
6. Facilities available at site of proposed installation
   a. Space
   b. Temperature, humidity, and cleanliness of air
   c. Available fuels
   d. Available electric power
   e. Permissible noise, vibration, dust, or heat losses
   f. Source of wet feed
   g. Exhaust-gas outlets

The physical nature of the material to be handled is the primary item for consideration. A slurry will demand a different type of dryer from that required by a coarse crystalline solid which, in turn, will be different from that required by a sheet material. Table 15-17 lists the various types of dryers best suited for handling eight different classes of feed material and facilitates the preliminary selection of the group of dryers which are suitable from the standpoint of material handling.

Initial Comparison of Dryers

Following preliminary selection of the suitable types of dryers, a high-spot evaluation of the size and cost should be made to eliminate those which are obviously uneconomical. Information for this evaluation can be obtained from material presented under discussion of the various dryer types and from Sec. 20. Where data are inadequate, preliminary cost and performance data can usually be obtained from the equipment manufacturer. In comparing dryer performance, the factors listed above which affect dryer performance should be properly weighed. The possibility of eliminating or simplifying processing steps which precede or follow drying, such as filtration, grinding, or conveying, should be carefully considered. The physical properties of the product may be of prime importance and will directly influence the choice of dryer.

Table 15-17. Classification of Commercial Dryers Based on Materials Handled

Type of dryer	Liquids	Slurries	Pastes and sludges	Free-flowing powders	Granular, crystalline, or fibrous solids	Large solids, special forms and shapes	Continuous sheets	Discontinuous sheets
	True and colloidal solutions; emulsions. Examples: inorganic salt solutions, extracts, milk, blood, waste liquors, rubber latex, etc.	Pumpable suspensions. Examples: pigment slurries, soap and detergents, calcium carbonate, bentonite, clay slip, lead concentrates, etc.	Examples: filter-press cakes, sedimentation sludges, centrifuged solids, starch, etc.	100 mesh or less. Relatively free flowing in wet state. Dusty when dry. Examples: centrifuged precipitates, pigments, clay, cement.	Larger than 100 mesh. Examples: rayon staple, salt crystals, sand, ores, potato strips, synthetic rubber.	Examples: pottery, brick, rayon cakes, shotgun shells, hats, painted objects, rayon skeins, lumber.	Examples: paper, impregnated fabrics, cloth, cellophane, plastic sheets.	Examples: veneer, wallboard, photograph prints, leather, foam rubber sheets.
Tray and compartment. Direct type, batch operation	Not applicable	For very small batch production. Laboratory drying	Suited to batch operation. At large capacities, investment and operating costs are high. Long drying times	Dusting may be a problem. See comments under Pastes and Sludges	Suited to batch operation. At large capacities, investment and operating costs are high. Long drying times	See comments under Granular solids	Not applicable	See comments under Granular solids
Batch through-circulation. Direct type, batch operation	Not applicable	Not applicable	Suitable only if material can be preformed. Suited to batch operation. Shorter drying time than tray dryers	Not applicable	Usually not suited for materials smaller than 30 mesh. Suited to small capacities and batch operation	Primarily useful for small objects	Not applicable	Not applicable
Tunnel. Continuous Tray. Direct type, continuous operation	Not applicable	Not applicable	Suitable for small and large-scale production.	See comments under Pastes and Sludges. Vertical-turbo applicable	Essentially large-scale, semicontinuous tray drying.	Suited to a wide variety of shapes and forms. Operation can be made continuous. Widely used	Not applicable	Suited for leather, wallboard, veneer.
Continuous through-circulation. Direct type, continuous operation	Not applicable	Only crystal filter dryer may be suited	Suitable for materials that can be preformed. Will handle large capacities. Roto-louvre not generally suited	Not generally applicable, except Roto-louvre in certain cases	Usually not suited for materials smaller than 30 mesh. Material does not tumble, except in Roto-louvre dryer. Latter operates at higher temperatures	Suited to smaller objects that can be loaded on each other. Can be used to convey materials through heated zones. Roto-louvre not suited.	Not applicable	Special designs are required. Suited to veneers. Roto-louvre not applicable
Direct rotary. Direct type, continuous operation	Not applicable	Not applicable	Suitable only if product does not stick to walls and does not dust. Recirculation of product may prevent sticking	Suitable for most materials and capacities, provided that dusting is not too severe	Suitable for most materials at most capacities. Dusting or crystal abrasion will limit its use	Not applicable	Not applicable	Not applicable
Pneumatic conveying. Direct type, continuous operation	Not applicable	Can be used only if product is recirculated to make feed suitable for handling	Usually requires recirculation of dry product to make suitable feed. Well suited to high capacities. Disintegration usually required	Suitable for materials that are easily suspended in a gas stream and lose moisture readily. Well suited to high capacities	Suitable for materials that are easily suspended in a gas stream. Well suited to high capacities. Product may suffer physical degradation	Not applicable	Not applicable	Not applicable
Spray. Direct type, continuous operation	Suited for large capacities. Product is usually powdery, spherical, and free-flowing. High temperatures can be used with heat-sensitive materials. Product may have low bulk density	See comments under Liquids. Pressure-nozzle atomizers subject to erosion	Requires special pumping equipment to feed the atomizer. See comments under Liquids	Not applicable	Not applicable	Not applicable	Not applicable	Not applicable
Continuous sheeting. Direct type, continuous operation	Not applicable	Not applicable	Not applicable	Not applicable	Not applicable	Not applicable	Different types are available for different requirements. Suitable for drying without contacting hot surfaces	Not applicable
Vacuum shelf. Indirect type, batch operation	Not applicable	Not applicable	Suitable for batch operation, small capacities. Useful for heat-sensitive or readily oxidizable materials. Solvents can be recovered	See comments under Pastes and Sludges	Suitable for batch operation, small capacities. Useful for heat-sensitive or readily oxidizable materials. Solvents can be recovered	See comments under Granular solids	Not applicable	See comments under Granular solids

Vacuum freeze. Indirect type, batch or continuous operation	Usually used only for pharmaceuticals such as penicillin and blood plasma. Expensive. Used on heat-sensitive and readily oxidized materials	See comments under Liquids	See comments under Liquids	See comments under Liquids	Expensive. Usually used on pharmaceuticals and related products which cannot be dried successfully by other means. Applicable to fine chemicals.	See comments under Granular solids	Applicable in special cases such as emulsion-coated films.	See comments under Granular solids
Pan. Indirect type, batch operation	Atmospheric or vacuum. Suitable for small batches. Easily cleaned. Solvents can be recovered. Material agitated while dried	See comments under Liquids	See comments under Liquids	See comments under Liquids	Suitable for small batches. Easily cleaned. Material is agitated during drying, causing some degradation	Not applicable	Not applicable	Not applicable
Vacuum rotary. Indirect type, batch operation	Not applicable	May have application in special cases	Use is questionable. Material usually cakes to dryer walls and agitator. Solvents can be recovered	Suitable for non-sticking materials. Useful for large batches of heat-sensitive materials and for solvent recovery	Useful for large batches of heat-sensitive materials or where solvent is to be recovered. Product will suffer some grinding action. Dust collectors may be required	Not applicable	Not applicable	Not applicable
Indirect rotary. Indirect type, continuous operation	Not applicable	Not applicable	Generally requires recirculation of dry product. Little dusting occurs	Chief advantage is low dust loss. Well suited to most materials and capacities, particularly those requiring drying at steam temperature	Low dust loss. Inexpensive at almost all capacities. Material must not stick or be temperature-sensitive	Not applicable	Not applicable	Not applicable
Screw conveyor. Indirect type, continuous operation	Not applicable	Not applicable	Can only be used if material does not stick or cake	Suitable for materials that will not stick. Usually used with low moisture content materials. Can be used to convey the material	Usually used with low-moisture-content materials. Can be used as conveyor and auxiliary dryer	Not applicable	Not applicable	Not applicable
Vibrating tray. Indirect type, continuous operation	Not applicable	Not applicable	Not applicable	Suitable for free-flowing materials that are dusty. Usually operated at steam temperatures	Suitable for free-flowing materials that can be conveyed on a vibrating tray. Usually operated at steam temperatures, but higher temperatures are feasible	Not applicable	Not applicable	Not applicable
Drum. Indirect type, continuous operation	Single, double, or twin. Atm. or vacuum operation. Product flaky and usually dusty. Maintenance costs may be high	See comments under Liquids. Twin-drum dryers are widely used	Can be used only when paste or sludge can be made to flow. See comments under Liquids	Not applicable	Not applicable	Not applicable	Not applicable	Not applicable
Cylinder. Indirect type, continuous operation	Not applicable	Not applicable	Not applicable	Not applicable	Not applicable	Not applicable	Suitable for thin or mechanically weak sheets which can be dried in contact with a heated surface. Special surface effects obtainable	Suitable for materials which need not be dried flat and which will not be injured by contact with hot drum
Infrared. Batch or continuous operation	Only experimental use has been reported. Expensive	See comments under Liquids	See comments under Liquids	Expensive. Has been used on expensive products. Danger of overheating	Primarily suited to drying surface moisture. Not suited for thick layers. Expensive	Specially suited for drying and baking paint and enamels	Usually used in conjunction with other methods. Useful when there are space limitations	Useful for laboratory work or in conjunction with other methods
Dielectric. Batch or continuous operation	Very expensive. Used commercially only on penicillin	See comments under Liquids	See comments under Liquids	Very expensive. No commercial use reported	Very expensive. No commercial uses reported	Rapid drying of large objects suited to this method. Power costs excessive	Applications not developed	Successful on foam rubber. Not fully developed on other materials

Drying Tests

The critical comparison suggested above usually eliminates all but three or four dryer types from further consideration. Final evaluation of the remaining dryers requires tests in experimental units which properly simulate each dryer type. These tests should establish the optimum operating conditions, the ability of the dryer to handle the material physically, product quality and characteristics, and dryer size. The principal manufacturers of drying equipment are usually prepared to perform the required tests on dryers simulating their equipment. Occasionally, simple laboratory experiments can serve to further reduce the number of dryers under consideration.

Since plant-scale dryers seldom cost less than $5000 and often cost more than $50,000, extensive test work is justified in establishing the correct type of dryer and optimum operating conditions. Once a given type and size of dryer is installed, the product characteristics and drying capacity can be changed only within relatively narrow limits. Thus it is more economical, and far more satisfactory, to experiment in small-scale units rather than on the dryer that is finally installed.

Final Selection

Based upon the results of the drying tests that establish size and operating characteristics, formal quotations and guarantees should be obtained from dryer manufacturers. Initial costs, installation costs, operating costs, product quality, dryer operability, and dryer flexibility can then be given proper weight in the final evaluation and selection.

SECTION 16

ADSORPTION AND ION EXCHANGE

BY

Nevin K. Hiester, Ph.D., Chairman, Chemical and High Temperature Technologies Department, Stanford Research Institute, and Lecturer in Chemical Engineering, Stanford University; Member, American Institute of Chemical Engineers, American Chemical Society, American Institute of Aeronautics and Astronautics.

Theodore Vermeulen, Ph.D., Professor of Chemical Engineering, University of California, and Chemical Engineer, Lawrence Radiation Laboratory; Member, American Institute of Chemical Engineers, American Chemical Society, Electrochemical Society, American Nuclear Society, American Institute of Aeronautics and Astronautics.

Gerhard Klein, M.S., Associate Research Engineer, Sea Water Conversion Laboratory, Institute of Engineering Research, University of California; Member, American Institute of Chemical Engineers, American Chemical Society. (Sorbent Properties)

CONTENTS

THEORY OF SORPTION

Nature of Sorbent Materials. Whether a sorbent solid is used in granular or in finely divided form, the outer surfaces of the particles usually have an impractically low sorption capacity. As indicated by Monet [*Chem. Eng. Progress, Symp. Ser.*, **55** (24), 1 (1959)], almost all sorbents can be considered to contain a significant fraction of **micropores,** ranging from 5 to 60 per cent by volume. If the typical diameter of such micropores is as large as 150 angstroms, the sorbent is said to be **microcrystalline** and porous; if as small as 5 angstroms, **resinous** and permeable. Intermolecular attraction between the solid and certain solutes (which have entered the micropores from a gas or liquid carrier) may cause such solute molecules to be retained selectively, resulting in their being separated from the carrier phase.

Table 16-1 identifies known **sorption operations** in terms of type of fluid and structure of sorbent. The different operations are each explained separately, as follows.

Table 16-1. Classification of Sorption Operations

Substrate (fluid phase)	Sorbent (solid phase)		
	Voids accessible to substrate		Voids filled with immiscible or nonvolatile liquid
	Resinous (dissolution)	Microcrystalline (penetration)	
Liquid....	Ion exchange	Adsorption (on surfaces or in lattices)	Partition extraction
	Extraction (permeation)	Dialysis	
Gas......	Absorption (permeation)	Adsorption	Partition absorption

Ion exchange involves a solid phase containing bound groups that carry an ionic charge, either positive or negative, in conjunction with free ions of opposite charge that can be displaced. Early ion exchangers were inorganic silicate polymers of microcrystalline type—zeolites or green sands. These were followed by oxidized (carboxylated) or sulfonated coals. Most ion exchangers currently in large-scale use are based on synthetic resins, usually polystyrene copolymerized with divinylbenzene (to provide the requisite amount of cross linking); they are permeable only at molecular dimensions, unless a network of coarser pores is deliberately superimposed. Figure 16-1 indicates the chemical structure of this particular composition. Cation-exchange resins generally contain bound sulfonic acid groups; less commonly, these groups are carboxylic, phosphonic, phosphinic, etc. Anionic resins involve quaternary ammonium groups (strongly basic) or other aminos (weakly basic).

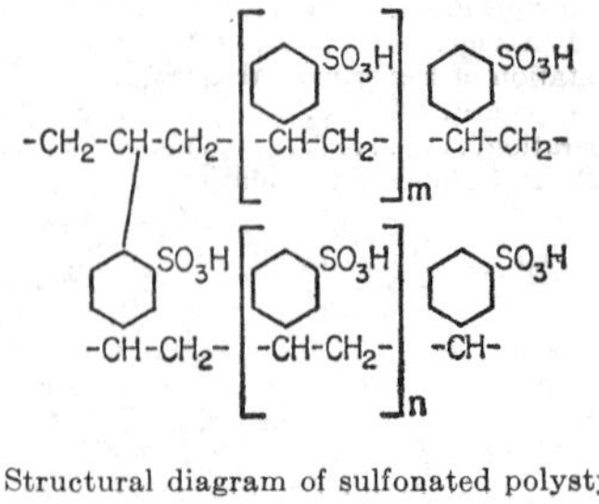

FIG. 16-1. Structural diagram of sulfonated polystyrene cation exchanger.

Ion exchange may be written as a **reversible reaction** involving chemically equivalent quantities; for example, for cation exchange,

$$Ca^{++}\,(aq.) + 2\,Na^{+}\,(resin) \rightleftharpoons Ca^{++}\,(resin) + 2\,Na^{+}\,(aq.)$$

or

$$Ca^{++} + 2\,NaR \rightleftharpoons CaR_2 + 2\,Na^{+}$$

where R represents a stationary univalent anionic site in the polyelectrolyte network of the exchanger phase. As in nearly all sorption operations, the solid sorbent must be conserved following its use, by a **regeneration** or revivification treatment with a solution containing the ion initially present in the solid. An ever-present excess of this ion during the regeneration step will cause the reaction equilibrium to reverse itself, restoring the resin to its initial condition.

Ion exchange between strong electrolytes can usually be carried out until the **stoichiometric capacity** of the exchanger has been used up; the total sorbent capacity is practically constant, regardless of the composition of the solution being treated. An apparent exception arises if a weak acid or base is involved, either in the resin or in solution (or in both), when the apparent capacity of the resin may be much less than its stoichiometric value; one example of this effect is the incomplete removal of silicic acid (H_2SiO_3) during the anionic stage of water demineralization.

Chelating ion-exchange resins have been synthesized that display unusually high selectivity for certain cations; some of these are commercially available. For a review of this field, see Hale [*Research (London)*, **9,** 104 (1956)]. The following types are representative:

1. Polystyrene matrix, containing imino-diacetate groups which are particularly selective for copper, nickel, cobalt, and iron (III) (Hale, Thomas, and Pepper, Brit. Patent 767,821. Morris, U.S. Patent 2,888,441).
2. Phenol-formaldehyde matrix, with 8-quinolinol replacing part or all of the phenol [Pennington and Williams, *Ind. Eng. Chem.*, **51,** 759 (1959)].
3. Phenol-formaldehyde matrix, with phenol replaced by *m*-phenylene diglycine or by *o*-aminophenol [Gregor, Taifer, Citarel, and Becker, *Ind. Eng. Chem.*, **44,** 2834 (1954)].
4. Polystyrene matrix impregnated with a solution of tributyl phosphate in perchloroethylene (Small, Dow Chemical Co., private communication).
5. Polyacrylate matrix, cross-linked with a small percentage of divinylbenzene, in which carboxyl groups are converted to enolizable diketones (McBurney, U.S. Patent 2,613,200).
6. Polymers containing bound porphyrin groups [Lautsch *et al.*, *J. Polymer Sci.*, **8,** 191 (1952)].
7. Polystyrene matrix, reduced and nitrated to produce a structure analogous to hexanitrodiphenylaminate which is selective for potassium in the presence of sodium (Skogseid, referred to by Kunin, "Ion Exchange Resins," p. 103, Wiley, New York, 1958).

Exploratory studies have been made of granular reagents for **electron-transfer** or **redox** reactions. Resins for this purpose have been synthesized by Cassidy and coworkers [*J. Am. Chem. Soc.*, **75,** 1610, 1615 (1953)], Manecke [*Angew. Chem.*, **71,** 646 (1959)], and Soloway and Schwartz [*Science*, **121**, 73 (1955)], incorporating hydroquinone groups into the polymer structure which enter into the following half reaction:

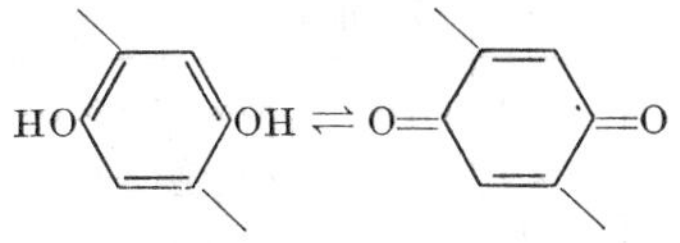

Gregor and coworkers [*J. Am. Chem. Soc.*, **77**, 3675 (1955)] have developed polythiolstyrenes for the same purpose:

$$2(\text{—SH}) \rightleftharpoons \text{—SS—} + 2H^+ + 2e^-$$

Resins of these two types are able to raise or lower the valence of susceptible metal ions without otherwise affecting the solution that is treated. They also appear suitable for oxygen removal from water supplies. Industrial development of such materials can therefore be expected.

Adsorption utilizes natural or synthetic materials of microcrystalline structure. Selective combination of solid and solute occurs on the pore surfaces throughout this structure; surface areas up to 100 sq. m./cc. are encountered, corresponding to an effective cylindrical pore diameter of less than 200 angstroms, or 2.0×10^{-6} cm. At higher temperatures (usually above 400°F.), adsorption may occur through a true reaction or chemical bonding; it is then termed **chemisorption.** Separations are usually carried out under conditions where the attractive forces are weaker and less specific than those of chemical bonds; here, the combining effect is identified as **physical adsorption.**

Hence, adsorption is usually analogous to a condensation of gas molecules, or to crystallization from a liquid. Its selective action is most pronounced in a monomolecular layer next to the solid surface, but at times selectivity may persist to a height of three or four molecules. Adsorption capacity of a solid for a solute tends to increase with the fluid-phase concentration of the solute.

Adsorbents in large-scale use include activated carbon, silica gel, activated alumina, fuller's earth, and other clays.

Molecular sieves, an important class of synthetic adsorbents, are alumosilicates that have undergone heating to remove water of hydration. They possess high porosity, with pores (in reality, lattice vacancies) of uniform size and essentially molecular dimensions. They adsorb small molecules only, are selective on molecular shape, and have a particular affinity for unsaturated and polar molecules. The lattice vacancy may have a diameter of 4 or 5 angstroms, depending on whether the alumosilicate is in the sodium or the calcium form. Molecular sieves are used primarily in gas treatment but also are effective for drying organic liquids [Milton, U.S. Patents 2,882,243–4. Breck, Reed, *et al.*, *J. Am. Chem. Soc.*, **78**, 5963, 5972 (1956). Griesmer, *Chem. Eng. Progress, Symp. Ser.*, **55** (24), 45 (1959)].

Particulate-gel dialysis provides another kind of separation based upon molecular size, carried out with a liquid substrate. It involves granules of a permeable and highly solvated material such as is used in membrane dialysis, *e.g.*, cellulose (Monet, U.S. Patent 2,773,028). The granule admits "crystalloid" solutes, either ionic or molecular, up to around 10 to 15 angstroms in diameter, but completely rejects "colloidal" material larger than this limiting size. Regeneration with solute-free liquid enables the crystalloid to quit the particle and be recovered in the effluent, leaving the solid ready for reuse.

Absorption- and extraction-type separations conducted with a sorbent solid are brought about by differences in solubility, rather than in molecular size. The solute undergoes a true phase change, on the molecular scale; in its "dissolved" state in the solid, each solute molecule is surrounded at close range by molecules of the sorbent material. The usual definitions of absorption and extraction are retained here: in absorption, the solute-carrying phase or substrate is gaseous; in extraction, liquid. Permeation of amorphous polymeric materials is an example of this effect, although usually carried out with membranes rather than with granules; examples are fixed gases or light organic molecules (CH_4, CH_3Br) through polyvinyl chloride, ethyl cellulose, or silicone rubber.

A specific instance of sorbent-extraction is the **ion-exclusion** (or electrolyte exclusion) operation which can be carried out with ordinary ion-exchange resins [Simpson and Wheaton, *Chem. Eng. Progress*, **50**, 45 (1954)]. The resin is presaturated with the same mobile ions (cations or anions, depending on resin type) as are in the solution. It will then repel the ionic components of the solution, while extracting neutral non-aqueous materials such as alcohols, carboxylic acids, and ketones of relatively low molecular weight.

Another case of sorbent extraction is encountered in **ion retardation.** For this purpose a cationic monomer is polymerized within the structure of a previously formed anion-exchange resin, or vice versa; the resulting structure is sometimes called a "snake-in-cage" polyelectrolyte. In its regenerated form, this matrix will have its cationic groups in hydrogen form and anionic groups in hydroxyl. Introduction of a strong electrolyte displaces the H^+ and OH^- and causes their neutralization; the resin thus becomes saturated with ionic species supplied by the process liquor. Regeneration with water causes the resin groups to hydrolyze, with liberation and recovery of the ions by reextraction into the substrate.

Another kind of phase-change sorption, used widely for chemical analysis, but with potential industrial applications, is **partition chromatography.** The sorbent is a true liquid, insoluble or non-volatile with respect to the substrate, contained in the pores of a granular solid supporting material that is usually relatively inert. Since such sorbents can be used for saturation-type operations as well, separations based upon them might well be termed **partition absorption** and **partition extraction.** In many cases the same solvent liquid could be used in conventional countercurrent tower equipment.

Physical Properties of Sorbent Materials. Data on commercially available materials for the two major types of sorption are given in Tables 16-2 and 16-3, with subsidiary sections. Table 16-2 lists adsorbents, while Table 16-3 covers cationic and anionic exchangers and other closely related materials. The purpose of these tables is twofold: to assist the engineer in identifying materials suitable for a needed application; and to supply typical physical property values, with sources of further data, on sorbents reported upon in the technical literature and identified there only by trade name. (Because of the latter purpose, the tables include some materials which have been discontinued and some which now carry another trade name or number.)

Interrelation of the various densities and porosities deserves some discussion. In general, data given on one basis by the manufacturers have not been converted to a different basis for present purposes; nevertheless, in using the tables, it will sometimes be desirable to estimate quantities that are not given explicitly.

For adsorbents, density values are usually reported as **bulk density** ρ_b, or weight of dry material per unit

Table 16-2. Physical Properties of Adsorbents

Material and typical uses	Shape of parti-cles[t]	Size range, U.S. Standard mesh	Internal porosity x, %	External void fraction ϵ, %	Bulk dry density, lb./cu. ft.	Avg. pore diam., ang-stroms	Surface area, sq. m./g.	Adsorptive capacity, g./g. dry solid	Trade designations
Aluminas									
Active alumina (transition alumina)	G	3–8, etc.	.....	.....	55	.....	210	0.14[a]	Alcoa F-1, F-3, F-7
Uses: drying gases and liquids;	G	20–60	.....	.....	47	.....	310	....	Filtrol 95
catalyst; catalyst support; de-	G	Various	25	49	50	34	250	0.14[a]	Reynolds R-2101 = RA-1, R-2102 = RA-3
fluoridation of alkylates; neutralization of lube oils	C	0.18 in.	.....	40	43	.....	310	....	Filtrol 86
	T	1 × 5/8 in.	60	.....	85	.....	0.5	0.14[a]	Porous Tabular Alumina T-71
	S	4–8, etc.	40	39	52	20–80	~350	....	Alumine Activée A, RA, S
	S	3–8, etc.	.....	45	45	64	360	0.20[a]	Kaiser Active Alumina KA-101
	S	150–400	.....	35	48	.....	400; 310	....	Filtrol 90, 106
	S	3–6	.....	.....	55	.....	350	0.21[a]	Alcoa Gel, Type H-151
	T	1–1/8 in.[c]	30; 47	~42	~51	136; 99	90; 190	....	Harshaw Al-0104T, Al-1404T
Desiccant (single-use), $CaCl_2$-impregnated	G	3–8, etc.	.....	.....	60	.....	.....	0.21[a]	Alcoa F-5
Catalytic alumina, low soda	S	3–8	.....	.....	55	~50	~250	....	Alcoa F-10; Alumine Activée CR
Activated bauxite	C, G	8–20, etc.	35	40	~53	~50	.....	0.04–0.2[d]	Florite; Florite Desiccant; Bauxite Activée
Chromatographic alumina	G	80–200	.....	.....	68	.....	210; 150	....	Alcoa Gamma Alumina F-20; XF-21
	S, P	30–140; P	.....	.....	~55	20–80	160	....	Alumine Chromatographique
Acid range (pH 4)	G	120–200[e]	.....	.....	54	.....	.....	....	Woelm acidic Al_2O_3; BioRad AG4
Neutral range (pH 7)	G	120–200[e]	.....	.....	54	.....	.....	....	Woelm neutral Al_2O_3; BioRad AG7
Alkaline range (pH 10)	G	120–200[e]	.....	.....	54	.....	.....	....	Woelm basic Al_2O_3; BioRad AG10
Siliceous Adsorbents									
Aluminosilicates	C, S, P	1/16 or 1/8 in.	45–55	36	~44	.....	770	....	Linde Molecular Sieves 4A, 5A, 13X
Use: selective adsorption based on molecular size and shape; drying;		Various	.....	34	~41	.....	.....	0.22[f]	Microtraps
catalyst support	P	200	.....	.....	50	.....	.....	0.65 meq[i]	Volclay
	C	1/16 or 1/8 in.	30	30	44	.....	550	....	Siliporite K10,[g] K20[h]
Acid-treated clay	P	....	.....	.....	30–45	.....	225–300	....	Clarsil PC, LC, LE; Filtrol 1, 4
Uses: refining petroleum fractions, vegetable oils, juices; catalyst base	C, S	0.15 in.	.....	40	53	.....	100	....	Filtrol 110, 120
Magnesia–silica gel	G	Various	33	25	~30	.....	300	....	Florisil; Magnesol
Fuller's earth	G	Various	~54	40	30–40	.....	130–250	....	Florex (regular; calcined); Clarsil PCS-G; Cecacite
Uses: same as for clay	P	....	.....	.....	38	.....	250	....	Clarsil PCS
Diatomaceous earth	C	Various	75–80	50	17–30	.....	1.2–20	....	Celite; Clarcel; Chromosorb; Dicalite
	P	....	.....	.....	9	.....	25–50	....	Tamms 680 Multicel; Celite; Clarcel; Dicalite
Silica gel	G, P	Various	~70	35–43	~25	140	~320	1.0[j]	Davison Silica Gel[k]
Uses: drying of gases, separation of hydrocarbons, catalyst base	G	Various	35–40	30–40	40–48	25–50	500–900	0.4–0.5[j]	Cecagel V, B; Sorbsil, UCC, CG 60 M; Davison; Eagle
	S	1/8 in., etc.	34	36	50	21	650	0.4	Mobil Sorbead R, W
	P	....	.....	.....	30	20	700	....	Davison; Cecagel P; Bio-Rad Silicic Acid
Carbons									
Shell-based; Uses (for all carbons): water treatment, gas purification, solvent recovery and purification, decolorizing natural products	G	Various	~50	~37	27–32	20	800–1100	45[l]	Acticarbone NC-35, NC-45; Barnebey-Cheney AC, KR, G, PC, PL; Cochranex FCB; Columbia L[u]; Girdler G-32;[r] Pittsburgh PCB
	P	....	60–80	45	20–22	~30	1200	....	Barnebey-Cheney YF-6, JF-6, JU-6 (high capacity)
Wood-based	G	Various	55–75	~40	10–35	20–40	625–1400	6–9[m]	Acticarbone (various grades); Cochranex FCN; Norit (various grades); Nuchar C
	P	....	.....	.....	10–35	.....	600–1200	....	Darco KB; Norit (various grades); Nuchar Aqua, WA, B, C
	P	....	.....	.....	22–28	.....	700–800	....	Darco G60
	P	....	43	40	19	32	800	....	Carboraffin
Peat-based	C, G, P	0.10 in., etc.	~55	40	15–32	30–40	500–1600	....	Norit (various grades); Sorbonorit III
	C	5–7	40–50	37	~21	~22	1300	....	Supersorbon IV, Solvorbon
Coal-based	G	Various	65–75	45–50	20–30	20–38	500–1200	~0.40[n]	Darco Granular
	G	10–30	.....	40	~30	60–65	800–1100	....	Cochranex FCP; Pittsburgh (various grades)
	G	....	80	40	28	22	1100	50[l]	Barnebey-Cheney MN-3
	C	50	45	40	30	.....	1500	....	Regesolv
	C	0.12, 0.2 in.	70–75	30	25–35	~25	~1400	....	Acticarbone (various grades); Benzocarb
	P	....	.....	.....	25–30	.....	600–700	....	Darco DC, S-51, BG; Hydrodarco B
Petroleum-based	C	Various	70–85	26–34	28–34	18–22	800–1100	0.6–0.7[o]	Columbia (various grades)
	P	....	~65	32	33	18–22	1000	0.65[o]	Columbia LC
Bone-based or simulated	G	Various	50–55	18	40	100	115	....	Bone Black, Bone Char
	G	Various	50–55	15	40	200	95	....	Synthad
Other Inorganic Materials									
Anhydrous $CaSO_4$ (desiccant)	G	Various	38	~45	60	.....	.....	0.12[p]	Drierite
Iron oxide adsorbent	C	4–6	22	37	90	.....	20	0.5[q]	Girdler G-42
Magnesia	P	....	70–80	~45	25	.....	~2	....	
Organic Materials									
Porous resin (decolorizing)	G	16–50	.....	.....	.....	.....	.....	....	Asmit 224; Decolorite; Wofatit E; Permutit DR; Duolite S-35[u]
Phenolic resin (decolorizing)	G	10–50	.....	35	~22	.....	3	....	Duolite S30
Aromatic-amine resin	G	16–50	~65	.....	40–50	.....	.....	....	Wofatit EW, EZ; Asmit 173, 173NP
Quaternary amine chloride resin	G, S	16–50	~65	.....	40–45	.....	.....	....	Asmit 259N, 261
Copper-amine resin (O_2 removal)	S	10–50	.....	35	30	.....	.....	0.12[s]	Duolite S-10

Table 16-2. Physical Properties of Adsorbents—(*Continued*)

[a] Water at 60 per cent relative humidity.
[b] Also available as spheres.
[c] Various specific sizes available within stated range.
[d] Water; test conditions not specified.
[e] Slightly different ranges for each manufacturer.
[f] Water, at 100 per cent relative humidity.
[g] Vacant sites have 4 angstrom diameter.
[h] Vacant sites have 5 angstrom diameter.
[i] Color bodies; test conditions not specified.
[j] Water, at 100 per cent relative humidity.
[k] "Intermediate-density" grade.
[l] Accelerated chloropicrin test.
[m] Phenol value.
[n] Benzene, at 20°C. and 7.5 mm. partial pressure.
[o] Carbon tetrachloride; test conditions not specified.
[p] Water; test conditions not specified.
[q] Sulfur.
[r] Impregnated with iron oxide.
[s] Oxygen.
[t] Shape of particles is indicated as follows: C, cylindrical pellets; G, granular; P, powder; S, spherical beads; T, tablets.
[u] Manufacture discontinued.

bulk volume as packed in a column. The dry **particle density** ρ_p is related to ρ_b and to the fraction of external voids ϵ in a packed bed as follows:

$$\rho_p(1 - \epsilon) = \rho_b \qquad (16\text{-}1)$$

The **crystalline density** of the solid ρ_c, as usually given in property tables for pure chemical compounds, is related to ρ_p and to the internal porosity x of the particles as

$$\rho_c(1 - x) = \rho_p \qquad (16\text{-}2)$$

Similarly, the **wet density** of an individual particle ρ_w is related to these factors and to the liquid density ρ_f by

$$\rho_w = \rho_p + \rho_f x \qquad (16\text{-}3)$$

A less exact relation can be drawn between the pore surface area per unit weight of dry solid σ and the mean pore radius $\bar{r}$, such as

$$\sigma = \frac{(\text{const.})\,x}{\rho_p \bar{r}} \qquad (16\text{-}4)$$

The "constant" in this equation may vary with different types of porous sorbents but is often of the order of 3.0.

For ion exchangers, the water-wet density is the usual value given. Ion-exchange materials are not considered porous unless they are inorganic and/or "mineral" (*e.g.*, sulfonated coal), or have had the usual resin structure interlaced with true internal pores (*i.e.*, continuous channels having an average diameter of at least 30 angstroms) by a separate step in the synthesis. For resinous exchangers in general, one can identify an **internal porosity** x which measures the uptake of water or other liquid and will vary somewhat with the ion held; but the particle phase approximates a true molecular-scale solution, and no surface area or pore diameter can be defined. Table 16-3 does not account specifically for the swelling that occurs upon wetting a dry resin, or the swelling or shrinkage caused by exchanging one ion for another.

Every effort has been made to provide these data in useful form, free from error. However, data from different sources may not be reported on the same bases and therefore cannot necessarily be taken to indicate the relative qualities of similar products.

EQUILIBRIUM RELATIONSHIPS

Performance of a solid sorption agent in treating a liquid or gas depends upon four factors: stoichiometric capacity of the solid, whenever it can be defined independently; equilibrium behavior, which limits the realization of full stoichiometric capacity; rate behavior, which often further restricts the performance of the system; and process arrangement, with its consequences for the material balance. Sometimes (*e.g.*, for ion exchange, adsorption from the liquid phase, and nearly irreversible adsorption from the gas phase) the realizable capacity of a solid has a nearly constant value. In other cases, the effective capacity varies with solute concentration in the feed and thus must itself be determined from the equilibrium behavior.

In systems with only two fluid-phase components—the solvent or carrier and the solute—a simple plot can be drawn of the solute concentration in the solid phase as a function of its concentration or partial pressure in the fluid phase. Each such curve usually holds at only one particular temperature, and hence is known as an **isotherm.** Figure 16-2 shows two isotherms. Solid-phase concentration q may be measured as moles per unit weight, and fluid-phase concentration c in moles per unit volume. Where the fluid is a gas, the partial pressure p of solute is often used as the abscissa; hence, in the following discussion, X is a generalized fluid-phase concentration that represents either c or p.

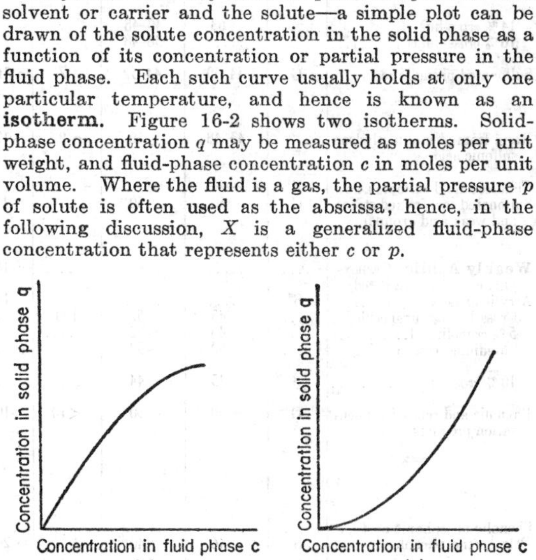

FIG. 16-2. Simplest shapes of adsorption isotherms. (*a*) Favorable equilibrium; (*b*) unfavorable equilibrium. [*J. Am. Chem. Soc.*, *65*, 532 (1943).]

Separation performance depends upon the curvature of a particular isotherm; this provides the basis for identifying a convex-upward curve as **favorable** (Fig. 16-2*a*) and a concave-upward one as **unfavorable** (Fig. 16-2*b*). Straight-line isotherms make up an intermediate class. Complex isotherms are possible that include both unfavorable and favorable portions.

For calculation purposes, isotherms may be treated in one of three ways: (1) a purely graphical recording of

Table 16-3. Physical Properties of Ion-exchange Materials

Material	Shape of particles[bb]	Bulk wet density (drained), lb./cu. ft.	Moisture content (drained), % by weight	Swelling due to exchange, %	Max. operating temp., °F.[aa]	Operating pH range	Exchange capacity: Dry, meq./g.	Exchange capacity: Wet, meq./ml.	Trade designations
Strongly Acidic	....	....	....	....	....	....	....	....	(Sodium-ion forms, 16–50 mesh; 40% external voids; except where noted)
Sulfonated polystyrene	S	....	....	i	~250	1–13			
1% cross-linked	....	44	91	....	....	....	5.8	0.35	Amberlite[a,d,o] IR-120, XE-176W; Diaion SK 1; Dowex[a,d,h] 50, 50W;[n] Permutit Q = Ionac C-240[h]
2% cross-linked	....	45	82	....	....	....	5.5	0.7	Diaion SK 1; Dowex[a,d,h] 50, 50W; Permutit Q = Ionac C-240[h]
4% cross-linked	....	47–51	68	35	....	....	5.3	1.3	Diaion SK 1; Dowex[a,d,h] 50, 50W; Duolite C-20; Imac C22;[h] Kastel C300, C300P;[q] Permutit Q = Ionac C-240;[h] Zeo-Karb 225 = Zerolit 225; Zeollex SA-LX
5 to 5.5% cross-linked	....	48–49	58–65	....	....	....	~5.1	1.4–1.6	Amberlite[f] IR-112,[dd] IR-120,[a,o] XE-100;[a] Dowex[a,d,h] 50, 50W; Duolite C-20, C-21,[cc] C-25[q]
8 to 8.3% cross-linked	....	49–53	44–53	7–10	....	....	4.8–5.1	1.9–2.2	Allassion GS;[h] Amberlite[a,d,e,f,h,o] IR-120;[d] XE-77 (H^+), XE-163 (Li^+), XE-169 (NH_4^+), XE-218(Li^+)[i]; Amberlyst 15;[q] Cochranex CRB, CRJ, CRZ-W; Diaion SK 1; Dowex[a,d] 50, 50W = Nalcite[h] HCR, HCR-W; Duolite C-20 = Chempro[dd] C-20; Duolite C-27; Imac C8P;[q] Ion-X;[b] Lewatit S100, S115;[g] Permutit Q = Ionac C-240;[h] Kastel C300; Wofatit KPS-200; Zeo-Karb 225 = Zerolit 225;[h] Zeollex SA-MX
Cross-linkage data not specified	....	50–56	48–50	....	....	....	4.5–5.2	1.9–2.2	Amberlite[f] IR-112,[dd] 200; Cation G-300; Cochranex CRV; Permutit RS; Permutit 50, C 50-D; Permutit QPHF = Ionac C-244; Resex P; Resina Cationica;[cc] Wofatit KPS[b]
9% cross-linked	....	~51	~48	....	....	....	5.1	~2.2	Allassion CM;[d,h] Duolite C-27
10% cross-linked	....	50–54	40–50	5	....	....	4.3–5.1	1.9–2.2	Amberlite[f] IR-120,[a] IR-122; Aminex M5;[e] Cochranex CRC, CRC-X; Dowex[a,d] 50,[h] 50W = Nalcite[h] HGR, HGR-W; Duolite C-20; Imac C12,[h,q] C26;[c,cc] Permutit QB = Ionac C-250
12% cross-linked	....	56	40–48	....	....	....	4.9–5.1	2.0–2.2	Amberlite[f] IR-120;[a] IR-124[g]; Diaion SK 1; Dowex[a,d,h] 50, 50W = Nalcite[h] HDR, HDR-W; Duolite C-20 = Chempro[dd] C-20; Imac C12P;[q] Kastel C300AGQ; Permutit Q = Ionac C-255
14% cross-linked	....	63	40–48	....	....	....	4.5	2.5–3.0	Allassion CM[d,h]
16% cross-linked	....	....	38–48	....	....	....	....	....	Diaion SK 1; Dowex[a,d,h] 50, 50W; Imac C16P;[q] Permutit QD = Ionac C-260;[h] Zeollex SA-HX
Sulfonated phenolic resin	G	44–50	44–52	7	~160	k	1.9–2.9	0.6–1.2	Amberlite IR-1;[cc] Diaion BK; Dowex 30[c] = Nalcite MX;[c] Imac C-11; Ionac C-200; Lewatit KS, KSN;[c] Resex; Wofatit D, F, K, KS; Zeo-Karb 215 = Zerolit 215; Zeo-Rex
Resin from phenol methylene sulfonic acid	....	43–48	50	~9	~170	k	1.9–2.9	0.6–0.9	Acuolite C-131; Amberlite IR-100,[cc] IR-105;[cc] Bio-Rex 40[c,d,h]; Duolite[h] C-3, C-10; Lewatit PN; Wofatit P; Zeo-Karb 315
Cellulose alkyl sulfonic acid	F	~20	....	k	....	4–10	~0.2	0.05	Cellex SE; Selectacel SM
Sulfonated coal (mixed strong and weak acid groups)	G	50	50	....	~130	2–12	1.7	0.7	Allassion C, CP; Cochranex CCA; Dusarit S (Na^+, H^+); Ionac C-150 = Zeo-Karb; Konvertat; Permutit S53 (Ca^{++}); Permutit C30-N, C40-P; Soucol; Zeo-Karb Na, HI
Weakly Acidic (Carboxylic, except where noted)	....	....	....	....	~180	....	....	....	(Hydrogen-ion form, 16–50 mesh, 40% external voids; except where noted)
Acrylic or methacrylic	S	....	....	....	~180				
Cross linkage unspecified	....	45	57	100	....	5–14	11.0	3.5	Amberlite IRC-50[a,d,e,f,o]
5% cross-linked	....	45	~52	....	....	5–14	10.0	3.5	Cochranex CRI; Permutit H-70 = Ionac C-270
"Medium" cross-linking	....	~50	~52	....	....	5–14	9.5	3.7	Allassion CC; Imac 25; Kastel C100; Permutit C; Wofatit CP[b] (Na^+); Zeo-Karb 226 = Zerolit 226
10% cross-linked	d	45	44	....	....	5–14	9.0	3.5	Bio-Rex 70; Duolite CS-101; Permutit H-70 = Ionac C-270
Phenolic and related condensation products	G	~50	~50	<10	~100	7–12			
							1.9	0.8	Duolite CS-100
							2.5	1.1	Wofatit CN (Na^+)[a]; Zeo-Karb 216 = Zerolit 216 (Na^+)
							4.0	~1.6	Imac C19; Lewatit CNO
							5.0	1.9	Permutit H = Ionac C-265
							k	k	Imac C-25; Lewatit C; Wofatit C
Phenolic phosphonic acid	....	....	....	....	....	....	3.3	1.4	Duolite ES-65
Polystyrene phosphonic acid	S	46	40	....	~200	4–12	6.6	3.0	Bio-Rex 63 (Na^+);[d] Duolite C-61,[cc] C-63; Nalcite X-219
Polystyrene phosphonous acid	S	46	40	....	~240	4–12	6.0	2.7	Bio-Rex 62 (Na^+);[d] Duolite C-60[cc], C-62
Polyvinyl sulfuric acid	....	....	....	....	210	....	....	....	Buggenheim CFB-P
Polystyrene aminodiacetic acid	S	....	71–76	....	....	4–14	1.1	0.33	Chelex 100; Dowex A-1
Inorganic materials	G								
Greensand (Na^+)	....	84	2	None	140	6–8	~0.14	~0.18	Cochranex CGH; Ionac C-50; Zeo-Dur; Zerolit
Aluminum silicate	G	35–60	....	None	90	7–8	....	0.4–0.6	Cochranex CSL; Decalso (H^+, Na^+); Decalso F, Y; Doucil (Na^+); Nalcolite; Permutit F, T (K^+) = Ionac C-101, C-102 (K^+); Zerwat; Zonolite Ore (Mg^+)
Same, gel form (Na^+)	....	52	~55	None	100	7–8	1.4	0.53	Decalso = Ionac C-100
Zirconium phosphate	....	56	....	....	....	....	....	1.8	Bio-Rad ZP-1[d]
Zirconium tungstate	....	100	....	....	....	....	....	0.8	Bio-Rad ZT-1[d]
Zirconium molybdate	....	50	....	....	....	....	....	0.5	Bio-Rad ZM-1[d]
Phosphomolybdate (NH_4^+)	....	....	....	....	....	....	....	0.2	Bio-Rad AMP-1[e]
Celluloses	F	~20	....	k	....	4–10	....	....	(Minus 100 mesh)
Phosphonic, low capacity	....	~20	....	....	....	....	~1.0	....	Cellex P (Na^+); Selectacel P (H^+, NH_4^+); Whatman P10
Medium capacity	....	....	....	....	....	....	4	....	Whatman P40
High capacity	....	....	....	....	....	....	7	....	Whatman P70
Methyl carboxylic	....	....	....	....	....	....	~0.7	....	Cellex CM, Selectacel CM, Whatman CM 70

[a] CP grades available.
[b] Other degrees of cross linking are available.
[c] Granular.
[d] Finer-mesh sizes available.
[e] Very fine powder available.
[f] Fine-particle grades carry XE or CG numbers.

Table 16-3. Physical Properties of Ion-exchange Materials—(*Continued*)

Material	Shape of particles[bb]	Bulk wet density (drained), lb./cu. ft.	Moisture content (drained), % by weight	Swelling due to exchange, %	Max. operating temp., °F.[aa]	Operating pH range	Exchange capactiy Dry, meq./g.	Exchange capactiy Wet, meq./ml.	Trade designations
Strongly Basic, ...	....	.....	.....	......	......	....	....	....	(Chloride-ion form, 16–50 mesh, 40% external voids; except where noted)
Polystyrene matrix, trimethyl benzyl ammonium type[m]	S	.....	.....	[l]	......	1–13			
1 to 2% cross-linked......	....	.....	.....	......	......	....	3.2	0.25	Dowex[a,d] 1[n]
4% cross-linked..........	....	42	60	......	100[p]	....	3.45	0.90	Amberlite[a,d,o] IRA-401,[q] IRA-401S, XE-75;[dd] Dowex[a,d] 1; Zeollex SB 1-LX
6% cross-linked..........	....	43	~58	......	100[p]	....	~4.0	1.1	Amberlite IRA-402; Kastel A500; Zeollex SB I-MX
8% cross-linked..........	....	45	56	15–20	120[p]	....	4.3	1.3	Amberlite[a] IRA-400, XE-78[r]; Cochranex AL-AT; De-Acidite[s] FF = Zerolit[s] FF; Dowex[a,d] 1 = Nalcite SBR
Cross linkage unspecified..	....	40–45	42–56	3–20	120[p]	....	4.1	1.3	Allassion AQ17; Amberlite IRA-405, IRA-425; Diaion SA 100; Duolite A-42; Imac S5-30,[cc] S5-40, S5-50; Lewatit M-500; Permutit ESB; Permutit S1 = Ionac A-540; Resanex HB; Wofatit SBW, SBI, SBU
Same, porous structure[q]...	....	~40	52–62	2–10	120	....	~4.0	1.0	Cochranex AM-AY; Diaion SA 101; Duolite A-101, A-101D; Lewatit MP-500; Dowex 21K = Nalcite SBR-M, SBR-P; Wofatit SBW
10 to 16% cross-linked....	....	43	.....	......	......	....	....	1.4–1.5	Dowex[a,d] 1; Zeollex SB I-HX
Polystyrene matrix, dimethyl-hydroxyethyl-benzyl ammonium type									
1 to 4% cross-linked.......	....	44	50[t]	......	......	....	3.2	0.8[t]	Dowex[a,d] 2; Zeollex SB II-LX (4%)
6% cross-linked..........	....	45	.....	......	......	....	....	1.2	Kastel A300; Zeollex SB II-MX
8% cross-linked..........	....	45	42	5–15	100[p]	....	3.4	1.4	Amberlite IRA-410; Cochranex AP-AQ; Dowex[a,d] 2 = Nalcite SAR
Cross linkage unspecified..	....	~44	~42	......	100[p]	....	3.5–4.5	1.2–1.5	Allassion AQ 27; Amberlite IRA 411, XE-98;[dd] Diaion SA 200; Duolite A40, A102; Imac S5-52; Lewatit M-II, M-600; Permutit ES; Permutit S2 = Ionac A-550; Permutit A300 D
Same, porous structure[q]...	....	~44	~42	......	100[p]	....	3.4	0.8–1.2	Allassion DC22; Diaison SA 201; Duolite A102D; Kastel A500P; Lewatit MP-600
10–12% cross-linked.......	....	45	.....	......	......	....	....	1.2–1.5	Dowex[a,d] 2; Zeollex SB II-HX
Condensation products, phenolic matrix..............	G	45	.....	......	100	....	2.3	0.8	Imac S-3; Lewatit MN; Wofatit L 165
Addition product with pyridinium groups...........	....	.....	50	10	100	....	4.3	1.4	Permutit SK; SKB = Ionac A-570, A-580; A-590
Trimethylaminoethyl cellulose....................	F	.....	.....	[k]	......	4–10	0.6	....	Cellex T; Selectacel TEAE
Weakly Basic									(Hydroxide-ion form, 16–50 mesh, 40% external voids, except where noted)
Aminopolystyrene..........	G; S	43	45	5–25	180	0–8	5.3–6.0	2.0–2.5	Allassion AS, ADM; Amberlite[a] IR-45; Cochranex AH(Cl^-); De-Acidite F, H; Dowex[a] 3 = Nalcite WBR; Duolite A-14,[cc] A-114;[cc] Imac A20, A21;[x] Kaken Kogaku KK12; Kastel A-200; Lewatit[w,x] M, M2, MI, MIH, MIH-59, MP-60;[q] Merck II; Permutit E; Permutit A240-A; Wofatit M. N, MD; Zerolit B[cc] = De-Acidite B[cc]
	G; S	25	52	5–20	200	0–8	~6.0	~1.1	Imac A19, A20;[v,w] Polyaminostyrene
	S	42	50	~10	100[p]	0–10	4.5	1.5	Imac A21;[x] Permutit W = Ionac A-315[v,w] (Cl^-, SO_4^{--})
	S	42	50	......	200	0–6	3.5	1.3	De-Acidite G = Zerolit G[x] (Cl^-)
Aminated acrylic (or other aliphatic) polymers	G; S	45	60	~10	100[p]	0–10	6.0–7.0	1.5–2.0	Deacidite = Ionac A-260 (SO_4^{--});[w,x] De-Acidite 735;[w,x] Amberlite XE-168[x]
	G	40	50	~10	140	0–6	9.2	2.9	Bio-Rex 5;[w,x] De-Acidite E = Zerolit E; Resanex
Aminated phenolic condensation products	G	32	45–50	15	100	0–8	9–10	2.5	Amberlite IR-4B; Duolite A-7[w] (SO_4^{--}); Imac A33, A34;[x] Permutit A230, A230-A
	G	30	45	~15	140	0–10	7–8	1.9–2.1	Duolite A4[x] (SO_4^{--}), A6[x] (SO_4^{--}); Permutit CCG = Ionac A-330 (Cl), (SO_4^{--})
Epoxy-polyamine...........	....	43	~55	......	170	....	9.1	2.9	Duolite A-30T[x]; Imac A13T[x], A17, A27
Zirconium oxide gel.........	G	50	.....	......	......	....	....	0.8	Bio-Rad H20-1
Celluloses..................	F	~20	.....	[k]					
Aminoethyl.............	....	.....	.....	......	......	....	1.0	....	Whatman AE-50
Diethylaminoethyl........	....	.....	.....	......	......	....	~0.8	....	Cellex D; Selectacel DEAE; Whatman DE-50; Macherley-Nagel DEAE
Tertiary amine...........	....	.....	.....	......	......	....	0.3	....	Cellex E; Selectacel Ecteola; Macherley-Nagel Ecteola
Para-aminobenzyl.........	....	.....	.....		......	....	0.4	....	Cellex PAB
Dextran polymer, diethylaminoethyl............	....	.....	.....	......	......	....	....	....	DEAE-Sephadex
Intermediate Basic									
Epoxy-polyamine (and related structures)...............	S	43	55	3	170	....	8.8	2.7	Allassion AW, AW3; Duolite A-30, A-30B (25%)[u], A-70[cc]; Kastel A100
	S	41	~55	......	......	....	8.0	2.5	Cochranex AV; Duolite A-41, A-43 (30%);[u] Permutit A = Ionac A-300 (Cl^-, SO_4^{--})
	S	38	~55	......	......	....	7.5	1.8	Duolite A-37 (35%)[u]
Amino polystyrene..........	....	~40	~40	......	......	....	8–10	3.0	Imac A13, A17, A19 (lower capacity); Wofatit L 150 (Cl^-), L 165 (Cl^-)
Aminated phenolic..........	....	~40	~45	......	......	....	~5	1.7	Cochranex AN(Cl^-); Duolite A-2[w], A-3[cc], A-4[x], A-6[x], A-7[w] (all SO_4^{--})

[g] Resistant to oxidizing agents.
[h] H^+ form available, or usual.
[i] Li^7 form available, or usual.
[j] Entries that follow are for H^+ form converted to Na^+ form.
[k] Uncertain.
[l] Entries that follow are for OH^- form converted to Cl^- form.
[m] May be unstable to reducing agents containing sulfur.
[n] Analytical grades of Dowex resins, in various size ranges, are available.
[o] Analytical grades of Amberlite resins, in various size ranges, are available.
[p] OH^- form; Cl^- form is stable to near 200°F.
[q] Porous bead structure with 15 to 25 per cent internal porosity.
[r] OH^- form usually supplied.
[s] Amine type uncertain.
[t] 4 per cent cross-linked.
[u] Per cent of strong base, relative to total capacity.
[v] Primary amines known to be present.
[w] Secondary amines known to be present.
[x] Tertiary amines known to be present.
[aa] Longer useful life is obtained at lower temperatures.
[bb] Shape of particles is indicated as follows: F, fiber; G, granular; P powder; S, spherical beads.
[cc] Manufacture discontinued.
[dd] Designation discontinued.

experimental measurements (use of this method is, of course, limited to graphical calculation procedures); (2) an empirical algebraic form fitted to the data, usually selected for its generality and for its simplicity of use in subsequent calculations; (3) an equation that truly reflects the molecular statistics of the particular solute-surface interactions involved (although this degree of rigor is not often possible, models based upon molecular theory do in fact provide many of the forms used for purely empirical data fitting).

In what follows, concentration values generally appear in a dimensionless form that is adapted to the individual system being described. This involves use of an upper-limit fluid-phase concentration X_0 and an upper-limit solid-phase concentration q_0^* that are in equilibrium with each other.

For **adsorption** with an initially empty solid, the incoming fluid-phase concentration is taken as the upper-limit value. The dimensionless fluid-phase concentration becomes

$$\mathbf{X} = \frac{X}{X_0} \tag{16-5}$$

and the dimensionless solid-phase concentration is

$$\mathbf{Y} = \frac{q}{q_0^*} \tag{16-6}$$

For **ion exchange** with modern industrial sorbents, which always involves two or more species of like charge, the solid capacity in gram (or pound) equivalents per unit weight generally remains constant as exchange proceeds; hence capacity is designated as a fixed value, Q. The total "equivalent" concentration of ions in the liquid, likewise a constant, is C_0. In terms of these reference concentrations, the dimensionless fluid-phase concentration is

$$\mathbf{x} = \frac{c}{C_0} \tag{16-7}$$

and the dimensionless solid-phase concentration is

$$\mathbf{y} = \frac{q}{Q} \tag{16-8}$$

These dimensionless concentrations will lie in the range of 0 to 1.

Empirical Equations for Adsorption. Seven representative forms of empirical isotherm are given in Table 16-4. The first column gives the isotherm equation in its dimensional form, without reference to a local upper limit. The second column is the equilibrium $\mathbf{Y}$ in terms of the coexisting $\mathbf{X}$, and the third column gives the equilibrium $\mathbf{X}$ as a function of the coexisting $\mathbf{Y}$. The last column gives the derivative $d\mathbf{Y}^*/d\mathbf{X}$, which is used in calculations (described below) of proportionate-pattern break-through curves.

In a system with completely homogeneous surfaces and negligible interaction between adsorbed molecules, the **Langmuir equation** suffices. The other equations represent different types of departure from the Langmuir conditions.

Calculated shapes of isotherms, using the equations in Table 16-4, are equivalent to four of the five types of curve shown in Fig. 16-3; that is, to all except type IV, which shows two inflection points. The classification of types in Fig. 16-3 is due to Brunauer, Deming, Deming, and Teller [*J. Am. Chem. Soc.*, **62**, 1723 (1940)], who supply an equation for fitting type IV. The constants of the equations in Table 16-4 must fall into a specific range, as given in Table 16-5, in order to fit the isotherm type indicated.

Empirical Equations for Ion Exchange. A general guide to ion-exchange equilibria is given by the Donnan membrane approach [*Chem. Revs.*, **1**, 73 (1924). Gregor, *J. Colloid Sci.*, **6**, 20 (1951). Rice and Harris, *J. Chem. Phys.*, **24**, 1258 (1956)]. If the exchange reaction is written in the general terms

$$mA + R_mB \rightleftharpoons mRA + B$$

Table 16-4. Adsorption Equilibria

Equation type	$\dfrac{q^*}{q_{\text{lim}}}$	$\mathbf{Y}^*$	$\mathbf{X}^*$	$\dfrac{d\mathbf{Y}^*}{d\mathbf{X}}$
Langmuir[a]	$\dfrac{K_LX}{1+K_LX}$	$\dfrac{(1+K_LX_0)\mathbf{X}}{1+K_LX_0\mathbf{X}}$	$\dfrac{\mathbf{Y}}{1+K_LX_0(1-\mathbf{Y})}$	$\dfrac{1+K_LX_0}{(1+K_LX_0\mathbf{X})^2}$
Sips[e]	$\left(\dfrac{K_SX}{1+K_SX}\right)^{\alpha_S}$	$\left[\dfrac{(1+K_SX_0)\mathbf{X}}{1+K_SX_0\mathbf{X}}\right]^{\alpha_S}$	$\dfrac{\mathbf{Y}^{1/\alpha_S}}{1+K_SX_0(1-\mathbf{Y}^{1/\alpha_S})}$	$\dfrac{\alpha_S(1+K_SX_0)^{\alpha_S}\mathbf{X}^{\alpha_S-1}}{(1+K_SX_0\mathbf{X})^{\alpha_S+1}}$
Koble-Corrigan[a]	$\dfrac{K_CX^{\alpha_C}}{1+K_CX^{\alpha_C}}$	$\dfrac{(1+K_CX_0{}^{\alpha_C})\mathbf{X}^{\alpha_C}}{1+K_CX_0{}^{\alpha_C}\mathbf{X}^{\alpha_C}}$	$\left[\dfrac{\mathbf{Y}}{1+K_CX_0{}^{\alpha_C}(1-\mathbf{Y})}\right]^{1/\alpha_C}$	$\dfrac{\alpha_C(1+K_CX_0{}^{\alpha_C})\mathbf{X}^{\alpha_C-1}}{(1+K_CX_0{}^{\alpha_C}\mathbf{X}^{\alpha_C})^2}$
Freundlich[e]	$K_FX^{\alpha_F}$	$\mathbf{X}^{\alpha_F}$	$\mathbf{Y}^{1/\alpha_F}$	$\alpha_F\mathbf{X}^{\alpha_F-1}$
Trinomial	[b]	$\mathbf{X}(1-\alpha_1-\alpha_2+\alpha_1\mathbf{X}+\alpha_2\mathbf{X}^2)$	$\mathbf{Y}(1-\bar{\alpha}_1-\bar{\alpha}_2+\bar{\alpha}_1\mathbf{Y}+\alpha_2\mathbf{Y}^2)$[c]	$1-\alpha_1-\alpha_2+2\alpha\mathbf{X}+3\alpha_2\mathbf{X}^2$
Jura-Harkins[d,e]	$[-\ln(p/P)]^{-1/K_J}$	$\left(\dfrac{-\ln a_0}{-\ln a_0\mathbf{X}}\right)^{1/K_J}$	$a_0{}^{(\mathbf{Y}^{-K_J}-1)}$	$\dfrac{(-\ln a_0)^{1/K_J}}{K_J\mathbf{X}(-\ln a_0\mathbf{X})^{1+(1/K_J)}}$
Brunauer-Emmett-Teller[e,f]	$\dfrac{(1+K_B)p/P}{[1+K_B(P/p)][1-(p/P)]}$	$\dfrac{\mathbf{X}(1+K_Ba_0)(1-a_0)}{(1+K_Ba_0\mathbf{X})(1-a_0\mathbf{X})}$	[g]	$\dfrac{(1+K_Ba_0)(1-a_0)(1+K_Ba_0{}^2\mathbf{X}^2)}{(1+K_Ba_0\mathbf{X})^2(1-a_0\mathbf{X})^2}$

[a] For gas-phase equilibria, K is proportional to total pressure; q_{lim} corresponds to $p \rightarrow \infty$.
[b] No comparable form is defined.
[c] Relate $\bar{\alpha}_1$ and $\bar{\alpha}_2$ to α_1 and α_2.
[d] Generally, K_J is 2 or 3, or between them; q_{lim} corresponds to $p = P/2.718$.
[e] First column gives q^*/q_{ref}.
[f] q_{lim} is measured at $p = (P/K_B)[(1+K_B)^{0.5}-1]$.
[g] Solve from $\mathbf{Y}$ relation as a quadratic equation.

References: Langmuir, *J. Am. Chem. Soc.*, **38**, 2221 (1916); Sips, *J. Chem. Phys.*, **18**, 1024 (1950); Koble and Corrigan, *Ind. Eng. Chem.*, **44**, 383 (1952); Freundlich, "Colloid and Capillary Chemistry," Dutton, New York, 1926; Polynomial Type, *Advances in Chem. Eng.*, **2**, 157 (1958); Jura and Harkins, *J. Chem. Phys.*, **11**, 430 (1943); Brunauer, Emmett, and Teller, *J. Am, Chem. Soc.*, **60**, 309 (1938).

Nomenclature:
$K_B, K_C, K_F, K_J, K_L, K_S$ = equilibrium constants.
$\alpha_C, \alpha_F, \alpha_S$ = constant exponents.
$\alpha_1, \alpha_2, \bar{\alpha}_1, \bar{\alpha}_2$ = constants in trinomial adsorption equation.
a_0 = ratio of solute partial pressure in feed stream to solute vapor pressure p_0/P.
p = partial pressure in fluid phase.
P = vapor pressure of solute in fluid phase.
$\mathbf{X} = X/X_0$; $\mathbf{Y} = q/q_0^*$; $\mathbf{X}^* = X^*/X_0$; $\mathbf{Y}^* = q^*/q_0^*$; see development of Eqs. (16-5) and (16-6).

in practice the equilibrium is usually given by

$$K_{AB} = \left(\frac{q_A}{c_A}\right)^n \left(\frac{c_B}{q_B}\right) = \left(\frac{\mathbf{y}_A}{\mathbf{x}_A}\right)^n \left(\frac{\mathbf{x}_B}{\mathbf{y}_B}\right) \left(\frac{Q}{C_0}\right)^{n-1} \qquad (16\text{-}9)$$

where n lies betweeen m and unity, $n = m$ representing the "mass-action" form; concentrations q and c are in gram- (or pound-) equivalent units, rather than in moles; for binary systems $\mathbf{x}_A + \mathbf{x}_B = 1$, and $\mathbf{y}_A + \mathbf{y}_B = 1$ [*cf.* Eqs. (16-7) and (16-8)].

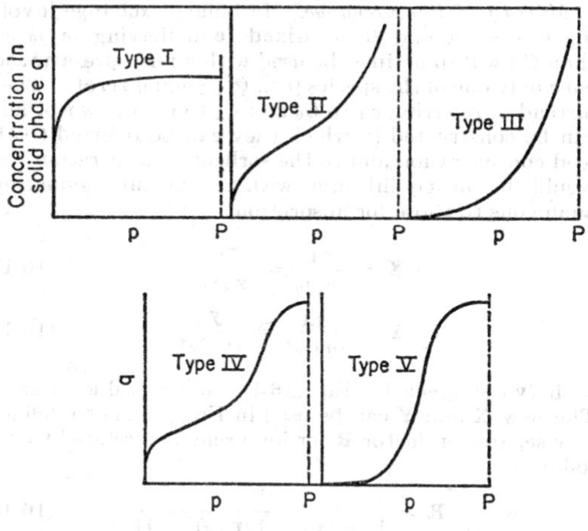

FIG. 16-3. Representative types of experimental isotherms for "physical" adsorption. [*J. Am. Chem. Soc.*, **62,** 1723 (1940).]

Constant-separation-factor Equations. Use of a constant separation factor, or equilibrium parameter, provides the same degree of generality in handling non-linear cases of adsorption and ion exchange that the use of a constant relative volatility gives in binary distillation. For **adsorption, a separation factor R** can be defined that becomes constant when the Langmuir isotherm is obeyed:

$$\mathbf{R} = \frac{\mathbf{X}(1 - \mathbf{Y})}{\mathbf{Y}(1 - \mathbf{X})} = \frac{1}{1 + K_L X_0} \qquad (16\text{-}10)$$

It is apparent that **R** is not invariant for a given adsorption system but will increase toward unity as the reference concentration X_0 decreases.

For **ion exchange,** the separation factor is

$$\mathbf{r}_{AB} = \frac{\mathbf{x}_A \mathbf{y}_B}{\mathbf{y}_A \mathbf{x}_B} = \frac{\mathbf{x}_A(1 - \mathbf{y}_A)}{\mathbf{y}_A(1 - \mathbf{x}_A)} \qquad (16\text{-}11)$$

The right-hand sides of Eqs. (16-9) and (16-11) are reciprocally identical when $n = 1$ (*e.g.*, in the exchange of ions of the same valence), so that

$$\mathbf{r} = \frac{1}{K_{n=1}} \qquad (16\text{-}12)$$

Equation (16-12), and Eqs. (16-7), (16-8), (16-9), and (16-11), apply also to **exchange adsorption,** where the fluid phase contains (or consists of) two adsorbable components which together entirely saturate the surfaces of the adsorbent so that $q_1 + q_2 = Q$ and $c_1 + c_2 = C_0$ (Ryan, Sc.D. Thesis in Chemical Engineering, M.I.T., 1951).

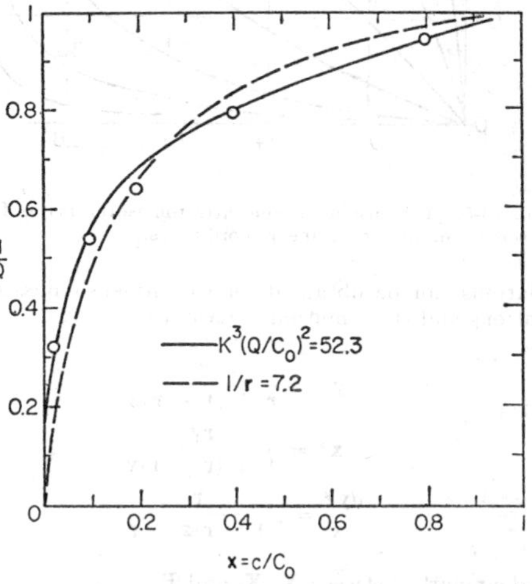

FIG. 16-4. Approximation to experimental equilibrium given by constant **r** curve; data are for Fe^{3+} replacing H^+ on Dowex 50 resin. [*Chem. Eng. Prog. Symp. Ser.*, **55,** No. 25, 113 (1959).]

When $n \neq 1$, a suitable average **r** can often be obtained by fitting the isotherm at a point where $\mathbf{y} = 1 - \mathbf{x}$. In this case,

$$\mathbf{r} = \left[\frac{1}{K}\left(\frac{Q}{C_0}\right)^{n-1}\right]^{\frac{2}{n+1}} \qquad (16\text{-}13)$$

This approximation is illustrated in Fig. 16-4 for data of Vasishth and David [*Am. Inst. Chem. Engrs. J.*, **5,** 391 (1959)] for the case where $m = n = \frac{1}{3}$.

From the definition given by Eq. (16-11), explicit

Table 16-5. Range of Constants for Equations in Table 16-4.

Equation type	Type I, favorable throughout	Type II, favorable at low, unfavorable at high concentrations	Type III, unfavorable throughout	Type V, unfavorable at low, favorable at high concentrations
Langmuir	$K_L > 0$	....	$0 > K_L X_0 > -1$	
Sips	$0 < \alpha_S < 1$ $\alpha_S < 2K_S X_0 + 1$ $K_S X_0 > -1$	$0 < \alpha_S < 1$ $\alpha_S > 2K_S X_0 + 1$ $K_S X_0 > -1$	$\alpha_S > 1$ $\alpha_S > 2K_S X_0 + 1$ $K_S X_0 > -1$	$\alpha_S > 1$ $\alpha_S < 2K_S X_0 + 1$ $K_S X_0 > -1$
Koble-Corrigan	$0 < \alpha_C < 1$ $\alpha_C < \frac{1 + K_C X_0}{1 - K_C X_0}$	$0 < \alpha_C < 1$ $\alpha_C > \frac{1 + K_C X_0}{1 - K_C X_0} > -1$	$\alpha_C > 1$ $\alpha_C > \frac{1 + K_C X_0}{1 - K_C X_0}$	$\alpha_C > 1$ $\alpha_C < \frac{1 + K_C X_0}{1 - K_C X_0}$ $K_C X_0 > -1$
Freundlich	$0 < \alpha_F < 1$ $K_F > 0$	....	$\alpha_F > 1$ $K_F > 0$	
Trinomial	$\alpha_1 < +3\alpha_2$ $\alpha_1 < 0$ $\alpha_1 + \alpha_2 < 1$	$\alpha_1 > +3\alpha_2$ $\alpha_1 < 0$ $\alpha_1 + \alpha_2 < 1$	$\alpha_1 > +3\alpha_2$ $0 < \alpha_1 < 3$ $\alpha_1 + \alpha_2 < 1$	$\alpha_1 < +3\alpha_2$ $0 < \alpha_1$ $\alpha_1 + \alpha_2 < 1$
Jura-Harkins	....	$K_J > 0$		
Brunauer-Emmett-Teller	$K_B a_0 > 1$ $0 > (3 + K_B a_0^2)\, a_0 < 1 - (1/K_B)$	$K_B a_0 > 1$ $(3 + K_B a_0^2) a_0 > 1 - (1/K_B)$	$1 > K_B a_0 > 0$	

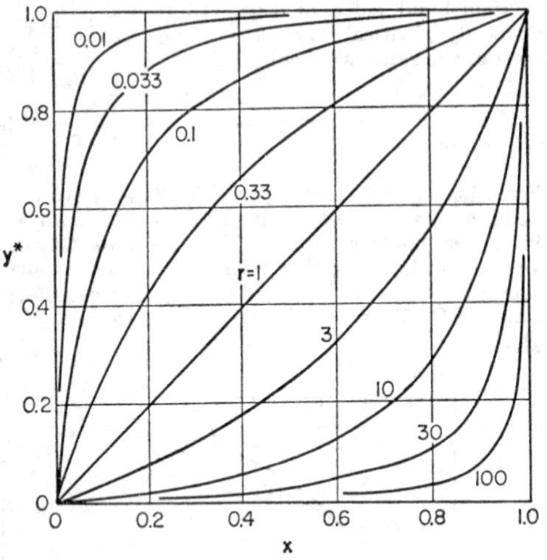

FIG. 16-5. Dimensionless-concentration isotherms as functions of separation factor on linear coordinates.

relations can be obtained for the dimensionless concentrations and their mutual derivative:

$$\mathbf{y}^* = \frac{\mathbf{x}}{\mathbf{r} + (1 - \mathbf{r})\mathbf{x}} \tag{16-14}$$

$$\mathbf{x}^* = \frac{\mathbf{r}\mathbf{y}}{1 + (\mathbf{r} - 1)\mathbf{y}} \tag{16-15}$$

$$\frac{d\mathbf{y}^*}{d\mathbf{x}} = \frac{\mathbf{r}}{[(1 - \mathbf{r})\mathbf{x} + \mathbf{r}]^2} \tag{16-16}$$

and similarly between **Y**, **X**, and **R**.

Variations in the shapes of isotherms, for a range of values of **r**, are shown in Fig. 16-5 on linear scales, and in Fig. 16-6 on logarithmic scales. In these figures **x**, **y***, and **r** can be replaced by **X**, **Y***, and **R**. Such plots can often be used for fitting **r** values to experimental data by

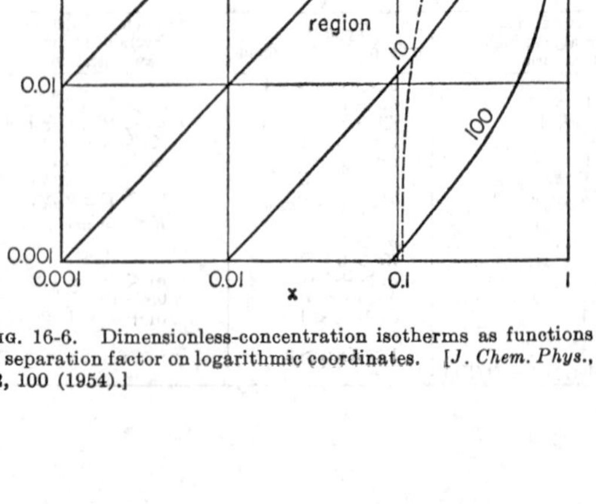

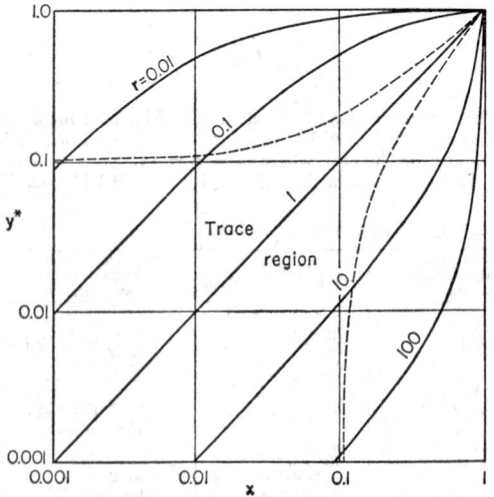

FIG. 16-6. Dimensionless-concentration isotherms as functions of separation factor on logarithmic coordinates. [*J. Chem. Phys.*, **22**, 100 (1954).]

empirical curve matching. It is seen that **r** values less than unity give "favorable" curves, whereas **r** values greater than unity give "unfavorable" curves.

Simplest of all sorption equilibria, and a special case of nearly all the types just considered but not often encountered, is the **linear isotherm** or Henry's-law case, $\mathbf{Y}^* = \mathbf{X}$; or, for exchange adsorption where $K(C_0/Q)^{n-1} = 1$, hence $\mathbf{y}^* = \mathbf{x}$. The ease of calculation for this case makes it a valuable reference condition, to which other cases may be compared. The linear case corresponds to $\mathbf{r} = 1$.

Mixed-feed Ion Exchange. In binary exchange involving species A and B, a **mixed feed** [having $(c_A)_0$ less than C_0] will sometimes be used with a resin presaturated with only one of the species [*i.e.*, $(q_A)_0$ equal zero]. Then, instead of referring c_A to C_0 and q_A to Q, a new isotherm can be constructed in which they can be referred to the feed concentration and to the sorbent concentration that would be in equilibrium with it, yielding equations analogous to those for adsorption:

$$\mathbf{X} = \frac{c_A}{(c_A)_0} = \frac{\mathbf{x}_A}{(\mathbf{x}_A)_0} \tag{16-17}$$

$$\mathbf{Y} = \frac{q_A}{(q_A)_0{}^*} = \frac{\mathbf{y}_A}{(\mathbf{y}_A)_0{}^*} \tag{16-18}$$

with $(\mathbf{y}_A)_0{}^*$ given by Eq. (16-14) at the value of $(\mathbf{x}_A)_0$. The new **X** and **Y** can be used in Eq. (16-11) to define a new separation factor **R** for ion exchange, related to **r** as follows:

$$\mathbf{R} = \frac{1}{1 + (\mathbf{x}_A)_0[(1/\mathbf{r}_{AB}) - 1]} \tag{16-19}$$

Note the similarity of Eq. (16-19) to the adsorption form [Eq. (16-10)].

An even more general case, corresponding to a mixed feed with a uniformly partially presaturated resin [$(q_A)_0$ between zero and Q], is described by Vermeulen and Hiester [*J. Chem. Phys.*, **22**, 96 (1954)].

The smaller $(\mathbf{x}_A)_0$ becomes, or the smaller $(c_A)_0$ is with respect to C_0, the more nearly **R** approaches unity. The chromatography of trace components often exhibits linear-isotherm behavior, as an example of this effect. An absolute value for $(\mathbf{x}_A)_0[(1/\mathbf{r}) - 1]$ of less than 0.1 is sufficient to approach this; this is known as the **trace criterion.** This region is shown inside the dotted lines on Fig. 16-6. In adsorption of a single solute species, the isotherm likewise approaches linearity as the feed-stream concentration of solute is reduced, as was noted in connection with Eq. (16-10). "Trace" systems have the further property that, if more than one solute is present in low concentration, each solute behaves as if the others were not present.

Examples. a. Thomas [*Ann. N.Y. Acad. Sci.*, **49**, 161 (1948)] provides the following Langmuir isotherm for the adsorption of anthracene from cyclohexane onto alumina:

$$q^* = \frac{22X}{1 + 375X}$$

with q^* in millimoles anthracene per gram when X is in millimoles anthracene per milliliter. What are the values of K_L and $q_{\lim}$ according to Table 16-4?

$K_L = 375$ ml./millimole anthracene (ans.)

$q_{\lim} = \dfrac{22}{K_L} = 5.87 \times 10^{-2}$ millimole anthracene/g. (ans.)

b. For the above isotherm and a feed concentration $X_0 = 8.11 \times 10^{-4}$ millimole/ml., what is the value of **R**?

$$\mathbf{R} = \frac{1}{1 + K_L(8.11 \times 10^{-4})} = 0.766 \quad \text{(ans.)}$$

c. For the above isotherm what feed concentration X_0 would give an **R** value greater than 0.9 according to Eq. (16-10)?

$$\mathbf{R} = \frac{1}{1 + 375X_0} > 0.9$$

$$X_0 < \frac{0.111}{375} = 2.96 \times 10^{-4} \text{ millimole anthracene/ml.} \qquad \text{(ans.)}$$

d. The equilibrium constant K for the exchange of A^+ with B resin is 3.16. According to Eq. (16-19) what mole fraction should A^+ be of the feed cations for **R** to be greater than 0.9?

$$\mathbf{r}_{AB} = \frac{1}{K_{AB}} = 0.316$$

$$\mathbf{R} = \frac{1}{1 + (\mathbf{x}_A)_0[(1/0.316) - 1]} > 0.9$$

$$(\mathbf{x}_A)_0 < \frac{0.111}{2.16} = 0.0515 \qquad \text{(ans.)}$$

Separation Factor for Reverse Processes. Mathematically, a **reverse process** is one where $\mathbf{x}_B$ replaces $\mathbf{x}_A$, and $\mathbf{y}_B$ replaces $\mathbf{y}_A$. The symbol † is used to designate the reverse step. From Eq. (16-11), the separation parameter becomes

$$\mathbf{r}^\dagger = \frac{1}{\mathbf{r}} \tag{16-20}$$

This is also true for **X**, **Y**, and **R**. Physically, this situation corresponds to desorption into a carrier phase of a previously adsorbed solute; or to a binary ion exchange which is precisely the reverse of the exchange for which **r** has been defined.

Multicomponent Equilibria for Adsorption. With the assumption of a constant separation factor for each component, it is possible to develop equilibrium equations that apply for a larger number of components. Such relations are derived below for one additional component; their further extension is fairly obvious. (Despite the formal similarity between single-component adsorption and two-component ion exchange, it seems desirable to use different frames of reference for multicomponent adsorption and for multicomponent ion exchange.)

For a pair of solute components 1 and 2, the respective reference fluid-phase concentrations $(X_1)_0$ and $(X_2)_0$ are determined; and the reference solid-phase equilibrium concentrations $(q_1)_0^*$ and $(q_2)_0^*$ and the separation factors $\mathbf{R}_1$ and $\mathbf{R}_2$ are defined for each component independently of the other. Then, if both species are present together, a Langmuir equation takes the form

$$\frac{q_1^*}{q_{\lim}} = \frac{K_1X_1}{1 + K_1X_1 + K_2X_2} \tag{16-21}$$

We set $X_1 = (X_1)_0\mathbf{X}_1$; $(q_1)_0/q_{\lim} = 1 - \mathbf{R}_1$; $K_1(X_1)_0 = (1 - \mathbf{R}_1)/\mathbf{R}_1$; with similar functions for component 2. Substitution in Eq. (16-21) then yields the result

$$\mathbf{Y}_1^* = \frac{q_1^*}{(q_1)_0^*} = \frac{\mathbf{X}_1}{\mathbf{R}_1 + (1 - \mathbf{R}_1)\mathbf{X}_1 + (\mathbf{R}_1/\mathbf{R}_2)(1 - \mathbf{R}_2)\mathbf{X}_2} \tag{16-22}$$

Multicomponent Equilibria for Ion Exchange. For these systems, the total concentrations C_0 and Q are retained as characteristics of the entire system, and the fractional concentrations are expressed with reference to them. We designate three components—A, B, and C. The dimensionless concentrations for A are

$$\mathbf{x}_A = \frac{c_A}{\Sigma c_i} = \frac{c_A}{C_0} \tag{16-23}$$

$$\mathbf{y}_A = \frac{q_A}{\Sigma q_i} = \frac{q_A}{Q} \tag{16-24}$$

Similar relations apply for components B and C. Also, for each pair of components, by analogy to Eq. (16-11), we can define the separation factor

$$\mathbf{r}_{AB} = \frac{\mathbf{x}_A\mathbf{y}_B}{\mathbf{y}_A\mathbf{x}_B} \tag{16-25}$$

with comparable equations for $\mathbf{r}_{AC}$ and $\mathbf{r}_{BC}$. We then utilize the relation $\Sigma\mathbf{y}_i = 1$ to obtain

$$\mathbf{y}_A^* = \frac{\mathbf{x}_A}{\mathbf{x}_A + \mathbf{r}_{AB}\mathbf{x}_B + \mathbf{r}_{AC}\mathbf{x}_C} \tag{16-26}$$

Note that Eqs. (16-22) and (16-26) reduce to the form of Eq. (16-14) when component 2 (or C) is absent. A modification of the same derivation will give equations for the **x**'s analogous to Eq. (16-15).

Distribution Ratio. For each process arrangement there is another useful equilibrium form—the dimensionless distribution ratio **D**. This term takes into account the relative amounts of each phase that would be in equilibrium:

$$\mathbf{D}_i = \frac{(q_i)_0^*W}{(X_i)_0v\epsilon} \tag{16-27}$$

where $W/v\epsilon$ is the ratio of solid weight W to fluids volume $v\epsilon$ in the system (v = volume of contactor, ϵ = fraction of external voids).

For simply binary ion exchange,

$$\mathbf{D}_\Sigma = \frac{QW}{C_0v\epsilon} \tag{16-28}$$

since the highest solid concentration that can be achieved in equilibrium with $(c_i)_0$, which is C_0 in such a case, will be Q, the ultimate capacity of the resin. When the "trace" criterion is met [see Eq. (16-19) and subsequent discussion], it can be seen from Eq. (16-14) that $(q_A)_0^*/(c_A)_0$ will approach $Q/\mathbf{r}_{AB}C_0$; so, in this case,

$$\mathbf{D}_A \cong \frac{QW}{\mathbf{r}_{AB}C_0v\epsilon} = \frac{\mathbf{D}_\Sigma}{\mathbf{r}_{AB}} \tag{16-29}$$

The distribution ratio **D** may be compared with $K_d(=Q/C_0)$ used by Boyd [*J. Am. Chem. Soc.*, **69**, 2818 (1947)], Mayer and Tompkins [*J. Am. Chem. Soc.*, **69**, 2866 (1947)], Glueckauf [*Trans. Faraday Soc.*, **51**, 34 (1955)], and others in considering ion-exchange chromatography.

RATE PROCESSES

The effective rate of adsorption or ion exchange is determined by one or more of several diffusional steps. In this section these steps are described mathematically for a single particle of sorbent. The performance of equipment containing large numbers of individual particles will evidently depend not only upon local particle behavior but also upon the type and size of apparatus and the over-all arrangement of the process.

Individual steps in the **transport mechanism,** any

one of which may restrict the over-all performance in a certain region of operating conditions, are:

1. Diffusion in the solid phase (or, for an adsorbent, diffusion in the adsorbed surface layer).
2. Reaction at the phase boundaries. (Although this process is usually very fast, the various modes of mass transfer are often expressed in terms of apparent reaction rates for purposes of mathematical simplicity. Discussion of this approach follows the treatment of all the diffusion mechanisms.)
3. Pore diffusion in the fluid phase, within the particles (for most adsorbents, inorganic zeolites, and certain ion-exchange resins).
4. Mass transfer from the flowing phase to the external surfaces of the sorbent particles.
5. Mixing, or lack of mixing, between different parts of the contacting equipment. For instance, in column operation with slow flow rates, the break-through curves may be broadened by eddy dispersion or molecular diffusion in the axial direction.

The essential difference between steps 1 and 3 is that they are separated by step 2 and hence occur in different phases. The rates of these three steps are independent of the particular process arrangement selected, for a given sorbent particle in a constant driving potential. By contrast, the contribution of steps 4 and 5 depends greatly upon the type of apparatus; rate values cited below for these steps apply only to fixed-bed columns.

The equations that follow refer to **point conditions** within the contacting equipment, such as may apply to the average concentrations in the neighborhood of a single sorbent particle; in certain cases they are localized in still greater detail. To reduce the algebra, they are expressed in dimensionless concentrations $\mathbf{y}$ and $\mathbf{x}$, rather than in q and X; throughout, $\mathbf{y}$, $\mathbf{x}$, $\mathbf{r}$, and $\mathbf{D}_\Sigma$ can be replaced jointly by $\mathbf{Y}$, $\mathbf{X}$, $\mathbf{R}$, and $\mathbf{D}$ without altering their validity.

Particle-phase Diffusion. Diffusion which results from a concentration gradient within the individual sorbent particles, after the solute concerned has moved away from the carrier phase, is called particle-phase, solid-phase, sorbent-phase, or internal diffusion. This type of transport includes diffusion through a homogeneous and permeable adsorbing solid, such as ion-exchange resin; or in a mobile adsorbed layer covering the internal pore surfaces of a porous solid; or in an absorbing liquid that is used to impregnate a porous solid particle. For perfect spherical symmetry, the rate is

$$D_p \left(\frac{\partial^2 \mathbf{y}_r}{\partial r^2} + \frac{2}{r} \frac{\partial \mathbf{y}_r}{\partial r} \right) = \frac{\partial \mathbf{y}_r}{\partial \tau} \tag{16-30}$$

Here, D_p is the particle-phase diffusivity, $\mathbf{y}_r$ is the dimensionless solid-phase concentration at any internal radius r, and τ is reaction time.

This equation is often approximated by the **linear-driving force** relation of Glueckauf and Coates [*J. Chem. Soc.*, **1947**, 1315; *Trans. Faraday Soc.*, **51**, 1540 (1955)]:

$$\left(\frac{d\mathbf{y}}{d\tau} \right)_{\text{particle}} = \frac{k_{pF} a_p}{\mathbf{D}_\Sigma \epsilon} (\mathbf{y}^* - \mathbf{y}) \tag{16-31}$$

where $\mathbf{y}$ is the dimensionless concentration of the solute of interest averaged over the entire particle; $\mathbf{y}^*$ is the value that would be in equilibrium with the instantaneous fluid-phase concentration outside the particle; mass-transfer coefficient k_{pF} has units of length per unit time and is designated with the subscript F to indicate that it refers to the fluid phase; such reference explains the need for the distribution ratio $\mathbf{D}_\Sigma \epsilon$; a_p is the outer-surface interfacial area of the sorbent particles per unit volume of contacting system. The product $k_{pF} a_p$ is related to the diffusivity and to the effective spherical particle diameter d_p through the equation

$$k_{pF} a_p = \frac{60 D_p \mathbf{D}_\Sigma \epsilon}{d_p^2} \tag{16-32}$$

A better approximation to the behavior of Eq. (16-30) is given by a **quadratic driving-potential** form [Vermeulen, *Ind. Eng. Chem.*, **45**, 1664 (1953)]:

$$\left(\frac{d\mathbf{y}}{d\tau} \right)_{\text{particle}} = \frac{k_{pF} a_p}{\mathbf{D}_\Sigma \epsilon} \psi \left(\frac{\mathbf{y}^{*2} - \mathbf{y}^2}{2\mathbf{y} - \mathbf{y}_0} \right) \tag{16-33}$$

with $\mathbf{y}_0$ the dimensionless solid-phase concentration levels at the start (often 0 or 1), and

$$\psi = \frac{1}{\mathbf{r} + 15(1 - \mathbf{r})/\pi^2} \tag{16-34}$$

Particle-phase diffusivity values, for use in Eq. (16-30) or Eq. (16-32), have been reported almost exclusively for ion-exchange resins. The equimolal counterdiffusion value of D_p will have the fluid-phase diffusivity D_f as its upper-limit value. However, the ratio D_p/D_f will usually lie in the range of 10^{-1} to 10^{-4} and is greatly affected by the precise nature of the exchanging ions. The exchange of hydrogen with other cations on weakly acidic cationic exchangers, for instance, is exceedingly slow. Multivalent ions show markedly lower mobility in the exchanger phase than do univalent ions, and this effect is intensified by increase in valence.

Tables 16-6 and 16-7 show typical **particle-phase diffusivities** in cation and anion resin, respectively. In addition to the effect of ion charge, the size of the hydrated ion (Cs^+ vs. Na^+) and the relative tendency to form a covalence (high in the case of Ag^+, I^-, and also H^+) appear to account for the observed variations.

Table 16-6. Self-diffusion Rates in Dowex 50 Cation Resin

Temp., °C.	Cross linking, % divinyl benzene	Diffusion rate, 10^{-7} sq. cm./sec.				
		Cs^+	Na^+	Ag^+	Zn^{++}	La^{3+}
0.3	4	.....	6.7	....	....	0.30
	8	6.6	3.4	2.62	0.21	0.03
	12	.....	1.15			
	16	1.11	0.66	1.00	0.03	0.002
25.0	4	.....	14.1	....	....	0.69
	8	13.7	9.44	6.42	0.63	0.092
	12	.....	....	....	0.29	
	16	3.10	2.40	2.75	0.14	0.005

Boyd and Soldano, *J. Am. Chem. Soc.*, **74**, 6091 (1953).

Table 16-7. Self-diffusion Rates in Dowex 2 Anion Resin

Units of 10^{-7} sq. cm./sec.

Ion	Cross linking, % divinyl benzene	Temperature	
		0.3°C.	25.0°C.
Br^-	1	4.35	9.12
	2	2.98	6.40
	3	2.03	4.52
	6	1.50	3.87
	8	0.68	2.04
	16	0.06	0.26
BrO_3^-	6	1.76	4.55
Cl^-		1.25	3.54
WO_4^{--}		0.60	1.80
I^-		0.35	1.33
PO_4^{3-}		0.16	0.57

Soldano and Boyd, *J. Am. Chem. Soc.*, **75**, 6099 (1953).

The self-diffusion values given in the tables were measured with mixtures of ordinary and radioactive isotopes. For mixtures of unlike ions, the diffusivities will be intermediate. For example, at 16 per cent cross linking, a small amount of Na^+ in a resin containing predominantly Zn^{++} has $D_p = 0.22 \times 10^{-7}$, and a small amount of Zn^{++} in a resin containing predominantly Na^+ has $D_p = 0.85 \times 10^{-7}$ sq. cm./sec. at 25°C. At 8 per cent cross linking, for resin mainly in the Na^+ form, H^+ shows a D_p of 8.82; and on resin mainly in the Cs^+ form, Na^+ has a D_p of 9.80, in the same units [Soldano and Boyd, *J. Am. Chem. Soc.*, **75**, 6107 (1953)]. Although particle-phase diffusivity tends to vary with composition, algebraic calculation methods based upon Eqs. (16-30) to (16-33) usually require the selection of a single average value.

Fluid-Phase Effects. *Pore Diffusion.* In the case where the amount of material held in the **pores** is negligible compared with that held by the solid, the **diffusion rate** is given by a relation analogous to Eq. (16-30):

$$\frac{\partial \mathbf{y}_r}{\partial \tau} = \frac{D_{\text{pore}}(1-\epsilon)}{\mathbf{D}\Sigma\epsilon}\left[\frac{\partial^2 \mathbf{x}_r}{\partial r^2} + \frac{2}{r}\left(\frac{\partial \mathbf{x}_r}{\partial r}\right)\right] \tag{16-35}$$

This equation has been solved analytically for only a few cases. Through the work of Wheeler [*Advances in Catalysis*, **3**, 250–327 (1951)] the pore diffusivity can be expressed

$$D_{\text{pore}} = \frac{D_f x}{2}\left\{1 - \exp\left[-\frac{4\,\bar{r}}{3D_f}\left(\frac{8RT}{M}\right)^{0.5}\right]\right\} \tag{16-36}$$

where x is the internal porosity of the particles, r is the average pore radius, and $(8RT/M)^{0.5}$ is the molecular velocity group based on gas constant, absolute temperature, and mean molecular weight of gas. For liquids the exponential term is dropped.

If a linear driving potential is used as a gross approximation, the rate equation is

$$\left(\frac{d\mathbf{y}}{d\tau}\right)_{\text{particle}} = \frac{k_{\text{pore},F}\,a_p(\mathbf{x} - \mathbf{x}^*)}{\mathbf{D}\Sigma\epsilon} \tag{16-37}$$

with
$$k_{\text{pore},F}\,a_p = \frac{60D_{\text{pore}}}{d_p^2}(1-\epsilon) \tag{16-38}$$

External Transport. The **transport rate** for solute between the bulk of the fluid phase and the outer surfaces of the sorbent granules is evidently governed by the molecular or ionic diffusivity and also, in turbulent flow, by the eddy diffusivity which controls the effective thickness of the boundary layer.

Here the rate of material transfer for the solute of interest is given by the classical form involving the driving potential between the bulk fluid and the granule surface:

$$\left(\frac{d\mathbf{y}}{d\tau}\right)_{\text{particle}} = \frac{k_{fF}a_p}{\mathbf{D}\Sigma\epsilon}(\mathbf{x} - \mathbf{x}^*) \tag{16-39}$$

where k_{fF} is the fluid-phase mass-transfer coefficient, $\mathbf{x}^*$ is the dimensionless fluid-phase concentration in equilibrium with the outer surface of the solid, and the other variables are as defined previously.

For **packed-bed** operations the following relation, adapted from Wilke and Hougen [*Trans. Am. Inst. Chem. Engrs.*, **41**, 445 (1945)], can be used for evaluating the mass-transfer coefficient:

$$k_{fF}a_p = \frac{10.9F(1-\epsilon)}{d_pS\eta}\left[\frac{D_f}{d_p(F/S)}\right]^{0.51}\left(\frac{D_f\rho_f}{\mu}\right)^{0.16} \tag{16-40}$$

where η is the logarithmic mean of $(1 - \mathbf{y})$ and $\mathbf{y}$ is the mole fraction of the diffusing component in the entire phase (usually η is near unity); F/S is superficial velocity, volumetric flow rate of fluid F per unit area S of contactor cross section; D_f is fluid-phase diffusivity; ρ is density; μ is viscosity.

Equation (16-40), developed for *laminar-flow* gas-solid contact, appears to give slightly low results for liquid-solid contact. For the latter case, the numerical values discussed below (Fig. 16-8) are fitted empirically by reducing the exponent on the right-hand (Schmidt-group) term from 0.16 to 0.12. For aqueous solutions, at 20°C., Eq. (16-40) then becomes

$$k_{fF}a_p = \frac{2.62(D_fF/S)^{0.5}}{d_p^{1.5}} \tag{16-41}$$

For accurate calculations, the external-transport rate must be corrected for the effect of ion-concentration gradients (that is, of electric charge) along the transport path. This effect has been examined by Schlögl and Helfferich [*J. Chem. Phys.*, **26**, 5 (1957)].

Axial Dispersion and Diffusion in Packed Beds. In fixed-bed operations, the effects of **longitudinal dispersion** and **molecular diffusion** can be expressed empirically by an **apparent conductance** k_{lF} which is a function of separation factor $\mathbf{r}$ [*cf.* Eq. (16-11)]:

$$k_{lF}a_p = \frac{F\bar{\mathbf{g}}}{SL} \tag{16-42}$$

where L is the axial "mixing length"; $\bar{\mathbf{g}}$, given in Eq. (16-60), is a correction factor that accounts for variation in this conductance with changes in $\mathbf{r}$ and in total conductance. With $\mathbf{r} \geq 1$, $\bar{\mathbf{g}} = 1$.

Axial mixing length is given by

$$L = \frac{d_p}{\mathbf{P}_l} + \frac{D_f}{\sqrt{2}(F/S)} \tag{16-43}$$

where the packing Péclet number for axial dispersion $\mathbf{P}_l$ is approximately 0.7 for liquids with laminar-flow behavior (when $d_p\rho_fF/S\mu$, the Reynolds number based on superficial velocity and particle diameter, is less than 200), 1.8 for liquids in turbulent flow, and 1.8 for gases in either flow regime [McHenry and Wilhelm, *Am. Inst. Chem. Engrs. J.*, **3**, 83 (1957). Ebach and White, *Am. Inst. Chem. Engrs. J.*, **4**, 161 (1958). Carberry and Bretton, *Am. Inst. Chem. Engrs. J.*, **4**, 367 (1958)].

The theory of axial dispersion has been developed by Lapidus and Amundson [*J. Phys. Chem.*, **56**, 984 (1952)], Lightfoot [*J. Phys. Chem.*, **61**, 1686 (1957)], Acrivos [*Chem. Eng. Sci.*, **13**, 1 (1960)], and others; but numerical **methods** based directly upon the theory had not been published as of 1961.

Combined Fluid-phase Coefficient. Where only fluid-phase resistances are involved, a **combined fluid-phase mass-transfer coefficient** k_{CF} can be defined by adding the resistances:

$$\frac{1}{k_{CF}a_p} = \frac{1}{k_{fF}a_p} + \frac{1}{k_{\text{pore},F}a_p} + \frac{1}{k_{lF}a_p} \tag{16-44}$$

The resulting coefficient $k_{CF}a_p$ can be used in a rate expression having the form of Eq. (16-39). It is recognized that the linearizing of pore diffusion and axial dispersion "conductances" is only approximate. Hence Eq. (16-44) will prove most satisfactory in those cases where the external-transport resistance is relatively large.

In the event a sorbent-phase resistance also is appreciable, the resistances will no longer be directly additive. This situation is treated in a following section.

Reaction-kinetic Treatment. For **adsorption** of a single component obeying a Langmuir isotherm, the rate is

$$\left(\frac{dq}{d\tau}\right)_{\text{particle}} = \kappa\left[X(q_{\text{lim}} - q) - \frac{1}{K_L}q\right] \qquad (16\text{-}45)$$

Substitution using Table 16-4 and Eqs. (16-5), (16-6), and (16-10) gives

$$\left(\frac{d\mathbf{Y}}{d\mathbf{t}_R}\right)_{\text{particle}} = \mathbf{X}(1 - \mathbf{Y}) - \mathbf{RY}(1 - \mathbf{X}) \qquad (16\text{-}46)$$

with

$$\mathbf{t}_R = \frac{\kappa_F \tau}{\mathbf{D}\epsilon} \qquad (16\text{-}46a)$$

and

$$\kappa_F = \frac{\kappa X_0 \mathbf{D}\epsilon}{1 - \mathbf{R}} \qquad (16\text{-}46b)$$

Use of subscript F as an identification for κ indicates that this coefficient, like the mass-transfer coefficients above, is expressed with reference to the fluid phase. This explains the need for introducing $\mathbf{D}\epsilon$ in Eqs. (16-46*a*) and (16-46*b*).

With **ion exchange** or **exchange adsorption** between two components, the reaction-kinetic relation is

$$\left(\frac{dq}{d\tau}\right)_{\text{particle}} = \kappa_\Sigma[c(Q - q) - \mathbf{r}q(C_0 - c)] \qquad (16\text{-}47)$$

or

$$\left(\frac{d\mathbf{y}}{d\mathbf{t}_R}\right)_{\text{particle}} = \mathbf{x}(1 - \mathbf{y}) - \mathbf{ry}(1 - \mathbf{x}) \qquad (16\text{-}48)$$

with $\mathbf{t}_R$ defined as above and

$$\kappa_F = \kappa_\Sigma C_0 \mathbf{D}_\Sigma \epsilon \qquad (16\text{-}48a)$$

Over-all Effect of Fluid- and Particle-phase Resistances. Reasonably exact solutions in the case where appreciable resistance exists on both sides of the phase change have been developed, for fixed beds, only in two limiting cases of separation-factor behavior: $\mathbf{r} = 1$ by Rosen [*Ind. Eng. Chem.*, **46**, 1590 (1954)] and $\mathbf{r} = 0$, for example, by Vermeulen [*Ind. Eng. Chem.*, **45**, 1664 (1953)].

At $\mathbf{r} = 1$, to a fairly high degree of accuracy, the **over-all fluid-phase mass-transfer coefficient** is

$$\frac{1}{\kappa_F} = \frac{1}{k_f F a_p} + \frac{1}{k_l F a_p} + \frac{1}{k_p F a_p + k_{\text{pore},F} a_p} \qquad (16\text{-}49)$$

For a general approach, recourse must be had to the methods of chemical-reaction kinetics just described.

By introducing the equilibrium relations [Eqs. (16-14) and (16-15), respectively], the linear driving-force relations of Eqs. (16-31) and (16-39) can also be transformed to Eqs. (16-46) or (16-48). In both these cases

$$\kappa_F = \mathbf{b} k_F a_p \qquad (16\text{-}50)$$

where k_F represents either k_{fF} or k_{pF}; correction factor $\mathbf{b}$ is not a constant (except at $\mathbf{r} = 1$, where it is unity). In order to solve the general case, it is necessary to use an average value (determined at $\mathbf{X} = 0.50$) as an approximate constant.

For **particle-phase diffusion** controlling,

$$\mathbf{b}_p = \frac{1}{\mathbf{r} + (1 - \mathbf{r})\mathbf{x}} \approx \frac{2}{1 + \mathbf{r}} \qquad (16\text{-}51)$$

For **fluid-phase transport** controlling,

$$\mathbf{b}_f = \frac{1}{1 + (\mathbf{r} - 1)\mathbf{y}} \qquad (16\text{-}52)$$

With $\mathbf{r} < 1$, approximately,

$$\mathbf{b}_f = \frac{1}{1 + (\mathbf{r} - 1)\mathbf{x}} \approx \frac{2}{1 + \mathbf{r}} \qquad (16\text{-}52a)$$

while with $\mathbf{r} > 1$, approximately,

$$\mathbf{b}_f = 1 - \left(1 - \frac{1}{\mathbf{r}}\right)\mathbf{x} \approx \frac{\mathbf{r} + 1}{2\mathbf{r}} \qquad (16\text{-}52b)$$

(These relations are obtained from the limiting behavior of fixed beds under either favorable or unfavorable equilibrium, as discussed later.)

In the case where fluid-phase and particle-phase resistances both influence the rate behavior, $\mathbf{b}$ can be determined as a function of k_{pF} and $\bar{k}_{CF}$; the latter is computed like k_{CF} but excludes $k_{\text{pore},F}$. From Eqs. (16-32) and (16-44), a **mechanism parameter** ζ can be calculated, such that

$$\zeta = \frac{k_{pF}}{\bar{k}_{CF}} \qquad (16\text{-}53)$$

The factor $\mathbf{b}$ has been given by Hiester *et al.* [*Am. Inst. Chem. Engrs. J.*, **2**, 404 (1956)] as a function of $\mathbf{r}$ and ζ, and is plotted in Fig. 16-7.

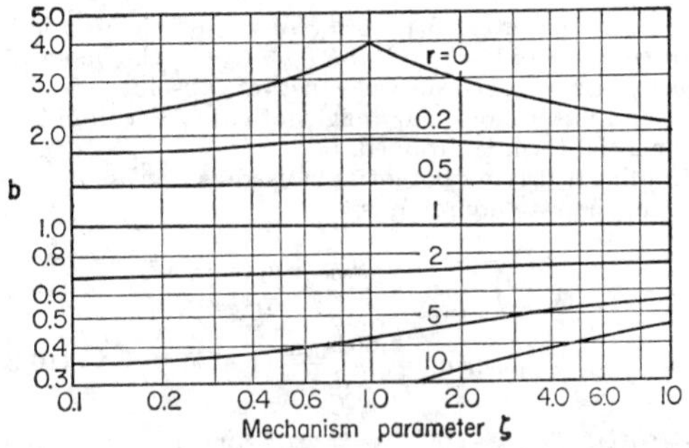

FIG. 16-7. Correction term for combining diffusional resistances. [*Am. Inst. Chem. Eng. J.*, **2**, 409 (1956).]

Experimental Resistances in Fixed-bed Ion Exchange. This factor can be used for a **general addition of resistances:**

$$\frac{\mathbf{b}}{\kappa_F} = \frac{1}{k_f F a_p} + \frac{1}{k_l F a_p} + \frac{1}{k_{\text{pore},F} a_p + k_p F a_p} \qquad (16\text{-}54)$$

In principle, this type of addition can be applied regardless of the particular process arrangement; in practice, as already indicated, k_{fF} and k_{lF} are generally available only for packed beds.

In addition to describing the combined resistance in terms of the apparent kinetic coefficient κ_F, it is sometimes practicable (with $\mathbf{r} \ll 1$) to use an **apparent over-all fluid-phase coefficient** k_{OfF} when the fluid-phase resistance predominates, or an **over-all particle-phase coefficient** k_{OpF} when the particle-phase resistance predominates. These over-all coefficients are related to κ_F, and hence to the individual coefficients, in the following way:

$$\frac{\mathbf{b}}{\kappa_F} = \left(\frac{\mathbf{b}}{\mathbf{b}_f}\right)\left(\frac{1}{k_{OfF} a_p}\right) \quad \text{or} \quad \left(\frac{\mathbf{b}}{\mathbf{b}_p}\right)\left(\frac{1}{k_{OpF} a_p}\right) \qquad (16\text{-}54a)$$

where $\mathbf{b}_f$ and $\mathbf{b}_p$, respectively, are the factors given by Eqs. (16-51) and (16-52).

For the case where neither longitudinal dispersion nor pore diffusion is a factor—that is, in ion-exchange systems at reasonable flow rates—the applicability of Eq. (16-54) to experimental data for fixed beds is shown in Fig. 16-8.

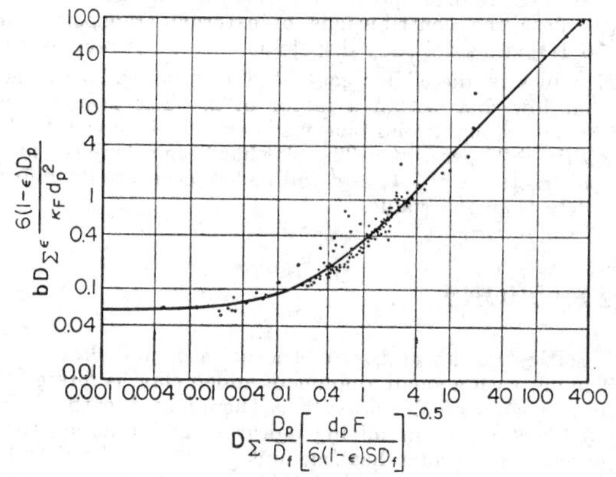

FIG. 16-8. Correlation of rate data for fixed-bed ion exchange. [*Am. Inst. Chem. Engrs. J.*, **2**, 410 (1956).]

This figure provides the experimental basis for Eq. (16-41), and the confirmation of the reliability of Eq. (16-32). This plot corresponds to the dimensionless relationship

$$\frac{\mathbf{b}}{\kappa_F} = \frac{d_p^2}{6(1-\epsilon)\epsilon}\left\{\frac{0.29}{D_f}\left[\frac{d_pF}{6(1-\epsilon)SD_f}\right]^{-0.5} + \frac{0.06}{\mathbf{D}_\Sigma D_p}\right\} \tag{16-55}$$

with the first right-hand term inside the brackets being the external-transport contribution and the second, the particle-diffusion contribution. Another form of this relation is

$$\frac{\mathbf{b}(F/S)}{\kappa_F d_p} = g_1\left(\frac{d_pF}{D_fS}\right)^{0.5} + g_2\frac{d_pF/D_fS}{\mathbf{D}_\Sigma\epsilon(D_p/D_f)} = \frac{\mathbf{b}h}{\mathbf{N}_R d_p} \tag{16-55a}$$

where
$$g_1 = \frac{0.29}{[6(1-\epsilon)]^{0.5}\epsilon} \tag{16-55b}$$

and
$$g_2 = \frac{0.06}{6(1-\epsilon)} \tag{16-55c}$$

with $g_1 = 0.382$ and $g_2 = 0.0167$ when $\epsilon = 0.40$; h = height or length of contactor; $\mathbf{N}_R$ is given by Eq. (16-56). Source of the data and their interpretation are given by Hiester *et al.* (*loc. cit.*).

General Correlation for Fixed Beds. As shown under Fixed-bed Operations (p. 16-29), the performance of sorbent columns can be characterized by an **over-all number of transfer units** $\mathbf{N}_{OF}$ (*i.e.*, either $\mathbf{N}_{OfF}$ or $\mathbf{N}_{OpF}$) or a related **number of reaction units** $\mathbf{N}_R$. These dimensionless parameters are each proportional to column height and to over-all rate coefficient; also inversely proportional to fluid-phase velocity and hence proportional to the apparent residence time of the fluid. They are defined as follows:

$$\mathbf{N}_R = \frac{\kappa_F v}{F} = \frac{\kappa_F h}{F/S} \tag{16-56}$$

where v is column volume and F is volumetric flow rate.

$$\mathbf{N}_{OfF} = \frac{k_{OfF}a_pv}{F} = \frac{k_{OfF}a_ph}{F/S} \tag{16-56a}$$

$$\mathbf{N}_{OpF} = \frac{k_{OpF}a_pv}{F} = \frac{k_{OpF}a_ph}{F/S} \tag{16-56b}$$

These relations also serve to define the familiar **height of transfer unit** H_{OF} or **height of reaction unit** H_R:

$$H_R = \frac{h}{\mathbf{N}_R} = \frac{F/S}{\kappa_F} \tag{16-57}$$

$$H_{OfF} = \frac{h}{\mathbf{N}_{OfF}} = \frac{F/S}{k_{OfF}a_p} \tag{16-57a}$$

$$H_{OpF} = \frac{h}{\mathbf{N}_{OpF}} = \frac{F/S}{k_{OpF}a_p} \tag{16-57b}$$

The foregoing correlation for κ_F, in terms of external transport and particle-phase diffusion [Fig. 16-8 and Eq. (16-55)], can be extended so as to account for all the effective resistances described above: axial molecular diffusion; axial eddy dispersion; external mass transport; and fluid-phase pore diffusion, particle-phase diffusion, or the sum of these two. The interrelation of these resistances, and their effect upon the dimensionless group $\overline{\mathbf{N}}_{OF}d_p/h$ or $\overline{\mathbf{N}}_Rd_p/\mathbf{b}h$, is given in Fig. 16-9 as a function of the Péclet number for flow d_pF/D_fS.

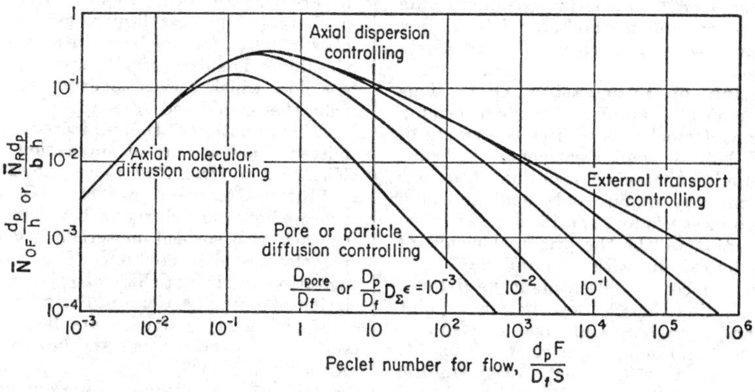

FIG. 16-9. Effects of Péclet group, distribution ratio, and diffusivity ratio on height of a transfer unit or reaction unit.

True objective of the correlation, the value of **N**, is found from $\overline{\mathbf{N}}$, which it equals when longitudinal dispersion effects are negligible. When they are not negligible, and when $\mathbf{r} < 1$, a factor of **g** corrects for the **non-additivity of the effective resistance** due to axial dispersion or diffusion:

$$\mathbf{N}_R = \mathbf{g}\overline{\mathbf{N}}_R \qquad (16\text{-}58)$$

and similarly for $\overline{\mathbf{N}}_{OfF}$ or $\overline{\mathbf{N}}_{OpF}$. In these relations, **g** may be estimated by the relation

$$\log \mathbf{g} = -\frac{1-\mathbf{r}}{2}\frac{L\overline{\mathbf{N}}_R}{h\mathbf{b}}\log\frac{\overline{\mathbf{N}}_R}{\mathbf{b}} \qquad (16\text{-}59)$$

with $\bar{\mathbf{g}} \leq 1$. In the case where axial diffusion is the controlling mechanism, **g** becomes equal to the factor $\bar{\mathbf{g}}$ used in Eq. (16-42):

$$\log \bar{\mathbf{g}} = -\frac{1-\mathbf{r}}{2}\log\frac{\overline{\mathbf{N}}_R}{\mathbf{b}} \qquad (16\text{-}60)$$

In Fig. 16-9, liquid-phase behavior has been used to calculate the contributions of external transport [Eq. (16-41)] and axial eddy dispersion. In these regions, the $\overline{\mathbf{N}}$ values predicted for gas-phase systems will be somewhat low, but within a factor of 2. The accuracy of predictions on liquid-phase systems is believed to be within ±20 per cent. The plot has been calculated for a void-fraction ϵ of 0.40 and will be less accurate if ϵ differs widely from this value.

SORPTION OPERATIONS

Three major types of solid-fluid sorption equipment are in use: (1) batch units; (2) semicontinuous units involving fixed beds of sorbent through which the process fluid passes, with periodic interruption for regeneration; and (3) fully continuous units which provide for countercurrent or cocurrent movement of sorbent and fluid.

BATCH OPERATIONS

It is often advantageous to carry out sorbent-liquid contact in batch equipment; such methods are less frequently employed for treatment of gases. Batch methods are well adapted to laboratory use, and have also been applied on a larger scale in several specific instances.

Laboratory Methods. In purifying the products of organic-chemical synthesis, decolorizing carbons and clays are frequently used as **contact adsorbents** (*i.e.*, they are stirred directly into a liquid-phase mixture or solution) and are subsequently separated by filtration.

Batch tests or measurements are often conducted on portions of adsorbent or ion-exchange material intended for larger-scale use. For example, either the equilibrium sorptive uptake of a solid or its ultimate sorption capacity can be determined in this way. The solid is presaturated with solution that contains the solute at a specified concentration level; or preequilibrated with a pair of solutes, whose final solution-phase concentrations are determined separately. The solid can then be drained or centrifuged or rinsed so as to be wholly free of the initial solution. After this it is suspended in a quantity of a different liquid or solution, for titration or other similar analysis. The American Water Works Association is undertaking to standardize procedures and methods for determining these and other properties of sorbents [*Water Works Manual*, **16**, 39 (1952)].

Contact Filtration of Lubricating Oils. This process is used to remove colored and carbon-forming materials from lubricant stocks, as well as the traces of products formed in sulfuric acid treatment. In some cases, either vacuum distillates or residuum fractions from crude petroleum may require only acid and clay treatment in order to meet product specifications. Elsewhere, solvent extraction will be the principal means of treatment, followed by refining with acid and clay.

Figure 16-10 shows a contact-filter plant used for a "long residuum" or "cylinder stock" having a flash point of 440° to 450°F. and a Saybolt Universal viscosity of 80 to 85 sec. at 210°F. [Kauffman, *Chem. & Met. Eng.*, **34**, 155 (1927)]. This residuum is first treated with sulfuric acid, at the rate of 40 to 45 lb. of 66°Bé. acid per barrel of oil, at 140° to 150°F. After this treatment, the sludge is settled at the bottom of the agitator and drawn off. The oil, with a small amount of added clay, is filtered to remove emulsified acid. It is then mixed with about 0.5 lb. clay/gal. in mixing agitators and pumped to a pipe still or similar heating unit where it is brought to about 450°F. It is held at this temperature for several minutes, then cooled to 300°F. and filtered.

Particle size of the clay is usually 80 to 100 mesh, substantially finer than can be used in the alternative method of percolation treatment in fixed beds. Diatomaceous earth may be used as a filter precoat or may be mixed with the slurry to improve its filtering properties. The clay cake from the filter is usually washed with naphtha and blown with inert (flue) gas before it is discarded; it can be revivified by heating in air at between 1000° and 1400°F.

Later practice in this field was surveyed by Kalichevsky and Kobe [*Petrol. Refiner*, **32** (9), 215 (1953)]. Filtration rates for clay-oil slurries were reported by Bible, Witte, and Donnell [*Ind. Eng. Chem.*, **31**, 1007 (1939)]. A correlation of equilibrium data on color removal from various oils by various adsorbents has been given by Rogers, Grimm, and Lemmon [*Ind. Eng. Chem.*, **18**, 164 (1926)], and the effect of times and temperatures of treatment has been studied by Kalichevsky and Ramsay [*Ind. Eng. Chem.*, **25**, 941 (1933)].

Mixer-settler Operations. Mixing and filtering can be accomplished in the same vessel by using large-particle sorbent material (50 mesh and coarser) through which a liquid can drain quite readily. The solid sorbent is reused a substantial number of times before it is regenerated or replaced. With the vessel filled with a charge of process liquor, gentle agitation is usually obtained by sparging the slurry with air. Draining of the liquor is subsequently hastened by use of a reverse gas flow which serves to expel the interstitial solution from the settled bed (Fig. 16-11).

A combination of these mixer-settlers to provide intermittent countercurrent operation was described by Hiester *et al.* [*Ind. Eng. Chem.*, **45**, 2402 (1953)].

Slurry–Granular Sorbent Contact. Where the process liquor is a slurry rather than a clear liquid, batch contact with sorbent materials is generally preferred to percolation-type contact. The latter involves less agitation and is more likely to give a progressive accumulation of slurry particles in the body of sorbent.

If the slurry particles are larger than those of the sorbent, the sorbent may be incorporated in the slurry. After sufficient contact, the process liquor may be centrifuged or filtered. Subsequently, the sorbent is recovered by hydraulic classification or by wet screening.

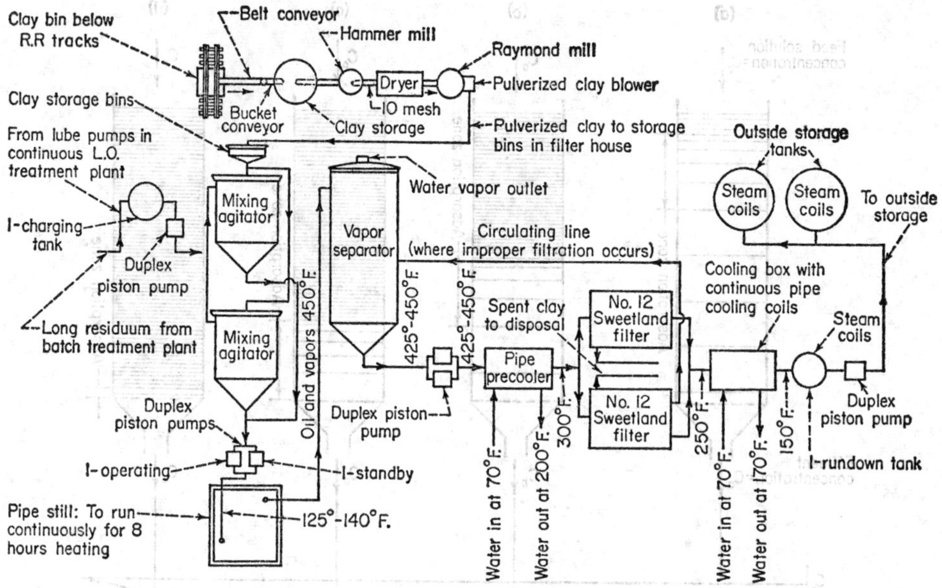

FIG. 16-10. Flow diagram for contact filtration.

Such a method has been used for pectin recovery from grapefruit peel [Myers and Rouse, U.S. Patent 2,323,483. Boehner and Mindler, *Ind. Eng. Chem.*, **41**, 448 (1949)].

The **resin-in-pulp method** was developed to utilize relatively coarse anion-exchange resin with a slurry of finely ground uranium ore in acid-leach liquor. The apparatus involved was described by Hollis and McArthur [*Proc. Intern. Conf. Peaceful Uses Atomic Energy*, **8**, 54 (1955)]. See also Sec. 19, p. 19-23.

A variation on this type of operation involves semi-continuous feed of fluid to an agitated vessel with fluid discharge through a screen that retains the resin (Davis, Ward, and Klinger, Inter-American Congress on Chemical Engineering, Puerto Rico, 1961).

FIXED BEDS

The most frequently used method of fluid-solid contact for sorption operations is in **columnar units**, with the solid particles closely packed in a relatively fixed arrangement. Adsorbent particle sizes in such equipment usually lie in a narrow range but may average from as large as 4 mesh to as small as 250 mesh. **Pressure drop** is often taken as a determining factor in particle-size specification; on the other hand, performance of adsorbent columns often improves rapidly with decreasing particle size. Thus in liquid-phase processing, total cost of the adsorption step can sometimes be reduced by designing for over-all pressure drops as large as 50 to 100 lb./sq. in. Calculation of pressure drop in packed beds is described in Sec. 5, p. 5-49.

An upper limit to column performance is set by the stoichiometry of the adsorbent solid in relation to the solute carried in the feed. Once this limit is approached, the process efficiency cannot be further improved except by changing to a different adsorbent having a larger stoichiometric capacity. Thus it is important to recognize whether performance is limited with respect to

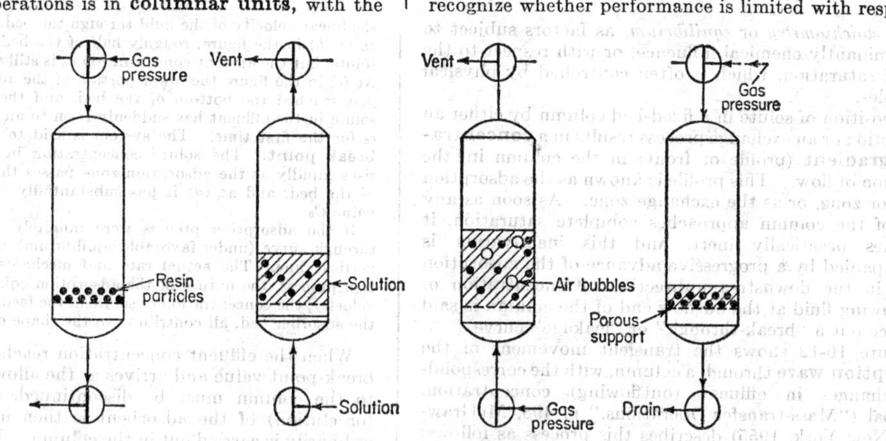

FIG. 16-11. Sequence of operations in a batch mixer-settler.

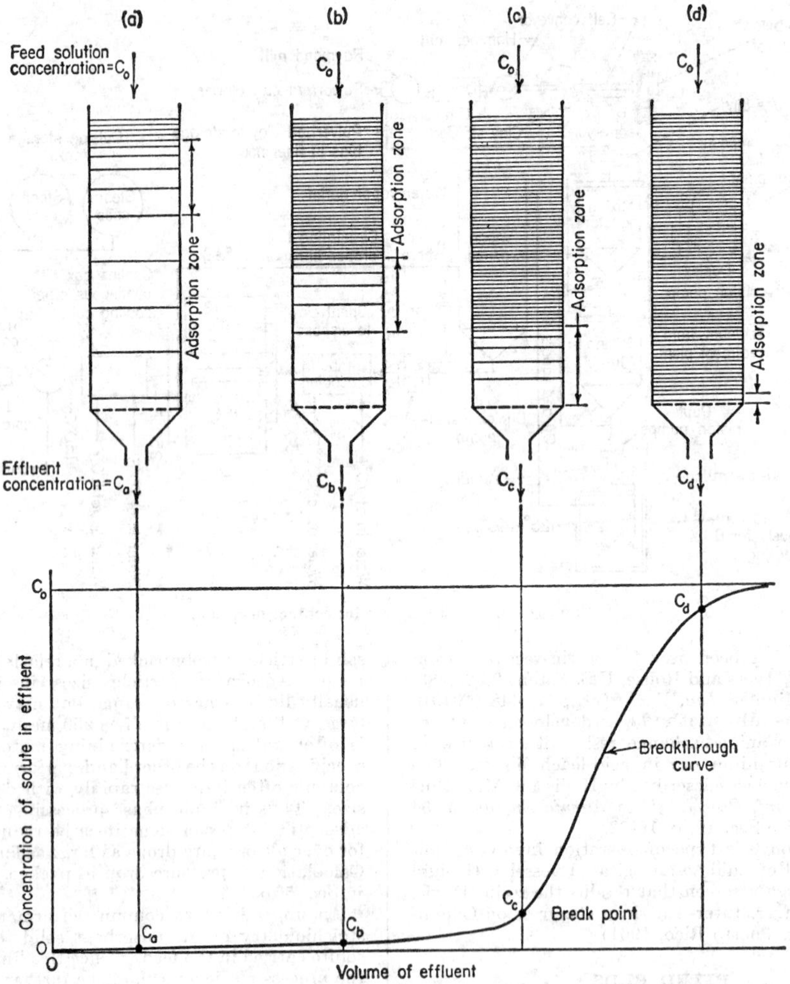

FIG. 16-12. Passage of adsorption wave through a fixed bed. (*Treybal, "Mass-transfer Operations," McGraw-Hill, New York,* 1955.)

either *stoichiometry* or *equilibrium*, as factors subject to predominantly chemical influence, or with respect to the *rate* of saturation, which is often controlled by physical variables.

Deposition of solute in a fixed-bed column by either an adsorption or an exchange process results in a **concentration gradient** (profile or front) in the column in the direction of flow. This profile is known as the adsorption wave or zone, or as the exchange zone. As soon as any part of the column approaches complete saturation, it becomes practically inert, and this inactivation is accompanied by a progressive advance of the adsorption wave in the downstream direction. Concentration of the flowing fluid at the outflow end of the column is said to trace out a "break-through" or "leakage" curve.

Figure 16-12 shows the transient movement of the **adsorption wave** through a column, with the corresponding changes in effluent (outflowing) concentration. Treybal ("Mass-transfer Operations," p. 498, McGraw-Hill, New York, 1955) describes this process as follows:

As solution continues to flow, the adsorption zone moves downward as a wave, at a rate ordinarily very much slower than the linear velocity of the fluid through the bed. At a later time, as at (*b*) in the figure, roughly half of the bed is saturated with solute, but the effluent concentration c_b is still substantially zero. At (*c*) in the figure the lower portion of the adsorption zone has just reached the bottom of the bed, and the concentration of solute in the effluent has suddenly risen to an appreciable value c_c for the first time. The system is said to have reached the **break point.** The solute concentration in the effluent now rises rapidly as the adsorption zone passes through the bottom of the bed, and at (*d*) it has substantially reached the initial value C_0.

If the adsorption process were infinitely rapid, the break-through curve (under favorable equilibrium) would be a straight vertical line. The actual rate and mechanism of the adsorption process, the nature of the adsorption equilibrium, the fluid velocity, the concentration of solute in the feed, and the length of the adsorber bed, all contribute to the shape of the curve.

When the effluent concentration reaches or passes the break-point value and arrives at the allowable limit, feed to the column must be discontinued. **Regeneration** (or elution) of the adsorbent is then necessary, which ordinarily is carried out in the column. Depending upon the precise nature of the adsorption and the equipment, either a forward or a reverse flow of regenerant may be

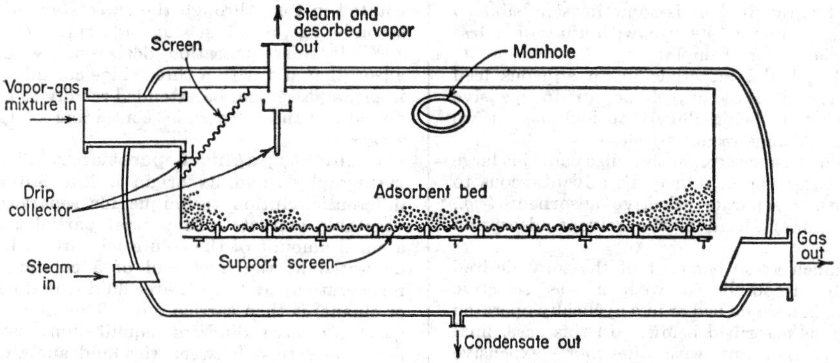

FIG. 16-13. Shallow-bed high-through-put adsorber equipped for steam heating. (*After Logan, in Treybal, "Mass-transfer Operations," McGraw-Hill, New York,* 1955.)

preferred; in either case, regeneration involves the passage of a **desorption wave** through the column as the regenerated section grows at the expense of the unregenerated part.

For certain adsorbents, such as activated carbon used for decolorizing sugar syrups, it may prove necessary or advantageous to discharge the adsorbent from the column and regenerate it externally (for carbon, this is accomplished in air-fed kilns, meanwhile reloading the column with a different batch of adsorbent to prepare it for reuse).

For **regenerating an adsorbent,** a change in the equilibrium is usually desirable in order to make solute removal more rapid and complete. This may involve a change in temperature, a change in carrier fluid, or frequently both. When steam or other hot gas is the regenerant and solvent vapor the adsorptive, the off-gas passes through a condenser where the solvent is recovered; any remaining fixed gas will not be completely free of solvent and is therefore recycled to the absorbers before being vented. Often, for regenerations in place, mixing of the saturant and regenerant fluids is undesirable; in such cases, the column will be purged with an appropriate inert fluid between regeneration and the next saturation step, and perhaps also between each saturation step and the following regeneration.

Figure 16-13 shows a design for an adsorber bed, for **recovering solvent vapors from air,** which provides a large cross section and relatively shallow bed depth in order to minimize pressure drop (Logan, U.S. Patent 2,180,712). Flow through such a bed is normally at a superficial gas velocity of 1 to 2 ft./sec. The bed of fairly coarse particles is supported on a reinforced heavy-gage screen; the containing vessel is equipped for regeneration with low-pressure steam, which serves at the same time as an external heating medium for the adsorbent.

An automatically operated unit for **water softening by ion exchange** is shown in Fig. 16-14 (Calmon and Kingsbury, in Nachod and Schubert, "Ion Exchange Technology," p. 243, Academic Press, New York, 1956). The contact meter closes a circuit each time a preset volume of water has passed through it; this interrupts the water flow and causes the regeneration steps to be carried out in sequence. First, the resin is backwashed (upward) at a rate which will fluidize it and carry off any accumulated dirt particles. Next, the brine regenerant is introduced in downflow. A short rinse period follows, in which the total salt concentration is reduced to feed-water level, and after this the column is ready for return to "saturation" service.

Joint Use of Two Adsorbents. When an expensive adsorbent is needed to bring about the full extent of

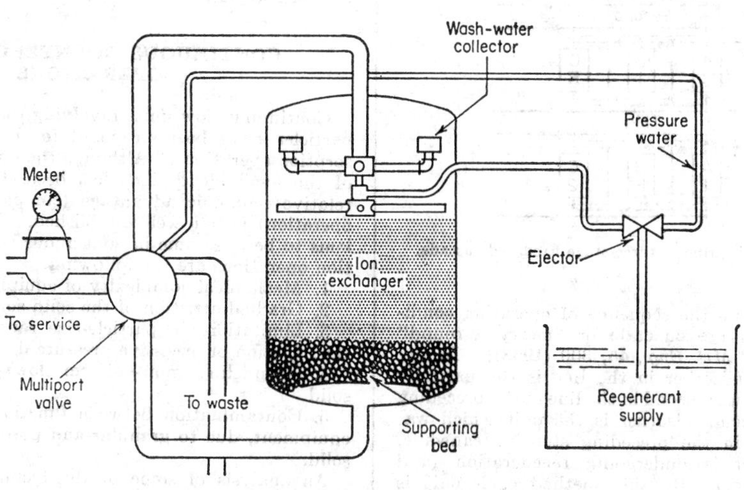

FIG. 16-14. Single-bed ion-exchange unit. (*Permutit Co.*)

purification that is required, it is sometimes possible to reduce costs by combining its use with that of a less expensive material. For example:

1. Suspended colloidal materials in an aqueous feed should be coalesced onto gravel or an inexpensive adsorbent, rather than being allowed to foul the surface of high-cost ion-exchange resin particles.

2. For a solvent-rich air stream that also contains large proportions of water vapor, it may be advantageous to dry the air with a separate selective adsorbent (*e.g.*, silica gel or alumina) ahead of the solvent-adsorption step.

3. Often as much as 90 per cent of the total desired removal can be accomplished with a less selective adsorbent, either in a single bed or in a cyclically operated cascade of beds, as described below. In this case, final purification is carried out with the more expensive material in a relatively small trimmer bed.

Mixed Beds. In water treatment by ion exchange, cationic and anionic resins can be combined in nearly equimolal proportions to given complete demineralization with somewhat better resin utilization and lower equipment cost than would result from using two separate beds. When the break point is reached, a gentle backwashing separates the lighter cationic resin from the denser anionic one, and each is regenerated and rinsed in a separate part of the column. After this, a more vigorous backwashing, with air mixing, restores the uniform mixture of resin for the next saturation step.

Cyclic Operations. Often two fixed-bed adsorber or exchanger units are provided, so that one is on stream while the other is being regenerated. If the break-through curve is quite shallow, and thus leaves a large proportion of unused capacity when the break point is reached, it may be desirable to use two or more beds in series, introducing a new bed at the downstream end each time a completely spent bed upstream is removed from service. In this way, by a valve arrangement that provides the proper succession of saturant and regenerant streams to each bed, a fixed-bed assembly can simulate a completely countercurrent system.

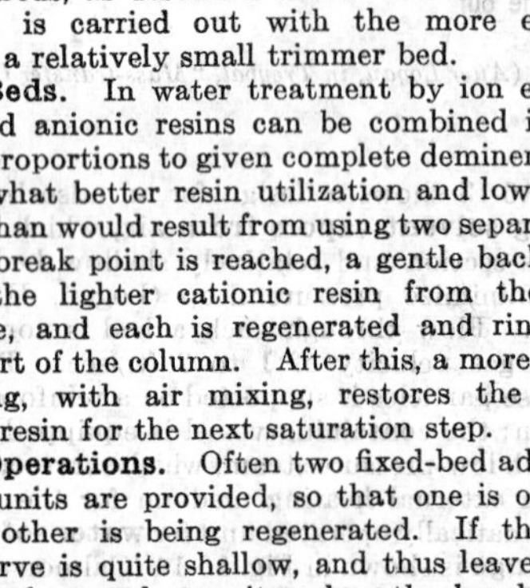

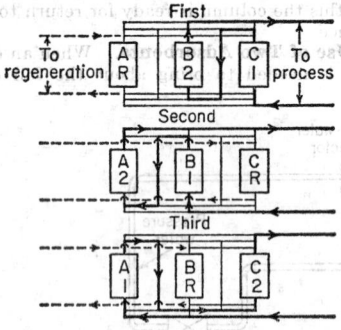

FIG. 16-15. Flow diagram of three-stage fixed-bed cascade.

Figure 16-15 shows the sequence of operating conditions in a **three-stage cascade** or "merry-go-round" [Bulkeley, *Chem. & Met. Eng.*, **45**, 300 (1938)]. In any one step the first adsorber in the line is the partially charged unit which was second in the line in the preceding step, while the second adsorber is the unit which was being regenerated in the preceding step. Meanwhile, the third adsorber is undergoing regeneration (and cooling, if necessary). By this method each unit is rotated in turn through the three steps of regeneration, second-stage, and first-stage adsorption.

While this illustration deals only with vapor-phase adsorption and with a three-stage cascade, the principles it encompasses can be extended readily to other fixed-bed operations and to cascades containing a larger number of stages.

Chromatographic Separations. The term "chromatography" had its origin in the initial use of this differential-elution technique for separation of colored vegetable extracts. In a brief partial-saturation step, a small amount of the solute mixture to be separated is deposited at the inlet end of a column. Elution (or regeneration) by a solute-free fluid (the elutant, elutriant, or eluant) is then carried out. The different solutes will generally have different equilibrium distributions (or partition ratios) between the fluid and the solid phase; those held less tightly by the solid will advance more rapidly through the bed during the elution. The longer the column, the more completely the individual bands or zones of solute will draw apart from one another and thus allow the solutes to be isolated in successive portions or fractions of the effluent.

Movement of a band or zone of solute occurs by the following mechanism: fluid on the upstream side of the zone is undersaturated with respect to that solute, and takes it into solution; overtaking and passing the peak of the zone, the fluid becomes supersaturated compared with the adsorbent then in contact with it and therefore redeposits the solute on the solid. For theory and design of chromatographic separation, see Vermeulen ("Advances in Chemical Engineering," vol. 2, Academic Press, New York, 1958).

Frontal Analysis. The different partition ratios for different solutes give rise to another effect that is used mainly for chemical analysis. If a mixture of two or more solutes is fed to a relatively short column in a saturation-type operation, the break-through curve of total solute will first indicate the arrival of the least strongly held component, which will often level off to a plateau at (or above) its feed-concentration value. The arrival of the other solutes, in their turn, can be noted similarly, until complete saturation is finally reached.

A related procedure, **displacement analysis,** is like chromatographic elution but uses an elutant with a steadily increasing concentration of displacing agent; the resulting break-through plateaus resemble those for frontal analysis.

CONTINUOUS COUNTERCURRENT OPERATIONS

Continuous-flow units involving the transport of solid particles have been proposed for both gas and liquid sorption operations. Although the operability of several of the available designs has been demonstrated, their relative economic advantage (compared with fixed-bed operation) is not well established. The primary problems to be overcome in continuous countercurrent sorption operations are the following:

1. Mechanical complexity of equipment.
2. Gradual attrition of the solid sorbent.
3. Limitations in particle-size range, to avoid either classification or excessive pressure drop.
4. Channeling (non-uniform flow) of either fluid or solid.
5. Contamination between functional sections of the equipment, due to granular and porous structure of the solid.

An analysis of some of the technical and economic

factors involved shows that there is generally no overwhelming basis for preferring a countercurrent system over fixed-bed units; see Hiester *et al.* [*Chem. Eng. Progress, Symp. Ser.*, **50** (14), 23 (1954)].

Hypersorption. This moving-bed process for adsorption has been applied especially to ethylene recovery from methane and other gases of lower molecular weight [Berg, *Trans. Am. Inst. Chem. Engrs.*, **42,** 665 (1946). Kehde, Fairfield, Frank, and Zahnstecher, *Chem. Eng. Progress*, **44,** 575 (1948)].

The adsorbent (usually activated carbon) moves downward in a tower through a cooler, a rectifying section, a reflux section, and a heated stripping section, into a discharge mechanism and a sealing leg. A gas lift then returns the adsorbent to the top of the tower, where its flow reverses in an impactless separator, and from which it passes through a storage hopper back into the column. The stripping section is fed with steam, and the mixture of steam and desorbed bottom product are disengaged from the bed at a tray just below the reflux section. A side stream of steam-free bottom product is introduced in the reflux section to displace any of the overhead components that may originally have been adsorbed.

Above the feed plate, the process gases undergo countercurrent contact with the main bed of adsorbent. The major part of this stream is disengaged below the cooler, while a minor part of it serves to dehydrate the stripped carbon and is then added to the lift-gas circulation stream. Part of the latter, in turn, is bled off with carbon dust at the top of the unit. External reactivation at higher temperature can be carried out continuously on a small part of the solid inventory.

Fluidized Adsorption. The use of silica gel in a continuous fluidized system for the drying of gases has been described by Ermenc [*Chem. Eng.*, **68** (10), 87 (1961)]. The adsorption tower was 10 ft. in diameter by approximately 70 ft. tall. The adsorption section contained a bubble-cap entrance tray and seven perforated trays, five of which were designated as adsorption plates and two as heat-transfer plates. The latter cooled the incoming hot gel, which was at a temperature of 250°F. The gel used was 6- to 12-mesh material when new, and moved downward at a rate of 80 lb./min. The superficial gas velocity was 4½ ft./sec.

The regenerator section consisted of four perforated plates and one bubble-cap entrance plate. The plates had a gel loading of 6 lb./sq ft. However, only 50 to 60 per cent of the quantity of gas used in the adsorber section was required. In this operating system part of the hot gas to be dried was first used as the regenerating medium, and a condensing cooler was provided between the regenerator and adsorber plate sections. The rest of the hot gas by-passed the regenerator plates going directly into the cooler.

Hydro-Softener. Continuous ion exchange offers the hope of using less resin, less regenerant chemical, less rinse water, and more compact equipment than in either batch or fixed-bed methods. Since saturation and regeneration are carried out in separate sections, each of these can be sized separately to give the most efficient operation. The Dorr-Oliver Hydro-Softener, an entirely continuous and countercurrent apparatus, is shown in Fig. 16-16 (Wilcox, Roberts, and Fitch, U.S. Patent 2,528,099).

In the Hydro-Softener, water softening is accomplished by fluidized contact between water and two separate beds of resin in the larger of two tanks. Exhausted resin is transferred continuously from the softening cell to the regenerating cell by means of ejectors. The brine fed to the regeneration unit has a much lower flow rate; hence the regeneration unit can have a smaller diameter. In this unit, the descending resin is washed free of salt in a rinsing zone before it is recycled to the softening cell.

Other Solution Upflow Arrangements. Many continuous ion-exchanger contactors involve solution upflow. A **rotating plug valve** at the bottom of the column is used for resin take-off, as developed by Stanton (M.S. Thesis, University of Washington, 1950). In

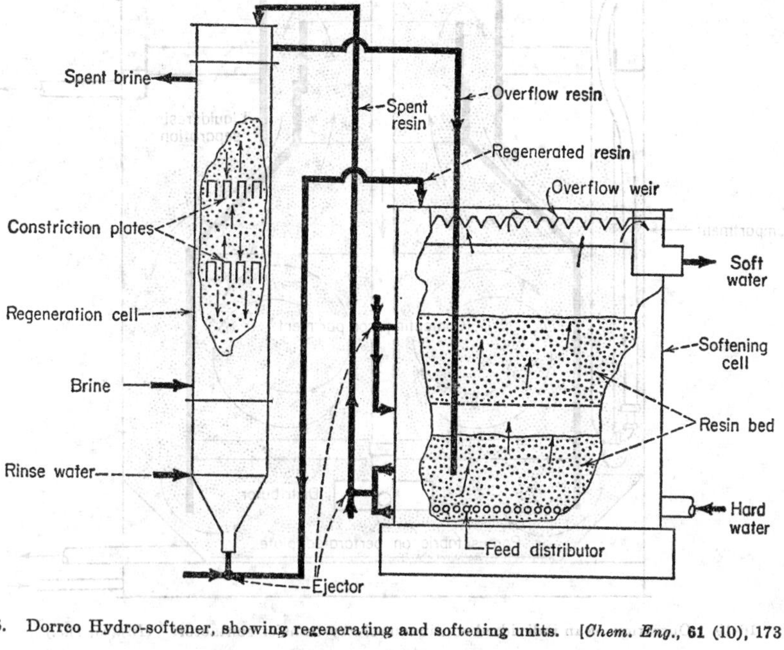

FIG. 16-16. Dorrco Hydro-softener, showing regenerating and softening units. [*Chem. Eng.*, **61** (10), 173 (1954).]

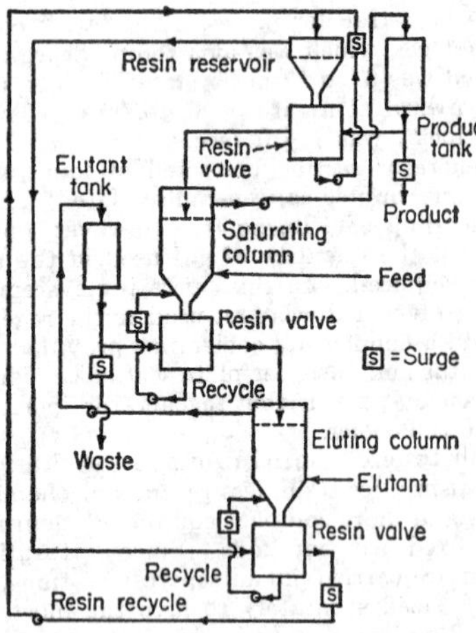

FIG. 16-17. Process flow sheet utilizing moving-bed contactors with downward flow of sorbent. [*Chem. Eng.*, **61** (10), 176 (1954).]

Stanton's apparatus, saturation and regeneration were carried out in separate zones of a single column, with regeneration-zone contact improved by the use of sieve plates.

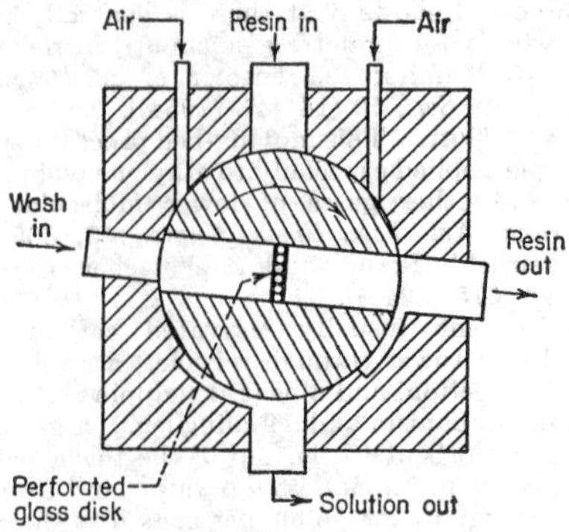

FIG. 16-18. Resin metering and dewatering valve. [*Chem. Eng.*, **61** (10), 174 (1954).]

Selke and Bliss [*Chem. Eng. Progress*, **47**, 529 (1951)] used a **rotating-disk feeder** to introduce a cation exchanger in the H^+ form (with relatively low density) at the top of a fluidized bed of the resin. Countercurrent operation was obtained by an increase in density of the resin, which caused it to settle to the bottom as it was converted to the heavy-metal form. Regeneration was also conducted with downflow of resin, but under dense-bed conditions.

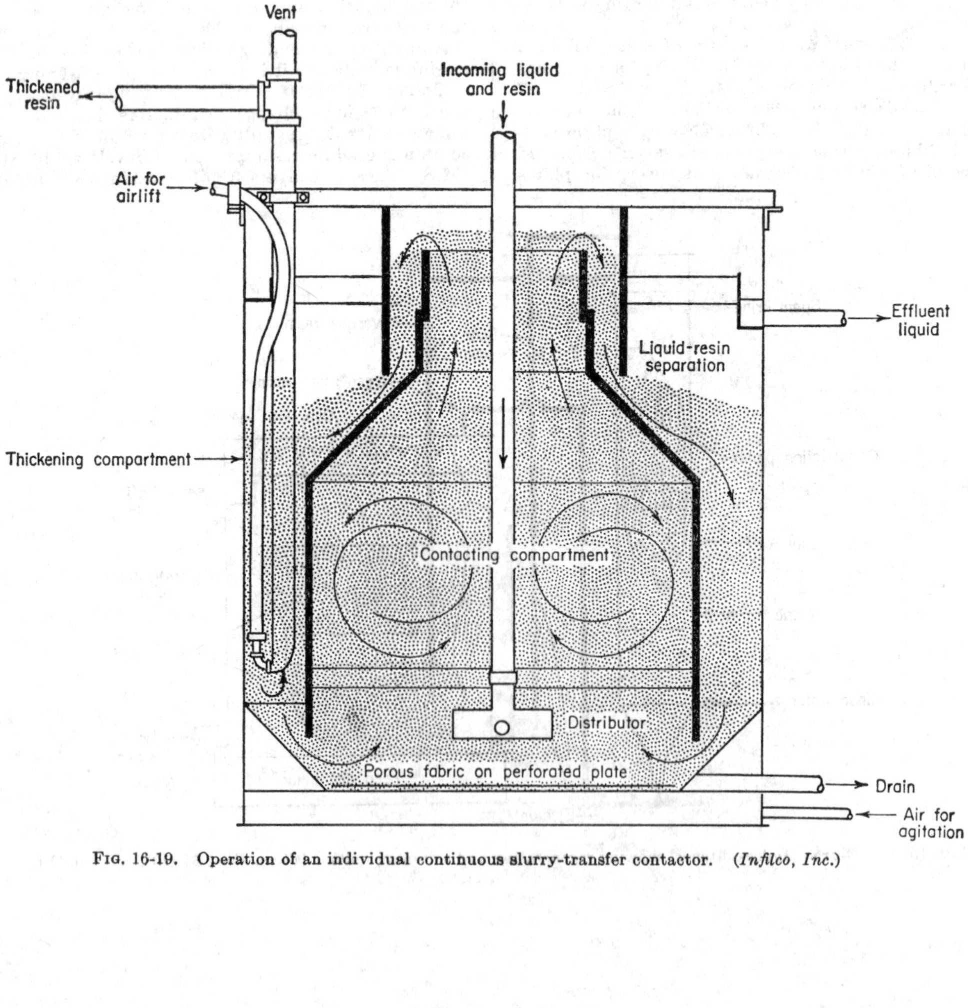

FIG. 16-19. Operation of an individual continuous slurry-transfer contactor. (*Infilco, Inc.*)

A **dense-bed column,** with downward piston flow of resin between two **motorized valves,** has been operated at Stanford Research Institute. Figure 16-17 shows the flow diagram for a complete exchange process using such columns. The upper valve continually supplies resin to the column, while the lower valve withdraws it at an equal rate. The valve design is shown in Fig. 16-18. Resin entering the valve is retained on the perforated glass disk at the mid-point of the bore, while free solution drains through the disk. Rotating clockwise, the bore passes under the right-hand air inlet, where air pressure (applied through a cam-actuated solenoid valve) dewaters the resin by forcing the interstitial liquid through the disk. The bore next becomes aligned with the resin outlet, and a wash solution aids in discharging the resin from the bore. Wash solution remaining is forced out by air from the left-hand inlet; and the cycle is ready to repeat [Hiester, Fields, Phillips, and Radding, *Chem. Eng. Progress*, **50,** 139 (1944)].

Apparently because of large axial-dispersion effects, the foregoing columns were found to give a more shallow gradient for the exchange zone (*i.e.*, a higher H.T.U.) than is observed in fixed beds. In spite of this defect, the resin inventory is sometimes less than that used in fixed beds.

A **spinner column,** with countercurrent flow of resin in the annular space between an inner rotating cylinder and a stationary glass pipe, has been investigated by Koenig, Olin, Babb, and McCarthy [*Chem. Eng. Progress, Symp. Ser.*, **50** (14), 102 (1954)]. Stable swirls of the resin slurry, evenly spaced through the entire column height, were induced by proper selection of flow rates and rotor speed. This column showed relatively low H.T.U. values under optimum operating conditions, but also a relatively small capacity of resin in any given tower.

A multideck **ore-dressing jig** of commercially available type has been investigated for countercurrent ion exchange. Pulsations of a diaphragm at the base of the jig induce alternate expansion and contraction of the resin bed on each screened deck. Although a low contact efficiency was found, the equipment is rugged, flexible, and easily maintained [McNeil, Swinton, and Weiss, *J. Metals*, **7,** 912 (1955)].

Continuous Slurry Transfer. Countercurrent movement of an ion-exchange resin slurry and of the liquor to be contacted, without the use of transfer valves, is provided in the Infilco continuous slurry transfer unit. As shown in Fig. 16-19, each unit functions as a mixer, decanter, and thickener, with contact time depending upon the residence period of the resin in the circulating system from the time it enters until it settles into the concentrator. Agitation of the unit is provided by air sparging at the bottom, and the thickened resin is also transferred by an **air lift.**

A typical cyclic system consists of two units used for loading and two for regeneration. The liquor flows by gravity from unit to unit with the fresh resin being moved from the regeneration section to the loading section by an air lift, as is the spent resin being moved to the elution section.

Hydraulic-ram Operations. Upflow without fluidization can be provided by equipping the top of a column with a "hydraulic ram" as developed at Oak Ridge National Laboratory. The "ram" is a portion of the bed through which liquid is passed continuously downflow and removed at the side, so as to exert a downward force on the lower-lying solid particles which thereby are maintained in a dense-bed arrangement. Equipment embodying this principle is shown in Fig. 16-20.

Downward movement of the bed occurs through **ejector action** at the bottom, which carries a recycle slurry of resin back to the top of the bed. With the aid of a well-controlled hydraulic balance of pressures within and between the column sections beneath the hydraulic ram, different sections in their turn are used for feed treatment, regeneration or stripping, and rinse, with almost no intercirculation of fluid between adjacent sections. Like the Hydro-Softener, this apparatus can be maintained in completely continuous steady-state operation, with the resin moving smoothly at low flow rates [Arehart, Bresee, Hancher, and Jury, *Chem. Eng. Progress*, **52,** 353 (1956)].

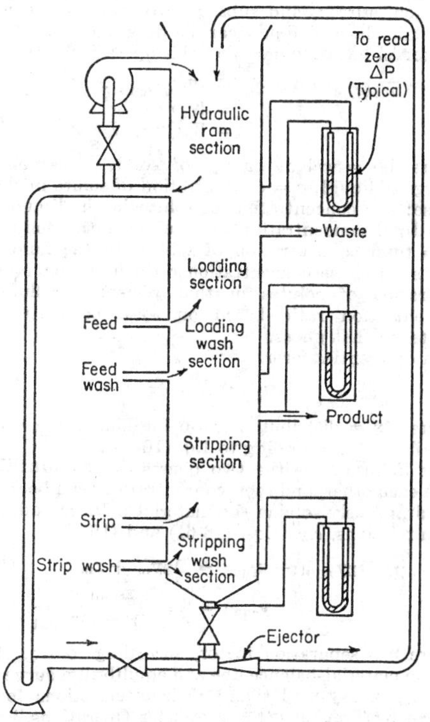

FIG. 16-20. Continuous ion-exchange column, with hydraulic ram. [*Chem. Eng. Prog.*, **52,** 354 (1956).]

Pulsed-bed Operations. The contactor developed by Higgins and coworkers at Oak Ridge National Laboratory utilizes downflow of solution; resin and solution flow alternately, in opposite directions. Upward movement of resin is accomplished by intermittent hydraulic impulses applied to the base of the column, each lasting a few seconds, after which the solution flow is resumed for several minutes. See further in Sec. 19, p. 19-23.

Moving-belt Operations. Cation-exchange resin enclosed in a permeable casing can be conveyed through counterflowing solution [McCormack and Howard, *Chem. Eng. Progress*, **49,** 404 (1953)]. An endless belt of phosphorylated cotton has been used in a similar manner [Guthrie, *Ind. Eng. Chem.*, **44,** 2187 (1952). Muendel and Selke, *Ind. Eng. Chem.*, **47,** 374 (1955)], as has wire gauze coated with ion-exchange resin (Mihara and Terasaki, Japanese Patent 2223).

SORPTION DESIGN METHODS

BATCH SYSTEMS

The following discussion deals with the mathematical analysis and design of representative process systems. As before, equations involving $\mathbf{x}$, $\mathbf{y}$, $\mathbf{r}$, and $\mathbf{D}_\Sigma$ will be equally valid if these variables are replaced, respectively, by $\mathbf{X}$, $\mathbf{Y}$, $\mathbf{R}$, and $\mathbf{D}$.

Approach to Equilibrium in a Single Stage. In one of the most elementary fluid-solid operations, decolorization of a liquid, the adsorbent is added to the solution, stirred, and subsequently allowed to settle so that the clarified liquid can be decanted off. A simple **material balance** describes this operation:

$$W_b(q)_{in} + V_b(c)_{in} = W_b(q)_{equil} + V_b(c)_{equil} = W_b q + V_b c = W_b Q\mathbf{y} + V_b C_0 \mathbf{x} \qquad (16\text{-}61)$$

where W_b = weight charge of solid; V_b = volumetric charge of liquid; q = concentration of solute in the solid phase; c = concentration of solute in the liquid phase; Q = total concentration of solutes in the solid phase; C_0 = total concentration of solutes in the fluid phase; $\mathbf{y}$ = solid-phase concentration ratio based on total concentration of solutes in that phase; $\mathbf{x}$ = fluid-phase concentration ratio based on total concentration of solutes in that phase.

In differential form,

$$\mathbf{D}_\Sigma \, d\mathbf{y} = -d\mathbf{x} \qquad (16\text{-}62)$$

where $\mathbf{D}_\Sigma$ = distribution ratio for binary ion exchange $= QW_b/C_0V_b$, according to Eq. (16-28).

At infinite time the two phases are in **equilibrium** with each other, and their concentrations can be found by simultaneously solving the material balance and equilibrium relations, *e.g.*, Eqs. (16-61) and (16-14):

$$\mathbf{D}_\Sigma \mathbf{y}_{equil} + \mathbf{x}_{equil} = \mathbf{D}_\Sigma \mathbf{y}_{in} + \mathbf{x}_{in} \qquad (16\text{-}63a)$$

$$\mathbf{y}_{equil} = \frac{\mathbf{x}_{equil}}{\mathbf{r} + (1 - \mathbf{r})\mathbf{x}_{equil}} \qquad (16\text{-}63b)$$

where $\mathbf{r}$ = separation factor, according to Eq. (16-11). Or the material-balance line and equilibrium curve can be drawn on a **y-x** plot and their intersections found as shown by Treybal ("Mass-transfer Operations," p. 470, McGraw-Hill, New York, 1955). Once the time for essentially complete equilibrium (say $\mathbf{x} = 0.99\mathbf{x}_{equil}$) is found for the contactor with the fluid-solid system to be used, a related graphical technique can be used to determine the number of countercurrent equilibrations required to provide the desired treatment of the feed, as pointed out below in the discussion of multiple-stage systems.

Reaction-kinetic Form. Equations (16-61) and (16-62), together with the appropriate rate (and, where necessary, equilibrium) equations, lead to prediction of the solid and fluid concentrations with time. For example, with the **reaction-kinetic rate relation** [Eq. (16-48)], which is of very general applicability, as discussed previously (p. 16-13), the resulting integral is analogous to that given by Hougen and Watson ("Chemical Process Principles," Part III, Kinetics and Catalysis, p. 825, Wiley, New York, 1947) for homogeneous second-order reversible reactions.

For the **solution phase,**

$$\mathbf{t}_R = \frac{1}{w} \ln \frac{(2g\mathbf{x} + f - w)(2g\mathbf{x}_{in} + f + w)}{(2g\mathbf{x} + f + w)(2g\mathbf{x}_{in} + f - w)} \qquad (16\text{-}64)$$

where
$$b = \mathbf{r}(\mathbf{D}_\Sigma \mathbf{y}_{in} + \mathbf{x}_{in})$$
$$f = (1 - \mathbf{r})(\mathbf{D}_\Sigma \mathbf{y}_{in} + \mathbf{x}_{in}) - \mathbf{D}_\Sigma - \mathbf{r}$$
$$g = \mathbf{r} - 1$$
$$w = (f^2 - 4bg)^{0.5}$$

since w is always real. A zero value is trivial, and the integral equation is not given here.

The equation for the **sorbent phase** is the same, except for replacing $\mathbf{x}$ by $\mathbf{y}$, but the definitions for $b, f,$ and g are different:

$$b = \mathbf{D}_\Sigma \mathbf{y}_{in} + \mathbf{x}_{in}$$
$$f = (\mathbf{r} - 1)(\mathbf{D}_\Sigma \mathbf{y}_{in} + \mathbf{x}_{in}) - \mathbf{D}_\Sigma - \mathbf{r}$$
$$g = (1 - \mathbf{r})\mathbf{D}_\Sigma$$

For $\mathbf{r} = 1$, or more particularly for trace conditions with $\mathbf{R} = 1$, Eq. (16-64) is indeterminate. By introducing this restriction before integrating, the result for the solution phase becomes

$$\mathbf{t}_R = -\frac{1}{(\mathbf{D}_\Sigma + 1)} \ln \frac{\mathbf{x} - \mathbf{x}_{equil}}{\mathbf{x}_{in} - \mathbf{x}_{equil}} \qquad (16\text{-}65)$$

For other rate-determining mechanisms the integral forms for the behavior of the sorbent system can be obtained in the same manner. Because of their complexity and limited use, except for determining precise rate constants in fundamental studies of the sorption process, these forms are not tabulated here.

Multiple-stage Systems. The design of a sorption system involving several consecutive batch equilibrations is analogous to that for any mixer-settler system involving mass transfer between dissimilar phases. In this case, $\mathbf{D}_\Sigma$ becomes the apparent relative molal flow rate of the two phases. Treybal ("Mass-transfer Operations," pp. 472–479, McGraw-Hill, New York, 1955) gives graphical techniques for predicting the behavior of several cocurrent and countercurrent sorption operations for any equilibrium curve as well as analytical solutions for a Freundlich equilibrium isotherm. The correspondence between the two sets of nomenclature is as follows:

Treybal	Symbols Used Here
Y	$cM/\rho_f = xc_0M/\rho_f$
X	$qM = yq_0{}^*M$
Ls/Gs	$W_b/V_b\rho_f = \rho_b/\epsilon\rho_f$
n	$1/\alpha_F$
m	$M/[\rho_f(Mq_{ref}K_F)^{1/\alpha_F}]$

where M equals molecular weight of solute.

Ion-exchange Separations. When more than one saturating and one eluting solute are involved (as, for example, in **ion exchange** where two saturating components are to be differentially eluted by a third, and thus separated), a **stepwise trial-and-error calculation,** suitable for any number of components, can be used, which is related to the Lewis and Cope method for multicomponent distillation [*Ind. Eng. Chem.*, **24**, 498 (1932)].

This calculation procedure is based on the assumption of a constant separation factor for each pair of components present, as pointed out in the section on Multicomponent Equilibria (p. 16-11). Thus, from Eq. (16-26) in terms of three components A, B, and elutant E, we can define the **equilibrium elutant ratio** β as

$$\beta = \frac{\mathbf{y}_E^*}{\mathbf{x}_E} = \mathbf{r}_{AE}\frac{\mathbf{y}_A^*}{\mathbf{x}_A} = \mathbf{r}_{BE}\frac{\mathbf{y}_B^*}{\mathbf{x}_B} = \frac{1 - \mathbf{y}_A^* - \mathbf{y}_B^*}{1 - \mathbf{x}_A - \mathbf{x}_B} \qquad (16\text{-}66)$$

where $\mathbf{y}$ and $\mathbf{x}$ are defined in terms of Q and C_0. Elimination of $\mathbf{x}$ in the latter, through its relation with $\mathbf{r}$, β, and $\mathbf{y}$, leads to

$$\beta = 1 - (1 - r_{AB})y_A - (1 - r_{BE})y_B \quad (16\text{-}67)$$

These equilibrium relations which are concerned with any stage, say the *n*th, in conjunction with the material balance [similar to Eq. (16-61)] can now be used to solve a specific problem. Considering the *n*th stage, as shown in Fig. 16-21, these conservation equations written in dimensionless form for a countercurrent system are

$$\mathbf{D}_\Sigma(y_A)_{in} + (x_A)_{n-1} = \mathbf{D}_\Sigma(y_A)_n + (x_A)_{out} \quad (16\text{-}68)$$

Example. An ion-exchange resin predominantly in the hydrogen form ($y_E = y_H = 0.9952$, $y_A = y_{Li} = 0.0025$, $y_B = y_K = 0.0023$) is to be used to fractionate an acid feed solution containing roughly equal amounts of Li^+ and K^+ ($x_A = x_{Li} = 0.308$, $x_B = x_K = 0.302$, $x_E = x_H = 0.390$). The value of $\mathbf{D}_\Sigma$, based on the relative quantities of the two phases and their ionic capacities, is 0.725; also $r_{AE} = 1$ and $r_{BE} = 0.316$. What is the degree of separation of Li^+ and K^+ in the effluent solution after two contacts?

a. First, assume values for the effluent solution concentrations from stage *N* (in this example, *N* = 2):

$$(x_A)_{out} = 0.160$$
$$(x_B)_{out} = 0.052$$

b. From a material balance over the entire system, calculate the effluent resin concentrations from stage 1:

$$(y_A)_{out} = (y_A)_{in} + \frac{1}{\mathbf{D}_\Sigma}[(x_A)_{in} - (x_A)_{out}] = 0.207$$

$$(y_B)_{out} = (y_B)_{in} + \frac{1}{\mathbf{D}_\Sigma}[(x_B)_{in} - (x_B)_{out}] = 0.347$$

c. Using Eq. (16-67) calculate β for stage 1:

$$\beta_1 = 1 - (1 - 1)\ 0.207 - (1 - 0.316)\ 0.347 = 0.763$$

d. From the equilibrium relations of Eq. (16-66), calculate the effluent solution concentrations from stage 1:

$$(x_A)_1 = \frac{r_{AE}}{\beta_1}(y_A)_{out}$$
$$= \frac{1}{0.763}(0.207) = 0.271$$
$$(x_B)_1 = \frac{r_{BE}}{\beta_1}(y_B)_{out}$$
$$= \frac{0.316}{0.763}(0.347) = 0.144$$

e. The material balance [Eq. (16-68)] can now be used to obtain the effluent resin concentration from stage 2:

$$(y_A)_2 = (y_A)_{in} + \frac{1}{\mathbf{D}_\Sigma}[(x_A)_1 - (x_A)_{out}] = 0.156$$

$$(y_B)_2 = (y_B)_{in} + \frac{1}{\mathbf{D}_\Sigma}[(x_B)_1 - (x_B)_{out}] = 0.129$$

f. Steps *c* and *d* are repeated for stage 2, leading to

$$\beta_2 = 0.910$$
$$(x_A)_2 = 0.171 = (x_A)_{out}$$
$$(x_B)_2 = 0.045 = (x_B)_{out}$$

g. The assumed values from step *a* are not the same as calculated in step *f*; hence new intermediate values are assumed:

$$(x_A)_{out} = 0.165$$
$$(x_B)_{out} = 0.049$$

and steps *b* to *f* are repeated.

h. Step *g* is repeated until the assumed values and the calculated values are identical; this leads to

$$(x_A)_{out} = 0.163$$
$$(x_B)_{out} = 0.049$$

Thus the Li^+/K^+ ratio has been increased to 3.33 in the effluent solution from stage 2, vs. 1.02 in the feed solution.

A comparison of similar calculations with experimental data has been given by Hiester, Phillips, and Cohen [*Chem. Eng. Progress, Symp. Ser.*, **50** (14), 51 (1954)].

Linear-isotherm Form. If the equilibrium curve is **linear**, well-known analytical solutions are available. For instance, for countercurrent operation, the **Kremser equation** [*Natl. Petrol. News*, **22** (21), 42 (1930)] applies:

$$\frac{(\mathbf{X}_A)_{in} - (\mathbf{X}_A)_{out}}{(\mathbf{X}_A)_{in} - (\mathbf{X}_A)^*_{out}} = \frac{\mathbf{D}_A{}^{N_c+1} - \mathbf{D}_A}{\mathbf{D}_A{}^{N_c+1} - 1} = \gamma_A$$
$$= \mathbf{D}_A \frac{(\mathbf{Y}_A)_{in} - (\mathbf{Y}_A)_{out}}{(\mathbf{Y}_A)_{in} - (\mathbf{Y}_A)^*_{out}} \quad (16\text{-}69)$$

Here $(\mathbf{X}_A)^*_{out} = (\mathbf{Y}_A)_{in}$. The ratio γ_A is the **degree of approach to equilibrium transfer** at the end of the multistage system where the solid enters. The degree of approach to equilibrium transfer at the fluid-entrance end is $\gamma_A/\mathbf{D}_A$ where $(\mathbf{Y}_A)^*_{out}$ is in equilibrium with and equal to $(\mathbf{X}_A)_{in}$. The form for calculating the **number of plates** is

$$N_c = \frac{1}{\ln \mathbf{D}_A} \ln \frac{\mathbf{D}_A - \gamma_A}{\mathbf{D}_A(1 - \gamma_A)} \quad (16\text{-}70)$$

Graphical solution of these equations is given in Treybal's Fig. 8.15 ("Mass-transfer Operations," p. 220, McGraw-Hill, New York, 1955). The relation between nomenclatures is

Treybal	Symbols Used Here
y	$\mathbf{X}x_0 = x$
x	$\mathbf{Y}y_0^* = y$
m	r
$\dfrac{y_2 - mx_2}{y_1 - mx_2}$	$\dfrac{(x)_{out} - (x)_{out}^*}{(x)_{in} - (x)_{out}^*} = 1 - \gamma$
A	$\mathbf{D}$
N_p	N_c

Use of these relations in the design of a two-section equilibrium-stage contactor, for the separation of several ions having linear isotherms with the elutant, is given by Hiester and coworkers [*Ind. Eng. Chem.*, **45**, 2402 (1953)].

All the procedures described above are based on the assumption that the amount of fluid mechanically retained with the solid after filtration or settling is negligible. In the event it is not, calculation methods applicable to leaching operations must be used (Treybal, *op. cit.*, pp. 612–622).

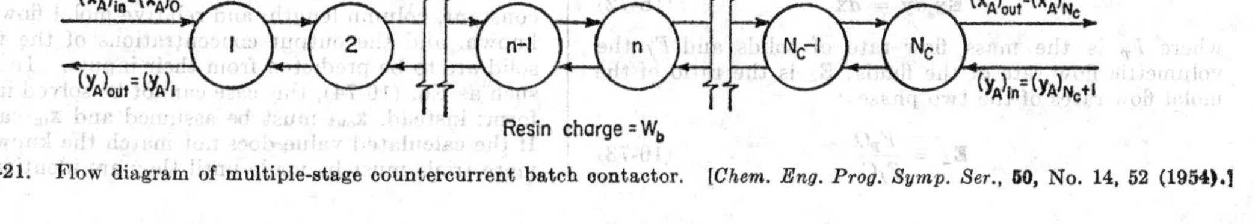

FIG. 16-21. Flow diagram of multiple-stage countercurrent batch contactor. [*Chem. Eng. Prog. Symp. Ser.*, **50**, No. 14, 52 (1954).]

CONTINUOUS COUNTERCURRENT MOVING BEDS

Sorption Efficiency of a Simple Moving-bed Unit. A continuous-flow system with countercurrent contact of fluid and solid phases resembles in many respects a constant-molal-overflow distillation column. Its most striking difference, which affects its design and operation, is that the two phases are not cross-convertible, as gas and liquid are in the condenser and reboiler of a distillation unit. Instead the adsorbent must be regenerated with an independent elutant in a separate operation before being returned to the system for reuse. Thus any complete unit must involve both sorption and desorption, with recycle of the solid phase, as shown in Fig. 16-22.

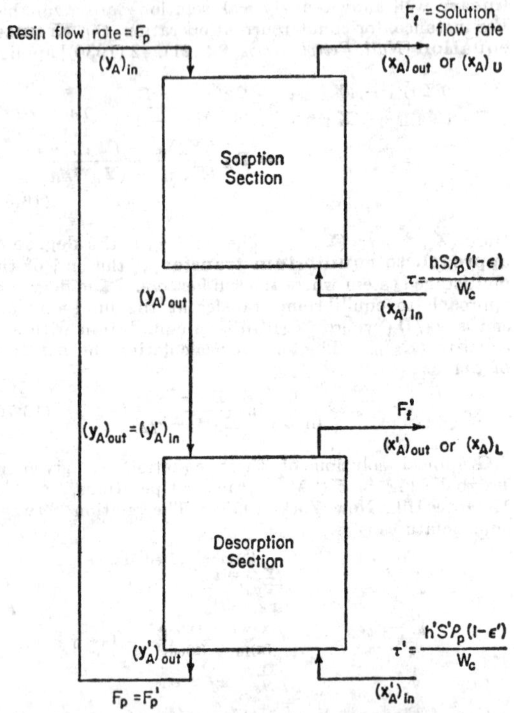

FIG. 16-22. Flow diagram of a two-section continuous countercurrent moving-bed system; primes denote elution variables.

In providing the mathematical model for this type of operation, either section can be used to develop the **material-balance equation**; the two sections are identical algebraically. Thus, for the sorption section, we have

$$F_p(q)_{\text{in}} - F_f(c)_{\text{out}} = F_p(q)_{\text{out}} - F_f(c)_{\text{in}} = F_p(q) - F_f(c) = F_pQ\mathbf{y} - F_fC_0\mathbf{x} \qquad (16\text{-}71)$$

or, in differential form,

$$\mathbf{E}_\Sigma\, d\mathbf{y} = d\mathbf{x} \qquad (16\text{-}72)$$

where F_p is the mass flow rate of solids and F_f the volumetric flow rate of the fluids; $\mathbf{E}_\Sigma$ is the ratio of the molal flow rates of the two phases:

$$\mathbf{E}_\Sigma = \frac{F_pQ}{F_fC_0} \qquad (16\text{-}73)$$

By analogy with Eqs. (16-28), (16-27), and (16-29), we may also define the ratio

$$\mathbf{E}_i = \frac{F_p(q_i)_0{}^*}{F_f(c_i)_0} \qquad (16\text{-}73a)$$

and, for "trace" conditions,

$$\mathbf{E}_A = \frac{F_pQ}{\mathbf{r}_{AB}F_fC_0} = \frac{\mathbf{E}_\Sigma}{\mathbf{r}_{AB}} \qquad (16\text{-}73b)$$

Only two rate relations will be considered in this section. The first, the reaction-kinetic form, is presented because of its general applicability, which was pointed out earlier. The second, the external-transport form, illustrates the familiar graphical technique for determining the number of transfer units in this type of system (the technique can also be applied to a linear or quadratic driving-force treatment of particle-phase diffusion).

Reaction-kinetic Form. Equation (16-72) can be solved in combination with the **kinetic-rate** Eq. (16-48), using the top of the moving bed (where the resin enters) to set the boundary conditions, with the result:

$$\mathbf{t}_R = \frac{1}{w}\ln\frac{(2g\mathbf{x} + f - w)(2g\mathbf{x}_{\text{out}} + f + w)}{(2g\mathbf{x} + f + w)(2g\mathbf{x}_{\text{out}} + f - w)} \qquad (16\text{-}74)$$

where $b = \mathbf{r}(-\mathbf{E}_\Sigma\mathbf{y}_{\text{in}} + \mathbf{x}_{\text{out}}) = \mathbf{r}(-\mathbf{E}_\Sigma\mathbf{y}_{\text{out}} + \mathbf{x}_{\text{in}})$
$f = (1 - \mathbf{r})(-\mathbf{E}_\Sigma\mathbf{y}_{\text{in}} + \mathbf{x}_{\text{out}}) + \mathbf{E}_\Sigma - \mathbf{r}$
$g = \mathbf{r} - 1$
and $w = (f^2 - 4bg)^{0.5}$ is real. It is physically possible for w to be imaginary, that is, for $4\,bg$ to be greater than f^2. In such a case

$$\mathbf{t}_R = \frac{1}{iw}\left(\tan^{-1}\frac{2g\mathbf{x} + f}{iw} - \tan^{-1}\frac{2g\mathbf{x}_{\text{out}} + f}{iw}\right) \qquad (16\text{-}75)$$

where $i = \sqrt{-1}$.

The close correspondence between Eq. (16-74) and the corresponding equation for the batch system [Eq. (16-64)] is not coincidental. If the material-balance differential equations and boundary conditions are compared, it is obvious that the solutions must be the same, except for the following minor changes in parameters:

Batch	Countercurrent
$\mathbf{x}_{\text{in}}$	$\mathbf{x}_{\text{out}}$
$\mathbf{D}_\Sigma = QW_b/C_0V_b$	$-\mathbf{E}_\Sigma = -QF_p/C_0F_f$

It therefore follows that any prediction equation for one system is applicable to the other (if the same equilibrium and kinetics hold) by making the changes indicated above. The two forms, however, are not equally easy to use.

In a batch system, the solute concentrations in the entering fluid and solid charges are known in advance, and the rate constant κ can be calculated from the solution concentration at any time.

For a countercurrent system, the fluid and solid concentrations leaving the column are not known unless they have been determined experimentally or have been specified for design purposes. In the former case the rate constant can be determined; in the latter, given the rate constant and the value of the molal flow rate ratio $\mathbf{E}_\Sigma$, the length of the column can be determined. A third case, however, is the more difficult one; here the rate constant, column length, and relative molal flow rate are known, and the output concentrations of the fluid and solid are to be predicted from their inputs. In relations such as Eq. (16-74), this case cannot be solved in explicit form; instead, $\mathbf{x}_{\text{out}}$ must be assumed and $\mathbf{x}_{\text{in}}$ calculated. If the calculated value does not match the known value, more trials must be made until they are identical.

External-transport Form. In the event that the over-all kinetics of the sorption step are controlled by **fluid-phase transport** external to the particle, combination of that rate [Eq. (16-39)] with the material-balance relation [Eq. (16-72)] leads, with the boundary conditions shown in Fig. 16-22, to the result:

$$\int_{\mathbf{x}_{\text{out}}}^{\mathbf{x}_{\text{in}}} \frac{d\mathbf{x}}{\mathbf{x} - \mathbf{x}^*} = k_{OfF}a_p \frac{\mathbf{E}}{\mathbf{D}_\Sigma \epsilon} \frac{hS\rho_p(1-\epsilon)}{F_p}$$

$$= \frac{k_{fF}a_p h}{F_f/S} = N_{OfF} \tag{16-76}$$

where $$\mathbf{D}_\Sigma = \frac{Q\rho_p(1-\epsilon)}{C_0\epsilon} \tag{16-76a}$$

and k_{OfF} = over-all mass-transfer coefficient based on fluid phase; k_{fF} = fluid-phase mass-transfer coefficient; N_{OfF} = over-all number of transfer units based on fluid phase; a_p = outer-surface interfacial area of the sorbent particles per unit volume of contacting system; h = height or length of contactor; S = cross-sectional area of contactor; ρ_p = dry-particle density; F_p = weight flow rate of solid; F_f = volumetric flow rate of fluid; ϵ = ratio of void space outside of solid particles to total volume of contactor; other symbols as defined previously.

This is the well-known **Chilton-Colburn equation** [*Ind. Eng. Chem.*, **27,** 255 (1935)] relating the sorption efficiency of a countercurrent contactor to its number of transfer units. Although an implicit analytical solution of this is possible for a given isotherm equation and material-balance relation between $\mathbf{y}$ and $\mathbf{x}$, it is much simpler to use a **McCabe-Thiele diagram** to obtain $(\mathbf{x} - \mathbf{x}^*)$ and then to integrate the above equation graphically as shown in Fig. 16-23.

If the number of transfer units is known and the output concentrations are desired, an operating line of slope $\mathbf{E}_\Sigma$ can be moved (with its ends at the proper values of $\mathbf{y}_{\text{in}}$ and $\mathbf{x}_{\text{in}}$) until the graphically determined number of transfer units equals the desired value. This trial-and-error positioning of the operating line then gives the proper values of $\mathbf{x}_{\text{out}}$ and $\mathbf{y}_{\text{out}}$ at its ends. A non-parallel displacement of the operating line is also possible, equivalent to a change in the relative flow rates of the two countercurrent phases.

Linear-isotherm Form. A **linear equilibrium isotherm** permits an explicit analytical solution to Eq. (16-76). This is the well-known **Colburn equation** [*Trans. Am. Inst. Chem. Engrs.*, **35,** 211 (1939)]. In terms of **approach to equilibrium transfer** at the top of the column γ_A, it is

$$\gamma_A = \frac{(\mathbf{X}_A)_{\text{in}} - (\mathbf{X}_A)_{\text{out}}}{(\mathbf{X}_A)_{\text{in}} - (\mathbf{X}_A)^*_{\text{out}}}$$

$$= \frac{\mathbf{E}_A(e^m - 1)}{e^m - \mathbf{E}_A}$$

$$= \mathbf{E}_A \frac{(\mathbf{Y}_A)_{\text{in}} - (\mathbf{Y}_A)_{\text{out}}}{(\mathbf{Y}_A)_{\text{in}} - (\mathbf{Y}_A)^*_{\text{out}}} \tag{16-77}$$

where $m = (1 - \mathbf{E}_A)\mathbf{N}_{OfF}/\mathbf{E}_A$ and the degree of approach to equilibrium transfer at the bottom is $\gamma_A/\mathbf{E}_A$.

Again $(\mathbf{X}_A)^*_{\text{out}} = (\mathbf{Y}_A)_{\text{in}}$; and $(\mathbf{Y}_A)^*_{\text{out}}$ is in equilibrium with and equal to $(\mathbf{X}_A)_{\text{in}}$. In terms of the **number of transfer units,**

$$(\mathbf{N}_A)_{OfF} = \frac{\mathbf{E}_A}{\mathbf{E}_A - 1} \ln \frac{\mathbf{E}_A - \gamma_A}{\mathbf{E}_A(1 - \gamma_A)} \tag{16-78}$$

These equations are given graphically in Treybal's Fig. 8.22 ("Mass-transfer Operations," p. 233, McGraw-Hill, New York, 1955). The relation to the nomenclature is the same as for Eqs. (16-69) and (16-70), except that Treybal's $N_{toG} = \mathbf{N}_{OfF}$.

Height of a transfer unit is easily obtained from these values of N_{OfF}:

$$H_{OfF} = \frac{h}{\mathbf{N}_{OfF}} = \frac{F_f/S}{k_{OfF}a_p} \tag{16-79}$$

and, as pointed out earlier, can be used for design purposes if the behavior of the mass-transfer coefficient k_{OfF} is known under various flow conditions. Such studies have been performed, for both linear and nonlinear isotherms, by Hiester and coworkers [*Chem. Eng. Progress*, **50,** 139 (1954); *Chem. Eng. Progress, Symp. Ser.*, **50** (14), 63 (1954)]. As pointed out by Monet and Vermeulen [*Chem. Eng. Progress, Symp. Ser.*, **55** (25), 109 (1959)], these mass-transfer resistances can also be related to the reaction-kinetic rate constant through the **b** factor of Eqs. (16-50) to (16-54).

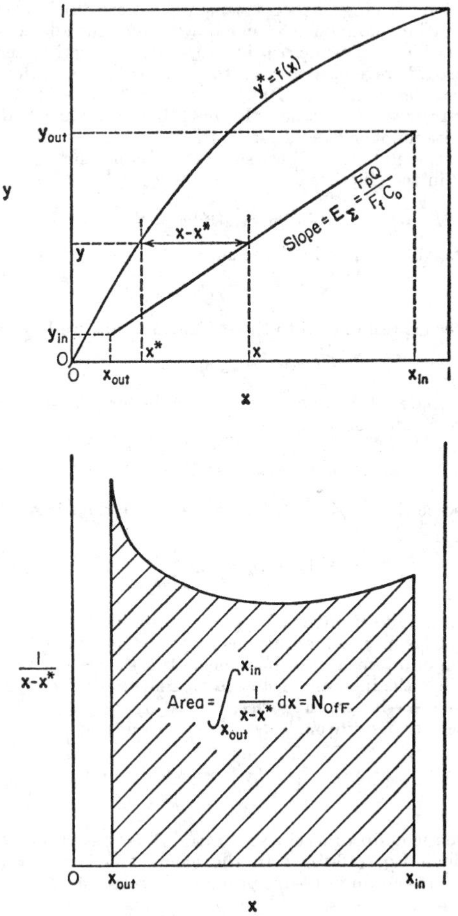

FIG. 16-23. Graphical determination of number of transfer units.

Height of a theoretical plate (H.E.T.P.), while not so fundamentally based, is also useful at times. It can be obtained from the column height and the number of equilibrium contacts N_c, as calculated by the techniques described under Multiple-stage Systems, p. 16-25. For linear isotherms the relation between the height of a transfer unit and the height of a theoretical plate can be obtained by eliminating γ_A between Eqs. (16-70) and

(16-78), since $\mathbf{D}_A$ and $\mathbf{E}_A$ will both represent the relative molal flow rate of the two phases:

$$\frac{\mathbf{N}_{OfF}}{N_c} = \frac{\mathbf{E}_A \ln \mathbf{E}_A}{\mathbf{E}_A - 1} \tag{16-80}$$

Ultimate Sorption Efficiency for a Regenerative Moving-bed System. For each set of column operating conditions and each sorption system, there is an ultimate degree of removal or separation possible. Such limits are achieved in an infinitely long column and are dependent on the equilibrium isotherms of the solutes involved and on the molal flow ratio of the two phases. In a two-unit system as shown in Fig. 16-22, with constant separation factors specified as defined in Eq. (16-76), the theoretical limits can be deduced analytically.

Maximum Recovery for a Pure Product Stream. As in the multiple-stage equilibrium-contact system above, the ion-exchange process considered here involves two saturating components which are differentially eluted by a third. The desorption (or elution) section serves to provide regenerated resin to the top of the sorption (or saturation) section. **Optimum desorption-unit performance** occurs when the outgoing resin has had an infinite number of solution contacts and is in equilibrium with the elutant. Thus, since there is no component A or B in the elutant, or

$$(\mathbf{x}_A')_{\text{in}} = (\mathbf{x}_B')_{\text{in}} = 0$$

there will be none in the resin, *i.e.*,

$$(\mathbf{y}_A')_{\text{out}} = (\mathbf{y}_B')_{\text{out}} = 0$$

Since this resin is fed to the saturation unit, we have also

$$(\mathbf{y}_A)_{\text{in}} = (\mathbf{y}_B)_{\text{in}} = 0$$

A material balance around the latter section under these conditions gives

$$\mathbf{x}_{\text{in}} - \mathbf{x}_{\text{out}} = \mathbf{E}_\Sigma(\mathbf{y}_{\text{out}} - 0) \tag{16-81}$$

or, since the recovery $\bar{R}_U$ in the upper product is $\mathbf{x}_{\text{out}}/\mathbf{x}_{\text{in}}$,

$$1 - \bar{R}_U = \mathbf{E}_\Sigma \frac{\mathbf{y}_{\text{out}}}{\mathbf{x}_{\text{in}}} \tag{16-82}$$

An infinite number of transfer units in the saturation column is most advantageous recoverywise if it produces an equilibrium at the bottom of the saturation section between the incoming solution $\mathbf{x}_{\text{in}}$ and the outgoing resin $\mathbf{y}^*_{\text{out}}$. In this limiting case, the ratio $\mathbf{y}_{\text{out}}/\mathbf{x}_{\text{in}}$ can be replaced by $\beta/\mathbf{r}$, through use of Eq. (16-66), to give

$$1 - \bar{R}_U = \mathbf{E}_\Sigma \frac{\beta}{\mathbf{r}} \tag{16-83}$$

The equilibrium elutant ratio β is based on $\mathbf{y}_{\text{out}}$, through Eq. (16-67). In the event $\mathbf{y}_{\text{out}}$ is not given, Eqs. (16-66) and (16-67) provide the relation

$$\beta = \frac{1}{1 + [(1 - \mathbf{r}_{AE})/\mathbf{r}_{AE}](\mathbf{x}_A)_{\text{in}} + [(1 - \mathbf{r}_{BE})/\mathbf{r}_{BE}](\mathbf{x}_B)_{\text{in}}} \tag{16-84}$$

From Eq. (16-19) this is identical to

$$\beta = \frac{1}{(1/\mathbf{R}_A) + (1/\mathbf{R}_B) - 1} \tag{16-84a}$$

so that β approaches unity under trace conditions.

The ratio of $\mathbf{r}_{AE}$ to $\mathbf{r}_{BE}$ is the separation factor $\mathbf{r}_{AB}$ for these two components, and when it is greater than unity, ion B is more strongly held on the resin than ion A. Thus,

$$1 - (\bar{R}_B)_U = \mathbf{E}_\Sigma \frac{\beta}{\mathbf{r}_{BE}} = \mathbf{r}_{AB}\mathbf{E}_\Sigma \frac{\beta}{\mathbf{r}_{AE}} = \mathbf{r}_{AB}[1 - (R_A)_U] \tag{16-85}$$

Another way of writing the recoveries is in terms of the ratios of the ions in each stream; so

$$\frac{(\mathbf{x}_A)_{\text{out}}}{(\mathbf{x}_A)_{\text{in}}}\frac{(\mathbf{x}_B)_{\text{in}}}{(\mathbf{x}_B)_{\text{out}}} = \frac{(\bar{R}_A)_U}{(\bar{R}_B)_U} = \frac{(\mathbf{x}_A)_{\text{out}}/(\mathbf{x}_B)_{\text{out}}}{(\mathbf{x}_A)_{\text{in}}/(\mathbf{x}_B)_{\text{in}}} \tag{16-86a}$$

From Eq. (16-85)

$$1 - \frac{(\bar{R}_A)_U}{(\phi_{AB})_{\text{out}}/(\phi_{AB})_{\text{in}}} = \mathbf{r}_{AB}[1 - (\bar{R}_A)_U] \tag{16-86b}$$

when $\phi_{AB} = \mathbf{x}_A/\mathbf{x}_B$.

The **relation between recovery and purity** $\bar{p}_A$ then is

$$(\bar{R}_A)_U = \frac{\mathbf{r}_{AB} - 1}{\mathbf{r}_{AB} - \{(\phi_{AB})_{\text{in}}[1 - (\bar{p}_A)_U]/(\bar{p}_A)_U\}} \tag{16-87}$$

$$\text{since} \quad (\bar{p}_A)_U = \frac{(\phi_{AB})_{\text{out}}}{1 + (\phi_{AB})_{\text{out}}} \tag{16-88}$$

Thus, if a pure stream of ion A is desired $[(\bar{p}_A)_U = 1]$, then

$$(\bar{R}_A)_U = \frac{\mathbf{r}_{AB} - 1}{\mathbf{r}_{AB}} \tag{16-89}$$

A material balance over the entire system shows that in the elution column

$$(\bar{p}_B)_L = \frac{(\mathbf{x}_B')_{\text{out}}}{(\mathbf{x}_B')_{\text{out}} + (\mathbf{x}_A')_{\text{out}}} = \frac{\mathbf{r}_{AB}}{\mathbf{r}_{AB} + 1} \tag{16-90}$$

$$(\bar{R}_B)_L = \frac{(\mathbf{x}_B')_{\text{out}}}{(\mathbf{x}_B)_{\text{in}}} = 1 \tag{16-91}$$

In the limiting case we are considering, ion B is completely removed from solution in the saturating column, and thus the outgoing solution is in equilibrium with the completely eluted resin that enters the saturation column. From Eq. (16-85) then, this case occurs when

$$\mathbf{E}_\Sigma \frac{\beta}{\mathbf{r}_{BE}} = 1 \quad \text{or} \quad \frac{1}{\mathbf{E}_\Sigma} = \frac{\beta}{\mathbf{r}_{BE}} = \frac{F_f C_0}{F_p Q} \tag{16-92}$$

The recovery-purity relation given in Eq. (16-87) holds when

$$\frac{1}{\mathbf{E}_\Sigma} > \frac{\beta}{\mathbf{r}_{BE}} \tag{16-93}$$

Operating Conditions for Various Recovery-purity Relations. Similar reasoning shows that the elution column will completely regenerate the resin, as required for maximum purity, if an infinite number of transfer units is provided and

$$\frac{\mathbf{E}_\Sigma'}{\mathbf{r}_{BE}} = \frac{F_p Q}{\mathbf{r}_{BE} F_f' C_0'} < 1 \tag{16-94}$$

For infinite NTU in the saturation column, the effect of the relative molal flow rates of the two phases on the recoveries and purities is recapitulated in Table 16-8.

In a two-section unit, the enrichment of ion B in the bottom product $(\phi_{BA})_L/(\phi_{BA})_{\text{in}}$ can never exceed the value of $\mathbf{r}_{BA}$. Thus, unless $\mathbf{r}_{BA}$ is considerably greater than unity, such a unit will not provide satisfactory separations. However, further enrichment of ion B can be obtained by using this bottom product stream as the feed to another two-section unit where more ion A would be removed in the top product, leaving the new bottom product more pure in ion B. The cascading of such units is discussed further by Hiester *et al.* [*Ind. Eng. Chem.*, **45**, 2402 (1953)].

These relations also apply to any countercurrent contacting system, such as distillation, in which the separation factors for carrier and solutes are each constant.

These same relations are applicable to multistage batch systems where solid is passed through a desorption group of stages prior to recycle, upon replacement of $\mathbf{E}$ by $\mathbf{D}$ in Eq. (16-94) and in Table 16-8.

Examples. *a.* The feed to a two-unit moving-bed separation system is $(x_A)_{in} = (x_{Li})_{in} = 0.308$ and $(x_B)_{in} = (x_K)_{in} = 0.302$, with the carrier $(x_E)_{in} = (x_H)_{in} = 0.390$. The separation factors are $r_{AE} = 1$ and $r_{BE} = 0.316$.

1. What is the maximum possible recovery of pure A from the saturation section, and at what relative molal flow rate of solid to fluid phase does this occur?

$$r_{AB} = r_{AE}/r_{BE} = 1/0.316 = 3.16$$

$$(\bar{R}_A)_U = \frac{r_{AB}-1}{r_{AB}} = \frac{3.16-1}{3.16} = 68.4 \text{ per cent} \qquad \text{(ans.)}$$

$$\beta = \frac{1}{1 + \dfrac{(1-r_{AE})(x_A)_{in}}{r_{AE}} + \dfrac{(1-r_{BE})(x_B)_{in}}{r_{BE}}}$$

$$= \frac{1}{1 + \dfrac{(1-1)(0.308)}{1} + \dfrac{(1-0.316)(0.302)}{0.316}} = 0.605$$

$$\mathbf{E}_\Sigma = \frac{r_{BE}}{\beta} = \frac{0.316}{0.605} = 0.522 \qquad \text{(ans.)}$$

2. What would be the recovery of A if a purity $(\bar{p}_A)_U$ of 98 per cent was acceptable, and what would be the molal flow ratio?

$$(\bar{R}_A)_U = \frac{r_{AB}-1}{r_{AB} - \{(\phi_{AB})_{in}[1-(\bar{p}_A)_U]/(\bar{p}_A)_U\}}$$

$$= \frac{3.16-1}{3.16 - \left[\dfrac{0.308}{0.302}(1-0.98)/0.98\right]} = 68.9 \text{ per cent} \qquad \text{(ans.)}$$

since

$$(\phi_{AB})_{in} = \frac{(x_A)_{in}}{(x_B)_{in}} = \frac{0.308}{0.302}$$

Then

$$\mathbf{E}_\Sigma = \frac{r_{AE}}{\beta}[1-(\bar{R}_A)_U] = \frac{1}{0.605}(1-0.689) = 0.514 \qquad \text{(ans.)}$$

3. At what molal flow ratio would all of component A be removed from the fluid phase, *i.e.*, $(\bar{R}_A)_U = 0$?

$$\mathbf{E}_\Sigma = \frac{r_{AE}}{\beta} = \frac{1}{0.605} = 1.65 \qquad \text{(ans.)}$$

b. The feed of problem *a* is changed to $(x_A)_{in} = (x_B)_{in} = 0.01$ and $(x_E)_{in} = 0.98$.

1. What would be the relative molal flow rate at maximum recovery?

$$\mathbf{R}_A = \frac{1}{1 + (\mathbf{X}_A)_{in}[(1/r_{AE}) - 1]} = \frac{1}{1 + 0.01(1/1 - 1)} = 1$$

$$\mathbf{R}_B = \frac{1}{1 + (\mathbf{X}_B)_{in}[(1/r_{BE}) - 1]} = \frac{1}{1 + 0.01[(1/0.316) - 1]} = 0.98$$

The trace criterion is met ($\mathbf{R} \approx 1$) so $\beta = 1$, and

$$\mathbf{E}_\Sigma = \frac{r_{BE}}{\beta} = 0.316 \qquad \text{(ans.)}$$

2. How many transfer units are required for equilibrium to be approached for component A (*e.g.*, $\gamma/\mathbf{E}_A = 0.99$) at the bottom of the saturation section for component A?

$$\mathbf{E}_A \cong \frac{\mathbf{E}_\Sigma}{r_{AE}} = \frac{0.316}{1} = 0.316$$

$$\gamma_A = 0.99\mathbf{E}_A = 0.313$$

$$(\mathbf{N}_A)_{OfF} = \frac{\mathbf{E}_A}{\mathbf{E}_A - 1}\ln\frac{\mathbf{E}_A - \gamma_A}{\mathbf{E}_A(1-\gamma_A)}$$

$$= \frac{0.316}{0.316-1}\ln\frac{0.316-0.313}{0.316(1-0.313)} = 1.96 \qquad \text{(ans.)}$$

FIXED-BED OPERATIONS

In simple fixed-bed operations the solute undergoing adsorption, or the ion being exchanged, is removed continuously from the carrier fluid and accumulated in the solid phase, as shown in Fig. 16-12. Such transfer proceeds until the concentration on the solid reaches a value corresponding to equilibrium with the concentration in the feed stream. At this point the fluid just leaving that solid layer reaches the feed concentration; however, until the last layer of the sorbent is nearly saturated, the column effluent remains practically free of the solute. This change in effluent concentration with time is known as the **break-through curve** or concentration history.

Table 16-8. Recoveries and Purities for Infinitely Long Saturation Column in a Two-unit Continuous Countercurrent System

Molal flow ratio $\mathbf{E}_\Sigma$	Recovery $(\bar{R}_A)_U$	Purity $(\bar{p}_A)_U$
$\mathbf{E}_\Sigma < \dfrac{r_{BE}}{\beta}$	$(\bar{R}_A)_U = \dfrac{r_{AB} - \mathbf{E}_\Sigma\beta/r_{BE}}{r_{AB}} > \dfrac{r_{AB}-1}{r_{AB}}$	$(\bar{p}_A)_U = \dfrac{(\phi_{AB})_{in}(1-\mathbf{E}_\Sigma\beta/r_{AE})}{1-(\mathbf{E}_\Sigma\beta/r_{BE}) + (\phi_{AB})_{in}(1-\mathbf{E}_\Sigma\beta/r_{AE})} < 1$
$\mathbf{E}_\Sigma = \dfrac{r_{BE}}{\beta}$	$(\bar{R}_A)_U = \dfrac{r_{AB}-1}{r_{AB}}$	$(\bar{p}_A)_U = 1$
$\dfrac{r_{BE}}{\beta} \le \mathbf{E}_\Sigma \le \dfrac{r_{AE}}{\beta}$	$(\bar{R}_A)_U = 1 - \dfrac{\mathbf{E}_\Sigma\beta}{r_{AE}}$	$(\bar{p}_A)_U = 1$
$\dfrac{r_{AE}}{\beta} = \mathbf{E}_\Sigma$	$(\bar{R}_A)_U = 0$	$(\bar{p}_A)_L = \dfrac{(\phi_{AB})_{in}}{(\phi_{AB})_{in}+1}$
$\dfrac{r_{AE}}{\beta} \le \mathbf{E}_\Sigma$	$(\bar{R}_A)_U = 0$	$(\bar{p}_A)_L = \dfrac{(\phi_{AB})_{in}}{(\phi_{AB})_{in}+1}$

Nomenclature:
$\mathbf{E}_\Sigma$ = relative equilibrium molal flow rate ratio for binary ion exchange
$\bar{p}$ = purity of solute in a given fraction or stream of the fluid
$\bar{R}$ = recovery of solute in a given fraction or stream of the fluid
r = separation factor, defined by Eq. (16-11)
β = equilibrium elutant ratio, defined by Eq. (16-66)
ϕ = ratio of solute concentrations in fluid stream

Its prediction or interpretation is the major purpose of the mathematical models given here.

Material-balance Relation. Because the solute concentration depends both on the time from beginning of flow and on the position in the column, the problem of fixed-bed design is much more complex than in the batch case (where time is the major independent variable) or the countercurrent case (where the column position is the critical variable). This complexity is reflected by the material-balance partial differential equation

$$-\frac{\partial c}{\partial v}(V - v\epsilon) = \rho_b\left[\frac{\partial q}{\partial(V - v\epsilon)}\right]_v \qquad (16\text{-}95)$$

$$-\left(\frac{\partial \mathbf{x}}{\partial v}\right)_{\mathbf{Z}v} = \left(\frac{\partial \mathbf{y}}{\partial \mathbf{Z}v}\right)_v \qquad (16\text{-}95a)$$

where c = concentration of solute in the fluid phase; v = volume of contactor; V = volume of fluid entering contactor; ϵ = ratio of void space outside of solid particles to total volume of contactor; ρ_b = bulk density of solid particles in contactor; q = concentration of solute in the solid phase; $\mathbf{x}$ = fluid-phase concentration ratio, based on total concentration of solutes in that phase; $\mathbf{y}$ = solid-phase concentration ratio, based on total concentration of solutes in that phase; $(V - v\epsilon)$ = amount of fluid that has flowed through column volume v.

The dimensionless through-put parameter $\mathbf{Z}$ is given by

$$\mathbf{Z} = \frac{C_0(V - v\epsilon)}{Q\rho_b v} = \frac{V - v\epsilon}{\mathbf{D}_\Sigma \epsilon v} = \frac{\tau}{\mathbf{D}_\Sigma \epsilon v/F} \qquad (16\text{-}96)$$

where C_0 = total concentration of solutes in fluid phase; Q = total concentration of solutes in solid phase; $\mathbf{D}_\Sigma$ = distribution ratio for binary ion exchange; τ = time; F = volumetric flow rate of fluid phase. Here the W/v ratio used in Eq. (16-28) to define $\mathbf{D}_\Sigma$ is ρ_b, bulk density of the solid. From the next-to-last ratio in Eq. (16-96), $\mathbf{Z}$ is seen to be the number of void volumes that have passed through the column, divided by the distribution ratio.

Proportionate-pattern Limit (Unfavorable Equilibrium). The proportionate-pattern case is a classical one in the theory of chromatography. By assuming that equilibrium is maintained everywhere in the column, De Vault [*J. Am. Chem. Soc.*, **65**, 532 (1943)] obtained the relation

$$\frac{d\mathbf{y}^*}{d\mathbf{x}} = \mathbf{Z} + \frac{\alpha}{v} \qquad (16\text{-}97)$$

where α is a constant of integration. Equation 16-97 is valid only in the range of positive $\mathbf{Z}$ values that give $0 \le \mathbf{x} \le 1$. The constant α may be evaluated with the aid of the generally applicable material-balance integral

$$\int_0^\infty (C_0 - c)\,d(V - v\epsilon) = q_0^*\rho_b v \qquad (16\text{-}98)$$

or, in dimensionless form,

$$\int_{\mathbf{Z}=0}^{\mathbf{x}=1} (1 - \mathbf{x})\,d\mathbf{Z} = 1 \qquad (16\text{-}99)$$

In the event that $\mathbf{x}$ leaves zero when $\mathbf{Z}$ is greater than zero, then the integration must be performed in two steps:

$$\int_{\mathbf{Z}=0}^{\mathbf{Z}\text{ at }\mathbf{x}=0} d\mathbf{Z} + \int_{\mathbf{Z}\text{ at }\mathbf{x}=0}^{\mathbf{Z}\text{ at }\mathbf{x}=1} (1 - \mathbf{x})\,d\mathbf{Z} = 1 \qquad (16\text{-}100)$$

For the case of a **constant separation factor r** [see Eq. (16-14)], first treated by Walter [*J. Chem. Phys.*, **13**, 229 (1945)], Eq. (16-97) leads to

$$\frac{d\mathbf{y}^*}{d\mathbf{x}} = \frac{\mathbf{r}}{[(1 - \mathbf{r})\mathbf{x} + \mathbf{r}]^2} = \mathbf{Z} + \frac{\alpha}{v} \qquad (16\text{-}101)$$

Determination of the $\mathbf{Z}$ values for $\mathbf{x} = 0$ and $\mathbf{x} = 1$ and solution of Eq. (16-101) for $(1 - \mathbf{x})$ permit the integration indicated in Eq. (16-100). In this case it is found that $\alpha = 0$, and Eq. (16-101) reduces to

$$\mathbf{x} = \frac{\mathbf{r} - (\mathbf{r}/\mathbf{Z})^{0.5}}{\mathbf{r} - 1} \qquad (16\text{-}102)$$

The limits of validity are $\mathbf{x} = 0$ at $\mathbf{Z} = 1/\mathbf{r}$: $\mathbf{x} = 1$ at $\mathbf{Z} = \mathbf{r}$.

This concentration history has been called the **proportionate-pattern break-through,** because $\mathbf{x}$ depends on $\mathbf{Z}$ only, and the relative sharpness of the curve cannot be increased by lengthening the column.

Where other isotherms apply, the same procedure may be applied; that is, the derivative from the fourth column of Table 16-4 can be introduced into Eq. (16-97), and the resulting value of $(1 - \mathbf{x})$ used in Eq. (16-100) in order to evaluate α. Note that the Freundlich isotherm with $n = 2$, in the form $\mathbf{y} = \mathbf{x}^2$, leads to a break-through line of constant slope.

If the equilibrium ceases to be unfavorable (that is, $\mathbf{r} < 1$), $d\mathbf{x}/d\mathbf{Z}$ from Eq. (16-102) takes on a negative slope. As this is prohibited by the material-balance relation, the break-through curve for "equilibrium" must be drawn continuously vertical at $\mathbf{Z} = 1$ in all instances where $\mathbf{r} < 1$. This theoretically vertical curve, therefore, is also a type of proportionate-pattern result.

Constant-pattern Limit (Favorable Equilibrium). It is an experimental fact that break-through curves are sometimes encountered which retain a constant shape, regardless of column length. This indicates that all parts of the exchange zone move through the column at a constant rate. This is equivalent to $(\partial\mathbf{Z}v/\partial v)_\mathbf{x}$ being constant; so from Eq. (16-95a), $(\partial\mathbf{y}/\partial\mathbf{x})_v$ is constant. However, since $\mathbf{y}$ and $\mathbf{x}$ have the same limits,

$$\mathbf{y} = \mathbf{x} \qquad (16\text{-}103)$$

and also

$$d\mathbf{y} = d\mathbf{x} \qquad (16\text{-}104)$$

at each given position in the column. Both the foregoing partial derivatives have a value of unity. This is the **continuity condition** for the constant-pattern case. The approach of $\mathbf{y}$ to $\mathbf{x}$ is possible only for $\mathbf{r}$ values less than unity, because equilibrium restrictions prevent the approach if $\mathbf{r}$ is unity or greater. The constant-pattern case was first identified and discussed by Bohart and Adams [*J. Am. Chem. Soc.*, **42**, 523 (1920)] for the irreversible reaction kinetics ($\mathbf{r} = 0$).

Particle-phase Diffusion. An exact solution for the **irreversible** constant-pattern break-through is obtained from the results of Wicke [*Kolloid-Z.*, **167**, 289 (1939)], as based on the rate relation given in Eq. (16-30):

$$\mathbf{x} = 1 - \frac{6}{\pi^2}\sum_{n=1}^{\infty}\frac{1}{n^2}e^{-u} \qquad (16\text{-}105)$$

with

$$u = n^2[\psi\mathbf{N}_{pF}(\mathbf{Z} - 1) + 0.64]$$

$$\mathbf{N}_{pF} = \frac{k_{pF}a_p v}{F} = \frac{60D_p\mathbf{D}_\Sigma\epsilon v}{Fd_p^2} \qquad (16\text{-}106)$$

where $\mathbf{N}_{pF}$ = number of transfer units based on particle phase; k_{pF} = mass-transfer coefficient based on particle phase; a_p = outer-surface interfacial area of the sorbent particles per unit volume of contacting system; v = volume of contactor; F = volumetric flow rate of fluid phase; D_p = particle-phase diffusivity; $\mathbf{D}_\Sigma$ = distribution ratio of solute concentrations in the solid and fluid phases; ϵ = ratio of void space outside solid particles to total volume of contactor; d_p = effective spherical diameter of sorbent particle; $\mathbf{Z}$ = through-put parameter, defined by Eq. (16-96); and, since $\mathbf{r} = 0$ [*cf.* Eq. (16-34)],

$$\psi = \frac{\pi^2}{15} \qquad (16\text{-}107)$$

Glueckauf and Coates (*J. Chem. Soc.*, **1947,** 1315) have provided the solution of the **linear-driving-force approximation** [Eq. (16-31)], which, for the irreversible case, is

$$\mathbf{x} = 1 - e^{-u} \qquad (16\text{-}108)$$

where $u = \mathbf{N}_{pF}(\mathbf{Z} - 1) + 1$

For favorable equilibrium and a constant separation factor, their result is

$$\frac{\mathbf{r}}{1-\mathbf{r}} \ln \frac{\mathbf{x}_2(1-\mathbf{x}_1)}{\mathbf{x}_1(1-\mathbf{x}_2)} + \ln \frac{1-\mathbf{x}_1}{1-\mathbf{x}_2} = \mathbf{N}_{pF}(\mathbf{Z}_2 - \mathbf{Z}_1) \qquad (16\text{-}109a)$$

This can also be written as

$$\frac{\mathbf{r}}{1-\mathbf{r}} \ln \mathbf{x} - \frac{1}{1-\mathbf{r}} \ln (1-\mathbf{x}) = \mathbf{N}_{pF}(\mathbf{Z} - 1) + \alpha_p \qquad (16\text{-}109b)$$

with α_p determined by graphically integrating Eq. (16-100). Values of α_p are shown in Table 16-9 as a function of $\mathbf{r}$, along with the lower limits of $\mathbf{N}_p$ for a constant exchange zone to be established and thus for Eq. (16-109) to be valid to ± 0.01 on $\mathbf{x}$.

Table 16-9. Constants and Limits for Eqs. (16-109*b*) **and** (16-115*b*)

r	α_p	α_f	$N_{min.}$
0	1.00	−1.00	4
0.2	1.05	−1.10	10
0.5	1.14	−1.17	25
0.8	1.17	−0.69	75
1.0	(1.19)	(−0.19)	∞

The Vermeulen **quadratic-driving-force approximation** [Eq. (16-30)] can also be integrated in the completely irreversible case to give

$$\mathbf{x} = (1 - e^{-u})^{0.5} \qquad (16\text{-}110)$$

where $u = \psi \mathbf{N}_{pF}(\mathbf{Z} - 1) + 0.61$

Integral solutions implicit in $\mathbf{x}$ are available for other values of $\mathbf{r}$.

Pore Diffusion. This problem has been solved for the irreversible case ($\mathbf{r} = 0$) under the assumption that the fluid-phase concentration in the pores is negligible compared with the solid-phase value (Acrivos, cited by Vermeulen, "Advances in Chemical Engineering," vol. 2, p. 177, Academic Press, New York, 1958). The explicit result is an empirical relation:

$$\mathbf{x} = 0.557[\mathbf{N}_{\text{pore},F}(\mathbf{Z} - 1) + 1.15] - 0.0774[\mathbf{N}_{\text{pore},F}(\mathbf{Z} - 1) + 1.15]^2 \qquad (16\text{-}111)$$

with $$\mathbf{N}_{\text{pore},F} = \frac{k_{\text{pore},F}a_p v}{F} = \frac{60\, D_{\text{pore}} v}{F d_p^2} \qquad (16\text{-}112)$$

At $\mathbf{r} = 0$ the external-transport curve (as will be seen) has a finite limit at $\mathbf{x} = 1$, and the solid-phase diffusion curve has a finite limit at $\mathbf{x} = 0$; however, the pore-diffusion curve has two such limits: at $\mathbf{x} = 0$, $\mathbf{Z} = 1 - (1.15/N_{\text{pore}})$, and at $\mathbf{x} = 1$, $\mathbf{Z} = 1 + (2.43/N_{\text{pore}})$. The pore-diffusion problem has not been solved analytically for other values of $\mathbf{r}$ between zero and one. Breakthrough curves in this region may be estimated graphically by use of the procedures suggested by Vermeulen and Hiester [*Chem. Eng. Progress, Symp. Ser.*, **55** (24), 61 (1959)].

External Transport. For irreversible adsorption ($\mathbf{r} = 0$), Drew, Spooner, and Douglas [*Klotz. Chem. Rev.*, **39**, 241 (1946)] obtained

$$\mathbf{x} = e^u \qquad (16\text{-}113)$$

where $u = \mathbf{N}_{fF}(\mathbf{Z} - 1) - 1$

and $$\mathbf{N}_{fF} = \frac{k_{fF}a_p v}{F} \qquad (16\text{-}114)$$

As $\mathbf{Z}$ approaches zero, $\mathbf{x}$ **becomes small but not identically** zero. At $\mathbf{Z} = 1 + (1/\mathbf{N}_{fF})$, $\mathbf{x}$ **approaches 1 and the** equation ceases to apply.

The method of integrating Eq. (16-39), taking into account Eq. (16-104) and replacing $\mathbf{x}^*$ by the appropriate function of $\mathbf{y}$ (hence, of $\mathbf{x}$), according to the isotherm, is applicable to partially reversible adsorption ($0 < \mathbf{r} < 1$). Michaels [*Ind. Eng. Chem.*, **44,** 1922 (1952)] has used this technique for the case of a **constant separation factor.** His result is

$$\frac{1}{1-\mathbf{r}} \ln \frac{\mathbf{x}_2(1-\mathbf{x}_1)}{\mathbf{x}_1(1-\mathbf{x}_2)} + \ln \frac{1-\mathbf{x}_2}{1-\mathbf{x}_1} = \mathbf{N}_{fF}(\mathbf{Z}_2 - \mathbf{Z}_1) \qquad (16\text{-}115a)$$

As with the Glueckauf relation, this can be expressed as

$$\frac{1}{1-\mathbf{r}} \ln \mathbf{x} - \frac{\mathbf{r}}{1-\mathbf{r}} \ln (1-\mathbf{x}) = \mathbf{N}_{fF}(\mathbf{Z} - 1) + \alpha_f \qquad (16\text{-}115b)$$

and α_f determined in the same manner. Table 16-9 also shows these values and the lower limits of $\mathbf{N}_f$ for Eq. (16-115) to be valid to within ± 0.01 on $\mathbf{x}$.

Reaction Kinetics. The replacement of $\mathbf{y}$ by $\mathbf{x}$ in the **reaction-kinetic** rate equation (16-48) permits integration to

$$\frac{1}{1-\mathbf{r}} \ln \frac{\mathbf{x}}{1-\mathbf{x}} = \mathbf{N}_R(\mathbf{Z} - 1) \qquad (16\text{-}116a)$$

or $$\mathbf{x} = \frac{1}{1 + e^{-u}} \qquad (16\text{-}116b)$$

where $u = (1 - \mathbf{r})\mathbf{N}_R(\mathbf{Z} - 1)$

$$\mathbf{N}_R = \frac{\kappa_F v}{F} = \frac{\mathbf{t}_R}{\mathbf{Z}} \qquad (16\text{-}117)$$

The result given in Eq. (16-116) was first derived by Sillen and Ekedahl [*Arkiv. Kemi., Mineral., Geol.*, **A22** (15, 16), (1946)]. As has been pointed out, this form is useful for treatment of the combined-mechanism region for favorable equilibria ($\mathbf{r} < 1$). The dimensionless quantity $\mathbf{N}_R$ has also been called the *column-capacity parameter* and $\mathbf{t}_R$ the *solution-capacity parameter* by Hiester and Vermeulen [*Chem. Eng. Progress*, **48,** 505 (1952)]; these correspond respectively to the thickness modulus and *time modulus* of Hougen and Marshall [*Chem. Eng. Progress*, **43,** 197 (1947)].

Velocity of Exchange Zone. Under constant-pattern conditions the rate of advance of the **exchange zone** assumes a particularly simple value. The ratio R_F of this rate (measured at a reference value of $\mathbf{x}$) to the velocity of the fluid is always

$$R_F = \left[\frac{\partial(v\epsilon/S)}{\partial(V/S)}\right]_{\mathbf{x}} = \left[\frac{\partial(v\epsilon)}{\partial V}\right]_{\mathbf{x}} \qquad (16\text{-}118)$$

Introduction of Eq. (16-96) in derivative form gives

$$\left[\frac{\partial(Zv)}{\partial v}\right]_{\mathbf{x}} = \frac{1}{\mathbf{D}_\Sigma}\left\{\left[\frac{\partial V}{\partial(v\epsilon)}\right]_{\mathbf{x}} - 1\right\} \qquad (16\text{-}119)$$

Since in the constant-pattern case the left-hand term is unity, there results

$$R_F = \frac{1}{1 + \mathbf{D}_\Sigma} \qquad (16\text{-}120)$$

This is merely a restatement of the continuity condition; it may be compared with a similar relation that applies to the center of gravity of chromatographic zones.

Linear-equilibrium Form. Linear equilibrium involves constant-separation-factor conditions, with the value of the factor $\mathbf{R}$ equal to unity. The conditions under which this is approached were discussed in connection with Eqs. (16-10) and (16-19); it is also approached, according to Eq. (16-12), when $K = 1$. As pointed out earlier, when $\mathbf{r}$ (or $\mathbf{R}$) $= 1$, the different rate-determining mechanisms combine to define the **fluid-phase rate constant** that occurs in the reaction-kinetic form

$$\frac{\partial \mathbf{Y}}{\partial \tau} = \frac{\kappa_F}{\mathbf{D}}(\mathbf{X} - \mathbf{Y}) \qquad (16\text{-}121)$$

Substitution of Eqs. (16-96) and (16-117) into Eqs. (16-95*a*) and (16-121) leads to the dimensionless form

$$-\left(\frac{\partial \mathbf{X}}{\partial \mathbf{N}_R}\right)_{\mathbf{ZN}_R} = \left(\frac{\partial \mathbf{Y}}{\partial \mathbf{ZN}_R}\right)_{\mathbf{N}_R} = \mathbf{X} - \mathbf{Y} \qquad (16\text{-}122)$$

Anzelius [*Z. angew. Math. Mech.*, **6**, 291 (1926)] and Schumann [*J. Franklin Inst.*, **208**, 405 (1929)] have integrated this for a heat-transfer case analogous to solute in the fluid ($\mathbf{x} = 1$ at $\mathbf{N}_R = 0$) but none on the sorbent ($\mathbf{y} = 0$ at $\mathbf{Z} = 0$) to obtain

$$\mathbf{X} = \mathbf{J}(\mathbf{N}_R, \mathbf{ZN}_R) \qquad (16\text{-}123a)$$
$$\mathbf{Y} = 1 - \mathbf{J}(\mathbf{ZN}_R, \mathbf{N}_R) \qquad (16\text{-}123b)$$

The function $\mathbf{J}$ of two variables s and t is given by

$$\mathbf{J}(s, t) = 1 - \int_0^s e^{-t-\xi} I_0 (2\sqrt{t\xi})\, d\xi \qquad (16\text{-}124)$$

where I_0 is a modified Bessel function of the first kind. It is related to Brinkley's function g, of which a punched-card table is available [*Math. Tables Aids Comp.*, **6**, 40 (1952)] in the following manner:

$$\mathbf{J}(s, t) = 1 - g(\sqrt{s}, \sqrt{t}) \qquad (16\text{-}125)$$

An approximation to Eq. (16-124), due to Onsager, has been reported by Thomas [*Ann. N.Y. Acad. Sci.*, **49**, 161 (1948)]:

$$\mathbf{J}(s, t) = \frac{1}{2}\left[1 - \operatorname{erf}(\sqrt{s} - \sqrt{t}) + \frac{e^{-(\sqrt{s} - \sqrt{t})^2}}{\pi(\sqrt{t} + \sqrt[4]{st})}\right] \qquad (16\text{-}126)$$

This is accurate to within 1 per cent when $\sqrt{st} \geq 6$, where (for any number z)

$$\operatorname{erf}(z) = \frac{2}{\sqrt{\pi}} \int_0^z e^{-\zeta^2}\, d\zeta \qquad (16\text{-}127)$$

as given in standard tables of the probability function. At $\sqrt{st} \geq 60$, the last term of Eq. (16-126) can be dropped, to give the simple Klinkenberg approximation [*Ind. Eng. Chem.*, **40**, 1970 (1948)].

Figure 16-24, on logarithmic-probability coordinates, shows the behavior of the $\mathbf{J}$ function. The concentration histories plotted against time on *linear* scales normally are S-shaped. The probability scale for $\mathbf{x}$ largely eliminates the curvature of such plots, and also makes it possible to plot accurately those values which are either very small or very near to unity. The logarithmic scale for $\mathbf{ZN}_R$ makes it possible to compare experimental $\mathbf{x}$ vs. time plots directly with the theoretical curves; this curve-fitting technique was utilized in analogous heat-transfer calculations by Furnas [*Trans. Am. Inst. Chem. Engrs.*, **24**, 1942 (1930)] and in ion-exchange work by Beaton and Furnas [*Ind. Eng. Chem.*, **33**, 1500 (1941)].

The $\mathbf{J}$ function is also given by Hougen and Marshall [*Chem. Eng. Progress*, **43**, 197 (1947)] on logarithmic coordinates, by Furnas (*loc. cit.*) on linear coordinates, and by Klinkenberg (*loc. cit.*) in nomographic form.

The mathematical behavior of $\mathbf{J}$ is given by Hiester and Vermeulen [*Chem. Eng. Progress*, **48**, 505 (1952)], Goldstein [*Proc. Roy. Soc.* (*London*), **A219**, 151, 171 (1953)], and Klinkenberg [*Ind. Eng. Chem.*, **46**, 2285 (1954)].

Constant-separation-factor Form. The most general relation that has been developed for break-through behavior is that of Thomas [*J. Am. Chem. Soc.*, **66**, 1664 (1944)], which includes the separation factor $\mathbf{r}$ as an independent variable along with the number of reaction units $\mathbf{N}_R$ and the through-put ratio $\mathbf{Z}$. Equations (16-48) and (16-95*a*) take the dimensionless form

$$-\left(\frac{\partial \mathbf{x}}{\partial \mathbf{N}_R}\right)_{\mathbf{ZN}_R} = \left(\frac{\partial \mathbf{y}}{\partial \mathbf{ZN}_R}\right)_{\mathbf{N}_R} = \mathbf{x}(1 - \mathbf{y}) - \mathbf{r}\mathbf{y}(1 - \mathbf{x}) \qquad (16\text{-}128)$$

These relations have been integrated for the same boundaries as Eq. (16-123) to give

$$\mathbf{x} = \frac{\mathbf{J}(\mathbf{rN}_R, \mathbf{ZN}_R)}{\mathbf{J}(\mathbf{rN}_R, \mathbf{ZN}_R) + e^u[1 - \mathbf{J}(\mathbf{N}_R, \mathbf{rZN}_R)]} \qquad (16\text{-}128a)$$

and
$$\mathbf{y} = \frac{1 - \mathbf{J}(\mathbf{ZN}_R, \mathbf{rN}_R)}{\mathbf{J}(\mathbf{rN}_R, \mathbf{ZN}_R) + e^u[1 - \mathbf{J}(\mathbf{N}_R, \mathbf{rZN}_R)]} \qquad (16\text{-}128b)$$

where $u = (\mathbf{r} - 1)\mathbf{N}_R(\mathbf{Z} - 1)$

It is apparent that Eq. (16-128) contains the $\mathbf{J}$ function as a limiting case, at $\mathbf{r} = 1$. This equation has also been shown to reduce into the constant-pattern result [Eq. (16-116*a*)] with $\mathbf{r} \ll 1$, and into the proportionate-pattern result [Eq. (16-102)] with $\mathbf{r} \gg 1$, in work by Hiester and Vermeulen (*loc. cit.*) and Gilliland and Baddour [*Ind. Eng. Chem.*, **45**, 330 (1953)]. Extensive numerical values of Eq. (16-128) have been computed and tabulated by Opler and Hiester ("Tables for Predicting the Performance of Fixed-bed Ion Exchange," Stanford Research Institute, Menlo Park, Calif., 1954).

Break-through Plots. The behavior of $\mathbf{x}$ ($= c/C_0$) as plotted against dimensionless time ($\mathbf{ZN}_R$, or $\mathbf{t}_R$) on linear scales is shown in Fig. 16-25 as a function of equilibrium behavior $\mathbf{r}$. Plots analogous to Fig. 16-25 have also been prepared by Hiester and Vermeulen (*loc. cit.*) for an extensive range of $\mathbf{N}_R$ values at $\mathbf{r} = 0$, 0.5, and 1, plus those shown in Fig. 16-26 for three higher values of $\mathbf{r}$.

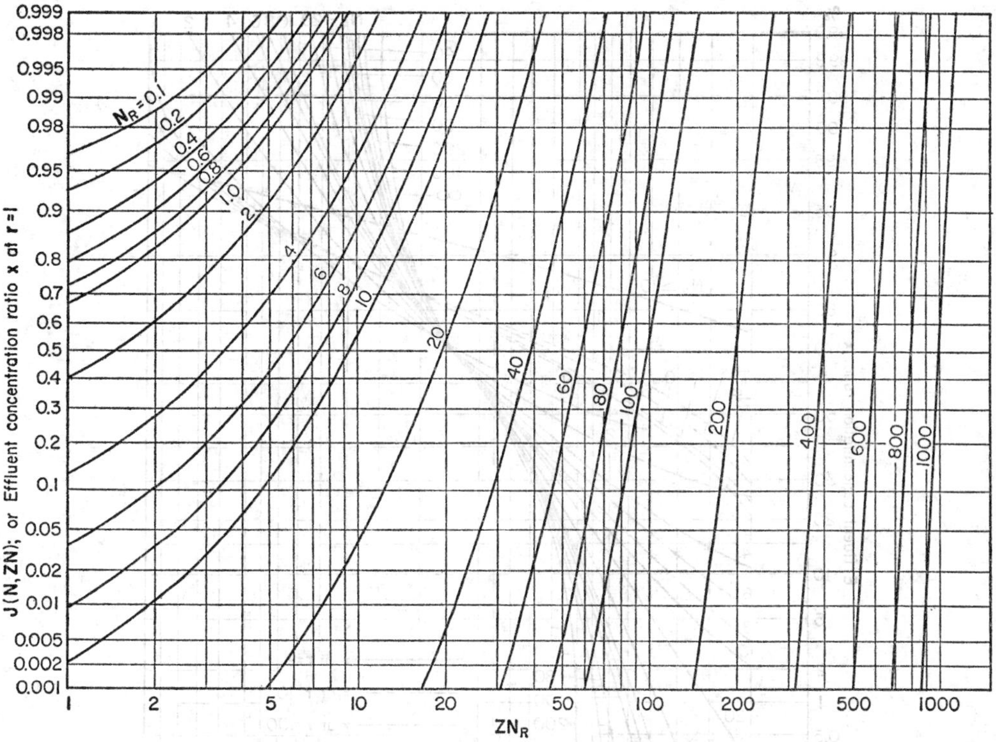

FIG. 16-24. Dependence of J function upon NTU and through-put ratio.

In this figure, **x** is plotted against the logarithm of **Z** to condense the abscissa scale.

For intermediate values of **r** and $\mathbf{N}_R$, the cross plots of Figs. 16-27 to 16-31 cover the working range of **r** values that apply in design calculations. These figures give $1 - \mathbf{Z}$ (or $\mathbf{Z} - 1$) as a function of **r**, at various values of $\mathbf{N}_R$, for five constant values of **x**. The five **x** vs. **Z** points obtained from these plots are sufficient to define completely a concentration history; this construction is shown

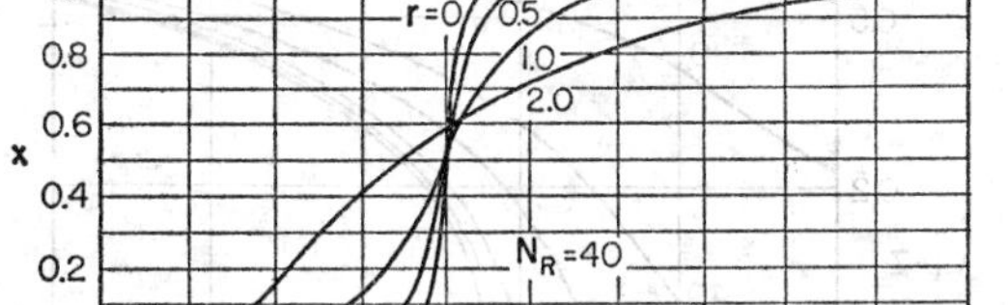

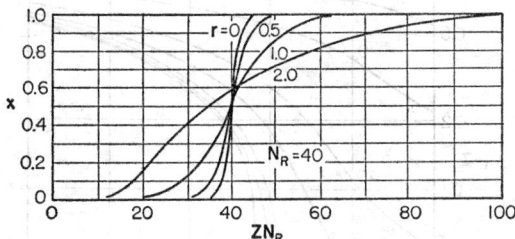

FIG. 16-25. Effect of equilibrium parameter **r** on break-through history.

in Fig. 16-35. [Photocopies of the just-mentioned figures prepared by Hiester and Vermeulen, plus another set of cross plots of $1 - \mathbf{Z}$ (or $\mathbf{Z} - 1$) as a function of $\mathbf{N}_R$ at various values for **r**, for constant **x** values, are for sale by the American Documentation Institute, Photoduplication Service, Library of Congress, Washington 25, D.C., as Document 3665.]

If either $\mathbf{N}_R$ or **r** varies with **x**, the **general reaction-kinetic solution** can still be used to develop a break-through curve for any given pattern of behavior. The curve to be calculated may be divided into several regions, each of which is small enough for the correction factor **b**, as defined by Eqs. (16-51) or (16-52), to be essentially constant. In terms of curve matching, this corresponds to matching different segments of a break-through curve to different reaction-kinetic curves. A detailed example of the use of this technique is given by Hiester and Vermeulen (*loc. cit.*). Families of break-through curves for particle-diffusion or external-transport controlling, based on such constructions, are available in their article and in ADI Document 3665.

Elution Behavior. Thomas's result has been applied mainly to two-component exchange-adsorption systems, in which a fluid containing one component interacts with a solid phase containing initially only the other component; or to one-component adsorption involving solid that is initially entirely free of adsorbed material. In addition, however, Thomas has shown that elution from a completely saturated bed and saturation of a completely eluted bed are complementary processes [*Ann. N.Y. Acad. Sci.*, **49**, 161 (1948)]; see also Eq. (16-20).

In the present nomenclature the break-through curve for this case ($\mathbf{x}' = 0$ at $\mathbf{N}_R = 0$ and $\mathbf{y}' = 1$ at $\mathbf{Z} = 0$) is given by

$$\mathbf{x}' = \frac{1 - J(\mathbf{r}\mathbf{N}_R, \mathbf{Z}\mathbf{N}_R)}{1 - J(\mathbf{r}\mathbf{N}_R, \mathbf{Z}\mathbf{N}_R) + e^{u}J(\mathbf{N}_R, \mathbf{r}\mathbf{Z}\mathbf{N}_R)} \qquad (16\text{-}129)$$

where $u = (\mathbf{r} - 1)\mathbf{N}_R(\mathbf{Z} - 1)$. The complementary nature of this relation and Eq. (16-128*a*) can be proved by replacing $\mathbf{x}'$ by $1 - \mathbf{x}\dagger$, **r** by $1/\mathbf{r}\dagger$, $\mathbf{N}_R$ by $\mathbf{r}\dagger\mathbf{N}_R\dagger$, and **Z** by $\mathbf{Z}\dagger$. As before, $\mathbf{x}'$ is the value of $\mathbf{x}_A$ and $\mathbf{x}\dagger$ the value of $\mathbf{x}_B$ during the elution step.

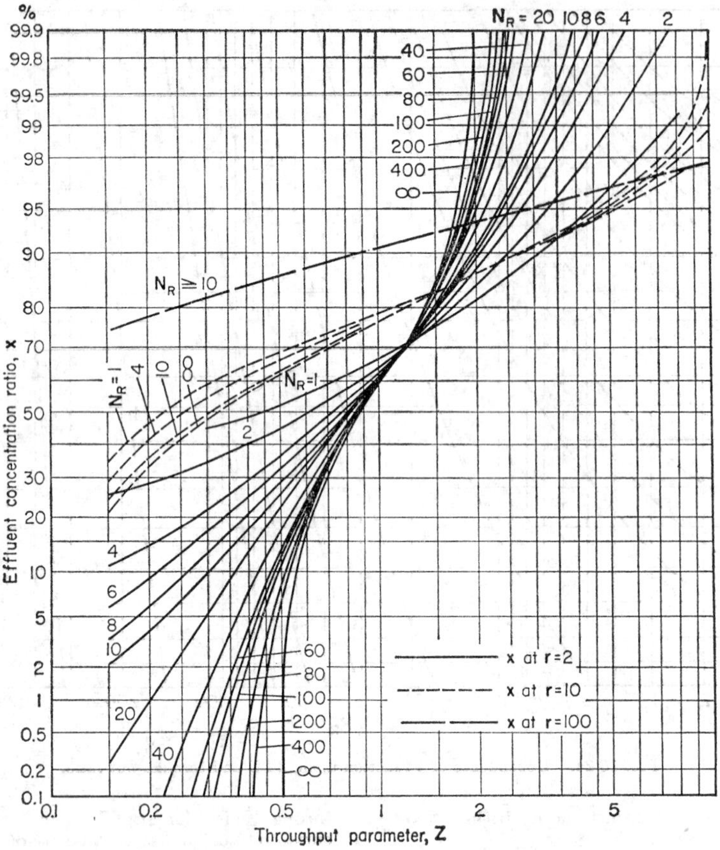

FIG. 16-26. Break-through histories at r = 2, 10, and 100 for the reaction-kinetic treatment. [*Chem. Eng. Prog.*, **48**, 509 (1952).]

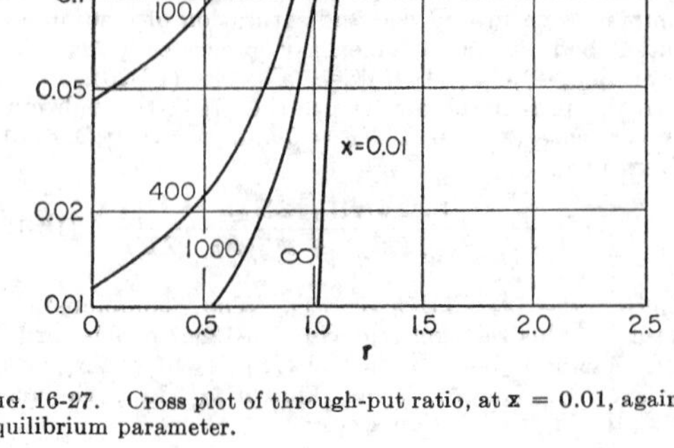

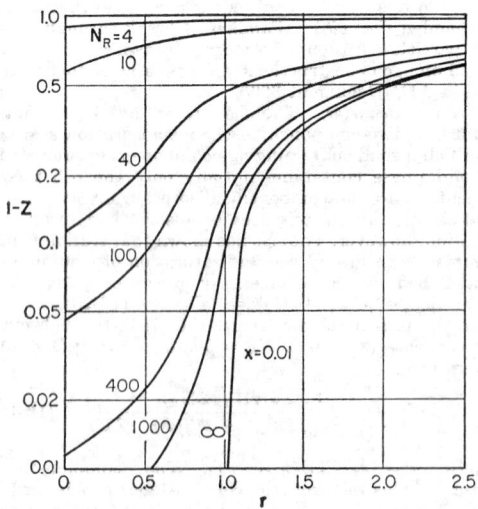

FIG. 16-27. Cross plot of through-put ratio, at x = 0.01, against equilibrium parameter.

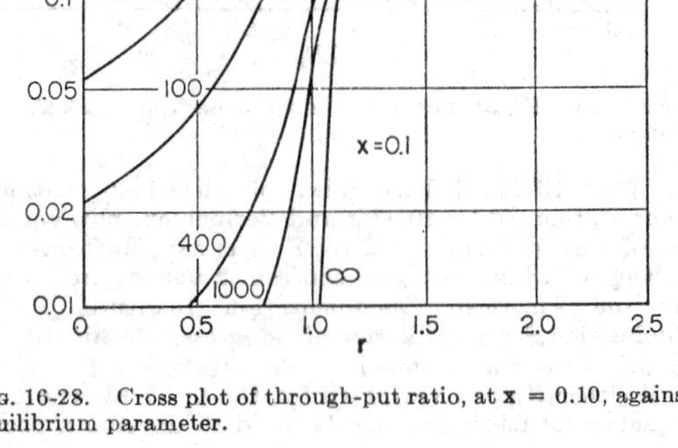

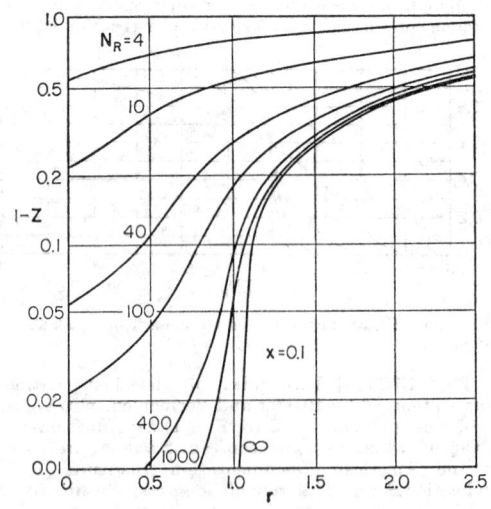

FIG. 16-28. Cross plot of through-put ratio, at x = 0.10, against equilibrium parameter.

A more general treatment, of which Eqs. (16-128), (16-129), and the trace form [Eq. (16-123)] are all special cases, is described by Vermeulen and Hiester [*J. Chem. Phys.*, **22,** 96 (1954)].

Interpretation of Experimental Data. The use of **experimental break-through data** to obtain rate values

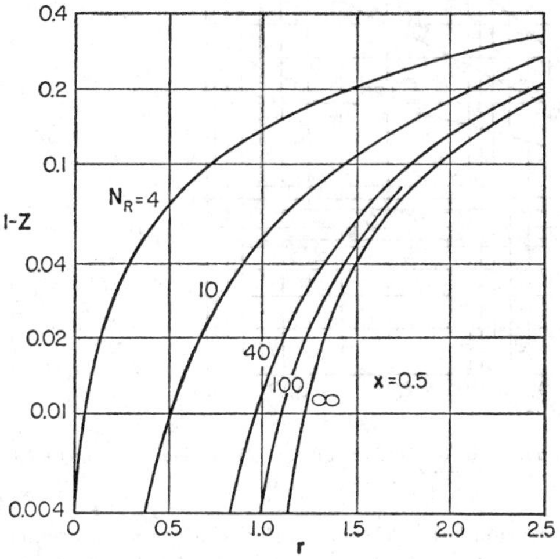

FIG. 16-29. Cross plot of through-put ratio, at $\mathbf{x} = 0.50$, against equilibrium parameter.

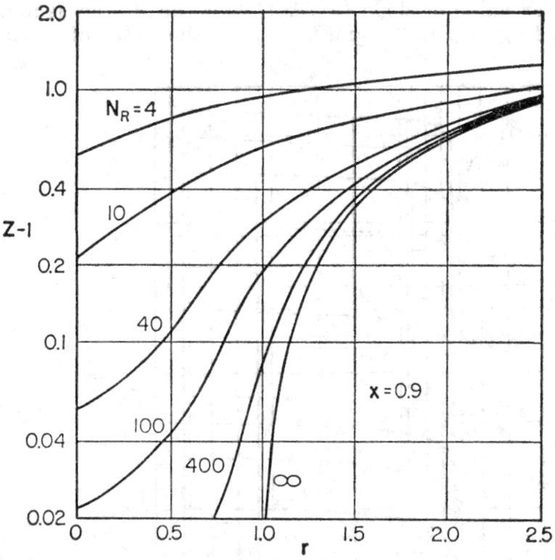

FIG. 16-30. Cross plot of through-put ratio, at $\mathbf{x} = 0.90$, against equilibrium parameter. [*Chem. Eng. Prog. Symp. Ser.*, **55,** No. 24, 64 (1959).]

(or, alternatively, $\mathbf{N}_R$ values) is straightforward, if the equilibrium constant K or K_L is known and hence the separation factor **r** can be calculated. In this case the experimental data can be plotted on a probability ordinate (for **x**) vs. a logarithmic abscissa (for time), and the graph can be shifted horizontally until it matches a specific curve on a theoretical plot of **x** vs. **Z** for various $\mathbf{N}_R$'s at the proper value of **r**. The matched curve will give the number of reaction units $\mathbf{N}_R$; and the **Z** value at any one **x** (for instance, $\mathbf{x} = 0.5$) can be used with the matching time (measured at the column exit) to calculate $\mathbf{D}_\Sigma$ from Eq. (16-96).

An even simpler technique, based on the slope of the break-through curve at $\mathbf{x} = 0.5$, has been suggested by

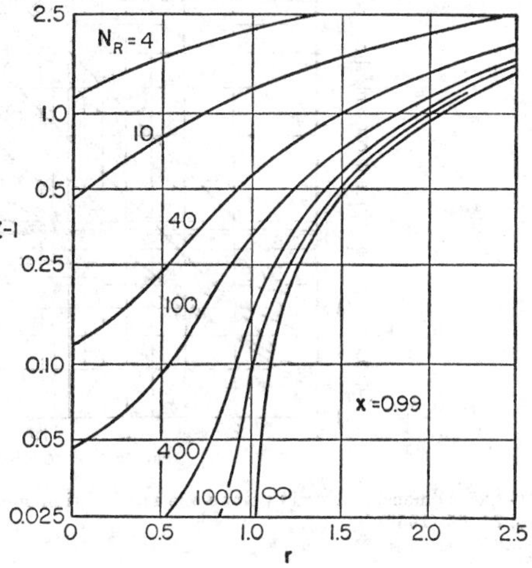

FIG. 16-31. Cross plot of through-put ratio, at $\mathbf{x} = 0.99$, against equilibrium parameter.

Thomas (*loc. cit.*) and Gilliland and Baddour (*loc. cit.*). In the proportionate-pattern region, for the reaction-kinetic model, differentiation of Eqs. (16-102) and (16-116*a*) shows that

$$\left(\frac{\partial \mathbf{x}_{0.5}}{\partial \mathbf{Z}}\right)_{\mathbf{N}_R} = \frac{(\mathbf{r}+1)^3}{16\mathbf{r}(\mathbf{r}-1)} \tag{16-130a}$$

This result, being independent of $\mathbf{N}_R$, does not give any rate data but does give the $\mathbf{D}_\Sigma$ value. However, in the constant-pattern region,

$$\left(\frac{\partial \mathbf{x}_{0.5}}{\partial \mathbf{Z}}\right)_{\mathbf{N}_R} = \frac{(1-\mathbf{r})\mathbf{N}_R}{4} \tag{16-130b}$$

Also, for $\mathbf{r} = 1$,

$$\left(\frac{\partial \mathbf{x}_{0.5}}{\partial \mathbf{Z}}\right)_{\mathbf{N}_R} = \frac{\sqrt{\mathbf{N}_R}}{2\sqrt{\pi}} \tag{16-130c}$$

These and other values of the **mid-point slope** are shown in Fig. 16-32. For **r** values less than unity, the slope is seen to depend upon the particular mechanism that is rate-determining.

The dimensionless mid-point slope $\partial \mathbf{x}_{0.5}/\partial \mathbf{Z}$ is related to the experimental mid-point slope, measured graphically on a linear plot of the concentration history, as follows:

$$\frac{d\mathbf{x}_{0.5}}{d\mathbf{Z}} = \mathbf{D}_\Sigma\, \epsilon v\, \frac{d\mathbf{x}_{0.5}}{d(V-v)} = \frac{\mathbf{D}_\Sigma \epsilon v}{F}\, \frac{d\mathbf{x}_{0.5}}{d\tau} \tag{16-131}$$

In the event the equilibrium constant, and thus **r**, is not known, the complementary nature of the saturation and elution processes [mentioned relative to Eq. (16-129)] can be used to advantage in the following procedure.

A saturation run is carried to completion ($\mathbf{x} \approx 1$); the column is then regenerated by a solution of the ion initially present on the resin, at the same concentration level C_0 and at the same flow rate as used in the saturating run. If the saturation data are fitted against one of the

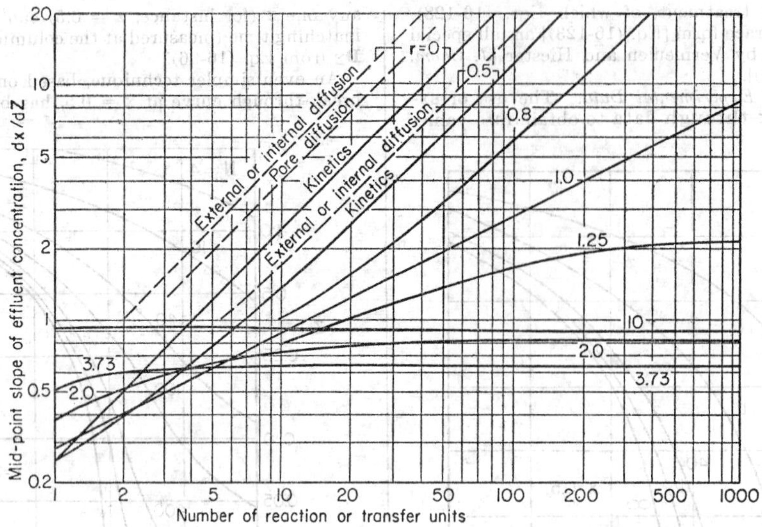

FIG. 16-32. Dimensionless mid-point slope as a function of equilibrium parameter, and of NRU or NTU. [*Chem. Eng. Prog. Symp. Ser.*, **55**, No. 24, 65 (1959).]

standard curves for a given **r** value, and the elution data are fitted similarly on the related **r**† chart, apparent values of $\mathbf{N}_R$ and $\mathbf{N}_R$† will be obtained. This procedure can be repeated for other **r** values. Then, if $\mathbf{N}_R$†/$\mathbf{N}_R$ is plotted against the assumed **r**, intersection of the curve with a line $\mathbf{N}_R$†/$\mathbf{N}_R$ = **r** will indicate the correct value of **r**.

The mid-point-slope method is even more direct when applied to such data. Because the designations of "saturation" and "elution" refer to process requirements rather than to the special problem of column performance, it is convenient to designate the exchange with favorable equilibrium as the *A* step ($\mathbf{r}_A < 1$; $K_A > 1$) and the reverse exchange as the *B* (or *A*†) step. Each value of $\mathbf{r}_A$ and $(\mathbf{N}_R)_A$ then corresponds both to a particular value of slope $(\partial \mathbf{x}/\partial \mathbf{Z})_{0.5}$ for the *A* step as indicated by Fig. 16-32; and to a particular value of $-(\partial \mathbf{x}/$

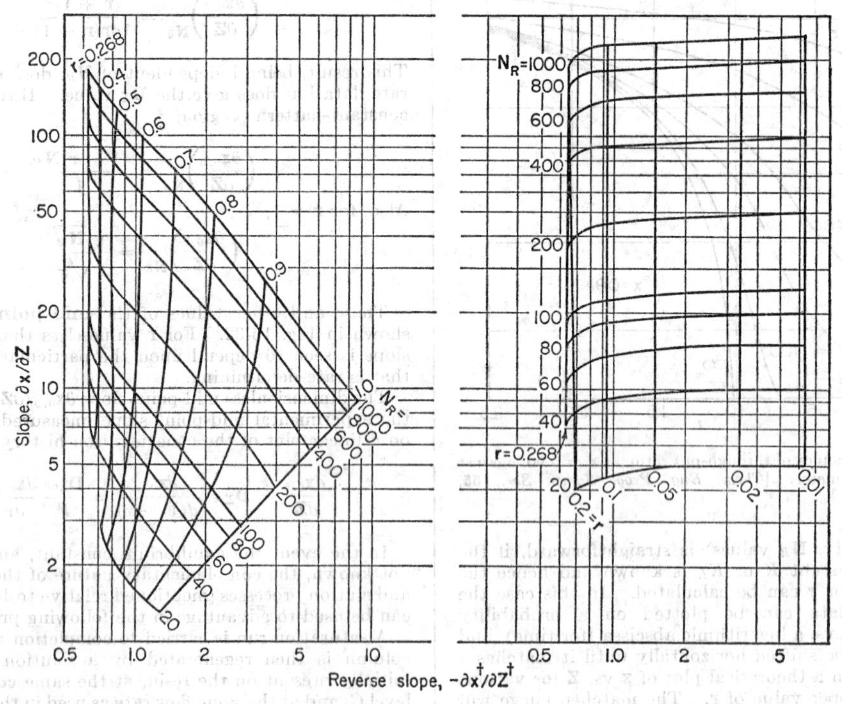

FIG. 16-33. Relation between mid-point slope and reverse slope, reaction-kinetic case. [*Am. Inst. Chem. Engrs. J.*, **2**, 406 (1956).]

Table 16-10. Sequence for Design Calculations

Given: flow rate, break-through limit, equilibrium parameter, particle diameter, diffusivities

Specified variable	Through-put ratio $\mathbf{Z}$	NTU parameter N	Apparent contact time hS/F	Bed volume v or hS	Bed content $hSQ_{\rho b}$	Fluid content $\mathbf{Z}hSQ_{\rho b}$ or $(V - hS\epsilon)C_0$	Fluid volume $V - hS\epsilon$	Running time $\frac{V}{F}$
(*A*) resin utilization	1	2	3	4	5	6	7	8
(*B*) run time	4*(9)	8	7	6	5	3	2	1
(*C*) column volume	4	3	2	1	5	6	7	8

* Assumed.

$\partial \mathbf{Z}\dagger)_{0.5}$, termed the reverse slope, for the B step. In Fig. 16-33 the slope and the reverse slope are plotted as ordinate and abscissa on log-log coordinates, and the values of $\mathbf{r}_A$ and $(\mathbf{N}_R)_A$ are taken as contours. Use of this plot involves calculating the dimensionless slopes from the experimental data for both A and B steps by Eq. (16-131); locating the corresponding point on Fig. 16-33; and reading off both the $\mathbf{r}_A$ and $(\mathbf{N}_R)_A$ values.

The minimum slope which occurs at $\mathbf{r} = 3.73$ produces a double plot in Fig. 16-33. The left side corresponds to $\mathbf{r}_A$ values between 0.268 (= 1/3.73) and 1.0, and the right side to $\mathbf{r}_A$ between zero and 0.268. A choice may be made between these two ranges by taking the ratio of the corrected experimental through-put volumes $[(V\dagger - v\epsilon)_{0.5}/(V - v\epsilon)_{0.5}]$ for the two steps. Figure 16-34 shows this ratio, which also equals $\mathbf{Z}\dagger_{0.5}/\mathbf{Z}_{0.5}$, as a function of $\mathbf{r}$ and $\mathbf{N}_R$. If $\mathbf{Z}\dagger_{0.5}/\mathbf{Z}_{0.5}$ is greater than 0.61,

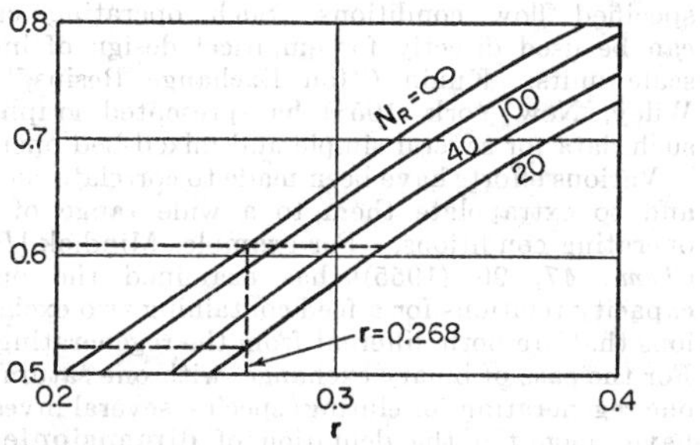

FIG. 16-34. Ratio of through-put volumes at the mid-point, for saturation and elution. [*Am. Inst. Chem. Engrs. J.*, **2**, 407 (1956).]

then $\mathbf{r}$ is greater than 0.268; likewise, if less than 0.52, $\mathbf{r}$ is less than 0.268. In the intermediate region, a trial-and-error procedure between Figs. 16-33 and 16-34 will indicate which $\mathbf{r}$ and $\mathbf{N}_R$ combination is consistent with both.

Similar curves for particle diffusion or external transport controlling are given by Hiester *et al.* [*Am. Inst. Chem. Engrs. J.*, **2**, 404 (1956)].

Design Sequence. Essence of the foregoing theory is that the break-through concentration $\mathbf{x}$ is known mathematically as a function of $\mathbf{N}$ and $\mathbf{Z}$ (for a given constant $\mathbf{r}$). Separately, $\mathbf{N}$ is related to rate factors and to residence time (hS/F or τ) and $\mathbf{Z}$ to capacity factors for the solid and the fluid.

As pointed out above, experimental data must be matched to theoretical curves or equations in order to determine the $\mathbf{Z}$ scale (hence $\mathbf{D}$) and the applicable $\mathbf{N}$ value (and thus the rate factor κ or k).

For design, the calculation sequence to be used depends on the variables that are specified. Three typical sequences are shown in Table 16-10. One of these is illustrated in the following example.

Examples. a. It is desired to decolorize 1.0 cu. ft./min. of sugar solution ($= F = 60$ cu. ft./hr.) to 5 per cent or less of its initial color level (which is 0.001 lb. color bodies/lb. liquid solution). An available column, 20 ft. high and 2 ft. in diameter, is charged with activated carbon. Adsorption on this material is described by a Langmuir isotherm, with $K_L = 1.0 \times 10^5$ lb. solution/lb. color bodies. Other properties of the carbon are $\epsilon = 0.40$; $d_p = 0.82$ mm. (average) $= 0.00269$ ft.; $Q_{\rho b} = 1.0$ lb. color bodies/cu. ft. of packed bed; and $D_{\text{pore}} = 1.5 \times 10^{-6}$ sq. cm./sec. $= 5.81 \times 10^{-6}$ sq. ft./hr. Pore diffusion provides the rate-limiting resistance. Solution density is 70.0 lb./cu. ft.

What is the on-stream time, between successive regenerations?

This problem corresponds to Case C of Table 16-10, and computation steps will be numbered in the same order. The equilibrium parameter $\mathbf{R}$, from Eq. (16-10), is 0.0099; this is essentially equivalent to $\mathbf{R} = 0$.

1. Column volume $v = 20(1)^2\pi = 62.8$ cu. ft.

2. Superficial linear velocity through the bed $F/S = 60/(1)^2\pi = 19.1$ ft./hr. Hence the apparent residence time $hS/F = 20/19.1 = 1.05$ hr.

3. NTU from Eq. (16-112):

$$\mathbf{N}_{\text{pore}} = \frac{60D_{\text{pore}}}{d_p^2}\frac{v}{F}$$

$$= \frac{(60)(5.81 \times 10^{-6})(62.8)}{(0.00269)^2(60)} = 50.3$$

4. Through-put ratio $\mathbf{Z}$, at $\mathbf{X} = 0.05$, is obtained from Eq. (16-111):

$$0.557b - 0.0772b^2 = 0.05$$

where $b = 50.3(\mathbf{Z} - 1) + 1.18$

Solving, $b = 0.09$ (or 7.13)

$\mathbf{Z} = 0.978$ (or 1.118)

(The latter value for $\mathbf{Z}$ is obviously wrong, since at $\mathbf{R} = 0$, $\mathbf{X} > 0.5$ for $\mathbf{Z} > 1$.)

5. Solute content of bed $vQ_{\rho b} = (62.8)(1.0) = 62.8$ lb. color bodies.

6. Solute content of fluid $\mathbf{Z}vQ_{\rho b} = 0.978(62.8) = 61.5$ lb. color bodies.

7. Fluid volume $= 61.5/(0.001)(70.0) = 879$ cu. ft. $= V - v\epsilon$. Column void volume $v\epsilon = (0.4)(62.8) = 25$ cu. ft.; thus total volume fed to the break-through-limit time $V = 879 + 25 = 904$ cu. ft.

8. On-stream time in any one cycle $= V/F = {}^{904}\!/_{60} = 15.1$ hr.

b. Adsorption of carbon dioxide on carbon was studied by Wicke [*Kolloid-Z.*, **86**, 295 (1939).] who obtained the concentration histories shown in Table 16-11. Both runs were made at an inlet flow rate F of 1.85 ml./sec., at 0°C., with a feed concentration C_0 of 52 mm. Hg, with a carrier gas making up another

Table 16-11. Experimental Data for Adsorption of Carbon Dioxide on Carbon

Sorption		Desorption	
$\mathbf{X}$	τ, sec.	$\mathbf{X}'$	τ', sec.
0.010	645	0.970	270
.030	660	.936	330
.140	690	.873	390
.290	710	.744	480
.377	720	.653	540
.464	730	.610	570
.540	740	.570	600
.610	750	.530	630
.726	770	.460	690
.833	800	.430	720
.864	810	.400	750
.940	870	.273	900
.974	960	.177	1080
		.103	1320
		.070	1500
		.023	1920

528 mm. Hg. Column height h was 72 cm., with a cross-sectional area S of 0.39 sq. cm. and a void volume $v\epsilon$ of 16.6 ml. so that the effective through-put time $v\epsilon/F$ was 9.0 sec.

1. On the assumption that the adsorption isotherm can be fitted by the Langmuir relation [Eq. (16-10)], and that the reaction-kinetic treatment of break-through applies, what are the values of $\mathbf{R}$ and $\mathbf{N}_R$ for each break-through curve?

A linear plot of each break-through curve in the vicinity of the mid-point reveals that, for sorption,

$$\frac{d\mathbf{X}_{0.5}}{d\tau} = 0.00745 \text{ sec.}^{-1} \quad \text{and} \quad \tau_{0.5} = 734 \text{ sec.}$$

so $\tau_{0.5} - v\epsilon/F = 734 - 9 = 725$ sec. and, for desorption,

$$\frac{d\mathbf{X}'_{0.5}}{d\tau'} = -0.00127 \text{ sec.}^{-1} \quad \text{and} \quad \tau'_{0.5} = 655 \text{ sec.}$$

so $\tau'_{0.5} - v\epsilon/F = 655 - 9 = 646$ sec. Separation factor $\mathbf{R} < 1$, since this adsorption process is assumed to follow a Langmuir isotherm. From Fig. 16-29 it can be seen that $\mathbf{Z}_{0.5} \cong 1$ if it is also assumed that $\mathbf{N}_R$ is greater than 40. On this basis, Eq. (16-96) shows that

$$\frac{\mathbf{D}\epsilon v}{F} = \frac{\tau - (v\epsilon/F)}{\mathbf{Z}} \cong \tau_{0.5} - (v\epsilon/F) = 725 \text{ sec.}$$

Then from Eq. (16-131)

$$\frac{d\mathbf{X}_{0.5}}{d\mathbf{Z}} = 725(0.00745) = 5.4$$

$$-\frac{d\mathbf{X}'_{0.5}}{d\mathbf{Z}\dagger} = -725(-0.00127) = 0.92$$

and

$$\frac{\mathbf{Z}\dagger_{0.5}}{\mathbf{Z}_{0.5}} = \frac{\tau'_{0.5} - (v\epsilon/F)}{\tau_{0.5} - (v\epsilon/F)} = \frac{646}{725} = 0.892$$

From Fig. 16-34, $\mathbf{R}$ is greater than 0.268; from Fig. 16-33 for sorption, at coordinates (0.92, 5.4),

$$\mathbf{R} = 0.58 \quad \text{and} \quad \mathbf{N}_R = 50$$

Therefore, for desorption

$$\mathbf{R}\dagger = 1/\mathbf{R} = 1.72$$

and

$$\mathbf{N}_R\dagger = \mathbf{R}\mathbf{N}_R = 29$$

The assumption of a high $\mathbf{N}_R$ and $\mathbf{R}$ less than 1 for the sorption process is thus validated, verifying that $\mathbf{Z}_{0.5}$ is essentially unity.

The above results can be checked further since, in the constant-pattern region that this case approaches (compare Table 16-9), Eq. (16-130b) shows that

$$\frac{d\mathbf{X}_{0.5}}{d\mathbf{Z}} = \frac{(1 - \mathbf{R})\mathbf{N}_R}{4} = \frac{(0.42)(50)}{4} = 5.25$$

which is close to the measured value of 5.4.

2. Determine the theoretical break-through curves and compare them with the experimental data.

Figures 16-27 to 31 can be used to determine the values for certain $\mathbf{X}$'s for each of the ($\mathbf{R}$, $\mathbf{N}_R$) combinations. The results are given in Table 16-12. Note that, if $\mathbf{D}\epsilon v/F$ is taken as 725 sec.,

Table 16-12. Calculated Data for Adsorption of Carbon Dioxide on Carbon

$\mathbf{R} = 0.58$, $\mathbf{N}_R = 50$				$\mathbf{R}\dagger = 1.72$, $\mathbf{N}_R\dagger = 29$			
$\mathbf{X}$	$\mathbf{Z}$	$\tau - (v\epsilon/F)$, sec.	τ, sec.	$\mathbf{Z}\dagger$	$\tau' - (v\epsilon/F)$, sec.	τ', sec.	$\mathbf{X}'$
0.01	0.775	558	567	0.28	202	211	0.99
0.1	0.892	642	651	0.46	331	340	0.9
0.5	1	720(725)	729	0.904	651(655)	660	0.5
0.9	1.11	800	809	1.66	1195	1204	0.1
0.99	1.23	885	894	2.33	1680	1689	0.01

$\tau_{0.5} - (v\epsilon/F) = 725$ sec. and $\tau'_{0.5} - (v\epsilon/F) = 655$ sec., as shown in parentheses. The latter value is 9 sec. longer than the experimental value. If this difference is split between the adsorption and desorption placement so that $\tau'_{0.5} - (v\epsilon/F)$ is 651 sec., then from the $\mathbf{Z}\dagger_{0.5}/\mathbf{Z}_{0.5}$ ratio of 0.904, $\tau_{0.5} - (v\epsilon/F)$ is 720 sec. This last number is therefore the best average value of $\mathbf{D}\epsilon v/F$ and is used in calculating the values of $\tau - (v\epsilon/F)$ shown in the table. The experimental points (open circles and triangles) and calculated points (solid circles and triangles) are both plotted in Fig. 16-35 and are found to have good correspondence.

3. What are the values of K_L, $\mathbf{D}$, and $q_{\lim}\rho_b$? From the ideal-gas law,

$$c_0 = \frac{52}{760 \times 359} = 1.91 \times 10^{-4} \text{ lb.-moles } CO_2\text{/cu.ft.}$$

Also

$$\epsilon = v\epsilon/hS = \frac{16.6}{(72)(0.39)} = 0.591$$

From Eq. (16-10)

$$K_L = \frac{1}{c_0}\left(\frac{1}{\mathbf{R}} - 1\right) = \frac{1.72 - 1}{1.91 \times 10^{-4}}$$

$$= 3.77 \times 10^3 \text{ cu. ft./lb.-mole}$$

From Eq. (16-96)

$$\mathbf{D} = \frac{[\tau_{0.5} - (v\epsilon/F)]F}{v\epsilon} = \frac{(725)(1.85)}{16.6} = 80.7$$

From Eq. (16-27)

$$(q_i)_0{}^*\rho_b = \mathbf{D}c_0\epsilon = (80.7)(1.91 \times 10^{-4})(0.591)$$
$$= 9.1 \times 10^{-3} \text{ lb.-mole/cu. ft.}$$

From Table 16-5

$$q_{\lim}\rho_b = \frac{(q)_0{}^*\rho_b(1 + K_Lc_0)}{K_Lc_0} = \frac{9.1 \times 10^{-3}(1.72)}{0.72}$$
$$= 2.41 \times 10^{-2} \text{ lb.-mole/cu. ft.}$$

Cyclic Operation. For the more common ion-exchange reactions, such as water softening, operating capacities are frequently quoted by resin manufacturers as a function of the **regenerant dosage,** applied under specified flow conditions. Such operating capacities can be used directly for empirical design of industrial-scale units. Kunin ("Ion Exchange Resins," 2d ed., Wiley, New York, 1958) has presented graphs giving such data for several simple and mixed-bed operations.

Various efforts have been made to correlate such results and to extrapolate them to a wide range of possible operating conditions. For example, Mindick [*Ind. Eng. Chem.*, **47**, 96 (1955)] has examined the operating-capacity relations for a feed containing two exchangeable ions that are both different from the regenerating species. For the case of binary exchange, with one saturating and one regenerating (or eluting) species, several investigators have suggested the definition of **dimensionless variables** that would apply to an **entire period or cycle of operation,** rather than to an instantaneous condition of a column [Hiester and Phillips, *Chem. Eng.*, **61** (10), 161 (1954). Farnham, M.S. Thesis in Chemical Engineering, Stanford University, 1955]. These variables are:

1. Resin utilization $\mathbf{U}$—the ratio of operating capacity (or amount of feed ion actually exchanged) to the ultimate capacity for that ion represented by the total amount of resin in the column.

2. Regenerant efficiency $\mathbf{G}$—the quantity of ions removed from the resin divided by the total quantity of regenerant ions fed to the column.

3. Average leakage $\mathbf{L}$—the amount of feed ion which escapes from the column during saturation periods, divided by the total amount of that ion fed.

4. Feed potential $\mathbf{Z}_{sat}$—the total amount of feed ion charged, divided by the ultimate capacity of the column.

5. Regenerant potential $\mathbf{Z}_{reg}$—the quantity of regenerant ions fed to the column, divided by the ultimate capacity of the column.

In terms of the symbols already used,

$$\mathbf{L} = \frac{1}{\mathbf{Z}_{sat}} \int_0^{\mathbf{Z}_{sat}} \mathbf{x}\, d\mathbf{Z} \qquad (16\text{-}132)$$

$$\mathbf{U} = \mathbf{Z}_{sat}(1 - \mathbf{L}) = \mathbf{Z}_{sat} - \int_0^{\mathbf{Z}_{sat}} \mathbf{x}\, d\mathbf{Z} \qquad (16\text{-}133)$$

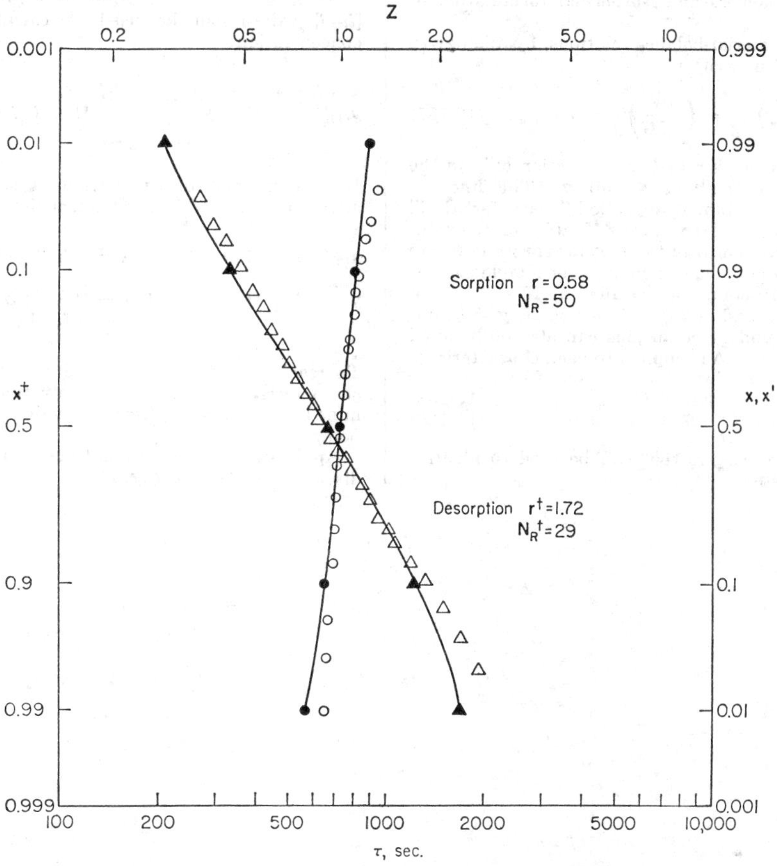

FIG. 16-35. Matching of theoretical break-through curves to experimental data of Wicke, for adsorption of carbon dioxide on activated carbon.

$$\mathbf{G} = \frac{1}{\mathbf{Z}_{\text{reg}}}\left[\int_0^{\mathbf{N}_R} y_{\mathbf{Z}(\text{sat})}\, d\mathbf{N}_R - \int_0^{\mathbf{N}_R} y_{\mathbf{Z}(\text{reg})}\, d\mathbf{N}_R\right] \qquad (16\text{-}134)$$

In an idealized cyclic operation, where all successive saturation and regeneration steps are identical, the concentration pattern in the column after the first saturation period will be duplicated only roughly by the concentration pattern after the second saturation period. The same will be true of the patterns at the end of the regeneration steps. In the following cycles these patterns will, however, converge into a steady-state behavior which is duplicated exactly at the corresponding stages in each successive cycle. For this **steady state,** the regenerant efficiency becomes

$$\mathbf{G} = \frac{\mathbf{Z}_{\text{sat}}(1 - \mathbf{L})}{\mathbf{Z}_{\text{reg}}} \qquad (16\text{-}135)$$

Cornaz and Hiester (unpublished work) have shown that a function **F**, first used by Thomas [*J. Am. Chem. Soc.*, **66**, 1664 (1944)] and designated by him as ϕ, can be used in calculating **L** and hence **U** and **G**. In this treatment the average leakage is

$$\mathbf{L} = \frac{1}{\mathbf{N}_R \mathbf{Z}_{\text{sat}}} \mathbf{F}(\mathbf{N}_R, \mathbf{Z}_{\text{sat}}) - \mathbf{F}\dagger(\mathbf{N}_R, \mathbf{Z}_{\text{reg}}) + \Xi \qquad (16\text{-}136)$$

where, for various values of **r**, the values of **F** and **F**† have been computed and tabulated for a range of values of $\mathbf{N}_R$ and **Z** along with other functions that are needed for evaluating the residual function Ξ. In this way a solution involving two time variables, $\mathbf{Z}_{\text{sat}}$ and $\mathbf{Z}_{\text{reg}}$, is split into terms each of which involves only one time variable ($\mathbf{Z}_{\text{sat}}$, $\mathbf{Z}_{\text{reg}}$, or $\mathbf{Z}_{\text{reg}} + \mathbf{Z}_{\text{sat}}$. It should be noted that this particular treatment applies only when the flow of regenerant is in the same direction as flow of saturant, and, in addition, the resin does not undergo much mixing as a result of backwashing. While the results are not yet in a form which will allow their rapid use, the basic principles of cyclic operation have been established, and the numerical efficiencies for any given cycle have been rendered calculable.

Framework for Computer Calculations

For complex rate or equilibrium behavior, numerical integration of the rate and material-balance equations (with enthalpy balances added, if necessary) may be carried out manually or on a digital computer. A particularly useful framework for such calculations, which is termed the **method of characteristics,** has been described by Acrivos [*Ind. Eng. Chem.*, **48**, 703 (1956)]. It is illustrated here only for the simplest of cases, involving a dimensionless and isothermal formulation of rates.

The rate and material-balance relations, by analogy to Eq. (16-128), can be written

$$-\left(\frac{\partial \mathbf{x}}{\partial \mathbf{N}}\right)_{\mathbf{NZ}} = \left(\frac{\partial \mathbf{y}}{\partial \mathbf{ZN}}\right)_{\mathbf{N}} = U(\mathbf{x}, \mathbf{y}) \qquad (16\text{-}137)$$

where the dimensionless rate U is a function only of the dimensionless concentrations **x** and **y**. The lines of constant **NZ** and constant **N** are called "characteristics." Characteristics of type I, constant **ZN**, are used to evaluate the **x** changes. Those of type II, for constant **N**, are then used to evaluate changes in **y**. For simple saturation, the boundary condition specified at $\mathbf{N} = 0$, for all **ZN**, is that $\mathbf{x} = 1$; and at $\mathbf{ZN} = 0$, for all **N**, $\mathbf{y} = 0$; but more complex boundary conditions can also be handled easily. An increment Δ is applied to each characteristic, such that

$$\mathbf{ZN} = i\Delta \qquad (16\text{-}138)$$
$$\mathbf{N} = j\Delta \qquad (16\text{-}139)$$

where i and j are integers that can be used to identify each calculation step.

As a first approximation, the rate at one set of $[i, j]$ values can be used to calculate an adjacent concentration:

$$\mathbf{x}_{(1)}[i, j+1] = \mathbf{x}[i, j] + U[i, j]\Delta \qquad (16\text{-}140)$$
$$\mathbf{y}_{(1)}[i, j+1] = \mathbf{y}[i-1, j+1] + U[i-1, j+1]\Delta \qquad (16\text{-}140a)$$

In this method of calculation, a second iteration is advantageous, and is often sufficient:

$$\mathbf{x}_{(2)}[i, j+1] = \mathbf{x}[i, j] + \tfrac{1}{2}U[i, j]\Delta + \tfrac{1}{2}U_{(1)}[i, j+1]\Delta \qquad (16\text{-}140b)$$
$$\mathbf{y}_{(2)}[i, j+1] = \mathbf{y}[i-1, j+1] + \tfrac{1}{2}U[i-1, j+1]\Delta + \tfrac{1}{2}U_{(1)}[i, j+1]\Delta \qquad (16\text{-}140c)$$

To reach the concentration values at an intersection of characteristics $[i, j]$, the concentrations must be determined at all underlying intersections, a total of $i \times j$ points.

Application of the method to more difficult problems is discussed by Acrivos (*loc. cit.*).

SECTION 17

OTHER DIFFUSIONAL OPERATIONS

BY

Karl Kammermeyer, Sc.D., Professor and Head, Department of Chemical Engineering, University of Iowa; Member, American Institute of Chemical Engineers, National Society of Professional Engineers, American Chemical Society, American Society for Engineering Education, American Association for the Advancement of Science; Registered Professional Engineer, Iowa, Pennsylvania. (Section Editor)

K. C. D. Hickman, Ph.D., Consultant, Technical Director, Aquastills, Inc.; Member, American Vacuum Society; Fellow, Royal Photographic Society, Chemical Society (London), New York Academy of Sciences, Rochester Academy of Sciences. (Molecular Distillation)

Coleman J. Major, Ph.D., Professor of Chemical Engineering, University of Iowa; Member, American Institute of Chemical Engineers, American Chemical Society, American Rocket Society; Registered Professional Engineer, Iowa, California. (Leaching, Sublimation, Freeze-Drying)

G. P. Monet, M.S., Research Associate, E. I. du Pont de Nemours & Co.; Member, American Chemical Society, American Institute of Chemical Engineers. (Electrodialysis)

James O. Osburn, Ph.D., Professor of Chemical Engineering, University of Iowa; Member, American Institute of Chemical Engineers, American Chemical Society, American Society for Engineering Education; Registered Professional Engineer, Iowa. (Crystallization)

John E. Powers, Ph.D., Professor of Chemical Engineering, University of Oklahoma; Member, American Institute of Chemical Engineers, American Chemical Society, American Society for Engineering Education, American Association for the Advancement of Science. (Thermal Diffusion)

J. W. Riggle, M.S., Research Engineer, E. I. du Pont de Nemours & Co.; Member, American Chemical Society, American Institute of Chemical Engineers, National Society of Professional Engineers; Registered Professional Engineer, Delaware. (Dialysis)

Lenard O. Rutz, Ph.D., Assistant Professor of Chemical Engineering, University of Iowa; Member, American Chemical Society, American Institute of Chemical Engineers, American Society for Engineering Education. (Gaseous Diffusion)

CONTENTS

LEACHING

Definition. Leaching is the process of removing a solute from a solid by the use of a liquid solvent. It is sometimes called **solvent extraction,** a term also applied loosely to liquid-liquid extraction (see Sec. 21).

Equipment Used. Many types of equipment are used to effect contact of the original solid with the solvent and subsequent separation of the resulting solution. One of the simplest forms of leaching vessel is a tank in which the solids and solvent are agitated and then allowed to separate. Separation may take place in the same tank or in another vessel, a settling unit. Another type of leaching equipment consists of an open tank equipped with porous or perforated bottom in which the solvent is allowed to percolate by gravity through the bed of retained solids. When volatile solvents are used or when gravity flow is too slow, a closed percolation vessel with a solvent feed pump may be used. Various types of filter presses are often employed for percolation-type leaching.

Descriptions and performance data on equipment used for leaching operations are given in Sec. 19, p. 19-17.

Types of Flow. The three principal types of flow used in leaching systems are indicated in Fig. 17-1. The **single stage** in Fig. 17-1*a* represents the complete operation of contacting the solids feed and fresh solvent and subsequent mechanical separation. In the **multistage cocurrent (parallel) system** shown in Fig. 17-1*b*, fresh solvent and solids feed are mixed and separated in the first stage. Underflow from the first stage is sent to the second stage, where more fresh solvent is added. This scheme is repeated in all the succeeding stages. In the **multistage countercurrent system** shown in Fig. 17-1*c* the underflow and overflow streams flow countercurrently to each other.

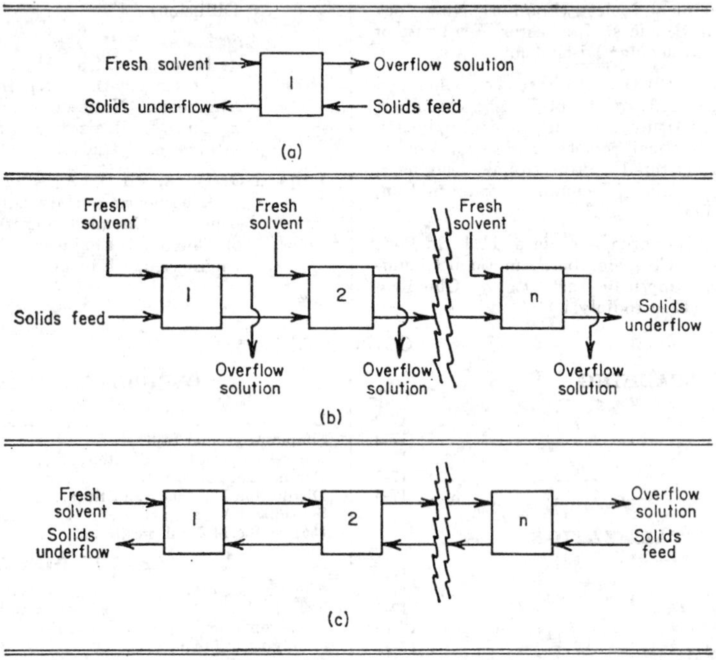

FIG. 17-1. Types of flow employed in leaching. (*a*) Single stage. (*b*) Multistage cocurrent. (*c*) Multistage countercurrent.

DESIGN CALCULATION METHODS

Analytical Methods. Baker's method [*Chem. & Met. Eng.*, **42,** 669 (1935)] was developed for multistage countercurrent leaching using the ideal-stage concept. It assumes that the solution adhering to the inert solids in the underflow in a given stage has the same composition as that in the overflow from that stage. Also, it assumes that the underflow rate between stages is constant or that the solvent-to-inerts ratio is constant between stages.

For constant underflow, the Baker equation may be put into the form

$$\frac{1}{f} = 1 + a_n + a_n a + a_n a^2 + \cdots + a_n a^{n-1} - \frac{W_f''}{w_d''}(1 + a_n + a_n a + a_n a^2 + \cdots + a_n a^{n-2}) \quad (17\text{-}1)$$

where f = ratio of solute in underflow discharged from first stage to solute in underflow fed to last stage; n =

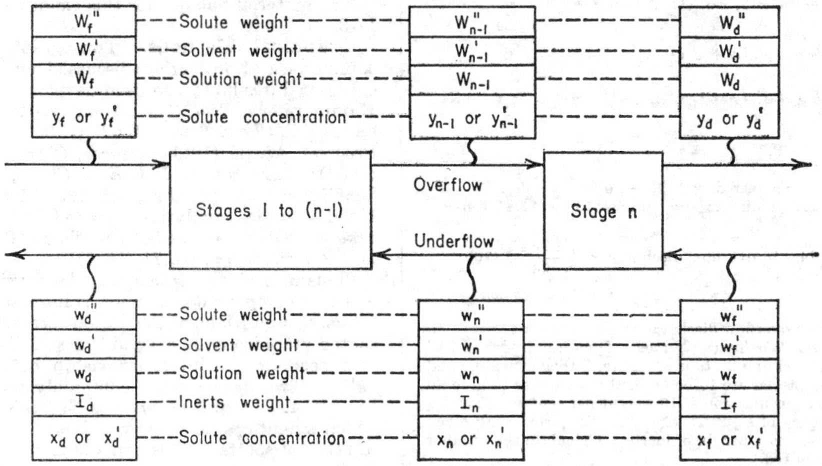

FIG. 17-2. Symbols used for analytical methods.

number of ideal stages; other symbols are defined as follows (see also Fig. 17-2):

$a = W_{n-1}/w_d$ = ratio of overflow solution leaving stage $(n-1)$ to solution in underflow leaving first stage
$a' = W'_{n-1}/w_d'$ = ratio of solvent in overflow leaving stage $(n-1)$ to solvent in underflow leaving first stage
$a_n = W_d/w_n$ = ratio of overflow solution leaving last stage to solution in underflow leaving last stage
$a_n' = W_d'/w_n'$ = ratio of solvent in overflow leaving last stage to solvent in underflow leaving last stage
w = weight of solution adhering to solids in underflow
w' = weight of solvent in underflow
w'' = weight of solute in underflow
W = weight of overflow solution
W' = weight of solvent in overflow
W'' = weight of solute in overflow
$x = w''/w$ = weight fraction of solute in underflow solution
$x' = w''/w'$ = weight ratio of solute to solvent in underflow
$y = W''/W$ = weight fraction of solute in overflow
$y' = W''/W'$ = weight ratio of solute to solvent in overflow

Subscripts:

d = discharge
f = feed
n = nth stage (refers to stream leaving that stage)

If the fresh solvent contains no solute ($W_f'' = 0$), Eq. (17-1) becomes

$$\frac{1}{f} = 1 + a_n + a_n a + a_n a^2 + \cdots + a_n a^{n-1} \tag{17-2}$$

For the case of constant solvent-to-inerts ratio, the quantity a is replaced by a' and a_n by a_n' in Eqs. (17-1) and (17-2).

The Baker method is particularly useful for calculating terminal concentrations if the number of ideal stages is known, although it may also be used for calculating the number of ideal stages if the terminal quantities are established.

A modification of the Baker method as applied to variable underflow has been developed by Grosberg [*Ind. Eng. Chem.*, **42**, 154 (1950)].

The **McCabe-Smith method** (McCabe and Smith, "Unit Operations of Chemical Engineering," p. 760, McGraw-Hill, New York, 1956) uses the same general assumptions as the Baker method but facilitates calculation of number of stages directly by use of the known solution concentrations.

For constant total underflow or constant solution-to-inerts ratio, the McCabe-Smith equation becomes

$$n - 1 = \frac{\log \dfrac{x_n - y_{n-1}}{x_d - y_f}}{\log \dfrac{x_n - x_d}{y_{n-1} - y_f}} \tag{17-3}$$

For constant solvent-to-inerts ratio, Eq. (17-3) becomes

$$n - 1 = \frac{\log \dfrac{x_n' - y'_{n-1}}{x_d' - y_f'}}{\log \dfrac{x_n' - x_d'}{y'_{n-1} - y_f'}} \tag{17-4}$$

Example 1. *Baker Method.* One hundred tons of ore containing 15 per cent solubles and 5 per cent moisture by weight are to be leached with 100 tons of water in a continuous countercurrent system consisting of three ideal stages. The underflow from each stage contains 0.3 lb. of solution per lb. of inerts. Determine the percentage of solubles recovered and the composition of the overflow discharge stream.

Solution. The underflow from each stage contains 80 tons of inerts and $(0.3)(80) = 24$ tons of solution. Total weight of underflow from each stage $= 80 + 24 = 104$ tons. By an over-all material balance, weight of solution leaving stage 3 is equal to $100 + 100 - 104 = 96$ tons. Material balances around stages 1 and 2 give overflows of 100 tons of solution from each of these stages. Since the fresh solvent contains no solute, Eq. (17-2) applies.

$$a = \frac{W_{n-1}}{w_d} = \frac{\text{lb. solution in overflow from stage 2}}{\text{lb. solution in underflow from stage 1}} = \frac{100}{24} = 4.167$$

$$a_n = \frac{W_d}{w_n} = \frac{\text{lb. solution in overflow from stage 3}}{\text{lb. solution in underflow from stage 3}} = \frac{96}{24} = 4.000$$

For the case where $n = 3$, Eq. (17-2) becomes

$$\frac{1}{f} = 1 + a_n + a_n a + a_n a^2$$

$$\text{Thus} \quad \frac{1}{f} = 1 + 4.0 + 4.0(4.167) + 4.0(4.167)^2 = 91.1$$

$$f = \frac{1}{91.1} = 0.0110$$

Per cent solubles recovered = 100(1 − 0.0110) = 98.90
Solubles in overflow discharge = (0.989)(15) = 14.84 tons

$$\text{Per cent solubles in overflow discharge} = \left(\frac{14.84}{96}\right)(100)$$
$$= 15.4 \text{ per cent}$$

Per cent water in overflow discharge = 84.6 per cent

Example 2. McCabe-Smith Method. One hundred tons of underflow feed containing 20 tons of solute, 2 tons of water, and 78 tons of inert material are to be leached with water to give an overflow effluent concentration of 15 weight per cent solute and a 95 per cent recovery of solute. The underflow from each stage carries 0.5 lb. of solution per lb. of inerts. Calculate the number of ideal stages required.

Solution. (Basis: 100 tons underflow feed.)

Since total underflow is constant, Eq. (17-3) applies.

Over-all solute material balance gives the following:

Solute in overflow discharge = W_d'' = (0.95)(20) = 19 tons.

Concentration of overflow discharge = 15 per cent. Therefore, weight of overflow discharge = 19/0.15 = 126.67 tons.

Weight of solution adhering to solids in underflow leaving each stage = (0.5)(78) = 39 tons.

Concentration of the overflow leaving stage n is equal to that of the solution adhering to the solids leaving this stage. Therefore, weight of solute in underflow leaving stage $n = w_n''$ = (0.15)(39) = 5.85 tons.

Solute material balance around stage n gives solute entering this stage = 19 + 5.85 − 20 = 4.85 tons = W''_{n-1}.

Concentrations are therefore as follows:

$$\text{Solute in underflow from stage } n\text{: } x_n = \frac{5.85}{39} = 0.15$$

$$\text{Solute in overflow to stage } n\text{: } y_{n-1} = \frac{4.85}{143.67} = 0.0338$$

$$\text{Solute in underflow discharge: } x_d = \frac{1}{39} = 0.0256$$

$$\text{Solute in solvent feed: } x_f = 0$$

Equation (17-3) becomes

$$n - 1 = \frac{\log \dfrac{0.15 - 0.0338}{0.0256}}{\log \dfrac{0.15 - 0.0256}{0.0338}} = 1.16$$

n = 2.16 ideal stages.

The material balance for this example is shown in Fig. 17-3.

Graphical Methods. Two graphical methods in common use at present are discussed here. Other graphical procedures have also been developed [Armstrong and Kammermeyer, *Ind. Eng. Chem.*, **34**, 1228 (1942); Blickle and Káldi, *Chem. Tech.*, **12**, 521 (1960); Fitch, *Chem. Eng. Progress*, **47**, 83 (1951); George, *Chem. Eng.*, **66** (3), 111 (1959); Ravenscroft, *Ind. Eng. Chem.*, **28**, 851 (1936); Scheibel, *Chem. Eng. Progress*, **49**, 354 (1953)]. A combined graphical-analytical method has been devised to take full advantage of both methods [Ruth, *Trans. Am. Inst. Chem. Engrs.*, **44**, 71 (1948)].

Since a leaching system may be considered to consist of three components, namely, solute, solvent, and inert solids, compositions of the various streams may be represented graphically on several types of diagrams that take into account the interrelationship between three variables. Two of the types commonly used are shown in Fig. 17-4. Figure 17-4*a* is a right-triangular plot in which weight fraction of solvent Y is plotted against weight fraction of solute. This type of plot has been shown to exhibit the same general properties (Major, "Extraction of Acetic Acid with Ethyl Ether in a Sieve-plate Column," Ph.D. Thesis, Cornell University, Ithaca, N.Y., 1941) as the equilateral triangle for representation of ternary systems [Elgin, *Trans. Am. Inst. Chem. Engrs.*, **32**, 457 (1936)].

Figure 17-4*b* is a plot of inerts-to-solution ratio Y' against solute-to-solution ratio. It can be considered a modification of the Ponchon-Savarit method used in distillation calculations [Maloney and Schubert, *Trans. Am. Inst. Chem. Engrs.*, **36**, 741 (1940)]. Either diagram permits choice of scales for the ordinate and abscissa. The right-triangular diagram is preferred by many because the concentrations of the various streams are somewhat easier to visualize than in the other diagram.

Referring to both Fig. 17-4*a* and *b*, *EF* represents the locus of overflow compositions for the case where the overflow stream contains no inert solids. *E'F'* represents overflow streams containing some inert solute either by entrainment or by partial solubility in the overflow solution. Lines *GF*, *GL*, and *GM* represent the loci of underflow compositions for the three different conditions shown on the diagrams. In Fig. 17-4*a*, the constant-underflow line *GM* is parallel to *EF*, the hypotenuse of the triangle whereas *GF* passes through the right-hand vertex representing 100 per cent solute. In Fig. 17-4*b*, underflow line *GM* is parallel to the abscissa. *GF* passes through the point on the abscissa representing the composition of the clear solution adhering to the inert solids.

If all the solute is in solution and if the solution adhering to the solids has the same composition as that of the

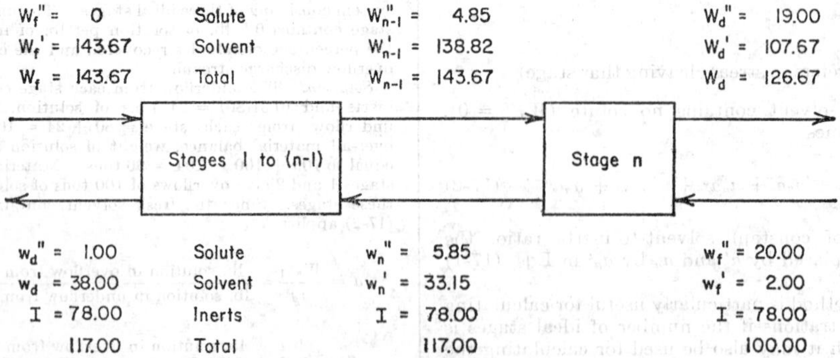

FIG. 17-3. Material balance for Example 2.

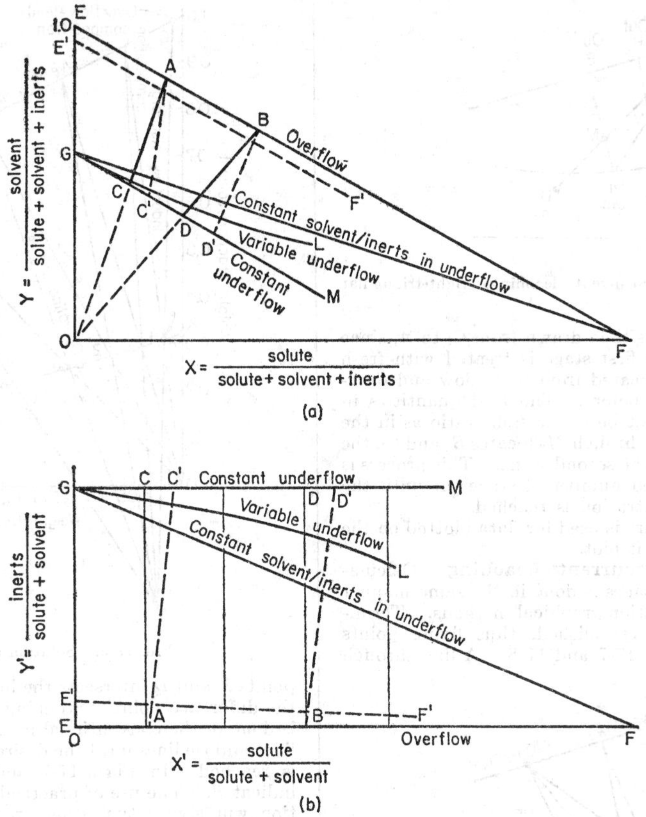

FIG. 17-4. Composition diagrams for leaching calculations. (*a*) Right-triangular diagram. (*b*) Modified Ponchon-Savarit diagram.

overflow stream, then lines such as *AC* and *BD* of Fig. 17-4*a* and *b* represent the ideal-equilibrium tie lines. In Fig. 17-4*a* these lines pass through the origin (representing 100 per cent inerts). In Fig. 17-4*b* the equilibrium tie lines are vertical. For non-equilibrium conditions or for equilibrium conditions with selective adsorption, the tie lines would be displaced, such as *AC′* and *BD′*. Point *C′* is to the right of *C* if the solute concentration in the overflow solution is less than that in the underflow solution adhering to the solids. Unequal concentrations in the two solutions indicate insufficient contact time to achieve equilibrium and/or preferential adsorption of one of the components on the inert solids. Tie lines such as *AC′* may be considered as "practical" tie lines if data on underflow and overflow compositions are obtained on samples contacted under conditions simulating actual operation, particularly as regards contact time, agitation, and particle size of solids.

Single-stage Leaching. Single-stage leaching may be represented graphically as in Fig. 17-5. Point *A* represents the solvent feed while point *D* represents the underflow or solids feed. A straight line drawn between these two points passes through point *M*, the average concentration of the two feeds combined. The position of point *M* on the line is determined from the lengths of the line segments as follows:

$$\frac{\text{Length } AM}{\text{Length } MD} = \frac{\text{weight of underflow feed}}{\text{weight of solvent feed}}$$

The tie line drawn through *M* intersects the overflow line at *B*, the final composition of the overflow. It intersects the underflow line at *C*, the final composition of the underflow stream. If *CB* is a practical tie line, the final concentrations represented by *C* and *B* represent actual rather than ideal values.

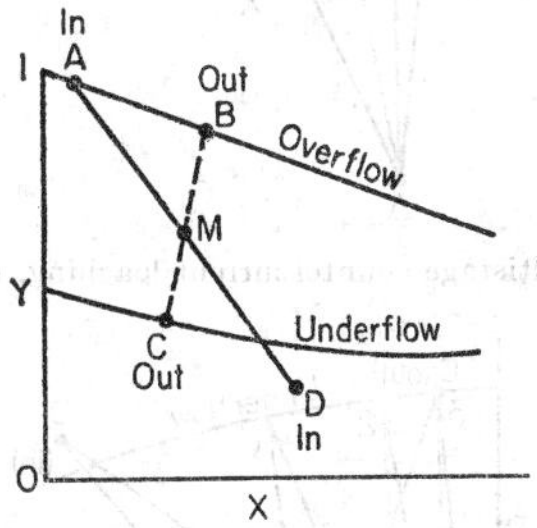

FIG. 17-5. Single-stage leaching, right-triangular diagram.

Single-stage leaching may also be represented on the modified Ponchon-Savarit diagram of the type shown in Fig. 17-4*b*.

Multistage Cocurrent Leaching. Figure 17-6 shows multistage cocurrent leaching on a right-triangular diagram. As in the single-stage operation described previously, point *A* represents the solvent feed while point *D* represents the underflow or solids feed. Point M_1 is located by the same method described for the single-stage operation. The tie line through M_1 locates overflow composition B_1 and underflow composition C_1 from

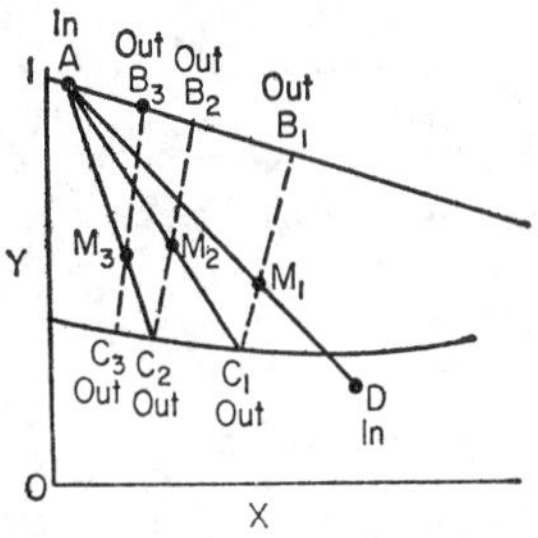

FIG. 17-6. Multistage cocurrent leaching, right-triangular diagram.

the first stage. A line is then drawn from C_1 to A, since the underflow from the first stage is treated with fresh solvent. Point M_2 is located from underflow and overflow feed quantities as before. The feed quantities in the second stage need not be in the same ratio as in the first stage. The tie line through M_2 locates B_2 and C_2, the final compositions from the second stage. This process is repeated for the required number of stages or until the desired terminal concentration is reached.

An analogous procedure is used for data plotted on the modified Ponchon-Savarit plot.

Multistage Countercurrent Leaching. Calculation of the number of stages is done in the same manner as in liquid-liquid extraction graphical methods. Terminal concentrations are established, thus fixing points A, B, C, and D of Figs. 17-7 and 17-8. A line through

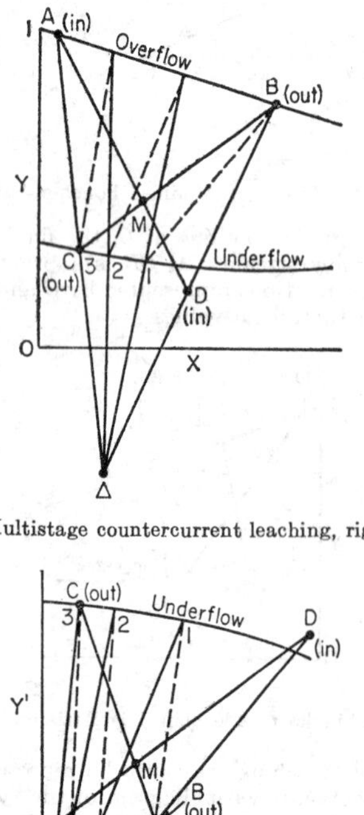

FIG. 17-7. Multistage countercurrent leaching, right-triangular diagram.

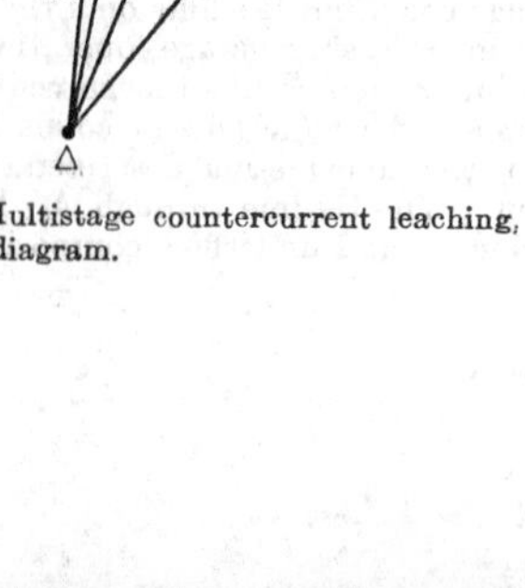

FIG. 17-8. Multistage countercurrent leaching, modified Ponchon-Savarit diagram.

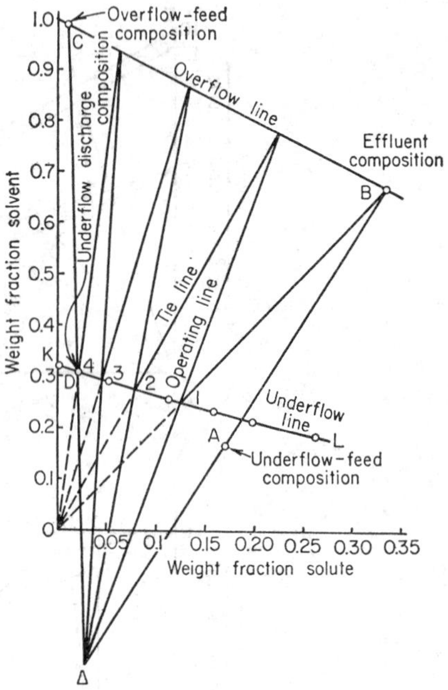

FIG. 17-9. Solution to Example 3.

points B and D intersects the line through A and C at Δ, the difference point. Stepping off the number of stages is done in the conventional manner by following Δ-point lines and tie lines until the desired terminal concentration is reached. In Figs. 17-7 and 17-8, three stages are indicated. The use of practical tie lines in the construction will give actual stages required. Similarly, ideal-equilibrium tie lines will yield ideal stages. If one of the terminal concentrations is the unknown quantity with the number of stages known, trial and error must be used.

Line CB intersects AD at point M, which represents the weighted average composition of all streams combined. The lengths of the line segments are proportional to the stream weights as follows:

$$\frac{AM}{MD} = \frac{\text{weight of underflow feed}}{\text{weight of overflow feed}}$$

$$\frac{CM}{MB} = \frac{\text{weight of overflow effluent}}{\text{weight of underflow effluent}}$$

Example 3 illustrates the graphical method.

Example 3. Graphical Method. A countercurrent process is to leach 420 tons of ore per day with 200 tons of wash water containing 1 per cent solute by weight. The ore contains 16.8 per cent solute, 16.5 per cent water, and the balance inerts. The overflow discharged from the process is to contain 33 weight per cent solute; 88 per cent of the solute in the underflow feed is to be recovered. Test data (Table 17-1) show that constant

Table 17-1. Calculation of Underflow Composition—Example 3

Test data		Calculated compositions				
		lb./lb. inerts			Weight fraction in underflow	
lb. solution / lb. inerts	lb. solute / lb. solution	Solute	Solvent	Underflow	Solute	Solvent
0.473	0	0	0.473	1.473	0	0.321
0.515	0.147	0.076	0.439	1.515	0.050	0.290
0.575	0.301	0.173	0.402	1.575	0.110	0.255
0.631	0.401	0.253	0.378	1.631	0.155	0.232
0.686	0.479	0.329	0.357	1.686	0.195	0.212
0.812	0.580	0.471	0.341	1.812	0.260	0.188

underflow cannot be assumed. Calculate the number of ideal stages required.

Solution. Underflow compositions are calculated using the test data given in Table 17-1. The data of the last two columns of this table are plotted as the underflow line *KL* in Fig. 17-9. Composition of the underflow discharge is determined as follows:

Basis: 100 lb. underflow feed.

$$\begin{aligned}\text{Solute in underflow feed} &= 16.8 \text{ lb.}\\ \text{Solvent in underflow feed} &= 16.5\\ \text{Inerts in underflow feed} &= \underline{66.7}\\ & \quad 100.0 \text{ lb.}\end{aligned}$$

Underflow discharge contains

$$(0.12)(16.8) = 2.016 \text{ lb. solute, } 66.7 \text{ lb. inerts}$$

or

$$\frac{2.016}{66.7} = 0.0302 \text{ lb. solute/lb. inerts}$$

From Table 17-1, by interpolation in column 4,

$$\frac{\text{lb. solvent}}{\text{lb. inerts}} = 0.473 - \left(\frac{0.0302}{0.076}\right)(0.034) = 0.459$$

Therefore, the underflow discharge composition is

	lb.	Wt. fraction
Solute =	2.02	0.02
Solvent = (0.459)(66.7) =	30.62	0.31
Inerts =	66.70	0.67
	99.34	1.00

An alternative procedure to establish the underflow discharge composition would be to mark the composition of the underflow discharge (on a water-free basis) on the abscissa of Fig. 17-9, then draw a straight line from this point to the one representing pure water. The point of intersection of this with the underflow line represents the composition of the underflow discharge.

The terminal compositions (points *A*, *B*, *C*, and *D*) are connected as shown in Fig. 17-9 to establish the Δ point. Stepping off the stages on the diagram in the conventional manner gives four ideal stages required.

CRYSTALLIZATION*

REFERENCES: Badger and Seavoy, "Heat Transfer and Crystallization," Swenson Evaporator Co., Harvey, Ill., 1946. Berthaud, *J. chim. phys.*, **10,** 625 (1912). Buckley, "Crystal Growth," Wiley, New York, 1951. Garrett and Rosenbaum, *Chem. Eng.*, **65** (16), 127 (1958). Griffiths, *J. Soc. Chem. Ind.*, **44,** 7T (1925). McCabe, *Ind. Eng. Chem.*, **21,** 30, 112 (1929). Miller, Phillips, and Saeman, *Chem. Eng. Progress*, **43,** 667 (1947). Seavoy and Caldwell, *Ind. Eng. Chem.*, **32,** 633 (1940). Svanoe, *Ind. Eng. Chem.*, **32,** 637 (1940); *Chem. Eng. Progress*, **55** (5), 47 (1959). Symposium on Nucleation Phenomena, *Ind. Eng. Chem.*, **44,** 1269–1328 (1952). Van Hook, *Ind. Eng. Chem.*, **36,** 1042, 1048 (1944); **37,** 782 (1945). Van Hook and Frulla, *Ind. Eng. Chem.*, **44,** 1305 (1952). Zachariasen, "Theory of X-ray Diffraction in Crystals," Wiley, New York, 1944.

Crystallization is important as an industrial process because of the number of materials that are marketed in the form of crystals. It is used widely as a purification step because of the high degree of purification produced in a single step. Crystallization is a practical method of obtaining a concentrated chemical substance in a form that is pure, attractive, and convenient for handling.

Crystallization from Solution Is Emphasized. Crystallization may be carried out from vapor, from a melt, or from solution. Most industrial uses of crystallization involve solutions. For this reason, most of this section is devoted to this subject. Crystallization from the molten state, as exemplified in zone refining, is treated briefly. Solidification of metals is basically a crystallization process, and much theory has been developed in relation to metal crystallization. This process, however, is outside the scope of this section.

Crystallization Problems. When a crystallization step is being considered in process design, certain problems must be faced. It is important first to understand the nature of crystals. Calculation of yield requires a study of equilibrium or solubility relationships; heat balances are solved by enthalpy diagrams. Practical problems of equipment design are approached by considering separately the problems of nucleation and crystal growth.

CRYSTALS

A crystal is the most highly organized type of nonliving matter. It is characterized by the fact that its constituent parts (atoms or ions) are arranged in orderly array in so-called **space lattices.** The interatomic distances in a crystal of any definite material are constant and characteristic of the material.

* This section makes liberal use of material from the previous edition, written by Warren L. McCabe.

Types of Crystals. (See Seitz, "The Modern Theory of Solids," McGraw-Hill, New York, 1940.) Crystalline solids can be classified into five main types. The types vary in the type and strength of the bond between the constituent atoms or ions, and in electrical, magnetic, and mechanical properties.

Metals are formed from the atoms of the electropositive elements. In alloys the atoms of each constituent may either occupy definite positions in the lattice, or each position in the lattice may be occupied by various kinds of atoms in turn. The excellent electrical and thermal conductivities of metals are due to the motions of free electrons through the space lattice.

Ionic crystals are formed by combinations of highly electropositive and highly electronegative elements, such as ordinary salts. The positions in the space lattices are occupied by ions rather than atoms, and such crystals are good ionic conductors of electricity at high temperature. The forces between the ions are coulomb electrostatic forces. Ionic crystals obey valence rules.

Valence crystals are formed by combinations of the lighter elements in the middle column of the periodic chart. Diamond and silicon carbide are examples. They are very hard, are poor conductors of electricity, and have poor cleavage. They conform to valence rules. The interatomic bonds are due to sharing of electron pairs.

Semiconductors such as zinc oxide add impurities easily, which modify the properties of the pure crystal and cause them to disobey valence rules. Pure crystals of this type have deficient space lattices.

Molecular crystals are characterized by weak bonds that consist essentially of weak residual forces of the van der Waals type. They have low melting points. Organic solids and elements with completed electron shells form such crystals. They are relatively soft and weak. Many can be evaporated molecularly.

Many crystals have characteristics and properties that place them in intermediate positions with respect to the above classification.

Crystal Forms. Law of Haüy. As a result of the space-lattice arrangement of the atoms composing them, crystals, if allowed to form without hindrance from outside bodies, appear in definite polyhedral shapes and exhibit varying degrees of symmetry. It has been found that, although the relative development of the different faces of two crystals of the same material may be widely different, the interfacial angles of corresponding faces of the two crystals are all equal and characteristic of that substance. This is the law of Haüy.

Isomorphism. The law of isomorphism states that, in certain series of chemically similar substances, the crystals are of the same crystalline form. Until refined methods were available for the measurement of crystal angles it was thought that isomorphic materials gave crystals with the same angles. It has been established, however, that there are small but regular differences in the corresponding angles of isomorphous substances. These differences are of the same sort that exist among other properties of elements in the same periodic group.

Crystallographic Systems. Since the crystals of a definite substance all show the same interfacial angles in spite of wide differences in the extent of development of the faces, crystal forms are classified on the basis of angles. Three important faces are chosen as **axial planes.** The **axes** are three lines parallel to the intersections of the axial planes.

In addition to the three axial faces, a fourth fundamental face, intersecting the three axes, is chosen. The lengths of the segments so cut off from the three axes are expressed as ratios, the length of one of them being taken as unity.

One class of crystals, showing a hexagonal cross section with 60-deg. angles between normals to the hexagonal sides, is most conveniently referred to four axes instead of the usual three. Three of the axes are at 60 deg. to each other and in the same plane; the fourth is perpendicular to the plane of the other three.

The combinations of angles and lengths of the axes give rise to seven classes of crystals:

1. Triclinic System. Three mutually inclined and unequal axes, all three angles unequal, and other than 90, 60, or 30 deg.

2. Monoclinic System. Three unequal axes, two of which are inclined, but the third is perpendicular to the other two.

3. Orthorhombic System. Three unequal rectangular axes.

4. Tetragonal System. Three rectangular axes, two of which are equal and different in length from the third.

5. Trigonal System. Three equal and equally inclined axes.

6. Hexagonal System. Three equal coplanar axes, inclined to 60 deg. to each other, and a fourth axis different in length from the other three and perpendicular to them.

7. Cubic System. Three equal rectangular axes.

EQUILIBRIUM

Phase Diagrams. Equilibrium relationships in crystallization are expressed in the form of solubility data, which are plotted as phase diagrams. Solubility data are ordinarily given as parts by weight of anhydrous material per 100 parts by weight of total solvent. If there is water of crystallization, the composition of the crystal is also specified. An example is shown in Fig. 17-10, the phase diagram for the $MgSO_4$-H_2O system.

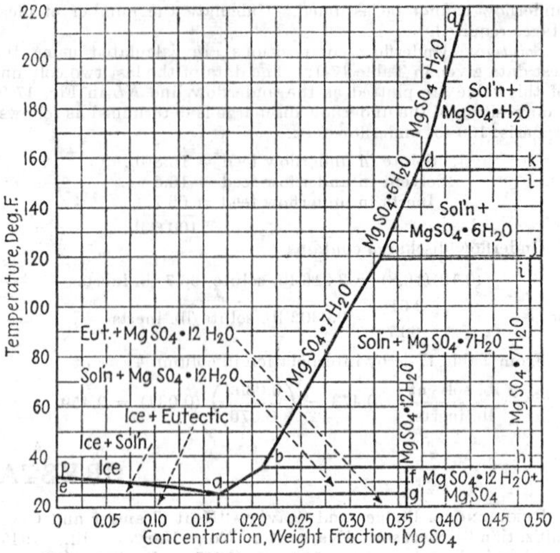

FIG. 17-10. Phase diagram, $MgSO_4$-H_2O system.

Referring to Fig. 17-10, one finds that ice is obtained when solutions whose composition is between p and a are cooled. Between a and b, the crystal form is $MgSO_4.12H_2O$; this form is also obtained by evaporation of water at a constant temperature between these two points, as, for example, 30°F. Between b and c the crystal is $MgSO_4.7H_2O$; between c and d, $MgSO_4.6H_2O$; and between d and q it is $MgSO_4.H_2O$.

Solubility data in the literature should be used with caution. Much of the published data are inexact and may have been influenced by impurities or by variations in pH. It is better to determine solubility data experimentally for the actual solvent and solute involved.

Yield of Crystallization Process. In many cases the process of crystallization is slow and the final mother liquor is in contact with a sufficiently large crystal surface so that concentration of the liquor is substantially that of a saturated solution at the final temperature of the process. In such a case the yield of the process is calculated from the composition of the initial solution and the solubility of the material at the final temperature. If appreciable evaporation has taken place during the process, this must, of course, be known or estimated.

When the rate of crystal growth is slow, a considerable time may be required to reach equilibrium. This is especially true where the solution is very viscous, or where the crystals collect in the bottom of the vessel so there is little crystal surface exposed to the supersaturated solution. In such cases the final mother liquor from the process may retain appreciable supersaturation, and the actual yield will be less than that calculated from the solubility curve unless considerable time is allowed for equilibrium to be reached. At any rate, the assumption that the mother liquor is a saturated solution gives the maximum yield of crystals that can be expected. The actual crop, after removal from the crystallizer, will in general retain some adhering mother liquor, which will give an increased weight.

In case the solid product is in the anhydrous form, the calculation of the yield is simple since the solid phase contains no water.

When the crop is hydrated, account must be taken of the water of crystallization in the crystals, since this water is withdrawn from the mother liquor and is not available for retaining the solute in solution.

The following formula can be used to calculate the **theoretical yield** of a crystallization process. It is valid for either hydrated or anhydrous crystals and assumes only that the mother liquor is saturated with solute at the final temperature, though this last restriction is removed if S (see below) is taken as the actual concentration of solute in the mother liquor at the end of the process. Equation (17-5) gives the weight of crystals as they exist in the final magma.

$$C = R\,\frac{100w_0 - S(H_0 - E)}{100 - S(R - 1)} \qquad (17\text{-}5)$$

where C = weight of crystals in final magma

$R = \dfrac{\text{molecular weight of hydrated solute}}{\text{molecular weight of anhydrous solute}}$

S = solubility (parts by weight anhydrous solute per 100 parts by weight total solvent) of material at final temperature

w_0 = weight of anhydrous solute in original batch

H_0 = total weight of solvent in batch at the beginning of the process

E = evaporation during the process

Example 1. A 30 per cent solution of Na_2CO_3 weighing 10,000 lb. is cooled slowly to 20°C. The crystals formed are sal-soda ($Na_2CO_3.10H_2O$). The solubility of Na_2CO_3 at 20°C. is 21.5 parts of anhydrous salt per 100 parts of water. During cooling 3 per cent of the weight of the original solution is lost by evaporation. What is the weight of $Na_2CO_3.10H_2O$ formed?

Solution. Since the molecular weight of $Na_2CO_3.10H_2C$ is 286.2, and that of Na_2CO_3 is 106, $R = 286.2/106.0 = 2.70$. Also, $w_0 = (0.30)(10{,}000) = 3000$ lb.; the evaporation is $(0.03)(10{,}000) = 300$ lb.; and, therefore, $H_0 - E = 10{,}000 - 3000 - 300 = 6700$ lb. The weight of the crop is, by Eq. (17-5),

$$C = 2.70\left[\frac{(100)(3000) - (21.5)(6700)}{100 - 21.5(2.70 - 1.0)}\right]$$

$$= 6636 \text{ lb.}$$

Purity of Product. Although a crystal itself is necessarily pure, it retains some mother liquor when removed from the final magma, and the adhering liquor will carry its share of the impurities present in the mother liquor. If the adhering mother liquor is dried on the crystal, contamination will result.

In practice, crystals usually are centrifuged or filtered. Residual mother liquor after centrifuging amounts to 2 to 5 per cent of the weight of the crystals. Large, uniform crystals from low-viscosity mother liquors will retain a minimum proportion of mother liquor, while non-uniform, small crystals from viscous solutions will retain a considerably larger proportion. Comparable statements apply to filtration of crystals. It is common practice to wash the crystals on the centrifuge or filter with fresh solvent; use of countercurrent washing in multiple stages may reduce loss of crystals by solution in the wash water. Purity can also be improved by recrystallization, but this method is not usually so satisfactory as proper washing of the crystals.

Heat Effects in a Crystallization Process. The heat effect of a crystallization process is calculated by means of a heat balance. Such a balance can be computed by two methods: the individual heat effects, such as sensible heats, latent heats, and heats of crystallization, can be computed and combined into a balance equation, or an enthalpy balance can be taken in which the total enthalpy of all leaving streams minus the total enthalpy of all entering streams is equal to the heat absorbed from external sources by the process.

In the first method, the heat removed from the crystallizing solution by external means is equal to the sum of the sensible heat lost by the cooling solution and the heat evolved in the formation of the crystalline crop (heat of crystallization) minus the radiation losses and minus the heat of vaporization of solvent evaporated during the process.

Heat of Crystallization. In heat-balance calculations on crystallization processes the heat of crystallization is usually important. The heat of crystallization is the latent heat accompanying the precipitation of crystals from a saturated solution. For most substances, heat of crystallization is exothermic; it varies with concentration and temperature. Heat of crystallization is related to heat of dilution of the solution and heat of solution of the crystal. The heat of solution is the heat evolved when a unit mass of solid is dissolved in a very large amount of water. A table of heats of solution is given in Sec. 3. Heats of dilution are scarce, especially for concentrated solutions, and it is usual to use the negative value of the heat of solution for the heat of crystallization. This is equivalent to neglecting heats of dilution. Ordinarily, the heat of dilution is small in comparison with that of solution, and the approximation is justified. Furthermore, the neglect of the heat of dilution leads to a conservative result because the heat of dilution is usually a heat evolution by the solution.

Example 2. The heat absorbed when 1 g.-mole of $MgSO_4.7H_2O$ is dissolved isothermally at 18°C. in a large amount of water is 3180 cal. What is the heat of crystallization of 1 lb. of $MgSO_4.7H_2O$ if heat of solution effects are negligible?

Solution. The molecular weight of $MgSO_4.7H_2O$ is 246.5. Since 1 cal./g.-mole = 1.8 B.t.u./lb.-mole, the heat of crystallization of $MgSO_4.7H_2O$ is $\dfrac{(3180)(1.8)}{246.5} = 23$ B.t.u./lb.

Enthalpy-concentration Chart. The enthalpy method of calculating heat balances over crystallization processes is facilitated by the use of the enthalpy-concentration chart so constructed as to show the solid phases [Bošnjaković, *Z. ges. Kälte-Ind.*, **39**, 182 (1932)]. This method rigorously accounts for the heats of dilution and is very simple arithmetically, once the chart has been constructed. The disadvantages of the enthalpy-concentration chart are as follows: (1) considerable data are required for its construction, and these data are often not available; (2) the initial construction of the chart is time-consuming and not justified for a single calculation. For substances commonly crystallized and for which adequate data are available, the enthalpy-concentration chart has considerable utility.

An enthalpy-concentration chart for the system $MgSO_4.H_2O$ is shown in Fig. 17-11. The use of the chart in heat-balance calculations involving solutions has been described [McCabe, *Trans. Am. Inst. Chem. Engrs.*, **31**, 129 (1935)]. In Fig. 17-11 the enthalpies of the solid phases from zero to 50 per cent $MgSO_4$ are shown, and the diagram can be correlated with the ordinary phase diagram shown in Fig. 17-10. The line *pa* represents the freezing points of ice from solutions of $MgSO_4$. Point *a* is the eutectic, and line *abcdq* is the solubility curve of various hydrates, as previously described for the phase diagram (Fig. 17-10).

The area *aep* of Fig. 17-11 represents the enthalpies of all equilibrium mixtures of ice and $MgSO_4$ solution. The isothermal (25°F.) triangle *age* gives the enthalpies of all combinations of ice and partly solidified eutectic and of $MgSO_4.12H_2O$ and partly solidified eutectic. Area *abfg* contains the enthalpy-concentration coordinates of all magmas consisting of $MgSO_4.12H_2O$ crystals and its mother liquor. The isothermal (35.7°F.) area *bhf* represents the isothermal transformation of $MgSO_4.7H_2O$ to $MgSO_4.12H_2O$, and this area represents mixtures consisting of a saturated solution of concentration 21 per cent, solid $MgSO_4.7H_2O$, and solid $MgSO_4.12H_2O$. The area *cihb* represents all magmas of $MgSO_4.7H_2O$ (epsom salt) and its mother liquor. The isothermal (118.8°F.) area *cji* represents mixtures consisting of a saturated solution containing 35 per cent $MgSO_4$, solid $MgSO_4.6H_2O$, and solid $MgSO_4.7H_2O$. Area *dljc* represents magmas of $MgSO_4.6H_2O$ and its mother liquor. The isothermal (154.4°F.) area *dkl* represents mixtures consisting of a saturated solution containing 37 per cent $MgSO_4$, solid $MgSO_4.H_2O$, and solid $MgSO_4.6H_2O$. Area *qrkd* is part of the field representing saturated solutions in equilibrium with $MgSO_4.H_2O$. Except for the isotherms in the liquid-solution field and the solubility and freezing-point curves, all lines on the enthalpy-concentration chart are straight.

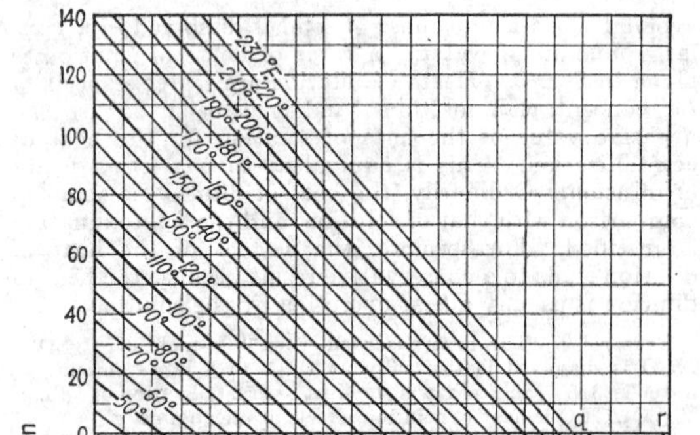

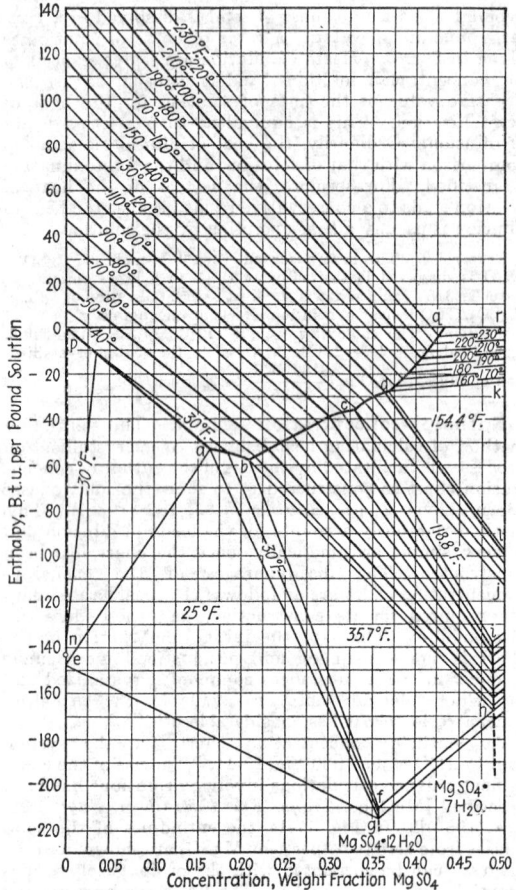

FIG. 17-11. Enthalpy-concentration chart, $MgSO_4$-H_2O system.

Example 3. 10,000 lb. of a 32.5 per cent $MgSO_4$ solution at 120°F. is cooled without appreciable evaporation to 70°F. in a crystallizer. How much heat must be removed from the solution, and what weight of $MgSO_4.7H_2O$ crystals will form?

Solution. The crystals and mother liquor are represented by terminals of the straight isothermal line for 70°F. in the field *cihb* of Fig. 17-11. The initial solution is represented by the point in the undersaturated-solution field on the 120°F. isotherm at a concentration of 0.325. The magma must have an average concentration of 0.325 and a temperature of 70°F. From Fig. 17-11, the coordinates of the four points are:

	Temp., °F.	Conc.	Enthalpy
Original solution	120	0.325	−33.0
Crystals	70	0.488	−144.0
Mother liquor	70	0.259	−47.3
Magma	70	0.325	−78.4

Heat removed from the solution is

$$10{,}000(-33.0 + 78.4) = 454{,}000 \text{ B.t.u.}$$

Yield of crystals is obtained by applying the "lever-arm principle" commonly used in calculations involving equilibrium diagrams.

$$\text{Weight of crystals} = 10{,}000\,\frac{0.325 - 0.259}{0.488 - 0.259} = 2880 \text{ lb.}$$

Fractional Crystallization. When two or more solutes are present in a solution, it is often possible to crystallize one of the solutes and leave the others in solution. Usually, such fractional-crystallization methods are based on differences in solubilities of the solutes.

The solubility of a material in a solution of another solute is, in general, widely different from its solubility in the pure solvent. For example, the solubility of sodium chloride at 20°C. is 36 parts per 100 parts water, and that of sodium nitrate is 88 parts per 100 parts water, but a solution saturated at 20°C. with respect to both these salts will contain only 25 parts sodium chloride and 59 parts sodium nitrate per 100 parts water.

The mutual solubilities of the above two salts can be shown diagrammatically, as in Fig. 17-12. The solubilities are plotted for two different temperatures: Line *DEF*

Coordinates of Points

Point	Na Cl	Na NO_3
A	36	0
B	0	88
C	25	59
D	40	0
E	17	160
F	0	176
G	17	68

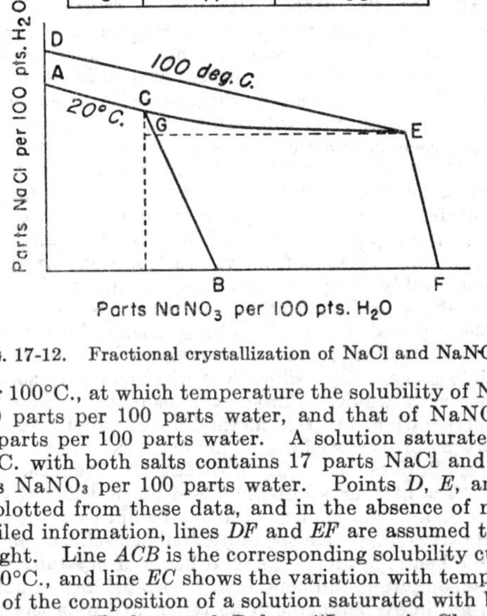

FIG. 17-12. Fractional crystallization of NaCl and $NaNO_3$

is for 100°C., at which temperature the solubility of NaCl is 40 parts per 100 parts water, and that of $NaNO_3$ is 176 parts per 100 parts water. A solution saturated at 100°C. with both salts contains 17 parts NaCl and 160 parts $NaNO_3$ per 100 parts water. Points *D*, *E*, and *F* are plotted from these data, and in the absence of more detailed information, lines *DF* and *EF* are assumed to be straight. Line *ACB* is the corresponding solubility curve for 20°C., and line *EC* shows the variation with temperature of the composition of a solution saturated with both components (Badger and Baker, "Inorganic Chemical Technology," 1st ed., p. 82, McGraw-Hill, New York, 1928).

If a solution at 100°C. has a composition represented by a point on line *DE*, the solution is saturated with respect to NaCl but not with respect to $NaNO_3$, while if the composition of the solution is represented by a point on line *EF*, the solution is saturated with $NaNO_3$ but not with NaCl. For a detailed treatment of such solubility relationships, see Blasdale ("Equilibria in Saturated Salt Solutions," Reinhold, New York, 1927).

Example 4. As an illustration of fractional crystallization, consider the separation of $NaNO_3$ and NaCl from a solution saturated at 100°C. with both salts and therefore represented by point *E*. If a basis of 100 lb. water is taken, the solution contains 17 lb. NaCl and 160 lb. $NaNO_3$. Suppose the solution is cooled to 20°C. The solution becomes supersaturated with respect to $NaNO_3$, and crystallization of the latter should take place. The composition of the solution moves along the path *EG*.

At 20°C., if equilibrium is reached, the composition of the solution is that represented by point *G*. If line *CB* is considered straight, the abscissa of *G* can be calculated from similar triangles as follows:

$$\text{Parts NaNO}_3 = 59 + \frac{(88 - 59)(25 - 17)}{25} = 68.3$$

On cooling along the line *EG*, there will separate 160 − 68.3 = 91.7 lb. $NaNO_3$, and all the NaCl will remain in solution. If the solution is now evaporated at 100°C. until the $NaNO_3$ concentration is brought back to 160 parts per 100 parts water. NaCl will be precipitated during the evaporation and can be removed. The concentration of the solution will again be represented by point *E*, and the cycle repeated. On each cooling, (91.7/160)(100) = 57.3 per cent of the nitrate in solution will crystallize, and, on each evaporation, the same percentage of the chloride will be precipitated. Various modifications of the method can be used. For example, the amount of water in the batch can be kept constant and the solution resaturated at 100°C. with fresh $NaNO_3$ after each cooling. The hot solvent will act as a selective solvent for the nitrate, since it is impoverished in $NaNO_3$, but saturated with respect to NaCl. Nitrate can therefore be dissolved and chloride left behind. The dissolved nitrate is recovered in the cooling part of the cycle.

Another method of fractional crystallization is sometimes used, where advantage is taken of different crystallization rates. Thus, a solution saturated with borax and potassium chloride will, in the absence of borax seed crystals, precipitate only potassium chloride on rapid cooling. The borax remains behind as a supersaturated solution, and the potassium chloride crystals can be removed before the slower borax crystallization starts.

CRYSTAL FORMATION

Crystallization involves two steps: the crystals must first form and then grow to the desired size. To examine the theory of the process each step is considered in turn. In both steps, the **degree of supersaturation** is the driving force.

Formation of new crystals is termed **nucleation.** Uniformity of the crop of crystals depends on the relationship between nucleation and growth. If new crystals form continuously and rapidly during the process, the crop will consist of many small crystals; if only a few nuclei form or are introduced at the beginning, and if the subsequent crystallization takes place on these nuclei without further formation of nuclei, a crop of large, uniform crystals will result.

A qualitative understanding of the factors affecting nucleation and crystal growth is important in controlling size and purity of crystal product.

Methods of Forming Crystals in Solutions. In any crystallization process, the formation of nuclei should be under control. In a batch process, if uniform crystals are desired, it is advisable to form as large a proportion as possible of the crystals at the same time. Otherwise, a non-uniform crop will be obtained. In a continuous process, the number of nuclei formed per unit time will be continuous and uniform and must equal the number of crystals that are withdrawn per unit time from the crystallizer. In a continuous crystallizer either most of the nuclei should form within a narrow zone in the unit so that all nuclei can receive the same time of growth (as in the Swenson-Walker crystallizer, for example) or there must be a classifying action in the crystallizer which will retain the small crystals under treatment until they have grown to the proper size before they are removed from the unit (as is done in continuous vacuum crystallizers, for example).

Nucleation can be accomplished by adding the desired number of nuclei, usually in the form of crushed crystals, to the crystallizer when the solution is either saturated or supersaturated, or nuclei may be formed *in situ*. New nuclei may originate *in situ* in one or more of the following ways:

1. By spontaneous nucleation from unseeded solutions.
2. By attrition of existing crystals. If crystals are agitated vigorously, small corners and fragments may be broken from existing crystals; fragmentation of crystals by spalling also takes place under the influence of heat. Such fragments and mutilated crystals quickly repair themselves, and the fragments become new nuclei.
3. Mechanical impact. Mechanical impact in a supersaturated solution has been shown to cause nucleation [Young, *J. Am. Chem. Soc.*, **33,** 148, 162 (1911)]. Vigorous stirring, the collision of crystals in the solution, with each other or with the walls of the crystallizers, may cause the formation of some new nuclei. This formation is over and above that resulting from the mechanical fracture of existing crystals. Its importance in industrial crystallization is questionable.
4. New crystals are formed because of the inoculating influences of crystals already present. This method of crystal formation is probably the most important single method and is the method that is subject to the most accurate control.
5. Local variations in the concentration of the solution may cause nucleation in restricted zones. For example, the withdrawal of heat through the containing wall will cause temperature gradients near the wall which can increase the supersaturation enough to accelerate nucleation. Evaporation from the surface may result in abnormally high concentrations in the solution at the surface and lead to nucleation. Even surfaces at solution temperature sometimes appear to catalyze nucleation near them.

In general, the above causes of nucleation are interwoven, and it is usually not possible to separate them completely in any given case. It is possible, however, to emphasize or to suppress individual nucleation effects and thereby to facilitate control.

Thus, method 1 is essentially an uncontrolled formation method. In general, it is preferable to use method 4 if possible, rather than method 1.

The formation of crystals by attrition (method 2) should be suppressed as much as possible. Such formation occurs at the expense of existing perfect crystals and is not subject to adequate control. For practical control purposes, methods 3 and 4 can be considered as equivalent. The mechanical impact of stirrers or of crystals on each other accounts for only a small proportion of the total nucleation and depends on stirring rate and the number and size of crystals existing in the equipment at any given time. The much more important inoculating effect is determined by these same variables. Increased stirring rate, for example, brings about more uniform distribution of crystals in the crystallizing solution, which will increase their inoculating influence. Such effects increase nucleation rate more than they do growth rate and are the logical explanation of the general observation that stirring tends to cause small crystals.

Nucleation by method 5 depends largely on the design of the crystallizer and the rate at which it is operated. For best control it is advisable to suppress this method by reducing as much as possible local variations in the temperature or concentration of the solution.

Spontaneous Nucleation. Under proper conditions nucleation takes place in an unseeded solution—one that has been carefully freed of all solid particles. The presence of dust particles, small solute crystals, or in some cases crystals of other materials, may lead to a second type of crystal formation, namely, that from seeded solutions. In practice, the seeded case is the more important. Except for closed batch crystallizers in which the solutions are heated well above the saturation temperatures before being sent to the crystallizers, completely unseeded solutions are not usually encountered. Batch vacuum crystallizers and special crystallizers, such as sugar-boiling apparatus, fall into the category of equipment that operates on unseeded solutions. On the other hand, crystallizers in which the solution has access to the atmosphere of the plant will in all probability be seeded by the plant dust which invariably will carry tiny crystals and dust particles and which will inoculate the solution.

In the case of an unseeded solution, it is possible in viscous solutions of relatively high molecular weight, such as those of sugars, to maintain a highly supersaturated solution indefinitely without the formation of nuclei. To obtain this result the solution must be carefully prepared, must be entirely free from dust particles, and must be "sterilized" or heated well above its saturation temperature for a time in a completely airtight container.

For such a solution, there is a metastable region in which spontaneous nucleation does not take place despite the fact that the solution is supersaturated. This is shown diagrammatically in Fig. 17-13. The normal-solubility curve is shown as line AB, and dotted line CD is

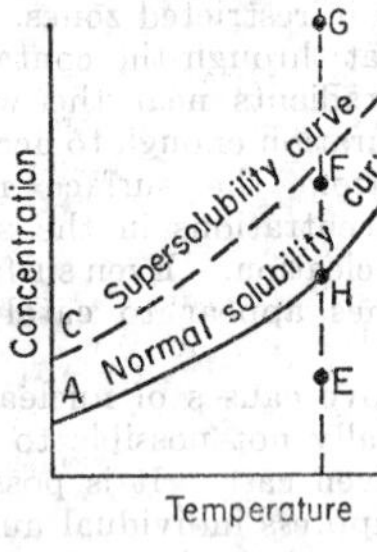

FIG. 17-13. Diagrammatic representation of supersaturation theory.

the **supersolubility curve.** Between these two curves, no spontaneous nucleation takes place. A solution represented by point E, below the solubility curve AB, is unsaturated. A solution at F is metastable and will remain at F unless seed crystals are added to it. It will drop to H if seed crystals are added. Any solution above line CD, such as that at G, will crystallize spontaneously, and its concentration will fall to point H.

There is disagreement as to whether solutions in the metastable region will ever crystallize, given enough time. Some solutions have remained in this state for years without crystallizing. On the other hand some workers, having observed slow nucleation in this region, regard the supersolubility curve as the point at which the rate rises rapidly to some arbitrary value. This situation is illustrated in Fig. 17-16. The suggestion has also been made that spontaneous nucleation at the supersolubility curve is caused by the energy of vibration normally present in any laboratory.

In spite of the controversy concerning the meaning of the phenomenon, the supersolubility curve has been a useful concept in the analysis of crystal formation from unseeded solutions.

Nucleation by Foreign Substances. Crystallization of one substance can be initiated by crystals of a different substance, if the crystal forms are similar in size and form of lattice. For this reason, it is necessary to take special pains to exclude dust if consistent supersolubility measurements are desired. Dust contains a variety of crystalline materials, some of which are likely to be similar to the material being crystallized.

If the similarity in crystal form exists in only one or

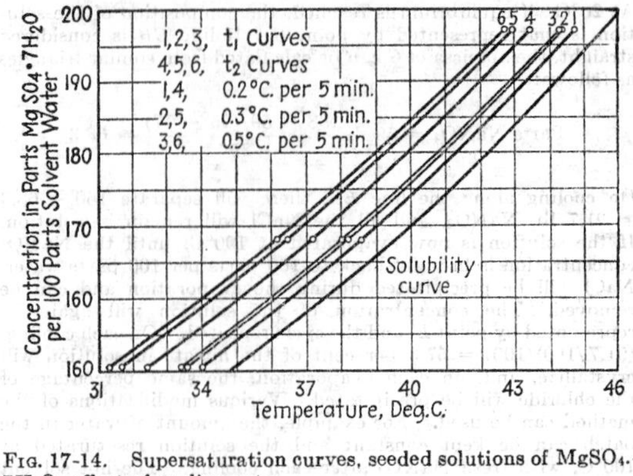

FIG. 17-14. Supersaturation curves, seeded solutions of $MgSO_4 \cdot 7H_2O$; effect of cooling rate.

two directions, crystallization takes place by oriented overgrowth, called *epitaxis.* According to Telkes [*Ind. Eng. Chem.*, **44**, 1308 (1952)] nucleation may occur when the crystallographic data of the foreign substance and the salt to be crystallized agree within 15 per cent. Turnbull and Vonnegut [*Ind. Eng. Chem.*, **44**, 1292 (1952)] report cases of nucleation catalysis where the difference is as large as 50 per cent.

On the other hand, impurities in solution may inhibit the formation of new nuclei. The effect of a given impurity cannot be predicted; in general, however, high-molecular-weight materials seem to be the most effective inhibitors.

Nucleation in Seeded Solutions. In most industrial processes using crystallization, solutions are seeded to obtain a more uniform product. Work carried out on the supersolubility relationships of seeded solutions has shown that, if a solution initially without seeds is cooled at a definite rate and if definite quantities of a definite size of seeds are added when the concentration of the solution reaches saturation, there is a definite degree of undercooling corresponding to the formation of new nuclei. Other reproducible supersaturation curves are found at which the rate of formation of crystals becomes a maximum. Results of such experiments on $MgSO_4 \cdot 7H_2O$ are shown in Fig. 17-14 [Ting and McCabe, *Ind. Eng. Chem.*, **26**, 1201 (1934)]. The t_1 curves show where new nuclei first formed, and the t_2 curves show where the rate of formation reaches a maximum. Supersaturated solutions of KCl show the same type of behavior. Curves of the type shown in the figure are quite readily reproducible. The positions of curves t_1 and t_2 were also found to depend on the weight of seeds, the screen size of the seeds, and the rate of stirring.

The supersaturations obtained in seeded solutions are considerably less than those found in crystallizing unseeded solutions. These results indicate that the ability of seed crystals to inoculate a solution and to cause the formation of new crystals is an important fundamental factor in crystallization.

Nucleation by Sonic Energy. Irradiation by sound waves tends to promote equilibrium. In supersaturated solutions, sonic and ultrasonic radiation is useful in causing crystallization of substances which are otherwise difficult to crystallize. Van Hook and Frulla [*Ind. Eng. Chem.*, **44**, 1305 (1952)] report some experiments with sugar solutions. Lower frequencies (8 kc. was used) are more efficient than higher ones. There is a minimum power threshold of about 100 watts/sq. cm. The sound waves exert a powerful shattering effect on crystals that are formed.

GEOMETRY OF CRYSTAL GROWTH

Preliminary to the subject of rate of growth of crystals, certain facts regarding the geometry of crystal growth are important.

Parallel Displacement of Faces. Geometrically, a crystal is a solid bounded by planes. Shape and size of such a solid are functions of the interfacial angles and of the linear dimensions of the faces. As a result of the constancy of its interfacial angles, each face of a growing or dissolving crystal, as it moves away from or toward the center of the crystal, is always parallel to its original position. This is known as the **principle of the parallel displacement** of faces. The rate at which a face moves in a direction perpendicular to its original position is called the **translation velocity** of that face.

Crystal Habit. From an industrial point of view, the term "crystal habit" refers to the relative sizes of the faces of a crystal. No general law controlling crystal habit has been discovered. This property is easily affected by conditions of crystal formation and growth. It is very difficult to prepare perfect crystals with all faces of the same form equally developed. Small amounts of foreign substances will often completely change the crystal habit of a material. The selective adsorption of dyes by the different faces of a crystal can greatly modify the habit of the crystal. Phenomena of this kind are so general that the prediction of crystal habit is difficult.

Overlapping Principle. Since the relative sizes of the individual faces of a crystal vary between wide limits, it follows that different faces must have different translation velocities. A geometric law of crystal growth known as the **overlapping principle** is based on these velocity differences and may be stated as follows: In the growing of a crystal, only those faces having the lowest translation velocities survive, and, in the dissolving of a crystal, only those faces having the highest translation velocities survive. For example, consider cross sections of a growing crystal, as in Fig. 17-15. The polygons

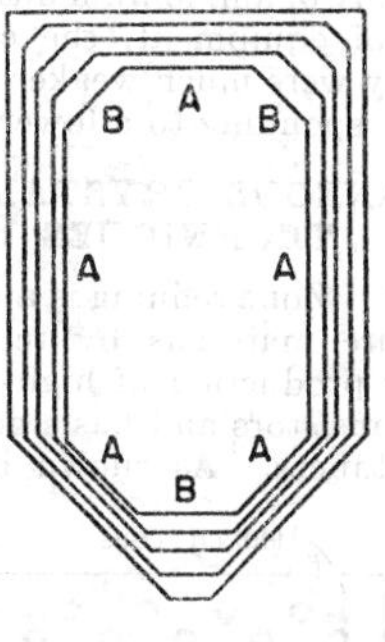

FIG. 17-15. Overlapping principle.

shown in the figure represent varying stages in the growth of the crystal. The faces marked A are slow-growing faces (low translation velocities), and the faces marked B are fast growing (high translation velocities). It is apparent from Fig. 17-15 that the faster B faces tend to disappear, as they are "overlapped" by the slower A faces.

The overlapping principle, if combined with the principle of the parallel displacement of faces, makes it possible to predict the final shape of a crystal when the initial shape and the relative translation velocities of the faces are known.

Crystal Growth. After initial seeding has been made, further nucleation should be avoided while the crystals are growing. In this way, crystals of uniform size are obtained.

Rate of deposition of crystalline material depends on the area of surface of the growing crystals and on the supersaturation. These must be matched to the rate of cooling or rate of solvent removal to keep the supersaturation below the point where nucleation takes place.

Rate of Crystal Growth. Rate of crystallization is determined by two processes which take place in series. Material is transferred from the solution to the surface of the crystal by diffusion; at the surface the material is incorporated into the crystal structure. The net rate depends on the rates of each of these processes. If the concentration of a saturated solution is C_0, that of the bulk of the solution C, and that of the solution in contact with the crystal surface C', the rate of deposition is

$$\frac{dW}{d\theta} = k'S(C' - C_0) = kS(C - C') \qquad (17\text{-}6)$$

where W is weight; θ is time; k is mass-transfer coefficient for diffusion; k' is reaction-rate constant for interfacial area; S is surface area.

When C' is eliminated from Eq. (17-6), the result may be written

$$\frac{dW}{d\theta} = \frac{S(C - C_0)}{(1/k') + (1/k)} \qquad (17\text{-}7)$$

Coefficient k is independent of supersaturation, but k' is not. Various results have been reported, but there is general agreement that k' is proportional to some power of the supersaturation. Values from the second to the fourth power have been reported for different systems.

The relative importance of the two steps depends on a number of factors:

1. When supersaturation is great, the ordering reaction at the surface is relatively rapid, and the diffusion step controls the rate.
2. Conversely, when supersaturation is small, the process at the surface is the rate-controlling step.
3. Sonic and supersonic vibrations increase the rate of diffusion, and thus the crystallization process, when the rate depends on the diffusion rate.
4. Small amounts of impurities modify the rate of growth at the surface. Dyes, acid, and various other ions have been found to inhibit the growth of crystals, as they are adsorbed on the crystal faces and interfere with the crystallization process. Different faces are affected to a different extent, and thus the crystal habit is modified by foreign substances. The face that adsorbs the greatest amount of impurity will have the lowest translation velocity and hence will increase in size relative to the other faces, in accordance with the overlapping principle.

The ΔL Law. It has been shown [McCabe, *Ind. Eng. Chem.*, **21**, 30, 112 (1949)] that all geometrically similar crystals of the same material suspended in the same solution grow at the same rate, if growth is measured as the increase in length of geometrically corresponding distances on all crystals. If ΔL is the increase in linear dimension of one crystal, it is at the same time equal to the increase in the corresponding dimension of each of the other crystals. On the other hand, it is independent of the initial size of the original crystals, provided that all crystals in the suspension are treated exactly alike.

This law permits the screen analysis of the product to be calculated from that of the seeds. If D is the size of the opening of a sieve that will just pass a given crystal, then D is proportional to linear dimension L, or

$$\alpha D = L$$

and

$$\alpha \Delta D = \Delta L \qquad (17\text{-}8)$$

where α is a proportionality constant that is identical for all crystals of the batch. It has been shown that

$$W_p = \int_0^{W_s} \left(1 + \frac{\Delta D}{D_s}\right)^3 dW_s \qquad (17\text{-}9)$$

where W_p is weight of product obtained from a unit weight W_s of seed crystals; D_s and W_s are coordinates of the cumulative screen-analysis curve (where W_s is total weight retained on the screen of opening size D_s).

Screen analysis of the product is calculated by graphical integration, given the weights of seed and product and screen size of the seed.

Different values of ΔD are assumed until one is found which satisfies Eq. (17-9). This value of ΔD is then added to each D of the seed screen size to give the product size.

An example of this calculation is given by McCabe and Smith ("Unit Operations of Chemical Engineering," p. 819, McGraw-Hill, New York, 1956).

Limitations of ΔL Law. The above analysis fails completely in any case where crystals are given preferential treatment based on size. If larger crystals have a higher velocity relative to the solution than do smaller ones, the larger crystals will grow more and the smaller crystals less than is predicted by the ΔL law. If there is a classifying action in the crystallizer by which small crystals are retained longer than large crystals, the ΔL law does not apply. It is applicable only if all crystals, regardless of size, are treated exactly alike as to conditions and time of growth. It also applies only to the growth of existing crystals and is not concerned with nucleation.

Simultaneous Growth and Formation of Crystals. In most industrial crystallizations, growth and nucleation occur simultaneously. The result of the combined process on the size distribution of the crystals depends on the relative rates of formation and growth. Actual experimental data for such rates are practically nonexistent; until suitable data are developed, only qualitative reasoning can be applied. Such reasoning may, however, be useful in analyzing the effects of the crystallization factors in industrial processes.

For aid in such an analysis, hypothetical curves such as those shown in Fig. 17-16 are useful. Figure 17-16

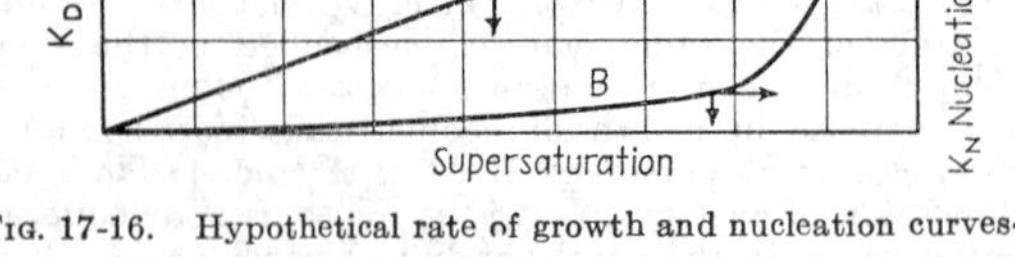

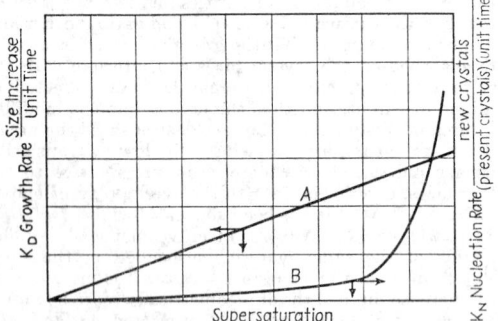

Fig. 17-16. Hypothetical rate of growth and nucleation curves.

shows two rate curves, both plotted against supersaturation. Curve A shows growth rate K_D expressed as a coefficient giving the rate of increase of linear dimension per unit time. Curve B shows nucleation rate expressed as coefficient K_N, defined as the number of new crystals produced per unit time per existing crystal. On the assumption that growth is approximately a first-order reaction, curve A is straight; on the other hand, the nucleation-rate curve B will start low and remain low in the metastable region but will rise sharply at supersaturations corresponding roughly to the point where the supersaturation curves are located. As mentioned above, however, the nucleation rate is not necessarily zero at low supersaturations.

Figure 17-16 shows that, at low supersaturations, growth will tend to predominate over nucleation, although both rates will be low. At high supersaturations, especially those in which the nucleation rate has passed the break point in the curve, nucleation will predominate strongly over growth.

The positions of curves such as those shown in Fig. 17-16 will undoubtedly vary considerably with changes in such operating variables as stirring rate, temperature, concentration, size and number of crystals present in the solution, impurities, and nucleation at interfaces.

In batch crystallization wherein the supersaturation varies with time, the final result of the crystallization process would depend upon the integrated effect along curves such as those shown in Fig. 17-16. Present knowledge of crystallization is not sufficient to provide a quantitative basis for such integrations. In a continuous crystallizer where conditions are constant at any given point in the apparatus, the rates at this point will be constant and correspond to a definite abscissa on Fig. 17-16. If large crystals are desired, low supersaturations must be used or too many nuclei will form. Low supersaturations necessarily mean low rates of deposition, and large crystals can be made only at the expense of low volumetric crystallizer capacity.

Usually, the objective of the crystallizer operator is to achieve maximum growth rate consistent with low nucleation rate. Such an operation should be conducted at a supersaturation just short of the zone of rapid rise of the nucleation rate, approximately as shown by the arrows on curve B in Fig. 17-16.

It is not always satisfactory to operate under such conditions, however, since factors other than capacity may enter. In some cases agglomeration tends to occur at supersaturations just short of that corresponding to a rapid increase in nucleation. Also, Miller, Phillip, and Saeman [*Chem. Eng. Progress*, **43**, 667 (1947)] report that, in a pilot-plant study of ammonium nitrate crystallization in Krystal type of equipment, the crystals formed at maximum capacity were much weaker than those formed at a capacity corresponding to a lower supersaturation.

MISCELLANEOUS CRYSTALLIZATION TECHNIQUES

Zone Refining. Zone refining is a method of producing extremely pure materials by recrystallization. It was first used for production of high-purity silicon and germanium for transistors and has since been applied to many other substances. As shown in Fig. 17-17, the

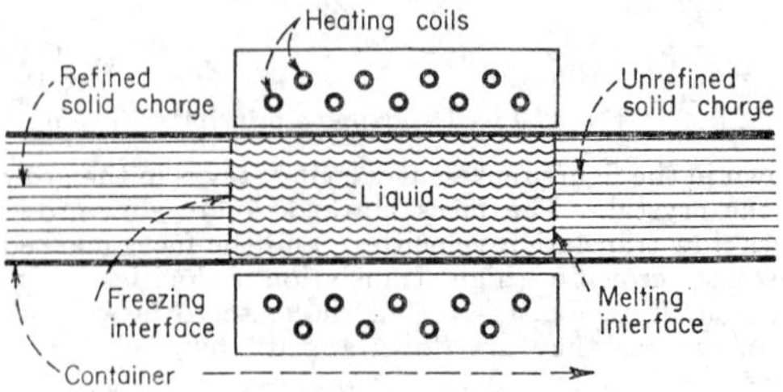

Fig. 17-17. Diagram of zone refining. [*Chem. Eng.*, **66** (8), 80 (1959).]

material to be purified is drawn slowly through alternate heating and cooling zones. The part in the heating zones is in the liquid state; that in the cooling zone is solid. Impurities tend to collect in the liquid phase, and since the liquid zone travels along the material to the end, the impurities collect in the trailing end.

For details of this process, see Pfann ["Zone Melting," Wiley, New York, 1958; *Chem. Eng. News*, **34,** 1440 (1956); *Trans. Am. Inst. Mining Met. Engrs.*, **194,** 747 (1952); *J. Metals*, **7,** 961 (1955)] and Hesse and Schildknecht [*Angew. Chem.*, **68,** 641 (1956)].

Extractive Crystallization. This process is based on the selective reaction of urea and thiourea with straight-chain hydrocarbons. Urea forms crystalline complexes with normal paraffins and can thus be used to remove them from other constituents of petroleum fractions.

See Bailey *et al.* [*Ind. Eng. Chem.*, **43,** 2125 (1951)]; Kobe [*Petrol. Refiner*, **31** (3), 106; (5), 151 (1952)]; Swenn [*Ind. Eng. Chem.*, **47,** 216 (1955)].

Hydrothermal Crystal Growth. A method for growing single crystals of quartz involves use of an alkaline solution at elevated temperatures and pressure. In a typical operation, an autoclave is operated with a 50°C. temperature differential between top and bottom and a pressure of 1000 atm. Linear growth rate is as much as 0.04 in./day. See Walker and Buehler [*Ind. Eng. Chem.*, **42,** 1369 (1950)] and Laudise and Sullivan [*Chem. Eng. Progress*, **55** (5), 55 (1959)].

CRYSTALLIZATION APPARATUS

A classification of crystallization equipment based on the means used to develop supersaturation and to control yield per pass follows:

1. Supersaturation produced by cooling without substantial evaporation:

a. Atmospheric cooling by natural convection. Examples: tank crystallizers, Wulff-Bock crystallizer.

b. Cooling by liquid cooling medium, absorbing heat through metal surface. Examples: agitated batch crystallizer, Howard crystallizer, double-pipe crystallizer, Swenson-Walker crystallizer, Krystal cooling crystallizer.

2. Supersaturation produced by evaporation without substantial cooling, where the heat for the evaporation is transferred to the solution through metal surfaces. Examples: crystallizing evaporators, Krystal evaporator crystallizer.

3. Supersaturation produced by adiabatic evaporation and cooling. Example: vacuum crystallizers.

Crystallizers may also be classified in the following manners: batch vs. continuous, agitated or non-agitated, classifying or non-classifying. Classifying crystallizers function in such a manner that crystals are retained in the crystallizer until they have reached a minimum size before discharge.

To force crystallization, it is necessary to maintain the crystallizing solution in a supersaturated condition. **Choice of equipment** usually depends on the solubility-temperature relation of the substance to be crystallized. For solutes with a small positive temperature coefficient of solubility, or a negative coefficient, supersaturation must be developed by **evaporation.** If the solute has a large positive temperature coefficient, **cooling without evaporation** can produce the required supersaturation.

Crystallization can also be induced by adding a second solvent to reduce the solubility. This method has not found extensive application.

Tank Crystallization. Common practice in producing crystals has been to prepare hot, nearly saturated solutions and to cool them, by natural convection, in open tanks. Sometimes rods or strings are hung in the tanks to give the crystals additional surface on which to grow and to keep at least a part of the product out of the sediment that might collect in the bottom.

When the tanks have cooled sufficiently, which is usually a matter of several days, any remaining mother liquor is drained off and the crystals are removed by hand. This involves much labor and often results in the inclusion, with the crystals, of any impurities that have settled to the bottom of the tank. The floor space and labor required and the amount of material tied up in the process are large. On the other hand, investment is low and the equipment is simple and quickly available. This makes tank crystallization attractive for use in process development.

Contact between crystals and solution is poor, cooling rate is low, and nucleation rate is relatively small; so growth predominates over formation. The crystals are usually large and tend to interlock. This interlocking may result in occlusion of mother liquor and introduction of impurities. Size of individual crystals is variable. Capacity of such a crystallizer is low because of the low rate of heat transfer obtainable by atmospheric cooling. Evaporation from the surface is sensitive to the relative humidity of the air.

In the operation of naturally cooled tank crystallizers, there is no way to control either nucleation or growth except by using suitable lagging, or by varying the ratio of tank surface to tank volume. The size of the unit can be so chosen that the rate of heat loss corresponds roughly to the cooling time necessary to give the desired crystal size.

Solar Evaporation. Similar in principle to tank crystallization is the production of crystals by solar evaporation. This process is carried on extensively in dry climates to recover salts from sea water or from other waters with high mineral contents. The tank is replaced by ponds, into which the salt-containing water flows by tidal action or is pumped.

Rate of evaporation depends on humidity of the air, wind velocity, and amount of solar energy absorbed. Addition of a small amount of dye to the solution results in an appreciable increase in absorption of solar energy, with a consequent increase in capacity [Bloch, Farkas, and Spiegler, *Ind. Eng. Chem.*, **43,** 1544 (1951)].

In a large installation near San Francisco, Calif. [Schrier, *Chem. Eng.*, **59** (10), 138 (1952)], separate ponds were used for concentrating and for crystallizing. The crystallizing ponds had a gentle slope and a rectangular shape, to allow the concentrated liquor to drain from the crystals and to permit mechanical harvesting. Five to seven years were required to make a pond system impervious, and capacity was 40 tons of salt per acre per year.

The Wulff-Bock Crystallizer. The Wulff-Bock [Griffiths, *J. Soc. Chem. Ind.*, **44,** 7*T* (1925)] type of crystallizer has been widely used in Germany and in England but has not been used extensively in the United States. It consists of a shallow trough set at a slight inclination and mounted on rollers so that it can be rocked from side to side. At frequent intervals along its length are partitions extending part way across, so that the liquid, instead of flowing directly from one end to the other, flows in a zigzag path. Cooling is by natural convection, and the crystallizer is continuously operated.

The slow rate of cooling inherent in the Wulff-Bock crystallizer results in a relatively low capacity, but this crystallizer gives uniform crystals of unusually large size.

Agitated Batch Crystallizers. Figure 17-18 shows an agitated batch crystallizer. Water is circulated through the cooling coils, and the solution is agitated by the propellers on the central shaft. This agitation performs two functions: (1) It increases the rate of heat transfer and keeps the temperature of the solution more nearly uniform, and (2) by keeping the fine crystals in suspension it gives them an opportunity to grow uniformly instead of forming large crystals or aggregates. Further, the agitation, combined with the more rapid cooling, results in the formation of a large number of

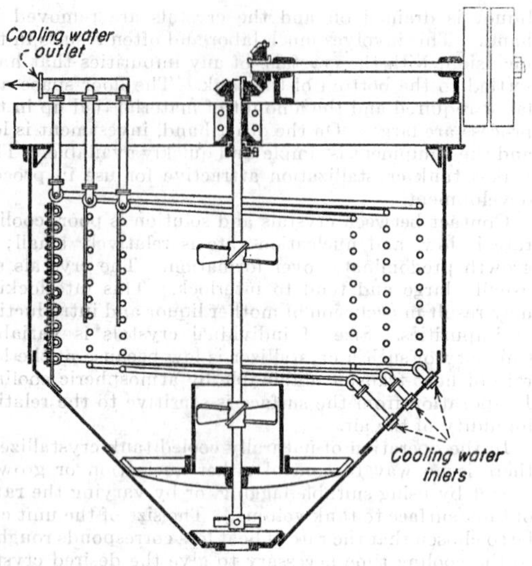

FIG. 17-18. Agitated batch crystallizer.

nuclei as compared with the tank methods, and therefore the product of this operation is not only more uniform but also very much finer than that from the older tanks. The difficulties with this apparatus are: first, that it is a batch or discontinuous method; and, second, that the solubility is least in the stagnant film on the surface of the cooling coils. Consequently crystal growth is most rapid at this point, and the coils rapidly build up with a mass of crystals which decreases the rate of heat transfer.

A certain amount of control can be exercised on the crystallization process occurring in a batch, artificially cooled crystallizer by varying the rate of cooling. As long as the solution is undersaturated, it may be cooled as rapidly as the temperature and rate of the cooling water and the area of the cooling surface permit. When the solution becomes supersaturated, the rate of temperature decrease should be retarded in order that the labile region is not entered. It is advisable to seed the solution at this point to prevent the uncontrolled initial nucleation characteristic of unseeded solutions. Once there is available considerable crystal surface for growth, the rate of heat removal can be increased, provided that the coils are not too badly salted. The rate of temperature decrease may be very small during the period of maximum crystallization rate, even if the rate of heat transfer is good, because of the necessity of withdrawing from the solution the latent heat of crystallization.

The Howard Crystallizer. This crystallizer (Fig. 17-19) consists essentially of a vertical conical device through which solution flows in an upward direction. The upper end of the crystallizer is the wide part of the cone. A concentric outer conical chamber serves as a cooling water channel. Crystals that are suspended in the upward-flowing stream of solution must grow to such a size that they will settle through the fastest part of the stream of solution at the apex of the cone (the bottom of the crystallizer) before they can escape. By regulating the velocity of flow at the bottom of the crystallizer, the size of the product is controlled. On the other hand, the cross section of the top of the crystallizer is large, the velocity of the solution is low, and the smaller crystals are not carried over the top. The apparatus functions both as a crystallizer and as a hydraulic classification device. The concentration of the solution is maintained by the inflow of strong solution from a storage tank, and the product is withdrawn continuously in a stream of mother liquor.

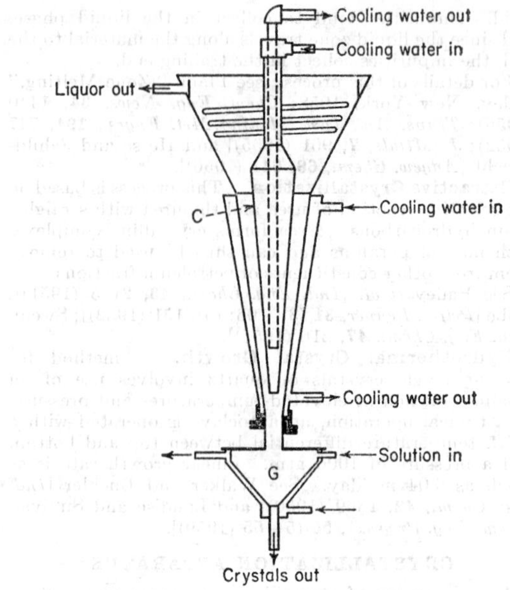

FIG. 17-19. Howard crystallizer.

Since the Howard crystallizer is a continuous one, conditions in it can reach a steady state. As the solution flows up through the crystallizing cone, its supersaturation increases because of the cooling brought about by the inner cooling cone *C*. Nucleation should start at a fairly definite point in the crystallizer. Nuclei will tend to drop through the incoming solution because of the action of gravity and are thereby continually contacted with fresh supersaturated solution. Growth therefore occurs, and, when the crystal is large enough, it will settle into vessel *G*. Nucleation due to the inoculating effect of existing crystals can accompany the growth in the same zone in which the growth is taking place.

The Double-pipe Crystallizer. [Seavoy and Caldwell, *Ind. Eng. Chem.*, **32**, 628 (1940).] This crystallizer consists essentially of a double-pipe heat exchanger fitted with internal helical ribbons. The cooling liquid passes through the annular space between the two pipes, and the crystallizing solution is pumped through the inner tube countercurrent to the cooling liquid. The helical ribbons act as scrapers to keep crystals from building up on the cooling surface. The scrapers make contact with the inner wall of the inside pipe. This crystallizer is ordinarily used in a continuous batch manner. It is placed in series with a large tank containing the solution to be cooled, and the solution is pumped through the double-pipe unit at a rate sufficient to ensure an adequate heat-transfer rate.

Units of about 40 ft. in length are common. These may be arranged in parallel or series to give the necessary capacity. They give positive heat transfer in cases where there is fouling of the heat-transfer surface or where the slurry is very thick. Because fouling is largely eliminated, large temperature differentials may be used, so that relatively small heat-transfer surface is needed. Heat-transfer coefficients of from 30 to 150 B.t.u./(hr.)(sq. ft.)(°F.) are obtained, with temperature differentials of over 30°F. [Garrett and Rosenbaum, *Chem. Eng.*, **65** (16), 127 (1958)].

The **Votator crystallizer** is a double-drum apparatus, similar to the scraped-pipe crystallizer. The inner drum rotates rapidly, and the liquid solution flows in the annulus between the two drums. The outer drum is cooled by coolant in a jacket. This gives moderately high heat-transfer coefficients, with small hold-up, but low capacity.

The Swenson-Walker Crystallizer. A popular continuous crystallizer using a liquid cooling medium is the Swenson-Walker crystallizer (Fig. 17-20). It consists of an open trough 24 in. wide, with a semicylindrical

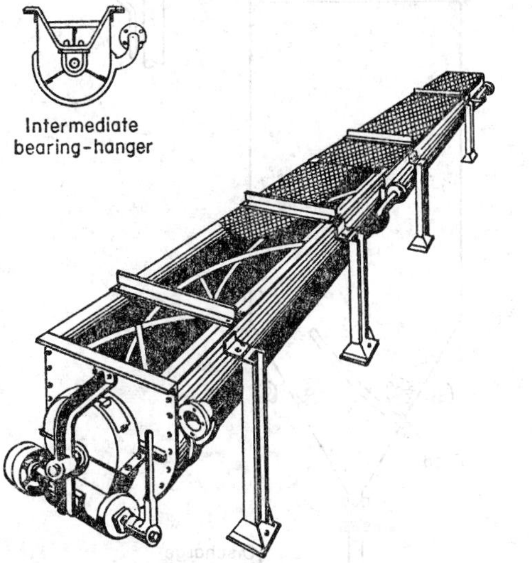

FIG. 17-20. Swenson-Walker crystallizer. [*Seavoy and Caldwell, Ind. Eng. Chem.*, **32**, 632 (1940).]

bottom, a water jacket welded to the outside of the trough, and a slow-speed, long-pitch, spiral agitator set close to the bottom of the trough, but not so close as to make contact with the trough. This apparatus is ordinarily built in units 10 ft. long, and a number of units may be joined together to give increased capacity. Forty feet is the maximum length usually driven from one shaft; and, if lengths greater than this are desired, it is usual to arrange several such crystallizers, one above the other, and allow the solution to cascade from one bank to the other.

The hot concentrated solution to be crystallized is fed at one end of the trough, and cooling water usually flows through the jackets, countercurrent to the solution. In order to control crystal size, it is sometimes desirable to introduce an extra amount of water into certain sections. When conditions are properly adjusted, nuclei begin to form a short distance from the point where feed is introduced; these nuclei grow regularly as the solution passes down the length of the crystallizer. The function of the spiral stirrer is not especially that of either agitation or conveying the crystals. Its purposes are (1) to prevent an accumulation of crystals on the cooling surface and (2) to lift the crystals which have already been formed and shower them down through the solution. In this manner the crystals grow while they are freely suspended in the liquid and therefore are usually fairly perfect individuals, reasonably uniform in size, and free from inclusions or aggregations.

At the end of the crystallizer there may be an overflow gate where crystals and mother liquor together overflow to a draining table or drain box, from which the mother liquor is returned to the process and the wet crystals are raked to a centrifuge. In other cases, a short section of an inclined-screw conveyor lifts the crystals out of the solution and delivers them to the centrifuge, while the mother liquor overflows at a convenient point. The advantages of this type over tank crystallization are high capacity, large saving in floor space and in material in process, and especially a saving in labor. To reach low final temperatures, cooling can be obtained by use of refrigerated brine instead of cooling water.

The supersaturation produced in the Swenson-Walker is primarily due to cooling and only incidentally to evaporation. Uniform cooling is desirable, especially through the range of temperature where nucleation first occurs. It is possible to seed the solution artificially, but ordinarily seeding is left to fortuitous seeding from the atmosphere. There is no classifying action, and therefore complete uniformity is not obtained in the product.

Capacity of a Swenson-Walker crystallizer is largely determined by heat transfer. An over-all coefficient based on a logarithmic average temperature difference of 10 to 25 B.t.u./(hr.)(sq. ft.)(°F.) is used and an effective heat-transfer area of 3 sq. ft./running foot of crystallizer assumed. The number of units to be used in parallel depends on the total capacity desired.

Example 5. A Swenson-Walker crystallizer is to cool a 23 per cent solution of Na_3PO_4 from a temperature of 104° to 77°F. During the cooling, $Na_3PO_4.12H_2O$ is crystallized. It is desired to produce 500 lb. product/hr. The solubility of Na_3PO_4 at 77°F. is 15.5 parts anhydrous salt/100 parts total water. The specific heat of the solution can be taken as 0.77, and the heat of crystallization of 1 lb. product is 63 B.t.u./lb. Cooling water is to enter the crystallizer jacket at 60°F. and is to leave at 68°F. The over-all heat-transfer coefficient is 25 B.t.u./(sq. ft.)(hr.)(°F.). What length of crystallizer should be used?

Solution. The weight of solution per hour that will give 500 lb. of crystals is calculated with the aid of Eq. (17-5). The molecular weight of $Na_3PO_4.12H_2O$ is 380.2, and that of Na_3PO_4 is 164.0; $R = 380.2/164.0 = 2.32$. If a basis of 100 lb. original solution is chosen, $w_0 = 23.0$; $S = 15.5$; and $H = 100 - 23.0 = 77.0$ lb. The product obtained from 100 lb. solution is, by Eq. (17-5),

$$C = 2.32 \frac{(100)(23.0) - (15.5)(77.0)}{100 - 15.5(2.32 - 1.0)} = 32.2 \text{ lb.}$$

In order that 500 lb./hr. of crop be obtained, a feed of (100/32.2)(500) = 1550 lb. is necessary. The heat to be removed from the crystallizing solution is:

To cool solution: (1550)(0.77)(104 − 77)	= 32,200 B.t.u./hr.
To crystallize: (500)(63)	= 31,500 B.t.u./hr.
Total = q	= 63,700 B.t.u./hr.

The logarithmic mean temperature drop is

$$(\Delta t)_m = \frac{(104 - 68) - (77 - 60)}{2.303 \log \frac{104 - 68}{77 - 60}} = 25°\text{F.}$$

The length of crystallizer is

$$\frac{q}{3U(\Delta t)_m} = \frac{63{,}700}{(3)(25)(25)} = 34 \text{ ft.}$$

Four 10-ft. sections should be used.

Crystallizing Evaporators. The development of supersaturation by means of evaporation without substantial cooling is often carried out in equipment that has the physical characteristics of an evaporator and, in fact, is designed essentially as an evaporator largely because the essential engineering problem is one of heat transfer. Usually the equipment employed is so nearly like that used in ordinary evaporation that it is considered to be an evaporator, although the crystallization may be the more difficult of the two parts of the problem. In the evaporation of a salting liquor (*e.g.*, the precipitation of NaCl from brine in the common-salt industry) the crystallization is usually incidental to the evaporation, and no particular control of size is exercised. On the other hand, the crystallizing of sugar is carried out in a vacuum evaporator, but the control is based entirely on building a correct crystal. In this case the operator brings the sirup to a definite density, shocks out the desired number of nuclei, and grows them to the correct size without forming new crystallization centers. The control is exercised entirely by varying the vacuum and steam supply.

A special case of evaporative crystallization is the **salt grainer** (Badger and Baker, "Inorganic Chemical Technology," 2d ed., pp. 15–18, McGraw-Hill, New York, 1941). In the salt grainer the solution is kept hot and supersaturation is developed by evaporation rather than by cooling. Nucleation occurs at the surface of the brine; the nuclei tend to be retained at the surface by surface-tension effects and to form hopper-shaped crystal agglomerates, which, when large enough, break away, drop to the bottom of the grainer, and are raked out by slow-moving rakes.

In a vacuum crystallizer a warm, saturated solution is fed to a lagged closed vessel that is maintained under a vacuum. The solution cools adiabatically to the boiling temperature corresponding to the vacuum in the vessel. The cooling results in crystallization, not only because of the cooling of the solution, but also because of evaporation. It is necessary to ensure that the incoming solution reaches the surface; otherwise the feed will tend to short-circuit to the discharge.

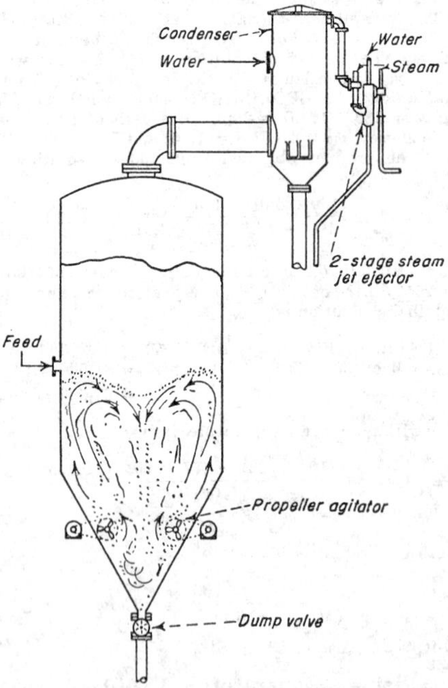

FIG. 17-21. Batch vacuum crystallizer without booster [*Seavoy and Caldwell, Ind. Eng. Chem.*, **32,** 628 (1940).]

Four forms of the vacuum crystallizer are shown in Figs. 17-21, 17-22, 17-23, and 17-24 [Seavoy and Caldwell, *Ind. Eng. Chem.*, **32,** 627 (1940)]. Figure 17-21 represents a simple type of batch vacuum crystallizer. Propeller agitators are used to develop a swirling action

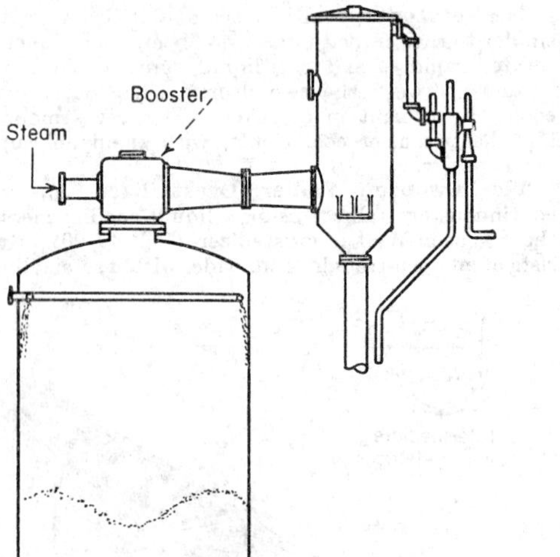

FIG. 17-22. Continuous vacuum crystallizer with booster. [*Seavoy and Caldwell, Ind. Eng. Chem.*, **32,** 628 (1940).]

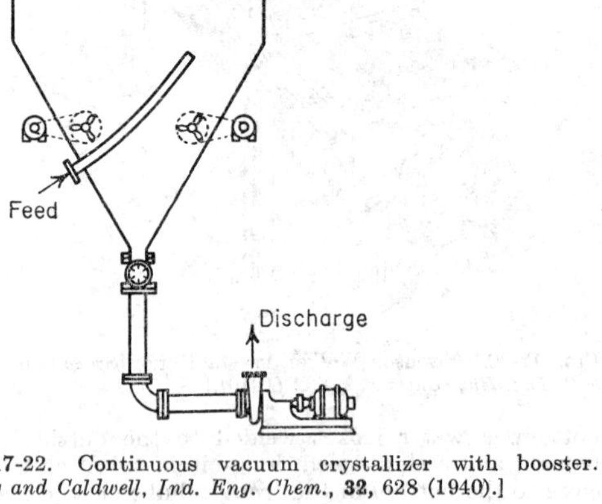

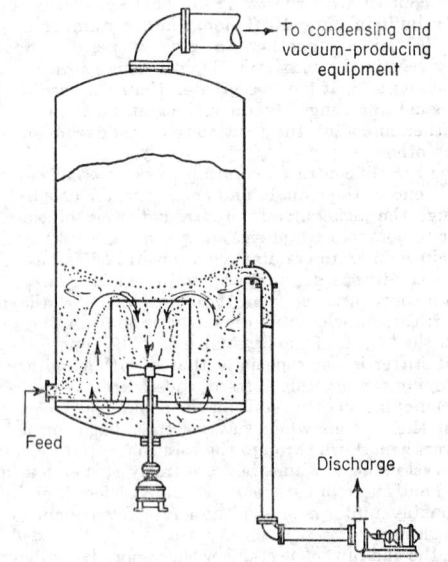

FIG. 17-23. Continuous vacuum crystallizer with vertical agitator. [*Seavoy and Caldwell, Ind. Eng. Chem.*, **32,** 629 (1940).]

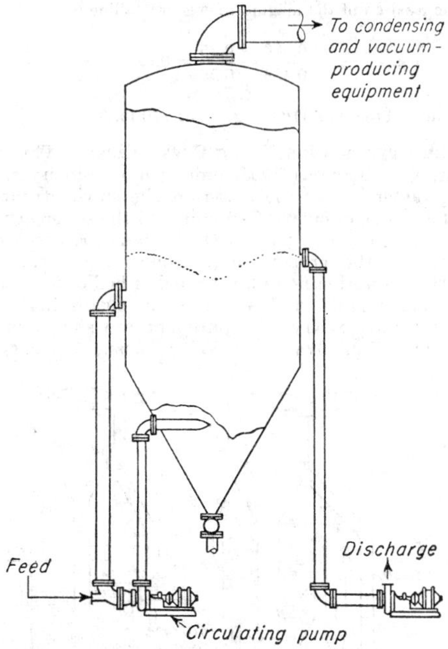

FIG. 17-24. Continuous vacuum crystallizer with pump circulation. [*Seavoy and Caldwell, Ind. Eng. Chem.*, **32**, 629 (1940).]

in the crystallizer. In case of temperature in the crystallizer high enough so that the vapor from it is condensable by the cooling water available, the vapors from the crystallizer pass directly to a condenser as shown in Fig. 17-21. In most cases, however, the cooling water is too warm to condense the vapor leaving a vacuum crystallizer at the desired temperature of operation in the crystallizer. In this case a steam-jet booster is used to compress the vapors to a point where they can be condensed by the cooling water available. The air and noncondensable gases from the condenser are commonly ejected to the atmosphere by further steam-jet equipment. A second type of vacuum crystallizer, operated by such a booster, is shown in Fig. 17-22. This type is operated continuously. The feed tube is so positioned that the feed solution is forced to the surface and flashes to equilibrium with the vapor. Propeller agitators aid in keeping the crystals in suspension and in preventing short circuiting.

The forms of crystallizer shown in Figs. 17-23 and 17-24 can be operated either as batch or as continuous units. The combination of propeller and draft tube shown in Fig. 17-23 is effective in preventing short circuiting of the feed. The form shown in Fig. 17-24 has an external circulating pump which takes suction from the side of the crystallizer and discharges tangentially into the cone. The agitators can be omitted from this unit. The feed is introduced into the circulation stream, and the circulation stream must be large enough that the mixed stream is not so supersaturated that it is in the labile condition.

Batch operation has the advantage of low steam consumption if a steam-jet booster is used. The steam required by a steam-jet booster to remove 1 lb. of low-pressure vapor from the crystallizer increases rapidly as the pressure in the crystallizer is reduced. In batch cooling much of the vapor is removed at a relatively high pressure because the solution charged to the crystallizer is essentially hot and only at the end of the batch is the full pressure differential over the booster required and only at the end of the process is the maximum steam consumption called for. The average steam consumption is therefore considerably lower than is the case for a continuous crystallizer where all vapor must be removed under conditions where the steam consumption is a maximum. On the other hand, a continuous crystallizer has the advantages of lower first cost per unit of capacity, ease of control, and constant mass of crystals in the unit. It is easier in the continuous unit to maintain supersaturations outside of the labile field.

Yield from a Vacuum Crystallizer. The calculation of the yield obtainable in a vacuum crystallizer depends upon the method used in the heat-balance calculations. A vacuum crystallizer operates essentially adiabatically. The heat liberated by the solution on cooling to the equilibrium temperature and the heat of crystallization are available for vaporizing water from the solution, and these thermal effects must balance. If the enthalpy-concentration chart is used, the total enthalpy of the vapors and magma leaving the crystallizer must equal the total enthalpy of the feed solution entering the unit.

In case the heat items are computed individually, which is the method to be used when the enthalpy-concentration chart is not available, the evaporation can be calculated by means of Eq. (17-10)

$$E = \frac{(w_0 + H_0)(c)(\Delta t)[100 - S(R-1)] + q_c R(100w_0 - SH_0)}{L_w[100 - S(R-1)] - q_c RS} \tag{17-10}$$

where w_0 is the weight of anhydrous solute; H_0 is the total weight of solvent in the feed solution; c is the specific heat of the feed solution; Δt is the temperature range through which the solution is cooled (temperature of feed to temperature of discharge); q_c is the heat of crystallization per unit weight of crystal; L_w is the latent heat of evaporation from the solution; S is the anhydrous solubility in parts solute per 100 parts total solvent; and R is the ratio of the molecular weight of the crystals to that of the anhydrous salt. When the value of E is known, the yield is calculated by means of Eq. (17-5). Calculation for batch vacuum crystallizers can be based on Eq. (17-10) by dividing the cooling range into steps and applying the equation to each step.

If the enthalpy-concentration chart is used, the simplest method of vacuum crystallizer calculation is one based on the "basic construction" applicable to the chart. Since the process is adiabatic, a single straight line on the chart must pass through the three points on the chart that represent feed solution, magma, and vapor, respectively. Furthermore, the point representing the magma must lie on the straight-line isotherm lying in the magma field and corresponding to the temperature of the vapor and magma. The point representing the magma is found by locating the intersection of these two lines as shown in Fig. 17-25. The ratio of crystals to mother liquor in the magma is found from the intersection by applying the lever-arm principle to the two line segments on the straight-line isotherm.

Example 6. A continuous vacuum crystallizer is fed with 100,000 lb./hr. of a 35 per cent solution of $MgSO_4$ at a temperature of 183°F. An absolute pressure of 0.2 lb./sq. in. is maintained in the crystallizer by the booster, and the solution has a 10°F. elevation in boiling point.

Calculate the yield of $MgSO_4.7H_2O$, and the evaporation for this crystallizer:

a. By means of Eqs. (17-5) and (17-10).

b. By means of Fig. 17-11.

Solution. Part *a*: For this take

$$c = 0.77 \text{ B.t.u./(°F.)(lb.)}$$
$$L_w = 1080 \text{ B.t.u./lb.}$$
$$q_c = 23 \text{ B.t.u./lb. } MgSO_4.7H_2O$$

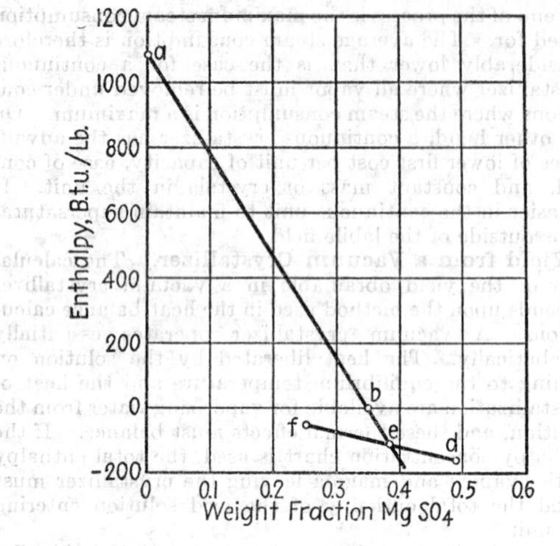

FIG. 17-25. Solution to Example 6b.

The temperature of boiling water at 0.2 lb./sq. in. abs. is 53°F., and the equilibrium temperature of the solution in the crystallizer is 53 + 10 = 63°F.

The remaining numerical values to be substituted in Eqs. (17-5) and (17-10) are:

$$w_0 = (0.35)(100{,}000) = 35{,}000 \text{ lb./hr.}$$

$$R = \frac{\text{mole wt. } MgSO_4.7H_2O}{\text{mole wt. } MgSO_4} = 2.045$$

S = solubility of anhydrous $MgSO_4$ at 63°F. = 33.33 parts $MgSO_4$/100 parts total water (Fig. 17-10)

$$\Delta t = 183 - 63 = 120°\text{F.}$$

$$H_0 = 100{,}000 - 35{,}000 = 65{,}000 \text{ lb./hr.}$$

then $(w_0 + H_0)(c)(\Delta t)[100 - S(R-1)]$

$$= (100{,}000)(0.77)(120)[100 - 33.33(2.045 - 1)] = 6.022 \times 10^8$$

$$(q_c)(R)(100w_0 - SH_0) = (23)(2.045)[(100)(35{,}000) - (33.33)(65{,}000)] = 0.627 \times 10^8$$

$$L_v[100 - S(R-1)] - q_cRS = 1080[100 - 33.33(2.045 - 1)] - (23)(2.045)(33.33) = 68{,}793$$

By Eq. (17-10) the evaporation is:

$$E = \frac{(6.022)(10^8) + (0.627)(10^8)}{68{,}793} = 9665 \text{ lb./hr.}$$

By Eq. (17-5) the yield is:

$$C = (2.045)\frac{(100)(35{,}000) - (33.33)(65{,}000 - 7842)}{100 - (33.33)(2.045 - 1)}$$

$$= 50{,}050 \text{ lb./hr.}$$

Solution, Part *b*: Figure 17-25 shows the graphical solution of this problem using values from the enthalpy-concentration chart of Fig. 17-11. From steam tables, the enthalpy of 1 lb. steam at a pressure of 0.2 lb./sq. in. abs. and a temperature of 63°F. is 1089.5 B.t.u. Point *a* has the coordinates $H = 1089.5$, $c = 0$. The enthalpy of the feed solution, which has a concentration of 0.35 and a temperature of 183°F., is 0. The coordinates of point *b* are $H = 0$, $c = 0.35$, and straight line *ab* can be drawn. The straight line *fd* is the 63°F. isotherm in the area *bcih* of Fig. 17-11. The coordinates of its terminals are: point *f*, $H = -49.5$, $c = 0.25$; point *d*, $H = -157.5$, $c = 0.488$. Lines *fd* and *ab* intersect at point *e*, which has the coordinates $H = -111.2$, $c = 0.386$. The average concentration of the final magma is, therefore, 38.6 per cent $MgSO_4$. The total magma is (100,000)(0.35/0.386) = 90,673 lb./hr. The evaporation is, therefore, (100,000)(1 − 0.35/0.386) = 9327 lb./hr. The discrepancy between this figure and that found in part *a* (9665 lb./hr.) is a result of the approximations made in the heat-balance items used in part *a*.

The fraction of the magma that is crystalline is

$$\frac{0.386 - 0.25}{0.488 - 0.25} = 0.571$$

and the yield is (0.571)(90,673) = 51,770 lb./hr.

The Krystal Classifying Crystallizer. This equipment, also known as the Jeremiassen or Oslo crystallizer, is characterized by the fact that the supersaturation is produced in a circulating stream, and the supersaturation is developed in one part of the unit and released in another. In the crystallizing element itself, the supersaturated solution flows up through a bed of forming and growing crystals and provides a classifying action. Three types of Krystal equipment are shown in Figs. 17-26 and 17-27 [Svanoe, *Ind. Eng. Chem.*, **32**, 636 (1940)].

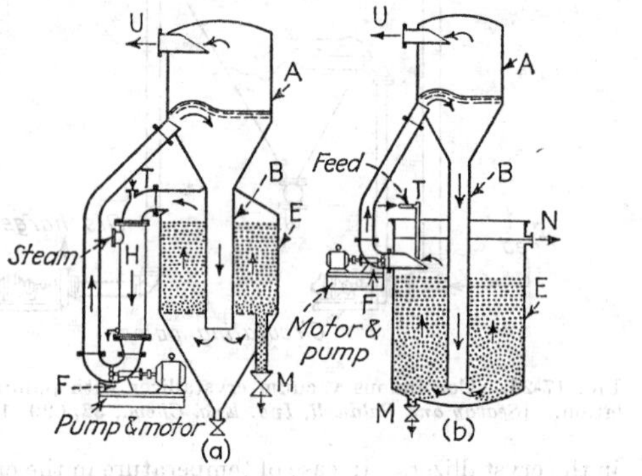

FIG. 17-26. Krystal crystallizers: (*a*) evaporator crystallize (*b*) vacuum crystallizer.

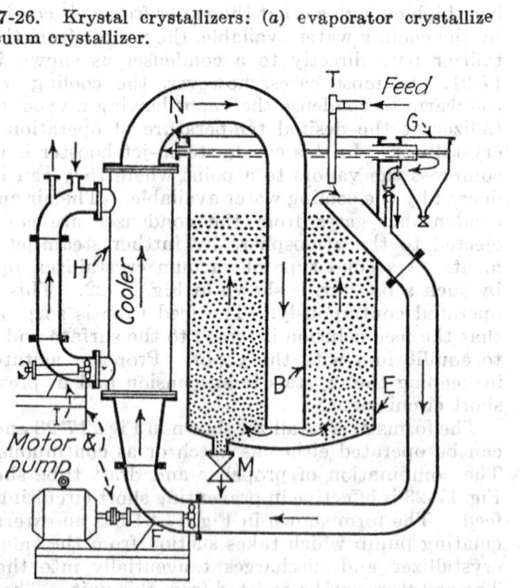

FIG. 17-27. Cooling crystallizer. [*Svanoe, Ind. Eng. Chem.*, **32**, 638 (1940).]

These three types differ primarily in the means used for developing supersaturation. In Fig. 17-26*a* the supersaturation is obtained by heating the circulating stream while under a static head great enough to prevent its vaporization and flashing of the heated solution in vessel *A*. The vapor released by the flash is removed through pipe *U*. The solution, supersaturated with respect to the temperature existing in crystallizing vessel *E*, leaves the flash vessel *A*, passes up through a screen in the bottom of vessel E, contacts crystals above the screen, and loses its supersaturation while in contact with them. The overflow stream, leaving vessel A and passing to heater H, should be practically saturated. Feed solution is mixed with this solution at T. Crystals are drawn off continuously or periodically through discharge M. Pump F, driven by the motor, forces the circulating stream through its circuit. Heater H is steam-heated. This type of crystallizer is used in cases where the supersaturation must be developed entirely by evaporation and not by cooling. Two or more of these units can be connected in multiple effect just as in the case of an ordinary evaporator. Figure 17-26*b* represents a vacuum type of Krystal unit. This unit is a true vacuum crystallizer, in that the supersaturation is developed by adiabatic pressure reduction on the hot, concentrated, feed solution. The feed enters at T, is incorporated in a circulating cycle stream, and the combined stream flashed in flash vessel A. Supersaturated solution passing through pipe B contacts growing crystals in crystallizer E, and the flow of liquid in vessel E performs a classifying action. Mother liquor is drawn off at N and the magma drawn off at M. Nucleation can occur in vessel E by the inoculation of the solution by the existing crystals and by any impact of the crystals on each other and on the wall of the vessel. In continuous operation the rate of nucleation must equal the number of finished crystals withdrawn as product.

The modification shown in Fig. 17-27 develops supersaturation entirely by liquid cooling. The circulating stream passes through the tubes of cooler H, and supersaturated solution flows through pipe B to the bottom of crystallizer E. The feed, which should be warm and concentrated, enters at T. It is incorporated immediately in the circulating stream, the combined stream is cooled in H, and supersaturation is thereby obtained. The diluting of the incoming feed with a comparatively large circulating stream of mother liquor allows the solution to be cooled in cooler H without entering the labile region and thereby allows this cooling to be accomplished without nucleation until the solution comes in contact with the crystals in E. Vessel G can be used to remove very small nuclei that reach the upper layers of the crystallizer E. If small nuclei are continually removed, the average size of the crystal crop is increased. The action of vessel G has substantially the same effect as a reduction in the rate of nucleation curve shown in Fig. 17-16. Mother liquor leaves the crystallizer at M.

In the travel of the supersaturated solution up through the crystal mass, the supersaturation, and therefore the rate of crystal growth, decreases from bottom to top. The average supersaturation and the average rate of growth at the top are both considerably lower than the supersaturation and growth rate at the bottom of the mass at the point of entrance of the supersaturated solution.

Crystallization Costs. Crystallizer costs vary greatly, because most crystallizers are custom-made for specific jobs. For rough preliminary estimates, Fig. 17-27*A* can be used. Data for this figure, which are based on 1958 prices, include cost of accessories.

Comparison of Vacuum and Liquid-cooled Crystallizers. In cases where the necessary supersaturation can be developed by cooling, the choice of a crystallizer usually lies between a mechanical unit, cooled by transmitting heat through a metal wall, and a vacuum unit that has no heat-transfer surface in the crystallizer itself. In such a comparison the Swenson-Walker may be taken as representative of the mechanical type, and the vacuum crystallizer shown in Figs. 17-21 to 17-24 as representative of the vacuum type [Seavoy and Caldwell, *Ind. Eng. Chem.*, **32**, 631 (1940)].

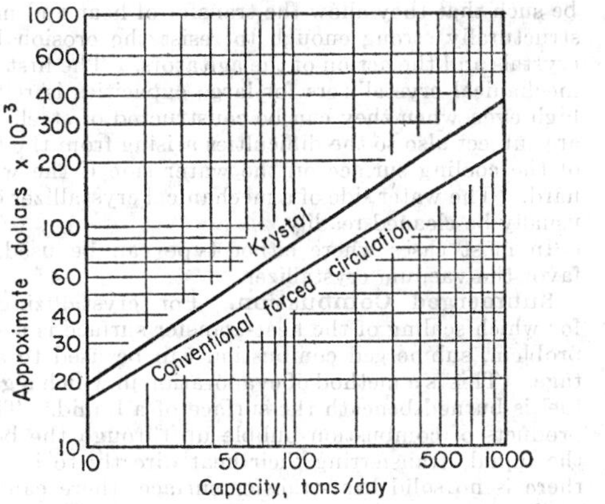

FIG. 17-27*A*. Costs of crystallization systems, 1958 prices. [*Garrett and Rosenbaum, Chem. Eng.*, **65** (16), 140 (1958).]

The main difference between the vacuum and mechanical crystallizers is that the heat is removed in the vacuum crystallizer without passing it through a heating surface. This gives the vacuum crystallizer several important advantages. The absence of large heat-transfer surfaces results in a lower first cost for the vacuum crystallizer and also allows the crystallizer to be built of corrosion-resisting materials. The absence of the cooling surface also eliminates the growth of crystals on a metal surface from which they must be removed mechanically during operation. The limitations of the vacuum crystallizer are: (1) it usually requires a steam-jet booster to obtain the low temperature desired, and the steam consumption may be large; (2) magma densities may be too heavy to circulate freely in the crystallizer; (3) it may not be possible to attain the desired final temperature. The first limitation of high steam consumption has been discussed. Magma density may limit the cooling region available because of the difficulty of discharge and the difficulties of developing adequate circulation in the crystallizer. The critical magma density is approximately 50 to 55 per cent by weight when the density of the crystals is not greatly different from the density of the mother liquor and 35 to 40 per cent by weight when the differences in densities are relatively large.

The difficulty of attaining the desired final temperature may be due to the inability of the booster to exhaust at a low enough pressure. The commercial limit of suction pressure obtainable with such equipment is about 0.11 in. Hg absolute. This corresponds to a water boiling point of 20°F. If the solution possesses an appreciable boiling-point elevation, the minimum temperature obtainable is increased by the amount of boiling-point elevation. For very high boiling-point elevations, such as those encountered in crystallizing caustic soda, vacuum crystallization is out of the question.

Two further disadvantages of the vacuum crystallizer are: (1) it requires more headroom than does a mechanical-type crystallizer and (2) rubber linings, which are commonly used for corrosive solutions, are unsatisfactory for hot acid solutions.

The mechanical crystallizer has the advantage in not requiring vacuum-producing equipment, in being independent of the vapor pressure of the solution, and in requiring no steam. It can also handle stiffer magmas than can the vacuum crystallizer because free circulation is not required.

The mechanical crystallizer is frequently limited by the materials of construction. The materials used must be such that they allow the transfer of heat and must be structurally strong enough to resist the erosion by the crystals and the action of the agitators. The first cost of mechanical crystallizers for large capacities is relatively high even when they can be constructed of steel. They are subject also to the difficulties arising from the fouling of the cooling surface on the water side if the water is hard. The water side of a mechanical crystallizer cannot usually be cleaned readily.

In most cases where either type can be used, costs favor the vacuum crystallizer.

Submerged Combustion. For crystallizing salts for which scaling of the heat-transfer surface is a serious problem, submerged combustion can be used to advantage. This is a method of evaporation in which a gaseous fuel is burned beneath the surface of a liquid. The hot products of combustion bubble up through the body of the liquid, transferring their heat directly to it. Since there is no solid heat-transfer surface, there can be no scaling.

Equipment for submerged combustion is simple, consisting of a tank and a burner [Lindsey, *Chem. Eng.*, **60** (4), 227 (1953)]. Careful burner design and control are necessary to avoid explosions. Burners are built with rated capacities of 30,000 to 5 million B.t.u./hr., and several may be used in one tank.

Prilling. A combination spray-drying and crystallizing technique is in widespread use for the production of ammonium nitrate as well as urea. Hot concentrated ammonium nitrate solution is sprayed into a tower, into the bottom of which is blown atmospheric air. The ammonium nitrate crystallizes into agglomerates, or "prills," which are conditioned with diatomaceous earth to reduce caking and are bagged for use.

Satisfactory ammonium nitrate crystals have been produced in Krystal equipment. The product so made is in the form of single crystals rather than aggregates [Miller, Phillips, and Saeman, *Chem. Eng. Progress*, **43**, 667 (1947)].

CAKING OF CRYSTALS

A problem that is often met in handling crystalline products is their tendency to cake or bind together. This is often troublesome in bulk storage or in barreled products but is most serious in those cases where crystals are sold in small packages. The difficulty may exist in degrees, varying from loose aggregates that fall apart between the fingers, to solid lumps that can be crushed only by considerable force. The demand of the average consumer that the material shall flow freely from the package makes the prevention of caking a serious problem for the manufacturer.

Critical Humidity. Just as the vapor pressure of water is fixed by its temperature, so the vapor pressure of any solution is fixed by its temperature at an amount somewhat lower than the vapor pressure of water at that temperature. If a saturated solution is brought into contact with air in which the partial pressure of water is less than the vapor pressure of the solution, the solution will evaporate. On the other hand, if the air contains more moisture than this limiting amount, the solution will absorb water until it is so dilute than its vapor pressure is equal to the partial pressure of the moisture of the air with which it is in contact. If a crystal of a soluble salt is in contact with air that contains less water than would be in equilibrium with the saturated solution, the crystal must stay dry, because if it were surrounded with a film of solution, that solution would necessarily evaporate. On the other hand, if the crystal is brought into contact with air containing more moisture than would be in equilibrium with its saturated solution, then the crystal will become damp and in time will absorb water until it is completely dissolved, and the solution is so dilute that it is in equilibrium with the air.

In the range of temperatures around ordinary room temperature, the vapor pressure of a given solution varies with temperature in such a way that it is nearly a constant percentage of the vapor pressure of water at the same temperature. Saturated sodium chloride, for instance, has a vapor pressure approximately 80 per cent of that of water at the same temperature. If sodium chloride, therefore, is brought into contact with air of more than 80 per cent relative humidity it will absorb moisture, while if it is brought into contact with air of less than 80 per cent relative humidity it will stay dry. From this follows the conception of **critical humidity** of a solid salt. This is the humidity above which it will always become damp and below which it will always stay dry. If the crystal should be coated with impurities derived from the mother liquor from which it was separated (in the case of sodium chloride such impurities would be calcium and magnesium chlorides), this may result in a critical humidity higher or lower than that of the pure salt, according to whether the impurities give solutions having greater or less vapor pressures than that of the salt in question. Consequently, the critical humidity of a commercial grade of a crystalline material may differ appreciably from the critical humidity of the pure substance.

Prevention of Caking. Suppose a sample of sodium chloride is exposed for a short time to an atmosphere more moist than its critical humidity and then that it is removed to an atmosphere less moist than its critical humidity. During the first period it will absorb more moisture, and during the second period it will lose this moisture. If the crystals are large, so that there are relatively few points of contact and there is a large free volume between the crystals, there will probably be no appreciable bonding of the crystals due to this solution and reevaporation, if the time of exposure is not too great. If, on the other hand, the crystals are fine, or have a small percentage of voids, or are in contact with a moist atmosphere for a long time, sufficient moisture may be absorbed to fill the voids entirely with saturated solution; and when this has been reevaporated the crystals will lock into a solid mass. Consequently, to prevent the caking of such salts, the following conditions are desirable: (1) the highest possible critical humidity; (2) a product containing uniform grains with the maximum percentage of voids and the fewest possible points of contact; (3) a coating of powdery inert material that can absorb reasonable amounts of moisture.

The first condition (maximum critical humidity) is often met by removing impurities, such as calcium chloride in the case of common salt, free acid where a salt is formed in acid solutions, etc. It often happens that the impurities have a lower critical humidity than the product desired, although this is entirely accidental. To increase the percentage of voids, it is not necessary to produce larger crystals but to produce a more uniform mixture. For a given crystal form, and for absolutely uniform crystals as to size, the percentage of voids is the same no matter what the size of the crystals. A variation in particle size, however, rapidly decreases the percentage of voids. On the other hand, a fine product has more points of contact per unit volume than a coarse one and, hence, a greater tendency to cake. The third remedy is not always applicable. Illustrations of its use are dusting of table salt with magnesia or tricalcium phosphate and the dusting of flake calcium chloride (25 per cent H_2O) with anhydrous calcium chloride.

Some hydrated salts have a melting point so near room temperature that they may sometimes be stored under conditions where fusion begins. Here again the same considerations hold, for, if the percentage of voids is large or the points of contact between adjacent crystals few, the amount of fused material may not be sufficient to lock crystals together on resolidification. If, because of extremely fine crystal size or a mixture of sizes, the percentage of voids is too far reduced or the number of points of contact too greatly increased, the crystals may be firmly locked on resolidification. In this case, also, caking may be partly prevented by dusting the crystals with powdered material. In the case of hydrated salts, this powdery material may be produced from the salt itself by drying under such conditions that a very thin surface layer is dehydrated.

SUBLIMATION

REFERENCES: Anon., *Ind. Eng. Chem.*, **48** (3), 19A (1956). Bakken, *Chem. Eng.*, **36**, 345 (1929). Bebie, *Chem. & Met. Eng.*, **41**, 247 (1934). Cremer, "Chemical Engineering Practice," vol. 6, Chap. 15, by Kemp, Academic Press, New York, 1958. Nord, *Chem. Eng.*, **58** (9), 157 (1951). Weissberger, "Technique of Organic Chemistry," vol. 4, Chap. VII, by Tipson, Interscience, New York, 1951. Wilke, *Chem. Inds.*, **63**, 34 (July 1948). British Patents 142,902, 173,789, 447,759, 644,941, 700,143. French Patent 948,039. U.S. Patents 1,324,716, 1,324,717, 1,464,844, 1,987,301, 2,214,838, 2,252,052, 2,310,188, 2,499.255, 2,583,013, 2,607,440, 2,608,472, 2,628,892, 2,676,092, 2,737,439, 2,740,527, 2,742,342, 2,743,169.

Definitions. *Sublimation* is the term used to describe one of the following operations:

1. Direct vaporization of a solid without the appearance of any liquid phase. (Solid → gas)
2. Direct condensation of a vapor to the solid state without the appearance of a liquid phase. This is also called *desublimation.* (Gas → solid)
3. The complete process of vaporizing a solid and then condensing the vapor directly to the solid state without the appearance of a liquid phase. (Solid → gas → solid)

Pseudo sublimation is the process of vaporizing a liquid and then condensing the vapor directly to the solid state. (Liquid → gas → solid)

Simple sublimation is a process in which the vapor phase consists essentially of the component being sublimed with only small amounts of other gaseous components present. When the vapor pressure of the solid during vaporization is below atmospheric pressure, as is the usual case, simple sublimation must be conducted under reduced pressure. Schematic diagrams of simple vacuum sublimations are shown in Fig. 17-28.

Entrainer sublimation or *carrier sublimation* is the process whereby an inert gas called the *entrainer* or *carrier* is passed over or through the product to be sublimed. The mixture of entrainer and product vapors is then cooled in a condensing section where solid product is recovered. Figure 17-29 is a schematic representation of this type of process. Entrainer sublimation with quenching is shown in Fig. 17-30.

The *triple point* of a substance is the point at which all three phases (solid, liquid, and vapor) coexist in equilibrium. It is represented by point *B* of Fig. 17-31. Line *AB* is the locus of all points representing temperature and corresponding vapor pressure at which solid and vapor are in equilibrium. Line *BC* is the locus for liquid-vapor equilibrium while *BD* is for solid-liquid equilibrium. Line *BE* is a continuation of curve *CB* and represents

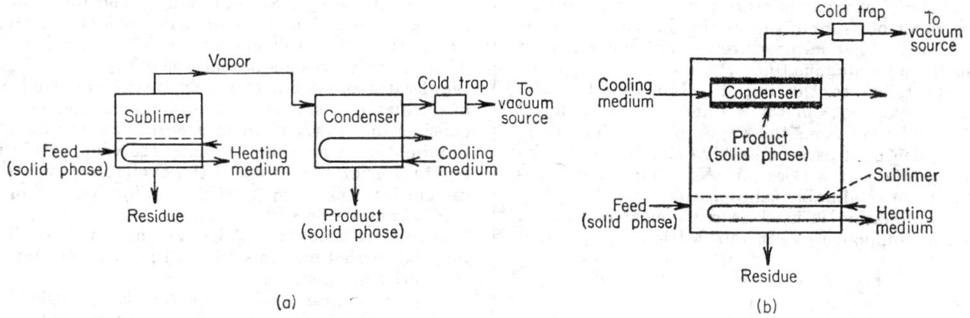

FIG. 17-28. Simple vacuum sublimation. (*a*) Separate sublimer and condenser. (*b*) Combined sublimer and condenser.

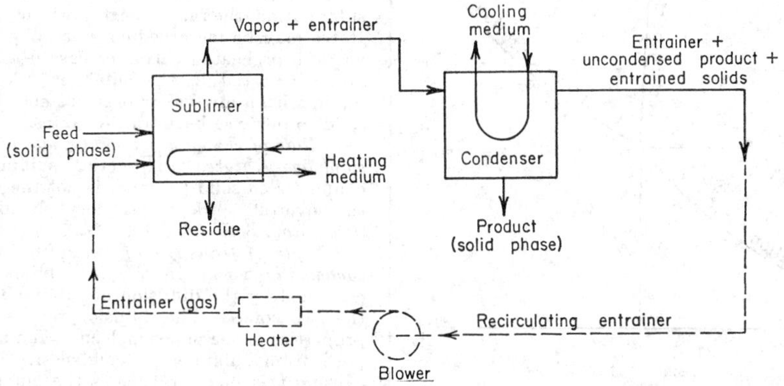

FIG. 17-29. Entrainer sublimation (with or without recirculation).

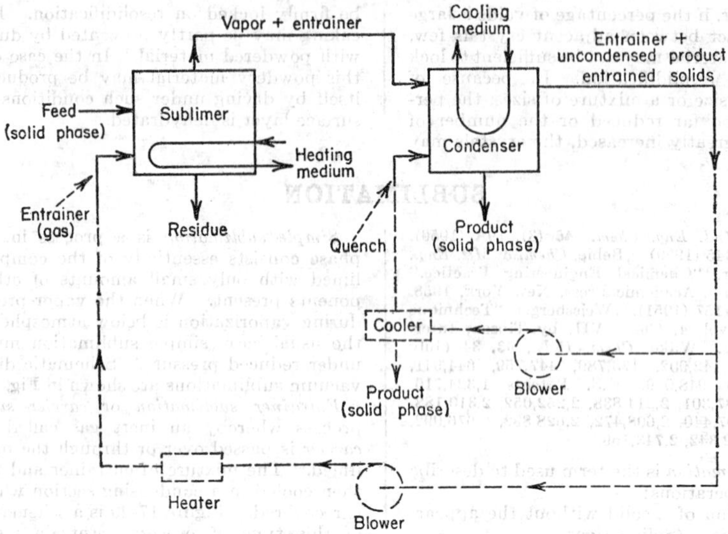

FIG. 17-30. Entrainer sublimation with quenching (with or without recirculation).

metastable equilibrium exhibited by certain substances in which the liquid phase can exist at a pressure below the triple-point pressure.

The *sublimation point* of a substance is the temperature at which the vapor pressure of the solid phase is equal to the total pressure of the gas phase in contact with it (analogous to boiling point of a liquid).

The *snow point* of a gas mixture is the temperature at which the vapor pressure of the sublimable component is equal to the actual partial pressure of that component in the gas mixture (analogous to dew point).

Sublimand refers to the initial sublimable material before it is vaporized; *sublimate* refers to the material after it is condensed from the vapor phase. The term *sublimate* is also used as an adjective that refers to the sublimable component. For example, sublimate vapor is the vapor of the sublimable component.

Uses. Sublimation is used as a physical method of separation of components. In purification, the product itself is usually the sublimable component, while the principal impurities remain as residue. In some cases, the impurities are sublimable, leaving the desired product as residue. Sublimation is useful as a means of removal of components from a reaction mixture or a process stream. It is used as a method of obtaining products of a particular crystal structure, particle size, or shape. It may also be used as a method for controlled introduction of a component into a reaction system by vaporization of the solid into a gas stream. Where product decomposition or corrosion becomes significant at distillation temperatures, sublimation may be the preferred method of purification, since operating temperatures are usually considerably lower than in a corresponding distillation. Sublimation sometimes replaces solvent extraction or crystallization operations if the available solvents create difficulties concerning safety, handling, purity, or physical characteristics of the product.

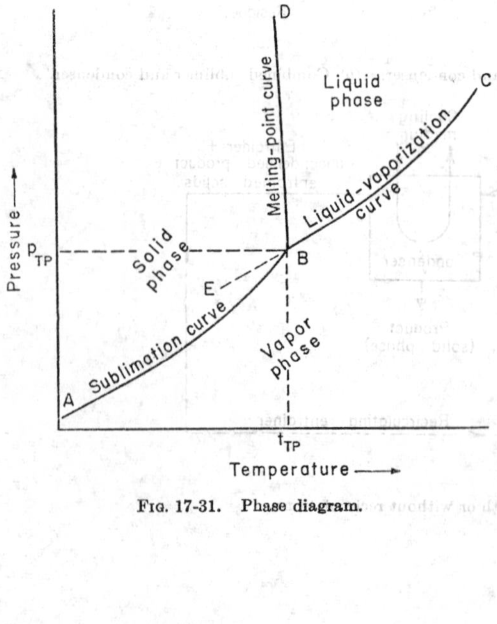

FIG. 17-31. Phase diagram.

Limiting Factors. The rate at which sublimation may be carried out depends on the rate-limiting process in a series of operations:

1. *Rate of heat flow to material in sublimer.* If the feed material is a solid at sublimer temperatures, as is the case for true sublimation, the rate of heat flow is apt to be low. If the material is a liquid, as in pseudo sublimation, the rate of heat flow is usually much greater. Rates may be increased considerably by agitation or by use of a preheated entrainer passed through the solid or liquid material in the sublimer. Sometimes an inert liquid with a low vapor pressure may be mixed with the solid to increase heat-transfer rates.

2. *Rate of change from solid phase to gas phase at constant temperature.* In practical sublimations, the phase change from solid to vapor is not the governing rate for the over-all process. Theory is discussed by Alty [*Proc. Roy. Soc.* (*London*), **A161**, 68 (1937)].

3. *Rate of transport of mass from vaporizing zone to condensing zone.* In simple sublimation, this rate is governed by the diffusion of sublimable vapors between the two zones. The diffusion rate is a function of the properties of the vapor molecules and also of the physical path from sublimer to condenser. The driving force causing this mass transfer is the difference between the partial pressure of the sublimable material in the sub-

limer and the vapor pressure of the material at the condenser temperature. In entrainer sublimation, this mass transfer is governed by the rate of flow of entrainer from the sublimer to the condenser.

4. *Rate of change from gas to solid phase.* This rate is determined by the rate at which heat is removed from the gas phase and from the solid phase that is subsequently formed. In a sublimation where no cold entrainer (quench) is added to the condenser, the gas-film coefficient between the vapor and condensing surface usually is governing. Over-all heat-transfer coefficients in this case are generally in the range of 0.5 to 2 B.t.u./(hr.)(sq. ft.)(°F.). Extremely rapid rates of cooling can be obtained by mixing cold entrainer directly with the vapor or by quenching the vapor stream by direct contact with an inert liquid.

5. *Rate of heat flow from the solid.* This rate is a function of the physical form (particle size, etc.) and thermal properties of the solid.

DESIGN CALCULATIONS

Simple Sublimation. In a simple vacuum sublimation, if the product is the sublimable component, some product will be lost because of removal of vapor along with the non-condensables by the pump. The fraction lost f_1 may be calculated by means of the equation

$$f_1 = \frac{N_L(p_c/E_c)}{E_s p_s(1 + N_L) - \Delta p - (p_c/E_c)} \qquad (17\text{-}11)$$

where N_L = total moles of gas leakage into system per mole of material vaporized in sublimer; p_c = vapor pressure of sublimate at condenser gas outlet temperature; p_s = vapor pressure of sublimate at sublimer temperature; E_c = relative saturation at condenser outlet ($= p_c/p_c'$); E_s = relative saturation at sublimer outlet ($= p_s'/p_s$); p_c' = actual partial pressure of sublimate in effluent stream from condenser; p_s' = actual partial pressure of sublimate in stream leaving sublimer; Δp = pressure drop due to gas and vapor flow between sublimer and condenser.

Equation (17-11) may be rearranged as follows to solve for allowable leakage into the system:

$$N_L = \frac{f_1[E_s p_s - \Delta p - (p_c/E_c)]}{(p_c/E_c) - f_1 E_s p_s} \qquad (17\text{-}12)$$

For the ideal case where pressure drop Δp between sublimer and condenser is zero and the solid and vapor phases are in true equilibrium with one another in both units ($E_c = 1$, $E_s = 1$), Eq. (17-11) reduces to

$$f_1 = \frac{N_L p_c}{p_s(1 + N_L) - p_c} \qquad (17\text{-}13)$$

Equation (17-13) is equivalent to that developed by Nord (*loc. cit.*).

Product losses can also occur as a result of entrainment of solid particles in the gas stream leaving the condenser. There is no convenient method of calculating these losses, since they are a function not only of the characteristics of the product in the condenser but also of the particular mechanical design of the equipment.

Example 1. A material is to be purified by simple vacuum sublimation at a sublimer temperature of 150°C. and a condenser outlet temperature of 80°C. The total amount vaporized is 10 lb.-moles/hr. Loss of product is to be limited to 0.1 per cent (f_1 = 0.001). Calculate the maximum allowable air leakage into the system in standard cubic feet per minute. Assume E_c = 0.98, E_s = 0.90, and Δp = 1.0 mm. Hg.

Vapor-pressure data on the material are as follows:

Temp., °C.	Vapor Pressure, mm. Hg, abs.
150	13 ($= p_s$)
80	0.06 ($= p_c$)

Solution. Substituting the proper values into Eq. (17-12) gives

$$N_L = \frac{0.001[(0.90)(13) - 1.0 - (0.06/0.98)]}{(0.06/0.98) - (0.001)(0.90)(13)}$$

$$= 0.215 \text{ mole/mole of product vaporized}$$

Since moles of product vaporized = 10/60 = 0.1667 mole/min., allowable air leakage = (0.1667)(0.215) = 0.0358 mole/min., or (0.0358)(359) = 12.9 standard cu. ft./min.

Entrainer Sublimation. The fraction f_2 uncondensed per pass is calculated from the equation

$$f_2 = \frac{p_c(N_c + N_s)}{E_c P_c - p_c} \qquad (17\text{-}14)$$

where N_s = moles of entrainer added to sublimer per mole of material vaporized,

$$N_s = \frac{P_s - E_s p_s}{E_s p_s} \qquad (17\text{-}15)$$

and P_c = total absolute pressure in condenser; P_s = total absolute pressure in sublimer; other symbols as for Eq. (17-11).

If the sublimer temperature is below the triple point, the sublimate collected in the condenser will always be in the solid state without the appearance of a liquid phase during any part of the condensation process. If the sublimer temperature is above the triple point and there is not sufficient pressure drop from the sublimer to the condenser, a certain minimum amount of entrainer must be added to the condenser in order to prevent sintering of the sublimate. Sintering is brought about by formation of solid from the liquid state. The minimum quantity of entrainer N_c to be added to the condenser to prevent sintering is

$$(N_c)_{\min} = \frac{P_c}{p_{TP}} - \frac{P_s}{E_s p_s} \qquad (17\text{-}16)$$

where p_{TP} = vapor pressure at the triple point.

If P_c/p_{TP} is equal to or less than $P_s/E_s p_s$, no cold entrainer is required for prevention of sintering. However, cold entrainer in amounts greater than minimum is often added to the condenser in order to increase the over-all cooling rate and/or to decrease the cooling surface required. The addition of cold entrainer tends to produce more of a snowlike or powdery sublimate, whereas condensation on a cooling surface tends to form a more crystalline deposit.

It can be shown that Eq. (17-14), which applies to entrainer sublimation, is quite similar to Eq. (17-11), which was developed for simple sublimation. Referring to Eq. (17-11), it will be noted that the quantity $[E_s p_s (1 + N_L) - \Delta p]$ is equal to the condenser pressure P_c. Thus, Eq. (17-11) may be written in the form

$$f_1 = \frac{p_c N_L}{E_c P_c - p_c} \qquad (17\text{-}17)$$

The similarity between Eqs. (17-17) and (17-14) is apparent. Thus the gas that leaks into a simple vacuum sublimation unit is analogous to the entrainer purposely added to an entrainer-type sublimation unit. For a given set of operating conditions, the fraction uncondensed is directly proportional to the quantity of entrainer passing through the condenser. Since $(N_c + N_s)$ is greater than N_L, it follows that the fraction uncondensed per pass through the condenser will be greater in entrainer sublimation than in simple sublimation for the same operating conditions. Thus recirculation of the entrainer is usually necessary in the former process in order to minimize over-all losses of product.

The principal **advantages** of entrainer over simple sublimation are that it is more easily adapted to continuous processing, permits more rapid evaporation rates, and produces a snowlike or powdery deposit.

Equipment. Many types of equipment are used in sublimation processes. Some types of equipment are designed specifically for sublimation while others are adaptations of existing types of drying, distillation, heat transfer, or solids-handling equipment. For example, tray, rotary, or turbodryers are often used as sublimers. Rotary dryers, jacketed vessels, tray dryers, air-cooled tanks, and scraped-wall vessels may be used as condensers. The general references previously cited give more complete details on specific designs used.

Example 2. A material is to be purified by sublimation using air as the entrainer. The sublimer is to operate at 140°C. at a pressure of 750 mm. Hg abs. The condenser is to operate at 80°C. and 740 mm. Hg abs. Vaporization rate is to be 5 lb.-moles/hr. The relative saturation in the sublimer is 0.75; that in the condenser is 0.98.

Vapor-pressure data:

Temp., °C.	Vapor Pressure
140	$p_s = 6.6$ mm. Hg
80	$p_c = 0.06$

Calculate (*a*) the percentage recovery of product per pass through the condenser if no cold entrainer is added to the condenser; (*b*) the air-circulation rate in standard cubic feet per minute.

Solution. From Eq. (17-15),

$$N_s = \frac{P_s - E_s p_s}{E_s p_s} = \frac{750 - (0.75)(6.6)}{(0.75)(6.6)}$$

$$= 151 \text{ moles air/mole product vaporized}$$

Applying Eq. (17-14),

$$f_2 = \frac{p_c(N_c + N_s)}{E_c P_c - p_c} = \frac{(0.06)(0 + 151)}{(0.98)(740) - 0.06} = 0.012$$

$$\text{Per cent recovery per pass} = 100 - (0.012)(100) = 98.8$$

$$\text{Air-circulation rate} = \frac{(151)(5)(359)}{60}$$

$$= 4520 \text{ standard cu. ft./min.}$$

Example 3. Vapor-pressure data on a certain compound are as follows:

Temp., °C.	Vapor Pressure, mm. Hg abs.
30	0.17
99 (triple point)	20.0
111	30.0

The sublimer is operated at 111°C. and 740 mm. Hg abs. and the condenser outlet gas stream is at 30°C. and 720 mm. Hg abs. Nitrogen is used as the entrainer. To prevent sintering, the actual quantity of nitrogen for quenching in the condenser is twice the minimum. The product is vaporized at a rate of 5 lb.-moles/hr. The relative saturation in the sublimer is 0.90 and that in the condenser is 0.98.

Calculate (*a*) the nitrogen required for quenching in standard cubic feet per minute; (*b*) the total nitrogen circulated in standard cubic feet per minute; (*c*) the percentage of product uncondensed per pass through the condenser.

Solution. (*a*) *Nitrogen required for quenching.* From Eq. (17-16),

$$(N_c)_{\min} = \frac{720}{20} - \frac{740}{(0.90)(30)}$$

$$= 8.59 \text{ moles nitrogen/mole product vaporized}$$

Actual amount used is twice the minimum, or $N_c = (2)(8.59) = 17.2$ moles/mole product vaporized.

$$\text{Flow rate of nitrogen} = \frac{(17.2)(5)(359)}{60}$$

$$= 515 \text{ standard cu. ft./min.}$$

(*b*) *Total nitrogen required.* From Eq. (17-15),

$$N_s = \frac{740 - (0.90)(30)}{(0.90)(30)}$$

$$= 26.4 \text{ moles nitrogen/mole product vaporized}$$

$$\text{Flow rate of nitrogen in sublimer} = \frac{(26.4)(5)(359)}{60}$$

$$= 790 \text{ standard cu. ft./min.}$$

$$\text{Total nitrogen requirement} = 515 + 790$$

$$= 1305 \text{ standard cu. ft./min.}$$

(*c*) *Product uncondensed per pass.* From Eq. (17-14),

$$f_2 = \frac{(0.17)(17.2 + 26.4)}{(0.98)(720) - 0.17} = 0.0105$$

$$\text{Per cent uncondensed per pass} = 1.05$$

FREEZE-DRYING

REFERENCES: Bradish, Brain, and McFarlane, *Nature*, **159**, 28 (1947). Burton, *Food Inds.*, **19**, 107, 617 (1947). Flosdorf, *J. Chem. Ed.*, **22**, 470 (1945). Flosdorf, "Freeze-Drying," Reinhold, New York, 1949. Flosdorf, Hull, and Mudd, *J. Immunol.*, **50**, 21 (1945). Flosdorf, Stokes, and Mudd, *J. Am. Med. Assoc.*, **115**, 1095 (1940). Friedman, *Ind. Eng. Chem.*, **39**, 20 (1947). Harris, "Biological Applications of Freezing and Drying," Academic Press, New York, 1954. Heiss and Schachinger, *Food Tech.*, **5**, 211 (1951). Ikan, *Chem. Eng. Progress*, **43**, 348 (1947). Sluder, Olsen, and Kenyon, *Food Tech.*, **1**, 85 (1947). U.S. Patents: A list of 58 patents is given by Flosdorf ("Freeze-Drying," p. 229, cited above).

Applications. Freeze-drying is used for a large variety of products which cannot be dried satisfactorily by the more usual methods. Some of its applications are shown in Table 17-2.

The principal **advantages** of freeze-drying have been summarized as follows by Flosdorf ("Freeze-Drying," Reinhold, New York, 1949):

1. Low temperatures avoid chemical changes in labile components.
2. Loss of volatile constituents (other than water) is minimized.
3. Product may be dried without foaming.
4. Constituents of the dried material remain dispersed.
5. Coagulation of the constituents is minimized.
6. Case-hardening is eliminated.
7. Sterility is maintained.
8. Oxidation of the product is minimized or eliminated.

Basic Principles. Freeze-drying is a special case of **sublimation.** In most applications water is the volatile constituent to be removed. Water in the frozen or solid state is sublimed and is removed from the material directly as a vapor. Since the vapor pressure of ice is considerably below atmospheric pressure, freeze-drying requires **high vacuum.** If the water present in the material were in the pure state, then theoretically

Table 17-2. Applications of Freeze-Drying

	Food Products	
Fruit juices	Clams	Tea extracts
Vegetables	Fish	Meats
Vegetable juices	Coffee extracts	Milk
Oysters		
	Medical	
Convalescent human serum	Human milk, goats' milk	
Human blood plasma	Antibiotics	
Normal blood serum	Hormones, amino acids, bile, etc.	
Animal sera	Vitamins, pharmaceuticals	
Concentrated globulins	Specimens for electron microscopy	
Bacterial and viral cultures	Histology and cytology	
Bacterial and viral vaccines	Bone, skin, membrane, and artery grafts	

it would be possible to freeze-dry materials at or near 0°C. at a pressure of about 4.6 mm. Hg abs. (4600 microns). However, the water usually exists in the form of a solution, a eutectic mixture, or in a combined state. It is therefore necessary to cool the material to temperatures below 0°C. in order to keep the water in the solid phase. In actual practice most freeze-drying is performed at temperatures of −10° to −40°C., with corresponding pressures of about 2000 to 100 microns (see Table 17-3).

Table 17-3. Vapor Pressure and Heat of Sublimation of Water Ice

Temp., °C.	Vapor pressure, mm. Hg	Vapor pressure, Microns Hg	Heat of sublimation, B.t.u./lb.
0	4.579	4579	1220
−10	1.950	1950	1210
−20	0.776	776	1200
−30	0.286	286	1192
−40	0.097	97	1186

Drying rates are divided into the usual constant-rate and falling-rate periods as shown in Fig. 17-32. During the constant-rate period, solid sublimes at a rate which is a function of the heat input and the heat of sublimation of the solid. The **sublimation rate** $dW/d\theta$ may be expressed in lb./hr. by the equation

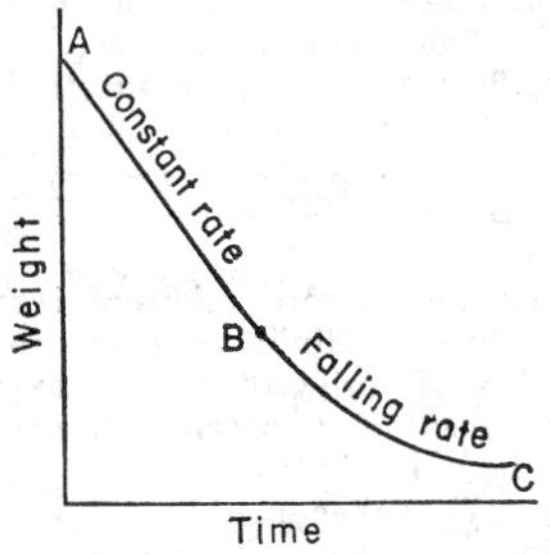

FIG. 17-32. Drying curve, freeze-drying.

$$\frac{dW}{d\theta} = \frac{Q}{\lambda_0} = \frac{UA\,\Delta t}{\lambda_0} \tag{17-18}$$

where Q = heat absorbed, B.t.u./hr.; λ_0 = heat of sublimation, B.t.u./lb.; U = over-all heat-transfer coefficient, B.t.u./(hr.)(sq. ft.)(°F.); A = heat-transfer area, sq. ft.; Δt = temperature difference between heat source and ice, °F.

Rate of heat input is proportional to the heat-transfer area and the temperature difference between the heat source and the ice temperature. The value of U depends on the method of heat transfer. With the usual heat-transfer media, conduction predominates if the material is in good physical contact with the heat-transfer surface. Radiation predominates if there is poor contact with the heat-transfer surfaces or when radiant-heat sources are intentionally employed. For conduction, values of U are sometimes in the range of 0.5 to 2.0 B.t.u./(hr.)(sq. ft.)(°F.). For radiation, values of U may be computed by the usual methods using a combined emissivity factor of 0.6 to 0.8.

Heat-transfer area is governed by mechanical design of the equipment. Temperature difference is governed by the temperatures of the heating medium and the ice. Maximum allowable temperature of the heating medium is such that none of the ice melts in any part of the material being dried.

If puffing does not occur, materials dried in layers of thicknesses of a few millimeters to about 30 mm. at temperatures of −10° to −20°C. give drying rates of about 1 mm. depth per hour during the constant-rate period (Flosdorf, *op. cit.*, p. 43). For thin layers of these same materials, the rate may be increased from two to four times; for the more difficult products the rate may be as low as 0.2 mm. depth per hour.

For many substances, 95 per cent of the total water that is removed requires about 80 per cent of the total drying time (constant-rate period). The remaining 5 per cent requires about 20 per cent of the total drying time (Flosdorf, *op. cit.*, p. 41).

Figure 17-33 is a schematic diagram of the **basic elements** of a freeze-drying process. The essential requirements are indicated by the numerals in the figure.

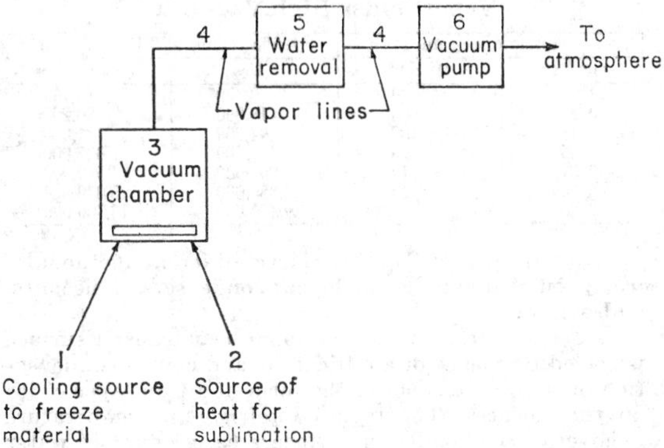

FIG. 17-33. Basic elements of freeze-drying process.

1. *Cooling Source to Freeze the Material to Be Dried.* This is accomplished by external cooling sources and/or by self-freezing. If the material is subjected quickly to a high vacuum, the material tends to cool itself by the evaporation of water. If the rate of heat loss by this means is appreciably greater than the rate of heat absorption by the material from its immediate surroundings, then self-freezing is practical. Otherwise, additional cooling must be used to freeze the material initially. Prefreezing of the material may be accomplished in a separate step externally or it may be performed *in situ* in the vacuum chamber by means of a refrigerant circulated through a jacket or cooling coils within the chamber.

2. *Source of Heat for Sublimation.* In order to sublime 1 lb. of ice, approximately 1200 B.t.u. of heat must be supplied (see Table 17-3). For small quantities to be dried the atmospheric surroundings may supply sufficient heat for this purpose. For most applications, however, external heat sources are required. Hot water circulated through coils and jackets, electric-resistance heating elements, and infrared heating are some of the methods used.

3. *Vacuum Chamber.* The vacuum chamber may be compared with the sublimer in an ordinary sublimation unit. It must be constructed so as to minimize air leakage into the system, to support properly the material to be dried, and to provide a source of heat for sublimation, and it must be equipped with a sufficiently large outlet for the water vapor to escape with a minimum pressure drop under peak-load conditions. It should also be designed for easy loading and unloading.

The vacuum chamber may take a variety of forms, depending on the amounts and characteristics of the material to be dried. In some cases, the chamber may consist merely of a glass bottle which also later serves as the marketing container for the product. In other cases, the vacuum chamber may be a large vacuum-shelf dryer equipped with cooling and heating coils or jackets. Rotary vacuum dryers and scraped-wall cylinders are also used. Air locks are often used on continuous systems for introduction and removal of the material in order to avoid breaking the vacuum.

4. *Vapor Line.* The vapor line conducts the water vapor and non-condensable gases away from the vacuum chamber to the water-removal system. Because of the high specific volumes of water vapor and air at the high vacuums employed, the vapor line is usually very large compared with most other fluid-transport lines. One pound of water vapor at 0°C. and 100 microns occupies a volume of 151,000 cu. ft. (see Table 17-4).

Table 17-4. Specific Volumes of Air and Water Vapor under High Vacuum

Absolute pressure		Specific volume at 0°C., cu. ft./lb.	
mm. Hg	Microns	Air	Water vapor
1	1000	9,420	15,100
0.5	500	18,800	30,200
0.1	100	94,200	151,000
0.05	50	188,000	302,000
0.01	10	942,000	1,510,000
0.005	5	1,880,000	3,020,000
0.001	1	9,420,000	15,100,000

5. *Water-removal System.* Three different methods of water removal may be employed: condensers, desiccants, and pumps.

a. Condensers. In this method a heat-transfer surface is cooled by means of a refrigerant and causes condensation of the water vapor in the form of a thin layer of ice on the surface. The required refrigerant temperature is governed by condenser surface area, amount of water vapor removed, thickness of the ice layer, temperature of the frozen material in the vacuum chamber, and amount of non-condensable gases in the system. Ice is removed intermittently by melting it with a heated fluid circulated through the condenser or on a continuous basis by means of scraper blades.

Hygroscopic liquids at low temperatures may also be used for direct condensation of water vapor. The liquid flows in a wetted-wall system or is sprayed into a condensing chamber where the water vapor condenses and is absorbed by the hygroscopic liquid. To operate satisfactorily, this type of system requires a liquid which has low vapor pressure, low viscosity, and high affinity for water.

b. Desiccants. Chemical desiccants remove water vapor by chemical combination. Phosphorus pentoxide reacts with water to form metaphosphoric acid. Calcium chloride, calcium sulfate, and lithium chloride form hydrates. These desiccants are generally used for small-scale applications.

Physical desiccants remove water vapor by adsorption on their active surfaces. Silica gel, alumina, and special zeolites ("molecular sieves," "microtraps") are the principal adsorbents used commercially.

When water is removed by the desiccant, heat is evolved. In order to avoid excessive temperature rise of the desiccant, external cooling is often necessary.

c. Pumps. Water vapor may be removed simultaneously with the non-condensable gases by means of pumps. These may be of the mechanical oil-sealed rotary or the steam-ejector type. For oil-sealed rotary pumps, provision must be made for removal of the condensed water from the oil. This is usually accomplished by recirculating the oil through a centrifuge, desiccant, or suitable filter. Water that is removed by a steam ejector combines with the cooling water used for condensation of the steam. Use of pumps for water-vapor removal is economical for relatively small installations but is not economical for systems where large volumetric capacities are required. For the larger installations a condenser or desiccant is usually used, followed by a pump to remove the non-condensable gases.

6. *Vacuum Pump.* Function of the vacuum pump is to maintain a low pressure in the main vacuum chamber where sublimation occurs. It must compress the low-pressure gases and vapors to slightly above atmospheric pressure for proper discharge to the atmosphere. Single-stage rotary pumps are used for pressures down to about 100 microns Hg. For very tight vacuum systems, the approximate required size of rotary vacuum pump may be estimated by assuming 1 cu. ft./min. pump displacement per cubic foot of total volume of the system evacuated (Flosdorf, *op. cit.,* p. 193). A four-stage steam ejector can evacuate to about 500 microns, while a five-stage ejector can attain about 100 microns.

Design of Vacuum Lines. Flow is laminar in vacuum lines at conditions encountered in freeze-drying applications. Pressure drop ΔP in lb./sq. ft. may be calculated by means of the Fanning equation

$$\Delta P = \frac{fL\rho u^2}{2gD} \tag{17-19}$$

where f = friction factor; L = length of line, ft.; ρ = density of fluid at average line temperature and pressure, lb./cu. ft.; u = fluid velocity, ft./sec.; g = acceleration of gravity, 32.2 ft./(sec.)^2; D = internal diameter, ft. Equation (17-19) reduces to

$$\Delta p = \frac{106VLZ}{d^4} = \frac{1.77WLZ}{\rho d^4} \tag{17-20}$$

where Δp = pressure drop, microns Hg; V = volume rate of flow at average fluid temperature and pressure, cu. ft./min.; Z = viscosity of fluid at average line temperature, centipoise; d = internal diameter, in.; W = weight rate of flow, lb./hr.

For air, Eq. (17-20) becomes

$$\Delta p = \frac{(1.81 + 0.0055t)VL}{d^4} = \frac{(1.81 + 0.0055t)WL}{60\rho d^4} \tag{17-21}$$

where t = average fluid temperature, °C. For water vapor, Eq. (17-20) becomes

$$\Delta p = \frac{(0.94 + 0.0037t)VL}{d^4} = \frac{(0.94 + 0.0037t)WL}{60\rho d^4} \tag{17-22}$$

Equations (17-21) and (17-22) are applicable at fluid temperatures of −50° to +50°C. They may be used for calculating pipe diameter if pressure drop is known. For design purposes, line size may be estimated by assuming that the pressure drop is equal to 10 per cent of the upstream absolute pressure. Line sizes may then be approximated by means of the following equations:

For air,

$$d = \left(\frac{1.8 \times 10^8 \rho VL}{p^2}\right)^{0.25} = \left(\frac{3 \times 10^6 WL}{p^2}\right)^{0.25} \tag{17-23}$$

For water vapor,

$$d = \left(\frac{1.5 \times 10^8 \rho VL}{p^2}\right)^{0.25} = \left(\frac{2.5 \times 10^6 WL}{p^2}\right)^{0.25} \tag{17-24}$$

where p = average line pressure, microns Hg.

Example. Calculate the pressure drop in a vacuum line 8.0 in. inside diameter, 10 ft. long, carrying 8.82 lb./hr. of water vapor at an average line pressure of 300 microns at −10°C.

Solution.

$$\rho = \left(\frac{18}{359}\right)\left(\frac{300}{760{,}000}\right)\left(\frac{273}{263}\right) = 0.0000205 \text{ lb./cu. ft.}$$

Using Eq. (17-22) gives a pressure drop of

$$\Delta p = \frac{[0.94 + (0.0037)(-10)](8.82)(10)}{(60)(0.0000205)(8)^4} = 15.8 \text{ microns Hg}$$

MOLECULAR DISTILLATION

Definitions. Three broad classes of high-vacuum distillation can be discerned (see Table 17-5): (1) *conventional* apparatus, generally consisting of a boiler, fractionating column, and condenser, operated under high vacuum; (2) *unobstructed-path* distillation operated under high vacuum; and (3) *molecular* distillation, where the vapor path is unobstructed and the condenser is separated from the evaporator by a distance less than the mean free path of the evaporating molecules. This section deals with categories 2 and 3; "high" vacuum is defined as a pressure of residual gas so low that further reduction does not change the performance of the apparatus.

Table 17-5. High Vacuum Manometric Range

Class of still	Laboratory size, mm.	Industrial size, mm. Hg
1. Conventional stills	0.01–0.1	0.1 –5.0
2. Unobstructed-path stills	0.01–0.1	0.001 –0.01
3. Molecular stills	0.001	0.0001–0.001

Molecular and short-path distillations are generally conducted at pressures of 1 to 7μ, rather less than 1μ being readily available in the laboratory, whereas about 3 to 30μ have proved economical in industry (μ = micron = 0.001 mm. Hg). The differences between unobstructed-path and molecular distillation lie in dimensions and operating conditions; thus one piece of apparatus can be either a short-path or a molecular still, according to the rate of distillation and the pressure of residual gas.

Simple Molecular Still. A simple and practical molecular still with an evaporative efficiency of about 0.5 is formed by an electrically heated tray suspended in an evacuated test tube (Fig. 17-34). An evaporative

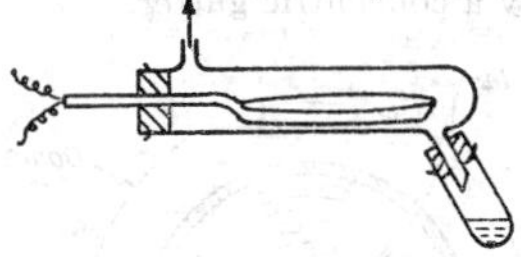

FIG. 17-34. Simple molecular still.

efficiency of 0.5 means that 50 per cent of all the molecules evaporating are able to leave the containing cup at first try and reach the condenser to be completely condensed without re-evaporation.

An all-glass molecular pot still is shown in heavy outline superimposed on a conventional still and condenser in Fig. 17-35. Heat is applied beneath the still, and the ceiling is cooled by ice or a blast of air. Liquid condenses on the ceiling and drops into the receiver. Considering any typical element of liquid surface *S*, a molecule can evaporate in any direction embraced by a solid angle of 180 deg. Those molecules which proceed within the wide cone *m*, *s*, *m′* will condense on the ceiling and be collected; the rest will condense on the walls and return to the still. Contrast this with the conventional still where only those molecules within the narrow cone *d*, *s*, *d′* will pass up the neck of the flask, and only an exceedingly small fraction *s*, *r*, *r′* will wander into the receiver.

Ordinary laboratory "vacuum" distillations are done at 1 to 10 mm. Hg in order to transfer the vapor rapidly enough to complete the distillation in reasonable time. The efficiency of transfer of the molecular pot still of Fig. 17-36 is 0.4 to 0.6; that of the conventional still is 0.001 to 0.0001. Stated another way, an evaporating

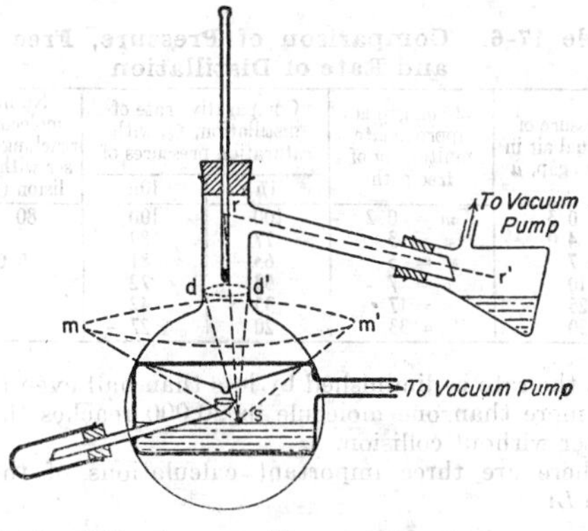

FIG. 17-35. Molecular pot still, superimposed on conventional still and condenser.

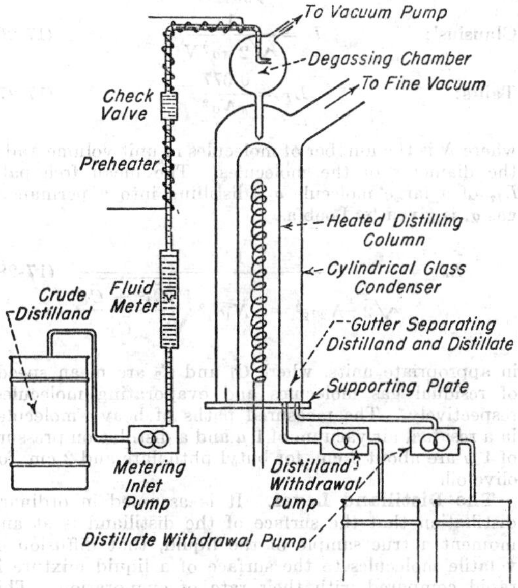

FIG. 17-36. Falling-film molecular still.

molecule is likely to escape permanently at the first or second try in a molecular still, whereas it may return to the distilland a thousand times before finally reaching the exit of an ordinary vacuum still. Temperature of distillation and hazard of decomposition are reduced in proportion to the lowered pressure of the molecular still.

Mean-free-path Considerations. The definition of molecular distillation as "within the mean free path of the emergent molecules" implies that, if the molecules suffer collision of any sort, particularly with molecules of residual gas, they will be delayed in reaching the condenser or may return to the distilland; distillation will be slowed and will become progressively more equilibrant in kind. Burch showed how the chance that a molecule will reach the evaporator at one strike should vary with the distances, in multiples of the free path. Cox and Hickman measured the change in rate of distillation with change in pressure of residual gas and found that collisions mattered less than formerly supposed. The comparison of pressure, free path, and rate of distillation is given in Table 17-6, which shows

Table 17-6. Comparison of Pressure, Free Path, and Rate of Distillation

Pressure of residual air in 2-cm. gap, μ	2-cm. gap is approximate multiple m of free path	Comparative rate of distillation, %, with saturation pressures of		Number of molecules, %, reaching condenser without collision (Burch)
		1μ	10μ	
0.3	m = 0.2	100	100	80
4.0	= 3	77	89	
7	= 5	63	81	0.005
10	= 7	53	72	
25	= 17	35	42	
50	= 33	20	27	

that the rate is diminished by less than half even though not more than one molecule in 20,000 reaches the condenser without collision.

There are three important calculations of the free path L:

Maxwell's: $$L = \frac{1}{\frac{4}{3}\pi\sigma^2 N} \tag{17-25}$$

Clausius': $$L = \frac{1}{\sqrt{2}\,\pi\sigma^2 N} \tag{17-26}$$

Tait's: $$L_T = \frac{0.677}{\pi N\sigma^2} \tag{17-27}$$

where N is the number of molecules in unit volume and σ the diameter of the molecules. The mean free path L_{σ_2} of a large molecule σ_2, distilling into a permanent gas σ, is given by Loeb as

$$L_{\sigma_2} = \frac{1}{\sqrt{2}\,\pi N_2\sigma_2^2 + \pi N_1\sigma_1^2\sqrt{\dfrac{\bar{C}_1^2 + \bar{C}_2^2}{\bar{C}_2}}} \tag{17-28}$$

in appropriate units, where C_1 and C_2 are mean speeds of residual gas molecules and evaporating molecules, respectively. The measured paths of heavy molecules in a residual air vacuum of 1 μ and a distillation pressure of 1 μ are about 3 cm. for butyl phthalate and 2 cm. for olive oil.

The Distilland Layer. It is assumed in ordinary distillation that the surface of the distilland is at any moment a true sample of the liquid, that diffusion of volatile molecules to the surface of a liquid mixture is rapid compared with their rate of evaporation. This condition is demonstrably unfulfilled in the molecular still, where convection due to ebullition is absent and high viscosities and high molecular weights impede diffusion. Efficient molecular distillation requires mechanical renewal of the surface film. This can be done in three ways: (1) by vigorous agitation of the liquid in bulk, *i.e.*, the stirred pot still; (2) by gravitational flow in cascade or vertical falling film; or (3) by mechanical spreading in thin films. The last is accomplished by transferring the distilland to a heated roller or traveling band or by using centrifugal force to spread it on a rotating disk, cone, or cylinder. The heated rotating cone and the wiped cylinder are currently the preferred forms of evaporator.

Commercial Apparatus. **Falling-film stills** have been made in single and multiple units, in sizes ranging from a few centimeters to 50 cm. diameter, 2 to 10 meters high, with through-puts ranging from 1 to 60 liters/hr. The elements of construction are shown in Fig. 17-36. The distilland is admitted through a metering device into the vacuum where it is degassed in one or more preliminary vessels and then allowed to pass on to the walls of a heated polished metal cylinder stationed within a concentric cooled condensing cylinder. The space between the two is maintained under high vacuum (1 to 5 μ) by fast pumps. Most falling-film stills use chromium-plated evaporators, housed within tall glass cylinders.

Centrifugal stills, shown diagrammatically in Fig. 17-37, consist of a housing or base plate covered by a lid

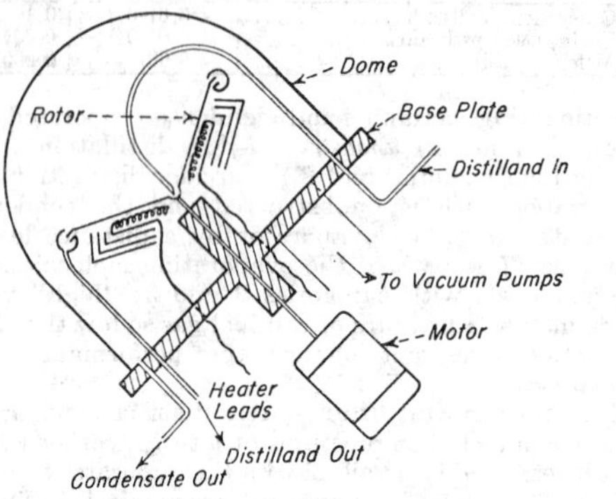

FIG. 17-37. Centrifugal molecular still.

or dome. A rotor is supported on a shaft that passes through a bearing and stuffing box attached in the base plate. A radiant electrical heater warms the rotor, and radiation is conserved by baffles placed at the back and sides of the heater. Distilland is admitted from a preliminary degasser through a feed pipe to a depression at the center of the rotor, whence it is spun rapidly outward in an exceedingly thin, uniform layer. At the edge, the distilland, spent after evaporation of the volatile constituents, is picked up by a scoop (Fig. 17-38) or collected by a concentric gutter.

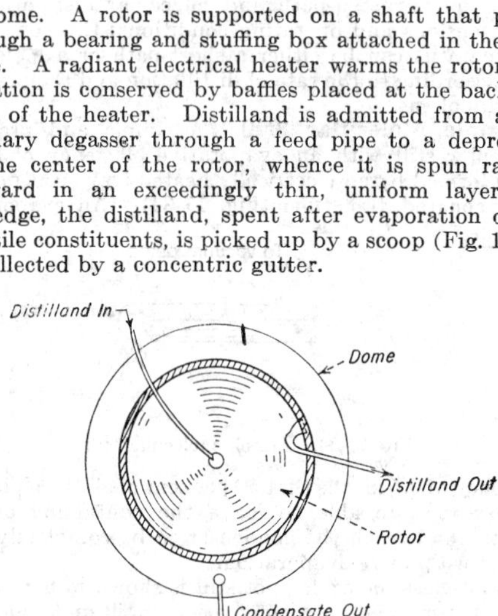

FIG. 17-38. Distilland flow in centrifugal still.

Since the distilland is held on the evaporator by centrifugal force, it is independent of gravity, and the rotor may be horizontal or vertical or even upside down. A convenient angle for small stills (12 to 36 in. diameter) is with the evaporator facing upward at about 45 deg. The rotors of larger stills are generally cones instead of plates, and they spin on vertical shafts. The condenser hangs within the cone, and means are provided for pumping the condensates, collected separately from three concentric zones, over the rim. Stills of this type have evaporating areas of about 4.5 sq. meters and handle 200 to 700 liters of distilland per hour, collecting 2 to 400 liters of distillate per hour, according to the object of treatment. The consumption of power is about 100 kw., 60 per cent for heating the still, the remainder for pumps and subsidiary equipment.

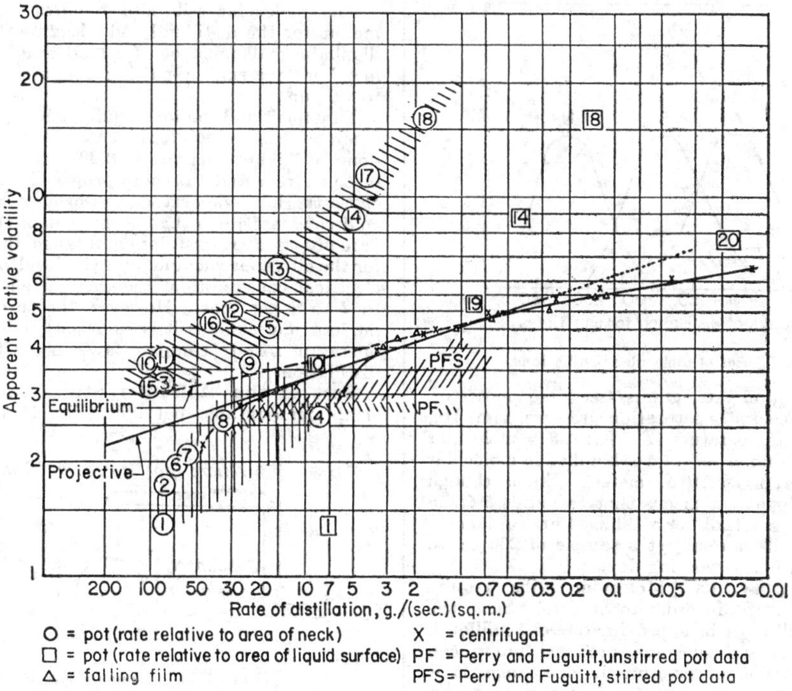

FIG. 17-39. Separatory power of various stills as a function of rate. [*Hickman and Trevoy, Ind. Eng. Chem.*, **44**, 1908 (1952).]

In the last few years the falling-film still has been improved greatly by the addition of **wipers**. The inside of the vertical tubular container is made the evaporator and the inner concentric tube the condenser. Carbon or Teflon wipers, held in a cylindrical cage, are rotated between evaporator and condenser and agitate the distilling surface many times each second. Because of a very slight splashing, it is customary to place a porous baffle between the two surfaces and rotate it with the scrapers. The general design, due to Arthur F. Smith, Rochester, N.Y., is in increasing use for petrochemicals and in heavy industry.

Distillation Efficiency and Rate. It is a safe generalization that all types of unobstructed-path stills provide non-equilibrant distillation. In ordinary distillation of a mixture, the quantities of constituents distilling are proportional to their partial pressures P_1, P_2, . . . , P_n, but, under molecular conditions, the quantities are $\frac{P_1}{\sqrt{M_1}}, \frac{P_2}{\sqrt{M_2}}, \ldots, \frac{P_n}{\sqrt{M_n}}$. Since substances of like molecular weight distill at similar temperatures in natural mixtures of organic substances (*e.g.*, plant or animal fats, sterols, or hormones) the kind of separation available from molecular distillation scarcely differs from equilibrant distillation. It is the degree of thermal exposure that is so markedly less in the molecular still.

The **maximum degree of separation** available in a single pass through a short-path still is "one theoretical molecular plate." Much argument and research have been devoted to defining this unit. It has become obvious that the unit is variable, dependent on conditions, being larger at slow rates of evaporation and most nearly approached when there is great surface agitation. Hickman and Trevoy [*Ind. Eng. Chem.*, **44**, 1908 (1952)] compiled a map (Fig. 17-39) of the behavior of two test fluids, 2-ethyl hexyl sebacate and 2-ethyl hexyl phthalate, in "ideal" high-vacuum stills and the practical stills of the laboratory. Centrifugal, falling-film, and stirred-pot stills all gave optimum separations, defined as one theoretical plate, at absolute rates of evaporation corresponding to vapor pressures of 0.005 mm. Hg or less, but only the centrifugal still yielded near optimum separation at the more usual rates of 0.01 to 0.1 mm. Hg, *e.g.*, in the yield range of 5 to 50 kg./(hr.)(sq. meter). The other types gave useful but lesser separations. The circled numbers of Fig. 17-39 refer to still constructions in the original paper.

The poor separations resulting from a simple act of molecular distillation mean that, in a series of distillates removed from a complex mixture, any given constituent will appear in *some concentration* in every fraction. If the fractions are withdrawn at equal time intervals and uniform increments of temperature, the variation of yield of a component *A* in the distillates follows a smooth probability curve, and this applies also to components *B*, *C*, . . . *N*, so that the concentrations of each overlap according to the scheme shown in Fig. 17-40. The position of the maxima of these curves on the temperature axis, obtained under rigidly standardized conditions, provides the molecular substitute of a boiling point and one that can be made accurate, or at least reproducible, within ±1°C.

The quantitative **rate of distillation,** under truly "projective" conditions of evaporation and complete non-return condensation, is equal to the quantity of material passing across an imaginary area in a saturated vapor of the distilland equal to the area of the evaporating surface and is given numerically by the Knudsen-Langmuir equation

$$w = 0.0583p \sqrt{\frac{M}{T}} \tag{17-29}$$

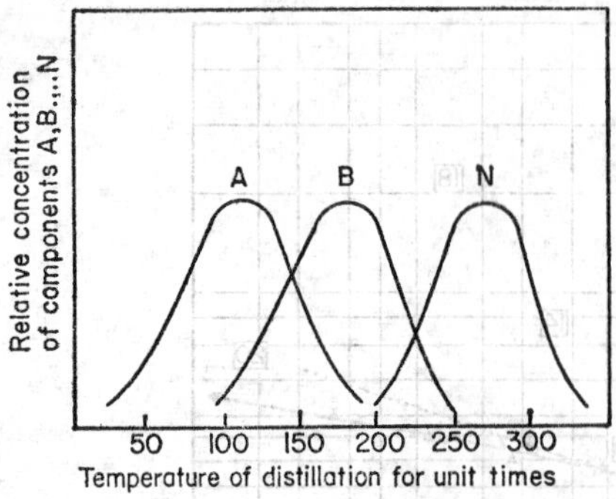

FIG. 17-40. Series of molecular distillations.

where w = distillation rate, grams/(sec.) (sq. meter of evaporating surface); p = saturation pressure, mm. Hg, at the solution temperature T °K.; M = molecular weight. For the kind of substances handled in molecular stills, $w = 0.5$ gram/(sec.)(sq. meter). Small though this figure may appear, it means that two stills 5 ft. in diameter can process a tank car of oil in 24 hr. A laboratory falling-film still can subject a sample of 200 cc. to 15 to 20 passes in half a working day.

Subsidiary Apparatus. Molecular stills require **high-vacuum pumps** in order to operate. Since the pressure in the still must be approximately one-millionth of an atmosphere, and since no practical pump can achieve this reduction of pressure in one stage, it is usual to employ two or more pumps in series, each unit being designed especially for its place in the series. A solitary exception is the laboratory micropot still, which can be evacuated sufficiently well by a rotary oil pump (8 to 12 μ in the still).

The pump that is used for the ultimate vacuum is by general choice the Langmuir **condensation pump.** The laboratory falling-film still, handling one liter/hr. of distilland, requires a condensation pump with a capacity of 100 liters/sec. at 1 to 2 μ, which gas it will pass on to a **mechanical forepump** at a pressure of 0.1 to 0.2 mm. The forepump must have an effective volumetric capacity of at least 1 liter/sec. If it is not desired to employ such a large mechanical pump, a **vapor booster pump** may be inserted between the condensation pump and the mechanical pump. The booster will take in gases at 0.2 mm. and 1 liter volume, compressing them to 0.5 mm. and 0.4 liter volume, which can be handled by the smallest commercial pump.

Industrial centrifugal stills can be operated by large condensation pumps in series with oil-sealed rotary mechanical pumps, capacity 100 to 200 cu. ft./min. The materials being distilled are almost always contaminated with impurities that are volatile at the temperatures and pressures prevailing in the still but condense to liquids under the conditions in the mechanical pump. The sealing fluid soon becomes fouled, the impurities re-evaporating to fill the suction space at each intake stroke of the pump and condensing again on each compression stroke. The volumetric capacity of the pump decreases to a small fraction of optimum. Furthermore, the contaminants, especially fatty acids, are likely to be corrosive, causing the rotor to jam after a few hours' use. Thus industrial stills employ **steam ejectors** as prime movers, which often have the advantage of flushing the odors away into the chimney or drain. A typical pumping train for a large still will consist of three stages of steam, two oil boosters, and a condensation pump, capacity 1000 to 5000 liters/sec., next to the still.

The molecular still also requires inlet pumps and meters for the distilland and withdrawal pumps for the distillate. All must be of a kind that will not "vapor-lock" or "overrun" in passing from atmospheric pressure to vacuum.

The final and major requirement is heat—now by common usage **electrical heat.** Because distillation is done at high temperature (200° to 300°C.) and must often be repeated to secure proper separations, and because the hot evaporator loses heat by radiation to the cold condenser, less than 5 per cent of the input heat is actually used by distillation. When the heat required for the oil-vapor vacuum pump is also debited against the electrical consumption, the thermal efficiency may fall to 2 to 3 per cent. However, the through-put of the modern molecular still is sufficiently high for the total operating cost to compare favorably with conventional distillation.

Uses of the Molecular Still. Laboratory. The small demountable pot still (Fig. 17-41) is an inter-

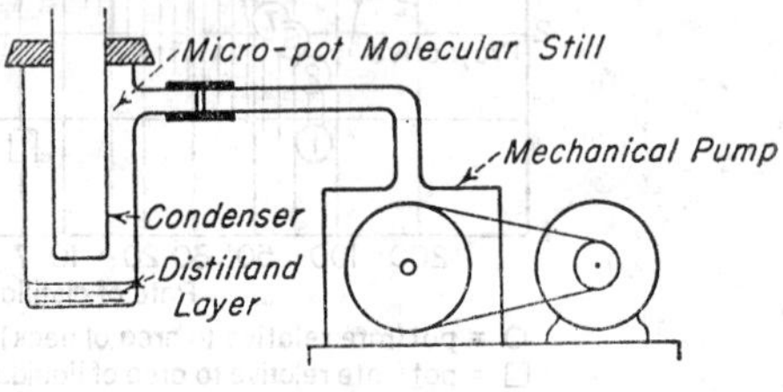

FIG. 17-41. Demountable pot still.

mediary step in the estimation of vitamin E in foods and oils. The same apparatus is useful for purifying small samples of drugs, dyes, sterols, and hormones. For the investigation of natural oils and waxes, the cyclic batch falling-film still is generally employed (Fig. 17-42). This instrument is designed for multiple

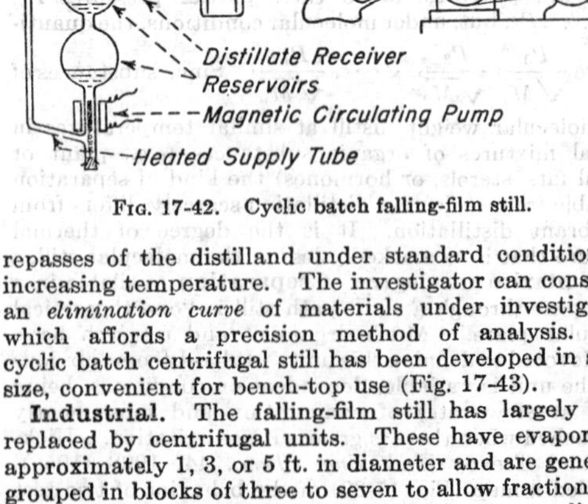

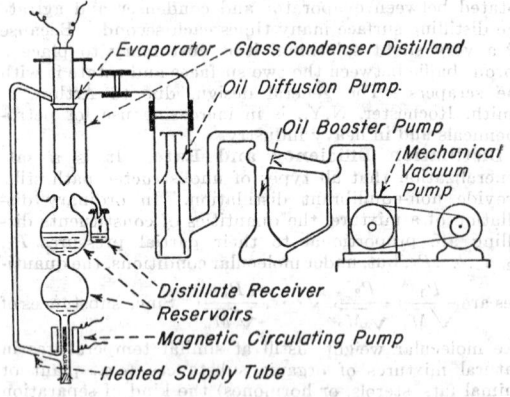

FIG. 17-42. Cyclic batch falling-film still.

repasses of the distilland under standard conditions of increasing temperature. The investigator can construct an *elimination curve* of materials under investigation which affords a precision method of analysis. The cyclic batch centrifugal still has been developed in small size, convenient for bench-top use (Fig. 17-43).

Industrial. The falling-film still has largely been replaced by centrifugal units. These have evaporators approximately 1, 3, or 5 ft. in diameter and are generally grouped in blocks of three to seven to allow fractionation by multiple redistillation. Their chief uses are distilla-

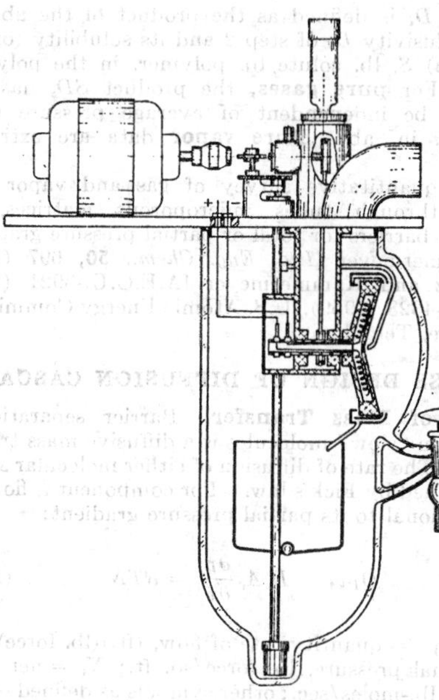

FIG. 17-43. Cyclic batch centrifugal still.

tion of vitamin A esters and intermediates, stripping of vitamins E (α-, β-, γ-, and δ-tocopherols) and sitosterols from vegetable oils, and the complete distillation of industrial high-boiling synthetics, plasticizers, fatty acid dimers, and the like. Recent uses are for separating mono- and di-glycerides for bread and paraffin wax for milk cartons.

Comparative Properties of Molecular Stills. Modern high-vacuum stills perform distillations at what are believed to be the lowest theoretically possible temperatures, and they accomplish this in the shortest times at present attainable in distillation equipment. For example, even an industrial flash distillation done at 10 mm. Hg involves a thermal exposure about 300,000 times greater than that caused by a high-speed molecular rotor. Against these advantages of the molecular still must be placed the poor separatory power of the unit act of distillation.

Fractionation. Separations better than unity—one molecular plate—can be secured by a series of redistillations done in a cascade of separate molecular stills. If the feed of a binary mixture is admitted at approximately the center of the cascade, and if distillates are blended

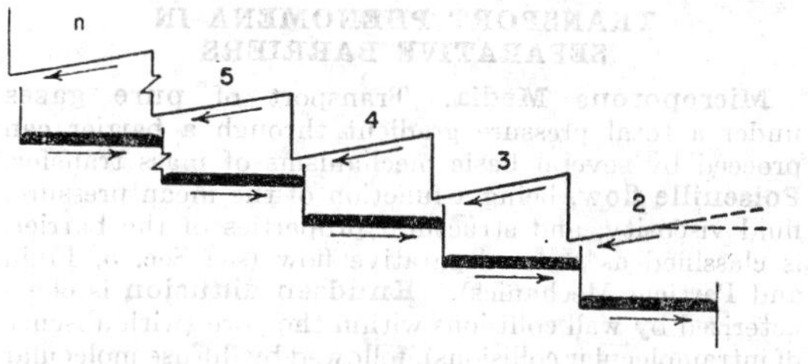

FIG. 17-44. Multicompartment molecular still.

with the residues one still backward and the residues with the distillates one still forward, purified components emerge at either end of the cascade. Two self-contained units have been described for doing this, the laboratory glass still of Wollner and associates and the steel 10-compartment still of Brewer and Madorsky (Fig. 17-44), which was devised for separating the isotopes of mercury.

GASEOUS DIFFUSION

REFERENCES: Barrer, "Diffusion in and through Solids," Cambridge, London, 1951. Benedict, *Trans. Am. Inst. Chem. Engrs.*, **43**, 41 (1947). Carman, "Flow of Gases through Porous Media," Academic Press, New York, 1956. Cohen, "The Theory of Isotope Separation," Chap. 1 and App. D, McGraw-Hill, New York, 1951. Manegold, "Kapillarsysteme," Band 1, Strassenbau, Chemie u. Technik, Heidelberg, 1955.

Scope of Subject. Barrier separation became a practical unit operation of chemical engineering with the creation and operation of the first commercial gaseous-diffusion plant at Oak Ridge, Tenn. Engineered specifically for the enrichment of $U^{235}F_6$ from a vapor mixture of the naturally occurring uranium hexafluorides, containing 99.3 per cent $U^{238}F_6$, the concentration of $U^{235}F_6$ to 99.0 per cent was effected with a multistage cascade of microporous nickel tubular barriers by the predominant flow mechanism of free-molecule transfer through pores or orifices, known as Knudsen flow or molecular effusion, respectively.

The general scheme of the barrier-separation process consists of passing a high-pressure (binary) gaseous mixture over a "separative" barrier. A fraction of the molar feed rate or cut $\theta(= V/F)$ diffuses through it into the low-pressure discharge chamber as enriched gas of composition y, while the remainder, $L/F(= 1 - \theta)$, discharges as high-pressure depleted fluid of concentration x. A flow diagram of a unit stage is shown in Fig. 17-45.

Basic **mass equation** for this process, for isothermal steady-flow operation, is

$$x_f = \theta y + (1 - \theta)x \tag{17-30}$$

The corresponding **rate equation** is

$$\theta y = \frac{D_i A_c}{RTFl}(\pi x - py) \tag{17-31}$$

where x = mole fraction of light component in undiffused gas stream; x_f = mole fraction of light component in feed gas stream; y = mole fraction of light component

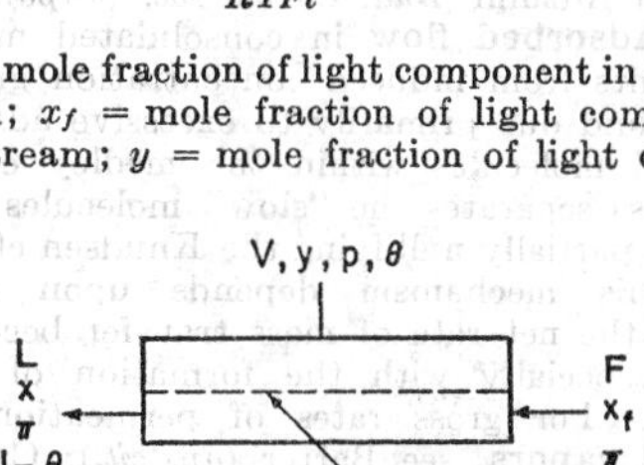

FIG. 17-45. Diagram of a unit stage.

in diffused gas stream; D_i = diffusivity of light component i, sq. ft./sec.; A_c = cross-sectional area of barrier, sq. ft.; R = universal gas constant, 1544 (ft.)(lb. force)/(lb.-mole)(°R.); T = absolute temperature, °R.; l = thickness of porous barrier, ft.; π = upstream pressure in barrier, lb. force/sq. ft.; p = downstream pressure in separation cell, lb. force/sq. ft.; F, V, and L = molar flow rates, lb.-moles/sec.

A **separative barrier** is defined as a structural matrix permitting the "fast" molecule to separate *within the barrier* according to the respective transfer mechanism. For an ideal porous barrier this is pure free-molecule diffusion within the pores. However, non-porous polymeric barriers operate on the principle of differential solubility of components within the polymer.

Recent separation techniques employing related separations are the jet process of Becker [*Chem. Ing. Tech.*, **29**, 365 (1957)]; centrifugal separation of Beyerle and Groth (*Proc. Symposium Isotope Separation*, Amsterdam, 1957); electromagnetic separation discussed by Becker ("Kerntechnik," Ed. by Riezler and Walcher, Teubner, Stuttgart, 1958); mass diffusion formulated by Cichelli *et al.* [*Chem. Eng. Progress*, **47**, 63, 123 (1951)] and Keyes and Pigford [*Chem. Eng. Sci.*, **6**, 215 (1957)]; and enrichment of helium through a glass barrier [Norton, *J. Am. Ceramic Soc.*, **36**, 90 (1953); also *Chem. Eng. News*, **35**, 7 (Sept. 9, 1957) and **36**, 42 (May 12, 1958)]. Few are, as yet, economically feasible for commercial production purposes.

TRANSPORT PHENOMENA IN SEPARATIVE BARRIERS

Microporous Media. Transport of **pure gases** under a total pressure gradient through a barrier can proceed by several basic mechanisms of mass transfer: **Poiseuille flow,** being a function of the mean pressure, fluid viscosity, and structural properties of the barrier, is classified as a non-separative flow (see Sec. 5, Fluid and Particle Mechanics). **Knudsen diffusion** is characterized by wall collisions within the pore (with absence of intramolecular collisions), followed by diffuse molecular reflections from it according to the Lambert cosine law. Such pure molecular behavior prevails for Knudsen numbers $N_{\text{Ku}}(=\lambda/\bar{d}_0)$ greater than 100. Since the mean free path λ of helium at 1 atm. and 0°C. is 1740 angstroms, it would diffuse through a 17.4 angstrom pore $(=\bar{d}_0)$ as a Knudsen fluid. Since Knudsen flow calculated by the "long-tube" formula is valid for $L_c/\bar{d}_0 > 100$, L_c being the length of capillary, the equation reduces to the case of orifice flow or **molecular effusion** at $L_c/\bar{d}_0 = 0$. However, for microporous media, the conductance of the barrier is restricted because of the short, tortuous flow paths.

Transition flow is characterized by a slip velocity at the pore wall. It represents a mixture of laminar and Knudsen flow which can be evaluated by the empirical equation of Adzumi [*Bull. Chem. Soc. (Japan)*, **12**, 304 (1937)]. **Adsorbed flow** in consolidated microporous media results from induced concentration gradients of adsorbed fluid due primarily to excessive adsorption of the "slow" molecules within the medley of "pores." This process separates the "slow" molecules *within the pores*, thus partially nullifying the Knudsen effect.

Since this mechanism depends upon adsorption equilibria, the net rate of mass transfer becomes most complex, especially with the formation of adsorbate azeotropes. For gross rates of permeation of **pure gases and vapors,** see Barrer (*op. cit.*); Carman (*op. cit.*); Kammermeyer [*Chem. Eng. Progress, Symp. Series* 24, **55**, 115 (1959)]; Manegold (*op. cit.*).

Polymeric Media. The transmission of fluids through polymeric barriers is known as **selective solubility diffusion.** Its rate-controlling mechanisms are considered to consist of (1) adsorption and solution of a component into the polymeric matrix; (2) diffusion of solute through the barrier under a concentration potential; (3) desorption and evaporation of solute from the surface of the polymer. The transmission rate of each component follows Eq. (17-32) below, where D_i is the gross diffusivity of the three afore-mentioned steps, provided the barrier diffusion process is flow-controlling.

Experimental evidence indicates that D_i of Eq. (17-32) increases exponentially with a linear change in barrier temperature. For this activation behavior of solute diffusion, D_i is defined as the product of the absolute solute diffusivity D_s of step 2 and its solubility (or concentration) S, lb. solute/lb. polymer, in the polymeric barrier. For **pure gases,** the product SD_s has been found to be independent of average pressure up to 58 lb./sq. in. abs. **Pure vapor** data are extremely meager.

For a quantitative survey of gas and vapor mass transfer through tubes, microporous matrices, and polymeric barriers for total or partial pressure gradients, see Kammermeyer [*Ind. Eng. Chem.*, **50**, 697 (1958)] and Rutz and Kammermeyer [A.E.C.U.-3921 (1958), A.E.C.U.-4328 (1959), U.S. Atomic Energy Commission, Oak Ridge, Tenn.].

PROCESS DESIGN OF DIFFUSION CASCADES

Rates of Mass Transfer. Barrier separation of "fast" from "slow" molecules is a diffusive mass-transfer process. The rate of diffusion of either molecular species is determined by Fick's law. For component i, flow rate is proportional to its partial pressure gradient:

$$Q_{PVi} = D_i A_c \frac{\partial p_i}{\partial x} = RTN_i \tag{17-32}$$

where Q_{PVi} = quantity rate of flow, (ft.)(lb. force)/sec.; p_i = partial pressure, lb. force/sq. ft.; N_i = net molar flow rate, lb.-moles/sec.; other symbols as defined earlier. In practice, the generalized diffusion coefficient D_i is replaced by effective diffusivity D_{ei} of the barrier, an experimentally determined value. Since many permeation rates P_{ei} (effective permeability) are tabulated in the literature as (standard cu. cm.)(cm. thickness)/(sec.)(cm. Hg pressure drop), see Manegold (*op. cit.*, p. 563) for conversion of P_{ei} to D_{ei} (sq. ft./sec.) as used in Eq. (17-32).

The transport of gas mixtures through **microporous media** by gaseous diffusion under a total pressure gradient is based upon the unequal collision frequency of each molecular species upon the walls of the pores. For an isothermal gas mixture, the kinetic theory of gases predicts that the average kinetic energy of both components is equal. Consequently, the swift, light molecule i "separates" from its slower, heavier neighbor j *within the barrier* since the arithmetic average speed of the ith component in a Maxwellian gas is $\bar{v}_i = \sqrt{8g_cRT/\pi M_i}$ or

$$\frac{\bar{v}_i}{\bar{v}_j} = \sqrt{\frac{T_iM_j}{T_jM_i}} = \frac{D_{Ki}}{D_{Kj}} = \beta_{ij} \tag{17-33}$$

where g_c = gravitational conversion constant, 32.17 (lb. mass)(ft.)/(lb. force)(sec.^{2}); M_i and M_j = molecular weights of components i and j; D_K = Knudsen diffusivity, sq. ft./sec.; β_{ij} = relative diffusivity for pure Knudsen flow.

In general, the experimental transfer rate (or separation) is a complex function of the degree of turbulence in discharge chambers, geometric structure of barrier, extent of "free-molecule" conditions, and the degree of adsorption in the multitude of pores. The net rate of mass transfer will depend upon the following sequence of processes: (1) laminar or turbulent flow in high- and low-pressure chambers; (2) molecular diffusion through high-pressure laminar boundary layer; (3) selective adsorption on high-pressure flow surfaces; (4) transport of adsorbate along "pore" walls by its induced potential; (5) transition or Knudsen flow in parallel with adsorbed flow through the residual core of each "pore"; (6) selective desorption in the low-pressure chamber; (7) emission by molecular diffusion through low-pressure boundary layer; and (8) turbulence of bulk fluid in the low-pressure chamber.

Consequently, the gross rate of transfer of component i through a barrier is based upon an effective diffusivity D_{ei} defined in Eq. (17-32). This equation is also valid for the diffusion of gas or vapor solute through **polymeric barriers.**

Barrier Equilibria. For a **microporous barrier,** definite equilibrium concentrations are obtained in each "phase" at a given temperature and pressure. The degree of concentration difference across the barrier stems from the relative arithmetic average speed of the respective molecular species:

$$\frac{\bar{v}_i}{\bar{v}_j} = \beta_{ij} = \frac{y_i}{x_i}\left(\frac{1 - x_i}{1 - y_i}\right) = \frac{Y}{X} \qquad (17\text{-}34)$$

where $(1 - y_i) = y_j$ for a binary mixture; $X = x/(1 - x)$ and $Y = y/(1 - y)$, mole ratio concentrations in the undiffused and diffused gas streams, respectively.

When adsorption occurs in the pores of the matrix in excess of that minimum necessary to sustain a diffusive flow behavior or Knudsen flow, adsorbed flow, which favors transmission of heavy component j, will effect a smaller molecular separation across the barrier. Consequently, the relative diffusivity of light component i will decrease substantially from its pure Knudsen flow value of β_{ij} and become β_{ij}^*, an experimental value measured under adsorbed flow conditions prevailing within the pores of the barrier. General correlations permitting an evaluation of the transmission of adsorbed layers for pure gases or binary mixtures are not yet available for design purposes for specific fluid-barrier systems.

Case I. If **turbulent conditions** (no longitudinal or transverse concentration gradients) exist in the high- and low-pressure chambers and if the downstream concentration equals that of the fluid flowing through the barrier, the relative diffusivity α_{ij} at the pressure ratio $p_r(= p/\pi)$ is evaluated from $\alpha_{ij} = Y/X$. Combining this relation with Eq. (17-31), α_{ij} at a pressure ratio p_r can be evaluated from

$$\alpha_{ij} = \beta_{ij} - (\beta_{ij} - 1)\frac{y}{x}p_r \qquad (17\text{-}35)$$

where $\beta_{ij} = \sqrt{M_j/M_i}$ for an isothermal Knudsen flow process. In addition, note that α_{ij} becomes $\alpha_{ij}^*(= D_{ei}/D_{ej})$ if adsorbed flow is substantial at the absolute pressure distribution *in* the barrier.

Case II. With **laminar-flow conditions** within the barrier chambers, the relative diffusivity is greater compared with the result from Case I. Combining the differential mass balance with the finite component balance across a stage, the Naylor-Backer equation [*Am. Inst. Chem. Engrs. J.*, **1,** 95 (1955)] in terms of the equilibrium diffusion ratio $K_i(= y_i/x_i)$ becomes

$$K_{in} = \frac{1 - \theta}{\theta}\left[\left(\frac{X_{n+1}}{X_n}\right)^{\alpha/\epsilon} - 1\right] \qquad (17\text{-}36)$$

where $x_{n+1} = \theta y_n + (1 - \theta)x_n$ when numbering the stages up the cascade and $\epsilon = \alpha - 1$.

For **polymeric barriers,** the equilibrium diffusion ratio $K_i(= y_i/x_i)$ depends upon the relative diffusivity $D_{si}/D_{sj}(= \alpha_{ij}^*)$ of the solute.

Case I. For **turbulent-flow conditions** of the bulk fluid in the high-pressure chamber, $V_{jo} = V_{jf}$ from Eq. (17-38) since no concentration gradients exist. (V_o = volumetric flow leaving high-pressure outlet of cell, cu. ft./sec.; V_f = volumetric flow entering high-pressure inlet to cell, cu. ft./sec.) Then the Weller-Steiner equation [*Chem. Eng. Progress*, **46,** 585 (1950)] for laminar conditions reduces to

$$\frac{y}{1 - y} = \alpha_{ij}\left[\frac{x - p_r y}{(1 - x) - p_r(1 - y)}\right] = Y \qquad (17\text{-}37)$$

where α_{ij} is evaluated from Eq. (17-35). This case will result in less enrichment than the laminar-flow mechanism of Case II. However, it would be a "design-safe" procedure since more theoretical stages are prescribed.

Huckins and Kammermeyer [*Chem. Eng. Progress*, **49,** 294 (1953)] demonstrated experimentally that Eq. (17-37) was also valid for microporous barriers if α_{ij} equaled the ratio of the respective permeabilities or pure gas diffusivities $(= D_{ei}/D_{ej})$. These experimental values were obtained for the identical operating temperature and pressure ratio of the separating barrier. Based upon the experimental data (see Fig. 17-48), turbulent-flow conditions prevailed and α_{ij} equaled D_{ei}/D_{ej} in Eq. (17-37).

Case II. With **laminar motion** within the barrier chambers, concentration gradients, both longitudinal and transverse, exist along the surface of the barrier. For such bulk fluid motion, the equilibrium curve should be calculated from the Weller-Steiner equation:

$$\frac{V_{jo}}{V_{jf}} = \left(\frac{t_f - C/A}{t_o - C/A}\right)^E \left(\frac{t_f - \alpha_{ij} + B}{t_o - \alpha_{ij} + B}\right)^G \left(\frac{t_f - B}{t_o - B}\right)^H \qquad (17\text{-}38)$$

where
$A = (\alpha_{ij} - \epsilon_{ij}p_r)/2$
$B = (1 + \epsilon_{ij}p_r)/2$
$C = (\alpha_{ij}/2) - AB$
$E = [\epsilon_{ij}(1 - p_r)]^{-1}$
$G = [\alpha_{ij}(A - 1) + B]/(2A - 1)(\alpha_{ij}/2 - B)$
$H = B/(B - AB - C)$
$t = [(Az)^2 + 2Cz + B^2]^{1/2} - Az$
$z = V_{if}/V_{jf}$

Subscripts f and o refer to the feed and outlet high-pressure streams of each stage. The enriched concentration y_i of the downstream chamber and the cut θ follow from the trial-and-error solution for V_{if}, V_{io}, V_{jf}, and V_{jo}:

$$y_i = \frac{V_{if} - V_{io}}{(V_{if} - V_{io}) + (V_{if} - V_{jo})} \qquad \theta = \frac{(V_{if} - V_{io}) + (V_{jf} - V_{jo})}{V_{if} + V_{ji}} \qquad (17\text{-}39)$$

Design Methods. Separation Principles. The general flow scheme for achieving a separation with solid barriers is shown in Fig. 17-45. This procedure is valid for gaseous diffusion through porous barriers or vapor solute diffusion through polymeric barriers. It should be emphasized that these methods are based on $(\alpha - 1) \gg 1$. For $(\alpha - 1) \ll 1$, "differential techniques" become justifiable for the isotope separation calculations.

The mechanics of evaluating the process design for a special degree of separation is identical to the finite stage-separation techniques developed for distillation, sorption, and extraction (see Table 17-7).

Single- and Multistage Diffusion. Single-stage diffusion represents the simplest design of gas or solute diffusion equipment. As shown in Fig. 17-46, the flow diagram includes a compressor and intercooler in each high-pressure feed stream. The unit can be operated at any pressure ratio or cut in a flow system, thereby giving various degrees of separation. Table 17-8 gives the equilibrium equations applicable to laminar- or turbulent-flow operations, thus its counterpart to an equilibrium still. Multistage diffusion implies the compounding of single units in series excluding any recycle techniques. Enrichment is attained at the sacrifice of wasting the undiffused fractions.

Table 17-7. Similarity of Gaseous Diffusion to Distillation

General unit	Fractional distillation	Gaseous (or solute) diffusion
Separator	Phase interface	Barrier
Separating unit	Plate	Stage
Separating assembly	Column	Cascade
Separator function	Rectify and strip	Enrich and strip
Enriched phase	Vapor	Diffused low-pressure fluid
Depleted phase	Liquid	Undiffused high-pressure fluid
Separation ratio	Relative volatility ($= \alpha$)	Relative diffusivity ($= \alpha_{ij}$)
Equilibrium ratio	Equilibrium vaporization ($= K_v$)	Equilibrium diffusion ($= K_i$)
Flow potential	Vapor phase (pressure) Liquid phase (gravity)	Gas phase (pressure)
Feedback	Internal reflux ratio	Recycle ratio
Flow ratio	....	Cut $= \theta = V/F$
Minimum number of stages	Fenske equation	Fenske equation
Finite number of stages ($\alpha \geq 2$)	McCabe-Thiele diagram	McCabe-Thiele diagram
Finite number of stages ($1 < \alpha < 2$)	Smoker or Kremser equation	Smoker or Kremser equation
Stage efficiency	40–80%	80–95%
Energy source	Reboiler (latent)	Compressor (work)
Energy sink	Condenser (latent)	Intercooler (heat)
Minimum separation energy	$(5/4)RT$	$-RT\ \Sigma y_i \ln (\gamma_i y_i)$ (γ_i = activity coefficient in vapor phase)
Thermodynamic efficiency, %	19 ($x_f = 0.05$)	Very small
Stage size	Area (allowable superficial vapor velocity)	Average area (rate equation)
Optimum plant size	Small or large	Very large

Countercurrent Multistage Diffusion. To improve the economics of the above separation process, the undiffused fractions are recycled to the feed stream of the previous stage. In general, the internal recycle ratio should be selected such that the recycle gas concentration from the nth stage equals that of the feed to the $(n - 1)$th stage. For such process designs, θ can vary continuously or irregularly in each stage depending upon the operating variables and equilibria. The recycle ratio generally decreases from the feed stage to the "tops" for $(\alpha - 1) \gtrsim 1$ giving a "hyperbolic envelope" of the barrier-flow-area requirement per stage (Fig. 17-47). Similar flow distribution occurs in the stripping section. See Table 17-8 for equilibria equations.

True Continuous Multistage Diffusion. Economic plant-scale operation requires a "straightening out" of the operating line. This permits the use of multiples of "standard stage units" to attain constant recycle ratio conditions. Although this "square cascade" design increases the compressor capacity above the minimum flow duty of the previous tapered or "curved" cascade, the over-all process economy will be increased. For design principles and equations using the scheme for porous or polymeric barriers, consult Tables 17-7 and 17-8 and Fig. 17-48. The design process principles require that $\Theta \gtrsim \frac{1}{2}$ in the rectifying section and $\Theta \lesssim \frac{1}{2}$ in the stripping section for continuous diffusion operation.

Table 17-8. Equilibrium-curve Relations

Stage design	Flow pattern	Barrier matrix	
		Microporous	Polymeric
Single	Laminar	Eq. (17-36); α_{ij}, Eq. (17-35)	Eqs. (17-38), (17-39)
	Turbulent	Huckins-Kammermeyer method	Eq. (17-37); experimental α_{ij}
Countercurrent multistage	Laminar	Eq. (17-36); α_{ij}, Eq. (17-35)	Eqs. (17-38), (17-39)
	Turbulent	$\alpha_{ij} = Y/X$; α_{ij}, Eq. (17-35)	Eq. (17-37); experimental α_{ij}
True continuous	Laminar	Eq. (17-36); α_{ij}, Eq. (17-35)	Eqs. (17-38), (17-39)
	Turbulent	$\alpha_{ij} = Y/X$; α_{ij}, Eq. (17-35)	$\alpha_{ij} = Y/X$; α_{ij}, Eq. (17-35)

Example 1. Separation of Uranium Isotopes. $U^{235}F_6$, occurring with $U^{238}F_6$ in nature at a concentration of 0.72 per cent, is enriched by gaseous diffusion to 95 per cent at a constant relative diffusivity of 1.004. For continuous multistage diffusion, evaluate the minimum number of theoretical enriching stages, and the number of stages required with a recycle ratio of 1.10 times the minimum if the stage efficiency is 90 per cent.

Solution. From the equilibrium curve calculated for $\alpha = 1.004$, the minimum recycle ratio was 0.999970 using a calculated y_f. The Smoker equation gives an actual stage requirement of 2879 stages. This is 1.457 times the stage requirement for total recycle operation.

Example 2. Gaseous Separation by Microporous Barriers. Experimental separation data were obtained for hydrogen-nitrogen mixtures using a porous Vycor glass barrier in a single-stage diffusion cell. With a feed gas at 0.32 mole fraction hydrogen flowing under turbulent conditions at $\pi = 64.4$ lb./sq. in. abs., determine the effect of the cut Θ on the permeated gas composition at $p = 14.39$ lb./sq. in. abs. if α_{ij} (experimental) is 3.48. Compare these results with laminar-flow behavior and experimental data. Determine horsepower, intercooler duty, and flow area to process 1 lb.-mole/sec. of a hydrogen-nitrogen mixture at 75°F., fed to a single-stage unit operating with a 0.5-in. (thick) barrier at a cut of 0.50. Assume adiabatic compression and compressor efficiencies of 0.75 and 0.85, respectively.

Solution (see Fig. 17-46). Having an experimental α_{ij} at the above pressure ratio, the Huckins-Kammermeyer method (*loc.*

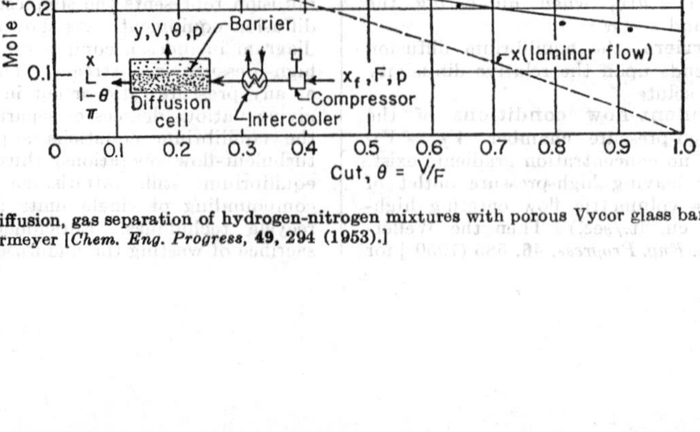

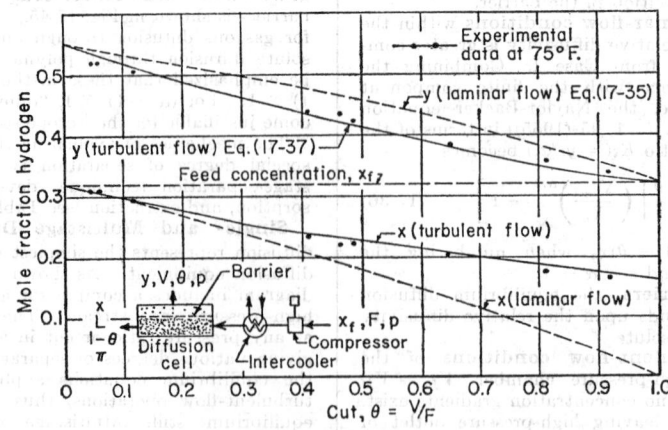

Fig. 17-46. Single-stage diffusion, gas separation of hydrogen-nitrogen mixtures with porous Vycor glass barriers. Experimental data from Huckins and Kammermeyer [*Chem. Eng. Progress*, 49, 294 (1953).]

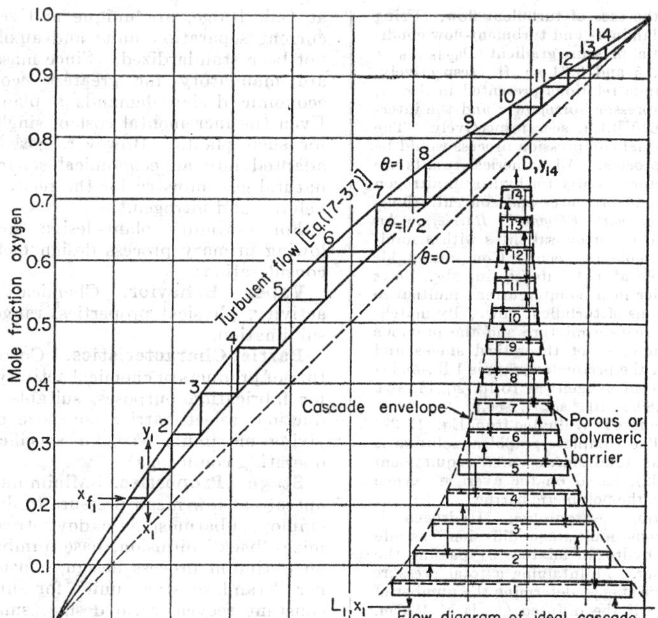

Fig. 17-47. Air separation by countercurrent multistage diffusion using polymeric barriers.

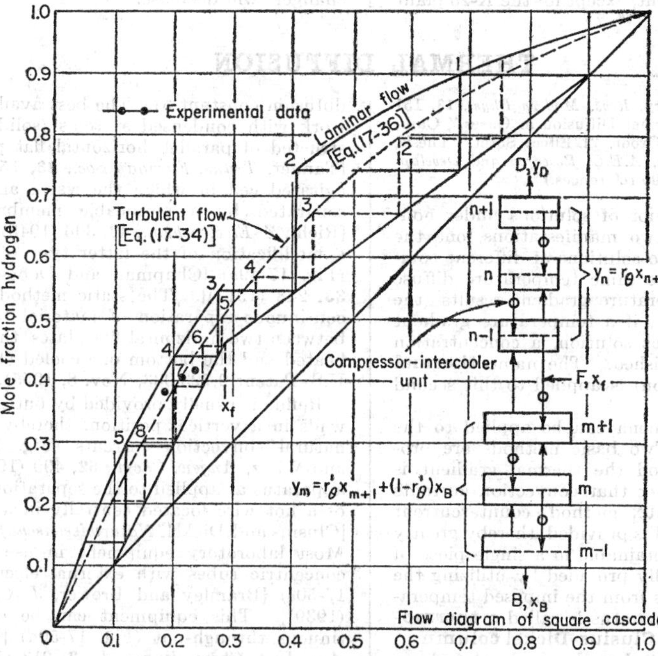

Fig. 17-48. True continuous multistage diffusion. Square cascade design using porous Vycor barriers. Experimental data from Huckins and Kammermeyer [*Chem. Eng. Progress*, 49, 294 (1953)].

cit.) should be employed for the case of turbulent flow. Using Eq. (17-32), the flow area for laminar- and turbulent-flow conditions based on the average partial pressure gradient (D_{hydrogen} = 1.51 × 10^{-6} sq. ft./sec.) is 5.85 and 3.64 sq. ft., respectively. According to the thermodynamic relations presented in Sec. 4, the adiabatic single-stage compressor horsepower and the intercooler duty is 3310 hp. and 2640 B.t.u./sec., respectively. The compressor duty for an isothermal compression process would be 80 per cent of the adiabatic process. All numerical results are based on a compressibility factor of unity for hydrogen-nitrogen gas mixtures within this range of pressures and concentrations.

Example 3. *Air Separation with Polymeric Barriers.* An enriched air reserve is required for space satellites with a minimum oxygen content of 95 mole per cent. Compressed air (21 per cent oxygen), available at 114.7 lb./sq. in. abs., flows through a 10-mil plastic barrier in a countercurrent multistage diffusion system under conditions of turbulent flow. By matching the concentrations of the recycle mixture and the previous feed stream, determine the number of theoretical stages and barrier area of the first stage if the production rate is 1 lb.-mole/day of enriched air (95.5 per cent oxygen) at 15 lb./sq. in. abs. [α_{ij} = 2.1 and $D_{e(\text{oxygen})}$ = 1.89 × 10^{-9} sq. ft./sec.]

Solution. The equilibrium curve is evaluated from Eq. (17-37) using an experimental α_{ij}. The complete graphical solution is presented in Fig. 17-47. The total barrier area requirement is 680 sq. ft. using Eq. (17-32), based on the average oxygen partial pressure gradient across the polymeric barrier.

Example 4. *Hydrogen-Nitrogen Separation.* Hydrogen is recovered in a true continuous multistage diffusion cascade process from a 28.5 per cent hydrogen mixture by passing the gas over a microporous barrier. Maintaining a total pressure drop of 3 atm. across successive stages, determine the number of enriching and stripping stages if the diffused gas is at 1 atm. pressure and β_{ij} = 3.74. Use an external recycle ratio of 2.51 if hydrogen is enriched to 90 per cent and stripped to 10 per cent, under laminar- and turbulent-flow conditions over the barrier.

Solution. Use Eq. (17-35) to evaluate α_{ij} at p_r = 0.25 and at each x value. Then calculate concentration y from Eq. (17-36). The McCabe-Thiele graphical method is satisfactory to determine the number of theoretical stages.

General Design and Economic Factors. Gaseous-diffusion plants and equipment, except for the K-25 plant at Oak Ridge, are unique and scarce. Consequently, current separation units and auxiliary equipment have not been standardized. Since mass-production methods are mandatory for greatest economy, the ultimate economic design demands a plant with many stages. Even the incremental cost of single units is rather high for such plants. However, gaseous diffusion may be adapted into an economical separative process by the natural-gas industry for the recovery of carbon dioxide, helium, and nitrogen.

For optimum plant-design specifications, the following primary process design factors require thorough consideration:

Vapor Behavior. Chemical stability, corrosion activity, physical properties, range of liquefaction and sublimation.

Barrier Characteristics. Corrosion resistance, structure of products of chemical activity, mechanical strength for fabrication purposes, suitable design for mass production; select barrier pore size or selective solubility giving maximum α_{ij}* for specific vapor mixture and operating conditions.

Stage Properties. Minimum hold-up capacity, operate at low mean pressure to decrease adsorbed flow, employ subatmospheric downstream pressure to minimize "back" diffusion, base number and area per stage on optimum process design, consider number of stages per "standard stage unit" for shutdown purposes and constant recycle ratio design, small cuts require large barriers, and for maximum stage performance design for laminar-flow conditions.

Process Economics. In general, the smaller the diffusivity, the greater will be the number of stages and α_{ij}, while the number of compressors and intercoolers and the barrier area will decrease. The smaller the mean pressure, the greater will be α_{ij} and vapor hold-up while the number of stages, compressors, and heat exchangers will decrease.

THERMAL DIFFUSION

REFERENCES: Jones and Furry, *Revs. Modern Phys.*, **18,** 151 (1946). Grew and Ibbs, "Thermal Diffusion in Gases," Cambridge, New York, 1952. De Groot, "L'Effect Soret," Thesis, Amsterdam, 1945. (Von Halle, *A.E.C. Research and Development Rept.* K-1420, 1959, lists 690 references.)

Definitions. The behavior of solutions under nonisothermal conditions has two manifestations, one the inverse of the other. If two solutions of different composition and initially at the same temperature diffuse together, a transient temperature gradient results (the Dufour effect). Conversely, if a temperature gradient is applied to a homogeneous solution, a concentration gradient is generally established. The name **thermal diffusion** (or thermodiffusion) is applied to this second effect.

Thermal-diffusion phenomena can be applied to the separation of materials. Two basic methods are provided: in the **static** method the thermal gradient is established in such a manner that convection currents are eliminated; in the **reflux** method, countercurrent flow of hot and cold material is provided, thereby greatly increasing the separation obtainable in a single piece of equipment. Reflux is usually provided by utilizing the density gradient that results from the imposed temperature gradient. Such an apparatus is called a **thermogravitational column** or a **Clusius-Dickel column.**

Equipment. Equipment has been developed to use both the static and reflux methods in **batch** and **continuous-flow** manners. The static method without bulk flow is used primarily to determine the thermal diffusion constant α. The best available equipment for work with condensed systems (solid or liquid) is constructed of parallel, horizontal flat plates (Fig. 17-49*c*) [Tanner, *Trans. Faraday Soc.*, **23,** 75 (1927)] or uses an agitated cell in which the warm and cold regions are separated by a permeable membrane (Fig. 17-49*a*) [Riehl, *Z. Electrochem.*, **49,** 306 (1943)]. For gas systems a modification of the latter type of apparatus is used (Fig. 17-49*b*) [Chapman and Dootsen, *Phil. Mag.* (6), **33,** 248 (1917)]. The static method has been used for continuous separation of material by flowing material between two horizontal flat plates, the upper plate being heated and the bottom one cooled (Fig. 17-49*d*) (Jones, U.S. Patent 2,723,033, Nov. 8, 1955).

Reflux is usually provided by putting the hot and cold walls in a vertical position, thereby producing laminar natural convection currents (Fig. 17-50*a*) [Korsching and Wirtz, *Angew. Chem.*, **52,** 499 (1939)]. The original apparatus as applied to the separation of gases consisted of a hot wire located centrally in a tube (Fig. 17-50*b*) [Clusius and Dickel, *Naturwissenschaften*, **26,** 546 (1938)]. Most laboratory equipment in use today is made of concentric tubes with external electrical heating (Fig. 17-50*c*) [Bramley and Brewer, *J. Chem. Phys.*, **7,** 553 (1939)]. This equipment can be operated with continuous through-put (Fig. 17-50*d*) [Powers and Wilke, *Am. Inst. Chem. Engrs. J.*, **3,** 213 (1957)]. Reflux can also be provided by external pumping (Fig. 17-50*e*) [Jury and Von Halle, *Chem. Eng. News*, **34,** 3606 (1956)]. In such an apparatus the hot and cold fluids are physi-

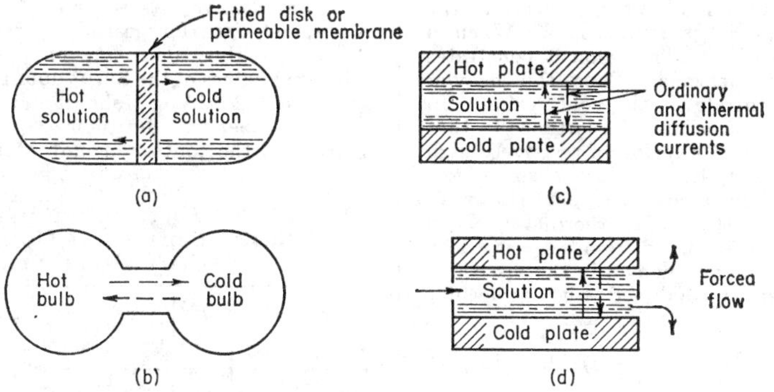

FIG. 17-49. Thermal-diffusion equipment, static methods. (*a*) Agitated cell. (*b*) Two-bulb apparatus. (*c*) Horizontal flat plates without bulk flow. (*d*) Horizontal flat plates with bulk flow.

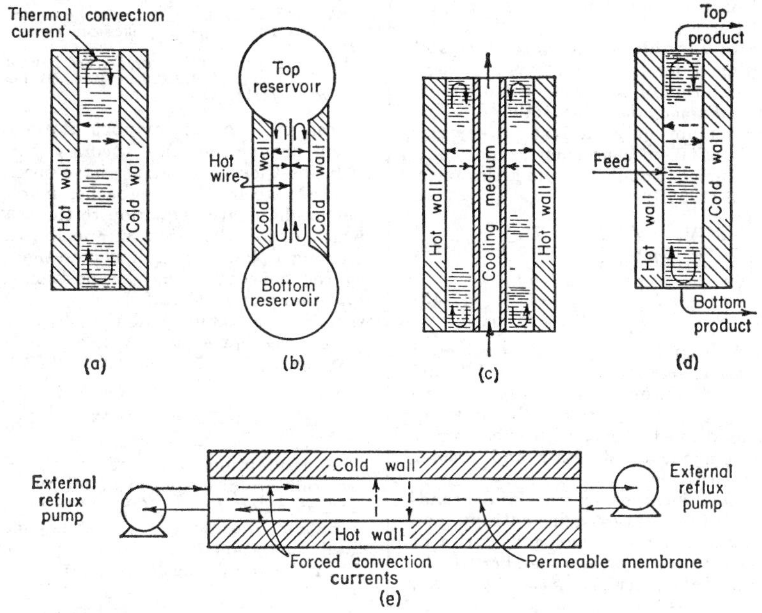

FIG. 17-50. Thermal-diffusion equipment, reflux methods. (*a*) Flat plate batch thermogravitational column without reservoirs. (*b*) Hot-wire batch thermogravitational column with reservoirs. (*c*) Concentric-cylinder batch thermogravitational column without reservoirs. (*d*) Continuous-flow thermogravitational column. (*e*) Horizontal forced-convection reflux thermal diffusion column.

cally separated by a permeable membrane, and mixing within each portion is provided by placing the hot plate on the bottom in addition to operating the reflux flow under turbulent-flow conditions.

THEORY

Basic Flux Expression. The flux J_{TD} of component 1 (the component of lower molecular weight in a binary solution) in ft./sec. is expressed in terms of the **thermal diffusion constant** α as

$$J_{TD} = \alpha X_1 X_2 D \frac{d \ln T}{dx} \qquad (17\text{-}40)$$

where X_1 and X_2 = mole fractions of components 1 and 2, respectively; D = coefficient of ordinary diffusion, sq. ft./sec.; T = absolute temperature, °R.; x = space coordinate in direction of flux, ft.

The kinetic theory of gases and the cage model of liquids have been applied to analysis of thermal diffusion and the estimation of α. Both theories account for the relative mass and size of the species being separated. In the absence of any appreciable size difference, the heavier species concentrates in the cold region. For substances of identical molecular weight the larger molecule will go to the cold region. For gas mixtures the mass effect is generally dominant, but for liquids the size factor is of primary importance.

Although thermal-diffusion effects are treated quantitatively for gases by kinetic theory and only qualitatively for liquids by the cage model, the latter provides a somewhat clearer picture of the factors influencing thermal-diffusion effects. The **cage model** considers that each molecule in the liquid is retained temporarily in an equilibrium position by the potential field of the surrounding molecules. At the same temperature all molecules have the same kinetic energy; therefore the heavier molecules have higher momentum. When a heavier molecule jumps to a colder region it penetrates farther than a lighter molecule. Thus the heavier molecules tend to concentrate in the cold region. In liquids the steric effect is of primary importance in that a large molecule moving from a region of relatively high temperature is able to force its way into a small hole and is thus trapped (concentrated) in the cold region.

Estimation of α for Gases. The thermal-diffusion constant α can be readily estimated from viscosity data of the form $\mu = kT^n$, where exponent n in the viscosity-temperature relationship is combined with molecular weights as follows:

$$\alpha \cong 1.5 \frac{M_2 - M_1}{M_2 + M_1} (1 - n) \tag{17-41}$$

This equation was developed for isotopic gas mixtures but is sufficiently accurate to yield a first approximation for α for other gas mixtures. Several other expressions, including one based on the Sutherland model, are presented by Jones and Furry (*loc. cit.*).

Estimation of α for Liquids. The more successful methods for estimating α for liquid systems are based on a molecular interpretation of the "net heat of transport" [Denbigh, *Trans. Faraday Soc.*, **48**, 1 (1952)]. The following equations require only activation energies determined from viscosity measurements, molecular weights, and molar volumes [Dougherty and Drickamer, *J. Phys. Chem.*, **59**, 443 (1955)]:

$$\alpha = \frac{M_1V_2 + M_2V_1}{2(M_1X_1 + M_2X_2)RT}\left(\frac{\Delta U_2}{V_2} - \frac{\Delta U_1}{V_1}\right) \tag{17-42}$$

$$\Delta U = R\left\{\left[\frac{\partial \ln (\mu V)}{\partial (1/T)}\right]_P - PT\left[\frac{\partial \ln (\mu V)}{\partial P}\right]_T\right\} \tag{17-43}$$

where V = molar volume, cu. ft./lb.-mole; R = universal gas constant, B.t.u./(lb.-mole)(°R.); ΔU = internal activation energy, B.t.u./lb.-mole; μ = absolute viscosity, lb. mass/(ft.)(sec.); P = pressure, lb. force/sq. ft.; other symbols as defined above, with subscripts 1 and 2 referring to components of lesser and greater molecular weights, respectively.

A similar development incorporates the Hildebrand-Scatchard theory, using the Flory-Huggins entropy, and permits one to estimate α for a homologous series of pairs from measurements on one or two members of the series [Dougherty and Drickamer, *J. Chem. Phys.*, **23**, 295 (1955)].

Phenomenological Theories. Development of theories to predict equipment performance based on the combination of the basic flux expression [Eq. (17-40)], Fick's law for diffusion, and the necessary hydrodynamic relations have been remarkably successful.

The Static Case. Static equipment operating without through-put (Fig. 17-49*a*, *b*, *c*) reaches steady-state conditions when the flux of material by ordinary diffusion is equal to that of thermal diffusion. Solution of the differential equation describing this condition yields an expression for α in terms of the static separation factor q_s:

$$\alpha = \frac{\ln q_s}{\ln (T_h/T_c)} \tag{17-44}$$

where T_h = absolute temperature of hot region, T_c = absolute temperature of cold region, °R., and q_s is defined as

$$q_s = \frac{X_h(1 - X_c)}{(1 - X_h)X_c} \tag{17-45}$$

where X = mole fraction and subscripts h and c refer to hot and cold regions, respectively.

Representative values for α are given in Table 17-9. Additional data for gaseous systems are tabulated by Grew and Ibbs (*loc. cit.*, p. 128). Thirty pages of tabulated values of the **Soret coefficient** $D'/D = \alpha X_1X_2$ are presented by Von Halle (*loc. cit.*, p. 271) [D' = coefficient of thermal diffusion, sq. ft./(sec.)(°R.)]. No analysis of the continuous-flow static case (Fig. 17-49*d*) is available.

Table 17-9. Representative Values of Thermal-diffusion Constant as Measured in Static Thermal-diffusion Cells

System component			Composition mole % (component 2)	ΔT, °F.	Arithmetic average temp., °F.	α*
1	2					
H_2	D_2	(g)	50	153	136	0.173†
He	N_2	(g)	50	155	135	0.36†
A	CO_2	(g)	50	¶	50	0.019†
C_6H_6	C_7H_{16}	(l)	50	22	102	−0.3‡
EtOH	CCl_4	(l)	50	5	95	3.69§
H_2O	HCl	(l)	0.18	11	73	1.28‡

* A negative sign indicates component 1 concentrates in the cold region.
† Grew and Ibbs, "Thermal Diffusion in Gases," Cambridge, New York, 1952.
‡ Huse, Trevoy, and Drickamer, *Rev. Sci. Instr.*, **21**, 60 (1950).
§ Whitaker and Pigford, *Ind. Eng. Chem.*, **50**, 1026 (1958).
¶ Extrapolated to $\Delta T = 0$.

Reflux. The Transport Equation. Several different phenomenological theories of thermogravitational (Clusius-Dickel) columns have been proposed. One of the more fruitful approaches involves reduction of a partial differential equation to the **transport equation** which relates the net flow τ in lb./sec. of component 1 crossing a plane perpendicular to the walls of the column to the concentration, the position coordinate in the direction parallel to the plates y, and the physical dimensions of the column and the physical properties of the system (as represented by H and K) [Furry, Jones, and Onsanger, *Phys. Rev.*, **55**, 1083 (1939)]:

$$\tau = HX_1X_2 - K\frac{\partial X_1}{\partial y} \tag{17-46}$$

The assumptions required in the derivation of this equation are discussed in detail by Powers [*Univ. Calif. Radiation Lab. Rept.*, UCRL-2618 (August, 1954)].

Batch Operation. For steady-state conditions the total separation factor q_T is expressed in terms of H^0, K^0, and column length L, ft.:

$$\ln q_T \equiv \ln \frac{X_t(1 - X_b)}{(1 - X_t)X_b} = \frac{H^0L}{K^0} \tag{17-47}$$

where $$H^0 = \frac{\alpha\beta_T\rho g(2\omega)^3B(\Delta T)^2}{6!\mu\bar{T}} \equiv aB(2\omega)^3 \tag{17-48}$$

$$K^0 = \frac{(\beta_T)^2\rho g^2(2\omega)^7B(\Delta T)^2}{9!D\mu^2} + 2\omega\rho DB \equiv a'B(2\omega)^7 + b'B(2\omega) \tag{17-49}$$

and $\beta_T = \partial\rho/\partial T$, lb. mass/(cu. ft.)(°F.); ρ = density, lb. mass/cu. ft.; g = gravitational acceleration parallel to plates of column, ft./sec.^{2}; ω = one-half the distance between the walls of a thermogravitational column, ft.; B = width of thermogravitational column, ft.; a, a', and b' are dimensional constants; subscripts t and b refer to top and bottom of column, respectively; other symbols as defined previously.

In developing these relations the effect of concentration on the density profile is ignored (De Groot, *loc. cit.*) and the various physical properties of the system are assumed constant at the arithmetic average temperature [Emery, *Ind. Eng. Chem.*, **51**, 651 (1959)]. The equations apply most directly to flat-plate columns

(Fig. 17-50*a*, *d*). Detailed treatments of hot-wire and concentric-cylinder apparatus (Fig. 17-50*b*, *c*) are available (Jones and Furry, *loc. cit.*). Equations (17-47) to (17-49) are satisfactory for the analysis of most concentric-cylinder columns.

The time required to reach steady-state operation depends very critically on the column dimensions. For a batch column with both ends connected to reservoirs (Fig. 17-50*b*) and operated such that $0.7 > X_1 > 0.3$, the relaxation time t_r in seconds is given by (Jones and Furry, *loc. cit.*)

$$t_r = \frac{m_t m_b L}{(m_t + m_b)K^0} \qquad (17\text{-}50)$$

where m_t and m_b = lb. mass of material in top and bottom reservoirs, respectively; L = length of column, ft.; K^0 is defined by Eq. (17-49). Other equations for estimating the time to approach equilibrium are available (Jones and Furry, *loc. cit.*; Powers, "Proceedings of the Joint Conference on Thermodynamic and Transport Properties of Fluids," p. 198, Institution of Mechanical Engineers, London, 1957).

It has been found that the above theoretical developments are in excellent *qualitative* agreement with experimental results but the values of H^0 and K^0 calculated from Eqs. (17-48) and (17-49) must be modified empirically to obtain agreement between calculated and experimental results. One such empirical modification has been developed using data obtained with gas systems [Drickamer, Mellow, and Tung, *J. Chem. Phys.*, **18**, 945 (1950)] and another is based primarily on data obtained with liquids (Powers, *loc. cit.*, 1954).

Continuous-flow Operation. Applying the transport equation (17-46) to the analysis of continuous-flow operation yields an exact general equation relating the concentration at the ends of the column to the flow rate σ, lb./sec., through the column and the physical parameters of the column (Jones and Furry, *loc. cit.*). The complicated form of this general solution has led to the development of several restricted solutions as presented by Jones and Furry. Only one of these will be considered here. For a column with identical dimensions (H and K) and through-put σ above and below the feed entry and in which $0.7 > X_1 > 0.3$

$$X_t' - X_b' = \frac{H}{2\sigma}\left(1 - \exp\frac{-\sigma L}{2K}\right) \qquad (17\text{-}51)$$

where X' = mass fraction. In applying this equation it is generally assumed that H and K are independent of the superimposed flow and therefore equal to H^0 and K^0. The form of the flow-rate dependence predicted by the resulting expression represents experimental data on continuous-flow columns very well [Powers and Wilke, *Am. Inst. Chem. Engrs. J.*, **3**, 213 (1957)]. However, in order to obtain quantitative agreement it is not only necessary to correct theoretical H^0 and K^0 values calculated from Eqs. (17-48) and (17-49), as discussed under batch operation, it is also necessary to consider the influence of flow rate through the column on H and K. Since H^0 and K^0 are the values of H and K at zero flow rate, the flow correction terms $h(\phi)$ and $k(\phi)$ are defined by the relations $H = h(\phi)H^0$ and $K = k(\phi)K^0$. The terms $h(\phi)$ and $k(\phi)$ have been obtained semiempirically and are presented in Fig. 17-51. The ϕ term is computed according to

$$\phi = -\frac{6!\mu\sigma}{2\beta_T\rho g(2\omega)^3 B\,\Delta T} \qquad (17\text{-}52)$$

The application of these flow-dependent correction terms is illustrated by Powers and Wilke (*loc. cit.*).

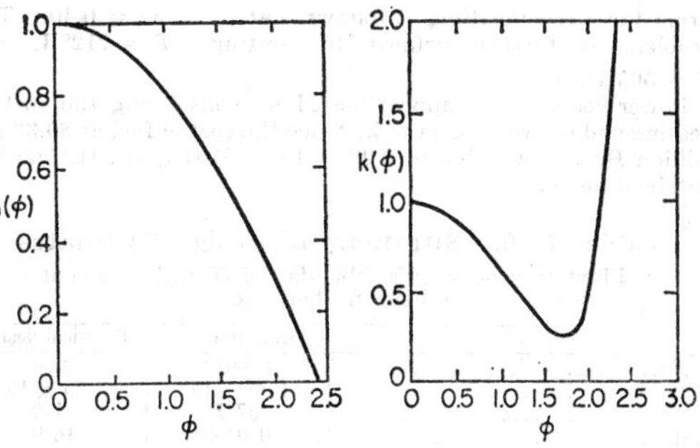

FIG. 17-51. Flow-correction terms $h(\phi)$ and $k(\phi)$ as functions of ϕ. [*Powers and Wilke, Am. Inst. Chem. Engrs. J.*, **3**, 213 (1957).]

Practical use of thermal diffusion for commercial separations will involve multistage apparatus. This subject is discussed in detail by Jones and Furry (*loc. cit.*).

DESIGN

Economic Design Equations. The uncorrected theoretical equations presented by Jones and Furry (*loc. cit.*) have been used [Krasney-Ergen, *Phys. Rev.*, **58**, 1078 (1940)] as the basis for the development of economic design equations for the special case in which $X_1 \ll 1$ throughout the column. This analysis has been extended to the case $0.7 > X_1 > 0.3$ [Powers and Wilke, *loc. cit.*]. For the latter case, considering fixed charges per unit area S and operating costs $p_c/2\omega$ to be independent of the design variables (distance between plates 2ω, column width B, and length L), it is determined that minimum total cost corresponds to design based on the following equations (symbols as defined previously):

$$(2\omega)^7 - 5\frac{b'}{a'}(2\omega) - 6\frac{b'}{a'}\frac{p_c}{s} = 0 \qquad (17\text{-}53)$$

$$\frac{b'}{a'} = 9!\left(\frac{D\mu}{\beta_T g\,\Delta T}\right)^2 \qquad (17\text{-}54)$$

$$B = \frac{(2.78)6!\mu\bar{T}\sigma(X_t - X_b)}{\alpha\beta_T\rho g(\Delta T)^2(2\omega)^3} \qquad (17\text{-}55)$$

$$L = \frac{2.54\rho D(2\omega)B}{\sigma}\left[\frac{a'}{b'}(2\omega)^6 + 1\right] \qquad (17\text{-}56)$$

Design Illustration. Krasney-Ergen (*loc. cit.*) and Jones and Furry (*loc. cit.*) have presented numerical examples of the design of thermal-diffusion equipment for concentrating dilute mixtures of isotopic gases. On the basis of the calculations presented by these authors, it would appear that Eqs. (17-53) to (17-56) can be used with reasonable success in the design of gaseous thermal-diffusion plants. The assumption that the fixed costs per unit area S are independent of the plate spacing is probably seriously in error for very small spacings ($2\omega < 0.05$ in.) and thus the design equations yield strange results when applied to the design of liquid thermal-diffusion plants as illustrated by the following:

Example. A thermal-diffusion plant to process 1000 bbl./day of a 50 mole per cent *n*-heptane–benzene mixture will be designed. (This particular design would have no commercial significance, as *n*-heptane and benzene are easily separated by distillation. However, the process is indicative of separation of aromatics and aliphatics, a difficult separation when applied to lubricating oils.)

The design equations presented here are based on Eq. (17-51) and therefore are restricted to $0.7 > X_1 > 0.3$ and equal flow rates in each section. Therefore, the overhead product rate is set at 500 bbl./day of 70 mole per cent *n*-heptane and the bottom product rate at 500 bbl./day of 30 mole per cent *n*-heptane.

From these specifications it follows that $X_t - X_b = 0.40$. The problem is further defined by setting $\Delta T = 212°R.$ and $\bar{T} = 565°R.$

Power costs p_c are approximated by considering the cost of heating and cooling media to be twice the cost of fuel at $0.30 per million B.t.u. A value of 2.23×10^{-4} ($)(ft.)/(sq. ft.)(day) is obtained for p_c.

Table 17-10. Summary of Design Estimates

Plant to process 1000 bbl./day of 50 mole per cent *n*-heptane–benzene

	Optimum design	Practical design
2ω, in.	0.0072	1/32
B, ft.	4.36×10^5	5.25×10^3
B, miles	82.7	1.0
L, ft.	0.0468	16.9
Total area: $B \times L$, sq. ft.	2.05×10^4	8.88×10^4
Heat load, B.t.u./hr	5.27×10^8	5.27×10^8
Capital investment	$1,230,000	$5,320,000
Daily operating costs:		
Fuel and cooling water	$7,670	$7,670
Fixed charges	743	3,230
Total	8,413	$10,900
Cost per barrel of feed processed	$8.41	$10.90
Cost per gallon of feed processed	$0.20	$ 0.26

Equipment costs are assumed to be indpendent of 2ω, and the cost per square foot of area of one plate is estimated to be $60 per square foot. This is ten times the value obtained from published cost curves [Chilton, *Chem. Eng.*, **56** (6), 97 (1949)] for heat-exchange surface and is intended to include cost of auxiliary equipment, design, increase in cost index, etc. On this basis a value of $0.364/(sq. ft.)(day) is obtained for S.

These cost data and values of the other system parameters as obtained from the literature are used in Eqs. (17-53) to (17-56) to obtain the dimensions for the "optimum" design listed in Table 17-10. Estimates of the total heat load, capital investment, and operating costs are included.

Even though a column 0.563 in. long and 82.7 miles wide with a plate spacing of 0.0072 in. may be optimum, it would hardly seem practical. An increase in plate spacing would decrease column width and increase column length. The cost would also be increased by an increase in plate spacing. (Actually a decrease in fabrication cost with an increase in 2ω would probably offset the predicted increase in cost due to the increased area.) A plate spacing of 1/32 in. was arbitrarily chosen as a minimum practical plate spacing, and values of B and L_T were calculated from Eqs. (17-55) and (17-56). The results of these calculations are listed under "practical" design in Table 17-10 for comparison with the optimum design. The value of the column length (17 ft.) for this arbitrary plate spacing represents a practical construction, and thus no other designs are considered.

The cost data used in these estimates are only approximate; yet the results should indicate the order of magnitude of the costs involved. It can be seen that thermal diffusion is an expensive process.

DIALYSIS

Introduction. Dialysis is a process by which various substances in solution having widely different molecular weights may be separated by diffusion through semipermeable membranes. Prior to about 1955 dialysis was used commercially to recover caustic soda from a mixture with hemicellulose as well as in the refining of beet sugar. Parchment paper was used as the semipermeable membrane. The apparatus in which the membranes were held, called a dialyzer, was manufactured by Brosites Machine Company (Figs. 17-52 and 17-53). Since then,

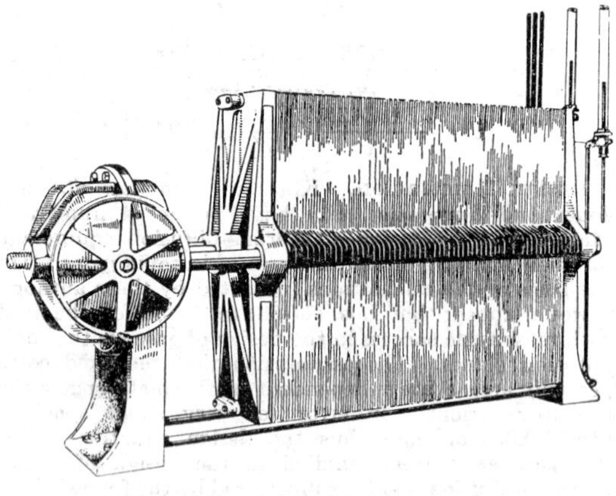

FIG. 17-52. Assembled dialyzer unit.

National Aluminate Company has introduced microporous polyvinyl chloride membranes, and Graver Water Conditioning Company has manufactured a dialyzer for use with these membranes. Current uses include recovery of mineral acids from aqueous solutions in metallurgical operations and of colloidal organics in the manufacture of pharmaceutical chemicals.

Dialysis, which depends on the **relative diffusion rates** of two solutes, is most effectively applied to separate low-molecular-weight substances in solution from very-high-molecular-weight substances. Complete separation is possible only if the latter substances are too large to pass through the membrane pores. The degree of separation or the extent of recovery of the low-molecular-weight solute may determine the capacity of the dialysis equipment. In most cases this capacity is very low because of the slow rate of transfer in dialytic cells. In the recovery of caustic, for example, one commercial dialyzer of 850 sq. ft. membrane area can handle 36 gal./hr. of 15 to 20 per cent caustic at about 90 per cent recovery.

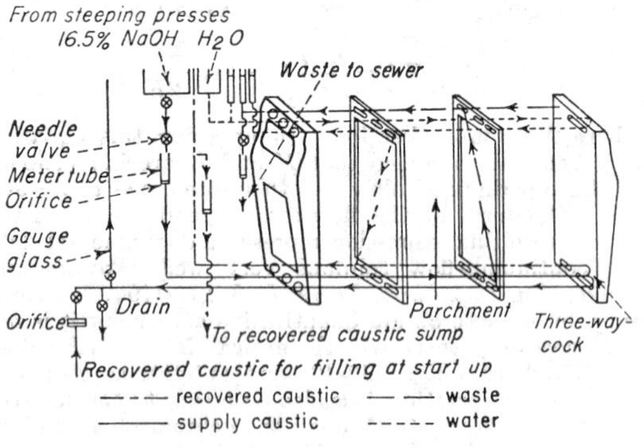

FIG. 17-53. Diagrammatic drawing of dialyzer.

Theoretical Background. If an aqueous solution containing substances of different molecular weights is kept separated from a more dilute solution of these substances by means of a semipermeable membrane such as cellophane or parchmentized paper, the **concentration gradient** thus established causes the substances to diffuse through the membrane from the concentrated to the more dilute solution at varying rates of transfer. At the same time, water will move through the membrane in a direction opposite to the movement of the solutes.

The rate of mass transfer through the membrane is given by the usual Fick's law equation as

$$\frac{dN}{dt} = -DA\frac{dC}{dZ} \qquad (17\text{-}57)$$

where N = number of moles of substance transferred; t = time, sec.; D = diffusion coefficient, sq. cm./sec.; A = area, sq. cm.; C = concentration, moles/cc.; Z = distance measured in the direction of diffusion flow, cm.

For steady-state mass transfer through a membrane with countercurrent flow of the process solutions adjacent to the membrane, the following equation can be derived from Eq. (17-57):

$$W = U_0 A\,\Delta C_{lm} \qquad (17\text{-}58)$$

where W = weight transferred, g./min.; U_0 = over-all dialysis coefficient, (g./min.)/(sq. cm.)(g./cc.) or cm./min.; A = membrane area, sq. cm.; ΔC_{lm} = logarithmic mean concentration gradient across the membrane, g./cc. = $(\Delta C_1 - \Delta C_2)/2.3 \log (\Delta C_1/\Delta C_2)$; ΔC_1, ΔC_2 = inlet and outlet concentration differences, respectively.

The above equation is valid only for **dilute** solutions. It can also be used for batch dialysis where ΔC_1 refers to the initial concentration difference and ΔC_2 to the final difference.

In the case of **concentrated** solutions, diffusion of the solute across the membrane is accompanied by diffusion of the solvent in the reverse direction. The counterdiffusion of solvent reduces the rate of transfer of the solute and thus increases the membrane area required for a given application. A comparison of the results calculated from Eq. (17-58) for dilute solutions with those calculated from an equation derived from concentrated solutions [Lane and Riggle, *Chem. Eng. Progress Symp. Series* 24, **55**, 127 (1959)] is given in Fig. 17-54.

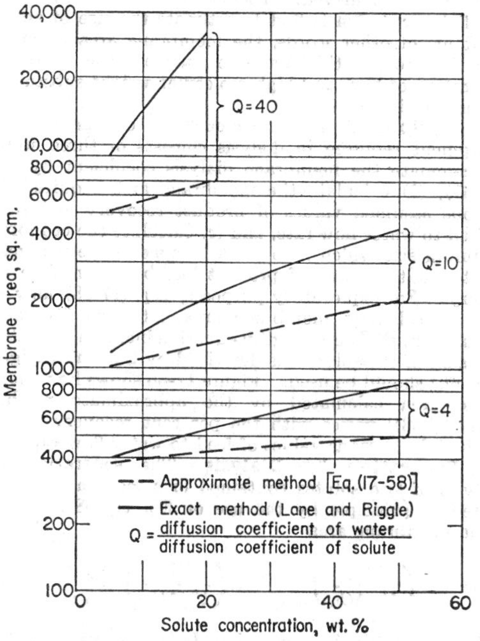

FIG. 17-54. Calculated membrane area to recover 90 per cent of solute at a feed rate of 100 g./min.

Here the membrane area calculated to recover 90 per cent of the solute dissolved in a feed flowing at a rate of 100 g./min. is shown for both the approximate method [Eq. (17-58)] and the exact method of Lane and Riggle. Parameter Q is the ratio of the diffusivity of the solvent, water, to that of the solute.

Calculation of Dialysis Coefficients. In order to apply Eq. (17-58) to design of dialysis equipment, a knowledge of the over-all dialysis coefficient of the solute is necessary. When experimental data are not available, the over-all dialysis coefficient may be estimated from the **diffusion coefficient** related to the properties of the solution, and from the **properties of the membrane** being used. Analogous to heat transfer, the over-all resistance to transfer through a membrane is given by a liquid film on each side of the membrane as well as the membrane itself. Thus

$$\frac{1}{U_0} = \frac{1}{U_1} + \frac{1}{U_2} \qquad (17\text{-}59)$$

The combined film coefficient U_1 has been found from laboratory experiments on solutions having viscosities in the order of that of liquid water to be calculable from the equation

$$U_1 = 1000D \qquad (17\text{-}60)$$

The membrane dialysis coefficient U_2 may be estimated from the equation

$$U_2 = \frac{60DFV'}{hz} \qquad (17\text{-}61)$$

where F = ratio of hindered diffusion rate to unhindered rate; V' = relative volume of membrane occupied by pores; h = tortuosity, ratio of capillary length to membrane wet thickness; z = membrane wet thickness, cm.

Values of V', h, and z should be determined by experiment for each application for highest accuracy, although Tables 17-11 and 17-12 present values for several types of membranes. This recommendation is based on the fact that swollen thickness z and, therefore, V' are affected by the dialyzing molecule. Tortuosity h varies with direction and shape of the capillaries in the membrane and is not necessarily the same for membranes

Table 17-11. Properties of Commercial Films
Do not use for caustic solutions

	Dry thickness, cm. × 10³	Wet thickness z, cm. × 10³	Relative volume occupied by pores V'	Ratio of capillary length to wet thickness (tortuosity) h	Pore diam., angstroms (cm. × 10⁸)
Du Pont cellophane:					
300 P.D.*	1.91	3.96	0.52	3.8	38
450 P.D.	2.67	4.95	0.46	3.4	46
600 P.D.	3.56	7.25	0.51	4.9	33
300 P.U.D.†	1.78	4.32	0.59	3.9	48
450 P.U.D.	2.54	6.10	0.58	3.5	51
Avisco cellophane:					
300 P.-1	2.54	5.07	0.50	4.1	31
450 P.-1	3.94	7.86	0.50	3.8	32
600 P.-1	9.90	17.80	0.44	2.4	29
Seamless tubing	1.91	3.56	0.46	4.3	33
Paterson parchment paper:					
30 lb.	5.08	6.85	0.26	2.0	36
40 lb.	5.97	8.50	0.30	3.4	30
60 lb.	9.00	12.70	0.29	3.0	22
Denitrated nitrocellulose:					
Light	5.34	9.40	0.43	2.6	35
Heavy	9.15	16.50	0.44	2.2	33

* P.D. refers to sized materials.
† P.U.D. refers to unsized materials.

of the same material but different thicknesses. A dialyzing molecule such as caustic affects both the swollen thickness and tortuosity. In performing experiments to measure the required membrane properties, the combined film coefficient U_1 either must be made negligible by high agitation rates or must be assumed to be given by Eq. (17-60).

Table 17-12. Swelling of Commercial Films

	Dry thickness, cm. × 10³	Thickness in water, cm. × 10³	Thickness in 1N NaOH cm. × 10³
Du Pont cellophane:			
300 P.D.*	1.91	3.96	7.10
450 P.D.	2.67	4.95	7.60
600 P.D.	3.56	7.25	9.65
300 P.U.D.†	1.78	4.32	
450 P.U.D.	2.54	6.10	
Avisco cellophane:			
300 P.-1	2.54	5.07	
450 P.-1	3.94	7.86	
600 P.-1	9.90	17.80	
Seamless tubing	1.91	3.56	
Paterson parchment paper:			
30 lb	5.08	6.85	11.20
40 lb	5.97	8.50	12.70
60 lb	9.00	12.70	18.20
Denitrated cellulose:			
Light	5.34	9.40	
Heavy	9.15	16.50	
Cellulose acetate:			
120-C.A.-43	2.54	2.54	

* P.D. refers to sized materials.
† P.U.D. refers to unsized materials.

The Faxen drag factor F may be evaluated from the following equation [Bacon, *J. Franklin Inst.*, **221**, 251–258 (1936)]:

$$F = 1 - 2.104\left(\frac{s}{S}\right) + 2.09\left(\frac{s}{S}\right)^3 - 0.95\left(\frac{s}{S}\right)^5 \qquad (17\text{-}62)$$

where s = diameter of diffusing molecule or particle and S = average diameter of membrane pores, angstroms. A plot of Eq. (17-62) is presented in Fig. 17-55.

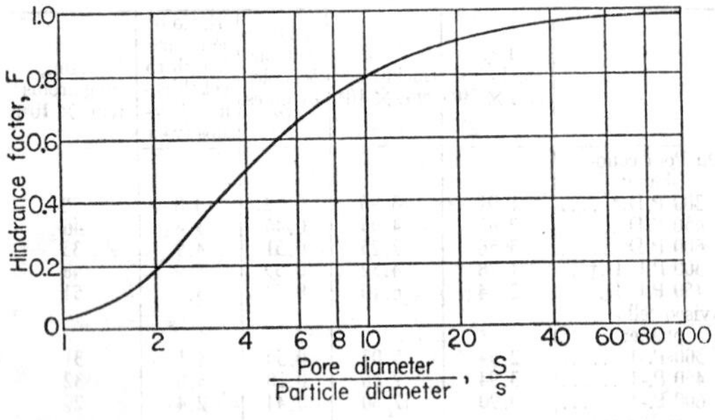

FIG. 17-55. Plot of Faxen's equation. [*Lane and Riggle, Chem. Eng. Progress, Symp. Ser.* 24, **55**, 127 (1959).]

The pore diameter should also be obtained from experiment using a molecule of known diameter, about 10 to 50 per cent of the pore diameter; the properties of the membrane; and Eqs. (17-60) to (17-62). Representative values, however, are presented in Table 17-11. The molecular diameter may be estimated, if necessary, from the following equations:

For solids such as sugar and urea,

$$s = 1.465 \times 10^{-8}\left(\frac{M}{\rho}\right)^{1/3} \qquad (17\text{-}63)$$

For liquids,

$$s = V_m^{1/3} \times 10^{-8} \qquad (17\text{-}64)$$

where M = molecular weight; ρ = density, g./cc.; V_m = molecular volume, cc., at boiling point.

Values of diffusion coefficients necessary for calculating dialysis coefficients from Eq. (17-60) are given in tabular form in Sec. 14. When necessary data are lacking, diffusion coefficients may be estimated from molecular weight of the solute by various equations given in the literature. The most notable of these are the Stokes-Einstein equation [von Wogan, *Ber. deut. physik. Ges.*, **6**, 542 (1908)], the Arnold equation [*J. Am. Chem. Soc.*, **52**, 3937 (1930)], and, more recently, that proposed by Powell, Rosevears, and Eyring [*Ind. Eng. Chem.*, **33**, 430 (1941)].

In general, diffusion coefficients may be estimated sufficiently accurately for dialysis design from the data given in Table 17-13. These data were obtained by

Table 17-13. Diffusion Coefficients and Molecular Diameters of Non-electrolytes

Molecular weight	D, sq. cm./sec. × 10⁵	Molecular diam., angstroms
10	2.20	2.9
100	0.70	6.2
1,000	0.25	13.2
10,000	0.11	28.5
100,000	0.05	62.0
1,000,000	0.025	132

plotting diffusion coefficients against molecular weight. Values of the average diameter of the solute molecules are also given.

In dealing with the diffusion of electrolytes, it should be pointed out that the effective diameter of the molecule depends on the extent of hydration of the electrolyte, and the molecular weight of the hydrated salt should be used [Washburn, *J. Am. Chem. Soc.*, **31**, 322 (1909)].

Applicability of Dialysis. Two factors are involved in determining the applicability of dialysis to a particular separation problem. First is the size of equipment required, and second, the degree of separation that may be achieved. The method usually employed for dialyzer design is first to estimate the size of equipment or, in other words, the membrane area required, and then to use this figure to calculate the degree of separation of low- and high-molecular-weight substances in the solution.

1. Equipment Size. Calculation of the size of equipment required in dialysis consists of three steps: (*a*) calculate the membrane dialysis coefficient by Eq. (17-61), (*b*) calculate the membrane area required for various assumed values of product recovery and ratio of feed to water flow rate, and (*c*) calculate the economic optimum size which involves a balance between investment and the value of product lost by incomplete recovery. For exploratory purposes, Eq. (17-58) may be used to calculate membrane area, although for exact calculation, the more lengthy equation including counter-diffusion of the solvent as described by Lane and Riggle (*loc. cit.*) should be used. Figure 17-56 shows how membrane area calculated by the approximate method [Eq. (17-58)] varies with the per cent recovery of the product for various values of feed to water flow rate.

2. Separation by Dialysis. The separation by dialysis of two solutes contained in a feed can be estimated in principle by the use of Eq. (17-58). For a given membrane area

$$\left(\frac{W}{U_0\,\Delta C_{lm}}\right)_{\text{Solute 1}} = \left(\frac{W}{U_0\,\Delta C_{lm}}\right)_{\text{Solute 2}} \qquad (17\text{-}65)$$

Lane and Riggle have calculated as an example the separation of sodium sulfate from sucrose. Their results are shown in Fig. 17-57, where it can be seen that the

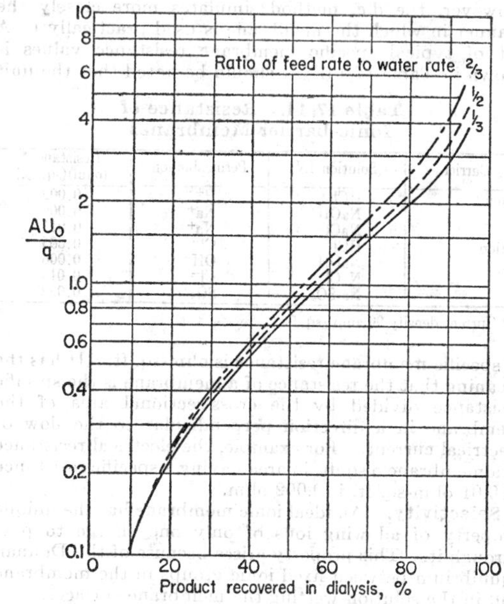

FIG. 17-56. Membrane area required vs. product recovered at various values of feed-to-water flow rates; A = area, sq. cm.; U_o = over-all dialysis coefficient, cm./min.; q = flow rate of feed solution, cu. cm./min.

recovery of an enriched sodium sulfate product decreases with an increase in enrichment. Furthermore, only a modest enrichment is possible because both solutes are small, less than 10 angstroms, with respect to the pore size, 30 to 50 angstroms. As can be seen from Fig. 17-55, the only way by which large enrichments can be obtained is to select a membrane pore diameter of about the same size as the larger solute.

The calculated separability of two solutes depends on the values chosen for the diffusivity of each solute. For a mixture, it is permissible to use the diffusivities of the pure materials only when there is no interaction between the solutes. An example of an interaction is the common ion effect such as exists in a mixture of sodium chloride and hydrochloric acid.

Dialysis Equipment. Commercial dialysis is best carried out by means of continuous countercurrent

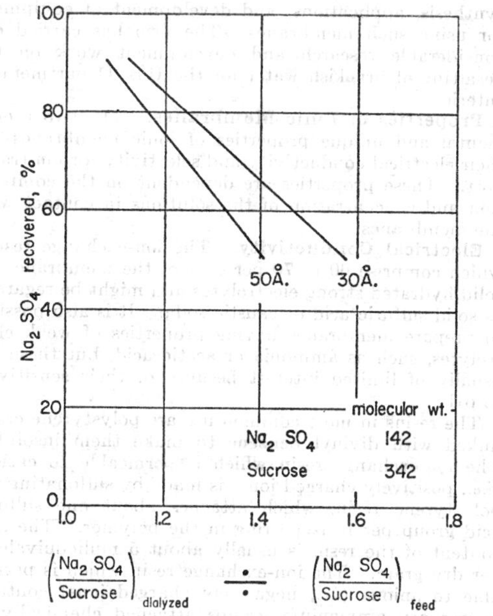

FIG. 17-57. Dialytic fractionation. [*Lane and Riggle, Chem. Eng. Progress, Symp. Ser.* 24, **55**, 127 (1959).]

dialyzers, which are discussed by Vollrath [*Chem. & Met. Eng.*, **43**, 303 (1936)], Eynon [*J. Soc. Chem. Ind.*, **52**, 173T (1933)], and Bassett [*Chem. & Met. Eng.*, **45**, 254 (1938)]. In general, these consist of a series of alternate water and solution cells connected in parallel and separated by membranes. The dialyzer frame is constructed similarly to a plate-and-frame filter press. A plant-size dialyzer manufactured by Brosites Machine Company, such as that shown in Fig. 17-52, has about 850 sq. ft. of membrane and costs $10,900 plus installation (February, 1960). A plant-size unit using polyvinyl chloride membranes and having 1000 sq. ft. of dialyzing area was available in 1960 from Graver Water Conditioning Co. for $9,000 plus installation costs. A laboratory model which can be used to evaluate the applicability of dialysis is available from Brosites. This model costs about $250 (February, 1960). Graver also markets a laboratory-size dialyzer equipped with 3.61 sq. ft. of polyvinyl chloride membrane for $300.

ELECTRODIALYSIS

Introduction. Electrodialysis is the use of an electromotive force to transport ionized materials through diaphragms separating two or more solutions. Although old in principle, it has become of potential commercial importance with the development of membranes made of ion-exchange materials. Such membranes have a low electrical resistance and are more or less selective in the transport of ionized materials of one charge, either positive or negative, and barriers to ionized materials of the opposite charge. While capable of a variety of applications, as discussed below, they have received most attention in the desalting of brackish water containing from 1000 to 5000 p.p.m. of salts. It is difficult at present (1960) to assess the potential impact of this new processing tool in the chemical industry because few data have been published. Membrane materials for experimental use are or have been available from Ionics, Inc., National Aluminate Company, Permutit Company, Rohm and Haas Company, and American Machine and Foundry Company.

The unique properties and uses of ionic membranes were predicted by biologists. The desalting process is described in principle by Meyer ("Natural and Synthetic High Polymers," vol. 4, p. 819, Interscience, New York, 1950). Early attempts at synthesizing membranes involved the gelation of ionic dyes in collodion [Sollner, *J. Electrochem. Soc.*, **97**, 139C (1950)]. In 1949, disks of ion-exchange materials were prepared by Wyllie and Patnode [*J. Phys. & Colloid Chem.*, **54**, 204 (1950)] consisting of commercial granular ion-exchange resins embedded in a polymer matrix. Also at this time, some of the properties of ion-exchange membranes were described by Juda and others of Ionics, Inc. Since then, Ionics has carried out a broad program on membrane synthesis, applications, and development of equipment for using such membranes. The firm has carried out considerable research and development work on the desalting of brackish water for the U.S. Department of Interior.

Properties of Ionic Membranes. The two fundamental and unique properties of ionic membranes are their electrical conductivity and selectivity for ion transport. These properties are dependent on the composition and concentration of the solutions in contact with the membranes.

Electrical Conductivity. The ion-exchange resins, which comprise 60 to 70 per cent of the membrane, are solid hydrated strong electrolytes and might be regarded as solid sulfuric acid or caustic soda. It is also possible to prepare membranes having properties of weak electrolytes, such as ammonia or acetic acid, but these are usually of limited interest because of their sensitivity to pH.

The resins in most common use are polystyrene cross-linked with divinyl benzene to make them insoluble. The ion-exchange resin which is permeable to cations (*i.e.*, positively charged ions) is made by sulfonating the polystyrene resin, which attaches about one sulfonic acid group per benzene ring in the polymer. The acid content of the resin is usually about 5 milliequivalents per dry gram. The ion-exchange resin which is permeable to anions (*i.e.*, negatively charged ions) contains quaternary ammonium groups attached chemically to the polystyrene resin to the extent of 1 to 3 milliequivalents per dry gram.

Electrical resistance of the membranes can be measured by immersing them in a given solution at a fixed distance from two electrodes as shown in Fig. 17-58. A d.c. e.m.f.

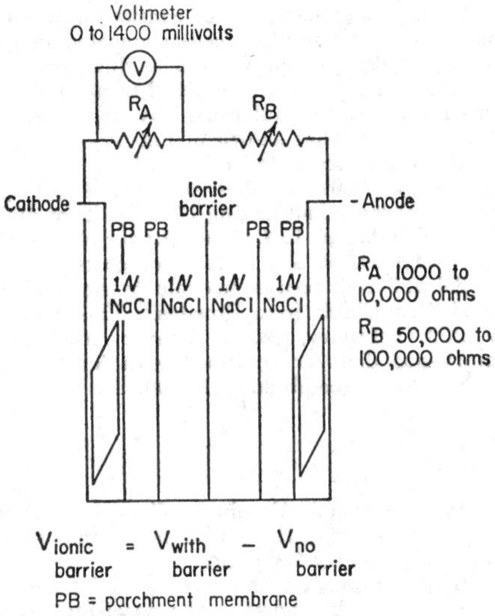

FIG. 17-58. Resistance of ionic-barrier membranes. [*Monet, Chem. Eng. Progress, Symp. Ser.* 24, **55**, 198 (1959).]

is applied across the electrodes and the current flow is adjusted to a desired level, say 10 to 100 amp./sq. ft. The potential drop across the electrodes is measured after a fixed time, say 1 min. The experiment is repeated with the membrane removed. The potential drop across the membrane alone is the difference in the two potential drops and the resistance is obtained by dividing by the current flow. (A simpler method is to measure the resistance by a 1000-cycle a.c. bridge. However, the d.c. method simulates more closely the manner in which the membrane is used practically.) A list of typical specific membrane resistance values is shown in Table 17-14. It should be noted that the unit

Table 17-14. Resistance of Ionic-barrier Membranes

Barrier	Solution 1*N*	Permeable ion	Resistance* (ohm)(sq. ft.)
Anion	HCl	H^+	0.002
	NaOH	Na^+	0.009
	NaCl	Na^+	0.015
Cation	HCl	Cl^-	0.005
	NaOH	OH^-	0.006
	NaCl	Cl^-	0.013
	Na_2SO_4	$SO_4^=$	0.022

* Current density 90 amp./sq. ft.

of specific membrane resistance is ohm-sq. ft. It has the meaning that the resistance of a membrane is the specific resistance divided by the cross-sectional area of the membrane in a direction perpendicular to the flow of electrical current. For example, the electrical resistance of a membrane 5 sq. ft. in area having a specific resistance of 0.01 ohm-sq. ft. is 0.002 ohm.

Selectivity. An ideal ionic membrane has the unique property of allowing ions of only one charge to pass through it. This property arises because of the Donnan equilibrium between fixed ionic groups in the membrane and in the solution wetting the membrane surfaces.

Selectivity can be described conveniently by the transport number of the ion toward which the membrane is supposedly impermeable. The transport number is the fraction of all the ions, both positively and negatively charged, carried through the membrane which have one given electrical charge. For example, a sulfonated polystyrene membrane should be impermeable to negative ions, and a perfect membrane would therefore have a transport number for negative ions, abbreviated t_-, equal to zero. Also a quaternary ammonium resin membrane should be impermeable to positive ions, with $t_+ = 0$. A transport number of 0.3 as defined here would mean that 30 per cent of the ions transported across a membrane, as calculated from Faraday's law, would be of the leakage ion toward which the membrane is supposedly impermeable.

Measurement of membrane selectivities is carried out using an apparatus similar to that shown in Fig. 17-58. The apparatus is filled with a solution of one composition on one side of the membrane and a solution of different composition on the other side. After passage of a given amount of electricity, the solutions adjacent to the membrane are drained and analyzed. The transport number of the leakage ion is the amount of this ion found by analysis divided by the total amount of ions transported as calculated from Faraday's law. Typical values of transport numbers of the leakage ion are shown in Table 17-15.

Table 17-15. Selectivity of Ionic-barrier Membranes

Barrier	Solutions 1*N*		Permeable ion	Leakage ion	Transport No.* leakage ion
Anion	NaCl	NaOH	Na^+	OH^-	0.31
	Na_2SO_4	NaCl	Na^+	Cl^-	0.05
	NaCl	Na_2SO_4	Na^+	$SO_4^=$	0.003
	$MgSO_4$	$MgCl_2$	Mg^{++}	Cl^-	0.12
Cation	NaCl	HCl	Cl^-	H^+	0.52
	HCl	NaCl	Cl^-	Na^+	0.009
	NaCl	$MgCl_2$	Cl^-	Mg^{++}	0.0002

* Current density 90 amp./sq. ft.

It is clear that leakage is low in neutral solutions. However, the leakage of hydrogen ion through cation barrier membranes (*i.e.*, the quaternary-ammonium type) is so high, about 50 per cent, that it would be difficult to use them in acidic solutions. The same is true for anion barrier membranes (*i.e.*, the sulfonic acid type) where the leakage of hydroxyl ion is about 30 per cent. Leakage appears to be high where the flow of a large slow-moving ion, such as sodium ion through an anion barrier membrane, is opposed by the flow of small fast-moving ions such as hydroxyl ions. The electrical leakage of membranes is a serious obstacle because of the commonness of acidic and basic solutions in industry. Recently, Ionics has stated that it is possible to prepare membranes having transport numbers for hydrogen and hydroxyl ions as low as 0.05. Such membranes, if economically feasible, should be of considerable interest in the chemical process industries.

Applications of Electrodialysis. Electrolysis. The potential application of ionic membranes to the electrolysis of aqueous sodium chloride solution has appeared attractive because salt-free caustic soda could be produced without requiring subsequent purification. The process, shown in Fig. 17-59, has not yet been successful

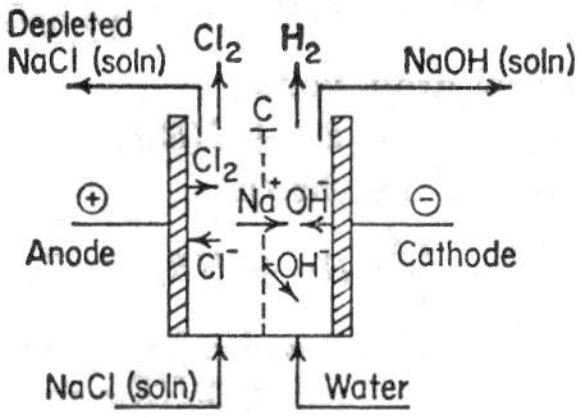

Cathode:	$H_2O + e^-$	$\longrightarrow$	$OH^- + \frac{1}{2} H_2(g)$
Anode:	Cl^-	$\longrightarrow$	$\frac{1}{2} Cl_2(g) + e^-$
Membrane:	Na^+	$\xrightarrow[\text{Membrane}]{\text{Cation}}$	Na^+
Net reaction:	$H_2O + Na^+ + Cl$		$Na^+ + OH^- + \frac{1}{2} Cl_2(g) + \frac{1}{2} H_2(g)$

FIG. 17-59. Oxidation and base production, caustic-chlorine cell. [*Mason and Juda, Chem. Eng. Progress, Symp. Ser.* 24, **55,** 161 (1959).]

commercially because of chlorine attack on the membrane. A second limitation would appear to be electrical leakage of hydroxyl ion. In the process shown, sodium ions move through the anion barrier membrane to the cathode where caustic soda is formed. Fresh sodium chloride solution is fed into the anode compartment where chlorine gas is formed at the anode.

Desalting of Sea Water. A schematic diagram for desalting of sea water is shown in Fig. 17-60. The Ionics, Inc., apparatus consists of about 300 to 600 compartments placed between two electrodes in a way resembling a filter press. The compartments are only about 0.04 in. thick to reduce electrical-resistance losses. As shown, every other membrane is permeable to positively charged ions and the remainder to negatively charged ions. The feed water flows through all compartments in parallel. Under the action of the applied d.c. e.m.f., all sodium ions move toward the cathode and all chloride ions to the anode. In every other compartment the salt is removed from the feed water and is trapped in the remaining compartments because of the impermeability of the adjacent membranes. Typical conditions for a brackish water of 2000 p.p.m. are a product containing 500 p.p.m. salt and a concentrate containing 10,000 p.p.m. salt. The consumption of electrical energy is 5 kw.-hr./1000 gal. of feed solution

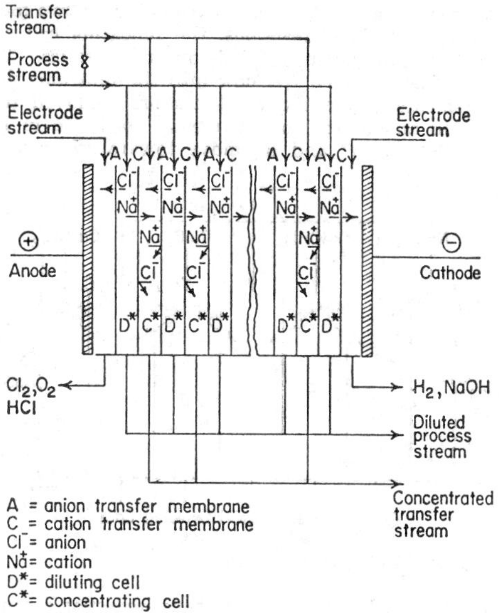

FIG. 17-60. Multimembrane concentrating and diluting cells. [*Mason and Juda, Chem. Eng. Progress, Symp. Ser.* 24, **55,** 156 (1959).]

for a current density of 15 amp./sq. ft. (data supplied by Ionics, Inc., March, 1960).

One of the unsuspected design factors involved is that it is possible to cause water to decompose when the amount of ions transported by the flow of electric current through the membrane exceeds the amount of ions transported from the solution to the membrane by diffusion and convection. A limiting current density for one apparatus is shown in Fig. 17-61. This makes multiple

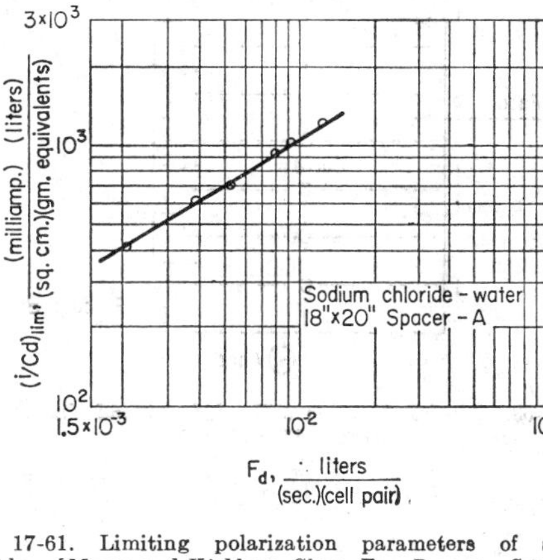

FIG. 17-61. Limiting polarization parameters of sodium chloride. [*Mason and Kirkham, Chem. Eng. Progress, Symp. Ser.* 24, **55,** 179 (1959).]

staging economically attractive to optimize salt removal, discussed by Mason and Kirkham [*Chem. Eng. Progress, Symp. Ser.* 24, **55,** 179 (1959)].

Metathesis Reactions. Metathesis or double-decomposition reactions are of the type $A^+C^- + B^+D^- \rightarrow A^+D^- + B^+C^-$. It is possible in principle to carry out such reactions continuously in apparatus used for desalting water. Whereas in desalting water, the repeating unit or cell consists of two compartments and two membranes, in metathesis reactions, the repeating cell consists of four compartments and four membranes. The feed solutions *AC* and *BD* flow into the first and third compartments, while the reactants are removed from the second and fourth compartments, as shown in Fig. 17-62. Cations A^+ and B^+ move toward the cathode

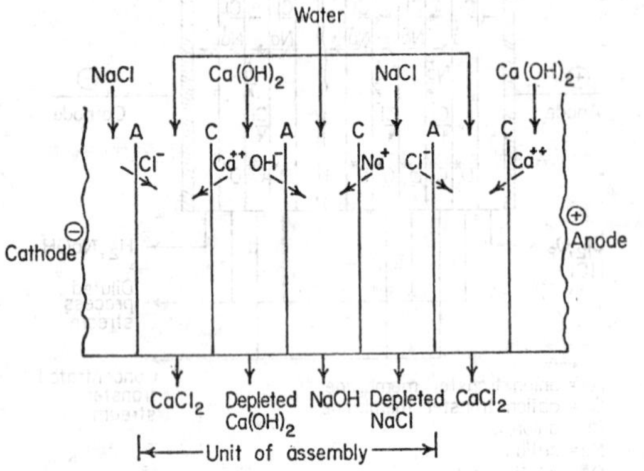

FIG. 17-62. Membrane cell for metathesis production of caustic from lime and salt. [*Mason and Juda, Chem. Eng. Progress, Symp. Ser.* 24, **55**, 159 (1959).]

under the action of the d.c. e.m.f., and anions C^- and D^- move toward the anode. Products *AD* and *BC* are

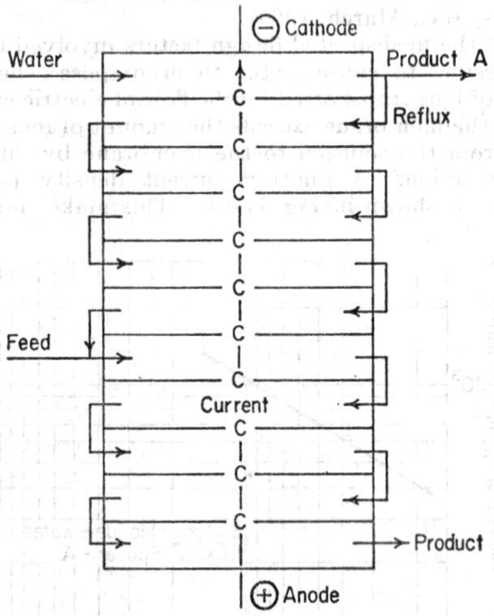

FIG. 17-63. Ion-fractionation still. [*Mason and Juda, Chem. Eng. Progress, Symp. Ser.* 24, **55**, 158 (1959).]

trapped in separate compartments by the selective action of the membranes. So far as is known, no reactions of this type have reached commercial application.

Fractionation of Ionic Mixtures. A schematic diagram for fractionation of cations is shown in Fig. 17-63. It consists of a number of compartments all of which are separated by cation permeable membranes. In this apparatus, the cations tend to move through all the membranes in series toward the cathode but are carried back by a flow of solution which acts as a reflux. At each membrane, the ionic flux is proportional to the product of the mobility times the concentration of the individual ions.

Design of Electrodialyzers. Detailed design of an electrodialyzer can best be done by the vendor because of the large amount of experience available (see Mason and Kirkham, *loc. cit.*); however, a few simple equations are useful for order-of-magnitude calculations. For an electrodialyzer containing *N* unit cells, where *N* might be greater than 100,

$$\text{Capacity, lb. equiv./hr.} = \frac{IAN}{12{,}000} \qquad (17\text{-}66)$$

Terminal potential drop, volts

$$= E_D + I(R_M + R_S)N \qquad (17\text{-}67)$$

Power consumption, kw.-hr./hr.

$$= \frac{IA}{1000} E_D + I(R_M + R_S)N \qquad (17\text{-}68)$$

Unit power consumption, kw.-hr./lb. equiv.

$$= 12I(R_M + R_S) \qquad (17\text{-}69)$$

where I = current density, amp./sq. ft.; A = membrane cross-sectional area, sq. ft.; N = number of unit cells; E_D = decomposition potential plus overvoltage at the electrodes, volts, assumed to be small compared with the voltage drop across N unit cells; R_M = membrane resistance, (ohm)(sq. ft.); R_S = solution resistance, (ohm)(sq. ft.).

In the above calculations, it is assumed that the potential drop required to transport ions from a low to a high concentration is small compared with the potential drop across the membranes and solution. The concentration potential drop E_C in volts is given by the Nernst equation:

$$E_C = \frac{RT}{nF} \ln \frac{C_2}{C_1} \equiv 0.059 \log \frac{C_2}{C_1} \qquad (17\text{-}70)$$

where R = gas constant, 1.99 cal./(g.-mole)(°K.); T = temperature, °K.; n = g.-equivalents/g.-mole; F = Faraday constant, 23,060 cal./(volt)(g.-equivalent); C = concentration, usually in g.-mole/liter.

There are no published data for comparison of this thermodynamic concentration potential with the potential existing across a membrane under electrodynamic conditions.

SECTION 18

LIQUID-GAS SYSTEMS

BY

Aaron J. Teller, Ph.D., Dean, College of Engineering, Cooper Union for the Advancement of Science and Art; Technical Director, Mass Transfer, Inc.; Member, American Institute of Chemical Engineers, American Chemical Society.

WITH

Shelby A. Miller, Ph.D., Professor and Head, Chemical Engineering Department, University of Rochester; Member, American Institute of Chemical Engineers, American Chemical Society.

AND

Edward G. Scheibel, Ph.D., Director of Engineering, Otto H. York Co., Inc.; Member, American Institute of Chemical Engineers, American Chemical Society.

CONTENTS

PHASE SEPARATION

INTRODUCTION

Liquid-gas transfer systems are utilized for the separation of materials based on phase-equilibria relationships, with the rate of transfer controlled by molecular and eddy-diffusion mechanisms. Process equipment utilized for liquid-gas transfer operations is designed for the purpose of achieving such transfer by providing optimum conditions of rate of transfer between the gas and liquid phases with a minimum expenditure of energy and capital investment.

The liquid-gas transfer systems are composed of

Distillation	Evaporation
Flashing	Humidification
Rectification	Dehumidification
Absorption	Dephlegmation
Stripping	Spray drying

Distillation is the separation of the constituents of a liquid mixture via partial vaporization of the mixture and separate recovery of vapor and residue. The process of vaporization is generally of a differential nature.

Flashing is a distillation process wherein the total vapor removed is in phase equilibrium with the residue liquid.

Rectification is the separation of the constituents of a liquid mixture by successive distillations (partial vaporizations and condensations) and is obtained via the use of an integral or differential process. Separations into effectively pure components may be obtained via this procedure.

Stripping or desorption is the transfer of a gas, dissolved in a liquid, into a gas stream. The term is also applied to that section of a fractionating column below the feed plate.

Absorption is the transfer of a soluble component in a gas-phase mixture into a liquid absorbent whose volatility is low under process conditions.

Evaporation generally refers to the removal of water, by vaporization, from aqueous solutions of non-volatile substances.

Humidification and dehumidification refer to the transfer of water between a gas stream and a water stream.

Dephlegmation, or partial condensation, refers to the process wherein a vapor stream is cooled to a desired temperature such that a portion of the less volatile components of the stream is removed from the vapor by condensation.

Spray drying is an extension of the evaporative process wherein almost all the liquid is removed from a solution of a non-volatile solid in the liquid.

All these processes are, in common, liquid-gas mass-transfer operations and thus require similar treatment from the aspect of phase equilibria and kinetics of mass transfer. The fluid-dynamic analysis of the equipment utilized for the transfer also is similar for many types of liquid-gas process systems.

Process equipment utilized for liquid-gas contacting is based on a combination of operating principles of the three categories:

Mode of Flow of Streams

Countercurrent
Cocurrent
Cross flow

Gross Mechanism of Transfer

Differential
Integral

Phase in Turbulence

Gas
Liquid

The combination of these characteristics utilized in the various types of process equipment is indicated in Table 18-1.

Table 18-1. Characteristics of Liquid-gas Systems

Equipment designation	Mode of flow	Gross mechanism	Phase in turbulence	Primary gas-liquid process applications
Packed tower	Countercurrent,* cocurrent, cross flow	Differential	Gas	Absorption, rectification, stripping, humidification, dehumidification
Plate tower	Countercurrent or cross flow	Integral	Liquid	Absorption, rectification, stripping, humidification, dehumidification
Falling film, wetted wall	Countercurrent* or cocurrent	Differential	Neither	Absorption, rectification
Spray system	Cocurrent* cross flow, countercurrent	Differential	Gas	Absorption, humidification, drying
Heat exchanger	Cocurrent or countercurrent	Differential	Gas	Evaporation, dephlegmation
Mixer	Single stage	Integral	Liquid	Absorption
Venturi	Cocurrent	Differential	Gas	Absorption

* Primary type.

VAPOR-LIQUID CONTACTING

TRAY COLUMNS

Tray Types. Plate columns utilized for liquid-gas contacting may be divided into two classifications:

1. Cross-flow plate
2. Counterflow plate

The cross-flow tray (Fig. 18-1*a*) requires a liquid downcomer and is more generally used than the counterflow tray (Fig. 18-1*b*) because of transfer-efficiency advantages and greater operating range.

The flow pattern of the liquid on a cross-flow tray may be controlled by variation in placement of downcomers in order to increase stability of operation or improve the mass-transfer efficiency.

Where the liquid loading on a column is less than 60 to 80 gal./(min.)(ft. of weir) a "normal" cross-flow

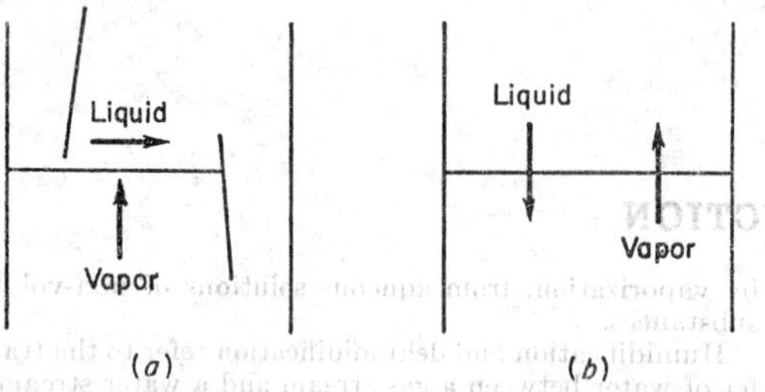

Fig. 18-1. (*a*) Cross-flow tray (side view). (*b*) Countercurrent tray (side view).

pattern with segmental outlet weir is generally used (Fig. 18-2*a*).

In the event of liquid loading exceeding 60 to 80 gal./(min.)(ft. of weir) in a column having sufficient vapor capacity, split flow (Fig. 18-2*b*) and sometimes radial flow (Fig. 18-2*c*) are used.

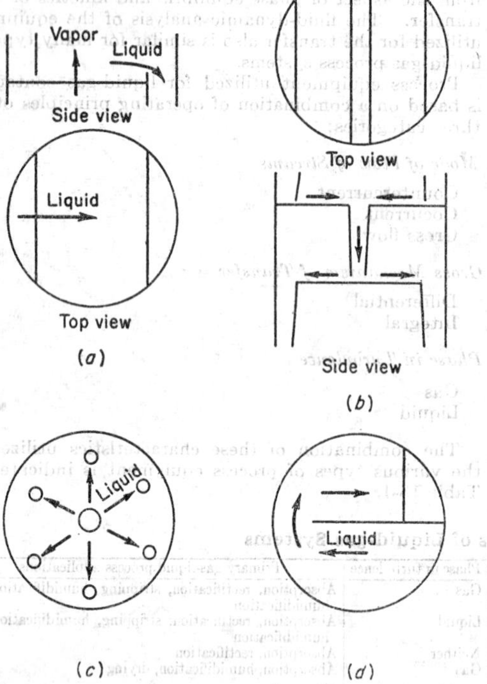

Fig. 18-2. (*a*) Cross-flow pattern. (*b*) Split-flow pattern. (*c*) Radial-flow pattern (top view). (*d*) Reverse-flow pattern (top view).

It should be noted that the fraction of column cross-section area available for gas-dispersion components (*e.g.*, caps or perforations) is significantly lower in split-flow design than in cross-flow design. Thus for the same vapor capacity split-flow design generally requires a larger column diameter than "normal" cross flow.

In the case of a liquid-phase controlling system, with low liquid flows, it may be required to increase the retention time and path of the liquid. This may be achieved by using a reverse flow plate (Fig. 18-2*d*).

The approximate range of operation for various flow patterns as proposed by Huang and Hodson [*Petrol. Refiner*, **37** (2), 104 (1958)] is indicated in Fig. 18-3.

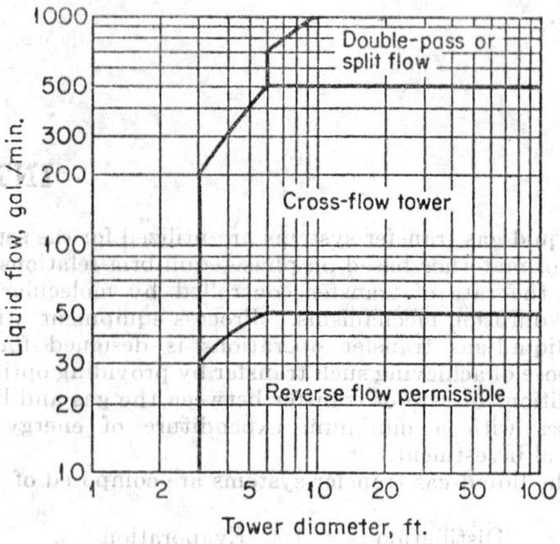

Fig. 18-3. Liquid loading—flow pattern relationship. [*Huang and Hodson, Petrol. Refiner*, **37**, 104 (1958).]

The internals used in plate towers for the purpose of gas dispersion are bubble caps, sieve perforations, or modifications thereof.

The physical-seal dispersion systems consist of the bubble cap and its modification. The bubble-cap seal consists of a riser which acts as a liquid seal and through which the vapor rises. The vapor then proceeds through a reversal path and is then dispersed via slots in the cap. The bubble cap and the basic modification, the tunnel cap, are shown in Fig. 18-4*a* and *b*. The vapor area of the slots varies between 8 and 15 per cent of the tray area.

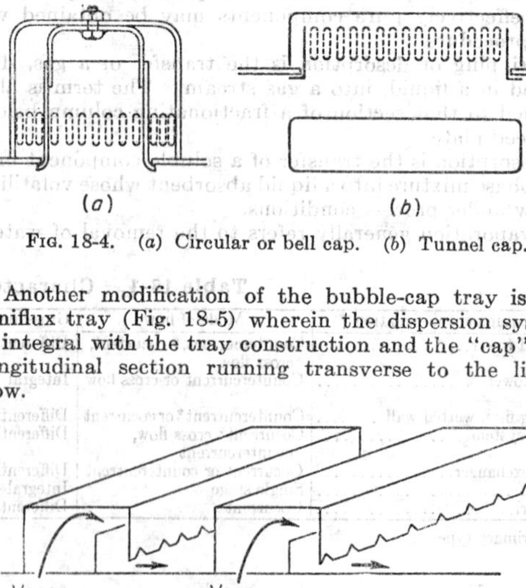

Fig. 18-4. (*a*) Circular or bell cap. (*b*) Tunnel cap.

Another modification of the bubble-cap tray is the Uniflux tray (Fig. 18-5) wherein the dispersion system is integral with the tray construction and the "cap" is a longitudinal section running transverse to the liquid flow.

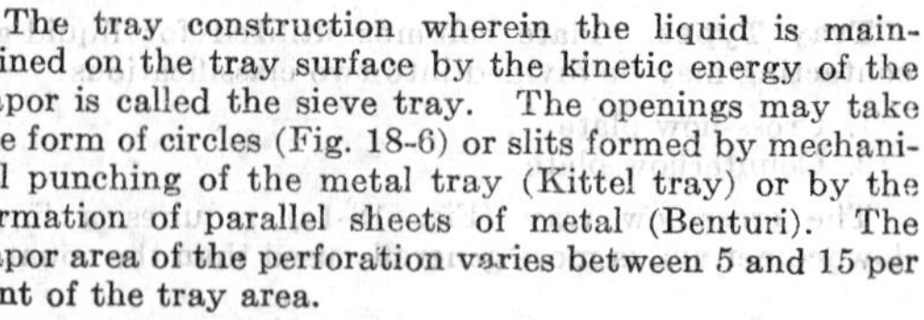

Fig. 18-5. Uniflux tray.

The tray construction wherein the liquid is maintained on the tray surface by the kinetic energy of the vapor is called the sieve tray. The openings may take the form of circles (Fig. 18-6) or slits formed by mechanical punching of the metal tray (Kittel tray) or by the formation of parallel sheets of metal (Benturi). The vapor area of the perforation varies between 5 and 15 per cent of the tray area.

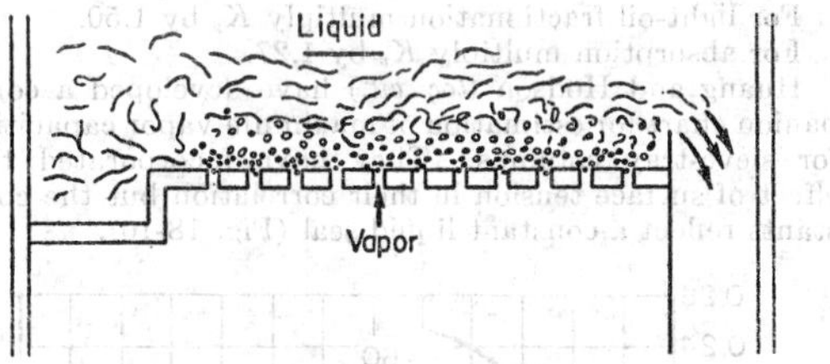

FIG. 18-6. Section through sieve tray.

Recent modifications combining the sieve-tray vapor-dispersion mechanism and a positive mechanical seal are the various types of valve trays with commercial designations of the Koch Flexitray (Fig. 18-7), Nutter tray

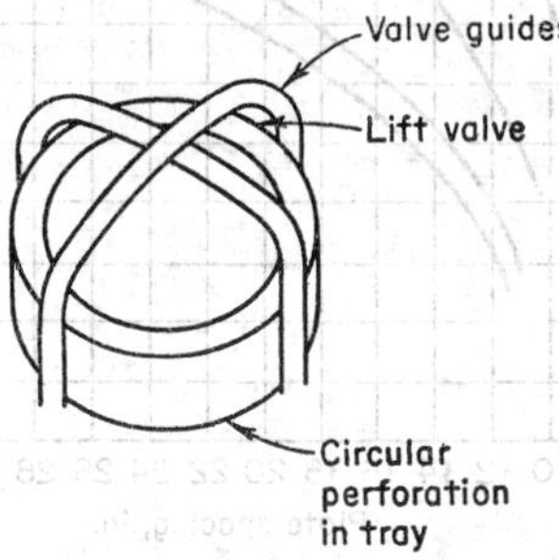

FIG. 18-7. Koch Flexitray.

(Fig. 18-8), and Glitsch ballast tray. These trays all consist of an open section on the tray and a lift-valve closing system providing a variable open area, thus inhibiting tray leakage at low vapor rates. The vapor area of the tray openings varies between 10 and 25 per cent of the tray area.

Counterflow trays such as the turbogrid, perforated, and Ripple trays have vapor-flow areas ranging from 10 to 30 per cent of the tray area.

Tray-column Capacity. *Introduction.* The stable operating ranges of the various types of trays are dependent on the criteria established for stability and therefore vary even for a given tray construction.

The minimum stable operating condition for trays is more easily defined than the maximum-flow condition. In mechanical-restriction trays (bubble-cap type), the minimum vapor flow occurs when only a portion of the vapor-dispersion units are in operation; that is, insufficient vapor flow exists to provide sufficient head for all slots to operate. This is called *pulsating operation.*

In the case of the sieve-tray type of tower, the minimum vapor flow is generally considered as a rate insufficient to maintain the liquid on the tray. The phenomenon that occurs is called *weeping.*

The maximum operating rate is less definable from specific criteria. Column instability may result from *flooding* or *priming.* A rapid decrease in column efficiency may result from *excessive entrainment.* Thus any one of three factors may establish the limiting capacity of a cross-flow tray column and these may not be completely interdependent.

Therefore, any relationship that has been proffered cannot be considered general in application and was developed on the basis of performance characteristics of a given series of columns studied. In column design each of the three factors must be studied to establish the upper limits of operation.

Flooding occurs when the pressure drop through a tray exceeds the liquid head available in the downcomer. In such a case the vapor will tend to short-circuit the normal path and rise through the downcomer.

Priming occurs when the foam on the tray reaches the tray above. This condition causes an additional resistance to the passage of gas through the vapor-dispersion section on the tray above. Thus excessive vapor-pressure drop losses occur and effective entrainment increases, resulting in a limiting column capacity due to either a rapid decrease in efficiency or flooding.

A *critical degree of entrainment* has often been used as the criterion for maximum operation and was the basis of the Souders and Brown relationship. Colburn indicated that entrainment was not the limiting factor.

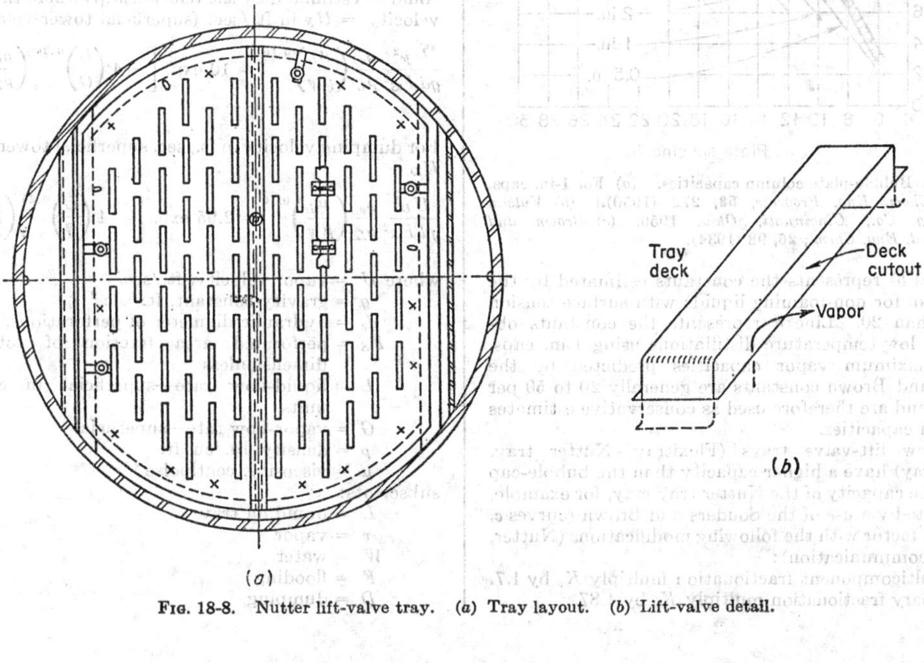

FIG. 18-8. Nutter lift-valve tray. (a) Tray layout. (b) Lift-valve detail.

However, foam level is closely related to entrainment and is probably closely related to the maxima established by Souders and Brown.

Cross-flow Towers. In general the range of operation utilized in industrial operations for cross-flow towers is

$$0.4 < U_{\text{superficial}} \sqrt{\rho_v} < 2.3 \text{ for bubble caps}$$
$$0.5 < U_{\text{superficial}} \sqrt{\rho_v} < 2.5 \text{ for sieve trays}$$

where U_s is the superficial tower velocity in ft./sec. and ρ_v is the gas density in lb./cu. ft.

These values were established for 18-in. tray spacing and the upper limit will vary with tray spacing. However, the stable range of operation is generally four- to fivefold for both bubble-cap and sieve trays.

Based on the correlation for limiting vapor flow related to entrainment, Souders and Brown proposed the relationship

$$U_{\max} = K_v \sqrt{\frac{\rho_L - \rho_v}{\rho_v}} \tag{18-1}$$

The constant K_v is a function of tray spacing and liquid seal. The curved lines (lines *c*) in Fig. 18-9 represent the constants of Souders and Brown. The shaded area (lines *b*) represents the constants estimated by the Vulcan Co. for non-foaming liquids with surface tension greater than 20. Line *a* represents the constants obtained in low-temperature distillations using 1-in. caps.

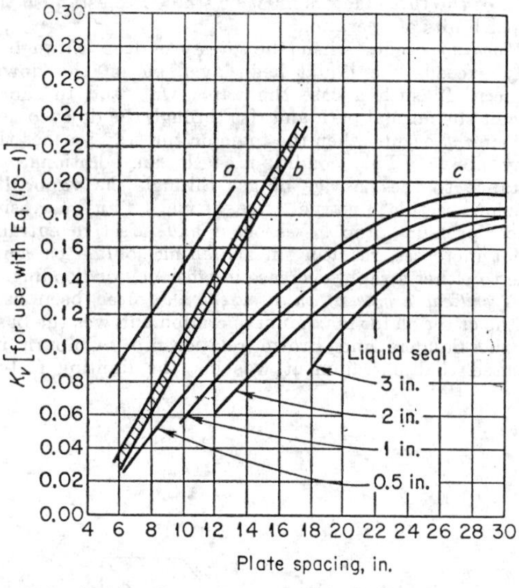

FIG. 18-9. Bubble-plate column capacities. (*a*) For 1-in. caps. [*Wenzel, Chem. Eng. Progress,* **53,** 272 (1950).] (*b*) *Vulcan Engineering Co., Cincinnati, Ohio,* 1956. (*c*) *Brown and Souders, Ind. Eng. Chem.,* **26,** 98 (1934).

The maximum vapor capacities predicted by the Souders and Brown constants are generally 20 to 50 per cent low and are therefore used as conservative estimates of column capacities.

The new lift-valve trays (Flexitray, Nutter tray, Glitsch tray) have a higher capacity than the bubble-cap tray. The capacity of the Nutter tray may, for example, be estimated via use of the Souders and Brown (curves *c*, Fig. 18-9) factor with the following modifications (Nutter, personal communication):

For multicomponent fractionation multiply K_v by 1.7.
For binary fractionation multiply K_v by 1.87.
For light-oil fractionation multiply K_v by 1.50.
For absorption multiply K_v by 1.27.

Huang and Hodson (*loc. cit.*) have developed a companion chart for estimation of maximum vapor capacities for sieve-tray columns. They have incorporated the effect of surface tension in their correlation but the constants reflect a constant liquid seal (Fig. 18-10).

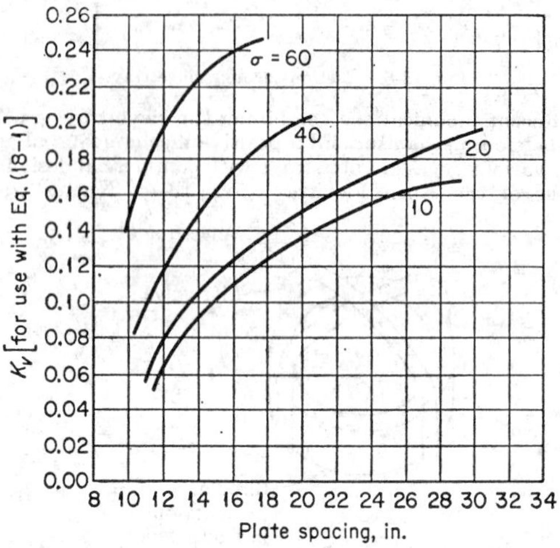

FIG. 18-10. Sieve-tray column capacities. σ = surface tension, dynes/cm.

Counterflow Towers. Counterflow trays have a higher vapor capacity than cross-flow trays but a narrower stable operating range. Majeweski [*Brit. Chem. Eng.*, **4** (6), 336 (1959)] correlated data reported on the behavior of countercurrent trays by various investigators. The stable operating range was found to be less than 2 to 1 compared with a conservative cross-flow stable operating range of 4 to 1.

Majeweski found that the flooding and dumping points could be estimated by the relationships where the flooding velocity $= U_F$ in ft./sec. (superficial tower velocity).

$$\frac{U_F{}^2}{g d_e F_S{}^2} \frac{\rho_v}{\rho_L} \left(\frac{\mu_L}{\mu_W}\right)^{0.16} = 10 \exp.\left[-4\left(\frac{L}{G}\right)^{0.25}\left(\frac{\rho_v}{\rho_L}\right)^{0.125}\right] \tag{18-2}$$

For dumping velocity in ft./sec. superficial tower velocity, U_D

$$\frac{U_D{}^2}{g d_e F_S{}^2} \frac{\rho_v}{\rho_L} \left(\frac{\mu_L}{\mu_W}\right)^{0.16} = 2.95 \exp.\left[-4\left(\frac{L}{G}\right)^{0.25}\left(\frac{\rho_v}{\rho_L}\right)^{0.125}\right] \tag{18-3}$$

where U = vapor velocity, ft./sec.
g = gravity constant, ft./sec.^{2}
d_e = hydraulic diameter of perforations, ft.
F_S = perforated area fraction of total area, dimensionless
L = liquid-flow rate—superficial in consistent units
G = vapor-flow rate—superficial
ρ = density, lb./cu. ft.
μ = viscosity, centipoise

subscripts:
L = liquid on tray
v = vapor
W = water
F = flooding
D = dumping

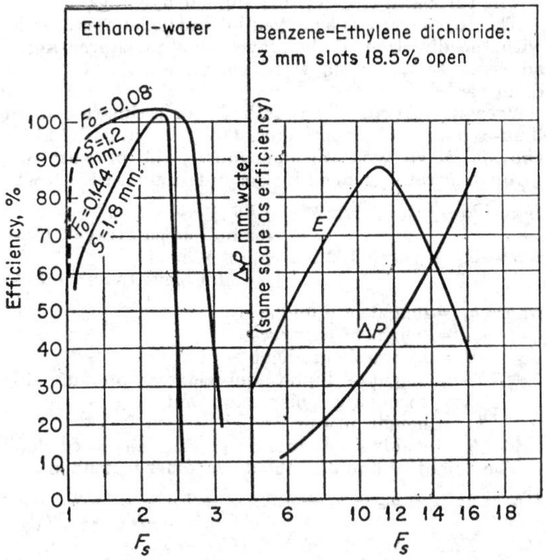

FIG. 18-11. Countercurrent tray efficiency and pressure drop as function of vapor flow. $F_S = U_{sup}\sqrt{\rho_v}$ = ft./sec. $\sqrt{\text{lb./cu. ft.}}$; F_o = fraction of tray open; S = perforation diameter. (*Nerov and Darowskich, Chem. Prom.*, 1957, *p.* 92; *Chim. Nauka i Prom*, 1957, *p.* 95. *Cervinka and Cerny, Chem. Premsyl*, 1955, *p.* 232.)

Equations (18-2) and (18-3) have been found to be valid over the range of variables

$$2.5 < L/G < 148$$
$$0.65 < U_S < 12.2$$

Countercurrent-tray spacing ranges from 8 to 16 in. as a function of anticipated froth height.

The basis for the narrow operating range compared with cross-flow trays results from the existence of an apparent narrow optimum range for attainment of high efficiency in mass transfer.

This phenomenon was noted by Nerov and Darowskich (*Chem. Prom*, 1957, p. 92; *Chim. Nauka i Prom*, 1957, p. 95) (Fig. 18-11) for the ethanol-water system and Cervinka and Cerny (*Chem. Premsyl*, 1955, p. 232) for the benzene–ethylene dichloride system (Fig. 18-11) where $F_S = U_S\sqrt{\rho_v}$.

The data on Ripple-tray performance indicated essentially constant efficiency over the range $1 < F_S < 2$ [Hutchinson and Baddour, *Chem. Eng. Progress*, **52**, 503 (1956)].

Tray Layouts. *Cross-flow trays*, whether bubble-cap or sieve type, are similar in layout (Fig. 18-12*a* and *b*). The tray consists of

1. Active or vapor-dispersion zone
2. Peripheral stiffening zone
3. Disengaging zone
4. Downcomer zone
5. Periphery waste

The downcomer zones generally occupy 10 to 30 per cent of the total tray area.

The peripheral stiffening zone is generally 1 to 2 in. wide and occupies from 2 to 5 per cent of the total area, the fraction decreasing with increase in tray diameter.

The fraction of tray area occupied by the disengaging and inlet distributing zone ranges from 5 to 20 per cent of the total area.

The weir length ranges from 55 to 80 per cent of the column diameter so that the downcomer zone on each end of the plate occupies from 5 to 15 per cent of the total tray area.

The periphery waste occurs primarily with bubble-cap trays and is due to the inability to fit the cap layout to the circular form of the tray.

Typical values of the fraction of total area available for vapor dispersion and contact with the liquid for sieve trays and bubble-cap trays with a weir chord equal to 75 per cent of the diameter are given in Table 18-2.

Table 18-2. Active Tray Area

Column diam., ft.	Cap diam., in.	Active area, fraction of total cross section	
		Bubble-cap tray	Sieve tray
3	3	0.60	0.65
4	4	0.57	0.70
6	4	0.66	0.74
8	6	0.70	0.76
10	6	0.74	0.78

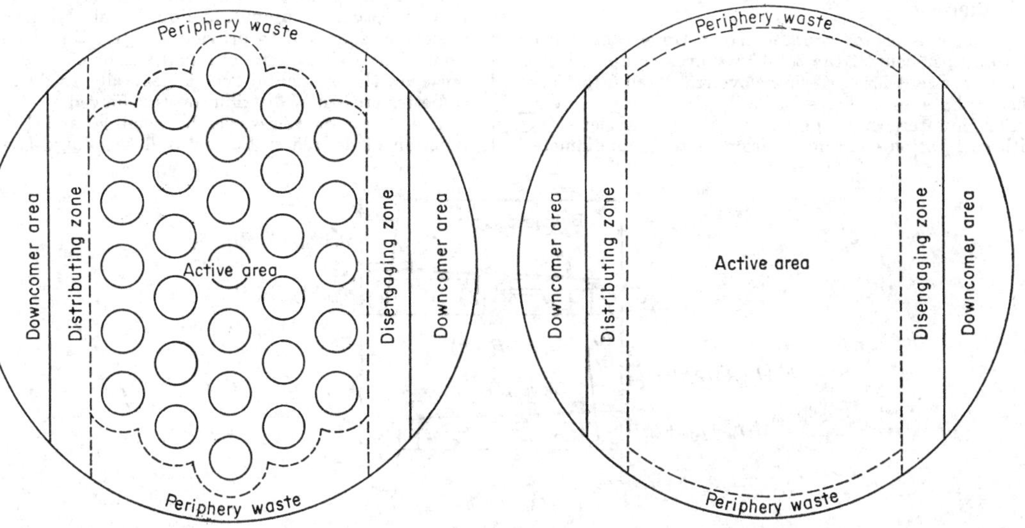

FIG. 18-12. Zone distribution. (*a*) Bubble-cap tower. (*b*) Sieve-tray tower.

The tray thickness, generally established by the mechanical design factors, does not affect the pressure drop of a bubble-cap tray. However, since the tray itself is an integral component of the vapor-dispersion system of the sieve tray, the thickness is significant.

In practice, it has been found that

$$0.1 < \frac{\text{tray thickness}}{\text{hole diameter}} < 0.7$$

However, the smaller the ratio, the higher the dry-plate pressure drop and recommended practice is that

$$0.4 < \frac{\text{plate thickness}}{\text{hole diameter}} < 0.7$$

Bubble caps are generally arranged on an equilateral-triangle layout. Cap spacing should not be less than the cap diameter plus 1 in., in order to avoid impact of vapor streams from adjacent caps. In practice spacing varies from cap diameter plus 1 in. to cap diameter plus 2 in. Cap diameters vary from 2 to 6 in. except in special applications such as low-temperature distillations where caps as small as 1 in. diameter are used.

Hole sizes for cross-flow perforated trays range from ⅛ to ½ in. diameter. The $\frac{3}{16}$-in. perforation is generally used since uniform punchings are difficult to obtain in the ⅛ in. diameter and weeping of the tray tends to increase with hole size.

The spacing of perforations, usually on an equilateral-triangle basis, ranges from 2.5 to 5 diameters. With closer spacing than 2.5 diameters excessive coalescence of bubbles occurs. At spacings greater than five diameters, tray capacity is limited and inactive liquid zones develop between the perforations, thus reducing transfer efficiency.

Countercurrent trays are of perforated or slotted construction and require no downcomers. The vapor and liquid pass countercurrent to each other through the openings on the tray.

Three types of countercurrent trays employed in industrial operation are

1. Perforated
2. Turbogrid
3. Ripple

The open area for countercurrent trays ranges from 10 to 30 per cent of the total tray area compared with 5 to 15 per cent for cross-flow sieve trays and 8 to 15 per cent for bubble-cap trays.

The countercurrent perforated tray is a sieve tray with perforation size ranging from ¼ to ½ in. diameter.

The turbogrid tray has rectangular openings.

The Ripple tray is arranged in sinusoidal cross section with the direction of the wave function alternating on adjacent trays. Hole sizes vary from ⅛ to ⅜ in. diameter.

Pressure Drop. The methods for estimation of the fluid-dynamic behavior of cross-flow trays of both bubble-cap and sieve type are analogous. The pressure drop through a tray is defined by the equation (see Fig. 18-13)

$$H_w = h_s + h_{ow} + 1/2\,\Delta H + h_D + h_r \quad \text{for bubble-cap trays} \qquad (18\text{-}4)$$

$$H_w = h_w + h_{ow} + 1/2\,\Delta H + h_D + h_r \quad \text{for sieve trays} \qquad (18\text{-}4a)$$

where h_s = height of liquid seal
h_{ow} = height of weir crest
ΔH = hydraulic gradient
h_D = height of liquid equivalent to pressure drop through gas-dispersion unit
h_w = height of weir
h_r = residual pressure drop (generally very small)

The height of liquid in the downcomer is defined by

$$H_D = 2h_{ow} + h_w + h_s + 1.5\,\Delta H + h_D + h_r + h_c \quad \text{for bubble-cap trays} \qquad (18\text{-}5)$$

$$H_D = 2(h_w + h_{ow}) + 1.5\,\Delta H + h_D + h_r + h_c \quad \text{for sieve trays} \qquad (18\text{-}5a)$$

where h_c = height of liquid equivalent to pressure drop resulting from flow under the downcomer

The determinations of the seal, weir crest, and loss due to flow under the downcomer are independent of the dispersion method.

Liquid Seal. The liquid seal is that height of liquid above the top of the vapor-dispersion orifice at zero liquid flow. In the case of bubble caps

h_s = height of weir minus height of top of slot above deck

In the case of sieve trays

$$h_s = \text{weir height} = h_w$$

General practice indicates that the seal or static submergence varies from 0 to ½ in. for vacuum service, ½ to 2 in. in atmospheric operation, and 1 to 4 in. for pressure operation.

Weirs and Weir Crest. Weirs are used in cross-flow trays in order to provide a liquid seal for the vapor-dispersion zone and to provide effective liquid distribution. The weir may be of segmental or circular design; however, the segmental type is generally used inasmuch as better cross-flow distribution is achieved.

The height of weir varies between ½ and 4 in. as a function of desired static seal and the liquid-flow rate.

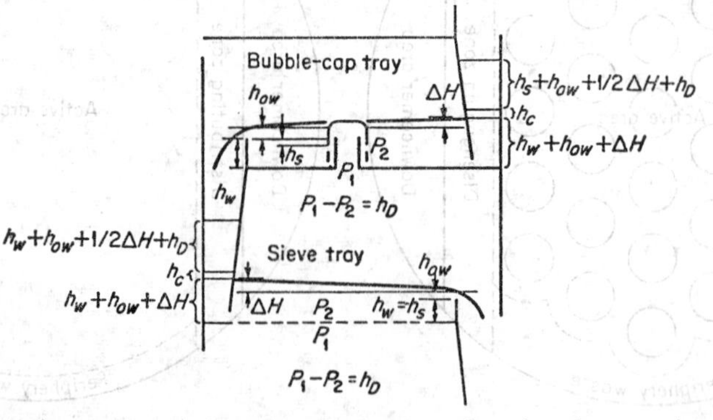

FIG. 18-13. Pressure-drop contributions for cross-flow trays. h_D = pressure drop through cap or sieve, equivalent height of tray liquid; h_w = height of weir; h_{ow} = weir crest; h_s = static liquid seal; ΔH = hydraulic gradient; h_c = loss under downcomer.

When the active total submergence of the vapor-distribution slots or perforations is less than 1 in. jetting of the vapor occurs and entrainment is magnified, thus leading to a decrease in tray efficiency. With increase of submergence, tray operation is stabilized. An increase in the liquid-phase efficiency occurs with increase in slot submergence as a result of increase in liquid-residence time. The choice of submergence is then a function of optimization of tray pressure drop and efficiency.

The weir crest may be calculated from the Francis Weir equation and its modifications for various weir types.

Segmental weir:

$$h_{ow} = 0.48\left(\frac{Q_w}{L_w}\right)^{2/3} \quad \text{in. of liquid} \tag{18-6}$$

where Q_w = liquid flow, gal./min.
L_w = length of weir, in.

Serrated weirs:

$$h_{ow} = 0.7\left[\frac{Q_w}{\tan(\theta/2)}\right]^{0.4} \tag{18-7}$$

where Q_w = liquid flow, gal./min./serration
θ = angle of serration

Circular weir:

$$h_{ow} = \left(\frac{Q_w}{10D}\right)^{0.704} \tag{18-8}$$

where Q_w = liquid flow, gal./min.
D = diameter of weir, in.

In the case of circular-cross-section columns a correction must be made for the distorted pattern of liquid-flow approach to the weir, and a correction factor for effective weir length may be made via use of Fig. 18-14, such that

$$h_{ow} = 0.48F_w\left(\frac{Q_w}{L_w}\right)^{2/3} \tag{18-6a}$$

The use of segmental weirs is generally accepted in process design because of good resultant liquid distribution. Even where circular downcomers are utilized the downcomer is often preceded by a segmental weir.

In cases where the weir crest over a straight segmental weir is less than ¼ in., it is desirable to use a serrated segmental weir to provide good liquid distribution. Inasmuch as fabrication standards permit the tray to be ⅛ in. out of level, weir crests less than ¼ in. can result in maldistribution of liquid flow.

Loss under Downcomer. The head loss under the downcomer may be estimated from the relationship

$$h_c = 0.06\left(\frac{Q}{A_d}\right)^2 \tag{18-9}$$

where Q = liquid flow, gal./min.
A_d = area of flow under downcomer, sq. in.

Although the loss of the downcomer is small, the clearance is significant from the aspect of tray stability and liquid distribution. The seal between the top of the liquid on the tray and the bottom of the downcomer should range between ½ and 1½ in.

Hydraulic Gradient. The hydraulic gradient, the head of liquid necessary to overcome the frictional loss created by liquid passage across the tray, is significant to tray stability inasmuch as it is the only liquid head that varies across the tray length. If the gradient is excessive, the upstream portion of the tray may be rendered inoperative because of increased resistance to vapor flow as a result of increase in liquid head in this zone (Fig. 18-13). In general, the empirical criterion for stable operation is $h_D > 2.5\,\Delta H$.

Bubble-cap trays or modifications thereof exhibit greater hydraulic gradients than sieve trays because of the greater number of flow resistances created by the bubble caps.

Davies [*Ind. Eng. Chem.* **39**, 774 (1947)] developed the basic relationship for hydraulic-gradient behavior for bubble-cap systems

$$\sqrt{\Delta H}\left\{\Delta H\left[3\left(\frac{r}{2}-1\right)+\frac{2}{1+\frac{1}{4}\beta^2}\right] + 3r[d_o + S(\alpha - 1)]\right\} = \frac{r\sqrt{r}\sqrt{1+\frac{1}{4}\beta^2 Q}}{2.4C_D l_l} \tag{18-10}$$

where

ΔH = hydraulic gradient, in. liquid
r = number of rows of caps perpendicular to liquid flow
$\beta = \dfrac{\text{distance between rows of caps}}{\text{minimum distance between caps}}$
d_o = total clear-liquid depth adjacent to weir, in.
S = cap-skirt clearance, in.
$\alpha = \dfrac{\text{total free space between risers in adjacent rows}}{\text{total free space between caps in adjacent rows}}$
Q = liquid flow, gal./min.
C_D = liquid-gradient constant
l_l = total free space between caps normal to liquid flow, in.

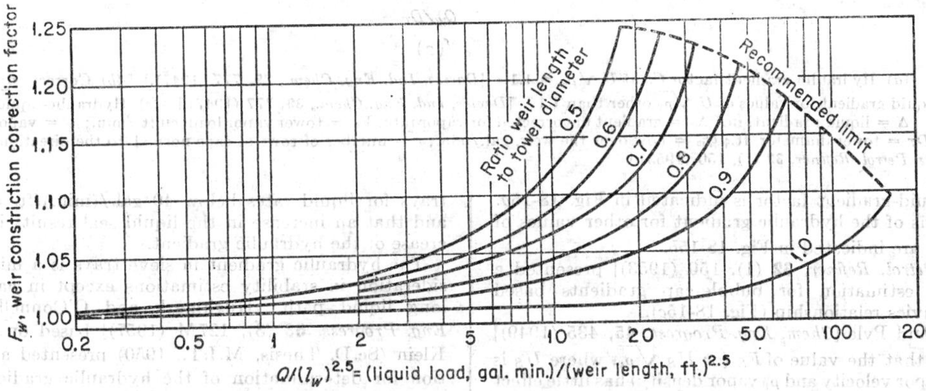

FIG. 18-14. Correction for effective weir length. (*Bolles, Petrol. Processing, February,* 1956.)

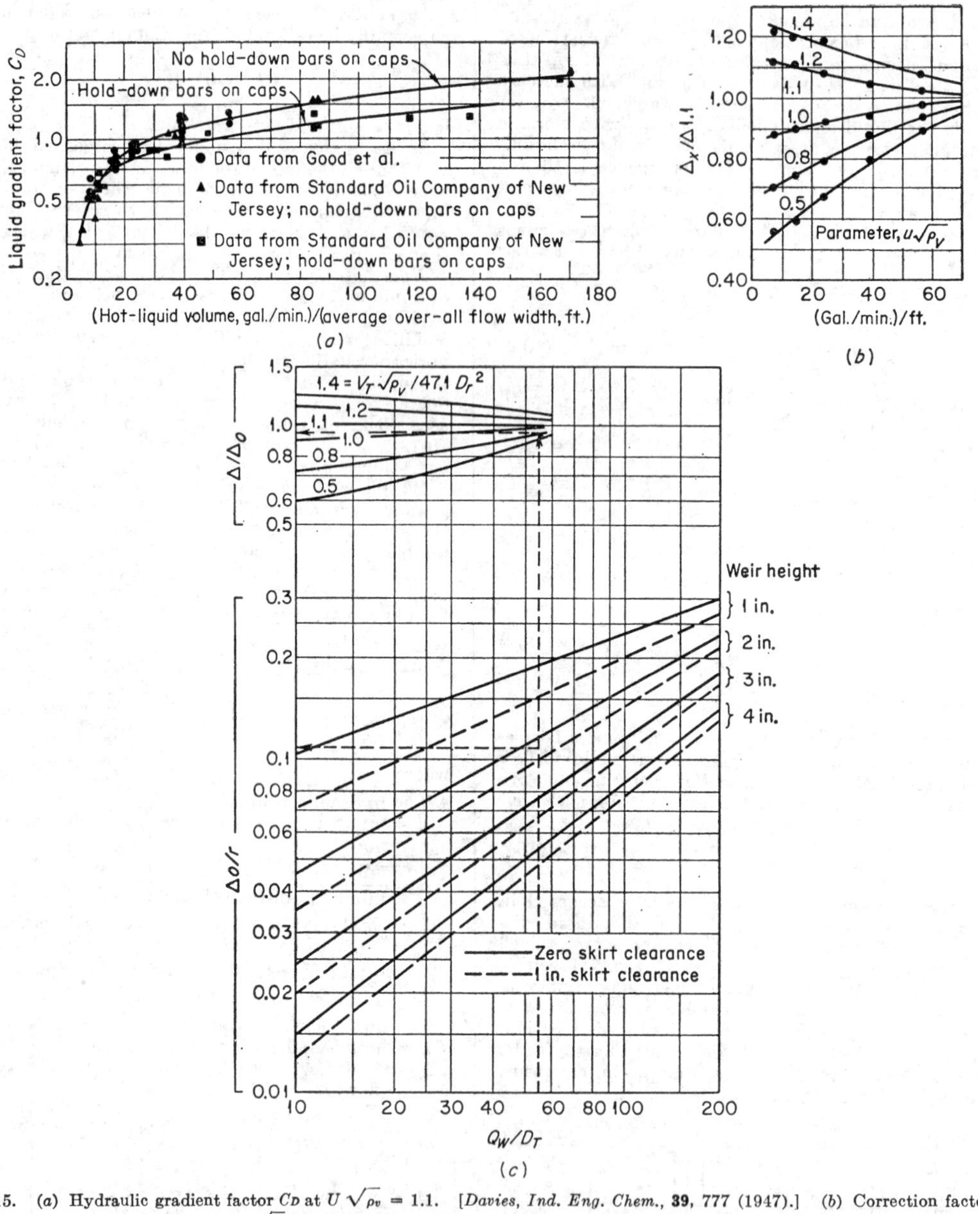

FIG. 18-15. (*a*) Hydraulic gradient factor C_D at $U\sqrt{\rho_v} = 1.1$. [*Davies, Ind. Eng. Chem.*, **39**, 777 (1947).] (*b*) Correction factor for adjusting liquid gradient for values of $U\sqrt{\rho_v}$ other than 1.1. [*Davies, Ind. Eng. Chem.*, **39**, 777 (1947).] (*c*) Hydraulic-liquid-gradient estimation. Δ = liquid gradient, in.; Δ_o = gradient uncorrected for vapor rate; V_t = tower vapor load, cu.ft./min.; ρ_v = vapor density, lb./cu.ft.; D_T = tower diameter, ft.; Q_w = flow over the weir, gal./min.; r = number of rows of caps normal to the direction of liquid flow. [*Zenz, Petrol. Refiner*, **32** (1), 150 (1953).]

The liquid-gradient factor is indicated in Fig. 18-15*a*. Corrections of the hydraulic gradient for other values of $F(u\sqrt{\rho_v})$ are indicated in Fig. 18-15*b*.

Zenz [*Petrol. Refiner*, **32** (1), 150 (1953)] presented a simplified estimation for bubble-cap gradients based on the Davies relationship (Fig. 18-15*c*).

Kemp and Pyle [*Chem. Eng. Progress*, **45**, 435 (1949)] indicated that the value of F_S (or $U_S\sqrt{\rho_v}$, where U_S is the slot vapor velocity and ρ_v vapor density) has little effect on the magnitude of the hydraulic gradient on bubble trays for liquid rates below 40 gal./(min.)(ft. of weir), and that an increase in the liquid seal results in an increase of the hydraulic gradient.

The hydraulic gradient in sieve trays is a minor consideration in stability estimations except in cases of a long liquid path. Hughmark and O'Connell [*Chem. Eng. Progress*, **53** (3), 127M (1957)] based on work of Klein (Sc.D. Thesis, M.I.T., 1950) presented a correlation for determination of the hydraulic gradient on a sieve tray. Although the relationship does not explicitly indicate the effect of vapor velocity the effect is implicit in the choice of the friction factor as a function of the degree of mixing on the tray. The hydraulic gradient, inches of liquid, is predicted by the relationship

$$\frac{\Delta H}{L} = 0.374 \frac{fV^2}{R_H} \tag{18-11}$$

where $R_H = \dfrac{bL_o}{b + 2L_o}$

$L_o = \dfrac{1}{6}(h_{ow} + h_w + 0.5\,\Delta H)$ (where weir height and weir crest are in inches of liquid)

b = average width of tray, ft.

$V = \dfrac{Q}{449 L_o \phi}$ = foam velocity

Q = flow of clear liquid, gal./(min.) (average width of tray, ft.)

ϕ = foam density, lb./cu. ft.

L = length of bubbling path, ft.

As indicated in Fig. 18-16*a*

$$f = 0.47 R_e^{-1} \quad \text{for poor mixing}$$

where $F_S < 9$ (where $F_S = U_S \sqrt{\rho_v}$ as defined above) and U_S = perforation velocity, ft./sec.

$$f = 1.95 R_e^{-1} \quad \text{for good mixing}$$

where $F_S > 9$ and $R_e = \dfrac{R_H V \rho_L}{\mu}$.

Downcomer Height. The downcomer height is one of the factors affecting limiting capacity of column operation. Insufficient downcomer height can result in flooding. The general rule of design for stable behavior is that the downcomer height be equal to twice the estimated clear-liquid height in the downcomer.

The maximum height of liquid in the downcomer consists of the contributions of the various pressure drops and liquid levels as indicated in Fig. 18-13. In the case of bubble-cap trays

$$\text{Liquid height in downcomer} = h_D + h_w + 2h_{ow} + h_s + h_c + 1\tfrac{1}{2}\,\Delta H \tag{18-12}$$

In the case of sieve trays

$$\text{Liquid height in downcomers} = h_D + 2(hw + h_{ow}) + h_c + 1\tfrac{1}{2}\,\Delta H \tag{18-12a}$$

Estimation of the height of liquid in the downcomer via this procedure is conservative, since via aeration the static heights of liquid h_w, h_{ow}, and h_s range from 110 to 125 per cent of the equivalent height during column operation.

Dry Pressure Drop. The pressure drop of the vapor stream through sieve and bubble-cap tray is based on the contraction and expansion losses through the restriction of the vapor-dispersing devices. A basic orifice equation can be applied to sieve trays

$$h_D = C U_o^2 \frac{\rho_v}{\rho_L} \tag{18-13}$$

where U_o = hole velocity, ft./sec.

The orifice coefficient varies with the ratio of perforation diameter to tray thickness and the per cent open area. Leibson, Kelley, and Bullington [*Petrol. Refiner*, **36** (2), 127 (1957)] correlated the pressure-drop data for sieve trays of $\frac{3}{16}$-in.-diameter perforation obtained by Arnold, Plank, and Schoenborn [*Chem. Eng. Progress*, **48**, 633 (1952)]; Hunt, Hanson, and Wilke [*Am. Inst. Chem. Engrs. J.*, **1**, 441 (1955)]; Jones and Pyle [*Chem. Eng. Progress*, **51**, 424 (1955)]; Kamer [*Chem. Eng., Japan*, **18**, 108 (1954)]; and Mayfield, Rasmussen, and Lee [*Ind. Eng. Chem.*, **44**, 2238 (1952)]

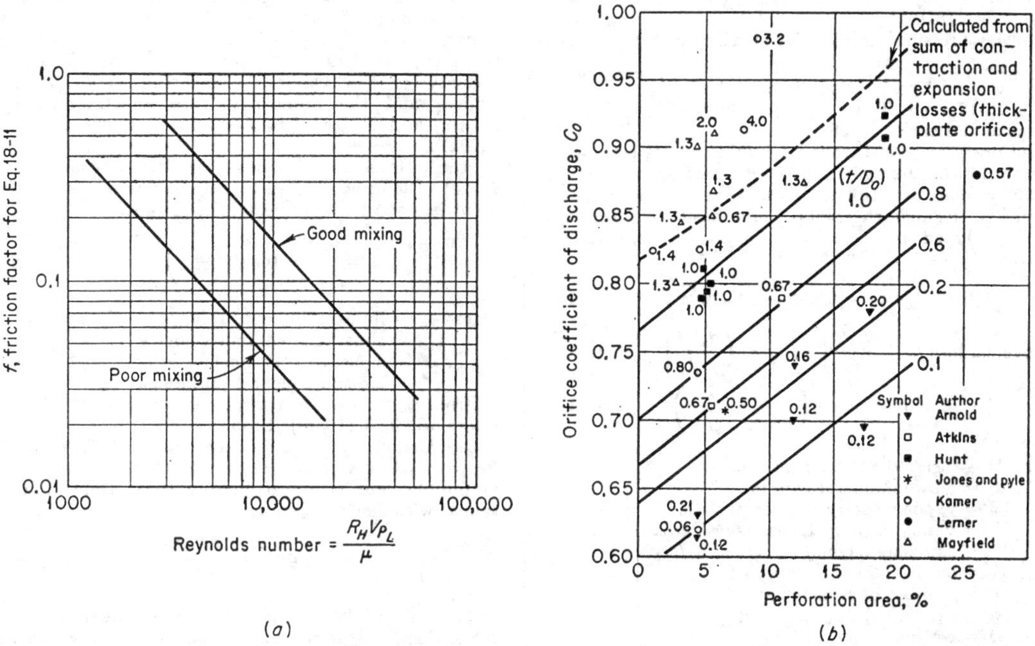

FIG. 18-16. (*a*) Friction factor for hydraulic gradient on sieve trays. [*Hughmark and O'Connell, Chem. Eng. Progress*, **53**, (3), 127M (1957).] (*b*) C_o for dry-tray pressure-drop calculation ($\frac{3}{16}$-in.-diameter holes). [*Leibson et al., Petrol. Refiner*, **36** (2), (1957).]

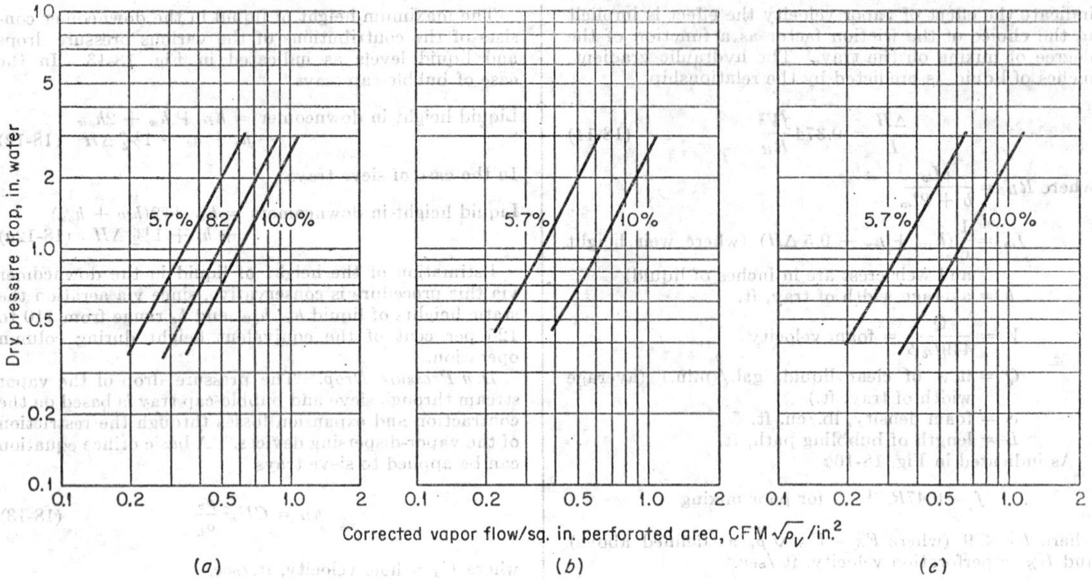

FIG. 18-17. Dry pressure drop for sieve trays. Per cent free area based on perforated zone only. (*Teller, "Allen's Handbook for Oil and Chemical Industries," Philadelphia, Pa., 1958.*) (*a*) $\frac{3}{16}$-in.-diameter perforations. (*b*) $\frac{1}{8}$-in.-diameter perforations. (*c*) $\frac{1}{4}$-in.-diameter perforations.

to determine the effect of these variables on the orifice coefficient for the relationship

$$h_D = 0.186\left(\frac{U_o}{C_o}\right)^2 \frac{\rho_v}{\rho_L} \tag{18-14}$$

where C_o = constant as a function of the ratio of tray thickness to perforation diameter t/D_o (Fig. 18-16*b*)

The dry pressure drop for sieve trays per unit of active area for $0.5 < \left(\frac{\text{tray thickness}}{\text{perforation diameter}}\right) < 0.7$ is indicated in Fig. 18-17*a*, *b*, *c* (Teller, "Allen's Handbook for Oil and Chemical Industries," 1958).

The pressure drop through a bubble cap is estimated from the loss occurring because of contraction in the riser, loss in reversing direction of flow and the contraction, and expansion through the slots. The basic relationships were developed by Dauphine (Sc.D. Thesis, M.I.T., 1939).

$$\text{Riser loss } h_u = 0.111\frac{d_u}{\rho_L}(V_u\sqrt{\rho_v})^{2.09} \tag{18-15}$$

$$\text{Reversal loss } h_r = \frac{2.22}{\rho_L}\left[V_r\sqrt{\rho_v}\left(\frac{d_u}{d_c}\right)^2\right]^{1.71} \tag{18-16}$$

$$\text{Slot blow } h_o = \left(\frac{2.43V_c}{nw\sqrt{\rho_L/\rho_v}}\right)^{2/3} \tag{18-17}$$

where d_u = inside diameter riser, in.
d_c = inside diameter cap, in.
V_u = vapor velocity in riser, ft./sec.
V_r = vapor velocity in narrowest cross section in cap zone beyond the riser, ft./sec.
V_c = cu. ft./min. vapor per slot
n = number of slots in cap
h = pressure drop, in. liquid
w = width of slot, in.

Inasmuch as all losses are related to the volume rate of flow and the square root of the vapor density, the estimation of dry pressure-drop loss is indicated as a function of cu. ft./min. $\sqrt{\rho_v}$ per square inch of active tray surface (Fig. 18-18).

Entrainment. Entrainment in tray columns adversely affects the over-all column efficiency and therefore is a limiting factor in establishing the column velocity; thus many of the correlations regarding limiting flow in columns are related to a maximum entrainment.

Work in entrainment has been of an empirical nature, relating over-all column velocity and effective tray spacing and entrainment, although it is believed that velocity of the vapor through the vapor-dispersion orifices and the liquid-flow rate affect entrainment [Cheng and Teller, *Am. Inst. Chem. Engrs. J.*, **7**, 282 (1961)].

Hunt, Hanson, and Wilke [*Am. Inst. Chem. Engrs. J.*, **1**, 441 (1955)] conducted an extensive study on entrainment in sieve trays and established that

$$e_w = 0.073\left(\frac{U_S}{S'}\right)^{3.2} \tag{18-18}$$

where e_w = lb. entrainment/lb. vapor
U_S = superficial column velocity, ft./sec.
S' = effective tray spacing = tray spacing minus 2.5 times clear-liquid height on tray, in.

From the data of Atteridge *et al.* [*Am. Inst. Chem. Engrs. J.*, **2**, 3 (1956)], Brooks *et al.* (*Petrol. Engr.*, vol. C-32, August, 1955), and Jones and Pyle [*Chem. Eng. Progress*, **51**, 424 (1955)] it appears that the entrainment in bubble caps is approximately three times that obtained with sieve trays and

$$e_w \cong 0.21\left(\frac{U_S}{S'}\right)^{3.2} \tag{18-19}$$

The data of Jones and Pyle reflect an extreme in the ratio of the entrainment in bubble-cap trays to those of sieve trays (Fig. 18-19*a*). In this specific evaluation the ratio varies from 6 to 12.

Simkin, Strand, and Olney [*Chem. Eng. Progress*, **50**, 565 (1954)] determined the entrainment for 5.5- and 5.7-in. bubble caps in a 14.75-in.-diameter column. The empirical relationship correlating their data and data for 2.75-, 4-, and 4.25-in. bubble caps obtained by Sherwood and Jenny [*Ind. Eng. Chem.*, **27**, 265 (1935)], Holbrook and Baker [*Trans. Am. Inst. Chem. Engrs.*, **30**, 520 (1934)], and Strang [*Trans. Inst. Chem. Engrs.*, **12**, 169 (1934)] is

$$\log_{10} \frac{e}{A_f(h_w + h_{ow} - h_e + h_z)} = -3.95 + \frac{27.3}{T} + 10.75 U_S \frac{\rho_v}{\Delta\rho} \quad (18\text{-}20)$$

where e = entrainment, lb./min.
A_f = column cross section available for vapor flow, sq. ft.
h_w = weir height, in.
h_{ow} = weir crest, in.
h_e = elevation of top of slots, in.
h_z = slot opening, in.
T = tray spacing, in.
U_S = column superficial velocity, ft./sec.
$\Delta\rho = \rho_L - \rho_v$

Eduljee [*Brit. Chem. Eng.*, **3** (9), 474 (1958)] correlated most of the previously accumulated data on entrainment in bubble-cap columns and proposed a correlation (Fig. 18-19*b*) correlating the degree of entrainment with superficial velocity, system physical properties, and the height of the plate above the foam level on the tray below.

Caution should be exercised in applying these relationships to columns with effective tray spacing less than 4 in. or greater than 16 in. since entrainment at these levels does not appear to vary significantly with variation in U/S', where S' is distance from top of foam to tray deck above. This phenomenon is due to the fact that at high levels the particle size is so small that drag effects predominate over gravity effects. At low levels the heavy particles are projected with sufficient velocity such that gravity and drag effects are relatively small.

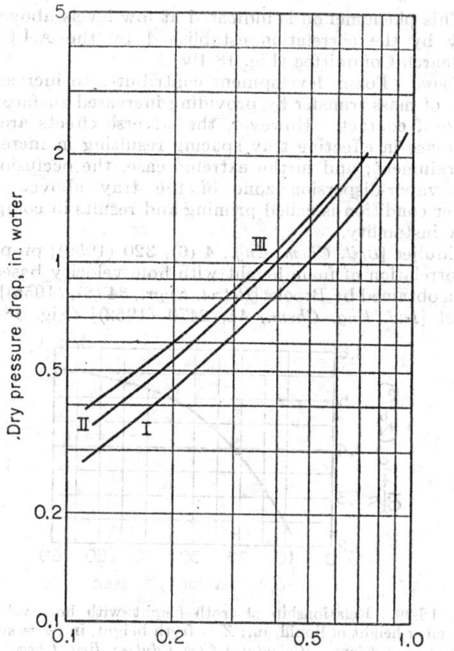

Fig. 18-18. Dry pressure drop through bubble caps.

Curve	Cap diam., in.	Spacing, triangular, in.
I	3	4½
II	4	6
III	6	8

Slots occupy 50 per cent of cap periphery. (*Teller, "Allen's Handbook for Oil and Chemical Industries," Philadelphia, Pa*, 1958.)

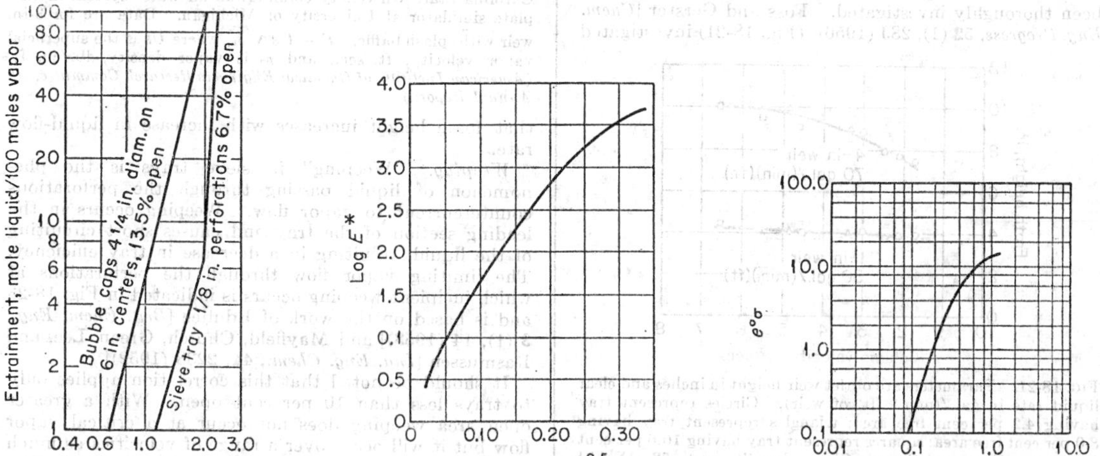

Fig. 18-19. (*a*). Entrainment on bubble cap and sieve trays (18-in. tray spacing). [Jones and Pyle, *Chem. Eng. Progress*, **51**, 424 (1955).] (*b*) Entrainment in bubble-cap trays. $E^* = E \cdot S^{2.59}\mu\sigma^{0.4}$; E = entrainment, lb./(hr.)(sq. ft. free area of plate); E^* = entrainment corrected for liquid properties and plate spacing; U = vapor velocity, ft./sec., based on free area of plate; σ = surface tension of liquid, dynes/cm.; μ = viscosity of liquid, centipoise; ρ_L = density of liquid, lb./cu. ft.; ρ_v = density of vapor, lb./cu. ft.; S = clear height, ft., given by plate-spacing − foam height. [Eduljee, *Brit. Chem. Eng.*, **3** (9), 474 (1958).] (*c*) Entrainment in bubble-cap trays. e° = entrainment, lb. liquid/lb. vapor; σ = surface tension, dynes/cm.; U = superficial column velocity, ft./sec.; S = distance between top of froth and tray above, in. (*"Bubble Tray Design Manual," vol.* 58, *American Institute of Chemical Engineers*, 1958.)

This phenomenon is indicated at low levels above the tray by the correlation established by the A.I.Ch.E. Research Committee (Fig. 18-19*c*).

Foam. Foam development contributes to increase in rate of mass transfer by providing increased surface and time of contact. However, the adverse effects are the decrease in effective tray spacing resulting in increased entrainment; and in the extreme case, the occlusion of the vapor-dispersion zone of the tray above. This latter condition is called priming and results in complete tray instability.

Eduljee [*Brit. Chem. Eng.*, **4** (6), 320 (1959)] proposed a correlation of foam height with hole velocity based on data obtained by Brooks [*Petrol. Engr.*, **34** (8), (1955)] and West [*Ind. Eng. Chem.*, **44**, 2470 (1952)] (Fig. 18-20).

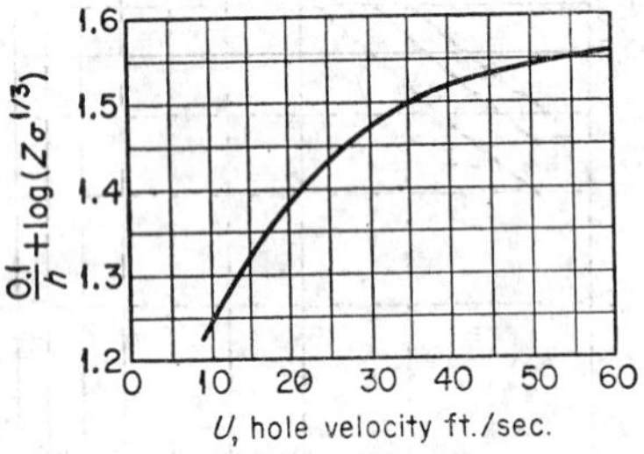

FIG. 18-20. Relationship of froth height with hole velocity. h = clear height of liquid, in.; Z = froth height, in.; σ = surface tension, dynes/cm. [*Calculated from Eduljee, Brit. Chem. Eng.*, **3** (1), 14 (1958).]

The author took into account the height of clear liquid in the correlation. However, it is questionable whether the relationship applies to clear-liquid heights (above the vapor-dispersion device) below ½ in. In such cases, "jetting" or projection of liquid by a gas flume occurs and true foaming is minimized. The entrainment is thus magnified by a physical-projection mechanism.

The effect of liquid velocity on foam height has not been thoroughly investigated. Foss and Gerster [*Chem. Eng. Progress*, **52** (1), 28J (1956)] (Fig. 18-21) investigated

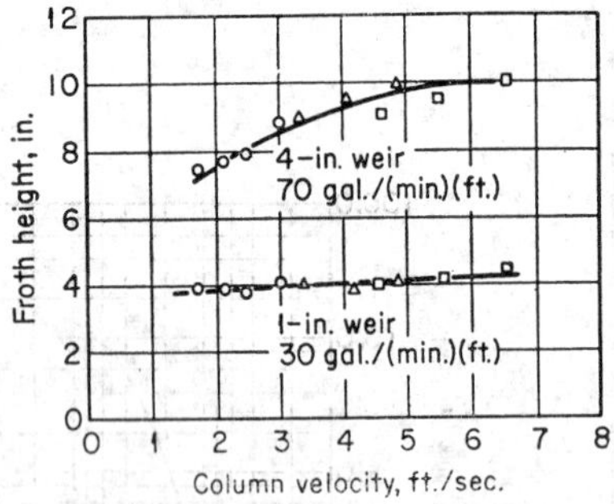

FIG. 18-21. Parameters are outlet weir height in inches and clear liquid rate in gal./(min.) (ft. of weir). Circles represent tray having 4.2 per cent free area; triangles represent tray having 8.0 per cent free area; squares represent tray having 10.6 per cent free area. [*Foss and Gerster, Chem. Eng. Progress*, **52** (1), 28J (1956).]

foam height on sieve trays at 30 gal./(min.)(ft. of weir) and 70 gal./(min.)(ft. of weir). The linear rate at 70 gal./(min.)(ft.), however, was 0.31 ft./sec., whereas the linear rate for 30 gal./(min.)(ft.) was 0.40 ft./sec. as a result of change in weir height. In both cases the foam height above clear liquid was of the same magnitude, 2 to 2½ in. Inasmuch as the linear velocity of the liquid was approximately the same in both cases, no general conclusions concerning the effect of liquid velocity can be drawn.

The froth development on bubble-cap trays has been extensively investigated by the A.I.Ch.E. Research Committee. The data for a range of systems of varying surface tension are correlated in Fig. 18-22. It appears

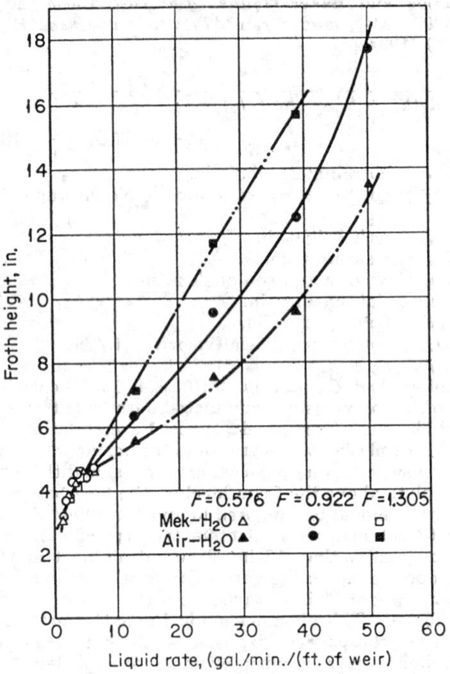

FIG. 18-22. Effect of liquid rate on froth height. Comparison of froth heights for methyl ethyl ketone–water system in North Carolina State University column and air-water system in one-plate simulator at University of Michigan. Data are for 3-in. weir with splash baffle. $F = Us\sqrt{\rho_v}$, where Us is the superficial vapor velocity, ft./sec., and ρ_v is vapor density, lb./cu. ft. (*American Institute of Chemical Engineers Research Committee, 4th Annual Report.*)

that foam height increases with increase in liquid-flow rate.

Weeping. "Weeping" in sieve trays is the phenomenon of liquid passing through the perforations countercurrent to vapor flow. Weeping occurs in the leading section of the tray and causes short circuiting of the liquid, resulting in a decrease in tray efficiency. The limiting vapor flow through the perforations at which incipient weeping occurs is indicated in Fig. 18-23 and is based on the work of Eduljee [*Brit. Chem. Eng.*, **3** (1), 14 (1958)] and Mayfield, Church, Green, Lee, and Rasmussen [*Ind. Eng. Chem.*, **44**, 2238 (1952)].

It should be noted that this correlation applies only to trays less than 10 per cent open. With a greater open area weeping does not occur at a critical vapor flow but it will occur over a range of velocities as much as 40 per cent above the critical flow indicated in Fig. 18-24.

Dumping. Dumping is the bubble-cap tray analogy to weeping but occurs primarily because of excessive liquid flow. When the hydraulic gradient becomes excessive, the leading row of caps ceases operating, and if the liquid level on the tray is greater than the riser height, liquid will tend to dump through the riser to the tray below.

Froth Density. Froth density generally ranges between

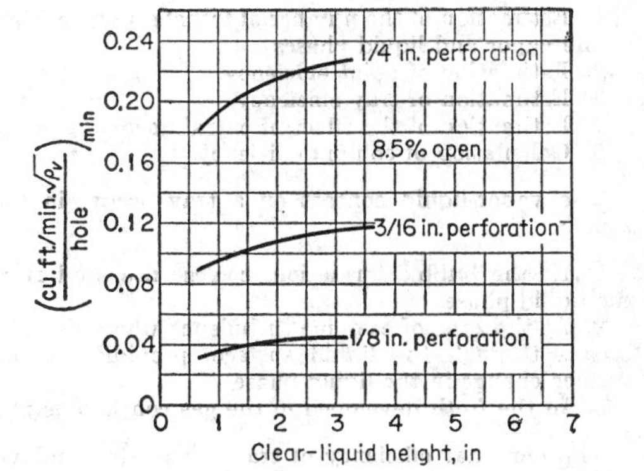

FIG. 18-23. Weep-point correlation. [Calculated from Eduljee, *Brit. Chem. Eng.*, **3** (1), 14 (1958).]

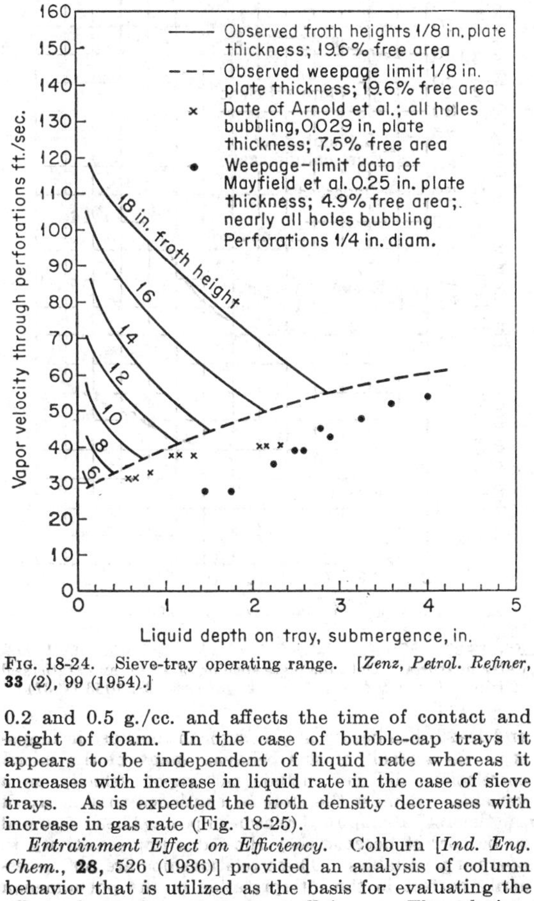

FIG. 18-24. Sieve-tray operating range. [*Zenz, Petrol. Refiner*, **33** (2), 99 (1954).]

0.2 and 0.5 g./cc. and affects the time of contact and height of foam. In the case of bubble-cap trays it appears to be independent of liquid rate whereas it increases with increase in liquid rate in the case of sieve trays. As is expected the froth density decreases with increase in gas rate (Fig. 18-25).

Entrainment Effect on Efficiency. Colburn [*Ind. Eng. Chem.*, **28**, 526 (1936)] provided an analysis of column behavior that is utilized as the basis for evaluating the effect of entrainment on tray efficiency. The relationship is

$$E_a = \frac{E_{MV}}{1 + (eE_{MV}/R)} \tag{18-21}$$

where E_a = apparent tray efficiency including effect of entrainment
E_{MV} = Murphree tray efficiency
e = entrainment, moles liquid/mole vapor
R = internal reflux ratio L/V

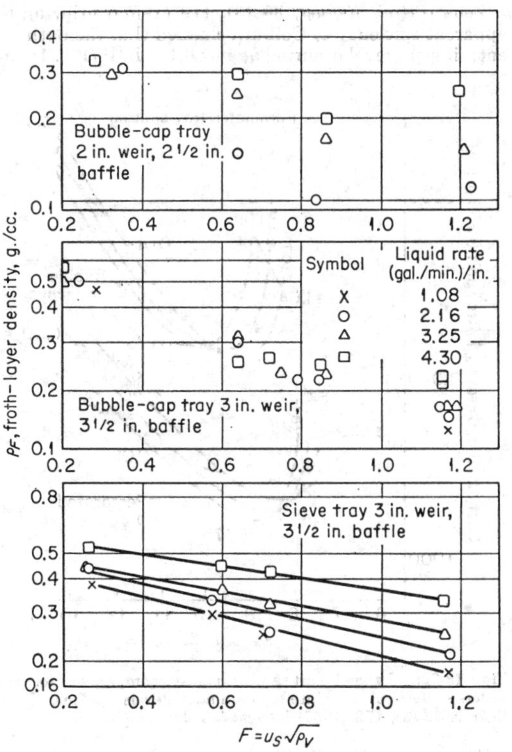

FIG. 18-25. Froth-density characteristics air-water system. (*American Institute of Chemical Engineers Research Committee on Tray Efficiencies in Distillation Columns, 4th Annual Rept.*, 1958.)

It was also indicated by Colburn that, at the economic optimum, $e = R/3E_{MV}$, and that the level of entrainment is so high at this condition that column stability factors will prevail prior to attaining this value of entrainment.

It should be noted that Colburn indicated a limitation in the relationship as reflected that E_a is the *apparent* efficiency at the level of entrainment e.

The limitation is based on the assumption that the differences in change of liquid compositions on successive trays are constant.

A more exact relationship representing the effect of entrainment requires a tray-to-tray analysis and can be expressed as

$$x_{n+2} = x_{n+1} + \frac{E_{MV}/R}{1 + (eE_{MV}/R)} [y^*_{n+1} - Rx_{n+1} - (1 - R)x_D] \tag{18-22}$$

where x = mole fraction in liquid phase of more volatile component of a binary mixture or equivalent binary in a multicomponent mixture
y^* = equilibrium composition (mole fraction) in vapor phase of liquid concentration x
E_{MV} = Murphree tray efficiency
e = entrainment, moles liquid/mole vapor
R = internal reflux ratio L/V

subscripts:
n = tray number
D = distillate

A comparison of trays required for the rectification zone of a benzene-toluene distillation indicated an 18 per cent error obtained with the application of E_a, the apparent efficiency (private communication, D. E. Danly).

Zenz [*Petrol. Refiner*, **36** (3), 179 (1957)] utilizing the apparent efficiency of Colburn claimed that the optimum entrainment level occurred at $e = 0.175L/V$ (Fig. 18-26).

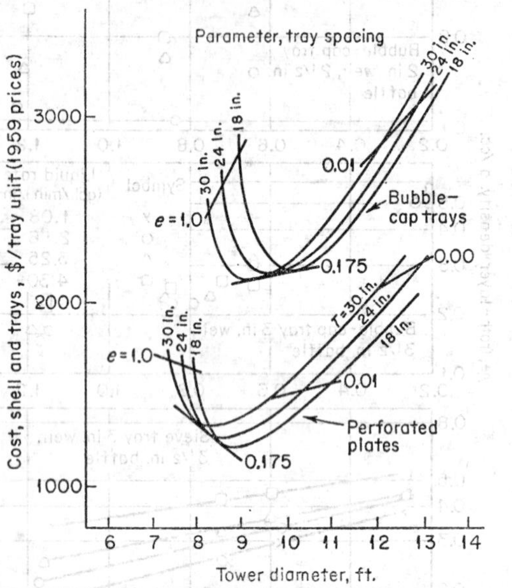

FIG. 18-26. Typical cost and capacity comparison for tray towers—effect of absolute entrainment levels. [*Zenz, Petrol. Refiner*, **36** (3), 179 (1957) *brought to* 1959 *costs.*]

The application of this generalization must be used with caution in that variation in the inherent tray efficiency does affect the additional number of trays required to overcome the effect of entrainment, since via Colburn's apparent efficiency equation

$$\frac{dE_a}{de} = \frac{-E_0/(L/V)}{\{1 + [eE_0/(L/V)]\}^2} \qquad (18\text{-}23)$$

In addition the Zenz generalization optima were obtained for carbon-steel construction and with the use of the Simkin empirical bubble-cap entrainment equation (including extrapolation) for estimation of entrainment.

The use of this relationship results in a higher level of entrainment than that obtained by the Fractionation Research, Inc. (Fig. 18-19*b*) (American Institute of Chemical Engineers, "Bubble Tray Design Manual," p. 59, Science Press, 1958).

Tray Efficiency. The estimation of tray efficiency is still in an empirical state. However, recent analyses have lead to a greater understanding of tray behavior, resulting in an increased accuracy in estimation of tray efficiency.

The Murphree efficiency is generally used for representation of effectiveness of transfer on trays. However, the number of transfer units attained is a more sensitive and fundamental indication of the effectiveness of mass transfer on a tray. The Murphree point efficiency is related to the transfer units achieved by the relationship

$$E_{OG} = 1 - \exp.\,(-N_{OG}) \qquad (18\text{-}24)$$

where E_{OG} = point efficiency based on the over-all vapor-phase concentration gradient
N_{OG} = number of gas-phase transfer units

Thus the more recent methods for the prediction of tray efficiency are based on the following pattern:

1. Estimation of the number of transfer units achieved in the vapor and liquid phases
2. Estimation of point efficiency
3. Estimation of tray efficiency
4. Estimation of the effect of entrainment
5. Calculation of column efficiency

The vapor-liquid contact on a tray occurs in three zones:

1. At the bubble formation, coalescence, and rise in the liquid phase
2. At the zone of extreme turbulence where the vapor breaks through the liquid surface, providing a rapid surface change in the liquid phase
3. In the froth developed in the gas continuous phase

The fact that efficiency of tray towers does not vary greatly over a range of vapor through-put (Figs. 18-27

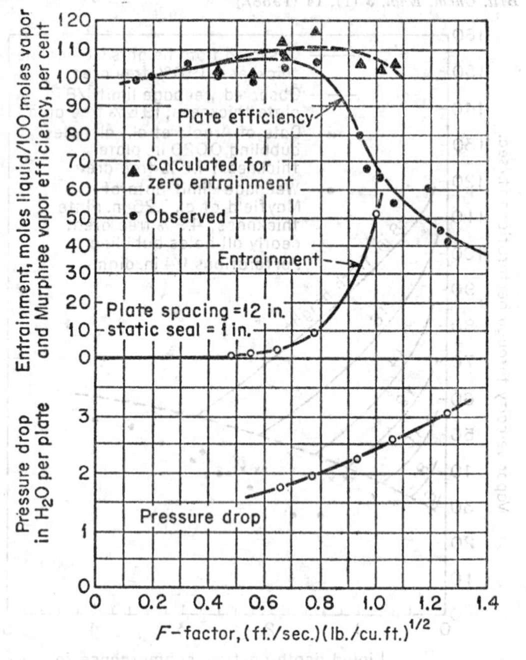

FIG. 18-27. Murphee plate efficiencies for distillation of ethanol-water mixtures. Data for plate spacing of 12 in. and static seal of 1 in. [*Peavy and Baker, Ind. Eng. Chem.*, **29**, 1056 (1937).]

and 18-28) has been a major factor in their use in industry. As a result of this behavior many of the initial correlations did not include the vapor velocity as a variable. It must therefore be cautioned that many of the theoretical-empirical relationships have been assumed to be correct because they showed a low sensitivity to operating variables. These relationships are not necessarily correct in the interpretation of the phenomenon of mass-transfer behavior on trays and therefore may be limited in application to design.

Correlations for tray efficiency fall into one of three categories:

1. Gross correlations
2. Correlations based on transfer in continuous liquid phase
3. Correlations based on transfer in both the liquid continuous and vapor continuous phases

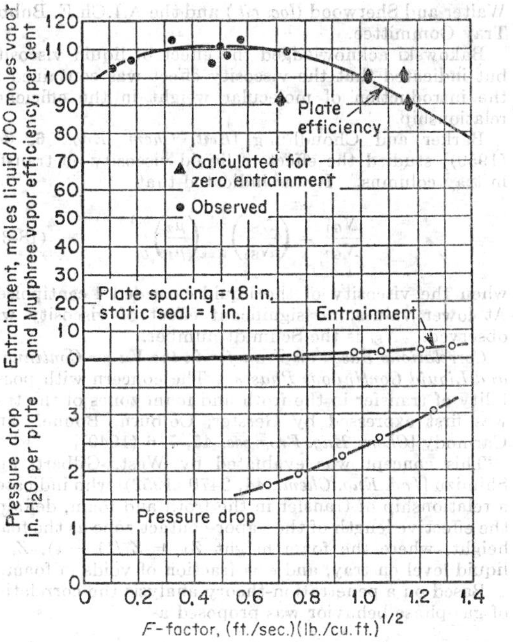

FIG. 18-28. Murphree plate efficiencies for distillation of ethanol-water mixtures. Data for plate spacing of 18 in. and static seal of 1 in. [*Peavy and Baker, Ind. Eng. Chem.*, **29**, 1056 (1937).]

Gross Correlations. In analysis of behavior of petroleum columns, Drickamer and Bradford (*Trans. Am. Inst. Chem. Engrs.*, vol. 39, 1943) were able to correlate tray efficiency with the viscosity of the feed stock and found that E_{MV} is proportional to $\mu^{-0.9}$. O'Connell [*Trans. Am. Inst. Chem. Engrs.*, **42**, 741 (1946)] indicated the effect of relative volatility on efficiency (which is reflected in the relative resistance of the vapor and liquid phases) in his correlation relating the efficiency of commercial and laboratory columns to the quantity $\alpha\mu$. The correlation fitted the experimental data to an accuracy of ± 10 per cent (Fig. 18-29), with 90 per cent of the points falling within 16 per cent of the curve values.

Correlations Based on Transfer within the Liquid Continuous Phase. Walter and Sherwood [*Ind. Eng. Chem.* **33**, 403 (1941)], in a correlation based on data obtained in a laboratory column, indicated that

$$E_{MV} = 1 - \exp.\left[-\frac{Z}{(2.50 + 0.370/HP)\mu^{0.68}W^{0.33}}\right] \tag{18-25}$$

or

$$N_{OG} \alpha \frac{Z}{\mu^{0.68}W^{0.33}} \tag{18-26}$$

where Z = liquid depth above mid-point of slots, in.
W = slot width, in.
μ = viscosity of liquid, centipoise
H = Henry's constant, lb.-moles/(cu. ft.) (atm.)
P = operating pressure, atm.

The correlation (average deviation ± 22 per cent) was established for the range of variables

$1 < Z < 1.8$ in.
$0.7 < \mu < 22$ centipoises

Significant in this work was the fact that efficiency appeared to be only slightly affected by the slot width.

Geddes [*Trans. Am. Inst. Chem. Engrs.*, **42**, 79 (1946)] assumed that the transfer occurred in the liquid continuous phase and that unsteady-state transfer occurred in both vapor and liquid in conformance with the penetration theory. He suggested that the transfer was made between spherical bubbles (equivalent to average bubble volume) and the liquid phase. The relationships proposed were

$$k_G = \frac{a}{3t}\ln F \tag{18-27a}$$

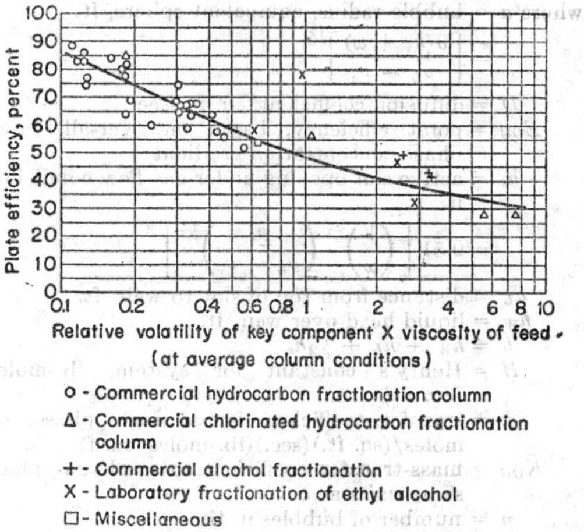

FIG. 18-29. Effect of relative volatility and viscosity on over-all plate efficiency of fractionating columns. [*O'Connell, Trans. Am. Inst. Chem. Engrs.*, **42**, 741 (1946).]

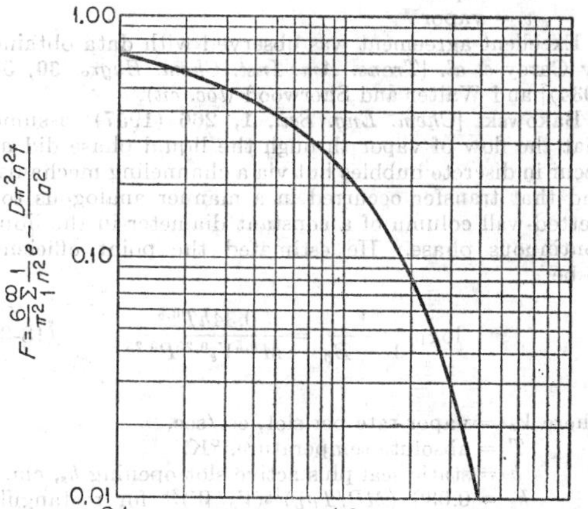

FIG. 18-30. F factor for use in Eq. (18-27a). [*Geddes, Trans. Am. Inst. Chem. Engrs.*, **42**, 88 (1946).]

where F = function of $\left(\frac{D_v\pi^2 t}{a^2}\right)$ (Fig. 18-30)

$$k_L = 1.13\left(\frac{D_L}{t_e}\right)^{1/2} \tag{18-27b}$$

$$K_{OG} = \frac{1}{k_G} + \frac{1}{Rk_L} \tag{18-28a}$$

$$R = zHT \tag{18-28b}$$

and

$$\ln(1 - E_{OG}) = \frac{3K_{OG}t}{a} \tag{18-29}$$

where a = bubble radius, equivalent sphere, ft.

$$= \left[\frac{\sigma(h_s + \omega)}{\rho_L - \rho_v}\right]^{1/3}$$

D = diffusion coefficient, sq. ft./sec.
E_{OG} = point efficiency, based on over-all vapor-phase-concentration gradient
h_s = active slot opening under gas-flow conditions, ft.

$$= 0.51\left[\left(\frac{V}{\omega}\right)^{2/3}\left(\frac{\rho_v}{\rho_L - \rho_v}\right)^{1/3}\right]$$

h_L = distance from top of slot to weir, ft.
h_W = liquid head over weir, ft.
h = $h_W + h_L + \frac{1}{2}h_s$
H = Henry's constant for system, lb.-moles/(cu. ft.)(atm.)
k = transfer coefficient for a single phase, lb.-moles/(sq. ft.)(sec.)(lb.-moles/cu. ft.)
K_{OG} = mass-transfer coefficient, over-all gas phase, same units as k
n = number of bubbles in time t
t = time of rise of a gas bubble through tray liquid, sec. $= \dfrac{h}{4a^{0.37}}$
t_e = average contact time of liquid surrounding bubble, sec. $= \dfrac{2at}{h}$
T = temperature, °R.
V = cu. ft. of gas at std. conditions in time t
z = gas-compressibility coefficient, dimensionless
ω = slot width, ft.
ρ = density, lb./cu. ft.

subscripts:
L = liquid
v = vapor

Excellent agreement was observed with data obtained by Carey *et al.* [*Trans. Am. Inst. Chem. Engrs.* **30**, 504 1934)] and Walter and Sherwood (*loc. cit*).

Bakowski [*Chem. Eng. Sci.*, **1**, 266 (1957)] assumed that the flow of vapor through the liquid phase did not occur in discrete bubbles but via a channeling mechanism and that transfer occurred in a manner analogous to a wetted-wall column of a constant diameter in the liquid continuous phase. He estimated the point efficiency to be

$$\log_{10}\frac{1}{1 - E_p} = \frac{0.34hT^{0.5}}{M^{0.5}V_s^{0.25}P^{0.25}} \qquad (18\text{-}30)$$

where V_s = vapor rate per slot, cc./sec.
T = absolute temperature, °K.
h = static seal plus active slot opening h_s, cm.
h_s = $0.038\,(MP/T\rho_L)^{1/3}(V_s/W)^{2/3}$ for rectangular slots
M = molecular weight of vapor
P = pressure, atm.
W = width of slot, cm.
ρ_L = density of liquid g./cc.
E_p = point efficiency

Good agreement was obtained with data obtained by Carey *et al.* (*loc. cit.*) and Langdon and Keyes [*Ind. Eng. Chem.* **35**, 464 (1943)].

The correlation was applied to data obtained with static submergences varying between ¼ and 1¼ in. The liquid head over the weir and hydraulic gradient were neglected since it was observed that the active liquid level on the tray due to the high degree of turbulence was generally below that of the weir.

The small indirect effect of slot width implied in Eq. (18-30) is in agreement with that observed by Walter and Sherwood (*loc. cit.*) and the A.I.Ch.E. Bubble Tray Committee.

Bakowski acknowledged the effect of liquid viscosity but indicated that the viscosity effect was contained in the introduction of molecular weight in the efficiency relationship.

Barker and Choudhung [*Brit. Chem. Eng.*, **6**, 348 (1959)] studied the effect of liquid viscosity on transfer in tray columns. It was indicated that

$$\frac{N_{G1}}{N_{G2}} = \left(\frac{N_{Sc}}{N_{Sc}}\right)_v^{0.5}\left(\frac{\mu_2}{\mu_1}\right)_L^{0.6} \qquad (18\text{-}31)$$

when the viscosity of the liquid exceeded 4 centipoises. At lower values, no significant effect of viscosity was observed. N_{Sc} is the Schmidt number.

Correlations Based on Transfer in the Vapor Continuous and Liquid Continuous Phases. The concern with possibility of transfer in the froth and foam zones of the tray was first expressed by Gerster, Colburn, Bonnet, and Carmody [*Chem. Eng. Progress*, **45**, 716 (1949)].

This concept was evaluated by West, Gilbert, and Shimizu [*Ind. Eng. Chem.*, **44**, 2470 (1952)] who indicated a relationship of transfer in the froth and foam, defining the effective length of the vapor-contact zone as the foam height, where the foam height $Z_V = Z_i/(1 - \epsilon)$, Z_i = liquid level on tray, and ϵ = fraction of voids in foam.

Based on a penetration-theory analysis the correlation of gas-phase behavior was proposed as

$$\ln\frac{1}{1 - E_G} = \frac{(2.39Z_i/r^{1.5})(D_v/V)^{0.5}[\epsilon^{0.5}/(1 - \epsilon)]}{1 + m(D_v/D_L)^{0.5}(C_{v\,avg}/C_{L\,avg})} \qquad (18\text{-}32)$$

where C_{avg} = conversion factor converting k from ft./hr. to lb.-moles/(hr.)(sq. ft.); conversion-factor units are lb.-moles/cu. ft.
D = diffusivity of solute, sq. ft./hr.
E_G = Murphree point efficiency, vapor concentrations
m = slope of equilibrium line
r = average radius of bubble in foam, ft.
V = superficial gas velocity based on active area in column, ft./hr.
Z_i = initial liquid level above gas-dispersion zone, ft.
ϵ = fraction of voids in foam above active area

subscripts:
v = vapor phase
L = liquid phase

The Distillation Subcommittee of the A.I.Ch.E. Research Committee in an extensive study of the behavior of bubble-cap columns related the number of transfer units achieved based on residence time in the tray zone. Thus,

$$N_G = k_G\bar{a}(RT)\frac{\beta}{U_G} = \frac{k_G\bar{a}t_G}{3600} \qquad (18\text{-}33)$$

and

$$N_L = \frac{k_L\bar{a}\rho_L}{L_m} = \frac{k_L\bar{a}t_L}{3600} \qquad (18\text{-}34)$$

where β = gas hold-up on tray, cu. ft./sq. ft. bubbling area
t_G = true gas residence time, sec.
t_L = true liquid residence time, sec.
R = gas constant in consistent units
T = temperature, °R.
U_G = superficial gas velocity, bubbling surface, ft./sec.
ρ_L = molal density of liquid phase, lb.-mole/cu. ft.

Based on an empirical analysis the time of contact was related to liquid rate, gas rate, and weir height. The final suggested correlations are

$$N_G = \frac{0.776 + 0.116W - 0.290F + 0.0217L}{N_{Sc}^{0.5}} \quad (18\text{-}35)$$

and $N_L = (1.65 \times 10^4 D_L)^{0.5}(0.26F + 0.15)t_L$ (18-36)

where $t_L = \dfrac{37.4 Z_c Z_L}{L}$

$Z_c = 1.65 + 0.19W - 0.65F + 0.020L$
D_L = liquid diffusivity, sq. ft./hr.
$F = U_S \sqrt{\rho_v}$ = ft./sec. (superficial) $\sqrt{\text{lb./cu. ft.}}$
L = gal./min. (average liquid-flow width, ft.)
L_m = liquid flow on bubbling-area basis, lb.-moles/(hr.)(sq. ft.)
W = weir height, in.
Z_L = length of liquid travel, ft.
Remainder of nomenclature as in Eqs. (18-33), (18-34)

The limitations of application of these equations suggested by the committee are

Gas-phase Equation

$N_{Sc} \cong 0.6$
$1.0 < F < 2.6$*
$5 < L < 25$ gal./(min.)(ft.)
$1 < W < 5$ in.
$0.5 < \pi < 6$ atm.

Liquid-phase Equation

$0.2 < F < 2.3$
$5 < L < 100$ gal./(min.)(ft.)
$1 < W < 5$ in.
$1.3 <$ tray length < 3.8 ft.

The correlations assume a completely mixed tray and a zero entrainment level.

The values of N_G and N_L can be combined to obtain the Murphree point efficiency via the relationship

$$\frac{-1}{\ln(1 - E_{OG})} = \frac{1}{N_G} + \frac{mG_m}{L_m}\frac{1}{N_L} \quad (18\text{-}37)$$

Effect of Liquid Mixing on the Tray. The Murphree tray efficiency assumes complete mixing of liquid on a tray. However, actual conditions on a cross-flow tray are such that complete mixing does not occur. A concentration gradient exists resulting in increased tray efficiency.

Lewis [*Ind. Eng. Chem.*, **28**, 399 (1936)] evaluated the relationship between the point efficiency and the plate efficiency for three extreme cases where no liquid mixing occurs. The three cases are

1. Vapor enters plate at uniform composition (Fig. 18-31).
2. Vapor unmixed, liquid flows in the same direction on successive plates (Fig. 18-32).
3. Vapor unmixed, liquid reverses direction on successive trays (Fig. 18-33).

Case 1 has found the widest application in practice and is represented by the relationship

$$E_{MV} = \frac{L_m}{mG_m}\left[\left(\exp.\frac{mG_m}{L_m}E_{OG}\right) - 1\right] \quad (18\text{-}38)$$

Equation (18-38) assumes the following in addition to the base conditions:

1. L/V is constant.
2. Slope of equilibrium curve m is constant for the range of tray concentrations.
3. Point efficiency is constant across the tray.

* Utilization of this relationship for vapor loadings less than the equivalent of $F = 1$ is questionable because of the rapid decrease in value of k_Ga below this rate.

Under actual operating condition, neither the Murphree nor the Lewis assumptions apply since partial back mixing of the liquid occurs. Gautreux and O'Connell [*Chem. Eng. Progress*, **51**, 232 (1955)], assuming, as did Kirchbaum ("Distillation and Rectification," Chemical Publishing, New York, 1948), that the mixing can

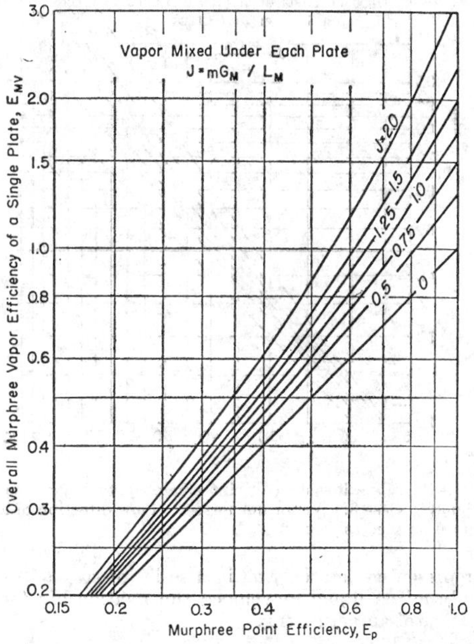

FIG. 18-31. Relationship of point efficiency to Murphree tray efficiency. Case 1. Vapor mixed under each plate.

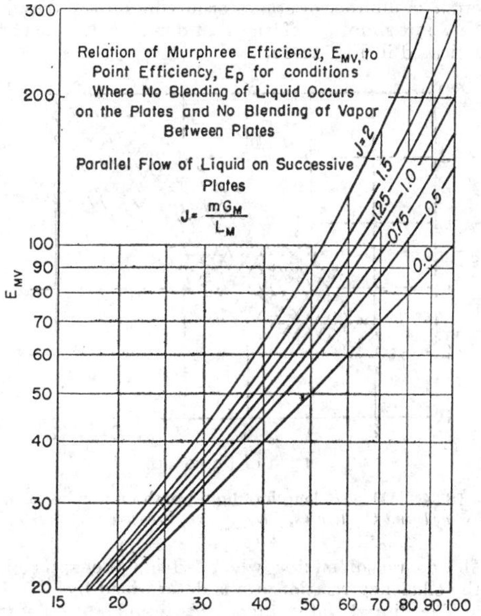

FIG. 18-32. Relationship of point efficiency to Murphree tray efficiency. Case 2. Vapor not mixed under each plate. Liquid flow in same direction on successive plates.

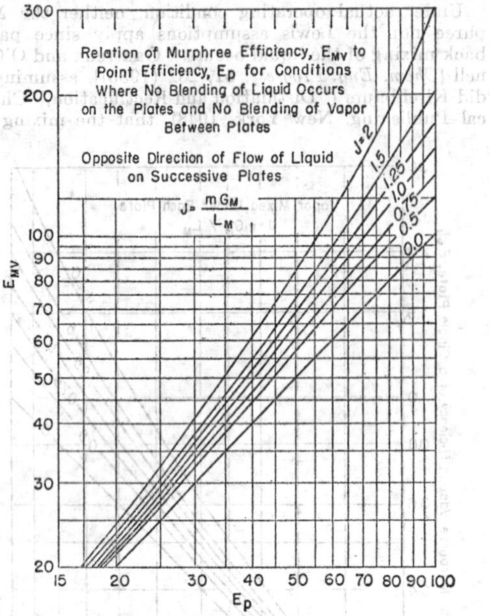

FIG. 18-33. Relationship of point efficiency to Murphree tray efficiency. Case 3. Vapor not mixed. Flow direction of liquid reversed on successive plates.

be represented as occurring in a series of stages of completely mixed liquid, developed the relationship for the behavior of an actual tray

$$E_{MV} = \frac{L_m}{mG_m}\left[\left(1 + \frac{mG_m}{L_m}\frac{E_{OG}}{n}\right)^n - 1\right] \tag{18-39}$$

where n = number of stages occurring on the tray.

An approximation of the number of stages occurring is indicated in Fig. 18-34.

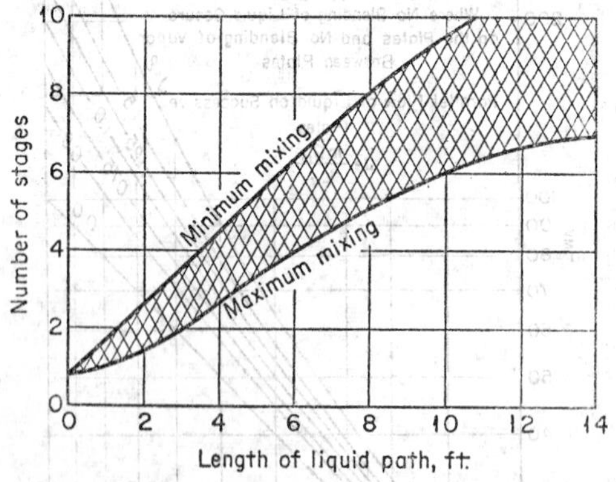

FIG. 18-34. Effect of length of liquid path on number of stages. [*O'Connell and Gautreaux, Chem. Eng. Progress*, **51**, 236 (1955).]

The degree of mixing which affects the applicability of the efficiency relationship is determined by

1. The liquid rate; increased liquid rate decreases back mixing.
2. Obstructions inherent in a tray; the use of a sieve tray will result in less back mixing than the use of a bubble-cap tray.
3. Vapor rate; increased vapor rate will increase turbulence and increase mixing.

An alternate approach, proposed by the A.I.Ch.E. Bubble Tray Committee (A.I.Ch.E. "Bubble Tray Design Manual," 1958), was based on experimental evidence of mixing on bubble-cap trays with water as the liquid phase. The correlation based on a Peclet-number variation is

$$\frac{E_{MV}}{E_{OG}} = \frac{1 - e^{-(n+\mathrm{Pe})}}{[n + \mathrm{Pe}]\{1 + [(n + \mathrm{Pe})/n]\}} + \frac{e^n - 1}{n\{1 + [n/(n + \mathrm{Pe})]\}} \tag{18-40}$$

where $n = \frac{\mathrm{Pe}}{2}\left(\sqrt{1 - \frac{4mG_m}{L_m}\frac{E_{OG}}{\mathrm{Pe}}} - 1\right)$

$\mathrm{Pe} = \frac{Z_L{}^2}{Dt_L}$

Z_L = length of liquid travel, ft.

$(D_e)^{0.5} = 0.0124 + 0.0171U_G + 0.00250L + 0.0150W$ for 3-in. bubble caps on 4½-in. triangular centers

For definition of other terms, see Eqs. (18-35) and (18-36).

The graphical representation for this relationship is indicated in Fig. 18-35*a* and *b*, where $\lambda = mG_m/L_m$

Comparison of Efficiencies of Various Types of Trays. The major emphasis in collating variables affecting column efficiency has been placed on bubble-cap columns primarily because the influx of new types of column internals has occurred only since 1940 and has achieved an accelerated pace only in recent years. The same basic principles of mass transfer apply to the new types of internals, the difference of efficiency due only to variation in vapor distribution and in availability of contact area.

In order to compare efficiencies of various types of internals effectively, the study should be made under the same conditions of flow and submergence. Studies of this nature are limited and comparison except on this basis is questionable.

Jones and Pyle [*Chem. Eng. Progress*, **51**, 424 (1955)] compared the efficiency of a bubble-cap tray (13.5 per cent free area and sieve tray 6.7 per cent free area) in a 18-in.-diameter column, using the acetic acid–water system. Under the conditions of operation, it was implied that entrainment did not significantly affect the tray efficiency. The sieve tray was found to have a wider range of stable operation than the bubble cap and provided a greater efficiency of mass transfer at values of $F = U_s\sqrt{\rho_v}$ less than 1.4 (Fig. 18-36). Mayfield *et al.* [*Ind. Eng. Chem.* **44**, 2238 (1952)] compared sieve-tray and bubble-cap-tray efficiencies for the n-propanol–sec-butanol system. Although the sieve-tray column was of a greater diameter than the bubble-cap column, the length of liquid path was essentially the same in both cases. Entrainment was not significant in either column. By correcting for differences in length of liquid path the sieve tray was found to be 5 to 15 per cent more efficient than the bubble-cap tray.

Gas-phase efficiencies obtained with a ⅛-in.-diameter by ⅜-in.-pitch sieve tray by Wolf (M.S. Thesis, University of Delaware, 1958) and with a 1.5-in.-diameter cap on 2.5-in.-square pitch for the ammonia-air-water system were compared by the A.I.Ch.E. Research Committee by Gerster, Hill, Hochgraf, and Robinson (Efficiencies in Distillation Columns, Final Report, University of Delaware, 1958) and are indicated in Fig. 18-37.

It appears that a change in F value of 0.9 to 1.7 has

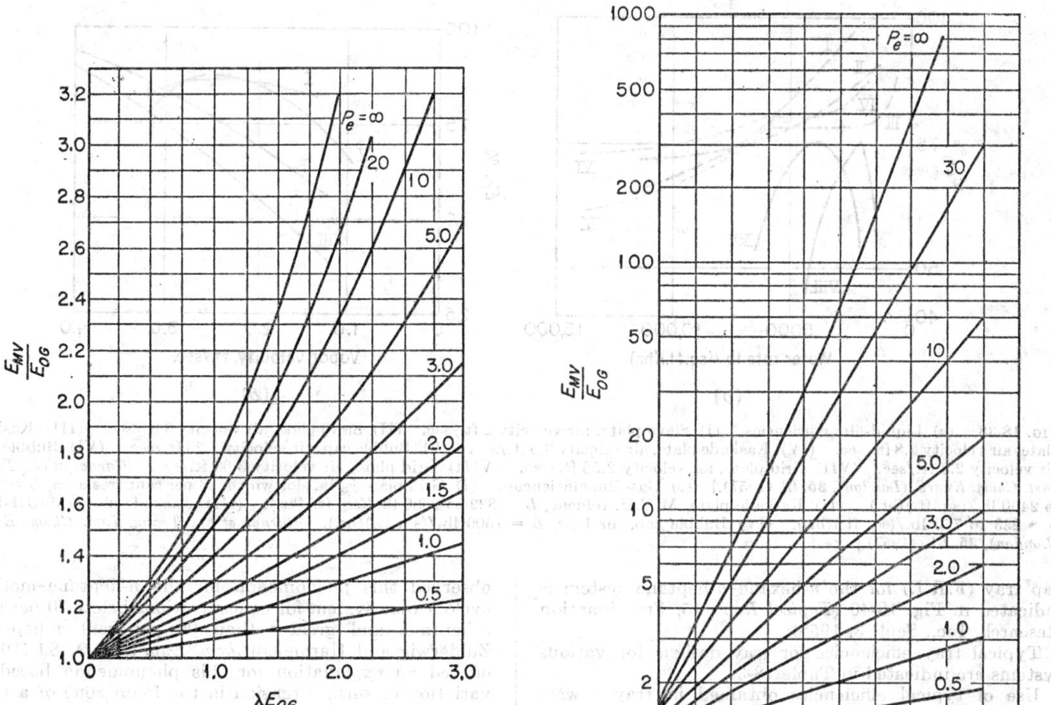

FIG. 18-35. Mixing curves. (*"Bubble Tray Design Manual," American Institute of Chemical Engineers,* 1958.)

little effect on sieve-tray efficiency at a given liquid rate, whereas a considerable change occurs in bubble-cap efficiency. At an F value of 1.7 the sieve tray provided from 5 to 10 per cent greater efficiency than did the 1½-in.-diameter bubble caps.

A comparison of the performance of several trays was made by Garner, Ellis, and Freshwater [*Trans. Inst. Chem. Engrs.*, **35**, 61 (1957)] from data obtained by various investigators for the humidification of air (gas

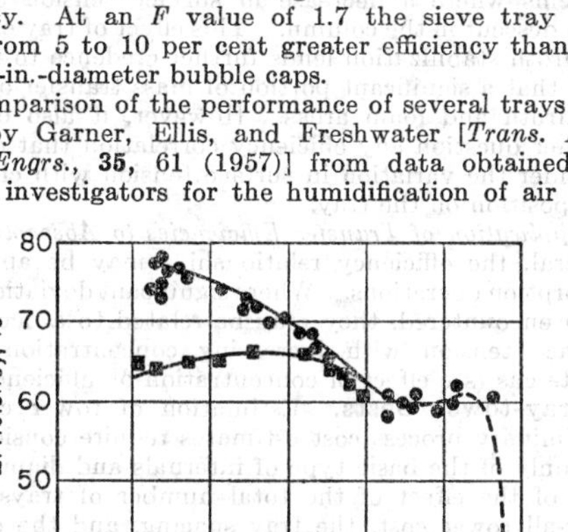

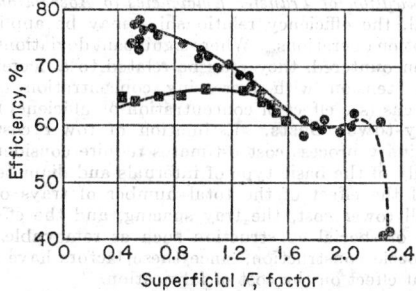

FIG. 18-36. Relative efficiency of sieve and bubble-cap plates. ● Sieve, ⅛-in.-diameter perforations on ⅜-in. triangular centers. Seal = 1.5 in.; plate spacing = 18 in. ■ Bubble cap, 4¼-in.-diameter caps on 6-in. triangular centers. Seal = 1 in.; plate spacing = 18 in. [*Jones and Pyle, Chem. Eng. Progress,* **51**, 424 (1955).]

phase controlling) and oxygen desorption (liquid phase controlling). Inasmuch as submergences and the length of liquid path were different in each case, the efficiencies are not comparable. However, the variation in efficiency with system-flow conditions is typical for the behavior of various types of internals (Fig. 18-38*a* and *b*).

Pollard [*Trans. Inst. Chem. Engrs.*, **35**, 69 (1957)] compared the performance of the Kittel tray with a bubble-cap tray for the β-chlorotoluene–*p*-chlorotoluene system at 30 to 40 mm. Hg (Fig. 18-39).

A comparison of the efficiency of the Glitsch ballast tray (1.53-in.-diameter orifice) and a standard bubble-

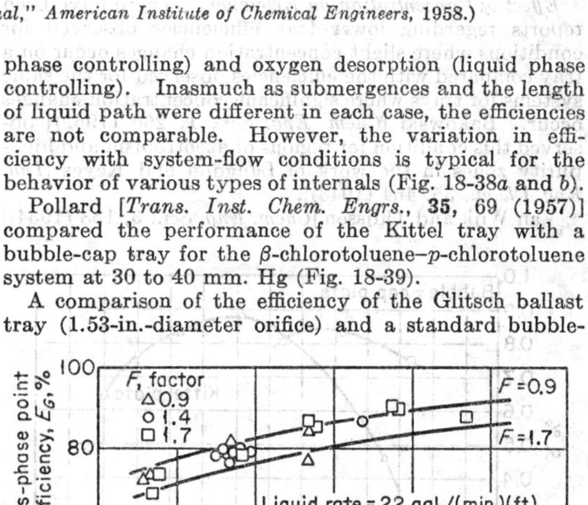

FIG. 18-37. Comparison of gas-phase point efficiency values for a sieve tray and for bubble-cap tray 1. Experimental points show result for the sieve tray; solid lines show the result for tray 1. Ammonia-air-water system at 1 atm. and 20°C. (*Gerster, Hill, Hochgraf, and Robinson, American Institute of Chemical Engineers Research Committee on Tray Efficiencies in Distillation Columns, Final Rept., Dec.* 1, 1958.)

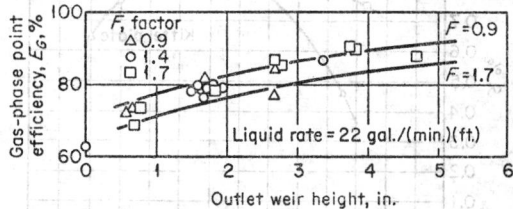

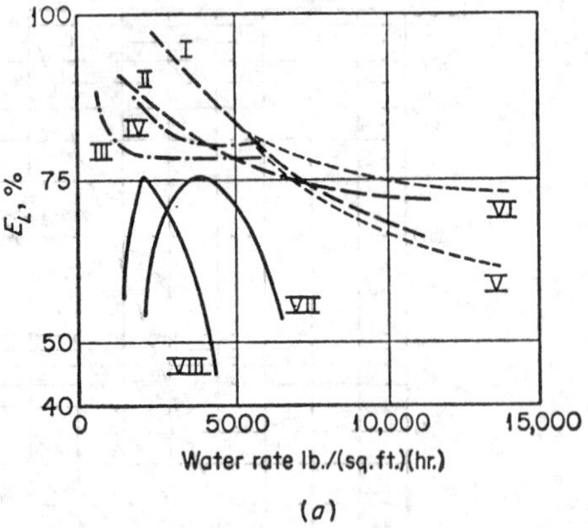

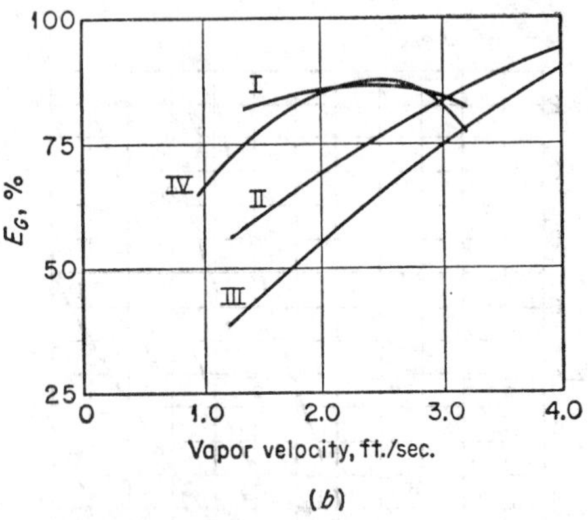

FIG. 18-38. (*a*) Liquid-film efficiencies. (I) Sieve plate, air velocity 2 ft./sec. (II) Sieve plate, air velocity 3 ft./sec. (III) Kaskade plate, air velocity 2.8 ft./sec. (IV) Kaskade plate, air velocity 3.9 ft./sec. (V) Bubble cap, air velocity 1.23 ft./sec. (VI) Bubble cap, air velocity 2.3 ft./sec. (VII) Grid plate, air velocity 2.56 ft./sec. (VIII) Grid plate, air velocity 3.63 ft./sec. [*Garner et al., Trans. Inst. Chem. Engrs. (London)*, **35**, 61 (1957).] (*b*) Gas-film efficiencies. (I) Grid plate ⅛ in. slot width, 23 per cent free area, L = 2380 to 2450 lb./(sq. ft.)(hr.). (II) Kaskade plate, M.C.H.-toluene, L = 822 to 2660 lb./(sq. ft.)(hr.). (III) Kaskade plate, MeOH-H_2O, L = 233 to 760 lb./(sq. ft.)(hr.). (IV) Bubble cap, air-H_2O, L = 1500 lb./(sq. ft.)(hr.). [*Garner et al., Trans. Inst. Chem. Engrs. (London)*, **35**, 61, (1957).]

cap tray (F.R.I.) for the *n*-hexane–*n*-heptane system is indicated in Fig. 18-40 (*Topical Rept.* 15, Fractionation Research, Inc., Sept. 3, 1958).

Typical tray efficiencies for tray designs for various systems are indicated in Table 18-3.

Use of typical efficiencies obtained in tray towers for estimation projections must be tempered with the knowledge of the compositions, liquid path, submergence, vapor and liquid velocities, and tray spacing, inasmuch as variation in any one of these quantities can vitally affect the magnitude of the tray efficiency. Values reported in Table 18-3 are useful, therefore, only to establish ranges of efficiency.

Effect of Concentration on Efficiency. There have been reports regarding lower tray efficiencies observed for conditions where slight concentration changes occur on a tray compared with the efficiencies observed for the same systems for trays where significant concentration changes occur. Bakowski [*Chem. Eng. Sci.*, **1**, 266 (1952)] observed this condition for regions of azeotropism and high-purity zones in the work of Langdon and Keyes [*Ind. Eng. Chem.*, **35**, 464 (1943)].

Van Wijk and Thijssen [*Chem. Eng. Sci.*, **3**, 153 (1954)]

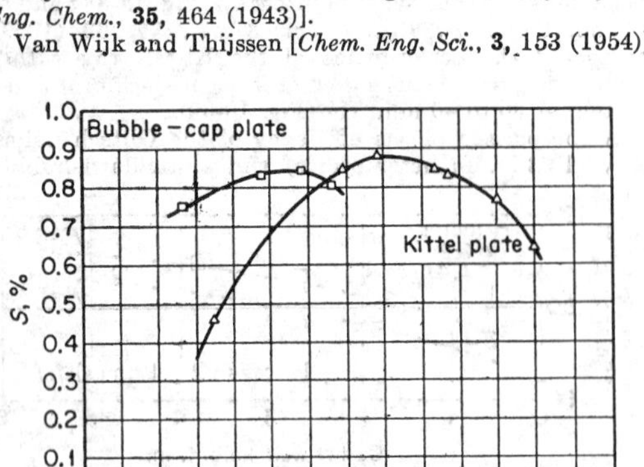

FIG. 18-39. Comparison of Kittle tray and bubble-cap plate. Efficiency against reduced vapor velocity. [*Pollard, Trans. Inst. Chem. Engrs. (London)*, **35**, 74 (1957).]

observed this phenomenon for the *n*-heptane–methylcyclohexane system for concentrations below 70 per cent *n*-heptane and greater than 99 per cent *n*-heptane. Zuiderwig and Harmens [*Chem. Eng. Sci.*, **9**, 89 (1958)] offered an explanation for this phenomenon based on variation of surface tension in the foam zone of a tray. It was indicated that stabilization of foam occurs as a result of variation of surface tension of the liquid phase with the high-surface-tension material concentrating at the interstices and preventing agglomeration. Where the concentration gradient in the liquid is small, foam instability occurs and it is indicated that the mass-transfer rate decreases concomitant with the decrease in stable surface.

The investigators also found that where an increase in surface tension occurred on the tray with descent down the column a higher tray efficiency was observed than for systems where a decrease in surface tension occurred with descent in the column. This effect of tray efficiency via froth stabilization lends further credence to the concept that a significant portion of mass transfer occurs in the froth and foam areas. However, it also opens to further question any efficiency correlation that does not consider the variation in surface tension with change in composition on the tray.

Application of Transfer Efficiencies to Absorption. In general, the efficiency relationships may be applied to absorption operations. Where significant deviations have been encountered, they may be related to a decrease in surface tension with increasing concentration of the solute gas (see effect of concentration on efficiency).

Tray-tower Costs. Estimation of tower costs for preliminary process cost estimates require consideration not only of the basic type of internals and diameter but also of the effect of the total number of trays on the over-all tower cost, the tray spacing, and the effect of choice of special construction such as removable trays and nozzle construction, since these factors have a significant effect on the cost of fabrication.

The approximate purchase prices (1960) of sieve-tray and bubble-cap towers based on welded tray construction (for 12- to 18-in. tray spacing) and a 50-tray-unit basis are indicated in Fig. 18-41*a* and *b*. The correction-cost factor for the total number of trays required in the column is indicated in Fig. 18-41*c*.

Table 18-3. Representative Tray Efficiencies

Type	Diam.	System and conc.	$U_s\sqrt{\rho_v}$*	Static submergence, in.	Liq. rate, gal./(min.)(ft. weir)	Efficiency E_{MV}	Efficiency Column	Pressure, psia	Remarks	Ref.
Bubble cap	15.7 in.	Ethanol 20–60%	0.2–0.4	1.18	...	92–80	...	14.7	Tray spacing 5.3 in.	1
		Water 80–40%	0.2–0.6	1.18	...	95–80	...	14.7	7.9 in.	
			0.2–0.8	1.18	...	87–83	...	14.7	10.6 in.	
			0.2–1.1	1.18	...	97–84	...	14.7	16.3 in.	
	6 in.	Ethanol-water	0.04–0.06	0.25	...	74	...	14.7	...	2
			0.04–0.06	0.5	...	82	...	14.7		
			0.04–0.06	0.75	...	88	...	14.7		
			0.04–0.06	1.25	...	96	...	14.7		
	5 by 9 in.	Methanol–*n*-propanol	0.2–1.0	1.5	...	87	...	14.7	...	3
	5 by 9 in.	Methanol–*i*-butanol	0.2–1.0	1.5	...	74	...	14.7		
	5 by 9 in.	Benzene-carbon tetrachloride	0.2–0.8	1.5	...	86	...	14.7		
	12 in.	Liquid air	0:5	0.41	...	77	...	17.0	...	4
			0.3	0.28	...	67	...	17.0		
	6 ft. 0 in.	C_1–C_6, keys C_3–C_5	0.7–1.0	0.07–0.1	...	...	77–84	47–368	...	5
		C_3–C_6, keys C_4–C_5	1.0–1.1	0.15–0.17	...	...	59–64	116–117		
		C_3–C_6, keys C_4–C_5	0.9–1.1	0.31–0.32	...	...	44–46	146–147		
	7 ft. 0 in.	Methyl cyclohexane, toluene, phenol	...	...	...	...	49–53	16–20	...	6
	4 ft. 0 in.	Cyclohexane–*n*-heptane								
		65.5 mole % C_6	0.97	1	17.5	80.6	...	35.05	Entrainment free basis	7
		30.05 mole % C_6	1.00	1	19.7	86.9	...	34.9		
		50.55 mole % C_6	1.92	1	22.9	71.8	...	23.64		
		28.4 mole % C_6	2.49	...	40.5	83.0	...	23.73		
	18 in.	Ethylene dichloride 20–80%	0.95	0.5	...	111	...	14.7	...	8
		Toluene 80–20%	0.95	0.5	...	89	...	14.7		
		Acetone 20–60%	0.4	0.5	...	40	...	14.7		
		Water 80–40%	0.5	0.5	...	88	...	14.7		
	13 in.	Methanol 10–90%	0.46	2	...	62	...	14.7	...	9
		Water 90–10%	0.6	2	...	92	...	14.7		
	5 ft. 6 in.	Methylene dichloride	0.92	...	17.1	84–91	...	36.7	...	10
		Ethylene dichloride	1.31	...	24.5	88–101	...	36.7		
Tunnel cap	13 ft. 0 in.	Butane-butylene-furfural	0.59	...	70	56	...	86.7–96.7	...	10
		(8–16% butane)	0.79		80	50				
Bubble cap	6 ft. 0 in.	C_6–C_7	0.8	...	...	...	78	24	...	11
			1.25	...	...	...	81	24		
			1.5	...	...	...	77	24		
			2.0	...	...	...	60	24		
Ballast tray	6 ft. 0 in.	...	0.8	3	...	...	78	24	...	11
			1.25	3	...	...	81	24		
			1.5	3	...	...	77	24		
			2.0	3	...	...	60	24		
Sieve tray	6 ft. 0 in. (2-ft. width perforated)	Methyl alcohol 0–10.7% *n*-propyl alcohol 49.2–72% sec-Butyl alcohol 50.2–17.3%	0.7	1½	20	...	58.7	...	...	12
Bubble cap	2 ft. 0 in.	Methyl alcohol 0–10.7% *n*-propyl alcohol 48–73% sec.-Butyl alcohol 52–17%	0.7	...	...	...	50.3	...	...	12
Sieve tray	6 ft. 0 in. (2-ft. width perforated)	Methyl alcohol 0–11.9% *n*-propyl alcohol 30.6–72.7% sec.-Butyl alcohol 52.2–15–4%	0.9	1½	30	...	67.3	...	...	12
Sieve tray	18 in.	Acetic acid–water	0.5	...	...	...	76	...	...	13
Bubble cap	18 in.	Acetic acid–water	0.5	...	...	...	65	...	...	13
Sieve tray	18 in.	Acetic acid–water	1.4	...	...	...	65	14.7	...	13
Bubble cap	18 in.	Acetic acid–water	1.4	...	...	...	65	14.7		
	24 in.	*n*-pentane–*m*-xylene	0.9	...	33	114.9	...	14.7	...	14
						118.0	...	14.7		
	8 ft. 0 in.	Benzene, toluene, xylene	2.31	1	17–26	...	54	17.5	...	14
Sieve tray	13 ft. 0 in.	Mixed xylenes + C_8, C_9, C_{10} paraffins, C_8, C_9, C_{10} naphthenes	2.12 (rect.) 1.81 (stripping)	...	45.5 (rect.) 51.6 (stripping)	...	85.5	25	...	14

* U_s = superficial vapor velocity, ft./sec.; ρ_v = vapor density, lb./cu. ft.

References:

[1] Kirschbaum, *Z. Ver. deut. Ing. Beih. Verfahrenstech.*, No. 5, p. 131, 1938; No. 3, p. 69, 1940.

[2] Carey, Sc.D. Thesis, M.I.T., 1930.

[3] Brown, Souders, Nyland, and Hesler, *Ind. Eng. Chem.*, **27**, 383 (1935).

[4] Lubo and Williams, Liquid Air Fractionation, *O.S.R.D. Rept.* 3768, 1944. Astan, Tests of Perforation of Portable Units for Liquid Air Rectifying, *O.S.R.D. Rept.* 1944.

[5] Cicalese, Davies, Harrington, Houghland, Hutchinson, and Walsh, *Petrol. Processing*, **1**, 296 (1946).

[6] Drickamer, Brown, and White, *Trans. Am. Inst. Chem. Engrs.*, **41**, 555 (1945).

[7] F.R.I. Tests, Fourth Annual Progress Rept., Research Committee, A.I.Ch.E., 1956.

[8] Oliver and Watson, *Am. Inst. Chem. Engrs. J.*, **2**, 18 (1956).

[9] Gerster, Bonnet, and Hess, *Chem. Eng. Progress*, **47**, 621 (1951).

[10] "Bubble Tray Design Manual," A.I.Ch.E. Research Committee, Science Press, 1958.

[11] Topical Report 15, Fractionation Research, Inc., 1958.

[12] Mayfield, Church, Green, Lee, and Rasmussen, *Ind. Eng. Chem.*, **44**, 2238 (1952).

[13] Jones and Pyle, *Chem. Eng. Progress*, **51**, 424 (1955).

[14] Gerster, Hill, Hochgraf, and Robinson, A.I.Ch.E. Research Committee, Tray Efficiency in Distillation Columns, Final Report, University of Delaware, 1958.

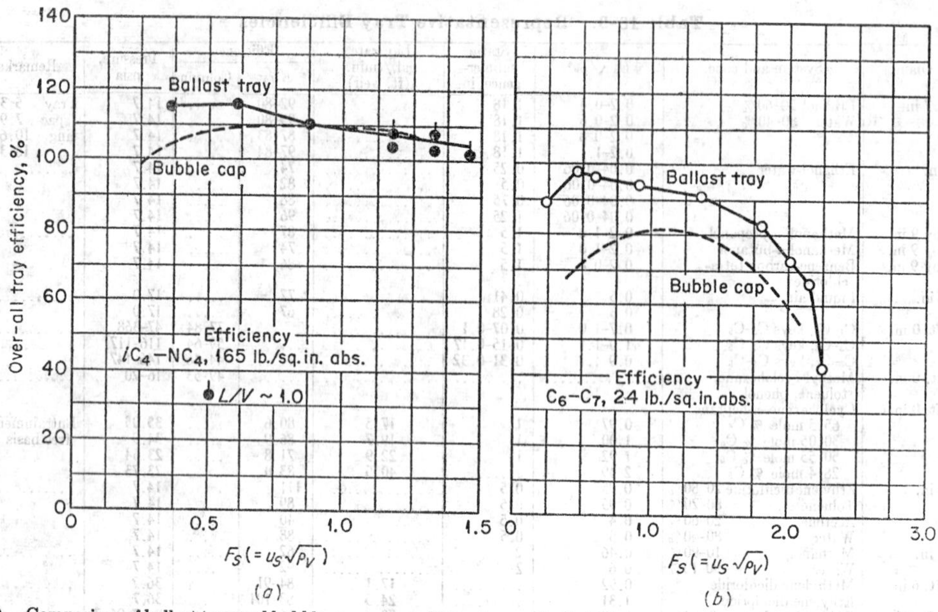

FIG. 18-40. Comparison of ballast tray and bubble-cap tray—efficiencies. (*Topical Rept.* 15, *Fractionation Research, Inc., Sept.* 3, 1958.)

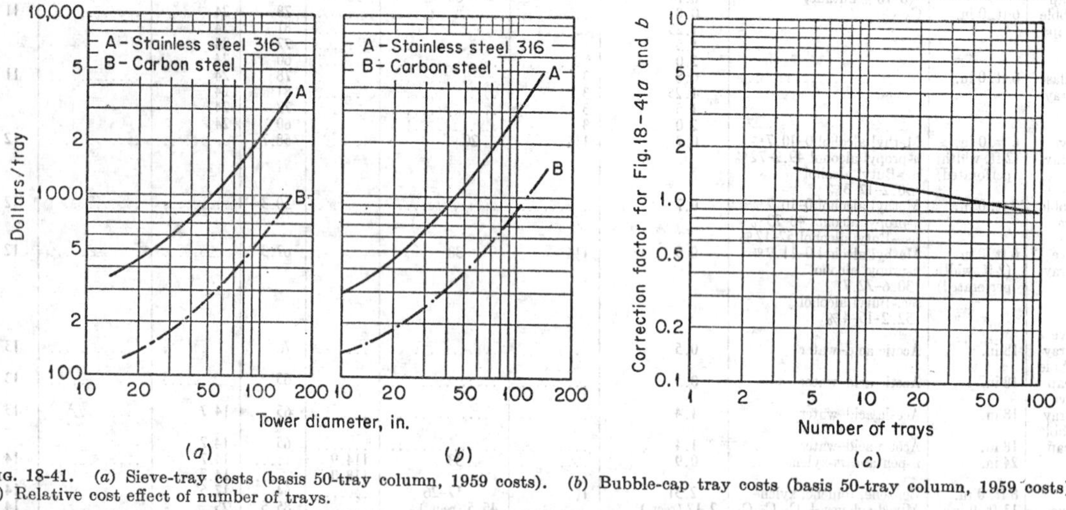

FIG. 18-41. (*a*) Sieve-tray costs (basis 50-tray column, 1959 costs). (*b*) Bubble-cap tray costs (basis 50-tray column, 1959 costs). (*c*) Relative cost effect of number of trays.

The costs of tray columns as a function of the material of construction may be roughly estimated from the following factors:

Carbon steel	1
410 stainless steel	1.6–2.4
304 stainless steel	2.0–2.7
316 stainless steel	2.3–3.2
Monel	3.0–4.0

Optimization of Design. The criterion for optimization of design of plate towers is based on the achievement of the desired separation at a minimum operating cost including amortization. The minimum cost of operation is obtained when

$$\frac{d(\text{over-all costs})}{d(\text{operation and design variables})} = 0$$

and
$$\frac{d^2(\text{over-all costs})}{d(\text{operation and design variables})^2} > 0$$

The optimization of the effect of design variables is generally determined for specific columns rather than by application of generalizations since variables associated with the design may be quite different from those proposed in generalized optimization equations. Process conditions which may be varied to achieve optima in design are

1. Ratio of liquid-stream flows (reflux ratio or liquid-gas ratio)
2. Operating pressure
3. Feed condition

Equipment and process characteristics which affect optimum design are

1. Materials of construction
2. Utility costs
3. Labor costs
4. Type of internals in column

5. Quantity and purity of overhead product
6. Tray efficiency
7. Type of vapor-liquid equilibrium relationship

An example of an optimization relationship where reflux ratio was used as the prime variable is indicated in Fig. 18-42.

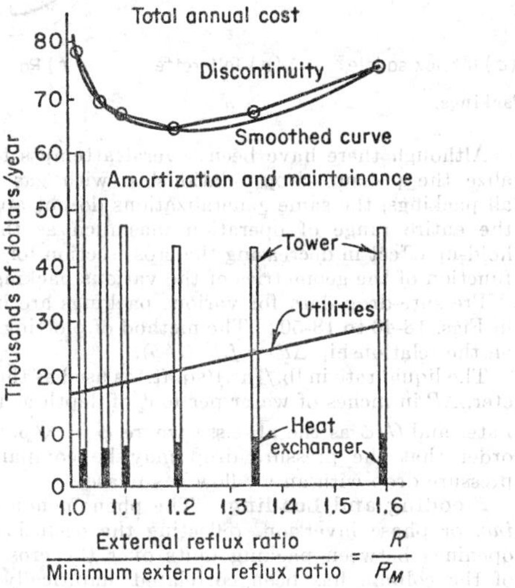

FIG. 18-42. Optimum-reflux-ratio determination.

Several generalized relationships are available for preliminary estimates. Colburn [Chemical Engineering Lecture Notes, University of Delaware, 1943] proposed that the optimum reflux ratio

$$R_{\text{opt}} = \frac{N + [(C_2/hG_b + C_3)/C_1] + (dN/dR)}{dN/dR} \tag{18-41}$$

where R = external reflux ratio $= L/D$
N = number of theoretical plates
G_b = allowable vapor velocity in heat exchangers, lb.-moles/(hr.)(sq. ft.)
h = hours of operation
C_1 = amortization rate for tower, dollars/(sq. ft.)(plate)(year)
C_2 = amortization rate for heat exchangers, dollars/(sq. ft.)(year)
C_3 = cost of utilities per mole of distillate, dollars/mole

Happel [*Chem. Eng.*, **65** (14), 144 (1958)] using a modification of the Colburn relationship found that the optimum number of trays varies from two to three times the number at total reflux. Gilliland [*Ind. Eng. Chem.*, **32**, 1220 (1940)] from the establishment of an empirical relationship between reflux ratio and theoretical trays based on a study of existing columns indicated that

$$0.1 < \frac{R_{\text{opt}} - R_{\min}}{R_{\min} + 1} < 0.3$$

and correspondingly

$$0.35 < \frac{N_{\text{opt}} - N_{\min}}{N_{\min} + 1} < 0.52$$

The effect of utilities costs on optimum operation was noted by Kiguchi and Ridgway [*Petrol. Refiner*, **35** (12), 179 (1956)], who indicated that in petroleum-distillation columns the optimum reflux ratio varies between 1.1 and 1.5 times the minimum reflux ratio. Where refrigeration is involved $1.1\,R_{\min} < R_{\text{opt}} < 1.2\,R_{\min}$ and where cooling-tower water is used in the condensers $1.2\,R_{\min} < R_{\text{opt}} < 1.4\,R_{\min}$.

The optimum entrainment level was evaluated by Colburn [*Ind. Eng. Chem.*, **28**, 526 (1936)] and Zenz [*Petrol. Refiner*, **36** (3), 179 (1957)]. Colburn indicated that $e = cu^m$ and that the optimum level of entrainment for determination of the optimum column diameter for established liquid-vapor flows was determined by the relationship

$$e_{\text{opt}} = \frac{R}{(m-1)E_{MV}} \tag{18-42}$$

where E_{MV} = Murphree tray efficiency
R = internal reflux ratio L/V
e = entrainment, moles vapor/mole liquid
c = constant for column
u = superficial column velocity
m = column characteristic constant

Zenz (*loc. cit.*) from a study of the characteristics of bubble-cap and sieve trays estimated that the optimum level of entrainment was equal to $0.175\,L/V$ (Fig. 18-26).

PACKED COLUMNS

Introduction. Packed columns have found extensive application in liquid-gas contact systems, primarily in the case of absorption operations but also in the case of distillation where small cross-sectional-area requirements preclude effective tray-tower performance. In general, they require a lower capital investment than do tray towers and provide turbulence in the gas phase, resulting in good mass-transfer efficiency for gas-phase-controlling systems. With the advent of packing constructed of plastic materials, the inherent disadvantage of weight of packed columns compared with tray columns has been overcome.

The packed column is a simple device compared with tray columns (Fig. 18-43). A typical column consists of a cylindrical shell containing a support plate and redistributor plates supporting the packing. A liquid distributor is set above the packing and designed to provide effective irrigation of the packing. Many packings are commercially available, each possessing specific advantages for liquid-gas contacting from the aspects of cost, surface availability, liquid-surface regeneration, pressure drop, weight, and corrosion resistance.

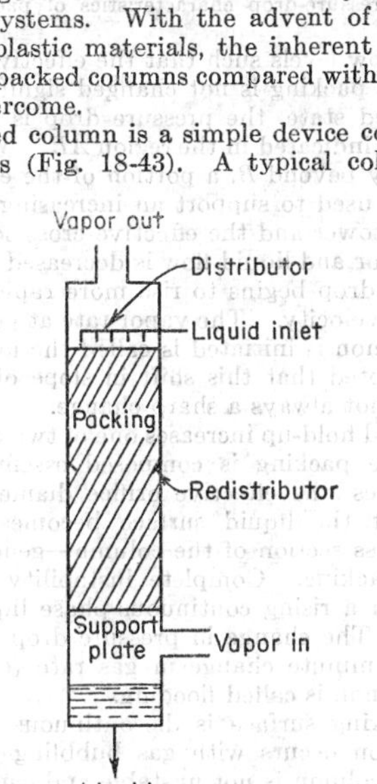

FIG. 18-43. Packed column (schematic).

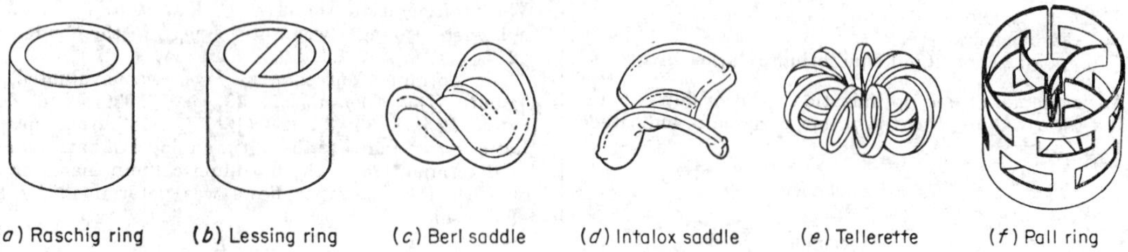

(a) Raschig ring (b) Lessing ring (c) Berl saddle (d) Intalox saddle (e) Tellerette (f) Pall ring

FIG. 18-44. Packings.

Typical packings used in packed towers are indicated in Fig. 18-44.

Pressure Drop and Stability. Pressure drop and instability phenomena in packed columns are illustrated in Fig. 18-45.

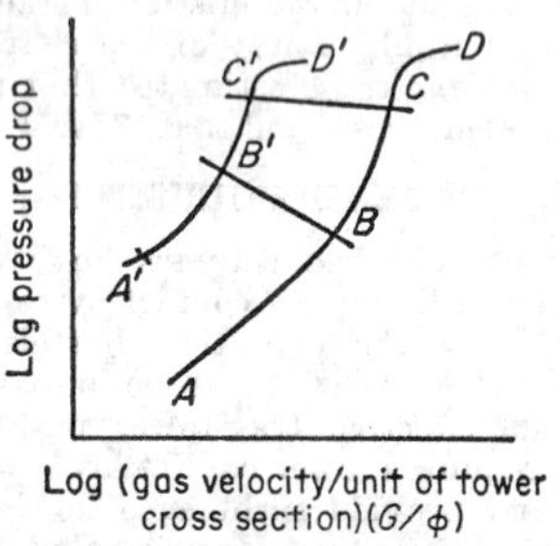

FIG. 18-45. Pressure-drop characteristics of packed columns.

At liquid-flow levels such that the effective open cross section of the packing is not changed significantly from the unirrigated state, the pressure drop is proportional to $G^{1.8 \text{ to } 2.0}$ as indicated in the region AB. With increase in gas velocity beyond B, a portion of the energy of the gas stream is used to support an increasing quantity of liquid in the tower and the effective cross section of the tower for vapor and liquid flow is decreased (region BC). The pressure drop begins to rise more rapidly than the square of the velocity. The vapor rate at point B where this phenomenon is initiated is called the loading point. It must be noted that this shift in slope of the ΔP vs. G/ϕ curve is not always a sharp change.

As the liquid hold-up increases one of two changes may occur. If the packing is composed essentially of extended surfaces, the effective orifice diameter becomes so small that the liquid surface becomes continuous across the cross section of the column—generally at the top of the packing. Complete instability occurs concomitant with a rising continuous-phase liquid body in the column. The change in pressure drop is extremely great with a minute change in gas rate (condition C). The phenomenon is called flooding.

If the packing surface is discontinuous in nature a phase inversion occurs with gas bubbling through the liquid. The column is not unstable and can be brought back to gas-phase continuous operation by merely reducing the gas flow. Analogous to the flooding condition the pressure drop rises rapidly as phase inversion occurs.

At high liquid-flow rates, the behavior is represented by curve $A'B'C'$ and the transition to loading is not so abrupt as in the case of lower liquid rates.

A stable operating condition beyond "flooding" (region CD) for non-extended surface packing with the liquid as the continuous and vapor as the dispersed phase has been reported by Lerner and Grove [*Ind. Eng. Chem.*, **43,** 216 (1951)] and Teller [*Chem. Eng.*, **61** (9), 168 (1954)].

Although there have been several attempts to generalize the pressure-drop relationship with gas flow for all packings, the same generalizations do not apply over the entire range of operation inasmuch as the liquid hold-up effect in decreasing the cross section for flow is a function of the geometries of the various packings.

Pressure-drop data for various packings are indicated in Figs. 18-46 to 18-50. The method of plotting is based on the relationship $\Delta P = f(L, G/\phi)$.

The liquid rate in lb./(hr.)(sq. ft.) is used as the parameter, ΔP in inches of water per foot of depth as the ordinate, and G/ϕ as the abscissa where $\phi = \sqrt{\rho_v/0.075}$ in order that the pressure drop may be compared with pressure drop with an air-flow gas phase.

Flooding and Loading. The phenomenon of *flooding*, or phase inversion, reflecting the occlusion of the openings between packing units over the cross section of the column has been correlated empirically for the various commercial packings. Inasmuch as the development of flooding proceeds for each packing by the same mechanism, it is expected and confirmed that the pressure drop at flooding is independent of the liquid-gas flow ratio and is dependent only on the physical properties of the system.

The pressure drops at flooding for various packings using the air-water system are indicated in Table 18-4.

Table 18-4. Flooding Pressure Drops

Packing	Size	Pressure drop at flooding, in. water/ft. packing	Source
Raschig rings	¼	4	Zenz, *Chem. Eng.*, **60** (8), 176 (1953)
	½	3.5	
	1	4	
	1½	2.5	
	2	2.5	
Berl saddles	½	2.5	
	1	2.5	
	1½	2.2	
Tellerettes (phase inversion)	1	2.5	Teller and Ford, *Ind. Eng. Chem.*, **50,** 12101 (1958)

A general correlation of the flooding condition for various packings was developed by Sherwood and Hollaway [*Ind. Eng. Chem.* **30,** 768 (1938)]. The correlation was based on the equation

$$\frac{U^2 a}{g F_d{}^3} \frac{\rho_v}{\rho_L} \mu^{0.2} = f\left(\frac{L}{G}\frac{\rho_v}{\rho_L}\right)^{1/2} \tag{18-43}$$

where U = superficial gas velocity at flooding, ft./sec.
a = total area of packing, sq. ft./cu. ft. packing
F_d = fractional voids in dry packing, cu. ft./cu. ft. tower volume
G = gas rate, lb./(hr.)(sq. ft.)
g = 32.2 (lb. mass) (ft.)/(lb. force)(sec.^{2})
L = liquid rate, lb./(hr.)(sq. ft.)
ρ_v and ρ_L = gas and liquid densities, lb./cu. ft.
μ = viscosity of liquid, centipoise

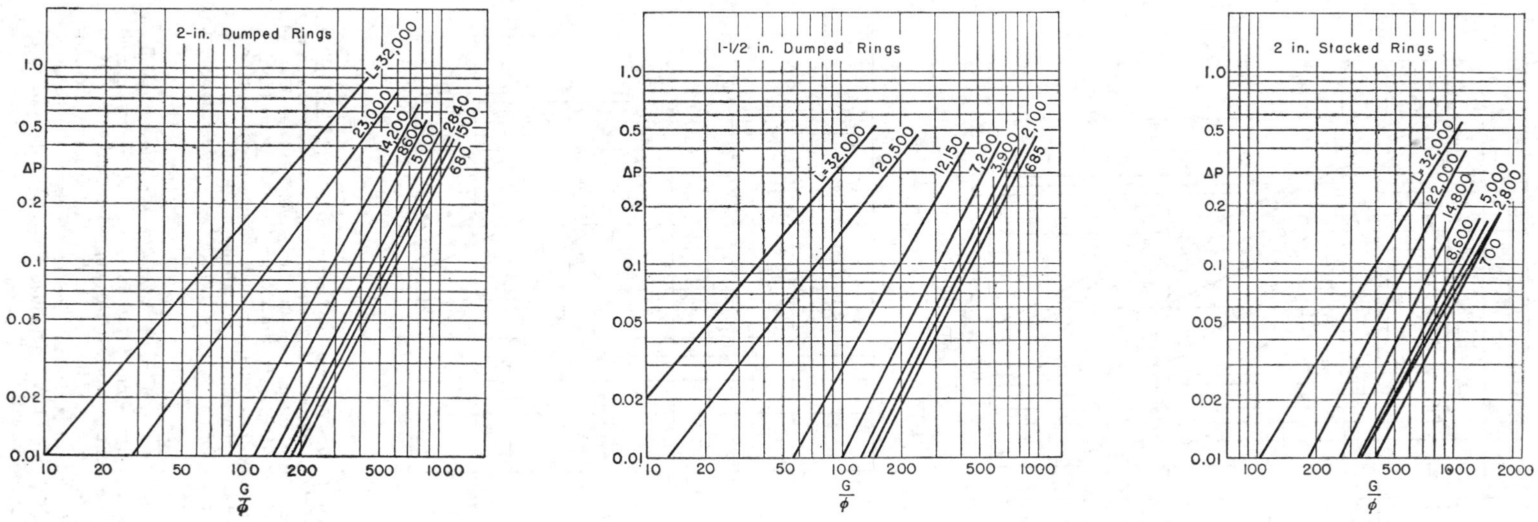

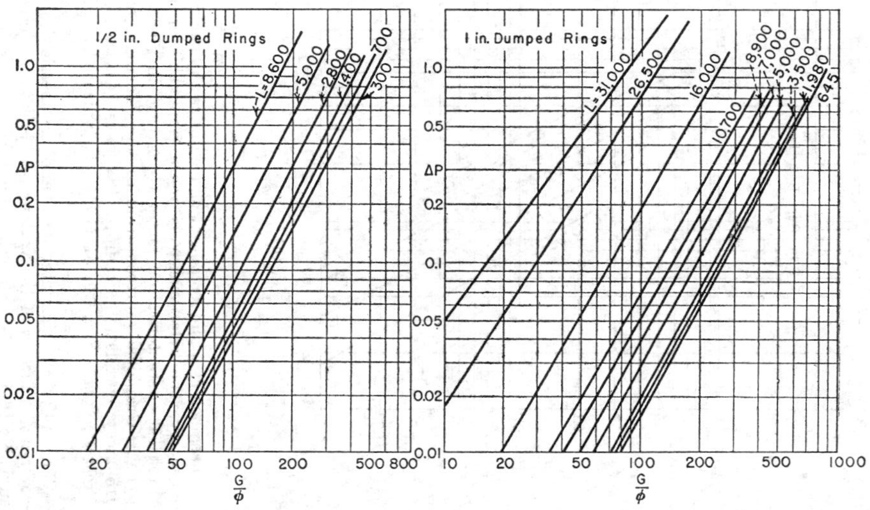

FIG. 18-46. Pressure-drop data for ceramic Raschig rings. (*Data of Tillson, S.M. Thesis, M.I.T.*, 1939.) ΔP = pressure drop, in. water/ft. of depth; G = gas rate, lb./(hr.)(sq. ft.); L = liquor rate, lb./(hr.)(sq. ft.); $\phi = (\rho/0.075)^{\frac{1}{2}}$; ρ = gas density, lb./cu. ft.

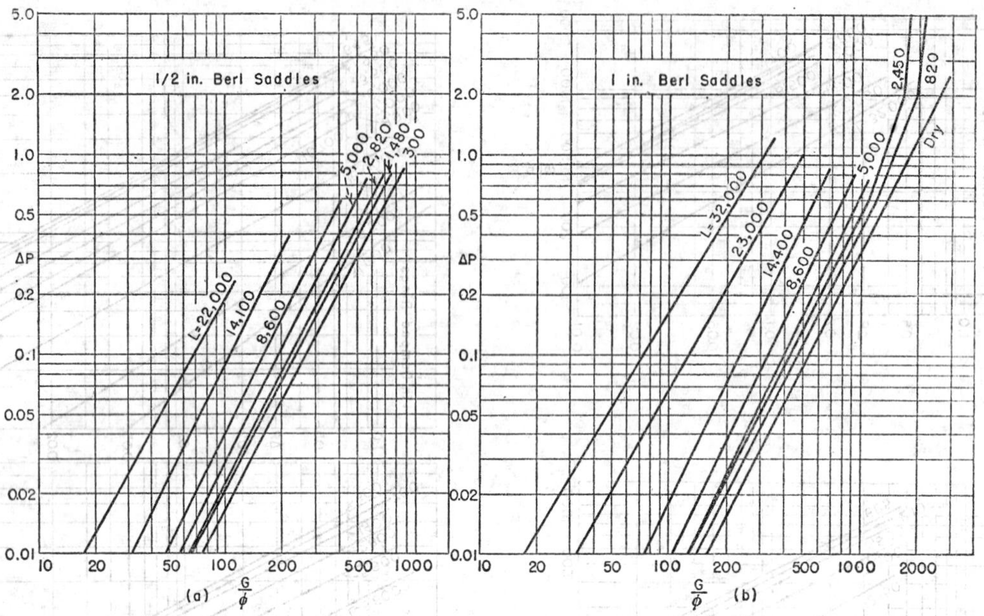

Inasmuch as a and F_D do not characterize the packing geometry, the relationship is more applicable if an empirical characterization factor C_f is used in place of a/F_d^3. Graphical representation of the Sherwood and Hollaway correlation modified by Leva [*Chem. Eng. Progress, Symp. Ser.*, **10**, 51 (1954)] is indicated in Fig. 18-51.

The physical characteristics and geometric characterization factors of the various packings are as given in Table 18-5.

Table 18-5. Characterization Factors of Packings

Packing	Nominal size	% free volume	Weight, lb./cu. ft.	Characterization factor C_f
Raschig rings, stoneware	¾	67	46	182*
	1	68	45	155*
	1½	68	45	97*
	2	75	24	75*
Raschig rings, steel (1⁄16 in. thick)	1	92	73	115*
	2	92	38.7	75*
Berl saddles, stoneware	¾	65	48	138*
	1	69	45	82.5*
	1½	70	38	76*
Intalox saddles, stoneware	1	70	34	77†
	1½	81	30	81†
Tellerettes, polyethylene HD	1	87	10	57‡
Polyethylene LD	1	83	10	65‡
Pall rings, carbon steel	1 (24 gage)	93	33	45§
	2 (20 gage)	94	28	17§

* Lubin, Ph.D. Thesis, University of Missouri, 1949.
† Leva, *Chem. Eng. Progress, Symp. Ser.*, **10**, 51 (1954).
‡ Teller and Ford, *Ind. Eng. Chem.*, **50**, 12101 (1958).
§ Echert *et al.*, *Chem. Eng. Progress*, **54**, 70 (1958).

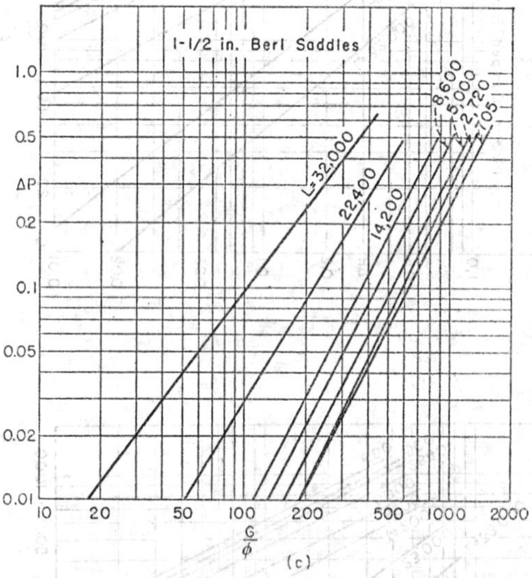

FIG. 18-47. Pressure drop for ceramic Berl saddles and spiral tile. (*Data of Rillson, S.M. Thesis, M.I.T.*, 1939) using air and water in a 20-in. tower except for 1-in. saddles at liquor rates below 5000 lb./(hr.)(sq. ft.) from Mach [*Dechema Monograph.*, **6**, 38 (1933); *Z. Ver. deut. Ing.*, *vol.* 375, 1935]. ΔP = pressure drop, in. water/ft. of depth; G = gas velocity, lb./(hr.)(sq. ft.); L = liquid rate, lb./(hr.)(sq. ft.); $\phi = (\rho/0.075)^{\frac{1}{2}}$; ρ = gas density, lb./cu. ft.

The effect of surface tension on flooding should be significant since it would affect the coalescence mechanism necessary for the creation of the continuous liquid phase. Investigations in this area of study have been limited. Newton *et al.* [*Petrol. Refiner*, **31**, 10, 141–143 (1952)] varied surface tension of the liquid phase by introduction of controlled quantities of surfactants and found that modification of the Sherwood-Hollaway correlation by using, as the abscissa, the quantity $L/G \sqrt{\rho_v/\rho_L}\,(\sigma/\sigma w)^3$, where σ = surface tension of liquid, dynes/cm.^{2}, and σw = surface tension of water, dynes/cm.^{2}, satisfied the emperimental data. It was, however, noted by the authors that foaming created by the use of surfactant had an effect on the flood point which may have magnified the contribution of surface-tension variation.

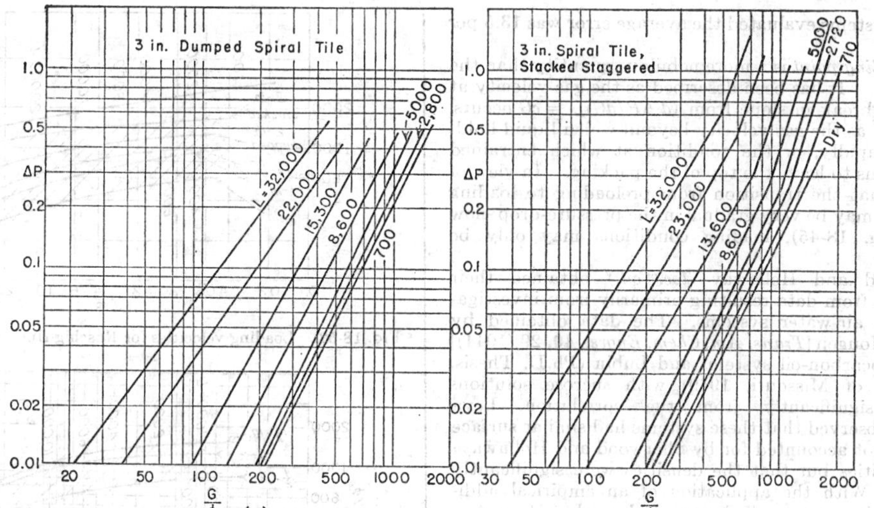

FIG. 18-48. Pressure drop for spiral tile packing. Nomenclature is same as for Fig. 18-47.

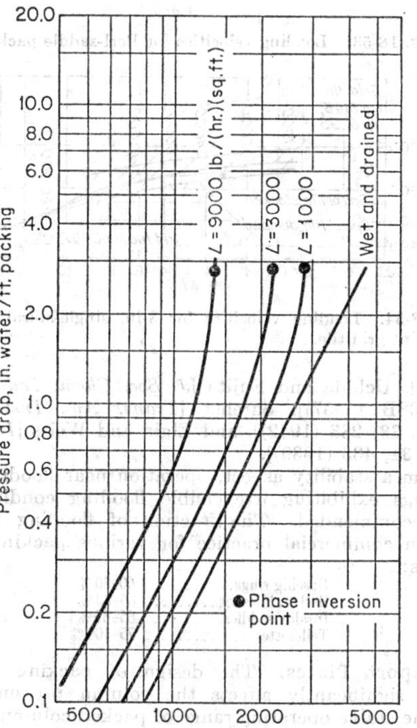

FIG. 18-49. Pressure drop ¾-in. by 2-in. Tellerettes (1 in. nominal). System: air–15 per cent monoethanolamine (viscosity 1.88 centistokes).

A generalized correlation of flooding rates for a two-fluid countercurrent system has been proposed by Sakiadis and Johnson [*Ind. Eng. Chem.*, **46**, 1229 (1954)] based on the relationship

$$1 + 0.835 \left[\left(\frac{\rho_D}{\rho_C} \right)^{1/4} \left(\frac{U_D}{U_C} \right)^{1/2} \right] = C_p \left(\frac{U_C^2}{g_c \epsilon^3} \frac{\rho_C}{\Delta \rho} \right)^{-1/4} \tag{18-44}$$

where ρ = density, lb./cu. ft.
U_C = superficial velocity, ft./hr.
g_c = acceleration due to gravity, 4.7×10^8 ft./hr.^{2}
ϵ = fractional void space, cu. ft./cu. ft. tower
C_p = packing constant (see original article)
subscripts:
D = dispersed phase
C = continuous phase

The form of equation bears a high degree of similarity to the Sherwood-Hollaway relationship. For a wide

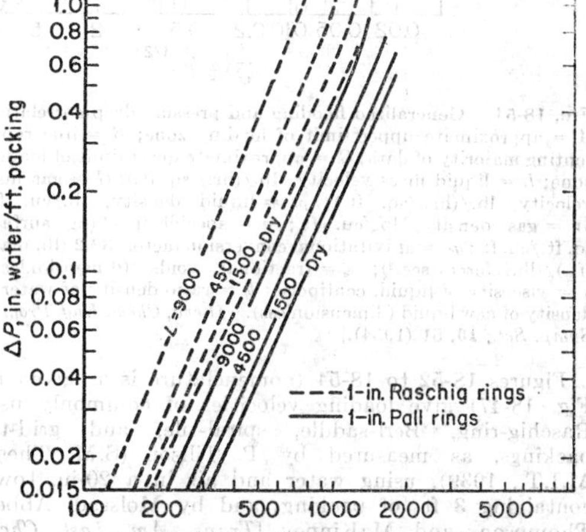

FIG. 18-50. Pressure drop for Pall rings and Raschig rings. Nomenclature is the same as for Fig. 18-47. [*Echert, Chem. Eng. Progress*, **54**, 71 (1958).]

range of systems evaluated the average error was 13.5 per cent.

The *loading point* is a more nebulous quantity than the flood point. It has been described as the gas velocity at which the break in slope from $(d\,\Delta P/dG)_L = cG$ occurs, alternately as the gas velocity beyond which liquid hold-up rises rapidly, or the condition at which entrained liquid begins to leave the top of the packing. In view of the fact that the transition from preloading to loading conditions may be very gradual in the pressure-drop–flow curve (Fig. 18-45), loading conditions may only be estimated.

Sherwood and Hollaway (*loc. cit.*) obtained their correlation from data resulting primarily from investigations with air-water systems. The data obtained by Bain and Hougen [*Trans. Am. Chem. Engrs.*, **40,** 29 (1944)] with hydrocarbon-oil systems and Lubin (Ph.D. Thesis, University of Missouri, 1949) with sucrose solutions deviated significantly from the correlation. Leva (*loc. cit.*) observed that these systems had similar surface tensions (not accounted for by Sherwood and Hollaway) and viscosities but that the densities were significantly different. With the application of an empirical additional density factor, all data were brought into agreement with the correlation. The empirically corrected flooding-condition estimating plot is indicated in Fig. 18-51.

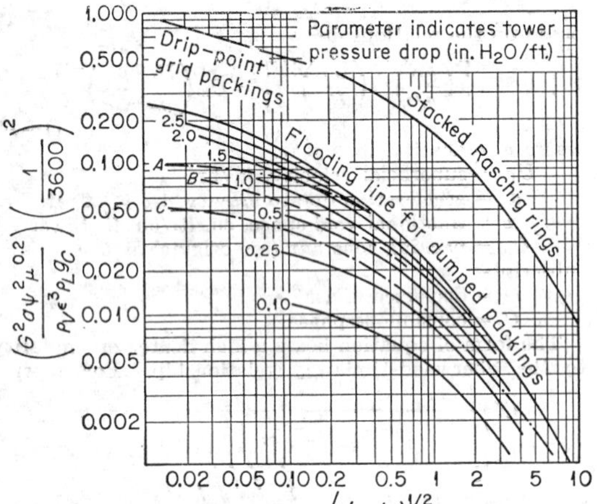

FIG. 18-51. Generalized flooding and pressure-drop correlation. A = approximate upper limit of loading zone; B = line representing majority of data; C = approximate lower limit of loading zone; L = liquid mass velocity lb./(hr.)(sq. ft.); G = gas mass velocity, lb./(hr.)(sq. ft.); ρ_L = liquid density, lb./cu. ft.; ρ_V = gas density, lb./cu. ft.; a = specific packing surface, sq. ft./cu. ft.; g_c = gravitational conversion factor, 32.2 (lb. mass)(ft.)/(lb. force)(sec.²); ϵ = fractional voids (dimensionless); μ = viscosity of liquid, centipoise; ψ = ratio density of water to density of new liquid (dimensionless). [*Leva, Chem. Eng. Progress Symp. Ser.*, **10,** 51 (1954).]

Figures 18-52 to 18-54 (nomenclature is as given for Fig. 18-47) give loading velocities of commonly used Raschig-ring, Berl-saddle, spiral-tile, and grid-tile packings, as measured by P. Tillson (S.M. Thesis, M.I.T., 1939), using water and air in a 20-in. tower containing 3 ft. of packing; and by Molstad, Abbey, Thompson, and McKinney [*Trans. Am. Inst. Chem. Engrs.*, **38,** 387 (1942)]. These data agree substantially with the more limited data of Mach [*Dechema Monograph.*, **6,** 38 (1933); *Z. Ver. deut. Ing.*, vol. 375, 1935], White [*Trans. Am. Inst. Chem. Engrs.*, **31,** 1 (1935)], Uchida and Fujita [*J. Soc. Chem. Ind. Japan*, **40,** 238B (1937)], Sarchet [*Trans. Am. Inst. Chem. Engrs.*, **38,** 283 (1942)], and Elgin and Weiss [*Ind. Eng. Chem.* **31,** 435 (1939)].

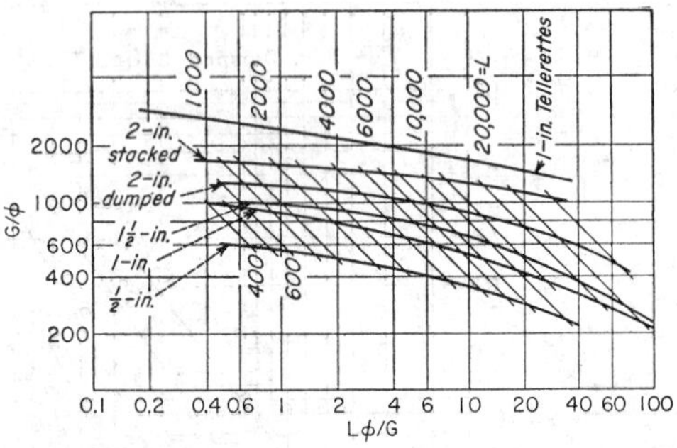

FIG. 18-52. Loading velocities for Raschig rings and Tellerettes.

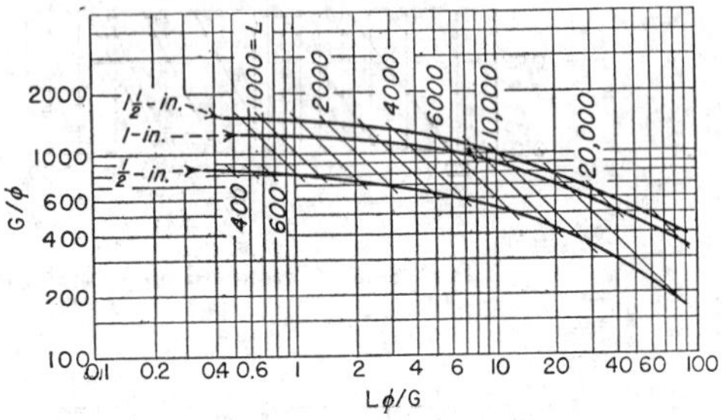

FIG. 18-53. Loading velocities for Berl-saddle packin g.

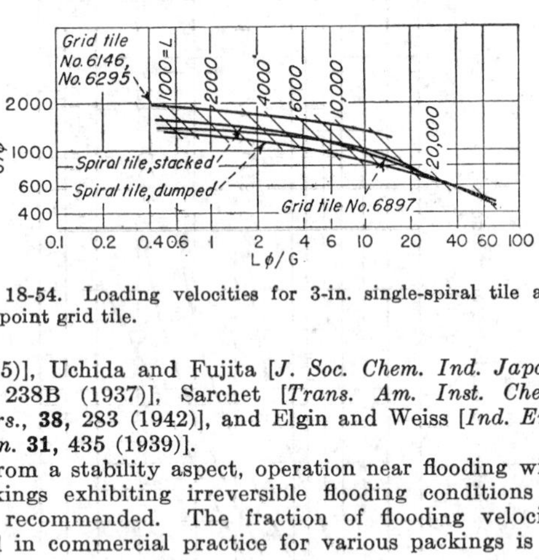

FIG. 18-54. Loading velocities for 3-in. single-spiral tile and drip-point grid tile.

From a stability aspect, operation near flooding with packings exhibiting irreversible flooding conditions is not recommended. The fraction of flooding velocity used in commercial practice for various packings is as follows:

Raschig rings	60–80%
Berl saddles	65–80%
Intalox saddles	65–85%
Tellerettes	75–100%

Support Plates. The design of packing support plates significantly affects the column pressure drop and the stable operating range of packed columns. The degree of open area on a support plate is the fraction of void inherent in the design of the plate minus that portion of the open area occluded by the packing. Thus the support plate should have a greater open area than that obtained with the packing stipulated, in order that the support area is not the critical region in the development of flooding.

Two basic types of support plates may be utilized:

1. Countercurrent
2. Separate flow passages for liquid and vapor

The two types of support plates are indicated, respectively, in Figs. 18-55 and 18-56. With the countercurrent type of support plate the per cent opening prior to occlusion can range up to 90 per cent open. With the separate-flow-passage support plate, free areas prior to occlusion may range up to 200 per cent open, providing a greater range of operating stability.

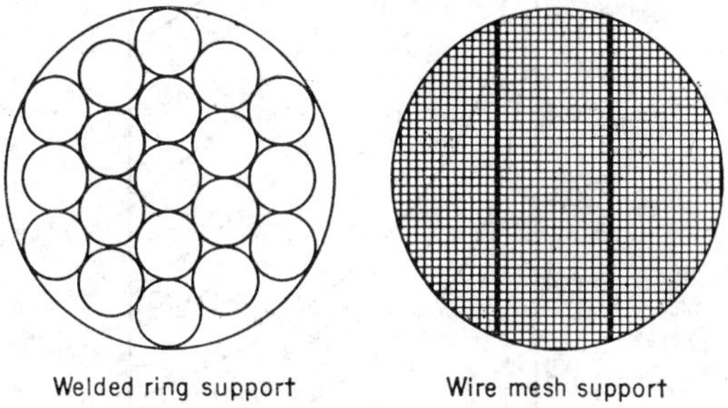

FIG. 18-55. Packing supports (countercurrent).

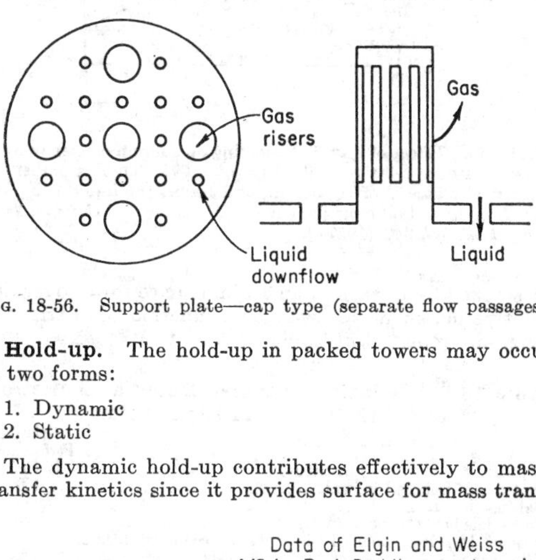

FIG. 18-56. Support plate—cap type (separate flow passages).

Hold-up. The hold-up in packed towers may occur in two forms:

1. Dynamic
2. Static

The dynamic hold-up contributes effectively to mass-transfer kinetics since it provides surface for mass transfer and surface regeneration via agglomeration and dispersion. Static hold-up is limited in its contribution to mass-transfer rates, as indicated by Thoenes and Kramers [*Chem. Eng., Sci.* **8**, 271 (1958)]. In laminar regions hold-up in general has a negative effect on the efficiency of separation.

The determination of dynamic and static hold-ups has not yet been accomplished since such evaluation requires an interpretation of the behavior of hold-up. Measurements, however, have been made of operational and inherent hold-ups. The operational hold-up consists of the dynamic and inherent hold-ups. The inherent hold-up may (in the interstices of the packing) consist of both dynamic and static hold-up.

Extensive data on operational hold-up have been obtained by Cooper, Christl, and Perry [*Trans. Am. Inst. Chem. Engrs.*, **37**, 979 (1941)]; Furnas and Bellinger [*Trans. Am. Inst. Chem. Engrs.*, **34**, 251 (1938)]; Elgin and Jesser [*Trans. Am. Inst. Chem. Engrs.*, **39**, 277 (1943)]; Elgin and Weiss [*Ind. Eng. Chem.*, **31**, 435 (1939)]; and Shulman, Ullrich, Weiss, and Proulx [*Am. Inst. Chem. Engrs. J.*, **1**, 247 (1955)].

Elgin and Jesser (*loc. cit.*) noted that operational hold-up appears to be independent of gas velocity until the region of loading is reached, in studies with ½- and 1-in. Berl saddles and ½- and 1-in. Raschig rings. Beyond the loading point hold-up rises rapidly (Fig. 18-57).

Leva ("Tower Packings and Packed Tower Design," U.S. Stoneware Corp., 1953) correlated the work of Jesser and Elgin (*loc. cit.*), Elgin and Weiss (*loc. cit.*), and Cooper Christl, and Perry (*loc. cit.*) for air-water systems and correlated the hold-up below loading with $L^{0.6}$ (Fig. 18-58).

Shulman *et al.* (*loc. cit.*) measured the operational and inherent hold-ups for 1-in. Raschig rings and 1-in. Berl saddles below the loading point and found the variation with system conditions as follows:

For viscosity less than 12 centipoise:
Operational hold-up $= h_o$
1-in. Raschigs

$$h_o = 0.00039L^{0.57}\mu^{0.13}\rho^{-0.84}\left(\frac{\sigma}{73}\right)^{0.925-0.262\log L} \qquad (18\text{-}45)$$

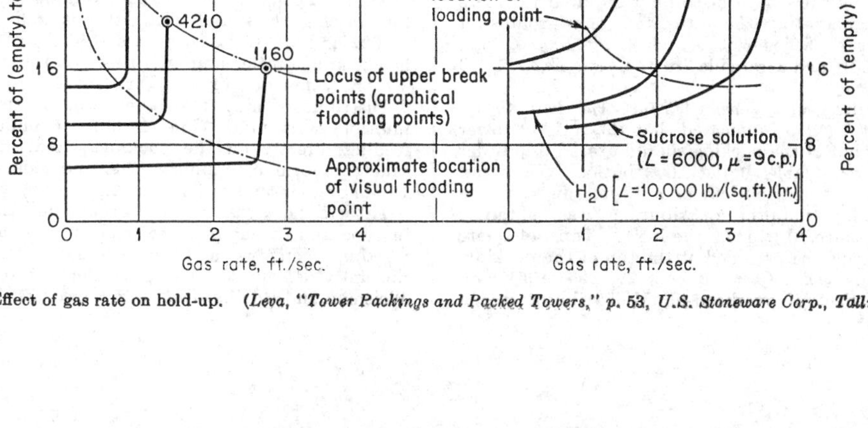

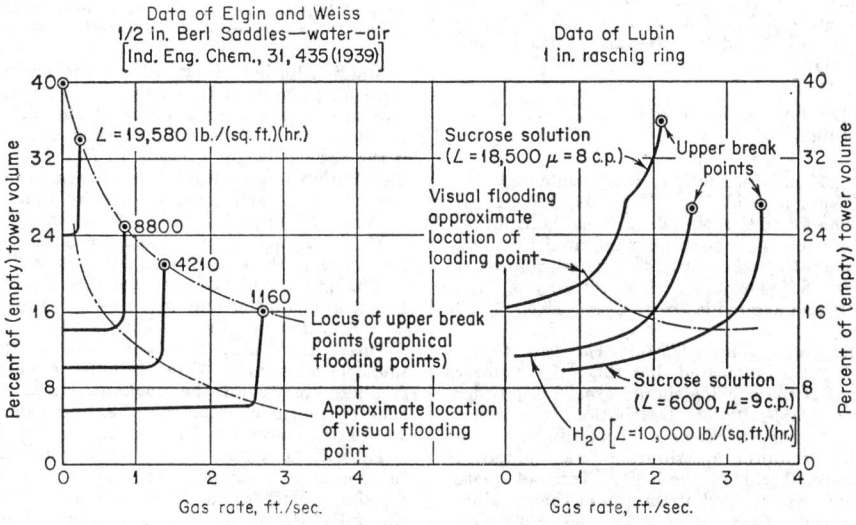

FIG. 18-57. Effect of gas rate on hold-up. (*Leva, "Tower Packings and Packed Towers," p. 53, U.S. Stoneware Corp., Tallmadge, Ohio.*)

1-in. Berl saddles

$$h_o = 0.00043L^{0.57}\mu^{0.13}\rho^{-0.84}\left(\frac{\sigma}{73}\right)^{1.033-0.262\log L} \quad (18\text{-}46)$$

Static hold-up $$h_s = C\mu^m\left(\frac{1}{\rho_L}\right)^{0.37\sigma h} \quad (18\text{-}47)$$

Packing	C	m	n
1-in. carbon Raschig rings	0.0185	0.02	0.23
1-in. porcelain Raschig rings	0.00020	0.02	0.99
1-in. porcelain Berl saddles	0.00119	0.04	0.55

where h_o = hold-up, cu. ft. liquid/cu. ft. packing
σ = surface tension, dynes/cm.
ρ = liquid density, g./ml
μ = liquid viscosity, centipoise
L = liquid rate, lb./(hr.)(sq. ft.)

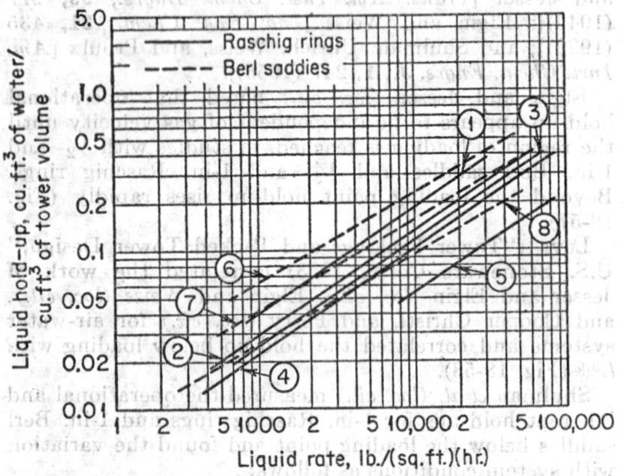

FIG. 18-58. Liquid hold-up data for rings and saddles. (1) 3/8-in. Raschig rings; (2) 1/2-in. Raschig rings; (3) 5/8-in. Raschig rings; (4) 1-in. Raschig rings; (5) 2-in. metal rings; (6) 1/4-in. Berl saddles; (7) 1/2-in. Berl saddles; (8) 1-in. Berl saddles. (*Leva, "Tower Packings and Packed Towers," p. 52, U.S. Stoneware Corp., Tallmadge, Ohio.*)

Distribution. The effectiveness of a packed column for mass transfer is highly dependent on effective distribution of the liquid and gas streams. Two factors affect distribution:

1. Initial liquid-distribution device
2. Length of liquid flow

The effect of maldistribution was evaluated by Manning and Cannon [*Ind. Eng. Chem.*, **49**, 347 (1957)] (Fig. 18-59), who found that the effect of maldistribution is magnified by the length of column required for mass transfer, corroborating the estimated relationships of packed-tower efficiencies of Murch [*Ind. Eng. Chem.*, **5**, 2616 (1953)] and Granville [*Brit. Chem. Eng.*, **2**, 70 (1957)].

Baker, Chilton, and Vernon [*Trans. Am. Inst. Chem. Engrs.*, **31**, 296 (1935)] indicated that the ratio of tower diameter to that of the packing should exceed 8 in order to achieve reasonable liquid distribution. However, with single-point distribution for a 12-in. tower with a 3/4-in. packing, uniform distribution was obtained only at a distance 10 ft. from the inlet. Thus adequate distribution must be provided at the top of the packing.

Pratt [*Trans. Inst. Chem. Engrs.*, **29**, 226 (1951)] reported the effect of overhead-liquid-distributor design for stacked 3-in. rings in an 18-in. square tower over-all. Relative mass-transfer rates as a function of distributor design are reported in Table 18-6.

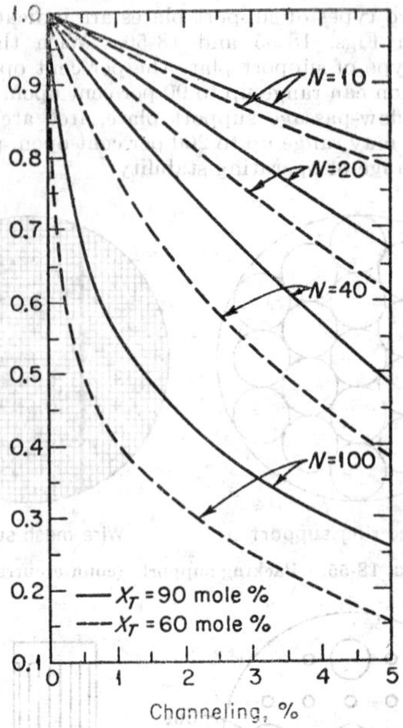

FIG. 18-59. Effect of liquid channeling on column efficiency for a system with a relative volatility of 1.07. Total number of theoretical plates N of 10, 20, 40, and 100 at top liquid composition X_T of 90 and 60 mole per cent. [*Manning and Cannon, Ind. Eng. Chem.*, **49**, 347 (1957).]

Table 18-6. Relative Transfer Rates as Function of Overhead Liquid Distributor

Distributor	Relative Performance of Packing
Serrated edge troughs 1 in. wide	100
Single nozzle entry	16
Splash plate below single nozzle	76
Single nozzle + 18-in. dumped 1-in. rings above stacked rings	63
Multiple nozzles + 18-in. dumped 1-in. rings above stacked rings	120

Maldistribution occurs within the packing bed with increasing length of liquid travel. The liquid tends to flow toward the walls and the gas up the center (Figs. 18-60, 18-61). Thus redistribution may be necessary if the packed height exceeds 15 ft. The effect of maldistribution due to liquid flow toward the walls of the columns was partially overcome by the use of a nonwetting wall liner by Teller [*Chem. Eng. Progress* **50**, 65 (1954)]. The effect of reflection of liquid from the walls for Raschig rings and Tellerettes is indicated in Fig. 18-62*a* and *b*. In these figures H.T.U.$_{OG}$ is the over-all height of a transfer unit (ft.) based on the gas phase and G is the vapor rate in (lb.)/(hr.)(sq. ft.).

Distributors may take the form of spray nozzles, multiple weir units (Fig. 18-63), or multiple nozzles feeding directly on the packing. Redistributors may take the form of support grids and side wipers (Fig. 18-64) or weir-type redistributors.

Interfacial Area. It has been found that variation in type and extent of interfacial area, as a function of packing geometry and system flow conditions, significantly affects the mass-transfer rates of systems. Weisman and Bonilla [*Ind. Eng. Chem.*, **42**, 1099 (1950)],

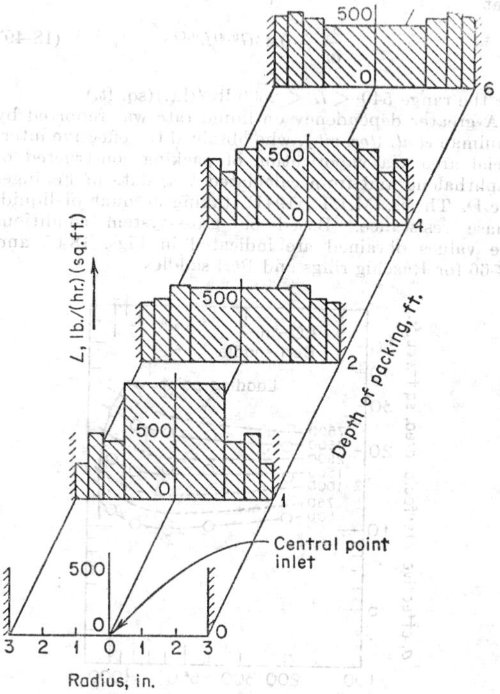

FIG. 18-60. Liquid distribution in a 6-in. column packed with ½-in. broken-stone packing. Increments of radius represent equal-annular-area segments of tower cross section. Central-point inlet. Water rate = 500 lb./(hr.)(sq. ft.). Air rate = 810 lb./(hr.)(sq. ft.). Data from Baker, Chilton, and Vernon. (*Sherwood and Pigford, "Absorption and Extraction," 2d ed., McGraw-Hill Book Company, Inc., New York,* 1952.)

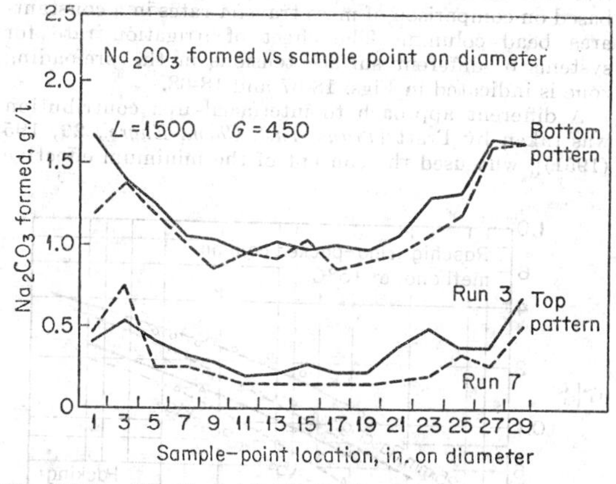

FIG. 18-61. Liquid distribution—effect on concentration distribution—1½-in. Pall rings. [*Eckert, Chem. Eng. Progress,* **54,** 70J (1958).]

Shulman *et al.* [*Am. Inst. Chem. Engrs. J.,* **1,** 253 (1955)], and Yoshida and Koyanagi [*Ind. Eng. Chem.,* **50,** 365 (1958)] have determined the effective area of interfacial transfer in columns, based on comparison with known area systems both unirrigated and irrigated. Via combination of the mass-transfer coefficient for a unit area of transfer and the effective area of mass transfer, effective prediction of mass transfer may be obtained.

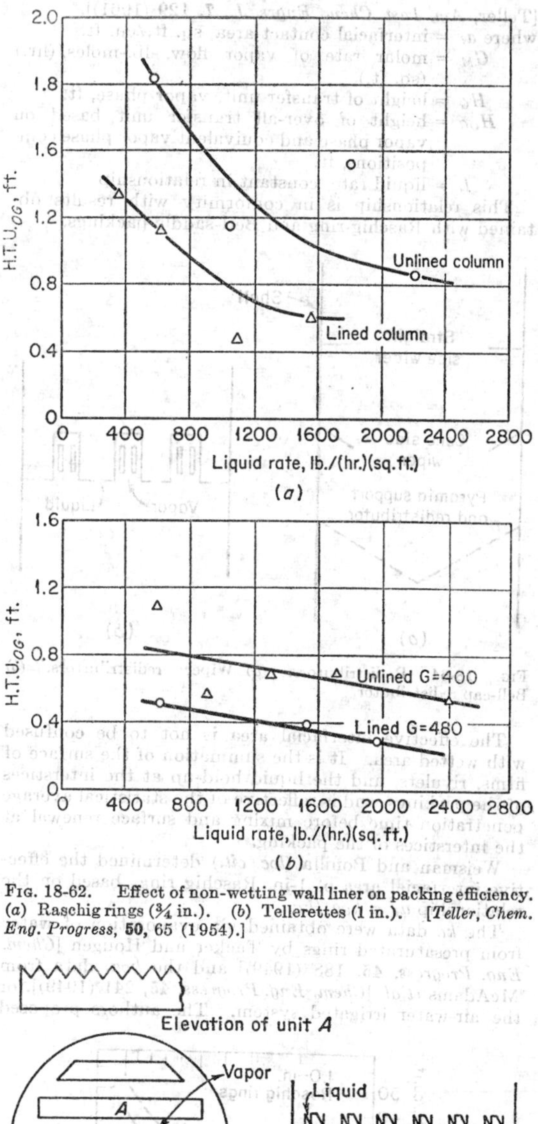

FIG. 18-62. Effect of non-wetting wall liner on packing efficiency. (*a*) Raschig rings (¾ in.). (*b*) Tellerettes (1 in.). [*Teller, Chem. Eng. Progress,* **50,** 65 (1954).]

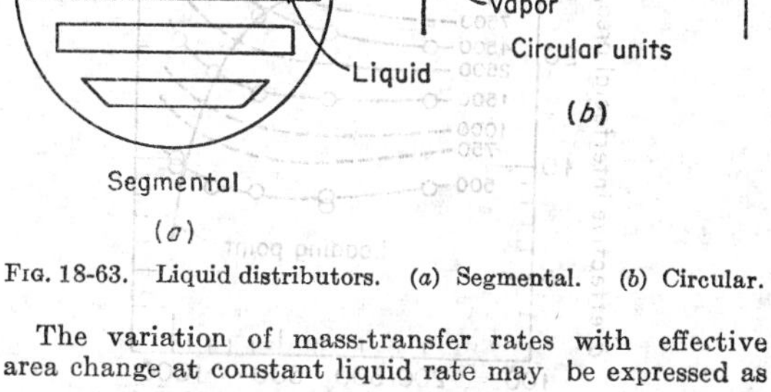

FIG. 18-63. Liquid distributors. (*a*) Segmental. (*b*) Circular.

The variation of mass-transfer rates with effective area change at constant liquid rate may be expressed as

$$\left(\frac{\partial H_{OG}}{\partial G_M}\right)_L = \frac{H_{OG} - H_G}{G_M} + \frac{1}{a_i}\left(\frac{\partial H_G a_i}{\partial G_M}\right)_L - \frac{H_{OG}}{a_i}\left(\frac{\partial a_i}{\partial G_M}\right)_L \qquad (18\text{-}48)$$

[Teller, *Am. Inst. Chem. Engrs. J.*, **7**, 129 (1961)].

where a_i = interfacial contact area, sq. ft./cu. ft.

G_M = molar rate of vapor flow, lb.-moles/(hr.)(sq. ft.)

H_G = height of transfer unit, vapor phase, ft.

H_{OG} = height of over-all transfer unit based on vapor phase and equivalent vapor phase compositions, ft.

L = liquid rate, constant in relationship

This relationship is in conformity with results obtained with Raschig-ring and Berl-saddle packings.

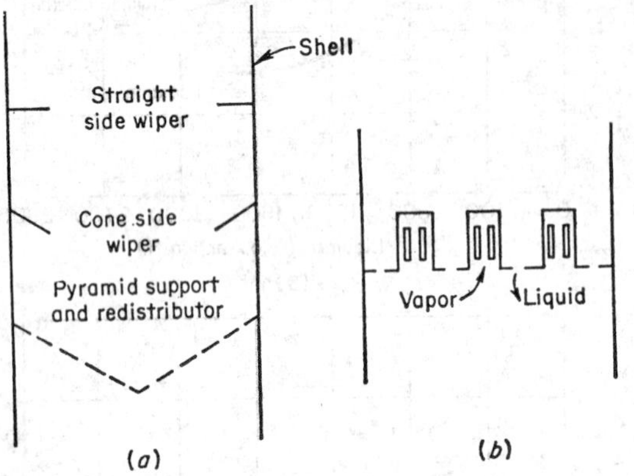

FIG. 18-64. Redistributors. (*a*) Wiper redistributors. (*b*) Bell-cap redistributor.

The effective interfacial area is not to be confused with wetted area. It is the summation of the surface of films, rivulets, and the liquid hold-up at the interstices of the packings, and is reflective of the statistical average penetration time before mixing and surface renewal at the interstices of the packing.

Weisman and Bonilla (*loc. cit.*) determined the effective interfacial area of 1-in. Raschig rings based on the relationship $a_i = k_G a_i / k_G$.

The k_G data were obtained via evaporation of water from presaturated rings by Tacker and Hougen [*Chem. Eng. Progress*, **45**, 188 (1949)] and the $k_G a_i$ data from McAdams *et al.* [*Chem. Eng. Progress*, **45**, 241 (1949)] for the air-water irrigated system. The authors proposed

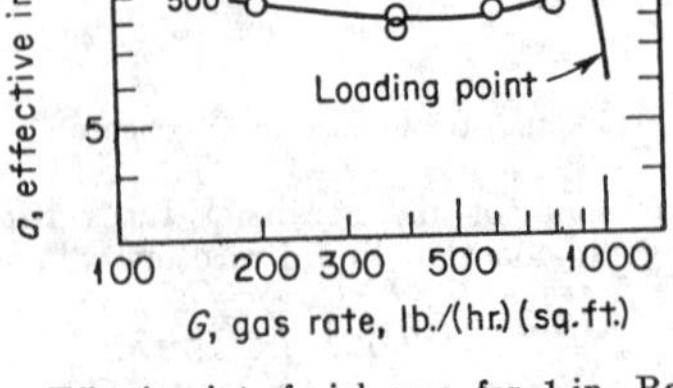

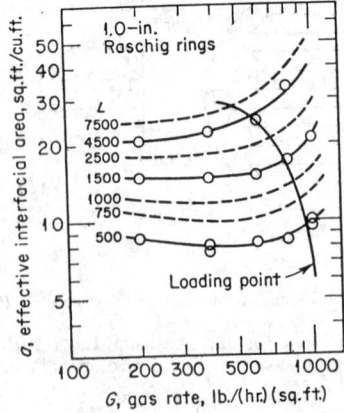

FIG. 18-65. Effective interfacial area for 1-in. Raschig rings based on data of Fellinger. [*Shulman et al., Am. Inst. Chem. Engrs. J.*, **1**, 257 (1955).]

that

$$\frac{a_i}{a_t} = 0.44G^{0.31}L^{0.07} \tag{18-49}$$

for the range $540 < L < 2600$ lb./(hr.)(sq. ft.).

A greater dependency on liquid rate was reported by Shulman *et al.* (*loc. cit.*), who obtained the effective interfacial area via vaporization of packing constructed of naphthalene and from calculated $k_G a_i$ data of Fellinger (Sc.D. Thesis, M.I.T., 1941), taking account of liquid-phase resistance. Based on gross-system conditions the values obtained are indicated in Figs. 18-65 and 18-66 for Raschig rings and Berl saddles.

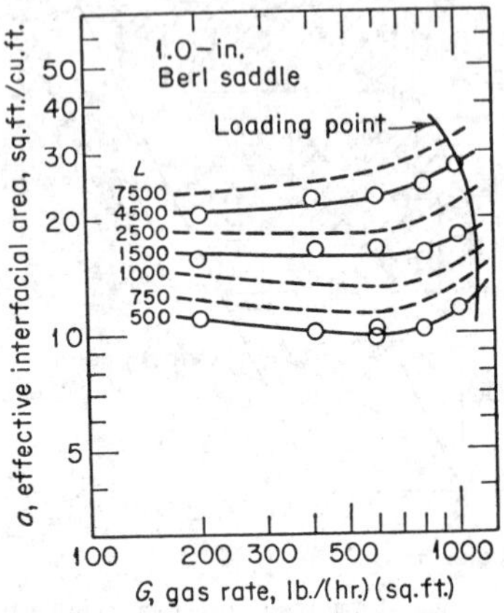

FIG. 18-66. Effective interfacial area for 1-in. Berl saddles based on data of Fellinger. [*Shulman, Am. Inst. Chem. Engrs. J.*, **1**, 257 (1955).]

Yoshida and Koyanagi (*loc. cit.*) calculated the effective interfacial area of Raschig rings and Berl saddles based on comparison of mass-transfer rates in a constant-area bead column. The effect of irrigation rate for systems of different surface tensions in the preloading zone is indicated in Figs. 18-67 and 18-68.

A different approach to interfacial-area contribution was taken by Pratt [*Trans. Inst. Chem. Engrs.*, **29**, 195 (1951)], who used the concept of the minimum effective

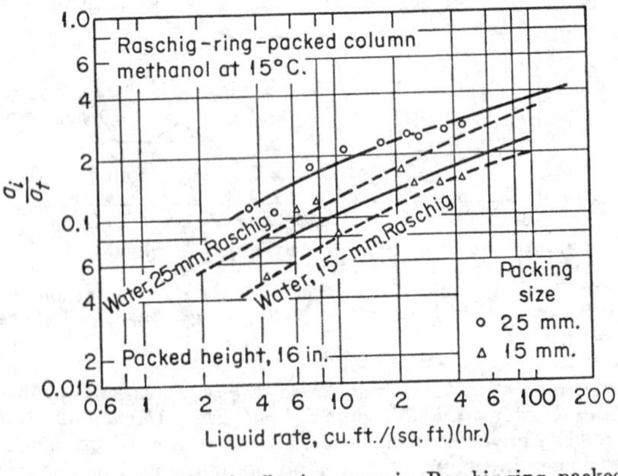

FIG. 18-67. Fractional effective area in Raschig-ring packed column irrigated with methanol. a_i = interfacial area; a_t = surface area—packing. [*Yoshida and Koyanagi, Ind. Eng. Chem.*, **50**, 372 (1958).]

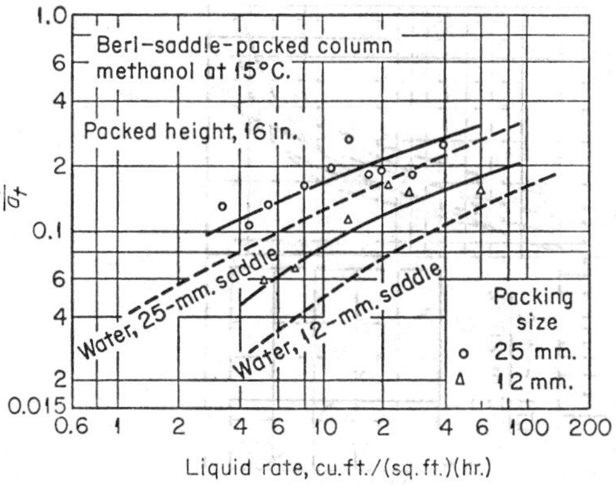

FIG. 18-68. Fractional effective area in Berl-saddle packed column irrigated with methanol. a_i = interfacial area; a_t = surface area—packing. [*Yoshida and Koyanagi, Ind. Eng. Chem.*, **50**, 372 (1958).]

liquid rate (M.E.L.R.). The author claimed, in contradiction to other investigators quoted, that a minimum liquid rate occurred for any type of packing beyond which the effective interfacial area (a maximum) did not vary. He assumed this on the basis that K_Ga did not vary beyond a given irrigation rate for the systems and ranges studied. The graphical determination of this M.E.L.R. is indicated in Fig. 18-69.

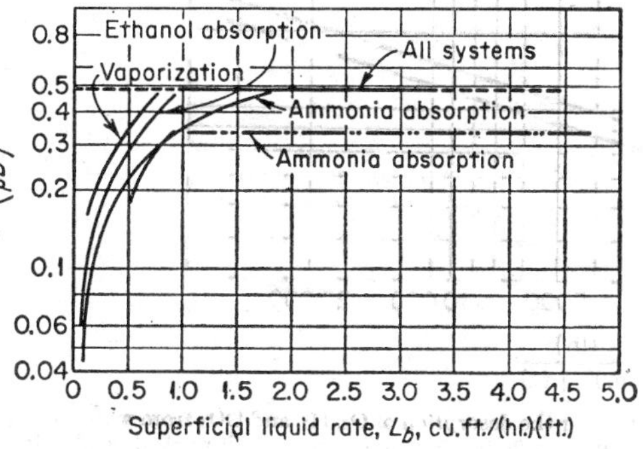

FIG. 18-69. Graphical determination of minimum effective liquid rate. Data for G = 500 lb./(hr.)(sq. ft.). L_b = liquid rate based on periphery of packing. [*Pratt, Trans. Inst. Chem. Engrs.*, **29**, 282 (1950).]

	Superficial area, sq.ft./cu.ft.	Periphery, ft./sq.ft.	Equivalent diam., ft.
Raschig rings:			
½ in.	114	91	0.0233
1 in.	58	49	0.0555
1½ in.	36	31	0.0878
2 in.	29	26	0.112
Berl saddles:			
½ in.	141	141	0.0193
1 in.	79	79	0.0350
1½ in.	50	50	0.0560

Liquid-phase Transfer. Based on a study of desorption of oxygen, hydrogen, and carbon dioxide, Sherwood and Hollaway [*Trans. Am. Inst. Chem. Engrs.*, **36**, 39 (1940)] found that H_L was independent of gas velocity below the loading range where a rapid change of area and turbulence occurs (Fig. 18-70).

It was also found that in preloading range H_L varied with an exponential power of L (Figs. 18-71, 18-72).

An empirical relationship was proposed correlating

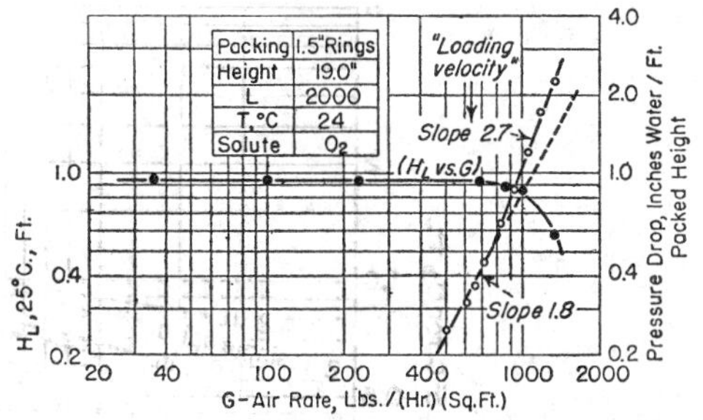

FIG. 18-70. Effect of gas velocity on H_L. [*Data of Sherwood and Holloway, Trans. Am. Inst. Chem. Engrs.*, **36**, 39 (1940).]

the liquid-film coefficient with operating and system variables

$$H_L = \frac{1}{\alpha}\left(\frac{L}{\mu}\right)^n\left(\frac{\mu}{\rho D}\right)^{0.50} \tag{18-50}$$

where α and n are characteristics related to the available surface and geometry of the packing. The constants are in Table 18-7.

Table 18-7. Values of Constants for Eq. (18-50)

	Packing, in.	α	n
Raschig rings	0.5	280	0.35
	1.0	100	0.22
	1.5	90	0.22
	2.0	80	0.22
Berl saddles	0.5	150	0.28
	1.0	170	0.28
	1.5	160	0.28
Tile	3.0	110	0.28

and H_L = height of liquid-phase transfer unit, ft.
L = liquid-flow rate, lb./(hr.)(sq. ft.)
μ = viscosity of liquid, lb./(ft.)(hr.)
ρ = density of liquid, lb./cu. ft.
D = diffusivity in liquid phase, sq. ft./hr.

Yoshida and Koyanagi [*Ind. Eng. Chem.*, **50**, 365 (1958)] indicated that Eq. (18-48) was limited in applicability in that the function L/μ did not effectively reflect the Reynolds number since the effective area of contact varied with irrigation rate. The Sherwood and Hollaway correlation implied that the area of contact was independent of liquid rate since the characterization factor of a given size of packing was constant.

A more exact relationship was obtained by Yoshida and Koyanagi (*loc. cit.*) by dimensional analysis

$$\frac{H_L}{(\mu^2/\rho^2 g)^{1/3}} = C(N_{Re})^p(N_{Sc})^q \tag{18-51}$$

which is similar in form to that proposed by van Krevelen and Hoftijzer [*Chem. Eng. Progress*, **44**, 529 (1948)]

$$\frac{H_L}{(\mu^2/\rho^2 g)^{1/3}} = \frac{1}{0.015}\left(\frac{L}{\alpha_t\mu}\right)^{1/3}(N_{Sc})^{2/3} \tag{18-52}$$

where H_L = height of liquid-phase-transfer unit, ft.
μ = viscosity of liquid, lb./(ft.)(hr.)
ρ = density of liquid, lb./cu. ft.
g = acceleration of gravity, 4.17×10^8 ft./(hr.)^2
N_{Re} = Reynolds number, dimensionless
N_{Sc} = Schmidt number, dimensionless
L = liquid rate, lb./(hr.)(sq. ft.)
α_t = effective interfacial area, sq. ft./cu. ft.

The effect of the Reynolds number on the height of a transfer unit indicates a variable exponent p in Eq. (18-51) as indicated in Fig. 18-72.

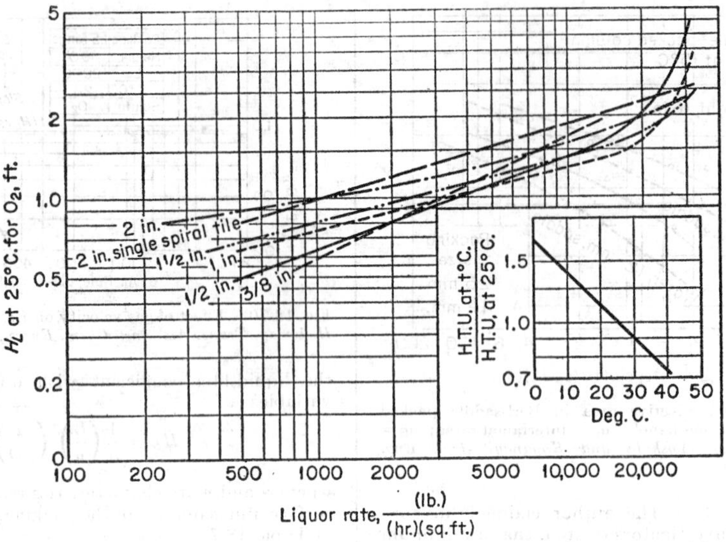

Fig. 18-71a. Liquor-film H.T.U. for ceramic ring packing. Based on data for the desorption of O_2, H_2, and CO_2 from water, compiled by Sherwood and Holloway [*Trans. Am. Inst. Chem. Engrs.*, **36**, 39 (1940)], using a 20-in.-diameter column with packed heights from 13 to 49 in. The plot gives values of H_L for oxygen at 25°C.; values at other temperatures may be obtained from the small ratio plot. The curves apply to dumped rings, except for 2- and 3-in. spiral tile, which apply to dumped or stacked staggered.

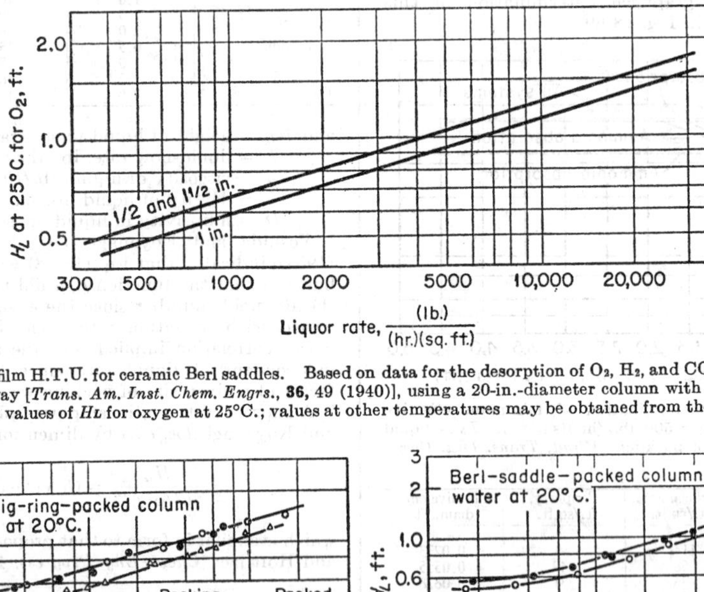

Fig. 18-71b. Liquid-film H.T.U. for ceramic Berl saddles. Based on data for the desorption of O_2, H_2, and CO_2 from water, compiled by Sherwood and Holloway [*Trans. Am. Inst. Chem. Engrs.*, **36**, 49 (1940)], using a 20-in.-diameter column with packed heights from 15 to 22 in. The plot gives values of H_L for oxygen at 25°C.; values at other temperatures may be obtained from the ratio plot in Fig. 18-71a.

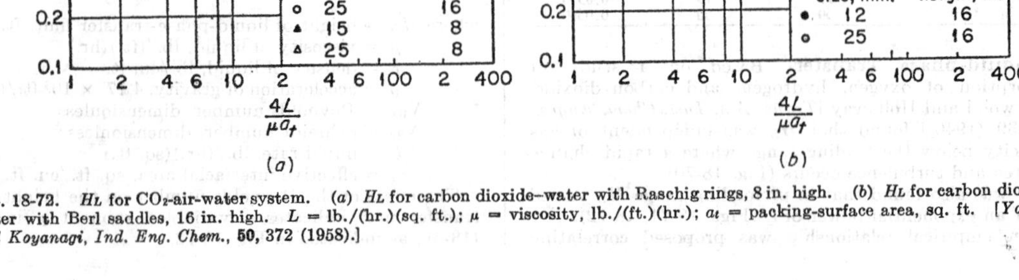

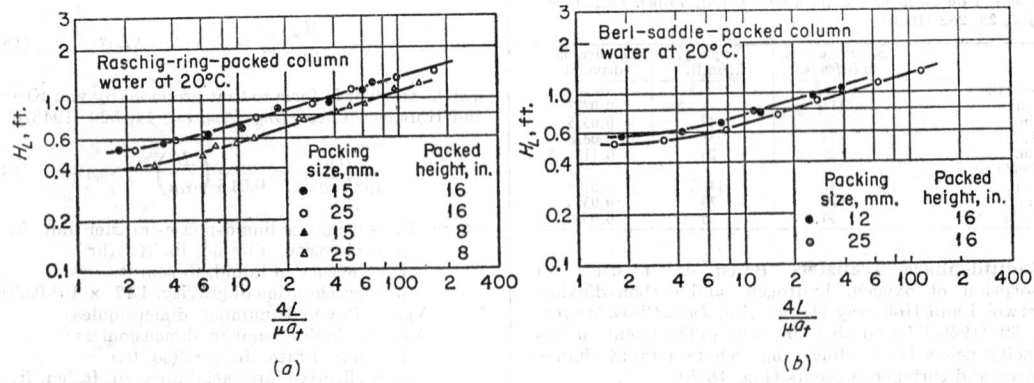

Fig. 18-72. H_L for CO_2-air-water system. (a) H_L for carbon dioxide–water with Raschig rings, 8 in. high. (b) H_L for carbon dioxide–water with Berl saddles, 16 in. high. L = lb./(hr.)(sq. ft.); μ = viscosity, lb./(ft.)(hr.); a_t = packing-surface area, sq. ft. [*Yoshida and Koyanagi, Ind. Eng. Chem.*, **50**, 372 (1958).]

In accordance with the j-factor analogy Onda, Sada, and Murase [*Am. Inst. Chem. Engrs. J.*, **5**, 235 (1959)] found, similar to the relationships proposed by van Krevelen and Hoftijzer (*loc. cit.*) and Yoshida and Koyanagi (*loc. cit.*) that

$$\frac{H_L}{(\mu^2/\rho^2 g)^{1/3}} = \frac{1}{0.021}\left(\frac{L}{\alpha_t \mu}\right)^{0.51}(N_{Sc})^{0.5} \quad (18\text{-}53)$$

for Raschig rings, where α_t is equal to the total geometric surface of the packing [see nomenclature, Eq. (18-52)].

Via development of liquid-film behavior on the basis of the penetration theory it was proposed that

$$\frac{H_L}{(\mu^2/\rho^2 g)^{1/3}} = \frac{1}{0.013}\left(\frac{L}{\alpha_t \mu}\right)^{0.5}(N_{Sc})^{0.5} \quad (18\text{-}54)$$

for Raschig rings [see nomenclature, Eq. (18-52)].

An agreement within ±20 per cent was found to exist between the liquid-phase height of transfer unit and data obtained for liquid films by Sherwood and Hollaway (*loc. cit.*) for ½- to 2-in. rings, Deed *et al.* [*Ind. Eng. Chem.*, **39**, 766 (1947)] for ½-in. rings, Vivian and Whitney [*Chem. Eng. Progress*, **43**, 691 (1947)] for 1-in. rings, and Hikita *et al.* [*Chem. Eng., Japan*, **20**, 113 (1956)] for 15- and 25-mm. rings.

It has been proposed by Shulman *et al.* [*Am. Inst. Chem. Engrs. J.*, **1**, 253 (1955)] that the area of transfer be treated independently of the mass-transfer coefficient k_L and that the interfacial area be obtained from available data in order to predict effective mass transfer. The authors suggest the use of the equation

$$\frac{k_L D_p}{D_L} = 25.1\left(\frac{D_p L}{\mu_L}\right)^{0.45}(N_{Sc})^{0.5} \quad (18\text{-}55)$$

for Raschig rings and Berl saddles.

where D_L = liquid-phase diffusivity, sq. ft./hr.
D_p = diameter of a sphere possessing the same surface area as a unit of packing, ft.
k_L = lb.-moles/(hr.) (sq. ft.) (lb-mole/cu. ft.)
L = liquid-flow rate, lb./(hr.)(sq. ft.)

Other nomenclature is the same as for Eq. (18-52).

Although no effect of gas velocity was observed by these investigators, the liquid rates utilized in the experimental evaluation for effect of gas velocity was less than 6000 lb./(hr.)(sq. ft.). At high liquid rates it was observed by Cooper, Christl, and Perry [*Trans. Am. Inst. Chem. Engrs.*, **37**, 979 (1941)] that the effect of gas velocity on H_{OL} was significant for the CO_2-air-water system, at liquid rates of 13,600 lb./(hr.)(sq. ft.) to 56,000 lb./(hr.)(sq. ft.). Data obtained with the use of 2-in. Raschig rings indicate that H_{OL} decreases with increase in gas velocities under these irrigation conditions. The authors suggest that, at the extremely high liquor velocities employed, considerable internal recirculation of vapor occurred, thus decreasing the over-all concentration potential. Thus lower mass-transfer rates resulted. The degree of backmixing is decreased by increase in the gas velocity. It is indicated that the back-mixing effect becomes significant when the ratio of the average velocities of liquid to gas exceeds 1 (Fig. 18-73*a* and *b*).

Knoedler and Bonilla [*Ind. Eng. Chem.*, **50**, 125 (1956)] presented an empirical relation for the liquid-phase coefficient for Stedman packing in a 6-in.-diameter column at low gas rates.

$$K_L a = 200 D_L L^{0.77}\left(\frac{\mu}{\rho D_L}\right)^{0.53} \quad (18\text{-}56)$$

where $K_L a$ = over-all coefficient based on liquid-phase concentrations and equivalent, lb.-moles/(hr.)(cu. ft.)(lb.-moles/cu. ft.)
D_L = liquid-phase diffusion coefficient, sq. ft./hr.
L = liquid-flow rate, lb./(hr.)(sq. ft.)
μ = viscosity of liquid, lb./(ft.)(hr.)
ρ = density of liquid, lb./cu. ft.

Gas-phase Transfer. There has been no satisfactory general relationship developed for the prediction of gas-phase behavior in packed columns having different packing geometries. The principal deterrents to the development of such a relationship have been (1) the variation in effective area of contact as a function of liquid rate and surface tension and (2) the lack of availability of a true gas-phase controlling system unencumbered by side effects of heat development or chemical reaction.

Investigations of the behavior of gas films have been conducted with

1. Vaporization of pure liquids into a gas stream
2. Absorption of a solute gas by solvent offering a high degree of solubility
3. Absorption of a solute gas in a liquid where the equilibrium partial pressure is zero as a result of an irreversible chemical reaction

In cases 1 and 2, heat of vaporization and heat of solution effect result in (1) localized temperature changes that are reflected in variable-equilibrium constants not typical of the bulk conditions and (2) local changes in surface tension that may result in film splitting and

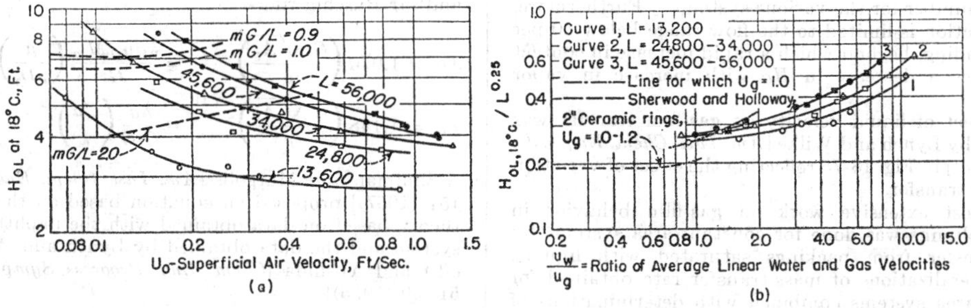

FIG. 18-73. (*a*) Effect of gas velocity on H_{OL} at high liquor rates. From data on CO_2 absorption in water, using 2-in. steel Raschig rings. On this graph G and L are for molar rates. [*Cooper, Christl, and Perry, Trans. Am. Inst. Chem. Engrs.*, **37**, 979 (1941).] (*b*) Absorption of CO_2 in H_2O at high liquid rates. Correlation of data of Cooper, Christl, and Perry [*Trans. Am. Inst. Chem. Engrs.*, **37**, 979 (1941)] with those of Sherwood and Holloway [*Trans. Am. Inst. Chem. Engrs.*, **36**, 49 (1940)].

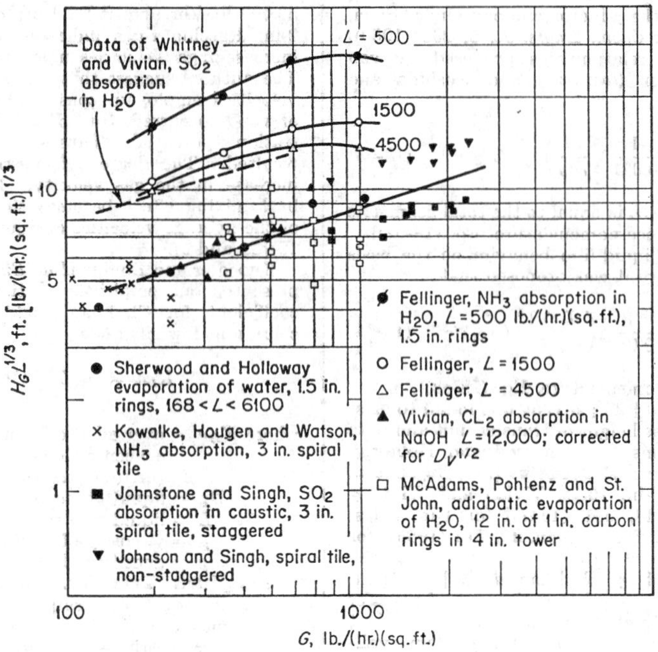

FIG. 18-74. Correlation of data on gas-film resistance to mass transfer in packed towers. (*Sherwood and Pigford, "Absorption and Extraction," 2d ed., McGraw-Hill Book Company, Inc., New York,* 1952.)

change of effective area of mass transfer as indicated by Bond and Donald [*Chem. Eng. Sci.*, **6**, 237 (1957)].

In case 3, the situation is complicated by the fact that the chemical reaction rate or diffusion of the reactive component of the solvent may be rate controlling and the absorption process may be liquid-phase controlling.

Sherwood and Hollaway [*Trans. Am. Inst. Chem. Engrs.*, **36**, 21 (1940)] attempted to correlate the gas-phase behavior in irrigated columns via the relationship

$$H_G = \frac{1.01G^{0.31}}{L^{0.33}} \quad \text{ft.} \tag{18-57}$$

indicated in Fig. 18-74.

where H_G = height of gas-phase transfer unit, ft.
G = gas rate, lb./(hr.)(sq. ft.)
L = liquid rate, lb./(hr.)(sq. ft.)

Deviations from observed data are significant and from that observed for the ammonia-air-water system is great. No correction was made for the variation in the Schmidt number for the various systems. Furthermore, the correlation is limited to the flow range below 60 per cent of loading, beyond which a rapid increase in contact area causes a decrease in H_G with increase in vapor velocity.

The effect of liquid velocity on gas-film transfer was indicated by Lynch and Wilke [*Am. Inst. Chem. Engrs. J.*, **1**, 18 (1955)] in Fig. 18-75 reflecting the effect of variation in area of transfer.

The most extensive work on gas-film behavior in packed columns was done for constant-area systems by mass transfer from packings saturated with liquids. From generalizations of mass-transfer rate obtained for constant-area systems combined with determinations of the area of mass transfer in packed columns, the effective mass-transfer-rate coefficient can be obtained.

Gamson, Thodos, and Hougen [*Trans. Am. Inst. Chem. Engrs.* **39**, 1 (1943)] evaluated the behavior in columns packed with spheres and saddles. It was found that

$$J_D = \frac{k_G p_{gf} M_m}{G}\left(\frac{\mu}{\rho D_v}\right)^{2/3} = 0.99\left(\frac{D_p G}{\mu}\right)^{-0.41} \tag{18-58}$$

and

$$J_H = \frac{h_G}{C_p G}\left(\frac{C_p \mu}{k}\right)^{2/3} = 1.064\left(\frac{D_p G}{\mu}\right)^{-0.41} \tag{18-59}$$

for values of N_{Re} exceeding 350.

Tacker and Hougen [*Chem. Eng. Progress*, **44**, 529 (1948)] found in the range of Reynolds numbers $70 < (N_{Re} = G\sqrt{A_p}/\mu) < 3000$ that for Berl saddles

$$J_D = 0.855\left(\frac{G\sqrt{A_p}}{\mu}\right)^{-0.34} = \frac{k_G p_{gf} M_m}{G}\left(\frac{\mu}{\rho D_v}\right)^{2/3} \tag{18-60}$$

$$J_H = 0.920\left(\frac{G\sqrt{A_p}}{\mu}\right)^{-0.34} = \frac{h_G}{C_p G}\left(\frac{C_p \mu}{k}\right)^{2/3} \tag{18-61}$$

and for Raschig rings

$$J_D = 1.070\left(\frac{G\sqrt{A_p}}{\mu}\right)^{-0.41} = \frac{k_G p_{gf} M_m}{G}\left(\frac{\mu}{\rho D_v}\right)^{2/3} \tag{18-62}$$

$$J_H = 1.148\left(\frac{G\sqrt{A_p}}{\mu}\right)^{-0.41} = \frac{h_G}{C_p G}\left(\frac{C_p \mu}{k}\right)^{2/3} \tag{18-63}$$

Shulman and Margolis [*Am. Inst. Chem. Engrs. J.*, **3**, 157 (1957)] proposed an equation based on the *J*-factor theory based on data obtained with the naphthalene-air system and the data obtained by Lynch and Wilke (*loc. cit.*) and Yoshida [*Chem. Eng. Progress Symp. Ser.* 16, **51**, 59 (1955)].

$$J_D = \frac{k_G M_m P_{BM}}{G}\left(\frac{\mu}{\rho D_v}\right)^{2/3} = 1.195\left(\frac{D_p G}{\mu(1-\epsilon)}\right)^{-0.36} \tag{18-64}$$

Combined with the availability of effective area of mass transfer, the authors believe that effective prediction of a physical type of gas-film mass-transfer coefficient can be made. The nomenclature for Eqs. (18-58) to (18-64) is as follows:

A_p = external surface of packing unit, sq. ft.
C_p = specific heat of gas stream, B.t.u./(lb.)(°F.)
J = dimensionless Chilton and Colburn J factor
D_v = gas-phase diffusion coefficient, sq. ft./hr.
D_p = equivalent diameter of packing, ft.
G = mass velocity of gas stream, lb./(hr.) (sq. ft.)
k = thermal conductivity of gas stream, B.t.u./(hr.)(sq. ft.)(°F./ft.)
k_G = gas-phase mass-transfer coefficient, lb.-moles/(hr.)(sq. ft.)(atm.)
M_m = average molecular weight of gas stream, lb./lb.-mole
p_{gf} = partial pressure of inserts in gas film, atm.
μ = viscosity of gas stream, lb./(ft.)(hr.)
ρ = density of gas, lb./cu. ft.
ϵ = void fraction, dimensionless

Thoenes and Kramers [*Chem. Eng. Sci.*, **8**, 271 (1958)] questioned the applicability of a generalized J function to packed columns indicating that the relative influence of the Reynolds and Schmidt characterization quantities varied significantly with the condition of transfer. This analysis was in agreement with that of Goffney and Drew [*Ind. Eng. Chem.*, **42**, 1126 (1950)] who investigated liquid-phase mass transfer in turbulent conditions in packed columns. Thoenes and Kramers (*loc. cit.*) divided the types of mass transfer into turbulent, laminar, and stagnant. The empirical relationship evolved for dense packings (spheres) was

$$N_{Sh} = \underbrace{(k_1 N_{Re}^{1/3} N_{Sc}^{1/3})}_{\text{laminar}} + \underbrace{(k_2 N_{Re}^{0.8} N_{Sc}^{0.4})}_{\text{turbulent}} + \underbrace{k_3 N_{Re}}_{\text{stagnant}} \qquad (18\text{-}65)$$

where N_{Sh} = Sherwood number = $\dfrac{Ekd}{(1 - E)\epsilon D_v}$

ϵ = fraction of voids
E = surface area $(\pi/4)d^2$
D_v = diffusion coefficient
d = particle diameter (equivalent of sphere)
k_1, k_2, k_3 = system constants

Absorption Accompanied by Chemical Reaction. For a more theoretical discussion of this subject, see Sec. 14. Absorption accompanied by chemical reaction provides three major advantages over that of physical absorption:

1. Greater capacity of solvent for the solute gas
2. Generally an increased rate of absorption
3. Increased utilization of stagnant zones of the liquid phase

Inasmuch as the equilibrium partial pressure of the solute in the solvent is generally zero prior to full utilization of the reagent solvent, the solvent capacity for the solute gas is greater than that obtained in physical absorption.

Analyses have been made for the effect of variables on the mass-transfer rate by a first-order reaction and a rapid second-order irreversible reaction via the possible mechanisms of the "Whitman" two-film theory, the Higbie penetration theory, and the Danckwerts surface-renewal modification of the penetration theory.

In the case of a first-order reaction accompanying absorption, analyses via the three mechanisms yield similar results. Danckwerts [*Am. Inst. Chem. Engrs. J.*, **1**, 456 (1955)] compared the effective liquid-phase mass-transfer coefficients (for a unit area) based on the three mechanisms:

Two-film model, Sherwood and Pigford:

$$k_L' = \frac{Dk_c}{\tanh (Dk_c/k_L)} \qquad (18\text{-}66)$$

Higbie penetration model:

$$k_L' = \sqrt{Dk_c}\left(1 + \frac{k_L^2}{8Dk_c}\right) \operatorname{erf} \frac{2}{k_L}\sqrt{\frac{Dk_c}{\pi}} + \frac{2}{k_L} Dk_c \exp.\left(\frac{-4Dk_c}{\pi k_L^2}\right) \qquad (18\text{-}67)$$

Danckwerts surface-renewal model:

$$k_L' = \sqrt{Dk_c + k_L^2} \qquad (18\text{-}68)$$

where k_L' = average effective absorption coefficient
k_c = reaction-velocity constant
k_L = liquid-film coefficient for physical absorption
D = diffusion coefficient in liquid phase

It was found that the effect of the reaction rate depended on a single parameter, Dk_c/k_L^2, for all three mechanisms. Comparison of the rate of absorption accompanied by chemical reaction to that of physical absorption was made on the basis of zero solute concentration in the bulk liquid phase. In all cases it was found at slow reaction rates where Dk_c/k_L^2 approaches zero that the rate is the same as in a physical absorption and at high reaction rates compared with k_L (at high values of Dk_c/k_L^2) the absorption became gas-phase controlling.

The case of absorption accompanied by a second-order reaction has not been solved analytically except with specific restrictions. Sherwood and Pigford ("Absorption and Extraction," 2d ed., McGraw-Hill, New York, 1952) developed analyses for both the two-film and penetration models for the case of a rapid second-order irreversible reaction. Application of the two-film model results in the relationship

$$k_L' = k_L\left(1 + \frac{D_B}{D_A}\frac{q}{c_{ai}}\right) \qquad (18\text{-}69)$$

Via the penetration model

$$k_L' = \frac{k_L}{\operatorname{erf} (\alpha/D_A)^{1/2}} \qquad (18\text{-}70)$$

where D_A = liquid-phase diffusivity for solute gas, sq. ft./hr.
D_B = liquid-phase diffusivity for reagent, sq. ft./hr.
c_{ai} = concentration of solute at the interface, lb.-moles/cu. ft.
q = concentration of unreacted reagent in bulk of liquid, lb.-moles/cu. ft.
x_e^1 = effective distance of liquid film from interface to the reaction zone, ft.
$\alpha = \dfrac{x_e^1}{4}$
k_L = liquid-film coefficient, physical absorption, lb.-moles/(hr.)(sq. ft.)(lb.-moles/cu. ft.)
k_L' = liquid-film coefficient in absorption accompanied by chemical reaction

For the simple case where the rates of diffusion of solute gas and reagent in the liquid phase are equal,

$$D_A/D_B = 1 \qquad \text{then} \qquad k_L' = k_L\left(1 + \frac{q}{c_{ai}}\right) \qquad (18\text{-}71)$$

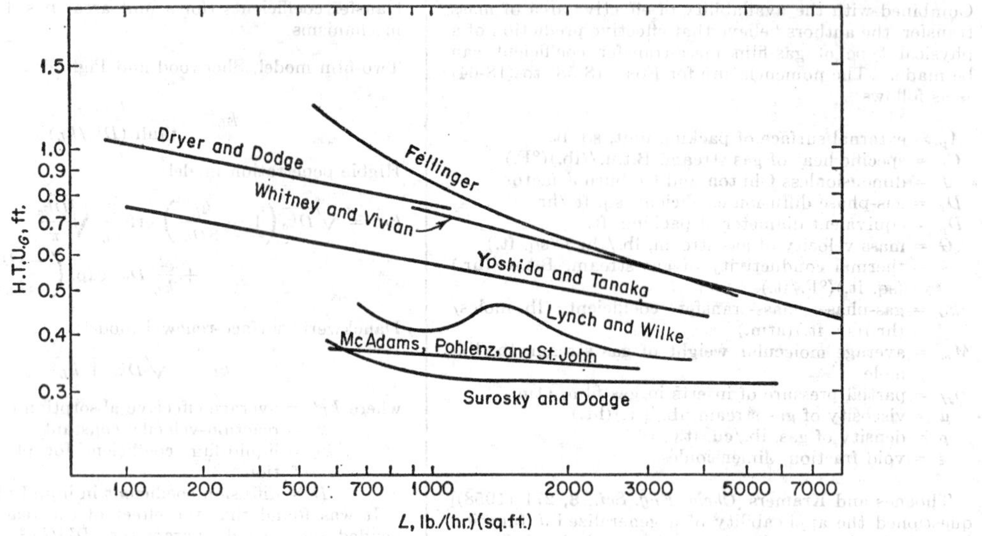

Fig. 18-75. H.T.U.$_G$ as a function of liquid rate by various investigators. [*Lynch and Wilke, Am. Inst. Chem. Engrs. J.*, **1**, 18 (1955).]

To a close degree of approximation it is indicated that

$$k_L' = k_L\left(1 + \frac{D_A}{D_B}\frac{q}{c_{ai}}\right) \qquad (18\text{-}72)$$

From Eqs. (18-69) and (18-70) it is noted that analyses by the two-film model and the penetration model again yield similar results.

From these relationships it is observed that the rate of absorption accompanied by a rapid second-order irreversible reaction is linear with the quantity q/c_{ai}, the concentration of reagent (in uncombined state) divided by the concentration of the solute at the interface.

A more general analysis of absorption accompanied by chemical reaction via the penetration model has been made by Perry and Pigford [*Ind. Eng. Chem.*, **45**, 1247 (1953)].

The increased utilization of stagnant-liquid zones in absorption accompanied by chemical reaction over that of physical absorption was indicated by Danckwerts

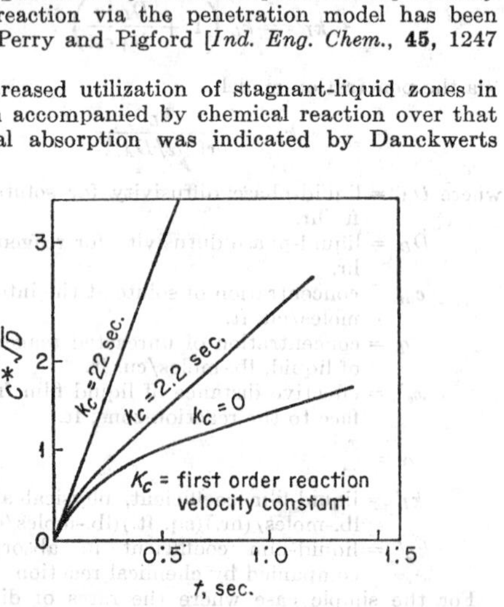

Fig. 18-76. Effect of first-order reaction of transient absorption Q = quantity of gas absorbed at time t; C^* = concentration of unreacted dissolved gas at surface of liquid; D = diffusivity of dissolved gas. [*Danckwerts, Am. Inst. Chem. Engrs. J.*, **1**, 456 (1955).]

(*loc. cit.*). With rapid removal of the absorbed gas by reaction, the development of a concentration gradient of the solute gas predicted by the penetration theory is negated. Thus the rate of absorption with chemical reaction is not affected to the same degree by time of contact prior to surface renewal as is the case with physical absorption (Fig. 18-76). As a result of this behavior the stagnant zones of liquid appearing in any liquid-gas contact device become effective in contributing to the active interface area when reaction accompanies absorption. Thus the rate of transfer is less sensitive to change in liquid rates in absorption accompanied by chemical reaction than the case of physical absorption (Fig. 18-77).

Behavior of Various Systems and Packings. In view of the incomplete development of the theory of mass-transfer behavior, much of the estimation of rate of transfer is based on comparison with systems already evaluated. Comparison is generally based on equivalent geometry and flow characteristics, the variation related primarily to the physical properties of the systems.

The following system behaviors are reported:

Ammonia-air-water	Liquid and gas phase contributing—chemical reaction contributing
Air-water	Gas phase controlling
Sulfur dioxide–air–water	Liquid and gas phase contributing
Carbon dioxide–air–water	Liquid phase controlling
Carbon dioxide–air–monoethanolamine	Absorption accompanied by chemical reaction
Carbon dioxide–air–carbonate	Absorption accompanied by chemical reaction
Ethanol-air-water	Liquid and gas phase contributing
SiF_4-air-water	Gas phase controlling—chemical reaction contributing
Distillation systems	Either phase may control—both contribute

Ammonia-Air-Water System. Transfer in the ammonia-air-water system has been studied extensively for a wide variety of packings, and results of these

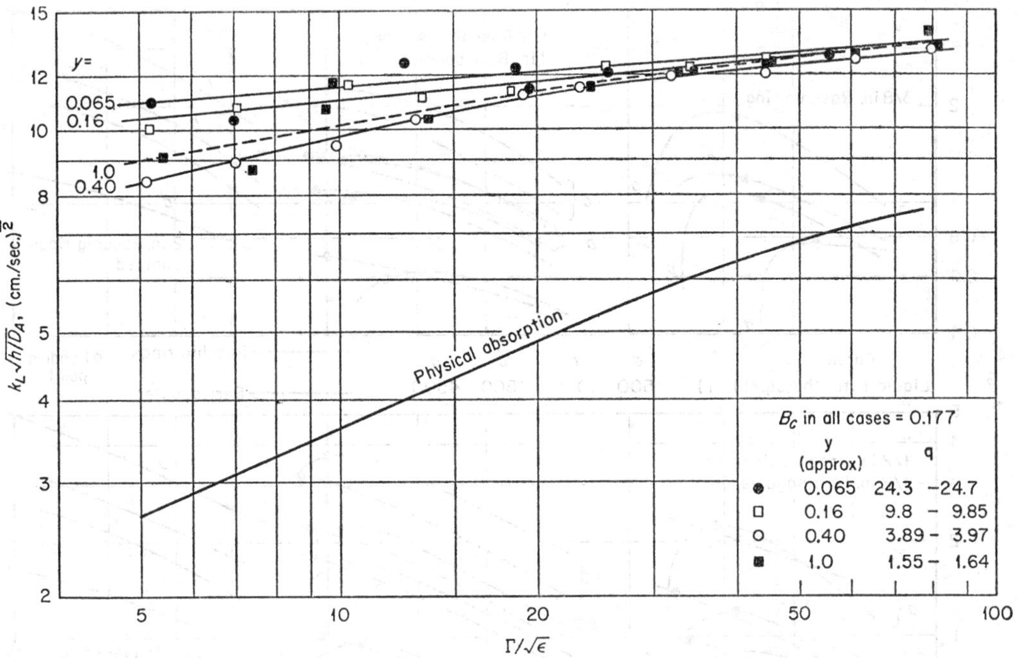

FIG. 18-77. Absorption of chlorine into 0.177*M* ferrous chloride. Γ = liquid flow rate, g./(cm.)(min.); $\epsilon = (\mu/\mu w)(P/P_w)$; k_L = liquid phase absolute coefficient, cm./sec.; h = height of wetted-wall column, cm.; D_A = liquid-phase diffusivity Cl_2, sq. cm./sec.; B_c = initial liquid phase concentration of nonvolatile solute reacting with absorbed gas; y = gas phase mol fraction of absorbing component $q = B_c/2C^*$. [*Gilliland and Baddour, Am. Inst. Chem. Engrs. J.*, **4,** 223 (1958).]

studies are valuable in estimation of comparative effectiveness of packing geometries. Although initial studies with this system were predicated on the hypothesis that it was gas-phase controlling, recent studies have indicated that the liquid may provide from 5 to 40 per cent of the resistance at 25°C. The heights of transfer unit obtained for the ammonia-air-water system are greater than that anticipated for physical-absorption systems. However, it is believed that this anomalous behavior is due to the effect of heat generation at the interface resulting in localized variations in surface tension that cause a decrease in effective area of contact, and local deviations in equilibrium concentrations from bulk-phase conditions.

Fellinger (Sc.D. Thesis, M.I.T., 1941) presented an extensive study of this system with Raschig rings, Berl saddles, and triple-spiral tiles (Fig. 18-78). The data indicate no distinct pattern of variation of mass-transfer efficiency with size of packing. In the cases of both Raschig rings and Berl saddles, the optimum size from the aspect of transfer efficiency appears to be the 1-in. normal size. As reported by Fellinger, the Berl saddle (in the 1- and 1½-in. sizes) provides approximately 25 per cent more efficiency than the comparable size of Raschig ring.

In all cases a maximum in H_{OG} is observed prior to the loading range. A rise in H_{OG} with gas rate is anticipated since $K_Ga\alpha G^{0.5-0.8}$ for constant surface and $H_G\alpha G_M/k_Ga(1-y)$. It appears that effective interfacial area increases rapidly at the preloading conditions overcoming the decrease of constant-area mass-transfer efficiency.

Parsely *et al.* [*Chem. Eng. Progress* **46,** 17 (1950)] and Molstad *et al.* [*Trans. Am. Inst. Chem. Engrs.*, **39,** 605 (1953)] performed an extensive evaluation for this system with drip-point grid packing. K_Ga was found to be proportional to $G^{0.83}$ and $L^{0.17}$ below an irrigation rate of 10,500 lb./(hr.)(sq. ft.) (Fig. 18-79). However, the transfer coefficient decreased with an increase in liquid rate to 15,000 lb./(hr.)(sq. ft.). This behavior may be attributed to the back-mixing phenomenon observed by Cooper, Christl, and Perry (*loc. cit.*).

A comparison of transfer efficiency of Intalox saddles with other packings was provided by Wen (M.S. Thesis, University of West Virginia, 1953) (Fig. 18-80), indicating the effect of more effective liquid distribution for Intalox saddles resulting in higher efficiencies. Williams, Akell, and Talbot [*Chem. Eng. Progress*, **43,** 585 (1947)] evaluated the efficiency of Fiberglas packing in a 6-in.-diameter column. It was observed (Fig. 18-81) that irrigation rates exceeding 2000 lb./(hr.)(sq. ft.) were necessary to achieve effective mass transfer.

Teller [*Chem. Eng. Progress*, **50,** 65 (1954)] compared the efficiency of 1-in. Tellerettes with ¾-in. Raschig rings. A smaller response to irrigation rates was noted with the Tellerettes (Fig. 18-82*a* and *b*). Inasmuch as the material of construction, polyethylene, was hydrophobic, it appeared that a major contribution to mass transfer was the rapid agglomeration and surface regeneration, adding further confirmation to the Higbie penetration theory. Further verification of this phenomenon was made by Khalif *et. al.* [*Referat. Zhur. Khim.*, No. 8843, 1955] who observed that the coefficient of mass transfer to droplets is 10 to 13 times larger than from a gas to a flat surface.

Air-Water System. The air-water-system behavior for various packings has been extensively investigated from both the aspect of a vapor-phase controlling system and for developing design information for cooling towers and humidification systems.

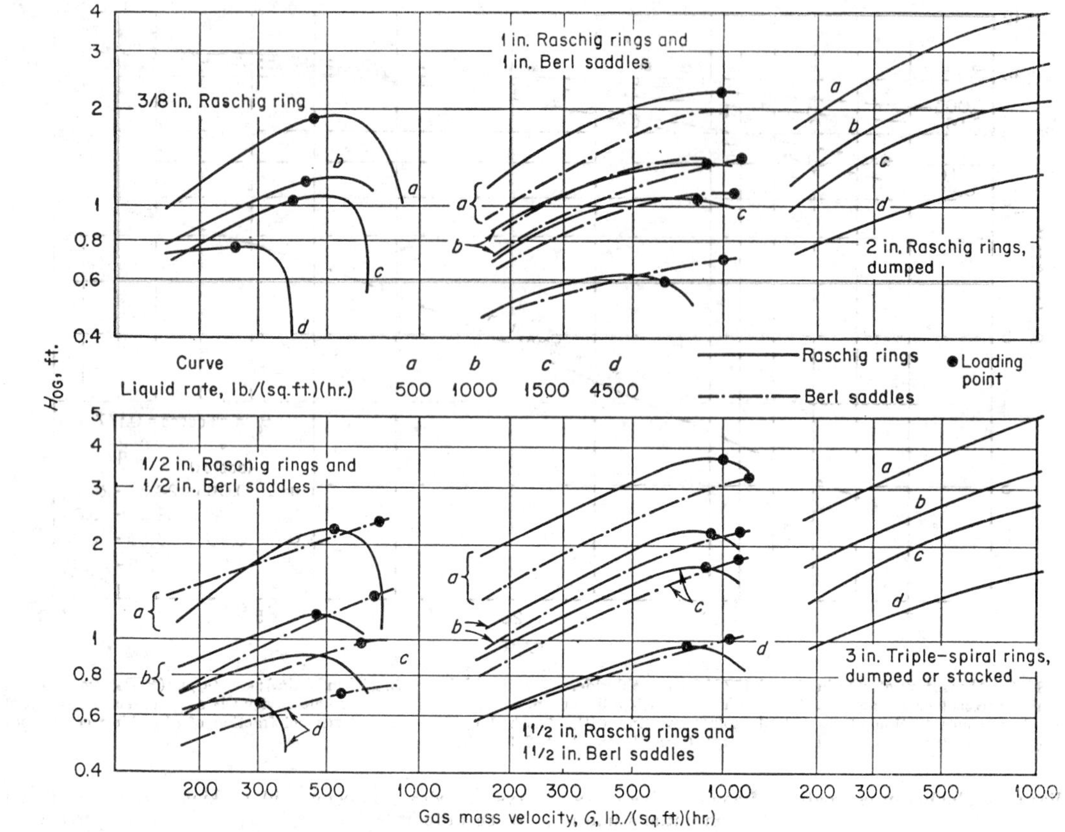

FIG. 18-78. Packed-column performance, ammonia-air-water system. (*Fellinger, Sc.D. Thesis, M.I.T.*, 1941.)

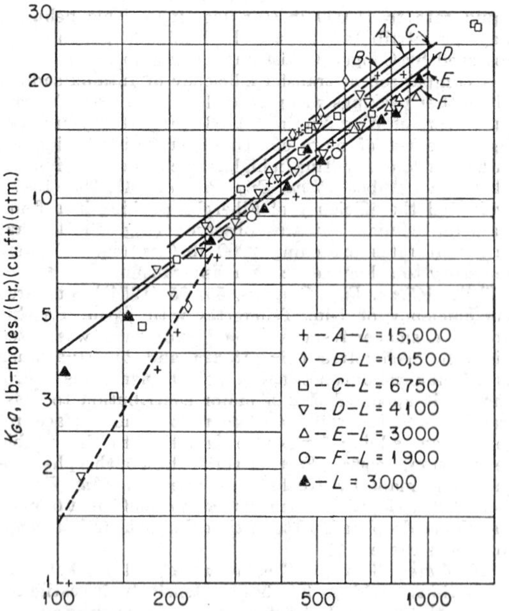

FIG. 18-79. K_Ga vs. G for ammonia absorption with 2.25 ft. of No. 6295 drip-point grid packing. [*Parsely et al., Chem. Eng. Progress*, **46**, 17 (1950).]

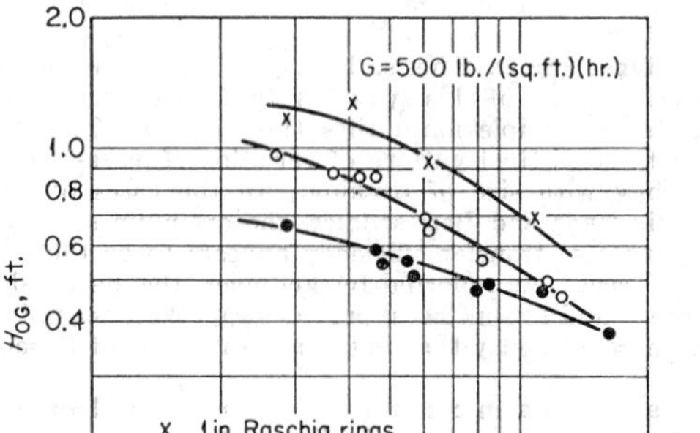

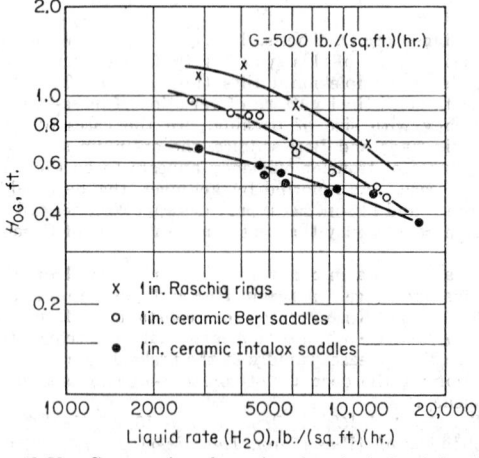

FIG. 18-80. Comparative absorption data in beds of Raschig rings, Berl saddles, and Intalox saddles, system NH_3-air-H_2O. (*Wen, M.S. Thesis, University of West Virginia*, 1953.)

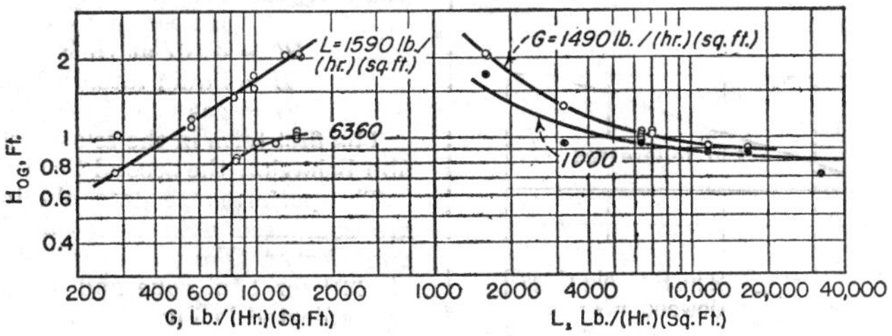

FIG. 18-81. Values of H.T.U. for absorption of NH_3 in water from air. Fiberglas pads, fibers vertical, bulk density of 4.7 lb./cu. ft. [*Data of Williams, Akele, and Talbot, Chem. Eng. Progress*, **43,** 585 (1947).]

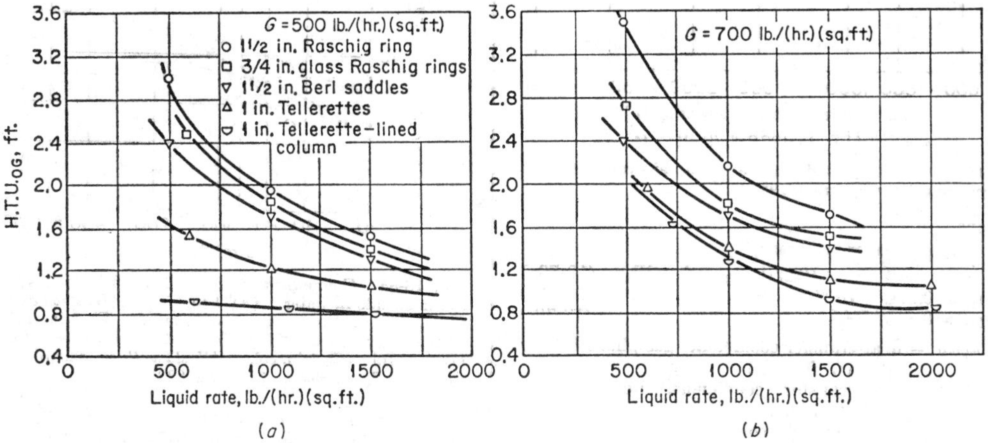

FIG. 18-82. Column packing comparison, NH_3-air-H_2O system. [*Teller, Chem. Eng. Progress*, **50,** 70 (1954).]

Norman [*Trans. Inst. Chem. Engrs.*, **29** (2) 226 (1951)] compared the data for performance of a variety of packings with that obtained for Paragrid packing. The packings reported were Raschig rings, Berl saddles, wood grid, and the Paragrid. A variation in the effect of the mass velocity of the gas is observed as a function of packing geometry. For the range of flow studied an increase in irrigation rates was reflected in an increase in efficiency of mass transfer (Fig. 18-83).

Ford (private communication) compared the efficiency of Raschig rings, Dowpac, and Tellerettes in cooling towers in the form of the thermal-transfer coefficient (Fig. 18-84). It should be noted that Hensel and Treybal [*Chem. Eng. Progress*, **48,** 362 (1952)] indicated that the thermal-transfer coefficient is higher than the mass-transfer coefficient. This phenomenon is probably related to the fact that thermal transfer is not so sensitive to the existence of stagnant pockets of liquid as is the penetration type of mass transfer.

Parsely, Molstad, Cress, and Bauer [*Chem. Eng. Progress*, **46,** 17 (1950)] evaluated the performance of drip-point grid tiles in the air-water system for the range $1900 < L < 15{,}000$ and $100 < G < 1000$ where flows are in lb./(hr.)(sq. ft.). It was found that, for this packing, k_Ga was independent of liquor rate and proportional to $G^{0.839}$. The performance of 1-in. carbon Raschig rings in this system was studied by McAdams, Pohlenz, and St. John [*Chem. Eng. Progress*, **45,** 241 (1949)]. Using an 8-in.-diameter tower for the flow range $350 < G < 1000$ and $500 < L < 2600$, it was found that end effects were equivalent to 7.2 in. of packing. The small effect of liquid rate on the gas-phase mass and heat-transfer coefficient was unusual, as indicated by the

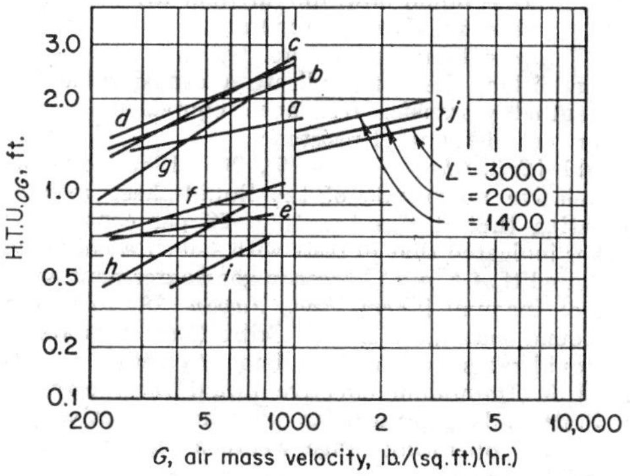

FIG. 18-83. Column-packing comparison, air-H_2O system.

Curve packing	Ref.	Liquid rate, lb./(hr.)(sq. ft.)
a. 6295 grid	1	3000
b. 6146 grid	1	3000
c. 6897 grid	1	3000
d. Wood grid	2	3000
e. 1-in. rings	1	3000
f. 1-in. saddles	1	3000
g. 1-in. rings	2	500
h. 1-in. rings	3	1500
i. 1-in. rings	3	3000
j. Carbon grid	4	3000

1. Molstad, McKinney, and Abbey, *Trans. Am. Inst. Chem. Engrs.*, **39,** 605 (1943); *Chem. Eng. Progress*, **46,** 17 (1950).
2. Carey and Williamson, *Proc. Inst. Mech. Engrs.* (*London*), **163,** 41 (1950).
3. Mehta and Parekh, M.S. Thesis, M.I.T., 1939.
4. Norman, *Trans. Inst. Chem. Engrs.*, **29** (2), **226** (1951).

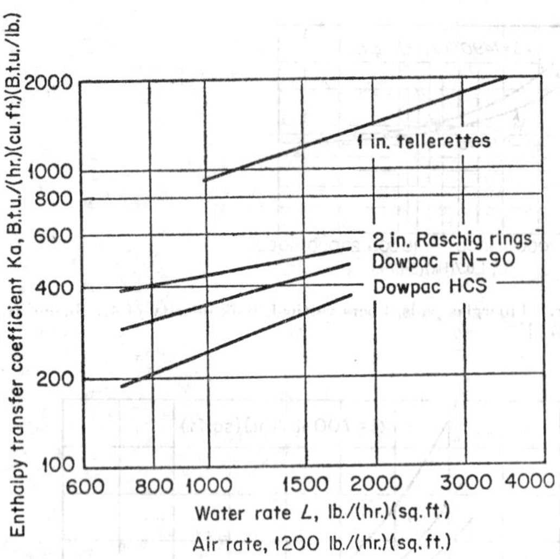

FIG. 18-84. Packing performance with air-water system. (*Ford, personal communication*, 1958.)

equations

$$(h_Ga_H)_{tf} = 1.78G^{0.70}L^{0.07}e^{0.0023t_f} \quad \text{Btu/(hr.)(sq. ft.)(°F.)} \quad (18\text{-}73a)$$

$$(k_Ga)_m = 0.89G^{0.70}L^{0.07} \quad (18\text{-}73b)$$

$$h_La = 0.82G^{0.7}L^{0.5} \quad (18\text{-}73c)$$

where h_Ga_H = heat-transfer coefficient, gas phase B.t.u./(hr.)(cu. ft.)(°F.)
h_La = heat-transfer coefficient, liquid phase B.t.u./(hr.)(cu. ft.)(°F.)
$(k_Ga)_m$ = mass-transfer coefficient, gas phase lb./(hr.)(cu. ft.)(unit enthalpy difference) unit enthalpy difference = B.t.u./lb.-mole bone-dry air
L = liquid flow, lb./(hr.)(sq. ft.)
G = gas flow, lb./(hr.)(sq. ft.)
t_f = film temperature, °F.

In addition, the data indicate a considerable liquid-film enthalpy-transfer resistance equivalent to 27 to 46 per cent of the total resistance.

Cribb [*Brit. Chem. Eng.* 4 (5), 264 (1959)] questioned the relative magnitude of the liquid-phase resistance, indicating that it was less than 20 per cent. It was further indicated that in tests with 4-in. Raschig rings it was found that $h_La \propto L^{1.5}$ was in good agreement with the data of Inazumi [*Chem. Eng., Japan*, **19**, 579 (1955)], who found that $h_La \propto L^{1.36}$. Cribb (*loc. cit.*) stated that the liquid rates used by McAdams *et al.* were below the M.E.L.R. (minimum effective liquid rate) established by Pratt and thus the data were not reflective of the commercial operating range where a higher sensitivity to liquid rate exists.

Sulfur Dioxide–Air–Water. Sulfur dioxide absorption by water represents a system in which both the liquid and vapor resistances are significant. Whitney and Vivian [*Chem. Eng. Progress*, **45**, 323 (1949)] evaluated the performance of 1-in. Raschig rings for the range $920 < L < 11{,}700$ lb./(hr.)(sq. ft.) and $65 < G < 800$ lb./(hr.)(sq. ft.). On the assumption that the gas rate did not affect the liquid-film transfer rate, the following relationship was developed:

$$\frac{1}{K_La} = \frac{1}{0.44L^{0.82}} + \frac{H'}{0.028G^{0.7}L^{0.5}} \quad (18\text{-}74)$$

$$H_{OL} = \frac{L^{0.18}}{27.4} + \frac{H'L^{0.5}}{1.75G^{0.7}} \quad (18\text{-}75)$$

where K_La = over-all mass-transfer coefficient, lb.-moles/(hr.)(cu. ft.)(lb.-moles/cu. ft.)
H' = 0.107 at 70°F.
L = liquid rate, lb./(hr.)(sq. ft.)
G = gas rate, lb./(hr.)(sq. ft.)

The first term in the relationship represents the liquid-film behavior, the second term the gas-film behavior.

The performance data obtained by the investigators are compared with those obtained by Haslam, Ryan, and Weber [*Trans. Am. Inst. Chem. Engrs.*, **15**, 177 (1923)] for 1-in. coke and 3-in. spiral tile packings and are indicated in Fig. 18-85.

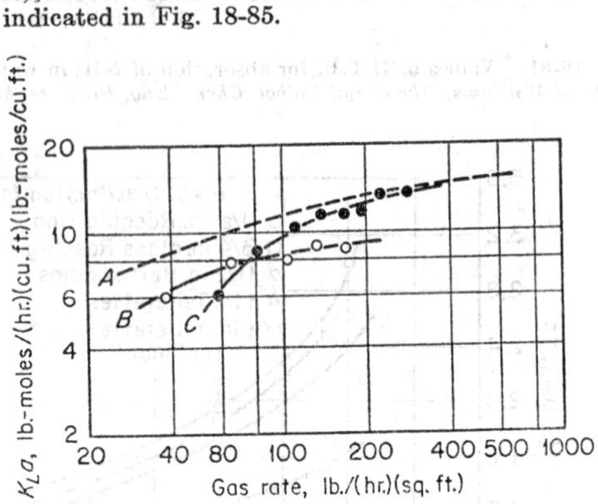

FIG. 18-85. Comparison of over-all coefficients absorption of sulfur dioxide in water. (*A*) 1-in. rings. [*Whitney and Vivian, Chem. Eng. Progress*, **45**, 335 (1949).] (*B*) 3-in. spiral tile. [*Haslam, Ryan, and Weber, Trans. Am. Inst. Chem. Engrs.*, **15**, 177 (1923).] (*C*) 1-in. coke. [*Haslam, Ryan, and Weber, Trans. Am. Inst. Chem. Engrs.*, **15**, 177 (1923).]

Pearson *et al.* [*Chem. Eng. Progress*, **47**, 257 (1951)] evaluated the performance of 24 ft. of 1-in. Raschig rings in a 12-in.-diameter tower for this system. The results were in good agreement with those obtained by Whitney and Vivian (*loc. cit.*), indicating that, with good distribution and accounting for end effects, laboratory data can be used for estimation of plant performance.

Absorption of CO_2. Carbon dioxide is recovered commercially by water (essentially physical absorption) in high-pressure systems and by alkaline solvents at operating pressures varying from 1 to 10 atm.

Carbon Dioxide–Air–Water System. Performance of packed columns for this system has been reported by Sherwood and Holloway (*loc. cit.*) (Figs. 18-70 and 18-71); Yoshida and Koyanagi (*loc. cit.*) (Fig. 18-72); Koch, Stutzman, Blum, and Hutchings [*Chem. Eng. Progress*, **45**, 677 (1949)]; and Cooper, Christl, and Perry (*loc. cit.*) (Fig. 18-73*a* and *b*). It was observed that H_L was independent of gas rate for values of $U_L/U_G < 1$. At values of $U_L/U_G > 1$, backflow of the gas caused a decrease in effective rate of mass transfer. Sherwood and Holloway indicated that H_L was proportional to $L^{0.22-0.46}$ as a function of the packing geometry and size (Fig. 18-70), Table 18-9.

Koch *et al.* (*loc. cit.*) investigated the behavior of Raschig rings (3/8, 1/2, 3/4, and 1 in.) in 6- and 10-in.-diameter columns packed to a height of 4 ft. In contradiction to the Sherwood and Holloway data, the authors proposed that H_L was independent of packing size and that

$$k_La = 0.25L^{0.96} \quad (18\text{-}76)$$

or

$$H_L \propto L^{0.04} \quad (18\text{-}76a)$$

where k_La = mass-transfer coefficient, liquid phase lb.-moles/(hr.)(cu. ft.)(lb.-moles/cu. ft.)
L = liquid flow, lb.-moles/(hr.)(sq. ft.)
H_L = height of transfer unit, ft.

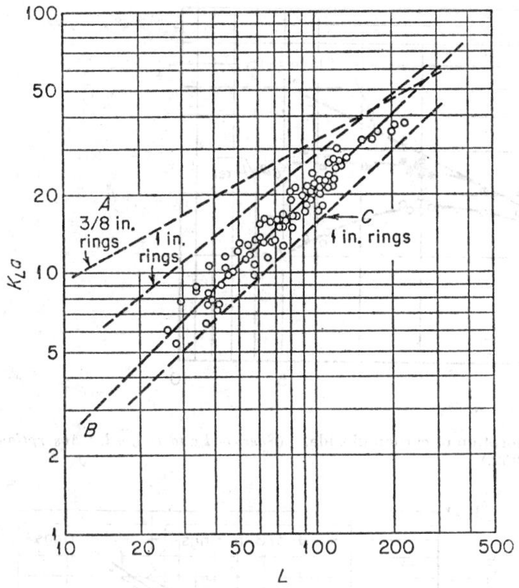

FIG. 18-86. K_La vs. L for carbon dioxide absorption. (A) Sherwood and Holloway, *Trans. Am. Inst. Chem. Engrs.*, **36,** 39 (1940). (B) Koch *et al., Chem. Eng. Progress*, **45,** 681 (1949). (C) Draemel and Ruckman *et al., Chem. Eng. Progress*, **45,** 677 (1949).

A comparison of the data of these investigators with those of others is indicated in Fig. 18-86.

Alkaline Solutions. The absorption of carbon dioxide by alkaline solutions is an example of absorption accompanied by chemical reaction. The complexity of analysis resulting from variation in reaction mechanism, reaction rate, viscosity, surface tension of the solvents, and the effective interfacial area has restricted analysis to essentially empirical relations. The alkaline solutions used commercially are sodium hydroxide, sodium and potassium carbonates, and the ethanolamines. A recent development is the hot carbonate method developed for CO_2 removal from pressurized gas systems (10 to 20 atm.) by the Bureau of Mines [Benson, Field, and Haynes, *Chem. Eng. Progress*, **52,** 33 (1956)]. The hot carbonate method appears to be limited to a concentration level of CO_2 in the gas phase above 0.5 per cent but provides economical operation in combination with other alkaline absorption processes. Mullowney [*Petrol. Refiner*, **36,** (12), 149 (1957)] compared the economics of various CO_2 recovery processes for a stream of 12 million surface cu. ft./day containing 34 per cent CO_2 at a total pressure of 350 lb./sq. in. gage. The CO_2 was removed to a level of 10 to 25 p.p.m. The comparison is given in Table 18-8.

Table 18-8. Comparison of Costs for Carbon Dioxide Removal*

Method of Absorption	Operating Cost, Dollars/ 11 × 10⁶ Standard Cu. Ft.
Aqueous monoethanolamine	0.15
Aqueous diethanolamine followed by caustic	0.19
Hot K_2CO_3 followed by aqueous monoethanolamine	0.11
Water followed by MEA	0.12
Hot K_2CO_3 followed by aqueous diethanolamine	0.12

* From Mullowney, *Petrol. Refiner*, **36** (12), 149 (1957).

Inasmuch as the rate of absorption of carbon dioxide is a function of the solvent used since rate of reaction, diffusion of the reagent, and solution viscosity are affected by the solvent, the rates in various solvent systems and packings are compared in Table 18-9.

The comparison of system performance in Table 18-9 is not exact since the transfer rate is a function of the partial pressure of the CO_2 in the gas phase and the concentration of unreacted reagent. These values vary from case to case as noted.

Sodium Hydroxide Solution. Tepe and Dodge [*Trans. Am. Inst. Chem. Engrs.*, **39,** 255 (1943)] evaluated the performance of this system using ½- and 1-in. Raschig rings. It was found that K_Ga was independent of gas rate and proportional to $L^{0.28}$. A significant effect of concentration was observed in that the mass-transfer coefficient increased with caustic concentration up to $2N$ and then decreased with increasing caustic concentration. Sherwood and Pigford ("Absorption and Extraction," 2d ed., McGraw-Hill, New York, 1952) indicate that the controlling step is a slow pseudo-first-order irreversible reaction between dissolved CO_2 and OH—, and that $K_Ga \propto (q/\mu_L)^{1/2}$, where μ_L is the viscosity of the liquid and q the concentration of unreacted reagent. Figure 18-87 illustrates the theoretical expectations and the actual performance. It is believed that the deviation is due to area decrease resulting from increasing viscosity at higher caustic concentrations. In Fig. 81-87, μ_{rel} is the viscosity of the absorbent referred to water.

Sodium Carbonate Solution. Comstock and Dodge [*Ind. Eng. Chem.*, **29,** 520 (1937)] found no effect of gas velocity on mass-transfer coefficients for CO_2 absorption by KOH solutions in a 10-mm. Raschig ring column. It was noted, however, that the increased conversion of the reagent resulted in a decrease in mass-transfer coefficient as indicated by the relationship for absorption

Table 18-9. Absorption-rate Coefficients for CO_2 in Various Solvent Systems

Solvent	Packing	L, lb./(hr.)(sq. ft.)	G, lb./(hr.) (sq. ft.)	K_Ga, lb. moles/(hr.)(cu. ft.) (ΔY)*	Ref.
Water	1-in. Raschig rings	2500	300	0.05	1
1N sodium carbonate, 20% of sodium as bicarbonate	1-in. Raschig rings	2500	300	0.03	2
2N diethanolamine, 50% conversion to carbonate	¾-in. Raschig rings	2500	300	0.4	3
2N sodium hydroxide, 20% conversion to carbonate	1-in. Raschig rings	2500	300	2.3	4
2N sodium hydroxide	1-in. Berl saddles	2500	263	1.9	5
2.5N monoethanolamine, 40% conversion to carbonate	1-in. Tellerettes	2500	861	4.9	6
			570	3.7	
	1-in. Berl saddles	2500	861	3.1	6
	1-in. Raschig rings	2500	861	3.1	6
				3.0	
40% potassium carbonate, 50% conversion to carbonate	½-in. Raschig rings	2500	400	0.1–0.6 + (P_{CO_2})	7

References:
[1] Sherwood and Hollaway, *Trans. Am. Inst. Chem. Engrs.*, **36,** 39 (1940).
[2] Furnas and Bellinger, *Trans. Am. Inst. Chem. Engrs.*, **34,** 251 (1938).
[3] Cryder and Maloney, *Trans. Am. Inst. Chem. Engrs.*, **37,** 287 (1941).
[4] Tepe and Dodge, *Trans. Am. Inst. Chem. Engrs.*, **39,** 255 (1943).
[5] Spector and Dodge, *Trans. Am. Inst. Chem. Engrs.*, **42,** 827 (1946).
[6] Teller and Ford, *Ind. Eng. Chem.*, **50,** 1201 (1958).
[7] Benson, Field, and Jimeson, *Chem. Eng. Progress*, **50,** 356 (1954).
* ΔY = mole fraction driving force.

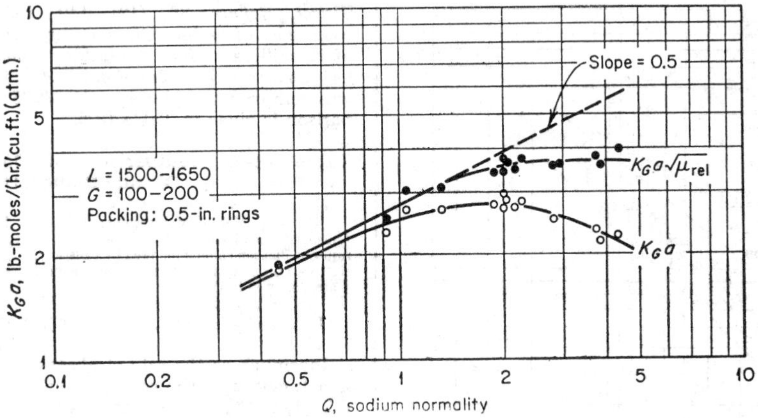

FIG. 18-87. Effect of sodium hydroxide concentration on rate of absorption of carbon dioxide. (*Sherwood and Pigford, "Absorption and Extraction," 2d ed., McGraw-Hill Book Company, Inc., New York,* 1952.)

accompanied by a second-order chemical reaction (Fig. 18-88).

Furnas and Bellinger [*Trans. Am. Inst. Chem. Engrs.*, **34,** 251 (1938)] studied the behavior of this system with ⅜- and 1-in. Raschig rings and 1-in. Berl saddles

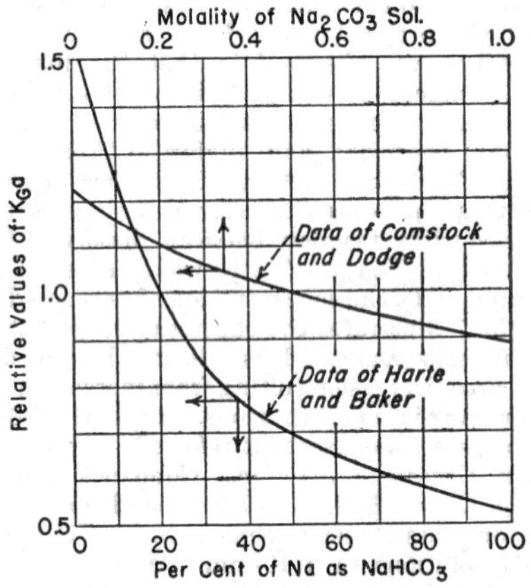

FIG. 18-88. Effect of molality, and percentage conversion to $NaHCO_3$ on K_Ga for the system Na_2CO_3, $NaHCO_3$, CO_2, H_2O, and air.

in a 12-in.-diameter column. Mass-transfer coefficients were found to be independent of gas rate. The data are compared with those of Comstock and Dodge (*loc. cit.*) and are indicated in Fig. 18-89. The significant effect of temperature on rate of absorption as a result of decrease in viscosity and increase in reagent diffusivity is indicated in Fig. 18-90.

Ethanolamine Solutions. The absorption of carbon dioxide by ethanolamine solutions appears to be accompanied by a second-order irreversible reaction. In general, amine concentrations vary between $2N$ and $5N$ and the operating temperature range is 100° to 130°F. based on optimum viscosity and equilibrium conditions.

Schneerson and Leibush [*J. Appl. Chem.* (*U.S.S.R.*), **19** (9), 869 (1946)] compared the rate of mass transfer for carbon dioxide in the various ethanolamines. The use of the comparison is limited to that of the relative

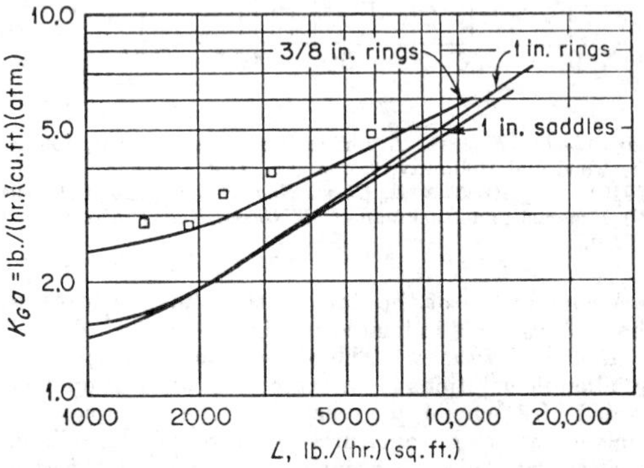

FIG. 18-89. Mass-transfer coefficient—CO_2-air, Na_2CO_3-H_2O system. [*Furnas and Bellinger, Trans. Am. Inst. Chem. Engrs.*, **34,** 251 (1938).]

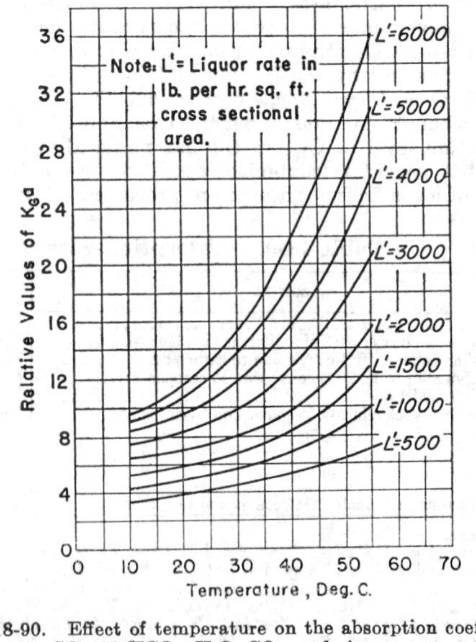

FIG. 18-90. Effect of temperature on the absorption coefficient system Na_2CO_3, $NaHCO_3$, H_2O, CO_2, and air.

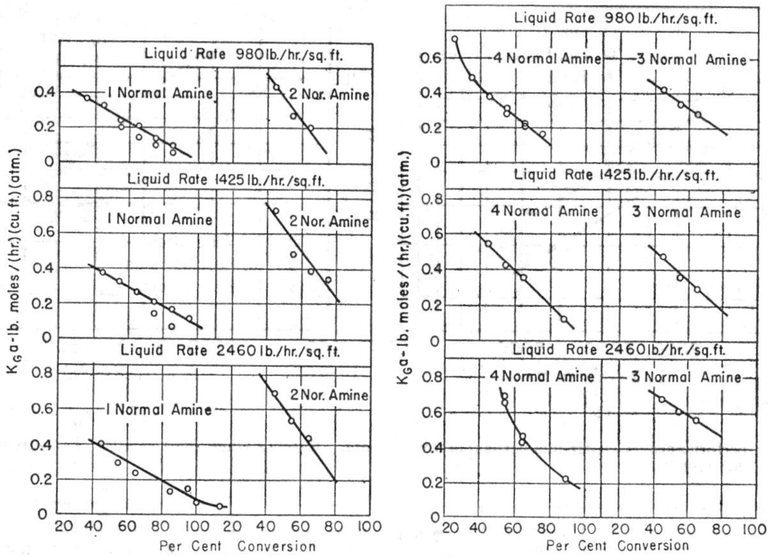

FIG. 18-91. Absorption of CO_2 by diethanolamine solutions at atmospheric pressure—absorption coefficient vs. per cent conversion of amine. [*From Cryder and Maloney, Trans. Am. Inst. Chem. Engrs.*, **37**, 827 (1941).]

rates of transfer since the work was done in a 1-in.-diameter column with 5- to 6-mm. Raschig rings.

Table 18-10. Relative Rates of CO_2 Absorption by the Various Amines

L = 695 lb./(hr.) (sq. ft.); T = 122°F; CO_2 conc., 0.03 to 0.05 moles CO_2/mole MEA 5% amine converted to carbonate

Amine	K_Ga, Lb-moles/(Hr.)(Sq. Ft.)(Atm.)
2*M* monoethanolamine	6.89
2*M* diethanolamine	2.83
3.5*M* triethanolamine	0.295

Cryder and Maloney [*Trans. Am. Inst. Chem. Engrs.*, **37**, 827 (1941)] evaluated the performance of ¾-in. Raschig rings in an 8-in.-diameter tower using the diethanolamine system. No significant effect of gas rate on the mass-transfer coefficient was observed. The authors noted a decrease in mass-transfer rate with increase in the partial pressure of CO_2 and with increase in degree of conversion of the ethanolamine in agreement with the anticipated behavior of a second-order reaction mechanism (Figs. 18-91 and 18-92).

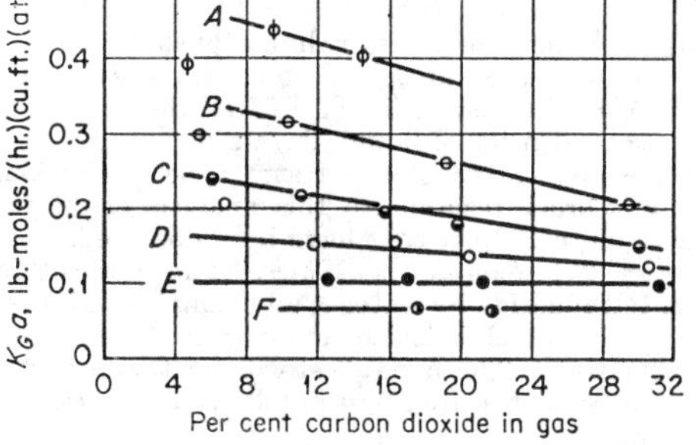

FIG. 18-92. Effect of CO_2 partial pressure on K_Ga during absorption by diethanolamine. [*Cryder and Maloney, Trans. Am. Inst. Chem. Engrs.*, **37**, 827 (1941).]

Kohl [*Am. Inst. Chem. Engrs. J.*, **2**, 264 (1956)] developed an empirical relationship for absorption of CO_2 by monoethanolamine solutions based on the data of Schneerson and Leibush (*loc. cit.*) and found that

$$K_Ga = \frac{B}{\mu^{0.68}}[1 - B'(0.5 - C)Me^{0.0067T-3.4P}] \qquad (18\text{-}77)$$

where B and B' = constants of the contacting system
C = moles CO_2/mole MEA in solution, less than 0.5
M = molarity of MEA
T = temperature, °F.
P = partial pressure of CO_2, atm.
μ = viscosity of solution, centipoise

The value $(0.5 - C)$ is equivalent to q, the concentration of unreacted reagent. The value of the constant 0.5 represents the maximum concentration of CO_2 in solution and is limited to atmospheric operation. The maximum value of the constant can be as high as 0.65 for pressure operation.

The effect of the partial pressure, of CO_2, $e^{-3.4P}$, is limited to CO_2 partial pressures below 0.6 atm. For this range of pressure the effect of CO_2 partial pressure is less than is indicated by the theoretical second-order reaction function $K_L \alpha (1/c_{ai})$ since the reaction becomes pseudo-first-order. Performance data obtained for high-pressure operation by Gregory and Scharman [*Ind. Eng. Chem.*, **29**, 514 (1937)] indicate that the inverse linear relationship may hold at partial pressures of CO_2 exceeding 1 atm.

Teller and Ford [*Ind. Eng. Chem.*, **50**, 1201 (1958)] compared the performance of Berl saddles, Raschig rings, and Tellerettes (all nominal 1 in.) for the CO_2-monoethanolamine system in an 8-in.-diameter polyethylene-lined tower (Figs. 18-93*a* and *b*, 18-94*a* and *b*); for these figures G_i is the inlet gas rate in lb./(hr.)(sq. ft.) and other terms are as defined for Eq. 18-77. It was observed that $H_{OG} \alpha L^{0.57}$ similar to that obtained by Furnas and Bellinger (*loc. cit.*) for the sodium carbonate solvent. A significant effect of gas rate was observed for the lean conditions of the system (CO_2 less than 0.11 atm.) in accordance with the observations of Spector and Dodge [*Trans. Am. Inst. Chem. Engrs.*, **42**,

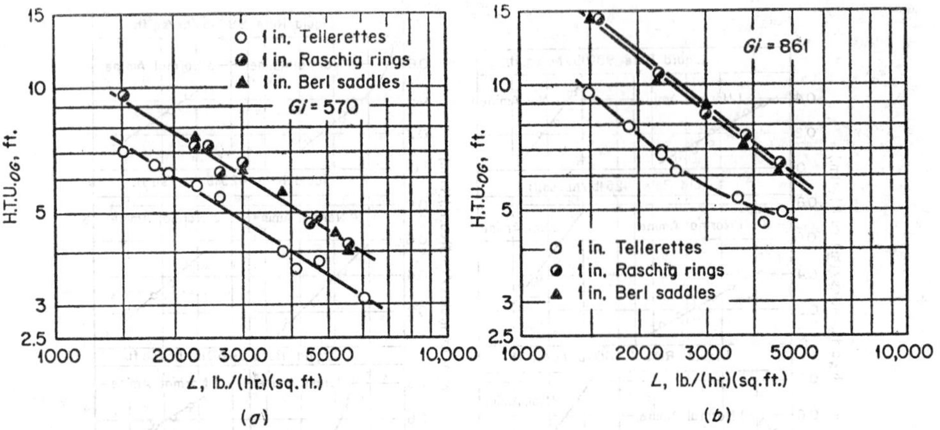

Fig. 18-93. Packing performance—CO_2-air-monoethanolamine system. Raschig rings, Berl saddles, Tellerettes. [*Teller and Ford, Ind. Eng. Chem.*, **50**, 1203 (1958).]

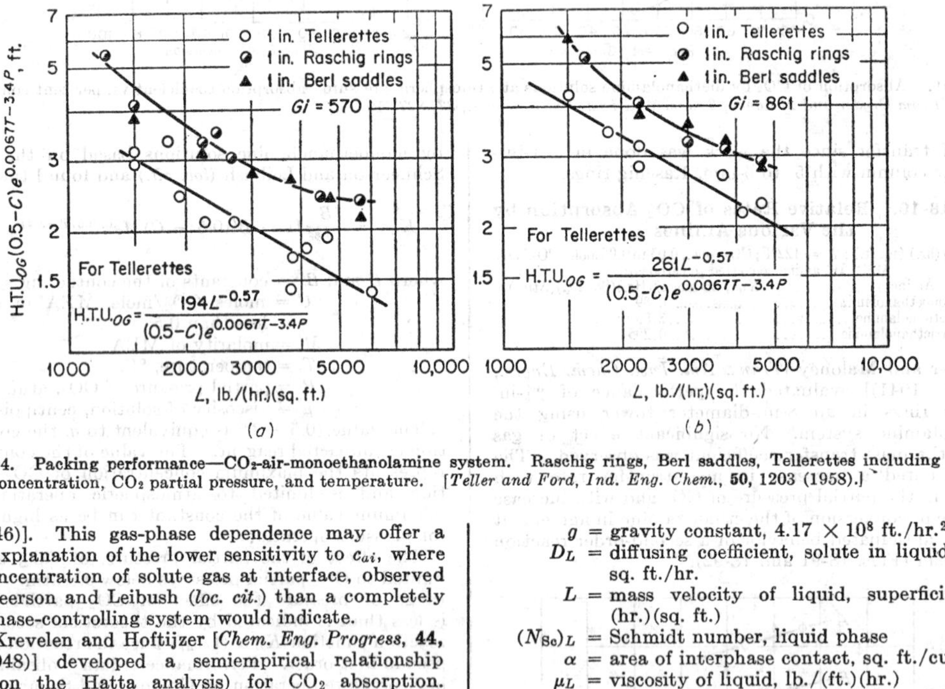

Fig. 18-94. Packing performance—CO_2-air-monoethanolamine system. Raschig rings, Berl saddles, Tellerettes including effect of reagent concentration, CO_2 partial pressure, and temperature. [*Teller and Ford, Ind. Eng. Chem.*, **50**, 1203 (1958).]

827 (1946)]. This gas-phase dependence may offer a partial explanation of the lower sensitivity to c_{ai}, where c_{ai} = concentration of solute gas at interface, observed by Schneerson and Leibush (*loc. cit.*) than a completely liquid-phase-controlling system would indicate.

Van Krevelen and Hoftijzer [*Chem. Eng. Progress*, **44**, 529 (1948)] developed a semiempirical relationship (based on the Hatta analysis) for CO_2 absorption. Although correlations were established with specific data by the relationship

$$\frac{k_L(\mu_L^2/g\rho_L^2)^{1/3}}{D_L} = 0.015\left(\frac{L}{\alpha\mu_L}\right)(N_{Sc})_L^{1/3} \qquad (18\text{-}78)$$

In the case of absorption, k_L is multiplied by the quantity $x/\tanh x$ to obtain the effective mass-transfer coefficient

$$x = \left(\frac{\mu_L^2}{g\rho_L^2}\right)^{1/3}\left(\frac{k_c}{D_L}\right)^{1/2}$$

where k_L = mass-transfer coefficient, liquid phase lb.-moles/(hr.)(sq. ft.)(lb.-moles/cu. ft.)

k_c = reaction-rate constant, first-order reaction, $hr.^{-1}$

g = gravity constant, 4.17×10^8 ft./hr.^{2}

D_L = diffusing coefficient, solute in liquid phase, sq. ft./hr.

L = mass velocity of liquid, superficial, lb./(hr.)(sq. ft.)

$(N_{Sc})_L$ = Schmidt number, liquid phase

α = area of interphase contact, sq. ft./cu. ft.

μ_L = viscosity of liquid, lb./(ft.)(hr.)

ρ_L = density of liquid, lb./cu. ft.

In the application of the Hatta type of relationship for a first-order reaction to this analysis errors in the range of 50 to 100 per cent have been observed.

Silicon Tetrafluoride in Water. The absorption of silicon tetrafluoride by water is an example of absorption accompanied by chemical reaction with a solid by-product formation. The over-all stoichiometry of the reaction may be represented by the following equation:

$$3SiF_4 + 2H_2O = 2H_2SiF_6 + SiO_2 \qquad (18\text{-}79)$$

Whynes [*Trans. Inst. Chem. Engrs.*, **34**, 117 (1956)] found that, if discrete liquid particles (such as in spray towers) were present as the absorbing liquid surface, encrustration of the surface with silica occurs, inhibiting further absorption. In wetted-wall experimental tests, the process was found to be gas-phase diffusion controlling and

$$K_G = 0.049 N_{Re}^{0.8} \qquad (18\text{-}80)$$

where K_G = lb.-moles/(hr.)(sq. ft.)(atm.)

N_{Re} = Reynolds number in wetted-wall tube

Sherwin [*Trans. Inst. Chem. Engrs.*, **32**, S129 (1954)] collated information obtained for silicon tetrafluoride in a number of British phosphate plants and presented performance data as in Table 18-11.

Table 18-11. Performance of Absorption Equipment, SiF_4-Air-Water System

Tower	L, moles/(hr.)(sq. ft.) water	GS, moles/hr. gas	K_Ga lb.-moles/(hr)(cu. ft.)(atm.)	K_Ga/L
Batch spray.......	3.1	417	0.49	0.16
Batch spray.......	8.97	292	0.638	0.0712
Batch spray.......	4.23	250	0.938	0.222
Continuous spray..	8.15	201	1.04	0.119
Packed tower......	62.5	501	3.68	0.0589
Jet scrubber.......	4020	501	15.6	0.00389

H. E. Ford and F. Arndt (personal communication) indicate that non-extended surface packings have been effective in this absorption problem because of stable operating conditions in the flooding region. As clogging develops localized phase inversions occur, resulting in washing down of the silica.

Distillation Applications. Distillation in packed columns has generally been limited to column diameters less than 2 ft. and column heights less than 20 ft. The diameter limitation is based on the difficulty of maintaining effective liquid distribution for columns with dimensions exceeding these quantities.

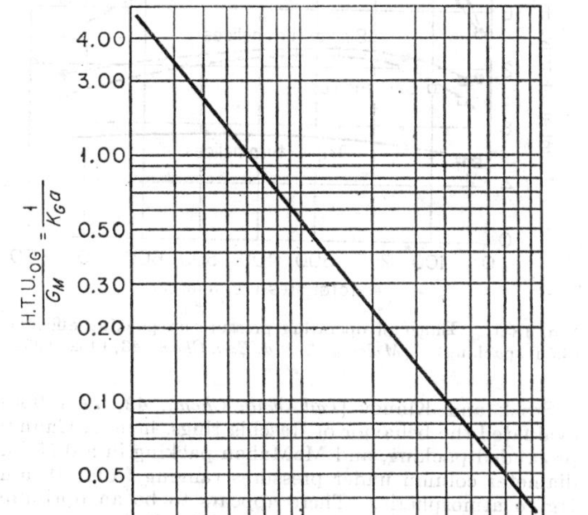

Fig. 18-95. Performance of packed columns (Raschig rings and Berl saddles) in the distillation of ethanol-water. H.T.U.$_{OG}/G_m$ vs. $(1/m)(L/u)$ for ethanol-water system. [*Furnas and Taylor, Trans. Am. Inst. Chem. Engrs.*, **36**, 135 (1940).]

A limited number of generalizations for estimation of packed-column behavior are available. Furnas and Taylor [*Trans. Am. Inst. Chem. Engrs.*, **36**, 135 (1940)] evaluated the performance of Raschig rings and Berl saddles with the ethanol-water system and found that the system behavior was independent of the type of packing. The empirical relationship presented is

$$K_Ga = 0.0069 \left(\frac{1}{m}\frac{L}{\mu}\right)^{1.21} \qquad (18\text{-}81)$$

where m = slope of equilibrium curve

L = liquid rate, lb./(hr.)(sq. ft.)

μ = viscosity, lb./(ft.)(hr.)

G_m = molar gas rate mols/(hr.) (sq. ft.)

The data are shown in Fig. 18-95. The relationship implies a liquid-phase-controlling behavior inasmuch as the transfer rate is independent of vapor flow.

Murch [*Ind. Eng. Chem.*, **45**, 2616 (1953)] analyzed previously accumulated data for distillation in packed columns and presented the relationship

$$\text{H.E.T.P.} = K_1 G^{K_2} d^{K_3} h^{1/3} \frac{\alpha\mu}{\rho} \qquad (18\text{-}82)$$

where G = superficial mass velocity of vapor, lb./(hr.)(sq. ft.)

d = column diameter, in.

h = height of packing, ft.

α = relative volatility

μ = liquid viscosity, centipoise

ρ = liquid density, g./cc.

H.E.T.P. = height of packing equivalent to one theoretical plate, in.

K_1, K_2, K_3 = constants as a function of the packing the packing

The constants for various packings are indicated in Table 18-12.

Table 18-12. Constants for Murch Equation

	Summary of packing constant			
	Size, in.	K_1	K_2	K_3
Rings	¼			
	⅜	2.10	−0.37	1.24
	½	8.53	−0.34	1.24
	1.0	0.57	−0.10	1.24
	2.0	0.42	0	1.24
Saddles	½	5.62	−0.45	1.11
	1.0	0.76	−0.14	1.11
McMahon	¼	0.017	+0.50	1.00
	⅜	0.20	+0.25	1.00
	½	0.33	+0.20	1.00
Protruded packing	0.16	0.39	+0.25	0.30
	0.24	0.076	+0.50	0.30
	0.48	0.45	+0.30	0.30
	1.0	3.06	+0.12	0.30
Stedman	2	0.077	+0.48	0.24
	3	0.363	+0.26	0.24
	6	0.218	+0.32	0.24

It is significant that the relationship includes the effect of liquid maldistribution in that it predicts an increase in H.E.T.P. with column diameter and height of packing.

The relationship may appear to be misleading in that no cognizance is taken of the liquid rate or diffusivity, although Furnas and Taylor (*loc. cit.*) indicate a liquid-phase-controlling mechanism in distillation. However, the data utilized were taken at high reflux ratios or at total reflux such that $G = L$ and the majority of data used in the Murch correlation were obtained with the ethylene dichloride–benzene and n-heptane–methyl cyclohexane systems whose diffusivities lie within 10 per cent of each other. Thus adequate correction for system diffusivities should be made prior to use of the relationship.

It was noted by Granville [*Brit. Chem. Eng.*, **2**, 70 (1957)] that a limitation of both the Furnas and Taylor and Murch relationships is that the H.E.T.P. normally decreases in the range of loading and then remains constant or increases in the preflooding zone as indicated in Fig. 18-96 [Teller, *Chem. Eng.*, **61** (9), 185, (1959)]. Thus the relationships [Eqs. (18-81) and (18-82)] which do not show a curve inflection are limited in application. Granville established an empirical relationship for behavior of packings in the loading region only for an 8-ft. packed height (assuming H.E.T.P. proportional to $h^{1/3}$) based on the following studies (Table 18-13):

Table 18-13

Investigator	Ref.	Type packing	System
Fischer and Bowen	*Chem. Eng. Progress*, **45**, 359 (1949)	½-in. McMahon	Benzene–ethylene dichloride
Deed, Schutz, and Drew	*Ind. Eng. Chem.*, **39**, 770 (1947)	½-in. Raschig rings	iso-PrOH–H_2O
Duncan, Koffolt, and Withrow	*Trans. Am. Inst. Chem. Engrs.*, **38**, 259 (1942)	½-in. Raschig rings	MeOH–H_2O, CCl_4–C_6H_6
Furnas and Taylor	*Trans. Am. Inst. Chem. Engrs.*, **36**, 135 (1940)	⅜- to 1-in. Raschig rings, ½-in. Berl saddles	EtOH–H_2O
Kirschbaum	"Distillation and Rectification," Chemical Publishing, New York, 1948	8- to 35-mm. Raschig rings	EtOH–H_2O
Johnson	Ph.D. Thesis, University of Birmingham, 1954	¼-in. Raschig rings	Methyl cyclohexane–toluene
Granville	Ph.D. Thesis, University of Birmingham, 1954	¼-in. Raschig rings, ⅜-in. Fenske helices	Methyl cyclohexane–toluene

It was proposed that

$$\text{H.E.T.P.} = 28D_pM_a\frac{G_m}{L_m} \qquad (18\text{-}83)$$

where H.E.T.P. = height, ft

D_p = nominal packing size, in.

M_a = average slope of equilibrium curve $= \dfrac{\Sigma nM}{\Sigma n}$

M = slope of equilibrium curve

n = number of plates

G_m, L_m = gas- and liquid-flow rates, moles/(hr.)(sq. ft.)

It is indicated that the reliability of the relationship is good for Raschig rings and should be applied with caution to other packings.

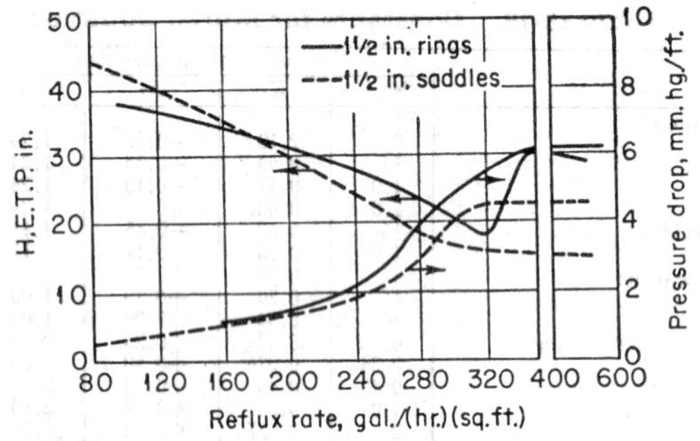

FIG. 18-96. Comparison of performance of 1½-in. rings and saddles—benzene–ethylene dichloride system at total reflux. [*Teller, Chem. Eng.*, **61** (9), 185 (1954).]

Robinson and Gilliland ("Elements of Fractional Distillation," McGraw-Hill, New York, 1950) proposed the general relationship for packed-column behavior.

$$\text{H.E.T.P.} = \frac{d}{M_v}\left[12G^{0.2} + \frac{G}{HPD_L(L/\mu)^{0.75}(\mu/\rho D_L)^{0.5}}\right] \qquad (18\text{-}84)$$

where H.E.T.P. = height equivalent to theoretical plate, ft.

d = tower diameter, ft.

M_v = average molecular weight of vapor

G, L = vapor and liquid rates, lb./(hr.)(sq. ft.)

H = Henry's constant, lb.-moles/(cu. ft.)(atm.)

P = total pressure, atm.

D_L = liquid-phase diffusivity, cm.²/sec.

μ = viscosity, poise

ρ = liquid density, g./cc.

Myles, Feldman, Wender, and Orchin [*Ind. Eng. Chem.*, **43**, 1452 (1951)] evaluated the effect of operating pressure on the fractionating efficiency of helices, heligrid packing, Berl saddles, and spheres using the *h*-heptane–methylcyclohexane system. It appeared that the optimum operating pressure was 200 mm. Hg for all packings (Fig. 18-97). The average irrigation rate was based on the mean of the flooding rate and minimum irrigation rates.

This observation was in disagreement with the data obtained by Berg and Popovic [*Chem. Eng. Progress*, **45**, 683 (1949)], who observed no effect of operating pressure for the range 20 to 760 mm. Hg using ⅛-in. Fenske helices with the *n*-octane–toluene system.

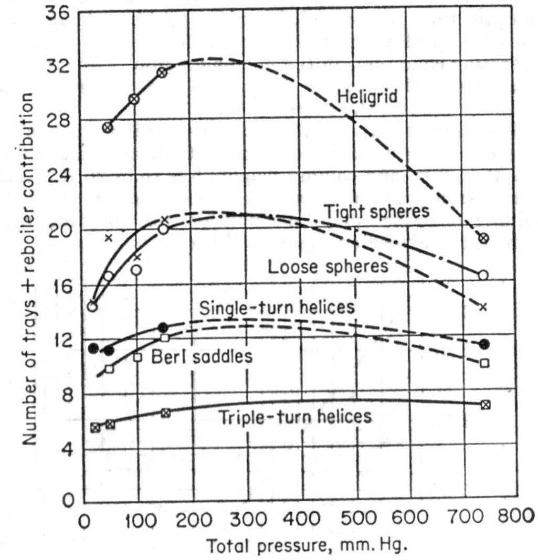

FIG. 18-97. Effect of operating pressure on packing efficiency (3.5 ft. packing). [*Myles et al., Ind. Eng. Chem.*, **43**, 1452 (1951).]

Stock and Kinney [*Ind. Eng. Chem.*, **42**, 77 (1950)] evaluated the behavior of Raschig rings, helices, Cannon protruded packing, and McMahon packing in a 0.75-in.-diameter column under pressures ranging from 10 mm. Hg to atmospheric. There appears to be an optimum in the range of 50 to 100 mm. Hg (Fig. 18-98).

The behavior of wire-mesh packings, both Stedman and Goodloe, have been reported by Morton [*Trans. Inst. Chem. Engrs.*, **29**, 240 (1951); **34**, 146 (1956)] and Bragg [*Ind. Eng. Chem.*, **49**, 1062 (1957)]. Morton indicated that column height had little or no effect on the H.E.T.P. of the Stedman packing, and a decrease in efficiency of only 20 to 25 per cent was observed when column diameter was increased from 1 to 12 ft. Both these packings exhibit low H.E.T.P.'s, usually less than 3 in. (Fig. 18-99). Bragg [*Ind. Eng. Chem.*, **45**, 1676 (1953)] correlated the separation characteristics of hexagonal-type Stedman packing for the systems benzene–ethylene dichloride, 2, 2, 4-methyl pentane and

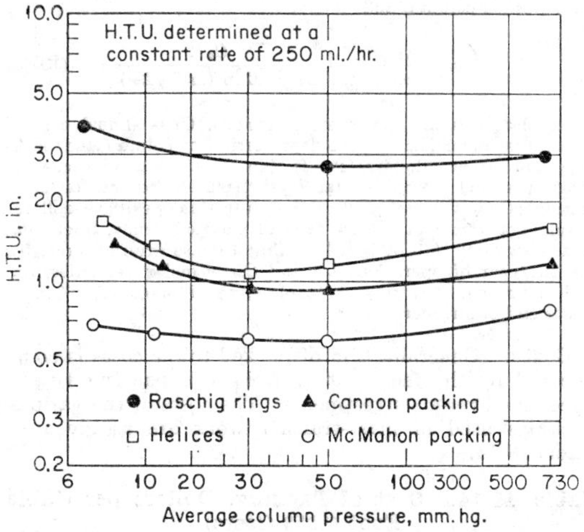

FIG. 18-98. Variation of H.T.U. with average column pressure at constant through-put. [*Struck and Kinney, Ind. Eng. Chem.*, **42**, 77 (1950).]

methylcyclohexane, and an isomeric heptane mixture. The relationship proposed is

$$p = 2.8 + \frac{6.5}{R^{0.27}} + \frac{0.5}{R^{0.9}} \qquad (18\text{-}85)$$

where p = theoretical plates per ft. of packing
R = reflux rate expressed as gal./hr. at reflux temperatures

Design Optima. Optima in packed-column construction depend on the proper selection of exit liquor and gas compositions as well as column diameter. Generalizations of optima must assume behavior patterns, such as constant slope of the equilibrium line, single-phase controlling operations, and simple power-function relationships for pressure drop, transfer rate, or costs.

Inasmuch as conditions obtained in practice do not permit such simplifications, the conclusions obtained with the use of the following generalizations for obtaining optima should be used primarily to establish only the magnitude of variables in process design.

The optimum gas velocity in a packed column was expressed by Colburn (Unit Operation Notes, University of Delaware, 1936)

$$G_{\text{opt}} = \left(\frac{C_1\rho_2}{MC_2{}^1\theta b^1}\right)^{\frac{1}{M+1}} \qquad (18\text{-}86)$$

$$G_{\text{opt}} = 2680\phi^{1/3}\left(\frac{C_1}{C_2\theta b}\right)^{1/3} \quad \text{approx.} \qquad (18\text{-}87)$$

where C_1 = annual cost of packing and shell, dollars/(years)(cu. ft.)
$C_2{}^1$ = cost of delivered energy, dollars/ft.-lb.
C_2 = cost of delivered energy, dollars/kw.-hr.
θ = operating time, hr./year
M = exponent in pressure-drop correlation with the assumption that $\Delta P = \dfrac{b^1G^M}{\rho}$
ρ = gas density, lb./cu. ft.
b = pressure drop, in., H_2O/ft. packing at G/ϕ = 1000 lb./(hr.)(sq. ft.)
$\phi = (\rho/0.075)^{1/2}$

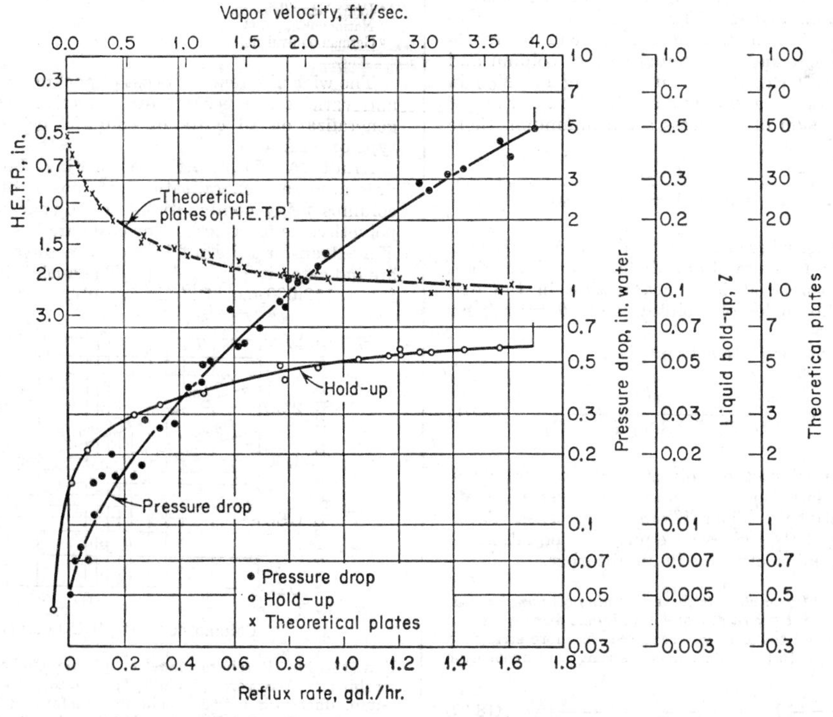

FIG. 18-99. Characteristics of 25-mm. Goodloe packing, 24-in. depth. [*Bragg, Ind. Eng. Chem.*, **49**, 1063 (1957).]

If the column operates at the economic gas velocity then

$$\frac{\text{Cost}}{\text{Transfer unit, lb./hr.}} = \frac{1.5H_{OG}C_1^{2/3}(C_2\theta b)^{1/3}}{2680\phi^{2/3}} \qquad (18\text{-}88)$$

It should be noted that the optimum indicated is established only on the basis of over-all operating costs independent of the effect of velocity of the process streams on the mass-transfer efficiency and therefore does not consider the interrelationship of optima of mass-transfer rate, system-flow rates, and cost.

Williamson [*Trans. Inst. Chem. Engrs.*, **29**, 215 (1951)] established a relationship for estimation of the economic optimum vapor velocity in packed columns

$$v_e = 8.5\left(\frac{C_T}{nC_p}\right)^{1/3} \qquad (18\text{-}89)$$

where v_e = optimum gas velocity, ft./sec.
C_T = capital cost of tower, dollars/cu. ft.
C_p = cost of electric power, dollars/kw.-hr.
n = number of velocity heads lost/ft. of packing

This relationship should be used only as a guide in estimating procedures in view of the assumptions made by the author in arriving at the equation. They are as follows:

1. The liquid rate must be in excess of the M.E.L.R. established by Pratt (p. 18-34).
2. The system is gas-phase controlling and operating with a constant H_G above the M.E.L.R.
3. Operation time 8400 hr./year.
4. Efficiency of fan and motors—50 per cent.

Column Height (Exit-gas Strength). At a given value of mG_M/L_M, the required column height is dependent upon the value chosen for the exit-gas strength. The latter quantity may be determined by an economic balance between the cost of lost solute and the cost of additional column height. The annual cost of solute per unit cross-sectional area of column can be represented as $C_4\theta G_M y_2$, and the annual cost of column and pressure drop as $C_3H_{OG}N_{OG}$. Substituting for N_{OG} in terms of mG_M/L_M, y_1, and y_2 and solving for the value of y_2 at which the sum of the costs are a minimum, there results, approximately,

$$y_2 - mx_2 = \frac{C_3H_{OG}}{C_4\theta G_M(1 - mG_M/L_M)} \qquad (18\text{-}90)$$

for packed towers, where C_3 = annual cost of apparatus and energy for pressure drop, dollars/(year)(cu. ft.); C_4 = value of solute at its concentration in the exit liquor, dollar/lb.-mole of solute; and θ = hr./year operation.

A similar result for plate columns is

$$y_2 - mx_2 = \frac{C_6}{C_4\theta G_M E(2.3 \log L_M/mG_M)} \qquad (18\text{-}91)$$

where C_6 = annual cost of column and pressure drop, dollars/(year)(plate)(sq. ft.), and E = over-all plate efficiency, fractional. Tiller [*Trans. Am. Inst. Chem. Engrs.*, **40**, 331 (1944)] gives an equivalent equation for the optimum number of plates in an absorber.

The optimum exit-liquor strength for a stripping column depends on a balance between the cost of lost solute in the exit liquor and the cost of additional tower height required for more stripping. Equations analogous to those for exit-gas strength in absorption are

$$\left(x_2 - \frac{y_2}{m}\right)_{\text{opt}} = \frac{C_3H_{OL}}{C_4L_M\theta(1 - L_M/mG_M)} \qquad (18\text{-}92)$$

for a packed column, and

$$\left(x_2 - \frac{y_2}{m}\right)_{\text{opt}} = \frac{C_6}{C_4L_M\theta E \ln (mG_M/L_M)} \qquad (18\text{-}93)$$

for a plate column. In these equations, C_3 = annual cost of apparatus (amortization and depreciation of column and packing) and power, dollars/(cu. ft.)(year); C_6 = annual cost of apparatus and power, dollars/(year)(plate) (sq. ft. of cross section); C_4 = value of solute at concentration of exit gas, dollars/lb.-mole of pure solute; E = over-all plate efficiency, fractional; H_{OL} = over-all H.T.U. based on liquid-phase driving force, ft.; θ = hr./year of operation; L_M and G_M = molar velocities, lb.-moles/(hr.)(sq. ft.); m = slope of equilibrium curve, y^*/x, at dilute end of stripper.

Costs. Generalization of packed-tower costs is complicated by the fact that variations in packing vitally affect the over-all investment. The costs of the various packings used in mass-transfer work are as given in Table 18-14.

Table 18-14. Cost of Packing, Dollars per Cubic Foot (1959 Costs)
Less than 100 cu. ft.

	Size			
	½ in.	1 in.	1½ in.	2 in.
Raschig rings, ceramic[b]	11.70	6.50	5.05	4.85
Raschig rings, carbon steel[e]	......	......	.....	5.95
Raschig rings, stainless steel 316[e]	......	50.75	.....	27.85
Raschig rings, carbon[f]	......	18.60	18.40	
Berl saddles, ceramic[a]	24.80	9.90	7.50	7.70
Intalox saddles, ceramic[b]	23.55	9.40	7.15	7.30
Tellerettes, L. D. polyethylene[c]	......	16.00		
Tellerettes, H. D. polyethylene[c]	......	18.50		
Pall rings, ceramic[d]	......	5.00[g]		
Pall rings, polypropylene[b]	41.00	26.00	20.75	18.50
Pall rings, stainless steel	186.50	96.00	83.00	69.00

[a] M. A. Knight Co.
[b] U.S. Stoneware Co.
[c] Colonial Iron Works Co.
[d] Bradische Anilin and Soda Fabrik.
[e] Johns-Manville Corp.
[f] National Carbon Co.
[g] German equivalent.

The wide differences in cost of packing per unit volume and variation in performance effectiveness restrict cost generalization to costs of columns using a particular type of packing.

Arndt (A.I.Ch.E. Atlanta meeting, February, 1959) presented a generalization of costs of plastic-shell columns using combinations of Dowpac and Tellerette polyethylene packings. The costs are based on provision of five transfer units or 95 per cent recovery efficiency and are indicated in Fig. 18-100. The author indicated that, for a 112,000 cu. ft./min. scrubber, 6 man-hr. were

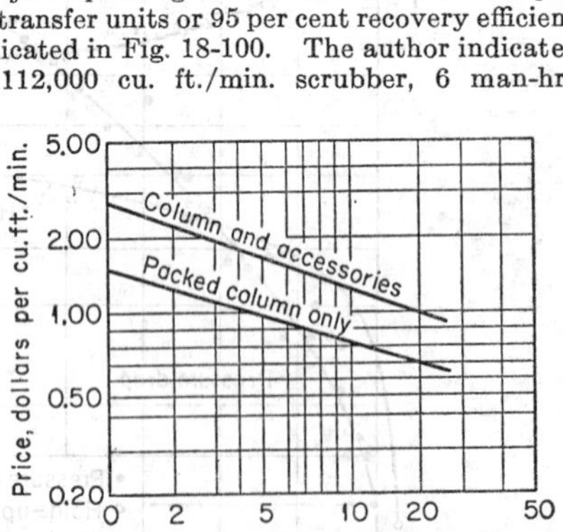

FIG. 18-100. Purchase price of plastic packed-column fume scrubbers. Accessories include fan, motor, drive, recirculation pump, ductwork between column and fan. (*Arndt, American Institute of Chemical Engineers Meeting, Atlanta, February,* 1959.)

required for packing the tower and installation costs were $90.

Chilton [*Chem. Eng.*, **56** (6), (1949)] estimated costs of packed towers as a function of diameter. The relationship (1959 basis) is indicated in Fig. 18-101.

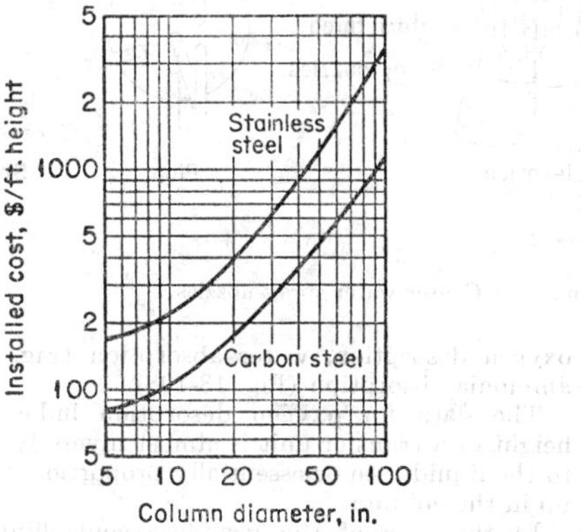

Fig. 18-101. Packed-column costs, 1959—M & S Index = 235. [*From Chilton, Chem. Eng.*, **56** (6), (1949).]

SPRAY SYSTEMS

Introduction. Spray contacting devices generally represent the least expensive installations for mass transfer. However, as a result of (1) mixing of the liquid sprays with the gas stream, (2) entrainment of spray by the gas stream, and (3) effectively parallel flow in most designs, spray-type absorption units are not generally applicable to systems where true countercurrent flow is required.

Thus, high gas solubilities are required in spray systems since the number of transfer units available are limited. Spray contacting units have been found to be uniquely applicable to systems where highly soluble gases accompany solids that must be removed from a gas stream.

Four types of spray systems are in commercial use. They consist of the spray column (Fig. 18-102*a* and *b*), the cyclonic spray (Fig. 18-103), the venturi scrubber (Fig. 18-104*a* and *b*) which is normally associated with a cyclonic spray removal, and the jet scrubber.

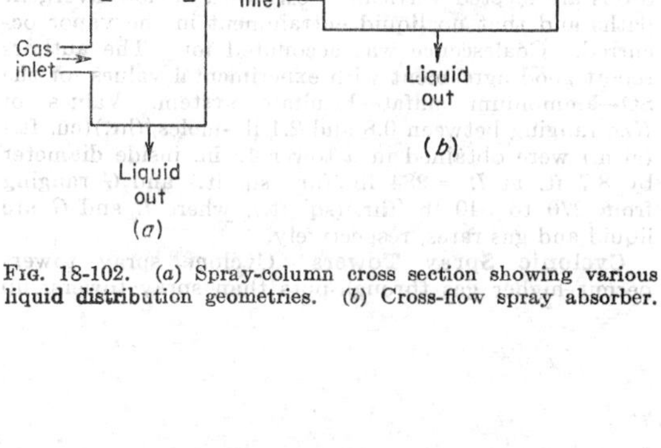

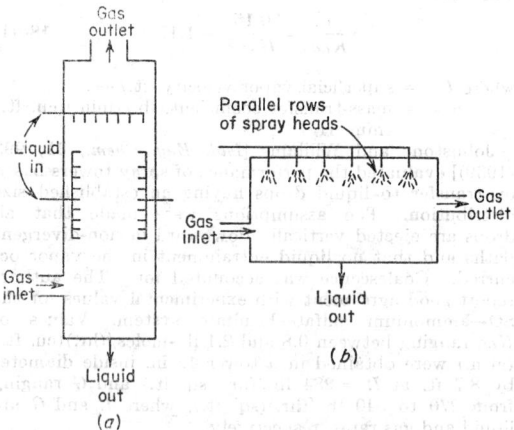

Fig. 18-102. (*a*) Spray-column cross section showing various liquid distribution geometries. (*b*) Cross-flow spray absorber.

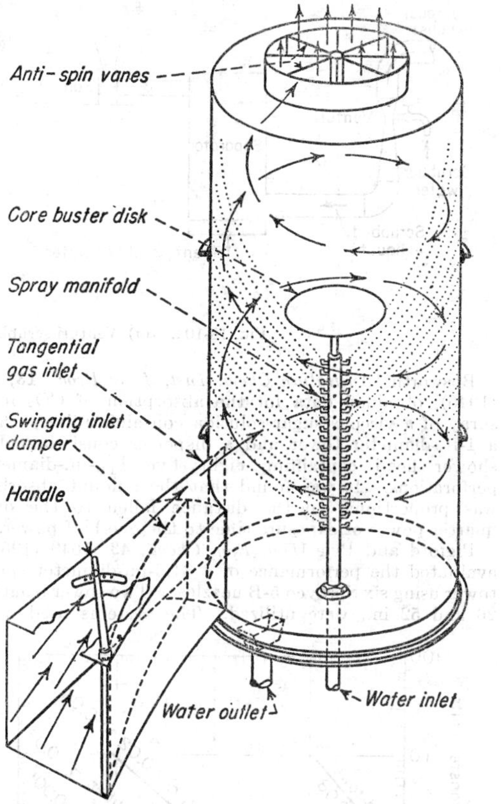

Fig. 18-103. Schematic view showing elements of cyclonic-spray scrubber. [*From Kleinschmidt and Anthony, Trans. Am. Soc. Mech. Engrs.*, **63**, 349 (1941).]

In spray towers and cyclone spray towers the liquid dispersion is created by mechanical power consumption in the liquid phase. In venturi scrubbers, the liquid dispersion is developed via power provided by the gas phase. In jet scrubbers both the liquid dispersion and the gas pumping are provided by the liquid-phase power input.

Lunde [*Ind. Eng. Chem.*, **50**, 293 (1958)] found that the number of transfer units obtained is related to the power input to the liquid and/or the gas phases in spray systems. The relationships are indicated in Table 18-15, where P_L is the power input into the liquid phase and P_G is the power input to the gas phase.

Table 18-15. Transfer Unit–Power Input Relationship in Spray Systems

Spray tower	$N_T \alpha \frac{P_L^{\sim 1}}{P_G^{0.1}}$
Cyclone spray tower	$N_T \alpha P_L^{0.9}$
Venturi scrubber	$N_T \alpha P_L^{0.3} P_G^{0.8}$

A comparison of power consumption for a cyclone scrubber and venturi scrubber by Lunde (*loc. cit.*) is indicated in Fig. 18-105 and that of a spray tower with a venturi in Fig. 18-106.

Spray Towers (see also spray nozzles in phase-dispersion portion of section). Mass transfer in spray towers, in which liquid droplets fall via gravity forces, would be anticipated to proceed in the liquid phase via the penetration phenomenon where $W \alpha t^{1/2}$ for liquid-phase-controlling systems, where W = mass transferred and t = time of contact of the two phases.

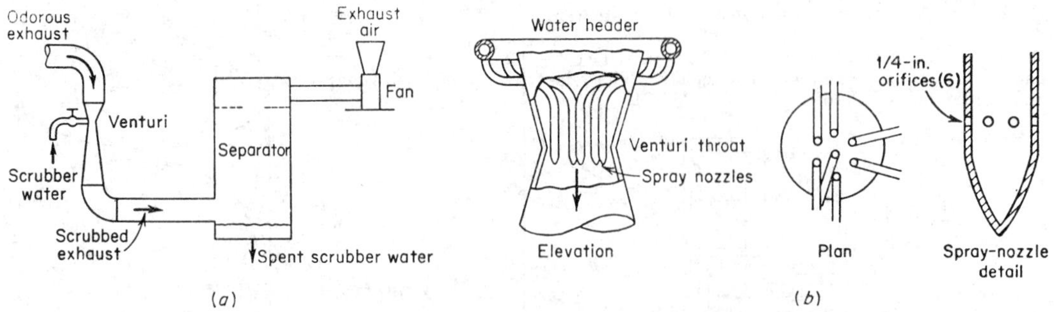

FIG. 18-104. (a) Venturi scrubber system. (b) Center water spray nozzles.

Bosworth [*Australian Chem. Inst. J. & Proc.*, **13**, 53 (1946)] obtained data for the absorption of CO_2 in a spray of a viscous sugar solution containing lime, using a 1-ft.-diameter tower and a disperser consisting of a shower head containing eighty-five 1/16-in.-diameter perforations. It was found that the amount absorbed was proportional to the distance fallen to the one-quarter power or exposure time to the one-half power.

Pigford and Pyle [*Ind. Eng. Chem.*, **43**, 1649 (1951)] evaluated the performance of a 31.5-in.-diameter spray tower using six Sprayco 5-B nozzles. Two tower lengths, 26 and 52 in., were utilized. The systems used were oxygen desorption, water absorption (Fig. 18-107) and ammonia absorption (Fig. 18-108).

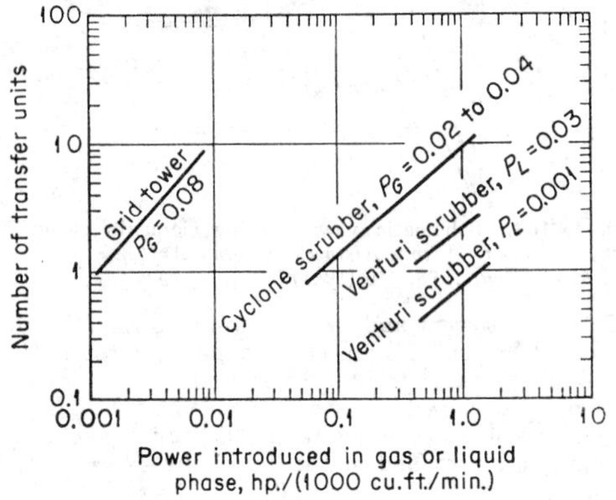

FIG. 18-105. Power consumed in absorbing SO_2. [*Lunde, Ind. Eng. Chem.*, **50**, 293 (1958).]

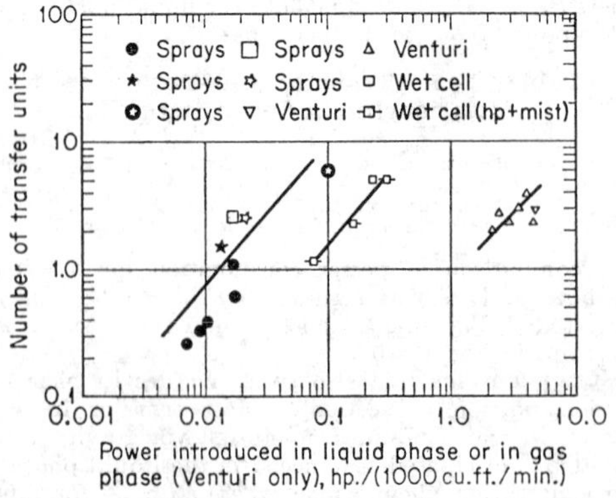

FIG. 18-106. Power consumed in HF absorption. [*Lunde, Ind. Eng. Chem.*, **50**, 293 (1958).]

The data for oxygen desorption indicate that the height of a transfer unit is almost inversely proportional to the liquid rate or essentially proportional to the hold-up in the column.

In the case of the gas-phase-controlling system of H_2O-air or the predominantly gas-phase transfer of NH_3-air-water system, for values of G less than 500 lb./(hr.)(sq. ft.), $H_{OG} \propto G^{0.6}$ and $H_{OG} \propto 1/L$. At values of G greater than 500 lb./(hr.)(sq. ft.), the effect of increase in gas velocity on H_{OG} diminishes.

A significant factor in the behavior of spray columns is illustrated in Fig. 18-108. The number of transfer units is not directly proportional to the height of the column. Only a 47 per cent increase in number of transfer units is achieved by doubling the column height from 26 to 52 in. This behavior is reflective of the inherent limitation of spray columns where no surface regeneration occurs and the rate of mass transfer decreases with exposure time. In addition back mixing results from open column turbulence, thus limiting the degree of countercurrent flow.

The limiting gas rate for the spray tower appeared to be 800 lb./(hr.)(sq. ft.) (Figs. 18-107 and 18-108), the velocity at which excessive entrainment occurs. Haslam, Ryan, and Weber [*Trans. Am. Inst. Chem. Engrs.*, **15**, 177 (1923)] obtained data on the performance of a spray column for the system SO_2-air-water in an 8-in.-diameter spray column 30 in. high.

A correlation was presented for operation at 15°C. and 1 atm.

$$\frac{1}{K_Ga} = \frac{0.15}{U_S^{0.8}} + 1.17 \qquad (18\text{-}94)$$

where U_S = superficial vapor velocity, ft./sec.
K_Ga = mass-transfer coefficient, lb./(min.)(cu. ft.)(mm. Hg)

Johnstone and Williams [*Ind. Eng. Chem.*, **31**, 993 (1939)] evaluated the performance of spray towers based on transfer to liquid drops having an established size distribution. The assumptions were made that all drops are ejected vertically downward in non-divergent paths and that no liquid entrainment in the vapor occurred. Coalescence was accounted for. The authors report good agreement with experimental values for the SO_2–ammonium sulfate–bisulfate system. Values of K_Ga ranging between 0.8 and 2.1 lb.-moles/(hr.)(cu. ft.)(atm.) were obtained in a tower 42 in. inside diameter by 8.7 ft. at L = 284 lb./(hr.)(sq. ft.) and G ranging from 270 to 540 lb./(hr.)(sq. ft.), where L and G are liquid and gas rates, respectively.

Cyclonic Spray Towers. Cyclone spray towers permit higher gas through-puts than spray towers, up

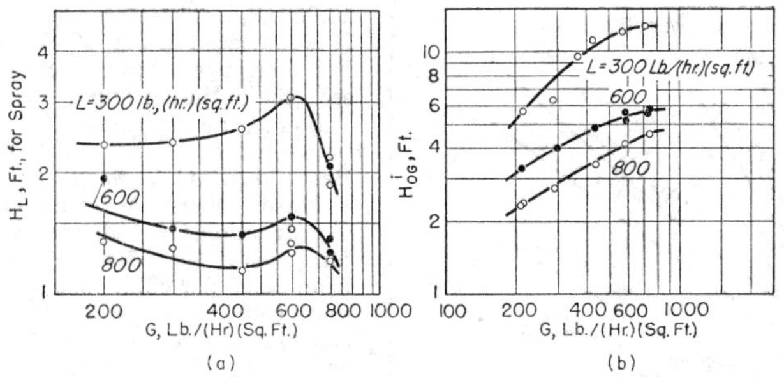

FIG. 18-107. Performance of spray absorber: (*a*) Desorption of O_2 from water at 30°C. (*b*) Heat transfer and condensation of water from air. Tower diameter = 31.5 in. Vertical distance from six Sprayco 5-B nozzles to air inlet = 52 in.

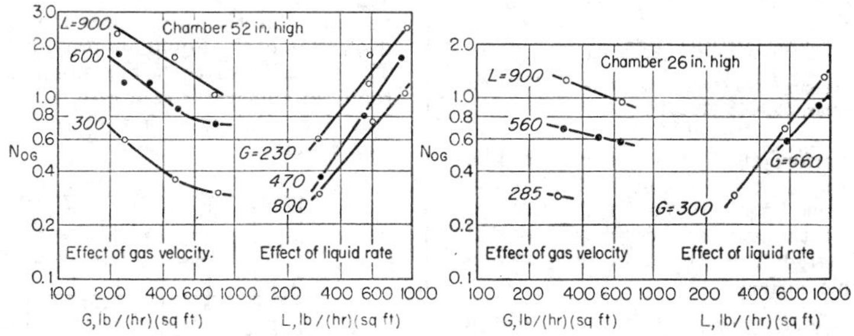

FIG. 18-108. Absorption of NH_3 in a spray-type column. Spray chamber 31.5 in. diameter, 52 or 26 in. from nozzles to base of chamber, six Sprayco 5-B nozzles on 12-in.-diameter circle at top of chamber. [*Data of Pigford and Pyle, Ind. Eng. Chem.*, **43,** 1649 (1952).]

to 2400 lb./(hr.)(sq. ft.) as reported by Kleinschmidt and Anthony [*Trans. Am. Soc. Mech. Engrs.* **63,** 349 (1941)]. This increase in capacity is achieved by forcing the gas into a spiral pattern of flow. Liquid spray entering the system from an axial distributor makes contact with the gas and then separates by the induced centrifugal force, striking the wall of the vessel and descending. Thus entrainment is minimized.

Johnstone and Silcox [*Ind. Eng. Chem.*, **39,** 808 (1947)] and Johnstone and Kleinschmidt [*Trans. Am. Inst. Chem. Engrs.*, **34,** 181 (1938)] evaluated the performance of the cyclone scrubber for the SO_2–air–sodium carbonate solution system. In the work by Johnstone and Silcox (*loc. cit.*) the spray was supplied along a 6-ft. axial distributor by 20 to 50 hollow-cone nozzles (0.046 in. diameter) in a 14-ft.-high unit varying from 28.5 in. diameter at the bottom to 20.5 in. inside diameter at the top. The performance of this unit is indicated in Fig. 18-109. Data from this unit as well as those from a

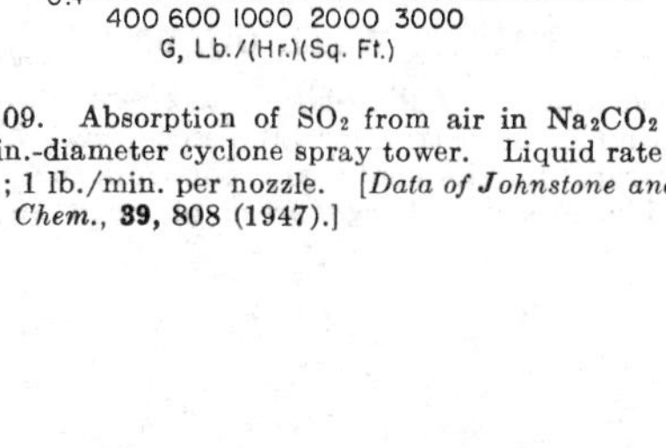

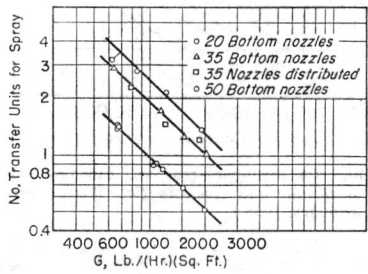

FIG. 18-109. Absorption of SO_2 from air in Na_2CO_2 solution using 28-in.-diameter cyclone spray tower. Liquid rate = 20 to 55 lb./hr.; 1 lb./min. per nozzle. [*Data of Johnstone and Silcox, Ind. Eng. Chem.*, **39,** 808 (1947).]

10.5-ft.-inside-diameter vessel investigated by Johnstone and Kleinschmidt (*loc. cit.*) were correlated by the equation

$$N_T = \frac{64.5LD_c\pi}{G^{0.8}SdN_{Sc}^{2/3}} + \frac{0.0071A_w\pi}{G^{0.37}SN_{Sc}^{2/3}} \qquad (18\text{-}95)$$

where N_T = number of transfer units, over-all gas phase
L = liquid rate, gal./min.
D_c = diameter of tower, ft.
π = total pressure, atm.
G = gas rate through duct at column entrance, lb.-moles/(min.)(sq. ft.)
S = cross section of inlet, sq. ft.
A_w = surface area of wetted wall in tower, sq. ft.
d = mass median diameter of drops, microns
N_{Sc} = Schmidt number

Venturi Scrubbers. Venturi scrubbers were developed for the purpose of dust and mist separation. As a result of the high degree of dispersion of liquid (injected into the venturi throat at pressures between 5 and 25 lb./sq. in. gage) by the high-velocity gas, large areas of liquid are exposed for vapor-phase contact. Thus mass transfer may be effectively accomplished. As a result of the back mixing and parallel-flow mechanism, the number of transfer units that can be achieved is limited.

Byrd and Dewey [*Chem. Eng. Progress*, **53,** 447 (1957)] indicated that the velocity of gas through the throat generally ranges between 125 and 300 ft./sec. and the liquid rate ranges between 2 and 9 gal./1000 surface cu. ft. of gas.

The pressure drop through a venturi scrubber is generally high, with a normal operating pressure drop of 8 to 20 in. of water across the unit. The pressure drop as a function of operating conditions is indicated in Fig. 18-110.

Johnstone and Roberts [*Ind. Eng. Chem.*, **41,** 2417

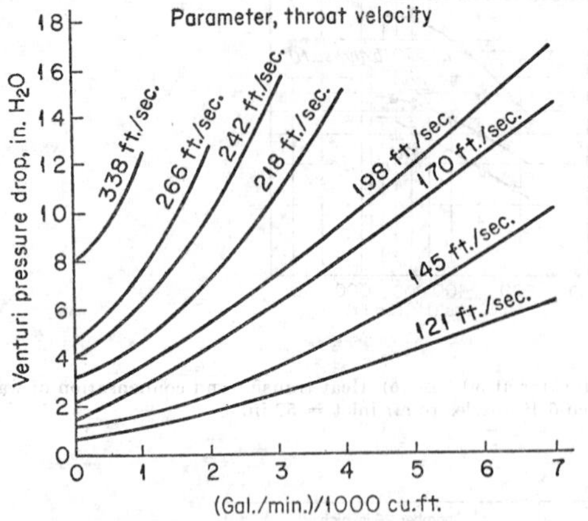

FIG. 18-110. Venturi pressure drop vs. water rate. [*Byrd and Dewey, Chem. Eng. Progress*, **53**, 448 (1957).]

(1949)] studied the performance of a venturi scrubber with the SO_2-air-water system. It was indicated that the optimum particle size for absorption is 100 μ.

The performance of the venturi scrubber with this system may be estimated from the data presented as related to the available surface.

$$N_S = 0.17S \tag{18-96}$$

where S = surface of particles, sq. ft./cu. ft. gas
N_S = number of transfer units obtained during atomization

Inasmuch as Johnstone and Roberts estimated the surface from the relationship with flow conditions established by Lewis, Edwards, Gogla, and Rice [*Ind. Eng. Chem.*, **40**, 67 (1948)] the number of transfer units achieved for this system in the venturi scrubber may be estimated as

$$N_S = \frac{41.5L}{(16{,}050/V_t) + 1.41L^{1.5}} \tag{18-97}$$

where L = liquid-gas ratio, gal./1000 cu. ft.
V_t = gas velocity at venturi throat, ft./sec.

For the velocity ranges involved in venturi scrubbers the quantity $1.41L^{1.5}$ is small compared with the quantity

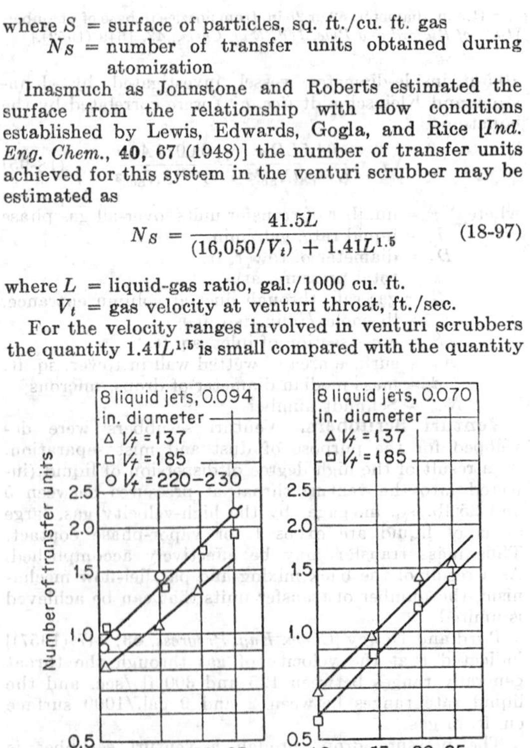

FIG. 18-111. Venturi scrubber performance. V_t = gas velocity at venturi throat (ft./sec.). (*Data from Johnstone and Roberts, SO_2 absorption by water.*)

$16{,}050/V_t$. Therefore, ka should be proportional to L. It is indicated in Fig. 18-111 that this relationship holds. For the range of gas velocities evaluated, 137 to 225 ft./sec., the optimum found was 185 ft./sec.

Power requirements for venturi scrubbers range between 2 and 5 hp. per 1000 cu. ft./min. according to Basee [J.A.P.C.A., **6**, 218 (1957)].

Mason (personal communication) of the Chemical Construction Co. indicated that the power consumption for venturi scrubbers is reported to vary (1959 costs) from $2.25 per cubic foot per minute for 500 cu. ft./min. units to $0.60 per cubic foot per minute for units having capacities larger than 25,000 cu. ft./min. for mild-steel construction. Stainless-steel costs for comparative-sized units are estimated at $3.35 and $2.25 per cubic foot per minute.

Jet Scrubbers. The draft-inducing venturi scrubber or jet scrubber reverses the procedure of the "standard" venturi. Motivating power for the gas and power for dispersion of the liquid are provided by the liquid stream. The capacity of the jet scrubber as a function of draft required and water feed rate is indicated in Fig. 18-112. Initial capital costs for jet scrubbers are indicated in Fig. 18-113.

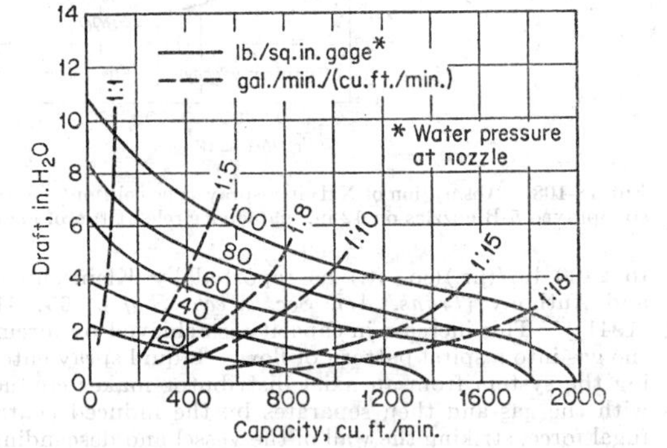

FIG. 18-112. Capacity curve—typical fume scrubber, jet type. (*Courtesy of Schutte and Koerting Co., Webb, Paint Industry Magazine, January,* 1958.)

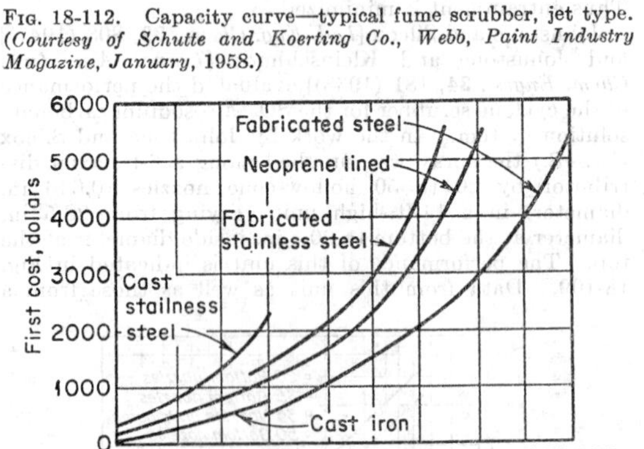

FIG. 18-113. Jet scrubber—cost vs. capacity (1959 costs). (*Courtesy of Schutte and Koerting Co., Webb, Paint Industry Magazine, January,* 1958.)

WETTED-WALL COLUMNS

Wetted-wall or falling-film absorbers have found application in mass-transfer problems where high heat-transfer-rate requirements are concomitant with the absorption process. Large areas of open surface are

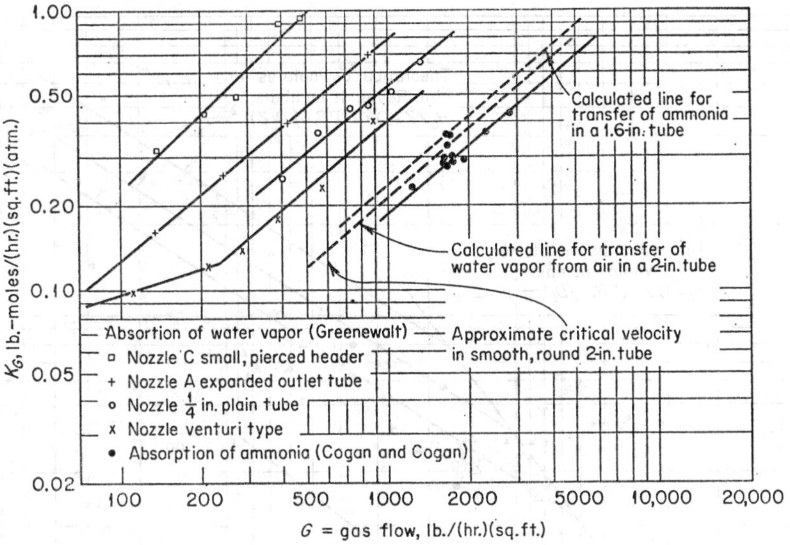

FIG. 18-114. Mass-transfer rates in wetted-wall columns having turbulence promotors. *(Data of Greenewalt and Cogan and Cogan.)* *(Sherwood and Pigford, "Absorption and Extraction," 2d. ed., McGraw-Hill Book Company, Inc., New York, 1952.)*

available for heat transfer for a given rate of mass transfer in this type of equipment because of the low mass-transfer rate inherent in wetted-wall equipment. In addition this type of equipment lends itself to annular-type cooling devices.

Gilliland and Sherwood [*Ind. Eng. Chem.*, **26**, 516 (1934)] found that, for vaporization of pure liquids in air streams for streamline flow,

$$\frac{k_G D}{D_v}\frac{P_{BM}}{\pi} = 0.023 N_{Re}^{0.83} N_{Sc}^{0.44} \qquad (18\text{-}98)$$

where D_v = diffusion coefficient, sq. ft./hr.
D = inside diameter of tube, ft.
k_G = mass-transfer coefficient, gas phase, lb.-moles/(hr.)(sq. ft.)(lb.-moles/cu. ft.)
N_{Re} = Reynolds number, gas phase
N_{Sc} = Schmidt number, gas phase
P_{BM} = logarithmic mean partial pressure of inert gas, atm.
π = total pressure, atm.

Where turbulence promoters are used at the inlet gas section an improvement in gas mass-transfer coefficient for absorption of water vapor by sulfuric acid was observed by Greenewalt [*Ind. Eng. Chem.*, **18**, 1291 (1926)]. A falling off of the rate of mass transfer below that indicated in Eq. (18-98) was observed by Cogan and Cogan (M.I.T. Thesis, 1932) where a calming zone preceded the gas inlet in ammonia absorption (Fig. 18-114).

In work with the hydrogen chloride–air–water system, Dobratz, Moore, Barnard, and Meyer [*Chem. Eng. Progress*, **49**, 611 (1953)] using a cocurrent-flow system found that $k_G \propto G^{1.8}$ (Fig. 18-115) instead of the 0.8 power as indicated by the Gilliland equation. Heat-transfer coefficients were also determined in this study. The radical increase in heat-transfer rate in the range of G = 20,000 lb./(hr.)(sq. ft.) was similar to that observed by Tepe and Mueller [*Chem. Eng. Progress*, **43**, 267 (1947)] in condensation inside tubes.

Gaylord and Miranda [*Chem. Eng. Progress*, **53**, 139M (1957)] using a multitube cocurrent-flow falling-film hydrochloric acid absorber for hydrogen chloride absorption found

$$K_G = \frac{0.0122}{M_m^{1.75}}\frac{DG}{\mu} \qquad (18\text{-}99)$$

where K_G = over-all mass-transfer coefficient, lb.-moles/(hr.)(sq. ft.)(atm.)
M_m = mean molecular weight of gas stream at inlet to tube
D = diameter of tube, ft.
G = mass velocity of gas at inlet to tube, lb./(hr.)(sq. ft.)
μ = viscosity of gas, lb./(ft.)(hr.)

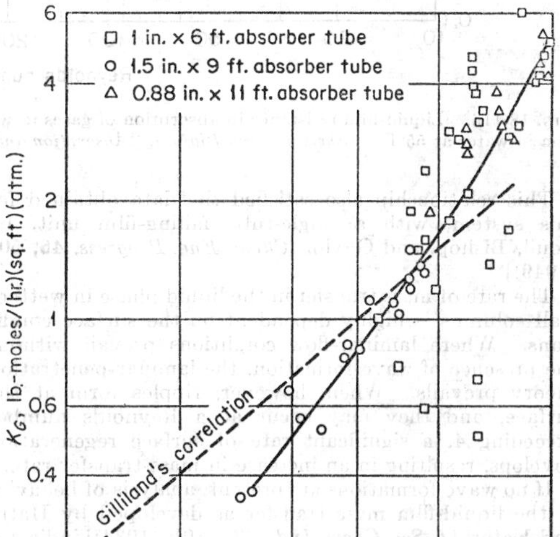

FIG. 18-115. Mass-transfer coefficients vs. average gas velocity —HCl absorption—wetted-wall column. [*Dobratz, Moore, Barnard, and Meyer Chem. Eng. Progress*, **49**, 611 (1953).]

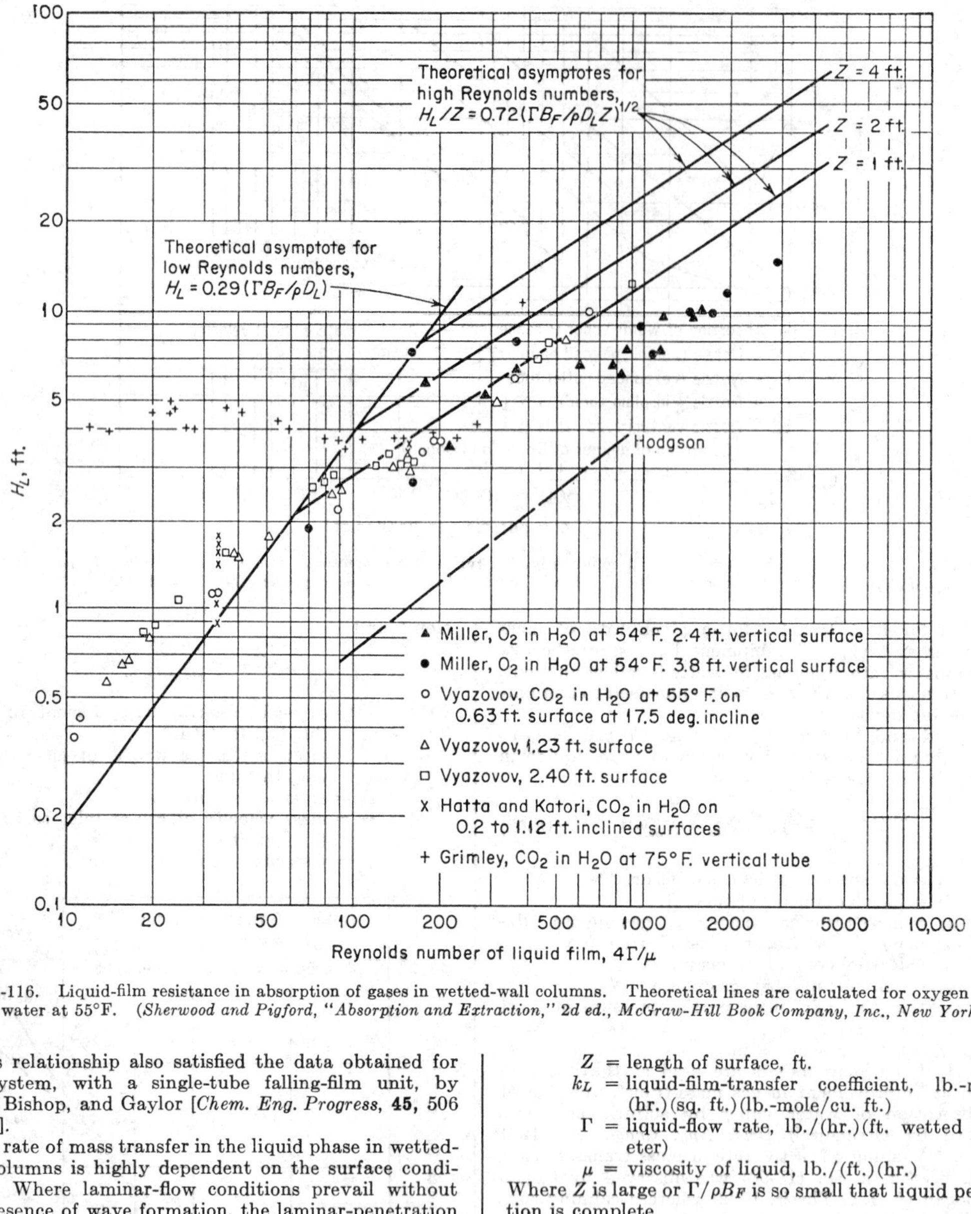

FIG. 18-116. Liquid-film resistance in absorption of gases in wetted-wall columns. Theoretical lines are calculated for oxygen absorption in water at 55°F. *(Sherwood and Pigford, "Absorption and Extraction," 2d ed., McGraw-Hill Book Company, Inc., New York,* 1952.

This relationship also satisfied the data obtained for this system, with a single-tube falling-film unit, by Coull, Bishop, and Gaylor [*Chem. Eng. Progress*, **45,** 506 (1949)].

The rate of mass transfer in the liquid phase in wetted-wall columns is highly dependent on the surface conditions. Where laminar-flow conditions prevail without the presence of wave formation, the laminar-penetration theory prevails. When, however, ripples form at the surface, and they may occur at a Reynolds number exceeding 4, a significant rate of surface regeneration develops, resulting in an increase in mass-transfer rate.

If no wave formations are present, analysis of behavior of the liquid-film mass transfer as developed by Hatta and Katori [*J. Soc. Chem. Ind.*, **37,** 280B (1934)] indicates that

$$k_L = \sqrt{\frac{6}{\pi}}\sqrt{\frac{D_L\Gamma}{\rho B_F{}^2}} \qquad (18\text{-}100)$$

where $B_F = (3u\Gamma/\rho^2 g)^{1/3}$

D_L = liquid-phase diffusion coefficient, sq. ft./hr.

ρ = liquid density, lb./cu. ft.

Z = length of surface, ft.

k_L = liquid-film-transfer coefficient, lb.-moles/(hr.)(sq. ft.)(lb.-mole/cu. ft.)

Γ = liquid-flow rate, lb./(hr.)(ft. wetted perimeter)

μ = viscosity of liquid, lb./(ft.)(hr.)

Where Z is large or $\Gamma/\rho B_F$ is so small that liquid penetration is complete

$$k_L = 3.41\frac{D_L}{B_F} \qquad (18\text{-}101)$$

and

$$H_L = 0.29\frac{\Gamma B_F}{D_L} \qquad (18\text{-}102)$$

A comparison of experimental data for carbon dioxide absorption obtained by Hatta and Katori (*loc. cit.*), Grimley [*Trans. Inst. Chem. Engrs.*, **23,** 228 (1945)], and Vyazov [*J. Tech. Phys. (U.S.S.R.)*, **10,** 1519 (1940)], and for absorption of oxygen and hydrogen by Hodgson (S.M. Thesis, M.I.T., 1949), Henley (B.S. Thesis, University of Delaware, 1949), Miller (B.S. Thesis, University of Delaware, 1949), and Richards (B.S.

Thesis, University of Delaware, 1950), was made by Sherwood and Pigford ("Absorption and Extraction," McGraw-Hill, New York, 1952) and is indicated in Fig. 18-116.

In general the observed mass-transfer rates are greater than those predicted by theory and may be related to the development of surface rippling, a phenomenon which increases in intensity with increasing liquid path.

Vivian and Peaceman [*Am. Inst. Chem. Engrs. J.*, **2**, 437 (1956)] investigated the characteristics of the CO_2-H_2O and Cl_2-HCl, H_2O system in a wetted-wall column and found that gas rate had no effect on the liquid-phase coefficient at Reynolds numbers below 2200. Beyond this rate, the effect of the resulting rippling was to significantly increase the liquid-phase transfer rate. The authors proposed a behavior relationship based on a dimensional analysis but suggest caution in its application concomitant with the use of this type of relationship. Cognizance was taken by the authors of the effects of column length, one to induce rippling and increase of rate of transfer, one to increase time of exposure which via the penetration theory decreases the average rate of mass transfer in the liquid phase. The equation is

$$\frac{k_L h}{D_L} = 0.433 \left(\frac{\mu_L}{\rho_L D_L}\right)^{1/2} \left(\frac{\rho_L{}^2 g h^3}{\mu_L{}^2}\right)^{1/6} \left(\frac{4\Gamma}{\mu_L}\right)^{0.4} \tag{18-103}$$

where D_L = diffusion coefficient of solute in liquid, sq. ft./hr.
g = gravity-acceleration constant, 4.17×10^8 ft./hr.^{2}
h = length of wetted wall, ft.
k_L = mass-transfer coefficient, liquid phase, ft./hr.
Γ = mass rate of flow of liquid, lb./(hr.)(ft. of periphery)
μ_L = viscosity of liquid, lb./(ft.)(hr.)
ρ_L = density of liquid, lb./cu. ft.

The effect of chemical reaction in reducing the effect of variation of the liquid rate on the rate of absorption in the laminar-flow regime was illustrated by the evaluation of the rate of absorption of chlorine in ferrous chloride solutions in a wetted-wall column by Gilliland, Baddour, and White [*Am. Inst. Chem. Engrs. J.*, **4**, 323 (1958)] (Fig. 18-77).

PHASE DISPERSION

REFERENCES: For general treatments of phase dispersion and disperse systems, see Birkhoff and Zarantonello, "Applied Mathematics and Mechanics," vol. II, "Jets, Wakes, and Cavities," Academic Press, New York, 1957. Hermans, "Flow Properties of Disperse Systems," Interscience, New York, 1953. Lane and Green, in Batchelor and Davis, "Surveys in Mechanics," Cambridge, Univ. Press, New York, 1956. Plateau, "Statique expérimentale et théoretique des liquides soumis aux seules forces moléculaires," Gauthier-Villars, Paris, 1873.

Industrial chemical manufacture is, whenever feasible, a fluids-handling process. The greater convenience and economy identified with the processing of fluids and more effective control of chemical reactions when they proceed in a fluid phase dictate such a choice. In view of the general insolubility among gases, liquids, and solids, therefore, it is not surprising that chemical engineering practice is replete with examples of multiphase systems. Systems involving a gas phase and one or more liquid phases in coexistence are an important group among these.

Gas-liquid mixtures are generally of three types. In one, the gas phase is continuous and the liquid is dispersed as drops or slugs. In a second, the reverse of the first, the liquid is continuous and the gas is dispersed as bubbles. In a third case, both phases are substantially continuous but attenuated to provide a relatively large interphase surface, or indeed both phases may appear to be discontinuous depending on local conditions within the mixture. An example of the latter is the highly turbulent cocurrent flow of a gas and a liquid in the appropriate proportions within a pipe.

LIQUID-IN-GAS DISPERSIONS

REFERENCES: For general discussions of liquid-in-gas dispersions, see Green and Lane, "Particulate Clouds: Dusts, Smokes, and Mists," Van Nostrand, Princeton, N.J., 1957. Avy, "Les Aerosols," Dunod, Paris, 1956. For classical treatment of jet disintegration, see Castleman, *Bur. Standards J. Research*, **6**, 369 (1931). Helmholtz, *Monatsber. Berlin Akad.*, **1868**, 215, *Phil. Mag.*, **36**, 377 (1868). Rayleigh, *Proc. London Math. Soc.*, **10**, 4 (1879). Vereschchagin and Semerchan, *Soviet Phys. Doklady*, **1**, 2484 (1957). Specific detailed exposition of sprays and spraying is found in Meyer and Ranz, in Kirk-Othmer, "Encyclopedia of Chemical Technology," vol. 12, pp. 703–721, Interscience, New York, 1954. Fraser, Eisenklam, and Dombrowski, *Brit. Chem. Eng.*, **2**, 414, 496, 536, 610 (1957). Giffin and Muraszew, "The Atomization of Liquid Fuels," Wiley, New York, 1953. Department of Engineering Research, Pennsylvania State University, "Bibliography on Sprays," 2d ed., The Texas Co., New York, 1953. See also Lewis, Edwards, Guglia, Rice, and Smith, *Ind. Eng. Chem.*, **40**, 67 (1948). Troesch, *Chem.-Ing.-Tech.*, **31**, 667 (1959). Excellent reviews of developments in spray drying and spray-drying equipment are given by Marshall, *Chem. Eng. Progress, Monograph Ser.*, **50** (2) (1954), who also discusses atomization and atomizers; and by Seltzer and Settelmeyer, in "Advances in Food Research," vol. 2, pp. 399–520, Academic Press, New York, 1949. For a critical summary of two-phase flow in pipes, see Isbin, Moen, and Mosher, *U.S. Atomic Energy Comm. Report*, A.E.C.U-2994, November, 1954.

Distribution or dispersion of a liquid phase in a gas phase is a phenomenon frequently encountered in chemical and related processing.

A liquid may be projected or released into a gaseous continuum in a number of forms. On the one hand it may flow or fall as a substantially continuous stream, jet, or sheet, or rest on a supporting surface as a static film with one face exposed to the gas. Alternatively, it may be produced into discrete drops or short filaments, usually small and frequently microscopic, that reside in a gas atmosphere transiently or that are maintained dynamically in a disperse state. There is no distinct boundary between these two extremes, but practically a jet or film is clearly distinguishable from a system of spray, mist, fog, or free drops. It is the latter with which this section is primarily concerned.

Theory of Drop Formation. A drop may form in one of two ways: by mechanical subdivision of a larger mass of liquid, or by condensation from the vapor phase. Mechanical subdivision may be achieved by individual removal of the quantity of material that will constitute a drop from the bulk of the liquid, or by the disintegration of thin jets or sheets of the liquid.

Condensation of a vapor to a finely dispersed liquid phase occurs upon supersaturation of a vapor-bearing gas, sometimes assisted by the presence of condensation nuclei or nucleating agents. Supersaturation may result from subcooling a saturated mixture (as by mixing with a cold stream of gas or by sudden expansion of the mixture) or from chemical reaction among gaseous components to form a liquid product (as in the formation of sulfuric acid droplets from water vapor and SO_3). The resulting droplets are initially very small ($<0.1\mu$) and the dispersion created is in the class of a true aerosol or "fog," often quite permanent. Familiar examples are rain clouds, "steam" plumes, ground fog and smog, oil smoke, and the sulfuric acid mist already mentioned. The latter constitutes an outstanding example of aerosol permanence, inasmuch as it can persist after being bubbled through water.

Filament and Sheet Disintegration. A filament of liquid is mechanically unstable, as demonstrated by Rayleigh [*Proc. London Math. Soc.*, **10**, 4 (1879)], and the smaller its diameter the greater its sensitivity to small disturbing forces. When a liquid jet disintegrates, it does so varicosely (by assuming a series of bulges and necks, with separation into sets of primary and satellite drops) or sinuously (by going into a wave, the humps of which become unstable and break). When a jet is first formed both types of disturbance are possible, but at low jet velocities the varicose form is likely to be the cause of disintegration. As velocity increases and the air resistance grows rapidly greater, sinuous break-up becomes more likely. At very high velocities, the jet inertia becomes too great to allow marked oscillations of either type to form along its surface (Richardson, in J. J. Herman's "Flow Properties of Disperse Systems," North-Holland Publishing Co., Amsterdam, 1953). Instead the two fluids interpenetrate, the gas forming bubbles within the liquid and drops of liquid escaping the surface into the gas. Disintegration of the jet rapidly ensues.

A jet may experience a disturbance from an outside source that aggravates its instability, hastens its destruction, and makes its atomization more thorough. If the jet is in laminar flow it indeed must be triggered. The filament may encounter the disturbance within the nozzle or after it has emerged.

Thin unsupported films of liquid, like jets, are unstable and break up into drops. Fraser (in "Sixth Symposium on Combustion," Reinhold, New York, 1956) has described four mechanisms of film disintegration:

1. Rim disintegration. Threads of fluid are pulled away from the edge of the film by escaping primary drops. The threads then disintegrate into much smaller droplets.
2. Perforated-sheet disintegration. Turbulent disturbances puncture thin portions of the film. Once a rupture occurs, it spreads rapidly by virtue of surface tension, and break-up of the film ensues.
3. Wavy-sheet disintegration. When a film is propelled at high velocity into a gaseous atmosphere, turbulence in the gas phase can cause the film to flap. The resulting violent stresses can tear away patches of liquid, or can cause the sheet to roll up into a hollow filament that is unstable and disintegrates into hollow droplets.
4. Thick-sheet disintegration. As the result of interaction with the atmosphere at high velocities, the sheet of liquid may break up near the orifice that produces it. Relatively large primary drops can result.

The mechanical properties of the liquid and of the atmosphere into which it is dispersed affect the disintegration of the filament or sheet. The viscosity and surface tension of the liquid are of particular importance. High viscosity favors a longer film, and high surface tension a more contracted and tougher one; both favor a less ruffled and more durable one. Other factors remaining the same, low viscosity and low surface tension are desirable for ease of dispersion and minimum size of drops. The effect of the properties of the gas into which the liquid is projected is less well defined. Fraser (*loc. cit.*), however, reported that the mean drop size produced by a simple pressure nozzle spraying water into air increased slowly as the pressure of the surrounding air decreased from atmospheric, took a sharp increase at 18 in. Hg, and then began to decrease with further decreases in pressure.

Energy Requirements. The disintegration of a mass of liquid into drops results in the enlargement of the interfacial area between the liquid and its atmosphere, the specific surface being inversely proportional to drop dimension for drops of the same shape. Thus a 1-mm. drop that is subdivided into a uniform colony of 1-μ droplets will experience an increase of surface area from 0.0314 to 31.4 sq. cm.

The amount of energy required for surface creation is the product of the specific surface energy for the liquid-gas system involved (numerically equal to the interfacial tension) and the area of the new surface formed. This is a relatively small quantity. For example, to subdivide massive water into 1-μ droplets involves on the order of 0.1 cal./g. or 1000 ft.-lb./gal. of water atomized.

The increase in surface energy is theoretically the only energy investment required for the creation of a liquid-in-gas dispersion. In practice, energy is expended in three additional ways during the process of disintegration:

1. Inertial losses. The liquid usually is accelerated in the course of its atomization, and the energy of acceleration is partly expended as unproductive inertial losses along the path of the liquid before atomization occurs and as residual kinetic energy of the drops after they are formed. Dissipation of energy in this way is slight: loss equivalent to acceleration to a velocity of 100 ft./sec. is on the order of 0.1 cal./g.
2. Viscous losses. The rate of liquid deformation is high during drop formation. On the assumption of a model sufficiently idealized to allow calculation, Monk [*J. Appl. Phys.*, **23**, 288 (1952)] has estimated the energy dissipated against viscous forces during the atomization of 1 g. of water to 1-μ droplets in 1 sec. to be in the range 10^4 to 10^6 cal. This represents power expenditure on the order of 100 to 10,000 hp.
3. Mechanical inefficiency. The application of the necessary energy to a liquid during its atomization is itself an energy-consuming process. Mechanical losses are associated with the pumps or rotating heads that may be used to produce disintegration, with the prime movers that drive them, and with the motion of the fluids involved in the system. Mechanical inefficiency is greatest for two-fluid nozzles and spinning disks, and least for a properly designed simple nozzle system in combination with an efficient pump.

As is illustrated above, energy losses identified with drop production usually are large compared with the basic energy required for new surface. They are generally incalculable, and the power requirement of an atomizing system must be predicted from experience.

Theoretical Drop Size and Coalescence. The mechanical behavior of drops is extremely complicated. A drop can disintegrate owing to inertial interaction with a surrounding gas in a manner described by Helmholtz [*Monatsber. Berlin. Akad.*, **1868**, 215; *Phil. Mag.*, **36**, 337 (1868)], and instability of this kind undoubtedly is important in the generation of sprays. The maximum size of a drop that is stable to inertial disturbance can be calculated in terms of the properties of the fluids and the relative velocity of the drop (Birkhoff and Zarantonello, "Jets, Wakes, and Cavities," p. 330, Academic Press, New York, 1957), provided that the effects of viscosity and gas turbulence are considered negligible. Drops falling at their terminal velocity exhibit Helmholtz stability up to relatively large diameters (for water in air, the order of magnitude is 1 cm.). Smaller drops, on the other hand, require high relative velocities for the onset of instability—for a 1-mm. globule of water in air, for example, on the order of 50 ft./sec., with velocity increasing by the factor $\sqrt{10}$ for each order of magnitude of decrease in drop size.

The simultaneous effects of other influences, notably viscous forces and gas turbulence, make the prediction of drop dimension from the principle of Helmholtz stability inaccurate and seriously complicate drop-size theory.

The effective size of the drops comprising a disperse system depends on the rate of coalescence of the drops relative to the length of time that they are in suspension. Drops will coalesce if they are allowed to make physical contact with one another, barring their mutual insulation, as in the case of dirt-coated mercury globules.

Physical contact among the droplets of aerosol mists can result from Brownian motion, and fogs coagulate at a steadily declining rate that is well approximated by a simple law proposed by Whytlaw-Gray and Patterson ["Smoke," E. Arnold, London, 1932]:

$$\frac{1}{n} - \frac{1}{n_o} = kt \qquad (18\text{-}104)$$

where n_o and n are the concentrations of dispersed particles, number per cc., at the initial time and at time = t sec., respectively. The coefficient k is characteristic of the particular aerosol which it describes, but for many systems its magnitude is 10^{-9} cc./sec. For a concentration of 10^5 particles per cc., therefore, the time to halve the particle population by coalescence is about 3 hr., and aerosols of this and smaller concentrations can be viewed as substantially stable.

Mechanically induced contact also will accelerate coalescence. Thus, Langstroth and Gillespie [*Can. J. Research*, **B25**, 455 (1947)] found a marked increase in the coagulation rate of ammonium chloride smoke with agitation of the smoke by a paddle. Of greater practical interest is Kleinschmidt's observation that, with pressure nozzles which project liquid into relatively still gas, the deceleration of particles after they leave the nozzle allows large drops to overtake small ones with consequent coalescence. On the assumption of Stokes's law, Kleinschmidt showed that knowledge of the drop-size distribution from a nozzle would allow estimation of the rate of collision and hence of coalescence among drops [*Chem. & Met. Eng.*, **46**, 487 (1939)]. Inasmuch as the size and distribution of droplets from a nozzle seldom are known accurately, such computation is not quantitatively helpful, but qualitatively it emphasizes the value of a positive bulk gas flow past a nozzle or other drop producer to minimize recombination.

Because of the dynamic differences associated with particle size, a swarm of uniform droplets is less likely to coalesce than one of mixed sizes. In this sense, the baffled construction of a therapeutic atomizer, by its removal of oversize drops, produces a mist that is not only relatively uniform but also relatively stable.

Sprays, Mists, and Fogs. Dispersions of liquids in gases are given a number of names intended to classify them, but precise exclusive intelligence is not conveyed by any of the terms used.

Definitions. Sprays generally imply mechanically produced dispersions, usually deliberately generated. Again, sprays are usually considered as unstable suspensions of relatively large drops, although therapeutic sprays comprise small drops in quite stable suspension. *Mists* and *fogs* are generally viewed as fortuitously, often undesirably, occurring dispersions, most often as atmospheric phenomena. The usual implication is that of stable, small-particle composition, but mists may be unstable. Fogs are optically dense mists that appreciably reduce the visual range. Mists and fogs generally are formed by condensation rather than by atomization.

A *smoke* may be either a dust or mist suspension, characterized by great stability and very small particles (less than 5 μ and often less than 0.1 μ) of condensation origin, particularly from combustion or other chemical reactions. In a quantitative technical sense, stable mists and fogs are properly termed smokes. The term *aerosol*, coined to describe colloidal aerial dispersions, is popularly and loosely applied to any suspension in air.

A *drop* is a small, discrete portion of liquid, roughly spheroidal in shape. A minute drop, substantially spherical, is called a *droplet*. Droplets usually are in the micronic or submicronic size range, but the distinction is not sharp. A *particle* is any individual portion of finely divided matter, solid or liquid, although the word is commonly reserved for solids; a *globule*, on the other hand, is exclusively a liquid particle.

Properties and Characteristics. Of the properties of the component phases the *density of the gas* and the *density, viscosity*, and *surface tension of the liquid* all affect the size and size distribution of the drops created. They relate also to the difficulty of disintegrating a jet or sheet. As has been mentioned, the exact role of these properties in the formation and behavior of drops is clear only in the most simplified of theoretical statements, but experience shows that they are significant. Qualitatively speaking, one may say that increasing liquid density favors jet persistence but also increases inertial forces and thus decreases maximum stable drop size in a gravitational field; increasing gas density increases the instability of both jets and drops and favors smaller drops; increasing viscosity, while making massive disintegration more difficult and considerably increasing the energy expenditure in such disintegration, favors the role of the viscous forces that are practically important to drop formation; increasing surface tension (or, more strictly, interfacial tension of the two-phase system) increases stability and the difficulty of producing small drops.

Vapor pressure does not directly affect drop mechanics but is indirectly of interest. For example, the liquid often passes from a zone of higher to one of lower pressure during its disintegration and under the right conditions may flash or boil rapidly. Such action would facilitate jet or sheet disintegration. A spray or mist, having large interfacial area, will rapidly approach physical equilibrium, and in gas initially unsaturated with the liquid extensive evaporation of drops of high-volatility material may occur. Drops of pure material may disappear completely, depending on the liquid-gas flow ratio, and drops of solution may be converted into particles of solid solute. Evaporation from drops is the principle behind humidifying sprays and spray dryers.

Very small droplets will continue to evaporate when larger ones have ceased, because of the *increase of vapor pressure with surface curvature.* According to the Thomson-Gibbs relation,

$$\ln\left(\frac{p}{p_\infty}\right) = \frac{2\gamma M}{RTr\rho} \qquad (18\text{-}105)$$

where p is the vapor pressure at temperature T exerted from a drop of radius r, containing liquid of molecular weight M, surface tension γ, and density ρ, and p_∞ is the vapor pressure of the same liquid at the same temperature over a flat surface. Equation (18-105) has been verified experimentally by La Mer and Gruen [*Trans. Faraday Soc.*, **48**, 410 (1952)] for drops of dioctyl phthalate–toluene and oleic acid–chloroform binaries in the diameter range 0.16 to 1.4 μ. For water drops greater than 0.1 μ, the vapor pressure is increased less than 4 per cent, but for liquids of high molecular weight, 1-μ drops can have a significantly increased vapor pressure.

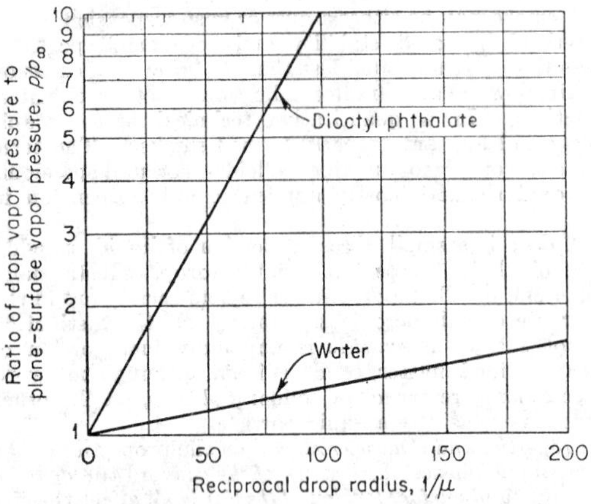

FIG. 18-117. Increase of vapor pressure with drop radius for low- and high-molecular-weight materials.

Figure 18-117 shows the calculated effect for dioctyl phthalate contrasted with that for water. The dependency of vapor pressure on curvature favors drop-size uniformity by the growth of larger drops in a cloud at the expense of smaller ones.

Temperature, pressure, and *composition* of liquid and gas determine the values assumed by the properties above, viscosity and vapor pressure being especially sensitive to temperature. Liquid composition may be of further importance in that drop size and shape may be affected as solutions or suspensions are concentrated by evaporation or have their properties changed by chemical reaction.

The characteristic features of mixtures of liquids in gases are their heterogeneity (particularly the nature of it) and their instability. Both features are closely related to the characteristics of the component drops, individually and as a population. The effective viscosity of the mixture is generally that of the continuum, whereas the density is the bulk density of the mixture. The optical characteristics, of interest as bases for analysis of dispersions, are complicated. Transmission, refraction, scatter, polarization, and spectral color all have been studied and applied more or less successfully to measurements of practical significance.

The shape, size, size distribution, spatial distribution, and charge are "properties" of drops and drop populations that contribute importantly to the characteristics and usefulness of sprays and mists. Although very coarse sprays may contain drops whose diameter is of the order of 1 cm., most sprays of industrial interest have drop diameters less than 1 mm., often less than 200 μ. The population of extremely fine aerosols may be as small as 0.01 μ. In this range of sizes, drops of all liquids are essentially spheres. The drop-size distribution varies widely depending on the source of the drops: condensation techniques can produce quite uniform droplets (monodisperse systems), whereas some atomization methods result in a wide range of sizes.

Drops brought into contact with one another readily coalesce, and this behavior is an outstanding and unique characteristic. Solid particles that collide may or may not agglomerate, and an aggregate that is formed may be relatively unstable. Drops that coalesce, on the other hand, completely lose their individuality and can never be exactly recreated. Except for coalescence and the ability of large drops to disintegrate while falling, the mechanics of liquid globules is substantially that of rigid solid particles of the same size range, a subject dealt with extensively in the literature.

Drops often carry a charge, and the distribution is usually random, in both magnitude and sign. Atomized drops may acquire their charge from ions in the parent liquid; condensed drops must acquire their charge from ions in their atmosphere, naturally (as by cosmic rays) or artificially induced. Natural fogs frequently carry high charges of preponderantly one or the other sign, which contribute to the stability of the fog [Elton, *Chem. & Ind. (London)*, **1953,** 407].

Examination of Dispersions. The understanding and effective use of sprays and mists require knowledge about one or more of such quantities as number and mass concentration, drop size and size related parameters, and distribution of size and concentration. Such determinations may be made by sampling and subsequent analysis of the collected particles, or by direct observation of the dispersion mass. Because accurate and representative sampling is always difficult, and drop populations pose especially awkward possibilities of coalescence, premature deposit or absorption, and disintegration, direct observation is much the preferred method. Unfortunately it is often impracticable.

Except for the special problems mentioned above, the sampling and examination of drops are achieved by methods used for dust specimens. In general, the sample is collected by impingement or filtration, weighed for mass concentration, counted for number concentration, and scaled for size. A waxed or greased slide often is used for the collection of drops with the minimum error. Collection of colored drops sometimes is made on filter or blotting paper, with allowance for the spread of the trace during absorption. Counting and scaling may be done from photographs or the original specimens and may be assisted by a lens, microscope, or electron microscope. This is at best undesirably tedious and time-consuming but in some cases has no adequate substitute. The method of Adler and coworkers [*Chem. Eng. Progress*, **50,** 14 (1954)], involving the electronic scanning of a photographic negative for drop-size-distribution data, shows promise of relief from optical counting. Ranz and Hofelt [*Ind. Eng. Chem.*, **49,** 288 (1957)] have developed a jet impacter for the rapid routine determination of cumulative volume distribution of a spray; it is recommended for drop sizes up to 100 μ.

Direct optical methods that have been used include unmagnified or microscopic observation of sedimentation rates, interpreted by the application of Stokes's law (for particle Reynolds numbers below 0.05) or of the Cunningham modification thereof (for particles of the same order as the molecular mean free path); measurement of the intensity of transmitted monochromatic light; measurement of the intensity or polarization of scattered light; observation of the number of sequences of the color spectrum in scattered light over an arc of 180 deg.; and use of an ultramicroscope to observe the number of scintillae (hence the concentration of particles) in a specimen. All these methods require suitable optical apparatus and special technique, and each suffers from its own set of limitations. Each, therefore, needs to be considered deliberately before it is adopted for a given application. A useful critical summary of these and other optical techniques is given by Green and Lane ("Particulate Clouds," Chaps. 4, 7, Van Nostrand, Princeton, N.J., 1957).

For the evaluation of monodisperse suspensions of droplets too fine to be treated directly by optical methods (of the order of 0.1 μ and less), La Mer and coworkers [*J. Colloid Sci.*, **5,** 471 (1950); *Science*, **118,** 516 (1953)] have developed an ingenious method that involves the growth of particles by condensation upon and in them of a volatile solvent. The method is restricted to relatively non-volatile materials.

Surveys of spray-estimation methods have been presented by Ranz ["Air Sprays and Spraying," Department of Engineering Research, Pennsylvania State University, University Park, Pa., Mar. 26, 1956] and by Troesch [*Chem.-Ing.-Tech.*, **31,** 667 (1959)].

Spray Nozzles. A spray nozzle is a device for breaking up a liquid into drops. The applications of spray nozzles are numerous and varied, and consequently a large number of different forms are in use. All spray nozzles may be classified under one of the following types:

1. *Pressure nozzles* in which the fluid is under pressure and is broken up by its inherent instability and its impact on the atmosphere or by its impact on another jet or a fixed plate.
2. *Rotating nozzles* (*spinning atomizers*) in which the fluid is fed at low pressure to the center of a rapidly rotating disk or cup. Centrifugal force causes the fluid to be broken up into drops.
3. *Gas-atomizing nozzles* (two-fluid nozzles, pneumatic atomizers) in which the fluid is subjected to the disrupting effect of a high-velocity jet of gas.

There are several forms of each of these types in common use, and these will now be described in turn.

Pressure Nozzles. *Hollow-cone Nozzles.* Pressure nozzles find the widest field of application and are available in a variety of forms and sizes. The most common of these is the so-called hollow-cone nozzle. In this nozzle the fluid is fed into a whirl chamber through tangential passages or through a fixed spiral so that it acquires a rapid rotation. The orifice is placed on the axis of the whirl chamber, and the fluid exits in the form of a hollow conical sheet which then breaks up into drops. Such nozzles are illustrated in Figs. 18-118, 18-119, and 18-120. Hollow-cone nozzles are made with orifices from 0.02 to 2 in. in diameter with corresponding discharge rates of

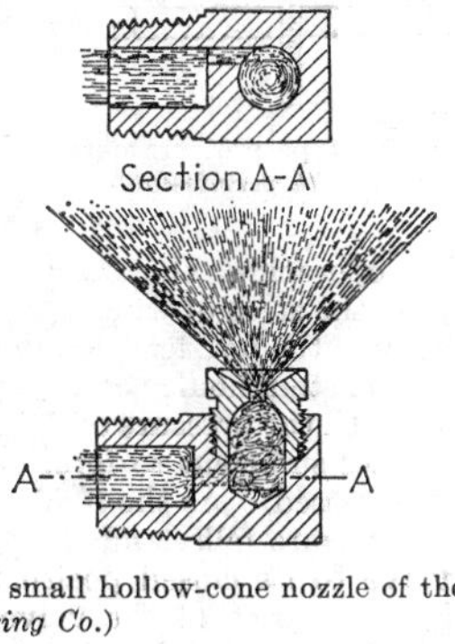

FIG. 18-118. A small hollow-cone nozzle of the tangential type. (*Spray Engineering Co.*)

from less than 0.01 to more than 200 gal./min. The larger sizes are used for cooling ponds, for washing gravel and sand, aerating water, etc., and are usually operated at relatively low pressures. Smaller nozzles may be used for spray drying, air washers and humidifiers, oil burners, gas absorption, etc., and are usually operated at somewhat higher pressures. In common with all pressure nozzles the capacity of a given nozzle is nearly proportional to the square root of the pressure except at extremely high pressures where friction limits the discharge. Operating pressures do not usually exceed 300 lb./sq. in. except in special cases such as milk-powdering sprays where pressures of from 1000 to 7000 lb./sq. in. are used. For a

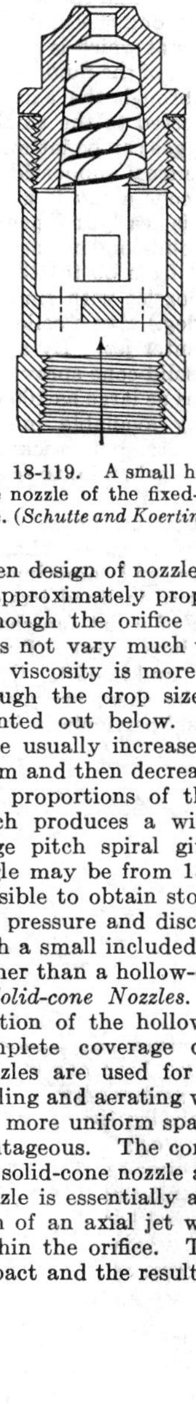

FIG. 18-119. A small hollow-cone nozzle of the fixed-spiral type. (*Schutte and Koerting Co.*)

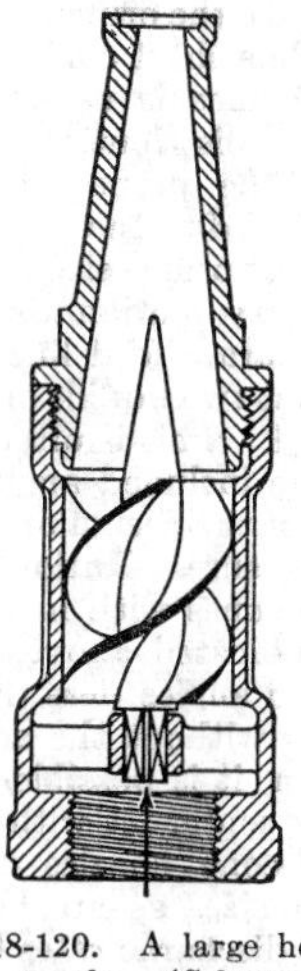

FIG. 18-120. A large hollow-cone nozzle. (*Schutte and Koerting Co.*)

given design of nozzle the discharge at constant pressure is approximately proportional to the area of the orifice, although the orifice does not run full. The discharge does not vary much with the viscosity of the fluid until the viscosity is more than ten times that of water, although the drop size is somewhat altered, as will be pointed out below. The included angle of the spray cone usually increases slowly with pressure to a maximum and then decreases, but it is largely determined by the proportions of the nozzle. A spiral with a short pitch produces a wide-angle spray, and conversely a large pitch spiral gives a small included angle. The angle may be from 15 to 135 deg., but it is not always possible to obtain stock nozzles of a desired angle when the pressure and discharge rate are also fixed. Nozzles with a small included angle tend to produce a solid-cone rather than a hollow-cone spray.

Solid-cone Nozzles. The solid-cone nozzle is a modification of the hollow-cone nozzle which is used when complete coverage of a fixed area is desired. Such nozzles are used for certain washing applications, for cooling and aerating water, and for other purposes where the more uniform spatial distribution of the drops is advantageous. The construction and operation of a typical solid-cone nozzle are illustrated in Fig. 18-121. The nozzle is essentially a hollow-cone nozzle with the addition of an axial jet which strikes the rotating fluid just within the orifice. The break-up is largely due to this impact and the resulting turbulence. The fluid appears

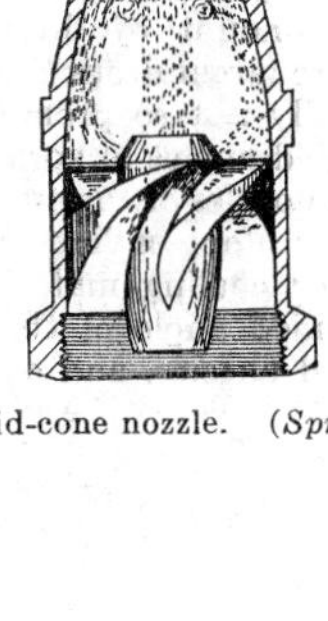

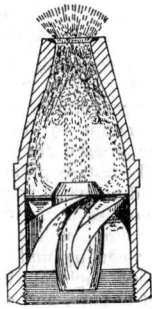

FIG. 18-121. Solid-cone nozzle. (*Spray Engineering Co.*

to leave the orifice in drop form, whereas in a hollow-cone nozzle a short conical fluid sheet which breaks up outside the orifice is usually observed. To obtain a uniform spatial distribution, it is necessary to design the nozzle so that the proper relation exists among the amount of liquid fed to the center jet, the amount which is rotated, and the orifice size. Normally, more of the fluid is given a rotary motion than is passed through the axial jet. A separate feed line may be connected to the axial jet so that two liquids or a liquid and a gas can be intimately mixed. This is often useful for chemical applications.

The included angle of the solid-cone spray is a function of the design of the nozzle and is nearly independent of pressure. Various commercial solid-cone nozzles produce cones with included angles of from 30 to 100 deg. As indicated above, hollow-cone nozzles with small included angles (less than about 30 deg.) give a solid-cone spray without the addition of a center jet. By special design, it is possible to produce a solid-cone spray without a center jet with included angles as large as 100 deg. Solid-cone nozzles are not usually available in such small sizes as are hollow-cone nozzles, but stock sizes have discharge rates from less than 1 gal./min. to several hundred gallons per minute.

Fan Nozzles. A third form of pressure nozzle is the so-called fan nozzle. By means of milled cuts or channels on the rear face of the orifice plate, and sometimes an elongated orifice, or by means of two inclined jets, the fluid is caused to exit in the form of a flat fan-shaped fluid sheet which then breaks up into drops. Typical fan nozzles are shown in Figs. 18-122 and 18-123. Owing to surface tension, the edges of the sheet are usually bounded by solid streams or "horns," particularly in the

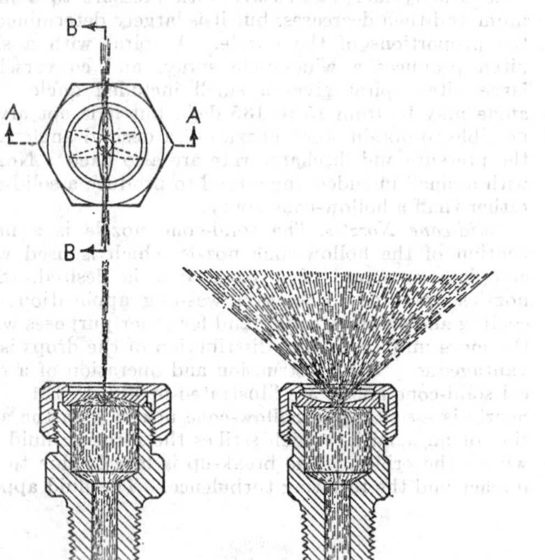

FIG. 18-122. One type of fan nozzle. (*Spray Engineering Co.*)

smaller sizes, which may comprise from one-fourth to one-half of the total amount of liquid sprayed. These streams break up into larger drops than the central sheet. The horns are usually not so pronounced in the larger sizes, and for included angles of spray that are less than about 50 deg. Fan nozzles are useful when it is desired to distribute the spray along a line such as in washing, cleaning, coating, or cooling material in a continuous process. The included angle of the fan is from 10 to 130 deg. in standard nozzles, and capacities range from 0.1 to 20 gal./min.

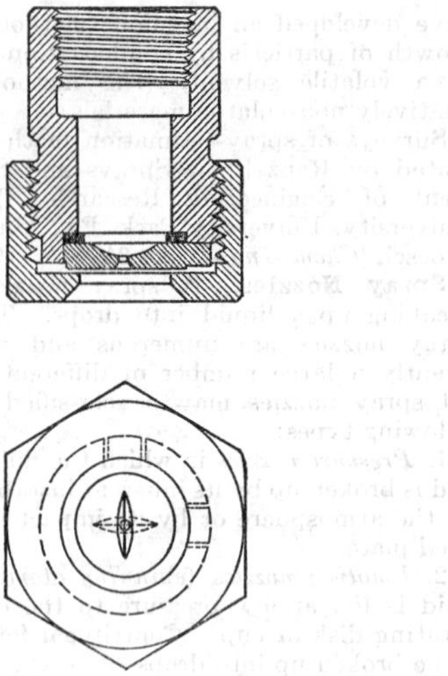

FIG. 18-123. Another design of fan nozzle. (*Schutte and Koerting Co.*)

Vibrating Nozzles. A vibrating pressure nozzle developed by Sliepcevich, Consiglio, and Kurata [*Ind. Eng. Chem.*, **42**, 2353 (1950)] is shown in Fig. 18-124. When

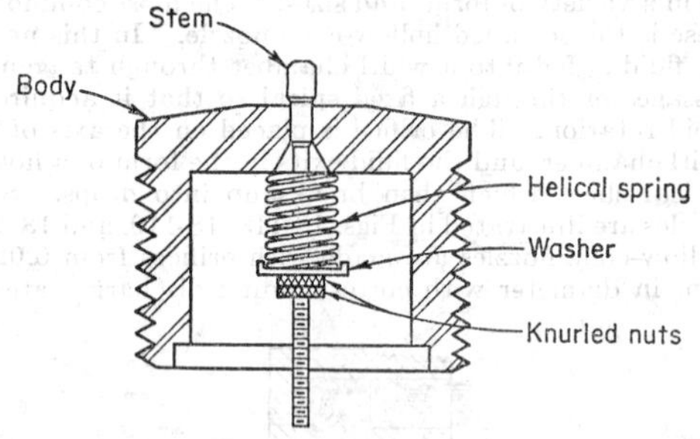

FIG. 18-124. Vibrating-type pressure nozzle. [*From Ind. Eng. Chem.*, **42**, 2353 (1950), *with permission.*]

the nozzle is not operating, the orifice is closed by a tapered-head valve, the stem of which passes through the orifice into the body of the nozzle. A compression spring attached to the valve stem holds the tapered head firmly against the orifice until the pressure of fluid being pumped to the nozzle becomes sufficient to force it away, leaving an annular orifice exposed. As the fluid escapes through this annulus, the pressure falls, and the spring attempts to restore the valve to its closed position; the pressure build-up is such, however, that the valve does not close completely. Thus the combined action of the spring and the fluctuating fluid pressure induces a state of self-excited vibration during which the valve head is maintained at some average position a small distance from the orifice such that the discharge of fluid from the nozzle is in the form of a continuous spray.

Sliepcevich *et al.* tested the vibrating nozzle at 400 to 2100 lb./sq. in. They found that the angle of spray is the angle of the valve taper at all pressures. The performance of the nozzle depends on spring constant and initial compression, area of the annular orifice, and ratio of valve-head diameter to orifice diameter, an optimum combination of which has not been reported. The finest and most uniform sprays are said to be delivered when the vibration of the valve is clearly audible. Advantages claimed for the vibrating nozzle are that it will produce a finer dispersion at a given capacity (or a higher capacity for a given fineness) than a conventional pressure nozzle, and that it is self-cleaning.

Impact Nozzles. Another type of nozzle which is used for certain special purposes is the impact nozzle. A solid stream of fluid under pressure is caused to strike a fixed surface or another similar stream. By a proper orientation and shape of the plate or by varying the size and direction of the two fluid streams, it is possible to obtain a hollow-cone-, fan-, or disk-shaped fluid sheet. It has been found possible to produce drops of more uniform size with an impact nozzle than with other types of pressure nozzles if laminar flow is maintained. It is extremely difficult to produce laminar flow in other types of pressure nozzles because of their essential interior parts. The orifices of impact nozzles, on the other hand, may be designed to produce laminar flow if proper precautions are taken. Such laminar-flow impact nozzles are applicable to continuous operations such as gas-washing and chemical reactions between a liquid and a gas, in which the more uniform drop size results in an over-all saving in spite of greater nozzle cost.

Small impact nozzles of the type shown in Fig. 18-125 are often used in air-moistening equipment.

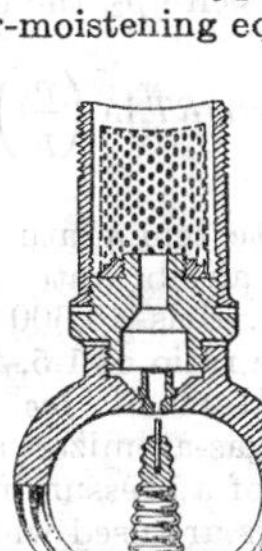

FIG. 18-125. A small impact nozzle as used in a direct humidifier. (*Parks-Cramer Co.*)

Pressure nozzles as a class are relatively simple, small, and inexpensive, and they usually consume less power than other types. They may be used with all fluids that have a viscosity less than about 300 to 500 sec. Saybolt and that do not contain solid particles larger than the passages in the nozzle.

Materials of Construction. Pressure nozzles are commonly furnished in cast iron and cast brass or bronze in the larger sizes and in steel, brass, and bronze in the smaller sizes. When corrosion or erosion is important, the nozzles may be formed from any material that can be either machined, cast, or molded. Some of the more common special materials are stainless steel, monel metal, hard lead, ceramics, hard rubber, and glass. When erosion is an important consideration, tips of stellite or other hard alloys may be used. Monel-metal nozzles are particularly useful for high-temperature applications. Typical pressure-capacity data for standard pressure nozzles are contained in Table 18-16.

Power. The power required to pump liquid through a pressure nozzle is calculated as

$$P = 5.82 \times 10^{-4} Qp \qquad (18\text{-}106)$$

where P = power consumed at the nozzle, hp., p = pressure drop across the nozzle, lb./sq. in., and Q = volumetric flow rate of liquid through nozzle, gal./min. The total power required will include in addition that dissipated because of pressure drop along the line to the nozzle and that equivalent to the inefficiency of the pump and drive used.

Table 18-16. Discharge Rates and Included Angle of Spray of Typical Pressure Nozzles*

Nozzle type	Orifice diameter, in.	Discharge, gal./min., and included angle of spray							
		10 lb./sq. in.		25 lb./sq. in.		50 lb./sq. in.		100 lb./sq. in.	
		Discharge	Angle, deg.	Discharge	Angle, deg.	Discharge	Angle, deg.	Discharge	Angle, deg.
Hollow cone	0.046	......	..	0.10	65	0.135	68	0.183	75
	.140	0.535	82	0.81	88	1.10	90	1.50	93
	.218	1.25	83	1.88	86	2.55	89	3.45	92
	.375	7.2	62	11.8	70	16.5	70		
Solid cone	.047	......	..	0.167	65	0.235	70	0.34	70
	.188	1.60	55	2.46	58	3.42	60	4.78	60
	.250	3.35	65	5.40	70	7.50	70	10.4	75
	.500	17.5	86	27.5	84	38.7	73		
Fan	.031	0.085	40	0.132	90	0.182	110	0.252	110
	.093	0.70	70	1.12	76	1.57	80	2.25	80
	.187	2.25	50	3.70	59	5.35	65	7.70	65
	.375	9.50	66	15.40	74	22.10	75	30.75	75

* Data furnished through the courtesy of the Spray Engineering Co.

Rotating Nozzles (Spinning Atomizers). The essential part of a spinning atomizer is a cup or more often a disk which is driven at a high speed (several hundred up to 50,000 r.p.m.). The principle of the spinning atomizer differs from that of pressure nozzles in that the fluid to be sprayed attains its velocity with little or no pressure increase. Thus the feed is brought at low pressure to the disk, at or near its center, and the feed rate can be controlled independently with respect to the atomizer operating conditions. The atomizer may be smooth, it may have peripheral vanes, or it may be hollow with equispaced radial vanes or channels in its interior along which the liquid to be dispersed is directed by the centrifugal head developed. The disk may be from 2 in. to 3 ft. in diameter, although most designs lie between 2 and 12 in.

The exact mechanism by which the mass of liquid is disintegrated as it is propelled across and away from the rotating disk is somewhat speculative. Photographs show that liquid may leave the atomizer as drops, as filaments, or in a sheet [Hinze and Milborn, *J. Appl. Mechanics*, **17**, 145 (1950)], the progression being in that order as feed rate is increased at a given disk speed. It is the filament and sheet stages that are of practical interest. Presumably uniformity of the drop population produced requires that the parent films or filaments be uniform, and Hinze and Milborn suggest that this condition is achieved by maintenance of a large centrifugal field compared with the gravitational, uniform feed rates, vibration-free disk operation, and smooth disk surfaces. Marshall [*Chem. Eng. Progress Monograph Ser.* **50** (2), (1954)] has shown that when these conditions are not met the disk discharge is quite non-uniform.

The spray pattern produced by a spinning atomizer is complicated by a number of simultaneous effects. The gravitational field and the drag from passage through the gas surrounding the nozzle tend to cause a drop-size trajectory spread, the smaller drops falling away more quickly. The currents produced by the deliberate circulation of the gas (*e.g.*, in a spray dryer) may oppose or augment the falling away. In addition there will be interaction between the disk and the surrounding gas, and between the spray and the gas that will affect the circulation. The result is a spray pattern impossible to calculate—a desirable pattern can be achieved only through experiment.

The power that is required by a spinning atomizer is the sum of the requirement to pump the liquid, the losses to mechanical inefficiency in the drive and bearing system, and the losses due to interaction between the disk and its gaseous environment. The liquid pumping power can be calculated for its maximum (*i.e.*, no-slip) condition:

$$P = 1.33 \times 10^{-11} wn^2 \left(\frac{D^2 - D_o^2}{2}\right) \quad (18\text{-}107)$$

when D = disk diameter, in., D_o = diameter at which feed is applied to disk, in., n = disk rotation rate, r.p.m., P = power, kw., and w = mass rate of liquid flow, lb./min. [Marshall, *loc. cit.*]. Adler and Marshall [*Chem. Eng. Progress*, **47**, 515, 601 (1951)] found that Eq. (18-107) would fit their power data for vaned-disk atomizers if the coefficient were 1.25×10^{-11}, only a 6 per cent reduction from the theoretical maximum. Smooth disks would be likely to draw less power than this because of the greater likelihood of slip.

The power consumed because of the disk's pumping air cannot be generalized, as it varies with disk design and operating conditions. Some disks can consume appreciable amounts of power in this way, as shown by the data of Adler and Marshall (*loc. cit.*) for dry disks rotating in air (Fig. 18-126). Mechanical losses can be

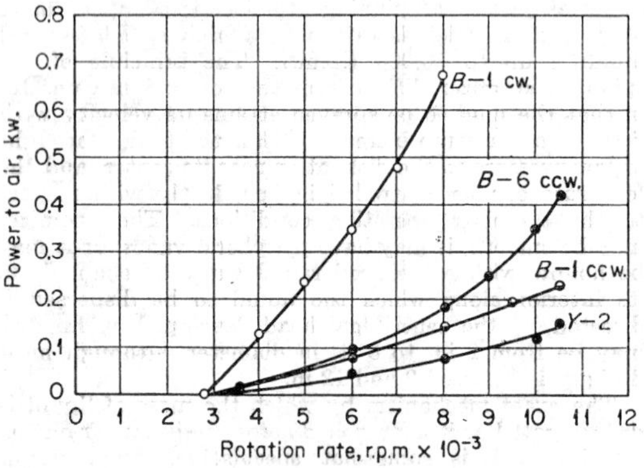

FIG. 18-126. Power consumed by vaned disks pumping air. B—1 cw: 7-in. disk with 60 1-in. vanes 0.406 in. high, clockwise. B—1 ccw: same, counterclockwise. B—6 ccw: 6-in. disk with 30 1.5-in. vanes 1 in. high. Y—2: 5-in. disk with 24 1-in. vanes 0.375 in. high. [*Chem. Eng. Progress Monograph Ser.*, **50** (2), 39 (1954), *with permission.*]

estimated from knowledge of the efficiency of the particular drive used.

Marshall (*loc. cit.*) calculated the spinning-disk speed and corresponding nozzle pressure that will impart the same velocity to an element of liquid leaving each atomizer. Typical values are shown in Table 18-17. For the same final velocity given to streams representing equal mass rates of flow, about the same amount of power should be required by disk and pressure nozzle.

Spinning atomizers are used in some air washers, in small air-moistening units, and in domestic oil burners. They can be adapted to a fuel of fairly high viscosity and they are primarily useful for spraying slurries and liquids containing solid particles which would clog other nozzles. Hence they are widely used in spray drying.

Gas-atomizing Nozzles. Gas-atomizing nozzles, also called pneumatic nozzles or two-fluid atomizers, break up a stream of liquid by contact with a high-velocity stream of gas, usually air or steam. The fluid may be fed under pressure or by a low hydrostatic head, or it may be sucked up by the injector action of the gas stream. Pressure feed, up to 50 or 60 lb./sq. in., is the more common technique in process applications. Perhaps the most familiar example of suction feed is in the well-known therapeutic spray such as is produced by a Collison atomizer (Collison, "Inhalation Therapy Technique," Heinemann, London, 1935. Green and Lane, "Particulate Clouds," p. 39, Van Nostrand, Princeton, N.J., 1957). The contact between the fluid and the gas may take place entirely outside the nozzle or within a chamber from which the spray exits through an orifice. In commercial nozzles the atomization usually takes place just at the point of discharge. The shape of the cloud of spray may be controlled by the shape of the orifice in the internal-mixing types and by additional gas jets in the external type.

Table 18-17. Nozzle Pressures and Disk Speeds Resulting in the Same Liquid Discharge Velocity*

Pressure, lb./sq. in.	Speed, r.p.m., of disk of diameter indicated		
	4 in.	6 in.	12 in.
10	1260	840	420
100	4160	2770	1385
400	9300	6200	3100
1000	13,100	8750	4375
5000	29,200	19,580	9790

* From Marshall, *Chem. Eng. Progress Monograph Ser.*, **50** (2), 40 (1954).

If m lb. of air is used to atomize 1 lb. of liquid in a pneumatic nozzle in which the air expands isothermally from pressure p_1 to pressure p_2, the energy used is

$$E = mRT \ln \left(\frac{p_1}{p_2}\right) \quad (18\text{-}108)$$

where T is the absolute temperature of the expansion. At a fluid ratio of 1 lb. air/lb. water and a pressure ratio of 4, the energy required is 40,600 ft.-lb./lb. of water atomized; at a pressure ratio of 1.5, this becomes 11,850 ft.-lb./lb. of water (Marshall, *loc. cit.*). At a given performance level, a gas-atomizer nozzle may require several-fold the power of a pressure nozzle.

Gas-atomizing nozzles are used when very small drops are desired. They are also capable of spraying more viscous fluids than pressure nozzles. They are commonly used for spray painting, for air and material moistening, for the application of insecticides, and in oil burners. Except for the oil-burner application the discharge rate of gas-atomizing nozzles is small, seldom exceeding 10 gal./hr. Considerably more power is required to spray at a given rate with a gas-atomizing nozzle than with a pressure nozzle.

Humidification. Gas-atomizing nozzles are often used for direct humidification in plants where controlled humidity is required, such as textile and paper mills. A number of atomizers are mounted on the supply pipes, which are attached to the ceiling. The nozzles are arranged to spray horizontally and are adjusted so that the spray will be completely evaporated before reaching the floor or machinery beneath them. Humidifying nozzles spray from 1 to 10 gal./hr. and require from 40 to 100 cu. ft. free air/gal. water. The air pressure is usually about 30 lb./sq. in., and the water may be delivered by suction from a level slightly below the atomizer or under a pressure of from 10 to 30 lb./sq. in.

Drop Size. Pressure nozzles of like capacity give a similar distribution of drop sizes when operated at a given pressure. The hollow-cone nozzles usually yield a somewhat smaller range of drop sizes than the solid-cone nozzles. The central sheet of small fan nozzles is also particularly good in this respect, but the "horns" at the edge of the sheet break up into much larger drops so that the advantage is largely lost. As already noted, the smallest range of drop size at a given pressure and capacity will be formed by an impact nozzle designed to produce a laminar fluid sheet. For applications which require the smallest possible range of drop sizes a large number of small nozzles should be used in preference to a few nozzles of large capacity. If a maximum number of small drops is required, nozzles of the smallest size practicable should be used and operated at the highest possible pressure.

It is frequently convenient to express the size of drops produced by a nozzle in terms of a mean or a median diameter, a single number that will be an index to the size range of the population. If a distribution function is known to be consistent, a mean diameter can be a useful interpretation criterion. However, because of the wide range of drop sizes formed by a spray nozzle, it is difficult to define an average drop size which will be significant for all purposes. It is usually better to have detailed information on the frequency distribution of the drop sizes. A few typical drop-size distributions which illustrate the effect of pressure variations and of the nozzle size are given in Table 18-18. These figures may

Table 18-18. Drop-size Distributions Produced by Three Hollow-cone Nozzles of the Same Design

Nominal drop diam., μ	Number of drops in each size group					
	0.063-in. orifice diam.			0.086-in. orifice diam.		0.128-in. orifice diam.
	50 lb./sq. in.	100 lb./sq. in.	200 lb./sq. in.	100 lb./sq. in.	200 lb./sq. in.	200 lb./sq. in.
10	375	800	1700	100	300	100
25	200	280	580	60	150	50
50	160	180	260	41	100	45
100	50	60	70	26	34	27
150	27	31	35	14	18	15
200	19	23	27	9	12	11
300	8	9	11	5	8	6
400	2	4	4	4	7	3
500	1	1	....	2	1	2
600	1	...	....	1		1

NOTE: 1 $\mu = 10^{-4}$ cm. = 0.0000394 in. The nominal diameter is the mid-diameter of a drop group which includes a finite range of sizes. The "25" group includes drops from 17.5 to 37.5 μ, the "50" group contains drops from 37.5 to 75 μ, etc. The number of drops has been adjusted in each case so that the total amount of fluid sprayed is the same for each size distribution.

be taken as a fair example of the performance of pressure nozzles. If liquids of different physical properties are sprayed, the same size distributions will be obtained but at different pressures.

For the graphical representation of drop-size distribution it is convenient to make use of the Rosin equation:

$$F_d = e^{-bd^n} \qquad (18\text{-}109a)$$

where F_d is the fraction of the mass of the sample contained in drops of diameter greater than d, and b and n are constants. Most size distributions appear to follow this equation, which yields a straight line if log d is plotted against log log $1/F_d$. The slope of the line is a measure of the breadth of the distribution. Normal probability and log probability plots also are often used, as are a number of other distribution functions. There is little or no theoretical justification for selecting one over another, and the simplest and most consistent for a given case should be selected (Marshall, *loc. cit.*).

For a number of applications the total surface area of the spray drops per unit volume of fluid sprayed is a significant factor. For a given nozzle design the exposed surface area in square feet per gallon sprayed is a function of the fluid pressure and the discharge rate. This relationship is illustrated in Fig. 18-127. These curves are based on a relatively small amount of data and for one type of hollow-cone nozzle. Although other standard nozzle types would probably give somewhat different results, the data of Fig. 18-127 may be taken as reasonably typical of the performance of well-designed nozzles.

A number of investigators have correlated the drop-size data obtained with pressure nozzles by an expression

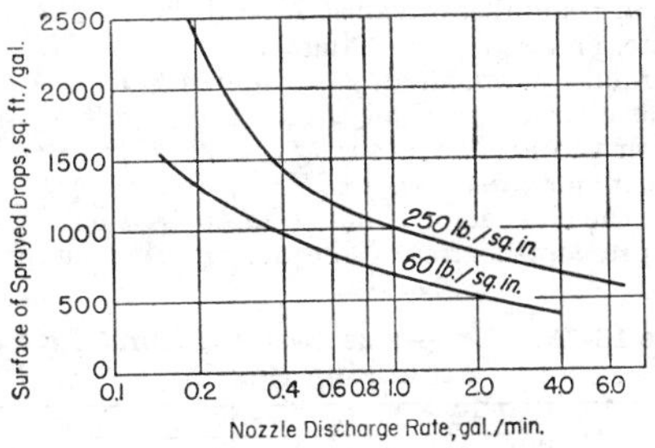

FIG. 18-127. Typical performance of well-designed nozzles.

of the form $D_o \propto \sigma^a \nu^b (FN)^c p^d$ where D_o is the volume-surface (Sauter) mean diameter, FN is the "flow index" $= Q/\sqrt{p}$, p is the pressure drop across the nozzle, Q is the volumetric rate of liquid atomization, ν is the kinematic viscosity, and σ is the surface tension, a, b, c, and d being empirical constants. For example, Knight [*Proc. Inst. Mech. Engrs. (London)*, **169**, 93 (1955)] was able to correlate data for a hollow-cone nozzle with an angle of 85 deg. and with an oil of σ = 24 dynes/cm. for values of FN up to 4 and for pressures up to 200 lb./sq. in. thus:

$$D_o = 220p^{-0.46}Q^{0.21}\nu^{0.22} \qquad (18\text{-}109b)$$

where Q is in lb./hr. and ν in centistokes.

From the standpoint of drop size, the only difference between a rotating nozzle and a pressure nozzle is that in the former the liquid is formed into a thin sheet of suitable velocity by centrifugal force instead of by direct fluid pressure. As a result, the drop-size distribution of a rotating nozzle is quite similar to that of a pressure nozzle. Because there are no small passages in a rotating nozzle, the flow is maintained at much higher viscosities than in a pressure nozzle. The effect of variations in viscosity, density, and surface tension on the drop size has not been investigated, and it is probable that somewhat different laws apply. It is undoubtedly true, however, that high rotational speed, low viscosity, and a small discharge will tend to produce small drops and a minimum range of drop size.

Herring and Marshall [*Am. Inst. Chem. Engrs. J.*, **1**, 200 (1955)] developed an empirical generalized drop-size distribution for vaned-disk atomizers as shown in Fig. 18-128. In the correlation D = disk diameter, b = vane

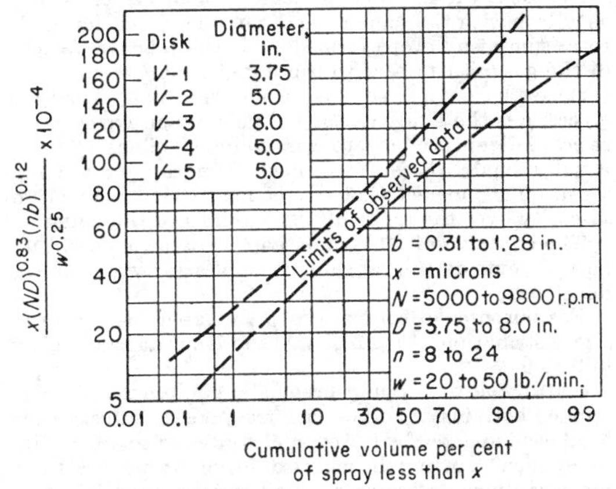

FIG. 18-128. Generalized drop-size distribution for vaned-disk atomizers. [*From Chem. Eng. Progress Monograph Ser.*, **50 (2)**, 69 (1954), *with permission.*]

height, n = number of vanes, N = disk speed, w = mass flow rate, and x = drop diameter.

As ordinarily operated, gas-atomizing nozzles produce much smaller drops than pressure or rotating nozzles. Although the smaller atomizing nozzles tend to give a somewhat narrower range of drop sizes than the larger nozzles, the size factor is not so important as in the case of the pressure nozzles. The determining factor is the relation between the quantities of gas and of liquid. When insufficient gas is used, large drops are formed which are readily visible since they are projected well beyond the cloud of small drops. The quantities of liquid and of gas should always be adjusted so that no such large drops are in evidence. Assuming that proper operation is maintained, the drop size can be controlled by varying the gas pressure, higher pressures yielding smaller drops. The liquid pressure has little effect on the drop size and for the most part only determines the quantity of liquid delivered, which is also a function of the gas pressure. An empirical equation for the mean drop size produced by a gas-atomizing nozzle has been given by Nukiyama and Tanasawa [*Trans. Soc. Mech. Engrs. (Japan)*, **5**, 18, 63 (1939)]. This equation, which is given below, is generally applicable when the liquid density is between 0.7 and 1.2 g./cc., the surface tension is from 19 to 73 dynes/cm., the viscosity is between 0.003 and 0.5 poise, and the gas velocity is subsonic.

Table 18-19. Drop-size Distribution of a Small Atomizing Nozzle

Drop diam., μ	Number of drops	Drop diam., μ	Number of drops
2	390,000	35	1,730
5	340,000	40	1,080
10	165,000	45	650
15	40,200	50	430
20	11,680	60	350
25	4,970	70	220
30	2,160		

NOTE: The fluid pressure and the gas pressure were each 15 lb./sq. in. The total quantity of fluid represented by this size distribution is the same as that in Table 18-21, so that the numbers of drops are directly comparable.

$$D_o = \frac{1920}{v}\sqrt{\frac{\sigma}{\rho}} + 597\left(\frac{\mu}{\sqrt{\sigma\rho}}\right)^{0.45}\left(\frac{1000Q_1}{Q_2}\right)^{1.5} \quad (18\text{-}110)$$

where D_o is the mean drop diameter in microns (defined as a drop with the same ratio of volume to surface as the total sum of all drops formed); v is the relative velocity of the gas with respect to the liquid in ft./sec.; σ is the surface tension in dynes/cm.; ρ is the fluid density in g./cc.; μ is the fluid viscosity in poises; and Q_1/Q_2 is the ratio of liquid volume to gas volume. Since Q_1/Q_2 is usually small, D_o is determined primarily by the first term. This means that D_o is nearly independent of viscosity over the range of applicability of the equation.

The equation of Nukiyama and Tanasawa should not be used outside the range of variables for which it was developed.

For purposes of comparison with Table 18-18 a drop-size distribution of a small air-atomizing nozzle is given in Table 18-19.

Applications. Spray-producing equipment is widely applied both inside and outside the process industries, as has been indicated by the examples cited in the preceding discussion. Among the most extensive extra-process uses for spray nozzles are as washers, coolers, fuel injectors, agricultural atomizers, and paint sprayers.

In chemical process applications, liquid-in-gas dispersions have four places of major importance: (1) spray drying, (2) spray towers for washing and absorption, (3) venturi scrubbers for gas-liquid contacting, (4) liquid distributors for packed beds. Spray dryers and prilling towers can dry or crystallize solutions, slurries, or melts, are particularly adaptable to high-capacity processes, and will handle many heat-sensitive materials without damage (Marshall, *loc. cit.*).

Details of the design and performance of spray dryers and spray absorbers are presented in Sec. 20. Table 18-20 lists and classifies the more common applications for spray nozzles.

Table 18-20. Common Applications for Spray Nozzles

First number:* type most used.
Second number: type frequently used.
Third number: type sometimes used.

Types

1. Solid-cone wide-angle spray.
2. Hollow-cone wide-angle spray.
3. Narrow-angle spray.
4. Pressure atomizing spray.
5. Tangential spray.
6. Flat spray.
7. Deflector or impact spray.
8. Air- or gas-atomizing spray.
9. Rotating-disk spray.

Pressure Nozzles

Cooling circulating water for condenser (5, 1, 6)
Spray-type condensers (1, 4, 3)
Aerating and purifying water supplies (5, 1, 6)
Scrubbing and washing gases (1, 3, 9)
Humidification and dehumidification (4, 8, 3)
Spray refrigeration (5, 1)
Gas absorption and adsorption (1, 3, 5)
Spray drying (4, 8)
Chemical processes where a large free surface is required (1, 4, 8)
Distributing oil over the fuel bed in gas machines (1)
Enriching gas with a liquid distillate (1, 4)
Oil burners (4, 8, 9)
Desuperheaters (4)
Washing or coating materials in process (4, 2, 8)
Washing liquids (1, 4)
Washing automobiles, railway coaches, etc. (6, 3)
Washing coal, sand, gravel, etc. (2, 6)
Beating down foam (1, 3, 6)
Cooling mill rolls (1, 4, 6)
Descaling hot billets (3, 6)
Quenching coke and pig iron (5, 1)
Settling dust (4, 1)
Applying insecticides, weed killers, etc. (1, 7, 8)
Applying asphalt to highways (1, 7, 6)
Fire protection (7)
Ornamental sprays

Rotating Nozzles

Spraying viscous liquids and slurries (7, 9, 8)
Oil burners (4, 8, 9)
Small air moisteners (8)
Spray drying (4, 8)
Air washing (4, 1, 9)

Gas-atomizing Nozzles

Spray painting (8)
Oil burners (4, 8, 9)
Spray drying (4, 8)
Air moistening (8, 4)
Moistening materials with water or other fluids (8, 4)
Spraying small quantities of insecticides, etc. (8, 4)
Metal coating (8)
Applying cements, refractories, etc. (8, 7)

* Classification kindly supplied by S. G. Ketterer.

GAS-IN-LIQUID DISPERSIONS

REFERENCES: Comprehensive treatments of bubbles or foams are given by Haberman and Morton, *Rept.* 802, David W. Taylor Model Basin, Washington, D.C., 1953. Benfratello, *Energia elettrica*, **30**, 80, 486 (1953). Berkman and Egloff, "Emulsions and Foams," pp. 112–152, Reinhold, New York, 1941. Bikerman, "Foams: Theory and Industrial Applications," Reinhold, New York, 1953. The influence of surface-active agents on bubbles and foams is summarized in selected passages from Schwartz and Perry, "Surface Active Agents," vol. I, Interscience, New York, 1949; and from Schwartz, Perry, and Berch, "Surface Active Agents and Detergents," vol. II, Interscience, New York, 1958. A review of foam stability also is given by de Vries, *Mededel. Rubber-Sticht. Delft*, No. 326, 1957. The following reviews of specific applications of gas-in-liquid dispersions are recommended: Industrial fermentations: Finn, *Bacteriol. Rev.*, **18**, 254 (1954). Aerobic oxidation of wastes: McCabe and Eckenfelder, "Biological Treatment of Sewage and Industrial Wastes," vol. I, part 2, Reinhold, New York, 1955. Cellular elastomers: Flint, "Natural Rubber Latex and Its Applications," No. 4, "The Preparation of Latex Foam Products," British Rubber Development Board, London, 1954. Gould, in "Symposium on Application of Synthetic Rubbers," pp. 90–103, American Society for Testing Materials, Philadelphia, 1944. Fire-fighting foams: Perri, in Bikerman, *op. cit.*, Chap. 12. Froth-flotation methods and equipment: Gaudin, "Flotation," 2d ed., McGraw-Hill, New York, 1957. Booth, in Bikerman, *op. cit.*, Chap. 13, and Taggart, "Handbook of Mineral Dressing," Sec. 12, pp. 52–84, Wiley, New York, 1945.

Objectives of Gas Dispersion. The dispersion of gas as bubbles in a liquid or in a plastic mass is effected for one of the following purposes: (1) gas-liquid contacting (to promote absorption or stripping, with or without chemical reaction), (2) agitation of the liquid phase, or (3) foam or froth production. Gas-in-liquid dispersions also may be produced or encountered inadvertently, sometimes undesirably.

Gas-liquid Contacting. Usually this is accomplished with conventional columns or with spray absorbers (see preceding portion, Sec. 18). For systems containing solids or tar likely to plug columns, for absorptions accompanied by strongly exothermic reactions, or for treatments involving a readily soluble gas or a condensable vapor, however, gas dispersers may be used to advantage.

Agitation. Agitation by a stream of gas bubbles (usually air) rising through a liquid is employed in tanks of such large volume or of such unsymmetrical shape as to make mechanical agitation ineffective or expensive. Gas spargers may replace mechanical agitators also for simple blending operations involving a liquid of low volatility or for applications in which it is difficult to seal around an agitator shaft.

Foam Production. This is important in froth-flotation separations, in the manufacture of cellular elastomers, plastics, and glass, and in certain special applications (*e.g.*, food products, fire extinguishers). Unwanted foam can occur in process columns, in agitated vessels, and in reactors in which a gaseous product is formed; it must be avoided, destroyed, or controlled. Berkman and Egloff ("Emulsions and Foams," pp. 112–152, Reinhold, New York, 1941) have pointed out that foam is produced only in systems possessing the proper combination of interfacial tension, viscosity, volatility, and concentration of solute or suspended solids. From the standpoint of gas comminution, foam production requires the creation of small bubbles in a liquid capable of sustaining foam.

Theory of Bubble and Foam Formation. A **bubble** is a globule of gas or vapor surrounded by a mass or thin film of liquid. By extension, globular voids in a solid are sometimes called bubbles. *Foam* is a group of bubbles separated from one another by thin films, the aggregation having a finite static life. Although non-technical dictionaries do not distinguish between foam and froth, a technical distinction is often made. A highly concentrated dispersion of bubbles in a liquid is considered a *froth*, even if its static life is substantially nil (*i.e.*, it must be dynamically maintained); thus all foams are also froth, whereas the reverse is not true. The term *lather* implies a froth that is worked up on a solid surface by mechanical agitation; it is seldom used in technical discussions. The thin walls of bubbles comprising a foam are called *laminae* or *lamellae*.

Bubbles in a liquid originate from one of three general sources: (1) they may be formed by desupersaturation of a solution of the gas or by the decomposition of a component in the liquid; (2) they may be introduced directly into the liquid by a bubbler or sparger, or by mechanical entrainment; (3) they may result from the disintegration of larger bubbles already in the liquid.

Generation. Spontaneous generation of bubbles of gas or vapor from a homogeneous liquid is theoretically impossible (Bikerman, "Foams: Theory and Industrial Applications," p. 10, Reinhold, New York, 1953). The appearance of a bubble requires a gas nucleus as a void in the liquid. The nucleus may be in the form of a small bubble or of a solid carrying adsorbed gas, examples of the latter being dust particles, boiling chips, and a solid wall. A void can result from cavitation, mechanically or acoustically induced.

Theory permits the approximation of the maximum size of a bubble that can adhere to a submerged horizontal surface, if the contact angle between bubble and solid (angle formed by solid-liquid and liquid-gas interfaces) is known [Wark, *J. Phys. Chem.*, **37**, 623 (1933). Jakob, *Mech. Eng.*, **58**, 643 (1936)]. Inasmuch as the bubbles that actually rise from a surface are always considerably smaller than those so calculated and inasmuch as the contact angle is seldom known, the theory is not directly useful.

Formation at a Single Orifice. The formation of bubbles at an orifice or capillary immersed in a liquid has been the subject of much study, experimental and theoretical (Bikerman, *op. cit.*, Secs. 3–7). There are three regimes of bubble production (Silberman, in "Proceedings of the Fifth Midwestern Conference on Fluid Mechanics," pp. 263–284, University of Michigan Press, Ann Arbor, 1957): (1) single-bubble, (2) intermediate, and (3) jet.

Single-bubble Regime. Bubbles are produced one at a time, their size being determined by the orifice diameter D, the interfacial tension of the gas-liquid film σ, the densities of the liquid ρ_L and gas ρ_G, and the gravitational acceleration g according to the relation

$$D_B^3 = \frac{6D\sigma}{g(\rho_L - \rho_G)} \cong \frac{6D\sigma}{g\rho_L} \qquad (18\text{-}111)$$

where D_B is the bubble diameter. The bubble size is independent of gas-flow rate; the frequency, therefore, is directly proportional to the rate. Equation (18-111) leads to

$$f = \frac{Qg(\rho_L - \rho_G)}{\pi D\sigma} \qquad (18\text{-}112)$$

where f is the frequency of bubble formation and Q is the volumetric rate of gas flow, in consistent units.

Equations (18-111) and (18-112) result from a balance of bubble buoyancy against interfacial tension. They recognize no inertia or viscosity effects. At low bubbling rates, they are quite satisfactory. Van Krevelen and Hoftijzer [*Chem. Eng. Progress*, **46**, 29 (1950)] and Guyer and Peterhaus [*Helv. Chim. Acta*, **26**, 1099 (1943)], for example, reported air-bubble diameters 0.84 to 1.02 times those calculated from Eq. (18-111), when the bubbles were formed at a frequency in the range 0.3 to 1.0 per sec. in water, transformer oil, ether, and carbon tetrachloride. Orifice diameters ranged from 0.004 to 0.95 cm., and the orifices discharged vertically upward.

In the single-bubble regime, the relationship between the size of the orifice and the size of the bubble produced is not simple, depending on the properties of the system. If Eq. (18-111) is expressed in metric units, when $D_B > 0.078\sqrt{\sigma/(\rho_L - \rho_G)}$ the bubble diameter is smaller than the orifice diameter, implying an unstable condition at the orifice. Conversely, when $D_B < 0.078\sqrt{\sigma/(\rho_L - \rho_G)}$, the bubble diameter exceeds the orifice diameter. For the case of bubbles being formed in water, the orifice diameter which permits bubbles of about its own size is calculated as 0.66 cm., or about 0.25 in. Davidson and Amick [*Am. Inst. Chem. Engrs. J.*, **2,** 337 (1956)] confirmed this estimate in their observation that stable bubbles in water were formed at a 0.64-cm. orifice but could not be formed at a 0.79-cm. one.

Intermediate Regime. As the gas rate through a submerged orifice increases beyond the limit of the single-bubble regime, the frequency of bubble formation increases more slowly and the bubbles begin to grow in size. Between the two regimes there may indeed be a range of gas rates over which the bubble size decreases with increasing rate, owing to the establishment of liquid currents that nip the bubbles off prematurely. The net result can be the occurrence of a minimum bubble diameter at some particular gas rate (Maier, *U.S. Bur. Mines Bull.* **260,** 1927. Bikerman, *op. cit.*, p. 4).

At the upper portion of this region, the frequency becomes very nearly constant with respect to gas rate, and the bubble size correspondingly increases with gas rate. In the range of gas velocities that represent Reynolds numbers at the orifice below 2000, Leibson and coworkers [*Am. Inst. Chem. Engrs. J.*, **2,** 296 (1956)] have shown from their data and those of Davidson and Amick (*loc. cit.*) that the bubble diameter may be approximated as

$$D_B = 0.18D^{0.5}N_{Re}{}^{0.33} \qquad (18\text{-}113)$$

The range of orifice diameters covered was 0.04 to 0.40 in.

Eversole, Wagner, and Stackhouse [*Ind. Eng. Chem.*, **33,** 1459 (1941)], who found a near constancy of bubbling frequency for a range of conditions, reported that at a frequency of 40 to 50 per sec. bubbles of approximately constant diameter (0.23 cm.) were produced by capillaries in the range 0.014 to 0.034 cm. in diameter. The observation of independence of bubble diameter with respect to orifice diameter has been made by many others.

The role of the volume of the orifice chamber and lines between control valve and orifice has been examined by Hughes and coworkers [*Chem. Eng. Progress*, **51,** 557 (1955)], who pointed out that above a critical value (0.2 to 0.8) for the capacitance number N_c, bubble size depends on chamber volume V_b. The capacitance number is defined thus

$$N_c = \frac{4gV_b(\rho_L - \rho_G)}{\pi D^2 \rho_G c^2} \qquad (18\text{-}114)$$

where c is the velocity of sound in the gas and where any consistent set of units may be used. In careful experimental work it is important that the chamber effect be defined or eliminated and that it be considered in the application of results to a scaled-up design, in which V_b may be large—for example, in a sieve tray (Brown, *U.S. Atomic Energy Comm. Rept.* UCRL-8558, 1959).

Theory is not well enough developed to elucidate fully the intermediate regime. The effect of the liquid and gas properties is not well defined either by theory or by experiment. Siemes and Kauffman [*Chem. Eng. Sci.*, **5,** 127 (1956)] found viscosity of considerable importance to the size and frequency of bubbles. The location and surroundings of the orifice are manifestly significant—thick-wall capillaries produce larger bubbles than thin ones, according to Siemes and Kauffman—but without precise definition.

Jet Regime. With further rate increases, turbulence at the orifice sets in, and the gas stream approaches the appearance of a continuous jet which breaks up 3 to 4 in. above the orifice. As a matter of fact, the stream consists of large, closely spaced, irregular bubbles with a rapid swirling motion. These bubbles disintegrate into a cloud of smaller ones of random size distribution between 0.01 in. (or smaller) and about 0.5 in. (Leibson *et al., loc. cit.*). There are many contradictory reports about this regime, and theory, although helpful (see, for example, Silberman, *loc. cit.*), is as yet unable to describe the phenomena observed.

Formation at Multiple Orifices. At high velocities coalescence of bubbles formed at individual orifices occurs; Helsby and Tuson [*Research (London)*, **8,** 270 (1955)], for example, observed the frequent coalescence of bubbles formed in pairs or in quartets at an orifice. Multiple orifices spaced by the order of magnitude of the orifice diameter increase the probability of coalescence, and when the magnitude is small (as in a sintered plate) there is invariably some. The broken lines of Fig. 18-132, p. 18-74, presumably represent zones of increased coalescence and relatively less effective dispersion as the gas rate through porous carbon tubes is increased.

Savitskaya [*Kolloid. Zhur.*, **13,** 309 (1951)] found that the average bubble size formed at the surface of a porous plate was such as to maintain constancy of the product of bubble specific surface and interfacial tension as the latter was varied by addition of a surfactant.

Entrainment and Mechanical Disintegration. Gas can be entrained into a liquid by a solid or a stream of liquid falling from the gas phase into the liquid, by surface ripples or waves, and by the vertical swirl of a mass of agitated liquid about the axis of a rotating agitator. Small bubbles probably form near the surface of the liquid and are caught into the path of turbulent eddies whose velocity exceeds the terminal velocity of the bubbles. The mechanism of entrainment is not well understood, however, and no confident calculations can be made about it (Birkhoff and Zarantonello, "Jets, Wakes, and Cavities," p. 327, Academic Press, New York, 1957).

The disintegration of a submerged mass of gas takes place by the turbulent tearing of smaller bubbles away from the exterior of the larger mass or by the influence of surface tension on the mass where it is attenuated by inertial or shear forces into a cylindrical or disk form. A fluid cylinder that is greater in length than in circumference is unstable and tends to break spontaneously into two or more spheres. These effects account for the action of fluid attrition and of an agitator in the disintegration of suspended gas, but they are not practically calculable.

Foam. A foam is formed when bubbles rise to the surface of a liquid and persist for awhile without coalescence with one another or without rupture into the vapor space. The formation of foam, then, consists simply of the formation, rise, and aggregation of bubbles in a liquid in which foam can exist.

The life of foams varies over many magnitudes—from seconds to years—but in general is finite. Maintenance of a foam, therefore, is a dynamic phenomenon.

Gravitational force favors the separation of gas from liquid in a disperse system, causing the bubbles to rise to the liquid surface and the liquid contained in the bubble walls to drain downward to the main body of the liquid. Interfacial tension favors the coalescence and ultimate disappearance of bubbles; indeed, it is the cause of bubble destruction upon the rupture of the lamina.

The viscosity of the liquid in a film opposes the drainage of the film and its displacement by the approach of coalescing bubbles. The higher the viscosity, the slower will be the film-thinning process; furthermore, if viscosity increases as the film grows thinner, the process becomes self-retarding. The viscosity of films appears to be greater than that of the main body of the parent liquid in many cases. Sometimes this is a simple temperature effect, the film being cooler because of evaporation; sometimes it is a concentration effect, dissolved or fine suspended solids migrating to the interface to produce classical or anomalous increases in viscosity; at yet other times, the effect seems to occur without explanation.

If the liquid laminae of a foam system can be converted to impermeable solid membranes, the film viscosity can be regarded as having become infinite and the resulting "solid foam" will be permanent. Likewise, if the laminae are composed of a Bingham plastic or a thixotrope, the foam will be permanently stable for bubbles whose buoyancy does not permit exceeding the yield stress. For other non-Newtonian fluids, however, and for all Newtonian ones, no matter how viscous, the viscosity can only delay but never prevent foam disappearance. The popular theory, held since the days of Plateau, that foam life is proportional to surface viscosity and inversely proportional to interfacial tension, is not correct, according to Bikerman (*op. cit.*, p. 161), who points out that it is contradicted by experiment.

Bikerman also rejects the idea that foam films drain to a critical thickness at which they spontaneously burst. Foam stability rather is keyed to the existence of a surface skin of low interfacial tension immediately overlying a solution bulk of higher tension, latent until it is exposed by rupture of the superficial layer [Maragoni, *Nuovo cimento*, No. 2, **5-6**, 239 (1871)]. Such a phenomenon of surface elasticity, resulting from concentration differences between bulk and surface of the liquid, accounts for the ability of bubbles to be penetrated by missiles without damage. With reference to it, it is conceivable that films below a certain thickness no longer carry any bulk of solution and hence have no capacity to "heal" surface ruptures, thus becoming vulnerable to mechanical damage that will destroy them. The Maragoni phenomenon is consistent also with the observation that neither pure liquids nor saturated solutions will sustain a foam, since neither extreme will allow the necessary difference in concentration between surface and bulk of solution.

The specific ability of certain finely divided, insoluble solids to stabilize foam has long been known (Berkman and Egloff, *op. cit.*, p. 133. Bikerman, *op. cit.*, Chap. 11). Bartsch [*Kolloidchem. Beih.*, **20**, 1 (1925)] found that the presence of fine galena greatly extended the life of air foam in aqueous isoamyl alcohol, and the finer the solids the greater stability. Particles on the order of 50 μ lengthened the life from 17 sec. to several hours. This behavior is consistent with theory, which indicates that a solid particle of medium contact angle with the liquid will prevent the coalescence of two bubbles with which it is in simultaneous contact. Quantitative observations of this phenomenon are scanty.

Berkman and Egloff explain that some additives increase the flexibility or toughness of bubble walls, rather than their viscosity, to render them more durable. They cite as illustrations the addition of small quantities of soap to saponin solutions, or of glycerin to soap solution to yield much more stable foam.

Characteristics of Dispersion. *Properties of Component Phases.* As discussed in the preceding section, dispersions of gases in liquids are affected by the viscosity of the liquid, the density of the liquid and of the gas, and the interfacial tension between the two phases. They also may be affected directly by the composition of the liquid phase. Both the formation of bubbles and their behavior during their lifetime are influenced by these quantities as well as by the mechanical aspects of their environment

Viscosity and density of the component phases can be measured with confidence by conventional methods, as can the interfacial tension between a pure liquid and a gas. The interfacial tension of a system involving a solution or micellar dispersion becomes less satisfactory, inasmuch as the interfacial free energy depends on the concentration of solute at the interface. Dynamic methods and even some of the so-called static methods involve the creation of new surface. Since the establishment of equilibrium between this surface and the solute in the body of the solution requires a finite amount of time, the value measured will be in error if the measurement is made more rapidly than the solute can diffuse to the fresh surface. Eckenfelder and Barnhart (A.I.Ch.E. 42d National Meeting, *Reprint* 30, Atlanta, Ga., 1960) found that measurements of the surface tension of sodium lauryl sulfate solutions by maximum bubble pressure were higher than those by DuNuoy tensiometer by 40 to 90 per cent, the larger factor corresponding to a concentration of about 100 p.p.m. and the smaller to a concentration of 2500 p.p.m. of sulfate.

Even if the interfacial tension is measured accurately, there may be doubt about its applicability to the surface of bubbles being rapidly formed in a solution of a surface-active agent, for the bubble surface may not have time to become equilibrated with the solution. Coppock and Meiklejohn [*Trans. Inst. Chem. Engrs.* (*London*), **29**, 75 (1951)] reported that bubbles formed in single-bubble regime at an orifice in a solution of a commercial detergent had a diameter larger than that calculated in terms of the measured surface tension of the solution [Eq. (18-111)]. The disparity probably is a reflection of unequilibrated bubble laminae.

One concerned with the measurement of gas-liquid interfacial tension should consult the useful reviews of methods prepared by Harkins (in Weissberger, "Techniques of Organic Chemistry," vol. I, part II, 2d ed., Chap. 9, Interscience, New York, 1949) and by Schwartz and coauthors ("Surface Active Agents," vol. I, pp. 263-271, Interscience, New York, 1949; "Surface Active Agents and Detergents," vol. II, pp. 389-391, 417-418, Interscience, New York, 1958).

Dispersion Characteristics. The chief characteristics of gas-in-liquid dispersions, like those of liquid-in-gas suspensions, are the heterogeneity and the instability.

Heterogeneity. The composition and structure of an unstable dispersion must be observed in the dynamic situation by looking at the mixture, with or without the aid of optical devices, or by photographing it, preferably in nominal steady state; photographs usually are required for quantitative treatment. Stable foams may be examined after the fact of their creation if they are sufficiently robust or if an immobilizing technique such as freezing is employed [Chang, Schoen, and Grove, *Ind. Eng. Chem.*, **48**, 2035 (1956)].

The rate of rise of bubbles has been discussed in many papers, including two that present good reviews of the subject [Benfratello, *Energia elettrica*, **30**, 80 (1953). Haberman and Morton, *Rept.* 802, David W. Taylor Model Basin, Washington, D.C., September, 1953]. Small bubbles (below 0.2 mm. in diameter) are essentially rigid spheres and rise through water at terminal velocities that place them clearly in the laminar-flow region; hence their rising velocity may be calculated from Stokes's law. As bubble size increases to about 2 mm., the spherical shape is retained, and the Reynolds number is still sufficiently small (<400) that Stokes's law should be nearly obeyed.

Two effects set in, however, that alter the velocity. At about $N_{Re} = 100$, a wobble begins that can develop into a helical path if the bubbles are not liberated too close to one another [Houghton, McLean, and Ritchie,

Chem. Eng. Sci., **7**, 40 (1957). Hougton, Ritchie, and Thomson, *ibid.*, p. 111]. Furthermore, for bubbles in the range 1 mm. and larger (until distortion becomes serious), internal circulation can set in, causing a considerably increased rising velocity. [Garner and Hammerton, *Chem. Eng. Sci.*, **3**, 1 (1954). Haberman and Morton, *loc. cit.*]. The presence of a surface-active material, even in extremely small concentration, can retard or stop this internal circulation. In this behavior may lie the explanation of the fact that the addition of long-chain fatty acids to water to produce a concentration of 1.5×10^{-4} molar markedly reduces the rate of rise of bubbles [Stuke, *Naturwissenschaften*, **39**, 325 (1952)].

Above about 2 mm., bubbles begin to change to ellipsoids, and above 1 cm. they become lens-shaped, according to Davies and Taylor [*Proc. Roy. Soc. (London)*, **A200**, 379 (1950)]. The rising velocity in water for the size range 1 mm. $< D_B <$ 20 mm. has been reported as 20 to 30 cm./sec. (Birkhoff and Zarantonello, *op. cit.*, p. 328.) Above a Reynolds number of the order of magnitude of 1000, the bubbles assume a helmet shape, with a flat bottom (Eckenfelder and Barnhart, *loc. cit.*; Leibson *et al.*, *loc. cit.*). After bubbles become large enough to depart from Stokes's law at their terminal velocity, behavior is generally complicated and erratic, and the data reported scatter considerably. The rise can be slowed, furthermore, by a wall effect if the diameter of the container is not greater than 10 times the diameter of the bubbles, as shown by Uno and Kintner [*Am. Inst. Chem. Engrs. J.*, **2**, 420 (1956)].

When bubbles are produced in clouds, as by a porous disperser, their behavior during rising is further complicated by interaction among themselves. In addition to the tendency for small bubbles to coalesce and large ones to disintegrate, there are two additional opposing influences on the rate of rise of bubbles of any particular size: (1) a "chimney" effect can develop in which a massive current upward appears at the axis of the bubble stream, leading to increased net bubble velocity; (2) the proximity of the bubbles to one another can result in a hindered-settling condition, leading to reduced average bubble velocity. Figure 18-129 shows the data of Houghton, McLean, and Ritchie (*loc. cit.*) for clouds of

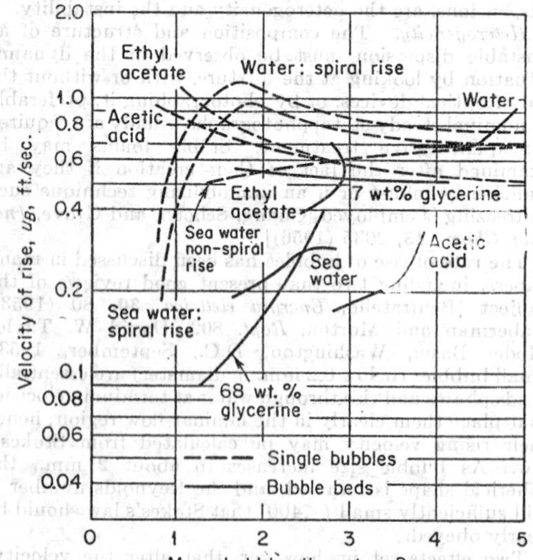

FIG. 18-129. Velocity of rise bubbles, singly and in clouds. [*From Chem. Eng. Sci.*, **7**, 48 (1957), *by permission.*]

bubbles compared with the single-bubble data of Houghton, Ritchie, and Thomson (*loc. cit.*) for pure water and sea water, and of Peebles and Garber [*Chem. Eng. Progress* **49**, 88 (1953)] for acetic acid and ethyl acetate. The bubble clouds were produced with a sintered-glass plate of mean pore size (inferred from air wet-permeability data) 81 μ, and they resulted in expansion of the liquid column as indicated by the dynamic bed densities reported in Table 18-21. The difference between the curves for pure water and sea water again illustrates the significance of small concentrations of solute with respect to bubble behavior.

Table 18-21. Bulk Density of Aerated Liquids*

Bubbles produced by a sintered-glass plate with a mean pore size of 81μ.

Superficial velocity of gas, cu. ft./(sq. ft.)(sec.)	Bulk density of bed, g./ml.					
	Water	Sea water	8% glycerin†	68% glycerin†	Acetic acid	Ethyl acetate†
0	1.00	1.00	1.02	1.18	1.05	0.90
0.10	0.85	0.65	0.80	0.42	0.58	0.71
0.15	0.83	0.50	0.70	0.39	0.50	0.65
0.20	0.83	0.43	0.66	0.59	0.55	0.63
0.30	0.83	0.57	0.70	0.74	0.55	0.64
0.40	0.83	0.64	0.70	....	0.55	
0.50	....	0.65	0.70	....	0.55	

* From Houghton *et al.*, *Chem. Eng. Sci.*, **7**, 40 (1957).
† Measured with a larger-pore (114-μ) plate. Density is probably lower than would have resulted from 81-μ plate.

The quantitative examination of bubble systems is aided by the use of proper illumination and photography. The formation of bubbles at single sources often is sufficiently periodic to be "stopped" by stroboscopic light. Clouds of rising bubbles are more difficult to assess and require careful technique. Satisfactory photographic methods have been developed by Vermeulen, Williams, and Langlois [*Chem. Eng. Progress*, **51**, 85 (1955)] and by Calderbank [*Trans. Inst. Chem. Engrs.*, **36**, 443 (1958)] and are described by these authors. Calderbank's technique resulted in particularly precise measurements that permitted a good estimation of the surface area of the dispersed bubbles.

Stability of Dispersions. The stability of non-foaming dispersions does not exist in even a quasi-static sense, and it can be described only in terms of the rate of separation of the phases relative to the rate of their dispersion.

Foam stability is gaged by two different observations, the persistence of the foam and the rate of drainage from the foam. Both are called by such names as "foam capacity" and "foaming power," but Bikerman emphasizes that they measure quantities that are different and generally independent. Bikerman has summarized the methods for both (*op. cit.*, Chaps. 2 and 4).

The persistence of foam may be inferred from measurement of the life of a single film (*e.g.*, on a loop), from the life of a single bubble (*e.g.*, floating on the surface of a liquid), or from observation of a three-dimensional foam. The last is the most usual. The life of the foam is described by (1) the rate of collapse (rather than the rate of drainage) of a static specimen, (2) the rate of increase of foam height during its formation, or (3) the steady-state height achieved by the foam under a particular condition of generation.

Foam drainage is determined by allowing a foam produced by blowing or agitation to stand and by observing the amount of liquid that collects below the foam as a function of time. There are two serious limitations to foam-drainage measurements: they cannot be used with short-lived foams (a minimum order of lifetime of 1 min. is necessary); they cannot discriminate between liquid drained from foam laminae and liquid yielded by the rupturing of laminae. Like foam-persistence indices, drainage indices depend upon the method and apparatus of their measurement.

Other Characteristics of Foams. The ability of a bubble wall to reflect interference patterns makes it possible to determine its thickness by use of monochromatic or white light (Bikerman, *op. cit.*, Chap. 6). The intensity of light transmitted through a foam mass can be used as an indication of mean bubble or cell size and of the number of cells present [Clark and Blackman, *Trans. Faraday Soc.*, **44**, 7 (1948)].

Foam density can be inferred also from comparison of the electrical conductivity of the foam with that of the parent liquid. Clark [*Trans. Faraday Soc.*, **44**, 13 (1948)] reported that the density ratio for solution/foam plotted against the conductivity ratio for solution/foam yielded one line applicable to data for five solutions of different materials whose conductivity covered a fourfold range.

Methods of Gas Dispersion. In general, the problem of dispersing gas in a liquid may be attacked in two ways: (1) the gas is introduced into the liquid initially in the form of bubbles of the desired size, or smaller bubbles that grow to the desired size; (2) a massive bubble or stream of gas is disintegrated within the liquid.

Spargers. Simple Bubblers. The simplest method of dispersing gas in a liquid contained in a tank is to introduce the gas through an open-end standpipe, a horizontal perforated pipe, or a perforated plate at the bottom of the tank. At ordinary gassing rates (corresponding to the jet regime) relatively large bubbles will be produced regardless of the size of the orifices.

Perforated-pipe or -plate spargers usually have orifices ⅛ to ½ in. in diameter. A perforated-pipe sparger should be so designed that the pressure drop across the individual orifices is large compared with the pressure drop down the length of the pipe; otherwise, the orifices most remote from the gas supply may not function.

Simple spargers are used as agitators for large tanks, principally in the cement and oil industries. Kauffman [*Chem. & Met. Eng.*, **37**, 178–180 (1930)] reported the following air rates for various degrees of agitation in a tank containing 9 ft. of liquid:

Degree of Agitation	Air Rate, Cu. Ft./(Sq. Ft. Tank Cross Section)(Min.)
Moderate	0.65
Complete	1.3
Violent	3.1

For a liquid depth of 3 ft. he recommended that the above rates be doubled.

An air lift consisting of a sparger jetting into a draft tube with ports discharging at several heights has been recommended by Heiser [*Chem. Eng.*, **55**, (1), 135 (1948)] for maintaining agitation in a heavy, coarse slurry the level of which varies widely. The design is illustrated in Fig. 18-130.

The ability of a sparger to blend miscible liquids might be described in terms of a fictitious diffusivity. Siemes did so, reporting that the agitation produced by a stream of bubbles rising in a tube with a superficial velocity of about 0.27 ft./sec. corresponded to an apparent diffusion coefficient as large as 75 sq. cm./sec. [*Chem.-Ing.-Tech.*, **29**, 727 (1957)]. The blending rate thus is several orders of magnitude higher than it would be by natural diffusive action.

According to Glinkov [*Compt. rend. acad. sci U.R.S.S.*, **51** (2), 99 (1946)], the turbulence induced by bubbles liberated beneath a liquid may be characterized by a dimensionless index *G*, which is the product of the Reynolds and Froude numbers (based on bubble diameter and velocity of bubble ascent) and the group $\rho_G Q/\rho S u_B$, where Q is the volumetric rate of gas liberation, cu. m./sec.; S is a cross section of the liquid perpendicular to the direction of bubble rise, sq. m.; u_B is the velocity of bubble rise, m./sec.; and ρ and ρ_G are the densities of the gas-free liquid and of the gas, respectively, kg./cu. m. Glinkov correlated the data from "boiling" slag baths of commercial size as a plot of the inverse Prandtl number against *G*.

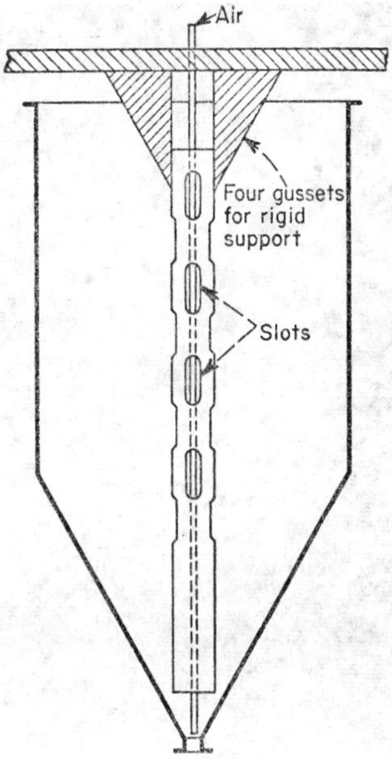

FIG. 18-130. Slotted air lift for agitation of variable-level charge. [*From Chem. Eng.*, **55** (1), 135 (1948), *by permission.*]

Open-end pipes or perforated plates sometimes are used without mechanical agitation to promote mass transfer, as in chlorinators. Apparently much of the mass transfer takes place during the creation of the new bubble surface. Guyer and Pfister [*Helv. Chim. Acta*, **29**, 1173 (1946)], investigating the absorption of carbon dioxide from single bubbles, reported that as much absorption took place during bubble formation and detachment as during a 0.33-ft. rise; Scouller and Watson (*Inst. Sewage Purif. J. Proc.*, 1934, part 1) reported about the same effect for the bursting of a bubble. In cases of easy absorption or low demand of solute gas, simple spargers produce an adequate dispersion; for most reactor-absorbers, however, they are inadequate. Cooper, Fernstrom, and Miller [*Ind. Eng. Chem.*, **36**, 504 (1944)] found that less than 1 per cent of the oxygen was absorbed from air bubbled at 0.54 cu. ft./min. from a ¼-in. tube through 9.5 in. of aqueous sodium sulfate, whereas 42 per cent was absorbed when the solution was agitated vigorously. For a perforated-plate sparger, Calderbank [*Trans. Inst. Chem. Engrs.*, **37**, 173 (1959)] observed that the interfacial area increased almost linearly with gas rate until a specific surface of 8 sq. ft./cu. ft. was reached. Above this level further increase in gas rate brought no further increase in specific surface.

Sieve trays may be viewed as special adaptations of perforated-plate spargers. Design details of sieve trays are found elsewhere in this section.

Porous Septa. Porous plates, tubes, disks, or other shapes are made by bonding or sintering together carefully sized particles of carbon, ceramic, polymer, or

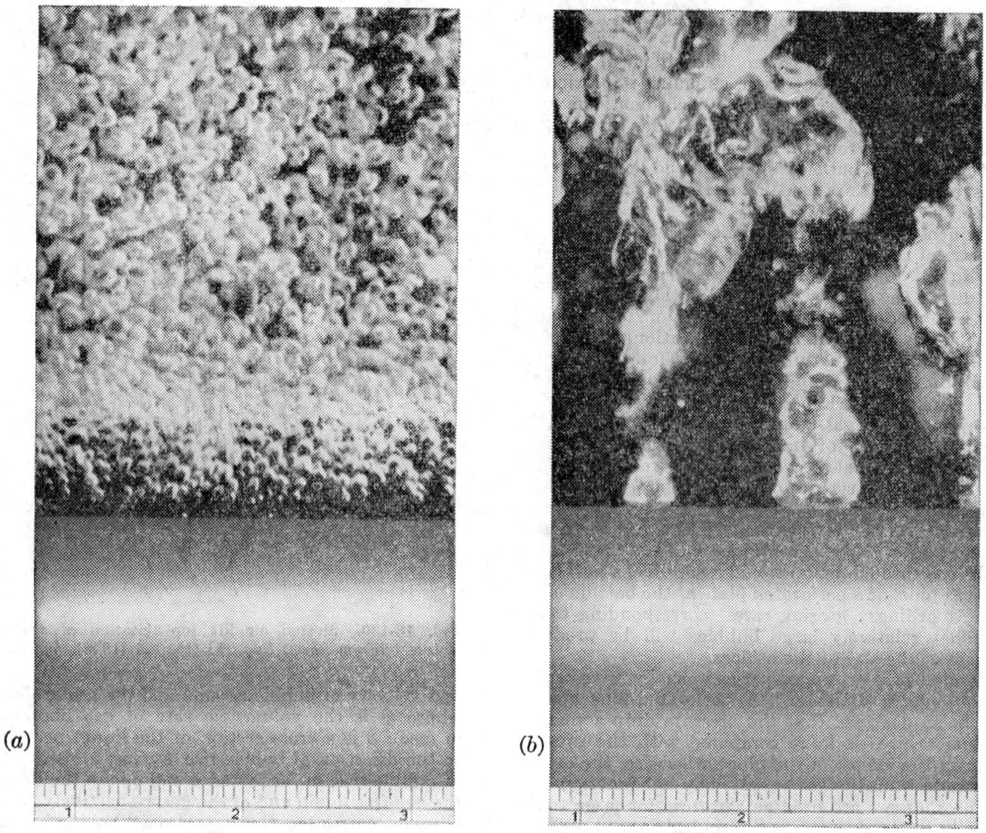

FIG. 18-131. Comparison of bubbles from porous septum and from a perforated-pipe sparger. Air in water at 70°F. (*a*) Grade 25 porous carbon diffuser operating under a pressure differential of 13.7 in. of water. (*b*) Karbate pipe perforated with 1/16-in. holes on 1-in. centers. (*National Carbon Co.*)

metal. The resulting septa may be used as spargers to produce much smaller bubbles than will result from a simple bubbler. Figure 18-131 shows a comparison of the bubbles emitted by a perforated-pipe sparger (0.062-in. orifices) and a porous carbon septum (120-μ pores). The gas flux through a porous septum is limited on the lower side by the requirement that for good performance the whole sparger surface should bubble more or less uniformly, and on the higher side by the onset of serious coalescence at the surface of the septum, resulting in poor dispersion. In the practical range of fluxes, the size of the bubbles produced depends on both the size of pores in the septum and the pressure drop imposed across it, being a direct function of both.

Table 18-22 lists typical grades of porous carbon, silica, alumina, stainless steel (type 316), and polymer commercially available. Porous media are manufactured also from porcelain, glass, silicon carbide, and a number of metals: monel, inconel, nickel, bronze, Hastelloy C, Stellite L-605, gold, platinum, and many types of stainless steel. The air permeabilities of Table 18-22 indicate the relative flow resistances of the various grades to homogeneous fluid but may not be used in designing a disperser for submerged operation, for the resistance of a septum to the flow of gas increases when it is wet. The air permeabilities for water-submerged porous carbon of some of the grades listed in the table are shown in Fig. 18-132. The data were determined with septa 0.625 in. thick in water at 70°F. Comparable wet-permeability data for 1-in. Alundum plates of two grades of fineness are given in Table 18-23. In the design use of Fig. 18-132 and Table 18-23, the hydrostatic head at the sparger must be added to the pressure drop estimated from the table or figure.

The gas rate at which coalescence begins to reduce the effectiveness of dispersion appears to depend not only on

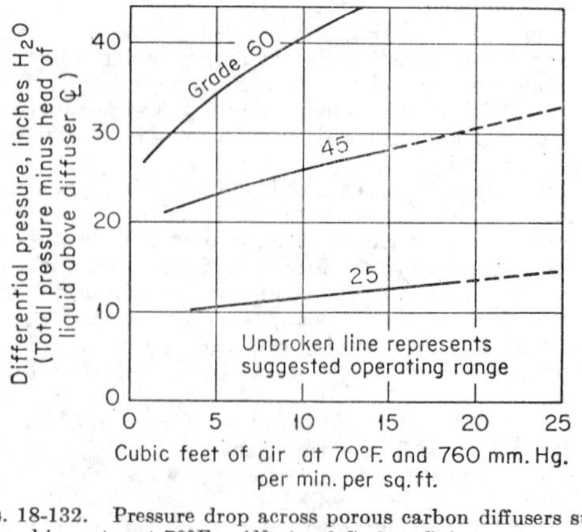

FIG. 18-132. Pressure drop across porous carbon diffusers submerged in water at 70°F. (*National Carbon Co.*)

Table 18-22. Characteristics of Porous Septa

Grade	Avg. % porosity	Avg. pore diam.	Air-permeablity data: Diaphragm thickness, in.	Pressure differential, in. water	Air flow, cu. ft./(sq. ft.)(min.)
Alundum porous alumina*					
P2220	....	25	1	2	0.35
P2120	36	60	1	2	2
P260	35	164	1	2	15
P236	34	240	1	2	40
P216	....	720	1	2	110
National porous carbon†					
60	48	33	1	2	
45	48	58	1	2	2
25	48	120	1	2	13
Filtros porous silica‡					
Extra fine	26.0	55	1.5	2	1–3
Fine	28.8	110	1.5	2	4–8
Medium fine	31.1	130	1.5	2	9–12
Medium	33.7	150	1.5	2	13–20
Medium coarse	33.8	200	1.5	2	21–30
Coarse	34.5	250	1.5	2	31–59
Extra coarse	36.5	300	1.5	2	60–100
Porous plastic§					
Teflon	....	9	0.125	1.38	5
Kel-F	....	15	0.125	1.38	13
Micro Metallic porous stainless steel§,¶					
H	45	5	0.125	1.38	1.8
G	50	10	0.125	1.38	3
F	50	20	0.125	1.38	5
E	50	35	0.125	1.38	18
D	50	65	0.125	1.38	60
C	55	165	0.125	27.7	990

* Data by courtesy of Norton Co., Worcester, Mass. A number of other grades between the extremes listed are available.
† Data by courtesy of National Carbon Co., Cleveland, Ohio.
‡ Data by courtesy of Filtros Inc., East Rochester, N.Y.
§ Data by courtesy of Pall Corp., Glen Cove, N.Y
¶ Similar septa made from other metals are available.

the pore size and pore structure of the dispersing medium, but also on the liquid properties, liquid depth, agitation, and other features of the sparging environment. For porous-carbon media, the manufacturer suggests that the best dispersion performance will result if the broken-line regions of Fig. 18-132 are avoided. For porous-stainless-steel spargers, which extend to a lower pore size than carbon, Micro Metallic Division, Pall Corp., recommends (Release 120A, 1959) a working limit of 8 cu. ft./(sq. ft.)(min.) to avoid serious coalescence.

Slabs of porous material are installed by grouting or welding together to form a diaphragm, usually horizontal. Tubes are prone to produce coalesced gas at rates high enough to cause bubbling from their lower faces, but they have the advantage of being demountable for cleaning or replacement (U.S. Patent 2,328,655). Roe [*Sewage Works J.*, **18**, 878 (1945)] claimed that silicon carbide

Table 18-23. Wet Permeability of Alundum Porous Plates 1 In. Thick*

Dry permability at 2 in. of water differential, cu. ft./(min.)(sq. ft.)	Pressure differential across wet plate, in. of water	Air flow through wet plate, cu. ft./(min.)(sq. ft.)
4.3	20.67	2.0
	21.77	3.0
	22.86	4.0
	23.90	5.0
55.0	4.02	1.0
	4.14	2.0
	4.22	3.0
	4.27	4.0
	4.30	5.0

* Data by courtesy of Norton Co., Worcester, Mass.

tubes are superior to horizontal plates, principally because of the wiping action of the liquid circulating past the tube. He reported respective maximum capacities of 5 and 3 cu. ft. gas/(sq. ft.)(min.) for a horizontal tube and a horizontal plate of the same material (unspecified grade). Mounting a flat-plate porous sparger vertically instead of horizontally seriously reduces the effectiveness of the sparger for three reasons: (1) the gas is distributed over a reduced cross section; (2) at normal rates, the lower portion of the sparger may not operate because of difference in hydrostatic head; (3) there is a marked tendency for bubbles to coalesce along the sparger surface. Bone (M.S. Thesis in chemical engineering, University of Kansas, 1948) found that the oxygen sulfite solution coefficient identified with a 1⅛- by 4-in. rectangular porous carbon sparger was 26 to 41 per cent lower for vertical than for horizontal operation of the sparger, the greatest reduction occurring when the long dimension was vertical.

Porous dispersers are used chiefly to promote gas absorption, particularly in sewage and waste aeration tanks. King [*Sewage and Ind. Wastes*, **54**, 826 (1952)] developed a specification procedure for porous aeration plates involving the rate of absorption of oxygen from air when the air is bubbled through a plate at a stipulated rate [about 1.9 cu. ft./(sq. ft.)(min.)] into a 3-ft. depth of aqueous sodium sulfite in a tank of stipulated design. King observed absorption rates for silica and alumina plates in the range 34 to 62 p.p.m./hr. [equivalent to coefficients of 3 to 6×10^{-4} lb.-moles/(hr.)(cu. ft.)(atm.)], decreasing linearly with increasing plate permeability. The dependency of absorption rate on permeability, hence on pore size, is consistent with Bone's observation that carbon tubes and slabs delivering 2.4 cu. ft./(sq. ft.)(min.) of air produced sulfite solution coefficients that were roughly inversely proportional to the nominal diameter of the septum pores. At 11.9 cu. ft./(sq. ft.)(min.), however, the inverse proportionality no longer obtained, presumably an indication of coalescence at the fine-pore spargers. This is in agreement with Houghton, McLean, and Ritchie [*Chem. Eng. Sci.*, **7**, 26 (1957)], who reported relatively little effect of sparger pore size on the rate of absorption of carbon dioxide in water, gas rates ranging from 12 to 17 cu. ft./(sq. ft.)(min.) and pore size ranging from 72 μ to 1.15 mm.

A comparison between porous septa and other types of dispersers is of interest. Chain and coworkers [First International Symposium Chemical Microbiology, World Health Organization, *Monograph Series* 10, Geneva, Switzerland, 1952] claimed that porous disks are about twice as effective as open-pipe and ring spargers for the air oxidation of sodium sulfite. Maloney (private communication, May, 1942) found that, in the absorption of carbon dioxide from a 9 per cent mixture with air into a 12-in. depth of 3N diethanolamine, a No. 20 National Carbon tube delivering 8.3 cu. ft./(sq. ft.)(min.) gave a coefficient of 3.3 lb.-moles/(hr.)(cu. ft.)(atm.), whereas a ⅜-in. open-end sparger gave a coefficient of 0.7 lb.-moles/(hr.)(cu. ft.)(atm.). Eckenfelder [*Sewage and Ind. Wastes*, **31**, 60 (1959)] proposed that dispersers for sewage-aeration tanks be compared on the basis of an oxygen-absorption number $N = K_La V/G_s^{1-n}h^{1-m}$, where K_La is the over-all oxygen-absorption coefficient, V is the absorbent volume, G_s is the air-flow rate, h is the absorbent depth, and m and n are empirical constants. His comparison of several types of dispersers evaluated by him or other investigators is shown in Table 18-24. Inasmuch as the absorption number is not dimensionless and Eckenfelder did not define the units of all his quantities, no absolute significance can be assigned to the values of N; the data of Table 18-24 are of relative interest only. The range of the index $(1 - n)$ apparently implies a notable difference in the dynamics or geometry among the several cases. This difference is reflected also in the values of the index $(1 - m)$, which probably depend as much on disperser placement and tank geometry as on disperser type.

Schulman and Molstad [*Ind. Eng. Chem.*, **42**, 1058

(1950)] and Houghton *et al.* [*Chem. Eng. Sci.*, **7**, 26 (1957)] studied the absorption of carbon dioxide in water in countercurrent unpacked columns fed with gas through a porous sparger at the bottom. Both papers note that true countercurrent contacting or single-stage perfect mixing could be observed, depending on the zone in the contactor and on the velocities involved. In Figs. 18-133 and 18-134 the results are compared with those

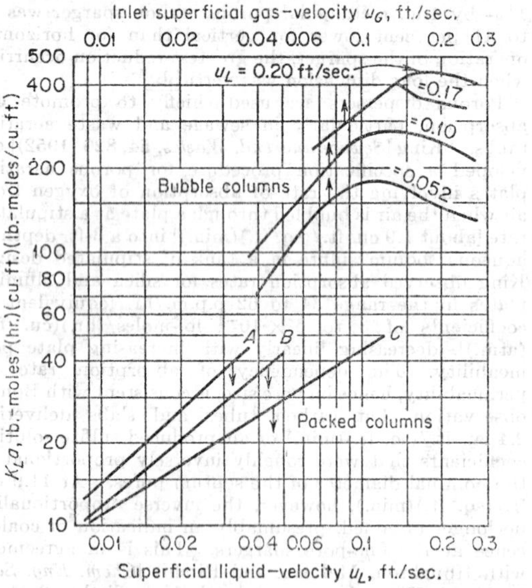

FIG. 18-133. Comparison of bubble columns with packed towers. Absorption of carbon dioxide in water. (*A*) Packing: 0.73-in. glass balls. [*Simmons and Osborn, Ind. Eng. Chem.*, **26**, 529 (1934).] (*B*) Packing: 1-in. coke. [*Adams and Edmonds, Ind. Eng. Chem.*, **29**, 447 (1937).] (*C*) Packing: Small glass rings. [*Cantello et al., Ind. Eng. Chem.*, **19**, 989 (1927).] (*D*) Bubble column, 1.5 ft. deep, 5.1 atm. total pressure, 15°C. [*G. Houghton et al., Chem. Eng. Sci.*, **7**, 26 (1957).] [*From Chem. Eng. Sci.*, **7**, 33 (1957), *by permission.*]

of earlier investigators for conventional packed columns. The sparged vessels permit absorption rates three to ten times greater than those for packed towers. The pressure drop, of course, also is greater. Andersen and Johnstone [*Am. Inst. Chem. Engrs. J.*, **1**, 135 (1955)] found that a fritted-glass sparger (pore size unspecified) allowed 90 per cent absorption of nitrogen dioxide in water from a 10 per cent mixture with air. The absorp-

Table 18-24. Aeration Effectiveness of Dispersers in Waste Treatment*

Disperser type	Type of waste	Absorption number N	Gas-rate index $1 - n$	Depth index $1 - m$	Lqiuid depth h, ft.
Porous Aloxite tube	Sulfite	270	0.85	0.45	15
Porous plastic tube	Sulfite	160	1.0		15
Porous carborundum plate	Water	65	0.80	0.74	26
Sparger (4 nozzles)	Sulfite	61	1.35	0.78	15
	Sewage	213	0.86		15
	Sewage	207	0.86		15
	Sewage	57	1.35		15
	Pulp and paper	279	0.81		15
Disk distributor	Sulfite	92	1.20		13
	Pulp and paper	168	0.95		15
Impingement	Sulfite	145	1.10	0.65	15
	Pulp and paper	195	1.10		15
	Pulp and paper	108	1.10		15
Jet	Pharmaceutical	110	1.00		4

* From Eckenfelder, *Sewage and Ind. Wastes*, **31**, 60 (1959).

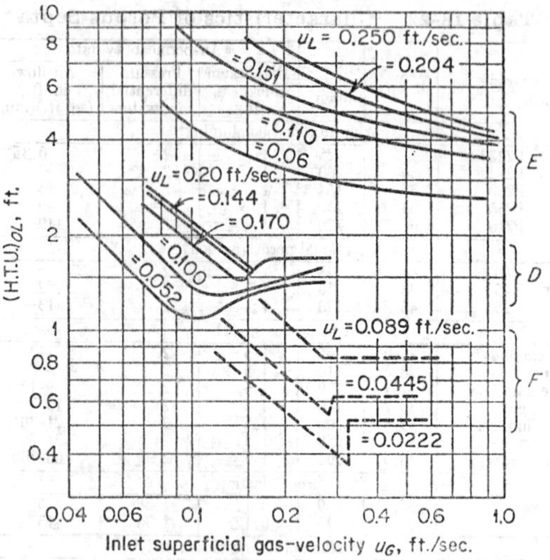

FIG. 18-134. Comparison of bubble columns with packed towers. Absorption of carbon dioxide in water. (*D*) Bubble column, 1.5 ft. deep, 5.1 atm. total pressure, 15°C. [*G. Houghton et al., Chem. Eng. Sci.*, **7**, 26 (1957).] (*E*) Packing: 2-in. steel rings. [*Cooper, Christl, and Perry, Trans. Am. Inst. Chem. Engrs.*, **37**, 979 (1941).] (*F*) Bubble column, 1.0 ft. deep, 1 atm. total pressure, 15°C. [*Shulman and Molstad, Ind. Eng. Chem.*, **42**, 1058 (1950).] [*From Chem. Eng. Sci.*, **7**, 33 (1957), *by permission.*]

tion in 7 in. of water was 90 per cent that in 28 in., indicating that porous spargers, like simple bubblers, are effective contactors largely because of the mass transfer that they promote during the process of bubble formation and liberation. Andersen and Johnstone reported that their recovery efficiencies were substantially higher than those obtainable for the same reaction in a bubble-cap tower.

The effect of surface-active agents on the performance of porous septa is not well defined. Eckenfelder, in the two papers already cited, reported odd effects of surface-active materials: surfactants, particularly when in a low concentration, generally reduced the absorption coefficients of oxygen in water, whereas foam breakers or retardants resulted in coefficients sometimes lower (50 per cent), sometimes higher (164 per cent) than the ones for pure water.

The tendency of porous spargers to plug, partially or totally, is one of their major disadvantages. Plugging is not limited to the obvious cases in which solids are carried into the septum by the gas in its passage or in which solids form on the exterior of the sparger—it also can occur because of chemical reaction or crystallization of solute from the absorbent within the pores of the porous medium. It is believed that the poor replicability of laboratory data on sulfite oxidations promoted by porous septa is at least partly caused by temporary plugging of the septa in random and unexplained sequences (Allen, M.S. Thesis in chemical engineering, University of Kansas, 1956). Gardner (M.S. Thesis in chemical engineering, University of Rochester, 1959) found that porous carbon spargers bubbling carbon-dioxide-bearing air into aqueous sodium carbonate plugged rapidly and irreversibly. Gardner showed that the plugging was caused by sodium bicarbonate, even when the concentration of this salt in the absorbent was considerably below the saturation level.

As stated above, porous septa enjoy their widest use in the aeration of activated sludge masses employed in the treatment of sewage and other oxidizable organic waste. King [*Sewage and Ind. Wastes*, **27**, 894, 1007, 1123 (1955)] presented a comprehensive statement of the design problem associated with the use of porous sparger plates in spiral-flow aeration tanks. Wiley *et al.* [*Paper Trade J.*, **124** (12), 59 (1947)] described the use of porous plates for aeration to relieve the low oxygen content of a river receiving sulfite-mill waste. Porous septa also may be used to promote the flocculation of finely divided solids in sludge-sedimentation tanks. They are thus installed as alternates to diffuser nozzles or air lifts in the Eimco Oxidator aerating clarifier (The Eimco Corp., *Bull.* SM-1005, October, 1959).

In one type of froth-flotation cell, air is distributed through a porous diaphragm, usually a canvas or a perforated rubber sheet, at a rate of 7 to 15 cu. ft./(sq. ft. diaphragm area)(min.). The pressure drop through a three-ply canvas is 1.5 to 4.0 lb./sq. in., depending on the degree of plugging existing. The rubber sheeting used is 5⁄64 to 5⁄32 in. thick and is perforated with 200 holes/sq. in., the pore diameter being 0.038 to 0.045 in. It is said to require only one-quarter to one-half the pressure drop of the canvas and to plug less readily.

Precipitation and Generation Methods. Precipitation. Precipitation of a gas from a supersaturated solution generally results in a fine dispersion of bubbles throughout the liquid [Bateman and Lang, *Can. J. Research*, **23E**, 22 (1945)].

Precipitation finds its widest use in the manufacture of cellular rubber. Uncured rubber (natural or synthetic) is heated and saturated with an inert gas at pressures as high as 4500 lb./sq. in. [Gould, *Rubber Age (N.Y.)*, **54**, 526; **55**, 65 (1944)]. The pressure is released before vulcanization, permitting liberation of the dissolved gas within the rubber and expansion of the elastomer. If partial vulcanization takes place before the pressure is released, closed-cell sponge rubber results. Taylor (U.S. Patent 2,372,695) applied this method to the manufacture of expanded thermoplastic materials by the use of a volatile solvent at 210°C. and 3000 lb./sq. in. pressure.

Precipitation is the principle underlying two designs of froth-flotation cell. In one, preaerated pulp is caused to froth by the application of a vacuum. An example is the Clemens cell. In another, the pulp is saturated with air at superatmospheric pressure and is flashed into the cell, which operates at atmospheric pressure. An example is the Juell cell. Neither of the flotation cells is extensively used in the mineral industries today.

Pressure saturation followed by flashing and bubble precipitation is the active principle in a combined flotation and thickening unit, the Eimco-Process Flotator, used by the process industries particularly for waste pretreatment and recovery (Fig. 18-135). The unit is a circular tank with the thickener and scraper mechanism supported on beams spanning the tank. The tank may be 6 to 40 ft. in diameter. The feed mixture is saturated with air at elevated pressure, usually about 30 lb./sq. in. gage. After passing through a back-pressure valve, the influent is introduced to the unit below the liquid level, where a mass of fine bubbles is released, carrying fine solids upward where they can be skimmed to the scum trough. Coarse, heavy solids meanwhile settle as in a conventional thickener. The method of influent introduction is said to be critical to the success of the Flotator's operation and must be specified for the particular problem being attacked. Examples of applications of the Flotator are sewage-sludge thickening, fat recovery from meat-packing waste, oil removal from refinery waste waters, and fiber recovery in the pulp and paper industry.

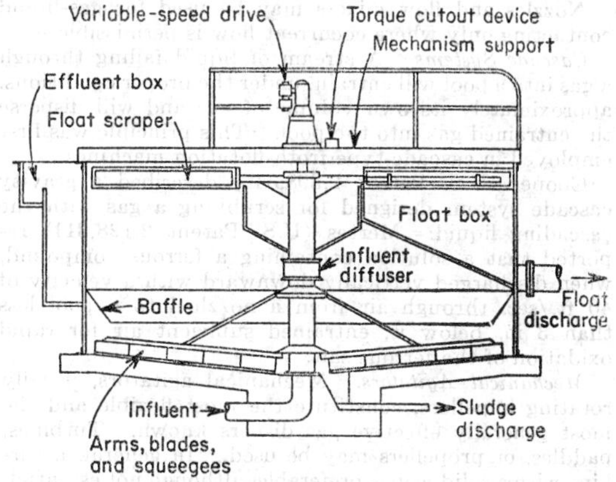

FIG. 18-135. The Flotator dissolved-air flotation thickener. (*Process Engineers, Inc., a division of the Eimco Corp.*)

Generation. Fine, well-dispersed bubbles are produced if a dissolved or finely divided suspended material is decomposed to yield a gas.

Generation methods are employed to prepare cellular elastomers or thermoplastics to which the resulting products of decomposition are not harmful. A number of "blowing agents" are used, the most common being sodium and ammonium bicarbonate, calcium carbonate, ammonium nitrate, diazo derivatives, and diisocyanates. Colin-Russ [*Chem. Trade J.*, **115**, 631 (1944)] suggested gas-saturated leather charcoal as a blowing agent. In the Talalay process for foam rubber, hydrogen peroxide is the source of gas, the oxygen being liberated by the action of catalase from yeast (Winspear and Waterman, in Morton's "Introduction to Rubber Technology," Chap. 18, Reinhold, New York, 1959). In every case, the blowing agent is compounded into a latex before it is gelled or into an elastomeric mass before it is cured, the material being uniformly dispersed throughout the plastic mass before gas generation occurs.

Leavening agents are gas-generation sources used to produce the light cellular structure of breads and pastries. Examples are baking powder and yeast, the latter effecting the decomposition of carbohydrate.

Fluid-attrition Systems. Nozzles and Pipe-line Contactors. The turbulence developed during the rapid flow of fluid through a nozzle or a pipe sometimes is utilized to disperse a gas in a liquid. Steam-water mixers of the venturi-nozzle type are manufactured by several companies. Excellent dispersions can be obtained with such devices, although for a gas-in-water dispersion the gas-to-liquid ratio is relatively low. In one design of nozzle, both air and steam are dispersed into the water to reduce further the vibration and noise resulting from collapsing steam bubbles.

Pipe-line contactors of gas-liquid mixtures usually involve orifices or baffles to redistribute the gas periodically. Pfirrmann (German Patent 740,674) described a pipe-line disperser with occasional short constrictions of such cross section that the fluid velocity through them would exceed 3 ft./sec. Tell [*Chem. & Met. Eng.* **52** (6), 115 (1945)] recommended an orifice of unstated dimension for dispersing continuously small quantities of a gas in a hydrocarbon.

A downflow pipe-line disperser for air and sewage was developed by Nordell (U.S. Patent 2,374,772). Initial dispersion was accomplished by a vortex above the downpipe into which the air was entrained as small bubbles.

Nozzles and flow mixers may be used for gas-liquid contacting only where cocurrent flow is permissible.

Cascade Systems. A stream of liquid falling through a gas into a pool will entrain, under the proper conditions, approximately its own volume of gas and will disperse the entrained gas into the pool. This principle was first employed in cascade-type froth-flotation machines.

Cooper (U.S. Patent 2,398,345) described a gravity cascade system designed for scrubbing a gas with the cascading liquid. Mertes (U.S. Patent 2,128,311) reported that a solution containing a ferrous compound, when discharged vertically downward with a velocity of 40 ft./sec. through air from a nozzle into a pool less than 3 in. below it, entrained sufficient air for rapid oxidation of the ferrous salt.

Mechanical Agitators. Mechanical agitators, usually rotating impellers, constitute the most flexible and the most generally effective gas dispers known. Turbines, paddles, or propellers may be used. In general, a turbine with a solid web is preferable, although not essential. For the best dispersions and the highest capacities, baffles or stator elements must be employed to minimize liquid swirl and increase the possible power input and shear rate at the agitator.

For agitators used as gas-liquid contactors, the most useful achievement criteria are rate of absorption promoted, efficiency of absorption, and extent of interface produced. For agitators used as frothers, the criteria are capacity and quality of froth produced. In both applications, the impeller speed, the shaft power, and the impeller and tank design required for satisfactory performance must be specified, as must the details of mechanical design requisite to dependable and economical operation.

The general basis for the design of gas-liquid contactors is that of model development: satisfactory operation is established on small scale, which is extrapolated to full size by proved scale-up techniques. Cooper, Fernstrom, and Miller (*loc. cit.*) investigated the absorption of oxygen from air into aqueous sodium sulfite contained in baffled tanks agitated with flat paddles or vaned-disk dispersers. They showed that it is possible to represent the performance of geometrically similar equipment, regardless of size, by the correlation of Fig. 18-136, where K_v is an over-all volumetric absorption coefficient, lb.-moles/(hr.)(cu. ft.)(atm.); and V_s is the superficial gas velocity based on inlet gas volume and cross section of the tank, ft./hr. The driving force is the logarithmic mean of the entering and leaving partial pressures of the solute gas. The power involved is that delivered to the agitator while gas is being dispersed, usually appreciably less than the no-gas power at the same impeller speed. Carlson [*Ind. Eng. Chem.*, **38,** 14 (1946)] used the data of Fig. 18-136 to compare the economics of a hypothetical agitated tank with a hypothetical packed tower promoting the absorption of oxygen in water. The costs of the two installations were of the same order, with the agitated tank slightly the more favorable at low gas rates.

A number of investigators have used the oxygen-sulfite reaction to study the design variables of disperser agitators on a small scale, with the following conclusions: the advantage of multiple impellers on the same shaft in an unstaged tank is dubious, for in some cases the absorption rate was decreased and the maximum increase over a single impeller was 10 per cent (Oldshue, *Proc. Bioengineering Symp.*, Rose Polytechnic Inst., Terre Haute, Ind., 1953); in the high-power range [3000 to 6000 ft.-lb./(min.)(cu. ft.)], wide differences in impeller shape produce little difference in the absorption effectiveness at a given power-input level [Karwat, *Chem.-Ing.-Tech.*, **31,** 588 (1959)], a conclusion consistent with the comparison of flat paddle and vaned disk in Fig. 18-136; for flat paddles and vaned disks, the effect of gas rate on absorption rate disappears as impeller diameter becomes greater than 40 per cent of tank diameter [Friedman and Lightfoot, *Ind. Eng. Chem.*, **49,** 1227 (1957)], a conclusion that may not extrapolate reliably to larger scale; at equal power input, unbaffled designs promote higher absorption rates than do baffled ones, particularly at high gas rates (Chain *et al.*, *loc. cit.*), but the maximum power deliverable to an unbaffled tank is relatively low; at all but low power levels, there is no advantage in introducing the gas to an agitator through a porous sparger instead of a simple open-end pipe (Chain *et al.*, *loc. cit.*). The absorption coefficients measured for air-sulfite are believed to be applicable to other oxygen-water systems, provided the mass-transfer resistance is the controlling one. They have been found suitable for the air oxidation of copperas to a precipitated iron oxide, for example.

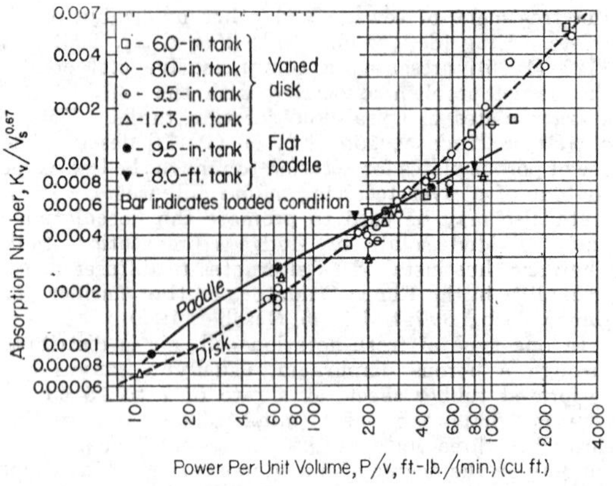

FIG. 18-136. Performance of mechanical agitator-dispersers. Absorption of oxygen from air into an aqueous solution originally 1.2N with respect to sodium sulfite (Na_2SO_3). Average temperature, 30°C. [*From Ind. Eng. Chem.*, **36,** 504 (1944), *by permission.*]

Johnson and coworkers [*Am. Inst. Chem. Engrs. J.*, **3,** 411 (1957)] investigated the effect of agitation intensity and gas velocity on the rate of a three-phase catalytic reaction, the hydrogenation of α-methyl styrene. They suggested the relationship

$$\frac{D_v}{kD^2}\left(\frac{\mu}{\rho_L D_v}\right)^{0.33} = A\left(\frac{\sigma}{V_s\mu}\right)^{0.75} N_{Re}^{-1.67} + B\frac{\rho_s}{m}N_{Re}^{-0.75} \qquad (18\text{-}115)$$

in which D = impeller diameter; D_v = diffusivity; k = mass-transfer coefficient; m = catalyst loading, g./liter; N_{Re} = agitation Reynolds number = $D^2n\rho_L/\mu$; n = agitator speed, rev./unit time; V_s = superficial gas velocity; μ = absolute viscosity of liquid; ρ_L = liquid density; ρ_s = solid (catalyst) density, g./ml.; and σ = surface tension of liquid. For the quantities not stipulated, any set of consistent units may be used. The coefficients A and B depend on the design of the agitation system; for the turbine used by these investigators, A = 29.0 and B = 6.55 × 10^{-4}. The role of the liquid properties was established largely by analogy, since they were not varied widely in the experiment. Equation (18-115) should be used cautiously as a design basis, particularly inasmuch as the last term may not apply to catalysts of different physical and chemical properties, but it emphasizes the importance of the agitator in the simultaneous functions of gas disperser and catalyst suspender.

The work of Wolf and Rushton [*J. Am. Oil Chemists' Soc.*, **30**, 147 (1953)] showed that a mechanical agitator can improve the capacity of steam-distillation units. Rate of stripping of free fatty acid from lard was 30 to 50 per cent higher when the steam was dispersed with a turbine than when a simple sparger was used without agitation.

Aerobic fermentations require a steady supply of oxygen and adequate dispersion of the active microorganism throughout the fermenting mass. Gaden and coworkers [*Ind. Eng. Chem.*, **42**, 1792 (1950); **48**, 2209 (1956); *J. Biochem. Microbiol. Tech. Eng.*, **1**, 163 (1959)] concluded that oxygen-sulfite simulations of fermentations were useful in the establishment of adequate air-dispersing conditions, but not in the prediction of rates. The absorption of oxygen by the yeast cells appears to be the controlling process, the rate of which is independent of dissolved oxygen concentration above 10^{-5} g.-mole/liter; hence above a minimum level, increasing agitation intensity has almost no effect on the rate of the fermentation. Bartholomew and coworkers [*Ind. Eng. Chem.*, **42**, 1801, 1827 (1950); *J. Agr. Food Chem.*, **1**, 302 (1953)] agreed with Gaden's analysis and stressed the importance of careful scale-model work in the laboratory and pilot plant to provide agitation information about the complex process of fermentation that can be scaled up with confidence. Using flat-blade turbines as agitators, they developed a rational system of geometrical scale-up from 5 to 200 to 15,000 gal. Wegrich and Shurter [*Ind. Eng. Chem.* **45**, 1153 (1953)] developed a similar fermentation scale-up procedure to 24,000 gal. Experimental fermentors of 20 to 50 liters in volume have been found useful—large enough to permit realistic simulation of plant equipment, but small enough to provide experimental convenience [Kroll and coworkers, *Ind. Eng. Chem.*, **48**, 2190 (1956); Nelson, Maxon, and Elferdink, *ibid.*, p. 2183]. Flat-blade turbines, curved-blade open turbines, paddles, and propellers (side and top entering) have been used as fermentor agitators [in addition to the preceding references, see Brown and Peterson, *Ind. Eng. Chem.*, **42**, 1769, 1823 (1950) and Pfeiffer *et al.*, *ibid.*, p. 1776]. Flat-blade turbines probably are slightly the better, but any of these designs can be used if care is exercised in their design and experimental use such that the results can be scaled up or down with assurance. In view of the moderate demand on the agitator, the 3 to 20 hp./1000 gal. of fermentor volume [700 to 5000 ft.-lb./(min.)(cu. ft.)] mentioned by Petty [*Chem. Inds.*, **66**, 184 (1950)] appears higher than necessary, at least on its high extreme. One approaching an aerobic fermentation from the engineering viewpoint, whether for design or operation, should consult Finn's excellent review [*Bacteriol. Rev.*, **18**, 254 (1954)].

Oldshue [*Ind. Eng. Chem.*, **48**, 2194 (1956)] investigated the aerobic oxidation of biological waste material (activated milk sludge) as promoted by a Mixco turbine and found that the oxygen uptake could be described quantitatively in terms of an absorption coefficient and the power input to the dispersing agitator. Figure 18-137 shows the data Oldshue obtained during the oxidation of milk sludge in a 20-ft.-diameter tank containing 12 ft. of liquid. The parameter of the lines is superficial air velocity, ft./sec. The data are said to be applicable within design limits for an impeller-to-tank diameter ratio of 0.2 and for all depths from 10 to 40 ft., provided that the power is maintained at the same power/depth ratio as in Fig. 18-137. Inasmuch as the rate of oxygen ingestion by the process becomes the ultimate controlling factor in the absorption rate, it is neither

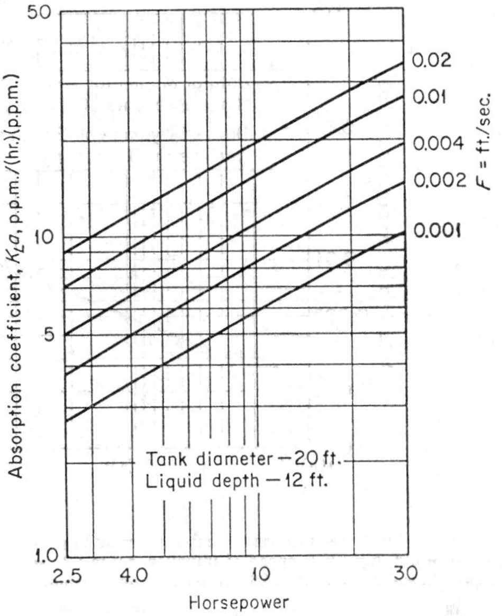

FIG. 18-137. Performance of mechanical agitator-disperser: Mixco turbine. Absorption of oxygen from air into milk-waste sludge. F = superficial air velocity. [*From Ind. Eng. Chem.*, **48**, 2196 (1956), *with permission.*]

necessary nor advisable to employ the high levels of agitator power input in aerations that are used in many chemical processes. Eckenfelder [*Chem. Eng. Progress*, **52**, 286 (1956)] reported turbine aerators operating in the range 0.3 to 0.4 hp./1000 gal. [70 to 93 ft.-lb./(min.)(cu. ft.)], and suggested that power levels above 0.7 hp./1000 gal. and impeller peripheral speeds above 10 ft./sec. should be avoided to prevent degradation of the sludge floc with related difficulties of floating and frothing.

Probably the most fundamental study to date of mechanical gas dispersion by agitators was made by Calderbank [*loc. cit.; Trans. Inst. Chem. Engrs.*, **37**, 173 (1959)]. Calderbank used geometrically similar vessels from 6 to 20 in. in diameter with flat-blade turbines similar to the Mixco type, with power input up to 6600 ft.-lb./(min.)(cu. ft.) and with relatively low gas rates (up to 3.6 ft./min. superficial). He measured bubble size, interfacial area, mass-transfer coefficients, and hold-up, with the following conclusions:

1. The liquid-phase mass-transfer coefficient is independent of bubble size and agitation rate. This apparently reflects a relationship between the size and slip velocity that results, fortuitously perhaps, in constancy of contact time. The conclusion should be checked on larger scale.

2. A tank in which gas is dispersed by an agitator acts as a single theoretical stage.

3. Interfacial area may be calculated as

$$a_o = 1.44\left(\frac{P}{V}\right)^{0.4}\rho_L{}^{0.2}\left(\frac{1}{\sigma}\right)^{0.6}\left(\frac{V_s}{V_t}\right)^{0.5} \qquad (18\text{-}116)$$

where a_o = gas-liquid interface/unit volume, cm.$^{-1}$; P = agitator shaft power during dispersion, ergs/sec.; V = volume of agitated mass, cu. cm.; V_s and V_t = superficial gas velocity and bubble terminal velocity, respectively, cm./sec.; ρ_L = liquid density, g./cu. cm.; σ = interfacial tension, dynes/cm. V_t generally will not be known, but for all but the finest bubbles, a mean value of 26 cm./sec. can be used with allowable error.

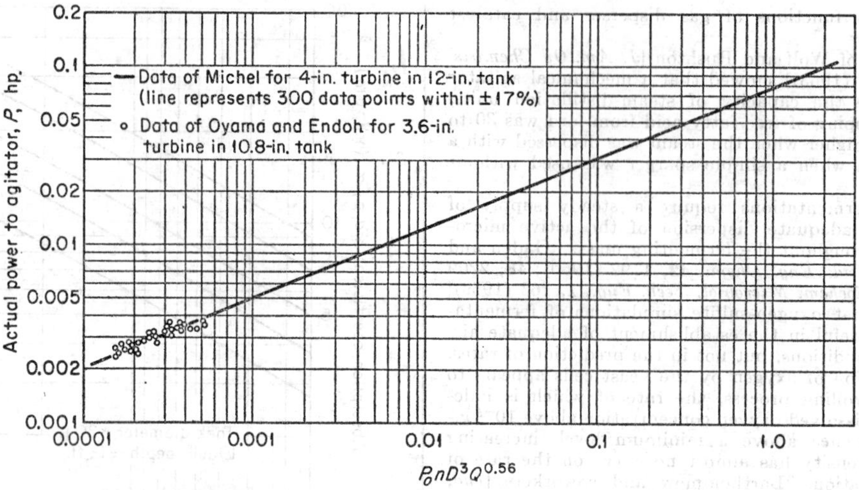

FIG. 18-138. Power requirement of gas-dispersing impellers. P = power consumed in the gassed liquid; P_o = power consumed in the ungassed liquid, h.p.; n = speed of impeller, r.p.m.; D = impeller diameter, ft.; Q = volumetric flow rate of gas, cu. ft./min. [*From Am. Inst. Chem. Engrs. J.*, **8**, 265 (1962), *by permission*.]

4. Gas hold-up can be calculated as

$$H = \left(\frac{V_s H}{V_t}\right)^{0.5} + 0.0216 \left(\frac{P}{V}\right)^{0.4} \rho_L{}^{0.2} \left(\frac{1}{\sigma}\right)^{0.6} \left(\frac{V_s}{V_t}\right)^{0.5} \quad (18\text{-}117)$$

where H = volume fraction of gas in suspension; other units are as in Eq. (18-116). At large values of P/V, this expression approximates the equation for contact time θ of air in water presented earlier by Foust, Mack, and Rushton [*Ind. Eng. Chem.*, **36**, 517 (1933)]:

$$\theta = c\left(\frac{P}{VV_s}\right)^{0.47} \quad (18\text{-}118)$$

When θ is in sec./ft., P/V in hp./cu. ft., and V_s in ft./sec., $1.26 \leq c \leq 1.65$.

All the correlations developed thus far for the performance of gas-liquid contactors have a common practical weakness, in that they involve the unknown agitator shaft power during gas dispersion. This is always likely to be less than the power required by the agitator rotating in gas-free liquid; at high gas rates it can be as low as 30 per cent of the no-gas power. Oyama and Endoh [*Chem. Eng., Japan*, **19**, 2 (1955)] correlated power data from geometrically similar equipment over a twofold size range using flat-blade turbines as a plot of P/P_o against $Q/(nD^3)$, where D is the impeller diameter, n the impeller rotational speed, P and P_o the agitator shaft power with and without gas, respectively, and Q the volumetric flow rate of the gas. The result was a gentle concave-upward curve of negative slope. Oyama and Endoh observed no values of P/P_o less than about 0.5. Calderbank [*Trans. Inst. Chem. Engrs.*, **36**, 463 (1958)] also correlated power data by the method of Oyama and Endoh. With a slightly different agitator design, he obtained data considerably below those of Oyama and Endoh which correlated reasonably well as two straight-line sections. Kalinske [*Sewage and Ind. Wastes*, **27**, 572 (1955)] presented a similar correlation for power in sludge-aeration tanks that is tantamount to a plot of $1 - (Q/(nD^3))$ against P/P_o.

Michel and Miller [*Am. Inst. Chem. Engrs. J.*, **8**, 262 (1962)] found that the Oyama-Endoh correlation failed for large ranges of P_o, generally predicting values of P higher than were measured. Their data were collected in a 12-in. baffled tank agitated by a 4-in. Mixco turbine dispersing air in one- and two-phase liquids ranging in density from 1 to 1.6 g./ml. and in viscosity from 1 to 28 centipoises. They proposed the correlation of Fig. 18-138. The line of Fig. 18-138 represents the data within ±17 per cent and, as shown, represents the data of Oyama and Endoh within the same limit. It spans an elevenfold range of Weber number but is not valid for dispersions containing a surfactant, which can further reduce the agitator power at a given speed.

Michel's correlation cannot be viewed as a scale-up device, but there is some evidence that it will be valid in geometrical models for at least a scale factor of 2. Like the correlations of Oyama and Calderbank, it has not been tested for high gas rates, and it should be used cautiously for superficial velocities above 0.06 ft./sec.

For moderate increases in gas rate at a constant impeller speed, the power reduction will be essentially linear with superficial gas velocity and may be so treated [Nelson *et al.*, *loc. cit.*]. In all cases, of course, the agitator drive must be capable of accepting the no-gas load.

In general, there is for each power level of a mechanical agitator-disperser a limiting gas-feed rate which may not be exceeded without danger of causing the tank to foam over. This limiting velocity has not been defined; at medium power levels, however, it is not likely to be higher than 25 cu. ft./(sq. ft. tank cross section)(min.), and at power intensities above 2000 ft.-lb./(min.)(cu. ft.) it may be 25 per cent of this maximum or less. Finn (*loc. cit.*) suggests that reasonable limits of superficial velocity in agitated fermentation tanks are 7 cu. ft./(sq. ft.)(min.) for flat-blade turbines and 1 cu. ft./(sq. ft.)(min.) for paddles. Kalinske (in "Biological Treatment of Sewage and Industrial Wastes," by McCabe and Eckenfelder, vol. I, Chaps. 2–10, Reinhold, New York, 1955) recommends an economical maximum of 10 cu. ft. of air/(sq. ft. impeller peripheral area)(min.) for vaned disks in aerobic oxidation tanks. Impeller peripheral area is the product of turbine circumference and height of vanes. Higher limits than this are likely to be desirable for chemical systems of higher reaction rate.

Mechanical dispersers that induce their own air supply are sometimes useful. The Turbo-Gas-Absorber, manufactured by Turbo-Mixer Division, General American Transportation Corp., is such a device (Fig. 18-139).

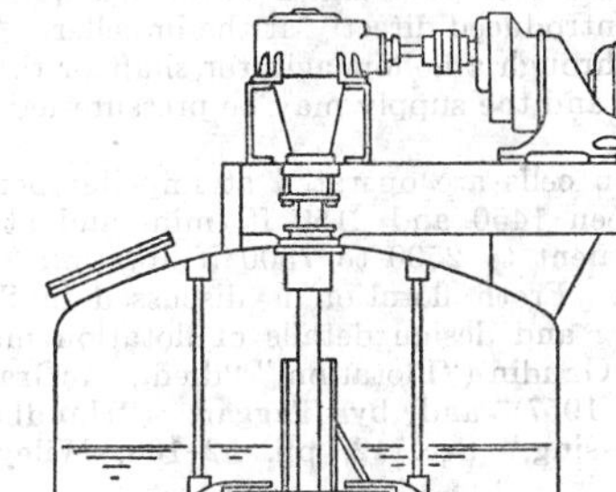

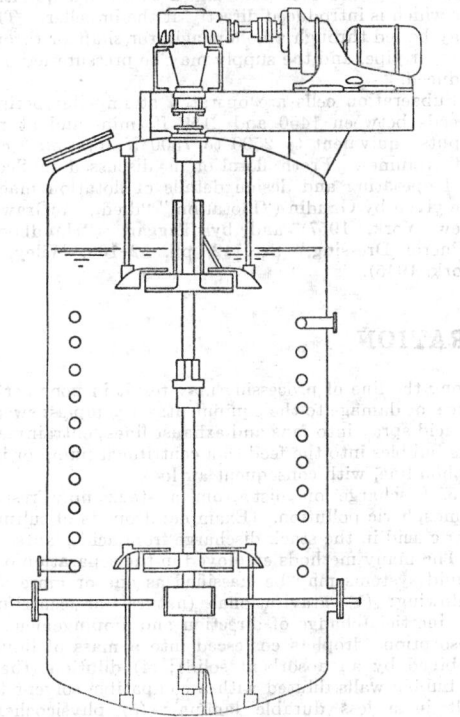

FIG. 18-139. Turbo-Gas-Absorber with combined pressure and self-induction impellers in hydrogenation vessel. The upper impeller is the gas entrainer. (*Turbo-Mixer Division, General American Transportation Corp.*)

Estimates of its gas-entraining capacity and of maximum effective gas rates for its operation as a pressure-fed disperser are given in Table 18-25. For gas rates greater than 160 cu. ft./min., a pressure-fed installation must be used. The five largest impellers are designed to operate only with positive-pressure gas feed.

A propeller in a draft tube or a properly designed turbine operating below a draft tube may induce a flow of freeboard atmosphere into the liquid. The Cavitator, made by Yeoman Brothers Co., employs a stator-enclosed turbine below a draft tube, as shown in Fig. 18-140, to induce gas at the rates indicated by the air-in-water data of Table 18-26. At these relatively low rates, high absorption efficiency is obtained; the Cavitator is said to absorb 46 per cent of the oxygen from air dispersed in sodium sulfite solution.

Table 18-25. Turbo-Gas-Absorber Gas-entraining Capacity*

Impeller diam., in.	Maximum gas-entraining capacity, cu. ft./min.	Maximum gas rate for pressure-fed operation, cu. ft./min.
4	2	3
6	10	15
9	15	20
12	25	40
18	60	100
22	100	180
27	160	300
34	...	600
42	...	1200
60	...	2500
72	...	3800
84	...	5000+

* Data by courtesy of Turbo-Mixer Division, General American Transportation Corp.

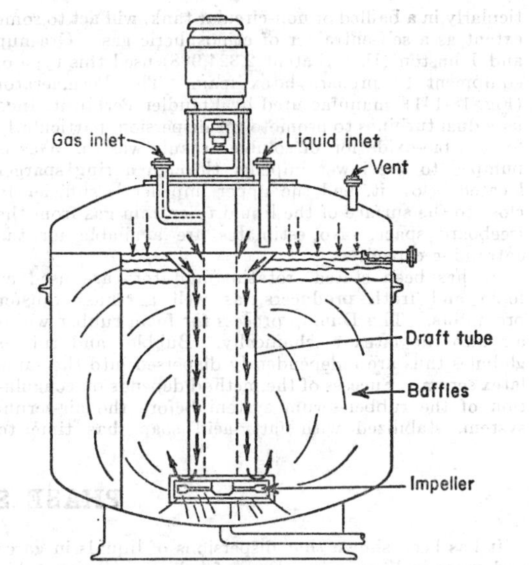

FIG. 18-140. The Cavitator agitated gas absorber. Gas is entrained by liquid flow through the draft tube and impeller. (*Yeomans Brothers Co.*)

An impeller operating near the surface of a liquid, par-

Table 18-26. Air-handling Capacity of the Cavitator*

Model	Motor hp.	Tank size: Square, side, ft.	Tank size: Round, diam., ft.	Approx. vol. of tank, gal.	Air rate, cu. ft./min.
C-27-2	2	8	9	4,600	8
C-27-3	3	10	11	7,100	12
C-37-5	5	12	13	10,200	18
C-37-7.5	7½	16	18	18,200	28
C-37-10	10	18	20	23,000	38

* Data by courtesy of Yeoman Brothers Co.

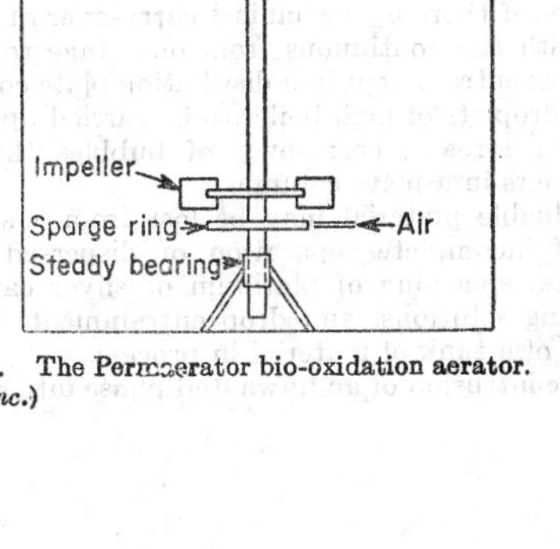

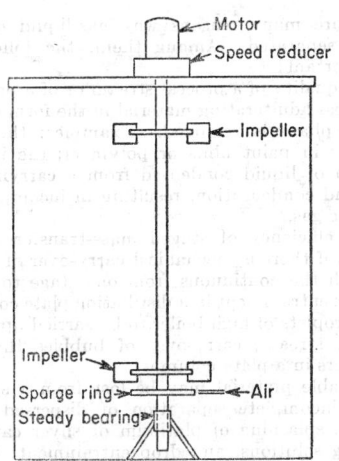

FIG. 18-141. The Permaerator bio-oxidation aerator. (*Pfaudler Permutit, Inc.*)

ticularly in a baffled or non-circular tank, will act to some extent as a self-entrainer of atmospheric gas. Greenup and Johnston (U. S. Patent 2,324,988) used this type of equipment to prepare latex foam. The Permaerator (Fig. 18-141), manufactured by Pfaudler Permutit, Inc., uses dual turbines to promote gas dispersion, particularly for the bio-oxidation of soluble organic wastes. Gas is pumped to the lower impeller through a ring sparger located below it, and the upper impeller is sufficiently close to the surface of the liquid to entrain gas from the freeboard space. No estimates are available for the entraining capacity.

As has been stated, rotating agitators are used as foam and froth producers, as well as mass-transfer promotors. The Dunlop process for foam rubber whips air into the latex mechanically. Bubbles and rubber globules thus are independently dispersed into the same latex serum. Success of the method depends on coagulation of the rubber-serum system before the air-serum system, stabilized with fatty-acid soap, has time to collapse. Mechanical agitators are used also for the preparation of such foods as meringue and whipped cream.

Rotating impellers are used extensively in froth-flotation machines. The flotation cell most widely used today, the subaeration machine, applies vigorous agitation to a mixture of pulp and a controlled quantity of air which is introduced directly at the impeller. The air may be fed through a hollow agitator shaft or through a sparger pipe, and the supply may be pressure-fed or self-induced.

Subaeration cells are operated at impeller peripheral speeds between 1450 and 2150 ft./min. and at power inputs equivalent to 2500 to 7500 ft.-lb./(min.)(cu. ft. cell volume). Froth flotation is discussed in Sec. 21, and operating and design details of flotation machines are given by Gaudin ("Flotation," 2d ed., McGraw-Hill, New York, 1957) and by Taggart ("Handbook of Mineral Dressing," Sec. 12, pp. 52–108, Wiley, New York, 1945).

PHASE SEPARATION

It has been shown that dispersions of liquids in gases and gases in liquids are always fundamentally unstable mixtures. Left to themselves, they will separate into massive collections of the component phases. When the disperse state is desirable process-wise, the natural separation tendency is combatted by the use of stabilizing materials and the selection of physical conditions that will lengthen the life of the dispersion. Under some circumstances, gas-in-liquid systems can remain almost permanently dispersed. A foam emulsion of crude oil, air, and water, for instance, whipped up with a high-shear mechanical agitator, has been known to persist as a semirigid gel for months with no apparent change in structure or composition and with no detectable phase separation.

Whether of intentional or inadvertent origin, gas-liquid dispersions nearly always must be ultimately separated. The separation may consist merely of removal of the aggregated and collected phases, or it may involve aggregation and collection as well as removal. Often the rate at which the process of separation would occur spontaneously is too low to be economically tolerable; in such cases the separation operation consists essentially of the artificial acceleration of the natural process.

There are many reasons why gas-liquid dispersions must be separated. Among them, the following are most important:

1. The quality of a process stream or of a product will suffer unless adulterating material in the form of another dispersed phase is removed. Examples: the presence of bubbles in paint films or polymers; the incomplete separation of liquid condensed from a carrying gas by cooling and condensation, resulting in incomplete "drying" of the gas.

2. The efficiency of staged mass-transfer operations is reduced if there is mechanical carry-over of a disperse phase with the continuous from one stage to the next. Examples: entrainment in a distillation plate column that permits droplets of high boiler to be carried upward with the vapor stream; carry-over of bubbles through the downcomers in a plate column.

3. Valuable material may be lost from a system because of incomplete separation of dispersed material. Examples: splashing of platinum or silver catalyst impregnating solutions, and drop entrainment; foam-over and loss of a tank of material in process.

4. The intrusion of an unwanted phase into equipment along the line of processing may result in poor performance, or damage to the equipment. Examples: sweeping of acid spray into fans and exhaust lines; entrainment of gas bubbles into the feed to a centrifugal pump or into a siphon line, with consequent air lock.

5. Discharge of mist from a stack may result in atmospheric pollution. Example: droplets of sulfuric or nitric acid in the stack discharge from acid plants.

The many methods employed in the separation of gas-liquid systems may be classified as one or more of the following: (1) gravitational (natural or centrifugal); (2) inertial (change of direction and impingement); (3) absorption (droplets coalesced into a mass of liquid or imbibed by an absorbent solid); (4) dilution (the film of bubble walls diluted with a compatible solvent to result in a less durable lamina); (5) physicochemical (aggregation aided by materials that alter the character of the phase boundary); (6) electrical (the surface charge on particles removed to eliminate dispersive forces of repulsion, or the particles charged to induce their migration to a collecting surface of the opposite charge); (7) thermal (a hot surface or an intense thermal field disrupting a foam structure). Often more than one method is effective, and the choice becomes one of economy or convenience.

The fundamentals underlying aggregation are those which underlie dispersion. They have been discussed briefly in earlier passages of this section. The techniques whereby they are applied differ widely, depending on whether the dispersion is liquid-in-gas or gas-in-liquid, and on the particular components of the system. Many separators and separating procedures are the product of invention or accumulated experience and have never been completely described scientifically.

This discussion will deal with the collection and separation of phases from both liquid-in-gas and gas-in-liquid dispersions, in that order. Those methods which are the same as or only slight modifications of ones used for solid-in-liquid or liquid-in-liquid dispersions will be given brief if any attention, most of the discussion centering about techniques of particular interest in the gas-liquid field.

LIQUID-IN-GAS SYSTEMS

The liquid-in-gas dispersions encountered in chemical operations are in the mist and fog range consisting of particles with diameters of 0.1 to 100 μ. Larger sizes are readily separated out in a reasonably sized settling tank since the terminal settling velocity in air for a 100-μ particle with a specific gravity of 1.00 is 1 ft./sec.

The forces acting on a dispersed liquid particle are identical to those acting on a solid particle suspended in a gas stream, and in general the same type of equipment is used for separation. One advantage that this separation has over the separation of solids is that the liquid droplets agglomerate immediately after separation and can be removed from the separator as a liquid stream. Thus bag filters have no specific application in separation of liquid from the gas although they may serve as coalescers. All other types of solid-gas separating devices can be operated continuously on liquid separation, eliminating the shutdown for discharging or cleaning required in the usual solid separations.

Liquid droplets coalesce much more readily than solid particles agglomerate; however, under adverse conditions they will also break up more easily than solids. These conditions are usually avoided in the design of liquid-entrainment separators. For particles in the size range of 3 to 100 μ Stokes's law applies and between 3 and 0.1 μ the Cunningham correction factor must be applied to the Stokes's-law velocity.

According to Stokes's law the drag on a spherical particle is given as

$$F_D = 3\pi\mu u D_p \tag{18-119}$$

where u is the velocity of a particle of diameter D_p relative to the gas, and μ is the absolute viscosity of the gas. At the terminal velocity the drag is equal to the force of gravity on the particle:

$$\frac{\pi}{6} D_p^3(\rho_L - \rho_G)g = 3\pi\mu u_t D_p \tag{18-120}$$

and

$$D_p = \sqrt{\frac{18\mu u_t}{g(\rho_L - \rho_G)}} \tag{18-121}$$

where ρ_L is the density of the liquid particle and ρ_G the density of the gas.

Since the terminal velocity varies as the square of the particle diameter, the difficulty of removing smaller particles increases rapidly. The benefit of a liquid spray to coalesce and thus trap the very fine particles is obvious. Many commercial separators operate on this principle.

To remove entrained liquid particles from a gas stream it is necessary to impart to them some velocity relative to the gas stream. Several forces may be brought to act on these particles such as by gravity, centrifugal force, momentum, electrical energy, or acoustical energy. The efficiency of removal in all cases increases with energy input and the most effective separator is that which gives the desired degree of separation with a minimum energy consumption.

Gravity Settlers. The simplest devices for separating liquid particles utilize gravity in a large vessel in which the velocity of the gas stream is reduced. If the gas passes vertically upward through the tank, all particles having terminal velocities equal to or greater than the vertical velocity of the gas stream will be removed. A 100-μ particle has a terminal velocity of 1 ft./sec. Thus very low velocities and consequently large equipment sizes are required for the removal of particles of less than 100 μ in diameter. Additional settling will be effected if the vertical component of the gas velocity is eliminated by causing the gas to flow horizontally through a long empty and generally rectangular chamber; however, even with this inexpensive design it becomes uneconomic to attempt to remove particles of less than 40 μ diameter.

The collection of the smaller dispersed particles can be improved by decreasing the distance through which the particle must fall to be removed. The Howard fume arrester (U.S. Patent 896,111) has been proposed on this basis and provides a series of horizontal vanes in the vessel to improve the efficiency of removal of small particles. Thus in a horizontal chamber L_s ft. long and B_s ft. wide and handling q cu. ft./sec. of gas, the terminal velocity of the smallest particle removed is given as

$$u_t = \frac{q}{L_s B_s} \tag{18-122}$$

However, if baffles to provide N_s horizontal compartments are installed in the same total height the terminal velocity for the smallest particle becomes

$$u_t = \frac{q}{N_s L_s B_s} \tag{18-123}$$

The minimum size of particle that can be settled in a given chamber is given according to Stokes's law as

$$D_{p\,\text{min}} = \sqrt{\frac{18\mu u_t}{g(\rho_L - \rho_G)}} = \sqrt{\frac{18\mu q}{g N_s L_s B_s(\rho_L - \rho_G)}} \tag{18-124}$$

and thus as the number of horizontal baffles or trays are increased in a given settling chamber the minimum particle size removed varies inversely as the square root of the number of trays. The hydraulic radius is equal to half the spacing between the baffles, and the pressure drop through the settling section of the chamber itself, *i.e.*, not considering the entrance and exit losses, is therefore very nearly proportional to the number of baffles in the chamber. It may be noted that, in a settling chamber of a given over-all size,

$$D_{p\,\text{min}} \propto (\Delta P)^{-1/2} \tag{18-125}$$

This same relationship prevails if the pressure drop is changed by increasing the length of the original void chamber to improve the collection efficiency.

Cyclone Separators. Centrifugal force may also be brought to act on the entrained particles, and by this means a force equal to several hundred gravities may be developed. The centrifugal force acting on a particle of mass M is equal to MV^2/r and the g term in the Stokes's-law equation may be replaced with V^2/r where V is the linear velocity at the radius r. In terms of angular velocity ω, the g term is replaced with $\omega^2 r$.

The flow pattern in a cyclone is complex, forming a double vortex, the outer one descending and the center one rising to the outlet head. In addition, owing to wall friction, the angular velocity increases from zero at the wall to a maximum value at the center and over a large section of the cyclone it varies inversely as the ½ to ⅓ power of the radius. Because of the complex flow pattern, simplifying assumptions cannot be made to calculate pressure drop. Pressure drop varies from 1 to 20 inlet velocity heads and large-sized cyclones are not generally designed to recover particles less than 5 μ in diameter.

Any cyclone separator for dust elimination can be used for elimination of liquid entrainment, and many companies supply centrifugal separators which can be installed in existing process vessels to solve the entrainment problem at its source. Figure 18-142 illustrates some of the units available for this application. Many

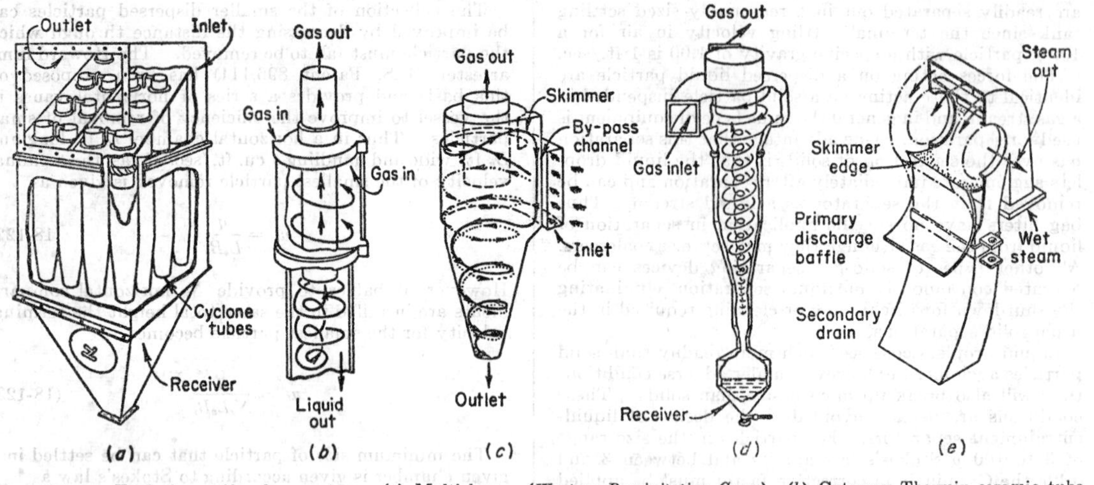

Fig. 18-142. Typical centrifugal separators. (*a*) Multiclone. (*Western Precipitation Corp.*) (*b*) Cutaway Thermix ceramic tube. (*Prat-Daniel Corp.*) (*c*) Van Tongeren cyclone. (*Buell Engineering Co.*) (*d*) Sirocco type D collector. (*American Blower Corp.*) (*e*) Horizontal steam separator. (*Foster Wheeler Corp.*) (*Montross, Chem. Eng., October*, 1953.)

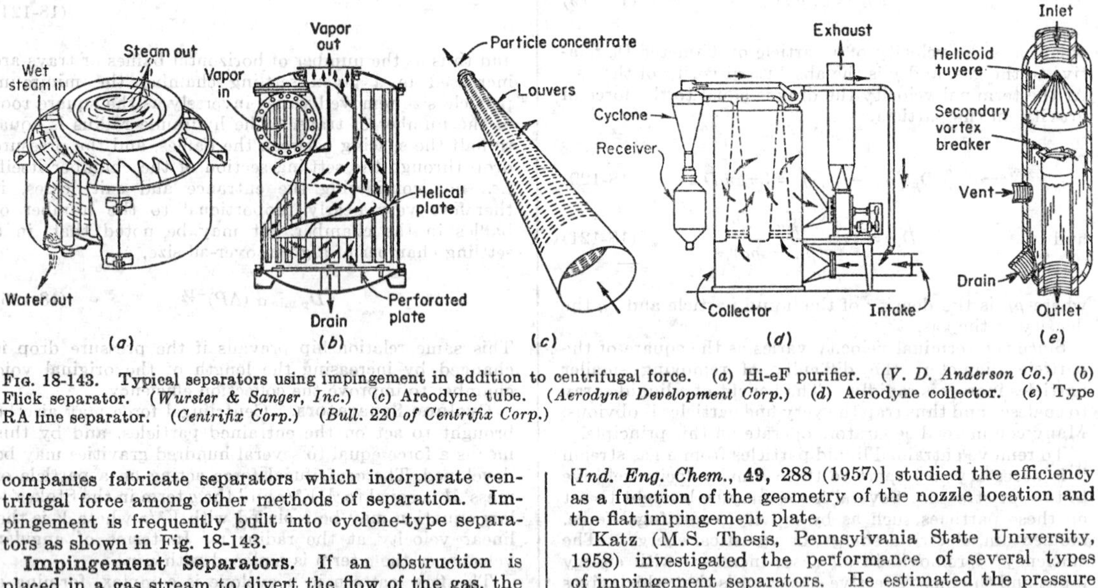

Fig. 18-143. Typical separators using impingement in addition to centrifugal force. (*a*) Hi-eF purifier. (*V. D. Anderson Co.*) (*b*) Flick separator. (*Wurster & Sanger, Inc.*) (*c*) Areodyne tube. (*Aerodyne Development Corp.*) (*d*) Aerodyne collector. (*e*) Type RA line separator. (*Centrifix Corp.*) (*Bull. 220 of Centrifix Corp.*)

companies fabricate separators which incorporate centrifugal force among other methods of separation. Impingement is frequently built into cyclone-type separators as shown in Fig. 18-143.

Impingement Separators. If an obstruction is placed in a gas stream to divert the flow of the gas, the entrained liquid droplets will be carried forward by their large momentum relative to the gas flow and will impinge upon the surface and be collected. The most effective impingement separation would be obtained by passing the gas at a high velocity through an orifice and impinging the stream on a large flat plate placed at right angles to the flow from the orifice and a short distance away.

Ranz and Wong [*Ind. Eng. Chem.*, **44**, 1371 (1952)] determined the efficiency of impaction for different nozzle shapes. Their purpose was to study the effectiveness of experimental equipment used in the evaluation of particle sizes in aerosols. Nozzle sizes are small and velocities high. Their data form the basis for the calculation of particle sizes collected in the successive stages of a cascade impaction system which can be applied to study the effectiveness of larger commercial entrainment separation equipment. Ranz and Hofelt [*Ind. Eng. Chem.*, **49**, 288 (1957)] studied the efficiency as a function of the geometry of the nozzle location and the flat impingement plate.

Katz (M.S. Thesis, Pennsylvania State University, 1958) investigated the performance of several types of impingement separators. He estimated the pressure drop in an impingement separator consisting of series of jets and target plates from available correlations of contraction and expansion losses of the gas phase, assuming that all the kinetic energy of the gas is expended on the target plate. His measured pressure drop was greater than calculated by about 0.3 to 0.5 gas velocity heads. In his tests kinetic energy of the entrained liquid particles in the jet would be equivalent to more than one gas velocity head if all particles were accelerated to the gas velocity in the jet. Thus it appears that the liquid particles issuing from the jet are not at the jet velocity, and the root mean square velocity for his particles, which were mainly in the range of 1 to 4 μ, was only 60 per cent of the jet velocity. The larger particles, which are easiest to collect, will be traveling at a lower velocity and the smaller particles will approach the jet velocity. This would explain why

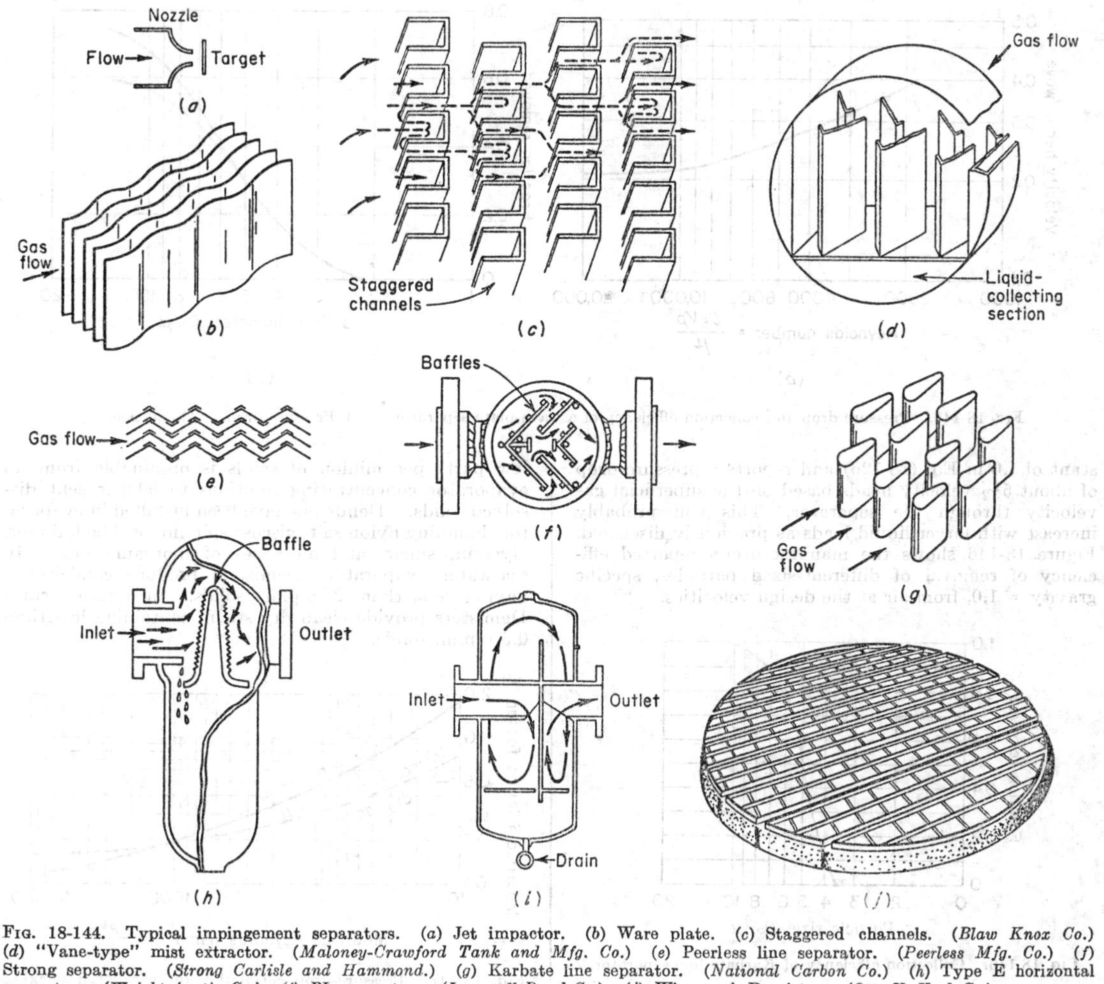

FIG. 18-144. Typical impingement separators. (a) Jet impactor. (b) Ware plate. (c) Staggered channels. (*Blaw Knox Co.*) (d) "Vane-type" mist extractor. (*Maloney-Crawford Tank and Mfg. Co.*) (e) Peerless line separator. (*Peerless Mfg. Co.*) (f) Strong separator. (*Strong Carlisle and Hammond.*) (g) Karbate line separator. (*National Carbon Co.*) (h) Type E horizontal separator. (*Wright-Austin Co.*) (i) PL separator. (*Ingersoll Rand Co.*) (j) Wire mesh Demister. (*Otto H. York Co.*)

the calculated effect of particle size on the impaction efficiency always gives a sharper cut than experimentally determined. The experimental curves frequently intersect the calculated curves at 50 per cent efficiency and thereby indicate that the uncertainty in the calculated efficiency may lie not in imperfections in the theoretical treatment but rather in our lack of knowledge of the velocity spectrum of the different-sized particles suspended in the moving gas stream. The same effect is also observed in data on centrifugal separators.

Katz also studied a wave-plate separator shown in Fig. 18-144. The pressure drop in this type of separator is a function of the geometry of the system and for a wave made up of a 90-deg. arc with a $\frac{7}{16}$-in. radius and an 0.15-in. clearance between sheets, the number of velocity heads per wave is given in Fig. 18-145. The figure also shows the collection efficiency for seven waves in this type of separator. The allowable velocity between the vanes of this unit is given as

$$V = K\sqrt{\frac{\rho_L - \rho_G}{\rho_G}} \tag{18-126}$$

where K is equal to 0.4, and V is in ft./sec.

Katz evaluated the efficiency of removal of different particle sizes and found no appreciable difference when operated at rates of half to three times that given in the equation. The efficiency was calculated assuming all particles in the stream developed radial motion about the center of the arc from which the separator sections were formed. However, the experimental efficiency shown in the figure is only about 20 per cent of that calculated and indicates that the 90 deg. arc is not long enough to develop a definite circular flow pattern in the gas stream. This could be improved by increasing the length of the arcs in the wave at the same radius or decreasing the radius at the same length, but these modifications would increase the pressure drop and one of the features of this design is its low pressure drop. The Tracyfier of Blaw Knox shown in Fig. 18-144 might be considered as the ultimate in this type of flow pattern in that gas may undergo two complete reversals for each bank of channels although in all probability the bulk of the gas follows a smooth wave pattern through the unit similar to that of the previous design.

The Karbate line separator shown in Fig. 18-144 consists of several layers of tear-drop-shaped rods of Karbate. The manufacturer recommends a design based on a con-

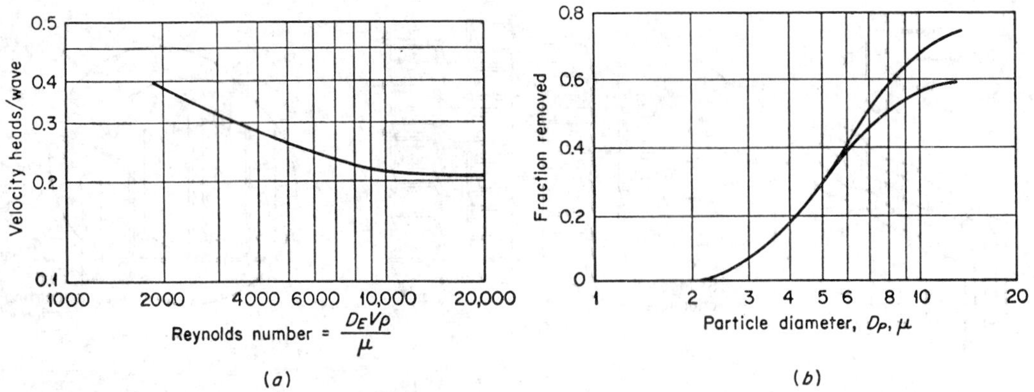

FIG. 18-145. Pressure drop and collection efficiency of a wave-plate separator. (*a*) Pressure drop. (*b*) Efficiency.

stant of 1.0 in Eq. (18-126) and reports a pressure drop of about 5½ velocity heads based on the superficial gas velocity through the separator. This will probably increase with larger liquid loads as previously discussed. Figure 18-146 shows the manufacturer's reported efficiency of removal of different-sized particles, specific gravity = 1.0, from air at the design velocities.

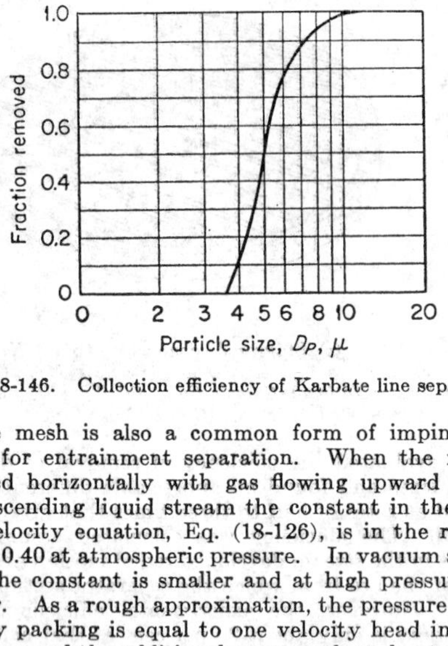

FIG. 18-146. Collection efficiency of Karbate line separator.

Wire mesh is also a common form of impingement target for entrainment separation. When the mesh is installed horizontally with gas flowing upward against the descending liquid stream the constant in the allowable velocity equation, Eq. (18-126), is in the range of 0.35 to 0.40 at atmospheric pressure. In vacuum applications the constant is smaller and at high pressures it is greater. As a rough approximation, the pressure drop in the dry packing is equal to one velocity head in a 4-in. thickness and the additional pressure drop due to wetted packing is equivalent to 0.8 velocity head at the normal design conditions. Figure 18-147 shows a more fundamental correlation of the dry-packing pressure drop as a function of Reynolds number and compared with the correlation of Carman [*Trans. Inst. Chem. Engrs.*, **15**, 150 (1937)] on solid granular packing. The data cover the normal operating range of Reynolds numbers from 400 to 6000, and for the lower values the friction factor probably approaches the Carman correlation.

One of the major applications of knitted wire mesh is the removal of entrainment in evaporators and in distillation columns. In evaporators, the mesh permits a several-fold increase in the evaporation rate of a unit of given size. The mesh also eliminates entrainment to the extent that an aqueous distillate containing only a few parts per million of solids is obtainable from an evaporator concentrating solutions to 50 per cent dissolved solids. Demisters have been installed in evaporators handling nylon salt, viscose spin liquor, black liquor, glycerin, sugar, and all types of inorganic salts. In sea-water evaporators Demisters produce condensates having less than 2 p.p.m. solids. In steam drums Demisters provide clean dry steam containing less than 0.5 p.p.m. solids.

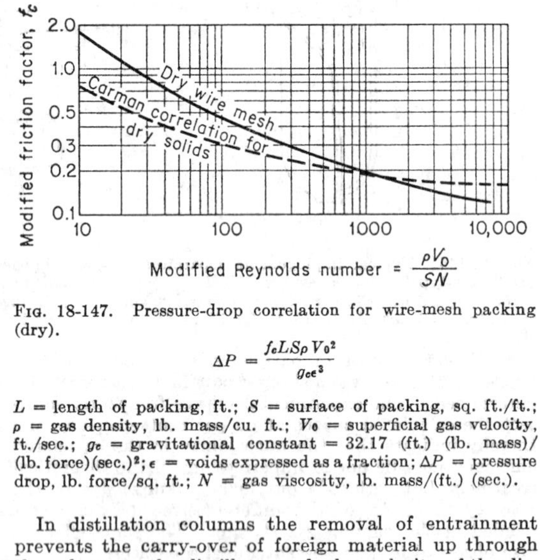

FIG. 18-147. Pressure-drop correlation for wire-mesh packing (dry).

$$\Delta P = \frac{f_e L S \rho V_0^2}{g_c \epsilon^3}$$

L = length of packing, ft.; S = surface of packing, sq. ft./ft.; ρ = gas density, lb. mass/cu. ft.; V_0 = superficial gas velocity, ft./sec.; g_c = gravitational constant = 32.17 (ft.) (lb. mass)/(lb. force)(sec.)^2; ϵ = voids expressed as a fraction; ΔP = pressure drop, lb. force/sq. ft.; N = gas viscosity, lb. mass/(ft.) (sec.).

In distillation columns the removal of entrainment prevents the carry-over of foreign material up through the column to the distillate, and where clarity of the distillate or freedom from foreign matter is a controlling factor the installation of mesh between the trays or at the top of the column will permit greater boil-up rates or the use of a more highly contaminated feed. The effectiveness of a Demister in removing entrainment in a vacuum distillation has been studied by radioactive tracers and reported by Hoekstra, Snow, Braille, and Curtice [*Oil Gas J.*, **58** (1), 70 (1960); **58** (2), 70 (1960)].

Massey [*Chem. Eng.*, **66** (14), 143 (1959)] has also presented performance data on the removal of sulfuric acid mist from exit stack gases using ½-in. Berl saddles, a Karbate separator, porous ceramic thimbles, and knitted wire mesh. He reported that the wire mesh gave the highest efficiency and lowest pressure drop of all types tested.

In these applications the mesh is wetted at the bottom, and Fig. 18-148 shows the additional pressure drop obtained under these conditions. The excess pressure

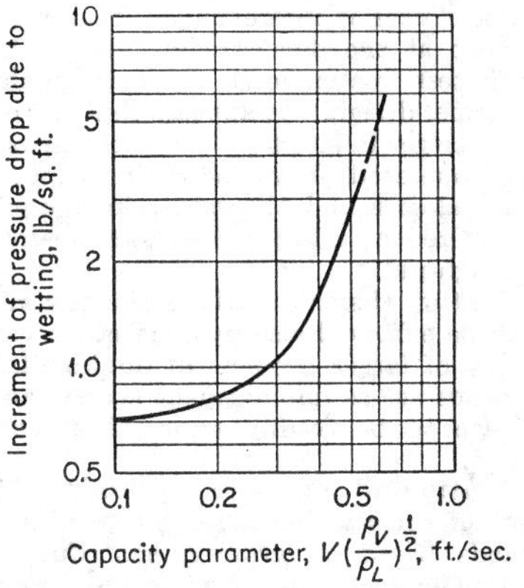

FIG. 18-148. Correction for wetted packing.

drop appears to be constant for different thickness of packing from 4 to 12 in. and can be attributed to the accumulation of liquid at the bottom of the packing. The removed liquid collects at this point until droplets can form which are of sufficient size to overcome surface tension and the frictional drag of the gas stream. The kinetic energy of the entrained droplets also contributes to the pressure drop when these particles are removed from the gas stream, but this factor is ignored in the theoretical treatment of the data. Visual inspection of the packing under normal operating conditions indicates that water accumulation penetrates only 0.6 to 0.7 in. into the packing, and on this basis it is possible to calculate an equivalent wetted wire size to give the excess pressure drop in this section of the packing. This equivalent wetted-wire size is shown in Fig. 18-149 and

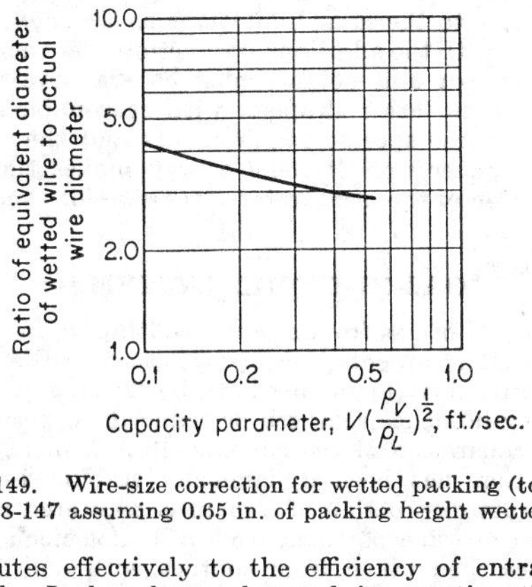

FIG. 18-149. Wire-size correction for wetted packing (to be used in Fig. 18-147 assuming 0.65 in. of packing height wetted).

contributes effectively to the efficiency of entrainment removal. It has been observed in practice that the effectiveness of the packing is greater when the liquid loading on the mesh is sufficient to keep the underside of the mesh thoroughly wetted.

Ranz and Wong (*loc. cit.*) also investigated the collection efficiency of different shapes of impaction surfaces, and Fig. 18-150 shows the efficiency for spherical and cylindrical surfaces. The empirical correction factor for the resistance of a gas to the movement of particles whose order of magnitude is a micron can be calculated thus:

$$C = 1 + \frac{2.5L}{D_p} \qquad (18\text{-}127)$$

where D_p is the particle diameter and L is the mean free path of the gas molecules, both expressed in the same units. This factor decreases with increasing particle size, and the value for a 1-μ particle in air at 25°C. is 1.19. The factor also approaches unity for gases of lower viscosity.

The empirical curves in Fig. 18-150 also exhibit a smaller slope than any of the theoretical equations which

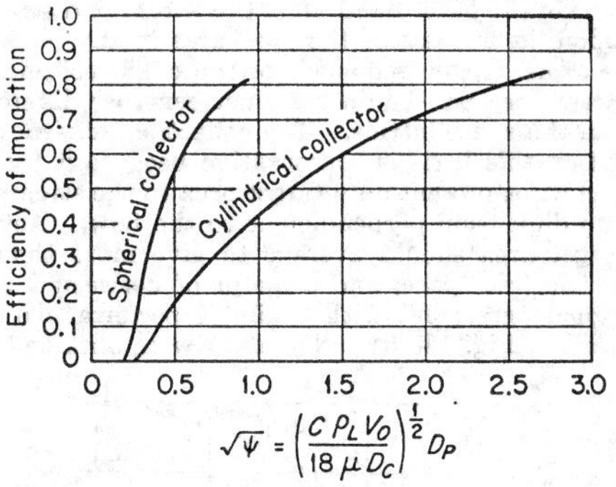

FIG. 18-150. Impaction efficiency of spherical and cylindrical targets. C = correction factor given by Fig. 18-127; ρ_L = particle density, g./cc.; V_0 = undisturbed velocity of aerosol stream, cm./sec.; μ = gas viscosity, poises; D_c = diameter of aerosol collector, cm.; D_p = diameter of aerosol particle, cm. Any system of units may be chosen so as to make ψ dimensionless.

are based on assuming all entrained particles have the same velocity as the gas stream. The curves give only the efficiency of impaction due to the inertia of the particle. To this must be added the efficiency of interception, since it is assumed that any particle whose center passes at a distance from the collecting surface less than its radius will be collected without the action of inertial forces. The interception efficiency for a cylinder of diameter D_c can be derived as

$$\eta_o = \frac{D_p}{D_c}\left[\frac{2 + (D_p/D_c)}{1 + (D_p/D_c)}\right] \qquad (18\text{-}128)$$

and for particle sizes small with respect to the diameter of the collecting cylinder the second term in brackets becomes 2.0.

The total collection efficiency is the sum of interception and impaction, namely,

$$\eta_T = \eta_o + \eta \qquad (18\text{-}129)$$

and the fraction of a given size of particle removed by a single collection layer is then calculated as

$$N_c = a_L \eta_T \qquad (18\text{-}130)$$

where a_L is the target area of the layer expressed as a fraction of the total cross-section area.

In Fig. 18-150, the experimental curve for cylindrical surfaces can be used to predict the collection efficiency of wire-mesh Demisters if the proper model is selected to represent the equivalent orientation of the wires in the mesh. Several models have been proposed, most of them giving higher efficiencies then obtained in practice. It is possible to deduce a model which predicts recoveries of different-sized particles consistent with experimental data. Wire-mesh packing can be considered as completely random wires such that the projection of the wires on surfaces in any direction will be identical. It can be assumed to consist of equal numbers of wires running in three directions all at right angles to each other and one set parallel to the direction of flow. Thus the reciprocal of the square root of one-third the linear feet of wire in a cubic foot of packing gives the spacing of an equivalent cubic lattice of the mesh. Applying this concept, which gives a target area of two wires per cube, the calculated efficiency is considerably greater than observed. A mesh with 97.5 per cent free space on a volume basis, made up of wires of 0.011 in. diameter, will provide 20.4 per cent target area in each lattice plane. On the other hand, if all the wires are distributed at random in this lattice the open area in any plane will be the same as the free space of the cubic volume, and the target area will be only 2.5 per cent per differential plane in the space lattice. The collection efficiency calculated on this basis is conservative because it assumes that the wires present only target area to the stream and have no dimension perpendicular to the flow. Actually the target area should average to give more than the volumetric free space, and a factor of between 2 and 3 gives good agreement with available performance data, as shown in Fig. 18-151. The data were obtained on a

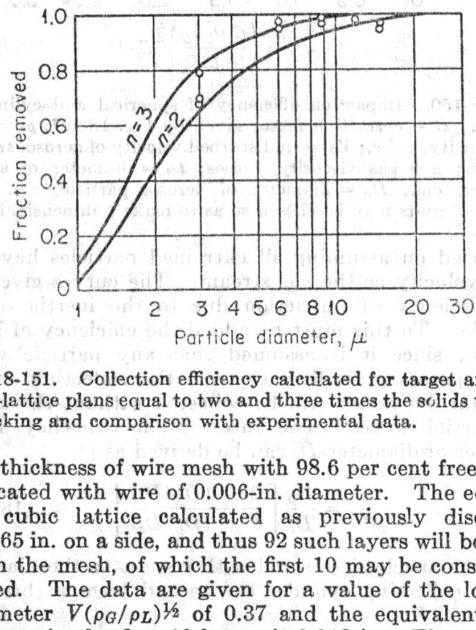

Fig. 18-151. Collection efficiency calculated for target area per space-lattice plans equal to two and three times the solids volume of packing and comparison with experimental data.

6-in. thickness of wire mesh with 98.6 per cent free space fabricated with wire of 0.006-in. diameter. The equivalent cubic lattice calculated as previously discussed is 0.065 in. on a side, and thus 92 such layers will be present in the mesh, of which the first 10 may be considered wetted. The data are given for a value of the loading parameter $V(\rho_G/\rho_L)^{1/2}$ of 0.37 and the equivalent wire diameter in the first 10 layers is 0.018 in. The over-all collection efficiency was calculated using a target area equal to two and three times the fraction of solids in the mesh and assuming complete mixing of the gas phase between intermediate layers in the space lattice. The collection efficiency in the wetted layers is determined by raising the fractional penetration in each layer to the tenth power, and the collection of the remaining mesh layers is determined by raising the penetration per layer to the 82d power. It should be recognized that this sharp line of demarcation between wet and dry packing does not exist, but the assumption of this hypothetical condition adequately reproduced the pressure-drop data. In all studies of the efficiency of entrainment separators, the first test of a theoretical model would be to determine the agreement of the calculated pressure drop with the observed. Only after such agreement is obtained can a valid application of the model be made to interpret the more complex mechanism of entrainment separation.

The experimental data appear to fall within the boundaries of the two curves shown, and thus a factor of 2.5 on the solids volume of the mesh will predict the efficiency of the mesh. This factor has been found applicable to other data on Demisters fabricated of 0.011-in.-diameter wire. The discrepancies of the data at the larger particle sizes is interesting. It may result from reentrainment at the downstream side of the packing because this test was made at a velocity slightly higher than the normal design. It appears that the reentrained particles are larger in size than the entering particles; so a mesh pad operated above the design capacity can be used as a coalescer and the reentrained liquid can be readily recovered in a larger Demister operated at the proper through-put.

The separation of small particles of a few microns and smaller can be achieved also by contacting a gas stream with a spray of larger droplets of liquid. In this case the large drops act as impingement targets and are of a sufficient size to be readily removed in conventional separators.

Electrostatic and Acoustic Methods. Liquid particles of submicron size do not respond readily to separation methods based on gravity, centrifugal force, or momentum. The energy required to accelerate them to velocities necessary for removal from a gas stream makes these methods uneconomic. They behave similar to solid particles of the same size and respond to electrostatic precipitation as described in Sec. 20 on solid-gas separations. However, excellent results have been obtained in removing sulfuric acid mist with a Demister of knitted mesh. It has been installed ahead of the electrostatic precipitator to decrease the load on this unit and has also been used alone with satisfactory results.

Coalescence of liquid particles by sonic and supersonic vibrations has been proposed but commercial operating units on this principle are not available. The vibrations are produced by either a vibrating rod or plate or by a pulsating gas stream from a siren or air whistle. A minimum field intensity of about 150 decibels is necessary to produce sufficient motion of the suspended particles to bring about coalescence. The coalescence depends upon the momentum imparted to the particles by the pulsations of the gas stream, and it is thus subject to the same limitations as the impingement separators with the additional restriction that the number of particles per unit volume must be adequate to effect coalescence to larger droplets with reasonable particle motion. These specific requirements and the low efficiency of generation of sonic energy makes the power consumption of these separators excessive for commercial application.

GAS-IN-LIQUID SYSTEMS

Separation of gas from a liquid continuum in which it is dispersed represents one of two cases. A relatively stable dispersion (foam) needs to be "broken," *i.e.*, the stabilizing influence removed or reduced, to permit subsequent separation of the components; an unstable dispersion that has been dynamically stabilized or that results from destruction of a foam is separated into discrete and massive portions, each a homogeneous phase, which are then taken from contact with one another. The latter case is relatively simple, whereas the former is difficult and practically impossible to generalize. The literature on the second case is very sparse. That on form breaking is extensive, specific, and often contradictory.

When a froth is used as the collection medium for a third (solid) phase, the froth is treated as if it were itself a distinct phase and is separated as cleanly as possible from the bulk of its parent liquid. It then can be considered as a foam that must be broken.

Separation of Unstable Systems. Unstable suspensions of bubbles in water are separated by the action of the buoyant force on the bubbles, a special case of gravity settling. The mixture is allowed to stand at rest or moves in laminar flow along a path until the bubbles have risen to the surface. Table 18-27 shows the calculated rate of rise of gas bubbles of various sizes in water at 20°C. For liquids other than water, the velocity of rise can be approximated by multiplying the rates of Table 18-27 by the specific gravity of the liquid and by the reciprocal of its viscosity. For bubbles larger than 100 μ this adjustment of velocity of rise for liquid properties is erroneous but for bubbles smaller than 1 mm. the error is less than 15 per cent.

A more serious error results from the assumption underlying the values of Table 18-27 that the bubbles are rigid spheres. As has been discussed, circulation within the bubble causes notable increases in its rising velocity in the range 100 μ to 1 mm., and flattening of bubbles 1 cm. and larger appreciably decreases their velocity. In the latter size range, however, the velocity of rise is so high as to make separation a trivial problem. The values of the table may be accepted as conservative, therefore, for the preliminary design estimates of separation vessels.

Separators may be static tanks or continuous-flow tanks or channels. Inasmuch as the separation rates (rates of rise of the bubbles) may be quite low, shallow tanks or troughs are usual. In the deaeration of high-viscosity dopes, the material is flowed in thin sheets along solid surfaces, and a vacuum may be applied to the stream to hasten the collection by virtue of increased bubble size. The Versator (Cornell Machine Co.) is a machine that spreads a thin film of viscous material by the centrifugal action of a rotating bowl through which the material flows. The system is under vacuum, and thus the liquid is degassed.

Table 18-27. Terminal Velocity of Bubbles Rising in Water at 20°C. (Calculated from Stokes's Law)

Bubble diam., μ	10	30	50	100	200	300
Terminal velocity, ft./sec	0.0002	0.0016	0.0047	0.018	0.072	0.162

Care obviously must be exercised to prevent the liquid from acquiring a velocity in excess of the velocity of rise of the bubbles and in the opposite direction.

Separation of Foam. Foam, an aggregation of bubbles separated by thin films, is destroyed by destruction of the film walls. As has been indicated, foams tend to drain, losing liquid from their laminae, which become thinner in the process. In general, foams are not destroyed by draining—that is, the draining usually continues only until a certain minimum wall thickness is achieved, when the gravitational force is no longer sufficient to cause liquid to run from the film. Rather they are destroyed because the films break, either spontaneously or not. Inasmuch as thinner films are characteristically more fragile than thicker ones, drainage abets or hastens the process of foam destruction, and the two are practically indistinguishable Any factor that favors drainage or film instability will assist in foam destruction.

Chemical Defoamers. Chemicals that will expedite the destruction of a foam when they are added to the gas-liquid dispersion are called defoamers. Commercial defoamers normally cause very rapid disintegration of the foam to which they have been added. Usually they are added in relatively small amounts, and it is not uncommon to measure their addition in parts per million.

Chemical defoamers generally fall in two classes, those soluble in the liquid of the foam system and those which are essentially insoluble. Soluble agents are polar-nonpolar compounds similar to aqueous surfactants; indeed, they may be the very agents that, under other conditions, will promote foam (Schwartz and Perry, "Surface Active Agents," vol. I, Chap. 29, Interscience, New York, 1949). For this reason, the concentration in which they are effective is critical and their use is restricted. They sometimes are used as carriers for insoluble defoamers.

Insoluble defoamers usually combine the characteristics of low volatility, ease of dispersion and strong spreading power, and surface attraction and orientation. Low volatility is important to prevent stripping of the material from the system before it can be dispersed and do its work. Dispersibility and spreading power are necessary for the quick effectiveness of small quantities of agent. The ability of the defoamer to concentrate itself in the film and to alter the nature of the film in the direction of reduced stability is the very essence of its function.

Classes of Defoamer Compounds. Currie (in Bikerman's "Foams," Chap. 15, Reinhold, N.Y., 1953) has divided chemical defoamers into the following classes:

1. Aliphatic acids and esters. These are usually moderately higher molecular weight compounds, although ethyl acetate and diethyl malonate have been used to control foaming in ore flotation [Lubman, *Tsvetyne Met.*, No. 7–8, 28 (1932)]. Examples of use: in the paper industry, where fatty acids and fatty-acid esters of polyhydric alcohols control foam in wood-pulp suspensions (Juriseh, U.S. Patent 2,923,687); in water-base paints, where 0.5 to 2 per cent diethyl phthalate destroys foam that would otherwise cause fish eyes and pinholes [Iddings and Kennedy, U.S.. Patent 2,045,551]; in the food industry, where egg-white foam is controlled during drying by glyceryl oleate in 0.01 per cent concentration (with a proteolytic enzyme) [Frey and Miller, U.S. Patent 2,358,324]; in engine-lubricant and other non-aqueous systems, where highly oxygenated organic compounds containing such groups as —COOR, —CO, and —OH in sufficient number to contribute at least 25 per cent oxygen in the molecule are claimed to be effective (Barsoff and Clayton, U.S. Patents 2,430,856–7; 2,528,465–6).

2. Alcohols. Moderate to high molecular weight alcohols, mono- and polyhydric, enjoy wide use as defoamers. Examples: octyl alcohol, long used as a defoamer in distillation columns, is also useful in fermentations (Steibelt, German Patent 602,087) and in many other industrial processes; the bottoms from the distillation of aliphatic alcohols in the C-12 to C-20 range destroy foam in papermaking processes (Hwa, U.S. Patent 2,903,432); 10 to 15 p.p.m. of oleyl alcohol in monoethanolamine solutions destroys foam during the absorption of hydrogen sulfide and carbon dioxide from natural gas [Reed, U.S. Patent 2,390,899; *Petrol. Processing*, **2**, 907 (1947)].

3. Sulfates and sulfonates. These are particularly useful in non-aqueous systems and in aqueous/non-aqueous mixtures but also find limited use in totally aqueous ones. Examples: in extracting hydrogen sulfide from sour gasoline (Nixon and Yarbroff, U.S. Patent 2,341,878); in engine-lubricant systems, where a mixture of a surfactant that will reduce the surface tension of an oil-insoluble polyhydric alcohol used with it below that of water is said to be effective (Trautman, U.S. Patent 2,603,599); in the hydrochlorination of aliphatic alcohols, where 5 to 25 p.p.m. of salts of alkyl-aryl sulfonic acid have been recommended (Carlson and Oakley, U.S. Patent 2,497,150).

4. Fatty-acid soaps. Alkali, alkaline earth, and other metal soaps are used. Examples: aluminum stearate at 0.05 to 3 per cent inhibits the foaming of gear oils (Zimmer, U.S. Patent, 2,338,613); sodium stearate defoams in the scrubbing of exit gases from an oxidation process yielding acetic acid (Osterloh, Voitille, Pyle, and Ficke, U.S. Patent 2,169,369).

5. Nitrogen-containing compounds. The amines, amides, and polyamides are excellent foam attackers and have been used particularly in preventing foam in boilers. Pyridinium, quinolinium, and quaternary compounds also are defoamers. Examples: alkyl amines are boiler-feed-water defoamers (Denman, U.S. Patent 2,363,923); high-molecular-weight materials with

N-substituted amide groups also are used in concentrations of 20 to 200 p.p.m. (Bird, U.S. Patent 2,428,775); polyamides, such as the acyl derivatives of piperazine are similarly effective (Jacoby, U.S. Patent 2,428,801); an aliphatic amine containing 8 to 18 carbon atoms, when mixed with a non-ionic surfactant in the ratio 0.01 to 0.05 parts of surfactant to amine and used as a 2 to 50 per cent solution in a carrier mineral oil, will suppress foam in sewage (Edwards and Rittershavsen, U.S. Patent 2,906,712); Gunderson and Bodach [*Ry. Eng. and Maintenance*, **47,** 447 (1951)] have reported an interesting instance in which the effectiveness of polyamides in locomotive-boiler defoaming is improved by the addition of chestnut extract. The latter is believed to be adsorbed preferentially on boiler sludge, and to prevent the adsorption of the polyamides.

6. Phosphates. Phosphates have found particular use in petroleum-oil systems but are not limited to this use. Examples: 0.01 to 1 per cent alkyl-alkylene diphosphate controls foam in lubricating oils (Smith and Cantrell, U.S. Patent 2,411,671); tributyl phosphate in isopropanol solution controls foam in soap solutions (Broderson and Quaedvlieg, U.S. Patent 2,220,485).

7. Silicones. Organo-silicon compounds are among the most effective of foam depressants and destructors. Analogous germanium compounds also can be used. Silicones are relatively new materials, and their ability to defoam is a quite recent discovery. They have nonetheless become a strong contender among commercial chemical defoamers, for their potency (ability to act in small concentration), wide range of effectiveness, and extreme chemical inertness are a combination of outstandingly attractive properties. Silicones may be of low or high viscosity, the best results in non-aqueous systems being obtained when a low-viscosity defoamer is used with a high-viscosity foaming system and vice versa. The silicone sometimes is applied by its being absorbed in a porous silica filler that distributes the defoamer broadly throughout the foam system (General Electric Co. *Bull.* CDS-204, "Silicone Antifoams," Waterford, N.Y., 1959). Examples: a proprietary silicone formulation controls foam in jam and wine making when used in permissible concentrations (<10 p.p.m.) (Dow Corning Corp., Ref. 1-107, "Dow Corning Silicone Products," Midland, Mich., 1954); tri- and tetra-alkyl silanes dissolved in a water-insoluble, water-soluble mixed solvent repress fermentation foam (Ciba, Ltd., Swiss Patent 257,713); a silicone polymer containing silica is effective at 0.05 per cent in varnish cooking [Vail, *Anal. Chem.*, **19,** 506 (1947)]; dimethyl silicone polymers assist in the foam-free distillation of volatile components from the latex of synthetic elastomers (Walker and Morrow, U.S. Patent 2,482,307); viscous methyl silicones present at 5 p.p.m. defoam lubricating oil [Trautman, *Lubricating Eng.*, **2,** 143 (1946)]; cyclic trimers of dialkyl germanium oxide are defoamers for gear oils (Trautman and Ambrose, U.S. Patent 2,416,360).

8. Sulfides and thio derivatives. These compounds are often mixed with other defoamers to produce a complex agent. Example: metallic derivatives of thio ethers, mixed with organic phosphite esters, inhibit foam in lubricating oils (Evans and Elliott, British Patent 596,150).

9. Halogenated compounds. All halohydrocarbons repress foam, but the lower-molecular-weight ones are less effective because of their high volatility. Highly halogenated and polymerized compounds are particularly used. Examples: highly fluorinated or fluoro-chloro hydrocarbon derivatives with 5 to 50 carbon atoms control foaming in lubricating oils and greases (Davis and Zimmer, U.S. Patent 2,394,596; Zimmer and Rosen, U.S. Patent 2,449,631).

10. Natural products. Vegetable oils and waxes, mineral oils, and sulfated derivatives of vegetable, mineral, and animal oils and fats have had a wide use as defoamers. The earliest defoamers were in this class. The examples of use are too numerous and diverse to be cited here; see Currie (*op. cit.*, pp. 299–301).

11. Inorganic compounds. Certain inorganic salts have found special applications as defoamers. Examples: monosodium phosphate, mixed with boric acid and ethyl carbonate, controls foam in the distillation of copolymers latex to remove styrene (Craig, U.S. Patent 2,432,386); 0.01 to 1 per cent bentonite reduces foaming of return water in sugar-extraction processes (Neumann and Beck, British Patent 580,620).

Chemical defoamers have the disadvantage that they constitute the addition of a contaminant to a process stream or to a product. They often are inert, however, and they are employed in such small quantities that their use frequently is permissible even when high standards of purity obtain, for example, in medicine manufacture and food processing.

For a comprehensive and helpful survey of chemical defoamers, the reader is referred to Currie (*loc. cit.*).

Foam Prevention. Certain specific agents added to materials that are potential foamers will prevent foam from forming [*Chem. Progress*, **6** (2), 3 (1960)]. These additives, called antifoam agents, are chemically in the same classes as defoamers but may differ in particulars of composition and use. They may be employed to forestall foam formation during manufacturing processes or to protect a product from undesirable foaming when the customer puts it to use.

Typical ingredients of antifoam agents are fatty-acid esters, metallic soaps, and hydrocarbons. The correct formulation and proportions generally must be determined by trial, as they will vary with the foamer.

Automatic Foam Control. In the processing of materials that produce foam in the course of their handling, automatic systems for sensing and controlling foam level can be installed to advantage. A notable example is in industrial fermentation processes, as in the manufacture of antibiotics.

Control-system designs have been described by Nelson, Maxon, and Elferdink [*Ind. Eng. Chem.*, **48,** 2183 (1956)] and by Kroll and coworkers [*Ind. Eng. Chem.*, **48,** 2190 (1956)]. They consist essentially of a sensing electrode that is activated by contact with the foam, a solenoid that opens to admit defoamer to the tank, and a reset timer to regulate the length (and hence the size) of addition. A delay control also can be used to prevent overaddition of defoamer in the event of slowly retreating or temporarily resurging foam. The design prepared by Nelson *et al.* is shown in Fig. 18-152.

Physical Methods of Defoaming. Instead of chemical defoamers, or in conjunction with them, physical methods may be used to accelerate the disintegration of foam. Foam structure can be attacked mechanically, thermally, or electrically.

Mechanical Methods. Static or rotating breaker bars are used with variable success to destroy foam or to

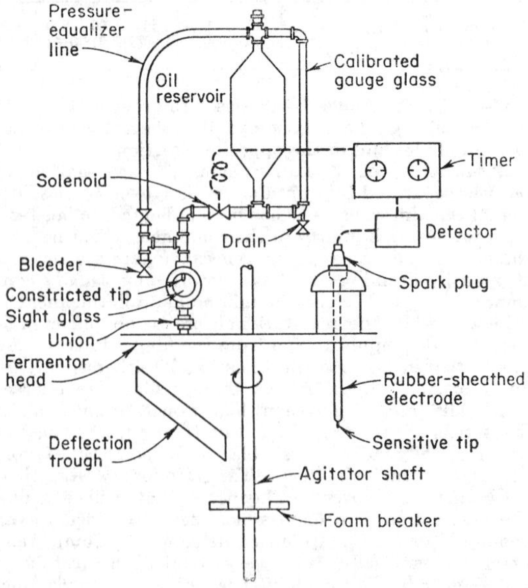

FIG. 18-152. System for automatic foam control in fermentors. [*From Ind. Eng. Chem.*, **48,** 2185 (1956), *with permission.*]

control its level. A rotating slinger that moves in the freeboard space will sometimes break foam masses as they arise, slinging the liberated liquid to the walls of the vessel and further shearing the body of the foam surrounding but outside the envelope of the slinger. In some instances stationary bars or closely spaced plates in contact with the rising foam will help to control its level. The wettability of the surface with respect to the liquid of the foam appears to be important. Shkodin [*Kolloid-Zhur.*, **14,** 213 (1952)] found that the foam on molasses was destroyed by contact with a wax-coated rod but was unaffected by a clean glass rod.

Acoustic vibrations sometimes will rupture foam. Impulses at the rate of 6000/sec. were found to break the froth generated in coal flotation [Sun, *Mining Eng.*, **3,** 865 (1958)], and Parlow [*Zucker*, **3,** 468 (1950)] reported the use of high-frequency air pulses to control the foam in sugar-sirup evaporators.

Thermal Methods. A hot surface in contact with or near a foam usually will destroy the foam. The action presumably is one of evaporation. When sufficient liquid is removed from a lamina it will collapse, exposing other laminae to the effect of the thermal source. Thus Gastrock and Reid [*Ind. Eng. Chem., Anal. Ed.*, **10,** 440 (1938)] observed that a hot wire placed above a boiling and foaming liquid dissipated the foam when the foam came within 1 cm. of the wire. A spark also will destroy foam [Schnurmann, *Ind. Eng. Chem., Anal. Ed.*, **11,** 287 (1939)], and this is probably a thermal action.

In a plant-size tank, a steam coil placed in the freeboard space often will discourage or eliminate foam formation. In this application, it should not be undesirable that solute cake on the heating surface, as this is likely to happen.

Electrical Methods. Although the mechanism is not understood, there is evidence that an electrical field will weaken or destroy foam. Gunderson (U.S. Patent 1,984,210) claimed that a pair of electrodes placed in a foam mass broke the foam by discharging the component bubbles. The destructive action of α particles [Chaminade, *Compt. rend.*, **228,** 480 (1949); Ader, *J. phys. radium*, **11,** 198 (1950)] may be electrical in principle, or a combination of the electrical and the mechanical.

Apparently little quantitative study has been devoted to mechanical techniques of defoaming, and no design data are available. A successful method requires experiment with the specific foam to be attacked.

SECTION 19

LIQUID-SOLID SYSTEMS

BY

Julian C. Smith, B.Chem., Ch.E., Professor of Chemical Engineering, Cornell University; Member, American Chemical Society, American Institute of Chemical Engineers. (Section Editor, Agitated-pan Dryers, Centrifuges, Leaching Equipment)

WITH

Charles M. Ambler, B.S.Ch.E., Director of Chemical Engineering, The Sharples Corp.; Member, American Institute of Chemical Engineers. (Centrifuges)

H. Leslie Bullock, B.M.E., Consulting Engineer; Member, American Society of Mechanical Engineers, Society of the Plastics Industry, American Ordinance Association. (Paste Mixing and Processing)

Donald A. Dahlstrom, Ph.D., Vice-president and Director, Research and Development, The Eimco Corporation; Member, American Chemical Society, American Institute of Chemical Engineers, American Institute of Mining, Metallurgical and Petroleum Engineers, Water Pollution Control Federation. (Gravity Sedimentation Operations)

Lawrence A. Dale, B.S.Ch.E., Project Engineer, The Eimco Corporation; Member, American Institute of Mining, Metallurgical and Petroleum Engineers. (Gravity Sedimentation Operations)

Robert C. Emmett, Jr., B.S.Ch.E., Research Engineer, The Eimco Corporation; Member, American Institute of Chemical Engineers, American Institute of Mining, Metallurgical and Petroleum Engineers. (Gravity Sedimentation Operations)

C. Fred Gurnham, D.Eng.Sc., Professor of Civil Engineering and Chemical Engineering, Illinois Institute of Technology; Member, American Chemical Society, American Institute of Chemical Engineers, American Institute of Mining, Metallurgical and Petroleum Engineers, American Society of Civil Engineers, Water Pollution Control Federation. (Expression)

Robert F. McNamara, M.S., Chemical Engineer, Ford, Bacon and Davis, Inc.; Member, American Gas Association. (Slurry Transportation)

A. W. Michalson, E.M., Sales Manager, Illinois Water Treatment Co. (Ion-exchange Equipment)

Shelby A. Miller, Ph.D., Professor and Chairman, Department of Chemical Engineering, University of Rochester; Member, American Association for the Advancement of Science, American Chemical Society, American Institute of Chemical Engineers, National Society of Professional Engineers, Society of Chemical Industry. (Filtration)

Julian Nardi, B.S.M.E., Late Chief Mechanical Engineer, Ford, Bacon and Davis, Inc.; Member, American Society for Testing Materials. National Society of Professional Engineers, (Slurry Transportation)

James Y. Oldshue, Ph.D., Director of Research, Mixing Equipment Co.; Member, American Chemical Society, American Institute of Chemical Engineers. (Circulation Mixers, Leaching Equipment)

J. Tom Roberts, Ph.D., Senior Chemical Engineer, Oak Ridge National Laboratory; Member, American Chemical Society, American Institute of Chemical Engineers, American Nuclear Society. (Ion-exchange Equipment)

Edward R. Vrablik, B.S.Ch.E., M.B.A., Project Engineer, The Eimco Corporation; Member, American Institute of Chemical Engineers, American Beet Sugar Technologists, American Marketing Association. (Gravity Sedimentation Operation)

CONTENTS

AGITATED PAN DRYERS

EXPRESSION

GRAVITY SEDIMENTATION OPERATIONS

FILTRATION

CENTRIFUGES

SLURRY TRANSPORTATION

REFERENCES: Durand and Condolios, "Hydraulic Transport of Coal and Other Solid Materials in Pipes," National Coal Board, Great Britain, Nov. 5–6, 1952. Lammers *et al.*, *U.S. Bur. Mines Rept. Invest.* 5404, 1958.

Introduction. It is possible to transport most bulk materials by mixing them with a suitable liquid and handling the resulting slurry in pipe or open channels by methods similar to those used with fluids. This method of transportation is not new, for applications date back to 1850. Today it is commonly used within processing plants and to a lesser extent in transporting solid materials for distances up to 100 miles. Within the process industries the coal, mining, and metal-refining industries have made more use of this method than any other group. Materials handled have included coal, anthracite sludge, ashes and clinkers, coal-washery refuse, phosphate matrix, phosphate pulp, clay, and nickel-copper concentrates. In addition, pipe lines have been completed or are in the planning stage to handle a range of products including brine, gilsonite, wood pulp, and nickel-cobalt crystals.

This section presents a review of this subject. It includes a discussion of the materials which can be transported, the equipment needed, and some economic factors which affect the use of this method of transportation. The existing theory of solids-liquids suspensions is covered in Sec. 5.

Several other unit operations are necessary in transporting solids by this method. When the solids are prepared they must be crushed and sized and mixed with a liquid. Recovery of the solid may require filtration and drying. A knowledge of these other processes is needed in any engineering study of slurry transportation. These unit operations are discussed in other sections of this handbook. In addition, it is assumed that the reader is familiar with the theories concerning the pumping and transportation of homogeneous fluids, as discussed in Sec. 6.

Materials Which Can Be Handled. In general it is technically possible to transport any solid by slurry transport if three conditions exist.

1. The solids must not undergo any undesirable chemical or physical change as a result of the mixing or separation of the solids and liquid or the actual transportation itself.

If any undesirable change occurs in the bulk material as a result of any step in the process, the method is obviously unsuitable. If an irreversible chemical reaction between the solid and the carrier fluid occurs, slurry handling cannot be used. Physical changes may also be undesirable. The Bureau of Mines, in a study of the transportation of a lignite (Lammers *et al.*, *U.S. Bur. Mines Rept. Invest.* 5404, 1958), found that the degradation in particle size as a result of the actual transportation made the project economically unattractive even though it was technically possible. Higher-rank coals do not degrade so much and therefore can be transported. Any agglomeration of particles during the transportation similarly affects the application of this method.

Not all chemical or physical change is undesirable. In some instances it is desirable. In the transportation of salt crystals in water, for example, the dissolving of some of the particles to form a brine is a desirable physical change. Sugar-cane stalks have been cut and transported in water solution. In this case the time of transit provides an opportunity for the partial solution of the sugars. Studies have also been made of a method of transporting wood chips in water and suitable chemicals so that partial pulping will occur during transit.

2. The slurry should not exhibit wide variations in viscosity.

In many cases a slurry exhibits variations in viscosity with changes in shearing stress. This phenomenon can be exhibited in any of these four ways:

a. Pseudoplastic suspensions exhibit a decrease in viscosity with increasing shear stress.

b. Dilatant suspensions exhibit an increase in viscosity with increasing shear stress.

c. Thixotropic suspensions possess a structure the breakdown of which is a function of time as well as shear stress. A plot of rate of shear against shear stress exhibits a hysteresis loop, the area of which is a measure of thixotropy.

d. Rheopectic suspensions are a form of a thixotropic suspension in which the suspension "sets up" (undergoes a rapid increase in viscosity) if it is rhythmically shaken or tapped.

Rheopectic suspensions cannot ordinarily be pumped through industrial pipe lines. Other suspensions can be handled as long as the variation of viscosity is not too great. Thixotropic suspensions such as milk and petroleum-drilling muds are handled as fluids without undue problems. The engineer responsible for the design of any slurry transportation system should be aware of the problems which can exist. As a rule some fairly simple tests of the suspension in a rotational viscometer give an adequate idea of the viscosity changes which will occur.

3. The particle size must not be too large.

Large particles, up to 4 in. or more in diameter, can be transported provided that

a. They are a relatively small percentage of the total.

b. They are spherical in shape.

c. High fluid velocities are used.

d. The specific gravity of the particle is close to the gravity of the liquid.

These four conditions are not always met. The closer they are approached, the larger the allowable particle size may be.

For a given solid material (with a fixed specific gravity and characteristic particle shape) and a given liquid, the selection of particle size must depend on an economic study. The larger the particle size, the greater is the cost of transporting the material. The smaller the particle size, the greater is the cost of grinding, mixing, separating, and drying the solid (if this is needed). If considerable crushing is needed, part of the bulk material may be so fine as to be useless.

Design Considerations. *Hydraulic Calculations.* No theory exists which completely describes all possible types of slurry flow, primarily because of the complexity of the system. Pressure drops are influenced by the properties of both liquid and solid as well as by their relative concentrations. Many of the properties of the solid, such as the size and particle shape, are not easily or accurately determined. The scarcity of research work in this field is another factor limiting the development of a consistent theory. It is therefore more accurate to describe the design of slurry-handling systems as an art rather than as a science.

Most studies to date have divided slurries into two different types:

1. A homogeneous colloidal suspension
2. A mixture of non-colloidal free-falling solids in an inert carrier

The first type is characterized by small particles and a high concentration of solids. The second type is characterized by larger particles and low solid concentrations. There are, of course, few cases in practice where such clear-cut differentiation is possible, but most slurries tend to behave like one or the other of these two ideal types.

For both types of slurry it has been found that two types of flow mechanism exist. These types of flow are referred to as viscous (or plastic) flow and turbulent flow. The calculations required to estimate pressure drops are different in each region of flow, as in the flow of true fluids. In slurry flow, however, the nature of these two regions is not so well understood as it is in true fluid flow, and the transition point from one to the other cannot be estimated with certainty. In the existing state of the art, it has not been established whether this division of the flow range into two regions is based on a real difference in the flow mechanism or is simply a convenient empirical method which facilitates the estimation of pressure drops.

Most colloidal homogeneous suspensions behave as non-Newtonian fluids. The theory of non-Newtonian fluid flow, presented in Sec. 5, can be used to calculate the pressure losses for this type of slurry. Both viscous and turbulent flow are important commercially. In some cases, such as cement manufacture, most of the flows normally encountered are within the viscous range.

Non-homogeneous suspensions can best be defined as those liquid-solid mixtures in which solids quickly settle out if there is no fluid velocity. With this type of slurry there is no practical purpose in considering viscous flow. In viscous flow there is no fluid motion at right angles to the direction of flow, and in the absence of such eddy currents there is nothing to keep a particle from settling out. With non-homogeneous slurries, therefore, it is of primary importance to keep the velocity so high that flow is turbulent.

The methods of calculating the pressure drop for this type of flow are presented in Sec. 5. The theory presented there points out two facts which are important in the design of slurry pipe lines:

1. For any system there exists a critical velocity below which particles will begin to settle out.
2. For any system there exists a velocity which will result in a minimum pressure gradient.

Most of the published literature indicates that these two velocities have approximately the same value. From an economic point of view this is very important. It indicates the desirability of operating a slurry pipe line under conditions which are as close as possible to the point at which settling out of the particles will take place.

Pipe Selection. A wide variety of material has been used in the construction of the existing slurry systems. Wood has been used widely in mining industries both in flumes and in pipes. Steel and cast iron have been used. In some short lines subject to extreme abrasion chrome-alloy materials have been used. Other materials are of course possible. If high pressures are to be encountered, however, carbon steel is probably the best choice, for it provides reasonable strength and erosion resistance and will probably be the least expensive installation.

Wall thickness is influenced by both the internal pressure and the possible erosion by the solid material. There are no codes or standards which give the wall thickness required to withstand internal pressure in slurry lines. The A.S.A. Code for Pressure Piping, B31.1, however, presents rules for the calculation of minimum wall thickness for many other fluids. This will provide a reasonable basis for the design of slurry lines as well. The allowance for erosion will depend upon the material to be handled. As an example, in the recent design of a slurry pipe line an erosion and corrosion allowance of about 0.250 in. was used. This was just about equal to the wall thickness required to withstand the internal pressure.

The diameter of the line depends on the size of particles to be carried in the line. Durand and Condolios ("Hydraulic Transport of Coal and Other Solid Materials in Pipes," National Coal Board, Great Britain, Nov. 5–6, 1952) recommend that to avoid plugging the diameter of the line be at least three times the diameter of the largest particle.

Care must also be taken in the slope of the pipe line. If the flow should stop for any reason, the solids will settle out. If provision can be made to drain or clean the line after these stoppages, there is no limit on the permissible slope. If, however, the line cannot be cleaned after an interruption in flow the slope of the line must be less than the angle of repose of the material which settles out.

Pumps. Both centrifugal and reciprocating pumps have been used to handle slurries. Centrifugal pumps have proved to be quite adequate for most slurry service. Impellers can be made of chrome or nickel alloys to give excellent abrasion resistance. They have been used to handle such diverse materials as sewage, gilsonite, coal, nitrocellulose, and fly ash. The head which can be developed by such a pump depends upon the nature of the slurry, but in general the developed head must be limited to 75 to 200 ft. of fluid per stage. To develop higher heads it is common to put several pumps in series. Six centrifugal units have been used in series to develop 900 ft. of head in pumping a gilsonite slurry.

This head restriction is the most serious limitation on centrifugal pumps. Where high heads are required, reciprocating pumps are normally used. Such units have been used on two long-distance slurry lines and are quite common in petroleum drilling-mud service.

Theoretical horsepowers are usually calculated using standard formulas. The efficiency, however, depends on the slurry and the pump itself. Any designs should be prepared only with the aid of pump manufacturers.

Economics. Most materials handled by slurry pipe lines are within plant limits. The reason for this is based on economics. Slurries often occur within process plants, containing a raw material or an intermediate product, and in such cases the only practical method of handling the material may be as a pseudo fluid. The cost of any other method of transferring the product from one point to another (such as separating the fluid and solid and transporting them separately) is prohibitive. Under such conditions high pressure drops can be tolerated which would be uneconomical in long-distance transportation. Similarly the design of the facilities need not be so precise as if long distances were involved. The engineer can use the best published data (or his own experience) as a foundation and apply a good factor of safety. The in-plant facilities may be overdesigned, but because the costs relative to total plant cost are usually small and because alternate methods of handling are more expensive, such excess capacity can be tolerated.

For long-distance transportation of solids, slurries are less frequently used. Again the reason is based upon economics and not a lack of technical data. In long-distance transportation other competitive methods of transportation are available. In most cases, these alternate methods, such as rail or ship, are cheaper. Even where financial studies indicate that pipe-line transportation would result in a cost saving, many companies do not consider these savings adequate to justify the research and development work and the inherent risk in using a relatively new transportation method.

A second economic consideration is the nature of pipe-line transportation itself. A pipe line is a high-fixed-cost low-operating-cost item. For a pipe line to be a good investment there must be a guaranteed through-put and a long useful life. This limits the use of pipe lines to intracompany transportation problems where the company intends to operate in the same manner for a long period of time or to sales agreements where the two companies are willing to enter into long-term agreements. These conditions are not common in the chemical process industries.

CIRCULATION MIXERS

REFERENCES: A.I.Ch.E. Equipment Testing Procedures, "Impeller Type Mixers," September, 1959. MacMullin and Weber, *Chem. & Met. Eng.*, **42**, 254 (1935). Rushton and Oldshue, *Chem. Eng. Progress*, **49**, 161, 267 (1953). Weisman and Efferding, *Am. Inst. Chem. Engrs. J.*, **6**, 419 (1960).

Introduction. Mixtures of solids and liquids are blended in a variety of equipment types, depending on the physical characteristics of the mixture. Relatively thin, pumpable suspensions are usually handled in tanks agitated with an impeller or fluid jet; non-flowing pastes are handled in slow-speed non-circulating mixers. This article deals with impeller mixers and jet mixers for pumpable slurries. Paste mixers are discussed on pp. 19-26 to 19-37.

MIXING EQUIPMENT

Impeller Mixers. An impeller mixer comprises a tank, usually vertical, one or more motor-driven impellers, and auxiliaries such as gear reducers, stuffing boxes, and baffles. Impellers may be roughly divided into two broad classes: axial-flow impellers and radial-flow impellers. The classification depends on the angle the blade makes with the mixer axis.

Axial-flow Impellers. Axial-flow impellers include all impellers in which the blade makes an angle of less than 90 deg. with the mixer axis. Propellers, fan turbines, and pitched paddles, as illustrated in Figs. 19-1 to 19-3, are representative axial-flow impellers. Most common for solid-liquid mixing, however, are propeller mixers, either portable or fixed mounted.

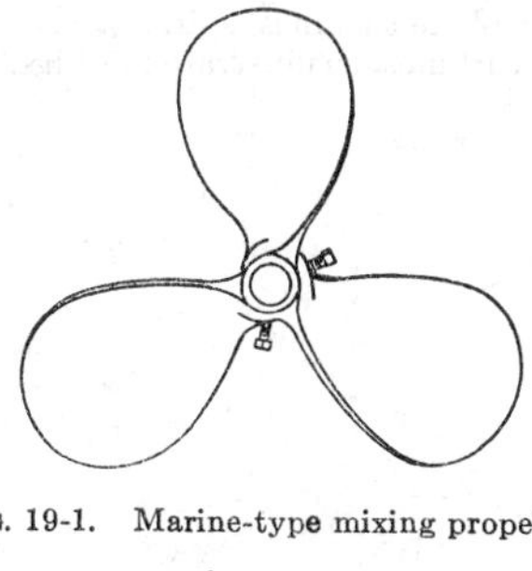

FIG. 19-1. Marine-type mixing propeller.

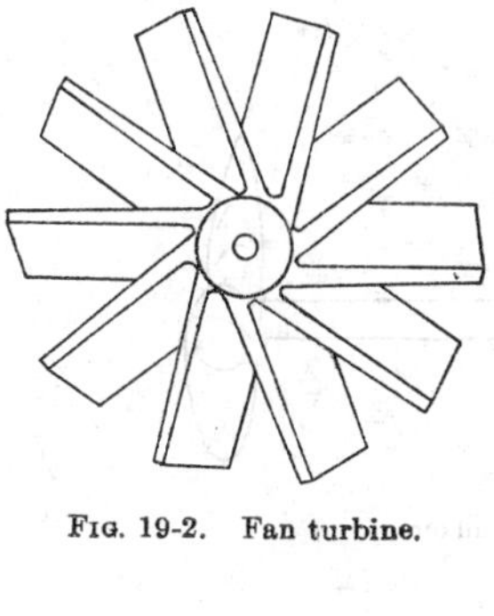

FIG. 19-2. Fan turbine.

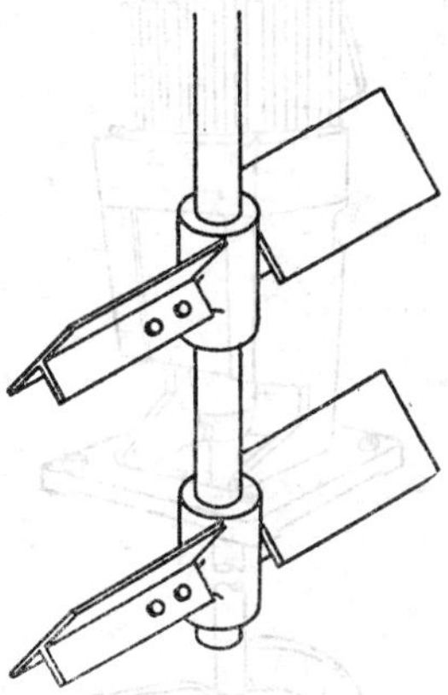

FIG. 19-3. Pitched paddle.

Portable mixers clamp on the side of a mixing vessel and are made in sizes up to 3 hp. To achieve a top-to-bottom flow pattern, they are commonly mounted angularly off center, as shown in Fig. 19-4, or they may be mounted vertically on center with baffles at the wall. Two basic speed ranges are available: either 1150 or 1750 r.p.m. with direct drive, and 350 to 420 r.p.m. with a gear drive.

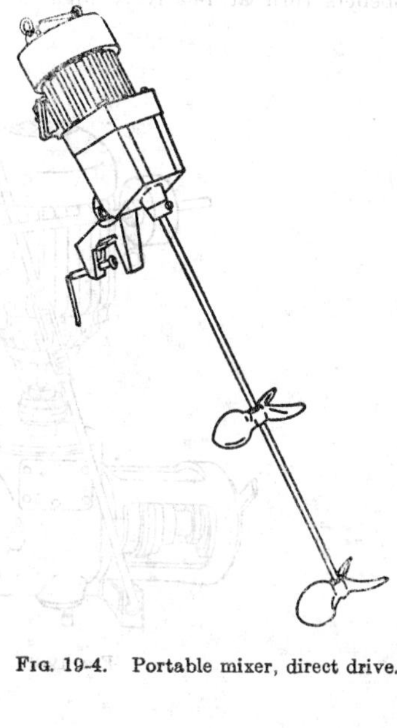

FIG. 19-4. Portable mixer, direct drive.

The high-speed units give a high level of fluid shear and relatively low pumping capacity throughout the tank; the low-speed units give a large pumping capacity, with less fluid shear. For suspension of solids it is common to use the gear-driven units, while for rapid dispersion or fast reactions, the high-speed units are usually used.

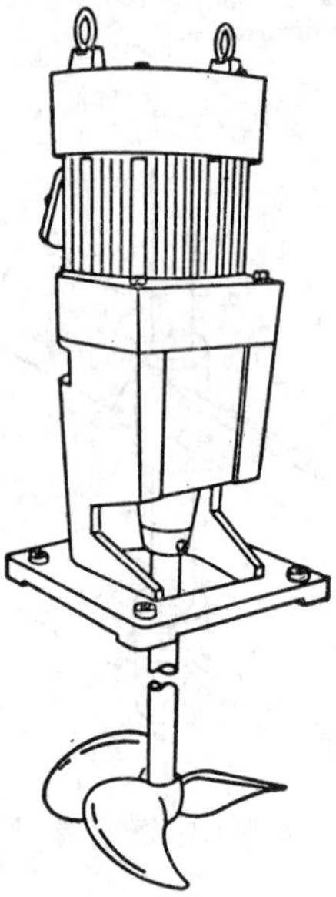

FIG. 19-5. Typical fixed-mounted propeller mixer.

For many medium-duty mixing applications, requiring up to 3 hp., the fixed-mounted propeller mixer shown in Fig. 19-5 is used. Such mixers are also mounted, as a rule, angularly off center to give top-to-bottom flow. They have the same speed ranges as portable mixers. They may be equipped with stuffing boxes or mechanical seals if the tank must be closed.

Since propellers turn at relatively high speeds, the drive required for a given power transmission is not expensive. Top-entering propeller mixers, however, cannot deliver more than about 3 hp., and the shaft length is limited to a maximum of about 6 ft.

Side-entering propeller mixers (Fig. 19-6) are used most commonly on applications where abrasive slurries are not present. Seals and stuffing boxes can be designed to operate in abrasive slurries but are best avoided if possible.

Standard impeller speeds are either 1150 or 420 r.p.m. Typical applications include suspension of sediment in petroleum pipe-line tanks, paper-pulp mixing, and other applications where the solids settle relatively slowly.

Wilson [*Oil Gas J.*, **53** (27), 165 (Nov. 8, 1954)] and Halpine [*World Oil*, No. 7, pp. 220H–220J (1953)] discuss the principles involved in this type of operation. The job of the side-entering mixer is to prevent the accumulation of particles that would occur over a period of weeks if the tank were not properly agitated.

Radial-flow Impellers. Radial-flow impellers all have blades which are parallel to the axis of the drive shaft. The smaller multibladed ones are known as "turbines"; larger, slower-speed impellers, often with two or four blades, are called "paddles." Still other designs are called "anchor" or "gate" agitators.

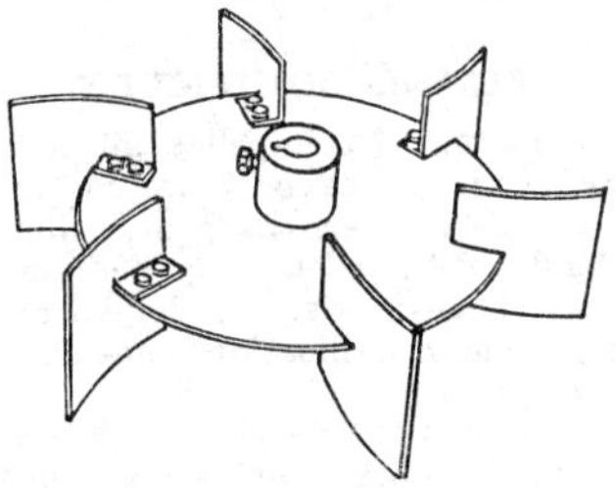

FIG. 19-7. Curved-blade turbine.

A turbine gives excellent circulation of the fluid throughout the mixing vessel. The diameter of the impeller is normally between 0.3 and 0.6 of the tank diameter. Turbine impellers come in a variety of types, such as curved-blade turbines, spiral backswept turbines, and flat-blade turbines, as illustrated in Figs. 19-7 to 19-9.

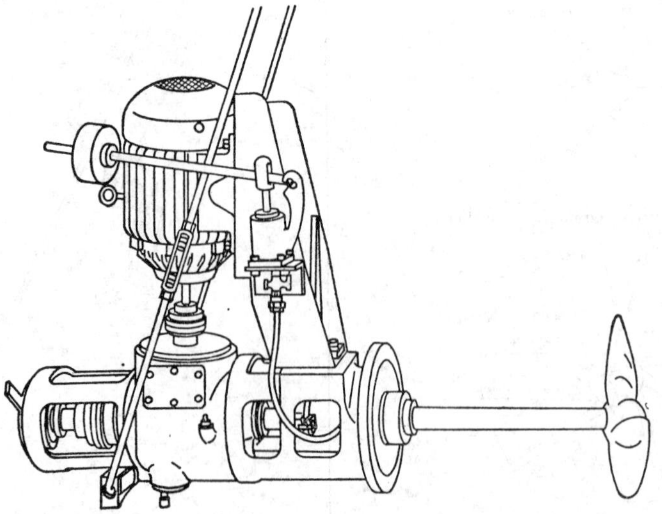

FIG. 19-6. Typical side-entering propeller mixer.

A paddle agitator has a diameter greater than 0.6 of the tank diameter. A typical paddle is shown in Fig. 19-10. Because of the large diameter, paddles turn at slow speeds. Anchor and gate impellers either sweep the tank bottom or, more commonly, sweep the entire peripheral area of the tank in contact with the fluid. These impellers are illustrated in Figs. 19-11 and 19-12. They are normally used where it is desired to have a close clearance between the impeller and the tank wall.

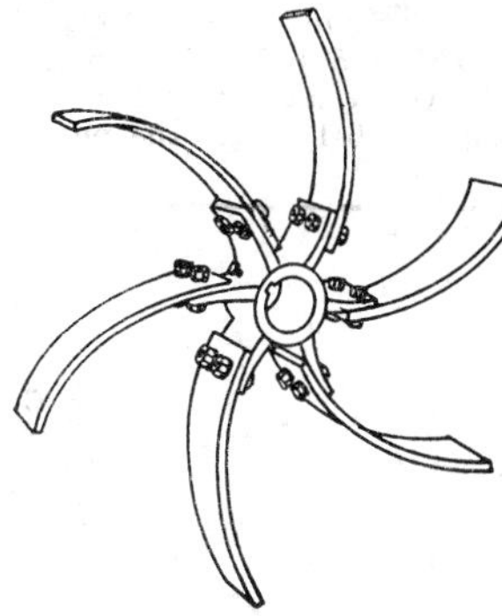

FIG. 19-8. Spiral backswept turbine.

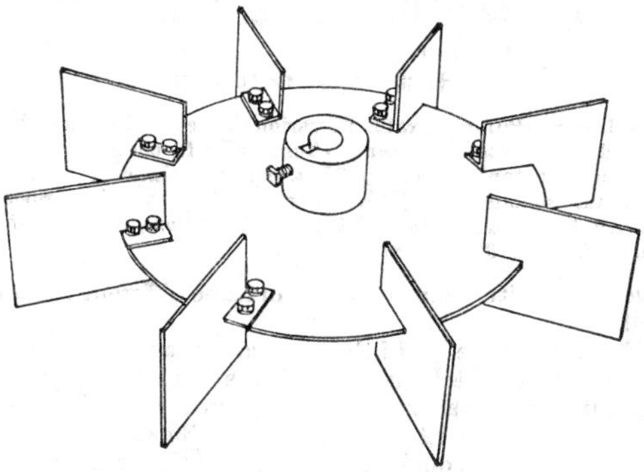

FIG. 19-9. Flat-blade turbine.

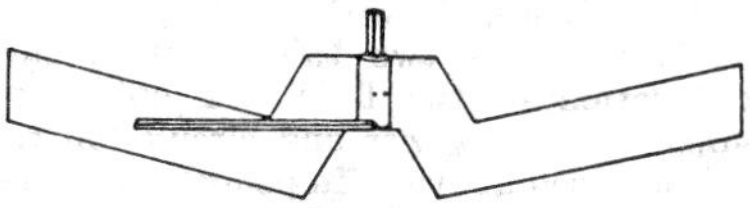

FIG. 19-10. Paddle.

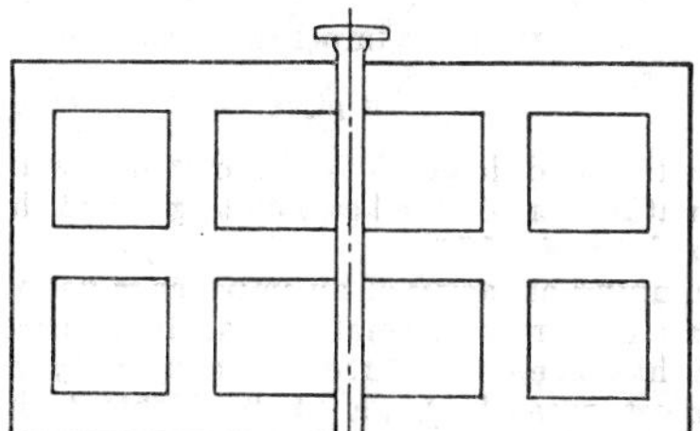

FIG. 19-11. Gate impeller.

Most large-scale mixing of solid-liquid suspensions is done with top-entering turbine or paddle agitators. A typical turbine agitator is shown in Fig. 19-13. Such units are made with any amount of power, from about 1 to as high as 500 hp. The impeller speed is typically between 50 and 150 r.p.m. but, depending on process conditions, may go as high as 400 or as low as 15 r.p.m.

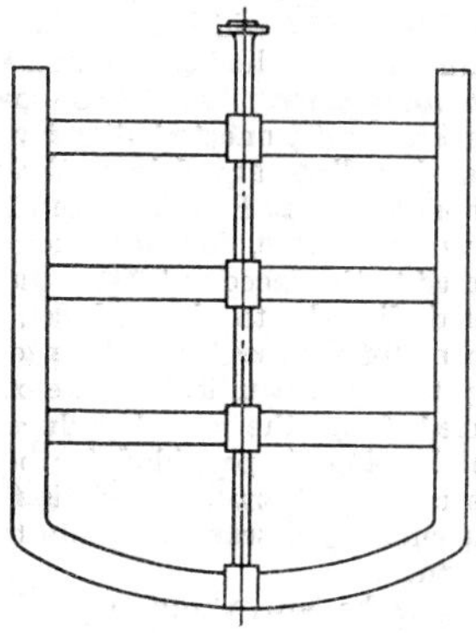

FIG. 19-12. Anchor impeller.

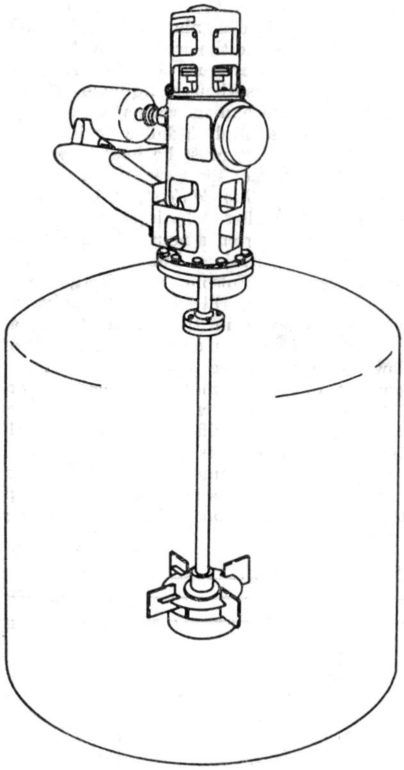

FIG. 19-13. Typical turbine unit.

Baffles. Mild agitation of slurries, especially viscous ones, may be done in unbaffled vessels. High impeller speeds, however, lead to an intense swirl and the formation of a vortex, often accompanied by air entrainment. For vigorous agitations of thin slurries the tank is provided with baffles which stop the swirl. Typical baffles are flat vertical strips set radially along the tank wall, as illustrated in Fig. 19-21. A tank which contains enough baffles so that the addition of more baffles does not significantly change the mixing characteristics of the equipment is said to be "fully baffled." Even in large tanks four baffles are almost always enough to give this condition. The standard baffle width is one-twelfth of the tank diameter. For agitating slurries the baffles are set out one-half the baffle width from the vessel wall to prevent accumulation of solids on the baffles.

Mixer Shafts and Drives. Small high-speed impellers, such as propellers, are connected directly to the drive motor. Slower impellers are driven through a speed reducer like those shown in Figs. 19-6 and 19-13. There are two basic types of drive, depending on how the drive shaft is connected to the speed reducer. In one type, the shaft is coupled directly to the reducer, so that any torsional or bending stresses or fluctuations are transmitted directly to the gear unit. In the other type, the shaft is isolated from the speed reducer. An independent set of bearings is provided for both shaft and reducer. The coupling between them is flexible, which eliminates transmission of transverse and torsional loads to the speed reducer.

Mixer-shaft lengths are a function of speed, shaft diameter, and impeller weight. Unsupported shafts 10 to 15 ft. long are not uncommon. In very deep tanks, foot bearings are sometimes needed, but they are best avoided if possible. In designing an impeller shaft, close attention must be paid to the critical speed of the assembly, for often the impeller must operate fully submerged, in air, and during periods when the liquid level is changing.

Stuffing boxes or mechanical seals are needed on closed tanks. In these cases the shaft deflection is an important design consideration. It must be held to within allowable limits for the type of shaft seal being used.

Injection Mixers. *Liquid Jets.* A jet of liquid may be produced by a propeller or by injecting liquid through a nozzle. Liquid jets from a nozzle are sometimes used in liquid-blending operations but are not common in solid-liquid systems. Folsom and Ferguson [*Trans. Am. Soc. Mech. Engrs.*, **71**, 73 (1949)] give some of the principles involved in the expansion of a liquid jet, and equations for the entrainment from a jet of liquid as it flows from an orifice of given diameter. For a given amount of power, more flow can be produced with a large orifice than with a small nozzle. The optimum diameter of the orifice is one-seventeenth of the distance that the liquid jet is to carry.

Air Mixing. Air is sometimes used for mixing in solid-liquid systems. Air is not effective for suspending free-settling solids but can be used in high-density slurries

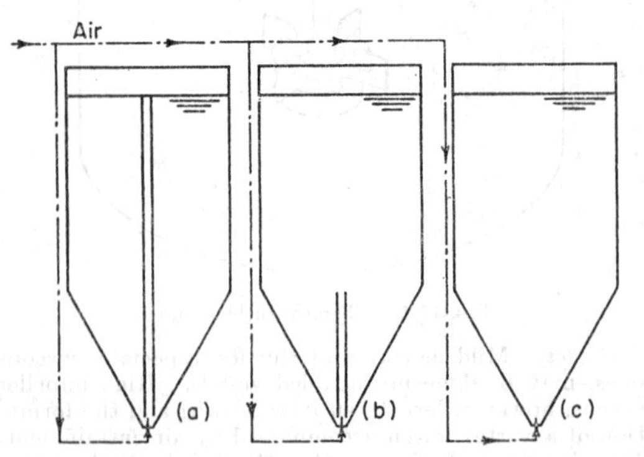

FIG. 19-14. Three different types of Pachuca tanks. (*a*) Full-center column, or Komata-Reefs tank. (*b*) Stub-column tank. (*c*) Free-air-lift tank. [*From Lamont, Can. J. Chem. Eng.*, **36**, 153 (1958), *by permission.*]

having hindered settling. The more common technique is to inject air in the center of a draft tube which causes the pulp to rise in the tube and flow down in the outer annular space. Such a vessel is called a Pachuca tank. Three types are shown in Fig. 19-14. Lamont [*Can. J. Chem. Eng.*, **36**, 153 (1958)] describes the flow patterns in such tanks and gives equations for calculating the circulation rate. Figure 19-15 gives the pumping rate of a

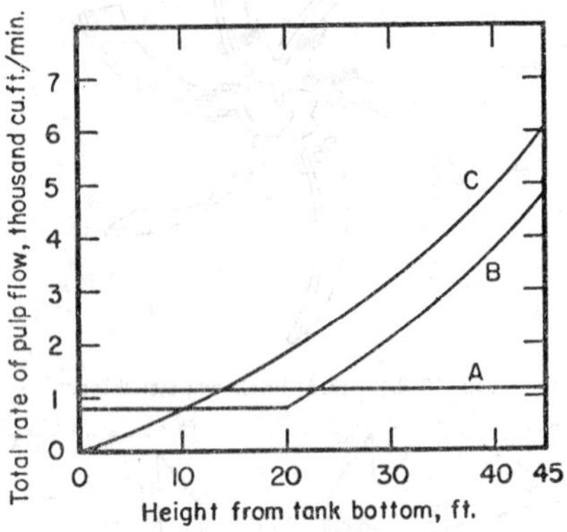

FIG. 19-15. Pumping rates in various types of Pachuca tanks. Line *A*. Komata-Reefs tank, 18-in. by 45-ft. column. Line *B*. Stub-column tank, 18-in. by 20-ft. column. Line *C*. Free-air-lift tank, no column. Notes: Air rate 300 cu. ft./min. Specific gravity 1.6. Pulp depth 45 ft. [*From Lamont, Can. J. Chem. Eng.*, **36**, 153 (1958), *by permission.*]

given pulp with a given air rate in three different Pachuca tanks.

From a knowledge of the circulation rate, it is possible to predict the effect that these tanks will have in smoothing out concentration fluctuations in a continuous-flow process. Gutoff [*Am. Inst. Chem. Engrs. J.*, **6**, 347 (1960)] presents some information in this regard.

FLUID MECHANICS OF MIXING

Circulation Rate, Power, and Head. Any circulation mixer creates two things within the mixing vessel: circulation of the fluid and fluid shear. The relationships between power and circulation rate in jet mixers are discussed above. Impeller mixers also supply energy to circulate the fluid. The power P consumed by an impeller is related to the volumetric circulation rate Q (also called the "pumping capacity") and the velocity head H from the impeller by the equation

$$P = \rho Q H \qquad (19\text{-}1)$$

where ρ is the fluid density. Symbols for this and subsequent equations are defined and units given in the nomenclature table, p. **19**-16.

The pumping capacity of an impeller is defined as the volumetric flow rate normal to the impeller discharge area. It has been measured for certain types of impellers, most recently by a photographic technique in which particles are suspended in the flowing liquid, a thin plane of light is passed through the tank, and photographs are made of the flow pattern. Figure 19-16 shows typical results of this procedure. Data on the pumping capacity of impellers are given by Rushton and Oldshue [*Chem. Eng. Progress*, **49**, 161, 267 (1953)] and Sachs and Rushton [*ibid.*, **50**, 597 (1954)].

The pumping capacities of a geometrically similar series of impellers are given by an equation of the form

$$Q \propto N D_a^3 \qquad (19\text{-}2)$$

where N is the speed and D_a is the impeller diameter.

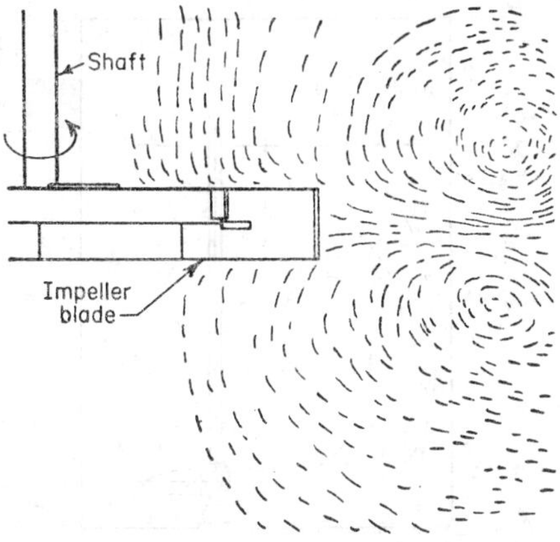

FIG. 19-16. Flow pattern from a 4-in. flat-blade turbine in a 12-in. tank. Fluid viscosity = 150 centipoises.

The impeller head H is proportional to the square of the velocity of the fluid leaving the impeller blades, which in turn is related to the pumping capacity Q. Equation (19-1) shows that there are many different combinations of impeller speed and impeller diameter which will give the same power consumption. For example, in a baffled tank the power consumed by any type of impeller turning at high speed in a low viscosity liquid is given by an equation of the form

$$P \propto N^3 D_a^5 \qquad (19\text{-}3)$$

If this is combined with Eqs. (19-1) and (19-2), the ratio of pumping capacity to impeller head at constant power consumption becomes

$$\frac{Q}{H} \propto D_a^{8/3} \qquad (19\text{-}4)$$

This leads to one of the basic principles of impeller operation: A large impeller running at a slow speed gives a large circulating capacity and a low fluid shear rate, while a small impeller running at high speed gives a high fluid shear rate and a low total circulating capacity. The power input may be distributed in different ways by the choice of the ratio of impeller size to tank size.

Shear Rate. The fluid velocity leaving the tips of the impeller establishes a fluid shear rate in the tank. This fluid shear rate is related to a fluid shear stress. Some processes are especially sensitive to the actual velocity of the fluid, in terms of both its direction and magnitude, while other systems are more influenced by the fluid shear stress in the system. It is important to distinguish between these two conditions.

Some processes are sensitive to the total flow through the tank, to the fluid velocity, and to the direction of flow. In such cases an axial-flow impeller gives a very different process result from a radial-flow impeller. If direction of flow is not important, axial and radial impellers give similar results.

If a process depends upon the pumping capacity of the mixer and the average fluid shear rate in the vessel, then the ratio of flow to fluid shear rate is usually controlling. In these systems, there is usually an optimum ratio of flow to fluid shear rate, and if data are taken with a given impeller type a curve such as that shown in Fig. 19-17 results. If a second impeller is tested, a curve of a similar shape, but somewhat displaced, is usually obtained. In comparing the two impeller types, it is

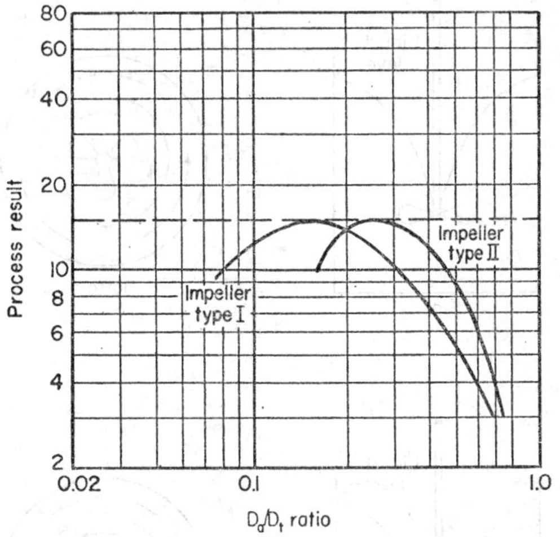

FIG. 19-17. Effect of D_a/D_t ratio (impeller head and flow both important).

found that the optimum points normally occur at approximately the same ratio of flow to fluid shear rate in the system.

The shear rate (or velocity gradient) produces shear stresses throughout the fluid in the tank. With non-Newtonian fluids in particular, the fluid shear rate is a key factor. With laminar flow, the shear stress can be calculated from the shear rate if the viscosity is known. With turbulent flow, however, this is not true. Turbulent shear stress results from the behavior of transient random eddies, including large-scale eddies which decay to small eddies or fluctuations. The scale of the large eddies depends on the tank size and is different in different systems. Small eddies, on the other hand, appear to be similar in both small and large systems. Small eddies dissipate energy primarily through viscous shear. Since their behavior is almost independent of tank size, processes which depend on this effect have similar characteristics in both small and large tanks.

The shear rate in the fluid is much higher near the impeller than it is near the tank wall. The difference is greater in large tanks than in small ones.

Flow Criterion. Reynolds Number. The chief criterion of the type of flow is the tank Reynolds number, defined by

$$N_{Re} = \frac{N D_a^2 \rho}{\mu} \qquad (19\text{-}5)$$

where N is the speed, D_a is the impeller diameter, ρ is the fluid density, and μ is the absolute viscosity. Since N_{Re} is dimensionless, it is important to use the same unit of time in calculating both N and μ.

Flow in the tank is turbulent whenever N_{Re} is greater than about 10,000. Thus viscosity alone is not a valid indication of the type of flow to be expected. Between Reynolds numbers of 10,000 and approximately 10 is a transition range in which flow is neither laminar nor fully turbulent; at Reynolds numbers below 10 flow is laminar only.

Unbaffled Tanks. In agitating a low-viscosity liquid in an unbaffled tank, there is a tendency for a swirling flow pattern to develop, regardless of the type of impeller. Figure 19-18 shows a typical flow pattern for either axial-flow or radial-flow impellers in unbaffled tanks. There is a vortex produced, and characteristically there is a considerable swirl. In spite of the swirl

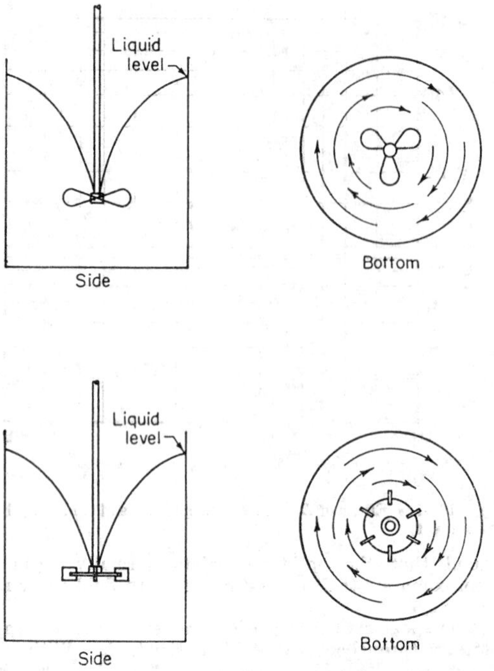

FIG. 19-18. Typical flow pattern for either axial- or radial-flow impellers in unbaffled tank.

and the tendency for particles to rotate about the shaft axis, however, there is sufficient interchange due to the low viscosity and high diffusion rate that satisfactory process results can often be obtained in an unbaffled vessel. However, there is a limit to the amount of power that may be applied in an unbaffled system, since once the vortex reaches the impeller, severe air entrainment occurs. In addition, the swirling mass of liquid often generates an oscillating surge in the tank, which coupled with the deep vortex may create a large fluctuating force reacting on the mixer.

In the transition range it is often possible to superimpose on a basic swirling flow pattern some top-to-bottom motion caused by the friction of the fluid on the tank walls and other obstructions in the system.

In the laminar region, surface drag at the wall of the tank becomes an important source of fluid friction, and it is often possible to superimpose considerable top-to-bottom flow on top of the swirling pattern. Critical comparison of small-scale and large-scale results is essential, since the surface wall area, compared with the volume of the liquid in the tank, has a marked effect on top-to-bottom turnover.

One way of achieving more top-to-bottom turnover in the transition or viscous range is to mount the impeller off center, as illustrated in Fig. 19-19. This position may be used with either turbines or propellers. The position is critical, since too far or too little off center in one direction or the other will cause greater swirling. Changes in viscosity and tank size also affect the flow pattern in such vessels.

Off-center mountings have been particularly effective in the suspension of paper pulp. The ranges of consistencies usually encountered and the level of power required to carry out effective mixing are such that the off-center position is strongly favored.

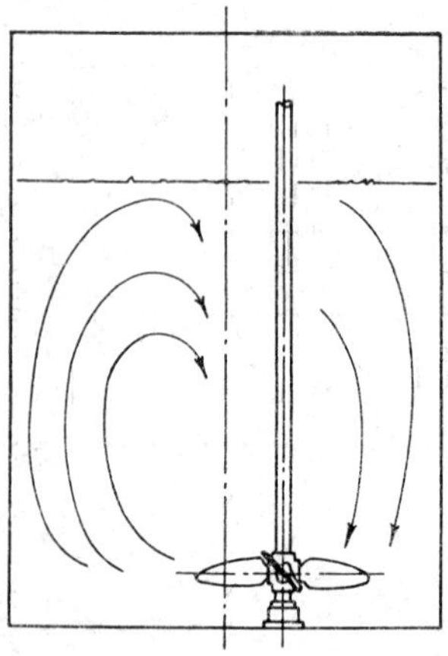

FIG. 19-19. Flow pattern with paper-stock propeller, unbaffled, vertical off-center position.

With axial-flow impellers an angular off-center position may be used. The impeller is mounted approximately 15 deg. from the tank center line and is moved to a quadrant off the tank center line in a direction the same as the direction of rotation. Figure 19-20 illustrates this type of mounting.

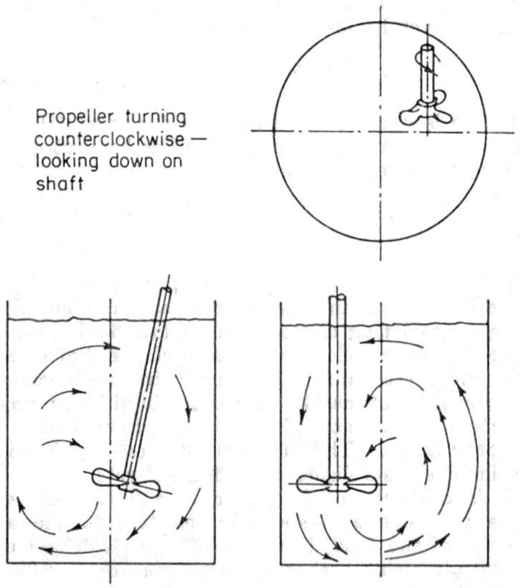

FIG. 19-20. Flow patterns for propeller in angular off-center position and in off-center position without baffles.

The angular off-center position used with propeller units is usually limited to the portable and fixed-mounted propeller types, drawing about 5 hp. or less. The unbalanced fluid forces generated by this angular off-center position can become severe with larger impellers than this.

Paddles, gates, and anchors normally operate in unbaffled tanks, since they have close clearance with the tank wall. Sometimes internal baffles are provided depending upon the degree of fluid shear needed and over-all blending requirements.

Baffled Tanks. The effect of baffles depends upon the type of flow. In the highly turbulent range, with Reynolds numbers greater than 10,000, baffles are commonly used with turbine impellers and with on-center propeller mixers. In these systems, propellers and radial-flow impellers show their true difference. The flow patterns are illustrated in Figs. 19-21 and 19-22. These differences in flow pattern are not significant if the mixing process is governed by both pumping capacity and fluid shear stress, but if direction of flow is important there may be a marked distinction in the performance of these two impeller types.

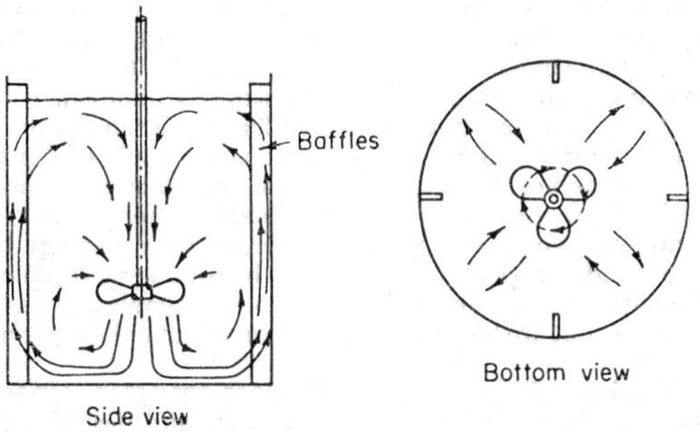

FIG. 19-21. Typical flow pattern in baffled tank with propeller positioned on center.

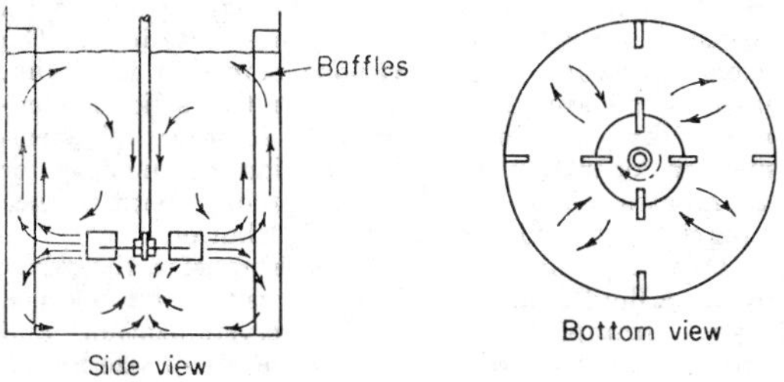

FIG. 19-22. Typical flow pattern in baffled tank with turbine positioned on center.

The use of baffles results in a large amount of top-to-bottom circulation. Many times more horsepower can be added to the system without vortexing or severely unbalanced fluid action.

In the transition region the width of the baffle may be reduced, often to one-half standard width. If the process result depends entirely on the over-all circulation pattern, without a marked requirement for top-to-bottom flow, the use of narrow baffles is satisfactory.

If the circulation pattern is satisfactory when the tank is unbaffled, but the vortex creates a problem, partial-length baffles may be used. These are standard width and extend from the surface into the upper third of the liquid volume.

In the region of laminar flow different authors have various comments about the use of baffles. The same amount of power is consumed by the impeller whether baffles are present or not. However, the flow pattern in the tank is often affected by the baffles. In these cases, the baffles are usually placed one or two baffle widths off the tank wall, the objective being to allow fluid to circulate behind the baffle but to produce some upward and downward deflection of flow. Often it is possible to get effective top-to-bottom flow without baffles in high-viscosity liquids, but there are other times that baffles are desirable.

PROCESS CRITERIA

Batch and Continuous Systems. Many agitated vessels operate batchwise and perform a wide variety of services. Vessels through which flow is continuous are also common, but their design is chiefly governed by one of four considerations. These are as follows:

1. *Provision for continuous reaction, controlled by chemical concentration.* In these processes the mixer often provides complete uniformity of tank contents so the tank acts as though it had a single uniform concentration, and the reaction rate corresponds to that concentration. If the mixing is not complete, allowance for this must be made in the calculations.

If the process result can be expressed in terms of a reaction rate which is a function of a chemical concentration raised to some exponent x, regardless of the number of steps involved, it is possible to analyze the system in terms of a single reaction rate. MacMullin and Weber [*Chem. & Met. Eng.*, **42** (5), 254 (1935)] and Greenhalgh, Johnson, and Nott [*Chem. Eng. Progress*, **55**, 44 (1959)] discuss continuous-flow processes in these terms.

The reaction rate in a well-mixed continuous reactor corresponds to the rate at the end of a batch reaction. In general, therefore, the total reaction volume that must be provided in a continuous system is greater than in a batch system. Figure 19-23 compares the volumes of a batch and a continuous reactor which give the same total conversion with a first-order chemical reaction. By providing several stages, each completely mixed, the volume of the continuous-flow tank is reduced, as shown in Fig. 19-23.

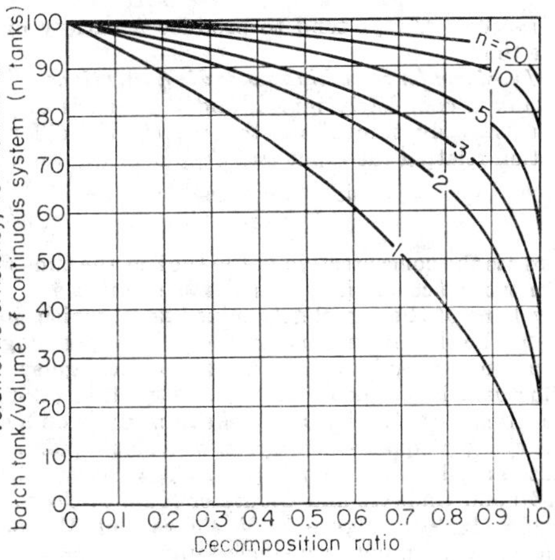

FIG. 19-23. Ratio of volume of a batch reactor compared with the volume of a continuous reactor required for the same degree of decomposition for the same order of reaction. [*From MacMullin and Weber, Chem. & Met. Eng.*, **42** (5), 254 (1935), *by permission.*]

If the only criterion of the process is the concentration of the product, the performance of a properly designed continuous system will be equal to that of a batch system.

2. *Provision for contacting controlled by residence time.* If a tank is perfectly mixed, the feed is dispersed instantaneously throughout the vessel. In a batch system, all particles are in the tank for approximately the same length of time. Since in a continuous tank there are different times for different particles, the product from a continuous reactor is usually not the same as from a batch reactor. Whether this is a better or poorer product depends upon the type of product.

Figure 19-24 shows the effect of the number of stages n. The more stages used in a continuous-flow system, the nearer the approach to a uniform residence time for all particles. It is usually desirable to set a limit on the minimum and maximum residence times in the system and then determine the volume for various numbers of stages.

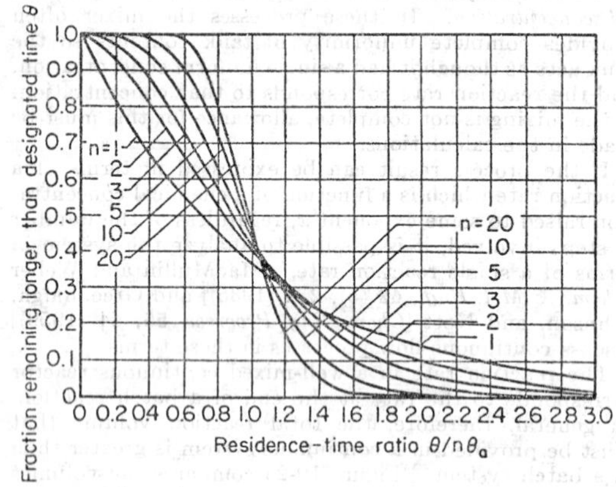

FIG. 19-24. Residence-time distribution in continuous-flow mixing tanks, assuming complete mixing in each tank. θ = designated time. $n\theta_a$ = total residence time (average). n = number of tanks. [*From MacMullin and Weber, Chem. & Met. Eng.*, **42** (5), 254 (1935), *by permission.*]

Plug flow is rarely achieved in a mixed tank because the impellers always tend to produce a variety of residence times.

3. *Provision for smoothing out cyclic fluctuations.* When the tank is completely mixed, and the feed is dispersed instantaneously throughout the vessel, the differential equation relating the input and output of the tank is

$$\frac{dc}{d\theta} = \frac{(c_i - c)F}{V_m} \qquad (19\text{-}6)$$

where c is the concentration in the tank at the time θ; c_i is the input concentration; F is the feed rate; and V_m is the volume of the completely mixed zone, which may or may not be the entire tank volume. The incoming concentration c_i may be constant, vary on a regular cycle, or fluctuate in a random fashion. Equation (19-6) has been integrated for the cases where c_i varies on a sinusoidal cycle, a square-wave cycle, or a single pulse. The results are given by Gutoff [*Ind. Eng. Chem.*, **48**, 1817 (1956)] and Cholette and Clouthier [*Can. J. Chem. Eng.*, **37**, 105 (1959)]. Figure 19-25 shows Gutoff's solution for a sinusoidal input to a single tank.

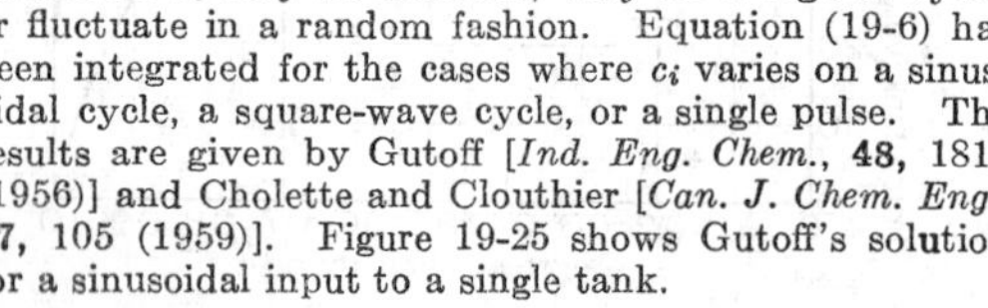

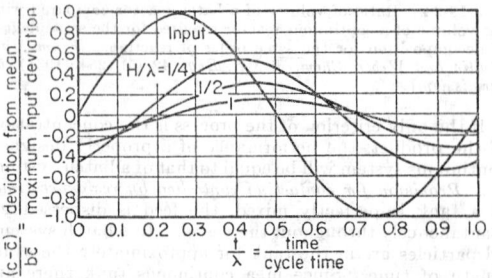

FIG. 19-25. Time variation in outflow concentrations from a completely mixed tank, assuming sinusoidal variations in input concentrations. H = hold-up time in tank; λ = cycle time. [*From Gutoff, Ind. Eng. Chem.*, **48**, 1817 (1956), *by permission.*]

A single tank is more effective than multiple tanks of the same total volume for small degrees of damping. If a large amount of damping is desired, the use of multiple stages becomes advantageous. In a multistage system the reagents may be admitted to the first stage and control points provided in subsequent stages to control the rate of addition.

If the tank is not perfectly mixed, it is still possible to predict what is likely to happen in the system. Gutoff [*Am. Inst. Chem. Engrs. J.*, **6**, 347 (1960)] assumes a flat velocity profile and a circulating flow pattern within the vessel. From an input varying sinusoidally he predicts the output from the tank and points out that, if the circulating time within the vessel is similar to the cycle fluctuation time, very little damping will result. If circulating time is very short compared with the fluctuation time, the fluctuations will be strongly damped.

4. *Maintenance of a Pumpable Slurry.* Often the only function of the mixer is to maintain the tank contents in a pumpable condition. For this, only enough motion in the fluid may be provided to ensure there is not a hard dense volume of packed solids, with no attempt to intermingle particles. It may also be desired to produce a flow pattern in which particles do not remain for days or weeks, but with no necessity for uniformity throughout the vessel.

Physical Dispersion and Mass-transfer Operations. In analyzing the performance and design of a mixer it is important to recognize the true function of the mixer in the process. In some processes physical dispersion is important; in others mass transfer dictates the mixer design. One type of dispersion operation is solid suspension, in which the performance criterion is the concentration of solids at various points in the tank. This may be studied by measuring the solid concentrations by multiple sampling. Another physical-dispersion operation is size reduction of particles or agglomerates. The measures of process performance are particle size and particle-size distribution.

In processes which depend on mass transfer, the mixer provides a fluid regime which promotes transfer between phases. Examples are dissolving, crystallization, and leaching. Some degree of solid suspension or size reduction may also be required, in which case both criteria are applied in analyzing mixer performance.

Solids Suspension. One characteristic of the solids encountered in liquid-solids operations is their settling velocity. Light materials such as filter aid, starch, activated sludge, and paper stock may have settling velocities as low as 1 ft./min. or less. Particles of these materials tend to follow the flow pattern of the fluid, and the slurry behaves as a relatively uniform material. Such slurries are often non-Newtonian.

The other extremes of settling velocities are found with such dense materials as nickel ore, uranium ore, or other metallic ores. Here the settling velocity is a function of the particle size, shape, and density as well as fluid viscosity and fluid density. The settling velocity of these particles in free settling usually ranges from 1 to 10 ft./min. and may go as high as 30 to 40 ft./min. In the middle range of 1 to 10 ft./min. it is possible to achieve a relatively uniform slurry in the tank. If the settling velocity is above 10 ft/min. it is difficult for an impeller to provide uniformity throughout the mixing vessel.

The settling velocity of the solids in the free state is important, but particles settle freely only in certain low ranges of weight or volume per cent solids. The volume per cent solids is often as important as weight per cent solids. Up to about 30 per cent by volume of solids, the particles are usually free-settling and settle rapidly once the mixer is turned off, provided they have a free settling velocity of 1 ft./min. or higher. When the solids concentration is between 30 and 50 volume per cent, there is a combination of free settling and hindered settling and the behavior depends upon the particular process.

At solids concentrations above 50 volume per cent hindered settling usually exists. The slurry then behaves more nearly like a viscous non-Newtonian fluid than like separate phases of fluid and solids. With hindered settling the main purpose of the mixer is to provide flow throughout the material, since once the solids are thoroughly suspended they normally settle out very slowly.

Free-settling Solids. The design of mixers to provide uniform suspension of free-settling solids involves specification of the power consumed, the impeller design, the impeller location, and the ratio of impeller size to tank size. Two criteria can be used for describing solid suspension: (1) the power required to give uniform suspension throughout a given height in a given liquid depth; (2) the power required just to get particles moving off the tank bottom.

Weisman and Efferding [*Am. Inst. Chem. Engrs. J.*, **6**, 419 (1960)], using the first criterion, studied the production of uniform suspensions in small tanks. Their equation for the power P required to give uniform suspension of height Z_s in a tank of diameter D_t with a single impeller operating in the turbulent range is

$$\frac{Z_s - B}{D_t} = 0.23 \ln \left[\frac{g_c P}{g \rho_m V_s u_s} (1 - \epsilon)^{-2/3} \left(\frac{D_a}{D_t} \right)^{1/2} \right] + 0.1 \qquad (19\text{-}7)$$

where B is the distance from the impeller to the tank bottom, ρ_m is the density of the slurry, V_s is the volume of the suspension, u_s is the free-settling velocity, ϵ is the volume fraction of the liquid in the suspension, and D_a is the impeller diameter. Equation (19-7) holds when $(Z_s - B)/D_t > 0.5$, $D_a/D_t < 0.5$. The coefficient 0.23 holds when $B/D_a > 0.5$ but increases to 0.27 when B/D_a is 0.20.

The second criterion has been used by Hirsekorn and Miller [*Chem. Eng. Progress*, **49**, 459 (1953)], Kuenhle [*Chem.-Ing. Tech.*, **28**, 221 (1956)], Zweitering [*Chem. Eng. Sci.*, **8**, 244 (1958)], and Weisman and Efferding. Weisman and Efferding conclude that the results of other authors agree reasonably well with their own using the second criterion. The power requirement P_s is given by the equation

$$\frac{1.74 g_c P_s}{g V_t u_s (\rho_s - \rho)} \left(\frac{1 - \epsilon}{\epsilon} \right)^{-1/2} \frac{D_a}{D_t} = 0.16 e^{5.3B/D_t} \qquad (19\text{-}8)$$

where V_t is the volume of the tank, u_s is the viscosity of the fluid, ρ_s is the density of the solid, and ρ is the density of the liquid. Equation (19-8) is valid for D_a/D_t ratios between 0.36 and 0.43, with the other conditions as specified for Eq. (19-7).

A mixture of particle sizes can often be subdivided into fractions of reasonably close particle size. At a given level of power, some of these solids may be in relatively uniform suspension while other particles may be moving only at lower levels in the tank. If the mixing tank is divided into several zones, as shown in Fig. 19-26, the performance of a tank may be illustrated by drawing profiles of the concentration of various fractions of the feed material as they exist in the various zones in the tank.

The suspension in the tank is not necessarily the same as the feed material, but under steady-state conditions the material drawn off from any given point must be the same as the material fed to the tank. In the case shown in Fig. 19-27, therefore, where the draw-off is at the bottom of the tank, the material drawn out from the tank has the same composition as the feed material. This gives a starting point, and from batch or continuous suspension data it is possible to sketch in profiles which show the zones occupied by the various particle-size fractions.

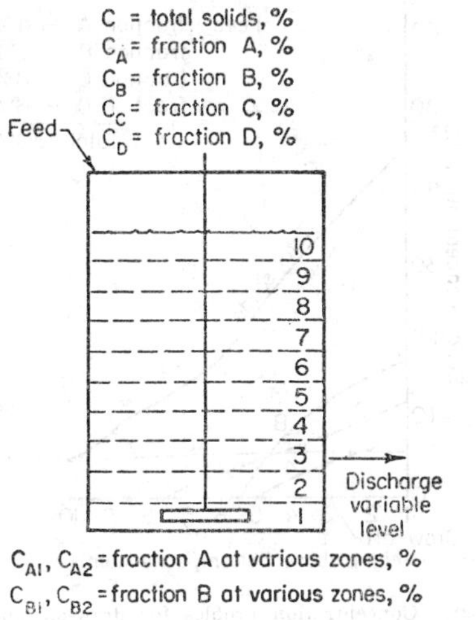

FIG. 19-26. Division of mixing tank into horizontal zones.

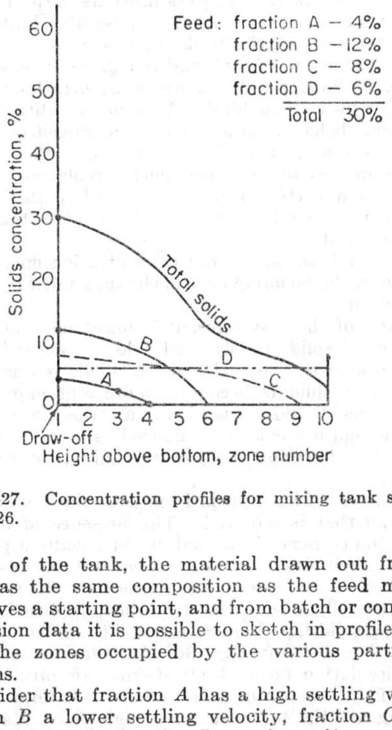

FIG. 19-27. Concentration profiles for mixing tank shown in Fig. 19-26.

Consider that fraction A has a high settling velocity, fraction B a lower settling velocity, fraction C a still lower velocity, and fraction D remains uniform with any appreciable agitation. Figure 19-27 shows that all the particles in the system do not have the same average residence time, as would be predicted from the feed rate and the volume of the tank. In designing tanks for chemical reactions this difference in residence times of the different fractions must be taken into account.

If the location of the draw-off point is changed, the composition of material at that point becomes the same as in the discharge and in the feed material, and the distribution of particles within the tank changes. Figure 19-28 indicates the conditions that exist when the draw-off is above the tank bottom.

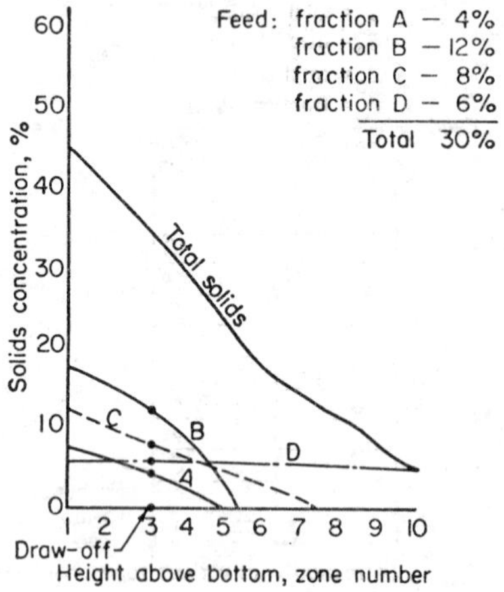

FIG. 19-28. Concentration profiles for draw-off point above tank bottom.

Many other practical aspects must be borne in mind, including the design of tank fillets, possible build-up of oversize particles in the tank, the location of draw-off tubes, and abrasion of tank and impeller surfaces.

Hindered Settling. At solids concentrations above 50 per cent by volume, hindered-settling conditions exist. The slurry behaves much like a homogeneous fluid, although often a non-Newtonian one. The process result desired is often a complete circulation of tank contents in a certain time interval. For this mixing impellers in unbaffled or partially baffled tanks are commonly used.

If the tank is to smooth out concentration fluctuations in the input, the blending time in the tank must be known and specified.

In many of these systems, it is observed that as the percentage of solids is increased a lower power input is needed to give the desired motion. This is due to the fact that the fluid is becoming more and more like a homogeneous liquid instead of a two-phase slurry. Often the high percentages of fine solids found in natural ores assist in lowering the power required for complete circulation.

The absence of hard packed solids on the tank bottom is often all that is required. The presence of fillets of solids in the corners of the tank is not usually a problem as long as their size does not progressively increase.

Compressed air is not often used for fluid mixing. When it is used, one of its most common applications is in circulating solid-liquid slurries with high solids content. Lamont [*Can. J. Chem. Eng.*, **36**, 153 (1958)] gives details of the circulation rates obtained from air mixers. Examples of the amount of air required for various degrees of mixing are the following values given by Kauffman [*Chem. & Met. Eng.*, **37**, 178 (1930)] for a liquid depth of 9 ft.:

Degree of Agitation	Air Flow, cu. ft./min./sq. ft. of Tank Cross Section
Moderate	0.65
Complete	1.3
Violent	3.1

Particle-size Reduction in Dispersion. Size reduction has to do with either reducing the basic particle size of the solid phase or breaking up agglomerates of particles. In either case, a major factor is the degree of fluid shear required. The higher the speed of the impeller, the greater the proportion of power that goes into the velocity head and consequently fluid shear. In some processes size reduction is undesirable, and it is necessary to make sure that it does not proceed beyond a certain point.

Typical operations involving size reduction are the dispersion of pigment in paints, the production of clays and coating materials, and the dispersion of lithium and sodium metals for chemical reaction.

In any given system, it is necessary to determine the fluid shear required. Conventional turbine impeller or paddle mixers may often be used. If higher fluid shear is required, then these impellers operating at high speed and small ratios of impeller size to tank size or some of the more specialized equipment types may be used.

Size-reduction operations are discussed in detail in Sec. 8.

Crystallization. Selection of a mixer to agitate a crystallizer is often critical. The impeller must circulate the material but not produce so much fluid shear that the growing crystals are degraded. Propellers and draft tubes are most common for this service. Crystallizers are described in Sec. 17.

Flotation Cells. Flotation cells are special agitated vessels common in the mining industry in conjunction with mechanical separations. Their job is to disperse air through the slurry and promote preferential attachment of air bubbles to the solid particles and so to cause some of the solids to rise into the froth at the top of the tank. Flotation is discussed in Sec. 21.

Dissolving and Leaching Operations. The dissolving and leaching of solids is often done in baffled or unbaffled vessels agitated with turbine impellers. Leaching is described on pp. 19–17 to 19–18.

A.I.Ch.E. Equipment Test Procedures. The American Institute of Chemical Engineers has published Equipment Test Procedures, Impeller Type Mixers, for testing mixing equipment in place in a process. These procedures cover equipment for liquid-solids contacting and describe the proper techniques for measuring power as well as process performance.

POWER CONSUMPTION OF IMPELLERS

Separate and distinct from process characteristics is the power consumption of a given impeller turning at a given speed. Several publications discuss the power drawn by an impeller under a given set of conditions in a mixing vessel. The power consumed by an impeller does not necessarily bear any relationship to process performance. It is, however, related to the speed and diameter of any given impeller type. Therefore, with a given impeller type in a given fluid system, there are only two independent choices of the three variables power, speed, and diameter. Once two of these have been chosen, the process performance is fixed.

The most useful correlation of power data has been to plot the power number $Pg_c/N^3D_a{}^5\rho$ against the impeller Reynolds number $ND_a{}^2\rho/\mu$. Various impeller types give curves illustrated in Fig. 19-29, from Rushton, Costich, and Everett [*Chem. Eng. Progress*, **46**, 395 (1950)]. The three basic ranges of flow pattern are illustrated by the power curve for a given impeller. In the turbulent region ($N_{\text{Re}} > 10{,}000$) the power is given by

$$P = KN^3D_a{}^5 \qquad (19\text{-}9)$$

where K is a constant characteristic of the impeller Values of K are tabulated in Table 19-1.

When $N_{\text{Re}} < 10$ laminar flow exists for all impellers. There is no effect of baffles on power consumption although there well may be an effect on process per-

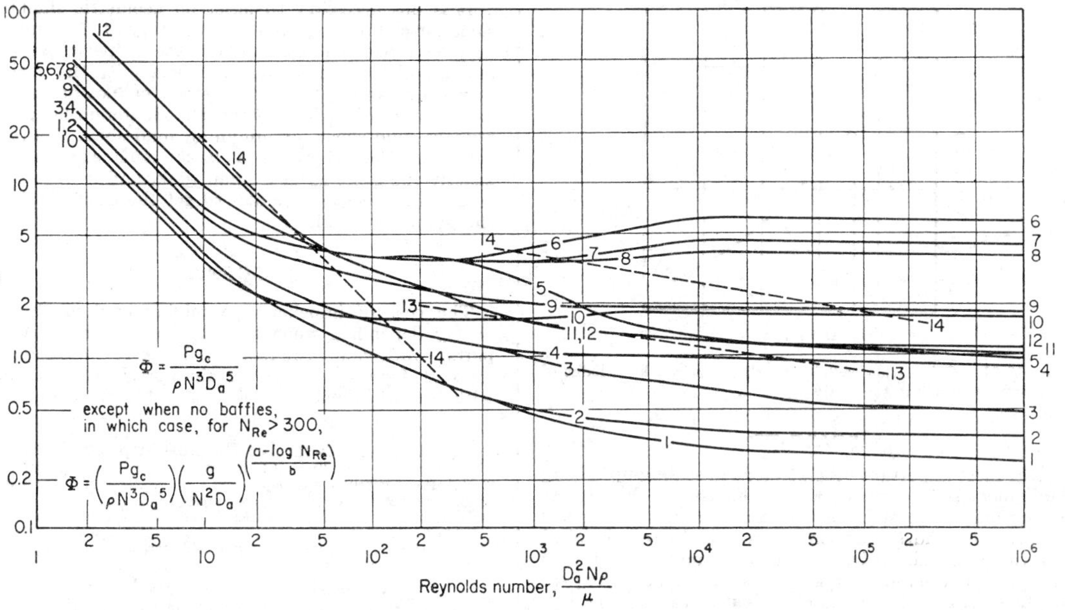

FIG. 19-29. Power characteristics of various mixing impellers: Curve 1, propeller, pitch equal to diameter, no baffles; Curve 2, propeller, pitch equal to diameter, four baffles, each 0.1 D_t; Curve 3, propeller, pitch twice the diameter, no baffles; Curve 4, propeller, pitch twice the diameter, four baffles, each 0.1 D_t—also same propeller, no baffles, but off-centered position; Curve 5, flat six-blade turbine, no baffles; Curve 6, flat six-blade turbine, four baffles, each 0.1 D_t; Curve 7, curved six-blade turbine, four baffles each, 0.1 D_t; Curve 8, arrowhead six-blade turbine, four baffles each, 0.1 D_t; Curve 9, eight-blade fan turbine, four baffles, each 0.1 D_t; Curve 10, two-blade flat paddle, four baffles, each 0.1 D_t; Curve 11, shrouded six-blade turbine, four baffles, each 0.1 D_t; Curve 12, shrouded six-blade turbine, stator ring with 20 blades; Curves 13 and 14, paddle, no baffles. [*From Rushton, Costich, and Everett, Power Characteristics of Mixing Impellers, Chem. Eng. Progress,* **46,** 470 (1950), *by permission.*]

formance. In this range, power varies in accordance with the equation

$$P = K'N^2D_a^3 \tag{19-10}$$

Table 19-1 gives values of the constant K' for several types of impellers.

At Reynolds numbers between 10 and 10,000 is a transition region in which the shape of the power number–Reynolds number curve is constantly changing, and no fixed exponents can be used in the equation.

Table 19-1. Values of K and K' for Eqs. (19-9) and (19-10)*

Type of impeller†	K' in Eq. (19-10), viscous range	K in Eq. (19-9), turbulent range
Propeller, square pitch, 3 blades	41.0	0.32
Propeller, pitch of 2, 3 blades	43.5	1.00
Turbine, 6 flat blades	71.0	6.30
Turbine, 6 curved blades	70.0	4.00
Turbine, 6 arrowhead blades	71.0	4.00
Fan turbine, 6 blades	70.0	1.65
Flat paddle, 2 blades	36.5	1.70
Shrouded turbine, 6 curved blades	97.5	1.08
Shrouded turbine, with stator (no baffles)	172.5	1.12

* From Rushton and Oldshue, Mixing—Present Theory and Practice, *Chem. Eng. Progress,* 49, 167 (1953), by permission.
† Four baffles at tank wall, each one-twelfth tank diameter.

With a Newtonian fluid there is no problem in determining the viscosity to use in the power correlation. With a non-Newtonian fluid, however, the viscosity is a function of the shear rate and sometimes of the time of mixing. In general, this is not sufficient information to calculate the average shear rate that the impeller "sees" through the mixing tank. Metzner and Reed [*Am. Inst. Chem. Engrs. J.,* **1,** 434 (1955)] and Metzner and Otto [*ibid.,* **3,** 3 (1957)] give data on small systems illustrating the fluid shear that results in non-Newtonian fluids. These shear rates were estimated by preparing power number–Reynolds number curves like Fig. 19-30 for a particular impeller and tank with a Newtonian fluid. From the power drawn with a non-Newtonian fluid the power number was computed. The Reynolds

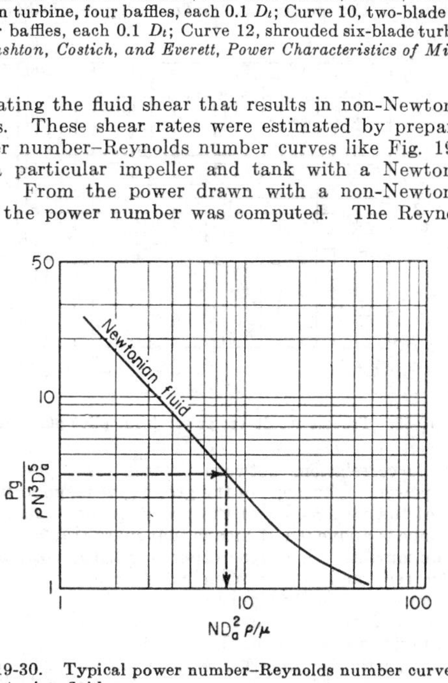

FIG. 19-30. Typical power number–Reynolds number curve for a Newtonian fluid.

number was then calculated from the curve, and the apparent viscosity computed. If data are available on viscosity vs. shear rate and time for the non-Newtonian fluid under consideration, the apparent shear rate in the mixing system may be estimated, as illustrated by Fig. 19-31.

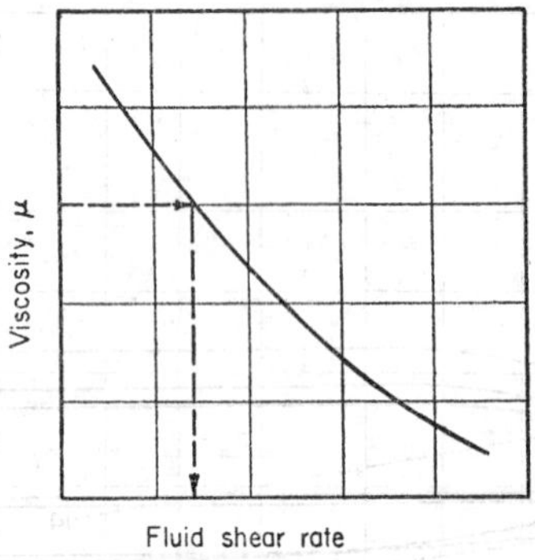

FIG. 19-31. Calculation of fluid shear rate from a knowledge of apparent viscosity in the mixing system.

SCALE-UP

The most important consideration in scaling up mixing equipment is to establish the mechanism of the process operation. It must be determined whether the process criterion is solid suspension, mass transfer, or chemical reaction. Usually a batch test is the most satisfactory for studying the process. During the study, the progress of the reaction is measured at various times to determine the effect of concentration of initial materials. By running at several different mixer speeds the mechanism of the over-all process can usually be determined.

Normally the most important single variable affecting scale-up is the power consumed. Figure 19-32 shows

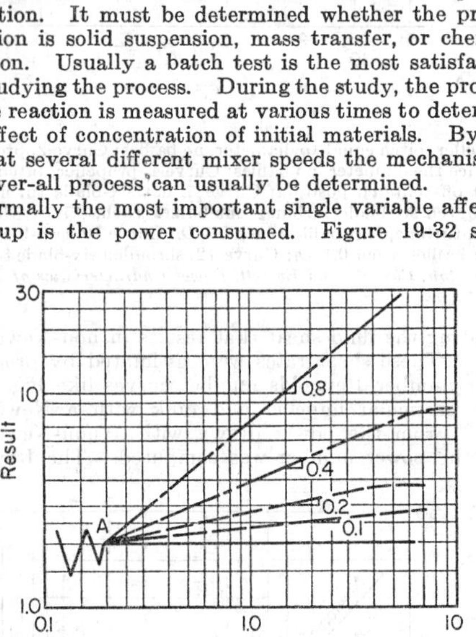

FIG. 19-32. Process result vs. power from pilot-plant studies.

possible correlations between process result and mixer horsepower. The slope of the graph gives a good indication of the mechanism of the process. For example, if the slope is above 0.4, it means that mass-transfer effects are important. If, on the other hand, the slope is between zero and 0.1, a chemical reaction or blending mechanism is usually involved.

If solid suspension controls it is important to study both radial-flow and axial-flow impellers.

Each particular process operation has its own scale-up characteristic. If pure suspension is involved, it will follow one particular pattern. If mass-transfer rates are involved, methods like those proposed by Barker and Treybal [*Am. Inst. Chem. Engrs. J.*, **6**, 289 (1960)] are applicable. If chemical reaction is controlling, the order of the reaction can be determined and the reaction-rate curves of MacMullin and Weber [*Chem. & Met. Eng.*, **42**, 254 (1935)] can be used to assist in the scale-up.

It is not necessary to insist on geometric similarity, since for certain purposes the geometry of the large unit may have been changed to keep the proper relationship among other parameters. For example, the ratio of power level in two different systems cannot be the same as the ratios of pumping capacity, maximum fluid shear, average fluid shear, or minimum fluid shear in the two systems. Conditions in a large tank can never be exactly the same as in a small tank, and it is necessary to examine all the variables to get the desired ratios in the proper proportions.

COSTS

The cost of impeller-type mixing equipment varies widely depending upon the alloy used for the wetted parts. As a guide, the ratios in Table 19-2 are suggested for cost figures. These pertain particularly to mixers with turbine impellers.

Table 19-2. Relative Cost of Impeller Mixers

Type of Unit	Relative Cost
Steel shaft and impellers, open tank	1.0
Stainless-steel shaft and impellers, open tank	1.3
Stainless-steel shaft and impellers, closed tank. Stuffing box up to 150 lb./sq. in. gage	1.7
Stainless-steel shaft and impellers, replaceable cartridge-type seal, up to 150 lb./sq. in. gage	2.1

The cost of mixing equipment is related to the horsepower and speed of the equipment and both of these must be considered in analyzing cost data. However, to find the cost of a mixer which will do a comparable job as a chemical process is scaled up, the following relation may be used as an approximation

$$\text{Mixer cost} \propto \text{tank volume}^{0.6}$$

Nomenclature

B = distance of impeller from tank bottom, ft., measured from lowest point on tank bottom to a point midway between upper and lower extremities of the impeller blades, excluding hub
c = concentration, lb./ft.^{3}: c_i of feed stream
D = diameter, ft.: D_a of impeller, D_t of tank
F = feed rate, ft.^{3}/sec.
g = acceleration of gravity, ft./sec.^{2}
g_c = Newton's-law conversion factor, ft.-lb./lb.$_f$-sec.^{2}
H = impeller head, ft.-lb.$_f$/lb.
K, K' = constants in Eqs. (19-9) and (19-10)
N = impeller speed, r.p.s.
N_{po} = power number $Pg_c/\rho N^3 D_a^5$
N_{Re} = Reynolds number $ND_a^2\rho/\mu$
n = number of mixing tanks
P = power, ft.-lb.$_f$/sec.: P_s, power to move particles off tank bottom
Q = volumetric fluid displacement of impeller (circulation rate or pumping capacity), ft.^{3}/sec.
u_s = free-settling velocity calculated from Stokes's law, ft./sec.
V = volume, ft.^{3}: V_m, volume of completely mixed zone; V_s, volume of completely mixed zone below solid-liquid interface; V_t, volume of tank
x = exponent in reaction-rate equation
Z_s = height of uniform suspension in agitated vessel, ft.

Greek letters:
ϵ = volume fraction of liquid in slurry
θ = time, sec.: θ_a, average residence time in tank
ρ = density of fluid, lb./ft.^{3}: ρ_m, density of slurry mixture; ρ_s, density of solid
μ = absolute viscosity, lb./ft.-sec.

LEACHING EQUIPMENT

REFERENCES: Cofield, *Chem. Eng.*, **38** (1), 127 (1951). Lamont, *Can. J. Chem. Eng.*, **36**, 153 (1958). McCabe and Smith, "Unit Operations of Chemical Engineering," Chap. 13, McGraw-Hill, New York, 1956.

Definition. Leaching is the removal of soluble material from an insoluble solid phase by dissolution in a liquid solvent. The soluble constituent may be a pure liquid or a liquid solution, or it may be another solid mixed more or less intimately with the insoluble material. The solid phase may be particulate matter such as a crystalline precipitate, or it may be a semipermeable cellular material such as wood or fish livers. Thus the solute may be readily separable from the insoluble solid and dissolve quickly upon contact with the solvent; it may also be held in pockets or inside cells and dissolve only after diffusion through the insoluble material. Still other components may become soluble only after chemical reaction with the solvent.

Leaching differs little from the washing of filtered solids, and much leaching equipment resembles the washing section of various filters. In leaching a larger amount of soluble material is usually removed from the solid than in filtration washing, and the properties of the insoluble residue may change considerably during the leaching operation. The rate of dissolution may be controlled by the mass-transfer coefficient between solvent and solute, or it may depend on the rate of diffusion through cell walls, the rate of a chemical reaction, or both. To improve diffusion rates it is desirable to subdivide the solid into as small particles as possible. This, however, may lead to severe problems in physically processing the fine particles.

Leaching Equipment. Leaching equipment is divided into two types: units which handle open permeable solid masses, usually by percolation of the solvent through an unagitated bed of solids; and units which handle impermeable solids or materials which disintegrate during leaching. In the second type the solids are agitated with the liquid and later separated from it. Both methods may be either batch or continuous.

Percolation Leaching Equipment. Equipment for leaching by percolation includes the following types:

Open tanks and vats
Diffusion batteries
Rake classifiers
Bucket-elevator contactors
Screw-conveyor contactors
Horizontal-disk contactors

In the first two types the solids are held stationary in a large tank with a false bottom. They are sprayed with solvent until their solute content is reduced to an economic minimum and are then excavated. Countercurrent flow of the solvent through a series of tanks is common, with fresh solvent entering the tank containing most nearly exhausted material. In a typical ore-dressing operation the tanks are 175 by 67 by 18 ft. in size and handle 9000 tons of ore on a 13-day cycle. Some tanks operate under pressure, to contain volatile solvents or increase the percolation rate. A series of pressure tanks operating with countercurrent solvent flow is called a *diffusion battery*.

Coarse solids are also leached by percolation in moving-bed equipment, including single-deck and multideck rake classifiers, bucket-elevator contactors, screw-conveyor contactors, and other types. The **Bollman extractor** shown in Fig. 19-33 is a bucket-elevator unit designed to handle 50 to 500 tons/day of flaky solids like soybeans. Buckets with perforated bottoms are held on an endless

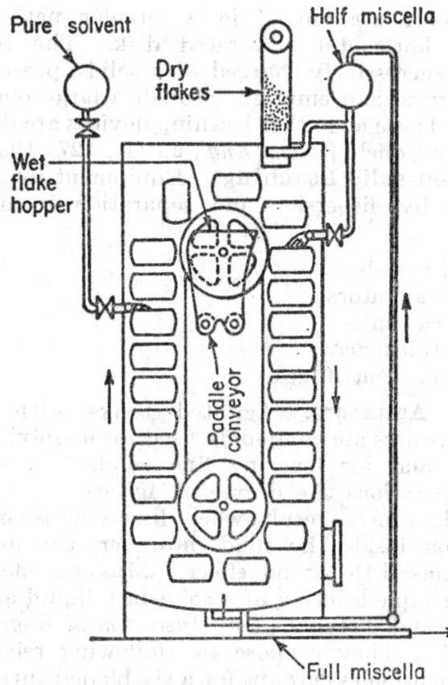

FIG. 19-33. Bollman extractor for leaching soybeans. *(From McCabe and Smith, "Unit Operations of Chemical Engineering," McGraw-Hill, New York, 1956, by permission.)*

moving belt. Dry flakes are fed into the descending buckets at the top of the machine and are sprayed with partially enriched solvent, the "half miscella." As the buckets rise on the other side of the unit the beans are sprayed with a countercurrent stream of pure solvent. Exhausted flakes are dumped from the buckets at the top of the unit into a paddle conveyor; enriched solvent, the "full miscella," is pumped from the bottom of the casing.

Another continuous unit for light permeable solids is the **Hildebrandt screw-conveyor extractor** shown schematically in Fig. 19-34. The screws turn at different

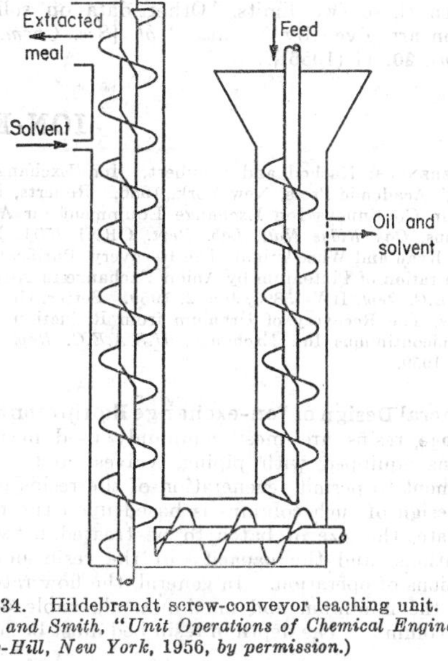

FIG. 19-34. Hildebrandt screw-conveyor leaching unit. *(From McCabe and Smith, "Unit Operations of Chemical Engineering," McGraw-Hill, New York, 1956, by permission.)*

speeds to compact the solids in the horizontal section. Solids and solvent move countercurrently through the U-shaped conveyor. In a **Rotocel extractor** several compartments are moved in a circular path over a stationary horizontal perforated disk. The compartments are successively charged with solids, passed under solvent sprays, and emptied through a large opening in the disk. These and other leaching devices are described in detail by Cofield [*Chem. Eng.*, **58** (1), 127 (1951)].

Dispersed-solid Leaching. Equipment for leaching fine solids by dispersion and separation includes the following:

- Agitated vessels
  - Simple agitators
  - Pachuca tanks
- Gravity thickeners
- Continuous centrifuges

Simple Agitators. Agitated tanks with central turbine impellers are commonly used for dissolving solids in liquids and for leaching fine solids. In ordinary solution operations the degree of agitation has a large effect on the process result; when dissolving is controlled by diffusion inside the solid, however, the degree of agitation has little or no effect. Mass-transfer coefficients for simple solution of a solid in a liquid are given by Barker and Treybal [*Am. Inst. Chem. Engrs. J.*, **6**, 289 (1960)]. They propose the following relationship among dimensionless groups for a six-bladed turbine in a baffled tank completely full of liquid, with no gas-liquid interface:

$$\frac{kD_t}{D_v} = 0.052 \left(\frac{D_a^2 n\rho}{\mu}\right)^{0.84} \left(\frac{\mu}{\rho D_v}\right)^{0.5} \qquad (19\text{-}11)$$

where k is the mass-transfer coefficient, D_t is the tank diameter, D_a is the turbine diameter, n is the rotational speed, and ρ, μ, and D_v are the density, viscosity, and volumetric diffusivity, respectively, of the liquid solution. Nagata, Adachi, and Yamaguchi [*Mem. Fac. Eng. Kyoto Univ.*, **20**, 72 (1958)] studied solution rates in unbaffled tanks agitated with four-blade pitched turbines. They present correlations for the minimum speed at which the solids are all suspended and for the speed at which air is pulled into the liquid by vortexing. Dissolving operations must be carried out at speeds between these two limits. Other data on solids dissolution are given by Nagata *et al.* [*Soc. Chem. Engrs. (Japan)*, **20**, 11 (1956)].

If the process is controlled by internal diffusion the residence time in the vessel is the only significant factor. The degree of agitation has little effect on the rate of solution, and the power supplied to the agitator need only be the minimum required for the desired level of suspension of the solid particles. The impeller may be a radial-flow or axial-flow turbine, a propeller, or a large-diameter paddle. In a continuous-flow process the residence time of some particles, especially the smallest or the largest ones in a mixture of sizes, may differ considerably from the average residence time of all the material in the tank. This should be recognized and allowed for in designing a leaching vessel or in scaling up from pilot-plant results.

Pachuca Tanks. Ores of gold, uranium, and other metals are often leached in large air-agitated vessels known as Pachuca tanks. A typical tank is a vertical cylinder with a conical bottom section, usually with a 60-deg. included angle, 22½ ft. in diameter and 45 ft. in over-all height. In some designs air is admitted from an open pipe near the bottom of the cone, but more commonly a central vertical tube, perhaps 18 in. in diameter, extends from the bottom of the tank almost to the liquid surface. (See Fig. 19-14.) Air is admitted to the bottom of this tube and pulls the liquid-solid suspension up through the tube with considerable velocity. Air disengages from the liquid surface; the agitated suspension finds its way down the outer part of the tank and eventually reenters the bottom of the central tube. Lamont [*Can. J. Chem. Eng.*, **36**, 153 (1958)] describes the operation of Pachuca tanks, both with and without the central tube. Shortening the tube length from 45 to 20 ft. has been found to increase the solution rate in treating gold ores by the cyanide process.

Continuous Leaching Systems. Simple agitators and Pachuca tanks are customarily operated batchwise. After leaching has proceeded to the desired degree the agitation is shut off and the solids separated by gravity sedimentation or by filtration through an external filter. Continuous countercurrent leaching is obtained with several gravity thickeners connected in series, as discussed under Continuous Countercurrent Decantation, p. 19–52. If contact in a thickener is inadequate an agitated tank is placed in the equipment train between each pair of thickeners. When the solids are too fine to settle by gravity, the thickeners may be replaced by continuous sedimentation centrifuges such as helical-conveyor units or nozzle-discharge machines.

ION-EXCHANGE EQUIPMENT

References: Nachod and Schubert, "Ion Exchange Technology," Academic Press, New York, 1956. Roberts, Developments in Continuous Ion Exchange Equipment for AEC Applications, *Oak Ridge Natl. Lab. Rept.* ORNL-2504, May 21, 1958. Ryan and Wheelwright, The Recovery, Purification, and Concentration of Plutonium by Anion Exchange in Nitric Acid, *U.S.A.E.C. Rept.* HW-55893, Jan. 2, 1959. Setter, Googin, and Marrow, The Recovery of Uranium from Reduction Residues by Semicontinuous Ion Exchange, *U.S.A.E.C. Rept.* Y-1257, July 9, 1959.

General Design of Ion-exchange Equipment. Ion-exchange resins are most commonly used in pressure columns equipped with piping, valves, and accessory equipment to permit regeneration of the resins in place. The design of such columns is based upon the required flow rate, the size of batch to be treated between regenerations, and the capacity of the resin under the conditions of operation. In general, the flow rate determines the minimum and maximum allowable diameter of the column. The depth of resin bed must be sufficient to include the necessary volume of resin and to provide for a minimum bed depth, for efficient operation. Required minimum bed depths have been empirically determined. If a bed is too shallow, distribution of the liquid is difficult, and complete exchange may not be achieved throughout a cycle. Inevitably, the lower two or three inches of resin will not be utilized fully because of uneven distribution, which represents an appreciable waste in a shallow bed. Distribution is particularly difficult if the equipment must operate over a wide range of flow rates. Usually, in water-treatment units a range of 4 to 1 is permissible. A smaller range is better when treating valuable products or when exchanging relatively high concentrations of ions.

If the volume of resin required is much larger than can be accommodated in a column suitable for the desired flow rate, storage of the product may be desirable, to permit operation at an acceptable minimum rate. If the desired flow rate requires a larger column than is needed for the necessary resin volume, there must be a compromise. Sometimes this second problem can be minimized by using smaller multiple columns equipped for automatic regeneration, with one column normally in regeneration and the remaining units sized to handle the flow rate. As discussed later, continuous moving-bed equipment is more easily adapted to these extremes and may permit a drastic reduction in resin inventory.

Before the sizes of ion-exchange equipment may be estimated, it is necessary to have a complete analysis of the water or other solution to be treated. The capacity of the resins for the ions to be exchanged must be known. Most currently available ion-exchange resins are relatively non-selective, so that all similar ions will be exchanged by a given resin, whether the process requires this or not. Large amounts of data are available in published literature and sales brochures on capacities and applications of the various resins, but these are generally not specific to a given practical application and should be used for design purposes only by specialists. For any process that is not already thoroughly proved in other plants under similar conditions, and for all major projects, laboratory and pilot-plant work is advisable to determine usable resin capacities, regenerant quantities, resin life, and quality of product. Firms which manufacture ion-exchange equipment will cooperate in such work, and have experience in scaling up equipment from small laboratory columns. It is usually feasible to scale up to almost any size of plant from results obtained in columns 1 or 2 in. in diameter, but such scale-up should not be attempted except by specialists.

Table 19-3 gives typical design data. These should be used for preliminary evaluation purposes only and should not be regarded as iron-clad rules.

Table 19-3. Design Data for Fixed-bed Ion Exchanger

Type of resin	Max. and min. flow, gal./min./sq. ft.	Min. bed depth, in.	Max. operating temp., °F	Usable capacity, kilograins $CaCO_3$ equivalents per cu. ft.	Regenerant quantity and chemical
Cation	7–12 max. 1– 2 min.	24–30	240	18–32 11–20 15–30	5–15 lb. NaCl 4–12 lb. 66°Bé. H_2SO_4 10 to 30 lb. 20°Bé. HCl
Weak and intermediate-base anions	4– 7 max. 1– 2 min.	30–36	100	18–24	3–4 lb. NaOH
Strong-base anions	5– 7 max. 1– 2 min.	30–36	100–120	8–16	4–8 lb. NaOH
Mixed cation and strong-base anion (chemically equivalent mixture)	8–12 max.*	36–48	100	5–8 (based on mixture)	Same as cation and anion individually

These figures represent the usual ranges of design for water-treatment applications and should not be regarded as absolute limits. In general, allowable flow rates and bed depths for chemical processing applications are on the conservative side of the figures given above.

* Flows up to 100 gal./min./sq. ft. have been used for polishing condensate or deionized water.

Typical Ion-exchange Column. A typical ion exchanger consists of a vertical cylindrical pressure vessel of lined steel or stainless steel. Linings are usually of natural or synthetic rubber. Sparge distributors are provided at the top and bottom, and frequently a separate distributor is used for regenerant solution. The resin bed, consisting of several feet of ion-exchange resin beads or particles, is supported by the screen of the bottom distributor or by a support bed of graded quartz or anthracite. A distributor may be designed to prevent escape of resin particles by wrapping perforated pipe laterals with stainless steel or Saran screen, or by placing a similar screen between perforated plates mounted in the top or bottom of the column. Externally, the unit is provided with a valve manifold to permit downflow operation, upflow backwashing, injection of regenerant, and rinsing of excess regenerant (Fig. 19-35). If the unit is to treat a product of greater value than water, provision is made to remove the product as thoroughly as possible before regeneration and to displace the rinse water thoroughly before refilling with the valuable fluid. These steps are commonly known as "sweetening off" and "sweetening on," respectively. Because the resin beads are porous some dilution of the product with water is unavoidable. This can be minimized by using air to help displace water or product from the resin, or by collecting dilute product obtained during the sweetening-off step and using it for sweetening on.

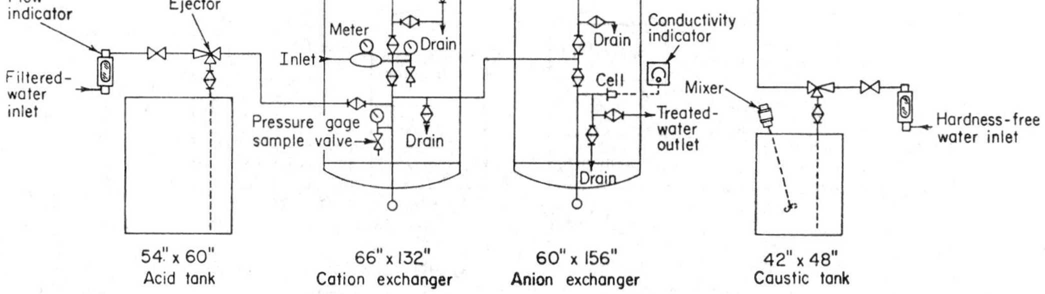

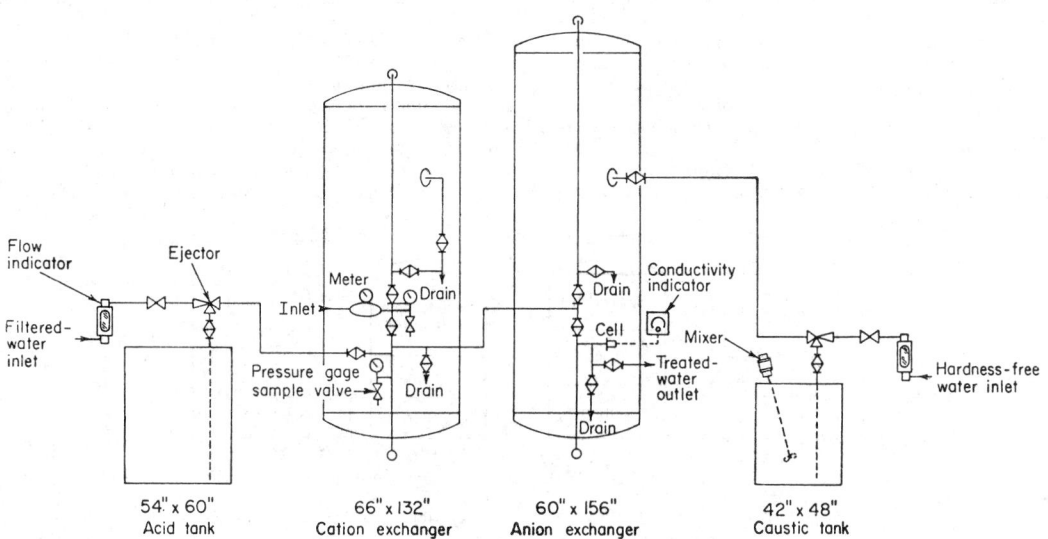

FIG. 19-35. Typical two-bed deionizing system.

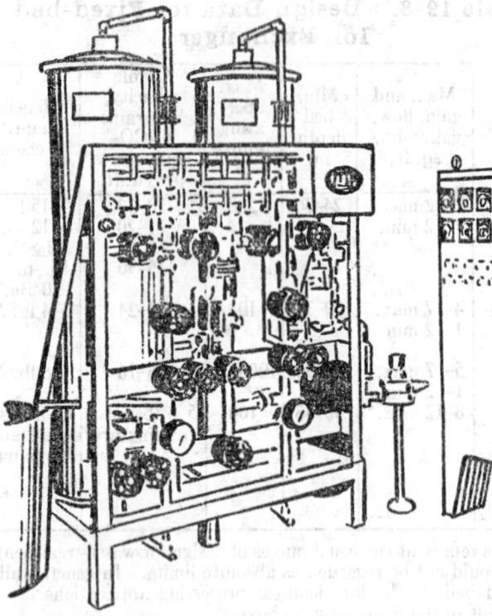

FIG. 19-36. Two-bed "package" automatic deionizer.

Freeboard is required above the resin bed to permit bed expansion during backwashing. Usually, the freeboard depth ranges from 50 to 100 per cent of the resin depth.

Since the regeneration process is accomplished by sequential operation of a number of valves, it is adaptable to automatic operation. Multiple units are commonly used to permit uninterrupted flow and to allow individual units to be taken out of service and regenerated fully automatically. The units are most commonly controlled by measurements of conductivity. For products where the ion-exchange process has little effect upon electrical conductivity, volume measurements may be suitable. Figure 19-36 shows a simple two-bed "package" type of automatic deionizer, with pneumatically operated valves controlled by timers.

Mixed-bed Ion Exchangers. The typical ion exchanger described above contains only one type of resin, either a cation resin or an anion resin, and regeneration is normally accomplished with one chemical solution, either a strong acid or a strong base. In a "mixed-bed" ion exchanger, a cation and an anion resin are contained in the same column. During the service, or loading, step they are intimately mixed. For regeneration, backwashing separates the lighter anion resin from the denser cation resin. The unit has a screened distributor at the plane of interface between the two resins, so that they may be separately regenerated without removing them from the column. The most common method of regeneration (Fig. 19-37) permits simultaneous regeneration of the two resins, with the alkali flowing downward through the anion resin to the interface distributor, and the acid upward through the cation resin. The regenerant solutions mutually restrict one another from penetration into the other resin, and neutralize one another before going to the drain. After regeneration and rinsing, the resins are remixed by compressed air. The bottom distributor is ordinarily of the screened type because of the difficulty of introducing compressed air into a support bed without upsetting graded layers, and to avoid the chance of contaminating the product. To permit uniform columnar exhaustion of the resin, the tank often has a flat bottom; in large-diameter columns this is accomplished by welding a flat false bottom in a conventional dished-head tank.

Automation of Ion Exchangers. As in other types of equipment, the term "automatic" is subject to various interpretations. A fully automatic deionizer has the following features: (1) bulk storage of regenerants; (2) automatic pumping and dilution of regenerants from bulk storage to ion-exchange units; (3) conductivity controllers, or other method for sensing the quality of effluent and taking corrective procedures when needed; (4) a method for distinguishing between the need for regeneration and a transitory drop in effluent quality, and ability to take appropriate steps in either case; (5) a fully automatic regeneration procedure, including automatic control of flows and dilution of regenerants; (6) fully automatic return to service, or to standby condition, as required; (7) fail-safe protection to eliminate any risk of contamination of effluent with regenerant solutions, drain-down of ion-exchange columns, or back-up of water or product into regenerant storage; (8) alarms to notify the operator of any malfunction, and provision to advise the operator of the nature and location of the malfunction.

Some installations, many of which are in power plants, have all these features. Recording instruments and elaborate graphic control panels enable the operator to visualize operating conditions and flows. The cost of such an installation depends more upon the instrumentation and controls than upon the size of the basic ion-exchange equipment, and consequently some compromises must usually be made, particularly if the ion exchangers are small. Even for a small job, however, automatic controls should be highly reliable. Automatic equipment is specified in part to reduce labor costs, but frequent maintenance work can exceed the cost of operation of manually operated equipment if the design is inadequate for the required service. Even for the smallest automatic installation items 3 through 7, above, are highly desirable and can be included at reasonable cost. Item 8 (alarms) must also be included but may be much simpler than for a large project. Thought should

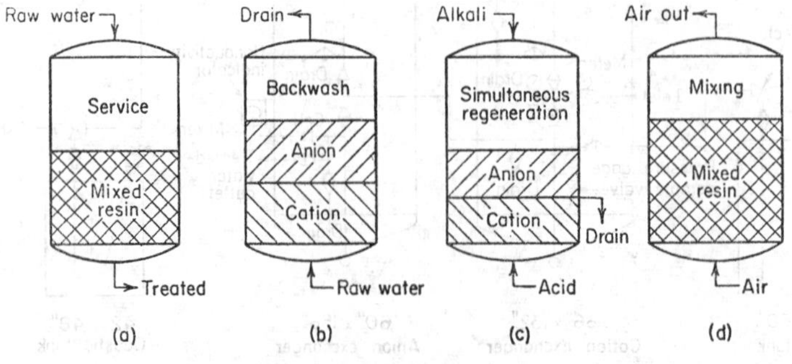

FIG. 19-37. Principle of mixed-bed ion exchange: (*a*) Service period. (*b*) Backwash period. (*c*) Simultaneous regeneration. (*d*) Resin mixing.

be given to the problems of handling strong chemicals, and a system designed that is acceptable to the particular plant. Chemical manufacturers can suggest suitable storage and handling facilities for any situation.

ION-EXCHANGE PROCESSES FOR WATER TREATMENT

Ion exchange is most widely used for water treatment. By the use of suitable ion exchangers, individually or in series, almost any natural water supply can be treated to make it suitable for any purpose, from simple washing operations requiring only a hardness-free water, to the most critical chemical and electronic uses which may require water with a resistance in excess of 10 megohms-cm. If the raw-water supply contains turbidity, iron, manganese, free chlorine, or organic matter, pretreatment by other methods may be necessary or desirable.

Base-exchange Softener. A familiar example of ion exchange is the base-exchange water softener, which uses a zeolite or cation exchange resin on the sodium cycle, regenerated with common salt. Such a unit merely exchanges sodium for calcium and magnesium, so that the effluent water contains no scale-forming hardness and will not interfere with the action of soap or other cleansers. Softeners are too common and well known to require detailed discussion here.

Cation Exchanger. Cation-exchange resins of the same types commonly used in water softeners may also be regenerated with sulfuric or hydrochloric acid. They then have hydrogen ions available for exchange and will remove sodium as well as calcium and magnesium, replacing all cations with hydrogen ions, so that the effluent water contains acids. If the water is high in carbonate alkalinity, the total dissolved solids may be reduced by cation exchange followed by aeration or degasification to remove free carbon dioxide. The remaining anions may be removed by anion exchange as described below.

Anion Exchangers. There are two general classifications of anion resins, weakly basic and strongly basic. The weakly basic resins (this term as used here includes certain resins sometimes classified as "intermediate bases") act as adsorbents for strong acids. Thus water which has been "decationized" and degasified may now be converted to "deionized" water by passage through such a resin. Anion resins are regenerated with caustic soda solution, or in some cases with soda ash or ammonia.

The weakly basic resins are most commonly used to provide deionized water for rinsing operations, and for makeup of plating solutions and other chemical and pharmaceutical solutions where extreme purity is not essential. They are also often used preceding strongly basic anion units, since they are more economical. Weakly basic resins, however, cannot remove weak acids such as dissolved carbon dioxide and silica from water. The strong-base resins, introduced in 1948, exchange hydroxyl ions even for these very weakly ionized acids, and they can even split neutral salts, such as sodium chloride.

Deionized Water. Decationized water after passage through the hydroxyl form of a strongly basic anion resin is completely deionized, since all cations have been replaced by hydrogen ions, and all anions by hydroxyl ions. Actually, a single pass through a cation exchanger followed by a strong-base anion exchanger leaves a small residual of dissolved solids in the water, normally about 2 to 5 p.p.m. of sodium hydroxide or carbonate. Silica will normally be reduced to 0.1 p.p.m. or less, and by special techniques used to produce makeup water for very high pressure boilers, to 0.02 p.p.m. or below.

Passage through a second cation-anion series will further reduce the impurities in the water. Such an arrangement can become quite cumbersome and costly, and the usual method of treatment where ultrapure water with a resistance of 1 megohm-cm. or higher is required is the mixed-bed deionizer, described above.

If a sulfonated polystyrene cation-exchange resin is intimately mixed with a quaternary ammonium anion resin, water passing through the bed in effect is treated by a multiple series of cation-anion exchangers. This reduces ions to a minimum. Such equipment is commonly used to produce "conductivity water" for production of electronic equipment, pure chemicals, high-pressure boiler makeup, nuclear reactors [Thompson and Reents, *Ind. Eng. Chem.*, **51**, 1259 (1959)], and numerous other applications.

In water treatment a mixed-bed exchanger has a number of advantages. In addition to producing water with resistances closely approximating theoretical perfection, it produces a more *uniform* purity and a more nearly constant pH than is possible with a cation-anion system. Silica can be reduced to the lower limits of analytical accuracy. Henderson (*Chem. Processing*, June, 1958) has reported 0.001 p.p.m. of silica, 0.1 p.p.m. total dissolved solids, and pH of 6.8 to 7.0. Often the product is of much higher quality than actually required, so that minor difficulties with the equipment show up well in advance of any serious trouble that could affect plant processes. Variations in quality of the entering water and in flow rate, even well beyond normal design rates, have little or no effect upon effluent quality. Where a mixed bed is not applicable directly for treatment of a raw-water supply, it is often used at the end of the flow sheet as a polisher.

Figures 19-38 and 19-39 give a comparison of the results to be expected from typical deionizers of the three basic types: two-bed weak base, two-bed strong base, and mixed bed.

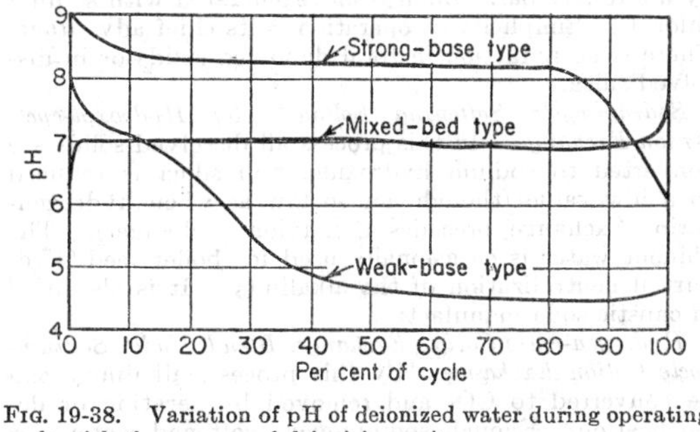

FIG. 19-38. Variation of pH of deionized water during operating cycle with three types of deionizing units.

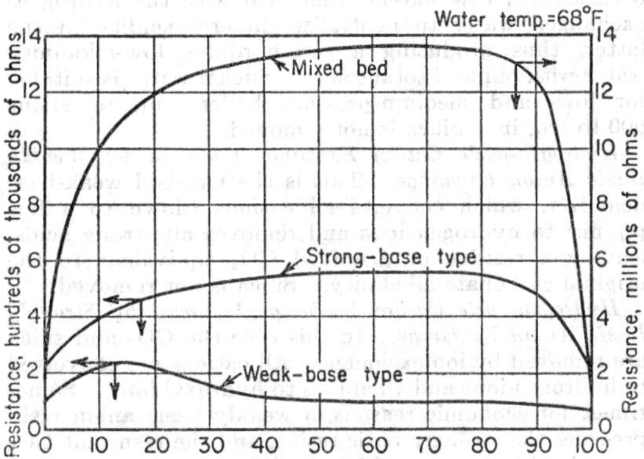

FIG. 19-39. Variation of electrical resistance of deionized water during operating cycle with three types of deionizing units.

As shown in Fig. 19-38, the two-bed deionizer with weakly basic anion resin produces a water with a lower pH than do deionizers with strong-base resin. This is due to the presence of dissolved carbon dioxide which results from the formation of unstable carbonic acid in the cation exchanger. The free CO_2 is removed by strong-base anion resins. The curve in Fig. 19-38 showing the pH variation from a two-bed unit with strong-base anion resin illustrates the leveling off of pH at a comparatively high level during the service cycle, followed by a drop in pH as the anion resin becomes exhausted. The pH would increase sharply if the cation resin were to become exhausted first. The mixed-bed deionizer, as shown, produces a more uniform effluent throughout the run with a pH very close to 7.0. The mixed-bed water is normally so pure that very slight variations in dissolved CO_2 affect the pH radically. The curves in Fig. 19-38 were all taken from readings obtained from in-line cells. A sample of deionized water exposed to air absorbs CO_2 so that the pH drops rapidly.

Summary of Water-treatment Applications of Ion Exchange. Following are some examples of applications of ion exchange to water treatment.

Sodium-cycle Cation Exchange. This is the familiar zeolite or base-exchange softener process. By passing hard water through a cation exchanger regenerated with sodium chloride, the calcium and magnesium which form scale and react with soap are removed and replaced by sodium, which forms extremely soluble salts. There is no reduction in dissolved solids.

Sodium Softening Followed by Chloride-cycle Anion Exchange. This process is used for low-pressure low-makeup boiler feed water to remove hardness and alkalinity. All anions are converted to chloride ions by a strongly basic anion resin regenerated with sodium chloride. Simplicity of operation is its chief advantage. There is no reduction in total dissolved solids or in dissolved silica.

Sodium-cycle Softening Followed by Hydroxyl-cycle Anion Exchange. In this process all dissolved solids are converted to sodium hydroxide, and silica is reduced to a low value (though not so low as when hydrogen-cation exchange precedes the anion exchanger). The effluent water is occasionally used for boiler feed, after partial neutralization of the alkalinity. It is also used in caustic soda manufacture.

Hydrogen-cycle Cation Exchange, Blended with Sodium-cycle Cation Exchange. By this process, alkalinity can be converted to CO_2 and removed by aeration or degasification. Enough sodium-cycle softened water (or, occasionally, raw water) is blended with the hydrogen-exchanged water to neutralize mineral acidity in the latter, thus producing a zero-hardness low-alkalinity water with reduced total solids. Such a water is suitable for low- and medium-pressure boilers, up to about 600 lb./sq. in. Silica is not removed.

Hydrogen-cycle Cation Exchange Followed by Weakly Basic Anion Exchange. This is the two-bed weak-base deionizer, which converts all cations (down to a few p.p.m.) to hydrogen ions and removes all strong acids, leaving a residue of dissolved CO_2 equivalent to the original carbonate alkalinity. Silica is not removed.

Hydrogen-cycle Cation Exchange Followed by Strongly Basic Anion Exchange. In this case the CO_2 and silica are removed by ion exchange. All cations are converted to hydrogen ions and all anions to hydroxyl ions. Sometimes, for economic reasons, a weakly basic anion resin precedes the strongly basic resins, and the resultant CO_2 is mechanically removed before the final anion exchange. The product is widely used for boiler feed and for process water.

Mixed Bed of Hydrogen-cycle Cation-exchange Resin and Strong-base Anion-exchange Resin. The mixed-bed deionizer produces ultrapure water for high-pressure boilers, nuclear-reactor systems, and innumerable processes and products.

Combinations of units other than those described above are often used. For example, for some applications a cation exchanger, a weak-base anion, aeration or mechanical degasification, and a mixed-bed deionizer may be more economical than the mixed bed alone. The choice rests upon the usual balance of capital investment vs. operating cost and must be calculated for any given set of operating conditions. Curves have been developed to assist in comparing the operating costs for the various stages of ion-exchange treatment of water [Kahler and Reents, *Chem. Eng.* **64** (1), 206 (1957)].

CHEMICAL PROCESS APPLICATIONS OF ION EXCHANGE

Economics of Ion Exchange vs. Conventional Chemical Treatment. In general, the chemical cost of removing solids by ion exchange is greater than the cost of chemical precipitation. For example, reduction of calcium alkalinity in water by precipitation with lime requires a smaller expenditure of chemicals than does its removal by ion exchange. For small volumes, however, the equipment cost may favor ion exchange, and operation is simpler. As a rule, it is uneconomical to deionize waters containing more than 600 p.p.m. total dissolved solids (as $CaCO_3$ equivalents), although there are exceptions, particularly where requirements are small and the alternatives are also expensive.

The quantities of regenerant chemicals required for ion exchange always exceed stoichiometric quantities, but this disadvantage is often overcome by the simplicity of operation and easy reproducibility of results, plus the elimination of precipitates which require filters or other liquids-solids separation equipment. In an economic evaluation of ion exchange vs. chemical precipitation, whether for water treatment or for chemical processes, the capital investment and labor requirements often favor ion exchange, while the chemicals consumed in operation favor precipitation. If the evaluation is based on ion exchange vs. distillation, when the concentrations of exchangeable ions are within limits suitable for ion exchange, the capital-investment cost is usually much in favor of ion exchange. Of course, in either situation, a total economic comparison must be made, and these statements are intended only as a general guide.

Fixed-bed Equipment Applied to Chemical Purification. Fixed-bed ion-exchange equipment has limitations for chemical processing applications, and moving-bed designs which are capable of relatively continuous operation seem likely to take over much of this field. Nevertheless, conventional fixed-bed equipment, very similar to that used in water treatment, has been highly successful in many applications. For batch removal of objectionable ions from a chemical solution, fixed-bed ion exchangers are quite suitable. As in water treatment, ion exchange is most effective for removing relatively small concentrations of ionized solids from a non-polar liquid. An example is the removal of salts from crude glycerin or from sugar solutions. In the case of glycerin containing about 1 per cent dissolved salts, a series of cation and anion exchangers followed by a mixed-bed exchanger produces a solution of sufficient purity to permit evaporation to the desired concentration of CP glycerin [Rahles, Reents, and Stromquist, *J. Am. Oil Chem. Soc.*, **29**, 133 (1952)]. In purifying sugar and glycerin solutions, color-adsorbent resins often precede the ion-exchange resins. Crude glycerin from saponification, containing 30 per cent glycerin and about 2 per cent sodium chloride is being purified by a combined process of ion exclusion and ion exchange followed by triple-effect evaporation to produce CP glycerin at a concentration of 99.5 per cent. (Ion exclusion is a process involving the use of ion-exchange resins but not requiring regenerant chemicals; the separation of solutes is achieved physically because of the characteristics of the resin of "excluding" the electrolyte from the interior of the resin bead, while permitting the non-electrolyte, or less ionized electrolyte, to enter the bead.)

There are many other similar applications. Salts are commonly removed by ion exchange from organic chemicals such as methanol, formaldehyde, ethylene glycol, and alcoholic beverages (Nachod and Schubert, "Ion Exchange Technology," p. 554, Academic Press, New York, 1956). Ion exchange is particularly effective when the concentrations of impurities to be removed are very small. This is in sharp contrast to the characteristics of other unit processes, and thus ion exchange is often the only feasible method for such purification problems. Ion-exchange resins are used to recover traces of gold from rinse waters in gold-plating operations. When the resin becomes loaded with gold, it is simply burned. This is a practical application even though the gold is present in such a low concentration that it cannot be recovered in any other way.

Valuable processing fluids which become contaminated in use by dissolving ionizable solids may be recovered by ion exchange. The most common example of this is the removal of metal oxides from chromic acid solutions used in chrome plating and anodizing of aluminum. [Gilbert, Morrison, and Kahler, *Proc. Am. Electroplaters' Soc.*, **39**, 31 (1952)].

Continuous Ion-exchange Equipment. Many potentially useful chemical processes can be performed in the laboratory by ion exchange but cannot be economically adapted to plant-scale operation in fixed-bed ion exchangers which are applicable to water treatment or to the simple purification processes described above. These more difficult processes are classified as involving *separation, recovery concentration, purification,* or *metathesis.* Ion exchange can separate two or more ions of the same sign by taking advantage of the differences in their relative distribution between the solution and an ion-exchange resin. The rare earths are commercially separated by chromatographic stratification in a long series of fixed-bed ion-exchange columns, a process which is justified by the high value of the rare-earth elements.

Recovery concentration, purification, and metathesis are all examples of a type of ion exchange in which an ion in one solution is first sorbed on an ion-exchange resin and then desorbed into another solution. If the ion is valuable, the emphasis is upon recovery and concentration. If the ion is an objectionable one, the emphasis is on purification of the solution. In metathesis, the emphasis is on conversion of one salt into another, as, for example, calcium hydroxide to sodium hydroxide. Where a few hundred parts per million of ions dissolved in water are to be converted to another form, as in the conversion of calcium and magnesium in water to sodium or hydrogen ions, it is feasible to design fixed-bed equipment which will operate on the service or loading cycle for many hours, or even for several days, and will be in the regeneration cycle for an hour or two. On the other hand, in a more complex sorption-desorption process involving relatively high chemical concentrations and a more involved regeneration or stripping operation, a few minutes on the loading cycle might be followed by several hours in regeneration. To provide continuous operation a large battery of units with a tremendous volume of resin would be required. The combination of high capital investment and high operating cost has often made such processes uneconomical.

Many attempts have been made to design equipment better suited to handle such chemical applications of ion exchange. Recent successful applications show that both capital investment and operating cost may be substantially reduced. By appropriate design and automatic control and instrumentation, separations can be accomplished that are not practical in any other way, and regeneration dosages can approach stoichiometric levels because of the more efficient utilization of the resin capacity.

Much of the continuous ion-exchange development work in recent years has been done in connection with U.S.A.E.C. chemical processing problems. One of the first, and largest, examples of this development is the Anaconda "Resin-in-Pulp" uranium mill at Grants, N.M., which processes 1125 tons of ore per day. After the leaching of western uranium ores, uranium is present in solution as an anionic sulfate complex which can be recovered, concentrated, and purified by anion exchange. The ores, however, also contain clay slimes which hydrate during the leaching process to give a slurry which is a viscous "pulp." To avoid filtration, which would be necessary with conventional ion-exchange beds, the Grants mill uses large-mesh resin loosely contained in stainless-steel screen "baskets" which oscillate up and down in troughs through which the pulp flows. This vertical action keeps the resin fluidized and prevents the slimes from fouling the resin. The pulp is fed through 10 series-connected troughs (each 50 ft. by 6 in. by 6 in.), each trough fitted with 10 baskets (each 4 by 4 by 4 ft.) and each basket containing 15 cu. ft. of resin. Desorption of the uranium is carried out simultaneously in four additional troughs in series. The baskets oscillate at five cycles per minute through a 15-in. stroke. The resin does not actually move countercurrently to the solutions, but the effect of continuous countercurrent flow is approximated by changing the feed and take-off points from one trough to the next in a 14-trough time cycle.

A later development is the Higgins contactor, used to recover uranium from reduction-residue sulfate leach slurries at the Oak Ridge Y-12 plant, plutonium from nitrate solutions at the Hanford Purex plant, uranium in chloride solution at the Japan Atomic Fuel Corporation uranium-metal production plant, and for non-nuclear applications by private commercial plants. Figure 19-40 illustrates the mode of operation of the contactor. Strictly speaking, the operation is intermittent rather than truly continuous; *i.e.*, the resin and solutions flow alternately rather than at the same time, but in practice the distinction is not important. The solutions flow against a packed bed of resin, eliminating the danger of fluidization and providing differential-countercurrent contact between the two phases, thus combining the high-through-put, low-H.E.T.S. advantages of fixed-bed operation with the operational advantages of continuous countercurrent flow. The solution flow period is typically several minutes long. Intermittently the resin bed is moved (pulsed) a short distance relative to its length by interrupting the solution flows for several seconds and hydraulically applying a pressure drop across the bed. The column of resin slides as a piston in a cylinder, lubricated by its contained liquid, with the individual particles closely maintaining their positions relative to each other.

The two valves in the resin loop and a source of hydraulic pressure difference are basic to the method of resin circulation. In Fig. 19-41 they are shown as open-port valves and a hydraulic piston which cyclically reverse their positions. The valves act as check valves

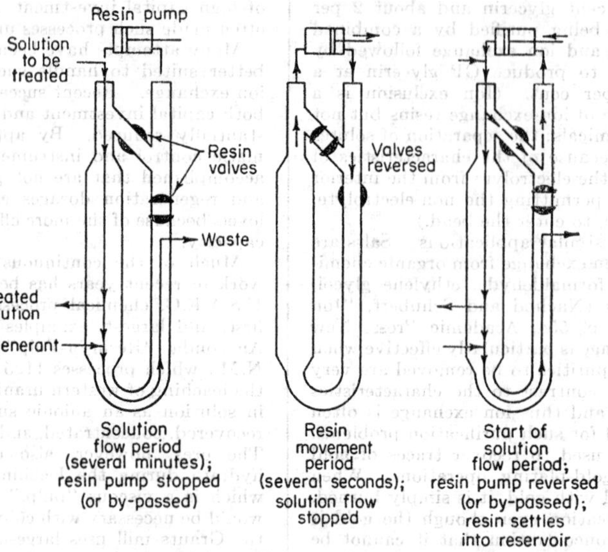

FIG. 19-40. Mode of operation of the Higgins contactor (ORNL-LR-Dwg. 27857R).

which permit the resin to move in one direction only. Thus the resin is moved around the loop with a remote pump in much the same manner as solutions are pumped using a check-valve assembly and a remote diaphragm or piston actuator. Additional valves in the resin loop can be used for positive isolation of solution flows in different sections of a contactor. Stopping the feed and take-off streams during the period of resin movement prevents these streams from interfering with the movement. This, however, is not always necessary.

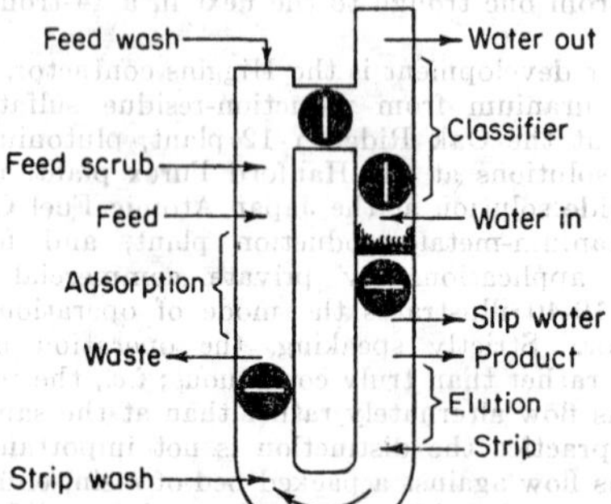

FIG. 19-41. Principle of operation of the Y-12 Higgins contactor. (*U.S.A.E.C. Rept.* Y-1257, *July* 9, 1959.)

Open-port valves of the ball or plug type have been used in contactors up to 8 in. in diameter and butterfly valves have been used in contactors up to 3 ft. in diameter. The diameter of the resin valve can be smaller than the contactor diameter if this is important economically. On large contactors valves as small as one-third the contactor diameter have been used successfully. For ease of resin movement, however, changes in diameter should be made gradually, as with a conical taper. The source of the hydraulic pressure difference which causes the resin to move may be a pump, a hydraulic accumulator, or simply the water main. A hydraulic accumulator may be powered by a pump (smaller than one used directly), the water main (requiring a smaller line than one used directly), or compressed air. A pump may operate on contactor solution or in oil acting on contactor solution. The resin movement actuator may be either single-ended or double-ended; *i.e.*, it may "push" the resin or both "push" and "pull" it. Small contactors have been operated with "pull" only, *e.g.*, by using a vacuum on the downstream side and letting atmospheric pressure do the pushing.

In the Y-12 uranium recovery contactor (Fig. 19-41), the sorption section is 33 ft. long by 24 in. in diameter. The gross height of the contactor is almost 60 ft. The other contactor sections are 12 in. in diameter. The four valves in the resin loop are of the butterfly type, nominally 8 in. in diameter. The system has proved satisfactory for processing tonnage quantities of uranium-bearing slag waste materials, which are leached with sulfuric acid, partially clarified, and fed to the contactor as slurries containing 2 to 10 volume per cent solids (magnesium fluoride, activated alumina, or carbon). Though the resin is a packed bed during the solution flow period, the fact that it is pulsed every few minutes to move the resin prevents it from filtering out the solids and plugging up. A dilute sulfate "feed-scrub" solution serves to remove any weakly sorbed anionic contaminants tending to follow the uranium with the resin. A water "feed wash" pushes the sulfate solution back and also removes most of any solids trying to follow the resin. The resin settles through a countercurrent stream of water in the "classifier" section, further removing any solids following the resin and also removing any broken resin beads which would otherwise increase the pressure drop in the sorption section, which operates at high solution flow rates. In the "elution" section the uranium is desorbed and recovered in concentrated and purified form by an acidified ammonium nitrate "strip" solution. The "slip water," which comes in with the resin, is kept separate from the "product" solution, to avoid unnecessary dilution, with the aid of a conductivity probe between the two outlets. The resin is given a water "strip wash," to push the nitrate solution back, before being returned to the sorption section. A hydraulic accumulator, powered by compressed air, moves the resin. The "bayonet" distributors for solution feed and take-off are perforated stainless-steel pipes wrapped with

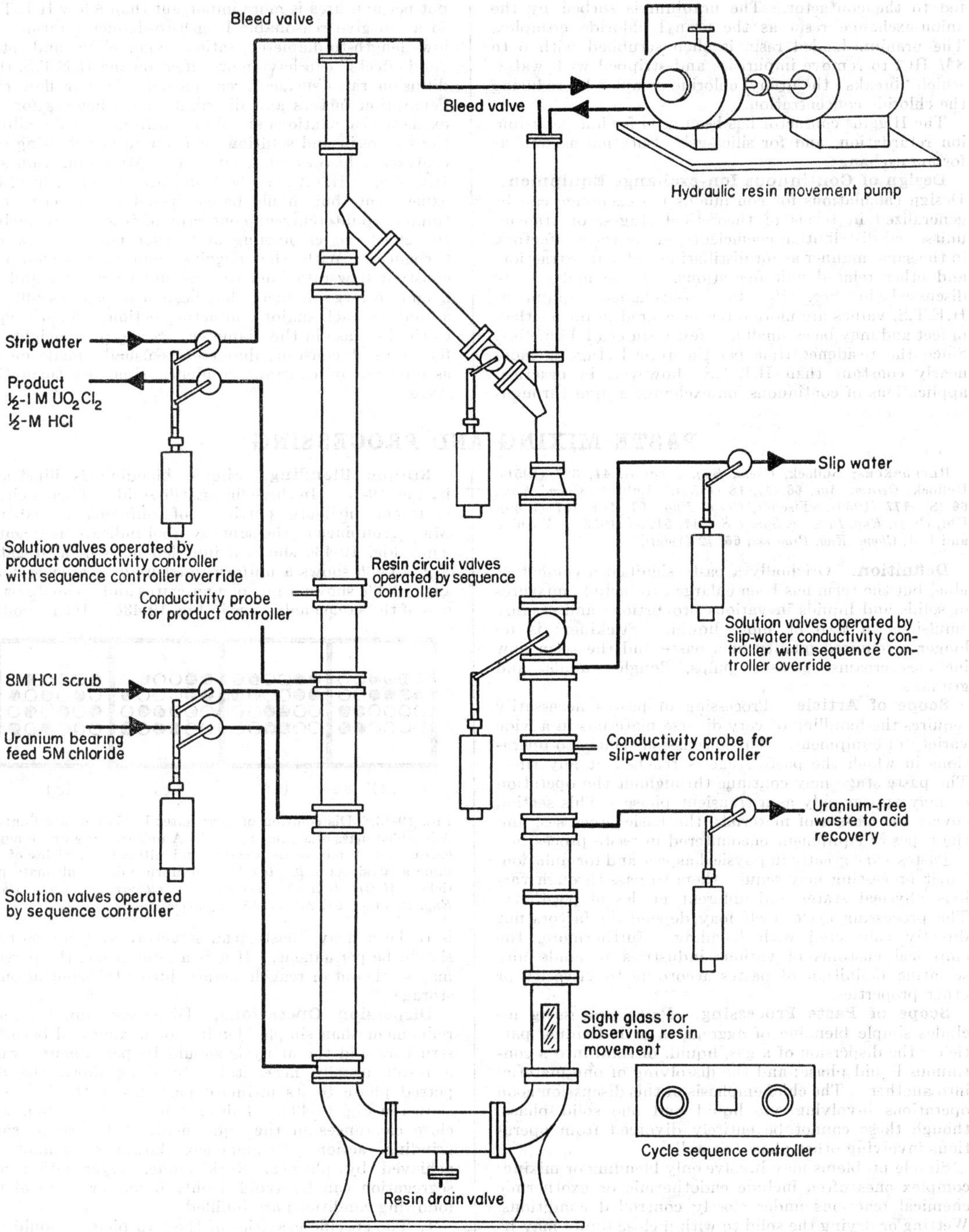

FIG. 19-42. Higgins contactor for uranium concentration and purification.

stainless-steel screen and inserted through a flanged opening. Three of these are set in parallel at each inlet or outlet in the 24-in. section, and two in parallel in the 12-in. sections.

Figure 19-42 shows the Japanese uranium purification contactor (built by Illinois Water Treatment Company). It is of rubber-lined construction, 8 in. in diameter by about 20 ft. high. Two ball valves are used in the resin loop, one 8-in. and one 6-in. The resin is moved by a turbine-type pump operating in a light oil. An ore concentrate is dissolved in hydrochloric acid, and the solution is concentrated by distillation and fed to the contactor. The uranium is sorbed by the anion-exchange resin as the uranyl chloride complex. The uranium-loaded resin is then scrubbed with 6 to 8*M* HCl to remove impurities and stripped with water, which "breaks" the uranyl chloride complex by reducing the chloride concentration.

The Higgins contactor has been used for ion exclusion, ion retardation, and for silica-gel adsorption as well as for ion exchange.

Design of Continuous Ion-exchange Equipment. Design calculations for continuous ion exchange can be generalized in terms of theoretical stages, or transfer units, and distribution coefficients, or spearation factors, in the same manner as for distillation, solvent extraction, and other related unit operations. These matters are discussed in Sec. 16. In ion-exchange equipment H.E.T.S. values are more often measured in inches than in feet and may be as small as a few resin bead diameters. Since the residence time per theoretical stage is more nearly constant than H.E.T.S., however, in practical applications of continuous ion exchange a high throughput per unit area is more important than a low H.E.T.S., so as to give reasonable length-to-diameter ratios. At low length-to-diameter ratios, channeling and other "end effects" can have more effect on the H.E.T.S. than diffusion rate, surface area, particle size, or flow rate. Separation factors and distribution coefficients for ion-exchange calculations are obtained from batch equilibrations of resin and solution, or from curves showing concentration history in fixed beds. Minimum values of H.E.T.S. or H.T.U. can be found from batch or fixed-bed experiments but should be confirmed in the actual continuous countercurrent contactor of interest, to include the effects of channeling and other possible flow disturbances. With the Higgins contactor scale-up at constant flow rate from runs at small diameter and full height to large diameter has been made successfully by adding to each major contactor section a length equal to the increase in the diameter. Scale-up in height and flow rate at constant diameter is usually made on the assumption of constant residence time per theoretical stage.

PASTE MIXING AND PROCESSING

REFERENCES: Bullock, *Chem. Eng. Progress*, **47**, 397 (1951). Bullock, *Ceram. Age*, **68** (4), 18 (1956). Bullock, *Chem. Eng.*, **66** (8), 177 (1959). Fischer, *Chem. Eng.*, **67** (16), 107 (1960). Uhl, *Chem. Eng. Progress Symp. Ser.* 17, **51**, 93 (1955). Voznick and Uhl, *Chem. Eng. Progress*, **56**, 72 (1960).

Definition. Originally a paste signified a cement or glue, but the term has been enlarged to include mixtures of solids and liquids in various proportions and creamy emulsions of two or more liquids. Stickiness is no longer a required quality of a paste and the term now includes creams, greases, pulps, doughs, muds, and grumes.

Scope of Article. Processing of pastes necessarily requires the handling of very diverse materials in a wide variety of equipment. This discussion relates to operations in which the paste stage is reached at any time. The paste stage may continue throughout the operation or may appear only as a transient phase. This section covers the classes of materials, the basic processes, and the types of equipment encountered in paste processing.

Pastes vary greatly in physical aspect and formulation. Their processing may require them to pass through various physical states and different grades of plasticity. The processing cycle itself may depend on factors not directly connected with blending. Furthermore, the empirical customs of various industries preclude any scientific definition of pastes according to viscosity or other properties.

Scope of Paste Processing. Paste processing includes simple blending of aggregates or individual particles; the dispersion of a gas, liquid, or solid into a continuous liquid phase; and the dissolving of one material into another. The chief emphasis of this discussion is on operations involving one liquid and one solid phase, though these cannot be entirely divorced from operations involving other phases as well.

Simple problems may involve only blending or mixing; complex ones often include endothermic or exothermic chemical reactions under closely controlled conditions. Wetting or drying the solid to within close limits may be required. Often the exact physical state of the end product is of primary importance and equipment is designed or selected not only to blend but also to produce a granular, flaked, powdery, or puttylike product of a certain density. When a certain physical state of a definite chemical mixture is the goal, careful selection of the equipment and exact control of the operating conditions are necessary.

Simple Blending. Simple blending is illustrated by Fig. 19-43. In these figures the solid and blank circles represent ultimate particles of different ingredients. Mass groupings of the same symbol indicate aggregates. Thus Fig. 19-43*a* shows a jumbled mass of aggregates; Fig. 19-43*b* shows a uniform mixture of aggregates; and Fig. 19-43*c* shows a mix of aggregates and ultimate particles of the same analysis as in Fig. 19-43*b*. If the product

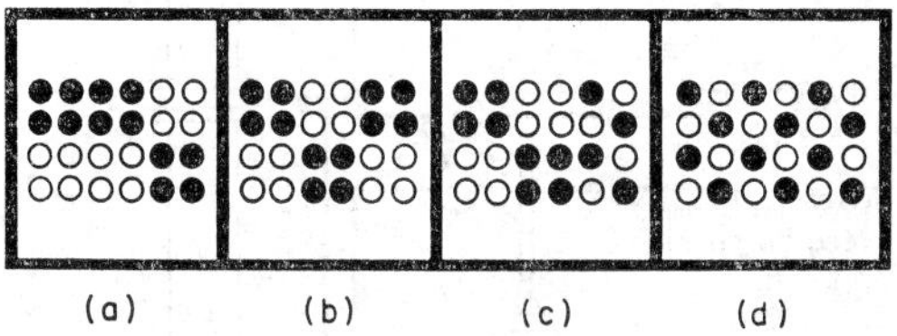

FIG. 19-43. Distribution of aggregates in simple blending: (*a*) A jumbled mass of aggregates. (*b*) A uniform mixture of aggregates. (*c*) A mix of aggregates and ultimate particles of the same analysis as in *b*. (*d*) Ideal uniform mix of ultimate particles. [*From Bullock, Mixing in Muller-type Mixers, Chem. Eng. Progress*, **51**, 243 (1955), *by permission.*]

is to be a heavy paste, the structure and composition should be permanent. If it is a light paste, the particle may settle out or reagglomerate during transportation or storage.

Dispersion Operations. Dispersion implies more refinement than simple blending or mixing and both the structure and the analysis should be permanent. Such a result usually necessitates breaking down the dispersed phase to its ultimate particles, with the result shown in Fig. 19-43*d*. This calls for considerable power, close clearances in the equipment, and perhaps some grinding action. Permanence, however, cannot be achieved by physical work alone. Aggregation and segregation can be avoided only if one or more of the following conditions are fulfilled:

1. The specific gravities of the two phases should not be widely different.
2. The particles of the dispersed or internal phase must be kept separate by a protective colloid.
3. The particles must be so small that Brownian movement occurs.
4. The continuous phase must have a high viscosity or strong set to support the particles against the action of gravity.

Uses of Dispersion. Dispersion may be required to produce permanent suspensions of commercial products during storage or transportation, to break down aggregates to produce a smooth coating as in paints, to grind particles under conditions which will avoid reaggregation, or to develop full color value of expensive pigments. The dispersion of pigments in making leather coatings or printing inks illustrates all these requirements. The use of protective colloids to prevent reaggregation of finely dispersed particles is very important. For instance, unprotected freshly dispersed colloidal sulfur may form aggregates larger than the original feed, and certain metallic pigments have been observed to form thin metallic plates when unprotected.

General Techniques. The selection of dispersing agents and protective colloids may be critical. The dispersing agent must be able to separate the particles making up the aggregates; the protective colloid must insulate the charged particles to avoid reagglomeration. If the dispersing agent is dissolved in the liquid phase, the solution must wet the particles of the material to be dispersed so that penetration of the mix is easy and uniform. If the dispersing agent is a finely divided solid, it should be mixed uniformly throughout the material to be dispersed so that an intricate series of paths is produced along which the liquid phase may penetrate the mass. A homely illustration of this action is the mixing of sugar in cocoa powder. Dry cocoa powder is very difficult to wet with either water or milk, but if sugar is first mixed with the cocoa the liquid penetrates quickly. Instant food powders are also examples of dry mixtures of this type.

Critical Limitations. The pH and ion concentration of the water phase are very important, especially in the manufacture of water-in-oil emulsions. Outside electrical effects must be considered and guarded against as stable dispersions and stable emulsions are possible only when in electrical equilibrium. A seemingly unimportant factor may cause imbalance. A small sharp projection at the edge of the stator in a colloid mill, for example, may have a high enough electrical potential to break the freshly made emulsion discharging from the mill. Such projections must be removed and the surface made as smooth as the surrounding metal.

Temperature Effects. Water emulsions and dispersions must, of course, be protected against extremes of temperature. The formation of ice crystals concentrates the water in a pure state and destroys the dispersion. Subsequent melting of the ice crystals will not restore the original structure. Also, high temperatures approaching the boiling point usually degrade the structure and actual boiling destroys it.

GENERAL EQUIPMENT DESIGN

Fundamental Action of Equipment. The processing of pastes is primarily a mixing or blending operation. About forty truly useful and practical types of mixer have been developed to cover the field of paste mixing. Regardless of the type of equipment used, however, the production of a smooth uniform paste calls for certain fundamental actions which influence the speed, shape, and size of the processing elements. Because of the flow properties of pastes, high-velocity impellers are not generally effective as they tend to bore holes in the mass without producing any circulation. Impact and shear forces must be developed adjacent to the mixer blades, not at a distance. This favors mixers with intermeshing blades and mixers having small clearances between the blades and the body. Some pastes cling so tightly to the working surfaces that a very slow-speed shearing action is required. Such slow speed allows the material time to work its way into the active zone. Slow-speed shear, coupled with a smearing or wiping action, usually produces good results on pastes. Folding over, stretching, and compression of the materials also help to produce an intimate and uniform mix. Pug mills, muller mixers, and kneaders combine these principles in their action.

Required Operating Conditions. To be effective, batch units of paste-processing equipment must fulfill four basic operating conditions:

1. The container section must satisfactorily hold the ingredients of the mix.
2. The materials must be moved progressively into the active working zone by the motion of the container or the blades or working surfaces.
3. The working elements must operate on the materials in the active zone in such a manner and with sufficient intensity to produce the desired degree of dispersion.
4. The product must leave the container quickly and cleanly at the end of the run.

In continuous mixers, unless part of the discharge is continuously recirculated, the desired characteristics of the product must be obtained in one passage through the active zone. To make this possible the feed hopper or inlet must discharge cleanly and uniformly into the active zone, without any hold-up of portions of the material. Also, there must be sufficient volume blending of the materials after they enter the active zone to produce a uniform product throughout the run. This is especially true with extruders in which the active zone has an extremely small cross section and the motion of the material is continuously in one direction, from inlet hopper to nozzle. Successful operation of such apparatus calls for extremely uniform preblending of the ingredients before they enter the feed hopper.

STANDARD TYPES OF EQUIPMENT

Change-can Mixers. Change-can mixers are vertical batch mixers in which the container is a separate unit which is easily placed in or removed from the frame of the machine. They are available in capacities from 1 to 150 gal. The most common type is the pony mixer illustrated in Fig. 19-44. Separate cans allow the batch to be carefully measured out or weighed before being brought to the mixer itself. The mixer can also serve to transport the finished batch to the next operation or to storage. The identity of each batch is preserved and weight checks are easily made.

Change cans are relatively cheap. A good supply of cans allows cleaning to be done in a separate department, arranged for efficient cleaning. In paint and ink plants, where the mixing precedes milling or grinding and where there may be a long run of the same formulation and color, the cans may be used for an extended period without cleaning, as long as no drying out or surface oxidation occurs.

In most change-can mixers, the mixing elements are raised from the can, by either a vertical lift, as in Fig. 19-44, or a tilting head; in others the can is dropped away from the mixing elements. After separation the mixing elements drain into the can and the blades can be wiped down. With the can out of the way, complete cleaning of the blades and their supports is simple. If necessary, a can of cleaning fluid may be placed in the frame and the blades may be cleaned by rotating them in the solution.

Intimate mixing is accomplished in change-can mixers in two ways. One method is to have the mixing unit assembly rotate with a planetary motion so that the rotating blades sweep the entire circumference of the can (Fig. 19-45). The other is to mount the can on a rotating turntable so that all parts of the can wall pass the blades at a point of minimum clearance (Fig. 19-46). In the Troy angular mixer (Fig. 19-47) the can is revolved

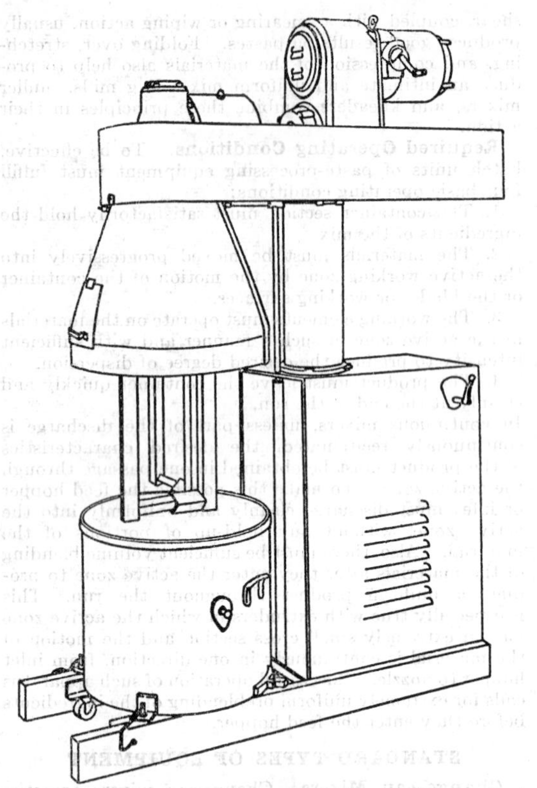

FIG. 19-44. Change-can mixer. (*Chas. Ross & Son Co., Inc.*)

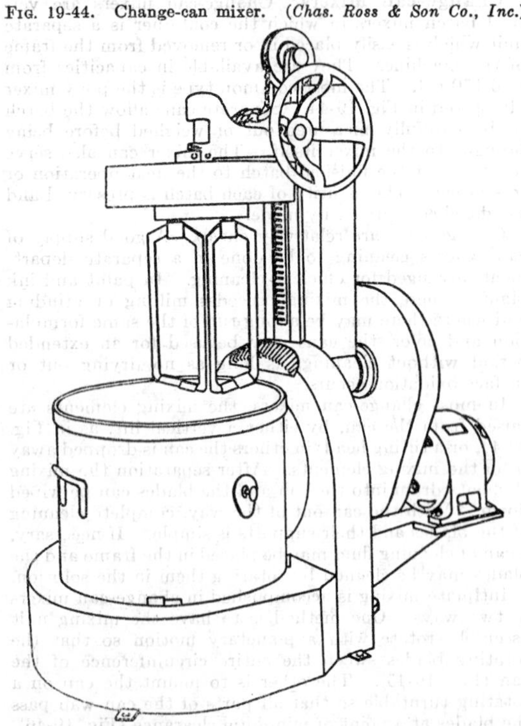

FIG. 19-45. Change-can mixer with planetary motion. (*Chas. Ross & Son Co., Inc.*)

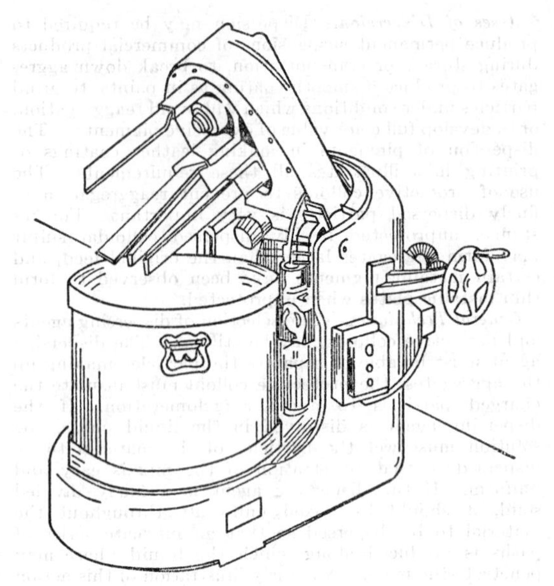

FIG. 19-46. Change-can mixer with rotating turntable. (*J. H. Day Co., Inc.*)

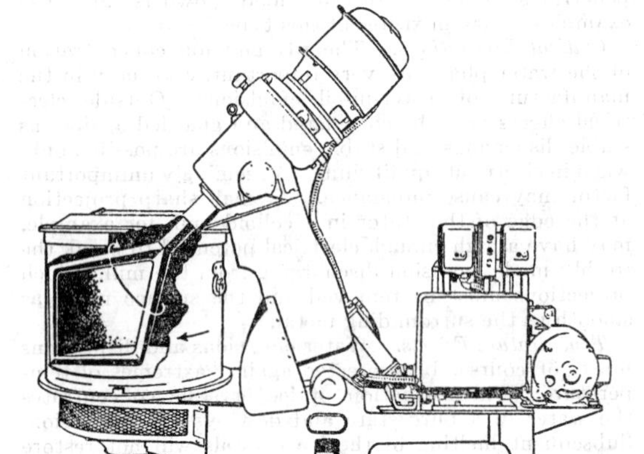

FIG. 19-47. Troy angular mixer. (*Patented; Skinner Engine Co.*)

on a turntable and a diamond-shaped rotating agitator is set at an angle so that the lower elements of the diamond sweep the bottom and side of the can with each revolution.

The rotating elements have many forms, ranging from smooth flat blades to intricate intermeshing paddles. The rotating turntable and the planetary motion of the mixing elements move material to and from the center of the can, but most of this motion is horizontal. The mixing elements are therefore shaped and sloped to induce motion from top to bottom. Where whisks and beaters are used, as in bakery products, vertical displacement is not needed and circulation depends on cavitation around the rotating shafts and backward turnover at the can wall.

As mixing proceeds in a change-can mixer, the flow characteristics usually change. Viscous vehicles often warm up, with a consequent reduction of viscosity. Thin vehicles wet out fine solids and form heavy pastes.

In making some paints and inks, excessive dusting or splashing may occur at the start of the cycle. To reduce the time cycle under these conditions, variable-speed or two-speed motors are used. Slow speed reduces dusting and splashing and may be necessary at the start of a run. In the absence of speed control, trouble may often be avoided by careful study of the order of addition of the mix ingredients.

Small change-can mixers are normally driven by a single motor. As size increases, however, the speed of the turntable drops faster than that of the agitators and it becomes economical to use two motors. This design also makes the operation more flexible, as the can may be revolved with the agitators stationary for rough preblending, or the agitators may be run in a stationary can to mix different strata before introducing centrifugal effects by rotation of the can.

The Duplex mixer shown in Fig. 19-48 uses three motors. This machine combines a small high-speed dispersing unit with the diamond agitator of the standard

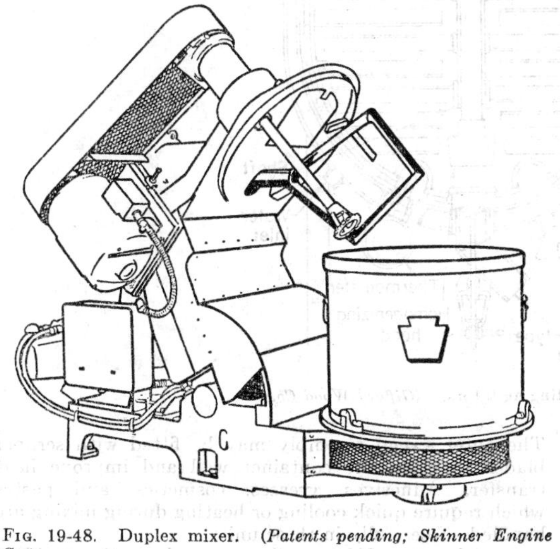

FIG. 19-48. Duplex mixer. *(Patents pending; Skinner Engine Co.)*

Troy mixer and the standard turntable. This combination gives a good illustration of the power requirements of different mixer components. In a 60-gal. mixer used to produce heavy inks, the turntable is driven by a 2-hp. motor, the agitator by a two-speed 7½-hp. motor, and the 6-in.-diameter high-speed dispersing head by a 15- or 20-hp. motor.

Can Design and Selection. Change cans may be purchased in various materials to avoid corrosion or product contamination. They are subject to rough usage and should be made of heavy-gage metal, with liberal reinforcement of base and rim. Efficient mixing depends on their retaining a true cylindrical shape to ensure uniform clearance of the mixing elements. The bottom should be designed so that the can is accurately centered on the machine base or turntable. Lugs, preferably three, should be provided for anchoring the can to the turntable. Lifting handles, lugs, or trunnions should be mounted well above the center of gravity of the loaded can. The surface in contact with the can should have sufficient area to distribute the weight and avoid distortion of the can wall. When a sling is used to lift a loaded can, the loops going under the trunnions or lugs should extend vertically down from a rigid horizontal crosspiece which spans the diameter of the can, and the chains or cables going to the crane or other lifting device should extend from the ends of the crosspiece to the hook. This protects the can from the crushing effect of chains going direct from the lugs to a lifting hook.

Most cans are unloaded by dumping but some are fitted with valves or gates so that they can supply a regulated feed to the next operation. Where valves or gates are used, they must be protected from damage or accidental opening.

Stationary-tank Mixers. Stationary-tank mixers are recommended when there is no advantage in having the change can for conveying or storage, when the batch size is above 150 gal., and when the feed and product may be conveniently handled by permanent piping or chutes. The same type of mixing actions must take place in tank mixers as in change cans. The contents of the tank must be moved progressively into the active zone of intensive action at close clearances. However, as the tank and the bearings holding the mixing elements are part of the same structure, very close clearances can be maintained to give intense shear.

Stationary tanks are used with all types of agitators for work with thin fluids, as discussed under Circulation Mixers, pp. 19-5ff. Paste-processing equipment, however, is limited to the following types:

Gate Mixers. One of the oldest stationary-tank mixers is the gate mixer illustrated in Fig. 19-11, p. 19-7. A flat rotating structure of horizontal and vertical bars cuts the paste at different levels and at the tank wall where

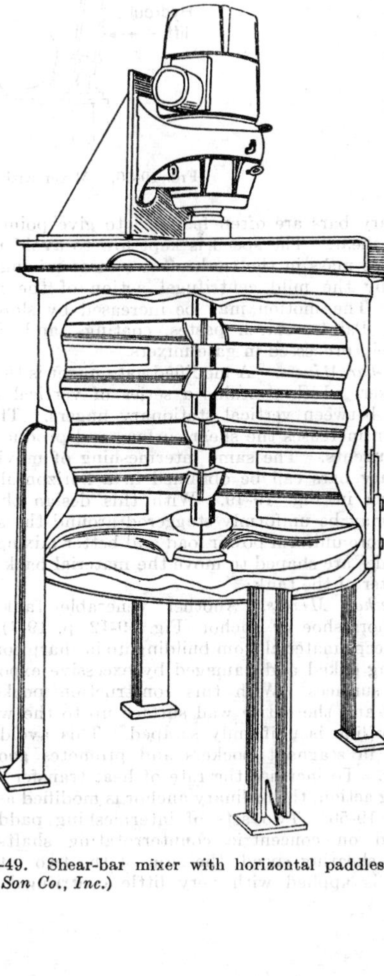

FIG. 19-49. Shear-bar mixer with horizontal paddles. *(Chas. Ross & Son Co., Inc.)*

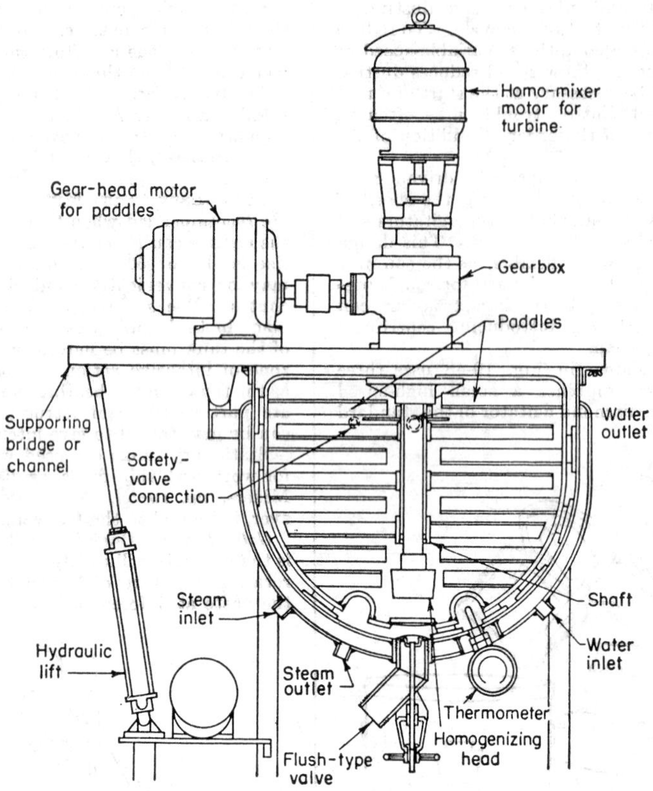

FIG. 19-50. Mixer with counterrotating agitators. (*Gifford-Wood Co.*)

stationary bars are often fastened to give points of intensive shear. The speed is kept low to avoid rotating the entire mass in the tank. Slow mass mixing is produced by the mild centrifugal action of the rotating blades. The motion may be increased by sloping the blades. Paints, starch pastes, coatings, and sizes are effectively processed in gate mixers.

Shear-bar Mixers. A modified gate mixer is the shear-bar mixer, which contains a series of vertical paddles passing between vertical stationary fingers. This construction increases the shear surface and produces more eddy currents. The same intermeshing of moving and stationary bars can be obtained in a horizontal mixer, as shown in Fig. 19-49. With this design the rotor blades may be uniformly staggered around the shaft to give a more uniform power load and better mixing. The end blades are shaped to move the material back toward the center of the tank.

Horseshoe Mixers. Another venerable tank mixer is the horseshoe or anchor (Fig. 19-12, p. 19-7). This mixer keeps material from building up in sharp corners or becoming caked and damaged by excessive exposure to heated surfaces. With this construction pockets are avoided and the entire wall surface up to the working-capacity line is uniformly scraped. This avoids overheating in stagnant pockets and promotes good heat transfer. To increase the rate of heat transfer and the shearing action, the ordinary anchor is modified as shown in Fig. 19-50. Two sets of intermeshing paddles are mounted on concentric counterrotating shafts. The relative shearing speed, the sum of the two rotational speeds, is applied with very little centrifugal action. The outer sweep assembly may be fitted with scraper blades to clean the container wall and improve heat transfer. Adhesives, greases, cosmetics, and pastes which require quick cooling or heating during mixing are handled successfully in these units.

Revolving-cone Mixers. Some pseudoplastic or thixotropic materials cannot be processed with ordinary blades, since even slow-moving elements only bore holes in the material. To produce adequate shear and mass motion it is necessary to hold the material against the shearing and transporting surfaces for an appreciable distance. This is done by the rotating cone shown in Fig. 19-51. The hollow cones are fitted with narrow

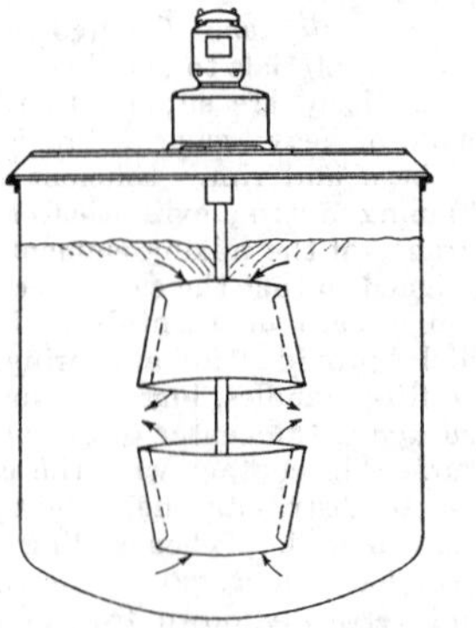

FIG. 19-51. Revolving-cone mixer.

vertical internal vanes extending from top to bottom of the cones or even beyond the cone boundaries, if vigorous action is needed. The narrow vanes have two purposes: first, to rotate the material in contact with the inner cone surface; second, to produce a shearing action. Centrifugal force holds the material against the inner cone surface and the slope of the cone walls produces mass movement from the small end of the cone to the larger end. Shear is produced along the inner edge of the vanes and at the ends where the material enters or leaves the cones. The pairs of cones may be mounted with the large ends facing each other, as shown, to move the material from the top and bottom of the tank toward the center, or they may be inverted to move the material from the center of the tank to the top and bottom.

Soap Crutchers. The soap crutcher was developed for mixing soap. It consists of a continuous helix mounted in a draft tube. Close clearance between the screw and the tube and the high rotational speed results in rapid motion of the material and high shear. The screw lifts the material through the tube and gravity returns it to the bottom of the tank. If the tank has well-rounded corners, this mixer may be used for fibrous materials. Heavy paper pulp containing 16 to 18 per cent solids is uniformly bleached in large mixers of this type.

Kneaders and Banbury Mixers. In hand kneading a doughy material, the dough is pulled out, folded back on itself, and pushed down to join the separate layers. This action is repeated until the desired uniformity is obtained. The mechanical device which most nearly duplicates this action is called a kneader, which consists essentially of two specially shaped blades set on parallel shafts, mounted with close clearances in a U-shaped trough. The bottom of the trough is curved upward to form a ridge between the blades. Figure 19-52 shows a medium-weight kneader.

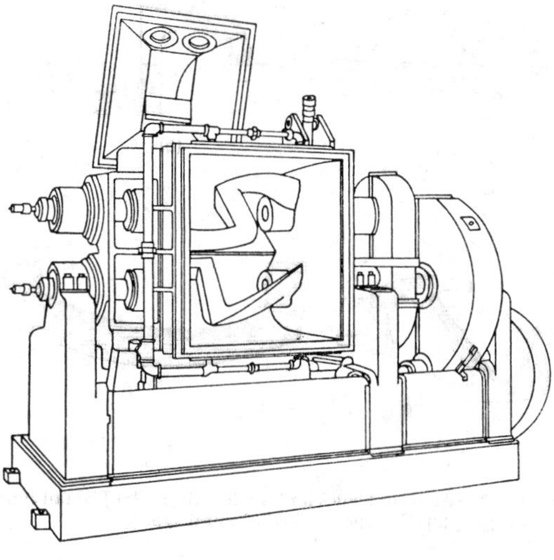

FIG. 19-52. Medium-weight kneader mixer. (*J. H. Day Co., Inc.*)

Kneaders are of two general types—standard or W & P mixers and intensive or Banbury mixers. In W & P

Table 19-4. Characteristics of Kneader Mixers*

Frame No.	Machine characteristics	Special duty	Tangential blades, extra heavy duty			Overlapping blades, heavy duty			Overlapping blades, standard duty		
500	Working capacity, gal.	1000	1600	2000	2500	2880	3600				
	Trough dimensions	100 × 80	100 × 80	100 × 100	100 × 125	113 × 100	113 × 125				
	Max. hp. input	1000	250	250	200	200	200				
400	Working capacity, gal.	500	800	1000	1250	1440	1800	2250	2560	3200	
	Trough dimensions	80 × 64	80 × 64	80 × 80	80 × 100	90 × 80	90 × 100	90 × 125	103 × 100	103 × 125	
	Max. hp. input	800	200	200	150	150	150	125	100	100	
320	Working capacity, gal.	250	400	500	625	720	900	1125	1280	1600	2000
	Trough dimensions	64 × 51	64 × 51	64 × 64	64 × 80	72 × 64	72 × 80	72 × 100	82 × 80	82 × 100	82 × 125
	Max. hp. input	600	150	150	125	125	125	100	75	75	60
253	Working capacity, gal.	125	200	250	313	360	450	563	640	800	1000
	Trough dimensions	51 × 41	51 × 41	51 × 51	51 × 64	57 × 51	57 × 64	57 × 80	65 × 64	65 × 80	65 × 100
	Max. hp. input	400	125	125	100	100	100	75	60	60	50
205	Working capacity, gal.	63	100	125	157	180	225	282	320	400	500
	Trough dimensions	41 × 33	41 × 33	41 × 41	41 × 51	46 × 41	46 × 51	46 × 64	52 × 51	52 × 64	52 × 80
	Max. hp. input	250	100	100	75	75	75	60	50	50	40
165	Working capacity, gal.	32	50	63	79	90	113	141	160	200	250
	Trough dimensions	33 × 26¼	33 × 26¼	33 × 33	33 × 41	37 × 33	37 × 41	37 × 51	41½ × 41	41½ × 51	41½ × 64
	Max. hp. input	150	75	75	60	60	60	50	40	40	30
132	Working capacity, gal.	16	25	32	40	45	57	71	80	100	125
	Trough dimensions	26¼ × 21	26¼ × 21	26¼ × 26¼	26¼ × 33	29½ × 26¼	29½ × 33	29½ × 41	33½ × 33	33½ × 41	33½ × 51
	Max. hp. input	100	50	50	40	40	40	30	25	25	20
106	Working capacity, gal.	8.0	13	16	20	23	29	36	40	50	63
	Trough dimensions	21 × 17	21 × 17	21 × 21	21 × 26¼	23½ × 21	23½ × 26¼	23½ × 33	26¾ × 26¼	26¾ × 33	26¾ × 41
	Max. hp. input	60	30	30	25	25	25	20	15	15	10
85	Working capacity, gal.	4.0	6.4	8.0	10	11	14	18	20	25	32
	Trough dimensions	17 × 13½	17 × 13½	17 × 17	17 × 21	19 × 17	19 × 21	19 × 26¼	21 × 21	21 × 26¼	21 × 33
	Max. hp. input	40	20	20	15	15	15	10	7½	7½	5
68	Working capacity, gal.	2.0	3.2	4.0	5.0	5.8	7.2	9.0	10	13	
	Trough dimensions	13½ × 11	13½ × 11	13½ × 13½	13½ × 17	15¼ × 13½	15¼ × 17	15¼ × 21	17 × 17	17 × 21	
	Max. hp. input	20	10	10	7½	7½	7½	5	3	3	
55	Working capacity, gal.	1.0	1.6	2.0	2.5	2.9	3.6	4.5	5.0		
	Trough dimensions	11 × 8¾	11 × 8¾	11 × 11	11 × 13½	12¼ × 11	12¼ × 13½	12¼ × 17	13½ × 13½		
	Max. hp. input	10	5	5	3	3	3	2	1½		
43	Working capacity, gal.	0.50	0.80	1.0	1.2	1.4	1.8	2.2			
	Trough dimensions	8¾ × 7	8¾ × 7	8¾ × 8¾	8¾ × 11	9¾ × 8¾	9¾ × 11	9¾ × 13½			
	Max. hp. input	6	3	3	2	2	2	1½			
35	Working capacity, gal.	0.25	0.40	0.50	0.63	0.70	0.90	1.1			
	Trough dimensions	7 × 5⅝	7 × 5⅝	7 × 7	7 × 8¾	7¾ × 7	7¾ × 8¾	7¾ × 11			
	Max. hp. input	4	2	2	1½	1½	1½	1			
28	Working capacity, gal.	0.12	0.20	0.25	0.32	0.35	0.45	0.55			
	Trough dimensions	5⅝ × 4½	5⅝ × 4½	5⅝ × 5⅝	5⅝ × 7	6¼ × 5⅝	6¼ × 7	6¼ × 8¾			
	Max. hp. input	2	1	1	¾	¾	¾	½			

The nominal or average working capacities listed in the table may vary plus or minus 10 per cent or more depending upon the form of blade and characteristics of the material.

* *Courtesy of Struthers Wells Corp.*

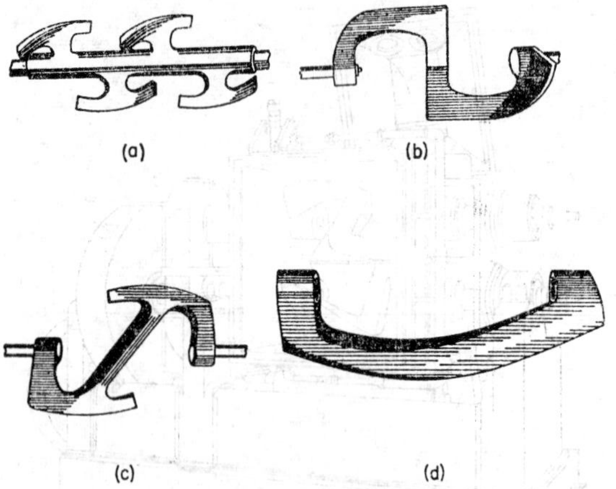

Fig. 19-53. Agitator blades for kneader mixers; (*a*) Fishtail type. (*b*) Z type. (*c*) El type. (*d*) 135° spiral type.

mixers the top of the charge is unconfined, there is considerable space in the mixer body above the blades, and work is done both between the rotors and between the rotors and the walls. These mixers are made for light, medium, and heavy duty, with power requirements ranging from ⅙ to 2 hp./gal. of capacity. The mixing blades cover the entire bottom of the mixing chamber, which conforms closely to their cylinders of rotation Smooth vertical walls allow little purchase for the material to hang up above the blades and the operating level is kept so low that material does not come into contact with the domed cover. The blades are given different forms for various materials (see Fig. 19-53*a*, *b*, *c*, and *d*), but all are shaped so that their rotation draws material down into the active zone. Relative positioning of the blades and suitable overlapping avoid build-up of sticky material on the blades. Discharge may be by tilting, by a door in the side, or by a door or doors in the bottom. Table 19-4 gives capacity and horsepower data on mixers ranging from $\frac{3}{10}$ to 1000 gal. capacity. The clearances are relatively large in these kneaders; so they cannot handle exceptionally tough materials.

Intensive mixers or Banbury mixers (Fig. 19-54) are extra-heavy-duty machines used mainly in the plastics and rubber industries. The top of the charge is confined by a cover shaped to conform to the cylinders of rotation of the blades, and mounted so that it can be forced down on the charge by mechanical or hydraulic means. For standard mixing the pressure on the charge is 15 to 20 lb./sq. in.; for rubber reclaim work pressures up to 150 lb./sq. in. are used. The clearance between the rotors and the walls is extremely small and it is here that the mixing action takes place. According to Comes (*India Rubber World*, May, 1950, p. 178) "Mixing action in the Banbury is obtained between the rotors and the walls of the chamber, not between the rotors themselves. Since no work is done between the rotors, the friction ratio between the rotors is unimportant. The operation

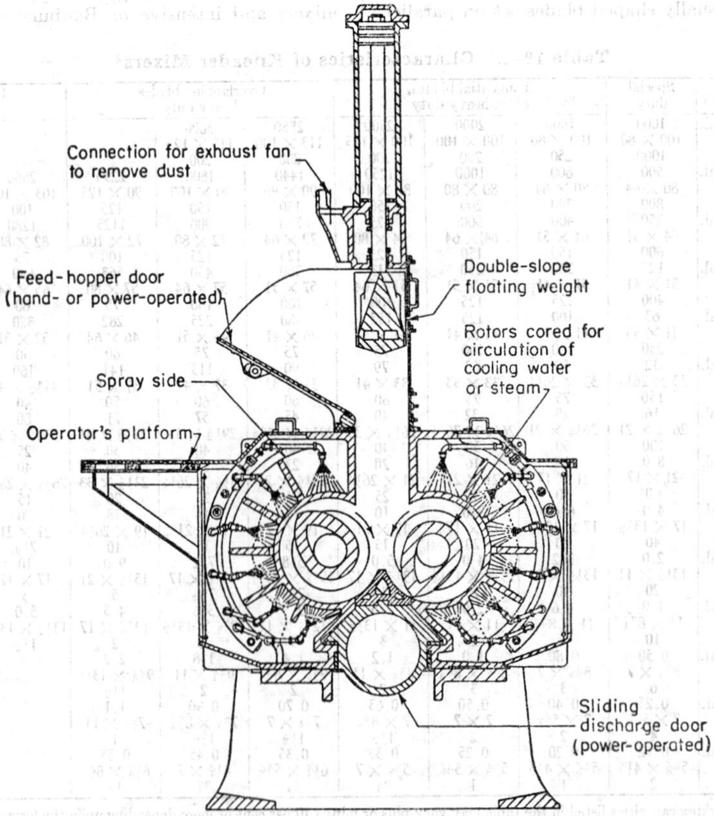

Fig. 19-54. Banbury mixer. (*The Farrel-Birmingham Co.*)

of the rotors of a Banbury at different speeds enables one rotor to drag the stock against the rear of the other and thus help clean ingredients from this area."

The extremely high power consumption of the machines operating at speeds of 40 r.p.m. or lower calls for rotor shafts of large diameter. The combination of heavy shafts, stubby blades, close clearances, and the confined charge limits the Banbury mixer to small batches. The production rate is increased as much as possible by using powerful drives and rotating the blades at the highest speed the material will stand. The friction produced in the confined space is great and with heat-sensitive materials cooling is a serious problem. As an example, a No. 11 Banbury operating at 20 r.p.m. and consuming 250 hp. may turn out a 9 cu. ft. batch in 10 min. The same mixer, operating at 40 r.p.m. and consuming 500 hp., turns out the same batch in 5 min.

Pan Mixers and Mullers. Early types of pan or muller mixers were known as edge runners or putty chasers. The first pan mixers consisted of a plain circular rotating pan containing two or more stationary plows. An early muller was the black powder mill in which large wide-face wooden mullers rotated on a stationary circular wooden floor around a center post.

The main application of muller mixers is now in the foundry industry, in mixing small amounts of moisture and binder materials with sand particles for both core and molding sand. In paste processing, pan and plow mixers are principally used for mixing putty and clay pastes, while muller mixers handle such diversified materials as clay, storage-battery paste, welding-rod coatings, and chocolate coatings.

In muller mixers the rotation of the circular pan or of the plows brings the material progressively into the path of the mullers, where the intensive action takes place. As it is the relative motion of the plows, muller wheels, and pan which produces the desired mixing action, the exact layout of the moving parts is chiefly a matter of individual manufacturer's preference. Figure 19-55 shows one type of mixer, in which the mullers and plows revolve around a stationary turret in a stationary pan. Figure 19-55*a* is a plan view and Fig. 19-55*b* is a sectional elevation of a typical unit. *C* is the crib; *M*1 and *M*2 the muller wheels; *A* the pressure area between the muller and the bed plate; *D* the distance setting of the muller above the bed plate; *B* screws for regulating *D*; and *S* the compression spring for regulating the pressure of the muller wheels. The unit shown is set for counterclockwise rotation. The outside plow *P*2 moves material from the crib wall to the path of the following muller; the inside plow *P*1 moves it from the central turret *T* to the path of the other muller. The mullers crush the material, breaking down lumps and aggregates. Also, as the mullers have wide faces and rotate around the turret in a curve of short radius, only one line on the circumference of the muller face meshes exactly with the material on the pan bottom. Inside this line, the surface of the muller drags material backward; outside it the material is pushed forward. This produces a rotary smearing action on the material and tends to blend the ingredients very intimately.

Extremely fluid mixes cannot be mulled as there is not sufficient friction to rotate the mullers and they swing around the turret as heavy, inefficient, slow-speed paddles. Viscous but non-sticky materials which can be deflected or folded over by the plows are effectively mixed, but extremely sticky materials bunch up in front of the plows and do not move over into the muller paths.

Standard muller mixers range in capacity from a fraction of a cubic foot to more than 60 cu. ft. with power requirements ranging from 1/8 to 75 hp. Muller wheels range in weight from 8 to 4000 lb. There are mullers with jacketed cribs and wear plates and with totally enclosed construction for solvent recovery or operation under vacuum or with a controlled atmosphere. A continuous muller is shown in Fig. 19-56. At the point of intersection of the two crib bodies, the outside plows give an approximately equal exchange of material from one crib to the other, but material builds up in the first crib until the feed rate and the discharge rate of material from the gate in the second crib are equal. The residence time is regulated by adjusting the outlet gate.

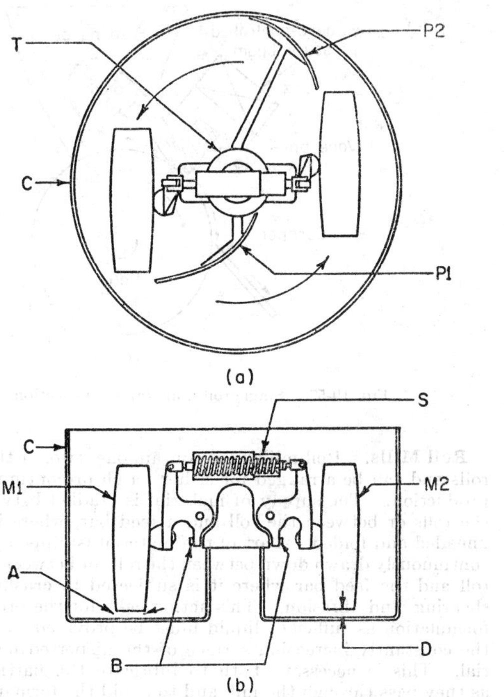

Fig. 19-55. Muller mixer: (*a*) Plan view. (*b*) Sectional elevation. [*From Bullock, Mixing in Muller-type Mixers, Chem. Eng. Progress*, **51**, 243 (1955), *by permission*.]

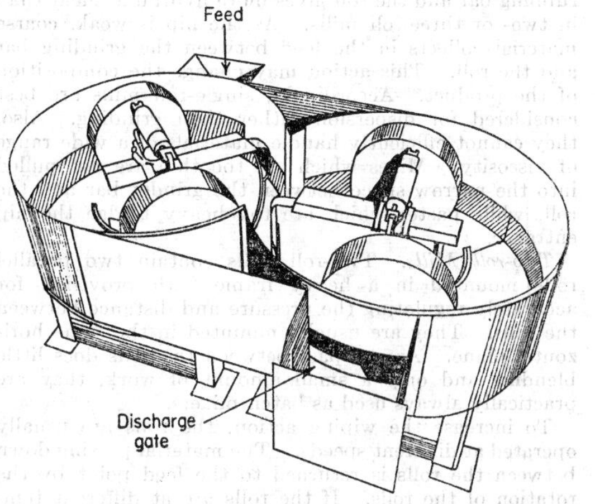

Fig. 19-56. Continuous muller mixer. (*National Engineering Co.*)

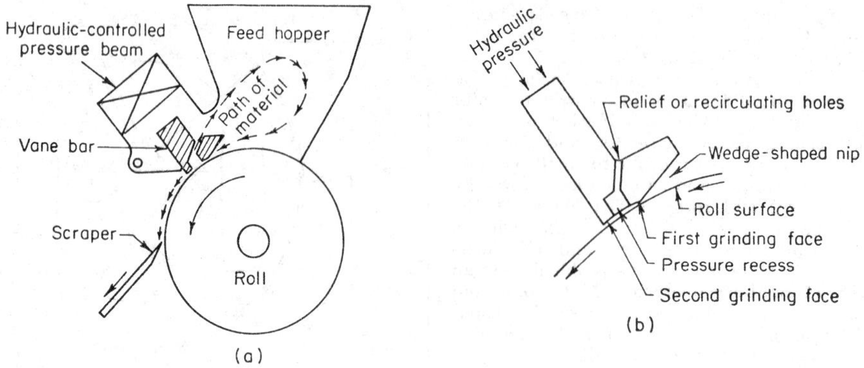

FIG. 19-57. Single-roll mill: (a) Cross section. (b) Enlarged view of vane bar. (*Vickers-Armstrong, Ltd.*)

Roll Mills. Roll mills may contain one, two, or three rolls and can be arranged for either batch or continuous production. The supply of material is cradled between the rolls or between the roll and a feed bar, where it is kneaded and folded. Part of the material is nipped and continuously drawn down between the rolls or between the roll and the feed bar where it is subjected to crushing, shearing, and abrasion. This action calls for the proper formulation as sufficient liquid must be provided to wet the constantly increasing surface of the dispersed material. This is necessary both to lubricate the particles as they pass through the mill and to avoid the formation of new agglomerates. Since all the broken or dispersed particles in the thin film must be immediately surrounded with a film of vehicle, the feed to the mill must be uniform and not contain lumps of dry material. Change-can mixers may be used for preliminary dispersion.

The roll or rolls may be heated or cooled as required. As the action varies with the number of rolls, the different types will be considered separately.

Single-roll Mills. The single-roll mill (Fig. 19-57) contains a wide-faced grinder bar working against a smooth hardened roll. Practically all the work done in single-roll mills results from abrasion. The nipping action is much weaker than between two rolls rotating in the same direction at the point of contact, and there is less crushing than in a two-roll mill. The larger contact area of the rubbing bar and the roll gives more hydraulic shear than in two- or three-roll mills. As the nip is weak, coarse material collects in the feed between the grinding bar and the roll. This action may change the composition of the product. Accordingly, single-roll mills are best considered for dispersion rather than grinding. Also, they cannot efficiently handle materials of a wide range of viscosity. Mixes which are too thin are not pulled into the narrow space between the grinder bar and the roll, while pastes which are too heavy bridge the nip entrance.

Two-roll Mills. Two-roll mills contain two parallel rolls mounted in a heavy frame with provision for accurately regulating the pressure and distance between the rolls. They are usually mounted in the same horizontal plane. As one pass between the rolls does little blending and only a small amount of work, they are practically always used as batch mixers.

To increase the wiping action, the rolls are usually operated at different speeds. The material passing down between the rolls is returned to the feed point by the rotation of the rolls. If the rolls are at different temperatures the material will usually stick to the hotter roll and return to the feed point as a thick layer. This avoids by-passing the feed by two thin films tightly held to the roll surfaces.

At the end of the period of batch mixing, heavy materials may be discharged by dropping between the rolls, while thin mixes may be removed by a scraper bar pressing against the descending surface of one of the rolls.

Two-roll mills are mainly used for preparing color pastes for the ink, paint, and coating industries. There are a few applications in heavy-duty blending of rubber stocks, for which corrugated and masticating rolls are often used.

Three-roll Mills. Three-roll mills are continuous units containing three parallel rolls of equal diameter mounted in a rigid framework. The rolls run at different speeds, the receiving roll being the slowest and the discharge roll being the fastest. The bearings of the middle roll are held stationary in the frame. The clearances between the front and back rolls and the middle roll are independently adjustable. Feed enters between the first and second rolls and a film of appreciable thickness is produced at the first nip, where aggregates and particles are crushed. They are then abraded through rubbing action of the rolls turning at different speeds, but since the film is thick there is probably no hydraulic shear. In the second nip a smaller clearance produces a thinner film and the speed of the take-off roll is increased to compensate for the reduction of cross-sectional area. In the thinner film there is more crushing, less internal abrasion, and—because of the higher speed—more external abrasion against the rolls. The higher speed produces some hydraulic shear in the thin film. At both nips there is a rotary motion of the stock lying in the nip, which produces some mass mixing. The finished product is removed from the last roll by a tapered delivery chute fitted with a scraper bar as shown in Fig. 19-58.

For satisfactory operation, the rolls must be ground to a uniform diameter throughout their length. Roll surfaces must be hard and ground to a mirror finish. As the pressures between the rolls are extremely high the roll diameters must be large to avoid bowing. High-grade bearings must be carefully mounted in rigid frames so that the axes of the rolls always lie in the same plane. Otherwise a uniform clearance at the nip is not possible.

The chief application of three-roll mills is in dispersing and grinding inks and pigment pastes, but they may be used whenever an extremely uniform dispersion is desired.

Pug Mills and Extruders. Pug mills and extruders are valuable for processing heavy plastic masses. Some pug mills are for extrusion, but the machines are usually classified according to the form of their working ele-

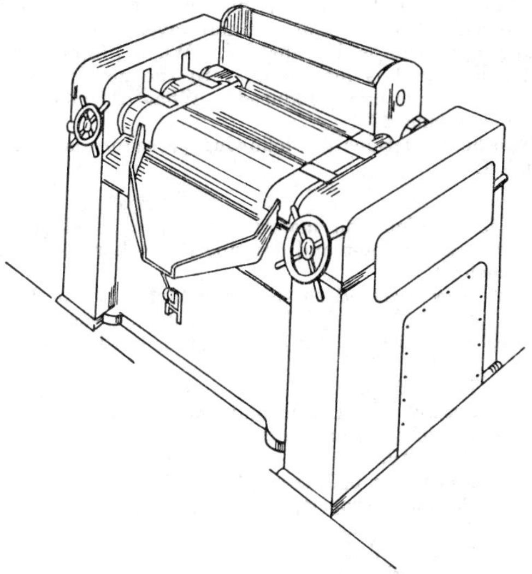

FIG. 19-58. Three-roll mill. (*J. H. Day Co., Inc.*)

ments. Machines using short stout paddles for mixing and moving the material are called pug mills; machines using a continuous screw or screws are called extruders.

Pug Mills. A pug mill (Fig. 19-59) contains one or two shafts fitted with short heavy paddles, mounted in a cylinder or trough which holds the material being processed. In two-shaft mills the shafts are parallel and may be horizontal or vertical. The paddles may or may not intermesh. Clearances are wide so that there is considerable mass mixing. Unmixed or partially mixed ingredients are fed at one end of the machine, which is usually totally enclosed. The paddles push the material forward as they cut through it, and carry the charge toward the discharge end as it is mixed. Product may discharge through one or two open ports or through one or more extrusion nozzles which give roughly shaped, continuous strips. Automatic cutters may be used to make blocks from the strips. Pug mills are most used in the ceramic field for mixing and tempering clay products.

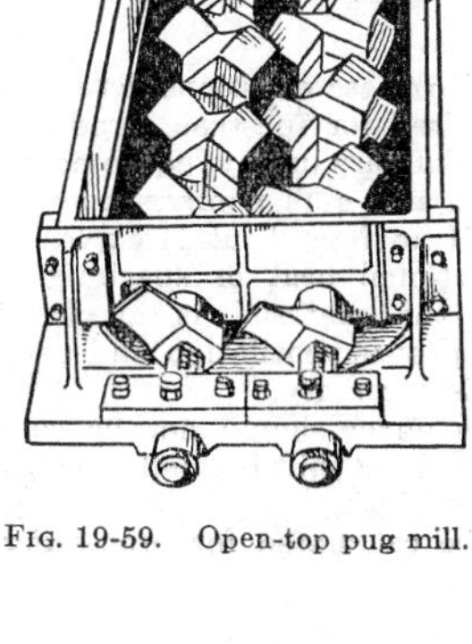

FIG. 19-59. Open-top pug mill.

Extruders. Extruders used for paste processing are of the screw type in which a continuous screw or screws rotate in a closely fitting barrel. (See Fig. 19-60.) To deaerate and compact the material and generate enough pressure to force the material through the extrusion die, the depth or pitch of the screw changes along its length.

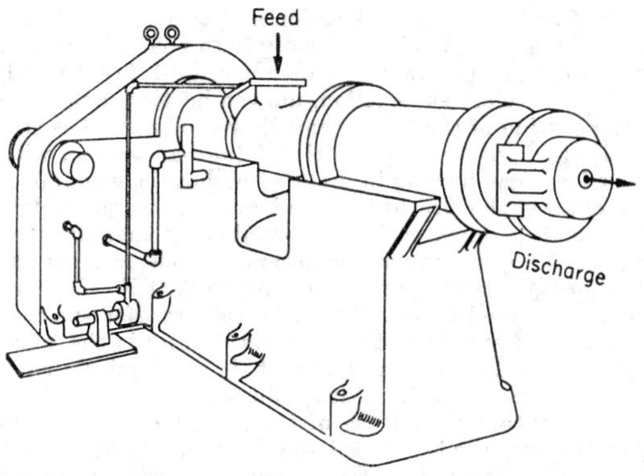

FIG. 19-60. Mixer-extruder. (*The Farrel-Birmingham Co.*)

Extruders are on the border line of paste processing, for material is fed as a dry solid, is fluxed in the barrel to a paste, and resolidifies at the discharge. In the barrel the material is subject to shearing, rubbing, and kneading. The direct work of the screw is supplemented by forcing the material through breaker screens and around breaker disks, just before it is forced out through the nozzle. As the mixing zone is of small cross section and the motion of the material is substantially in one direction only there is little volume blending. The ingredients should therefore be blended uniformly before entering the feed hopper.

Multiple-screw extruders produce greater smearing and shearing of the material and a slight reverse motion which improves the blending action.

Applications of extruders range from the extrusion of soft food and chemical mixes which do not require fluxing, to the extrusion of hard plastics, some of which must be fluxed at temperatures above 440°F. Wires are covered and shapes of intricate cross section are produced; also, large tonnages of plastics resins are blended in extruders to form pellets for press and injection molding.

Carley *et al.* [*Ind. Eng. Chem.*, **45**, 970, 974, 978, 989 (1953)] discuss the theory of extrusion and present data for scaling up from tests in small equipment.

HEAT TRANSFER

Pastes are often heated or cooled by heat transfer through the walls of the container or hollow mixing arms. Good agitation, a large ratio of transfer surface to mixer volume, and frequent removal of material from the surface are essential for high rates of heat transfer. Sometimes evaporation of part of the mix is used for cooling. Radiant heating, occasionally used for supplementary heating, is affected by the reflecting power of the mix surface.

In most mixers the metal wall has a negligible thermal resistance. The films of heating or cooling medium and especially of the paste usually have high resistance. It is important, therefore, to minimize the resistance of the heating or cooling medium and to move the paste up to and away from the smooth wall surface as steadily and rapidly as possible. This is best achieved by having the paste flow so as to follow a close-fitting scraper which wipes the film from the wall with each rotation. Typical over-all heat-transfer coefficients are between 5 and 40 B.t.u./(hr.)(sq. ft.)(°F.).

Heating Methods. The most economical heating method varies with plant location and available facilities. *Direct firing* may be done cheaply with coal, oil, or gas, but with the disadvantages of a constant fire hazard, the need for close supervision, uneven heating, oxidation of the outside of the kettle, and slow cooling. It is still widely used with varnish kettles. *Indirect heating,* with air or inert gas flowing in a closed circuit, is economical and reduces the fire hazard and damage to the kettle wall. Fairly quick cooling is possible by changing the path of the gas through the circuit. Such systems are used for operating temperatures above 300°F. If temperatures exceed 900°F. the ducts and transfer surfaces should be of stainless steel. *Steam heating* is the most widely used heating method. It is economical, safe, and easily controlled. With thin-walled mixers there must be automatic release of the vacuum that results when the pressure is reduced and the steam in the jacket condenses. Otherwise weak sections will collapse. *Transfer-liquid heating* using water, oil, special organic liquids, or molten inorganic salts permits good temperature control and provides insurance against overheating the processed material. *Electrical heating* is accomplished with resistance bands or ribbons which must be electrically insulated from the machine body but in good thermal contact with it. The heaters must be carefully spaced to avoid a succession of hot and cold areas. Sometimes they are mounted in aluminum blocks shaped to conform to the container walls. Their effective temperature range is 300° to 1000°F. Temperature control is precise, maintenance and supervision costs are low, and conversion of electrical energy to heat is almost 100 per cent. The cost of electrical energy is usually large, however, and may be prohibitive. *Frictional heat* develops rapidly in some units such as a Banbury mixer. The first temperature rise may be beneficial by softening the materials and accelerating chemical reactions. High temperatures detrimental to the product, however, may easily be reached, and provision for cooling or frequent stopping of the machine must be made. Frictional heating may be controlled by reducing the number of working elements, their area, and their speed. This increases the mixing time but facilitates cooling the charge.

Cooling Methods. In *air cooling,* air may be blown over the machine surfaces, the area of which is best extended with fins. Air or cooled inert gas may also be blown over the exposed surface of the mix, provided care is taken to avoid contamination or oxidation of the charge. *Evaporation* of excess water or solvent under vacuum or at atmospheric pressure provides good cooling. A small amount of evaporation produces a large amount of cooling. Removing too much solvent, however, may damage the charge. *Direct addition of ice* to the mixer provides rapid convenient cooling, provided the resulting dilution of the mix is permissible. *Addition of dry ice* is more expensive but results in lower temperatures, and the CO_2 gas evolved provides a good inert atmosphere. Many mixers are cooled by *circulation of water or refrigerants* through jackets or hollow agitators. In general this is the cheapest method.

SELECTION OF PROCESS AND EQUIPMENT

Equipment for a New Product. If a new product is being considered the preliminary study must be highly detailed. Laboratory or pilot-plant work must be done to establish the controlling factors. The problem is then to select and install equipment which will operate for quantity production at minimum over-all cost.

One approach is by analogy. What product currently produced is most similar to the new product? How is this material produced? What difficulties are being experienced?

In other situations the following procedure is recommended:

1. List carefully all materials to be handled at the processing point and describe their characteristics, such as
   a. How received at the processing unit: in bags, barrels, drums, in bulk, by pipe line, etc.?
   b. Must storage and/or weighing be done at the site?
   c. Physical form.
   d. Specific gravity and bulk characteristics.
   e. Particle size or size range.
   f. Viscosity.
   g. Melting or boiling point.
   h. Corrosive properties.
   i. Abrasive characteristics.
   j. Is material poisonous?
   k. Is material explosive?
   l. Is material an irritant to skin, eyes, or lungs?
   m. Is material sensitive to exposure to air, moisture, or heat?
2. List pertinent data covering production:
   a. Quantity to be produced per 8-hr. shift.
   b. Formulation of finished product.
   c. What accuracy of analysis is required?
   d. Will changes in color, flavor, odor, grade (as on lead for pencils) require frequent cleaning of equipment?
   e. Is this operation independent, or does it serve other apparatus with which it must be synchronized?
   f. Is there a change in physical state during processing?
   g. Is there a chemical reaction? Is it endothermic or exothermic?
   h. What are the temperature requirements?
   i. What is the form of the finished product?
   j. How must the material be removed from the apparatus (by pumping, free flow through pipe or chute, dumping, etc.)?
3. Describe in detail the controlling characteristics of the finished product:
   a. Permanence of the emulsion or dispersion.
   b. Degree of blending of aggregates or of ultimate particles.
   c. Ultimate color development required.
   d. Uniformity of the dispersion of active ingredient or ingredients, as in a drug product.
   e. Degree of control of moisture content for pressing, extrusion, etc.

The answers to these questions determine the type of equipment required for full-scale production. Thus, if the feed ingredients are lumpy, equipment having crushing powers, such as a muller mixer, kneader, or roll mill, is indicated. If an ingredient is explosive, there must be no high frictional heat or sparking created in the apparatus. If the material is an irritant, enclosed operation with proper ventilation and perhaps a dust or fume collector is necessary.

A continuous mixer should not be considered if the quantity produced per shift is small. If there is a change in physical state during processing, the power requirements should be calculated for processing the heaviest and most viscous stage. If there is an endothermic or exothermic reaction, jacketed equipment for heating or cooling is indicated.

To produce an intimate blend of ultimate particles, the equipment must embody close clearances and intensive action. If one ingredient is present in very small concentrations it may be advisable to consider master batching in which that ingredient is separately mixed with part of some other ingredient of the mix, and then added to the rest of the mix for final dispersion. Master batching is especially valuable in adding tinting colors, antioxidants, and the like. The master batch may be made up with laboratory accuracy, while at the mixing station weighing errors are minimized by the dilution of the important ingredient.

Answers to these questions may make it desirable to consider automatic weighing and batch accumulation, metering of liquid ingredients, and automatic control of various time cycles.

Careful study of all controlling factors can save costly alterations to equipment and materially shorten the startup time. The latter is important as the cost of off-grade or spoiled material mounts very rapidly.

Preparation and Addition of Materials. To ensure maximum production of high-grade material, the physical preparation of the material must be correct and the ingredients of the mix must be added in the proper order. The ingredients of the mix must be examined carefully. Some finely powdered materials, such as carbon black, contain much air. If possible they should be compacted or wet out before being added to the mix. If a sufficient quantity of light solvent is a part of the formula, it may be used to wet the powder and drive out the air. If the powder cannot be wetted, it may be possible to densify it somewhat by mechanical means. Removal of adsorbed gas under vacuum is sometimes necessary.

Many ingredients such as vulcanizers, antioxidants, and antiacids are present in small amounts. These substances often tend to form aggregates when dry. Before entering the mixer they should be fluffed, either by screening as herein if the aggregates are soft, or by passage through a small hammer mill, roll mill, or muller if they are hard. The mixing time is cut down and the product is more uniform if all ingredients are freed from aggregates before mixing.

If any solids present in small amounts are soluble in a liquid portion of the mix, it is well to add them as a solution, making provision to distribute the liquid uniformly throughout the mass. When a trace of solid material which is not soluble in any other ingredient is to be added, it may be necessary to add it as a solution in a neutral solvent, with provision to evaporate the solvent at the end of the mixing cycle.

AGITATED PAN DRYERS

Description. Agitated pan dryers consist of a fairly shallow flat-bottomed cylindrical pan covered by a dished or conical cover. The bottom and walls of the pan are jacketed for heating with steam or other medium. A central vertical shaft carries a slow-moving heavy-duty agitator which stirs the material in the dryer and moves it toward and away from the heat-transfer surfaces. The agitator is usually set to a very close clearance and may carry spring-loaded scrapers to clean the heat-transfer surface. The drive shaft may enter the pan from above through the cover or from below through the floor. Nearly all pan dryers, even when operated at atmospheric pressure, are closed with a cover containing a manhole, sight glasses, and an outlet through which heated vapors escape by natural draft. Vacuum pan dryers have a dished or dome-shaped cover fitted with a manhole, sight glasses, and a vacuum connection. Both types have a port in the side, flush with the pan floor, through which dry product is discharged. In drying sticky materials which tend to rotate with the agitator as a single mass, stationary fingers just clearing the agitator are set in the pan from the top or side.

An atmospheric pan dryer is sometimes called a **graining bowl.** One type of pan dryer incorporates a screen filter in the pan floor for dewatering crystalline solids prior to drying. Other special units employ Thermocoil construction in the jacket, in which a coil carrying heat-transfer fluid is cast in a heavy cast-iron shell. An atmospheric dryer is shown in Fig. 19-61; a vacuum pan dryer is shown in Fig. 19-62. Typical units range from 3 to 10 ft. in diameter and contain from 15 to 300 sq. ft. of heating surface. They are generally loaded about two-thirds full. Agitator speeds range from 2 to 20 r.p.m.

Fields of Application. Agitated pan dryers handle batches of material which must be agitated during drying. They are fairly easily cleaned and are therefore adaptable to handling successive batches of a number of different materials. They are most useful for batchwise drying of hard-to-handle materials for which continuous drying would be uneconomical, as when solvents must be vaporized from the solids and recovered; drying must be under high vacuum; or where evaporation, crystallization, and drying, with consequent large changes in physical properties, must be done in a single unit. They are not suitable for materials which suffer particle-size degradation during drying or which form into balls and caseharden.

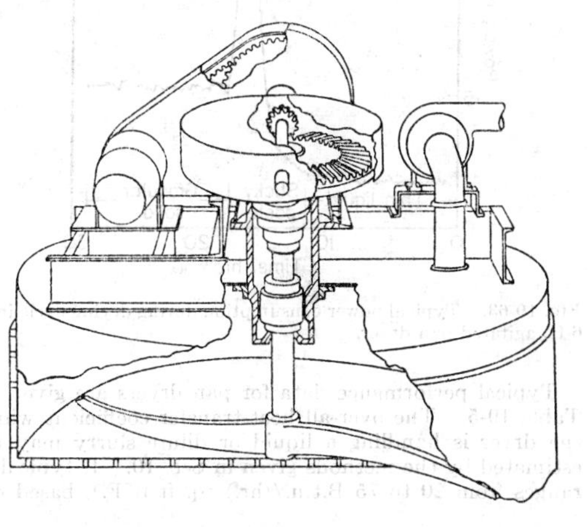

FIG. 19-61. Atmospheric pan dryer. (*C. O. Bartlett and Snow Co.*)

Design and Performance Data. The chief factors governing the operation of an agitated pan dryer are the rate of heat transfer and the degree of agitation. Of these, agitation is the more critical, for it must be effective enough to keep all the material active, to prevent damage by overheating stagnant material, and to give satisfactorily rapid heat transfer. With some materials the degree of agitation is limited by the amount of power that can be supplied to the dryer. Often the contents of the pan pass through several stages: starting perhaps

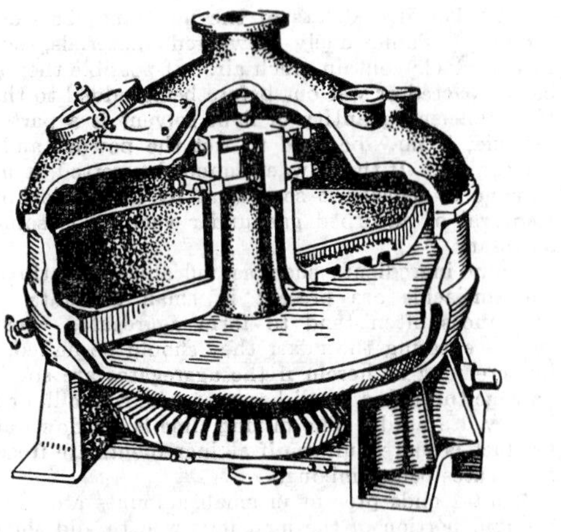

FIG. 19-62. Vacuum pan dryer. (*Buflovak Equipment Division.*)

as a thin solution they become progressively more viscous, change to a sticky paste, and finally become a free-flowing granular solid. Heat-transfer rates and agitation requirements change markedly during the drying cycle. The dryer must be designed to handle the material in the most difficult stage.

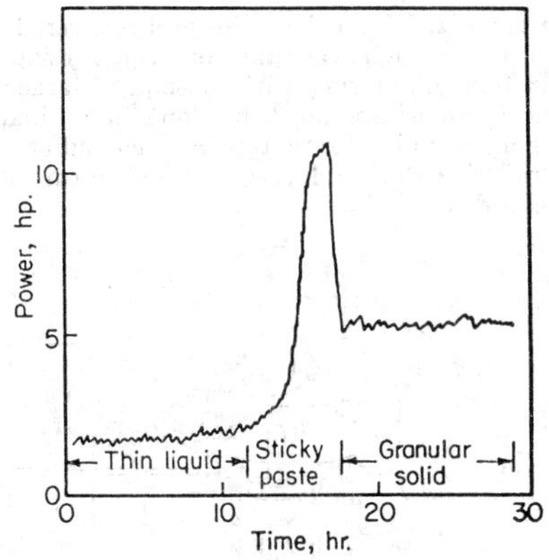

FIG. 19-63. Typical power consumption during drying cycle in a 6-ft. agitated pan dryer.

Typical performance data for pan dryers are given in Table 19-5. The over-all heat-transfer coefficient while the dryer is handling a liquid or dilute slurry may be estimated by the methods given in Sec. 10. It typically ranges from 20 to 75 B.t.u./(hr.)(sq. ft.)(°F.), based on the heat-transfer area in contact with the liquid. Similar values are obtained in heating viscous pastes using scraper agitators. In drying pastes and granular solids the average over-all coefficient ranges from 5 to 40 B.t.u./(hr.)(sq. ft.)(°F.). It changes throughout the cycle, depending on the density and moisture content of the material. It also depends strongly on the agitator speed. Under given operating conditions the total drying time is about proportional to the volume of charge per unit area of heating surface.

The power consumption also varies throughout the drying cycle. Figure 19-63 shows typical data for drying a material in a 6-ft. pan dryer with an agitator turning at 11 r.p.m. During the first half of the cycle the material was a thin liquid and the power consumption was low. When the material became a sticky paste the power consumed rose to a peak; when it changed to a granular solid the power fell to about half the peak value. Power consumption when the material is a liquid may be estimated by the methods outlined under Circulation Mixers. No adequate methods exist for estimating the peak power. For scale-up it is suggested that pilot-plant data be correlated by an equation of the form

$$\frac{P_m g_c}{n^3 D^5 \rho_s} = K \left(\frac{Mg}{\rho_s n^2 D^4} \right)^m \qquad (19\text{-}12)$$

where P_m = peak power consumption; n = agitator speed; D = pan diameter; ρ_s = bulk density of material; M = mass of charge; g_c = Newton's-law conversion factor; g = acceleration of gravity; K and m are empirical constants. The groups in Eq. (19-12) are dimensionless, and any consistent set of units may be used. Equation (19-12) is based on the assumption that shear forces in

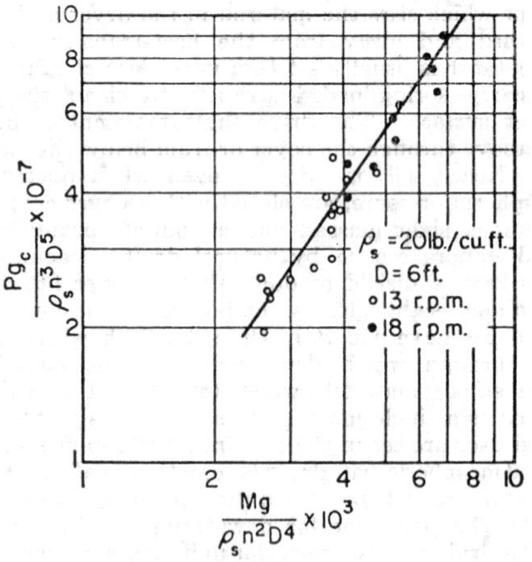

FIG. 19-64. Power correlation for an agitated pan dryer.

Table 19-5. Performance Data for Agitated Pan Dryers*

Material	Solvent	Wt. % solvent		Pan diam., ft.	Agitator speed, r.p.m.	Operating pressure, lb./sq. in. abs.	Over-all coefficient U, B.t.u./(hr.)(sq. ft.)(°F.)	Over-all cycle time, hr.
		Initial	Final					
Sodium sulfate	Water	45	0.5	3	2	14.7	18	11
Sodium carbonate	Water	74	14.4	3	2	14.7	38	6
Sodium carbonate	Water	83.5	0.1	3	2	14.7	38	
Calcium carbonate	Water	37.2	0.1	3	3	14.7	35	4
Ore sludge	$TiCl_4$	70	1.0	...	...	14.7, 0.9	10	
Sodium sulfate	Water	57.1	7.5	3	2	1.2	23	5.5
Sodium sulfate	Organic	39.0	1.0	...	...	0.9	15	
Sodium chloride	Water	81.5	0.6	3	2	1.2	51	10
Calcium phosphate	Water	46.8	2.6	3	2.5	0.8	19	3
Lithium chloride	Water	49.0	0.1	...	...	0.5	12.5	

* From Harcourt, A.S.M.E. meeting, Niagara Falls, Sept. 17–23, 1936; and from Bethlehem Foundry and Machine Co.

the material are negligible in comparison with the lifting forces. Figure 19-64 shows data from a 6-ft. dryer correlated according to Eq. (19-12).

In a vacuum dryer the exit velocity of the vapor should not exceed 2 ft./sec., to minimize dust carry-over. Time must be provided in the cycle for charging the material, heating it to temperature, and discharging it when dry. Discharging normally takes 15 to 30 min. Thermal efficiencies usually range from 70 to 80 per cent with vacuum dryers and 65 to 75 per cent with atmospheric dryers.

Costs. Purchase prices of agitated pan dryers (f.o.b. Bethlehem, Pa., June, 1960) are given in Fig. 19-65. Operating costs vary considerably, depending on the nature of the material and the length of the drying cycle. Power costs typically range from 10 cents to $1 per ton of dry material. Annual maintenance costs average 2 to 3 per cent of the total installed cost. Operating labor requirements vary greatly, depending on the amount of instrumentation and automation provided. With minimum instrumentation, 1 to 2 man-hr. per batch is required for loading and unloading, and about half a man's time is needed while the dryer is in operation.

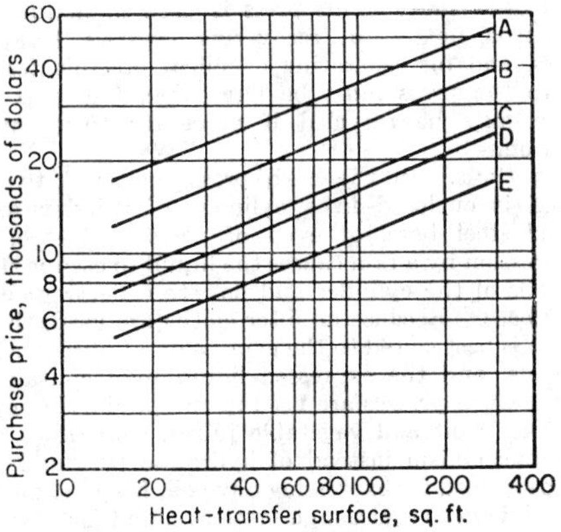

FIG. 19-65. Purchase price of agitated pan dryers. Curve *A*, for nickel-clad steel; *B*, for Thermocoil construction; *C*, for stainless steel, type 316, clad; *D*, for stainless steel, type 304, clad; *E*, for carbon steel. (*Bethlehem Foundry and Machine Co.*)

EXPRESSION

REFERENCES: Bailey, "Industrial Oil and Fat Products," pp. 469–479, Interscience, New York, 1945. Dickey and Bryden, "Theory and Practice of Filtration," Chap. 9, Reinhold, New York, 1946.

Definition. Expression is the separation of liquid from a two-phase solid-liquid system by compression under conditions that permit the liquid to escape while the solid is retained between the compressing surfaces. Expression is distinguished from filtration in that pressure is applied by movement of the retaining walls instead of by pumping the material into a fixed space.

Purpose. Expression has the same purpose as filtration: to separate liquid and solid phases from a mechanical mixture of the two. In filtration, the original mixture is sufficiently fluid to be pumpable; in expression this is not usually true, and the material may appear entirely solid. Expression is therefore employed to separate systems that are not readily pumpable. It is also used instead of filtration when a more thorough removal of liquid from the cake is desired.

In some applications, as the dewatering of paper, expression is competitive with drying. Mechanical removal of water is usually far cheaper than any thermal method; hence expression is almost universally employed for one stage of water removal. In vegetable-oil production, expression and solvent extraction are competitive; expression is less thorough but may yield both oil and meal products of higher quality. In the recovery of juice from sugar cane, expression on three-roll mills is combined with solvent extraction using water, in a series of alternating or simultaneous operations.

EXPRESSION EQUIPMENT

Hydraulic presses of the batch type have been used for centuries but are diminishing in importance. The principal batch presses are the box, platen, pot, curb, and cage. For continuous operation, the screw press and various types of roller mills are in common use.

Batch Presses. *Box Press.* The material to be expressed is wrapped in canvas cloths and placed in a series of steel boxes fitting between the fixed and movable heads of a vertical hydraulic press. Each bag lies on a perforated mat over a grid of drainage channels and is covered and enclosed by the next higher box. The series of loaded boxes is compressed as a unit under hydraulic pressure.

A 15-box press will handle 8 tons of conditioned cottonseed meats in a 24-hr. period, reducing the oil content from 30 to about 6 per cent. The operating cycle is from 20 to 30 min. per batch. The press is first closed rapidly under low pressure until flow of oil starts at about 200 lb./sq. in. pressure on the cake; then high-pressure fluid is used to close the press slowly to the maximum of 1600 lb./sq. in. pressure on the cake, with 4000 lb./sq. in. on the hydraulic fluid. The maximum pressure is continued for a few minutes to permit drainage.

Platen Press. The platen press is similar to the box press, but the cloth bags are not enclosed on the sides during pressing. The platens or plates are sometimes cored for heating and usually have gutters to collect the expressed liquid. The whole press may be tilted backward slightly to provide better drainage. This type of press is also built in horizontal form. With steam-heated platens, a cold-pressed oil of superior quality can be obtained first, followed by a further yield of poorer-quality hot-pressed oil.

Pot Press. Material to be pressed is enclosed in a cylindrical pot, with filter pads or screens beneath and on top, and is compressed by a ram entering from above. The filter medium is flat and covers only the top and bottom of the material; hence it is not subject to stretching or tearing as in box or platen presses. Because the material is entirely enclosed, it may be more fluid than in other types of press. In practice a series of pots is used in each press, the bottom of each pot serving as the ram for the pot below.

The largest use of pot presses is in the chocolate industry, but they also find application for pressing olives, palm, and similar nuts, and for separating liquid from slushy materials such as chemical products. In a typical cycle, from 500 to 600 lb. of chocolate liquor, produced by grinding cocoa nibs, is pumped to the press chambers, which are then closed under a pressure of 6000 lb./sq. in. Cocoa butter is expressed, leaving a cake of cocoa powder.

A development of the pot press is the Carver combined filter and hydraulic press, used as a conventional filter press until the chambers are full, and then closed under hydraulic pressure to obtain a further yield of liquor and a drier cake. This press is used in making cocoa and cocoa butter, in recovering crystals from other liquors, and for separating chemical precipitates. The feed to the press must be pumpable, but part of the filtrate may be recycled if necessary to obtain this condition.

Curb Press. In the curb press, material to be expressed is enclosed in a cylinder of wooden slats or beveled steel bars, or even of perforated steel plate. Compression by a ram causes the liquid to escape through the walls of the cylinder and flow to collecting channels at the base. Because no filter cloths are used, this type of press is best suited to the expression of fibrous non-oily materials, and the expressed liquid may contain some solids. Curb presses are used in the production of cider and other fruit and vegetable juices, sometimes with a screw mechanism instead of hydraulic pressure. They have been used for expressing olive oil, fish oils, and other oils that do not require high pressures, and for dewatering and recovering grease from garbage before incineration.

Cage Press. The cage press is similar to the curb press except that the inside of the cylinder has fine longitudinal grooves leading through the cylinder walls to larger drainage channels. It is suitable for oilier and less fibrous materials than the curb press. Intermediate drain plates and cloths are sometimes used within the cake. Cage presses are not extensively used in America but are employed in Europe for expressing castor beans and copra.

Continuous Presses. *Screw Press.* The continuous screw press, typified by the Anderson expeller (Fig. 19-66), consists of a rotating screw fitting closely inside a

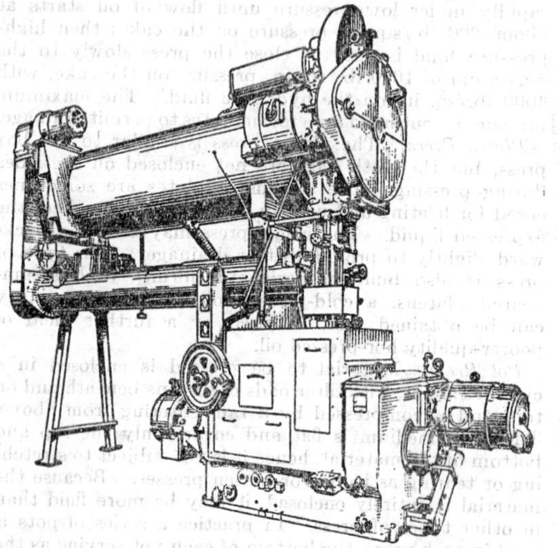

FIG. 19-66. Anderson expeller with oil-seed tempering unit. (*The V. D. Anderson Co.*)

horizontal slotted curb. The curb and screw may be tapered toward the discharge end to increase the pressure on the material. This may also be achieved by varying the pitch on the screw in a uniform cylinder. The discharge end of the curb is partly closed by an adjustable cone or other device to change the size of the opening and thus to vary the pressure on the material. Rotation of the screw moves the material forward; and, as the pressure increases, liquid is expelled and escapes through lengthwise slots in the curb. The operation is continuous, and labor and other operating costs are lower than for hydraulic pressing. This type of equipment is extensively used in the vegetable- and animal-oil industries and is applied to the dewatering of such materials as paper pulp, plastics, synthetic rubber, garbage, and paunch manure. During dewatering, washing or dilution water may be injected at one or more points in the cage. Shear action in the mass effectively disintegrates the solid without damaging individual fibers. The capacity of commercial screw presses for oils ranges from 3 to 1000 tons of raw material per 24 hr. The residual oil content may vary from 2 to 18 per cent, depending on the oil seed pressed and the type of press.

Roller Mills. Continuous roller mills (Fig. 19-67), as used in the cane-sugar industry, combine a mechanical

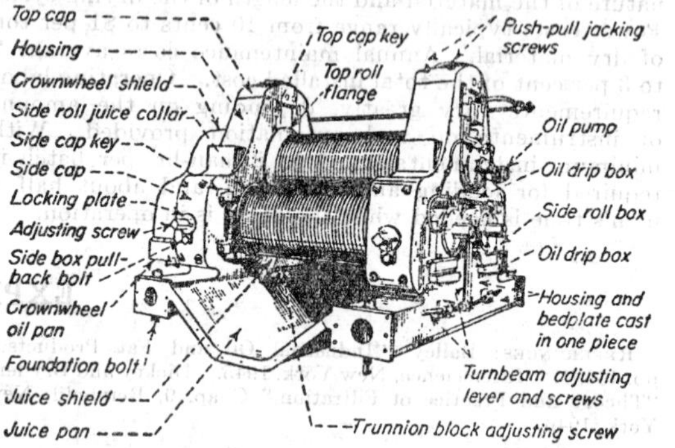

FIG. 19-67. Three-roll sugar mill. (*The Farrel-Birmingham Co.*)

breaking and crushing action with the application of pressure to express juice. Three-roll mills are common, with the top roll above and between the other two, and pressed against them by hydraulic rams at each end. Material is squeezed between the top and first rolls and is then directed by a turnplate into the nip of the top and second rolls for a second pressing. The rolls are made of cast iron, corrugated or grooved in various patterns. A feed roll is sometimes used to force-feed the first pair of rolls, permitting the use of a smaller mill opening or a higher rate of feed.

In the cane-sugar industry, trains of four to seven of these mills are used, with the blanket of crushed cane carried between them by apron conveyors. The cane is first crushed dry; but, at selected points in the later mills, water or weak liquor is added as a spray or bath, to improve sugar recovery. This process is known as maceration and is equivalent to leaching of the cane combined with expression in the mills.

Two-roll mills cause expression of liquid without the crushing and tearing action of three-roll units. Double rolls are widely used for dewatering paper, usually supported on a felt, in papermaking machines. Similar two-roll units, often with padded surfaces instead of steel, squeeze water or process liquids from textiles after kiering, dyeing, bleaching, and related operations. In the padding process of dyeing, the cloth is thoroughly impregnated with small quantities of dye by successive squeezings with padded rolls.

Disk Press. Continuous disk presses are in use for the mechanical removal of moisture from various materials, including fruit and vegetable pulps, spent grains, packinghouse wastes, reclaimed and synthetic rubber, and wood pulp. The press includes two rotating disks, facing each other but not parallel; material to be pressed is fed into the widest part of the opening and is discharged after about a four-to-one squeeze. Pressures up to 180 lb./sq. in. may be obtained.

Auxiliary Equipment. Hydraulic pumps of various capacities and pressures are used, frequently with high- and low-pressure units on the same drive. Large-capacity low-pressure pumps are required for closing the presses and for miscellaneous services such as cake forming and opening the presses. Low-capacity high-pressure fluid is needed for the final pressing. Sometimes the hydraulic fluid is the same as the liquid being expressed, to avoid possible contamination.

Accumulators are used to reduce the load on the pumps, by building up a reservoir of fluid under pressure when the pumps are not serving the presses directly. Weighted accumulators contain a cylinder and piston, carrying a load of iron, stone, or concrete. Air-ballasted accumulators have the advantages of lessened line shock and lighter weight and hence simpler foundations. Separate accumulators are needed for the high- and low-pressure systems.

Automatic change valves have been developed which, with a single manual operation, supply low-pressure fluid to close the press and start the flow of oil and then supply high-pressure fluid slowly to the maximum pressure of the system. Choke valves prevent too rapid an application of the higher pressure.

EXPRESSION THEORY

Theory of the expression operation is far from complete. Most experimental work has been done on a particular material and has led to the development of empirical equations which lack general application.

Equilibrium Conditions. Gurnham and Masson [Theses, New York University (1940 and 1942); *Ind. Eng. Chem.*, **38**, 1309 (1946)] have studied the equilibrium conditions of expression, *i.e.*, the conditions after a constant pressure has been maintained until no further flow occurs. They consider a knowledge of this state prerequisite to an investigation of rates of expression and recommend that the quantity of liquid expressed be considered as the difference between the quantity originally present and the quantity remaining in the cake after pressing. The amount of liquid remaining in the press cake after partial expression can presumably be determined from the measured volume of the cake and the known or estimated volume of the solid portion.

The volumes of various materials were measured under a series of pressures, and the hypothesis presented that an increase in pressure on a system of expressible material, considered as a fractional increase over the previous pressure, causes a proportional increase in the bulk density of the solid portion of the system:

$$\frac{dp}{p} = K\,d\rho_s = Kd\,\frac{1}{V}$$

or

$$\frac{dp}{d(1/V)} = Kp \qquad (19\text{-}13)$$

In integrated form, this is

$$\log p = k + \frac{k'}{V} \qquad (19\text{-}14)$$

where p is pressure on the system, ρ_s is bulk density of the solid portion of the system, V is specific volume of the system based on the solid content, and K, k, and k' are constants depending on the nature of the material and the conditions of expression. These investigations were carried out in the Carver test cylinder, equivalent to a pot press 1 sq. in. in area, and in a cage press 10 sq. in. in area. Materials tested included cotton fiber, woolen yarn, wool felts, asbestos fiber, paper pulp, wood sawdust, and other fibrous substances, pressed in dry condition or wetted with water, oils, and other liquids. Pressures used ranged from 250 to 20,000 lb./sq. in. Most of Deerr's data on sugar cane and bagasse, discussed below, also confirm this theory.

Empirical Equations. Deerr investigated the expression of juice from sugar cane and bagasse, using apparatus equivalent to small pot presses (*Hawaiian Sugar Planters' Assoc. Expt. Sta., Agr. and Chem. Ser., Bulls.* 22, 1908; 30, 1910; 38, 1912). He suggested the formula

$$V_c = \frac{C}{p^n} \qquad (19\text{-}15)$$

in which V_c is volume of cake (fiber plus unexpressed juice) under pressure p, C is a constant for a given experiment, and n is a constant or a function of p depending on pressing conditions. Equation (19-15) is entirely empirical, but it fits the observed data with fair accuracy. Using this equation, Deerr made theoretical calculations of pressures on the rolls and of work done in expression. It has been observed that the equation of Gurnham and Masson fitted Deerr's original data closely except with pots of small diameter, in which the wall effect was large, and in low-pressure tests during which air was probably entrapped in the sample.

Koo and coworkers studied the expression of seven different oils over a range of pressures, temperatures, pressing times, and moisture contents, using a laboratory cage press 70 cu. in. in capacity [Koo and Chen, *Ind. Research (China)*, **6**, 9 (1937). Koo, *J. Chem. Eng. China*, **4**, 15, 207 (1937); **5**, 47, 69 (1938); **7**, 1, 23 (1940); **8**, 1, 5 (1941); *Ind. Eng. Chem.*, **34**, 342 (1942)]. They developed a formula of the type

$$W = C'W_o\,\frac{p^{1/2}\theta^{1/6}}{\nu^a} \qquad (19\text{-}16)$$

in which W is weight of oil expressed, W_o is weight of oil in the original material, C' is a "press constant" depending on the type of material, p is pressure, θ is time of pressing, ν is kinematic viscosity of the oil at press temperature, and a is a constant that depends on the type of oil seed. Pressures from 1000 to 4500 lb./sq. in. were employed, with temperatures from 15° to 125°C. (giving a fifteenfold variation in kinematic viscosity), and times from ½ to 9 hr. Moisture content of the seed was important, the optimum being between 5 and 13 per cent depending on the type of material and the temperature.

Continuous Expression. No comprehensive theory has been developed for expression in a continuous screw press, although there is some similarity to feed screws and extrusion presses. Worm efficiency, or forward movement of solids referred to a projected worm area, may range from 25 to 80 per cent. The unaccounted-for displacement appears to be consumed in shear motion within the mass and perhaps in a rolling movement near the periphery or cage wall. A fibrous structure or some other type of cake which possesses internal tensile strength is necessary for successful expression; thus paper pulp or coal can be dewatered, but mud or clay slurries slip ineffectually past the rotating screw. Pressures inside the screw press may reach 10 to 20 tons/sq. in. at some points but are far lower in many applications, *e.g.*, 1000 to 2000 lb./sq. in. in pulp dewatering.

Expression of liquids from continuously moving webs in a roller press has been studied with paper and paper-makers' felts. The principal variables have been defined, although quantitative conclusions are largely empirical. Total pressure applied by means of the upper roll is an important variable, but its effect is not simple; increased pressure increases the force, causing dewatering, but may more than counteract this effect by compacting and lengthening the flow channels. Roll hardness is a factor, as soft rolls cause an increase in nip area, hence a diminished force per unit area on the material, and also an increased distance of flow; soft rolls thus perform a less thorough dewatering than hard rolls. Similarly, rolls of large diameter distribute the pressing force and increase the flow distance, so are less effective than small rolls. At high peripheral roll speed, time in the nip is diminished, and dewatering is less thorough.

An important but not well understood variable is resistance to flow within the material. This property varies manyfold as the material advances into the roll nip and is compressed. Transverse flow is necessary to remove liquid from the interior of the mass; flow parallel to the web but opposite in direction is the only possible liquid movement in the nip itself. The structure of the material and the variation of structure with pressure are controlling factors. Use of a perforated roll, sometimes with suction from the inside, permits transverse flow even at the nip and greatly increases the degree of liquid removal. Additional research is needed on all these variables. Three-roll mills presumably act like two successive pressings on two-roll mills; further dewatering occurs in the second nip because equilibrium is never reached in a single pass.

GRAVITY SEDIMENTATION OPERATIONS

REFERENCES: Coe and Clevenger, *Trans. Am. Inst. Mining. Engrs.*, **55**, 356 (1916). Kynch, *Trans. Faraday Soc.*, **48**, 166 (1952). Talmage and Fitch, *Ind. Eng. Chem.*, **47**, 38 (1955). Roberts, *Trans. Am. Inst. Minihg. Engrs.*, **1**, 61 (1949). Counselman, *Trans. Am. Inst. Mining. Engrs.*, **187**, 223 (1950).

Definition. Sedimentation is the removal of suspended solid particles from a liquid stream by gravitational settling. Sedimentation operations may be divided into thickening and clarification. The primary purpose of thickening is to increase the concentration of the feed stream; that of clarification is to remove solids from a relatively dilute stream.

CLASSIFICATION OF PULPS. TESTING METHODS

Table 19-6 gives descriptive classification of pulps and includes the most common methods employed to size a sedimentation basin. Clarifiers handle Class 1 and some Class 2 pulps, whereas thickeners handle some Class 2 and all Class 3 and Class 4 pulps.

The empirical testing methods indicated in Table 19-6 are designed to evaluate, for sizing purposes, the forces of gravity, buoyancy, and frictional drag which act on a particle as it settles in a fluid medium. Empirical sizing methods are necessary because of the many factors which influence the settling of a particle. These include the densities of liquid and particle, the viscosity, particle size, particle shape, particle concentration, and amount of flocculation.

The two primary criteria in specifying a sedimentation basin are surface area and depth. The surface area must be large enough so that the upward velocity of liquid leaving the basin is not greater than the settling velocity of the slowest-settling particle which is to be recovered. The upward velocity of liquid leaving the basin is usually recorded as ft./hr. or gal./min., sq. ft. of surface area.

In a sedimentation basin the solids concentration varies from that of the solids-free overflow leaving the basin to that of the concentrated underflow stream. Although the variation in concentration is continuous, the concentrations at various depths may be grouped into four zones as shown in Fig. 19-68. This figure illustrates a continuous thickener in which feed pulp continuously enters at the center of the tank, clear liquid leaves at the periphery of the tank, and thickener pulp discharges at the bottom.

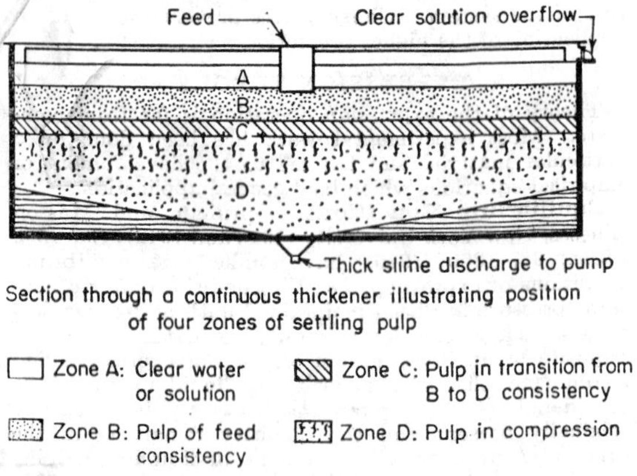

FIG. 19-68. Four zones of settling pulp, illustrating continuous thickening.

Determination of Surface Area. As indicated in Table 19-6, the method used to estimate the surface area of a settling basin depends on the type of pulp. The *long-tube method* is used for materials which settle without a clearly defined interface. This includes all Class 1 pulps and some Class 2 pulps. The method is especially applicable if flocculation is a function of retention time.

Flocculation is often employed to overcome the effect of Brownian movement by increasing the apparent particle size by agglomeration and reduction of surface charge. Flocculation may be either mechanical or

Table 19-6. Classification of Sedimentation Pulps and Methods of Testing

Pulp description	Description of initial sedimentation	Example	Methods to determine unit area	Methods to determine height of compression zone
Dilute, Class 1; independent particle subsidence	Particles or flocs settle independently. No definite line of subsidence. Settling unhindered. Settling rate mainly dependent upon size of particle or floc	Turbid water and trade wastes. Silt	Long tube	Coe and Clevenger, Roberts
Intermediate, Class 2; phase subsidence	Upper zone of independent particle subsidence. Lower zone of collective subsidence. Line of demarcation not sharp	Chemical and metallurgical pulps. Raw sewage. Flue dust	Long tube, Coe and Clevenger, Kynch (Talmage and Fitch)	Coe and Clevenger, Roberts
Concentrated, Class 3; collective subsidence or mass subsidence	Definite line of subsidence. Settling rate decreases with increasing concentration of solids. Settling rate retarded by particle or floc interference	Chemical and metallurgical pulps. Activated sludge	Coe and Clevenger, Kynch (Talmage and Fitch)	Coe and Clevenger, Roberts
Compact, Class 4; compact subsidence	Flocs or particles in intimate contact subsidence due to compression	All pulps by sedimentation pass to this	Coe and Clevenger	Coe and Clevenger, Roberts

chemical. Mechanical flocculation is accomplished by gentle circulation of the particles to provide time for flocs to build up. Chemical flocculation may be induced by changes in pH or by addition of high-valence ions or organic reagents such as starch and glue.

If the amount of flocculation is significant, the detention time becomes important in controlling the solids content of the overflow. Flocculation of solids may be comparatively slow, and flocs may continue to grow at the expense of smaller flocs as fast-settling particles unite with slower-settling ones. In general, for any given overflow rate the overflow clarity will improve markedly as the detention time is increased.

The long-tube apparatus consists of a plastic tube approximately 3 in. in inside diameter and about 8 ft. long. Taps inserted into the tube every foot of height permit samples to be withdrawn from the tube and analyzed for suspended solids.

Static testing with the long tube consists of filling the tube with a feed sample and withdrawing at specified time intervals 200-cc. samples with a clarity which is better than, equal to, or slightly below the desired overflow clarity, starting with the uppermost tap and continuing downward. Samples are withdrawn until all remaining solids are in the bottom of the tube in the compression zone.

The long-tube method determines the suspended solids in the overflow as a function of overflow rate and detention time by analyzing suspended solids in a settling pulp at various heights and at various times. The data recorded in this static testing procedure are position, time, and solids concentration. From these results the detention time and overflow rate in ft./hr. or gal./min., sq. ft. can be calculated. The detention time is the total time elapsed since the feed was introduced; the overflow rate is the corrected depth of the tap divided by the detention time. The depth of the tap must be corrected for the lowering of the contents of the long tube due to withdrawal of the samples.

A plot is made of suspended solids in the overflow as a function of overflow rate, with detention time as a parameter. This plot may show that the flocculation of solids in the pulp is not a function of detention time. From the graph it is possible to select the proper combination of clarification-zone detention time and overflow rate which would yield the desired overflow clarity.

The results of static testing with the long tube may be dynamically verified by periodically injecting samples into the long tube and analyzing for suspended solids the liquid which is displaced as overflow. The rate and position at which the feed should be introduced into the tube are based on the selected overflow rate and detention time. The feed point should be chosen so that the overflow withdrawn is retained for the proper time interval before removal.

The tap depth at which the sample is to be injected is equal to the overflow rate in feet per hour multiplied by the proper detention time. For example, if the overflow rate is 3 ft./hr. and the desired detention time is 2 hr., a volume of feed sample equal to 1 ft. of long-tube height should be injected into a tap which is 6 ft. below the uppermost liquid surface every 20 min. Before injection of any sample, the uppermost foot of liquid is drained through the uppermost tap and analyzed for suspended solids.

Simplified Method. A simpler method also used in studying Class 1 and some Class 2 pulps is to determine the proper detention time in the clarification zone by holding a number of samples of feed pulp in graduated cylinders for various detention times and withdrawing the uppermost liquid for suspended-solids analysis. This type of investigation gives a plot of suspended solids in the overflow as a function of detention time The procedure gives only the required detention time; the overflow rate must be selected from experience.

When materials settle with a definite interface, as with some Class 2 pulps and all Class 3 and Class 4 pulps, the solids-handling capacity determines the surface area. In a sedimentation basin there exist various dilutions (pounds of liquid per pound of solid) ranging from the dilution of the overflow to that of the underflow. Each dilution may be considered to correspond to a solids-handling capacity. This is defined as the capacity of a material of given dilution to reach a condition such that the mass rate of solids leaving a region is equal to or greater than the mass rate of solids entering the region. The attainment of this condition with a specific dilution depends on the mass subsidence rate being equal to or greater than the corresponding rise rate of displaced liquid. A properly sized sedimentation basin containing material of many different dilutions has adequate area such that the rise rate of displaced liquid at any region never exceeds the subsidence rate.

Coe and Clevenger Method. The method developed by Coe and Clevenger [*Trans. Am. Inst. Mining. Engrs.*, **55**, 356 (1916)] is most commonly employed to determine surface area when the material settles with a definite interface. This method utilizes the following formula for a material balance around a region of given dilution in equilibrium:

$$A = \frac{1.333(F - D)}{RS} \qquad (19\text{-}17)$$

where A = cross-sectional area of basin, sq. ft./(ton dry solids)(24 hr.); R = settling rate, ft./hr., of a feed dilution F; S = specific gravity of liquid; F = dilution of feed, mass ratio of liquid to solids; and D = dilution of underflow discharge.

R is a function of F for unflocculated pulps. From a complete set of R and F values the area required for various dilutions may be found by recording the initial settling rate of materials with dilutions ranging from that of the feed to that of the discharge. The dilution corresponding to the maximum value of A represents the minimum solids-handling capacity and is the critical dilution.

In using this method the initial constant sedimentation rate is found through tests in graduated cylinders using dilutions ranging from the feed dilution to the underflow dilution. Samples of various dilutions are obtained by decanting clear liquor and thoroughly mixing the remaining pulp.

Kynch Method. The Kynch method [*Trans. Faraday Soc.*, **48**, 166 (1952)] is also designed to determine the solids-handling capacity at the critical condition. The Coe and Clevenger method involves separate measurements of the initial settling rate at many dilutions. The Kynch method differs in that it stipulates that solids concentrations ranging from the initial concentration of pulp to its ultimate concentration exist momentarily at the interface of a settling pulp, and that the slope of a tangent drawn to the settling curve represents the settling velocity corresponding to the solids concentration existing at the interface.

Note that the Kynch method was originally developed on the basis of particles having the same size and shape. Any method based on this assumption has limited application. However, in flocculated pulps the size and shape of the agglomerates approach uniformity. The Kynch method is therefore more applicable to flocculated pulps than to pulps having a wide range of particle size and shape. Modification of the Kynch method [Talmage and Fitch, *Ind. Eng. Chem.*, **47**, 38 (1955)] led to the fol-

lowing formula for unit area:

$$A = \frac{t_u}{C_0 H_0} \qquad (19\text{-}18)$$

where A is the unit area, sq. ft. per ton of dry solids per 24 hr.; t_u is time in days found from the intersection of the tangent to the settling curve and the ordinate scale value of the height H_u that the solids in the graduated cylinder would have if all the solids were at the desired underflow dilution; C_0 is the initial feed pulp concentration, tons of dry solids per cu. ft. of feed pulp; and H_0 is the initial height of the entire pulp in the graduated cylinder, ft.

Unlike the Coe and Clevenger method, the Kynch method has the disadvantage that it does not indicate a maximum unit area, for Eq. (19-18) is not valid at dilutions less than the critical dilution. Therefore, it becomes mandatory that the critical dilution be determined on the settling curve. Various empirical methods have been employed to determine this critical point.

Determination of Basin Depth. A sedimentation basin includes the following zones: free-settling or clear-solution zone, feed zone, transition zone, and compression zone. Of the methods employed for determining surface area only the long-tube method gives any estimate of sedimentation depth, and this is only partial. The detention time and overflow rate found by the long-tube method are used to determine the height required in the free-settling or clear-solution zone and in the feed zone. The height of the transition zone is always empirically established; that of the compression zone can be determined by laboratory tests with graduated cylinders.

In the compression zone of a sedimentation basin, the dilution ranges from the dilution which is analogous to the start of compression to the dilution at which solids are withdrawn from the basin. The dilution at the start of compression is thought to be the dilution at which the solids have formed a structure such that additional concentration occurs not by the settling of the structure but by the collapsing of it. This phenomenon is the reason why in test work rakes rotated at about 0.1 r.p.m. must be used in determining the height of the compression zone.

The height of the compression zone is determined by dividing the volume of the compression zone by the area of sedimentation. The compression-zone volume is calculated from the time interval between the moment the solids enter the compression zone and the moment they leave the zone as underflow. If the average volume of slurry per weight of dry solids in the compression zone is known, then the volume of the compression zone is found by multiplying this average value by the total weight of solids in the compression zone.

The dilution at the start of compression is arbitrarily determined by inspecting a settling curve of pulp height vs. settling time. This curve is found from tests with graduated cylinders equipped with rakes rotating at 0.1 r.p.m. The straight-line portion of the compression-zone settling curve is extrapolated until it intersects the ordinate or height axis. The distance between this intercept and the height of the pulp at zero time is divided in half, and the determined point is moved horizontally until it intersects the settling curve. The height of the settling cylinder indicated by this intersection indicates the solids concentration that would exist at the start of compression if the solids were homogeneously distributed over the entire height.

The selected concentration of the underflow must be less than the ultimate obtainable concentration. This selection may be based on previous experience with regard to the pumping characteristics of the slurry, required filter-feed concentration, or the economics involved in building a larger thickener to obtain a higher underflow concentration. The height that the solids would occupy in the graduated cylinder if the solids were homogeneously mixed at the desired underflow concentration is calculated, based on the selected underflow value and the known solids content of the cylinder (the specific gravity of slurry as a function of solids concentration simplifies this calculation). This height is indicated on the settling curve. The difference between times corresponding to the desired underflow concentration and the start of compression represents the solids-retention time required in the compression zone.

The average compression-zone volume per weight of dry solids is found by integrating the settling curve between the limits of entering and leaving the compression zone. From the average volume of the compression zone per weight of dry solids the compression-zone volume and finally the compression-zone height are calculated.

Roberts Method. Another way of estimating compression-zone height is the Roberts method [*Trans. Am. Inst. Mining. Engrs.*, **1**, 61 (1949)]. This is a modification of the Coe and Clevenger method and is applicable to all types of pulps. The compression-zone portion of a settling curve usually represents a logarithmic variation. The Roberts method graphically integrates this logarithmic function using a semilogarithmic plot. The average compression-zone volume is found from the area under a straight line plotted on semilogarithmic paper whereas the Coe and Clevenger method employs the area under a curved line plotted on arithmetic paper. Properly used, both methods indicate the same compression-zone height. In the Coe and Clevenger method, time-interface readings are necessary only up to and including the point of desired underflow concentration. With the Roberts method, however, sedimentation readings are required up to the ultimate compression point because the logarithm of $D - D_\infty$ is plotted against time, where D is the dilution at any finite time and D_∞ is the dilution at infinite time.

Final Sizing of a Sedimentation Basin. Once the required surface area is established, a combination of safety factors is applied to the calculated area. One factor covers any variations in feed characteristics such as temperature, solids concentration, pH changes, and particle size. This safety factor varies from 1.10 to 1.25 depending upon the degree of fluctuation of these variables and their effect on sedimentation. A second factor allows for the ineffective volume of the sedimentation basin caused by turbulence at the inlet. This factor is greatly dependent upon the size of the sedimentation basin and ranges from 1.10 for units about 100 ft. in diameter or larger to 1.50 for units less than 15 ft. in diameter. The product of the two safety factors is applied in calculating the design surface area.

The depth of the sedimentation basin is the sum of the depths of four zones: the free-settling or clear-solution zone, the feed zone, the transition zone, and the compression zone. The long-tube method determines the volume and height of the clear-solution zone and the feed zone. Testing methods not employing the long tube must provide for a depth of 1 to 6 ft. for the clear-solution zone, with the shallower depths employed for fast-settling materials such as metallurgical concentrates. Generally, a depth of about 2 ft. is provided for the feed zone. Allowance for the transition zone must be made even when the long-tube method is employed. This allowance is usually 2 ft.

The compression zone is calculated and multiplied by a safety factor of 1.75 to ensure maximum sludge concentration and permit a limited amount of sludge

storage. The sum of the four zone depths is the final side water depth of the sedimentation basin.

THICKENERS

Batch Thickeners. *Batch Settling Tanks.* Batch settling tanks are the simplest and oldest devices for thickening. Fig. 19-69 depicts a typical unit. The

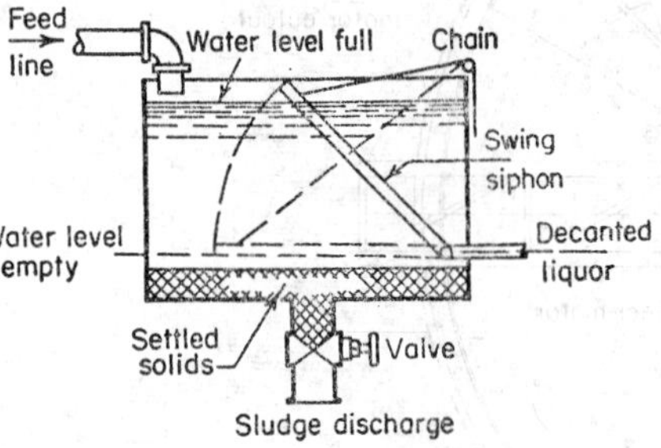

Fig. 19-69. Batch settling tank.

tank is first filled with pulp to be thickened. After a predetermined time which depends on the settling characteristics, clear supernatant liquid is withdrawn through a swing siphon or suitable draw-off connections on the tank wall. After the desired volume of clear liquor is decanted, thickened sludge is removed through the discharge valve or gate.

Batch settling tanks are normally made at the plant and may be of any convenient shape or size. Cylindrical tanks are the most common. Frequently a group of tanks is installed to stagger the fill-settle-withdrawal cycle.

Settling Cones. The settling cone consists of a conical tank with an apex angle of 45 to 60 deg. It is usually batch but may be made continuous by providing an automatically or manually controlled sludge-metering valve at the apex.

Allen Cone. An Allen cone is shown in Fig. 19-70. Feed enters through the central loading well. Clarified solution *A* overflows to a peripheral trough *C*. Solids settle into zone *K* and a baffle *B* prevents disturbance of the sludge bed.

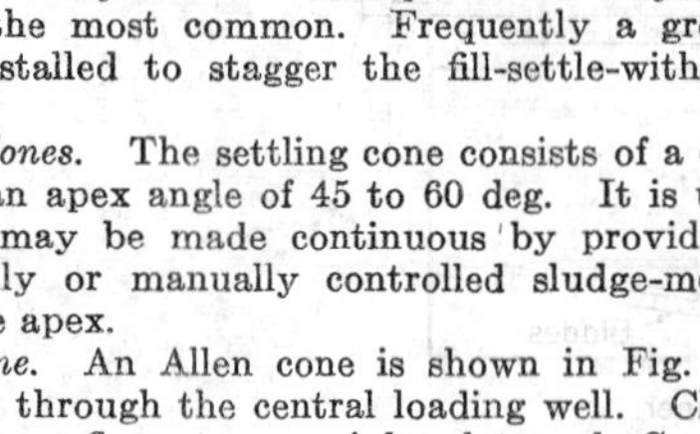

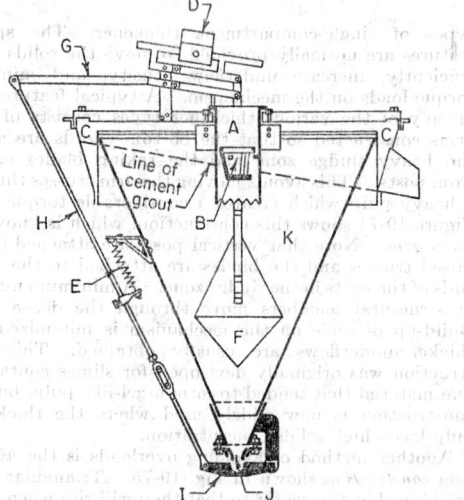

Fig. 19-70. The Allen settling cone.

As the sludge density increases, actuator *F* begins to rise and transmits this information through connecting parts *G*, *H*, and *I* to the ball valve *J*. This valve opens and permits sludge to escape. Adjustments are made by means of the weight *D* and its position.

Continuous Thickeners. By far the most common type of sedimentation device is the mechanical continuous thickener with sludge-raking arms. The tanks are most often cylindrical, although rectangular thickeners are used. The basic feature of the continuous thickener is the sludge collection and removal system, which is designed to move the settled material continuously across the tank floor to the discharge point. Feed enters a cylindrical thickener through a central feed well designed to distribute the flow to the basin. Clarified liquor overflows into a launder around the periphery. Thickened sludge, raked toward the center by the slowly revolving mechanism, enters a central collecting trough or cone and is discharged through a spigot or removed by a sludge pump.

Single-compartment Thickeners. The three basic types of unit or single-compartment thickeners differ primarily in the method of supporting and driving the mechanism. These are (1) the type with a superstructure-supported mechanism; (2) the type with a center-column-supported mechanism with a central drive; and (3) the type with a center-column-supported mechanism but with the drive on a driving arm at the tank periphery. Type 3 is also known as a traction thickener.

Superstructure-supported thickeners are most common in diameters under 60 ft., although special units have been built in excess of 120 ft. in diameter. Figure 19-71 shows a typical unit. The drive consists of a worm or spur gear normally mounted on a large-diameter ball bearing and generally driven through one or more gear reductions by a motor or gear motor. A vertical driving shaft is keyed to the main gear. Two raking arms are attached to the center shaft through steel spiders. The long arms have sufficient blades to scrape the bottom twice per revolution, and when desirable, two additional short arms are provided to rake the inner area four times per revolution to remove large quantities of coarse particles settling out near the center. Cone scrapers bolted to the center shaft prevent plugging of the bottom-discharge cone. The superstructure spanning the tank may be the beam type, as shown in Fig. 19-71, or a truss type for larger mechanisms. The superstructure supports the thickener mechanism, the walkway, and the feed pipe or launder.

The units can be provided with a lifting device to provide relief for excessive loads. The simplest of these devices is a manual type. A yoke mounted on the main gear supports a handwheel; the shaft is connected to a lifting screw suspended from the handwheel. As the handwheel is rotated the mechanism is raised or lowered. The standard lift is 12 in. The drive head is designed so that the worm shaft can move laterally with the thrust absorbed in a calibrated spring. As the torque on the mechanism varies, the movement of the worm is transmitted to a pointer which gives visual evidence of the torque load. This movement also may actuate switches that ring a warning bell when the load nears the design limit, turn off the drive motor, or both.

Figure 19-72 depicts a *center-column-supported thickener*. This type of construction often is used in sizes of about 50 ft. but is economically more attractive with diameters of 60 ft. and above. The mechanism is supported by a stationary center column of concrete or steel. The raking arms are attached to a driving cage which revolves around the center column. The cage is bolted to the main drive gear which is mounted on a large ball bearing. One or more sets of reduction gears may be

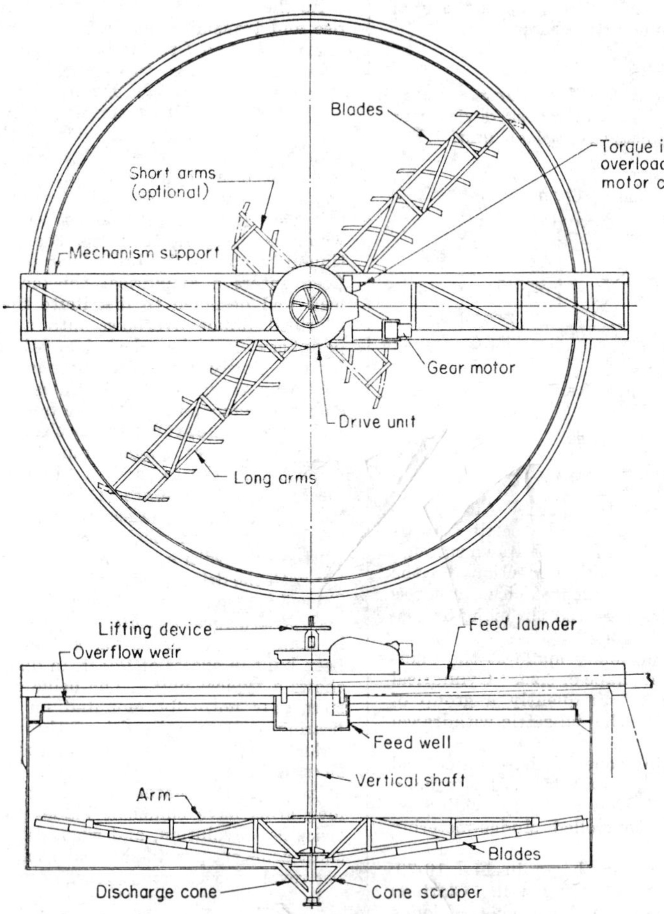

FIG. 19-71. Unit thickener with superstructure-supported mechanism. (*The Eimco Corp.*)

used, with two main pinions utilized in a balanced arrangement for the larger mechanisms requiring torque capacities of up to 1,800,000 ft.-lb. Lifting devices are available for center-column-supported thickeners that will lift the raking arms from 12 to 36 in. Center-column thickeners are made in sizes up to about 375 ft. in diameter.

A traction thickener is shown in Fig. 19-73. While the superstructure and center-column-supported units have centrally located drives, the traction thickener utilizes a motorized carriage riding on the tank wall. A driving truss extends from the stationary center column to the peripheral carriage. This truss serves as one long raking arm with one or more shorter arms used to rake the center area more frequently. Blades secured to the arms rake the settled solids to the annular sludge-discharge trench located around the center column. Electrical power is supplied to the moving carriage through slip rings connected to the center column, with contact made through brushes on the truss. If an overload occurs, the carriage loses speed and an alarm rings. The traction thickener is particularly adaptable to large tanks with heavy underflows. The only major limitation is that operation may be difficult in climates where snow and ice are common.

Special Design Features. Many special construction features may be provided for the three basic types of single-compartment thickener. The special features are normally provided to move the solids more efficiently, increase underflow density, and minimize torque loads on the mechanism. A typical feature used on any of the various thickener types consists of rake arms constructed so that the bottom chords are above the heavy sludge zone and the raking blades extend from posts. This avoids moving the arm trusses through a heavy pulp which creates a considerable torque load. Figure 19-74 shows this construction, which is known as *thixo arm.* Note that vertical posts are attached to the raised trusses and the blades are attached to the lower ends of the posts in the sludge zone. A minimum number of structural members move through the dense pulp. Build-up of scale on the mechanism is minimized and thicker underflows are usually obtained. This construction was originally developed for slimes containing fine material that tended to form a gel-like pulp, but the construction is now widely used where the thickened pulp has a high solids concentration.

Another method of avoiding overloads is the *hinged-arm construction* shown in Fig. 19-75. Triangular arms are hinged at the center so that they will rise when overloaded and return to the normal raking position when the load is reduced. Hinged arms can be employed on either superstructure- or center-column-supported mechanisms, but they have normally been used on the latter types.

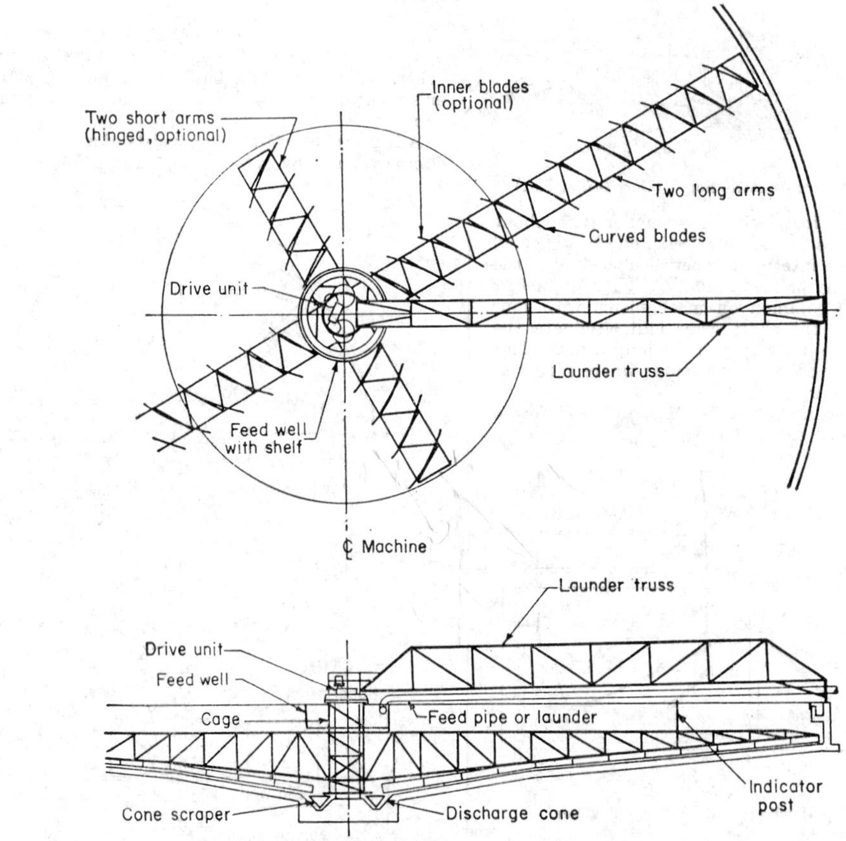

Fig. 19-72. Unit thickener with center-column-supported mechanism. (*The Eimco Corp.*)

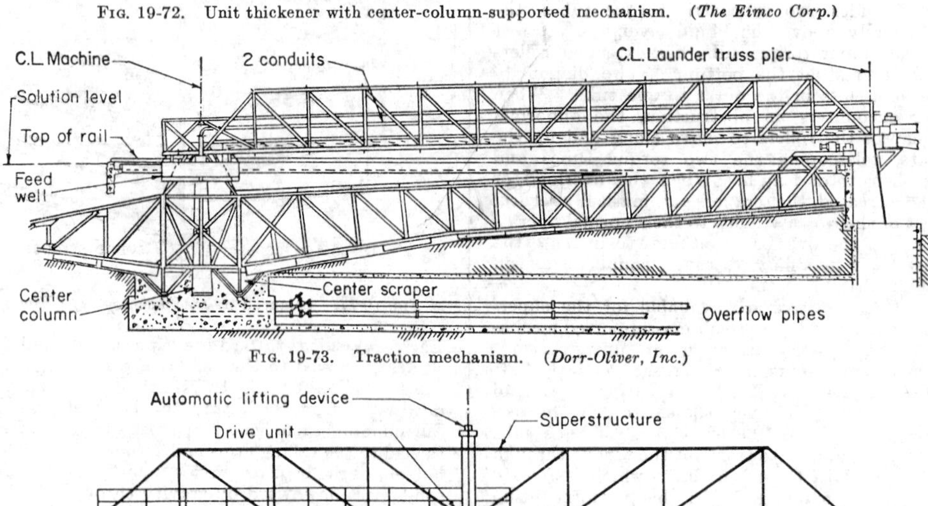

Fig. 19-73. Traction mechanism. (*Dorr-Oliver, Inc.*)

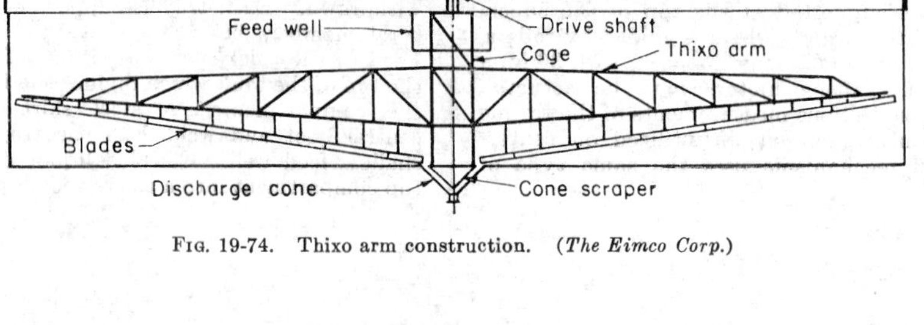

Fig. 19-74. Thixo arm construction. (*The Eimco Corp.*)

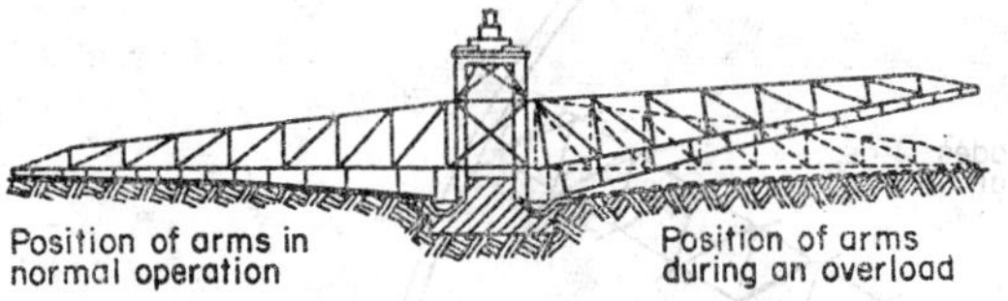

FIG. 19-75. Hinged-arm construction. (*Dorr-Oliver, Inc.*)

The design is most effective in units smaller than about 100 ft. in diameter, as considerable relief can be obtained at the center without interference between the end of the arm and the walkway or feed launder. With diameters above 100 ft. it is common on mechanisms with four arms to hinge only the short arms and eliminate the raking blades on the inner area of the long arms. This provides more torque relief at the center where the overloaded condition occurs.

Another automatic lifting device is used in the *Hardinge Auto-Raise Thickener* shown in Fig. 19-76. The auto

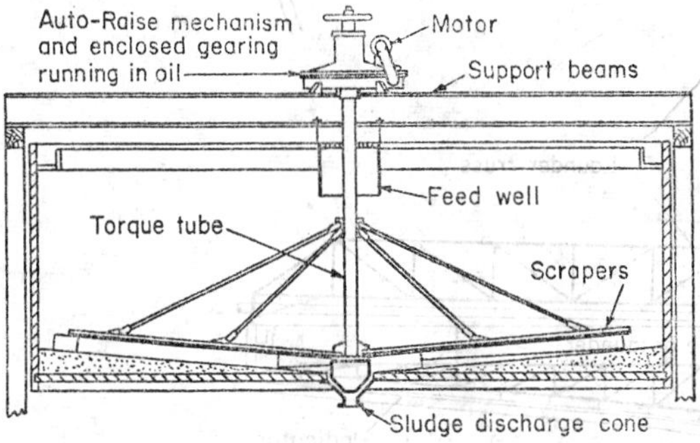

FIG. 19 76. The Hardinge Auto-Raise Thickener.

mechanism includes two concentric torque tubes, the outer one entirely above the liquid level. A yoke at the top of the inner torque tube has extended rollers which normally rest at the bottom of two diagonally opposed sloping slots in the outer torque tube. When the scraper encounters an obstruction, the abnormal resistance causes the rollers to move along and up the sloping slots, telescoping the two torque tubes and shortening their total length. When the overload or resistance is decreased, the scrapers automatically return, by the effect of their own weight, to their normal operating position. If the overload continues to increase the scrapers rise their maximum distance, sound an alarm, and cut off the driving motor.

Motorized lifting devices are available for the superstructure-supported and center-column-supported mechanisms. Two basic types are used on superstructure-supported thickeners—one in which the vertical shaft is lifted through the drive head by a lifting screw and gear unit, and another in which the entire drive head is raised on a platform. In the first type, a torque tube is bolted to the main gear to transmit the torque through driving lugs keyed to the main shaft, which is free to move through the main gear. In the platform-lifting device, the drive is mounted on a platform suspended from lifting screws supported at the top of the superstructure. The lifting frame, which is guided by rollers, can be designed to lift almost any distance, with 36 in. a normal maximum. Lifting motors may be actuated automatically by continuous measurements of the torque on the mechanism. A similar lift utilized on center-column-supported mechanisms uses the same type of controls.

Tray Thickeners. Often, to save floor space, tray thickeners are installed. In essence, a tray thickener is a series of unit thickeners one mounted on top of the other. There are three basic types: balanced tray thickeners, washing tray thickeners, and the combination type.

A balanced tray thickener consists of a tank divided into compartments by steel trays, as shown in Fig. 19-77.

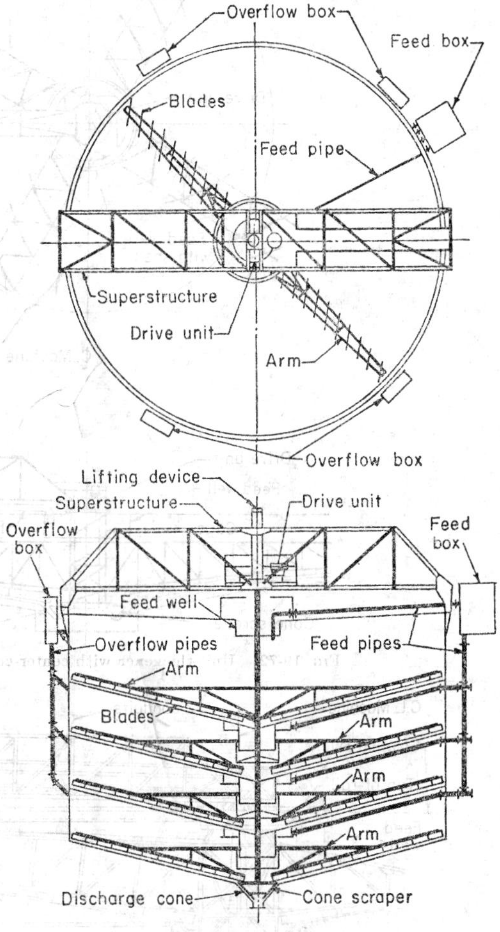

FIG. 19-77. Balanced tray thickener. (*The Eimco Corp.*)

Each tray slopes toward the tank center, and thickened sludge is moved to the center of each compartment by rakes parallel to the trays. A central boot extends downward from each tray to the next compartment. Surrounding each boot is a steel cylinder which is attached to the raking arms and extends slightly above the bottom of the boot to provide a partial seal. Thickened solids pass downward by gravity through the boots and cylinders to the bottom compartment where they are withdrawn. Each tray is supported from radial structural members below the plate and at the tank wall. Feed to the thickener first enters a feed-splitter box at the top of the tank which divides the flow equally among the compartments. A steel skirt surrounding each central boot and welded to the tray bottom forms a shallow feed well. Clarified liquor overflows from the top compartment into a conventional peripheral launder;

overflow from each lower compartment leaves through one or more peripheral outlets just below the tray above. Overflow pipes terminate in an overflow box at the top of the tank. Each pipe carries a manually adjustable vertical sleeve, which is required to adjust the superelevation of the overflow pipes and balance the head of pulp and liquor in each compartment. Superelevation is defined as the distance from the liquid level in the top compartment to the level in the overflow pipe. It is greatest for the bottom compartment because of the tall column of solids in the center that must be equalized.

The washing tray thickener is frequently used for countercurrent decantation systems. Its function is to thicken and wash the solids to remove the soluble material in the liquor. Fresh feed enters the top compartment through a standard feed well; the overflow is the strong liquor or pregnant solution. In all compartments except the bottom, settled pulp is raked to a central washing seal where the pulp is mixed with wash fluid from the next washing stage. The rediluted slurry then flows to the next lower compartment for thickening. Fresh water is added to the bottom washing seal, and the overflow from the bottom compartment flows to the next higher compartment, and so on. The design of the washing seal is critical as it must provide thorough mixing of the wash fluid with the pulp as well as an effective seal between compartments, and yet permit a uniform flow of pulp without plugging. Under proper conditions, a good seal will permit washing efficiencies as high as 95 per cent of the theoretical.

A combination tray thickener consists of a combination of several compartments in one tank operating both in parallel and in series, *i.e.*, as both balanced and washing stages. Several combinations are possible; in the most common the two top compartments act in parallel as balanced compartments and the lower compartments in series as washing stages.

Auxiliary Equipment. Underflow from a continuous thickener is sometimes discharged by gravity through a spigot but most often is removed by a pump directly connected to the discharge cone. For large tonnages, centrifugal sand pumps commonly are used. However, whenever practical, a diaphragm or positive-displacement pump is recommended if the maximum underflow density is desired, to assure a positive metered withdrawal rate. Diaphragm pumps are used with most thickeners since they are easily adapted to changing flow rates (by adjusting the stroke), relatively inexpensive, and simple to operate. Diaphragm pumps are available in capacities up to about 600 gal./min.

When flocculants are required for pretreatment of the thickener feed, the chemicals generally are stored as stock solutions considerably more concentrated than used for treatment. Organic polymers are normally stocked at strengths of 0.5 to 1.0 per cent in storage tanks suitable to supply one-half to three shifts. Before mixing with the feed, the stock solution is diluted to 0.025 to 0.1 per cent. The diluted flocculant is generally metered directly into the feed pipe or launder at several points just prior to entry into the feed well. Thorough mixing is required to provide intimate contact without localizing flocculation; too much turbulence after addition of the chemicals, however, may destroy a delicate floc. Flexibility should be designed into an installation to permit optimum chemical addition after startup.

Selecting a Thickener Type. Selection of the type of single-compartment or unit thickener depends primarily on the installation and operating costs. Most manufacturers have overlapping sizes in the superstructure-supported, center-column-supported, and traction types even though certain economical size ranges exist. For example, if the thickener must be covered to conserve heat, the superstructure-supported type may be more economical up to about 125 ft. in diameter although 60 ft. may be the limit for an uncovered unit. Traction thickeners often are least expensive in sizes over 250 ft. in diameter if the ground conditions permit installing proper supporting walls to carry the loads.

A tray thickener is generally preferred when floor space is a primary concern and heat retention is important. However, a unit thickener is normally used because of its simplicity of design and ease of operation. Better control of underflow density, clearer overflows, and thicker underflows usually can be obtained with a unit thickener.

Materials of Construction. A wide variety of materials of construction is available for most thickeners depending on local cost conditions. Steel and wood tanks are the most common for the smaller sizes. Concrete tanks are usually used for thickeners over 100 ft. in diameter but specific conditions often dictate otherwise. For large diameters, where liquor retention is not critical, earthen basins are often utilized. Most thickener mechanisms are made of steel. However, submerged parts may be made of wood, stainless steel, rubber- or epoxy-coated steel, or special alloys depending on the environment.

It is always best to conduct bench-scale tests to determine the proper thickener size, using methods previously discussed. Table 19-7 lists typical area requirements for thickeners but it has been included for illustrative purposes only.

Table 19-7. Typical Thickener-area Requirements*

	% solids		Unit area, sq. ft./ton, day
	Feed	Underflow	
Alumina, Bayer process:			
Red-mud primary settlers	3-4	10-25	20-30
Red-mud washers	6-8	15-20	10-15
Red-mud final thickener	6-8	20-35	10-15
Trihydrate seed thickener	2-8	30-50	12-30
Cement, West process	16-20	60-70	15-25
Cement kiln dust	9-10	45-55	3-18
Coral	12-18	45-55	15-25
Cyanide slimes	16-33	40-55	5-13
Lime mud:			
Acetylene generator	12-15	30-40	15-33
Lime-soda process	9-11	35-45	15-25
Paper industry	8-10	32-45	14-18
Magnesium hydroxide from brine	8-10	25-50	60-100
Metallurgical (flotation or gravity concentration):			
Copper concentrates	14-50	40-75	2-20
Copper tailings	10-30	45-65	4-10
Lead concentrates	20-25	60-80	7-18
Zinc concentrates	10-20	50-60	3-7
Nickel:			
Leached residue	20	60	8
Sulfide concentrate	3-5	65	25
Potash slimes	1-5	6-25	40-125
Uranium:			
Acid leached ore	10-30	25-65	2-10
Alkaline leached ore	20	60	10
Uranium precipitate	1-2	10-25	50-125

* These figures are general averages for illustrative purposes only. Bench-scale tests should be conducted for specific thickener applications.

Thickener Costs. Costs vary widely for a given diameter because of the many types of construction. As a general rule, the total installed cost will be about three to four times the cost of the mechanism. Table 19-8 lists the approximate installed cost of thickeners up to 100 ft. in diameter. These costs are to be used only

Table 19-8. Approximate Single-compartment Thickener Cost*

Diam., ft.	Cost/sq. ft.
10	\$50-\$60
30	\$15-\$20
50	\$12-\$14
75	\$ 9-\$11
100	\$ 8-\$10

* Cost complete including installation; based on steel mechanisms, steel tanks to 50 ft. and concrete tanks from 50 to 100 ft. Consult manufacturer for accurate costs and for sizes above 100 ft.

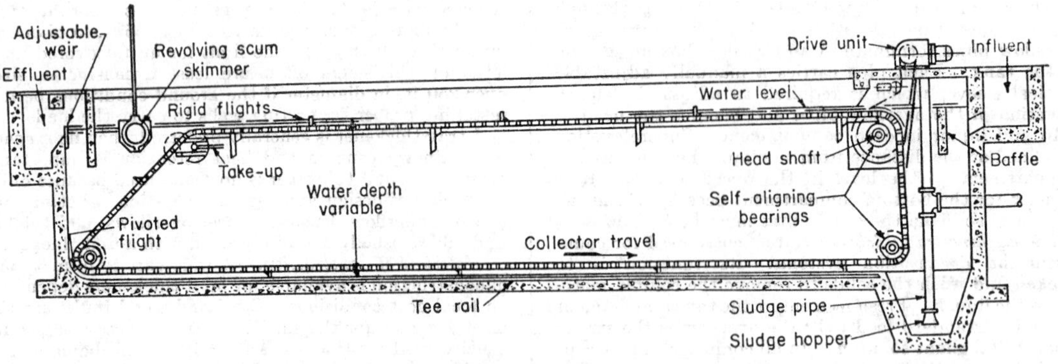

FIG. 19-78. Rectangular clarifier. (*The Chain Belt Co.*)

as a guide and do not include the cost of special design modifications. They are based on steel mechanisms and steel tanks for small thickeners, up to 50 ft. in diameter, and concrete tanks for the larger units.

Operating Costs. Power cost for a continuous thickener is an almost insignificant item. For example, a unit thickener 200 ft. in diameter with a torque rating of 800,000 ft.-lb. will normally require a 15-hp motor. The low power consumption is due to the very slow rotative speeds. Normally, a mechanism will be designed for a peripheral speed of about 25 ft./min. which corresponds to only 0.04 r.p.m. for a 200-ft unit. This slow speed also means very low maintenance costs. Operating labor is also low because little attention is normally required after initial operation has balanced the feed and underflow. If chemicals are required for flocculation, the chemical cost frequently dwarfs all other operating costs.

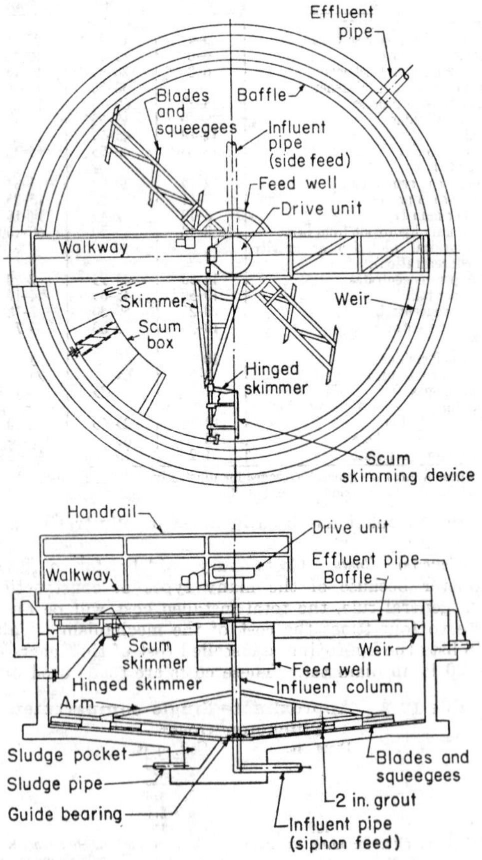

FIG. 19-79. Cylindrical clarifier. (*The Eimco Corp.*)

CLARIFIERS

Clarifier Types. Continuous clarifiers handle trade wastes, domestic sewage, or other dilute suspensions. They are similar to thickeners in that they are sedi-

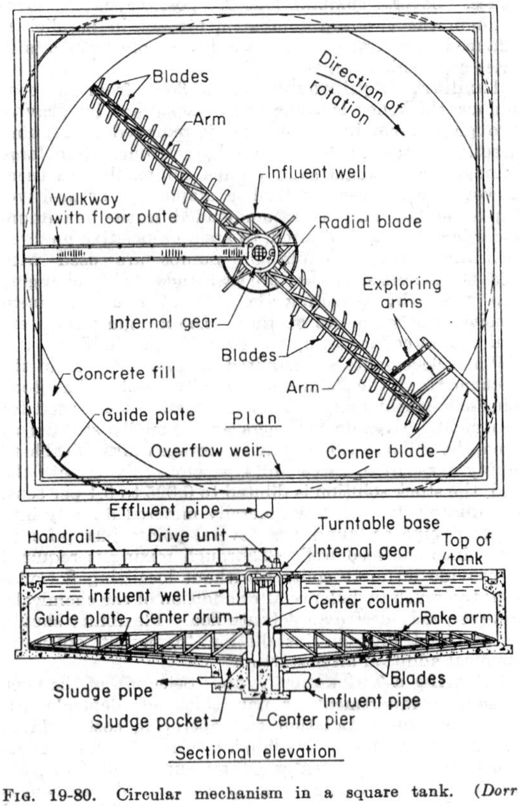

FIG. 19-80. Circular mechanism in a square tank. (*Dorr Oliver, Inc.*)

mentation tanks or basins with a mechanical sludge-raking mechanism. However, the amount of solids and weight of the thickened sludge are usually much lower than in thickener applications, and the raking mechanisms generally are not so heavy. For this reason, the installed cost of a clarifier is generally about 5 to 10 per cent less than that of a thickener of equal tank size, as given in Table 19-8.

Rectangular Clarifiers. Clarifiers are available in rectangular and cylindrical shapes in a multitude of sizes. One type of rectangular clarifier is pictured in Fig. 19-78. The raking mechanism in a rectangular unit is referred to as a drag and may be either the chain or bridge type. With a chain-type drag, sludge is raked to one end of the tank by scrapers fixed to endless chains. The chains are driven by a motor mounted outside the tank. The bridge system employs scrapers suspended from a traveling bridge mounted on rails. This bridge travels the length of the tank, reversing direction through the action of limit switches. Both chain-type and bridge-type rectangular clarifiers may be equipped with skimming devices for removal of surface scum. Rectangular clarifiers are available in widths from 6 to 70 ft. Their length is generally three to five times the width.

Cylindrical Clarifiers. Cylindrical units are available in diameters from 8 to 325 ft. As with single-compartment thickeners, there are three basic types: the superstructure-supported mechanism, the center-column-supported mechanism with central drive, and the center-column-supported mechanism with peripheral traction drive. The superstructure-supported type is generally limited to tanks less than about 45 ft. in diameter.

Figure 19-79 shows one of the many types of cylindrical clarifiers. In this superstructure-supported type of unit the feed enters up through the hollow central column or shaft. This is known as a *siphon feed* system. Feed enters the central feed well through slots near the top of the hollow shaft. With a siphon feed, the velocity of the feed stream is greatly reduced as it enters the basin proper, minimizing undesirable currents in the settling area of the tank. The unit illustrated is equipped with a surface skimming device, which includes a rotating skimmer, a scum baffle, and scum box assembly. The skimmer is attached to the central shaft (or revolving cage in center-column units) and has an adjustable scraper provided with synthetic-rubber wipers on its outer end. This scraper can be set for various skimming depths. Although most cylindrical units are equipped with peripheral weirs, radial weirs may also be provided to decrease the exit velocity and minimize weir loadings.

Circular mechanisms may be installed in square tanks as shown in Fig. 19-80. This mechanism differs from

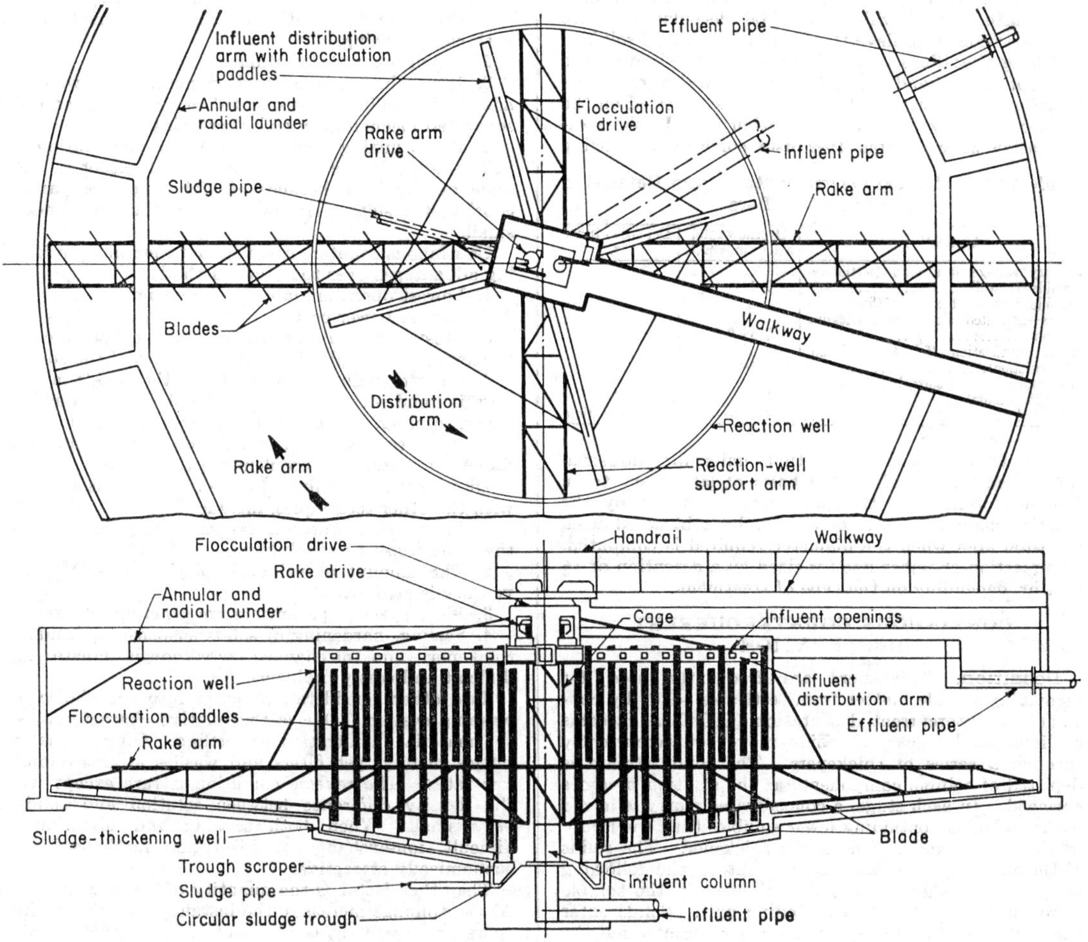

FIG. 19-81. Reactor-clarifier. (*The Eimco Corp.*)

the standard circular mechanism in that a hinged corner blade is provided to sweep the corners which lie outside the path of the main mechanism. This unit may be centrally fed to give radial flow, or cross flow may be used; that is, feed may enter along one wall and effluent overflow the opposite wall.

Reactor-Clarifiers. When desirable, mixing, flocculation, and sedimentation may all be done in a single cylindrical tank. As shown in Fig. 19-81, this type of unit contains a large center compartment which provides the necessary time for flocculation before the feed enters the basin proper.

The particular unit shown in Fig. 19-81 contains two sets of meshing vertical paddles. One set is attached to the raking mechanism, which rotates slowly; the other set is attached to the feed-distribution launders, which are rotated at a greater speed by a separate drive. Gentle agitation and complete flocculation are provided by this system. Other types of flocculating chambers with turbine impellers are available. Reactor-clarifiers are particularly advantageous for clarifying turbid waters where coagulation and flocculation are required to remove bacteria, suspended solids, or color. Similar units are used for softening water by lime addition. The center compartment provides the necessary reaction time to complete the precipitation. Similar units are often used in clarifying industrial process streams, sewages, and waste waters which must be flocculated before sedimentation to achieve the desired removal of solids.

Sizing Clarifiers. While thickeners are sized on the basis of solids-handling capacity (sq. ft. of cross-sectional area per ton per 24 hr.), clarifiers are sized on the basis of overflow rates and detention time in the sedimentation zone. Table 19-9 lists some typical sizing factors for clarifiers. Note that units for industrial wastes must be sized on the basis of laboratory tests. For reactor-clarifiers the tank area taken up by the reaction chamber must, of course, be subtracted from the total area when the diameter required is computed. The reaction chamber itself is sized on a detention of ½ to 1 hr. depending on the type of treatment.

Table 19-9. Typical Overflow Rates and Detention Times in Clarifiers

Application	Overflow rate, gal./min., sq. ft.	Detention time, hr.
Primary sewage treatment (settleable-solids removal)	0.4	2
Secondary sewage treatment (final clarifiers—activated sludge and trickling filters)	0.55–0.7	1.5–2
Water clarification (following 30-min. flocculation)	0.4–0.55	3
Lime and lime-soda softening (high rate —upflow units)	1.5	2
Industrial wastes	Must be tested for each application	

CONTINUOUS COUNTERCURRENT DECANTATION

Definition. Thickeners are frequently used for recovering soluble matter from settleable solids by continuous countercurrent decantation (C.C.D.). Streams of liquid and thickened solids move countercurrently through a series of thickeners. The solids stream is depleted of soluble components as the solution becomes enriched. In each stage, a concentrated slurry is mixed with a solution containing fewer solubles than the liquor in the slurry, and is fed to the thickener. The solids settle and are withdrawn to be sent to the following stage; the overflow solution, now richer in the soluble component, moves to the preceding unit. Solids enter the system in the first-stage thickener, from which the final concentrated solution is withdrawn. Wash water or barren solution is added to the last stage, and washed solids are removed in the underflow of this unit. The basic circuit is shown in Fig. 19-82, illustrating a simple three-stage C.C.D. system. Feed F is shown entering stage 1 after mixing with the overflow O_2, from thickener 2. The overflow of concentrated solution O_1 is withdrawn from thickener 1. The first-stage underflow U_1 is mixed with third-stage overflow O_3 and fed to thickener 2. Similarly, the second-stage underflow U_2 is mixed with wash water and fed to thickener 3. The washed solids are removed as the final underflow U_3.

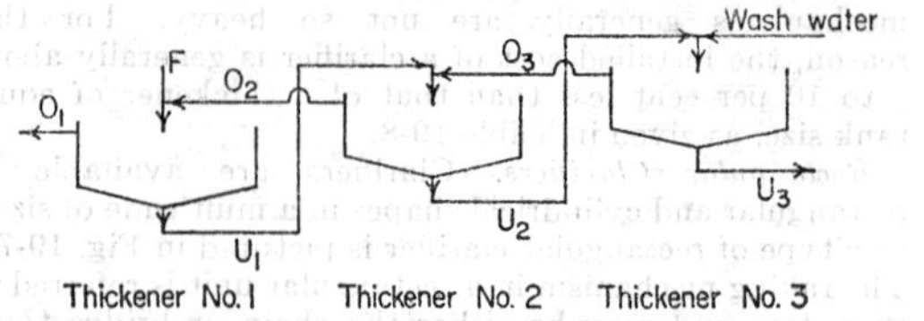

Fig. 19-82. Simple C.C.D. flow sheet.

Applications and Advantages of C.C.D. As described, C.C.D. is used to separate soluble matter from inert or insoluble solids. Alternative methods to accomplish this purpose include the following:

1. One or more continuous filters in series, usually with cake washing.
2. Batch pressure filtration and washing.
3. Ion-exchange or adsorption methods in which the adsorbing medium is suspended in the slurry and then separated mechanically as by screening.
4. Batch mixing, sedimentation, and decantation.

The last of these is now rarely used except in small-scale applications, because of high labor cost and inconsistent results. However, the initial investment is small.

Continuous countercurrent decantation has the following advantages over the other methods:

1. Lowest operating labor requirements.
2. Lowest power costs.
3. Most consistent performance with fewest upsets due to changes in the physical characteristics of the solids.
4. Lowest maintenance costs if the solids are not abrasive and present no unusual problems such as hardening, scaling, or crusting. Corrosive solutions and tendencies to scaling or crystal deposition can create difficult maintenance problems on thickeners.

Disadvantages or limitations of C.C.D., as compared with the other techniques, include

1. More wash water is normally required to effect the same recovery of solubles.
2. The amount of valuable solution or solids in inventory is greater.
3. Floor-space requirements are generally greater.
4. Scaling, hardening of solids suspensions inside the thickener, and mechanical breakdowns create more difficult and costly problems.

Two other considerations enter into the choice of a washing system. One is the relative characteristics of the material in filtration or settling. Often a material settles readily, yet filters and washes at uneconomical low rates. The reverse condition is rare except where the density difference between solution and solids is very small. When both settling and filtration are difficult, ion-exchange or adsorption methods become economically attractive.

The other factor is the quantity of material involved. As the tonnage increases, the installed cost of the thickeners per ton of material handled is reduced. This is possible because a single series of large thickeners will probably be sufficient to handle the entire tonnage. On the other hand, many filters, operating in parallel, would be necessary for the same job because of the relatively low capacity of the largest filters. Hence the capital cost of the filtering equipment will be in proportion to the tonnage handled, with no significant decrease in unit cost for larger plants.

Variables Affecting Recovery. Two main variables control the soluble recovery in C.C.D.: the ratio of the volume of overflow to the volume of liquor in the underflow, and the number of stages.

In practice, the former is affected by the settling conditions (characteristics of the solids, temperature, flocculation, and spare thickening capacity available) which can change the underflow solids concentration and thus alter the wash ratio.

The number of stages, once determined, will be affected only by loss of a unit for mechanical reasons or by reduction in mixing efficiency between stages. The predicted recovery by the C.C.D. system is generally based on complete mixing of underflow and overflow. In most cases, this assumption is valid. However, loss of efficiency will result if either of these conditions exist:

1. Inadequate time or inadequate turbulence in the mixer.
2. Strongly flocculated solids where the floc particles do not break down to release entrained liquid.

Design Factors. The following should be considered in designing a C.C.D. circuit:

1. Sufficient mixing of underflow and overflow. Usually mixing will be adequate if the combined stream flows turbulently a distance equal to the thickener radius. If a launder is used, baffles should be included. Where large stable flocs are formed, or where the viscosity and density of the underflow retard mixing, mechanical agitation may be required. However, excessive shear must be avoided so the flocculation condition can be restored with a small amount of reagent. If adequate mixing is not possible design should be based on a lower efficiency, determined from data on similar systems, and more stages should be included if required.
2. The thickener size is critical; sufficient area and depth are necessary to give the maximum underflow density under variable operating conditions.
3. The feed to the system should be uniform with respect to flow rate, particle size, dilution, and soluble concentration.
4. Provisions to recirculate underflow and overflow or to by-pass a thickener should sometimes be included. Pumps on underflow and overflow, with appropriate piping, are required for this.

The simplest arrangement of a C.C.D. circuit employs a gradual elevation increase from first to last thickener. Only the underflow must be pumped; the overflow moves by gravity. However, this system lacks flexibility. Since the underflow is more difficult to pump, it is preferable, especially on large thickeners, to utilize a downward slope from first to last unit and reduce the head on each underflow pump. Overflow pumps then become necessary.

5. If flocculation is required, the reagent is generally added to all units to maintain uniform settling conditions. Usually one-half to three-fourths of the total flocculant is added to the first thickener with the balance distributed evenly among the remaining units.

The cost of a C.C.D. system may be estimated from the installed cost of the thickeners plus 10 to 25 per cent additional for piping.

Flow-sheet Variations. In addition to the system illustrated in Fig. 19-82, a number of other flow systems are employed. Figure 19-83 shows an example of a circuit where the overflow from the second-stage thickener is mixed with dry feed as a leach solution. This procedure is useful if the volume of final overflow solution is critical. The recovery of solubles is greater than that possible with the standard circuit, for the same volume of strong liquor. The use of second-stage overflow as leach liquor may be restricted if (1) it requires special materials of construction in processing steps following leaching, or (2) the degree of saturation of the overflow significantly affects the leaching operation.

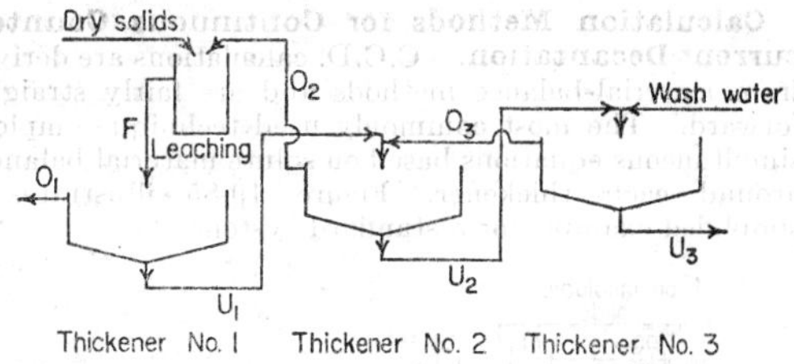

FIG. 19-83. C.C.D. and leaching circuit with all wash water added to the final thickener.

In some cases, leaching is employed between some or all thickening stages. This is generally required when the amount of soluble matter that can be dissolved is controlled by the chemical equilibrium. It is also used if an excess of leaching reagent is to be avoided in the final overflow. In that case only part of the leaching is done before the first-stage thickener by maintaining a deficiency of reagent. The balance of the reagent required is then added to the intermediate leaching step between first and second stages.

A third variation, shown in Fig. 19-84, is a series of thickeners with a continuous filter as the final stage.

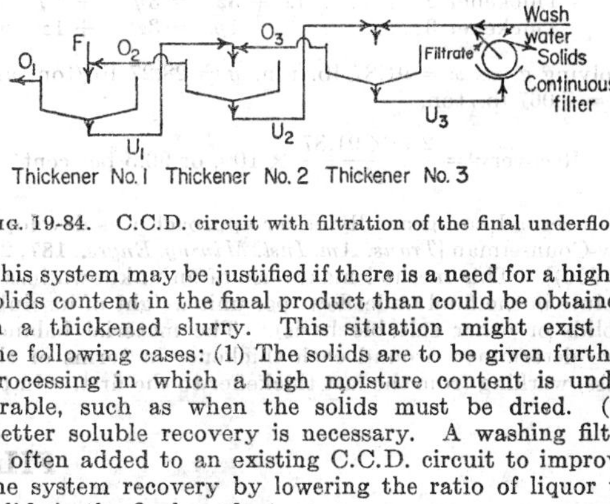

FIG. 19-84. C.C.D. circuit with filtration of the final underflow.

This system may be justified if there is a need for a higher solids content in the final product than could be obtained in a thickened slurry. This situation might exist in the following cases: (1) The solids are to be given further processing in which a high moisture content is undesirable, such as when the solids must be dried. (2) Better soluble recovery is necessary. A washing filter is often added to an existing C.C.D. circuit to improve the system recovery by lowering the ratio of liquor to solids in the final product.

Equipment. Unit thickeners or washing tray thickeners are used for continuous countercurrent decantation. Unit thickeners are easier to operate and maintain, and permit better washing for the same number of stages and the same volume of wash liquor. Tray thickeners are selected where heat loss or floor space is important.

For pumping the underflow, diaphragm pumps are frequently used because the gentle action does not destroy the floc structure, and the pumping rate can be precisely regulated. Their disadvantages are the low discharge head and the pulsating action which aggravates plugging of the suction lines. Centrifugal slurry pumps are often preferred on larger units. A spare underflow pump is recommended for large thickeners to ensure against loss of a washing stage, as well as possible damage to the thickeners due to pump failure.

Calculation Methods for Continuous Countercurrent Decantation. C.C.D. calculations are derived from material-balance methods and are fairly straightforward. The most commonly used technique employs simultaneous equations based on solute material balances around each thickener. Figure 19-85 illustrates a simplified example for a standard system.

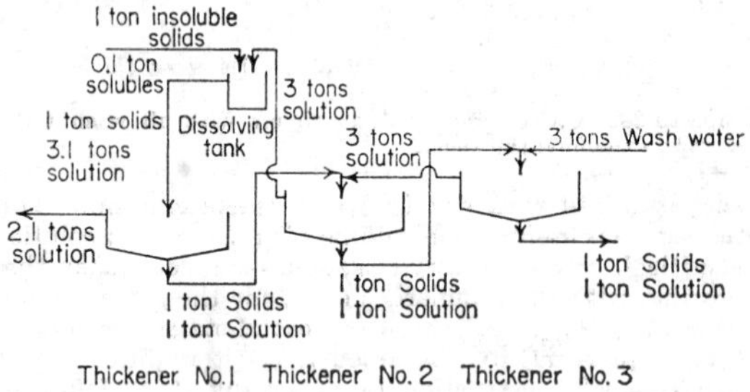

FIG. 19-85. Calculation of C.C.D. system performance.

Conditions:

1. Feed to system: 1.1 tons of total solids containing 0.1 ton of soluble matter (200 lb.).
2. Underflow insoluble-solids concentration: 50 per cent for all stages.
3. Wash water added: 3 tons/ton insoluble solids.

Let x, y, and z equal the pounds of solute per ton of solution in thickeners 1, 2, and 3, respectively.

Simultaneous equations equating the amount of solids into and out of each thickener are:

	Input	=	Output
Thickener 1........	$3y + 200$	=	$2.1x + 1x$
Thickener 2........	$1x + 3z$	=	$3y + 1y$
Thickener 3............	$1y$	=	$3z + 1z$

Solving gives $x = 91.87$ lb./ton, $y = 28.27$ lb./ton, and $z = 7.067$ lb./ton.

$$\text{Recovery} = \frac{2.1 \times 91.87}{200} \times 100, \text{ or } 96.5 \text{ per cent}$$

A second and generally easier approach was developed by Counselman [*Trans. Am. Inst. Mining. Engrs.*, **187**, 223 (1950)]. This method makes use of an unknown loss of solute in the final underflow (per unit weight of insoluble solids or other suitable basis). The material balances are determined around each thickener in terms of this loss, working from the last thickener to the first. In the example in Fig. 19-85, the amount of solute in the third underflow is designated as X lb./ton of insoluble solids. Since the total solution entering this thickener is 4 tons, the amount of solubles entering is $4X$. All of this amount is present in the underflow from the second thickener. As the proportion of feed to underflow solution is the same in the second stage, the amount of solute entering this unit is $16X$. The quantity added in the overflow from thickener 3 is $3X$. The balance, $13X$, therefore comes from the underflow of thickener 1. By similar methods, the solute content of the final overflow is determined to be $27.3X$, and thus the amount entering in the raw feed, 0.1 ton, equals $27.3X$ plus X. Recovery is $27.3/28.3 \times 100$, or 96.5 per cent. The concentration of the final solution is $(27.3X/28.3X)(200/2.1)$, or 91.87 lb./ton.

This method has the advantage of being rapid, less subject to mathematical error, and less difficult to use for complex circuits with varying underflow concentrations, with changing solution densities, or with other streams entering or leaving the system.

When the type of circuit shown in Fig. 19-85 is employed, and wash water enters only in the final thickener, the recovery may be predicted by the formula

$$R = 1 - \left(\frac{D}{F - D}\right)^n \tag{19-19}$$

where R = fraction of solute recovered
D = underflow dilution, lb. solution/lb. insoluble solids
F = feed dilution in all thickeners except the first, lb. solution/lb. insoluble solids
n = number of stages

In the example shown,

$$R = 1 - \left(\frac{1}{4 - 1}\right)^3 \text{ or } 0.963$$

The deviation from the actual value of 96.5 per cent is due to the amount of solute dissolved and entering the first-stage thickener. This has the same effect as adding wash water at this stage. Obviously, if a large proportion of the feed were soluble, this method would be much less accurate.

Graphical methods are also used for simplifying C.C.D. calculations. These are valuable where extensive study of C.C.D. flow sheets in the design stages is needed. In practice, the methods are less accurate and are useful only for approximate results because of the variations in underflow solids concentrations, solution densities, and feed dilution to each thickener.

FILTRATION

REFERENCES: Chalmers, Elledge, and Porter, *Chem. Eng.*, **62** (6), 191 (1955). Fuhrmeister, *Chem. Eng. Progress*, **47**, 550 (1951). Grace, *Chem. Eng. Progress*, **49**, 303, 367 (1953). Grace, *Am. Inst. Chem. Engrs. J.*, **2**, 307, 316 (1956). Smith, *Chem. Eng.*, **62** (6), 177 (1955).

Liquid-solids separations carried out under the impetus of pressure or vacuum are achieved in filters, strainers, or presses. Conducted in filters and strainers, the operation is called variously filtration, clarification, polishing, and straining; although technical differences have become associated with these terms, filtration usually is accepted as a generic word that includes the others. Conducted in presses, the separation is called expression.

Definition. Filtration may be defined as the separation of undissolved, particulate, suspended solids from a fluid mixture by passage of most of the fluid through a septum or membrane that retains the solids on or within itself. The mixture to be separated is called the feed slurry or prefilt, the fluid that passes through the septum is called the filtrate, and the septum is called the filter medium; when the separated solids accumulate in amounts that visibly cover the medium, they are called the filter cake or simply the cake. The equipment assembly that provides housing for the medium, a chamber for cake accumulation (if needed), space for the desired prefilt and filtrate hold-up, drainage surfaces and channels for the filtrate, and means for the supply and removal of the appropriate streams is called a filter.

In the broadest sense of filtration the fluid may be a liquid, a gas, or a mixture of the two. In practice, however, liquid filtration and gas clarification (the latter including methods of separation other than and in addition to filtration) are treated as distinct unit operations, each served by its own technical experts and equipment designers that only infrequently work simultaneously in both fields.

Filtration is conventionally differentiated from certain other mechanical separations that in their extremes are indistinguishable from filtration. Expression, for instance, has already been mentioned. Here the mixture to be separated is a solid or a paste too dry to be pumped, rather than a fluid. Examples are an apple entering a cider press and a ball of stiff potter's clay from which water can be squeezed by hand. If the solids-containing product of the separation is a concentrated slurry rather than a moist solid, the operation is called thickening, as in the sedimentation of sewage to produce sewage sludge. Thickening usually is preliminary to further mechanical separation, often accomplished by filtration. When a slurry is passed over a relatively coarse medium such that a part of the solids is retained by the medium while a considerable part passes through with the liquid in the form of a suspension, the term wet screening is applied to the separation. An illustration is the dewatering of washed coal by means of a vibrating screen, through which the fines pass with the wash water. In screening the view is primarily one of separating solids from solids rather than solids from liquid.

Classification of Filters. Filtration and filters may be classified in a number of ways:

1. By driving force. The filtrate is induced to flow through the septum by hydrostatic head (gravity), superatmospheric pressure applied upstream of the septum, subatmospheric pressure applied downstream of the septum, or centrifugal force across the septum. Centrifugal filtration is customarily associated with centrifugal sedimentation in the general subject of centrifugation, being regarded first as an application of the centrifugal phenomenon and second as a particular filtration. It is discussed later under **Centrifuges.**

2. By filtration mechanism. Although the mechanism for the arrest and accumulation of solids is not clearly understood, two model pictures of the filtration process provide a theory that is consistent with the majority of filtration rate and resistance data. The model wherein filtered solids are stopped at the surface of the medium and pile upon one another to form a cake of increasing thickness leads to cake-filtration equations; that wherein the solids are trapped within the pores or body of the medium leads to filter-medium-filtration equations. Filter-medium filtration sometimes is called blocking, sometimes clarification.

3. By function. The process goal of filtration may be dry solids (the cake is the product of value), clarified liquid (the filtrate is the product of value), or both. The former is achieved only in cake filtration, but clarification is accomplished in both filter-medium and cake operations.

4. By operating cycle. Filters may be intermittent (batch) or continuous, and batch filters may be operated with constant-pressure driving force, at constant rate, or in cycles that are variable with respect to both pressure and rate.

5. By nature of the solids. Cake filtration may involve an accumulation of solids that is compressible or substantially incompressible, corresponding roughly in filter-medium filtration to particles that are deformable and to those that are rigid. The particle or particle-aggregate size may be of the same order of magnitude as the minimum pore size of most filter media (1 to 10 microns and greater), or may be smaller (1 micron down to the dimension of bacteria and even large molecules). Most filtrations involve solids of the former size range; those of the latter range can be filtered, if at all, only by filter-medium-type filtration or by ultrafiltration, unless they are converted to the former range by aggregation prior to filtration.

These methods of classification are not mutually exclusive. Thus filters usually are divided first into the two groups of cake and clarifying equipment, then into groups of machines using the same kind of driving force, then further into batch and continuous classes. This is the scheme of classification underlying the discussion of filters of this section. Within it, the other aspects of operating cycle, the nature of the solids, and additional factors (*e.g.*, types and classification of filter media) will be treated explicitly or implicitly.

The following pages discuss filters, both cake-producing and clarifying, activated by hydrostatic head, pressure, and vacuum, and the filter media employed by these filters. Such filtration theory as is a practical guide to the selection and operation of filters is reviewed. The equipment is described and its operation elaborated. Included are certain thickeners of the filter type; not included are sedimentary thickeners, centrifugal filters, expression equipment, and electrophoretic separators, as these are dealt with in other portions of the handbook.

THEORY OF FILTRATION

Filtration has been developed as a practical art rather than as a science, but the theory of filtration has received more and more attention in industry during the past years.

Filtration theory, although seldom used in the actual design of a filter for a given operation, is valuable in interpreting laboratory tests, in seeking the optimum conditions for filtration, and in predicting effects of changes in operating conditions. The use of filtration theory is limited by the fact that the filtering characteristics must always be determined on the actual slurry in question, data obtained on one slurry being inapplicable to another.

Filtration usually results in the formation of a layer (or cake) of solid particles on the surface of the porous body, frequently a textile fabric, that forms the filtering medium. Once this layer has formed, its surface acts as the filter medium, solids being deposited and adding to the thickness of the cake while the clear liquor passes through. The cake is therefore composed of a bulky mass of particles of irregular shape, among which run small capillaries. The flow of liquor through the capillaries is always streamline and may therefore be represented by Poiseuille's equation, which may be adapted in the following form:

$$\frac{dV}{A\,d\theta} = \frac{P}{\mu[\alpha(W/A) + r]} \tag{19-20}$$

[Carman, *Trans. Inst. Chem. Engrs. (London)*, **16,** 174 (1938); also, McCabe and Smith, "Unit Operations of Chemical Engineering," McGraw-Hill, New York, 1956], expressing the differential or instantaneous rate of filtration per unit area as the ratio of a driving force, pressure, to the product of viscosity by the sum of cake resistance and filter medium resistance.

The rate of filtration can usually be expressed in terms of volume of filtrate collected V, area of filtering surface A, and time θ. The pressure P is the total drop through the filter medium and the cake upon it. The viscosity μ is that of the filtrate. (Any convenient units may be used, inconsistencies being absorbed in the cake and cloth resistances.)

W is the weight of dry-cake solids, which may be replaced by one of several equivalent terms, since

$$W = wV = \left(\frac{\rho c}{1 - mc}\right) V$$

where w is the weight of dry-cake solids per unit volume of filtrate, ρ is the density of the filtrate, c is the weight fraction of cake solids in the solute-free slurry, and m is the weight ratio of washed wet cake to washed dry cake.

The symbol α represents the average specific cake resistance, which is a constant for the slurry in its immediate condition. In the usual range of operating conditions it is related to the pressure by the expression

$$\alpha = \alpha' P^s$$

where α' is a constant determined largely by the size of the particles forming the cake; s is the cake compressibility, varying from 0 for rigid incompressible cakes, such as fine sand and kieselguhr, to 1.0 for very highly compressible cakes. For most industrial slurries, s lies between 0.1 and 0.8. The symbol r represents the resistance of unit area of filter cloth, as well as pressure drop in lines, etc.

Equation (19-20) can be integrated as follows for **constant-pressure** filtration, giving the relationship between the total time and filtrate measurements:

$$\frac{\theta}{(V/A)} = \frac{\mu\alpha}{2P}\left(\frac{W}{A}\right) + \frac{\mu r}{P} \qquad (19\text{-}21)$$

$$\frac{\theta}{(V/A)} = \frac{\mu\alpha w}{2P}\left(\frac{V}{A}\right) + \frac{\mu r}{P} \qquad (19\text{-}21a)$$

For a given constant-pressure filtration, these may be simplified to

$$\frac{\theta}{(V/A)} = K_p\left(\frac{W}{A}\right) + C = K_p'\left(\frac{V}{A}\right) + C \qquad (19\text{-}21b)$$

where K_p, K_p', and C are constants for the conditions employed.

Equation (19-20) may be integrated for **constant rate** of filtrate flow (or cake deposition) to give the following equation, in which filter-medium resistance is treated as a constant pressure to be deducted from the rising total pressure [Ruth, *Ind. Eng. Chem.*, **27**, 717 (1935)]:

$$\frac{\theta}{(V/A)} = \frac{1}{(\text{rate per unit area})} = \frac{\mu\alpha}{(P - P_1)}\left(\frac{W}{A}\right) \qquad (19\text{-}22)$$

which may also be written

$$\frac{\theta}{(V/A)} = \frac{1}{(\text{rate per unit area})} = \frac{\mu\alpha w}{(P - P_1)}\left(\frac{V}{A}\right) \qquad (19\text{-}22a)$$

In these equations P_1 is the pressure drop through the filter medium.

$$P_1 = \mu r\left(\frac{V}{A\theta}\right)$$

For a given constant-rate run, the equations may be simplified to

$$\frac{V}{A\theta} = \text{rate per unit area} = \frac{P}{K_r} + C' \qquad (19\text{-}22b)$$

where K_r and C' are constants for the given conditions.

In the filtration of small amounts of fine particles from liquids by means of bulky filter media (absorbent cotton, felt, etc.), it has been found that the above equations based upon the resistance of a cake of solids do not hold, since no cake is formed. For these cases, where filtration takes place in the capillaries of a thick medium, Hermans and Bredee [*J. Soc. Chem. Ind.*, **55T**, 1–4 (1936)] have developed equations which they have found applicable to the constant-pressure filtration of viscose, sugar solutions, etc. Comparable constant-rate equations are presented by Grace [*Am. Inst. Chem. Engrs. J.*, **2**, 323 (1956)].

Practical Significance of the Filtration Equations. The differential form [Eq. (19-20)] of the filtration equation yields interesting information on the mutual effects of the operating variables.

When the cake is composed of hard granular particles that make it rigid and incompressible, an increase in pressure results in no deformation of the particles or their interstices, whereby $s = 0$, and, neglecting filter-medium resistance, Eq. (19-20) becomes

$$\frac{dV}{d\theta} = \frac{AP}{\mu\alpha'(W/A)} \qquad (19\text{-}20a)$$

For incompressible cakes, therefore, the flow rate is directly proportional to the area and pressure and inversely to the viscosity, to the total amount of cake (or filtrate), and to α'.

When the cake consists of extremely soft, easily deformed particles, such as ferric and other metal hydroxides, s approaches 1.0, whereby Eq. (19-20), again neglecting the filter medium, reduces to

$$\frac{dV}{d\theta} = \frac{A}{\mu\alpha'(W/A)} \qquad (19\text{-}20b)$$

For very compressible cakes, therefore, the rate is independent of pressure.

The *effect of pressure* shown above is modified in most industrial filtrations, where the cake compressibility usually lies between 0.1 and 0.8. Furthermore the resistance of the filter medium reduces the effects of the respective variables. It has been found true, however, that in the filtration of granular or crystalline solids an increase in pressure causes a nearly proportionate increase in flow rate. Flocculent or slimy precipitates have their filtration rates increased only slightly by an increase in pressure. Some materials have a critical pressure above which a further increase results in an actual decrease in flow rate.

In the filtration of certain non-homogeneous sludges, such as those of slimy solids to which filter aids have been added, it has been found that a constant flow rate during filtration is more satisfactory than a constant pressure, for the latter results in poor initial clarity of the filtrate and a rapid build-up of cake resistance. As a matter of fact, filtration of any but the most incompressible sludges is more satisfactory when a low pressure is used at the beginning of the run. This is especially important in filtering slurries of low solid content.

Since most pressure filters are fed by centrifugal pumps, their operation is seldom either constant pressure or constant rate but, in accordance with the characteristic of the pump, is essentially constant rate during its early stages and constant pressure during much of the latter part of the cycle. Pumps having steep head-discharge characteristics do not operate at either constant rate or constant pressure during any part of the cycle, but always under intermediate conditions of increasing pressure and decreasing flow rate. Tiller [*Am. Inst. Chem. Engrs. J.*, **4**, 170 (1958)] shows a method of dealing with such a cycle.

Cake thickness is an important factor in determining the capacity and design of a filter, and upon it the cycle of operation depends. Filtration theory shows that, cloth resistance neglected, the average flow rate during a filtration is inversely proportional to the amount of cake deposited.

If the cake has a high resistance relative to that of the filter medium, therefore, the highest capacity of a given filter is reached with zero cake thickness. Consideration of the fact that a thin cake does not usually discharge easily, however, together with the important factor of time required to clean the filter, leads to the selection of an appreciable cake thickness. Filter capacity is often measured in terms of dry solids handled per unit of filtering area.

If the cake has a low resistance compared with that of the filter medium, the economic cake thickness will be increased.

In washing filter cakes it is usually found that there is a definite cake thickness at which a given ratio of wash water to cake solids will produce a minimum soluble salts content of cake. Conversely, the ratio of wash water to cake solids which is found necessary to produce a given soluble content of the cake is a minimum at this cake thickness. In many cases, however, the effect of cake thickness on washing efficiency is not marked. Minimum volume of wash water is desirable since excessive volumes may derange plant procedure.

The *effect of viscosity* is as indicated by the rate equations: the filtrate flow rate at any instant is inversely proportional to the filtrate viscosity. The high viscosity of some filtrates (for example, oils or concentrated solutions) can be reduced by the dilution of the prefilt with low-viscosity solvent, sometimes with a net gain in the filtration rate in spite of the increased volume of filtrate [Reeves, *Ind. Eng. Chem.*, **39**, 203 (1947); *Petroleum Processing*, **4**, 885 (1949); *Göttner, Erdol u. Kohle*, **7**, 287 (1954)]. If the filtrate is required in high concentration for subsequent treatment or as a product, dilution will be feasible only if the cost of reconcentration does not make the economics of the filtration unfavorable.

The *effect of temperature* on the filtration rate of incompressible solids is evident principally through its effect on viscosity. The viscosity of most liquids decreases markedly with increasing temperature. Higher temperatures thus permit higher filtration rates; if the filtrate were water, for example, an increase of temperature from 20° to 60°C. would double the rate of flow. Compressible sludges are affected in more complicated ways by temperature increase, but the general effect is apt to be increased filtration rate. Limits to the extent to which a prefilt may be heated are imposed by the cost of heating and, in vacuum filtration, by the vapor pressure of the filtrate.

The *effect of particle size* on cake and cloth resistances is marked. Even small changes in particle size affect the coefficient α' in the equation for cake resistance, $\alpha = \alpha' P^s$, and larger changes affect the compressibility s. Decreased particle size results in lower filtration rates and higher moisture content of the cake but sometimes in better washing efficiency. It is important, therefore, that close control be kept of the particle size in the feed to the filter. On the one hand, degradation of particle size by violent pump action or agitation must be avoided; on the other, preconditioning of the slurry by digestion or by chemical treatment may result in the flocculation of fine particles to agglomerates that are larger and more filterable. Practically unfilterable slurry may thus become filterable, as in the case of sewage sludge upon coagulation by alum or ferric chloride. The importance of preconditioning and of a number of other filtration variables is discussed by Furhrmeister [*Chem. Eng. Prog.*, **47**, 550 (1951)].

The *effect of the type of filter medium* is often not fully recognized. In selecting the medium for a given filtration, a balance must be struck between as open a weave as possible in order to reduce plugging and as tight a weave as is necessary to prevent excessive "bleeding" of fine particles. After a small thickness of cake has formed on the medium, bleeding often stops, fine particles being caught in the cake.

Of the weaves of filter cloths described under a following section, the number-duck weaves have the greatest ability to retain fine solids, followed in decreasing ability by chains (broken twills), twills, and hose ducks. The tendency to plug, however, is in the reverse order. Thick, stiff cloths tend to plug more readily than thin, pliable ones. The effect of cloth plugging on filtration rate is so appreciable that it will ultimately be the cause of replacement of the cloth. It also results in a need for using a safety factor in predicting filter capacities.

The *effect of solid content* of the slurry on the rate of filtration is shown in Eqs. (19-21*a*) and (19-22*a*), where it is expressed as w, the weight of cake-forming solids per unit volume of filtrate. These equations show that, filter-medium resistance neglected, the rate of filtrate flow is inversely proportional to the ratio of solids to filtrate but that the rate of cake deposition is directly proportional to this ratio. If a slurry is thickened before filtration, time required for its filtration on a given filter area will be reduced in direct proportion to the decrease in ratio of liquid to solids in the slurry.

Application of Filtration Theory to the Interpretation of Data

The filtration equations are useful in predicting the effect of a change in any variable if the constants are determined from data taken on the slurry in question. For example, vacuum test data can be extrapolated to show the approximate filtering rates that could be obtained if the slurry were filtered under pressure. Another problem often of interest is the effect of cake thickness or time cycle on over-all filtration rate.

If a *constant-pressure test* is run on a slurry, care being taken that not only the pressure but also the temperature and the solid content remain constant throughout the run and that time readings begin at the exact start of filtration, one can observe values of filtrate volume or weight and time. With the use of the known filtering area, values of $\theta/(V/A)$ can be calculated for various values of (V/A) which, when plotted with $\theta/(V/A)$ as the ordinate and (V/A) as the abscissa (Fig. 19-86*a*), result in a

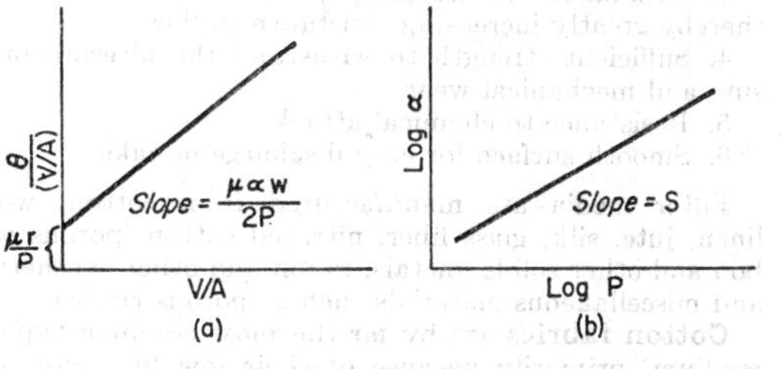

FIG. 19-86. Typical plots of filtration data.

straight line having the slope $\mu\alpha w/2P$ and an intercept on the vertical axis of $\mu r/P$. Since μ, w, and P are known, α and r can be calculated from

$$\alpha = \frac{2P}{\mu w} \times \text{(slope)}$$

and $$r = \frac{P}{\mu} \times \text{(vertical intercept)}$$

The effect of a change in any variable except P (which affects α) may now be estimated.

To determine the effect of a change in pressure, it is necessary to run a test under one or more other pressures, and to calculate α and r at those pressures in the same way. By plotting α and r against P on loglog paper (or by plotting log α and log r vs. log P), straight lines result from which it is possible to determine α and r at any reasonable pressure (Fig. 19-86*b*). In many cases it has been found that r does not vary appreciably with pressure, in which case an average value can be used at all pressures. This is often due to the fact that a low filtering pressure is used at the start of filtration.

When a low pressure is used for any appreciable time at the start of filtration, the beginning of time and filtrate readings should be delayed until the constant pressure is reached, in which case r is the resistance of the filter medium plus that of the cake deposited at low pressure. When the weight of the dry cake is measured vs. time, as is usually done in vacuum leaf tests, two or three tests are sufficient to permit plotting the straight-line function of θ/V vs. W. The ability to interpolate or extrapolate on this line eliminates the need for a large number of tests.

In *constant-rate filtration* it is suggested that the method of Bonilla [*Trans. Am. Inst. Chem. Engrs.*, **34**, 243 (1938)] be used, involving the determination of P_1 and α_0 in the equation

$$\alpha = \alpha_0 + \alpha'(P - P_1)^s$$

and plotting $(\alpha - \alpha_0)$ vs. $(P - P_1)$ to determine α' and s.

FILTER MEDIA

The choice of the filter medium is often the most mportant consideration in assuring efficient operation of a filter. This is true in spite of the fact that in most filtrations the medium does not do the actual filtering but merely acts as a support for the cake of solids that is deposited and on which the separating process takes place.

The filter medium should be selected primarily for its ability to retain the solids, without plugging and without undue bleeding of particles at the start of filtration. However, all the following attributes of a good filter medium should be sought in varying degrees depending on the specific problem:

1. Ability to bridge solids across its pores within a reasonable time after beginning to feed
2. Minimum resistance to flow of filtrate
3. Avoidance of wedging particles into its pores, thereby greatly increasing resistance to flow
4. Sufficient strength to withstand the filtering pressure and mechanical wear
5. Resistance to chemical attack
6. Smooth surface for easy discharge of cake

Filter media are manufactured from cotton, wool, linen, jute, silk, glass fiber, nitrated cotton, porous carbon and other solids, metals, rayon and other synthetics, and miscellaneous materials such as porous rubber.

Cotton fabrics are by far the most common type of medium, primarily because of their low first cost and availability in a wide variety of weaves. Cotton is attacked by all mineral acids and by many organic acids that can crystallize at operating temperatures, but it is not usually affected by volatile organic acids. Strong alkalies, acidic salts, and metallic ammonium salts also attack cotton. Operating temperatures should always be kept below 200°F. In describing cotton fabrics, reference is made to (1) weave, (2) style number, (3) weight, (4) count, (5) ply, and (6) yarn number. Of these, only the *style number* is completely definitive, but unfortunately it is a purely arbitrary number assigned by each manufacturer, except in the case of the so-called "number ducks." *Yarn number*, defining the weight of the original twisted filaments, is set by the weight of the fabric and its other characteristics and so is seldom a factor for the user to consider. *Ply* is defined as the number of small yarns twisted together to form the final thread, whereas *count* expresses the number of threads per inch in each direction. *Weight* is best given in terms of ounces per square yard. Fabrics of heavy weight and low count, in multi-ply construction, make the strongest cloths but in general show more tendency either to plug readily or to retain coarse solids. A wide variety of weaves is available, of which the simplest is the *plain weave*, in which the cross threads (filling) are woven over and under the long threads (warp) alternately, giving a somewhat square appearance.

Cotton ducks are the most common of the plain weaves, the term covering a wide range of constructions. They are low in first cost, have good mechanical strength and resistance to wear, and discharge cakes readily; but, when sufficiently tight to retain fine solids, they have high resistance to flow and plug rather quickly. The number ducks listed in Table 19-10 are frequently used in filter presses. Also of interest are other plain-weave cloths such as "ounce ducks," *e.g.*, 10-oz. duck, having a loose open weave useful only for coarse solids; "hose ducks," rather heavy and still more open in weave; cider-press cloths of about ⅛-in. thread spacing, useful as a backing cloth; sheetings, lightweight (2 to 8 oz./sq. yd.) open weaves for mild service; and specially finished weaves for straining "dopes," etc., such as cambrics, nainsooks, combed lawns, balloon cloths, and voiles.

Table 19-10. Cotton Number Ducks

Style No.	Construction			Description
	Weight/ sq. yd., oz.	Count	Ply	
12	11.5	50 × 34	2 × 2	Lightweight, tight weave
10	14.7	50 × 30	3 × 3	Light medium weight, more open
8	18.0	45 × 28	3 × 4	Medium weight, tight weave
6	21.3	36 × 26	3 × 3	Medium heavy weight
4	24.5	31 × 24	4 × 4	Heavy weight, very tight weave

Cotton twills are characterized by a diagonal weave resulting from interlacing the warp and filling yarns with a progression of one at the point of interlacing. They have less resistance to flow and less tendency to plug than ducks but consequently are more likely to pass fine particles at the start of filtration. Table 19-11 lists the six most common weaves, which serve for the average filtering problem. In the selection of a twill, the weight is important for strength and mechanical wear, while increasing count improves the ability to retain fine solids. Heavy cloths are necessary in large filter presses to provide satisfactory gasketing, also. *Drills* are a lightweight variation of the twill weave, while *canton flannel* has a nap on one side, making it useful in clarifying operations not requiring easy cake removal.

Table 19-11. Representative Cotton Twills

Classification		Construction (approx.)			Uses
Weight	Count	Weight/ sq. yd., oz.	Count	Ply	
Light	Low	15.5	38 × 28	4 × 4	For light service, *e.g.*, vacuum filters
Light	High	15.5	66 × 44	2 × 2	For light service, *e.g.*, vacuum filters
Medium	Low	17.5	36 × 25	3 × 3	For general use, including leaf filters
Medium	High	18.0	67 × 36	2 × 4	For general use, including leaf filters
Heavy	Low	22	34 × 24	4 × 4	For severe service, *e.g.*, filter presses
Heavy	High	20	58 × 42	3 × 4	For severe service, *e.g.*, filter presses

Cotton chain weaves, or broken twills, are woven with a 1-2-4-3 interlacing of warp and filling threads. They are usually intermediate between twills and number ducks in tightness, plugging tendencies, and other properties. At moderate or low operating pressures, they are superior to number ducks from most standpoints. Here again, high-count weaves are tighter than low-count fabrics of equal weight. Data are given in Table 19-12.

Wool cloths are sometimes used in filtering dilute acid solutions and in clarifying viscous liquids. They are characterized by severe plugging tendencies and rapid attack by alkalies, however. *Jute* cloths have been used extensively for filter pressing of coarse solids.

Fibrous-glass fabrics have been used for severe acid or temperature conditions where physical strength and wear resistance are not required, as in leaf filters. The flexing strength of glass fabrics has been improved by admixture of asbestos. *Silk* has been used in a very light, plain weave on string-discharge filters, where its free-filtering properties are utilized under mild mechanical conditions.

A wide variety of synthetic fibers is used in filter media, primarily because of their chemical resistance and resistance to bacterial attack. Representative materials include nylon, Dacron, Vincel, Orlon, Dynel, Saran, polyethylene, polypropylene, and Teflon. In addition, non-woven synthetic textiles are finding applications as filter media.

Metal fabrics are available in steel, stainless steel, monel, nickel, copper, brass, bronze, aluminum, and Everdur, and in several types of weave. In the plain weave, 400 mesh is the closest wire spacing available, thus limiting the use of this weave to coarse crystalline slurries, pulps, etc. The so-called "Dutch weaves," employing straight warp wires and crimped filling, can be woven much closer, providing a good medium for filtering fine crystals and pulps. However, this type of weave tends to plug readily when soft amorphous particles are filtered, making the use of filter aid desirable. The long life of the proper wire cloth in corrosive and high-temperature filtrations makes it desirable to install them more or less permanently.

Metals also are used in the form of rigid porous media. Sheets and tubes of sintered stainless steel and other metal are used in clarifying filters (especially in aircraft engines) and as a base for precoat filters.

Other porous media are made from a number of materials. *Carbon and graphite* in the form of plates, tubes, and special shapes are available in a wide range of porosities and are resistant to all acids and alkalies under non-oxidizing conditions. *Aloxite, alundum, silica,* and *porcelain* are similarly utilized and are resistant to all acids except hydrofluoric, but not to strong alkalies.

Plastic materials, including Teflon, are also available. The characteristics of a number of commercial grades of porous media are listed in Sec. 18.

Cotton batting finds extensive use in filtering gelatinous particles from paints, spinning solutions, and other viscous liquids, and for removal of dirt from milk, etc., the batting being discarded after use. Filtration takes place by deposition of the particles on the fibers throughout the mat, which is usually supported on both sides by gauze or light sheeting. Filter cotton is available in various stages of refinement and purification, from soft absorbent cotton to wool-like material with low filtering resistance. *Cotton table felt* is also used in clarifying liquids.

Wool felts and cotton-wool mixtures are available in both pressed and woven types. The former are less expensive, but the latter can be reused after cleaning or washing.

Filter papers and pulps are often used for the retention of very fine solids and for the clarification of liquids containing small amounts of solids. They are available in various degrees of permeability, thickness, and strength, and some are resistant to strong acids and alkalies. They must be well supported in the filter; and, if a cake is to be removed without destroying the paper, they must be covered with a sheeting.

Table 19-12. Representative Cotton Chains (Broken Twills)

Classification		Construction (approx.)			Uses
Weight	Count	Weight/sq. yd., oz.	Count	Ply	
Very light	High	12	56 × 50	2 × 2	Vacuum filters, etc.
Light	High	15	68 × 42	2 × 4	Vacuum and low-pressure work
Medium	High	18	57 × 37	3 × 3	For general use
Heavy	Low	22	34 × 30	3 × 4	For filter-press service, etc.
Heavy	High	20	67 × 38	3 × 5	For filter-press service, etc.

Granular beds, such as sand and coal filters, are widely used for filtration of water and chemical solutions to remove small quantities of easily coagulated solids. They are cleaned by backwashing at a rate sufficient to disrupt the bed and carry out the fine solids.

An extensive discussion of the structure of various filter media, their performance, and methods of measuring their porosity and other characteristics is given by Grace [*Am. Inst. Chem. Engrs. J.*, **2**, 307, 316 (1956)].

FILTRATION LEAF TESTS

It is unusual to be able to forecast what may be accomplished in the filtration of an untested product, and even the results obtained upon known products vary greatly with the conditions of filtration. Therefore, unless exact data have already been established, preliminary tests should be made to determine the filter requirements for a given filtration problem. Such tests are easy to make and require very simple, small-scale test equipment. Whether vacuum or pressure filtration is to be used is generally known beforehand. Occasionally tests are made for comparison.

Vacuum Tests. The leaf shown in Fig. 19-87 is connected to a filtrate receiver equipped with a vacuum gage. The receiver is connected to an aspirator. Different filter media may be used on this leaf for comparative tests.

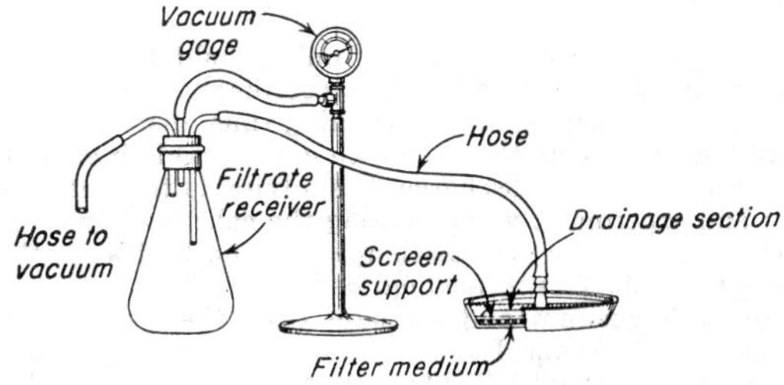

FIG. 19-87. Small-scale vacuum-filtration testing unit. (*Dorr-Oliver, Inc.*)

In making leaf tests, the operation of a continuous vacuum filter should be kept in mind. The cycle is divided into three periods, **cake formation** (or "pickup"), **drying,** and **discharge.** Sometimes pickup is followed by a period of displacement washing, and the cake may also be subjected to compression during drying. These factors should be considered, and a plan of the cycle or cycles to be tested should be formed.

If the object of filtration is simply the removal of solids from the liquor, the cycle may be: one-third pickup, one-third drying, and one-third discharge and reentry time. While under vacuum, the test leaf is submerged for the pickup period in the material to be tested. The leaf is then removed and held with the drain pipe down for the drying time allotted. Observations should be made during the test such as vacuum readings during pickup and drying; time at which cracks in the cake appear; temperature of the material; percentage of cake-forming solids present; acidity or alkalinity.

Usually a few preliminary tests will indicate the time range. Careful tests may then be made and, in these, variations in temperature, dilution, conditioning agents, etc., should be tried, and capacities and clarity of filtrate noted.

Pressure Tests. For plate-and-frame press work, tests are best made with a laboratory-size model. This will give representative "cake packing," etc. The apparatus shown in Fig. 19-88 is used for tests to obtain data for operation with a shell-type pressure filter.

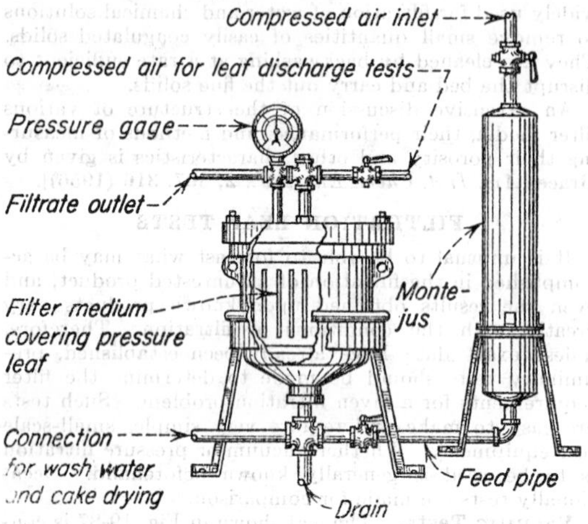

FIG. 19-88. Small-scale pressure-filtration testing unit. *(Dorr-Oliver, Inc.)*

Operation of the commercial unit should be kept in mind and the cycle arranged accordingly. After determining the cake-building or filling time, displacement washing and drying the cake with compressed air should be tried. For wet discharge it is advisable to open the cell and experiment upon washing the cake away with a jet of water. For dry discharge the effect of a gentle air blast in the test leaf should be tried.

In both vacuum and pressure tests the daily filter capacity is determined by the dry weight of cake per unit area of test leaf multiplied by cycles per 24 hr. and multiplied by the filter area. Capacity in solids is usually expressed in pounds per square foot per day and filtrate in gallons per square foot per minute or per day.

The material tested should be representative, and samples should be tested immediately after they are taken. In some instances, samples stored for several days have given results very different from those obtained when tested immediately because of changes that occur upon standing. All tests should be made under conditions that represent large-scale operations so far as possible.

Results obtained by leaf tests for capacity are irregular with extremely free-filtering materials, such as crystals in mother liquor. In such cases it is better to employ small-scale equipment.

Before undertaking test work it is advisable to consult a manufacturer of filtration equipment, giving as much data on the materials as possible, together with the objects of filtration.

Instead of model leaf tests, compression-permeability experiments permit the collection of data of the equivalent of a series of constant-pressure filtrations in a single run, and avoid the data-treatment complexity of constant-rate tests. The experimental procedure and method of data treatment are explained by Grace [*Chem. Eng. Progress*, **49**, 303, 427 (1953)].

FILTER AIDS

It is sometimes possible to increase filtration rate by adding to the prefilt a filter aid, material containing larger non-compressible particles. Filter aids are particularly useful with finely divided solids and slimy, deformable flocs. The particles of a good filter aid should be of low bulk density to minimize their settling tendency; they also should be porous and must be chemically inert to the filtrate.

Kieselguhr or diatomaceous earth having a high silica content is little affected by solutions, is free filtering, and is of light gravity. It is the most widely used of all filter aids in the filtration of sugar juices, vegetable oils, petroleum products, fruit juices, beverages, etc. Paper pulp is also used in the clarification of wine and beer.

The amounts of filter aid added are comparatively small, and the expense is more than counterbalanced by increased filter efficiency. Both paper pulp and kieselguhr can be washed and revivified so that they may be reused several times. Fuller's earth, carbon, pearlite, asbestos, sawdust, magnesia, salt, and gypsum are used as filter aids in special cases.

Decolorizing carbons and earths and activated clays act both as decolorizers and as filter aids for oils, fats, etc. In many cases, a coating of the filter aid is applied to the filter medium to act as a clarifying agent and to prevent blinding of the filter medium.

The commonly used filter aids of diatomaceous earth are prepared by various manufacturers. This material, being skeletal remains of diatoms, has a very high filter rate, does not fill the pores of filter media, and is used either as a precoating of the filter medium itself, or as a pulp mixture which must be filtered. Various degrees of purification used on the raw diatomaceous earth provide a material with varying filtration properties. These different types are given various trade names identifying them for certain work, as Filter-cel, Dicalite, etc.

For specific amounts of filter aid, the producers of various grades give their own recommendations.

FILTRATION EQUIPMENT

Cake Filters

Filters that accumulate appreciable visible quantities of filtered solids on the surface of the filter medium are called cake filters. The prefilt feed usually contains at least 1 per cent suspended solids and may have 40 per cent or more. After the first instant of filtration, the accumulated cake becomes the true filter medium, and the filtration proceeds according to the cake laws. The cake, the filtrate, or both may be the primary product of the filtration. When the filtrate is the product, the degree to which it is removed from the cake by washing and blowing becomes an economic choice. When the cake is the product, virtually complete filtrate removal may be necessary, and there often is economic incentive to achieve as dry a cake as possible in the filter; this may be accomplished by air or gas blowing.

Inasmuch as the cake is itself the effective filter medium, the base on which it is deposited need not be a particularly retentive medium; in fact, to minimize its resistance and thus to maximize the capacity of the filter, the medium usually is so open that some solids come through it at the beginning of a cycle. For this reason, a cake filtration seldom yields a completely clear filtrate and filtrate clarity, if required, must be achieved by such means as segregation of the cloudy portions (often a very small part of the total), recycle of the cloudy portions, or second-stage filtrate polishing.

Implicit in cake-filter operation is the removal of the solids, for the cake is normally so dry and compacted that it is no longer a fluid but a moist and sometimes sticky solid, the most difficult of all kinds of material to handle. Indeed, the ability to effect a clean separation of the cake from the filter medium and to discharge the cake economically from the filter is one of the important criteria determining the choice of filtration equipment.

Cake filters operate under the impetus of hydrostatic head, pressure imposed by a pump or a blow case, or vacuum.

Gravity (Hydrostatic Head) Filters. In a gravity filter, the flow of filtrate results from the hydrostatic pressure of the column of prefilt that stands above the surface of the filter medium or the cake. This pressure is always relatively low, ranging from a maximum of a few centimeters of fluid in a laboratory funnel to a maximum of a few feet of fluid in a plant filter. Gravity filters are used, therefore, only for relatively freely filtering materials and in cases where the highest rates are not required.

The advantages of gravity filters are

1. Their extreme simplicity.
2. Their dependency on only the simplest of accessories.
3. Therefore, their low first cost.
4. Their amenability to construction from almost any material, *e.g.*, porcelain or chemical stoneware.
5. The advantages of any horizontal, upper-surface filter: large particles settle quickly to the filtering surface to provide a low-resistance precoat for the finer particles; washing of the cake is effective and efficient.

The disadvantages are

1. The relatively low rates of filtration.
2. The excessive floor area occupied per unit of filtration area.
3. The high labor charges incurred.
4. Difficult housekeeping problems.

Except in the chemist's laboratory, in the semi-works, or on very small plant scale, gravity filters are seldom used in the process industries.

The Gravity Nutsche. A nutsche is a tank equipped with a false bottom, perforated or porous, that may support a filter medium or may itself act as the septum. In a gravity nutsche, the slurry contained in the tank is filtered under its own hydrostatic head, the filtrate collecting in a sump beneath the filter or running directly to the sewer.

Thorough displacement washing is possible in a nutsche if the desired amount of wash solvent is added before any of the original filtrate has been displaced from the cake by air. If washing is difficult, the nutsche may be equipped with an agitator that will reslurry the cake and maintain it in suspension until sufficient diffusion and dilution of cake contaminant has occurred.

When it is not necessary that the cake be discharged dry, equipping the nutsche with a discharge line flush with the filtering surface and with a reslurrying agitator permits rapid, easy cake removal. A dry cake, however, can be removed only by hand scooping, an operation that is costly in labor and that produces excessive wear of any filter fabric used. The cake may be shoveled through a manhole in the lower portion of the tank wall or, if the nutsche is small, the top shell or the bottom head may be retractable to provide access to the cake.

Nutsches frequently are plant-constructed from metal or wood, and wooden false bottoms for this purpose can be purchased from the manufacturers of wood tanks. The false bottoms of metal nutsches may be of perforated plate, porous sintered metal, or porous ceramic slabs or blocks (*e.g.*, silica, alumina, or porcelain). All-ceramic nutsches are made by manufacturers of chemical stoneware (*e.g.*, General Ceramics Corp., The U.S. Stoneware Co.), and at least one filter manufacturer offers custom-designed nutsches of metal (Enzinger Division of the Duriron Co.). Nutsches are seldom larger than 8 ft. in diameter (about 2000 gal. capacity and 50 sq. ft. of filtering area), and ceramic equipment is limited to a diameter of about 3 ft. (about 100 gal. capacity and 7 sq. ft. of filtering area).

Nutsches may be enclosed and, with the proper structural design, operated as pressure or vacuum filters.

The Delpark Industrial Filter. The Delpark filter (Delpark Division, Indiana Commercial Filters Corp.) is a semicontinuous self-cleaning gravity filter for use with freely filtering suspensions of relatively large solids. It consists of a flat endless conveyor of open screen that operates over carrying and driving rolls between sloping sides and up the ramped ends of a rack that sits above a receiving tank (see Fig. 19-89). The conveyor carries

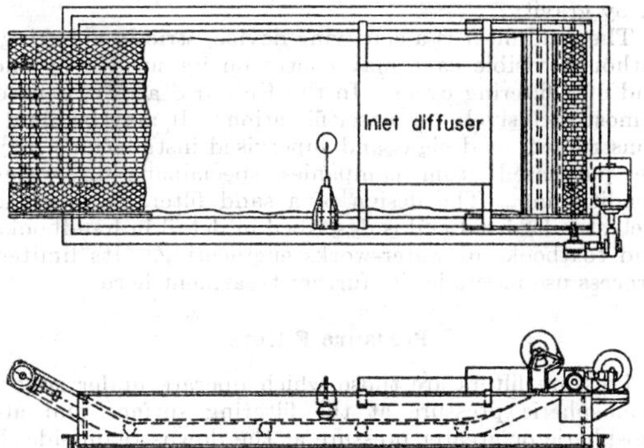

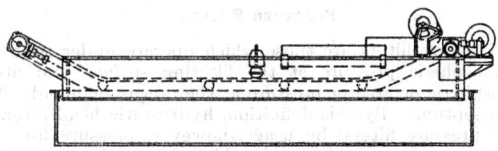

FIG. 19-89. Delpark filter. (*Indiana Commercial Filters Corp.*)

on its top surface a continuous covering of a loose-construction filter medium fed from a roll at one end of the filter. The horizontal and ramped sections of the medium and the sloping walls of the rack thus constitute a shallow trough (6 in. or less deep) into one end of which the prefilt is fed from a distributing device. The filtrate passes through the medium into the receiver, the solids being retained on the medium. As the cake becomes thicker and more resistant, the level of prefilt rises in the trough until, at a preset value, a float-activated switch causes the conveyor to advance, carrying fresh filter medium from the roll into the trough and discharging cake-laden medium over the opposite end of the filter into a waiting container. As soon as sufficient fresh surface has been provided for the level to fall the required amount, the float stops the driving mechanism. The cycle is repeated as often as the rate and solids content of the feed dictate.

Delpark filters range in size from about 3 to 130 sq. ft. of filtering area, and use filter media in widths of 16 to 48 in. The rated capacities are 2 to several hundred gal./min. They are most widely used for the reconditioning of machine-tool coolants and cutting oils, but they have been applied also to the filtration of spray-paint water, quenching and drawing oils, seed and other edible oils, plating solutions, and canning waste. An installation removing sludge from the quenching oil from various heat-treating and carbonizing furnaces processes 50 gal. of oil per minute and uses filter medium at the rate of about 1 yd./hr.

Bag Filters. Gravity bag filters, consisting of bags or pouches of filter fabric, felt, or chamois hung from suspending frames, largely have been displaced by more efficient filters. They are still occasionally used, however, for such simple straining operations as the removal of lumps from paint or dirt from lubricating oil. They are not recommended for process filtrations. Gravity bag filters for oil filtration (Wm. W. Nugent & Co., Inc.) have rated capacities ranging from 6 to 2000 gal./hr., based on oil with a viscosity of 200 S.S.U. (about 400 centipoises).

Sand Filters. The commonest type of gravity filter is the sand- or anthracite-bed filter. It consists of a tank or bin in which graded strata of gravel and sand or pulverized anthracite are placed, the size of the bed particle decreasing from the bottom of the bed to the top. The granular bed is the filter medium, to the top of which the prefilt is fed. The filtrate is removed through a false bottom or through perforated drainage pipes embedded in the medium near the bottom. The filter may be enclosed and operated under pressure instead of by gravity.

The sand filter is a clarifying device, strictly speaking, although visible cake may collect on its surface by the end of a filtering cycle. In the United States it is used almost exclusively for water filtration. It may be plant-constructed, or designs and supervised installations may be purchased from companies specializing in water conditioning. The design of a sand filter has become well standardized and is described in detail in handbooks and textbooks of water-works engineering. Its limited process use precludes its further treatment here.

Pressure Filters

Pressure filters are those which operate under super-atmospheric pressure at the filtering surface and atmospheric or greater pressure at the downstream side of the septum. By this definition, hydrostatic head filters are pressure filters; by usage, however, pressure filters have come to mean devices in which the filtering pressure is imposed by a liquid pump or by compressed gas. Thus pressure filters are fed by plunger, diaphragm, screw, and centrifugal pumps, by blow cases, and by streams that come from a pressure reactor. Except in the early stages of a cycle, cake pressure filters seldom are operated at less than 25 lb./sq. in. gage. Operating pressures of 50 to 75 lb./sq. in. are not uncommon, and special pressure filters are built to accommodate pressure drops of 500 lb./sq. in. or more.

For many years pressure filters were exclusively batch or intermittent apparatus. Continuous pressure filters now exist, but the difficulty of cake discharge from a pressure environment and the disadvantage of inaccessibility still considerably limit their use. The preponderant number of pressure filters, therefore, continue to be batch-operated.

The advantages of pressure filters are

1. Their use of high filtration pressure permits relatively rapid filtrations and enables difficult separations that otherwise would be prohibitively slow.
2. Their compactness provides large filtration area per unit of floor space occupied by the filter.
3. Batch pressure filters offer greater flexibility than any other kind, at relatively low first cost.

The disadvantages are

1. The well-developed, dependable batch pressure filter is difficult to adapt to continuous processes and, in many applications, is costly to operate.
2. Continuous pressure filters, on the other hand, are somewhat inflexible and the equipment is expensive.

Batch cake pressure filters are perhaps the most widely used solid-liquid separators in the process industries. Continuous pressure filters, less widely used, have important applications and are gaining acceptance.

Batch Pressure Filters

Pressure Nutsches and Sand Filters. As has been mentioned, nutsches and sand filters may be enclosed and converted into pressure filters by applying to the surface of the prefilt such compressed-gas pressure as the construction of the filter will tolerate safely. For ceramic pressure nutsches the limit is 30 lb./sq. in. or less. The same comments as for their gravity counterparts apply to these filters, with the additional observation that the closure of the filter necessary for the maintenance of pressure makes it even more awkward and undesirable to operate.

The Filter Press. The filter press is the simplest of all pressure filters and it is still one of the most widely used. There are two basic designs of filter press: the flush-plate, or plate-and-frame press, of which there are now several interesting major modifications; and the recessed-plate press. The plates of both types can be made from a wide variety of materials of construction: almost any metal (cast iron, cast steel, Ni-Resist, aluminum, lead, bronze, copper, nickel, monel), coated metal (galvanized, plastic-coated, rubber-covered), wood, wood coated with epoxy resin, and solid polymers (hard rubber, cast and laminated phenolic, glass-reinforced polyester).

A **plate-and-frame press,** as the name implies, is an assembly of alternate solid plates, the faces of which are studded, grooved, or perforated to permit drainage, and hollow frames, in which the cake collects during filtration (Fig. 19-90). A filter medium, usually a fabric,

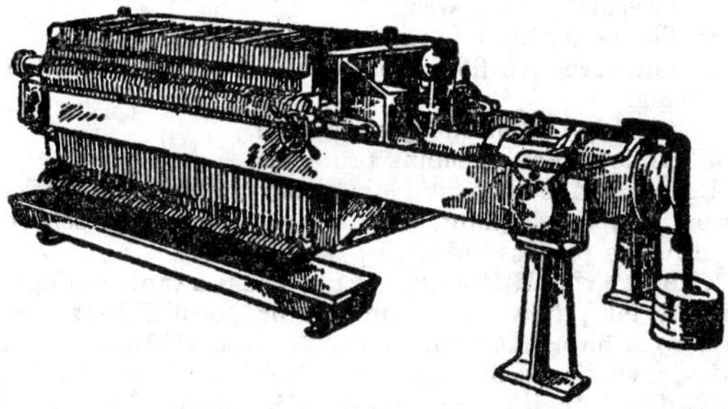

FIG. 19-90. Plate-and-frame filter press. (*T. Shriver & Co., Inc.*)

covers both faces of each plate. The plates and frames are usually rectangular, although they may be triangular or circular; the latter shape is used, with internal reinforcing of the frames, when the press is made of fabricated rather than cast metal (Fig. 19-91). They are hung

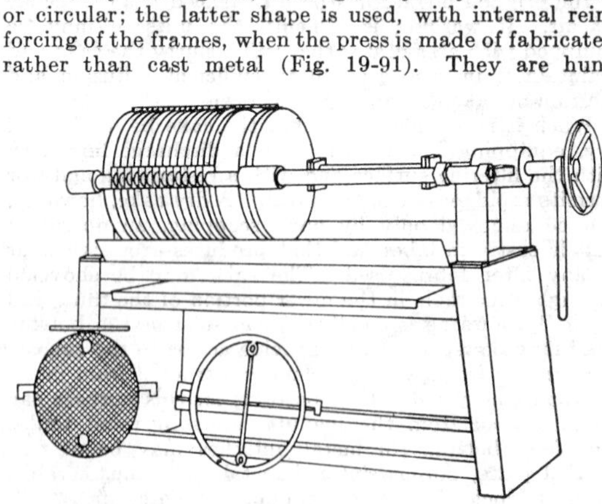

FIG. 19-91. Circular-plate fabricated-metal filter press. (*Star Tank and Filter Corp.*)

in a vertical position on a pair of parallel support bars. During filtration they are compressed to a substantially watertight closure between two end half plates, one fixed and one movable by capstan screw, ratchet and tommy bar, gear and pinion, or hydraulic ram.

Presses are fed and the filtrate is discharged through channels in the corners of the plates and frames or in lugs projecting from the sides of plates and frames. The latter arrangement eliminates the channel holes in the filter cloth, sometimes a source of alignment difficulties and leakage. The filtrate channel may run the entire length of the press into a discharge pipe at one end (closed discharge), or it may discharge through individual cocks, one on the side of each plate, into an open trough below the press (open discharge). Cocks are useful if absolutely clear filtrate is required, inasmuch as the cock of a leaky plate that is passing solids can be shut off to remove the plate from service. Otherwise, closed discharge is preferred, and is essential if toxic or volatile materials are being filtered. Several feed and discharge arrangements are possible: bottom feed and top discharge allows quick displacement of air and produces a cake of maximum uniformity with normal solids; top feed and bottom discharge provides maximum recovery of filtrate and maximum cake dryness and is most suitable for heavy, settling solids that may tend to clog bottom inlet ports; double feed and double discharge accommodates materials that filter at high rates and materials of high viscosity and is particularly suitable for precoating and for draining product out of the filter at the end of a run. One manufacturer offers a "roll-over" design that allows switching from top to bottom feed between or during filtrations (Star Tank and Filter Corp.).

Two techniques of washing are employed in filter presses, illustrated in Fig. 19-92. In simple washing the wash liquor follows the same path as the prefilt and filtrate. Unless the cakes are extremely uniform and highly permeable, simple washing is ineffective in a well-filled press. A more effective technique is thorough washing, a process during which wash liquor is admitted to the faces of alternate plates (whose discharge channels are cut off), whence it passes through the entire cake thickness to drain away on the faces of the other plates. Obviously the ports and channels of a thorough-washing press must be suitably designed and the plates correctly assembled. To assist in quick, proper assembly, plates and frames are identified by "buttons" cast on their sides: one button marks a filtering (non-washing) plate, two buttons mark a frame, and three buttons mark a washing plate. The assembly order thus is 1-2-3-2-1. Thorough washing should be used only when the frames are well filled, since an incompletely filled one will allow cake rearrangement or collapse during washing, and the wash will by-pass the solids through cracks or channels opened in the cake.

Filter presses are made in plate sizes ranging from 4 by 4 in. to 61 by 71 in. Frame thickness ranges from 0.125 to 8 in. Operating pressures up to 100 lb./sq. in. are common, and with special construction metal presses may be operated up to 1000 lb./sq. in. Metal plates may be cored for steam heating or for refrigerant circulation. The filtration rates achieved in filter presses vary widely, inasmuch as a broad variety of materials are filtered in this kind of equipment and a wide span of pressures is used. In chemical plants filtrate delivery rates from plate-and-frame presses often fall in the range 1 to 100 gal./(sq. ft. filtering area)(hr.). Typical filtering areas, cake capacities, and working pressures for various frames are shown in Table 19-13.

Table 19-13. Typical Filter-press Data*

Size of filter plate, in.			Effective filter area per filter chamber, sq. ft.		Holding capacity per 1 in. of chamber thickness, cu. ft.		Max. operating pressure for standard sizes, lb./sq. in.	
Recessed (center feed)	Side feed	Corner (eyed) feed	Metal	Wood or rubber	Metal	Wood or rubber	Metal	Wood
		4	0.14	....	0.006			
7	....	7	0.5	....	0.023	....	250	
12	12	12	1.7	0.9	0.07	0.04	150	100
18	18	18	3.9	2.3	0.16	0.10	150	100
24	24	24	7.0	4.8	0.29	0.20	100	100
26	....	26	8.0	....	0.33	....	100	
30	30	30	10.5	7.3	0.44	0.30	100	75
32	32	32	12.1	8.3	0.50	0.34	100	75
36	36	36	15.6	10.5	0.65	0.43	100	65
43¼	43¼	43¼	22.2	15.1	0.93	0.63	100	65
48	48	48	28.8	19.7	1.20	0.80	75	55
		56	.....	28.4	.....	1.18	...	50

* T. Shriver & Co., Inc.

The thickness of cake and the filtering area required for filtration of a particular slurry at a particular rate can be determined only from tests with the material to be filtered, preferably carried out in a small filter press, although Sperry [*Ind. Eng. Chem.*, **36**, 323 (1944)] has reported the specific resistance of a number of materials during filter-press filtration to provide guide lines for

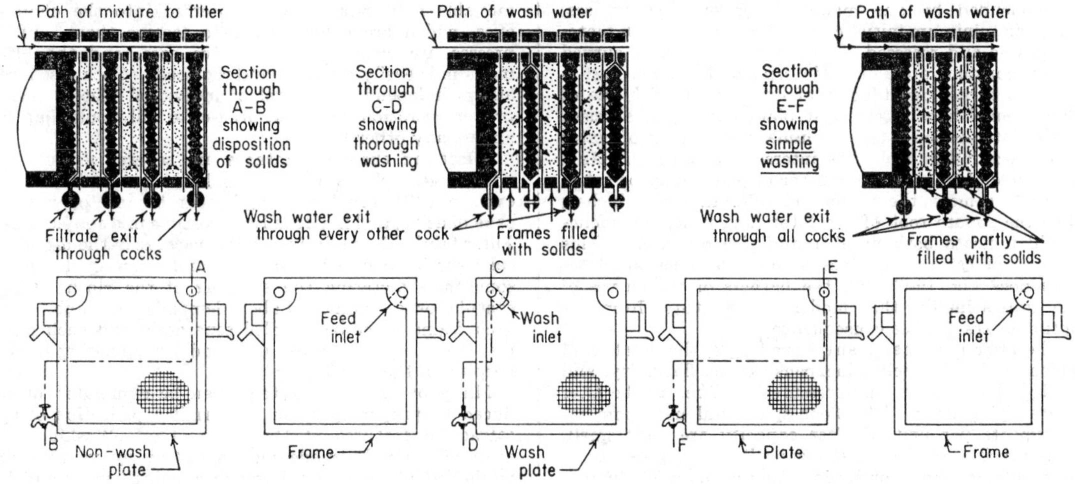

FIG. 19-92. Filling and washing flow patterns in a filter press. (*D. R. Sperry & Co.*)

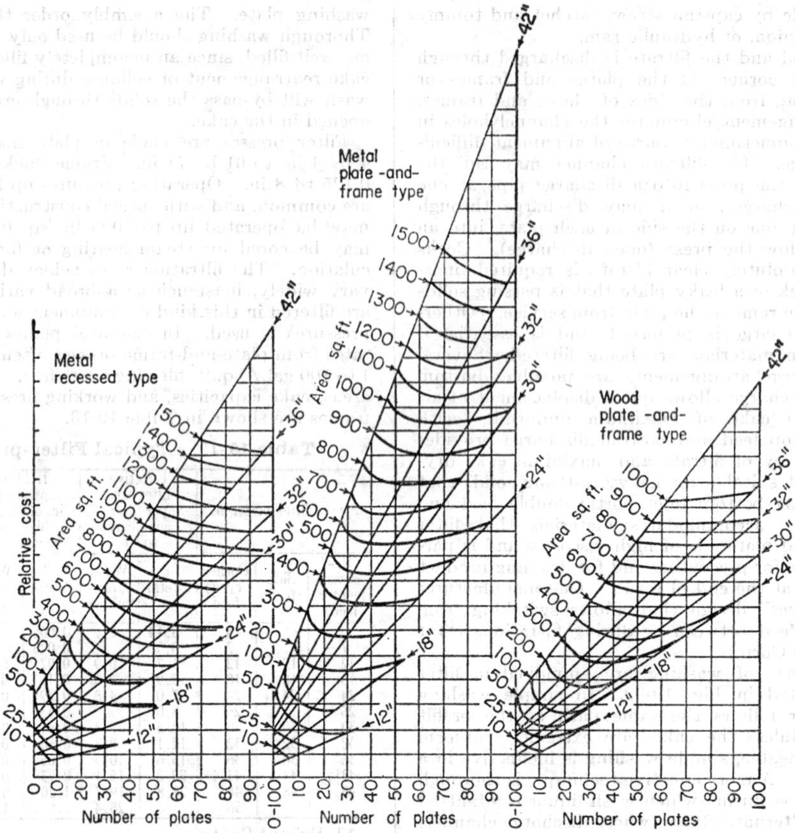

FIG. 19-93. Optimum combinations of size and number of filter-press plates. (*D. R. Sperry & Co.*)

first estimates. Even after the area is determined, the designer still must decide what combination of number and size of plates to use. This becomes a decision of convenience and economy, a press of neither extreme length nor extreme plate size being desirable. The graphs of Fig. 19-93 present the method of selection recommended by one manufacturer of filter presses, based on minimum initial cost and applied to both plate-and-frame and recessed-plate designs. A heavy curved line of constant area, or an interpolated parallel line, is followed to its lowest point of intersection with one of the diagonal lines of constant plate size. The abscissa of this intersection is the recommended number of plates of the size indicated by the intersected diagonal. As a quick rule of thumb, the number of plates may be taken to be the same as the nominal plate dimension in inches; thus the square root of the filter area in square inches would indicate both number and size of plates. This method of estimating gives a lower number of plates than does Fig. 19-93, but the flatness of the curves of the graphs implies that moderate departures from the optimum are of little consequence.

The filter press has many advantages, the greatest of which are its simplicity, inexpensiveness, flexibility, and ability to operate at high pressures as either a cake filter or clarifying filter. The floor space and headroom requirements per unit of filter capacity are very small. It is possible to reduce the capacity of a given press by removing frames or by inserting a blank-off dummy plate, and longer support bars can be purchased to increase capacity. If a press is to be used frequently at each of several different cake capacities, permanent dummy plates drilled with all the proper channels and ports and carrying drainage surfaces on both faces can be inserted in the plate line-up at the appropriate places. Whichever one is to blank off the press then has removable rubber-faced plugs inserted into the channel eyes, which are counterbored to receive them. Filter presses are cleaned with relative ease, and the filter medium is easily removed and replaced. Cock discharge allows independent control of individual plates. With proper operation, a denser, drier cake will result than for almost any other filter.

Offsetting these advantages are several serious disadvantages. Cake washing is likely to be imperfect, even in a "thorough-washing" press, because of variable cake density, and is virtually impossible in a simple press. Filter fabric life is relatively short because of the mechanical wear incidental to emptying and cleaning the press, sometimes dictating the scraping of the cloth with a spatula or a paddle. Labor demands are high, since each frame must be handled separately and each cloth inspected. Presses often drip and leak, making housekeeping in the area a problem.

Many of the disadvantages can be eliminated or reduced by proper operation to permit exploitation of the attractive features of the filter press. Washing, for example, may be made more effective by venting the wash-feed plates of a "thorough-washing" press and by discharging the wash from the top. Cloth wear can be minimized by choice of heavy, tight fabrics, by avoidance of sharp edges on plates, and by use of smooth wooden paddles to scrape the cloth. Labor expense can be reduced by the use of mechanical plate retractors and frame jacks that lift the frame above the press so that the operator can easily spatula the cake from it. With such devices it is reported that two girls empty and reassemble twenty-two 36-in. 60-plate presses in 8 hr. Leakage and dripping often result from dirty gasketing areas or sprung wooden plates, readily corrected defects.

The driest cake results from air blowing the filled filter press to purge the filtrate or wash from the cake and press channels. In some applications, steam or warm air is blown through the press to recover vapors from the cake and partially dry it. If the temperature of the purge gas is too high, however, cloth deterioration will be hastened; moreover, caution must be observed in air blowing a press containing a flammable filtrate.

A high-spot estimate of the uninstalled cost of plate-and-frame filter presses can be obtained from the nomograph of Fig. 19-94. Fiberglas-reinforced polyester

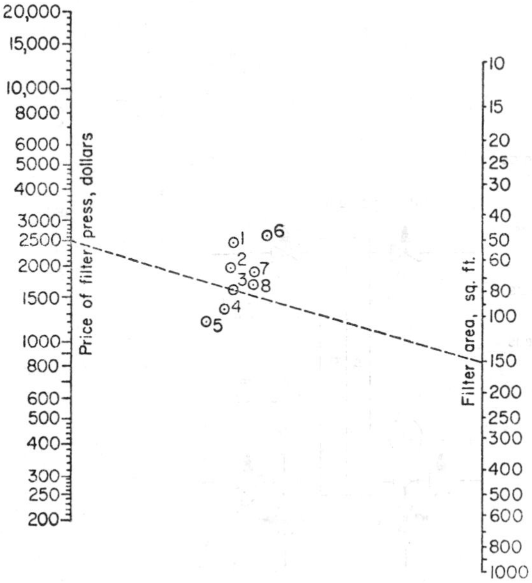

Fig. 19-94. Uninstalled cost of plate-and-frame filter presses. 1. Rubber-covered (⅛-in.) iron. 2. Polyvinyl-chloride-coated iron. 3. Aluminum. 4. Iron. 5. Wood. 6. Type CF8, stainless steel. 7. Bronze. 8. Ni-Resist 2. (*T. Shriver & Co., Inc.*)

plates cost about one-third as much as stainless steel, and epoxy-resin coating of wood plates and frames adds about 30 per cent to their cost.

A **recessed-plate filter press** resembles a plate-and-frame press in appearance but consists only of plates. Both faces of each plate are hollowed to form a chamber for cake accumulation between each two plates. The feed enters through a center orifice and the filtrate is discharged at one corner. A filter fabric with a central hole covers the plate and is connected through the feed port to the fabric on the opposite face of the plate by clips or by a fabric tube to which both cloths are sewed.

Recessed-plate presses cost about 15 per cent less than equivalent plate-and-frame models, but the wear and tear on filter media is much greater and therefore increases the operating cost. The entrance to a recessed plate is less likely to become clogged by a thick feed than is the port to a frame, and the reduced number of joints makes tight closure more certain. On the other hand, the cake is not uniform in thickness and the portion adjacent to the feed orifice usually remains mushy. Thorough washing therefore is not possible. Otherwise, recessed-plate and plate-and-frame presses behave generally alike.

The **Carver hydraulic filter press** (Fred S. Carver, Inc.) combines the principles of a filter and a hydraulic press. Slurry to be filtered is pumped into the press through a feed manifold and filtered at pressures up to several hundred pounds per square inch. After the filter cakes have formed, they are compressed hydraulically to pressures as high as 6000 lb./sq. in., the result being a very dry cake. At the end of the cycle, the cake is automatically ejected and dropped into a short conveyor that carries it from beneath the press. Hydraulic filter presses are made with chambers up to 32 in. in diameter. A 32-in. 12-chamber press will process on the order of a ton of cake per cycle. The cycle can be fully automated.

The **Eimco-Burwell filter** is an adaptation of the plate-and-frame press that allows automatic cycle control and reduces outage time to a matter of minutes. It consists of a number of circular frames supported on arms that rotate them into or out of the press (Fig. 19-95).

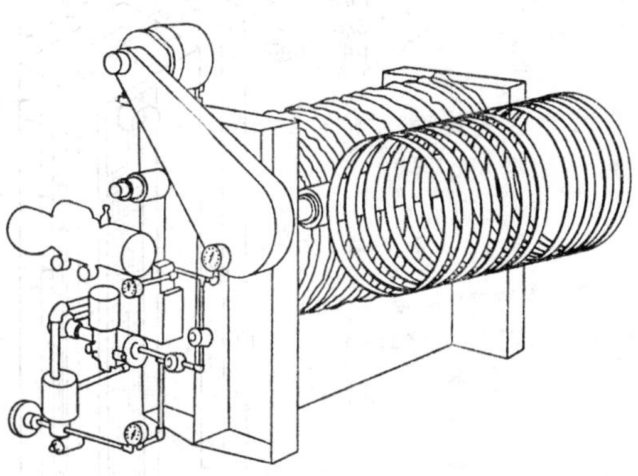

Fig. 19-95. Eimco-Burwell filter. (*The Eimco Corp.*)

Between each two frames in the press is a pair of movable plates fitted together to form in essence a large-diameter short-stroke piston and cylinder (Fig. 19-96). The plate surface is a drainage screen, over which a filter fabric is held by a retaining hoop. The press is closed by admitting air to the plate assemblies, which thereby expand, the male and female members moving away from one another and closing against their respective frames. At the end of the cycle, the press is opened by the release of the pressure inside the plate assembly and by the application of a slight vacuum (generated by an aspirator in the air line) that causes the plates to retract. The frames then can be swung out of the press for emptying.

Eimco-Burwell presses are made with frame diameters of 26 and 32 in. and with frame thicknesses of 1 to 3 in., in 0.5-in. increments. Standard presses have 7, 10, 14, 20, or 30 frames. The filtering area and cake capacity for a 26-in. press of thirty 2-in. frames are 221 sq. ft. and 18.4 cu. ft., respectively; corresponding values for a 32-in. press are 335 sq. ft. and 27.9 cu. ft. They are said to be adaptable to any filtration that can be carried out in a conventional plate-and-frame press at moderate pressures. Their forte, however, obviously is fairly rapidly filtering material for which the outage-time saving becomes highly significant.

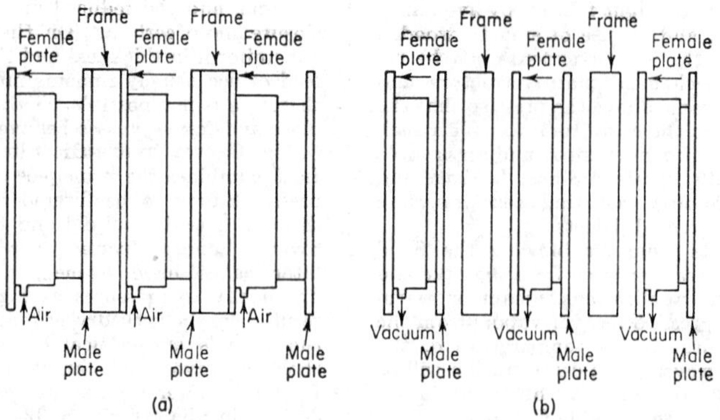

FIG. 19-96. Eimco-Burwell plates and frames. (*a*) Plate and frame positions after air pressure is applied to actuate the plate cylinder and piston assembly for closing the press. Air pressure holds the plates snugly against frames to provide a positive seal. (*b*) Plate and frame positions after air pressure is released, at end of filtration cycle. An evactor creates vacuum in air line, bringing plates to their retracted position and leaving filled frames clear for rotation.

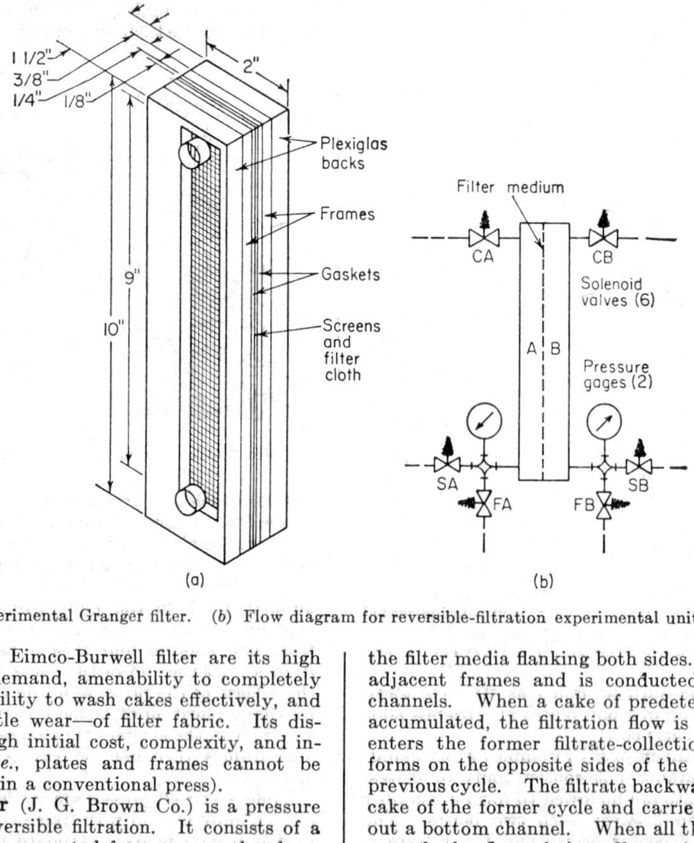

FIG. 19-97. (*a*) Experimental Granger filter. (*b*) Flow diagram for reversible-filtration experimental unit. (*J. G. Brown Co.*)

Advantages of the Eimco-Burwell filter are its high capacity, low labor demand, amenability to completely automatic control, ability to wash cakes effectively, and protection—hence little wear—of filter fabric. Its disadvantages are its high initial cost, complexity, and inflexibility of size (*i.e.*, plates and frames cannot be removed or added as in a conventional press).

The **Granger filter** (J. G. Brown Co.) is a pressure filter designed for reversible filtration. It consists of a row of parallel frames separated from one another by a panel of filter medium, usually a fairly tight fabric, and held between metal headers by stainless-steel strapping. The frames are made of a transparent plastic and are designed for a maximum pressure of 150 lb./sq. in. at 74°F. (their strength falls off at higher temperatures). The construction is illustrated by the two-chamber experimental model shown in Fig. 19-97*a*.

The operation of the Granger filter is as follows: Prefilt is admitted to alternate frames, and filtration occurs on the filter media flanking both sides. The filtrate fills the adjacent frames and is conducted from them by top channels. When a cake of predetermined thickness has accumulated, the filtration flow is reversed: prefilt now enters the former filtrate-collection frames, and cake forms on the opposite sides of the filter media from the previous cycle. The filtrate backwashes and removes the cake of the former cycle and carries the resulting sludge out a bottom channel. When all the sludge has been removed, the flow of clear filtrate is diverted to the top filtrate channel until the cake has again built up. This reversible operation permits filtration to very thin cakes (⅛ in. the recommended maximum, and $\frac{1}{16}$ in. feasible) and, therefore, at high rates. With this advantage of the low-resistance portion of a batch cycle, the average rate of filtration may be increased, even after allowance is made for the outage time and wasted filtrate due to the backwash periods. This is illustrated by Fig. 19-98, in which the data are for conventional and reversible

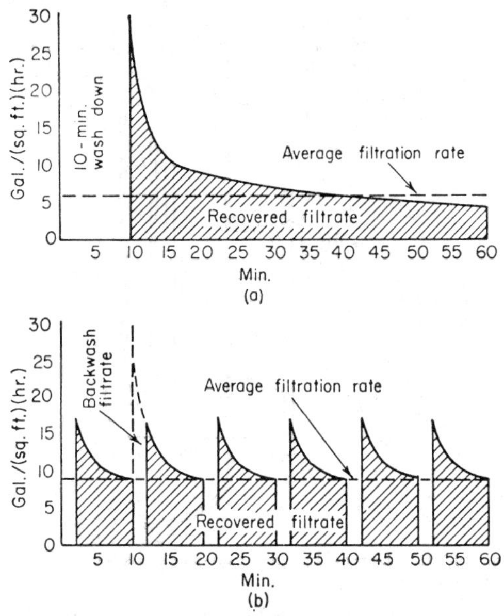

FIG. 19-98. Rates of normal and reversible filtration. (*a*) Direct standard vertical leaf filtration. One 60-min. cycle. (*b*) Reversible filtration. Six 10-min. half cycles. [*Chem. Eng. Progress*, **52**, 240 (1958) *with permission*.]

filtration of an 0.8 per cent Asbestine slurry at 30 lb./sq. in.

The advantages of the Granger filter are its simple and inexpensive construction; its low operating cost because of relatively high filtration rates, low filter-aid demand, and low labor charge; its small space requirements; its amenability to automatic control; and the visibility of its internals. Its disadvantages are its limitation to cases where the cake is to be discarded or where a slurry discharge is allowable; the possibility of contamination of filtrate by virtue of its passing through the same path taken by prefilt, and the difficulty of determining the optimum cutoff point for the backwash cycle.

The Granger filter is made with a single frame size (24 by 6.25 by 0.76 in.), providing a filtering area of 0.67 sq. ft. per face. Units have been assembled containing up to 60 chambers. The filter cost is about $10 per chamber. Filtration rates up to 6 gal./(sq. ft.)(min.) can be expected.

The **Readco short-cycle filter** (Capitol Products Corp.) also takes advantage of the thin-cake low-resistance period at the start of a conventional cake filtration. The heart of the filter is a single plate-and-frame assembly, two of which, operating separately, comprise the machine. The frame filters only on the face adjacent to the plate. It closes onto a continuous-belt filter fabric that covers the plate, being held in position by a compressed-air piston. A rubber gasket on the joint surface permits pressures up to 150 lb./sq. in. without leakage.

The filtration cycle is illustrated schematically in Fig. 19-99. After filtration the press is opened by the inward retraction of the frames. The cake adheres to the filter media, which are then rotated such that they carry the cake downward and over small rolls that discharge it from the media. This moves a cleaned section of the medium into position over the plates, and the frames are closed again. The length of the entire cycle may be less than 2 min., and the outage time is almost negligible. The Readco filter thus achieves, through a series of short cycles, a high average rate of filtration somewhat as illustrated for the Granger filter in Fig. 19-98.

The advantages of the Readco short-cycle filter are its high productivity, its amenability to automatic control, its low labor demand, its small requirement of floor space, and its ability to filter and wash solids that form cakes of high specific resistance. The disadvantages are the high cost of the filter, its small filtering area, and its mechanical complexity.

The Readco dry-discharge filter is made in only one size, with two plates and frames and a total filtering area of 1.6 sq. ft. It is claimed to produce filtered product at a rate equivalent to that produced in a conventional filter press with thirty times the area. The cost of a filter in stainless steel is about $6000, including valving and a control panel.

The Pressure Leaf Filter. The pressure leaf filter consists of an assembly of flat filtering elements (leaves) supported vertically in a pressure shell. The leaves are circular, arc-sided, or rectangular, and they have filtering surfaces on both faces. The shell is a cylindrical tank and its axis may be horizontal or vertical, the filter being described correspondingly as horizontal or vertical. In vertical filters the leaves may be replaced by cylindrical tubular elements.

A filter leaf consists of a heavy screen or grooved plate over which a filter medium of woven fabric or fine wire cloth may be fitted. Textile fabrics are more com-

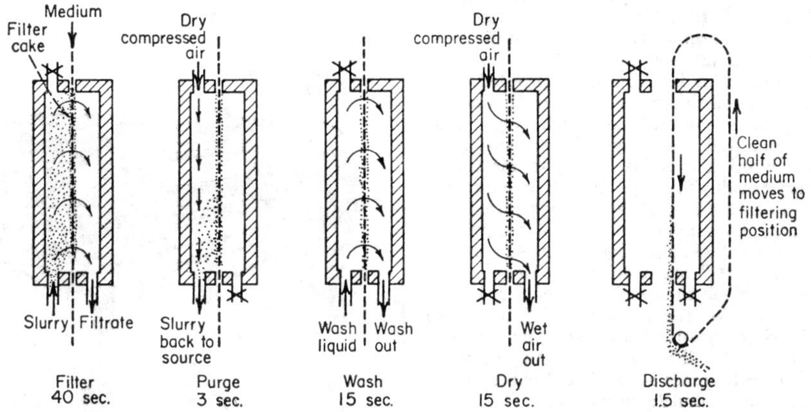

FIG. 19-99. Schematic representation of filtration cycle in a Readco short-cycle filter. Times shown are representative of typical operation. (*Capitol Products Corp.*)

monly used for chemical service and are usually applied as bags that may be sewn, zippered, stapled, or snapped. Wire screen cloth is frequently used for diatomite filtrations, particularly if a precoat is applied. It may be attached by welding, riveting, bolting, or calking, or by the clamped engagement of two 180-deg. bends in the wire cloth under tension, as in Multi-Metal's Rim-Lok leaf. Leaves may also be of all-plastic construction. The filter medium, regardless of material, should be as taut as possible to minimize sagging when it is loaded with a cake; excessive sag can cause cake cracking or dropping. Leaves may be supported at top, bottom, or center and may discharge from any of these locations. Figure 19-100 shows the elevation section of a precoated bottom-support wire leaf.

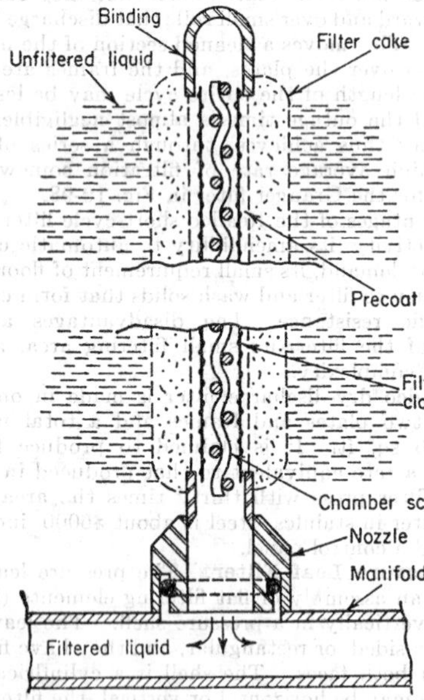

FIG. 19-100. Section of precoated wire filter leaf. (*Multi-Metal Wire and Cloth Co.*)

Pressure leaf filters are operated batchwise. The shell is locked and the prefilt slurry is admitted from a pressure source (pump or monte-jus). The slurry enters in such a way as to minimize settling of the suspended solids. The shell is filled and filtration occurs on the leaf surfaces, the filtrate discharging through an individual delivery line or into an internal manifold, as the filter design dictates. Filtration is allowed to proceed only until a cake of the desired thickness has formed, since to overfill will cause cake consolidation with consequent difficulty in washing and discharge. The decision of when to end the filtering cycle is largely a matter of experience, guided roughly by the rate in a constant-pressure filter or pressure drop in a constant-rate filter. This judgment may be supplanted by the use of the Durco-Enzinger cake-thickness detector, shown in Fig. 19-101, which "feels" the thickness of cake on a representative leaf. When the sensing element *B* begins to be surrounded by cake, the pressure on *B* begins to fall below the filtering pressure because of the gradient through the cake. The differential set up between elements *A* and *B* thus becomes a signal that can activate an alarm or an automatic shutdown control.

If the cake is to be washed, the slurry heel can be blown from the filter and wash liquor can be introduced to refill the shell. If the cake tends to crack during air blowing, it may be necessary to displace the slurry heel with wash gradually so as never to allow the cake to dry. Upon the completion of filtration and washing, the cake is discharged by one of the methods described below.

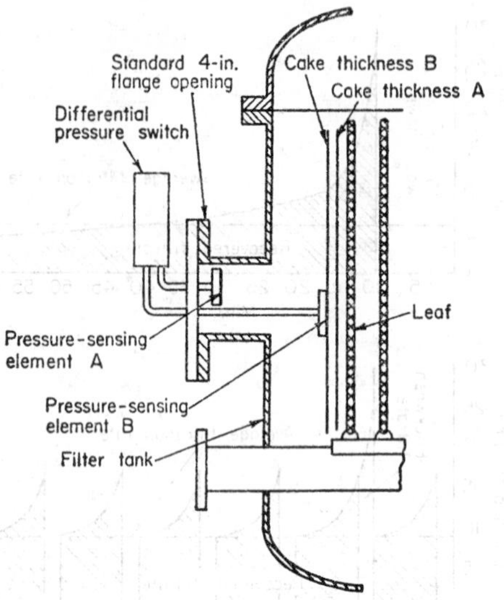

FIG. 19-101. Durco-Enzinger cake-thickness detector. (*The Duriron Co.*)

In horizontal pressure leaf filters longitudinal rectangular leaves may run parallel to the axis and in the plane of chords of the shell; or transverse leaves may run parallel to the head of the shell. In the former case, the leaves may be of several sizes, diminishing in height as their distance from the shell diameter increases; in the latter, they are all of the same size. In either case the leaves may be supported from the filter head, from an independent rack, or individually from the shell or from a filtrate manifold. Horizontal filters are particularly suited to dry-cake discharge.

An example of the longitudinal-leaf design is the **Kelly filter** (Dorr-Oliver, Inc.), from which the leaf assembly can be withdrawn by retraction of the head along rails (Fig. 19-102). A Kelly filter can be operated at pressures up to 250 lb./sq. in., whereas most pressure leaf filters are designed for a limit of about 60 lb./sq. in. It is also easily jacketed or insulated.

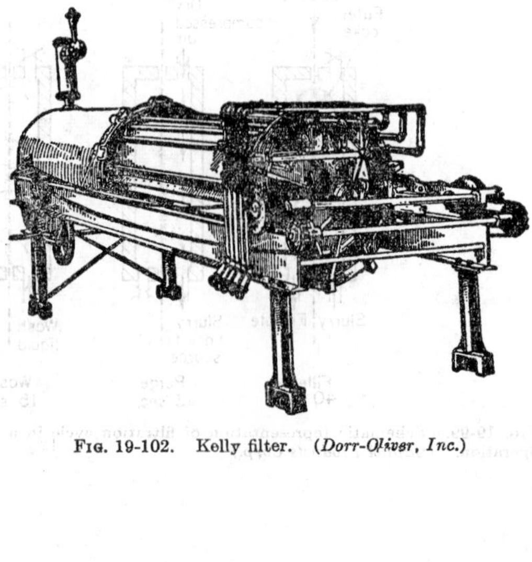

FIG. 19-102. Kelly filter. (*Dorr-Oliver, Inc.*)

The transverse-leaf filter is illustrated by several different designs. The **Sweetland filter** (Dorr-Oliver, Inc.) has circular leaves in a cast-iron shell that is split along its horizontal center line such that the counterweighted lower leaf can swing downward to open the press (Fig. 19-103). The shell is lined with stainless

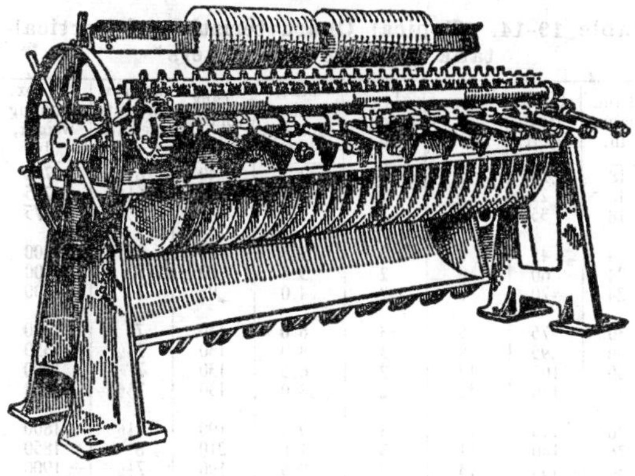

Fig. 19-103. Sweetland filter (open). (*Dorr-Oliver, Inc.*)

steel or other corrosion-resistant material if appropriate. The leaves are suspended from the top of the shell and are connected individually to an exterior header by sight glasses and cocks that allow inspection of the discharge from each leaf and the removal from service of any faulty leaf. The shell is opened for dry-cake discharge, assisted by backblowing air. Wet-cake discharge can be achieved without opening the filter. A sluicing nozzle that can be oscillated through 120 deg. and simultaneously moved longitudinally is located above each leaf and effects the cake discharge with a high-velocity water stream.

Some horizontal pressure leaf filters have circular leaves mounted on an axial discharge manifold designed to rotate them during filtration. The **Vallez filter** (Goslin-Birmingham Manufacturing Co.) is an example (Fig. 19-104). The leaves rotate at about 1 r.p.m. and thereby offer greater assurance of a filter cake of uniform thickness and density. The shell, which is split longitudinally, need not be opened even for dry-cake discharge if the cake discharges cleanly with blowback, for a discharge scroll in the bottom of the shell running the length of the filter will convey dry cake or thick reslurry outward. Wet discharge is effected by the use of stationary sluicing jets that play against the rotating leaves. In other designs the leaves are stationary during filtration but can be rotated at about 3 r.p.m. during sluicing discharge; examples are Hercules Filter Corp.'s Roto-jet and United States Filter Co.'s Auto-jet filters.

Simple designs of horizontal filters used particularly widely for diatomite filtration involve a retractable rack of circular, rectangular, or arc-side leaves communicating with a top or bottom filtrate manifold. The design is illustrated by the Niagara H style design, portrayed open in Fig. 19-105. A scavenger leaf is shown below

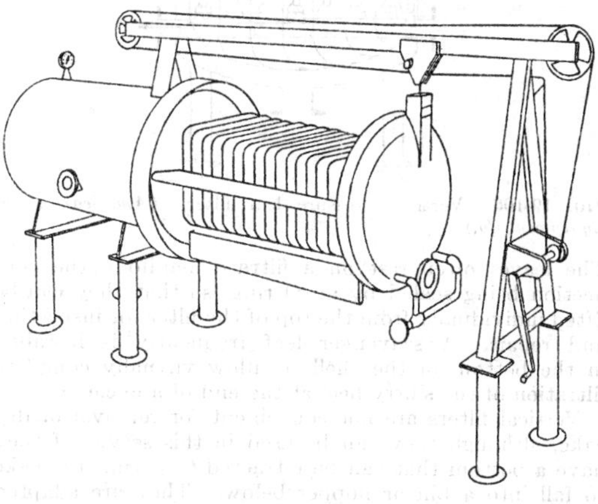

Fig. 19-105. Horizontal-tank pressure leaf filter. (*Ametek, Inc.*)

the leaf pack. This type of filter, like the Kelly, is suitable primarily for dry-cake removal, the cake being discharged into a hopper, chute, or car after the filter-leaf assembly has been drawn out. A follower plate at the end of the leaf pack scrapes out any cake that drops before the leaves are withdrawn.

Vertical pressure leaf filters have vertical, parallel, rectangular leaves mounted in an upright cylindrical

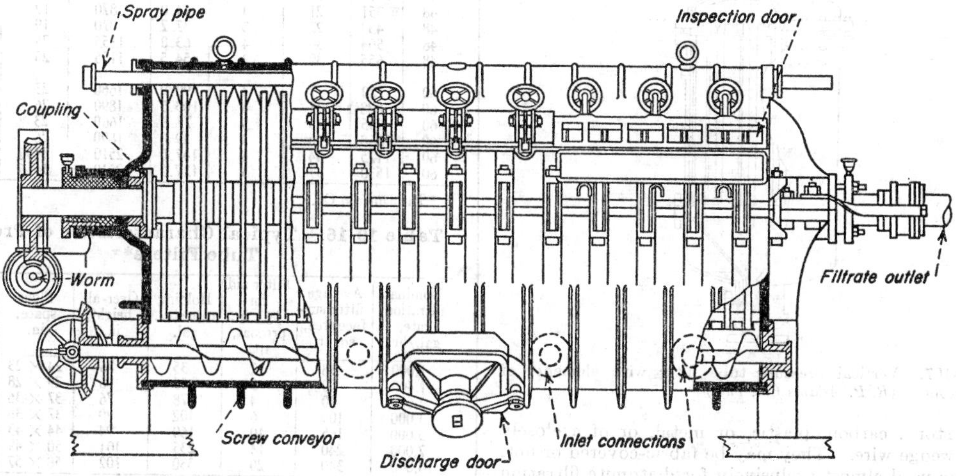

Fig. 19-104. Vallez filter (elevation and section). (*Goslin-Birmingham Mfg. Co.*)

pressure tank (Fig. 19-106). The leaves usually are of such different widths as to allow them to conform to the curvature of the tank and to fill it without waste space.

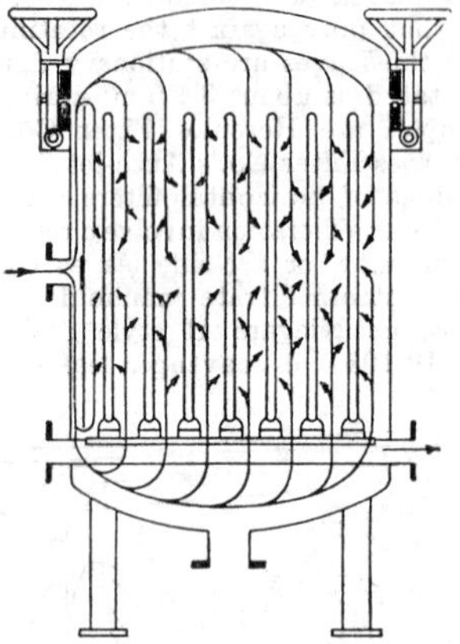

Fig. 19-106. Vertical pressure leaf filter. (*American Plant Equipment Co.*)

The leaves often rest on a filtrate manifold, the connection being sealed by an O ring, so that they can be lifted individually from the top of the filter for inspection and repair. A scavenger leaf frequently is installed in the bottom of the shell to allow virtually complete filtration of the slurry heel at the end of a cycle.

Vertical filters are not convenient for removal of dry cake, although they can be used in this service if they have a bottom that can be retracted to permit the cake to fall into a bin or hopper below. They are adapted rather to wet-solids discharge, a process that may be assisted by leaf vibration, air or steam sparging of a filter full of water, sluicing from fixed, oscillating, or traveling nozzles, and blowback. They are made by many companies, and they enjoy their widest use for diatomite precoat filtration.

Instead of flat leaves, cylindrical tubes may be used as the filtering elements in vertical pressure filters, the tubes being supported from a filtrate manifold (Fig. 19-107). The tubes may be made of wire cloth, of

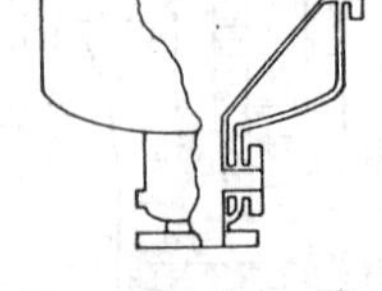

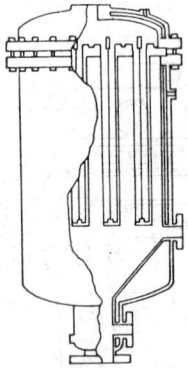

Fig. 19-107. Vertical pressure tube filter with elements of porous stone. (*R. P. Adams Co., Inc.*)

porous stone, carbon, plastic, or metal, or of a closely wound wedge wire. They may be fabric-covered or not. They are used almost exclusively for diatomite filtration and they are nearly always discharged wet by backwashing, sometimes assisted by agitation of water in the filter and by mechanical disturbance of the elements or of the deposited cake.

The advantages of pressure leaf filters are their considerable flexibility (up to the permissible maximum, cakes of various thickness can be formed successfully), their low labor charges, particularly when the cake may

Table 19-14. Typical Characteristics of Vertical-tank Pressure Leaf Filters*

Tank diam., in.	Filter area, sq. ft.	No. of leaves	Leaf spacing, in.	Max. cake capacity, cu. ft.	Tank volume, gal.	Approx. height over-all, ft.	Approx. shipping weight, lb.
18	20	5	3	1.5	40	6	700
18	25	5	3	2.0	45	6½	725
18	35	7	2	2.0	45	6½	775
24	45	7	3	3.5	80	7	1000
24	60	8	2	3.5	80	7	1100
24	70	8	2	4.0	95	7	1200
30	75	9	3	6.0	130	7	1300
30	95	9	3	8.0	130	7½	1350
30	105	12	2	6.5	130	7	1500
30	130	12	2	8.0	130	7½	1700
36	115	11	3	9.5	190	7½	1800
36	140	11	3	11.0	210	8	1850
36	155	14	2	9.5	190	7½	1900
36	190	14	2	12.0	210	8	2050
42	230	13	3	19.0	330	9	2100
42	270	17	2	17.0	300	8½	2800
42	315	17	2	20.0	330	9	3000
48	370	16	3	31.0	500	9½	3400
48	450	21	2	28.0	440	9	3600
48	510	21	2	32.0	500	9½	3800

* T. Shriver & Co., Inc.

Table 19-15. Typical Characteristics of Horizontal-tank Pressure Leaf Filters*

Tank diam., in.	Net filter area, sq. ft.	No. of leaves	Leaf spacing, in.	Cake space, cu. ft.	Tank volume, U.S. gal., gross	Approx. over-all length, ft.	Approx. shipping weight, lb.
36	52	6	4	6.5	210	9	1,900
36	60	7	3	5.0	210	9	1,950
36	86	10	4	10.8	280	12	2,100
36	103	12	3	8.6	280	12	2,200
36	129	15	4	16.2	370	15	2,350
36	163	19	3	13.6	370	15	2,500
36	155	18	4	19.4	435	17½	2,500
36	215	25	3	17.9	435	17½	2,800
48	252	15	4	31.5	685	15	4,000
48	319	19	3	26.6	685	15	4,150
48	351	21	4	44.0	870	19	4,500
48	453	27	3	37.7	870	19	4,750
48	504	30	4	63.0	1155	25	5,850
48	655	39	3	54.5	1155	25	6,200
60	720	27	4	90.0	1660	23	8,400
60	828	31	4	103.5	1890	26	9,000
60	935	35	3	77.8	1660	23	8,750
60	1068	40	3	89.0	1890	26	9,400
60	1175	44	4	147.0	2510	34½	11,000
60	1530	57	3	127.5	2510	34½	11,600

* The Duriron Co.

Table 19-16. Typical Characteristics of Pressure Tube Filters*

Nominal filtration rate, gal./hr.	Average filter surface area, sq. ft.	Filter aid for 1/32 in. precoat, qt.	Holding capacity, gal.	Over-all height, in.	Floor space, in.	Approx. shipping weight, lb.
1,000	38	2	35	76	24 × 23¾	575
1,400	50	3	55	76	29 × 28	775
2,000	70	4	78	76	37 × 36	950
3,000	105	6	102	90	37 × 36	1175
5,000	165	10	160	94	44 × 43	1400
7,000	240	14	235	101	50 × 49	1800
10,000	340	20	330	102	58 × 57	2400

* Olson Filtration Engineers, Inc.

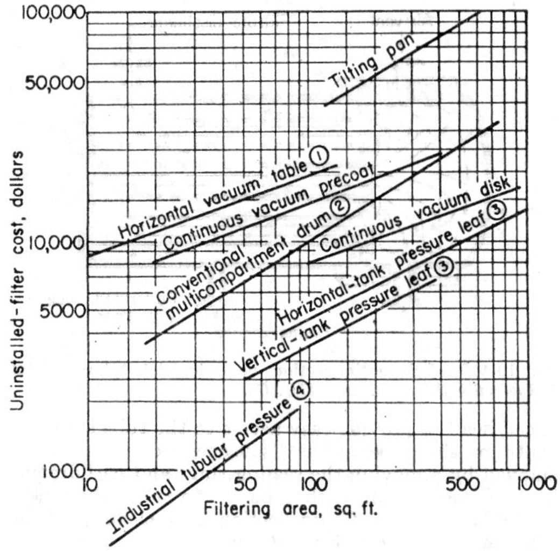

FIG. 19-108. Costs of filters, uninstalled. [*Adapted from Chalmers, Elledge, and Porter, Chem. Eng.*, **63** (6), 200 (1955).] All figures are for carbon-steel construction unless otherwise indicated. 1. Open type. Wash apparatus and variable-speed drive included. Double cost for stainless or rubber-covered construction. 2. Open type. Normal submergence (approximately 40 per cent). Swing-type agitator; drum paneled or wire-wound. Wash apparatus and variable-speed drum drive included. Double for stainless-steel or rubber-covered construction. 3. Carbon-steel tank, 304 stainless leaves. Increased by 50 per cent for all-stainless construction. Figures are for simplest construction with no accessories such as sluice nozzles, etc. 4. Double for 316 stainless, increase by 50 to 60 per cent for rubber covering.

be sluiced off or the dry cake discharges cleanly by blowback, the basic simplicity of many of the designs, and their adaptability to quite effective displacement washing. Their disadvantages are the requirement of exceptionally intelligent and watchful supervision to avoid cake consolidation or dropping, their inability to form as dry a cake as a filter press, their tendency to classify vertically during filtration and to form misshapen nonuniform cakes unless the leaves rotate, and the restriction of most models to 60 lb./sq. in.

Pressure leaf filters are used to separate much the same kinds of slurries as are filter presses and are used much more extensively than filter presses for diatomite filtrations. They should be seriously considered whenever uniformity of production permits long-time operation under essentially constant filtration conditions, when thorough washing with a minimum of liquor is desired, or when vapors or fumes make closed construction desirable. Under such conditions, if the filter medium does not require frequent changing, they may show a considerable advantage in cycle and labor economy over a filter press, which has a lower initial cost, and advantages of economy and flexibility over continuous vacuum filters, which have a higher first cost.

Pressure leaf filters are available with filtering areas of 1 sq. ft. (laboratory size) up to about 600 sq. ft. for vertical filters and 1600 sq. ft. for horizontal ones. Leaf spacings range from 2 to 6 in. but are seldom less than 3 in., since 0.5 to 1 in. should be left open between cake surfaces. When tubes instead of leaves are used, the maximum area is somewhat less (about 300 sq. ft.). Tables 19-14, 19-15, and 19-16 list typical data for pressure leaf and tube filters. Approximate uninstalled costs of pressure leaf filters are indicated in Fig. 19-108.

The Horizontal Plate Filter. The horizontal multiple-plate pressure filter consists of a number of horizontal circular drainage plates and guides placed one above another in a coaxial cylindrical shell and connected in parallel (Fig. 19-109). This filter somewhat resembles a filter press stood on end with only one face of each plate used for drainage. In certain special designs, both plate surfaces are filtering areas, but usually only the top face is used. The stack of plates is completely enclosed within the pressuretight shell and may be lifted out as a unit for cleaning or sterilization. Pressures as high as 300 lb./sq. in. can be used with some designs. A filter medium (paper or cloth, with or without a diatomaceous-earth precoat) is placed on each plate, much as in a laboratory Büchner funnel. Slurry under pressure is conducted to the plates through a central or annular feed manifold and filtration is continued until the cake capacity of the filter is reached or until the rate becomes prohibitively slow because of cake resistance. Some models have a scavenger plate at the bottom, as in Fig. 19-109, but in any event there is little slurry hold-up when filtration is stopped; what there is can

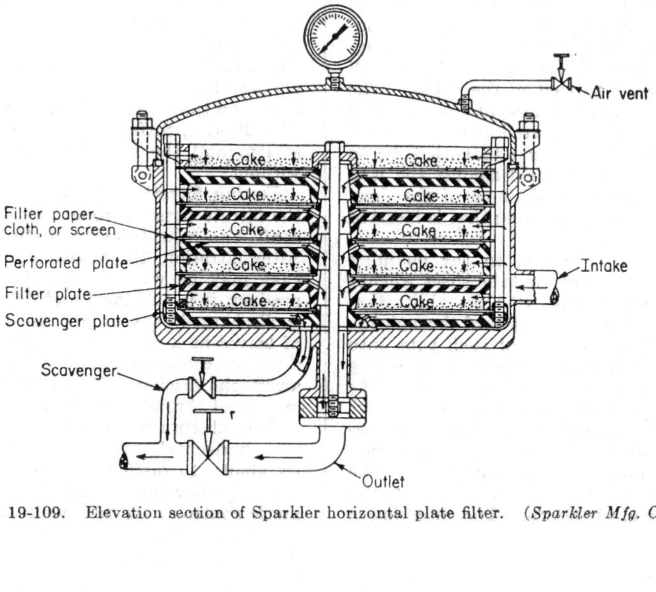

FIG. 19-109. Elevation section of Sparkler horizontal plate filter. (*Sparkler Mfg. Co.*)

be carried into the filter by the wash liquor or by an air blow. Washing and air blowing proceed as in a pressure leaf filter, except that no care is required to maintain air pressure in the shell. The cake is removed by removal of the plate stack from the tank.

The advantages of the horizontal pressure filter are its compactness, its cleanliness, its easy amenability to sterile cleaning, and the horizontal plate position that permits uniform cake deposit, satisfactory cake formation without achieving a cake of preordained thickness, and effective washing. Disadvantages are the relatively small size of the filters, the relatively large headroom and floor space required, and the labor demands for cleaning and filter medium removal (although not necessarily higher than for filter presses).

In view of these advantages and limitations, the horizontal plate filter makes its greatest contribution in applications where relatively small quantities of cake or intermittent flow rates are involved (*e.g.*, as a scavenger filter) and where cleanliness or sterile conditions are essential (*e.g.*, as in the food and pharmaceutical industries). It has been used for lard filtration and edible-oil recovery, and for varnish and petroleum-oil filtration. In its smaller sizes it is particularly valuable in the pilot plant and the small chemical works where demands are likely to vary from day to day and where the cleanliness of the filters makes them more desirable than a filter press.

Horizontal plate filters are made with plate sizes in the range 8 to 33 in. There may be as many as 24 plates in one filter, to give a filtering area of about 150 sq. ft. Any machinable metal may be used as a material of construction. An estimate of their cost may be made from Fig. 19-94. When complete tank enclosure of the filter is not necessary a somewhat less expensive model is available in sizes up to 400 sq. ft.; it consists of a stack of plates that form closure seals on gasket surfaces, as in a filter press, and that are connected by internal feed and filtrate lines.

The Model HR Sparkler filter is a horizontal pressure filter the plates of which, upon completion of filtration, can be rotated 90 deg. to allow cake discharge without opening the filter. The cake removal can be made by tapping an external agitator bar or by use of mechanical vibration. The dropped cake is conveyed out of the shell by a longitudinal conveyor scroll in the bottom of the shell.

The Industrial Tubular Filter. This product of the Industrial Filter and Pump Manufacturing Co. consists of one or more (up to 36) horizontal tubes supported by a transverse tube sheet in a cylindrical shell the axis of which is parallel to that of the tubes. The end of the tubes farthest from the head of the shell and from the header is closed by an inverted dome. A sheet of filter paper is rolled and inserted into each tube to form a filter-medium liner that is held against the wall of the tube because of the inverted dome of the dead end and because of a tapered sealing ring that is inserted at the entry end.

Slurry under pressure is admitted to the chamber between the head of the shell and the tube sheet whence it enters and fills the tubes (Fig. 19-110). Filtration occurs as the filtrate passes radially outward through the paper liner and the perforated walls of each tube into the shell and on out the filtrate discharge line, depositing cake on the liner. The filtration cycle is ended when the tubes have filled with cake or when the media have become so plugged as to render the filtration rate unacceptably low (at constant pressure) or the filtration pressure unacceptably high (at constant rate). The cake can be washed (if it has not been allowed to fill the tubes completely) and air-blown. The filter has a

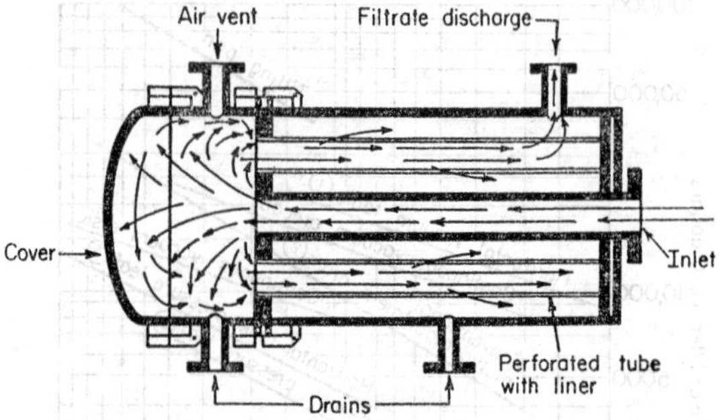

FIG. 19-110. Schematic section of industrial tubular filter. (*Industrial Filter and Pump Mfg. Co.*)

hinged head to provide easy access to the tube sheet and mouth of the tubes; thus "sausages" of cake can be removed by removing the sealing rings and withdrawing the filter paper from each tube. The tubes themselves are easily removed for inspection and cleaning, being sealed into the header by an O ring.

The advantages of the tubular filter are that it uses an easily replaced and inexpensive disposable filter medium, its filtration cycle can be interrupted and the shell can be emptied of prefilt at any time without loss of the cake, the cake is readily recoverable in dry form, and the inside of the filter is conveniently accessible. Disadvantages are its relatively small size, the necessity and attendant labor requirements of emptying by hand and replacing the filter media, the relatively small cake space, and the tendency for heavy solids to settle out in the header chamber and in the mouths of the tubes. Its applications are as a scavenger filter to remove fines not removed in a prior filtration stage with a different kind of equipment, or to handle the runoff from other filters, or in semiworks and small-plant operations in which its size, versatility, and cleanliness recommend it.

Industrial tubular filters are made with filtering areas ranging from 2.4 to 86.4 sq. ft. The cost of the equipment is shown in Fig. 19-108.

The Rodney Hunt Pressure Filter. The Rodney Hunt pressure filter (known in Europe as the Funda filter and made in the United States by the Rodney Hunt Machine Co.) is a horizontal plate filter, but the plate construction and assembly are suggestive of a horizontal leaf filter with filtration occurring only on the top surface of each leaf (Fig. 19-111). It consists of a pressure vessel enclosing a number of circular filter elements that are attached to and communicate with an axial drainage shaft and that are separated from one another by spacers. The filtering surface may be a woven textile or a wire screen, and the filter may operate with a precoat or without.

During filtration the vessel is filled with prefilt and the filtrate passes through the plates and out the hollow shaft, the cake forming on the top face of the plates. After filtration, the vessel is drained of prefilt and the cake may be washed, if desirable. If the cake is the product, it is air-blown and dried by hot air. The cake is discharged, wet or dry, by rotation of the assembly of leaves at a sufficiently high speed to sling away the solids by centrifugal action. If the cake may be flushed away, the discharge is assisted by a backwash of water or solvent through the filtrate channels and the plates.

The advantages of the Rodney Hunt filter are those of a horizontal plate filter, and the additional ones of its ability to discharge cake without being opened and hence its low labor demands and amenability to automatic control. Its disadvantages are primarily its com-

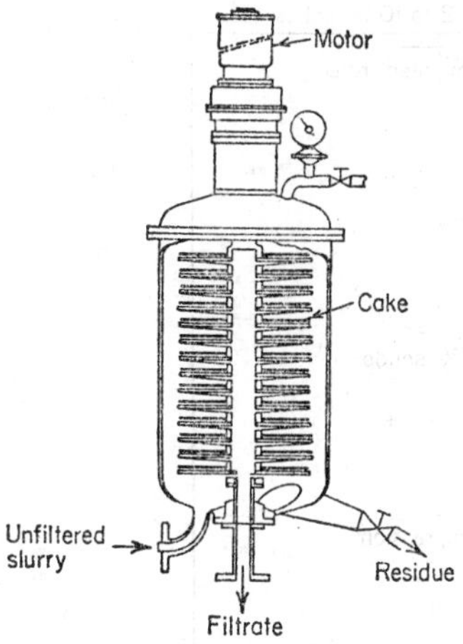

FIG. 19-111. Rodney Hunt pressure filter. (*Rodney Hunt Machine Co.*)

plexity and maintenance (stuffing boxes, high-speed drive) and its cost. It is made in sizes that cover the area range 2 to 250 sq. ft.

The Burt Filter. The Burt filter is a rotating batch pressure filter that looks something like a cement kiln (Fig. 19-112). It has a hollow trunnion at the feed end,

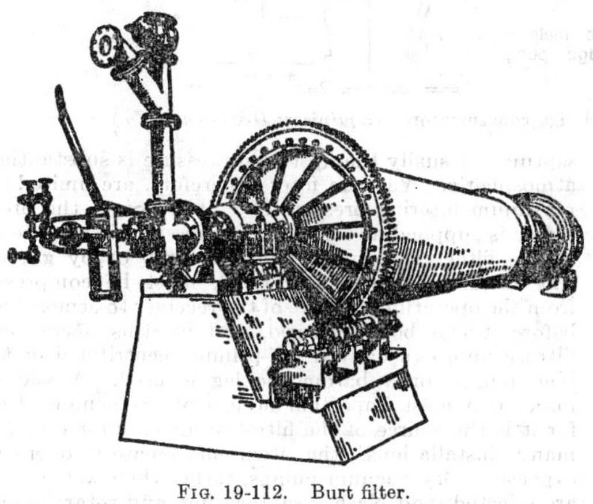

FIG. 19-112. Burt filter.

and a tire and rollers toward the other end. It is revolved by a pinion drive, and its speed is varied according to the nature of the material being filtered. The cylinder is lined on its inner periphery with drainage panels covered by filter cloth. Each panel has one or more outlet nipples passing through the cylinder shell, and external stationary launders receive the filtrate dropping from each circle of nipples. The rear end is closed by a cast-iron door equipped with a quick-opening outlet for discharge.

The material to be filtered is fed through the hollow trunnion at the head end, as the filter revolves. When the required charge has been introduced, the feed inlet is closed, air is admitted under pressure, and this pressure is maintained in order to force filtrate through the filter while forming and holding the cake in place. During rotation the filter cake forms while the filter medium is submerged by the feed. For discharge, the air pressure is cut off, water is admitted, the discharge ports are opened, and rotation is continued.

The Burt filter has found its major application in the metallurgical industry, where it has been used for extraction residues and for zinc sulfate liquors in electrolytic zinc refining.

Continuous Pressure Filters

Continuous Pressure Drums and Disks. Multicompartment drums and sectored disks controlled by a rotary valve and discharged by a knife are the essential elements of continuous pressure filters. They are exactly like their drum and disk vacuum filter counterparts except that they are enclosed within a pressure shell and they are designed to accept the greater stresses associated with their operation from superatmospheric levels of at least 30 lb./sq. in. upstream to substantially atmospheric pressure downstream. The later description of the basic continuous vacuum filter applies to them; therefore, it is not repeated here.

A major difference between continuous pressure and continuous vacuum filters is in the discharge of cake from the filter. Whereas in the vacuum filter it is at atmospheric pressure and drops from the filtering surface into a tank, bin, or trough, in the pressure filter it is removed from the drum or disk at full filtering pressure and must be throttled to atmospheric pressure during its discharge from the filter enclosure. With a certain type of cake it is possible to effect a continuous removal from the pressure system by a self-sealing screw conveyor, but most materials must be discharged into a receiver that is under filtration pressure. The use of two such alternate receivers and an arrangement of pressure locks makes it possible to take the solids from the system without interrupting the filter, but it nevertheless considerably frustrates the continuity of the process.

Continuous pressure filters are limited to lower-pressure maxima than are batch filters and to smaller sizes than are continuous vacuum machines. In their larger sizes, continuous pressure drums and disks must not exceed about 40 lb./sq. in. working pressure, although Goslin-Birmingham has built a small drum filter that can operate at 200 lb./sq. in. Even at these relatively low pressures, however, there is a real gain in production capacity over the highest achievable with a vacuum filter for substantially incompressible solids.

From these remarks, the advantages and disadvantages of continuous pressure drums and disks are apparent. On the credit side are the benefits connected with continuous machines (*i.e.*, labor saving and steady flow of materials) and with pressure filters (ability to operate at higher pressures than vacuum filters and ability to handle volatile liquids unsuited to vacuum filtration). On the debit side are mechanical complexity, difficulty in discharge of solids, high price (somewhat higher than vacuum filters unless the latter must be enclosed), increased maintenance cost because of the lack of access to the filter during its operation, and limitation to relatively low pressures. The field of application is a steady, fairly large flow of slurry that requires higher pressure than 15 lb./sq. in. for its economic filtration.

Both drum and disk filters are limited to 300 to 400 sq. ft. of area. Up to this limit they use the same sizes of drums and disks employed in continuous vacuum filters.

Continuous Precoat Pressure Filters. Precoat filters that operate on a long transient cycle, not actually continuous but so called, may be operated under pressure or vacuum. The latter is the more usual, and a description of this kind of filter is given in a subsequent passage on continuous vacuum filters. Inasmuch as the two types of filters are nearly identical except for the pressure at which they operate and for the necessity of enclosing the pressure filter, the description is not repeated here.

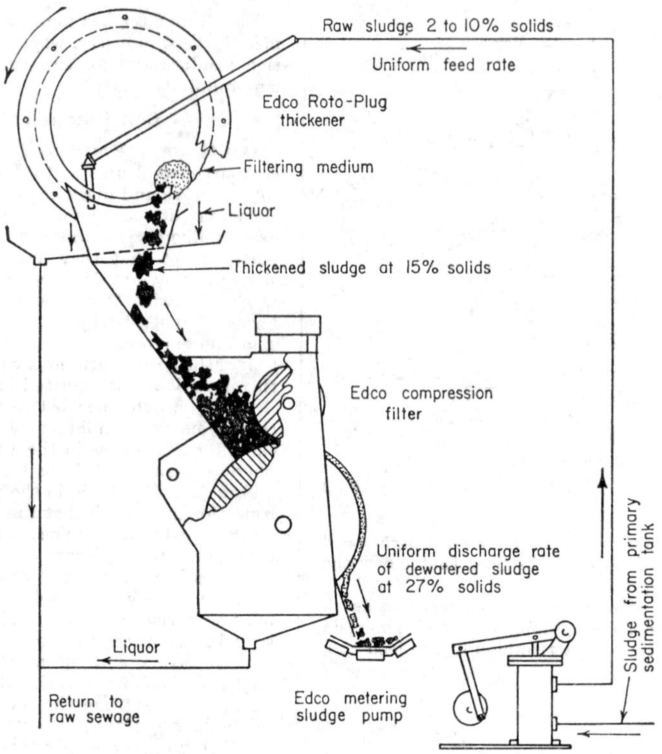

FIG. 19-113. Schematic arrangement, Carter-Edco sludge concentrator. (*Equipment Development Co.*)

The general comments made above about continuous drum pressure filters apply. Continuous pressure precoat filters do not exceed about 165 sq. ft. in area.

Carter-Edco Sludge Concentrator. This device, designed by the Equipment Development Co. for the concentration of primary sewage sludge from a 2 per cent slurry to a soft solid containing 70 per cent water, can be regarded as a kind of continuous pressure filter, although in the purest view it could be considered as the combination of a gravity thickener and an expression press.

With reference to Fig. 19-113, raw sludge is fed continuously to the Roto-Plug thickener, a rotating perforated-wall cylinder carrying a filter medium. Some liquor drains through the filter medium, and the slightly thickened sludge rolls up into a cylinder or plug which by its own weight further dewaters itself and the solids from new sludge being added to the thickener. When the rolling plug has increased to a certain critical size it begins to distend in the direction of its axis and over the edge of the thickener cylinder, where it is continuously cut away and falls in chunks to the unit below, the Edco compression filter. This consists of a set of rolls that compress the sludge against a drainage surface, expelling more liquor and delivering a continuous ribbon of moist filtered solids. The thickener can increase the consistency of the sludge from 2 to 15 per cent, and the compression filter can further increase it to 27 to 32 per cent. The concentrator is supplied in a range of capacities from 1 to 8 tons of dry solids per 24-hr. day.

Vacuum Filters

Vacuum filters are those which operate with less than atmospheric pressure on the downstream side of the filter septum. Usually the upstream pressure is substantially atmospheric. Vacuum filters, therefore, are limited to a maximum filtering pressure of 1 atm. Since the prefilt slurry is supplied at atmospheric pressure, it may be fed to the filter tank by a low-head pump or by gravity. The filtrate, on the other hand, must be compressed from the operating pressure of the receiver to atmospheric before it can be discharged, and for this operation a filtrate pump (usually a self-priming centrifugal or turbine pump) or a barometric leg is used. A vacuum pump is a most important accessory to vacuum filters, for it is the source of the filtration driving force and, in many installations, the item of greatest operating expense. Dry vacuum pumps, rather than wet, usually are selected, and Nash, reciprocating, and rotary pumps and ejectors all are used. The choice is principally economic and depends on the details of the service. In some cases, a barometric leg discharging into a sump seal eliminates the necessity of a vacuum pump.

Both batch and continuous filters are employed in process applications, but by far the predominant number of installations are the latter. The chief justification for vacuum filtration, in fact, is its adaptability to continuous systems.

The advantages of vacuum filters are

1. They can be designed as effective continuous filters.
2. As such, they are low labor users and efficient adjuncts to continuous processes.
3. The filtering surface can be open to the atmosphere and therefore easily accessible for inspection and repair.
4. Maintenance costs are usually low.

The disadvantages are

1. A vacuum system must be maintained.
2. Vacuum filters cannot be used with filtrates that are volatile, whether because of a low normal boiling point or a high operating temperature.

3. Most vacuum filters cannot handle difficultly filterable compressible solids.

4. Continuous vacuum filters are inflexible and do not perform well if their feed stream changes with respect to rate, consistency, or character of solids.

Other advantages and disadvantages are peculiar to particular types of equipment and will be discussed in that context.

Continuous vacuum filters probably handle more tonnage of solids than do all other kinds of filters combined. Batch vacuum filters, on the other hand, are of limited local use in chemical processing.

Batch Vacuum Filters

Vacuum Nutsches. If it is built to withstand the differential pressure, the filtrate-collection sump of a nutsche may be connected to a vacuum system to convert the nutsche into a vacuum filter. Except for the increased filtration capacity that results from the vacuum, the advantages and disadvantages of a vacuum nutsche are those of its gravity counterpart, and the same comments apply to both (see p. 19-61). Vacuum nutsches are useful in semiworks and small fine-chemicals operations.

The Galigher tilting filter (Galigher Co.) is a horizontal vacuum table, a shallow pan with a drainage grid and a medium support for a floor. The vacuum is provided by a pump which, with a filtrate receiver, is an integral part of the filter station. The filter pan is so supported as to allow its rotation through 180 deg. after the filtration has been finished in order to facilitate the cake removal. The filter is tilted by a handwheel.

The Galigher filter is really a short-walled vacuum nutsche, a bit more flexible and convenient than the nutsche but working on the same principle. It has been used primarily in minerals processing (*e.g.*, for filtering flotation concentrates). The filter is available in standard models ranging from 7 to 19 sq. ft.

Vacuum Leaf Filters. The Moore filter (Fig. 19-114) is a battery of leaves connected to a vacuum manifold in a portable rack. Each leaf consists of a rectangular frame of perforated pipe over which a bag of filter medium is stretched. Collapse of the bag is prevented and drainage provided for by wooden slats sewed vertically into the bag. The battery of frames is transported by crane to slurry tank, wash tank, and discharge bin successively. Vacuum is applied during filtration and washing, and air is back-blown to aid cake discharge.

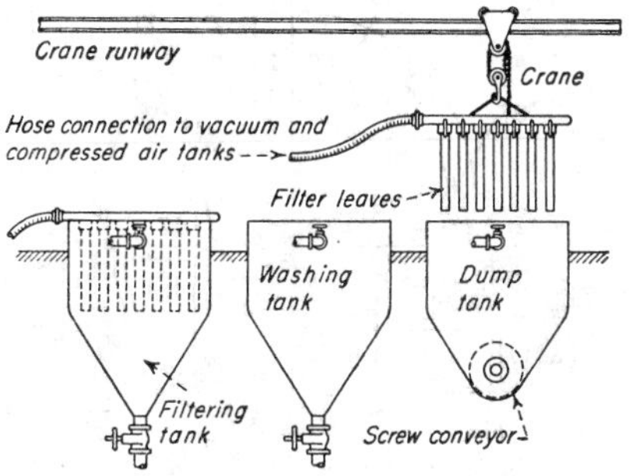

FIG. 19-114. Moore filter.

The advantages of the Moore filter are simplicity of operation, ready inspection of leaves after cake discharge, and ease with which a new leaf may be installed in place of a defective one. Further advantages are its adaptability to long cake-forming cycles and thorough washing. Disadvantages are crudeness, space requirements, and disorder and hazard identified with the possibility that sections of the cake may drop from the leaves during transport from tank to tank. Moore filters have been used in the metallurgical industry and in the manufacture of certain pigments.

The **Vacu-Flow suction leaf filter** (Hercules Filter Corp.) is a simple tank-mounted vacuum leaf filter that is a counterpart of vertical pressure leaf equipment. The filter consists of an open-top rectangular tank in which parallel rectangular leaves are mounted vertically, being supported on and draining into a filtrate manifold running along the tank bottom (Fig. 19-115). The manifold is connected directly to the suction side of a centrifugal pump that substitutes for a vacuum pump.

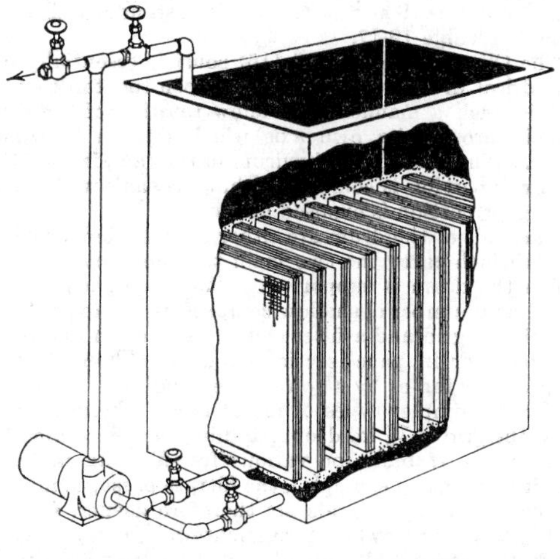

FIG. 19-115. Tank-mounted vacuum leaf filter. (*Hercules Filter Corp.*)

The tank is filled with slurry and filtration proceeds until a cake of maximum desirable thickness has developed. The pump is then shut off, the tank is drained, and the cake is hosed out the drain. Dry cake recovery is not recommended.

A tank-mounted vacuum leaf filter has the advantage of extreme simplicity and economy of first cost. Its disadvantage is that it is amenable only to rapid filtrations involving cake to be discarded, *i.e.*, filtrations involving filter aid, and even then at considerable labor expense. It can be made in almost any size and proportions. Hercules units range from 5-leaf, 10-sq.-ft. filters to 30-leaf, 1200-sq.-ft. models.

Continuous Vacuum Filters

Continuous vacuum filters, widely used throughout the process industries, fall into three classes: drums, disks, and horizontal filters, the latter being represented by table, pan, and belt types. Although there are striking differences among the designs and applications of continuous vacuum filters used commercially today, they all have the following features in common: a filtering surface that moves from a point of slurry application, where a cake is deposited under the impetus of a vacuum, to a point of solids removal, where the cake is discharged by mechanical and pneumatic methods, and thence back to the point of slurry application; a valve (or the equivalent) that regulates the pressure below the surface at various stages of its travel; an apparently continuous cycle of operation that is sometimes in fact an endless series of closely spaced batch events that approximate a continuous pattern. Details of continuous vacuum filters follow. Estimated uninstalled costs of several types of filters are given in Fig. 19-108.

Multicompartment Drum Filters

The Conventional Rotary Drum. The oldest and most popular continuous vacuum filter is the conventional rotary drum. The Oliver filter (Dorr-Oliver, Inc.) was the first machine of this kind, and it will be used as a typical example in the following description. Conventional drums that differ only in detail are made by many other companies, however, such as Ametek, Inc. (Filtration Engineers Div.), Denver Equipment Co., the Eimco Corp., Goslin-Birmingham Manufacturing Co., Komline-Sanderson Engineering Corp., Peterson Filters and Engineering Co., and the Whiting Corp. (Swenson Evaporator Co. Div.). Drum filters range in area from 1 to 800 sq. ft. Typical standard sizes are shown in Table 19-17.

The Oliver filter (Fig. 19-116) consists essentially of a cylindrical drum supported in an open-top tank or vat and in such a manner as to allow rotation of the drum therein around its own axis which is in a horizontal plane. The position of the drum in the tank is such that its lower portion is confined within the tank walls, while the upper portion is exposed above.

The ends of the drum are either open spiders or closed heads which carry the two main trunnions by means of which the drum is supported. The drum shell is composed of a number of shallow compartments covered with a drainage grid and a filter cloth. The cloth may be in one piece or in panel sections and is held in place by lateral caulking or by a spiral wire winding.

For the simpler types of minerals and chemical products, the grid is ⅞ in. deep, handling moderate amounts of filtrate. If built for various free-filtering materials (sulfite pulp as an example), the filtrate passages must be ample and drainage grids are therefore deeper, *i.e.*, 1½ to 1¾ in. For slowly filtering materials requiring sharp separation of initially cloudy filtrate, a grid ⅛ in. or less in depth is used. Grids are made of wood, perforated metal sheet, cast metal, or plastic.

The interior of each compartment communicates through a separate conduit (28), to a valve mechanism (31) which, during operation, automatically applies either suction or positive air pressure to the several conduits in rotation and through them in turn to the interior of the compartments. The automatic valve (31) is connected to a vacuum system and to a source of compressed air.

Under the drum, barely clearing the bottom of the

Table 19-17. Standard Sizes of Dorr-Oliver Filters*

Oliver Rotary Vacuum Filters, Areas in Square Feet Filtration Area

Diam., ft.	Length, ft.									
	1	2	4	6	8	10	12	14	16	18
3	9	18	36	54						
4	...	25	50	75	100					
5¼	...	...	65	100	130	165				
6	...	...	75	113	150	181				
8	...	...	...	...	200	250	300	350	400	
10	...	...	...	...	...	310	375	440	500	560
11½	...	...	...	...	...	...	430	500	570	640
14	...	...	...	...	...	...	...	610	700	790

Oliver Horizontal Filters

Diam., ft.	3	4	6	8	10	11½	13	15	19
Area, sq. ft.	3.5	10	25	47	65	90	120	165	275

American Disk Filters

Diam., ft.	No. of disks											
	1	2	3	4	5	6	7	8	9	10	11	12
4	22	44	66	88								
6	...	100	150	200	250	300	350	400				
8½	...	...	...	375	465	560	650	745	835	925		
10½	...	...	...	...	...	900	1050	1200	1350	1500	1650	1800
12	...	...	...	...	...	1200	1400	1600	1800	2000	2200	2400

* Dorr-Oliver, Inc.

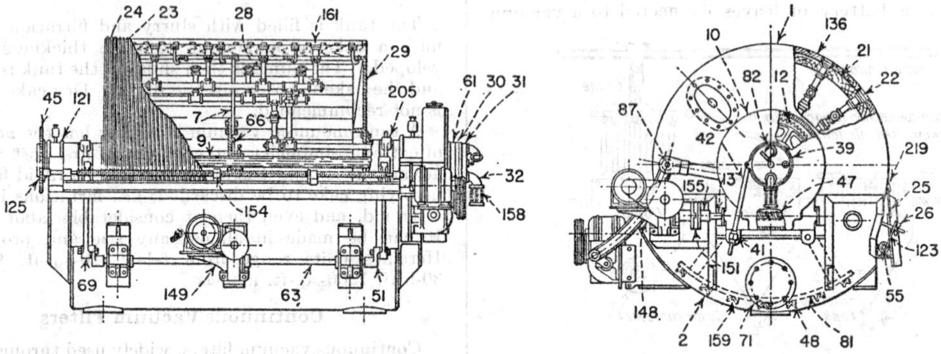

PARTS LIST

1. Filter drum
2. Filter tank
7. Drum arms
9. Drum shaft
10. Housed bearing
12. Worm-drive gear
13. Worm shaft
21. Wood staves
22. Division strips
23. Filter medium
24. Wire winding
25. Scraper blade
26. Scraper adjuster
28. Drum piping
29. Closed drum head
30. Wear plate
31. Automatic valve
32. Vacuum connection
39. Felt washer
41. Valve-adjusting pivot
42. Valve-adjusting rod
45. Wiring sprocket
47. Worm
48. Agitator rakes
51. Agitator crank
55. Scraper bearing
61. Pipe plate
63. Crankshaft
66. Center spider
71. Handhole cover
81. Agitator arc
82. Automatic valve flange
87. Connecting-rod pin
121. Rear bearing
123. Scraper plate
125. Feed-screw sprocket
136. Filter cover support
148. Type A drum drive
149. Type A agitator drive
151. Shaft coupling link
154. Wiring center dolly box
155. Shaft coupling
158. Diaphragm vacuum connections
159. Saddle clips
161. Drum nipples
205. Oscillating spider
219. Scraper tip

FIG. 19-116. Oliver continuous vacuum drum filter. (*Dorr-Oliver, Inc.*)

tank, is suspended a framework (81) supporting horizontal rakes (48) which, during operation, slowly oscillate, thus agitating the feed. Alternatively, paddle and propeller stirrers may be used.

The filter cake is usually discharged from the drum surface by a scraper blade which is set in a vertical position. On the edge of the scraper is affixed a detachable rubber tip. The scraper itself is mounted upon the edge of the filter tank. The low-discharge point of the Oliver filter cake permits cake discharge by pressure reversal, in most cases the scraper serving as a diversion plate only. Alternative means of cake removal include roll and wire discharge. The former, particularly useful for thin cakes of sticky or thixotropic material, consists of a roller operating close to the filter drain at the point of cake discharge. Cake is transferred to the roll from the filter and can be scraped from the roll by a cutting blade. A taut piano wire is used for the discharge of thin, friable cakes. The wire should be guarded to prevent human injury from the snap of the wire, should it break.

The Oliver filter is made of steel, wood, cast iron, cast lead, coated steel, stainless steel, monel metal, other alloys, and combinations of these materials. Lead-lined steel filter tanks are built, and in some cases a sheathing of brass or copper is used over the wood and steel portion. Any practical material of construction may be used in building the Oliver filter, and filter covers are provided in a wide variety of natural and synthetic textiles, woven-wire cloth, as well as finely perforated metal sheets.

During operation, the drum rotates slowly while the tank is supplied with the material to be filtered and the level is maintained to ensure a constant depth of submergence of the lower portion of the filter drum. In some types this depth may be set between limits ranging from zero to almost complete submersion of the drum. Once chosen, the valve is set for the given conditions.

Through the action of the automatic valve, vacuum is applied to those compartments of the drum passing through the sludge. The vacuum created within the compartments causes a flow of filtrate through the filter medium, conduits, and automatic valve, and a layer of cake solids is deposited upon the filter medium covering the submerged portion of the drum.

As the drum revolves, the vacuum in the compartments is maintained, and the layer of cake solids emerges and passes through the arc included by the upper or exposed portion of the drum. It is subjected to washing by water from spray nozzles; the wash water permeates the cake and displaces the liquid contained.

Following the washing period the cake is dewatered and discharged. The cleaned filter surface then rotates into the tank and the cycle is repeated.

String-discharge Filter. Instead of a doctor blade or a roller, a system of endless strings 0.5 in. apart that pass around the filter drum and off tangentially may lift the cake and discharge it. A drum using this kind of discharge is shown in Fig. 19-117. The valve is annular, enclosing the hub, and connections are made at its periphery rather than at its face. It is so set as to break the vacuum when the strings lift the cake from the drum.

String-discharge filters can operate successfully with a much thinner cake (1/16 in.) than can the conventional drum, which requires a minimum of 0.25 to 0.5 in. for the proper discharge. They thus can filter more difficult materials than a conventional drum. They achieve this result at the expense of greater dead area than in the conventional design. Their success, of course, depends on the susceptibility of the cake to removal by the strings, a point of behavior that must be confirmed experimentally before such a filter is chosen.

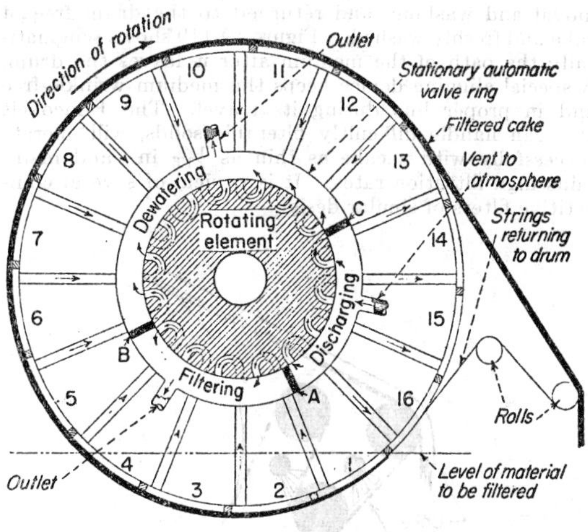

FIG. 19-117. Diagram of continuous vacuum filter operation. Sections 1 to 4 are filtering; sections 5 through 12 are dewatering; and section 13 is discharging the cake with the string discharge. Sections 14, 15, and 16 are ready to start a new cycle. The "hub" of this drawing illustrates the automatic valve, where *A*, *B*, and *C* represent members in the valve. (*Ametek, Inc.*)

Removable-medium Filters. Some drum filters provide for the filter medium to be removed and reapplied as the drum rotates. The purpose of this feature is to permit the complete discharge of thin or sticky cake and the regenerative washing of the medium.

The Coilfilter (Komline-Sanderson Engineering Corp.) is a drum filter of which the filter medium consists of two layers of stainless steel, helically coiled springs 0.41 in. in diameter, placed in corduroy pattern around the drum (Fig. 19-118). During filtration, the springs

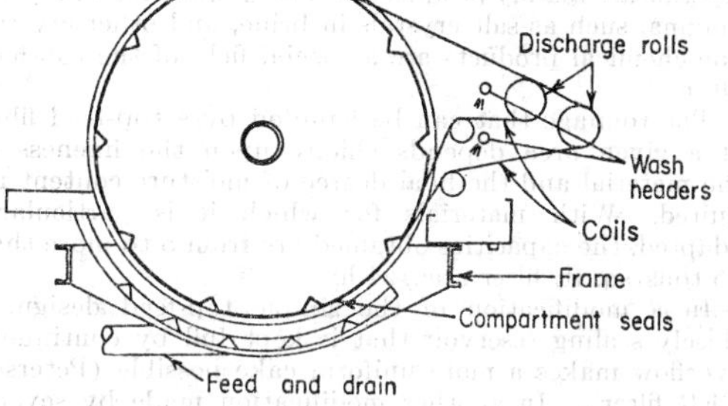

FIG. 19-118. Schematic elevation of Coilfilter. (*Komline-Sanderson Engineering Corp.*)

are wrapped around the drum and the cake is formed over them, the filtrate passing between coils and between turns of each coil. At the discharge position, the two layers of springs are taken off the drum on respective tangents and passed over discharge rolls when, with the help of a tyne bar, the cake is removed from them. The springs are spray-washed as they are flexed before the return to the drum.

The Coilfilter will filter slimy, difficult solids such as raw sewage sludge. It was developed particularly for the latter material, but it is of broader interest for difficult-to-filter materials in the chemical industry.

The Eimcobelt (Eimco Corp.) is a drum filter carrying a textile or fabric that is removed tangentially at the point of cake discharge, run over rollers for cake removal and washing, and returned to the drum free of cake and freshly washed. Figure 19-119 shows schematically the path of the medium after it leaves the drum. A special aligning device keeps the medium wrinkle-free and in proper line during its travel. The Eimcobelt also can handle difficultly filterable solids, will operate successfully with a cake as thin as $\frac{1}{16}$ in., and maintains high filtration rates. It is typical of several competitive filters of similar design.

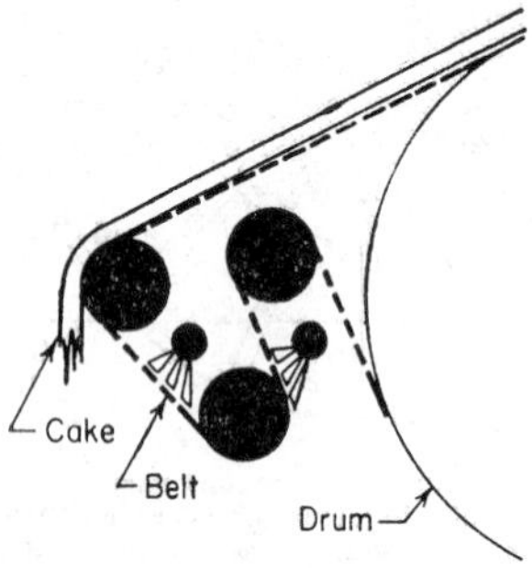

Fig. 19-119. Cake discharge and medium washing on an Eimcobelt filter. (*The Eimco Corp.*)

Top-feed Filter. Coarse, rapidly settling solids that would not form a satisfactory cake on a conventional drum can be filtered by a modification of the drum filter wherein the slurry is fed near the top of the drum to its ascending face. The cake is discharged at the bottom, falling into a chute. Little more than half of the drum is available for filtering and drying.

Since very low moisture concentration in a filtered product is usually required, the design of top-feed filters has evolved methods for the application of heat to the filter cake in various convenient ways. "Bone-dry" salt crystals are readily produced. The dewatering of crystal magma, such as salt crystals in brine, and other crystalline chemical products are a special field of the top-feed filter.

The tonnage that can be handled by a top-feed filter of a given area depends chiefly upon the fineness of the material and the final degree of moisture content required. With materials for which it is particularly adapted, the capacities obtained are from 5 to more than 35 tons/sq. ft. filter area/24 hr.

In a modification of the simple top-feed design, a closely sealing reservoir that is kept full by continuous overflow makes a more uniform cake possible (Peterson TFR filter). In another modification made by several companies, the drum surface is divided into panels, each of which has retaining sides at least 6 in. deep. The drum thus is sectioned into cubicles or hoppers into each of which slurry feeds as the hopper approaches the top of the drum. The hopper dewaterer will handle even more porous cakes of larger solids than will the top-feed filter. Less than half of its surface is available for filtering and drying.

Top-feed and hopper filters generally do not exceed 95 sq. ft. in area (5-ft. diameter).

Internal Feed: The Dorrco Filter (Fig. 19-120). This is a vacuum filter of the rotary-drum type with the filter medium placed on the inner surface of the drum as a series of panels parallel to the drum axis. The drum serves also as the container for the pulp, and no supplementary tank is used. Except for the annular retaining ring which creates the bath, the drum is open at one end for convenient inspection.

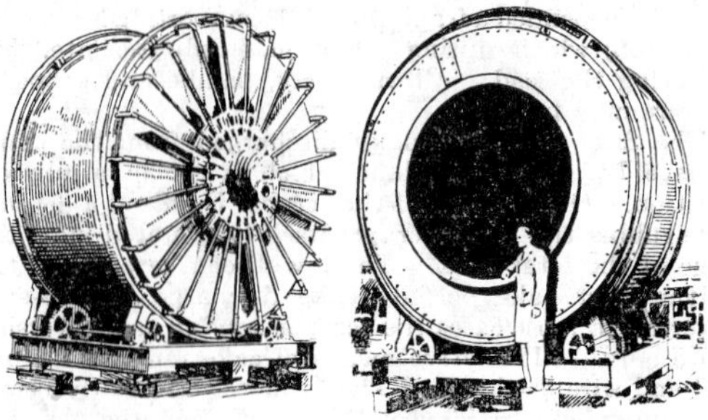

Fig. 19-120. Dorrco filter. (*Dorr-Oliver, Inc.*)

A troughed belt conveyor runs through the machine at one side of the center line collecting the cake as it is discharged and delivering it through the end of the machine at the center-line elevation. The drive arrangement is such that the speed of the filter drum can be adjusted independently of the speed of the conveyor. In some cases cake is removed by a spiral scroll in a trough.

As the filter revolves, the cloth passes down into the pulp bath underneath the line of feed and the cake-forming vacuum is applied automatically as adjusted by the setting of bridges in the head valve, permitting, where desired, the precoating of the cloth with the coarsest, most rapidly segregating material in the feed. As the cloth emerges from the bath, the cake is drained out and washing sprays may be brought to bear upon it while it is still resting in an inclined position against the drum. Following this early application of washing sprays, the cake is dried by vacuum until discharge.

As the cake passes over the hopper which guards the discharge conveyor, the drying vacuum is cut off and the panel is brought into direct connection with the special discharge port. This port leads by separate piping from the filter valve to a small four-way valve bringing the port into direct connection with the inlet and outlet of a small blower, and at the same time alternately opening the outlet and inlet connections of the blower to the atmosphere. This imparts to the panel an alternating pulsation with a gentle breathing action, freeing the cake and permitting it to drop away by gravity to the collecting conveyor, at the same time repeatedly flexing the cloth as a reconditioning step for further operation. When cake discharges readily and cleanly from the cloth, the "pulsating" discharge is changed to simple low-pressure "blow" discharge.

In the case of free-filtering materials, permitting high speeds of filter operation and handling of large tonnages on comparatively small drums, the face of the filter is short in proportion to its diameter and a simple chute is substituted for the belt conveyor. The short-faced filter lends itself particularly well to the distribution of extremely heterogeneous feeds where any appreciable depth of bath is difficult to maintain, the coarse material being merely sluiced onto the narrow path of filtering surface revolving under it. When operating conditions prevent the use of textile filter cloth, a special type of Dorrco filter has been designed to use woven-wire cloth.

Continuous Vacuum Precoat Filter. This filter is a major modification of the conventional continuous drum-type filter. Its unique principle of filtration and method of cake discharge have opened up many opportunities for the continuous filtration or clarification of products that have hitherto been difficult to handle. Precoat filtration is particularly adapted to handling solutions with pasty, gummy, or colloidal substances, or solutions with small amounts of solids held in suspension.

The vacuum precoat filter actually operates on a long transient cycle instead of continuously, but since the order of length of the cycle is days and since during this time filtration takes place without interruption and virtually at constant rate, the filter is usually thought of as continuous. First, a heavy layer of filter aid is formed on the drum, and then the solution to be clarified is fed into the tank which has been drained of excess filter aid. As the drum rotates, a thin film of solids is continuously formed on the surface of the filter aid and is rotated through the washing and drying zone to the discharge point. Here, an advancing knife-edge shaves off the film of solids and usually some filter aid. The cleaned surface of filter aid rotates on into the tank for further cake deposition (see Fig. 19-121). Flow rates

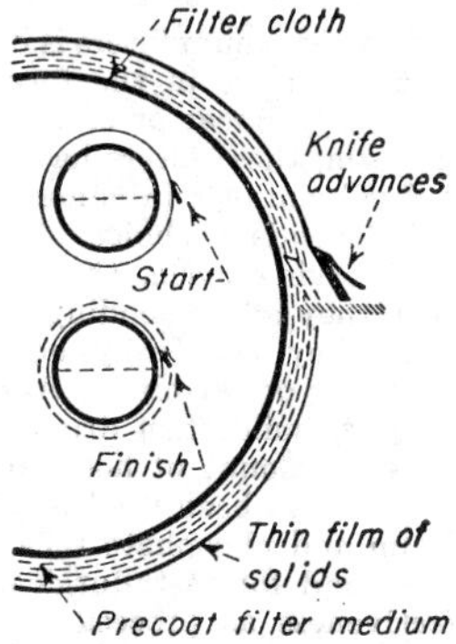

FIG. 19-121. Operating method of vacuum precoat filter. (*Dorr-Oliver, Inc.*)

are sustained and high. Satisfactory clarification usually takes place in one step. Precoating takes less than an hour; filtering or clarifying continues for periods ranging from 16 hr. to a week, depending upon how much precoat is removed with the cake.

Single-compartment Drum Filters

The Bird-Young filter (Bird Machine Co.) has no internal drum piping nor automatic rotary valve; the entire inside of the drum is subject to vacuum, and cake is discharged by a pulsating-air blowback, without help of either scraper or strings. This filter's special purpose is handling slow-filtering slurries, because of its ability to operate with very thin cakes.

The filter is shown in Fig. 19-122, in combined elevation and in section. The drum is made to bear atmospheric pressure and is supported, with axis horizontal, by trunnions at the drum ends.

The filter-feed bowl (3) is mounted so that from 5 to 50 per cent of the drum surface will be submerged in the slurry. Mounted inside the drum at the point desired for cake discharge is a shoe arrangement (4) which supplies compressed-air blowback to the surface sections of the drum as they pass the cake discharge point. This shoe is supported within a few thousandths of an inch from the inner drum surface by a radial supporting pipe (5) which is in turn supported by a stationary axial pipe (6) which passes through packing rings at the trunnions. The axial pipe acts as the channel for blowback air (7), the channel for evacuated air (8), the channel for filtrate removal (9) except at low submergence, when the siphon pipe (10) is used for filtrate removal, and the channel for wash filtrate.

The drainage surface of the metal drum shelf is divided into 50 to 100 longitudinal surface sections by slotted division strips. The filter cover is applied as a single piece, being held in place by crosswires in each cross-division strip. This gives the effect of separate sections of surface. Filtrate from each section drops to the bottom of the drum and flows out via the axial pipe, or by pumping out through the siphon pipe.

Drum speeds range from 0.03 to 6 min./rev. Sizes range from 1 to 140 sq. ft. of filtering area, the maximum drum diameter being 5.5 ft. The filter may be made of metal or coated metal; wood is unsuitable. The first cost of a Bird-Young filter is about twice that of a conventional rotary vacuum filter of the same area.

The major advantage of the Bird-Young filter is its ability to handle very thin cakes and hence to operate at high speeds and high production capacities and to afford good washing. Other advantages are its ability to effect sharp separations of filtrate and wash streams and its low internal resistance to air and filtrate flow. Its chief disadvantages are its high initial cost and the limit imposed upon its flexibility by its not having a valve.

Continuous Vacuum Disks

The continuous rotary vacuum disk filter, typified by Dorr-Oliver **American filter** (Fig. 19-123), is offered by most makers of vacuum drum filters. It is a continuous

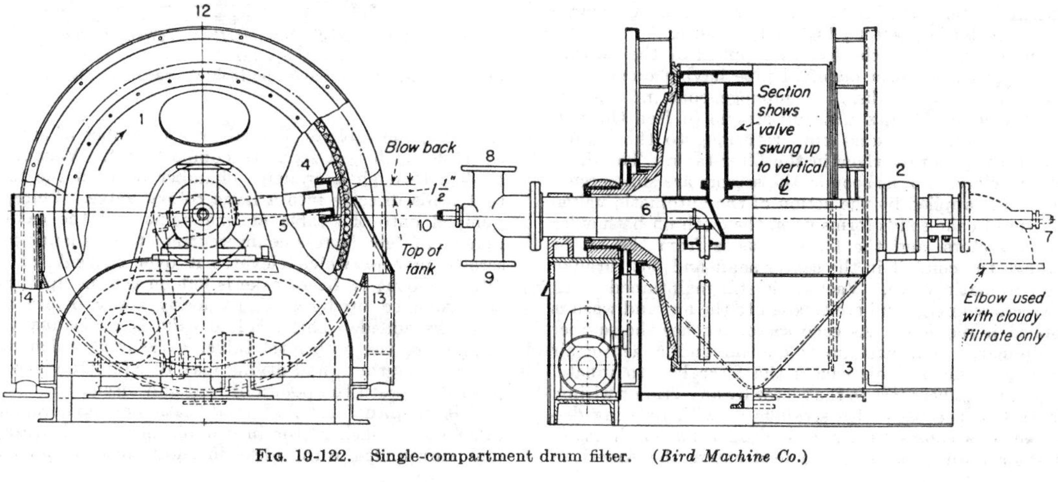

FIG. 19-122. Single-compartment drum filter. (*Bird Machine Co.*)

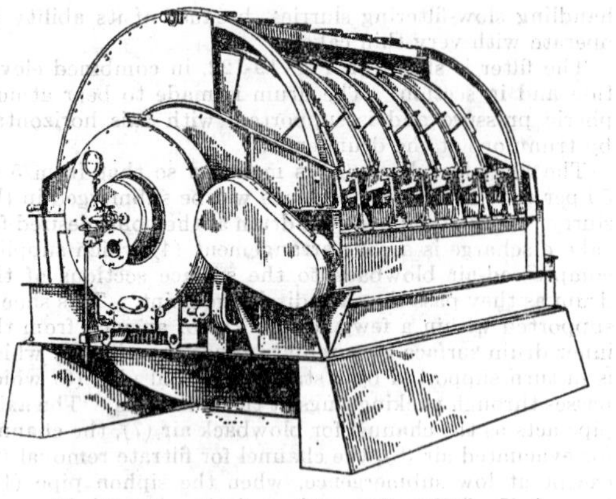

Fig. 19-123. American filter. (*Dorr-Oliver, Inc.*)

rotary vacuum filter consisting essentially of a number of filter disks mounted at regular intervals around a hollow center shaft. Rotation is by a gear drive. Each disk consists of a sector of wood, iron, or bronze, ribbed on both sides to support the filter cloth and to provide drainage.

Each sector has an outlet nipple that passes through an opening in the cast-iron center shaft joining a conduit running the entire length of the shaft and terminating in a port at the automatic valve. Each serves as a filtrate channel for all sectors along the shaft on that line. The automatic valve is similar to those used for other continuous rotary vacuum filters. Sectors are held in place by radial rods, each rod having a clamp and nut on the outer end that holds two adjacent sectors in place. Any sector can be replaced without disturbing the others, and at slow speeds it is not necessary to stop the filter to make the change.

Filter covers are in the form of bags slipped over the sectors, and the outer edges are folded under the clamps. At the filtrate nipple, a cord is tied round the neck of the bag and a rubber washer makes a tight joint between the nipple and the center shaft. The assembly of filter disks on the center shaft is mounted in a feed tank so that the sectors are completely submerged during the cake-building portion of the cycle. On the discharge side, the filter tank is crenelated to accommodate the disks. The space between these divisions is utilized for cake discharge; scrapers or tapered discharge rolls for each disk are mounted at the top of the tank. In some cases discharge is effected by fine water jets under pressure.

During operation, the feed is supplied at the bottom of the tank through a manifold pipe having one supply nozzle under each disk. A homogeneous mixture is maintained by forcing a steady stream of feed through these nozzles, the excess pulp returning to the supply tank through an overflow in the filter tank. The disks rotate slowly, and, as soon as the sectors are submerged, vacuum is applied by the action of the automatic valve. A layer of cake solids forms upon the cloth on both sides of the sectors, and the filtrate passes from the sector through the conduit in the center shaft and out through the automatic valve. Vacuum is still maintained when the sectors emerge and are exposed to the air, and wash is applied if required. As each sector reaches the scraper or discharge roll, vacuum is cut off and a gentle air blast is applied. This causes the filter bag to inflate, since it is not held fast to the sector by any grid or wiring. Contact of the bags with scrapers or with rotating discharge rolls causes the cake to drop between the tank divisions. In some uses, the feed enters the American filter from a launder placed along the rim of the filter tank.

Similar disk filters are made by other manufacturers. Among the modifications they have adopted are trapizoidally shaped sectors that enter the slurry tank at a more efficient angle, and paddle or propeller agitators to maintain the suspension in the slurry tank.

As indicated in Fig. 19-108, disk filters are the least expensive of all continuous filters; their low cost, indeed, and their extreme compactness are their greatest advantages. Their major disadvantage is their inadaptability to effective wash. Standard models range in diameter from 4 to 12.5 ft. and in area from 20 to 2400 sq. ft. Table 19-17 lists the standard sizes offered by one manufacturer.

Horizontal Continuous Vacuum Filters

A class of continuous vacuum filters is characterized by a horizontal filtering surface in the form of a table, a belt, or multiple pans in linear or circular arrangement. Regardless of the form, these filters have certain generic advantages and disadvantages in common. As credits, they permit an independent choice of cake thickness, washing time, and drying cycle, they effectively filter heavy dense solids, they allow flooding of the cake with wash solvent, and they are easily adaptable to true countercurrent leaching or washing. As liabilities, they are more expensive to build than drum filters and they use a relatively large amount of floor space per unit of filtering area. They have been used particularly for the filtration of gypsum and phosphate rock residues in the H_3PO_4 wet process and for metallurgical sludges. Recently their effectiveness as process apparatus for the solvent extraction of oil seeds has been strikingly demonstrated.

Horizontal Table. This filter is a rotating annular table whose top surface is a filter medium (Fig. 19-124).

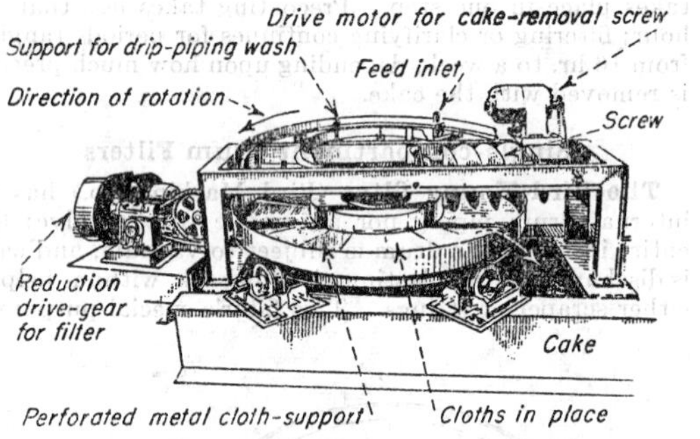

Fig. 19-124. Continuous horizontal vacuum filter. (*Dorr-Oliver, Inc.*)

Actually, the table is divided into a number of sectors, each of which is a separate compartment. Vacuum is applied through a drainage chamber beneath the table that leads directly into a large rotary valve. Slurry is pumped onto the table at one point and the cake is removed a few degrees countercurrent to this point by a scroll conveyor which elevates it over the side of the filter. About ⅛ in. of cake is left on the medium, and it is roughed up by a high-velocity spray before new slurry is added. This residual cake is a disadvantage peculiar to the horizontal table. Washing, which may be countercurrent, and drying may be effectively accomplished between the points of feed and discharge.

Tilting-pan Filter. A modification of the horizontal table makes each sector into a physically independent unit surrounded with sides—in short, into a pan con-

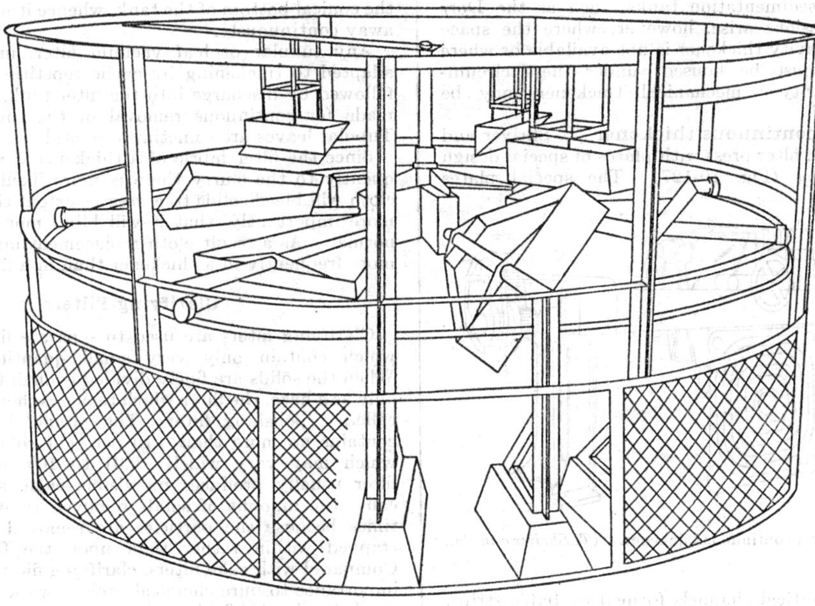

FIG. 19-125. Bird-Prayon tilting-pan filter. (*Bird Machine Co.*)

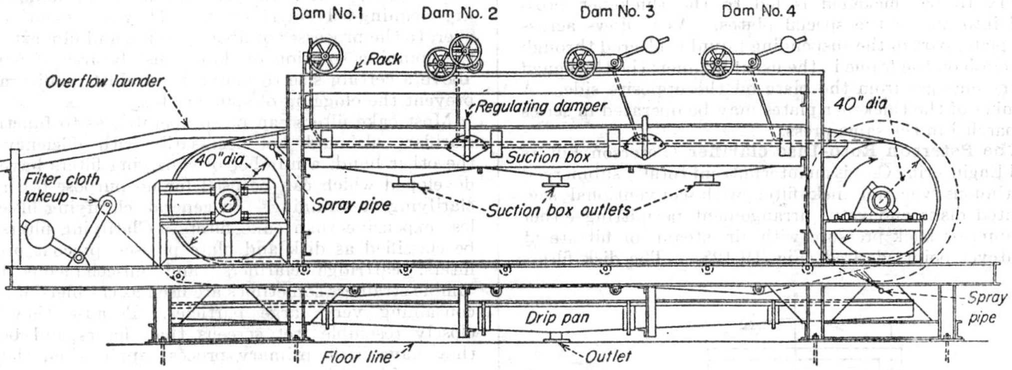

FIG. 19-126. Lurgi belt filter. (*Mercer-Robinson Co., Inc.*)

nected by a radial arm to a central vacuum valve. The pan is carried on a roller that rides a circular track around the filter. At the point of cake discharge, a mechanism inverts the pan and, with the help of a short blast of air if needed, the cake is dumped. The pan is then righted and is ready to receive its next charge of prefilt. One model of tilting-pan filter is shown in Fig. 19-125. Tilting-pan filters have the relative advantages of complete wash containment and good cake discharge, and the relative disadvantages of high cost and mechanical complexity.

Belt Filter. A perforated endless-rubber-belt conveyor supporting a filter fabric and traveling across a suction box comprises a third kind of continuous horizontal vacuum filter. An example of such a filter, the Lurgi, is shown in Fig. 19-126. The slurry is pumped onto the filter at one end, wash liquor is added along the path of the belt travel, as needed (rubber dams wiping against the cake separate the filtering zone and washing zones from one another), and the cake is dumped from the other end of the filter as the belt descends over the pulley. On the lower (return) side the belt and filter cloth are separated for the laundering action of water spray. The peculiar advantage of the belt filter, in fact, is the opportunity to wash the filter medium that it offers. Its peculiar disadvantage is the fact that half of its filtering surface is always idle.

A recent adaptation of the belt filter uses the belt as the valve, as before, but eliminates its function as a drainage deck. Instead the belt carries a linear series of pans, each of which is enclosed by sides and carries a piece of filter medium on its bottom, which is a drainage surface.

Filter Thickeners

Thickeners are devices which remove a portion of the liquid from a slurry to increase the concentration of solids in suspension. Thickening is done to prepare a dilute slurry for more economical filtration or to change the consistency or concentration of the slurry for process reasons.

Generally the most economical method of thickening is

to use gravity sedimentation tanks, such as the Dorr thickener. Occasions arise, however, where the space required by a gravity thickener is not available or where the thickener must be housed; under these circumstances, a filter-type mechanical thickener may be useful.

The Shriver continuous thickener (T. Shriver and Co.) is a modified filter press with plates of special design instead of frames (Fig. 19-127). The special plates

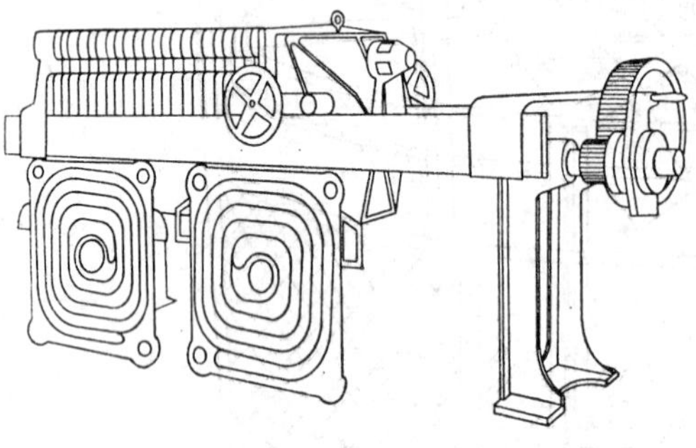

Fig. 19-127. Shriver continuous thickener. (*T. Shriver and Co., Inc.*)

carry spiral or vertical channels formed by baffle strips, the latter so arranged as to feed a liquid from left to right across the plate by successive vertical traverses. Slurry to be thickened is fed to the thickener press and into one of the special plates. As it flows across the plate, part of the suspending liquid is filtered through the cloth on the frame in the usual manner; the thickened slurry emerges from the plate on the opposite side. A number of the thickener plates may be operated in series or parallel in the same press.

The Peterson Roto-Disc clarifier (Peterson Filters and Engineering Co.) is an intermittent totally submerged continuous vacuum disk filter with conventional segmented disks and valve arrangement permitting either vacuum or back pressure with air, steam, or filtrate at whatever points desired (Fig. 19-128). The disk filters

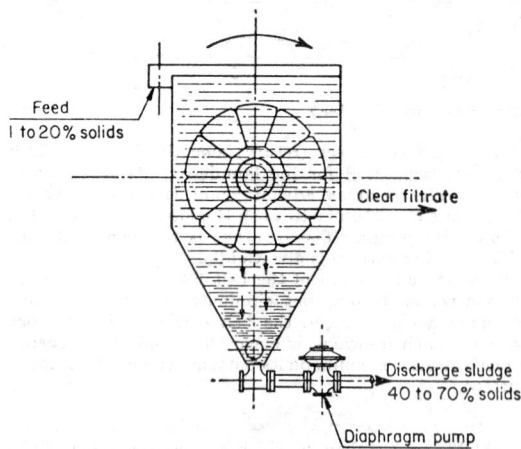

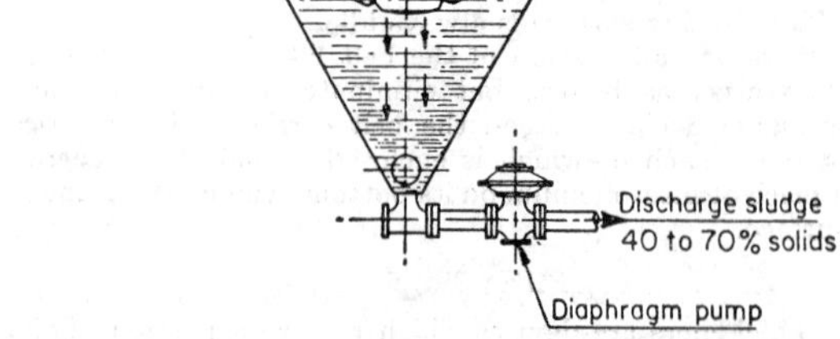

Fig. 19-128. Peterson Roto-Disc clarifier. (*Peterson Filters and Engineering Co.*)

until it has accumulated cake of suitable thickness whereupon it discharges its cake into the tank and is ready to repeat the cycle. The cake settles rapidly to the conical bottom of the tank, whence it may be pumped away continuously.

Any tubular or leaf vacuum filter, in fact, can be adapted to thickening by cyclic repetitions of filtration followed by discharge into the filter tank, if provision is made for continuous removal of the thickened solids. Tubular leaves are sometimes so used.

Since the filter fabric of a thickener is exposed so frequently to the slurry there is more likelihood that the cloth will bleed solids to a greater extent than usual and, more importantly, that it will blind more quickly than normal. As a result cloth replacement may be required more frequently in a thickener than in a filter.

Clarifying Filters

Clarifying filters are used to separate liquid mixtures which contain only very small quantities of solids. When the solids are finely divided enough to be observed only as a haze, the filter which removes them is sometimes called a polishing filter. The prefilt slurry generally contains no more than 0.10 per cent solids, the size of which may vary widely (0.01 to 100 microns). The filter usually produces no visible cake, sometimes because the amount of solids removed is so small, sometimes because the particles are removed by being entrapped within rather than upon the filter medium. Compared with cake filters, clarifying filters are of minor importance to pure chemical process work, their greatest use being in the fields of beverage and water polishing, pharmaceutical filtration, fuel- and lubricating-oil clarification, electroplating-solution conditioning, and dry-cleaning-solvent recovery. They are essential, however, to the processes of fiber spinning and film extrusion; the spinning solution or dope must be free of particles above a certain size to maintain product quality and to prevent the clogging of spinnerettes.

Most cake filters can be so operated as to function as clarifiers, although not necessarily with efficiency. On the other hand, a number of clarifying filters have been developed which can be used for no purpose other than clarifying or straining. In general, clarifying filters are less expensive than cake filters. Clarifying filters may be classified as disk and plate presses, precoat pressure filters, cartridge clarifiers, and miscellaneous types. Simple strainers sometimes are used as clarifiers of liquids containing very large particles. Because they more closely resemble wet screens than filters and because they have little primary process application, they are not considered here.

Disk Filters and Plate Presses. Filters employing asbestos-pulp disks, cakes of cotton fibers (filtermasse), or sheets of paper, pulp, or asbestos are used widely for the polishing of beverages, plating solutions, and other low-viscosity liquids containing small quantities of suspended matter. The term *disk filter* is applied to assemblies of pulp disks made of asbestos and cellulose fibers and sealed into a pressure case. The disks may be preassembled into a self-supporting unit (Fig. 19-129), or each disk may rest on an individual screen or plate against which it is sealed as the filter is closed (Fig. 19-130); the latter arrangement is similar to that of a horizontal-plate pressure filter. The disk assembly is compressed into the case when the cover is tightened, or by a separate screw inside the case. The liquid flows through the disks, and into a central or peripheral discharge manifold. Flow rates are on the order of 3 gal./(min.)(sq. ft.), and the operating pressure does not normally exceed 50 lb./sq. in. (usually it is less). Disk filters, like sheet and plate clarifiers, are almost always operated as pressure rather than vacuum filters, however. Individual filters are built to deliver up to 6000 gal./hr. of low-viscosity liquid.

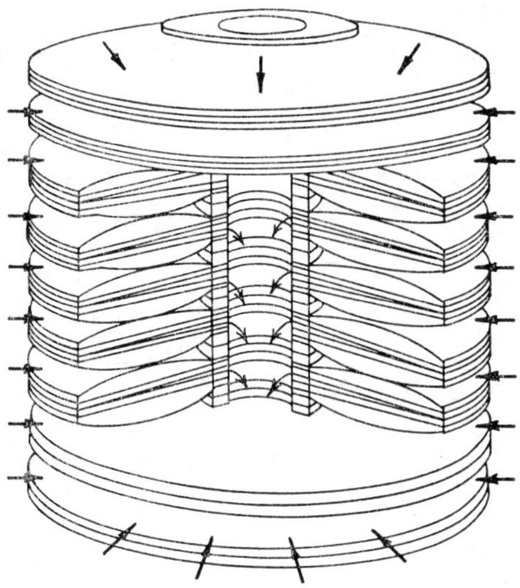

Fig. 19-129. Preassembled pack of clarifying-filter disks. (*Alsop Engineering Corp.*)

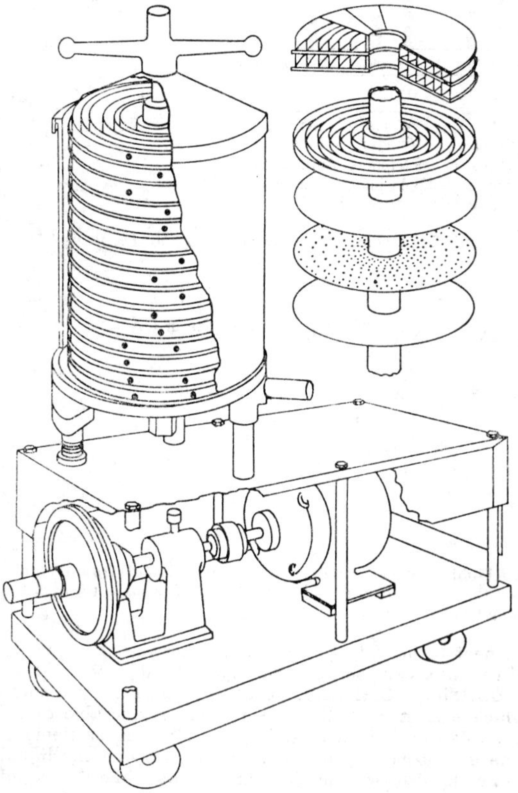

Fig. 19-130. Disk-and-plate clarifying-filter assembly. (*Alsop Engineering Corp.*)

Pulp filters employ one or more packs of filtermasse (cotton fibers compressed to a compact cylinder) stacked into a pressure case. The packs are sometimes supported in individual trays which provide drainage channels and sometimes rest on one another with a loose spacer plate between each two packs and with a drainage screen buried in the center of each pack. The liquid being clarified flows under a pressure of 50 lb./sq. in. or less through the pulp packs and into a drainage manifold. Flow rates are somewhat less than for disk filters, on the order of 0.5 gal./(min.)(sq. ft.). Pulp filters are used chiefly to polish beverages. The filtermasse may be washed in special washers and reformed into new cakes.

Plate presses, sometimes called sheet filters, are assemblies of paper or asbestos sheets, plates, and sometimes screens or frames. They are essentially modified filter presses with practically no cake-holding capacity. A press may consist of many plates or of a single filter sheet between two plates, the plates may be rectangular or circular, and the sheets may lie in a horizontal or in a vertical plane. The operation is similar to that of a filter press, and the flow rates are about the same as for disk filters. The operating pressure usually does not exceed 20 lb./sq. in. The presses are used most frequently for low-viscosity liquids, but an ordinary filter press with thin frames is often used as a clarifier for 1000-poise rayon-spinning solution. In the latter case, the filter medium is usually a layer-built carded-cotton web or a sandwich pack of pulp sheets, canton flannel, and muslin. The filtration pressure may be 1000 lb./sq. in.

Disk, pulp, and sheet filters accomplish extreme clarification, removing particles larger than 0.01 micron and smaller than 5 microns (particles larger than 5 microns normally are removed by a roughing filter which precedes the polishing operation). Such a wide spectrum of particle size dictates a considerable variety of filter media, as is illustrated by Fig. 19-131. Indicated are the grades of asbestos pad offered by one manufacturer, the approximate particle size retained by each, the water permeabilities at 10 lb./sq. in. differential, and some of the clarifying applications.

Precoat Pressure Filters. Precoat pressure filters consist of one or more leaves, plates, or tubes upon which a coat of diatomaceous earth or other filter aid is deposited to form a filtering surface for clarification. Filter paper is often substituted for a precoat. Additional filter aid may be mixed with the liquid to be filtered, particularly if the solids are gelatinous or sticky, in order to maintain a higher average filtration rate. Precoat pressure clarifying filters are essentially no different from pressure cake filters, except for the purpose to which they are put. Although with the proper choice of diatomaceous earth and filtration rate they may become essentially a polishing filter, they are more often used with "faster" filter aid and at higher rates as roughing clarifiers. Thus they may precede the polishing filters in beverage processing, they are widely used as dry-cleaning-solvent-recovery units, and they have been adapted for swimming-pool-water clarification.

The filtering elements may be screen-covered vertical rectangular leaves in a vertical cylindrical tank, screen-covered vertical circular leaves in a horizontal cylindrical tank, circular porous ceramic leaves, wire-wound cylindrical leaves, or hollow tubes of porous stone, porous carbon, wire cloth, or porous stainless-steel sheet. They may be fabric-covered. One arrangement permits sampling of each individual leaf discharge and also allows the operator to remove any one leaf from service. Plate-and-frame presses also have been adapted to precoat-clarification use.

Much of the novelty in precoat pressure filters lies in the methods employed to remove the cake at the end of a cycle. Since the cake discharges cleanly from the

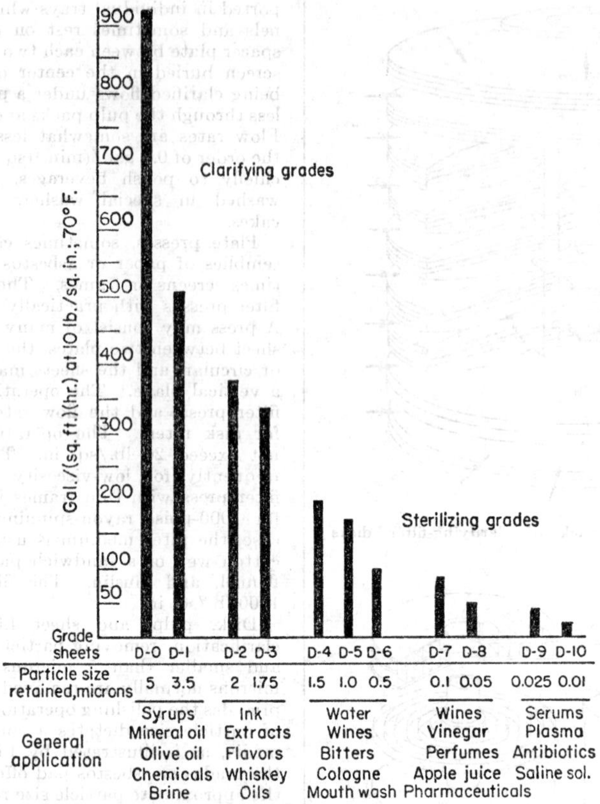

Fig. 19-131. Permeabilities and particle retention of asbestos clarifying media. (*F. R. Hormann & Co., Inc.*)

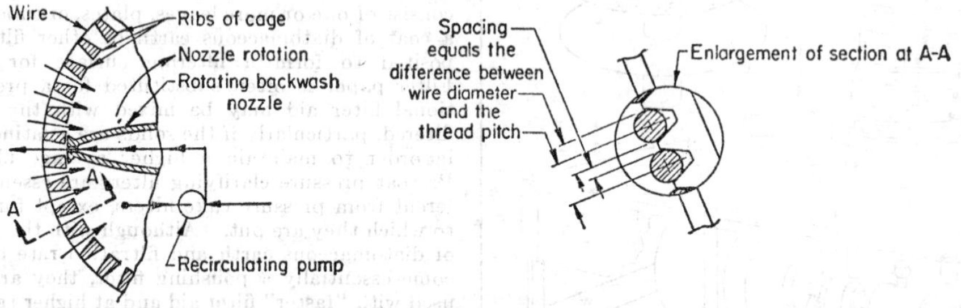

Fig. 19-132. Sectional view of Cuno Flo-Klean backwashing edge filter. Fluid pumped through the nozzle loosens solids from the filter surface and clears the filtering area. The pump draws filtered fluid from the filter dishcarge and returns it to the system through the nozzle. Thus there is no loss of backwash fluid. (*Cuno Engineering Corp.*)

filtering elements and normally is discarded, there is opportunity to remove it without opening the filter shell. Thus precoat clarifiers exactly resemble wet-discharge cake filters of the pressure-leaf type, the same design features and operating procedures applying to both (see pp. 19-67ff). Cake is discharged by simple backwash, by blowback of air, by sparging, by vibration, by scraping, by centrifugal action, and by a variety of sluicing-spray arrangements. Many of these methods are patented and are the chief sales point discriminating among highly competitive and otherwise remarkably similar equipment.

Care must be taken in operating precoat filters that a complete uniform layer of filter aid is deposited on the element before filtration starts. Otherwise the capacity of the filter can soon be seriously reduced.

Cartridge Clarifiers. Cartridge clarifiers are units which consist of or use one or more replaceable or renewable cartridges containing the active filter element. The unit usually is placed in a line carrying the liquid to be clarified; clarification thus occurs while the liquid is in transit. Mechanical or edge filters consist of stacks of metal disks separated to precise intervals by spacer plates, or a wire wound on a cage in grooves of a precise pitch, or a combination of the two. The liquid to be filtered flows radially between the disks, wires, or layers of paper, and particles larger than the spacing are screened out. Edge filters can remove particles down to 0.001 in.

(25 microns) but more often have a minimum spacing of twice this value. They have small solids-retaining capacity and hence must be cleaned often to avoid plugging. Continuous cleaning is provided in some filters. For example, Cuno's Flo-Klean (Fig. 19-132), a wire-wound unit, employs a slowly rotating nozzle which backwashes the element with filtered liquid; and Cuno's Auto-Klean (Fig. 19-133) is equipped with a scraper that

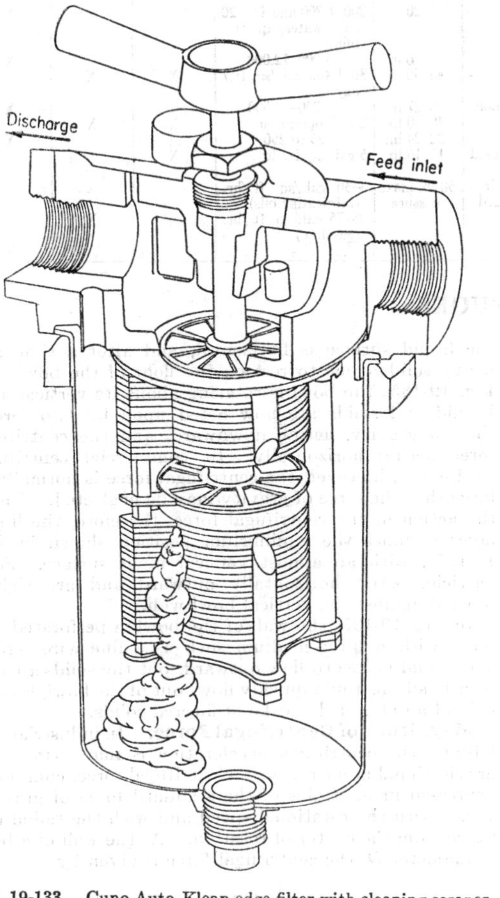

Fig. 19-133. Cuno Auto-Klean edge filter with cleaning scraper. (*Cuno Engineering Corp.*)

fits into the interdisk slots to comb away accumulated solids. In either case, the dislodged solids fall into a sump that may be drained at intervals.

The greatest number of cartridge clarifiers are of the micronic class, with elements of fiber, resin-impregnated filter paper, porous stone, or porous stainless steel of controlled porosity. Other rustless metals are also available. The elements may be chosen to remove particles larger than a fraction of a micron, although many are made to pass 10-micron solids and smaller. By proper choice of multiple-cylinder cartridges or multiple cartridges in parallel any desired flow rate can be obtained at a reasonable pressure drop (often less than 20 lb./sq. in.). A multi-element filter using wound-yarn tubes is shown in Fig. 19-134.

When the pressure rises to the permissible maximum, the cartridge must be opened and the element replaced. Micronic elements of the fiber type cannot be cleaned

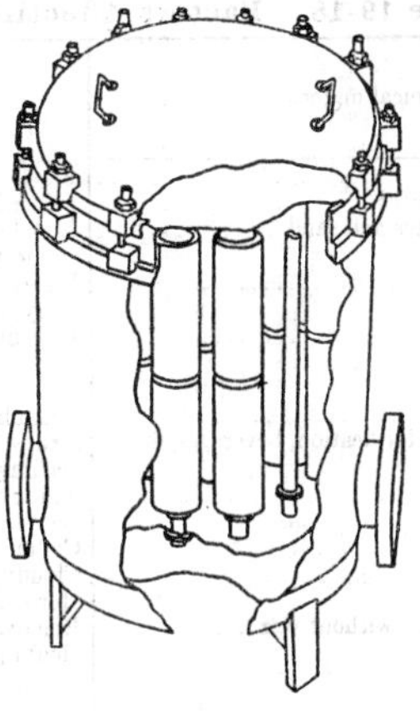

Fig. 19-134. Multi-element cartridge clarifier. (*Commercial Filter Corp.*)

and are so priced that they can be discarded or the filter medium replaced economically. Stone elements usually must be cleaned, a process best accomplished by the manufacturer of the porous ceramic or in accordance with his directions. The user can clean stainless-steel elements by chemical treatment.

Some cartridges are packed with adsorbent carbon or fuller's earth for oil purification and some are combinations of paper or cloth and wire screen. Fuller's earth or other adsorbent filter media should be used with caution if lubricating or cutting oil is being filtered. The adsorbent action of the media may remove valuable additives from the oil.

Miscellaneous Clarifiers. Certain oil clarifiers pump or percolate the oil through chambers packed with waste, non-metallic fiber, adsorbent solids, or through a cloth bag. The slow rate of gravity percolation makes it generally unsuitable for chemical process work.

For the selective removal of iron or other magnetic particles from a liquid (*e.g.*, from a clay slip), several magnetic separators are available. The Frantz Ferrofilter consists of a stack of soft-steel grids strongly magnetized by a direct-current coil or by a permanent magnet. The liquid to be filtered is flowed over the grids, which collect any magnetic solids present. Particles as small as 1 micron are said to be removed. The grids are cleaned by demagnetization and flushing. The Stearns magnetic-screen filter and the Eriez ferrous filter, which uses a permanent magnet, employ the same general principle. The Barnes Drill magnetic coolant separator flows the liquid around a magnetized rotating drum to which magnetic particles adhere. These are removed by a scraper blade.

Selection of Filtration Equipment

Proper selection of filtration equipment involves consideration of a large number of factors. In most problems it is necessary to make small-scale tests, as described earlier, after which a balance must be made among factors such as productive capacity, initial cost, operating costs (including maintenance), and reliability in service. Table 19-18 lists performance data and suitable types of filters for a number of representative materials. Smith and Chalmers *et al.* [*Chem. Eng.*, **62** (6), 177, 191 (1955)] discuss in detail the factors influencing the selection of filtration equipment.

Table 19-18. Factors Affecting Selection of Type of Filter and Character of Pulps Handled

Typical materials	Character	In. Hg vacuum or lb. pressure	Approx. filter capacity, lb./sq. ft./day	Type of filter suitable		
				Plate and frame	Shell type	Continuous vacuum
Cyanide slime	Finely ground quartz ores	18–25 in.	400– 2,000	..	..	X
Flotation concentrates	Minerals, finely ground	18–25 in.	400– 1,800	..	..	X
Gravity concentrates and sand	Metallic and non-metallic minerals almost free from slime	2– 6 in.	10,000–70,000	..	..	X
Cement slurry	Finely ground limestone and shale, or clay, etc.	18–25 in.	400– 2,000	..	..	X
Pulp and paper	Free-filtering fibers	6–20 in.	200–1,200 and 1½–20 gal. water/sq. ft./min.	..	..	X
Crystals, salt, etc.	Granular, crystalline	2– 6 in.	3,000–12,000	..	..	X
Cane-sugar-liquor clarification, beverages, etc.	Sirups and solution with small percentage of solids with filter aid	40–50 lb.	36–1,400 gal./sq. ft./day	X	X	
Pigments	Smeary, sticky, finely divided, non-crystalline	20–27 in.	200– 500	..	..	X
		40–50 lb.	Batch operation	X	X	
Sewage sludge	Colloidal and slimy	22–24 in.	25 to 250			X
Varnish	Cloudy viscous liquid, filter aid used for clarification. Filtered hot	15–16 lb.	5 gal./sq. ft./hr.	X	..	
Mineral oils, with or without wax	Removal of bleaching clay from petroleum products. 1 to 20% clay used	50 lb. max. pressure	3–30 gal./sq. ft./hr. (lubricating oils)	..	X	
			25–75 gal./sq. ft./hr. (gasoline)	..	X	
Cane mud	Vegetable fiber and cane juice	....	....	..	..	X

CENTRIFUGES

References: Ambler, *Chem. Eng. Progress*, **48**, 150 (1952). Flood, *Chem. Eng.*, **62** (6), 217 (1955). Grace, *Chem. Eng. Progress*, **49**, 427 (1953). Haruni and Storrow, *Chem. Eng. Sci.*, **2**, 164, 203 (1953). Smith, *Chem. Eng.*, **62** (6), 177 (1955).

General Principles. In liquid-solids separations centrifugal force is employed in both settling and filtration operations. In both cases it replaces the weaker force of gravity, resulting in more rapid settling and filtration and solid cakes containing less liquid.

Centrifugal separators make use of the familiar principle that an object whirled about a center point at a constant radial distance from that point is acted on by a force. The object is constantly changing direction and is thus accelerating even though the scalar magnitude of its velocity may be constant. This "centripetal acceleration" is caused by the centripetal force acting in the direction toward the center of rotation. If now the object is a cylindrical container, its contents exert an equal and opposite force—the "centrifugal force"—outward on the container walls. It is this force which causes sedimentation of heavy solid particles through a layer of liquid or filtration of a liquid through a bed of porous solids held inside a perforated rotating container.

These principles are illustrated in Fig. 19-135. In Fig. 19-135*a* a stationary cylindrical bowl contains a quantity of liquid and some particulate solids of greater density than the liquid. Since the bowl is not rotating the liquid surface is horizontal, and after a time any heavy solids come to rest on the floor of the bowl. In Fig. 19-135*b* the bowl is rotating about its vertical axis. Liquid and solids are now acted upon by two forces: that of gravity, acting downward, and the centrifugal force acting horizontally. In commercial centrifugal equipment, however, the centrifugal force is normally so large that the force of gravity may be neglected. Under the action of the centrifugal force, therefore, the liquid layer assumes the equilibrium position shown in Fig. 19-135*b*, with an almost vertical inner surface. Solid particles settle horizontally outward and are tightly pressed against the vertical bowl wall.

In Fig. 19-135*c* the wall of the bowl is perforated and lined with a filter medium such as a fine wire screen. The liquid is free to flow outward, but the solids are not. Nearly all the liquid quickly flows out of the bowl, leaving behind an almost dry cake of filtered solids.

Magnitude of Centrifugal Force. In industrial centrifuges the centrifugal acceleration is many times the gravitational acceleration. Centrifugal force, commonly expressed in multiples of the standard force of gravity, varies with the rotational speed and with the radial distance from the center of rotation. At the wall of a bowl of diameter D_b the centrifugal force is given by

$$F_c = 0.0000142 n^2 D_b \tag{19-23}$$

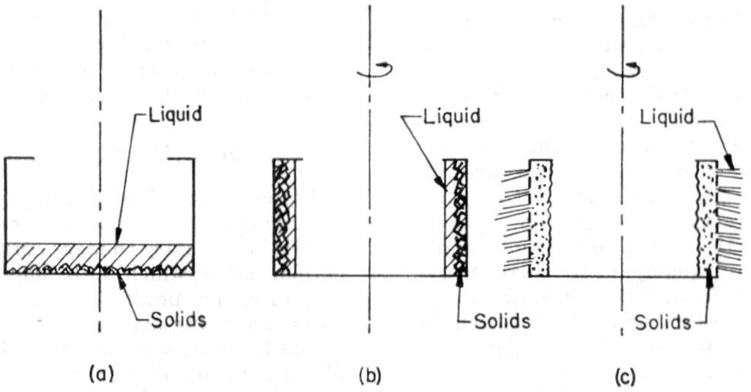

Fig. 19-135. Principles of centrifugal sedimentation and filtration: (*a*) Bowl stationary. (*b*) Sedimentation in rotating imperforate bowl. (*c*) Filtration in rotating perforated basket.

where F_c is the centrifugal force, multiples of gravity, n is the speed of rotation, r.p.m., and D_b is the bowl diameter, in.

Stress in Bowl Wall. Rotation of a centrifuge bowl generates a stress, known as the *self-stress*, in the bowl wall. In a thin-walled centrifuge bowl this stress is given by

$$S_s = 4.11 \times 10^{-10} n^2 D_b^2 \rho_m \tag{19-24}$$

where S_s is the self-stress, lb.$_f$/sq. in., and ρ_m is the density of the material of the bowl, lb./cu. ft.

The liquid layer in a centrifuge bowl exerts a pressure on the inner surface of the bowl. This pressure is found from the equation

$$P = 2.05 \times 10^{-9} \rho n^2 (D_b^2 - D_i^2) \tag{19-25}$$

where P is the pressure, lb.$_f$/sq. in., ρ is the liquid density, lb./cu. ft., and D_i is the diameter of the inner surface of the liquid, in. The liquid head causes an additional stress in the bowl wall S_e, which is

$$S_e = 1.03 \times 10^{-10} \frac{n^2 \rho D_b (D_b^2 - D_i^2)}{\delta} \tag{19-26}$$

where δ is the wall thickness, in. The total stress in the bowl wall S_T lb.$_f$/sq. in., is given by the equation

$$S_T = S_s + S_e$$

$$= 4.11 \times 10^{-10} n^2 D_b \left[\rho_m D_b + \frac{\rho (D_b^2 - D_i^2)}{4\delta} \right] \tag{19-27}$$

The liquid pressure in a high-speed centrifuge may be considerable, but usually the stress in the bowl wall is greater than the stress resulting from the liquid. For example, in a 16-in. bowl rotating at 5000 r.p.m. and containing a layer of water 3 in. thick, the liquid pressure at the bowl wall is 500 lb.$_f$/sq. in. If the bowl is made of stainless steel ½ in. thick, the total stress in the wall is 2090 lb.$_f$/sq. in., of which 62 per cent is self-stress and 38 per cent stress from the liquid head.

Equations (19-23) and (19-27) show that the centrifugal force increases with the diameter D_b and that the self-stress varies with D_b^2. Since the allowable self-stress normally limits the safe operating speed of a centrifuge, this means that with a given material of construction a high centrifugal force can be obtained with a small-diameter bowl but that in a large bowl the maximum centrifugal force is comparatively small. Figure 19-136 shows the range of diameter of commercial centrifugal equipment and the approximate maximum centrifugal force developed. The highest forces are produced in sedimentation centrifuges which do not discharge solids by mechanical conveyors.

Materials of Construction. Centrifuges are made from any machinable alloy strong enough to withstand the stresses. The strength required for a low-speed basket centrifugal is much less than for a high-speed sedimentation centrifuge so that the choice of material is much broader for the slower machine. Steel, rubber-covered steel, stainless steel, and monel are common materials of construction for basket centrifugals. With high-speed centrifuges the choice is much more limited, with most rotors made of high-strength carbon steel, tinned steel, or stainless steel, usually type 316. Other stainless steels such as types 302, 304, and 431, and K monel, inconel, Hastelloy C, and titanium are occasionally used. The casing and feed and discharge lines, since they are stationary, can be made of any suitable corrosion-resistant material.

Critical Speed. In the design of any high-speed rotating machinery attention must be paid to the

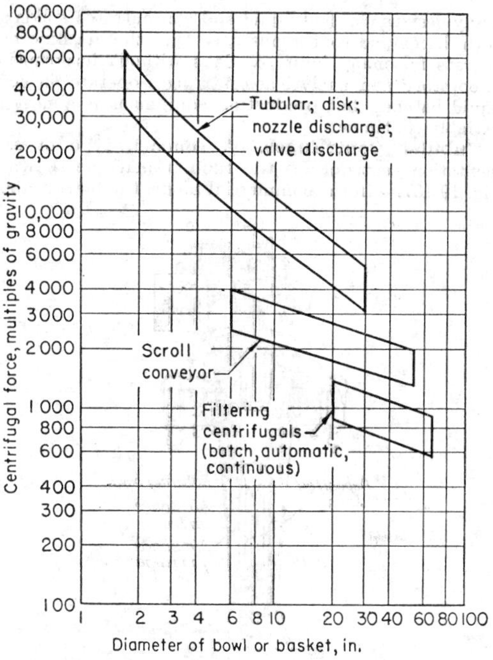

FIG. 19-136. Variation of centrifugal force with diameter in industrial centrifuges.

phenomenon of critical speed. This is the speed at which the frequency of rotation matches the natural frequency of the rotating part. At this speed any vibration induced by slight unbalance in the rotor is strongly reinforced, resulting in large deflections, high stresses, and even failure of the equipment. Speeds corresponding to harmonics of the natural frequency are also critical speeds but give relatively small deflections and are much less troublesome than the fundamental frequency. Critical speed of simple shapes may be calculated from the moment of inertia; with complex elements such as a loaded centrifuge bowl it is best found by experiment. Nearly all centrifuges operate at speeds well above the primary critical speed and must therefore pass through this speed during acceleration and deceleration. This is not a problem, however, provided the bowl is not seriously unbalanced.

SEDIMENTATION CENTRIFUGES

Sedimentation centrifuges remove solids from liquids by causing solid particles to "settle" through the liquid radially toward or away from the center of rotation. If the solids are less dense than the liquid they move inward to the liquid surface. If they are more dense than the liquid they "sink" outward and deposit on the inner surface of the bowl, from which they are removed manually, or mechanically, by a conveyor or a knife. In some centrifuges heavy solids are not allowed to deposit on the bowl wall but escape continuously through nozzles as a thick slurry. Sedimentation centrifuges are usually comparatively small in diameter and may operate at extremely high speeds.

Continuous Equipment. Most sedimentation centrifuges operate continuously, or nearly so, with respect to the feed and liquid discharge. In some applications it is necessary to interrupt the flow periodically to permit removal of accumulated solids. This interruption may be as long as 30 min. or as short as a few seconds. In many designs clarified liquid and concentrated solids are both discharged continuously, so that the machine may operate for many hours or days without interruption. Laboratory and analytical centrifuges operate on small liquid batches, but production equipment is almost invariably continuous.

Tubular Centrifuges. A common type of sedimentation centrifuge is the tubular machine shown in Fig. 19-137. In the commercial model the bowl is about

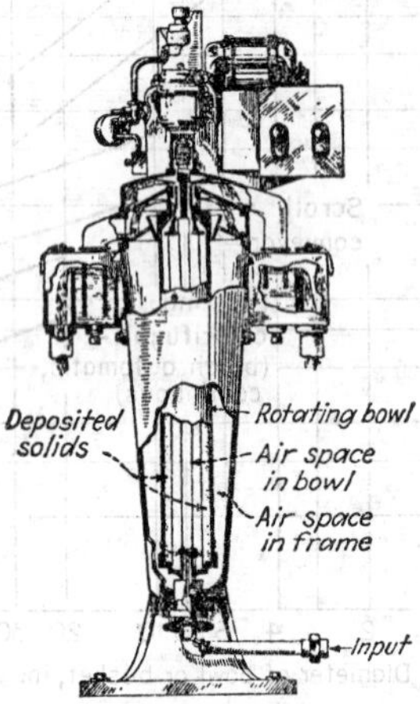

FIG. 19-137. Tubular-bowl high-speed centrifuge.

4 in. in diameter and 30 in. long. It turns about a vertical axis at 15,000 r.p.m., generating a force 13,200 times that of gravity. The bowl is suspended from the top and hangs free with only a loose guide at the bottom; thus the bowl can find its own center of mass as its axis of rotation if it becomes slightly unbalanced from accumulated solids. Such provisions for unbalance must be made in all centrifuges except slow-speed units for special purposes, for even a small unbalance can quickly destroy the centrifuge if no compensation is made for the enormous forces resulting from the unbalance.

Feed enters the bottom of the tubular centrifuge through a stationary nozzle, under sufficient pressure to jet upward into the bowl. It is accelerated to bowl speed and forms a layer on the inner wall of the bowl. Solids are drawn upward by the liquid flow, so that their trajectory in the bowl is curved toward the wall. If the trajectory of a given particle intersects the bowl wall, the particle is removed from the liquid; if it does not, the particle appears in the effluent. Successful clarification therefore requires the correct balance among many factors, as discussed later under Theory of Centrifugal Sedimentation.

The liquid layer does not always completely fill the bowl. When it does not, the depth of the layer is controlled by the position of the overflow port at the top of the bowl. To prevent "slip" of the liquid, and to accelerate it rapidly to full bowl speed, an assembly of three vertical blades called a "three-wing" is inserted in the bowl.

Liquid escapes from the top of the bowl into the stationary casing and leaves the machine through a discharge pipe. It leaves the bowl at high velocity and strikes the casing with considerable force. During discharge, it breaks up into tiny droplets and is often partially vaporized. Some models therefore have a completely enclosed discharge section to prevent loss of volatile liquids. In other operations the liquid foams on discharging, or contact of the liquid with air must be minimized, as in the clarification of fruit juices. Under such conditions the liquid is removed from tubular centrifuges by collector tubes which extend into the liquid layer, which "scoop out" liquid under pressure with little or no air inclusion. Other devices for removing liquid without aeration are described under Disk Centrifuges.

By providing two liquid outlets at different radial distances from the bowl axis, as shown in Fig. 19-137, it is possible to remove two immiscible liquids simultaneously from the centrifuge bowl. The lighter liquid forms a layer near the center of the bowl and discharges as in a clarifier centrifuge; the heavy liquid forms an outer layer and discharges into a separate part of the casing. Solids are removed by sedimentation from both liquids, and collect in the bowl as with a single liquid. Liquid-liquid separators of this kind are described in Sec. 21.

The liquid-handling capacity of a tubular clarifier depends on the relative densities of solids and liquid, the size and shape of the solid particles, the liquid viscosity, and the degree of clarification desired. A 4-in.-diameter centrifuge typically handles 30 to 60 gal./hr. on difficult separations and up to 1200 gal./hr. on easier separation problems. Detailed performance characteristics are listed in Table 19-19.

Solids are removed manually from this type of centrifuge. Sometimes a parchment-paper liner is placed in the bowl to facilitate removal of the solids. Only 5 to 10 lb. of solids may normally be collected in a tubular bowl before the quality of the clarified product is affected. Since it is rarely economical to clean a centrifuge by hand more than once an hour, the concentration of solids in the feed must therefore be less than 0.5 to 1 per cent by weight.

Multichamber Centrifuges. To increase the distance the liquid must travel in passing through the centrifuge, the bowl is sometimes divided into several—from two to as many as six—annular chambers. Figure 19-138

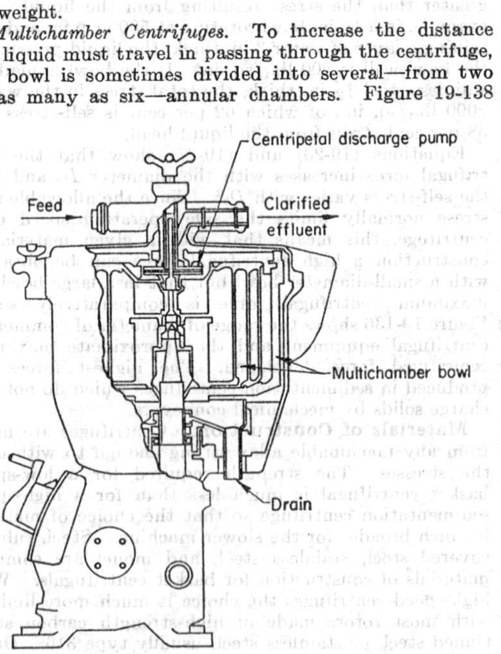

FIG. 19-138. Multichamber centrifuge. (*The De Laval Separator Co.*)

shows a three-chamber bowl. Feed enters the top of these bowls through a central pipe, and flows outward through the bowl. Coarse solids are thrown down against the inner surface of the innermost chamber;

finer ones are carried to the outer chambers. Eventually, as the inner chambers become filled, more and more solids are carried into the outer chambers. The total dirt-handling capacity of a given bowl is not increased by division into chambers, but the separate removal of coarse and fine particles, in different parts of the bowl, gives more complete removal in some separations than with a simple tubular bowl. In addition, as long as the outer chamber is free of solids the liquid leaving the centrifuge is subjected to the maximum centrifugal force developed by the machine. In a simple chamber the accumulation of solids progressively reduces the effective diameter of the bowl and lowers the centrifugal force.

Disk Centrifuges. The most common type of clarifier centrifuge is the disk machine illustrated in Fig. 19-139. Feed is admitted to the center of the bowl near its floor and rises through a stack of sheet-metal "disks"—actually truncated cones—spaced 0.022 to 0.050 in. apart. The half angle made by the disks with the vertical is typically between 35 and 50 deg. Each disk carries several holes, ¼ to ½ in. in diameter, which form, when the disks are assembled in place in the bowl, several channels through which the liquid rises.

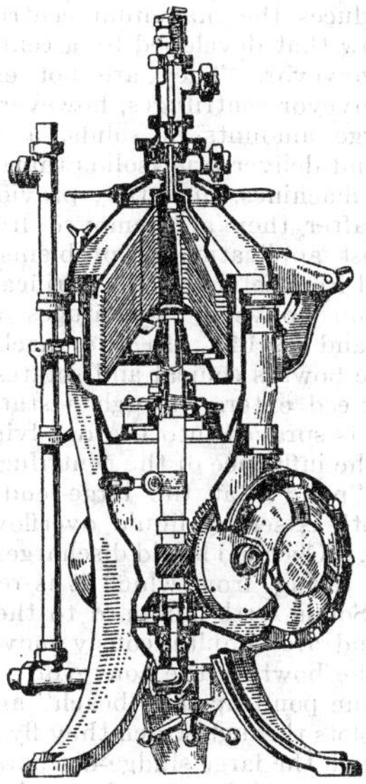

FIG. 19-139. Disk centrifuge with closed feed and discharge.

The purpose of the disks is primarily to reduce the sedimentation distance, since a solid particle must travel only a short distance before it reaches the underside of one of the disks. Once there it is in effect removed from the liquid, for the chance of its reentrainment in the effluent is small. It continues to move outward, however, because of the centrifugal force and also the liquid flow, until it is deposited on the wall of the bowl.

In the simple disk machine shown in Fig. 19-139 the accumulated solids must be removed periodically by hand, as in a tubular centrifuge. This requires stopping and disassembling the bowl and removal of the disk stack. Although the individual disks rarely require cleaning, manual removal of solids is economical only when the percentage of solids in the feed is very small. In the machines described later the solids are removed automatically without reducing the bowl speed.

Liquid may be discharged from the bowl through overflow ports as in a tubular centrifuge. Other ways of removing the liquid have been devised to avoid foaming and contact with air and to allow liquid removal under pressure. In the "hermetic centrifuge" shown in Fig. 19-139 feed enters the bowl through a hollow spindle at the bottom, and clarified liquid leaves through the central pipe at the top. Rotary seals between the bowl and the stationary feed and discharge pipes permit operation under pressures of 80 to 100 $lb._f$/sq. in. A valve in the discharge line keeps this pressure constant. Other designs contain a centripetal pump or "paring ring," with a vaned pump impeller mounted on the stationary feed pipe. Such a pump is illustrated in Fig. 19-138. Rotating liquid enters the outside of the impeller and flows inward between the stationary vanes to the annular chamber surrounding the feed pipe, and from there to the discharge. In the impeller the kinetic energy of the liquid is largely converted into pressure energy, so that the liquid leaves the bowl at pressures up to 100 $lb._f$/sq. in.

Disk centrifuges range in diameter from 7 to 30 in. and develop 4000 to 10,000 times the force of gravity. Their sedimenting effectiveness is very nearly the same as that of a tubular centrifuge, despite the lower centrifugal force. With some solids they are slightly less effective, on others slightly more effective, than a tubular machine. They are effective also as liquid-liquid separators, and especially so for the concentration of emulsions. By far the largest number of centrifuges sold for one purpose are "cream separators" for the concentration of butterfat in milk. These machines are all of the disk type.

Nozzle-discharge Centrifuges. Solids are removed continuously from the centrifuges shown in Fig. 19-140.

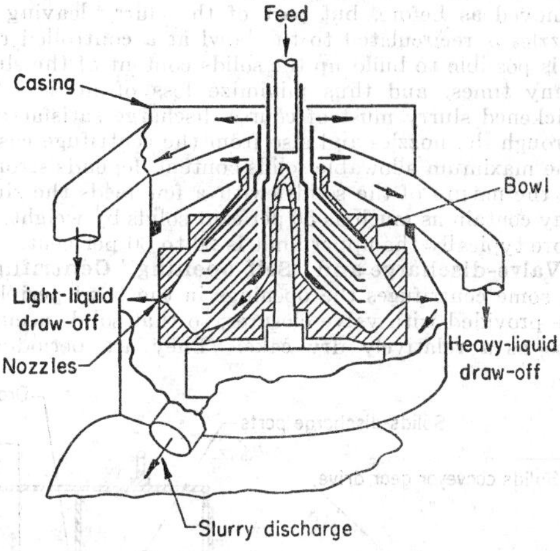

FIG. 19-140. Nozzle-discharge centrifuge. (*From McCabe and Smith, "Unit Operations of Chemical Engineering," McGraw-Hill, New York,* 1956, *by permission.*)

The bowl is much like that of a disk centrifuge except that it is more massive and carries several peripheral nozzles, typically 1 to 3 mm. in diameter. Clarified liquor is removed from the top of the bowl as in a simple disk machine; a slurry of concentrated solids continuously flows through the nozzles. By directing the nozzles tangentially away from the direction of rotation the power needed to drive the rotor is almost cut in half, because of the recovery of most of the kinetic energy from the discharge through the nozzles.

Many nozzle-discharge machines provide for only a single passage of the solids through the centrifugal field. The solids content of the discharged slurry, for a given feed rate and bowl speed, then depends on the size and

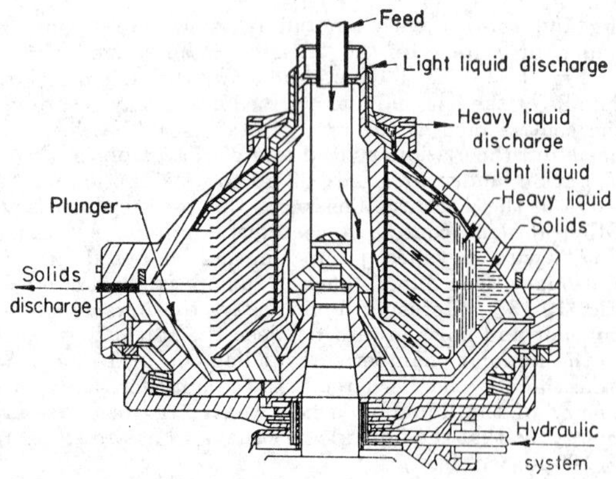

FIG. 19-141. "Self-opening" peripheral-annulus discharge. centrifuge. (*De Laval Separator Co.*)

the number of nozzles. In such a machine the slurry concentration is usually low, and relatively large amounts of liquid are withdrawn with the solids. Once-through nozzle machines are therefore most used when clarification is accompanied by liquid-liquid separations, as in the removal of water and pulp from citrus oil. Here the liquid leaving with the pulp is water; the valuable clarified oil is removed from the light-liquid discharge without loss.

For clarification of a single liquid and controlled concentration of the discharged slurry a nozzle machine with recirculation is commonly used. Clarified liquid is removed as before, but part of the slurry leaving the nozzles is recirculated to the bowl at a controlled rate. It is possible to build up the solids content of the slurry many times, and thus minimize loss of liquid. The thickened slurry must of course discharge satisfactorily through the nozzles and also from the centrifuge casing. The maximum allowable solids content depends strongly on the nature of the solids; with a few feeds the slurry may contain as much as 50 per cent solids by weight, but more typically the upper limit is 20 to 30 per cent.

Valve-discharge and "Self-opening" Centrifuges. In some centrifuges the openings in the bowl periphery are provided with valve closures, so that solids accumulate as a relatively dry cake. They are periodically discharged, along with some liquid, by opening the valves. The valves are commonly opened by a hydraulic mechanism which injects liquid into the valve body; the mechanism is activated by external timers which control the frequency and duration of the open period. In other designs (Fig. 19-141) a hydraulically operated plunger within the bowl is periodically lowered to uncover a peripheral slit through which accumulated solids are discharged. Both machines deliver somewhat drier solids than does a once-through nozzle machine, and they can be designed to handle coarser particles, up to ¼ in. in diameter.

Mechanical-conveyor Centrifuges. Continuous mechanical removal of solids from a sedimentation centrifuge is done by one or more helical conveyors revolving in the same direction as the bowl, usually at a slightly lower speed. As shown in Fig. 19-136, this additional complexity reduces the maximum centrifugal force to somewhat below that developed by a centrifuge without an internal conveyor. They are not especially good clarifiers. Conveyor centrifuges, however, process feeds containing large amounts of solids, a wide range of particle size, and deliver drier solids than other types of sedimentation machines, since they provide for drainage of the solids after they are removed from the liquid. They find most application in problems involving removal of liquid from solids, not in clarification of liquids.

Two common conveyor centrifuges are shown in Figs. 19-142 and 19-143. In the machine shown in Fig. 19-142 the bowl is conical and rotates about a horizontal axis. Feed enters through a stationary central inlet pipe and is sprayed into the revolving bowl. The liquid, under the influence of the centrifugal force, forms a layer—the "pond"—at the large end of the bowl. The pond depth is set by liquid overflow ports in the bowl end plate. Clarified liquid discharges through these ports into the casing, from which it is removed by the outlet pipe. Solids settle outward to the inner surface of the bowl and are simultaneously moved toward the small end of the bowl by the conveyor. They are conveyed out of the pond up the "beach" and delivered to the discharge slots through which they fly into the casing and drop through the large sludge-discharge line. Wash liquid may be sprayed from wash nozzles on the solids as they are conveyed up the "beach"; this liquid flows toward the large end of the bowl and mixes with the clarified liquor.

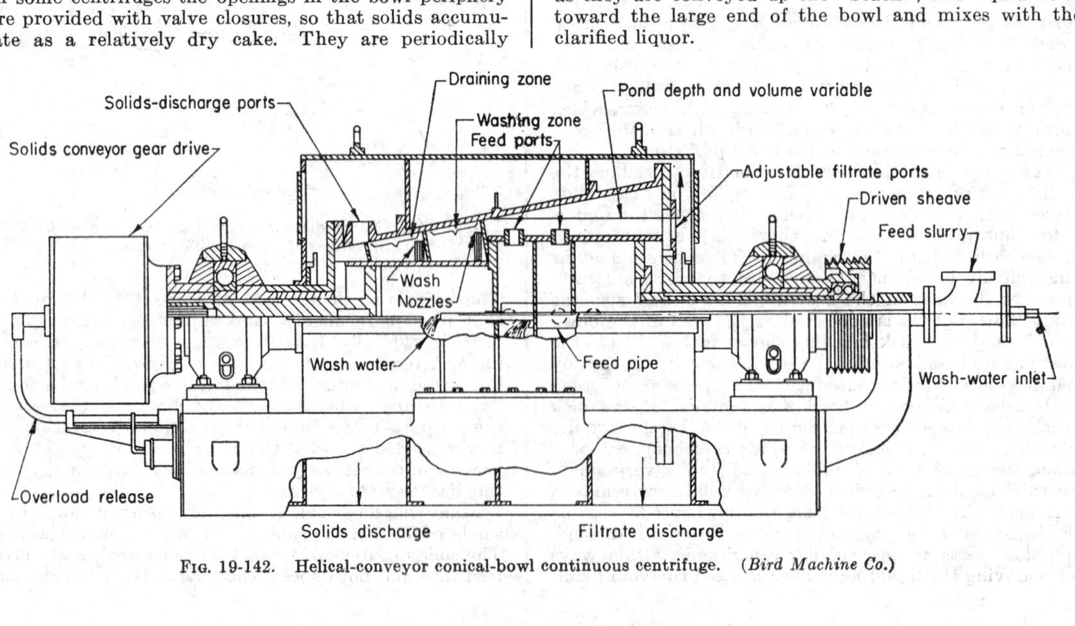

FIG. 19-142. Helical-conveyor conical-bowl continuous centrifuge. (*Bird Machine Co.*)

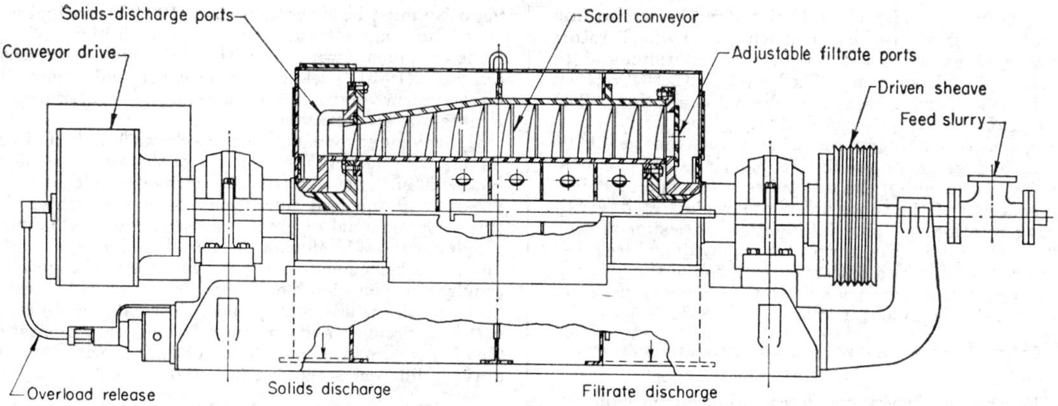

FIG. 19-143. Cylindrical-conical helical-conveyor centrifuge. (*Bird Machine Co.*)

A major problem in such a centrifuge is satisfactory clarification of the liquor. For the solids to convey properly there must be just the correct balance between the frictional force of the solids on the conveyor and the frictional force on the bowl wall. If the solids slide too easily on the bowl wall they turn freely with the conveyor, building up on the helix without moving toward the discharge. When the solids are under the liquid surface, in the "pond," the buoyancy of the liquid may greatly reduce the radial force, so that the frictional force is small. When the solids have been lifted out of the liquid into the "beach," the buoyant force no longer acts on them, and even though the centrifugal force is less than where the diameter is large, the net radial force on the solids may be greatly increased. Thus solids which convey well under the liquid may not convey up the "beach," and those which move readily on the dry "beach" may not convey well in the "pond." In extreme cases the solids are so buoyant they float on the liquid or at the interface between two liquid layers of differing densities.

Sometimes strips about 1/8 in. thick are attached to the bowl wall to increase the frictional resistance and permit the helix to convey the solids. In more stubborn problems the solution may be found in a machine with a bowl which is cylindrical, not conical, and in which the liquid layer extends almost from one end of the bowl to the other. Nearly all the conveying, therefore, is done on submerged solids. Near the solids discharge the diameter of the helix is reduced, so that deposited solids form a layer increasing in thickness toward the discharge ports. This stationary layer of solids becomes a steep "beach," up which even recalcitrant solids can often be conveyed. The same effect may also be obtained by inserting a metal filler piece of the proper shape, which minimizes the inventory of solids in the bowl.

Floating solids are readily moved toward the beach by the conveyor, provided dip weirs are included to prevent them from passing through the liquid-discharge ports. Similar weirs are also used with solids which collect at a liquid-liquid interface.

A design in which the bowl is partly cylindrical and partly conical is illustrated in Fig. 19-143. This machine combines some of the features of the centrifuges just discussed and has a wide range of application.

Washing in a helical conveyor centrifuge is usually fairly effective as long as most of the solid particles are larger than 74 microns (200 mesh) in diameter. Wash liquid does not pass through the solids directly; it flows in a stream over the solid layer in front of the helix, in a spiral path in the direction opposite to the motion of the conveyor, and eventually into the "pond." The solids must be sufficiently permeable for the wash liquid to displace residual liquor and leach out soluble material. With solid particles smaller than 43 microns (325 mesh) in diameter washing is completely ineffective.

Knife-discharge Clarifiers. Small amounts of coarse solids may be removed from large volumes of liquid in a knife-discharge clarifier, which in external appearance is much like the top-suspended filtering centrifugal shown in Fig. 19-145. It contains a solid "imperforate" bowl, 30 to 48 in. in diameter, in which solids accumulate. Liquid fills the bowl and overflows a lip at the top. Horizontal ring-shaped baffles inside the bowl keep the liquid from oscillating. When enough solids have collected the feed is shut off and the bowl speed reduced. Excess liquid is removed from the bowl by a manually adjusted skimmer pipe, and the wet solids are cut out by a knife and dropped through openings in the bowl floor.

Knife-discharge clarifiers with a horizontal bowl and fully automatic operation are also on the market. The sequence is the same as in manually operated vertical clarifiers, except that skimming and unloading are done at full basket speed. With very dilute feeds the liquid may be skimmed off several times before the solids are removed. Commercial machines of this type range in diameter from 12 to 96 in., with performance characteristics as shown in Table 19-19. In general knife-discharge clarifiers do not give perfect clarification and are often used to classify coarse or heavy solid particles from fine light ones.

Batch Laboratory Equipment. Sedimentation centrifuges handling discrete batches of liquid are nearly always for laboratory or analytical use, rarely for production. Representative types are test-tube centrifuges and ultracentrifuges.

Test-tube Centrifuges. In a test-tube centrifuge several tubes containing 10 to 1000 cc. of liquid are placed in a special head and spun at high speed about a vertical axis. Solids are thrown outward to the small end of the bottle, where their volume may be read on a graduated scale. By reading the volume of sediment after various known lengths of spinning time, the rate of sedimentation may be found. Ordinary test-tube centrifuges turn at speeds up to 12,000 r.p.m. and generate as much as 10,000 times the force of gravity at the bottle tip.

Ultracentrifuges. An ultracentrifuge is a special high-speed test-tube centrifuge, designed for sedimentation and analysis of very small particles such as viruses, proteins, high polymers, and pigments. Particles as small as 100 millimicrons in diameter can be settled in a reasonable time in such a machine. Typical rotors contain 12 celluloid test tubes, each containing 5 to 40 cc. of liquid, spun at a fixed angle with the vertical or allowed to swing free in a horizontal position. The rotor chamber is evacuated during operation. Commercial ultracentrifuges rotate at speeds up to 40,000 r.p.m. and generate up to 173,000 times the force of gravity at the end of the test tubes. In some machines the contents of the tubes are photographed at intervals during rotation, to give information on sedimentation rates. Originally the term "ultracentrifuge" referred to a machine in which optical observation of the progress of sedimentation was possible, but in current usage of the term this is no longer true.

Performance Characteristics of Sedimentation Centrifuges

The range of centrifugal force produced by commercially available sedimentation centrifuges is indicated in Fig. 19-136, and performance data for typical machines are given in Table 19-19. Excepting laboratory test-tube centrifuges, the highest forces are generated by simple tubular and disk machines. The addition of nozzles reduces the maximum force somewhat; conveyors or discharge knives reduce it considerably. The capacity ranges indicated are broad yet do not cover the complete operating range. The usual economical range of operation of a 4-in. tubular centrifuge, for example, is from 1 to 5 gal./min. of liquid, but with easy separations the machine may satisfactorily handle 20 gal./min., while in some difficult clarification problems the through-put may be limited to 0.5 gal./min. or even less. A nozzle-discharge centrifuge normally handles large volumes of liquid, but a 14-in. machine typically processes only 1 to 2 gal./min. when concentrating rubber latex. The power required, in addition, may vary by a factor of 2 or more from that indicated in Table 19-19.

Table 19-19. Specifications and Performance Characteristics of Typical Sedimentation Centrifuges

Type	Bowl diam., in.	Speed, r.p.m.	Max. centrifugal force × gravity	Through-put		Typical motor size, hp.
				Liquid, gal./min.	Solids, tons/hr.	
Tubular	1¾	50,000	62,000	....	....	*
	4¼	15,000	13,600	1–10	....	3
	5	15,000	16,000	1.5–15	....	3
Disk	7	12,000	14,300	0.1–1	....	⅓
	11½	6,000	5,900	4–40	....	5
	24	4,000	5,500	20–200	....	7½
Nozzle discharge	13¾	6,250	7,600	15–150	0.1–0.5	20
	30	3,000	3,830	40–400	0.5–2.5	125
Helical conveyor	6	6,000	3,070	10–20	0.25	3
	14	4,000	3,180	40	0.5–1.5	15
	18	3,500	3,130	50	0.5–1.5	15
	24	2,800	2,670	100	1.5–3	30
	32	1,800	1,470	250	3–6	60
	40	1,600	1,450	375	10–18	100
	54	1,000	770	750	35–90	150
Knife discharge	20	1,800	920	†	1.0‡	20
	36	1,200	740	†	4.1‡	30
	66	850	680	†	20.5‡	40

* Turbine drive, 100 lb./hr. steam at 40 lb./sq. in.

† Liquid through-put varies widely, depending on feed concentration and clarity desired.

‡ Maximum volume of solids in bowl, cu. ft.

Successful applications of continuous sedimentation centrifuges have been made at temperatures between −100° and 350°F., and pressures between atmospheric, or slightly below, to 150 lb.$_f$/sq. in. The feed must be fluid enough to flow into the machine, and the concentrated sludge must flow out, which means their viscosity must be lower than about 100,000 centipoises at operating temperatures. Capacities with highly viscous feeds are much lower than with thin liquids, as indicated by Eq. (19-31) below. Explosive liquids, including nitroglycerin, have been successfully centrifuged in remote-operated machines.

Helical-conveyor centrifuges rarely work well in viscous liquors. Preferably the viscosity of the solids-free liquid phase should not exceed 20 centipoises, although the viscosity of the feed slurry may be much greater than this. Commercial machines can separate solid particles ranging from ½ in. down to 1 micron in diameter. Satisfactory performance with very fine particles, however, requires a considerable difference in specific gravity between the solids and liquid. Normally a difference of 0.1 in specific gravity means relatively easy separation. Good performance has been obtained with specific-gravity differences ranging from 0.02 to 3.2.

Theory of Centrifugal Sedimentation

A solid particle settling through a liquid in a centrifugal-force field is subjected to a constantly increasing force as it travels away from the axis of rotation. It therefore never reaches a true "terminal" velocity. However, at any given radial distance r its settling velocity u_t is very nearly given by the Stokes's-law relation

$$u_t = \frac{\omega^2 r(\rho_p - \rho)D_p^2}{18\mu} \tag{19-28}$$

where ω is the rate of rotation, radians/sec.; ρ_p and ρ are the densities of solid and liquid, respectively, lb./cu. ft.; D_p is the equivalent diameter of a spherical solid particle, ft.; and μ is the liquid viscosity, lb./ft.-sec.

If settling takes place in a cylindrical or tubular bowl of radius r, ft., containing a thin layer of liquid of thickness s, ft., the flow rate at which half the solid particles will be removed from the liquid is given by

$$Q_c = \frac{(\rho_p - \rho)D_p^2 V\omega^2 r}{9\mu s} \tag{19-29}$$

where Q_c is the volumetric flow rate, in cu. ft./sec., and V is the volume, in cu. ft., of liquid held in the bowl. With a given flow rate Q, the *critical diameter*, or "cut point," D_{pc} is given by

$$D_{pc} = \sqrt{\frac{9Q\mu s}{(\rho_p - \rho)V\omega^2 r}} \tag{19-30}$$

Most particles with diameters larger than D_{pc} will be eliminated by the centrifuge; most particles with smaller diameters will appear in the effluent.

When the space for sedimentation is not cylindrical or the liquid layer is thick, Eq. (19-30) must be written

$$Q_c = \frac{(\rho_p - \rho)D_p^2 V\omega^2 r_e}{9\mu s_e} \tag{19-31}$$

where r_e and s_e are the appropriate averaged values of radius and layer thickness, in ft., for the given conditions. Equation (19-31) may be written

$$Q_c = \frac{2(\rho_p - \rho)D_p^2 g}{18\mu}\,\frac{V\omega^2 r_e}{g s_e} = 2u_g\Sigma$$

where u_g is the terminal settling velocity, in ft./sec., of the solid particle in a gravitational field and Σ is a characteristic of the centrifuge [Ambler, *Chem. Eng. Progress*, **48**, 150 (1952)]. Physically Σ is the area, in sq. ft., of a gravity settling tank of equivalent sedimentation characteristics to the centrifuge. For a tubular centrifuge it is approximately given by the equation

$$\Sigma = \frac{\pi b \omega^2}{4g}(3r_2^2 + r_1^2) \qquad (19\text{-}32)$$

where r_2 is the radius of the inner wall of the bowl, r_1 is the radius of the liquid surface, and b is the length of the bowl. For a disk centrifuge the equation is

$$\Sigma = \frac{2\pi(N-1)(r_b^3 - r_a^3)\omega^2}{3g \tan \theta} \qquad (19\text{-}33)$$

where N is the number of disks in the stack, r_a and r_b are the inner and outer radii of the disk stack, and θ is the conical half angle.

Typical Σ values for three types of sedimentation centrifuges are given in Table 19-20. In scaling up from laboratory tests or in comparing one type of centrifuge with another, sedimentation performance should be the same if the value of Q/Σ is the same for the two machines. Thus a 4-in. tubular centrifuge should have $^{27,100}\!/_{3080}$ or 8.8 times the capacity of a 1.75-in. laboratory machine.

Table 19-20. Scale-up Factors for Sedimentation Centrifuges*

Type of centrifuge	Diam., in.	Speed, r.p.m.	Σ value, sq. ft. Calculated	Σ value, sq. ft. Recommended for scale-up
Tubular	1¾	23,000	3,080	1,300
Tubular	4⅛	15,000	27,100	27,100
Disk	11½	6,000	133,700	68,000–133,000
Helical conveyor	14	3,250	8,930	6,000

* From Ambler, The Evaluation of Centrifuge Performance, *Chem. Eng. Progress*, 48, 150 (1952), by permission.

At low feed rates this is borne out by experiment; at high feed rates the large machine has about twenty times the capacity of the small one, because of fluid-dynamic effects in the small centrifuge which are not considered in the simple theory. The capacities of a disk machine and a helical-conveyor sludge separator are, in general, somewhat lower than predicted by theory. The conveyor tends to resuspend solid particles in the liquid; in a disk centrifuge the liquid issuing from the holes in the disk stack is swirled vigorously in a direction opposite to the rotation of the bowl, creating a complex flow path which is not allowed for in the derivation of Eq. (19-33).

FILTERING CENTRIFUGALS

Centrifuges which filter—that is, cause the liquid to flow through a bed of solids held on a screen—are commonly called "centrifugals." They are sometimes known by the other names "whizzers," "wringers," "extractors," or "dryers." They include batch machines, manually operated or partially automated, completely automatic batch machines designed to fit into continuous processes, and continuous machines. In principle they are all the same: in each type a cake of granular solids is deposited on a filter medium held in a rotating basket, washed, and spun "dry." The types differ chiefly in the way in which the solids are removed from the basket.

Batch Equipment. Batch filtering centrifuges, other than some fully automatic machines, contain a metal basket, usually perforated, rotating about a vertical axis. Inside the basket is a metal support screen, and inside that a filter medium of fabric or fine metal cloth. In small machines the basket may be held rigidly by a bearing in the base of a solid casing or curb; larger baskets must be allowed freedom to seek their own center of rotation. This is done by suspending the entire machine from rods or link chains, or by suspending the basket from above so that it turns freely in a rigidly mounted casing.

Base-bearing Centrifugals. Small heavy-duty centrifugals with a basket rigidly held in a base bearing are used chiefly for special operations such as wringing cutting oil from metal chips in machine shops, painting, enameling, and impregnation of porous solids. The basket often has a solid wall, not perforated, and is slightly larger at the top than at the bottom. Liquid is thrown outward, percolates upward through the solids, and overflows the top of the basket. Solids to be processed are shoveled into the basket or placed in it by hand, and are often unloaded manually also.

The rotational speed is fairly low but because the loaded basket is usually somewhat unbalanced the stresses are high and the machinery must be ruggedly built. A typical heavy-duty chip-oil extractor contains a basket 23 in. in diameter at the bottom, 26 in. in diameter at the top, and 18 in. deep. It holds 5 cu. ft. or 500 lb. of crushed steel chips and will process 20 loads per hour. It is driven at 1025 r.p.m. by a 10-hp. motor. Other base-bearing centrifugals range from 6 to 30 in. in diameter.

Link-suspended Centrifugals. A link-suspended centrifugal is shown in Fig. 19-144. Casing, basket, and drive assembly are suspended from three posts set on the floor. Solids are placed in the basket after the hinged cover is opened and are removed from the top when

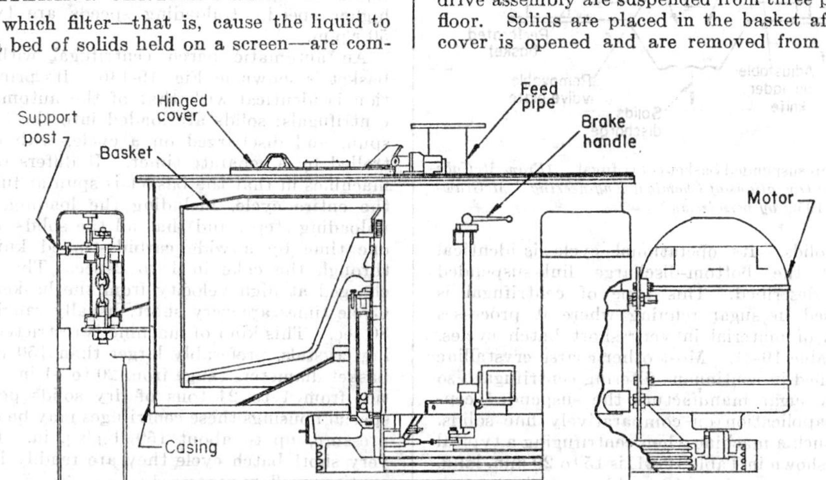

Fig. 19-144. Link-suspended batch centrifugal. *(Tolhurst Division, Ametek, Inc.)*

centrifuging is complete. For this the basket may be stopped or may revolve slowly in the reverse direction. A safety switch prevents starting the machine until the cover is locked in place. Liquid spun from the solids is removed from the casing by a discharge pipe. This design is commonly used for spinning liquids out of textiles as in dyeing and dry-cleaning operations. Sizes range from 30 to 108 in. in diameter.

Granular solids are processed in link-suspended centrifuges with bottom discharge. Feed slurry is admitted through a large pipe to build up a thick layer of solids, which is washed and spun "dry." After the spinning the basket speed is reduced from 900 to 50 to 75 r.p.m. The solids are peeled out of the basket by a manually operated unloader knife. They drop through large openings in the floor of the basket and through the open bottom of the casing. Typical machines handle 6 to 10 cu. ft. of solids per batch.

Top-suspended Centrifugals. Figure 19-145 shows a top-suspended centrifugal designed to handle crystalline

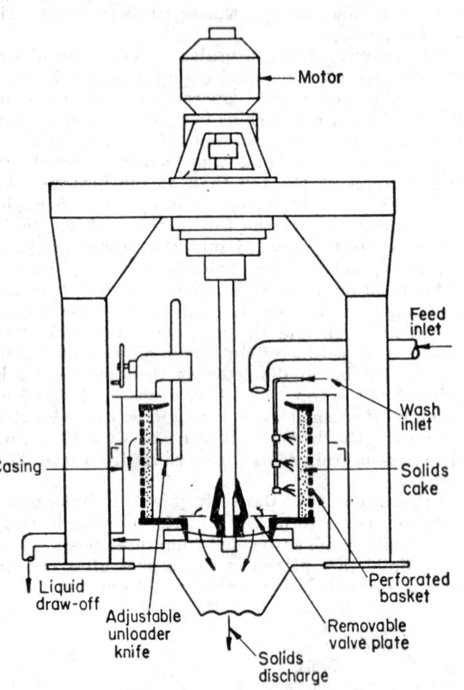

FIG. 19-145. Top-suspended basket centrifugal. *(From McCabe and Smith, "Unit Operations of Chemical Engineering," McGraw-Hill, New York, 1956, by permission.)*

or granular solids. Its operational cycle is identical with that of the bottom-discharge link-suspended machine just described. This type of centrifugal is extensively used in sugar refining where it processes large amounts of material in very short batch cycles, as shown in Table 19-21. Most other coarse crystalline solids are handled in continuous filtering centrifugals, so that except in sugar manufacture the suspended centrifugal finds application on comparatively fine solids. The cycle for such a machine when centrifuging a typical precipitate, as shown in Table 19-21, is 15 to 20 min. long. Basket diameters range from 12 to 48 in., with the centrifugal force diminishing with increased diameter as indicated by Fig. 19-136. These machines handle 0.2 to 11 cu. ft. of solids per batch. Fumetight casings are available to minimize loss of volatile liquids and to contain toxic substances.

Manual operation of a batch centrifuge requires almost constant attention by an operator, although with proper arrangement of the equipment it is possible for one man to operate several machines. Often parts of the cycle, such as washing and spinning, are automatically controlled. In some high-volume processes, such as sugar manufacture, it is economical to make the entire cycle automatic, as described below.

Table 19-21. Typical Capacities of Basket Centrifugals

Basis: 40-in.-diameter basket, 7.8 cu. ft. per load

Product	Cycle time, min.	Basket load, lb.	Capacity, tons/hr.
Top-suspended machine:			
Sugar	2–5	350–500	2–5
Inorganic salts	10–15	350–700	0.7–2.5
Organic crystals	10–20	250–350	0.4–1.0
Fine powders	30	350	0.35
Link-suspended machine:			
Waste	10	80	0.4
Textile piece goods	15	70–120	0.15–0.25
Salts, crystals, and powders	Same as top-suspended machine		

Automatic Batch Centrifugals. Both link-suspended and top-suspended centrifugals, 25 to 48 in. in diameter, are available with completely automatic operation, so that direct attendance by an operator is unnecessary. Electric timers control the various parts of the cycle, activating pneumatic valves in the feed line and wash liquid line. After the basket is spun and slowed down to the unloading speed, a hydraulically operated unloader cuts out the cake of solids and drops it through openings in the basket floor. In some designs the basket is turned in the opposite direction for unloading, to ensure that the knife cannot dig into the cake during high-speed operation. The various parts of the cycle are separately controlled and easily changed, so that the cycle found to give the best results may be repeated exactly, and yet varied, if necessary, to meet new conditions. In many operations the solids are fed and washed with the basket rotating at moderate speed, perhaps 980 r.p.m., and the final spinning or "extraction" is done at a higher speed of 1180 r.p.m. In other processes, depending on the characteristics of the solid and liquid, all operations except unloading are done at the higher speed. Unloading speeds are typically 35 to 50 r.p.m.

An automatic batch centrifugal with a horizontal basket is shown in Fig. 19-146. Its principle of operation is identical with that of the automatic suspended centrifugals: solids are loaded into the basket, washed, spun, and discharged on a cycle, with each step controlled by a separate timer. It differs from suspended machines in that the basket is spun at full speed during the entire cycle, including the loading, washing, and unloading steps, and that all the solids are removed at one time by a wide carbide-tipped knife which cuts through the cake in 1 to 2 sec. The solids are discharged at high velocity from the basket into a chute. Cycle times are very short, usually ranging from 30 to 80 sec. This kind of machine is restricted to free-draining crystals, preferably larger than 150 mesh. Typical basket diameters range from 20 to 41 in.; typical capacities from 1 to 24 tons of dry solids per hour. With special housings these centrifuges may be operated under pressure, up to about 150 $lb._f$/sq. in. Because of the very short batch cycle they are readily incorporated in continuous-flow processes.

Continuous Filtering Centrifugals. Truly continuous filtering centrifugals are also restricted to free-draining granular solids and in general do not yield a

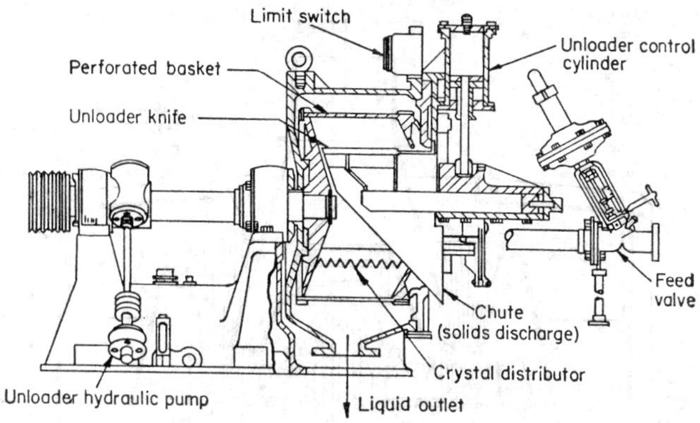

FIG. 19-146. Automatic batch centrifugal. (*Sharples Corp.*)

completely solids-free effluent. The filter medium is a metal screen, often 150 mesh or coarser; for some separations the wall of the bowl is slotted. Fine slow-filtering solids either pass through the filter medium or drain so slowly that the capacity of the centrifuge is uneconomically low. The most common types are horizontal screen-conveyor centrifuges and reciprocating-conveyor centrifugals; other types, such as the vertical conveyor and oscillating-screen centrifuges, developed for coal dewatering, find some applications in the process industries.

Horizontal Screen-conveyor Centrifuges. These machines are similar in general appearance to the cylindrical solid-bowl helical-conveyor centrifuges described earlier. Liquor does not drain into a pond, however; instead it passes through the layer of crystals and leaves the bowl through slots in the wall. The helical conveyor moves the solids in an axial direction to discharge openings at one end of the bowl. Wash liquid is sprayed on the solids as they are moved by the conveyor. Crystal breakage by the conveyor may be considerable, as may the loss of fine solids in the effluent liquor. These severely limit the range of applicability of this kind of centrifuge.

Reciprocating-conveyor Centrifuges. The centrifugal shown in Fig. 19-147 contains a horizontal perforated basket lined with a special metal screen. Slurry feed is admitted from a stationary feed pipe to a rotating cone, which accelerates it before depositing it on the inner wall of the basket next to the basket "floor." Deposited coarse solids are almost instantly freed of their liquor, which passes through the screen into the casing. A reciprocating piston moves the solids an inch or two toward the open end of the basket, then moves back exposing the screen to another increment of feed slurry. The feed cone is connected to and reciprocates with the piston. As the solids move in a layer over the screen

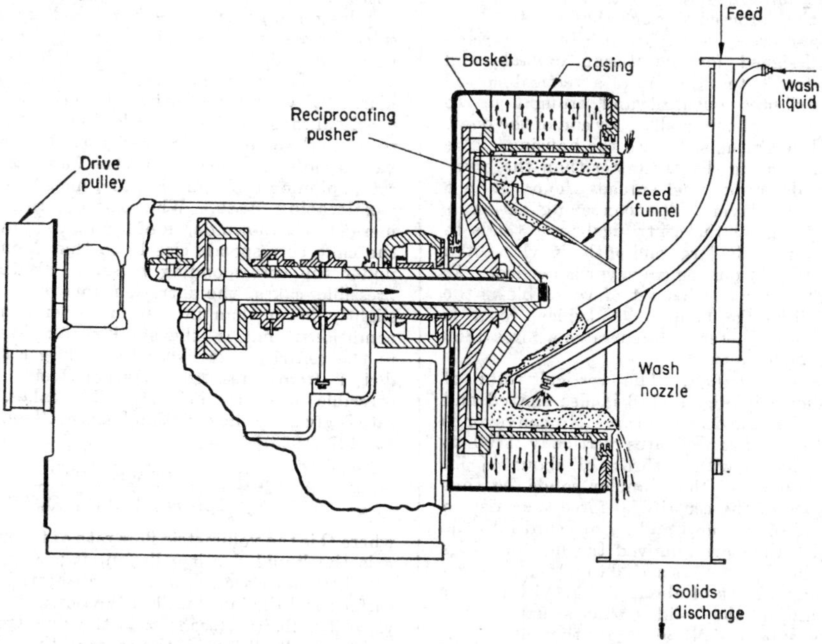

FIG. 19-147. Reciprocating-conveyor continuous centrifuge. (*Baker Perkins, Inc.*)

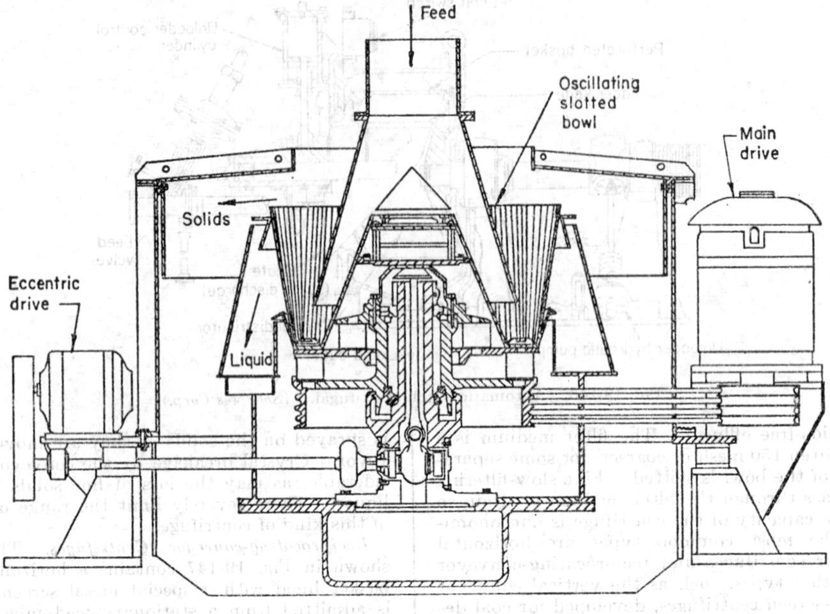

FIG. 19-148. Oscillating-basket centrifuge. (*Bird Machine Co.*)

they may be washed from one or more spray nozzles. At the end of their travel they reach the basket lip and fly off into an enlarged section of the casing from which they fall into the solids-discharge line. Reciprocating-conveyor centrifuges range in basket diameter from 12 to 48 in. and have nominal capacities of 1 to 25 tons/hr. of coarse crystalline solids. Some designs have a basket containing three stages or steps of different diameters, so that the solids are subjected to an increasing centrifugal force as they proceed through the machine.

Vertical Screen-conveyor Centrifuges. In a screening centrifuge designed for dewatering crystals and fibrous pulp the feed enters the top of a vertical slotted bowl. It is distributed outward and brought up to speed by a set of vanes at the small upper end of the bowl. Filtrate passes through the slots into the housing. The helical conveyor, rotating slightly faster than the bowl, moves the solids downward and spreads them out in a progressively thinner layer. The conveying action is comparatively gentle, for the centrifugal force tends to move the solids toward the large end of the bowl. Often only a little assistance from the conveyor is needed. At the bottom of the rotor another set of vanes blows the solids into the discharge hopper. A typical rotor is 16 in. in maximum diameter and generates a force 1800 times gravity at 2800 r.p.m.

Oscillating-screen Centrifuge. The vertical rotor of the centrifuge shown in Fig. 19-148 is also slotted and tapered, with the large end at the top. No conveyor is used; instead, the basket oscillates vertically 1700 to 2300 times per minute with a throw of about ¼ in. The oscillation "fluidizes" the granular solids, so that under the influence of the centrifugal force they rise to the large open end of the bowl and fly outward into the casing from which they are removed through openings in the bottom. Bowl diameters are 20 to 40 in., generating a low centrifugal force of about 120 gravities. For satisfactory operation the solid particles fed to the machine must be substantially all larger than 100 mesh (147 microns) in diameter. On such coarse feed capacities range from 25 to 100 tons/hr. of solids. Moderately effective washing is possible. Crystal breakage is very small, and the screen life is long. Designed for coal, these machines have found few applications in chemical manufacture.

Theory of Centrifugal Filtration

Theoretical predictions of the behavior of solids-liquid mixtures in a centrifugal filter have met with limited success. The problem is more complicated than filtration by gravity or under an impressed pressure difference, since the area for flow and the driving force both increase with radial distance from the centrifuge axis, and the specific cake resistance and porosity may also change markedly within the cake. Filtering centrifugals are nearly always selected by scale-up from tests in a laboratory machine on the material to be processed. The values most often needed are the filtration rate, washing rate, spinning time, and residual moisture content.

Filtration Rate. When the centrifuge cake is submerged in a known depth of liquid, the flow rate through the cake corresponds closely to that found in filtration under the corresponding pressure. With highly compressible cakes, the filtration rate in a centrifugal is slightly lower than in a filter under similar operating conditions; that is, the specific cake resistance found in the centrifuge is likely to be larger than that predicted from pressure filtration tests. With incompressible or nearly incompressible cakes, the filtration rate is given by the equation [Grace, *Chem. Eng. Progress*, **49**, 427 (1953)]

$$Q = \frac{\rho\omega^2(r_2^2 - r_1^2)}{2\mu(\alpha m_c/\bar{A}_L\bar{A}_a + R_m/A_2)} \qquad (19\text{-}34)$$

where Q is the volumetric flow rate of filtrate, cu. ft./sec.; ρ is the liquid density, lb./cu. ft.; ω is the rotational speed, radians/sec.; r_1 and r_2 are the radii of the liquid surface and the inner wall of the bowl, ft.; μ is the liquid viscosity, lb./(ft.)(sec.); α is the average specific cake resistance, ft./lb.; m_c is the mass of the solid cake in the basket, lb.; $\bar{A}_L$ and $\bar{A}_a$ are the logarithmic and arithmetic mean cake areas, defined by Eqs. (19-35) and (19-36), sq. ft.; R_m is the resistance of the filter medium, lb./ft.; and A_2 is the area of the filter medium, sq. ft.

The mean cake areas are defined by

$$\bar{A}_L = \frac{2\pi b(r_2 - r_i)}{\ln r_2/r_i} \tag{19-35}$$

$$\bar{A}_a = (r_2 + r_i)\pi b \tag{19-36}$$

where b is the height of the basket, ft., and r_i is the radius of the inside surface of the cake, ft.

Even with incompressible cakes, Eq. (19-34) applies exactly only when the cake is of uniform thickness. Most solids cannot easily be deposited in a uniform layer on a rotating centrifuge basket but instead yield a cake which is wedge-shaped in cross section. Such a cake gives a filtration rate 5 to 20 per cent greater than a cake of constant thickness having the same volume and permeability [Haruni and Storrow, *Chem. Eng. Sci.*, **2**, 164 (1953)].

Residual Moisture Content. The prediction of spinning time and residual moisture content of a centrifuge cake is even more complex than predicting filtration rates. Coarse crystalline solids can be spun to final moisture content in 10 to 20 sec.; fine solids may require 5 to 15 min. or more. No satisfactory theoretical correlations are available.

The residual moisture content obtainable in a centrifuged cake is considerably lower than in a pressure or vacuum filter, even when the filter cake is blown with air after deposition. The centrifugal force removes all liquid from the interstices of the centrifuge cake except that held by capillary forces. In general this is 40 to 60 per cent of that remaining after simple filtration. For example, if the cake from a filter press contains 35 per cent moisture (wet basis), the same solids after centrifuging would be expected to contain about 20 per cent moisture; if filtered crystals contain 7 per cent moisture, the same crystals from a centrifuge would contain about 3 per cent moisture.

Increasing the basket speed reduces the residual moisture content, sometimes slightly, sometimes very greatly. If the cake is spun at speeds below that at which it was formed, the variation may be predicted from the empirical relation

$$R - R_m = K(n_m - n)^x \tag{19-37}$$

where R is the residual moisture content, lb. moisture/lb. dry solid, obtained at n r.p.m.; R_m is the residual moisture found by spinning at the deposition speed n_m; and K and x are empirical constants [Haruni and Storrow, *Chem. Eng. Sci.*, **2**, 203 (1953)]. When the cake is spun at speeds greater than the deposition speed n_m, consolidation often occurs and the residual moisture content can no longer be predicted by an equation in the form of Eq. (19-37).

CENTRIFUGE AUXILIARIES

The centrifugal machine is the heart of the separation process, but many auxiliary pieces of equipment must be provided for the centrifuge to perform its function. These include the drive mechanism, feed and discharge facilities, feed-treatment equipment such as settlers or agglomerating tanks, and sometimes clean-up equipment such as a filter in the filtrate line.

Drive Mechanisms. Nearly all centrifuges are now provided with individual drives. Continuous centrifuges are usually driven by single-speed electric motors, often designed to provide a high starting torque. Otherwise the acceleration time, especially for a high-speed machine such as a nozzle-discharge centrifuge, would be inordinately long. Automatic controls may be included to bring the machine safely up to speed as rapidly as possible. Open, enclosed, or explosionproof motors are used as required.

Batch centrifugals which must frequently be stopped and started nearly always require a special heavy-duty drive. Electric motors are most common, although hydraulic drives and occasionally steam-turbine drives are also used. The drive must be able to accelerate the basket to full speed every few minutes in as short a time as possible, provide the power needed for full-speed operation, and yet not be any larger than necessary. For power unloading the drive must provide torque at a constant low speed of about 30 r.p.m. This may be obtained from an hydraulic drive, a d.c. electric motor, or a centrifugally controlled "jogging" switch on an a.c. motor. In some designs a small separate motor turns the basket during the unloading cycle, often in the direction opposite to the usual direction of rotation.

Brakes are required for the deceleration step. Electrical braking is often used for the first part of the deceleration, followed by mechanical braking after the basket speed has dropped to a safely low value.

Feed and Discharge Lines. A centrifuge, like any separator, cannot work effectively unless it is supplied with feed slurry at the correct rate, and the separated liquids and solids are properly removed. Unsatisfactory performance often results from poorly designed feed and discharge facilities, not from inadequacies in the centrifuge itself.

Feed lines must be large enough to handle the desired flow of slurry without blocking or excessive pressure drop, yet small enough to keep the fluid velocity high so as to minimize settling (see Slurry Transportation, pp. 19-3ff). Bends should be of long radius, not sharp. There should be no pockets where solids can accumulate during temporary interruptions in flow. Whenever possible the feed slurry should be kept moving at all times, even when the separator is intermittent in its operation. This may be done by continuously recycling a large stream of slurry to the feed tank and feeding the centrifuge through a short take-off pipe attached to the recirculation line. In some stubborn cases pulsed jets of stream or filtrate have been injected at controlled intervals into the take-off line to keep it open.

Discharge lines for the filtrate normally pose no problem unless the vapor pressure is high or the liquid tends to foam. The lines should be large enough to permit disengagement of any evolved gas and should be designed to avoid trapping gas. A much more difficult problem is presented by the wet solids, especially if they are in the form of a wet sludge. Chutes must be large and should be vertical if at all possible. Mechanical conveyors are sometimes required to keep the solids moving; sometimes the solids can be reslurried or even dissolved in a process fluid and pumped to the next processing step.

Slurry pumps should be selected with care. The steady discharge from a centrifugal pump is highly desirable, but low-speed oversize pumps should in general be used. High-speed pumps tend to degrade the solids, often making the separation difficult or even impossible.

Feed Treatment. Pretreatment of the feed slurry before separation often greatly improves the performance of the centrifuge. The capacity of a filtering centrifugal depends largely on the amount of liquid that must be passed through the cake of solids. It is desirable to reduce this to as small an amount as possible by thickening the feed in a settling tank or a liquid cyclone. Preliminary thickening is also desirable in most applications of mechanical-discharge sedimentation centrifuges.

Flocculating agents such as starch, alum, or Separan added to the feed may or may not be beneficial. Sometimes the flocs are fragile and break up in the centrifuge. Sometimes, however, they persist and make the separation more rapid and more complete. It is difficult to predict the value of a flocculant without tests on the actual centrifugal machine. In general flocculants are much less effective in a centrifugal separator than in gravity equipment, in which flocs settle gently and are not subjected to the high shear forces that occur in a centrifuge.

Few centrifugal separators give a sparkling clear liquid effluent, especially with finely divided solids. Continuous and automatic batch filtering centrifugals can be expected to pass 0.5 to 2 per cent of the feed solids through the filter screen. These solids may be recycled or sent on to another process step, or they may require removal in a pressure or vacuum filter. A clean-up filter is usually small, but it can rarely be avoided altogether if the separated liquid must be completely free of solids.

COSTS

Neither investment nor operating costs of centrifugal separators can be correlated with any single characteristic of a given machine, since they depend on the difficulty of the separation, the physical and chemical nature of the materials being separated, the auxiliary equipment required, and many other factors. The cost figures presented in this section are representative of typical installations in the chemical process industries. In other installations the costs might be somewhat less or very much greater than those indicated here.

Purchase Price. Typical purchase prices of high-speed sedimentation centrifuges, without mechanical conveyors for solids removal, are given in Table 19-22. These prices are as of December, 1959, and correspond to E.N.R. construction cost index of 800. A given type of machine may vary considerably in purchase price because of differences in materials of construction, type of enclosure (open discharge, fumetight, pressuretight), or portability.

Table 19-22. Costs of High-speed Centrifuges

Type	Bowl diam., in.	Designation	Purchase price, dollars	Remarks
Tubular	4-6	Oil purifier	1,800-4,500	Steel
		Chemical separator	3,500-8,000	Stainless steel
		Lacquer clarifier	5,800	Portable
Disk	12	Oil purifier	2,000-5,000	Steel
	24	Hermetic	10,000-25,000	Stainless steel
Nozzle discharge	12	....	8,000	Stainless steel
	18	....	16,000-25,000	
	18	Pressure operation	30,000-60,000	
Self-opening	12	....	8,000	Stainless steel
	18	....	15,000	
	24	....	23,000	

The purchase prices of scroll-conveyor sedimentation centrifuges are shown in Fig. 19-149. Prices of top-suspended filtering centrifugals are given in Fig. 19-150; of bottom-driven centrifugals in Fig. 19-151; of automatic batch centrifugals in Fig. 19-152; and of reciprocating-conveyor centrifuges and oscillating-screen centrifugals in Fig. 19-153. Top-suspended sedimentation centrifuges with imperforate bowls cost about 10 per cent more than similar machines with perforated baskets. A fume hood adds about 15 per cent to the cost of a top-suspended centrifugal; an explosionproof motor adds 15 to 35 per cent to the cost of the machine in steel construction.

Installation Costs. The cost of installing a centrifuge varies over an enormous range, depending on the kind of machine and also on what is meant by "installation." Some machines, such as portable disk and tubular centrifuges, may be shipped almost as packaged units, and require little or no foundation and a minimum of

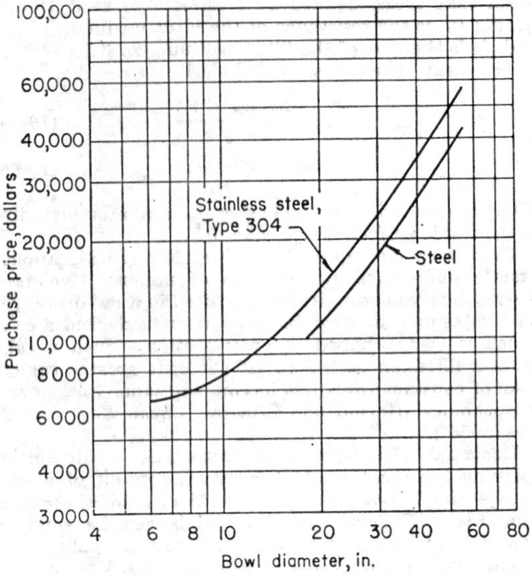

Fig. 19-149. Costs of helical-conveyor centrifuges.

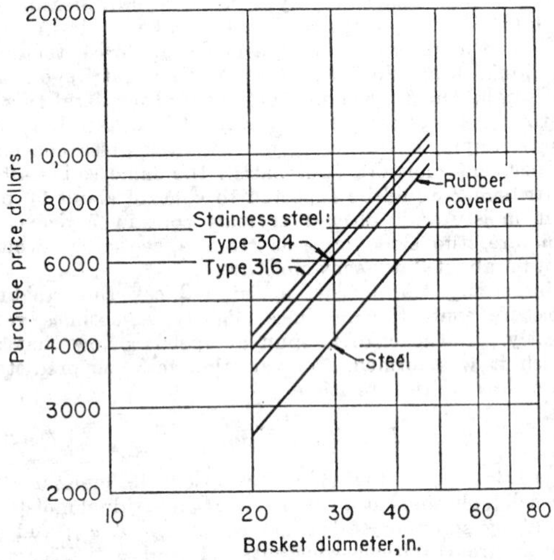

Fig. 19-150. Costs of top-suspended centrifugals.

piping and electric wiring. Other machines require extensive foundations, auxiliary feed tanks, special feed and discharge facilities, and elaborate electrical equipment.

Minimum installation costs, covering a simple foundation, and minimum wiring and piping are about as follows: 6 to 10 per cent of purchase price of tubular and disk centrifuges; 10 to 25 per cent for bottom-driven centrifuges, automatic batch centrifugals, and mechanical-conveyor centrifuges; and 25 to 30 per cent for top-suspended batch centrifugals. If the cost of all auxiliaries —special foundations, tanks, pumps, conveyors, etc.—is included, the installation cost may range from 100 to 400 per cent of the purchase price of the centrifuge itself.

Maintenance Costs. Despite the high speed of centrifugal equipment, maintenance costs are not usually high. For machines in light to moderately severe service, annual maintenance and repairs cost 5 to 10 per cent of the purchase price, exclusive of filter media when they

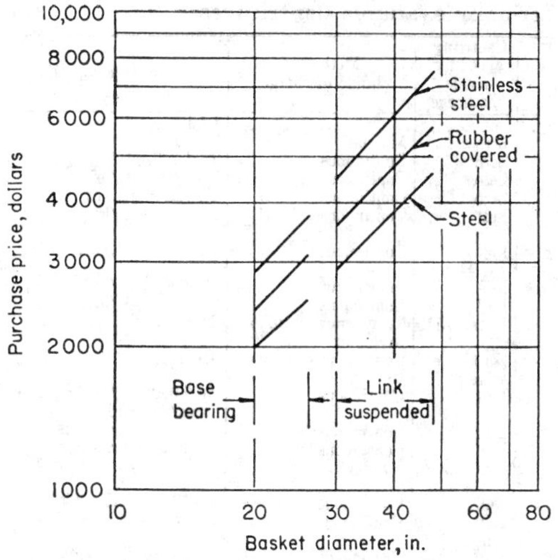

FIG. 19-151. Costs of bottom-driven batch centrifugals.

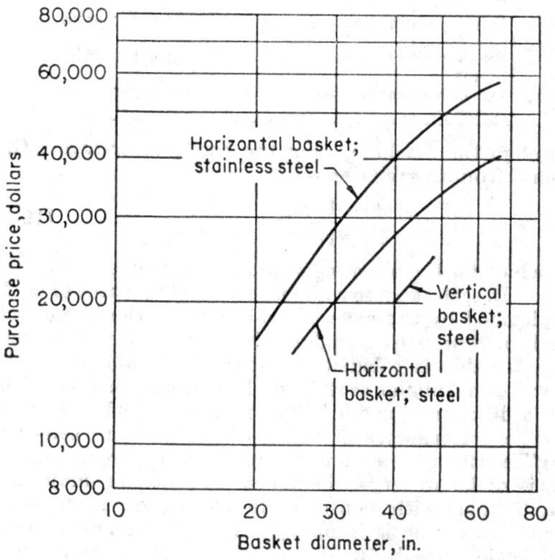

FIG. 19-152. Costs of automatic batch centrifugals.

are required. Bearings and spindles are most subject to wear. Unloader knives in automatic batch machines suffer from erosion, as do helical conveyors in many continuous centrifuges. For machines in severe service on highly corrosive fluids the maintenance costs may be several times the value for ordinary duty.

Operating Labor. Ordinary batch centrifugals require the most direct operating labor. A single man can tend one to three machines without extensive automatic controls. Fully automatic machines and continuous centrifuges need little attention. For estimating purposes such a centrifuge may be considered to need 0.05 to 0.2 of one man's time during operation.

Power. The power required per unit quantity of material passing through a centrifuge depends greatly on the difficulty of separation, especially with high-speed tubular and disk centrifuges. A given machine may process only one-tenth as much liquid in some separation problems as in others, but the amount of power drawn by the separator will be almost the same in both cases. Conveyor-discharge centrifuges require considerable

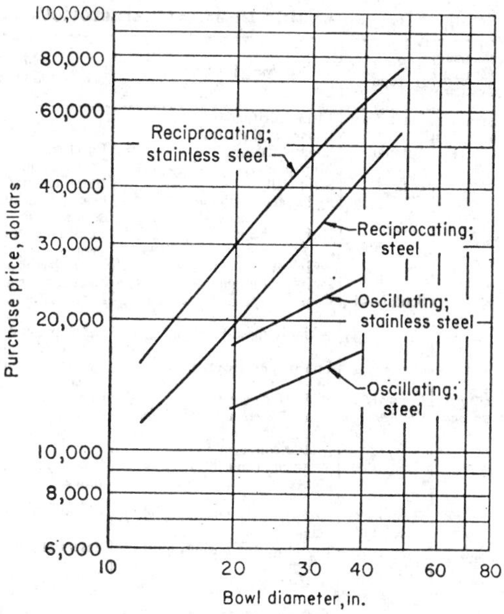

FIG. 19-153. Costs of reciprocating and oscillating centrifuges.

power to move the solids, but this power is almost directly related to the amount of solids being handled. The larger, slower-speed machines require somewhat less power per ton of material separated than do smaller ones of the same type, but the difference is not great.

Typical values for centrifugal separators handling dilute slurries are as follows, in kw.-hr./1000 gal. of feed: for disk and tubular centrifuges, 1 to 10; for nozzle-discharge centrifuges, 2 to 12; for helical-conveyor centrifuges, 2 to 4. Nozzle-discharge centrifuges typically draw 15 to 40 kw.-hr./ton of solid discharged through the nozzles.

Representative values for centrifuges handling concentrated slurry feeds and discharging heavy sludges or "dry" crystals, in kw.-hr./ton of dry solids, are: for helical-conveyor centrifuges, 12 to 15 for sizes up to 24 in., 2 to 10 for larger sizes; for automatic batch centrifugals, 4 to 6; for reciprocating-conveyor centrifugals, 2 to 4; for oscillating-screen centrifugals, 0.2 to 0.3. Batch centrifugals draw between 5 and 25 kw.-hr./ton of solid, depending on the length of the batch cycle and on the size of the basket load.

Even with a delivered power cost of 1¢ per kw.-hr., the power cost of a centrifuge in ordinary chemical service is very small, of the order of 5¢ per 1000 gal. of liquid or 5 to 10¢ per ton of solids separated. In many problems this cost is insignificant. When very large quantities of inexpensive materials must be separated, the power cost may be a significant part of the total operating cost.

SELECTION OF CENTRIFUGAL SEPARATORS

Choosing a centrifugal separator for a given problem involves striking a balance among a number of factors. The chief consideration is that the machine be able to perform the separation at the desired production rate. It must also perform reliably with undiminished effectiveness over long periods of time and operate economically with a minimum of maintenance and operating labor. Only after these criteria are satisfied does the initial investment become significant; with centrifugal equipment in particular it is false economy to use an inexpensive machine in corrosive or otherwise demanding service.

Table 19-23. Characteristics of Commercially Available Centrifuges

Mechanism of primary separation	Rotor type	Machine type	Method of solids discharge	Centrifuge speed for solids discharge	Method of liquid discharge	Relative capacity
Sedimentation	Batch	Ultracentrifuge	....	....	....	1 ml
		Laboratory, clinical	Batch manual	Zero	Manual	To 6 liters
	Tubular	Supercentrifuge	Batch manual	Zero	Continuous	To 1,200 gal./hr.
		Multipass	Batch manual	Zero	Continuous	To 2,400 gal./hr.
	Disk	Solid wall	Batch manual	Zero	Continuous	To 1,2000 gal./hr.
		Light-phase skimmer	Continuous for light-phase solids	Full	Continuous	To 1,200 gal./hr.
		Peripheral nozzles	Continuous for heavy-phase solids	Full	Continuous	To 18,000 gal./hr.
		Peripheral valves	Intermittent automatic	Full	Continuous	To 3,000 gal./hr.
		Peripheral annulus	Intermittent automatic	Full	Continuous	To 3,000 gal./hr.
	Solid bowl	Constant speed (horizontal)	Batch automatic	Usually full	Skimmer or continuous overflow	To 60 cu. ft.
		Variable speed (vertical)	Batch manual or batch automatic	Zero or reduced	Continuous or batch	To 16 cu. ft.
		Continuous decanter	Continuous screw conveyor	Full	Continuous	To 5,000 gal./hr. liquid, to 75 tons/hr. solids
Centrifugal filtration	Conical "screen"	Wide-angle screen	Continuous, no regulation	Full	Continuous	To 40 tons/hr. solids
		Conical "screen" with differential conveyor	Continuous	Full	Continuous	To 40 tons/hr. solids
		Vibrating conical screen	Essentially continuous	Full	Continuous	To 20 tons/hr. solids
		Reciprocating pusher	Batch	Full or reduced	Continuous	Limited data
	Cylindrical "screen"	Reciprocating pusher, single stage	Essentially continuous	Full	Continuous	To 25 tons/hr. solids
		Reciprocating pusher, multistage	Essentially continuous	Full	Continuous	To 44 tons/hr. solids
		Horizontal	Batch, automatic, unloader knife	Full	Intermittent	To 25 tons/hr. solids
		Vertical, underdriven	Batch, fully manual, manual knife, or automatic	Zero or reduced	Intermittent	To 3 tons/hr. solids
		Vertical, suspended	Batch, fully manual, manual knife, or automatic	Zero or reduced	Intermittent	To 10 tons/hr. solids

The overwhelming majority of centrifugal separators are made by equipment manufacturers, although a few machines have been plant-fabricated to solve unusual problems [see Meyers, Smith, and Smith, *Chem. Eng. Progress*, **51**, 415 (1955)]. Problems are normally solved, therefore, through application of one or more of the commercially available machines. In selecting one of these it must first be established whether the discharge of solids and liquid, or of either stream, is to be intermittent or continuous. This is largely a matter of the productive capacity desired, for continuous equipment can rarely be justified when the production rate is small. Note, however, that short-cycle automatic batch centrifuges have high capacities and are readily incorporated into continuous-flow processes.

Table 19-23 lists the various types of available centrifuges, their method of solids and liquid discharge, their unloading speed, and their relative productive capacity.

Sedimentation centrifuges are chosen on the basis of small-scale tests, made either in a laboratory bottle centrifuge or in a small tubular or disk machine. Performance in a bottle centrifuge is established by making a series of runs with different sedimentation times and observing the time required for satisfactory separation. The results may be scaled up using the Σ (sigma) concept discussed on pp. 19-92 and 19-93. The Σ values for tubular and disk centrifuges are given by Eqs. (19-32) and (19-33); for a bottle centrifuge Σ is given by the equation [Ambler and Kieth, "Organic Analysis," vol. 3, Chap. 4, Interscience, New York, 1956]

$$\Sigma = \frac{\omega^2 V}{4.6g \log_{10}[2r_2/(r_1 + r_2)]} \qquad (19\text{-}38)$$

in which ω is the rotational speed, radians/sec.; V is the volume of liquid in the bottle, cu. ft.; g is the gravitational acceleration, ft./sec.^{2}; r_1 is the radial distance, in ft., from the centrifuge axis to the liquid surface when the bottle is spinning; and r_2 is the radial distance to the bottom of the bottles. Σ is in sq. ft. The performance of a continuous centrifuge is predicted from batch data using the quantity Q/Σ, where Q is the flow rate, in cu. ft./sec., through the machine. For the bottle centrifuge Q/Σ is found from the relation

$$\frac{Q}{\Sigma} = \frac{4.6g}{\omega^2 t} \log_{10} \frac{2r_2}{r_1 + r_2} \qquad (19\text{-}39)$$

in which t is the observed sedimentation time required, in sec. In scaling up to a larger machine this value of Q/Σ is multiplied by the expected efficiency of the larger unit, and the flow rate through the larger machine found using the Σ value is calculated from Eq. (19-32) or (19-33). For a 4-in. tubular centrifuge the efficiency is about 1.00; for a disk centrifuge it is approximately 0.45.

The performance of nozzle-discharge and "self-opening" centrifuges is almost impossible to predict on the basis of laboratory tests alone. A specialist may make predictions with considerable confidence from small-scale tests, but it is nearly always necessary to make full-scale tests before performance can be guaranteed. Full-scale tests should be of as long a duration as possible, conducted either at the laboratory of the centrifuge manufacturer or through rental or loan of a test machine to the processing company. Sedimentation centrifuges with internal solids conveyors, similarly, cannot be selected in the absence of full-scale tests without considerable experience, although information from a bottle centrifuge or a laboratory model of the proposed machine is helpful for preliminary calculations.

Filtering centrifugals are selected on the basis of batch tests in a laboratory unit, preferably at least 12 in. in diameter. The method of conducting such tests is outlined by Smith [*Ind. Eng. Chem.*, **39**, 474 (1947)]. The selection of centrifugal separators is also discussed by Flood [*Chem. Eng.*, **62** (6), 217 (1955)]. Data from small compression-permeability cells may be interpreted to predict the performance of filtering centrifugals under a wide variety of operating conditions, as described by Grace [*Chem. Eng. Progress*, **49**, 427 (1953)]. Full-scale tests are again desirable. They may often be made in the laboratories of the centrifuge manufacturers, many of whom have extensive test facilities and a staff of specialists.

SECTION 20

GAS-SOLID SYSTEMS

BY

Paul Y. McCormick, P.E., B.S., Chemical Engineer, E. I. du Pont de Nemours & Co.; Member, American Institute of Chemical Engineers.

Robert L. Lucas, P.E., B.S., Chemical Engineer, E. I. du Pont de Nemours & Co.; Member, American Institute of Chemical Engineers, American Society of Mechanical Engineers. (Gas-Solids Separations)

David F. Wells, P.E., B.S., Chemical Engineer, E. I. du Pont de Nemours & Co.; Member, American Institute of Chemical Engineers. (Fluidized-bed Systems)

CONTENTS

GAS-SOLIDS SEPARATIONS

INTRODUCTION

In the organization of this section, equipment is classified by the condition in which the solids bed exists and the method by which gas-solids contacting is achieved, without regard to its application for a specific unit operation. At the same time, when describing a process vessel, the name currently in common use is retained. In most cases, this is taken from the unit operation in which the vessel historically has found its major applications. Furthermore, when discussing operating procedures and design methods, emphasis is placed upon design and operation for the unit process in which the vessel usually is employed.

In solids-gas contacting equipment, the solids bed can exist in any of the following four conditions:

Static. This is a dense bed of solids in which each particle rests upon another at essentially the settled bulk density of the solids phase. Specifically, *there is no relative motion among solids particles* (Fig. 20-1).

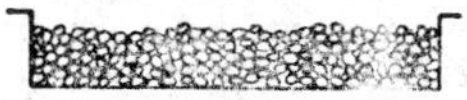

FIG. 20-1. Solids bed in static condition (tray dryer).

Moving. This is a slightly expanded bed of solids in which the particles are separated only enough to flow, one over another. Usually the flow is downward under the force of gravity, but upward motion by mechanical lifting or agitation may also occur within the process vessel. In some cases, lifting of the solids is accomplished in separate equipment and solids flow in the presence of the gas phase is downward only. The latter is a moving bed as usually defined in the petroleum industry. In this definition, *solids motion is achieved by either mechanical agitation or gravity force* (Fig. 20-2).

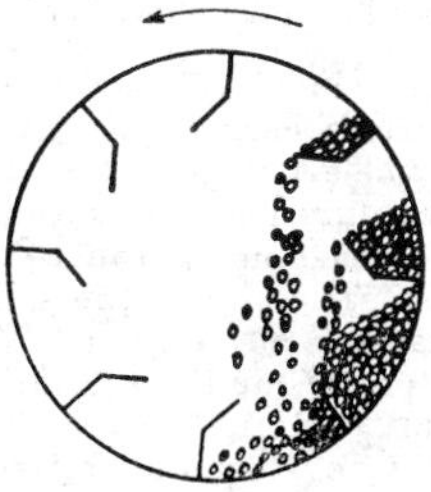

FIG. 20-2. Moving solids bed in a rotary dryer with lifters.

Fluidized. This is an expanded condition in which the solids particles are supported by drag forces caused by the gas phase passing through the interstices among the particles at some critical velocity. It is an unstable condition in that the superficial gas velocity upward is less than the terminal settling velocity of the solids particles; the gas velocity is not sufficient to entrain and continuously convey all the solids. At the same time, there exist, within the stream of gas, eddies traveling at high enough velocities to lift the particles temporarily. Particle motion is continually upward and falling back. Specifically, the solids phase and gas phase are intermixed and *together behave like a boiling fluid* (Fig. 20-3).

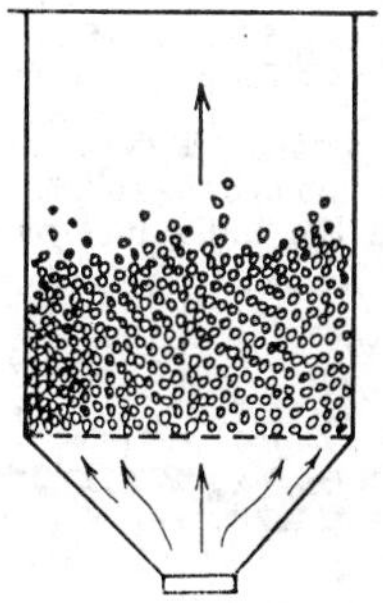

FIG. 20-3. Fluidized solids bed.

Dilute. This is a fully expanded condition in which the solids particles are so widely separated that they exert essentially no influence upon each other. Specifically, the solids phase is so fully dispersed in the gas that *the density of the suspension is essentially that of the gas phase alone* (Fig. 20-4). Commonly, this situation exists when the gas velocity at all points in the system exceeds the terminal settling velocity of the solids and the particles can be lifted and continuously conveyed by the gas; however, this is not always true. Gravity settling chambers such as prilling towers and countercurrent-flow spray dryers are two exceptions where the gas velocity is insufficient to entrain the solids completely.

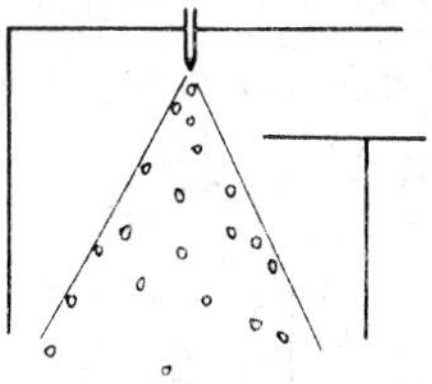

FIG. 20-4. Solids in dilute condition near the top of a spray dryer.

In the dilute condition a bed of solids does not truly exist, and because a dilute condition is usually associated with an extremely high gas velocity and pneumatic conveying of the solids, the equipment discussed is here termed **pneumatic equipment.**

Terms used in this section to describe the method by which gas may contact a bed of solids are the following:

1. *Parallel Flow.* The direction of gas flow is parallel to the surface of the solids phase. Contacting is primarily at the interface between phases, with possibly some penetration of gas into the voids among the solids near the surface. The solids bed is usually in a static condition (Fig. 20-5) but may in some instances be moving.

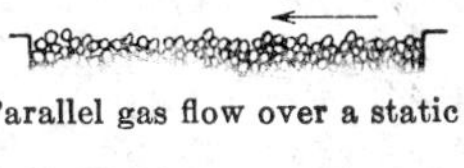

FIG. 20-5. Parallel gas flow over a static bed of solids.

2. *Perpendicular Flow.* The direction of gas flow is normal to the phase interface. The gas impinges on the

solids bed. Again the solids bed is usually in a static condition (Fig. 20-6) but also may be moving.

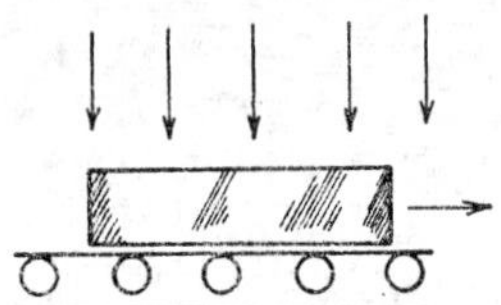

FIG. 20-6. Circulating gas impinging on a large solid object in perpendicular flow, in a roller-conveyor furnace.

3. *Through Circulation.* The gas penetrates and flows through interstices among the solids, circulating more or less freely around the individual particles (Fig. 20-7).

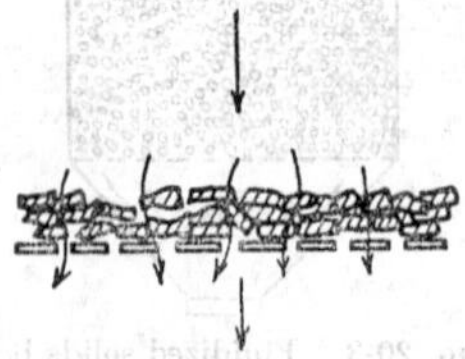

FIG. 20-7. Gas passing through a bed of preformed solids, in through-circulation on a perforated-apron conveyor.

This may occur when solids are in static, moving, fluidized, or dilute conditions; however, gas flow is always by through circulation when the latter two conditions exist.

Three additional terms require definition.

1. *Cocurrent Gas Flow.* The gas phase and solids particles both flow in the same direction (Fig. 20-8).

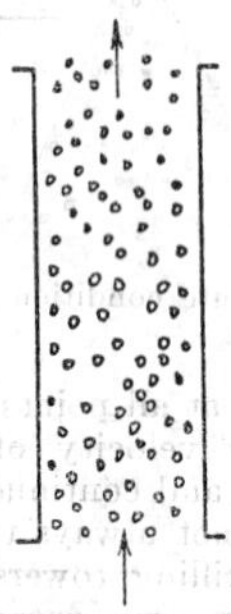

FIG. 20-8. Cocurrent gas-solids flow in a vertical-lift dilute-phase pneumatic conveyor.

2. *Countercurrent Gas Flow.* The direction of gas flow is exactly opposite to the direction of solids movement (Fig. 20-9).

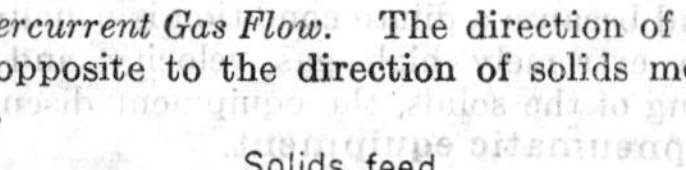

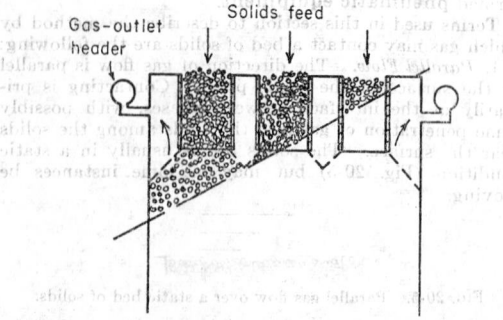

FIG. 20-9. Countercurrent gas-solids flow at the top disengaging section of a moving-bed catalytic reactor.

3. *Cross Flow of Gas.* The direction of gas flow is at a right angle to that of solids movement, across the solids bed (Fig. 20-10).

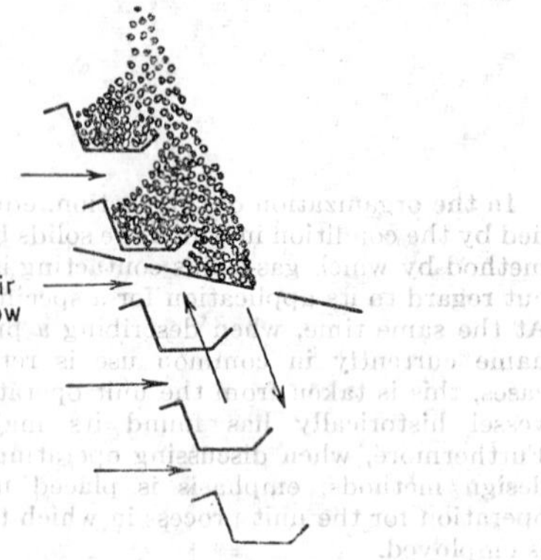

FIG. 20-10. Cross flow of gas and solids in a cascade-type gravity dryer (Link-Belt Company, Multi-Louvre principle).

These three conditions are important in the design and performance of continuous-process equipment only.

Because in a gas-solids contacting operation, heat transfer and mass transfer take place at the solids' surfaces, maximum process efficiency can be expected with a *maximum exposure of solids surface* to the gas phase, together with *thorough mixing* of gas and solids. Both are important. Within any arrangement of particulate solids, gas is present in the voids among the particles and contacts all surfaces except at the points of particle contact. When the solids bed is in a static or slightly moving condition, however, gas within the voids is cut off from the main body of the gas phase. Some transfer of energy and mass may occur by diffusion, but it is usually insignificant. Gas in the voids may usually be considered as not existing at all as far as the process is concerned.

Equipment design and selection are governed by two factors.

1. Mechanical considerations
2. Solids flow and surface characteristics

The former usually involves process temperature or isolation. Solids surface characteristics are important in that they control the extent to which an operation is diffusion limited, *i.e.*, diffusion into and out of the pores of a given solids particle, not through the voids among separate particles. The size of the solids particles, the surface-to-mass ratio, is also important in the evaluation of surface characteristics and the diffusion problem.

Gas-Solids Separations. After the solids and gas have been brought together and mixed in a gas-solids contactor, it becomes necessary to separate the two phases. If the solids are sufficiently coarse, and the gas velocity sufficiently low, it is possible to effect a complete gravitational separation in the primary contactor. Applications of this type are rare, however, and supplementary dust-collection equipment is commonly required. The recovery step may even dictate the type of primary contacting device selected. For example, when treating an extremely friable solid material, a deep fluidized-solids contactor might overload the collection system with fines, whereas the more gentle contacting of a traveling-screen contactor would be expected to produce a minimum of fines by attrition. Therefore, although gas-solids separation is usually considered as separate and distinct from the primary contacting operation, it is usually desirable to evaluate the separation problem at the same time contacting methods are evaluated.

This section will consider methods and equipment employed to recover entrained solids from a gas stream *in a dry state.* It will include means for removing fine dispersoids from atmospheric air. Wet-dust collectors, or scrubbers, as well as equipment for removing entrained liquid mist from gases, are discussed in Sec. 18.

STATIC-BED SYSTEMS

INTRODUCTION

The most elementary form of gas-solids contactor is a *static bed.* Here, particulate solids are held in *fixed positions,* one particle resting upon another, with *no relative motion among particles.* Gas is made to flow over, impinge upon, or flow through the voids among the particles. Except in the last case, contacting takes place only at the *interface* between the gas phase and solids phase. Much higher contacting efficiencies are obtained with through circulation; however, in the case of a static bed, *channeling* and *short-circuiting* of gas, because of non-uniformities in bed packing or density, can represent a serious operating problem. Once channeling begins, no means exist to correct the condition. Among other inherent disadvantages of static-bed systems is the difficulty of adding or removing solids during operation. Cyclic operations introduce valving and purging problems which may be complicated by very high temperatures. Because of relatively poor heat-transfer characteristics, excessive temperature gradients often exist in the solids bed.

On the other hand, static-bed processes have certain advantages over those in which solids move continuously through the system. There is no appreciable solids loss due to *abrasion,* and mechanical auxiliary equipment is not usually required to circulate, separate, or recover solids from the gas stream.

The use of static-bed contactors is quite common. In general, they are suitable for both particulate solids, ranging in size from 1/40 to 3 in., and large formed objects. Applications include *adsorption and gas drying, heat-treating, catalytic* (as in fixed-bed re-forming) and *non-catalytic chemical reactions,* and *solids drying.* Some of the principal applications of ordinary packed columns for gas-solids contacting are in gas adsorption and drying. These are discussed in detail in Sec. 16. Use of static-bed equipment in petroleum refining is reported in detail in the Petroleum Refiner Process Handbook [*Petrol. Refiner,* **37,** 9 (1958)]. Specific equipment which will be discussed here includes the following:

Batch trays and compartments
- Direct-heat dryers
- Vacuum-shelf dryers
- Batch furnaces

Continuous tunnels
- Continuous through-circulation dryers
- Belt-vacuum dryers
- Continuous furnaces

BATCH TRAYS AND COMPARTMENTS

Description. A tray or compartment contactor is an enclosed, insulated housing in which solids are placed upon tiers of trays in the case of particulate solids, or stacked in piles or upon shelves in the case of large objects. Heat transfer may be *direct* from gas to solids by circulation of large volumes of hot gas, *or indirect* by use of heated shelves, radiator coils, or refractory walls inside the housing. In indirect-heat units, excepting vacuum-shelf equipment, circulation of a small quantity of gas is usually necessary to sweep moisture vapor from the compartment and prevent gas saturation and condensation, or to otherwise control the compartment atmosphere. Compartment units are employed for heating and drying of lumber, ceramics, sheet materials (supported on poles), painted and metal objects, and all forms of particulate solids.

Field of Application. Because of the high labor requirements usually associated with loading or unloading the compartments, batch compartment equipment is rarely economical except in the following situations:

1. A long heating cycle is necessary in any event because the size of the solid objects or permissible heating temperature *requires a long hold-up* for internal diffusion of heat or moisture. This case may apply when the cycle will exceed 12 to 24 hr. Lumber drying is an example.
2. The production of *several different products* requires strict batch identity and thorough cleaning of equipment between batches. This is a situation existing in many small color-pigment drying plants.
3. *The quantity of material* to be processed does not justify investment in more expensive, continuous equipment. This case would apply in many pharmaceutical drying operations or processes involving heat-treating of small lots and varying sizes of metal articles.

Further, because of the nature of solids-gas contacting, which is usually by parallel flow and rarely by through circulation, heat transfer and mass transfer are comparatively inefficient. For this reason, use of tray and compartment equipment is restricted primarily to ordinary drying and heat-treating operations. Despite these harsh limitations, where the above situations do exist, economical alternatives are difficult to develop. Tray and compartment dryers and batch furnaces remain among the most widely used forms of gas-solids contacting equipment.

Auxiliary Equipment. If noxious gases, fumes, or dust are given off during the operation, *dust- or fume-recovery equipment* will be necessary in the exhaust-gas system. *Wet scrubbers* are employed for recovery of valuable solvents from dryers. In order to minimize heat losses, *thorough insulation* of the compartment with brick, asbestos, or other insulating compounds is necessary. Modern, fabricated, dryer-compartment panels usually have 3 to 6 in. of blanket insulation placed between the internal and external sheet-metal walls. Doors and other access openings should be gasketed and tight. In the case of tray and truck equipment, it is usually desirable to have available *extra trays and trucks* (or cars), so that they can be preloaded for rapid emptying and loading of the compartment between cycles. *Air filters* and *gas dryers* (Sec. 16) are occasionally employed on the inlet-air system for direct-heat units.

Vacuum-shelf dryers require auxiliary stream jets or other vacuum-producing devices, intercondensers for vapor removal, and occasionally wet scrubbers or (heated) bag-type dust collectors.

Uniform depth of loading in dryers and furnaces handling particulate solids is essential to consistent operation, minimum heating cycles, or control of final moisture. After a tray is loaded, the bed should be leveled to a uniform depth. Special *preform devices,* noodle extruders, pelletizers, etc., are employed occasionally for preparing pastes and filter cakes so that screen bottom trays can be used and the advantages of through circulation obtained.

Control of tray and compartment equipment is usually maintained by control of the *circulating-air temperature* (and humidity) and rarely by solids temperature. On vacuum units, control of the *absolute pressure* and *heating-medium temperature* is utilized. In direct dryers, cycle controllers are frequently employed to vary the air temperature or velocity across the solids during the cycle; *e.g.*, high air temperatures may be employed during a constant-rate drying period while the solids surface remains close to the air wet-bulb temperature. During the falling-rate periods, this temperature may be reduced to prevent casehardening or other degrading effects caused by overheating the solids surfaces. In addition, higher air velocities may be employed during early drying stages to improve heat transfer; however, after surface drying has been completed, this velocity may need to be reduced to prevent dusting. Two-speed circulating fans are employed commonly for this purpose.

Direct-heat Tray Dryers

A modern tray dryer usually consists of a well-insulated enclosure, fans and heating coils integrally installed, and suitable supports for the material. These dryers are more efficient and permit closer control of the drying operations than older, loft dryers in which air circulated over the material by natural convection. Satisfactory operation of tray-type dryers depends on maintaining a constant temperature and a uniform air velocity over all the material being dried.

Circulation of air at velocities of 200 to 2000 ft./min. is desirable to improve the surface heat-transfer coefficient and to eliminate stagnant air pockets. Proper air flow in tray dryers depends on sufficient fan capacity, on the design of ductwork to modify sudden changes in direction, and on properly placed baffles. *Non-uniform air flow is one of the most serious problems in the operation of tray dryers.*

Tray dryers may be of the tray-truck or stationary-tray type. In the former, the trays are loaded on trucks which are pushed into the dryer; in the latter, the trays are loaded directly into stationary racks within the dryer. Trucks may be fitted with flanged wheels to run on tracks, or with flat swivel wheels. They may also be suspended from and moved on monorails. Trucks usually contain two tiers of trays, with 18 to 48 trays per tier, depending upon the tray dimensions.

Trays may be square or rectangular, with 4 to 8 sq. ft./tray, and may be fabricated from any material compatible with corrosion and temperature conditions. When the trays are stacked in the truck, there should be a clearance of not less than 1½ in. between the material in one tray and the bottom of the tray immediately above. Where material characteristics and handling permit, the trays should have screen bottoms for additional drying area. Metal trays are preferable to non-metallic trays, since they conduct heat more readily. Tray loadings range usually from 0.5 to 4.0 in. deep.

Steam is the usual *heating medium* and a standard heater arrangement consists of a main heater before the circulating fan. When steam is not available or the drying load is small, electrical heat can be used. For temperatures above 400°F., products of combustion from coal, oil, or gas can be used, or indirect-fired air heaters.

Air is circulated by propeller or centrifugal fans; the fan is usually mounted within or directly above the dryer. Above 400°F., external or water-cooled bearings become necessary. *Total pressure drop* through the trays, heaters, and ductwork is usually in the range of 1 to 2 in. of water. *Air recirculation* is generally in the order of 80 to 95 per cent, except during the initial drying stage of rapid evaporation. Fresh air is drawn in by the circulating fan, frequently through dust filters. In most installations, air is exhausted by a separate small exhaust fan with a damper to control air-recirculation rates.

Design Methods. When evaporation takes place from a completely wetted surface, the true surface temperature can be evaluated by Eq. (15-31), Sec. 15. When there are no radiation effects and when the trays are well insulated, the surface temperature of the solids approaches the wet-bulb temperature of the drying air. This can be assumed for the *constant-rate drying period*, provided the heat-transfer coefficient is not corrected for radiation and conduction through non-wetted tray surfaces. The result probably will be conservative. The convection heat-transfer coefficient can be calculated using the following equation for parallel flow:

$$h_c = 0.013(G)^{0.8} \qquad (20\text{-}1)$$

where h_c = convection heat-transfer coefficient, B.t.u./(hr.)(sq. ft. of surface)(°F.)
G = air-mass velocity, lb./(hr.)(sq. ft. of cross-sectional flow area)(°F.)

In the case when flow is perpendicular to the wetted surface,

$$h_c = 0.37(G)^{0.37} \qquad (20\text{-}2)$$

This procedure usually is suitable for estimating purposes on new applications. For more precise calculations, the convection heat-transfer coefficient must be corrected for radiation and heat conduction through non-wetted surfaces and dryer geometry (see Sec. 15).

When the air passes over a long series of trays at low velocity, the temperature drop may be significant. At high velocity in two-truck or three-truck dryers, it will rarely exceed a few degrees. A suitable air velocity and inlet temperature must be chosen for each specific application. If, upon assuming no air-temperature drop, the calculated rate of evaporation during each air pass is high, it will be necessary to correct the effective air temperature to an average between inlet and outlet, by equating the heat loss from the air with that calculated as required for evaporation [see Sec. 15, Eq. (15-36)].

During the *falling-rate period*, the surface temperature begins to rise as movement of moisture from the solids interior is controlling. The *effect of loading depth* becomes apparent as the drying rate may be proportional to the square of the depth of loading [Eq. (15-39), Sec. 15]. On the other hand, capillarity and shrinkage may be active during this period, with the result that the drying time may remain linear with loading depth. For accurate design, experimental tests are necessary.

For estimating purposes, if the critical moisture content can be assumed or is known (see Tables 15-15 and 20-5), design can be based upon approximate equations given in Sec. 15 [Eqs. (15-48) and (15-49)], using Table 15-14 for material class determination.

Performance and Cost Data. A standard two-truck dryer is illustrated in Fig. 20-11. Adjustable baffles or a perforated distributor plate are normally employed to develop 0.1 to 0.2 in. of water-pressure drop at the wall through which air enters the truck enclosure. This will enhance uniformity of air distribution, from top to bottom, among the trays. In three (or more) truck ovens, air-reheat coils may be placed between trucks if the evaporative load is high. Means for reversing air-flow direction may also be provided in multiple truck units.

Purchase cost of truck compartments will range from $8 to $25 per cubic foot of effective volume; the higher cost is for approximately 75 cu. ft. compartments, and the lower for units in excess of 300 cu. ft. Price includes an aluminized steel housing, with 2 in. of insulation,

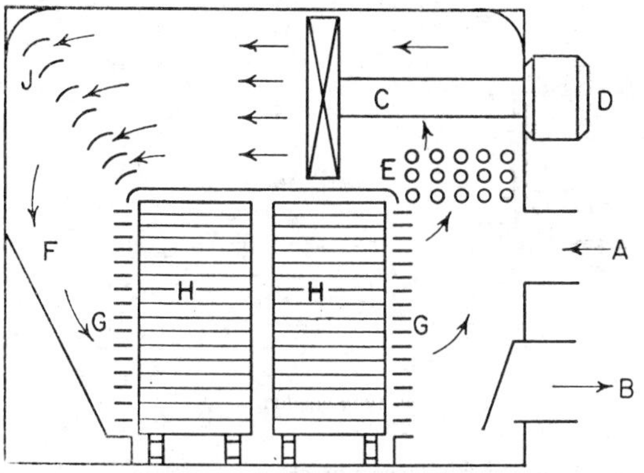

Fig. 20-11. Double-truck dryer. (*A*) Air-inlet duct. (*B*) Air-exhaust duct with damper. (*C*) Adjustable-pitch fan, 1 to 15 hp. (*D*) Fan motor. (*E*) Fin heaters. (*F*) Plenum chamber. (*G*) Adjustable air-blast nozzles. (*H*) Trucks and trays. (*J*) Turning vanes (*National Drying Machinery Co.*)

circulating fan, and an air heater. The prices vary somewhat among steam, direct-fired, indirect-fired, and electric-heat compartments. Control instruments will add $200 to $800 to the dryer cost (costs of 1959). Stainless-steel interior panels will increase the cost by roughly 30 per cent. Trucks of ordinary steel fabrication cost in the order of $200 to $400 each, depending on size. Trays cost $2 to $4 per square foot for carbon steel, $3 to $8 per square foot for stainless steel. Less expensive, fiberglass-reinforced plastic trays are also used in these dryers. Installed equipment cost will be 100 to 200 per cent of the carbon-steel purchase cost.

Performance data on some typical tray and compartment dryers are tabulated in Table 20-1. These indicate

Table 20-1. Manufacturer's Performance Data for Tray and Tray-truck Dryers*

Material	Color	Chrome yellow	Toluidine red	Half-finished Titone	Color
Type of dryer	2 truck	16-tray dryer	16-tray dryer	3 truck	2 truck
Capacity, lb. product/hr	24.6	35.5	4.1	125	10.5
Number of trays	80	16	16	180	120
Tray spacing, in.	4	4	4	3	3½
Tray size, in.	24 × 30 × 1½	26 × 38 × ⅞	26 × 38 × ⅞	24 × 27 × 1½	24 × 26½ × 1
Depth of loading, in.	1–2	1⅛–1¼	1⅛–1½	1⅛	
Initial moisture, % dry basis	207	46	220	223	116
Final moisture, % dry basis	4.5	0.25	0.1	25	0.5
Air temp., °F	185–165	212	122	200	80–210
Loading, lb. product/sq. ft.	2.05	6.9	1.6	3.05	1.9
Drying time, hr	33	21	41	20	96
Air velocity, ft./min	175	450	450	590	500
Air volume, cu. ft./min	8000	....	....	10,000	
Over-all drying rate, lb. water/(hr.)(sq. ft.)	0.12	0.134	0.084	0.24	0.023
Steam consumption, lb./lb. water evaporated	2.5	3.0	....	2.75	
Total installed power, hp	2.0	1.0	1.0	3.00	2.0

* Courtesy of Proctor & Schwartz, Inc.

that an over-all rate of evaporation of 0.03 to 0.30 lb. water/(hr.)(sq. ft. of tray area) may be expected from tray and tray-truck dryers. The thermal efficiency of this type of dryer will vary from 20 to 50 per cent, depending on the drying temperature used and the humidity of the exhaust air. In drying to very low moisture contents under temperature restrictions, the thermal efficiency may be in the order of 10 per cent. The major *operating cost* for a tray dryer is the labor involved in loading and unloading the trays. About 2 man-hr. is required to load and unload a standard two-truck tray dryer. In addition, about one-third to one-fifth of a man's time is required to supervise the dryer during the drying period. *Power* for tray and compartment dryers will be approximately 1.5 hp./truck in the dryer. *Maintenance* will run from 3 to 5 per cent of the installed cost per year.

Table 20-2. Performance Data for Batch Through-circulation Dryers*

Kind of material	Granular polymer	Vegetable	Vegetable seeds
Capacity, lb. product hr	270	93.8	61
Number of trays	16	24	24
Tray spacing, in.	17	17	17
Tray size, in. × in.	36 × 41	36 × 41	33.5 × 38.5
Depth of loading, in.	2.5	2.4	1.5
Physical form of product	Crumbs	0.25-in. diced cubes	Washed seeds
Initial moisture content, % dry basis	11.1	669.0	100.0
Final moisture content, % dry basis	0.1	5.0	9.9
Air temp., °F	190	170 dry-bulb, 120 wet-bulb to 145 dry-bulb	97
Air velocity, superficial, ft./min.	180	120 to 190	200
Tray loading, lb. product/sq. ft.	3.30	1.06	1.38
Drying time, hr	2.0	8.5	5.5
Over-all drying rate, lb. water evaporated/(hr.)(sq. ft.)	0.182	2.43	0.233
Steam consumption, lb./lb. water evaporated	4.0	2.42	6.8
Installed power, hp	10.0	25.0	25.5

* Courtesy of Proctor & Schwartz, Inc.

Compartment Through-circulation Equipment

In one type of batch through-circulation dryer, heated air passes through a stationary permeable bed of the wet material placed on removable *screen-bottom* trays suitably supported in the dryer. This type is similar to a standard tray dryer except that hot air passes through the wet solid instead of across it. The *pressure drop* through the bed of material does not usually exceed about 1 in. of water. In another type, *deep perforated-bottom trays* are placed on top of plenum chambers in a closed-circuit hot-air-circulating system. Gunpowder is dried this way. In some food-dehydration and grain-drying plants, the material is placed in *finishing bins* with perforated bottoms; heated air passes up through the material and is removed from the top of the bin, reheated, and recirculated. The latter types involve a pressure drop through the bed of material of 2 to 18 in. of water at relatively low air rates. Table 20-2 gives performance data on three applications of batch through-circulation dryers. Batch through-circulation dryers are restricted in application to *granular* materials that permit free through circulation of air. Drying times are usually much shorter than in parallel-flow tray dryers.

Vacuum-shelf Dryers

Vacuum-shelf dryers are *indirect-heated batch dryers* consisting of a *vacuumtight chamber* usually constructed of cast iron or steel plate, *heated, supporting shelves* within the chamber, a vacuum source, and usually a condenser.

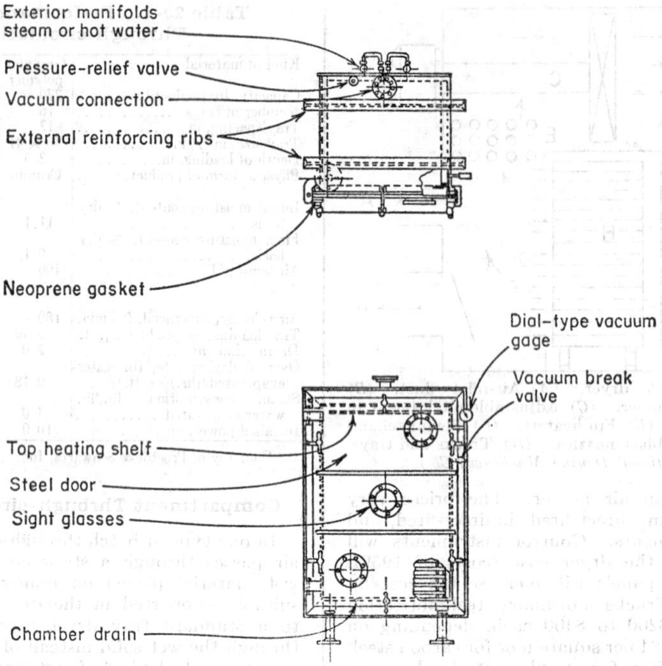

FIG. 20-12. Vacuum-shelf dryer. (*Courtesy of the F. J. Stokes Corp.*)

One or two doors are provided, depending on the size of the chamber. The doors are sealed with resilient gaskets of rubber or similar material (Fig. 20-12).

Hollow shelves of flat steel plate are fastened permanently inside the vacuum chamber and are connected in parallel to inlet and outlet headers. The heating medium, entering through one header and passing through the hollow shelves to the exit header, is generally steam, ranging in pressure from 100 lb./sq. in. gage to subatmospheric pressure for low-temperature operations. Low temperatures can be provided by circulating hot water, and high temperatures can be obtained by circulating hot oil or Dowtherm. Some small dryers employ electrically heated shelves. The material to be dried is placed in *pans or trays* on the heated shelves. The trays are generally of metal to ensure good heat transfer between the shelf and the tray.

Vacuum-shelf dryers may vary in size from 1 to 24 shelves, the largest chambers having over-all dimensions of 9 ft. wide, 18 ft. long, and 8 ft. high.

Vacuum is applied to the chamber and vapor is removed through a large pipe which is connected to the chamber in a manner such that, if the vacuum is broken suddenly, the inrushing air will not greatly disturb the bed of material being dried. This line leads to a condenser where moisture or solvent that has been vaporized is condensed. The non-condensable exhaust gas goes to the vacuum source, which may be a wet or dry vacuum pump or a steam-jet ejector.

Vacuum-shelf dryers are used extensively for drying pharmaceuticals, *temperature-sensitive* or *easily oxidizable* materials, and materials so valuable that labor cost is insignificant. They are particularly useful for handling small batches of materials wet with *toxic* or *valuable solvents*. Recovery of the solvent is easily accomplished without danger of passing through an explosive range. *Dusty materials* may be dried with negligible dust loss. *Hygroscopic materials* may be completely dried at temperatures below that required in atmospheric dryers. The equipment is employed also for *freeze-drying* processes (Sec. 17), for *metallizing-furnace* operations, and for the manufacture of *semiconductor* parts in controlled atmospheres. All these latter processes demand much lower operating pressures than do ordinary drying operations.

Design Methods. Heat is transferred to the wet material by *conduction* through the shelf and bottom of the tray, and by *radiation* from the shelf above. The critical moisture content will not be necessarily the same as for atmospheric tray drying [Ernst, Ridgway, and Tiller, *Ind. Eng. Chem.*, **30**, 1122 (1938)]. During the constant-rate period, moisture is rapidly removed. Often 50 per cent of the moisture will evaporate in the first hour of a 6- to 8-hr. cycle. The drying time has been found to be proportional to between the first and second power of the depth of loading. Shelf vacuum dryers operate in the range of 1 to 25 mm. Hg pressure. For size estimating purposes, a heat-transfer coefficient of 4 B.t.u./(hr.)(sq. ft.)(°F.) may be used. The area employed in this case should be the shelf area in direct contact with the trays (J. F. Maguire, F. J. Stokes Co., personal communication, June, 1960). Trays should be maintained as flat as possible to obtain maximum area of contact with the heated shelves. For the same reason, the shelves should be kept free from scale and rust. Air vents should be installed on steam-heated shelves to vent non-condensable gases. The heating medium should not be applied to the shelves until after the air has been evacuated from the chamber, to reduce the possibility of material overheating or boiling at the start of drying. *Casehardening* can sometimes be avoided by retarding the rate of drying in the early part of the cycle.

Performance and Cost Data. The *purchase price* of a vacuum-shelf dryer depends upon the cabinet size and number of shelves per cabinet. For estimating purposes, purchase prices range from $200 per square foot for a 16 sq. ft. dryer, $120 per square foot for a 36 sq. ft. unit, $100 per square foot for 50 sq. ft., to $60 per square foot for 200 sq. ft. Tray costs are the same as indicated for compartment dryers (p. 20-7). Dryer prices include cabinet, shelves, and a suitable condenser and vacuum pump (prices of 1960). Plastic (Heresite) coating of the shelves and interior of the cabinet will add roughly 20 per cent to the above prices. Stainless-steel shelf fabrication may double these costs. Installed cost of the equipment will be roughly 200 per cent of carbon-steel purchase cost.

The *thermal efficiency* of a vacuum-shelf dryer is usually on the order of 60 to 80 per cent. Table 20-3 gives operating data for one organic color and two inorganic compounds. Labor may constitute 50 per cent of the *operating cost*, and maintenance 20 per cent. Annual maintenance costs amount to 5 to 10 per cent of the total installed cost. Actual labor costs will depend on drying time, facilities for loading and unloading trays, etc. The *power required* for these dryers is only that for the vacuum system; for vacuums of 27 to 29 in. Hg the power requirements are in the order 0.007 to 0.015 hp./sq. ft. tray surface.

Table 20-3. Performance Data of Vacuum-shelf Dryers

Material	Sulfur black	Calcium carbonate	Calcium phosphate
Loading, lb. dry material/sq. ft.	5.25	4.1	6.7
Steam pressure, lb./sq. in. gage	60	60	30
Vacuum, in. Hg	27–28	27–28	27–28
Initial moisture content, % (wet basis)	50	50.3	30.6
Final moisture content, % (wet basis)	1	1.15	4.3
Drying time, hr	8	7	6
Evaporation rate, lb./(hr.)(sq. ft.)	0.66	0.58	0.49

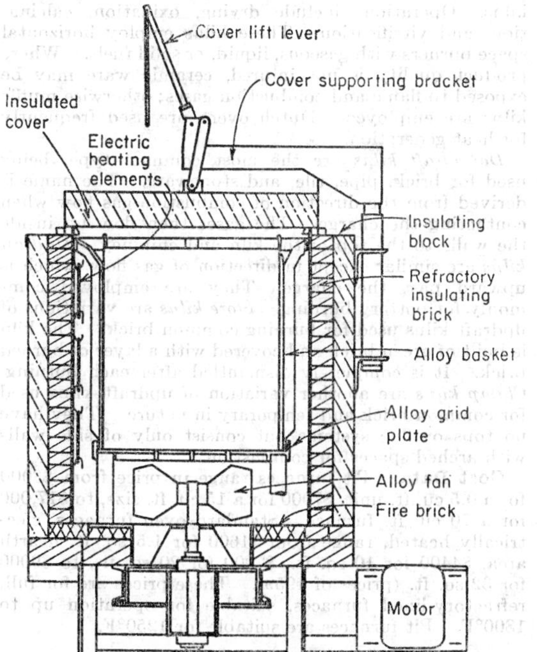

FIG. 20-13. Pit furnace. (*Courtesy of the W. S. Rockwell Co.*)

Batch Furnaces

These are employed mainly for the heat-treating of metals, such as annealing, normalizing, and "drawing" (tempering), and for the drying and calcination of ceramic articles. Many specialized furnaces have been designed for these purposes and may be either batch or continuous in operation. Batch furnaces are used in chemical processing for the same purposes as batch tray and truck dryers, where the drying or process temperature exceeds that which can be tolerated by unlined metal walls; ordinary tray and truck dryers are rarely employed where the circulating-gas temperature will exceed 600° to 800°F. They are employed for small batch calcination, thermal decompositions, and other chemical reactions; these are the same as those performed on a larger scale in rotary kilns, hearth furnaces, and shaft furnaces.

Design procedures and information on heat release in furnaces are given in Sec. 11. Tables indicating normal operating temperatures in various heating furnaces and the more common process furnaces are also included. Specialized designs of batch furnaces are shown in Figs. 20-13 to 20-16 and are described briefly below. All may be heated by gas, oil, or electricity. *Standard oven furnaces* are similar in design to the small muffle furnace depicted in Fig. 20-16, but with the muffle housing eliminated.

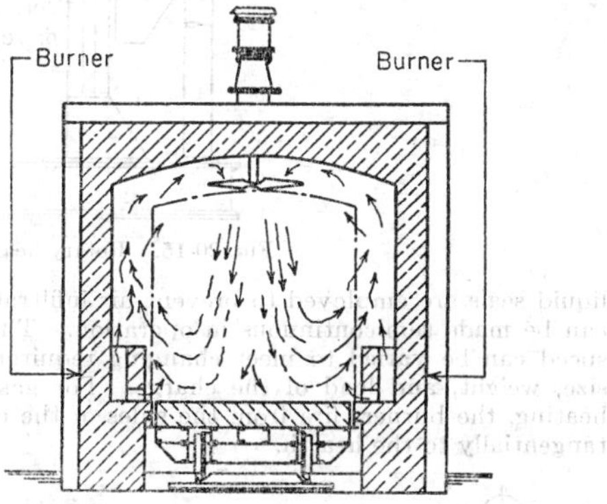

FIG. 20-14. Car-bottom furnace. (*Courtesy of the W. S. Rockwell Co.*)

Description. *Forced-convection pit furnaces* are employed for heat-treating small metal parts in bulk. Small pieces are suspended in a mesh-bottom basket, while larger pieces are placed on racks. Air heating is by means of Nichrome electric coils set in refractory walls around the periphery of the pit. A high-velocity fan beneath the basket circulates heated air up past the coils and then down through the basket. Some heat is radiated to the outer basket shell, but most is transferred by direct convection from the circulating gas to the solids.

Car-bottom furnaces differ from standard types in that the charge is placed upon movable cars for running into the furnace enclosure. The top of the car is refractory-lined and forms the furnace hearth. The top only is exposed to heat, the lower metal structure being protected by the hearth brick, sand, and water seals at the sides and ends, and circulation of cooling air around the car structure below the hearth. For use where floor space is limited, *elevator furnaces* serve similar purposes.

The *rotary-hearth furnace* consists of a heating chamber lined with refractory brick within which is an annular-shape refractory-lined rotating hearth. Around the periphery of the rotating hearth, sand or circulating

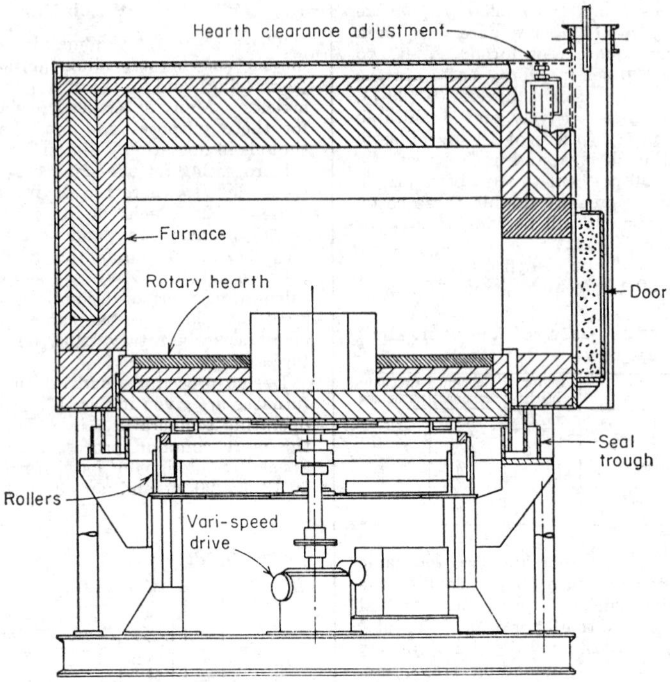

FIG. 20-15. Rotary-hearth furnace. (*Courtesy of the W. S. Rockwell Co.*)

liquid seals are employed to prevent air infiltration. It can be made semicontinuous in operation. The hearth speed can be varied to meet changing requirements in size, weight, and load of the charge. For gas and oil heating, the burners fire from the sides of the chamber, tangentially to the hearth.

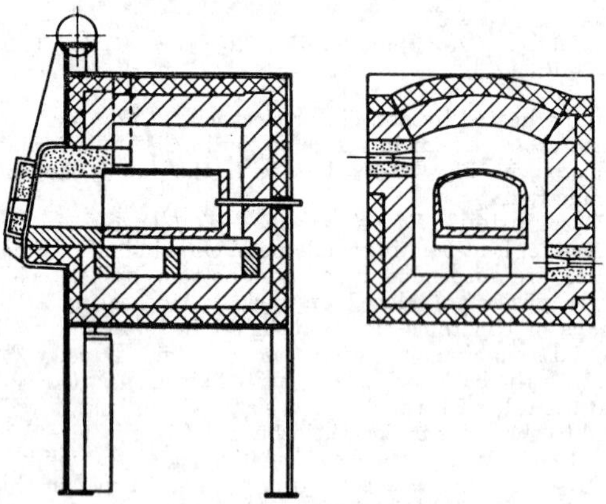

FIG. 20-16. Small muffle furnace. (*Courtesy of the W. S. Rockwell Co.*)

Standard furnaces are usually direct-heated, in that the burner combustion gases circulate directly over the charge; occasionally the flame may be permitted to impinge on the charge. For bright annealing, tool hardening, powdered-metal sintering, and other work requiring protection of the charge by special atmospheres, *muffle-type furnaces* are frequently employed. In these, the charge is separated from the burners and combustion gases by a refractory arch. Heat is transferred by hot-gas radiation and convection to the arch, and by radiation from the arch to the charge.

When used for *ceramic heating*, furnaces are called kilns. Operations include drying, oxidation, calcination, and vitrification. These kilns employ horizontal space burners with gaseous, liquid, or solid fuels. Where product quality is not injured, ceramic ware may be exposed to flame and combustion gases; otherwise muffle kilns are employed. Dutch ovens are used frequently for heat generation.

Downdraft kilns are the most common type, being used for brick, pipe, tile, and stoneware. The name is derived from the direction of combustion-gas flow when contacting the charge. The gases then flow up inside the walls to the top of the kiln and chimney. *Updraft kilns* are similar except in direction of gas flow, which is upward past the charge. They are employed commonly for pottery burning. *Stove kilns* are variations of updraft kilns used for burning common brick. The kiln is built of green brick and covered with a layer of burned brick. It is completely dismantled after each burning. *Clamp kilns* are another variation of updraft kilns used for common brick and temporary in nature. They have no tops or flue systems but consist only of side walls with arched spaces for combustion.

Cost Data. Pit furnaces range in price from $3000 for a 0.5 cu. ft. unit, $7000 for a 15 cu. ft. size, to $17,000 for a 70 cu. ft. furnace. Standard oven furnaces, electrically heated, range from $1600 for 1.5 sq. ft. hearth area, $4400 for 10 sq. ft., $7000 for 20 sq. ft., to $9000 for 32 sq. ft. (prices of 1959). These prices are for full, refractory-lined furnaces, suitable for operation up to 1800°F. Pit furnaces are suitable for 1250°F.

CONTINUOUS TUNNELS

Description. Continuous tunnels are in many cases *batch truck or tray compartments, operated in series.* The

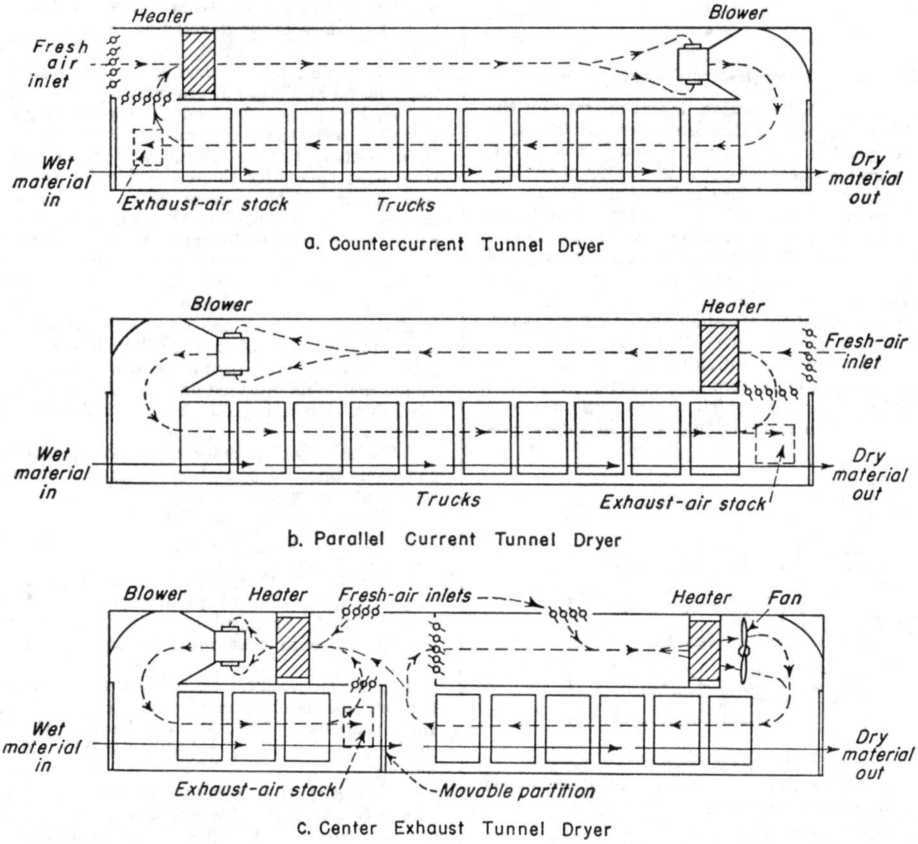

FIG. 20-17. Three types of tunnel dryers. [*Van Arsdel, Food Ind.*, **14** (10), 43 (1942).]

solids to be processed are placed in trays or on trucks which move progressively through the tunnel in contact with hot gases. Usually each truck occupies successively all positions in the tunnel for a given period of time. Operation is *semicontinuous;* when the tunnel is filled, one truck is removed from the discharge end as each new truck is fed into the inlet end. In some cases, the trucks move on tracks or monorails, and they are usually conveyed mechanically employing chain drives connecting to the bottom of each truck. Schematic diagrams of three typical tunnel arrangements are shown in Fig. 20-17. *Belt-conveyor and screen-conveyor tunnels are truly continuous* in operation, carrying a layer of solids on an endless conveyor, feeding continuously at one end and discharging continuously at the other end.

Air flow can be totally *cocurrent*, *countercurrent*, or a combination of both as shown in Fig. 20-17. In addition, *cross-flow* designs are employed frequently, with the heating air flowing back and forth across the trucks in series. Reheat coils may be installed after each cross-flow pass to maintain constant-temperature operation; large propeller-type circulating fans are installed at each stage and air may be introduced or exhausted at any desirable points. Tunnel equipment possesses maximum flexibility for any combination of air flow and temperature staging. When handling granular, particulate solids which do not offer high resistance to air flow, perforated or screen-type belt conveyors are employed with *through circulation* of gas to improve heat- and mass-transfer rates.

In tunnel equipment, the solids are usually heated by direct contact with hot gases. In high-temperature operations, radiation from walls and refractory lining may be significant also. Vacuum-type tunnel dryers, semicontinuous in operation, employ steam-heated-drums under the conveyor belt and electrical radiant heaters above. The air in a direct-heat unit may be heated directly or indirectly by combustion of oil, gas, or coal or, at temperatures below 400°F., by finned steam coils.

Applications of tunnel equipment are essentially the same as for batch tray and compartment units previously described; namely, practically all forms of particulate solids and large solid objects. In operation, they are more suitable for *large-quantity production*, usually representing investment and installation savings over (multiple) batch compartments. In the case of truck and tray tunnels, labor savings for loading and unloading are not significant compared with batch equipment. Belt and screen conveyors which are truly continuous represent major labor savings over batch operations but require additional investment for automatic feeding and unloading devices.

Auxiliary equipment and the special design considerations discussed for batch, trays, and compartments (pp. 20-5ff) apply also to tunnel equipment. For size-estimating purposes, tray and truck tunnels and furnaces can be treated in the same manner as discussed for batch equipment.

Continuous Through-circulation Dryers

Continuous through-circulation dryers operate on the principle of blowing hot air through a permeable bed of wet material passing continuously through the dryer. Drying rates are high because of the large area of contact and short distance of travel for the internal moisture.

The most widely used type is the *horizontal conveying-screen dryer* in which wet material is conveyed as a layer, 1 to 6 in. deep, on a horizontal mesh screen or perforated apron, while heated air is blown either upward or downward through the bed of material. Its drying characteristics were studied by Marshall and Hougen [*Trans. Am. Inst. Chem. Engrs.*, **38**, 91 (1942)]. This dryer consists usually of a number of individual sections, complete with fan and heating coils, arranged in series to form a housing or tunnel through which the conveying screen travels. As shown in the sectional view in Fig. 20-18,

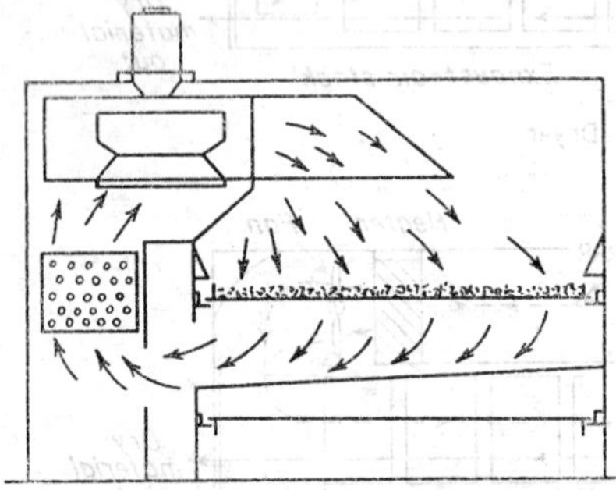

Fig. 20-18. Sectional view of a continuous through-circulation conveyor dryer. (*Courtesy of Proctor & Schwartz, Inc.*)

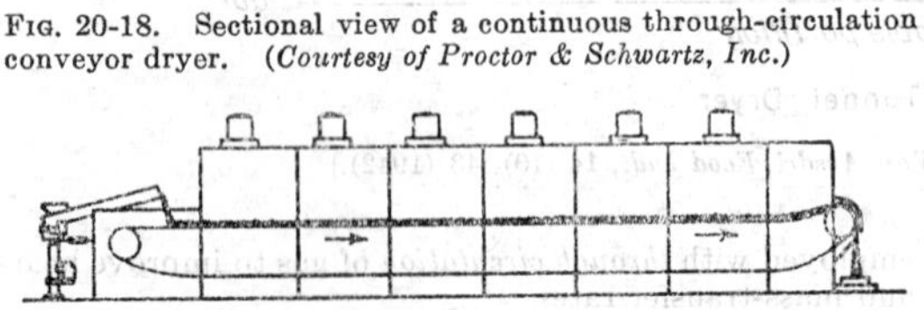

Fig. 20-19. Section assembly of a continuous through-circulation conveyor dryer. (*Courtesy of Proctor & Schwartz, Inc.*)

the air circulates through the wet material and is reheated before reentering the bed. It is not uncommon to circulate the hot gas upward in the wet end and downward in the dry end. A portion of the air is exhausted continuously by one or two exhaust fans, not shown in the sketch, which handle air from several sections. Since each section can be operated independently, extremely flexible operation is possible, with high temperatures usually at the wet end, followed by lower temperatures; in some cases a unit with cooled or specially humidified air is employed for final conditioning. The *maximum pressure drop* that can be taken through the bed of solids without developing leaks or air by-passing is roughly 2.0 in. of water.

Through-circulation drying requires that the wet material be in a state of granular or pelleted subdivision so that hot air may be readily blown through it. Many materials meet this requirement without special preparation. Others require special and often elaborate pretreatment to render them suitable for through-circulation drying. The process of converting a wet solid into a form suitable for through circulation of air is called *preforming*, and often the success or failure of this contacting method depends on the preforming step. Fibrous, flaky, and coarse granular materials are usually amenable to drying without preforming. They can be loaded directly onto the conveying screen by suitable spreading feeders of the oscillating-belt or vibrating type, or by spiked drums or belts feeding from bins. When materials must be preformed, several methods are available, depending on the physical state of the wet solid.

1. Relatively dry materials such as centrifuge cakes can sometimes be *granulated* to give a suitably porous bed on the conveying screen.
2. Pasty materials can often be preformed by *extrusion* to form sphaghettilike pieces, about ¼ in. in diameter and several inches long.
3. Wet pastes that cannot be granulated or extruded may be predried and preformed on a steam-heated *finned drum.* Preforming on a finned drum may be desirable also in that some predrying is accomplished (see Sec. 11).
4. Thixotropic filter cakes from rotary vacuum filters that cannot be preformed by any of the above methods can often be *scored by knives* on the filter, the scored cake discharging in pieces suitable for through-circulation drying.
5. Material that *shrinks* markedly during drying is often *reloaded* during the drying cycle to two to six times the original loading depth. This is usually done after a degree of shrinkage which, by opening the bed, has destroyed the effectiveness of contact between the air and solids.
6. In a few cases, powders have been *pelleted* or formed in *briquettes* to eliminate dustiness and permit drying by through circulation. Table 20-4 gives a list of materials classified by preforming method suitable for through-circulation drying.

Steam-heated air is the usual heat-transfer medium used in these dryers, although combustion gases may be used also. Temperatures above 600°F. are not usually feasible because of the problems of lubricating the conveyor, chain, and roller drives. Recirculation of air is in the range of 60 to 90 per cent. Conveyors may be made of wire-mesh screen or perforated-steel plate. The minimum practical screen opening size is about 30 mesh.

Design Methods. Theoretical equations suitable for estimating drying rates when hot gas is circulated

Table 20-4. Methods of Preforming Some Materials for Through-circulation Drying

No preforming required	Scored on filter	Granulation	Extrusion	Finned drum	Flaking on chilled drum	Briquetting and squeezing
Cellulose acetate	Starch	Kaolin	Calcium carbonate	Lithopone	Soap flakes	Soda ash
Silica gel	Aluminum hydrate	Cryolite	White lead	Zinc yellow		Cornstarch
Scoured wool		Lead arsenate	Lithopone	Calcium carbonate		Synthetic rubber
Sawdust		Cornstarch	Titanium dioxide	Magnesium carbonate		
Rayon waste		Cellulose acetate	Magnesium carbonate			
Fluorspar		Dye intermediates	Aluminum stearate			
Tapioca			Zinc stearate			
Breakfast food						
Asbestos fiber						
Cotton linters						
Rayon staple						

Table 20-5. Experimental Through-circulation Drying Data for Miscellaneous Materials

Material	Physical form	Moisture contents, lb./lb. dry solid			Inlet-air temp., °F.	Depth of bed, in.	Loading, lb. product/ sq. ft.	Air velocity, ft./min.	Experimental drying time, min.
		Initial	Critical	Final					
Alumina hydrate	Briquettes	0.105	0.06	0.00	355	2.5	12.3	120	30
Alumina hydrate	Scored filter cake	9.60	4.50	1.15	140	1.50	0.332	220	150
Alumina hydrate	Scored filter cake	5.56	2.25	0.42	140	2.75	.934	220	180
Aluminum stearate	¼-in. extrusions	4.20	2.60	.003	170	3.0	1.33	250	60
Asbestos fiber	Flakes from squeeze rolls	0.47	0.11	.008	280	3.0	2.78	175	9.3
Asbestos fiber	Flakes from squeeze rolls	.46	.10	.0	280	2.0	1.28	170	6.0
Asbestos fiber	Flakes from squeeze rolls	.46	.075	.0	280	1.5	0.92	220	4.5
Calcium carbonate	Preformed on finned drum	.85	.30	.003	280	1.5	3.27	225	20
Calcium carbonate	Preformed on finned drum	.84	.35	.0	280	3.5	5.26	230	30
Calcium carbonate	Extruded	1.69	.98	.255	280	0.5	1.00	280	15
Calcium carbonate	Extruded	1.41	.45	.05	280	.75	1.18	200	20
Calcium stearate	Extruded	2.74	.90	.0026	170	3.00	1.8	110	95
Calcium stearate	Extruded	2.76	.90	.007	170	2.00	1.2	180	70
Calcium stearate	Extruded	2.52	1.00	.0	170	1.5	0.9	200	40
Cellulose acetate	Granulated	1.14	0.40	.09	250	0.5	.29	250	3
Cellulose acetate	Granulated	1.09	.35	.0027	250	.75	.55	170	12
Cellulose acetate	Granulated	1.09	.30	.0041	250	1.00	.83	110	18
Cellulose acetate	Granulated	1.10	.45	.004	250	1.5	1.25	100	30
Clay	Granulated	0.277	.175	.0	212	2.75	9.45	200	32
Clay	½-in. extrusions	.28	.18	.0	212	5.00	20.5	210	73
Cryolite	Granulated	.456	.25	.0026	230	2.0	7.0	150	40
Fluorspar	Pellets	.13	.066	.0	300	2.0	10.5	220	13
Lead arsenate	Granulated	1.23	.45	.043	270	2.0	3.7	230	30
Lead arsenate	Granulated	1.25	.55	.054	270	2.5	4.5	230	40
Lead arsenate	Extruded	1.34	.64	.024	260	2.0	3.7	200	60
Lead arsenate	Extruded	1.31	.60	.0006	260	3–3.5	5.5	180	70
Kaolin	Formed on finned drum	0.28	.17	.0009	214	3.0	9.0	210	35
Kaolin	Formed on finned drum	.297	.20	.005	214	4.5	11.5	240	25
Kaolin	Extruded	.443	.20	.008	215	2.75	9.2	200	30
Kaolin	Extruded	.36	.14	.0033	250	3.5–4	8.3	300	20
Kaolin	Extruded	.36	.21	.0037	250	7.5	16.5	210	50
Lithopone (finished)	Extruded	.35	.065	.0004	275	3.2	13.0	200	30
Lithopone (crude)	Extruded	.67	.26	.0007	250	3.0	8.4	180	85
Lithopone	Extruded	.72	.28	.0013	250	2.25	5.9	230	30
Magnesium carbonate	Extruded	2.57	.87	.001	285	3.0	2.24	225	29
Magnesium carbonate	Formed on finned drum	2.23	1.44	.0019	290	3.0	2.7	170	40
Mercuric oxide	Extruded	0.163	0.07	.004	200	1.5	13.6	220	40
Silica gel	Granular	4.51	1.85	.15	250	1.5–0.25	0.66	170	25
Silica gel	Granular	4.49	1.50	.215	150	1.5–0.25	.69	180	105
Silica gel	Granular	4.50	1.60	.218	125	1.5–0.25	.7	180	110
Soda salt	Extruded	0.36	0.24	.008	280	1.5	4.66	100	85
Starch (pot.)	Scored filter cake	.866	.55	.069	250	2.75	5.38	200	45
Starch (pot.)	Scored filter cake	.857	.42	.082	250	2.0	3.62	185	25
Starch (corn)	Scored filter cake	.776	.48	.084	160	2.75	5.4	146	90
Starch (corn)	Scored filter cake	.78	.56	.098	225	2.75	5.6	150	40
Starch (corn)	Scored filter cake	.76	.30	.10	160	0.75	1.57	131	25
Titanium dioxide	Extruded	1.02	.60	.10	310	1.5	1.38	270	10.5
Titanium dioxide	Extruded	1.07	.65	.29	310	3.2	3.28	170	10
White lead	Formed on finned drum	0.238	.07	.001	180	2.5	15.7	220	50
White lead	Extruded	.49	.17	.0	200	1.5	6.9	200	45
Zinc stearate	Extruded	4.63	1.50	.005	190	1.75	0.85	170	60

through a granular bed of solids are given in Sec. 15; however, in actual practice, design of a continuous through-circulation dryer requires pilot-plant tests. Because loading and distribution of solids on the screen are rarely as uniform in commercial installations as in test dryers, 50 to 100 per cent may be added to the test drying time for commercial design.

Performance and Cost Data. Experimental *performance data* are given in Table 20-5 for numerous common materials. Performance data from several commercial through-circulation conveyor dryers are given in Table 20-6. *Labor requirements* will vary from ⅙ to 1 man, depending on time required for feed adjustments, inspection, etc. Annual *maintenance costs* range from 5 to 10 per cent of installed cost. These dryers will consume from 2.0 to 2.5 lb. of steam/lb. of water evaporated. Thermal efficiency is a function of final moisture required and per cent air recirculation.

Conveying-screen dryers are fabricated with conveyor widths from 1 to 12 ft., in sections 5 to 8 ft. long. Each section consists of sheet-metal enclosure, insulated side walls and roof, heating coils, circulating fan, inlet-air distributor baffles, fines catch pan under the conveyor, and conveyor screen (Fig. 20-19). The following tabulation indicates approximate purchase costs for equipment with type 304 stainless steel, hinged conveyor screens and includes steam-coil heaters, fans, motors, and a variable-speed conveyor drive. Cabinet and auxiliary-equipment fabrication is of standard aluminum or carbon-steel materials. (Costs of 1960)

8-ft.-wide Conveyor		10-ft.-wide Conveyor
$140/sq. ft.	(20–30 ft. long)	$120/sq. ft.
130/sq. ft.	(30–40 ft. long)	110/sq. ft.
120/sq. ft.	(40–50 ft. long)	100/sq. ft.
110/sq. ft.	(50–60 ft. long)	90/sq. ft.

Courtesy of National Drying Machinery Company, 1960.

Prices do not include temperature controllers, motor starters, preform equipment, or auxiliary feed and discharge conveyors; the latter may add $5000 to $15,000 to the dryer purchase cost.

Vacuum-belt Dryer

A vacuum-belt dehydrator manufactured by the Chemetron Corp. is currently the closest commercial approach to a truly continuous vacuum dryer. Feeding of liquid or slurry to the dryer is continuous and operation of the dryer conveyor is continuous. Dry product is removed from the vacuum chamber through two batch product-receivers, alternately filled and emptied. A schematic view of the Chemetron vacuum dehydrator is given in Fig. 20-20.

The drying system is housed in a cylindrical chamber approximately 12 ft. diameter by 52 ft. long. The

Table 20-6. Performance Data for Continuous Through-circulation Dryers*

Kind of material	Organic material	Inorganic pigment	Inorganic pigment	Gel product	Organic material		Fiber	Fiber
Capacity, lb. product/hr	2775	3330	4000	1440	400		2500	1500
					Stage A	Stage B		
Approx. dryer length, ft	60	108	62	130	30	34	62	62
Depth of loading, in	1	2	4	2.5	2.75	5	3	2
Air temp., °F	200–240	300	250	212–238–240–246	95 dry bulb, 79 wet bulb	125–180	250	240
Loading, lb. product/sq. ft	1.82	5.66	9.2	1.62	7.10	10.82	0.318	0.170
Type of conveyor	18 mesh	6 mesh	3⁄64- by 3⁄16-in. slots	50 mesh	0.068-in. holes, perforated plate		3⁄16-in. perforated plate	⅛-in. holes, perforated plate
Preforming method or feed	Filtered and scored	Rolling extruder	Finned drum	Granulator and oscillating feed	Oscillating feed		Rotary feed	Wet stock opener, rotary feed
Type and size of preformed particle.	Scored filter cake	¼-in.-diameter extrusions	5⁄16-in. square short sticks	Granules through 2-mesh screens	Approx. ⅛-in.-diameter globules		Long fiber	Cut fiber
Initial moisture content, % dry basis	78.6	94.5	55.0	488.0	42.9		50.0	100.0
Final moisture content, % dry basis	13.6	0.25	0.5	1.8	10.5		8.0	5.5
Commercial drying time, hr	0.26	1.20	0.81	1.0	4.95		0.032	0.043
Drying rate, lb. water evaporated/(hr.)(sq. ft.)	5.20	4.44	6.20	7.82	0.333		3.58	4.95
Air velocity (superficial), ft./min	180	170	250	235	220	180–190	240	240
Steam consumption, lb./lb. water evaporated	1.93	1.92	2.03	2.24	7.03		2.06	2.01
Installed power, hp	34.5	61.0	48.0	122.0	52.0		56.0	62.75

* Courtesy of Proctor & Schwartz, Inc.

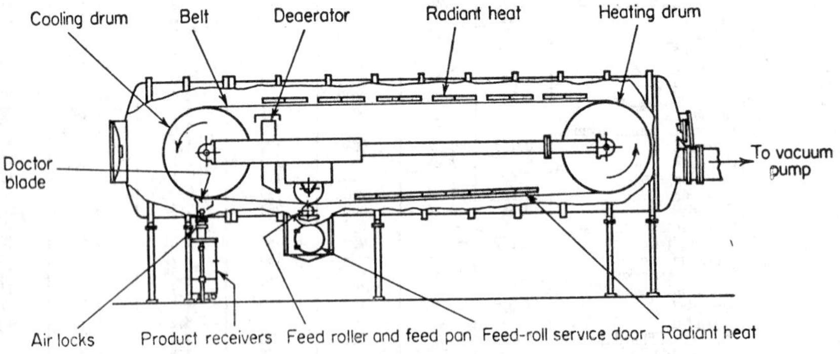

FIG. 20-20. Vacuum dehydrator. (*Courtesy of the Chemetron Corp.*)

chamber is designed for full vacuum and is provided with two large access ports, two product receivers, and numerous sight glasses. A four-stage steam-ejector system is employed to maintain low internal operating pressures. The dryer belt is of stainless steel, 4 ft. wide and roughly 100 ft. long over-all. It is supported on two 7.5- to 8.5-ft.-diameter steel drums. The slurry or liquid feed is picked up from a feed pan by a feed roller which applies a layer of uniform thickness on the belt. This layer is preheated by electrical radiant heaters, passes over the steam-heated drum where the major energy for evaporation is supplied, and is subjected to final heating and drying by additional radiant heaters mounted above the belt (near the top of the chamber). Before doctoring of the dried product, it is cooled as the belt passes over a cooling drum at the discharge end. Cooling usually reduces adherence of the product to the belt, for easier doctoring. Also, it obviates removing oxygen-sensitive and heat-sensitive products from the vacuum chamber while they are still warm from the drying operation. Dryers of similar design are manufactured in Europe also, where they have been employed for the production of milk powders and other food products.

The nature of the equipment requires a *liquid* or *slurry* feed, preconcentrated as much as possible. Control of the physical characteristics of the feed material is essential to uniform production and quality. To date, major applications have been in the drying of food products to produce flavorful and easily reconstituted powders, and pharmaceuticals. Table 20-7 contains a list of applications and approximate drying costs, estimated by the manufacturer. It should be understood that the equipment is not intended to be competitive directly in cost with other dryer types, except possibly spray dryers, vacuum-shelf, and vacuum-drum equipment. It is applicable primarily to heat-sensitive materials, where value of the product reduces the relative importance of drying cost compared with product quality requirements.

Continuous Furnaces

Continuous furnaces for metal treating are employed for the same general duties cited for batch furnaces. Units are gas, oil, or electrically heated and utilize direct circulation of combustion gases or muffles for heat transfer. Continuous furnaces frequently have an extension added for *cooling* of the charge before exposure to atmospheric air.

Conveyors may be of parallel chain, mat, slat, woven wire-mesh belt, or cast-alloy type. Automatic tensioning devices are used to maintain belt tension during heating and cooling. The product may rest directly on the conveyor or on special supports built into it. Roller-conveyors are used for large pieces. *Flame*

Table 20-7. Summary of Drying Processes and Costs Established at Chemetron Corp.

Product	% solids of feed	Dryer pressure, mm. Hg. abs.	Production rate, lb./hr.	Approx. cost per lb. of solid, ¢
Fruit and vegetable juices:				
Lemon juice	49.0	4.0	255	
Orange juice*	60	1–1.5	400	5.5
Prune juice	70	6–8	450	2
Elderberry juice	16.6	3.5–4.0	200	
Raspberry juice	59.4	3.0	500	2
Fruit punch	62.2	3.0	360	
Tomato juice	35	3.5	400	4–4.5
Banana puree	40	4.0	400	4.2
Beverages:				
Coffee*	45–50	6–8	800	1.5
Tea	45–50	7	750	2
Dairy products:				
Eggs:				
Whole	28.1	4.0	270	
Yolk	45.4	4.0	320	
Whites	10.6	4.0	100	
Whole milk	37.5	5.0	500	2–2.5
Skim milk	43	5.0	500	2–2.25
Malted milk	45	6.0	1060	1–1.5
Chocolate malted milk	70	6.0	900	1–1.5
Heat-sensitive products:				
Vitamin D_3	38	10	520	
Yeast	16	4.5	200	
Molasses firsts	77	5.5	450	
Streptomycin	40			
Citrus bioflavonoid*	34.9	5.6	600	

* Production items.
Equipment: 10 per cent/year.
Steam: $1.00/1000 lb.
Water: $0.10/1000 gal.
Electricity: $0.01/kw.
Labor: Operators $2/hr., maintenance $4/hr.
Installation and maintenance.

curtains are provided for sealing of the ends and protection of special treating atmospheres.

The pusher-type furnace is relatively free from mechanical problems because all mechanical parts are located outside the hot zone. It employs a roller-conveyor usually and will handle charges weighing considerably more per square foot than a belt-conveyor furnace. Pushers are driven by electric motors, compressed air, or hydraulic systems and can be automatically timed and synchronized with door-opening timers. For small solids, trays of perforated metal alloys are used to carry the product. These carriers ride through the tunnel on rollers, skid rails, and occasionally refractory skids, one tray pushing the next ahead. The charge may travel in a straight line or in counterflow movement in single or multiple chambers.

In counterflow movement, heat from the outgoing solids is transferred directly to cold incoming solids, reducing heat losses and fuel requirements. Continuous conveyor ovens are employed also for drying refractory shapes, and drying and baking of enameled pieces. In many of these latter, the parts are suspended from overhead chain conveyors.

Ceramic tunnel kilns handling large irregular-shaped objects must be equipped for precise control of temperature and humidity conditions, to prevent *cracking* and *condensation* on the product. The internal mechanism causing cracking when drying clay and ceramics has been studied extensively. Information on ceramic tunnel-kiln operation and design is reported fully in publications such as *The American Ceramic Society Bulletin*, *Ceramic Industry*, and *Transactions of the British Ceramic Society*.

MOVING-BED SYSTEMS

INTRODUCTION

In solids-gas contacting operations, the next advance in contacting efficiency and uniformity of mixing after the static bed is the moving bed. Here the solids are maintained still in an essentially settled-bed condition, but relative movement among the solids particles exposes new surface to gas contacting, prevents short circuiting, and reduces the chance for existence of stagnant, unmixed pockets. Moving-bed equipment is most readily classified by the mechanical method by which solids movement is achieved. Equipment forms are grouped here as follows:

Rotating vessels
Stirred vessels
Gravity vessels

ROTATING VESSELS

Description. A rotating vessel consists of a *cylinder*, *rotated* upon suitable bearings and usually *slightly inclined* to the horizontal. The length of the cylinder may range from four to more than ten times its diameter, which may vary from less than 1 to more than 10 ft. Feed solids fed into one end of the cylinder progress through it by virtue of rotation, head effect, and slope of the cylinder and discharge as finished product at the other end. Gases flowing through the cylinder may retard or increase the rate of solids flow, depending upon whether gas flow is countercurrent or cocurrent with solids flow.

Rotating vessels have been classified as *direct*, *indirect-direct*, *indirect*, and *special types* [Smith, *Ind. Eng. Chem.*, **30**, 993 (1938)]. The terms refer to the method of heat transfer, being "direct" when heat is added to or removed from the solids by direct exchange between flowing gas and solids, and being "indirect" when the heating medium is separated from physical contact with the solids by a metal wall or tube.

Only totally direct and totally indirect types will be discussed extensively here, as it must be recognized that an infinite number of variations between the two are possible. The basic units are commonly referred to as *rotary dryers*, *calciners*, and *kilns*. Their operating characteristics when performing heat- and mass-transfer operations make them suitable for accomplishment of *drying*, *chemical reactions*, *solvent recovery*, *thermal decompositions*, *mixing*, *sintering*, and *agglomeration* of solids. The specific types included are the following:

Direct Rotary Dryer (Cooler). This is usually a bare metal cylinder, with or without flights. It is suitable for low- and medium-temperature operations, the operating temperature being limited primarily by the strength characteristics of the metal employed in fabrication.

Direct Rotary Kiln. This is a metal cylinder lined on the interior with insulating block and/or refractory brick. It is suitable for high-temperature operations.

Indirect Steam-tube Dryer. This is a bare metal cylinder provided with one or more rows of metal tubes installed longitudinally in the shell. It is suitable for operation up to available steam temperatures, or in processes requiring water cooling of the tubes.

Indirect Rotary Calciners. This is a bare metal cylinder surrounded on the outside by a fired or electrically heated furnace. It is suitable for operation at medium temperatures up to the maximum which can be tolerated by the metal wall of the cylinder, usually 700° to 800°F. for carbon steel, 1000° to 1400°F. for stainless steel.

Direct Roto-Louvre Dryer. This is one of the more important special types, differing from the direct rotary unit in that true *through circulation* of gas through the solids bed is provided. Like the direct rotary, it is suitable for low- and medium-temperature operation.

Field of Application. Rotating equipment is applicable to batch or continuous processing solids which are relatively *free-flowing* and granular when discharged as product. Materials which are not completely free-flowing in their feed condition are handled in a special manner, either by *recycling* a portion of final product and *premixing* with the feed in an external mixer to form a uniform granular feed to the process, or by maintaining a bed of free-flowing product in the cylinder at the feed end and, in essence, performing a premixing operation in the cylinder itself. A properly designed recycle process will permit processing of many forms of slurry and solution feeds in rotating vessels. Direct rotary kilns and indirect calciners without internal flights or other obstructions are often provided with *hanging link chains* also. These may serve as surfaces upon which material can accumulate until it is no longer sticky, at which time it will break off as a granular solid and continue its movement through the cylinder. *Scraper chains* may also be provided on indirect calciners to maintain clean internal walls.

As a general rule, but not without exception, the direct-heat units are the simplest and most economical in construction and are employed where direct contact between the solids and flue gases or air can be tolerated. Because the total heat load must be introduced or removed in the gas stream, *large gas volumes* and *high gas velocities* are usually required. The latter will be rarely less than 100 ft./min. in an economical design. Therefore, employment of direct rotating equipment with solids containing extremely fine particles is likely to result in excessive *entrainment losses* in the exit-gas stream.

The indirect forms, being somewhat more complicated and expensive to construct, require, on the other hand, only sufficient gas flow through the cylinder to remove vapors or otherwise complete the internal process. In addition, these can be *sealed* for processes requiring *special gas atmospheres* and exclusion of outside air. Indirect forms, vacuum equipment excepted, are rarely suitable for heat-sensitive materials because the heating-surface temperature must be maintained below the decomposition temperature of the product and the resulting loss of temperature driving force usually results in very poor heat-transfer rates.

Auxiliary Equipment. On direct-heat rotating equipment, a combustion chamber is required for high temperatures and finned steam coils are used for low temperatures. If contamination of the product with combustion gases is undesirable on direct-heat units, indirect gas- or oil-fired air heaters may be employed to achieve temperatures in excess of available steam.

The *method of feeding* rotating equipment depends upon material characteristics and the location and type of upstream processing equipment. When the feed comes from above, a chute extending into the cylinder may be employed. For sealing purposes, or if gravity feed is not convenient, a screw feeder is normally used. On cocurrent direct-heat units, cold-water jacketing of the feed chute or conveyor may be desirable if it is contacted by the inlet hot-gas stream. This will prevent overheating of the metal wall with resultant scaling or overheating of heat-sensitive feed materials.

Any type of solids conveyor may be suitable for *recycle* mixing; however, the most universally applicable is the double-shaft pug-mill-type paddle mixer (see Fig. 20-77). This conveyor or mixer should be insulated to prevent excessive heat losses from the hot dry recycle product. To ensure uniformity in the recycle operation, a *surge storage* reserve of recycle solids should be installed for startup purposes and in the event of interruption of product discharge from the cylinder. In recycle operations, 50 to 60 per cent product recirculation is found economical in many instances.

One method of feeding direct cocurrent drying equipment utilizes dryer exhaust gases to convey, mix, and predry wet feed. The latter is added to the exhaust gases, at high velocity, from the dryer. The wet feed, mixed with dust entrained from the dryer, separates from the exhaust gases in a cyclone and drops into the feed end of the cylinder. The technique combines pneumatic and rotary drying. High thermal efficiency results from two cocurrent-flow stages operating countercurrently.

The product from rotating equipment can be discharged directly into storage or packaging bins or removed to another place for processing. Pneumatic conveyors are frequently employed as both conveyors and coolers. Other cooling equipment often used are screw conveyors, vibrating conveyors, and direct, or indirect, rotating coolers.

Dust entrained in the exit-gas stream is customarily removed in cyclone collectors. This dust may be discharged back into the process or separately collected. For expensive materials or extremely fine particles, bag collectors may follow a cyclone collector, assuming fabric temperature stability is not limiting. When toxic gases or solids are present, the exit gas is at a high temperature, the gas is close to saturation as from a steam-tube dryer, or gas recirculation in a sealed system is involved, wet scrubbers may be used independently or following a cyclone. Cyclones and bag collectors in drying applications frequently require insulation and steam tracing. The exhaust fan should be located downstream from the collection system. In association with rotating processing equipment, the *pressure drop* in the dust-recovery equipment will be 50 to 90 per cent of the total pressure drop through the entire contacting system.

Rotating equipment, except brick-lined vessels, operated above ambient temperatures is usually *insulated* to reduce heat losses. Exceptions will be direct-heat units of bare metal construction and operating at high temperatures, on which heat losses from the shell are necessary to prevent overheating of the metal. Insulation is particularly necessary on cocurrent direct-heat units. It is not unusual for product cooling or condensation on the shell to occur in the last 10 to 50 per cent of the cylinder length if it is not well insulated.

For best operation, the feed rate to rotating equipment should be closely controlled and uniform in quantity and quality. Because solids temperatures are difficult to measure, and changes slowly detected, most rotating-equipment operations are *controlled* by indirect means; inlet and exit gas temperatures are measured and controlled on direct-heat units such as direct dryers and kilns; steam temperature and pressure, and exit-gas temperature and humidity, are controlled on steam-tube units; direct shell temperature measurements are taken on indirect calciners. Product temperature measurements are taken for secondary control purposes only in most instances.

On modern rotating vessels, drive motors are electric. Despite the fact that prolonged electrical failures are in general less frequent than formerly, equipment which is electrically driven and operated with metal temperatures exceeding 300°F. should be provided with auxiliary drives or power sources. *Loss of rotation* of a heated calciner or high-temperature dryer carrying a heavy bed of hot solids will quickly result in *sagging* of the cylinder due to non-uniform cooling. Where close-fitting rotary seals must be maintained for process purposes, this loss of symmetry in the cylinder may represent a major disaster.

Direct-heat Rotary Dryers

The direct-heat rotary dryer is usually equipped with *flights* on the interior for *lifting* and *showering* the solids through the gas stream during passage through the cylinder. Although these flights may be continuous through the cylinder, they are usually offset every 2 to 6 ft. to ensure more continuous and uniform curtains of solids in the gas. The shape of the flights depends upon the handling characteristics of the solids. For free-flowing materials, a radial flight with a 90-deg. lip is employed. For sticky materials, a flat radial flight without any lip is used. When materials change characteristics during drying, the flight design is changed along the dryer length. In fact, because in drying operations this is frequently the case, many standard dryer designs employ flat flights with no lips in the first one-third of the dryer measured from the feed end, flights with 45-deg. lips in the middle one-third, and flights with 90-deg. lips in the final one-third of the cylinder. *Spiral flights* are usually provided in the first few feet at the feed end to accelerate forward flow from under the feed chute or conveyor and prevent leakage over the feed-end retainer ring into the gas seals. Current commercial practice for flight design is a compromise among construction economy, accessibility to the cylinder for maintenance, and showering efficiency.

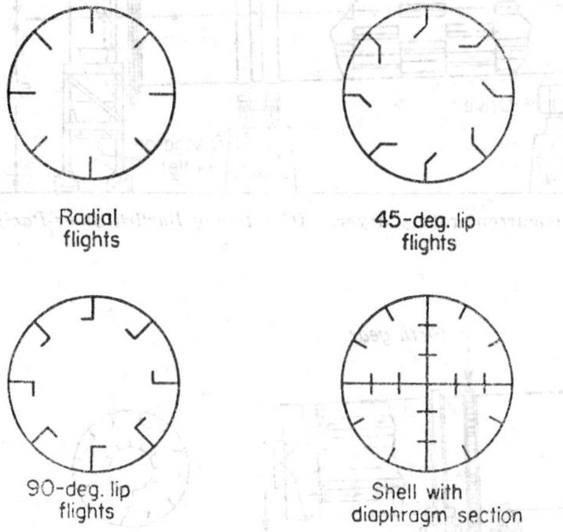

FIG. 20-21. Alternative direct-heat rotary-dryer flight arrangements.

When cocurrent gas-solids flow is used, flights may be left out of the final few feet at the exit end to reduce entrainment of dry product in the exit gas. Showering of wet feed at the feed end of a countercurrent dryer will, on the other hand, frequently serve as an effective means for scrubbing dry entrained solids from the gas stream before it leaves the cylinder. Some dryers are provided with sawtooth flights to obtain uniform showering, while others use lengths of chain, attached to the underside of the flights, to scrape over and knock the walls of the cylinder, thereby removing sticky solids which might normally adhere to it. In kilns, the chains may contribute significantly to heat transfer; however, their use contributes to maintenance costs when flights are present in direct dryers. *Solids sticking* on flights and walls are usually removed more efficiently by installation of *external shell knockers.* In dryers of large cross section, internal elements or partitions are sometimes used to increase the effectiveness of material distribution and reduce dusting and impact grinding. Use of internal members increases the difficulty of cleaning and maintenance unless sufficient free area is left between partitions for easy access of a man. Some examples of the more common flight arrangements are shown in Fig. 20-21. Component arrangements of countercurrent direct rotary dryers are shown in Fig. 20-22, and those of a cocurrent unit in Fig. 20-23.

Countercurrent flow of gas and solids gives greater *heat-transfer efficiency* with a given inlet-gas temperature, but cocurrent flow can be used more frequently to dry heat-sensitive materials at higher inlet-gas temperatures because of the rapid cooling of the gas during initial evaporation of surface moisture. The *indirect-direct* type depicted in Fig. 20-24 almost always employs

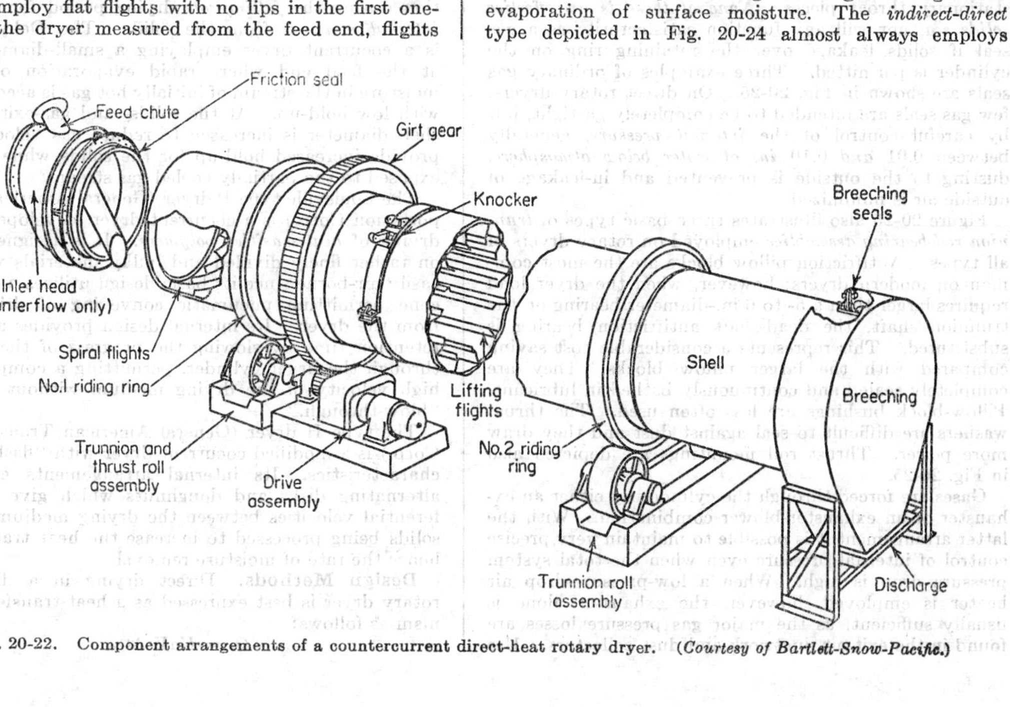

FIG. 20-22. Component arrangements of a countercurrent direct-heat rotary dryer. (*Courtesy of Bartlett-Snow-Pacific.*)

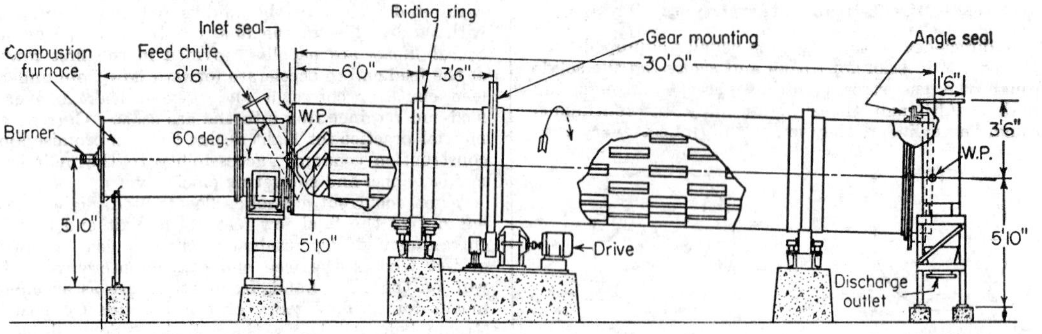

FIG. 20-23. Elevation of a 60 in. diameter by 30 ft. long direct-heat cocurrent rotary dryer. (*Courtesy of Bartlett-Snow-Pacific.*)

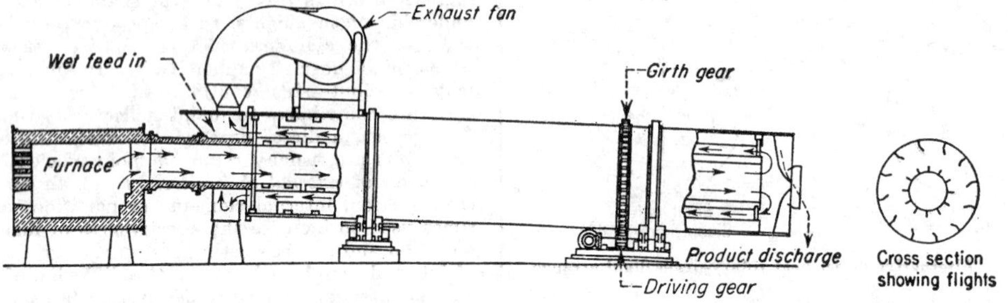

FIG. 20-24. Double-shell indirect-direct rotary dryer. (*Hardinge Co.*)

countercurrent flow during direct drying because of the higher thermal efficiency thereby obtained. The drying of heat-sensitive materials is precluded in this type because the hot surface of the inner cylinder may overheat the product.

A number of different methods are employed to *seal* the rotating cylinder and prevent gas leakage through the annular opening between the rotating cylinder and the stationary throat pieces. *None of these is an effective solids seal* nor will any function satisfactorily as a gas seal if solids leakage over the retaining ring on the cylinder is permitted. Three examples of ordinary gas seals are shown in Fig. 20-25. On direct rotary dryers, few gas seals are intended to be completely gastight, but by careful control of the *internal pressure*, generally between 0.01 *and* 0.10 *in. of water below atmosphere*, dusting to the outside is prevented and in-leakage of outside air is minimized.

Figure 20-25 also illustrates three basic types of *trunnion roll-bearing assemblies* employed on rotary dryers of all types. Antifriction pillow blocks are the most common on modern dryers; however, when the dryer load requires larger than a 5- to 6-in.-diameter bearing on the trunnion shaft, the dead-shaft antifriction bearing is substituted. This represents a considerable cost saving compared with the larger pillow blocks. They are completely sealed and continuously bathed in lubricant. Pillow-block bushings are less often used. The thrust washers are difficult to seal against dust and they draw more power. Thrust roll mountings are depicted also in Fig. 20-25.

Gases are forced through the cylinder by either an exhauster or an exhauster-blower combination. With the latter arrangement it is possible to maintain very precise control of internal pressure even when the total system pressure drop is high. When a low-pressure-drop air heater is employed, however, the exhauster alone is usually sufficient, as the major gas pressure losses are found in the exit-air ductwork and dust collectors. Use of a blower by itself to force gas through the cylinder is an unusual practice, because the internal pressure is above atmospheric and hot air and dust may be blown into the gas seals or out into the surrounding working areas.

Special designs of direct rotary dryers, such as the Renneburg DehydrO-Mat (Edw. Renneburg & Sons Co.), are constructed especially to provide longer retention during the *falling-rate* drying period for escape of *internal moisture* from the solids. The DehydrO-Mat is a cocurrent dryer employing a small-diameter shell at the feed end where rapid evaporation of surface moisture in the stream of initially hot gas is accomplished with low hold-up. At the solids- and gas-exit end, the shell diameter is increased to reduce gas velocities and provide increased hold-up for the solids while they are exposed to the partially cooled gas stream.

The Louisville type P dryer (General American Transportation Corp.) is a cocurrent dryer, developed for the drying of *heat-sensitive polymers*. It is designed for use on rather finely divided and bulky materials which are easily air-borne since its basic design utilizes a discharge cone permitting pneumatic conveying of dried solids from the dryer. Its internal design provides additional retention time by slowing the progress of the material through the dryer cylinder, permitting a comparatively high velocity of the drying medium without excessive "blow-through."

The type H dryer (General American Transportation Corp.) is a modified cocurrent dryer with "flash-drying" characteristics. Its internal arrangements consist of alternating disks and doughnuts which give high differential velocities between the drying medium and the solids being processed to increase the heat transfer and hence the rate of moisture removal.

Design Methods. Direct drying in a direct-heat rotary dryer is best expressed as a heat-transfer mechanism as follows:

$$Q_t = UaV(\Delta t)_m \qquad (20\text{-}3)$$

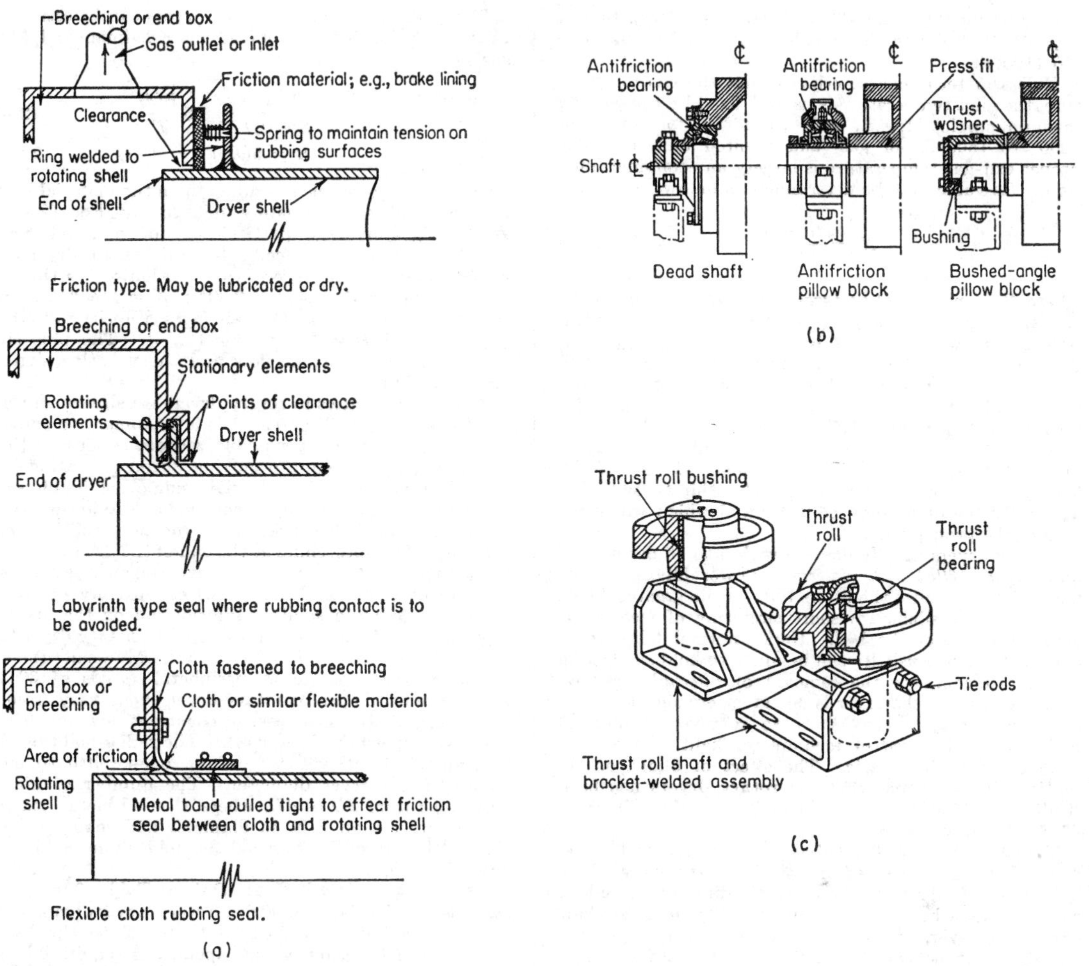

FIG. 20-25. Rotary-dryer components. (*a*) Alternative rotary gas seals. (*b*) Alternative trunnion roll bearings. (*Courtesy of Bartlett-Snow-Pacific.*) (*c*) Alternative thrust roll assemblies. (*Courtesy of Bartlett-Snow-Pacific.*)

where Q_t = total heat transferred, B.t.u./hr.; Ua = volumetric heat-transfer coefficient, B.t.u./(hr.)(cu. ft. dryer volume)(°F.); V = dryer volume, cu. ft.; and $(\Delta t)_m$ = true mean temperature difference between the hot gases and material, °F. When a considerable quantity of surface moisture is removed from the solids and the solids temperatures are unknown, a good approximation $(\Delta t)_m$ is the logarithmic mean between the wet-bulb depressions of the drying air at the inlet and exit of the dryer.

Data for evaluating Ua were given by Friedman and Marshall [*Chem. Eng. Progress*, **45**, 482, 573 (1949)], who reported tests on a small rotary dryer. Although they showed Ua as a complex function of the feed rate, air rate, and physical properties of the material being dried, a conservative design was recommended based on the following equation:

$$Ua = \frac{10G^{0.16}}{D} \qquad (20\text{-}4)$$

where G = air-mass velocity, lb./(hr.)(sq. ft. of dryer cross section); and D = dryer diameter, ft. This equation was developed from data taken from small test dryers, however, and its validity for application to dryers larger than 1 *or* 2 *ft. in diameter* has been questioned (Halldorsson, paper presented at Conference of American Fertilizer Industry, Oct. 12, 1956).

Typical performance data for low-temperature warm-air direct rotary dryers are given in Table 20-8 for cocurrent flow of gas and solids. Analysis of these data indicates Ua ranging from a maximum of 15 B.t.u./(hr.)(cu. ft.)(°F.) in the 4-ft.-diameter unit, to a minimum of 7 B.t.u./(hr.)(cu. ft.)(°F.) in the 10-ft.-diameter unit. Substitution in Eq. (20-4) shows a correction is then required in the constant which would raise it from 10 to 20 to 25. The equation should read as follows when applied to dryers of *commercial sizes between* 3 *and* 10 *ft.* diameter operating at fillage levels of 5 to 15 per cent of total shell volume:

$$Ua = \frac{20G^{0.16}}{D} \qquad (20\text{-}5)$$

In most cases, direct rotary dryers are still sized on the basis of test data and experience; however, the above method may be employed for estimating purposes. Other expressions for rotary-dryer heat transfer have been published by Miller [*Trans. Am. Inst. Chem. Engrs.*, **38**, 841 (1942)] and Saeman [*Chem. Eng. Progress*, **50**, 467 (1954)].

Unless material characteristics limit the gas temperature, the inlet temperature is usually fixed by the heating medium employed; *i.e.*, 250° to 350°F. for steam, or 1000° to 1500°F. for gas- and oil-fired burners. The proper exit-gas temperature is largely an economic function. Its value may be determined as follows:

$$N_t = \frac{t_1 - t_2}{(\Delta t)_m} \tag{20-6}$$

where N_t = *number of heat-transfer units* based upon the gas; t_1 = initial-gas temperature, °F.; t_2 = exit-gas temperature allowing for heat losses, °F.; and $(\Delta t)_m$ is as defined for Eq. (20-3). Equation (20-6) can be used to select an exit-gas temperature since it has been found (empirically) that rotary dryers are most economically operated between $N_t = 1.5$ and $N_t = 2.5$.

The L/D ratio (length/diameter) found most efficient in commercial practice lies between 4 and 10. If the length calculated above does not fall within these limits, another value of N_t may be computed which will place L/D in the proper range.

Rotary dryers usually operate with 5 to 15 per cent of *their volume filled with material*. Lower fillage will be insufficient to utilize the lifters fully, while greater fillage creates the possibility of short circuiting of feed solids across the top of the bed. Under normal fillage conditions, the dryer usually can be made to hold solids long enough to complete the removal of *internal moisture*. If the hold-up in the dryer is not great enough, the time of passage may be too short to remove all internal moisture, or because of incomplete flight fillage, performance may be erratic. The effect of fillage on retention time and uniformity in rotary dryers has been studied by Miskell and Marshall [*Chem. Eng. Progress*, **52**, 1 (1956)].

Time of passage is defined as hold-up divided by feed rate. It can be measured directly in rotary dryers if the hold-up and feed rate can be measured directly. Hold-up cannot always be measured conveniently on large plant dryers, however, unless a period of shutdown occurs when the dryer can be discharged and its contents weighed. Other methods have been resorted to, one of which consists of adding a pound or two of an inert detectable solid or a radioisotope of a feed constituent to the feed and analyzing for it in the discharged product. The time required for the maximum concentration to occur represents the average time of passage.

The time of passage in rotary dryers can be estimated by the relationships developed by Friedman and Marshall (*loc. cit.*), as given below:

$$\theta = \frac{0.23L}{SN^{0.9}D} \pm 0.6\frac{BLG}{F} \tag{20-7}$$

$$B = 5(D_p)^{-0.5} \tag{20-7a}$$

where B = a constant depending upon the material being handled and approximately defined by Eq. (20-7*a*); D_p = weight average particle size of material being handled, microns; F = feed rate to dryer, lb. dry material/(hr.)(sq. ft. of dryer cross section); θ = time of passage, min.; S = slope, ft./ft.; N = speed, r.p.m.; L = dryer length, ft.; G = air-mass velocity, lb./(hr.)(sq. ft.); and D = dryer diameter, ft. The plus sign refers to countercurrent flow and the negative sign to cocurrent flow.

Air-mass velocities in rotary dryers usually range from 400 to 4000 lb./(hr.)(sq. ft.). It is customary to employ the highest air velocity possible without serious dusting. The amount of dusting occurring during operation is a complex function of the material being dried, its physical state, the air velocity employed, the hold-up in the dryer, the number of flights, the rate of rotation, and the construction of the breeching at the end of the dryer. It can be predicted accurately only by experimental tests. An air rate of 1000 lb./(hr.)(sq. ft.) can usually be safely used with 35-mesh solids. Information on the dusting of a number of materials in a 1- by 6-ft. rotary dryer has been presented by Friedman and Marshall (*ibid.*). Rotary dryers operate at peripheral speeds of 30 to 100 ft./min. Slopes of rotary-dryer shells vary from 0 to 1.0 in./ft. In some cases of cocurrent-flow operation, negative slopes have been used. The radial flight height in a direct dryer will range from one-twelfth to one-eighth of the dryer diameter. The number of flights will range from 2*D* to 4*D*, where D = diameter, ft., for dryers larger than 2 ft. in diameter and should be designed to carry and shower all the hold-up and minimize any kiln action.

Performance and Cost Data. Table 20-8 gives *estimating-price* data for direct rotary dryers employing steam-heated air. Add $4000 to $8000 to the listed prices for higher-temperature operations requiring combustion chambers and fuel burners. The total installed cost of rotary dryers including instrumentation, auxiliaries, allocated building space, etc., will run 150 to 300 per cent of the purchase cost. Simple erection costs average 10 to 20 per cent of purchase cost.

Operating costs will include 20 to 35 per cent of one

Table 20-8. Warm-air Direct-heat Cocurrent Rotary Dryers, Typical Performance Data*

Material: heat sensitive solid
Maximum solids temperature: 150°F.
Feed conditions: 25 per cent moisture, 80°F.
Product conditions: 0.5 per cent moisture, 150°F.
Inlet air temperature: 330°F.
Exit-air temperature: 160°F.

Dryer size, in. × ft.	48 × 25	54 × 25	60 × 30	72 × 35	84 × 40	96 × 45	120 × 55
Evaporation, lb./hr.	300	400	500	700	900	1200	1900
Work, B.t.u./hr.	342,000	436,000	540,000	780,000	1,060,000	1,384,000	2,160,000
Steam, lb./hr. at 150 lb./sq. in. gage	700	900	1150	1600	2200	2900	4500
Discharge, lb./hr.	900	1150	1400	2100	2800	3600	5700
Exhaust velocity, ft./min.	200	200	200	200	200	200	200
Exhaust volume, cu. ft./min.	2250	2850	3550	5100	6950	9100	14,100
Exhaust fan, hp.	5	7.5	7.5	10	15	25	30
Dryer drive, hp.	3	5	7.5	10	20	25	50
Dryer r.p.m.	5.5	5	4.5	4	3.5	3	2.5
Ship wt., lb.	17,000	24,000	32,000	42,000	79,000	88,000	132,000
Shipping price, f.o.b. Sharon, Pa.	$15,500	$17,000	$18,000	$23,000	$37,000	$44,000	$56,000

Assumed pressure drop in system: 8.0 in. w.g.
System includes finned air heaters, transition piece, dryer, drive, product collector, duct, and fan.
Prices are for carbon-steel construction and include entire dryer system; dryer includes shell, tires, gear bases, seals, and feed conveyor.
For 304 stainless-steel fabrication, multiply the above prices by a factor of 1.7 (1960).
* General American Transportation Corp.

man's time, plus power and fuel required. Yearly maintenance costs will range from 5 to 10 per cent of total installed costs. Total horsepower for fans, dryer drive, feed and product conveyors will be in the range of $0.5D^2$ to $1.0\ D^2$. Thermal efficiency of a high-temperature direct-heat rotary dryer will range from 55 to 75 per cent and, with steam-heated air, from 30 to 55 per cent.

Direct-heat Rotary Kiln

One of the most important of the high-temperature process furnaces is the direct-fired rotary kiln. It replaces the ordinary rotary dryer when the wall temperature exceeds that which can be tolerated by a bare metal shell (700° to 800°F. for carbon steel). Rotary-kiln shells are lined in part or for their entire length with a *refractory brick* to prevent overheating of the steel with resulting weakening. Occasionally two linings are used, the one next to the shell being an *insulating brick*. Insulation is infrequently used on the outside of the shell, and caution must be observed not to overheat the shell metal by this confinement. Where wet feeds are applied to a kiln lining at the cold end, there may be leakage of liquid through the lining to the shell, which will cause trouble if the liquid is corrosive.

The feed is introduced into the upper end of the kiln by various methods, *i.e.*, inclined chutes, overhung screw conveyors, slurry pipes, etc. Sometimes *ring dams* or chokes of a refractory material are installed within the kiln to build a deeper bed at one or more points, thus changing the flow pattern. The hot product is discharged from the lower end of the kiln into quench tanks, onto conveyors, or into cooling devices which may or may not recover its heat content. These cooling and heat-recovery devices include rotating inclined cylinders, inclined slow-moving grates, shaking grates, etc.

Some kilns have *two* or *three diameters*, part of the length being one diameter and the remainder being another diameter. It is claimed that this arrangement increases kiln capacity, decreases fuel consumption, and improves product quality. Two types of kilns are depicted in Fig. 20-26. An enlarged cross section near

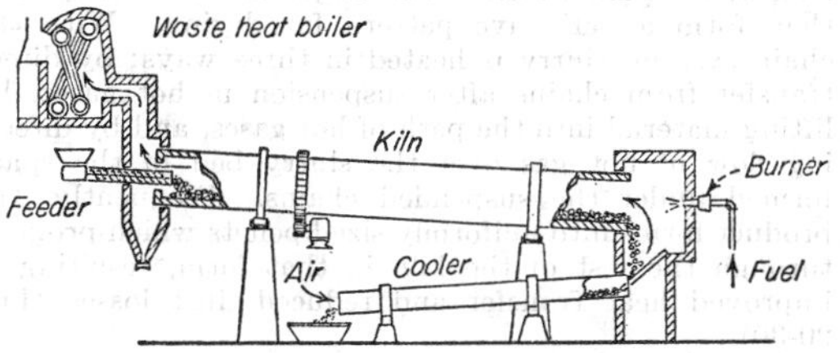

(a) Single diameter

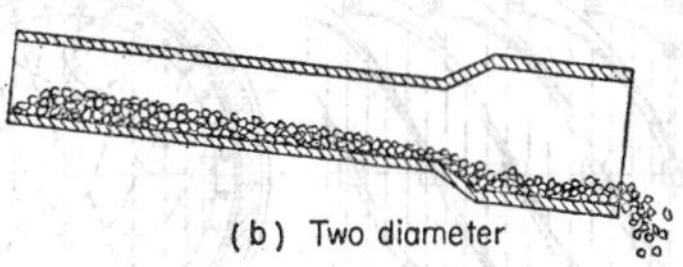

(b) Two diameter

FIG. 20-26. Rotary kilns.

the discharge end (and hot-gas inlet) reduces the gas velocity and provides *increased hold-up* for a "soaking" period at high temperature.

The first rotary kilns used in the United States were very small, 6 ft. 0 in. by 60 ft. 0 in. Sizes gradually increased and seemed to stop for a period at a maximum size of 12 ft. 0 in. by 450 ft. 0 in. In recent years, a few much larger units have been installed for cement production.

Modern rotary-kiln shells are of all-welded construction. Riding rings are forged or cast steel; support rollers are forged or cast steel and, on rare occasions, tool steel. Main bearings are sleeve-type, normally bronze. Antifriction bearings are frequently used on very small kilns, but never on the large units. Bearings on the pinion shafts are normally antifriction type, however.

Gearing is single helical or spur; gear lubrication usually is an automatic spray type. *Single drives* are used up to 200 hp. Kilns requiring more than 200 hp. may be equipped with dual drives, *i.e.*, two driving pinions and two motors, both driving one bull gear. In this manner, the power load is split through two separate driving mechanisms, meshing with one and the same gear.

Kiln inclination varies with processes from ¼ to ¾ in./ft. *Speed of rotation* also varies from very slow, *i.e.*, a peripheral speed of 3 ft./min. for a TiO_2 pigment kiln, or 45 ft./min. for a cement kiln, to 125 ft./min. for a unit calcining phosphate materials.

Special features include the discharge end designed for *air cooling* on kilns that operate at high temperatures, such as cement, dead-burned dolomite, and magnesia. Firing hoods are designed with retractable fronts, large side doors, and mounted on wheels. *Internal heat recuperators* are of numerous designs and are becoming more popular as fuel prices increase. *Thermocouple collector rings* are placed at various points on the shell for indicating and recording internal temperatures.

Scoop systems are provided for introducing collected dust, or in some cases a feed component through the shell at some intermediate point or points. Ports are installed in the shell for admitting combustion air at points beyond the hot zone; these are used in reducing kilns for burning carbon monoxide and volatiles from materials being processed.

Firing may be accomplished at either end, depending on whether cocurrent or countercurrent flow of the charge and gases is desired. Sometimes a solid fuel is mixed with the charge and burned as it moves down the kiln. Gaseous, liquid, or powdered fuels may be used. The burner may be installed directly at the end of the kiln with combustion occurring inside of it. In this case, the discharge-end housing usually consists of a fixed or movable kiln hood through which the fuel pipe enters the kiln. A center position for the fuel pipe is used when the flame is wanted off the charge. Some users prefer an off-center position toward the trough between the charge chord and the descending kiln lining. The kiln and the hood (combustion chamber) usually have open ends which coincide with each other with the gap being closed by a sliding seal (Fig. 20-27). Sometimes a special offset chamber for the introduction of secondary tempering air is provided on dryers and kilns (Fig. 20-28).

The exhaust gases are generally discharged into dust and fume knockdown equipment to avoid contamination of the atmosphere. Sometimes dust recovery is desired because the recovered material has an economic value. Gas-cleaning equipment includes cyclones, settling chambers, scrubbing towers, and electrical precipitators. Heat-recovery devices are utilized both within and outside the kiln. These result in an increase in kiln capacity, or a decrease in fuel consumption. Waste-heat boilers, grates, coil systems, and chains are used for this purpose.

The feed end of a rotary kiln is partially closed by a ring-shaped *feed head* which retains the end brick and dams backflow of solids. On the discharge end, a brick retaining-ring casting is made up to suit the application. For low temperatures, segmental alloy-iron rings may be employed. For high-temperature processes, either

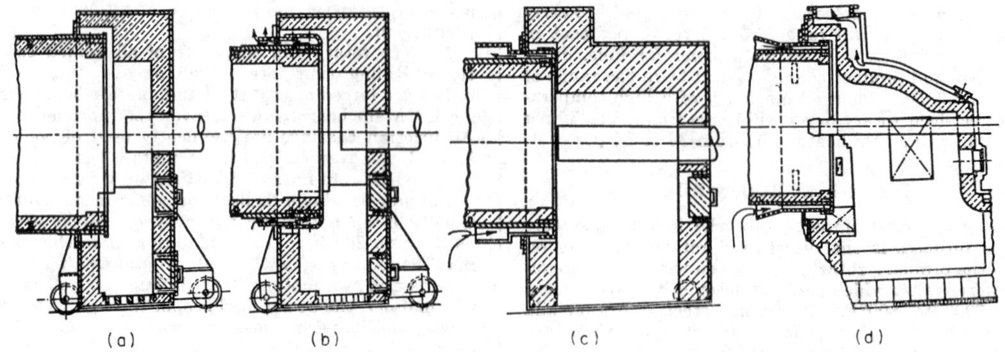

FIG. 20-27. Alternative kiln firing hoods. (*a*) Plain firing hood. (*b*) Hood for high temperatures. (*c*) Hood with enlarged combustion air passage. (*d*) Hood with cooler connection. (*Allis-Chalmers Manufacturing Co.*)

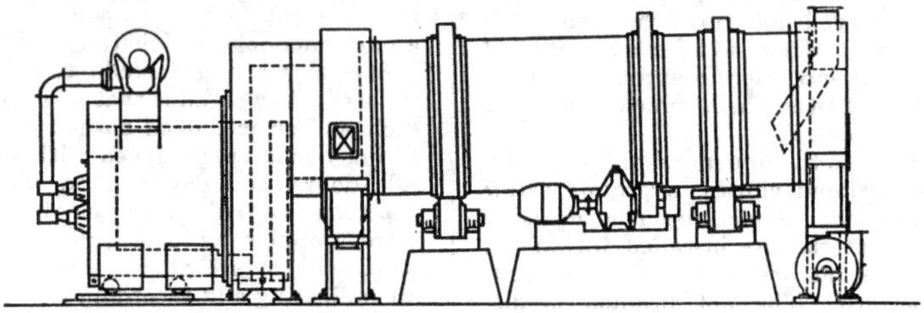

FIG. 20-28. Dryer firing hood with air-tempering chamber. (*Courtesy of Bartlett-Snow-Pacific.*)

segmental alloy-steel rings or kiln ends of the air-cooled type are employed; the latter provides longer life for both kiln end and the brick ring.

Efficient *air seals* are essential for the controlled and economical operation of kilns. They reduce outside air entrance; certain types effectively prevent entrance of all outside air. The simplest type of air seal is a floating T-section ring mounted on a wearing pad around the feed end of the kiln and free to slide with expansion of the kiln shell. The web of the T-ring is confined within

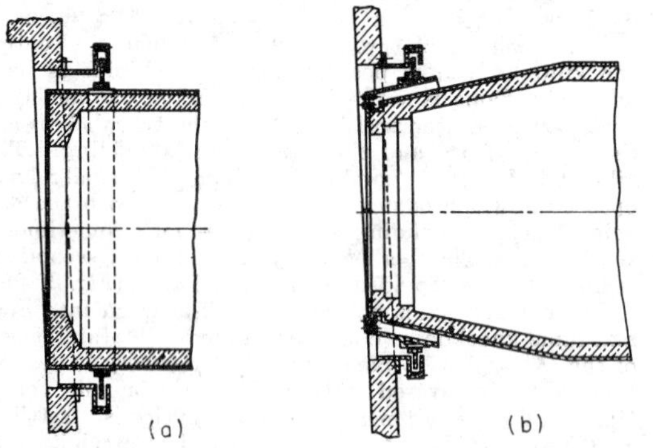

FIG. 20-29. Kiln-seal arrangements. (*a*) Single-floating-type feed-end air seal. (*b*) Single-floating-type air seal on air-cooled tapered feed end. (*Allis-Chalmers Manufacturing Co.*)

circular retainer plates. Figure 20-29 shows two arrangements. The floating-type discharge-end air seal consists of a circular bar which floats on a wearing pad and which can be moved to provide the desired operating clearance between air seal and firing hood. The floating ring and the fixed portion of these seals can be furnished with renewable wearing surfaces. Air infiltration through this type of seal is usually less than 10 per cent (Allis-Chalmers Manufacturing Co.). For further reduction of air infiltration, lantern-ring-type floating seals, pressurized with inert gas or stack gases, are employed.

Accelerated drying of slurries in the feed end of rotary kilns in wet-process operations is achieved by *installation of hanging chains.* Conveying spirals support suspended lengths of chain which are arranged in such a way that they form an effective pattern for drying. With the chain system, slurry is heated in three ways: by direct transfer from chains after suspension in hot gases, by lifting material into the path of hot gases, and by directing flow of hot gas over the slurry bed in the space formed under the suspended chains. Frequently, the product forms into uniformly sized pellets which progress through the rest of the kiln in that form, resulting in improved heat transfer and reduced dust losses (Fig. 20-30).

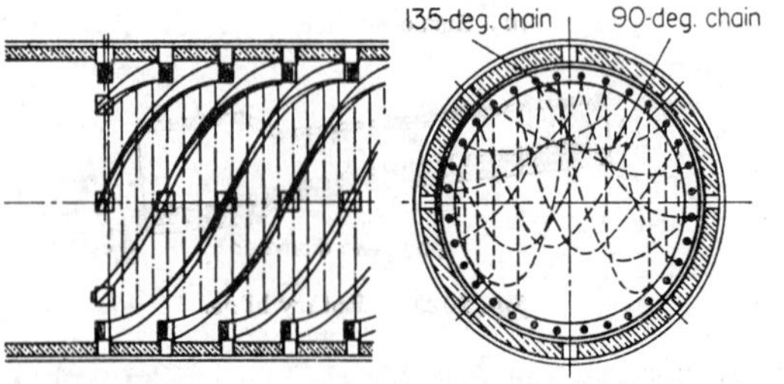

FIG. 20-30. Kiln chain installation (patented). (*Courtesy of the Allis-Chalmers Manufacturing Co.*)

Design Methods. In rotary kilns, the material is not showered through the air stream but is retained in the lower part of the cylinder. Gas-solids contacting is much less efficient than in flighted units. Heat transfer is by convection from the flowing gas to the kiln brick and exposed bed surface, and by radiation from the brick to the bed. For units employing separate combustion chambers, it can be assumed that at high temperatures the wall-film resistance to convection heat transfer from the gas to the brick is limiting and that at any point the bed temperature approaches the wall temperature. Hence the effective heat-transfer area is the inner kiln surface. For kilns under these conditions, the following empirical relationship is recommended for the convection heat-transfer coefficient from gas to brick:

$$Us = 0.05G^{0.67} \qquad (20\text{-}8)$$

where Us = heat-transfer coefficient, B.t.u./(hr.)(sq. ft. kiln surface)(°F.); and G = gas mass flow rate, lb./(hr.)(sq. ft. kiln cross section).

The above equation *does not account for gas radiation* at high temperature when the kiln charge can "see" the burner flame; hence the method will yield a conservative design. An analysis of heat transfer occurring in direct-fired rotary kilns is given by Gilbert [*Cement*, **5**, 417 (1932); **6**, 79, 189, 262, 327, 369 (1933); **7**, 1, 123 (1934)]. When a kiln is fired internally, the major source of heat transfer is radiation from the flame and hot gases. This occurs directly to both the solids surface and the wall, and from the latter to the product by reradiation (with some conduction).

Generally, a dry-feed kiln will have three zones of heating, and a wet-feed kiln will have four.

1. *Drying zone* at feed end removes moisture.
2. *Heating zone* where the charge is heated to the reaction temperature, *i.e.*, the decomposition temperature for limestone or "burning" temperature for cement.
3. *Reaction zone* in which the charge is burned, decomposed, reduced, oxidized, etc.
4. *Soaking zone* where the reacted charge is superheated or "soaked" at temperature or, if desired, cooled before discharge. The rates of heat transfer in each zone will be different. The detailed method of analyzing heat transfer in cement kilns as outlined by Gilbert can be used as a guide for estimating the performance of a kiln on other materials with reasonably satisfactory results.

Rotary kilns operate at various temperatures throughout their length. A graph of approximate gas and charge temperatures for wet-process cement is shown in Fig. 20-31. The maximum charge temperature is 2600° to 2800°F., and for the gases 2800° to 3000°F. Over-all

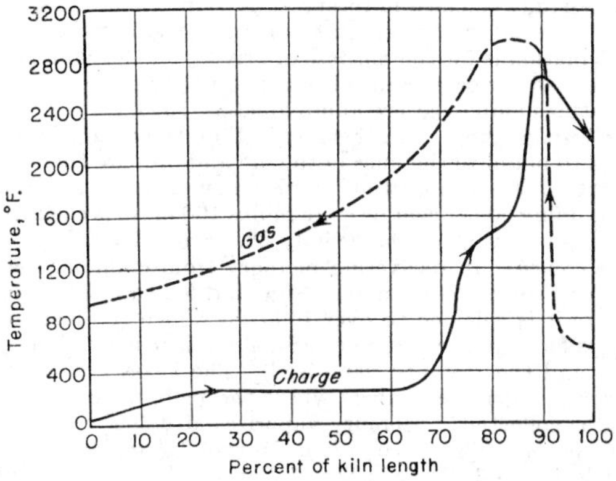

FIG. 20-31. Temperatures in rotary kiln on wet-process cement.

heat-transfer rates have been estimated to be in the range of 2500 to 6000 B.t.u./(hr.)(cu. ft.), based upon total kiln volume.

Several short-cut methods for estimating kiln capacity have been published but all have limitations in use. The following equation offered by Gibbs [*Rock Prods.*, **45** (11), 58 (1942)] gives an approximation of commercial practice for single-diameter kilns:

$$\text{Tons of product/day} = \frac{kLD^2}{100} \qquad (20\text{-}9)$$

This equation relates production capacity to kiln volume, where L is kiln length, ft.; D is diameter, ft.; and k is a factor whose magnitude depends on the charge material and other variables. It was formulated in connection with the observations of dolomite kilns, for which the data are given in Table 20-9. The very high ratio

Table 20-9. Dolomite Kiln Data

Size of kiln		Average production, tons/day	Secondary air	Shell volume/capacity ratio, cu. ft./(ton/day)	k [Eq. (20-9)]
$D \times L$, ft.	Shell volume, cu. ft.				
6 × 110	3,110	30(40)	Hot	104(78)	0.76(1.01)
7 × 115	4,420	60	Hot	74	1.06
8 × 125	6,280	90	Hot	70	1.12
8 × 125	6,280	80*	Cold	79	1.00
9 × 250	15,880	210(230)	Hot	76(69)	1.04(1.15)
Average value of k					1.00
Value of k under favorable conditions					1.15

* Note the difference in production from the same kiln which results from using either hot or cold secondary air.

of shell volume to capacity for the smallest kiln is believed to be due to the larger percentage effect of ring build-up in small diameters as compared with large diameters, the value in parentheses indicating the kiln's performance when clean. The largest kiln is stated to be operating on a more sticky material, which tends to coat the walls more seriously, thus decreasing its capacity. The value in parentheses indicates the performance of this kiln under good conditions. These data indicate that the kiln-volume requirements to produce 1 ton of burned dolomite per day range from 69 to 104 cu. ft., with 70 to 80 cu. ft. representing most of the data.

Publications by Gibbs [*Chem. & Met. Eng.*, **50** (8), 117 (1943); **53** (4), 99 (1946); **53** (5), 139 (1946)] modify this equation and present graphs which give recognition to the individual effects of various operating variables. The above-cited papers cover both wet and dry lime kilns, while others cover lime sludge [*Paper Trade J.*, **121** (10), *Tappi*, Sec. 91, Sept. 6, 1945; **122** (18), *Tappi*, Sec. 189, May 2, 1946].

Publications by Azbe [*Rock Prods.*, **49** (2), 90; (7), 80; (8), 90 (1946)] give data on the performance of rotary lime kilns, also.

Some commercial performance data for cement and lime kilns are shown in Table 20-10.

Some of the other major uses of direct rotary kilns are in the following processes (C. W. Spears, Traylor Eng. and Mfg. Div., Fuller Company; personal communication, Apr. 19, 1960).

Roasting. Rotary kilns are used for oxidizing and driving off sulfur and arsenic from various ores, including gold, silver, iron, etc. Temperatures employed will vary from 1000° to 2500°F.

Chloridizing. Silver ores are chloridized in rotary kilns successfully. Temperatures must be closely controlled between 1400° and 1500°F.

Black Ash. Barium sulfide (BaS) is produced by calcining a mixture of barite ($BaSO_4$) and carbon at a temperature of 2000°F. in continuous rotary kilns.

Table 20-10. Typical Rotary-kiln Installations*

Size, diam. × length	Usual No. of supports	Range of motor hp. to operate†	Nominal 24-hr. capacities‡ Portland cement, 376-lb. bbl.		Lime, net tons	
			Dry process	Wet process	Lime sludge	Limestone
5 × 80 ft.	2	5–7.5	140	100	10	16
6 × 70 ft.	2	7.5–15	190	135	15	24
7 × 70 ft.	2	15–20	275	200	20	35
5 ft. 6 in. × 180 ft.	4	15–20	285	250	30	45
7 × 120 ft.	2	15–25	475	340	35	55
7 ft. 6 in. × 125 ft.	2	20–30	575	415	40	70
6 × 220 ft.	4	20–30	420	375	45	65
8 × 140 ft.	2	25–30	750	540	55	90
9 × 160 ft.	2	30–50	1100	800	80	130
8 ft. 6 in. × 185 ft.	4	30–50	1125	810	80	135
10 × 150 ft.	2	40–75	1300	950	...	145
10 × 175 ft.	2	50–75	1500	1100	...	155
8 × 300 ft.	5	50–75	1150	1000	110	160
7 ft. 6 in. × 8 ft. 6 in. × 320 ft.	5	50–75	1175	1020	115	165
7 ft. 6 in. × 10 ft. × 8 ft. 6 in. × 300 ft.	5	50–75	1175	1020		
10 × 11 × 175 ft.	2	50–75	1650	1200	120	180
10 ft. 6 in. × 185 ft.	2	50–75	1800	1300	130	190
11 × 175 ft.	2	60–100	1850	1375	...	205
8 ft. 6 in. × 10 ft. × 8 ft. 6 in. × 300 ft.	5	50–75	1400	1200		
8 × 10 × 300 ft.	5	50–75	1425	1225	140	200
9 ft. 6 in. × 265 ft.	4	60–100	1500	1300	150	215
9 × 10 ft. 6 in. × 9 ft. × 325 ft.	5	60–100	1700	1500		
10 ft. 6 in. × 250 ft.	4	60–100	1750	1525	175	240
9 ft. 6 in. × 11 ft. × 9 ft. 6 in. × 300 ft.	5	60–100	1800	1550		
10 × 300 ft.	5	75–125	1900	1650	190	250
9 ft. 6 in. × 11 ft. × 9 ft. 6 in. × 375 ft.	6	75–125	2025	1800		
11 × 300 ft.	5	75–125	2400	2100	225	300
11 ft. 6 in. × 300 ft.	4	100–150	2600	2250	240	320
10 ft. 6 in. × 375 ft.	5	100–150	2700	2400	250	325
11 ft. 3 in. × 360 ft.	5	125–175	2900	2500	275	350
11 ft. 6 in. × 475 ft.	7	150–250	4000	3500	375	450
12 × 500 ft.	8	200–300	4600	4000	425	500

* Allis-Chalmers Manufacturing Co.

† Power requirements vary according to size of kiln, character of material handled, and method of operation.

‡ Capacities indicated are conservative, and apply to normal operation at sea level. Corrections would apply at increased altitudes, and for differing methods of operation.

Spodumene. A mixture of quartz, feldspar, and spodumene is being calcined in rotary kilns at 2200°F. to produce lithium aluminum silicate.

Vermiculite. A micaceous mineral is roasted to cause exfoliation for use as an insulating material.

Revivification. Temperatures of 1000° to 1400°F. are used to revivify fuller's and diatomaceous earth, although in the case of some earths, lower temperatures are employed.

Zinc. Oxidized ores are calcined to drive off water of hydration and carbon dioxide. The sulfide ore is always roasted before smelting.

Titanium oxide (TiO_2) is produced from ilmenite ore by mixing ore with carbon and heating in a rotary kiln. Also, the rotary kiln is used in the process of recovery of titanium oxide from hydrated titanium precipitate at about 1825°F.

Roofing Granules. Crushed quartz or sand of definite size is treated with various minerals, borax, soda ash, etc., and calcined at temperatures ranging from 1800° to 2500°F. Glass of different colors forms on the surface of the granules at various temperatures. An oxidizing or reducing flame is used to influence the final coloring.

Alumina (Al_2O_3) is produced by calcining either bauxite or aluminum hydroxide in rotary kilns at temperatures from 1800° to 2500°F. In obtaining the highest-purity alumina, the bauxite is digested with alkali to remove impurities; the resultant aluminum hydroxide [$Al_2(OH)_3$], of approximately 200-mesh size, is then calcined in rotary kilns at 2000°F.

Potassium Salts. In this operation, potassium chloride (KCl) is introduced to the rotary kiln at a fineness of minus 100 mesh and containing 9 per cent water. The salt is brought to the fusion temperature of 1427°F.

Magnesium Oxide. The natural minerals, *i.e.*, magnesite ($MgCO_3$), brucite [$Mg(OH)_2$], etc., after being crushed to predetermined size, are calcined at temperatures varying from 1440° to 3200°F., depending upon whether a caustic or dead-burned product (periclase) is being produced. Magnesium hydroxide, recovered from sea water or salt brine, is also being treated in a similar manner except that it is added in the form of a sludge.

Sodium Aluminum Sulfate. This product is now being successfully calcined in rotary kilns. In this process, the salt cake is broken up just prior to entering the kiln. Calcination is for the purpose of driving off the combined water (45 per cent) and sulfuric acid (3 per cent). Temperatures employed are approximately 1000°F.

Phosphate Rock. In this application, the rotary kiln is used to nodulize the fines in the ore and prepare them for electric-furnace operation. Ore under 2 in. in size and containing 50 per cent or more minus 100 mesh is calcined. Ore nodulizes at approximately 2200° to 2400°F.

Mercury. In recovering mercury from cinnabar ores, the ore is crushed to minus ½ in. and fed to rotary kilns where it is calcined to over 1000°F. Since the mercury exists as mercuric sulfide (HgS), the sulfur is oxidized to SO_2 and the mercury vaporized. The gases are passed through cooling chambers where the mercury condenses and is collected. Mercury vaporizes at 680°F.

Gypsum. The rotary kiln is rapidly replacing the kettle in producing plaster of Paris. Great care is required as the temperatures for reaction are low and within narrow limits, 228° to 267°F. Gypsum ($CaSO_4 \cdot 2H_2O$) is heated to drive off three-fourths of the water of crystallization to produce plaster of Paris [$(CaSO_4)_2 \cdot H_2O$]. Any overheating drives off all the water, producing gypsite ($CaSO_4$), which is unsatisfactory.

Clay. To produce lightweight aggregate for concrete, clay is calcined in rotary kilns. Temperatures employed vary from 2000° to 2500°F. The apparent density of the clay is reduced by 50 to 75 per cent.

Iron Ores. Crushed iron ores are partially reduced in rotary kilns to obtain nodules which are used in blast-furnace charges.

Manganese. Manganese ore, rhodochrosite, or manganese carbonate ($MnCO_3$) is calcined at about 2300°F. to produce the oxide (Mn_3O_4). Where the oxide ore is available but is in a finely divided state, the rotary kiln is used only for nodulizing.

Petroleum Coke. In order to eliminate excess volatile matter, petroleum coke is calcined at temperatures of 2200° to 2400°F. This is a sensitive material and temperature control is difficult to maintain.

When it is desired to increase the capacity of an existing kiln installation, consideration should be given to the following changes:

1. Increase charge volume held in kiln.
2. Increase temperature and quantity of combustion gases.
3. Decrease quantity of air in excess of combustion needs.
4. Increase speed of rotation of kiln.
5. Install ring dams at intermediate and discharge points.
6. Increase capacity of feeding and discharge mechanisms.
7. Decrease moisture content of feed material.
8. Increase temperature of feed material.
9. Install chains or flights, etc., in feed end.
10. Preheat all combustion air.
11. Reduce leakage of cold air into kiln at hot end.
12. Increase stack draft by increasing height or by use of jets.
13. Install instrumentation to control the kiln at maximum-capacity conditions.

The *time of passage* in rotary kilns (from which hold-up can be calculated) can be estimated by the following formula (*U.S. Bur. Mines Tech. Paper* 384, 1927):

$$\theta = \frac{0.19L}{NDS} \tag{20-10}$$

where θ = time of passage in the kiln, min.; L = kiln length, ft.; N = rotational speed, r.p.m.; S = slope of the kiln, ft./ft.; and D = diameter inside the brick, ft. Other equations for estimating the time of passage employing internal dams and a discharge dam are given by Bayard [*Chem. & Met. Eng.*, **52** (3), 100–102 (1945)].

The total power required to drive a rotary kiln, or dryer with lifters, can be calculated by the following formulas (courtesy of Bartlett-Snow-Pacific Co.): For a rotary kiln or calciner, *without lifters,*

$$\text{b.h.p.} = \frac{N[18.85y(\sin B)w + 0.1925DW + 0.33W]}{100{,}000} \tag{20-11}$$

For a rotary dryer or section of a kiln, *with lifters,*

$$\text{b.h.p.} = \frac{N(4.75dw + 0.1925DW + 0.33W)}{100{,}000} \tag{20-12}$$

where b.h.p. = brake horsepower required; N = rotational speed, r.p.m.; y = distance between the center line of the kiln and the center of gravity of the material bed, ft.; B = angle of repose of the material; W = total rotating load (equipment plus material), lb.; w = live load (material), lb.; D = riding-ring diameter, ft.; d = shell diameter, ft. For estimating purposes, let $D = (d + 2)$.

Drive motors should be of the high-starting-torque type and selected for 1.33 times maximum rotational speed. For two- or three-diameter kilns, the brake horsepower for the several diameters should be calculated separately and summed. Auxiliary drives should be provided to maintain shell rotation in event of power failure. These are usually gasoline or diesel engines.

Thermal Efficiency of Rotary Kilns. Kiln length is a major factor in determining thermal efficiency, and kilns with a high ratio of length to diameter have a greater thermal efficiency than those with a low ratio. The use of chains inside the kiln and of heat-recovery equipment on the gases and product leaving the kiln can increase substantially the thermal efficiency of a kiln installation. Efficiencies ranging from 45 to more than 80 per cent have been reported. A reasonably satisfactory range based on present fuel prices and construction costs would be 65 to 75 per cent utilization and recovery of the heat content of the fuel plus any heat of reaction of the charge. No distinction is made from an efficiency-calculation standpoint between the heat utilized in the kiln and that recovered (or utilized) outside the kiln. With countercurrent flow of the combustion gases and the charge material, an exceptionally long kiln will give high efficiencies within itself. However, good economics may dictate that a shorter kiln be installed with a waste-heat boiler on the hot gases to obtain an equivalent thermal efficiency at a lower investment. The heat in the hot product usually is recovered as preheat in the combustion air.

Size Segregation in Kilns. When an assemblage of solid particles, not very closely screened, is rotated within a cylinder, the solids assume a lunar shape, as shown in Fig. 20-32. This causes serious size segregation. The finest sizes remain at the bottom, in contact

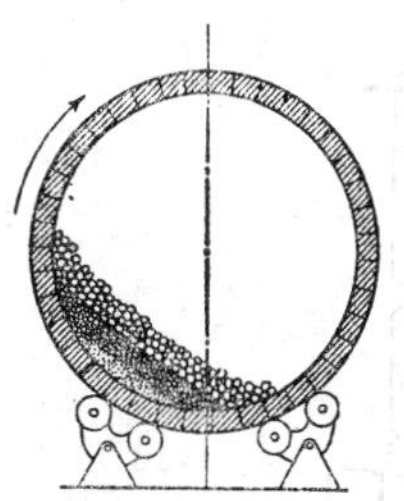

FIG. 20-32. Size segregation of solids in rotary kiln.

with the hot brick. The coarser particles form the upper layer of the agitated mass. As the kiln completes a revolution, the exposed brick, in an upper position, absorbs sensible heat from the gas mass. As the heated brick completes its circuit, it passes under and is in conductive contact with the fine particles. These fines are thus effectively heated by direct solid-to-solid transfer. The larger particles are heated by direct radiation from gas and brick, and become adequately calcined. The particles of size intermediate between the fine and coarse remain, throughout a complete revolution, "sandwiched" between the coarse and fine layers and are protected from heat by the excellent insulation properties of these layers, thus perhaps escaping complete calcination. This factor of segregation is offset by some kiln operators who classify or screen the kiln feed so that only

Table 20-11. Approximate Purchase Costs and Weights of Rotary Kilns (1960)*

Kiln size, diam. × length	No. riding rings	Kiln weight (does not include brick lining)	Total purchase price includes drive, burner, and controls (not including brick)	Motor hp.	Weight of 6-in. brick lining
8 ft. 0 in. × 80 ft.	2	210,000	$ 96,350	20	131,000
8 ft. 0 in. × 140 ft.	2	309,000	118,150	30	230,000
8 ft. 0 in. × 200 ft.	3	491,000	175,300	40	328,000
8 ft. 0 in. × 300 ft.	5	650,000	219,450	60	493,000
9 ft. 0 in. × 250 ft.	4	720,000	248,800	60	467,000
9 ft. 0 in. × 300 ft.	5	814,600	278,100	100	560,000
10 ft. 0 in. × 100 ft.	2	332,000	122,650	40	209,000
10 ft. 0 in. × 150 ft.	2	476,000	168,000	50	314,000
10 ft. 0 in. × 250 ft.	4	792,700	267,400	75	523,000
10 ft. 0 in. × 300 ft.	5	910,600	300,350	100	627,000
10 ft. 0 in. × 350 ft.	5	1,025,800	331,100	125	730,000
10 ft. 6 in. × 175 ft.	2	610,000	215,200	60	385,000
10 ft. 6 in. × 250 ft.	4	905,000	303,600	75	550,000
10 ft. 6 in. × 350 ft.	5	1,129,200	369,600	100	770,000
11 ft. 0 in. × 160 ft.	2	615,600	218,500	60	370,000
11 ft. 0 in. × 250 ft.	4	950,200	321,500	100	578,000
11 ft. 0 in. × 300 ft.	5	1,090,900	368,500	125	694,000
11 ft. 0 in. × 350 ft.	5	1,370,500	446,400	125	810,000
11 ft. 0 in. × 400 ft.	5	1,481,300	477,600	150	925,000
11 ft. 6 in. × 160 ft.	2	664,000	230,300	75	387,000
11 ft. 6 in. × 250 ft.	4	1,063,500	350,900	125	605,000
11 ft. 6 in. × 350 ft.	5	1,440,800	465,300	150	847,000
11 ft. 6 in. × 425 ft.	6	1,609,600	512,800	200	1,025,000
12 ft. 0 in. × 250 ft.	4	1,101,300	366,500	125	632,000
12 ft. 0 in. × 325 ft.	5	1,575,000	507,500	150	822,000
12 ft. 0 in. × 400 ft.	5	1,635,900	511,700	200	1,010,000
12 ft. 0 in. × 450 ft.	6	2,224,200	675,300	200	1,140,000
13 ft. 0 in. × 500 ft.	7	2,746,700	819,400	250	2,020,000 (9-in. brick)
14 ft. 0 in. × 400 ft.	5	2,600,000	762,200	400	1,750,000 (9-in. brick)
16 ft. 6 in. × 600 ft.	7	5,243,000	1,467,300	600	3,120,000 (9-in. brick)

* Traylor Engineering and Manufacturing Div., Fuller Company.

a narrow range of particle size is fed at one time. Also, faster kiln speeds which give a better agitation of the charge are used.

Rotary kilns are usually operated with between 3 and 12 per cent of their volume filled with material; 7 per cent is considered normal.

Cost Data. Purchase prices, weights, and horsepower requirements of typical units are given in Table 20-11. Installed costs will run 300 to 500 per cent of purchase cost. Maintenance will average 5 to 10 per cent of the total installed cost per year but is dependent largely on the life of the refractory lining.

Indirect-heat Rotary Steam-tube Dryer

Probably the most common type of indirect-heat rotary dryer is the steam-tube dryer (Fig. 20-33). Steam-heated tubes running the full length of the cylinder are fastened symmetrically in one, two, or three *concentric rows* inside the cylinder and rotate with it. Tubes may be simple pipe with condensate draining by gravity into the discharge manifold or *bayonet type.* Bayonet-type tubes are also employed when units are used as *water-tube coolers.* When handling sticky materials, one row of tubes is preferred. These are occasionally *shielded* at the feed end of the dryer to prevent build-up of solids behind them. Lifting *flights* are usually inserted behind the tubes to promote *solids agitation.*

Wet feed enters the dryer through a chute or screw feeder. The product discharges through peripheral openings in the shell in ordinary dryers. These openings also serve to admit purge air to sweep moisture or other evolved gases from the shell. In practically all cases, gas flow is *countercurrent* to solids flow. To retain a deep bed of material within the dryer, normally 10 to 20 per cent fillage, the discharge openings are supplied with *removable chutes* extending radially into the dryer. These, on removal, permit complete emptying of the dryer.

Steam is admitted to the tubes through a revolving steam joint into the steam side of the manifold (Fig. 20-34). Condensate is removed continuously, by

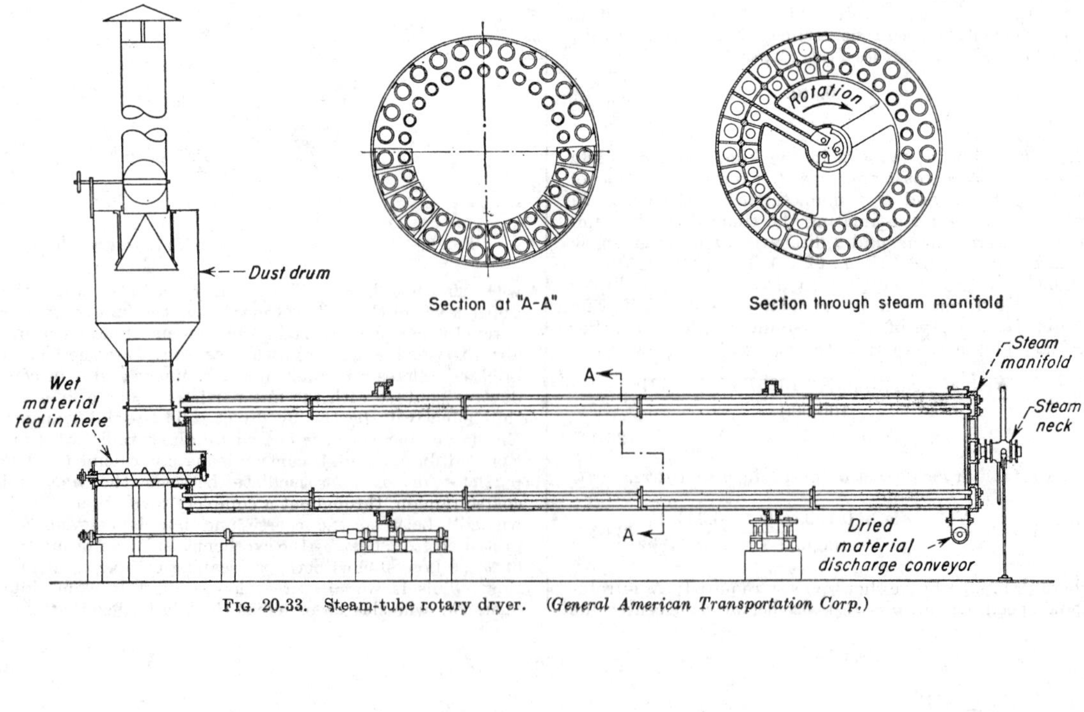

Fig. 20-33. Steam-tube rotary dryer. (*General American Transportation Corp.*)

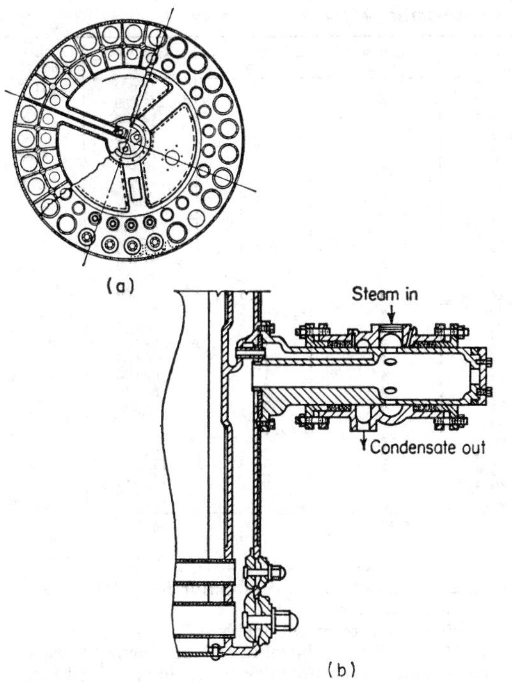

FIG. 20-34. Rotary steam joint for a standard steam-tube dryer. (*a*) Section of cast steam manifold. (*b*) Section of manifold and steam joint. (*Patented, General American Transportation Corp.*)

gravity through the steam joint to a condensate receiver, by means of lifters in the condensate side of the manifold. Employing simple tubes, non-condensables are continuously vented at the other ends of the tubes through Sarco-type vent valves mounted on an *auxiliary manifold ring*, also revolving with the cylinder.

Vapors (from drying) are removed at the feed end of the dryer, usually to the atmosphere through a natural-draft stack and settling chamber or wet scrubber. When employed in simple drying operations with 50 to 150 lb./sq. in. gage steam, draft is controlled by a damper to admit only sufficient outside air to sweep moisture from the cylinder, discharging the air at 150° to 200°F. and 80 to 90 per cent saturation. In this way, shell gas velocities and dusting are minimized. When used for solvent recovery or other processes requiring a sealed system, *sweep gas is recirculated* through a scrubber-gas cooler and blower.

Steam manifolds for pressures up to 150 lb./sq. in. gage are of cast iron. For higher pressures, the manifold is fabricated from *plate steel*, stay-bolted and welded. The tubes are fastened rigidly to the manifold face plate and are supported in a close-fitting annular plate at the other end to permit expansion. Packing on the steam neck is normally graphite-asbestos. Ordinary rotating seals are similar in design to those depicted in Fig. 20-25, with allowance for admission of small quantities of outside air when the dryer is operated under a slight negative internal pressure.

Steam-tube dryers are used for the *continuous heating or cooling* of granular or powdery solids which cannot be exposed to ordinary atmospheric or combustion gases. They are especially *suitable for fine dusty particles* because of the low gas velocities required for purging of the cylinder. Steam-tube units represent the lowest-cost heat-transfer surface of any indirect rotating equipment. Tube sticking is avoided or reduced by employing recycle, shell knockers, etc., as previously described; tube scaling by sticky solids is one of the major hazards to efficient operation. The dryers are suitable for drying, solvent recovery, and chemical reactions. Recently, steam-tube units have found effective employment in soda-ash production, replacing more expensive indirect-heat rotary calciners.

Special types of steam-tube dryers employ packed and purged seals on all rotating joints, with a *central solids-discharge manifold* through the steam neck to reduce the seal diameter. This manifold contains the product discharge conveyor and a passage for admission of sweep gas. Solids are removed from the shell by special volute lifters and dropped into the discharge conveyor. Units have been fabricated for operation at 3 in. of water, internal shell pressure with no detectable air leakage.

Design Methods. Heat-transfer coefficients in steam-tube dryers range from 5 to 15 B.t.u./(hr.)(sq. ft. total tube area)(°F.). Coefficients will increase with increasing steam temperature because of increased heat transfer by radiation. In units carrying saturated steam at 300° to 350°F., the heat flux $U\,\Delta T$ will range from 600 to 1200 B.t.u./(hr.)(sq. ft.) for difficult-to-dry and organic solids, and up to 2000 B.t.u./(hr.)(sq. ft.) for finely divided inorganic materials. The effect of steam pressure on heat-transfer rates up to 125 lb./sq. in. gage is illustrated in Fig. 20-35. *Time of passage* or

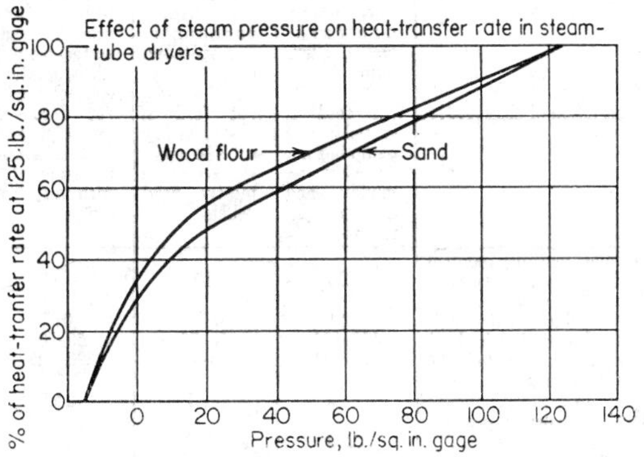

FIG. 20-35. Effect of steam pressure on heat-transfer rate in steam-tube dryers. (*Courtesy of the General American Transportation Corp.*)

hold-up of material can be estimated employing the kiln formula [Eq. (20-10)].

Performance and Cost Data. Table 20-12 contains data for a number of standard sizes of steam-tube dryers. *Prices* tabulated are for ordinary carbon-steel construction; multiply by 2.1 for type 304 stainless-steel fabrication. Installed costs will run 150 to 300 per cent of purchase cost.

The *thermal efficiency* of steam-tube units will range from 70 to 90 per cent, assuming a well-insulated cylinder. This does not allow for boiler efficiency, however, and is therefore not directly comparable with direct-heat units, like the direct-heat rotary dryer or indirect-heat calciner.

Operating costs for these dryers include 20 to 35 per cent of one man's time. *Maintenance* will average 5 to 10 per cent of total installed cost per year.

Table 20-13 outlines typical performance data from three drying applications in steam-tube dryers.

Table 20-12. Standard Steam-tube Dryers*

Size, diam., in. × length, ft.	Tubes No. o.d., in.	Tubes No. o.d., in.	Sq. ft. of surface	Sq. ft. of free area	Dryer speed, r.p.m.	Motor size, hp.	Shipping wt.	Est. price (1960)†
38 × 15	14-4½		230	6.3	6	3	12,000	$11,845
38 × 20	14-4½		315	6.3	6	3	13,000	
38 × 25	14-4½		395	6.3	6	5	14,200	
38 × 30	14-4½		480	6.3	6	5	15,200	
38 × 35	14-4½		560	6.3	6	5	16,400	14,005
54 × 20	18-4½	18-2½	625	13.3	4.4	5	22,500	17,430
54 × 25	18-4½	18-2½	790	13.3	4.4	5	24,500	
54 × 30	18-4½	18-2½	955	13.3	5	7.5	26,700	
54 × 35	18-4½	18-2½	1120	13.3	5	7.5	28,800	
54 × 40	18-4½	18-2½	1285	13.3	5	7.5	31,300	
54 × 45	18-4½	18-2½	1450	13.3	5.5	10	33,100	21,325
72 × 25	27-4½	27-3	1270	24	4	7.5	42,500	24,600
72 × 30	27-4½	27-3	1540	24	4	7.5	45,400	
72 × 35	27-4½	27-3	1800	24	4	10	48,900	
72 × 40	27-4½	27-3	2070	24	4	10	52,400	
72 × 45	27-4½	27-3	2335	24	4	15	56,600	
72 × 50	27-4½	27-3	2600	24	4	15	60,600	
72 × 55	27-4½	27-3	2865	24	4	20	64,500	
72 × 60	27-4½	27-3	3130	24	4	20	67,700	33,780
96 × 40	90-4½		4240	40.4	3	15	110,000	50,660
96 × 56	90-4½		5300	40.4	3	20	124,000	
96 × 60	90-4½		6350	40.4	3	20	140,000	
96 × 70	90-4½		7415	40.4	3	30	154,000	
96 × 80	90-4½		8465	40.4	3	40	166,000	64,320

* General American Transportation Corp.
† Carbon-steel fabrication; multiply by 2.1 for 304 stainless steel.

Table 20-13. Steam-tube Dryer Performance Data*

	Class 1	Class 2	Class 3
Class of materials handled.	High moisture organic, distillers' grains, brewers' grains, citrus pulp	Pigment filter cakes, blanc fixe, barium carbonate, precipitated chalk	Finely divided inorganic solids, water-ground mica, water-ground silica, flotation concentrates
Description of class......	Wet feed is granular and damp but not sticky or muddy and dries to granular meal	Wet feed is pasty, muddy or sloppy. Product is mostly hard pellets	Wet feed is crumbly and friable. Product is powder with very few lumps
Normal moisture content of wet feed, % dry basis	233	100	54
Normal moisture content of product, % dry basis	11	0.15	0.5
Normal temp. wet feed, °F.	100–120	50–70	50–70
Normal temp. product, °F.	175–185	225–275	200–225
Evaporation per lb. product, lb...............	2	1	0.53
Heat load per lb. product, B.t.u................	2250	1190	625
Steam pressure normally used, lb./sq. in. gage....	125	125	125
Heating surface required per lb. product, sq. ft...	1.67	2.00	0.35
Steam consumption per lb. product, lb............	3.33	1.72	0.85

* Courtesy of General American Transportation Corp.

Indirect-heat Calciners

Indirect-heat *calciners*, either batch or continuous, are employed for heat-treating and drying at higher temperatures than can be obtained in steam-heated rotating equipment. They require a minimum flow of gas to purge the cylinder which, when handling granular solids, reduces dusting; they are suitable for gas-sealed operation with oxidizing, inert, or reducing atmospheres. Indirect calciners are widely and successfully used in the following specific applications:

1. Activating wood charcoal
2. Reducing mineral high oxides to low oxides
3. Drying fluoride precipitates in a hydrogen fluoride atmosphere
4. Calcination of silica gel
5. Drying and removal of sulfur from cobalt, copper, and nickel powders
6. Reduction of metal oxides
7. Oxidizing and "burning off" of organic impurities
8. Reclamation of foundry sand from the shell-molding process

This unit consists essentially of a cylindrical retort, rotating within a stationary refractory-lined cylindrical furnace. The latter is arranged so that fuel combustion occurs within the annular ring between the retort and the furnace. The retort cylinder extends at both ends beyond the furnace. These end extensions carry the riding rings and drive gear. Material may be fed continuously at one end and discharged continuously at the other. Feeding and solids discharging are usually accomplished with screw feeders or other positive feeders, to prevent leakage of gases into or out of the retort with the solids.

In some cases where it is desirable to *cool the product* before removal to the outside atmosphere, the discharge end of the cylinder is provided with an additional extension, the exterior of which is water-spray cooled. *In cocurrent-flow calciners*, hot gases from the interior of the heated portion of the cylinder are withdrawn through a special exit tube. This tube extends centrally through the cooled section to prevent flow of gas near the cooled-shell surfaces and possible condensation. Frequently a *separate cooler* is used, isolated from the calciner by an air lock.

Operating temperatures in indirect-heat calciners are limited only by structural considerations, normally 800°F. for carbon steel and 1200°F. for stainless steels. Use of special metals may permit operation up to 2000°F., however.

To prevent *sliding of solids* over the smooth interior of the shell, *lifting bars* running longitudinally and welded to the inside wall are frequently provided. These normally do not shower the solids as in a direct-heat vessel but merely prevent sliding so that the bed will turn over and constantly expose new surface for heat and mass transfer. To prevent *scaling of the shell interior* by sticky solids, a scraper "chain" is occasionally employed. This may, for example, consist of a series of I-beam sections, pinned together. These will be fastened at

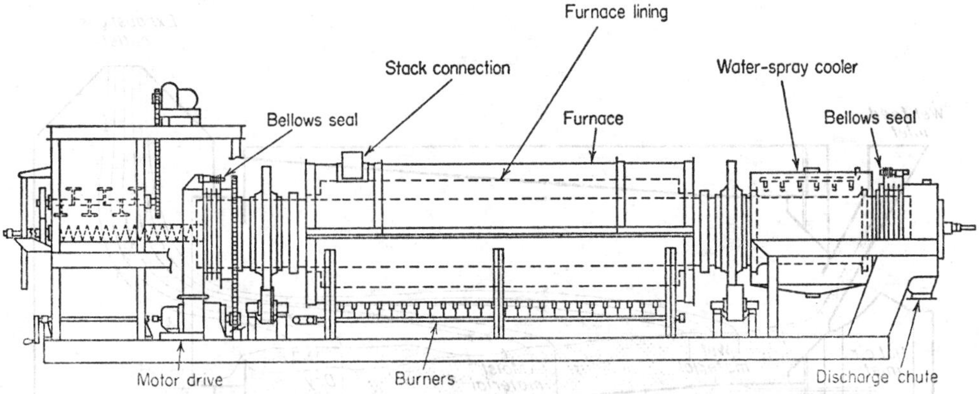

FIG. 20-36. Gas-fired indirect-heat rotary calciner with a water-spray extended cooler and feeder assembly. (*Courtesy of Bartlett-Snow-Pacific.*)

each end to rigid swivels by link chain to permit turning and prevent wrapping of the beam chain upon itself. The beam sections must be sufficiently heavy to sink through the solids bed, so that they ride directly on and scrape the shell. In this instance, lifting bars would not be used, agitation being provided by chain motion. The use of a scraper chain is a fairly common practice in, for example, indirect-heat soda-ash calciners. For precise control of retention, approaching plug flow, *continuous spiral flights* may be attached to the inside of the shell.

Because indirect-heat calciners frequently require close-fitting gas seals, it is customary to support all parts on a self-contained steel base, for sizes up to approximately 48 in. diameter by 30 ft. long. Electric, gas, or oil heating is used on modern units, with multiple-burner arrangements beneath the shell to ensure uniform heating. Process control is normally by shell temperature, measured by radiation pyrometers or similar devices. When a special gas atmosphere must be maintained inside the cylinder, positive rotary gas seals, with one or more pressurized and purged annular chambers, are employed. The diaphragm-type bellows seal (Bartlett-Snow-Pacific Co.) is suitable for pressures up to 2.0 in. of water, with no detectable leakage.

Design Methods. In indirect-heater calciners, heat transfer is primarily by *radiation* from the cylinder wall to the solids bed. The *thermal efficiency* ranges from 35 to 65 per cent. The limiting factors in heat transmission lie in the conductivity and radiation constants of the shell metal and solids bed. Knowing the characteristics of these, equipment may be accurately sized employing the Stefan-Boltzmann radiation equation. Apparent heat-transfer coefficients will range from 3.0 B.t.u./(hr.)(sq. ft. of cylinder surface)(°F.) in low-temperature operations to 15.0 B.t.u./(hr.)(sq. ft.) (°F.) in high-temperature processes. For comparison, *indirect-direct heat* dryers, such as that depicted in Fig. 20-24, yield extremely high thermal efficiencies, frequently up to 80 per cent in double-shell units, and up to 85 per cent in furnace-encased units. The reason is that the spent and partially cooled flue gases, rather than being discharged to atmosphere, are further utilized in convection heat transfer directly to the solids. Analysis of several indirect-direct units shows that 15 to 25 per cent of the heat input is by indirect heat transfer through the metal and 75 to 85 per cent by direct convection from gas to solids.

Cost Data. Power, operating, and maintenance costs are similar to those previously outlined for direct- and indirect-heat rotary dryers. Estimating purchase costs for continuous rotating calciners with carbon-steel and type 316 stainless-steel cylinders are given in Table 20-14, together with size, weight, and motor requirements. Sale price includes cylinder, *ordinary angle seals*, furnace, drive, feed and discharge conveyors, burners, etc. Installed cost may be estimated at 200 to 300 per cent of the purchase cost. A layout of a typical continuous calciner with an extended cooler section is illustrated in Fig. 20-36.

Table 20-14. Indirect-heat Rotary Calciners, Sizes and Purchase Costs (1960)*

Diam., ft.	Over-all cylinder length	Heated cylinder length	Motor hp. based on 2 r.p.m. of cylinder, 10% loading, 100 lb./cu. ft. material	Shipping wt., lb., exclusive of refractories	Approx. sale price in carbon-steel construction	Approx. sale price in No. 316 stainless construction
4	37 ft. 6 in.	31 ft. 0 in.	5	25,000	$19,000	$28,000
5	44 ft. 4 in.	36 ft. 8 in.	7.5	50,000	27,000	40,000
6	45 ft. 0 in.	37 ft. 4 in.	10	55,000	30,000	48,000
7	60 ft. 0 in.	52 ft. 3 in.	25	85,000	40,000	65,000

* Bartlett-Snow-Pacific Co.

Small batch retorts, electrically or combustion heated, are widely used as carburizing furnaces and are applicable also to chemical processes involving heat-treating of particulate solids. These are mounted on a structural-steel base, complete with cylinder, furnace, drive motor, burner, etc. Units are commercially available in diameters from 9 to 48 in. and lengths of 36 to 72 in. Continuous retorts with helical internal spirals are employed also for metal heat-treating purposes. Precise retention control is maintained in these operations. Standard diameters are 12, 18, and 24 in., with effective lengths up to 10 ft. Although designed originally for metal-treating purposes, these vessels are employed also in many small-scale chemical process operations which require accurate control of retention. Their operating characteristics and applications are identical to the larger indirect-heat calciners.

Direct-heat Roto-Louvre Dryer

One of the more important special types of rotating equipment is the *Roto-Louvre* dryer. As illustrated in Fig. 20-37, hot air (or cooling air) is blown through louvers in an essentially double-wall rotating cylinder and *up through* the bed of solids. The latter moves continuously through the cylinder as it rotates. Constant

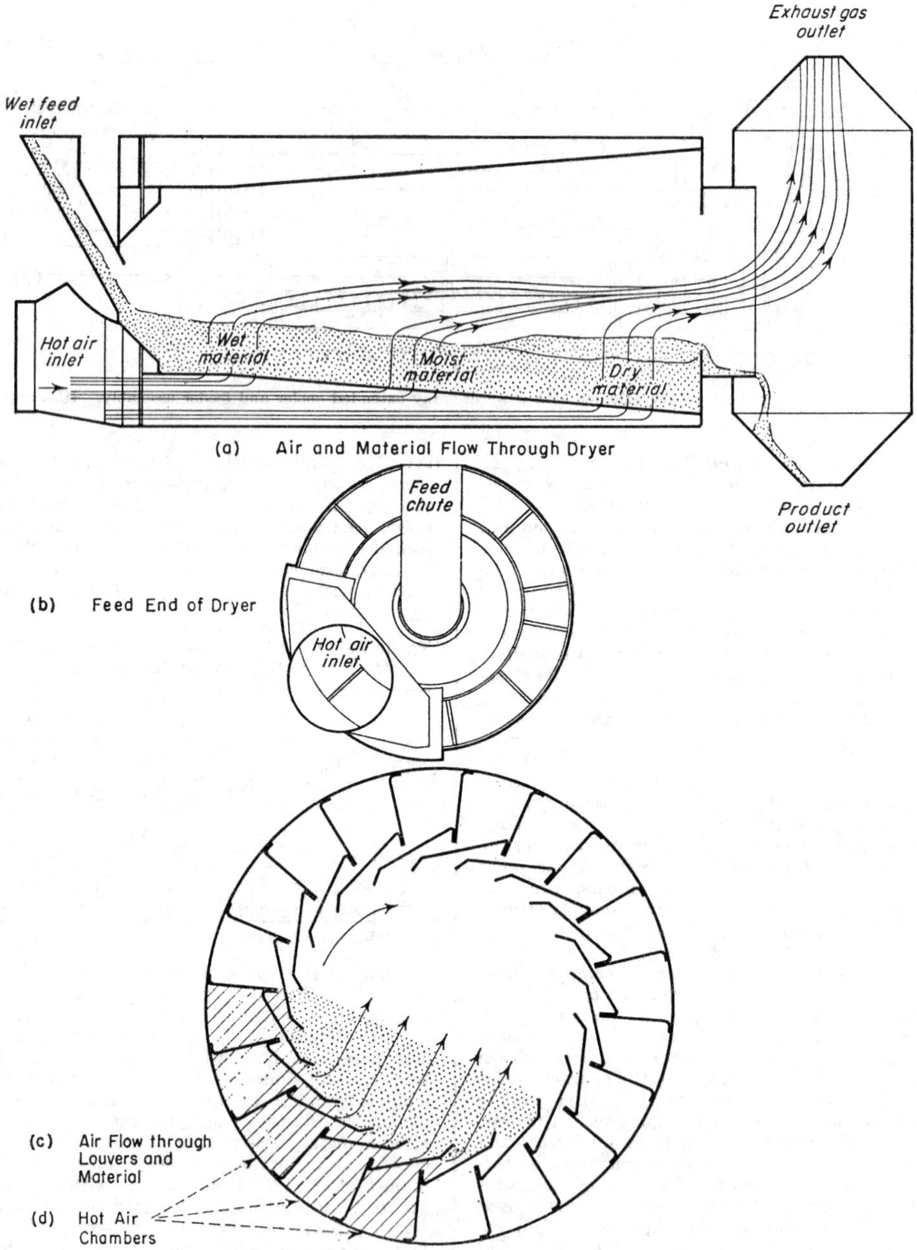

FIG. 20-37. Link-Belt Roto-Louvre dryer. (*Link-Belt Co.*)

turnover of the bed ensures uniform gas contacting for heat and mass transfer. The annular gas passage behind the louvers is partitioned, so that contacting air enters the cylinder only beneath the solids bed. The number of louvers covered at any one time is roughly 30 per cent. Because air circulates through the bed, fillages of 13 to 15 per cent or greater are employed.

Roto-Louvre dryers range in size from 2½ to 11½ ft. in diameter and from 8 to 35 ft. long. The largest unit is reported capable of evaporating 12,000 lb./hr. of water. Hot gases from 250° to 1000°F. may be employed. Because gas flow is through the bed of solids, extremely high pressure drop, from 3 to 20 in. of water, may be encountered within the shell. For this reason, both a pressure inlet fan and an exhaust fan are provided in most applications to maintain the static pressure within the equipment as close as possible to atmospheric. This prevents excessive in-leakage, or blowing of hot gas and dust to the outside. For pressure control, one fan is usually operated under fixed conditions, with an automatic damper control on the other, regulated by a pressure detector-controller.

In heating or drying applications, when cooling of the product is desired before discharge to the atmosphere, cool air is frequently blown through a second annular space, outside the inlet hot-air annulus, and released through the louvers at the solids-discharge end of the shell.

Roto-Louvre dryers are suitable for processing *coarse granular solids* which do not offer high resistance to air flow, require intimate gas contacting, and do not contain significant quantities of dust. Because showering of the solids particles is not necessary, impact breakage of crystals and large particles may be less in some cases than encountered in direct-heat rotary equipment with showering flights.

Because gas flow is through the constantly moving bed of solids, heat and mass transfer, at least from the gas to the surface of the solids, is extremely efficient; hence the equipment size required for a given duty is frequently less than required when an ordinary direct-heat rotary vessel with lifting flights is used. Purchase-price savings are partially balanced, however, by the more complex construction of the Roto-Louvre unit. A Roto-Louvre dryer will have a capacity roughly 1.5 times that of a single-shell rotary dryer of the same size under equivalent operating conditions. Because of the cross-flow method of heat exchange, the average Δt is not a simple function of inlet and outlet Δt's. There are currently no published data which permit sizing of equipment without pilot tests as recommended by the manufacturer, and because each unit may require some custom design, standard purchase prices are not available. Three specific applications of Roto-Louvre dryers are outlined in Table 20-15 [Lapple, Clark, and Dybdal, *Chem. Eng.*, **62**, 11, 177 (1955)]. Installation, operating, power, and maintenance costs will be similar to those experienced with ordinary direct-heat rotary dryers. *Thermal efficiency* will range from 30 to 70 per cent.

Table 20-15. Manufacturer's Performance Data for Link-Belt Roto-Louvre Dryers*

Material dried	Ammonium sulfate	Foundry sand	Metallurgical coke
Dryer diameter	2 ft. 7 in.	6 ft. 4 in.	10 ft. 3 in.
Dryer length	10 ft.	24 ft.	30 ft.
Moisture in feed, % wet basis	2.0	6.0	18.0
Moisture in product, % wet basis	0.1	0.5	0.5
Production rate, lb./hr.	2500	32,000	38,000
Evaporation rate, lb./hr.	50	2130	8110
Type of fuel	Steam	Gas	Oil
Fuel consumption	255 lb./hr.	4630 cu. ft./hr.	115 gal./hr.
Calorific value of fuel	857 B.t.u./lb.	1000 B.t.u./cu. ft.	150,000 B.t.u./gal.
Efficiency, B.t.u., supplied per lb. evaporation	4370	2170	2135
Total power required, hp	4	41	78

* Link-Belt Company.

STIRRED VESSELS

Description. In gas-solids contacting operations, a stirred vessel is defined as one on which the *housing enclosing the process is stationary*, while stirring and *movement of solids is accomplished by an internal mechanical agitator*. Innumerable forms of this equipment are in commercial use; however, this discussion includes only three types, representative of those in common use for chemical processing.

Vacuum-rotary Dryer. This is a horizontal jacketed cylindrical vessel containing a ribbon-type mechanical agitator. Heat transfer is *indirect*. To be complete, the discussion will include also rotating vacuum dryers which are similar in design, operation, and application. The latter are by definition truly rotating vessels, however.

Turbo-tray Dryer. This consists of a vertical polygonal shell containing a series of annular rotating shelves. Solids enter at the top and are agitated and mixed by a wiper during passage from one shelf to the next, lower down. Heat transfer usually is direct, gas to solids.

Hearth Furnaces. These may be single or multiple hearth in construction. The housing is a vertical cylindrical shape. Agitation and movement of solids from one hearth to the next, lower down, in multiple units is accomplished employing horizontal rotating rabble arms turning on a central shaft. Heat transfer is usually *direct* gas to solids by *convection* and by radiation from the walls. They are suitable for *high-temperature* operations and are refractory-brick lined.

Field of Application. Stirred vessels are applicable to processing solids which are relatively free-flowing and granular when discharged as product. Materials which are not free-flowing in their feed condition can be treated by recycle methods as described in the section on Rotating Vessels (p. 20-15ff). In general, stirred vessels have applications similar to rotating vessels. Their chief advantages compared with the latter lie in the fact that (1) large-diameter rotary seals are not required at the solids and gas feed and exit points because the housing is stationary, and for this reason *gas-leakage problems are essentially eliminated.* Rotary seals are required only at the points of entrance of the mechanical agitator shaft. (2) Use of a mechanical agitator for solids mixing introduces shear forces which are helpful for *breaking up lumps and agglomerates.* Balling and pelleting of sticky solids, an occasional occurrence in rotating vessels, can be prevented by special agitator design. The problems concerning dusting of fine particles in direct-heat units are identical to those discussed in the Rotating Vessel section (p. 20-15ff).

Vacuum-rotary Dryers

Vacuum-rotary dryers are *batch dryers*, at least in currently available commercial forms. Design of continuous equipment awaits development of continuous solids-discharging (and feeding) devices which will continuously convey particulate solids across a 15 lb./sq. in. gage pressure barrier, with no back leakage of air into the vessel. So-called continuous equipment now available is continuous in the drying stage but requires two or more batch hoppers to serve as air locks; the product output remains batch.

The more common type of vacuum-rotary dryer consists of a stationary cylindrical shell, mounted horizontally, in which a set of agitator blades mounted on a revolving central shaft stirs the solids being treated. Heat is supplied by circulation of hot water, steam, or Dowtherm through a *jacket surrounding the shell* and, in larger units, through the *hollow central shaft.* The agitator is either a single discontinuous spiral or a double continuous spiral. The outer blades are set as close as possible to the wall without touching, usually leaving a gap of ⅛ to ¼ in. Modern units occasionally employ spring-loaded shell scrapers mounted on the blades. The dryer is charged through a port at the top and emptied through one or more discharge nozzles at the bottom. Vacuum is applied and maintained by any of the conventional methods, *i.e.*, steam jets, vacuum pumps, etc.

Another type of vacuum-rotary dryer consists of a rotating horizontal cylindrical shell, suitably jacketed. Vacuum is applied to this unit through hollow trunnions

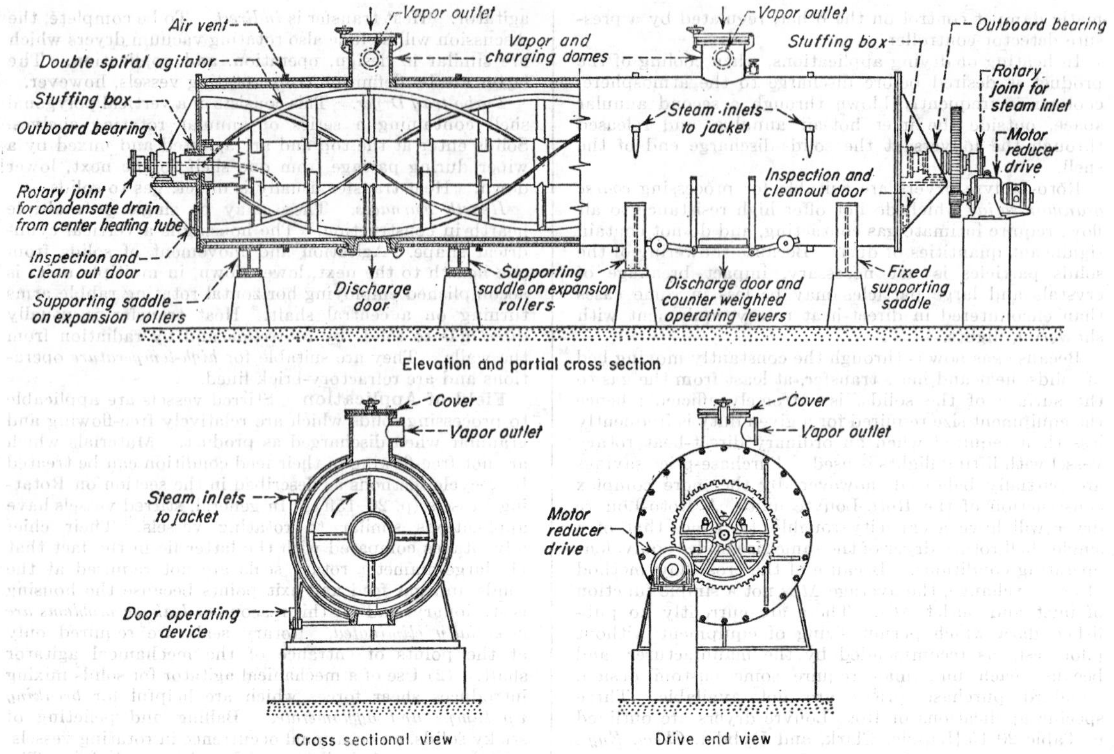

FIG. 20-38. A typical vacuum-rotary dryer. (*Blaw-Knox Co.*)

with suitable packing glands. Rotary glands must be used also for admitting and removing the heating medium from the jacket. The inside of the shell may have lifting bars, welded longitudinally, to assist agitation of the solids.

Recently, this latter design has been gradually replaced by the *double-cone rotating vacuum dryer*. Although identical in operating design, the sloping walls of the cones permit more rapid emptying of solids when the dryer is in a stationary position. The older cylinder shape required continuous rotation during emptying to convey product to the discharge nozzles. As a result, a circular dust hood was frequently necessary to enclose the discharge-nozzle turning circle and prevent serious dust losses to the atmosphere during unloading.

On all rotating dryers, the vapor-outlet tube is stationary; it enters the shell through a rotating gland and is fitted with an elbow and upward extension so that the vapor inlet, usually protected by a felt dust filter, will be at all times near the top of the shell.

A typical vacuum-rotary dryer is illustrated in Fig. 20-38 and a double-cone vacuum dryer in Fig. 20-39.

Vacuum is used in conjunction with drying or other chemical operations when *low solids temperatures* must be maintained because heat will cause damage to the product or change its nature, where *air combines with the product* when it is heated causing oxidation or an explosive condition, where *solvent recovery* is required, and when materials must be dried to extremely *low moisture levels.*

In vacuum processing and drying the objective is to create a large temperature-driving force between the jacket and the product. In order to accomplish this purpose at fairly low jacket temperatures, it is necessary

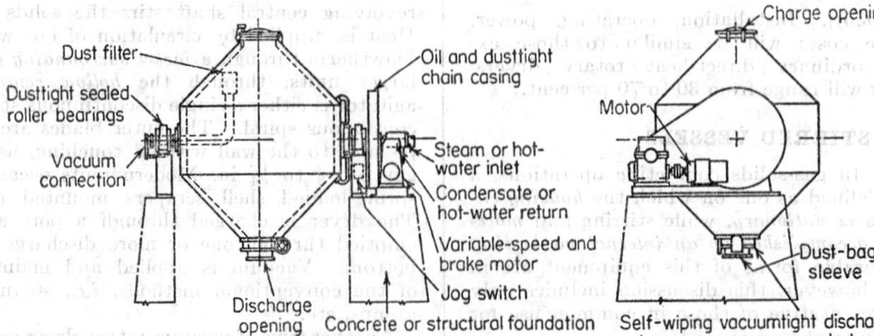

FIG. 20-39. Rotating (double-cone) vacuum dryer. (*Courtesy of the F. J. Stokes Corp.*)

Table 20-16. Performance Data of Vacuum-Rotary Dryers

Material	Diam. × length, ft.	Initial moisture, %	Steam pressure, lb./sq. in.	Agitator speed, r.p.m.	Batch dry weight, lb.	Final moisture, %	Vacuum, in. Hg	Time, hr.	Evaporation, lb. H_2O/(hr.)(sq. ft.)
Cellulose acetate	5 × 30	87.5	14	5.25	1350	8	26.5–27	7	0.3
Starch	5 × 30	45–48	15	4	8000	12	26 –27	4.75	1.2
Sulfur black	5 × 30	50	30	4	7000	1	27	6	0.9

to reduce the internal process pressure so that the liquid being removed will boil at a lower vapor pressure. It is not always economical, however, to reduce the internal pressure to extremely low levels because of the large vapor volumes thereby created. It is necessary to compromise on operating pressure, considering leakage, condensation problems, and the size of the vapor lines and pumping system. Very few vacuum dryers operate below 10 mm. Hg pressure on a commercial scale. Air in-leakage through gasket surfaces will be in the range of 0.15 lb./(hr.)(lin. ft. gasketed surface) under this condition.

Design Methods. The rate of heat transfer from the heating medium through the dryer wall to the solids can be expressed by

$$Q = UA\,\Delta t_m \tag{20-13}$$

where Q = heat flux, B.t.u./hr.; U = the over-all heat-transfer coefficient, B.t.u./(hr.)(sq. ft. of jacket area)(°F.); A = total jacket area, sq. ft.; and Δt_m = log-mean temperature driving force from heating medium to the solids, °F. The over-all heat-transfer rate is almost entirely dependent upon the film coefficient between the inner jacket wall and the solids, which depends to a large extent on the solids characteristics. Over-all coefficients may range from 5 to 35 B.t.u./(hr.)(sq. ft. of total area)(°F.) if the dryer walls are kept reasonably clean. Coefficients as low as 1 or 2 may be encountered if caking on the walls occurs.

For estimating purposes without tests, a reasonable coefficient for ordinary drying, and without taking the product to absolute dryness, may be assumed at U = 10 B.t.u./(hr.)(sq. ft.)(°F.) for rotary agitator dryers, and 6 B.t.u./(hr.)(sq. ft.)(°F.) for rotating units (J. F. Maguire, F. J. Stokes Corp., personal communication, June 7, 1960).

Table 20-17. Standard Rotary Vacuum Dryers*

Diam., ft.	Length, ft.	Heating surface, sq. ft.	Working capacity, cu. ft.	Agitator speed, r.p.m.	Weight, lb.	Purchase cost (carbon steel)	Purchase cost (304 stainless steel)
1.5	3.5	18	3.0	7.5	1,200	$ 5,500	$ 7,000
3.0	15	165	53.0	7.5	12,000	14,000	21,000
4.0	20	314	126.0	6.0	25,000	22,000	34,000
5.0	25	518	245.0	6.0	35,000	30,000	47,000
5.0	30	621	294.0	6.0	42,000	34,000	54,000

Prices include shell, agitator, drive, and jacket suitable for 30 to 50 lb./sq. in. gage steam; prices do not include auxiliary dust collectors, condensers, or vacuum pumps.

* F. J. Stokes Corp., 1960.

Table 20-18. Standard Rotating (Double-cone) Vacuum Dryers*

Working capacity, cu. ft.	Total volume, cu. ft.	Drive, hp.	Weight, lb.	1960 purchase price† Carbon steel	1960 purchase price† 304 stainless steel
3	4.5	0.50	1,750	$ 4,000	$ 5,200
10	15.4	0.75	2,400	4,600	6,000
25	38.5	3.0	3,200	5,200	7,000
75	115.0	7.5	7,700	9,500	15,000
100	165.0	10.0	11,500		
150	230.0	15.0	12,700	15,000	25,000

* F. J. Stokes Corp.

† Prices include dryer, drive and motor, and structural support for mounting on customer's concrete foundation. Horsepower is established for dryer loading of 65 per cent of total volume, with 50 lb./cu. ft. material.

Vacuum dryers are usually filled to 50 to 65 per cent of their total shell volume. Agitator speeds range from 3 to 8 r.p.m. Faster speeds yield a slight improvement in heat transfer but consume more power. Power requirements for an agitator drive average 0.2 LD, where L = length of the shell, ft.; D = diameter, ft.

Performance and Cost Data. Typical performance data for vacuum-rotary dryers are given in Table 20-16. *Size and cost data* for rotary agitator units are given in Table 20-17. Data for double-cone units are in Table 20-18.

Turbo-tray Dryers

The turbo-tray dryer is *continuous dryer* consisting of a stack of *rotating annular shelves* in the center of which turbo-type fans revolve to circulate the air over the shelves. Wet material enters through the roof, falling onto the top shelf as it rotates beneath the feed opening. After completing one revolution, *the material is wiped by a stationary wiper through radial slots* onto the shelf below where it is spread into a uniform pile by a stationary leveler. The action is repeated on each shelf, with transfers occurring once each revolution. From the last shelf, material is discharged through the bottom of the dryer (Fig. 20-40). The steel-frame housing con-

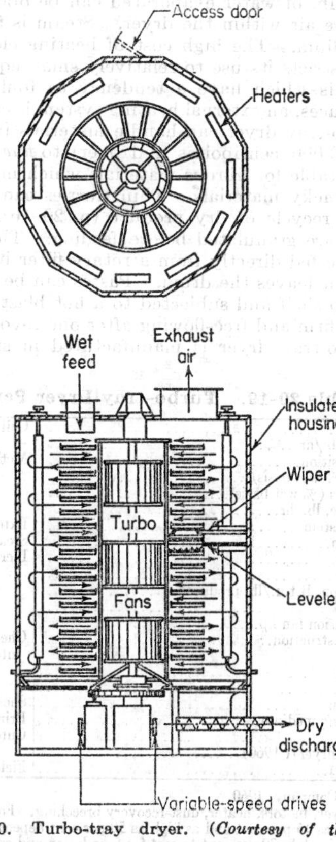

FIG. 20-40. Turbo-tray dryer. (*Courtesy of the Wyssmont Company.*)

sists of removable insulated panels for access to the interior. All bearings and lubricated parts are exterior to the unit with the drives located under the housing. Parts in contact with the product may be of steel or special alloy. The trays can be of any sheet material, such as enameled steel, asbestos-cement composition board, or plastic-glass laminates.

Air is made to flow over the product on the trays by the turbo-type fan wheels The rate at which each fan circulates air can be varied by changing the pitch of the fan blades. In final drying stages, in which diffusion controls or the product is light and powdery, the circulation rate is considerably lower than in the initial stage where high evaporation rates prevail. In the majority of applications, air flows through the dryer upward in counterflow to the material. In special cases, the required drying conditions dictate that air flow be cocurrent, or both countercurrent and cocurrent with the exhaust leaving at some level between solids inlet and discharge. A separate cold-air-supply fan is provided if the product is to be cooled before being discharged.

By virtue of its vertical construction, the turbo-type tray dryer has a stack effect, the resulting draft being frequently sufficient to operate the dryer with natural draft. Pressure at all points within the dryer is maintained close to atmospheric, as low as 0.005, usually less than 0.020 in. of water. Most of the roof area is used as a breeching, lowering the exhaust velocity to settle dust back into the dryer.

Heaters can be located in the space between the trays and the dryer housing where they are not in direct contact with the product, and *thermal efficiencies* up to 1500 B.t.u./lb. of water evaporated can be obtained by reheating the air within the dryer. Steam is the usual heating medium. The high cost of heating electrically generally restricts its use to relatively small equipment. For materials which have a tendency to foul internal heating surfaces, an external heating system is employed.

The turbo-tray dryer can handle materials from *thick slurries* (100,000 centipoises and over) to *fine powders.* It is not suitable for fibrous materials which mat, or for doughy or tacky materials. Thin slurries can often be handled by recycle of dry product (p. 20–16). Filter-press cakes are granulated before feeding. Thixotropic materials are fed directly from a rotary filter by scoring the cake as it leaves the drum. Pastes can be extruded onto the top shelf and subjected to a hot blast of air to make them firm and free-flowing after one revolution.

The turbo-tray dryer is manufactured in sizes from package units 6 ft. in height and 6 ft. in diameter to large outdoor installations 65 ft. in height and 35 ft. in diameter. Tray areas range from 60 to 18,000 sq. ft. in a single unit. The number of shelves in a tray rotor varies according to space available and minimum rate of transfer required, from as low as 12 shelves to as many as 58 in the largest units. Standard construction permits operating temperatures up to 650°F.

Design Methods. The heat- and mass-transfer mechanisms are similar to those in batch tray dryers, except that constant turning over and mixing of the solids significantly improves drying rates. Design must be based usually on previous installations or pilot tests by the manufacturer, unless the application is of a very simple type; apparent heat-transfer coefficients will range from 5 to 10 B.t.u./(hr.)(sq. ft. of exposed area)(°F.) for dry solids to 12 to 20 B.t.u./(hr.)(sq. ft.)(°F.) for wet solids (S. Stern, Wyssmont Co., personal communication, July 21, 1960). Turbo-tray dryers have been employed successfully for drying and cooling of calcium hypochlorite, urea crystals, calcium chloride flakes, and sodium chloride crystals. The Wyssmont "closed-circuit" system, as shown in Fig. 20-41, consists of the

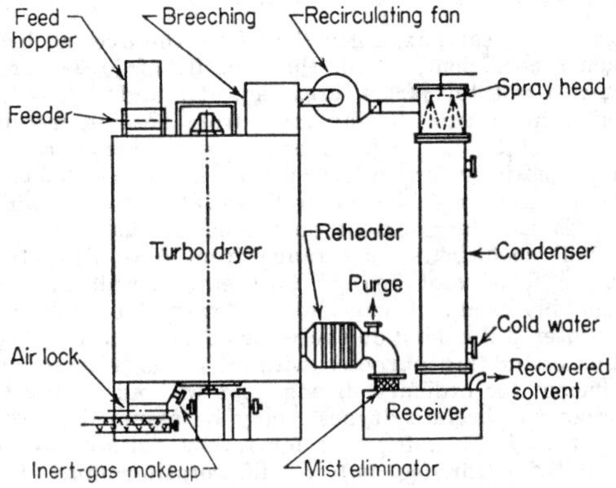

Fig. 20-41. Turbo-tray dryer in closed circuit for continuous drying with solvent recovery. (*Courtesy of the Wyssmont Co.*)

turbo-tray dryer with or without internal heaters, recirculation fan, condenser with receiver and mist eliminators, and reheater. Feed and discharge are through a sealed wet feeder and lock, respectively. This method is used

Table 20-19. Turbo-tray Dryer Performance Data in Wyssmont Closed-circuit Operations

Material dried	Cellulose gum	Antibiotic filter cake	Paraformaldehyde
Dried product, lb./hr	275	1200	300
Volatiles composition	Methanol and water	Butanol	Formaldehyde vapor and water
Feed volatiles (% wet basis)	60	50	35
Product volatiles (% wet basis)	2	0.5	4
Evaporation rate, lb./hr	390	1200	150
Type heating system	External	Internal	External
Heating medium	Steam	Steam	Steam
Drying medium	Inert gas	Inert gas	Inert gas
Dryer temp., °F	170	220	150
Heat consumption, B.t.u./lb. produced	1650	960	1250
Power, dryer hp	5	8	2
Power, recirculation fan hp	5	20	3
Materials of construction	Chemstone trays, remaining dryer interior stainless	Everdur with Chemstone trays	Stainless steel
Dryer height, ft	19	23	12
Dryer diam., ft	15	15	9
Recovery system	Shell-and-tube condenser	Shell-and-tube condenser	Direct-contact condenser
Condenser cooling medium	Brine and tower water	Chilled water	Chilled water
Location	Outdoor	Outdoor	Outdoor
Approx. cost of dryer† (1960)	$65,000	$67,000	$25,000
Dryer assembly‡	Field erected	Field erected	Packaged unit

* Wyssmont Company, 1960.

† Includes dryer, motors, heater, dust-recovery breeching. For recirculation fan, condenser, sealing feeder, discharge lock and instrumentation, additional costs may run as low as 15 per cent and as high as 50 per cent depending on condensing load, cooling medium, and material of construction for auxiliaries.

‡ Add approximately 20 per cent to cost for foundation and erection of field-erected units.

for continuous drying, without leakage of fumes, vapors, or dust to atmosphere.

Performance and Cost Data. Performance data for three applications of closed-circuit drying are included in Table 20-19. Operating, labor, and maintenance costs compare favorably with direct-heat rotating equipment. Purchase costs range from $9000 for a 60 sq. ft. packaged dryer, $50,000 for a 2000 sq. ft. unit, to $140,000 for a 10,000 sq. ft. dryer, all in carbon steel. Stainless-steel and aluminum fabrication run slightly higher.

Hearth Furnaces

A special design of a circular hearth furnace is the *Mannheim furnace*, in which sulfuric acid is reacted with sodium chloride to produce salt cake and hydrochloric acid. It consists of a refractory hearth, up to 18 ft. in diameter, with a silicon carbide arch. Hot flue gases are circulated around the muffle. The major portion of heat is transmitted through the arch and radiated to the product on the hearth. Feed materials are mixed and charged continuously to the center of the hearth where they are stirred by underdriven rabble arms. The charge is gradually worked toward the periphery as the reaction generates hydrogen chloride gas. This gas is withdrawn through a separate duct to an absorption system. The salt cake is discharged at the periphery. Figure 20-42 shows a diagrammatic cross section of a

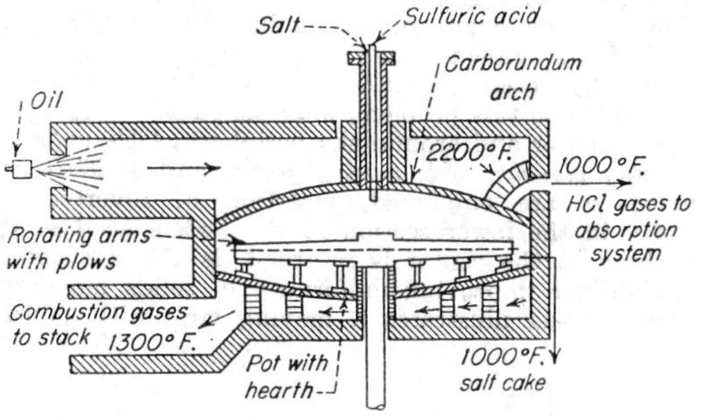

FIG. 20-42. Mannheim-type mechanical hydrochloric acid furnace.

Mannheim furnace. Combustion-chamber temperatures of about 2200°F. are used for heating. The salt cake is discharged from the hearth at about 1000°F.

Multiple-hearth Furnaces

Multiple-hearth furnaces have been in use for many years for ore processing. Modifications are known under various names, the Herreshoff, McDougall, Wedge, Nichols, etc. Figure 20-43 shows a general design. It consists of a number of annular-shaped hearths mounted one above the other. There are rabble arms on each hearth driven from a common center shaft. The feed is charged at the center of the upper hearth. The arms move the charge outward to the periphery where it falls to the next hearth. Here it is moved again to the center from which it falls to the next hearth. This continues down the furnace. The hollow center shaft is cooled internally by forced-air circulation.

Burners may be mounted at any of the hearths, and the circulated air is used for combustion. These furnaces handle granular materials and provide a long countercurrent path between the flue gases and the charge material. Industrial sizes are built from 6 to 22 ft. in diameter and include 4 to 16 hearths. Total hearth areas range from 70 to over 4000 sq. ft. They are used for roasting ores; drying and calcining lime, magnesite,

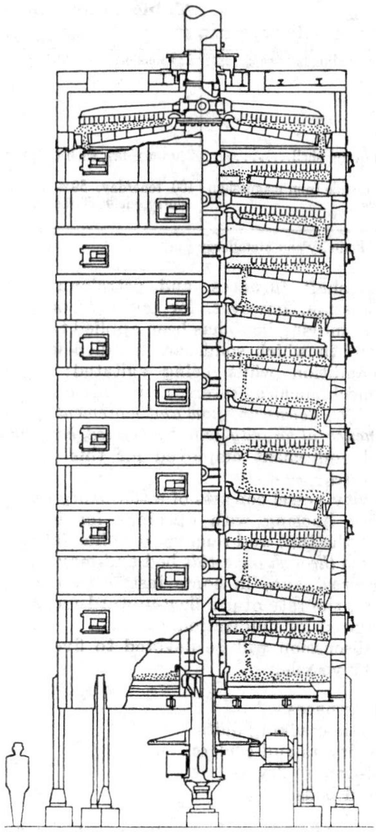

FIG. 20-43. Multiple-hearth furnace. (*Courtesy of Bartlett-Snow-Pacific.*)

and carbonate sludges; reactivation of decolorizing earths, and burning of sulfides to produce sulfur dioxide. The following is a partial list of applications.

1. Lime (*a*) from crushed limestone, (*b*) from oyster or sea shell, (*c*) from dolomitic limestone
2. Lead and zinc, roasting of sulfides
3. Mercury from cinnabar ores by volatilization
4. Gold and silver (*a*) chloridizing roast of gold-silver ore, (*b*) removal of arsenic
5. Sulfuric acid from iron pyrites
6. Paint pigments, roasting of metallic oxides
7. Refractory clays, calcination of refractory clay to reduce shrinkage
8. Foundry sand, removal of carbon from used foundry sand
9. Fuller's earth, calcination of fuller's-earth material
10. Sewage disposal, calcination of sewage slurry.

Table 20-20 lists three specific applications with a brief description of the furnaces as to design and operating conditions.

GRAVITY VESSELS

Description. A body of solids in which the particles, consisting of granules, pellets, beads, or briquettes, flow downward by gravity at substantially their normal settled bulk density through a vessel in contact with gases is defined frequently as a moving bed. This specific moving-bed technique finds application in blast

Table 20-20. Applications of Multiple-hearth Furnaces*

Product	Production rate	Furnace size	Special features
Mercury from cinnabar ore	225 tons ore/day (95% recovery)	(2) 18.0 ft. diam., 8 hearth furnaces	Furnaces fired on hearths 3 to 7, inclusive; retention time of 1.0 hr.; furnaces are oil-fired with low-pressure atomizing air burners; all air, both primary and secondary, introduced through the burners; draft control by monel cold-gas fans downstream from Mercury condensers
Lime from oyster shell	240 tons/day, shell (120 tons/day, lime)	(1) 22 ft., 3 in. diam., 12 hearth furnace	
Magnesium oxide from magnesium hydroxide	100 tons/day, 50% magnesium hydroxide slurry; yields 50 tons/day magnesium oxide	(2) 22 ft., 3 in., 10 hearth furnaces	Furnace walls of 4.5-in. firebrick, 9 in. insulation for 1550°F. operating temp. Furnace fired on hearths 4 to 10, inclusive

* Pacific Foundry and Metallurgy Co.

furnaces, shaft furnaces, and petroleum refining. In this discussion, however, for purposes of organization, the term "moving bed" has been applied to all processing equipment in which solids are handled in essentially a dense condition while being agitated; by rotational forces, mechanical agitators, or in this instance, gravity forces. The *downward flow and movement of solids under the influence of gravity will be defined here as a gravity bed,* and equipment employed for this operation as a *gravity vessel.*

A gravity vessel consists of a *stationary vertical usually cylindrical* housing with openings for introduction of solids (at the top) and removal of solids (at the bottom). Gas flow is *through the solids* bed and may be *cocurrent or countercurrent* and, in some instances, *cross flow.* By definition, the rate of gas flow upward must be less than that required for fluidization.

This discussion will be devoted to five specific types of gravity vessels:

- Shaft furnaces
- Catalytic-cracking units
- Pellet dryers and coolers
- Multi-Louvre dryers
- Spouted beds

The fourth is not a true gravity vessel as defined above, in that, during downward flow under the influence of gravity, the solids particles are partially dispersed in the gas stream. It is a cascade-type dryer. However, in operation it more closely approaches gravity movement than any other.

Fields of Application. One of the major advantages of the gravity-bed technique is that it lends itself well to true intimate countercurrent contacting of solids and gases. This provides for more efficient heat transfer and mass transfer. Gravity-bed contacting also permits use of the solid as a heat-transfer medium, as in pebble heaters.

Gravity vessels are applicable to *coarse granular free-flowing solids* which are comparatively *dust-free.* The solids must possess physical properties in size and surface characteristics so that they will not stick together, bridge, or segregate during passage through the vessel. The presence of significant quantities of fines or dust will close the passages among the larger particles through which the gas must penetrate, increasing pressure drop. Fines may also *segregate* near the sides of the bed or in other areas where gas velocities are low, ultimately completely sealing off these portions of the vessel. The high efficiency of gas-solids contacting in gravity beds is due to *uniform distribution of gas* throughout the solids bed; hence choice of feed and its preparation are important factors to successful operation. Preforming techniques such as *pelleting* and *briquetting* are employed frequently for preparation of suitable feed materials.

Gravity vessels are suitable for *low-, medium-,* and *high-temperature* operation; in the latter case, the housing will be lined completely with refractory brick. Dust-recovery equipment is minimized in this type of operation since the bed actually performs as a dust collector itself, and dust in the bed will not, in a successful application, exist in large quantities.

Other advantages of gravity beds include flexibility in gas and solids flow rates and capacities, variable retention times from minutes to several hours, space economy, ease of startup and shutdown, the potentially large number of contacting stages, and ease of control using the inlet- and exit-gas temperatures.

Maintenance of a *uniform rate of solids movement downward* over the entire cross section of the bed is one of the most critical operating problems encountered. For this reason gravity beds are designed as high and narrow as practical. In a vessel of large cross section, discharge through a conical bottom and center outlet will usually result in some degree of "rat-holing" through the center of the bed. Flow through the center will be rapid while essentially stagnant pockets are left around the sides. To overcome this problem, *multiple outlets* are provided in the center and around the periphery; *table unloaders, rotating ploughs, wide moving grates,* and *multiple-screw unloaders* are employed; insertion of inverted *cone baffles* in the lower section of the bed, spaced so that flushing at the center is retarded, is also a successful method for improving uniformity of solids movement. Figure 20-44 illustrates a moving tray with multiple

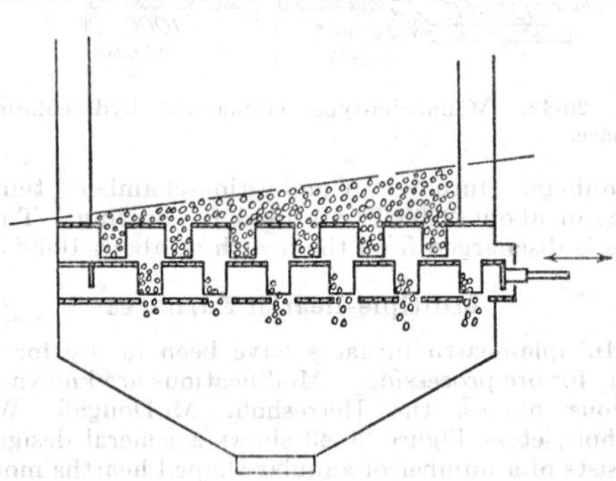

FIG. 20-44. Gravity-bed reactor; solids-discharge mechanism.

downspouts used to remove a precise amount of solids from each increment of area across the base of a gravity-bed reactor. The various pockets are filled at one extremity of its motion and emptied at the other. It is suitable primarily for fine non-abrasive solids. Figure 20-45 depicts a perforated-plate design, taking advantage of the flow characteristics and angle of repose of the solids to control the unloading rate. Still another design of this general type involves the use of a nest of inclined pipes, discharging into a common header, and placed to draw solids at geometrically spaced points across the base of the reactor.

Gas disengaging from the solids may represent another

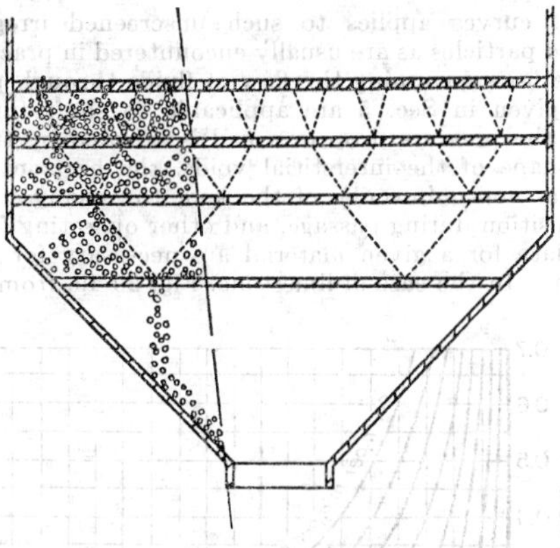

FIG. 20-45. Perforated-tray type of reactor discharge control.

serious operating problem in a gravity-bed reactor. One method, employing downspouts at the top for solids feeding while leaving an open space in the vessel above the downspout outlet for gas disengaging, is illustrated in Fig. 20-9. Another uses a series of inverted V-shaped channels inserted into the top of the solids bed. Gas and vapor are collected and removed from under the V's, while the solids flow over the top and around the channels (Fig. 20-46). These methods for both gas and

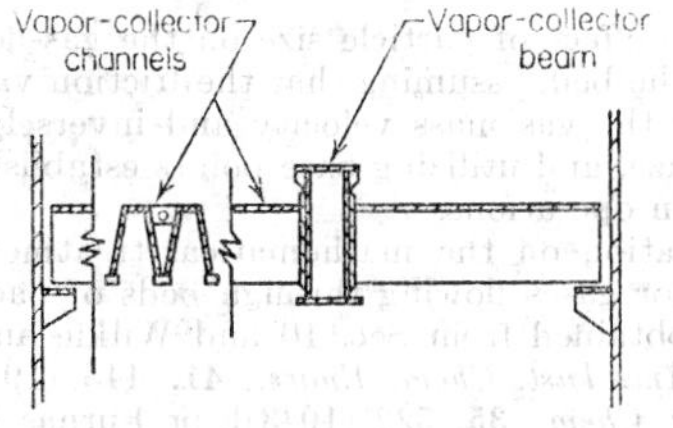

FIG. 20-46. Vapor disengaging tray at the top of a gravity-bed catalytic reactor. (Alternatively, this design may be employed for the addition of gas to a bed of solids.)

solids removal were developed initially for use in petroleum-refining catalytic reactors.

Shaft Furnaces

The oldest and most important application of the shaft furnace is the *blast furnace* used for production of pig iron. Another use is in the manufacture of *phosphorus from phosphate rock*. Formerly lime was calcined exclusively in this type of furnace, but many have been replaced by rotary kilns and hearth furnaces. Shaft furnaces are widely used also as *gas producers*. *Chemicals* are manufactured in shaft furnaces from briquetted mixtures of the reacting components.

A shaft furnace is a vertical refractory-lined cylinder in which a stationary (fixed bed) or descending column of solids is maintained, and through which an ascending stream of hot gas is forced. Three methods of fuel application may be employed: (1) one in which a solid fuel is added alone or mixed with the reacting solids, (2) one in which the fuel is burned in a separate combustion chamber with the hot gases being blown into the furnace at some level of the column, (3) one in which the fuel is introduced and burned in the bottom of the shaft. These differences affect the manner of heat transfer. In the first, heat is generated and immediately consumed directly within the bed. In the second, hot gases serve to carry heat into the furnace; heat transfer is by convection and hot-gas radiation. The third modification falls between the other two but approaches the first since heat generation occurs in direct contact with the lower portion of the bed. For maximum heat economy, recovered exhaust heat is employed for preheating of the incoming solids and combustion air. The fuels used may be gas, oil, or pulverized coal introduced through nozzles.

Bucket elevators, skip hoists, and cranes are used for top feeding of the furnace. Retention and downward flow are controlled by timing of the bottom discharge. Solids discharge may be manual, through mechanical gates on a time schedule, or continuous. Gases are propelled by a blower or induced draft from a stack or discharge fan. In normal operation, the downward flow of solids and upward flow of gas is constant with time, maintaining ideal "steady-state" conditions.

Shaft furnaces (or shaft kilns) employed for lime burning have been described by V. J. Azbe (*Rock Prods.*, August, September, October, November, 1945, and January, 1946). Figure 20-47 illustrates a shaft lime

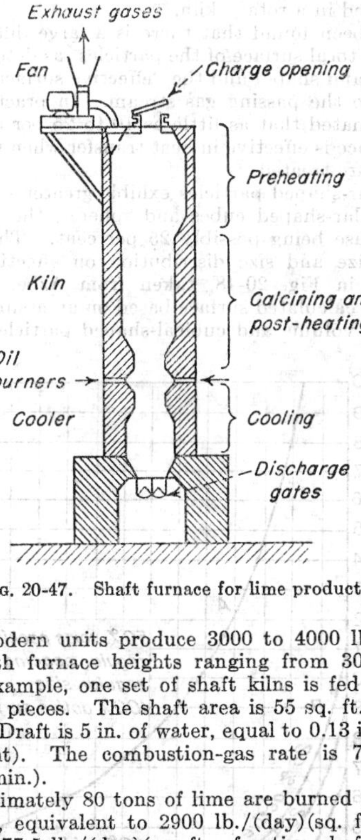

FIG. 20-47. Shaft furnace for lime production.

kiln. Modern units produce 3000 to 4000 lb./(sq. ft.)(day) with furnace heights ranging from 30 to 80 ft. For an example, one set of shaft kilns is fed with 5-in. limestone pieces. The shaft area is 55 sq. ft.; height is 37.5 ft. Draft is 5 in. of water, equal to 0.13 in. (draft)/ft. (height). The combustion-gas rate is 73 cu. ft./(sq. ft.)(min.).

Approximately 80 tons of lime are burned per day in each kiln, equivalent to 2900 lb./(day)(sq. ft. of shaft area), or 77.5 lb./(day)(cu. ft. of active shaft volume). The heat required for burning limestone has been estimated by Azbe, as shown in Table 20-21.

Table 20-21. Heat Requirements for Calcining Limestone*

1.785 lb. of $CaCO_3$/1.0 lb. of CaO

	B.t.u./lb. CaO
Preheat of limestone to 1648°F	862
Heat of dissociation of limestone	1212
Postheating of lime to 2400°F	175
Total heat put into lime in kiln	2249
Heat removed from lime in cooler	557

* Azbe, *Rock Prods.*, 48 (10), 102 (1945).

Design Methods. The *size and shape of the charge particles* control the amount of surface over which heat may be transmitted to the particle and also the depth of penetration through which the heat must pass to reach the center of each particle. Also, this size and shape control the nature of the random packing in the shaft and the extent of voids for gas passage. As particle size is decreased, the surface area of the particles increases. At the same time, the depth of heat penetration decreases. Both these factors tend to improve furnace performance. With *small particle size*, however, the charge column presents *high resistance to the passage of gas*, resulting in an increase in the power required for maintaining gas flow.

With closely screened material, the percentage of voids (usually 37 per cent) is independent of particle size. With unscreened particles showing a wide variation in size, the void volume is decreased; irregularity in gas flow results. Since the time required for heat penetration varies with particle size, small particles are overburned, while the large particles are left with uncalcined cores. In lime burning, large particles (4 to 8 in.) are preferably heated in a shaft kiln, while sizes below 3 in. are calcined in a rotary kiln.

It has been found that there is a large difference between the total surface of the particles (as determined by their size and shape) and the "effective surface" actually exposed to the passing gas stream. In practice, it has been estimated that as little as 10 to 25 per cent of the total surface is effective in heat transfer when unscreened particles are treated.

Irregular-shaped particles exhibit greater surface area than regular-shaped cubes and spheres, the amount of this increase being possibly 25 per cent. The effect of particle size and size distribution on effective surface is shown in Fig. 20-48, taken from Azbe. Curve *A* shows the calculated surface based on an assumed 50 per cent void volume and cubical-shaped particles. The *B* set of curves applies to such unscreened irregularly shaped particles as are usually encountered in practice.

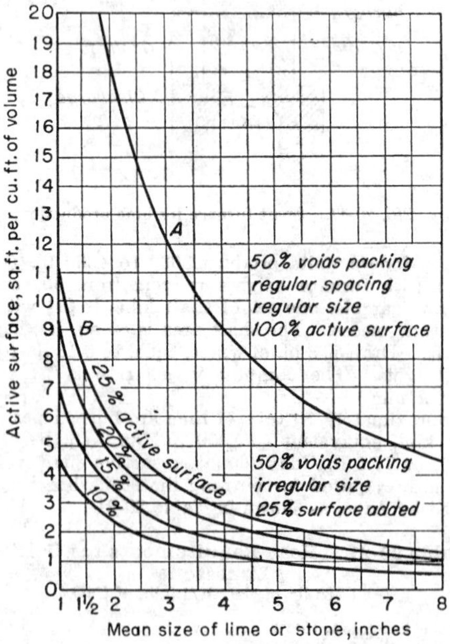

FIG. 20-48. Curve *A* shows surface variation with stone size, 100 per cent active surface. Curves in group *B* show effect of irregular stone size. [*Azbe, Rock Prods.*, **48**, 81 (*September*, 1945).]

The laws governing the flow of fluids through packed beds given in Sec. 5 are applicable to shaft furnaces. Since the pressure drop in a bed is affected by the size and shape of the interstitial voids, the horizontal and vertical non-uniformity of the bed, the changes in gas composition during passage, and other operating factors, test data for a given material are necessary for proper design. In the case of limestone, Fig. 20-49, from Azbe,

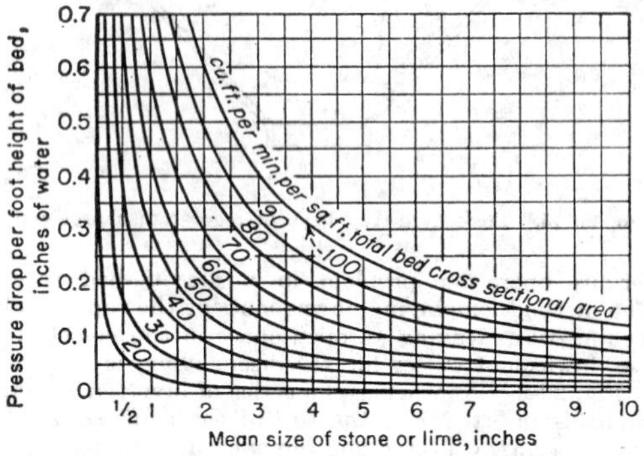

FIG. 20-49. Variation in gas friction with size of stone. [*Azbe, Rock Prods.*, **48**, 82 (*September*, 1945).]

shows the effect of particle size on the gas-flow friction through the bed, assuming that the friction varies as the square of the gas mass velocity and inversely with the particle size, and utilizing base points established during actual kiln operations.

Information on the mathematical treatment of heat transfer for gases flowing through beds of packed solids may be obtained from Sec. 10 and Wilkie and Hougen [*Trans. Am. Inst. Chem. Engrs.*, **41**, 445 (1945)], Hurt [*Ind. Eng. Chem.*, **35**, 522 (1943)], or Furnas (*U.S. Bur. Mines Bull.* 309, 1929).

The approximate charge and gas temperatures existing in a shaft furnace when burning limestone are shown in Fig. 20-50. In practice, the amount of excess combustion

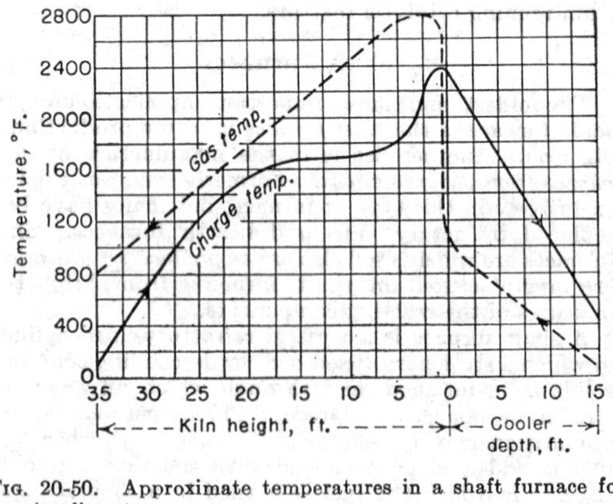

FIG. 20-50. Approximate temperatures in a shaft furnace for burning limestone.

air is limited generally to below 20 per cent, with 5 per cent representing the best performance.

The thermal efficiencies for well-equipped and well-operated kilns will exceed 80 per cent.

Catalytic-cracking Units

The Thermofor catalytic cracking unit (TCC) was developed by the Socony Mobil Oil Company and is employed to produce high-quality gasoline, increase yields of distillate fuel fractions, and reduce yields of residual fuels. It is one of many types of gravity-bed reactors developed for petroleum refining. A detailed summary of this and other important refining processes is included in the Petroleum Refiner Process Handbook [*Petrol. Refiner*, **37**, 9 (1958)].

The first commercial TCC unit was placed in operation in 1943. In 1950, the first air-lift TCC was started up, in which the original design was modified by superimposing the reactor over the kiln and replacing the bucket elevator with a pneumatic catalyst air lift.

Referring to Fig. 20-51, the charge is first heated with fractionator streams, combined with recycle, and charged to the reactor as a mixture of vapor and liquid. In the catalytic section, regenerated catalyst slowly flows by gravity down the seal leg from the surge hopper to the reactor. Sealing steam or flue gas flows countercurrent upward, permitting the pressure to increase from atmospheric in the hopper to as much as 15 lb/sq. in. gage in the reactor. In the reactor, catalyst flows slowly down a reaction bed of uniform depth, past vapor-collecting grids, through a purge zone, and out of the reactor. The purged spent catalyst gravitates into the kiln where it first contacts flue gas of low oxygen content in the upper section (countercurrent flow). As the catalyst passes downward in the kiln, its temperature is raised by coke combustion, then reduced by incoming air. In the lower kiln section, the air and catalyst flow cocurrently downward, the flue gas is disengaged, and the catalyst passes to the coolers. The coolers remove excess heat of coke combustion by generating steam and cool the catalyst to the desired temperature for return to the reactor. The regenerated catalyst flows into the lift pot where it is entrained in low-pressure air (2 to 3 lb./sq. in. gage) and conveyed to the surge hopper. The catalyst separates from the air in the surge hopper and flows back into the seal leg, completing the cycle. Synthetic bead catalyst is employed.

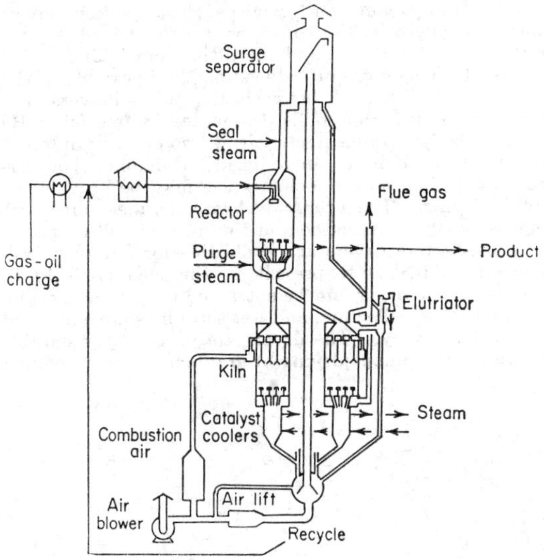

FIG. 20-51. Airlift Thermofor catalytic-cracking unit. (*Courtesy of the Socony Mobil Oil Company, Inc.*)

Unit sizes range from 1600 to 30,000 bbl./day in fresh feed capacity, and from 1600 to 30,000 lb./hr. carbon-burning capacity. Typical operating conditions are reactor space velocity 1 to 2.5 volumes/(hr.)(volume), catalyst-to-oil ratio 2 to 5 (volume), average reactor temperature 840° to 950°F.

Pellet Coolers and Dryers

Gravity beds are employed for cooling and drying of extruded pellets and briquettes from size-enlargement processes. The Sprout-Waldron rotary cooler illustrated in Fig. 20-52 consists of a stationary steel tank having a wear cylinder at the top for entry of gas and solids (usually from a pneumatic conveyor), with air holes staggered around the outer wall to admit additional air for optimum circulation. The tank encloses a rotating cage for retention of the solids bed. This cage consists of an inner cylinder of wire mesh and an outer perforated shell. Air entering the tank is circulated in cross flow through the pellet bed and discharges through the center column. Usually a rotary unloading gate and air lock are located underneath the cage.

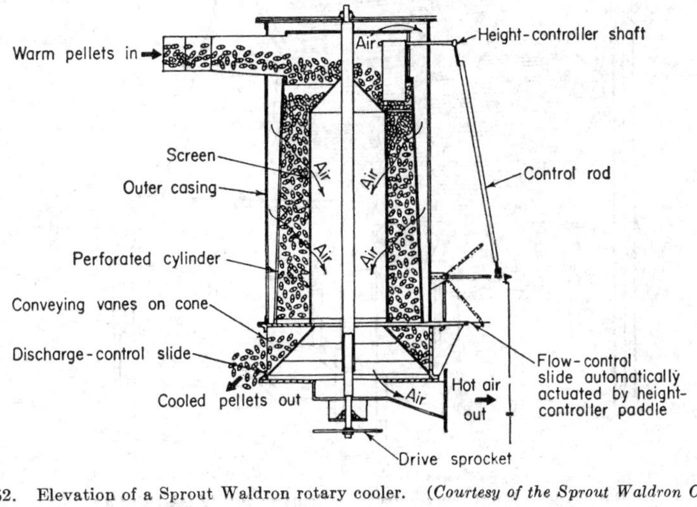

FIG. 20-52. Elevation of a Sprout Waldron rotary cooler. (*Courtesy of the Sprout Waldron Company.*)

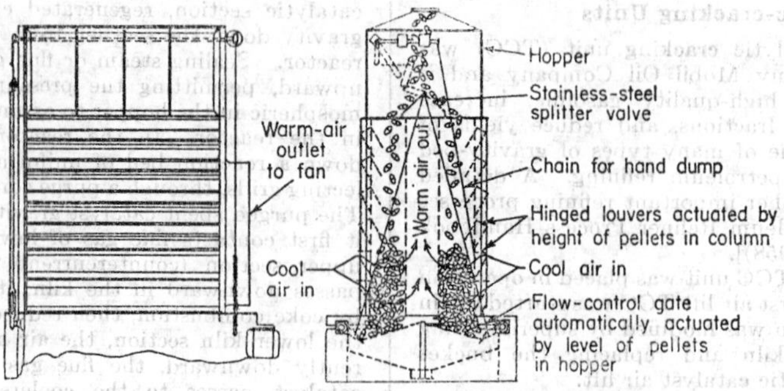

FIG. 20-53. Vertical gravity bed cooler with louvers. (*Courtesy of the Sprout Waldron Company.*)

Another cross-flow design employs a rectangular housing, partitioned into three vertical sections (Fig. 20-53). Solids move downward in the two outer sections, while cooling or drying air is drawn through the louvered outer walls, through the solids bed, and is discharged through the center section. Solids are discharged over a baffled, shaking shoe. Units of this general type are used for drying wheat and other grain products, and numerous forms of pelleted feeds. Gravity-bed dryers are most suitable for drying of granular *heat-sensitive products* employing moderate air temperatures. These require *extended hold-up* during the falling-rate drying period.

Multi-Louvre Dryer

The Multi-Louvre dryer is illustrated in Fig. 20-54. It is a gravity vessel but differs significantly from those previously described. Solids to be dried are fed by a screw conveyor into one side of the housing. They are picked up and conveyed to the top of the housing by a louver-conveyor, at which point they are dumped and fall in a thin stream over the face of the ascending louver; they are caught by the conveyor trough, moved slightly farther into the dryer, and the lifting and falling action repeated. Gases are introduced on the back side of the conveyor and passed between the filled louvers and through the layer of solids descending in free fall. By suitable baffle arrangements, air at two or three different temperatures may be introduced to simulate counter-current drying, and a cooling stage may be provided to follow drying. The air may be heated by any convenient means, steam or direct combustion of coal, oil, or gas.

Multi-Louvre dryers are applicable for granular free-flowing solids. Dust present in the feed is likely to *classify* in the dryer and be entrained in exit-gas stream. Cyclones, bag collectors, and wet scrubbers are employed for dust recovery. The dryers are particularly suitable for rapid continuous drying of granular solids, removing

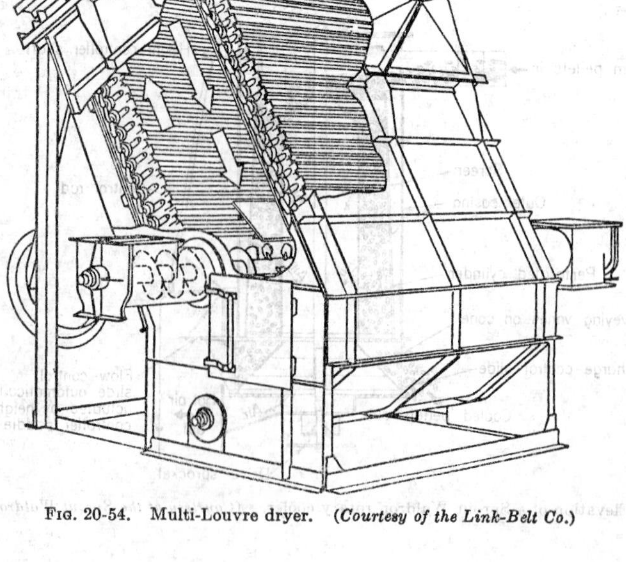

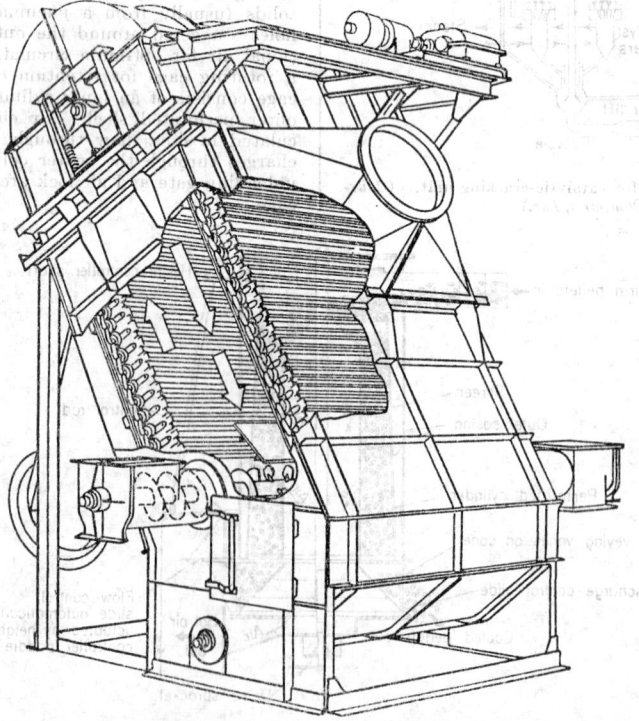

FIG. 20-54. Multi-Louvre dryer. (*Courtesy of the Link-Belt Co.*)

mainly *surface moisture.* Data from two typical applications of the Multi-Louvre dryer are given in Table 20-22 [Lapple, Clark, and Dybdal, *Chem. Eng.*, **62**, 11, 177 (1955)]. Drying of coal was one of the first and major uses of Multi-Louvre dryers. Other applications include treatment of ceramic compounds and plastic granules. There are few published data on performance, and because of the cross-flow nature of air circulation, there are no published methods permitting size estimation without pilot tests.

Table 20-22. Manufacturer's Performance Data for Link-Belt Multi-Louvre Dryers*

Material dried	Soybean meal	Bituminous coal (3/8 × 0)
Width, ft.	6 ft.	12 ft.
Chain centers, ft.	14 ft.	24 ft. 2 in.
Moisture in feed, %, wet basis	18.0	7.0
Moisture in product, %, wet basis	10.7	2.0
Production rate, lb./hr.	14,110	275,550
Evaporation rate, lb./hr.	1255	14,770
Type of fuel	Steam	Coal
Fuel/hr., lb.	2480	3040
Efficiency, B.t.u. supplied per lb. evaporated	1715	2410
Total power, hp.	29.5	137.5

* Link-Belt Company.

Spouted Bed

The spouted-bed technique was developed primarily for solids which are too coarse to be handled in fluidized beds. Although their applications overlap, the methods of gas-solids mixing are completely different. A schematic view of a spouted bed is given in Fig. 20-55.

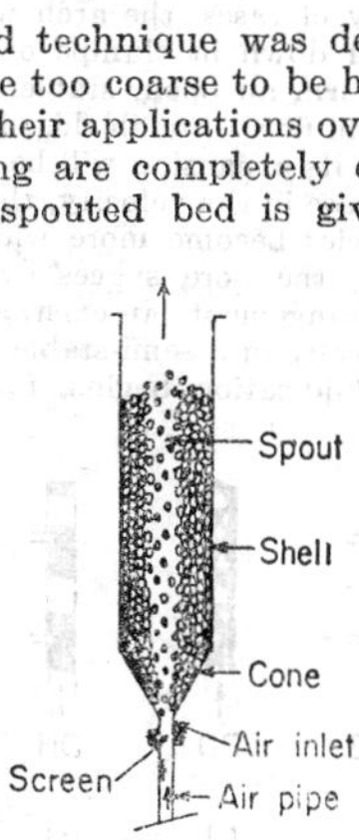

FIG. 20-55. Schematic diagram of a spouted bed. [*Mathur and Gishler, Am. Inst. Chem. Engrs. J.*, **1**, 2, 157–164 (1955).]

Mixing and gas-solids contacting are achieved first in a fluid "spout," flowing upward through the center of a loosely packed bed of solids. Particles are entrained by the fluid and conveyed to the top of the bed. They then flow downward in the surrounding annulus as in an ordinary gravity bed, countercurrent to gas flow. The mechanisms of gas flow and solids flow in spouted beds were first described by Mathur and Gishler [*Am. Inst. Chem. Engrs. J.*, **1**, 2, 157–164 (1955)]. Drying studies have been carried out by Cowan [*Eng. J.*, **41**, 5, 60–64 (1958)], and a theoretical equation for predicting the minimum fluid velocity necessary to initiate spouting was developed by Madonna and Lama [*Am. Inst. Chem. Engrs. J.*, **4**, 4, 497 (1958)].

Gas flow in a spouted bed is partially through the spout and partially through the annulus. About 30 per cent of the gas entering the system immediately diffuses into the downward-flowing annulus. Near the top of the bed, the quantity in the annulus approaches 66 per cent of the total gas flow; the gas flow through the annulus at any point in the bed equals that which would flow through a loosely packed solids bed under the same conditions of pressure drop. Solids flow in the annulus is both downward and slightly inward. As the fluid spout rises in the bed, it entrains more and more particles, losing velocity and gas into the annulus. The volume of solids displaced by the spout is roughly 6 per cent of the total bed.

Based upon experimental studies, Mathur and Gishler derived an empirical correlation to describe the minimum fluid flow necessary for spouting, in 3- to 12-in.-diameter columns:

$$u = \frac{D_p}{D_c}\left(\frac{D_o}{D_c}\right)^{0.33}\left[\frac{2gL(p_s - p_f)}{p_f}\right]^{0.5} \tag{20-14}$$

where u = superficial fluid velocity through the bed, ft./sec.; D_p = particle diameter, ft.; D_c = column (or bed) diameter, ft.; D_o = fluid-inlet orifice diameter, ft.; L = bed height, ft.; p_s = absolute solids density, lb./cu. ft.; p_f = fluid density, lb./cu. ft.; and g = 32.2 ft./sec.^{2}, gravity acceleration. The inlet orifice diameter, air rate, bed diameter, and bed depth were all found to be critical and interdependent:

1. In a given diameter bed, deeper beds can be spouted as the gas-inlet orifice size is decreased. Using air, a 12-in.-diameter bed containing 0.125- by 0.250-in. wheat can be spouted at a depth of over 100 in. with an 0.8-in. orifice, but at only 20 in. with a 2.4-in. orifice.

2. Increasing bed diameter increases spoutable depth. Employing a bed/orifice diameter ratio of 12 for air spouting, a 9-in.-diameter bed was spouted at a depth of 65 in. while a 12-in.-diameter bed was spouted at 95 in.

3. As indicated by Eq. (20-14), the superficial fluid velocity required for spouting increases with bed depth and orifice diameter and decreases as the bed diameter is increased. Data on minimum air flow required for spouting in a 6-in.-diameter bed are given in Table 20-23 [Mathur and Gishler, *Am. Inst. Chem. Engrs. J.*, **1**, 2 (1955)].

Employing wood chips, Cowan's drying studies indi-

Table 20-23. Spouting Behavior of Various Materials in a 6-in.-diameter Glass Column with a 3/8-in. Standard Air Inlet*

Material	Size, in.	Absolute density, lb./cu. ft.	Max. spoutable bed depth, in.	Min. air flow for spouting (superficial, ft./sec.)
Brucite	0.0232	156.5	27.5	0.56
Coffee beans	0.30 × 0.45	39.5	20.0	3.22
Lima beans	0.50 × 0.75	83.0	11.4	4.43
Mustard seeds	0.0855	75.7	34.0	2.57
Rape seeds	0.0691	68.9	30.0	2.01
Sunflower seeds	0.315 × 0.473	.....	15.0	3.06
Oats	0.118 × 0.394	.....	19.0	2.42
Wheat	0.125 × 0.250	85.9	30.0	3.53
Peas	0.250	86.6	12.0	5.31
Ottawa sand	0.0232(−20 + 35)	145.0	27.0	0.75
Shale	0.0390(−14 + 20)	128.8	36.0	1.21
Gravel	0.139(−4 + 8)	166.6	25.0	4.31
Gravel	0.0695(−8 + 14)	164.0	46.0	3.27

* Mathur and Gishler, *Am. Inst. Chem. Engrs. J.*, **1**, 2, 157–164 (1955).

cated that the volumetric heat-transfer coefficient obtainable in a spouted bed is at least twice that in a direct-heat rotary dryer. Using 20- to 30-mesh Ottawa sand, fluidized and spouted beds were compared. The volumetric coefficients in the fluid bed were four times those obtained in a spouted bed. Mathur dried wheat continuously in a 12-in.-diameter spouted bed, followed by a 9-in.-diameter spouted-bed cooler. A drying rate of roughly 100 lb./hr. of water was obtained using 350°F. inlet air. Six hundred pounds per hour of wheat was reduced from 16 to 26 per cent to 4 per cent moisture. Evaporation occurred also in the cooler using sensible heat present in the wheat. The maximum drying-bed temperature was 118°F. and the over-all thermal efficiency of the system was roughly 65 per cent. Some aspects of the spouted-bed technique are covered by patent (U.S. Patent 2,786,280).

The spouted bed is applicable for *free-flowing* granular solids which are too coarse for fluidization yet too fine to permit efficient contacting in an ordinary gravity bed. Cowan reported that significant size reduction of solids occurred when cellulose acetate was dried in a spouted bed, indicating its possible limitations for handling other friable particles.

FLUIDIZED-BED SYSTEMS

Fluidized-solids usage has developed since the advent of the Winkler process for gasification of coal [Newman, *Ind. Eng. Chem.*, **40,** 559 (1948)] and the original fluid-bed petroleum-cracking units (Gohr "Fluidization," p. 102, D. F. Othmer, ed., Reinhold, New York, 1956) into a much-used method of gas-solids contacting with many commercially successful applications in widespread fields, a great number of potentially large- and small-scale applications and surprisingly few misapplications or failures. As in most relatively new fields, some of the published information is contradictory, much is incomplete, many patents are "paper" patents and have not been commercially demonstrated, and many usages have been shrouded in secrecy. As an example of magnitude of use, over 1,500,000 bbl./day of petroleum are cracked in fluidized-bed catalytic crackers and about 10,000 tons/day of sulfuric acid are produced from SO_2 generated in fluidized-bed units roasting sulfur-containing ores.

Fluidization. An excellent description of dense-phase gas fluidization has been given by Morse [*Ind. Eng. Chem.*, **41,** 1117 (1949)]:

Consider a bed of granular particles through which a stream of gas is slowly flowing upward. Friction produces a pressure drop which increases with velocity in a manner expressed by the Carman-Kozeny fixed-bed correlation. Finally, as the velocity is increased, a point is reached where the pressure drop becomes equal to the sum of the weight of the bed per unit of cross-sectional area plus the friction of the bed against the walls. When this point is reached, one of two things may happen: either the bed expands and assumes a more open arrangement, so that the gas can flow without the pressure drop exceeding the unit bed weight, or the entire bed is lifted by the gas stream and rises like a piston. This alternative occurs with the materials that are not freely flowing and can therefore form an arch from wall to wall. In the majority of cases, the arch will break away, and the underside will fall down in clumps or aggregates. If the clumps fall so as to form an open, stable channel of sufficient size, most of the gas will flow through this channel, and although the bed has expanded, its expansion will be far from uniform.

With a further increase in gas velocity, the pores and channels enlarge and the particles become more widely separated. For free-flowing materials, the pore spaces eventually become so large that no stable arrangement can exist, and the particles will vibrate or circulate locally in a semi-stable arrangement; this is the point at which fluidization begins, forming the quiescent fluidized bed.

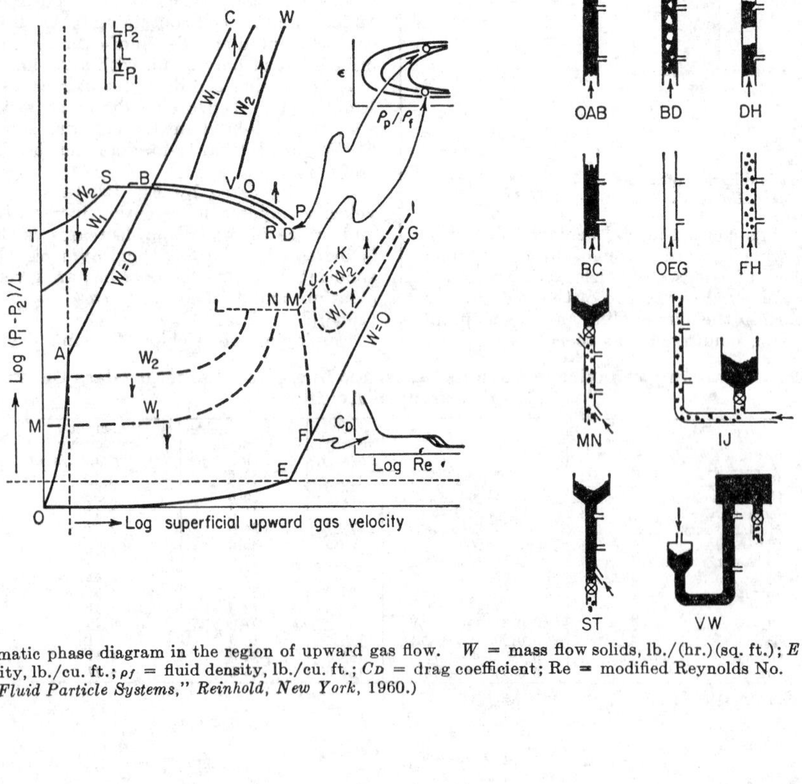

FIG. 20-56. Schematic phase diagram in the region of upward gas flow. W = mass flow solids, lb./(hr.)(sq. ft.); E = fraction voids; ρ_p = particle density, lb./cu. ft.; ρ_f = fluid density, lb./cu. ft.; C_D = drag coefficient; Re = modified Reynolds No. (*Zenz and Othmer, "Fluidization and Fluid Particle Systems," Reinhold, New York,* 1960.)

Another increment of velocity results in over-all circulation of the bed, often with transient gas streams flowing upward in channels that contain relatively few particles, with clumps of particles flowing downward.

The type of gas fluidization of solids described in the last paragraph above is *dense-phase fluidization* called *aggregative fluidization* by Wilhelm and Kwauk [*Chem. Eng. Progress*, **44**, 201 (1945)]. However, the term fluidized or fluidization pertains to many gas-solids and liquid-solids systems acted upon by the forces of gravity and fluid friction.

Zenz and Othmer ("Fluidization and Fluid Particle Systems," Reinhold, New York, 1960) have graphically represented (Fig. 20-56) all such gas-solids systems where the gas is flowing counter to gravity. The dense-phase fluidized-bed differs from most of the systems noted by Zenz in that the net solids flow is zero or nearly zero. Unless specifically mentioned to the contrary, any subsequent use of the term fluidization or fluidized bed pertains to dense-phase gas fluidization.

The size of solid particles which can be fluidized varies greatly from less than 1 micron to 2½ in. It is generally concluded that particles distributed in size between 65 mesh and 10 microns are the best for smooth fluidization (least formation of large bubbles). Large particles cause instability and result in slugging or massive surges. Small particles (less than 10 microns) frequently, even though dry, act as if damp, forming agglomerates or fissures in the bed, or spouting. Adding finer-sized particles to a coarse bed or coarser-sized particles to a bed of fines usually results in better fluidization.

The upward velocity of the gas is usually between 0.5 and 10 ft./sec. This velocity is based upon the flow through the empty vessel and is frequently referred to as the *superficial velocity*.

For details beyond the scope of this section, references should be made to Leva ("Fluidization," McGraw-Hill, New York, 1959), Zenz and Othmer (*loc. cit.*), as well as other sections of this volume.

The use of the fluidization technique requires in almost all cases the employment of a fluidized-bed system rather than an isolated piece of equipment. Figure 20-57 illustrates the arrangement of components of a system used in cases where the flow of solids is small, such as is

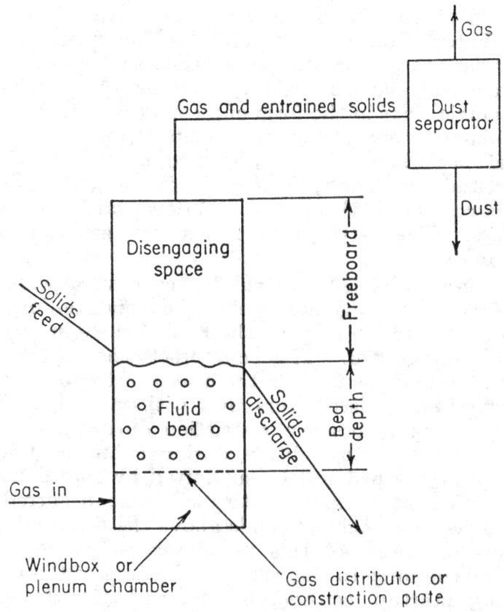

Fig. 20-57. Non-catalytic fluidized-bed system.

generally encountered in non-catalytic usages of the fluidized bed or in catalytic units where there is little or no deactivation of the catalyst. Figure 20-58 illustrates

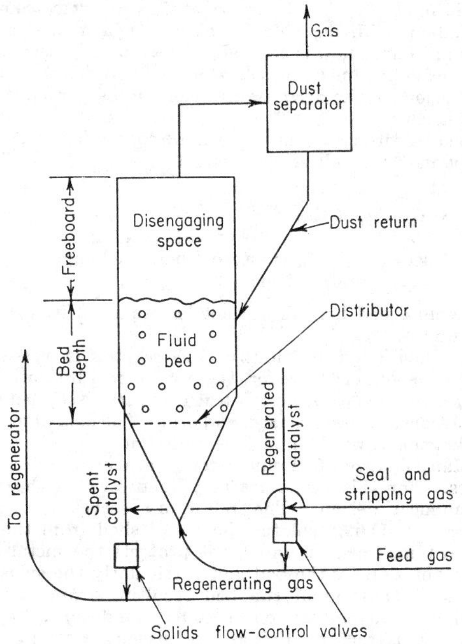

Fig. 20-58. Catalytic fluidized-bed system.

a catalytic-type unit such as is used for petroleum cracking where large quantities of solids flow into and out of the reactor, and to and from the catalyst regenerator, which also is usually a fluidized bed. It is obvious that, in the simplified form, the only difference between a fluidized catalytic-cracking unit and fluidized-bed units used in most other cases is the method and point of solids feed.

The major parts of a fluidized-bed system can be listed as follows:

1. Reaction vessel
   a. Fluidized-bed portion
   b. Disengaging space or freeboard
   c. Gas distributor
2. Solids feeder or flow control
3. Solids discharge
4. Dust separator for the exit gases
5. Instrumentation
6. Gas supply

Reaction Vessel

Fluidized-bed Portion. The process of fluidizing converts a bed of solid particles into an expanded suspended mass that resembles a boiling liquid. This mass has a zero angle of repose, seeks its own level, and assumes the shape of the containing vessel. Just as in a vessel designed for boiling a liquid, space must be provided for vertical expansion of the solids and for disengaging splashed and entrained material. The usual shape is a vertical cylinder. The total cross-sectional area is determined by the volumetric flow of gas and the allowable or required fluidizing velocity of the gas at operating conditions. In some cases, the smallest permissible flow of gas is used and in others the greatest permissible flow is used. The minimum velocity or mass flow rate is best determined by test in equipment where visual observations of the action of the bed can be made. The flow required to maintain a completely homogeneous bed of solids, whereby coarse or heavy particles will not segregate from the fluidized portion, is very different from the minimum fluidizing velocity discussed in many papers. The maximum flow is generally determined by the carry-over or entrainment of solids, and this is related to the dimensions of the disengaging space (cross-sectional area and height).

Bed height is determined by a number of factors, either individually or collectively, such as

1. Space-time yield
2. Gas-contact time
3. L/D ratio required to provide staging
4. Space required for internal heat exchangers
5. Solids-retention time

Generally, bed heights are not less than 12 in. or more than 50 ft.

As mentioned previously, the reactor is usually a vertical cylinder; however, there is no real limitation on shape. The specific design features vary with operating conditions, available space, and use. The lack of moving parts lends toward simple, clean design.

Many fluidized-bed units operate at elevated temperatures. For this use, refractory-lined steel is the most economical design. The refractory serves two main purposes: (1) it insulates the metal shell from the elevated temperatures, and (2) it protects the metal shell from abrasion by the bed and particularly the splashing solids at the top of the bed resulting from bursting bubbles. Depending on specific conditions, several different refractory linings are used. Generally, for the moderate temperatures encountered in catalytic cracking of petroleum, a reinforced gunnite lining has been found to be satisfactory. This also permits the construction of larger units than would be permissible if self-supporting ceramic domes were to be used for the roof of the reactor.

When heavier refractories are required because of operating conditions, insulating brick is installed next to the shell and firebrick is installed to protect the insulating brick. Industrial experience in many fields of application has demonstrated that such a lining will successfully withstand the abrasive conditions for many years without replacement. Most serious refractory wear occurs with coarse particles at high gas velocities and is usually most pronounced near the operating level of the fluidized bed.

Gas leakage behind the refractory has plagued a number of units. Care should be taken in the design and installation of the refractory to reduce the possibility of the formation of "chimneys" in the refractories. A small flow of solids and gas can quickly erode large passages in soft insulating brick. Gas stops are frequently attached to the shell and project into the refractory lining. Care in design and installation of openings in shell and lining is also required.

In many cases, cold spots on the reactor shell will result in condensation and high corrosion rates. Sufficient insulation to maintain the shell and appurtenances above the dew point of the reaction gases is necessary.

The violent motion of a fluidized bed requires ample foundations and sturdy supporting structure for the reactor. Even a relatively small differential movement of the reactor shell with the lining will materially shorten refractory life. The lining and shell must be designed as a unit.

Freeboard. The freeboard or disengaging height is frequently chosen rather arbitrarily or based on experience. It has been established that carry-over of solids entrained by the gases is reduced as the vertical distance between the top of the dense-phase fluidized bed and gas-outlet port is increased. Small-scale experiments have also shown that the size distribution of the solids entrained by the gases is reduced as the freeboard height or cross-sectional area is increased. However, for some distance (from a few inches to a number of feet) the size distribution of the solids in the dilute suspension just above the fluid bed is the same as the size distribution of the solids in the fluid bed.

At progressively greater distances above the bed, the size of the entrained particles becomes smaller and the weight of solids per unit volume of gas decreases. Attempts have been made to provide a basis for predicting entrainment or for properly specifying the freeboard height and cross section. No generalized correlation has been developed that can be used with assurance. Zenz and Othmer (*loc. cit.*) present a method; however, this should be substantiated for a particular problem with data on the gas-solid system under consideration. A plot of log E vs. log V^2/gZ or Froude number is useful in interpolating and correlating data. E = entrainment, lb./cu. ft. of gas; g = acceleration of gravity, ft./sec.^{2}; Z = disengaging height, ft.; V = gas velocity, ft./sec.; $V^2/gZ = N_{Fr}$. In the performance of tests to secure entrainment data, it must be remembered that the fluidized bed may be considered a classifier, and just as in the classification of solids in liquid suspensions, flocculation may exert considerable influence. Therefore, if possible, continuous tests should be run at the same conditions of temperature, pressure, solids particle-size distribution, gas composition, and gas velocities as expected in the larger unit. (Refer to Sec. 5, Particle Dynamics.)

Gas Distributor. The gas distributor has a considerable effect on proper operation of the fluidized bed. Basically there are two types: (1) for use where the inlet gas contains solids, (2) for use where the inlet gas is clean. In most cases, the distributor is designed to prevent backflow of solids during normal operation, and in many cases it is designed to prevent backflow during shutdown. In order to provide distribution, it is necessary to restrict the gas or gas and solids flow so that pressure drops across the restriction amount to from a few inches of water to a few lb./sq. in. As a general rule, pressure drops in excess of 2 lb./sq. in. are not used.

In cases where both solids and gases pass through the distributor, such as in catalytic-cracking units, a number of variations are or have been used, such as concentric rings in the same plane, with the annuli open (Fig. 20-59*a*), concentric rings in the form of a cone (Fig. 20-59*b*), grids of T-bars or other structural shapes (Fig. 20-59*c*), flat metal perforated plates supported or reinforced with structural members (Fig. 20-59*d*), dished and perforated plates concave both upward and downward (Fig. 20-59*e* and *f*). The latter two forms are generally more economical.

Experience has shown that the concave-upward type is a better arrangement than the concave-downward type as it tends to increase the flow of gases in the outer portion of the bed. This counteracts the normal tendency of higher gas flows in the center of the bed.

Structurally, distributors must withstand the differential pressure across the restriction during normal and abnormal flow. In addition, during a shutdown all or a portion of the bed will be supported by the distributor until sufficient backflow of the solids has occurred both to reduce the weight of solids above the distributor and to support some of this remaining weight by transmitting the force to the walls and bottom of the reactor. During startup considerable upward thrust can be exerted against the distributor as the settled solids under

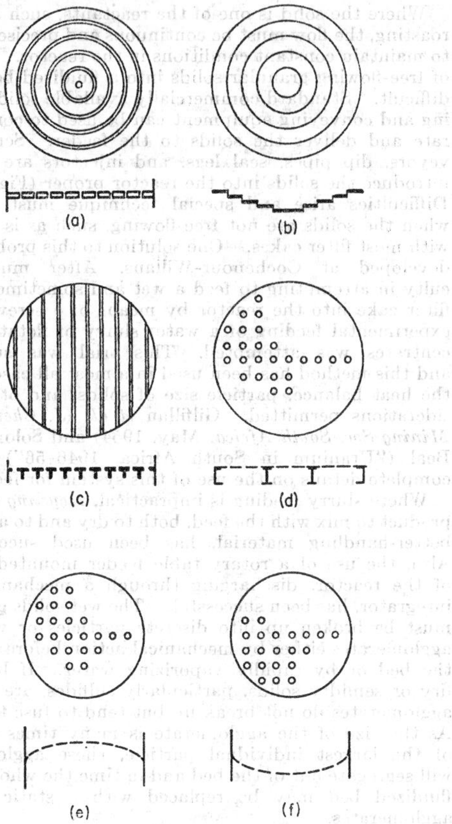

FIG. 20-59. Gas distributors for gases containing solids.

the distributor are carried up into the normal reactor bed.

Where the feed gas is devoid of or contains only small quantities of fine solids, more sophisticated designs of gas distributors can be used to effect economies in initial cost and maintenance. This is most pronounced when the inlet gas is cold and non-corrosive. When this is the case, the plenum chamber, gas distributor, and distributor supports can be fabricated of mild steel using normal temperature design factors. The first commercial fluidized-bed ore roaster [Mathews, *Trans. Can. Inst. Mining & Met.*, **L11**, 97 (1949)], supplied by the Dorr Co. (now Dorr-Oliver, Inc.) in 1947 to Cochenour-Willans, Red Lake, Ontario, was designed with a mild-steel constriction plate covered with castable refractory to insulate the plate from the calcine bed and also to provide cones in which refractory balls were placed to act as ball checks. The balls eroded unevenly and the castable cracked. However, when the unit was shut down by closing the air-control valve, the runback of solids was negligible because of bridging. If, however, the unit was shut down by deenergizing the centrifugal blower motor, the higher pressure in the reactor would relieve through the blower and fluidizing gas plus solids would run back through the constriction plate. Figure 20-60 illustrates two designs of gas inlets which have been successfully used to prevent flowback of solids. For best results, irrespective of the design, the gas flow should be stopped and pressure-relieved from the bottom upward through the bed.

Some units have been built and successfully operated

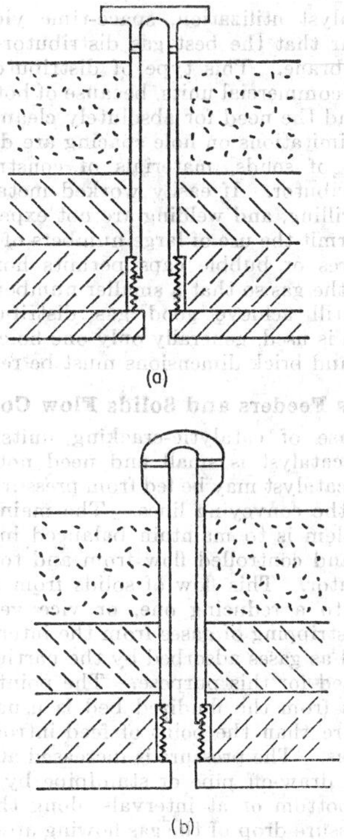

FIG. 20-60. Gas inlets designed to prevent backflow of solids. (*a*) Mortar board. (*b*) Club head. (*Courtesy of Dorr-Oliver, Inc.*)

with simple slot-type distributors made of heat-resistant steel. This requires a heat-resistant plenum chamber but eliminates the frequently encountered problem of corrosion caused by condensation of acids and water vapor on the cold metal of the distributor.

In cases where the inlet gas is hot, such as in dryers or in the upper distributors of multibed units, ceramic arches or heat-resistant metal grates are generally used.

Self-supporting ceramic domes have been in successful use for over 10 years as gas distributors where temperatures range up to 2000°F. Some of these domes are fitted with alloy-steel orifices to regulate air distribution. However, the ceramic arch presents the same problem as the dished head positioned concave downward. Either the holes in the center must be smaller so that the sum of the pressure drops through the distributor plus the bed is constant across the whole cross section, or the top of the arch must be flattened so that the bed depth in the center and outside is equal. This is especially important when shallow beds are used.

In some cases, it is impractical to use a plenum chamber under the constriction plate. This condition arises where a flammable or explosive mixture of gases is being introduced to the reactor. One solution for this is to pipe the gases to a multitude of individual gas inlets in the floor of the reactor. In this way it may be possible to maintain the gas velocities in the pipes above the flame velocity or to reduce the volume of gas in each pipe to the point where an explosion can be safely contained. Another solution is to provide separate inlets for the different gases and depend on mixing in the fluidized bed.

Much attention has been given to the effect of gas distribution on bubble growth in the bed and the effect of this on catalyst utilization, space-time yield, etc. It would appear that the best gas distributor would be a porous membrane. This type of distributor is seldom practical for commercial units, because of both structural limitation and the need for absolutely clean gas. Practically, the limitations on hole spacing are dependent on particle size of solids, materials of construction, and type of distributor. If easily worked metals are used, punching, drilling, and welding are not expensive operations and permit the use of large numbers of holes. The use of tuyères or bubble caps permits horizontal distribution of the gas so that a smaller number of gas-inlet ports can still achieve good gas distribution. If a ceramic arch is used, generally only one hole per brick is permissible and brick dimensions must be reasonable.

Solids Feeders and Solids Flow Control

In the case of catalytic-cracking units where the addition of catalyst is small and need not be steady, the makeup catalyst may be fed from pressurized hoppers into one of the conveying lines. The main solids-flow-control problem is to maintain balanced inventories of catalyst in and controlled flow from and to the reactor and regenerator. This flow of solids from an oxidizing atmosphere to a reducing one, or vice versa, usually necessitates stripping of gases from the interstices of the solids as well as gases adsorbed by the particles. Steam is usually used for this purpose. The point of removal of the solids from the fluidized bed is usually under a lower pressure than the point of feed introduction into the carrier gas. The pressure is increased at the bottom of the solids draw-off pipe or standpipe by introducing gas at the bottom or at intervals along the length so that the pressure drop of the gas flowing upward counter to the solids flow downward results in a higher pressure at the bottom as compared with the top. This standpipe may be fluidized or the solids may be flowing with no appreciable expansion. In any event, the pressure above the solids control valve must be maintained at the same or greater pressure than at the point of solids introduction into the carrier gas stream.

Several designs of valves for solids flow control are used. These should be chosen with care to suit the specific conditions. Usually, block valves are used in conjunction with the control valves. Figure 20-61 shows schematically some of the devices used for solids flow control. Not shown in Fig. 20-61 is the flow-control arrangement used in the Esso Research and Engineering Co. model IV catalytic-cracking units. This device consists of a U-bend. A variable portion of regenerating air is injected into the riser leg. Changes in air-injection rate change the fluid density in the riser and thereby achieve control of the solids flow rate. Catalyst circulation rates of 70 tons/min. have been reported.

Where the solid is one of the reactants, such as in ore roasting, the flow must be continuous and precise in order to maintain constant conditions in the reactor. Feeding of free-flowing granular solids into a fluidized bed is not difficult. Standard commercially available solids weighing and conveying equipment can be used to control the rate and deliver the solids to the feeder. Screw conveyors, dip pipes, seal legs, and injectors are used to introduce the solids into the reactor proper (Fig. 20-61). Difficulties arise and special technique must be used when the solids are not free-flowing, such as is the case with most filter cakes. One solution to this problem was developed at Cochenour-Willans. After much difficulty in attempting to feed a wet and sometimes frozen filter cake into the reactor by means of a screw feeder, experimental feeding of a water slurry of flotation concentrates was attempted. This trial was successful and this method has been used in almost all cases where the heat balance, particle size of solids, and other considerations permitted. Gilfillan *et al.* (*J. Chem., Met. Mining Soc. South Africa*, May, 1954) and Soloman and Beal ("Uranium in South Africa, 1946–56") present complete details on the use of this system for feeding.

Where slurry feeding is impractical, *recycling* of solids product to mix with the feed, both to dry and to achieve a better-handling material, has been used successfully. Also, the use of a rotary table feeder mounted on top of the reactor, discharging through a mechanical disintegrator, has been successful. The wet solids generally must be broken up into discrete particles or very fine agglomerates either by mechanical action before entering the bed or by rapidly vaporizing water. If lumps of dry or semidry solids, particularly sulfides, are fed, the agglomerates do not break up but tend to fuse together. As the size of the agglomerate is many times the size of the largest individual particle, these agglomerates will segregate out of the bed and in time the whole of the fluidized bed may be replaced with a static bed of agglomerates.

Solids Discharge

The type of discharge mechanism utilized is dependent upon the necessity of sealing the atmosphere inside the fluidized-bed reactor and the subsequent treatment of the solids. The simplest solids discharge is an overflow weir. This can be used only when the escape of fluidizing gas does not present any hazards due to nature or dust content, or when the leakage of gas into the fluidized-bed chamber from the atmosphere into which the bed is discharged is permitted. Solids will overflow from a fluidized bed through a port even though the pressure above the bed is maintained at a slightly lower pressure than the exterior pressure. Where it is necessary to restrict the flow of gas through the opening, a simple

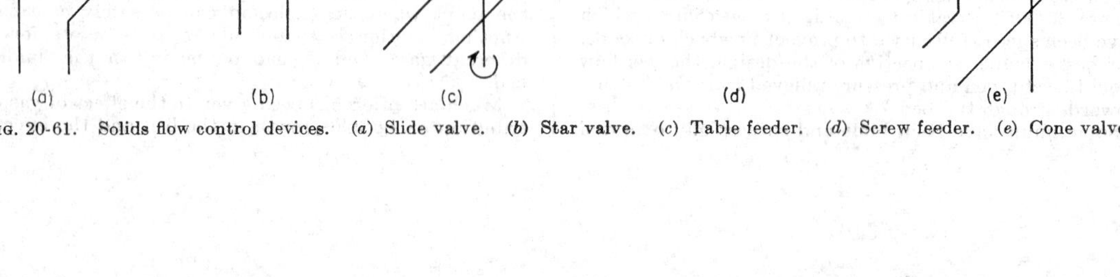

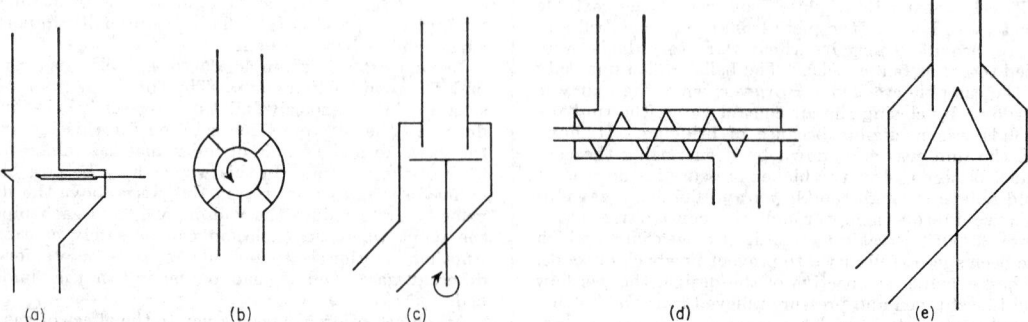

FIG. 20-61. Solids flow control devices. (*a*) Slide valve. (*b*) Star valve. (*c*) Table feeder. (*d*) Screw feeder. (*e*) Cone valve.

flapper valve is frequently used. Overflow to combination seal and quench tanks (Fig. 20-62) is used where

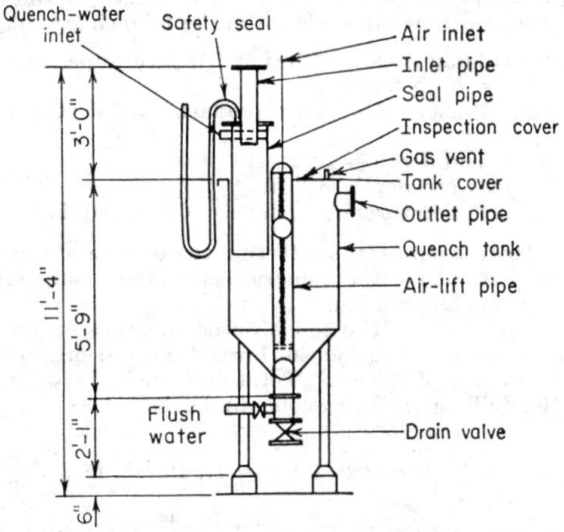

FIG. 20-62. Quench tank for overflow or cyclone solids discharge. (*Gilfillan et al., The Fluosolids Reactor As a Source of Sulphur Dioxide, J. Chem. Met. Mining Soc. South Africa, May,* 1954.)

it is permissible to wet the solids and where disposal or subsequent treatment of the solids in slurry form is desirable. The FluoSeal is a simple and effective way of sealing and purging gas from the solids where an overflow-type discharge is used (Fig. 20-63).

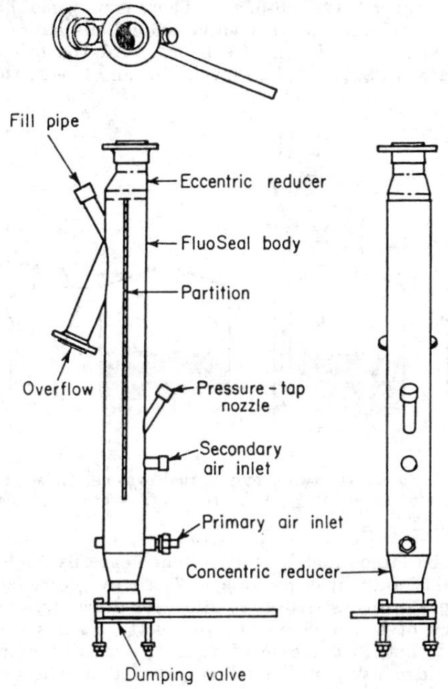

FIG. 20-63. Dorrco FluoSeal, type UA. (*Courtesy of Dorr-Oliver, Inc.*)

Seal legs are frequently used in conjunction with solids-flow-control valves to equalize pressures and to strip trapped or adsorbed gases from the solids. The operation of a seal leg is shown schematically in Fig. 20-64. The solids settle by gravity from the fluidized

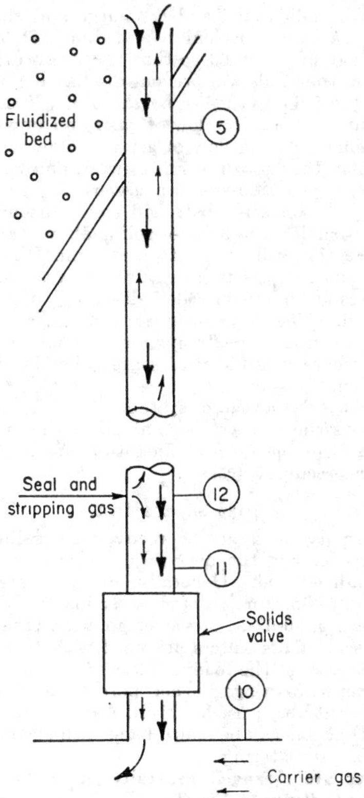

FIG. 20-64. Fluidized-bed seal leg.

bed into the seal leg or standpipe. Seal and/or stripping gas is introduced near the bottom of the leg. This gas flows both upward and downward. Pressures indicated in the illustration have no absolute value but are only relative. The legs are designed for either fluidized or settled solids.

The "ICI" valve shown schematically in Fig 20-65 serves better as a seal device than a solids-flow-control

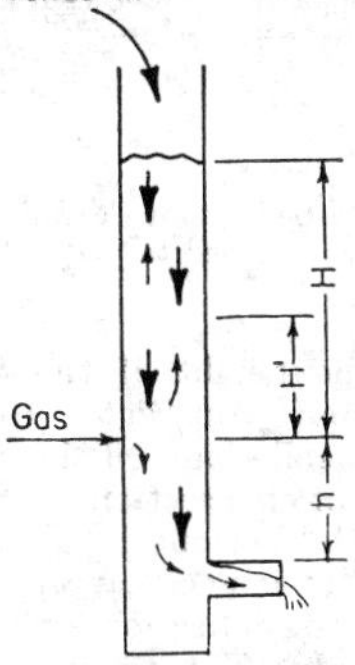

FIG. 20-65. ICI valve. (Imperial Chemical Ind., Br. 607723.)

valve. Gas introduced below the normal solids level and above the discharge port will flow upward and downward. The relative flow in each direction is self-adjusting, depending upon the differential pressure between the point of solids feed and discharge and the level of solids in the leg. The length and diameter of the discharge spout are selected so that the undisturbed angle of repose of the solids will prevent discharge of the solids. As solids are fed into the leg, height H of solids increases. This in turn reduces the flow of gas in an upward direction and increases the flow of gas in a downward direction. When the flow of gas downward and through the solids-discharge port reaches a given rate, the angle of repose of the solids is upset and solids discharge commences. Usually, the level of solids above the point of gas introduction will float between H and H'. Changes in conditions such as temperature or pressure can frequently result in uncontrolled discharge of solids and loss of seal. The fixed opening also makes it subject to pluggage from stray lumps, etc. Bottom draw-offs are used where possibility of segregation in the bed is encountered.

In most catalytic-reactor systems, no solids removal is necessary as the catalyst is retained in the system and solids loss is in the form of fines that are not collected by the dust-recovery system.

Dust Separation

It is usually necessary to recover the solids carried by the gas leaving the disengaging space or freeboard of the fluidized bed. Generally, cyclones are used to remove the major portion of these solids (see Gas-Solids Separations, p. 20-62). However, in a few cases, usually on small-scale units, filters are used without the use of cyclones to reduce the loading of solids in the gas. For high-temperature usage, either porous ceramic or sintered metal has been used. Multiple units must be provided so that one can be blown back with clean gas while one or more are filtering.

Cyclones are arranged generally in any one of the arrangements shown in Fig. 20-66. The effect of cyclone arrangement on the height of the vessel and over-all height of the system is apparent. Details regarding the cyclone design and collection efficiencies are to be found in another portion of this section.

Discharging of the cyclone into the fluidized bed requires some care. It is necessary to seal the bottom of the cyclone so that the collection efficiency of the cyclone will not be impaired by the passage of appreciable quantities of gas up through the solids-discharge port. This is usually done by sealing the dip leg in the fluid bed. Experience has shown, particularly in the case of deep beds, that the bottom of the dip pipe must be protected from the action of large gas bubbles which, if allowed to pass up the leg, would carry quantities of fine solids up into the cyclone and cause momentarily high losses. This can be done by attaching a plate larger in diameter than the pipe to the bottom. The length of the seal leg can be estimated as shown in the following example:

Given: Fluid density of bed at 1 ft./sec. superficial gas velocity = 70 lb./cu. ft.

Fluid density of cyclone product at 0.5 ft./sec. = 40 lb./cu. ft.

Settled bed depth = 6 ft.

Fluidized-bed depth = 8 ft.

Pressure drop through cyclone = 0.2 lb./sq. in.

In order to assure seal at startup, the bottom of the seal leg is 5 ft. above the constriction plate or submerged 3 ft. in the fluidized bed.

The pressure at the solids outlet of a gas cyclone is usually about 0.1 lb./sq. in. lower than the pressure at the discharge of the leg. Total pressure to be balanced by the fluid leg in the cyclone dip leg is

$$\frac{3 \times 70}{144} + 0.2 + 0.1 = 1.7 \text{ lb./sq. in.}$$

Height of solids in dip leg $= \frac{1.7 \times 144}{40} = 6.1$ ft.; therefore, the bottom of the separator pot on the cyclone must be at least 6.1 + 5 or 11.1 ft. above the gas distributor. To allow for upsets, changes in size distribution, etc., use 15 ft.

In addition to the simple dip leg, various other devices have been used to seal cyclone solids returns, especially for the second-stage cyclones. A number of these are shown in Fig. 20-67. One of the most frequently used is the flapper valve (20-67a). There is no general agreement as to whether this valve should discharge below the bed level or in the freeboard. All the others are discharged above the bed level. In any event, the legs must be large enough to carry momentarily high rates of solids and must provide seals to overcome cyclone pressure drops as well as to allow for differences in fluid density of bed and cyclone products. It has been reported that, in the case of catalytic-cracking catalysts, the fluid density of the solids collected by the primary cyclone is essentially the same as that in the fluidized bed. However, as a general rule the fluidized density of solids collected by the first cyclone is less than the fluidized density of the bed. Each succeeding cyclone collects finer and less dense solids. The velocity of gas up the tailpipe of a cyclone is less than the velocity in the bed, frequently being one-half that of the bed. Mrs. Peter D. Shroff has developed a nomograph for use in

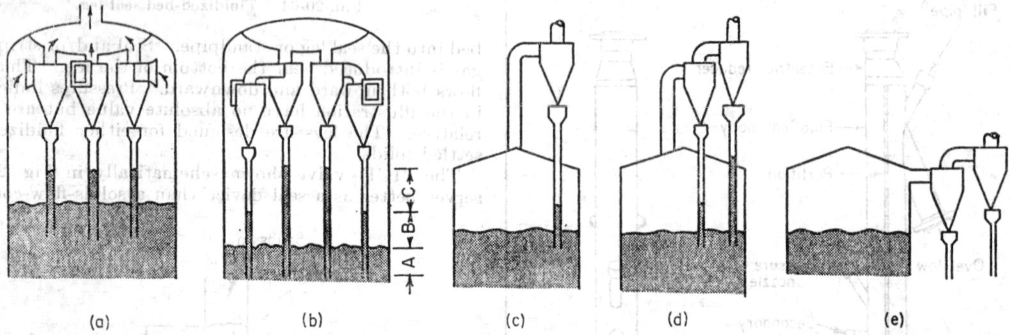

FIG. 20-66. Fluidized-bed cyclone arrangements. (a) Single-stage internal cyclone; (b) two-stage internal cyclone; (c) single-stage external cyclone, dust returned to bed; (d) three-stage external cyclone, dust returned to bed; (e) three-stage external cyclone, dust collected externally.

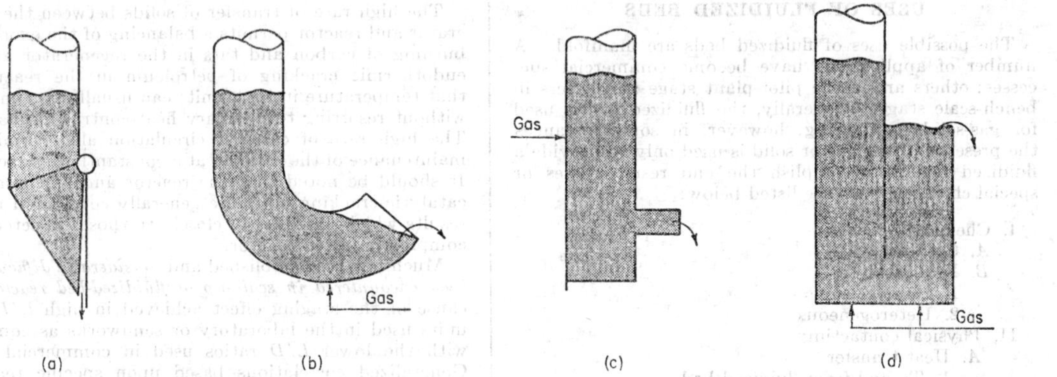

FIG. 20-67. Cyclone solids-return seals. (a) Flapper valve. (*Ducon Company.*) (b) J valve. (c) ICI valve (Imperial Chemical Ind., Br. 607723). (d) Fluid-seal pot (see Fig. 20-63).

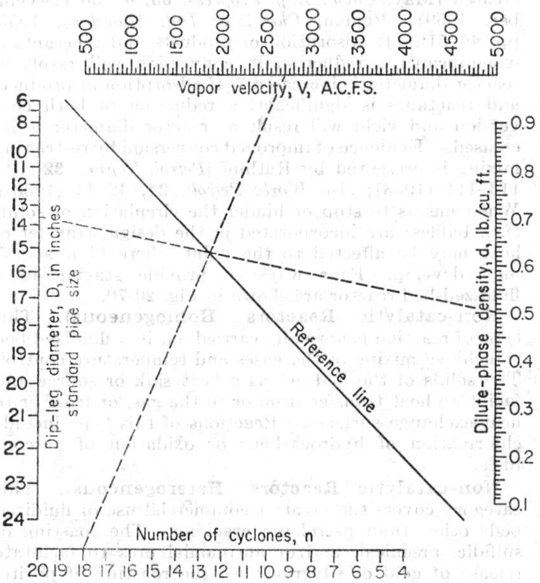

FIG. 20-68. Sizing of cyclone dip legs. (*Chem. Processing, August,* 1959.) The chart is based on the equation

$$\frac{n}{144}\frac{\pi D^2}{4} = \frac{3600\,Vd}{G}$$

For normal design catalyst mass velocity of 270,000 lb./(hr.)(sq. ft.), the equation rearranges to

$$D = \left(\frac{7.68\,Vd}{\pi n}\right)^{1/2}$$

where D = diameter of dip legs, in.
V = vapor velocity, actual cu. ft./sec.
d = dilute phase density, lb./cu. ft.
n = number of primary cyclones
π = constant, 3.1416

Example: Size the primary dip legs of the cyclones in a regenerator with 18 primary stages, handling 2700 actual cu. ft./sec. of vapors with a catalyst entrainment density of 0.5 lb./cu. ft.

Connect 2700 on the V scale with 18 on the n scale to intersect the reference line. Join 0.5 on the d scale with the reference-line intersection point and read on the D scale a dip leg diameter between 13 and 14 in.; therefore, select 14-in. standard pipe for the primary dip legs.

sizing cyclone dip legs (Fig. 20-68) in reactors and regenerators of fluidized catalytic-cracking units.

As cyclones are less effective as the particle size decreases, secondary collection units are frequently required, *i.e.*, filters, electrostatic precipitators, scrubbers. In cases where dry collection is not required, elimination of cyclones is possible if allowance is made for heavy solids loads in the scrubber (see Gas-Solids Separations, p. 20-62; see also Sec. 18, Scrubbers).

Instrumentation

Temperature Measurement. This is usually simple, and standard temperature-sensing elements are adequate for continuous use. Because of the high abrasion wear on horizontal protection tubes, vertical installations are frequently used. In highly corrosive atmospheres where metallic protection tubes cannot be used, short heavy ceramic tubes have been used successfully.

Pressure Measurement. Although successful pressure-measurement probes or taps have been fabricated using porous materials, the most universally accepted pressure tap consists of a purged tube projecting into the bed as nearly vertical as possible. Minimum internal diameters are ½ to 1 in. A purge rate of at least 1 cu. ft./min. is usually required. Pressure measurements taken at various heights in the bed are used to determine bed level. This is done by plotting the differential pressure between two or more points in the bed and the freeboard pressure against the level at which the pressure taps are located and extrapolating to zero differential pressure. The intercept will be the nominal bed level for constant fluid density. However, the splashing zone at the top of the bed is more dilute than the bed; therefore, solids will actually occur at greater elevations than indicated by the plot.

Because of pulsations in the bed, damping of the measurement instrument (manometer, draft gage, etc.) is frequently required. Experienced operators can frequently predict operating troubles by observing the motion of the measuring instrument.

Flow Measurement. Measurement of flow rates of clean gases presents no problem. Flow measurement of dirty gases is usually avoided. The flow of solids is usually controlled but not measured except externally to the system. Solids flows in the system are usually adjusted on an inferential basis (temperature, pressure level, catalyst activity, gas analysis, etc.). In many roasting operations the color of the calcine indicates solids feed rate.

USES OF FLUIDIZED BEDS

The possible uses of fluidized beds are manifold. A number of applications have become commercial successes; others are in the pilot-plant stage and others in bench-scale stage. Generally, the fluidized bed is used for gas-solids contacting; however, in some instances the presence of the gas or solid is used only to provide a fluidized bed to accomplish the end result. Uses or special characteristics are listed below:

- I. Chemical reactions
  - *A.* Catalytic
  - *B.* Non-catalytic
    1. Homogeneous
    2. Heterogeneous
- II. Physical contacting
  - *A.* Heat transfer
    1. To and from fluidized bed
    2. Between gases and solids
    3. Temperature control
    4. Between points in bed
  - *B.* Solids mixing
  - *C.* Gas mixing
  - *D.* Drying
    1. Solids
    2. Gases
  - *E.* Size enlargement
  - *F.* Size reduction
  - *G.* Classification
    1. Removal of fines from solids
    2. Removal of fines from gas
  - *H.* Adsorption-desorption
  - *I.* Heat-treatment
  - *J.* Coating

Catalytic Chemical Reactors. This use has provided the greatest impetus for use, development, and research in the field of fluidized solids. Some of the details pertaining to this use are to be found in the preceding pages of this section. Reference should also be made to Sec. 4. The evolution of fluidized cracking from the early 1940's has resulted in five arrangements as shown in Fig. 20-69. Units of this type are built or licensed for use by others.

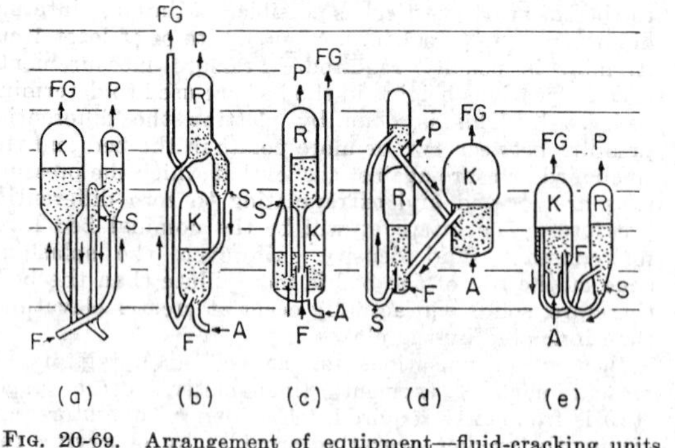

Fig. 20-69. Arrangement of equipment—fluid-cracking units (*a*) Standard Oil development model III. (*b*) Union Oil Products stacked design. (*c*) Model A, M. W. Kellogg Orthoflow. (*d*) Shell Development Co. (*e*) Esso Research and Engineering Co., model IV. (*Sittig, Chem. Eng., May*, 1953.)

F = feed
FG = flue gas
K = kiln (regenerator)
R = reactor
P = product
S = steam
A = air

The high rate of transfer of solids between the regenerator and reactor permits a balancing of the exothermic burning of carbon and tars in the regenerator and the endothermic cracking of petroleum in the reactor, so that temperature in both units can usually be controlled without resorting to auxiliary heat-control mechanisms. The high rate of catalyst circulation also permits the maintenance of the catalyst at a constantly high activity. It should be noted that the reactor and regenerator of catalytic-cracking units are generally considered to give results which agree fairly closely to those expected for a completely mixed reactor.

Much has been published and *considerable difficulty has been encountered in scale-up of fluidized-bed reactors* because of the staging effect achieved in high L/D ratio units used in the laboratory or semiworks as compared with the lower L/D ratios used in commercial units. Generalized correlations based upon specific reactions and catalysts or catalyst supports indicate reduced conversion and yield as the L/D ratio is decreased. Both gas and solids mixing increase as the L/D ratio is decreased [May, *Chem. Eng. Progress*, **55**, 49–56 (December, 1959). Reman, *Chem. & Ind.* (*London*), 1955, pp. 46–51]. If adsorption of products and reactants is insignificant, a reduction in conversion will result as reactor diameter is increased. If adsorption of products and reactants is significant, a reduction of both conversion and yield will result as reactor diameter is increased. Evidence of improved conversion by restricting mixing is presented by Ruthuff [*Petrol. Refiner*, **32** (10), 113–114 (1953); also *World Petrol.*, **24**, 42–44 (1953)]. When means to stop or hinder the circulation of solids (*i.e.*, baffles) are incorporated in the design, transfer of heat may be affected to the point where "hot spots" may develop. Four ways to provide staging in a fluidized-bed reactor are shown in Fig. 20-70.

Non-catalytic Reactors (Homogeneous). This type of reaction is normally carried out in a fluidized bed to achieve mixing of the gases and temperature control. The solids of the bed act as a heat sink or source and facilitate heat transfer from or to the gas, or from or to heat-exchange surfaces. Reactions of this type include chlorination of hydrocarbons or oxidation of gaseous fuels.

Non-catalytic Reactors (Heterogeneous). This category covers the greatest commercial use of fluidized beds other than petroleum cracking. The roasting of sulfidic, arsenical, and/or antimonial ores to facilitate release of gold or silver values; the roasting of pyrite, pyrrhotite, or naturally occurring sulfur ores to provide SO_2 for sulfuric acid manufacture; and the roasting of copper, cobalt, and zinc sulfide ores to solubilize the metal values are the major metallurgical uses. Figure 20-71 shows basic items in the system.

Calcination of lime and dolomite and clay in a commercial unit has been successfully demonstrated (Fig. 20-72). Fuels are burned in a fluidized bed of the product to produce the required heat. Bunker C oil, natural gas, and coal are used in commercial units. Temperature control is accurate enough to permit production of lime of very high availability with close control of slaking characteristics. Also, half calcination of dolomite is an accepted practice. The requirement of large crystal size for the limestone limits the application. Small-sized crystals in the limestone result in low yields due to high dust losses.

Phosphate rock is calcined to remove carbonaceous material before digesting with sulfuric acid. Several pilot plants have successfully demonstrated the direct reduction of hemotite to iron. Foundry sand is also calcined to remove organic binders and release fines.

An interesting feature of these high-temperature cal-

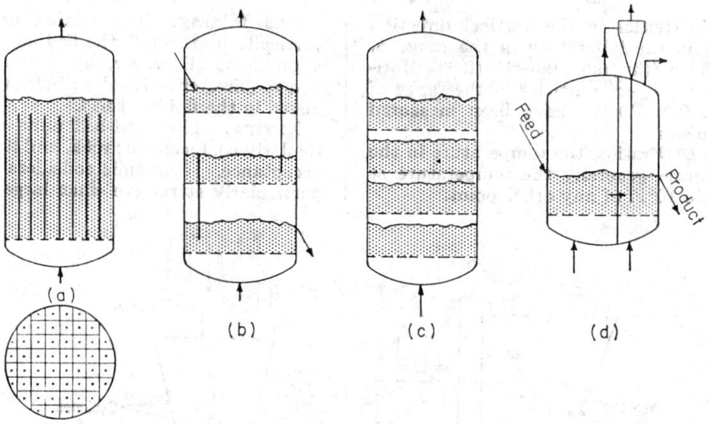

FIG. 20-70. Methods of providing staging in fluidized beds.

cination applications is the direct injection of either heavy oil, natural gas, or fine coal into the fluidized bed. Combustion takes place at well below flame temperatures without atomization or ignition. Considerable care in the design of the fuel- and air-supply system is necessary to take full advantage of the fluidized bed, which serves to mix the air and fuel.

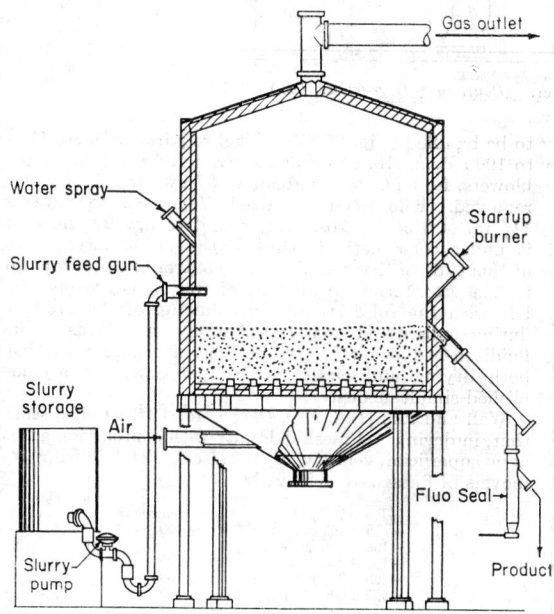

FIG. 20-71. Dorrco FluoSolids reactor, single-compartment, slurry feed. (*Courtesy of Dorr-Oliver, Inc.*)

Heat Transfer. Heat-exchange surfaces have been used to provide means of removing or adding heat to fluidized beds. Usually, these surfaces are provided in the form of vertical tubes manifolded at top and bottom. Other shapes have been used such as horizontal bayonets. In any such installations adequate provision must be made for abrasion of the exchanger surface by the bed.

The prediction of the heat-transfer coefficient is covered in Secs. 10 and 11. Normally, the transfer rate is between five and twenty-five times that for the gas alone.

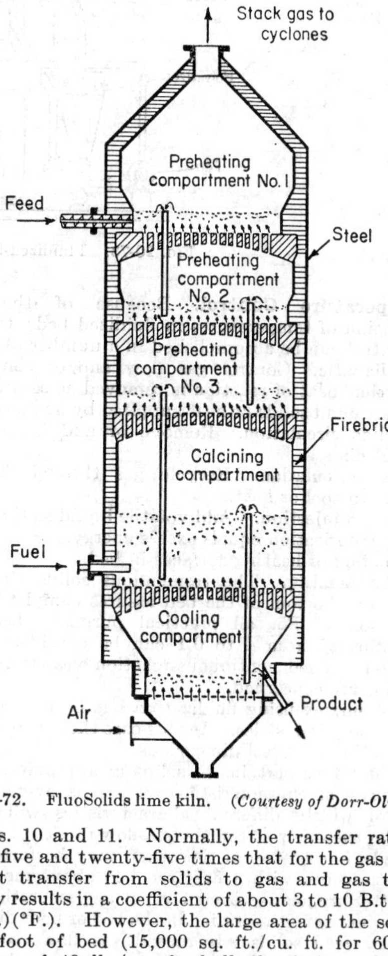

FIG. 20-72. FluoSolids lime kiln. (*Courtesy of Dorr-Oliver, Inc.*)

Heat transfer from solids to gas and gas to solids usually results in a coefficient of about 3 to 10 B.t.u./(hr.)(sq. ft.)(°F.). However, the large area of the solids per cubic foot of bed (15,000 sq. ft./cu. ft. for 60-micron particles of 40 lb./cu. ft. bulk density) results in the rapid approach of gas and solids temperatures. With a fairly good distributor, essential equalization of temperatures occurs within 1 to 3 in. of the top of the distributor.

Bed thermal conductivities in the vertical direction have been measured in the laboratory in the range of 20,000 to 30,000 B.t.u./(hr.)(sq. ft.)(°F.)(ft.). Horizontal conductivities for ⅛-in. particles in the range of 1000 B.t.u./(hr.)(sq. ft.)(°F.)(ft.) have been measured in large-scale experiments.

Except in extreme L/D ratios, the temperature in the fluidized bed is uniform—generally the temperature at any point being within 10°F. of any other point.

Gas Mixing. The mixing of gases as they pass vertically up through the bed has never been considered a problem. However, horizontal mixing is very poor and requires effective distributors if two gases are to be mixed in the fluidized bed.

Drying. Fluidized-bed units for drying solids, particularly coal, cement, rock, and limestone, are in general acceptance. Economic considerations make these units particularly attractive when large tonnages of solids are

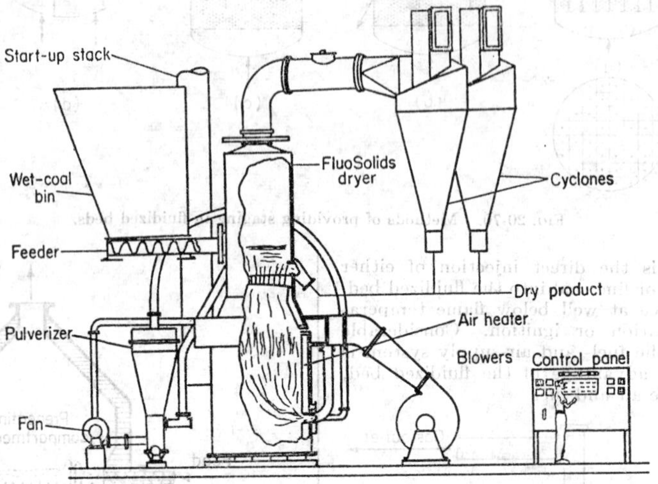

FIG. 20-73. Fluidized-bed coal dryer. (*Courtesy of Dorr-Oliver, Inc.*)

to be handled (Fig. 20-73). Fuel requirements are 1500 to 1900 B.t.u./lb. of water removed and total power for blowers, feeders, etc., is about 0.037 kw.-hr./lb. of water removed. The maximum-sized feed used to date is 1½ in. × 0 coal. However, a unit to dry 2½-in. coal is under construction. One of the major advantages of this type of dryer is the close control of conditions so that a predetermined amount of free moisture may be left with the solids to prevent dusting of the product during subsequent material-handling operations. The fluidized-bed dryer is also used as a classifier so that both drying and classification operations are accomplished simultaneously.

Wall and Ash [*Ind. Eng. Chem.*, **41**, 1247 (1949)] state that, in drying −4 mesh dolomite with combustion gases at a superficial velocity of 4 ft./sec., the following removals of fines were achieved:

Particle Size	% Removed
− 65 +100 mesh	60
−100 +150 mesh	79
−150 +200 mesh	85
−200 +325 mesh	89
−325 mesh	89

Temperature Control. Because of the rapid equalization of temperatures in fluidized beds, temperature control can be accomplished in a number of ways.

1. Adiabatic. Control gas flow and/or solids feed rate so that heat of reaction is removed as sensible heat in off gases and solids or heat supplied by gases or solids.
2. Solids circulation. Remove or add heat by circulating solids.
3. Gas circulation. Recycle gas through heat exchangers to cool or heat.
4. Liquid injection. Add volatile liquid so that latent heat of vaporization equals excess energy.
5. Cooling or heating surfaces in bed.

Solids Mixing. The tremendous solids circulation from top to bottom of the bed assures complete mixing of the solids. For all practical purposes, beds with L/D ratios of from 4 to 0.1 can be considered to be completely mixed continuous-reaction vessels as far as the solids are concerned.

Batch mixing using fluidization has been successfully used in many industries. In this case there is practically no limitation to vessel dimensions.

All the above pertains to solids of approximately the same physical characteristics. There is evidence that solids of widely different characteristics will classify one from the other at certain gas-flow rates. Two fluidized beds, one on top of the other, may be formed or a lower static bed with a fluidized bed above may result. The latter frequently occurs when agglomeration takes place because of either fusion in the bed or poor dispersion of sticky feed solids. Increased gas flows sometimes overcome the problem; however, improved feeding techniques or change in operating conditions may be required. Another solution is to remove agglomerates either continuously or periodically from the bottom of the bed.

Size Enlargement. Under proper conditions, particles of solids can be caused to grow. That is sometimes advantageous and at other times disadvantageous. Growth is associated with the liquefaction or softening of some portion of the bed material (*i.e.*, addition of soda ash to calcium carbonate feed in lime reburning, tars in fluidized-bed coking, or lead or zinc sulfates in zinc roasting causes agglomeration of dry particles in much the same way as binders act in rotary pelletizers). The motion of the particles, one against the other, in the bed results in spherical pellets. If the size of these particles is not controlled, segregation of the large particles from the bed will occur.

Size Reduction. Three major size-reduction mechanisms occur in the fluidized bed. These are attrition, impact, and thermal decrepitation.

Because of the random motion of the solids, some abrasion of surface occurs. This is generally quite small, usually amounting to about one-fourth to 1 per cent of the solids per day.

In areas of high gas velocities, greater rates of attrition will occur as well as fracture of particles by impact. This type of jet grinding is employed in some of the coking units to control particle size (Griffin *et al.*, presented at A.I.Ch.E. National Meeting, December, 1957). It also occurs to a lesser degree at the point of gas introduction when the pressure drop to assure gas distribution is taken across an orifice or pipe that discharges directly into the bed.

Thermal decrepitation occurs frequently when crystals rearrange because of transition from one form to another or where new compounds are formed (*i.e.*, calcination of limestone). Sometimes the strains, in cases such as this, are sufficient to reduce the particle to the basic crystal size.

All the above mechanisms will cause completion of fractures that were started previous to the introduction of the solids into the fluidized bed.

Classification. The separation of fine particles from coarse can be effected by use of a fluidized bed (see Drying). However, for economic reasons (*i.e.*, initial cost, power requirements for compression of fluidizing gas, etc.), it is doubtful except in special cases if a fluidized-bed classifier would be built for this purpose alone.

It has been proposed that fluidized beds be used to remove fine solids from a gas stream. This is possible under certain conditions.

Adsorption-Desorption. An arrangement for gas fractionation is shown in Fig. 20-74.

The effects of adsorption and desorption on the performance of fluidized beds are discussed under catalytic chemical reactors.

Heat-treatment. Certain solids require heat-treatment either to enhance their value or to make them more amenable to further processing. There are successful applications; however, details are not available. Generally, in this type of application multicompartment units are used to conserve heat (Fig. 20-72).

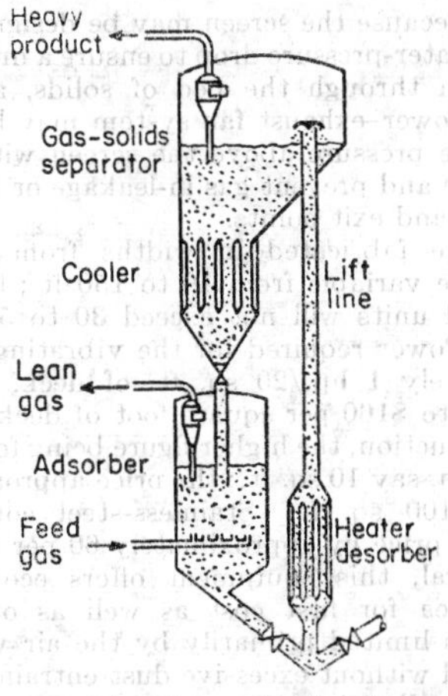

Fig. 20-74. Fluidized bed for gas fractionation. (*Sittig, Chem. Eng., May,* 1953.)

Coating. Fluidized beds of thermoplastic resins have been used to facilitate the coating of metallic parts. A properly prepared, heated metal part is dipped into the fluidized bed, which permits complete immersion in the dry solids. The heated metal fuses the thermoplastic, forming a continuous uniform coating.

DIRECT-HEAT VIBRATING CONVEYOR DRYERS

Information on vibrating conveyors and their mechanical construction is given in Sec. 7. The vibrating conveyor dryer is a modified form of *fluidized-bed equipment*, in which fluidization is maintained by a combination of pneumatic and mechanical forces. The heating gas is introduced into a plenum beneath the conveying deck through ducts and flexible hose connections, passes up through the screen conveying deck, through the fluidized bed of solids, and into an exhaust hood (Fig. 20-75). If ambient air is employed for cooling, the sides of the plenum may be open and a simple exhaust system used;

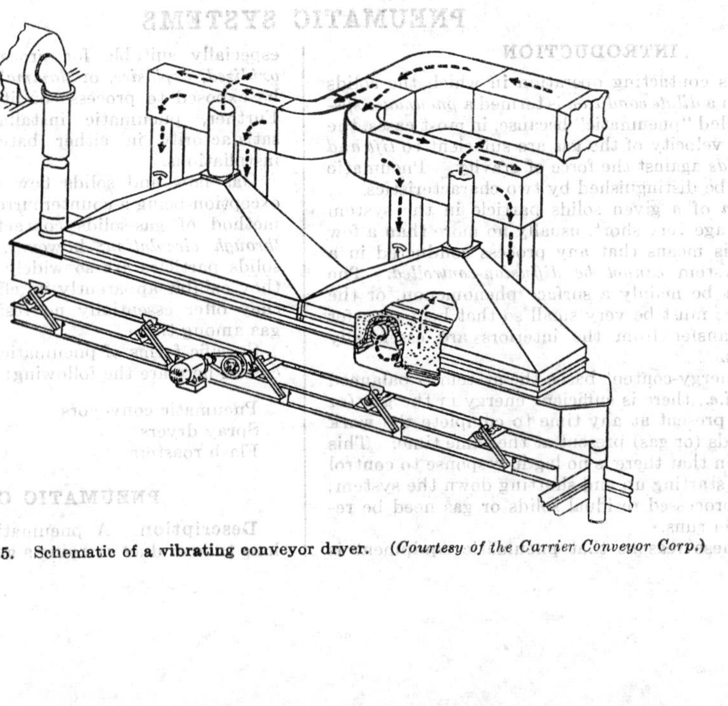

Fig. 20-75. Schematic of a vibrating conveyor dryer. (*Courtesy of the Carrier Conveyor Corp.*)

however, because the screen may be designed for several inches of water-pressure drop to ensure a uniform velocity distribution through the bed of solids, a combination pressure blower–exhaust fan system may be desirable to balance the pressure above the screen with the outside atmosphere and prevent gas in-leakage or blowing at the solids feed and exit points.

Units are fabricated in widths from 12 to 48 in. Lengths are variable from 10 to 150 ft.; however, most commercial units will not exceed 30 to 50 ft. long per section. Power required for the vibrating drive will be approximately 1 hp./20 sq. ft. of deck. Prices range from $100 to $160 per square foot of deck area in mild-steel construction, the higher figure being for units having a small area, say 10 sq. ft.; the price approaches the $100 figure at 100 sq. ft. Stainless-steel construction increases the price by approximately 60 per cent (1960).

In general, this equipment offers economical heat-transfer area for first cost as well as operating cost. Capacity is limited primarily by the air velocity which can be used without excessive dust entrainment. Table 20-24 shows limiting air velocities suitable for various solids particles. Usually, the equipment is satisfactory for particles larger than 100 mesh in size. [The use of indirect-heated conveyors eliminates the problem of dust entrainment, but capacity is limited by the heat-transfer coefficients obtainable on the deck (see Sec. 11).]

When a stationary vessel is employed for fluidization, all solids being treated must be fluidizable; non-fluidizable fractions fall to the bottom of the bed and may eventually block the gas distributor. The addition of mechanical vibration to a fluidized system offers the following advantages:

1. Equipment can handle non-fluidizable solids fractions. Although these fractions may drop through the bed to the screen, directional-throw vibration will cause them to be conveyed to the discharge end of the conveyor. Prescreening or sizing of the feed is less critical than in a stationary fluidized bed.

2. Because of mechanical vibration, incipient channeling is reduced.

3. Fluidization may be accomplished with lower pressures and gas velocities. This has been evidenced on vibratory units by the fact that fluidization stops when the vibrating drive is stopped.

Vibrating conveyor dryers are suitable for *free-flowing* solids containing mainly *surface moisture.* Retention is limited by conveying speeds which range from 5 to 25 ft./min. Bed depth rarely exceeds 3.0 in., although units are currently being fabricated to carry 12- to 18-in.-deep beds; these also employ plate and pipe coils suspended in the bed to provide additional heat-transfer area. Vibrating dryers are *not suitable for fibrous materials* which mat or for *sticky solids* which may ball or adhere to the deck.

For estimating purposes for direct-heat drying applications, it can be assumed that the *average exit-gas temperature* leaving the solids bed will approach the *final* solids discharge temperature on an ordinary unit carrying a 2- to 6-in.-deep bed. Calculation of the heat load and selection of an inlet-air temperature and superficial velocity (Table 20-24) will then permit approximate

Table 20-24. Table for Estimating Maximum Superficial Air Velocities through Vibrating Conveyor Screens*

Mesh size	Velocity, ft./min.	
	2.0 sp. gr.	1.0 sp. gr.
200	45	25
100	135	75
50	270	175
30	510	360
20	630	490
10	1350	900
5	2250	1560

* Carrier Conveyor Corp.

sizing, provided an approximation of the minimum required retention time can be made.

Vibrating conveyors employing direct contacting of solids with hot humid air have also been developed recently for *agglomeration* of fine powders, chiefly for preparation of agglomerated water-dispersible food products. Control of inlet-air temperature and dew point permits uniform addition of small quantities of liquids to solids by condensation on the cool incoming-particle surfaces. The wetting section of the conveyor is followed immediately by a warm-air-drying section and particle screening.

PNEUMATIC SYSTEMS

INTRODUCTION

A gas-solids contacting operation in which the solids phase exists in a *dilute condition* is termed a *pneumatic system.* It is called "pneumatic" because, in most cases, the quantity and velocity of the gas are sufficient to *lift and convey the solids* against the force of gravity. Pneumatic systems may be distinguished by two characteristics.

1. *Retention* of a given solids particle in the system is on the average very short, usually no more than a few seconds. This means that any process conducted in a pneumatic system *cannot be diffusion-controlled.* The reaction must be mainly a surface phenomenon, or the solids particles must be very small so that heat transfer and mass transfer from the interiors are essentially instantaneous.

2. On an energy-content basis, the system is balanced at all times; *i.e.*, there is sufficient energy in the gas (or solids) phase present at any time to complete the work on all the solids (or gas) present at the same time. This is significant in that there is no lag in response to control changes or in starting up and shutting down the system; no partially processed residual solids or gas need be retained between runs.

It is for these reasons that pneumatic equipment is especially suitable for processing *heat-sensitive, easily oxidized, explosive,* or *flammable* materials which cannot be exposed to process conditions for extended periods. Further, pneumatic installations may be operated satisfactorily in either batch- or continuous-process installations.

Gas flow and solids flow are usually *cocurrent,* one exception being a countercurrent-flow spray dryer. The method of gas-solids contacting is best described as *through circulation;* however, in the dilute condition, solids particles are so widely dispersed in the gas that they exhibit apparently no effect upon one another and they offer essentially no resistance to the passage of gas among them.

Specific forms of pneumatic equipment which are discussed here are the following:

Pneumatic conveyors
Spray dryers
Flash roasters

PNEUMATIC CONVEYORS

Description. A pneumatic conveyor consists of a long tube or duct carrying a gas at high velocity, a fan to propel the gas, a suitable feeder for addition and dispersion of particulate solids in the gas stream, and a cyclone collector or other separation equipment for final recovery of solids from the gas. In addition to ordinary solids-transport applications, pneumatic conveyors are employed for *heating, cooling,* and *drying* of particulate solids.

The solids feeder may be of any type; screw feeders, venturi sections, high-speed grinders, and dispersion mills are employed. For pneumatic conveyors, *selection of the correct feeder* to obtain thorough initial dispersion of solids in the gas is of major importance. For example, employing an air-swept hammer mill in a drying operation (such as the Raymond Imp mill), 65 to 95 per cent of the total heat may be transferred within the mill itself if all the drying gas is passed through it [Gordon, *Chem. Eng. Progress,* **45,** 8, 477–481 (1949)]. Fans may be induced-draft or forced-draft type. The former is preferred usually because the system can then be operated under a slight negative pressure. Dust and hot gas will not be blown out of system through leaks in the equipment. Cyclone separators are preferred for low investment and ease of cleaning; they are employed usually as primary collectors at least. If maximum recovery of dust or noxious fumes is required, the cyclone may be followed by a wet scrubber or bag collector.

Conveying air is heated by steam, electricity, direct combustion of fuels, or by an indirect-fired air heater. Cooling operations use ambient air or air cooled by refrigeration. In ordinary heating and cooling operations, during which there is no moisture pick-up, continuous recirculation of the conveying gas is frequently employed. Also, solvent-recovery operations employing continuously recirculated inert gas with intercondensers and gas reheaters are carried out occasionally in pneumatic conveyors.

Pneumatic conveyors are suitable for materials which are *granular and free-flowing when dispersed in the gas stream,* so they do not stick on the conveyor walls or agglomerate. Sticky materials such as filter cakes may be dispersed and partially dried by an air-swept disintegrator in many cases. Otherwise, dry product may be *recycled,* mixed with fresh feed), and then the two dispersed together in a disintegrator. Coarse material containing internal moisture may be subjected to fine grinding in a hammer mill. Not only is drying made possible by particle reduction, but the system may produce a fine dry product in one step, eliminating the additional handling required when drying and grinding are accomplished separately. The main requirement in all applications is that the operation must be instantaneously completed; internal diffusion of moisture must not be limiting in drying operations and particle sizes must be small enough so that the thermal conductivity of the solids does not control during heating and cooling operations. Pneumatic conveyors are not suitable for abrasive solids. Although they are not employed for grinding purposes, pneumatic conveying can result in significant *particle-size reduction,* particularly when handling crystalline or other friable materials. This may or may not be desirable but must be recognized if the system is selected. Its action is similar to that of a fluid-energy grinder.

Pneumatic conveyors may be *single-stage* or *multistage.* The former is employed for ordinary heating and cooling operations and drying processes requiring evaporation of small quantities of surface moisture. Multistage installations are used for difficult drying processes, *e.g.,* drying heat-sensitive products containing large quantities of moisture and drying materials initially containing internal as well as surface moisture. A typical two-stage drying system is illustrated in Fig. 20-76. It incorporates an ordinary single-stage dryer with a second stage

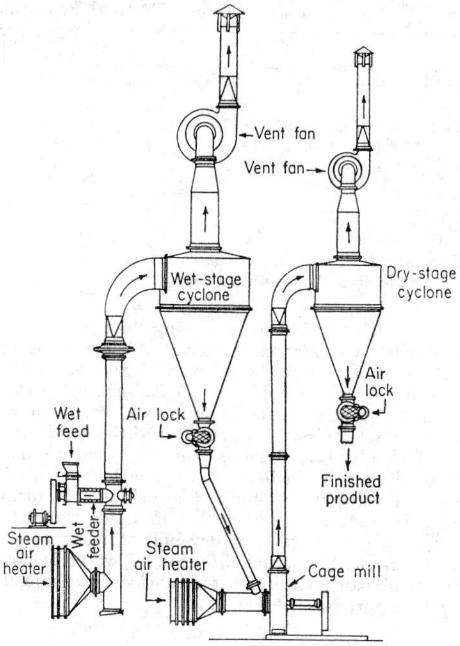

FIG. 20-76. Two-stage air stream and cage mill, pneumatic conveyor dryer. (*Courtesy of the Raymond Div., Combustion Eng., Inc.*)

containing a C-E Raymond cage-mill disintegrator. The second stage ensures complete drying after thorough dispersion of lumps and agglomerates. If disintegration is required to disperse the wet feed, the stages can be reversed, or disintegration can be employed in both stages. Systems of the type illustrated are employed for drying synthetic resins, of which low-pressure polyethylene and polypropylene are examples.

Figure 20-77 illustrates a single-stage dryer employing a paddle mixer, recycle, and a C-E Raymond Imp mill for fine grinding and dispersion of the mixed feed in the air stream. These units are designed to handle filter and centrifuge cakes and other sticky or pasty feeds. Employment of a cage mill in this system is very common also.

Several typical products dried in pneumatic conveyors are described in Table 20-25. The air-stream type referred to is an ordinary single-stage dryer like the first stage of Fig. 20-76.

Design Methods. Depending upon temperature sensitivity of the product, inlet-air temperatures between 300° and 1300°F. are employed. With a heat-sensitive solid, a high initial moisture content should permit use of a high inlet-air temperature. Evaporation of surface moisture takes place at essentially the wet-bulb air temperature. Until this is completed, by which time the air will have cooled significantly, the surface moisture film prevents the solids temperature from exceeding the wet-bulb temperature of the air. Pneumatic conveyors are used for solids having initial moisture contents ranging from 3 to 90 per cent, wet basis. The air quantity required and solids-to-gas loading are fixed by the moisture load, inlet-air temperature, and, frequently, the exit-air humidity. If the last is too great to permit complete drying, *i.e.,* if the exit-air humidity is above that in equilibrium with the product at required dryness, the solids-to-gas loading must be reduced together with the inlet-air temperature (see Table 15-9, Sec. 15).

Table 20-25. Typical Products Dried in Pneumatic Conveying Dryers*

Material	Initial moisture, wet basis, %	Final moisture, wet basis, %	Rate, lb./hr. product	Remarks
Clay, acid treated	60	18	8,500	Cage-mill type
Coal, ⅜-in. × 0	11.5	1.5	160,000	Air-stream type
Corn gluten feed	65	20	12,000	Cage-mill type
Kaolin (H_2O washed and partially dried)	10	0.5	16,000	Imp-mill type, grind to 99.9%, −325 mesh
Gluten (vital wheat)	70	10	500	Imp-mill type, grind to −80 mesh
Clay, ball	25	0.5	8,000	Imp-mill type, grind to 95%, −100 mesh
Gypsum, raw	25 total	5	7,000	Imp-mill type, grind and calcine to stucco
Pharmaceuticals	15	4	1,000	Air-stream type
Silica-gel catalyst	53	10	11,000	Cage-mill type
Synthetic resin	50	0.5	2,000	Two-stage system
Carboxylmethylcellulose	40	3	900	Imp-mill type, grind to 80%, −200 mesh
Sewage sludge	82	0	18,500	Multiple-cage-mill-type systems, dry and incinerate

* Raymond Division, Combustion Engineering, Inc.

The gas velocity in the conveying duct must be sufficient to convey the largest particle. This may be calculated accurately by methods given in Sec. 5. For estimating purposes, a velocity of 75 ft./sec., calculated at the exit-air temperature, is employed frequently. If mainly surface moisture is present and the solids are not reduced to ultimate dryness, the temperature driving force in the system will approach the log mean of the inlet- and exit-gas wet-bulb depressions. If ultimate dryness is reached (or passed), the solids temperature will approach the exit-gas dry-bulb temperature. In most cases where internal diffusion of water is not believed significant, the former situation is assumed for estimating purposes.

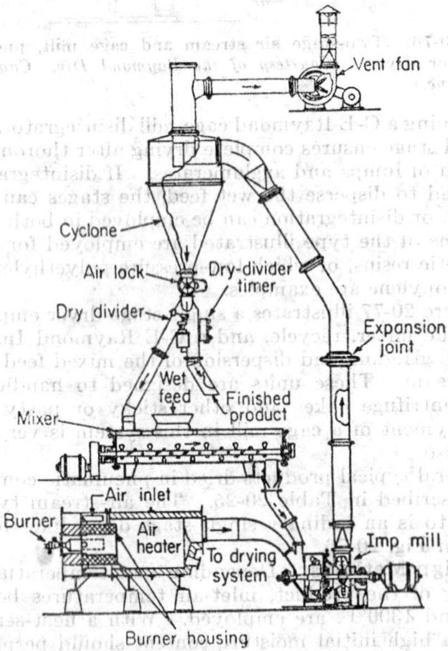

FIG. 20-77. Single-stage pneumatic conveyor dryer. *(Courtesy of the Raymond Div., Combustion Eng., Inc.)*

In spite of the fact that pneumatic conveying is considered dilute-phase contacting, and that in heating, drying, and cooling processes solids-to-gas loadings are very low, observation of operating conveyors indicates that the solids are rarely uniformly dispersed in the gas phase. With infrequent exceptions, the particles move in a laminar pattern, following a streamline along the duct wall where the flow velocity is at a minimum. Complete or even partial diffusion in the gas phase is rarely experienced, even with low-specific-gravity particles. Air velocities may approach 4000 to 6000 ft./min. It is doubtful, however, that even finer and lighter materials reach more than 80 per cent of this speed, while heavier and larger fractions may travel at much slower rates [Fischer, *Mech. Eng.*, **81**, 11, 67–69 (1959)]. Very little information and operating data have been published on pneumatic-conveyor dryers which would permit a true theoretical basis for design. Therefore, *firm design always requires pilot tests.* It is believed, however, that the significant velocity effect in a pneumatic conveyor is the difference in velocities between gas and solids.

One manner in which size may be computed, *for estimating purposes,* is by employing a volumetric heat-transfer concept as used for rotary dryers. If it is assumed that contacting efficiency is in the same order as that provided by efficient lifters in a rotary dryer, and the velocity difference is between gas and solids controls, Eq. (20-4) may be employed to estimate a volumetric heat-transfer coefficient. Assuming a duct diameter of 1.0 ft. (D), and assuming a gas velocity of 75 ft./sec., if the solids velocity is taken as 80 per cent of this speed, the velocity difference between the two would be 15 ft./sec. or 900 ft./min. If the exit gas has a density of 0.065 lb./cu. ft., the relative mass flow rate of the gas G becomes 3510 lb./(hr.)(sq. ft); the volumetric heat-transfer coefficient is 37 B.t.u./(hr.)(cu. ft.)(°F.). This is not far different from many found in commercial installations; however, it is usually not possible to predict accurately the actual difference in velocity between gas and solids. Furthermore, the coefficient is also probably influenced by the solids-to-gas loading and particle size, which control the total solids surface exposed to the gas in each cubic foot of conveyor. Therefore, *the above is only an approximation.*

For estimating purposes, the conveyor cross section is fixed by the assumed air velocity and quantity. The volume, hence the length, can then be calculated by the above method, employing the log-mean, air wet-bulb depression for the temperature driving force in Eq. (20-3). When air-swept grinders and dispersion mills or efficient venturi feeders are employed, a significant fraction of the total drying may occur instantaneously in the feeder. Apparently complete dispersion of solids in the gas is obtained momentarily at this point; however, means do not exist which permit prediction of the true effect here without pilot trials.

Pressure drop in the system may be computed by methods described in Sec. 5, or those outlined in the literature [Fischer, *Chem. Eng.*, **65**, 11, 114–118 (1958)]. To prevent excessive leakage into or out of the system, which may have a total pressure drop of 8 to 15 in. of water, rotary air locks or screw feeders are employed at the solids inlet and discharge.

The conveyor and collector parts are thoroughly *insulated* to reduce heat losses in drying and other heating operations. *Operating control* is maintained usually by control of the exit-gas temperature, with the inlet-gas temperature varied to compensate changing feed conditions. A constant solids feed rate should be maintained.

Cost Data. *Purchase costs* vary widely; many pneumatic-conveyor installations are assembled units, each component purchased from a different supplier. Representative prices are given in Table 20-26. These include

Table 20-26. Cost of C-E Raymond Flash-drying Systems,* September, 1960

Cage-mill type with disintegration, complete with dry-type secondary dust collector and motors. Mild-steel construction and 1200°F. inlet temperature†

Evaporative capacity, lb. water/hr.	Approx. building space width, ft. × length, ft. × height, ft.	Price, f.o.b. shops
1,000	15 × 20 × 25	$ 40,000
2,000	25 × 25 × 35	57,000
4,000	30 × 28 × 40	77,000
6,000	34 × 30 × 50	91,000
9,000	38 × 40 × 50	106,000
12,000	42 × 42 × 55	121,000
16,000	45 × 45 × 55	137,000
20,000	48 × 50 × 60	154,000

* Raymond Division, Combustion Engineering, Inc.

† With inlet temperature of 600° to 700°F., consider the water evaporation approximately double the actual to use the above table (*i.e.*, if capacity is 2000 lb./hr. H_2O, use price of unit for 4000 lb./hr. H_2O). Considerably lower inlet temperatures are also frequently used for many materials.

a cage mill for disintegration, primary cyclone, and bag-type secondary collector. In general, pneumatic conveyors for similar duties will compete in cost with cocurrent rotary dryers. Space economies may reduce the total installed investment slightly below that of the rotary unit. *Operating costs, thermal efficiency*, etc., are similar to cocurrent rotary units sized for the same duty (p. 20-20). When other operations, such as conveying, grinding, or classifying, are simultaneously performed, operating and investment costs may be reduced for the pneumatic-conveyor process itself by being partially written off on the secondary function. In this situation, a pneumatic conveyor becomes particularly attractive.

SPRAY DRYERS

Description. A spray dryer consists of a large cylindrical, and usually vertical, chamber into which material to be dried is sprayed in the form of *small droplets*, and into which is fed a *large volume of hot gas* sufficient to supply the heat necessary to complete evaporation of the liquid. Heat transfer and mass transfer are accomplished by direct contact of the hot gas with the dispersed droplets. After completion of drying, the cooled gas and solids are separated. This may be accomplished partially in the drying chamber itself by classification and separation of the coarse dried particles. Fine particles are separated from the gas in external cyclones, frequently with secondary bag collectors. When only the coarse-particle fraction is desired for finished product, fines may be recovered in wet scrubbers; the scrubber liquid is concentrated and returned as feed to the dryer. *Horizontal spray chambers* are manufactured also, with a longitudinal screw conveyor in the bottom of the drying chamber for continuous removal of settled coarse particles.

The principal gas-solids contacting operation employing spray dryers is *ordinary drying* of water solutions and slurries. They are used also in combined *drying and heat-treating operations*, and for *melt fusion and cooling of molten materials, e.g.*, ammonium nitrate "prilling." The latter may be considered a solids size-enlargement process. Recently, spray dryers have been developed for *wet-agglomeration processes* to produce rapidly dispersible forms of concentrated food products, another form of size enlargement. Spray drying is a second form of gas-solids contacting in which the solids phase is in a dilute condition. In contacting performance, it is similar to pneumatic conveying. It differs in application in that the feed material is usually a liquid solution, slurry, or paste capable of being dispersed in a fluidlike spray (rather than being composed of free-flowing particulate solids).

Spray drying involves three fundamental unit processes: (1) *liquid atomization*, (2) *gas-droplet mixing*, and (3) *drying from liquid droplets*. Atomization is accomplished usually by one of three atomizing devices: (1) high-pressure nozzles, (2) two-fluid nozzles, and (3) high-speed centrifugal disks. With these atomizers, thin solutions may be dispersed into droplets as small as 2 microns. The largest drop sizes rarely exceed 500 microns (35 mesh). Because of the large total drying surface and small droplet sizes created, the actual drying time in a spray dryer is measured in fractions of a second. Total residence of a particle in the system is on the average not more than 30 sec. A review by Marshall [Atomization and Spray Drying, *Chem. Eng. Progress Monograph Ser.*, **50**, 2 (1954)] considers spray-drying theory in detail, as well as the design and operating characteristics of modern spray dryers. Liquid atomization and dispersion are discussed in detail in Sec. 18. Atomizers commonly employed on spray dryers are described briefly below.

Special designs of spray dryers may provide for *cooling air* to enter around the chamber, closed systems for recovery of solvents, and *air sweepers or mechanical rakes* to remove dry product from the walls and bottom of the chamber. Some are followed by *pneumatic conveyors* as depicted in Fig. 20-78, in which drying air is diluted with cool air for product cooling before separation. Spray dryers may operate with *cocurrent, mixed*, or *countercur-*

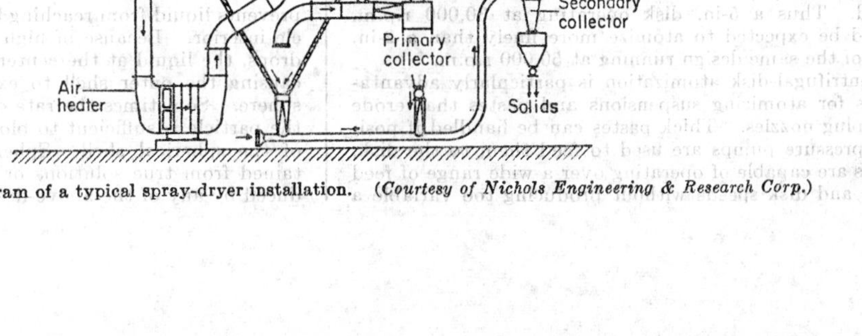

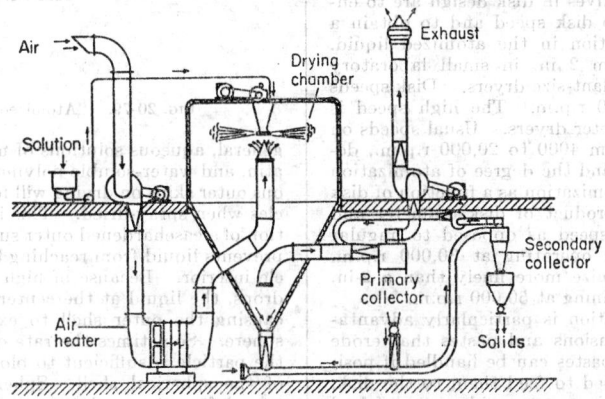

FIG. 20-78. Diagram of a typical spray-dryer installation. (*Courtesy of Nichols Engineering & Research Corp.*)

rent flow of gas and solids. Air may be heated by steam, direct-, or indirect-fired air heaters. Inlet-gas temperatures may range from 300° to 1500°F.

1. *Pressure nozzles* effect atomization by forcing the liquid under high pressure and with a high degree of spin through a small orifice. Pressures may range from 400 to 10,000 lb./sq. in., depending on the degree of atomization, capacity, and physical properties. Nozzle orifices may range in size from 0.010 to 0.15 in. diameter, depending on the pressure desired for a given capacity and the degree of atomization required. For high pressures and when solids are in suspension in the liquid, the nozzle orifice will be subject to wear by erosion and the orifice should be made of a hard alloy such as tungsten carbide or Stellite. Orifice inserts have been made from synthetic jewels such as sapphires. Maintenance on pressure nozzles is always a problem since erosion occurs with even the hardest inserts, and once the orifice has become scratched and non-uniform, good atomization is no longer possible. Likewise, incrustation and plugging by particles of foreign matter cause trouble. Piston pumps furnish the liquids at high pressure; erosion of the valves in these pumps is another maintenance problem.

Spray characteristics of pressure nozzles depend on the pressure and nozzle-orifice size. Pressure affects not only the spray characteristics but also the capacity. If it is desired to reduce the amount of liquid sprayed by lowering the pressure, then the spray may become coarser. To correct this, a smaller orifice would be inserted, which would then require a higher pressure to produce the desired capacity, and a spray might result that would be finer than desired. Multiple nozzles tend to overcome this inflexible characteristic of pressure atomization, although several nozzles on a dryer complicate the chamber design and air-flow pattern and cause collision of particles, resulting in non-uniformity of spray and particle size.

2. *Two-fluid nozzles* do not operate efficiently at high capacities and consequently are not used widely on plant-size spray dryers. Their chief advantage is that they operate at relatively low pressures, the liquid being under 0 to 60 lb./sq. in. pressure, while the atomizing fluid is under only 10 to 100 lb./sq. in. pressure. The atomizing fluid may be steam or air. Recently, a two-fluid nozzle has been developed especially for dispersion of thick pastes and filter cakes not previously capable of being handled in ordinary atomizers [*Chem. Eng.*, **67**, 6, 83–84 (1960)].

3. *Centrifugal disks* atomize liquids by extending them in thin sheets which are discharged at high speed from the periphery of the rapidly rotating specially designed disk. The principal objectives in disk design are to ensure bringing the liquid to disk speed and to obtain a uniform drop-size distribution in the atomized liquid. Disk diameters range from 2 in. in small laboratory models to 12 or 14 in. for plant-size dryers. Disk speeds range from 3000 to 50,000 r.p.m. The high speed is usually used in small-diameter dryers. Usual speeds on plant-size dryers range from 4000 to 20,000 r.p.m., depending on disk diameter and the degree of atomization desired. The degree of atomization as a function of disk speed is affected by the product of disk diameter and speed, *i.e.*, by peripheral speed as opposed to angular speed. Thus a 5-in. disk operating at 30,000 r.p.m. would be expected to atomize more finely than a 2-in. disk of the same design running at 50,000 r.p.m.

Centrifugal-disk atomization is particularly advantageous for atomizing suspensions and pastes that erode and plug nozzles. Thick pastes can be handled if positive-pressure pumps are used to feed them to the disk. Disks are capable of operating over a wide range of feed rates and disk speeds without producing too variable a product. Centrifugal disks may be belt-driven, direct-driven by a high-speed electric motor powered by a frequency changer, or driven by a steam turbine. Direct drive by an electric motor appears to have advantages where very high speeds are required and where closely controlled speed variations are necessary. The life of high-speed bearings in centrifugal-disk atomizers depends on the conditions of operation. Average life may be 2000 hr. A spare spray machine should be standard equipment.

The particle-size distribution obtained by any one of the three methods of atomization depends on a number of factors. In general, the size distribution will depend on atomizer design, liquid properties, and the degree of atomization. If the finest atomization possible is attempted, a limiting condition is approached, and the particle-size range, regardless of the method of atomization, will be narrow. This is particularly true of pressure nozzles, in which uniformity of size increases with pressure. On the other hand, for the production of a coarse product with a high percentage of large particles, the method of atomization will have a large effect on the particle-size distribution. Production of uniform coarse particles from centrifugal disks frequently can be obtained by careful design.

One of the principal advantages of spray drying is the production of a *spherical particle*, which is usually not obtainable by any other drying method. This spherical particle may be solid or hollow, depending on the material, the feed condition, and the drying conditions. In

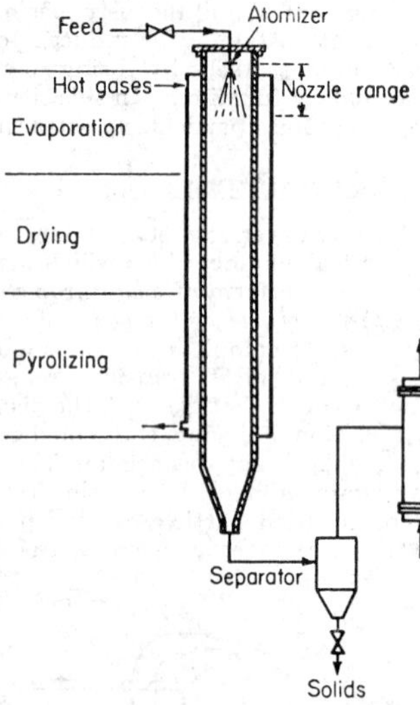

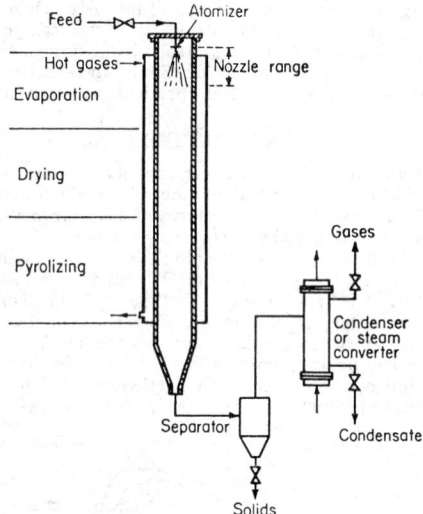

FIG. 20-79. "Atomized suspension" dryer.

general, aqueous solutions of materials such as soap, gelatin, and water-soluble polymers which form tough tenuous outer skins on drying will form hollow spherical particles when spray-dried. This is attributed to the formation of a casehardened outer surface on the particle which prevents liquid from reaching the surface from the particle interior. Because of high heat-transfer rates to the drops, the liquid at the center of the particle vaporizes, causing the outer shell to expand and form a hollow sphere. Sometimes the rate of vapor generation within the particle is sufficient to blow a hole through the wall of the spherical shell. Spherical particles may be obtained from true solutions or slurries and may be produced by any of the above-described atomizers.

The physical properties of spray-dried materials are subject to considerable variations, depending on the direction of flow of the inlet gas and its temperature, the degree and uniformity of atomization, the solids content of the feed, the temperature of the feed, and the degree of aeration of the feed. The properties of the product usually of greatest interest are (1) *particle size*, (2) *bulk density*, and (3) *dustiness*. Generally the required final moisture is easily obtained. The *particle size* is a function of atomizer operating conditions and also of the solids content, liquid viscosity, liquid density, and feed rate. In general, particle size increases with solids content, viscosity, density, and feed rate.

The *bulk density* of spray-dried solids is frequently the critical property subject to close control. The bulk density of material from a spray dryer may usually be increased by the following operating changes: (1) reducing droplet size, (2) reducing inlet-air temperature, (3) increasing air through-put, (4) increasing air turbulence, (5) employing countercurrent rather than cocurrent gas flow, and (6) effecting a wide range of size distribution from the atomizer. Chaloud *et al.* have evaluated qualitatively the effects of operating variables on the bulk density of particles from detergent spray dryers [*Chem. Eng. Progress*, **53**, 12, 593–596 (1957)].

A dusty product is caused by fine atomization or particle degradation after drying. Thin-wall hollow particles are susceptible to breakage during classification. Fine atomization and a high gas temperature contribute to high production rates in small drying chambers; they also generate fine particles and thin-wall spheres. Spray-drying installations yielding exceedingly fine and dusty products are often the result of an honest effort to design equipment for maximum capacity at a minimum investment. Large solids particles or heavy-wall spheres require longer drying cycles, hence larger drying chambers. Careful design in the pilot plant is necessary. In commercial installations, classification of particles and separation of a fine fraction from coarse product are carried out frequently by employing countercurrent flow of gas and solids. Mixed-flow chambers of some types are also adaptable for this purpose.

The majority of spray dryers in commercial use employ cocurrent flow of gas and solids. Countercurrent-flow dryers are used primarily for drying of soaps and detergents. Their classifying ability is useful in these applications. Air flow is upward, carrying entrained fines from the top of the chamber. The coarse product settles and is removed separately from the bottom of the chamber. Horizontal spray dryers always employ cocurrent flow of gas and solids. A swirling motion is imparted to the air to improve mixing. Mixed-flow dryers take a variety of forms which combine countercurrent and cocurrent drying. The flow patterns are complex with a high degree of turbulence in the drying chamber. In one type, air flow is similar to that in a cyclone. It is introduced tangentially at the top of a conical chamber, travels in a spiral pattern down the chamber wall, and returns in a column up the center to exhaust at the top. Feed is introduced at the center of the top, travels outward and downward countercurrent to the exit-gas stream, and then as it nears the wall is picked up and is carried downward cocurrent with the inlet-gas stream. Many variations of air-flow patterns are employed commercially; most are intended primarily to produce turbulence and thorough mixing of gas and droplets and to achieve the most effective use of the chamber volume.

Applications. The major and most successful drying applications of spray dryers are for solutions, slurries and pastes which (1) *cannot be dewatered mechanically* (2) *are heat-sensitive* and cannot be exposed to high-temperature atmospheres for long periods, or (3) *contain ultra-fine particles* which will agglomerate and fuse if dried in other than a dilute condition. In other applications, spray drying is rarely competitive on a cost basis with two-step dewatering and solids-drying processes. The cost of bag collectors for solids recovery from large volumes of exit gas may double the cost of a spray-dryer installation. Additional costs must usually be justified on the basis of some improvement in product quality, such as particle form, size, flavor, color, or heat stability. Spray drying is applicable to heat-sensitive products such as milk powders and other foods and pharmaceuticals because of the short contact time in the dryer hot zone. Further, the water film on the liquid drop protects the solids from high gas temperatures. Drying is carried out at essentially the drying-air wet-bulb temperature. Color pigments are examples of the class of products where it is desired to maintain as closely as possible the original solids particle size. Table 20-27 lists a variety of materials which have been successfully spray-dried. One other class of products particularly applicable to spray dryers is solids slurries containing extremely fine particles which are non-Newtonian in flow characteristics and remain fluid at very low moisture contents. Certain classes of clays are found in this category. Also, spray dryers have been developed for encapsulation processes to convert liquid, volatile flavors, and perfumes to particulate solids forms [Maleeny, *Soap Chem. Specialties*, **34**, 1, 135–141 (1958)]. Spray cooling has been employed for sodium bisulfate, ammonium nitrate, and phenothiazene.

Table 20-27. Some Materials That Have Been Successfully Spray-dried in an 18-ft.-diameter by 18-ft.-high Chamber with a Centrifugal-disk Atomizer*

Material	Air temp., °F. In	Air temp., °F. Out	% water in feed	Evaporation rate, lb./hr.
Blood, animal	330	160	65	780
Yeast	440	140	86	1080
Zinc sulfate	620	230	55	1320
Lignin	400	195	63	910
Aluminum hydroxide	600	130	93	2560
Silica gel	600	170	95	2225
Magnesium carbonate	600	120	92	2400
Tanning extract	330	150	46	680
Coffee extract *A*	300	180	70	500
Coffee extract *B*	500	240	47	735
Magnesium chloride	810	305	53	1140 (to dihydrate)
Detergent *A*	450	250	50	660
Detergent *B*	460	240	63	820
Detergent *C*	450	250	40	340
Manganese sulfate	600	290	50	720
Aluminum sulfate	290	170	70	230
Urea resin *A*	500	180	60	505
Urea resin *B*	450	190	70	250
Sodium sulfide	440	150	50	270
Pigment	470	140	73	1750

NOTE 1: The fan on this dryer handles about 11,000 cu. ft./min. at outlet conditions.

NOTE 2: The outlet-air temperature includes cold air in-leakage, and the true temperature drop caused by evaporation must therefore be estimated from a heat balance.

* Courtesy of Bowen Engineering, Inc.

If the product in no way adheres to the dryer parts and simple cyclone collectors are sufficient for gas-solids separation, batch operation of a spray dryer may be considered. Otherwise, the time and costs for cleaning the large equipment parts make them rarely economical for other than continuous processing of a single material.

A standard cocurrent-flow spray dryer is illustrated in Fig. 20-78. It includes a primary cyclone for separation of fines from the dryer exit gas and a pneumatic conveyor following the dryer used for product cooling. Large-diameter drying chambers are required when disk atomization is employed. Small-diameter high vertical chambers are used with two-fluid and pressure atomizers.

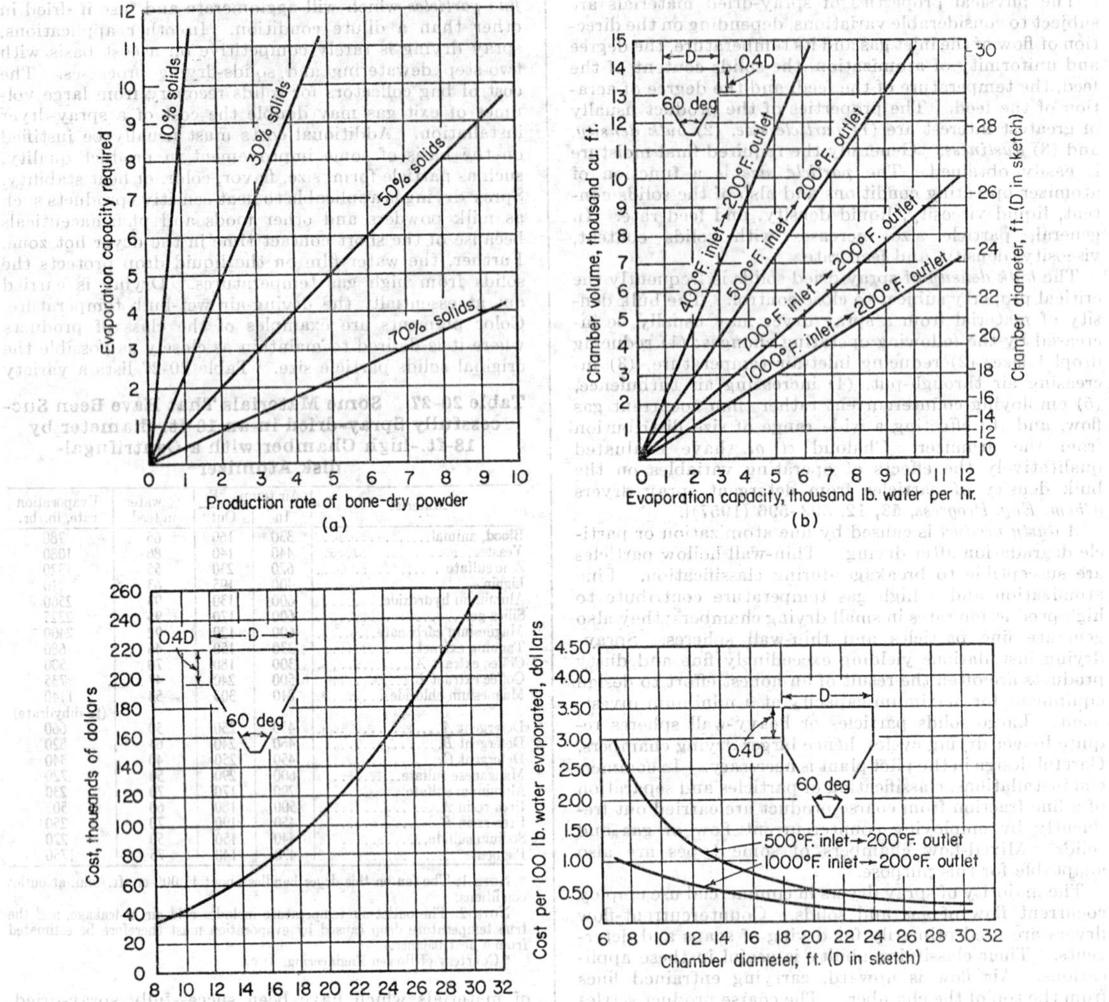

FIG. 20-80. Charts for estimating sizes and purchase costs of spray dryers. (*a*) Curves for determining the evaporation capacity of spray dryers from the production rate and solids concentration. (Use consistent units for production rate and evaporation capacity.) (*b*) Relationship between chamber volume and evaporation capacity of spray dryers. (Data based on retention time of 20 sec.) (*c*) Cost of spray-drying equipment as a function of drying chamber size. (See text for items included.) (*d*) Operating costs for spray-drying equipment. [*Courtesy of Chem. Eng. Costs Quart.*, **6**, 4 (1956).]

The *chamber shape* must conform to the atomizer *spray pattern* so that sprayed particles will not contact the walls before they are completely dry.

A considerably different type of spray contactor is illustrated in Fig. 20-79. Developed in Canada for recovery of sulfur from waste sulfite pulping liquor, the walls of the chamber are heated electrically or by hot combustion gases at 1100° to 1500°F., and heat transfer is by radiation from the walls to the droplets. Dry product is conveyed from the chamber by steam generated by evaporation of the droplets.

Design Methods. Design variables must be established by experimental tests before final design of a chamber can be carried out. In general, chamber size, atomizer selection, and separation auxiliaries will be determined by the desired *physical characteristics of the product.* Drying by itself is rarely a problem. An installed spray dryer is relatively inflexible in meeting changing operating requirements while maintaining a constant production rate. Important variables which must be fixed before design of a commercial dryer are the following:

1. The form and particle size of product required
2. The physical properties of the feed: moisture, viscosity, density, etc.
3. The maximum inlet-gas and product temperatures

A considerable quantity of published literature exists in which theoretical methods are described for calculating spray-dryer requirements on the basis of heat and mass transfer to liquid drops suspended in an air stream. For estimating purposes, one method employs the volumetric

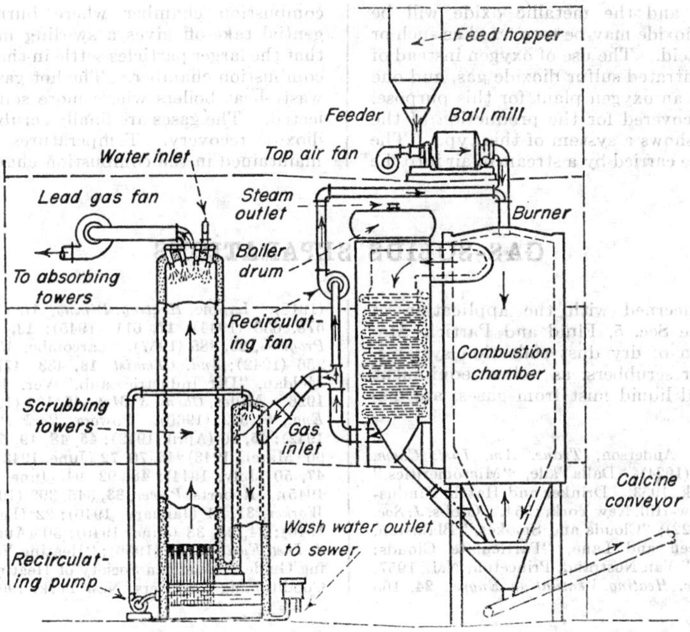

FIG. 20-81. Nichols-Freeman flash roasting system for making sulfur dioxide gas. *(Griswold, "Fluids, Combustion, and Furnaces," p. 425, McGraw-Hill, New York, 1946.)*

heat-transfer concept described previously for direct-heat rotary and pneumatic dryers. The log-mean air wet-bulb depression is assumed for the process driving force. Unfortunately, air flow and droplet patterns in commercial dryers are very complex and the effective velocity profiles are difficult to predict. The over-all coefficient is found to vary from 1 to 20 B.t.u./(hr.)(cu. ft. of chamber volume)(°F.). This depends on feed material, inlet-air temperature, droplet size distribution, and numerous other unpredictable variables. Use of Fig. 20-80 is suggested for *estimating purposes for preliminary design* of equipment size without the benefit of pilot trials.

Cost Data. Drying chambers, ductwork, and cyclone separators are usually constructed of stainless steel. Savings of roughly 20 per cent may be achieved on total purchase cost using carbon steel; the increasing tendency toward use of heat-resistant and corrosion-resistant plastic coatings (epoxy resins) makes the future appear promising for greater use of carbon-steel construction. Wide differences in cost may be experienced in the selection of the basic equipment. Air heaters vary in price range according to the selection of steam, electricity, direct-fired, and indirect-fired oil or gas heaters. Dust-collection equipment may consist of cyclone collectors or bag-type filters and may include a wet scrubber. Costs of nozzle and centrifugal atomizers are usually comparable. While the centrifugal atomizer requires mechanical gearing and motor drive, a high-pressure nozzle requires a high-pressure pump which will usually more than offset the cost of gearing and motor for the centrifugal atomizer. Auxiliary equipment which may be included are air filters, drying-chamber insulation, and mechanical or pneumatic cooling conveyors. A minimum of instrumentation consists of indicating and recording thermometers for inlet-air and outlet temperatures, ammeter for atomizer motor drive (or pressure gage for nozzle atomization), flowmeter, manometers, high-temperature alarm, and a panel board with push-button stations for all equipment. The drying process may be completely controlled automatically with some additional instrumentation. An approximation of the initial cost of spray-drying equipment may be obtained from Fig. 20-80*c*. The costs are based on drying chambers of the proportions shown, and they include the following:

1. Drying chamber with insulation, door, double-hung inspection port, windows and floodlights, ductwork and air disperser, stainless-steel construction
2. Stainless-steel cyclone dust collectors and carbon-steel stack
3. Miscellaneous ductwork
4. Oil or gas direct-fired air heater
5. All motors and fans
6. Air filters
7. Centrifugal atomizer and drive
8. Panel board and instrumentation for automatic control
9. Engineering services for design and fabrication of items 1 to 8
10. Erection in customer's plant of items 1 to 8
11. Engineering startup service

Total installed investment will range from 200 to 300 per cent of the costs indicated when buildings, foundation, access platforms, piping, wiring, etc., are added. Operating costs range from 0.2 to 3.0¢ per pound of water evaporated as indicated in Fig. 20-80*d*. Annual maintenance costs in addition will average 5 to 10 per cent of total installed cost.

Spray dryers may operate under positive, negative, or neutral pressures. In general, pressure drop in a complete system will range from 6 to 20 in. of water, depending on duct size and separation equipment employed.

FLASH ROASTERS

Flash roasters are especially suitable for very fine particles such as sulfides of zinc, iron, copper, and nickel which react with the oxygen in air with generation of heat. Sulfur dioxide and the metallic oxide will be formed. The sulfur dioxide may be recovered as such or be made into sulfuric acid. The use of oxygen instead of air gives a more concentrated sulfur dioxide gas, and one company has installed an oxygen plant for this purpose. The metal oxide is recovered for the production of the metal. Figure 20-81 shows a system of this type. The fine-charge particles are carried by a stream of air into the combustion chamber where burning occurs. A tangential take-off gives a swirling motion to the gases so that the larger particles settle in the hopper bottom of the combustion chamber. The hot gases are passed through waste-heat boilers where more solids settle and are collected. The gases are finally scrubbed and sent to sulfur dioxide recovery. Temperatures of about 1800°F. are maintained in the combustion chambers.

GAS-SOLIDS SEPARATIONS

This section is concerned with the application of particle mechanics (see Sec. 5, Fluid and Particle Mechanics) to the design of dry dust collection systems. Wet dust collectors, or scrubbers, as well as equipment for removing entrained liquid mist from gases, are discussed in Sec. 18.

REFERENCES: *General.* Anderson, *Trans. Am. Inst. Chem. Engrs.*, **16**, Part I, 69 (1924). DallaValle, "Micromeritics," 2d ed., Pitman, New York, 1953. Drinker and Hatch, "Industrial Dust," 2d ed., McGraw-Hill, New York, 1954. Gibbs, *J. Soc. Chem. Ind.*, **41**, 189T (1922); "Clouds and Smokes," Blakiston, Philadelphia, 1924. Green and Lane, "Particulate Clouds: Dusts, Smokes and Mists," Van Nostrand, Princeton, N.J., 1957. Knowles, *Trans. Am. Soc. Heating Ventilating Engrs.*, **24**, 165 (1918). Lapple, *Heating, Piping, Air Conditioning*, **16**, 410, 464, 578, 635 (1944); **17**, 611 (1945); **18**, 108 (1946); *Chem. Eng. Progress*, **53**, 385 (1957). Larcombe, *Mining Mag.*, **66**, 143, 206, 256 (1942); *Ind. Chemist*, **18**, 433, 477 (1942); **19**, 25 (1943). Meldau, "Der Industriestaub," Ver. deut. Ing. Verlag, Berlin, 1926. Miller, *Chem. & Met.*, **45**, 132 (1938). Pilpel, *Brit. Chem. Eng.*, **5**, 542 (1960). Powers, *Rock Prods.*, **45**, 58 (February, 1942); **45**, 46 (April, 1942); **45**, 48, 49, 51 (September, 1942); **46** 66 (March, 1943); **46**, 70, 72 (June, 1943); **47**, 74, 94 (May, 1944); **47**, 50 (July, 1944); **48**, 92, 94 (June, 1945); **48**, 84, 94 (July 1945). Roberts, *Power*, **83**, 345, 392 (1939). Anon., *Sheet Metal Worker*, **31**, 51 (January, 1940); 22 (February, 1940); 29 (May, 1940); 24, 25, 38 (June, 1940); 30 (August, 1940). Stairmand, *J. Inst. Fuel*, **29**, 58 (1956); "Heating Ventilating Air Conditioning Guide," American Society of Heating, Refrigeration and Air Conditioning Engineers, New York, 1960.

Nomenclature

In equations employing electrical quantities, only the c.g.s. system may be used, since there are no comparable electrical units in the English system.

Symbol	Definition	System of consistent units		Special units
		Metric (c.g.s.)	English	
A_c	Cyclone inlet area $= B_cH_c$ for cyclone with rectangular inlet	sq. cm.	sq. ft.	
A_e	Area of collecting electrode (side on which particles collect only)	sq. cm.	sq. ft.	
A_p	Area of particle projected on plane normal to direction of flow or motion $= (\pi D_p^2/4)$ for spherical particles	sq. cm.	sq. ft.	
B_c	Width of rectangular cyclone inlet duct	cm.	ft.	
B_e	Spacing between wire and plate or rod and curtain, or between parallel plates in electrical precipitators	cm.	ft.	
B_s	Width of gravity settling chamber	cm.	ft.	
c_d	Dust concentration in inlet or approach gas stream	....	....	grains/cu. ft.
c_h	Specific heat of gas	(cal.)/(°C.)(g.)	(B.t.u.)/(°F.)(lb.)	
c_{hb}	Specific heat of collecting body	(cal.)/(°C.)(g.)	(B.t.u.)/(°F.)(lb.)	
c_{hp}	Specific heat of particle stream	(cal.)/(°C.)(g.)	(B.t.u.)/(°F.)(lb.)	
C	Over-all drag coefficient $= F_d/(\rho u^2/2)(A_p) = 4g_LD_p(\rho_s - \rho)/3\rho u^2$ for spherical particles	dimensionless	dimensionless	
D_b	Representative dimension or diameter of body impinged upon	cm.	ft.	
D_{b1}, D_{b2}	Other characteristic dimensions of collecting body or device	cm.	ft.	
$(D_b)_{av.}$	Arithmetic average fiber diameter	cm.	ft.	
$(D_b)_s$	Surface average fiber diameter	cm.	ft.	
D_c	Cyclone diameter	cm.	ft.	
D_d	Outside diameter of wire or discharge electrode of concentric-cylinder type electrical precipitator	cm.	ft.	
D_e	Cyclone gas exit duct diameter	cm.	ft.	
D_L	Diameter of drops	cm.	ft.	
D_p	Diameter of particle	cm.	ft.	
$D_{p\mu}$	Diameter of particle	....	....	microns
D_{pc}	Cut size, diameter of particles of which 50% of those present are collected	cm.	ft.	
$D_{pc\mu}$	Cut size, diameter of particles of which 50% of those present are collected	....	....	microns
$D_{p,min}$	Minimum diameter of particle which is completely collected	cm.	ft.	
D_{ps}	Equivalent Stokes's law diameter of particle having a terminal settling velocity of u_t	cm.	ft.	
$D_{ps\mu}$	Equivalent Stokes's law diameter of particle having a terminal settling velocity of u_t	....	....	microns

Nomenclature—(*Continued*)

Symbol	Definition	System of consistent units		Special units
		Metric (c.g.s.)	English	
D_t	Inside diameter of collecting tube of concentric-cylinder type electrical precipitator	cm.	ft.	
D_v	Diffusion coefficient for particle	sq. cm./sec.	sq. ft./sec.	
DF	Decontamination factor = $\log_{10} [1/(1 - \eta)]$	dimensionless	dimensionless	
e	Natural or Naperian logarithmic base	2.718 . . .	2.718 . . .	
E	Electrostatic potential difference	statvolts		
E_c	Electrostatic potential difference required for corona discharge to commence	statvolts		
E_s	Electrostatic potential difference required for sparking to commence	statvolts		
F_{cv}	Cyclone friction loss, expressed as number of cyclone inlet velocity heads, based on area A_c	dimensionless	dimensionless	dimensionless
F_d	Drag or resistance to motion of a body in a fluid	dynes	poundals	
g_c	Conversion factor	$980.6 \left(\frac{\text{g. mass}}{\text{g. force}}\right)\left(\frac{\text{cm.}}{\text{sec.}^2}\right)$	$32.17 \left(\frac{\text{lb. mass}}{\text{lb. force}}\right)\left(\frac{\text{ft.}}{\text{sec.}^2}\right)$	
g_L	Local acceleration due to gravity	(cm./sec.)/sec.	(ft./sec.)/sec.	
h_{vi}	Cyclone inlet velocity head	....	....	in. water
H_c	Height of rectangular cyclone inlet duct	cm.	ft.	
H_s	Height of gravity settling chamber	cm.	ft.	
I	Electrical current per unit of electrode length	statamp./cm.		
k_ρ	Gas density relative to its density at 0°C., 760 mm.	dimensionless	dimensionless	dimensionless
k_t	Thermal conductivity of gas	(cal.)/(sec.)(sq. cm.)(°C./cm.)	(B.t.u.)/(sec.)(sq. ft.)(°F./ft.)	
k_{tb}	Thermal conductivity of collecting body	(cal.)/(sec.)(sq. cm.)(°C./cm.)	(B.t.u.)/(sec.)(sq. ft.)(°F./ft.)	
k_{tp}	Thermal conductivity of particle	(cal.)/(sec.)(sq. cm.)(°C./cm.)	(B.t.u.)/(sec.)(sq. ft.)(°F./ft.)	
k_{sg}	True particle specific gravity referred to water at 4°C.	....	....	dimensionless
K	Empirical proportionality constant, for cyclone pressure drop or friction loss	dimensionless	dimensionless	dimensionless
K_1	Filter-cake resistance factor = $\Delta p_c/V_f(w)$	....	....	(in. water)/(ft./min.)(lb. mass/min.-sq. ft.)
K_α	Proportionality constant, for collection efficiency of a single filter in a bed of fibers.	dimensionless	dimensionless	
K_c	Proportionality constant, for cloth pressure drop	....	....	$\left[\frac{\text{(in. water)}}{\text{(centipoise)(ft./min.)}}\right]$
K_d	Proportionality constant, for pressure drop through collected dust	....	....	$\left[\frac{\text{(in. water)}}{\text{(centipoise)(grain/sq. ft.)(ft./min.)}}\right]$
K_e	Electrical precipitator constant	(sec./cm.)	(sec./ft.)	
K_o	"Energy-distance" constant for electrical discharge in gases	cm.		
K_m	Stokes-Cunningham correction factor	dimensionless	dimensionless	dimensionless
K_{me}	Proportionality factor in Stokes-Cunningham correction factor	dimensionless	dimensionless	dimensionless
K_s	Proportionality factor in "slip flow" correction factor	dimensionless	dimensionless	dimensionless
L	Thickness of fibrous filter	cm.	ft.	
L_e	Length of collecting electrode in direction of gas flow	cm.	ft.	
L_s	Length of gravity settling chamber in direction of gas flow	cm.	ft.	
ln	Logarithm to the base e; natural logarithm	dimensionless	dimensionless	dimensionless
m_c	Dust capacity of air filter cell	....	....	lb.
m_p	Mass of particle	g.	lb.	
m_s	Mass of solids per unit of cloth area	....	....	grains/sq. ft.
M	Molecular weight	g./mole	lb./mole	
n	Exponent	dimensionless	dimensionless	dimensionless
N	Number of gas molecules in a mole	6.06×10^{23} molecules/g.-mole	2.76×10^{26} molecules/lb.-mole	
N_e	"Effective" number of turns made by gas stream in a cyclone separator	dimensionless	dimensionless	dimensionless
N_{Kn}	Knudsen number = λ_m/D_b	dimensionless	dimensionless	
N_{Ma}	Mach number	dimensionless	dimensionless	
N_o	Number of elementary electrical charges acquired by a particle	dimensionless	dimensionless	
N_{Pr}	Prandtl number = $c_h\mu/k_t$	dimensionless	dimensionless	
N_{Re}	Reynolds number = $(D_p\rho u/\mu)$ or $(D_p\rho u_t/\mu)$	dimensionless	dimensionless	
N_s	Number of shelves parallel to gas flow in gravity settling chamber	dimensionless	dimensionless	dimensionless
N_{sc}	Interaction number = $18\mu/K_m\rho_p D_v$	dimensionless	dimensionless	
N_{sd}	Diffusional separation number	dimensionless	dimensionless	
N_{sec}	Electrostatic-attraction separation number	dimensionless	dimensionless	
N_{sei}	Electrostatic-induction separation number	dimensionless	dimensionless	
N_{sf}	Flow-line separation number	dimensionless	dimensionless	
N_{sg}	Gravitational separation number	dimensionless	dimensionless	
N_{si}	Inertial separation number	dimensionless	dimensionless	
N_{st}	Thermal separation number	dimensionless	dimensionless	
N_t	Number of transfer units = $\ln [1/(1 - \eta)]$	dimensionless	dimensionless	
N_{tc}	Number of turns made by gas stream in a cyclone separator	dimensionless	dimensionless	dimensionless
Δp_c	Pressure drop across the dust layer in a bag filter	....	....	in. water
Δp_i	Pressure drop	....	....	in. water
Δp_{cv}	Pressure drop, expressed as number of cyclone inlet velocity heads, based on area A_c	dimensionless	dimensionless	dimensionless
q	Gas-flow rate	cc./sec.	cu. ft./sec.	

Nomenclature—(*Concluded*)

Symbol	Definition	System of consistent units: Metric (c.g.s.)	System of consistent units: English	Special units
q_m	Gas-flow rate per air filter cell	....	....	cu. ft./min.
Q_p	Electrical charge on particle	coulombs		
r	Radius; distance from center line of cyclone separator; distance from center line of concentric cylinder electrical precipitator	cm.	ft.	
R	Gas constant	$84{,}800 \left[\dfrac{(\text{cm.-g. force})}{(\text{g.-mole})(°\text{C.})}\right]$	$1546 \left[\dfrac{(\text{ft.-lb. force})}{(\text{lb.-mole})(°\text{F.})}\right]$	
t	Time	sec.	sec.	
t_d	Length of operating cycle	....	....	days
t_m	Time	....	....	min.
T	Absolute gas temperature	°K. or °C. abs.	°R. or °F. abs.	
T_b	Absolute temperature of collecting body	°K.	°R.	
T_p	Absolute temperature of particle	°K.	°R.	
u	Relative velocity between particle and main body of fluid	cm./sec.	ft./sec.	
u_e	Velocity of migration of particle toward collecting electrode	cm./sec.	ft./sec.	
u_t	Terminal settling velocity of particle under action of gravity	cm./sec.	ft./sec.	ft./sec.
u_{ts}	Terminal settling velocity of particle as calculated from Stokes's law	cm./sec.	ft./sec.	
V_c	Cyclone inlet velocity, average, based on area A_c	cm./sec.	ft./sec.	ft./sec.
V_e	Average velocity of gas flowing through electrical precipitator	cm./sec.	ft./sec.	
V_f	Superficial velocity of gas through cloth	....	....	ft./min.
V_o	Average velocity of dust-laden gas	cm./sec.	ft./sec.	
V_s	Average gas velocity in gravity settling chamber	cm./sec.	ft./sec.	
V_{ct}	Tangential gas-velocity component in a cyclone	cm./sec.	ft./sec.	
w	Mass velocity of dust approaching the filter cloth in a bag filter	....	....	(lb.)/(min.-sq. ft.)
α	Fractional free area (for screens, perforated plates, grids)	dimensionless	dimensionless	
δ	Dielectric constant	dimensionless		
δ_g	Dielectric constant at 0°C., 760 mm.	dimensionless		
δ_o	Permittivity of free space	(coulombs)²/(dyne)(sq. cm.)		
δ_b	Dielectric constant of body	dimensionless		
δ_p	Dielectric constant of particle	dimensionless		
ϵ	Elementary electrical charge	4.80×10^{-10} electrostatic units		
ϵ_b	Characteristic potential gradient at collecting surface	volts/cm.		
ϵ_v	Fraction voids in bed of solids	dimensionless	dimensionless	dimensionless
ζ	$= \left[1 + 2\dfrac{(\delta - 1)}{(\delta + 2)}\right]$; ranges from a value of 1 for materials with a dielectric constant of 1 to 3 for conductors	dimensionless		
γ	Figure of merit for dust collector $= \ln [1/(1 - \eta)]/\Delta p_t$	....	....	$(\text{in. water})^{-1}$
η	Collection efficiency, weight fraction of entering dispersoid collected	dimensionless	dimensionless	dimensionless
η_o	Collection efficiency of an isolated fiber, weight fraction of entering dispersoid collected	dimensionless	dimensionless	
η_α	Collection efficiency of a single fiber in a bed of fibers, weight fraction of entering dispersoid collected	dimensionless	dimensionless	
η_t	Target efficiency, fraction of dispersoid in swept volume collected on target	dimensionless	dimensionless	dimensionless
λ_i	Ionic mobility	(cm./sec.)/(statvolt/cm.)		
λ_m	Mean free path of gas molecules	cm.	ft.	
λ_p	Particle mobility $= u_e/\mathcal{E}$	(cm./sec.)/(statvolt/cm.)		
μ	Fluid viscosity	poise	(lb.)/(ft.)(sec.)	
μ_c	Fluid viscosity	....	....	centipoise
ρ	Fluid density	g./cc.	lb./cu. ft.	lb./cu. ft.
ρ_s	True (*not* bulk) density of solids; also density of liquid drops	g./cc.	lb./cu. ft.	lb./cu. ft.
σ	Ion density	number/cc.		
σ_{avg}	Average ion density	number/cc.		
ϕ	Cumulative weight fraction larger than size	dimensionless	dimensionless	dimensionless
ϕ_s	Particle-shape factor (number less than 1.0)	dimensionless	dimensionless	dimensionless
$\mathcal{E}$	Electrostatic potential gradient	statvolts/cm.		
$\mathcal{E}_c$	Electrostatic potential gradient required for corona discharge to commence	statvolts/cm.		
$\mathcal{E}_i$	Average electrostatic potential gradient in ionization stage	statvolts/cm.		
$\mathcal{E}_o$	Electrical breakdown constant for gas	statvolts/cm.		
$\mathcal{E}_p$	Average electrostatic potential gradient in collection stage	statvolts/cm.		
$\mathcal{E}_s$	Electrostatic potential gradient required for sparking to commence	statvolts/cm.		

Conversion factors:
- Multiply statvolts (or e.s.u.) by 300 to obtain volts.
- Multiply statamperes (or e.s.u.) by 3.34×10^{-10} to obtain amperes.
- Multiply centimeters by 10,000 to obtain microns.
- Multiply inches by 25,400 to obtain microns.
- Multiply pounds by 7000 to obtain grains.

PURPOSE OF DUST COLLECTION

Dust collection is concerned with the removal or collection of solid dispersoids in gases for purposes of:

1. Nuisance elimination—as in cleaning of ventilation air or fly-ash removal from power-plant combustion gases.
2. Equipment-maintenance reduction—as in filtration of engine-intake air or pyrites furnace-gas treatment prior to its entry to a chamber sulfuric acid system.
3. Safety- or health-hazard elimination—as in collection of siliceous and metallic dusts around grinding and drilling equipment and in some metallurgical operations and flour dusts from milling or bagging operations.
4. Product-quality improvement—as in air cleaning in the production of pharmaceutical products and photographic film.
5. Recovery of a valuable product—as in collection of dusts from dryers and smelters.
6. Powdered-product collection—as in pneumatic conveying; the spray drying of milk, eggs, and soap; and the manufacture of high-purity zinc oxide and carbon black.

MECHANISMS OF DUST COLLECTION

The forces or mechanisms utilized for dust collection may be classified as (1) gravity settling, (2) inertial deposition, (3) flow-line interception, (4) diffusional deposition, (5) electrostatic deposition, (6) thermal precipitation, and (7) sonic agglomeration. Recent papers by Chen [*Chem. Revs.*, **55**, 595 (1955)], Ranz (Principles of Inertial Impaction, *Penn. State Univ. Eng. Research Bull.* B-66, December, 1956), and Lapple [*Chem. Eng. Progress*, **53**, 385 (1957)] discuss the basic mechanisms and utilize dimensionless groups which measure their effectiveness. Table 20-28 lists the mechanisms and characteristic parameters.

PERFORMANCE OF DUST COLLECTORS

The performance of a dust collector is commonly termed collection efficiency, designated η, the weight ratio of dust collected to dust entering the apparatus. In some applications, such as the filtration of radioactive aerosols, the fraction escaping the collector is of greatest interest, and since this fraction is usually exponentially related to the properties of the filter, it is sometimes convenient to express efficiency in terms of log $[1/(1-\eta)]$, which is numerically equal to the logarithm of the ratio of inlet to outlet dust concentration. This quantity has been termed "decontamination factor," symbol DF, by Blasewitz and Judson [*Chem. Eng. Progress*, **51**, 6-J (1955)], who used logarithms to the base 10; and "number of transfer units," symbol N_t, by Wright, Stasny, and Lapple (High Velocity Air Filters, *WADC Tech. Rept.* 55-457, ASTIA No. AD-142075, October, 1957) who used natural logarithms and drew an analogy with the similar term used in heat and mass transfer. Perhaps the most logical performance figure is the one adopted by Chen [*Chem. Revs.*, **55**, 595 (1955)], which relates collection efficiency to the pressure drop expended:

$$\gamma = \frac{\ln [1/(1-\eta)]}{\Delta p_i} \qquad (20\text{-}15)$$

PROPERTIES OF PARTICLE DISPERSOIDS

Regardless of the figure of merit used, it should be kept in mind that performance is not a specific characteristic of a given collector but depends on the physical properties of the dispersoid handled. Figure 20-82 shows characteristics of particles and dispersoids together with the types of gas-cleaning equipment which are applicable.

Particle Size. The primary distinguishing feature of gas dispersoids is particle size. The most widely used unit of particle size is the micron, defined as 1/1000 mm. (1/25,400 in.), which is often designated by the symbol μ. This symbol should not be confused with the same symbol used for viscosity or the symbol mμ (millimicron) often used to designate 1/1000 micron. Particle size of a gas dispersoid is usually taken as the average or equivalent diameter of the particle in the United States, though

Table 20-28. Summary of Mechanisms and Parameters in Aerosol Deposition*

Deposition mechanism	Origin of force field	Deposition mechanism measurable in terms of: Basic parameter	Deposition mechanism measurable in terms of: Specific modifying parameters	System parameters
Flow-line interception‡	Physical gradient‡	$N_{sf} = \left(\frac{D_p}{D_b}\right)$	$N_{sc} = \left(\frac{N^2_{sf}}{N_{st}N_{sd}}\right) = \left(\frac{18\mu}{K_m\rho_p D_v}\right)$¶	Geometry: (D_{b1}/D_b), (D_{b2}/D_b), etc. ϵ_v α
Inertial deposition	Velocity gradient	$N_{si} = \left(\frac{K_m\rho_s D_p^2 V_o}{18\mu D_b}\right)$		
Diffusional deposition	Concentration gradient	$N_{sd} = \left(\frac{D_v}{V_o D_b}\right)$		
Gravity settling	Elevation gradient	$N_{sg} = \left(\frac{u_t}{V_o}\right)$		Flow pattern: N_{Re}‖ N_{Ma} N_{Kn}
Electrostatic precipitation	Electric-field gradient § a. Attraction	$N_{sec} = \left(\frac{K_m Q_p \epsilon_b}{\mu D_p V_o}\right)$	δ_p, δ_b†	Surface accommodation
	b. Induction	$N_{sei} = \left(\frac{\delta_p - 1}{\delta_p + 2}\right)\left(\frac{K_m D_p^2 \delta_o \epsilon_b^2}{\mu D_b V_o}\right)$		
Thermal precipitation	Temperature gradient	$N_{st} = \left(\frac{T - T_b}{T}\right)\left(\frac{\mu}{K_m \rho D_b V_o}\right)\left(\frac{k_t}{2k_t + k_{tp}}\right)$	(T_b/T), (T_p/T),† (N_{Pr}), (k_{tp}/k_t), (k_{tb}/k_t),† (c_{hp}/c_h), (c_{hb}/c_h)†	

* Lapple, *Chem. Eng. Progress*, **53**, 385 (1957).
† Not likely to be significant contributors.
‡ This has also commonly been termed "direct interception" and in conventional analysis would constitute a physical boundary condition imposed upon particle path induced by action of other forces. By itself it reflects deposition that might result with a hypothetical particle having finite size but no mass or elasticity.
§ In cases where the body charge distribution is fixed and known, ϵ_b may be replaced with Q_{bs}/δ_o.
¶ This parameter is an alternate to N_{sf}, N_{si}, or N_{sd} and is useful as a measure of the interactive effect of one of these on the other two. It is comparable with the Schmidt number.
‖ When applied to the inertial deposition mechanism, a convenient alternate is $(K_m\rho_s/18\rho) = N_{si}/(N^2_{sf}N_{Re})$.

Most forms of dust-collection equipment use more than one of these forces, and it is not uncommon for the controlling mechanism to change when the collector is operated over a wide range of conditions. It is therefore more convenient to classify dust-collection equipment according to type rather than according to the underlying mechanisms.

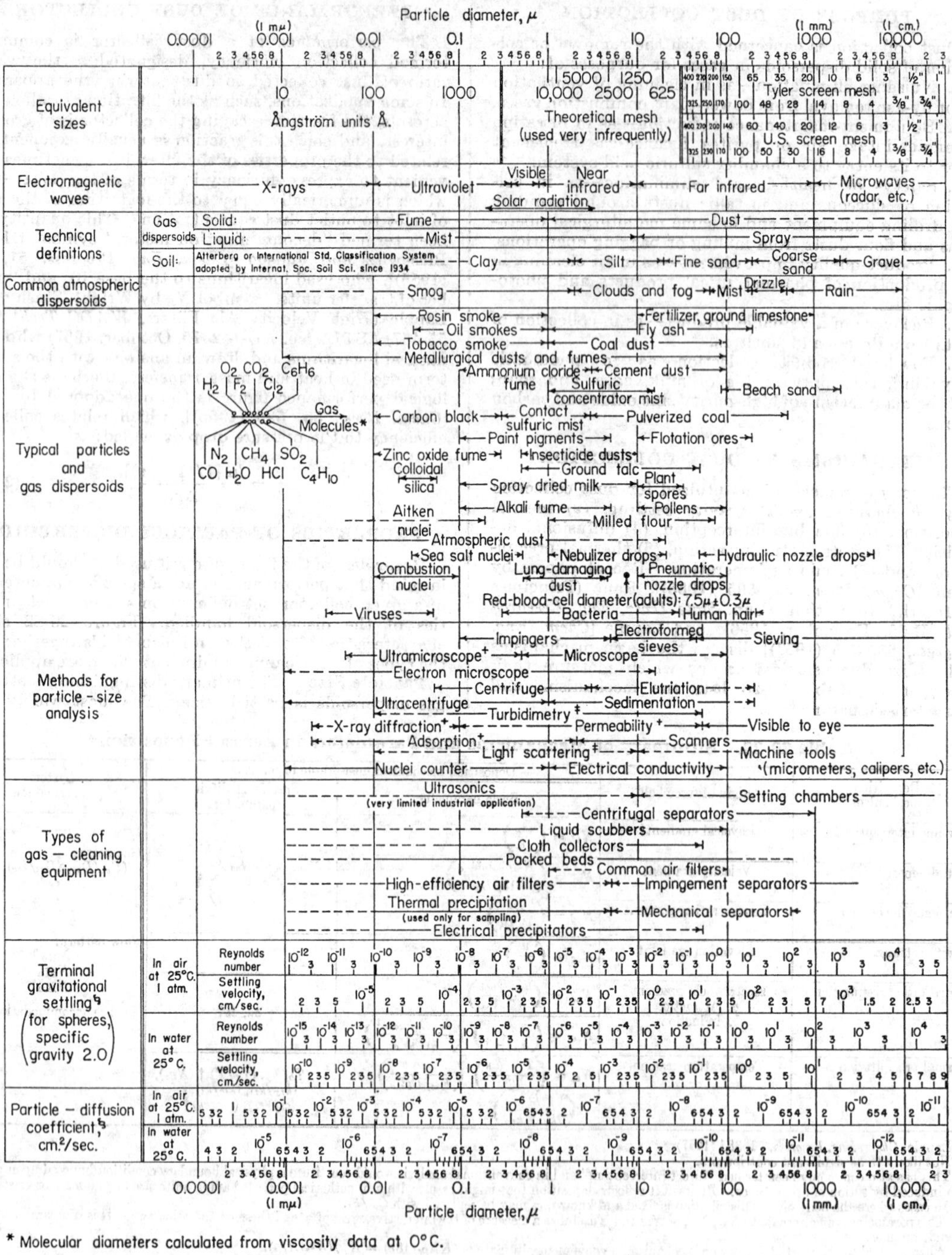

* Molecular diameters calculated from viscosity data at 0°C.

\+ Furnishes average particle diameter but no size distribution.

‡ Size distribution may be obtained by special calibration.

§ Stokes-Cunningham factor included in values given for air but not included for water.

FIG. 20-82. Characteristics of particles and particle dispersoids. *(Courtesy of the Stanford Research Institute, prepared by C. E. Lapple.)*

some writers (particularly German) specify particle size by the radius. Another common method is to designate the screen mesh (see p. 20-66) that has an aperture corresponding to the particle diameter. This method may lead to confusion unless the screen scale involved is specified.

COLLECTION EQUIPMENT

Gravity Settling Chambers. The gravity settling chamber is probably the simplest and earliest type of dust-collection equipment, consisting of a chamber in which the gas velocity is reduced to enable dust to settle out by the action of gravity. Its simplicity lends it to almost any type of construction. Practically, however, its industrial utility is limited to removing particles larger than 325 mesh (43 μ diameter). For removing smaller particles, the required chamber size is generally excessive.

Gravity collectors are generally built in the form of long, empty, horizontal, rectangular chambers with an inlet at one end and an outlet at the side or top of the other end. Assuming a low degree of turbulence relative to the settling velocity of the dust particle in question, the performance of a gravity settling chamber is given by

$$\eta = \frac{u_t L_s}{H_s V_s} = \frac{u_t B_s L_s}{q} \quad (\text{for } \eta \leqq 1.0) \qquad (20\text{-}16)$$

Expressing u_t in terms of particle size (equivalent spherical diameter), the smallest particle that can be completely separated out corresponds to $\eta = 1.0$ and, assuming Stokes's law, is given by

$$D_{p,\min} = \sqrt{\frac{18\mu H_s V_s}{g_L L_s(\rho_s - \rho)}} = \sqrt{\frac{18\mu q}{g_L B_s L_s(\rho_s - \rho)}} \qquad (20\text{-}17)$$

For a given volumetric air-flow rate, the collection efficiency depends on the total plan cross section of the chamber and is independent of the height. The height need be made only large enough so that the gas velocity V_s in the chamber is not so high as to cause reentrainment of separated dust. Generally V_s should not exceed about 10 ft./sec.

Horizontal plates arranged as shelves within the chamber will give a marked improvement in collection. This arrangement is known as the Howard dust chamber (Fume Arrester, U.S. Patent 896,111, 1908). The disadvantage of the unit is the difficulty of cleaning due to the close shelf spacing and warpage at elevated temperatures.

The pressure drop through a settling chamber is small, consisting primarily of entrance and exit losses. Settling chambers are occasionally used on natural-draft exhausts from kilns, but they are gradually being replaced by low pressure-drop cyclones or other more compact dust collectors.

Impingement Separators. When a dust-laden fluid impinges on a body, the fluid will be deflected around the body, whereas the dust particles, by virtue of their greater inertia, will tend to be collected on the surface of the body. The basic principles of impingement separators can be presented in terms of so-called "target" efficiencies. Target efficiency represents the fraction of particles in the fluid volume swept by the body which will impinge on the body. Thus, for flow around a cylinder, as shown in Fig. 20-83, all particles that are initially carried in the fluid between streamlines A and B will be collected on the body, and the target

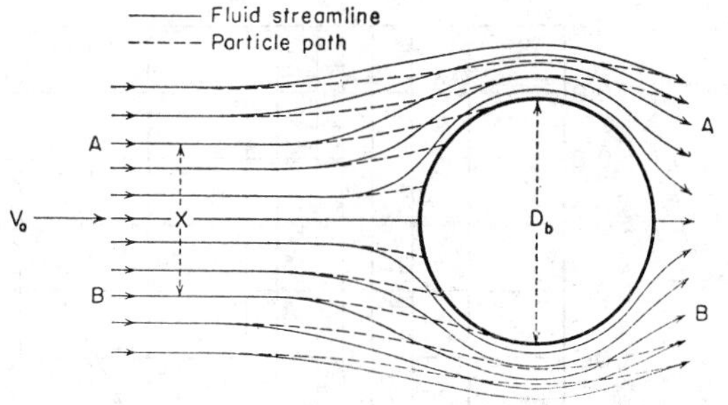

FIG. 20-83. Impingement separation.

efficiency will be (X/D_b). It can be shown [Albrecht, *Physik. Z.*, **32,** 48 (1931). Sell, *Forsch. Gebiete Ingenieurw.*, **2,** Forschungsheft 347, August, 1931. Langmuir and Blodgett, *U.S. Army Air Forces Tech. Rept.* 5418, Feb. 19, 1946 (U.S. Dept. of Commerce, Office of Technical Services PB 27565)] that the target efficiency η_t should be a function of the dimensionless group $(u_t V_o / g_L D_b)$. For simple shapes, this relationship can be derived from classical hydrodynamics; for more complex shapes, experimental determinations are required. While the relationships given by the above investigators for various collecting-body shapes are somewhat conflicting, the values reported by Langmuir and Blodgett (Fig. 20-84) are believed to be reliable. Although these relationships are derived for conditions of potential (streamline) flow around the body, they should hold closely even if the flow around the body is turbulent, since conditions on the upstream side of the body should approach those of potential flow in any case. It should also be noted that these relationships should apply whether the body moves through the fluid or whether the fluid moves around the body as long as V_o is taken as the relative velocity between the body and the bulk of the fluid.

Although the curves of Fig. 20-84 apply to collecting bodies in an infinite fluid, they may be applied for the direct calculation of collection efficiency of units employing such bodies in parallel and series, provided that adjacent collecting members are not so close as to cause an appreciable distortion of the flow pattern. This is substantially the case in many types of air filters. Where collecting members are relatively close, these curves would give a conservative approximation of collection efficiency. For collecting members having shapes differing widely from those shown in Fig. 20-84, additional experimental determinations are desirable, although order-of-magnitude estimates can be made by judicious interpolation of these curves. The paper by Ranz (*op. cit.*) provides means for predicting target efficiencies for a number of geometrical arrangements such as jets impacting on flat plates and channels; impaction on elbows, spheres, and cylinders. The target efficiencies are related to dimensionless groups of the operating variables. Methods are given for estimating collection efficiencies of some typical impingement separators.

In Fig. 20-85 is shown a typical commercial impingement collector. In general, impingement collectors are designed for a pressure drop in the range of 0.1 to 1.5 in. water, depending on the type and application, and are limited to removing dusts that are predominantly larger than 10 to 20 μ diameter. Rappers are sometimes provided to shake the collected dust off the collecting bodies at definite intervals. The chief advantage of such units lies in their greater adaptability to existing flues or ducts than other types of collectors. They may be used at

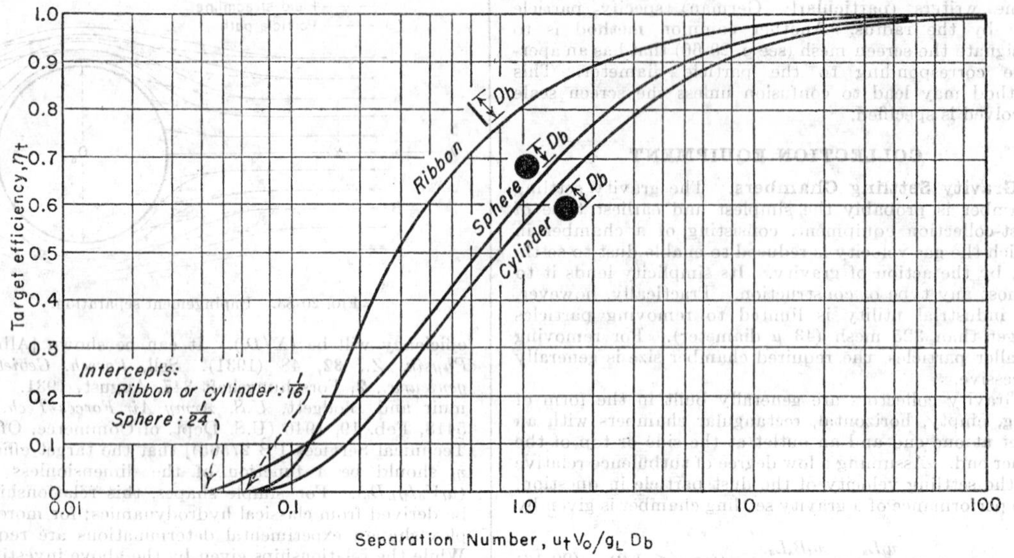

FIG. 20-84. Target efficiency of spheres, cylinders, and ribbons. The curves apply for conditions where Stokes's law holds for the motion of the particle. Langmuir and Blodgett have also presented similar relationships for cases where Stokes's law does not apply. [*Langmuir and Blodgett, U.S. Army Air Forces Tech. Rept.* 5418, *Feb.* 19, 1946 (*U.S. Department of Commerce, Office of Technical Services* PB 27565).]

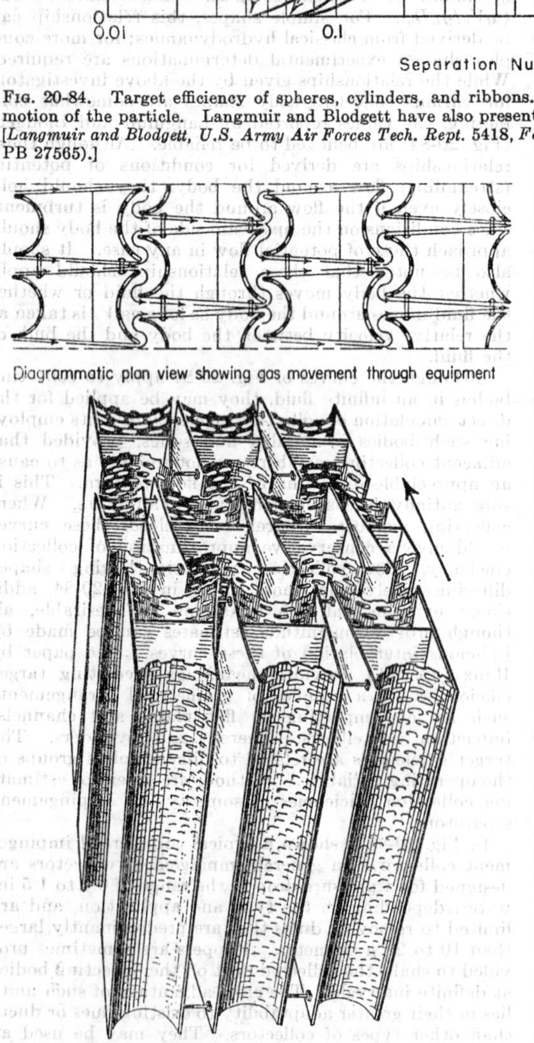
Diagrammatic plan view showing gas movement through equipment

FIG. 20-85. Reverse nozzle impingement separator. (*By-Products Recoveries, Inc.*)

elevated temperatures but not if the dust becomes tacky, although for the latter case some types are available in which circulating-water films are used to keep the elements clear. Purchase costs of impingement units are generally in the range of $0.15 to $0.30/(cu. ft./min.) of gas handled for installations of over 10,000 cu. ft./min. capacity in steel (prices in 1960). Further description will be found in Powers [*Rock Prods.*, **46**, 70, 72 (1943)] and Roberts [*Power*, **83**, 345, 392 (1939)].

Cyclone Separators. The most widely used type of dust-collection equipment is the cyclone, in which dust-laden gas enters a cylindrical or conical chamber tangentially at one or more points and leaves through a central opening (Fig. 20-86). The dust particles, by virtue of their inertia, will tend to move toward the outside separator wall from which they are led into a receiver. A cyclone is essentially a settling chamber in which gravitational acceleration is replaced by centrifugal acceleration. At operating conditions commonly employed, the centrifugal separating force or acceleration may range from five times gravity in very large diameter, low-resistance cyclones, to 2500 times gravity in very small, high-resistance units. The immediate entrance to a cyclone is usually rectangular.

Fields of Application. Cyclone collectors offer one of the least expensive means of dust collection from both an operating and an investment viewpoint. Cyclones have been employed to remove solids and liquids from gases and solids from liquids and have been operated at temperatures as high as 1000°C. and pressures as high as 500 atm. Cyclones for removing solids from gases are generally applicable when particles of over 5 μ (0.0002 in.) diameter are involved, although some of the multiple-tube parallel units attain 80 to 85 per cent efficiencies on particles of 3 μ diameter. In collecting particles of over 200 μ diameter, cyclones may be used, but gravity settling chambers are usually satisfactory and less subject to abrasion. In special cases where the dust shows a high degree of agglomeration, or where high dust concentrations (over 100 gr./cu. ft.) are involved, cyclones will remove dusts having a much smaller particle size. In certain cases efficiencies as high as 98 per cent have been realized on dusts having an ultimate

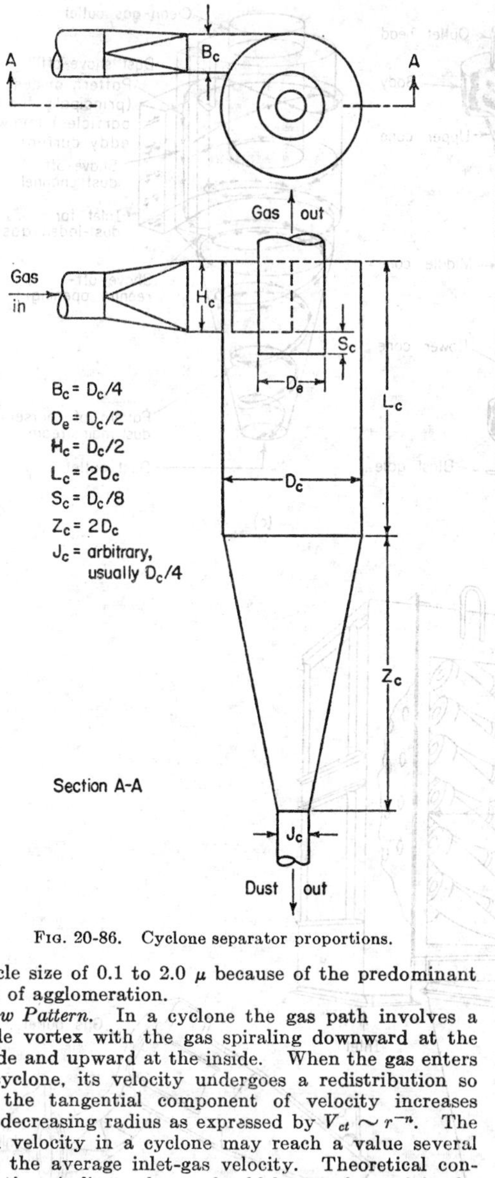

FIG. 20-86. Cyclone separator proportions.

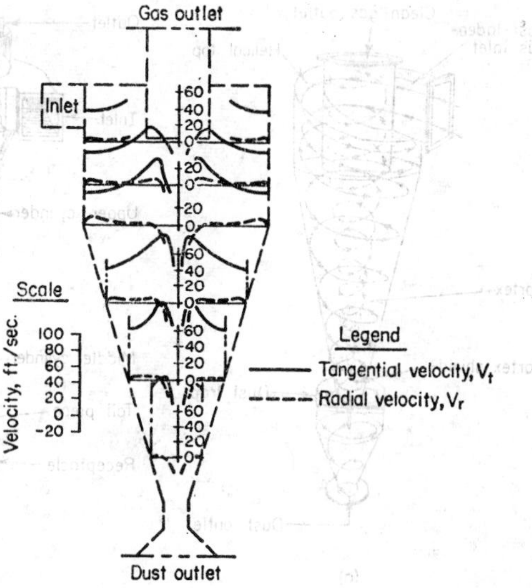

FIG. 20-87. Variation of tangential velocity and radial velocity at different points in a cyclone. [*Ter Linden, Inst. Mech. Engrs. J.*, **160,** 235 (1949).]

particle size of 0.1 to 2.0 μ because of the predominant effect of agglomeration.

Flow Pattern. In a cyclone the gas path involves a double vortex with the gas spiraling downward at the outside and upward at the inside. When the gas enters the cyclone, its velocity undergoes a redistribution so that the tangential component of velocity increases with decreasing radius as expressed by $V_{ct} \sim r^{-n}$. The spiral velocity in a cyclone may reach a value several times the average inlet-gas velocity. Theoretical considerations indicate that n should be equal to 1.0 in the absence of wall friction. Actual measurements [Shepherd and Lapple, *Ind. Eng. Chem.*, **31,** 972 (1939); **32,** 1246 (1940)], however, indicate that n may range from 0.5 to 0.7 over a large portion of the cyclone radius. Ter Linden [*Inst. Mech. Engrs. J.*, **160,** 235 (1949)] found n to be 0.52 for tangential velocities measured in the cylindrical portion of the cyclone at positions ranging from the radius of the gas-outlet pipe to the radius of the collector. Although the velocity approaches zero at the wall, the boundary layer is sufficiently thin that pitot-tube measurements show relatively high tangential velocities there, as shown in Fig. 20-87. The radial velocity V_r is directed toward the center throughout most of the cyclone, except at the center, where it is directed outward.

Superimposed on the "double spiral," there may be a "double eddy" [Van Tongeran, *Mech. Eng.*, **57,** 753 (1935). Wellmann, *Feuerungstech.*, **26,** 137 (1938)] similar to that encountered in pipe coils. Measurements on cyclones of the type shown in Fig. 20-86 indicate, however, that such double eddy velocities are small compared with the spiral velocity (Shepherd and Lapple, *op. cit.*).

Pressure Drop. The pressure drop through a cyclone as well as the friction loss is most conveniently expressed in terms of the velocity head based on the immediate cyclone inlet area. The inlet velocity head, expressed in inches of water, is related to the average inlet-gas velocity and density by

$$h_{vi} = 0.0030\rho V_c^2 \tag{20-18}$$

The cyclone friction loss is a direct measure of the static pressure and power that a fan must develop and is related to the pressure drop by

$$F_{cv} = \Delta p_{cv} + 1 - \left(\frac{4A_c}{\pi D_e^2}\right)^2 \tag{20-19}$$

Although there have been several attempts to calculate the friction loss or pressure drop from fundamental considerations [Feifel, *Forsch. Gebiete Ingenieurw.*, **9,** 68, 306 (1938); **10,** 212 (1939); *Arch. Wärmewirt.*, **20,** 15 (1939)], none is very satisfactory, since the simplifying assumptions made have not allowed for entrance compression, wall friction, and exit contraction, all of which have a major effect. Gonsequently, no general correlation of cyclone pressure-drop data is available as yet.

The friction loss through cyclones encountered in practice may range from 1 to 20 inlet velocity heads, depending on the geometric proportions (Alden, "Design of Industrial Exhaust System," 3d ed., Chap. VII, Industrial Press, New York, 1959. Shepherd and Lapple, *op. cit.*). For a cyclone of specific geometric proportions, however, F_{cv} and Δp_{cv} are substantially constant, independent of the actual cyclone size. The following discussion deals with reported equations for the pressure drop or friction loss of a cyclone when handling dust-free gases.

Miller and Lissman ["Calculation of Cyclone Pressure Drop," paper presented at December, 1940, meeting of A.S.M.E., New York (not published)], investigating

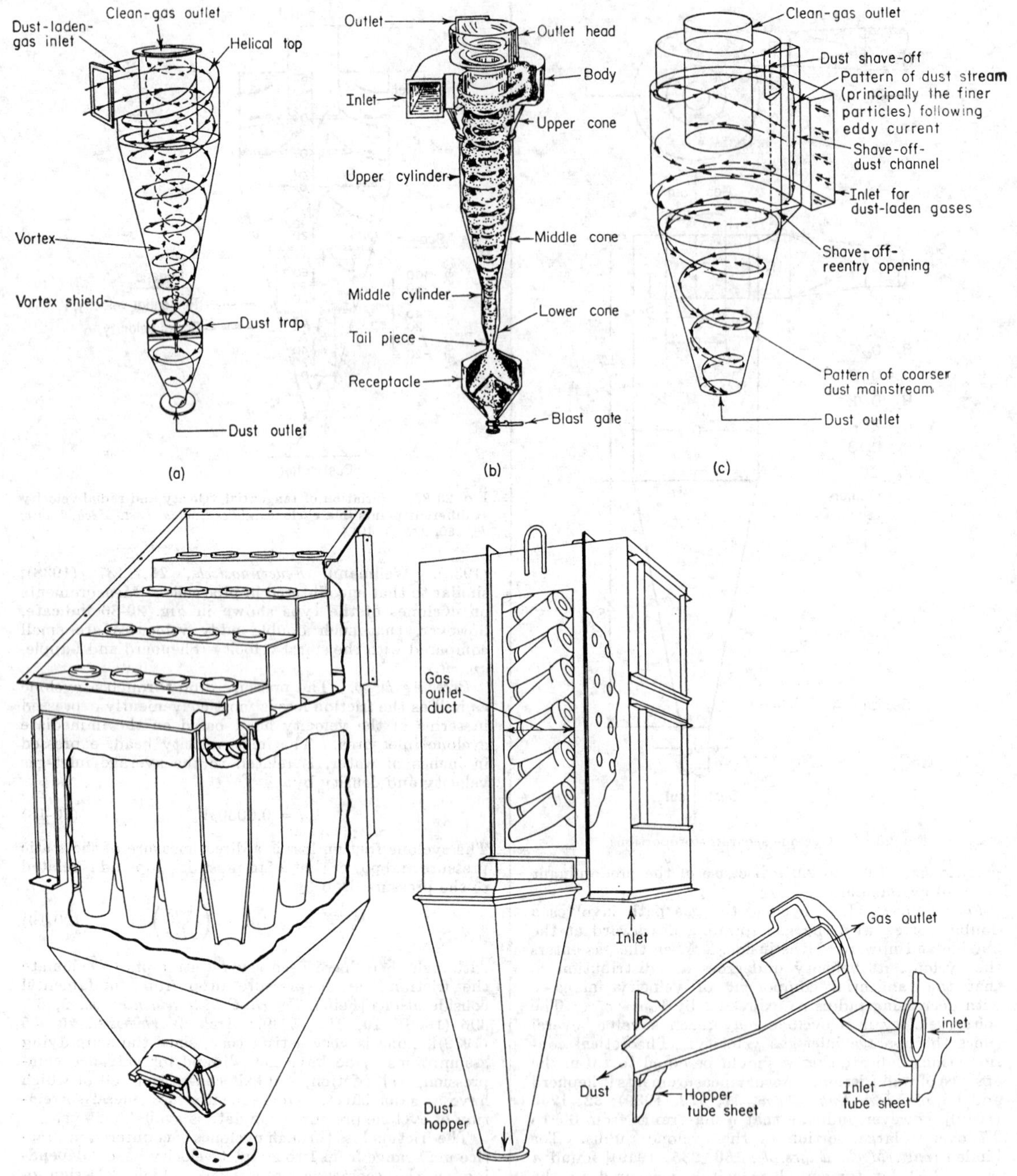

FIG. 20-88. Typical commercial cyclones. (a) Duclone collector. (*Ducon Company.*) (b) Sirocco type D collector. (*American Blower Co.*) (c) Van Tongeran cyclone. (*Buell Engineering Co.*) (d) Multiclone collector. (*Western Precipitation Corp.*) (e) Dustex miniature collector assembly. (*Dustex Corp.*) (f) Cutaway of the Dustex cyclone tube.

cyclones with an involute entrance, obtained the following empirical expression:

$$\Delta p_{cv} = K\left(\frac{D_c}{D_e}\right)^2 \qquad (20\text{-}20)$$

The value of K was found to be substantially constant with a value of 3.2 over the following range in proportions: $(B_c/D_c) = \frac{1}{8}$ to $\frac{3}{8}$; $(H_c/D_c) \cong 1.0$; $(D_e/D_c) = \frac{1}{4}$ to $\frac{3}{4}$. For smaller values of (D_e/D_c), the value of K increased, while for smaller values of (B_c/D_c), it decreased. In these tests D_c, D_e, and B_c were varied but not H_c.

Shepherd and Lapple (*op. cit.*), investigating cyclones of the general type shown in Fig. 20-86, obtained the following empirical expression:

$$F_{cv} = \frac{KB_cH_c}{D_e^2} \qquad (20\text{-}21)$$

These tests covered the following range in proportions: $(B_c/D_c) = \frac{1}{12}$ to $\frac{1}{4}$; $(H_c/D_c) = \frac{1}{4}$ to $\frac{1}{2}$; $(D_e/D_c) = \frac{1}{4}$ to $\frac{1}{2}$. With the normal arrangement in which the rectangular inlet terminates at the outer elements of the cyclone body or cylinder, K was found to have a value of 16.0. If the inner side of the inlet duct was extended past the cyclone cylinder wall and into the annular space halfway to the opposite wall to form an "inlet vane," the friction loss was reduced by over 50 per cent and K was found to be 7.5. Pressure-drop values calculated by means of Eq. (20-21) for a value of K of 13.0 will check the Miller and Lissman data within ±30 per cent for the most part. For the specific proportions shown in Fig. 20-86, $F_{cv} = 8.0$, and the pressure drop is given by

$$\Delta P_i = 0.024\rho V_c^2 \qquad (20\text{-}22)$$

Data reported in the trade literature for the type of cyclone shown in Fig. 20-88*b* can be closely represented by Eq. (20-21) for a value of K of 18.4. The proportions covered by this design are approximately: $(B_c/D_c) = \frac{5}{8}$; $(H_c/D_c) = \frac{5}{8}$; $(D_e/D_c) = \frac{1}{2}$ to 1. The term D_c, as specified here, is the diameter of the main or upper cylinder. The large diameter of the upper cone is $1\frac{5}{8}$ times as large. The cyclone shown in Fig. 20-88*a* has a reported (trade literature) pressure drop as follows:

$$\Delta P_i = 0.013\rho V_c^2 \qquad (20\text{-}23)$$

Iinoya [*Mem. Faculty Eng., Nagoya Univ.*, **5** (2) (September, 1953)] investigated the effect of wall roughness on pressure drop and found that pressure drop *decreased* with increased surface roughness. He pasted sand particles of various sizes on the wall of the cyclone and obtained pressure-drop data as shown in Table 20-29.

Table 20-29. Effect of Surface Roughness on Cyclone Pressure Drop

Size of Sand Particles on Wall	Pressure Drop, No. of Inlet Velocity Heads
None	8.0
147 to 175 microns, light coat	5.8
147 to 175 microns, heavy coat	4.9
500 to 1000 microns	4.1

First ("Fundamental Factors in the Design of Cyclone Dust Collectors," Doctoral Thesis, Harvard University, May, 1950) independently concluded that wall friction was a negligible part of the total pressure drop. Wall friction apparently reduces the vortex intensity, thereby decreasing pressure drop.

Collection Efficiency. Various authors [Davies, *Proc. Inst. Mech. Engrs.*, **B.1B**, 185 (1952). Lapple and Shepherd, *Ind. Eng. Chem.*, **32**, 605 (1940)] have investigated the theoretical time of movement of particles of dust toward the wall of the cyclone, and Ter Linden [*Proc. Inst. Mech. Engrs.*, **160**, 233 (1949)] has attempted a theoretical prediction of cyclone performance, but at the present time there is no generally accepted fundamental relationship. The most satisfactory expression for cyclone performance is still the empirical one by Rosin, Rammler, and Intelmann [*Z. Ver deut. Ing.*, **76**, 433–437 (1932)]. They derived the following equation for the minimum diameter particle that should be completely separated from the gas stream in a cyclone:

$$D_{p,\min} = \left[\frac{9\mu B_c}{\pi N_{tc} V_c(\rho_s - \rho)}\right]^{0.5} \qquad (20\text{-}24)$$

Smaller particles are removed to an extent proportional to the initial distance of the particles from the wall. Their derivation is based on Stokes's law, assuming the gas stream undergoes a fixed number of turns at constant spiral velocity without any mixing action or turbulence. The Rosin, Rammler, and Intelmann relationships can be conveniently presented in the form shown in Fig. 20-89, which gives the collection efficiency to be expected for a given particle size, expressed as a ratio to the cut size D_{pc}, where D_{pc} is defined by

$$D_{pc} = \left[\frac{9\mu B_c}{2\pi N_e V_c(\rho_s - \rho)}\right]^{0.5} \qquad (20\text{-}25)$$

This type of plot is essentially a generalized form of the "fractional" efficiency plot frequently found in commercial literature, and the cut size D_{pc} is the particle size corresponding to a fractional efficiency of 50 per cent. For the Rosin, Rammler, and Intelmann curve, the term N_e is identical with N_{tc}. Actually, as previously described, however, the flow pattern is considerably more complex, and the separation or classification efficiency curve is not nearly so sharp as would be predicted by this curve. Consequently, an experimental determination of this relationship must be relied upon. In the absence of reentrainment, such a curve, as well as the value of the term N_e, should be unique for a cyclone of given geometric proportions, and the value of N_e may be regarded as an approximate measure of the effectiveness of a given type of cyclone design. Where reentrainment is appreciable, the value of N_e will tend to decrease with increasing gas velocity and density.

In Fig. 20-89 is given a curve, based on experimental data for a variety of dusts, for a cyclone of the proportions given in Fig. 20-86. In this case reentrainment appeared to be minor, and based on a few plant and laboratory data, N_e has been found to be approximately 5.0. Although these data were not very accurate, the value given is probably conservative since some of the

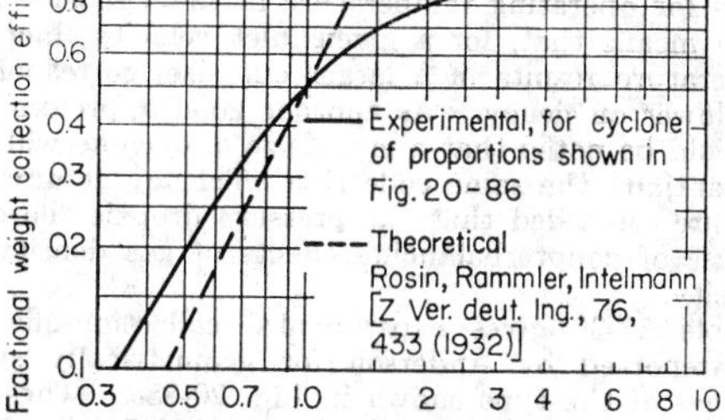

FIG. 20-89. Separation efficiency of cyclones.

data indicated the value of N_e to be as high as 10. If an inlet vane, as described above, is used with this cyclone, reentrainment becomes appreciable, and the apparent value of N_e has been found to be approximately 2 for cyclone inlet velocities on the order of 50 ft./sec. with air at atmospheric pressure. The above values of N_e were determined under conditions for which relatively little flocculation of dust in the gas stream would be expected.

Figure 20-89 gives the separation efficiency to be expected for a given particle size, whereas any dust or mist encountered in practice is comprised of particles covering a range of sizes. Consequently, the over-all collection efficiency is a summation of the efficiency on each particle size prorated according to the fraction of the total dispersoid in that size range. If the particle-size distribution is known, the over-all collection efficiency can be calculated graphically by plotting values of η and ϕ, corresponding to the same particle size, as ordinate and abscissa, respectively, on arithmetic graph paper as shown in Fig. 20-90. The over-all collection

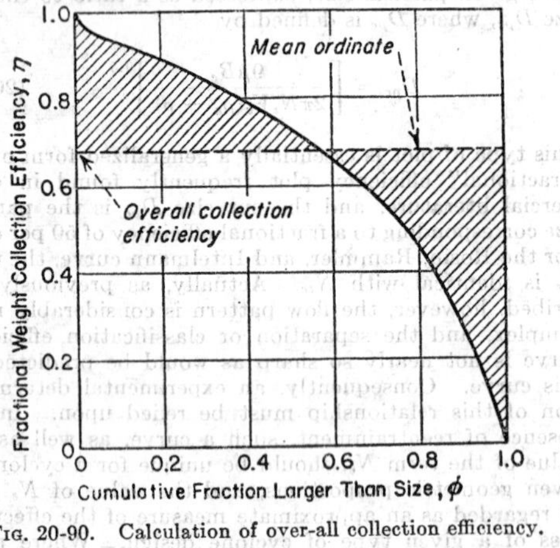

FIG. 20-90. Calculation of over-all collection efficiency.

efficiency is then given by the mean ordinate of the plot, *i.e.*, the ordinate for which the two shaded areas are equal.

In many cases a good approximation is obtained if the over-all collection efficiency is taken as equal to the cumulative percentage of material ϕ larger than the cut size D_{pc} in the dust fed to the cyclone. Equation (20-25) allows for operating temperature in the viscosity term, which means that, for a given inlet velocity, increased temperature results in a larger cut size, corresponding to a lower efficiency. As another good approximation, it should be noted that a given size of cyclone will have substantially the same collection efficiency at any temperature, provided that the pressure drop is the same, because of counterbalancing effects of gas density and viscosity.

Table 20-30 gives experimental collection-efficiency data reported by Anderson for geometrically similar cyclones of the type shown in Fig. 20-88*d*. These will serve to illustrate the order of magnitude of the collection efficiency to be expected for various particle sizes.

Cyclone Design Factors. Cyclones are generally designed to meet specified pressure-drop limitations. For ordinary installations, operating at approximately atmospheric pressure, fan limitations generally dictate a maximum allowable pressure drop corresponding to a cyclone inlet velocity in the range of 20 to 70 ft./sec. Consequently, cyclones are usually designed for an inlet

Table 20-30. Experimental Cyclone Collection Efficiencies*

Cyclone inlet velocity: 44 ft./sec.
Cyclone pressure drop: 4 in. water
Inlet dust concentration: 2–5 grain/cu. ft.
Specific gravity of dust: 3.0 g./cc.
Cyclone proportions: $B_c \cong D_c/6$
Gas: atmospheric air

Inlet Dust Particle-size Analysis

Particle Diam., μ	Cumulative % Larger Than Size
5	74
10	64
20	43

Cyclone diam., in.	Dust collected, %		
6	Total 90	− 5 μ 66	+ 5 μ 98
9	Total 83	−10 μ 60	+10 μ 99
24	Total 70	−20 μ 47	+20 μ 98

* Data reported by Anderson in Perry, "Chemical Engineers' Handbook," 2d ed., p. 1860, McGraw-Hill, New York, 1941.

velocity of 50 ft./sec., though this need not be strictly adhered to.

In the removal of dusts, the collection efficiency can be changed by only a relatively small amount by a variation in the operating conditions. The primary design factor that can be utilized to control collection efficiency is the cyclone diameter, a smaller-diameter unit operating at a fixed pressure drop having the higher efficiency [Anderson, *Chem. & Met.*, **40**, 525 (1933). Drijver, *Wärme*, **60**, 333 (1937). Whiton, *Power*, **75**, 344 (1932); *Chem. & Met.*, **39**, 150 (1932)]. Small-diameter cyclones, however, will require a multiple of units in parallel for a specified capacity. In such cases the individual cyclones can discharge the dust into a common receiving hopper [Whiton, *Trans. Am. Soc. Mech. Engrs.*, **63**, 213 (1941)]. The final design involves a compromise between collection efficiency and complexity of equipment. It is customary to design a single cyclone for a given capacity, resorting to multiple parallel units only if the predicted collection efficiency is inadequate for a single unit. Cyclones in series may be justified in cases where the dust has the following properties:

1. It has a broad size distribution including a sizable portion of particles finer than 15 microns, in which case a single large-diameter cyclone is used to collect the coarse fraction and reduce the loading to a small-diameter multiple-tube unit.

2. It has a high tendency to flocculate in the equipment preceding the cyclones as well as in the cyclones themselves.

In the latter case efficiencies predicted on the basis of ultimate particle-size distribution will be highly conservative. Also, although efficiency is normally increased by increasing the gas through-put (Drijver, *op. cit.*), in such cases the reverse may be true because of the deflocculating effect of higher velocities. Similarly, design proportion variations that result in increased collection efficiency with dispersed dusts may be detrimental in the case of flocculated dusts. Insufficient data are available to permit any generalization for this case, however. The flocculation factor is probably also the chief cause for inconsistency of data reported in the literature.

Reducing the gas-outlet duct diameter will increase both collection efficiency and pressure drop. Increasing the length of a cyclone is generally conceded to increase collection efficiency, though there are no reliable supporting data. There is also no reliable information on the effect of inlet proportions, although the Rosin, Rammler, and Intelmann relationship indicates that for a given cyclone inlet velocity the inlet width should be minimized. The cyclone developed by the Mill Mutual Fire Prevention Bureau has a relatively narrow rectangular inlet which is sized on the basis of the particle size of dust to be collected. The expense of fabricating the transition duct for a cyclone inlet having a high depth-to-width ratio must be weighed against the possible improvement in efficiency. It is essential that the inlet transition be relatively gradual in order to avoid excessive pressure drop due to gas jetting into the cyclone chamber. There is disagreement among cyclone designers regarding the optimum cone angle, but most "high-efficiency" cyclones have cone lengths in the range of 1.6 to 3.0 cyclone diameters.

A cyclone will operate equally well on the suction or pressure side of a fan if the dust receiver is airtight. Probably the greatest single cause for poor cyclone performance, however, is the leakage of air into the dust outlet of the cyclone. A slight air leak at this point can result in a tremendous drop in collection efficiency, particularly with fine dusts. For a cyclone under pressure, air leakage at this point is objectionable primarily from the local dust nuisance created. For batch operation, an airtight hopper or receiver may be used. For continuous withdrawal of collected dust, a rotary star valve, a double-lock valve, or a screw conveyor may be used, the latter only with fine dusts. A collapsible, open-ended rubber tube can be used for cyclones operating under slight negative pressure; mechanical flap-gate valves and fluidized seal legs can be used (see p. 20-48). Special pneumatic unloading devices can also be used with dusts. Figure 20-91 shows a cyclone in which the gas and solids

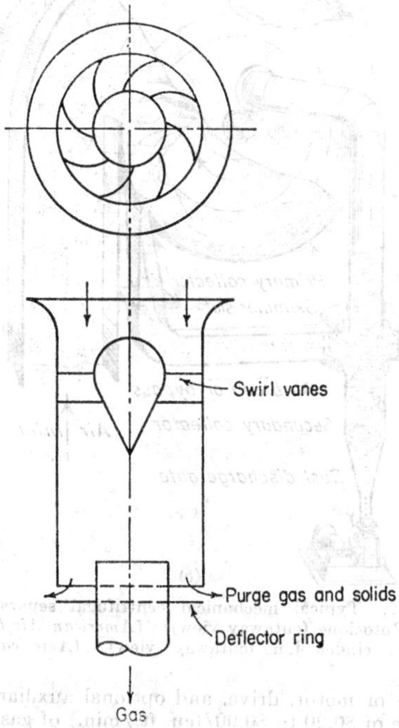

FIG. 20-91. Uniflow cyclone. [*Ter Linden, Inst. Mech. Engrs. J.*, **160**, 233 (1949).]

discharge at the same end. The solids are removed at the periphery together with a gas-purge rate of 5 to 20 per cent of the inlet-gas flow. In any case it is essential that sufficient unloading and receiving capacity be provided to prevent collected material from accumulating in the cyclone.

Generally cone-and-disk baffles, helical guide vanes, etc., placed inside a cyclone, will have a detrimental effect on performance. A few of these devices do have some merit, however, under special circumstances. Although an inlet vane will reduce pressure drop, it causes a correspondingly greater reduction in collection efficiency. Its use is recommended only where collection efficiency is normally so high as to be a secondary consideration and where it is desired to decrease the resistance of an existing cyclone system for purposes of increased air-handling capacity or where floor-space or headroom requirements are controlling factors. If an inlet vane is used, it is advantageous to increase the gas-exit-duct length inside the cyclone chamber. A disk or cone baffle located beneath the gas-outlet duct may be beneficial if air in-leakage at the dust outlet cannot be avoided. A heavy chain suspended from the gas-outlet duct has been found beneficial to minimize dust build-up on the cyclone walls. Such a chain should be suspended from a swivel so that it is free to rotate without twisting. At present there are no known devices that will recover the gas spiral-velocity energy in the gas-outlet duct. Substantially all devices that have been reported to reduce pressure drop do so by reducing spiral velocities in the cyclone chamber and consequently result in reduced collection efficiency.

At low dust loadings the pressure in the dust receiver of a single cyclone will generally be lower than in the gas-outlet duct. Increased dust loadings will increase the pressure in the dust receiver. Such devices as cones, disks, and inlet vanes will generally cause the pressure in the dust receiver to exceed that in the gas-outlet duct. A cyclone will operate as well in a horizontal position as in a vertical position. However, departure from the normal vertical position results in an increasing tendency to plug the dust outlet. If the dust outlet becomes plugged, collection efficiency will, of course, be low. If the cyclone exit duct must be reduced to tie in with proposed duct sizes, the transition should be made at least five diameters downstream from the cyclone and preferably after a bend. In the event that the transition must be made closer to the cyclone, a Greek cross should be installed in the transition piece in order to avoid excessive pressure drop.

Increased dust loadings will result in both decreased pressure drop and increased collection efficiency (Drijver, *op. cit.*; Shepherd and Lapple, *op. cit.*). At dust loadings of over 200 gr./cu. ft., the pressure drop may be as low as half that calculated in the absence of dust.

Commercial Equipment. Simple cyclones are available in a wide variety of shapes ranging from long slender units similar to that shown in Fig. 20-86 to short large-diameter units. The body may be conical or cylindrical, and entrances may be involute or tangential and round or rectangular.

In Fig. 20-88 are shown some of the special types of commercial cyclones. In the Multiclone a spiral motion is imparted to the gas by annular vanes, and it is furnished in multiple units of 6 and 9 in. diameter. Its largest field of application has been in the collection of fly ash from steam boilers. The tubes are commonly constructed of cast iron and other abrasion-resistant alloys. The Ducon cyclone utilizes a scroll inlet and a helical roof, both of which should reduce pressure drop. A major field of application has been in series and parallel installations in connection with fluidized-solids contactors in the petroleum and metallurgical industries. It is commonly fabricated of welded steel or stainless steel and may be lined with ceramic materials. The manufacturer claims an improvement in efficiency resulting from a conical baffle which is sometimes placed in the bottom of the cone. This device is used only on free-flowing dusts, since it has been found to cause plugging when handling sticky materials. The Van Tongeran cyclone claims to utilize the "double eddy" for increased collection efficiency by providing a by-pass from the top to the conical portion of the cyclone. It is made of welded steel and alloy plates and has had broad application. The Sirocco type D cyclone has an exit-duct collar that can be changed to increase or decrease collection efficiency with a corresponding increase or decrease in pressure drop. It is of welded steel or alloy construction and may be furnished with a cast-iron cone for abrasive applications. A wide range of sizes and types are offered for applications requiring various cut sizes. The Dustex unit employs multiple 5-in.-diameter cyclones in parallel for applications in which the dust loading does not exceed 10 gr./cu. ft. A cut size (50 per cent fractional efficiency point) of 1.3 microns is claimed for dust having a specific gravity of 2.4 suspended in air at ambient conditions. Efforts to avoid dust build-up, plugging, and subsequent maldistribution of gas flow in this collector include the use of vertical tube sheets, individual tangential inlets, and a design which permits circulation of the cleaned gases around the outside of the cyclones so as to minimize condensation from gases at temperatures close to the dew point. Standard construction materials are cast iron, cast aluminum, and welded stainless steels.

Cyclone Costs. The purchase cost, excluding design, of simple single-unit cyclones of 10- to 14-gage steel ranges from \$0.08 to \$0.20/(cu. ft./min.) of gas handled or \$0.30 to \$0.70/lb. steel. Special types of commercial cyclones generally involve a purchase cost in the range of \$0.12 to \$0.50/(cu. ft./min.) for steel cyclones made of 14-gage to $\frac{1}{4}$-in. plate. The larger commercial cyclones (above 3000 cu. ft./min.) fall into the lower end of the range, since the engineering charge is relatively independent of the size of the collector. Very small diameter multiple cyclone units in steel or cast-iron construction cost on the order of \$0.30 to \$1.00/(cu. ft./min.), depending on the size of the collector and the thickness of metal (prices of 1960).

Mechanical Centrifugal Separators. A number of collectors are commercially available in which the centrifugal field is supplied by a rotating member. Typical units are shown in Fig. 20-92. In the unit shown in Fig. 20-92*a*, the exhauster or fan and dust collector are combined as a single unit. The blades are especially shaped to direct the separated dust into an annular slot leading to the collection hopper while the cleaned gas continues to the scroll. The unit shown in Fig. 20-92*b* is usually used on the inlet side of a fan with the rotor connected to the fan shaft. The dust-laden gas enters on the periphery of the scroll, passing radially inward through the rotor and out the center, which point is normally coincident with the fan inlet port. Dust thrown to the scroll wall is concentrated in a small stream of gas which is by-passed through a cyclone collector, where the dust is finally collected.

Although no comparative data are available, the collection efficiency of units of this type is probably comparable with that of the single-unit high-pressure-drop cyclone installation. The clearances are smaller and the centrifugal fields higher than in a cyclone, but these are probably compensated for by the shorter gas path and greater degree of turbulence with its inherent reentrainment tendency. The chief advantage of these units lies in their compactness, which may be a prime consideration for large installations or plants requiring a large number of individual collectors. Caution should be exercised when attempting to apply this type of unit to a dust that shows a marked tendency to build up on solid surfaces, because of the high maintenance costs that may be encountered from plugging and rotor unbalancing. The purchase cost of steel units of this type,

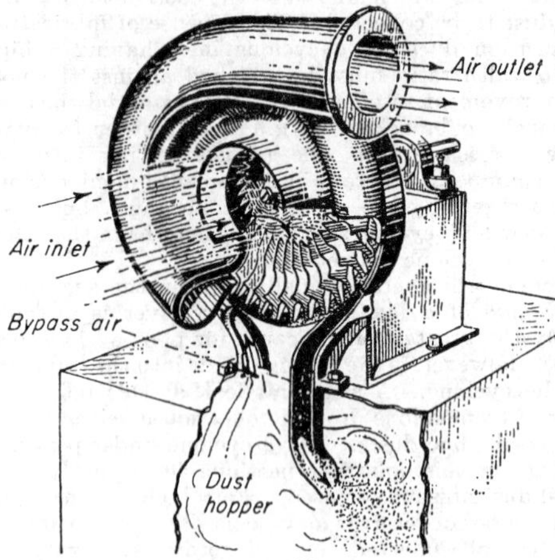

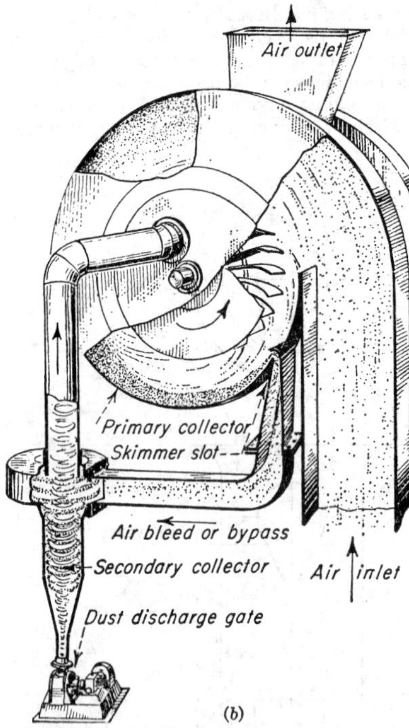

FIG. 20-92. Typical mechanical centrifugal separators. (*a*) Type D Rotoclone (cutaway view). (*American Air Filter Co.*) (*b*) Sirocco cinder fan (cutaway view). (*American Blower Corp.*)

exclusive of motor, drive, and optional auxiliaries, is in the range of \$0.20 to \$0.90/(cu. ft./min.) of gas handled depending on type and size (prices of 1960).

Granular-bed Separators. Although no dust collectors employing beds of granular solids are available as standard commercial units, such equipment has been designed for specific applications.

The Lynch granular filter [Anon. (Lynch), *Fuel Economist*, **12**, 47 (October, 1936)] utilizes a packed bed of gravel. The gravel is withdrawn from the bottom of the bed continuously and passed over a screen to remove collected dust before the gravel is returned to the top of the bed. Superficial gas velocities employed are on the order of 3 ft./sec. with bed depths of 1 to 4 ft. The gravel ranges from ½ to 1 in. diameter, and the pressure drop is on the order of 1 in. water. Steel units have been used up to 850°F. and temperatures up to 1500°F. can be handled with high-chrome steel, and up to 2000°F. with brick.

Granular packed-bed filters have been used in the removal of submicron radioactive particles from waste gases at the Hanford, Washington, plants operated by the General Electric Company for the U.S. Atomic Energy Commission. [Waste Disposal Symposium, *Nucleonics*, **4,** 11 (1949). Work, "Decontamination of Separation Plant Ventilation Air," General Electric Co., Hanford Atomic Products Operation, Document HW 11529, Nov. 10, 1948. Lapple, "Stack Contamination, Interim Report," General Electric Co., Hanford Atomic Products Operation, Document HDC-611 (Aug. 6, 1948). Blasewitz and Judson, *Chem. Eng. Progress*, **51,** 7-J (1955).] The filter consists of successively finer gradations of sand placed in a large underground container. A typical collection efficiency is 99.7 per cent when collecting particles having a geometric mean diameter in the range of 0.2 to 0.7 micron.

Electrostatically charged fluidized beds have been successfully used in aerosol filtration. Zenz and Othmer ("Fluidization and Fluid-particle Systems," Chap. 1, Reinhold, New York, 1960) describe several applications. One involved the use of polystyrene beads, on which surface-charge densities as high as 2.4 electrostatic units/sq. cm. were developed simply by shaking. Fluidization of 40- to 50-mesh beads resulted in charges up to 30 e.s.u./g. in a 12-g. bed. Efficiency of separation of atmospheric dust in a 1-in.-deep bed of 200-micron polystyrene beads bearing a surface charge of 0.086 e.s.u./sq. cm. was 97 to 98 per cent when fluidized at 0.5 ft./sec. A 0.5-micron gentian violet aerosol was collected at efficiencies of 95 to 99 per cent, using a 40- to 50-mesh bed fluidized at 0.83 ft./sec. and bearing a negative charge of 1.0 to 35.0 e.s.u./g. (Anderson and Silverman, paper presented at the Fifth Air Cleaning Seminar, Harvard School of Public Health, Boston, Mass., June 24–27, 1957.) Meissner and Mickley [*Ind. Eng. Chem.*, **41,** 1238 (1949)] reported similar results in removing 0.25 to 2.5 micron ammonium nitrate dusts in fluidized beds of alumina and silica gel.

The separation of dust in a bed of granular solids is due to (1) gravity settling, (2) diffusional deposition, (3) inertial deposition, (4) flow-line interception, and (5) electrostatic precipitation. This last factor is important when the bed, made up of particles with high electrical resistivity, is agitated, as in the above references, to develop a high surface charge. With fine packed beds operated at low gas velocities, gravity settling and diffusional deposition will predominate, and collection efficiency would be expected to decrease as the gas velocity increased. With coarse packed beds, operating at higher velocities, but still below fluidizing velocities, separation by inertial deposition and interception is controlling, and increased velocities would be expected to increase collection efficiency, provided that the gas velocity is not so high as to reentrain collected material. This is in accord with general observation, though data are scarce.

Bag Filters. There are two general types of bag filters, both capable of collection efficiencies upward of 99 per cent, and both suitable for fully automatic operation. The first, and older, type employs a relatively thin woven fabric as the filter medium, and the second uses felt.

Woven-fabric Filters. In operation, the dust-laden gases are passed through a woven fabric which "filters" out the dust, allowing the gases to pass on. Actually the separation is not a simple filtration, since the pores in the cloth are usually many times the size of the particles separated. When the dust-laden gases first pass through the cloth, the efficiency of separation will be low until enough particles have been removed to build up what corresponds to a "precoat" in the fabric pores. This initial deposition of dust takes place because of interception and impingement on the cloth fibers and by gravity settling and Brownian movement in the pores. With dusts normally encountered in industrial processes, this precoat layer will form in a few minutes, usually only a matter of seconds. Once this layer has formed, the efficiency of separation will usually be well over 99 per cent.

Although direct filtration plays a more important role at this stage, it is not the sole means of separation, since the pores in the collected dust may be considerably larger than some of the dust particles separated. In special cases, *e.g.*, fresh tobacco smoke in a room, the particle size and concentration are so small that an excessive time would be required to form a precoat layer. Normally, however, failure to achieve a very high collection efficiency is due entirely to improper equipment maintenance, from such sources as torn bags, poorly installed bags, or stretched bags.

For conditions encountered in practice, the flow through both the cloth and the collected dust will be streamline in character. The pressure drop through the cloth can be expressed by

$$\Delta p_i = K_c \mu_c V_f \qquad (20\text{-}26)$$

where K_c is a constant dependent on the nature of the cloth. Values of K_c for specific clean cloths are given in Table 20-31. When the pores of the cloth become filled with dust, the value of K_c may be over ten times that for the clean cloth. For dry dusts, however, if the dust layer on the cloth is deeper than about $\frac{1}{16}$ in. (on the order of 0.1 lb. dust/sq. ft. cloth), the over-all pressure drop across the dust-laden cloth will usually be that across the dust layer, the drop across the cloth itself, including the dust in the pores, being comparatively negligible.

The term "air permeability" is commonly used to characterize the porosity of a filter fabric. Air permeability is defined as the flow rate of air (at 70°F., 1 atm.) in cu. ft./min., which 1 sq. ft. of clean filter fabric will pass when the applied differential pressure is ½ in. water. The value of K_c may readily be calculated from the air permeability using Eq. (20-26) and substituting for V_f the air permeability, for Δp_i the value ½ in. H_2O, and for μ_c the viscosity of air at 70°F., 1 atm., which is 0.0181 centipoise. This leads to the relationship $K_c = 27.8/(\text{air permeability})$. Values of air permeability and K_c are given for a number of woven fabrics in Table 20-31.

The pressure drop through the separated dust layer may be expressed as

$$\Delta p_i = K_d \mu_c m_s V_f = K_d \mu_c c_d V_f^2 t_m \qquad (20\text{-}27)$$

The last equality gives the pressure-drop increase due to the accumulation of dust in time t_m. The resistance factor K_d can be calculated by means of Carman's [*Trans. Inst. Chem. Engrs.* (*London*), **15,** 150 (1937)] equation, which may be expressed in the form

$$K_d = \frac{160.0(1 - \epsilon_v)}{\phi_s^2 D_p \mu^2 \rho_s \epsilon_v^3} \qquad (20\text{-}28)$$

Unfortunately sufficient data are not normally available to permit utilization of Eq. (20-28), and an experimental determination of K_d is required. The range in the

Table 20-31. Resistance Factors and Air Permeabilities for Typical Woven Fabrics

Cloth	Pore size,† in.	Threads/in.	Weight, oz./sq. yd.	Thread† diam., in.	K_c§	Air permeability, (cu. ft./min.)/sq. ft. at $\Delta p_i = ½$ in. H_2O
Osnaburg cotton	0.01	32 × 28	.....	0.02	0.51	55
Osnaburg cotton (soiled)*	.....	32 × 28	.....	.....	4.80	5.8
Drill cotton	0.01	68 × 40	5.28	0.01	0.093	300
Cotton‡	.....	46 × 56	.....	.....	1.39	20
Cotton‡	.....	104 × 68	.....	.....	1.54	18
Cotton sateen (unnapped)	0.007	96 × 56	6.88	0.009	0.27	103
Cotton sateen (unnapped)	0.005	96 × 64	8.23	0.01	0.88	32
Cotton sateen (unnapped)	.....	96 × 60	.....	0.012	1.63	17
Cotton sateen (unnapped)	0.004	96 × 56	10.2	0.011	1.12	25
Wool	.....	....	.....	.....	0.25	111
Wool	.....	40 × 50	11.5	0.014	0.33	84
Wool, white‡	.....	36 × 32	.....	.....	0.15	185
Wool, black‡	.....	28 × 30	.....	.....	0.25	110
Wool‡	.....	30 × 26	.....	.....	0.51	55
Vinyon‡	.....	37 × 37	.....	.....	0.12	23
Nylon tackle twill	.....	72 × 196	.....	0.010	0.66	42
Nylon sailcloth	.....	130 × 130	.....	0.007	1.66	17
Nylon‡	.....	37 × 37	.....	.....	1.74	16
Nylon‡	.....	....	.....	.....	3.71	7.5
Asbestos‡	.....	....	.....	.....	0.56	50
Orlon‡	.....	72 × 72	.....	.....	0.66	42
Orlon‡	.....	74 × 38	.....	.....	0.75	37
Orlon‡	.....	....	.....	.....	1.16	24
Orlon‡	.....	....	.....	.....	1.98	14
Smoothtex nickel screen	.....	(300 mesh)	.....	.....	0.16	174
Glass	.....	32 × 28	.....	0.03	1.60	17
Dacron	.....	60 × 40	5.8	.....	0.84	33
Dacron	.....	76 × 48	13.4	.....	0.29	9.5
Teflon	.....	76 × 70	8.7	.....	1.39	20

* Cloth, similar to previous one, that had been in service and contained dust in pores although free of surface accumulation.
† Estimates based on microscopic examination.
‡ Data from R. T. Pring, "Air Pollution," p. 280, McGraw-Hill, New York, 1952.
§ Measured with atmospheric air. This value will be constant only for streamline flow, which is the case for values of $\rho V_f/\mu_c$ of less than approximately 100.

$$K_c = \frac{\Delta p_i}{\mu_c V_f}$$

where Δp_i = pressure drop, in. water; μ_c = gas viscosity, centipoise; V_f = superficial gas velocity through cloth, ft./min.; ρ = gas density, lb./cu. ft.

value K_d that may be encountered in practice is illustrated in Fig. 20-93, in which available experimental determinations of K_d reported in the literature for a variety of dusts are plotted against particle size. In most cases no accurate particle-size data were reported, and the curves represent the estimated range of particle size involved. The Williams, Hatch, and Greenburg data comprise a wide variety of dusts, and only the approximate limits enclosing these data are shown. Also included are curves predicted from Eq. (20-28) for specific values of ϕ, ρ_s, and ϵ_v. It is apparent from these curves that smaller particles tend toward higher values of ϵ_v, which is also borne out by the observation that fine dusts have a lower bulk density than coarser fractions of the same material, apparently because of the greater surface forces involved. For sizes under 10 μ, the value of K_d appears to become constant, increased voids compensating for the reduction in size. For coarse dusts, K_d varies approximately inversely as the square of the particle diameter, which implies that the voidage (or bulk density) does not change with particle size.

Equation (20-28) applies only where the mean free path of the gas molecules is small compared with the particle size of the dust particles. Where the particle size approaches the mean free path of the gas molecules, a correction factor must be applied to allow for the so-called "slip flow" and the resistance factor K_d will be less than given by Eq. (20-28). For atmospheric-pressure work, this correction factor becomes appreciable when the particle size of the collected dust is less than 5 μ diameter. To correct for "slip flow," the value K_d calculated from Eq. (20-28) must be divided by the factor

$$\left[1 + K_s\left(\frac{1-\epsilon_v}{\epsilon_v}\right)\left(\frac{\lambda_m}{\phi_s D_p}\right)\right]$$

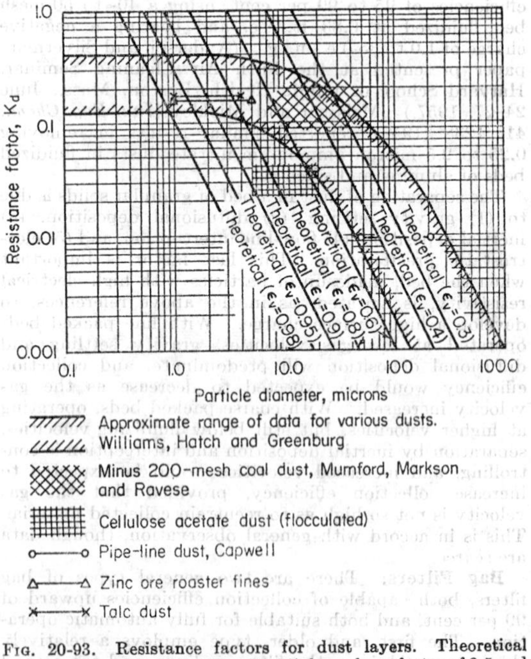

FIG. 20-93. Resistance factors for dust layers. Theoretical curves given are based on Eq. (20-28) for a shape factor of 0.5 and a true particle specific gravity of 2.0. [*Williams, Hatch, and Greenburg, Heating, Piping & Air Conditioning*, **12**, 259 (1940). *Mumford, Markson, and Ravese, Trans, Am. Soc. Mech. Engrs.*, **62**, 271 (1940). *Capwell, Gas*, **15**, 31 (*August*, 1939).]

The term K_s is essentially a constant having the approximate value 15 [Carman and Arnell, *Can. J. Research*, **26(A)**, 128 (1948)] when λ_m is calculated from kinetic theory. The relative constancy of experimental values of K_d at particle sizes under 5 μ (Fig. 20-93) is due to the "slip-flow" correction factor in addition to the increased voidages encountered with smaller particles.

Williams *et al.* [*Heating, Piping Air Conditioning*, **12**, 259–263 (1940)] define a cake resistance factor K_1 as follows:

$$K_1 = \frac{\Delta p_c}{V_f(w)} \tag{20-29}$$

Δp_c is the pressure drop in inches of water across the dust layer and does not include the drop across the cloth. w is the mass velocity of the dust approaching the filter cloth, in lb. mass/(min.)(sq. ft.) of filter area. These authors were concerned with filtering air at ambient conditions; so gas viscosity was omitted from the correlation. Since pressure drop is directly proportional to gas viscosity [see Eq. (20-26)], corrections for viscosities other than that of ambient air can readily be made. Values for K_1 are given in Table 20-32.

Table 20-32. Cake-resistance Factors for Certain Dusts*

Dust	K_1‡ for particle size less than						
	20 mesh	140 mesh	375 mesh	90 μ	45 μ	20 μ	2 μ
Granite	1.58	2.20	....	....	.....	19.8	
Foundry	0.62	1.58	3.78				
Gypsum	....	....	6.30	....	.....	18.9	
Feldspar	....	....	6.30	....	.....	27.3	
Stone	0.96	....	....	6.30			
Lampblack	....	....	....	....	.....	....	47.2
Zinc oxide	....	....	....	....	.....	....	15.7†
Wood	....	....	....	6.30			
Resin (cold)	....	0.62	....	....	.....	25.2	
Oats	1.58	....	....	9.60	11.0		
Corn	0.62	....	1.58	3.78	8.80		

* Data from Williams *et al.*, *Heating, Piping, Air Conditioning*, **12**, 259–263 (1940).

† Flocculated material, not dispersed; size actually larger.

‡ K_1 is a cake resistance factor.

$$K_1 = \frac{\Delta p_c}{V_f(w)}$$

where K_1 = cake resistance factor, in. water/(ft./min.)(lb. mass/sq. ft.), Δp_c = pressure drop, in. water; V_f = superficial air velocity, ft./min., w = mass velocity of dust approaching filter cloth, lb. mass/(min.)(sq. ft.). The above data were obtained when filtering air at ambient conditions. For gases other than atmospheric air, the Δp_c values predicted from Table 20-32 should be multiplied by the actual gas viscosity divided by the viscosity of atmospheric air.

Mechanical filters are available as standard commercial units. These comprise two general types. One utilizes cloth envelopes supported by screens (see Fig. 20-94*a* and *b*); the other uses either oval or round vertically mounted bags (see Fig. 20-94*c* and *d*), usually 5 to 8 in. in diameter and 8 to 17 ft. long. Access platforms for bag maintenance are usually provided on the clean-air side. These units may be shaken manually, although, except for the smaller sizes, motor shaking is generally provided. Complete automatic operation is also possible by providing a timer, shaker motor, and air- or motor-operated gas-discharge valves. The small sizes (under 1000 sq. ft. of cloth area) are available as "unit" filters and are shipped completely assembled. Portable unit filters are also available. Large units are built up of standardized rectangular sections in parallel. Each section contains on the order of 1000 to 2000 sq. ft. of cloth, and the sections are assembled in the field to form a single filter housing. In this manner, the filter can be partitioned so that one or more sections at a time can be cut out of service for shaking or general maintenance. Additional capacity can be provided at a later date by adding more sections. The purchase cost of fully automatic filters, complete with shakers, air-reversing valves, timer, manifolds, and supports, but without main fan and motor, is in the range of \$1.30 to \$3.00/sq. ft. of cloth area, depending on type and size. Normally these filters are furnished with rectangular housings, since these are more economical. However, circular units are available where greater strength is required as in pressure or vacuum service (prices of 1960).

Mechanical filters generally have a pressure drop of 2 to 6 in. water and are rated at 1 to 8 cu. ft./(min.)(sq. ft.) cloth area. For very fine dusts or high dust loadings the rating should not exceed 3 cu. ft./(min.)(sq. ft. cloth), and it may be desirable to reduce the rating to one-half. For very fine tacky dusts, bag-type filters are better than screen or envelope types, because of more effective shaking provisions. When dust loadings are high, cyclone precleaners may be employed to reduce the load on the filter.

Ordinary mechanical filters may be shaken every ¼ to 8 hr., depending on the service. A manometer connected across the filter is useful in determining when the filter should be shaken. Fully automatic filters may be shaken every 2 min., but bag maintenance will be greatly reduced if the time between shakings can be increased to 15 or 20 min. without developing excessive pressure drop. It is essential that the gas flow through the filter be stopped when shaking in order to permit the dust to fall off. With very fine dust, it may even be necessary to equalize the pressure across the cloth [Mumford, Markson, and Ravese, *Trans. Am. Soc. Mech. Engrs.*, **62**, 271 (1940)]. In practice this can be accomplished without interrupting the operation by cutting one section out of service at a time, as shown in Fig. 20-94*e*. In automatic filters this operation involves closing the dampers, shaking the filter units, either pneumatically or mechanically, sometimes accompanied by a reverse flow of cleaned gas through the filter, and lastly reopening the dampers. For compressed-air-operated automatic filters, this entire operation may take only 2 to 10 sec. For the ordinary mechanical filters equipped for automatic control, the operation may take as long as 3 min.

Filter fabrics in the earlier cloth-bag filters were generally cotton sateens. Cotton is still used to a major extent because of its low cost, but its use is limited to low-temperature applications. Many fabrics are now available. Table 20-33 lists some of the more common ones together with their properties. Early applications of glass and asbestos resulted in excessive bag failures, but these fibers are now successfully employed. Kling [*Blast Furnace Steel Plant*, **34**, 1257 (1946)] reports application of a combination glass-asbestos fabric in blast-furnace gas cleaning. The Dracco Division of Fuller Co. reports (trade literature) successful applications of glass cloth for metal oxides and cement dust. The latter application employed bag cleaning by combination of reverse gas flow and sonic vibration as shown in Fig. 20-94*f*. It is necessary to use relatively gentle bag-cleaning methods to avoid flexural failure of glass fibers.

It is generally economical to be conservative in specifying cloth area. Since pressure drop for a given service varies as the square of the velocity through the cloth, greater cloth area results in considerable reduction in shaking frequency and in increased bag life; incremental cloth costs are also relatively small, particularly in small installations. In operation, it is essential that the gas be kept above its dew point to avoid plugging of the bag pores. Cloth filters, however, have been successfully used in steam atmospheres, such as those encountered in vacuum dryers. In such cases the housing is generally steam-chased.

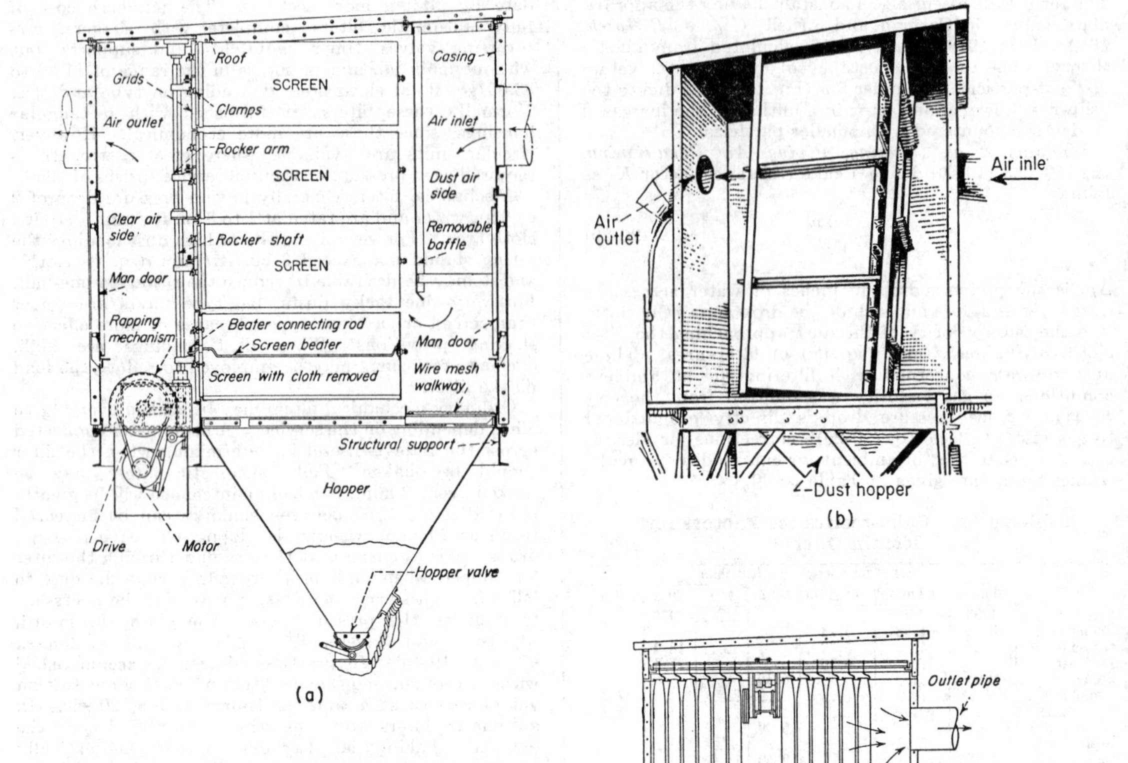

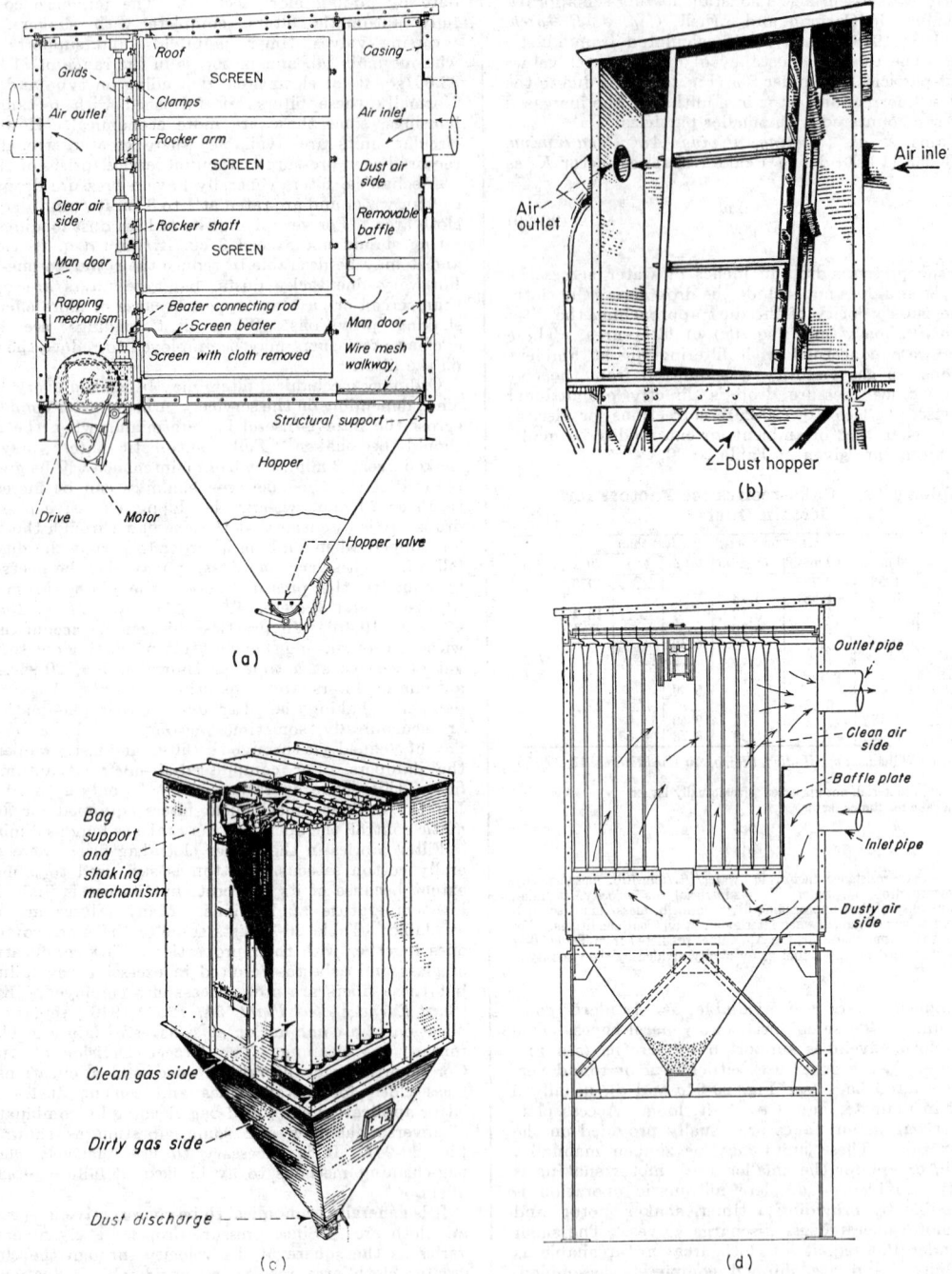

FIG. 20-94. Typical cloth filters. (*a*) Screen or envelope type (sectional view). (*Pangborn Corp.*) (*b*) Screen or envelope type (cutaway view). (*W. W. Sly Mfg. Co.*) (*c*) Bag type (cutaway view). (*Northern Blower Co.*) (*d*) Bag type (sectional view). (*Wheelabrator Corp.*) (*e*) Three-compartment bag collector at various stages in the cleaning cycle. (*Wheelabrator Corp.*) (*f*) Glass-fabric bag cleaning with reverse gas flow and sonic vibration. (*Dracco Div., Fuller Company.*)

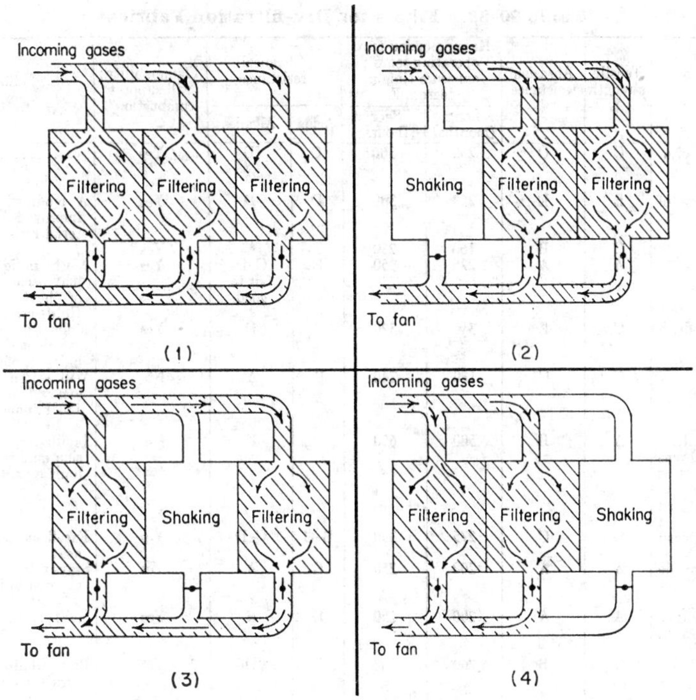

(e)

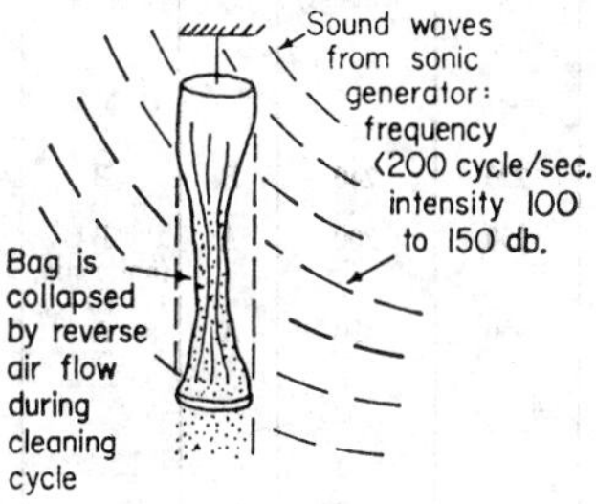

(f)

FIG. 20-94. (*Continued*).

Felt-fabric Filters. The ratings of woven-fabric filters are limited to the previously mentioned 1 to 8 cu. ft./(min.)(sq. ft. of cloth) by the compacting action of the higher velocities. This leads to high pressure drop and, finally, local breakdown of the filter cake, thereby permitting excessive penetration. The use of felt as the filter medium permits somewhat higher velocities, on some dusts, without excessive penetration, since the filter cake plays less of a role in filtration with this type of collector than it does with the woven-fabric filters.

The Hersey filter [Hersey, *Ind. Chemist*, **31**, 138 (1955)] was the first felt fabric filter to be developed commercially. It is shown in Fig. 20-95*a*. Figure 20-95*b* and *c* shows two commercial reverse-jet filters which were developed under Hersey patent rights. Cleaning is accomplished continuously or periodically, in response to pressure drop or a timer, without shutting off the gas flow, by a ring that travels up and down the outer surface of the bag. Compressed air is blown from a 1/32-in. slot on the inner edge of the ring through the filter fabric in a direction opposite to the flow of the dust-laden gas. The blow ring contacts and indents the felt, thereby helping to "seal" the blow ring so that the jet passes directly through the felt. The indenting action also serves to dislodge the dust layer. The filter bag is made of 1/16- to 1/8-in. felt in diameters of 8 to 18 in. and lengths up to 19 ft. Gas-handling capacities are high, in the range of 5 to 30 cu. ft./(min.)(sq. ft. of cloth area), but the trend in recent applications has been to avoid filter ratios higher than 15. More and more collectors are now being sized in the range of 5 to 10 cu. ft./(min.)/(sq. ft. of cloth area). The reason for this is again pressure drop. High pressure drop calls for more frequent cleaning, which results in more bag maintenance. Pressure drop should not exceed 6 in. water. Dust loadings as high as 2 lb. dust/lb. gas have been reported, but most applications involve inlet dust loadings of less than 40 gr. dust/cu. ft. gas.

A compilation (Hersey, *op. cit.*) of data on units in operation shows that of 88 units the pressure drop of 90 per cent of the units was between 1.1 and 6.3 in. water, with a median of 2.6 in water; of 95 units the

Table 20-33. Fibers for Dry-filtration Fabrics*

Fiber	Manufacturer	Tensile strength ‡	Abrasion resistance ‡	Recommended max. operating temp.; exposure time in degrees F. Long (months)	Short (hours)	Chemical resistance Acids	Alkalies	Flammability; will support combustion?	Special properties	General chemical classification
Acrilan	Chemstrand Corp.	C	C	250	300	D	D	Yes	....	Polyacrylonitrile (acrylic)
Arnel	Celanese Corp. of America	E	E	250	300	D	D	Yes	A modified cellulose, has improved heat and bacterial resistance	Triacetate
Cotton	Natural fiber	C	B	160	250	E	A	Yes	....	Cellulose
Dacron	E. I. du Pont de Nemours	A	A	275	350	B	C–D fair to good	Yes	More rapid de-gradation may occur in the presence of heat and moisture. Holds crease	Polyester
Darvan	B. F. Goodrich Chemical	C	E	310	320	B	D	Yes	Melts above 330°F. Has excellent dimensional stability at 300°F.	Nytril
Dynel	Union Carbide Chemical Co.	C	C	180	240	B	A	No	Will soften and distort if exposed to temp. above 180°F. unless heat-set	Copolymer of acrylonitrile and vinyl chloride
Glass	Pittsburgh Plate Glass Co.; Owens Corning Fiberglas Corp.; Libby Owens; Ford Glass Fiber Co.	A	E	500	650	C	E	No	Limited by poor flex-abrasion qualities. Finishes limit max. temp. range	Glass
Kodel	Eastman Chemical Products, Inc.	C	C	275	350	B–C	C–D	Yes	Excellent stability under heat	Polyester
Nylon 66	E. I. du Pont de Nemours; Chemstrand	A	A	200	250	E	A	Yes	Stays soft and pliable when exposed to heat	Polyamide
Nylon 6	American Enka; Industrial Rayon; National Aniline	A	A	200	250	E	B	Yes	....	Polyamide
Orlon 42	E. I. du Pont de Nemours	C	B	260	300	C	D	Yes	Best all-around high-temperature fiber	Polyacrylonitrile (acrylic)
Polyethylene	Union Carbide Chemical Co.	A	A	150	212 (heat-set)	A	A	Yes	Affected by some organic solvents. Can be heat-set to operate at about 212°F. If subjected to load for a long time, it will continue to stretch. Lighter than water	Polyethylene
Q957	Dow Chemical	C	X	220	240	B	B	No	Fibers made from film. They are flat ribbons	Vinylidene chloride
Saran	Saran Yarn Co. and others	D	C	150	200	A	B (ammonia, E)	No	Outstanding chemical resistance, but severe temp. limitation	Vinylidene chloride
Teflon (multifilament)	E. I. du Pont de Nemours	C	D	450	550	A	A	No	Very expensive. Best chemical resistance, good heat resistance. When exposed to temp. in excess of 400°F. toxic fumes are given off. Strength decreases rapidly at high temp.	Polyfluoroethylene
Verel	Eastman Chemical Products, Inc.	C	E	200	250	C	D	No	Verel FR has better flame resistance than wool	Modified acrylic
Wool	Natural fiber	Wet, E Dry, D	Wet, C Dry, C	200	250	E	E	No	When wet has excellent elastic recovery. Can be felted	Protein
Zefran	Dow Chemical	C	C	220	270	C	D	Yes	....	Acrylic alloy

* Courtesy of the Albany Felt Company; This company offers information as best currently available; no obligation or liability whatsoever is assumed in connection with its use. Data apply only to staple fibers, although continuous-filament yarns are also made; Teflon is excepted as test fabric was made from filament yarn.

‡ A = excellent; B = above average; C = good, average; D = fair; E = poor; X = unknown.

filter rates of 90 per cent of the units were between 5.3 and 32.5 cu. ft./(min.)(sq. ft. of filter area), with a median of 13.5; and of 68 units the dust load of 90 per cent of the units was between 0.05 and 8.0 gr./cu. ft. with a median of 0.6 gr./cu. ft. Of 32 units, the collection efficiency of 13 was above 99.99 per cent, 24 above 99.90 per cent, and of the remaining 8, between 97.2 and 99.9 per cent. Figure 20-96 shows some typical performance data.

Disturbance of the dust deposit causes some particles to sift through dense felt. Therefore, the less reverse-jet activity there is, the higher will be the average collection efficiency.

Tests at the Harvard air-cleaning laboratory showed approximately four times the penetration of talc through felt with reverse-jet cleaning on 100 per cent of the time as compared with 45 per cent jet operation; 1.5 times as much vaporized silica penetrated the felt with 100 per cent as compared with 10 per cent jet operation time; and 3.5 times as much electrically precipitated fly ash penetrated with 100 per cent operation as compared with 7 per cent operation of the reverse jet. Particle size was not the determining factor in penetration. The talc was 2.5 micron mass-median diameter, the vaporized silica 0.6 micron, and the fly ash 16.0 micron. The lowest efficiency was with the fly ash, but all three were above 99.9 per cent.

Figure 20-95*d* shows a reverse-jet filter employing no moving mechanical parts. The dust is deposited on the outside of the felt tubes, which are 4½ in. diameter

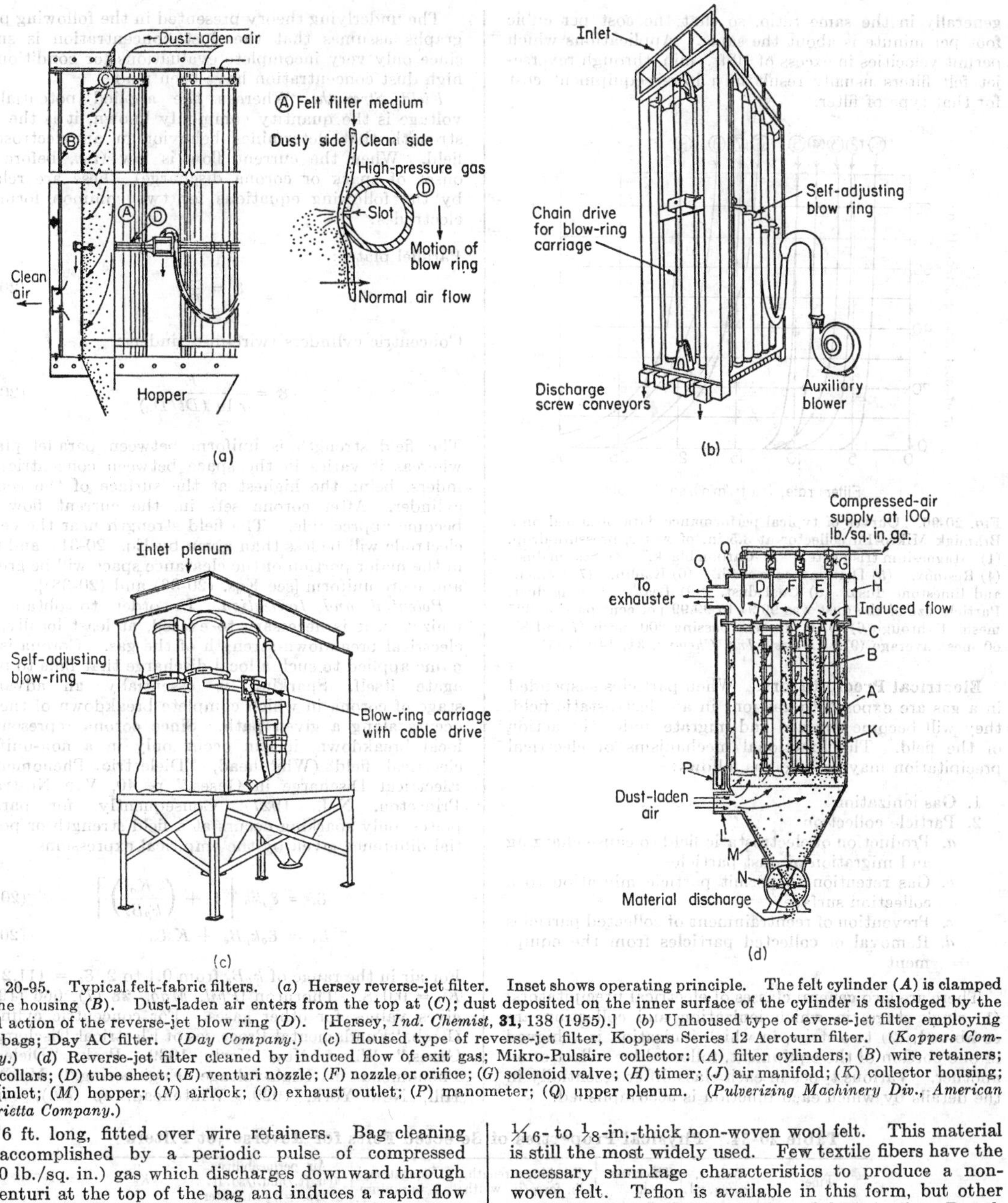

FIG. 20-95. Typical felt-fabric filters. (*a*) Hersey reverse-jet filter. Inset shows operating principle. The felt cylinder (*A*) is clamped in the housing (*B*). Dust-laden air enters from the top at (*C*); dust deposited on the inner surface of the cylinder is dislodged by the dual action of the reverse-jet blow ring (*D*). [Hersey, *Ind. Chemist*, **31**, 138 (1955).] (*b*) Unhoused type of everse-jet filter employing felt bags; Day AC filter. (*Day Company.*) (*c*) Housed type of reverse-jet filter, Koppers Series 12 Aeroturn filter. (*Koppers Company.*) (*d*) Reverse-jet filter cleaned by induced flow of exit gas; Mikro-Pulsaire collector: (*A*) filter cylinders; (*B*) wire retainers; (*C*) collars; (*D*) tube sheet; (*E*) venturi nozzle; (*F*) nozzle or orifice; (*G*) solenoid valve; (*H*) timer; (*J*) air manifold; (*K*) collector housing; (*L*) inlet; (*M*) hopper; (*N*) airlock; (*O*) exhaust outlet; (*P*) manometer; (*Q*) upper plenum. (*Pulverizing Machinery Div., American Marietta Company.*)

by 6 ft. long, fitted over wire retainers. Bag cleaning is accomplished by a periodic pulse of compressed (100 lb./sq. in.) gas which discharges downward through a venturi at the top of the bag and induces a rapid flow of the clean process gas back through the filter tube. This snaps the bag outward and discharges the dust, which then falls to the hopper. The bags are cleaned in sequence regulated by a timer which operates the solenoid valve above each filter tube at a specified time in the cycle. The cycle time can be adjusted to give some control over pressure drop. The duration of the cleaning pulse is $1/10$ sec., and the compressed-gas requirement is 9 to 14 cu. ft./min. (measured at atmospheric conditions) for a collector having 510 sq. ft. of filter area.

The original filter medium for reverse-jet filters was $1/16$- to $1/8$-in.-thick non-woven wool felt. This material is still the most widely used. Few textile fibers have the necessary shrinkage characteristics to produce a non-woven felt. Teflon is available in this form, but other synthetic fibers, including nylon, Orlon, Acrilan, Dynel, Dacron, and Arnel, are available in the form of grid felts, made by mechanically interlocking fibers through and around a woven grid of the same material. Physical properties of some felts are listed in Table 20-34.

The installed cost of felt-fabric filters equipped for automatic reverse-jet cleaning is usually lower than that of fully automatic woven-bag filter installations because of the lower space requirements of the former. Bare equipment costs are comparable. The cost per square foot of filter area is two- to fourfold higher for the felt filter, but the allowable filter velocities are generally in the same ratio, so that the cost per cubic foot per minute is about the same. Applications which permit velocities in excess of 10 ft./min. through reverse-jet felt filters usually result in a lower equipment cost for that type of filter.

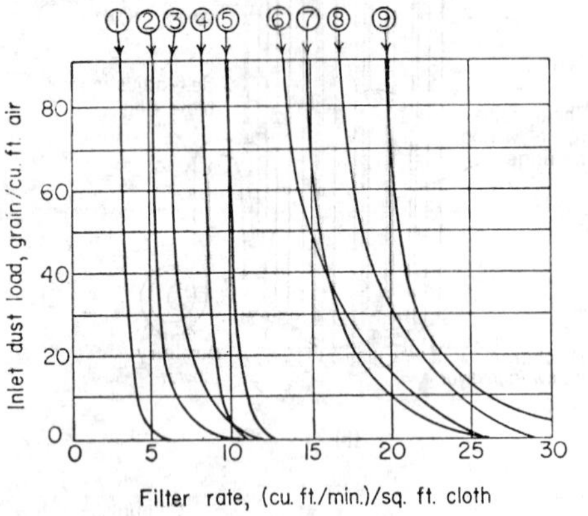

FIG. 20-96. Curves of typical performance data obtained on a Bramigk Mikro-Fil collector at 3.5 in. of water, pressure-drop. (1) Magnesium trisilicate. (2) Carbon black. (3) Starch dust. (4) Resinox. (5) Diatomaceous earth. (6) Kaolin. (7) Cement and limestone dust. (8) Coal dust. (9) Leather-buffing dust. Particle size of the dust was 99.94 to 99.99 per cent passing 325 mesh (1 through 6); 95.0 per cent passing 200 mesh (7 and 8); 60 mesh average (9). [*Hersey, Ind. Chemist*, **31**, 140 (1955).]

Electrical Precipitators. When particles suspended in a gas are exposed to gas ions in an electrostatic field, they will become charged and migrate under the action of the field. The functional mechanisms of electrical precipitation may be listed as follows:

1. Gas ionization
2. Particle collection
   a. Production of electrostatic field to cause charging and migration of dust particles
   b. Gas retention to permit particle migration to a collection surface
   c. Prevention of reentrainment of collected particles
   d. Removal of collected particles from the equipment

There are two general classes of electrical precipitators: (1) single-stage, in which ionization and collection are combined; (2) two-stage, in which ionization is achieved in one portion of the equipment, followed by collection in another. Various types in each class differ essentially in the details by which each function is accomplished.

The underlying theory presented in the following paragraphs assumes that the dust concentration is small, since only very incomplete evaluations for conditions of high dust concentration have been made.

Field Strength. Whereas the applied potential or voltage is the quantity commonly known, it is the field strength that determines behavior in an electrostatic field. When the current flow is low (*i.e.*, before the onset of spark or corona discharge), these are related by the following equations for two common forms of electrodes:

Parallel plates:

$$\mathcal{E} = \frac{E}{B_e} \tag{20-30}$$

Concentric cylinders (wire-in-cylinder):

$$\mathcal{E} = \frac{E}{r \ln (D_t/D_d)} \tag{20-31}$$

The field strength is uniform between parallel plates, whereas it varies in the space between concentric cylinders, being the highest at the surface of the central cylinder. After corona sets in, the current flow will become appreciable. The field strength near the center electrode will be less than given by Eq. (20-31), and that in the major portion of the clearance space will be greater and more uniform [see Eqs. (20-36) and (20-38)].

Potential and Ionization. In order to obtain gas ionization it is necessary to exceed, at least locally, the electrical breakdown strength of the gas. Corona is the name applied to such a local discharge that fails to propagate itself. Sparking is essentially an advanced stage of corona in which complete breakdown of the gas occurs along a given path. Since corona represents a local breakdown, it can occur only in a non-uniform electrical field (Whitehead, "Dielectric Phenomena—Electrical Discharge in Gases," p. 40, Van Nostrand, Princeton, N.J., 1927). Consequently, for parallel plates, only sparking occurs at a field strength or potential difference given by the empirical expressions

$$\mathcal{E}_s = \mathcal{E}_o k_\rho \left[1 + \left(\frac{K_o}{k_\rho B_e}\right)\right] \tag{20-32}$$

$$E_s = \mathcal{E}_o k_\rho B_e + K_o \mathcal{E}_o \tag{20-33}$$

For air in the range of $k_\rho B_e$ from 0.1 to 2, $\mathcal{E}_o = 111.2$ and $K_o = 0.048$. Thornton [*Phil. Mag.*, **28** (7), 666 (1939)] gives values for other gases. For concentric cylinders (Loeb, "Fundamental Processes of Electrical Discharge in Gases," Wiley, New York, 1939. Peek, "Dielectric Phenomena in High-voltage Engineering," McGraw-Hill, New York, 1929. Whitehead, *op. cit.*), corona

Table 20-34. Physical Properties of Selected Felts for Reverse-jet Filters

Fiber	Weight, oz./sq. yd.	Thickness, in.	Breaking strength, lb. force/in. width	Elongation, % to rupture	Air permeability (cu. ft./min.)/sq. ft. at $\Delta p_i = \frac{1}{2}$ in. water	K_c
Wool	23.1	0.135	...	...	27.1	1.03
Wool	21.2	0.129	...	...	29.8	0.93
Orlon*	10.9	0.045	65	18	20–25	1.11–1.39
Orlon*	17.9	0.088	85	18	15–20	1.39–1.85
Orlon*	24	0.125	110	60	10–20	1.39–2.78
Acrilan*	17.9	0.075	100	22	15–20	1.39–1.85
Dynel*	24	0.125	60	80	30–40	0.70–0.93
Dacron*	17.9	0.080	125	22	15–20	1.39–1.85
Dacron*	9.9	0.250	20	150	200–225	0.11–0.14
Dacron*	24	0.125	175	80	20–30	0.93–1.39
Nylon*	24	0.125	100	100	30–40	0.70–0.93
Arnel*	24	0.125	60	80	30–40	0.70–0.93
Teflon	15.6	0.053	...	...	82.5	0.34
Teflon	43.5	0.119	...	...	21.6	1.29

* These data courtesy of American Felt Co.

sets in at the central wire when

$$\mathcal{E}_c = \mathcal{E}_o k_\rho \left(1 + \sqrt{\frac{K_o}{k_\rho D_d}}\right) \qquad (20\text{-}34)$$

$$E_c = \left(\frac{\mathcal{E}_o k_\rho D_d}{2}\right)\left(1 + \sqrt{\frac{K_o}{k_\rho D_d}}\right) \ln\left(\frac{D_t}{D_d}\right) \qquad (20\text{-}35)$$

For air approximate values are $\mathcal{E}_o = 110$, $K_o = 0.18$. Corona, however, will set in only if $(D_t/D_d) > 2.718$. If this ratio is less than 2.718, no corona occurs, and only sparking will result, following the laws given by Eqs. (20-34) and (20-35) (Peek, *op. cit.*).

In practice, precipitators are usually operated at the highest voltage practicable without sparking, since this increases both the particle charge and the electrical precipitating field. The sparking potential is generally higher with a negative charge on the discharge electrode and is less erratic in behavior than a positive corona discharge. It is the consensus, however, that ozone formation with a positive discharge is considerably less than with a negative discharge. For these reasons negative discharge is generally used in industrial precipitators, and a positive discharge is utilized in air-conditioning applications. In Table 20-35 are given some typical values for the sparking potential for the case of small wires in pipes of various sizes. The sparking potential varies approximately directly as the density of the gas but is very sensitive to the character of any material collected on the electrodes. Even small amounts of poorly conducting material on the electrodes may markedly lower the sparking voltage. For positive polarity of the discharge electrode, the sparking voltage will be very much lower. The sparking voltage is greatly affected by the temperature and humidity of the gas, as shown in Fig. 20-97.

Table 20-35. Sparking Potentials* (Small Wire Concentric in Pipe)

Pipe diameter, in.	Sparking potential,† volts	
	Peak	Root mean square
4	59,000	45,000
6	76,000	58,000
9	90,000	69,000
12	100,000	77,000

* Data reported by Anderson in Perry, "Chemical Engineers' Handbook," 2d ed., p. 1873, McGraw-Hill, New York, 1941.

† For gases at atmospheric pressure, 100°F., containing water vapor, air, CO_2, and mist, and negative-discharge–electrode polarity.

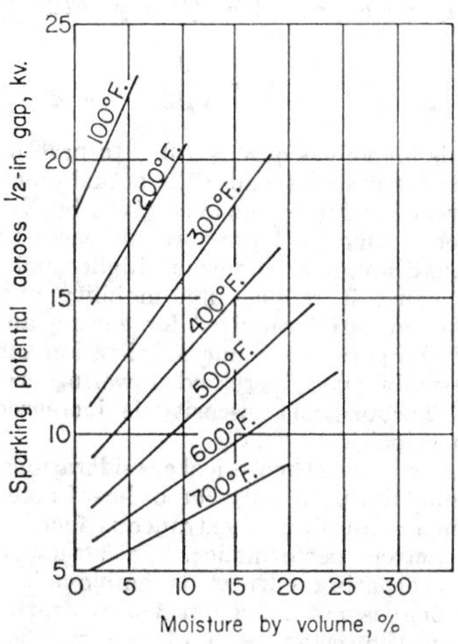

FIG. 20-97. Sparking potential for negative point-to-plane, ½-in. gap, as function of moisture content and temperature of air at 1.0 atm. pressure. [*Sproull and Nakada, Ind. Eng. Chem.*, **43**, 1356 (1951).]

Current Flow. Corona discharge is accompanied by a relatively small flow of electric current, typically 0.1 to 0.5 milliamp./sq. m. of collecting electrode area (projected, rather than actual area). Sparking usually involves a considerably larger flow of current which cannot be tolerated except for occasional periods of a fraction of a second duration, and then only when suitable electrical controls are provided to limit the current. However, when suitable controls are provided, precipitators have been operated continuously with a small amount of sparking to ensure that the voltage is in the correct range to ensure corona. Besides disruptive effects on the electrical equipment and electrodes, sparking will result in low collection efficiency because of reduction in applied voltage, redispersion of collected dust, and current channeling. Although an exact calculation can be made for the current flow for a d.c. potential applied between concentric cylinders, the following simpler expression, based on the assumption of a constant space charge or ion density, gives a good approximation of corona current [Ladenburg, *Ann. Physik*, **4** (5), 863 (1930)]:

$$I = \frac{8\lambda_i E(E - E_c)}{D_t^2 \ln (D_t/D_d)} \qquad (20\text{-}36)$$

and the average space charge is given by (Whitehead, *op. cit.*)

$$\sigma_{avg} = \frac{4(E - E_c)}{\pi D_t^2 \epsilon} \qquad (20\text{-}37)$$

In the space outside the immediate vicinity of corona discharge, the field strength is sensibly constant, and an average value is given by

$$\mathcal{E} = \sqrt{\frac{2I}{\lambda_i}} \qquad (20\text{-}38)$$

which applies if the potential difference is above the critical potential required for corona discharge so that an appreciable current flows.

Ionic mobilities are given by Loeb ("International Critical Tables," vol. 6, p. 107, McGraw-Hill, New York, 1929). For air at 0°C., 760 mm. Hg, $\lambda_i = 624$ (cm./sec.)/(statvolt/cm.) for negative ions. Positive ions usually have a slightly lower mobility. Loeb ("Basic Processes of Gaseous Electronics," p. 53, Univ. of California Press, Berkeley and Los Angeles, 1955) gives a theoretical expression for ionic mobility of gases which is probably good to within ±50 per cent.

$$\lambda_i = \frac{100.0}{k_\rho \sqrt{(\delta_g - 1)M}} \qquad (20\text{-}39)$$

In general ionic mobilities are inversely proportional to gas density. Ionic velocities in the usual electrostatic precipitator are on the order of 100 ft./sec.

Electric Wind. By virtue of the momentum transfer from gas ions moving in the electrical field to the surrounding gas molecules, a gas circulation is set up between the electrodes, known as the "electric" or "ionic" wind. For conditions encountered in electrical precipitators, the velocity of this circulation is on the order of 2 ft./sec. Also, as a result of this momentum transfer, the pressure at the collecting electrode is slightly higher than at the discharge electrode (Whitehead, *op. cit.*, p. 167).

Charging of Particles. [Deutsch, *Ann. Physik*, **68** (4), 335 (1922); **9** (5), 249 (1931); **10** (5), 847 (1931). Ladenburg, *op. cit.* Mierdel, *Z. tech. Physik.*, **13**, 564 (1932).] Three forces act on a gas ion in the vicinity of a particle: attractive forces due to the field strength and the ionic image; and repulsive forces due to the Coulomb effect. For spherical particles larger than 1 μ diameter, the ionic image effect is negligible, and charging will continue until the other two forces balance according to the equation

$$N_o = \left(\frac{\zeta \mathcal{E} D_p^2}{4e}\right)\left(\frac{\pi\sigma e t\lambda_i}{1 + \pi\sigma e\lambda_i t}\right) \tag{20-40}$$

The ultimate charge acquired by the particle is given by

$$N_o = \frac{\zeta \mathcal{E} D_p^2}{4e} \tag{20-41}$$

and is very nearly attained in a fraction of a second. For particles smaller than 1 μ diameter, the initial charging will occur according to Eq. (20-40). However, owing to the ionic-image effect, the ultimate charge will be considerably greater because of penetration resulting from the kinetic energy of the gas ions. For charging times of the order encountered in electrical precipitation, the ultimate charge acquired by spherical particles smaller than about 1 μ diameter may be approximated ($\pm$30 per cent) by the empirical expression

$$N_o = 3.4 \times 10^3 D_p T \tag{20-42}$$

Values of N_o for various sized particles are listed in Table 20-36 for 70°F., $\zeta = 2$, and $\mathcal{E} = 10$ statvolts/cm.

Particle Mobility. By equating the electrical force acting on a particle to the resistance due to air friction, as expressed by Stokes's law, the particle velocity or mobility may be expressed by

(*a*) For particles larger than 1 μ diameter:

$$\lambda_p = \left(\frac{u_e}{\mathcal{E}_p}\right) = \frac{\zeta D_p \mathcal{E}_i K_m}{12\pi\mu} \tag{20-43}$$

(*b*) For particles smaller than 1 μ diameter:

$$\lambda_p = \left(\frac{u_e}{\mathcal{E}_p}\right) = \frac{360 K_m e T}{\mu} \tag{20-44}$$

For single-stage precipitators, $\mathcal{E}_i$ and $\mathcal{E}_p$ may be considered as essentially equal. It is apparent from Eq. (20-44) that the mobility in an electrical field will be almost the same for all particles smaller than about 1 μ diameter, and hence, in the absence of reentrainment, collection efficiency should be almost independent of particle size in this range. Very small particles will actually have a greater mobility because of the Stokes-Cunningham correction factor. Values of u_e are listed in Table 20-36 for 70°F., $\zeta = 2$, and $\mathcal{E} = \mathcal{E}_i = \mathcal{E}_p = 10$ statvolts/cm.

Table 20-36. Charge and Motion of Spherical Particles in an Electrical Field

For $\zeta = 2$, and $\mathcal{E} = \mathcal{E}_i = \mathcal{E}_p = 10$ statvolts/cm.

Particle diam., μ	Number of elementary electrical charges, N_o	Particle migration velocity,* u_e, ft./sec.
0.1	10	0.27
.25	25	.15
.5	50	.12
1.0	105	.11
2.5	655	.26
5.0	2,620	.50
10.0	10,470	.98
25.0	65,500	2.40

* Includes Stokes-Cunningham correction factor.

Collection Efficiency. Although the actual particle mobilities may be considerably greater than would be calculated on the above basis because of the action of the electric wind in single-stage precipitators, the latter acts in a compensating fashion, and the over-all effect of the electric wind is probably to provide an equalization of particle concentration between the electrodes similar to the action of normal turbulence (Mierdel, *op. cit.*). On this basis Deutsch (*op. cit.*) has derived the following equations for collection efficiency, the form of which had previously been suggested by Anderson on the basis of experimental data:

$$\eta = 1 - e^{-(u_e A_e / q)} = 1 - e^{-K_e u_e} \tag{20-45}$$

For the concentric-cylinder (or wire-in-cylinder) type of precipitator, $K_e = 4L_e/D_t V_e$; for rod-curtain or wire-plate types, $K_e = L_e/B_e V_e$. Strictly speaking, Eq. (20-45) applies only for a given particle size, and the over-all efficiency must be obtained by an integration process for a specific dust distribution, as described on p. 20-72. However, over limited ranges of performance conditions, Eq. (20-45) has been found to give a good approximation of the over-all collection efficiency, with the term for particle migration velocity representing an empirical average value. Such values, calculated from over-all collection-efficiency measurements, are given in Table 20-37 for specific installations.

Table 20-37. Performance Data on Typical Single-stage Electrical Precipitator Installations*

Type of precipitator	Type of dust	Gas volume, cu. ft./min.	Average gas velocity, ft./sec.	Collecting electrode area, sq. ft.	Over-all collection efficiency, %	Average particle migration velocity, ft./sec.
Rod curtain.....	Smelter fume	180,000	6	44,400	85	0.13
Tulip type......	Gypsum from kiln	25,000	3.5	3,800	99.7	.64
Perforated plate.	Fly ash	108,000	6	10,900	91	.40
Rod curtain.....	Cement	204,000	9.5	26,000	91	.31

* Courtesy Research Corp.

For two-stage precipitators with close collecting-plate spacings (Figs. 20-107, 20-109), the gas flow is substantially streamline, and no electric wind exists. Consequently, neglecting reentrainment, collection efficiency may be expressed as [Penny, *Elec. Eng*, **56** 159 (1937)]

$$\eta = \frac{u_e L_e}{V_e B_e} \tag{20-46}$$

which holds for values of $\eta \leqq 1.0$. In practice, however, extraneous factors may cause the actual efficiency to approach a relationship of the type given by Eq. (20-45).

In general, increased pressure increases precipitation efficiency, although a somewhat higher potential is required, because it reduces ion mobility and hence increases the potential required for corona and sparking. Increased temperature reduces collection efficiency because ion mobility is increased, lowering critical potentials, and because gas viscosity is increased, reducing migration velocities.

Application. The theoretical considerations expounded above should be used only for order-of-magnitude estimates, since a number of extraneous factors may enter into the actual performance. In actual installations rectified alternating current is employed. Hence the electrical field is not fixed but varies continuously, depending on the wave form of the rectifier, although Schmidt and Anderson [*Elec. Eng.*, **57**, 332 (1938)] report that the wave form is not a critical factor. Allowances for high dust concentrations have not been fully studied, although Deutsch (*op. cit.*) has presented a theoretical approach. In addition, irregularities on the discharge electrode will result in local discharges. Such irregularities can readily result from dust incrustation on the discharge electrodes due to charging of particles with opposite polarity within the thin but appreciable glow or ionization layer surrounding this electrode. Very high dust loadings increase the potential difference required for corona and reduce the current due to the space charge of the particles. This tends to reduce the average particle charge and reduces collection efficiency. This can be compensated for by increasing the potential difference when high dust loadings are involved.

If the collected dust is not a good conductor, a high potential may develop across this dust layer. This not only reduces the potential across the gas stream but may result in spark discharge with resultant back ionization and reentrainment of dust. Schmidt and Anderson (*op. cit.*) and Anderson [*Physics*, **3**, 23 (July, 1932)] claim that this may be a controlling factor in the collection of all but conducting dust or mists. They state that an increase in relative humidity of 5 per cent may double the precipitation rate because of its effect on the conductivity of the collected dust layer. Mierdel and Seeliger [*Trans. Faraday Soc.*, **32**, 1284 (1936)] further discuss the problem and suggest the following remedies:

1. Avoid thick dust accumulation by using perforated or slotted electrodes.
2. Add moisture or conductive salts to increase the conductivity of the collected dust layer.
3. Change the wave form, using, for example, an alternating current superimposed on the direct current.

Beaver [*Trans. Am. Inst. Chem. Engrs.*, **42**, 251 (1946)], based upon work done by White, indicates that the critical resistivity above which such difficulties may be anticipated is on the order of 10^{10} ohm-cm. Steam, sodium chloride, and ammonia have all been successfully used as conditioning agents to increase conductivity in specific cases. Conditioning as used in the metallurgical field is discussed by Welch [Metallurgy of Lead and Zinc, *Trans. Am. Inst. Mining Met. Engrs.*, **121**, 304 (1936)]. Sproull and Nakada [*Ind. Eng. Chem.*, **43**, 1350–1363 (1951)] found that most dusts reach their maximum resistivity around 200° to 250°F., and that temperatures less than 200°, and greater than 500°F., were better than intermediate temperatures. This is shown in Fig. 20-98. Also shown is the large effect of moisture on the dust resistivity. Moisture is beneficial in two ways: it reduces the electrical resistivity of most dusts (an exception is powdered sulfur, which apparently does not absorb water), and it increases the voltage which may safely be employed without sparking, as shown in Fig. 20-97. In the great majority of applications, however, the resistivity of the dust and water-vapor content of the gases is such that good precipitation is obtained without the addition of any such agents (Beaver, *op. cit.*).

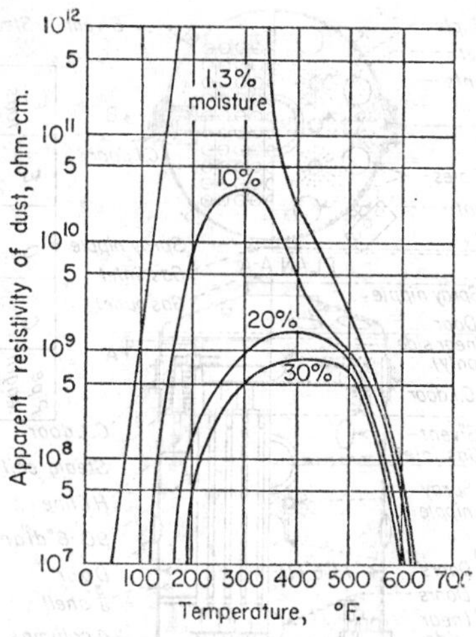

FIG. 20-98. Apparent resistivity of fume from an open-hearth furnace, as a function of temperature and various percentages of moisture content (volume). [*Sproull and Nakada, Ind. Eng. Chem.*, **43**, 1355 (1951).]

In order to achieve a maximum collection efficiency, electrical precipitators are operated as close to the sparking voltage as practicable without appreciable sparking. The following gives the order of magnitude of current, field strength, and ion density usually encountered in practice:

$I = 3 \times 10^3$ to 3×10^4 statamp./cm. (0.001 to 0.01 milliamp./cm.)

E = 5 to 20 statvolts/cm. [(1500 to 6000 volts/cm.)]

$\sigma = 10^8$ to 10^9/cc.

Single-stage Precipitators. The single-stage type of unit, commonly known as a Cottrell precipitator, is most generally used for dust or mist collection from industrial process gases. The corona discharge is maintained throughout the precipitator and, besides providing initial ionization, also serves to prevent redispersion of precipitated dust and recharges neutralized or discharged particle ions. Cottrell precipitators may be divided into two main classes, the so-called plate type (Fig. 20-99), in which the collecting electrodes consist of parallel plates, screens, or rows of rods, chains, or wires; and the

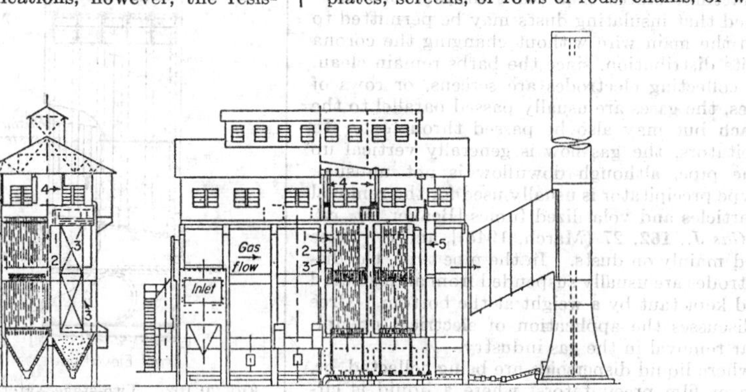

FIG. 20-99. Horizontal-flow plate precipitator used in cement plant. (*Western Precipitation Corp.*)

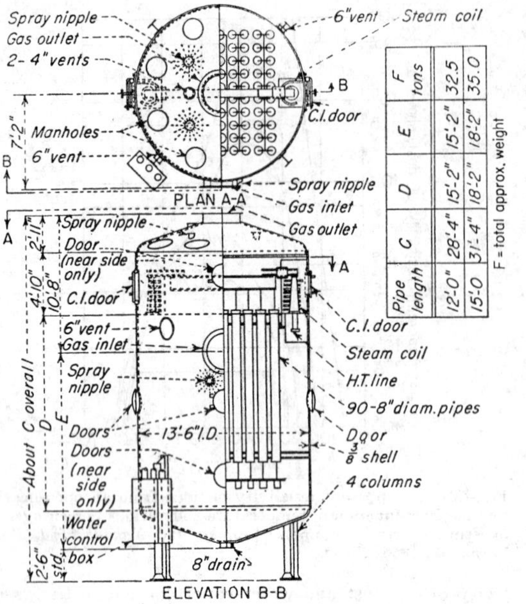

Pipe length	C	D	E	F tons
12'-0"	28'-4"	15'-2"	15'-2"	32.5
15'-0"	31'-4"	18'-2"	18'-2"	35.0

F = total approx. weight

FIG. 20-100. Blast-furnace pipe precipitator. (*Research Corporation.*)

pipe type (Fig. 20-100), in which the collecting electrodes consist of a nest of parallel pipes which may be square, round, or any other shape. The discharge or precipitating electrodes in each case are wires or rods, either round or edged, which are placed midway between the collecting electrodes or in the center of the pipes and may be either parallel or perpendicular to the gas flow in the case of plate precipitators. On some applications the Koppers Co. uses a discharge electrode which closely resembles barbed wire, as shown in Fig. 20-101*a*. This design is based on the principle that the sharper the electrode shape, the lower the voltage required to produce a given corona current. Since efficiency of dust collection is directly related to the rate of delivering electrical energy to the gas, it is said that this type of electrode will produce the same collection efficiency at a lower voltage than other electrode types. Comparative data are plotted in Fig. 20-101*b*. The data from Fig. 20-101*b* reduce to a single curve when plotted in Fig. 20-101*c* as input energy in watt-sec./cu. ft. of gas treated. The manufacturer states that plant installations have demonstrated that insulating dusts may be permitted to build up on the main wire without changing the corona current or its distribution, since the barbs remain clean. Where the collecting electrodes are screens, or rows of rods or wires, the gases are usually passed parallel to the plane of each but may also be passed through it. In pipe precipitators, the gas flow is generally vertical up through the pipe, although downflow is not unusual. The pipe-type precipitator is usually used for the removal of liquid particles and volatilized fumes [Beaver, *op. cit.* Cree, *Am. Gas J.*, **162**, 27 (March, 1945)], and the plate type is used mainly on dusts. In the pipe type, the discharge electrodes are usually suspended from an insulated support and kept taut by a weight at the bottom. Cree (*op. cit.*) discusses the application of electrical precipitators to tar removal in the gas industry.

Except where liquid dispersoids are being collected, or, in the case of film precipitators, where a liquid is circulated over the collecting electrode surface (Fig. 20-102),

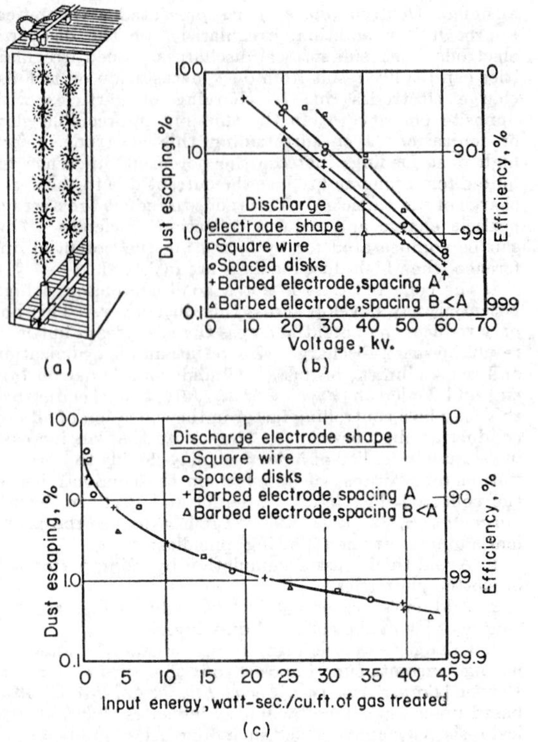

FIG. 20-101. Barbed-wire discharge electrode. (*a*) Illustration of corona location at barbs. (*b*) Efficiency of precipitator vs. voltage for several discharge electrode types. (*c*) Efficiency vs. input energy. (*Lagarias, Paper 59-51, presented at the meeting of the Air Pollution Control Assoc., June* 21–26, 1959.)

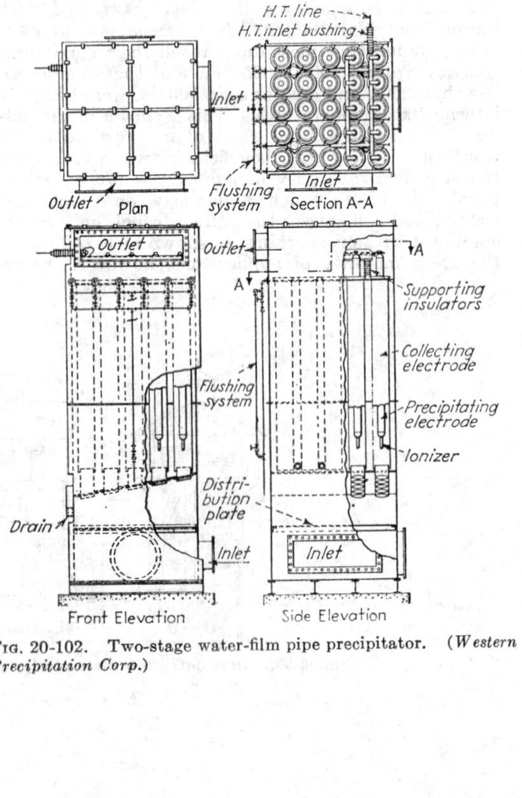

FIG. 20-102. Two-stage water-film pipe precipitator. (*Western Precipitation Corp.*)

thus continuously removing the precipitated material, the collected dust is dislodged from the electrodes either periodically or continuously by mechanical rapping or scraping, which may be performed automatically or manually. Perforated-plate or rod-curtain precipitators are frequently rapped without shutting off the gas flow and with the electrodes energized. This procedure, however, results in a tendency for reentrainment of collected dust. Sectional or composite-plate collecting electrodes (sometimes known as hollow, pocket, or tulip electrodes) are used to minimize this tendency in the continuous removal of the precipitated material, provided that it is free-flowing. These are generally designed for vertical gas flow and comprise a collecting electrode containing a dead air space and provided with horizontal protruding slots that guide the dust into this space (see Fig. 20-103) although some types use horizontal flow.

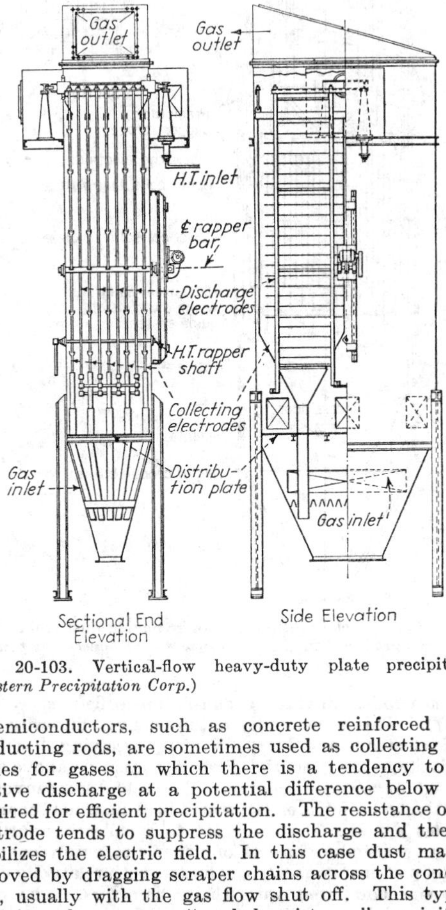

Fig. 20-103. Vertical-flow heavy-duty plate precipitator. (*Western Precipitation Corp.*)

Semiconductors, such as concrete reinforced with conducting rods, are sometimes used as collecting electrodes for gases in which there is a tendency to disruptive discharge at a potential difference below that required for efficient precipitation. The resistance of the electrode tends to suppress the discharge and thereby stabilizes the electric field. In this case dust may be removed by dragging scraper chains across the concrete slab, usually with the gas flow shut off. This type is sometimes known as a "graded resistance" precipitator because of the spacing of the reinforcing rods relative to the discharge electrodes in order to provide a maximum electrode resistance across the largest air gap [Schmidt, *Trans. Am. Inst. Chem. Engrs.*, **21,** 11 (1928)]. This type generally permits greater capacity and greater dust accumulation than other types, the dust in some cases being allowed to build up until it drops off by its own weight. However, it is not effective in its intended capacity for very conductive gases or collected materials, since surface creepage tends to destroy the graded resistance effect. Although collecting electrodes are usually metallic, carbon has been used for special corrosive service. Where the precipitated material is a liquid that forms a conducting film, insulators such as glass, terra cotta, or wood have also been used as collecting electrodes.

The choice of size, shape, and type of electrode is based on economic considerations and is usually determined by the characteristics of the gas and suspended matter and by mechanical considerations, such as flue arrangement, the available space, and previous experience with the electrodes on similar problems. The spacing between collecting electrodes in plate-type precipitators and the pipe diameter in pipe-type precipitators usually ranges from 6 to 15 in. The smaller the spacing the lower the necessary voltage and over-all equipment size, but the greater the difficulties involved in maintaining proper alignment and resulting from disturbances due to collected material. Large spacings are usually associated with high dust concentration in order to minimize spark-over due to dust build-up. For very high dust concentrations, such as those encountered in fluid catalyst plants, it is advantageous to use greater spacings in the first half of the precipitator than in the second half. Precipitators, especially of the plate type, are frequently built with groups of collecting electrodes in series in a common housing. Collecting electrodes are generally on the order of 3 to 6 ft. wide and 10 to 18 ft. high in plate-type precipitators and 6 to 15 ft. high in pipe types. It is essential for good collection efficiency that the gas be evenly distributed across the various electrode elements. Although this can be achieved by proper gas-inlet transitions and guide vanes, perforated plates or screens located on the upstream side of the electrodes are generally used for distribution. Perforated plates or screens located on the downstream side may be used in special cases.

Electrical precipitators are generally designed for collection efficiency in the range of 90 to 99.9 per cent. It is essential, however, that the units be properly maintained in order to achieve the required collection efficiency. Electrical power consumption is generally 0.2 to 0.6 kw./1000 cu. ft./min. of gas handled, and the pressure drop across the precipitator unit is usually less than 0.5 in. water, ranging from ¼ to 1 in. and representing primarily distributor and entrance-exit losses. Applied potentials range from 30,000 to 100,000 volts. Gas velocities and retention times are generally in the range of 3 to 10 ft./sec. and 1 to 15 sec., respectively. Velocities are kept low in conventional precipitators to avoid re-entrainment of dust. There are, however, precipitator installations on carbon black in which the precipitator acts to flocculate the dust so that it may be subsequently collected in multiple small-diameter cyclone collectors. By not attempting to collect the particles in the precipitator, higher velocities may be used with a correspondingly lower investment cost. A recent development is a fly-ash precipitator which operates at a gas velocity of 40 ft./sec. (see p. 20-89).

Electrical precipitators are generally energized by rectified alternating current of commercial frequency. The voltage is stepped up to the required value by means of a transformer and then rectified. The most common type of rectifier is the synchronous motor-driven mechanical rectifier, which requires more maintenance than the newer vacuum-tube or solid-state rectifiers employing selenium or silicon. Most new installations employ one of these electronic types. Half-wave rectification is sometimes used because of its lower equipment requirements and power consumption. The electrical equipment is usually housed in a separate substation, which can be located either adjacent to the precipitator or at some remote distance. In certain cases the electrical equipment may be included in a separate compartment

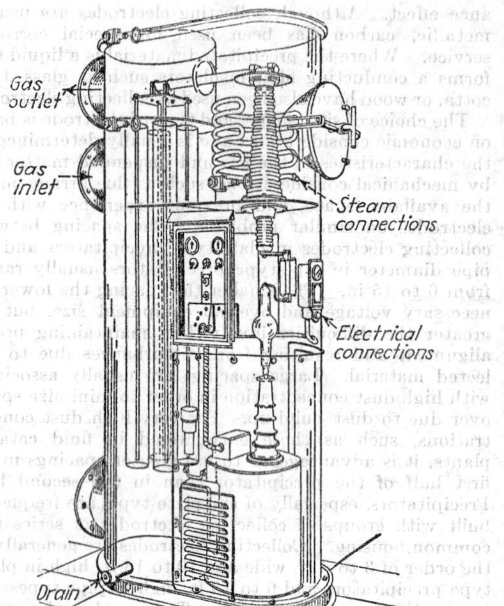

FIG. 20-104. Pipe precipitator with built-in electron-tube power unit. (*Research Corporation.*)

of a common shell of the precipitator unit (Fig. 20-104). The transformer and rectifying equipment may also be housed in a cabinet located near or on the precipitator with the controls located at some convenient operating point.

Electrode insulators must also be designed for a particular service. The properties of the dust or mist and gas determine their design as well as the physical details of the installation. Conducting mists require special allowances such as oil seals, energized shielding cups, or air bleeds. With saturated gas, steam coils are frequently used to prevent condensation on the electrodes.

Typical applications in the chemical field (Beaver, *op. cit.*) include detarring of manufactured gas, removal of acid mist and impurities in contact sulfuric acid plants, recovery of phosphoric acid mists, removal of dusts in gases from roasters, sintering machines, calciners, cement and lime kilns, blast furnaces, carbon-black furnaces, regenerators on fluid catalyst units, chemical-recovery furnaces in soda and sulfate pulp mills, and gypsum kettles. Figure 20-103 shows a vertical-flow steel-plate-type precipitator similar to a type used for catalyst-dust collection in certain fluid-catalyst plants.

Electrical precipitators are probably the most versatile of all types of dust collectors. Very high collection efficiencies can be obtained regardless of the fineness of the dust, provided that they are given proper maintenance. They can be used with moist or wet gases and have been successfully employed at temperatures as high as 1200°F. and at pressures up to 10 atm. The chief disadvantages are in the high initial cost and, in some cases, high maintenance costs. Furthermore, caution must be exercised with dusts that are combustible in the carrier gas. The *cost* of electrical precipitators varies widely with the application, the size, and the efficiency desired. Some representative figures are shown in Fig. 20-106.

Two-stage Precipitators. In two-stage precipitators, corona discharge takes place in the first stage between

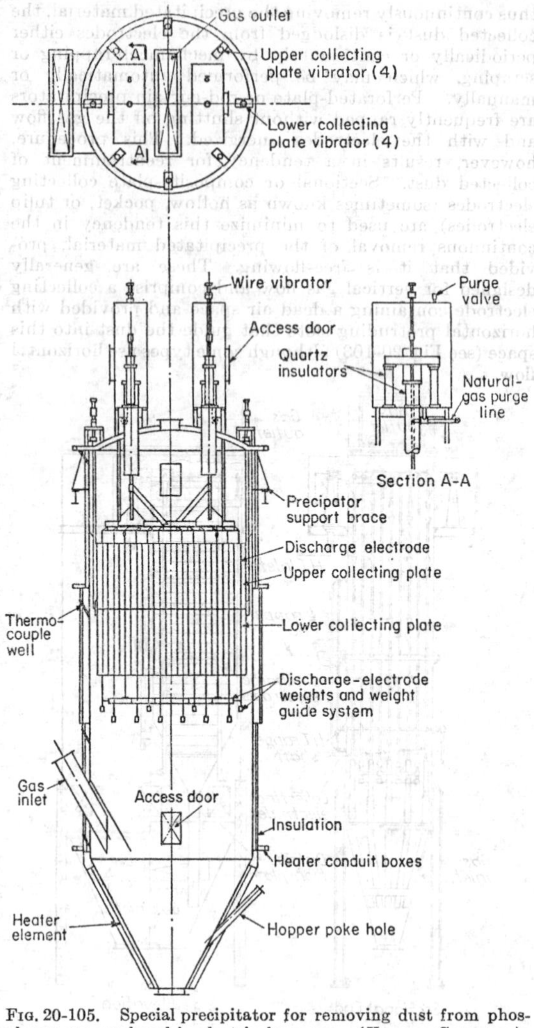

FIG. 20-105. Special precipitator for removing dust from phosphorus gas produced in electric furnaces. (*Koppers Company.*)

two electrodes having a non-uniform field (see Fig. 20-107). This is generally obtained by a fine-wire discharge electrode and a large-diameter receiving electrode. In this stage the potential difference must be above that required for corona discharge. The second stage involves a relatively uniform electrostatic field in which charged particles are caused to migrate to a collecting surface. This stage usually consists of either alternately charged parallel plates or concentric cylinders with relatively close clearances compared with their diameters. The only voltage requirement in this stage is that no sparking occur, though higher voltages will result in increased collection efficiency. Since collection occurs in the absence of corona discharge, there is no way of recharging reentrained and discharged particles. Consequently, some means must be provided for avoiding reentrainment of particles from the collecting surface. It is also essential that there be sufficient time and mixing between the first and second stages to secure distribution of gas ions across the gas stream and proper charging of the dust particles.

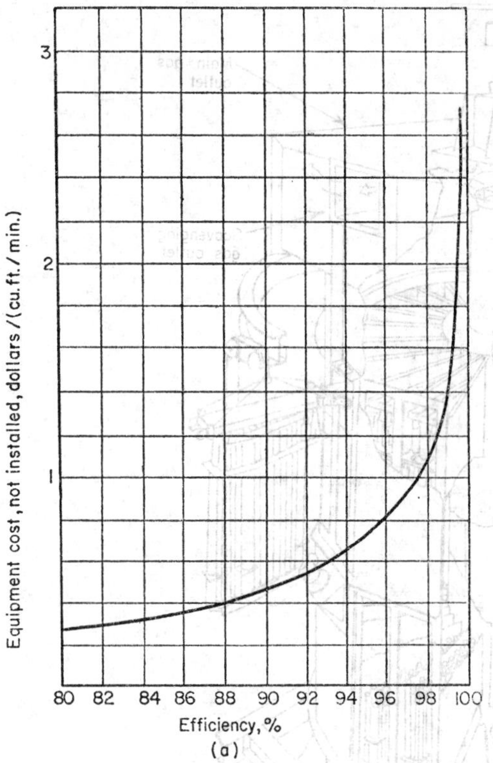

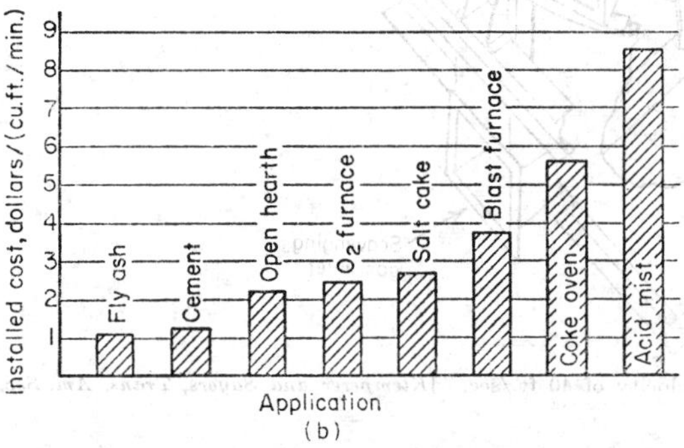

Fig. 20-106. Cost of electrical precipitators. (*a*) Equipment cost vs. efficiency based on gas volumes exceeding 500,000 cu. ft./min. in a fly-ash or similar application. (*b*) Installed cost (excluding ductwork, dust-handling equipment, and insulation) for various applications, based on handling gas volumes which are typical for each application. [*Stastny, Power*, **104**, 61 (*January*, 1960).]

In Fig. 20-102 is shown one of the earlier types of two-stage precipitators used for cleaning process gases. In this unit the ionizing electrode in the first stage is simply a small-diameter extension of the precipitating electrode of the second stage. Reentrainment is avoided and continuous cleaning of the collecting electrode is achieved by circulating a water film down the inside of the collecting electrode.

A recent development in the field of two-stage precipitators is a fly-ash precipitator which operates at a gas velocity of 40 ft./sec. A joint development program

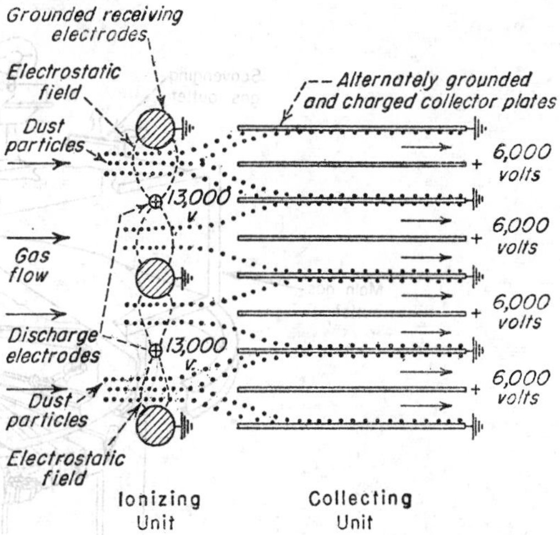

Fig. 20-107. Two-stage electrical precipitation principle.

undertaken by the Air Preheater Corp. and the Raytheon Manufacturing Co. at Waltham, Mass., resulted in demonstration of the principle [Tigges and Karlsson, *Trans. Am. Soc. Mech. Engrs.*, **78**, 305 (1956)]. A commercial scale (120,000 cu. ft./min. gas flow at 500° to 750°F., 1 atm.) unit was then developed at the Barking power generating station near London, England [Klemperer and Sayers, *Trans. Am. Soc. Mech. Engrs.*, **78**, 317 (1956)].

It was found that fine fly ash could be precipitated at velocities up to 50 ft./sec. in a concentric two-stage ionizing and collecting tube arrangement, but only if reentrainment and back emission could be eliminated by keeping the depth of dust deposit to a minimum (less than 0.03 in.). This is accomplished by periodically cleaning a section of the collecting elements by means of a high-velocity (80 to 120 ft./sec.) scavenging gas flow while other sections of the precipitator are kept in operation. The scavenging gas carries the dust to a secondary cyclone collector. The combined efficiency of the precipitator and secondary collector is approximately 95 per cent when treating fly ash with the following particle size distribution:

D_p, Microns	Weight, %
0–10	45
10–20	27
20–30	11
30–40	7
Over 40	10

The commercial-scale unit is shown in Fig. 20-108. The nests of ionizing and collecting cells are arranged in two 360 deg. banks, one above the other, in a vertical cylindrical stator shell 17 ft. in diameter. Each bank is divided into twelve 30-deg. sectors, and each sector is subdivided in two by a vertical radial sector division plate so that there are 24 sector-shaped tube nests in each 360-deg. bank. The over-all height of the precipitator is 30 ft. The grounded collecting tubes are hexagonal in shape, arranged in honeycomb formation, and the central combined ionizing/collecting electrodes are supported by two grids mounted above and below each tube nest on high-temperature insulators. At the bottom and top of the precipitator are two sector-shaped hoods which are mechanically rotated and sealed so that a flow of scavenging gas can be drawn upward through the two sets of cell nests in one half sector and out through the top hood. During the scavenging of each sector, the high-voltage electric power supply to that sector is automatically

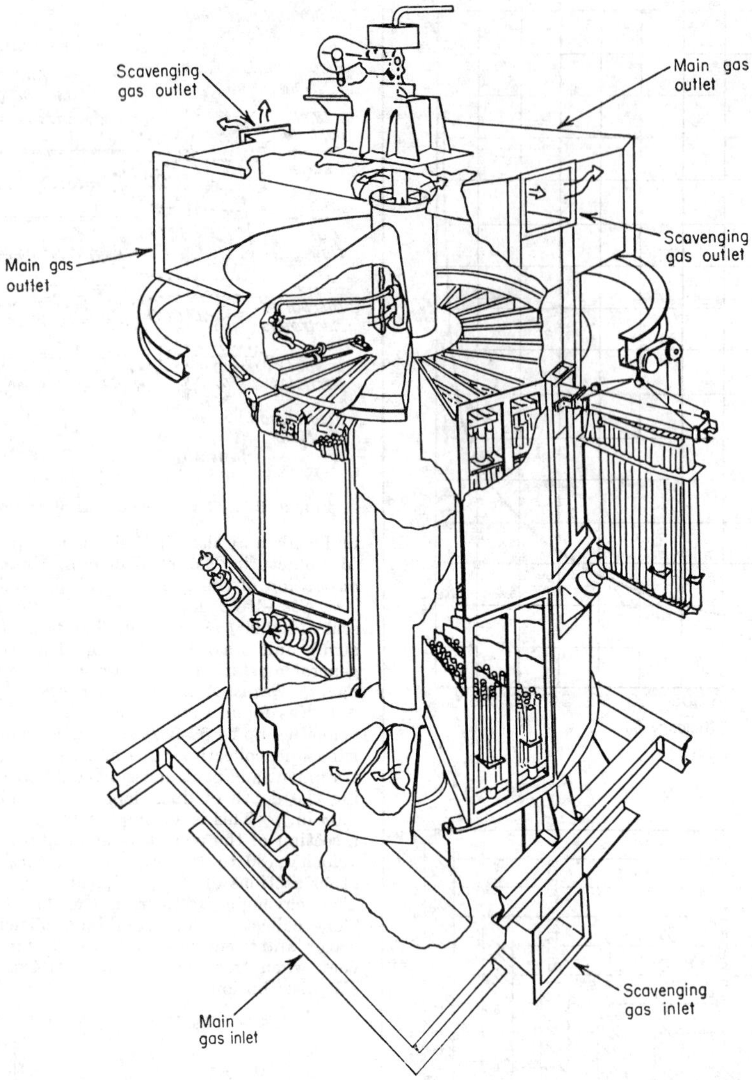

FIG. 20-108. General view of a precipitator which operates at a gas velocity of 40 ft./sec. [*Klemperer and Sayers, Trans. Am. Soc. Mech. Engrs.*, **78**, 317 (1956).]

suppressed to facilitate blowing off the dust. Each sector is powered individually by a selenium rectifier. Control of output voltage (12 to 13 kv.) and spark suppression is by saturable reactors on the a.c. supply.

A check with the Deutsch formula [Eq. (20-45)] using a transverse velocity based on a 1-micron particle diameter results in a predicted efficiency for this collector, which employs two precipitating stages in series, equal to 97.7 per cent, which compares favorably with the measured efficiency of 96 per cent.

The large-scale application of two-stage precipitators is, however, a comparatively recent development that has taken place in the air-conditioning field. Several units of the same general type are on the market, a typical one being shown in Fig. 20-109, whose primary application has been in the cleaning of atmospheric air. In these units the ionizing and collecting stages are built in separate sections of standardized size, and multiple units of each stage are assembled in parallel to meet a specific capacity. The ionizer unit is generally built up of vertical grounded tubes, circular or streamline in cross section and $1\frac{1}{4}$ in. nominal diameter, spaced about $3\frac{1}{2}$ in. apart. Between these tubes are stretched parallel discharge or ionizer electrodes, consisting of approximately 0.008-in.-diameter tungsten wire. The collecting unit, located on the downstream side of the ionizer unit, consists of 20 B.W.G. plates arranged parallel to the gas flow (see Fig. 20-107), usually vertical, with alternate plates grounded. These plates are spaced on approximately a $\frac{5}{16}$-in. pitch and are about 12 to 18 in. deep.

Both ionizer and collector sections are generally made in 24- and 36-in.-wide units, the heights being variable depending on the specific type or make. The plates are generally either zinc-coated steel or aluminum. A d.c. potential of 13,000 volts is applied between the ionizer wire and tubes, the wires being positive. A positive d.c.

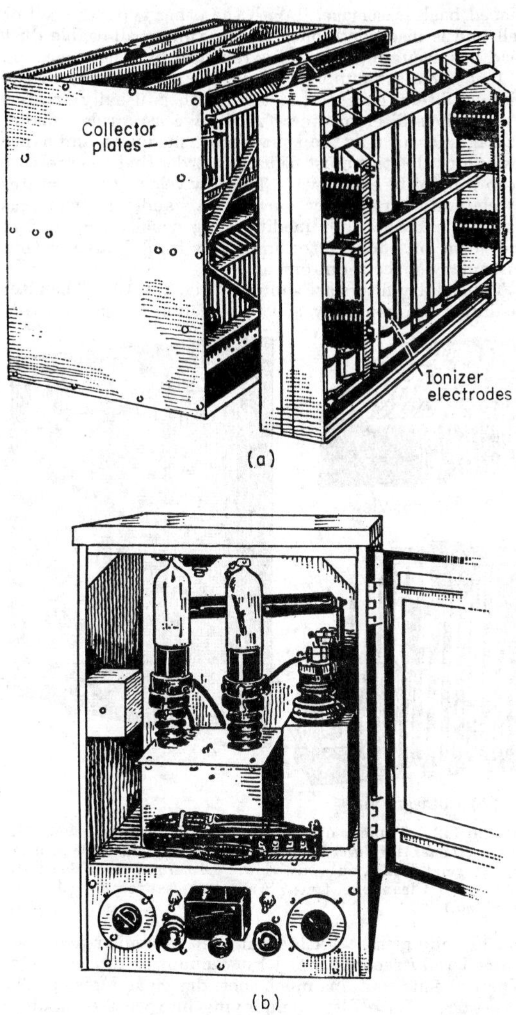

FIG. 20-109. Typical two-stage electrical precipitator used in air conditioning. (*Westinghouse Electric Corp.*) (*a*) "Precipitron" unit cells. (*b*) Power pack.

potential of 6000 volts is applied between adjacent collector plates. The necessary voltages for the ionizer and collector plates are obtained through a compact, self-contained vacuum-tube rectifier unit operated directly off of a 110-volt a.c. supply line.

The plates are coated with a viscous oil to avoid re-entrainment of collected dust. When the dust build-up exceeds a depth of approximately 1/16 in., the plate sections must be taken out, washed, and reoiled. Automatic means for cleaning and reoiling in place are also available. Depending on dust concentrations, cleaning may be required every 2 weeks to 3 months. Installations are usually provided with guarded doors that automatically cut off the power when the unit is entered. Where poor approach conditions are involved, perforated-plate air distributors may be employed. The units are rated at 85 to 90 per cent efficiency (U.S. Bureau of Standards Discoloration Test Method) at superficial velocities in the range of 300 to 550 ft./min. Electrical power consumption is approximately 0.02 kw./(1000 cu. ft./min.), and pressure drops range from 0.1 to 0.2 in. water. Purchase costs, complete with power packs and frames, but excluding housings, generally range from $0.10 to $0.25/(cu. ft./min.) of air handled, depending on the type and size of installation (prices of 1960).

A unit is available in which electrostatic precipitation is combined with a dry-air filter of the type shown in Fig. 20-112*b*. In another unit an electrostatic field is superimposed on an automatic filter of the type shown in Fig. 20-113*b*. In this case the ionizer wires are located on the leading face of the unit, and the collecting electrodes consist of alternate stationary and rotating parallel plates. Cleaning in this case is automatic and continuous. Both these units cost in the range of $0.10 to $0.30/(cu. ft./min.), or approximately three to four times as much as the comparable simple units without the electrostatic provisions.

Although intended primarily for air-conditioning applications, these units have been successfully applied to the collection of relatively non-conducting mists such as oil. However, other process applications have been limited largely to experimental installations. The large cost advantage of these units over the Cottrell precipitator lies in the smaller equipment size made possible by the close plate spacing, in the lower power consumption due to the two-stage operation, and primarily in the mass production of standardized units. In process applications, the close plate spacing is objectionable because of the relatively high dust concentrations involved. Special material or weight requirements for the structural members may eliminate the mass-production advantage except for individual wide applications. Consequently, application to process gases would appear to be limited. A possible outstanding field of application may be that of sulfuric acid mist collection although there are, to date, no commercial installations. The chief difficulty encountered in this case is the short-circuiting of the insulation.

Alternating-current Precipitators. High-voltage alternating current may be employed for electrical precipitation. Corona discharge will result in a net rectification, provided that no spark gaps are used in series with the precipitator. The equipment capacity for a given efficiency is considerably lower than for direct current, however. In addition, difficulties due to induced high-frequency currents may be encountered. The simplicity of an a.c. system, on the other hand, has permitted very satisfactory adaptation for laboratory and sampling purposes [Drinker, Thomson, and Fitchet, *J. Ind. Hyg.*, **5**, 162 (September, 1923)].

Air Filters. The equipment previously described is intended primarily for the treatment of process dusts. Air filters are employed in the elimination of atmospheric dust. The difference in application is not so much one of quality of dust as it is of quantity. Process dust concentrations may run as high as several hundred grains per cubic foot, although usually not exceeding 20 gr. Atmospheric-dust concentrations are generally below 5 gr./1000 cu. ft. Table 20-38 gives average atmospheric-dust concentrations that may be expected in various districts.

In the elimination of atmospheric dust, no attempt to recover the dust is usually made. Air washers may also

Table 20-38. Average Atmospheric-dust Concentrations*

1 gr./1000 cu. ft. = 2.3 mg./cu. m. = 0.065 mg./cu. ft.

Location	Dust Concentration, Gr./1000 cu. ft.
Rural and suburban districts	0.02–0.2
Metropolitan districts	0.04–0.4
Industrial districts	0.1 –2.0
Ordinary factories or workrooms	0.2 –4.0
Excessive dusty factories or mines	4.0 –400

* "Heating Ventilating Air Conditioning Guide," p. 77, American Society of Heating, Refrigerating and Air Conditioning Engineers, New York, 1960.

be employed for cleaning air, but these are installed primarily for humidifying or cooling the air, and dust removal is of only secondary importance.

Air filters may be classified in three groups on the basis of the type of filter medium employed: viscous, dry, or automatic.

Viscous filters are so called because the filter medium is coated with a viscous material to retain the dust. The filters are supplied in units of convenient size (generally of the order of 20- by 20-in. face area) to facilitate installation, maintenance, and cleaning. Each unit consists of an interchangeable cell or replaceable filter pad and a substantial frame that may be bolted to the frames of other similar units to form an airtight partition between the source of dusty air and its destination (Fig. 20-110).

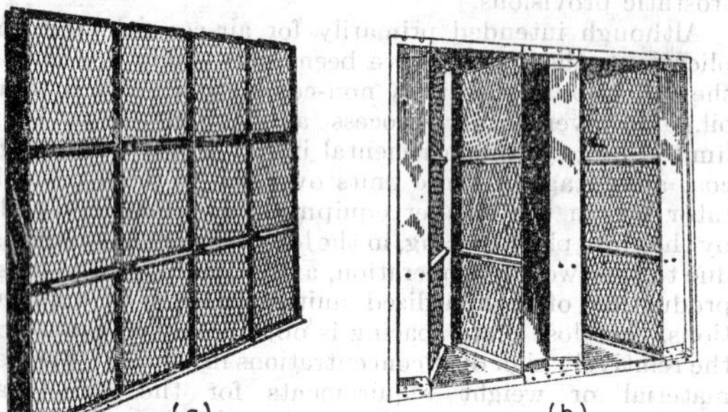

FIG. 20-110. Typical types of filter-bank installation. (*a*) Flat or L-type installation. (*b*) V-type installation.

Felt liners are sometimes used to make the assembly of individual cells airtight. Some types of cell may not have a separate cell frame but are clamped directly to the superstructure.

Typical commercial viscous-filter units are shown in Fig. 20-111. The filter pad may consist of one of a wide

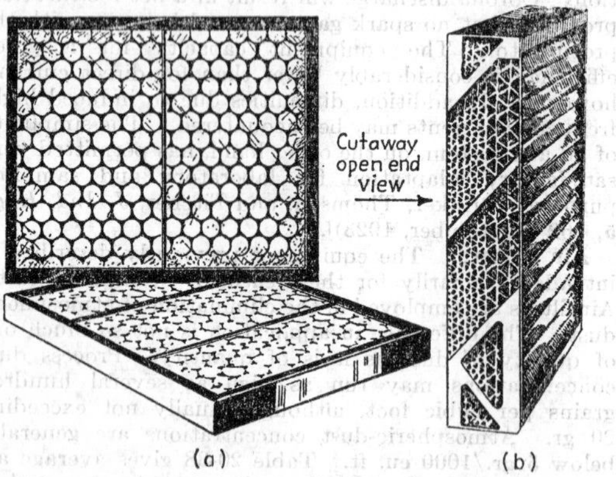

FIG. 20-111. Typical viscous unit filters. (*a*) Throwaway type, Dustop. (*Owens Corning Fiberglas Corporation.*) (*b*) Cleanable type, Air-Maze type B, cutaway open-end view. (*Air-Maze Corporation.*)

variety of materials, including glass fibers, animal hairs, wood shavings, corrugated fiberboard, split wire, or metal screening. These are coated with a dust-collecting liquid, such as mineral oil, and chemicals of high viscosity and flash point to act as a dust holder.

In the matter of servicing or reconditioning, the viscous-type filters fall into two classes. With most units employing a metallic medium, the unit cells are taken out and washed or steamed, reoiled, and then placed back in service. With the other type, the cell or cell pad is discarded, once the maximum allowable dust load has accumulated, and is replaced by a new one.

Dry filters are supplied in units similar in size to the viscous filters, except that the depth is usually greater. The various filter mediums used have, as a rule, smaller passages for air flow than the viscous mediums, and hence lower air velocities must be used in order that the pressure drop will not be excessive. This low velocity necessitates a relatively large filter surface to handle a given gas volume, and the filter mediums are usually arranged in the form of pockets to bring the frontal area within customary space requirements.

Typical dry filters are shown in Fig. 20-112. The filter mediums are generally sheets of cellulose pulp, cotton,

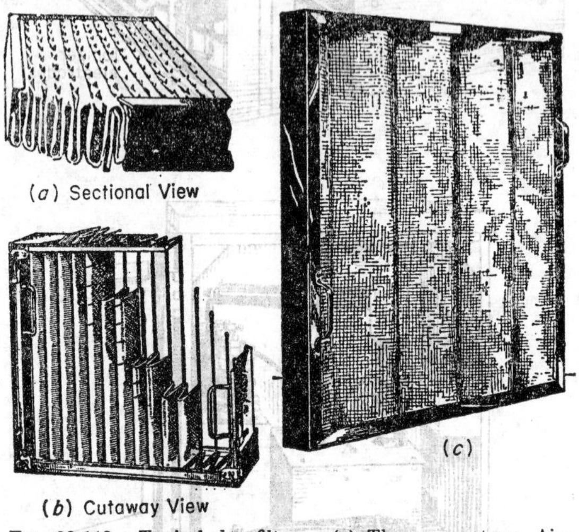

FIG. 20-112. Typical dry filters. (*a*) Throwaway type, Airplex. (*Davies Air Filter Corporation.*) (*b*) Replaceable medium type, Airmat PL-24, cutaway view. (*American Air Filter Company.*) (*c*) Cleanable type, Amirglass sawtooth. (*Amirton Company.*)

felt, or spun glass. Filters using felt or similar materials are generally reconditioned by vacuum or dry cleaning. Where the air contains much soot, dry cleaning is usually necessary. With filters employing inexpensive cellulose mediums, reconditioning is most economically accomplished by replacing the filter medium. Mechanical loading devices are often supplied to replace the filter sheets in the frames. In some cases the complete unit cell is discarded when the maximum dust load is reached.

Automatic filters might readily be classed under one or another of the previous groups, since they employ either a viscous-coated or dry-filter medium. They form a distinctive group in the air-filter field, however, in that the cleaning operation is essentially continuous and automatic. Most commercial automatic filters are of the viscous type and consist of perforated, crimped, or woven metallic screens in series (see Fig. 20-113*b* and *c*). The apertures are graded so that the air first meets the larger openings and is subjected to the finest filtering action just before it leaves. The screen curtains are drawn around in a vertical direction, either continuously or intermittently. The oil bath serves to rinse out the dust and coat the screen with a fresh film of oil. The dust is then allowed to settle out as a sludge in the bottom of the hopper. Such filters may be furnished with a hand crank or motor drive as desired.

The Airmat dust arrestor (Fig. 20-113*a*) is a dry automatic filter. It can, however, be considered automatic

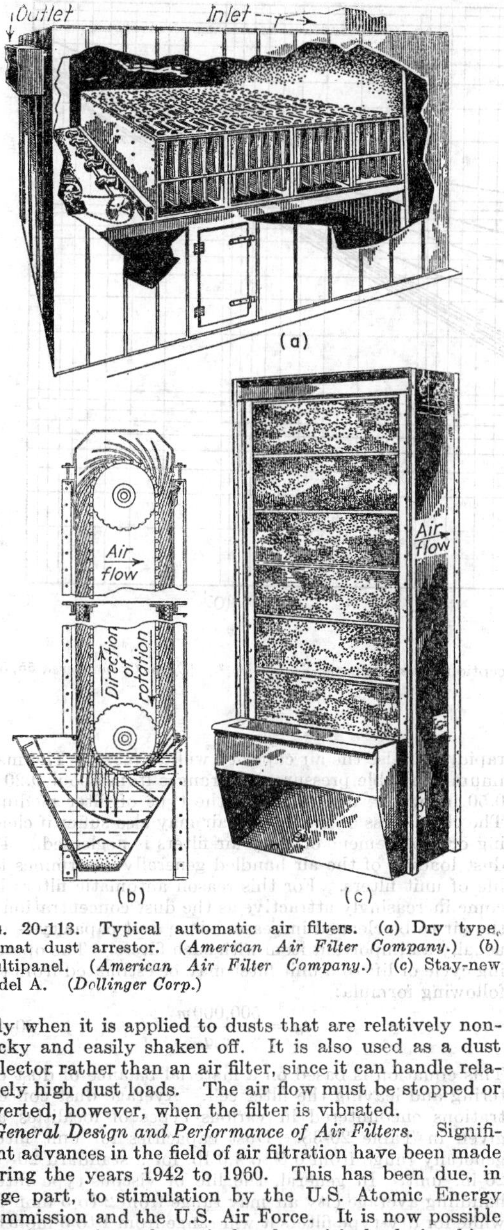

FIG. 20-113. Typical automatic air filters. (*a*) Dry type Airmat dust arrestor. (*American Air Filter Company.*) (*b*) Multipanel. (*American Air Filter Company.*) (*c*) Stay-new model A. (*Dollinger Corp.*)

only when it is applied to dusts that are relatively nonsticky and easily shaken off. It is also used as a dust collector rather than an air filter, since it can handle relatively high dust loads. The air flow must be stopped or diverted, however, when the filter is vibrated.

General Design and Performance of Air Filters. Significant advances in the field of air filtration have been made during the years 1942 to 1960. This has been due, in large part, to stimulation by the U.S. Atomic Energy Commission and the U.S. Air Force. It is now possible to estimate, from theoretical and empirical relationships, the approximate collection efficiency, pressure drop, and filter life that will result when a given monodisperse aerosol is filtered in a fibrous mat of uniform fiber diameter. [Blasewitz and Judson, *Chem. Eng. Progress*, **51**, 6-J (1955). Davies, *Proc. Phys. Soc.* (*London*), **B63**, 268 (1950). Davies, *Proc. Inst. Mech. Engrs.* (*London*), **B1**, 185 (1952). Langmuir, *O.S.R.D. Rep.* 865, 1942. Ramskill and Anderson, *J. Colloid Sci.*, **6**, 416 (1951). Ranz, *Tech. Rep.* 3, Contract AT-(30-3)-28, University of Illinois, 1951. Wong, Ph.D. Thesis in Chemical Engineering, University of Illinois, 1954. Chen, *Ann. Rep.* Contract DA18-108-CML-4789, Engineering Experiment Station, University of Illinois, Jan. 30, 1954. Chen, *Chem. Revs.*, **55**, 595 (1955). Wright, Stasny, and Lapple, *WADC Tech. Rept.* 55-457, ASTIA No. AD-142075, October, 1957.]

Chen (*op. cit.*) gives a comprehensive review of filtration theory and experiment. After noting that the efficiency η of an isolated fiber depends on inertial separation, flow-line interception, diffusional deposition, and Reynolds number, he made the assumption that the isolated fiber efficiency is equal to the sum of the efficiencies arising from the combined effects of inertia and interception and the combined effects of diffusion and interception. For the combined inertia and interception mechanisms he used the equation of Davies (*op. cit.*), which is plotted for $N_{\text{Re}} = 0.2$ as Fig. 20-114. For the diffusion and interception mechanisms he used a modification of the equation of Langmuir (*op. cit.*). This is plotted as Fig. 20-115. Chen then developed the following empirical relationship for predicting the efficiency of a single fiber in a bed of fibers:

$$\eta_\alpha = \eta_o[1 + K_\alpha(1 - \epsilon_v)] \qquad 20\text{-}47)$$

This indicates that the proximity of other fibers increases the collection efficiency of the isolated fiber. The value of K_α averaged 4.5 for values of ϵ_v ranging from 0.90 to 0.99. Extrapolation to ϵ_v lower than 0.90 may result in large errors.

The final step was the calculation of over-all collection efficiency of the fibrous mat filter:

$$\ln\left(\frac{1}{1-\eta}\right) = \frac{4}{\pi}\eta_\alpha\left(\frac{1-\epsilon_v}{\epsilon_v}\right)\left(\frac{(D_b)_{\text{avg}}L}{(D_b)_s^2}\right) \qquad (20\text{-}48)$$

Theoretical predictions of η were compared with measured efficiencies. The theory was found to overestimate the efficiency at large values of the inertial parameter N_{si} and underestimate it at large values of the diffusional parameter N_{sd}.

Wright, Stasny, and Lapple (*op. cit.*) conducted an extensive investigation of fibrous filters for air conditioning in aircraft applications. The significant mechanisms were found to be inertia, diffusion, and interception. Three aerosols were studied. Two of them were composed of relatively uniform supercooled liquid spheres 0.3 and 1.4 microns in diameter, respectively. The third was a more heterogeneous solid aerosol averaging 1.2 microns particle diameter. The fibers used were glass and tungsten, varying in diameter from 3 to 30 microns. Filter velocities ranged from 0.3 to 100 ft./sec. For clean, unloaded pads, all the experimental data were correlated on theoretical bases. The collection-efficiency data for the liquid aerosols agreed well with the theoretical predictions, even at velocities as high as 70 ft./sec., where efficiencies as high as 98 per cent were measured on unloaded pads. The solid-aerosol data agreed with those of the liquid aerosols at velocities less than 1 ft./sec., but for higher velocities the efficiencies were much lower than would be expected (20 per cent efficiency was typical for an unloaded pad at a velocity of 10 ft./sec.). This was apparently due to a failure of solid particles to adhere to the filter. As the pad became loaded with particles the collection efficiency and pressure drop increased. A sample design calculation showed that a filter having a non-loaded efficiency of 57 per cent when initially installed in liquid-aerosol service would have an average efficiency during its usable life equal to 98 per cent, because of the filtering action of the collected aerosol. Theoretical and semiempirical relationships were developed for the design of fibrous air filters.

The characteristics of the various types of air filters are compared in Table 20-39. The pressure drop through a filter increases as dust accumulates. The filter should be replaced when the pressure drop starts to increase

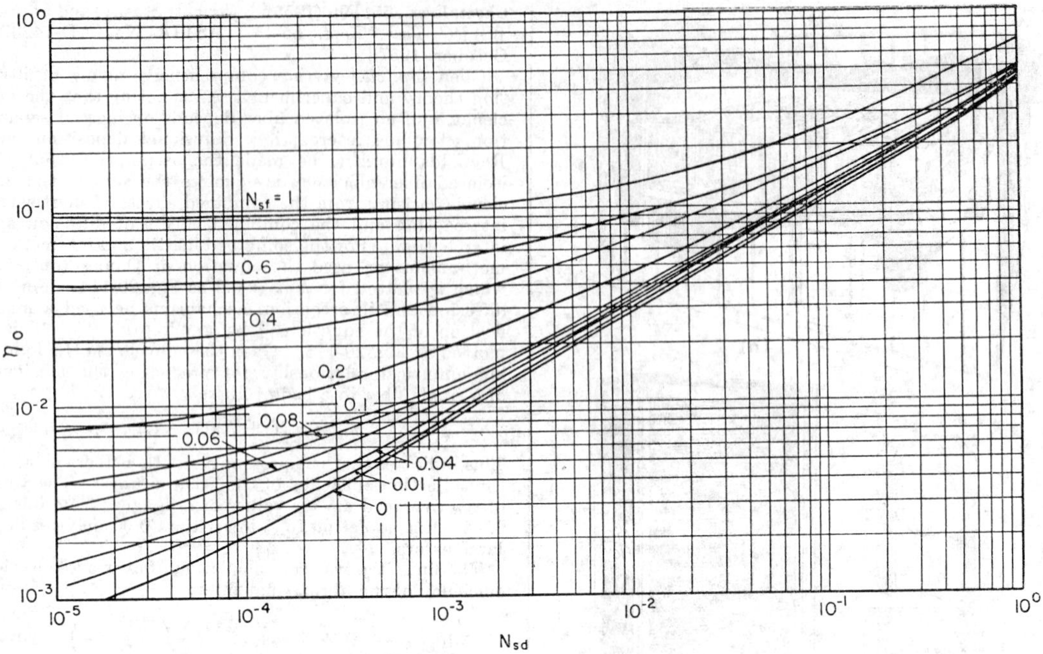

FIG. 20-114. Isolated fiber efficiency for combined diffusion and interception mechanisms at $N_{\text{Re}} = 10^{-2}$. [*Chen, Chem. Revs.*, **55**, 595 (1955).]

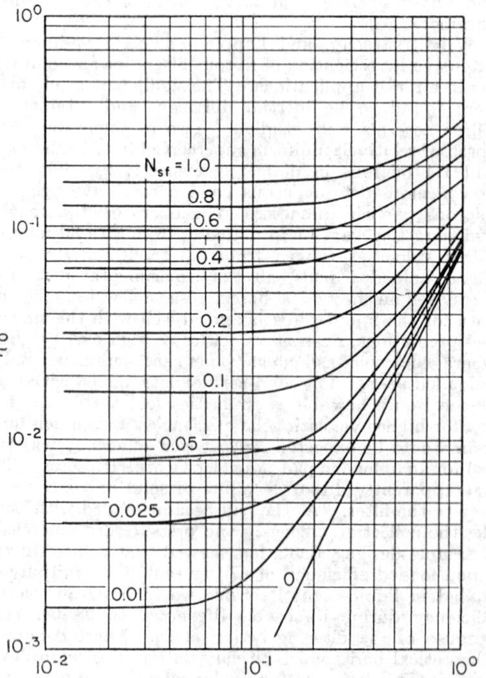

FIG. 20-115. Isolated fiber efficiency for combined inertia and interception mechanisms at $N_{\text{Re}} = 0.2$. [*Chen, Chem. Revs.*, **55**, 595 (1955).]

rapidly, or else the air capacity will decrease. The maximum allowable pressure drop ranges from about 0.20 to 0.50 in. water, depending on the type of filter medium. The cleanliness of the filtered air may also suffer if cleaning or replacement of dirty air filters is neglected. The dust loading of the air handled generally determines the life of unit filters. For this reason automatic filters become increasingly attractive as the dust concentration of the air to be cleaned increases, since dust capacity is not usually an important item with such filters. The operating cycle or life of a unit filter may be estimated from the following formula:

$$t_d = \frac{500{,}000 m_c}{\eta c_d q_m} \qquad (20\text{-}49)$$

This equation is based on a material balance of dust entering and leaving the filter cell. Average dust concentrations encountered in various types of localities are given in Table 20-38. Dust capacities for unit filters generally range from 0.5 to 4.0 lb. for a standard 20- by 20-in. unit. In general, the life of viscous-type filters handling average city air may range from 2 to 5 months, while for dry-type filters it will range from 1 to 3 months. For the average chemical plant the life will be from one-half to one-third that of the same filter handling "average" city air and may at times be considerably less because of the higher dust loadings involved.

The matter of a proper schedule for servicing filters cannot be too strongly stressed if satisfactory operation is to be obtained. The over-all time cycle for reconditioning washable viscous filters is generally about 24 hr. Unless they are allowed to drain sufficiently, an entrainment of oil by the filtered air may result.

In viscous air filters, dust collection is achieved by the impingement of particles on the filter surface, with the viscous coating serving to prevent reentrainment of separated dust. Collection efficiency generally increases as

Table 20-39. Comparative Air-filter Characteristics

	Unit filters				Automatic filters
	Viscous type		Dry type		
	Cleanable	Throwaway	Throwaway	Cleanable	
Dust capacity	1. Well adapted for heavy dust loads (up to 2 grain/1000 cu. ft.) due to high dust capacity		1. Well adapted to light or moderate dust loads of less than 1 grain/1000 cu. ft.		1. Well adapted for heavy dust loads (> 2 grain/1000 cu. ft.) since it is serviced automatically
Filter size	1. Common size of unit filter is 20- × 20-in. face area handling 800 cu. ft./min. at rated capacity 2. Face velocity is generally 300–400 ft./min. for all types				1. Automatic viscous units supplied to handle 1000 cu. ft./min. and over 2. Face velocity is 350–750 ft./min.
Air velocity	1. Rated velocity is 300–400 ft./min. through the filter medium 2. Entrainment of oil may occur at very high velocities		1. Rated velocity is 10–50 ft./min. through the medium. (Some dry glass types run as high as 300 ft./min.) 2. Higher velocities may result in rupture of filter medium		1. Rated velocity is 350–750 ft./min. through the filter medium for viscous types. For dry types, it is 10–50 ft./min.
Resistance	1. Resistance ranges from 0.05–0.30 in. when clean to 0.4–0.5 in. when dirty 2. When the resistance exceeds a given value, the cells should be replaced or reconditioned 3. Cycling cells in large installations will serve to maintain a nearly constant resistance				1. Resistance runs about 0.3–0.4 in. water
	4. High resistance due to excessive dust loading results in channeling and poor efficiency		4. Excessive pressure drops resulting from high dust loading may result in rupture of filter medium		
Efficiency	1. Commercial makes are found in a variety of efficiencies, these depending roughly on filter resistance for similar types of medium 2. Efficiency decreases with increased dust load and increases with increased velocity up to certain limits		1. In general, give higher efficiency than viscous type, particularly on fine particles 2. Efficiency increases with increased dust load and decreases with increased velocity		
Operating cycle		1. Well adapted for short-period operations (less than 10 hr./day) due to relatively low investment cost			1. Well adapted for continuous operation
	2. Operating cycle is 1–2 months for general "average" industrial air conditioning		2. Operating cycle is 2–4 weeks for general "average" industrial air conditioning		
Method of cleaning	1. Washed with steam, hot water, or solvents and given fresh oil coating	1. Filter cell replaced. Life may in some cases be lengthened by shaking or vacuum cleaning, but this is not often successful		1. Vacuum cleaned, blown with compressed air, or dry cleaned	1. Automatic. Filter may clog in time and cleaning by blowing with compressed air may be necessary
Space requirement	1. Well adapted for low headroom requirements 2. Form of banks can be chosen to fit any shaped space 3. Space should be allowed for a man to remove filter cells for cleaning or replacement				1. Have a high headroom requirement 2. Take up less floor space than other types
	4. Requires space for washing, reoiling, and draining tanks			4. Requires space for mechanical loader in some cases	
Type of filter medium	1. Crimped, split, or woven metal, glass fibers, wood shavings, hair—all oil coated		1. Cellulose pulp, felt, cotton gauze, spun glass 2. Dry medium cannot stand direct wetting. Oil-impregnated mediums are available to resist humidity and prevent fluff entrainment		1. Metal screens, packing, or baffling. One type uses cellulose pulp
Character of dust	1. Not well suited for linty materials			1. Not well suited for handling oily dusts	1. Not suited for linty material if of viscous types
	2. Well adapted for make-up air and granular materials		2. Well adapted for linty material 3. Better adapted for fine dust than other types		
Temperature limitations	1. All metal types may be used up as high as 250°F. if suitable oil or grease is used. Those utilizing cellulosic materials are limited to 180°F.		1. Limited to 180°F. except for glass types which may be used up to 700°F. if suitable frames and gaskets are used		1. Viscous may be used up to 250°F. if suitable oil is used. Dry type limited to 180°F.
Initial cost	1. Higher first cost than throwaway	1. First cost is relatively low. Frames are generally permanent but cells are replaced		1. Higher first cost than throwaway	1. Highest first cost of all
Operating cost	1. Power costs are comparable for all unit-type filters				1. Power costs are somewhat higher for automatic types 2. Little labor required to inspect, replace oil, or hand crank filter
	2. Labor cost to remove, clean, and replace the cells is comparable with the cost of replacement of throwaway-type cells for medium-sized installations of 10,000–50,000 cu. ft./min.	2. Replacement costs are comparable with labor costs for cleanable types for medium-sized installations (10,000–50,000 cu. ft./min.)		2. Same as for Viscous Cleanable	
	3. Maintenance exclusive of filter cells and depreciation are roughly comparable and vary more between different commercial makes in these groups than between different types				3. Depreciation and maintenance costs are the highest for automatic filters
Purchase cost (including frames), cost per 1000 cu. ft./min. (1960)	$10 to $35	$5 to $10	$5 to $10 for complete throwaway unit $8 to $30 for units with replaceable medium	$7 to $40	$35 to $100

the gas velocity increases unless the velocity becomes so high as to reentrain the dust together with the viscous coating. Efficiency also tends to decrease with increasing dust accumulation because of a saturation of the viscous coating with dust.

Ordinary air filters will have a low efficiency in separating particles below 1μ diameter. For particle sizes over 10μ, the filter efficiency for most makes is generally over 85 per cent. An oil impregnation of dry-filter media has also proved useful in eliminating any possibility of lint carry-over from the medium itself. Many of the dry media have also been fireproofed by suitable treatment.

Power costs may be computed by the following formula with reasonable accuracy (based on an over-all fan-motor efficiency of 63 per cent):

$$\text{Hp.} = \frac{\text{cu. ft. per min.} \times \text{resistance (in. of water)}}{4000} \qquad (20\text{-}50)$$

The additional power required for the operation of automatic filters is proportionately very small and may be neglected.

The approximate purchase-cost ranges for commercial steel filters are given in Table 20-39 (1960 costs). For special service, filters may be obtained of stainless steel, galvanized iron, cadmium-plated steel, brass, or aluminum. The American Railroads Association, Mechanical Division (Report on Relative Performance of Air Filters, Jan. 15, 1938, Chicago) and Rowley and Jordan [*Heating, Piping Air Conditioning*, **7**, 293–299 (1935); **10**, 539 (1938); **11**, 388, 633 (1939); **12**, 61, 699 (1940); **13**, 99, 246, 304, 524 (1941); **14**, 19, 438 (1942); **15**, 487 (1943)] report especially complete quantitative and comparative performance data, and Carrier, Cherne, Grant, and Roberts ("Modern Air Conditioning, Heating, and Ventilating," 3d ed., Chap. XV, Pitman, New York, 1959) give more detailed installation and operating-cost information.

Miscellaneous Air-filter Equipment. In Fig. 20-116 is shown a typical unit in which water is sprayed over a glass-fiber filter cell to combine the functions of dust removal and humidification. The wetted cells are followed by entrainment eliminators which may consist of 1-in.-thick glass-fiber mats or zigzag metal plates. Water is circulated at a rate of approximately 3 (gal./min.)/(1000 cu. ft./min.) of air handled and at a pressure of about 6 lb./sq. in. gage, while superficial cell gas velocities are on the order of 300 ft./min. The purchase cost of such units is on the order of \$50 to \$100/(1000 cu. ft./min.) of air handled, not including piping, ductwork, or auxiliary equipment. Complete evaporative-cooling installations of this type will cost about \$150 to \$300/(1000 cu. ft./min.) of air handled (prices of 1960).

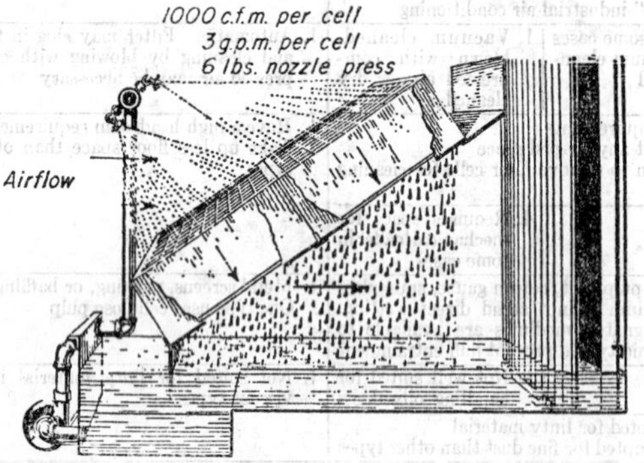

FIG. 20-116. Typical wetted-glass-fiber filter, "Capillary Conditioner." (*Air & Refrigeration Corp.*)

Air cleaners containing up to six wet cells, similar to that shown in Fig. 20-116, and three dry glass-wool pads in series have been developed to remove radioactive particles as small as 0.6 micron mass median diameter. [Hammond and Leary, Los Alamos Scientific Laboratory, *Rept.* LAMS-970, October, 1949. First, Moschella, Silverman, and Berly, *Ind. Eng. Chem.*, **43**, 1363 (1951).]

A number of units have been developed in which air cleaning is achieved by means of an electrostatic field either by itself or in conjunction with either a dry or viscous-coated filtering medium. These units are considerably more effective than dry or viscous air filters in removing particles smaller than 5μ diameter and are discussed in detail on pp. 20–90ff.

Air filters are available in special forms for use on engine and compressor air intakes as well as for removing dust, scale, and oil in compressed-air or process pipe lines (so-called "pipe-line" filters). A variety of domestic filter units are available for use in window ventilators, room conditioners, or central air-circulation systems. A domestic electrostatic air-cleaning unit, similar to the industrial types discussed on p. 20–91, is available.

Miscellaneous Collectors. High-intensity acoustic vibrations will cause collision and thereby tend to flocculate fumes and mists, whereupon they can be readily collected in conventional apparatus. There is an optimum frequency, generally in the range of 1000 to 10,000 cycles/sec., below and above which effective flocculation will not occur, depending on the size and density of the particle and the viscosity and density of the medium. The U.S. Bureau of Mines has sponsored extensive investigation in the field of ultrasonics [St. Clair *et al.*, *U.S. Bur. Mines Rept. Invest.* 3400, May, 1938; 4218, March, 1948; *Mining and Met.*, **18**, 244 (1937); *Ind. Eng. Chem.*, **41**, 2434 (1949)]. It was not until an economical source of acoustic energy was developed recently, however, that commercial application of this principle became feasible. The gas-siren generator (Ultrasonic Corp., Cambridge, Mass.) has permitted the conversion of compressed-gas energy into acoustic energy at 50 to 70 per cent efficiency in units developing up to 100 kw. acoustic output. With this type of generator a compressed-gas pressure of 6 lb./sq. in. gage is normally used for atmospheric-pressure applications and frequency can be varied continuously. A total range in frequency from 1000 to 200,000 cycles/sec. can be covered in several steps. The power consumption for aerosol agglomeration is normally in the range of 2 to 5 kw./(1000 cu.ft./min.) of gas handled. Sonic precipitation is limited to cases where the particle concentration is greater than 1 gr./cu. ft. For cases involving a lower particle concentration, sonic precipitation is feasible only if the particle concentration is raised by the introduction of additional particles as with the injection of steam. Pilot-plant or full-scale installations have been made or are under construction for the collection of carbon black, black liquor fumes, sulfuric acid mist, pulp-mill salt cake and soda cement dust, smelter fumes, and fly ash, and development work is under way on the precipitation of fog from airport atmospheres. However, it should be emphasized that sonic precipitation is still in the development stage, and several plants had to be dismantled after a short period of operation after it was found that exposure to the intense vibration was having a harmful effect on personnel in the vicinity [Walter, *Staub*, **36**, 228 (1954)]. Although in principle the sonic agglomerator and cyclone systems are about 20 per cent cheaper to install and operate than electrostatic precipitators of similar capacity, the need for heavy sound insulation raises the cost considerably [Pilpel, *Brit. Chem. Eng.*, **5**, 550 (1960)]. Further details are given by Jones [*J. Acoust. Soc. Am.*, **48**, 371 (1946)], Porter [*Chem. Eng.*, **55**, 100, 101, 115 (March, 1948)], Pilpel [*Ind. Chem.*, **32**, 327 (1956)], and Crawford ("Ultrasonic Engineering," Butterworth, London, 1955).

Molecular impacts tend to repel dispersoids away from a heated body. In thermal precipitation this principle is utilized to clean gas of suspended particles by passing the gas through or over a heated grid at low velocity [Blacktin, *J. Soc. Chem. Ind.*, **58**, 334 (1939). Watson, *Trans. Faraday Soc.*, **32**, 1073 (1936)]. Although this method has not yet been applied to industrial-dust collection, it has been very successful for atmospheric-dust sampling.

SECTION 21

GAS-GAS, LIQUID-LIQUID, AND SOLID-SOLID SYSTEMS

BY

Sherman S. Weidenbaum,* Ph.D., Research Chemical Engineer, Corning Glass Works; Member, American Institute of Chemical Engineers, American Chemical Society, American Ceramic Society, American Society for Quality Control, The Electrochemical Society. (Section Editor and Solid-Solid Mixing)

WITH

F. William Bloecher, Jr., S.M., Assistant Manager, Mining Chemicals Department, Cyanimid International; Member, American Institute of Mining, Metallurgical and Petroleum Engineers. (Flotation)

William J. Bronkala, B.Met.E., Chief Metallurgist, Stearns Magnetic Products; Member, American Institute of Mining, Metallurgical and Petroleum Engineers. (Dense Media and Magnetic Separation)

Edwin E. Cockrell, B.S., Application Engineer, Machinery Division, and Director, Customer Service Laboratory, W. S. Tyler Co.; Member, American Institute of Mining, Metallurgical and Petroleum Engineers. (Screening)

Paul E. Cook, Director of Technical Publications, Denver Equipment Company. (Sampling Solids)

*At present, United Nations Project Manager and Director, Israel Ceramic and Silicate Institute, Technion City, Haifa, Israel.

Fred D. DeVaney, M.S., Director of Metallurgy and Research, Pickands Mather and Co.; Member, American Institute of Mining, Metallurgical and Petroleum Engineers, American Iron and Steel Institute. (Jigging and Tabling)

William P. Dyrenforth, M.E., Registered Professional Engineer, Florida and Illinois; Vice President and Technical Director, Carpco Research and Engineering, Inc.; Member, American Institute of Mining, Metallurgical and Petroleum Engineers, Mining Club of New York. (Electrostatic Separation)

Morgan C. Sze, Sc.D., Registered Professional Engineer, New York; Executive Staff Engineer, The Lummus Company; Member, American Institute of Chemical Engineers. (Gas-Gas Systems)

Robert E. Treybal, Ph.D., Registered Professional Engineer, New York; Professor of Chemical Engineering, New York University; Member, American Institute of Chemical Engineers, American Chemical Society, American Society for Engineering Education. (Liquid-Liquid Systems)

Glenn O. Wilson, Registered Professional Engineer, Colorado and Connecticut. Director, Technical Coordination, Dorr-Oliver Inc.; Member, American Institute of Mining, Metallurgical and Petroleum Engineers. (Classification)

CONTENTS

GAS-GAS SYSTEMS

Contacting Devices

Jet mixers, such as oxyhydrogen torches, rely on the impingement of a jet against another jet, usually with both jets fed under pressure. This mixer is sometimes used for liquid mixing but finds its greatest application in the mixing of combustible gases just before ignition (see Fig. 21-1).

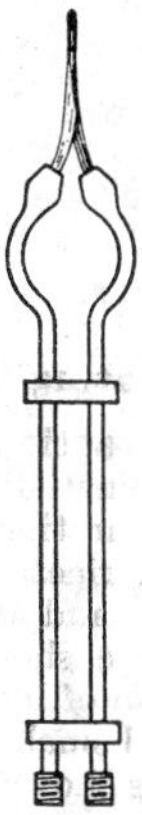

FIG. 21-1. Jet mixer for gases.

Injectors consist essentially of a main pipe and an auxiliary pipe, jet, nozzle, tube, or orifice through which a second stream is injected into the main stream. In some cases the velocity of flow in the main pipe induces a flow of material in the auxiliary pipe. In other cases, material is fed through the auxiliary pipe under sufficient pressure and velocity to cause the flow through the main pipe. This may be material recirculated from the tank itself by means of an outside pump. A requisite of rapid thorough mixing in this type is that the mass velocity in the auxiliary stream be considerably higher than in the main stream. Chilton and Genereaux [*Trans. Am. Inst. Chem. Engrs.*, **25**, 102 (1930)] found that, when mixing two gases with this type of mixer, good mixing can be obtained by making the mass velocity of the added stream two or three times that in the main stream.

Typical mixers of this type are shown as *a* and *b* in Fig. 21-2. Figure 21-2*b* is really a jet compressor with a built-in check valve. It is widely used today by public-utility companies for mixing propane and air to supply peak shaving gas under some pressure (Hammond, "Jet Compressor as Applied to Gas Industry," presented before New England Gas Assoc., June, 1958). Its advantages are (1) simplicity, (2) low cost, and (3) the combining of mixing and compressing operation into one Its limitation is that it does not readily adapt itself to operation under varying flow conditions.

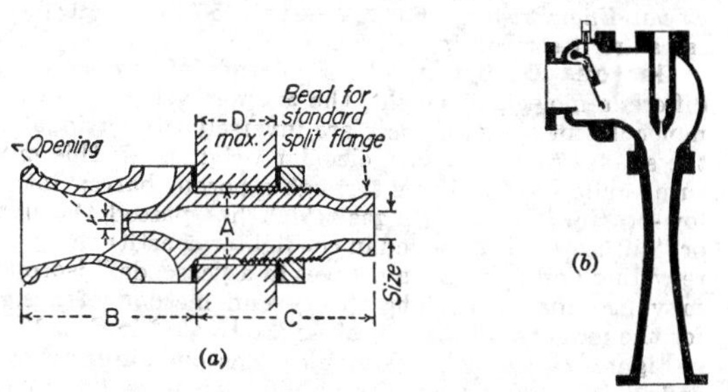

FIG. 21-2. (*a*) Injector mixer. (*b*) Jet compressor. (*Schutte and Koerting Co.*)

Baffled-flow Mixers used for gas mixing are simple in construction and easy to install. A typical mixer may be as shown in Fig. 21-3. These mixers rely for their

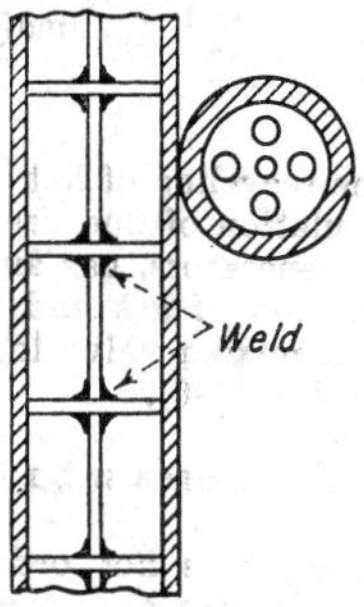

FIG. 21-3. Baffle-plate mixer.

action on the translation of pressure into turbulent velocity, thus permitting the desired mixing to be completed with the very short holding time available. A typical industrial application is the mixing of ammonia with air to give a 10 per cent ammonia in air mixture for ammonia oxidation to produce nitric acid.

Fans or blowers will mix gases intimately when the gases are supplied in desired proportions under continuous-flow conditions. They are also used for batch mixing, being located inside or outside the mixing chamber. Figure 21-4 shows a propeller-type fan and Fig. 21-5 a

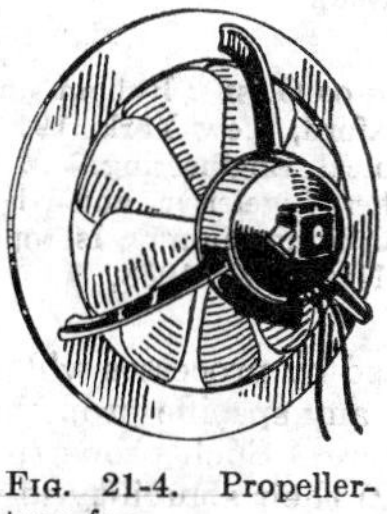

FIG. 21-4. Propeller-type fan.

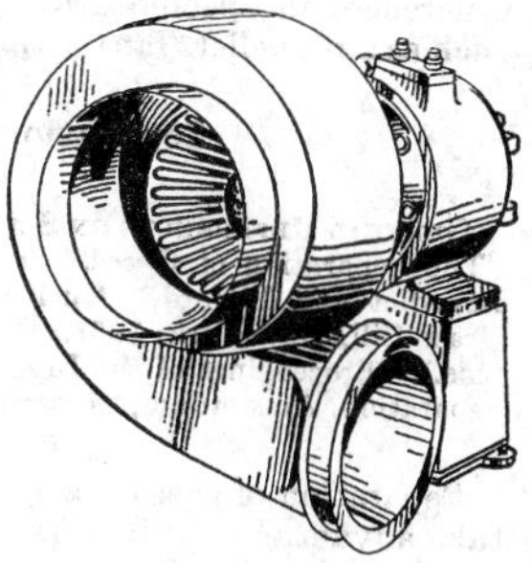

FIG. 21-5. Turbine blower.

turbine blower. This type of equipment has the advantage of being able to handle large volumes of gases with low power consumption. However, they are more complicated than the first three types of gas mixers and they need mechanical moving parts. Typical industrial appli-

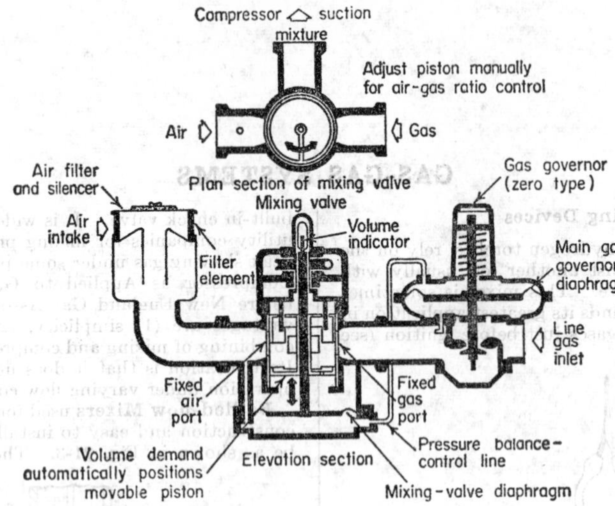

FIG. 21-6. Mixing valve. (*Sealas Corp.*)

cations include the recycling of hot gases in dryers (Sec. 20) and the recirculation of flue gas in certain furnaces. In most inert-gas generators, gas and air are mixed in a blower, the proportion of gas and air being controlled automatically by a mixing valve located at the suction of the blower (see Fig. 21-6).

Mixing Gases with Gases

The mixing of gases is not ordinarily considered a difficult operation. Gases are readily moved and can be made to flow together without elaborate equipment. Nearly all mixing of gases is done as a continuous process by any of the above-mentioned types of mixers.

If a relatively small mass of one gas is to be mixed with a relatively large mass of another gas which is static or moving at low velocity, the best approach to homogeneity lies in the provision of sparging devices with a large plurality of small passageways for entry of the small volume to the large volume at or as close as possible to critical-flow condition and spread over as great an area as is possible (Reed, John Zink Co., private communication).

Where batch mixing is desired, especially in cases where differences in specific gravity exist, a mechanical type such as a propeller (fan) within the container is advisable.

Separation of Gases

GENERAL REFERENCES ON SEPARATION OF GASES: Ruhemann, "The Separation of Gases," 2d ed., Oxford, New York, 1949. Benedict and Pigford, "Nuclear Chemical Engineering," McGraw-Hill, New York, 1957. Kistemaker, Bigeleisen, and Nier (eds.), "Proceedings of the International Symposium on Isotope Separation, Amsterdam," Interscience, New York, 1958.

Separation of gases is accomplished by processes which take advantage of the difference in any specific property exhibited by the gases in the mixture. Such properties may be (1) their vapor pressure, (2) their solubility in a solvent, (3) their affinity to a solid adsorbent, (4) their diffusion coefficients, (5) their molecular weight or atomic weight, (6) their density, and (7) their chemical properties. How separation is made and what equipment is used are briefly outlined in the following discussion on Separating Devices.

Separating Devices

Low-temperature Fractional-distillation Towers. Low-temperature fractional distillation is a technique used widely for gas separation. Distillation principles and low-temperature refrigeration are treated in Secs. 13 and 12, respectively, and will not be repeated here. For equipment, reference should be made to Sec. 18. The main special feature of low-temperature columns is the low tray spacing and small bubble caps used even for large-diameter towers as shown in Table 21-1.

Table 21-1. Commercial Air-rectification Trays

Type	Cap dimension, or hole diam.	Tray spacing	Company
Perforated plates....	0.8- to 0.9-mm. holes on 3.25-mm. triangular centers	90–100 mm.	Linde, Germany
Bubble-cap trays....	8.8- to 10.2-mm.-diam. caps	54–60 mm.	Messer, Germany
Bubble-cap trays....	1.0-in.-diam. caps	4–6 in.	Hydrocarbon Research, Inc. U.S.A.

Absorbers. The fundamentals of this technique for gas separation are treated in Sec. 14, while gas-liquid contacting equipment is discussed in Sec. 18.

Solid Adsorbers, Hypersorbers, Fluid Char Column. Another technique for gas separation is by means of a solid adsorbent. This may be accomplished in a fixed bed or in a moving bed, such as the hypersorber [Berg, Fairfield, and Multer, *Petrol. Refiner*, **28**, (11), 113–120 (1949)], or in a fluid bed, such as the fluid char process [Etherington, Fritz, Nicholson, and Scheeline, *Chem. Eng. Progress*, **52**, 274–280 (1956)]. These processes are described in Sec. 20.

Gaseous Diffusion. In a mixture of two gases of different molecular weight, the average velocities of the molecules of the two gases are inversely proportional to the square root of their molecular weights. If this mixture is allowed to diffuse through a porous barrier into a low-pressure space, the gas which has passed through, or "diffusate," is enriched in the lighter constituent. By recycling and using many stages in a "cascade," isotopes may be separated. The theory and method of design for the gaseous-diffusion process are treated in Sec. 17.

Figure 21-7 shows a simplified gaseous-diffusion cascade. The mixture entering a diffusion stage flows past a barrier while a portion flows through the barrier into

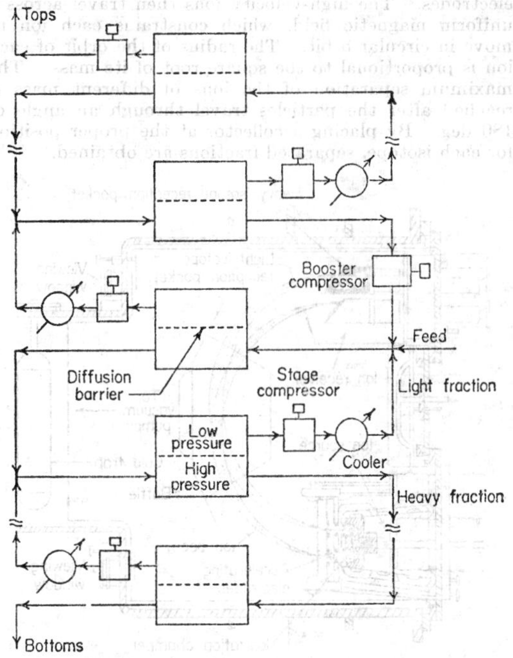

FIG. 21-7. Gaseous-diffusion cascade. (*Benedict and Pigford, "Nuclear Chemical Engineering," McGraw-Hill, New York,* 1957.)

the lower-pressure region. The diffusate is enriched in the lighter constituent and constitutes the lighter feed to the next stage near the top of the cascade. The gas which does not flow through the barrier is enriched in the heavier constituent and becomes the feed to the stage nearer the bottom of the cascade. On each stage a compressor compresses the diffusate from the downstream pressure of the barrier to the upstream pressure and the heat of compression is removed by a cooler. In a cascade of many stages, at intervals a booster compressor is needed to compensate for pressure drop of the higher-pressure gas.

This process has been applied commercially to the separation of $U^{235}F_6$ from the natural mixture of $U^{235}F_6$ and $U^{238}F_6$ [Keith, *Chem. Eng.*, **53**, 112–122 (1946). Hogerton, *Chem. Eng.*, **52**, 98–101 (1945)]. The heart of the process is the diffusion barrier. It must meet many requirements. In order that the bulk of the flow through such a barrier be by true diffusion, or molecule by molecule, and not by ordinary mass flow, the pores must be very small and their diameter must be of the order of the mean free path of the gas molecules or about 0.01 micron at about atmospheric pressure. The permeability should be high. The mechanical strength should be high so it can withstand the differential pressure across it. It must be made of material highly resistant to UF_6 so that the pores will not plug as a result of corrosion and that the product $U^{235}F_6$ cannot be lost through corrosion.

Because the mean free path of the gas molecules is larger at lower pressure, the entire $U^{235}F_6$ enriching plant operates at subatmospheric pressure. This imposes a most stringent requirement that the entire plant must be made as tight as possible to prevent in-leakage of air. In addition, the holding volume of the entire plant must be kept small. High-speed centrifugal gas pumps are provided with special shaft seals to limit in-leakage down to an extremely low and tolerable figure. Smaller reciprocating vacuum purge pumps are made vacuum-tight as single-stage valve-in-head machines with gas lubrication between piston and cylinder and sylphon bellows seals between piston rod and cylinder. This tightness requirement also applies to all valves and piping of the plant.

Thermal Diffusion. When a temperature gradient is set up in a mixture of uniform composition, weak diffusion currents are established with one component transported in the same direction as heat and the other in the opposite direction. No practical use was made of this effect, because it is so weak, until Clusius and Dickel [*Z. physik. Chem.*, **B44**, 397,451 (1939)] developed the thermal-diffusion column, which is shown schematically in Fig. 21-8. The gas mixture to be separated is confined in the annular space between two vertical cylinders,

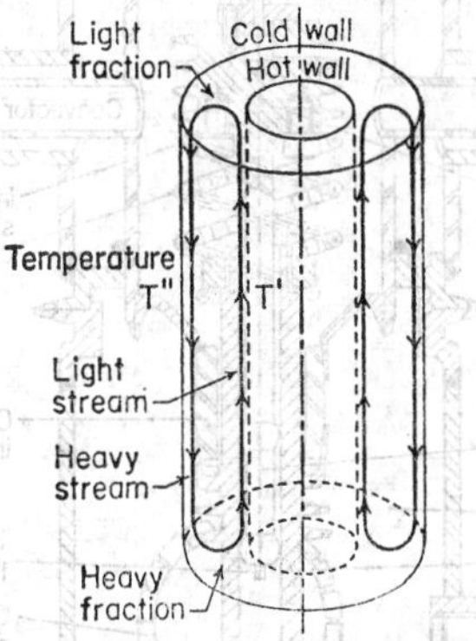

FIG. 21-8. Thermal-diffusion column. (*Benedict and Pigford, "Nuclear Chemical Engineering," McGraw-Hill, New York,* 1957.)

the inner one heated and the outer one cooled. The lighter constituent of the gas mixture concentrates in the heated area adjacent to the inner hot cylinder. Convection currents are established moving as indicated by the arrows. This counterflow multiplies the concentration difference obtained by simple thermal diffusion and practical application of this principle becomes possible. (A more detailed treatment of the theory of thermal diffusion is given in Sec. 17.)

Thermal diffusion is used mainly for small-scale separation of isotopic mixtures. There is no large-scale gaseous thermal-diffusion plant in operation, because on a large scale, a straight gaseous-diffusion plant is more economical. However, for small-scale isotope separation, thermal-diffusion columns are simplest and most inexpensive. Among the isotopes separated are those of chlorine, hydrogen, carbon, oxygen, and particularly the noble gases.

In order to have a high-temperature difference for maximum output, the inner cylinder is often an electrically heated hot wire or a G.E. Calrod heater. This is practical as long as the gases processed are very stable and do not decompose at the temperature of the hot surface. The outer cylinder may be a water-jacketed metal tube. A single column may be 10 ft. or longer in height and ½ to over 2 in. in diameter (inside diameter of outer tube). Two or more columns may be connected together in series to give the equivalent of a very high column. Connections are often made by a pair of coupling pipes from the bottom of one column to the top of the next one. If one of the two coupling pipes is heated, a convection current is set up and the two pipes form a convector loop. In a thermal-diffusion column, the hot and cold surfaces are preferably as close as possible without introducing large relative variations in spacing. Thus spacers are usually provided along the hot wire or Calrod to center the hot cylinder. Any off centering results in poor separation factor. In addition to centering, it has been found that spacers actually increase markedly the separation in a given column (Watson, The Performance of Thermal Diffusion Columns, "Proceedings of the International Symposium on Isotope Separation, Amsterdam," Interscience, New York, 1958).

As the central wire or Calrod is heated, it tends to expand, and if no allowance is made in the design, the hot wire or heater will bend. It is therefore necessary to attach a weight to the wire or heater to keep it taut and provide space below to allow for the expansion. One design used with success is shown in Fig. 21-9 (Boorman

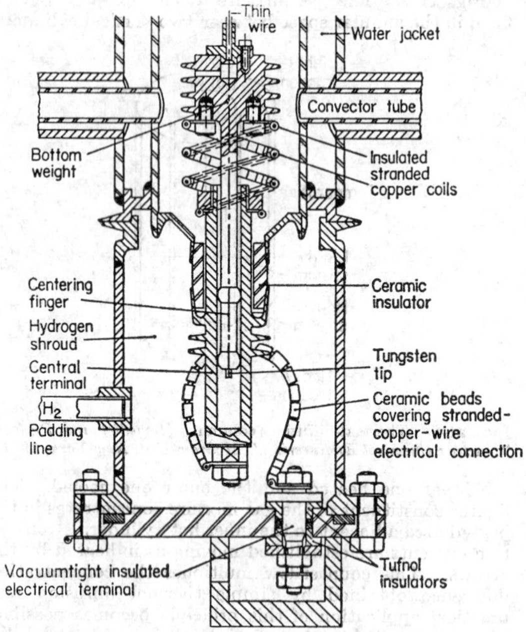

FIG. 21-9. Details of the bottom electrical seal of a thermal-diffusion column. (*Boorman and Kronberger, "The Separation of Hydrogen and Tritium by Thermal Diffusion," Proceedings of the International Symposium on Isotope Separation, Interscience, New York,* 1958.)

and Kronberger, The Separation of Hydrogen and Tritium by Thermal Diffusion, "Proceedings of the International Symposium on Isotope Separation, Amsterdam," Interscience, New York, 1958). The electrical seal consists of a ceramic insulator bonded at each end to metal. Power was brought into the column through the hollow central terminal and through copper coils to a weight attached to the bottom of the wire. This arrangement permitted expansion with the wire heated to 850°C. and maintained accurate centering of the wire. The seal is rugged and vacuumtight. Optimum operating pressure for most gases is generally near or somewhat below atmospheric pressure.

Electromagnetic Separator. The electromagnetic separator is really a large-capacity mass spectrometer developed for isotope separation. When an element or a compound is introduced as a vapor into an ionization chamber under vacuum, the compound is dissociated and the elemental particles are ionized by a stream of electrons from an electrically heated tungsten or tantalum filament. The positively charged ions thus produced are accelerated through a negative potential difference and emerge through corresponding slits in the accelerating electrodes. The high-velocity ions then travel across a uniform magnetic field, which constrains each ion to move in circular orbit. The radius of the orbit of each ion is proportional to the square root of its mass. The maximum separation of the ions of different mass is reached after the particles travel through an angle of 180 deg. By placing a collector at the proper position for each isotope, separated fractions are obtained.

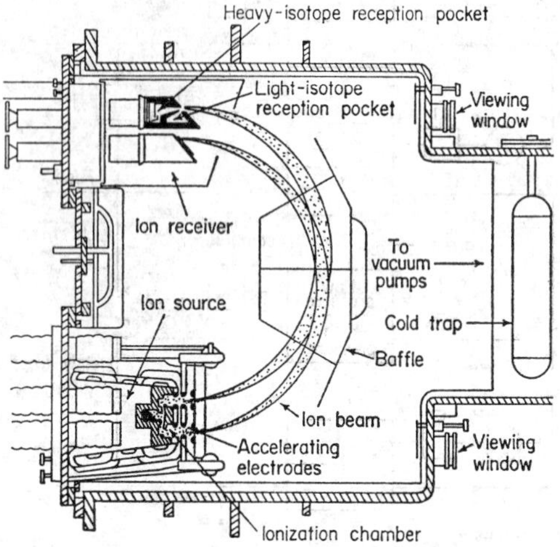

FIG. 21-10. An electromagnetic separator (Calutron) assembly in which two ionization arcs are employed. [*Keim, J. Appl. Phys.*, **24** (10), 1259 (1953).]

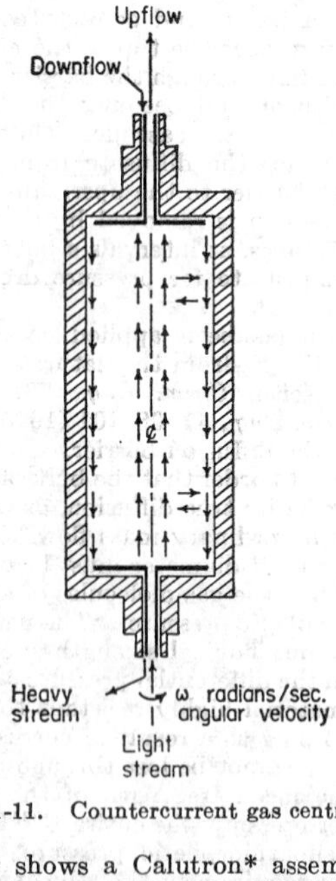

FIG. 21-11. Countercurrent gas centrifuge.

Figure 21-10 shows a Calutron* assembly [Keim, *J. Appl. Phys.*, **24** (10), 1255–1261 (1953)] in which two ionization chambers and two product collectors in parallel are provided inside a single vacuum tank with a single large magnet. The feed to an electromagnetic separator

* Name given to electromagnetic separator developed by California University Cyclotron Laboratory.

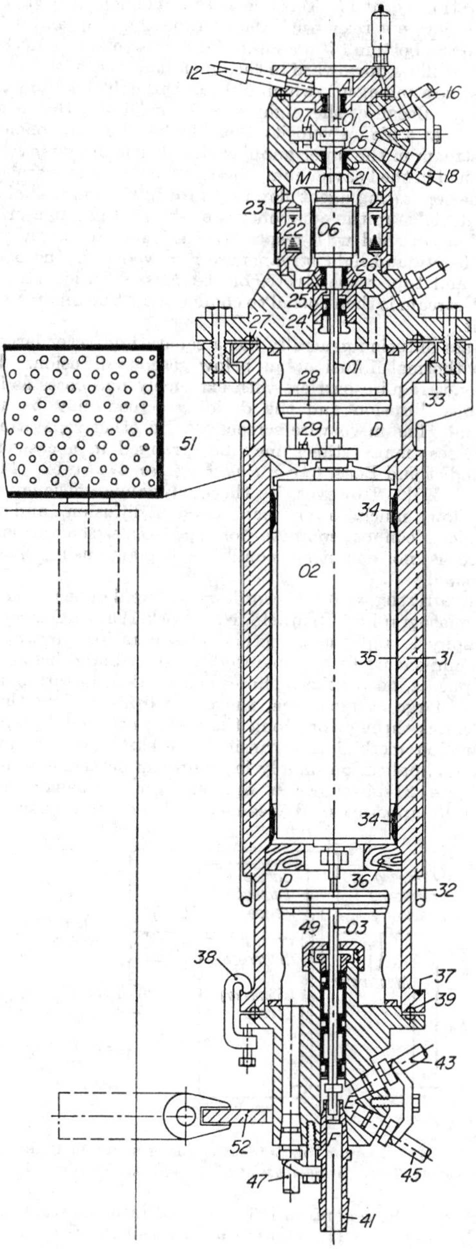

FIG. 21-12. Vertical section of gas centrifuge.

Rotating system:
01 Upper tube shaft
02 Rotor
03 Lower tube shaft
05 Motor shaft
06 Motor armature

Upper gas seal:
A Gas chamber
C Seal chamber
12 Gas inlet
16 Evacuation line (also hydrogen inlet)
18 Oil outlet

Motor:
M Motor space
21 Upper bearing
22 Stator
23 Cooling jacket of stator
25 Seal sleeve
26 Lower bearing

Safety guard:
31 Safety cylinder
32 Cooling coil
34 Catch rings (plastic)

Lower gas seal:
E Seal chamber
F Gas chamber
41 Connection for gas outlet
43 Evacuation line
45 Oil outlet
47 Oil outlet

Foundation:
51 Support for the installation
52 Safety catch against torsion
53 Concrete foundation

(*Beyerle and Groth, "Anreicherung der Uranisotope nach dem Gaszentrifugenverfahren," Proceedings of the Symposium on Isotope Separation, Interscience, New York,* 1958.)

may be a gas, a volatilizable element, or a volatile compound, such as the chloride of many metals. The operating pressure is in the order of 2×10^{-5} mm. Hg. Thus, any solid charge material used would be heated to a temperature sufficiently high to cause vaporization at this pressure. The ion source is regulated to vaporize the charge at a controlled rate. The receivers or collectors are normally cooled so as to retain the condensed isotope fraction. In case the product is a gas, the collector must contain some material which can hold the product in non-volatile form. For example, for nitrogen, a graphite collector with magnesium is used to retain nitrogen as magnesium nitride. Such collector material must also be easily separated from the product by chemical means. Thus the electromagnetic separator is not readily applicable to noble gases.

Operation of electromagnetic separators is batchwise. A cycle involves start-up, production, and cool-down. The same collector pockets usually used for a number of consecutive runs of an element must be sent to the chemical laboratory for product recovery. Sometimes in order to obtain high purity, the recovered product must be processed again in the electromagetic separator. Thus, while this apparatus is most versatile in separating small quantities of isotopes and it has a high separation factor, it is not economical for large-scale operation, since the output of each machine is limited and production involves batch operation and chemical recovery. Furthermore, the recovery of separated isotope per pass is poor. This is due to the fact that only a fraction of the charge vaporized is ionized and only a fraction of ions formed reach the collectors.

Gas Centrifuge. When a vertical cylinder containing a gas mixture is rotated about its axis at high angular velocity, the contained mixture will tend to separate, with the higher-molecular-weight component concentrating near the wall of the cylinder and the lower-molecular-weight component concentrating toward the axis. If the lighter stream is made to flow upward near the axial region and the heavier stream downward near the wall of the cylinder, a longitudinal composition gradient can be established as shown schematically in Fig. 21-11. The longer the cylinder, the greater the difference in gas composition, other conditions being constant.

The separation factor of a gas centrifuge depends on the difference between the molecular weights of the two constituents and not on the square root of the ratio of the molecular weights as in diffusion processes. This factor is much more favorable for isotopic mixtures of the heavy elements than for those of the light elements. Thus the gas centrifuge should be very economical for large-scale separation of uranium isotopes. However, because of the many engineering problems involved, no large-scale plant has ever been built.

Figure 21-12 shows the vertical cross section of a gas centrifuge developed for isotope separation (Beyerle and Groth, Anreicherung der Uranisotope nach dem Gaszentrifugenverfahren, "Proceedings of the Symposium on Isotope Separation, Amsterdam," pp. 667–694, Interscience, New York, 1958). The rotor has an accurately machined outside diameter of 150 mm. Its wall thickness is 8 mm. and its length is 700 mm. It is fabricated of an aluminum alloy called Bondur which has high elastic limit and tensile strength. The shaft is hollow so that gas can be fed and removed through it. The motor delivers 2.1 kw. at 60,000 r.p.m. All bearings are lubricated by a forced circulation system. The centrifuge has been tested to separate isotopes of xenon, krypton, selenium (as hydrogen selenide), and uranium (as uranium hexafluoride). It has been found that, under certain conditions, better separation is obtained when the feed is blended with hydrogen. It appears that the presence of hydrogen minimizes radial pressure gradients and, therefore, radial currents, because of its low molecular weight.

A gas centrifuge may also be operated with the temperature at the top and at the bottom maintained at different levels by means of suitable heating or cooling devices. When this is done, the separation obtained is dependent on this temperature gradient, which causes convection circulation inside the centrifuge.

Mass Diffusion. A simple mass-diffusion gas-separating apparatus is illustrated in Fig. 21-13 [Maier,

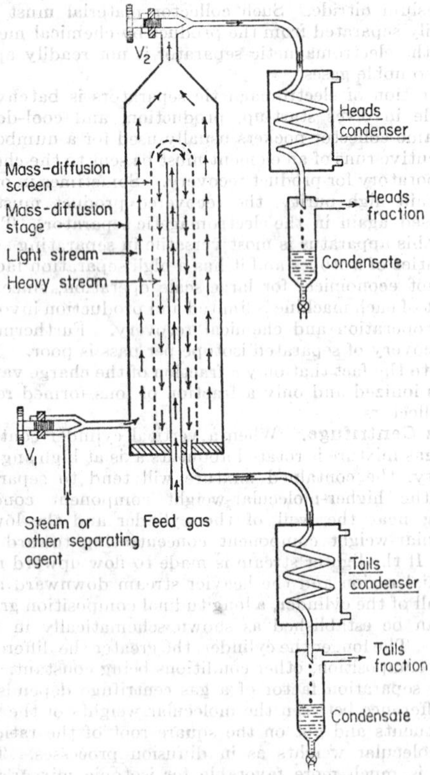

FIG. 21-13. Mass-diffusion apparatus used by Maier.

J. Chem. Phys., **7**, 854 (1939); *U.S. Bur. Mines Bull.* 431, 1940]. The heart of this apparatus is the cylindrical mass-diffusion stage, which consists of two annular chambers separated by a cylindrical mass-diffusion screen. The feed-gas mixture is fed through a central riser to the top of the inner annular chamber. The separating agent is a selected readily condensable vapor which does not react with the gases in the feed, and it is fed to the bottom of the outer annular chamber. As the feed gas flows downward in the inner chamber, it picks up the separating agent, which diffuses through the dividing screen. Because the lighter component in the feed diffuses at a higher velocity then the heavier component, the stream in the inner annular chamber is progressively enriched in the heavier component. For the same reason, as the separating agent flows upward in the outer chamber, it picks up the components of the feed gas at a proportion enriched with respect to the lighter component. The heavy and light streams are removed from the bottom and top, respectively, of the mass-diffusion stage. Each stream is then cooled to condense out the separating agent.

Mass diffusion generally has a separating factor larger than thermal diffusion but below gaseous diffusion. It does not require barriers with extremely fine pores as in gaseous diffusion and the dividing screen may be an ordinary fine-mesh wire screen. As in other separating processes, many stages may be arranged in a cascade [Benedict and Boas, *Chem. Eng. Progress*, **47**, 51–62, 111–122 (1951)]. However, its thermodynamic efficiency is very low, much lower than gaseous diffusion, and it therefore cannot compete for large-scale separations. There is no operating commercial plant using mass diffusion.

Chromatograph. According to Keulemans ("Gas Chromatography," Reinhold, New York, 1959), "Chromatography is a physical method of separation, in which the components to be separated are distributed between two phases, one of these phases constituting a stationary bed of large surface area, the other being a fluid that percolates through or along the stationary bed." This separation method is intrinsically a batch process and finds its application mainly in analytical determinations.

Figure 21-14 shows a diagram for a gas-chromatography apparatus. By some suitable device, a sample

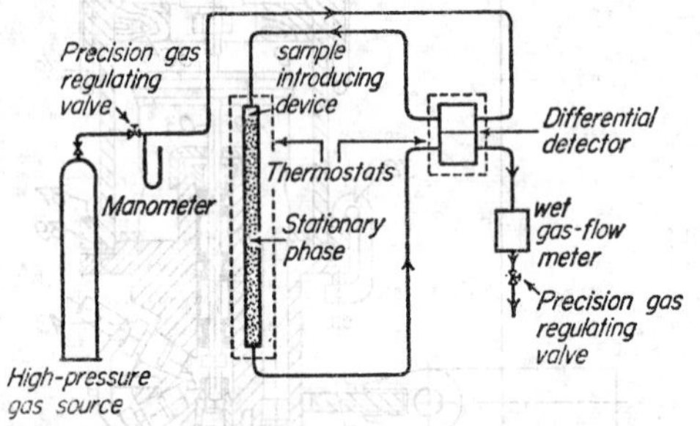

FIG. 21-14. Diagram of apparatus for gas chromatography. (*Keulemans, "Gas Chromatography," Reinhold, New York,* 1959.)

mixture to be separated is introduced into the front end of the column. The column is maintained at a certain temperature and a constant flow of an inert carrier gas is passed through it. This gas, the "eluent," transports the components of the mixture in vapor or gaseous form through the column. Since the components are retained by the stationary phase to different degree, their effective speeds in flowing through the column therefore differ. The column is always sufficiently long, so that when the components emerge from the outlet end, they emerge as individual "bands" separated by zones of the carrier gas. Composition of the effluent is then sensed by a delicate detecting device, capable of indicating the presence of the components qualitatively and quantitatively.

The efficiency of this method of separation is very high

and a high number of theoretical plates is obtained in a reasonably short column.

Stationary Phase. The stationary phase may be either a liquid supported on a solid or a solid. Table 21-2 gives a list of materials commonly used as the stationary phase.

Table 21-2. Liquids and Solids Commonly Used as a Stationary Phase for Gas Chromatography

Compound	Applications
Dimethyl sulfolane, on firebrick	For light hydrocarbon gases
Tricresyl phosphate, on firebrick	For chlorinated hydrocarbons
Squalene (2, 6, 10, 15, 19, 23-hexamethyltetracosane, $C_{30}H_6$), on firebrick. Obtained by hydrogenating squalene from shark's-liver oil	For light hydrocarbon gases
Palladium black (on asbestos)	For hydrogen isotopes
Activated charcoal	For O_2, N_2, CO, CH_4, C_2H_4, and C_2H_6
Silica gel	For O_2, N_2, CO, CH_4, C_2H_4, and C_2H_6

Support for a Liquid. The most common support is ground firebrick of 30/50 or 50/80 mesh size.

Column. A column for an analytical apparatus usually lies between 4 to 8 mm. inside diameter and 6 to 60 ft. long. It may be vertical or horizontal but usually is bent into a coil. The coiled column is immersed in a thermostat.

Carrier Gas. Most frequently used are helium, hydrogen, nitrogen, and carbon dioxide.

Detector. Best detectors are of the differential type in which a physical property of the carrier gas is compared with that of the carrier gas containing the transported component. The most commonly used detector makes use of thermal conductivity which is measured by a Wheatstone bridge.

The application of gas chromatograph for gas separation is limited to analytical determinations because the method is a "batch process" and the volume of gas processed is small. The only other application, other than analysis, is to use it to concentrate small quantities of impure but rare isotopes, such as tritium from hydrogen [Glueckauf and Kitt, Gas Chromatographic Separation of Hydrogen Isotopes, "Proceedings of the Symposium on Isotope Separation, Amsterdam," pp. 210–225, Kistemaker, Bigeleisen, and Nier (eds.), Interscience, New York, (1958)]. No large-scale equipment of this type is used in industrial gas separation.

Chemical Reactions. Table 21-3 lists the common commercial applications of separating a constituent from a gas mixture by means of chemical reactions.

Condensers. When the boiling point of one component of a gas mixture is very much different than those of the other components, the condensation method may be used to separate this component from the gas mixture. Described below is the equipment used in three commercial applications of this separating principle.

Helium from Natural Gas. Natural gas processed for helium recovery generally contains less than 2 per cent of helium. Thus, in separating helium, the feed gas is approximately 98 per cent condensed to yield a remaining gas of crude helium and nitrogen with very little methane. In plants operated by the U.S. Bureau of Mines [Mullins, *Chem. Eng. Progress*, **44**, 567–572 (1948)], condensation of natural gas is accomplished in custom-built shell-and-tube heat exchangers fabricated of copper and its alloys. Small-diameter tubes are joined to the tube sheets by sweating in place with 50 to 50 tin-lead solder. This construction has been found to give leakproof joints when the exchanger is operated at temperatures of −230° to −240°F. and at pressures of 200 to 300 lb./sq. in. gage.

Recovery of Phthalic Anhydride. Phthalic anhydride is obtained by the oxidation of naphthalene or orthoxylene with air in the vapor phase in the presence of a vanadium pentoxide catalyst. The hot reactor effluent containing the phthalic anhydride vapor is usually cooled in large air-cooled boxlike chambers, often called barns, to crystallize out the phthalic anhydride as long needlelike crystals. As the crystals grow, they fall down to the bottom and are removed. Periodically the boxes have to be cleaned.

In the former I. G. Ludwigshafen phthalic anhydride plant (Hunter, B.I.O.S. *Final Rept.* 753, Item 22, H.M. Stationery Office, London), the condensing system consisted of 15 sets of receiver boxes in series (see Fig. 21-15)

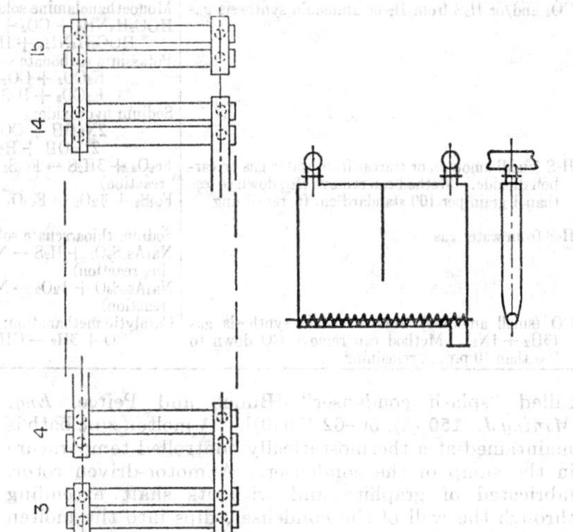

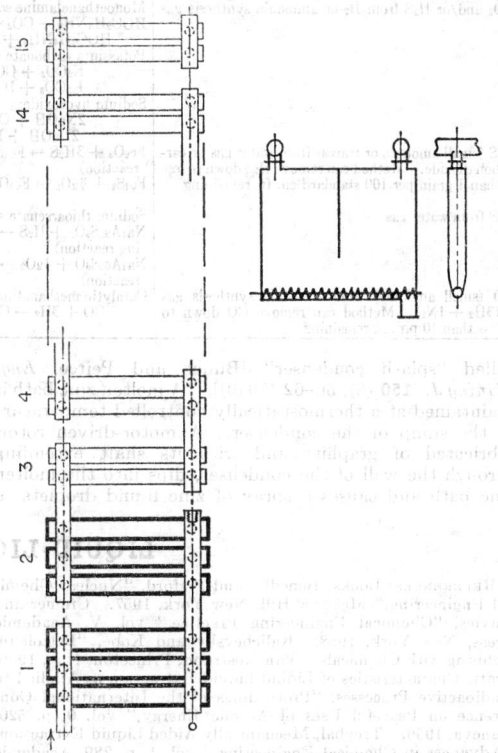

FIG. 21-15. Crude phthalic anhydride condensing system. (*Hunter, B.I.O.S. Final Rept. 753, H. M. Stationery Office, London.*)

each box approximately 18 ft. long, 12 ft. high, and 2 ft. wide with a dividing baffle. The first two sets were water-cooled and the remaining 13 sets air-cooled. Since at least two boxes are in parallel in each set, any one may be cleaned while the other was collecting product. A screw conveyor at the lower end of each receiver box delivered the product to a discharge chute.

In a recently built English plant, phthalic anhydride is crystallized out on the outside surface of spiro-gilled finned tubes cooled on the inside by a circulating oil stream (Riley, *Chem. & Ind.*, 1956, pp. 1464–1468). Periodically, by means of proper controls, the circulating-oil temperature is raised and the phthalic anhydride crystals are melted. Thus for each plant a multiple condensing system is provided so that, while some condensers are crystallizing out product, the remainder are melting the crystals.

Recovery of Zinc. In the commercial production of zinc, zinc oxide is reduced by carbon in a heated vertical retort. The products of reaction from the retort are mainly zinc vapor and carbon monoxide. Zinc is separated from carbon monoxide by condensation in the so-

Table 21-3.

Constituent removed	Chemical reaction involved	Equipment used
O_2 (small amounts or traces) from H_2 or $3H_2 + 1N_2$ mixture. Method removes O_2 down to less than 1 p.p.m. remaining	Catalytic deoxidation: $2H_2 + O_2 \rightarrow 2H_2O$ Catalysts: Palladium catalyst active at room temperature Nickel catalyst active at 350°F.	Vertical cylindrical vessels packed with suitable catalyst
O_2 from argon in high-purity argon production. Method removes O_2 down to less than 1 p.p.m. remaining	Add sufficient H_2 to react according to following equation: $2H_2 + O_2 \xrightarrow{\text{Pd cat.}} 2H_2O$	Vertical cylindrical vessels packed with suitable catalyst
Ammonia from coke-oven gas. Essentially quantitative ammonia removal with less than 1 grain of NH_3 per 100 standard cu. ft. of gas remaining	$2NH_3 + H_2SO_4 \rightarrow (NH_4)_2SO_4$	Single-stage spray chamber or single-contact sparger pipe in vessel containing ammonium sulfate solution with excess H_2SO_4
CO_2 and/or H_2S from H_2 or ammonia synthesis gas	Monoethanolamine solution: $HOC_2H_4NH_2 + CO_2 + H_2O \rightarrow (HOC_2H_4NH_3)HCO_3$ $HOC_2H_4NH_2 + H_2S \rightarrow (HOC_2H_4NH_3)HS$ Potassium carbonate solution: $K_2CO_3 + CO_2 + H_2O \rightarrow 2KHCO_3$ $K_2CO_3 + H_2S \rightarrow KHCO_3 + KHS$ Sodium hydroxide: $2NaOH + CO_2 \rightarrow Na_2CO_3 + H_2O$ $2NaOH + H_2S \rightarrow Na_2S + 2H_2O$	Countercurrent absorption towers provided with either packing or trays
H_2S (small amounts or traces) from water gas or carbon dioxide. Method can remove H_2S down to less than 1 grain per 100 standard cu. ft. remaining	$Fe_2O_3 + 3H_2S \rightarrow Fe_2S_3 + 3H_2O$ (sulfur-removal reaction) $Fe_2S_3 + \frac{3}{2}O_2 \rightarrow Fe_2O_3 + 3S$ (regeneration reaction)	Three or four large boxes with rectangular cross section packed with wood chips coated with iron oxide powder, two or three on stream in series, the remaining box being regenerated by air oxidation
H_2S from water gas	Sodium thioarsenate solution: $Na_4As_2S_5O_2 + H_2S \rightarrow Na_4As_2S_6O + H_2O$ (absorbing reaction) $Na_4As_2S_6O + \frac{1}{2}O_2 \rightarrow Na_4As_2S_5O_2 + S$ (revivifying reaction)	Absorption accomplished in countercurrent packed towers. Revivification is by a blowing of the solution with air also in tall towers. Sulfur precipitated is removed by filtration with continuous vacuum filters
CO (small amounts) from ammonia synthesis gas ($3H_2 + 1N_2$). Method can remove CO down to less than 10 p.p.m. remaining	Catalytic methanation: $CO + 3H_2 \rightarrow CH_4 + H_2O$ Fe or Ni cat.	Vertical cylindrical reactor packed with catalyst. Operating pressure ranges from 350 to 15,000 lb./sq. in. gage

called "splash condenser" [Bunce and Peirce, *Eng. Mining J.*, **150** (3), 56–62 (1949)]. A molten zinc bath is maintained at a thermostatically controlled temperature in the sump of the condenser. A motor-driven rotor, fabricated of graphite and with its shaft extending through the wall of the condenser, dips into the molten zinc bath and causes a spray of zinc liquid droplets to fill the condenser chamber and wash the condenser walls. Since the liquid zinc droplets are cooler, zinc vapor condenses on these droplets and on the walls and then falls back into the bath. Molten zinc is continuously removed from the condenser by overflowing through an external well. Heat is removed from the zinc bath by water-cooled coils in the outer wall of the sump.

LIQUID-LIQUID SYSTEMS

REFERENCES: Books: Benedict and Pigford, "Nuclear Chemical Engineering," McGraw-Hill, New York, 1957. Cremer and Davies, "Chemical Engineering Practice," vol. V, Academic Press, New York, 1958. Kalichevsky and Kobe, "Petroleum Refining with Chemicals," Van Nostrand, Princeton, N.J., 1956. Pratt, Characteristics of Liquid-Liquid Extraction as Applied to Radioactive Processes, "Proceedings of the International Conference on Peaceful Uses of Atomic Energy," vol. 9, p. 520, Geneva, 1956. Treybal, Mechanically Aided Liquid Extraction, "Advances in Chemical Engineering," vol. 1, p. 289, Academic Press, New York, 1956. Treybal, "Liquid Extraction," 2d ed., McGraw-Hill, New York, 1963.

Journals: Davis, Hicks, and Vermeulen, *Chem. Eng. Progress*, **50,** 188 (1954). Elgin, *Ind. Eng. Chem.*, **38,** 26 (1946); **39,** 23 (1947); **40,** 53 (1948); **41,** 35 (1949); **42,** 47 (1950). Freshwater, *Ind. Chemist*, **29,** 451 (1953); *Chem. Age*, **71,** 647 (1954). Hecker, *Österr. Chemiker-Ztg.*, **50,** 3 (1955). Morello and Poffenberger, *Ind. Eng. Chem.*, **42,** 1021 (1950). Pratt, *Ind. Chemist*, **30,** 437, 475, 597 (1954); **31,** 63, 505, 552 (1955). Quillen, *Chem. Eng.*, **61,** (6), 178 (1954). Rushton, *Ind. Eng. Chem.*, **44,** 2931 (1952). Thornton, *Nuclear Eng.*, **1,** 156, 204 (1956). Treybal, *Ind. Eng. Chem.*, **43,** 79 (1951); **44,** 53 (1952); **45,** 55 (1953); **46,** 91 (1954); **47,** 536 (1955); **48,** 518 (1956); **49,** 514 (1957); **50,** 463 (1958); **51,** 378 (1959); **52,** 262 (1960). Von Berg and Wiegandt, *Chem. Eng.*, **59** (6), 189 (1952); **61** (7), 183 (1954). Woodwark, *Trans. Inst. Chem. Engrs.*, **31,** 175 (1953).

Introduction. This section is concerned primarily with the operating characteristics, design, and selection of equipment used for the direct contact of two insoluble liquids for the purpose of causing a transfer of dissolved substance or heat from one to the other, or causing a chemical reaction between them.

Objectives. Insoluble liquids may be brought into direct contact with each other for any of four principal purposes, of which several may be under simultaneous consideration:

1. *Separation of solution components.* This includes the ordinary objectives of liquid extraction, wherein the constituents of a solution are separated by causing their unequal distribution between two insoluble liquids, the washing of a liquid with another to remove small amounts of a dissolved impurity, and the like. The theoretical principles governing the phase relationships, material balances, and the number of ideal stages or transfer units required to bring about the desired changes are to be found in Sec. 14. Dimensions of equipment, with which this section is concerned, are governed by considerations of the quantities of liquids to be handled, and the efficiency and operating characteristics of the type of equipment chosen.

2. *Chemical reaction between insoluble liquids.* The reagents may be the liquids themselves, or they may be dissolved in insoluble liquid solvents. The reaction rates to be expected, which are generally included in the study of reaction kinetics, and the time required for the desired degree of reaction are treated in Sec. 4.

3. *Cooling or heating a liquid by direct contact with another.* This is an infrequently used technique when heat transfer is the sole purpose of the operation. It is more customary to find applications which include chemical reaction or liquid extraction as simultaneous requirements.

4. *Creating permanent emulsions.* The problem here is the mechanical one of dispersing one liquid in another in such finely divided form that subsequent mechanical separation by settling either does not occur, or occurs at most only with extreme slowness. The ultimate goal is the emulsion itself, and neither extraction nor chemical reaction between the liquids is ordinarily contemplated.

Liquid-liquid contacting equipment may be generally

classified into two categories: **stagewise** and **continuous** (**differential**) contact.

STAGEWISE EQUIPMENT—MIXER-SETTLERS

The function of a stage is to contact the liquids, allow equilibrium to be approached, and to make a mechanical separation of the liquids. The contacting and separating correspond to mixing the liquids and settling the resulting dispersion; so that these devices are usually called **mixer-settlers.** The operations may be carried out in batch fashion or with continuous flow. If batch, it is likely that the same vessel will serve for both mixing and settling, whereas if continuous, separate vessels are usually but not always used.

Notation

a = specific interfacial surface between liquids, sq. ft./cu. ft.
a' = activity of a solute in solution
a_p = specific packing surface, sq. ft./cu. ft. packed section
b = a constant
C = a constant
C_O = orifice coefficient, dimensionless
C_R = the smaller of d_S^2/T^2 or $(T^2 - d_i^2)/T^2$, dimensionless
c = concentration, lb.-moles/cu. ft.
D = diffusivity, sq. ft./hr.
d = differential operator
d_F = packing size, ft.
d_{FC} = critical packing size, ft.
d_i = impeller diameter, ft.
d_O = nozzle, perforation, or orifice diameter, ft.
d_p = size of drop = diameter of a sphere of same volume/surface ratio, ft.
d_S = diameter of opening in circular baffle, ft.
E = stage efficiency of a single stage, fractional
E_{MD} = Murphree dispersed-phase stage efficiency, fractional
E_{ME} = Murphree extract stage efficiency, fractional
E_{MR} = Murphree raffinate stage efficiency, fractional
E_O = over-all stage efficiency of a cascade, fractional
e = 2.7183
f = pulse frequency, cycles/hr.
g = acceleration due to gravity $\doteq 4.18(10^8)$ ft./sq. hr.
g_c = conversion factor, $4.18(10^8)$ (lb. mass) ft./(lb. force) (sq. hr.)
H_{tOC} = over-all height of a transfer unit, continuous phase, ft.
H.E.T.S. = height equivalent to a theoretical stage, ft.
h = head loss due to friction; depth of dispersed phase on a perforated plate, ft.
h_C = contribution to h due to continuous phase, ft.
h_D = contribution to h due to dispersed phase, ft.
h_O = contribution to h_D due to orifice, ft.
h_σ = contribution to h_D due to interfacial tension, ft.
K = over-all mass-transfer coefficient, lb.-moles/hr. (sq. ft.)(mole fraction)
K' = over-all mass-transfer coefficient, lb.-moles/hr. (sq. ft.)(lb.-mole/cu. ft.)
K_a = over-all mass-transfer coefficient, lb./moles/hr. (sq. ft)(activity)
k' = individual phase mass-transfer coefficient, lb.-moles/hr. (sq. ft.)(lb.-moles/cu. ft.)
m = slope of equilibrium distribution curve dy/dx, mole fraction/mole fraction
m' = slope of equilibrium distribution curve, dc_E/dc_R, (lb.-moles/cu. ft.)/(lb.-moles/cu. ft.)
m_{CD}' = slope of equilibrium distribution curve, dc_C/dc_D, (lb-moles/cu. ft.)/(lb-moles/cu. ft.)
N = impeller speed, r.p.h.
N_{Fr} = Froude number d_iN^2/g, dimensionless
N_{Po} = power number $Pg_c/\rho N^3 d_i^5$, dimensionless
N_{Re} = Reynolds number of an impeller $d_i^2N\rho/\mu$, dimensionless
N_{Sc} = Schmidt number $\mu/\rho D$, dimensionless
n = number of orifices or perforations per plate
P = power for one real stage, ft. (lb. force)/hr.
Δp = pressure drop, lb. force/sq. in.
Q = total flow rate, cu. ft./hr.
q = rate of mass transfer, lb.-moles/hr. (sq. ft.); for batch operation, total mass transfer, lb.-moles
S = cross-sectional area of a tower, sq. ft.
s = average of the mutual solubilities of solute-free contacted liquids, weight per cent
T = diameter of mixing vessel or extraction tower, ft.
V = superficial velocity, ft./hr. = cu. ft./hr. (sq. ft.)
V_d = velocity in a downspout, ft./hr.
V_K = characteristic drop velocity, ft./hr.
V_O = velocity through an orifice or nozzle, ft./hr.
V_O' = velocity through an orifice or nozzle, ft./sec.
V_S = slip velocity, ft./hr.
V_t = terminal settling velocity at $\varphi_D \doteq 0$, ft./hr.
v = volume of liquid, cu. ft.
w = pulse amplitude, ft.
Z = height of liquid in vessel (mixer), ft.; for towers, height of packed section, ft.
Z_t = distance between trays, ft.
Z_t' = distance between trays, in.
z = a distance, ft.
Δp = pressure drop, lb./sq. in.
$\Delta\rho$ = difference in densities, lb. mass/cu. ft.
ϵ = fraction void volume in packed section
θ = time of contact, hr.
μ = viscosity, lb. mass/ft. hr. = 2.42 (centipoises)
ρ = density, lb./cu. ft.
σ = interfacial tension, lb. mass/sq. hr. = $28.7(10^3)$(dynes/cm.)
σ' = interfacial tension, dynes/cm.
φ = volume fraction of liquid in a vessel or extractor
ψ = frictional power absorbed by liquids in perforations of a sieve plate, sq. ft./cu. hr.

Subscripts:
C = continuous phase
D = dispersed phase
E = extract
e = at equilibrium
F = flooding
H = heavy liquid
L = light liquid
o = organic liquid
R = raffinate
w = water or aqueous liquid
1 = before
2 = after

Mixer-Settler Equipment. The equipment for extraction or chemical reaction may be classified as follows:

I. Mixers
  A. Flow or line mixers
    1. Mechanical agitation
    2. No mechanical agitation

B. Agitated vessels
1. Mechanical agitation
2. Gas agitation

II. Settlers
A. Non-mechanical
1. Gravity
2. Centrifugal (cyclones)

B. Mechanical (centrifuges)

C. Settler auxiliaries
1. Coalescers
2. Separator membranes
3. Electrostatic equipment

Morello and Poffenberger [*Ind. Eng. Chem.*, **42**, 1021 (1950)], Davis, Hicks, and Vermeulen [*Chem. Eng. Progress*, **50**, 188 (1954)], and Pratt [*Ind. Chemist*, **30**, 475 (1954)] have provided other classifications.

In principle, at least, any mixer may be coupled with any settler to provide the complete stage. There are several combinations which are especially popular. Continuously operated devices usually, but not always, place the mixing and settling functions in separate vessels. Batch-operated devices may use the same vessel alternately for the separate functions.

Mixers

Flow or Line Mixers. These are mixers through which the liquids to be contacted are passed, characterized principally by the very small time of contact for the liquids. They are used only for continuous operations or semibatch (where one liquid flows continuously and the other is continuously recycled). If holding time is required for extraction or reaction, it must be provided for by passing the mixed liquids through a vessel of the necessary volume. This may be a long pipe of large diameter, sometimes fitted with segmental baffles, but frequently the settler which follows the mixer serves. The energy for mixing and dispersing usually comes from pressure drop resulting from flow.

There are many types, and only the most important can be mentioned here. See also Hunter in "Science of Petroleum," [Dunstan (ed.), vol. 3, pp. 1779–1797, Oxford, New York, 1938]. They are used fairly extensively in treating petroleum distillates, in vegetable-oil refining, in extraction of phenol-bearing coke-oven liquors, in some metal extractions, and the like. Kalichevsky and Kobe ("Petroleum Refining with Chemicals," Elsevier, New York, 1956) discuss detailed application in refining of petroleum.

Jet Mixers. These depend upon impingement of one liquid on the other for obtaining a dispersion, and one of the liquids is pumped through a small nozzle or orifice into a flowing stream of the other. Both liquids are pumped. They can be used successfully only for liquids of low interfacial tension. See Fig. 21-16 and also Hunter and Nash [*Ind. Chemist*, **9**, 245, 263, 317 (1933)]. Treybal ("Liquid Extraction," 2d ed., McGraw-Hill, New York, 1963) describes a more elaborate device.

Trice (U.S. A.E.C. ANL-5741, 1957) used two cylindrical vessels, $T = Z$, $T = 0.333$ and 0.5, through which insoluble liquid pairs were pumped. The arrangement was a form of jet mixer. The droplet size was measured by a light-transmittance scheme, and for two systems, $d_p V_D \rho_C / \mu_C$ was a function of $(T V_D \rho_C / \mu_C)$ $(T V_D^2 \rho_C / \sigma)^{2/3} \varphi_D^{0.5}$. The mass-transfer coefficient for the continuous phase in two systems k_C' was given by

$$\frac{k_C' T}{D_C} = 0.03 \left(\frac{T V_D \rho_C}{\mu_C}\right)^{0.88} N^{0.5}_{ScC} \qquad (21\text{-}1)$$

Injectors. The flow of one liquid is induced by the flow of the other, with only the majority liquid being

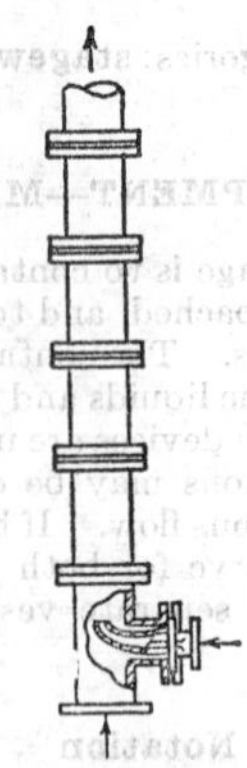

Fig. 21-16. Elbow jet mixer with orifice column. (*Treybal "Liquid Extraction," 2d. ed., McGraw-Hill, New York, 1963, with permission.*)

pumped at relatively high velocity. Figure 21-17 shows a typical device used in semibatch fashion for washing oil with a recirculated wash liquid. It is installed directly in the settling drum. See also Hampton (U.S. Patent 2,091,709, 1933), Sheldon (U.S. Patent 2,009,347, 1935), Ng (U.S. Patent 2,665,975, 1954). Folsom [*Chem. Eng.*

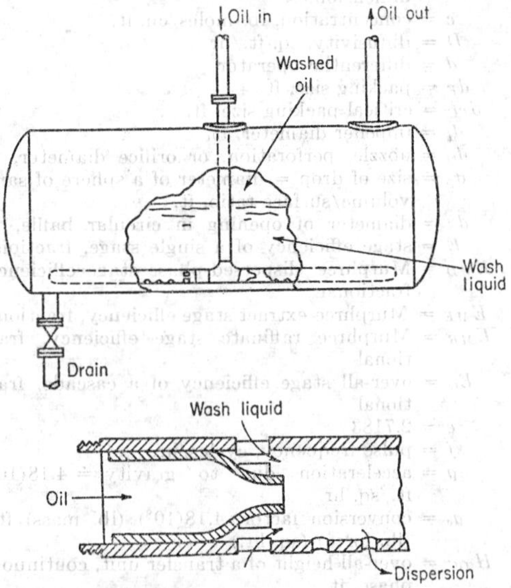

Fig. 21-17. Injector mixer. (*Ayres, U.S. Patent* 2,531,547, 1950.)

Progress, **44**, 765 (1948)] gives a good review of basic principles. The most complete study for extraction is provided by Kafarov and Zhukovskaya [*Zhur. Priklad Khim.*, **31**, 376 (1958)], who used very small injectors. With an injector measuring 73 mm. from throat to exit, with 2.48 mm. throat diameter, they extracted benzoic acid and acetic acid from water with carbon tetrachloride at the rate of 58 to 106 liters/hr., to obtain a stage efficiency $E = 0.8 - 1.0$. Data on flow characteristics are also given.

Orifices and Mixing Nozzles. Both liquids are pumped through constrictions in a pipe, the pressure drop of which is partly utilized to create the dispersion (see Figs. 21-3 and 21-18). Single nozzles or several in series may be used. For the case of orifice mixers, as

Fig. 21-18. Orifice mixer and nozzle mixer.

many as 20 orifice plates each with 2 lb./sq. in. pressure drop may be used in series [Morell and Bergman, *Chem. & Met. Eng.*, **35**, 211 (1928)]. In the Dualayer process for removal of mercaptans from gasoline, 39,000 bbl./day of oil and treating solution are contacted with 10 lb./sq. in. pressure drop per stage [Greek *et al.*, *Ind. Eng. Chem.*, **49**, 1938 (1957)]. Scott, Hayes, and Holland [*A.I.Ch.E. J.*, **4**, 346 (1958)] report on the interfacial area produced when water was dispersed in kerosene through single square-edged orifices in a 1-in. pipe.

Valves may be considered to be adjustable orifice mixers. In desalting crude petroleum by mixing with water, Hayes *et al.* [*Chem. Eng. Progress*, **45**, 235 (1949)] used a globe-valve mixer operating at 16 to 32 lb./sq. in. pressure drop for mixing 416 bbl./hr. oil with 50 bbl./hr. water, with best results at the lowest value. Simkin and Olney [*A.I.Ch.E. J.*, **2**, 545 (1956)] mixed kerosene and white oil with water, using 0.05 to 0.09 lb./sq. in. pressure drop across a 1-in. gate valve, at 10 gal./min. flow rate for optimum separating conditions in a cyclone, but higher pressure drops were required to give good extractor efficiencies (see Table 21-5, item 6).

Pumps. Centrifugal pumps, where the two liquids are fed to the suction side of the pump, have been used fairly extensively, and they offer the advantage that they provide interstage pumping at the same time. They have been commonly used in extraction of phenols from coke-oven liquors with light oil [Gollmar, *Ind. Eng. Chem.*, **39**, 596 (1947). Carbone, *Sewage and Ind. Wastes*, **22**, 200 (1950)], but the intense shearing action causes emulsions with this low interfacial tension system. Modern plants use other types of extractors. They are useful in extraction of slurries, as in the extraction of uranyl nitrate from acid-uranium ore slurries [*Chem. Eng.*, **66**, 30 (Nov. 2, 1959)]. Shaw and Long [*Chem. Eng.*, **64** (11), 251 (1957)] obtain a stage efficiency of 100 per cent ($E = 1.0$) in a uranium-ore slurry extraction with an open impeller pump. In order to avoid emulsification difficulties in these extractions, it is necessary to maintain the organic phase continuous, if necessary by recycling a portion of the settled organic liquid to the mixer. See Fig. 21-37 for costs.

Agitated line mixer. See Fig. 21-19. This device, which combines the features of orifice mixers and agitators, is used extensively in treating petroleum and vegetable oils. It is available in sizes to fit ½- to 10-in. pipe. See Table 21-6 for costs.

Agitated Vessels. These may be used for either batch or continuous service and for the latter may be sized to provide any holding time desired. They are useful for liquids of any viscosity up to 750,000 centipoises, although in contacting two liquids for reaction or extraction purposes, viscosities in excess of 100 centipoises are only rarely encountered.

Mechanical Agitation. This type of agitation utilizes a rotating impeller immersed in the liquid to

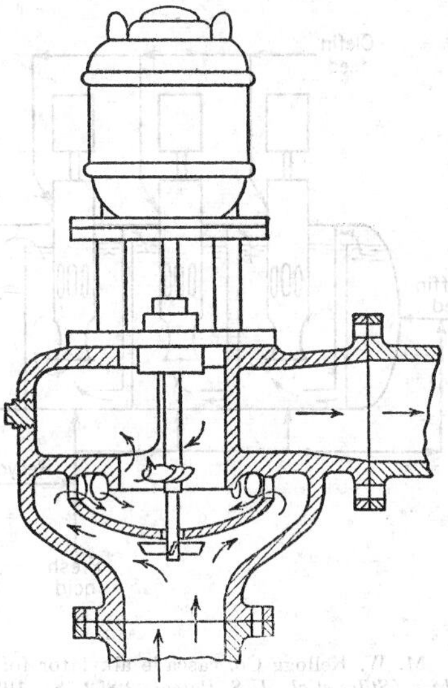

Fig. 21-19. Nettco Corp. "Flomix." (*Chase, U.S. Patent* 2,183,859, 1939.)

accomplish the mixing and dispersion. There are literally hundreds of devices using this principle, the major variations being found in cases where chemical reactions are carried out. The basic requirements regarding shape and arrangement of the vessel, type and arrangement of the impeller, and the like are essentially the same as those for dispersing finely divided solids in liquids, which are fully covered in Sec. 19. Figure 21-20

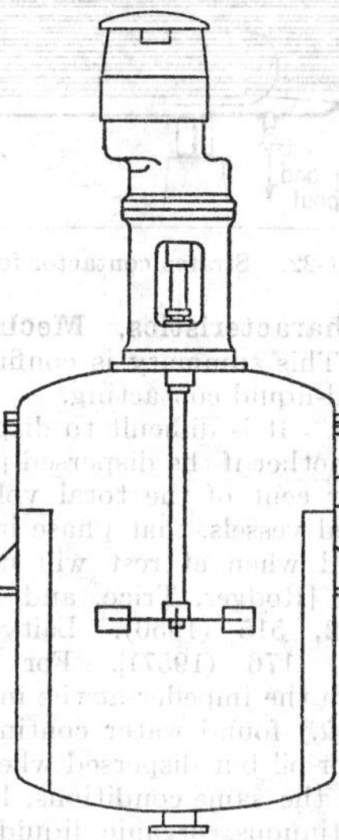

Fig. 21-20. Baffled mixing vessel.

shows a typical single-compartment vessel for extraction or chemical reaction. Back mixing may be reduced, and the extraction stage efficiency thereby increased, by the use of multicompartmented vessels such as those of Fig. 21-31 or, for chemical reactions, in the manner of Fig. 21-21. Figure 21-22 shows an example of a reaction vessel where extensive heat-transfer surface is also required.

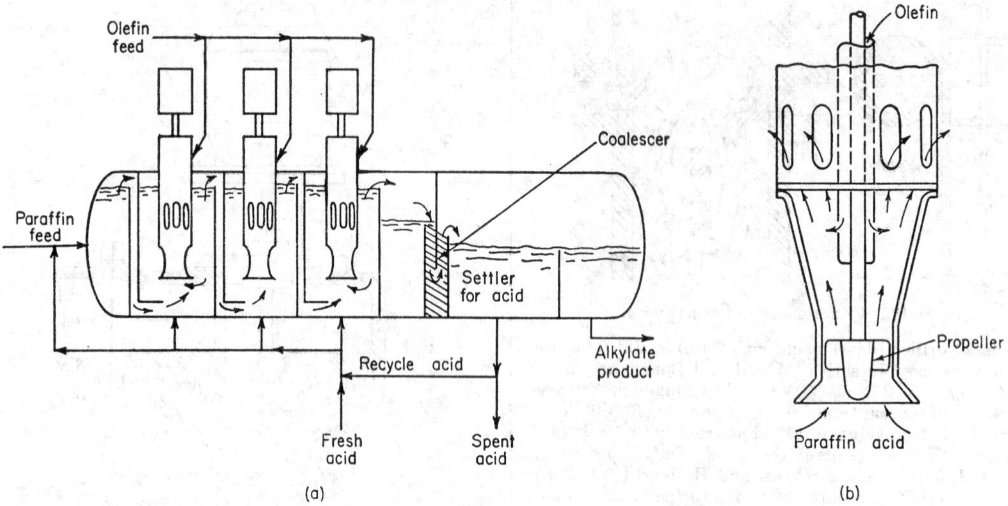

FIG. 21-21. M. W. Kellogg Co. cascade alkylator for sulfuric acid alkylation of paraffins and olefins, simplified (*a*). Mixer detail, simplified (*b*). (*Stiles et al., U.S. Patents* 2,852,581, 1958, and 2,920,124, 1960.)

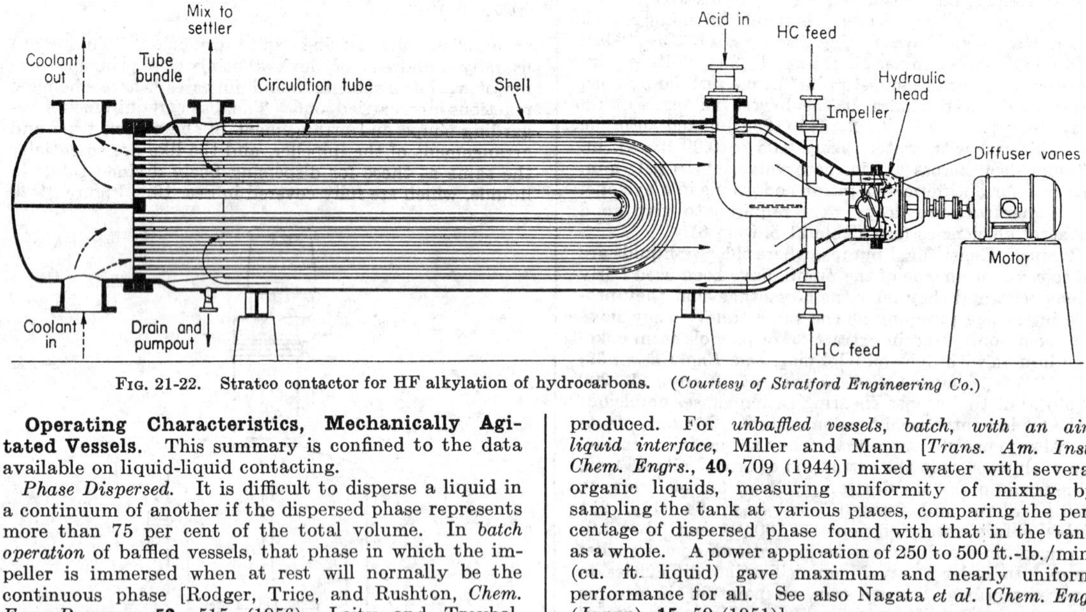

FIG. 21-22. Stratco contactor for HF alkylation of hydrocarbons. (*Courtesy of Stratford Engineering Co.*)

Operating Characteristics, Mechanically Agitated Vessels. This summary is confined to the data available on liquid-liquid contacting.

Phase Dispersed. It is difficult to disperse a liquid in a continuum of another if the dispersed phase represents more than 75 per cent of the total volume. In *batch operation* of baffled vessels, that phase in which the impeller is immersed when at rest will normally be the continuous phase [Rodger, Trice, and Rushton, *Chem. Eng. Progress,* **52,** 515 (1956). Laity and Treybal, *A.I.Ch.E. J.,* **3,** 176 (1957)]. For equal volumes of liquids and with the impeller at the interface when at rest, Laity (*loc. cit.*) found water continuous when agitated with a motor oil but dispersed when agitated with kerosene. Under the same conditions, Rodger (*loc. cit.*) found water continuous, organic liquids dispersed, at low agitator speeds but inversion to organic continuous at high speeds, and this occurred more readily for large values of $\Delta\rho/\rho_C$. With water dispersed, dual emulsions (continuous phase found in small droplets within large drops of dispersed phase) were frequently formed. *In continuous operation,* first the vessel is filled with the liquid to be continuous, then agitation is begun, following which the liquid to be dispersed is introduced.

Uniformity of Mixing. This refers to gross uniformity throughout the vessel and not to size of the droplets produced. For *unbaffled vessels, batch, with an air-liquid interface,* Miller and Mann [*Trans. Am. Inst. Chem. Engrs.,* **40,** 709 (1944)] mixed water with several organic liquids, measuring uniformity of mixing by sampling the tank at various places, comparing the percentage of dispersed phase found with that in the tank as a whole. A power application of 250 to 500 ft.-lb./min. (cu. ft. liquid) gave maximum and nearly uniform performance for all. See also Nagata *et al.* [*Chem. Eng. (Japan),* **15,** 59 (1951)].

For *baffled vessels operated continuously, no air-liquid interface,* Treybal [*A.I.Ch.E. J.,* **4,** 202 (1958)] presents a few miscellaneous data, but no complete studies have been made.

Degree of Dispersion. The fineness of dispersion as measured by the interfacial area produced by agitation has been gaged by a light-transmittance technique. Data and correlations for batch-operated vessels up to 18 in. diameter will be found in the works of Rodger *et al.* [*Chem. Eng. Progress,* **52,** 515 (1956); U.S. A.E.C. ANL-5575, 1956)], Calderbank [*Trans. Inst. Chem. Engrs.,* **36,** 443 (1958)], Vermeulen *et al.* [*Chem. Eng. Progress,* **51,** 85F (1955)], Kafarov and Babanov [*Zhur. Priklad. Khim.,* **32,** 789 (1959)], and Shinar and Church [*Ind. Eng. Chem.,* **52,** 253 (1960)].

Power for Agitation. The data for single liquids in

baffled and unbaffled vessels with an air-liquid interface are very extensive and are summarized by Rushton, Costich, and Everett [*Chem. Eng. Progress*, **46**, 395, 467 (1950)]. See also Sec. 19. In general, for baffled vessels, N_{Po} is a function of N_{Re}, while for unbaffled vessels operated with a vortex, N_{Po} is a function of N_{Re} and N_{Fr}. The data for two-liquid-phase mixtures are very limited.

Unbaffled vessels, air-liquid interface. Miller and Mann [*Trans. Am. Inst. Chem. Engrs.*, **40**, 709 (1944)] measured power requirements using water and a variety of insoluble liquids, $T = 0.5$ to 1.5 ft., with flat- and pitched-blade turbines, a two-bladed propeller, and a spiral turbine. Data for each impeller for both single- and two-phase liquids (water continuous) were correlated, in cases where vortexing did not produce aeration, by the same relationship for both, N_{Po} = function of N_{Re} for $N_{Re} < 10^4$. This required that for two-liquid mixtures the density and viscosity of the mixture be computed as

$$\rho = \rho_C\varphi_C + \rho_D\varphi_D \tag{21-2}$$

and

$$\mu = \mu_C^{\varphi_C}\mu_D^{\varphi_D} \tag{21-3}$$

The Froude number N_{Fr} was not used. At high values of N_{Re}, some difficulty in correlation developed, possibly because of an inversion of the dispersion to water-in-oil, which Eq. (21-3) does not account for.

Baffled vessels (with or without an air-liquid interface). Figure 21-23 shows a correlation of power for two-phase liquids and single liquids, using a six-bladed flat-blade turbine [Laity and Treybal, *A.I.Ch.E. J.*, **3**, 176 (1957)]. The two-liquid data are correlated by the single-liquid curve provided the density is computed by Eq. (21-2) and the viscosity by [Vermeulen *et al.*, *Chem. Eng. Progress*, **51**, 85F (1955)]

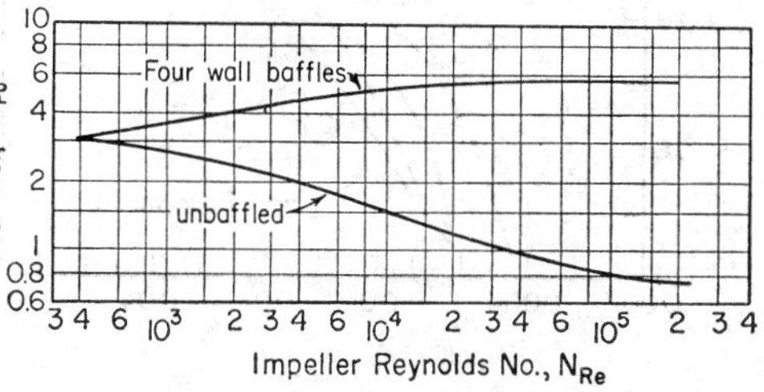

FIG. 21-23. Agitator power for two-liquid mixtures, baffled and unbaffled vessels, no air-liquid interface. $T = 1.0$ to 1.5 ft., $d_i/T = 0.333$ six-bladed flat-blade turbines. [*Laity and Treybal, A.I.Ch.E. J.* **3**, 176 (1959).]

$$\mu = \frac{\mu_C}{\varphi_C}\left(1 + \frac{1.5\mu_D\varphi_D}{\mu_D + \mu_C}\right) \tag{21-4}$$

There is essentially no effect of liquid flow rate when the vessel is operated continuously. Olney and Carlson [*Chem. Eng. Progress*, **43**, 473 (1947)] report power data for an arrowhead disperser used with wall baffles and for a spiral turbine (Turbo-Mixer) with a stator-ring baffle but no wall baffles, with single- and two-phase liquids. Although the data were originally correlated through Eqs. (21-2) and (21-3), it can be shown that a better correlation results if the viscosity is computed through Eq. (21-4).

At least until more data are obtained, it is therefore recommended that the general correlations for single liquids in baffled vessels (Sec. 19) be used for two-liquid mixtures, with density and viscosity computed through Eqs. (21-2) and (21-4), respectively.

Unbaffled vessels, no air-liquid interface. Figure 21-23 shows the results of batch agitation of one- and two-liquid mixtures in 12- and 18-in.-diameter vessels with a six-bladed flat-blade turbine (Laity and Treybal, *loc. cit.*). The correlation shown requires that densities for two liquids be calculated by Eq. (21-2), and viscosities by

$$\mu = \frac{\mu_w}{\varphi_w}\left(1 + \frac{6\varphi_o\mu_o}{\mu_w + \mu_o}\right) \tag{21-5}$$

for $\varphi_w > 0.40$, and

$$\mu = \frac{\mu_o}{\varphi_o}\left(1 - \frac{1.5\varphi_w\mu_w}{\mu_w + \mu_o}\right) \tag{21-6}$$

for $\varphi_w < 0.40$. Below $N_{Re} = 10^4$, the liquids were not uniformly mixed. There is no effect of impeller height from d_i to $2d_i$ from the vessel bottom, and a small effect of liquid flow rate at very high liquid rates when operated continuously. Owing to the lack of data, no generalizations regarding other impeller types may be made. Additional power data are provided by Wingard *et al.* [*Alabama Polytech. Inst. Eng. Expt. Sta. Bull.* **17**, p. 3, 1952].

Rates of Mass Transfer. There have been only a few investigations. A major difficulty in isolating the effects of the agitated vessel is the extraction which occurs during withdrawal of samples of the vessel contents taken for analysis; so that there are probably some effects of settling in many of the available data. In the following work, this is believed to be minimized.

Extraction in unbaffled vessels. Hixson and Smith [*Ind. Eng. Chem.*, **41**, 973 (1949)] batch-extracted iodine from water into a one-tenth volume of carbon tetrachloride in unbaffled glass vessels agitated with an axially arranged three-bladed propeller, $d_i/T = 0.5$, $Z = T$. Data may be correlated by plotting the logarithm of $(1 - E)$ against time, which yields straight lines for any system, vessel size, impeller, and impeller speed. The addition of very small amounts of a surface-active agent has been shown to have a profound effect on the rate of extraction in this system [Holm and Terjesen, *Chem. Eng. Science*, **4**, 265 (1955)].

Karr and Scheibel [*Chem. Eng. Progress*, *Symp. Ser.*, **50** (10), 73 (1954)] studied one of the mixer sections of the extractor shown in Fig. 21-49, arranged for continuous countercurrent flow in such a fashion that the packed sections did not contribute to the extraction. It is not possible to present the detailed results here, but the data of Fig. 21-24 are typical for a narrow range of solute

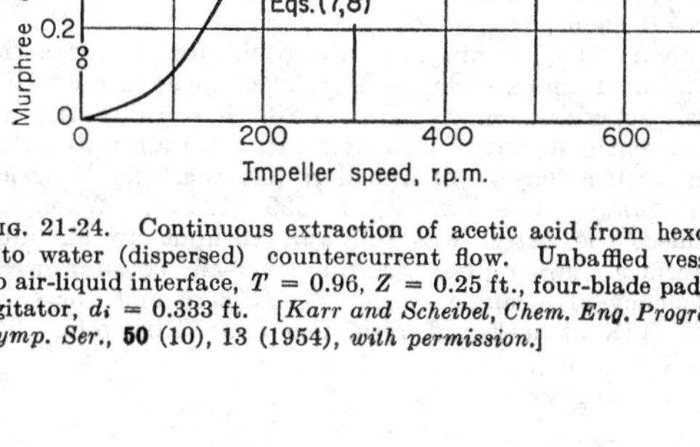

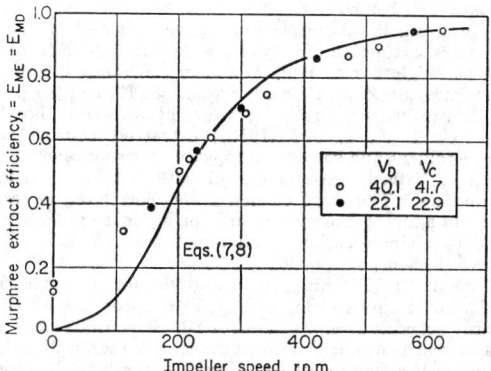

FIG. 21-24. Continuous extraction of acetic acid from hexone into water (dispersed) countercurrent flow. Unbaffled vessel no air-liquid interface, $T = 0.96$, $Z = 0.25$ ft., four-blade paddle agitator, $d_i = 0.333$ ft. [*Karr and Scheibel, Chem. Eng. Progress, Symp. Ser.*, **50** (10), 13 (1954), *with permission.*]

concentrations. The curve shown is calculated from Eqs. (21-7) and (21-8). The data show that some extraction occurs even when the agitator is not turning. The importance of the direction of extraction and which phase is dispersed is emphasized by Karr and Scheibel. Thus, with all other conditions the same, the mass-transfer coefficient when the organic liquid is dispersed is very much larger (up to ten times) if the organic liquid is the extractant than it is if the water is the extractant. In the former case, the droplets are much smaller and the dispersed-phase hold-up larger. These effects, similar to those noted in other systems by others, may be attributed to disturbances of the interface due to interfacial tension, the Marangoni effect [see, for example, Sternling and Scriven, *A.I.Ch.E. J.*, **5**, 514 (1959)]. Since the mixing sections were operated full, there was no vortex, and both dynamic and geometric similarity for a given system is possible for two sizes of mixers. Most of the data for two geometrically similar mixer sections (T = 0.25 and 0.958 ft., Z/T = 0.261, four-bladed flat-paddle agitators, d_i/T = 0.348) and the systems acetic acid–water–hexone (methylisobutyl ketone), acetic acid–water–xylene, and acetone–water–xylene at 77°F. are well correlated empirically by the following (only the first system was used in the smaller extractor):

$$K_a a = \alpha (N d_i)^{\beta} V_D{}^{\gamma} d_i{}^{\delta} \left(\frac{\Delta\rho}{\sigma}\right)^{1.5} \tag{21-7}$$

where the constants are

Dispersed phase	Extractant	α	β	γ	δ	Range of V_D
Organic........	Organic	1.43(10⁻⁷)	4.0	1.0	−1.0	6.1–44.5
Organic........	Water	4.41(10⁻⁷)	4.0	0	−1.0	11.5–41.9
Water.........	Organic or water	2.95(10⁻⁴)	3.0	1.0	−0.3	21.6–42

$K_a a$, which was computed on the assumption that both phases in the vessel were uniformly mixed, is independent of the continuous-phase velocity, at least in the range of values similar to those for V_D above. $K_a a$ may be converted to stage efficiency as follows:

$$E_{MD} = \frac{K_a a}{(V_D/Z)(dc_D/da') + K_a a} \tag{21-8}$$

Overcashier, Kingsley, and Olney [*A.I.Ch.E. J.*, **2**, 529 (1956)] also provide data for unbaffled vessels which are considered below.

In a small laboratory autoclave agitated with flat paddles, extraction of a dye between two liquids occurred at the highest rate if d_i/T was in the range 0.5 to 0.7 [Vishnevsky, *Zhur. Priklad. Khim.*, **28**, 1071 (1955)].

Extraction in baffled vessels. Flynn and Treybal [*A.I.Ch.E. J.*, **1**, 324 (1955)] extracted benzoic acid from toluene and kerosene into water in two geometrically similar baffled vessels agitated with flat-blade turbine impellers. The stage efficiency was correlated in terms of the agitator energy per unit of liquid treated, which led to a single curve for all flow rates and both vessel sizes at each phase ratio.

Figure 21-25 summarizes the results for the extraction of n-butyl amine from kerosene into water in a continuously operated mixer (T = 1.23, Z = 1.562 ft.) fed cocurrently upward, with and without four wall baffles and with a variety of impellers [Overcashier, Kingsley, and Olney, *A.I.Ch.E. J.*, **2**, 529 (1956)]. When unbaffled, the vessel was full and without an air-liquid interface. E_O represents the over-all countercurrent efficiency of a single stage. E_O at zero agitator speed was 0.18 at a liquid residence time 1.08 min. The

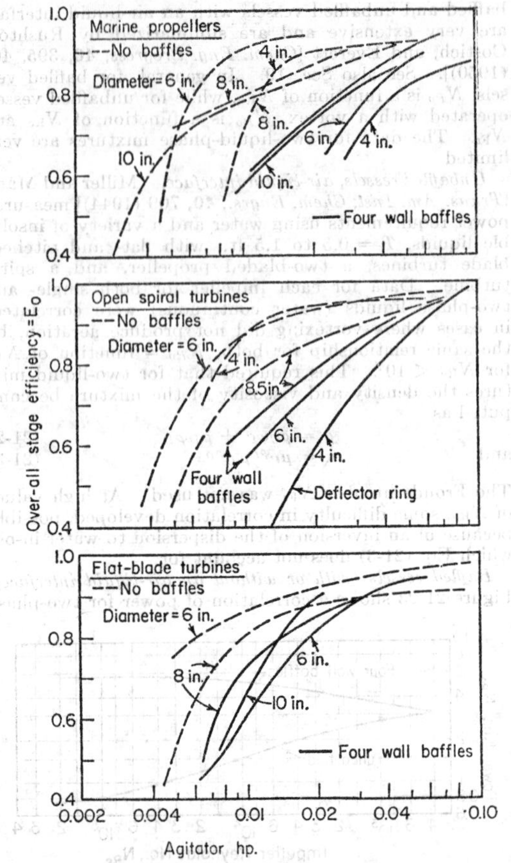

FIG. 21-25. Continuous extraction of n-butyl amine from kerosene into water, T = 1.23, Z = 1.56 ft., no air-liquid interface, impellers centered, V_R/V_E = 1.57, residence time = 1.08 min. [*Overcashier, Kingsley, and Olney, A.I.Ch.E. J.*, **2**, 529 (1956), *with permission.*]

improved performance in the absence of baffles may be attributed to the reduction in back mixing and to the reduced power requirement for a given impeller speed. In the absence of baffles, vertical location of the impeller is immaterial. With baffles, the best performance is given with the impeller at 0.667Z from the bottom, the worst at 0.25Z from the bottom. For the spiral turbine, wall baffles and stator-ring baffles produced the same power-efficiency relationship. Off-center unbaffled operation of a propeller was intermediate between centered baffled and centered unbaffled operation. The data for propellers, spiral turbines, and flat-blade turbines, d_i = 0.333 to 0.833 ft., in both unbaffled and baffled tanks, with a flow rate to produce a residence time θ = 0.18 hr., kerosene/water = 1.57 by volume, are empirically correlated by

$$E_O = 1 - \frac{0.318(10^{15})(d_i/T)^{\alpha}}{N_{\text{Re}}{}^{3.2} N_{Po}{}^{1.37}} \tag{21-9}$$

where α = 0 for baffled operation and 1.6 for unbaffled operation. For Eq. (21-9), the viscosity and density were computed through Eqs. (21-2) and (21-3).

Ryon, Daley, and Lowrie [*Chem. Eng. Progress*, **55** (10), 70 (1959)] extracted uranium from sulfate ore leach liquors into kerosene containing tributyl phosphate and di(2-ethyl hexyl) phosphoric acid, which react with uranyl ion and carry it into the organic phase. Baffled vessels of several sizes were agitated with six-blade flat-blade turbines and were operated batchwise and continuously. When operated continuously, the coefficient is reasonably independent of residence time, and the average values for mixing vessels of $T = 0.5$ to 3 in Fig. 21-26, calculated on the basis of complete back mixing of

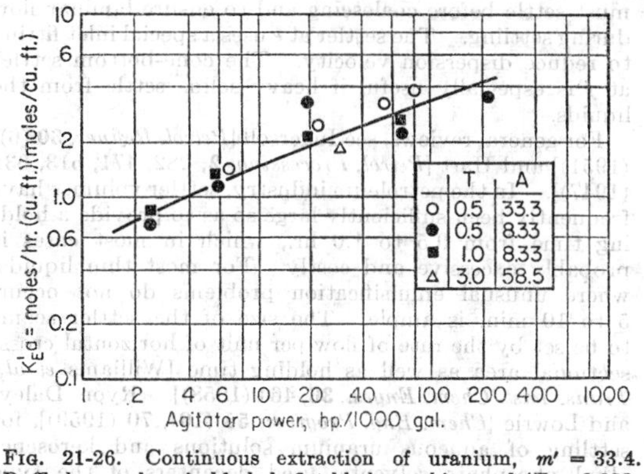

FIG. 21-26. Continuous extraction of uranium, $m' = 33.4$. Baffled vessels, six-bladed flat-blade turbines, $d_i/T = 0.333$. Average coefficients for 0.17 to 4.8 min. residence time. [*Data of Ryon, Daley, and Lowrie, Chem. Eng. Progress*, **55** (10), 70 (1959).]

both phases, correlate reasonably well with applied power/volume of vessel. The coefficient for the 3-ft. vessel, averaged for each of a three-stage cascade, corresponds to a total flow rate of 110 gal./min., a residence time in the mixer 1.2 min., and a stage efficiency $E = 0.789$. The settlers for these mixers had a residence time of 1.4 min., and extraction occurring during settling raised the average stage efficiency to $E = 0.926$.

Rates of Heterogeneous Chemical Reaction. Detailed studies of the role of agitation are practically non-existent. Most kinetic studies merely report that "efficient agitation" was used, with no details. In the case of one more detailed study [McKinley and White, *Trans. Am. Inst. Chem. Engrs.*, **40**, 143 (1944)], the effect of agitator speed in the continuous nitration of toluene with mixed acids in a laboratory-size stirred vessel was measured. Below 800 r.p.m. the degree of agitation was insufficient to produce appreciable interfacial surface for rapid mass transfer of the reagents to the reaction site, while above 1200 r.p.m., mass-transfer equilibrium was reached so rapidly that further increase in agitator speed no longer appreciably influenced the reaction rate. The data are specific for the particular apparatus used but presumably are typical of the sort to be obtained for most heterogeneous liquid reactions.

Kircher, Miller, and Geiser [*Ind. Eng. Chem.*, **46**, 1925 (1954)] specify that agitated vessels for sulfonation reactions should be equipped with turbine agitators, $d_i/T = 0.35$ to 0.5, operated at a peripheral speed of 650 to 700 ft./min. For many practical details of the use of the apparatus of Fig. 21-22, see "Hydrofluoric Acid Alkylation," Phillips Petroleum Co., Bartlesville, Okla., 1946. For details of heterogeneous reactions generally, see Groggins, "Unit Processes in Organic Synthesis," 5th ed., McGraw-Hill, New York, 1958.

Gas Agitation. The gas may be a vapor such as steam which is generated in place by boiling the liquids to be contacted, or which may be admitted through spargers at the bottom of the vessel.

Permanent gases such as air may also be used. Air, for example, has been used extensively for the mixing of reagents such as sulfuric acid with all but the most volatile of petroleum liquids. It can provide the gentlest of agitation, as in the washing of nitroglycerin with water, as well as vigorous mixing. There is danger of oxidation of product with air, and with any gas there will necessarily be some volatilization of the liquids being mixed. Gas agitation in the extraction of radioactive liquids offers the advantages of no maintenance-requiring moving parts, but it may require decontamination of the effluent air.

Although gas agitation has usually been considered an uneconomical method of applying mixing power, there is little in the way of quantitative data with which to judge its effectiveness in contacting immiscible liquids. Mathers and Winter [*Can. J. Chem. Eng.*, **37**, 99 (1959)] describe a mixer-settler in which air is used as an air-lift type of mixer. With a mixer of 5 liters volume, aqueous acetic acid (3.48 liters/min.) was extracted with hexone (6.9 liters/min.), using 0.3 cu. ft./min. of air. The average stage efficiency (including the effect of a 10-liter settler) was $E_{MR} = 0.93$, and the power for air was 0.001 hp., corresponding to 90 ft.-lb. energy expended/cu. ft. liquids treated. Thornton [*Nuclear Eng.*, **1**, 156, 204 (1956)] describes a somewhat similar air-agitated mixer.

Settlers

Emulsions and Dispersions. The mixture of liquids issuing from a mixer is a form of emulsion which must be settled, coalesced, and separated into its constituent liquid phases in bulk in order to withdraw the separated liquids from a stage. In order for a dispersion to "break" into its separate phases in bulk, both sedimentation and coalescence of the drops of the dispersed phase must occur. **Permanent** or **stable emulsions** are those whose droplets of dispersed phase are so small that settling and coalescence take place only over long periods of time, if at all. They are characterized by particle diameters of the order of 1 to 1.5 microns or less. **Unstable** or **temporary emulsions,** or **dispersions,** whose particle diameters are of the order of 1 mm. or larger, usually settle rapidly. Only the latter kind are tolerable in liquid-extraction operations and in conducting two-liquid chemical reactions where the phases are ultimately to be separated. Emulsions and dispersions are usually characterized by the terms **water-in-oil** (meaning an aqueous liquid dispersed, organic continuous) and **oil-in-water** (organic dispersed, aqueous continuous). **Dual emulsions** are those where the continuous phase is also present as very small drops dispersed within larger drops of the other liquid. See Becher, "Emulsions, Theory and Practice," A.C.S. Monograph 175, Reinhold, New York, 1957.

Meissner and Chertow [*Ind. Eng. Chem.*, **38**, 856 (1946)] show that the "breaking" of a dispersion under undisturbed batch conditions may be divided into two periods: (1) primary break, or rapid settling and coalescence of the bulk of the dispersed phase, which usually leaves a fog or haze of very small droplets suspended in dilute concentration in the majority liquid; and (2) secondary break, which represents the slow settling of the fog. For most purposes of multistage extraction, settlers designed for the slow secondary break would be too large; the small amount of interstage entrainment represented by the secondary fog hardly influences stage efficiency. For purposes of conserving solvent, however, it may be necessary to clarify as completely as possible the effluent from the final stage of a cascade. The use of coalescers (see below) can frequently eliminate the secondary fog.

Sedimentation. There are inadequate data on the settling of clouds of liquid drops through a liquid medium. Very small, isolated drops, settling in stagnant liquids under the force of gravity, move more rapidly than solid spheres. It is known that settling of dispersions is more rapid the larger the drop size and density difference, and the smaller the continuous-phase viscosity. This is confirmed by Felix and Holder [*A.I.Ch.E. J.*, **1,** 296 (1955)] in the case of petroleum-oil dispersions in water and phenol, who show also the reduced settling time required if the continuous-phase viscosity is decreased by increasing the temperature.

Coalescence. The principal driving force for coalescence of the settled drops is interfacial tension, which must be large if coalescence is to be rapid. Stabilizing agents or surfactants, which lower interfacial tension, lower the rate of coalescence and may also interfere by increasing the surface viscosity of the drops [see, for example, Nielsen, Wall, and Adams, *J. Colloid Sci.*, **13,** 441 (1958)]. Finely divided solids tend to accumulate at liquid interfaces and also retard coalescence thereby.

Gravity Settlers, Decanters. These are tanks wherein the dispersion is continuously settled and coalesced, and from which the settled liquids are continuously withdrawn. There is no well-established shape or best arrangement. Figure 21-27 shows some typical settlers. See also Treybal ("Liquid Extraction," 2d ed., McGraw-Hill, New York, 1963) for more elaborate designs. The modern trend is to keep them simple and as small as possible in order to reduce their cost. The decanter at *a*, Fig. 21-27, is a horizontally arranged cylindrical tank, where the liquid velocity is kept sufficiently low so as to minimize disturbance of the settling drops. An impingement baffle *A* is sometimes used to prevent a jet of incoming dispersion from disturbing the settling liquids. The valve at *B* is used periodically to withdraw "rag," an accumulation of dust and dirt particles which interfere with coalescence. An ordinary gage glass, not shown, may be installed to permit observation of the interface position. For an uninstrumented settler, the height of the effluent pipe for heavy liquid is set by

$$z_2 = \frac{(h_L + z_1 - z_3)\rho_L}{\rho_H} + z_3 - h_H \qquad (21\text{-}10)$$

where h_L and h_H represent the head losses through the piping for the light and heavy liquids, respectively. The siphon break at *C* prevents automatic emptying of the vessel by siphoning. Alternatively, the heavy-liquid leg and siphon break may be eliminated, and the flow of heavy liquid controlled by a valve at *D*. Such a valve may be activated by a liquid-liquid level-control instrument. At *b* is a settler arranged as a vertical cylinder. The settlers at *c* and *d* are fitted with internal baffles to reduce the distance through which the droplets must settle before coalescing and to ensure laminar flow during settling. The settler at *e* uses a special inlet fitting to reduce dispersion velocity. The cone-bottom settler at *f* is especially useful if heavy solids settle from the liquids.

For general reviews, see Ingersoll [*Petrol. Refiner*, **30** (6), (1951)] and Hart [*Petrol. Processing*, **2,** 282, 471, 513, 632 (1947)]. In the petroleum industry, settler volumes have frequently been sufficiently large so as to provide a holding time from 0.5 to 1.0 hr., which in most cases is probably excessive and costly. For most thin liquids, where unusual emulsification problems do not occur, 5 to 10 min. is ample. The size of the settler seems to be set by the rate of flow per unit of horizontal cross-sectional area as well as holding time [Williams *et al.*, *Trans. Inst. Chem. Engrs.*, **36,** 464 (1958)]. Ryon, Daley, and Lowrie [*Chem. Eng. Progress*, **55** (10), 70 (1959)], for settling of aqueous uranium solutions and kerosene-alkyl phosphate solvents, used decanters of the type shown at *b*, Fig. 21-27. The depth of the decanter having been chosen, these authors recommend that the horizontal cross section for the prevailing flow rate be set at twice the value which would give a dispersion-band thickness equal to the depth of the tank. In this manner dispersions of 40 gal./min. aqueous + 70 gal./min. solvent were successfully settled in a decanter of 1.4 min. holding time

In the extraction of uranium from ore leach liquors with kerosene-reagent solvents, there is a savings in the cost of thickeners and filters if the aqueous liquors are not clarified before extraction. If such slurries are extracted, however, it is necessary to increase the solvent/

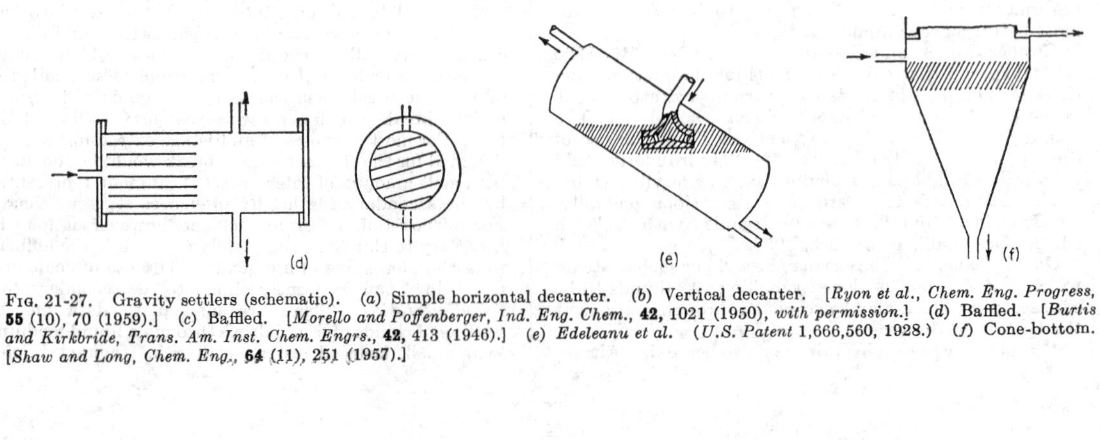

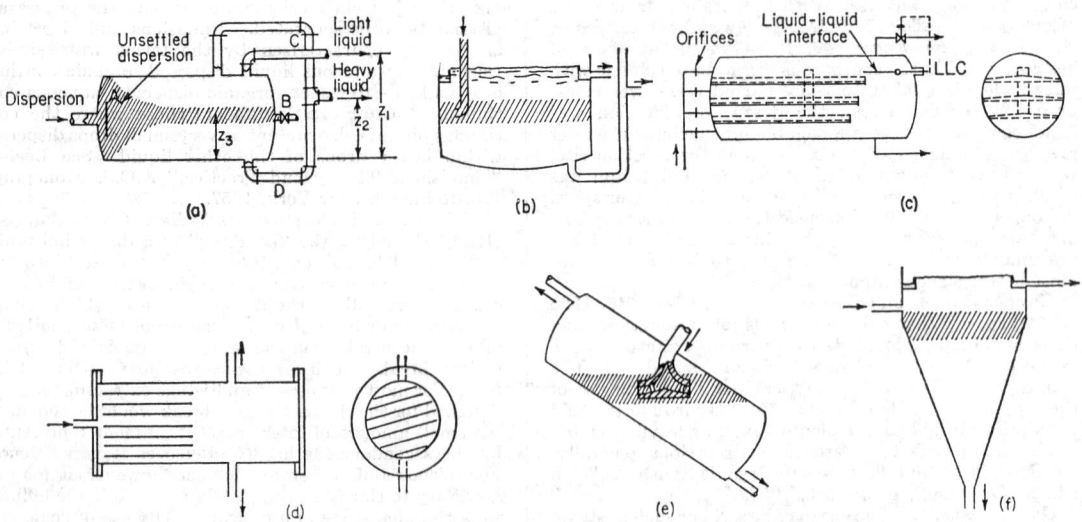

FIG. 21-27. Gravity settlers (schematic). (*a*) Simple horizontal decanter. (*b*) Vertical decanter. [*Ryon et al., Chem. Eng. Progress,* **55** (10), 70 (1959).] (*c*) Baffled. [*Morello and Poffenberger, Ind. Eng. Chem.*, **42,** 1021 (1950), *with permission.*] (*d*) Baffled. [*Burtis and Kirkbride, Trans. Am. Inst. Chem. Engrs.*, **42,** 413 (1946).] (*e*) *Edeleanu et al.* (*U.S. Patent* 1,666,560, 1928.) (*f*) Cone-bottom. [*Shaw and Long, Chem. Eng.*, **64** (11), 251 (1957).]

aqueous ratio in the extractors in order to make the organic phase continuous, else unsettleable emulsions are produced. Table 21-4 gives the data of Shaw and Long [*Chem. Eng.*, **64** (11), 251 (1957)] for settling areas required for such extractions. The high organic/aqueous ratios are obtained by recycling settled organic phase from the settler to the mixer. Entrainment of organic solvent with the settled solids represents a serious problem in such operations.

Table 21-4. Settling of Aqueous Uranium Leach Liquors with Kerosene–Alkyl Phosphate Solvent*

Nature of aqueous feed	Organic/aqueous ratio required	Permissible settler flow rate, gal./min./sq. ft. horizontal area
Clear liquor....................	4	1.4–1.6
Slimes (5% solids)..............	8	0.6
Dense pulps (50–60% solids)......	10	0.3

* Shaw and Long, *Chem. Eng.*, **64** (11), 251 (1957).

Cyclones. Cyclones have been suggested as simple means of enhancing by centrifugal force the rate of settling of liquid dispersions. Tepe and Woods (U.S. A.E.C. AECD-2864, 1943) report a few data for the separation of isobutanol-water dispersions in such devices, but the results were poor. The most complete study is that of Sinkin and Olney [*A.I.Ch.E. J.*, **2**, 545 (1956)], who conclude that high extraction efficiencies (requiring high degrees of dispersion) and good clarification of both effluents cannot be obtained in one stage involving a valve mixer and one cyclone. Tepe and Woods (*loc. cit.*) also tried *helical coils of pipe* for separating isobutanol-water mixtures with poor results.

Centrifuges. Mechanical centrifuges, high-speed machines, have been used for many years for separating liquid-liquid dispersions, for example, in the separation of caustic solutions and oils in the soap-making process, more recently in uranium extractions, and many others. By enhancing the settling rate (without, however, influencing coalescence), they reduce the settling time considerably. For details, see Sec. 19.

Settler Auxiliaries. These include the use of coalescers, separating membranes, electrical devices, and the addition of emulsion-breaking reagents. These last are used for treating permanent emulsions and will not be discussed here.

Coalescers. The small drops of a fine dispersion may be caused to coalesce and thus become larger by passing the dispersion through a coalescer. The enlarged drops then settle more rapidly. Coalescers are mats, beds, or layers of porous or fibrous solids whose properties are especially suited for the purpose at hand. Their action appears to be twofold: (1) protective, high-viscosity films surrounding the dispersed-phase droplets are ruptured and wiped away by the coalescers; (2) the droplets preferentially wet the solid, attach themselves thereto, and grow in size by coalescing with others similarly caught. The enlarged drops are then carried away by the flowing stream of continuous phase. The coalescer must therefore be a solid of large surface/volume ratio, with uniformly small passages to ensure action on all the dispersion, of low pressure drop for flow, and for best results it should be preferentially wet by the dispersed phase. It must also be mechanically strong enough to resist the pressure drop prevailing, and chemically inert toward the liquids. Beds of granular solids such as sand and diatomaceous earth, and bats of excelsior, steel wool, copper turnings, glass wool, Fiberglas, and the like have been used. Materials such as mineral wool may be especially coated with substances such as silicones and resins in order to provide the preferential wetting characteristics [see Jordan, *Trans. Am. Soc. Mech. Engrs.*, **77**, 393 (1955)]. The most complete data for the performance of such coalescers are those of Burtis and Kirkbride [*Trans. Am. Inst. Chem. Engrs.*, **42**, 413 (1946)] and Hayes, Hays, and Wood [*Chem. Eng. Progress*, **45**, 235 (1949)], who passed emulsions of water and salt in petroleum oils through beds of Fiberglas of several inches thickness. Superficial velocities of from 0.25 to 1 ft./min. proved best, although their results are specific for the system studied and may not be generally applicable. Other less bulky manufactured membranes are also available (see Jordan, *loc. cit.*). See also Kirkbride (U.S. Patent 2,522,378, 1950), Miller [*Petrol. Refiner*, **29** (5), 135 (1950)], and Hess (U.S. Patent 2,746,607, 1956).

Separating Membranes. If the capillary size of a porous substance is very small, then the liquid which preferentially wets the solid may flow through the capillaries readily, but strong interfacial films block the capillaries for flow of non-wetting liquid. Sufficient pressure will cause disruption of the films and permit passage of the non-wetting liquid, but regulation of the pressure commensurate with the pore size permits perfect phase separation. Separating membranes of this type are made of a variety of materials such as porcelain, paper which has been coated with special resins, and the like, and may be either hydrophilic or hydrophobic in character. They are made thin to permit maximum passage of the wetting liquid [see Jordan, *Trans. Am. Soc. Mech. Engrs.*, **77**, 393 (1955)]. In practice, the dispersion is usually first passed through a coalescer so as to permit settling of the bulk of the dispersed phase prior to presenting the mixture to the separating membrane, thus relieving the load on the membrane.

Figure 21-28 shows a combination device containing coalescers and both hydrophobic and hydrophilic separating membranes. Coalescers and separating membranes are fashioned in the form of hollow cylinders, and flow is radially through the wall. After passage through the

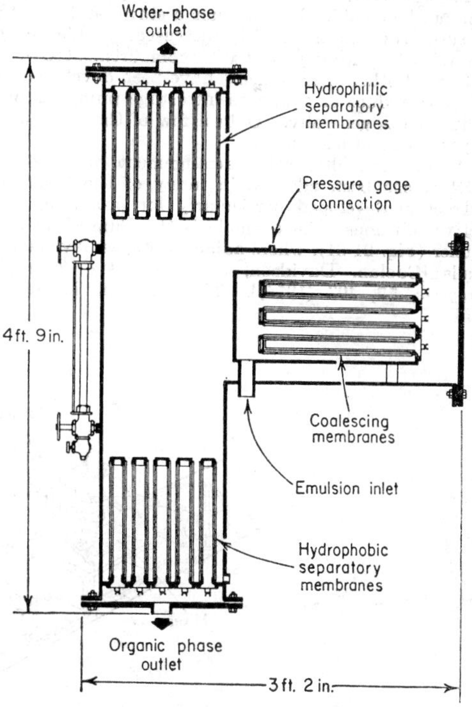

FIG. 21-28. Combination coalescer, settler, and membrane settler. (*Courtesy of Selas Corporation of America.*)

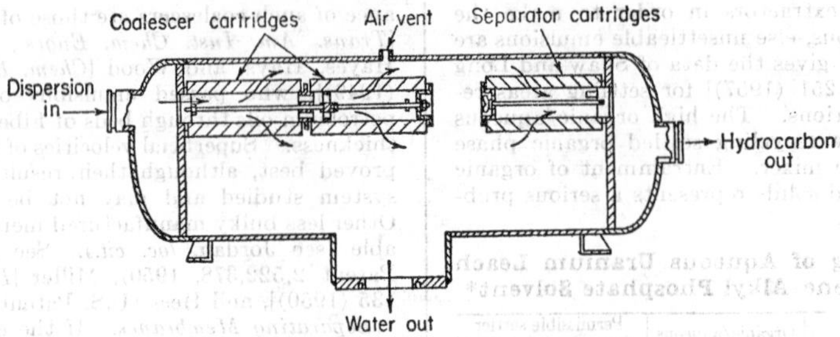

FIG. 21-29. Fuel-water separator. (*Courtesy of Warner-Lewis Co. Division, Fram Corp.*)

coalescers, settling of the bulk of the bulk of the liquids occurs in the vertical member of the device, after which the settled phases are passed through their respective separating membranes. Devices of this type are designed to handle from 150 to 1800 gal./hr., delivering completely separated phases, and further settling is unnecessary. Figure 21-29 shows another design for removing dispersed water from jet fuel or gasoline, available in sizes to handle from 300 to 1100 gal./min., and delivering clear effluents. In this case, only a hydrophobic membrane is required.

Electrical Devices. Subjecting electrically conducting emulsions or dispersions to high-voltage electric fields may cause rupture of the protective film about a droplet, and thus induce coalescence. This has been used particularly for the desalting of petroleum emulsified with brine, and for similar applications. See Albright [*Petrol. Engr.*, **13**, 2 (1941)], Turner (U.S. Patent 2,527,690, 1950), and Pearce [*Brit. J. Appl. Phys.*, **5**, 136 (1954); *Chem. Eng.*, **66**, 26 (Nov. 2, 1959)].

Mixer-Settler Combinations. Any mixer and settler can be combined to produce a stage, and the stages in turn arranged in a multistage cascade. Figure 21-30 shows such an arrangement with compartmented vessels.

Several other arrangements have been developed in an effort to reduce or eliminate interstage pumping and to reduce costs generally. Only a few of the more unique types are mentioned here.

A compact, alternating arrangement of mixers and settlers has been adopted in many of the "box-type" extractors developed particularly for processing radioactive solutions. An example is the Pump-Mix mixer-settler (Fig. 21-31), where adjacent stages have common walls [Coplan, Davidson, and Zebroski, *Chem. Eng. Progress*, **50**, 403 (1954)]. The impellers in this case pump as well as mix by drawing the heavy liquid upward through the hollow impeller shaft and discharging it at a higher level through the hollow impeller. These extractors or variants of them have been built not only in relatively large sizes but also in miniature for bench-scale work.

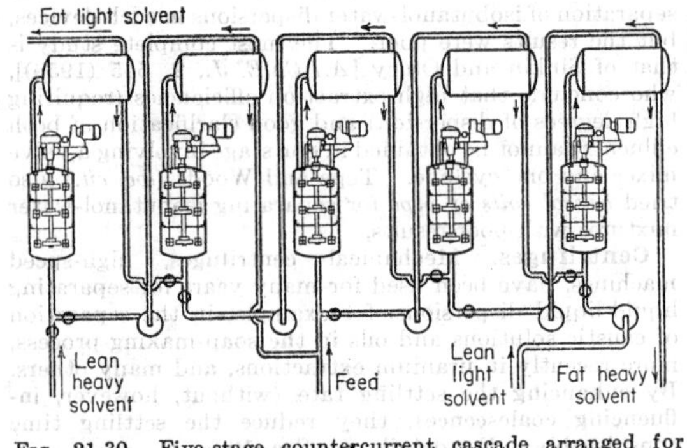

FIG. 21-30. Five-stage countercurrent cascade arranged for fractional extraction. Mixers compartmented, fitted with Turbo-Mixer agitators. (*Courtesy of Turbo-Mixer Division, General American Transportation Corp.*)

Figure 21-32 represents still further modification for low cost [Hazen and Henrickson, *Mining Eng.*, p. 994, 1957. Quinn, *Trefoil* (Denver Equipment Co.) *Bull.* M4-B90, 1957]. At *a* and *b* in the figure, the settler is a circular tank $T = 16$, $Z = 7$ ft., with the mixing vessel, 4 by 4 ft., contained inside. Agitators are turbines, $d_1 = 1.5$ ft., operated at 150 r.p.m. (1.5 hp.) and 200 r.p.m. (2.7 hp.).

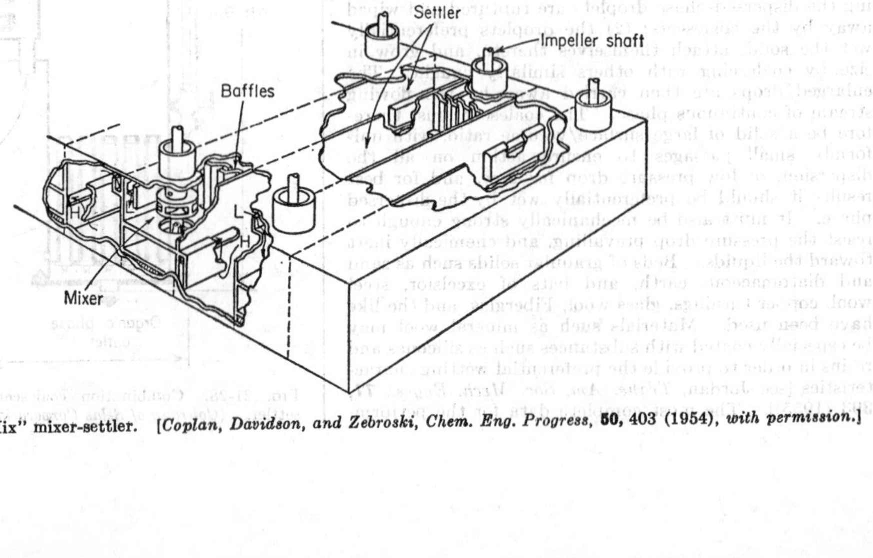

FIG. 21-31. "Pump-Mix" mixer-settler. [*Coplan, Davidson, and Zebroski, Chem. Eng. Progress*, **50**, 403 (1954), *with permission.*]

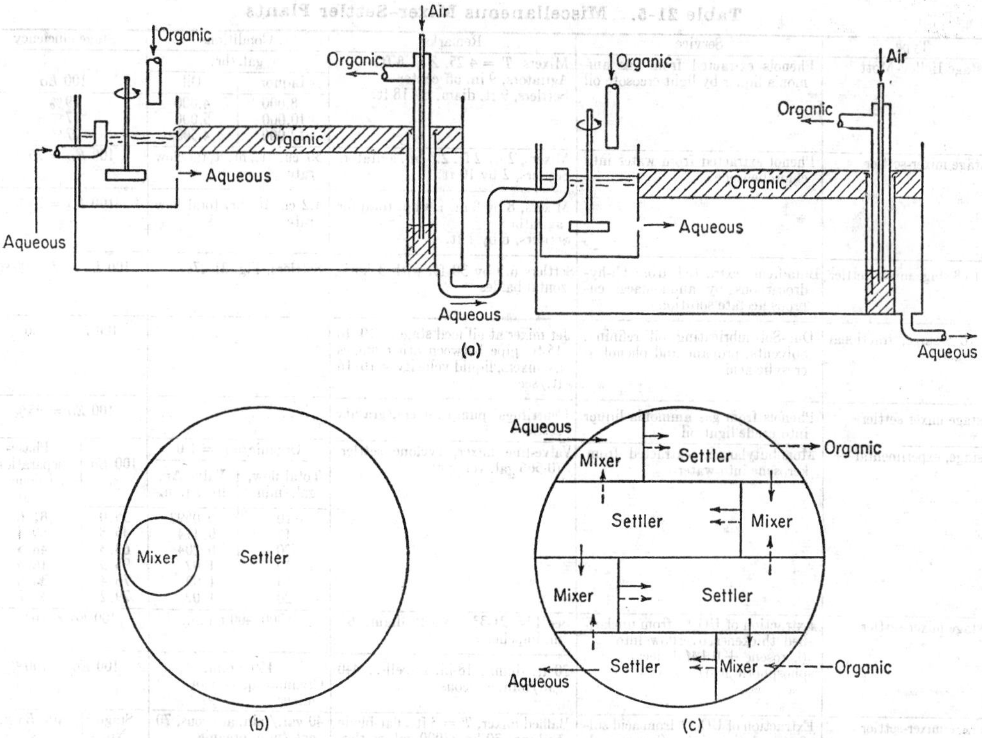

Fig. 21-32. Kerr-McGee multistage mixer-settler. (*a*) and (*b*) For uranium. (*c*) For vanadium extraction.

The aqueous feed is 100 gal./min. uranium-bearing ore leach liquor, the organic solvent 20 gal./min. of alkyl phosphate solutions in kerosene. Adjacent stages are at 1-ft. elevation difference, allowing gravity flow of the aqueous liquor, while the organic phase is pumped in countercurrent by air lifts. Provision is made for recycle of settled organic phase by overflow to the mixer, the amount of which can be adjusted by changing the height of the organic-overflow pipe. The vanadium extractor at *c* in the figure is a box type, built into a circular tank, $T = 32$, $Z = 7$ ft. The 18-in.-diameter turbines draw 7.5 hp.

Figure 21-33 shows a shrouded mixer impeller placed in a vessel which serves simultaneously for mixing in the upper part and settling in the lower [Lash, *Mining Eng.*, **10**, 1161 (1958)], used for extraction of uranium from unclarified thickener overflow. The major problems in the extraction of slurries are the settling of the disper-

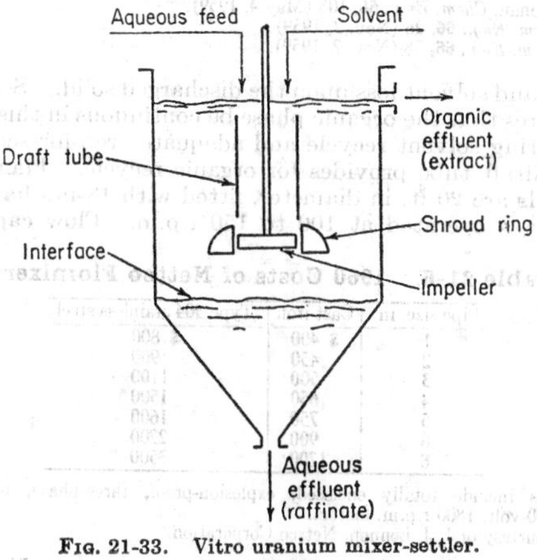

Fig. 21-33. Vitro uranium mixer-settler.

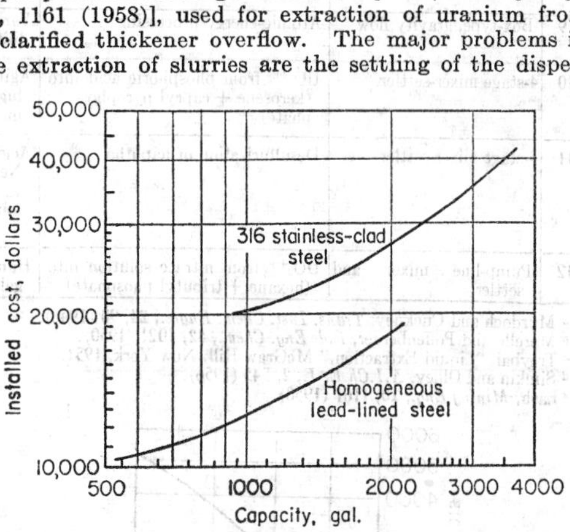

Fig. 21-34. Costs of jacketed kettles, 1958. (*Gushin, Chem. Eng., Sept.* 8, 1958, *p.* 142, *with permission.*) Lead-lined: 100 lb./sq. in. kettle, 100 lb./sq. in. jacket; cost includes kettle-cover, jacket, agitator, drive, shaft, thermometer well, blowpipe, insulation, material, labor, overhead, design. Stainless-clad kettles: 50 lb./sq. in. internal, 100 lb./sq. in. external; cost includes kettle, cover, jacket, agitator, thermometer well, blow-pipe, safety valves, insulation, material, labor, overhead, design but no motor reducer-starter; includes 316SS coils as follows:

Capacity, gal.	Length, ft.	Diam., in.
1000	300	2
1500	330	2
3000	540	2.5
3500	552	2.5

Table 21-5. Miscellaneous Mixer-Settler Plants

Item	Type	Service	Remarks	Conditions	Stage efficiency	Ref.
1	5-stage Holley-Mott	Phenols extracted from gas ammonia liquor by light creosote oil	Mixers, $T = 4.25$, $Z = 8$ ft. Agitators, 9 in. off center Settlers, 9 ft. diam. by 18 ft.	gal./hr. Liquor / Oil 8,000 / 4,000 10,000 / 5,000 12,000 / 4,500	100 Eo 79% 77% 77%	*a*
2	8-stage mixer-settler	Phenol extracted from water into chlorobenzene	Mixers, 2 by 2 ft. 2.3-hp. agitators Settlers, 2 by 10 ft.	50 cu. ft./hr. total flow rate	100 Eo = 75%	*b*
			Mixers, 8 by 8 in. 1.5 hp. total for agitators Settlers, 6 by 1 ft.	4.2 cu. ft./hr. total flow rate	100 Eo = 75%	
3	7- to 8-stage mixer-settler	Butadiene extracted from C_4-hydrocarbons by ammoniacal cuprous acetate solution	Settlers 6.5 by 30 ft. with 3 horizontal baffles	Settlers, Fig. 21-27*c*	100 Eo = 71–100%	*b*
4	7- to 9-stage, fractional extraction	Duo-Sol lubricating oil refining. Solvents: propane and phenol + cresylic acid	Jet mixer at oil feed stage. 10- to 15-ft. pipe between other stages as mixers, liquid velocity = 10–16 ft./sec	....	100 Eo = 100%	*c*
5	3-stage mixer-settler	Phenols from gas ammonia liquor into crude light oil	Centrifugal pump mixers, gravity settlers	....	100 Eo = 95%	*c*
6	1-stage, experimental	Monobutylamine extracted from kerosene into water	Valve-line mixer, cyclone settler (0.566 gal. volume)	Organic/aq. = 1.0 Total flow, gal./min. / Valve Δp, lb./sq. in. 10 / 0.0592 15 / 0.114 20 / 0.204 10 / 1.02 15 / 1.00 20 / 1.02	100 Eo % / Phase-separation efficiency, % 35.0 / 81.6 45.8 / 69.4 63.3 / 46.5 95.5 / 16.3 76.4 / 36.6 79.2 / 30.7	*d*
7	4-stage mixer-settler	Extraction of UO_2^{++} from unclarified thickener overflow into (kerosene + 0.1M dodecyl phosphoric acid)	See Fig. 21-33. 3.5 ft. diam., 6-in. impeller	300–400 r.p.m.	100 Eo = 90%	*e*
			20 ft. diam., 18-in. impeller, 440 gal./min. aqueous	150 r.p.m. Organic/aq. = 3 in mixer	100 Eo = 100%	
8	3-stage mixer-settler	Extraction of UO_2^{++} from acid sulfate solution into (kerosene + alkyl phosphoric acid)	Baffled mixer, $T = 3$ ft., flat-blade turbine, 30 hp./1000 gal. settler, see Fig. 21-27*b*	40 gal./min. aqueous, 70 gal./min. organic	Stage No. / 100 E_{MR}, % 1 / 93 2 / 91.6 3 / 93.2	*f*
9	Box-type, gravity flow	Atomic-energy processing	Various sizes, capacities from milliliters/hr. to 5 cu. m./hr.	....	100 Eo = 95–98%	*g*
10	4-stage mixer-settler	UO_2^{++} from phosphoric acid into (kerosene + capryl pyrophosphate)	Agitated mixers, disk-bowl centrifuge settlers, holding time in mixers = 2 min.	3 settlers/stage in parallel	....	*h*
11	3-stage mixer-settler	Desulfurization of naphtha	Acid treating, agitated mixer. Neutralization and washing, valve-line mixer. Electrostatic mixing-settling	8000 bbl./day naphtha, 400 bbl./day caustic, Δp = 8 lb./sq. in. 400 bbl./day water wash, Δp = 4 lb./sq. in.	90–95% sulfur removal	*i*
12	Pump-line mixer and settler	UO_2^{++} from nitrate solution into (hexane + tributyl phosphate)	Handles slurries. Settler = 2500 gal., tangential entrance	Organic phase recycled to pump mixer	....	*j*

[a] Murdoch and Cuckney, *Trans. Inst. Chem. Engrs.*, **24**, 90 (1946).
[b] Morello and Poffenberger, *Ind. Eng. Chem.*, **42**, 1021 (1950).
[c] Treybal, "Liquid Extraction," McGraw-Hill, New York, 1951.
[d] Simkin and Olney, *A.I.Ch.E. J.*, **2**, 545 (1956).
[e] Lash, *Mining Eng.*, **10**, 1161 (1958).
[f] Ryon, Daley, and Lowrie, *Chem. Eng. Progress*, **55**, (10), 70 (1959).
[g] Williams, Lowes, and Tanner, *Trans. Inst. Chem. Engrs.*, **36**, 464 (1958).
[h] Cronan, *Chem. Eng.*, **66**, 108 (May 4, 1959).
[i] *Chem. Eng.*, **66**, 26 (Nov. 2, 1959).
[j] *Chem. Eng.*, **66**, 28 (Nov. 2, 1959).

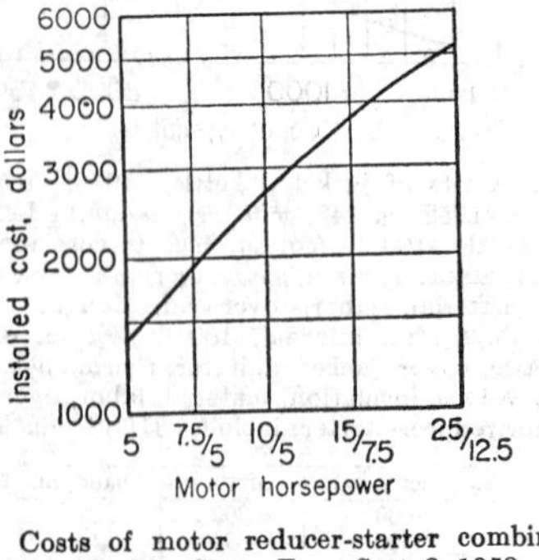

Fig. 21-35. Costs of motor reducer-starter combinations for agitators, 1958. (*Gushin, Chem. Eng., Sept. 8, 1958, p. 142, with permission.*)

sion, and solvent loss upon the discharged solid. Settling requires that the organic phase be continuous in this case, requiring solvent recycle and adequate area for settling. The draft tube provides for organic recycle. Plant-size vessels are 20 ft. in diameter, fitted with 18-in.-diameter turbines operated at 100 to 150 r.p.m. Flow capacity

Table 21-6. 1960 Costs of Nettco Flomixers*

Pipe size, in.	Cast iron	Type 304 stainless steel
1	$ 400	$ 800
2	450	900
3	500	1100
4	650	1500
5	750	1600
6	900	2200
8	1200	3500

Costs include totally enclosed, explosion-proof, three-phase, 60-cycle, 220/440-volt, 1800 r.p.m. motors.
* Courtesy of J. J. Lennon, Nettco Corporation.

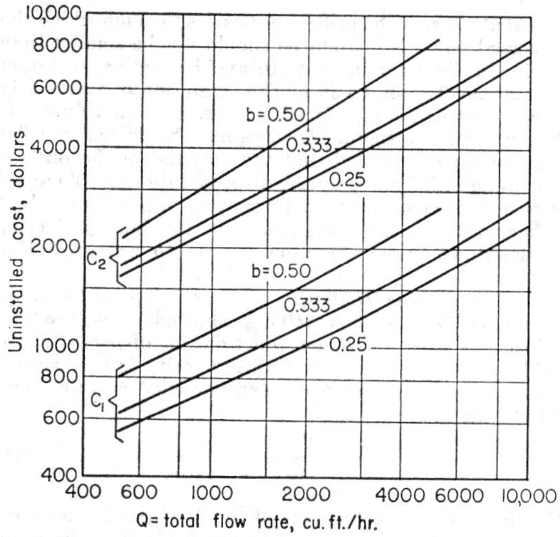

Fig. 21-36. Costs (1958) for major equipment, continuous mixer-settlers, single stage, with geometrically similar scale-up [*Treybal, A.I.Ch.E. J.* **5**, 474 (1959), *with permission*.] Basis: $T = Z = 1.5(Q/100)^b$; $d_i = T/3$, agitator power = 1000 Q ft.-lb./hr. C_1 includes stainless-steel flat-blade turbine, shaft, stuffing box, explosion-proof motor, geared speed reducer, mounting, support. C_2 includes C_1 + steel baffled mixer and settling vessel (10-min. holding time). Note: For equal superficial velocities through mixer, $b = 0.50$; for equal holding time in mixer, $b = 0.333$.

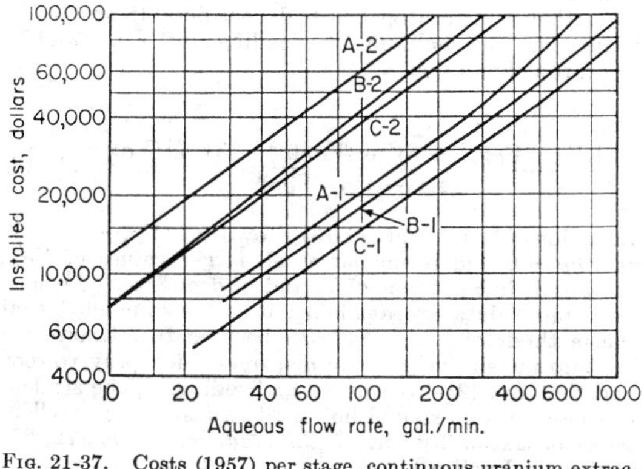

Fig. 21-37. Costs (1957) per stage, continuous uranium extraction. (*Shaw and Long, Chem. Eng., November*, 1957, *p.* 251, *with permission*.) Basis: Installed costs for tanks, pumps, agitators, foundation, installation, interstage piping, electric services, instruments; process equipment with 3/16-in. rubber lining, process piping with Saran or rubber lining. For steel multiply by 0.6, for stainless steel by 1.2.

1: clarified liquors, org./aq. = 4, settling area = 1.4 − 1.6 gal./min. (sq. ft.).
2: slimes, 5 per cent solids, org./aq. = 8, settling area = 0.6 gal./min. (sq. ft.).
A: centrifugal pump mixer + settler, 20 ft. pumping head.
B: combination mixer-settler (see Fig. 21-33), impeller tip velocity = 570 ft./min.
C: conventional mixer-settler, impeller velocity = 300 ft./min.

is 440 gal./min. of aqueous feed, with organic/aqueous = 3 in the mixer, fixed by settling rates.

Table 21-5 summarizes stage efficiencies of typical mixer-settler installations.

Costs. Costs for Nettco Flomixers (Fig. 21-19) are listed in Table 21-6. Costs of jacketed, agitated kettles are given in Fig. 21-34, and motor-starter combinations for agitators in Fig. 21-35. Figure 21-36 shows major equipment costs for mixer-settlers, arranged for geometrically similar scale-up. Figure 21-37 shows complete stage costs for certain uranium extractors. Economic selection of mixer-settler equipment and conditions for scale-up are discussed by Treybal [*A.I.Ch.E. J.*, **5**, 474 (1959)].

CONTINUOUS (DIFFERENTIAL) CONTACT EQUIPMENT

Equipment in this category is usually arranged for multistage countercurrent contact of the insoluble liquids, without repeated complete separation of the liquids from each other between stages or their equivalent. Instead, the liquids remain in continuous contact throughout their passage through the equipment.

General Characteristics. Countercurrent flow is maintained by virtue of the difference in densities of the liquids, and if the force of gravity is the motivating force, the equipment takes the form of a vertical tower, with the heavy liquid entering at the top and flowing downward, the light liquid entering at the bottom and flowing upward. Alternatively, a larger force (centrifugal) may be generated by rapidly revolving the device, in which case the general direction of flow is radial with respect to the axis of revolution. In either case, only one of the liquids may be pumped through the equipment at any desired velocity; the maximum velocity for the other is then necessarily limited at least by the difference in densities and the motivating force (gravitational or centrifugal). If an attempt is made to exceed the limiting velocity of the second fluid, it will be rejected by the equipment, which is then said to be **flooded.** For a given volumetric rate for each of the two liquids, as fixed by the process requirements, therefore, the **cross section for flow** must be sufficiently large so as to avoid velocities which result in flooding.

The **length of path for flow,** or the **height of a vertical tower,** is governed by the extent and rate of mass transfer or chemical reaction and is independent of the total quantities to be handled (see Sec. 14).

It cannot be overemphasized that knowledge of the characteristics of such equipment is very undeveloped. Rates of extraction in a given type of apparatus are known to vary not only from one chemical system to another but, for any chemical system with rates of flow of either phase, with direction of extraction (whether from dispersed phase to continuous, whether from organic to aqueous, and vice versa), with concentration of solute, with the presence or not of minute amounts of impurities, and with the degree of mechanical agitation. These effects are not well established. Furthermore, most of the available data are taken from small laboratory devices, frequently only a few inches in diameter and a few feet high. For these reasons, the generalizations given here should be used only for very rough estimates, with allowances for generous factors of safety. All processes should be pilot-planted before large-scale equipment is designed, and scale-up to larger sizes should be done with great caution.

Equipment Classification. Equipment can be broadly classified into the following categories, generally in order of increasing complexity of internal construction:

I. Gravity-operated extractors

A. No mechanical agitation
1. Wetted-wall towers and similar types
2. Spray tower
3. Baffle towers
4. Packed towers
5. Perforated-plate (sieve-plate) towers

B. Mechanically agitated extractors
  1. Towers agitated with rotating stirrers
  2. Pulsed towers
    a. Liquid contents pulsed
    b. Reciprocating plates

II. Centrifugal extractors

Gravity-operated Exractors (No Mechanical Agitators)

Wetted-wall Towers. These devices have been used in theoretical studies of the rates of mass transfer under conditions of controlled interfacial area. They are difficult to operate and have had no commercial application.

Spray Towers. These are the simplest of multistage counterflow extractors, consisting only of an empty tower, with provision for introducing and removing the liquids to be contacted. Figure 21-38 shows one design. Ordinarily straight-sided towers are used, but that shown in

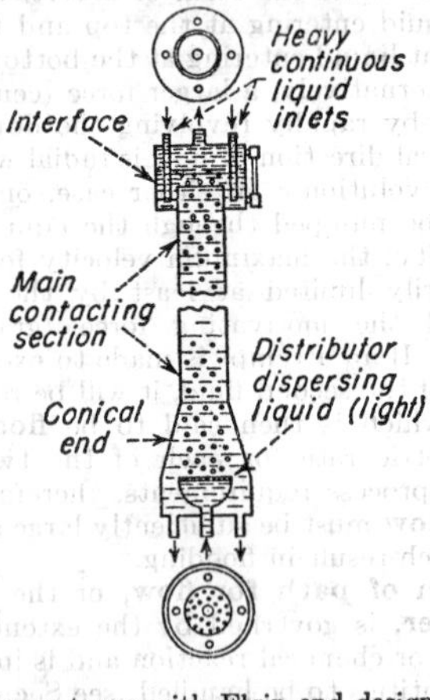

FIG. 21-38. Spray tower with Elgin end design. (*U.S. Patent* 2,364,892, 1944.) Arranged for light liquid dispersed.

the figure has been found particularly useful in eliminating restrictions in the flow areas at the points of introduction of liquids, and hence is not so readily flooded [see Blanding and Elgin, *Trans. Am. Inst. Chem. Engrs.*, **38**, 305 (1942). Elgin, U.S. Patent 2,364,892, 1944]. Essentially all the performance data available for spray towers come from laboratory-size devices of this design. As shown in the figure, it is arranged for the light liquid to be dispersed, and droplets of light liquid form at the lower distributor, rise through the downwardly flowing heavy liquid, and coalesce into a layer at the top, where the light liquid is withdrawn. For dispersing the heavy liquid, the tower is best turned upside down.

The spray tower is inexpensive to build, easy to keep clean, and has relatively high flow capacity. The freedom with which the continuous phase can circulate from top to bottom, however, leads to reduced extraction efficiency by destruction of the true countercurrent concentration differences between the phases [see Gier and Hougen, *Ind. Eng. Chem.*, **45**, 1362 (1953). Kreager and Geankoplis, *Ind. Eng. Chem.*, **45**, 2156 (1953). Cavers and Ewanchyne, *Can. J. Chem. Eng.*, **35**, 113 (1957)]. The towers will be most efficient if the length/diameter ratio is quite large, but it is difficult ordinarily to obtain the equivalent of more than one or two theoretical stages or transfer units at the most in single installations. However, the towers are not readily clogged with small amounts of solids.

Distributors. The orifices or nozzles through which the dispersed phase is introduced should not be smaller than 0.1 in. in diameter in order to avoid clogging, or larger than about 0.25 in. to avoid the formation of excessively large drops whose interfacial area for a given volumetric flow rate will be small. Orifices may be drilled in a flat plate or pipe, provided that the material of the plate is not preferentially wet by the dispersed liquid. To avoid wetting and consequent malformation of drops, it is best either to punch the holes and leave the burr projecting in the downstream direction or else to use projecting nozzles.

Dispersed-phase Hold-up. Elgin *et al.* [*A.I.Ch.E. J.*, **3**, 63 (1957); **5**, 533 (1959)] showed that the slip velocity V_S is a unique function of dispersed-phase hold-up in a given system. Slip velocity is the relative velocity of continuous phase and particles, and for countercurrent flow,

$$V_S = \frac{V_D}{\varphi_D} + \frac{V_C}{1 - \varphi_D} \qquad (21\text{-}11)$$

For liquid-liquid systems not at the flood point, they have shown that the ratio of slip velocity V_S to particle terminal velocity V_t (at $\varphi_D = 0$) can be estimated for any hold-up from Zenz's correlation for fluid-solid particulate systems [*Petrol. Refiner*, **36** (8), 147 (1957)]. Thornton [*Chem. Eng. Sci.*, **5**, 201 (1956)] claims that the function is

$$V_S = V_K(1 - \varphi_D) \qquad (21\text{-}12)$$

where V_K, a "characteristic velocity," equals V_t for the drops in the case of spray towers. This is not entirely compatible with the relationship recommended by Elgin. Nevertheless Thornton has had considerable success in estimating the hold-up at flooding by Eq. (21-12). Thornton shows that

$$\varphi_{DF} = \frac{[(V_{DF}/V_{CF})^2 + 8V_{DF}/V_{CF}]^{0.5} - 3V_{DF}/V_{CF}}{4(1 - V_{DF}/V_{CF})} \qquad (21\text{-}13)$$

Equations (21-12) and (21-13) show that (1) $\varphi_{DF} = 0.50$ at $V_{CF} = 0$ and is smaller at all larger values of V_{CF}; (2) φ_{DF} is independent of V_t and of drop size. At least until more data are available, it is recommended that the methods of Elgin (*loc. cit.*) be used to estimate the hold-up in relatively dilute dispersions in spray towers, and that Eq. (21-13) be used at flooding. [The student of these matters should not fail to consult the excellent paper of Harmathy, *Acta Tech. Acad. Sci. Hung.*, **12**, 209 (1955) (in English)].

Flooding. In addition to references of the preceding paragraph, see Mertes and Rhodes [*Chem. Eng. Progress*, **42**, 1021 (1950)], Fujita *et al.* [*Chem. Eng.* (*Japan*), **15**, 164 (1951)], Minard and Johnson [*Chem. Eng. Progress*, **48**, 62 (1952)], Sakiadis and Johnson [*Ind. Eng. Chem.*, **46**, 1229 (1954)]. Equations (21-11) to (21-13) provide one basis for estimating flooding velocities, but on the basis of purely statistical comparison of observed and calculated data, the correlation of Minard and Johnson (*loc. cit.*) is recommended. With slight simplification this becomes

$$V_{CF} = \frac{10{,}000\,\Delta\rho^{0.28}}{[0.453\mu_C^{0.075}\rho_C^{0.5} + d_p^{0.56}\rho_D^{0.5}(Q_D/Q_C)^{0.5}]^2} \qquad (21\text{-}14)$$

Drop sizes d_p may be estimated through Fig. 21-39. Since Eq. (21-14) was established from data for small towers, of the design of Fig. 21-38, it is recommended that actual values of V_C be taken at no more than 30

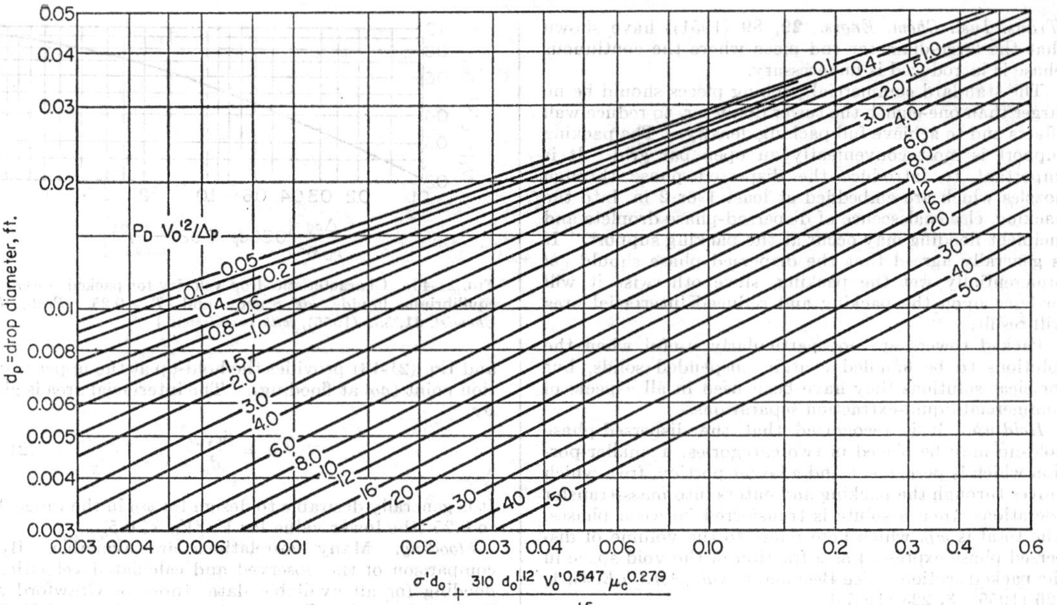

FIG. 21-39. Drop diameters for dispersion of insoluble liquids through nozzles and perforations. Uniform diameter, V_0' = 0 to 0.3 ft./sec.; maximum drop diameter, V_0' = 0.3 to 1 ft./sec.; V_0' not to exceed 1 ft./sec. [*Hayworth and Treybal, Ind. Eng. Chem.*, **42**, 1174 (1950).]

to 40 per cent of the calculated V_{CF}. This then establishes the cross section of the tower:

$$S = \frac{Q_C}{V_C} \qquad (21\text{-}15)$$

Mass Transfer. It is recognized that, in addition to the mass transfer which occurs during the passage of the dispersed-phase droplets through the continuous phase, there are important contributions during formation of the drops at the distributor and during coalescence at the principal interface (end effects).

The greater part of the data taken from spray towers, usually relatively short, includes all three of the transfer-rate contributions mentioned above. If, as has been shown, the end effects are large, it follows that data for a given system from a short tower, uncorrected for end effects, cannot be applied safely to taller towers: the total transfer per unit height will be much smaller than the uncorrected data would predict. This, together with the large circulation effects within the continuous phase, is probably responsible for the observation that it is difficult to obtain more than the equivalent of one or two stages at most in even very tall spray towers. The following brief list of references will provide an introduction into the literature of spray towers: Fleming and Johnson, *Chem. Eng. Progress*, **49**, 497 (1953); Gier and Hougen, *Ind. Eng. Chem.*, **45**, 1362 (1953); Vogt and Geankoplis, *Ind. Eng. Chem.*, **46**, 1763 (1954); Johnson *et. al.*, *A.I.Ch.E. J.*, **3**, 101 (1958); Smith and Beckmann, *A.I.Ch.E. J.*, **4**, 180 (1958). Summaries of earlier data are given by Treybal, "Liquid Extraction," McGraw-Hill, New York, 1963.

Baffle Towers. These are cylindrical shells in which horizontal baffles force the liquids to follow a zigzag path through the tower. Baffles may be segmental (side-to-side), disk-and-doughnut, or center-to-side, usually arranged at a vertical spacing of from 2 to 6 in. See Thompson, U.S. Patent 2,400,962, 1946. The dispersed liquid flows along the baffles in a thin film and falls (or rises) over the edge of the baffles in a broken sheet through the continuous liquid. If interfacial tension is low, the dispersed liquid will break up into drops, and the tower behaves much like a spray tower, with the baffles suppressing considerably the vertical circulation of the continuous phase. They have had application in the extraction of acetic acid from pyroligneous liquors and the solutions used in cellulose acetate rayon manufacture, and to a small extent in petroleum-refining processes. The flow capacities indicated in Table 21-7 may be considered as typical; flooding rates will actually depend upon the properties of the liquids, which phase is dispersed, and the detailed geometry of the towers. For various services, 8 to 11 baffles per theoretical stage have been reported [Morello and Poffenberger, *Ind. Eng. Chem.*, **42**, 1021 (1950)].

Table 21-7. Capacities of Baffle Towers*

Tower diam., in.	No. of baffles	Baffle spacing, in.	Baffle arrangement	$\Delta\rho$, lb./cu. ft.	Total flow, cu. ft./(hr.)(sq. ft.)
78	103	5	Center-to-side	12.72	65
42	104	5	Center-to-side	13.10	81.1
24	7	1.75	Center-to-side	14.35	121
26	96	4	Segmental	5.99	92.5

* Treybal, "Liquid Extraction," McGraw-Hill, New York, 1951, with permission.

Packed Towers. The empty shell of a spray tower is filled with packing to reduce the vertical circulation of the continuous phase. The standard commercial packings used in gas absorption, such as Raschig rings, Berl saddles, and the like, are generally used, but lumps of coke and wooden hurdles have been used on occasion. The packing, which reduces the available free space for flow, thereby reduces the flow capacity of the tower but also materially reduces the height required. Industrial applications generally use straight-sided towers, but most laboratory studies have come from packed towers whose shell design resembles that of Fig. 21-38. Dell and Pratt

[*Trans. Inst. Chem. Engrs.*, **29,** 89 (1951)] have shown that the large-diameter end piece where the continuous phase is introduced is unnecessary.

The standard commercial packing pieces should be no larger than one-eighth the tower diameter, to reduce wall effects and to achieve full packing density. The packing support is most conveniently an open bar grid. It is important to introduce the dispersed phase through nozzles which are embedded at least 1 or 2 in. into the packing, else coalescence of dispersed-phase droplets and incipient flooding may occur at the packing support. It is generally agreed that the dispersed phase should *not* preferentially wet the packing, since otherwise it will coalesce upon the packing and reduced interfacial area will result.

Packed towers are not particularly useful when the solutions to be handled contain suspended solids, but for clear solutions they have been used in all aspects of commercial liquid-extraction separations.

Hold-up. It is recognized that the dispersed-phase hold-up may be placed in two categories: a smaller portion which is permanent and a larger portion, free, which moves through the packing and enters into mass-transfer operations when a solute is transferred between phases. The total is φ_D, which here refers to the volume of dispersed phase expressed as a fraction of the void space in the packed section. See Beckmann *et al.* [*A.I.Ch.E. J.*, **1,** 426 (1955); **3,** 223 (1957)].

What follows is a very brief summary of the extensive work of Pratt and his coworkers, Dell, Gayler, Lewis,, Jones, Roberts, and White [*Trans. Inst. Chem. Engrs.*, **29,** 89, 110, 126 (1951); **31,** 57, 69 (1953); *Chem. & Ind.*, 1952, p. 358]. For the standard commercial packings of ½-in. size and larger, at low values of V_D, φ_D varies linearly with V_D up to values of $\varphi_D \doteq 0.10$. With further increase of V_D, φ_D increases sharply up to a "lower transition point," resembling "loading" in gas-liquid contact. At still higher values of V_D an upper transition point occurs, the drops of dispersed phase tend to coalesce, and V_D can increase without corresponding increase in φ_D. This regime ends in flooding. Drops of the dispersed phase reach a characteristic size within a short distance after leaving the distributor nozzles, regardless of their initial size. For each system there is a critical packing size above which the mean drop size is a minimum. For smaller packing, the drop size is larger (and interfacial area smaller). The critical size of packing, usually ½ in. or more, is given by

$$d_{FC} = 2.42\left(\frac{\sigma}{\Delta\rho g}\right)^{0.5} \qquad (21\text{-}16)$$

For packing larger than d_{FC}, the characteristic drop diameter, for liquids which are in concentration equilibrium, is given by

$$d_p = 0.92\left(\frac{\sigma}{\Delta\rho g}\right)^{0.5}\frac{V_K\epsilon\varphi_D}{V_D} \qquad (21\text{-}17)$$

For liquids which are not in concentration equilibrium and where an unequilibrated solute is present, the characteristic drop size will generally be larger. If the drops formed at the distributor nozzle are smaller than this, there may be a tendency to flood until they grow to size. It is therefore best to design the nozzles, through Fig. 21-39, to give drop sizes which are larger than that given by Eq. (21-17). V_K is a characteristic drop velocity (at $V_C = 0$, V_D approaching 0), and is given by Fig. 21-40. Below the upper transition point, the hold-up is given by

$$\frac{V_D}{\varphi_D} + \frac{V_C}{1 - \varphi_D} = \epsilon V_K(1 - \varphi_D) \qquad (21\text{-}18)$$

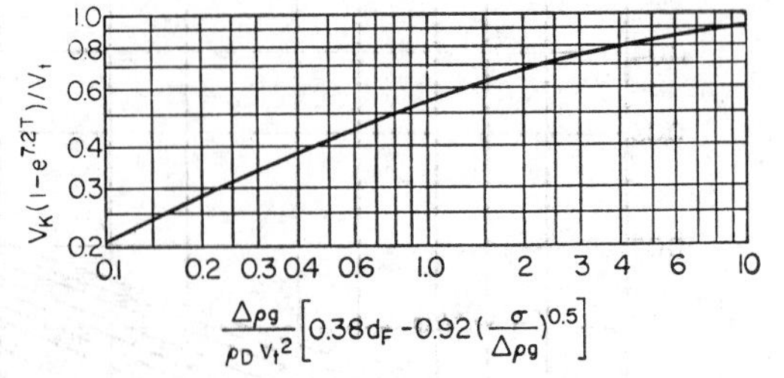

FIG. 21-40. Characteristic drop velocity for packed towers, for equilibrium liquids, $d_F > d_{FC}/$ and $T > 0.25$. [*Pratt, Ind. Chemist*, **31,** 552 (1955), *with permission.*]

and Eq. (21-13) provides the hold-up at the upper transition point (*not* at flooding). The interfacial area is given by

$$a = \frac{6\epsilon\varphi_D}{d_p} \qquad (21\text{-}19)$$

It is generally desirable to design for φ_D in the range 0.15 to 0.25 (the lower value for $V_D/V_C < 0.5$).

Flooding. Many correlations are available. By a comparison of the observed and calculated velocities at flooding for all available data, those of Crawford and Wilke [*Chem. Eng. Progress*, **47,** 423 (1951)] and Hoffing and Lockhart [*Chem. Eng. Progress*, **50,** 94 (1954)] are best and about equally effective. The Crawford-Wilke correlation is the simpler and is given in Fig. 21-41. See

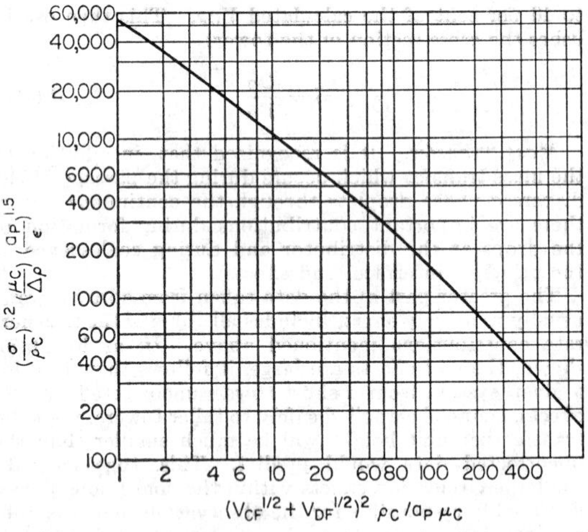

FIG. 21-41. Flooding in packed towers. [*Crawford and Wilke, Chem. Eng. Progress*, **47,** 423 (1951). *with permission.*]

also Dell and Pratt [*Trans. Inst. Chem. Engrs.*, **29,** 89, 270 (1951)], Fujita *et al.* [*Chem. Eng.* (*Japan*), **17,** 230 (1957)], Sakiadis and Johnson [*Ind. Eng. Chem.*, **46,** 1229 (1954)], Kafarov and Dytnerskii [*Zhur. Priklad. Khim.*, **30,** 1698 (1957)]. It is recommended that flow rates be set at no more than 50 per cent of the flooding values, less if the interfacial tension of the liquids is high.

Mass Transfer. Extraction rates for packed towers are usually excellently correlated for a given situation on the coordinate system of Fig. 21-42. In connection with the data on this figure, it should be noted that economical values of $m'V_E/V_R$ will usually lie in the range between 1 and 2, so that over-all heights of transfer units are not too unreasonable even for this high-interfacial-

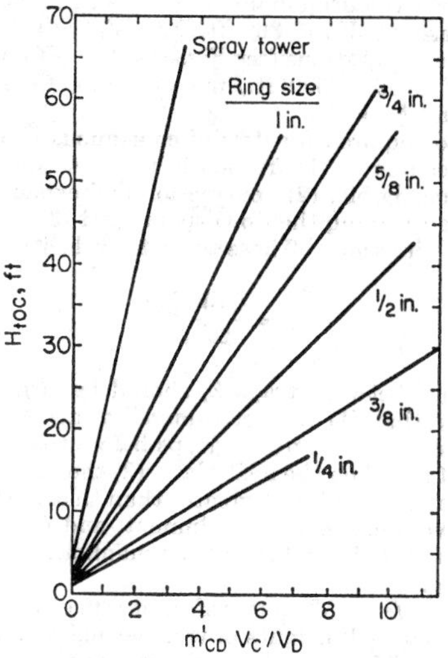

FIG. 21-42. Extraction of diethylamine from water into toluene (dispersed) in towers packed with unglazed porcelain Raschig rings. [*Leibson and Beckmann, Chem. Eng. Progress,* **49,** 405 (1953), *with permission.*]

tension system. For lower interfacial tensions, H_{tOC} will ordinarily be appreciably less.

Pratt [*Ind. Chemist,* **31,** 552 (1955)] notes that direction of transfer of solute has a noticeable effect, owing principally to alteration of drop size and hold-up, and that oscillation of the droplets is an important factor. Ellis [*Ind. Chemist,* **28,** 483 (1952)] shows that, for *rough estimates,* the following empirical relationships are useful for towers packed with Raschig rings larger than ⅜ in.

1. Transfer of solute from aqueous continuous to dispersed organic phase,

$$\text{H.E.T.S.} = \frac{94.5\mu_C(12d_F)^b(V_C/V_D)^{0.5}}{10^{0.0683s}\,\Delta\rho} \tag{21-20}$$

2. Transfer of solute from dispersed organic to aqueous continuous phase,

$$\text{H.E.T.S.} = \frac{69\mu_C(12d_F)^b}{10^{0.0535s}\,\Delta\rho} \tag{21-21}$$

where $b = 2.15/10^{0.096s}$. Here s is the average of the mutual solubilities of the solute-free contacted liquids in each other, expressed as weight per cent, and provides a rough measure of interfacial tension. For liquid pairs as insoluble as toluene and water, s may be taken as zero.

End effects (extraction during drop formation and final coalescence) are present in packed towers but are apparently of much less importance than in spray towers. Vertical circulation of the continuous phase is largely but not entirely repressed by the packing [see Gier and Hougen, *Ind. Eng. Chem.,* **45,** 1362 (1953)] but may assume major importance particularly in cases where V_C is small and V_D large (Vermeulen, Jacques, Cotter, and Miyauchi, U.S.A.E.C. UCRL-8029, 1957; paper at A.I.Ch.E. Meeting, Atlantic City, N.J., March, 1959). Scale-up must be done with great caution.

Table 21-8 lists the sources of recent mass-transfer data. Treybal ("Liquid Extraction," McGraw-Hill, New York, 1951) has summarized earlier data.

Perforated-plate (Sieve-plate) Towers. A schematic diagram for the most common design, arranged for light liquid dispersed, is shown in Fig. 21-43. The light

Table 21-8. Recent Packed-tower Mass-transfer Data

System	Tower diam., in.	Packing		Ref.
		Type	Size, in.	
Water–acetic acid–ethyl acetate, cyclohexane, methylcyclohexane, ethyl acetate + benzene	1	Saddles	0.25	*a*
Water–acetic acid–methylisobutyl ketone	1.95	Rings	0.23	*f*
Water–adipic acid–ethyl ether	6	Rings	0.5, 0.75	*d*
		Spheres	0.375	
Water–benzoic acid–carbon tetrachloride	1.95	Rings	0.25	*e*
Water–diethylamine–toluene	3, 4, 6	Rings	0.25 – 1	*g*
Water–ethyl acetate	4	Rings	0.5	*b*
Water–methylisobutyl carbinol	4	Rings	0.5	*i*
Water–methylethyl ketone	4	Rings	0.5	*i*
Acetone (aq.)–soybean oil, linseed oil	2	Saddles	0.25	*j*
		Rings	0.5	
Petroleum–furfural	2	Rings	0.25	*c*
	1.2	Rings	0.16	*h*

a Eaglesfield, Kelly, and Short, *Ind. Chemist,* **29,** 147, 243 (1953).
b Gaylor and Pratt, *Trans. Inst. Chem. Engrs.,* **31,** 78 (1953).
c Garwin and Barber, *Petrol. Refiner,* **32** (1), 144 (1953).
d Gier and Hougen, *Ind. Eng. Chem.,* **45,** 1362 (1953).
e Guyer, Guyer, and Mauli, *Helv. Chim. Acta,* **38,** 790 (1955).
f Guyer, Guyer, and Mauli, *Helv. Chim. Acta,* **38,** 955 (1955).
g Liebson and Beckmann, *Chem. Eng. Progress,* **49,** 405 (1953).
h Sef and Moretic, *Nafta (Yugoslavia),* **5,** 125 (1954).
i Smith and Beckmann, *A.I.Ch.E. J.,* **4,** 180 (1958).
j Young and Sullans, *J. Am. Oil Chemists' Soc.,* **32,** 397 (1955).

liquid flows through the perforations of each plate and is thereby dispersed into drops which rise through the continuous phase. The continuous liquid flows horizontally across each plate and passes to the plate beneath through the downspout. For heavy liquid dispersed, the same design may be used, but turned upside down. The plates serve to eliminate essentially completely the vertical recirculation of continuous phase characteristic of the spray tower. Furthermore, extraction rates are enhanced by the repeated coalescence and redispersion into droplets of the dispersed phase. Towers of the simple design suggested by Fig. 21-43 have been used successfully in a

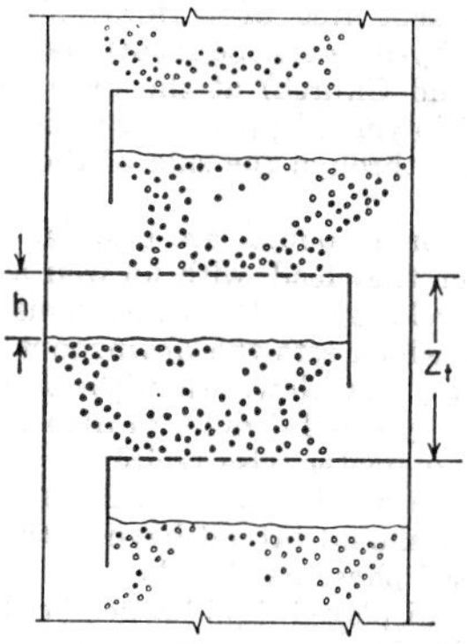

FIG. 21-43. Portion of a perforated-tray tower, arranged for light liquid dispersed.

great variety of services and for petroleum-refining processes have commonly been built to diameters of 12 ft. With careful design, these towers may have excellent flow capacities, and with systems of low interfacial tension equally excellent mass-transfer characteristics.

Many variations in design have been suggested and tried, for example, the use of tower packing in the downspouts to prevent entrainment of dispersed phase, arrangements in which both liquids must pass through perforations at each plate, arrangements with vertical perforated plates, etc. As recent examples of these, see Bradley (U.S. Patent 2,642,341, 1953), Williams (U.S. Patent 2,652,316, 1953), Maycock and Hartwig (U.S. Patent 2,729,550, 1956), and Pohlenz (U.S. Patent

2,872,295, 1959). Data are available only for arrangements of the sort shown in Fig. 21-43. In general, caplike sieve plates, bubble caps, and vertical perforated plates have not been so satisfactory as horizontal plates.

Plate Design.

REFERENCES: Pyle, Duffey, and Colburn, *Ind. Eng. Chem.*, **42**, 1042 (1950). Mayfield and Church, *Ind. Eng. Chem.*, **44**, 2253 (1952). Bussolari, Schiff, and Treybal, *Ind. Eng. Chem.*, **45**, 2413 (1953). Fujita and Tanizawa, *Chem. Eng. (Japan)*, **17**, 111 (1953). Major and Hertzog, *Chem. Eng. Progress*, **51**, 17 (1955). Garner, Ellis, and Hill, *A.I.Ch.E. J.*, **1**, 185 (1955); *Trans. Inst. Chem. Engrs.*, **34**, 223 (1956).

For best tray efficiency with a given system, it is well established that the dispersed phase must issue cleanly from the perforations. This requires that the material of the plates be preferentially wet by the continuous phase (requiring the use of plastics or plastic-coated plates in some instances) or that the dispersed phase issue from nozzles projecting beyond the plate surface. These may be formed by punching the holes and leaving the burr in place, or otherwise forming the jets (see Mayfield and Church, *loc. cit.*). The liquid flowing at the larger volume rate should be dispersed.

Perforations are usually 1/8 to 1/4 in. diameter, set 1/2 to 3/4 in. apart, on square or triangular pitch. There appears to be relatively little effect of hole size on extraction rate, except that with systems of high interfacial tension smaller holes will produce somewhat better rates. The entire hole area is suitably set at 15 to 25 per cent of the column cross section, subject, however, to check through calculations as outlined below. The velocity through the holes should be such that drops do not form slowly at the holes, but rather that the dispersed phase streams through the openings to be broken up into droplets at a slight distance from the plate. This generally requires average linear velocities through the holes of from 0.5 to 1.0 ft./sec. The plate area directly opposite downspouts is kept free of perforations. A scum or "interface-rag" by-pass can be incorporated in the trays (see Mayfield and Church) at the expense of tray efficiency, or provision may be made for periodic withdrawal of accumulations through the side of the tower between plates.

Downspouts (or upspouts) are best set flush with the plate from which they lead, with no weir as in gas-liquid contact. The velocity of the continuous phase in the downspout V_d, which sets the downspout cross section, should be set at a value lower than the terminal velocity of some arbitrarily small droplet of dispersed phase, say 1/32 or 1/16 in. diameter, else recirculation of entrained dispersed phase around a plate will result in flooding. The downspouts should extend beyond the accumulated layer of dispersed phase on the plate.

The depth of dispersed liquid h accumulating on each plate is determined by the pressure drop required for flow of the liquids,

$$h = h_C + h_D \tag{21-22}$$

For the dispersed phase,

$$h_D = h_\sigma + h_O \tag{21-23}$$

The available data indicate that, for the orifice effect,

$$h_O = \frac{(V_O^2 - V_D^2)\rho_D}{2g_c(0.67)^2\,\Delta\rho} \doteq \frac{V_O'^2\rho_D}{28.9\,\Delta\rho} \tag{21-24}$$

and that h_σ to overcome interfacial-tension effects may be estimated for drop formation at a low velocity through the holes,

$$h_\sigma = \frac{6\sigma}{d_{p0.1}\,\Delta\rho g_c} \tag{21-25}$$

where $d_{p0.1}$ = the drop diameter produced by flow of dispersed phase at V_O = 360 ft./hr. (V_O' = 0.1 ft./sec.) through the perforations (see Fig. 21-39). At hole velocities of 1 ft./sec. (3600 ft./hr.) or more, h_σ should be omitted, and $h_D = h_O$.

The head required for flow of continuous phase h_C includes losses due to (1) friction in the downspout, which should be negligible, (2) contraction and expansion upon entering and leaving the downspout, and (3) two abrupt changes in direction. These total 4.5 velocity heads:

$$h_C = \frac{4.5V_d^2\rho_C}{2g_c\,\Delta\rho} \tag{21-26}$$

The distance between trays Z_t should be larger than h, sufficient so that (1) the "streamers" of dispersed liquid from the holes break up into drops before coalescing into the layer of liquid on the next plate, (2) the linear velocity of continuous liquid is not greater than that in the downspout to avoid excessive entrainment, and (3) the tower may be entered through hand- or manholes in the sides for cleaning.

Mass Transfer. Mass-transfer rates may be expressed in terms of over-all heights of transfer units and successfully correlated for any tower and system as in Fig. 21-44. No significance in terms of individual heights of transfer units for the separate phases should be given to the slope and intercept of such lines. The advantage gained by dispersing the liquid flowing at the larger rate, which results in low values for the abscissa of Fig. 21-44 and consequently low transfer-unit heights, is clear. Alternatively, since the plates resemble and basically behave in the manner of stages, the performance is frequently expressed in terms of stage efficiency, either over-all E_O for the entire tower, or more satisfactorily as Murphree efficiencies for each tray.

The system of Fig. 21-44 is one of high interfacial tension, so that the heights of transfer units are relatively high and stage efficiency low. For systems of low interfacial tension, on the other hand, stage efficiencies may be very much improved. Table 21-9 lists sources of mass-transfer data.

Coulson and Skinner [*Chem. Eng. Sci.*, **1**, 197 (1952)] and Pratt [*Ind. Chemist*, **31**, 552 (1955)] suggest methods of

Table 21-9. Mass-transfer Data for Perforated-tray Towers

System	Tower diam., in.	Tray spacing, in.	Ref.
Benzene–acetone–water	3	4, 8	*h*
Benzene–benzoic acid–water	3	4	*h*
Ethyl acetate–acetic acid–water	2	8, 16, 24	*f*
Ethyl ether–acetic acid–water	8.63	4.63, 7, 20	*i*
Gasoline–methylethyl ketone–water	3.75	4.5, 6	*g*
Kerosene–acetone–water	3	4, 8	*h*
Kerosene–benzoic acid–water	3.63	4.75	*a*
Methylisobutyl ketone–adipic acid–water	4.18	6	*d*
2,2,4-trimethylpentane–methylethyl ketone–water	3.75	4.5, 6	*g*
Toluene–benzoic acid–water	8.75	6	*j*
	3.63	4.75	*a*
	3.56	3, 6, 9	*k*
	2.72	9	*e*
	2	24	*f*
Toluene–diethyl amine–water	4.18	6	*b, c*

[a] Allerton, Strom, and Treybal, *Trans. Am. Inst. Chem. Engrs.*, **39**, 361 (1943).
[b] Garner, Ellis, and Fosbury, *Trans. Inst. Chem. Engrs.*, **31**, 348 (1953).
[c] Garner, Ellis, and Hill, *A.I.Ch.E. J.*, **1**, 185 (1955).
[d] Garner, Ellis, and Hill, *Trans. Inst. Chem. Engrs.*, **34**, 223 (1956).
[e] Goldberger and Benenati, *Ind. Eng. Chem.*, **51**, 641 (1959).
[f] Mayfield and Church, *Ind. Eng. Chem.*, **44**, 2253 (1952).
[g] Moulton and Walkey, *Trans. Am. Inst. Chem. Engrs.*, **40**, 695 (1944).
[h] Nandi and Ghosh, *J. Indian Chem. Soc., Ind. & News Ed.*, **13**, 93, 103, 108 (1950).
[i] Pyle, Duffey, and Colburn, *Ind. Eng. Chem.*, **42**, 1042 (1950).
[j] Row, Koffolt, and Withrow, *Trans. Am. Inst. Chem. Engrs.*, **37**, 559 (1941).
[k] Treybal and Dumoulin, *Ind. Eng. Chem.*, **34**, 709 (1942).

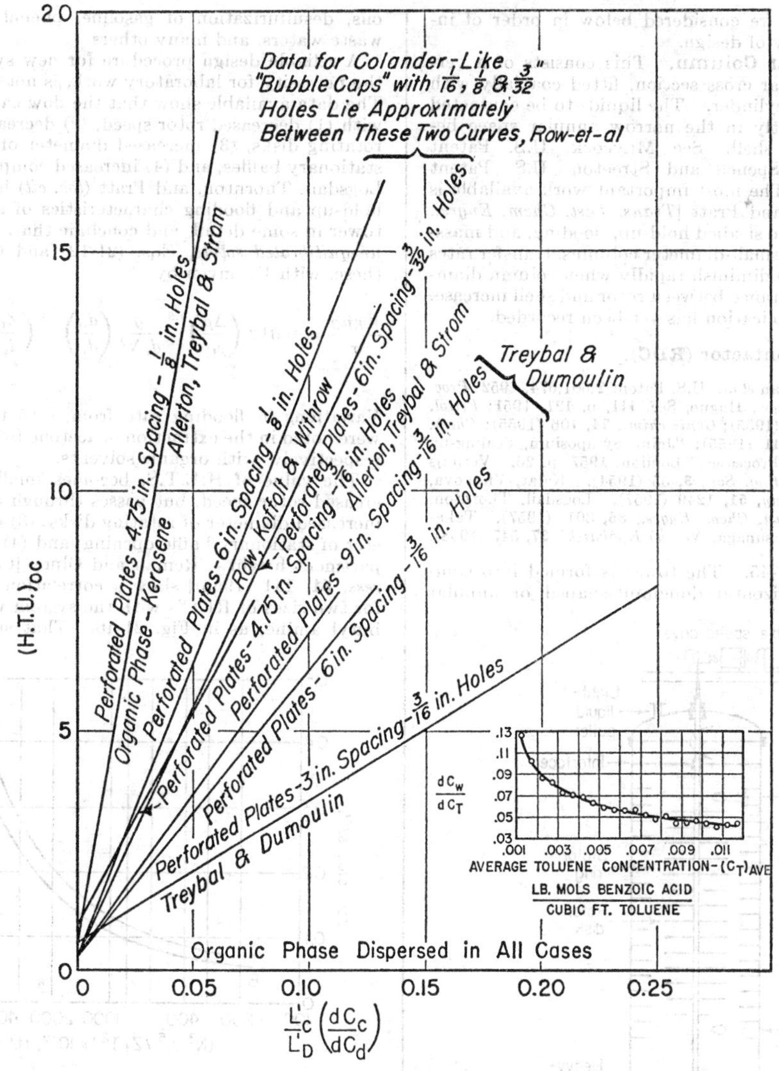

FIG. 21-44. Extraction rates for sieve-plate and modified bubble-plate columns. System benzoic acid, water, toluene except where noted. [*Allerton, Strom, and Treybal, Trans. Am. Inst. Chem. Engrs.*, **39**, 361 (1943); *Row, Koffolt, and Withrow, ibid.*, **37**, 559 (1941); *Treybal and Dumoulin, Ind. Eng. Chem.*, **34**, 709 (1942).]

estimating the rate of extraction. These have not been used successfully to predict the rates except in certain cases, owing, it is believed, to lack of adequate means of estimating extraction occurring during drop formation. The following empirical expression has been found to represent all the available data reasonably well, however, considering the great variety of circumstances and the considerable scatter in many of the original data:

$$E_O = \frac{89{,}500 Z_t^{0.5}}{\sigma}\left(\frac{V_D}{V_C}\right)^{0.42} = \frac{0.9 Z_t'^{0.5}}{\sigma'}\left(\frac{V_D}{V_C}\right)^{0.42} \quad (21\text{-}27)$$

where E_O is the over-all efficiency expressed as a fraction.

Koch Kascade Tower. See Koch, U.S. Patent 2,401,561, 1946; Fuqua, *Petrol. Processing*, **3**, 1050 (1948); Kjellman, *Sewage and Ind. Wastes*, **27**, 854 (1955). This is a form of perforated tray in which the perforations are arranged in vertical plates, of moderately complex design resembling a similar design used for gas-liquid contact. It has had application in the extraction of sulfur compounds from gasoline and in dephenolizing aqueous wastes, among other processes.

Gravity-operated Extractors (Mechanically Agitated)

Owing to the usual small density differences between the contacted liquids, the energy available from simple counterflow under the force of gravity is insufficient to disperse one liquid in the other and to establish turbulence levels to the extent necessary for rapid mass transfer, particularly for systems of high interfacial tension. Application of energy, mechanically applied through stirring devices, pulsations, etc., assists. The devices of major importance are considered below in order of increasing complexity of design.

Rotary Annular Column. This consists of a vertical shell of circular cross section, fitted coaxially with an inner, rotating cylinder. The liquids to be contacted flow countercurrently in the narrow annular space between rotor and shell. See Maycock, U.S. Patent 2,474,007, 1949; Spence and Streeton, U.S. Patent 2,742,348, 1956. The most important work available is that of Thornton and Pratt [*Trans. Inst. Chem. Engrs.*, **31**, 289 (1953)], who studied hold-up, flooding, and mass-transfer rates. In small-diameter columns, transfer rates are good, but these diminish rapidly when column diameter or annular clearance between rotor and shell increase. No commercial application has yet been recorded.

Rotary-disk Contactor (RDC).

REFERENCES: Reman *et al.*, U.S. Patent 2,601,674, 1952; *Proc. 3d World Petrol. Congr.*, Hague, Sec. III, p. 121, 1951; *Petrol. Refiner*, **34**, (9), 129 (1955); *Génie chim.*, **74**, 106 (1955); *Chem. Eng. Progress*, **51**, 141 (1955); "Joint Symposium, Scaling-up Chemical Plant and Processes," London, 1957, p. 26. Vermijs and Kramer, *Chem. Eng. Sci.*, **3**, 55 (1954). Kalat, Vnukova, and Rapis, *Chem. listy*, **51**, 1249 (1957). Logsdail, Thornton, and Pratt, *Trans. Inst. Chem. Engrs.*, **35**, 301, (1957). Takahashi, Suzuki, and Yasunaga, *Nenryô Kyôkaishi*, **37**, 547 (1958).

Refer to Fig. 21-45. The tower is formed into compartments by horizontal doughnut-shaped or annular

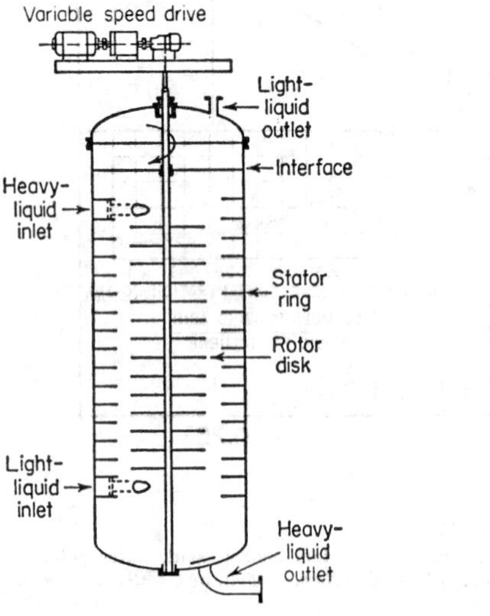

FIG. 21-45. Rotating-disk (RDC) extractor. (*Courtesy of General American Transportation Corp.*)

baffles, and within each compartment agitation is provided by a rotating, centrally located, horizontal disk. Somewhat similar devices have been known for some time. The features here are that the rotating disk is smooth and flat and of a diameter less than that of the opening in the stationary baffles, which facilitates fabrication and apparently improves extraction rates. Typical proportions are: tower diameter/rotating-disk diameter = 1.5 to 3; tower diameter/distance between disks = 2 to 8. The general proportions may be varied from one end of the tower to the other to accommodate changing liquid volumes and physical properties. These towers have been used in diameters ranging from a few inches for laboratory work, up to 8 ft. diameter by 40 ft. tall for purposes of deasphalting of petroleum. Other commercial services include furfural extraction of lubricating oils, desulfurization of gasoline, phenol recovery from waste waters, and many others.

A reliable design procedure for new systems, without the necessity for laboratory work, is not yet established. The data available show that the flow capacity increases with (1) decreased rotor speed, (2) decreased diameter of rotating disks, (3) increased diameter of opening in the stationary baffles, and (4) increased compartment height. Logsdail, Thornton, and Pratt (*loc. cit*) have studied the hold-up and flooding characteristics of a 3-in.-diameter tower in some detail, and conclude that, *in the absence of unequilibrated solute*, Eqs. (21-12) and (21-13) describe these, with V_K given by

$$\frac{V_K \mu_C}{\sigma} = 0.012 \left(\frac{\Delta\rho}{\rho_C}\right)^{0.9} \frac{g}{d_i N^2} \left(\frac{d_S}{d_i}\right)^{2.3} \left(\frac{Z_t}{d_i}\right)^{0.9} \left(\frac{d_i}{T}\right)^{2.7} \tag{21-28}$$

Variations in flooding rate from −15 to 200 per cent were noted in the extraction of acetone from and to water, respectively, with organic solvents.

The value of H.E.T.S. becomes smaller with (1) increased rotor speed, but passes through a minimum; (2) increased diameter of rotating disks; (3) decreased diameter of stationary baffle opening; and (4) decreased compartment height. Reman and Olney [*Chem. Eng. Progress*, **51**, 141 (1955)] show a correlation of stage height for two sizes of RDC's with the system water–kerosene–butyl amine, as in Fig. 21-46. That such correlations

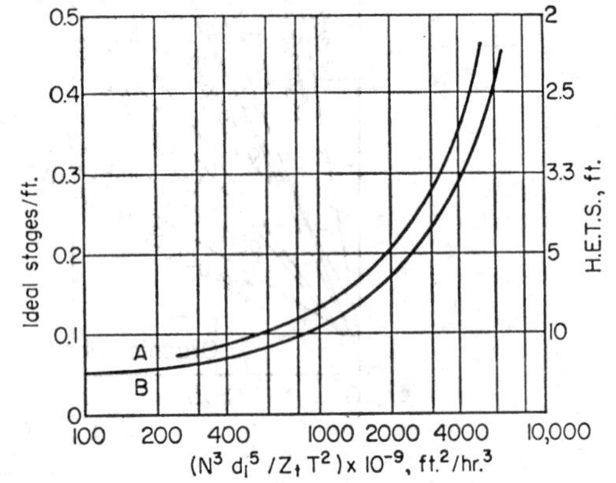

FIG. 21-46. Extraction in RDC columns, water–butyl amine–kerosene (continuous); T = 0.33 and 1.33 ft. Curve A: V_D = 50.7, V_C = 78.9 ft./hr.; curve B: V_D = 25.4, V_C = 78.9 ft./hr. [*Data of Reman and Olney, Chem. Eng. Progress*, **51**, 141 (1955).]

cannot be general is indicated by these authors' data on caustic extraction of gasoline, which show quite different curves. Logsdail, Thornton, and Pratt (*loc. cit.*) tentatively suggest that data can be correlated through

$$\frac{H_{tOC}}{V_C} \left(\frac{g^2 \rho_C}{\mu_C}\right)^{1/3} \varphi_D = C \left[\frac{\mu_C g}{V_K^3 (1 - \varphi_D)^3 \rho_C}\right]^{2\beta/3} \frac{\Delta\rho}{\rho_C}^{2(\beta-1)/3} \tag{21-29}$$

the constants C and β to be determined for each system. For toluene-water-acetone, β = 0.13; for butyl acetate–water–acetone, β = 0.4; in both cases, transfer was from water to organic solvent. For transfer in the reverse direction, V_K could not be computed (see above).

Miscellaneous uncorrelated data are offered in the references at the beginning of this discussion.

Mixco (Lightnin CMContactor) (Oldshue-Rushton) Column.

REFERENCES: Oldshue and Rushton, *Chem. Eng. Progress*, **48,** 297 (1952). Dykstra, Thompson, and Clouse, *Ind. Eng. Chem.*, **50,** 161 (1958). Gustison, Treybal, and Capps, *Chem. Eng. Progress, Symp. Ser.*, in press.

Refer to Fig. 21-47. The extractor is an extension of the simple baffled mixing vessel into a multistage column.

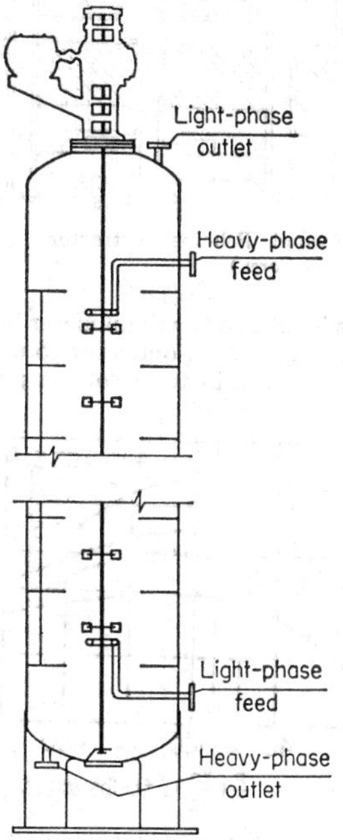

FIG. 21-47. Mixco (Oldshue-Rushton) extractor.

Although commercial application has been made, data are scarce and limited to towers of small diameter. The preferred proportions are $Z_t = 0.5T$, $d_S > d_i$.

Figure 21-48 presents some of the data of Oldshue and Rushton (*loc. cit.*) which show an optimum agitator speed for each configuration studied. The optimum would be expected to vary with physical properties of the liquids contacted. H.E.T.S. is improved, although capacity is decreased, by smaller openings in the stationary baffles. In the more difficult (because of high interfacial tension) extraction of uranium between kerosene-diluted solvents and aqueous solutions, Dykstra *et al.* (*loc. cit.*) have also shown the development of an optimum impeller speed. Gustison *et al.* (*loc. cit.*) have found it possible to correlate the stage efficiency with the ratio of flow rates (V_D/V_C) and the distribution coefficient, which varies considerably with concentration in the extraction of uranium. They also found it possible to scale up performance from 6 to 12 in. diameter geometrically, on the assumption that the continuous phase was thoroughly mixed in each compartment, by applying equal power per unit volume of liquids treated on the large and small scale, and using the same mass velocities of flow. Under these conditions it was anticipated, assuming K_Da to remain essentially constant, that

$$E_{MD2} = 1 - (1 - E_{MD1})^{Z_{t2}/Z_{t1}} \qquad (21\text{-}30)$$

where the subscripts 2 and 1 refer to large and small scale, respectively. This implies an increase of stage efficiency on scale-up, and this was confirmed.

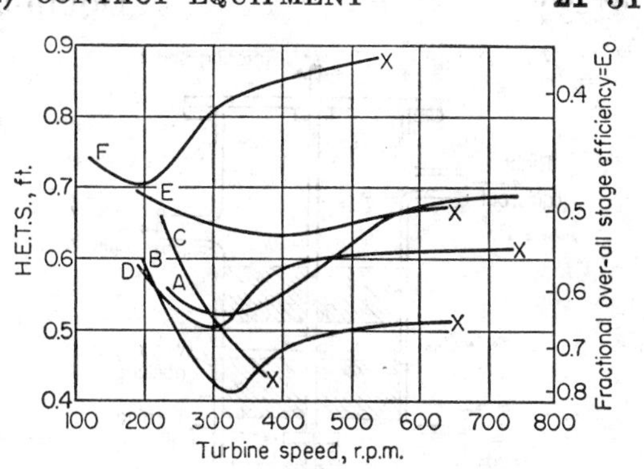

FIG. 21-48. Extraction in Mixco columns, methylisobutyl ketone–acetic acid–water (continuous); $T = 0.5$, $Z_t = 0.333$ ft. X = flooded condition.

Curve	d_i, ft.	d_s, ft.	V_D, ft./hr.	V_C, ft./hr.
A	0.1667	0.1775	15.2	7.1
B	0.1667	0.1775	26.8	12.8
C	0.1667	0.1775	26.8	18.6
D	0.1667	0.270	38.2	17.7
E	0.1667	0.270	26.8	12.8
F	0.250	0.270	15.2	7.1

[*Data of Oldshue and Rushton, Chem. Eng. Progress*, **48,** 297 (1952).]

A somewhat related design has been studied by Nagata, Eguchi, and coworkers [*Chem. Eng.* (Japan), **17,** 20 (1953); **20,** 2 (1956); *Mem. Faculty Eng., Kyoto Univ.*, **19,** 102 (1957); *Kagaku Kogaku*, **22,** 483 (1958)]. This column is characterized by the relatively small, separate openings between compartments for passage of liquids and the eccentric location of the impeller shaft. In a pilot-plant column, $T = 0.983$ ft., phenol was extracted from water ($V_C = 38.1$ ft./hr.) into benzene ($V_D = 21$ ft./hr.) at a fractional-stage efficiency of 0.618.

Scheibel (York-Scheibel) Columns.

REFERENCES: Scheibel, U.S. Patents 2,493,265, 1950; 2,850,362, 1958; British Patent 791,025, 1958; *Chem. Eng. Progress*, **44,** 681, 771 (1948); *A.I.Ch.E. J.*, **2,** 74 (1956). Scheibel and Karr, *Ind. Eng. Chem.*, **42,** 1048 (1950).

There are two designs. Figure 21-49 shows the earlier model. Alternate compartments are agitated with centrally located impellers, and the others are packed with an open woven wire mesh, per cent voids about 97 to 98. There are neither horizontal compartment plates nor vertical baffles, and the relative height of packed and mixed sections may be varied to suit prevailing conditions. This was one of the first mechanically agitated extractors to receive widespread application in both the laboratory and the industrial plant in a wide variety of services, and it is ordinarily still specified for 12 in. diameters or less.

There are relatively few data from the larger sizes. Scheibel and Karr (*loc. cit.*) present data on a 12-in.-diameter column, a part of which forms the basis of Fig. 21-50, for systems which are difficult (high interfacial tension) and easy (low interfacial tension) to extract. It is established that excellent values of H.E.T.S. are obtained under a wide variety of conditions. Low throughput and ratios of flow rates greatly different from unity require high agitator speeds for best results, and both direction of extraction and which phase is dispersed evidently influence the rates. No general correlation of flow capacities or of mass-transfer rates has been developed.

Figure 21-51 represents the newer design, developed not only to reduce the value of H.E.T.S. but also to permit more direct scale-up. In this arrangement, the impeller is surrounded by a shroud baffle, and the ratio of

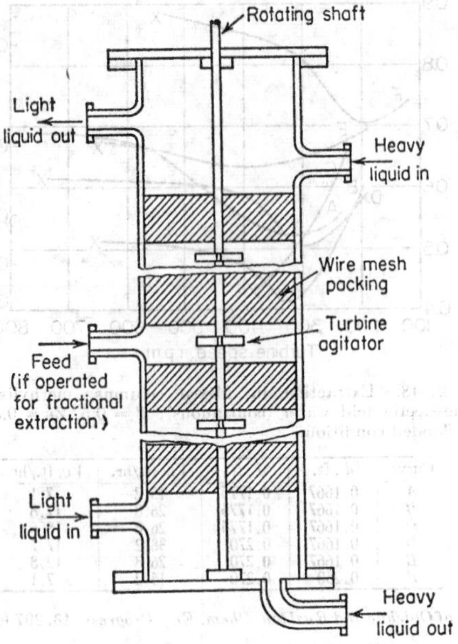

FIG. 21-49. First Scheibel column.

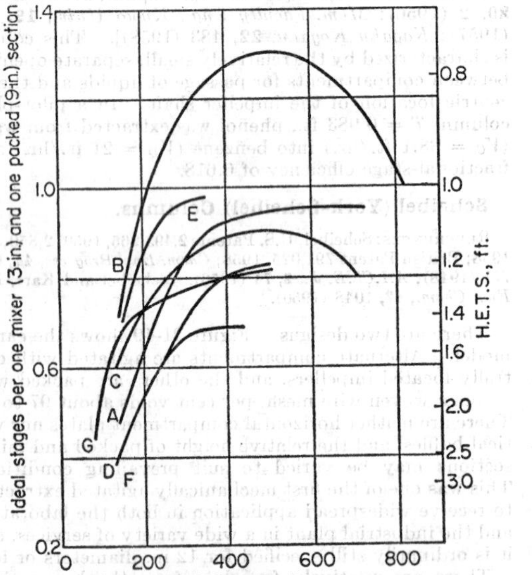

FIG. 21-50. Extraction in first Scheibel column, T = 0.94, d_i = 0.333 ft., height mixer section = 3 in., of packed section = 9 in. [*Data of Scheibel and Karr, Ind. Eng. Chem.*, **42**, 1048 (1950).]

Curve	System	V_D, ft./hr.	V_C, ft./hr.
A	MIBK(C)–water(D,E)–acetic acid	41.7	41.7
	MIBK(D)–water(C,E)–acetic acid		
B	MIBK(C,E)–water(D)–acetic acid	41.7	41.7
C	MIBK(C)–water(D,E)–acetic acid	23.2	23.2
	MIBK(C,E)–water(D)–acetic acid		
	MIBK(D)–water(C,E)–acetic acid		
D	*o*-Xylene(D)–water(C,E)–acetone	25.9	17.3
E	*o*-Xylene(D,E)–water(C)–acetone	22.1	21.2
F	*o*-Xylene(C)–water(D,E)–acetone	25.9	17.3
G	*o*-Xylene(C,E)–water(D)–acetone	21.1	22.1

(MIBK = methylisobutyl ketone; C = continuous; D = dispersed; E = extractant.)

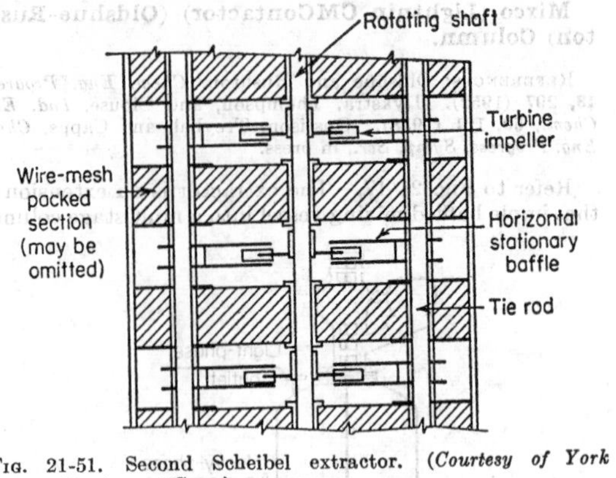

FIG. 21-51. Second Scheibel extractor. (*Courtesy of York Process Equipment Corp.*)

compartment height to tower diameter has been reduced. Data taken from a 12-in.-diameter column are shown in Fig. 21-52, correlated in terms of the power applied per

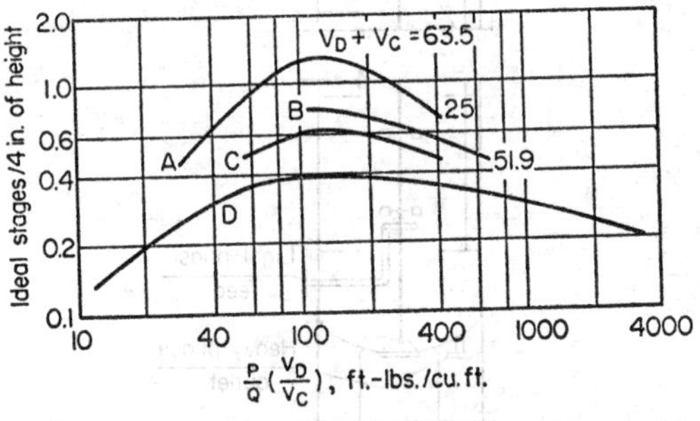

FIG. 21-52. Extraction in second Scheibel column, T = 0.94 ft., d_i = 0.333 ft., height of packed section = height of mixer section = 2 in. [*Data of Scheibel, A.I.Ch.E. J.*, **2**, 74 (1956).]

Curve	System
*A,B**	Methylisobutyl ketone–water–acetic acid
*C**	*o*-Xylene–water–acetic acid
D†	*o*-Xylene–water–phenol
	Methylisobutyl ketone–water–acetic acid
	o-Xylene–water–acetic acid

* Alternate mixing and packed sections.

† Packing omitted. Agitators in alternate and also every section.

unit volume of liquids handled per compartment. For the impeller used, the power number at turbulent Reynolds numbers is N_{Po} = 1.85. The data show that, while packing in alternate sections may increase mass-transfer rates, it decreases flow capacity. For systems of low interfacial tension and low viscosity, the alternate packed sections are specified for columns 36 in. diameter or less. For systems of high interfacial tension and viscosity, consecutive mixing sections without intermediate packed sections are more economical. Either arrangement is available in columns of diameter 3 in. and up, and columns of 7 ft. diameter are in service.

Pulsed Columns. These are extractors wherein a rapid reciprocating motion of relatively short amplitude is applied to the liquid contents. The agitation so produced has been found to give improved rates of extraction. The principle originated with van Dijck (U.S. Patent 2,011,186, 1935). Because agitation was necessary to reduce tower heights and consequently the expense of massive shielding, and because pulsing provided a means of agitation not requiring moving parts, bearings, and the like in contact with highly corrosive, dangerously radioactive liquids, pulsed columns have been freely applied in extraction and separation of metals from the solutions of the atomic-energy operations. Applications appear thus far to be limited to this area. There are two major types of columns: (1) ordinary (spray, packed, etc.) extractors on which pulsations are imposed, and (2) a special sieve-plate design. Their characteristics are quite different.

Pulsing Devices. Refer to Fig. 21-53. At *a*, a reciprocating plunger or piston pump from which the check

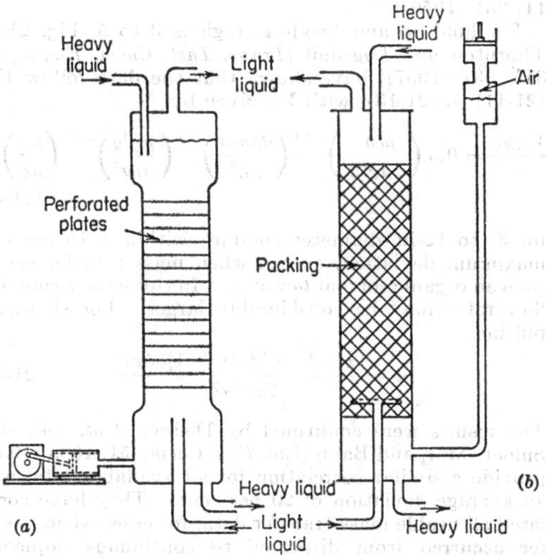

FIG. 21-53. Pulsed columns. (*a*) Perforated plate column with pump pulse generator; (*b*) packed column with air pulser.

valves have been removed is connected to the space containing continuous phase, as shown. This arrangement is mechanically reliable and can easily be arranged for varying the amplitude and frequency of the pulsations, but suffers the disadvantages that (1) the corrosive liquid may be in direct contact with the piston, and (2) too rapid pulsing, especially with volatile organic liquids, may cause cavitation. The pipe connecting column and pulser may be of any length to pass through shielding, barriers, and the like, but high pressure drop in the transfer pipe contributes to cavitation difficulties. An alternative arrangement using an air pulse is shown at *b* in the figure [Thornton, *Chem. Eng. Progress, Symp. Ser.*, **50** (13), 39 (1954); U.S. Patent 2,818,324, 1957]. This keeps corrosive liquids out of contact with the pulsing device and obviates the cavitation problem but because of the compressibility of the gas requires greater application of pulsing power for the same results. Flexible bellows or diaphragms of reinforced rubber, plastic, or metal in contact with the liquids may be flexed mechanically or by an electromagnetic transducer (Thornton, *loc. cit.*). If hydraulically activated, these may have a life of up to 30,000,000 cycles or more [Jealous and Johnson, *Ind. Eng. Chem.*, **47**, 1159 (1955)]. With suitable cam mechanisms, pulsations whose amplitude-time characteristics appear as sine, square, or saw-tooth wave shapes are possible.

Pressure at the pulsing device and the conditions for cavitation and "water hammer" may be estimated by the methods of Williams and Little [*Trans. Inst. Chem. Engrs.*, **32**, 174 (1954)] provided the pressure-drop characteristics of the tower internals are known. Jealous and Johnson (*loc. cit.*) have had good success in computing the power required for pulsing. During a test of a 2-ft.-diameter, 40-ft.-tall tower packed with 20-mesh screens and filled with kerosene, maximum power at 176.4 cycles/min., ¼-in. amplitude, was about 6 hp. Since power requirement alternates, the use of a flywheel on the pulse mechanism to act as an energy reservoir is suggested as a means of reducing power requirements. Alternatively, two columns could be pulsed 180 deg. out of phase with one pulse generator (Griffith, Jasney, and Tupper, U.S.A.E.C. AECD-3440, 1952). Irvine (U.S.A.E.C. ORNL-2377, 1957) devised a pulse pump to utilize part of the pulse energy. Concatenated columns (long extractors built as several short columns, with liquids led from one to the other in strictly countercurrent fashion) may be pulsed by a single pulse generator to advantage, since less power is required owing to reduced static head [Jealous and Lieberman, *Chem. Eng. Progress*, **52**, 366 (1956)].

The following terms are generally used to describe the pulse action: *Frequency* is the rate of application of the pulse action, cycles/time. *Amplitude* is the linear distance between extreme positions of the liquid in the column (not of the pulser) produced by pulsing. *Pulsed volume* = amplitude × frequency × column cross-sectional area = volumetric rate of movement of liquid, expressed as volume/time or volume/(time)(area).

Pulsed Spray Columns. Billerbeck *et al.* [*Ind. Eng. Chem.*, **48**, 183 (1956)] applied pulsing to a laboratory (1.5-in.-diameter) column. At pulse amplitude 7/16 in., rates of mass transfer improved slightly with increased frequency up to 400 cycles/min., but the effect was relatively small. Shirotsuka [*Kagaku Kogaku*, **22**, 687 (1958)] provides additional data. There is not believed to be commercial application.

Pulsed Packed Columns. Any of the ordinary packings may be used, although random packings tend to orient on pulsing, which may lead to channeling. For this reason, Thornton [*Chem. Eng. Progress, Symp. Ser.*, **50**(13), 39 (1954); *Brit. Chem. Eng.*, **3**, 247 (1958)] recommends fixed packing made from plates of corrugated expanded metal. Pulsing reduces the size of dispersed-phase droplets, increases hold-up, and increases interfacial area for mass transfer. There is a greater tendency toward emulsification, and maximum through-put is decreased, but H.E.T.S. is reduced considerably, by the pulsing. Pulsing can be applied on existing, non-pulsed packed towers to good mass-transfer advantage, provided limiting flow rates are not exceeded.

Feich and Anderson [*Ind. Eng. Chem.*, **44**, 404 (1952)], with ⅜-in. Raschig rings and ½-in. McMahon saddles in a 1.5-in. laboratory column, found the height of a transfer unit in the extraction of benzoic acid between toluene and water decreased from 13.4 ft. with no pulsing to 0.6 ft. with 400 cycles/min. at 3/16-in. amplitude. This is their best case but indicates what can be done. Somewhat less spectacular improvement resulted when acetic acid was the extracted solute. They concluded that the improvement is largely due to increase in interfacial surface resulting from pulsing, rather than major change in the mass-transfer coefficients. Chantry, von Berg, and Wiegandt [*Ind. Eng. Chem.*, **47**, 1153 (1955)] obtained the results of Fig. 21-54, indicating an optimum amplitude (lowest H.E.T.S.) for each pulse frequency. Pulsing made H.E.T.S. essentially independent of the continuous-phase flow rate. Somewhat similar improvements by pulsing are shown by Potnis *et al.* [*Ind. Eng. Chem.*, **51**, 645 (1959)], Crico [*Génie chim.*, **73**, 57 (1955)], Oyama and Yamaguchi [*Kagaku Kogaku*, **22**, 668 (1958)], Shirotsuka, Honda, and Yasuno [*Kagaku Kikai*, **21**, 645 (1957)], and Honda and Yamamoto [*Kagaku Kogaku*, **22**, 97 (1958)]. No means of predicting the effect of pulsing in the general case is now available.

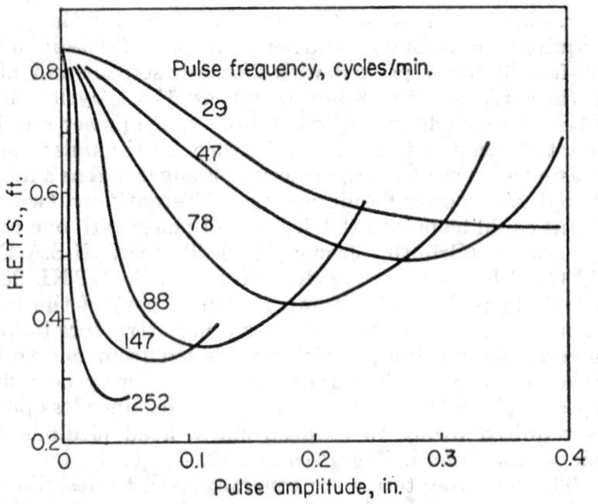

FIG. 21-54. Effect of pulsing on extraction in a packed column, methylisobutyl ketone–acetic acid–water (continuous). Tower diameter = 1.58 in., 27-in. depth of ¼-in. Raschig rings, $V_D \doteq V_C = 7.5$ to 10. [*Data of Chantry, von Berg, and Wiegandt, Ind. Eng. Chem.*, **47,** 1153 (1955), *with permission.*]

A small perforated-plate column of conventional design was pulsed by Goldberger and Benenati [*Ind. Eng. Chem.*, **51,** 641 (1959)] with marked improvement in mass-transfer rates.

Pulsed Sieve-plate Columns. The standard arrangement (see Fig. 21-53*a*) consists of a tower fitted with horizontal sieve plates which occupy the entire cross section of the column. There are *no downspouts* as in ordinary sieve-plate columns. Typical arrangements use ⅛-in.-diameter perforations sufficient to provide 20 to 25 per cent free space, with 2-in. plate spacing, pulse amplitudes in the range 0.25 to 1 in., and frequencies of 100 to 250 cycles/min., although the pulse characteristics will be dependent upon the system and flow rates under consideration.

Sege and Woodfield [*Chem. Eng. Progress, Symp. Ser.*, **50**(13), 179 (1954)] provide a good description of the operational characteristics. Refer to Fig. 21-55. Since

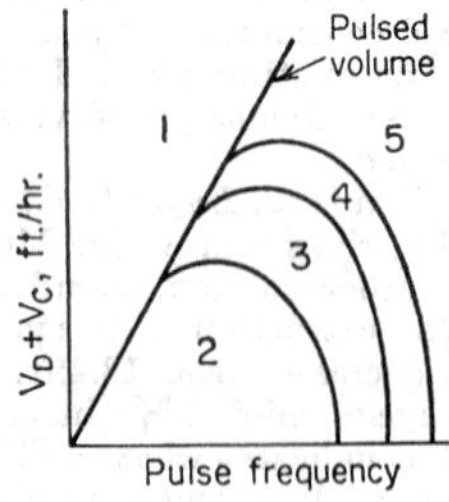

FIG. 21-55. Pulsed column characteristics. [*Sege and Woodfield, Chem. Eng. Progress, Symp. Ser.*, **50** (13), 179 (1954).]

in many cases the perforations are too small to permit flow owing to interfacial tension of the liquids, the total pulsed volume must ordinarily approximate the volumetric rate of flow of the liquids [Edwards and Beyer, *A.I.Ch.E. J.*, **2,** 148 (1956), show that slightly higher rates than $V_D + V_C$ = pulsed volume may be obtained]. In *region* 1 of the figure, the column is flooded because of insufficient pulsed volume. In *region* 2, discrete layers of liquid appear between plates during the quiet portion of the pulse cycle. During upward pulsing, the light liquid is forced through the perforations and forms drops which rise to the plate above. During downward pulsing, the heavy liquid behaves similarly. Flow is stable, but mass-transfer rates are generally poor. In *region* 3 there is little change in phase dispersion throughout the pulse cycle and a fairly uniform dispersion of small droplets persists throughout. This region provides the best mass-transfer rates. *Region* 4 is characterized by irregular coalescence into fairly large drops, and periodic reversals of the continuous phase (local flooding). Extraction rates are generally poor. Further increase in frequency results in flooding owing to emulsification, *region* 5. Transition between regions is gradual and continuous, not abrupt. Excellent photographs of these phenomena are provided by Defives, Durandet, and Gladel [*Rev. inst. franç. pétrole et Ann. combustibles liquides*, **11,** 231 (1956)].

For hold-up and flooding, regions 3 to 5, Fig. 21-55, Thornton and Logsdail [*Trans. Inst. Chem. Engrs.*, **35**, 316, 331 (1957)] have shown that the data follow Eqs. (21-11) to (21-13), with V_K given by

$$\frac{V_K \mu_C}{\sigma} = 0.6 \left(\frac{\rho_C \sigma^4}{\psi \mu_C^5 g_c}\right)^{0.24} \left(\frac{d_O \rho_C \sigma}{\mu_C^2}\right)^{0.9} \left(\frac{\mu_C^4 g}{\Delta\rho \sigma^3}\right)^{1.01} \left(\frac{\mu_D}{\mu_C}\right)^{0.30} \tag{21-31}$$

for 3- to 12-in.-diameter columns within ±15 per cent maximum deviation, except when mass transfer occurs *from* an organic solvent *to* water. In this case permissible flow rates may be considerably larger. For sine-wave pulsing,

$$\psi = \frac{\pi^2[(T^4/n^2 d_O^4) - 1](fw)^3}{2g_c C_O Z_t} \tag{21-32}$$

The results were confirmed by Defives *et al.* (*loc. cit.*). Smoot, Mar, and Babb [*Ind. Eng. Chem.*, **51,** 1005 (1959)] provide a similar correlation for all available data, with an average deviation of 20 per cent. They have correlated all usable mass-transfer data, for cases where transfer occurred from dispersed to continuous (aqueous) phase, the major resistance residing within the dispersed phase (average deviation 20 per cent):

$$\frac{H_{tOC}}{Z_t} = 0.20 \left(\frac{fwT^2}{nd_O^2}\right)^{0.434} \left(\frac{\Delta\rho}{\rho_D}\right)^{1.04} N_{ScD}{}^{0.865} \left(\frac{\sigma}{\mu_C V_C}\right)^{0.096} \left(\frac{V_C}{V_D}\right)^{0.636} \left(\frac{T}{Z_t}\right)^{0.317} \left(\frac{\mu_C}{\mu_D}\right)^{4.57} \tag{21-33}$$

They further provide an excellent bibliography of sources of data. Mar and Babb [*Ind. Eng. Chem.*, **51,** 1011 (1959)] provide a correlation for the back-mixing effect in these columns.

On scale-up to 2-ft.-diameter towers, Woodfield and Sege [*Chem. Eng. Progress, Symp. Ser.*, **50**(13), 14 (1954)] have indicated that serious channeling may reduce mass-transfer rates appreciably. By removing plates from a 12-in. length of the column and installing a specially designed redistributor instead, H_{tOC} was improved from 5 to 1.2 ft. in the extraction of uranium.

Reciprocating Plate Columns. These were suggested by van Dijck (U.S. Patent 2,011,186, 1953), who proposed moving the plates of a perforated-plate extractor up and down rapidly over a short distance. Isaac and DeWitte [*A.I.Ch.E. J.*, **4,** 498 (1958)] indicate some success with this arrangement. Karr [*A.I.Ch.E. J.*, **5,** 446 (1956)] used large-diameter (⅝-in.) perforations with 63 per cent free space in the plates, and also plates of expanded metal in a 3-in.-diameter column, thereby maintaining high flow capacity with high mass-transfer rates.

Centrifugal Extractors

The force of gravity for counterflow of liquids of different density may be replaced and in effect increased, many

Table 21-10. Podbielniak Centrifugal Extractors and Clarifiers*

Series	Diam., in.	Width, in.	Total vol. hold-up,[a] gal.	Flow capacity,[a,b] gal./min.	Power required,[a] continuous operation, hp.	Pressure required, lb./sq. in.		Approx. wt.,[a,e] lb.	Space required,[f] in.		
						Light liquid in[c]	Heavy liquid in[d]		Length	Width	Height
5000	17	0.25–0.50	0.16–0.4	0.066–0.132	1	80–175	20–125	200	36	24	24
6000	17–25	0.5–2.0	1–2	1–5	1–2	80–165	20–125	200–400	36	24–28	24
9600	36	2–4	7–10	1–10	3–4	65–150	20–100	600–1500	72	28–36	48
9700	36	4–36	10–80	10–175	3–10	65–150	20–100	2500–5000	72	36–72	48
9800	42–48	4–48	25–200	20–750	10–20	65–150	20–100	8000–24000	96	36–96	60

* Courtesy of Podbielniak, Inc.
[a] Depends on width.
[b] Combined streams, average systems.
[c] Depends on density difference, rotor speed, and position of feed.
[d] Depends on back pressure placed on light liquid effluent.
[e] Exclusive of drive.
[f] Including drive, normal installation.

thousandfold if desired, by centrifugal machines. These then become especially useful for handling liquids of low density difference and those with tendencies to form emulsions.

Podbielniak Extractor (Podbielniak, U.S. Patent 2,044,996, 1935, and many others). This is the most important of the group. Refer to Fig. 21-56. Rotation

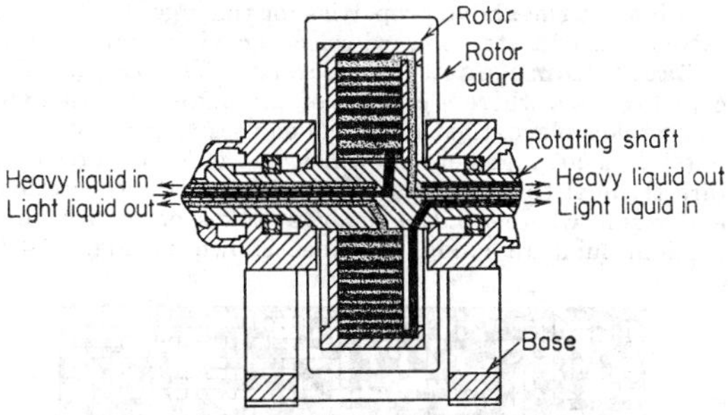

FIG. 21-56. Podbielniak centrifugal extractor, schematic. (*Treybal, "Liquid Extraction," 2d ed., McGraw-Hill, New York, 1963, with permission.*)

is about a horizontal shaft. The body of the extractor is a drum, the early models of which contained a spiral metal sheet. Later models have been built with concentric perforate cylinders. The liquids are introduced through the rotating shaft with the help of special mechanical seals; the light liquid is led internally to the drum periphery and the heavy liquid to the axis of the drum. Rapid rotation (up to several thousand r.p.m., depending on size) causes radial counterflow of the liquids, which are then led out through the shaft. Materials of construction include steel, stainless steel, Hastelloy, and other corrosion-resistant alloys. The machines are particularly characterized by extremely low hold-up of liquid per stage, and this led to their extensive use in the extraction of antibiotics, such as penicillin and the like, where multistage extraction and phase separation must be done rapidly to avoid chemical destruction of the product under conditions of extraction. They have been used extensively in all phases of pharmaceutical manufacture and are increasingly being used in other fields: petroleum processing, both solvent refining and acid treating, dephenolization of waste waters, extraction of uranium from ore leach liquors, as well as for clarification and phase-separation work. See *Chem. Eng.*, **66,** 99 (Mar. 23, 1959); Kaiser, *Sewage and Ind. Wastes*, **27,** 311 (1955); Podbielniak, Gavin, and Kaiser, *J. Am. Oil Chemists' Soc.*, **36,** 238 (1959); Doyle and Rauch, *Petrol. Engr.*, **27**(5), C-49 (1955); Anderson and Lau, *Chem. Eng. Progress*, **51,** 507 (1955). Low hold-up corresponds to low solvent inventory and rapid attainment of steady state on startup. Table 21-10 lists some of the characteristics of the machines.

During operation, a liquid-liquid interface position must be maintained, as with any extractor, by control of the pressure of the effluents. For this machine, a high pressure on the light-liquid-out line corresponds to a light-liquid-continuous situation, low pressure to light-liquid-dispersed.

With a laboratory model (18 in. diameter, 2 in. wide, 18 concentric cylinders slotted at 180-deg. intervals), Barson and Beyer [*Chem. Eng. Progress*, **49,** 243 (1953)] obtained from two to eight ideal stages with isoamyl alcohol–boric acid–water at 5000 r.p.m. The number of stages increased with ratio of light-to-heavy liquid flow but with varying position of the interface and consequently varying fraction of the machine devoted to light-liquid-dispersed. At constant flow rate, the number of stages was essentially independent of rotational speed. Jacobson and Beyer [*A.I.Ch.E. J.*, **2,** 283 (1956)] obtained about the same results. Alexandre and Gentilini [*Rev. inst. franç. pétrole et Ann. combustibles liquides*, **11,** 389 (1956)] similarly obtained five ideal stages with benzene–acetic acid–water, and 3.4 to 12.5 ideal stages with methylisobutyl ketone–acetic acid–water. Anderson and Lau [*Chem. Eng. Progress*, **51,** 507 (1955)] describe a model handling 10 to 15 per cent suspended solids in the liquids, and report a fraction to two ideal stages when extracting penicillin and chloromycetin, 1860 to 2300 gal./hr. total flow rate.

Luwesta (Centriwesta) Extractor. This is a development from Coutor (U.S. Patent 2,036,924, 1936). See also Eisenlohr [*Ind. Chemist*, **27,** 271 (1951); *Chem.-Ing.-Tech.*, **23,** 12 (1951); *Pharm. Ind.*, **17,** 207 (1955); *Trans. Indian Inst. Chem. Engrs.*, **3,** 7 (1949–1950)]. This centrifuge revolves about a vertical axis and contains three actual stages. It operates at 3800 r.p.m. and handles approximately 1300 gal./hr. total liquid flow at 12 kw. power requirement. Provision is made in the machine for accumulation of solids separated from the liquids, for periodic removal. It is used, more extensively in Europe than in the United States, for extraction of acetic acid, pharmaceuticals, and similar products.

SOLID-SOLID SYSTEMS

SOLID-SOLID MIXING

REFERENCES: 1. A.I.Ch.E. Standard Testing Procedure for Solids Mixing Equipment, American Institute of Chemical Engineers, 345 East 47 St., New York 17, N.Y. 2. Bullock, *Chem. Eng.*, Apr. 20, 1959. 3. Danckwerts, *Research*, **6,** 355–361 (1953). 4. Fischer, *Chem. Eng.*, Aug. 8, 1960. 5. Kirk and Othmer (eds.), "Encyclopedia of Chemical Technology," vol. 9. Reinhold, New York, 1952. 6. Lacey, *J. Appl. Chem.*, **4,** 257–268 (1954). 7. Quillen, *Chem. Eng.*, June, 1954. 8. Scott, Chapter on Mixing of Solids in "Chemical Engineering Practice," Cremer and Davies (eds.), vol. 3, p. 362, Butterworth, London.

1957. 9. Weidenbaum, Chapter on Mixing of Solids in "Advances in Chemical Engineering," Drew and Hoopes (eds.), vol. II, Academic Press, New York, 1958. 10. Work, *Chem. Eng. Progress*, **50** (9), (September, 1954).

A comprehensive bibliography is available in ref. 9. Equipment photographs and details are available in refs. 2, 4, 5, 7, 8, and 10. References 3 and 6 give excellent theoretical work. Reference 5 gives a tabulation and summary of many mixer types and applications. References 8 and 9 are book chapters dealing with mixing of solids and cover both the theoretical and equipment aspects. Interpretive summaries of the literature in various areas (state of mixedness, theoretical frequency distributions, rate equations, and equipment) are included in ref. 9. Reference 1 gives a procedure for testing solids-mixing equipment.

Fundamentals

Objectives of Solid-Solid Contacting. Equipment in which solid materials are mixed may be used for a number of operations. Blending of ingredients may be the main objective as, for example, in the preparation of feeds, insecticides, fertilizer, glass batches, packaged foods, and cosmetics. Other objectives may include cooling or heating such as in the cooling of limestone or sugar, or the preheating of plastic prior to calendering. Drying or roasting of the solids is sometimes desired. In some applications, such as polymerization of plastics, catalyst manufacture, or the preparation of cereal products, the solids mixture may be reacted. Coating is desired in some cases as in the manufacture of pigments, dyes, minerals, candy and other food products, and the preparation of feeds. In certain of these cases, small amounts of liquid may be added, but the end product is a solids mixture. Sometimes agglomerates are desired as in the preparation of food products, pharmaceuticals, detergents, and fertilizer. Often size reduction is desired while solids are being mixed. In all cases, the mixing of solids occurs. However, in some of these operations, the details of the equipment to accomplish operations other than pure blending may become a major problem. This portion of Sec. 21 will deal with equipment whose major function is to give a thorough mixture of solids. Specialized equipment to perform the other functions is discussed in other sections of the handbook and will not be dealt with here. Thus, for example, Sec. 8 is devoted to size reduction and enlargement, although equipment mentioned there may also accomplish mixing.

Batch Ingredient Properties Affecting Solids Mixing. Wide differences among properties such as particle-size distribution, density, shape, and surface characteristics (such as electrostatic charge) may make blending very difficult. In fact, the properties of the ingredients dominate the mixing operation. The most commonly observed characteristics of solids are: (1) *Particle-size distribution.* This tells the percentages of the material in different size ranges. (2) *Bulk density,* which is weight per unit of volume of a quantity of solid particles; this is usually expressed in lb./cu. ft. It is not a constant and can be decreased by aeration and increased by vibration or mechanical packing. (3) *True density* of the solid material; usually expressed in lb./cu. ft. This, divided by the density of water, equals specific gravity. (4) *Particle shape.* Some types are pellets, egg shapes, blocks, spheres, flakes, chips, rods, filaments, crystals, or irregular shapes. (5) *Surface characteristics* such as surface area and tendency to hold a static charge. (6) *Flow characteristics. Angle of repose* and *flowability* are measurable characteristics for which standard tests are available (*e.g.*, A.S.T.M. Test B213-48 on Flow Rate of Metal Powders, etc.). A steeper angle of repose would indicate less flowability. The term "lubricity" has sometimes been used for solid particles to correspond roughly to viscosity of a fluid. (7) *Friability* (also see grindability, Sec. 8). This is the tendency of the material to break into smaller sizes in the course of handling. There are quantitative tests specially devised for certain materials such as coal which can be used to estimate this property. Abrasiveness of one ingredient upon another should also be considered. (8) *State of agglomeration.* This refers to whether the particles exist independently or adhere to one another in clusters. The kind and degree of energy employed during mixing and the friability of the agglomerates will affect the extent of agglomerate breakdown and particle dispersion. (9) *Moisture or liquid content of solids.* Often a small amount of liquid is added for dust reduction or special requirements (such as oils for cosmetics). The resultant material may still have the appearance of a dry solid rather than a paste. (10) *Density, viscosity, and surface tension* at operating temperature of any liquid added. (11) *Temperature limitations of ingredients.* Any unusual effects due to temperature changes which might occur (such as heat of reaction) should be noted.

A look at the above properties for the ingredients to be mixed is a first step toward selecting mixing equipment.

Batch Homogeneity. *Measuring Uniformity.* Except for cases where a coating of one ingredient with another takes place, the theoretical end result of mixing will not be an arrangement in which one type of particle is directly next to a different type. Rather, the theoretical end result where *random tumbling* takes place will be a random mixture along the lines shown in Fig. 21-57.

FIG. 21-57. A random arrangement of black and white particles. (*Lacey, Trans. Inst. Chem. Engrs. (London)*, **21**, 52–59 (1943).)

With easily distinguishable particles which can be counted, the variation between spot samples of a known size (*i.e.*, number of particles) can be theoretically predicted for a random mixture and used as a guide to determine how closely random blending of the ingredients is approached. Where individual particles cannot be easily distinguished and particle counts are not practical, various types of analyses can be made on spot samples to determine batch uniformity. Recent advances in instrumental analysis have made it much easier to give rapid and numerous analyses which are of great benefit for statistical analyses. Some of these methods are X-ray fluorescence, flame spectrometry, polarography, and emission spectroscopy. Also, radioactive-tracer methods have been used. Regardless of the analytic methods chosen, whether gravimetric, volumetric, electrometric, particle counts, optical or other, it is very important that the data be objectively analyzed via statistical methods should there be any question as to the adequacy of the mixture. The analytical error should be very small compared with the variation in the composition (or other property) between spot samples.

Reference 9 describes many different ways of measuring uniformity.

Evaluation. Whether the desired end product is satisfactory can be used as a practical criterion of the adequacy of the solids mixture. A further consideration is the effect of the solids mixture on the over-all economics of the manufacturing process. Studies of the type mentioned in the previous paragraph *may* be part of such an evaluation. Where the solids mixture is made directly into a product, as in the case of feed pellets or pharmaceutical tablets, uniformity tests on these items will speak for themselves. In cases where the solids mixture must be further processed, such as in the manufacture of glass or plastics, the efficiency and costs of the subsequent operations can often be related to the starting solids mixture. In such cases, knowledge of the homogeneity of the solids mixture is needed to determine its effect on the manufacturing process.

Regardless of the method of evaluating the solids mixture, the sampling procedure is vital. Often a sampling thief, or other special device, is used to remove samples from the mixture without excessive disturbance of the batch. If an easier method of sampling is obvious and will bring less contamination to the batch, it should be used.

Method of sampling, location, size and number of samples, method of sample analysis, and fraction of the batch removed for sampling all contribute to how well the sampling study reflects the actual conditions.

A standard testing procedure for solids-mixing equipment is available (Ref. 1). This contains details and references pertaining to sampling from solids mixtures for both batch and continuous mixing.

Segregation Problems. Previously it was pointed out that wide differences among properties may make blending very difficult. For example, natural segregating tendencies will be observed with extreme differences in specific gravity, size, or shape. The heavier, smaller, or smoother and rounder particles tend to sink through the lighter, larger, or jagged ones, respectively. In some cases, preparation of the materials to avoid extreme differences in such ingredient properties can avoid segregation problems.

There are also other factors which can cause segregation.

Electrostatic charges may cause particles to repel each other. In cases where continued blending may cause such charges to build up, it is important to determine the precise blending time required and not to overblend.

Loss of material as dust must be considered as a possible means of segregation and should not be aggravated by too strong suction in the dust-collection apparatus.

If there are smeary particles which have an almost pastelike behavior and barely flow (high angle of repose), frictional anchorage of these onto the other particles in the mixture may be necessary in order to achieve good mixing.

Where a batch ingredient is in agglomerate form, some device to break up the agglomerates should be used to prevent them from segregating from the rest of the mixture and to ensure the intimate dispersion of this ingredient throughout the mixture.

The use of a liquid such as water (possibly with a surface-active agent) can have remarkable effects in overcoming segregation which may appear inevitable otherwise.

Although the above applies to the actual *solids-mixing* operation, thought must also be given to the subsequent processing steps. Thus, the solids-mixing operation must be checked from the point of view of delivering a well-mixed batch to a certain point. The system must be scrutinized for possible segregating points such as transfer points, long drops, flow through silos, and vibratory equipment. Where a liquid is used, the amount that can be added without getting into caking problems which may upset the later processing of the solids mixture should be determined.

Equipment

Mixing Mechanisms. There are several basic mechanisms by which solid particles are mixed. These include small-scale random motion (diffusion), large-scale random motion (convection), and shear.

Motions which increase the mobility of the individual particles will promote diffusive mixing. If there are no opposing segregating effects, this diffusive mixing will in time lead to a high degree of homogeneity. Diffusive mixing occurs when particles are distributed over a freshly developed surface and when individual particles are given increased internal mobility. A plain tumbler gives the former while an impact mill gives the latter.

For most rapid mixing, in addition to diffusive (fine-scale) mixing, there should be a means by which large groups of particles are intermixed. This can be accomplished by either the convective or shear mechanism. A ribbon mixer illustrates the former whereas a plain tumbler gives the latter.

Types of Solids-mixing Machines. There are several types of solids-mixing machines. In some machines the container moves. In others a device rotates within a stationary container. In some cases, a combination of rotating container and rotating internal device is used. Sometimes baffles or blades are present in the mixer. Table 21-11 classifies solids-mixing machines via the characteristics given in the column headings. Illustrations of several of the machines listed there are shown in Fig. 21-58. The various types listed in Table 21-11 will be briefly discussed below, with paragraph numbers referring to the columns.

1. *Tumbler.* Suitable for gentle blending; capable of handling large volumes; easily cleaned; suitable for dense powders and abrasive materials. Not for breaking up agglomerates.

Figure 58*a* and *b* (without broken-line portions) shows some unbaffled tumblers.

Figure 58*c* and *d* shows some baffled tumblers.

2. *Tumbler with Agglomerate Breaker.* (See Sec. 8 for ball mill, rod mill, and vibratory pebble mill which will accomplish mixing along with size reduction.)

Several tumblers are available with separately driven internal rotating devices for breaking up agglomerates. The tumbler itself can be used for gentle blending if agglomerate breakdown is not required.

The broken-line portions of Fig. 58*a* and 58*b* show some types of agglomerate-breaking devices for tumblers.

Table 21-12 includes impact velocities for some internal rotating devices in tumblers as well as other mixers. Contamination and wear problems of internal rotating devices are discussed under Performance Characteristics.

3. *Stationary Shell or Trough.* There are a number of different types of mixers in which the container is stationary and material displacement is accomplished by single or multiple rotating inner mixing devices.

Ribbon mixer (Fig. 58*e*). Within this subgroup there are several types. Ribbon cross section and pitch, clearances between outer ribbon and shell, and number of spirals on the ribbon are some features which can be varied to accommodate materials ranging from low-density finely divided materials that aerate rapidly to fibrous or sticky materials that require positive discharge aid. Other construction variations are either center or end dis-

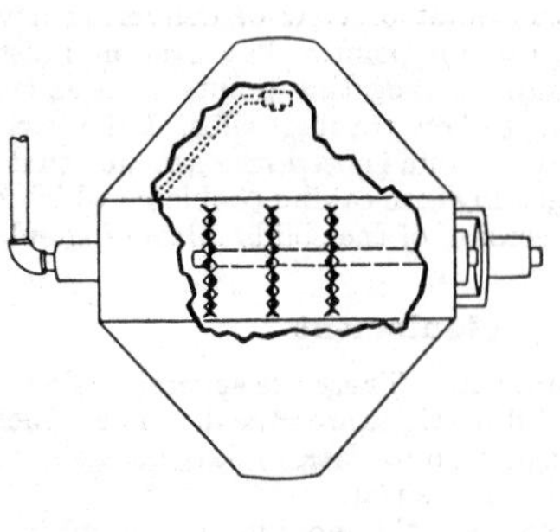

(a) Double cone

Agglomerate breaking device shown in broken line. Spray nozzle shown in dotted line. Tumblers of this type available plain or with either or both of the above features.

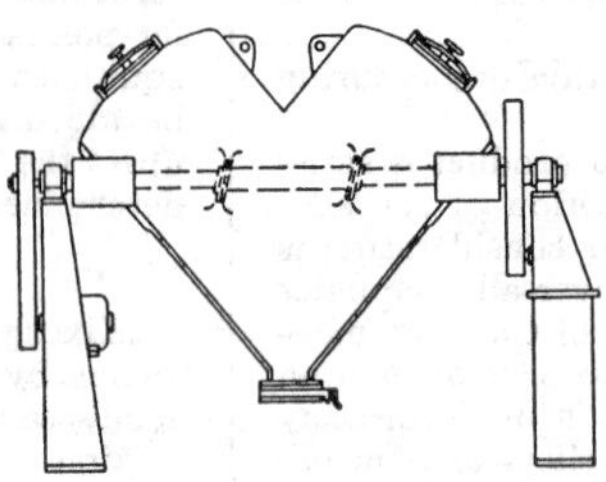

(b) Twin shell (Vee)

Agglomerate breaking and liquid feeding device shown in broken line. Where no liquid feeding is necessary, a pin-type agglomerate breaking device is used. Tumblers of this type are available plain or with any of the above features.

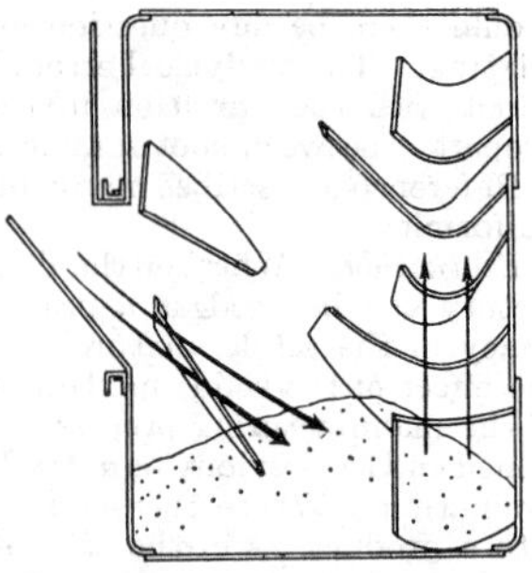

(c) Horizontal drum (with baffles)

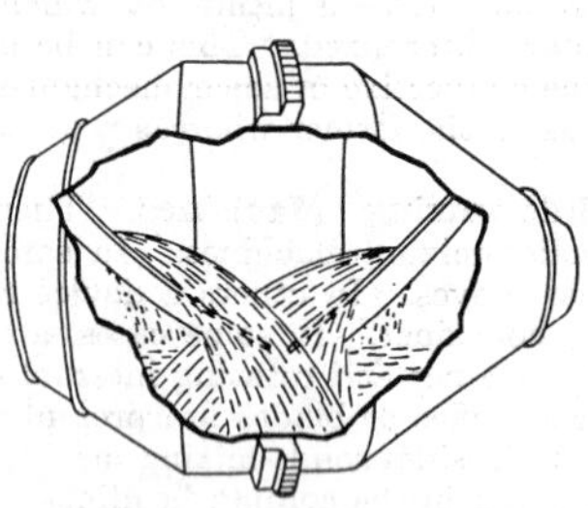

(d) Double-cone revolving around long axis (with baffles)

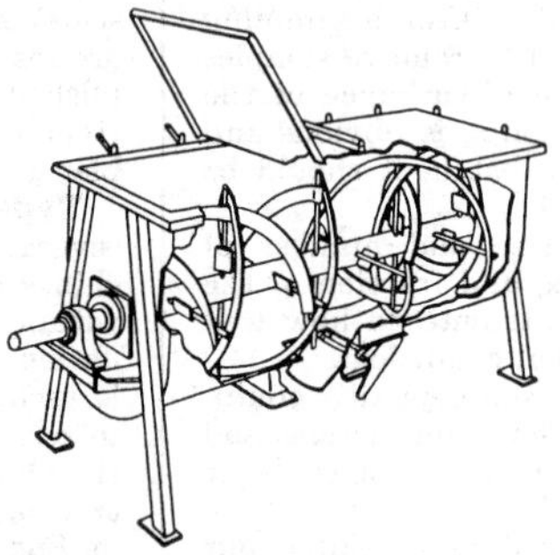

(e) Ribbon

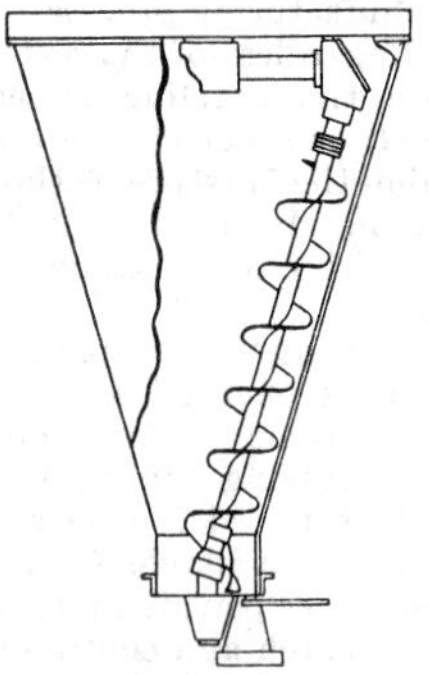

(f) Vertical screw (orbiting type)

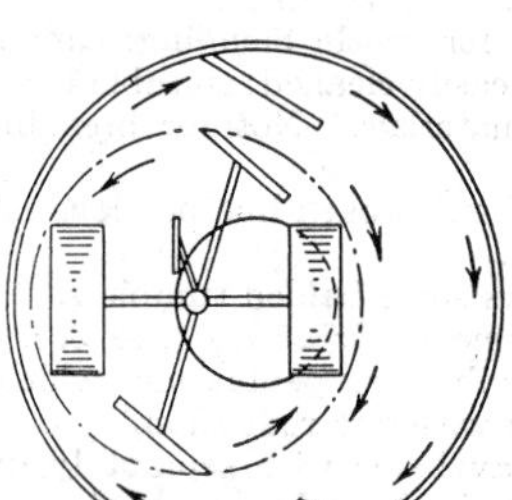

(g) Batch muller

Three types are available:
(1) pan is stationary and muller turret rotates;
(2) muller turret is stationary and pan rotates;
(3) pan rotates clockwise, muller turret rotates counterclockwise.
Type 3 is illustrated above

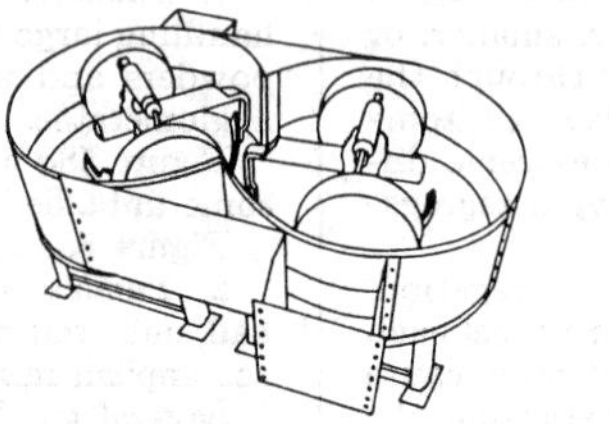

(h) Continuous muller (stationary shell)

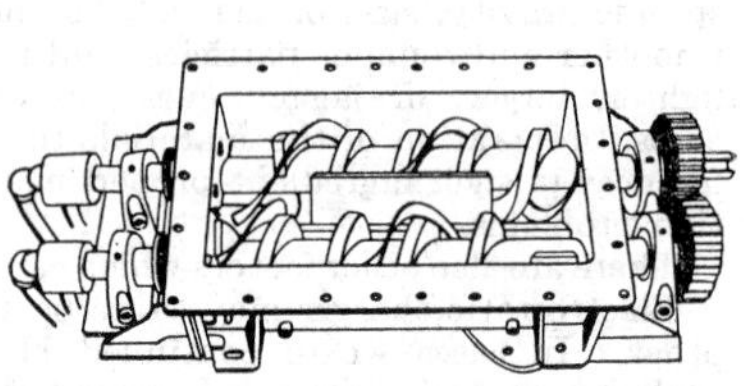

(i) Twin rotor (adapted to heat transfer-jacketed body and hollow screws)

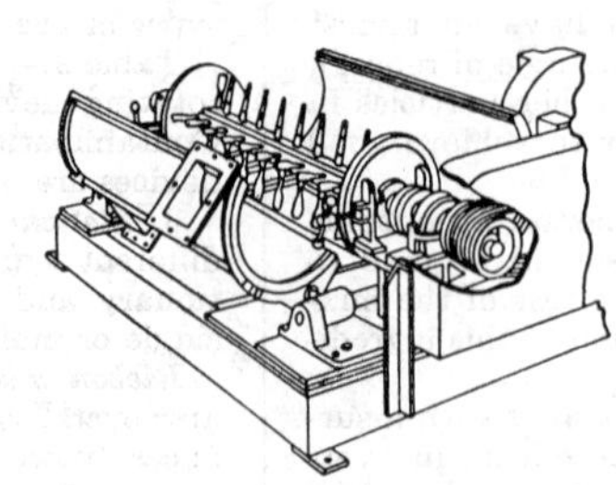

(j) Single rotor

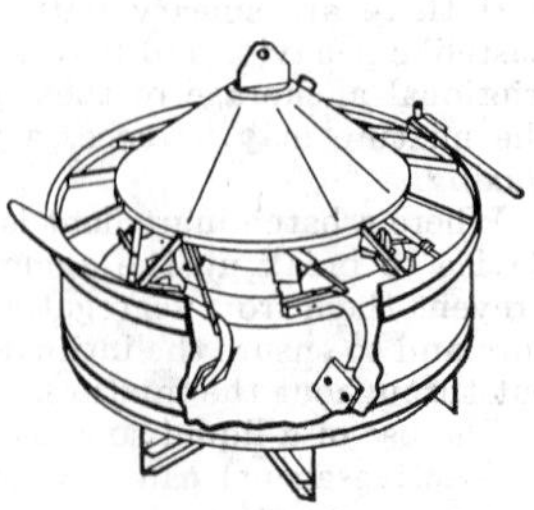

(k) Turbine

FIG. 21-58. Several types of solids-mixing machines. (See Table 21-11.)

Table 21-11. Types of Solids-mixing Machines*

Tumbler (1)	Tumbler with internal agglomerate breaker (2)	Stationary shell or trough (3)	Both shell and internal device rotate (4)	Impact mixing (5)	Process steps which can affect solids mixing (6)
Without baffles:					
Drum, either horizontal or inclined	Ball mill Pebble mill	Ribbon	Countercurrent, muller turret and pan rotate in opposite directions	Hammer mill	Filling of hoppers
Double cone...........	Rod mill	Stationary pan, rotating muller turret†		Impact mill	Fluidization
Twin shell............. Cube	Vibratory pebble mill	Vertical screw	Planetary types	Cage mill	Screw feeders
Mushroom type........	Double cone Twin shell Cube	Single rotor Twin rotor		Jet mill Attrition mill	Conveyor-belt loading Elevator loading
		Turbine Paddle mixer			Pneumatic conveying Vibrating
With baffles: Horizontal drum........ Double cone revolving around long axis		Sifter (turbosifter)			

* Diagrammatic sketches of many of these machines are shown in Fig. 21-58.
† There is also a muller in which the turret is stationary but the pan rotates.
‡ Although these steps, when carefully selected, can aid mixing, caution must be exercised with pneumatic conveying and vibrating as they may tend to separate materials.

charge, and the mounting of paddles or cutting blades on the center shaft. A broad ribbon can be used for lifting as well as conveying while a narrow one will cut through the material while conveying. The ribbon is adaptable to batch or continuous mixing.

Vertical screw mixer. This subgroup also has several variations. One type is shown in Fig. 58*f*. In this type, the screw rotates about its own axis while also orbiting around the center axis of the conical tank. In another variation, the screw does not orbit but remains in the center of the conical tank and is tapered so that the swept area steadily increases with increasing height. In another type, the central screw is contained in an inner cylindrical casing. This type of mixer is primarily suitable for free-flowing dry solids.

Muller mixer. The stationary-pan muller with rotating turret is one of several types. Other muller types are the countercurrent in which the pan and muller turret rotate in opposite directions, and the rotating-pan type in which the muller turret is stationary.

The heavy, wide roller rides over the material. There is some skidding action where the rollers engage the mass of materials. This gives local shearing plus coarse scale mixing which is aided by the plows and scrapers.

The muller is useful for mixing problems requiring certain types of aggregate breakdown, frictional anchorage of particles to one another, and densification of the final mix. Materials which are excessively fluid or sticky should be avoided. The muller mixer is generally used for batch operations (Fig. 58*g*) although 58*h* shows a continuous muller.

Twin rotor (Fig. 58*i*). This consists of two shafts with either paddles or screws encased in a cylindrical shell. There are various types available with shaft speeds ranging from moderately low to relatively high (see Table 21-12). It is useful for continuously mixing non-free-flowing solids; liquids can be added; there is minor product attrition; materials can be added beyond the inlet. Easily adaptable to heating or cooling. Some machines are specifically designed for heat transfer during mixing. The pug mill is one type of twin rotor.

Single rotor (Fig. 58*j*). This consists of a single shaft with paddles, encased in a cylindrical shell. This type is available with relatively high speeds (see Table 21-12) although in certain cases lower speeds are used. A high-speed single rotor gives the maximum impact short of a grinding mill. It is used for intensive dispersion and disintegration; available with split casing; suitable for heating or cooling and for small amounts of liquid addition.

Turbine mixer (Fig. 58*k*). This is a circular trough with a housing in the center around which revolves a spider or a series of legs with plow shares or mold boards on each leg. The mold boards spin around through the circular trough; suitable for free-flowing dry materials or semiwet materials which do not flow well; also adaptable to liquid-solid mixing and coating problems.

Table 21-12. Approximate Impact Velocities of Some Rotating Internal Devices in Mixers

Type of Mixer (See Table 21-11)	Tip Speed, ft./min.
Ribbon..............................	280
Turbine.............................	600
Twin-shell tumbler with:	
Pin-type intensifier..................	1700
Liquid-feed bar......................	3300
Twin rotor...........................	Up to 1300
Single rotor..........................	6000–9000
Mills of various types.................	2500–20,000

4. *Shell and Internal Device Rotate.* The countercurrent muller (Fig. 58*g*), which is in this category, is mentioned under Muller Mixer. This machine has a clockwise rotating mixing pan with a counterclockwise rotating mixing tool head mounted off center of the pan, thus providing a planetary mixing pattern. For mixing of free-flowing solids not requiring the shearing and compressive action of the mullers, plows are sometimes used alone. When used with mullers, the plows deflect material into their path. Special mixing tools are also available.

5. *Impact mixing,* which includes size reduction, is covered in Sec. 8.

6. The process steps listed in Table 21-11 can sometimes be used to promote mixing (see Ref. 10). However, they are primarily for functions other than solids mixing. (Note precautions for pneumatic conveying and vibrating in Table 21-11.)

Since paste mixing is not within the scope of this section, such widely used paste mixers as the sigma blade and banbury types will not be covered here but instead are taken up in Sec. 19.

Performance Characteristics. Before selecting solids-mixing equipment, a careful study should be made of various performance characteristics. These are given below.

Uniformity of Mixture. The proper type of mixer should be chosen to assure the desired degree of batch homogeneity. This cannot be compromised for other conveniences. Information is given under Types of Solids Mixing Machines about the special abilities of various kinds of machines to blend different types of materials.

Mixing Time. The actual time during which the batch is being mixed is usually less than 15 min. if the proper type of machine and working capacity have been chosen. In some cases much more lengthy mixing times are tolerated so as to avoid the cost of purchasing more efficient equipment. However, there is usually a machine which can properly homogenize almost any type of mixture in less than 15 min. provided one is willing to pay the price.

Besides actual mixing time, however, the total cycle time should be optimized.

Charging and Discharging. The total handling system must be considered in order to obtain optimum charging and discharging conditions. This includes the efficient use of weigh hoppers and surge bins, minor ingredient premixing, location of discharge gates, etc.

Power. In general, power requirements are not a major consideration in choosing a solids mixer since other requirements usually predominate. However, sufficient power must be supplied to handle the maximum needs should there be changes during the mixing operation. Also, where a variety of mixes may be required, power must be sufficient for the heaviest bulk-density materials. If the loaded mixer is to be started from rest, there should be sufficient power for this. Where speed variation may be desirable, this should be taken into account in planning power requirements.

Horsepower requirements of several types of mixers are listed in Table 21-13.

Cleaning. The ease, frequency, and thoroughness of cleaning may be crucial considerations where incompatible batches are to be mixed at different times in the same machine. Plain tumbling vessels are easy to clean provided that adequate openings are available. Areas that may present cleaning problems are (1) seals or stuffing boxes, (2) crevices at baffle supports, (3) any corners, and (4) discharge arrangement. Where cleaning between different batches may be time-consuming, several small mixers should be considered. Special sanitary construction can usually be provided at extra expense.

Agglomerate Breakdown and Attrition. The two meth-

Table 21-13. Horsepower Requirements and Speeds of Rotation for Some Commercial Solids Mixers (Approximately 50 cu. ft. Working Capacity)

Type of solids-mixing machine	Approx. working capacity, cu. ft.	Horsepower		Rotational speed, r.p.m.		Comments
		Shell	Internal device	Shell	Internal device shaft speed	
1. Tumbler						
Without baffles:						
Double cone	54	7½	....	18	....	Based on 100 lb./cu. ft. material
Twin shell	50	5	....	13.7	....	Max. bulk density of material = 55 lb./cu. ft.
With baffles:						
Horizontal drum						
Manufacturer E	50	20	....	11.1	....	Heavy duty (material 100 lb./cu. ft). For extremely heavy duty (150–200 lb./cu. ft. material), the maximum working capacity with 20-hp. motor is 35 cu. ft.
Manufacturer F	50	10	....	14	....	For material of 40 lb./cu. ft. max. bulk density
Double cone revolving about horizontal axis	56	25	....	11.5	....	Mixer can be tilted. Rear end charger. Capacity based on mixed concrete
2. Tumbler with agglomerate breaker:						
Double cone	54	7½	See Comment	18	See Comment	Hp. requirement for internal device depends on character of material, type and speed of agitator. These are to be determined by adequate testing
Twin shell	50	5	5 (pin-type intensifier bar) 7½ (liquid-solids intensifier bar)	13.7	945 (1730 ft./min. tip speed) 1055 (3320 ft./min. tip speed)	Max. bulk density of material = 55 lb./cu. ft.
3. Stationary shell or trough						
Ribbon:						
Manufacturer C	50	....	12	....	28	Hp. required based on material of 50–60 lb./cu. ft. bulk density, medium free-flowing, using 10 hp./ton for average mix cycle of 3–10 min. (depending on material, range can be 3–18 hp./ton)
Manufacturer A	46	....	10	....	37	Based on material of 30 lb./cu. ft. bulk density
Manufacturer D	50	....	15	....	45	Based on material of 40–50 lb./cu. ft. bulk density
3-shaft ribbon	50	....	Blender shaft 20 Feeder shaft 7½ (total)		Variable-speed drives on all shafts	This blender is rated at 300 cu. ft./hr. on batch-mixing basis; 900 cu. ft./hr. on continuous-mixing basis. Materials rated at 70 lb./cu. ft. bulk density
Vertical screw	52.9	....	5	....	Screw, 64.4 Orbit, 2.2	Hp. based on 37 lb./cu. ft. bulk density. This may vary with different materials. Max. hp. = 10, max. weight = 4410 lb.
Muller:						
Batch; stationary pan, rotating turret	40		60	....	24 (turret speed)	Based on material of 60–75 lb./cu. ft. bulk density
Continuous; stationary pan, rotating turret	Basically, the continuous mullers are merely two batch mullers joined together at the cribs, making a figure 8 design. Thus, the 40 cu. ft. batch muller rated at 60 hp. becomes an 80 cu. ft. working capacity continuous muller requiring 125 hp. This would give 125 tons/hr. with a 2½-min. residence time (see Table 21-14 for further information on continuous capacities). Turret speeds are 24 r.p.m.					
Single rotor	....	See Comments		....	....	In this *continuous* unit, the output can range from 25–600 lb./min. with hp. from 5–100 and r.p.m. of 500–4000 depending on the materials mixed
Double rotor	....	See Comments		....	....	In this *continuous* unit the output can range from 200–500 lb./min. with hp. from 5–40 and r.p.m. from 200–300 depending on the materials mixed
Twin-rotor heat-exchanger mixer	49.2	....	5–15	....	20–100	Amount of conveying and mixing action affected by amount of pitch and type of ribbons mounted on exterior of hollow screws
Turbine	50	....	50	....	Peripheral speed of 600 ft./min.	
4. Both shell and internal device rotate						
Countercurrent muller	45 60–90†	* 20	* 25	6.75–8.75 5.65	28–35 20	

* One 25-hp. motor drives both the shell (mixing pan) and internal device (mixing star).
† Batch capacity range depends on nature of materials to be mixed.

ods of producing agglomerate breakdown and attrition are: (1) *Impact.* The major factor is the peripheral speed of the rotating internal device. Table 21-12 gives impact-velocity data for various mixers. (2) *Shearing and compressive action,* which in mullers depends upon the clearance between muller and pan, and the muller weight or spring load, respectively.

Where an attrition device is necessary to break down aggregates but may also produce too much size reduction on other batch ingredients, the tolerable attrition should be determined by tests.

Dust Formation. Loss of dust can seriously affect batch composition, particularly where vital minor ingredients are lost. Methods of minimizing dust formation are: (1) Use of less dusty but equally satisfactory batch ingredients. Sometimes a pelletized form of an extremely dusty material is available. (2) Proper venting so as to enable filtering of displaced air rather than unregulated loss of dust-laden air. (3) Dust-tight arrangements for loading and unloading the mixer. (4) Addition of liquids where tolerable. Water is not only effective in minimizing dust upon discharging from the mixer, but if properly added, it will also render the batch less dusty in subsequent handling steps. The addition of a small quantity of surface-active agent will improve the penetration of the water throughout the batch and enable it to wet even such materials as coal dust. The method of adding water is important (See Method of Adding Liquids).

Care should be taken to avoid powerful suction on the mixer or the weigh hopper from which the ingredients feed into the mixer. If the dust-collection suction on the mixer is too strong, vital ingredients may be sucked out. If the dust-collection system on the weighing system is too strong, errors in weighing may result.

Electrostatic Charge. Certain batch materials such as plastics tend to accumulate a charge easily. Work input will affect the charge on the batch. Coating of the inside of the mixer shell or rotating elements may occasionally result because of electrostatic charge. This can present a cleaning problem. Possible aids in overcoming this are (1) addition of special solid materials with very high surface area to weight ratios, (2) addition of liquids (see Dust Formation and Method of Adding Liquids), (3) proper choice of material of construction of the mixer, (4) controlling humidity, (5) preparation of the batch ingredients so as to minimize accumulated charge.

Equipment Wear. Simple tumbling mixers give the least wear. Attrition devices in tumblers may present serious abrasion problems with certain materials such as sand and abrasive grinding-wheel grains. Abrasion-resistant coating such as rubber coating, special alloys, or platings should be considered for these cases. An internal agitator device may wear even though its speed is low. Particularly where highly abrasive materials are to be mixed, the benefits of an agglomerate-breaking device must be weighed against the potential contamination and replacement and maintenance costs.

Contamination of Product. This has been partially covered under Cleaning and Equipment Wear. Other sources of contamination are lubricants and repair materials. Types which are not compatible with the batches to be mixed should be avoided.

Heating or Cooling. Nearly all commercial mixers can be heated or cooled. Some can be provided with heated or cooled agitators. Where temperature rise during mixing is detrimental, cooling facilities should be provided. The various manufacturers can provide details on the means of heating their machines. Most common heating means are (1) water or steam in the jacket and in hollow-screw or paddle-type internal agitator, (2) hot oil, (3) Dowtherm liquid or vapor, (4) electric heaters, contact or radiant, (5) hot air in direct contact with product (suitable only for revolving-drum-type mixers), (6) exterior heating of drum by direct or indirect firing. For cooling, the most common means are (1) water or refrigerated fluid in the jacket and in hollow-screw or paddle-type internal agitator, (2) an evaporant such as liquid ammonia, (3) direct air contact (for rotating-shell mixers), (4) oil or Dowtherm (or equivalent) for cooling high-temperature materials.

Flexibility. Where batches of widely different size must be mixed, flexibility of operating capacity may enable use of fewer mixers. Certain features may require a non-flexible capacity requirement. For example, ordinarily an internal agitating device in a tumbling mixer does not function effectively unless the batch is loaded to a certain level. The need for such features must be weighed against the limitations imposed by a narrow operating-capacity range when choosing equipment for an operation where batch size will vary considerably.

In general, the effect of per cent of mixer volume occupied by the batch on the adequacy of mixing should be borne in mind, particularly when any change from the recommended volume per cent is considered.

Vacuum or Pressure. Most tumbling mixers can have provision for vacuum or pressure. Mixers which cannot be adapted to these conditions are mullers with rotating pans. Continuous mixers introduce problems of sealing the charge and discharge ends.

Method of Adding Liquids. Where the addition of liquids may be desirable (see Dust Formation and Electrostatic Charge), this should be considered when designing the mixing system rather than hastily improvised. The purpose of the liquid should be considered, whether for (1) dust suppression; (2) product; (3) heating and cooling. If a viscous liquid must be well distributed, this should be considered when choosing the mixer.

Liquid should be directed into the batch materials and not onto bare mixer surface since this could cause build-up. Nozzle spray pressure should be sufficient to penetrate the batch but not so high as to cause heavy splashing.

Automated equipment for the addition of liquids can be worked into the over-all mixing plant where necessary. For dust-reduction purposes, a volumetric method of metering is satisfactory. However, should a critical batch ingredient be added in liquid form, a more precise method of metering may be necessary.

Other considerations are (1) proper ventilation and discharge enclosures, (2) provision for relief of internal explosion, (3) vibration isolation (shock mounts), (4) remote operation of charge and discharge, (5) noise during operation.

Equipment Selection. *General Comments.* Types of mixers and performance characteristics are given above. Segregating tendencies among solid materials were described previously. A sound approach to solids-mixer selection starts with a careful examination of these areas. However, mixer selection should also involve consideration of the mixer's place in the over-all process. Possible consolidation of many solids-processing steps, or the opposite (splitting up one operation into several), deserves scrutiny at this time. If no one standard machine has all the necessary requirements, thought should be given as to which machine can best be modified to achieve the most desirable combination of features. One should look at the over-all process objectives as well as the equipment details when selecting a solids mixer.

Pilot Tests. In some cases, it is possible to perform pilot tests on a small-scale version of the equipment to be used in production. Much useful information can be found here but the following must be borne in mind:

1. In general, the larger the pilot unit, the more reliable the prediction of large-scale performance. The pilot

Table 21-14. Costs of Several Types of Solids-mixing Machines (See Table 21-11)

The figures given below are derived from log-log graphs of cost ($) on the ordinate vs. working capacity, cu. ft., on the abscissa. The cost in dollars = c_2 of a mixer of working capacity = Q_2 (cu. ft.) can be estimated from the equation $c_2 = c_1(Q_2/Q_1)^n$. The column entitled "Range" gives the working-capacity range over which this equation holds. Where several ranges are listed for any type of machine, care must be taken to use the proper c_1 and n for the range shown. c_1 is the ordinate intercept at the lowest working capacity Q_1; n is the slope of the log-log plot and represents the exponent of the relationship: capacity^n = cost. This type of relationship is commonly used in order-of-magnitude estimation. Further information on it can be found in Aries and Newton, "Chemical Engineering Cost Estimation," Chemonomics, New York, 1950, and Chilton, "Cost Engineering in the Process Industries," McGraw-Hill, New York, 1960.

The following qualifications must be borne in mind when using this method of estimating solids-mixer costs:

1. The cost figures pertain to 1960.
2. Special features will increase the cost. Similar machines may differ in cost depending upon construction and other differences (type of drive, maximum bulk density which can be handled, etc.). Therefore, careful attention should be paid to the comments.
3. In order to simplify the tabulation of costs, the best straight line was drawn for each log-log graph, even though there was scatter about these lines and sometimes a slight curvature.

Therefore, the cost figures should be used only for order-of-magnitude estimations and not as exact quotes. This point cannot be stressed too heavily, since virtually every manufacturer who was contacted expressed misgivings about the advisability of including any cost figures because of the ease with which these can be misused so as to give misleading impressions. Despite these misgivings, the manufacturers did cooperate to help the engineer to obtain rapid "guesstimates" of solids-mixer costs.

When a definite quote on a solids mixer is needed, this should be obtained from the manufacturer after the type of machine which will be needed has been discussed with him in detail.

Many machines are available in much larger capacities than those included in the ranges in this table. For example, 700 cu. ft. working capacity ribbon mixers and 1000 cu. ft. working capacity tumbling mixers are available; even larger-capacity machines can be built.

Type of solids-mixing machine	Range, cu. ft.	c_1	n	General comments; check with equipment manufacturer if precise figure is needed
1. Tumbler				
Without baffles:				
Double cone (Fig. 21-58*a*)				
Manufacturer A:				
Mild steel	13–40	1500	0.36	For working-capacity range of 13–40 cu. ft., construction is for bulk density of 100 lb./cu. ft.
	54–325	2700	0.65	For working-capacity range of 54–165 cu. ft., construction is for bulk density of 75 lb./cu. ft.
304 stainless steel (reg. commercial finish)	13–40	2300	0.32	For working-capacity range of 240–325 cu. ft., construction is for bulk density of 50 lb./cu ft.
	54–325	3800	0.77	Prices do not include motor drives
316 stainless steel (reg. commercial finish)	13–40	2600	0.30	
	54–325	4400	0.77	
Twin shell (vee) (Fig. 21-58*b*) Manufacturer B (Note: These figures apply also to double cone for Manufacturer B):				
Carbon steel	1–200	600	0.47	Above 30 cu. ft. working capacity, bulk densities of 50–65 lb./cu. ft.
Stainless steel	1–200	800	0.49	Below 30 cu. ft. working capacity, some bulk densities may go as high as 135–165 lb./cu. ft. although most are in the 65–75 lb./cu. ft. range. Check with manufacturer. Type of drive also has bearing on this
With baffles:				
Horizontal drum carbon steel (Fig. 21-58*c*)	....	....	....	Electric motors included
Without liner	15–70	3000	0.52	Light duty, bulk densities to 70 lb./cu. ft.
With liner	13–110	3800	0.73	Heavy duty, bulk densities of 100 lb./cu. ft.
	35–170	5950	0.72	Extremely heavy duty, bulk densities of 150–200 lb./cu. ft.
Double cone rotating around long axis (Fig. 21-58*d*)	56–210	12,000	0.65	Includes motor without starter, liners and blades, and rear-end charger
2. Tumbler with agglomerate breaker				
Twin shell:				
Pin-type intensifier (carbon steel)	1–75	1200	0.41	Above 30 cu. ft. working capacity, bulk densities of 55–65 lb./cu. ft.
Pin-type intensifier (stainless steel)	1–75	1400	0.45	Below 30 cu. ft. working capacity, bulk densities as high as 115 lb./cu. ft. with smaller sizes but mostly in the 65–75 lb./cu. ft. range
Liquid-solids feed-bar type of intensifier (carbon steel)	1–50	1900	0.39	Bulk densities in 50–65 lb./cu. ft. range
Liquid-solids feed-bar type of intensifier (stainless steel)	1–50	2100	0.43	
3. Stationary shell or trough ribbon (Fig. 21-58*e*)				
Manufacturer A:				
Mild steel	7.5–186	840	0.54	Does not include motor drive. Double spiral blade. 30 lb./cu. ft. bulk density material
304 stainless steel	7.5–186	1560	0.57	
Manufacturer C:				
Standard carbon steel	25–300	1500	0.52	Double ribbon, inner and outer; motor and drive not included. Capacities based on 50–60 lb./cu. ft. bulk density material although mixer can be used with other bulk densities with necessary power adjustment
Standard 304 stainless steel	25–300	3100	0.59	
Manufacturer D:				
Carbon steel without drive and motor	11–94	1930	0.56	Batch capacity and range based on bulk density of 40–50 lb./cu. ft. Other densities will affect capacities accordingly
With drive and motor	11–94	2650	0.56	
3-shaft ribbon (includes motor and variable drives):				
Carbon steel, heavy duty	25–50	8900	0.31	May be used for wetted materials with angle of repose up to 60 deg. and weighing up to 60 lb./cu. ft. or for free-flowing materials weighing up to 70 lb./cu. ft.
Stainless steel, heavy duty	3–50	3800	0.48	
Carbon steel, medium duty	These are available in 25 and 50 cu. ft. models. The difference in price as compared with heavy duty would be due to the use of smaller motors			May be used for wetted materials with angle of repose of 60 deg. and weighing up to 30 lb./cu. ft. and for free-flowing materials weighing up to 35 lb./cu. ft.
Stainless steel, medium duty				
Vertical-screw mixer (Fig. 21-58*f*) with orbiting screw:				
Mild steel	3.5–12.5	3100	0.11	Motor and motor controls (not mounted) are included. Will handle materials up to 189 lb./cu. ft. depending on volume to be mixed.
304 stainless steel	3.5–12.5	4300	0.12	Does not have universal joint at bottom of screw
Mild steel	7–100	4100	0.10	Does have universal joint at bottom of screw
304 stainless steel	7–100	6000	0.14	
Muller:				
Rotating muller turret, stationary shell carbon steel	6–60	5100	0.69	Stainless steel approximately 200–240% of carbon-steel prices

Table 21-14. Costs of Several Types of Solids-mixing Machines (See Table 21-11)—*(Continued)*

Type of solids-mixing machine	Range, cu. ft.	c_1	n	General comments; check with equipment manufacturer if precise figure is needed
Continuous muller with rotating turret and stationary shell (Fig. 21-58*h*)	6–120 (actual batch capacity) 11–170 tons/hr. continuous mixing through-put for 2½ min. residence time	8700	0.66	Based on material bulk density of 60–75 lb./cu. ft. and continuous mixing comparable with approximately 2½ min. batch mulling cycle (residence time). Residence time will affect tons/hr.; it can vary from 1–5 min.
Twin rotor—heat exchanger, mixer (Fig. 21-58*i*):				
Carbon steel	2.7–49 (actual batch capacity)	5100	0.44	Used where heat transfer is needed along with mixing. Does not include motor and drive; hollow screws with mixing ribbons; heavy-duty construction; mixing action depends on pitch and type of ribbon mounted on exterior of hollow screw. Material density assumed = 70 lb./cu. ft.
Stainless steel	2.7–49 (actual batch capacity) (cap. in tons/hr. = 0.6 to 10 assuming 10 min. residence time)	9300	0.34	Heat-transfer capacities 20,000 to 1,000,000 B.t.u./hr. assuming 300°F. heat-transfer medium, over-all heat-transfer coeff. of 8–30 and solids over-all coeff. of 8–15 B.t.u./(sq. ft.)(hr.)(°F.)
Turbine (Fig. 21-58*k*)	2½–100	1770	0.70	Includes basic mixer with motor with one manually operated discharge gate. 12½ cu. ft. and above have replaceable liners as standard equipment
4. Both shell and internal device rotate	....	....	....	Batch capacity range established on basis of material bulk density of 100 lb./cu. ft.
Countercurrent mixer (Fig. 21-58*g*)	....	....	....	Other densities will affect capacities accordingly
Carbon steel, plows only	5.5–45	4000	0.50	(Not including motor drive)
With mullers	5.5–45	4300	0.55	(Not including motor drive)
Stainless steel:				
Plows only	5.5–45	6400	0.54	(Not including motor drive)
With mullers	5.5–45	7200	0.60	(Not including motor drive)
Larger capacity				
Carbon steel:				
Plows only	90	24,500	....	(Not including motor drive)
With mullers	60	26,500	....	(Not including motor drive)
Stainless steel:				
Plows only	90	44,000	....	(Not including motor drive)
With mullers	60	53,000	....	(Not including motor drive)

unit should be a prototype with all dimensions properly scaled down.

2. Published solids-mixing scale-up data are rare. Equipment suppliers can provide scale-up information for their particular type of equipment based on past experience. With geometrically similar tumblers, if the speeds are adjusted to give comparable motion and the mixer volume fraction occupied by the charge is the same, scale-up of results will be straightforward. The presence of a rotating internal device presents problems in the scaling up of clearances, blade area to mixture volume, and sizes and speeds of the rotating devices. For agglomerate breakers, the key factor in scaling up is impact velocity. Scale-up in cylinders is discussed on pp. 290–292 of Ref. 9. Solids-processing scale-up is discussed in a paper by Sterret (*Chem. Eng.*, Sept. 21, 1959).

3. The actual process materials should be used if possible. If substitute materials must be used, they should have the same mixing characteristics. Tests with differently colored but otherwise identical beads can be misleading and so can tracers. The reason is that the flow properties of the specific materials to be mixed in the plant may not be the same as these demonstration materials. Regardless of how the mixer contents appear to be moved around, the properties of the actual batch ingredients may cause segregation or other problems.

4. Differences in materials of construction between the pilot unit and the production unit should be considered. This may have a bearing on caking, abrasion, and electrostatic effects.

Continuous Mixing. Although batch mixing has been the predominant method of mixing of solids, consideration is being given to the use of continuous mixing in many industries. There are two types of continuous-mixing operations. The first type has a low hold-up volume and will provide fine-scale blending of the particles via impact and shear elements such as are used in grinding machines. Some machines of this type are the hammer, impact, cage, and jet mills. It is essential that the feed to these machines be properly proportioned and premixed in order to achieve a uniform product.

The second type of continuous mixer involves high hold-up machines which contain agitating and conveying mechanisms. These rearrange the individual particles and also displace large volumes of material and move the batch through the machine. Mixers of this type can produce both fine-scale and coarse-scale blending. The ribbon-type mixer is frequently used for continuous mixing although this is also used for batch mixing. Recently a continuous muller mixer has been developed as shown in Fig. 21-58*h*.

The average composition of the stream leaving a continuous mixer is the same as the average of the added entering streams. Variations in proportions of the entering streams will be damped out by the mixing action of a continuous mixer. These effluent-stream variations will become smaller as average solids residence time is increased and the frequency of the variations become larger.

Certain general criteria can be used to determine whether continuous flow will be beneficial. Continuous flow is worth consideration if (1) a single formulation can be run for an extended period, (2) the fluctuations of the outgoing product are within process requirements, (3) sufficiently accurate metering of ingredients can be achieved, (4) the rest of the process warrants continuous mixing. Continuous flow is of doubtful benefit if (1) frequent changes of formulations are anticipated, (2) fluctuations of product composition will be outside the permitted range, (3) the ingredients cannot be metered with the necessary level of accuracy, (4) complex temperature or pressure cycles are involved.

Sometimes a system of mixing and dispersing is composed of one or more batch units providing a feed to a continuous intensive dispersion unit. Another possibility would be a batch mixer and surge bin which provide a continuous feed to a final dispersion unit. Various combinations of this type with adequate sampling at the proper points may be used where continuous flow would be beneficial provided that certain features could be overcome.

Costs.

Table 21-14 gives costs of several types of solids-mixing machines.

SOLIDS SAMPLING

REFERENCES: Taggart, "Handbook of Mineral Dressing," Wiley, New York, 1945. Gy, "A New Theory of Ore Sampling," A.I.M.E. Annual Meeting, Feb. 24–28, 1957. "Economics of Automatic Sampling," Third Stevens Symposium on Statistical Methods in the Chemical Industry, Jan. 24, 1959, American Society for Quality Control.

Sampling dry solids, slurries, sampling equipment and costs, pitfalls to avoid, determining size of sample, and examples of sampler installations are covered in this section. For the theory of sampling one of the best textbooks is Taggart's "Handbook of Mineral Dressing." Sources of various sampling devices can be found in "Thomas' Register" and "Chemical Engineering Catalog."

Sample Reliability. Process and quality control require sampling at various points in the flow sheet. It can be accomplished in several ways. The earlier practice of manual sampling has yielded to mechanical automatic sampling which is impersonal, low-cost, consistent, and statistically reliable.

Modern laboratory facilities and technically trained personnel represent large investments. Therefore, it is poor economy to analyze samples whose reliability is subject to question. *The analysis can be no more reliable than the sample on which it is based.*

Wet and Dry Sampling. Slurries and dry materials normally present no real sampling problems. Dust seals make sampling possible in pneumatic conveying systems without "salting" or contaminating the resulting samples with material previously handled. Water sprays can be used to clean sample cutters to flush remaining solids that would adhere to the inside of cutters. Sticky materials which do not readily clean from sample cutters present problems which require individual study.

Hand Sampling. Hand sampling is the process of manually withdrawing a sample from the stream. By comparison to mechanical sampling it is costly and statistically unreliable. Coning and quartering is a long-established practice of mixing and splitting to reduce the bulk of a sample for more convenient analysis.

Types of Mechanical Samplers. There are several types of standard mechanical samplers and many more non-standard units which have been developed for limited special applications. Some of the more common mechanical samplers are illustrated in Fig. 21-59. The automatic straight-line samplers offer both the lowest cost and greatest flexibility of operation. The Vezin-type and Snyder-type samplers are arc-type samplers which normally operate continuously and are for sampling dry materials.

Automatic straight-line samplers are available in both normal-duty and heavy-duty construction. Generally speaking a normal-duty sampler mechanism will handle any problem where a standard-duty sample cutter is used.

Table 21-15. Cost of Sampling Equipment*

Cutter travel, in.	Size and type of sampler	Speed of cutter, in./sec.	Price	Add for cutter
16	Straight-line automatic	7.5	$ 500	$30 (wet type)
21	Straight-line automatic	12	525	$150 (dry type, front travel)
30	Straight-line automatic	18	675	$270 (dry type, end travel)
36	Straight-line automatic (heavy-duty)	30	950	$100 up for special cutter
20 diam.	Vezin type (simplex)	Continuous operation	1200	Cutters included
20 diam.	Vezin type (duplex)	Continuous operation	2300	Cutters included
24 diam.	Snyder type (simplex)	Continuous operation	875	Cutters included
24 diam.	Snyder type (duplex)	Continuous operation	1675	Cutter included
	Riffler type sample splitter	18 by 18 in. top opening	80	

* 1960 costs.

Heavy-duty construction is required only where heavy special-design cutters are required or where the cutter travel is unusually long (36- to 120-in. travel, etc.).

Sampling Pitfalls to Avoid. In solids sampling each step must be engineered to eliminate accidental classification by size or gravity. Different sizes usually have different analyses.

A true sample is a portion that represents the whole stream. Split-stream types of sampling, grab samples, improperly designed sample cutters, or sampling techniques which do not take the entire portion of the stream uniformly cannot be truly representative. The best and accepted sampling technique is to move the sample cutter at a uniform speed completely through the entire stream when the stream is in a free-fall state, keeping the cutter at right angles to the stream.

Automatic samplers require very little maintenance but the mechanisms should be accessible for routine maintenance checks. Central control panels to signal location of samplers not operating properly are helpful in large operations.

Size of Sample. A sample volume or bulk should be small enough for convenient laboratory analysis. Four factors govern the amount of material taken with each pass through the stream:

1. Tonnage of feed (usually fixed by the process and cannot be varied for convenience of sampling).
2. Size of cutter opening (not variable as it is based on size of particles in the stream) (see Fig. 21-60).
3. Speed of cutter through the stream (a variable factor which is used to control volume of sample).
4. Frequency of sample cut (a variable factor used to control volume of sample).

Various cutter speeds approximating 7.5, 12, 18, and 30 in./sec. are available from manufacturers of automatic

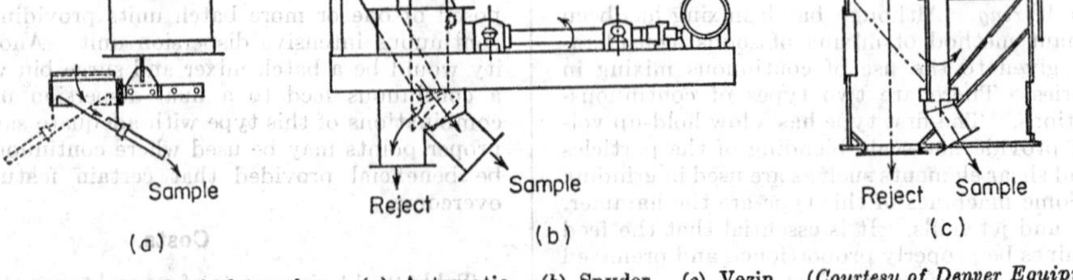

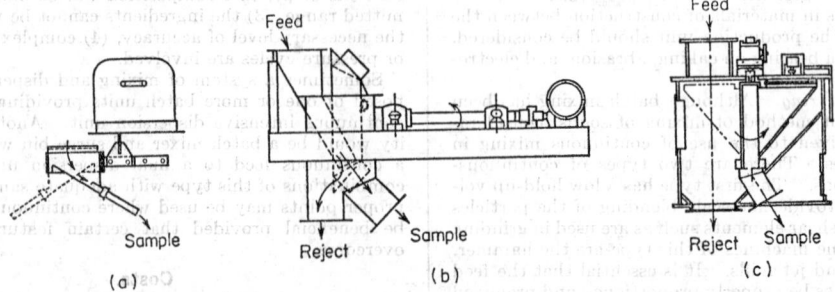

FIG. 21-59. Types of mechanical samplers. (*a*) Automatic. (*b*) Snyder. (*c*) Vezin. (*Courtesy of Denver Equipment Co.*)

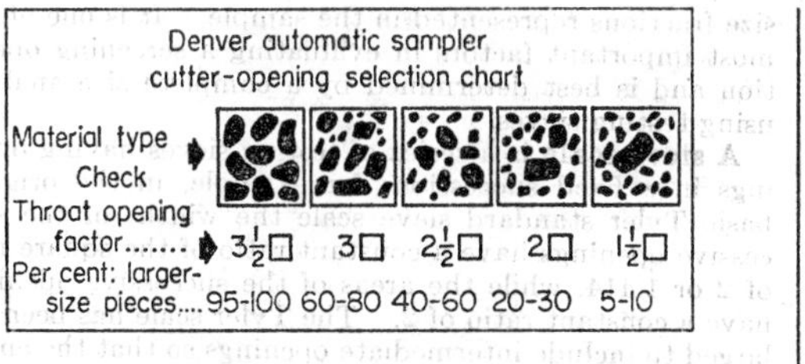

Fig. 21-60. Cutter opening must be two to three times the diameter of largest particle to prevent "bridging." (*Courtesy of Denver Equipment Co.*)

samplers. A cutter passing through the stream at 30 in./sec. will cut a sample of one-fourth the bulk as the same cutter passing through the same stream at 7.5 in./sec. (Fig. 21-61.) The higher cutter speed does not

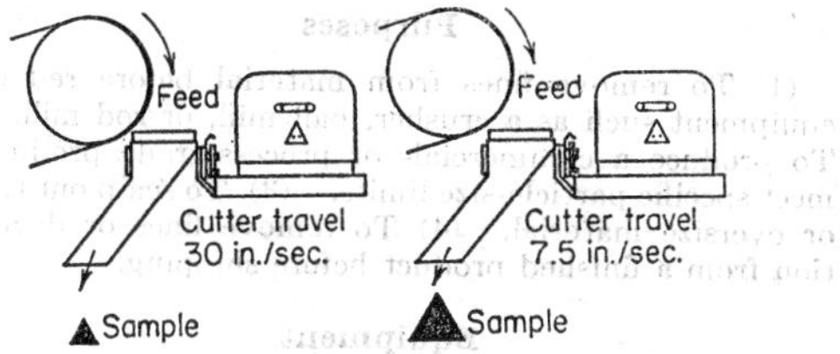

Fig. 21-61. Cutter speeds. (*Courtesy of Denver Equipment Co.*)

affect the sample reliability and the smaller volume sample resulting will often eliminate the need for secondary sampling.

The formula for determining the amount of sample per cut is

$$\frac{(\text{lb. of feed/sec.}) \times (\text{cutter opening, in.})}{(\text{Speed of cutter, in./sec.})} = (\text{lb. of sample per cut})$$

Frequency of the cut through a stream is variable but the more frequent the cut the more representative the sample.

The amount of material taken per cut and the frequency of the sampling interval are usually determined by the amount or volume of material required for sample analysis as well as from on-the-job experience.

There are no formulas for arriving at the percentage of material to be taken as a sample or frequency of sampling interval. Such calculations have been developed for some specific and individual problems, but they are not applicable to most sampling problems. Some industries have established sampling standards based on experience, but the practice of one plant may not entirely apply to the problems in a similar plant. Uniform material normally requires less frequent intervals while material of a known variable composition requires more frequent cuts. Automatic samplers can be secured which operate at intervals of 1 min. or even seconds between sample cuts. These same samplers can be modified to operate continuously if necessary.

Secondary Dry Sampling. Frequently the bulk of a primary sample is so large that secondary sampling is required to provide a sample of proper size for laboratory analysis. Where secondary sampling is used on dry materials it is often desirable to incorporate a size-reduction step between the primary and secondary samplers.

Crushing provides a more uniform size distribution of the feed to the secondary sampler and provides a more reliable sample. Since the primary sample increments will cause surges to the secondary sampler a hopper and positive-type feeder should be used to provide a constant and uniform stream of feed to the secondary sampler (Fig. 21-62). In high-tonnage operations it is practical to consider sampling towers with several size-reduction and sampling stages.

Secondary Slurry Sampling. Secondary sampling of slurry or pulps requires that several secondary cuts must be made during the short time the primary cutter is in the stream. On a slow-speed 21-in.-travel primary sampler, operating at 7.5 in./sec., the cutter is in the stream less than 3 sec. To accomplish this multiple cut of the primary sample discharge during this short period of time a Vezin-type secondary sampler equipped with four sample cutters is often used (Fig. 21-63).

Continuous Analysis of Samples. X-ray analysis of materials has made possible continuous process control which provides answers much faster than detailed chemical analysis yet with a high degree of accuracy. Automatic samplers which operate continuously in the stream are used to provide a continuous primary sample. The primary sample is pumped or conveyed to the central X-ray analyzer. Here a secondary sample is cut which is then used for the analysis. The sampling techniques used for continuous analysis are the same as those used

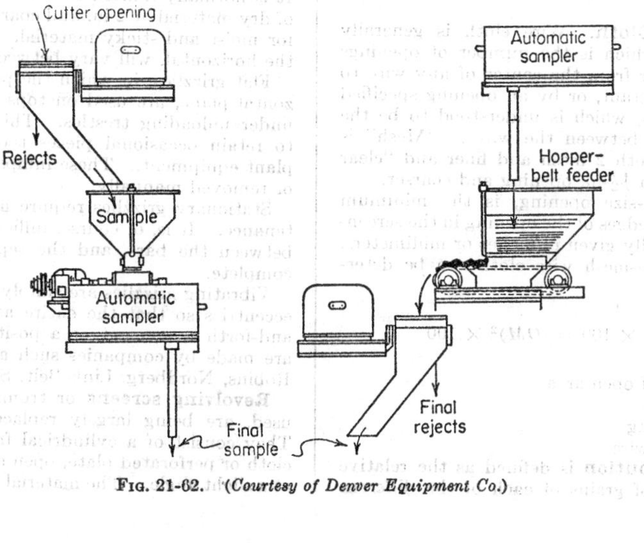

Fig. 21-62. (*Courtesy of Denver Equipment Co.*)

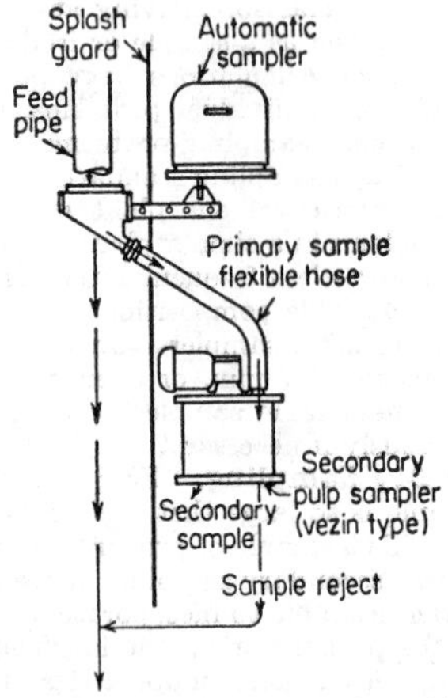

FIG. 21-63. Vezin-type secondary sampler with four sample cutters. (*Courtesy of Denver Equipment Co.*)

for other sampling problems and the same continuous sampling system is often used to supply samples to a central chemical laboratory for simple quick determinations.

SCREENING

REFERENCES: Kuenhold, Factors to Consider in Vibrating Screen Installations, *Mining Eng.*, June, 1957, pp. 650–653. Reed, The Story behind the New Sieve Specifications, *The Testing World*, October, 1959. Taggart, "Handbook of Mineral Dressing," Wiley, New York, 1945.

Definitions

Screening is the separation of a mixture of various sizes of grains into two or more portions by means of a screening surface, the screening surface acting as a multiple go and no-go gage, and the final portions consisting of grains of more uniform size than those of the original mixture.

Material that remains on a given screening surface is the oversize or plus material; that material passing through the screening surface is the undersize or minus material; and that material passing one screening surface and retained on a subsequent surface is the intermediate material.

The screening surface may consist of woven wire, silk, or plastic cloth; perforated or punched plate; grizzly bars; or wedge wire sections.

Mesh and Space Cloth. Wire cloth is generally specified by "mesh," which is the number of openings per linear inch counting from the center of any wire to a point exactly 1 in. distant, or by an opening specified in inches or millimeters, which is understood to be the clear opening or space between the wires. "Mesh" is generally favored for cloth 2 mesh and finer and "clear opening" for space cloth ½-in. opening and coarser.

Aperture, or screen-size opening, is the minimum clear space between the edges of the opening in the screening surface and is usually given in inches or millimeters.

Open area of square-mesh wire cloth can be determined by the formula

$$P = \frac{O^2}{(O + D)^2} \times 100 = (OM)^2 \times 100$$

where P = percentage of open area
M = mesh
O = size of opening
D = diameter of wire

Particle-size distribution is defined as the relative percentage by weight of grains of each of the different size fractions represented in the sample. It is one of the most important factors in evaluating a screening operation and is best determined by a complete size analysis using testing sieves.

A sieve scale is a series of testing sieves having openings in a fixed succession; for example, in the original basic Tyler standard sieve scale the widths of the successive openings have a constant ratio of the square root of 2 or 1.414, while the areas of the successive openings have a constant ratio of 2. The Tyler scale has been enlarged to include intermediate openings so that the entire scale has the successive openings according to the fourth root of 2 or 1.189. The sieve series adopted by the National Bureau of Standards, American Society for Testing Materials, American Standard Association, and many foreign countries applies the fourth-root-of-2 principle, and the openings are fully compatible with the Tyler standard scale even though the sieve designations may vary (Table 21-16).

Purposes

(1) To remove fines from material before reduction equipment such as a crusher, ball mill, or rod mill. (2) To produce a commercial- or process-grade product to meet specific particle-size limits. (3) To scalp out tramp or oversize material. (4) To remove fines or degradation from a finished product before shipping.

Equipment

Screening machines may be divided into five main classes: grizzlies, revolving screens, shaking screens, vibrating screens, and oscillating screens. Grizzlies are used primarily for scalping at 2 in. and coarser, while revolving screens and shaking screens are generally used for separations above ½ in. Vibrating screens cover this coarse range and also down into the fine meshes. Oscillating screens are confined in general to the finer meshes below 4 mesh.

Grizzly screens consist of a set of parallel bars held apart by spacers at some predetermined opening. Bars are frequently made of manganese steel to reduce wear. A grizzly is widely used before a primary crusher in rock- or ore-crushing plants to remove the fines before the ore or rock enters the crusher. They can be a stationary set of bars or a vibrating screen.

The stationary grizzly is the simplest of all separating devices and the least expensive to install and maintain. It is normally limited to the scalping or rough screening of dry material at 2 in. and coarser and is not satisfactory for moist and sticky material. The slope, or angle with the horizontal, will vary between 20 and 50 deg.

Flat grizzlies, in which the parallel bars are in a horizontal plane, are used on tops of ore and coal bins and under unloading trestles. This type of grizzly is used to retain occasional pieces too large for the following plant equipment. These lumps must then be broken up or removed manually.

Stationary grizzlies require no power and little maintenance. It is, of course, difficult to change the opening between the bars, and the separation may not be too complete.

Vibrating grizzlies are simply bar grizzlies mounted on eccentrics so that the entire assembly is given a back-and-forth movement or a positive circle throw. These are made by companies such as Allis-Chalmers, Hewitt Robins, Nordberg, Link-Belt, Simplicity, and Tyler.

Revolving screens or trommel screens, once widely used, are being largely replaced by vibrating screens. They consist of a cylindrical frame surrounded by wire cloth or perforated plate, open at both ends, and inclined at a slight angle. The material to be screened is delivered at the upper end and the oversize is discharged at the lower end. The desired product falls through the wire cloth openings. They revolve at relatively low speeds of 15 to 20 r.p.m. Their capacity is not great and efficiency is relatively low.

Mechanical shaking screens consist of a rectangular frame, which holds wire cloth or perforated plate and is slightly inclined and suspended by loose rods or cables, or supported from a base frame by flexible flat springs. The frame is driven with a reciprocating motion. The material to be screened is fed at the upper end and is advanced by the forward stroke of the screen while the finer particles pass through the openings. In many screening operations they have given way to vibrating screens.

Shaking screens, such as the mechanical-conveyor type made by Syntron Co., may be used for both screening and conveying.

Advantages of this type are low headroom and low power requirement. The disadvantages are the high cost of maintenance of the screen and the supporting structure due to the vibration and its low capacity compared with inclined high-speed vibrating screens.

Vibrating screens are used as standard practice where large capacity and high efficiency are desired. The capacity, especially in the finer sizes, is so much greater than any of the other screens that they have practically replaced all other types where the efficiency of the screen is an important factor. Advantages include accuracy of sizing, increased capacity per square foot, low maintenance cost per ton of material handled, and a saving in installation space and weight.

There are a great number of vibrating screens on the market but basically they can be divided into two main classes: (1) mechanically vibrated screens, (2) electrically vibrated screens.

Mechanically Vibrated Screens. The most versatile vibration for medium to coarse sizing is generally conceded to be the vertical circle produced by an eccentric or unbalanced shaft, but other types of vibration may be more suitable for certain screening operations, particularly in the finer sizes. One well-known four-bearing mechanically vibrated screen, installed in an inclined position, is the Ty-Rock (Fig. 21-64). This is a

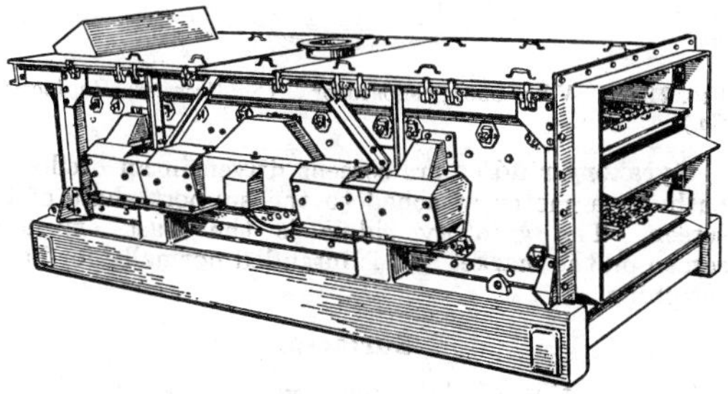

FIG. 21-64. Ty-Rock screen with air seal enclosure. (*W. S. Tyler Company.*)

balanced circle-throw machine mounted on a base frame, having a full-floating body mounted on shear rubber mounting units which absorb the shocks of heavy material and allow the shaft to revolve around its own natural center of rotation.

Two-bearing screens, of which there are many types, have the same screen body as the four-bearing type but without the two outer bearings and the base frame. The gyrating motion is caused by eccentric weights on the shaft, and the screen itself is supported by overhead cables or springs on the floor.

Screening machines actuated by rotating unbalanced weights have a symmetrical shaft through the screen body with an unbalanced flywheel on each end. Counterweights on each flywheel, which may be moved in relation to the shaft, permit adjustment of the amplitude of vibration. On some makes of machines the complete shaft assembly is contained in a unit bolted to the top of the screen body.

The horizontal-type screen is actuated by an enclosed mechanism consisting of off-center weights geared together on a pair of short horizontal shafts. The mechanism is usually mounted between the side plates and above the screen body.

Electrically vibrated screens are particularly useful in the chemical industry. They handle very successfully many light, fine, dry materials and metal powders from approximately 4 mesh to as fine as 325 mesh. Most of these screens have an intense, high-speed (1500 to 7200 vibrations/min.) low-amplitude vibration supplied by means of an electromagnet.

Typical of these is the Hum-mer screen used throughout the chemical industry. Figure 21-65 shows one used throughout the fertilizer industry for handling mixed chemical fertilizers. A smaller unit (Fig. 21-66) is frequently used for laboratory testing and pilot-plant work.

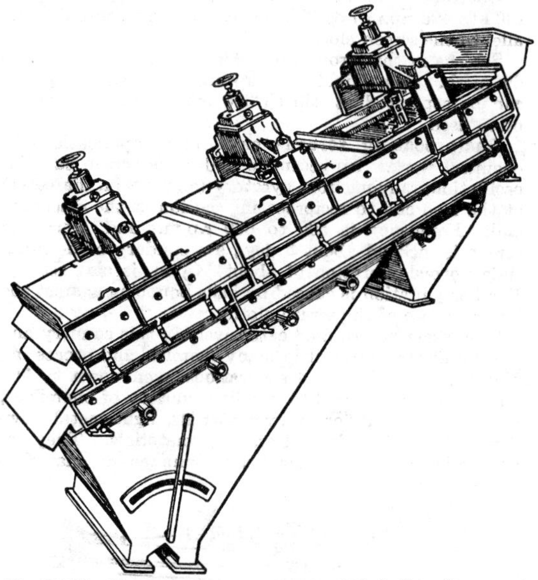

FIG. 21-65. Type 38 Hum-mer screen. (*W. S. Tyler Company.*)

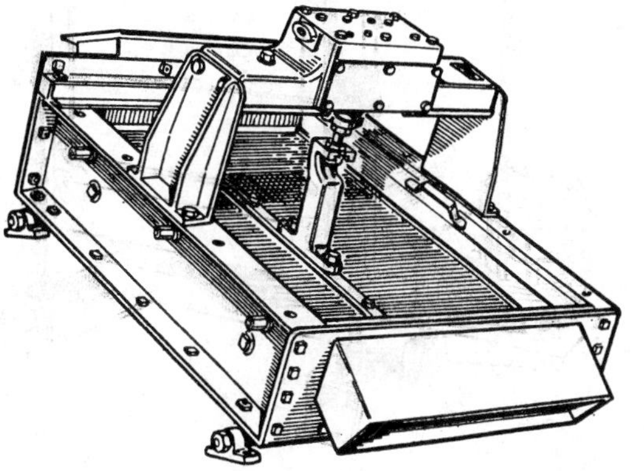

FIG. 21-66. Type 38 Jr. Hum-mer screen. (*W. S. Tyler Company.*)

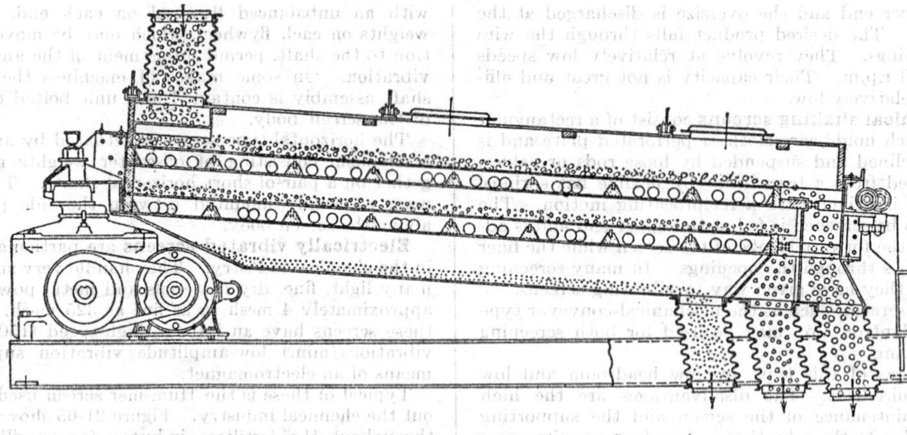

FIG. 21-67. Rotex screen. (*Orville Simpson Company.*)

Oscillating screens are characterized by low-speed (300 to 400 r.p.m.) oscillations in a plane essentially parallel to the screen cloth.

Screens in this group are usually used from ½ in. to 60 mesh. Some light free-flowing materials, however, can be separated at 200 to 300 mesh. Silk cloths are often used.

Reciprocating screens have many applications in chemical work. An eccentric under the screen supplies oscillation, ranging from gyratory (about 2 in. diameter) at the feed end to reciprocating motion at the discharge end. Frequency is 500 to 600 r.p.m.; and, since the screen is inclined about 5 deg., a secondary high-amplitude normal vibration of about ¹⁄₁₀ in. is also set up. Further vibration is caused by balls bouncing against the lower surface of the screen cloth.

These screens are used extensively in this country and are standard equipment in many chemical and processing plants for handling fine separations even down to 300 mesh. They are used to handle a variety of chemicals, usually dry, light, or bulky materials, light metal powders, powdered foods, and granular materials. They are not designed for handling heavy tonnages of materials like rock or gravel. Machines of this type are typified by Fig. 21-67.

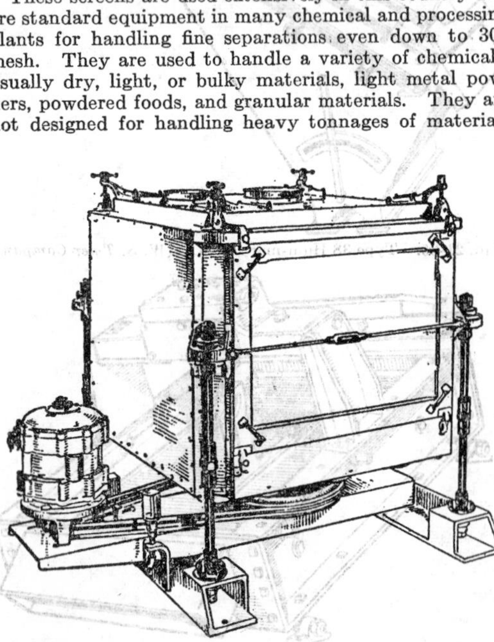

FIG. 21-68. Gyratory screen. (*Allis-Chalmers Manufacturing Company.*)

Gyratory screens are a boxlike machine, either round or square, with a series of screen cloths nested atop one another. Oscillation, supplied by eccentrics or counterweights, is in a circular or near-circular orbit. In some machines a supplementary whipping action is set up. Most gyratory screens have an auxiliary vibration caused by balls bouncing against the lower surface of the screen cloth. Typical machines are Fig. 21-68 and Fig. 21-69.

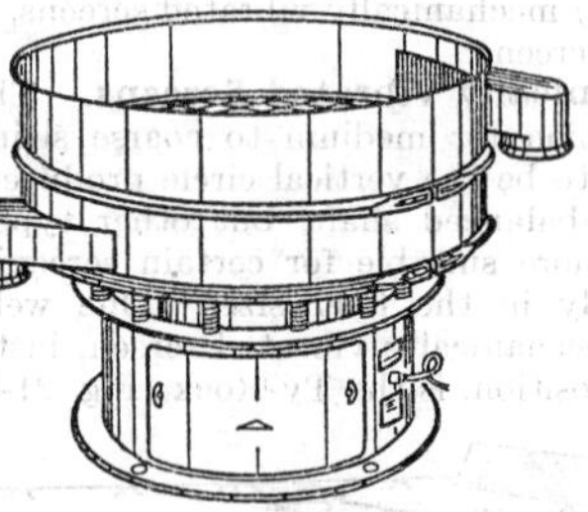

FIG. 21-69. Vibro-energy separator. (*Southwestern Engineering Co.*)

Gyratory riddles are screens driven in an oscillating path by a motor attached to the support shaft of the screen. The gyratory riddle is the least expensive screen on the market and is intended normally for batch screening.

Surfaces

The selection of the proper screening surface is very important and the opening, wire diameter, and open area should all be carefully considered. The four general types of screening surfaces are woven wire cloth, silk bolting cloth, punched plate, and bar or rod screens.

Woven wire cloth has by far the greatest selection as to screen opening, wire diameter, and percentage of open area. Thousands of specifications are available from over 4 in. clear opening to 500 mesh. Woven wire screens are obtainable in a variety of metals and alloys. Steel and high-carbon steel are generally favored for the coarser openings because of their abrasion-resistant qualities, and other materials, such as phosphor bronze, monel, and stainless steel, are used for their corrosion-resisting or non-contamination qualities.

Square-mesh cloth is the conventional type of screen

cloth but there are many types of cloth with an oblong weave. This latter construction provides greater open area and capacity and in addition makes it possible to use stronger wire for the same size of screen opening and for the same percentage of open area.

In choosing a wire-cloth specification there must be a compromise between sharpness of separation, capacity, freedom from blinding, and life of the wire cloth. The square-mesh cloth will give the closest control of the maximum size particle in the undersize material; but the effective size of the openings will be reduced, because of the foreshortening when used at an angle of inclination, with consequent reduction in capacity. It should be realized that it is often necessary to use a cloth specification with an aperture larger than the smallest size material acceptable in the oversize, in order to ensure thorough removal of the undersize. A screen with a rectangular opening will increase the capacity with but little loss of sharpness when handling rounded or cubical grains. Slabby or flat material may also be handled on rectangular-opening cloth if the final product specification will allow in the undersize a certain percentage of flat pieces having one dimension greater than the specified square-opening sieve. In other words pieces that might fall through a rectangular cloth and be allowed in the product might not go through the limiting square-mesh sieve on which the specification is based. If the through product is to be further ground or processed a small amount of this material will not be objectionable.

Screen-cloth specifications having a relatively large length-to-width ratio are desirable where moisture or sticky material tends to cause blinding with square or short rectangular openings.

The finer the diameter of the wire from which a given specification is woven the greater will be its screening capacity, although its screening life will be less. Since production capacity is generally more important than screen surface cost, care should be taken to avoid using too heavy a specification which might restrict the capacity of the screening unit on which it is used and thus create a bottleneck in the flow.

Catalogues of the wire-cloth manufacturers should be consulted for further study of the different types of wire-cloth specifications.

Silk bolting cloth originated in Switzerland and is generally woven from twisted multistrand natural silk. The system of numbers and grades for both bolting cloth and gritz gauze has been handed down from the original Swiss weavers. In recent years, nylon and similar synthetic materials have been introduced woven largely from monofilaments. The nylon grades are generally designated by their micron opening and are available in light, standard, and heavy weights.

Comparative Openings of Silk, Nylon, and Wire Bolting Cloth. In screening any material, the size of the particles going through the screen is determined by the actual opening and not by the number of meshes per linear inch. A table showing the comparative openings can be obtained from either The Orville Simpson Co. or The W. S. Tyler Co. As a rule, the lighter grades of wire-screen cloth, having greater percentages of open area, screen more freely and accurately and should be used wherever they will give satisfactory length of service. The table of comparative openings is convenient for selecting a screen specification with a specific opening, or to pick a specification having a heavier or lighter wire but having the same opening.

Punched plates are available in a variety of perforations including round, square, hexagonal, and elongated openings. Punched metal will generally wear longer than wire cloth and has more rigidity, which is an advantage in certain applications. However, it usually does not give the capacity per square foot that wire cloth does and is generally heavier per square foot. Its use is normally limited to the coarser separations.

Bar screens are generally used in handling large and heavy pieces of material. They are formed from rails, rods, or bars, suitably shaped; made from rolled steel or castings; fixed in parallel position and held by crossbars and spacers. Bars, which taper in thickness from top to bottom and may also taper in width from one end to the other, are recommended because they tend to avoid blinding.

Rod decks are also available composed of spring-steel rods approximately 2 ft. long, sprung into position between molded rubber blocks, and held in position by means of rubber spacers.

Performance Formulas

There is some confusion concerning the meaning of screen efficiency, as a uniform method for figuring efficiency has never been established. A sound method of evaluating screen performance is given by the W. S. Tyler Company, Cleveland, Ohio, in their "Sieve Handbook" No. 53. In this formula when material put through the screen is the desired product "efficiency" is the ratio of the amount of undersize obtained to the amount of undersize in the feed.

$$E = \frac{R \times d}{b}$$

where E = efficiency, R = per cent of fines through the screen, d = per cent finer than designated size in screen fines, and b = per cent finer than designated size in screen feed.

When the object is to recover an oversize product from the screen the efficiency may be expressed as a ratio of the amount of oversize obtained to the amount of true oversize.

$$E = \frac{O \times c}{a}$$

where O = per cent of oversize over the screen, c = per cent coarser than designated size in screen oversize, and a = per cent coarser than designated size in screen feed.

Other formulas for the derivation of screen efficiency are used. Taggart in his "Handbook of Mineral Dressing" gives the formula

$$E = 100 \times \frac{100(e - v)}{e(100 - v)}$$

where E is the efficiency, e is the percentage of undersize in the feed, and v is the percentage of undersize in the screen oversize.

Graphical methods of evaluating efficiency, using sieve analyses, are also used and are recommended when serious research on screening is done.

Data Affecting Screen Problems

When attempting to pick a screening machine to do a specific screening problem it should be fully understood that there are no formulas or charts that establish screen capacities as there are too many variables which may affect performance. Screen consultants will readily admit that they must depend largely on laboratory tests and previous field experience. In attempting to choose a screening machine for a particular screening application the customer and manufacturer should consider the following: (1) Full description of material involved including the name and type of material, weight per cubic foot, and physical characteristics such as hardness, particle shape, flow characteristics (free-flowing, sluggish, or sticky), per cent of moisture and temperature. (2) Normal and maximum total rate of feed to screen. (3) Complete sieve analysis of screen feed, including maximum lump size, and sieve analysis of desired product. (4) Separation or separations required and the purpose of screening. Can slotted or rectangular openings be used in place of square openings. (5) Is screening to be accomplished dry or wet, and what amount of water is available. (6) Other important factors include method of delivering feed to the screen, open or closed circuit, open or enclosed screens, previous screening experience with the material, flow sheet or description of related equipment, operating hours per day, power available, and space limitations.

Variables in Screening Operations

It will readily be seen that many variables in a screening operation can easily be changed in the field, and the practical operator will always be trying to improve his operation or adapt it to new products or processes. Capacity and efficiency in screening operations are closely related. The capacity may be large if low efficiency is not objectionable. Usually, as the tonnage to a screen is increased, the efficiency is decreased.

Method of Feed. The screening machine must be fed properly in order to obtain the maximum capacity and efficiency. The feed should be spread evenly over the full width of the screen cloth and should approach the screen surface in a direction parallel to the longitudinal axis of the screen and at as low a practical velocity as is possible.

Screening Surfaces. It is generally agreed that the most efficient screening results when a series of single-deck screens is used. This is because lower decks of multiple-deck screens are not fed so that their entire area is used and because each separation requires a different combination of angle, speed, and amplitude of vibration for maximum performance.

Angle or Slope. The optimum slope of inclined vibrating screens is that which will handle the greatest volume of oversize and still remove the available undersize required by the standards of the particular operation. To separate a material into coarse and fine fractions, the bed thickness must be limited so that vibration can stratify the load and allow fines to work their way to the screen surface and pass through the opening. Increased slope naturally increases the rate of travel, and at a given rate it reduces the bed thickness.

In the oscillating screen the angle of inclination must be coordinated with the speed and stroke for best results.

Direction of Rotation. In circle-throw screens somewhat greater efficiency can be obtained by counterflow rotation, that is, having the material move down the screen against the rotation. Screens rotating with the flow of material will handle greater tonnage and operate at a lower angle.

Vibration Amplitude and Frequency. Speed and amplitude of vibration should be designed to convey the material properly and to prevent blinding of the cloth. They are somewhat dependent upon the size and weight of the material being handled and are related to the angle of installation and the type of screen surface. The object, of course, is to see that the feed is properly stratified for the most efficient separation.

Testing Sieves

Many product specifications now call for definite sizes of material in terms of given percentages passing or retained on specified test sieves. Test sieves are also generally used to determine the efficiency of screening devices and the work of crushing and grinding machinery.

It is essential that standard sieves, with standard size openings, be used for sieve analyses. The time of screening and the method of agitating the material on the sieve should also be standard, and in many industries the practice of specifying the test-sieve designation and the time and method of sieving is followed. An excellent booklet on the theory and use of standard testing sieves is given in the "Testing Sieve Handbook" No. 53 published by the W. S. Tyler Company, Cleveland, Ohio.

U.S. Sieve Series. The American Society for Testing Materials in cooperation with the National Bureau of Standards and the American Standards Association has further refined the U.S. sieve series combining the former coarse and fine series into a single series with a fourth-root-of-2 ratio (Table 21-16). The openings in the individual sieves have remained unchanged except for minor adjustments in sieves coarser than 6.73 mm. In the revised series, sieves 1 mm. and coarser are identified by openings in millimeters, and those finer than 1 mm. by their openings in microns.

Tyler Standard Sieve Series. Many users have their standards and tests based on using Tyler standard screen scale testing sieves (Table 21-16). The only difference between the U.S. sieves and the Tyler screen scale sieves is the identification method. Tyler screen scale sieves are identified by the nominal meshes per linear inch while the U.S. sieves are identified by millimeters or microns, or by an arbitrary number which does not necessarily mean the mesh count. The Tyler standard sieve scale series has as its base a 200-mesh screen in which the opening is 0.0029 in. and the wire diameter 0.0021 in.

International Test Sieve Series. The International Standards Organization has been intensifying its efforts to establish an international test sieve series. At a meeting held at The Hague in October, 1959, the I.S.O. provisionally recommended for adoption as an international standard 19 sieves as shown by the * in (Table 21-16). These sieves correspond to every alternating sieve in the fourth-root-of-2 U.S. sieve series from ⅞-in. opening to 325 mesh.

Testing Sieve Shakers

The Ro-Tap testing sieve shaker (Fig. 21-70) manufactured by the W. S. Tyler Company is the standard

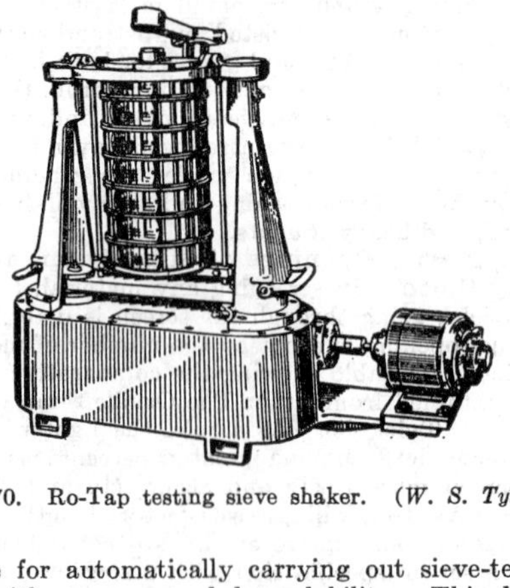

FIG. 21-70. Ro-Tap testing sieve shaker. (*W. S. Tyler Company.*)

machine for automatically carrying out sieve-test procedure with accuracy and dependability. This device is built to hold a series of 8-in.-diameter Tyler standard scale testing sieves and imparts to the sieves both a circular and a tapping motion. In effect, it reproduces the circular and tapping motion given testing sieves in hand sieving but does it with a uniform mechanical action. An important feature of the Ro-Tap is that both speed

Table 21-16. U.S. Sieve Series and Tyler Equivalents A.S.T.M.—E-11-61

Sieve designation: Standard	Sieve designation: Alternate	Sieve opening: mm.	Sieve opening: in. (approx. equivalents)	Nominal wire diam.: mm.	Nominal wire diam.: in. (approx. equivalents)	Tyler equivalent designation
107.6 mm.	4.24 in.	107.6	4.24	6.40	0.2520	
101.6 mm.	4 in.†	101.6	4.00	6.30	.2480	
90.5 mm.	3½ in.	90.5	3.50	6.08	.2394	
76.1 mm.	3 in.	76.1	3.00	5.80	.2283	
64.0 mm.	2½ in.	64.0	2.50	5.50	.2165	
53.8 mm.	2.12 in.	53.8	2.12	5.15	.2028	
50.8 mm.	2 in.†	50.8	2.00	5.05	.1988	
45.3 mm.	1¾ in.	45.3	1.75	4.85	.1909	
38.1 mm.	1½ in.	38.1	1.50	4.59	.1807	
32.0 mm.	1¼ in.	32.0	1.25	4.23	.1665	
26.9 mm.	1.06 in.	26.9	1.06	3.90	.1535	1.050 in.
25.4 mm.	1 in.†	25.4	1.00	3.80	.1496	
22.6 mm.*	⅞ in.	22.6	0.875	3.50	.1378	0.883 in.
19.0 mm.	¾ in.	19.0	.750	3.30	.1299	.742 in.
16.0 mm.*	⅝ in.	16.0	.625	3.00	.1181	.624 in.
13.5 mm.	0.530 in.	13.5	.530	2.75	.1083	.525 in.
12.7 mm.	½ in.†	12.7	.500	2.67	.1051	
11.2 mm.*	7/16 in.	11.2	.438	2.45	.0965	.441 in.
9.51 mm.	⅜ in.	9.51	.375	2.27	.0894	.371 in.
8.00 mm.*	5/16 in.	8.00	.312	2.07	.0815	2½ mesh
6.73 mm.	0.265 in.	6.73	.265	1.87	.0736	3 mesh
6.35 mm.	¼ in.†	6.35	.250	1.82	.0717	
5.66 mm.*	No. 3½	5.66	.223	1.68	.0661	3½ mesh
4.76 mm.	No. 4	4.76	.187	1.54	.0606	4 mesh
4.00 mm.*	No. 5	4.00	.157	1.37	.0539	5 mesh
3.36 mm.	No. 6	3.36	.132	1.23	.0484	6 mesh
2.83 mm.*	No. 7	2.83	.111	1.10	.0430	7 mesh
2.38 mm.	No. 8	2.38	.0937	1.00	.0394	8 mesh
2.00 mm.*	No. 10	2.00	.0787	0.900	.0354	9 mesh
1.68 mm.	No. 12	1.68	.0661	.810	.0319	10 mesh
1.41 mm.*	No. 14	1.41	.0555	.725	.0285	12 mesh
1.19 mm.	No. 16	1.19	.0469	.650	.0256	14 mesh
1.00 mm.*	No. 18	1.00	.0394	.580	.0228	16 mesh
841 micron	No. 20	0.841	.0331	.510	.0201	20 mesh
707 micron*	No. 25	.707	.0278	.450	.0177	24 mesh
595 micron	No. 30	.595	.0234	.390	.0154	28 mesh
500 micron*	No. 35	.500	.0197	.340	.0134	32 mesh
420 micron	No. 40	.420	.0165	.290	.0114	35 mesh
354 micron*	No. 45	.354	.0139	.247	.0097	42 mesh
297 micron	No. 50	.297	.0117	.215	.0085	48 mesh
250 micron*	No. 60	.250	.0098	.180	.0071	60 mesh
210 micron	No. 70	.210	.0083	.152	.0060	65 mesh
177 micron*	No. 80	.177	.0070	.131	.0052	80 mesh
149 micron	No. 100	.149	.0059	.110	.0043	100 mesh
125 micron*	No. 120	.125	.0049	.091	.0036	115 mesh
105 micron	No. 140	.105	.0041	.076	.0030	150 mesh
88 micron*	No. 170	.088	.0035	.064	.0025	170 mesh
74 micron	No. 200	.074	.0029	.053	.0021	200 mesh
63 micron*	No. 230	.063	.0025	.044	.0017	250 mesh
53 micron	No. 270	.053	.0021	.037	.0015	270 mesh
44 micron*	No. 325	.044	.0017	.030	.0012	325 mesh
37 micron	No. 400	.037	.0015	.025	.0010	400 mesh

* These sieves correspond to those proposed as an international (I.S.O.) standard. It is recommended that wherever possible these sieves be included in all sieve analysis data or reports intended for international publication.

† These sieves are not in the fourth-root-of-2 series, but they have been included because they are in common usage.

and stroke are fixed and not adjustable. This ensures the comparability between a number of sieve tests, not only in a manufacturer's plant but between tests of a supplier and his customer.

The Ro-Tap is equipped to handle from 1 to 13 sieves at a time and is equipped with a timer that automatically terminates the test after any predetermined time.

Another mechanical shaker is the End-Shak (Fig. 21-71) made by the Newark Wire Cloth Company. Sieves used are Newark test sieves, made to conform with the U.S. standard series.

A number of less expensive sieve shakers are on the

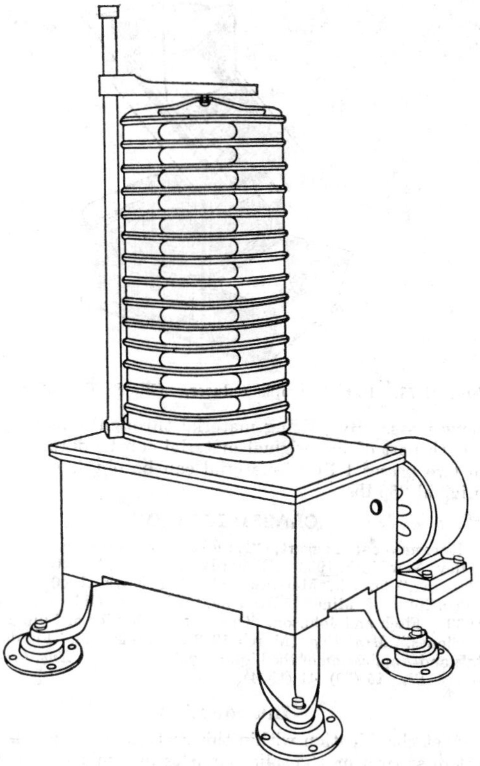

FIG. 21-71. End-Shak testing sieve shaker. (*Newark Wire Cloth Company.*)

market, such as the Dynamic (Fig. 21-72) by Soiltest Co., Chicago, Ill.; the Cenco-Meinzer by Central Scientific Co., Chicago, Ill.; the Tyler Portable by the W. S. Tyler Company, Cleveland, Ohio; and also a number of electromagnetic vibratory shakers. The latter should be used only where strict comparability with other tests is not required, since it is difficult to be sure that identical intensity of vibration was present in the tests being compared.

The 16-to-1 sample reducer (Fig. 21-73) greatly reduces the time necessary to cut out a representative sample for

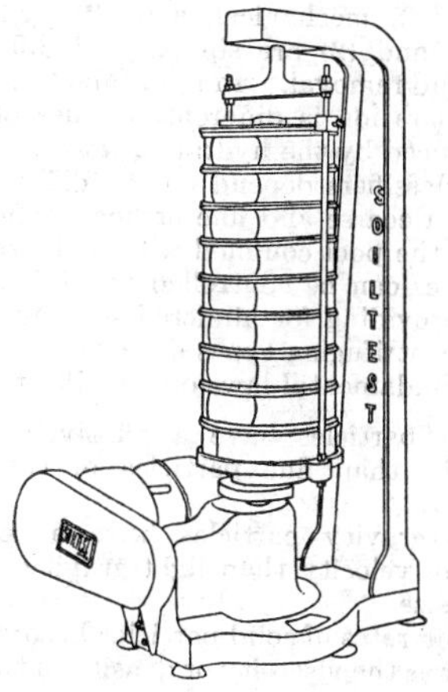

FIG. 21-72. Dynamic sieve shaker. (*Soiltest Incorporated.*)

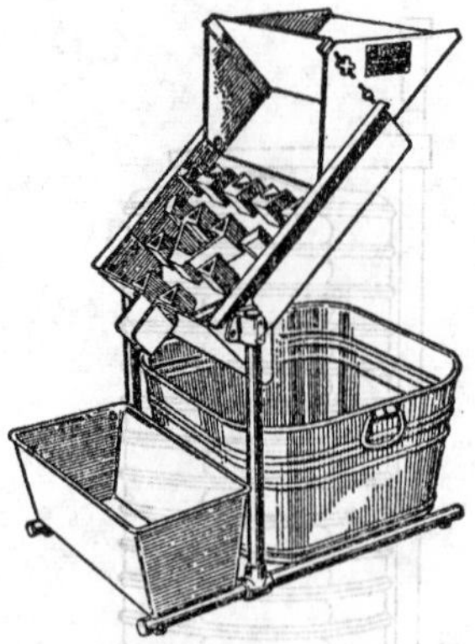

FIG. 21-73. 16-to-1 sample reducer. (*W. S. Tyler Company.*)

sieve tests. By passing material through it once, a sixteenth part of the original material can be obtained, and in two passes 1 lb. of material can be obtained from an original 256 lb.

CLASSIFICATION

REFERENCES: Taggart, "Handbook of Mineral Dressing," Wiley, New York, 1953. Richards and Locke, "Textbook of Ore Dressing," 3d ed., McGraw-Hill, New York, 1940. Gaudin, "Principles of Mineral Dressing," McGraw-Hill, New York, 1939. Fitch and Johnson, "Operating Behavior of Liquid-Solid Cyclones," *Min. Eng.* (March 1953). Dahlstrom, "Fundamentals and Application of the Liquid Cyclone," *Chem. Eng. Progress, Symp. Ser.*, **15** (50), 41 (1954).

Introduction

Wet classification within this section is defined as that art of separating the solid particles in a mixture of solids and liquid into fractions according to particle size or density by methods other than screening. In general the two products resulting are (1) a partially drained fraction containing the coarse material (called the sand) and (2) a fine fraction along with the remaining portion of the liquid medium (called the overflow).

Classifying operation is carried out in a pool of fluid pulp confined in a tank arranged to allow the coarse solids to settle out, whereupon they are removed by gravity, mechanical means, or induced pressure. Solids which do not settle report as overflow from the pool. Mesh of separation as used in this text is the screen size retaining 1½ per cent of the overflow solids.

Classifier types fall into three basic categories: (1) nonmechanical, (2) mechanical, and (3) hydraulic. Functionally (1) and (2) are similar and differ only in the means of sand removal. In hydraulic types (3) the character of separation is different because of the hindered settling induced by the hydraulic water.

All wet classifiers depend on the difference in settling rate between coarse and fine or heavy and light gravity particles in the pool confined within the tank of the machine. Rates can be controlled to some extent by mild agitation, providing for hindered settling, and power vs. gravity in centrifuging types of units.

Several fundamental laws on classification are:

1. Coarse particles have a relatively faster settling velocity than fine particles of the same specific gravity.
2. Heavy-gravity particles have a relatively faster settling velocity than light-gravity particles of the same size.
3 Settling rates of solid particles become progressively slower as the viscosity or density of the fluid medium increases.
   a. There is a point (called critical dilution) where the lowering of density or viscosity in the pool by addition of more liquid creates a velocity effect which overcomes normal classification settling velocity, thereby coarsening the separation.
   b. Conversely at this point less liquid will cause a viscosity and buoyancy effect which will also coarsen the separation.

Typical problems to be solved by wet-classification means fall into several broad categories such as (1) to effect a simple sand-slime separation resulting in two products; (2) to effect a concentration of smaller heavy-gravity particles in a product containing larger light-gravity particles; (3) an operation to obtain a washing effect by successive dewatering, repulping in weaker solution, and further dewatering; (4) to sort solids having a full range of screen sizes into a number of partials each having a short range of screen sizes; and (5) for closed-circuit control of grinding mills.

Classification is by definition used preponderantly in the treatment of raw materials. However, these raw materials find their way into chemical processing per se and thus become of interest to the chemical engineer, particularly so when the products to be treated react better when of a defined cleanliness, size, gravity, or moisture content.

There are numerous machines and machine types to effect the separations and products under consideration and there is much overlapping in the possibilities. Usually, only one type will stand up under close scrutiny for the operating or economic problem involved.

Approximate cost figures shown are for July, 1960, and subject to variation. All such classifiers can be furnished in acid- or causticproof construction of stainless and rubber-covered steel at appropriately higher prices. All the machines discussed have been developed for 24-hr. continuous trouble-free duty and nearly all have built-in overload assistance devices.

The quick reference Table 21-17 will help by way of rapid elimination of poor possibilities. Following that the brief comments and cuts will help pinpoint most probable selections. Further study of the more elaborate data in the references and contact with the usual suppliers are recommended, as there are many possible modifications of equipment which can improve operating results from any type of machine finally selected.

Non-mechanical Classifiers

Cone Type. Cone classifiers are one of the oldest types but are still used for relatively crude work because of low cost of installation. They are limited in diameter because of high headroom requirements caused by the ±60-deg. sloping sides. Units are simple and are often fabricated locally with millwright ingenuity fashioning the apex opening arrangement for adjustment or control of the spigot (sand) product. Cones are not suitable for pulps having a tendency to hang up or build mud banks. Operating attention is often necessary to greater degree than for the more positive mechanical types. Cost figures are not available.

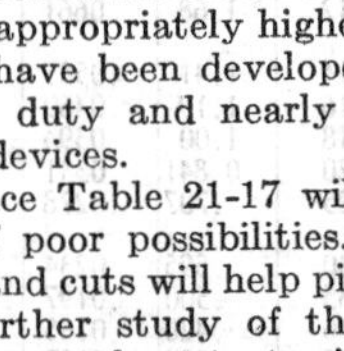

FIG. 21-74. Cone classifier. F = feed, O = overflow product, S = sand product, H.W. = hydraulic water.

Table 21-17. Sizes, Limitations, and Major Applications of Wet Classification Machines

Figure	Type of classifier	Normal size range, ft.			Normal mesh of separation range*	Normal feed tonnage range	Max. over-size in feed	Normal over-flow, % solids range	Normal feed density, % solids range	Normal sand product, % solids range	Motor range, hp	Typical applications
		Width	Diam.	Max. length								
	Non-mechanical:											
21-74	Cone classifier	......	2-12	....	28-325	2-100 tons/hr.	¼ in.	5-30	Not critical	35-60	None	For desliming and primary dewatering
21-75	Liquid cyclone	......	10 mm. to 4 ft.	9	48 mesh to 5 microns	½-1500 gal./min.	14-325 mesh	5-30	10-60	55-70	Power for pressure head 5-60 lb./sq.in.	For medium or fine separations and closed-circuit grinding
	Mechanical:											
21-76	Drag classifier	1-10	....	Not critical	28-200	5-350 tons/hr.	1½ in.	5-30	Not critical	70-83	1-10	For desliming, conveying, and closed-circuit grinding
21-77 and 21-78	Rake and spiral classifiers	1-20	....	40	20-200	5-350 tons/hr.	1 in.	5-30	Not critical	75-83	½-25	Closed-circuit grinding, washing and dewatering, desliming, process feed control
21-79	Bowl classifier	1½-20	4-28	40	100-325	5-200 tons/hr.	½ in.	5-25	Not critical	75-80	Bowl: 1-7½ Rake: 1-25	Closed-circuit grinding usually in secondary circuits
21-80	Bowl desiltor	4-16	20-50	40	100-325	5-250 tons/hr.	½ in.	1-15	Not critical	75-83	Bowl: 1-10 Rake: 5-25	Recovery of fine sand, limestone, coal, and fine phosphate rock from large flow volumes
21-81	Hydroseparator	......	10-150	....	100-325	5-700 tons/hr.	¼ in.	1-20	Not critical	30-50	1-15	For fine separation where large feed volumes are involved and drainage not critical
21-82	Solid-bowl centrifuge	......	18-54 in.	70 in.	200 mesh to 1 micron	10-600 gal./min.	¼ in.	1-40	5-50	10-70	15-150	For fine-size fractionating
21-83	Sand washer	......	7-12	....	28-65	25-125 tons/hr.	1 in.	5-15	Not critical	75-80	5-10	For desliming and dewatering large tonnages of solids
21-84	Countercurrent classifier	......	1½-10	40	35-100	1-600 tons/hr.	3 in.	5-30	Not critical	75-83	¼-25	Sand-slime separations, washing, closed-circuit grinding
	Hydraulic:											
21-85	Sizer	1½-20	....	5-20	8-150	2-100 tons/hr.	3/16 in.	1-10	30-60	40-60	1-2 for air pressure	Multiproduct unit for exceptionally clean sands fractionated into narrow size ranges. Min. 3 tons hydraulic water per ton sand
21-86	SuperSorter†	6	....	40	8-150	40-150 tons/hr.	⅜ in.	1-10	30-60	40-60	1 to operate pincer valves	Multiproduct unit for exceptionally clean sands fractionated into narrow size ranges. Min. 3 tons hydraulic water per ton sand
21-87	SiphonSizer‡	......	3-30	....	14-150	1-100 tons/hr.	1 in.	1-10	30-60	40-60	None	Two-product unit efficient for desliming and exceptionally clean sands, washing, closed-circuit grinding. Min. 2 tons hydraulic water per ton sand
21-88	Hydroscillator‡	4-12	4-14	40	20-150	5-250 tons/hr.	½ in.	5-30	Not critical	75-83	Oscillator: 3-10 Rakes: 5-20	Two-product unit for exceptionally clean sand having low moisture content. Closed-circuit grinding, washing. Min. 0.5 ton hydraulic water per ton sand

* Size of screen retaining 1½ % of the overflow solids.
† Trade-mark of Deister Concentrator Co., Inc.
‡ Trade-mark of Dorr-Oliver Inc.

Liquid Cyclone. The wet cyclone classifier has rapidly achieved prominence during the last 10 years and continues to gain popularity throughout chemical and ore-dressing industries. Standout virtues are its low capital cost and ability to make extremely fine separations and to deliver a given separation at high overflow per cent solids.

In simplest terms the unit has a top cylindrical section and a lower conical section terminating in an apex opening, often adjustable. The unit operates under pressure induced by a static hydraulic head or by means of a pump forcing new feed into the cylindrical portion tangentially, thus producing centrifuging action and vortexing. The cover has a downward-extending pipe to cut the vortex and remove the overflow product. Coarse solids travel down the sides of the steeply sided cone section and are removed in a partially dewatered form at the apex.

Liquid cyclones such as the DorrClone* are available in numerous sizes and types ranging from pencil-sized 10 mm. diameters of plastic or aluminum oxide to 48 in. diameter of rubber-protected mild or stainless steel. Porcelain units 1 to 4 in. diameter are becoming popular and in the 6-in. size the starch industry has standardized on special molded nylon types. Small units for fine-size separations are usually manifolded in multiple units in parallel with up to 480 ten-mm. cyclones in a single case. Larger sizes may be used singly or manifolded by outside piping as necessary.

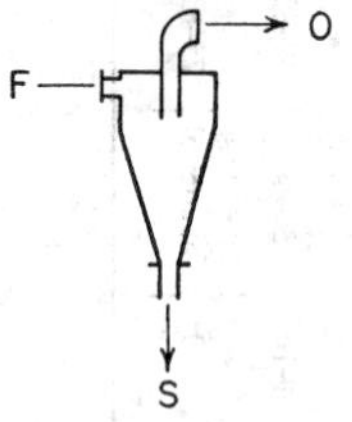

FIG. 21-75. Liquid cyclone.

For closed-circuit grinding, particularly for regrind operations and fine separations, the liquid cyclone is replacing more expensive bowl classifiers. To some extent it is serving for 48- to 65-mesh separations in closed-circuit grinding work, but the cases are not so clear-cut.

Typical uses more in line with chemical applications are degritting milk of lime and of red mud in alumina production, removal of carbonaceous material in upgrading gypsum produced in making phosphoric acid, open-circuit washing of fine uranium pulps, classification of crystal magma such as lactose and sodium bisulfite, and classifying pigment and plastic beads into size ranges.

Costs run from a few dollars each for single 10-mm. units to many thousands for multiples in closed housings and from a few hundred dollars to $2000 for the conventional 3-, 6-, 12-, and 24-in.-diameter ore-dressing types. Unless static head is available the cost of the pumping system must be added.

Mechanical Classifiers

Drag Classifiers. Single endless belt or chain suspensions with cross flights running in an inclined trough have long been used for draining and classifying. Many styles, sizes, and shapes have resulted from locally built units, and operating results on a scientific basis are meager. In general they have served their purpose consistent with the type of engineering and cost included.

The new Hardinge Overdrain† classifier is of the belt

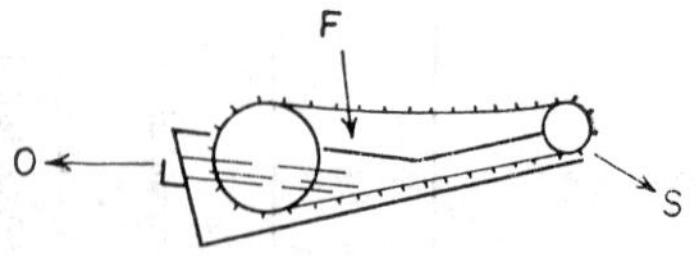

FIG. 21-76. Drag classifier.

type but it embodies the innovation of allowing entrapped water and slimes to escape through holes in the belt just uphill of the cross flights in an upwardly direction and thence flow down on top of the belt into the pool without again intermingling with the sand product being advanced by the cross flights. Sands with lower moisture and fines content result from this action. Modern design and materials of construction permit sizes up to 10 ft. wide and 41 ft. long on steeper than average slopes and for very high tonnages.

Approximate f.o.b. factory costs range from $1500 to $2500 per foot of belt width, including tanks but without drives or accessories.

Rake and Spiral Classifiers. Rake-type classifiers such as the Dorr* classifier and spiral types such as the Akins† have been the workhorses for general-classification problems for half a century, and their names describe the mechanisms installed in sloping-bottom tanks. Mechanically the machines are powerfully built and functionally they are most versatile and flexible. They were the first classifiers used successfully for closed-circuit grinding. Separations as fine as 325 mesh can be accomplished at reduced tonnage rates. Quite likely a greater tonnage of material is treated in these types than in all other classifiers combined.

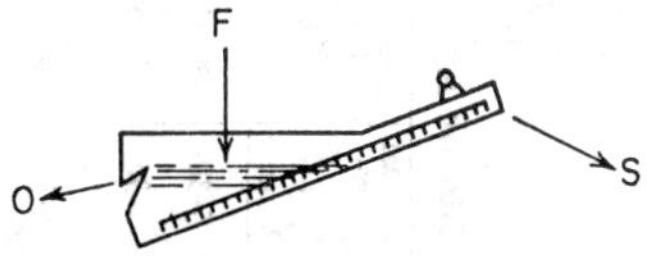

FIG. 21-77. Rake classifier.

Control of water into the classifiers is important since separation into overflow and sand products is made largely by the buoyancy, viscosity, and degree of agitation in the pool.

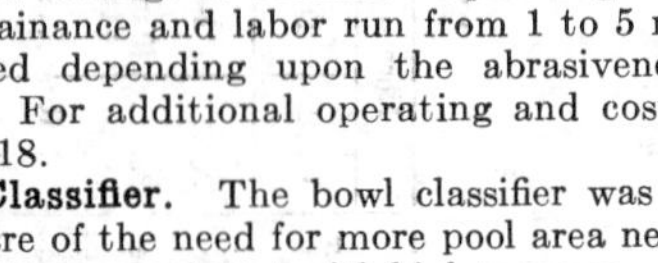

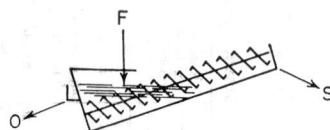

FIG. 21-78. Spiral classifier.

Both types of machines will produce rake products of consistent moisture content even with considerable variation in feed tonnage or volume. Operating costs including maintainance and labor run from 1 to 5 mils/ton of sand raked depending upon the abrasiveness of the material. For additional operating and cost data see Table 21-18.

Bowl Classifier. The bowl classifier was developed to take care of the need for more pool area necessary for fine separations consistent with high tonnage. In essence a shallow bowl with revolving plows is superimposed over a rake or screw dewatering section. Feed enters at the center of the bowl and fine solids overflow at the periphery. Coarse solids collected on the bowl bottom are raked to the center for discharge into the dewatering

* Trade-mark of Dorr-Oliver Inc.
† Trade-mark of Hardinge Co., Inc.

* Trade-mark of Dorr-Oliver Inc.
† Trade-mark of Mine and Smelter Supply Co.

Table 21-18.

Duty	Typical size	Raking capacity 2.7 sp. gr. solids, tons/day per stroke/min.			Approx. per ft. of width in mild-steel construction, F.O.B. factory	
					Wt., lb.	Cost
Rake classifiers						
Light.......	4 by 20 ft.	25	max. speed	30	2,000	$ 1,650
Medium....	6 by 25 ft.	80	max. speed	30	2,600	1,800
Heavy......	8 by 30 ft.	320	max. speed	25	3,700	2,500
Spiral classifiers						
					Complete machine	
Heavy.....	36 in. diam. by 20 ft.	110 tons/day per r.p.m.			9,000	$ 5,500
Heavy.....	78 in. diam. by 36 ft.	1130 tons/day per r.p.m.			51,000	20,000

compartment below where wash water may be added for counterflow.

Liquid cyclones are rapidly taking over the functions formerly handled by bowl classifiers because of lower capital costs and floor-area requirements. However, where drained sand products are wanted, there is still a place for bowls in ore-dressing practice.

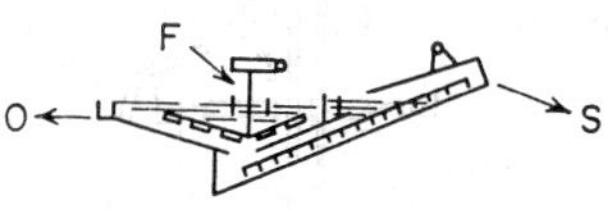

Fig. 21-79. Bowl classifier.

Costs including tanks and drives range from $1000 to $1500 per foot of bowl diameter depending upon raking capacity needed.

Bowl Desiltor. The bowl desiltor provides for pool surface areas well beyond those areas possible in bowl classifiers where larger sizes are limited by mechanical design. Its use is in operations involving large flow volumes and fine separations. Rake tonnages can be great or small with a dewatering compartment to suit the conditions.

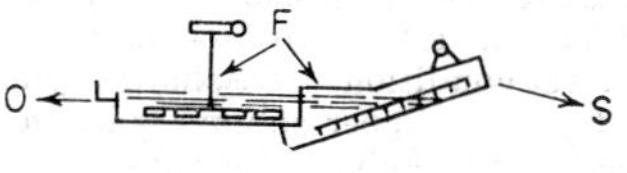

Fig. 21-80. Bowl desiltor.

In the bowl desiltor the rotating blades in the bowl plow outward and discharge settled coarse material at the periphery where it drops into the drainage compartment. This configuration does away with the long cantilevered rake construction necessary in bowl classifiers.

Widest application has been for the recovery of and drainage of very fine material overflowing coarser washing units in glass sand, concrete sand, coal, and limestone processing plants.

Costs including steel tanks and drives range from $750 to $1250 per foot of bowl diameter depending upon the raking capacity needed.

Hydroseparator. The hydroseparator is merely a thickener-type machine receiving more flow than can be clarified in the area provided. Thus the overflow contains fine solids and the greater the feed rate per unit of area the coarser the solids in the overflow.

Classification efficiency of the hydroseparator compares with that of the cone classifier and is appreciably lower than obtained from mechanical or hydraulic units. The chief virtue of the hydroseparator is its ability to receive and slough off great quantities of water at low per-unit-volume cost.

Typical applications include primary dewatering of phosphate rock matrix and silica sand products following wet screening. In ore dressing it is used mainly to protect large-diameter thickeners by scalping out +65-mesh material.

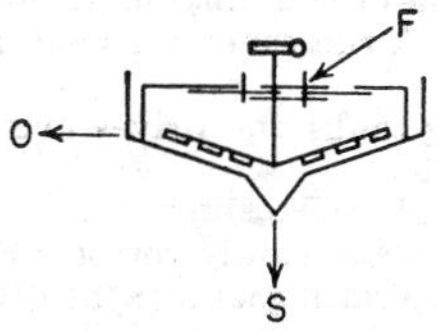

Fig. 21-81. Hydroseparator.

Mechanism costs range from $170 to $500 per 100 sq. ft. of pool area not including tanks, which may be steel, wood, or concrete.

Solid-bowl Centrifuge. The Bird solid-bowl centrifuge uses power instead of gravity and can develop up to 1800 *g*. It is therefore a unique type in classification practice.

The unit consists essentially of two rotating elements, the outer being a solid-shell conical-shaped bowl and the inner comprising a helical-screw conveyor revolving at a speed slightly lower than that of the bowl. Raw feed slurry is delivered through a stationary feed pipe to the conveyor where, urged by centrifugal force, it is transferred to the revolving bowl. A circumferential classifying pool is formed and contained at the larger diameter of the cone shell. The ports for oversize material are located closer to the axis of rotation than the ports for the overflow to effect a beach line and drainage.

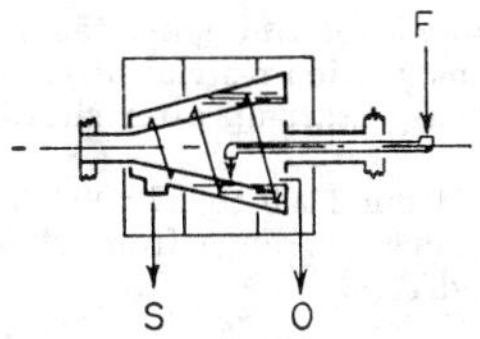

Fig. 21-82. Solid-bowl centrifuge.

Centrifugal force deposits the oversize particles against the bowl wall from which they are conveyed by the helix. The overflow fractions flow around the helix to the liquid-discharge ports. Size of separation is controlled by feed rate and degree of centrifugal force.

Several prime features of this totally enclosed unit are its high capacity per square foot of floor area, small volume of material in process, high degree of separation, and shear action for dispersion of solids. Typical applications are desliming to upgrade cement rock, sizing of abrasives, fractionating for reagent control, and classification of pigments.

Costs and weights including motors run from $11,000 and 3300 lb. to $45,000 and 35,400 lb. f.o.b. factory in plain-steel construction.

Sand Washer. The sand washer has a circular line of buckets rotating in a circular tank having a sloping bottom to form the pool. The buckets dip into the pool and drag out settled sand for drainage and discharge. As a classification device it is limited to 28- to 65-mesh separations owing to the pool area afforded by the design.

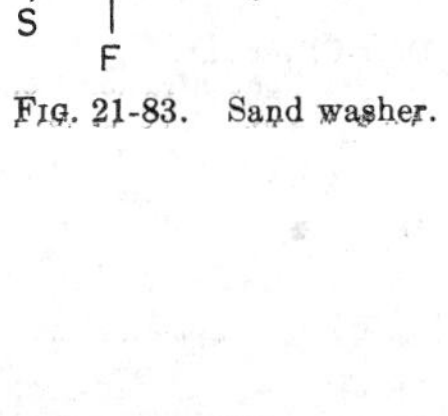

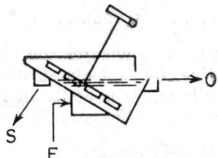

Fig. 21-83. Sand washer.

As the name implies the normal use is for removal of silt and clay from bank-run sand and sand deposits dredged from underwater.

Costs including tanks and drives average about $650 per foot of diameter.

Countercurrent Classifier. The countercurrent classifier is an inclined, slowly rotating cylindrical drum with continuous spiral flights attached to the interior of the shell forming helical troughs. Direction of rotation is such that material in the troughs is impelled toward the higher end. The lower end of the shell is closed except for a central overflow opening. Attached to the upper end is a sand-dewatering elevator which rotates with the shell. Wash water introduced at the upper end drains from the lifting flights above the normal water level and progresses countercurrent to the sand toward the overflow.

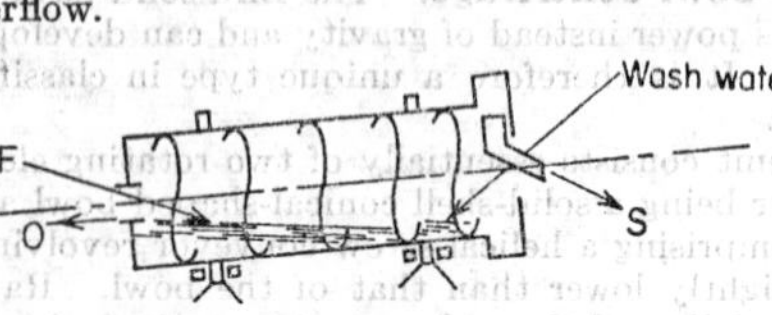

FIG. 21-84. Countercurrent classifier

Usual application is for sand-slime separations, washing and for closed construction restricting escape of heat and chemical fumes, easy start-up after shutdown, and general simplicity.

Weights range from 1100 to 120,000 lb. and approximate costs f.o.b. factory range from $1.50 to $0.50 per pound including drives.

Hydraulic Classifiers

Jet Sizer* and SuperSorter.† The Jet Sizer and SuperSorter are multicompartment and, therefore, multiproduct classifiers operating on the basis of hindered settling. The classification pockets are arranged in series for through flow with parallel pockets to take care of high tonnage fractions in the range of sizes. Each compartment is served with low-pressure hydraulic water.

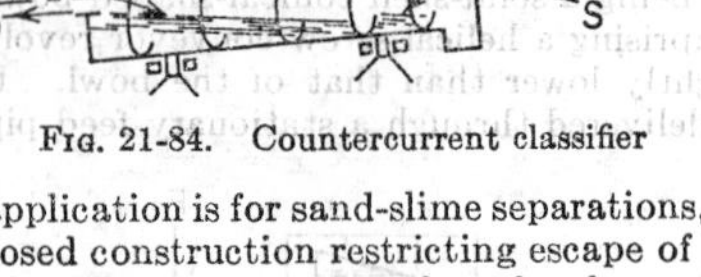

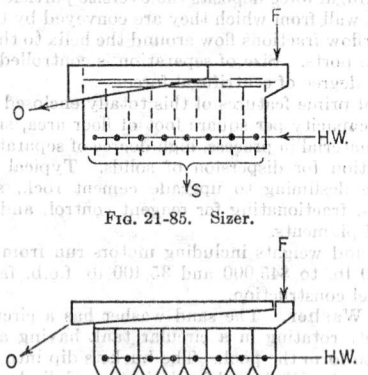

FIG. 21-85. Sizer.

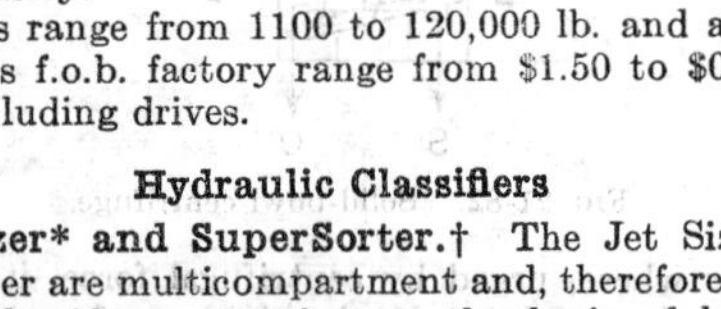

FIG. 21-86. SuperSorter.

Hydraulic classification ensures the highest separating efficiency obtainable by wet-classication means. The amount of hydraulic water is controlled so that in each succeeding compartment the coarsest particles are maintained in hindered-settling condition and the finer fractions pass along for similar treatment. Two compartments will normally capture 90 per cent of a two-screen-size fraction. Spigot discharge is controlled by air-actuated valves in the Jet-Sizer and motor-driven pincer-type valves in the SuperSorter. Sand fractions can be taken from single or combinations of compartments as desired.

Typical applications include careful sizing of silica-glass sand, washing phosphate rock, sizing of abrasives, smokeless powder, sodium aluminate, etc.

Jet sizer costs average approximately $1500 per compartment.

D-O SiphonSizer.* The D-O SiphonSizer is a high-efficiency hydraulic classifier developed originally for washing and sizing of phosphate rock. In ore-dressing work it is normally a two-product unit buy by use of an upper column sealed at the top but open at the bottom three products are possible, being the coarse, intermediate, and fine fractions.

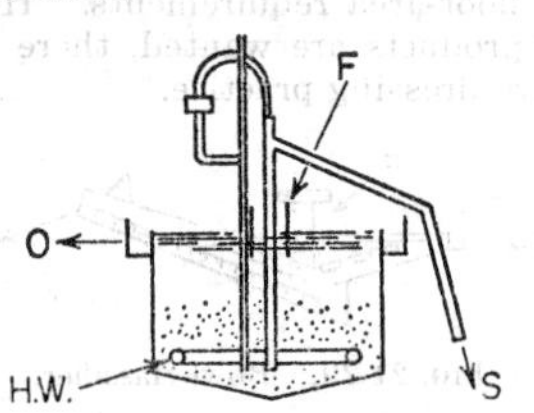

FIG. 21-87. D-O SiphonSizer (two-product type).

Feed to be sized is put into hindered-settling condition by hydraulic water in quantity only sufficient to teeter the smallest particle wanted in the sand product. Thus the sand will contain all solids coarser in size and the finer fractions report to the overflow or pass into the upper column for removal in a three-product unit.

Sands are discharged by siphons extending to the bottom of the hindered-settling zone. Siphon control is obtained by a novel hydrostatically actuated valve which makes or breaks the siphon to flow only when the teeter zone is in correct condition. Discharge by an intermediate fraction from the upper column is by means of additional siphons. Hydraulic-water consumption is considerably lower than required for multipocket sizers.

Costs including steel tanks average approximately $700 per foot of diameter.

Hydroscillator.* The Hydroscillator as a two-product machine combines hydraulic action with a mechanical oscillating assist which greatly reduces consumption of hydraulic water. Rake-sand products are exceptionally clean and well drained as compared with other hydraulic units.

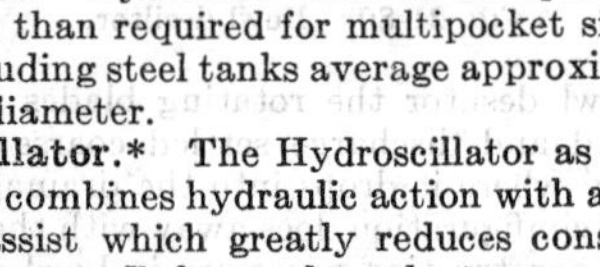

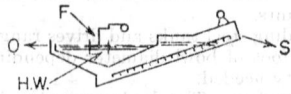

FIG. 21-88. Hydroscillator.

Outside appearance resembles a bowl classifier but within the bowl of a Hydroscillator an oscillating plate of nearly full diameter accepts the feed and jiggles the coarse solids into a shallow zone while they travel toward the periphery. The oscillating plate is perforated to allow upward flow of hydraulic water which passes through the settled solids causing a semihindered-settling condition in the shallow moving bed. Overflow is removed over a circular weir and the sand product passes under a submerged weir and into the rake compartment for drainage.

* Trade-mark of Dorr-Oliver Inc.
† Trade-mark of Deister Concentration Co., Inc.

It has been most widely used to date for closed-circuit grinding of copper and iron ore but recent applications are for open-circuit washing and sizing of phosphate rock.

The Hydroscillator is comparatively expensive, with costs including tanks and drives averaging approximately $2800 per foot of bowl diameter.

DENSE-MEDIA SEPARATION

REFERENCES: Taggart, "Handbook of Mineral Dressing," Wiley, New York, 1945. Mitchell, "Coal Preparation," A.I.M.E., New York, 1950. Lowe, Heavy Density Flow Sheets, *Mining Congr. J.*, June, 1957.

Dense-media separation is employed to beneficiate many mineral products including coal, iron ore, aggregate materials, etc. Preparation of a liquid suspension of finely divided high-gravity solids can produce a stable high-gravity bath in which separation of solids can be effected. Many types of solids have been used to obtain this high-gravity medium, but the magnetic solids ferrosilicon and magnetite are used most extensively. These two solids, either alone or in combination, can obtain a suitable dense medium over a gravity range of 1.25 to 3.4. A special new spheroidal ferrosilicon medium offers potential extension of 3.7 gravity.

Dense media is applicable on any ore in which the valuable constituent has an appreciable gravity difference from the gangue constituents. In coarse-ore heavy-media separation plants the limiting bottom size of dense-medium feed is 10 mesh and the upper size limit is 12 in.

The dense-media process perform one or more of the following functions: (1) rejection of a finished waste product and an enriched concentrate for further concentration, (2) production of a finished concentrate and a rejectable waste, (3) production of a finished concentrate and a low-grade reject for additional treatment, or (4) production of a finished concentrate and a finished reject, plus a middling for additional treatment.

Magnetic-media Characteristics and Costs. The gravity selected will depend on individual ore characteristics. Coal plants operate on magnetite medium which can develop gravities to 2.20. In the gravity range of 2.20 to 2.90, mixtures of magnetite and ferrosilicon media are used. Above 2.85, ferrosilicon medium alone is used. Ground ferrosilicon pig will permit gravities up to 3.4. Above 3.4 the spheroidal ferrosilicon medium has been used successfully.

In general, ferrosilicon and magnetite media will be finer than 65 mesh although several grades of fineness are available. Magnetite is priced at $25 to $40* per ton, f.o.b. grinding plant. Price depends on the grade of medium required. For higher operating gravities a ferrosilicon alloy has good magnetic responsiveness combined with good stability in plant practice. Ferrosilicon prices will vary from $100 to $150* per ton depending on the grade of product required. Spheroidal media command a premium price.

Dense-media Plant Operation. Primary slimes and fines are objectionable because they dilute the medium and increase its viscosity. Such slimes should be removed prior to heavy-media separation.

Figure 21-89 illustrates a modern dense-media flow sheet as applied in coal cleaning. The separatory vessel illustrated is a commonly used scraper type. The feed is preconditioned on screen (1) to remove fines and to wet the product thoroughly. Excess water is drained off on this screen before the feed enters the separatory vessel (2) which is filled with medium at a preselected gravity. Float material rises to the surface and overflows a weir and is transferred to drain screen (3). Sink material is removed and elevated above the medium surface by a flight conveyor (4). The dense medium is continuously returned from the circulating vessel (6) and from the heavy-medium storage sump (8) as required.

Float and sink products are fed to separate rinse screens (3) and (9) or, in some small plants, to partitioned compartments of a common rinse screen. The products are first rinsed with recirculated rinse water and finally with fresh-water sprays. About 1 gal./min. of rinse water/ton/hr. of rinsed product is usually needed for +½-in. products and up to 2 gal./(min.)(ton)(hr.) for +10-mesh material. The separated products are dewatered on their respective screens.

The medium rinsed from the products on screens (3) and (9) has been diluted with water and is too low in gravity to be returned directly to the separatory vessel. The material is collected in sump (10) and pumped by a dilute medium pump (11) to the feed box of a permanent-drum magnetic separator (12). The drum-type magnetic separator with a permanent-magnet assembly is commonly used for medium recovery. The recovered medium is returned through a demagnetizing coil (16) to the media-storage sump. In coal plants, the magnetic separator discharges a magnetic concentrate of sufficiently high gravity to go directly to the storage sump. In other dense-media plants, where higher operating gravities are required, it is sometimes necessary to incorporate a densifier between the magnetic separator and the media circuit to bring the recovered medium to a higher gravity for reuse.

The separator tailing (14) and/or overflow (15) can be used as a rinse on the preconditioning screen (1). To conserve water, settling tanks (17) or cyclones are used to clarify the underflow from screen (1). The clarified water is recycled to the primary rinse troughs (19) by rinse-water pump (18). If the rinse water cannot be clarified sufficiently for effective rinse in a settling tank or cyclone, thickeners may be used.

The type of dense-media vessel shown in Fig. 21-89 has a capacity of 30 tons/hr. of raw coal feed per foot of vessel width when the feed material is +¼ in. in size and with the usual size distribution in the +¼-in. product. Other types of separatory vessels will vary from this capacity figure, and the individual ore characteristics will influence capacity ratings. The separatory vessel illustrated is designed to handle 12-in. maximum size. The usual size is 3 to 6 in.

A plant feed with a large amount of fine sizes, or a plant feed sized initially at ⅛ in., must be fed to the separatory vessel at a reduced rate to obtain high efficiency. Feed rates as low as 20 tons/hr./ft. of vessel width would be used for 3- by ⅛-in. coal feed having 50 per cent of the feed in the ¼- by ⅛-in. size range. The capacity of separatory-vessel accessory equipment is increased when handling finer plant feeds.

As particle gravities of the heavy and light fractions differ from the operating gravity of the vessel, the ease of separation at a statistical efficiency increases and the inefficiency as measured by the weight of the "misplaced particles" decreases.

A typical analysis of sink and float products gives equal weight percentages (0.9 per cent) of misplaced particles at a gravity of 1.342, which is considered to be the operating gravity. The misplaced particles in both products will then be 0.9 per cent of the feed and the efficiency will be 99.1 per cent.

Efficiencies as measured above will average about 99.5 per cent, when handling +½-in. coal under the conditions indicated. The efficiency drops to about 98 per cent for +⅛-in. coal.

The operating cost of the vessel shown in Fig. 21-89 will include one operator, power for the screens, pumps,

* 1960 prices.

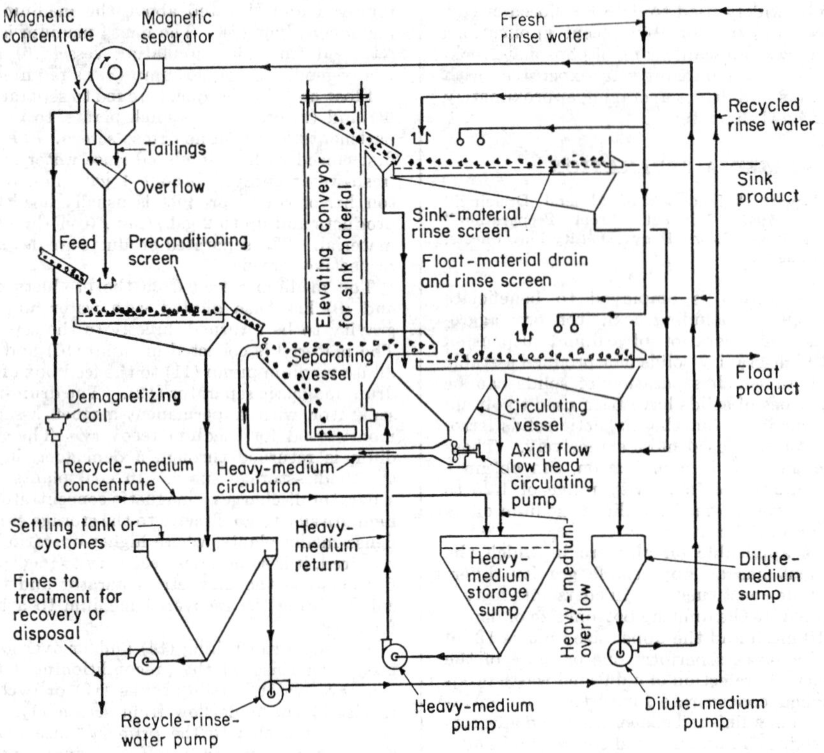

FIG. 21-89. Typical dense-media flow sheet for coal-cleaning plant. (*Courtesy of Fuel Process Co.*)

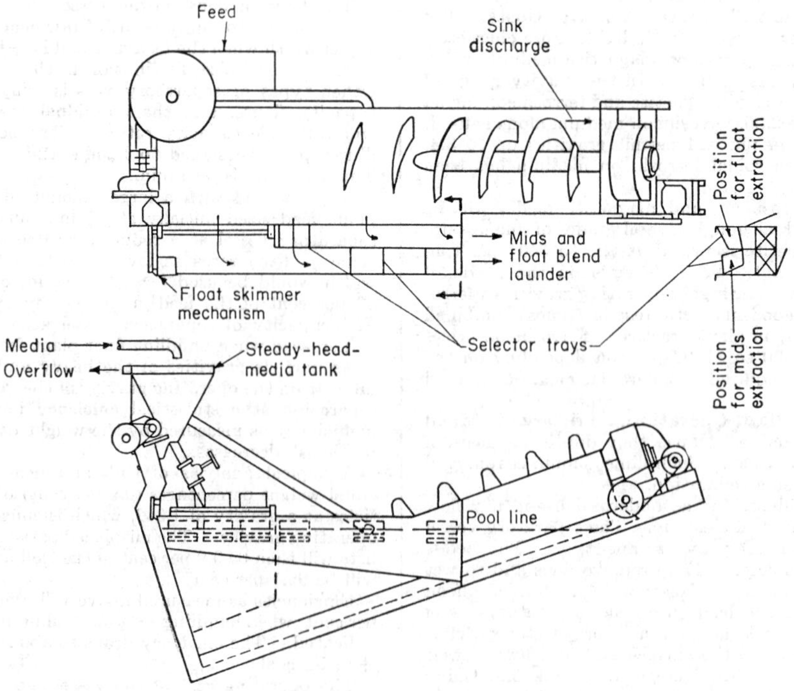

FIG. 21-90. Modified spiral classifier-type dense-media separatory vessel. (*Courtesy of Mine Smelter Supply.*)

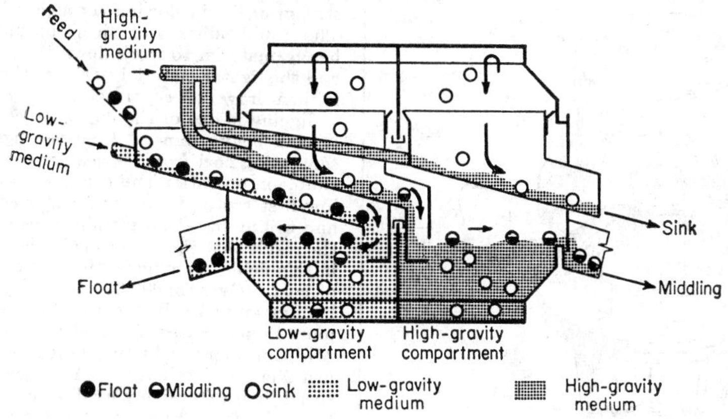

FIG. 21-91. Revolving-drum-type dense-media separatory vessel. *(Courtesy of Western Machinery Co.)*

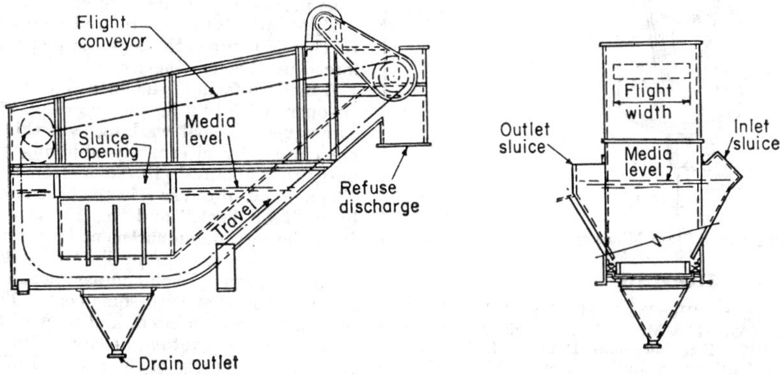

FIG. 21-92. Drag-tank-type dense-media separatory vessel. *(Courtesy of Link-Belt Co.)*

etc., of 0.5 to 1.0 hp./ton-hr. of capacity and magnetic medium losses of 0.3 to 1.0 lb. of magnetite for each ton of coal processed.

The complete installation cost of this vessel in a coal-preparation plant, without preliminary dry-screening facilities and without loading facilities, will range from $800 to $1500* per ton-hour capacity on plants in the 100 to 400 tons/hr. size.

Separatory-vessel Types. In coarse dense-media work three basic types are most commonly applied. They include (1) modified-spiral-classifier-type vessel (Fig. 21-90), (2) revolving-drum-type vessel (Fig. 21-91), and (3) drag-tank-type vessel (Fig. 21-92). The classifier- and drum-type vessels have been used extensively in treating iron ores. The drag-tank type is used in coal treatment. Each of these types has individual advantages and manufacturers should be consulted for recommendations on specific problems for selection of the most suitable vessel. Other types of vessels are available and are equally applicable to separations handled by the equipment illustrated.

Fine-particle Cleaning with Dense-media Cyclones. The material to be treated is pulped with the medium, and this pulp is fed tangentially through the feed inlet (1) of Fig. 21-93 to the short cylindrical section (2). The short cylindrical section (2) carries the central "vortex finder" (3) which prevents short circuiting within the cyclone. Separation is made in the cone-shaped part of the cyclone (4) by the action of centrifugal and centripetal forces. The heavier portion of the material leaves the cyclone at the apex opening (5) and the lighter portion leaves at the overflow top orifice (6).

* 1960 prices.

The sharpness of separation of the mineral from the gangue is dependent on (1) the specific gravity of the media, (2) the cleanliness of the media, (3) the size of the internal openings in the cyclone (feed inlet, apex, and vortex) and (4) the pressure at which the pulp is introduced into the cyclone. Included cone angle on dense-media cyclones has been increased to around 40 deg. in many iron-ore cyclone plants. There is a trend toward the use of smaller multiple cones (10 and 12 in. diameter) rather than fewer and larger cones.

Dense-media cyclones are generally operated 12 to 35 lb./sq. in. Higher pressures increase capacity but accelerate wear. Residence time of the ore particles is very short in the cyclone, and a larger volume of medium is circulated with each ton of ore fed to the cone. Loss of medium is higher in cyclone plants (5 to 10 lb./ton of ore treated) as compared with coarse-ore dense-media plants (0.5 to 1.5 lb./ton). Cyclone-plant manpower requirements are low and efficiency is high. Two 10-in.-diameter cyclones can handle over 100 tons/hr. of $-\frac{1}{4}$-in. feed.

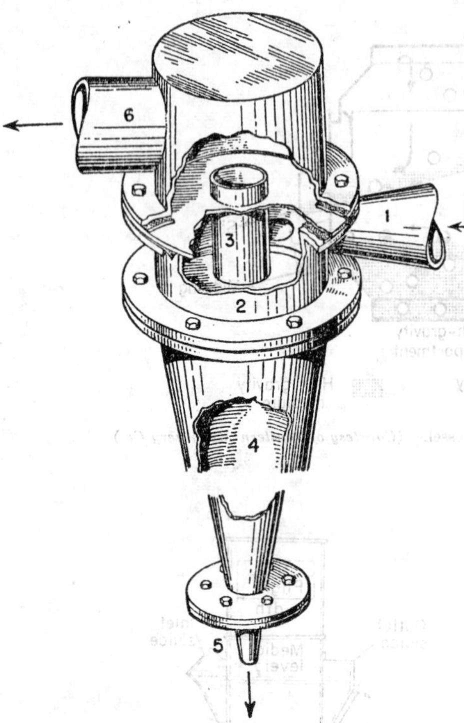

FIG. 21-93. The Dutch State Mines cyclone separator.

JIGGING

REFERENCES: Taggart, "Handbook of Mineral Dressing," Wiley, New York, 1953. The Mechanism of Jigging, *Mining Technol.*, March, 1943. Kirchberg and Hentzschel, A Study of the Behavior of Particles in Jigging, *Trans. Intern. Mineral Dressing Congr.*, 1957. Marincel, Use of Jigs in the Concentration of Iron Ores, 14th Annual Mining Symposium, 1953, University of Minnesota, Minneapolis. Bogert, Fine Coal Cleaning with the Feldspar Jig, *Mining Congr. J.*, July, 1960.

A jig is a mechanical device used for separating materials of different specific gravities by the pulsation of a stream of liquid flowing through a bed of the materials. The liquid pulsates or "jigs" up and down, causing the heavy material to work down to the bottom of the bed, and the lighter material to rise to the top. Each product is then drawn off separately.

Jigging is one of the oldest processes used for concentrating heavy mineral from the lighter gangue and for separating coal from its heavier contaminants. Jigs are simple in operation and can be constructed locally with a low first cost. Power and water consumption are high, and tailing losses on metallic ores are usually high, with the result that the use of jigging is now somewhat limited in this field. Jigging is widely used in the concentration of coal. Over 50,000,000 tons of coal are concentrated by jigs annually in the United States. It is used to a more limited extent in treating the lead-zinc ores of the Mid-Continent field, iron ores, and some heavy nonmetallic ores like barite. A relatively new type of high-speed jig is extensively used in the recovery of fine values from placer gold and tin and tungsten deposits, and for recovering a portion of the metallic values liberated in ball-mill grinding circuits. Jigging has been superseded in many milling operations by the adoption of the sink-float process or by fine grinding followed by flotation.

Types of Jigs. There are two principal types of jigs. In the first type, the sieve is stationary, and water is forced up through the screen.

A modern form of the fixed-sieve-type jig is the Jeffrey air-operated Baum jig shown in Fig. 21-94, which is used extensively in coal washing. In this jig the pulsations are caused by alternately applying and exhausting air pressure at about 2½ lb./sq. in. from the pulsion chamber. The amount of refuse rejected is controlled automatically by a "flash float," and this refuse is ejected positively from the screen compartment by a ratchet-operated star gate. Such jigs customarily are built with a number of compartments. Each compartment or cell rejects waste material together with some coal. These middlings can be crushed, recirculated, and some of the coal recovered.

A further advantage of circulating these middlings is to raise the density of the material in the jig bed, giving the effect of a heavy-medium process and thus sharpening the separation. A mechanical jig that has come into widespread use since 1950 is the Wemco-Remer jig. This jig is used mainly in concentrating materials such as iron and barite ores and in removing impurities such as wood, shale, and lignite from sand and gravel. These jigs are

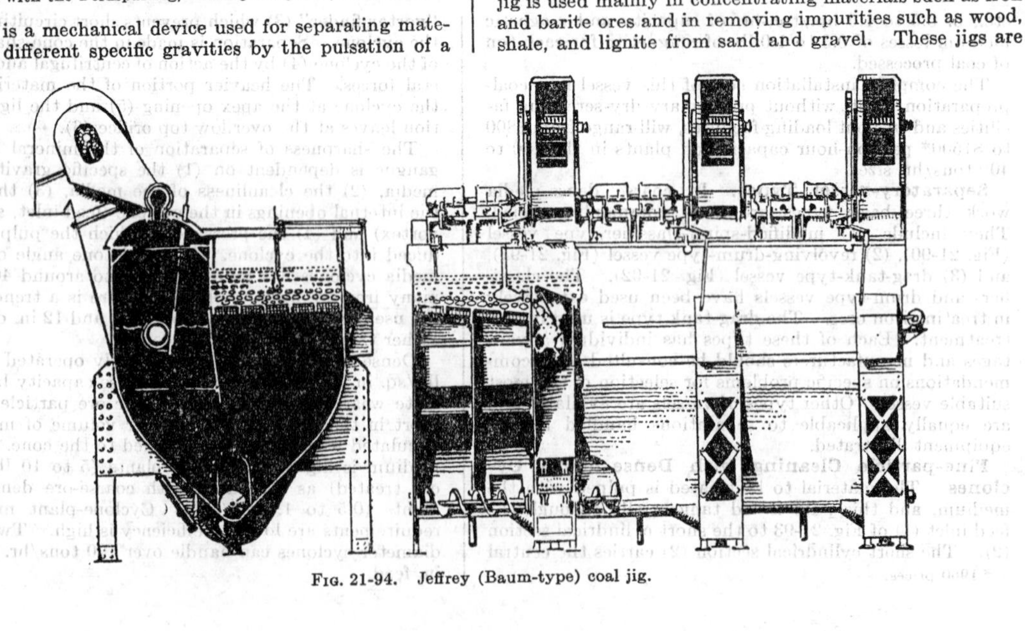

FIG. 21-94. Jeffrey (Baum-type) coal jig.

unusual in that they use a stroke of approximately 3/8 in. at 150 r.p.m. with a secondary motion superimposed having a 1/16-in. stroke with a frequency of 400 strokes/min. Jigs of the type where the sieve moves up and down such as the Hancock jigs are now in little use. A type of high-speed jig in rather common use is the Denver mineral jig. This is usually a two-compartment all-steel diaphragm-actuated jig. This jig is sometimes used in grinding circuits to recover heavy minerals as soon as they are liberated. These minerals are recovered as a hutch product. This jig is used mostly in the treatment of gold, tungsten, and chromite ores.

Jig Feed. In coal washing jigging is practiced on unsized material as coarse as 7 in. In metal-milling practice jigging is now seldom employed on material coarser than 3/4 in. Float-and-sink methods have largely superseded jigs as a way of concentrating metallic ores in the −3- to +1/2-in. range. Shaking tables usually are considered more efficient than jigs for treating ores finer than 2 mm. (10 mesh). Jigs are used in some plants to obtain flow-sheet simplicity since they can handle a wide range of sizes. Jigs, except when extremely heavy minerals are treated, such as gold, galena, cassiterite, or tungsten minerals, recover only a small percentage of the sizes finer than 65 mesh (1/4 mm.).

Capacity. The Jeffrey-Baum will treat 3 tons/hr./sq. ft. of active screen area of −4-in. coal. For fine sizes the capacity decreases. A standard 5- by 16-ft. Wemco-Remer jig will treat 30 to 45 tons/hr. of −3/8-in. iron ore. A Cooley jig, a variation of the Harz jig consisting of six compartments 42 by 48 in., will handle 25 to 30 tons/hr. of −1/2-in. Mid-Continent zinc ore.

Power Requirements. The power required in jigging depends on the screen area, the size of material treated, the percentage of opening in the jig screen, the depth of the bed, the length of stroke, and the number of strokes per minute. The power required for plunger-type jigs treating 1/2-in. material is about 0.1 hp./sq. ft. jig screen surface.

Water Consumption. Jigs require much water. In most installations, the Harz-type jig uses 1500 to 2500 gal. water/ton material treated. Water requirements for treating −3/8-in. iron ore in a Wemco-Remer rougher-cleaner jig circuit are approximately 1200 gal. water/ton of material processed.

Cost. The direct operating cost of jigging depends on the nature and size of material to be treated, the number of jigging stages required, and the size of the plant. In large-tonnage plants treating coal or iron ore, this unit cost will vary from 4 to 15 cents per ton of feed.

TABLING

References: Taggart, "Handbook of Mineral Dressing," Wiley, New York, 1953. Kirchberg and Berger, *Trans. Intern. Mineral Processing Congr.*, 1960, London. Taggart and Lechmere-Oertel, Elements of Operation of the Pneumatic Table, *Am. Inst. Mech. Engrs. Tech. Publ.* 196, 1929. Dickson, Trepp, and Nichols, Virginia Plant Concentrates Sulphide Ore with Air Tables, *Eng. Mining J.*, **160** (4), (April, 1959). Anon., Linka Mill Added to Nevada WO_3 Output, *Mining World*, June, 1956. McLeod, Tungsten Milling and Current Metallurgy at Canadian Exploration Limited, *Can. Mining Met. Bull.*, March, 1957. Anon., Automation Keys Two Stage Precision Washing at Moss No. 3, *Coal Age*, April, 1959. Anon., Upgrading Fragile Coal to Premium Metallurgical Product, *Coal Age*, September, 1959. Stahl, Milling Practice of the St. Joseph Lead Co., *Mining Technol.*, May, 1943. Mitchell, The Recovery of Pyrite from Coal Mine Refuse, *Mining Technol.*, July, 1944. Burdick, Beneficiation of Scheelite Ores by Gravity Concentration, *Mining Technol.*, November, 1942. Ralston, Flotation and Agglomerate Concentration of Non-metallic Minerals, *U.S. Bur. Mines Rept. Invest.* 3397, p. 42, May, 1938. Diener, Clemmer, and Cooke, Beneficiating Cement Raw Materials by Agglomeration and Tabling, *U.S. Bur. Mines Rept. Invest.* 3247, 1935. Coghill, DeVaney, Clemmer, and Cooke, Concentration of Potash Ores of Carlsbad, N.M., by Ore Dressing Methods, *U.S. Bur. Mines Rept. Invest.* 3271, 1935. Selective Oiling and Table Concentration of Phosphatic Sands in the Land Pebble District of Florida, *U.S. Bur. Mines Rept. Invest.* 3195, 1932. O'Meara, Norman, and Hammond, Froth Flotation and Agglomerate Tabling of Feldspars, *Bull. Am. Ceram. Soc.*, **18**, 286 (1939). Normal and O'Meara, Froth Flotation and Agglomerate Tabling of Mica, *U.S. Bur. Mines Rept. Invest.* 3558, 1941.

Wet Tables. Tabling is a concentration process whereby a separation between two or more minerals is effected by flowing a pulp across a riffled plane surface inclined slightly from the horizontal, differentially shaken in the direction of the long axis and washed with an even flow of water at right angles to the direction of motion. A separation between two or more minerals depends mainly on the difference in specific gravity between the minerals and to a lesser degree on the shape and size of the particles. The process is best suited for the concentration of ore and coal where there is a considerable difference between the effective specific gravity (sp. gr. mineral minus sp. gr. water) of the valuable and the waste material. Tables treat metallic ores effectively in the size range from 6 to 150 mesh but can be used to treat lighter materials such as coal of a considerably larger size.

Shaking tables were developed first about 1896 by Wilfley for concentrating metallic ores, and the peak of their development coincided with the installation of the first oil flotation plants about 1914. Since that time the field of these two more or less competitive processes has been fairly well defined. Tabling is best suited for the treatment of material containing only one valuable mineral that is free at a granular size and where a considerable difference exists between the effective specific gravities of the mineral constituent. Flotation has been found to be best in treating complex ores containing several valuable minerals, those requiring fine grinding for liberation, and those having small gravity differentials.

The heaviest particles in a table feed are the least affected by the current of water washing down over the tables, and they collect in the riffles along which they move to the end of the table. The lighter materials ride above the heavy minerals and tend to be washed over the riffles to the low side of the table. Suitable launders are placed at the end of the low side of the table to catch the various products as they are discharged. These launders are provided with movable dividing devices to separate the concentrates from the middlings and the middlings from the tailings. Since these devices are quickly movable, a rapid adjustment may be made to suit variations in the rate and grade of material treated. It seldom is possible in tabling to make a sharp separation of the feed into a high-grade concentrate and a low-grade tailing with one pass. Some material of intermediate grade is almost invariably present as a band between these products, and it is customary to return such middlings either with or without additional grinding to the head of the circuit for retreatment. The amount of middling recirculated may amount to 25 per cent of weight of the feed to the table.

Tables usually are surfaced either with heavy battleship linoleum or with rubber. The riffles may be a clear grade of sugar pine or may be rubber strips. Such riffles are usually 3/8 in. wide and taper from the feed end of the table to the discharge end. If the table is used for concentrating coarse material (−8 mesh), the riffles may be as high as 1 in. at the feed end. For fine material the riffles are not over 1/4 in. at the feed end of the table. Almost every mill operator employs a different style of riffling a table, which he believes best for his particular separation. The usual method of riffling is shown in Fig. 21-95.

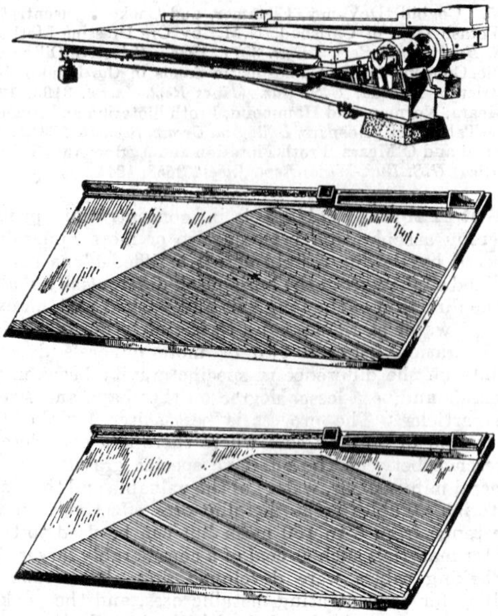

FIG. 21-95. Deister-Overstrom diagonal deck table. Center, diagonal deck with pool riffle system for sand. Bottom, diagonal deck with pool riffle system for fine sand and slime.

If the object of tabling is to produce as clean a concentrate as possible, a diagonal area in the upper discharge side corner is left unriffled. This area is known as the cleaning deck. If the table is to be used in making only a rough concentrate and a finished tailing, the riffling is extended by many operators. Tables are provided with adjustable tilting devices so that the transverse slope may be varied. The head motion is such that the deck reverses its direction with a maximum velocity at one end and a minimum velocity at the other end of the stroke. It is the quickness of the return that causes the material to migrate toward the discharge end. The length of stroke may be adjusted. A longer stroke is required for coarse material than for fine material. This will vary from 1¼ in. for coarse material to ½ in. for fines. Modern tables operate at considerably higher speed than formerly, the range being from 270 for coarse to 350 strokes/min. for fines.

Present table practice is to use multiple decks. Multiple-deck tables consisting of from two to three decks effect space saving proportionate to the number of decks employed. They also have the advantage in that no heavy floor supports need be supplied since such tables are supported by suspended mountings. Multiple-deck installations reduce capital expenditures since a single motor and less piping and fewer launders are required than for a comparable number of single-deck installations.

General information for standard-size tables operating on various-sized feeds is shown in Table 21-19. The No. 6 table of the Deister Concentrator Co. (Fort Wayne, Ind.) has a diagonal deck approximately 6 ft. wide and 14 ft. long. The No. 7 table used primarily for coal work is approximately 8 ft. wide and 16 ft. long. It should be remembered in reading this table that the figures given apply to single-deck installations. In modern practice, each table, whether it be a single-deck or multiple-deck installation, is driven by a single motor which is connected to the actuating mechanism by a V-belt drive. The installed horsepower for the large No. 7 deck is 1.5 hp. A comparable figure for the smaller No. 6 deck is 1 hp. per deck. The actual power consumed in operation is somewhat less.

An essential factor for good table operation is that the rate of feed must be uniform, both as to tonnage and as to physical properties. No one factor will cause more trouble to the table operator than to have a surging feed. The feed to tables may be unsized or it may be either screened or hydraulically classified. For treating fine coals a common procedure is to use hydrocyclones both to deslime the material and to give a cyclone underflow of about 40 per cent solids which constitutes the table feed.

Tabling is a relatively cheap operation, and in large installations the direct operating cost will be in the order of from 2 to 6¢ per ton of feed. If the feed is uniform one operator can take care of many tables. In a modern coal plant with multiple-deck tables, a single operator can handle the tabling of as much as 1200 tons/hr. In an ore-tabling plant such as a lead or zinc operation, a table operator can watch as many as 50 tables with a total capacity in the order of 200 tons/hr. Labor is the principal item of cost. Power requirements and maintenance are both low. The installed cost of a table including supports and launders is from $6000 to $8000 per deck. In the past, one of the disadvantages of table installation is the relatively large floor space required for the tonnage treated. This disadvantage has now largely been overcome by the use of multiple-deck tables. Their main advantage is that, in the size range for which they are suited, it is a cheap and effective method of concentrating simple ores and coal.

Dry Tables. Tabling may be done dry as well as wet and for such use tables of special design are used. The Sutton, Steele and Steele table is an example of this type of equipment. It has a shaking motion somewhat similar to that of a wet table, except that the direction of motion is inclined upward from the horizontal, and instead of water acting as the medium of distribution, a blast of air is driven through a perforated deck. The table has application in cases where it is desirable to treat material dry, either because of water shortage or because it is undesirable to wet the materials. The table supplements other dry methods of concentration, such as electrostatic and electromagnetic methods. An advantage of this table is the ability to handle material coarser than that treated on most wet tables. Ores as coarse as ¼ in. and coal as coarse as 3 in. can be treated.

Close sizing is necessary to give good results, and until recently this has militated against adoption of the table for fine sizes, owing to the difficulties of screening most ores dry below about 40 mesh. The development of improved dry methods for sizing fine material by the use of

Table 21-19. Generalized Operating Data Superduty Diagonal-deck Concentrating Table

Table No.	Feed	Feed size	Feed capacity, tons/hr.	Speed, r.p.m.	Stroke, in.	Water with feed, gal./min.	Dressing water, gal./min.	Size of deck
6	Ore	¼ in.–35 mesh	2.0 –10.0	275	1.25	30–150	10–100	6′5″ × 14′1″
6	Ore	35–150 mesh	1.0 – 2.5	285	0.75	16– 40	5– 20	6′5″ × 14′1″
6	Ore	Minus 150 mesh	0.25– 1.0	300	.50	3– 12	3– 10	6′5″ × 14′1″
7	Coal	1½ in.	15.0–25.0	270	1.25	125–210	55– 90	8′¼″ × 16′9¼″
7	Coal	¾ in.	10.0–15.0	280	1.00	60– 85	20– 35	8′¼″ × 16′9¼″
7	Coal	½ in.	7.5–12.0	285	1.00	42– 65	18– 31	8′¼″ × 16′9¼″
7	Coal	⅛ in.	5.0– 7.5	290	0.75	28– 42	12– 18	8′¼″ × 16′9¼″
7	Coal	1⁄16 in.	3.0– 5.0	290	.75	15– 28	9– 12	8′¼″ × 16′9¼″

various cyclonelike devices has tended to increase the use of this apparatus on finer sizes.

Dry tables are used commercially in the separation of many types of minerals. Their greatest use is in the treatment of coal but ilmenite, various tungsten ores, and even copper ores are so treated. Another important use is the cleaning of industrial materials such as seeds, cork, bagasse, fiber, nuts, wood chips, and coffee. One interesting use is in the sorting of silicon carbide by grain shapes. Flat and splintery grains are removed from others of more nearly equal dimensions.

Agglomeration Tabling. Agglomeration tabling is a process whereby selective flocculation or agglomeration of grains of one mineral in an aggregate is caused by the addition of an agglomerating agent in a conditioning cell or in the ball-mill circuit, the slurry containing the agglomerated grains then being fed across gravity tables. The larger size, the oil-filmed surface, and the feathery texture of the floccules cause them to be washed over the side of the table by the current of cross water while the unflocculated discrete particles remain on the table and are carried off the end in the position followed normally by the concentrate in the usual table feed. An oiled particle will tend to ride on the surface of the water and thus is more readily carried across the side of the table than an unoiled particle. Agglomeration tabling has had more application in the concentration of phosphate minerals than in any other field, although successful tests have been run on limestone, potash, mica, and other ores.

The process is limited to granular material in the size range from 10 to 100 mesh. In this respect it differs from flotation which functions best on material 48 mesh and finer. For best results the material should be well deslimed and should be conditioned with the agglomerating reagents at a high percentage of solids, 65 per cent or greater. A collector is used that will selectively film the mineral to be agglomerated. In phosphate and limestone practice, this collector is usually a cheap fatty acid such as talloel. In potash separation long-chain amines are used to film sylvite (KCl).

A bulk oil is always used in addition to the collector to give body to the film and to assist in forming agglomerules. In Florida practice, it is customary to use 0.3 to 0.5 lb./ton talloel and 4 to 5 lb./ton of a 22°Bé. fuel oil. Operating data for the agglomerate tabling of phosphate and potash ore are shown in Table 21-20.

Table 21-20. Operating Data Agglomerate Tabling of Phosphate and Potash Ore

Type of table	Feed size	Feed capacity, tons/hr.	Table speed, r.p.m.	Table stroke, in.	Water with feed, gal./min.	Dressing water, gal./min.	Size of deck
No. 6 super-duty diagonal deck	10–48 mesh	2.5–3.5	295	1.0	20–40	8–15	6′5″ × 14′1″

Agglomerate tabling works best on simple ores consisting of two free minerals. It has several advantages over the usual tabling method in that it can be used to separate two minerals the difference in specific gravity of which is so small that an effective separation cannot be made by gravity separation alone. Tables treating an agglomerated feed have a considerably larger capacity than tables using untreated feeds, since the capacity of a table treating an agglomerated feed is limited only by the carrying capacity of the riffles. Disadvantages of the method that must be considered are the cost of the reagents used and the fact that, if the mineral fraction filmed is the one to be sold, the oily film may be objectionable and must be burned off.

MAGNETIC SEPARATION

References: Dean and Davis, Magnetic Separation of Ores, *U.S. Bur. Mines Bull.* 425, 1941. Taggart, "Handbook of Mineral Dressing," Wiley, New York, 1953. DeVaney, New Developments in the Magnetic Concentration of Iron Ores, *Proc. Intern. Mineral Processing Congr.*, Institution of Mining & Metallurgy, London, Paper 31, Group VI, April, 1960. Forcia, Hendrickson, and Palasvirta, Magnetic Separation in Beneficiation of Mesabi Range Magnetic Taconite, *Mining Eng.*, December, 1958.

Any solid placed in a magnetic field is affected by it in some way. Solids may be classified into two broad categories: (1) diamagnetic solids which are repelled and (2) paramagnetic solids which are attracted by a magnetic field. For practical consideration the more common paramagnetic solids are classified into three groups, namely, (1) strongly magnetic (ferromagnetic), (2) weakly magnetic, and (3) non-magnetic. The art of separating one solid from another by means of a magnetic field is called magnetic separation. The principal uses of magnetic separators can be discussed in two broad categories: (1) tramp-iron removal and (2) concentration and purification.

Tramp-iron Magnetic Separators. Tramp-iron magnetic separators are used to protect handling and processing equipment such as crushers and pulverizers and conveyor systems. They are usually applied on dry material or on material which contains only surface moisture. Iron coarser than $\frac{1}{8}$ in. is usually defined as tramp iron. Following are the most commonly applied separators:

Magnetic-head Pulleys. Magnetic pulleys are used to remove tramp iron from products handled on belt conveyors. Both electromagnetic pulleys and the new radial-pole permanent-magnetic-head pulleys are used in conveyor systems requiring pulley diameters up to 60 in. and widths up to 60 in. Either type can be used at belt speeds to 600 ft./min. Table 21-21 shows typical information used in selecting an electromagnetic pulley. Enter the table with the belt width of the conveyor. Follow the belt-width column to the capacity equal or

Table 21-21. Capacities of Electromagnetic Pulleys in Cubic Feet per Hour for Tramp-iron Removal on Normal Conveyor Operation*

Pulley diam., in.	Width of belt, in.												Normal belt speed, ft./min.
	12	14	16	18	20	24	30	36	42	48	54	60	
12	790	1,080	1,460	1,880	2,330	3,500	....	....	....	....	....	....	175
15	900	1,240	1,670	2,150	2,660	4,000	6,300	....	....	....	....	....	200
18	1,010	1,390	1,880	2,420	3,000	4,500	7,100	10,500	....	....	....	....	225
20	....	1,550	2,090	2,690	3,330	5,000	7,900	11,700	16,600	....	....	....	250
24	....	....	2,380	3,060	3,800	5,700	9,000	13,300	19,000	26,200	....	....	285
30	....	....	....	3,540	4,400	6,600	10,400	15,400	22,000	30,400	....	....	330
36	....	....	....	....	4,860	7,300	11,500	17,000	24,300	33,600	43,300	....	365
42	....	....	....	....	....	8,000	12,600	18,700	26,700	36,800	47,500	59,000	400
48	....	....	....	....	....	8,700	13,600	20,300	29,000	40,000	51,600	64,200	435
54	....	....	....	....	....	....	....	22,200	31,700	43,700	56,400	70,100	475
60	....	....	....	....	....	....	....	....	33,300	46,000	59,300	73,800	500

* Courtesy of Indiana General Corporation Magnetic Equipment Division.

Table 21-22. Correction Factors for Inclined Conveyors*

Degrees incline	5	6	7	8	9	10	11	12	13	14	15	16	17	18	19	20
Correction factor	0.955	0.946	0.937	0.928	0.919	0.910	0.901	0.892	0.883	0.874	0.865	0.856	0.847	0.838	0.829	0.820

* Courtesy of Indiana General Corporation Magnetic Equipment Division.

next larger to that being handled. Follow the appropriate horizontal column to the left side of the table to determine the diameter of magnetic pulley required. Check the right-hand column in this same horizontal column to determine normal recommended belt speed. If a higher speed is required, a larger-diameter pulley must be selected. In selecting magnetic pulleys for inclined-conveyor installation a correction factor must be applied to belt speed and capacity in cubic feet as indicated in Table 21-22.

Suspended Magnets. Suspended tramp-iron magnets are installed flat over a conveyor or at an angle over the conveyor head pulley. Height of suspension is determined by particle size and conveyor loading. Nominal burden is determined by the formula $D_c = 25.2C/WV$ where D_c = center burden depth, in., on 20-deg. troughed conveyor; C = capacity, cu. ft./min.; W = width of belt, ft.; and V = belt speed, ft./min. The size of the tramp iron will influence magnet selection. The depth D_c plus a 2- to 4-in. clearance for collected magnetics determines suspension height. Select installation factors from Table 21-23 for tramp size, belt speed, and burden depth to obtain application rating. Enter selection chart (Fig. 21-96) with application rating and suspension height to select the magnet for application. For continuous removal of tramp iron, cross-belt or para-belt models are used.

Table 21-23. Suspended-magnet Installation Factors*

Installation factors	Suspension position: Parallel over belt	Suspension position: Tilted over pulley
Min. size tramp iron, in.		
Less than ½	100	80
½–1	60	50
1–2	30	20
2–4	10	5
Over 4	0	0
Belt speed, f.p.m.:		
0–350	20	0
350–500	40	0
500–650	60	10
Over 650	80	20
Avg. burden depth, in.		
0–3	20	0
3–6	40	10
6–9	60	30
9–12	80	60
Over 12	100	80

* Courtesy of Indiana General Corporation Magnetic Equipment Division.

Magnetic Drums. Drum separators are used where space is insufficient for other tramp-iron magnets or where chutes and ducts rather than conveyors are used to handle the flow of material. The magnetic-field pattern developed by this drum is much like a radial magnetic-pulley pattern. An outer rotating cylinder carries the feed material through the magnetic field developed by the stationary-magnet assembly.

Plate Magnets. Tramp iron is removed from bulk solids handled in chutes by trapping it against a magnetized plate as material flows down the chute. This type of magnet must be periodically cleaned. A chute angle of 45 deg. is recommended, and the plate magnet should be installed close to the feed point to eliminate velocity influences.

Grate Magnets. A grate magnet consists of a series of magnetized bars and is used to remove fine iron as well as tramp iron. The grate is an accumulating-type magnet and the collected magnetics must be periodically removed. Feed is usually vertical through the grate. Normally the grates are 1 in. in diameter and are spaced on 2-in. centers.

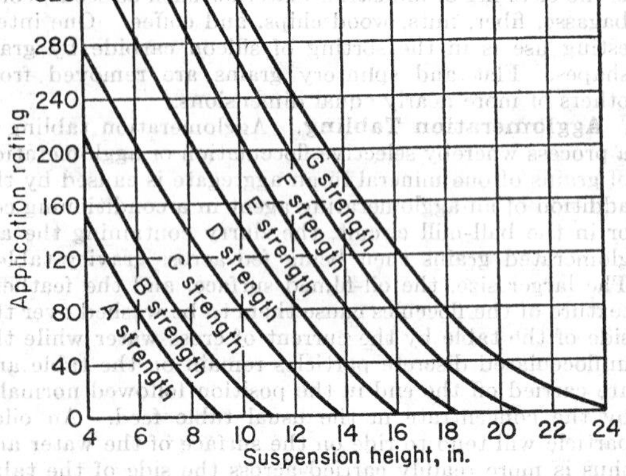

FIG. 21-96. Rectangular suspended-magnet selection chart. Operating principle of magnetic pulley. (*Courtesy of Indiana General Corporation, Magnetic Equipment Division.*)

Metal Detectors. In those cases where the tramp metal is not magnetically responsive, an electronic detector is used to indicate its presence. Magnetic detectors are available and are sometimes installed where tramp-iron-removal devices cannot be installed.

Magnetic Separators as Concentrators and Purifiers. Special magnetic separators have been designed for concentration and purification of solids. Generally, "concentration" involves magnetic separation of a large amount of magnetic-feed product, whereas "purification" involves the removal of small amounts of magnetic particles from a large amount of non-magnetic feed material. For practical application and selection, magnetic concentrators and purifiers are divided into (1) wet types and (2) dry types.

Wet Magnetic Separators. Two of the most frequently applied wet magnetic separators are (1) permanent and electromagnetic drum separators and (2) permanent and electromagnetic filters. Wet-drum separators are applied as medium recovery units in dense-media plants and in the concentration of magnetic iron ores. Magnetic filters are commonly applied to remove fine magnetic particles from liquids or liquid suspensions. Wet magnetic drums are designed for continuous magnetic discharge. Magnetic filters accumulate magnetics, and the filter element must be periodically removed and cleaned.

Wet-magnetic-drum separators. Magnetic-drum separators are applied to concentrate finely divided, strongly magnetic materials. Three basic types of drum concentrators are available: (1) concurrent drums for cobbing operations on −¼-in. ore, (2) counterrotation drums for roughing operations on −10-mesh ore, and (3) countercurrent drums for finishing operations on −65-mesh ore. Operation consists of introducing the feed into a feed trough which in turn introduces the pulp to the magnetic field. Magnetics in the feed are attracted to the rotating drum shell where they are cleaned by the agitating action created by the alternating polarity of the magnet as-

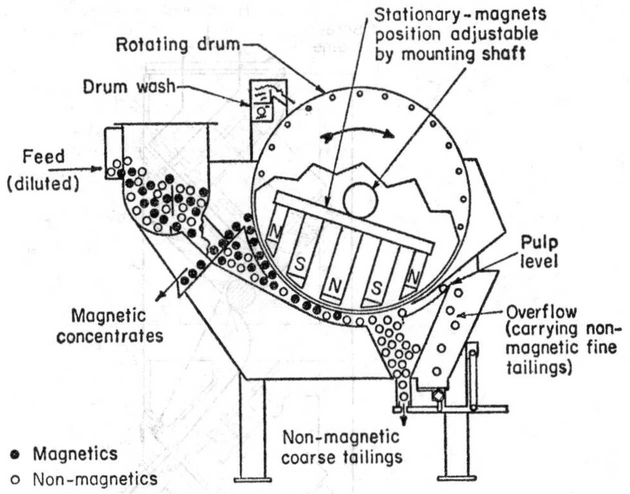

FIG. 21-97. Counterrotation wet-drum separator. *(Courtesy of Jeffrey Manufacturing Co.)*

sembly. Basic principle of operation of the concurrent wet separator is shown in Fig. 21-97 and the counterrotation wet separator in Fig. 21-98.

Wet-magnetic-drum specifications. Wet magnetic drums are constructed in both permanent and electromagnetic types. Permanent drums are finding increasing acceptance because of their greater dependability and lower operating and maintenance costs. The electromagnetic wet drum is applied where extremely high intensity magnetic fields are required and where a wide range of magnet control is necessary. Adjustable permanent-magnet wet drums with 30 per cent control are now available. Most wet drums are 30 or 36 in. in diameter with magnet widths to 6 ft. Multiple-drum separators are selected on the basis of the individual separation under consideration. Cobbing drums are usually double drums. Finishing drums are commonly double- or triple-drum separators. Satisfactory feed volume for cobbing separators is 75 to 125 gal./min./ft. of magnet width—for roughers, 75 to 100 gal./min./ft.—for finishers, 40 to 60 gal./min./ft.

Wet-drum-separator operating costs. Wet-magnetic-drum separators (particularly the permanent type) are low in operating cost. Maintenance costs will vary widely but a figure of 3 to 5 per cent of initial cost per year is used in estimating maintenance costs. Initial cost of permanent drums will usually be slightly higher than electromagnetic drums, even with their required accessory equipment (d.c. power supply and control panels). A 30-in.-diameter single-drum wet magnetic separator has a cost of about $1500* per foot of magnet width. A 36-in.-diameter single-drum wet magnetic separator has a cost of $2200* per foot of magnet width. Multiple-drum costs increase in almost direct proportion to the number of drums required.

Dry Magnetic Concentrators and Purifiers. Dry magnetic separators can be classified on the basis of the magnetic-field intensity they develop. They include (1) high-intensity separators, (2) moderate-intensity separators, (3) low-intensity separators, and (4) high-speed high-intensity drum separators. The individual applications

* 1960 prices.

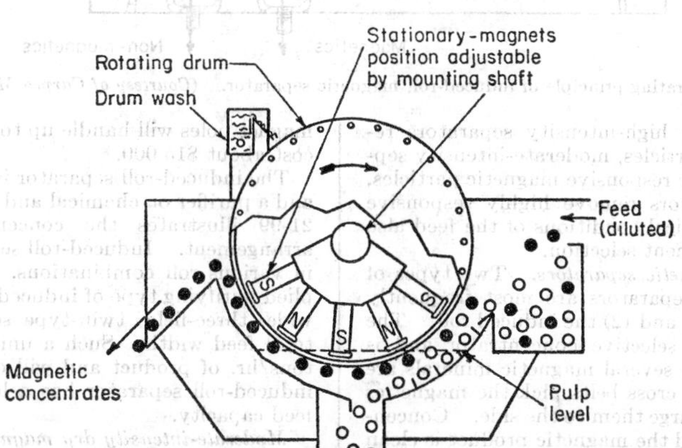

FIG. 21-98. Concurrent wet-drum separator. *(Courtesy of Jeffrey Manufacturing Co.)*

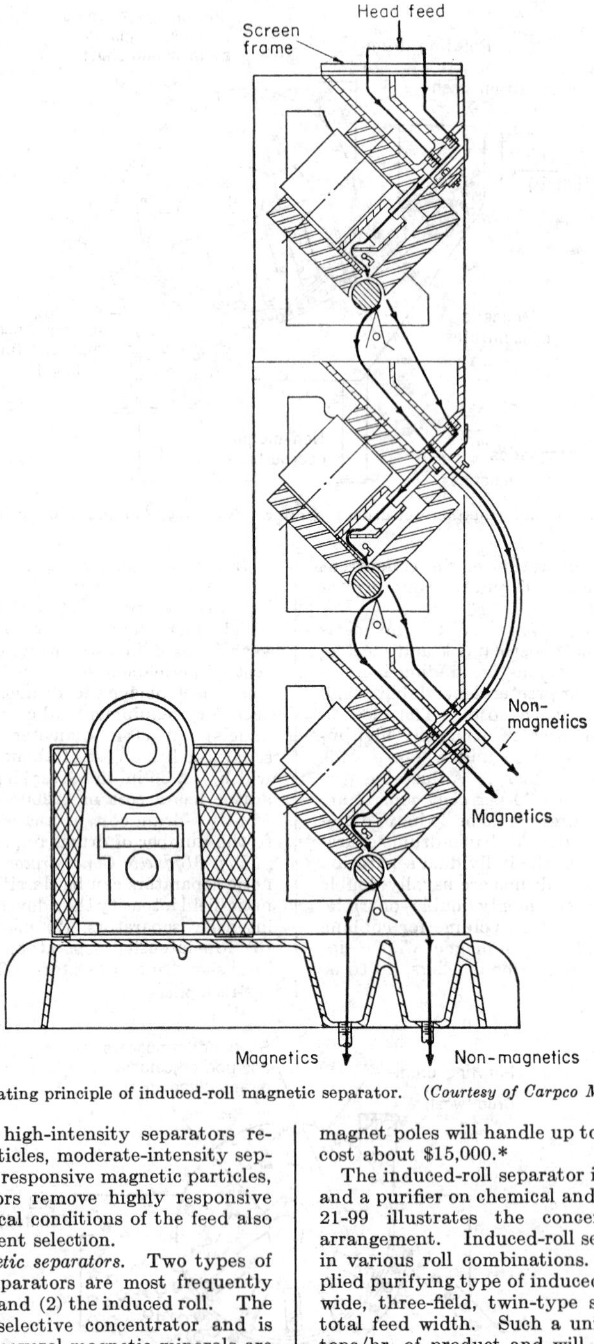

FIG. 21-99. Operating principle of induced-roll magnetic separator. (*Courtesy of Carpco Manufacturing Co.*)

are diverse but generally high-intensity separators remove weakly magnetic particles, moderate-intensity separators remove moderately responsive magnetic particles, and low-intensity separators remove highly responsive magnetic particles. Physical conditions of the feed also influence magnetic-equipment selection.

High-intensity dry magnetic separators. Two types of high-intensity magnetic separators are most frequently applied: (1) the cross-belt and (2) the induced roll. The cross-belt separator is a selective concentrator and is sometimes preferred when several magnetic minerals are present in the feed. The cross belts pick the magnetics off the feed belt and discharge them to the side. Concentration is by direct lift and the magnetic product is clean and free of entrapped non-magnetic material. The cross belt has been used to concentrate wolframite, monazite, and other high-value mineral products. Cross-belt capacity is low and initial cost is high relative to feed capacity. An 18-in.-wide cross-belt separator with two magnet poles will handle up to 2 tons/hr. of feed and will cost about $15,000.*

The induced-roll separator is applied as a concentrator and a purifier on chemical and mineral products. Figure 21-99 illustrates the concentrating-type induced-roll arrangement. Induced-roll separators are manufactured in various roll combinations. The most frequently applied purifying type of induced-roll separator is the 30-in. wide, three-field, twin-type separator having 60 in. of total feed width. Such a unit will clean from 3 to 7½ tons/hr. of product and will cost about $15,000.* The induced-roll separator has a low initial cost per unit of feed capacity.

Moderate-intensity dry magnetic separators. The moderate-intensity magnetic separators include (1) the alternating-polarity drum separator and (2) the Uni-gap drum separator. The alternating-polarity drum was designed to treat a feed having a large amount of magnetics while

* 1960 prices.

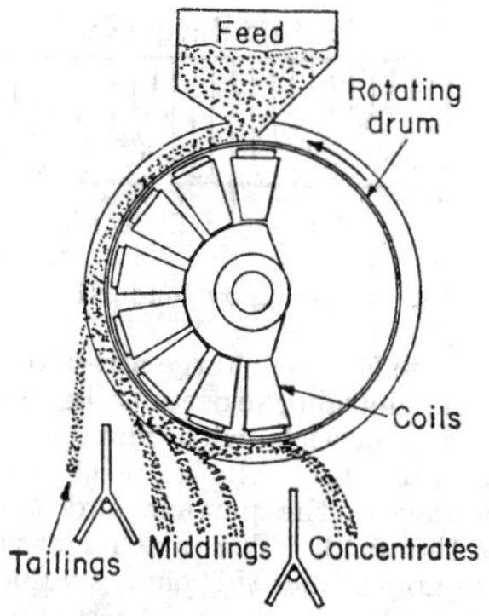

FIG. 21-100. Operating principle of alternating-polarity ball-Norton separator. (*Courtesy of Indiana General Corporation, Magnetic Equipment Division.*)

obtaining a high-grade concentrate (see Fig. 21-100). This separator has been used to concentrate magnetite ores in the 1½-in. by 100-mesh size range. The magnetic field of this drum will hold a large load of magnetics while providing sufficient agitation of the magnetics during treatment to shake out impurities entrapped in the initial magnetic pick-up. Capacity of this alternating-polarity separator will vary inversely with the size of the feed. On coarser ores, capacities of 30 tons/hr./ft. of magnet width have been obtained. A 30-in.-diameter by 60-in.-wide magnetic drum will cost about $10,000.*

The Uni-gap drum is designed to produce a moderately high intensity magnetic gap across the entire drum width at a single position on the drum circumference. This type of magnet is useful in removing finely divided magnetic particles and is applied on material finer than ¼ in. at feed rates of 3 tons/hr./ft. of magnet width or less.

Low-intensity dry magnetic separators. Low-intensity magnetic separators are applied in concentration and purification where the magnetic particles to be removed are large in size and the magnetic responsiveness of the magnetics is high. Magnetic pulleys and low-intensity tramp-iron drum separators are used in these applications although the magnetics to be removed may be lower in responsiveness than tramp iron. Modified versions of these tramp-iron separators are usually applied. Feed rates for these low-intensity separators are lower than those used in a tramp-iron application.

High-speed dry magnetic separators. The high-speed alternating-polarity magnetic-drum separator has been introduced to American industry in recent years. It is designed to treat very finely divided material—100 mesh and down—and to produce a high-grade magnetic-concentrate product free of entrapped non-magnetics. It has been used in concentrating dry magnetite ores, fly ash, etc. Several variations of construction are available but Fig. 21-101 shows the general principle of operation.

Types of Material Used in Magnet Manufacture. Magnetic separators are conventionally classified as (1) electro or (2) permanent. Electromagnets use insulated copper-wire windings around a soft-iron core energized with d.c. Permanent-magnet types do not require external energization. They employ special-alloy cores which after initial charging continue to produce a magnetic field permanently. There are a wide variety of permanent magnet alloys but only the highest-energy grade, Alnico V, had been used until about 1958. A newer permanent-magnet material, oriented barium ferrite, was introduced in separators at this time. This new ceramic permanent magnet produces equivalent energy to Alnico V on an equivalent-weight basis. Lighter separators can be produced with ceramic magnets and this material is used wherever possible.

* 1960 prices.

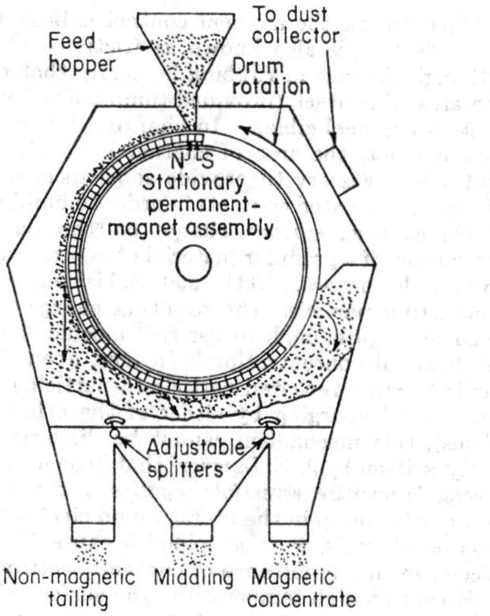

FIG. 21-101. Operating principle of dry-fines permanent-magnet separator. (*Courtesy of Indiana General Corporation. Magnetic Equipment Division.*)

ELECTROSTATIC SEPARATION

REFERENCES: 1. Gillson, Electrostatic Methods of Concentration, "Chemical Engineers' Handbook," 3d ed., 1950. 2. Lawver, Fundamentals of Electrical Concentration of Minerals, *Am. Inst. Mining & Met. Engrs., Tech. Paper*, February, 1957. 3. Mora, "Study of Electrical Concentration of Minerals," M.I.T. Thesis, 1958. 4. Loeb, Recent Developments in Analysis of Positive and Negative Coronas in Air, *J. Appl. Phys.*, **19**, 882, (1948). 5. Carpenter, "Technical Aspects of High Tension Separation," A.I.M.E., Tampa, Fla., December, 1949.

Principle. The principle of electrostatic separation is based on the fact that, if one or more of the materials in a granular mixture can receive a surface charge on or before entering an electrostatic field, the grains of that material will be repelled from one of the electrodes and attracted toward the other, depending upon the sign of the charge on the grain. By causing such grains to fall into separate chutes, a separation or concentration results.

This "principle" is rather simply and yet broadly stated, and in view of the tremendous increase in the use of variations of it in industry today, it should be described more fully. Actually, the term electrostatic is a misnomer. In some processes the energy applied is almost entirely electrostatic; but in others, more commonly used, the energy is applied in the form of current flow and could more properly be called "electrodynamic."

The major electrification mechanisms of separation or beneficiation of solid substances can be divided into three groups:

1. Contact electrification
2. Electrification by conductive induction
3. Electrification by ion bombardment

Each of the above mechanisms gives rise to a surface charge on the solid particles, and although each is a distinctly separate mechanism, two or more occur, more or less, in every separation and thus none can be neglected.

Charging by Contact Electrification. It has been observed that, when the surfaces of two dissimilar materials are brought into contact, each surface will bear exchange charges the moment contact is broken. Contact electrification is also known as frictional electrification, although the role of rubbing is merely that of increasing the area of contact (provided temperature effects due to friction are negligible). In charging by particle-to-particle contact, the area of contact is usually quite small and it is necessary to provide some mechanical method of causing repeated contacts in order to build up an appreciable average surface charge on the particles. Any movement of a granular material causes repeated particle-to-particle contact. If the material is composed of poorly conducting particles, the resulting charge density often becomes high enough to use this mechanism as a means of electrical concentration. In fact, even if no effort is made to cause repeated particle-to-particle contact (as in the case of charging by either of the other two mechanisms), this mechanism cannot be disregarded. It was aptly written by J. E. Lawver[2] that "the misleading terms *reversible positive, reversible negative, and non reversibility,* commonly found in the literature on electrical concentration of minerals, were so coined because of the failure to recognize the importance of contact electrification."

Except at high temperature, the surface charge due to contact electrification of dry minerals can probably be attributed to the transfer of electrons. Coehn's rule states that "when two dielectric materials are contacted and separated, the material with the higher dielectric constant becomes positively charged." Although Coehn's rule is reported to have been verified for more than 400 substances, it is of limited value in the separation of solids because the contact potentials of the solids are related to the work functions of the solids, and impurities or lattice defects can reverse the predicted situation. The theory of contact electrification is complex, and certainly, a great deal more needs to be learned about the electrification properties of solids. No two triboelectrification series have been found to be identical, which can probably be attributed to the fact that the substances used to form the various series may have entirely different electrical properties because of previous temperature and chemical histories. The practical problem facing the engineer interested in controlling and thus using contact electrification is that of finding a means of altering (thermally, physically, or chemically) the surface of the materials so that a selective electrification, and hence a separation, can be made. In many simple cases, it is only necessary to have discrete surfaces in order to obtain suitable contact electrification. The treatment is then merely dedusting or desliming. (Removal of a common surface from materials to be separated is necessary in any case in the use of any of the three basic electrification mechanisms.)

Charging by Conductive Induction. This mechanism is simpler and more readily explained than contact electrification. If a solid particle is placed on a grounded conductor in the presence of an electric field, the particle will rapidly develop a surface charge by induction. Whether the particle is conductive or dielectric, it can be considered to have become more or less polarized. However, a conductive particle will, in an extremely brief interval of time, become an equipotential surface through its contact with the grounded conductor and thus become charged to the same potential as the grounded conductor. A dielectric particle is difficult to define in terms of its potential, because of the variation of charge on its surface. It is sufficient to say that the dielectric particle remains essentially polarized because of its inability to redistribute electrons and thus no net charge is generated (see Fig. 21-102). However, no substance is either a perfect conductor or a perfect dielectric. All real particles will require finite intervals of time to become polarized and conductive particles will also require

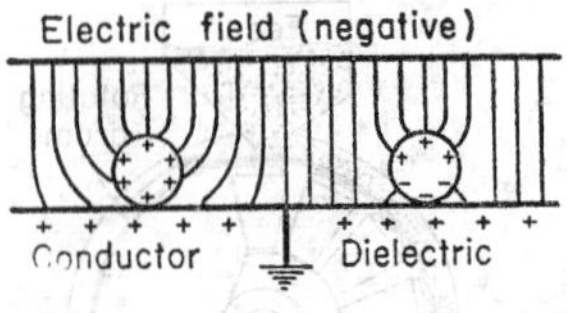

FIG. 21-102. Charging by conductive induction.

finite time to transfer this charge stress to ground. One may assume the charging process to be equivalent to an *RC* circuit and a particle with finite conductivity will eventually obtain a total charge of $Q = C_pV$, where C_p is the capacitance of the particle and V is the voltage difference in the field. The mathematics of how the particle finally approaches this charge value can be found in Lawver[2] and Mora.[3] It can be reasonably assumed that a non-conductive particle will have a high enough resistivity and therefore a low enough capacity to remain essentially uncharged under the *RC* circuit equation. Practically speaking, charging by conductive induction can be used to make a finite separation between relative conductors and non-conductors. If a grounded rotor is used to feed the material into the electric field, such as in Fig. 21-103, the following results will more or less take

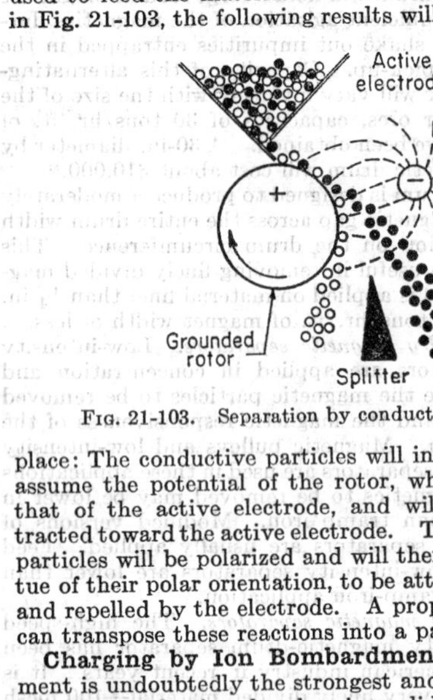

FIG. 21-103. Separation by conductive induction.

place: The conductive particles will in a very short time assume the potential of the rotor, which is opposite to that of the active electrode, and will therefore be attracted toward the active electrode. The non-conductive particles will be polarized and will therefore tend, by virtue of their polar orientation, to be attracted to the rotor and repelled by the electrode. A properly placed cutter can transpose these reactions into a particle separation.

Charging by Ion Bombardment. Ion bombardment is undoubtedly the strongest and perhaps the most effective mechanism for charging solid particles, but the selectivity of this mechanism is practically nil. However, when it is combined with the mechanism of conductive induction the selectivity of the compound process becomes very good. Charging by the use of mobile ions is definitely not an "electrostatic" process even though engineers generally use the term to describe any beneficiation process that uses a high-voltage electric field. In the past few years the term "high tension" has, through constant usage, become the generally accepted name for the processes involving ionic bombardment. In the high-tension process, mobile ions are provided by a beamed electrode* that produces a corona discharge while simultaneously concentrating this source of mobile ions in a given direction. If a dielectric particle and a conductive particle are placed in the path of these mobile ions, a portion of the surface of each particle will be given a strong electrical charge. On the conductor this charge is redistributed almost instantaneously, whereas on the

* Patent 2,548,771, Carpco.

non-conductor the redistribution of the same charge will be very slow. If a group of these particles are placed on a grounded surface in the path of these mobile ions, it will be found that, when the source of mobile ions is stopped, the conductors are free to leave the surface because they have shared their charge with the ground. On the other hand, the dielectric or non-conductor particles, which are not capable of readily losing their charge, are held to the surface by their own image force (Lawver[2]). The electrostatic-image theory is merely a method of solving Laplace's or Poisson's equations by inspection of symmetry conditions. In other words, these equations can be satisfied if a particle of equal and opposite charge is assumed to be placed at a mirror-image position with respect to the grounded surface and the particle in question. This image force is given as $F = QQi/4\pi e_o(2s)^2$, where $-Q = +Qi$ = total surface charge on the mineral and s = the distance from the charge to the grounded surface. e_o = field strength of ionic field. For a detailed discussion of image theory, see Sommerfeld ("Electrodynamics," Academic Press, New York, 1952).

The mechanisms for producing a working corona discharge are quite complex. Loeb,[4] Bandel, and Amin have probably investigated these mechanisms more completely than any other group and have published some very informative papers on the subject. It has been established that the "point" in point-to-plane corona discharge should not actually be a point as such. According to Loeb's work, the optimum configuration is that of a small-diameter hemisphere, or for laterally extended corona, a fine wire gives a hemispherical cross section in the direction of ion flow. Both positive and negative corona discharges are useful and each has special application for certain separations. However, a negative electrode can produce a more intense corona in air before arcing because the flash-over voltage is higher.

Industrial high-tension separators make use of a grounded rotor for the "grounded surface" mentioned above in order to have a continuous surface that will introduce the particles to the source of mobile ions and then take them away. All particles are charged while under ion bombardment, but shortly after the particles are removed from this area, the conductors are free to leave the rotor and the non-conductors are pinned by their image force. This is the primary charging step and the initial separation step in this process. High-tension separation becomes extremely selective; however, when a static electrode (large enough in diameter to preclude corona discharge) is used following the ionic electrode (see Fig. 21-104). The dielectrics have been highly charged and

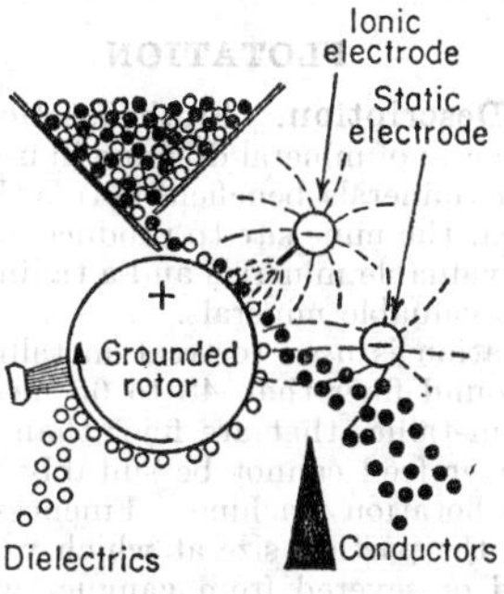

FIG. 21-104. Separation by ion bombardment.

strongly pinned to the rotor and, for the sake af simplicity, can be considered to be henceforth out of the system. The conductive particles, however, have shared their charge with the ground and are now being charged oppositely by conductive induction. This compound process produces very wide and distinct separations between discrete conductive and non-conductive particles and greatly increases the capacity over processes using conductive induction only.

Types of Equipment. The two main types of equipment in use today are the plate type and the rotor type. The plate type is, as it sounds, merely two vertical plates (with all edges sufficiently rounded to prevent corona discharge) suspended relatively close to each other and having either a high voltage impressed on one and the other grounded, or one charged positively and the other negatively. Chutes, of course, are used below these to collect the various products, and a method of feeding the material at the top is required. This type is especially useful for separating two non-conductive substances from each other after charging by contact electrification. Although the equipment itself is quite simple, the processes of charging the particles are usually not so simple. The engineer's main problem in using plate separators is in finding the most efficient method of treating the surfaces of the substances to be separated in order to facilitate and enhance particle-to-particle charging. Plate separators, to the author's knowledge, are not manufactured for sale and the user is forced to design and build his own; however, International Minerals & Chemical Corp., holds patents on several configurations of electrodes as well as on several charging processes.

The rotor type, conversely, is a machine that actually performs the charging step during its operation and therefore is not completely dependent on prior treatment. As mentioned under the mechanism of ionic bombardment, the rotor is used to expose the particles to the ionic charge and then remove them while simultaneously acting as a continuous grounded surface. The bulk of the high-tension separators used in industry are manufactured by Carpco Research and Engineering, Inc. The Carpco machine is a very versatile separator of modular design wherein rotor units can be stacked vertically or horizontally in a single machine and any type of flow sheet can be performed in a single machine. Figure 21-105 shows a cross section of a Carpco six-rotor vertically stacked machine, and it will be noted that the machine has been field-oriented on the right-hand side for parallel operation. In other words, each rotor is getting the same feed such as would be the case in an all "rougher" unit. On the left side, the machine is shown oriented for series operation such as would be the case with a small operation, wherein one rotor gives sufficient rougher capacity but the material needs more than one pass to make a final product. Although it is not shown, this high-tension separator can also be oriented to repass middlings or tailings products. Capacities of these machines are generally high and range from about 1000 to 2000 lb./hr./ft. of rotor length. A Carpco 12-rotor machine (10-ft. rotors) can, for example, handle up to 120 tons/hr. of specular hematite ore in a one-pass operation. As of 1960 the cost of this type of equipment, complete with all accessories, runs about \$500 to \$600 per foot of rotor length.

Effect of Humidity. It is imperative that all particles to be separated (under any one of the three basic electrification mechanisms) be completely surface-dry. This is not a serious problem in itself since drying of surface moisture is quite straightforward. However, a problem is encountered, at high humidities, of *keeping* the surfaces dry. Tests on specular hematite and silica have shown that a reasonable separation can be made on predried mineral, under high-tension conditions, at 70°F. if the relative humidity is less than about 35 per cent. These same tests have shown that at 60 per cent relative humidity an ore temperature of 110°F. is required to

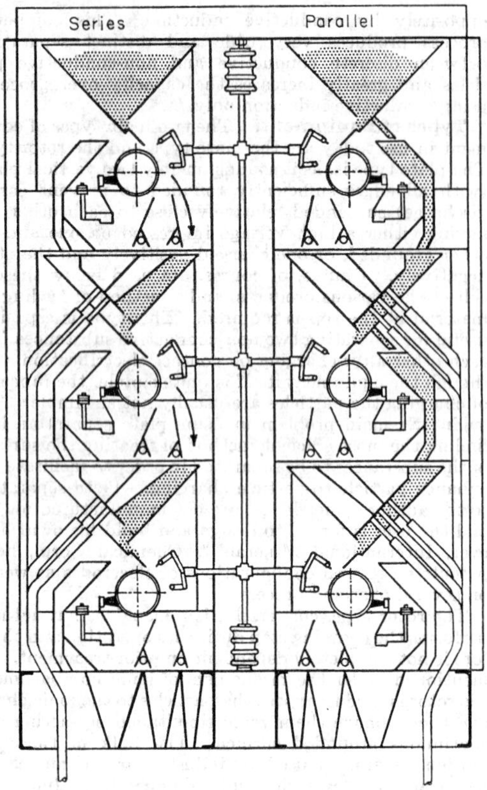

FIG. 21-105. Carpco high-tension separator.

effect a separation, and at 90 per cent relative humidity, a minimum temperature of 190°F. is required. This is not a rule of thumb or a curve that can be applied to minerals in general, however. In the case of an ilmenite-rutile-zircon separation it will be found that the ilmenite and rutile (especially the rutile) must be kept at 200°F. or above to perform an efficient separation, regardless of the relative humidity. In contact electrification, Florida phosphate rock contacted against Florida quartz will charge the quartz highly negatively and the phosphate equally positively over a temperature range of −10° to 600°F. Sylvite, however, requires a contact temperature of about 900°F. to exchange charges with Halite but will not begin to separate until cooled to about 300°F. and discontinues separating below 190°F. if the relative humidity is around 90 per cent. It is sufficient to say that each case is individual and in each case ambient humidity plays a more or less significant part.

Applications of Processes. International Minerals & Chemical Corp. has a plant in Topsham, Maine, separating feldspar from quartz and concentrating potassium feldspar from sodium feldspar. This is a plate-type separation using contact electrification for a charging mechanism. J. R. Simplot Co. in Idaho is separating quartz, feldspar, and mica by the use of the high-tension process. Almost every major tin-mining company in Malaya and Nigeria uses the high-tension process to separate columbite, ilmenite, and cassiterite from gangue minerals. There are few titanium-mineral-producing plants in the world today that do not use the high-tension process for the separation of ilmenite and rutile from monazite and zircon and other non-conductors. Umgababa Minerals, Ltd., a division of Anglo American Corp., in Durban, South Africa, is producing approximately 100,000 tons/year of ilmenite by this means. E. I. du Pont de Nemours has two plants in Florida, each capable of processing up to 1000 tons/day of heavy mineral bulk concentrates and producing mainly ilmenite, rutile, leucoxene, and zircon by the combined use of high-tension separation and high-intensity magnetic separation.

No typical flow sheets are given here because each case is quite individual. Some general conditions can be mentioned, however, to guide the engineer in the use of these processes: Generally speaking, most ores or substances must be ground to −8 mesh in order to have a sufficient charge-to-mass ratio to effect a separation. The size range of the particles has a definite bearing on the separation efficiency, and it may be said that the closer the size range, the more efficient the separation, particularly with respect to the separation of conductors from non-conductors. As stated previously, all particles must have discrete surfaces. This necessitates a relative degree of desliming. For example, a −8-mesh grind would probably need desliming at 200 mesh, a −20-mesh grind at 325 mesh, and a −35-mesh grind at 400 mesh, etc. Difficult ores may require classification at intermediate meshes in order to be successfully separated. Specific gravity of the various minerals in an ore can greatly increase or decrease the efficiency of separation of conductors from non-conductors. For example, hematite (specular) has a much greater gravity than silica, and since it is the conductor and is to be thrown from the rotor, its greater mass aids the separation. On the other hand, in a separation of monazite from ilmenite, the non-conductive monazite has a greater gravity than the conductive ilmenite, which makes the separation more difficult. A chart compiled by Carpco Research & Engineering, Inc., can be found in "Engineering & Mining Journal Guidebook," vol. 158, No. 6A, pp. 26, 85, June, 1957. This chart is a relative "gravity–conductivity–magnetic susceptibility" reference and is true for the particular minerals tested. It may be used as a rough guide but should not be construed as a chart consistently specifying general mineral behavior.

ADDITIONAL READING: Fraas and Ralston, Electrostatic Separations of Solids, *Ind. Eng. Chem.*, **32,** 600 (May, 1940). Fraas, The Conductance Electrostatic Separator, *Am. Inst. Mining Met. Engrs. Tech. Publ.* 1511, 1942. Fraas, Notes on Drying for Electrostatic Separation of Particles, *Am. Inst. Mining Met. Engrs. Tech. Publ.* 2257, 1947. Fraas and Ralston, Dielectric Constant in Air-ambient Electrostatic Separation, *U.S. Bur. Mines Rept. Invest.* 4278, April, 1948. Long, New Dry Concentrating Equipment, *U.S. Bur. Mines, Rept. Invest.* 4286, May, 1948. Bullock, Scope and Economics of Electrostatic Separation, *Ind. Eng. Chem.*, **33** (9) (September, 1941).

FLOTATION

General Description. Froth flotation is by far the dominant process of mineral dressing in use today. Mineral dressing (minerals beneficiation) is the treatment of ores at or near the mine site to produce one or more concentrates of valuable minerals and a tailings composed of waste or less valuable minerals.

Froth flotation is used to treat metallic ores that are generally ground finer than 48 to 65 mesh, or coal and certain non-metallics that are finer than 20 to 28 mesh. Usually coarser feed cannot be suitably mixed and suspended by a flotation machine. Fineness of grind is determined by the particle size at which valuable minerals are liberated or severed from gangue (waste) particles. In flotation machines the ore is suspended in water at a pulp density generally from 15 to 35 per cent solids by means of mechanical or air agitation. The surfaces of specific mineral particles are treated with chemicals called promoters or collectors which render those particles air-avid and water-repellent. With vigorous agitation and aeration in the presence of a frother, a layer of froth or foam forms at the top of the flotation machine. The air-avid minerals become attached to air bubbles and rise to the surface where they collect in the froth and are skimmed off. Undesired minerals are depressed or rendered non-floatable either by leaving their surfaces unaltered by collector adsorption or through the use of modifying agents.

The valuable concentrates from froth flotation may be either the froth product which collects at the top, or the underflow product. In the case of metallic sulfide ores of copper, lead, zinc, nickel, mercury, and molybdenum, and native gold and silver, the values collect in the froth. In glass-sand flotation, iron-bearing minerals are floated off in the froth, while high-grade silica values report as underflow.

Flotation Reagents. *Promoters* or *collectors* provide minerals which are to be floated with a water-repellent air-avid coating that will adhere to an air bubble. Typical collectors for flotation of metallic sulfides and native metals are xanthates, 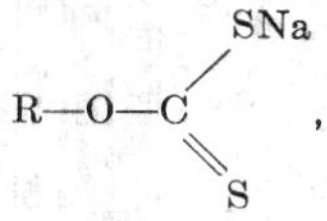 , and dithiophosphates, 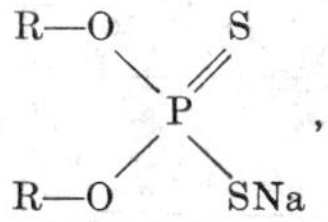 , where R is an alkyl group of two to six carbon atoms. The ionized collector is adsorbed on a sulfide mineral surface with bonding through the sulfur atoms. The alkyl group provides the water-repellent coating. Quantities of the order of 0.01 to 0.2 lb. reagent/ton of ore are generally used.

Crude or refined fatty acids and their soaps, petroleum sulfonates, and sulfonated fatty acids are widely used as collectors in flotation of fluorspar, phosphate rock, iron ore, and other non-metallics. In these operations reagent dosages are much higher, of the order of 0.2 to 2 lb./ton ore.

Cationic collectors such as fatty amines and amine salts are widely used for flotation of quartz, potash, and silicate minerals in quantities of 0.1 to 1.0 lb./ton.

Fuel oil and kerosene are used as collectors for coal, graphite, sulfur, and molybdenite since they are readily adsorbed by such naturally hydrophobic minerals. In fact, a frother alone can often be used to float these minerals. These hydrocarbons are also used as extenders or diluents in non-metallic flotation with sulfonates, fatty acids, and fatty amines.

Widely used *frothers* are pine oil, cresylic acid, and five to eight carbon aliphatic alcohols such as methylisobutyl carbinol and *n*-heptanol. Water-soluble frothers containing several solubilizing groups (polypropylene glycol derivatives) were introduced about 6 years ago and now are used extensively. Quantities of frothers required are usually from 0.01 to 0.2 lb./ton.

Modifiers. Flotation modifiers include several classes of chemicals as described below.

Activators are used to make a mineral surface amenable to collector coating. Copper ion is used, for example, to activate sphalerite (ZnS), rendering the sphalerite surface capable of adsorbing a xanthate or dithiophosphate collector. Sodium sulfide is used to coat oxidized copper and lead minerals so that they can be floated by a sulfide mineral collector.

Alkalinity regulators such as lime, caustic soda, soda ash, and sulfuric acid are used to control or adjust pH, a very critical factor in many flotation separations.

Depressants assist in selectivity (sharpness of separation) or stop unwanted minerals from floating. Typical are sodium or calcium cyanide to depress pyrite (FeS_2), while floating galena (PbS), sphalerite (ZnS), or copper sulfides; zinc sulfate to depress ZnS while floating PbS; sodium ferrocyanide to depress copper sulfides while floating molybdenite (MoS_2); lime to depress pyrite; sodium silicate to depress quartz; quebracho to depress calcite ($CaCO_3$) during fluorite (CaF_2) flotation; lignin sulfonates and dextrins to depress graphite and talc during sulfide flotation.

Dispersants or *deflocculants* are important for control of slimes which sometimes interfere with selectivity and increase reagent consumption. Soda ash, lime, sodium silicate, and lignin sulfonates are used for this purpose.

Quantities of modifying agents used vary widely, ranging from as little as 0.05 lb./ton to as high as 5 or 10 lb./ton, depending upon the reagent and the metallurgical problem.

Mining Applications. Well over 90 per cent of the world's copper, lead, zinc, molybdenum, antimony, and nickel are produced from ores that are concentrated first by froth flotation. Most of the phosphate rock fines in Florida are recovered by flotation and the potash ores of the Carlsbad, N.M., area are also concentrated by flotation.

Some typical examples of froth-flotation separations are shown in Table 21-24.

Table 21-24. Typical Froth-flotation Separations

Ore	Reagents	Flotation product	
		% recovery	Assay
Zinc sulfide in carbonate gangue, 4% Zn, 5% pyrite	0.44 lb./ton $CuSO_4 \cdot 5H_2O$ 0.07 lb./ton dithiophosphate 0.14 lb./ton NaCN 0.02 lb./ton frother	98.4	63.5% Zn
Phosphate rock, 30% BPL with silica gangue	Phosphate flotation 1.0 lb./ton tall oil 2.3 lb./ton fuel oil 0.8 lb./ton NaOH	Phosphate rougher conc.	12% insol. 65% BPL
	Silica flotation from phosphate conc. 0.1 lb./ton fatty amine 0.4 lb./ton kerosene	Silica tailings (final phosphate conc.) 85	75–77% BPL 3% insol.
Fluorite, 40% CaF_2 in $CaCO_3$, SiO_2, iron oxide gangue	7.0 lb./ton Na_2CO_3 1.5 lb./ton Na_2SiO_3 0.8 lb./ton refined fatty acid 0.1 lb./ton alcohol frother 0.15 lb./ton quebracho	95	99% CaF_2
Iron ore assaying, 30–35% Fe with siliceous gangue	3.0 lb./ton H_2SO_4 1.9 lb./ton petroleum sulfonate 0.7 lb./ton fuel oil 0.4 lb./ton tall oil 1.4 lb./ton Na_2SiO_3	70	58–60% Fe 6–8% SiO_2
Copper sulfide ore, 0.9% Cu with pyrite and silicate gangue	6.0 lb./ton lime 0.03 lb./ton dithiophosphate 0.02 lb./ton alcohol frother	91	24% Cu

Industrial Applications. Froth flotation has only a limited use outside of minerals beneficiation For example, it is used for clarifying rayon-spinning baths and for treating water-soluble oils used in grinding operations. Impurities are floated from chicle, a base for chewing gum. Deinking and dewaxing of waste paper, floating gluten and fiber from cornstarch, and separation of good peas from bad are other industrial applications.

The so-called "dissolved-air" flotation machines used for sewage or industrial-waste treatment dissolve air under pressure in the waste stream. Upon release of pressure the dissolved air forms bubbles which float solid matter in a scum on the surface of a tank where it is removed by a skimming mechanism. This is not froth flotation as described in this article.

Flotation Machines. The machines which are most widely used today in sulfide, coal, and non-metallic flotation operations in the western hemisphere are the Fagergren,* the Denver Sub-A* and the Agitair flotation* machines. Often one type of machine will be used for roughing and another for cleaning.

These machines provide mechanical agitation and aeration by means of a rotating impeller on an upright shaft. In addition, the Agitair, and sometimes the Denver Sub-A, also utilize "pneumatic air" from a blower to help aerate the pulp.

In the Fagergren machine (Fig. 21-106) pulp is drawn upward into a rotor (*A*) by the rotor's lower portion (*B*).

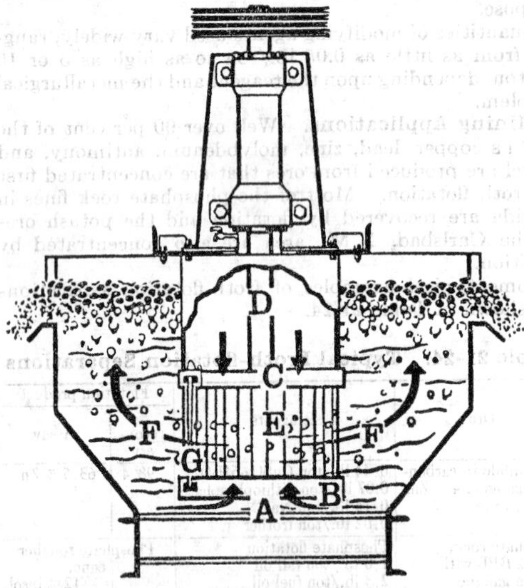

FIG. 21-106. Fagergren flotation machine.

Simultaneously, the rotor's upper end (*C*) draws air down the standpipe (*D*) for thorough mixing with the pulp inside the rotor (*E*). The aerated pulp is then expelled by a strong centrifugal force (*F*). The shearing action of the stator (*G*), a stationary cage fitting closely around the rotor, breaks the air into minute bubbles. This action uniformly distributes a large volume of air in the form of minute bubbles in all parts of the cell.

In the Sub-A machine (Fig. 21-107) the pulp flows into the machine by gravity through the feed pipe, dropping directly on the top of the rotating impeller below the stationary hood. This is the mixing and aeration zone (1) where air is drawn in by positive suction down the standpipe into the heart of the cell. Zone 2 is the separation zone where the mineral-laden air bubbles separate from the worthless gangue. Zone 3 is the concentrate zone where cell action is very quiet. Here concentrates, partly separated from the discharge side of the machine by a baffle, are enriched, moving forward to be removed by the paddles.

In the Agitair flotation machine (Fig. 21-108) the impeller is a flat rubber-covered disk with steel fingers extending downward from the periphery. A rubber-covered stabilizer or "bubble peeler" eliminates dead spots in the agitation zone and improves bubble-ore contact. Degree of aeration is controlled by regulating air

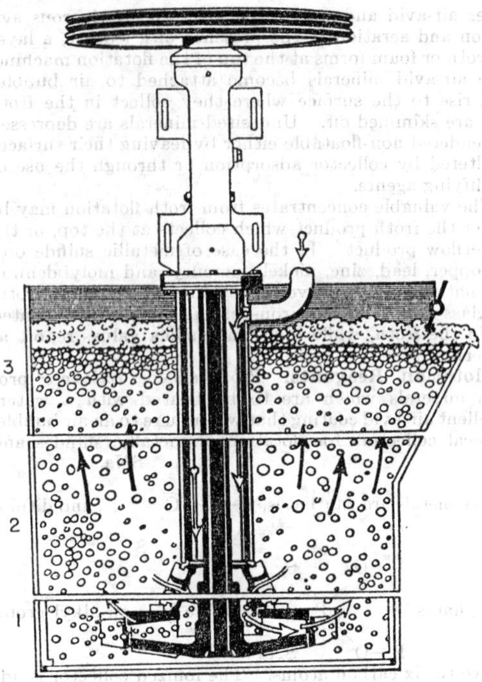

FIG. 21-107. Denver Sub-A flotation machine.

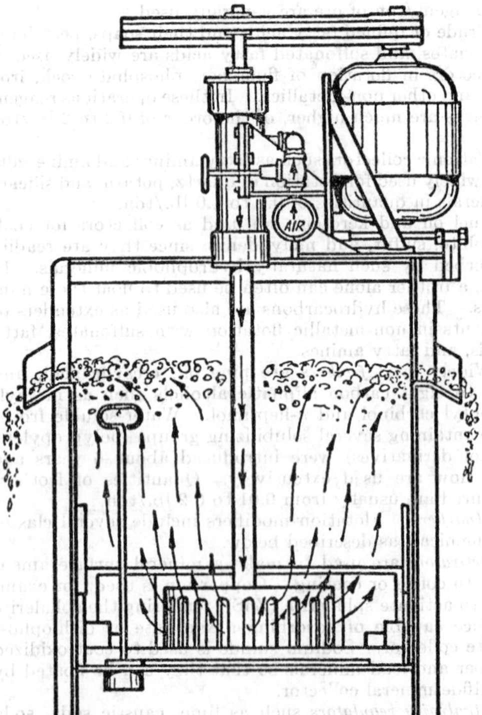

FIG. 21-108. Agitair flotation machine.

* Agitair Flotation is a registered trade-mark of The Galigher Company. Sub-A machines are sold by the Denver Equipment Company and Fagergren machines by Western Machinery Company.

pressure on each cell with an individual air valve. Air is supplied at 1.5 lb./sq. in.

Many other types of flotation cells will be found in older mills. The Callow cell has no mechanical parts. Ore pulp is suspended and aerated by air bubbles coming through a porous medium (usually a cloth mat) forming the bottom of the cell. In the MacIntosh cell air is introduced through a porous medium wrapped around a rotating pipe near the bottom of a V-shaped trough. The Forrester cell is a V-shaped trough with air introduced through ½- to 1-in. vertical pipes spaced at 4- to 6-in. intervals lengthwise. A modification of the Forrester cell is used at a large phosphate flotation plant in Florida. Maintenance costs on it are considerably less than for mechanical cells in the same service.

Capacities. Tonnage handled by flotation equipment will vary with the pulp density of feed and flotation time (residence time) required for roughing and cleaning. Number of cells required for a specific job can be calculated as follows:

$$\text{No. cells} = \frac{T \times \text{tpd} \times d}{V \times 1440}$$

where T = flotation time, min.
tpd = dry tons ore treated per 24-hr. day
d = volume, cu. ft. of pulp (ore and water) containing 1 ton dry solids
V = volume, cu. ft. of one cell

Typical data for three types of machines are shown in Table 21-25.

Table 21-25. Approximate Capacities of Flotation Cells, Tons Dry Feed per 24 Hr. with Pulp at 33 Per Cent Solids, Specific Gravity Ore at 3.0

Cell	Cell volume, cu. ft.	Hp. per cell	4 cells			8 cells			12 cells		
			Flotation time, min.								
			4	8	12	4	8	12	4	8	12
Fagergren 66 by 66 in.....	60	10	1140	570	380	2280	1140	760	3420	1710	1140
Agitair 48 by 48 in.....	40	7.5	760	380	254	1520	760	510	2280	1140	760
Denver Sub-A No. 24 43 by 43 in.....	50	5	950	475	317	1900	950	635	2850	1430	950

Capacities shown in Table 21-25 are based solely on volume of flotation cells. Major flotation-equipment installations today will also be designed from energy-input considerations as well. For example, if laboratory and pilot-plant tests have indicated 3 kw.-hr./ton are required to achieve desired metallurgical results on a certain ore, doubling or tripling contact time with energy input remaining below 3 kw.-hr./ton will not improve inferior results.

The trend today in new or remodeled flotation installations is to use the largest-size units, particularly in larger mills where amounts of ore to be treated are 50 tons/hr. or greater. Smaller machines are sometimes preferred for cleaning operations, however.

Plant Operation. Ores must be ground to a point of complete or nearly complete liberation. Even though this might possibly be accomplished by coarse crushing, grinding to finer than 20 mesh is necessary in all cases and to finer than 48 mesh in most, prior to flotation. Grinding is done in ball or rod mills in closed circuit with classifiers.

In many instances, superior flotation results are obtained by conditioning the ore with the reagents before the flotation step. Oily-type collectors are sometimes added to the grinding circuit to ensure dispersion. For proper selectivity, a definite contact time is sometimes required between reagent and ore, and this is usually secured by mixing the reagent and ore pulp in a "conditioner" consisting of a cylindrical tank with a vertical impeller.

Flotation machines are built in multiple units, and the flow of the pulp through various units is adjusted for the best results. Common practice is to feed the pulp to several cells known as "roughers," which produce a barren tailing and low-grade concentrate. The concentrate is treated, sometimes after regrinding, in "cleaner" cells and "recleaner" cells for final concentration. The tailings from the cleaner and recleaner cells are recirculated back through the system or concentrated separately in additional cells. Regrinding of these middlings is necessary in many ores.

Important auxiliary equipment in a flotation plant includes reagent feeders and controls, sampling and weighing devices, slurry pumps, filters and thickeners for dewatering solids, reagent storage and makeup equipment, and analytical devices for process control.

Figure 21-109 is a flow sheet of a typical simple flotation plant.

Equipment Costs. Typical costs (August, 1960) for a four-cell bank of the three most widely used machines are shown in Table 21-26. These units are the largest made by each manufacturer.

Plant Costs. Froth-flotation plants generally will be completely integrated concentrating operations, with equipment also installed for crushing, grinding, sizing, materials handling, and perhaps water recovery. Hence the actual cost of the flotation section of a milling plant will be a small part of the over-all capital cost. Large sulfide mills (2000 tons/day and up) will cost approximately $2000 per ton per day (August, 1960). Smaller plants will run higher than this. This approximation includes an allowance for a complete milling installation with wiring, piping, auxiliaries, ore bins, mill water tank, but no shops or warehouses. Of the $2000 per ton per day total, about $20 per ton per day is the cost of flotation equipment alone in larger mills. In small mills (100 to 500 tons/day) total cost may run as high as $3000 to $4000 per ton per day with flotation machines running to $60 per ton per day. The largest item in mill capital costs will usually be crushing and grinding equipment.

Table 21-26. Typical Flotation-machine Costs (August, 1960) for Four-cell Bank

Type, size	Pulp volume, cu. ft.		Total installed hp.	F.o.b. factory		Remarks
	Per cell	Total		Total	Per cu. ft. cell volume	
Fagergren 66 in..............	61	244	40 (range 40–60)	$7,600	$31.15	Mild-steel construction with rubber wearing parts. Excludes froth launders, includes boxing, tankage, four 10-hp. motors and drives
Denver Sub-A 56 in.........	100	400	40 (range 40–50)	$10,018	$25.05	Mild-steel construction with molded rubber wearing parts. Includes two 20-hp. motors and drives, ⅓-hp. paddle shaft drive, supercharged air header but no blower. Free-flow type, no intermediate weirs
Agitair 48 in...............	40	160	30 (range 20–30)	$5,418	$33.86	Mild-steel construction with rubber-covered wearing parts. Includes two 15-hp. motors and drives, excludes feed box, junction box, and blower

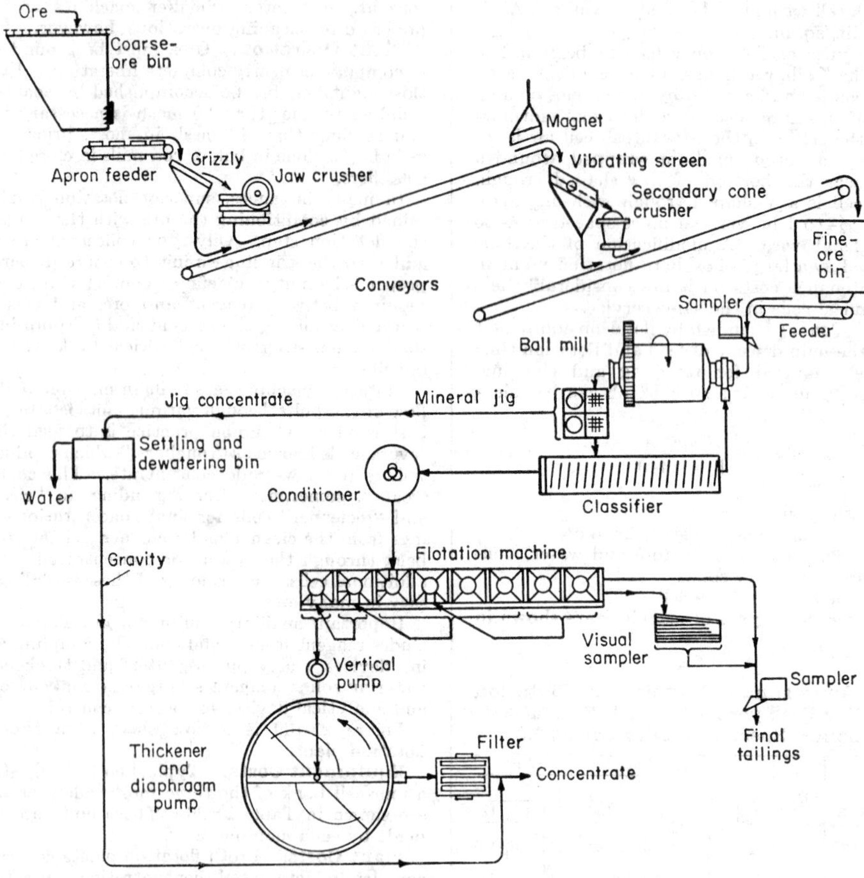

FIG. 21-109. Flow sheet of a simple flotation plant.

Important variables influencing total cost of a flotation mill are:

1. Hardness of ore and mineralogical associations (determine ease and fineness of grinding)
2. Metal content of ore (non-metallics require much greater materials-handling investment for concentrates than do base-metal sulfides, for example)
3. Soil conditions at mill site
4. Weather conditions
5. Estimated life of plant
6. Degree of automation
7. Type of construction required or preferred
8. Safety factor for capacity

To obtain a rough estimated maximum cost of a sulfide-concentrating plant, a rule of thumb used by some engineering companies is to multiply the total mill equipment cost (f.o.b. factory) by four. This is for a de luxe job. Less elaborate mills may cost 3× f.o.b. factory cost of equipment.

Power Requirements. Power consumption for most sulfide ores will range from 2 to 3 kw.-hr./ton of feed (for flotation alone). Easy-to-float ores such as the well-deslimed Florida phosphate ores can be floated for about 1 kw.-hr./ton. A typical copper sulfide ore will require 2½ to 3 kw.-hr./ton.

Chief factors influencing power requirements are (1) amount of cleaning done, (2) pulp density (dilution) of feed, (3) flotation time, and (4) froth and middling pumping requirements.

Labor Requirements. In modern sulfide flotation plants one operator can readily handle flotation sections treating up to 12,000 to 14,000 tons/day of feed, provided

Table 21-27. Operating Costs (1959–1960) per Ton of Ore Treated at 22 Sulfide-flotation Plants Treating 211,621 Tons/Day of Cu, Pb, Zn, Pb-Zn, Cu-Pb-Zn, Cu-Mo, and Cu-Ag Ores at Rates from 800 to 45,000 Tons/Day

Item	High	Low	Weighted average*	%	Arithmetic average†	%
Unloading, crushing	$0.391	$0.050	$0.067	10.7	$0.101	8.4
Grinding	0.650	0.100	0.220	35.3	0.272	22.6
Flotation‡	0.860	0.062	0.108	17.3	0.276	22.9
(reagents)	(0.50)	(0.017)	(0.052	(8.3)	(0.149)	(12.4)
Filtration, drying, loading	0.260	0	0.018	2.9	0.051	4.2
Tailings disposal	0.060	0.002	0.016	2.6	0.026	2.2
Misc.	0.680	0	0.036	5.8	0.136	11.3
Total direct	2.20	0.319	$0.465	74.6	$0.862	71.6
Indirect	1.66	0.056	0.159	25.4	0.342	28.4
Grand total	3.86	0.375	$0.624	100.0	$1.204	100.0

* Based on total daily tonnage.
† Based on number of mills.
‡ Including reagent cost. Reagent costs are shown in parentheses.

ore is not too complex and treatment is fairly simple. In some new coal-flotation operations, incorporation of a flotation circuit for fines recovery has been made in an existing preparation plant without addition of any extra manpower. Machines run automatically with a brief check several times a day. An average labor requirement (first half of 1960) for large porphyry–copper sulfide concentrators is one man shift per 800 tons of ore, including maintenance and repair.

Operating Costs. Operating costs were collected from 22 sulfide-flotation plants treating 211,621 tons/day of Cu, Pb, Zn, Pb-Zn, Cu-Pb-Zn, Cu-Mo, and Cu-Ag ores in the United States, Canada, and Latin America. These costs covered either the year 1959 or the first 6 months of 1960. Summary is shown in Table 21-27.

Certain of these milling costs can be broken down another way as follows:

Maintenance......	\$0.093–\$0.14/ton	(5 mills, 40,000 tons/day feed)
Power............	0.18 –0.47/ton	12 mills, 53,320 tons/day feed
Labor............	0.049–0.69/ton	12 mills, 53,320 tons/day feed
Supplies..........	0.017–1.27/ton	12 mills, 53,320 tons/day feed

BIBLIOGRAPHY: Gaudin, "Flotation," 2d ed., McGraw-Hill, New York, 1957. Sutherland and Wark, "Principles of Flotation," Australasian Institute of Mining and Metallurgy, Melbourne, 1955. Taggart, "Handbook of Mineral Dressing," Wiley, New York, 1945. Taggart, "Elements of Ore Dressing," Wiley, New York, 1951. Gaudin, "Principles of Mineral Dressing," McGraw-Hill, New York, 1939. American Cyanamid Company, Mineral Dressing Notes No. 21, "Froth Flotation," 1955; No. 25, "Flotation Reagents," 1960.

SECTION 22
PROCESS CONTROL

BY

Douglas M. Considine, B.S. Chem. Eng., Director, Marketing Planning, Hughes Aircraft Co., Culver City, Calif.; Member, American Institute of Chemical Engineers, Instrument Society of America, American Marketing Association, American Management Association, National Sales Executives. (Section Editor and Process Measurements)

WITH

Louis Bertrand, B.Sc., M.Sc. Chem. Eng., Consultant on Chemical Engineering, Engineering Department, E. I. du Pont de Nemours & Co., Inc., Wilmington, Del.; Member, American Institute of Chemical Engineers, American Society of Mechanical Engineers, American Ordnance Association. (Control of Distillation Columns)

Glenn F. Brockett, B.S., Vice-President—Sales, Fisher Governor Co., Marshalltown, Iowa; Member, American Society of Mechanical Engineers, Fellow Instrument Society of America. (Final Control Elements)

Steven Danatos, M.E., M.S., Associate Editor, Engineering Practice, *Chemical Engineering*, McGraw-Hill Publishing Co., Inc., New York; Member, American Chemical Society. (Process Measurements)

Richard C. Gillette, B.S., Elec. Eng., M.A., Account Executive, Wilson, Haight and Welch, Inc., Hartford, Conn.; Member, American Economic Association. (Telemetering, Automatic Controllers)

George A. Hall, Jr., B.S., Advanced Systems Development, Westinghouse Electric Corp., Pittsburgh, Pa. (Fundamentals of Automatic Control)

Wilfred H. Howe, B.S. Elec. Eng., M.B.A., Chief Engineer, The Foxboro Co., Foxboro, Mass.; Member, American Institute of Electrical Engineers, American Society of Mechanical Engineers. (Indicators and Recorders)

John Johnston, Jr., B.S. in M.E., Engineering Manager, Instrument Products Division, Engineering Department, E. I. du Pont de Nemours & Co., Inc., Wilmington, Del.; Member, American Society of Mechanical Engineers, American Association for the Advancement of Science, Instrument Society of America. (Economics of Chemical Process Instrumentation, Organizing and Training for Instrumentation Responsibility)

J. B. Jones, B.Sc., M.Sc., Chem. Eng., Consultant on Mass Transfer, Engineering Department, E. I. du Pont de Nemours & Co., Inc., Wilmington, Del.; Visiting Lecturer, Columbia Univ.; Member, American Institute of Chemical Engineers. (Control of Distillation Columns)

Alfred H. McKinney, B.S., Consultant, Engineering Services Division, Engineering Department, E. I. du Pont de Nemours & Co., Inc., Wilmington, Del.; Member, American Institute of Chemical Engineers, American Chemical Society, Instrument Society of America. (Dryer Instrumentation)

Neal Richter, Ph.D., Assistant Professor of Chemical Engineering, California Institute of Technology, Pasadena, Calif.; Member, American Institute of Chemical Engineers. (Fundamentals of Automatic Control)

Sanford M. Roberts, Ph.D., Bonner and Moore Associates, Inc., Houston, Tex.; Member American Institute of Chemical Engineers. (Computer Process Control)

Carl W. Sanders, B.S. Chem. Eng., Consulting Engineer, Engineering Services Division, Engineering Department, E. I. du Pont de Nemours & Co., Inc., Wilmington, Del.; Member, Instrument Society of America. (Heat-exchanger Instrumentation)

Thomas M. Stout, Ph.D., Manager, Process Analysis Department, TRW Computers Co., Division of Thompson Ramo Wooldridge, Inc., Canoga Park, Calif.; Member, American Institute of Electrical Engineers, Institute of Radio Engineers. (Computer Process Control)

CONTENTS

PROCESS MEASUREMENTS

INDICATING AND RECORDING INSTRUMENTS

TELEMETERING

COMPUTER AND DATA PROCESSING

FUNDAMENTALS OF AUTOMATIC PROCESS CONTROL

AUTOMATIC CONTROLLERS

FINAL CONTROL ELEMENTS

INSTRUMENTATION OF UNIT OPERATIONS

References: Baker, Ryder, and Baker, "Temperature Measurement in Engineering," vol. I, Wiley, New York, 1953. American Institute of Physics, "Temperature: Its Measurement and Control in Science and Industry," vol. 2, Reinhold, New York, 1955. Hall, "Fundamentals of Thermometry," Chapman & Hall, London, 1953. Combes, Temperature Measuring Devices, *Automation*, **7** (5), 87–88 (May, 1960). Carroll, "Industrial Instrument Servicing Handbook," McGraw-Hill, New York, 1960. Eckman, "Industrial Instrumentation," Wiley, New York, 1950. Considine, "Process Instruments and Controls Handbook," McGraw-Hill, 1957. Leck, "Pressure Measurement in Vacuum Systems," Reinhold, New York, 1957. Moynihan, Circuits for High-ambient, Differential Pressure Measurement, *Control Eng.*, **7** (4), 163 (April, 1960). Caddell, "Fluid Flow in Practice," Reinhold, New York, 1956. Smith, Metering and Proportioning Flow, *Automation*, **6** (11), 82 (November, 1959). Stearns, "Flow Measurement with Orifice Meters," Van Nostrand, Princeton, N.J., 1951. Basic Types of Industrial Mass Flowmeters, *J. Instr. Soc. Am.*, Parts I, II, and III, June, 1960. Considine, "Industrial Weighing," Reinhold, New York, 1948. Kirwan and Demler, "Continuous Weighing Meters and Feeders," A.S.M.E. Instruments and Regulators Conf. Paper 53-IRD-9, 1953. Owen, "A Treatise on Weighing Machines," Griffin, London, 1922. Smith, "Testing of Weighing Equipment," Natl. Bur. Standards (U.S.) Handbook H37, 1945. Revesz, Process Instrumentation for Measurement and Control of Level, *Inst. Radio Engrs. Trans.* PGIE-7, 11 (August, 1958). Greenwood, Electronic Techniques in Liquid-level Measurement, *Inst. Radio Engrs. Trans.* **1-7** (1), 65 (March, 1958). Denyes and Fox, Continuous Specific Gravity Measurement, *Instrumentation*, **4** (4), 11–12 (1950). "The Instrument Manual," Sec. X, United Trade Press, London, 1953. Bates, "Electrometric pH Determinations," Wiley, New York, 1954. Brode, "Chemical Spectroscopy," Wiley, New York, 1954. Harley and Wiberley, "Instrumental Analysis," Wiley, New York, 1954. Kolthoff and Laitinen, "pH and Electro-titrations," Wiley, New York, 1941. Milner, "Polarography and Other Electro-analytical Processes," Longmans, New York, 1957. Delahay, "Instrumental Analysis," Macmillan, New York, 1957. Smith, "Inorganic Chromatography," Van Nostrand, Princeton, N.J., 1953. Willard, Merritt, and Dean, "Instrumental Methods of Analysis," Van Nostrand, Princeton, N.J., 1958. Britton, "Hydrogen Ions," Van Nostrand, Princeton, N.J., 1956. Brimley and Barrett, "Practical Chromatography," Chapman & Hall, London, 1958. Nachtrieb, "Principles and Practice of Spectrochemical Analysis," McGraw-Hill, New York, 1950. Townes and Schawlow, "Microwave Spectroscopy," McGraw-Hill, New York, 1955. Continuous pH Control of Process Solutions, *Automation*, **6** (10), 72–75 (October, 1959). Glasser, Refractometers in Process-stream Analysis, *Control Eng.*, **4** (12), 96–101 (December, 1957). Cost Conscious Chromatographs, *Chem. Eng. Progress*, **6** (4), 102–106 (April, 1959). Farrar, What's New in Continuous-stream Monitors? *Oil Gas J.*, **57** (41), 127 (Oct. 5, 1959). Siggia, "Continuous Analysis of Chemical Process Streams," Wiley, New York, 1959. Cassidy, "Fundamentals of Chromatography," Interscience, New York, 1957. Bower, Survey of Analog-to-Digital Converters, *N.B.S. Rept.* 2755, July, 1953. Lucas, Data Processing and Inventory Control, *Control Eng.*, September, 1955. Hall, Data Reduction Applied to the Chemical Industry, *Control Eng.*, July, 1956. Hix, Factors in Selecting Data Handling Systems, *J. Instr. Soc. Am.*, June, 1956. Perkins and Cooper, Data Handling in the Process Industries, *Control Eng.*, July, 1956. Harris, "Electrical Measurements," Wiley, New York, 1955. Drysdale and Jolley, "Electrical Measuring Instruments," Chapman & Hall, London, 1958. Banner, "Electronic Measuring Instruments," Chapman & Hall, London, 1958. Ceaglske, "Automatic Process Control for Chemical Engineers," Wiley, New York, 1956. Farrington, "Fundamentals of Automatic Control," Wiley, New York, 1951. Grabbe, Ramo, and Woolridge, "Handbook of Automation, Computation and Control," Wiley, New York, 1958. Jones, "Electrical Control Systems," Wiley, New York, 1953. Grabbe, "Automation in Business and Industry," Wiley, New York, 1957. Wiener, "Cybernetics," Wiley, New York, 1948. Holzbock, "Automatic Control: Principles and Practices," Reinhold, New York, 1958. Murphy, "Basic Automatic Control Theory," Van Nostrand, Princeton, N.J., 1957. Ahrendt and Savant, "Servomechanism Practice," McGraw-Hill, New York, 1960. Ahrendt and Taplin, "Automatic Feedback Control," McGraw-Hill, New York, 1951. Bruns and Saunders, "Analysis of Feedback Control Systems," McGraw-Hill, New York, 1955. Evans, "Control-system Dynamics," McGraw-Hill, New York, 1954. Gille, Pélegrin, and Decaulne, "Feedback Control Systems," McGraw-Hill, New York, 1959. Goode and Machol, "System Engineering," McGraw-Hill, New York, 1957. James, Nichols, and Phillips, "Theory of Servomechanisms," McGraw-Hill, New York, 1947. Lauer, Lesnick, and Matson, "Servomechanism Fundamentals," McGraw-Hill, New York, 1960. Smith, "Feedback Control Systems," McGraw-Hill, New York, 1958. Ledgerwood, "Control Engineering Manual," McGraw-Hill, New York, 1957. McCracken, "Digital Computer Programming," Wiley, New York, 1957. Wilkes, "Automatic Digital Computers," Wiley, New York, 1948. Jacobson and Roucek, "Automation," Philosophical Library, New York, 1959. British College of Science and Technology, "Modern Computer Methods," Philosophical Library, New York, 1959. Berkeley and Wainwright, "Computers: Their Operation and Appliances," Reinhold, New York, 1956. Chapin, "Introduction to Automatic Computers," Van Nostrand, Princeton, N.J., 1957. Davis, "Computability and Unsolvability," McGraw-Hill, New York, 1958. Engineering Research Associates, "High-speed Computing Devices," McGraw-Hill, New York, 1950. Fifer, "Analogue Computations," vols. I, II, McGraw-Hill, New York, 1959. Johnson, "Analog Computer Techniques," McGraw-Hill, New York, 1956. McCormick, "Digital Computer Primer," McGraw-Hill, New York, 1959. Smith, "Electronic Digital Computers," McGraw-Hill, New York, 1959. Wrubel, "A Primer of Programming for Digital Computers," McGraw-Hill, New York, 1959. Analog Computers Solve Many Problems, *Oil Gas J.*, **57** (41), 138–140 (Oct. 5, 1959). Stein, The Outlook for Computer Control, *Chem. Eng. Progress*, **55** (4), 86–90 (April, 1959). Boycks, Priestley, and Taylor, "The Performance of a Computer Controlled Pilot Plant," A.I.Ch.E. Symposium, St. Paul, September, 1959. "Computer Techniques in Chemical Engineering," A.I.Ch.E. Monograph, New York, 1959. Bertram, "The Role of Computers in Process Control," No. 40, A.I.Ch.E. Symposium, Mar. 16, 1959. Archer, "An Optimalizing Process Control," A.I.Ch.E. Symposium No. 43. Alt, "Electronic Digital Computers in Science and Engineering," Academic Press, New York, 1958. Braun, Comparing Integral and Incremental Process Control Computers, *Control Eng.*, **7** (1), 113 (January, 1960). Rosen, Characteristics of Digital Codes, *Control Eng.*, **6** (12), 115 (December, 1959). Computers: Revolution in Process Control, *Automatic Control*, **12** (5), 13 (May, 1960). Gotlieb and Hume, "High-speed Data Processing," McGraw-Hill, New York, 1959. Shaw, Techniques and Equipment for Digital Data Conversion, *Control Eng.*, **7** (3), 107 (March, 1960). Ceaglske, "Dynamics and Control of an Absorption Column," A.I.Ch.E. Symposium, St. Paul, September, 1959. Tolin and Fluegel, "An Analog Computer for On-line Control of a Chemical Reacter," A.I.Ch.E. Symposium, St. Paul, September, 1959. Morris, Dynamic Response of Shell and Tube Heat Exchangers to Temperature Disturbances, A.I.Ch.E. Symposium, St. Paul, September, 1959. Solheim, Guide to Controlling Continuous Flow Chemical Reactors, *Control Eng.*, **7** (4), 107 (April, 1960). Rose and Rose, "Distillation," Interscience, New York, 1957. Zuiderweg, "Manual of Batch Distillation," Interscience, New York, 1957. Carney, "Laboratory Fractional Distillation," Macmillan, New York, 1949. Parkins, Continuous Distillation Plant Controls, *Chem. Eng. Progress*, **56** (7), 60–68 (July, 1959). Ryle, Gamma Density Controls Extraction Column, *Chem. Eng. Progress*, **53** (11), 551–553 (November, 1957). Fractionator Control with High-speed Chromatography, *Automatic Control*, **12** (5), 23 (May, 1960). Johnson, Simulation and Analysis Improve Evaporator Control, *J. Instr. Soc. Am.*, **7** (7), 46 (July, 1960). Fanning and Bryan, What about Pilot Plant Instrumentation? *Automatic Control*, **7** (7), 85 (July, 1960). Mayer, Characteristics of Impulse Communications and Control Systems, *Trans. Am. Inst. Elec. Engrs.*, **73** (13), 3-977-84 (Aug. 1954). Equipment for Telemetering Systems, *FM-TV*, **12**, Nos. 7–9, 17–19, July, 1952; 26–29, August, 1952; 24–26, 32, September, 1952. Iberall, Attenuation of Oscillatory Pressures in Instrument Lines, *Bur. Standards J. Research*, vol. 45, July, 1950. Grogan and Rohmann, "On the Dynamics of Pneumatic Transmission Lines," A.S.M.E. Paper 56-SA-1, Cleveland, June 17–21, 1956.

NOTE: Special reference must also be made to the comprehensive Guide to Process Instrument Elements by Theodore R. Olive and Steven Danatos, *Chem. Eng.*, **64** (6), 285–320 (June 1957); and to "Process Instruments and Controls Handbook," edited by Douglas M. Considine, McGraw-Hill, New York, 1957. Both text material and illustrations have been used freely in the preparation of this section of this handbook. In acknowledging the cooperation of contributors to the foregoing publications, the editor wishes to express his appreciation and gratitude to Mrs. Cathy Kasten, who typed and supervised preparation of most of the manuscripts that comprise this section.

PROCESS MEASUREMENTS

Measurement is a fundamental requisite to process control whether that control be effected automatically, semiautomatically, or manually. The quality of control obtainable also bears a relationship to the accuracy, reproducibility, and reliability of the measurement methods which are employed. Therefore, selection of the most effective means for measurements is an important first step in the design and formulation of any process-control system.

Because of the rather disproportionate emphases which have been afforded to the data-processing and automatic-controller aspects of process instrumentation over the past two decades of automation progress, there has been a tendency among process engineers to pay too little attention to the selection of measurement means. And the instrument designers and builders have often overlooked the development of new and improved measurement methodologies.

Progress in the science of measurement has been substantial, but this progress has not kept pace with the other facets of instrumentation. For example, the standards of measurement terminology have lagged the development of the rather sophisticated nomenclature of automatic control. Principal advancements in the measurement field during the last two decades have occurred in the area of continuous chemical analysis. But measurements of the more frequently occurring variables, such as temperature, pressure, flow, and liquid level, have undergone relatively few major changes.

Aside from design refinements, for example, the use of thermocouples, resistance thermometers, filled-system thermometers, and radiation pyrometers remains the prime temperature-detecting means, just as they were a quarter century ago. Orifice and venturi flowmeters, the science of which was well established 50 years ago, still account for the largest portion of process-flow instrumentation. Several critical process variables, such as viscosity, consistency, color, moisture, and humidity, although now subject to continuous process measurement, still await scientific break-throughs for the attainment of completely satisfactory results. Chemical and process engineers have a heavy responsibility to encourage greater scientific attention to the development and application of better measurement means.

Table 22-1. Relative Order of Occurrence of Various Types of Measurements in the Process Industries

Process Variable and Type of Measurement		Estimated % of Installations
Temperature		34.7
Electrical methods, such as thermocouple potentiometers, millivoltmeter pyrometers, and resistance thermometers	20.5	
Mechanical methods, such as filled-system thermometers	12.4	
Radiation pyrometers	1.8	
Flow		17.5
Mechanical methods	14.6	
Electrical methods	2.9	
Liquid level		11.8
Mechanical methods	10.2	
Electrical methods	1.6	
Pressure		11.7
Mechanical methods	9.8	
Electrical methods	1.9	
Chemical composition		5.6
Electrical variables such as current, voltage, resistance, and power		4.6
Humidity		3.5
Speed (linear and rotational)		2.1
Density and specific gravity		1.8
Moisture		0.7
All other variables such as viscosity, consistency, weight, and color		6.0
		100.0

As guidance to the process engineer in the establishment of an instrumentation laboratory, standards, calibration, and repair facilities, and instrument departments and training programs, the relative order of occurrence of the different types of measurements in the process industries is shown in Table 22-1. These trade estimates are based on a broad survey and will vary from one segment of industry to the next.

TEMPERATURE MEASUREMENTS

Fixed Points for Standardization. For standardization throughout science and industry, it is essential

Table 22-2. Fixed Points for Thermometer and Pyrometer Standardization

Substance	Phase change	Temperature °C.	Temperature °F.
Helium	Melts	<−271	<−456
Hydrogen	Boils	−253	−423
Oxygen	Melts	−227	−377
Nitrogen	Boils	−196	−321
Oxygen	Boils	−183	−297
Isopentane	Melts	−160	−256
Methyl cyclohexane	Melts	−126	−195
Carbon bisulfide	Melts	−112	−170
Toluene	Melts	−95.0	−139.0
Carbon dioxide	Sublimes	−78.5	−109.3
Chloroform	Melts	−63.5	−82.3
Mercury	Melts	−38.9	−38.0
Carbon tetrachloride	Melts	−22.9	−9.2
Water	Melts	00.0	+32.0
Glauber's salt	Melts	+32.4	90.3
Acetylene dichloride	Boils	55.0	131.0
Ethyl alcohol	Boils	78.3	172.9
Water	Boils	100.0	212.0
Toluene	Boils	110.0	230.0
Chlorobenzene	Boils	132.0	269.6
Brombenzene	Boils	156.6	313.9
Aniline	Boils	184.5	364.1
Nitrobenzene	Boils	209.0	408.2
Tin	Melts	231.9	449.4
Diphenyl	Boils	254.6	490.3
Naphthol (α)	Boils	278.0	532.4
Diphenylamine	Boils	302.0	575.6
Lead	Melts	327.4	621.3
Mercury	Boils	357.3	675.1
Potassium dichromate	Melts	397.5	747.5
Zinc	Melts	419.4	786.9
Sulfur	Boils	444.6	832.3
Lead chloride	Melts	501.0	933.8
Calcium nitrate	Melts	561.0	1041.8
Antimony	Melts	630.0	1166.0
Aluminum	Melts	658.7	1217.7
Manganous sulfate	Melts	700.0	1292.0
Potassium chloride	Melts	770.3	1418.5
Sodium chloride	Melts	800.4	1472.7
Sodium carbonate	Melts	852.0	1565.6
Sodium sulfate	Melts	884.7	1624.5
Silver	Melts	960.5	1760.9
Gold	Melts	1063	1945
Potassium sulfate	Melts	1069	1956
Copper	Melts	1083	1981
Stannic oxide	Melts	1127	2061
Lithium silicate	Melts	1201	2194
Barium fluoride	Melts	1280	2336
Nickel	Melts	1452	2646
Cobalt	Melts	1480	2696
Iron	Melts	1530	2786
Palladium	Melts	1549	2820
Platinum	Melts	1755	3191
Alumina	Melts	2000	3632
Tungsten	Melts	3400	6152

that temperature measurements have the same meaning from one laboratory to the next and from one factory to the next. This has been made possible through the adoption of consistent temperature standards and scales. Reproducible fixed points have been selected and the temperature intervals between them have been divided into convenient numbers of degrees. The most important of these fixed points are the boiling points and freezing points of pure substances at specified pressures. Fixed points for thermometer and pyrometer standardization are given in Table 22-2.

International Temperature Scale. To provide a basis for precise and convenient temperature measurements, a temperature scale, known as the international temperature scale, has been established which covers the range from the boiling point of oxygen to the highest temperatures of incandescent bodies and flames. This scale is based on six reproducible equilibrium temperatures, or fixed points, to which numerical values have been assigned, and on specified interpolation formulas which relate temperatures between or above these points to the indications of standard temperature-measuring instruments.

The international temperature scale was first adopted in 1927 by the Seventh General Conference on Weights and Measures and was revised in 1948 by the Ninth General Conference. At this last conference, the name *Celsius* was recommended to designate the scale having 0 degrees as the ice point and 100 degrees as the steam point. Celsius thus replaces the word *centigrade* as was commonly used in the United States. The abbreviation remains unchanged, namely, °C.

The six fixed points, the instruments used for interpolation between fixed points, and the interpolation equations are given in Table 22-3.

In addition to the definition of the international temperature scale of 1948, the conference recommended the procedures to be used in realizing the fixed points and the requirements which the instruments must fulfill if they are to be standard instruments.

Temperature Scale below the Oxygen Point. There is no international temperature scale below the oxygen point, but a scale based on the resistance of several capsule-type platinum resistance thermometers, which were calibrated with a gas thermometer, is maintained at the National Bureau of Standards (Washington, D.C.). This scale is distributed to other laboratories by calibrating similar thermometers by comparison methods. For the temperature range from approximately 10° to 4°K., there is nothing to correspond to the international scale except a gas thermometer. From 4.2° to 1°K., the vapor pressure of helium is used for the measurement of temperatures in laboratories throughout the world. Below 1°K., the magnetic properties of paramagnetic salts provide both the means of attaining temperatures in the range and the indication of the temperature of the salt.

Temperature-scale Conversion Formulas. Conversion tables can be found in Sec. 1 of this handbook. The basic formulas for converting from one temperature scale to the next are as follows:

Degree Fahrenheit = $\frac{5}{9}$ degree Celsius
Degree Fahrenheit = $\frac{4}{9}$ degree Reaumur
Degree Celsius = $\frac{9}{5}$ degree Fahrenheit
Temperature (degrees Fahrenheit) = $\frac{9}{5}$ × (degrees Celsius) + 32
Temperature (degrees Fahrenheit) = $\frac{9}{4}$ × (degrees Reaumur) + 32
Temperature (degrees Celsius) = $\frac{5}{9}$ × (degrees Fahrenheit) − 32
Temperature (degrees Celsius) = $\frac{5}{4}$ × (degrees Reaumur)
Temperature (degrees Reaumur) = $\frac{4}{9}$ × (degrees Fahrenheit) − 32
Temperature (degrees Reaumur) = $\frac{4}{5}$ × (degrees Celsius)
Temperature (degrees Kelvin) = (degrees Celsius) + 273.16

Establishing and Maintaining a Temperature Scale. The problem of establishing and maintaining a temperature scale is not confined to the National Bureau of Standards, but it is necessary that this be done in industrial and research laboratories as well. In the preceding description of temperature scales, a definition was given of the international temperature scale on which practically all temperature measurements are based. By setting up apparatus suitable for realizing the fixed points and by calibrating the three standard instruments used for interpolating between these fixed points, the primary temperature scale may be established. To do this requires a considerable investment in equipment and time. Three different methods or combinations of them are commonly used in maintaining temperature scales in laboratories:

The first method involves the setting up of equipment for primary calibrations of the three standard measuring instruments: (1) the resistance thermometer, (2) the platinum vs. platinum-rhodium thermocouple, and (3) the optical pyrometer. This method provides a primary

Table 22-3. Basis for the International Temperature Scale of 1948

Temp. range, °C.	Fixed points, °C.	Interpolation equation	Standard instrument	Notes
−182.97 to 630.5	Oxygen (b.p.) (−182.970) Ice (f.p.) (0) Steam (b.p.) (100) Sulfur (b.p.) (444.600)	$R_t = R_0[1 + At + Bt^2 + C(t - 100)t^3]$	Platinum resistance thermometer	1
0 to 630.5		$R_t = R_0(1 + At + Bt^2)$ where R_t = resistance of thermometer resistor at temp. t, R_0 = resistance at 0°C., and A, B, and C are constants		
630.5 to 1063	Antimony (f.p.) (630.5) Silver (f.p.) (960.8) Gold (f.p.) (1063.0)	$E = a + bt + ct^2$ where E = e.m.f. of standard thermocouple and a, b, and c are constants	Platinum vs. platinum–10% rhodium thermocouple	2
1063 to ∞	Gold (f.p.) (1063.0)	$\frac{J_t}{J_{Au}} = \frac{e^{\frac{C_2}{\lambda(t_{Au}+T_0)}} - 1}{e^{\frac{C_2}{\lambda(t+T_0)}} - 1}$ where J_t and J_{Au} are the radiant energies per unit wave-length interval at wave length λ emitted per unit time by a unit area of a black body at the temperature t and at the gold point t_{Au}, respectively; c_2 = 1.438 cm. deg.; T_0 = temp. of ice point, °K.; λ = wave length	Optical pyrometer	3

f.p. = freezing point; b.p. = boiling point.
1. For measurements of the highest precision, the triple point of water may be used with the assigned value of 0.0100°C.
2. The temperature of the antimony to be determined with a standard resistance thermometer.
3. No standard instrument is explicitly specified, but the optical pyrometer is commonly used.

calibration of all three instruments with the opportunity to repeat these calibrations as required.

The second and most frequently used method is to submit the three standard instruments to the National Bureau of Standards for calibration. In this case, the platinum resistance thermometer and the platinum vs. platinum-rhodium thermocouple may be given primary calibrations; and the optical pyrometer is given a comparison calibration through the use of the standard optical pyrometer at the bureau. The instruments which are calibrated in this manner and those calibrated in the previous procedure then become the standards of the laboratory and are normally used, in turn, to calibrate the secondary instruments, such as other thermocouples or liquid-in-glass thermometers.

The third procedure which may be used is to rely entirely upon what may be called secondary standards, namely, base-metal thermocouples and liquid-in-glass thermometers. Such instruments are certified by the National Bureau of Standards if they meet certain specifications, and they may be used to maintain a temperature scale although not with the same accuracy as the primary instruments.

Further information on the establishment and maintenance of temperature standards can be found in Considine (ed.), "Process Instruments and Controls Handbook" (McGraw-Hill, New York, 1957).

Thermocouples

The history of the thermocouple dates back to the discovery by Seebeck in 1821 that an electric current flows in a continuous circuit of two metals if the two junctions are at different temperatures. Such a thermocouple may be represented diagrammatically as shown in Fig. 22-1. A and B are the two metals, and T_1 and T_2

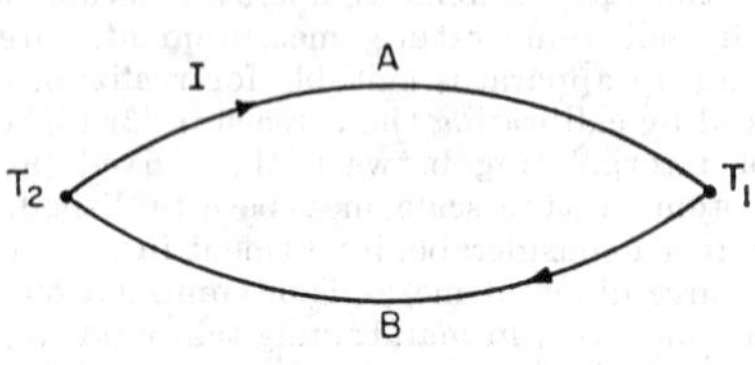

FIG. 22-1. Simple thermocouple circuit.

are the temperatures of the junctions. I represents the thermoelectric current which flows in the circuit. A is customarily referred to as thermoelectrically positive to B if T_1 is the colder junction.

Thermoelectric Laws. *Law of the Homogeneous Circuit.* An electric current cannot be sustained in a circuit of a single homogeneous metal, however varying in section, by the application of heat alone.

Law of Intermediate Metals. If in any circuit of solid conductors the temperature is uniform from any point P through all the conducting matter to a point Q, the algebraic sum of the thermoelectromotive forces in the entire circuit is totally independent of this intermediate matter and is the same as if P and Q were put in contact.

Law of Successive or Intermediate Temperatures. The thermal e.m.f. developed by any thermocouple of homogeneous metals with its junctions at any two temperatures T_1 and T_3 is the algebraic sum of the e.m.f. of the thermocouple with one junction at T_1 and the other at any other temperature T_2 and the e.m.f. of the same thermocouple with its junctions at T_2 and T_3.

Thermocouple Size. For a given composition, the smaller the thermocouple wire and junction, the faster the response to changes of temperature. In many applications, the mechanical strength of the wires themselves is required to support the thermocouple. Other factors being equal, the larger the diameter of the wires, the greater is the effect of heat conduction on the temperature of the measuring junction. This may be significant, particularly under conditions permitting only a small immersion. In addition, small wires are easily kinked and broken and more readily develop inhomogeneities. In cases involving corrosion, thermocouples of large wires normally require replacement less frequently than those of small wires.

Thermocouple Selection. To assist in the selection of a proper thermocouple, in accordance with the composition, size, and construction factors, summary tables and curves are given in Table 22-4, Figs. 22-2 and 22-3, and Table 22-5.

Table 22-4. Common Types of Thermocouples and Temperature Ranges in Which They Are Used

I.S.A. type	Positive element	Negative element	Usual temp. range		Max. temp.	
			°C.	°F.	°C.	°F.
S	90% Pt–10% Rh	Platinum	0 to 1450	32 to 2650	1700	3100
R	87% Pt–13% Rh	Platinum	0 to 1450	32 to 2650	1700	3100
K	Chromel-P	Alumel	−200 to 1100	−300 to 2000	1200	2200
J, Y	Iron	Constantan	−200 to 750	−300 to 1400	1000	1800
T	Copper	Constantan	−200 to 350	−200 to 650	600	1100
	Chromel-P	Constantan	−100 to 1000	−150 to 1800	1000	1800

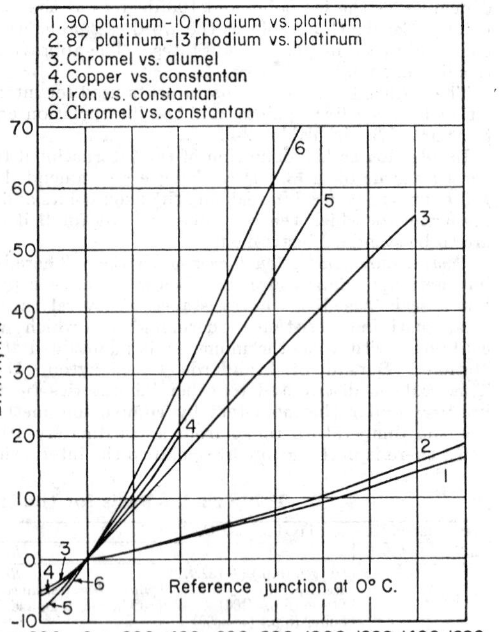

FIG. 22-2. Temperature–thermal e.m.f. curves for common types of thermocouples.

Thermocouple Junctions. The measuring junction of a thermocouple may be formed by any method providing the necessary strength and electrical contact (law of intermediate metals). Wires may be either twisted together before soldering or welding to increase junction strength, or they may be butt-welded (see Table 22-6). The cut wires usually will be curved from having been coiled and should be carefully straightened. In this operation, hammering or excessive twisting and

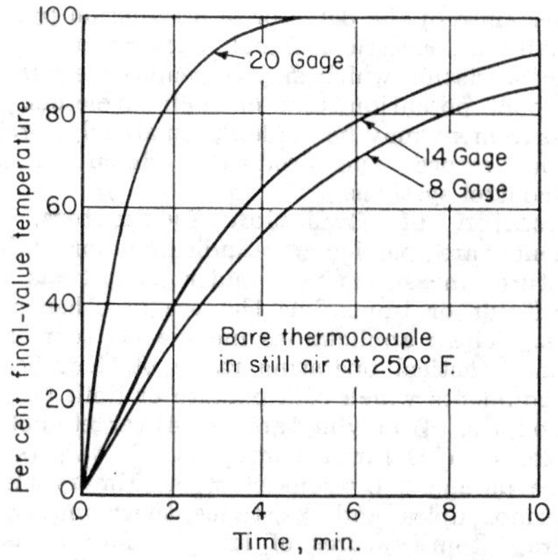

FIG. 22-3. Response of bare thermocouples of different sizes.

Table 22-5. Corrosion Characteristics of Common Thermocouples

Type of Thermocouple	Influence of Temperature and Gas Atmospheres
Platinum vs. platinum-rhodium	1. Resistance to oxidizing atmosphere: very good 2. Resistance to reducing atmosphere: poor 3. Platinum corrodes easily above 1000°C. Should be used in gastight ceramic protecting tube
Chromel-P vs. Alumel	1. Resistance to oxidizing atmosphere: good to very good 2. Resistance to reducing atmosphere: poor 3. Affected by sulfur, reducing or sulfurous gas, SO_2, and H_2S
Iron vs. Constantan	1. Oxidizing and reducing atmospheres have little effect on accuracy. Best used in dry atmospheres 2. Resistance to oxidation: good up to 400°C. but poor above 700°C. 3. Resistance to reducing atmosphere: good (up to 400°C.) 4. Protect from oxygen, moisture, sulfur
Copper vs. Constantan	1. Subject to oxidation and alteration above 400°C. due to copper, above 600°C. due to Constantan wire. Contamination of copper affects calibration greatly 2. Resistance to oxidizing atmosphere: good 3. Resistance to reducing atmosphere: good 4. Requires protection from acid fumes
Chromel-P vs. Constantan	1. Chromel attacked by sulfurous atmosphere 2. Resistance to oxidation: good 3. Resistance to reducing atmosphere: good

Table 22-6. Methods of Joining Thermocouple Wires

Type of thermocouple	Method of joining	Flux
Platinum vs. platinum-rhodium	Oxygas flame weld	None
	Electric-arc weld	None
Chromel-P vs. Alumel	Oxyacetylene or oxygas flame weld	Borax, fluorite
	Electric-arc weld	None
	Silver solder	Borax
	Electric-resistance weld	None
Iron vs. Constantan	Oxyacetylene or oxygas flame weld	Borax, fluorite
	Electric-arc weld	None
	Silver solder	Borax
	Soft solder	Rosin
	Electric-resistance weld	None
Copper vs. Constantan	Electric-arc weld	None
	Silver solder	Borax
	Soft solder	Rosin
Chromel-P vs. Constantan	Oxyacetylene or oxygas flame weld	Borax, fluorite
	Electric-arc weld	None
	Silver solder	Borax

bending of the wires must be avoided. Excessive cold working or tool handling may alter the thermal e.m.f. or damage the surface and contribute to short life.

Thermocouple Protecting Tubes. Platinum vs. platinum-rhodium thermocouples are particularly susceptible to contamination and should be protected by ceramic tubes which are impervious to gases and vapors at all operating temperatures. Metal protecting tubes usually provide sufficient protection for base-metal thermocouples. The oxide coatings on the thermocouple wires are fairly effective in protecting the wires from contamination by metallic vapors. Metal tubes which provide sufficient protection in an oxidizing atmosphere may be entirely unsatisfactory if large amounts of furnace gases are present. In some installations it has been found advisable to ventilate the interior of the protecting tube with a slow stream of air or an inert gas in order to minimize the deleterious effects of gases.

The primary ceramic tubes which meet most requirements of stability and imperviousness to gases are highly refractory porcelain (Sillimanite, Mullite) for temperatures up to about 1500°C., fused silica for temperatures up to about 1050°C. in an oxidizing atmosphere, and Pyrex glass for temperatures up to about 500°C.

The secondary or metal tube most suitable for a particular application depends to a large extent upon the type of corrosion encountered. Nickel-chromium-iron tubes are particularly useful in oxidizing atmospheres, chromium-iron tubes in atmospheres containing sulfur, and nickel and iron tubes in hot caustic and molten-metal baths, respectively. The temperature limits given in Table 22-7 for the various types of tubes are those which will, in general, result in a reasonably long life. The tubes may be used at higher temperatures than those given, but higher operating temperatures will result in a shorter life. Fire clay, silicon carbide, and graphite meet certain requirements of secondary tubes at temperatures above the useful limits of metal tubes. Numerous other types of tubes have been developed for specific purposes. [For further information on thermocouples, see Sec. 2-1, by Wilson and Evans, in "Process Instruments and Controls Handbook" (McGraw-Hill, New York, 1957).]

Table 22-7. Recommended Maximum Operating Temperature of Protecting Tubes

Type of tube	Recommended max. temp. °C.	°F.
Metal Tubes		
High silicon iron	425	800
Seamless steel	550	1000
Carbon steel	550	1000
Cast iron	700	1300
Wrought iron	700	1300
18 Cr-8 Ni stainless steel	950	1800
28 Cr iron	1100	2000
Chromel T	1100	2000
Nichrome	1100	2000
Nickel	1100	2000
20 Cr-32 Ni-48 Fe (Incoloy)	1100	2000
Inconel	1260	2300
Ceramic Tubes		
Fused silica	1050	1900
Fire clay	1550	2800
Sillimanite	1550	2800
Mullite	1550	2800
Silica	1600	2900
Silicon carbide	1650	3000

Radiation Pyrometers. The method of measuring the temperature of an object by means of the quantity and characteristics of the energy which it radiates has been designated "radiation pyrometry." This field of pyrometry has produced several different primary elements which may be broadly classified in two groups: (1) optical pyrometers, those instruments in which the brightness (for a narrow wave-length interval) of a hot object is manually compared by the operator's eye with that of a source of standard brightness, and (2) radiation pyrometers, those instruments which measure the rate of energy emission per unit area over a relatively broad range of wave lengths. In the past, the latter devices have been classified as total-radiation pyrometers, since in theory they are sensitive to the entire spectrum of energy radiated by the hot object. Actually, practical devices are sensitive to a limited wave-length interval and should be designated partial-radiation pyrometers or, as is followed in this section, simply be referred to as radiation pyrometers.

Operating Principles. Radiation pyrometers measure the intensity of radiation emitted by a hot object over a range of wave lengths. The Stefan-Boltzmann equation indicates that the rate at which energy is emitted from a unit area by a black body is a function of the difference of the fourth powers of the absolute temperatures of a hot source and a receiver. Thus the temperature of a suitably arranged receiver (radiation pyrometer) may be theoretically related to the temperature of a hot target. An elementary form of such a pyrometer is shown in Fig. 22-4. It comprises (1) a

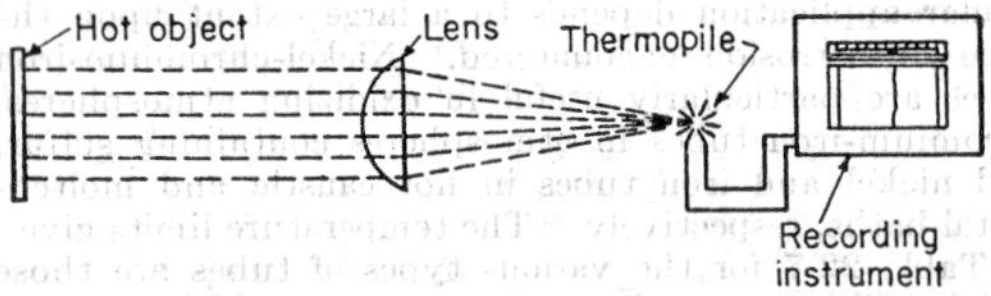

FIG. 22-4. Elementary radiation pyrometer.

lens (or mirror) optical system for focusing radiated energy on a detecting element and (2) a detector, which may be a photocell, bolometer, vacuum thermocouple, thermopile, or other element which varies an electrical quantity as a function of its temperature. The optical system and detector must be protected with a housing and an auxiliary instrument provided for measuring the pyrometer signal. [For further information see Sec. 2-2, by Forsythe and Hornor, in "Process Instruments and Controls Handbook" (McGraw-Hill, New York, 1957).]

The temperature change of the detector depends not only on the source temperature but also on the thermal equilibrium established by the detector with its surroundings. Thus, while the detector is absorbing energy from the hot object, it is also losing heat by radiation, conduction, and convection to its housing, enclosing atmosphere, and supports. The equilibrium will also depend on the temperature of the housing and thus on the ambient temperature. It is necessary then that the housing temperature be stabilized or, better, that the detector response be compensated for changes in housing temperature. As a consequence of all these factors, an industrial radiation pyrometer usually responds to a slightly different power of the object temperature than the fourth (as in the Stefan-Boltzmann law), and its calibration equation is empirical.

The detecting elements for the most widely used industrial radiation pyrometers are thermopiles composed of several thermocouples connected in series. Thermistor-, platinum-, and copper-element bolometers also serve as detectors. Phototubes of various types have been employed as detecting elements. The barrier-layer photovoltaic cell and the cesium vacuum photocell have been used in steel-industry pyrometry in the United States. The photovoltaic cell is widely used in England for radiation pyrometry. German pyrometers utilize lead sulfide photoconductive tubes. At least two commercial pyrometers have vacuum thermocouples as detectors.

The response of the detector of a radiation pyrometer is normally an electrical signal, such as an e.m.f. or resistance variation which may be readily measured with conventional potentiometers or millivoltmeters. Thus the measurement may be made automatically, provide a continuous record, and produce a signal for use in process-control systems.

Application of Radiation Pyrometers. These instruments are particularly indicated for industrial temperature measurements under conditions which make difficult or impossible the use of other primary elements. These applications include (1) temperatures above the practical operating range of thermocouples, (2) environments which contaminate or limit the life of thermocouples, (3) moving targets, (4) targets not easily accessible, such as furnace interiors, (5) targets which would be damaged by contact with primary elements like thermocouples and resistance thermometers, and (6) average temperatures of large surface areas. Although these conditions are also satisfactorily met with an optical pyrometer, a distinction may be made because the latter must be manually operated. If the application demands automatic measurement, or a continuous record, or adaptability to process control, then a radiation pyrometer should be used.

Range of Temperature Measurement. Conventional designs of radiation pyrometers may be obtained for measurement of temperatures between 400°F. and any conceivable high temperature. The type previously described for low-temperature measurement has a normal range of 125° to 700°F. and may be used on some applications down to 32°F. In order to obtain adequate sensitivity, a single instrument design is not applicable to the entire range of temperature indicated above. An arbitrary classification, as shown in the accompanying list, has been made to establish the range of operation over which a single type of instrument is recommended for use.

Type of Pyrometer	Temp. Range, °F.
High range..................	1500 and higher
Intermediate range...........	1000–2500
Low intermediate range	400–1200
Low range..................	125–400

Because a radiation pyrometer develops a signal proportional to approximately the fourth power of the temperature, the scale of the measuring instrument will be contracted at the low end and expanded at the high end. As a result, the readability and control sensitivity usually required will be obtained only on the upper 40 per cent of the measuring-instrument range span. When selecting a radiation pyrometer and measuring instrument for a particular application, specifications should be drawn so that the temperatures to be measured will be within 60 to 100 per cent of the instrument range.

Direct Observation of the Target. This method is applicable whenever an unobstructed sighting path can be provided and direct measurement of temperature of an object is required. If the medium between the target and pyrometer is clean air (for example, the target is the billet in an induction heater), the instrument may be used directly without accessory equipment. If absorbing or radiating gases intervene, the pyrometer should have an air-purged sighting tube. The sighting tube may be of Inconel when exposed to temperatures up to 2000°F. Ceramic tubes are available for temperatures to 4500°F. The tube should extend to within 1 or 2 in. of the target. The purging air should be clean and dry and each radiation pyrometer should be provided with its own air filter. A minimum quantity of air should be employed to avoid cooling the target. For furnaces at pressures slightly above atmospheric, a flow of 20 to 30 cu. ft./hr. has been found adequate. If the purge supply pressure is unsteady, a low-cost differential regulator and indicating flowmeter may be used to maintain a steady purge rate.

Sighting on Target Tube. In this method, the pyrometer observes the interior of a tube which has a closed end inserted in the chamber whose temperature is to be measured. This method is employed whenever a suitable target cannot be obtained or flame, smoke, dust, and combustion products interfere. These target tubes are sized so that the pyrometer will observe only the bottom of the tube. Ceramic tubes are usually employed for this purpose. However, the entire tube need not be ceramic—a wrought-iron extension may be employed for that section whose temperature will be less than 500°F. Because ceramic tubes exhibit appreciable porosity, it is often necessary to air-purge the tubes if the furnace gases foul the optical system.

Optical Pyrometers

Instruments designated as optical pyrometers are those which measure the intensity of the radiant flux emitted in a narrow wave-length interval in the visible spectrum. The temperature of the target is then determined from its spectral radiant intensity. The radiant energy is measured by photometric comparison of the relative brightness of the object of unknown temperature with a source of standard brightness, such as the tungsten filament of an electric lamp designed for this purpose. The brightness comparison is made by the observer and is dependent upon the extreme sensitivity of the human eye to differences in brightness between two adjacent surfaces of the same color. The latter requirement is satisfied by providing the optical system of the pyrometer with a glass color filter which is nearly monochromatic for the wave length of red radiation (0.65 micron). An outstanding advantage of the optical pyrometer results from the high ratio of change in brightness of the source being measured, as seen through the filter, to the corresponding change in source temperature. Under favorable conditions, brightness matches can be made to a fraction of 1 per cent.

Modern optical pyrometers effect the brightness comparison by either of two methods: (1) varying the current through the filament of the standard brightness source, until its brightness matches that of the target image, or (2) optically varying the observed brightness of the image, until it matches that of the standard lamp filament, while maintaining a constant current through the lamp. The condition of matched brightness is evidenced by blending the standard lamp filament with the image of the hot target. This effect has created the general designation of *disappearing-filament* optical pyrometers for these instruments.

Application of Optical Pyrometers. The optical pyrometer is employed in both laboratory and industrial operations for measuring temperature above 1400°F. The high order of precision and accuracy obtainable by careful operation has caused it to be accepted as the standard means for determining temperatures on the international temperature scale from the gold point upward and permits its use as a secondary standard of temperature for laboratory work. Industrial applications of the optical pyrometer depend upon its ability to measure accurately temperatures of objects which are remote and inaccessible, other than visually, such as molten metals or furnace interiors or the temperature of surfaces or of incandescent filaments. It is also used for process calibration of other temperature-measuring devices such as radiation pyrometers and thermocouples in protection tubes. It is portable, and skill in its operation may be readily acquired. The optical pyrometer must be manually operated, and thus its measurements cannot be continuously recorded or used to control automatically.

Range of Temperature Measurement. The normal limits of application lie between 1400° and 5200°F. With special absorbing screens, the calibration has been extended to 10,000°F. The instruments are frequently supplied with a double- or triple-range calibration, *i.e.*, 1400° to 2250°F., 1950° to 3200°F., and others.

Target Size and Distance. Measurements with this instrument are independent of the distance between the target and the observer, provided the image of the target is sufficiently large to make it possible to secure a definite brightness match with the filament or test spot. It is necessary that the cone of rays proceeding from the measured area of the source, with the telescopic objective as its base, be unobstructed.

Resistance Thermometers

The resistance thermometer depends upon the inherent characteristics of metals to change in electrical resistance when they undergo a change in temperature. Although industrial resistance-thermometer bulbs are usually made of platinum, copper, or nickel, the temperature-resistance phenomenon also applies to semiconductors, and it is quite possible that, as improved semiconducting materials are developed, they may find an increasing use in resistance thermometry. The theory of the temperature-resistance phenomenon in semiconductors is adequately treated in many texts, some of which are listed in the References (see also Sec. 2-2 by Adams in "Process Instruments and Controls Handbook," *loc. cit.*).

Basically, a resistance thermometer is an instrument for measuring electrical resistance, but which is calibrated in units of temperature instead of in units of resistance. In this respect, the resistance thermometer is not unlike many other electrical transducers which convert an electrical measurement into units of a process variable, such as temperature or pressure (*cf.* Sec. 25 of this handbook).

One of several common forms of bridges can be employed in resistance thermometry. These include (1) Wheatstone bridge, presently the most common type used in industrial resistance thermometers, (2) Callendar-Griffiths bridge, (3) double slide-wire bridge, (4) capacitance bridge, and (5) Mueller bridge. These bridges may be operated with either direct or alternating current and may be (1) the null-balance type or (2) the deflection type.

Temperature Coefficient of Resistance. The change in electrical resistance of a material with a change in temperature is termed the "temperature coefficient of resistance" for the material. The coefficient is expressed as a change in ohms resistance per ohm per degree of temperature at a specified temperature. For most metals, the temperature coefficient is positive. For pure metals, the change in resistance with temperature is practically linear, at least over a portion of the resistance-temperature curve.

Typical curves for platinum, copper, and nickel are given in Fig. 22-5.

Resistor-bulb Design. Resistor bulbs are available in many forms and shapes, depending upon their intended application. A common form as shown in Fig. 22-6 comprises a tubular-shaped metal stem, the lower end of which is sealed, while the upper end terminates in the head or terminal housing. The resistance winding is located in the lower end of the stem. The winding always must be in good thermal contact with the inner surface of the stem or housing so that proper heat transfer from the medium being measured will occur and result in an acceptable speed of response. For obvious reasons, the winding must be electrically insulated from the stem.

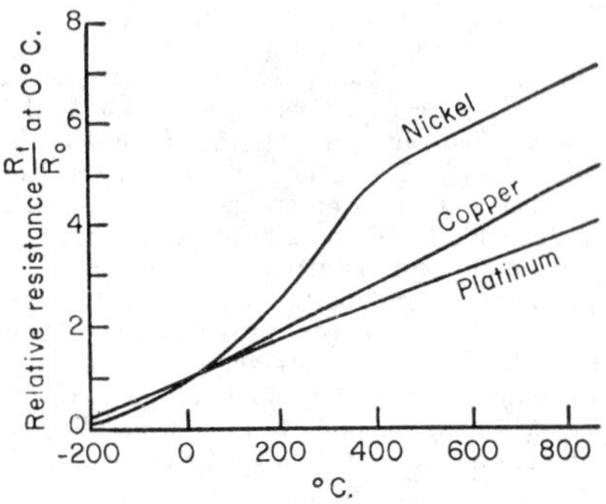

FIG. 22-5. Typical resistance-thermometer curves for platinum, copper, and nickel wire used in resistor bulbs.

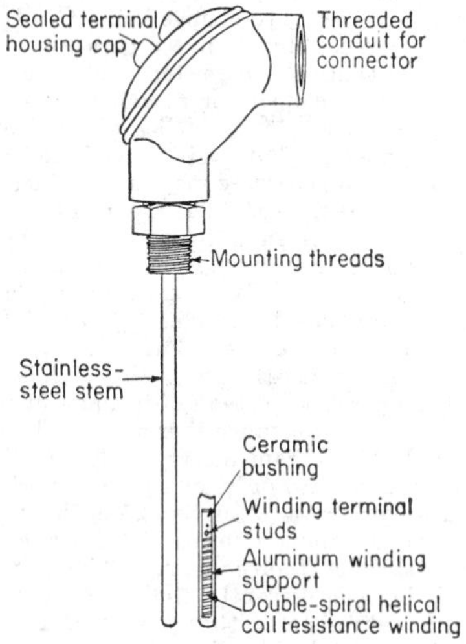

FIG. 22-6. Industrial-type resistance-thermometer bulb.

Thus one of the fundamental design problems is that of achieving the desired electrical insulation with minimum thermal insulation.

Principal factors in resistance-thermometer bulb design include (1) shape, (2) size, (3) material used in resistance winding, (4) insulation of the winding, and (5) type of winding. The first two factors are largely a matter of mechanical design. A complete delineation of the many available bulb shapes and sizes is beyond the scope of this section.

Resistance vs. temperature of various metals used in resistor-bulb windings are given in Table 22-8.

Types of Resistor-bulb Applications. *Spot-temperature Measurement.* Most resistor bulbs are used for the measurement of spot temperatures as opposed to average-temperature measurement. For spot-temperature measurement, the resistance winding usually is concentrated into the annular space located 1 or 2 in. from the lower end of the stem. The end of the stem is tightly sealed to protect the winding and prevent the entrance of contaminating or damaging elements. The upper end of the stem usually is welded or brazed into a head or terminal housing which contains the means for making connections. Where the resistance winding is a flat frame or arbor, the temperature-sensitive portion of the bulb housing may be flattened to conform more nearly to the shape of the winding. This construction gives a faster response to temperature changes.

Average-temperature Measurement. In applications of this type, the resistance winding is distributed over a portion of the length of the stem. This length varies from about 1 in. from the tip to as much as 4 in. or more from the tip. The latter type of bulb is particularly useful for the measurement of liquids in vessels or pipe lines, for example, the coolant liquids and lubricating oil in aircraft engines.

A bulb is available for measuring the average temperature of large vessels containing liquids, such as petroleum-product storage tanks. This bulb comprises a long, uniformly stretched helical coil of fine copper wire mounted and sealed into a thin-walled flexible plastic tube. For mechanical protection, this tube is mounted in a long flexible metal hose for suspension from the roof to the bottom of the tank. Since the resistance winding is uniformly stretched and distributed over the vertical height of the liquid, the resistance of the winding is proportional to the average temperature of the tank even though there may be a considerable temperature gradient from the bottom to top.

Free-air resistor bulbs, as the name implies, are designed for the measurement of air temperatures. They are of numerous types and designs, depending upon whether still air or air moving at high velocity is involved. If still or slowly moving air is the object of measurement, especially where fast response is required, the simplest form of bulb is that of a self-supporting helical coil of bare wire, mounted to a light supporting frame. For high-velocity air measurements, as encountered in high-speed aircraft, the designer must guard against the influence of radiation from external sources, such as the sun, and errors due to friction of air against the bulb.

Surface-temperature Measurement. An interesting surface-temperature resistor bulb is in the form of a small wafer. This unit comprises a winding of fine nickel wire, sealed between two sheets of plasticized paper, and has a total thickness of about 0.005 in., a width of 0.5 in., and a length of 1.5 in. Two heavier wire leads extend from one end of the unit. When tightly cemented to the surface whose temperature is to be measured, it has a useful range of −100° to 400°F., with an accuracy of ±1°F. Its very small mass and good thermal contact result in very fast response speeds.

Resistor-bulb Connections. Three methods are commonly used for making electrical connections from the resistance winding to the measuring instrument, namely, the use of two, three, or four leads.

Table 22-8. Resistance vs. Temperature of Various Metals

Metal	Resistivity, microhm-cm.	Relative resistance R_t/R_0 at 0°C.*											
		−200	−100	0	100	200	300	400	500	600	700	800	900
Alumel	28.1	.....	.....	1.000	1.239	1.428	1.537	1.637	1.726	1.814	1.899	1.982	2.066
Copper	1.56	0.117	0.557	1.000	1.431	1.862	2.299	2.747	3.210	3.695	4.208	4.752	5.334
Iron	8.57	.....	.....	1.000	1.650	2.464	3.485	4.716	6.162	7.839	9.790	12.009	12.790
Nickel	6.38	.....	.....	1.000	1.663	2.501	3.611	4.847	5.398	5.882	6.327	6.751	7.156
Platinum	9.83	0.177	0.599	1.000	1.392	1.773	3.142	2.499	2.844	3.178	3.500	4.810	4.109
Silver	1.50	0.176	0.596	1.000	1.408	1.827	2.256	2.698	3.150	3.616	4.094	4.586	5.091

* R_t = resistances at temperature T_0 ohms.
R_0 = resistance at 0°C., ohms.

Two-lead Method. This method, shown in Fig. 22-7, is the simplest, consisting of two relatively low-resistance leads *a* and *b* connecting the bulb resistance winding with the measuring apparatus. In this case, the leads are copper and a Wheatstone bridge is shown.

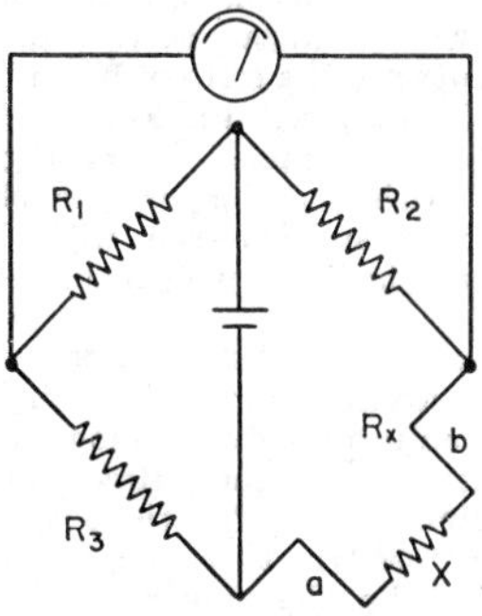

FIG. 22-7. Two-lead method for connecting resistor bulb to measuring instrument.

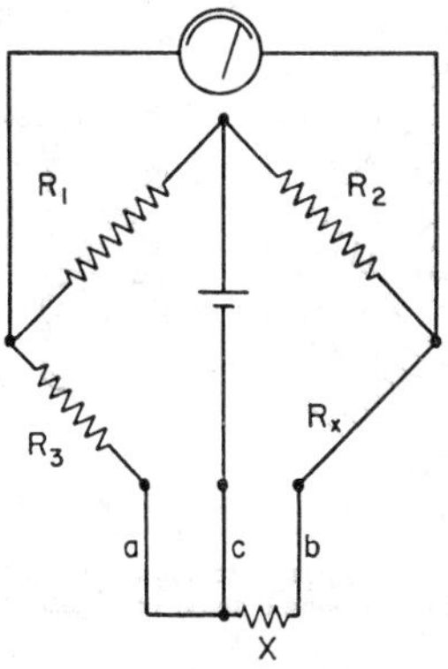

FIG. 22-8. Three-lead method for connecting resistor bulb to measuring instrument.

Three-lead Method. This method, shown in Fig. 22-8, is the most practical and widely used method in industrial resistance thermometry.

Four-lead Method. This method is used only where the highest degree of accuracy is required, as in the case of a platinum resistance thermometer used as a laboratory standard. Two circuit arrangements, as shown in Fig. 22-9*a* and *b*, are required when this method is employed.

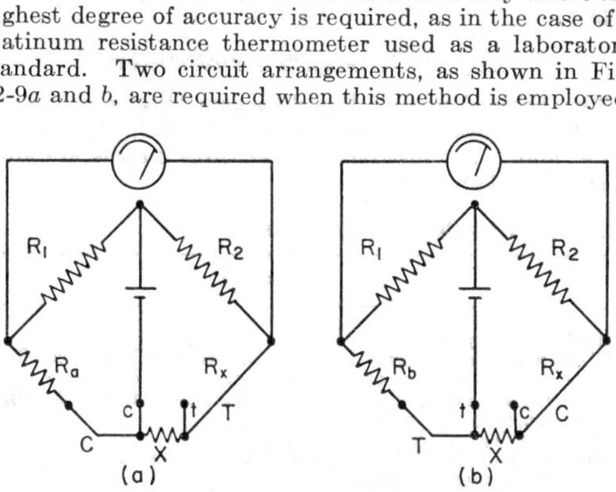

FIG. 22-9. Four-lead method for connecting resistor bulb to measuring instrument.

Filled-system Thermometers

The filled-system thermometer is designed to provide an indication or record of temperature some distance

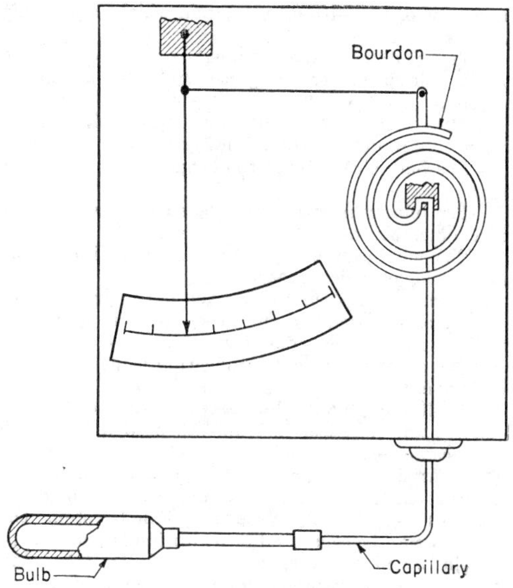

FIG. 22-10. Filled-system thermometer.

removed from the point of measurement (see Fig. 22-10). There are exceptions, however. In some cases, the capillary length approaches zero, and designs exist where the bourdon is itself the bulb of the system. The sensitive or measuring element (bulb) contains a gas or fluid which changes in physical characteristics with temperature. This change is communicated to the bourdon through a capillary tube. The bourdon responds to the signal from the bulb to provide a motion related in some definite way to the bulb temperature. This motion is generally amplified by a mechanical linkage or gear system to drive a pointer for temperature indication or to drive a pen for recording the temperature signal. The angular motion is frequently used directly without amplification in the manufacture of dial gages and is also frequently used directly for control purposes.

Applicational Advantages of Method. Filled-system thermometers are used extensively in most industrial processes for a number of reasons:

1. Fundamental simplicity of the system allows rugged construction, minimizing the possibility of damage or failure in shipment, installation, and use. The amount of upkeep is generally minor. However, the cost of replacement of thermal systems is generally higher than that of the simplest electrical devices.

2. Simplicity of the system allows inexpensive over-all design.

3. As used in the process industries, sensitivity, response time, and accuracy (expressed in per cent of span) are generally the equal of any of the other high-quality industrial-type temperature-measuring instruments available (see item 5 under Limitations, p. 22-12).

4. The capillary allows considerable separation between the point of measurement and the point of temperature indication. Although the system length is usually limited to 250 ft., applications up to 400 ft. are in successful operation. It is frequently more economical to employ transmitters for signal transmission beyond 100 ft.

5. The system is self-contained, that is, it needs no auxiliary power supply, such as compressed air or electricity. It is, however, frequently combined with a pneumatic or an electric transmission system of either

the motion or force-balance types, in which case auxiliary power is required.

6. The system delivers enough power to drive not only a pointer or recording pen but also a controller mechanism.

Application Limitations of Method. Thermal systems are limited in the following ways:

1. The bulb size may be too large to fit the available space.
2. The minimum spans are not so narrow as in electrical temperature-measuring systems.
3. The maximum temperature is more limited than that in some electrical measuring systems.
4. In case of system failure, the entire unit must be replaced or repaired. Some large users have found it practicable to set up repair facilities. In electrical systems, the primary element, connecting leads, and instrument are independently replaceable.
5. Sensitivity and absolute accuracy are not the equal of short-span electrical instruments used in connection with resistance-thermometer bulbs.
6. Separation of the measuring element and bourdon of more than 250 ft. generally is not recommended.

Classes of Filled Systems. Filled-system thermometers may be separated into two fundamental types, those in which the bourdon responds to (1) volume changes and (2) pressure changes. Those which respond to volume changes are completely filled with a liquid. The liquid expansivity with temperature is greater than that of the bulb metal, the net volume change being communicated to the bourdon. An internal-system pressure volume change is always associated with the bourdon volume change, but this effect is not of primary importance. The systems that respond to pressure changes are either filled with a gas or are partially filled with a volatile liquid. Changes in gas or vapor pressure with changes in bulb temperature are communicated to the bourdon. The bourdon will increase in volume with increase in pressure, but this effect is not of primary importance.

Filled-system thermometers have been classified by instrument manufacturers as follows:

Volumetric principle:	
Liquid filled..........	Class I
Mercury filled........	Class V
Pressure principle:	
Vapor filled...........	Class II
Gas filled.............	Class III

For further information on thermometers, see Sec. 2-4 by Zuehlke and Sec. 2-5 by Kebbon in "Process Instruments and Controls Handbook," *loc. cit.*

Bimetal Thermometers

Thermostatic bimetal can be defined as a composite material, made up of strips of two or more metals fastened together, which, because of the different expansion rates of the components, tends to change its curvature when subjected to a change in temperature.

With one end of a straight strip fixed, the other end deflects in direct proportion to the temperature change and the square of the length, and inversely as the thickness, throughout the linear portion of the deflection characteristic curve. If a strip of bimetal is wound into a helix or spiral and one end is fixed, the other end will rotate when heat is applied. The angular deflection varies directly with the temperature change and the length of the strip, and inversely with the thickness of the material, over the linear part of the deflection characteristic curve.

Bimetals show uniform deflection only over part of the deflection characteristic curve. Therefore, for a thermometer with uniform scale divisions, a bimetal must have linear deflection over the desired temperature range.

Types of Elements. The three types of elements most commonly used in thermometers, the flat spiral, the single helix, and the multiple helix, are shown in Fig. 22-11.

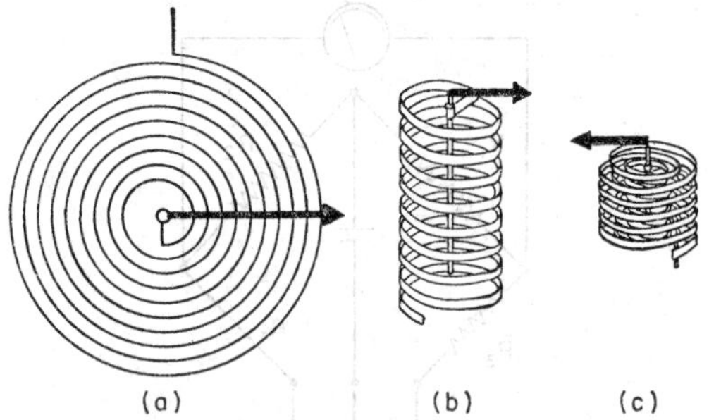

FIG. 22-11. Principal types of elements used in bimetal thermometers: (*a*) flat spiral, (*b*) single helix, (*c*) multiple helix.

Ranges. Bimetal thermometers are made in ranges from 1000°F. down to −300°F. and lower. However, at these low temperatures the rate of deflection drops off quite rapidly. While bimetal thermometers are made in ranges up to 1000°F., they do not have long-time stability at these temperatures. Usually thermometers of this range are not recommended for continuous use above 800°F.

Liquid-in-Glass Thermometers

The three forms of liquid-in-glass thermometers are (1) all-glass (etched stem or enclosed scale), (2) tube and scale, and (3) industrial. These three classes are summarized in Table 22-9.

Table 22-9. Characteristics of Liquid-in-Glass Thermometers

Class and type	Range °F.	Range °C.	Accuracy	Application
All glass:				
Einchluss..............	−328 to +680	−201 to +360	Usually 1 scale division	Laboratory testing
Beckmann..............	−22 to +392	−30 to +200	±0.002° to ±0.005°C.	Scale indicates only 0° to 5° or 6°C. with 0.01°C. division. Thermometer must be set to be on scale for any given temperature. Used for laboratory testing to check temperature variations or deviations, *i.e.*, from a known temperature
Clinical..............	+96 to +106	+35 to +41	±0.2°F. (0.1°C.)	Checking body temperature (index at 98.6°F.)
Laboratory or chemical...	−328 to +1200	−201 to +648	Usually 1 scale division	General testing. Also available with protecting armor
Max. or min. registering..	−40 to +400	−40 to +204	1 to 2 scale division	Ovens, kilns, meteorology
Tube and scale:				
Cup case..............	−30 to +500	−22 to +260	Usually 1 scale division	Oil-tank-temperature testing
Tin, copper, or stainless-steel case..........	−40 to +400	−40 to +204	Usually 1 scale division	Breweries, confectioners, warehouses, household
Industrial:				
Spirit filled..............	−150 to +120	−100 to +50	Usually 1 scale division	Oil, paint, dairy, rubber, diesel engine, candy, refrigeration, chemical industries
Mercury filled..........	−40 to +1200	−40 to +648		

Pyrometric Cones. Pyrometric cones, used mainly in the ceramic industry, are slender trihedral pyramids of ceramic materials. They soften and bend under advancing kiln temperatures, indicating heat conditions in the kiln, the rate of advance of temperature, and the finishing point of the ware. The fusion and bending of the cones are a time-temperature phenomenon and do not indicate any definite temperature. Approximately 60 cones are used to cover the temperature range from 585°C. (1085°F.) to 2015°C. (3659°F.). In use the cones are usually set in a plaque at an angle of 8 deg. from vertical. Observation of a fired cone shows the experienced operator if the furnace atmosphere was oxidizing or reducing or if carbonizing of the ware has taken place.

PRESSURE MEASUREMENTS

Measurement of absolute pressure, gage pressure, vacuum or draft pressure, and differential pressure may be accomplished by three principal classes of measuring elements: (1) the liquid column, where the density and height of a liquid are utilized to measure pressure, (2) the metallic formed pressure element, with or without an opposing force, such as a spring or opposing pneumatic or hydraulic force, and (3) various electrical and electronic methods, such as strain gages, thermal-conductivity gages and ionization gages (see Sec. 3-1 by Smith, Sec. 3-2 by Arobone and Fyffe, and Sec. 3-3 by Lawrence in "Process Instruments and Controls Handbook," *loc. cit.*).

Mechanical Sensing Elements

A summary of the basic types of mechanical pressure-measuring elements is given in Table 22-10 and in the series of diagrams (Figs. 22-12 through 22-31).

Elastic Elements. There are three main types of elastic pressure elements: (1) diaphragm, (2) bellows, and (3) bourdon tube. Basically they are designed to follow the physical law that, within the elastic limit, stress is proportional to strain (Hooke's law), that is, deflection is proportional to the pressure applied. Pressure and vacuum ranges available are listed in Table 22-11.

Seals. In many pressure-measuring applications, it is desirable to prevent the process fluid from contacting or seeping into the pressure-measuring element or connecting line for either of two reasons:

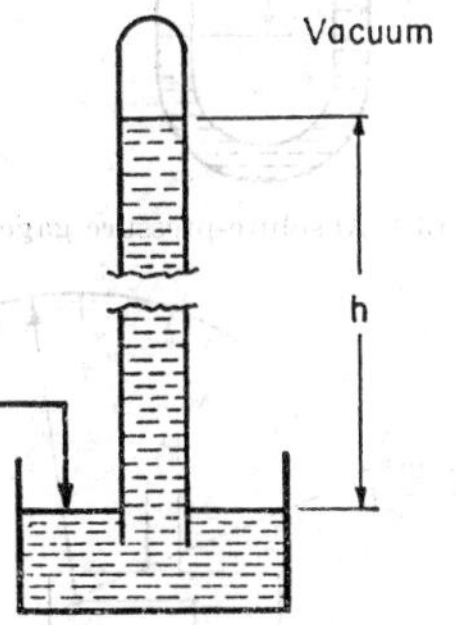

FIG. 22-12. Fixed-cistern barometer.

1. To prevent inaccuracies in measuring-element indication due to changes in static head
2. To protect the measuring element from corrosive fluids or congealing, viscous fluids

Protecting seals involve the use of either a protecting fluid or membrane between the process fluid and the measuring element.

Table 22-10. Industrial Pressure-measuring Instruments Which Utilize Mechanical Sensing Elements

Type of instrument	Basic element used	Refer to Fig.	Pressure range
Fixed-cistern barometer	Mercury column	22-12	Atmospheric
U-type absolute pressure gage	Liquid column	22-13	5 to 50 in. mercury
Differential mercury barometer	Mercury column	22-14	10 to 500 in. water
Manometer well	Liquid column	22-15	6 to 130 in. liquid
Inclined-tube manometer	Liquid column	22-16	½ to 50 in. mercury
Ring-balance manometer	Force on ring	22-17	20 to 420 in. water
Bell-type gage	Force on bell	22-18	0.2 to 40 in. water
Bell-type differential gage	Force on bell	22-19	0.2 to 40 in. water
Pressure gage	Diaphragm (metallic)	22-20	2.0 in. water to 30 lb./sq. in. (some to 400 lb./sq. in.)
Absolute pressure gage	Diaphragm	22-21	6 to 760 mm. mercury abs. 3.2 to 405.6 in. water
Absolute pressure gage	Bellows	22-22	200 mm. to 60 in. mercury abs.
Pressure, draft, or differential gage	Diaphragm (non-metallic, spring-loaded)	22-23 and 22-24	0.2 to 120 in. water
Pressure gage	Bellows (spring-loaded)	22-25	5 in. water to 30 lb./sq. in. (some to 800 lb./sq. in.)
Differential gage	Bellows (spring-loaded)	22-26	20 to 400 in. water
Differential gage	Double bellows	22-27	20 to 400 in. water
Pressure gage	C bourdon	22-28*a*	12 to 100,000 lb./sq. in.
Pressure gage	Helical bourdon	22-28*b*	12 to 80,000 lb./sq. in.
Pressure gage	Spiral bourdon	22-28*c*	12 to 40,000 lb./sq. in.
Force-balance seal gage	Bourdon, metallic, diaphragm, or bellows	22-29	12 in. water to 100 lb./sq. in.
Gage (air seal)	Bourdon, metallic, diaphragm, or bellows	22-30	20 in. to 100 ft. water (primarily for liquid-level applications)
Volumetric-seal gage	Bourdon	22-31*a* 22-31*b* 22-31*c*	50 to 10,000 lb./sq. in.

Table 22-11. Ranges of Elastic Elements

Element	Application	Min. range	Max. range
Diaphragm	Pressure	0-0.2 in. H_2O	0-400 lb./sq. in. gage
	Vacuum	0-0.2 in. H_2O vacuum	0-30 in. Hg vacuum
	Compound vacuum and pressure	Any span within pressure and vacuum ranges with total span of 0.2 in. H_2O	
Bellows	Pressure	0-5 in. H_2O	0-800 lb./sq. in. gage
	Vacuum	0-5 in. H_2O vacuum	0-30 in. Hg vacuum
	Compound vacuum and pressure	Any span within pressure and vacuum ranges with total span of 5 in. H_2O	
Bourdon	Pressure	0-12 lb./sq. in. gage	0-100,000 lb./sq. in. gage
	Vacuum	0-30 in. Hg vacuum	
	Compound vacuum and pressure	Any span within pressure and vacuum ranges with total span of 12 lb./sq. in.	

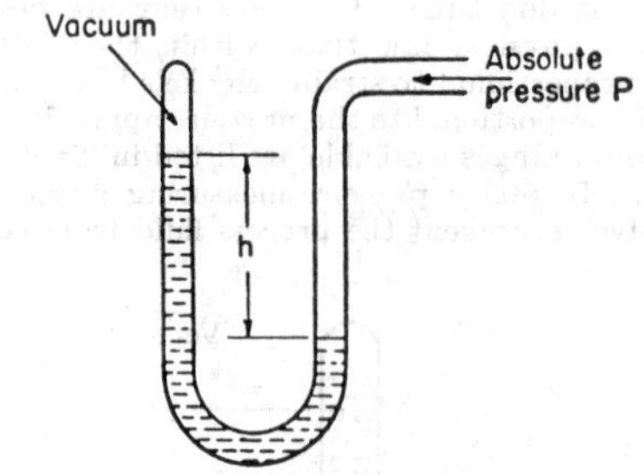

FIG. 22-13. Absolute-pressure gage with end closed.

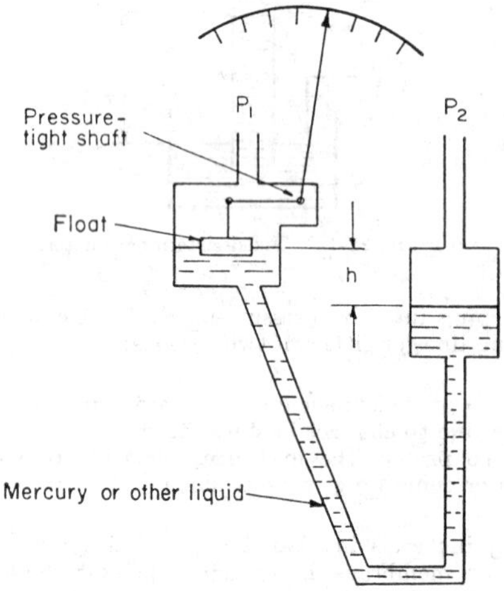

FIG. 22-14. Differential-pressure manometer.

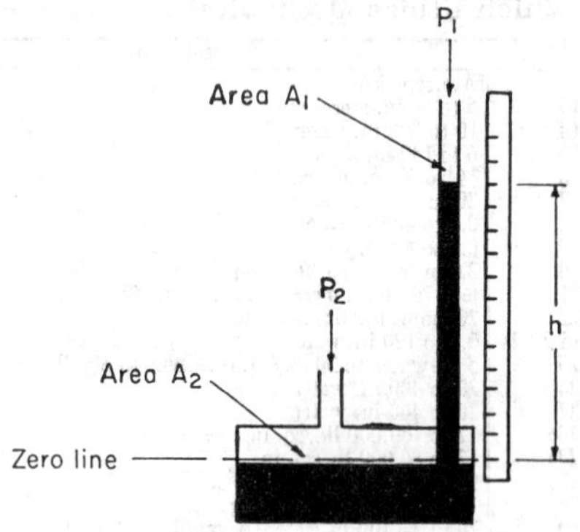

FIG. 22-15. Manometer well. $P_2 - P_1 = d\left[1 + \frac{A_1}{A_2}\right] h.$

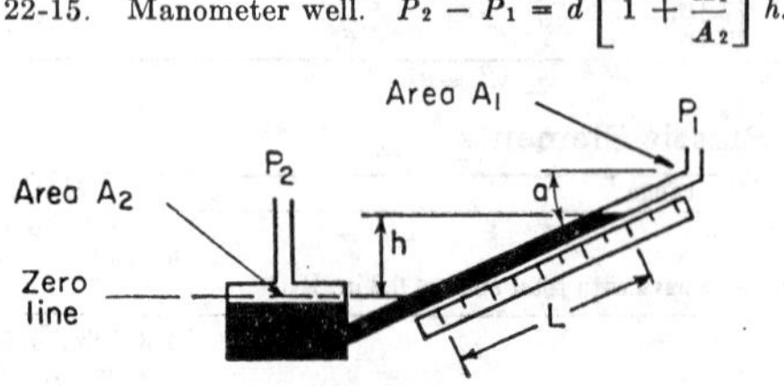

FIG. 22-16. Inclined-tube manometer.

$$P_2 - P_1 = d\left[1 + \frac{A_1}{A_2}\right] L \sin \alpha.$$

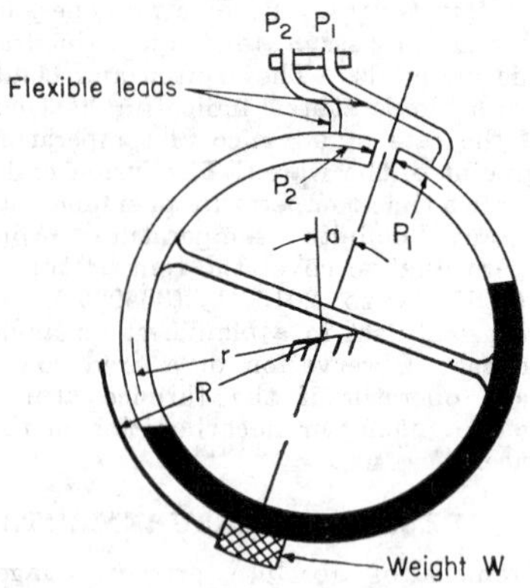

FIG. 22-17. Ring-balance manometer. $P_2 - P_1 = \frac{RW \sin \alpha}{rA}.$

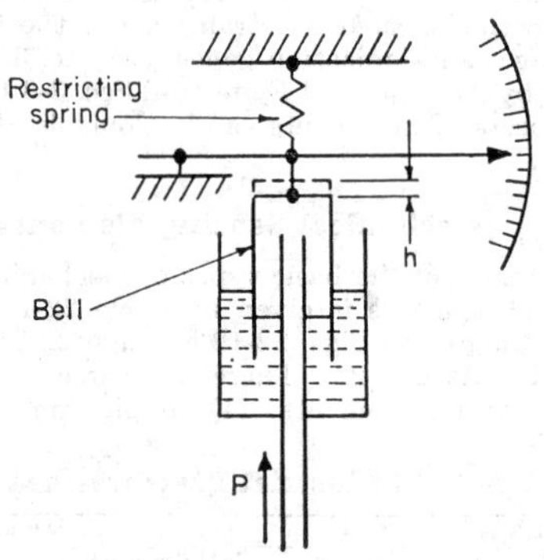

FIG. 22-18. Liquid-sealed bell. $P = \frac{F_c h}{A}.$

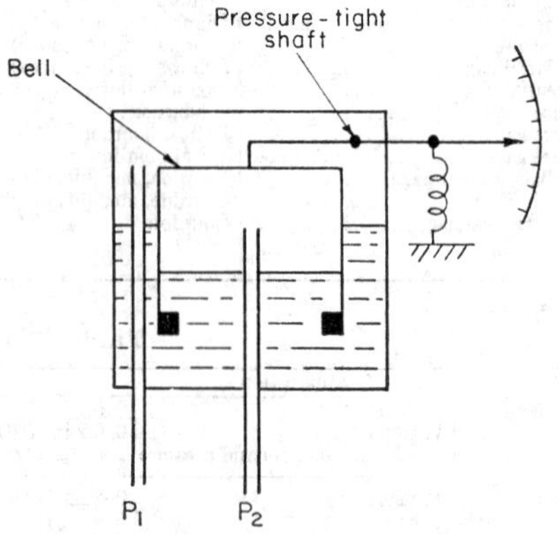

FIG. 22-19. Bell-type differential-pressure gage.

$$P_2 - P_1 = \frac{F_c h}{A}.$$

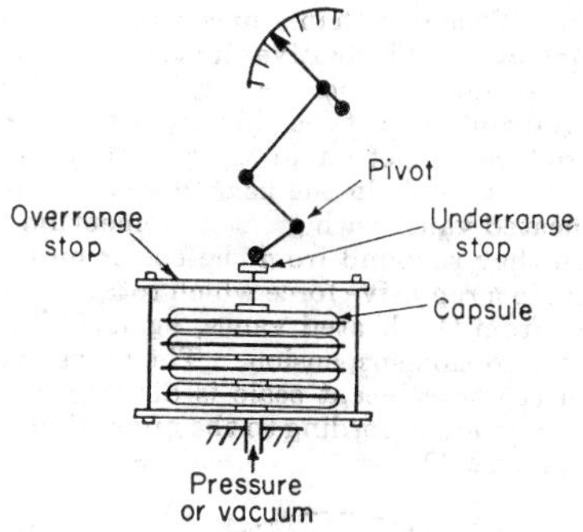

FIG. 22-20. Diaphragm element.

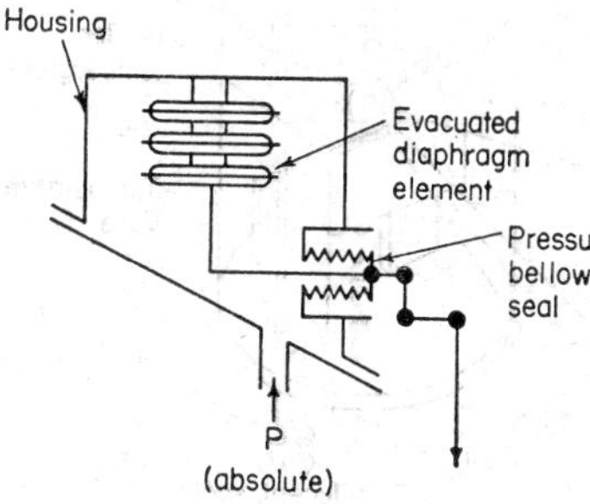

FIG. 22-21. Absolute-pressure gage.

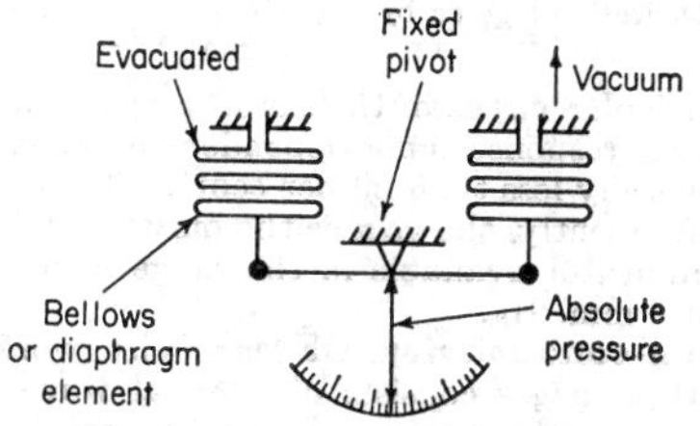

FIG. 22-22. Bellows absolute-pressure gage.

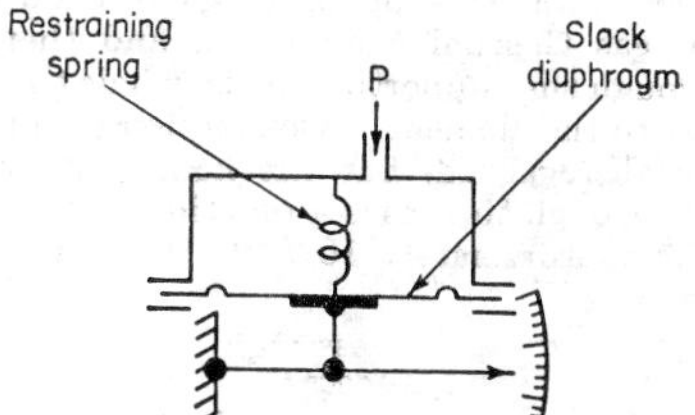

FIG. 22-23. Slack-diaphragm gage.

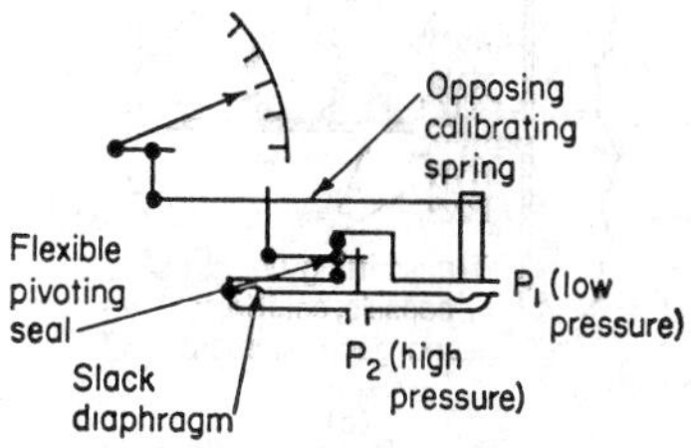

FIG. 22-24. Slack-diaphragm differential unit.

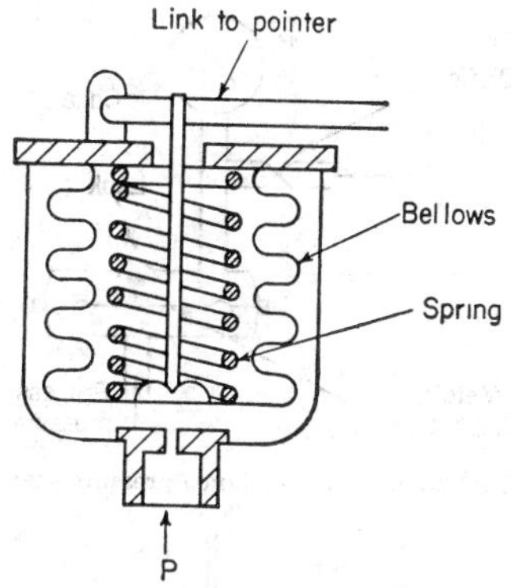

FIG. 22-25. Spring-loaded bellows gage.

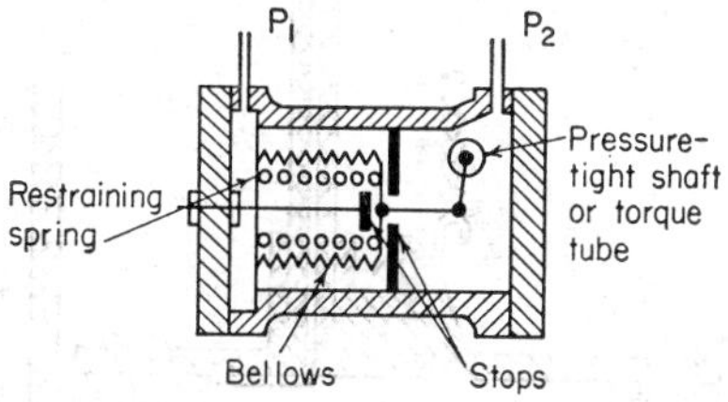

FIG. 22-26. Bellows differential gage.

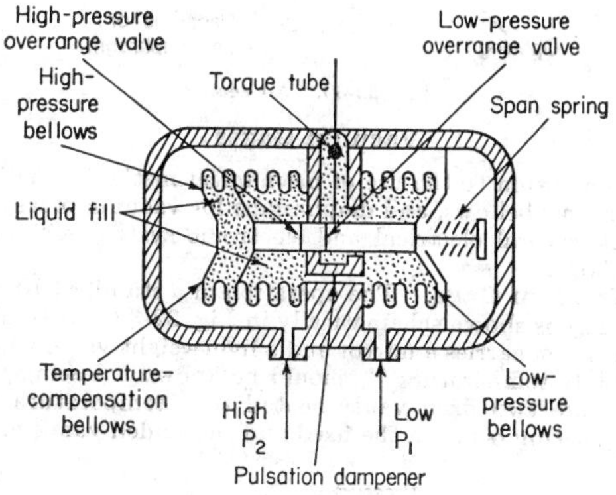

FIG. 22-27. Double-bellows differential gage.

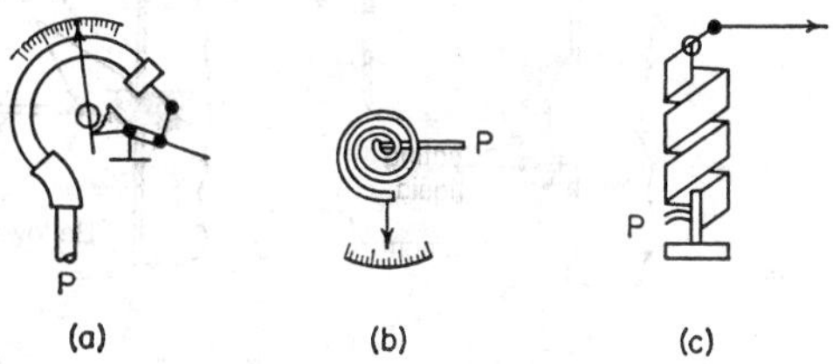

FIG. 22-28. Types of bourdon gages: (*a*) C type, (*b*) spiral, (*c*) helical.

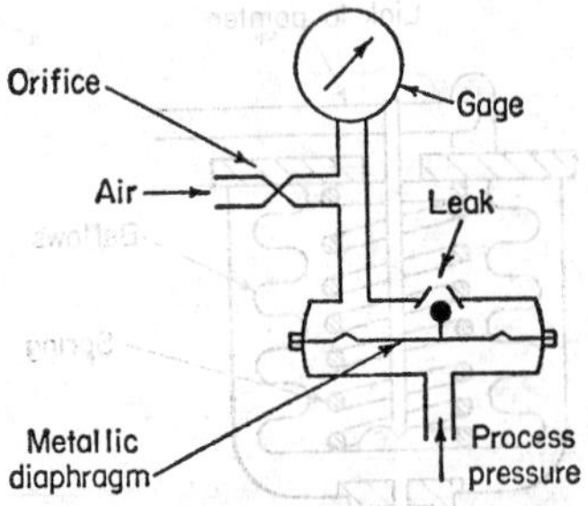

Fig. 22-29. Force-balance pressure seal.

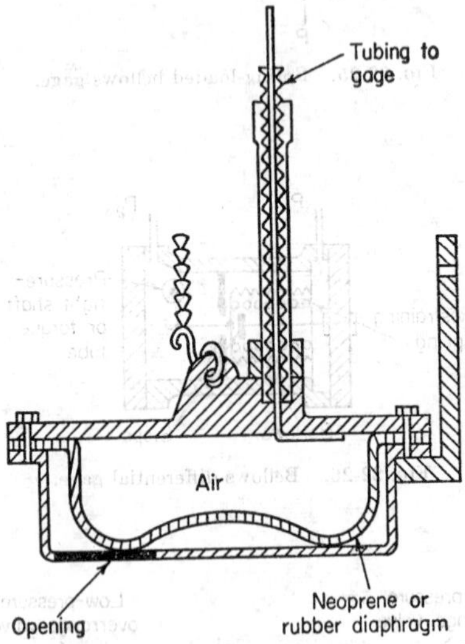

Fig. 22-30. Air seal.

Vacuum Gages

In addition to the use of mechanical methods, such as bourdons, bellows, and diaphragms for vacuum measurement, several electrical and electronic systems are now available.

Knudsen Gage. The operation of a standard Knudsen gage is shown schematically in Fig. 22-32. A torsion suspension carries a mirror and a lightweight vane, whose absolute temperature T_1 should be known. Facing this vane are two fixed vanes heated to a temperature T_2. The spacing between the fixed and suspended vanes must be considerably smaller than a mean free path in order to achieve linearity and relative independence from the effects of gas composition. A light beam directed toward the galvanometer-type mirror carried by the suspension produces a spot on an external translucent scale. Gas molecules present in the gage chamber will rebound from the heated vanes with greater momentum than that with which they rebound from the cooler movable vane. This results in a repulsive force which rotates the movable vane away from the heated vanes, against the restoring torque of the torsion suspension. The angular deflection as read on the translucent scale is directly proportional to the gas pressure, according to the approximate formula shown in Fig. 22-32.

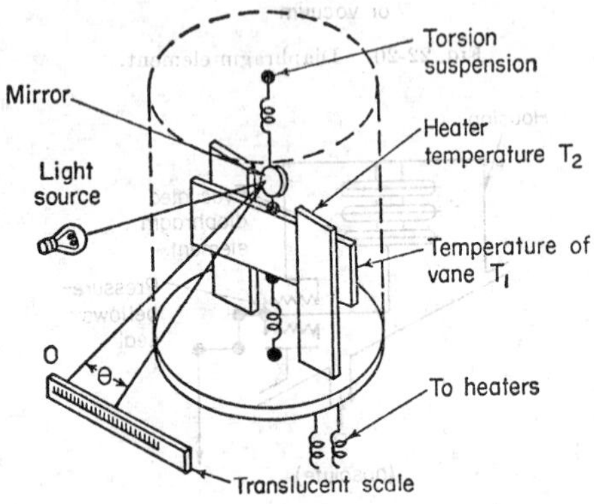

Fig. 22-32. Knudsen gage.

Deflection θ given by $\theta \approx KP\left(\sqrt{\frac{T_2}{T_2}} - 1\right)$

The particular virtue of the Knudsen-gage principle is that the gage response is not dependent upon gas composition (generally less than 20 per cent). Thus, although not used frequently, the gage is the only reasonably pure pressure indicator available in the range below approximately 10^{-4} mm. Hg.

Thermal-conductivity Gages. The working element of these gages consists of a metal wire or ribbon exposed to the unknown pressure and heated by an electric current. The temperature attained by the heater is such that the total rate of heat loss by radiation, gas convection, gas thermal conduction, and thermal conduction through the supporting leads equals the electrical power input to the element. Convection is unimportant and can be disregarded, but the heat loss by thermal conduction through the gas is a function of pressure. At pressures of approximately 10 mm. Hg and higher, the

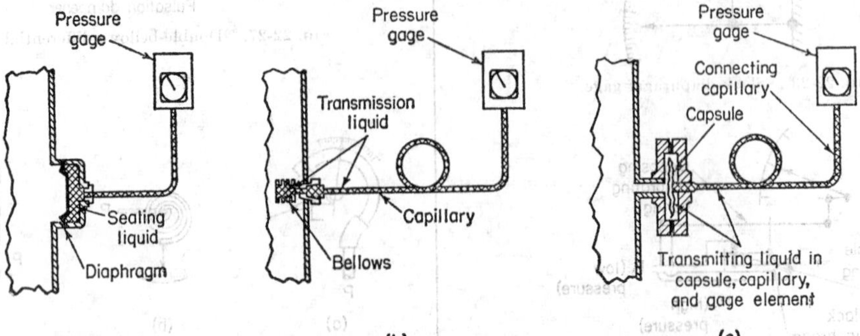

Fig. 22-31. Types of volumetric seals: (a) diaphragm, (b) bellows, (c) capsule.

thermal conductivity of a gas is high and roughly independent of further pressure increases. At pressures below 1 mm. Hg, on the other hand, the thermal conductivity decreases with decreasing pressure, eventually in linear fashion and reaching zero at zero pressure. At pressures below a few millimeters Hg, therefore, the cooling by thermal conduction in the gas limits the temperature attained by the heater to a relatively low value. As the pressure is reduced below a few hundred microns, the heater temperature rises, and at the lowest pressures, the heater temperature reaches an upper value established by heat radiation and by thermal conduction through the supporting leads.

The principal sources of inaccuracy in thermal-conductivity gages arise from the difficulty in keeping constant two different surface conditions. First of these is the accommodation coefficient, which is a measure of the closeness with which a gas molecule rebounding from a heated or cooled surface has acquired the temperature of that surface. More troublesome is the emissivity of the surface, which controls the relation between temperature and rate of radiant-energy emission. The emissivity of a new clean heater is low and results in high temperatures at low gas pressures, but after a period of service the metal surface becomes oxidized, carbonized, or otherwise slightly dirty. When this occurs, the low-pressure range is particularly subject to error, frequently reading high by as much as 20 microns Hg.

The two types of thermal-conductivity gage utilize different means for converting the temperature variations of the heater into meter readings. As shown in Fig. 22-33, Pirani gages are customarily used in a Wheatstone

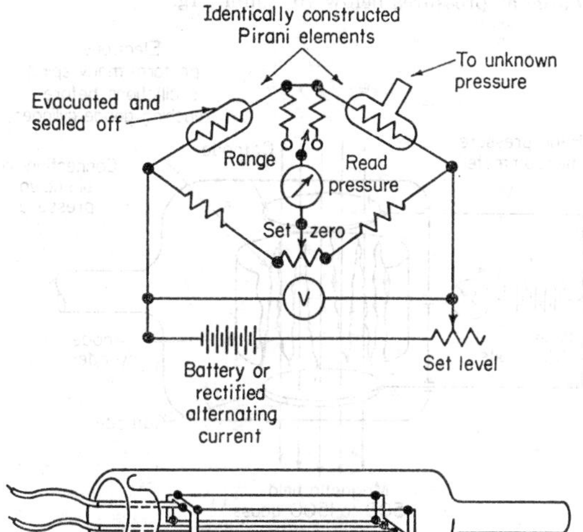

FIG. 22-33. Pirani gage: (top) gage in fixed-voltage Wheatstone bridge, (bottom) sensing element (Sylvania).

bridge having two scales; the lower scale covering from zero to perhaps 20 or 40 microns is approximately linear; while the higher scale, covering from a few microns to nearly 1 mm. Hg, is roughly logarithmic. The two scales of the meter are customarily calibrated directly in terms of pressure of air.

Rotating Viscometer Gage. Figure 22-34 shows a considerably simplified sketch of the rotating viscometer gage. The commercial unit has a pivoted and horizontally mounted armature rather than being hung from

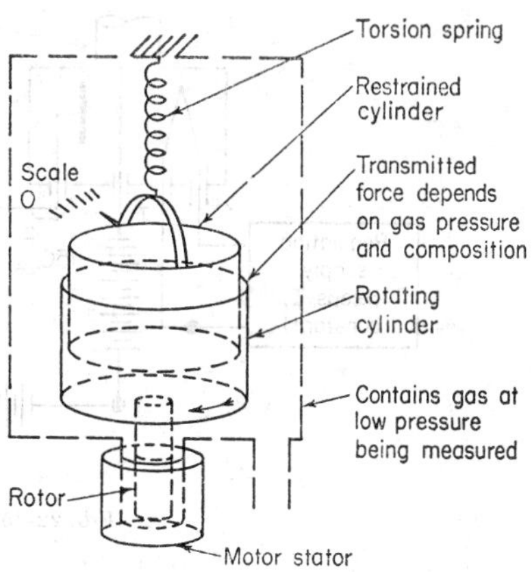

FIG. 22-34. Simplified sketch showing operating principle of rotating viscometer gage (General Electric molecular gage).

a torsion spring. The rotating cylinder is turned by a synchronous clock-type motor.

The gage deflection results from momentum transfer between the fast-moving rotating cylinder and the spring-restrained armature cylinder. It is known experimentally and from the kinetic theory of gases that the viscosity of a rarefied gas behaves very much like the thermal conductivity, being linearly proportional to pressure for very low pressures and substantially independent of pressures so high that the mean free path is much less than the dimensions of the apparatus. Accordingly, it would be expected that the torque on the armature would be proportional to pressure for pressures below a few tens of microns and substantially independent of pressure for pressures greater than about 1 mm. In order to extend the useful range beyond a few hundred microns, the gage has been designed with vanes in the viscometer cylinders, so that turbulent momentum transfer takes place for pressures above approximately 1 mm. Above a few millimeters, the response is again linear with pressure, but the transition region between modes of operation, in the region of 1 mm. for air, is cramped and subject to rather severe temperature sensitivity and other sources of error.

Hot-filament Ionization Gage. In the hot-filament ionization gage, which is shown schematically in Fig. 22-35, a prescribed current of electrons is emitted thermionically from an incandescent filament and attracted to an adjacent grid electrode which is maintained at a positive potential of approximately 150 volts. Some of the electrons are collected at the grid, but the majority pass through the interstices and enter a region bounded by the grid and a negatively biased ion-collecting electrode. The electrons execute curved paths which eventually terminate on the grid; during their travel, however, they ionize a fraction of whatever gas molecules may be present. Those ions formed in the region between the electron-collecting grid and the ion-collecting plate are attracted to the plate, and the ion current is measured in an external microammeter or vacuum-tube voltmeter circuit. This ion current will be different for different gases at the same pressure; *i.e.*, a hot-filament ionization gage is dependent on composition. Over a wide range of molecular density, however, the ion current from a gas of constant composition will be directly proportional to the molecular density of the gas in the gage element.

Alpha-source Ionization Gage. The alpha-source ionization gage of the type identified as Alphatron uti-

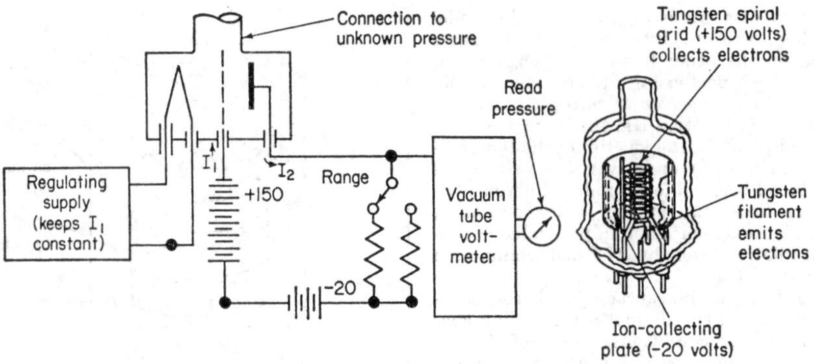

FIG. 22-35. Hot-filament ionization gage.

lizes radioactively emitted alpha particles as an efficient agent for ionizing the gas in the sensing element. These ions are collected and measured in a circuit similar to that used with a hot-filament ionization gage, but which is more sensitive since the available current is lower. Figure 22-36 shows schematically one arrangement of an alpha-source gage.

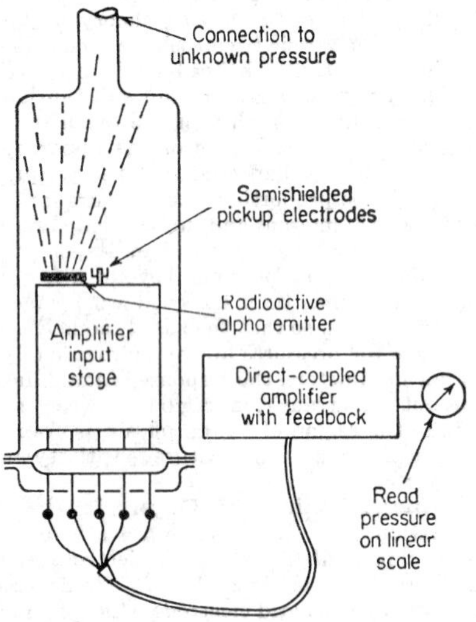

FIG. 22-36. Alphatron ionization gage.

The alpha-source ionization gage shares with the hot-filament ionization gage the feature that the ionizing agent (alpha particles from a radioactive source) operates independently of the amount of ionization produced. This feature, taken in conjunction with certain considerations of ion formation, recombination, and collection, serves to make the current of ions an inherently linear function of the molecular density of the gas in the chamber.

Philips Cold-cathode Ionization Gage. This ingenious gage, invented by Penning of the Philips Company (Holland), possesses many of the advantages of the hot-filament ionization gage without the difficulty of being susceptible to burn-out. Ordinarily, an electrical discharge between two electrodes in a gas cannot be sustained below a few microns pressure. To state simply a complicated set of relationships, it is because of collection at the electrodes that the birth rate of new electrons capable of sustaining ionization is smaller than the death rate of electrons and ions. In the Philips gage this difficulty is overcome by the use of a collimating magnetic field which forces the electrons to traverse a tremendously increased path length before they can reach the collecting electrode. In traversing this very long path, they have a correspondingly increased opportunity to encounter and ionize molecules of gas in the interelectrode region, even though this gas may be extremely rarefied. It has been found possible by use of a magnetic field and appropriately designed electrodes, as indicated in Fig. 22-37, to maintain an electrical discharge at pressures below 10^{-6} mm. Hg.

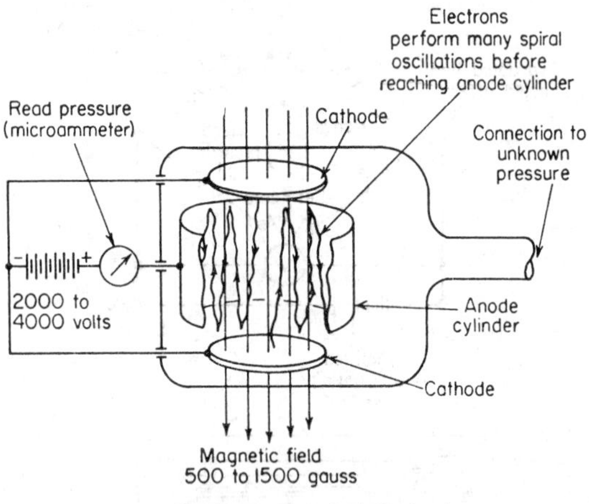

FIG. 22-37. Philips cold-cathode ionization gage.

Electrical Pressure Transducers

Although available in a large variety of types and constructions, the primary sensing element of an electrical pressure transducer generally takes the form of a (1) bourdon, (2) spiral, (3) helix, (4) diaphragm, (5) bellows or (6) a modification of one of these.

Since the output of these transducers is electrical, classification by the different electrical parameters and transposals offers an arrangement which gives logical subsections. Principal among these classes are (1) strain gage, (2) resistive, (3) magnetic, (4) capacitive, (5) piezoelectric, and (6) oscillometric. To cover in detail all the modifications possible within each class of transducer is of course beyond the scope of this section.

Therefore, the units must be considered only as typical of each class.

Strain Gages. When a wire is stretched elastically, its strength and diameter are altered, resulting in a change in its electrical resistance. Measurement of this change of resistance is the principle upon which the wire strain gage is based. For example, stretching a wire 0.1 per cent diminishes its diameter (with constant volume) by 0.3 of 0.1 per cent, in accordance with Poisson's ratio, and theoretically should produce a change in resistance of 0.17 per cent. "Change in resistance" of a strain gage is considered in terms of "change in strain" and is expressed as a ratio called strain sensitivity or gage factor. Symbolically, gage factor becomes

$$\text{Gage factor } G = \frac{\Delta R/R}{\Delta L/L}$$

where ΔR represents the resistance change in a total gage resistance R, divided by the corresponding change in length ΔL in a total length of conductor L. In actual practice, for reasons unknown, measured gage factors differ from the theoretical value, which according to the foregoing example should be 1.7. Gage factors vary from one type of resistance wire to the next, but the gage factor of a given wire is the same whether the gage is used in compression or tension.

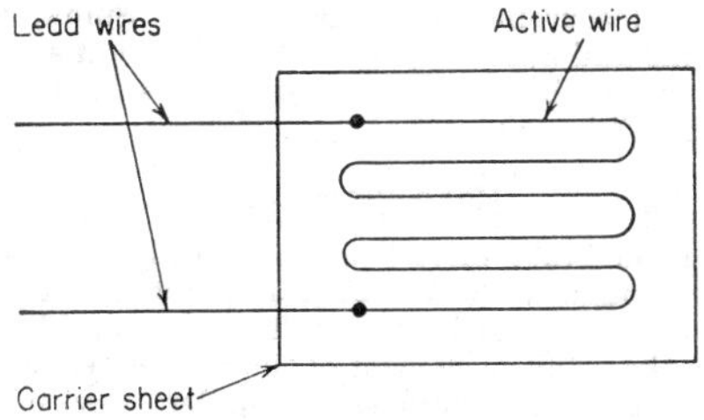

FIG. 22-38. Bonded strain gage (usually takes the form of a flat grid cemented to a carrier sheet).

Bonded Strain Gage. The bonded gage usually takes the form of a flat grid, as shown in Fig. 22-38. To obtain maximum performance, the active element of resistance wire must be as near as possible to the surface of the member under study. The most effective method is to cement the wire directly to the surface of the member.

Wire sizes of 1 to 1½ mils are generally used. This practice results in a convenient wire length to obtain a desired gage resistance without resulting in a grid of excessive area. The basic standard gage has a resistance of approximately 120 ohms and passes about 25 ma. of current in a 6-volt bridge circuit. The 120-ohm resistance is large compared with the nominal resistance of extension wires and is high enough not to be greatly affected by resistance of high-quality switches. Many different types of bonded gages are available with resistance values of 60 to 5000 ohms and effective gage lengths from 1⁄16 to 6 in.

Unbonded Strain Gage. The unbonded-wire strain gage (Fig. 22-39) consists of a stationary frame which supports a movable armature through thin cantilever plates. The strain-sensitive wire is strung under initial tension as a filament between pins located on the frame and armature. When the armature is displaced longitudinally, the filament is elongated or shortened, depending on the direction of displacement, causing an increase or decrease in resistance, respectively.

Armature travel is limited by a stop which protects the wires against overload, the maximum displacement being about 0.0015 in. each side of center. As stated, the nominal bridge resistance can be from 60 to 5000 ohms. Input voltage varies from 5 to 60 volts a.c. or d.c. with open-circuit outputs of 6 to 175 mv. full range and closed-circuit outputs of 30 to 200 microns at full range. Unbonded gages have an accuracy and linearity of 1 per cent full scale or better, and their resolution is 0.1 per cent of full scale or better.

Wheatstone-bridge Circuits. Strain gages are usually connected so as to unbalance a four-arm Wheatstone-bridge circuit when their resistance is changed by stress (see Fig. 22-40*a*). If a strain gage is connected as shown therein, so that the only source of unbalance is the change of resistance in the gage resulting from the application of strain to the gage, the difference in potential across the output terminals becomes a measure of that strain. This potential can be measured by a sensitive voltmeter.

The circuits shown in Fig. 22-40 are useful for measuring static strains or the static component of a varying strain and will operate with d.c. or a.c. power. Using direct current, battery-powered, the circuit may take

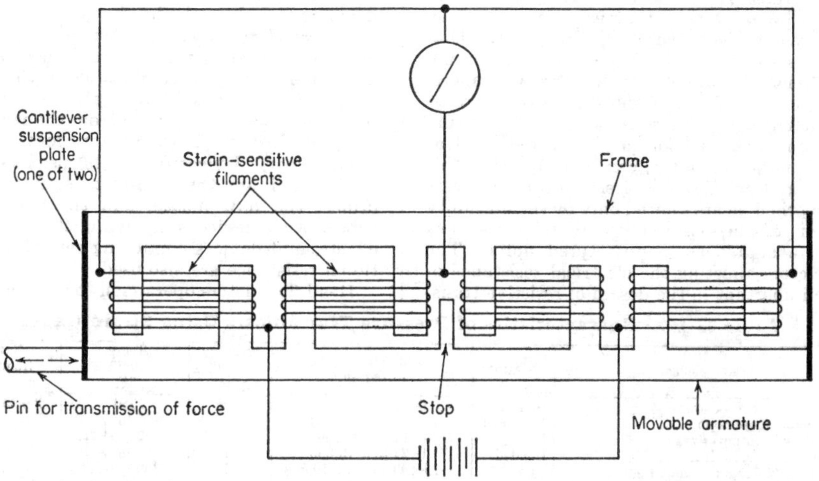

FIG. 22-39. Schematic drawing of unbonded strain gage (incorporates a stationary frame that supports a movable armature through two cantilever plates).

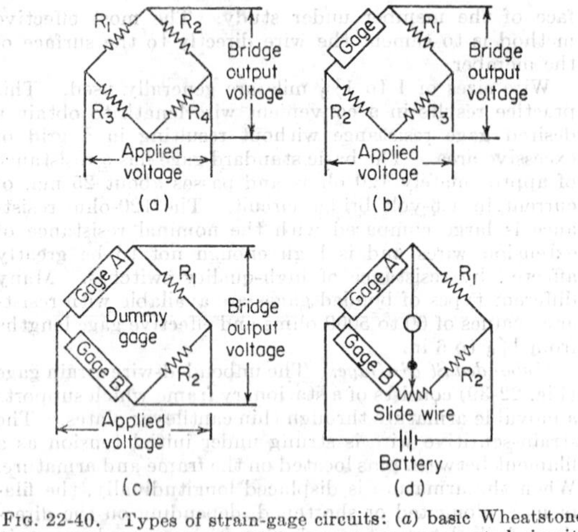

FIG. 22-40. Types of strain-gage circuits: (*a*) basic Wheatstone bridge, (*b*) simple circuit, (*c*) temperature-compensated circuit, (*d*) basic d.c. direct-indicating circuit.

the form of Fig. 22-40*d*, with a small slide-wire introduced between the fixed resistors to balance the bridge at the start of the test. A light-spot galvanometer can be used for indicating unbalance. For direct reading, a sensitive microammeter or millivoltmeter with proper characteristics can be used without amplifier to replace the galvanometer. These systems are limited to steady strain or strain that changes no faster than 1 cycle/sec. Characteristics of bonded-strain-gage pressure transducers are summarized in Table 22-12. The unbonded strain-gage pressure transducer is available in a variety of factory-built assemblies. Normally, the units consist of a frame and an armature that moves with respect to the frame.

In the unbonded-strain-gage pressure transducer, pressure usually is converted to force by a flexible metallic bellows for the range from 0 to 50 lb./sq. in. The bellows insulates the gage-measuring elements from the fluid under pressure, yet at the same time transmits the force to the gage armature. At pressures above 50 lb./sq. in. diaphragms are used instead of metallic bellows. These diaphragms are actually rigid disks of great strength, which represent a safety factor far in excess of normal engineering practice. In this case, diaphragm characteristics govern gage response. Diaphragm materials are selected and treated for maximum stability, and dimensions are held within close tolerances.

Resistive Pressure Transducers. Pressure transducers which include a pressure-sensitive device operating to change to ohmic resistance of an electrical element as a function of changes in pressure can be included in this area. While variations in the design of transducers using this basic principle are limited only by the ingenuity and imagination of the user, there are relatively few different types available as manufactured units. The fundamental factors affecting the electrical resistance of conductors are important in the design of resistive transducers. Resistance is increased, for example, if the length of the conductor is increased or if its cross-sectional area is decreased. These are changes in the dimensions of the material. Changing a property of the material can also produce the same effect as when a change in temperature causes a change in the resistivity of the material. Changes in dimensions and in properties may occur simultaneously. For example, heat applied to a copper wire will cause an increase in its dimensions and in its resistivity; likewise, if a wire is subjected to hydrostatic pressure (or to strain), both its dimensions and its resistivity are changed.

Other Electrical Pressure Transducers. Other types of transducers include (1) transducers that are sensitive to internal structure or dimension changes, such as the carbon pile and pressure-sensitive wire; (2) moving contact elements; (3) temperature-resistance elements; (4) magnetic systems, such as the inductance and reluctance types; (5) capacitive systems; (6) piezoelectric systems; and (7) oscillator systems.

FLOW MEASUREMENTS

The principal classes of instruments used in the process industries are (1) head flowmeters, (2) area flowmeters, (3) positive-displacement meters, (4) weirs and flumes for flow measurement in open channels, and (5) mass and magnetic flowmeters. The latter types of meters have not yet been applied widely. (For further information of Flow Measurements, see Sec. 4-1 by Spink, Sec. 4-2 by Collins and Sprenkle, Sec. 4-3 by Terry, and Sec. 4-4 by Gephardt in "Process Instruments and Controls Handbook," *loc. cit.*)

Head Flowmeters

The term "rate meter" applies to all types of flowmeters through which the fluid does not pass in isolated quantities. Movement of the fluid stream which flows through the primary element of the rate meters is directly or indirectly used to actuate a secondary device, and the rate of flow is inferred from known physical laws or from empirical relations. Head meters form a subdivision of rate meters and operate by measurement of the pressure differential or head across a suitable restriction to flow in the pipe line.

A head meter, shown schematically in Fig. 22-41, comprises:

1. *Primary Element.* Some form of restriction in the flow line to induce the head.
2. *Secondary Element.* Connected to the differential head and measures it as a means of determining flow rate. The shaded vertical columns along the top of the pipe show the relationship of static pressures existing at points up- and downstream from the restriction.

Operation of Head Flowmeters. The most common primary devices (elements) used to induce a differential head are the thin-plate square- or sharp-edged orifice, the flow nozzle, and the venturi tube. Pitot tubes, other devices employing either impact or suction effects, and devices employing centrifugal forces or frictional resistance are also used.

Head flowmeters operate on the principle of converting

Table 22-12. Characteristics of Pressure Transducers Using Strain Gages

Sensing elements	Type strain gage	Available ranges, lb./sq. in.	Accuracy, % full range	Temp. limit, °F.	Natural frequency, cycles/sec.
Bourdon tube and bellows	Bonded	0–10 to 0–50,000	±¼	250	300 to 2000
Bellows and diaphragm	Unbonded	0–0.05 to 0–10,000	±½	−65 to +250	270 to 10,000
Bellows and cantilever beam	Bonded	0–10 to 0–2,500	±¼	−50 to +170	
Ring type	Bonded	0–25 to 0–10,000	±1	−50 to +170	Above 1500
Catenary diaphragm or diaphragms	Bonded	−15–100 to −15–10,000	±1	−300 to 6000 High-air or water cooling supplied	To 45,000

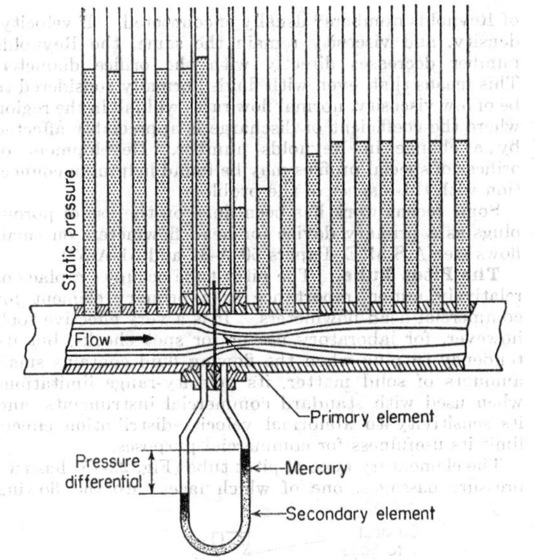

FIG. 22-41. Elements of head flowmeter. Shaded vertical columns along top of pipe show relationship of static pressure existing at points up- and downstream from restriction.

energy from one form to another. In the case of liquid flows only two forms are considered, namely, kinetic energy and energy due to static pressure. Orifice meters, venturi meters, and similar types depend on the conversion of energy in the form of static pressure into the kinetic energy of velocity. In the case of the pitot tube, the conversion is from kinetic energy to pressure at the impact tube.

In the case of gas or vapor, a third form of energy is involved in the interchange, namely, the internal energy of the compressed fluid. A close approach to an exact mathematical analysis, based on the laws of thermodynamics, may be made for venturi tubes and flow nozzles. But for orifice plates and other primary devices, with which the throat or jet area is indefinite, very little is gained over use of the hydraulic formula with experimentally determined correction factors.

Orifice Plate. Perhaps the most important characteristic of the orifice plate (Fig. 22-42) favoring its choice as a primary device for head meters is its ease of installation and replacement. The economy of manufacture and ease with which it may be reproduced are other important considerations. Because of its many advantages, it has been the subject of a great deal of research work, with the result that there is probably a greater mass of empirical test data and knowledge of performance for the orifice plate, under all varieties of operating conditions, than for any other head flowmeter primary device. From the analysis of test results it would appear that, when used on clean fluids, its performance is at least as reproducible as that of any other device used to induce a differential head.

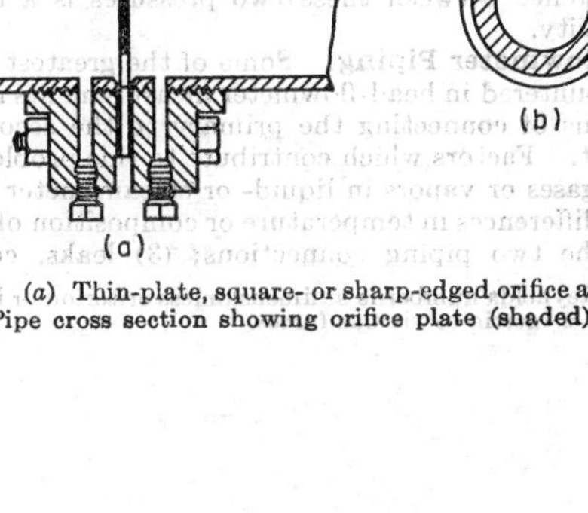

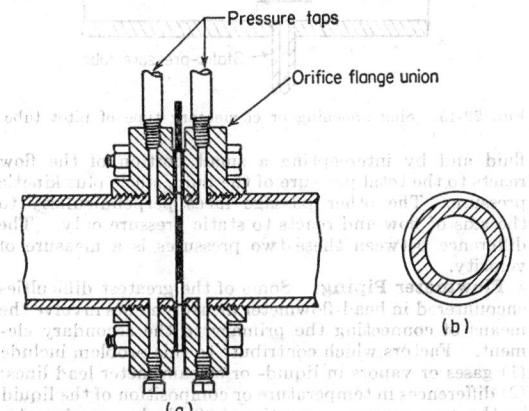

FIG. 22-42. (*a*) Thin-plate, square- or sharp-edged orifice assembly. (*b*) Pipe cross section showing orifice plate (shaded).

Flow Nozzle. This device (Fig. 22-43) consists of a bell-shaped approach section of elliptical profile followed by a cylindrical throat tangent to the ellipse. The axes of the A.S.M.E. long-radius nozzle are d and $2/3d$, respectively, for low diameter ratios, $D/2$ and $\frac{1}{2}(D - d)$ for high diameter ratios (D equals the pipe diameter and d is the throat diameter). Tests for other contours were included in the A.S.M.E. analysis of the coefficient data, and the difference due to contour was found to be less than the difference in tests at separate laboratories on the same nozzle.

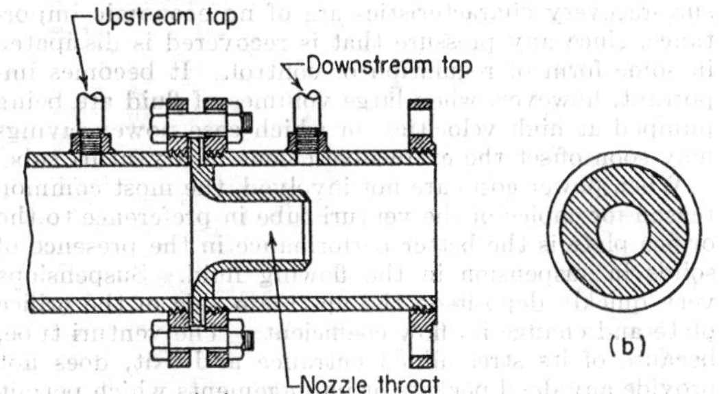

FIG. 22-43. (*a*) Flow nozzle with pipe-line taps. (*b*) Pipe cross section showing nozzle (shaded).

The smoothness of the approach to tangency, the length of the cylindrical portion of the nozzle, and the locations of the pressure taps were shown to have an important bearing on the discharge coefficient. Throat lengths exceeding 60 per cent of the diameter upstream and one-half pipe diameter downstream from the inlet face of the nozzle gave best results. Either taps drilled into the throat of the nozzle or corner taps as used with the I.S.A. nozzle were found to give less consistent readings.

Compared on a diameter-ratio basis, the flow nozzle would appear to give a higher pressure recovery than an orifice, but as used in commercial practice this is not the case. Because the coefficient of the flow nozzle is approximately 63 per cent higher than that of the orifice plate, a lower diameter ratio is required to give the desired reading on the differential pressure-measuring device. When the pressure recovery for this lower diameter ratio is checked, it will be found to be practically identical with that of the orifice plate designed for the same installation. A decrease in the effective overall loss is accomplished only by manipulation of the section downstream from the restriction.

Venturi Tube. In the venturi tube (Fig. 22-44), the ultimate in pressure recovery is attained by the long cone

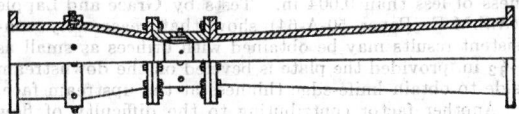

FIG. 22-44. Venturi tube of Herschel design.

exit, commonly designated in this country as the Herschel design and in Europe as the classical venturi-tube design. This implies approximately a 10 to 1 taper or a 20 to 1 slope of the profile of the cone with respect to the axis of the venturi. A greater or lesser slope results in a greater percentage pressure loss.

Since most of the pressure is recovered in the region of high velocity, a large part of the possible pressure recovery can be obtained by using a truncated recovery cone having an outlet diameter somewhat smaller than the inlet to the venturi. The shape or length of the outlet section has no effect on the coefficient of discharge of the tube.

In industrial flow measurement, quite frequently pressure-recovery characteristics are of no economic importance, since any pressure that is recovered is dissipated in some form of regulation or control. It becomes important, however, when large volumes of fluid are being pumped at high velocities, in which case power savings may soon offset the extra investment in a venturi tube.

When power costs are not involved, the most common reason for choice of the venturi tube in preference to the orifice plate is the better performance in the presence of solids in suspension in the flowing fluid. Suspensions very quickly deposit on the upstream side of the orifice plate and change its flow coefficient. The venturi tube, because of its streamlined entrance and exit, does not provide any dead pockets or impingements which permit these solids to settle out. Frequently, in the measurement of fluid catalysts, clay and oil mixtures, paper stock, and similar fluids, single-pressure tap holes at the inlet and throat section are substituted for the usual piezometer rings to permit the solids to be purged back into the stream by continuous flow of clean purging liquid.

Either the flow nozzle or the venturi tube will permit accurate measurement of approximately two-thirds more fluid at the same differential head as the thin-plate sharp-edged orifice of the same size. This is a frequent reason for the choice of the flow nozzle, especially on high-velocity steam lines.

Primary Devices for Small Flows. The need for flowmeters and flow controllers for pilot plants and plants manufacturing such materials as pharmaceuticals and rare chemicals, where extremely low flow rates are encountered, has recently aroused considerable interest in the investigation of small orifices and flow nozzles. Much of the work that has been done in the past on this subject is worthless because insufficient attention was paid to the ratio of thickness at the orifice edge to orifice diameter.

Tests on orifices in 2-in. and larger pipes indicate that, unless the orifice thickness is less than (1) one-eighth the orifice diameter, (2) one-thirtieth to one-fiftieth the pipe diameter, and (3) one-fourth the projection of the orifice rim beyond the wall of the pipe or dam height, the discharge coefficient becomes a function of thickness. Furthermore, when the ratio of diameter to thickness approaches the proportions of a short tube, the discharge is "broomy" at low flows of a short tube, the discharge is "broomy" at low flows and jumps free at high flows. In this process, the coefficient of discharge drops abruptly as much as 25 per cent.

An orifice of $\frac{1}{32}$-in. bore, in order to fulfill the requirements for a thin-plate orifice, must be reduced to a thickness of less than 0.004 in. Tests by Grace and Lapple (A.S.M.E. Paper 50-A-64) show that reasonably consistent results may be obtained with orifices as small as $\frac{1}{32}$ in. provided the plate is beveled on the downstream side to obtain knife-edge thinness at the upstream face.

Another factor contributing to the difficulty of flow measurement with small primary devices is the low range of Reynolds numbers* usually encountered. If velocity, density, and viscosity remain the same, the Reynolds number decreases directly with the orifice diameter. This means that, even with fluids normally considered to be of low viscosity, normal flow rates will fall in the region where the coefficient of discharge is appreciably affected by a change in Reynolds number. Development of orifices of special profiles may be found helpful in connection with this aspect of the problem.

Some recent work has been done on the use of porous plugs as a primary device for head flowmeters on small flows (see A.S.M.E. Papers 50-A-37 and 51-A-57).

The Pitot Tube. The pitot tube occupies a place of relatively minor importance as a primary element for commercial head flowmeters. It is a very effective tool, however, for laboratory use or for spot checks, but its tendency to plug when the flowing fluid contains small amounts of solid matter, its velocity-range limitations when used with standard commercial instruments, and its sensitivity to abnormal velocity-distribution effects limit its usefulness for commercial purposes.

The elementary type of pitot tube (Fig. 22-45) has two pressure passages, one of which faces into the flowing

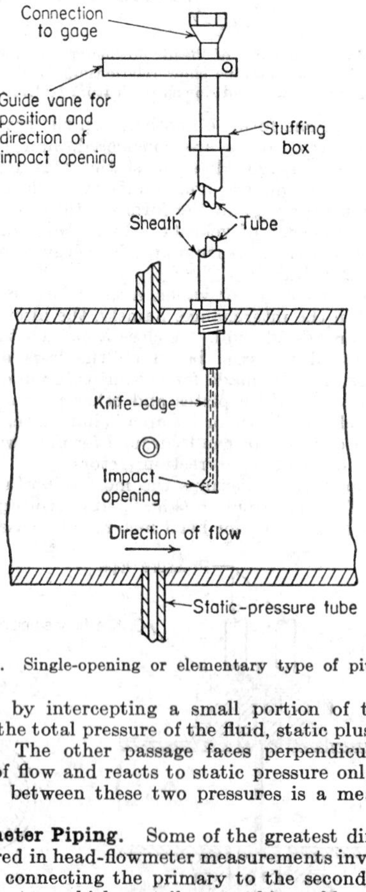

FIG. 22-45. Single-opening or elementary type of pitot tube.

fluid and by intercepting a small portion of the flow reacts to the total pressure of the fluid, static plus kinetic pressure. The other passage faces perpendicularly to the axis of flow and reacts to static pressure only. The difference between these two pressures is a measure of velocity.

Flowmeter Piping. Some of the greatest difficulties encountered in head-flowmeter measurements involve the means of connecting the primary to the secondary element. Factors which contribute to this problem include (1) gases or vapors in liquid- or stream-meter lead lines; (2) differences in temperature or composition of the liquid in the two piping connections; (3) leaks, condensate,

* Reynolds number is a dimensionless criterion or index of the ratio of inertia to viscous forces.

hydrates, and similar conditions in gas-meter lead lines. Such difficulties have contributed to the trend toward greater use of electric and pneumatic transmission, with a transmitter located as close to the level of the pressure taps as is possible.

Differential-pressure Meters. Common meters for converting the fluid head into indication or recording of flow rates include (1) liquid-filled manometers, (2) mercury float-type manometers, (3) bell-type meters, (4) weight-balance-type meters, (5) bellows-type meters, and (6) force-balance-type meters. Because of the square-root relationship between the measured differential pressure and corresponding flow rate, for evenly graduated scales, the square-root function must be extracted either by means of square-root calibration of the meter or by other means which permit linear calibration with respect to flow. Most designs can be supplied for pneumatic control, either by addition of a suitable unit in the instrument case or by use in a system with pneumatic transmission. Electric control is not commonly available in most types.

Additional mechanisms to provide integration of flow rates for cost-accounting purposes are available in many indicating and recording designs of both intermittent and continuous types.

Force-balance-type Meters. The instruments previously described are of the motion-balance type in that, as the differential pressure changes, considerable motion must occur to restore equilibrium. Another type that has come into widespread use during recent years is the force-balance type. These instruments are used as pneumatic transmitters to give an air output pressure proportional to the differential pressures. An industrial mercury-float-type flow manometer is shown in Fig. 22-46.

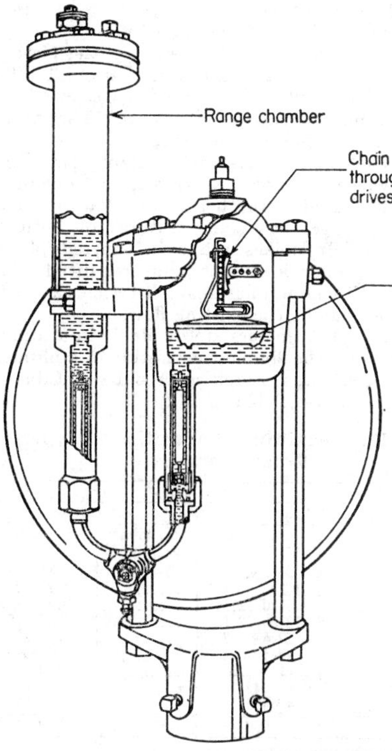

FIG. 22-46. Mercury-float-type manometer.

Electric Types of Head Flowmeters. Electric flowmeters are of two predominant types: (1) inductance- or impedance-bridge meters and (2) electrical-resistance meters. These meters have the advantage of not requiring a pressure-tight bearing as required in the mechanical meters (except the type employing a magnetic coupling). Their application may be limited in some hazardous locations, however, because of explosion proofing requirements.

An inductance system is shown in Fig. 22-47, an impedance system in Fig. 22-48, and a resistance-rod system in Fig. 22-49.

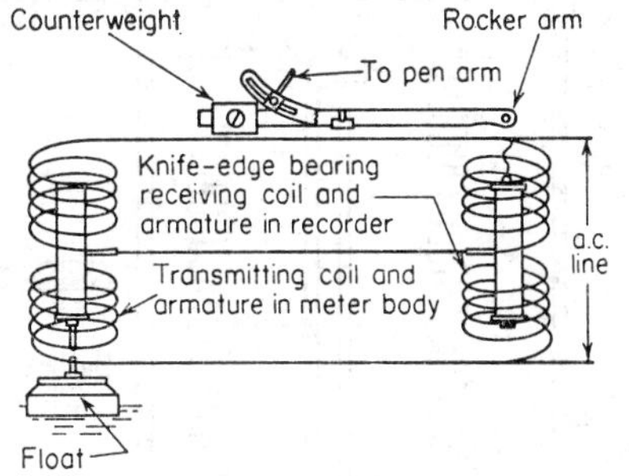

FIG. 22-47. Inductance-bridge system used in head flowmeter.

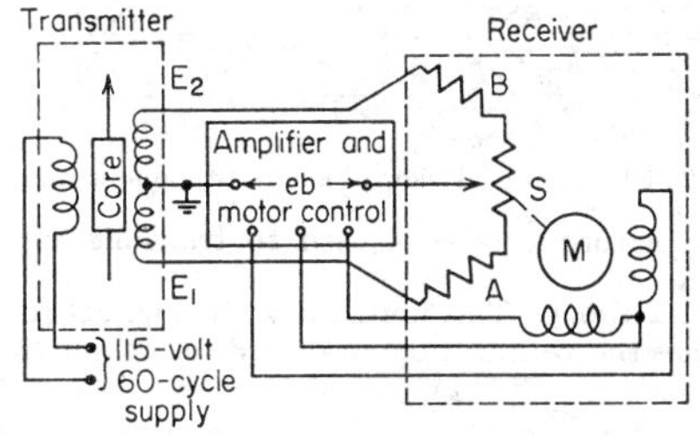

FIG. 22-48. Impedance-bridge system used in electric flowmeter.

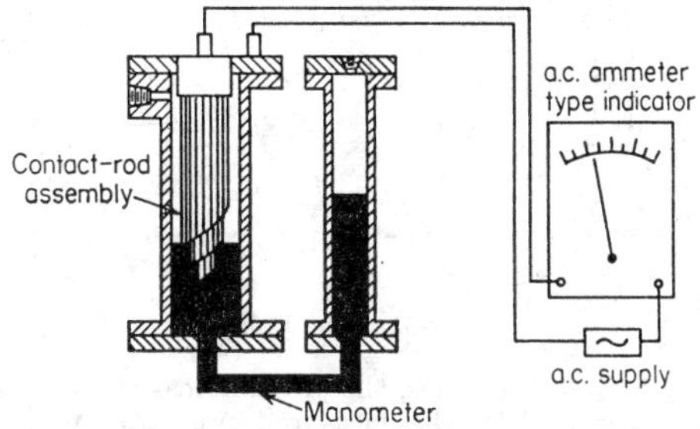

FIG. 22-49. Resistance-rod system used in electric flowmeter.

Bellows-type Meters. In the bellows-type meter, the differential pressure acts against a metal bellows, where the unbalanced force produced is counterbalanced by the spring characteristics of the bellows plus (usually) an external spring load. The cross section of a meter of this type is shown in Fig. 22-50.

This meter uses a flexible torque tube to transmit the bellows motion to the pen arm. Other designs use a stuffing-box construction and pressure-tight bearing to transmit the bellows motion. In still another design, the space between bellows is filled with a liquid to prevent distortion of the bellows in the event of overrange and to provide a means for damping the meter. In this

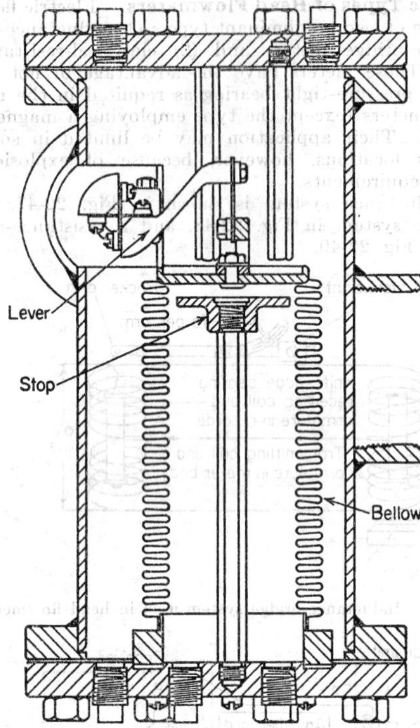

FIG 22-50. Sectional view of aneroid-type flow manometer.

design, a torque tube is used to transmit the bellows motion.

Dall Tube.* This unit, shown in Fig. 22-51, far outperforms the venturi tube in regard to pressure recovery.

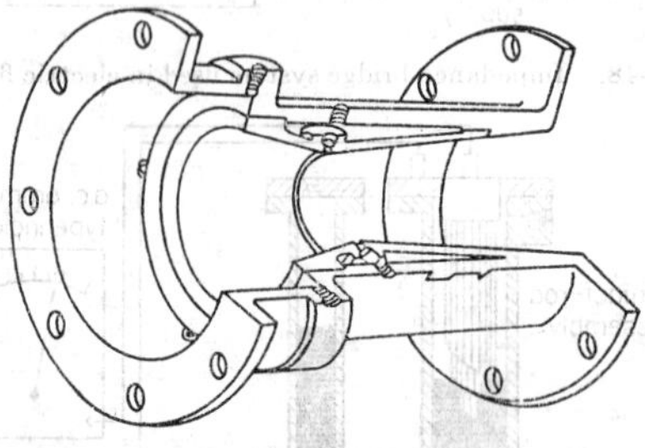

FIG. 22-51. The Dall tube.

On high diameter ratios, the pressure loss may be as low as 2.5 per cent of the measured pressure drop. The short length of the unit and its light weight make it easier to handle and to install than the venturi tube. Its use, however, should be confined to fluids which do not contain appreciable amounts of settleable solids.

Target Meter.† This unit, shown in cross section in Fig. 22-52, is an application of the principle of the annular orifice. A disk *A* located centrally in the flow conduit is supported by the force bar *B* of a force-balance transmitter *C*, allowing free flow for sediment or heavy liquids at the bottom of the pipe and for vapors or light liquids at the top of the pipe.

The difference in pressure on the two sides of the disk produces a force which is counteracted by the force of the transmitted signal pressure acting on a small bellows.

* George Kent Ltd. † The Foxboro Company.

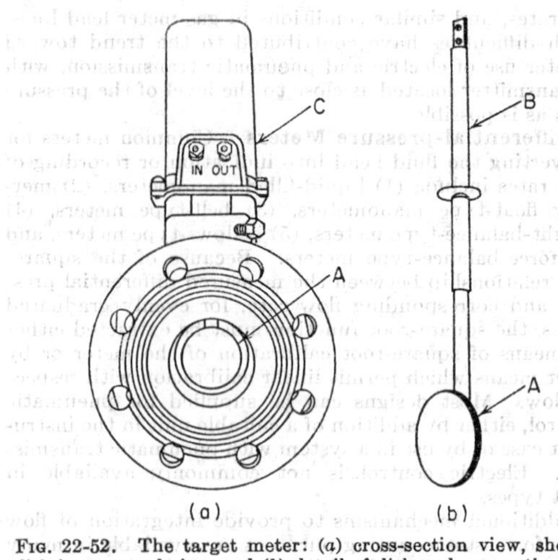

FIG. 22-52. The target meter: (*a*) cross-section view, showing disk in center of pipe, and (*b*) detail of disk and connecting arm.

The two forces are maintained in null balance by the usual flapper-and-nozzle position-sensing mechanism.

Area Flowmeters

Area meters are of two general types:

1. *Rotameters.* In the usual rotameter a weighted plummet contained in an upright tapered tube, large end up, is lifted to the position of equilibrium between the downward force of the plummet and the upward force of the fluid flowing past the plummet through the annular orifice. In smaller sizes the tube is made of glass which is graduated so that the flow can be read directly by observing the position of the plummet.

2. *Piston-type Meters.* In these meters, the piston is accurately fitted inside a sleeve and is lifted by fluid pressure until sufficient port area in the sleeve is uncovered to permit passage of the flow. The flow is indicated by the position of the piston.

Both types of area meters are available for remote indication, where electric, electronic, or pneumatic transmitters are used. Another meter, known as the orifice-and-plug type, has some features of both the foregoing types. It makes use of a tapered plunger inserted into a fixed orifice. The plunger is lifted axially by the fluid until the annular space between the orifice and plunger can handle the existing flow.

Rotameters. Rotameters are available in a number of different designs, the simplest consisting of a plummet in a tapered graduated Pyrex glass tube suitable for moderate pressure (see Table 22-13).

Table 22-13. Maximum Capacities of Typical Rotameters*

Nominal pipe size, in.	Capacity			
	Water		Air	
	cc./min.	gal./min.	cc./min.†	cu. ft./min.†
⅛	5–320	....	85–610	
⅛, ¼	5–3,560	0.94	85–42,500	1.5
½	....	1.298–5.04	....	4.70–22.12
¾	....	5.70–12.34	....	10.40–52.7
1	....	12.60–28.10	....	25.05–119.7
1½	....	22.6–52.85	....	60.5–223
2	....	47.5–90.4	....	103–373
3	....	110–178	....	300–716
4	....	245	....	400
5	....	450	....	500
6	....	900	....	1000

* Source: Schedules of three manufacturers.
† At standard temperature and pressure.

The term rotameter was derived from the fact that plummets were originally produced with slots to give them rotation for the purpose of centering and stabilizing the float. The present trend, however, is toward guided non-rotating floats. The rotation of such floats is now interpreted as an indication of an unfavorable entrance condition.

The essential elements of any rotameter are clearly shown in Fig. 22-53 and, in addition to suitable inlet and

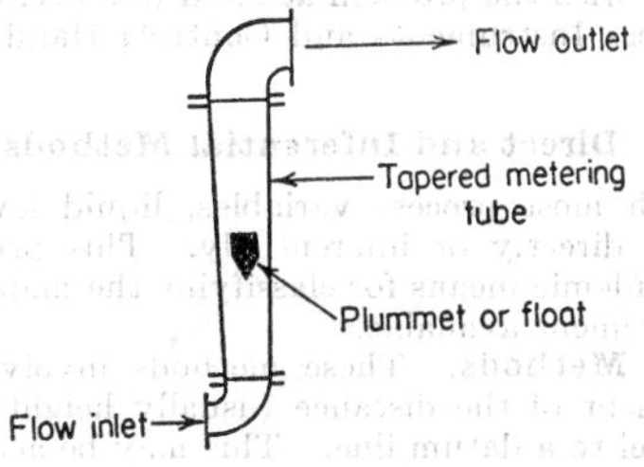

FIG. 22-53. Basic components of rotameter.

outlet connections, comprise (1) a metering tube and (2) a float. Rather complex devices can be built up, starting with these basic components.

The maximum capacities of typical rotameters are given in Table 22-13.

Piston-type Area Meters. While there are variations in design, the usual piston-type meter comprises (1) a sleeve or cylinder held rigidly in a cast body and (2) a well-fitted piston or metering plug. Orifices, usually rectangular, are cut into the sleeve. These orifices are uncovered by the piston or plug until sufficient area is opened to permit passage of the flow being measured. The metering edges consist of the port edges and the bottom edge of the plug. The position of the piston or metering plug, therefore, provides a direct indication of the orifice area and, consequently, the rate of flow. One design is shown in Fig. 22-54.

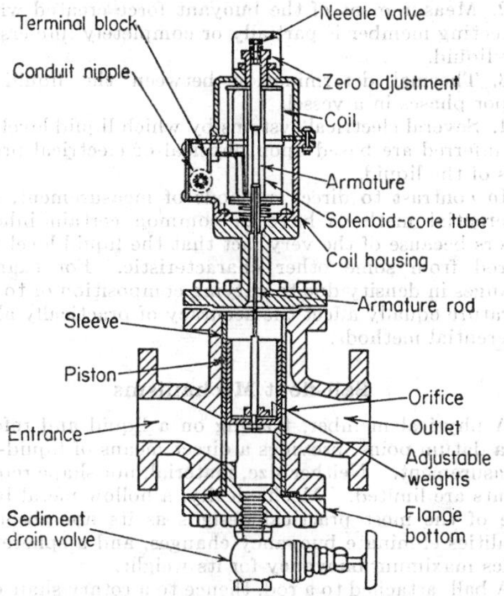

FIG. 22-54. Weight-loaded area flowmeter.

Positive-displacement Meters

Displacement meters are commonly divided into four basic types: (1) reciprocating, (2) rotating, (3) oscillating, and (4) nutating-piston meters. Of major importance is the last of these, which is used in greater quantities than all others combined.

Basic requirements for positive-displacement meters in industrial service are (1) simplicity of design, required to make maintenance possible without specially trained personnel; (2) accuracy within stated limits; users seldom have facilities for checking this characteristic; (3) availability in a wide variety of sizes to satisfy various flow conditions; (4) availability in different materials and calibrations for the measurement of widely different fluids; and (5) reasonably low pressure loss.

Nutating-piston Meter. This device, which is also known as the disk type of meter, is the most widely used positive-displacement meter in the United States. Figure 22-55 shows a sectional view of a typical meter of

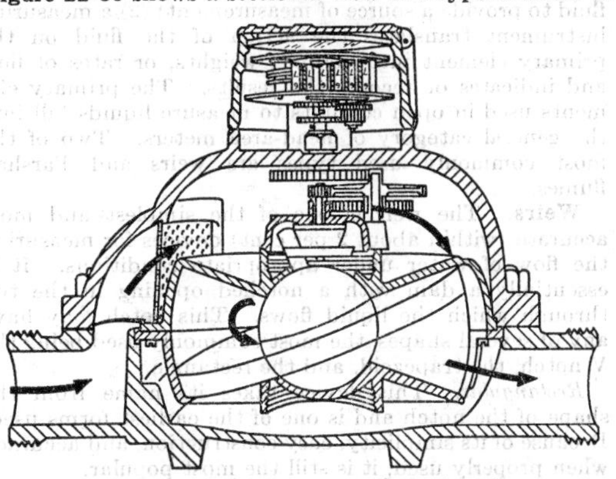

FIG. 22-55. Sectional view of typical nutating-piston meter.

this type. Each cycle (complete movement) of the measuring piston or disk displaces a fixed volume of liquid. Note that there is only one moving part in the measuring chamber, namely, the piston. The liquid enters through the inlet port and fills the spaces above and below the piston, which fits closely and precisely in the measuring chamber. The advancing volume of liquid moves the piston in a nutating motion until the liquid discharges from the outlet port.

Rotating Meters. These are commonly known as *current* meters or *velocity* meters. They operate on the turbine principle; *i.e.*, the volume is measured by the movement of a wheel or turbine type of impeller which is actuated by the velocity of the liquid flowing through it. They are used to measure continuous high flow rates with minimum pressure loss.

Figure 22-56 shows a typical velocity meter. There

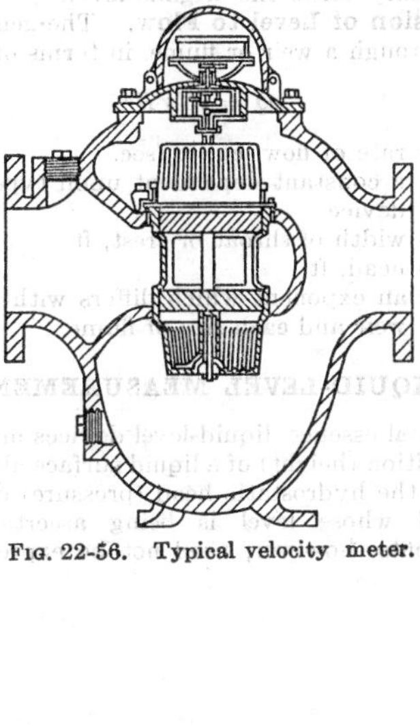

FIG. 22-56. Typical velocity meter.

are two propellers, mounted on a vertical spindle which is carried on an agate bearing. One propeller is a right-hand and the other is a left-hand helix. The incoming liquid is divided into two equal streams which flow through their respective propellers in equal volume and at the same velocity.

The speed of rotation of the impellers is then a function of the velocity of the liquid through the chamber, which in turn is a function of the flow volume.

Weirs and Flumes

To measure the rate of flow in open channels, especially in streams and rivers, two distinct operations are necessary: (1) a primary element is acted upon directly by a fluid to provide a source of measurement; (2) a measuring instrument translates the action of the fluid on the primary element into volume, weights, or rates of flow and indicates or records the results. The primary elements used in open conduits to measure liquids fall into the general category of head-area meters. Two of the most commonly used types are weirs and Parshall flumes.

Weirs. The weir is one of the simplest and most accurate (within about 2 per cent) devices for measuring the flow of water under appropriate conditions. It is essentially a dam with a notched opening in the top through which the liquid flows. This notch may have any of several shapes, the most commonly used being the V notch, the trapezoid, and the rectangle.

Rectangular. This device takes its name from the shape of the notch and is one of the earliest forms used. Because of its simplicity, easy construction, and accuracy when properly used, it is still the most popular.

Triangular (V-notch). This weir has a greater practical range of capacity than any other type for a given size. Since it requires a greater loss of head, however, it is most suitable for measuring flows of less than 4 cu. ft./sec.

Cipolletti. This is a trapezoidal weir in which the sides of the notch slope one horizontal to four vertical. Its popularity is based on the belief that these side slopes are just sufficient to correct for the side contractions of the nappe (overfalling sheet of water), and the flow is therefore proportional to the length of the weir crest.

Flumes. Basically, a flume is an open channel through which the fluid has free flow. Upstream, the entrance converges to the throat whose sides are parallel and then diverges downstream after passing through it. The Parshall flume has supplanted all other types and is therefore the only one to be considered here. It is a special case where the floor slopes downward from the level floor of the entrance section and is then inclined to a level slightly below the original level.

Conversion of Level to Flow. The general formula for flow through a weir or flume, in terms of head, is

$$Q = KWH^n$$

where Q = rate of flow, cu. ft./sec.
K = a constant dependent upon type and size of device
W = width of throat or crest, ft.
H = head, ft.
n = an exponent which differs with each type of weir and each size of flume

LIQUID-LEVEL MEASUREMENTS

In the final essence, liquid-level devices measure either (1) the position (height) of a liquid surface above a datum line or (2) the hydrostatic head (pressure) developed by the liquid whose level is being ascertained. Level measurements, however, need not be expressed strictly in terms of inches or feet above a datum line, or in terms of the hydrostatic head developed, but can be conveniently interpreted (thus calibrated) in terms of the volume of liquid contained, provided that the dimensional and contour characteristics of the containing vessel are known. Further, with information concerning the specific gravity of the liquid, level measurements can be expressed in terms of the weight of liquid in the vessel. The choice of units for a given level measurement varies, of course, with the problem at hand (see Sec. 5 by Elfers in "Process Instruments and Controls Handbook," *loc. cit.*).

Direct and Inferential Methods

As with most process variables, liquid level can be measured directly or inferentially. This provides one rather academic means for classifying the many methods of measurement available.

Direct Methods. These methods involve a direct measurement of the distance (usually height) from the liquid level to a datum line. This may be accomplished by

1. Direct visual observation of distance on a suitably calibrated scale, as with a gage stick, hook gage, or gage glass
2. Determination of the position of a detecting member which rides on the liquid surface, such as a ball or other type of float
3. Contact of electrode probes with a liquid surface
4. Interruption of a light beam to a photoelectric cell
5. Reflection of radio and radar frequency waves or sonic waves from a liquid surface

Inferential Methods. Effects other than the changing position of a liquid surface can be used to advantage in determining the liquid level in a vessel. Some of these effects are

1. Measurement of the fluid or hydrostatic head developed by the liquid.
2. Measurement of the buoyant force created when a detecting member is partially or completely immersed in the liquid.
3. Thermal determination between the liquid and vapor phases in a vessel.
4. Several electrical systems by which liquid level may be inferred are based upon physical or electrical properties of the liquid.

In contrast to direct methods of measurement, most inferential methods have in common certain inherent errors because of the very fact that the liquid level is inferred from some other characteristic. For example, changes in density due to varying composition or to temperature equally affect the accuracy of practically all the inferential methods.

Ball-float Mechanisms

A physical member, floating on a liquid and referred to a datum point, provides a direct means of liquid-level measurement. Neither size, material, nor shape requirements are limited. Mechanically, a hollow metal ball is one of the most practical designs as its non-absorbent qualities eliminate buoyancy changes, and a sphere provides maximum buoyancy for its weight.

A ball, attached to a rod, thence to a rotary shaft operating in a bearing, trunnion, or packing gland, with a pointer and scale, is shown in Fig. 22-57. Requirements for this device are simple. For maximum sensitivity, the ball float should be weighted so that it will sink to its largest (center) section. As the level rises or falls around the sphere, this produces the largest amount of available

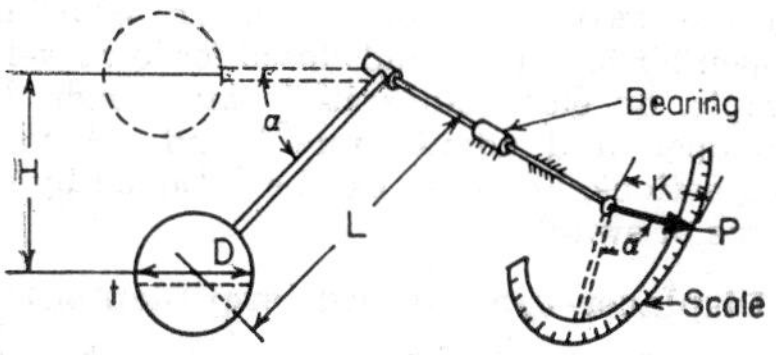

FIG. 22-57. Ball-float mechanism, operating principle.

power in both directions needed to overcome friction of shafts and bearings, plus inertia of component parts.

Float Valves

From measurement, it is a simple transition step to a closely coupled controller—the float valve as shown in Fig. 22-58. In these devices, the float directly and mechanically positions a valve mechanism, to open and close

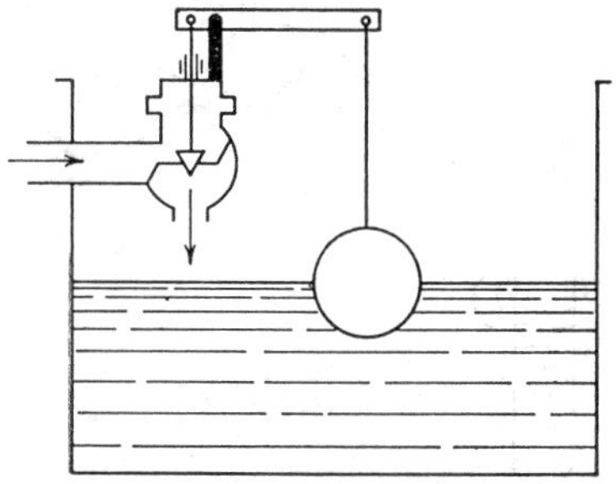

FIG. 22-58. Schematic diagram of float valve.

it and allow more or less flow of liquid into the vessel, thereby controlling its level at an established point. These devices have a long history of use for open tanks, reservoirs, sumps, domestic plumbing fixtures, and the like and are still popularly used.

The control device, usually a valve, must be located close or adjacent to the float device since transmission of level measurement is developed by simple direct mechanical linkage. The stroke or travel of the valve in practice is usually about ½ or ¾ in.

Applications also are limited because floats do not develop sufficient torque to overcome kinetic unbalance forces, such as velocity forces caused by differential or pressure drop across the valve member. This generally limits the use of these devices to a pressure drop across the valve of 100 lb./sq. in. or less with conventional size floats.

Pilot-operated Cage-type Gages. Limitations imposed on measurement and control of liquid level by direct mechanically operated ball-float devices introduced the need for a pilot- or relay-operated device for measurement and control action.

The float-cage and tank stuffing-box type of level measurement and control device has a relay or pilot member added to it in the manner shown schematically in Fig. 22-59. The rotation of the shaft produced by a change of liquid level within the vessel or float cage translates motion to the relay pilot and through its action allows an operating-medium impulse such as air to be sent to an indicating gage for level measurement or to a remote diaphragm motor valve for liquid-level control.

Chain or Tape Float Gages. In gages of these types, the float is connected by means of a flexible chain or tape to a rotating member (which is connected to the indicating mechanism). A counterweight, as shown in Fig. 22-60, is employed to keep the chain or tape taut as

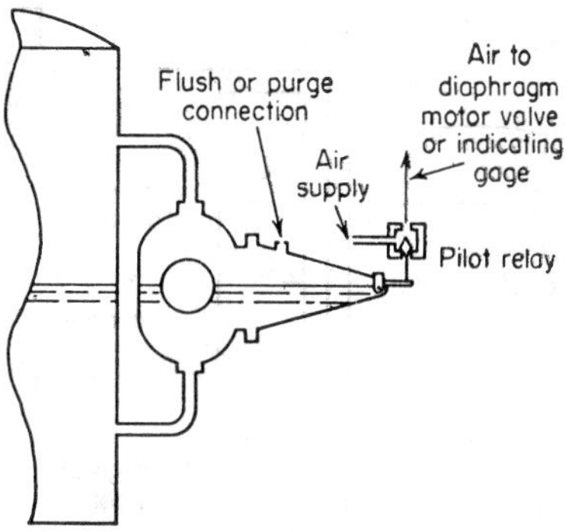

FIG. 22-59. Float-cage-type gage with pilot relay.

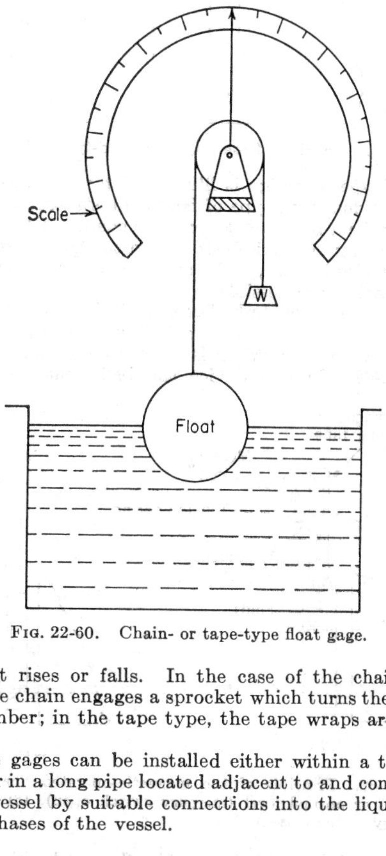

FIG. 22-60. Chain- or tape-type float gage.

the float rises or falls. In the case of the chain-type gage, the chain engages a sprocket which turns the rotating member; in the tape type, the tape wraps around a drum.

These gages can be installed either within a tank or vessel or in a long pipe located adjacent to and connected to the vessel by suitable connections into the liquid and vapor phases of the vessel.

Magnetic-type Float Gages

The problems of stuffing boxes in ball-float gages led enterprising researchers to develop designs which employ magnetic forces to follow or sense the float position. Two such designs are described below: (1) the magnetic-bond method and (2) the magnetic-operated float switch.

Magnetic-bond Method. A float mechanism employing the magnetic-bond method of measuring liquid level utilizes a magnetic member which floats on the surface of the liquid. A magnetic-flux field is transmitted from the magnetic float to a suitable pick-up device, which actuates the indicator or controlling device. A

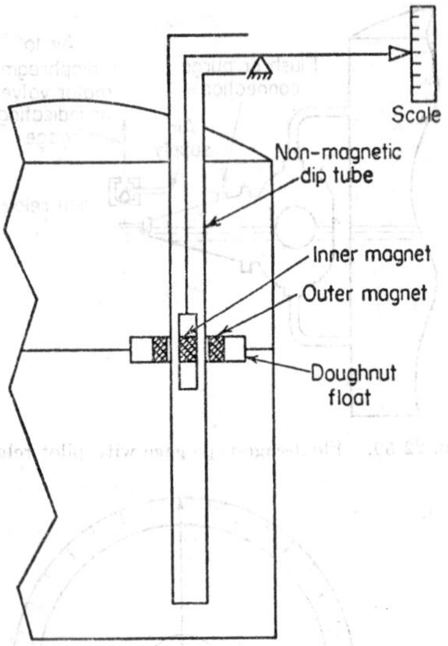

FIG. 22-61. Principle of the magnetic-bond-type ball-float gage.

typical type of design is illustrated by Fig. 22-61. Although a doughnut type of float is illustrated, this member may be a ball, a disk, or other shape. Other means of conveying magnetic-bond action to the pick-up member may also be used, and many mechanical variations of this principle are possible.

Magnetic-operated Float Switch. Another type of ball-float mechanism employing magnetic force to operate a mercury switch is illustrated schematically in Fig. 22-62. In this device the ball float positions a

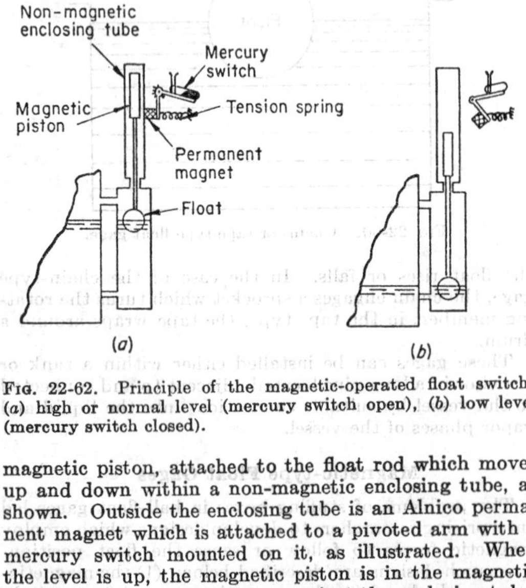

FIG. 22-62. Principle of the magnetic-operated float switch: (a) high or normal level (mercury switch open), (b) low level (mercury switch closed).

magnetic piston, attached to the float rod which moves up and down within a non-magnetic enclosing tube, as shown. Outside the enclosing tube is an Alnico permanent magnet which is attached to a pivoted arm with a mercury switch mounted on it, as illustrated. When the level is up, the magnetic piston is in the magnetic field and the magnet is drawn against the enclosing tube, thereby tilting the mercury switch to one position (to open or close a circuit as desired). When the level drops to a predetermined point, the piston is moved down out of the magnetic field and the magnet is pulled out by the tension spring, thereby tilting the mercury switch to its other position. Figure 22-62*a* and *b* illustrates these two conditions with an SPST mercury switch open for high level and closed for low level, where, for example, an electric-operated valve might be energized to open and admit more liquid. A variety of switching actions, however, can be obtained by selection of the type of switch.

Displacer-type Liquid-level Elements

Since the introduction of the displacer type of liquid-level gage and controller, its use has continued to increase, and currently in process operations it is the most widely used. This, of course, is easily understood when the many design and application advantages are considered. Gages of the displacement-float type of construction fall into two principal categories: (1) torque-tube units and (2) force-balance units.

Torque-tube Unit. A schematic diagram of this design is shown in Fig. 22-63. The displacer *A* is supported at one end of a support rod *B*, while the other end

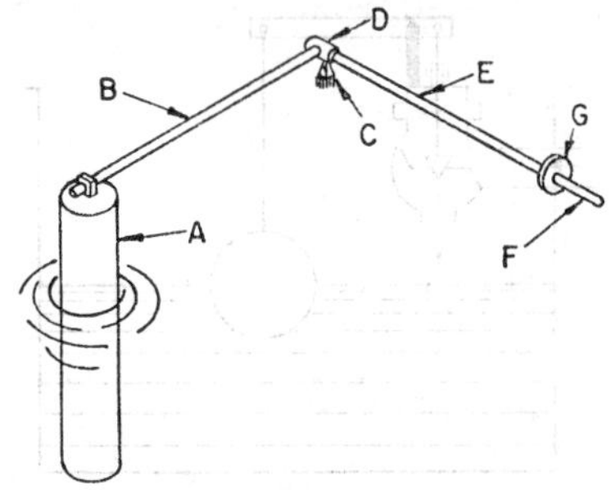

FIG. 22-63. Schematic diagram of torque-tube displacer unit.

of the rod is carried by a pivot bearing assembly *C*. A torque tube *E* is located at 90 deg. to the support rod and is attached to it at the pivot point. This tube has a pressure-tight inner end fitting *D* and a flange member *G* bolted or suitably held in place to form a pressure seal with a housing which encloses the above parts. A shaft *F* is inserted into the hollow torque tube and is attached to the fitting *D*. Before the outer torque tube flange *G* is bolted or sealed, it is manually rotated by an amount necessary to twist the tube, rotating the support rod about its pivot point, and completely supporting the weight of the displacer.

A rise in liquid about the displacer causes it to become effectively lighter by the amount of the weight of the liquid being displaced. This change of weight then permits the twisting spring action of the torque tube to raise the displacer and rotate the support rod *B* about its pivot point along with the torque end fitting *D*. Since the operating shaft *F* is attached to fitting *D*, it too is rotated by a similar amount, thus giving a measurable shaft rotation which is directly proportional to the liquid-level change.

A pointer may be attached to the operating shaft *F* of the torque tube of the above construction to give a direct scale reading of the liquid level, but it is not generally used because the amount of shaft rotation is small and the scale range is very narrow.

Force-balance Unit. Another design employing the displacer principle and known as the force-balance system is shown in Fig. 22-64. Here a change in buoyant force is transmitted through a float arm and flexible-disk (or flexure-tube) pressure seal to a force-balancing pilot system. A rise in liquid level causes the displacer to become effectively lighter by the amount of the additional liquid displacement, which in turn permits the balance spring to move a flapper arm closer to a nozzle.

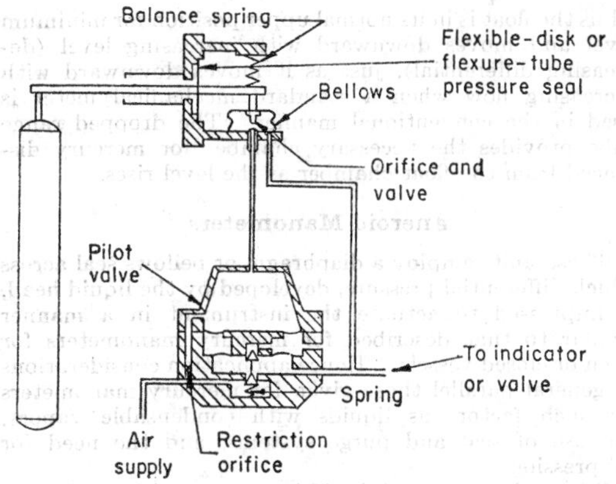

FIG. 22-64. Schematic diagram of force-balance displacer unit with flexible-disk pressure seal.

This action increases the nozzle pressure to an air relay, causing an increase in output pressure of magnitude sufficient to balance the force of the loading spring with a feedback bellows and return the displacer to its original position.

Hydrostatic Methods

Basic methods of utilizing hydrostatic head in a vessel as a basis for liquid-level measurement and control generally employ commercially available pressure gages, as well as standard models of differential-pressure meters commonly used for flow or differential-pressure measurement. Thus coverage of hydrostatic methods primarily centers around proper installation of instruments and the use of suitable accessory equipment for liquid-level applications.

Although instruments which measure pressure are limited to use on vessels open to the atmosphere, it does not follow that differential-pressure-type instruments are employed solely for level measurements in vessels under pressure. In open vessels one leg of the manometer is simply left open to atmosphere, whereas in closed vessels it is used to compensate for the vessel pressure which acts equally on both legs and therefore cancels out, leaving only the head effect as a variable related to liquid level.

In application, hydrostatic methods of liquid-level measurement for open or closed vessels may be classified as follows: (1) direct connection of hydrostatic head to measuring device, (2) diaphragm-box system, (3) air-trap system, (4) bubble-tube or purge system, (5) force-balance system, and (6) opposed-diaphragm types.

Various diaphragm systems are shown in Fig. 22-65; an air-purge system is shown in Fig. 22-66.

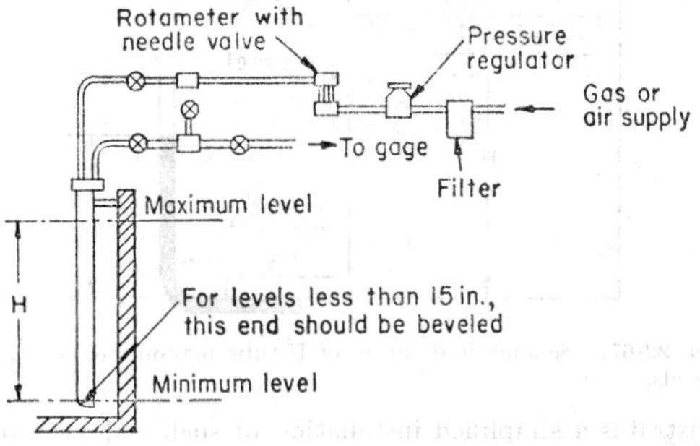

FIG. 22-66. Gas or air-purge system for open vessels.

Mercury Manometers

Various forms of instruments designed for measurement of differential pressure or liquid flow are readily adapted for liquid-level measurement by the hydrostatic method. These include mercury manometers and various types of "dry" flowmeters described elsewhere in this section. The application problems and the principles of operation of systems employing these instruments are distinctly different for *open-vessel service* as compared with *closed-vessel service* and are therefore covered separately under these two headings for mercury manometers. Dry-type manometers are covered separately later to avoid confusion in terminology.

Two general considerations apply to all manometer-type instruments employed for liquid-level measurements, namely: (1) maximum and minimum ranges available and (2) compensation for changes in specific gravity of the vessel liquid. The second consideration is inherent in all hydrostatic methods because specific-gravity changes affect the measured head. In some manometer-type instruments, compensation for changes in specific gravity is provided by an adjustment (sometimes termed a "sensitivity slider") which multiplies pen or pointer travel in an exact ratio of the initial specific gravity to the actual working specific gravity. In other cases, any necessary gravity corrections are simply in the form of a factor.

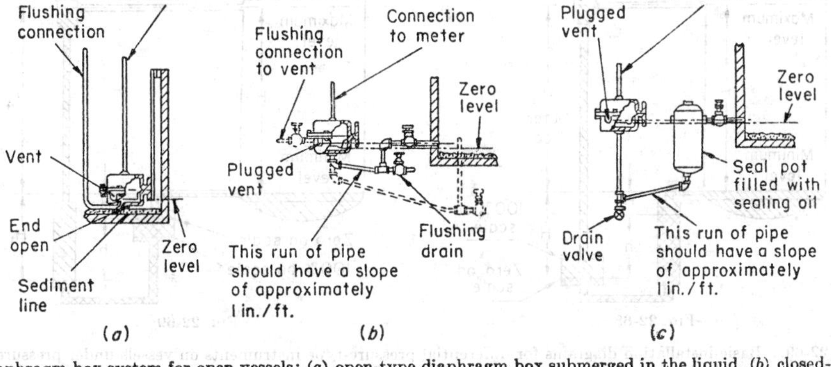

FIG. 22-65. Diaphragm-box system for open vessels: (*a*) open-type diaphragm box submerged in the liquid, (*b*) closed-type diaphragm box located outside of tank, (*c*) closed-type diaphragm box for use with corrosive liquids.

Open-vessel Service. A simple U-tube manometer can serve to measure the pressure due to hydrostatic head in an open vessel by connection to a minimum-level tap, as described for the pressure gage. Figure 22-67

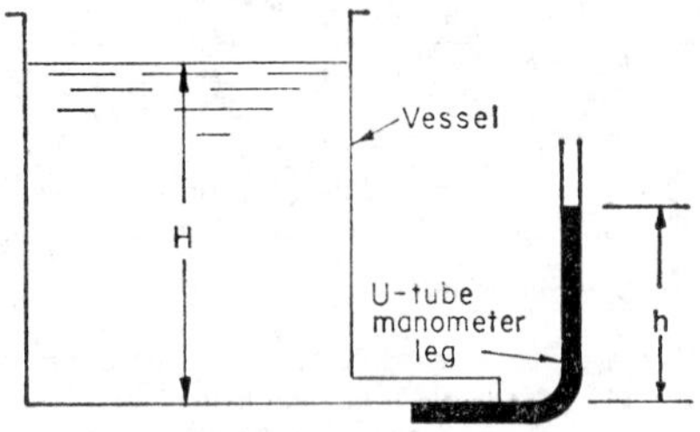

FIG. 22-67. Schematic diagram of U-tube manometer for open vessels.

illustrates a simplified installation of such a device and serves to explain the basic operating principle of differential-pressure-type instruments for open-vessel service.

Closed-vessel Service. As shown by the schematic diagram (Fig. 22-68) for a basic system, mercury-manometer installations for vessels operating under pressure differ from those for open vessels in one fundamental respect, namely, the outer leg connected to the maximum-level point has a relatively constant head which creates the greatest differential pressure across the manometer when the vessel liquid is at its minimum value. As the level rises in the vessel, this differential pressure decreases to zero at the maximum-level connection. Such a relationship is seen to be the reverse of that found in open-vessel service where the differential increases with hydrostatic head; it is also the reverse of that found in flow measurement for which most manometers are designed.

In the case of an electric meter, it is only necessary to reverse the power leads of the inductance-bridge circuit to reverse the response of the meter. Thus, the float-chamber (high-pressure) side of the meter body can be connected to the outer leg, as illustrated, but the instrument will read zero level when the vessel is empty and respond in the normal manner with level changes, the float moving upward for increasing level.

In the case of the mechanical meter, reversal of the instrument response is accomplished by "dropping" the range tube below the float chamber and connecting the latter to the minimum-level tap, as shown in Fig. 22-69. Thus the float is in its normal upper position for minimum level and moves downward with increasing level (decreasing differential), just as it moves downward with increasing flow when a standard mechanical meter is used in the conventional manner. The dropped range tube provides the necessary chamber for mercury displaced from the float chamber as the level rises.

Aneroid Manometers

These units employ a diaphragm or bellows seal across which differential pressure, developed by the liquid head, is impressed to actuate the instrument in a manner similar to that described for mercury manometers for open or closed vessels. Hence application considerations in general parallel those given for mercury manometers for such factors as liquids with condensable vapors, the use of seal and purge systems, and the need for suppression.

Where the measured liquid is non-corrosive to the seal of the aneroid-type manometer, this liquid or its condensed vapors can be connected directly to the manometer, as shown in Fig. 22-70. The device illustrated is a

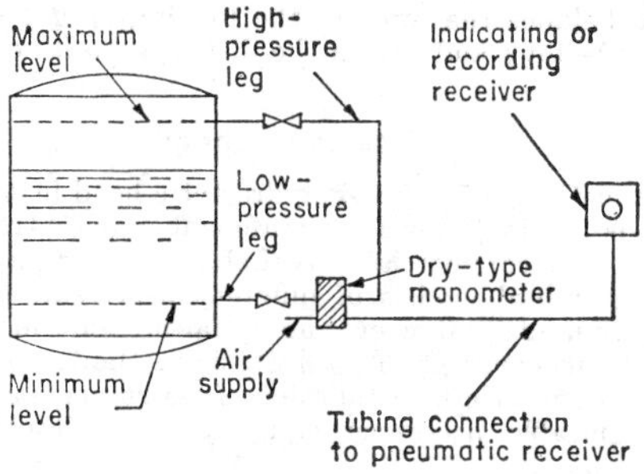

FIG. 22-70. Aneroid manometer installed on closed vessel with vessel liquid connecting lines.

non-indicating pneumatic transmitter which is connected to a remote liquid-level indicator or recorder.

The pneumatic-transmitter design is basically arranged for flow measurement, providing an increase in differential pressure. Thus, as discussed for the use of mercury manometers for closed-vessel service on liquid-filled systems (all except gas- or air-purge systems), the differential pressure due to the difference between the fixed outer leg and the hydrostatic head is maximum at zero

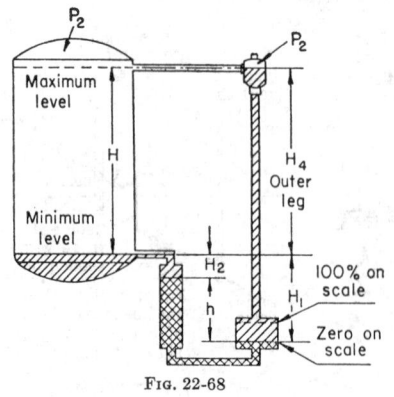

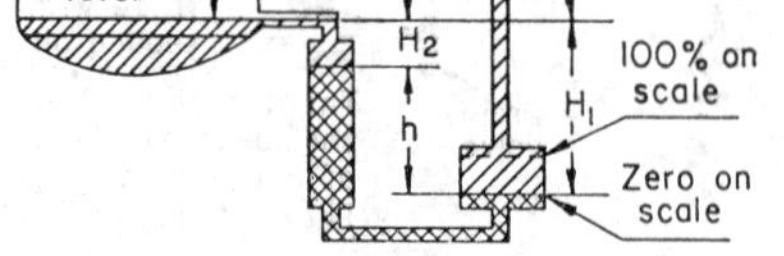

FIG. 22-68

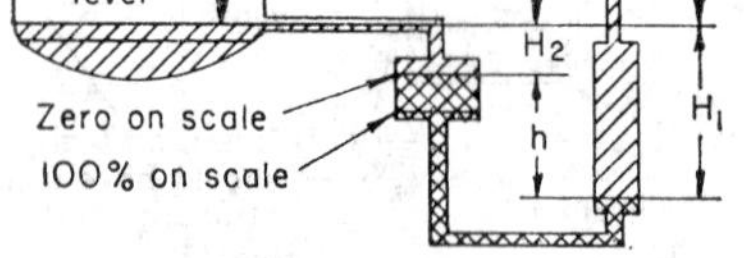

FIG. 22-69

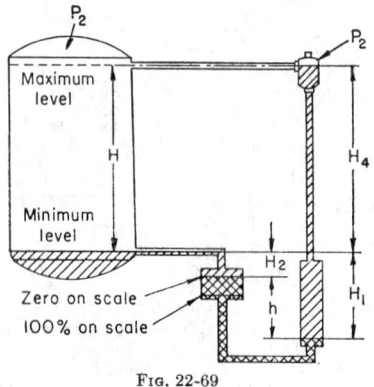

FIGS. 22-68 and 22-69. Basic installation diagrams for differential-pressure-type instruments on vessels under pressure:
Fig. 22-68. Electric meter body.
Fig. 22-69. Mechanical-type meter body with dropped range tube.

level and decreases with increase in level. To provide direct reading of level on the indicator or recorder, therefore, the pneumatic receiver must be equipped with a reverse movement, or means must be incorporated in the aneroid manometer to compensate for the fixed head and provide a direct relationship between the transmitter output air pressure and level changes.

Other Liquid-level Systems

Less frequently used liquid-level measurement systems include (1) expansion-tube units, (2) thermal-hydraulic systems, (3) thermometer-bulb immersion methods, (4) sonic-type detectors, (5) nuclear-radiation-type detectors, (6) oscillator-type detectors, (7) electrode or probe systems, (8) photoelectric-cell systems, and (9) capacitance systems.

CHEMICAL-COMPOSITION MEASUREMENTS

The principal means now in use for measurement of chemical composition have been summarized as follows by C. M. Albright, Jr., of the Du Pont Company (see Sec. 6 in "Process Instruments and Controls Handbook," *loc. cit.*).

Measurements Based on Electromagnetic Radiation

The following methods involve either the emission, reflection, transmission, or diffraction of electromagnetic radiation by the sample.

Emission Spectroscopy. Used mostly for solids and metals analysis, but applicable to gases and liquids. Elemental composition of sample thermally excited by bombardment with electrons and ions in an arc or spark is determined by characteristic wave length and amount of emitted radiation.

Flame Photometry. Commonly used for determination of alkali metals by flame excitation. Similar to emission spectroscopy except may employ simpler optical system with filters instead of monochromator.

Fluorescence. May be employed in visible and ultraviolet regions for identification and measurement of pigments, dyes, petroleum products, and phosphors. Amount and spectral distribution of emitted radiation is related to presence of certain atoms, crystals, or molecules.

Raman Spectrophotometry. Useful for analysis of clear aqueous solutions free of suspended solids. Assists in identification and measurement of molecules on basis of structure similar to infrared techniques but depends upon analysis of reradiated light upon photo-excitation of sample.

Induced Radioactivity. Applicable to identification of some elements in any kind of sample by analysis and measurement of radioactive decay products after nuclear irradiation of sample.

X-ray Fluorescence. Analysis of solids, such as metals and alloys, for elements by observing characteristic X-ray radiation spectra from sample exposed to high-energy electron or X-ray bombardment.

X-ray Analysis.

1. Absorption measurements detect heavy elements in presence of lighter ones, such as lead or bromine in gasoline.
2. Critical edge absorption measurements identify and determine elemental composition.
3. Diffraction patterns identify crystal structure and hence composition of crystalline solids.

Ultraviolet Spectrophotometry. For analysis of many molecules in gases or liquids, such as Cl_2, SO_2, NO_2, CS_2, ozone, mercury vapor, and various unsaturated organic substances. Although not always so specific as infrared, sometimes preferable because stronger absorption bands permit detection of smaller quantities of unknown.

Conventional Photometry (Transmission Colorimetry). Similar to ultraviolet, but usually involves simple optical photometers employing filters to detect and measure colored compounds and light-absorbing precipitates.

Colorimetry. Used for opaque solids and liquids wherein color, or spectral distribution, of reflected light can be measured and related to composition.

Light Scattering. Used for molecular-weight measurements in liquids and particle size in dilute suspensions of gases and liquids.

Optical Rotation (Polarimetry). Specialized technique employing polarized light for measuring concentration of sugar and similar solutions.

Refractive Index. Useful to determine concentration of binary solutions that are optically clear or that do not form deposits on cell windows or prisms. Used also to grade optical solids such as glasses and plastics.

Infrared Spectrophotometry. Used to identify and measure concentration of heteroatomic compounds in gases, many non-aqueous liquids, and some solids. Infrared analyzers employ simplified optical systems and are useful for continuous analysis of one component in gas or liquid streams.

Microwave Spectroscopy. New technique having limited flexibility and sensitivity, but enormous resolution in terms of molecular determination in gases and vapors.

Nuclear Quadrupole Moment. Research technique holding promise for structural identification and quantitative measurement in many gases, liquids, and solids. Involves narrow-band radio-frequency resonance absorption.

Measurements Based on Chemical Reactions

The following methods involve the measurement of the results of reaction with other chemicals in terms of amount of sample or reactant consumed, product formed, or thermal energy liberated; or determination of equilibrium attained.

Orsat Analyzers. Employ quantitative selective chemical absorption of gases from sample on volumetric basis. Usually of batch type, but in special cases may be continuous-flow types employing pneumatic bridge and differential gas-flow measurement.

Automatic Titrators. Employ quantitative reaction with measured flow of reactant or electrically generated reactant and potentiometric, amperometric, or colorimetric end-point or null determination. May be sequential batch type or continuous. For gas and liquid samples.

Impregnated Paper-tape Device. Primarily for gases. Consist of chemically treated paper tapes that are continuously unreeled, exposed to sample, and viewed by phototube to measure color change that is empirically related to unknown in sample. These can be assembled to operate on a large number of colorimetric analytical techniques.

Chromatography. Essentially consists of passing a mixture through an adsorption or partition column. It represents a two-phase system in which advantage is taken of the different equilibria existing between the two phases to separate components differing in equilibrium constants. The sample and carrier are generally called the mobile phase whereas the column material is referred to as the stationary (or static) phase. The mobile phase can be a gas, liquid, or solid in solution whereas the stationary phase can only be a liquid or solid.

Continuous Chemical-reaction Types. For gas and liquid samples. Can employ a series of steps like a miniature automatic chemical plant, to carry out many analytical laboratory techniques where electrical-conductivity changes, color changes, or precipitates can be measured and related to concentration of unknown in sample.

Combustion Types. Used for flammable gases and vapors in air or other medium that will support combustion reaction to completion. Wires electrically heated to just above the ignition temperature and having a large temperature coefficient of resistance are employed. The change in resistance, measured in a bridge circuit, indicates the amount of combustion, and hence the amount of flammable gas or vapor.

Other Reaction Types. Generally limited to gases and vapors. Quantitative exothermic reaction of unknown in sample with reactant causes temperature rise that can be measured by conventional means. Useful for H_2O, O_2, CO_2, H_2, and some alcohols.

Redox Potentiometry. Used for solutions in which both oxidized and reduced forms of the unknown may exist. The relative concentration of the two forms can be measured by inert probing electrodes as a solution potential is developed that differs from the standard potential.

pH or Hydrogen-ion Concentration. Special case of potentiometry for measuring hydrogen-ion concentration when one component of the redox system (the hydrogen electrode) is a solid. Used extensively for weak aqueous solutions of acids and bases.

Metal-ion Equilibria. Another special case of potentiometry where one component of the redox system, the metal electrode, is a solid and is sensitive to concentration changes in the particular ion involved.

Measurements Based on Current, Voltage, or Flux Changes Produced in Energized Electric and Magnetic Circuits Containing the Sample

Mass Spectroscopy.

1. *Nier Type.* The conventional mass spectrometer employing electronic ionization of a low-pressure gas or vapor sample, electrostatic ion acceleration, magnetic-field deflection to separate masses, and ion-current measurement to establish quantitative analysis.

2. *Omegatron.* Specialized technique in which ions are caused to seek characteristic mass-related orbits in a powerful uniform magnetic field.

3. *Time of Flight.* A newer method employing pulse techniques to accelerate ion bunches into a drift space and determine mass separation by relative arrival time at the ion collector.

Controlled-potential Electrolysis. The basic electrochemical technique for quantitative analysis, usually on batch basis, of conducting solutions containing oxidizable or reducible material. Measurement is based upon weight of material plated out on electrode.

Polarography. Similar to bulk electrolysis but applicable to aqueous and non-aqueous solutions, molten salts, and organic salts. Not limited to batch determinations. Employs microelectrode so that current is "diffusion-limited" and proportional to concentration of reducible (or oxidizable) ions in solution. Applied potential to achieve one-half of diffusion-limited current is related to chemical identity of ion measured.

Coulometry. Similar to bulk electrolysis and applicable to some solution systems except quantity of electricity that flows at constant potential is measured. Several modifications of this technique are employed in automatic titrators, but the basic method is not widely used except where quantitative accuracy is desired.

Amperometry. Similar to bulk electrolysis and applicable to same solution systems as polarography. Depends on current measurement at a fixed applied potential corresponding to a diffusion-current plateau for the substance being measured. Current changes are then proportional to concentration changes. Sometimes used in conjunction with automatic titrators.

"Dead-stop" Methods. A specialized measurement wherein the current that flows between inert platinum microelectrodes at a fixed potential, less than 0.5 volt, is proportional to the concentration of the minority species in a reversible redox system. Useful for halogen and iron systems.

Electrical Conductivity. Used for solutions, slurries, and wet solids. Especially useful for water-purity determination. Employs resistance-bridge type of measurement with alternating current to avoid polarization effects. Conductivity depends on type, mobility, and concentration of ions.

Dielectric Constant and Loss Factor. Provides similar information to that obtained by electrical conductivity but does not require electrode contact with sample. Useful for determining very small amounts of water in organic systems or solids.

Oscillometry. Similar to dielectric constant measurements but measures complex impedance of sample at radio frequencies by the load the sample reflects into the coil of an oscillator circuit. Useful for following titration end points and for determining small concentrations of salt in water.

Gaseous Conduction. Specialized technique for detecting vapors of organic halides in air by measuring the change in current that flows between a heated platinum anode and a concentric platinum cathode upon exposure to the sample.

Paramagnetism. Uncommon physical property exhibited to a significant extent only by oxygen and oxides of nitrogen. These gases will displace other substances from strong magnetic fields, permitting their determination either by measuring the displacement force directly or by the effect of some other physical property, such as thermal loss.

Nuclear Magnetic Resonance. Nuclear spin in elements and isotopes having odd atomic numbers causes radio-frequency absorption in uniform magnetic field. Very sensitive technique for gases, liquids, and some solids. Uses rather complex equipment.

Measurements Based upon the Results of Applying Thermal or Mechanical Energy to a System

Measurements are expressed in terms of energy transmission, work done, or changes in physical state.

Thermal Conductivity. Useful for a number of common gases in essentially binary systems wherein the thermal conductivity of the component being sought differs from that of the background. CO, CO_2, H_2, NH_3, SO_2, and H_2S can be readily measured in air, O_2, or N_2 by this means. Measurement is usually made by observing the change in temperature of a fine heated wire that is conduction-cooled by the gas or vapor sample stress.

Melting and Boiling Points. These are basic physical constants that are usually measured on a batch basis by observing the temperature rise or fall at a constant heating or cooling rate for an inflection point. These measurements are commonly specified for purity limits of many chemical products.

Ice Point (Crystallization). Many solutions, upon cooling, reach a point at which one component crystallizes. Determination of this component can be made on a batch basis by collecting and weighing the amount separated, assuming that the balance of the solution is saturated with that component, or by supercooling and observing by optical means the quantity of crystals formed or the temperature at which they are formed.

Dew Point. Similar to ice point but applicable to gas and vapor systems. Used extensively for water-vapor determination. Measurement is made by observing temperature to which a surface exposed to sample must be lowered to just form a condensate. This method is available in automatic form.

Vapor Pressure. The composition of a simple system can be determined by equilibrium vapor-pressure measurements at a known temperature of vapor-liquid interface.

Fractionation. The separation of liquid samples by distillation into their component fractions, with quantitative determination of composition on a volume or weight basis provided auxiliary data are available for identification of the fractions.

Thermal Expansion. Composition of solids and liquids can sometimes be determined, on known systems, by characteristic changes in volume or length with respect to temperature.

Viscosity. Measurement of fluid friction by mechanical drag between driven and free members immersed in the sample, damping of longitudinal or torsional vibration, or resistance to flow. These measurements can be related to such composition variables as molecular weight or concentration of simple solutions and suspensions.

Sound Velocity. Composition of gas, liquid, and solid mixtures, especially binary systems, can be characterized by attenuation and/or change in velocity of propagation of sound waves through the sample. The propagation of sound is related to molecular structure and intermolecular interactions.

Density. Composition of simple systems involving gases and liquids can be determined by density measurement. Techniques employed may involve restoring force on buoyant bobs or measurement of forces transmitted by a mass of the substance being analyzed as in viscous-drag gas-density meter.

pH-MEASURING SYSTEMS

Because of the importance of pH measurement to the process industries and its frequency of occurrence as compared with other chemical-composition determinations, a basic review is given here. Two methods are in general use for the direct determination of pH: (1) chemical indicators (color change), and (2) potentiometric instruments, *i.e.*, pH meters. The first method is largely confined to the laboratory.

Potentiometric pH Measurement. A potentiometric pH-measurement system consists of

1. pH-responsive electrode, such as glass, antimony, quinhydrone, or hydrogen electrode
2. Reference electrode, usually calomel or silver-silver chloride
3. Potential-measuring devise, such as a pH meter, usually some form of vacuum-tube voltmeter. Such a basic system is shown in Fig. 22-71

pH Instruments. Electronic pH meters are voltmeters with scale divisions in pH units which are equivalent at 25°C. to 59.15 mv. per pH unit. These meters fall into two general classes: (1) those utilizing a potentiometer circuit in which the electronic amplifier output is registered on a null-reading galvanometer and (2) those which register the amplifier output on a direct-reading meter. Meters are available in portable, battery-operated models as well as models operating on line current. Many are equipped to switch from pH to millivolt scale readings for measurement of oxidation-reduction potentials. The growing interest in oxidation-reduction systems makes this a desirable feature.

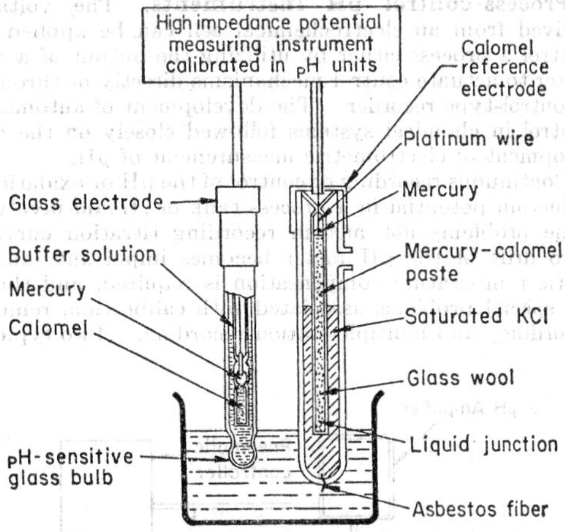

FIG. 22-71. A potentiometric pH-measuring system.

The voltage of a specific pair of electrodes of a given type will not be exactly zero when checked in a buffer solution of the proper value for which the instrument is designed. This is the asymmetry potential, which is not the same for all electrodes. Since the glass-electrode response to change in pH is in agreement with the theoretical value, the asymmetry potential may be corrected for by an adjustment of the asymmetry control provided in the instrument. This sets the meter to read the correct pH when the electrodes are immersed in a buffer of known pH. Measurements are then made with respect to this reference point. When electrodes and meter have stabilized in operation, it is necessary only to recheck standardization occasionally. When it is necessary to use "fresh" electrodes, more frequent adjustment of the controls may be required. One of the most commonly used buffers for the standardization of pH meters is potassium acid phthalate, 0.05 molar or 0.05 molal. The pH values of this solution have been determined at the National Bureau of Standards by Hamer, Pinching, and Acree and are the fundamental pH standards accepted by the British Standards Institution (see British Standard 1647:1950) and the National Bureau of Standards. The pH values of 0.05 molal solutions of potassium acid phthalate at 0° to 60°C. for the calibration of pH meters are given in the following table:

Temp. t, °C.	pH*	pH†
0	4.012	4.01
5	4.005	4.01
10	4.001	4.00
15	4.000	4.00
20	4.001	4.00
25	4.005	4.01
30	4.011	4.01
35	4.019	4.02
40	4.030	4.03
45	4.043	4.04
50	4.059	4.06
55	4.077	4.08
60	4.097	4.10

* As determined by Hamer, Pinching, and Acree.
† Rounded values, *Bur. Standards J. Research*, **36**, 47 (1946).

Process-control pH Instruments. The voltage derived from an electrochemical cell can be applied to control a process either by utilizing the output of a pH meter to actuate control mechanisms directly or through a control-type recorder. The development of automatic control in chemical systems followed closely on the development of electrometric measurement of pH.

Continuous recording or control of the pH or oxidation-reduction potential in a process tank or stream involves some problems not met in recording titration curves. Zero drift of the pH meter becomes important, automatic temperature compensation is required, and there are special problems associated with calibration, remote recording, and multiple-station recording. Two typical pH-control applications are shown in Figs. 22-72 and 22-73.

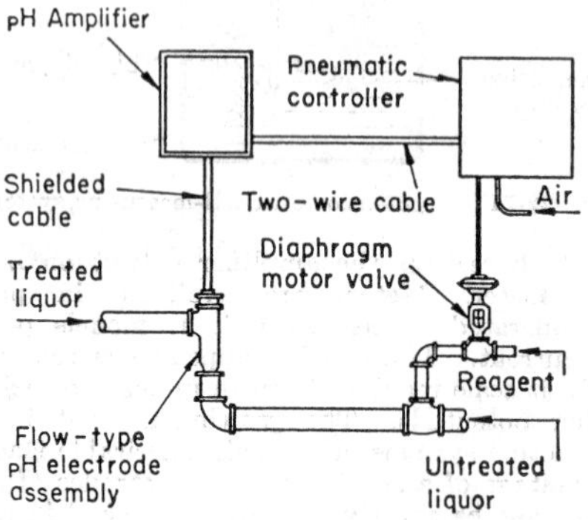

FIG. 22-72. Basic automatic pH control system.

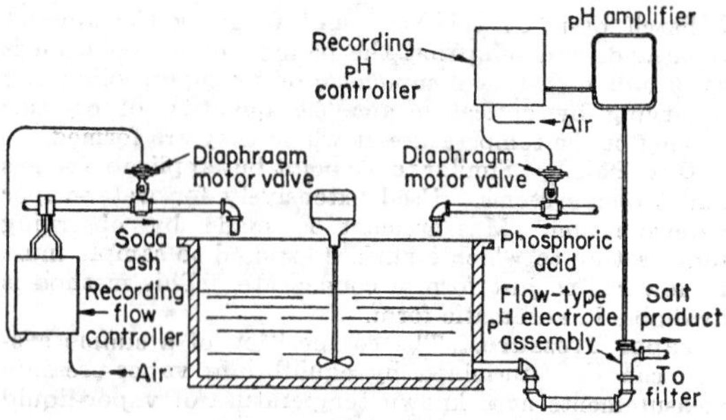

FIG. 22-73. Continuous automatic neutralization in the manufacture of disodium phosphate is made possible through the use of automatic flow and pH controllers. The fine control afforded by this system protects purity of salt product and prevents waste of either reagent.

OTHER PROCESS MEASUREMENTS

Space does not permit detailed description of control and instrumentation of other process variables. In Tables 22-14 to 22-18, however, are brief listings of the major instrument types for the measurement of the most important of these variables. The illustrations and data therein are from the "Guide to Process Instrument Elements," by Theodore R. Olive and Steven Danatos, appearing as a special report in the June, 1961, issue of *Chemical Engineering* and copyrighted by McGraw-Hill Publishing Co., Inc., New York, N.Y.

Table 22-14. Instruments for Weight and Weight Rate of Flow

Diagram	Principle	Applications and remarks
	Fixed-load Weighing	
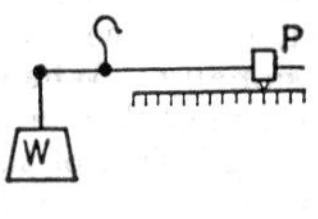	Fig. 22-74. Uneven-balanced scale. Simplest form, the steel-yard shown here, illustrates principle of most weight-balanced industrial scales. Unknown weight on a short moment arm is balanced by movable known poise (or known weights plus poise) on a long moment arm. Industrial scales (*e.g.*, Fig. 22-76) introduce additional levers between unknown weight and beam which increase ratio of unknown to poise	Most widely used weighing method for industrial use. Includes manual and automatic types. Indications on dial available. Some types print weight automatically
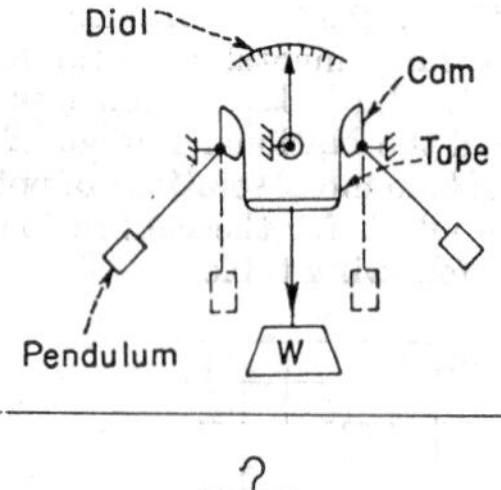	Fig. 22-75. Pendulum-balanced scale. One or more pendulums balance increasing loads as they move from vertical (zero) to horizontal (maximum). Because load balanced varies as sine of displacement angle, cams are used to give linear scale graduation. Cam may be on pendulum or on pointer. Metal tape transmits motion	Commonly used in both commercial and industrial scales, especially where dial indication of weight is desired. Available in recording and printing types also with photoelectric cutoff. Toledo Scale Co. has developed remote digital recording for scale
	Fig. 22-76. Spring-balanced scale. Spring deflecton within limits is directly proportional to load, so deflection can be used as a measure of weight supported. Hydraulic (spring) balanced scales. Force produced by load is detected by liquid-filled capsular element, transmitted to spring-loaded pressure-sensitive element	Commonly used for small commercial scales but is also used to balance beam in automatic industrial scales. Used in crane-hook scales and other industrial applications

Table 22-14. Instruments for Weight and Weight Rate of Flow—(*Continued*)

Diagram	Principle	Applications and remarks
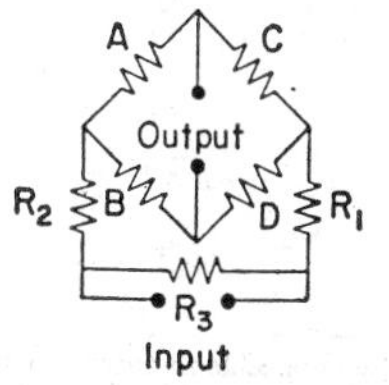	Fig. 22-77. Tension-balanced load cell (strain gage) (Baldwin-Lima-Hamilton Corp.). Strain gages bonded to calibrated tension element measure load in terms of lengthening of element. Resistance change in strain gage is measured by a bridge circuit. Unbonded strain gages may be used for smaller loads.	Used for both stationary and moving loads. Easily weighs tanks, bins, and hoppers. Made also in automatic printing type (Streeter-Amet Co.). Up to 50,000 lb. per load cell
	Moving-load Weighing	
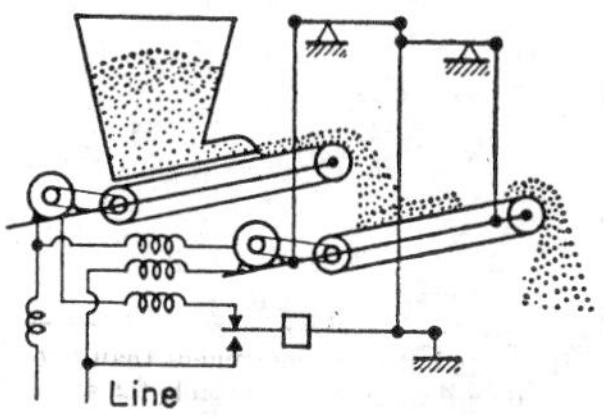	Fig. 22-78. Semicontinuous feed-belt weigher (Richardson Scale Co.). Scale-balanced weigh belt controls operaton of a feed belt. Scale belt runs continuously but is fed intermittently with loads shorter than its full length so that a definite increment is weighed. Increments come close together, approximate continuous flow. Scale-mounted feed tank (liquids). Feed tank on scale is filled to set point, after which feed valve is closed. Tank discharges automatically, weight is registered, and cycle repeats. Variation used for accurate weight rate of feed allows liquid to discharge only as fast as weight setting of scale decreases through action of motor-driven beam poise (Proportioneers Inc.)	Used to record receipt and withdrawal of bulk materials and for batching of solids. Used where accuracy of other methods such as volumetric or head-type flow metering, or pump displacement, is insufficient
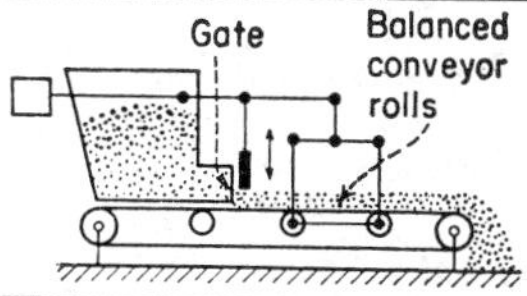	Fig. 22-79. Continuous conveyor scale. Scale-balanced section of belt conveyor used to totalize continuous loads is made in many variations. Various forms of automatic weighers used including spring-balanced beams, strain gage load cells, and motor-driven-poise self-balancing scales. Totalizer integrates instantaneous loads with belt speed to take care of possible belt-speed variations	Commonly used on bulk materials where continuous record is needed for inventory purposes. Such scales give quick response to load variations. Some subtract weight of material sticking to return belt
	Weigh Feeders	
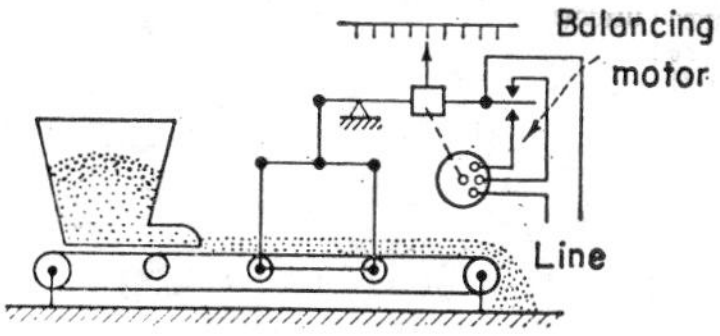	Fig. 22-80. Scale-balanced belt feeder (Schaffer Poidometer). Scale-balanced feed belt controls setting of feed hopper gate to maintain constant weight on belt	Used for feeding solids at constant rate to process
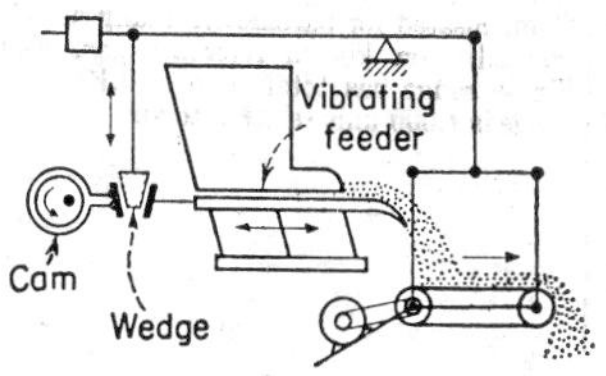	Fig. 22-81. Balanced weigh belt, mechanical feeder (Omega Machine Co.). Short feed belt carried on a scale is fed by a mechanically vibrated tray (smaller than shown, in later models). Oscillation of tray, controlling feed rate, is governed by scale beam through raising or lowering of a resilient wedge	Used on all types of free-flowing solids for both feeding and proportioning. Variable-speed star feeder may be substituted for vibrator. Feed range adjustable. 100 to 1 range. Up to 10,000 lb./hr.
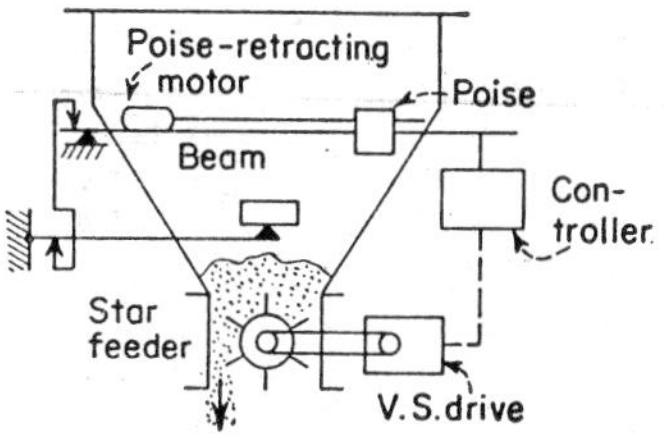	Fig. 22-82. Loss-in-weight feeder (Omega Machine Co.). Scale hopper is discharged by a star feeder driven by a variable-speed drive. Scale beam counterpoise is retracted continuously by a constant-speed motor. Pneumatic controller acts to hold beam in balance by matching discharge rate to feed rate set by retracting poise	Handles dry materials in chemical, fertilizer, plastic, and other industries. Can be granular, lumpy, stringy, etc. Poise retraction speed is adjustable. 100 to 1 feed range. Up to 40,000 lb./hr.

Table 22-15. Instruments for Fluid-density and Specific-gravity Controls

<table>
<tr><th>Diagram</th><th>Principle</th><th>Applications and remarks</th></tr>
<tr><td></td><td>Fig. 22-83. Hand hydrometer. Weighted float with small-diameter stem at top sinks in liquid to depth proportional to specific gravity, scale is read at liquid level</td><td>Widely used where automatic operation is not needed</td></tr>
<tr><td>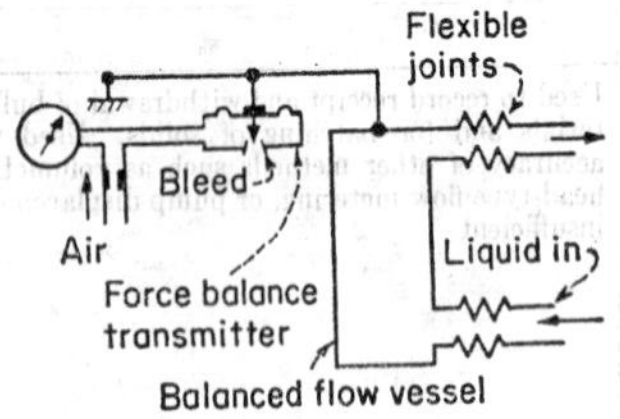
</td><td>Fig. 22-84. Balanced-flow vessel. Fixed-volume vessel through which liquid flows continuously is weighed automatically by scale or force-balance transmitter</td><td>Generally applicable to automatic density control. Any specific gravity of liquids</td></tr>
<tr><td>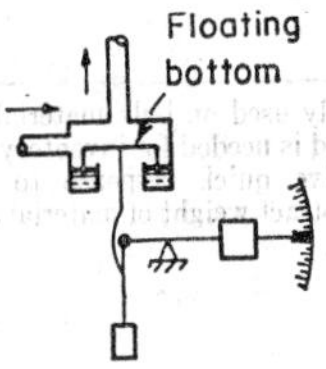
</td><td>Fig. 22-85. Gas specific gravity balance (Alpha-Lux). Weight of tall gas column is measured against air by floating bottom of gas vessel, which is scale-balanced</td><td>Similar to but more convenient than two-pipe system described above. Suitable for any gas. Can be made recording</td></tr>
<tr><td>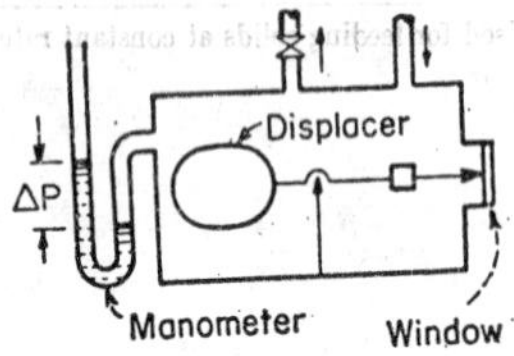
</td><td>Fig. 22-86. Buoyancy gas balance (Edwards). Displacer on balance beam in vessel is balanced for air and manometer reading noted at exact balance pressure. Air then displaced by gas and pressure adjusted until balance again attained. Ratio of pressures in density relative to air</td><td>Used mainly for high-precision laboratory measurements. Cannot be adapted to continuous measurement</td></tr>
<tr><td>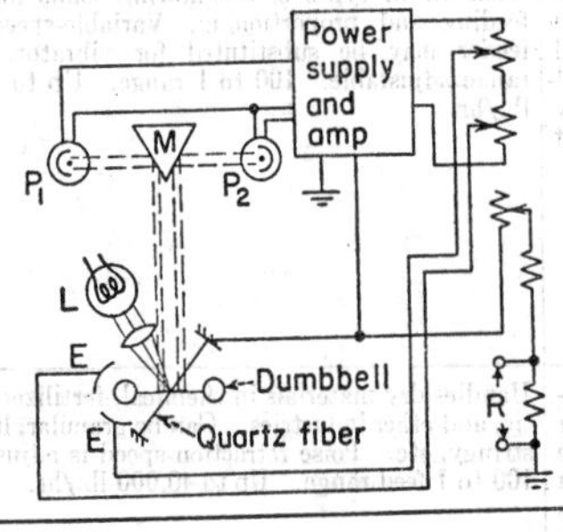
</td><td>Fig. 22-87. Gas density balance (Beckman Instruments, Inc.). A null-balance instrument. Gas density measured by buoyancy of one ball of dumbbell compared to other ball which is punctured and is not subject to buoyancy effects. Rotation of rhodium-coated dumbbell about horizontal quartz fiber produces electrostatic force between electrodes and the suspension. Balancing potential is obtained and measured by the amount of light received by phototubes P_1 and P_2. Rebalance potential nulls balance, is recorded as gravity relative to air</td><td>Continuous measurement of a process stream. Compensated for barometric changes. Calibrated manually on known reference gas, usually air. Single range has total span of 0.100 unit; multirange is 1.000 unit relative to air</td></tr>
</table>

Table 22-15. Instruments for Fluid-density and Specific-gravity Controls—(*Continued*)

Diagram	Principle	Applications and remarks
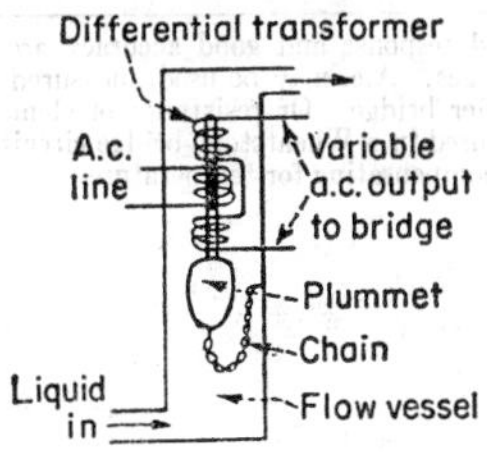	Fig. 22-88. Chain-balanced-float density recorder (Precision Thermometer & Instrument Co.). Bob in continuous-flow vessel is weighted to carry half the weight of a light chain when submerged in median-density liquid at mid-point in its range. Chain attached to bottom of float and to vessel wall at half height. Density increase causes float to rise, supporting more chain; decrease, to sink, supporting less chain. Float position transmitted by differential transformer	Can be used for recording and/or control. Available to resist most corrosive conditions. Suitable for practically any liquid. Note this is a method of actually weighing fixed volume of liquid. Can be corrected for temperature variations
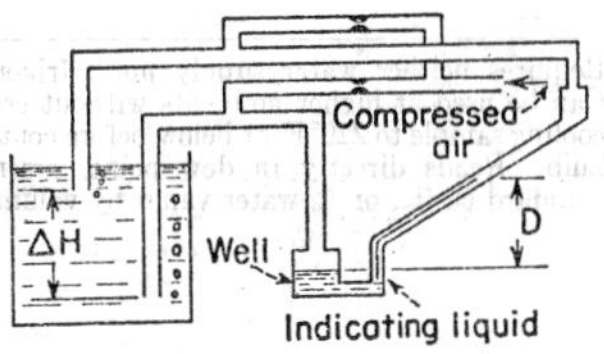	Fig. 22-89. Differential air bubbler (Petrometer Corp.). Air at regulated pressure and quantity is bubbled through two dip tubes of different lengths submerged in liquid. Differential pressure is a measure of the weight of liquid column between dip-tube ends, hence of specific gravity of the liquid. Head D of indicating liquid is directly proportional to specific gravity of liquid in tank	Suitable for practically all liquids except those which will crystallize in the measuring pipes. Can be used on suspensions, on stationary or flowing liquids. Can use liquid instead of air
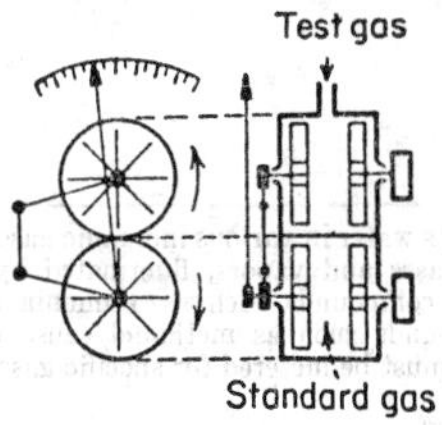	Fig. 22-90. Viscous-drag gas density meter (Ranarex type, Permutit Co.). Driven impellers in standard and test gas chambers produce opposite rotation in gas columns. Non-rotating impellers coupled together by linkage measure relative drag, balance point depending on relative density	Often used for determining compensation of binary gas mixtures—an analysis rather than a density instrument. Calibrated on gases to be measured

Table 22-16. Instruments for Controlling Humidity of Gases

Diagram	Principle	Applications and remarks
	Wet-bulb Depression	
	Fig. 22-91. Sling psychrometer. Based on measurement of wet-bulb depression. Two thermometers are fastened together. One measures dry-bulb. The other, covered with a water-saturated wick, measures wet-bulb, provided that sling is whirled to produce rapid air flow for maximum evaporative cooling. From psychrometric tables the relative humidity and dew point can be determined. Recording psychrometer. Principle same as that of sling psychrometer except that bulbs of a two-pen recording thermometer are installed in an air stream of at least 900 ft./min. velocity. Wet-bulb wick kept saturated by water reservoir	Most accurate simple and low-cost device for measuring relative humidity of air. Probably the most used method for recording wet-bulb, dry-bulb temperatures for industrial humdity determination. Hazard is that wet bulb may run dry
	Hygrometers	
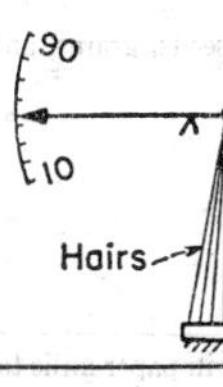	Fig. 22-92. Dimensional-change hygrometers. Various organic materials change in linear (or volume) dimensions with changes in relative humidity. Among them are human hair, which makes one of the most accurate hygrometers, various woods, animal membranes. Wood shaving cemented to spring made of screen wire and coiled like a bimetallic thermometer makes a simple direct-reading indicator	Advantage is direct reading in relative humidity. Slow response and somewhat temperature-sensitive

Table 22-16. Instruments for Controlling Humidity of Gases—(*Continued*)

Diagram	Principle	Applications and remarks
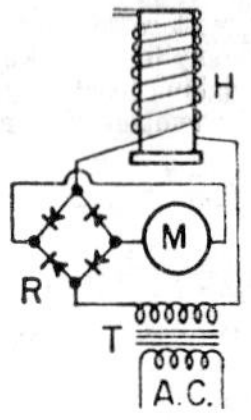	Fig. 22-93. Electric resistance hygrometers. Double wire winding on light insulator is coated with hygroscopic film containing lithium chloride which becomes more conductive as its equilibrium moisture content increases. Ambient humidity determines conductivity of coating and this governs current flow between the wires	Rapid response and good accuracy are main advantages. A.c. may be used, measured as d.c. by rectifier bridge. Or resistance of element can be measured in a Wheatstone-bridge circuit. Can be self-compensating for temperature
	Dew Point	
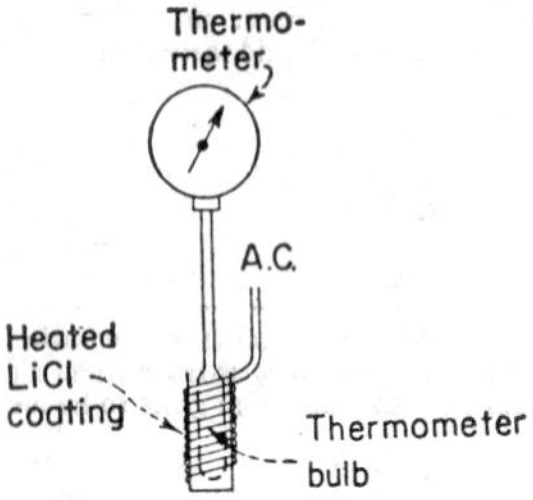	Fig. 22-94. Electric hygrometer-type dew-point meter (Foxboro Co.). Superficially resembles Fig. 22-93 but works on different principle. Double wire winding on insulating tube is coated with a hygroscopic conducting coating (lithium chloride solution). Inside the tube is a thermometer bulb. Low-voltage current supplied to wires heats the coating thereby driving out moisture until equilibrium is reached between moisture leaving and moisture returning. Temperature of the equilibrium point as measured by the thermometer is related to dew point of air at bulb	Requires neither water supply nor refrigeration. Can be used at higher ambients without error by cooling sample to 220°F. or below before contacting bulb. Reads directly in dew point, grains per standard cu ft., or % water vapor by volume
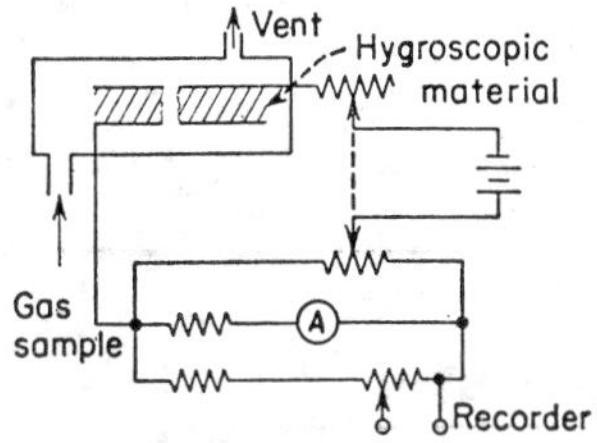	Fig. 22-95. Electrolytic water analyzer (Du Pont design) (Manufacturers Engineering & Equipment Corp., and others). Water vapor in gas stream is continuously passed over and absorbed on a film of partially hydrated phosphorus pentoxide. The absorbed water is quantitatively electrolyzed between platinum electrodes in the detector cell. The current required for electrolysis is directly proportional (Faraday's law) to the absorbed water. Meter *A* in series with the cell reads proportional to the water content of gas stream	Detects water in various inorganic gases, hydrocarbon gases and vapors, fluorinated hydrocarbons. Basic compounds such as ammonia and organic compounds such as methanol cause interference. Flow must be metered for specific gases

Table 22-17. Instruments for Controlling Moisture Content of Solids

Diagram	Principle	Applications and remarks
	Resistance meters. Resistance of massive solids is read between prongs mounted a fixed distance apart, thrust into material. Resistance of pulverized materials is read by applying standard compression between plates, measuring resistance across plates. Uses Wheatstone-bridge circuit and indicator	Used for powders, lumber, leather, tobacco, similar materials. Calibrated against materials of known moisture content
	Dielectric-constant meter. Since water has 15 to 20 times the dielectric constant of most materials, small changes in water content mean relatively large dielectric changes. Weighed material is put into test condenser, oscillation frequency of test cell circuit is set to standard frequency as produced in a second, crystal-controlled oscillating circuit. Null position represents moisture content	Used chiefly on seeds, grains, and powdered chemicals
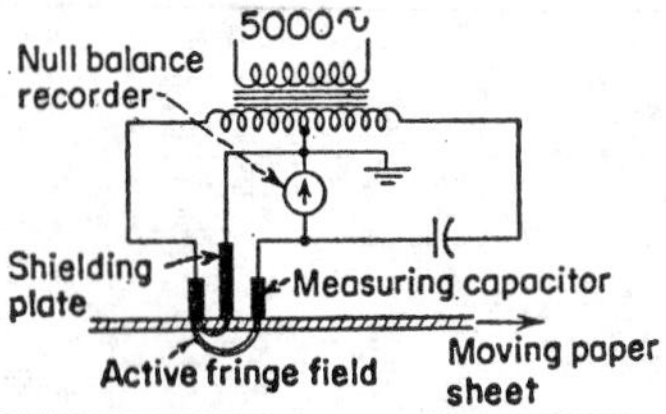	Fig. 22-96. Dielectric constant moving-web meter (Foxboro Co.). Box over moving web of moist material contains hygroscopic dielectric between condenser plates. Air in box and in dielectric attains moisture equilibrium with web material. This equilibrium and hence moisture content of web determined as capacitance in high-frequency bridge	Used extensively in paper mills to measure moisture content of paper as it progresses through paper machine

Table 22-18. Instruments for Controlling Viscosity and Consistency

Diagram	Principle	Applications and remarks
	Fig. 22-97. Timed discharge through nozzle. Method of viscometers such as the Saybolt. Vessel with short capillary tube has discharge timed at desired temperature	Commonly used for expressing viscosities of oils
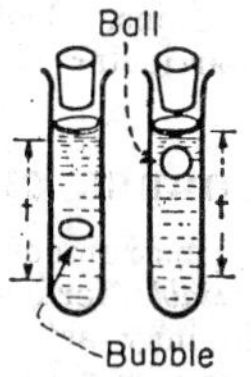	Fig. 22-98. Timed fall of ball or rise of bubble. Time for fall of metal ball or rise of bubble through liquid confined in tube is proportional to absolute viscosity since in either case liquid flows in viscous flow through a definite restriction	Both are laboratory methods commonly used in measuring oil viscosity. Ball method can be timed with great accuracy by field coils at start and finish
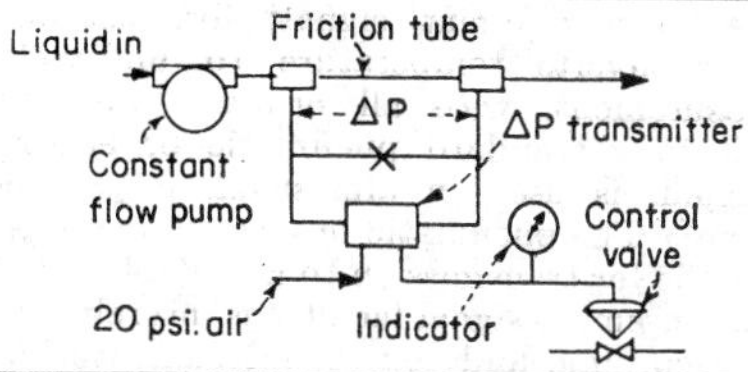	Fig. 22-99. Pressure drop through friction tube. Liquid pumped at constant rate through friction tube in viscous flow. Pressure drop across ends of tube is measured by pneumatic force-balance type differential pressure transmitter in terms of absolute viscosity. Gives direct solution to Poiseuille's equation	Can be used for wide range of industrial liquids, for remote recording and control. Extremely simple and foolproof. Requires no attention
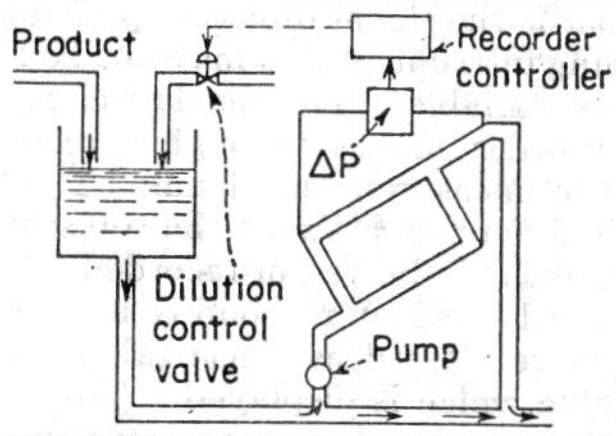	Fig. 22-100. Continuous consistency meter (Fischer & Porter Co.). Gear pump diverts a portion of product stream through flow bridge where a pressure differential between two reference points is established. The differential pressure is a direct measure of the consistency of the material	Measures, records, and controls the consistency of fibrous or pulpy slurries
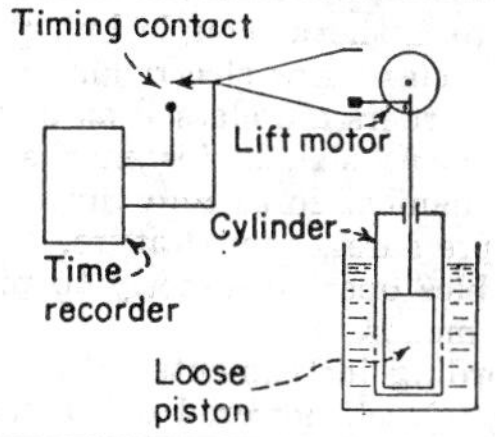	Fig. 22-101. Viscometer (Norcross Corp.). Piston is raised in a timed sequence and falls by gravity through liquid. Clearance between piston and cylinder forms measuring orifice. Time of fall is recorded as a measure of viscosity	Can be used in Newtonian liquids, non-Newtonian liquids, and on high polymers. Probe can be immersed in any process vessel as well as in laboratory equipment
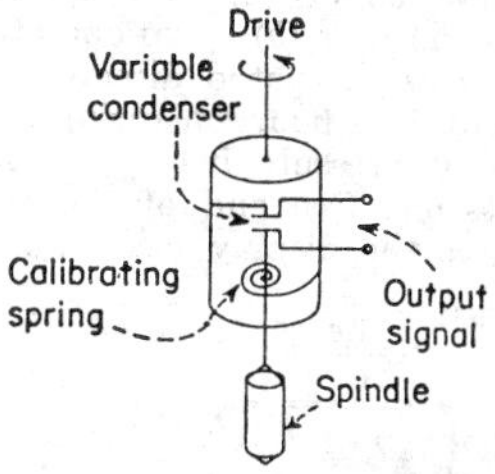	Fig. 22-102. Torque to rotate a torque element in a liquid (Brookfield Eng. Co.). Synchronous motor drives vertical spindle with disk, paddle or cylinder submerged in test liquid. Drive is through calibrated spring. Angular lag of spindle behind motor is proportional to viscosity and is measured in various ways. Controller detects angle of displacement by periodic electric contact. Recorders adapted to this device by several instrument makers measure angle three ways: capacity change, resistance change, and timed impulse	Can be used in open or closed vessels, under pressure or vacuum, at high or low temperatures. Used for both Newtonian and non-Newtonian liquids or suspensions
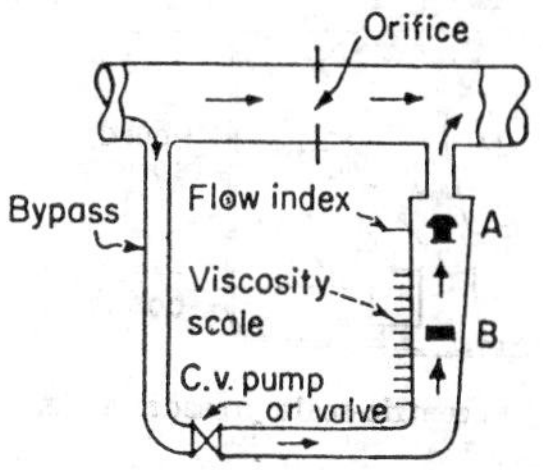	Fig. 22-103. Viscosity-sensitive rotameter (Fischer & Porter Co.). Rotameter bobs can be designed for either sensitivity or immunity to viscosity. With constant flow rate a sensitive bob can be calibrated for viscosity. One method is to use immune bob to set flow rate at index mark	Suitable for both Newtonian and non-Newtonian liquids and suspensions in continuous flow. Used for visual and remote readings and control

INDICATING AND RECORDING INSTRUMENTS

The function of indication and recording is to present information to a human operator. Hence the form of the display is a major factor, and should be seriously considered in selecting instruments. Although factors enter into the choice and may appear decisive, they should not be permitted to override the requirements for adequate display.

Indication and recording may be in analog or digital form. Analog display is characterized by a continuously variable response. The display of a pointer against a scale, a pen line on a chart, or a photographic record of an oscilloscope trace is analog. Digital display is numerical in form. A number-type counter, a typed or printed record sheet, or a record in numerical code on a paper or magnetic tape is digital.

Analog display is by far the most common in chemical processing and similar operations. The mechanisms for analog display are almost invariably simpler, less expensive, less subject to wear, and in many instances more useful than digital display. Specifically, the position of an indicating pointer provides at a glance an accurate presentation of the value of a variable. Numbers are less easy to read quickly and correctly. Analog chart records give continuous graphic presentation of both the value and the trend of process variables. This continuity is important; trends are vital in process operation and are more easily visualized from chart records than from columns of figures.

Digital display has distinct advantages where the primary objective is to obtain a numerical record at regular intervals, either by an operator entering indicated values on a log sheet or by direct digital recording. By using several digit numbers, basic reading error can be reduced to any desired level. (Integrated total values can be displayed to a single gallon reading out of a million total figure—but note that this does not imply that the measured quantity is correct to that accuracy.) For accounting and computing purposes, data must be in digital form.

Digital display has limited application in process-industry applications except for integrator or totalizer values. There is some use of digital indicators where a number of variables are read and manually logged one at a time on a single instrument using a manual switching mechanism. Many electrical laboratory bridge-type instruments and similar test equipment use decade (digital) type variable resistance and other impedance units.

Electronically operated digital indicators are available, including high-speed electronic counters, digital voltmeters, and indicators developed in connection with digital computing machines; these are generally expensive and complex devices. They find limited use in industrial processing.

Digital recording of chemical process variables is a specialzed procedure. Number print recording of the value of a single variable is common on weighing scales but has found little application in other measurements in chemical processing. Data logging, where the numerical values of a large number of variables are typed or printed sequentially, has been applied in a number of pilot plants, and to a limited extent in process operations. Data are usually printed out at regular intervals, with facilities for print-out on demand, or if values are outside tolerance limits. Data loggers can produce punched-tape records simultaneously with typed records. In many cases, a logging unit is combined with an automatic scanning alarm system. The basic cost of transducing, programming, scanning, and print-out is considerable and is relatively independent of the number of variables handled; the cost per variable recorded is correspondingly high unless a large number of variables are recorded. The display is in the form of either an adding-machine tape or a log sheet. Various display patterns have been developed for specific applications. Data loggers are specifically engineered for particular applications, including details of the display.

INDICATOR AND RECORDER OPERATION

Indicating and recording instruments display the measured value of a *process variable*, for instance, temperature. This process variable may act directly on the instrument, or a *transducer* may be used to convert the process variable to a different signal; for instance, a thermocouple converts temperature to millivolts. Transducer measurement, with all primary measurements converted to a standard pneumatic or electric measurement signal, is used in almost all large-scale process operations. The pneumatic or electric measurement signals provide for transmission to a control center. The standard measurement signal facilitates interchangeable indicating, recording, and control instrumentation.

Measurement signal is the signal directly applied to the indicating or recording instrument and may not be identical with the process variable. The display element of the indicator or recorder moves through a *scale span* corresponding to the measurement signal. The scale span is the algebraic difference between the top scale and bottom scale values of the indicated or recorded variable.

Indicators and recorders which respond to an electrical measurement signal are classed as electrical, regardless of the process variable which is displayed. Thus a self-balancing potentiometer recorder which measures the millivoltage produced by a thermocouple but records in terms of temperature is classed as electrical. Non-electrical indicators and recorders are classed as mechanical instruments. Measurement signals for mechanical instruments include mechanical force and motion, pneumatic and hydraulic pressures, temperature, humidity, etc., when these variables operate directly to provide a display by mechanical means.

Indicating and recording instruments may be of (1) deflection type, either (*a*) self-powered or (*b*) auxiliary-powered. Or they may be of (2) null-balance type, either (*a*) manually balanced or (*b*) servo-operated.

Deflection instruments are actuated directly from the measurement signal; thus in a bourdon spring-type pressure gage, the measured pressure inside the flattened C-shaped tube deflects the free end of the tube; the motion directly operates the display (see Fig. 22-104).

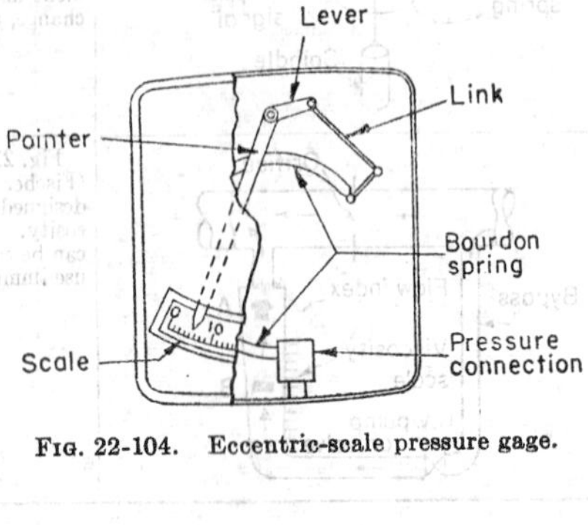

FIG. 22-104. Eccentric-scale pressure gage.

When available energy of the measurement signal is limited, auxiliary power from an external source may be used. A typical example is the amplifier commonly employed in oscilloscopes to increase low-voltage measurement signals to a level suitable for deflection of the beam.

In general, deflection instruments are simple, rugged, and low in first cost and maintenance. The power required to operate an indicating display is small, favoring the use of self-powered instruments. Many mechanical recorders are self-powered, deflection type, including both those directly operated from primary variables, such as pressure and differential pressure, and also recorders operated from pneumatic transmission systems. Self-powered electrical recorders are available for operation from electrical measurement signals of moderate or high power levels. The power level available from thermocouples, resistance thermometers, strain gages, and from many types of analytical instruments is usually insufficient for satisfactory operation of self-powered recorders. For these applications, either auxiliary amplification or null-balance instruments are commonly used.

Amplifiers for use with deflection instruments are usually of the feedback type, with a large feedback ratio to provide exact correspondence between input and output signals.

Null-balance instruments compare the measurement signal to a feedback signal generated in the instrument and controlled by the position of the display. In operation, the display is manipulated, thereby varying the feedback signal so as to make it equal to the measurement signal. On manually operated null-balance instruments deviation from null (difference between measurement and feedback signals) is presented in suitable form to an operator who then manipulates the control to obtain a null balance; with the feedback signal equal to the measurement signal, the indication of the display gives the value of the measurement signal. In servo operation, the null detector operates through an amplifier and servomotor to move the display and vary the corresponding feedback signal. This provides continuous adjustment to maintain null and thereby a continuous indication of the value of the measurement signal (Fig. 22-105).

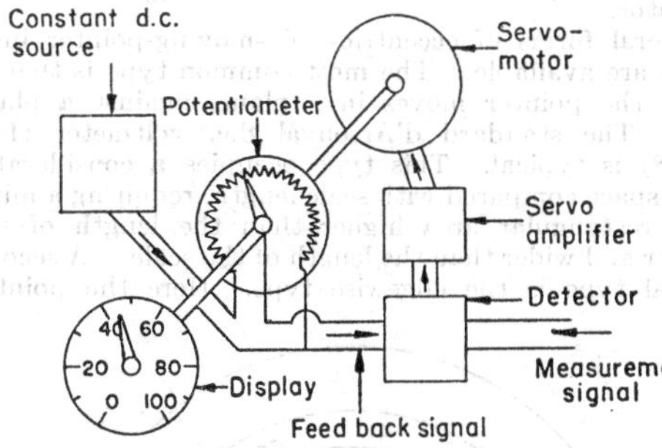

FIG. 22-105. Typical self-balancing instrument.

Where highest accuracy is required, null-balance indicators and recorders are usually selected. Laboratory-type high-accuracy measurement bridges of various types are typical. Servo operation is advantageous where continuous display is required, and either the power available from the measurement signal is inadequate or the power needed to operate the recording or indicating mechanism is considerable. Many strip-chart recorders with rectilinear chart coordinates are servo operated; wide strip-chart recorders (approximately an 11-in. scale length is common) are almost always of servo type. The power available from the servo drive facilitates direct operation of alarms and signals and other functions in addition to indicating and recording (see also p. 22-45 for operation of the 12-in.-wide strip-chart recorder).

Speed of Response. The speed of response of modern deflection and null-balance instruments is entirely adequate for chemical and similar process applications. Mechanical instruments are limited primarily by the measuring element. Null-balance instruments are limited by servo characteristics. Full chart travel in 2 to 3 sec. is standard, with speeds to 1/4 sec. available on special order. For higher speeds, special high-speed direct-writing deflection instruments and also oscillographs and oscilloscopes are used. Transducers are also available which will convert almost all mechanical variables to electrical signals, with special versions having extremely high response speeds.

Accuracy and Readability. American Standard Definitions of Electrical Terms states "The accuracy of an instrument is the number or quantity which defines its limit of error." . . . "The error is the difference between the indication and the true value of the quantity being measured." In defining accuracy, it is customary to assume negligible error in observation of the indication and negligible error in the "true" value.

The conditions under which error is measured are vital. A.S.A. standards exist for specific instruments. The Scientific Apparatus Manufacturers Association define S.A.M.A. accuracy rating on the basis of specified test conditions. In selecting instruments, it is important to ascertain the conditions under which accuracy is defined, since different manufacturers use the same terms with enough different shades of meaning to create confusion when specifications or calibration data are compared.

Repeatability or, as it is sometimes called, *precision* of measurement is closely akin to accuracy. In many applications, major objectives are to repeat operating conditions known to produce satisfactory product, to obtain information on trends, or to compare results under prescribed variations of operating conditions. For these objectives, repeatability rather than absolute accuracy is the decisive criterion. Since repeatability may be up to an order of magnitude better than absolute accuracy, it is important to distinguish the real requirements when selecting instruments.

It is important to select instruments whose accuracy and repeatability are adequate. It is equally important to recognize practical accuracy limitations. Specification of instruments with a higher accuracy than is actually necessary can materially increase first cost and may lead to the selection of more complex instrumentation with lower true reliability and much greater maintenance. This is particularly true of specifications calling for accuracy beyond manufacturers' standard tolerances, thus requiring special design, manufacture, and calibration.

Readability. Since the objective of indicating and recording instruments is to present information to human operators, readability of the display is a major consideration. As previously mentioned, accuracy is customarily stated without reference to readability; the final reading of the display includes the instrumental errors (accuracy) as well as the human errors (readability).

The requirements for readability depend upon application. A broad pointer, bold scale divisions, and a location at or above eye level facilitate ease of reading at a distance. On the other hand, for maximum accuracy of reading, a knife-edge pointer, many fine scale graduations, and a location at or below eye level are essential. A large instrument with a long scale—taken alone—is easiest to read In contrast, where a large number of variables are displayed, compact instruments which can be located close to each other present a maximum amount of information in a minimum total area and facilitate observation of the condition of the system.

For applications where maximum reading accuracy is required, the instrument must be conveniently located, with adequate lighting. Under these conditions, the position of a knife-edge pointer or a pen line can easily be seen to 1/32 in.; with care, the position can be read to 1/100 in. Figure 22-106 shows a full-scale reproduction

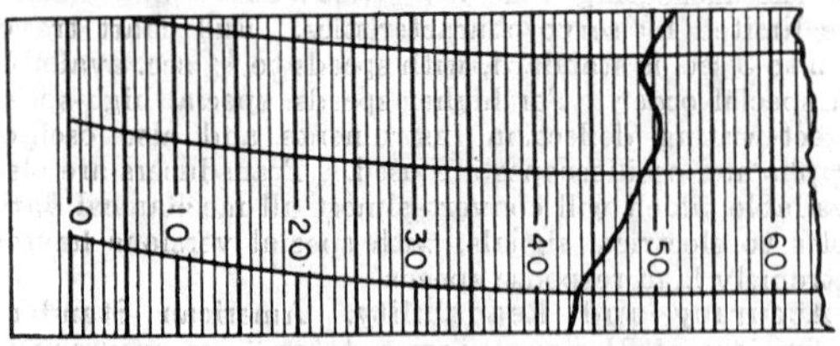

FIG. 22-106. Full-scale chart record.

of a section of standard chart record. The chart is graduated 25 lines to the inch. The position of the pen line is readily estimated to a quarter of a division. On this basis, a scale length of 4 in. gives a readability of 1/4 per cent. This is adequate for most process measurements, especially since the basic accuracy of measurement seldom exceeds 1/2 per cent.

Expanded-scale Instruments. Readability can be increased by using an expanded-scale (suppressed-zero) instrument. Thus a temperature instrument may read 0° to 1000° with a readability of 2° to 3° on a 4-in. scale. If the working temperature range lies between 600° and 800°, an instrument with a 600° to 800° scale may be employed, giving a readability to 1/2 deg. The expanded scale increases readability and may or may not improve accuracy. On measurements such as gage pressure, where a "natural" zero value of the measured variable is readily available, an instrument with a zero reading on scale can be checked at this zero point. This zero check procedure can materially aid in maintaining accuracy. It is not available on suppressed-zero instruments. On mechanical instruments, where expanded scales are obtained by increased mechanical multiplication, expanded scales do not increase absolute accuracy and may result in a decrease if the increased mechanical loading from increased multiplication affects the performance of the primary element. On the other hand, many instruments operating from a measurement signal produced by a transducer have an accuracy in per cent of scale span which within certain limits is independent of the measurement signal. For example, a self-balancing potentiometer recorder measuring temperature as sensed by a thermocouple should have the same 99.5 per cent accuracy on a 0° to 1000°F. (30.46 mv.) scale span and on a 600° to 800°F. (7.15 mv.) scale span. For the 1000°F. span, the instrument error may be as large as 5°F., while for the 200° span, the maximum error is 1°F. This is of course in addition to any reading error and to the error of the thermocouple.

Parallax. On indicating instruments, there is a working separation between the pointer and the scale. If the reading of the instrument is taken from a direction other than true perpendicular, a "parallax" error will result. Where accuracy of readings is important, this parallax error must be considered in the selection of the instrument, its location, and in operator training.

INDICATING INSTRUMENTS

Indicating instruments can be (1) moving-pointer indicators, either (*a*) concentric scale (pointer moves through an angle greater than 180 deg., usually about 270 deg.), or (*b*) eccentric scale (pointer moves through an angle less than 180 deg., usually less than 90 deg.); (2) moving-scale indicators; or (3) moving-material indicators.

The moving-pointer indicator is by far the most common. The standard pressure gage (Fig. 22-107) illustrates the concentric-scale type. A pointer moves

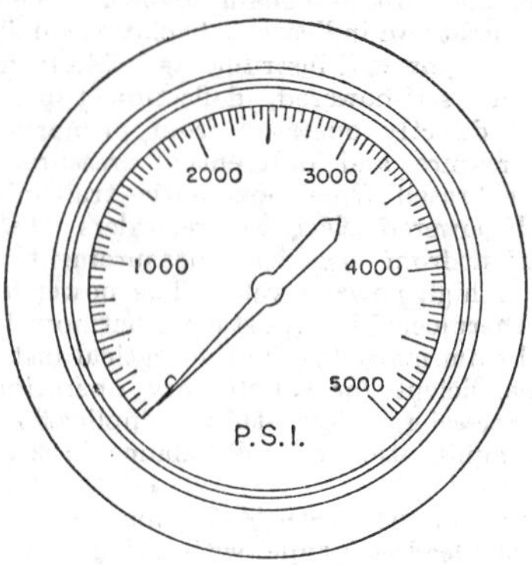

FIG. 22-107. Typical pressure gage.

through a large angle, usually between 240 and 330 deg. This type provides a compact instrument with a relatively long scale in comparison with the total area. This type does not readily lend itself to more than a single pointer. The concentric-scale indicator is common in both the electrical and mechanical types.

Eccentric-scale-moving-pointer indicators cover a wide variety of displays. Indicators with an angular motion of the pointer between 10 and 100 deg. are very common. On electrical indicators, the pointer is customarily connected directly to the moving element. Scale span is usually adjusted electrically. Mechanical indicators may have the pointer connected directly to a primary element moving through a corresponding angle; more often a link and lever connection between moving element and pointer is provided. This construction is simple; adjustments of zero and span are readily provided; two or more pointers are easily installed in a single indicator.

Several forms of eccentric-scale-moving-pointer indicators are available. The most common type is that in which the pointer moves in a plane, against a plane scale. The standard d'Arsonval d.c. voltmeter (Fig. 22-108) is typical. This type occupies a considerable panel space compared with scale length, requiring a minimum rectangular area higher than the length of the pointer and wider than the length of the scale. A second general type is the edgewise type. Here the pointer

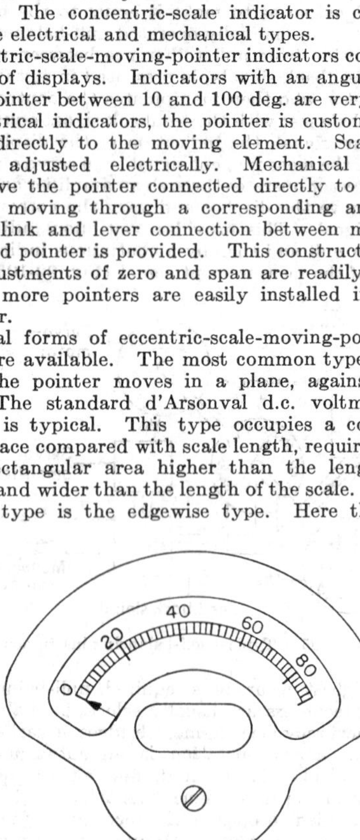

FIG. 22-108. Voltmeter.

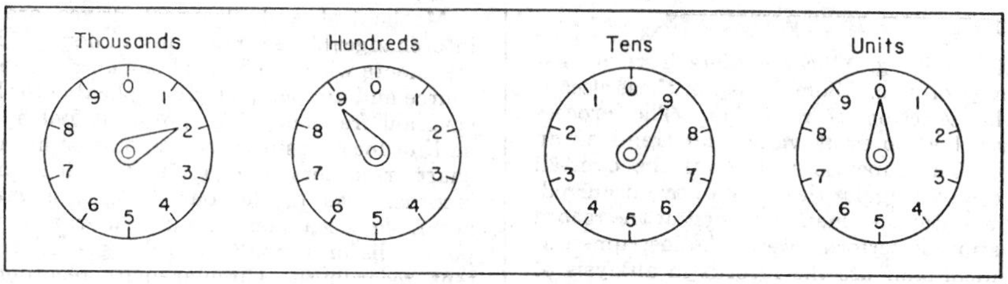

Fig. 22-109. A multiple-pointer integrator display.

rotates around an axis located behind a cylindrical scale. The pointer can move either up and down (vertical edgewise) or in a horizontal plane (horizontal edgewise). By using a long pointer (compared with the scale length), a display is produced which approximates straight-line motion. Compact displays can be provided since the length of the pointer does not affect the frontal space required. This type of display lends itself particularly to multiple scale indications; two, three, four or more pointers can be provided with related variables displayed in close proximity to each other in a relatively small total space.

Straight-line pointer motion is relatively uncommon in plain indicating instruments; a straight-line pointer motion is frequently provided in connection with rectilinear-coordinate strip-chart recorders.

Multiple-pointer Indicators. Watt-hour meters and similar totalizing instruments often use several separate pointers for units, tens, and hundreds (see Fig. 22-109). This display is simple and inexpensive and puts very little load on the driving mechanism (in contrast to a digital counter, which imposes a considerable load in going from, say, 199,999 to 200,000). To an experienced operator, the multiple-pointer display is easily and accurately read but the novice is very prone to error. For example, in Fig. 22-109 the correct reading is 1890 and not 2990 as might appear at first glance.

In addition to the simple moving mechanical pointer, there are a number of other types of moving display element. Typical are the instruments with a moving light beam—both the light-beam galvanometer and the oscilloscope. Another form consists of a vertically moving two-colored tape where the division line between the two colors is the effective pointer (Fig. 22-110). This is commonly used for indication of level. The extent of the dark-colored tape exposed indicates the amount of liquid in a vessel, with the white tape above indicating the vapor space, thereby providing a graphic indication of level.

Moving-scale Indicators. In a moving-scale indicator the scale itself moves past a fixed index. The graduated dial is typical. The reading is always at the same physical location. Parallax errors are minimized. This type is particularly useful where a number of variables are connected by switches to a single indicator, with the values read off and logged at regular intervals. The display may be on a rotating drum, with its axis parallel to the front of the instrument, which permits a long scale length with a small frontal area. Or even greater scale length can be provided by use of a moving-scale tape instead of a moving drum. Optical-display indicators are often of the moving-scale type. Optical projection systems can provide long effective scale length in small total space.

Except for optical systems, moving-scale mechanisms tend to be larger and heavier than moving pointers, and require more driving power. They are frequently servo-operated. The approximate value of the indicated variable is much more obvious from a moving-pointer display as compared with a moving-scale indication.

Moving-material Indicators. The sight glass for liquid level, the glass-tube manometer for pressure or differential pressure, the direct-indicating variable-area flowmeter (glass-tube rotameter) and the mercury-in-glass thermometer are the principal moving-material type of indicator. These direct-reading instruments are very simple, reliable, and economical. Within their scope of application, they are extremely satisfactory.

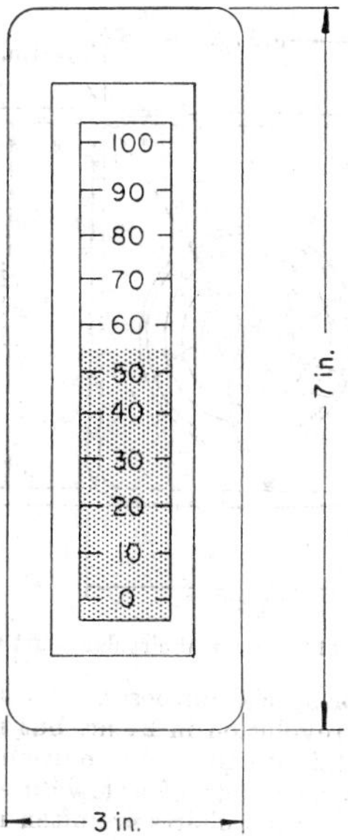

Fig. 22-110. Two-color ribbon display.

The limitations of direct-reading moving-material indicators are readily apparent. Operation directly connected to the process fluid requires a location adjacent to the process. The sight glass must be at the level of the measured liquid; the glass-stem thermometer must be directly immersed, or located in a thermal well in the process vessel or the process flow line; the rotameter must be in the process flow line. Most applications of moving-material indicators are for low or moderate pressures and temperatures and for non-hazardous fluids. Special units are available for difficult applications but lack the inherent simplicity of a glass tube in the open or behind a plain glass window. Manometers are normally limited to a 50-in. scale length, which provides a maximum 25 lb./sq. in. scale span. Direct-reading moving-material indicators are limited to indication without recording.

RECORDING INSTRUMENTS

Records produced by graphic recorders have an extremely wide range of uses. Some grasp of these uses is important in the selection of recorders. The process operator observes both present value and trend as an operating guide. The supervisor observes the over-all performance and any irregularities which have occurred. The instrument maintenance man looks first at the record if there is a question of performance of the instrumentation. The technical staff use the records in analysis of system operation. Totalized flow and other accounting data are computed from the chart data. These and many other functions are served by graphic records.

Graphic recorders may be grouped in accordance with the type of chart used, as (1) circular-chart and (2) strip-chart recorders. Or they may be grouped in accordance with the recording mechanism: (1) single and multiple continuous record using pen and fluid ink, (2) multipoint intermittent record using stylus or print wheel and semifluid ink, or (3) special recording mechanisms.

Circular-chart recorders are extensively used in the process industries. The so-called 12-in. circular chart with approximately 4-in. scale length is generally selected for process records (Fig. 22-111); smaller circular charts

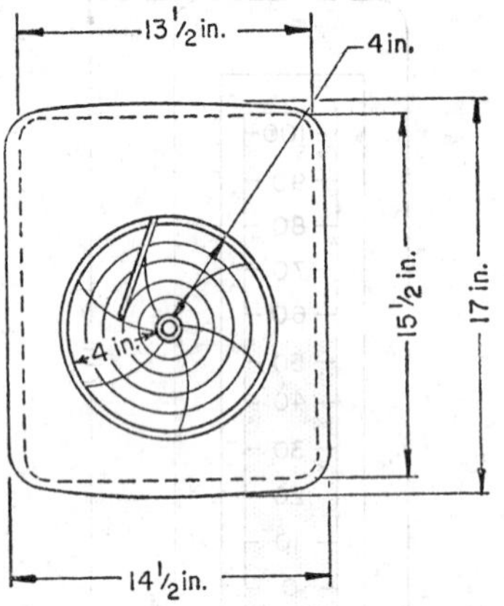

FIG. 22-111. Typical circular-chart recorder.

are available for special purposes. Most circular charts operate at one revolution in 24 hr. but speeds from one revolution per minute to one revolution per month are available. A wide variety of scale values and time scales are available. Special charts are often made. There is little or no interchangeability between charts for instruments of different manufacturers.

Circular-chart recorders are available for practically every type of process operation; both mechanical and electrical, deflection and servo-operated are available with a full complement of auxiliary functions, including control and transmission.

The circular chart has a number of advantages. The display is eminently satisfactory for most process applications. The 4-in. scale length for the process variable, and the ¾ in./hr. chart speed at mid-scale on a 12-in. chart operating one revolution per day are both quite adequate for most process records. The 12-in. circular chart is easily handled, easily filed; when removed from the recorder, it lies flat with no tendency to curl. Circular charts are put on and taken off the recorder much more simply than any other type. Basic chart accuracy is excellent (see following discussion). The chart support and chart-drive mechanism are very simple, reliable, and economical.

Mechanical and electrical drives are standard and interchangeable in most instruments. Mechanical instruments with mechanical clock drives require no power source and are particularly applicable for locations where constant-frequency a.c. power is not readily available and for locations involving explosion hazards. Circular-chart recorders are available with single continuous records, with up to four continuous multiple records, and from at least one manufacturer, with up to six multipoint (discontinuous) records (see multipoint intermittent recording). Circular-chart recorders are made in many forms, including flush-panel-mounting types, and full weatherproof types for field mounting in the open.

Circular-chart recording has limitations. The first is recorder size; this can be important in central control rooms where many variables must be displayed. Considerations of readability limit standard recorder mounting on a panel to three high, with two high preferred. Recorders of different manufacture differ in width; a horizontal center distance of at least 15 in. is required and 16 to 17 in. is preferred for a typical recorder (Fig. 22-111). The large panel space increases cost and disperses the display, materially reducing the operator's ability to monitor the process.

The changing of one-revolution-per-day charts at about the same time each day involves difficulties in some applications. It is no problem in the many applications where charts are collected daily for supervisory and accounting purposes. But it can be a major factor on recorders in remote and inaccessible locations. Where the measured variable does not change rapidly, 7-day or even 30-day charts can be used. Automatic chart changers are available for use with standard circular-chart recorders. These provide a month's supply of charts with provision for changing charts automatically at 24-hr. intervals.

For records for analytical purposes, for test data, and the like, rectilinear strip-chart records are often preferred. On circular charts both time lines and process-variable lines are usually circular arcs. For special purposes, the difference in distance moved per unit time near the center and near the outside of circular charts can be objectionable. Finally, for records of specific tests of varying duration, the fixed time for one revolution of a circular chart is often not optimal. It should be noted that, for most continuous process operations, computing techniques and apparatus are fully developed for use with circular charts. Typical is the gas-flow computer which provides continuous integration of the square root of the product of static and differential gas pressure as recorded on standard circular charts.

Strip-chart recorders are made in great variety. The most common for industrial process application are the so-called "12-in.-wide strip-chart" type, and the so-called "miniature" process recorders, although a great variety of other types are used for particular applications.

The 12-in.-wide strip-chart recorder has a scale length of about 11 in., is invariably electrical and servo-operated, has rectilinear coordinates, and is available with one or two continuous records and with a variety of multipoint (discontinuous) recording arrangements. This type was developed for thermocouple temperature measurement and is widely applied to recording of primary electrical quantities and of electrical output of transducers from non-electrical variables. It is not available for direct operation from mechanical or pneumatic measurement signals. The instrument is accurate and reliable; it is very flexible, with provision for auxiliary functions including control, alarm, and signal contacts, and retransmission systems. A variety of chart speeds is available from a few inches per day up to feet per minute. Pen speeds of a second or two for full scale are standard, with speeds to ¼ sec. also available. Several manufacturers have servo drives available for the chart, providing a record which is a direct function of two variables, rather than of one or more variables with respect to time.

Wide strip-chart instruments of different manufacture vary in size. All are large; a typical recorder is 21 in. wide by 16 in. high (Fig. 22-112). These recorders are

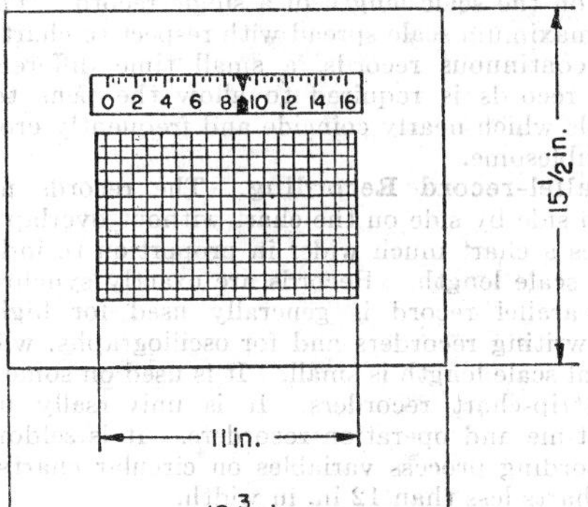

FIG. 22-112. Strip-chart controller.

relatively expensive and are generally designed for indoor mounting since they are not weatherproof. They operate with a standard 100-ft. roll chart, with provision for chart tear-off, or for continuous chart rewind. An electrical power supply is required for chart drive and for servo operation.

Wide strip-chart recorders are used extensively in industrial process operations as temperature recorders and recorder-controllers in connection with thermocouples. They find wide application in pilot-plant operations, in analysis and test recording, and on many specialty applications where the basic accuracy of the instrument and the readability of the rectangular-coordinate wide-strip record are important. For central control rooms, the applications are generally limited to multipoint thermocouple temperature measurements.

Miniature strip-chart process recorders are designed to meet the demand for a recorder requiring small panel space for use in central process-control rooms and similar applications. The performance is the same as that of the 12-in. circular-chart recorder. While some variety in sizes has been offered, a roughly 6-in.-high by 6-in.-wide recorder with a chart scale length of 4 in. is common (Fig. 22-113). The miniature recorders are at present available only as recorder-receiver elements, operating from

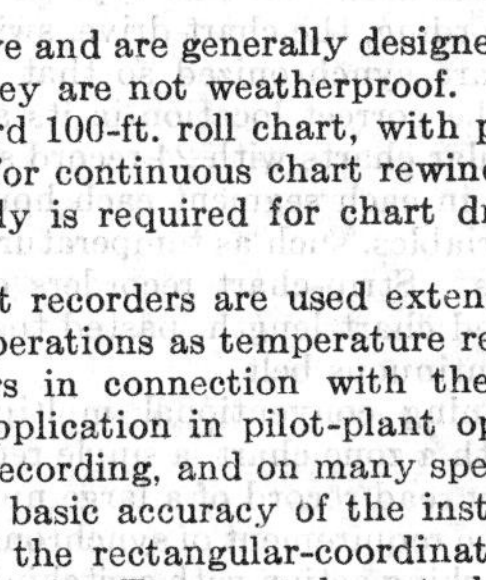

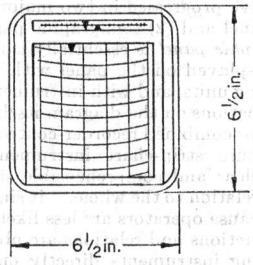

FIG. 22-113. A Consotrol miniature recorder.

3 to 15 lb./sq. in. (or 3 to 27 lb./sq. in.) pneumatic transmission signals or from 1 to 5 ma., 4 to 20 ma., and 10 to 50 ma. d.c. transmission signals (or in some cases, from equally specific a.c. voltage signals). These recorders have rewind mechanisms for the charts, and high-capacity ink systems to operate for a full month; alternatively, the chart can be torn off and removed daily, if desired. Up to three continuous records are available. Electrical chart drives are standard, with pneumatic chart drives for locations where constant-frequency a.c. electric power is not available or presents an explosion hazard. Chart speed is usually in the vicinity of ¾ in./hr. Most miniature strip-chart recorders have recording pens carried on long pen arms moving through a small angle. Roughly 15 deg. angular motion is usual. This results in charts with time arcs having relatively little curvature. Some manufacturers provide linear pen motion and rectilinear charts, but this pen structure is necessarily somewhat more complex. Recorders of this type are not made for multipoint (discontinuous) recording. Miniature strip-chart recorders are usually designed for operation indoors and are not fully weatherproof.

Both electrical and pneumatic transducers are available to convert practically every process measurement to a measurement signal suitable for operation of miniature strip-chart recorders.

Miniature strip-chart recorders are almost universally panel-mounted and are usually applied where groups of instruments are required. Their primary application is in central control rooms. At least one manufacturer supplies a continuous strip chart in folded form rather than in roll form. The chart is furnished as a folded package with each fold 1½ in. long. The chart feeds from the folded package through a modified strip-chart transport and recording mechanism and automatically refolds into a space in the bottom of the recorder. This folded chart has two important advantages: (1) Any part of any length of chart is immediately available for inspection either in the instrument or after removal without need for unwinding and rewinding. (2) The record chart automatically folds into place in the recorder without requiring attachment to a rewind drum. This is true for the entire chart length or for any section of chart left in the recorder.

In addition to wide strip and miniature strip-chart recorders, electrical strip-chart recorders are made in both servo-operated and deflection types in a wide range of sizes and types. Servo recorders similar to the 12-in.-wide strip type are made with narrower charts (7-in.-width chart is typical), resulting in savings both in instrument cost and in panel space. Deflection-type recorders are made from 2- to 6-in. scale length, for a wide range of electrical variables.

High-speed Recorders. For test and analytical measurements, direct-writing high-speed deflection-type recorders are available with speed of response up to 100 cycles/sec. or more. Pen motion is generally less than 2 in. Simultaneous continuous records are available, with parallel non-overlapping record channels on a wide chart. Matching amplifiers are available, so that low-level signals can be recorded. Chart speeds up to feet per second are available.

Recording Mechanisms

Pen-and-ink recording using a water-base ink with suitable pen and chart paper is the most common type. The combination of ink, pen, and paper is coordinated by the manufacturer to produce an uninterrupted sharp record line under a wide range of ambient temperature and humidity. Pen-and-ink recording is simple, reliable, and economical. The pen need impose very little load on the driving mechanism.

Single and multiple continuous records are produced. Where two or more records are made on the same chart span, different colors of ink identify the different variables. On this type colored record lines tend to blend for

½ in. or more when record lines cross. It is desirable to avoid record lines normally running close together and with frequent crossings on a pen-and-ink record.

Two principal types of pens are used: (1) unit pens, where the pen point and ink supply are integral, moving together, and (2) capillary pens, with a capillary-tube connection between the writing point and an ink supply at a fixed location in the instrument.

Intermittent multipoint recording is used to record sequentially a number of variables. A dot or a dot and identifying number are printed on a chart for each measured variable at regular intervals. The printing mechanism consists of an ink pad saturated with an oil-base semifluid ink (similar to stamp-pad ink) which applies this ink to a stylus or print wheel. The stylus or print wheel then is pressed against the chart at a location corresponding to the value of the measurement signal. The mechanism provides for synchronizing color of print, print wheel number, or both, with the connected measurement signal, so that a number of readily identified records are produced on a single chart span.

In terms of cost per point recorded, multipoint recorders are generally the simplest and least expensive method of data gathering for a moderate number of items. This is specially true for multiple temperature measurements using thermocouple or resistance-thermometer primary elements. Alarms and signals can be included in most types. Although considerable mechanism is involved in the synchronized switching and printing, this has been well worked out and is in general quite rugged and reliable and requires little maintenance.

Recorder Charts

Practically all recorder charts are printed on paper specially manufactured for desired record properties. Although all paper is hygroscopic and varies dimensionally with ambient humidity, the moderately thick paper used in circular charts should change in dimension less than 0.1 per cent per 10-deg. change in relative humidity. The thin paper used for strip charts has a greater coefficient of expansion.

Circular charts are located from the punched center hole. This hole should be held within 0.002 in. tolerance on both hole size and concentricity with the printed lines. The chart hub should be equally precise in size and location. Where extreme accuracy is required under severe variations in humidity, special circular charts are available from some manufacturers, made from a sheet with a non-hygroscopic plastic base.

Strip charts are located from holes in one edge which register with sprocket pins in the driving drum (holes, if any, in the other edge are oval to allow for chart expansion). Precision in hole size, in the relation between holes and chart printing, and in location of sprocket pins is more difficult to maintain in strip charts.

Multiple records, either continuous or multipoint intermittent, save on instrument cost and on panel space. For measurements such as humidity using wet- and dry-bulb temperature, and gas flow with differential and static pressures, it is desirable to have the records on a single chart.

Overlapping-record Charts. Two or more records using the same chart space are very common in process recording. This is ideal for wet- and dry-bulb hygrometry, where both records use the same temperature scale and the wet-bulb temperature is always less than the dry-bulb temperature. In gas-flow measurement, pressure and differential pressure usually require different scales.

Three options are available:

1. A zero to 100 chart may be used, with a multiplying factor applied to obtain actual values.
2. A single set of chart graduations can be used, with numbers for pressure and differential-pressure calibration printed on alternate major time lines.
3. Where different scale layouts for the different variables are required, such as a square-root-graduated flow scale, alternate time zones on the chart may be printed with static-pressure calibration and differential-pressure calibration.

With overlapping records, the width of the chart is based on the scale length of a single record. This provides maximum scale spread with respect to chart width. With continuous records, a small time difference between records is required to allow the pens to pass. Records which nearly coincide and frequently cross may be troublesome.

Parallel-record Recording. The records may be located side by side on the chart without overlap. This requires a chart much wider in proportion to individual record scale length. Records are exactly synchronized. This parallel record is generally used for high-speed direct-writing recorders and for oscillographs, where individual scale length is small. It is used on some 12-in.-wide strip-chart recorders. It is universally used in on-off time and operation recorders. It is seldom used for recording process variables on circular charts or on strip charts less than 12 in. in width.

Zone (Time-sequenced) Recording. Several records may be made on a single chart, separated into zones along the time axis. In this type of multipoint (intermittent) recording, the chart drive, switching, and marking system are synchronized so that each record point appears at the correct location in its appropriate record zone. Circular charts with 24 record segments, with one record point in each segment each hour, monitor slowly changing variables, such as temperature and humidity in storage areas. Strip-chart recorders of this type use a predetermined chart length, pasted together at the ends to form a continuous belt.

By combining conventional multipoint intermittent recording with a zone chart, a single recorder can provide a clear, easily read record of a large number of variables. Because of the requirement of synchronizing chart motion as well as marking action with switching of variables, this combination is usually employed with variables which change slowly.

SYSTEM DISPLAY

Well-engineered display, important in individual indicating and recording instruments, becomes crucial in central-control-room design where complete data on large and often critical process operations must be presented to a human operator. Indications and records must be coordinated with controls, switches, alarms, and auxiliary equipment, to present a clear, easily visualized display of the process operation. Developments in control centers have progressed in two major directions: (1) full graphic panel and (2) semigraphic panels.

The *full graphic panel* is essentially a flow diagram of the process displayed on the panel with representations of the processing units, and with instruments mounted in appropriate locations on the diagram itself (Fig. 22-114). The recorders or combined recorder-controllers are almost always miniature strip-chart instruments. This presents a very clear and comprehensible showing of each element in its relation to the whole. It simplifies training procedures because operators are less likely to make mistakes when functions and relations are obvious.

But mounting instruments directly on the flow diagram also has disadvantages. A good graphic display takes a lot of panel space; in general, it is limited to a vertical panel. It must be fully custom-engineered. Graphic panels tend to be expensive and because of their

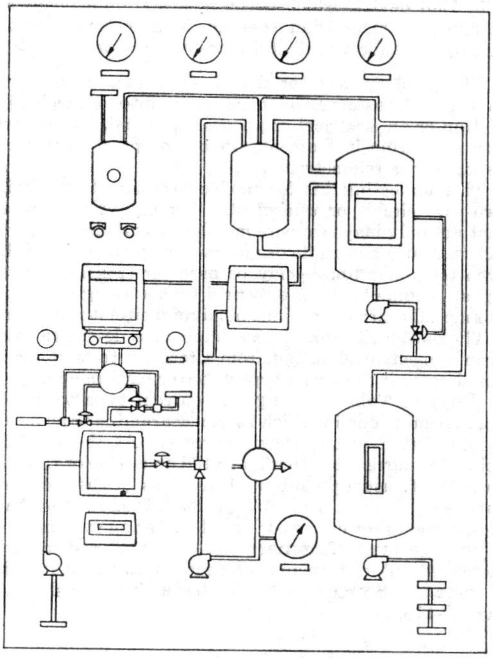

FIG. 22-114. Full graphic panel.

size add to the cost of the control house. The display, dispersed over a large panel area, is less easy for the operator to follow just because of its size, especially where several related operations are grouped in a single control setup. Full graphic display is inflexible. From the time the graphic layout is started, any change in the process involves considerable expense and delay in bringing the display up to date. Thus there is some question as to the real advantage to the operators of full graphic display. The point is made that, by the time an operator has enough competence to operate the process, he does not need to have the instruments mounted on a flow diagram to show him their relationships.

Semigraphic panels provide process control with minimum panel space. Combined vertical and sloping panel surfaces give maximum useful working space per foot of panel length. Indicators, recorders, controllers, and auxiliary equipment are grouped as closely together as mechanical considerations permit. The graphic display is usually a small-scale pictorial flow diagram mounted above the working surfaces. This may be simply a line drawing, or colors and lights may be included to relate the operating instruments, switches, and valves to their diagrammatic representations.

Figure 22-115 illustrates a typical standard unit specifically designed for use with electrical indicating and recording instruments. As shown, 12 miniature two-pen strip-chart recorders and 24 indicating controllers are mounted in a cabinet with an over-all length of 44 in. Space is available inside the cabinet for thermocouple transducers and alarm and signal devices. The cabinets are designed for use in groups for large process operations. Matching cabinets are provided for switches, indicators, annunciators, and auxiliary devices.

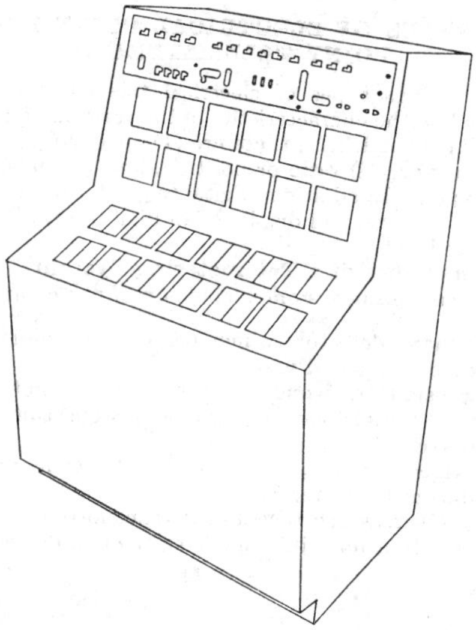

FIG. 22-115. Semigraphic console.

The arrangement shown combines compactness and great flexibility in a standardized unit. Any desired combination of recorders and controllers can be used. A central terminal bank in each cabinet provides all interconnections; standard cables run from this terminal bank to each instrument location. Space for additional instruments can be allowed for in the initial layout. Any change in process control requires simply a change in connections at the terminal board and redrawing the small section of the flow diagram affected. This general approach takes full advantage of the basic compactness and flexibility of all electrical instrumentation.

TELEMETERING

According to the American Standards Definition C42.30-1957, telemetering involves "the aid of intermediate means which permit the measurement to be interpreted at a distance from the primary detector." American Standards Association makes no mention of distance between the transmitting and receiving stations but does recognize the distinctive feature of telemetering as the nature of the translating means, which includes provision for converting the measured value into a signal that can be transmitted conveniently.

Telemetering can be divided into two types: (1) mobile and (2) point-to-point. A.S.A. defines mobile telemetering as "electric telemetering between points which may have relative motion where the use of interconnecting wires is precluded." Point-to-point telemetering is that type where the relative positions of the transmission and receiving stations remain fixed and is, of course, the type of telemetering with which the chemical engineer is most frequently concerned.

Mobile telemetering, particularly that type used in missile and aircraft applications, usually is characterized by small size and weight for the amount of data transmitted. With the requirements of high reliability under severe environmental conditions, this type of equipment has received much attention during recent years and has reached a high degree of sophistication. Most of these systems are highly specialized, however, and are too refined for industrial applications.

Point-to-point telemetering has been developed with the industrial user in mind and has the advantage of being a highly versatile and dependable means of data transmission. Major users are in the utility fields where transmission and distribution networks are very large. The pneumatic version of point-to-point telemetering is used widely in the process industries.

TYPES OF ELECTRICAL POINT-TO-POINT TELEMETERING

The various types of electrical telemetering can be classified by the characteristics of the transmission signal. According to A.I.E.E., these are (1) current, (2) voltage, (3) frequency, (4) ratio or position, and (5) pulse or impulse types. In addition, digital telemetering, where the data are received and displayed in digital form, has been introduced.

Components of a Telemetering System. A complete telemetering system is made up of five components:

1. Primary detector, which detects the value of the measurand (measured value)
2. Transmitter, which converts the output of the primary detector into an analog system suitable for transmission
3. Connecting link, which is the transmission path from transmitter to receiver
4. Receiver, which accepts the transmitted signal and converts it to a form intelligible to the end device
5. End device, which is the final system element and displays the measurand as either an indication, a recording, or some form of digital read-out or code

The primary detector may be any measuring device that can transform the measurand into a mechanical motion or an electrical or pneumatic signal. In general, any measuring instrument can be equipped to transmit its signal via telemetering.

The connecting link for an electrical signal usually is a two-wire circuit or *equivalent.* "Or equivalent" means that not only may two-wire metallic circuits be employed, but that also any radio or microwave transmission link—even telephone lines—may be used for transmitting the signal. Some types of electrical telemetering do require full metallic circuits or limit maximum circuit impedance.

The end device may be as simple as a device to transform a mechanical output from a receiver to an indicator position, or it may be a typewriter or card punch.

Current Telemetering. A current-type telemetering system is one in which the measurand is transmitted as a function of an electric current. At the receiving point, the current is either indicated on a scale or recorded on a chart, usually calibrated in terms of the measured variable. Figures 22-116 and 22-117 show the basic requirements for current-type telemetering systems.

Voltage-type Telemetering. A voltage-type telemetering system transmits the measurand as a function of voltage. Schematically, the basic circuit is shown in Fig. 22-118.

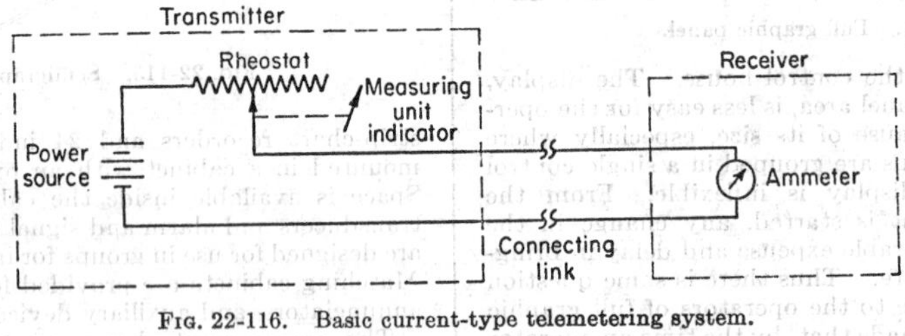

Fig. 22-116. Basic current-type telemetering system.

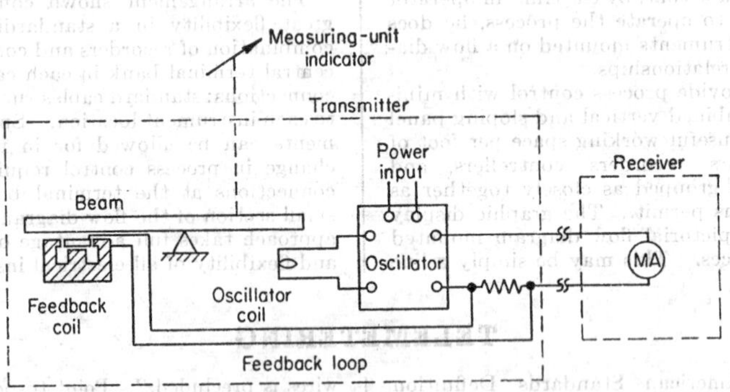

Fig. 22-117. Current-type balanced telemetering system (Microsen).

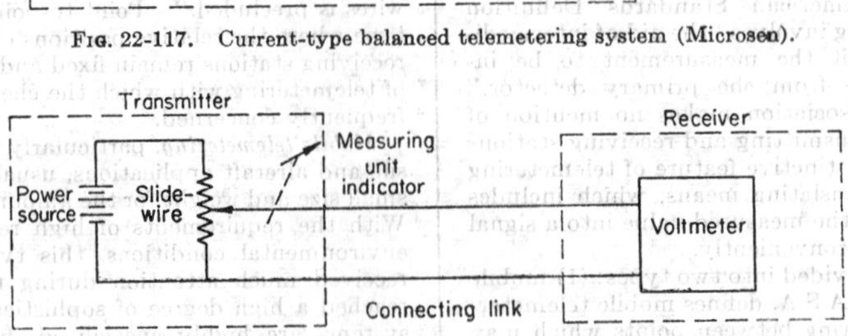

Fig. 22-118. Voltage-type telemetering system.

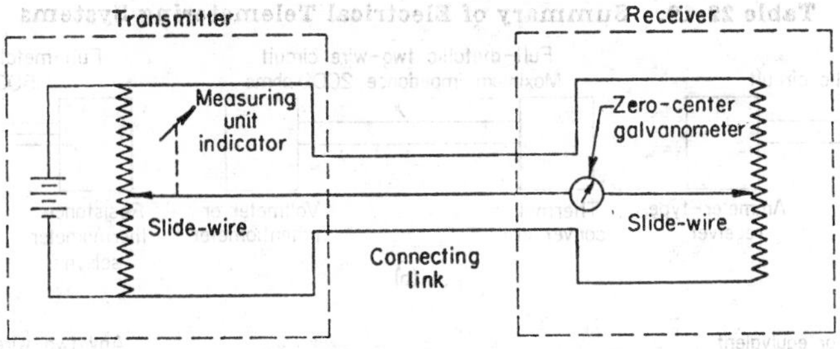

FIG. 22-119. Position-type telemetering system.

A change in measured variable causes the sliding contact to move across the slide-wire, changing the voltage supplied to the circuit. The receiver is in the form of a voltmeter, or a potentiometer, calibrated in units of the measured variable.

Typical of the voltage telemetering systems in use are those employed to measure electrical power. A thermal converter measures the power by converting a small proportional part of total power to heat, then measuring this heat with thermocouples, which provide the millivoltage output to be transmitted to the receiver. The receiver normally is a self-balancing millivoltmeter. These systems require a full metallic two-wire circuit, fully shielded against parasitic currents.

Position-type Telemetering. Position-type telemetering is a variation of voltage telemetering, but this system transmits the measurand by positioning variable resistors or other electrical components in a bridge circuit so as to produce relative magnitudes of electrical quantities or phase relationships. Figure 22-119 shows the basic circuit for this type of system.

A change in the measured variable will cause the slide-wire contact on the transmitter to move, upsetting bridge balance, as indicated on the galvanometer. In order to rebalance the bridge, the slide on the receiver slide-wire must be moved, and its indicator scale, calibrated in units of the measured variable, shows the reading. Other units of this type include Selsyn motors and various inductance bridges. These circuits require a three-wire full metallic circuit, limited generally to 1500 ft. The leads should be shielded to prevent pick-up of stray signals. Temperature-measuring systems using resistance thermometers are generally included as position-type telemetering systems.

Frequency-type Telemetering. In the frequency type, changes in the measured variable cause changes in the frequency of the transmitted a.c. signal. Basically, all that is required is a transducer to change the measured variable to an analogous frequency, electronic amplification and transmission signal, and a discrimination at the receiving end that can sense the frequency variations and indicate or record them. Descriptions of a few commercially available systems follow:

One type (Minneapolis-Honeywell) requires that a current proportional to the measured variable be fed into a current-to-frequency converter. Another (Westinghouse Freq-O-Tron) accepts a millivoltage signal and transforms it into a 15 to 35 cycles/sec. signal over the range of the measured variable. Still another system (General Electric type TFO), especially applicable to the transmission of electrical parameters, uses a 2- or a 2½-element watt-hour mechanism that will rotate at a speed proportional to the input. The Leeds and Northrup high-speed telemetering system receives a millivoltage input and measures it on a null-balance type of instrument that positions the contacts on two slide-wires, which are part of a resistance-capacitance network.

Pulse-type Telemetering Systems. Pulse-type systems utilize various electric-pulse techniques transmitted as a function of time, and independent of electrical magnitude. The most widely used are the pulse-counting systems, in which the number of pulses transmitted corresponds to the measured variable, and the pulse-width or pulse-duration types, in which the length of the pulse is determined by the measured variable.

The pulse-count system uses a device to change the number of pulses transmitted in a given time as a function of the measured variable. The receiver is capable of counting these pulses and of indicating the total. This system finds major use on transmission of total flow and generally is not used for instantaneous rate readings. This simplifies the system as the total number of pulses will be a function of total flow and no exact timing of intervals is required.

The pulse-width systems are the most widely used types in industrial telemetering, particularly in the fields of oil and gas pipe lines and water systems. The systems available have the advantages of simplicity, dependability, and ruggedness.

Generally, these systems use a "live zero," a transmitted pulse that indicates zero reading so that, in the absence of any pulse, the receiver will indicate off scale. The transmission link can be any two-wire circuit or equivalent of any length.

All the pulse-duration systems use a mechanically rotated cam to produce the timed interval. This has the advantage that, for special circumstances, such as flow measurement where a square-root factor is required, the cam can be contoured to conform to any mathematical law.

DIGITAL TELEMETERING

Digital telemetering combines techniques from other fields. Somewhere in the circuit, the measurement analog has to be converted into a digital code. If this is done at the transmission end, the output of the measuring system is fed to a translator that encodes the reading, which is then transmitted by any convenient means to a receiver that will accept the code used. The output from the decoder-receiver is fed to a digital read-out, card punch, or other appropriate apparatus.

The pulse-duration type of telemetering can be employed to feed the signal to a device that will translate the pulse width to a digital code. This method does not transmit a pulse code, so that technically it is a pulse-duration system, but the trend has been to classify all digital read-out systems as digital telemetering.

MULTIPLEXING

Multiplexing is a method of transmitting several signals over one transmission channel. Its use is restricted to those methods of telemetering which can employ a two-wire equivalent circuit. It can result in a saving of trans-

Table 22-19. Summary of Electrical Telemetering Systems

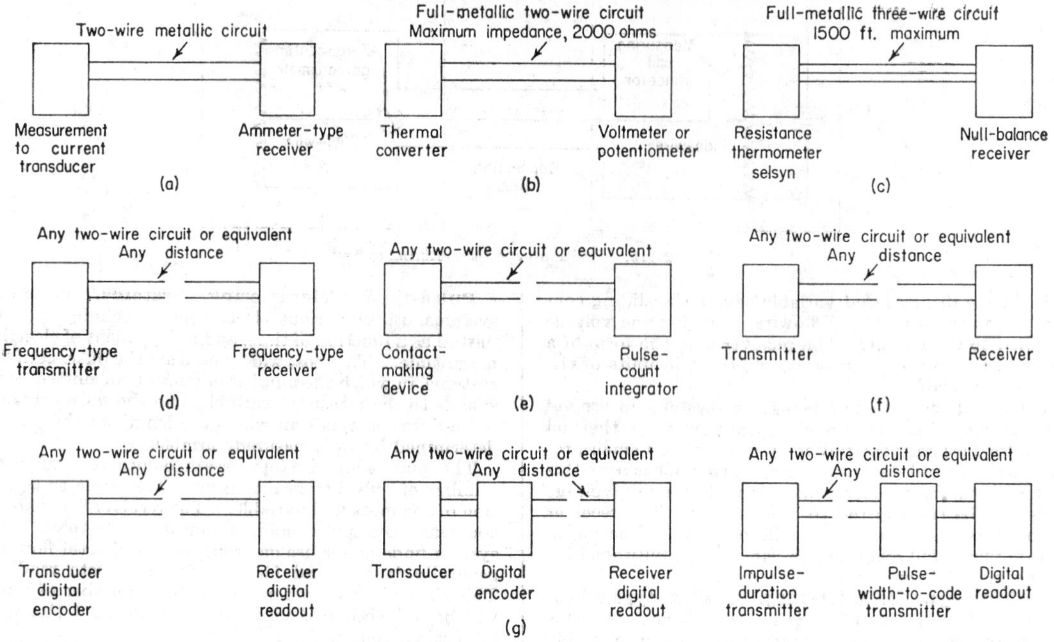

Type	Simplified block diagram	Advantages and limitations	Major applications
Current	(a)	Instantaneous transmission of d.c. over two-wire circuit. Limited to 5 miles. Can operate into electronic control systems	Analog transmission of mechanical measurements
Voltage	(b)	Instantaneous transmission. Limited to full metallic circuits of 2000 ohms, free of parasitic currents	Analog transmission of electrical quantities
Position	(c)	Instantaneous transmission. Requires three wires (full metallic circuit) not exceeding 1500 ft.	Temperature measurement with resistance thermometer; other analog transmissions
Frequency	(d)	Practically continuous. For millivolt or milliampere input. Will operate over wire circuit, carrier, or microwave links	Primarily for transmission of electrical measurements but may be adapted to non-electrical quantities where high-speed transmission is required
Pulse count	(e)	Simple. Will transmit over wire circuit, carrier, or microwave links	Primarily for total flow transmission. Not used for instantaneous readings
Impulse duration	(f)	Simple electromechanical device. Will transmit over wire circuit, carrier, or microwave links	Analog transmission of all measurands
Digital	(g)	Transmission over wire circuits, carrier, or microwave links	For digital read-out of all measurands, especially where supervisory control (pulse width) is available or where digital records are required or digital computing is to be used

mission equipment or telephone-rental costs and is especially useful where several transmitters are placed at the same location. There are two general types of multiplexing: (1) frequency and (2) time-division.

Frequency multiplexing provides simultaneous transmission of data on all measurands to the receiving point. This is accomplished by modulating several carrier frequencies by several telemeter transmitters. At the receiving end, there must be a group of tuned filters to discriminate between the different carrier frequencies and key the various telemeter receivers.

Time-division multiplexing employs a switch at the transmitting end that sequentially switches several transmitters onto a single transmission circuit. At the receiving end is another switch whose operation is synchronized with the first that will switch the data into the proper telemeter receiver. This does not give continuous monitoring of each channel but is useful where this is not important, such as when used with telephone lines. The system then permits use of the cheapest-grade line at substantial savings in rental costs.

A summary of electrical telemetering systems is given in Table 22-19.

PNEUMATIC TRANSMISSION OR TELEMETERING

For many years, the use of pneumatic methods for transmitting readings from primary elements to centralized instrument control panels in process plants was by far the most common method of telemetering. Although pneumatic transmission is still extremely popular, trends toward the use of more sophisticated methods of data handling and processing have to some degree increased the interest in electrical telemetering methods as just described (see Sec. 8-5 by Higgins in "Process Instruments and Controls Handbook," McGraw-Hill, New York, 1957).

Characteristics of Pneumatic Systems. Industrial pneumatic devices commonly operate over a 3 to 15 lb./sq. in. gage range with signals transmitted through small-bore metal or plastic tubing. The bore diameters of this tubing are usually between 0.188 and 0.305 in., with lengths varying from a few feet up to 2000 ft. or more. Pneumatic receivers, controller measuring elements, and valve positioners usually have receiving-end volumes up to approximately 5 cu. in. Diaphragm or piston valve motors have receiving-end volumes ranging from about 100 to 6000 cu. in. equivalent volume.

In some applications, a flow-transmission system must respond to small cyclic signals of a few tenths of a pound per square inch amplitude at frequencies up to several cycles per second. A temperature-transmission system, however, may be required to follow slow cyclic changes of 1/10 lb./sq. in. amplitude and frequencies from a few cycles a minute to a fraction of a cycle per minute. The transmission dynamics are seldom a problem in the latter case unless transmission is over hundreds of feet. Where recovery following disturbances is expected to be about 10 sec. or less, the dynamics of the pneumatic system must be considered.

Pneumatic Transmission Lag. The transmission lag affects the pneumatic line in two ways: First, the line introduces lag because of the delays in the propagation of pressure waves through the tubing. Second, the transmitting device has a resistance to air flow. This resistance modifies the lag inherent in the line. For a simple pneumatic system, this effect is shown by the analogous electrical system of Fig. 22-120. The time constant of the transmission system is RC sec.; the time constant of the system with signal generator (transmitter) is $(R + R_g)C$ sec. The transmitter may have insufficient capacity to supply and exhaust air. This corresponds to

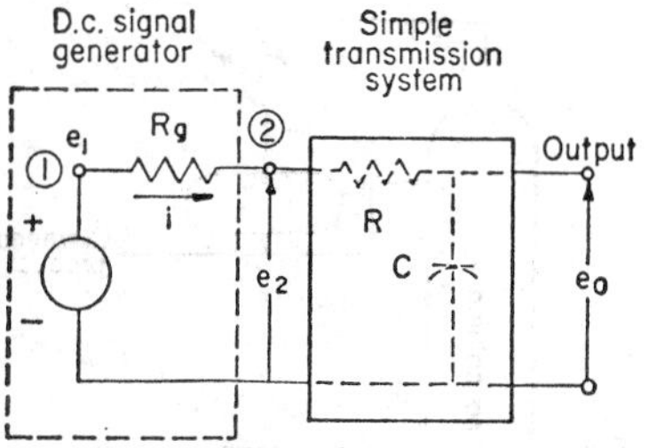

FIG. 22-120. Electrical analog showing the effect of transmitter on transmission lag.

e_1 = signal to be transmitted, volts
e_2 = signal at generator output, volts
e_0 = signal as received, volts
R_g = internal resistance of generator (transmitter)
i = current from signal generator

a limiting of current i in Fig. 22-120 and further distorts dynamic signals. This same approach can be extended to apply to more complex transmission systems.

Pneumatic Transmitting Devices. The flapper-nozzle or vane-nozzle types of mechanisms used in pneumatic transmitters and the bellows arrangements used in pneumatic receivers are quite similar to mechanisms that are described later in this section under Automatic Controllers. In essence, the transmitter employs a device which modulates the instrument air supply into pressure signals which vary from 3 to 15 lb./sq. in. gage and which are in proportion to the measured variable. The receiver, in turn, translates these pressure signals into movement of an indicator or recorder or controller mechanism.

COMPUTER AND DATA PROCESSING

In the simplest process-control systems, a number of standard controllers are used. Each controller receives a signal representing the measured value of a process variable, compares this actual value with the desired value of the variable, and actuates a valve or other control device to cause the difference between the measured and desired values to be reduced toward zero. In a temperature-control system, for example, a gas-filled bulb may be used to generate a pressure signal corresponding to the actual process temperature. This pressure signal is compared with another pressure, established by an operator through rotation of a knob on the front of the controller, and the amplified pressure difference is used to position a valve regulating, say, the flow of steam to a heat exchanger. In most applications of such controllers, of which there are now many types and manufacturers, each controller is intended to maintain a *single* variable at a specified value.

In somewhat more sophisticated control systems, two or more controllers and various auxiliary devices may be used in combination. Examples are shown in Figs. 22-121 and 22-122. The first example (Fig. 22-121) is a ratio control system employing three flow transmitters, two ratio relays, and two controllers to maintain flows B and C in fixed ratios to flow A. The ratio relays can be adjusted to vary the ratios $k_1 = B/A$ and $k_2 = C/A$. The second example (Fig. 22-122) is a cascade control system used for accurate temperature regulation of a distillation column. In the system shown, the temperature at an intermediate point in the column provides the set point for a controller regulating steam flow to a reboiler. This scheme has an important advantage over direct actuation of the valve by the temperature controller: disturbances (such as steam-header pressure changes) which would tend to produce a steam-flow change and therefore a change in the heat input without a signal from the temperature controller are effectively counteracted.

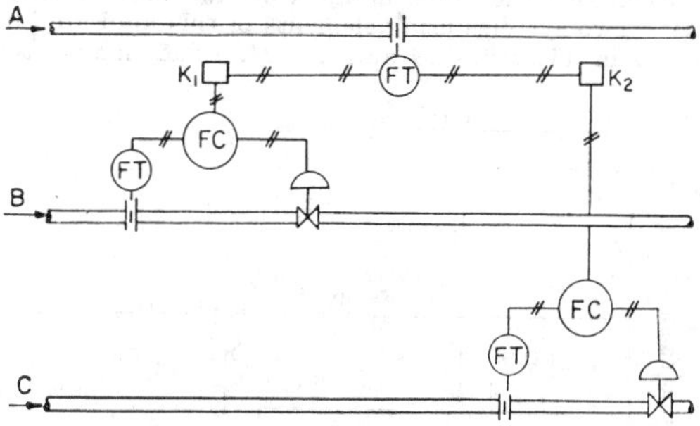

FIG. 22-121. Ratio control system.

Computing elements have been used to make the temperature and pressure corrections which convert a differential-pressure signal from an orifice into a mass-flow signal. The equation evaluated is

$$Q = k\sqrt{\frac{Pp}{T\rho Z}}$$

where Q = mass-flow rate, standard cu. ft./hr.
p = differential pressure, lb./sq. in.
P = static pressure, lb./sq. in.
T = temperature, °R.
ρ = specific gravity
Z = supercompressibility factor
k = a constant

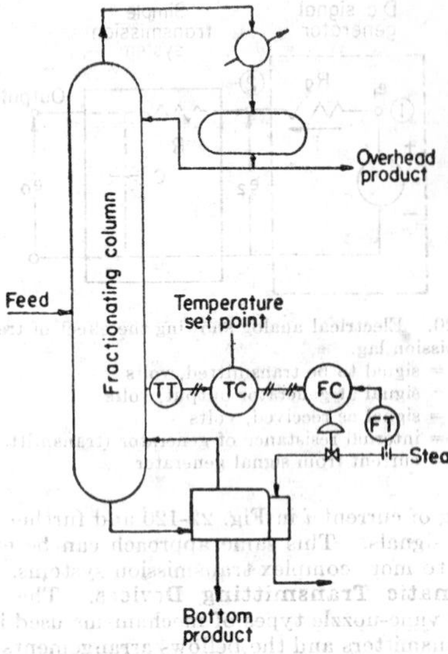

FIG. 22-122. Cascade control system.

For a given gas, ρ and Z are constants which can be considered part of the instrument calibration; the computing elements needed are devices for performing multiplication, division, and square root. When the mass-flow signal is compared with a reference and the difference is used to actuate a valve, the resulting control system can be called a computing control system.

The conventional controller can be regarded as an analog computing device, since it always embodies means for subtracting two signals and amplifying the difference, and it frequently provides output signals which also include the integral or derivative of the difference. However, analog computing devices have only recently been introduced under this designation for process-control use. Two systems using elements of this kind are illustrated in Figs. 22-123 and 22-124. The first system,

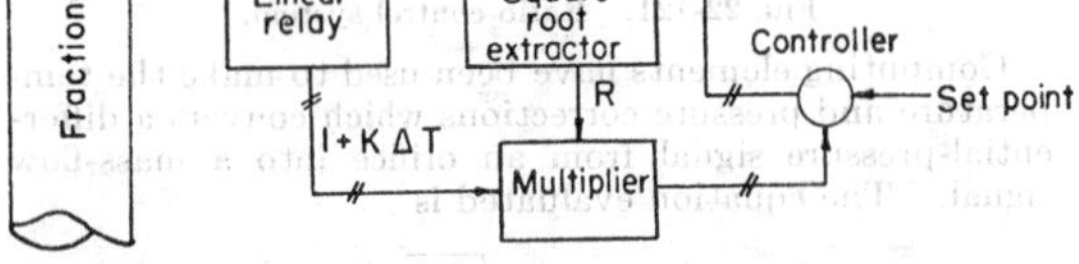

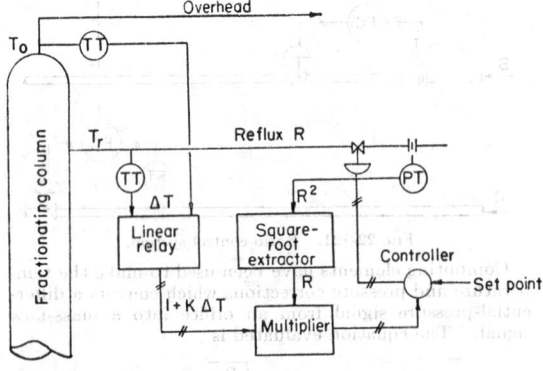

FIG. 22-123. Computing equipment for internal reflux control.

devised by D. E. Lupfer and D. E. Berger of the Phillips Petroleum Company [(*Oil Gas J.*, **57** (34), 68–72 (1959)], implements a method of control for a fractionating column based on material and energy balances for the top tray (see also pp. 22-94ff.). It uses a linear relay, a square-root extractor, and a multiplier to compute internal reflux

$$R_i = R[1 + K(T_0 - T_r)]$$

where K is the ratio of the specific heat of the liquid on the top tray to its heat of vaporization. This quantity is compared with a set point and the difference changes the external reflux in such a way that the internal reflux is held constant.

A fairly elaborate analog computing system has been designed for control of a chemical reactor. This system, shown in Fig. 22-124, was also devised by Phillips Petroleum Co. personnel [Tolin and Fluegel, *J. Instr. Soc.*

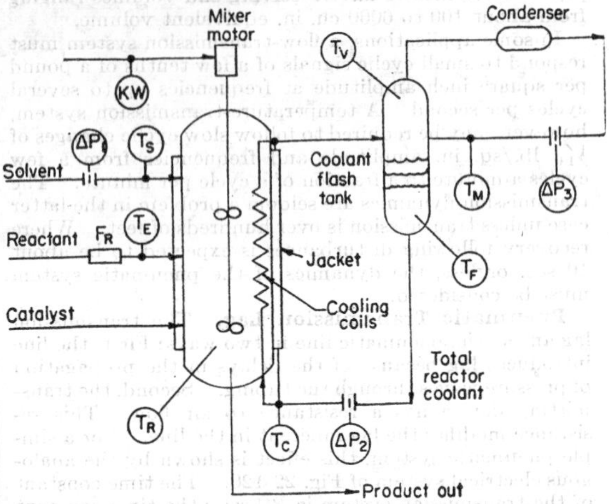

FIG. 22-124. Variables for computer control of a chemical reactor.

Am., **6**, 32–38 (October, 1959)] and employs a heat-balance calculation to determine the amount of product made in an exothermic reaction. Computer inputs include the flow rates of reactants and coolants, temperature differences between feed streams and the reactor itself, power supplied to a stirrer, and heat loss through the reactor walls. Specific heats, heats of reaction and vaporization, and other factors are inserted manually. The computer output can be used to operate the reactor at a constant production rate.

From systems of the type just described, it is only a short extension to systems whose purpose is to maximize or minimize some measure of process performance. This measure may be the production rate or a more complicated function of the process variables (see subsequent sections of this chapter). Various devices have been proposed and built for this purpose.

Suppose that the measure of process performance shows a maximum when plotted as a function of one of the process variables, as sketched in Fig. 22-125. If small variations are imposed around an average value of the variable m, the performance variable p will vary as shown in Fig. 22-126. With the average value of m to the left of the peak in Fig. 22-125, the variation in p with

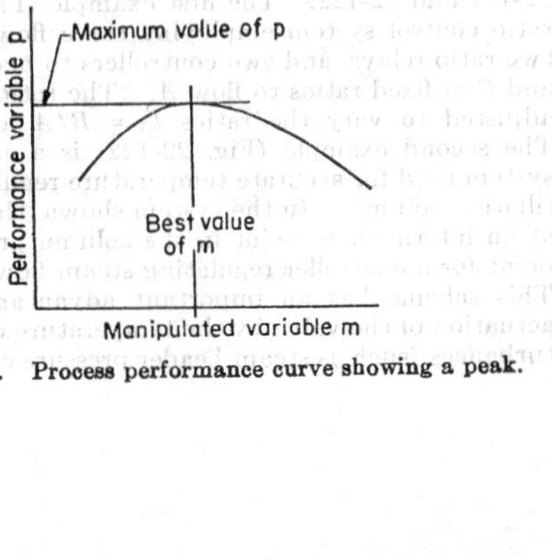

FIG. 22-125. Process performance curve showing a peak.

time will be similar to the variation in m and "in phase" with it, *i.e.*, the maximum values of p and m occur simultaneously and likewise for the minimum values. If deviations from the respective averages are considered, positive deviations in p correspond to positive deviations in m and negative deviations in p correspond to negative deviations in m. If the deviations of p and m from their respective average values are multiplied algebraically, the result is positive at all times in the cycle; the average value of the product is therefore also positive. This result identifies a point at the left of the peak.

If the same procedure is applied with the average value of m to the right of the peak in Fig. 22-125, the two curves will be "out of phase" as shown in Fig. 22-126. Here

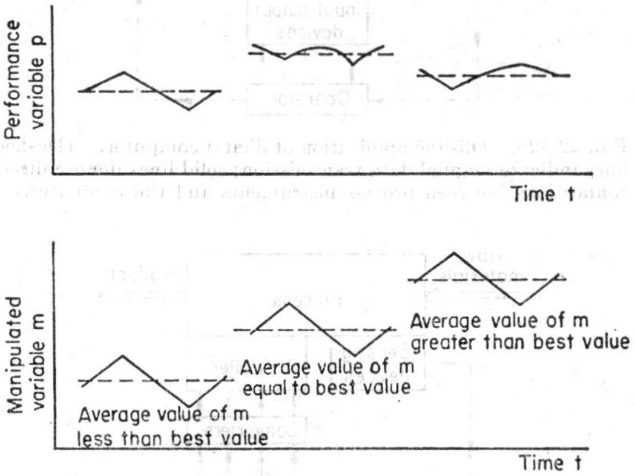

Fig. 22-126. Relationships of variables in one type of peak-seeking system.

negative deviations of p correspond to positive deviations of m and conversely. The instantaneous product of the deviations is now negative at all times, and the average value of the product is now negative. This result is characteristic of a point to the right of the peak.

As might be expected and as can be established from inspection of the center curves in Fig. 22-126, the average value of the product of the deviations of p and m from their respective average values will be zero when the average value of m matches the best value shown in Fig. 22-125.

The calculations required for locating the best value of m in this way can be carried out continuously and automatically by filtering devices which effectively subtract the average values from signals corresponding to p and m, a multiplier to give the product of the resulting differences, and another filter to average the product. The output from the calculating devices, whether it is electric or pneumatic, can then be used to alter the average value of m in such a way that it moves toward the best value. A related scheme, reversed so as to find the minimum of a performance curve, was used by Vasu [*Trans. Am. Soc. Mech. Engrs.*, **79**, 481–490 (1957)] to control an engine for minimum fuel consumption.

Another method for accomplishing the same result also employs a continuous variation of m but uses a memory device to store the maximum value of p. When p decreases a specified amount from the maximum value, the direction of change in m is reversed. As with the previous system, this system will cause a variation of p about its maximum value as suggested by Fig. 22-127. As the figure indicates, the average value of p in this system—as in the previous system—is less than the possible maximum value. This loss in performance, the size of

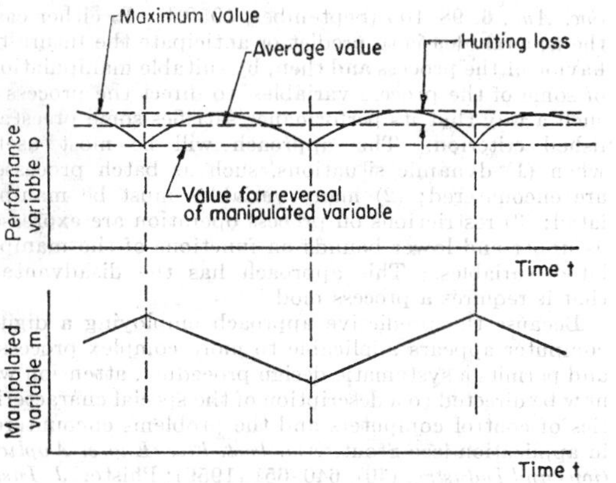

Fig. 22-127. Relationships of variables in another type of peak-seeking system.

which depends on the amplitude of the variation in m, cannot be avoided in a system of this type.

The systems just described perform satisfactorily when no process-time delays are present to obscure the relationships between p and m. When delays are important, another kind of peak-seeking system can be employed. In this system, a step change in m is made and the resulting value of p is measured after a suitable time interval. If the change observed in p is positive, another change in m is made in the same direction. If the change in p is negative, the next change in m is made in the opposite direction. This process continues until the peak is found. Provisions can be made for varying the step size as the peak is approached or for extending the basic scheme to processes in which the performance variable depends on two or perhaps more variables which can be manipulated [Bernard and Soderquist, *Control Eng.*, **6**, 124–129 (November, 1959)].

A number of other special-purpose devices for accomplishing the same results have been invented and discussed in the literature, but space limitations do not permit describing all of them here. As a group, these devices exemplify an approach known as "exploratory control" or "direct optimization" since they involve peak seeking carried out directly on the process. This approach can be expected to be most successful when (1) the process is continuous; (2) only a limited number of variables (m's) can be manipulated; (3) restrictions on process operations are expressed as upper and lower bounds on the m's, rather than on functions of these variables. It has the advantage that little knowledge of the process is required.

For processes to which the exploratory approach is not applicable, another approach called "predictive control" can be taken. In this approach, the process is represented by a mathematical model, and high-speed calculations are used to determine the best set of operating conditions. The model may be an analog simulation of the process operated on an accelerated time scale (Ziebolz and Paynter, *Proc. Natl. Electronics Conf.*, vol. 9, 1954) or a collection of equations solved by a digital computer (Grabbe and Phister, *Control Eng.*, June, 1957). If a digital computer is used, the calculations performed may involve iterative or trial-and-error computations resembling very closely the peak-seeking procedures described above. They may also be simple evaluations of formulas for determining the best values of the manipulated variables from measured process quantities, representing either an analytic solution of the control problem or a summary of previous iterative solutions [Stout, *J. Instr.*

Soc. Am., **6**, 98–103 (September, 1959)]. In either case, the general idea is to predict or anticipate the future behavior of the process and then, by suitable manipulations of some of the process variables, to direct the process in such a way that its performance satisfies some preestablished criterion. This approach will be most useful when (1) dynamic situations, such as batch processes, are encountered; (2) many variables must be manipulated; (3) restrictions on process operation are expressed as upper and lower bounds on functions of the manipulated variables. This approach has the disadvantage that it requires a process model.

Because the predictive approach employing a digital computer appears applicable to more complex processes and permits a systematic design procedure, attention will now be directed to a description of the special characteristics of control computers and the problems encountered in application [see Stout, *Am. Inst. Elec. Engrs. Applications and Industry*, (40), 640–651 (1959); Phister, *J. Instr. Soc. Am.*, vol. 6, January, 1959; and James and Boksenbom, *Control Eng.*, **4** (9), 148–159 (September, 1959)].

ON-LINE PROCESS-CONTROL COMPUTERS

A digital computer used for process control is a general-purpose digital computer which has been equipped with means for receiving and transmitting analog signals. In addition to performing every function of the general-purpose computers used for scientific calculations (such as solving algebraic and differential equations or doing statistical analyses), the process-control computer can receive signals directly from process instruments of all types, convert these signals into a form suitable for its internal uses, reconvert the results of its calculations into continuous signals, and transmit these signals to controllers which are regulating process conditions.

The digital process-control computer is a stored-memory machine, often using a magnetic drum. Upon the magnetic drum are stored the instructions or computer program to guide the process, constants needed in the calculations, and measured values of process variables reflecting current process performance. Data and instructions are stored in a binary-coded digital form, and both arithmetic and logical operations are carried out by transistor, diode, and magnetic-core circuits. By carrying out a long series of additions, subtractions, multiplications, divisions, comparisons, and other basic operations, each requiring an individual step in the program, the computer can perform a wide variety of calculations.

COMPUTER FUNCTIONS

Computers can assist in process control in a number of ways, not all of which can be called "computer control." Shown schematically in Figs. 22-128 to 22-131, the possible uses range from periodic off-line calculations to continuous closed-loop control.

An off-line application of a computer is shown in Fig. 22-128. In a system of this kind, readings from process instruments and laboratory analyses are collected by an operator for use in control calculations. The computer in schemes of this kind is often a slide rule or desk calculator, but full-fledged digital computers are being used in growing numbers. The results of these calculations are then the basis for adjustments of process conditions. When disturbances are relatively infrequent and the requisite calculations are complex, an off-line computer may be satisfactory.

Use of a computer as a program or sequence controller is illustrated in Fig. 22-129. In this application, the computer receives its information from an operator but is connected to the process so that it may exercise direct

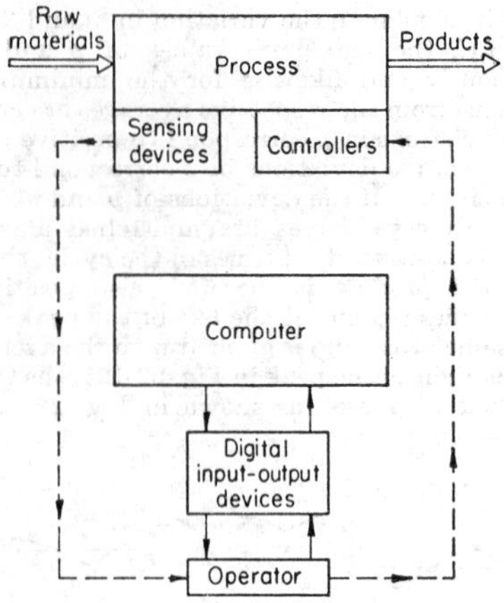

FIG. 22-128. Off-line application of digital computer. (Dashed lines indicate manual data transmission; solid lines denote direct connections between process instruments and the computer.)

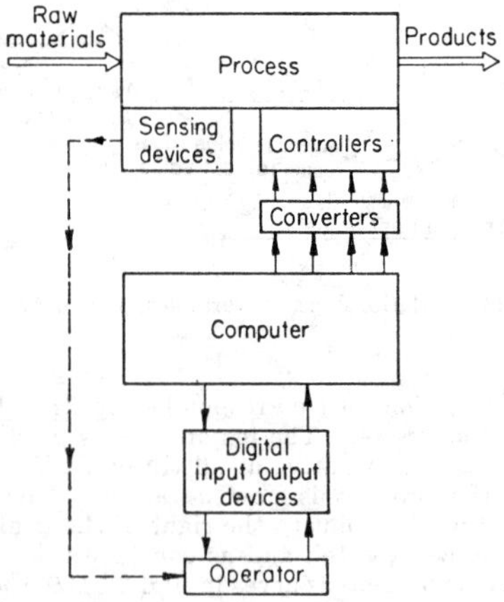

FIG. 22-129. Use of a computer as a program or sequence controller. (Dashed lines indicate manual data transmission; solid lines denote direct connections between process instruments and the computer.)

control. Various systems of this type have been installed for blooming and rolling-mill control in the steel industry. In the simplest of these systems, a punched card may contain complete information on the number of passes through the mill, the roll speed and separation for each pass, edger speed, and position. In more elaborate systems, the card may contain only the initial dimensions of the ingot or slab, the final dimensions desired, the initial temperature of the metal, and the type of steel. By referring to its memory, the computer is expected to find a suitable mill program. These systems require a minimum number of process measurements but do not fully utilize the capabilities of a general-purpose digital control computer. As far as is now known, no program or sequence controllers built around a general-purpose computer have been installed in the chemical industry, but they are being used for starting and shutting down steam power plants [*Control Eng.*, **6**, 38, July, 1959)].

A computer used as a data logger and operating guide calculator is shown in Fig. 22-130. Process-sensing devices are connected, through converters which change

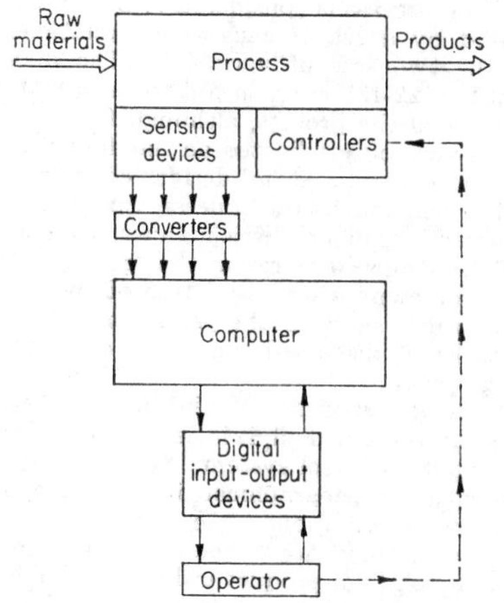

FIG. 22-130. Use of a computer as a data logger and operating guide calculator. (Dashed lines indicate manual data transmission; solid lines denote direct connections between process instruments and the computer.)

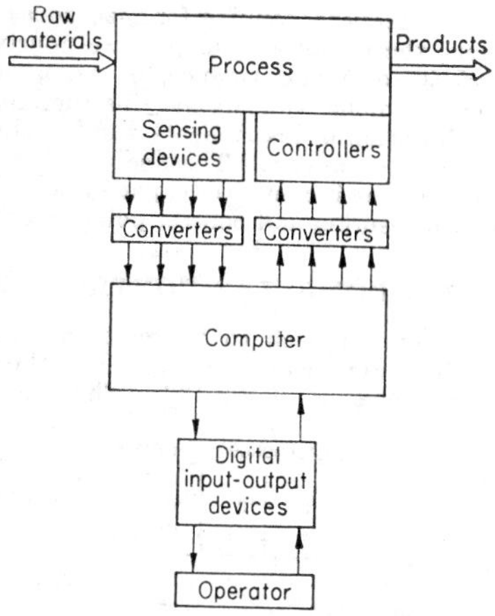

FIG. 22-131. Use of a computer for closed-loop control. (Dashed lines indicate manual data transmission; solid lines denote direct connections between process instruments and the computer.)

the original signals into a form acceptable to the computer, directly to the computer in this system. The computer outputs are raw process data or functions of the original readings, such as yields or efficiencies, which may help the operator to adjust the process to a better set of conditions. A number of systems of this kind have been installed in chemical plants. This approach is useful when process relationships are being established, but as a control scheme, it perpetuates many of the deficiencies of conventional systems.

A closed-loop computer control system is shown in Fig. 22-131. In a system of this kind, the computer reads instruments, calculates the best operating conditions, and resets the process controllers automatically. In normal operation, the operator receives data on performance of the process-computer system via a typewriter or special signaling devices and can modify system operation by inserting new constants or complete programs via a tape reader, switches, or other input devices. In emergencies, the operator can assume control, running the process in the same way as before installation of the computer. Systems of this kind have been installed by Texaco (catalytic polymerization) [*Chem. Eng.*, **66**, 102–104 (Oct. 29, 1959)], B. F. Goodrich Chemical Co. (vinyl chloride) [*Chem. Eng. Progress*, **56**, 63–67 (May, 1960)], Monsanto Chemical Co. (ammonia), and others in the chemical process industries.

Control systems employing digital computers usually combine the functions of optimization, scanning, logging, and sequence control. The various functions are executed in turn under the direction of an executive program of the kind sketched in Fig. 22-132. In effect, the computer continually traverses the outside loop, watching a clock and comparing the actual time with the scheduled time for the performance of each function. When the time comes, the computer leaves the main loop, performs the appropriate calculations, resets the time at which the particular function should be repeated, and returns to the main loop. The control functions generally require more time than the other functions and can be carried out in

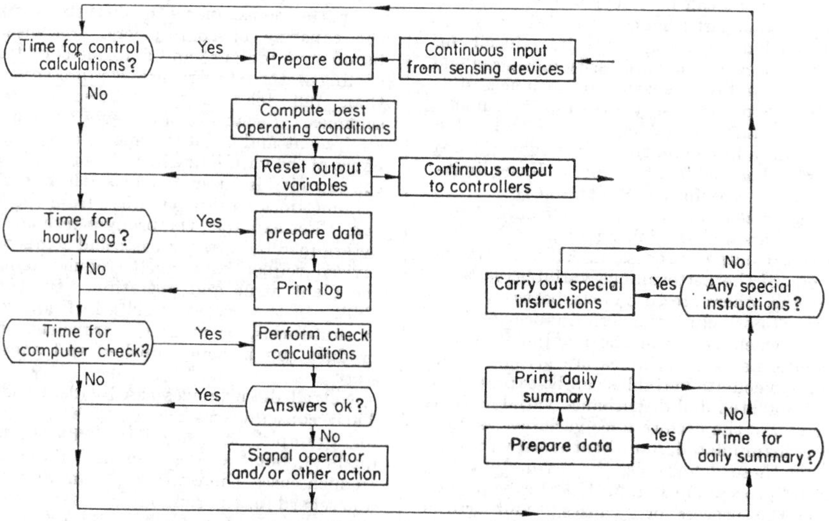

FIG. 22-132. Executive program for a computer control system.

parts to allow frequent scanning for hazardous conditions. At intervals, the computer can prepare hourly or daily logs, check its own performance, or carry out special instructions. Among the special instructions can be included calibration of instruments and startup or shutdown of process equipment. These sequencing operations can be programmed if computer capacity is available and if necessary measuring and control points are provided.

DESIGNING COMPUTER CONTROL SYSTEMS

An organized approach to design of predictive computer control systems can be derived from the schematic diagram presented in Fig. 22-133. This diagram is intended to show cause-effect relationships between the following types of variables:

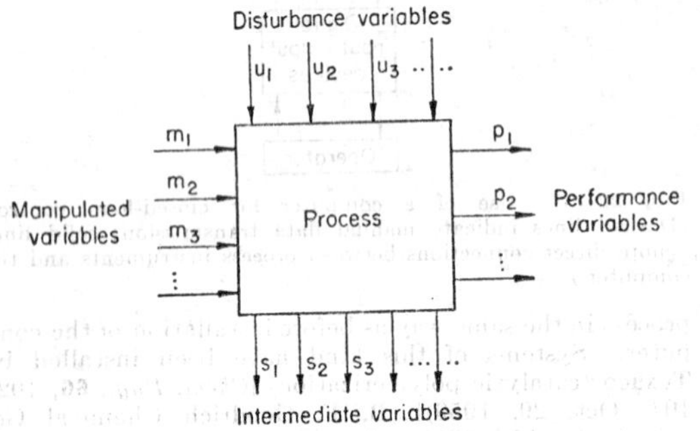

FIG. 22-133. Schematic description of process control problem.

1. *Disturbance variables* are those variables which are not subject to control by the computer. They describe changes imposed on the process which necessitate some kind of deliberate action by the control system.

2. *Manipulated variables* are those variables which are directly adjusted by the computer. The term "manipulated" is used because these variables often, but not always, consist of set points which were adjusted by manual positioning of a knob on a controller prior to installation of a computer.

3. *Intermediate variables* are variables which appear at some intermediate point in the process or in the calculations. In principle, they can be calculated when values of the manipulated and disturbance variables are specified. The intermediate variables are introduced for convenience, either because they are easily measured and therefore provide an indirect measure of an inaccessible disturbance variable or because they simplify calculation of the performance variables (see below). The intermediate variables have no other significance; if any variables of this kind are subject to upper or lower limits, they are listed with the performance variables.

4. *Performance variables* are variables or combinations of variables which assume special significance by their appearance in statements of process objectives. As discussed below, one of the performance variables is to be maximized, and the others are to be held between upper and lower limits. In principle, the performance variables can be computed when values of the manipulated, disturbance, and intermediate variables are given. However, since the intermediate variables can be expressed in terms of the manipulated and disturbance variables, it is also possible to regard the performance variables as functions only of the manipulated and disturbance variables.

In the light of these definitions, the arrows entering the block labeled "process" in Fig. 22-133 represent variables acting on the process or "causes," and arrows leaving the block represent response variables or "effects." The process is considered to be capable of being represented by a set of cause-effect relationships connecting the two sets of variables. The diagram presented in Fig. 22-133 is *not* meant to show material flows into and out of the process, although flow rates may be among the variables indicated on the diagram.

Computer-control-system design consists largely of identifying the important process variables, specifying process objectives in a realistic manner, developing cause-effect relationships to represent the process, and devising a scheme for computing the values of the manipulated variables which satisfies the process objectives. These various tasks are discussed in greater detail in the following paragraphs.

Identifying Process Variables. Before process variables can be identified, it is necessary to fix the limits of the computer control system. These boundaries may coincide with the geographical limits of the process, or they may be drawn about some unit within the process. In some cases, they may extend to sources of raw materials or to points of product utilization. Wherever the boundaries are placed, they must be set with care so that improvements in one process do not inadvertently have adverse effects elsewhere.

Disturbance variables are a crucial element in any control system. A disturbance can be defined as a change of a process variable from a past or normal value, either abrupt or gradual. Many kinds of disturbances can be enumerated.

Variability can be found in the characteristics of raw materials, in the flow rates from upstream processes, in catalyst activities, in ambient-air temperature and humidity, in barometric pressure, and in cooling-water temperature. Other sources of variability include coking of reactors, fouling of heat exchangers, erosion of orifice plates, drifting of instruments, and plugging of pipes or vessels.

An important area of variability occurs in processes having multiple reactors which normally handle the same feed material. In general, the units do not behave identically in their ability to handle the same amount of material and to produce the same product. These differences may be traced to variations in the quantity of the catalyst, channeling through the catalyst, the initial condition of the catalyst, the history of the catalyst, the mechanical design of the units, and differences in the piping runs to and from the units.

Another consequence of disturbances is variability in the capacity of compressors. Because of changes in barometric pressure and ambient conditions which affect cooling-water temperature, compressors often run at less than full load under conventional instrumentation schemes. Because compressors are expensive pieces of equipment and often the main bottleneck in a plant, the effect of the variability in ambient conditions on compressor capacity is an area well worth investigation.

Sometimes variability arises from the way the plant is run. For example, the product rate and quality may be determined by sales forecasts and commitments which are revised frequently enough to require numerous changes in the plant goals and operation. In this case, the variability in the process results in frequent plant startups or shutdowns, or numerous transient periods when one product run is being finished and another is about to start.

Not all disturbances can be identified with certainty. Their consequences may be clearly evident (appearing, for example, as unexplained fluctuations in product quality), but the source may be impossible to pinpoint. In such cases, the control system must be designed with due regard for the random variations which remain when the major disturbances have been accounted for.

In general, the manipulated variables are easily identified. They are often the variables whose values have been left to the discretion of operators or supervisory personnel. Ordinarily, however, many variables of this kind require adjustment only infrequently, and it may not be economical to provide the control computer with means for making these adjustments directly; it may be better to continue manual adjustment of some controller set points, possibly based on advice from the computer, than to install hardware for this purpose.

In certain cases, it may not be easy to distinguish manipulated variables from intermediate or performance variables. For example, suppose that a temperature is to be adjusted. A change in temperature is usually effected by changing the flow of a heating or cooling medium. Depending on the nature of the control system, it might be necessary to regard this flow as the manipulated variable and the resulting temperature as an intermediate or performance variable. Generally speaking, the term "manipulated" implies a near-instantaneous correspondence between the process variable and the computer output signal.

Intermediate variables can be introduced in unlimited numbers, but each variable must be expressed as a function of the manipulated and disturbance variables before it can be useful. In addition to flows, temperatures, pressures, and other operating conditions at intermediate points in the process, the list of intermediate variables may include such quantities as yields or conversions used to compute production rates and operating returns, calculated concentrations and reactant ratios, average production rates from parallel units needed to allocate raw material, and a host of other auxiliary quantities.

Specifying Process Objectives. Because of their importance, the performance variables deserve close attention. These variables are necessary in order to make a precise quantitative statement of process objectives in a form which can be used by a control computer. One of the performance variables, p_1, called the *objective function,* is an expression for the dollar operating return D written as

$$p_1 = D = v_{P_1}P_1 + v_{P_2}P_2 + \cdots - v_{M_1}M_1 - v_{M_2}M_2 - \cdots - D_0 \quad (22\text{-}1)$$

where D_0 is the fixed costs in dollars; $P_1, P_2 \ldots$ are the amounts of the various products or by-products; M_1, M_2, . . . are the amounts of raw material, energy, catalyst, solvents, and so on; and the v's are incremental values or costs. If the P's and M's are the amounts of product made and material consumed in an hour or a day, D is the operating return for the corresponding period. For a batch process, the operating return should be expressed as dollars per unit time and integrated over the time of each batch; the dollars for a number of batches should then be summed to get the total dollars for a month or year. In semicontinuous processes, such as those involving a steady flow of raw material and a periodic replacement of catalyst, the cost of the catalyst should be added as a number of dollars per occurrence, not averaged over the amount of product made. This practice is necessary because the number and timing of catalyst changes may be among the control decisions to be made by the computer, and the calculations are more easily carried out on this basis.

When process operating conditions are fixed by such considerations as raw-material availability or equipment capacities, the exact values and costs used in the expression for operating return may be unimportant. In many cases, the same set of "best" operating conditions is obtained for a significant range of some of the values and costs, particularly for the costs of utilities. In such cases, minor utility costs can be ignored with consequent simplifications in the control calculations.

The objective function can be multiplied or divided by a constant without changing the location of the best operating point. This emphasizes the fact that relative rather than absolute costs and values are important and suggests that scaled figures can be used for convenience. However, when the payout from installation of a control computer is evaluated, fairly exact figures must be used.

The values and costs used in the expression for operating return may be functions of raw material or product quality. Examples are found in the chemical industry, where some products are sold at prices which depend on the amounts of impurities or diluents present, and in the petroleum industry, where the values of gasoline blending stocks depend on the octane rating and other characteristics. Values and costs may likewise be functions of the amount of material, as with contracts for purchase of natural gas or electrical energy. To reach realistic conclusions, these details must be built into the objective function.

The objective function is to be maximized by a suitable choice of the manipulated variables. At the same time, a number of other objectives must be achieved. These objectives are known as constraints and can be expressed by inequalities

$$p_{il} \le p_i \le p_{iu} \qquad i = 2, 3, 4, \ldots \quad (22\text{-}2)$$

or equalities

$$p_i = p_{is} \qquad i = 2, 3, 4, \ldots \quad (22\text{-}3)$$

The constraints arise from requirements on product rates set by market conditions or availability of storage space, from product quality specifications, from bounds on the availability of raw materials or utilities, from limits on the capacity of equipment, from safety considerations, and from other sources. Flows, pressures, temperatures, levels, concentrations, and other variables in any part of a process may be constrained to fall within upper and lower limits or to take a specified value in order to prevent actual damage to equipment, to avoid operating difficulties which do not actually damage equipment but which do lead to wasted time or materials, or to protect plant personnel.

It is sometimes convenient to view an equality constraint as two inequalities, the upper and lower limits being very close or even coinciding. By this device, all constraints can be expressed by inequalities. In practice, if a constrained variable is not at a limiting value, it is as if the limit did not exist; in this sense, it can be said that the only important constraints are equality constraints. The choice depends in part on the techniques being used to calculate the best process conditions.

Whether or not inequalities are expressed as "less than" or "less than or equal to" is immaterial. If the computer is told that a certain temperature must be less than 200°, for example, it is free to select 199, or 199.9, or 199.99. Whatever value is actually allowed can be taken as the limit, interpreted really as "not more than." Analogous statements apply to lower limits.

An extremely important part of computer-control-system design is setting down the proper number of realistic constraints. If too few are specified, the results of the control calculations will be ridiculous; for example, the computer might decide that a reactor should be run at infinite temperature and infinite feed rate. Since conclusions like these frequently result from extending process equations into regions where they do not apply, constraints should be applied at the very least to limit operation to regions for which the equations used by the computer are valid. If too many constraints are specified, on the other hand, the choices open to the computer are unduly restricted, and it may be forced into saying that the present way of running the process is the only way. Because intelligence has been applied in the past, it may be assumed that the present operations are reasonably good and that the computer should not call for radical changes in operating conditions. Nevertheless, some latitude for change must be provided or the potential benefits from computer control will be legislated away.

In connection with constraints, it should also be noted that the upper and lower limits frequently vary with time. When constraints such as raw-material availability or equipment capacity play an important role in fixing the best process conditions, a major control function may be following shifts in the limits in order to maximize the dollar return from plant operation.

Operating return may appear to be a rather special form of process objective. It is used, of course, because profit is the ultimate aim of most process operations. However, various tricks permit the operating return as defined above to be applied in other situations of importance to process managements. In periods when maximum production is desired, for example, the computer can be told that the raw-material costs are zero; in maximizing D, the computer will then maximize the total value of the products or, if the product values are all made equal, the total amount of all the products. If the production rate is fixed (by stating suitable constraints), maximizing D corresponds to minimizing the major variable costs. If the major raw-material rates are fixed, maximizing D corresponds to maximizing yields. Most other special requirements can be handled by similar methods.

Process operators have a natural tendency to ask for a maximum amount of product at the least cost and the maximum quality. Except in special circumstances, it is not possible to maximize or minimize more than one function of the process variables at a single set of the manipulated variables. The problem is illustrated in two variables in Fig. 22-134. The maximum yield

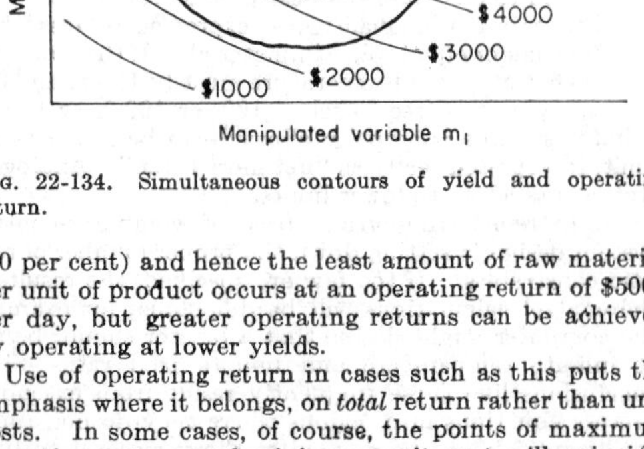

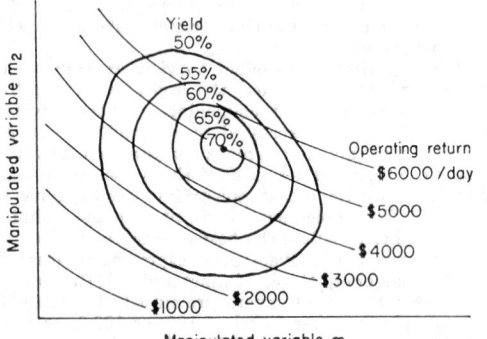

FIG. 22-134. Simultaneous contours of yield and operating return.

(70 per cent) and hence the least amount of raw material per unit of product occurs at an operating return of $5000 per day, but greater operating returns can be achieved by operating at lower yields.

Use of operating return in cases such as this puts the emphasis where it belongs, on *total* return rather than unit costs. In some cases, of course, the points of maximum operating return and minimum unit cost will coincide. If so, nothing is lost by using operating return as the single objective. When product quality is governed by economic considerations rather than rigid "go" or "no go" specifications, the best compromise between product quantity and quality can be achieved by placing a dollar value on product quality and thereby reducing both objectives to a common denominator. The objective function is well adapted to this approach.

Finally, it might be noted that the constraints can be combined with the objective function by including terms to represent the costs of violating the constraints. These costs might be real, such as cost of reworking off-specification product or damaging process equipment; if so, the possibility must be faced that the maximum operating return is obtained by producing a small amount of unacceptable material or sustaining a definite equipment-maintenance charge. The costs may also be artificial and set so high that the computer will never call for conditions violating the constraint. This approach might be used with constraints arising from the limited availability of raw materials or utilities, where a high incremental cost above the limiting value would effectively prevent a demand for more material than is available. The same tactic could be applied to avoid operating equipment beyond its ratings.

Developing Cause-Effect Relationships. The cause-effect relationships by which process performance can be predicted are known as *process equations* or the *mathematical model* of the process. Depending on the uses made of the process equations, they may or may not have to provide a complete description of process performance. In general, equations are necessary only for each of the performance and intermediate variables as functions of the manipulated and disturbance variables. While it has been implied that one equation is needed for each of the dependent variables, the usual mathematical model consists of a series of equations leading to values of the performance variables. Many of the quantities obtained along the way could be called intermediate variables, but it is not customary to dignify them in this fashion.

The use of many simple equations, rather than a few long and complicated equations, is a natural technique for digital computation since, in any event, the calculations must be broken up into a series of elementary mathematical operations.

The process equations can be classified in various ways: by the kind of operation which they describe, by the kind of equations employed, or by the techniques used for their development. Various kinds of equations can be used to express process relationships. In continuous processes, feed and product rates are expected to be relatively constant, as are pressure, temperatures, concentrations, and other variables throughout the process. Disturbances may consist of occasional steplike changes resulting, for example, from an abrupt shift in the source of raw material or in the product specifications. The important control problem here may be determination of the best process conditions during periods of steady-state operation which prevail for a greater part of the available time. For this purpose, a mathematical model consisting of *algebraic equations* is generally sufficient. This model is composed of energy and material balances, yield or conversion correlations, phase relationships, state equations, and other kinds of equations familiar to chemical engineers.

In batch processes, flows of raw materials are deliberately intermittent, and process conditions are generally varied in a planned manner with time. A batch process is never in a steady-state condition. The mathematical model necessarily consists of differential or difference equations which represent process behavior as a function of time. Similar models are required to represent the response of continuous processes in the intervals immediately following major disturbances or during startup and shutdown. The common approach is to write *differential equations* derived from principles of energy, momentum, and mass transfer, and chemical-reaction kinetics. Looking to the use of a digital computer which can repeat a series of calculations in a finite time, it is convenient to use *difference equations* which give the dependent variables at multiples of some basic time interval.

Mathematical models can be derived by either *theoretical* or *empirical methods.* A theoretical analysis, even approximate, often provides an indication of the important variables and a clue to their functional relationships [Anderson, *Chem. Eng. Progress,* **55,** 61–67 (April, 1959) and Pinchbeck, *Chem. Eng. Sci.,* **6,** 105–111 (March, 1957)]. These results may be very helpful in guiding a statistical analysis of experimental data. If a small number of data taken over a limited range of the variables is used, a statistical analysis can give slopes or exponents which are impossible from theoretical considerations. Because such errors are avoided, models based on a theoretical foundation can be extrapolated with greater confidence than a strictly empirical model.

Experimental methods for developing dynamic-process models include step and frequency-response techniques which are widely known [Laspe, *J. Instr. Soc. Am.,* **3,** 134–138 (April, 1956). Young, "Introduction to Process Control Design," Instruments Publishing Co., Pittsburgh, 1955]. Correlation techniques, not yet developed fully or used generally, have also been tried (Florentin, Hainsworth, Reswick, and Westcott, Joint Symposium Instrumentation and Computation in Process Development and Plant Design, London, May 11–23, 1959). Analog-computer simulation is an effective means for producing dynamic models of complex processes because many experiments can be run quickly, varying computer parameters until its responses match those of the process [Batke, Franks, and James, *J. Instr. Soc. Am.,* **4,** 14–18 (January, 1957). Woods, *Ind. Eng. Chem.,* **50,** 1627–1630 (November, 1958). Williams, *Chem. Eng.,* **67,** 121–126, Feb. 8; 131–136, Mar. 7; 139–244, Apr. 4; 121–126, May 2; 97–102, May 30; 113–118, June 27, 1960].

Statistical techniques for converting suitable process data into steady-state models have been discussed in great detail in the literature (Davies, "Design and Analysis of Industrial Experiments," Hafner, New York, 1954). However, it may not be amiss to call attention to the possible use of statistical techniques for adjusting data before starting a routine correlation or regression study. If process variables such as production rate or yield can be calculated in several independent ways from different sets of variables, all measured but subject to random errors, it may be possible to compute the most likely values of the measured variables by a least-squares procedure (Deming, "Statistical Adjustment of Data," Wiley, New York, 1948).

Having obtained a mathematical model by one means or another, the system designer should insist that it be checked with data not used in its development. Such checks may require that special tests be performed in which process variables are set at prescribed values so their effects can be observed, preferably but not necessarily one at a time. Alternately, by exercise of great will power, some of the original data may be set aside for this purpose. In any event, a check on the accuracy of the model is a necessary step in system design. Statistical methods will have to be used to judge how accurately predicted and measured process behavior agree.

Devising a Control Scheme. In a computer control system, the mathematical model or process equations are used to calculate the best values of the manipulated variables at a given time or as functions of time. These values have the characteristic that any departure from them would cause an unfavorable change in the objective function or a constraint to be violated. Various means, classified as to whether the model is steady-state or dynamic, can be employed to find the values of the manipulated process variables which meet these objectives.

Considering first only steady-state process situations and ignoring the existence of constraints for a moment, a natural technique for finding the values of the manipulated variables which maximize the objective function is to differentiate it with respect to each of the variables and to equate the resulting functions to zero. This technique can seldom be employed in a purely analytical fashion because of the number and complexity of the process equations. However, vanishing of the partial derivatives is a necessary condition for a maximum value of the objective function and can be made the basis for a numerical procedure for finding the best process conditions. Using the mathematical model and starting at any arbitrary set of conditions, a small change is made in each of the manipulated variables in turn and approximate partial derivatives are computed. When all the partial derivatives are calculated, new values of the manipulated variables are obtained from the previous values by adding increments proportional to the partial derivatives and of the same sign; when the derivative is positive, the manipulated variable is increased, and conversely. This cycle can be repeated just as described or, to reduce the amount of computing needed, the increments in the manipulated variables can be added again without a reevaluation of the partial derivatives until a maximum value is reached; at this point, new partial derivatives are calculated. Known as "gradient methods" or "methods of steepest ascent," these procedures are the subject for a considerable amount of literature which can be consulted for further details (Tompkins, "Modern Mathematics for the Engineer," Beckenbach, Ed., Chap. 18, McGraw-Hill, New York, 1956).

In practice, of course, constraints cannot be ignored. When the constraint is a direct upper or lower limit on a manipulated variable, the solution is easy: stop increasing or decreasing the variable when it reaches its limit. When the constraint is a limit on a function of two or more manipulated variables, the problem is more complicated. In step-by-step calculations of the kind described above, a test after each step will show whether or not a constraint is violated. If not, no action is needed. If a constraint is violated, the manipulated variables must be changed so as to bring the constrained quantity back within its limits. These changes can be accomplished by adding incremental changes which are proportional but *opposite in sign* to the partial derivatives of the constrained quantity with respect to the manipulated variables. In special situations, other techniques are available for dealing with constraints on functions of the manipulated variables.

Constraints on functions can be treated using Lagrangian multipliers (Hildebrand, "Methods of Applied Mathematics," Prentice-Hall, Englewood Cliffs, N.J., 1952). A common, although special, application of this method is found in allocation of raw material to a number of parallel units which are slightly different in their performance [Stout, *J. Instr. Soc. Am.,* **6,** 98–103 (September, 1959)]. (A related problem in another field is allocation of load to a number of parallel electrical generating stations.) (Kirchmayer, "Economic Control of Interconnected Systems," Wiley, New York, 1959.) For example, if the total production rate is

$$P_t = P_1 + P_2 + P_3 + \cdots \qquad (22\text{-}4)$$

with each of the individual production rates a function of the corresponding feed rate (and other variables), indicated as

$$P_i = p_i(F_i, \ldots) \qquad (22\text{-}5)$$

and if the total feed rate is fixed at a value

$$F_t = F_1 + F_2 + F_3 + \cdots \qquad (22\text{-}6)$$

then the feed allocation giving the maximum production rate is found by forming a new function

$$\phi = P_t + \lambda(F_t - F_1 - F_2 - F_3 - \cdots) \qquad (22\text{-}7)$$

and proceeding in the usual way. In this expression, λ is the Lagrangian multiplier. Equation (22-7) is differentiated with respect to the various flow rates and the resulting partial derivatives are equated to zero:

$$\frac{\partial\phi}{\partial F_1} = \frac{\partial P}{\partial F_1} - \lambda = 0$$

$$\frac{\partial\phi}{\partial F_2} = \frac{\partial P_2}{\partial F_2} - \lambda = 0 \qquad (22\text{-}8)$$

$$\frac{\partial\phi}{\partial F_3} = \frac{\partial P_3}{\partial F_3} - \lambda = 0$$

and so on. These expressions are satisfied when

$$\frac{\partial P_1}{\partial F_1} = \frac{\partial P_2}{\partial F_2} = \frac{\partial P_3}{\partial F_3} = \cdots = \lambda \qquad (22\text{-}9)$$

i.e., when a small change in the feed rate to one unit produces a gain which is exactly balanced by a loss in another unit.

In cases where the objective function and the constraints are all linear combinations of the variables, a special technique called linear programming can be used. Not many process-control problems are adapted to this tool, but it has been used to solve problems of refinery scheduling (Manne, "Scheduling of Petroleum Refinery Operations," Harvard University Press, Cambridge, Mass., 1956), for mixing materials (Gass, "Linear Programming," McGraw-Hill, New York, 1958), in cement manufacture, etc. (Weeks, *Rock Prods.*, April, 1960).

Dynamic problems, in which the objective function is an integral involving quantities which vary with time, present more difficulties. One approach is the calculus of variations (Hildebrand, "Methods of Applied Mathematics," Prentice-Hall, Englewood Cliffs, N.J., 1952) concerned in the simplest cases with integrals of the form

$$I = \int_0^T f(x', x, t)\, dt \qquad (22\text{-}10)$$

where x' is dx/dt. The question here is to find the best pattern of variation for x with time in order to maximize the integral. A solution is found from the relation

$$\frac{\partial f}{\partial x} - \frac{d}{dt}\frac{\partial f}{\partial x'} = 0 \qquad (22\text{-}11)$$

Extensions of the basic procedures permit consideration of problems in several variables, and the technique of Lagrangian multipliers can be used to include constraints written as equalities. The calculus of variations does not lend itself readily to problems involving inequality constraints. It was used to develop control relationships for a batch-hydrogenation reactor by Eckman, Lefkowitz, and their associates at Case Institute [Eckman, *Control Eng.*, **4**, 197–204 (September, 1957)].

For batch process or other cases where process dynamics are an essential element of the control problem, another technique for developing control relationships is available and now widely used. Devised by R. Bellman and called dynamic programming (Bellman, "Dynamic Programming," Princeton University Press, Princeton, N.J., 1957), it can be applied to the same problems that are treated by the calculus of variations and to other problems as well. The methods are, however, quite different. In dynamic programming, the process is represented by difference equations which permit calculation of successive states of the process. Selection of the best values of the manipulated variables is then regarded as a multistage decision process. The primary concept of the method is the principle of optimality, stated as: "An optimal policy has the property that whatever the initial state and initial decision are, the remaining decisions must constitute an optimal policy with regard to the state resulting from the first decision."

When any decision is made regarding the values of the manipulated variables, it is assumed that subsequent decisions will be optimum. This assumption reduces considerably the number of calculations needed to establish the best operating conditions. Suppose, for example, that a chemical process is to operate for 30 days before it is shut down and that 20 combinations of flow rate and temperature are possible each day. To examine all the possibilities, the objective junction would have to be evaluated for 20^{30} combinations of flow rate and temperature, which would obviously be an impossible task under any circumstances.

Using dynamic programming, the calculations are started by first considering the last stage of operation. For the example suggested in the previous paragraph, the last stage would be the final day of operation. For various states of the process at the start of the final day, perhaps representing the possible catalyst-activity values which might result from differing prior treatments, the 20 combinations of flow rate and temperature would be examined and the best one selected. The calculations would then be repeated for the next-to-the-last day, using the previously determined optimum values for the final day. The same steps are repeated for the next previous day and so on, at each stage making use of the fact that the best policies for subsequent stages are known. As can easily be seen, this approach effects a great saving in computer effort.

Dynamic programming has been applied to a number of problems connected with the operation of chemical processes. One problem considered is the operation of a process employing a catalyst whose activity declines with time and the treatment it receives; here the question is selection of the process conditions and the times of catalyst replacement which will maximize the long-term profit (Roberts, A.I.Ch.E. Symposium on Computers, 1960). Other examples have been presented by Kalman, Lapidus, and Shapiro [*Chem. Eng. Progress*, **56** (2), 55–61 (February, 1960)] and by Aris, Bellman, and Kalaba (*Rand Corp. Rept.* P-1798, Santa Monica, Calif., September, 1959). Additional applications and more widespread use of this method can be expected in the foreseeable future.

EVALUATING COMPUTER CONTROL SYSTEMS

As is the case with any other process improvement, a computer control system is expected to pay for itself promptly through increases in yield or production rate, reductions in operating costs, or better control of product quality. At various stages in the design of a computer control system, its costs must therefore be compared with the expected benefits in order to judge the attractiveness of the investment.

In 1962, at least, the cost of a computer control system could be expected to fall between \$200,000 and \$400,000. These figures include the cost of the computer itself, associated input-output equipment for connecting the computer to process instruments and controllers, a few sensing devices not previously installed, modifications to the control room or the process itself needed to make space for the computer and to take full advantage of its capabilities, and the cost of engineering services involved in system design, computer programming, and installation. System costs, which might increase or decrease in the future depending on changes in the design of equipment or in the scope of the systems installed, are sufficiently large that careful attention is given to their economic justification.

In the early stages of system design, before mathematical models of the process are developed, it is impossible to make any accurate predictions of the benefits to be expected. Only rough guesses can be made. One can, for example, examine operating records to determine the difference between presently observed yields and the theoretical maximum yields. If this difference is small, its complete elimination might not justify a computer control system. If it is large, however, and grounds can be found for thinking that a computer control system would reduce the difference, further effort on system design is at least warranted. Similar considerations apply to operating costs which might be reduced by installation of a control computer.

Improvements in product quality, another potential source of benefits, may be difficult to translate into dollar earnings. In some cases, if off-specification product entails a direct cost for scrapped material, reprocessing, or transportation from a customer back to the producer, estimates can be made as described earlier by examination of past records. On the other hand, if better quality is expected to lead to getting a larger share of a limited market, the resulting dollar earnings may be largely guesswork. It should also be noted that inadequate control of a process, which often leads to wide variations in product quality, may result in the average product quality being held at a high level so that the lowest-quality material produced will meet specifications. Tighter process control in such cases would mean a reduction in the quality variations, permitting a *lower* average quality and consequent savings in some operating costs.

After a mathematical model and a control scheme are developed, more exact estimates of expected benefits can be made. At this point, it is possible to simulate process operation mathematically. The procedure consists essentially of collecting data for a representative period of past operation without the computer control system and calculating what the yield, production rate, product quality, and important operating costs would have been *if* the computer control system had been working. If repeated enough times to reduce the possible misleading effects of errors in the data or an unrepresentative selection of data, this procedure gives as good a prediction of expected benefits as can be obtained. At this point, system costs can be estimated with considerable accuracy, and the economic justification for installation can be judged with some confidence.

The most accurate measure of system justification is obtained, of course, following installation when actual costs and benefits are available. A few words of caution should be inserted, however, in connection with post-installation evaluations. Because processes are already operated reasonably well, the benefits to be expected are often not great; for example, 2 to 5 per cent is a typical estimate for an improvement in yield. Process measurements are frequently subject to errors of the same magnitude. As a result, a chance exists that the measurements will show a loss in process performance even though an improvement was actually realized. This chance can be reduced by using more data and applying some statistical tests. As would be expected, the smaller the average improvement and the greater the measurement errors, the larger the number of data needed. The appropriate statistical tests are described in nearly all texts on the subject, and an example of their application to a problem of this kind has been published [Stout, *Control Eng.*, **7**, 93–97 (February, 1960)].

Finally, comparisons of operation with and without a computer control system assume that all other influences on process performances have been constant. If changes have occurred, such as use of a new feed material or a new piece of process equipment, suitable allowances must be made. This point must be considered before requesting or granting guarantees of computer-control-system performance.

INSTALLATION OF A COMPUTER CONTROL SYSTEM

While the process model is being developed, the constraints defined, and the optimization procedure worked out, the system designers can determine the number of variables which must be measured or adjusted by the control computer. Typical systems may require 25 to 100 inputs to the computer and 5 to 30 outputs. In estimating these numbers, it is good practice to provide that all variables adjusted by the computer will also be measured as a check on system performance. Some flexibility should be provided for later expansion of the system. An early determination of the number of computer inputs and outputs, even approximate, permits the computer manufacturer to begin assembly of the input-output devices for the control system.

The system designers must also select primary sensing devices to measure variables needed by the computer. Many measurements—flow, pressure, temperature, level, speed, and position, for example—are relatively easy unless unusual ranges or environmental conditions are encountered. Other variables, such as physical or chemical properties of raw materials and products, can present considerable difficulty. Sometimes, as with certain kinds of spectrometers, the computer must solve a set of simultaneous equations to obtain the information desired. In some cases, readings from several instruments can be transmitted to the computer which then computes the desired quantity from a formula. In other cases, where suitable on-line instruments are not available, laboratory determinations must be used with the results being supplied to the computer by means of knobs, switches, or punched tape. In any event, the system designers must devise ways of getting whatever data are required by the control system.

Even for relatively straightforward measurements such as flows, pressure, or temperature, careful consideration must be given to the data-transmission system. If pneumatic instruments are used, the air signal must be converted by a pneumatic-to-electric transducer to give an electrical signal compatible with the computer. Conversion in the opposite direction is necessary when electric signals from the computer are used to actuate pneumatic controllers or valves. Thermocouple output voltages are small and must be amplified for use by the computer. Signals of all types may require filtering to remove extraneous signals originating in the sensing device itself or picked up in the data-transmission system. To save equipment, relay or electronic commutators are used to transmit the various signals in sequence to the analog-to-digital converter associated with the computer.

In planning computer functions, the system designers and programmers must allocate space in the computer memory and reserve computer time for its various duties. Distribution of memory space requires estimating the number of instructions and data storage locations needed for control, scanning, logging, sequencing, and auxiliary routines used, for example, to operate a typewriter or tape punch. The program must be planned well enough that modifications to parts of the program can be made from time to time without disrupting all the past space allocations.

A digital computer necessarily carries out its calculations one step at a time. This fact imposes a limit on the frequency with which any particular set of calculations can be repeated. On the other hand, the quality of control is generally improved if the control calculations are made very often. At one extreme, if the control calculations are made only infrequently, no benefit is derived from the computer. At the other extreme, if the control calculations are repeated as often as possible, no time is left for the performance of other functions. Fortunately, "often" is a relative term, depending on the process, and it is usually possible to determine a repetition rate for the basic control calculations which achieves almost all the benefit theoretically available with continuous control and leaves some time for auxiliary functions.

Programming for on-line control differs from programming for scientific calculations in the emphasis which must be given to time- and space-allocation problems. Generally speaking, the time required for execution of a program can be minimized by being somewhat extravagant with instructions and memory space, while space can be saved by writing programs which take a comparatively long running time. Since both time and space may be severely limited, considerable effort can be expended in reaching the best possible compromise between maximum speed and minimum program length.

Another important consideration is system reliability. In any complex system which is expected to operate with a minimum of human intervention, extensive safeguards must be provided against the possibility of equipment failure. In a computer control system, the points of possible failure include heavy process equipment, primary sensing devices, data-transmission links, transducers, controllers, and the computer itself. Within the time and space limits mentioned above, a number of important steps can be taken to reduce the probability of calamitous system failure.

The computer can be programmed to look for heavy-equipment failures in a number of ways. Sudden flow or pressure changes may signify breakage of a pipe or vessel, and growing discrepancies between flows into and out of equipment may be an indication of a developing leak. Failure of a sensing device may be manifested by a sudden zero or full-scale reading which will be noticed by the computer; these signs may also be a clue to a faulty data-transmission link. A drifting or defective transducer can be detected by providing a standard input signal which must be processed by the pneumatic-to-electric and analog-to-digital converters for comparison with an expected value stored in the computer memory. Faulty controllers can be located by an independent measurement of the variable being controlled; if the measured value does not match the controller set point within a specified tolerance, a reasonable ground exists for believing that the controller is not functioning properly.

Computer failures must be expected, even though equipment now being installed for control of chemical processes has established an excellent reputation for reliability. To catch the infrequent failures which do occur, several steps can be taken. Check problems can be run as a regular part of the control program, the answers from each execution of the program being compared with previously stored answers. In addition to checking data for reasonableness, the computer can check the results of an evaluation of the control equations against the last previous set of answers; a large discrepancy is an indication of possible trouble in the computer. When such troubles occur, the calculations can be repeated automatically to determine if random error was responsible. If the results continue to show a fault in the computer, the process outputs can be held at their previous values or returned to a safe level. Similar actions can be taken in case of an electric-power failure that disables the computer.

While considering the actions to be taken in emergencies, the system designers must also provide for computer-operator communication under normal conditions. Knobs, switches, or other devices must be provided by which the operator can insert data into the computer; for quantities which are needed only infrequently, the tape punch and reader can be used for this purpose. Display and alarm devices are needed. A logging typewriter is the primary means for recording and displaying routine process performance data, while another typewriter may be provided to give a record of program changes, special instructions, certain alarm conditions, or other infrequent events. Ideally, the computer and its associated equipment are installed in the main control room where operators can readily keep an eye on the complete system.

When a computer and its input-output equipment are delivered, the input connections to the computer are made first. The performance of the transducers and converters is checked, and exact scale factors are established for the various instruments. While this step is being carried out, the computer is checked using regular check problems. When the input-output system and the computer are both working, the control program is rechecked using actual signals from process instruments but with the outputs merely displayed on analog indicating or recording devices or typed out on the typewriter. This check may continue for several weeks to establish the correctness of the control scheme under a variety of process conditions. It may go on even longer if part of the control program could not be written without data acquired after connecting the computer to the process. In any event, after process-operating personnel have gained confidence in the computer, the connections from the computer to the process can be completed and the system placed in routine operation.

Computer maintenance can be performed by the manufacturer under a maintenance contract or by user personnel who have received special training for this assignment. The former arrangement will probably be preferred by most users since the manufacturer assumes the responsibility for providing test equipment and spare parts. In addition, because computer failures are relatively rare and seldom occur at the same point, a manufacturer's representative who services several machines and has the benefit of maintenance reports from other installations and his home office is generally better able to recognize and correct defects when they do show up.

FUNDAMENTALS OF AUTOMATIC PROCESS CONTROL

By means of automatic control, processes can be controlled continuously and precisely to give more uniform and higher-quality products. This leads to higher profits due both to less waste and to greater value from better quality. Very fast processes with short response times, such as aircraft-guidance systems, which proceed much too rapidly to be controlled manually, can be operated automatically, thus opening new fields of operations. Many routine or hazardous jobs can be done, freeing men from drudgery and danger. Machines with enormous memories and abilities to calculate can be built to operate control systems that would be too complicated for direct human operation. But there are limits to any control system. It must be designed and constructed, which places many practical limits on it, and it cannot think, but only does what it is told to do. However, by use of the proper engineering techniques, automatic control systems can be built and successfully applied to any process.

THE GENERAL CONTROL SYSTEM*

The essential idea of any automatic control system is that the process and controller form a closed loop of action and response. There is a feedback of information from the output of a process to a controller which regulates the process in order to hold the output to any desired value, hence the often-applied name of "feedback control." The components of a control system, either automatic or manual, can best be seen in a block diagram of a simple generalized system shown in Fig. 22-135.

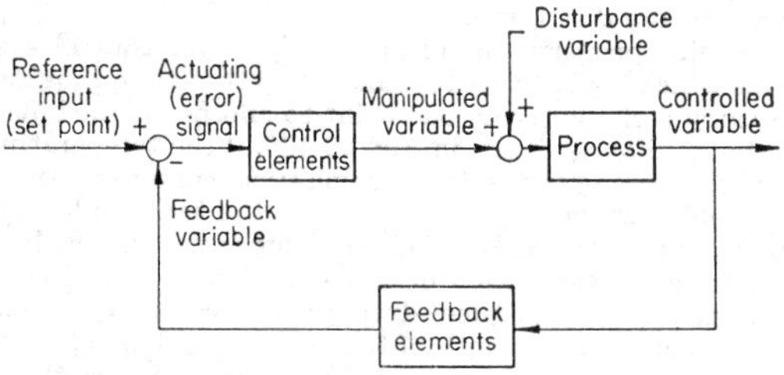

FIG. 22-135. Block diagram of a feedback control system subject to a disturbance.

Block Diagrams. These show the relations among the system variables and are the standard method of illustrating the behavior of a system. Conventions for their construction have been established. Lines represent signals, which may be flows of information as well as flows of material and energy. A circle is a summing point, representing an algebraic addition or subtraction of the input signals to the point. The operation to be performed is indicated by the algebraic sign by the signal. A branch point, or a line branching from another line, indicates a division of a signal into more than one path without modification. Rectangles are system elements representing some dynamic function or relationship between input and output, such as the process or the control elements. These system functions are commonly called transfer functions. The entire block diagram is a mapping of the differential equation of the system.

* The terminology used here conforms largely with the Industrial Instruments and Regulators Division of A.S.M.E. However, to provide the broadest possible understanding, many synonyms commonly used in control terminology are also included. A glossary of common terms is given on pp. 22–75 to 22–76.

The function of the control system is to hold the output of the process to some desired level, which is the reference input or set point. As disturbances move the output from this point some characteristic of the output or controlled medium, the controlled variable, changes. The value of the controlled variable is measured by the feedback elements and a signal proportional to it is fed back to the control system where it is compared with its desired value, the reference input, in the error detector, or summing point. The difference in these two signals, the actuating or error signal, actuates the control elements to adjust the manipulated variable so as to change the operation of the process in a way that will reduce the actuating or error signal to zero. The action of the disturbance variable on the process may be represented as a change in the input signal, as in Fig. 22-135, or in other, equivalent ways. There is no unique way of constructing any block diagram, but there are always variations within the framework of the symbolism used.

There are some special classes of control systems worth considering in the present context. One such class is the group of automatic control systems which are open-loop in character. That is, there is no direct linkage between the controlled variable and the control elements through the feedback elements. The block diagram would differ from Fig. 22-135 by having the lower portion of the loop, including the feedback elements and error detector, removed.

Examples of such systems could be those used in neutralizing wastes or mixing grains. The analysis and design of such an open-loop system is considerably different from that embodying a closed loop. But in a more generalized view they can be considered the same, because there must be some periodic feedback in the form of inspections or analyses of the results of the operation of the system.

Likewise manual control can be thought of as a class of feedback operation. The human operator observes the output of a process either by use of his senses or by watching measuring instruments. As he notes variations in output he takes corrective action on the process inputs. This mode of feedback control is less sensitive, slower, and less reproducible and predictable than automatic action. But because of human ability to comprehend a complicated over-all picture of an operation, capacity to learn and reason, and adaptability to changes, there are many areas where manual control still is and will continue to be used. A block diagram can also be made for a manual control system. In it the operator takes the place of all the system components except the final control element and the process.

Typical Process. The significance of the various parts of the general control system can be best seen by considering what they correspond to in a simple example, such as the heat exchanger shown in Fig. 22-136, in

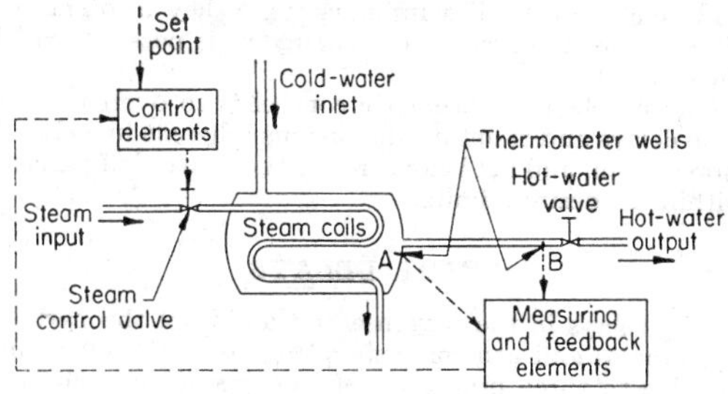

FIG. 22-136. Typical heat-exchange process.

which water is heated by steam condensing in coils. The controlled medium is the energy transferred in the heater and the controlled variable is the temperature of the hot water. The reference input, or set point, is the desired temperature of the water delivered by the heater.

The heat exchanger is the equipment in which the process takes place, and its transfer function relates the outlet-water temperature to the flow rate of steam, which is the manipulated variable. The form of the transfer function can be complicated and in this case depends on the design of the exchanger, the states of the steam and the water, and the water- and steam-flow rates.

The feedback elements include some means of measuring the controlled variable, the temperature, and some method of transmitting this information to the error detector where it is compared with the set point. In this case the measuring element could be a liquid-filled thermometer bulb mounted at either *A*, the outlet of the heater, or at *B*, some point in the pipe downstream from the heater. The error detector, or summing point, in the controller compares the two signals it receives and transmits their difference, the actuating signal, to the control elements. This signal is utilized to change the final control element so as to alter the manipulated variable. In this case it is used to change the position of the steam valve to control the steam-flow rate. The result of the manipulation is to reduce the error in the value of the controlled variable, or to bring the water temperature back to the set-point value.

The disturbance is any change in the surroundings or system that tends to move the controlled variable from the reference input value. It could be a change in ambient conditions that alters the heat losses through the tank walls, a change in the steam pressure, or a change in the water-flow rate. For purposes of classification, disturbances are broken down into two types, load disturbances, such as the first and third examples, and supply disturbances, such as the second example where steam pressure varies.

Performance Criteria. There is a criterion of performance for every operation. It may be a desired product quality, a maximum conversion or yield, or one of many other types of evaluation. The purpose of a control system is to hold the variables within limits so that the process output falls within the range dictated from the performance criterion.

If there were no disturbances, there would be no need for controls, but there always will be some. Likewise, if all parts of a process responded immediately, that is, if a change in the value of the controlled variable due to a disturbance could be immediately detected, corrective action instituted at once, and the error brought back to zero with no time passing, the problem of automatic control would be greatly simplified. However, processes and all parts of their control systems have characteristics that retard changes and the responses initiated by the changes. And as will be shown, not only do these delaying characteristics shift the time scale of the response of a system element to a input change, they also cause a distortion of the form of the change as it passes through the element.

The problem of automatic control is to overcome the time delays and resultant distortions inherent in a closed-loop system, and hold the value of the controlled variable within the desired limits.

TIME DELAYS

The delays in the response and action of the parts of the process and control system are called time lags and are due to three properties of the system: capacitance, resistance, and transport or dead time.

Those parts of a process which have the ability to store a flow, such as energy, material, or electricity, are termed capacities. In Fig. 22-136, for example, the walls of the steam coils and the water in the tank can store energy, thus are capacities. This storage property gives the ability to retard change. For instance, if the temperature of the incoming steam to the heat exchanger increases, it requires some time for more energy to be added to the coils and to the water in the tank so as to bring it up to a new, higher temperature.

Those parts of a process which resist transfer between capacities are termed resistances. In Fig. 22-136, the walls of the steam coils and the insulating effect of the layers of steam and water on either side of them resist the transfer of energy between the steam in the coils and the water on the outside of the coils. The combined effect of supplying a capacitance through a resistance produces characteristic time retardations in the transport between capacities. Such resistance-capacity, *RC*, time retardations are often called capacity lags or transport lags.

It is desirable to classify processes by the number and arrangement of their resistance-capacity pairs, since processes containing a similar number and arrangement of *RC* pairs tend to exhibit similar behavior and controllability.

In order to classify processes in this manner, it is necessary to assume that their resistance-capacities are separated into discrete units. This way of analyzing processes is called the lumped-capacity or lumped-parameter method. In some processes resistance-capacity is distributed. These are termed distributed-capacity or distributed-parameter processes, and a different form of analysis must be adopted. A natural-gas pipe line is an example where both resistance and capacity are distributed.

A third property found in processes and control systems which contributes to time lags is that time required to carry a change from one point to another point in the system. For example, in Fig. 22-136, if the temperature of the incoming water drops, some time will elapse before the colder water can travel through the tank and reach the thermometer bulb. This time lag is not just a slowing down or retardation of a change, but it is a discrete time delay, or dead time, during which no change whatever occurs. The length of this dead time depends both on the velocity with which the change is transported and on the distance over which it is carried. Thus in Fig. 22-136, the dead time would be much larger if the thermometer bulb were located at *B* some point downstream in the output line, instead of at *A* near the tank outlet. Thus dead time is also termed distance-velocity lag or transportation lag.

PROCESS DYNAMICS

In the analysis of a control system, the most important point is to understand the dynamics of the system components. Before a rational control scheme can be applied, it must be known how the output of any element will respond to input changes in both magnitude and form of response and what the time lag will be. Mathematical methods have been developed to assist in this analysis.

The response of any element is given in terms of its transfer function *G*, which is defined as the ratio of output signal θ_o to the input signal θ_i.

$$G = \frac{\theta_o}{\theta_i} \qquad (22\text{-}12)$$

The transfer-function equation is the differential equation representing the dynamics of the system component.

The simplest possible case is where the transfer function is a constant, which represents a proportional element.

$$G = K = \frac{\theta_o}{\theta_i} \qquad (22\text{-}13)$$

This is a zero-order system, or one whose dynamics is represented by a zero-order differential equation. It represents a system with no time delays, only a multiplication of the signal. The multiplication factor K is called the gain of the system. In order to have a zero time lag the capacitance of the system must be zero, and the constant is equal to the resistance. One example might be the laminar flow of an incompressible fluid through a pipe, where the gain in fluid head is directly proportional to the flow rate, with the laminar, frictional resistance the gain. The response of such a system to a unit step change in the input variable is shown in Fig. 22-137. Such diagrams, the reaction curves of systems

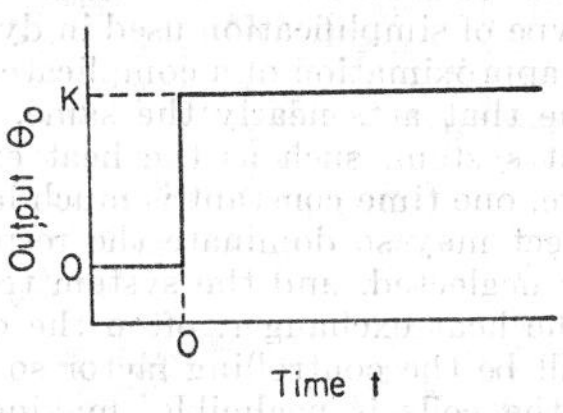

FIG. 22-137. Response of a proportional or pure resistance element to a unit step input change at time 0.

initially at a steady-state condition to a unit step increase of the input variables, are conventional methods of picturing system dynamics.

Another simple system is a pure capacitance system. This might be an ideal electrical condenser or a liquid storage tank. For this case the differential equation is

$$C\frac{d\theta_o}{dt} = \theta_i \qquad (22\text{-}14)$$

where C is the capacitance and t is time. Using the operationals notation for differential equations of

$$D = \frac{d}{dt} \qquad (22\text{-}15)$$

the transfer function is

$$G = \frac{1}{CD} \qquad (22\text{-}16)$$

Figure 22-138 illustrates the reaction curve for a step input to a pure, simple capacitance element. Consideration of the transfer function and its reaction curve shows that a pure capacitance element acts as an integrator, a function which is useful in analysis.

Most real systems involve resistance-capacitance pairs, giving rise to transfer lags as mentioned earlier.

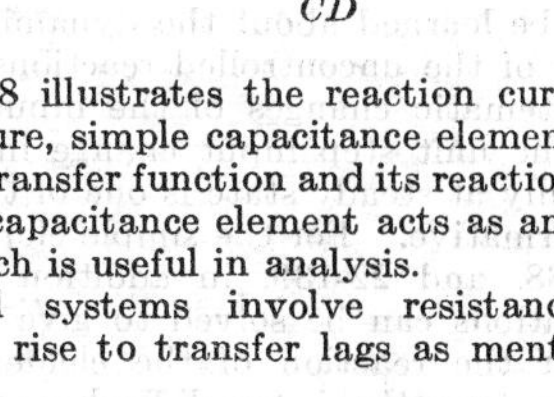

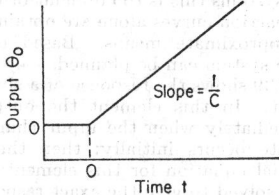

FIG. 22-138. Response of a pure capacitance element to a unit step input change at time 0.

The simplest case is a single resistance-capacitance lumped-parameter system.

The differential equation for this system is derived by equating the rate of transfer into the system to the rate of storage. The transfer rate is equal to the difference in input and output signals multiplied by the reciprocal of the resistance, or the conductance. The rate of storage is the product of the capacitance and the rate of change of output. So, the differential equation is

$$\frac{1}{R}(\theta_i - \theta_o) = C\frac{d\theta_o}{dt} \qquad (22\text{-}17)$$

This may be rearranged to give the transfer function

$$G = \frac{1}{RCD + 1} \qquad (22\text{-}18)$$

The resistance-capacitance product occurs in the analysis of any system exhibiting time lag. It has the dimensions of time and is commonly replaced by the single symbol T, called the time constant. The concept of time constants is both convenient and important. This one parameter is sufficient to describe the dynamics of a system, eliminating the necessity of determining both the resistance and the capacitance. This represents a considerable gain in analysis and determination of the characteristics of elements. Systems with the same time constants have the same response to changes; so analogy becomes an important tool in understanding dynamics.

Figure 22-139 gives an example of the response of a single time constant, or resistance-capacitance, element,

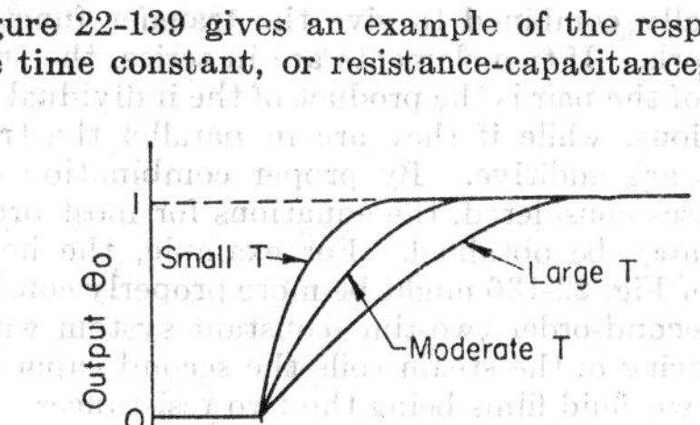

FIG. 22-139. Response of a single-time-constant element to a unit step input change at time 0, showing effect of size of time constant T on time lag.

with the time constant as a parameter. For the case of the heat exchanger of Fig. 22-136, the time constant, hence behavior of the system, would change in the same way if the capacitance, the bulk of water, or the resistance, the thermal resistance of the steam-coil walls and the fluid films changed. In calling this a single-time-constant lumped-parameter element, it is assumed the heat capacity, or capacitance, of the coils, tank, and other parts is zero, and the water is perfectly mixed so that its state is represented by a single temperature. The time constant can be determined by response of the system to a simple change, such as a step function or a steady sinusoidal oscillation. Then the response of the system to more complicated inputs is determined from the time constant.

There are two more simple transfer functions that will be presented for completeness. The first is that of a second-order oscillatory system with damping. The most common example is a mass on a spring with frictional resistance for damping. This type of action can be found in many physical situations, perhaps most often in the measuring elements of a system. It is represented by a second-order differential equation giving rise to the transfer function

$$G = \frac{1}{T^2D^2 + 2T\zeta D + 1} \tag{22-19}$$

in which ζ is the damping ratio. The other simple transfer function is that for dead time, which is, in terms of the dead time L,

$$G = e^{-LD} \tag{22-20}$$

These transfer functions can be obtained by deriving the differential equations for the element or action they represent.

The transfer functions which have been presented are for simple ideal cases, and unfortunately most real systems are not described well by them. Few elements have zero resistance or capacitance, and a true single-time-constant system is hard to realize. Also the assumptions of lumped parameters, such as uniform temperature in the heat-exchanger tank, while convenient, are generally only approximations. However, these simple transfer functions are still very useful in analyzing real systems.

The derivation of the exact differential equations for the dynamics of actual systems can be very difficult and is many times impossible, and even when they can be derived, they may be too complicated to solve even in an approximate way. In many cases a complicated process can be broken down into a group of simple components in a series and parallel network. If the transfer functions of the components are known, they can be algebraically combined to give the transfer function of the network. If two elements are in series, the transfer function of the pair is the product of the individual transfer functions, while if they are in parallel the transfer functions are additive. By proper combination of the simple cases considered, the equations for most practical systems may be obtained. For example, the heat exchanger of Fig. 22-136 might be more properly considered to be a second-order two-time-constant system with the heat capacity of the steam coils the second capacitance, and the two fluid films being the two resistances. Then the transfer function would be the product of two single-time-constant functions.

$$G = G_1G_2 = \frac{1}{(T_1D + 1)(T_2D + 1)} \tag{22-21}$$

where T_1 is the time constant for heating the walls of the coil and T_2 for heating the water.

Derivation of the differential equation is only the first step to an understanding of the dynamics of a system; to know how the system responds to changes, the equation must be solved. And solution of the equation to give the mode of response is very difficult and for some types of inputs or systems it cannot be obtained.

In order to obtain solutions to control-system problems, the systems are generally linearized. That is, the differential equation is made to be a linear ordinary differential equation with constant coefficients, which means none of the coefficients, such as time constants, can be functions of the variables. This assumption is necessary to obtain the solution of many practical problems in a reasonable form and in a reasonable length of time. Over some limited range of values of the variables this approximation is valid. This range may include the whole region of interest, or it may be a quite small area, making the results obtained of limited value. This method has been the basis of most work done in control-system theory and is a very valuable tool because it makes solutions possible that have proved to be useful. Continuing work is being done to extend the field of non-linear control theory so that it may be more widely applied in the areas where linearizing falls short.

Examples of non-linearity may be found in all parts of a system, and they give rise to two types of changes in response: both the gain of an element, that is, the multiplication of signal, and the response in time, which is either transfer lag or dead time, may be altered. The resistance to flow through a pipe depends on the velocity; so the gain is non-linear. The heat-transfer coefficient in a heat exchanger depends on the velocity of the fluid in the exchanger; so the time constant and transfer lag are functions of the energy-transfer rate, as is the dead time in a situation such as Fig. 22-136 when the thermometer bulb is located at point B so that the transportation lag depends on the velocity of the fluid. Very few systems are truely linear if examined closely; even the electrical resistor changes value with some changes, such as temperature or loads that cause heating. But over some range of operation all systems can be linearized sufficiently well to secure results of some value.

Another type of simplification used in dynamics analysis is that of approximation of a complicated system with a simpler one that acts nearly the same. If in a two-time-constant system, such as the heat exchanger considered before, one time constant is much larger than the other, its effect may so dominate the response that the other can be neglected, and the system treated as first-order. In the heat exchanger, often the capacitance of the water will be the controlling factor so that the heat capacity of the coils is negligible, making Eq. (22-18) essentially as good as representation of the dynamics as is the more complicated Eq. (22-21). Analysis shows that the response of any multiple-time-constant system is similar in form to a second-order-time-constant system offering a convenient simplification in many cases. In addition the behavior of any complex system can be approximated sufficiently well for some purposes by the behavior of a one-time-constant system with dead time.

From this it is seen that simple systems with simple transfer functions are useful both as aids in synthesizing transfer functions of some complicated systems and as approximate models for the study of the behavior of other still more complicated systems under some limited range of values of the variables. Much valuable information about system dynamics needed in system design and analysis can be obtained from these admittedly approximate models because they do offer some solution in a usable form.

RESPONSE OF SYSTEMS

Much can be learned about the dynamics of systems from a study of the uncontrolled reactions of their elements to systematic changes of the input and output variables. The unit step input change imposed on an element initially at steady state is one of the most common and informative. For the simple elements of Figs. 22-137, 22-138, and 22-139, in addition the transfer-function equations can be solved to give an analytical expression for the reaction of the element. In more complicated systems this is too difficult or tedious to do. So instead, reaction curves alone are obtained by experimental or approximate means. Based on them, the control of the system can be planned.

Figure 22-139 shows the response of a single-time-constant element. In this element the output starts to respond immediately when the input changes, and the maximum rate occurs initially; then the rate drops. The differential equation for this element [Eq. (22-17)] can be easily solved to give the exact response to a step input change.

$$\theta_o = \theta_i(1 - e^{-t/T}) \tag{22-22}$$

This solution permits a physical interpretation of the time constant. It is the time required for the output of this element to make 63.2 per cent of its final change, when it is disturbed from a steady state by a step change of input.

The controllability of a system of this type is illustrated in Fig. 22-140. If, at time t_0, the demand load on the system is suddenly increased with no compensating correction made, the output will respond as in curve *a*. Likewise if, at time t_0, the input supply alone is increased suddenly, the output will react as in curve *b*. Now if the increase in supply is considered to be a correction to compensate for the load increase, and the correct amount is supplied precisely at t_0, the output of the system remains constant. So with a single-time-constant system, ideal control eliminates any output fluctuations.

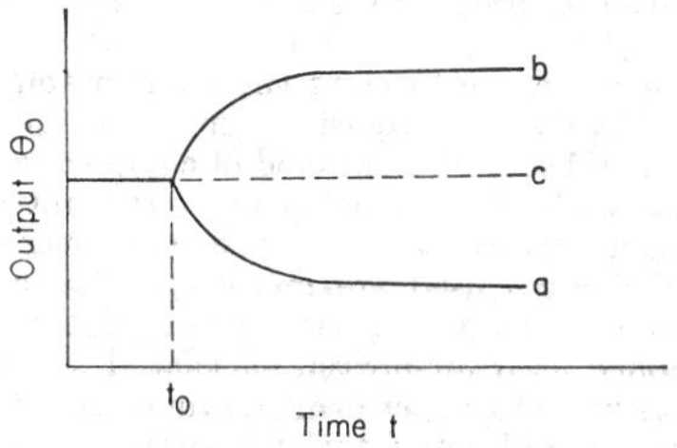

FIG. 22-140. Reaction curves of a single-time-constant element to step changes of the demand alone (curve *a*); of the supply alone (curve *b*); and of simultaneous demand change and exact supply correction (curve *c*).

Turning from the single-time-constant element, which as pointed out, is not a good model of reality, a different type of behavior is seen. Figure 22-141 shows the reaction of a two-time-constant element, in which the time constants are taken to be equal, for simplicity, to a step input change. The size of the time constants is taken as a parameter. For this element the response also begins immediately, but the rate increases from zero to a maximum and then falls off, making an S-shaped reaction curve. Figure 22-142 illustrates the reaction of this type of system when the demand is suddenly increased and the supply exactly corrected, as Fig. 22-140 did for a single-time-constant system. When the demand only is increased, the output responds as a first-order-time-constant element, as shown by curve *a*. But when the supply alone is increased by an amount that will exactly compensate for the increased load, the response is the second-order S-shaped curve *b*. So when the two changes occur simultaneously as in curve *c*, the output is not held constant. In contrast to a first-order system, for a system including a second-order-time-constant element there is a change in output that has a considerable time duration after a sudden load increase, even though the supply is instantaneously, exactly corrected. This is a major difference in controllability of real, multiple-time-constant systems compared with ideal, first-order systems.

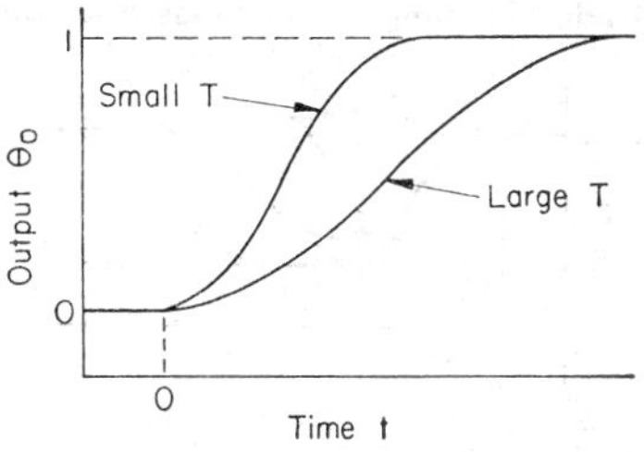

FIG. 22-141. Response of a two-time-constant element to a unit step input change at time 0, showing effect of size of time constant *T* on time lag.

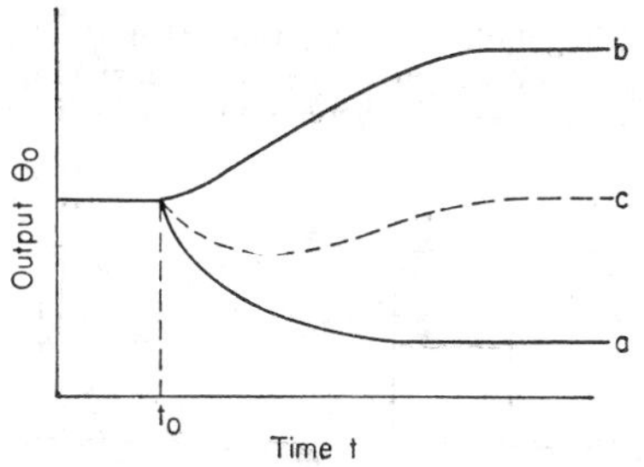

FIG. 22-142. Reaction curves of a two-time-constant element to step changes of the demand alone (curve *a*); of the supply alone (curve *b*); and of simultaneous demand change and exact supply correction (curve *c*).

The reaction curves of elements with several equal time constants when subject to unit step input changes are shown in Fig. 22-143. The curves have the same S shape as the two-time-constant element shown in Fig. 22-141, but the time lags become longer as the order of the element increases.

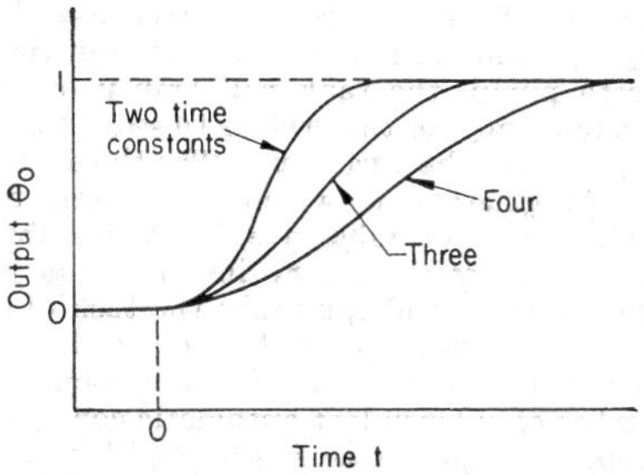

FIG. 22-143. Response of multiple-time-constant elements to a unit step input change at time 0, showing effect of increasing number of time constants.

The effect of dead time on a multiple-time-constant element is shown in Fig. 22-144. The response to the step change at time t_0 is delayed by the dead time L but is not otherwise affected. Dead time can occur in any part of a system, and here it is assumed it delays the time at which the element becomes aware of the change in input signal.

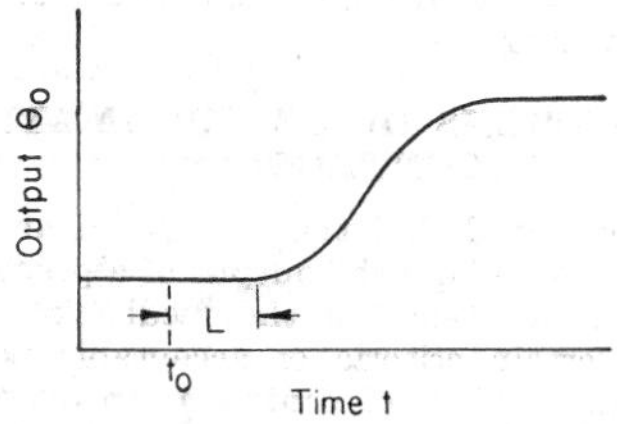

FIG. 22-144. Effect of dead time *L* on the response of a multiple-time-constant element subject to a step input change at time t_0.

FACTORS AFFECTING CONTROLLABILITY

Some processes have an inherent tendency to stay in balance. They have internal properties that limit the range of the variables when the operation of the process is upset by any type of change. Such a property is termed self-regulation, and systems that display it are said to have positive self-regulation. In the liquid-level tank *A* of Fig. 22-145, there is positive self-regulation

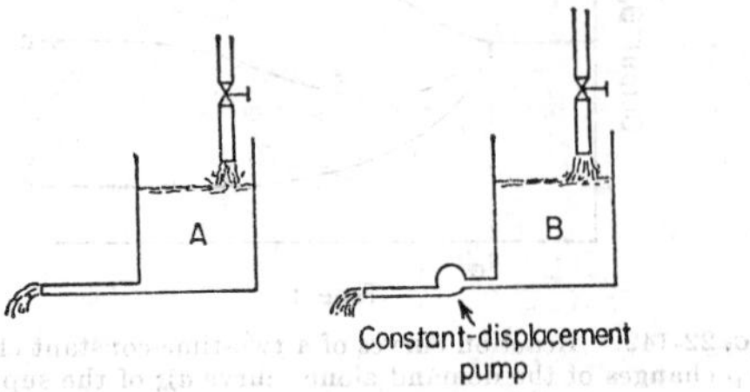

FIG. 22-145. Liquid tank systems showing (*A*) positive self-regulation and (*B*) neutral self-regulation.

with regard to the fluid head. As the rate of influx changes the head will change, but it tends to come to a new steady-state position since the outflow rate is determined by the head. There are some limits to the changes in variables that positive self-regulation can balance; in this case the size of the tank is the source of limitation.

In contrast to this is tank *B*, which has neutral or no self-regulation. There is only one influx rate which produces a steady head. For any other rate but that of the constant-rate pump, the tank will empty or overflow. There is no tendency for the process to stay in balance or limit the changes of the variables. The third possibility, negative self-regulation, in which the process reacts in the direction of greater unbalance, is also possible. The degree of self-regulation is very important in applying controls to a process and can make the task of securing good control difficult or impossible by leading to very poor time response and stability in the system.

The number of independent automatic controllers that may be applied to any process is limited by the process itself. The state of a process is fixed once all its degrees of freedom are specified, or controlled. Extra controllers, or control redundancy, will produce a system that will not work properly, thus defeating itself. The number of degrees of freedom in a process is equal to the number of variables minus the number of independent relationships or equations among the variables. This is the maximum number of controllers that may be applied, and in many real cases the number will be less. The number actually applied is determined by the characteristics and behavior of the particular process.

FUNCTIONS OF AN AUTOMATIC CONTROLLER

It has been stated that the purpose of an automatic control system is to hold the output of a process to some desired value, by means of the feedback principle of operation. Certain criteria of acceptable performance exist, and the problem of control is to overcome time delays and distortions to keep the operation within the prescribed limits. In order to accomplish this, the controller must perform four primary functions: (1) measurement of some characteristic of the process output, (2) comparison of this to the desired value or set point, (3) analysis of the error signal and computation of the appropriate correction, and finally, (4) correction of the manipulated, process input variable.

The measuring means of the controller must first embody a sensing or primary element. The types of measurements that are made and the various devices used to make each of them cannot be enumerated easily. Many standard sensing devices and methods exist, and new techniques are constantly being adopted.

The signal from the sensing element must be carried to the controller by the transmitting means. Air pressure is probably the most common transmitting medium, but others, especially electrical signals and mechanical linkages, have been used.

Finally, there must be a receiving element within the controller. It accepts the transmitted signal from the sensing element and converts it into chart or scale readings and the appropriate signal for the comparison element.

The element for performing the comparison function must first have some provision for accepting the set-point value, and second, a method of comparing the feedback signal with the set point and transmitting their difference, the error signal, to the computer element. The actual devices used are many and depend on the nature of the mechanical or electrical signals used. For the commonly used air-pressure-actuated systems, baffles and jets or bellows perform the function.

The analysis and computation function is the key to successful attainment of quality control. Based on the information it receives, the computer determines the amount of adjustment and how it is applied, following its built-in methods of analysis. Time lags of both the resistance-capacitance and dead-time types can arise in all parts of the controller, as well as the process; so there are delays both between the time a process is subject to a change and the controller becomes aware of the presence and extent of the change, and between the time a controller initiates a change and the process responds to it. The type of corrective actions, or mode of control, applied may be varied, and by varying the type, the control quality changes. In manual control an operator learns by experience the optimum manner of making process corrections to hold output to the desired value. In an automatic controller, this function is built into the computer.

Figure 22-146 illustrates how the quality of control can be upgraded by simple alterations of the method of

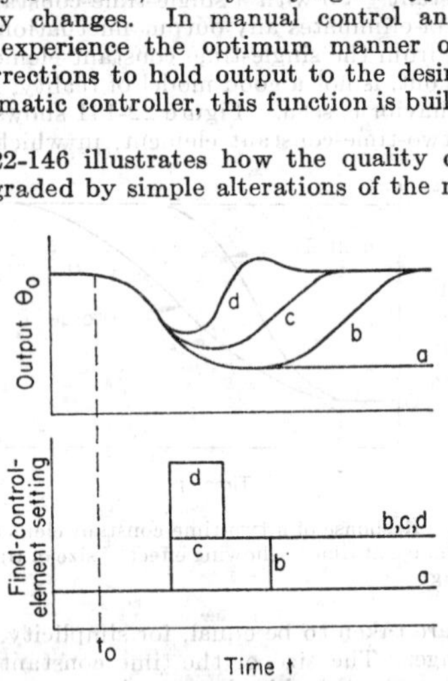

FIG. 22-146. Effect on reaction to controller of decreasing time delay in applying correction and applying excess correction to a multiple-time-constant process after a step load increase: (*a*) no correction; (*b*) exact correction—long delay; (*c*) exact correction—short delay; and (*d*) excess correction—same delay as (*c*).

controller action. The modes shown are idealized but serve to illustrate the principle. At time t_0 the output load of the process is subject to a step increase. If no correction is made, the process output will come to a new steady state because of positive self-regulation, as shown in curve *a*. If the controller delays making a correction until the new value is attained, the result would be as in curve *b*, assuming an exact correction is made. This type of operation, or any type with long time lags, is unsatisfactory because of both large and long-duration output deviations. If the controller can be made to react to the initial part of the output change and compute the exact correction from it, the reaction is as shown in curve *c*. There are some lags that will always prevent the change from being applied immediately. This mode results in quicker recovery and smaller deviation. But the recovery can be made still faster, and the maximum deviation reduced further, by application of excess correction, as in curve *d*. Some cycling will occur, but if the excess is not too large, it is not a problem.

As is illustrated by the foregoing example, excess correction is a desirable quality for controller reaction to display, as long as the stability limits of the process are not exceeded. It will act to reduce the time lag, or in effect, partially catch up for the time lost due to lags. As such, excess control provides a partial answer to the problem of automatic process control, overcoming the time delays in a system. It is not applicable in processes with very small capacities, such as most flow-rate control systems.

By proper selection and adjustment of the mode of control which the computer function embodies, good response can be secured for nearly any control system. Several conventional modes of control, which will give good performance for nearly any process, have been developed, and are used for all standard controllers.

The final control element adjusts the value of the manipulated variable. Its nature depends on what the manipulated variable is, and it is activated by the computer signal which may be a pressure, an electrical signal, or some mechanical impulse. Normally the final control element is positioned by a motor operator for speed and accuracy of adjustment rather than being positioned by the error signal directly. Error signals often are weak, because the error-detecting or comparison means cannot take much power from the measuring means without decreasing its sensitivity or accuracy. So most controllers contain one or two stages of amplification to increase the power of the error signal.

Some control systems obtain all needed operating power from the controlled medium through the primary sensing element and the measuring means. Such systems are termed self-operated controllers. Systems that use an auxiliary source of power in addition are termed relay-operated systems. The auxiliary power may be introduced at any convenient point, such as the measuring means or the error detector, or by the amplifiers.

In essaying the analysis of an automatic control system, the time lags of the control elements may be found to be significant, especially when high-speed processes and feedback loops are considered. Both time-constant and dead-time lags occur in the controller and have the same bad effects on the quality and stability of control as lags in the process itself.

Much of the delay occurs in the measuring means and is of the resistance-capacitance pair variety. There must be a flow of some quantity from the controlled output to the sensing element to have it respond, and the flow occurs through a resistance to the capacitance of the element. In the case of a thermometer, there is resistance, due to finite thermal conductivities, to the energy flux needed to raise the temperature of the mercury and glass; or in an air-pressure gage, there is resistance to flow in the lines that feed air to the bourdon tube. If care is not exercised in design and installation of the measuring element, the time constant may easily become significant in comparison with that of the process. Shields and other protective devices can cause very large increases in resistance and must be used with this consideration in mind.

There can be significant delays in transmission of signals, especially in the case of long pneumatic lines, where both the resistance and capacitance can become large. The use of electrical signals and components is desirable from the standpoint of lags, but they have other drawbacks which limit their use.

The error detector, computer, amplifiers, and similar parts of the controller generally have small enough time constants so as to make negligible resistance-capacitance lag. However there can be dead time in them caused by friction in parts, poor fits, and electrical contact gaps.

Frictional resistance and physical inertia in final control elements can cause time lags, as can mechanical flaws such as gear backlash or worn parts. Proper maintenance is needed in all parts of a control system, but particularly here. Special equipment, such as valve positioners in fluid-flow systems, may be needed to ensure proper action.

MODES OF CONTROL

The essential part of any automatic control system is the mode of control, or type of action the computer function takes in response to error signals, or departures of the controlled variable from the set point. For, as was shown, by application of some excess correction appropriately applied, the magnitude and duration of output deviations can be minimized. But improper application of correction, either in the form of the correction or the time of its application, can lead to greater and longer departures from set point or continually increasing deviations or oscillations of the controlled variable until it reaches its possible limits, or some part of the system fails. Thus the forms of response of a controlled system to disturbances can be divided into two classes, stable and unstable. In a stable system, the effects of disturbances, or the transients in a system, die out with time, and in an unstable system the disturbances increase until limits are reached or failure results. There are, of course, degrees of stability; that is, a system may be rapidly or slowly returned to its set point. By proper selection of the mode of control followed by proper adjustment of it, the stability of a system can be ensured and the response can be made rapid.

In manual control the operator learns to manage a process by experience, thus developing his individual modes of control. Automatic controllers work by predetermined relations; which may be expressed mathematically, so that a rational system of control can be developed for any process by established design techniques. Several basic modes of control have been developed and accepted as the standard types of controller action.

Two-position Control. The simplest, and perhaps most common, mode of control is two position, or on-off. In it the computer function of the controller changes the value of the controller output, or the manipulated variable, from one extreme to the other as the measured value of the controlled variable goes above and below the set point. Figure 22-147 shows the operation of an ideal controller of this type on a process. As the controlled variable drops below the set point the manipulated variable is turned on to its maximum value and it is turned completely off as the controlled variable rises above the set point. The indicated oscillations result for a real system with several resistance-capacitance pairs. As the values of the time constants grow smaller, that is, as the system considered becomes a more rapidly responding one, the amplitude of the oscillations will decrease but the frequency of controller action will increase. Actual on-off controllers operate in a somewhat modified fashion. There is a small interval, known as a differential gap, between the points where the manipulated variable changes from on to off or off to on. This is illustrated in Fig. 22-148 for the same type of system. The manipulated variable does not go on until the lower limit of the

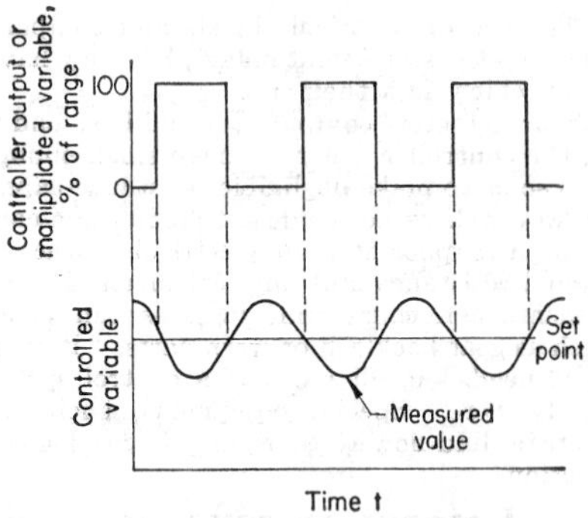

FIG. 22-147. Operation of a two-position controller without differential gap.

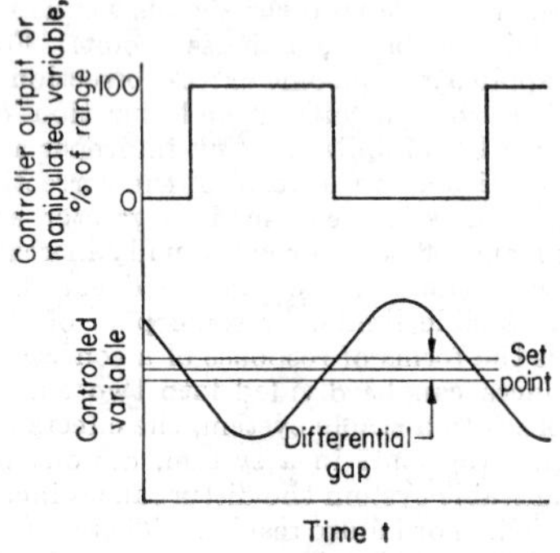

FIG. 22-148. Operation of a two-position controller with differential gap.

differential gap is reached and is not turned off until the upper limit is exceeded. The amplitude of the oscillations of the controlled variable is increased, but this loss of control sensitivity is more than compensated for by decreased wear of the control mechanisms due to the lower frequency of operation.

One other attribute of two-position control can be seen by considering how the operation is affected by load changes, as illustrated in Fig. 22-149. When the process

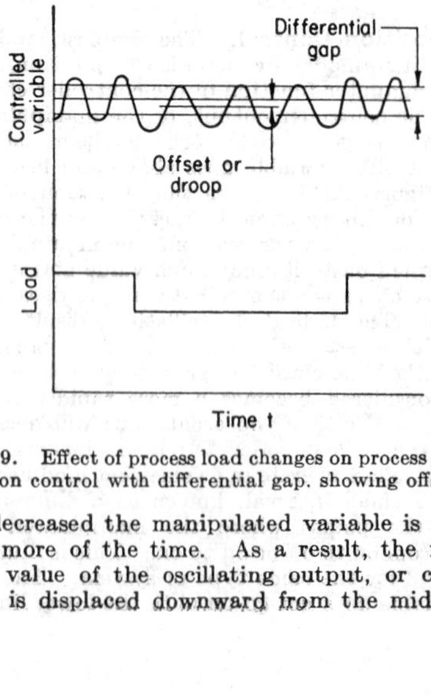

FIG. 22-149. Effect of process load changes on process control by two-position control with differential gap, showing offset.

load is decreased the manipulated variable is in its off position more of the time. As a result, the mean, or average, value of the oscillating output, or controlled variable, is displaced downward from the mid-point of the differential gap, or control point. Such shifts are called offset or "droop."

Two-position control can be seen to be a drastic type of action that gives imperfect control as evidenced by both cycling and offset. The response of the controller is not a function of the magnitude of the error signal. To eliminate some of the worst effects of this extreme on-or-off action, some modification can be made.

In multiposition control, the position of the final control element, and hence the value of the manipulated variable, is moved between three or more positions at predetermined values of the controlled variable. While this has somewhat better action than two-position control, because of less drastic corrections, exact corrections are not made, and cycling and offset still result.

Other applications control only part of the input to a process, with the rest by-passing the final control elements. Thus smoother operation results since the manipulated variable changes over a smaller range, never going to a completely off position. This improvement is also limited in benefit since, again, exact corrections are not made.

Average-position mode embodies a predetermined relationship between the value of the controlled variable and the time-average position of a two-position controller. The controlled variable is held within a specified range by alternating the manipulated variable between its two extremes, with the relative time in each determined by the relative position of the controlled variable between the limits of the selected range. If the controlled variable moves out of the range, the manipulated variable remains at one limit. Thus some attempt is made to make the controlled output a function of the magnitude of the error signal. The result is somewhat better control at the expense of increased cycling of the final control elements.

Two-position control, and its modifications, are often used because they are cheap, simple, and easily applied. They are common both in home applications, such as furnaces, hot-water heaters, and appliances, and in industry, in such places as air conditioning and refrigeration. But in many cases the relatively slow response, the cyclic nature of the control, or the offset are undesirable, and control of sufficient quality is not provided. In still other cases, especially when there are high process response rates and significant lags in other parts of the system, two-position control cannot hold the process output within limits.

Functional Modes of Control. Most of the control of processes and other complicated phenomena is done by use of one or several of three more refined modes of control. These are distinguished from various types of two-position control in two ways: first; their output is a function of the error signal, and second, their output changes in a smooth, continuous manner over the range of the manipulated variable. These modes are:

1. Proportional or throttling or modulating
2. Integral or proportional-speed floating or reset
3. Derivative or rate or lead component

The first name for each mode describes the functional relationship between the output and error signal, and the other names are descriptive titles commonly used which are derived from the nature of the control action. Their actions can likewise be specified in two ways, mathematically and in terms of the response to various forms of inputs. Three types of inputs are generally considered a step function: (1) where the input is suddenly changed from one steady value to another; (2) a ramp function, where the input is increased at a constant rate; and (3) a steady sinusoidal function. In the first two types the transient behavior of the output is of interest, that is, how fast and in what manner does the output reach its steady value. For a sinusoidal input, the steady-state response, which is usually termed the frequency response, is studied. In all cases the delay of the signal and its gain or amplification characterize the system behavior. For a sinusoidal input these take special forms. The output for a linear system is also a sine with the same frequency and is related to the input by an amplitude ratio, that is, the ratio of the amplitude of the output sine to the input sine, and the phase shift, or the displacement in time of the output sine from the input sine usually measured in units of degrees or radians instead of time.

Proportional Mode. In the proportional mode of control, the controller output is proportional to the input or error signal. This may be expressed mathematically as

$$M = \frac{1}{b}E + M_0 \qquad (22\text{-}23)$$

where M is the controller output, E the error signal, b the proportional band or throttling range, and M_0 the zero error signal of the controller. The proportional band is the change in value of the controlled variable needed to produce a 100 per cent change in the output signal. It is usually measured in per cent of the range of the particular instrument that the input must change to give a 100 per cent output change. In practical controllers the proportional band may cover less than 1 per cent to 400 per cent or more. Figure 22-150 illustrates

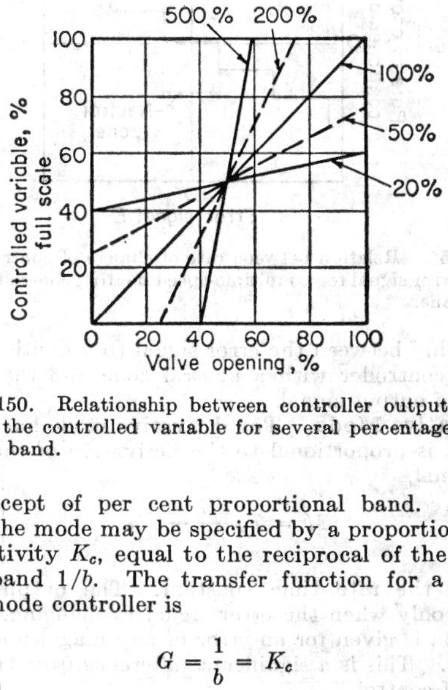

FIG. 22-150. Relationship between controller output and the value of the controlled variable for several percentages of proportional band.

the concept of per cent proportional band. Alternatively, the mode may be specified by a proportional gain or sensitivity K_c, equal to the reciprocal of the proportional band $1/b$. The transfer function for a proportional-mode controller is

$$G = \frac{1}{b} = K_c \qquad (22\text{-}24)$$

Figure 22-151 shows the response of a proportional-mode controller to a step function and a sinusoidal input. The controller responds immediately to a step change and gives a multiplication of signal of $1/b$ or K_c. The phase shift is zero, that is, the output sine follows the input sine exactly with no lag, and the amplitude ratio is $1/b$ or K_c.

Two points of interest in applying proportional control can be seen in Fig. 22-151. First, the output signal changes only when the input signal changes, and second, the output signal can change from its zero value M_0 only when there is an error signal, or there is no corrective action unless there is a deviation of the controlled variable from the set point. Because of this second attribute, there is a steady-state error, offset, or droop in the controlled output of a process regulated by a proportional-mode controller if the load on the process changes. The controller supplies an exact correction, or has no offset, for only one process load. Many controllers have provisions for manually resetting the set point to bring the output back to the desired level, but if there are frequent changes it is not practical to keep resetting the controller.

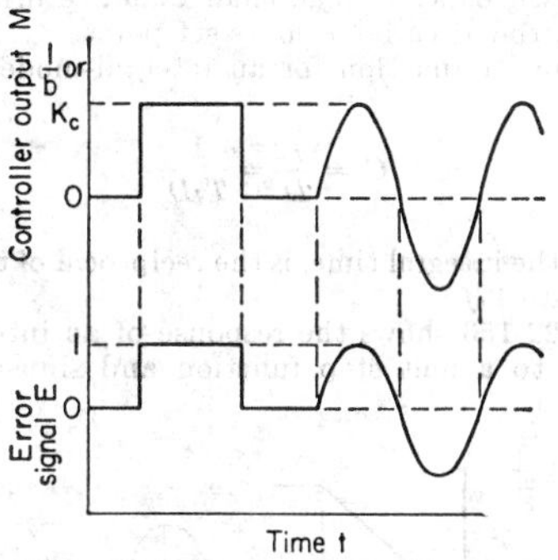

FIG. 22-151. Response of proportional-mode controller to step-function and sinusoidal-error inputs.

In summary, the proportional mode has good response characteristics and can stabilize processes that have significant inherent lags, and so it is widely used. But it does give rise to offset in the process output; so load changes should be small and infrequent. The offset can be reduced by using a narrow proportional band, or high gain, bu this gives rise to an undesirable, underdamped cycling output. Figure 22-152 illustrates application of proportional control to a process when it is disturbed by a sudden load change.

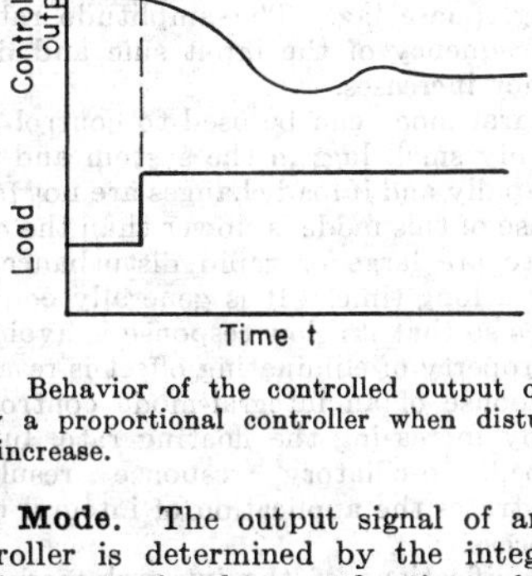

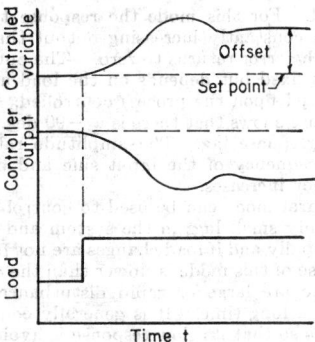

FIG. 22-152. Behavior of the controlled output of a process regulated by a proportional controller when disturbed by a sudden load increase.

Integral Mode. The output signal of an integral-mode controller is determined by the integral of its input, or the error signal, over the time of operation. Mathematically the output is given by

$$M = f\int E\,dt + M_0 \qquad (22\text{-}25)$$

where f is the floating or reset rate and has the units of reciprocal time. The floating rate is commonly expressed as repeats per time. The rate at which the controller adjusts the output is given by

$$\frac{dM}{dt} = fE \qquad (22\text{-}26)$$

so this mode also makes corrections that are dependent on the magnitude of the error. In addition, and most important, from Eq. (22-25) it can be seen that the controller continues to make adjustments or corrections until the error signal is brought to zero. The integral mode is unique in this respect; it can make an exact correction for any disturbance or load change and return the value of the controlled variable to its set point.

The transfer function for an integral-mode controller is

$$G = \frac{f}{D} = \frac{1}{T_i D} \qquad (22\text{-}27)$$

where T_i, the integral time, is the reciprocal of the floating or reset rate $1/f$.

Figure 22-153 shows the response of an integral-mode controller to a unit step function and sinusoidal-input

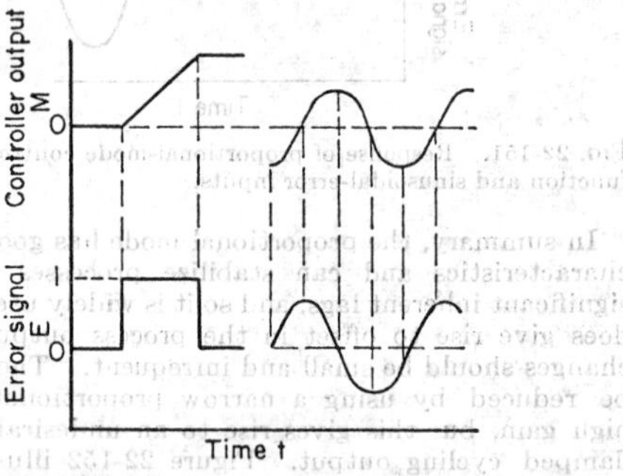

Fig. 22-153. Response of integral-mode controller to step-function and sinusoidal-error inputs.

error signal. For this mode the response to a sudden change is a constantly increasing output that levels off only after the error returns to zero. The output at zero error is not fixed but depends on the load and disturbances imposed upon the process controlled. The sinusoidal response shows that there is a −90 deg. phase shift or a 90-deg. phase lag. The amplitude ratio depends upon the frequency of the input sine and decreases as the frequency increases.

The integral mode can be used to control processes if there are only small lags in the system and the process responds rapidly and if load changes are not fast or large. The response of this mode is slower than the other types, and if there are large or rapid disturbances the error persists for a long time. It is generally combined with other modes so that its slow response is avoided but the desirable property of eliminating offset is retained. The rate of response of an integral-mode controller can be increased by increasing the floating rate, but again an underdamped, oscillatory response results. Figure 22-154 illustrates the application of integral control to a typical process.

Some modifications of the integral mode which are used include single- or multiple-speed floating control. In these the rate of change of the controller output is fixed at one or several values instead of being proportional to the error. In single-speed floating control, when the controlled variable is away from the set point, the controller output changes at a fixed rate regardless of the magnitude of the error. In multiple-speed floating

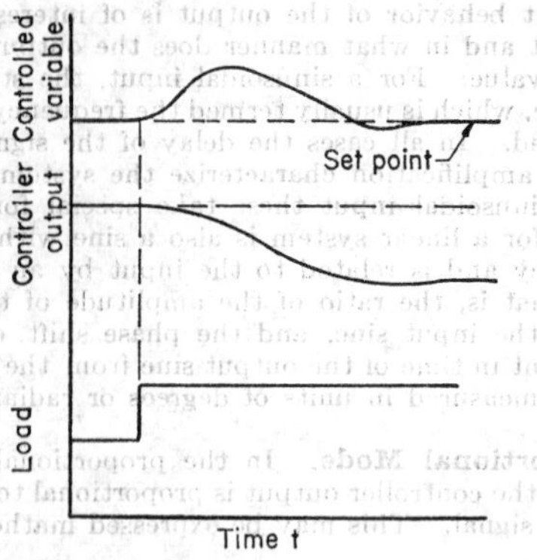

Fig. 22-154. Behavior of the controlled output of a process regulated by an integral controller when disturbed by a sudden load increase.

control there are several fixed floating speeds, each corresponding to a range of values of the error signal. In general, controllers of these types have a neutral zone, a range of error signal around the set point, in which they do not operate. This corresponds to the differential gap of a two-position controller. Figure 22-155 shows the

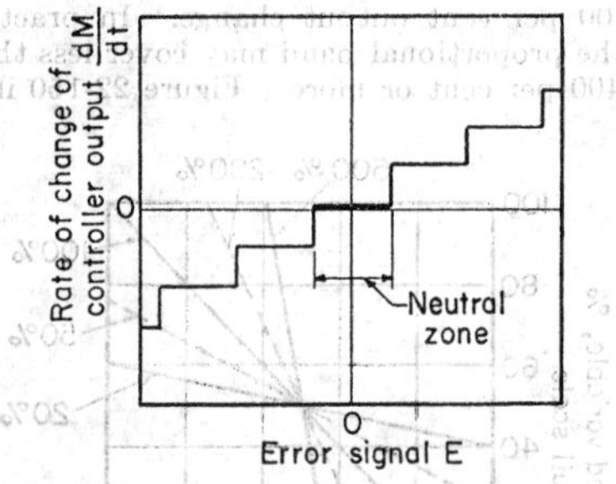

Fig. 22-155. Relation between rate of change of controller output and error signal for a multiple-speed floating controller with a neutral zone.

relationship between the error signal to a multiple-speed floating controller with a neutral zone and the rate of change of output signal.

Derivative Mode. The derivative mode has an output that is proportional to the derivative of the input-error signal,

$$M = T_d \frac{dE}{dt} + M_0 \qquad (22\text{-}28)$$

with T_d the rate time constant. The output signal changes only when the error signal is changing, and no correction is given for an error of any magnitude if it is constant. This is a significant difference from the other modes of control.

The transfer function for the drivative mode of control is

$$G = T_d D \qquad (22\text{-}29)$$

Figure 22-156 illustrates the relationship between the controller input-error signal and the output of a derivative-mode controller for a ramp function and sinusoidal error signal. The response to a step function input is not defined, since the derivative of the error signal is infinite. The attribute of making corrections only during periods of change of error and making no correction for steady errors is seen. The frequency response has the

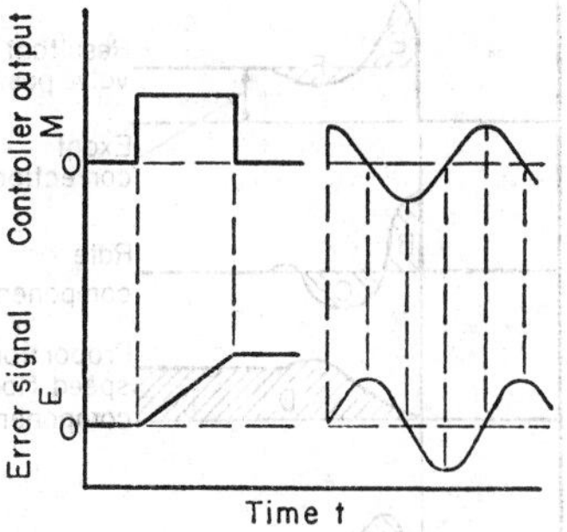

FIG. 22-156. Response of derivative-mode controller to ramp-function and sinusoidal-error inputs.

properties of a +90 deg. phase shift, or a 90-deg. phase lead, and an amplitude ratio that is again a function of frequency but increasing with increasing frequency.

Because of its characteristic of giving a corrective signal only when the error signal is changing, the derivative mode is not satisfactory as a control function by itself. It is used only in combination with other modes. Used in this way it has a very strong stabilizing effect on processes because of its fast response to all types of changes. Its output is always in a direction to oppose changes, both toward and away from the set point. It is especially effective where there are lags in any part of the system, and can be used to counteract some of the effects of dead time. The modification of inverse derivative mode, in which the output is proportional to the negative derivative of error, has some useful applications.

Combination Modes. Most of the process-control work, especially where good quality control is desired under conditions of significant load changes or large lags, is done by use of combinations of the three basic modes. As has been indicated, advantage can thus be taken of the best features of each. Three combinations are normally encountered: (1) proportional plus integral, (2) proportional plus derivative, and (3) proportional plus integral plus derivative.

Proportional plus Integral. The addition of integral mode to proportional mode constitutes one of the most widely used control systems. The proportional mode has good response to most changes and can be used where there are moderate time lags. The integral mode compensates for large load changes, eliminating offset. So, except for cases where there are very rapid disturbances to the processes or there are very large lags, this type of controller gives very good performance. This mode is sometimes called automatic reset since it automatically resets the set point of the proportional mode.

Figure 22-157 illustrates the reaction of a proportional plus integral, or proportional plus reset, mode controller to a unit step function load change. The total response can be seen to be the sum of the individual responses of the two modes. In this case the reset rate is taken to be a function of the proportional gain, which means the two modes operate in series. In some instances the two are operated in parallel so that the reset rate is independent of the proportional gain. For the type of system illustrated, the integral time, or reciprocal reset rate, is seen to be the time needed for the integral mode to repeat the correction made by the proportional mode.

Figure 22-158 presents the behavior of a system under proportional plus integral control. The response of each mode and the total controller correction following a step load change are illustrated and the behavior of the controlled process output indicated. Unless the load changes are fast or the lags large this method of control will give satisfactory performance. The integral mode

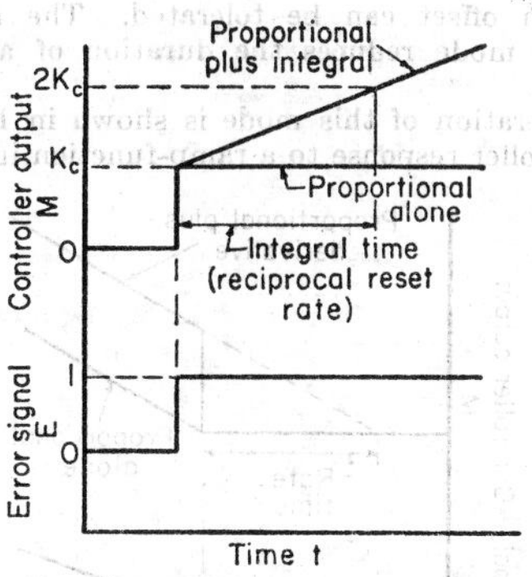

FIG. 22-157. Output response of a proportional-plus-integral-mode controller to a unit-step-function input, where the proportional gain is K_c (proportional band $b = 1/K_c$).

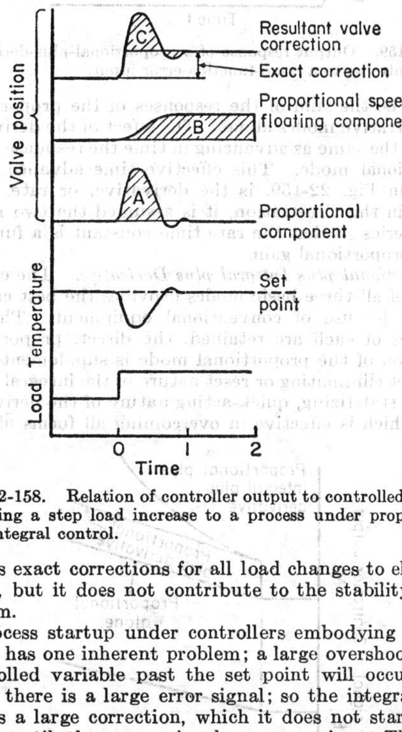

FIG. 22-158. Relation of controller output to controlled variable following a step load increase to a process under proportional-plus-integral control.

makes exact corrections for all load changes to eliminate offset, but it does not contribute to the stability of the system.

Process startup under controllers embodying integral mode has one inherent problem; a large overshoot of the controlled variable past the set point will occur. Initially there is a large error signal; so the integral mode makes a large correction, which it does not start to remove until the error signal reverses sign. This is a manifestation of the lag of the integral-mode response. Several manufacturers have developed means of minimizing this difficulty, which can also occur if there are large error signals. The addition of derivative, or rate, mode is beneficial in this respect, since its output leads the error signal, hence cancels out the lag effect of the integral mode.

Proportional plus Derivative. This combination mode does not have the utility of the other types and so is not widely used. The addition of derivative mode, with its characteristics of rapid response and an output that leads its input, makes it possible to control processes that have rapid load changes and disturbances and large time lags. The derivative mode's tendency to oppose all changes helps to increase the stability of a system when it is added to proportional-mode control, but the often undesirable offset remains. So this combination can be used only when offset can be tolerated. The addition of derivative mode reduces the duration of all types of deviations.

The operation of this mode is shown in Fig. 22-159. The controller response to a ramp-function input can be

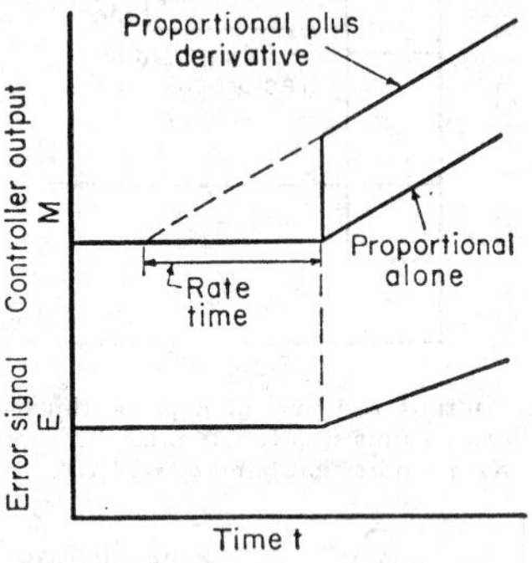

FIG. 22-159. Output response of a proportional-plus-derivative mode controller to a ramp-function-error input.

seen to be the sum of the responses of the proportional and derivative modes alone. The effect of the derivative mode is the same as advancing in time the response of the proportional mode. This effective time advance, illustrated in Fig. 22-159, is the derivative, or rate, time. Again, in this illustration, it is assumed the two modes are in series so that the rate time constant is a function of the proportional gain.

Proportional plus Integral plus Derivative. The combination of all three basic modes provides the best control possible by use of conventional equipment. The advantages of each are retained; the direct, proportional correction of the proportional mode is supplemented by the offset eliminating or reset nature of the integral mode and the stabilizing, quick-acting nature of the derivative mode which is effective in overcoming all forms of lags.

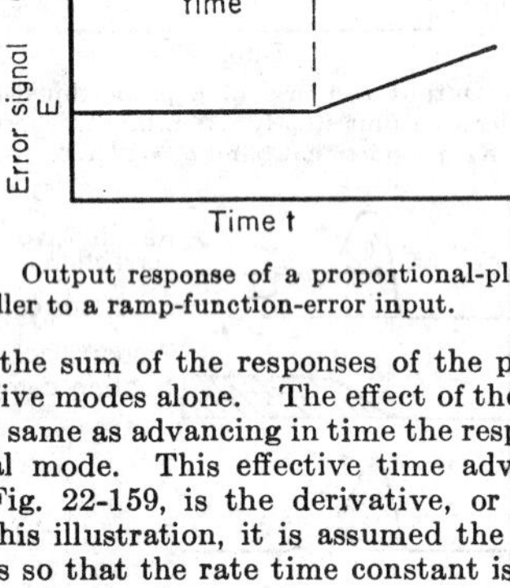

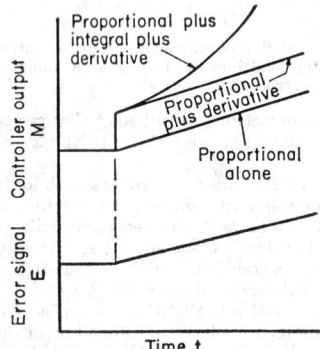

FIG. 22-160. Output response of a proportional-plus-integral-plus-derivative mode controller to a ramp-function-error input.

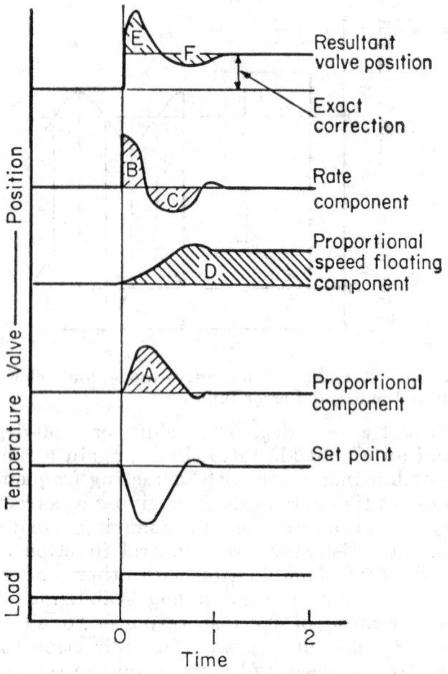

FIG. 22-161. Relation of controller output to controlled variable following a step load increase to a process under proportional-plus-integral-plus-derivative control.

The response of the output of a proportional plus integral plus derivative controller to a ramp-function input error is shown in Fig. 22-160. Figure 22-161 illustrates the behavior of the controller output, the contribution of each mode, and the resulting controlled variable deviation of a process controlled by a proportional plus integral plus derivative controller. These figures show how each mode makes its characteristic contribution to the control of a process.

SELECTION OF MODE OF CONTROL

Probably the most troublesome decision in design and instrumentation of an automatic-process-control system is that of selecting an adequate yet economical mode of control. The solution is usually a compromise between the quality of control obtained and the cost of the control system. The control system must be sufficient to meet all the quality criteria of the system but should not include refinements beyond those required. Unneeded additions make the cost excessive, and the added problems of adjustment and maintenance may become large. But, if there is any doubt, completely adequate instrumentation and controls should be chosen, because the economic loss due to overinstrumentation is slight compared with quality and quantity loss resulting from penny pinching on the control equipment.

Table 22-20 gives the forms of control suited to processes of various characteristics. This table is a general

Table 22-20. Process Characteristics vs. Mode of Control

No. of process capacities	Process reaction rate	Process time lags		Load changes		Suitable mode of control
		Resistance capacitance	Dead time	Size	Speed	
Single	Slow	Moderate to large	Small	Any	Any	Two-position or modifications
Single (self-regulating)	Fast	Small	Small	Any	Slow to moderate	Integral or modifications
Multiple	Slow to moderate	Moderate	Small	Small	Moderate	Proportional
Multiple	Moderate	Moderate	Small	Large	Slow to moderate	Proportional plus integral
Multiple	Any	Any	Moderate	Small	Any	Proportional plus derivative
Multiple	Any	Any	Moderate	Large	Any	Proportional plus integral plus derivative
Any	Faster than that of control system	Small or nearly zero	Small to moderate	Any	Any	Wide-band proportional plus fast integral

guide only and must not be construed as more than an approximate aid in selecting control modes. In this there is no substitute for actual experience on identical or related processes, or a rigorous frequency-response analysis and its interpretation by a competent control engineer. It should be recalled here that single-capacity processes are those whose dynamics are dominated by one of their resistance-capacity pairs, while multiple-capacity processes have two or more resistance-capacitance pairs of significant size.

Processes with very small capacity, notably flow processes, are successfully controlled by integral mode alone, or by wide-band proportional control combined with very fast integral action.

ABRIDGED GLOSSARY OF AUTOMATIC-CONTROL TERMINOLOGY

Actuating Signal. The difference at any time between the reference input and a signal related to the controlled variable, *e.g.*, the reference input minus the primary feedback.

Aperiodic. Not showing oscillation.

Automatic Controller. Any device which measures the value of a variable quantity or condition and operates to correct or to limit deviation of this measured value from a selected reference.

Automatic Control System. Any operable combination of one or more automatic controllers connected in closed loops with one or more processes.

Average-position Action. Action in which there is a predetermined relation between value of the controlled variable and the time-average position of a final control element which is moved periodically from one of two fixed positions to the other.

Capacitance. The change in quantity contained per unit change in a reference variable. Capacitance is measured in units of quantity, divided by the reference variable.

Capacity. A measure of the maximum quantity of energy or material which can be stored within the confines of a stated piece of equipment. Capacity is measured in units of quantity.

Closed-loop or Feedback Control System. A control system in which the controlled quantity is measured and compared with a standard representing the desired performance. Any deviation from the standard is fed back into the control system in such a sense that it will reduce the deviation of the controlled quantity from the standard.

Control Accuracy. The degree of correspondence between the ultimately controlled variable and the desired value.

Control Agent. That process energy or material of which the manipulated variable is a condition or characteristic.

Control Point. The value of controlled variable which, under any fixed set of conditions, the automatic controller operates to maintain.

Control System. An assemblage of control apparatus coordinated to execute a planned set of control functions.

Controlled Medium. That process material in which a variable is controlled.

Controlled Variable. That quantity or condition of the controlled system which is directly measured and controlled.

Controlling Means. Those elements of an automatic controller which are involved in producing a corrective action.

Corrective Action. The variation of the manipulated variable produced by the controlling means.

Cycling. A periodic change of the controlled variable.

Dead Band. The range of values through which the measured variable can be varied without initiating effective response.

Dead Time. Any definite delay between two related actions. This is measured in units of time; *e.g.*, in counters, the time interval, after a count, during which a radiation detector and/or its circuit are insensitive to ionizing events.

Dead Zone. The largest range of values of the measured variable to which the instrument will not effectively respond.

Deviation. The difference between the instantaneous value of the controlled variable and the value of the controlled variable corresponding to the set point.

Differential Gap. Applying to two-position controller action the smallest range of values through which the controlled variable must pass in order to move the final control element from one to the other of its final positions.

Feedback Controller. A mechanism which measures the value of the controlled variable, accepts the value of the command, and as a result of a comparison, manipulates the controlled system in order to maintain an established relationship between the controlled variable and the command.

Final Control Element. That portion of the controlling means which directly changes the value of the manipulated variable.

Floating Action. That in which there is a predetermined relation between the deviation and the rate of motion of a final control element.

Floating Rate. In proportional-speed floating controller action, the rate of motion of the final control element corresponding to a specified deviation.

Floating Speed. In a single- or multispeed controller action, the rate of motion of the final control element.

Hunting. The undesirable oscillation of an automatic control system such that the controlled variable swings on both sides of the predetermined reference value without seeming to approach it.

Integral Action. That in which the final control element is positioned in accordance with a time integral function of the controlled variable.

Lag. Any deviation from instantaneously complete response to input signal.

Linearity. Conformity to a straight line.

Measuring Means. Those elements of an automatic controller which are involved in ascertaining and communicating to the controlling means the value of the controlled variable.

Motor Operator. A portion of the controlling means which applies power for operating the final control element.

Multiple Action. That in which two or more controller actions are combined.

Multipostion Action. That in which a final control element is moved to one of three or more predetermined positions, each corresponding to a definite range of values of the controlled variable.

Noise. Any unwanted disturbance, such as a signal which tends to interfere with reception of the desired signal.

Non-linearity. The deviation of any functional relationship from direct proportionality.

Offset. The steady-state difference between the control point and the value of the controlled variable corresponding to the set point.

Open-loop Control System. A control system in which the controlled quantity is permitted to vary in accordance with the inherent characteristics of the control system and the controlled power apparatus for any given adjustment of the controller.

Positioning Action. That in which there is a predetermined relation between value of the controlled variable and position of a final control element.

Process. The collective functions performed in and by the equipment in which a variable is to be controlled.

Proportional-position Action. That in which there is a continuous linear relation between value of the controlled variable and position of a final control element.

Rate Action. That in which there is a continuous linear relation between rate of change of the controlled variable and position of a final control element.

Rate Time. In proportional plus rate controller action and proportional plus reset plus rate controller action, the time interval by which the rate action advances the effect of the proportional-position action upon the final control element.

Reset Rate. Applying to proportional plus reset controller action and proportional plus rate controller action, the number of times per minute that the effect of the proportional-position action upon the final control element is repeated by the proportional-speed floating action.

Resistance. Opposition to flow, measured in units of potential change required to produce unit change in flow.

Self-operated Controller. A device in which all the energy to operate the final control element is derived from the controlled medium through the primary element.

Self-regulation. An inherent characteristic of the process which aids in limiting deviation of the controlled variable.

Set Point. The position to which the control-point-setting mechanism is set.

Two-position Action. That in which a final control element is moved from one of two fixed positions to the other.

AUTOMATIC CONTROLLERS

PNEUMATIC CONTROLLERS

Basically, the purpose of any pneumatic controller is to supply air to the diaphragm of a pneumatic control valve. For most control systems this pressure will be in the 3 to 15 lb./sq. in. range, standardized by agreement between instrument manufacturers and users. Some special systems use other pressure ranges. With varying pressures applied to the diaphragm motor of the valve, the valve will assume different positions. This control action is accomplished through the use of a restriction in the line supplying air to a nozzle which can be covered or uncovered by a flapper that is positioned by the measuring system. With the nozzle open, back pressure in the line will be a minimum; with the nozzle closed, the pressure will be greatest.

Two-position Control Model. With a two-position control system, it is necessary only to allow full or minimum pressure to be supplied to the diaphragm moving the valve to the full-open or full-closed position.

The various manufacturers have different mechanical approaches to the problem, but the basic idea remains the same. Figure 22-162 shows the basic system. The

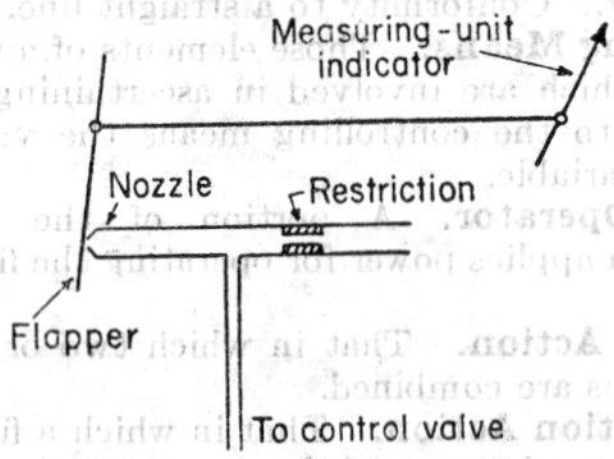

FIG. 22-162. Schematic of two-position pneumatic controller with flapper-nozzle arrangement.

speed of response of the system shown would be very slow. The diameter of the nozzle hole must be quite small so that the force exerted on the vane is negligible compared with the force exerted by the measuring system. One manufacturer overcomes this by splitting the air into two jets and moving a vane between the two. This is done on the theory that the force on the vane will be balanced and thus have no effect on the measuring system. Other manufacturers use a spring-loaded ball baffle in place of the nozzle flapper to overcome this difficulty. With the nozzle diameter small, the restriction diameter also must be small. The result is that pressure changes will occur slowly within the line, introducing a lag into the control system. This is especially true if the line capacity is large. A pilot valve (relay), located close to the control unit, overcomes this problem by cutting system capacity to a minimum.

Bleed and Non-bleed Pilots. The relay valve may be of the bleed or non-bleed type. The bleed-type valve allows air to bleed to atmosphere or to be transmitted to the control valve. The non-bleed type does not waste the air. Figures 22-163 and 22-164 show schematically the bleed and non-bleed types of pilot valves.

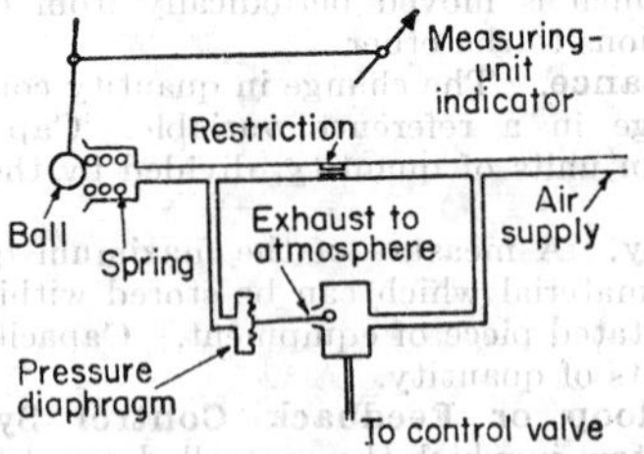

FIG. 22-163. Schematic of two-position pneumatic controller, showing a bleed-type relay and ball-baffle displacement-sensing device.

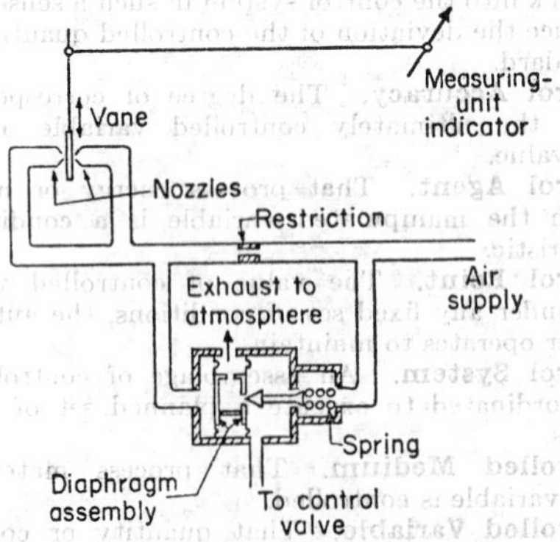

FIG. 22-164. Schematic of two-position pneumatic controller, showing split-nozzle error detector and a non-bleed-type relay.

The control point is set by a manual control that positions an indicator on the scale and repositions the flapper in relation to the nozzle. This is adjusted so that when the measuring unit indication is aligned with the control-system indicator no movement of the control valve will result. For simplicity, this adjustment is not included on the sketches used to illustrate the various modes of control.

Proportional-position Control Mode. Proportional control action is generated by adding a proportioning bellows and a feedback mechanism to the basic on-off controller. For the sake of simplicity, only the flapper-nozzle type of control unit will be shown, and details of the relay valves will be omitted.

Generally, proportional control is achieved by modulating the movement of the flapper over the nozzle with a force supplied by another bellows, as shown in Fig. 22-165. The air actuating this proportioning bellows is

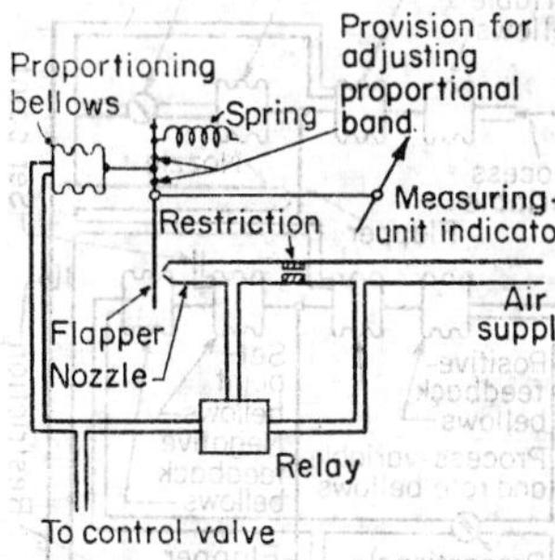

Fig. 22-165. Schematic of proportional-position pneumatic controller.

the output of the relay which also supplies the valve actuator. The proportioning bellows is connected to an arm that repositions the flapper in relation to the nozzle in a manner that lessens the effect of the change in the measured variable. Thus a greater change is required to move the valve through its full travel.

The proportional-band adjustment is easily accomplished by incorporating a means for changing the fulcrum point of the arm that repositions the flapper so that it moves more or less for a given change in the bellows position.

This arrangement, which allows the output of the device to affect the input, is the feedback principle.

Proportional plus Reset Control Mode. Reset action is obtained by adding another bellows, a capacity, and a bleed arrangement to the proportional controller. In the arrangement shown in Fig. 22-166, a change that

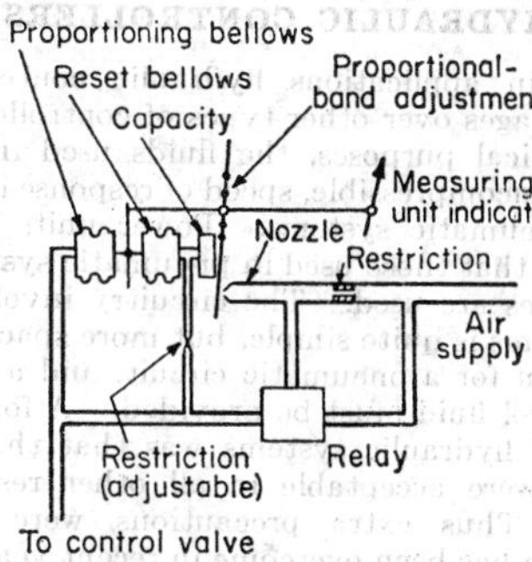

Fig. 22-166. Schematic of a proportional-plus-reset pneumatic controller.

causes the flapper to move will change the output pressure from the relay. If this movement is in a direction to reduce output it will, in turn, reduce pressure in the proportioning bellows, but because of the restriction in the line to the reset bellows, the pressure here momentarily will stay high, accentuating the movement of the flapper away from the nozzle, thus causing an even greater movement of the control valve. If the error is in the opposite direction, the pressure in the reset bellows will be higher than that in the proportioning bellows and the flapper will tend to close more, again accentuating the correction.

Other methods of obtaining reset action are shown in Fig. 22-167*a* and *b*. The purpose of the reset bellows remains the same, namely, to add an additional correction

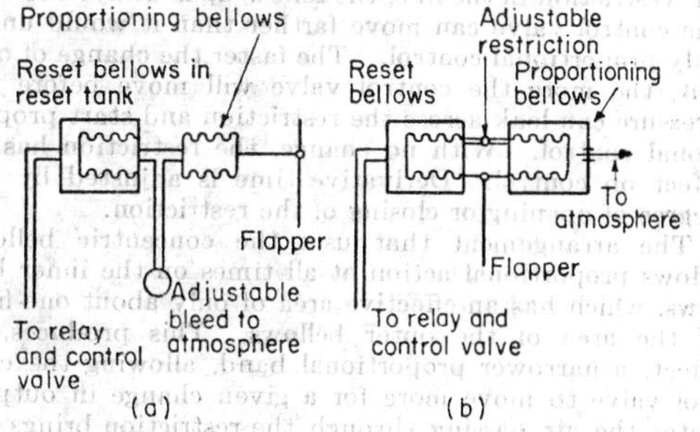

Fig. 22-167. Proportional-plus-reset pneumatic controllers: (*a*) proportional-plus-reset control unit with bleed to atmosphere, (*b*) proportional-plus-reset control unit with bleed between the bellows.

so long as any deviation exists. This correction disappears when the controlled variable is at the set point.

Proportional Position plus Rate Control Mode. Rate (derivative) action is important because it helps stabilize a process more quickly after a change has occurred. It is added to the proportional controller by interposing a restriction and a capacity in the feedback loop to the proportioning bellows. This may be done as shown in Fig. 22-168. Alternate means of accomplishing this same effect are shown in Fig. 22-169*a* and *b*.

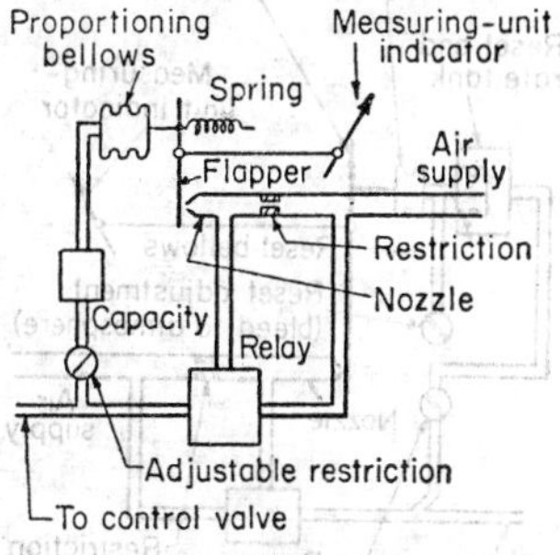

Fig. 22-168. Proportional-plus-rate pneumatic controller.

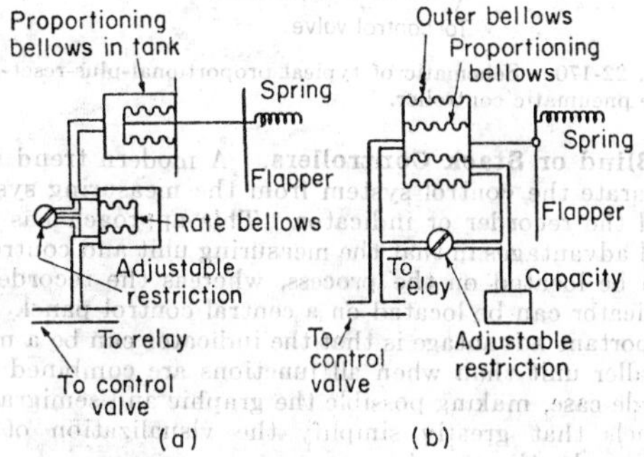

Fig. 22-169. Proportional-plus-rate pneumatic control units: (*a*) bellows in rate-action tank, (*b*) concentric bellows.

In the proportional controller, the pressure in the proportioning bellows is always equal to the output pressure of the relay. By adding a restriction in the line leading to the proportioning bellows, a time delay can be introduced that will allow the relay output pressure to change before the effect is noted by the proportioning bellows. If, for example, the flapper approached the nozzle, increasing relay output pressure, the proportional controller would sense the change and react immediately. With the restriction in the line, the follow-up is delayed so that the control valve can move farther than it would under only proportional control. The faster the change of output, the more the control valve will move before the pressure can leak across the restriction and start proportional control. With no change, the restriction has no effect on control. Derivative time is adjusted by the degree of opening or closing of the restriction.

The arrangement that uses the concentric bellows allows proportional action at all times on the inner bellows, which has an effective area of only about one-fifth of the area of the outer bellows. This produces, in effect, a narrower proportional band, allowing the control valve to move more for a given change in output. Later the air passing through the restriction brings the larger outer bellows into play and regular proportional control resumes until a further change in output occurs.

Proportional plus Reset plus Rate Control Mode. The proportional plus reset plus rate controller combines into one unit all the functions already discussed. This can be accomplished without major revision to the pneumatic circuit or placement of the components through careful design. The action of the various elements making up the complete controller is the same as when they are used in the less complex arrangements. Figure 22-170 shows schematically a typical proportional plus reset plus rate controller.

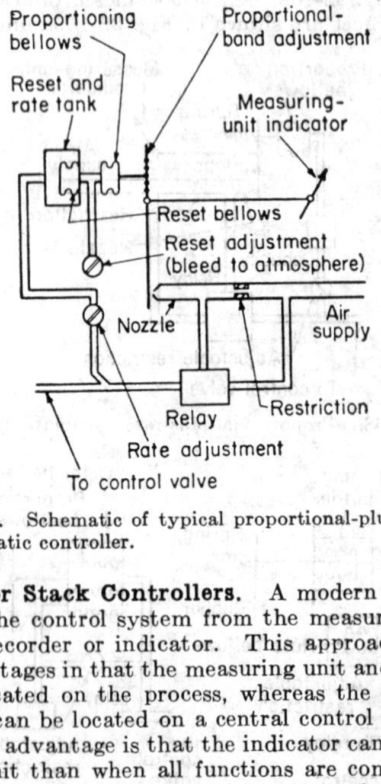

FIG. 22-170. Schematic of typical proportional-plus-reset-plus-rate pneumatic controller.

Blind or Stack Controllers. A modern trend is to separate the control system from the measuring system and the recorder or indicator. This approach has several advantages in that the measuring unit and controller can be located on the process, whereas the recorder or indicator can be located on a central control panel. An important advantage is that the indicator can be a much smaller unit than when all functions are combined in a single case, making possible the graphic and semigraphic panels that greatly simplify the visualization of the process by the operator.

Certain changes are necessary in the make-up of this type of controller, because it may be inaccessible or inconvenient to reach while the process is in operation. A pneumatic set-point signal, usually in the 3 to 15 lb./sq. in. range, is transmitted to the controller. The measured variable is transmitted in the form of another 3 to 15 lb./sq. in. signal instead of as a mechanical input. These variations result in a controller of a slightly different form that has three rather than one feedback loop. Study of Fig. 22-171 will show that the principles

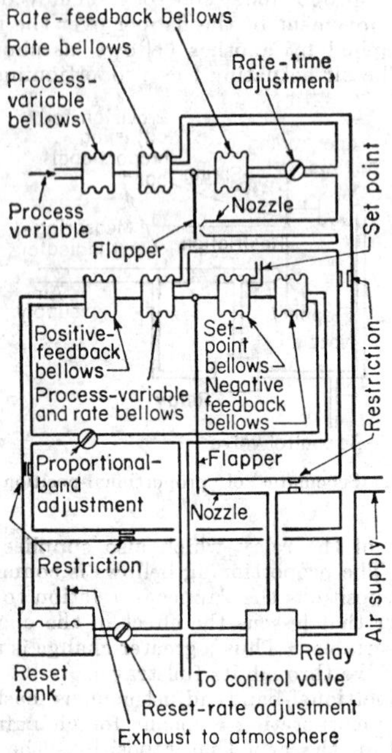

FIG. 22-171. Schematic of typical stack-type blind pneumatic controller.

involved have not changed. Figures 22-172*a*, *b*, and *c* show how various manufacturers have approached this problem; these controllers are representative of the variations in mechanical form.

HYDRAULIC CONTROLLERS

For certain applications hydraulic controllers offer some advantages over other types of controllers. Since, for all practical purposes, the fluids used in hydraulic systems are incompressible, speed of response is far higher than for pneumatic systems. Power units may be of smaller sizes that those used in pneumatic systems where high pressures are used. The circuitry involved in hydraulic systems is quite simple, but more space usually is required than for a pneumatic circuit, and a return line for the control fluid must be provided. A former major drawback of hydraulic systems was that the hydraulic fluids that were acceptable in all other respects were flammable. Thus extra precautions were necessary. This problem has been overcome in recent years with the introduction of non-flammable control fluids.

Hydraulic Control Relays

All the principles involved in pneumatic control also apply to hydraulic control. Of course, some changes in mechanical design will be necessary because of the different medium used. One major change will be that, because of the cost of the hydraulic control fluid, all pilots

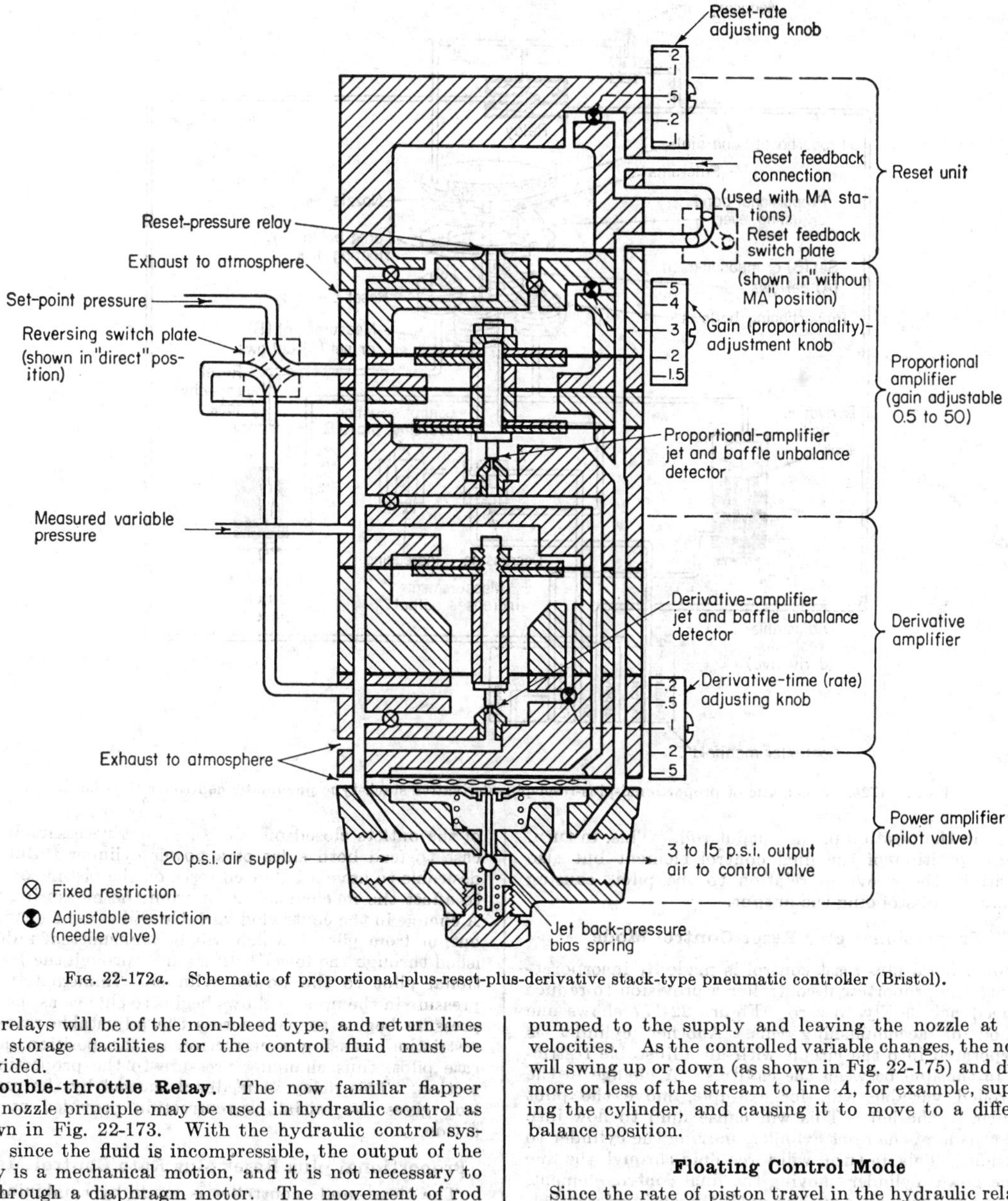

FIG. 22-172*a*. Schematic of proportional-plus-reset-plus-derivative stack-type pneumatic controller (Bristol).

and relays will be of the non-bleed type, and return lines and storage facilities for the control fluid must be provided.

Double-throttle Relay. The now familiar flapper and nozzle principle may be used in hydraulic control as shown in Fig. 22-173. With the hydraulic control system, since the fluid is incompressible, the output of the relay is a mechanical motion, and it is not necessary to go through a diaphragm motor. The movement of rod *A* (the flapper) changes the relative area of the nozzle and orifice, upsetting the pressure balance in the double-acting cylinder. This causes the piston to move to a new balance point and moves the output shaft, which may be coupled to the control valve.

Four-way Pilot Valve. More widely used is the four-way pilot valve shown in Fig. 22-174. A change in the controlled variable moves rod *A* in or out, displacing spools 3 and 4 into parts 1 and 2. This upsets the balance of pressure in the double-acting cylinder, causing the piston to seek a new balance position, and moving the shaft connected to the final control element.

Jet Pipe. Another type of relay commonly used in hydraulic control circuits is the jet pipe. The jet-pipe relay uses fluids at high pressures (up to 500 lb./sq. in.) pumped to the supply and leaving the nozzle at high velocities. As the controlled variable changes, the nozzle will swing up or down (as shown in Fig. 22-175) and direct more or less of the stream to line *A*, for example, supplying the cylinder, and causing it to move to a different balance position.

Floating Control Mode

Since the rate of piston travel in the hydraulic relay is easily adjustable, hydraulic control is especially adapted to pure floating (proportional-speed) control where the speed of correction is proportional to the error signal. Any of the arrangements in Figs. 22-173, 22-174, and 22-175 can be used.

Proportional-position Control Mode

Proportional control can be generated by providing a feedback loop so that there is a force that will counteract the motion of the input rod. Figure 22-176 shows a typical setup of this type.

In this case, the pilot "spools" and sleeve are both shown to be movable, a concept often incorporated into hydraulic controls. A change in the controlled variable will move the pilot relative to the sleeve, causing a

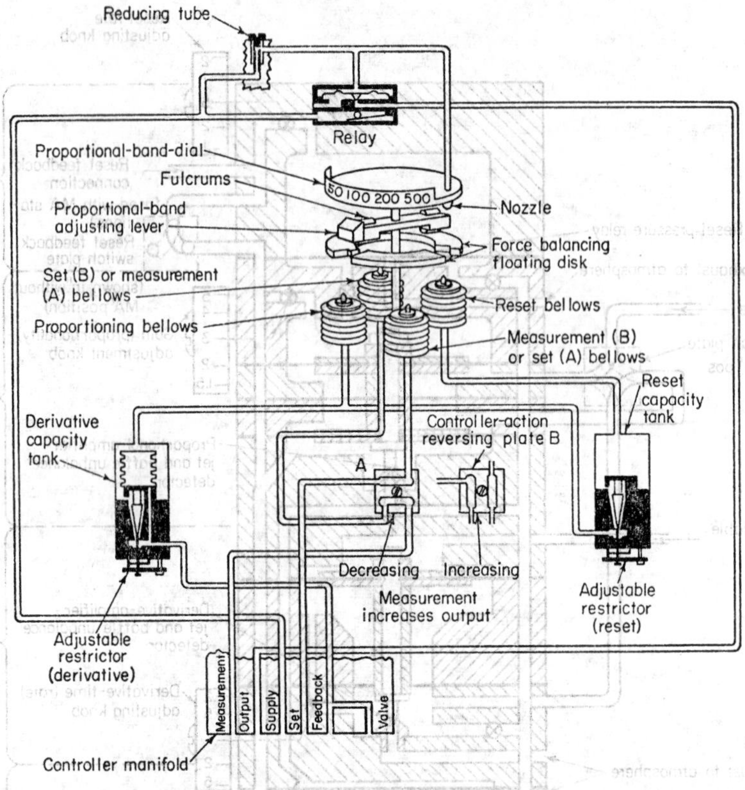

FIG. 22-172*b*. Schematic of proportional-plus-reset-plus-derivative stack-type pneumatic controller (Foxboro).

change in the position of the output rod. This, in turn, changes position of the final control element but also repositions the sleeve in relation to the pilot, causing rebalance and stopping the output.

Proportional plus Reset Control Mode

Proportional plus reset control is made by incorporating into the proportional controller a provision to reduce the feedback slowly to zero. Figure 22-177 shows one method of accomplishing this. Another cylinder is incorporated into the circuit with an adjustable restriction in the line between the cavities. A change in the controlled variable will, for example, move the pilot cylinder to the left. This will cause fluid to flow into the left side of the reset cylinder, moving the cylinder to the right. This, in turn, will force fluid through the line to the power cylinder, moving the final control element. This movement will continue until the spring force balances the hydraulic force. At this point the hydraulic pressures on opposite sides of the rest cylinder will be unequal, but leakage past the adjustable restriction will occur to equalize the pressure. This will slowly cancel the feedback, and when the pressures are fully equal, straight proportional control will result.

Proportional plus Rate Control Mode

Rate action can be added to the hydraulic proportional controller by combining the proportional-speed floating control already shown and the proportional-position control. Figure 22-178 shows a typical controller of this type.

Pilot 1 is the proportional-speed (rate) pilot, with one of the outlets closed off, since it is not necessary in this case to feed both sides of a power cylinder. But it is desirable to have a balanced force on the piston so as not to affect the mechanical input from the measuring unit. A change in the controlled variable will cause a change in output from pilot 1 which will be transmitted undiminished through the lower bellows and through the proportional pilot to the power cylinder. Immediately, the pressure in the upper bellows begins to change as the fluid pressure begins to pass across the adjustable rate-time restriction, causing a correction in the position of the rate pilot, thus changing pressure to the proportioning section. This delay in feedback caused by the restriction gives the initial overcorrection provided by rate action.

Proportional plus Reset plus Rate Control Mode

The three-mode controller is made by combining the modes already discussed. The action of the separate modes of control is not changed by the combination. Figure 22-179 shows a typical example of this type of controller.

ELECTRIC AND ELECTRONIC CONTROLLERS

The differentiation between electric and electronic controllers usually is that the electronic controller will incorporate vacuum tubes (or solid-state devices) instead of straight wire circuits.

Often the electrical-type controllers will be used to operate an electrical final control element, but for many applications the pneumatic-valve operator has advantages over its electrical counterpart, and in these cases

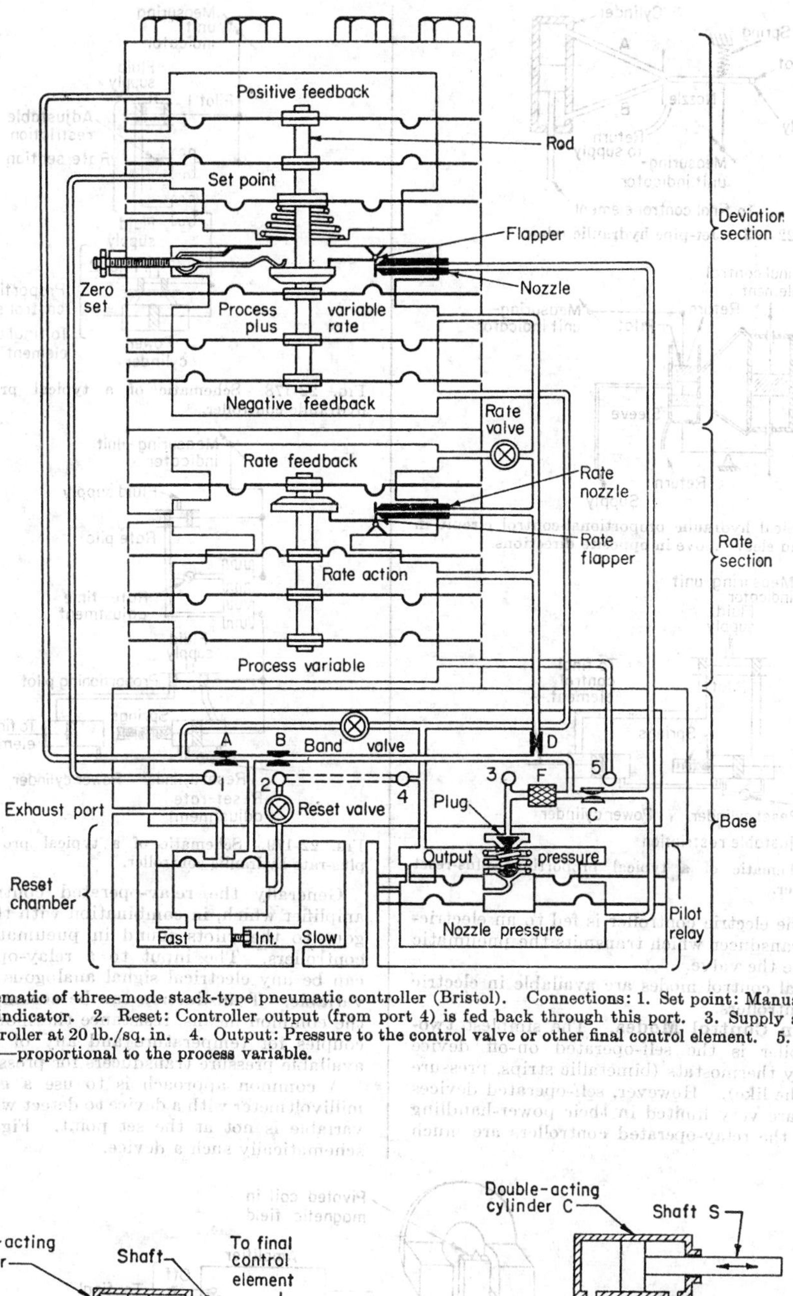

Fig. 22-172c. Schematic of three-mode stack-type pneumatic controller (Bristol). Connections: 1. Set point: Manually set by a knob on the recorder or indicator. 2. Reset: Controller output (from port 4) is fed back through this port. 3. Supply air: Dry clean air supplied to the controller at 20 lb./sq. in. 4. Output: Pressure to the control valve or other final control element. 5. Process variable: From a transmitter—proportional to the process variable.

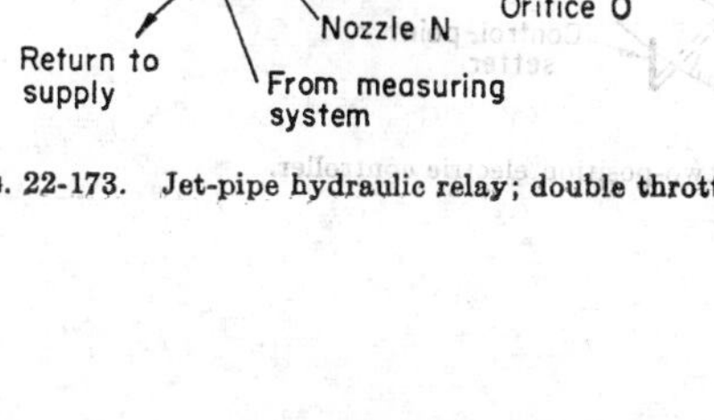

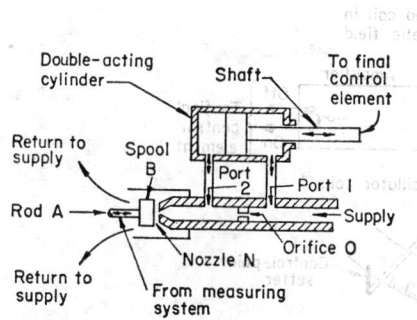

Fig. 22-173. Jet-pipe hydraulic relay; double throttle.

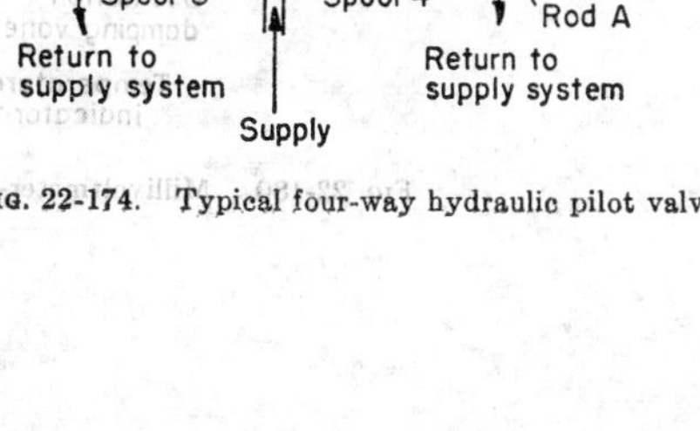

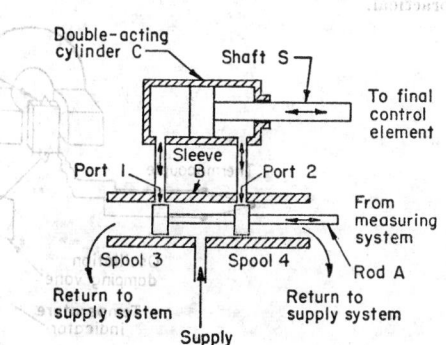

Fig. 22-174. Typical four-way hydraulic pilot valve.

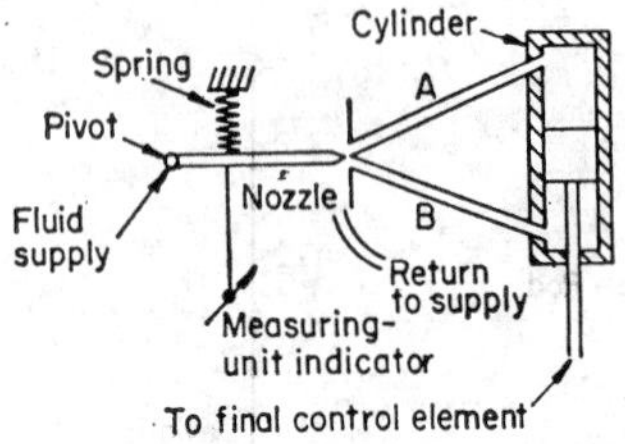

FIG. 22-175. Jet-pipe hydraulic relay.

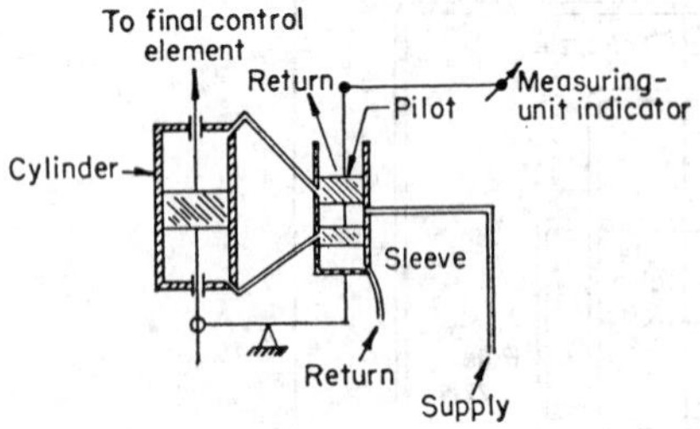

FIG. 22-176. Typical hydraulic proportional-control circuit in which the pilot and sleeve move in opposite directions.

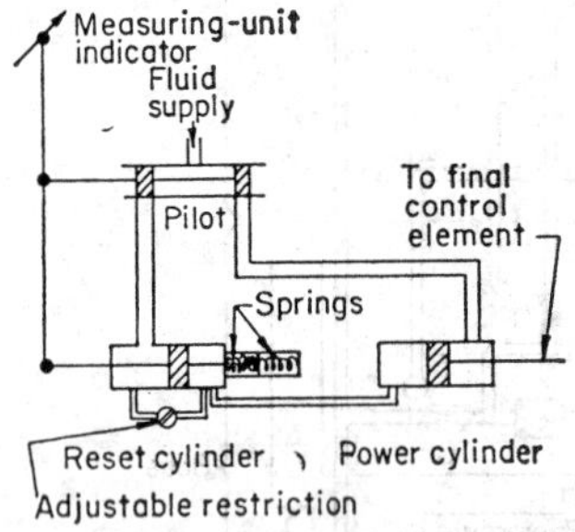

FIG. 22-177. Schematic of a typical proportional-plus-reset hydraulic controller.

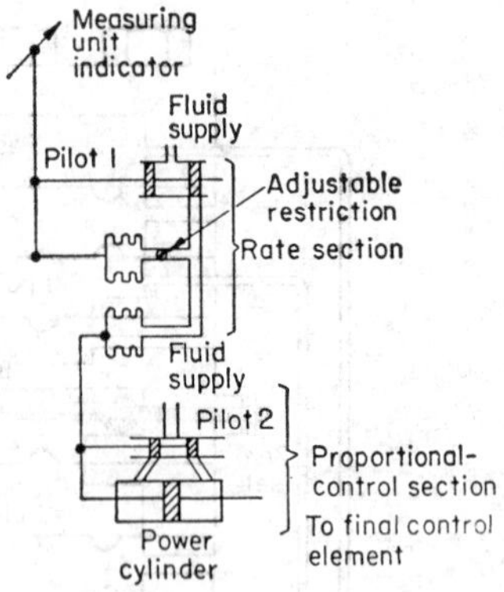

FIG. 22-178. Schematic of a typical proportional-plus-rate hydraulic controller.

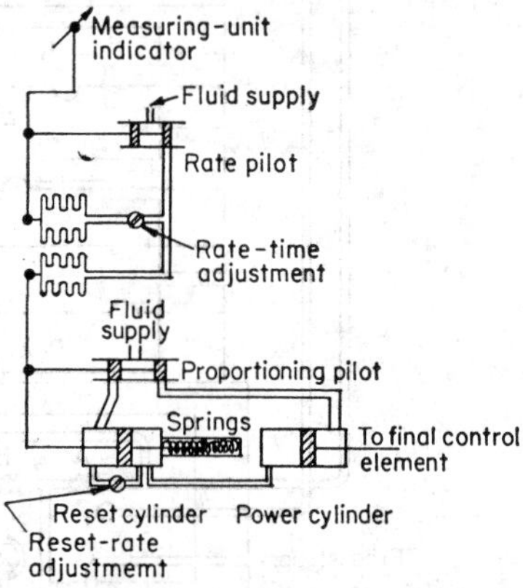

FIG. 22-179. Schematic of a typical proportional-plus-reset-plus-rate hydraulic controller.

the output of the electric controller is fed to an electric-to-pneumatic transducer which transmits the pneumatic signal to operate the valve.

All the normal control modes are available in electric or electronic controllers.

Two-position Control Modes. The simplest two-position controller is the self-operated on-off device characterized by thermostats (bimetallic strips, pressure switches, and the like). However, self-operated devices of this nature are very limited in their power-handling capabilities; so the relay-operated controllers are much more practical.

Generally the relay-operated controller utilizes an amplifier which, in combination with the relay, is analogous to the pilots found in pneumatic and hydraulic controllers. The input to a relay-operated controller can be any electrical signal analogous to the controlled variable. Transduction can be accomplished by any of the common means, resistance thermometers or thermocouples for temperature and any of the commercially available pressure transducers for pressure and flow.

A common approach is to use a galvanometer-type millivoltmeter with a device to detect when the controlled variable is not at the set point. Figure 22-180 shows schematically such a device.

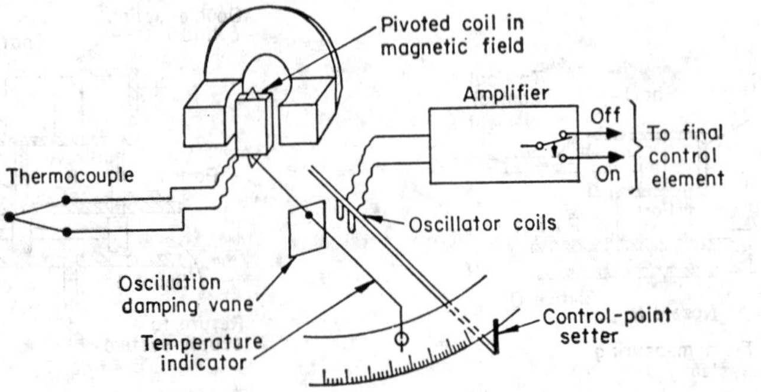

FIG. 22-180. Millivoltmeter-type relay-operated two-position electric controller.

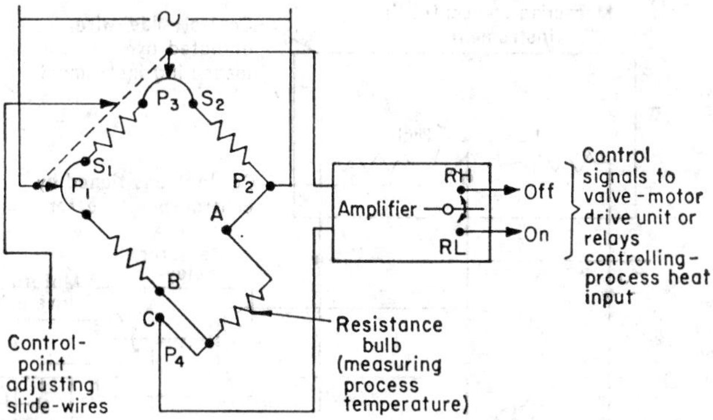

FIG. 22-181. Bridge-type relay-operated two-position electric controller.

Another common approach to the problem of two-position electric control is to use a bridge-type detector. Such a controller is shown schematically in Fig. 22-181. The set point in this case is determined by adjusting the position of contacts on slide-wires S_1 and S_2. An unbalance in the bridge, which will occur when the controlled variable is not at the set point, will result in a millivoltage output which is amplified and drives the final control element.

Floating-control Mode. Floating control requires a reversible control motor driving the final control element. Simply, all that is required is a circuit, such as in Fig. 22-180, with a "low" and a "high" contact that will drive the motor to open or to close the final control element on command from one of these contacts or detectors.

Proportional-speed floating control can be accomplished with a circuit as shown in Fig. 22-181 if a variable-speed reversible motor is used to drive the final control element. The output from the bridge circuit is proportional to the error; so motor speed will vary proportionally with the error. Polarity of the error signal will change as the controlled variable passes through the control point; so the direction of the motor can be changed.

Proportional Control Mode. A common approach to the problem of proportional control with electric controllers is to use a fixed-time-cycle type of action. A typical application of this type of controller would be on an electric furnace where, to maintain temperatures at a desired level, the heating elements are turned on and off according to a timed cycle. When more heat is necessary, the elements are turned on for a longer portion of the cycle. An arrangement that will accomplish this is shown schematically in Fig. 22-182. Contact *A* is positioned mechanically by the temperature-measuring system. Contact *B* reciprocates as a function of time; so the time of closing will be a function of the magnitude of the measured variable in relation to the control-point setting.

Proportional-position Control Mode. Proportional-position controllers act to position the final control element as a function of the measured variable. This takes basically the form of the Wheatstone bridge, but instead of having the output of the bridge drive a motor at a speed proportional to the signal, the motor-driven final control element is connected mechanically to a slide-wire contact that moves in such a manner as to bring the bridge back into balance; so the output signal once again is zero. Figure 22-183 is typical of this type of controller.

Dual- and Three-mode Controllers. Electric and electronic multimode controllers are a relatively recent development, and as yet, no clearly defined "best way" has been achieved. As a result, the methods of achieving the various modes of control are at least as numerous as the number of manufacturers offering this type of equipment. As yet there has been no standardization on a signal as is the case of the 3 to 15 lb./sq. in. pneumatic signal. Thus components from several manufacturers often cannot be combined into a signal system.

The newest development in the field is functionally unitized instrumentation which is of a size that compares with the unitized pneumatic instrumentation. All these systems are able to produce an electrical signal to operate a final control element, but electric-to-pneumatic transducers are available for pneumatically operated final control elements. Some circuits use vacuum-tube amplifiers, others use magnetic amplifiers, and some use transistor amplifiers. Some systems use a.c. transmission signals; others use d.c. signals.

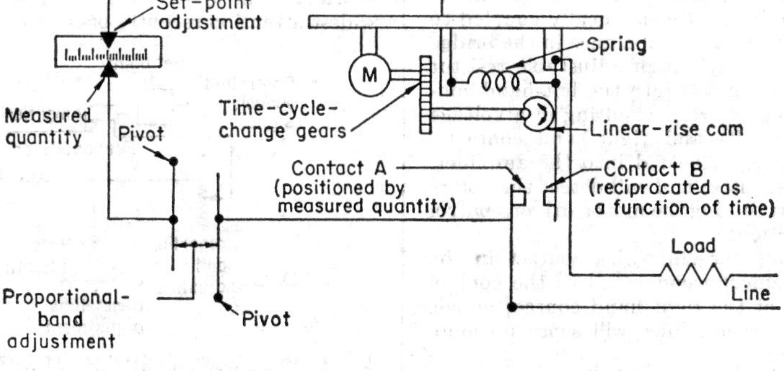

FIG. 22-182. Typical proportional average-position electric controllers with fixed time cycle.

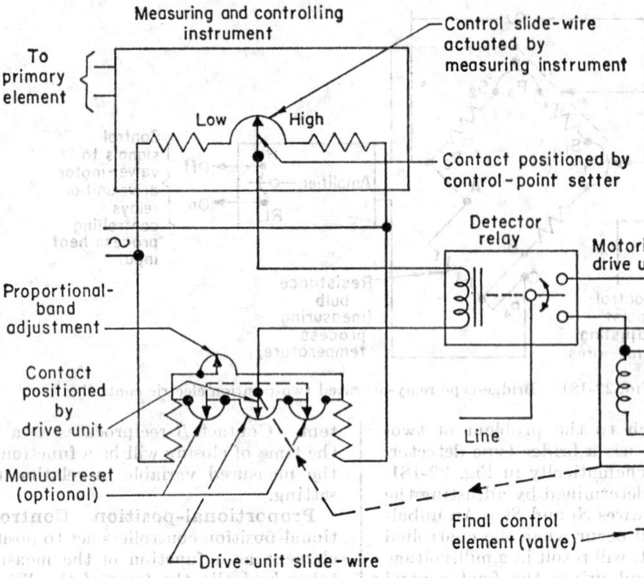

FIG. 22-183. Typical proportional-position electric controller.

With the wide diversity of types available, it is difficult to define any one as typical. The intricacies of the individual electronic circuits cannot be explored here with sufficient thoroughness to be of real value. However, it may be worthwhile to explore briefly a few of the types of controls available and to point out how some of the problems may be solved.

Three-action Position-adjusting Controllers. Figure 22-184 shows a method of obtaining three modes of

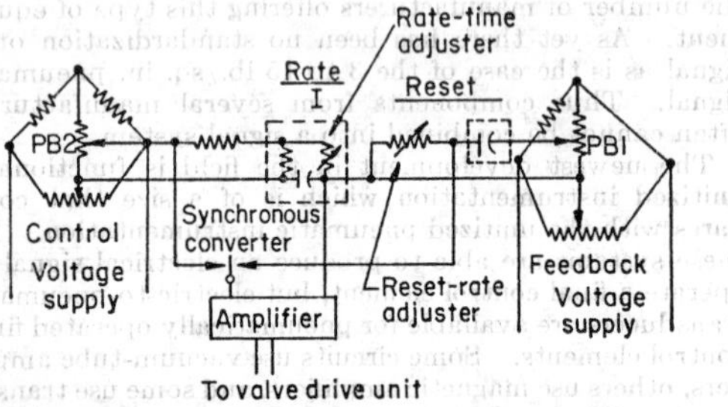

FIG. 22-184. A position-adjusting-type electronic controller.

control on a position-adjusting type of controller. When a change in the measured variable occurs, the adjustable slide-wire in the control bridge (mechanically coupled to the measuring unit) will cause an unbalance in the bridge and therefore a current flow through adjustable resistor PB2 (proportional band control) into the left-hand contact of the synchronous converter, resulting in a voltage difference between the left- and right-hand contacts. This would cause a signal to be fed into the amplifier. The amplifier is phase-sensitive and will detect the polarity of the signal and start driving the motor-driven control unit in the proper direction.

This will start moving the slide-wire contact in the feedback bridge (mechanically connected to the control unit) until the voltage at the right-hand contact equals that at the left, when the amplifier will sense no more error signal and will stop.

Reset action is obtained by introducing a capacitor (shown in dotted area) in the line to the feedback bridge. When the controlled variable is away from the set point, the control-bridge output is other than zero. To balance this, the feedback voltage must also be other than zero; so there will be a current flow through the line containing the capacitor, causing build-up of a charge. As it charges, current in the feedback bridge tends to diminish. To keep the voltage on both sides of the synchronous converter equal despite the charge on the capacitor, the valve slide-wire must move farther. Thus an additional correction will always be introduced until the controlled variable reaches the set point and control-bridge output is zero.

Rate action, dependent on the rate of change of the variable, is generated by a resistance-capacitance circuit shown in the diagram which senses the changing voltage from the control bridge, building up a charge on the capacitor and on the adjustable rate-time resistor. This voltage is added to the voltage, seen by the left-hand contact on the synchronous converter, so that the feedback bridge must provide an extra large correction. The charge on the condenser, hence on the resistor, is a function of the rate of change of the voltage; so when there is no change in voltage (*i.e.*, in the controlled variable), this part of the circuit does not affect operation.

Three-mode Current- or Voltage-adjusting Controller. The type of controller that has been receiving widest attention recently uses as an output a voltage or a

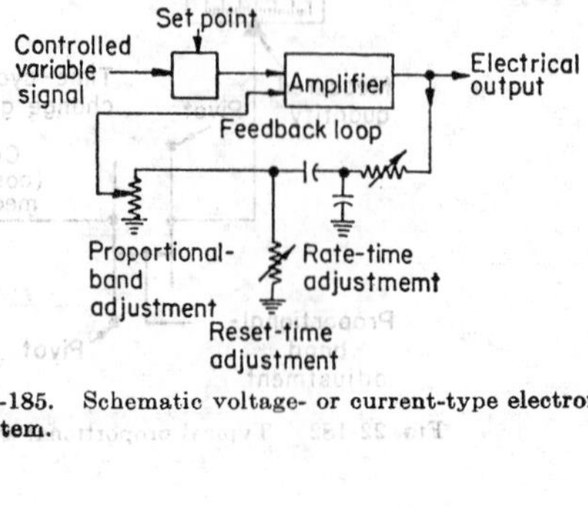

FIG. 22-185. Schematic voltage- or current-type electronic control system.

current. Voltage types use signals from the millivoltage range to 25 or more volts. Current types use signals as low as 0 to 5 ma. to 50 ma. or more. Reduced to the simplest schematic type of diagram they are all similar. Figure 22-185 shows a schematic of this type of system.

There are different methods of producing the input signal to the controller section. With the unitized types, these will be within an arbitrary range. The set point also will be received from the control station in the form of an electrical signal.

More sophisticated forms may have more than one amplifier included for phase discrimination, rate signal, etc. The output is in the form of an electrical signal proportional to the proper controller action. This can be fed to an electric-to-pneumatic transducer to operate a pneumatic control valve, or to an electrical operator. Some end devices will accept this signal in the form of the varying signal, but most positioning devices, such as electric valve operators, must have a circuit to compare the signal received from the controller with a reference. This becomes, in effect, a circuit similar to Fig. 22-184 without the feedback back to the control circuit.

FINAL CONTROL ELEMENTS

In automatic process control, the control valve is the final element in the control loop. It serves as a continuously variable orifice to change the rate of flow of the control agent. The complete control valve consists of an actuator and a valve body. A typical control valve is shown in cross section in Fig. 22-186.

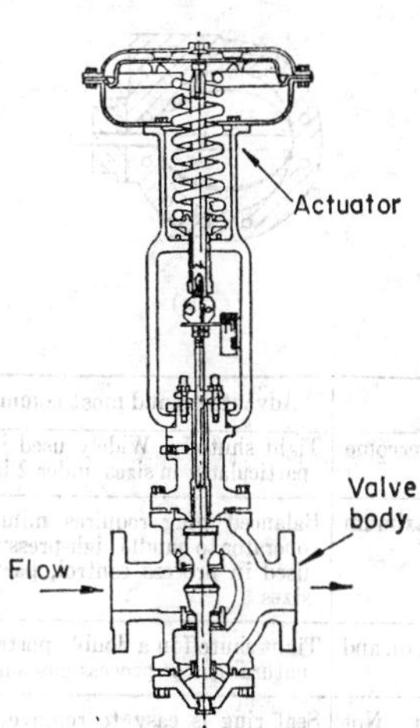

Fig. 22-186. Typical control valve.

The body is a pressuretight fitting that contains the variable orifice; the actuator provides the power to move a plug or baffle to vary the flow area of the orifice. The motion of the operator is transmitted through a stuffing box or bellows seal in the body wall to move the valve plug.

VALVE BODIES

Control-valve bodies may be screwed, flanged, or welded into the flow line. Screwed ends usually are threaded with American Standard female tapered pipe threads. The dimensions, design details, and pressure-temperature ratings of flanged ends are in accordance with American Standards Association Specification B16.5-1961. Socket- or butt-welding ends may be specified, although socket welding is not recommended in pipe sizes above 2 in.

Most common body materials are cast iron and carbon steel. Low-alloy steels, such as chrome-molybdenum, are used for high temperatures. Various grades of stainless steels, bronze, monel, nickel, Inconel, Hastelloys, and all castable alloys are available for corrosive chemical service, or for very high- or low-temperature applications. Trim parts, consisting of seat rings, valve plug, stem, bushings and stuffing-box parts usually are furnished in stainless steel but are available in any of the afore-mentioned alloys. Seating surfaces often are hard-surfaced with Stellite or its equivalent.

Several of the common types of control-valve design and construction are illustrated in Table 22-21, with a brief description of valve-body construction, design limitations, advantages, and applications.

CONTROL-VALVE ACTUATORS

Actuators may be pneumatically, electrically, or hydraulically powered. Pneumatic operation is the most widely used method in process control. Self-contained, electrically powered electrohydraulic actuators are used occasionally but are not generally considered economical.

Simple diaphragm and spring-type actuators are most widely used, although their power is limited. Pressure-balanced pneumatic piston-type actuators with built-in "positioners" are gaining in popularity, particularly in the chemical industry. These devices use high-pressure air and deliver relatively high thrusts. The design and characteristics of several common actuators are summarized in Table 22-22.

VALVE POSITIONERS

A valve positioner is really a closed-loop controller, powered by an auxiliary air supply with instrument signal as input, diaphragm pressure as output, and the feedback from the valve stem. It is usually mounted on the side of the valve but may be on top of the diaphragm casing. The basic purpose of the positioner is to assure a valve-plunger position that is exactly proportional to the instrument signal; this is accomplished by utilizing the power of the auxiliary air supply to overcome any hysteresis, friction, or unbalance in the valve assembly.

The relation between instrument signal and valve stem movement is usually linear, but some models are available with a cam and the feedback linkage that can be used to change the characteristics of the valve. This may be a useful tool in stabilizing complex control systems.

Valve positioners are normally specified on single-ported valves requiring high stem thrusts, on large valves requiring a high volume of air to operate, on systems where process requirements make exact valve positioning essential, on split-range applications, and in cases where special valve characterization is desirable.

Figure 22-187 shows exterior and sectional views and a schematic diagram of a typical valve positioner.

Table 22-21. Control-valve Bodies

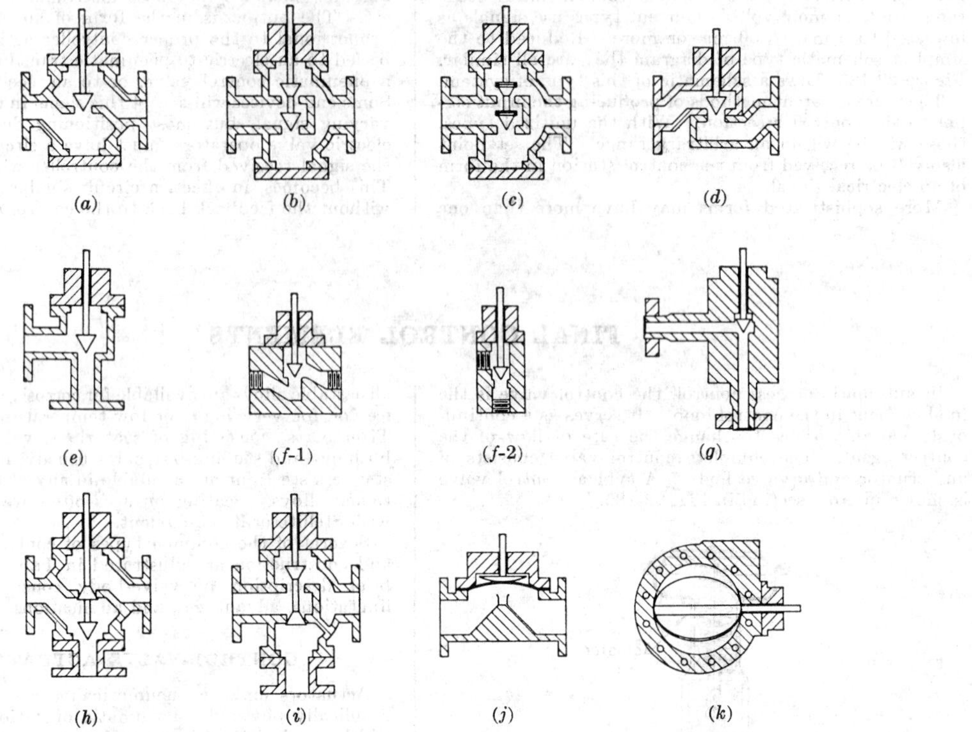

Schematic illustration	Type of construction	Design limitations	Advantages and most common applications
(a)	Single-port, sliding-stem reversible globe body	Operator must have power enough to overcome port unbalance	Tight shutoff. Widely used in process control, particularly in sizes under 2 in.
(b)	Double-port, sliding-stem reversible globe body	Will not shut off tight. 2% leakage maximum should be anticipated	Balanced plug requires minimum force from operator to handle high-pressure drops. Widely used in process control, particularly in larger sizes
(c)	Double-port, sliding-stem reversible globe body with O-ring or molded composition seats	Pressure drop limited to about 200 lb./sq. in. and temperature to about 160°F.	Tight shutoff in a double-ported valve. Used in natural gas or process gases and liquids
(d)	Single-port, sliding-stem, split body	Body bolting must withstand line stresses. Not furnished with welding ends	Seat ring is easy to remove. Widely used in chemical processes
(e)	Single-port, sliding-stem, angle body	If installed as "flow-closing" has tendency to slam when operating near the seat with high-pressure drop. Will cavitate at outlet when handling liquids	Unobstructed flow passages and high efficiency. Used in handling slurries and sometimes on flashing liquids
(f)	Single-port, bar stock globe (f-1) or angle body (f-2)	Maximum size 2 in. Screwed or welding ends only	Popular in alloys not readily castable such as nickel and monel. Inexpensive
(g)	Single-port, forged angle body with lens ring flanged connections	Generally furnished with orifice sizes under 1 in. only	Used on ammonia or polyethylene reactor letdown; or other very high pressure service
(h)	Three-way body. Adaptation of single-ported globe body	Port unbalance same as for single-ported body	Two inlets and single outlet. Used on flow-mixing applications such as temperature control
(i)	Three-way body. Adaptation of double-ported globe body	Port unbalance same as for single-ported body	Single inlet and two outlets. Used on flow-splitting applications such as heat-exchanger by-pass
(j)	Saunders patent diaphragm body	Temperature limited by availability of diaphragm material. Static pressure limited by available force from operator	May be plastic-lined. Used on slurries and corrosive chemicals
(k)	Butterfly valve. Flanged or wafer-type body with rotary shaft	Not suitable for extremely high pressure drops	Economical in large sizes. Can be rubber-lined to give tight shutoff

Table 22-22. Valve Actuators

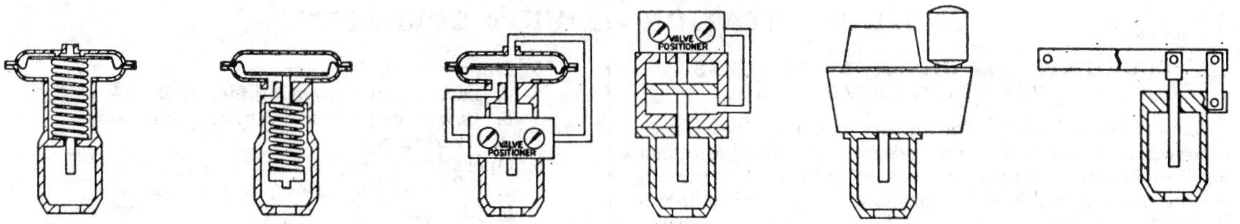

(a) (b) (c) (d) (e) (f)

Schematic diagram	Type of construction	Design limitations	Advantages and most common applications
(a)	Spring and diaphragm air pressure moves stem downward	Thrust is limited. Spring absorbs power	Simple and dependable. Fails upward with loss of operating air. Widely used in process control
(b)	Spring and diaphragm air pressure moves stem upward	Thrust is limited. Spring absorbs power	Fails upward with loss of operating air
(c)	Pressure-balanced or springless diaphragm	Requires a positioner. Does not fail safe	Has more power than spring types
(d)	Pressure-balanced piston	Requires a positioner. Does not fail safe	Uses high-pressure air and has maximum power. Widely used in chemical industry
(e)	Electrohydraulic	High initial cost and potential maintenance. Heavy and bulky	Requires electric power only. Often used with long-distance signal transmission
(j)	Mechanical lever	Requires considerable motion and force at end of lever	Generally operated by a ball float in open tank or low-pressure level control

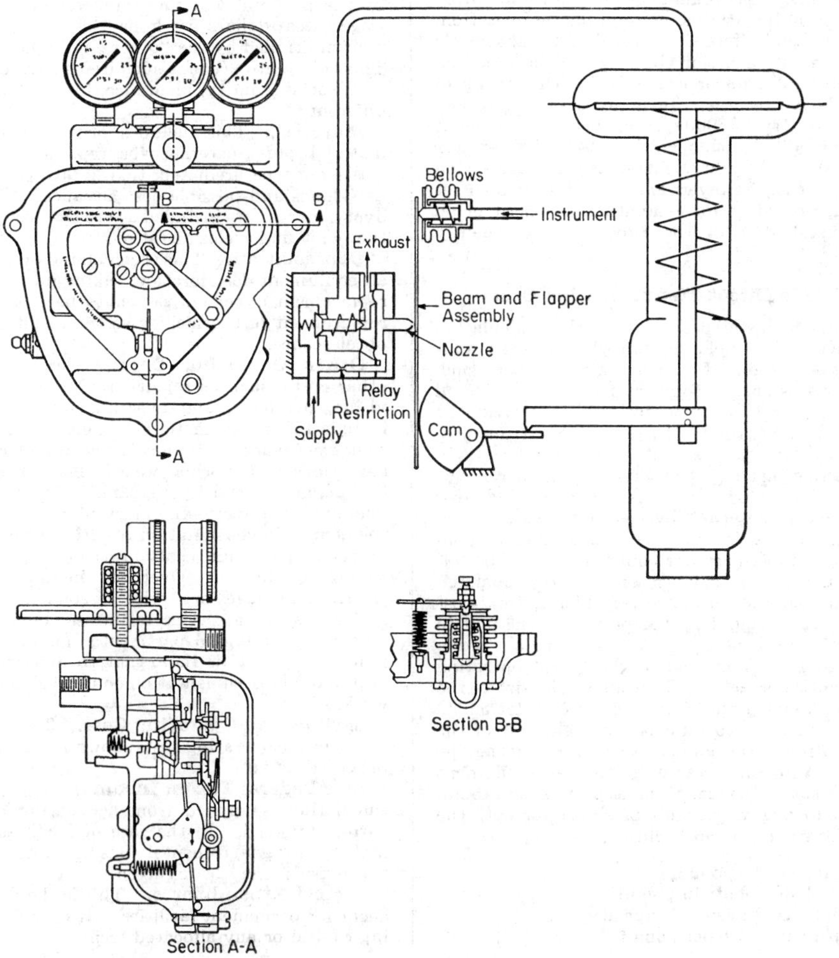

Fig. 22-187. Side-mounted positioner on spring-and-diaphragm operator.

INSTRUMENTATION OF UNIT OPERATIONS

ECONOMICS OF CHEMICAL PROCESS INSTRUMENTATION

Financial justification for an investment in instrumentation must be calculated on the same basis used for other equipment in a chemical processing facility. Instrumentation usually will incur a proportionately large increment of engineering-design cost because of the extensive analysis and relatively large amount of detail associated with the intelligent specification of even the lowest-cost instrument item. This, coupled with the high cost of installation and the increasingly large percentage of the equipment investment represented by instrumentation, emphasizes the need for close scrutiny into the essentiality of every element in the instrumentation system.

The fact that chemical operations are, in a sense, "blind" operations (in that they cannot be easily observed as is the case in metalworking operations, for example) establishes that a major segment of the instrumentation investment is justified as necessary for safe, effective operation. Another segment of the instrumentation investment can be classed as integral with or an essential part of certain items of operating equipment. The justification for these is calculated as lumped with the operating unit. The remaining portion representing choices between automatic vs. non-automatic operation, or choices between different approaches to automatic operation, represents a major challenge to the imagination of the process engineer confronted with the job of calculating relative returns. In many case histories in the chemical industry a $5000 quality-control instrument can be clearly credited with operating cost reductions exceeding $100,000 per year. These are the exception rather than the rule, however, and it is desirable to set forth a formal procedure for evaluating the merit of an instrument installation of the type more frequently encountered.

Reduction in Direct Manufacturing Costs

Most instrument installations for which a calculation is made are justified as tools through which direct manufacturing costs are reduced. In order to evaluate such savings, it is necessary to compare the costs with and without the proposed instrumentation. In arriving at the cost of operation without the proposed instrumentation, it is necessary to consider the improvements in operating practice that might be expected in the absence of the proposed installation. This should extend over the period (usually one year) covered by the calculation.

Anticipated changes in equipment also must be considered if an equitable basis for comparison is to be followed. Instrumentation savings usually are calculated on an incremental-cost basis rather than a total-cost basis; *i.e.*, the costs related to that portion of the unit in which the savings are being realized is shown as "incremental operating cost" instead of the "total operating cost" for the entire process. This reduces the size of the numbers being handled and simplifies the calculation.

It is general practice to tabulate each element of the savings calculation on an annual basis of cost using the first year's operation after startup of the new equipment for the comparison. Typical of the items in such tabulation are the following which must be shown for both the present and for the proposed facilities:

1. Total capacity in pounds
2. Estimated shipments in pounds
3. Shipments as per cent of capacity
4. Unit operating cost per pound
5. Depreciation rates for:
   a. Direct manufacturing facilities
   b. Power, general and service facilities
   c. Over-all rate
6. Operating costs:
   a. Labor and other employment costs
   b. Material
   c. Depreciation
   d. Other operating costs
7. Total operating cost
8. Savings and operating cost
9. Less Federal tax on income
10. Net savings
11. Investment
    a. Project expenditures
    b. Allocated facilities
    c. Working capital
12. Return on investment

Many of the foregoing items will now be discussed in detail.

Labor and Other Employment Costs. The savings in operating and maintenance labor are determined by estimating the hours reduction in labor to be obtained by the proposal and then multiplying by the corrected wage rates (dollars per hour-base rate equals dollar per hour multiplied by the "other employment cost factor"). This takes into account such items as vacation pay, pension, social security, insurance, hospitalization, and shift differential.

Material. This includes process material and raw material plus materials for repairs and maintenance. Costs must be predicted, taking into consideration market trends and possible cost advances. Freight and delivery charges are included as are the cost of processing to the point under consideration.

Depreciation. This is calculated on the basis of over-all equipment deterioration, taking into account physical replacement of the entire facility because of wear and/or replacement of the facility as the result of technological obsolescence.

Other Operating Costs. Here are consolidated other costs, such as repairs, replacement, power, supervision, overhead, and miscellaneous supplies. Repairs include labor and material. Replacement covers items that are replaced periodically because of severe operating conditions or abnormal wear. The term power is used to include electricity, steam, water, air, inert gas, vacuum, and fuel. Incremental costs are used unless the change in consumption resulting from the proposal is of such magnitude that powerhouse labor or facilities would be affected. Overhead includes such items as salaries and wages of service personnel, cost of operating and maintaining service facilities, plant administration, plant engineering, departmental management, and administration. It is important to investigate the effects of proposed instrumentation on clerical and other indirect work.

Savings and Operating Cost. This is the difference between the operating costs shown for the present and the proposed basis.

Less Federal Tax on Income. The rate used in this calculation is applied from accounting records for the period involved. In the case of facilities for producing material for governmental consumption, renegotiation of this expense may be involved.

Project Expenditures. This is the new money to be spent for permanent facilities. It does not include working capital or any allocated facilities.

Allocated Facilities. The proposed instrumentation may affect a portion of the available capacity of the existing power or service facilities. Thus it is necessary to earn a return only on a fraction of the investment that is consumed as a result of the installation.

Working Capital. In addition to the money represented by physical facilities, a certain amount is represented by inventories and cash on hand. Savings through reductions in working capital often are possible as a result of automatic control. It should be recognized that a reduction in investment will have a powerful influence on the criterion "per cent return on investment," since it is not subject to the dilution suffered by "operating costs," savings subject to Federal income tax, and other factors.

Return on Investment. The percentage represented by the net annual savings to be expected from the proposed investment is the criterion that will be used for evaluation of the proposal. Different companies have different requirements for the percentage return necessary to obtain authorization for a proposed installation. This varies, depending on the nature of the savings (whether in labor or material), the nature of the product and its market, the competitive position of the company and other factors.

Economic Effects of Installing Instrumentation

Instrumentation that is installed on a savings basis will usually affect chemical-plant operation in one of the following ways:

1. Reduction of equipment investment by the elimination of intermediate storage, excess capacity, standby machinery, and unnecessary purification steps, or by making possible an operation that would otherwise be inoperable
2. Reduction of working capital by speeding production adjustments and by reducing inventory
3. Reduction of materials cost by minimizing waste and increasing yields
4. Maintenance of product quality at minimum acceptable level
5. Readjustment of operating conditions to suit variations in raw-material quality
6. Reduction in operating costs by increasing labor efficiency and simplifying operations
7. Increase in continuity of operation at lowered maintenance
8. Conservation of utilities and supplies consumed
9. Increase in production rates per dollar invested in plant equipment
10. Revitalization of obsolescent operations through modernization

More than half of the instruments used in chemical plants today did not exist 10 years ago. Currently, instruments are controlling the composition of process streams and the quality of product. The next logical step will be that of keeping the plant at its economic optimum, which is frequently different from the engineering optimum.

ORGANIZING AND TRAINING FOR INSTRUMENTATION RESPONSIBILITY

Organization

In all but the smallest chemical manufacturing companies, the responsibility for instrumentation or control-systems engineering, operation, and maintenance is vested in a separately identified segment of the organization. This segment usually is best allied with the operating rather than the service side of the organization. This is because process control is so intimately a part of the operating responsbility and because the interpretation of process measurements and the adjustment of control set points or other operating parameters is so essential to the achievement of production goals, the maintenance of operating continuity, and the adherence to measured standards of product quality.

The instrumentation segment must, at a minimum, provide a variety of talents and services, including instrumentation development, process-control systems analysis, and project engineering and maintenance.

Among the qualifications which may be considered essential to the chemical company's instrumentation staff are the need for knowledge in (1) physical chemistry, fluid dynamics, heat and mass transfer, and reaction systems; (2) analytical techniques required in the definition of the static and dynamic relationships between operating variables in complex chemical reactions; and (3) use of advanced mathematics and statistics in evaluating relationships between variables. These requirements are in addition to a fundamental knowledge of the physics and mechanics of instrumentation systems per se.

Functions and Responsibilities. One organizational approach to fitting the process control or instrumentation department (section or group) into the over-all plant management organization is shown in Fig. 22-188. The nature of the work performed depends on the nature of the operation, the depth of dependence on instrumentation, the value of the product, and other factors. In a situation such as that shown by Fig. 22-188, the instrumentation functions, exclusive of supervision, might take the classifications shown on the abbreviated job descriptions given in Table 22-23.

Some of the major items of work of the instrumentation organization, as shown in Fig. 22-188, are now described briefly:

Instrument Development. An instrument development facility in the chemical manufacturing organization is needed to supply the specialized equipments required in connection with research work and plant operations for which no commercial source may exist. These equipments take the form of (1) custom-designed inspection apparatus; (2) detection devices based on physical or chemical principles which are unique to the situation involved; (3) completely new forms of instrumentation whose development represents a potentially superior operating basis; (4) special combinations of commercially available instruments modified in capability more closely to satisfy the needs of a particular application; (5) proprietary developments which, if purchased outside the company, would reveal know-how of value to competitors; and (6) some research efforts which may not have obvious relevance to current operations but may be of potential importance.

Equipment usually necessary for the conduct of an effective instrument-development program includes the following types and categories: (1) sets of primary and secondary standards, plus laboratory calibration and checking apparatus for weight, temperature, voltage, resistance, pressure, capacitance, and gas constants; (2) infrared spectrophotometer; (3) mass spectrometer; (4) emission spectrometer; (5) vapor chromatograph; (6) radiation sources and detectors; (7) precision electrical measuring instruments; (8) pH and oxidation-reduction measuring equipment; (9) chemical analysis instruments; and (10) electrical and electronic test equipment.

Plant Test and Process Analysis. A means for collecting and organizing laboratory, pilot-plant and full-scale plant operating data is an important ingredient in the development of sound engineering design and the diagnosis of obscure operating anomalies. Many organizations have assembled mobile complements of test

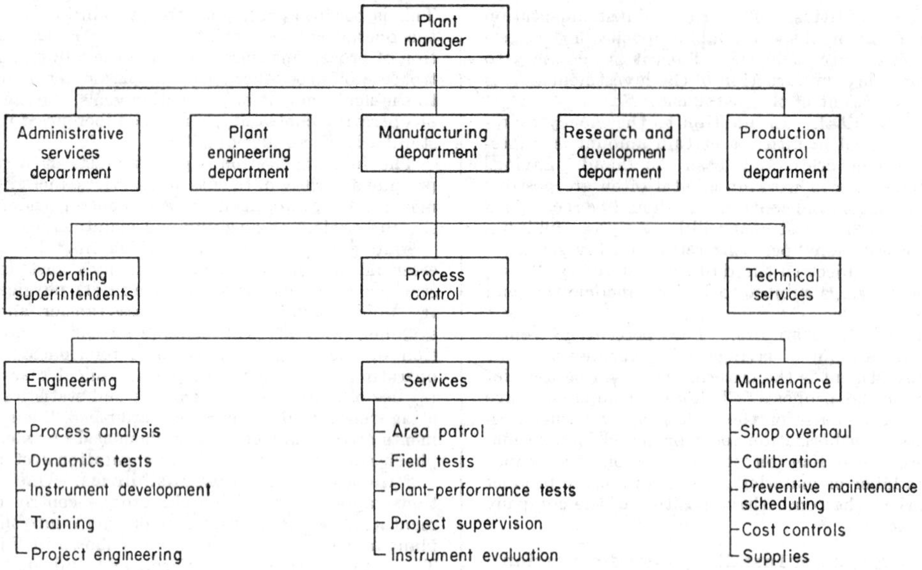

FIG. 22-188. Location of instrumentation and process-control facility in a large process-industry corporation.

Table 22-23. Chemical-plant Instrumentation Manpower

Position	Qualities	Schooling	Experience	Function	Relationship
Mechanic.......	Mechanical aptitude, manual dexterity, inquisitive, and ability to learn rapidly	Use of tools, arithmetical operations, mechanical, electrical, and physics fundamentals. Interpretation of drawings	Repair and calibration, trouble shooting and adjustment of broad range of instruments on variety of processes	Assure satisfactory availability and performance of installed instrumentation	Cooperates with plant operator and coordinates through technician and supervisor
Technician......	Alert, stable, progressive, ability to diagnose logically and correctly	Use of test equipment, mathematics, electronics, chemistry, process behavior, instrument measurement, and control technology	Process equipment operation, diagnosis of instrument and process troubles, repair of complex instrument systems, close association with experienced engineers	Maintain special equipment. Diagnose operating troubles, assure peak performance and maximum operating continuity	Cooperates with plant operator; initiates corrective actions
Maintenance engineer	Systematic, careful, sound judgment, rapid diagnostician, persuasive leader	Engineering fundamentals, plant operations, measurement and control principles, supervision, equipment operation	Responsibility for work of instrument craft organization of maintenance procedures, supervision of unit start-up and operation	Organize maintenance effort for most economic preservation of operating continuity and adaptation to changing conditions	Coordinates maintenance program for maximum over-all economy consistent with operating requirements
Project engineer	Meticulous, decisive, cooperative, quick to understand and to use help intelligently	Engineering fundamentals, equipment operation, measurement and control, processes and unit operations, construction	Operation of instrumented processes, design of major process- control installations, close association with manufacturers' engineers	Provide adequate instrumentation for economic operation of proposed plants and processes	Derives information from process engineers; specifies instruments as required
Applications engineer	Authoritatively informed on many subjects, analytical, inquisitive, systematic, thoughtful, persuasive, confident	Chemical engineering, automatic-control theory, methods of measurement, advanced mathematics, use of computers	Process engineering, equipment operation, instrument evaluation and uses, plant tests, use of analog computers, frequency response and correlation analysis	Investigate and evaluate suitability of instrument systems to process requirements. Specify approach and system most appropriate for needs	Determines process needs in cooperation with process engineer. Defines needs for guidance of project engineer
Development engineer	Patient, inquisitive, ingenious, creative, scientifically inclined	Mechanics, physical chemistry, electronics, dynamics, advanced mathematics	Development of electronic circuits, analytical instruments, automatic inspection systems, and special measurement techniques	Conceive and develop workable instrument systems to suit process requirements not satisfied by commercially available devices	Sets program based on advice of application engineer and analysis of operating needs
Specialist—control systems	Analytical, logical, intuitive, realistic, sound judgment, able to formulate ideas clearly	Mathematics, statistics, chemical engineering, use of computers, process analysis, advance control-systems analysis	Use of analog and digital computers, dynamics analysis of chemical processes, correlation techniques, application engineering	Quantitatively analyze process controls required for optimum operation of existing and proposed units	Investigates process operability and defines control approach in cooperation with research engineers
Instrumentation analyst	Scientifically inclined, ingenious, patient, systematic, deep interests in physics and chemistry	Physics, chemistry, physical chemistry, nuclear techniques, electronics, mathematics, advanced analytical chemistry	Laboratory analysis, electronic-circuit development, fabrication, installation, and use of special analytical instruments	Define analytical approach and specify suitable instruments for process-stream analysis	Works cooperatively with project engineer or plant technical group to define analytical needs

instrumentation with which experimental data can be obtained from a number of operating facilities. Others have provided a variety of portable units which can be carried or shipped to the test site. Still others make a practice of installing special instrumentation on a temporary basis at new facilities and pilot plants. This equipment is used during initial operation to record the results of experiments carried on during acceptance tests and periods of the greatest difficulty of operation. The test equipment is disassembled after having served it purpose and stored for reuse on subsequent constructions. The second of these practices is most prevalent and offers the greatest flexibility for meeting multiple commitments.

Supporting the portable test facility, a data-reduction center with computation equipment is desirable. Also needed are test facilities for checking the performance characteristics of control apparatus and the frequency response of control-loop assemblies. The analog computer is invaluable for exploration of process-control alternatives and for investigating the basis for design of plant equipment.

In the usual case, the following equipment should be a part of the requirement to serve this need: (1) infrared analyzer with a variety of sources and cells; (2) ultraviolet analyzer with a variety of sources and cells; (3) refractometer; (4) gas chromatograph; (5) pH meters; (6) thermal-conductivity analyzer; (7) oxygen analyzer (paramagnetic); (8) Orsat apparatus; (9) Explosimeter; (10) electrical-conductivity bridge and cells; (11) set of fast-response flow transmitters, pressure transmitters, and temperature transmitters; (12) radiation sources and detectors; (13) recording viscometer; (14) miscellaneous transducers and converters; (15) speed recorders; (16) power supplies; (17) multichannel recorders for electrical voltage and pneumatic pressure; (18) X-Y recorder; (19) signal generators; (20) scalers; (21) oscilloscopes; (22) radiation pyrometers; (23) load cells; (24) densitometers; and (25) timers and program controllers.

Computation Center. Supplementing the test facility but available for use on work outside the region of instrumentation, the computer center will usually include the following complement of equipment (since no computer facility ever proves large enough to accommodate the needs that arise as the competence and facility in its use increase and become known, any such installation should be made with adequate provision for expansion):

1. An analog computer with the following components:

100 to 200	operational amplifiers
50 to 100	multiplication channels
25 to 50	operational relays
25 to 50	function generators
25 to 50	operational switches
2 to 3	separate consoles
3 to 4	X-Y recorders
12 to 18	recording channels

2. A digital-computer facility of the maximum size and capability that can be afforded

Work related to instrumentation engineering for which the computation center is needed ranges from the calculation of flow-orifice diameters to the simulated operation of a complete processing system, including its chemical kinetics, energy and material balance, and controller characteristics. Aside from the uses which involve the solution of mathematical equations on a routine or purely objective basis, the greatest use for computers is by chemical engineers who are searching out the mechanism of a physical or chemical phenomenon in order that improved understanding will increase their confidence for design and operation.* Exploratory work of this nature is gradually developing a body of knowledge which is increasingly needed for quantitative design of controlled processes.

* *Cf.* pp. **22**-54 to **22**-61 on computer controls.

In addition to the development of these mathematical models, the computation center is an invaluable aid to training. Dynamic models of an operating entity can be made to reproduce almost every type of operating difficulty, thus providing opportunity for realistic trial of alternative procedures for overcoming the difficulty. Experience can be gained before the fact in dealing with emergency situations with maximum safety. Alternative choices can be fully evaluated and demonstrated. This is important in the design phase of a new facility, where by demonstration, unanimous agreement on a course of action and the elimination of endless controversy results from dramatic exploration and comparative evaluation of all suggested alternatives.

Project Engineering

The instrumentation portion of a new construction project in the process industries involves details of engineering, specification, and procurement out of all proportion to the purchase value of the instrument equipment.† Numerous procedures for streamlining the operation have been originated and incorporated by groups faced with the problem. Essentially, these take the form of engineering standards for specification and installation. Price agreements are negotiated for repetitive items. Standard symbols and terminology simplify drafting. Repetitive situations are supplied with identical combinations and to the extent possible, all requirements are simplified to enable the repetitive use of a minimum variety of instrument types and models.

Project requirements are evolved as the design progresses. Basic data become available and decisions on operating strategy are reached in a series of steps wherein instrumentation engineering is nearly always subservient and consequently undergoes many fluctuations from one alternative to another. Consideration of the controllability aspects of proposed designs early in their development does much to alleviate this difficulty. Investigation of alternatives and establishment of quantitative bases for control decisions using analog and digital computation is the most powerful combatant against vacillation. An additional tool of proved value is the scale model. Development of design layout for most efficient and utilitarian arrangement is enhanced by this means. Additional dividends accrue to the use of models in the avoidance of interferences and the coordinated visualization by all who are involved.

At the outset, a very inexpensive representation using blocks and sheets can be used to obtain agreement on general layout. At the intermediate stage, it is profitable to build with approximate shapes and to assign pipe, duct, and conduit routes. Questions on process sequence, hydraulic and mechanical efficiency, operator access, maintenance ease, safety, and expansibility will have been resolved at this stage. In the final model, replicas are used; piping, duct and electrical cabling are placed; measurement- and control-equipment locations are chosen; possible modifications are visualized and provided for; agreement is reached on the size and location of service facilities; and plans are evolved for the most efficient sequence of construction steps. Special cameras are used to make photographs of the model which will serve as substitutes for drawings and which, when duplicated, will serve each craft in developing bills of material and in sketching installation details.

A project engineering section must work with speed and decisiveness in order to minimize engineering costs.

† *Cf.* pp. **24**-2 to **24**-8.

This is best achieved by separating all specialized engineering and science functions from the project organization without making the separation so effective as to bar ready access to the use of such specialized talent where needed. Usually, the specialists and their equipment are being used in programs of research and plant assistance, which often are financed from corporation funds, thus reducing the costs which might otherwise be allocated to project engineering on a distributed basis.

With nearly one thousand new instrument items being introduced each year, no project engineering group can operate effectively without provision for keeping abreast of new developments. The instrument-evaluation facility, which may be operated by the plant performance test group, may include in its program the comparative evaluation of instruments being considered for project purposes as well as the evaluations normally conducted for development of dynamic characteristics in control-loop analysis.

Maintenance

Instrument maintenance in a chemical plant can operate under two entirely different philosophies. Consistent with the accepted pattern for care of operating equipment, one philosophy attempts to reduce all work to patterns of systematic jobs and schedules, with success measured in terms of maintenance-cost reduction and decreasing shutdown frequency attributable to instrument-maintenance failure. The other philosophy directs attention to continuity of the operating process even at the expense of maintenance, and success is spelled in terms of plant production vs. capacity.

Wherever possible, an intelligent compromise between the two extremes is sought. It is necessary for management to be alert to the forces that are constantly at work to cause unbalance and it must be empowered to exert the necessary restraining influence. The first, or maintenance-efficiency philosophy, is served by those who imagine that most problems can be eliminated by the establishment of a procedure for every possible eventuality and who are least happy when something is handled independently of the system. The second, or operational philosophy, is served by those who are less interested in the cost of repair than they are in the cost of lost production. They constantly observe behavior in order to detect the beginnings of imperfect function and work continuously to prevent the need for repair. Naturally, such constant surveillance is costly in terms of maintenance labor but is counterbalanced by the prevention of major repair or extended interruption to plant operation.

Maintenance Manpower. Some organizations consolidate the operating supervisor and control technician function into one, making operating responsibility a highly technical one. Controller adjustment, field calibration, trouble shooting, and in-place repair are the function of this area control team, which is responsible to operating management but is controlled by the central instrumentation organization. Admittedly, this dual responsibility can generate misunderstandings, but it has the advantage that it is conducive to a strong cooperative relationship instead of a schism between maintenance and operation.

As a craft, instrumentation maintenance suffers an eternal struggle because it is one that is never completely mastered. New techniques, new instrument designs operating on new principles confront the instrument craftsman continuously. Training programs, factory refresher courses, and shop talks go on constantly. Volumes of descriptive literature and lesson material are always in the process of digestion. Flow diagrams and process descriptions follow basic programs in mathematics, physics, and chemistry in a never-ending effort to master the changing patterns of plant operations.

Training for Maintenance. Where the installation is new, training for instrument maintenance begins 6 months before the plant starts operation. A typical program covers the material outlined in Table 22-24. This is conducted by experienced instrumentation engineers who have had additional instruction in the principles of teaching. The course furnishes a refresher in mathematics, physics, chemistry, and electronics; then covers the principles of operation, installation practices, care, and maintenance of each of a number of kinds of instruments suited to each of a number of chemical

Table 22-24. Instrumentation Training Program for Advancement from Trainee to Control-Mechanic

Subject	Class hours	Shop hours
Mathematics:		
Use of fractions and decimals	2	0
Use of ratio, proportion, and per cent	2	0
Use of square root and squares	2	0
Calculation of area and volume	2	0
Use of graphs and calibration curves	2	0
Conversions of units	2	0
Pressure:		
Fundamentals of pressure	2	0
Use of manometers	4	2
Use of elastic-deformation instruments	2	4
Use of pressure calibrators	4	2
Maintenance of pressure gages	6	4
Maintenance of pressure recorders	4	4
Maintenance of pressure transmitters	20	16
Temperature:		
Application of temperature fundamentals	2	0
Use of glass-stem and industrial thermometers	4	2
Use of bimetallic thermometers	4	2
Application of filled-system thermometers	2	0
Installation of liquid-filled thermometers	2	2
Installation of gas-filled thermometers	2	2
Use of temperature-calibrating equipment	4	2
Maintenance of temperature transmitters	4	4
Maintenance of temperature recorders	6	4
Flow:		
Flow-measurement fundamentals	2	0
Use of orifice plates	4	2
Use of differential manometers	6	2
Use of flow calibrators	6	4
Maintenance of flowmeters—general	2	4
Maintenance of mercury manometers	6	4
Maintenance of ring-type manometers	6	4
Maintenance of bell-type manometers	6	4
Maintenance of bellows-type manometers	6	4
Use of area-type meter	2	2
Maintenance of glass-tube rotameters	6	4
Maintenance of metal-tube rotameters	6	4
Maintenance of flow transmitters	18	6
Maintenance of displacement meters	6	4
Level:		
Fundamentals of level measurement	2	0
Hydrostatic-instrument maintenance	2	2
Bubbler-type-instrument practice	6	2
Ball-float-instrument practice	4	4
Displacement-float-instrument practice	8	6
Mechanical-float-instrument practice	6	4
Weight:		
Fundamentals of weighing	2	0
Load-cell practice	8	6
Gravimetric-feeder practice	8	6
Automatic control:		
Instrument-air-supply practice	4	0
Concepts in pneumatic control	2	0
Pneumatic-controller operation	2	2
Maintenance of pressure regulators	2	2
Maintenance of temperature regulators	2	2
Controller-relay operation	2	4
Controller mechanisms	4	4
Controller circuitry	4	3
Controller test and calibration	4	4
Maintenance of position-balance controllers	6	4
Maintenance of force-balance controllers	6	4
Maintenance of specialized controllers	6	4
Control-valve principles	2	0
Maintenance of diaphragm actuators	8	4
Maintenance of piston actuators	8	4
Maintenance of valve positioners	6	4
Maintenance of control accessories	8	2

Table 22-24. Instrumentation Training Program for Advancement from Trainee to Control Mechanic—(*Continued*)

Subject	Class hours	Shop hours
Process-control practice	6	4
Control-loop diagraming	6	2
Controller adjustment	16	10
Process-control trouble shooting	16	10
Time-cycle controllers	4	2
Interlock systems	4	2
Alarm and signal systems	4	2
Specialized control-loop checking	8	0
Control-center check-out and maintenance	16	0
Electricity and Electronics:		
D.c. electricity	8	0
D.c. series circuits	2	2
D.c. parallel circuits	2	2
Application of Ohm's law	2	2
Measurement of d.c. power	2	2
A.c. electricity	4	2
A.c. voltage and current relationships	4	2
Inductance, capacitance, impedance	2	2
Trouble shooting a.c. circuits	6	4
Electromagnetic theory	8	2
Transformers	2	2
Vacuum-tube-voltmeter use	2	2
Oscilloscope use	8	4
Resistor-capacitor coding	8	2
Capacitance circuits	8	4
Diode characteristics and use	8	4
Filter circuits	2	2
Rectifier circuits	2	2
Voltage-divider circuits	2	2
D.c. power supplies	2	2
Triode characteristics and use	4	4
RC amplifier coupling	2	2
Amplifier-coupling practice	2	2
Control-grid operation	2	2
Amplifier trouble shooting	6	3
Power-supply trouble shooting	2	2
Feedback effects	2	2
Cathode-follower circuits	2	2
Application of tetrodes and pentodes	2	2
Oscillator trouble shooting	6	3
Use of tube tester	2	4
Thermoelectric principles	2	2
Use of portable potentiometer	6	4
Operation of electronic potentiometers	8	4
Trouble shooting electronic potentiometers	8	8
Trouble shooting resistance bridges	8	4
Trouble shooting capacitance bridges	8	4
Trouble shooting interconnected systems	4	2
Electrical-instrument installation practice	8	0
Electronic-control-systems theory	4	0
Electronic-controller operation	16	4
Controller adjustments	4	2
Controller trouble shooting	12	6
Electrical actuators for control valves	4	2
Electropneumatic transducers	2	2
Control-loop checking	2	2
Control-loop trouble shooting	16	8
Control-center check-out and maintenance	16	0
Analyzers:		
Principles of pH measurement	4	4
Trouble shooting pH measurement	4	4
Trouble shooting electrical-conductivity meters	2	2
Trouble shooting photoelectric instruments	2	2
Fundamentals of chemical analysis	16	2
Thermal-conductivity analyzers	8	4
Photoelectric analyzers	8	4
Infrared analyzers	16	8
Gamma- and beta-radiation instrumentation	16	8

plant situations. Sources of error are illustrated and evaluated. Methods for circumventing commonly encountered difficulties are shown. Test procedures and diagnostic practices are taught.

During the final phase, agreement is reached for participation in the contractor's final installation work and for check-out of the installed equipment. This and the actual startup are the most critical and often the most valuable training stages. Close cooperation between student, instructor, operating supervision, and construction worker is necessary. Each student must be exposed to the widest possible variety of experience. Each must be checked out in the logical deduction of cause related to a full range of simulated effects.

A training device of inestimable value for both the instrumentation technician and the operator is the simulated control center. With it, the instructor can construct every conceivable operating situation. The operator can be taught to diagnose the situation and to plan and execute the proper steps for correction. The technician must be similarly versed, with the added requirement that he cannot assume that all instruments are operating correctly.

Motion pictures, sound slides, exploded working models, construction kits, and practice instruments are needed for the instrumentation training program. Course materials in the form of lecture guides, texts, films, and demonstrations can be obtained from professional organizations, such as the Instrument Society of America, from instrument manufacturers, numerous technical institutes, vocational schools, and colleges. Invariably, the course content will have to be reorganized and supplemented in order to satisfy the requirements of each plant situation. Only after the completion of a program is it profitable to spend time at one or more of the excellent factory-conducted courses dealing with a manufacturer's particular line of equipment.

Maintenance Facilities. The instrumentation-maintenance shop depends on the magnitude, type, and frequency of work it is expected to handle. Most organizations prefer to have an instrument shop that is self-sufficient. The requirements for a typical large plant will be considered. The shop should be located close to other maintenance facilities and to central materials storage. Heavy items of instrumentation can be unloaded at the entrance, decontaminated, cleaned, and handled by a chain hoist to the central work area. Special vises and jigs have been developed for holding control valves, meters, and other heavy units. Cleaning baths may use solvent vapor and ultrasonic agitation. Calibration stands for flowmeters should be equipped for gas and liquid service.

All work stands should be designed to suit specific needs. The majority of these stations should have precision air-supply regulators and calibration gages of multiple range. Quick connectors of various size and a variety of special connectors and jigs for the most common instrument types should be on hand. Electrical power supply and calibration stands should be installed at numerous locations, although the main electrical repair facility may be located in a separate room.

Calibration assemblies for flowmeters used in chemical service generally are for smaller capacity than those for petroleum refineries and power plants. A manifolded assembly of rotameters of different ranges, dry-gas meters, a wet test meter, a weigh scale, and a pair of calibration tanks plus one gasometer-type meter prover can be arranged to suit almost any condition likely to be met. Pressure-calibration stands using double-well manometers, precision gages, and dead-weight testers can serve the dual purpose of checking static-pressure and differential-type instruments. Temperature calibration usually requires one small muffle furnace, an oil bath, a molten salt bath, and a checking system composed of certified thermometers, resistance bulbs, thermocouples, a precision resistance bridge, and pontentiometer.

Separation of the electrical and electronics repair facility from other shop work is recommended in the interest of cleanliness, freedom from noise and vibration, and to prevent accidents which may result from the presence of liquids and gases in an area where high voltages may be grounded through a worker's wet feet. Special jigs and racks usually are required for handling the explosionproof housings which are used in most chemical-plant instruments of the electrical type. A chemical hood and ventilator also are needed, inasmuch as many of the electronic instruments used for process-stream analysis will require calibration with standard mixtures of process fluids, some of which may be toxic, flammable, and/or explosive. Mobile radio equipment and radio telemetering systems also are usually the responsibility of the instrument shop. Standard test equipment is needed for these and for many of the other miscellaneous plant apparatus, such as fire-alarm systems, plant-protection systems, wired television, weather stations, teletype systems, and computers.

Maintenance Records. Despite the difficulty of segregating instrument-repair costs from what might be termed "plant continuity insurance," there are numerous advantages in addition to cost control for keeping good maintenance records. To be useful, the records must be factual and religiously maintained with their purpose clearly in mind.

Functions other than cost control, which a readily accessible maintenance-record system affords, include

1. Central source of original data and specifications
2. Complete history of alterations, range changes, corrosion and wear resistance, performance under differing process conditions, replacement, and repair
3. Cross comparison between different makes and models of instruments and of similar instruments in different types of service
4. Automatic recheck and preventive-maintenance schedule
5. Quantitative basis for evaluating designs and for supporting the need for redesign or change
6. Basis for estimating reliability and for predicting shutdown schedules

To serve these purposes, even a moderate-sized plant will find it worthwhile to code its instrument units on punched cards or other mechanized data forms. A code for critical types of adjustment, replacement, or repair then can be used and a history developed which can be explored by machine search. Patterns and trends thus are discovered which would otherwise remain hidden in a mass of miscellaneous data. Cost information also can be organized on such a system and will provide meaningful guidance for supervision, provided it is remembered that the time devoted to process analysis and control-system adjustment cannot be equated to maintenance costs.

Standards of Instrumentation Practice. The larger the contractor who builds plants for the chemical industry, the stronger will be the tendency to simplify project work by means of standardization. Instrument manufacturers have cooperated with the chemical industry in the evolution of standard practices. Trade associations such as the Scientific Apparatus Makers Association and the Fluid Controls Institute have active programs for standardization. They work closely with appropriate units of the Instrument Society of America and the Chemical Industry Advisory Board for the determination of standardization needs peculiar to chemical-plant uses.

It is the user who can benefit most from intelligently following an adequate standards program. Uniformity in the establishment of units of measurement throughout the plant is an excellent starting point. Too often, one finds a Fahrenheit thermometer located adjacent to a Celsius (centigrade) calibrated unit simply because one is part of a power unit and the other is part of a chemical unit. Agreement on measuring units among all agencies responsible for the use of instruments can be followed by agreement on types of instruments for each class of application; *e.g.*, bimetallic vs. filled-system, glass stem vs. dial, industrial vs. laboratory, and ½-in. connection vs. ¾-in. These represent only a few of the choices open to the selection of a simple indicating thermometer.

Standardization on the minimum combination of variations can increase safety, save time and money, and contribute significantly to versatility and ease of replacement.

Connections to piping and vessels, piping and wiring between instrument units, manifolds and mountings, enclosures and winterizing, vents and purges, air supply and power supply—all are subject to improved utility where standard practices and procedures have been adopted and followed.

A uniform basis for conducting tests and a uniform nomenclature and terminology for describing instrument performance is an important result of cooperation between chemical-plant instrumentation engineers. This is particularly pertinent with respect to the dynamic characteristics of instruments and to such terms as accuracy, linearity, and resolution.

Standard methods for treating data in the calculation of fluid flow are critical to the chemical plant. Different flowmeter manufacturers use different reference pressures and temperatures, and it is necessary to be careful in selecting conversion factors for energy and material-balance calculations. Most plants reduce all flows to weight units, *e.g.*, pounds per hour, and adopt a standard reference for base conditions. All orifice-meter installations follow standard patterns, usually employing flange taps, and the orifice diameter is calculated in accordance with one procedure throughout.

A standardized program for handling orifice calculations is published under the auspices of A.I.Ch.E. for use on Univac I. A standard method for calibrating area-type meters and current meters is necessary, along with uniform treatment for factors correcting for viscosity and density. The capacity of automatic control valves is calculated in accordance with whatever standards the manufacturer employs, and it is necessary for the chemical plant to recalculate all these to a common standard.

Laboratory analysis, so often used to check the accuracy of process-stream analysis, is itself subject to critical examination as a source of discrepancies. Standard practices must be established for the collection of representative samples and for the conduct of each step in the analysis. Care must be taken to ensure that units are reduced correctly to a comparable basis.

CONTROL OF DISTILLATION COLUMNS

The problems of distillation control relate directly to the relative volatility of the materials being separated. For example, water and ethylene glycol are easily separated because of the high volatility of water relative to that of glycol. But closer boiling mixtures, such as the isomers of xylene, are more difficult to separate by distillation.

Whether separations are fundamentally easy or difficult, the distillation equipment is usually designed for a particular separation with provision for only modest margins of performance ability. Thus it is the responsibility of the distillation-control system to safeguard the purity of distilled products. Reference will be made here to control of composition, temperature, pressure, and level. These are elements of the control system designed to maintain purity of product. Other controls may regulate productivity and economy, but it would be difficult to suggest an example where composition of product is subordinate to either.

The more elusive aspects of distillation control relate to control of product composition and its responses to disturbances, such as feed rate, feed composition, or feed enthalpy, that originate external to the distillation column. The McCabe-Thiele diagram (see Sec. 13) was originally devised as an aid in designing distillation columns. It is helpful in visualizing the effects of disturbances, several of which are covered here by way of illustration.

The majority of distillation columns produce two product streams: (1) one rich in *low boilers, i.e.*, distillate, and (2) one rich in *high boilers, i.e.*, bottoms. In this sense, their operation parallels that of a simple binary distillation. The concept of "key" component separation represents a means of treating a complex separation in terms of a simple binary separation.

Degrees of Freedom in Control Specifications. It is important to recognize the degrees of freedom of choice in specifying the variables to be controlled. The choice of variables open is the natural consequence of the column heat and material balance and is analyzed as follows:

Figure 22-189 represents a typical distillation column. The over-all material balance can be represented by the following two equations:

$$F = W + D \tag{22-30}$$

$$Fx_F = Wx_W + Dx_D \tag{22-31}$$

where F = feed rate, lb.-moles/unit of time
W = bottom product, lb.-moles/unit of time
D = distillate, lb.-moles/unit of time
x_F = mole fraction of low boiler in the feed
x_D = mole fraction of low boiler in the distillate
x_W = mole fraction of low boiler in the bottom product

The assumption is made that the molar heat capacities and the latent heats of vaporization of all components are

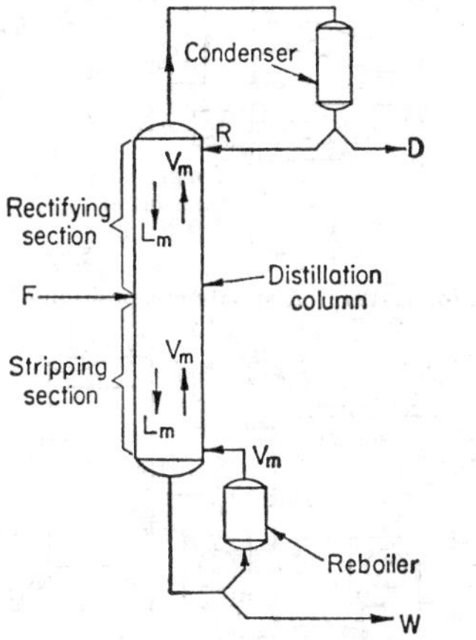

FIG. 22-189. Typical distillation-column arrangement.

the same. It is assumed also that (1) heat losses from column are negligible and (2) heats of mixing are negligible. In consequence, the upward vapor flow and the downward liquid flow in both the rectifying and stripping sections are invariant within the sections. Also, the accounting for the column heat balance is independent of the compositions of the product streams.

With these qualifications, the internal material balance and the heat balance can be accounted for by the following equations:

$$L_n = (1 + b)R \tag{22-32}$$

$$V_n = D + (1 + b)R \tag{22-33}$$

$$L_m = L_n + qF \tag{22-34}$$

$$V_m = L_m - W \tag{22-35}$$

$$x_W = f\frac{L_m}{V_m} \tag{22-36}$$

$$x_D = g\frac{L_n}{V_n} \tag{22-37}$$

where V_n = vapor rate in the rectifying section, lb.-moles/unit of time
V_m = vapor rate in the stripping section, lb.-moles/unit of time
L_n = liquid rate in the rectifying section, lb.-moles/unit of time
L_m = liquid rate in the stripping section, lb.-moles/unit of time
D = distillate rate, lb.-moles/unit of time
R = external reflux, lb.-moles/unit of time

b is a numerical factor depending on the reflux enthalpy of temperature. Note: $b > 0$ whenever the reflux temperature is below that at the top of the column.

q is a numerical factor dependent on feed enthalpy whose value satisfies the following constraints: $q > 1$ when the feed temperature is below that of the feed plate. $q = 1$ when the feed temperature and composition are identical to those of the feed plate. $1 > q > 0$ when the feed enters the column partially vaporized. $q = 0$ when the feed is completely vaporized and is at saturated temperature $q < 0$ when the feed is superheated vapor.

In Eqs. (22-36) and (22-37), f and g account for functional relationships which are dependent on column-design factors, such as (1) number of plates in the column, (2) location of control plates, (3) location of feed plate, and (4) temperature or other criteria specified for the control plates.

From the standpoint of controls, these factors are fixed. For example, the automatic controls are unable to shift the injection of feed up or down the column in response to departures from optimum column operation. Neither is the location of the control plates ordinarily regarded as variable. Even the control-plate temperatures are ordinarily considered as fixed, although it would be possible to regard them as variable and arrange feedback controls for their regulation.

The consequence of fixing all the factors on which the functionals f and g depend is to fix the functionals in turn. Therefore, they will be excluded from the list of variables in the analysis to follow. Excluding f and g, Eqs. (22-30) through (22-37) include 13 variables. One possible classification of the 13 is as follows:

Free variables (22-32) (*usually not controllable*): x_F, q, and b

Variables whose values are usually controlled (22-31): F and x_D or alternately F and x_W

Dependent variables (22-37): W, D, V_n, V_m, L_n, L_m, R, and x_W or alternately x_D

Thus 5 of the 13 variables are defined, which leaves 8 unknowns in 8 independent equations. There exists a unique solution for this set, and thereby the column performance is completely determined.

It is necessary to assign values to 5 of the 13 variables in order to reduce the system to 8 equations in 8 unknowns. Usually some of the 5 represent conditions imposed by preceding process steps, such as feed composition, feed rate, and feed enthalpy. Usually the overhead or the bottoms composition is specified. It is not permissible to overdefine the system. The sum of *free* and *controlled* variables must equal 5. Conversely, the *dependent* variables must equal 8. Within this framework, there are a number of possible combinations open that characterize different modes of column control. Several of these combinations are shown in Table 22-25.

Table 22-25. Possible Modes of Column Control

Distillate and feed	Distillate and bottoms	Distillate and boil-up	Distillate bottoms and boil-up	Bottoms and boil-up	Bottoms boil-up and reflux	Feed-rate distillate and boil-up	Distillate bottoms and boil-up	Distillate bottoms and feed enthalpy
Free Variables								
x_F, q, b	x_F, q, b	x_F, q, b	x_F, b	x_F, q, b	x_F, b	x_F, b	F, x_F, b	x_F, b
Specified Variables								
F, x_D	x_D, x_W	x_D, V_m	x_D, x_W, V_m	x_W, V_m	x_W, V_m, L_n	x_D, F, V_m	x_D, x_W, V_m	x_D, x_W, q
Dependent Variables								
$W, D, R, V_m, L_m, V_n, L_n, x_W$	$W, D, R, V_m, L_m, V_n, L_n, F$	$W, D, R, L_m, V_n, L_n, x_W, F$	$W, D, R, L_m, V_n, L_n, F, q$	$W, D, R, L_m, V_n, L_n, x_D, F$	$W, D, L_m, V_n, x_D, F, q$	$W, D, R, L_m, V_n, L_n, q$	$W, D, R, L_m, V_n, L_n, q$	$W, D, R, L_m, V_m, V_n, L_n, F$

Composition Measurement. Distillation is invariably concerned with composition control, of either the distillate or bottom product, or both. Because composition bears an unvarying relationship to boiling temperature (assuming fixed pressure), it is natural that product composition usually is controlled via temperature.

Other possible methods of control exist, of course, and may assume more importance in the future. For example, product-stream composition could be measured continuously by other physical measurements, such as vapor-phase chromatography, ultraviolet photometry, or infrared photometry. Also, automatic chemical analyzers may find application in distillation-product quality control.

Differential Vapor-pressure Measurement. The actual boiling temperature at the temperature-control point will change with changes in column pressure. This can be troublesome, particularly in low-pressure columns where minor variations in absolute pressure are substantial compared with the operating pressure.

A differential-vapor-pressure-type temperature-measuring system (known as "$d\ V_p$" transmitter) avoids this problem (see Fig. 22-190). To one of two opposing

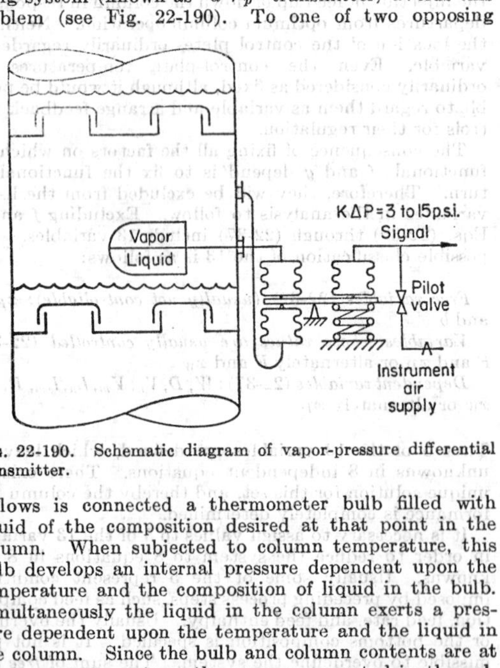

FIG. 22-190. Schematic diagram of vapor-pressure differential transmitter.

bellows is connected a thermometer bulb filled with liquid of the composition desired at that point in the column. When subjected to column temperature, this bulb develops an internal pressure dependent upon the temperature and the composition of liquid in the bulb. Simultaneously the liquid in the column exerts a pressure dependent upon the temperature and the liquid in the column. Since the bulb and column contents are at the same temperature, the pressures exerted in the column and in the bulb are each a function of the liquid composition, *i.e.*, that in the bulb and that in the column. Comparing the two pressures in the differential force-balance system shown affords a sensitive index of composition in the column as referred to the fixed composition in the bulb, which is independent of minor variations in absolute operating pressure.

Composition Control. The following discussion is based on use of temperature to indicate the composition of material, but the techniques described apply equally well to control loops based on other methods of composition measurement. Regulation of product composition is normally accomplished by manipulating boil-up and/or reflux rates, which change the relative rates of vapor and liquid flow throughout the column.

Typical Composition-control Systems. Figures 22-191, 22-192, and 22-193 show only those controls

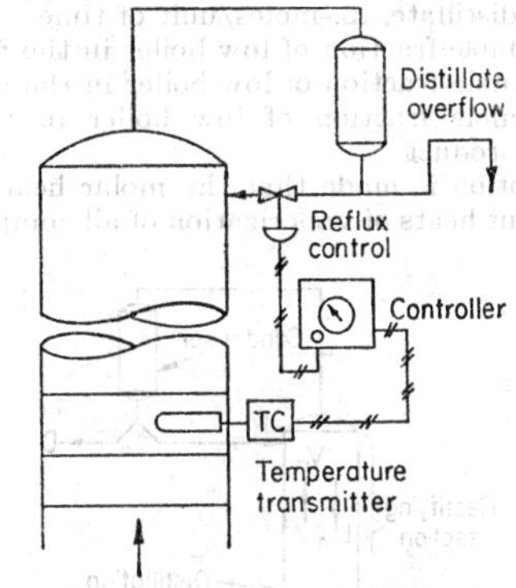

FIG. 22-191. Distillate-composition control.

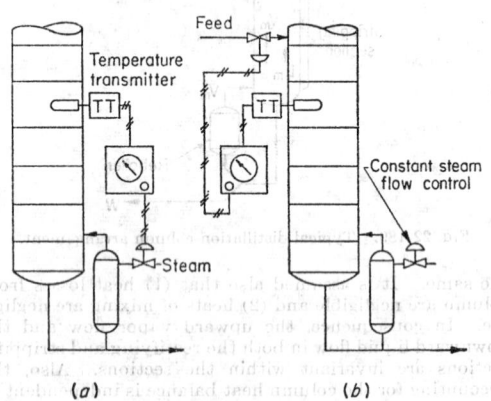

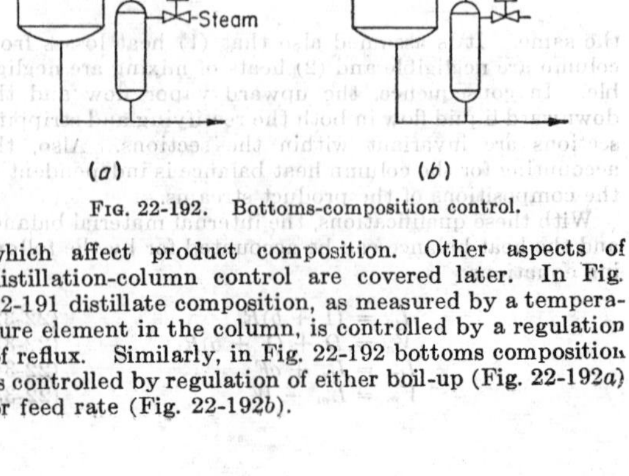

FIG. 22-192. Bottoms-composition control.

which affect product composition. Other aspects of distillation-column control are covered later. In Fig. 22-191 distillate composition, as measured by a temperature element in the column, is controlled by a regulation of reflux. Similarly, in Fig. 22-192 bottoms composition is controlled by regulation of either boil-up (Fig. 22-192*a*) or feed rate (Fig. 22-192*b*).

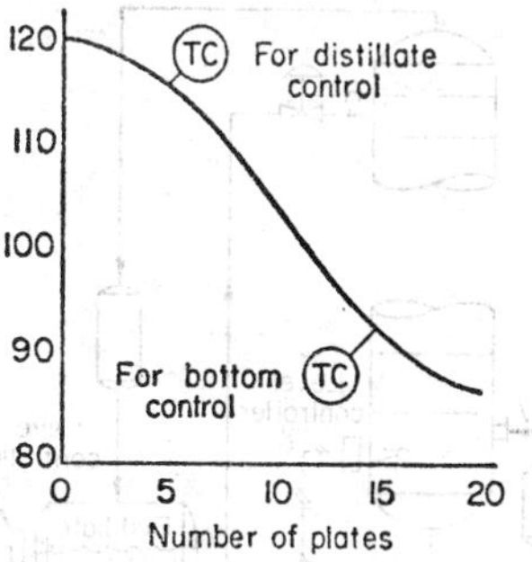

FIG. 22-193. Typical column temperature profile.

It would appear advantageous to maintain both reflux and boil-up on automatic control. If a simple binary separation is being controlled, this presents no problem, but rarely is this the case. If the feed contains an impurity having a volatility between those of the distillate and bottoms, automatic control on both reflux and boil-up presents problems. The reflux control operates to return the impurity down the column, while the boil-up control operates to send the impurity up the column. The result is that the intermediate boiler accumulates in mid-column and displaces the composition to such an extent that separation fails.

It is possible to devise controls, either continuous or intermittent, to sense mid-column temperature and purge the accumulated impurity (as in the so-called "pasteurization column"). Unless the accumulation is minor, however, it would be uneconomical to discard the purge without redistillation. An alternative is to allow the intermediate boiler to be discharged with either bottoms or distillate and, if justified, provide an additional column for its separation. The final choice rests, of course, on a comparison of the economics of the methods.

The foregoing discussion was based upon consideration of binary mixtures contaminated with intermediate-boiling impurities. It applies equally to the separation of key components from multicomponent mixtures.

Location of Composition Temperature-sensing Element. Common to both distillate- and bottoms-temperature controllers is the fact that the pertinent temperature measurement is made not on the product directly but in the column a number of plates away. Usually a product stream that is relatively pure is being separated from the binary mixture, so that boiling point or any other quality test of the product is often insensitive to changes in its concentration. Location of the temperature-sensing element some plates away makes it possible to obtain a greater change in temperature for a fixed change in final composition. Fixing the composition at such a point in the column suffices to control the column-product composition within narrow limits, even with wide variations in other factors, such as vapor and liquid flows.

Selecting the optimum location can best be done based on the column temperature profile, which the distillation designer should provide. Figure 22-193 shows a typical temperature profile in a distillation column. As indicated, the temperature-sensing element should be located where the temperature profile is steep but not too far removed from the end of the column. The rectifying-section temperature measurement must be located above the feed plate, the stripping-section temperature measurement below the feed plate.

Inventory-control Arrangements. Distillation columns provide little or no surge capacity, so that it is necessary to remove the distillate and bottoms as fast as they accumulate. Controls for product draw-off should be as simple as possible. In columns operating at atmospheric pressure, loop-sealed overflows may be all that are required. At positive pressures, level-controlled let-down valves are suitable. For vacuum operation, discharge pumps in combination with liquid-level-controlled valves are required.

Figures 22-194 and 22-195 suggest the various means of obtaining column inventory control. Figure 22-194

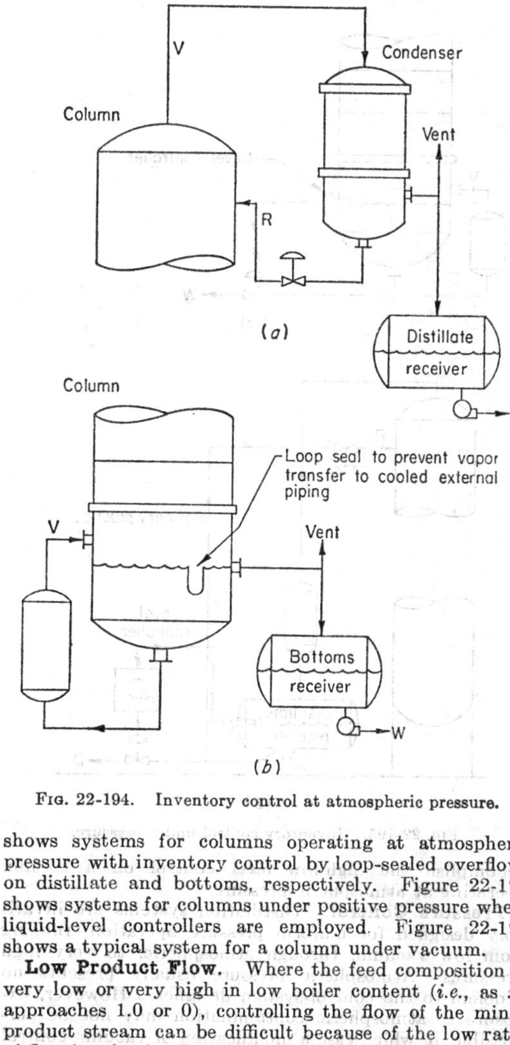

FIG. 22-194. Inventory control at atmospheric pressure.

shows systems for columns operating at atmospheric pressure with inventory control by loop-sealed overflows on distillate and bottoms, respectively. Figure 22-195 shows systems for columns under positive pressure where liquid-level controllers are employed. Figure 22-196 shows a typical system for a column under vacuum.

Low Product Flow. Where the feed composition is very low or very high in low boiler content (*i.e.*, as x_F approaches 1.0 or 0), controlling the flow of the minor product stream can be difficult because of the low rates of flow involved. In such cases, a high-low level-control system can be used, allowing the product to accumulate in a receiver until the upper limit of level is reached. Then the system opens a valve fully to discharge until the lower limit of level is reached. For pressure or vacuum operation, Fig. 22-197 shows a typical control system employing a float switch with magnetic pick-up to sense the high- and low-level points and to actuate electrically the discharge valve through a solenoid valve on the air-to-valve line. Note that, in the case of vacuum operation where a discharge pump is used, a sequence controller is employed to start the pump. Figure 22-197 shows the use of an intermittent siphon to

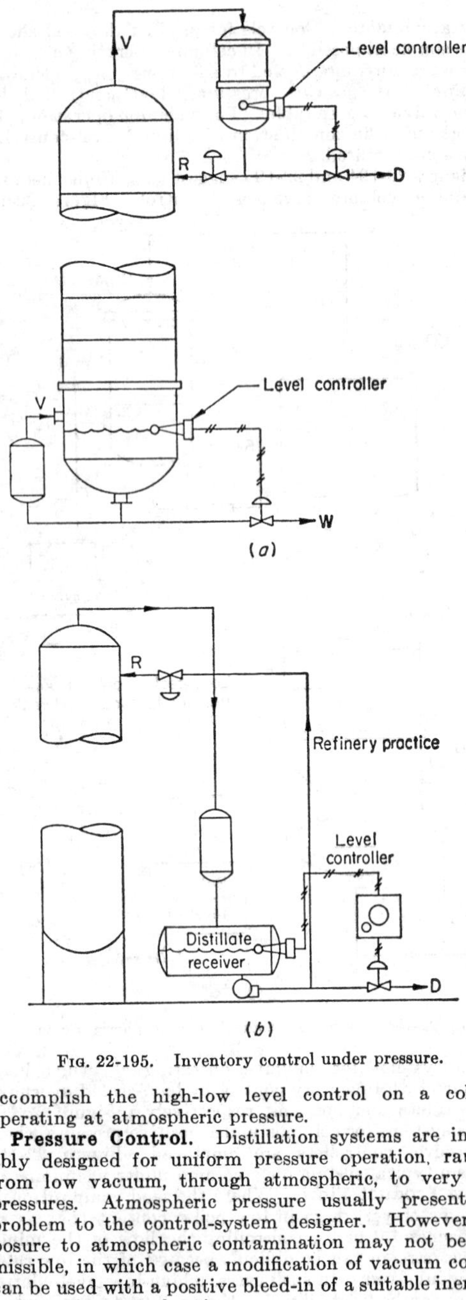

FIG. 22-195. Inventory control under pressure.

accomplish the high-low level control on a column operating at atmospheric pressure.

Pressure Control. Distillation systems are invariably designed for uniform pressure operation, ranging from low vacuum, through atmospheric, to very high pressures. Atmospheric pressure usually presents no problem to the control-system designer. However, exposure to atmospheric contamination may not be permissible, in which case a modification of vacuum control can be used with a positive bleed-in of a suitable inert gas to keep the control active.

Figure 22-198*a* shows a typical pressure-control system for a distillation column. Here control is obtained by regulation of the amount of venting on the condenser. Figure 22-198*b* shows a vacuum control system with control based on the use of a vacuum tempering bleed valve ahead of the vacuum source.

Effects of Column Dynamic Behavior. Most of the individual control loops referred to in the previous discussions are of standard design and are covered in standard texts on instrumentation.

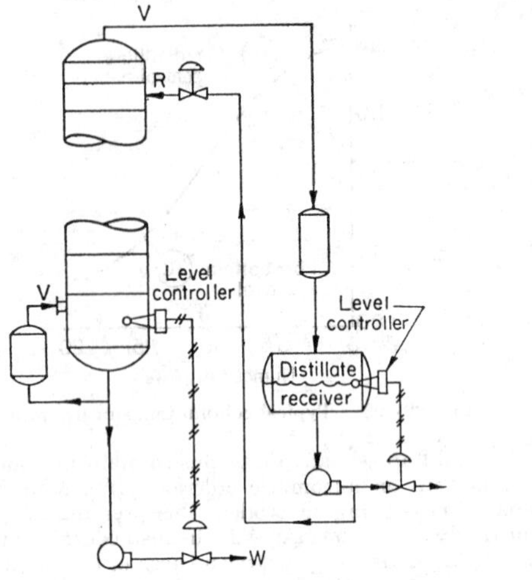

FIG. 22-196. Inventory control under vacuum.

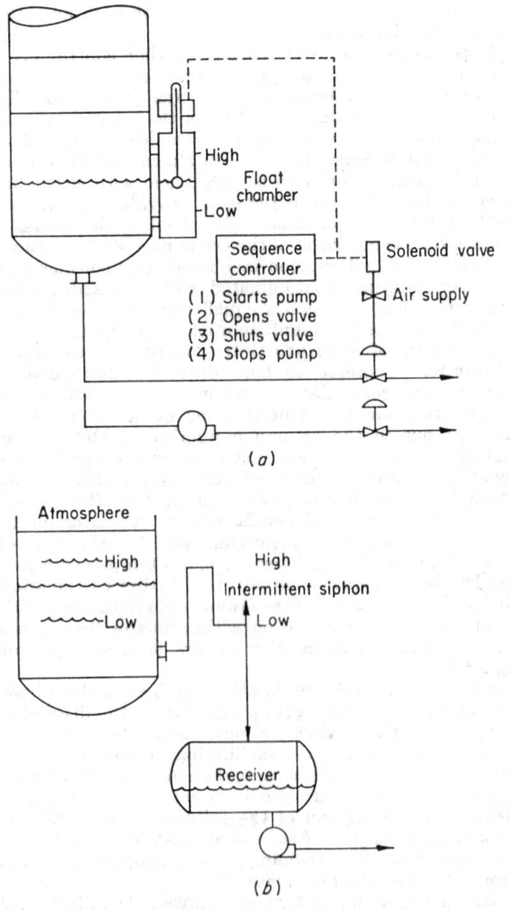

FIG. 22-197. Inventory control at very low production rates.

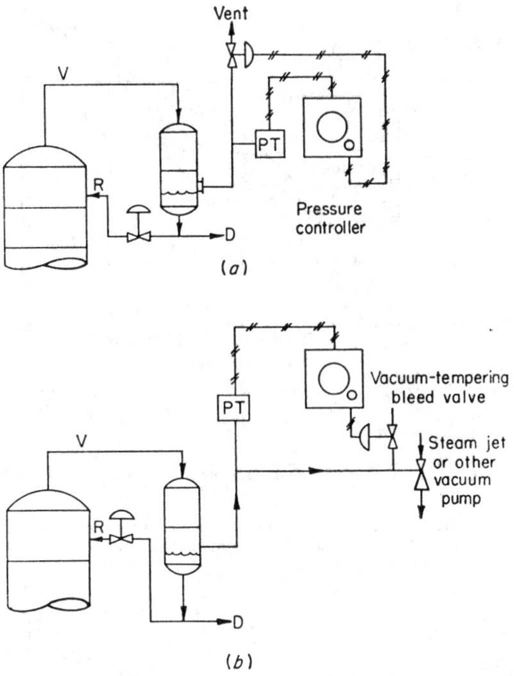

FIG. 22-198. Column pressure control.

In the application of such systems to distillation columns, however, the particular dynamic behavior of such columns can often cause problems. These are discussed briefly in the following paragraphs.

Column temperatures respond in a relatively sluggish manner to operational disturbances and to corrective control action. Improper selection and application of controls can produce sustained oscillation of operating variables. The result can easily be off-standard products. There is the ever-present danger that the controls will fail to provide the required liquid-to-vapor ratios in the column, whereupon operation suffers. Indeed it is relatively easy to lose separation entirely.

Experience in the application of automatic-control theory to distillation columns is limited. One approach to the problem of designing satisfactory controls, which has proved successful, is to design a reserve of performance ability into the distillation system and to place all but one of the controllable variables on fixed-value control. For example, make the column higher (more plates) and larger in diameter (higher allowable reflux and vapor rates), place the feed and boil-up on fixed-rate control, and control the reflux by temperature at a rate to guarantee satisfactory rectification. Thus the only disturbances to which the column is subjected are feed composition and feed enthalpy. With adequate reserve in reflux capacity, the feed disturbances would have negligible effect. It must be recognized that there is a capital cost penalty in the overdesigned column and that the excess reflux rates and boil-up increase heat and coolant consumption.

Effect of External Disturbances. Within the material-handling capacity range of a given distillation column, *i.e.*, between the excessive loadings at which flooding occurs and the very low loading at which draindown occurs, the quality of separation depends to an important degree upon the column heat balance. The point at which the heat is applied is also of importance. For example, heat introduced at the base of the column as boil-up operates through a greater number of plates than does heat entering as feed enthalpy. Consequently, it is possible for separation to become poorer if boil-up heat supply is decreased by controls to compensate for an increase in feed enthalpy due to external conditions. External disturbances, therefore, are quite significant, to the extent that they upset column heat balance.

The composition controls are designed to mitigate the effects of such disturbances, but because of their customary location in the column, some number of plates removed from either the top or bottom of the column, they are deceived to a minor extent in assessing the purity of product and, in fact, deceived to a major extent in assessing the quantitative result of external disturbances.

The effects of several typical disturbances have been analyzed and will now be discussed. A 15-plate toluene-benzene distillation was chosen for illustration. Plate-by-plate calculations were made using a digital-computer program. Alternatively, the analysis can be made using the McCabe-Thiele graphical solution. The McCabe-Thiele diagrams of the disturbances analyzed are presented here because they convey a clearer picture of the effects of disturbances than does a tabulation of column operating data.

McCabe-Thiele Diagram. The McCabe-Thiele diagram as an aid to distillation design has been adequately covered in the chemical engineering literature (see Robinson and Gilliland, "Elements of Fractional Distillation," 4th ed., pp. 123–125, McGraw-Hill, New York, 1950). It is pertinent to recall those aspects of its construction which relate to distillation-control analysis.

Figure 22-199 represents a typical McCabe-Thiele diagram of a binary distillation. Reference has been made above to the location of the composition-control temperature measurement in the column. The feedback regulation of the composition on the control plate has the effect of maintaining the composition at that point in the column at a preselected value. Once chosen, this composition is constant. Also fixed are the number of plates above and below the control plate and, of course, above and below the feed plate.

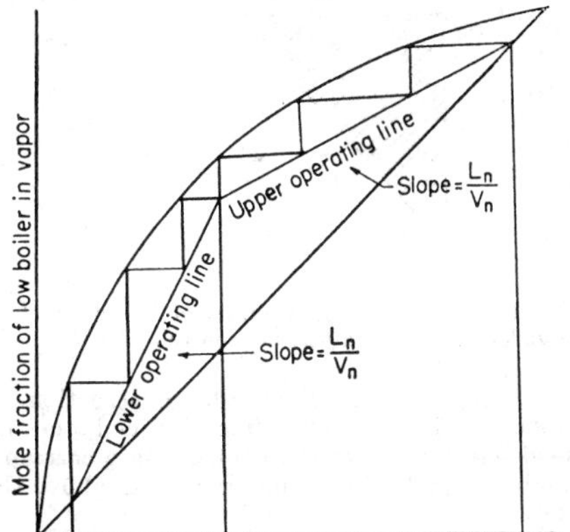

FIG. 22-199. McCabe-Thiele diagram of simple binary distillation.

As indicated in Fig. 22-199, the product composition corresponds to the intersection of the operating lines with the 45-deg. diagonal, the upper operating line for distillate composition, and the lower operating line for bottoms composition. The effect on the McCabe-Thiele diagram of external column heat-balance disturbances is to shift the location of the operating lines on the diagram.

The McCabe-Thiele diagram construction implicitly solves the column heat balance so that this requirement, in analyzing the effect of heat-balance disturbances on composition control, is adequately accounted for. Two other criteria must be met in the graphical solution of the effect of disturbances: (1) As previously noted, the composition on the control plate is held invariant by the composition controls; and (2) the number of plates and the locations of the feed and control plates remain unchanged.

Any response of a distillation column to external disturbances must entail shifts in the location of the column operating lines; in fact, the slopes will change. Moreover, it is clear that the slope changes of the upper and lower operating lines are opposite in sign. The requirement that the control-plate composition remain unchanged and that the number of plates between it and the end of the column remain unchanged requires that the construction of the perturbed operating line be accomplished by displacing it about the control plate in such a way that the number of plates between it and the end of the column remain unchanged. This construction of displacing the operating line is illustrated in Fig. 22-200, which shows the construction of the upper column diagram for effect of reduced reflux.

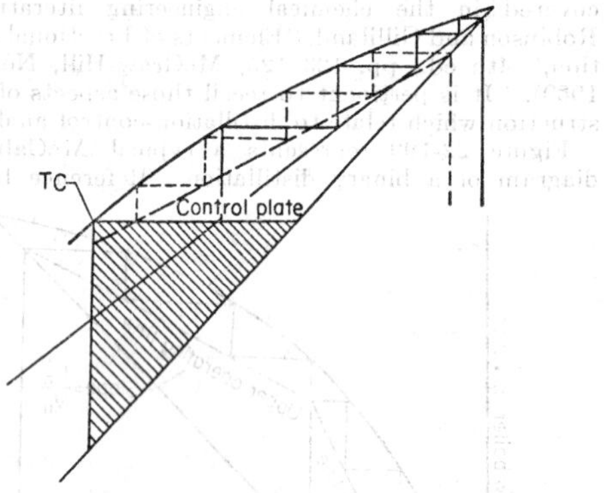

Fig. 22-200. McCabe-Thiele diagram of the effect of a reflux change under distillate-composition control.

The constraints fulfilled by the construction are (1) the slope of the operating line declined and (2) the graphical solution above the control plate correspond to the number of plates in the upper column above the control plate.

Obviously, the decrease in slope of the upper column line can only cause a drop in distillate purity. A similar analysis holds for the effect of altering the slope of the lower operating line where bottoms-composition control is in operation.

Therefore, to estimate the effect of external disturbances on separation, it remains only to determine the slope change on the operating lines and construct the complete diagram, upper and lower, in such a way as to account for the total number of plates and their deployment.

Figures 22-201 through 22-203 represent the analysis of several typical external disturbances. Although the examples shown were precisely calculated by computer, a graphical analysis by means of the McCabe-Thiele construction is just as informative and can be obtained in the absence of a digital computer or a plate-by-plate calculation.

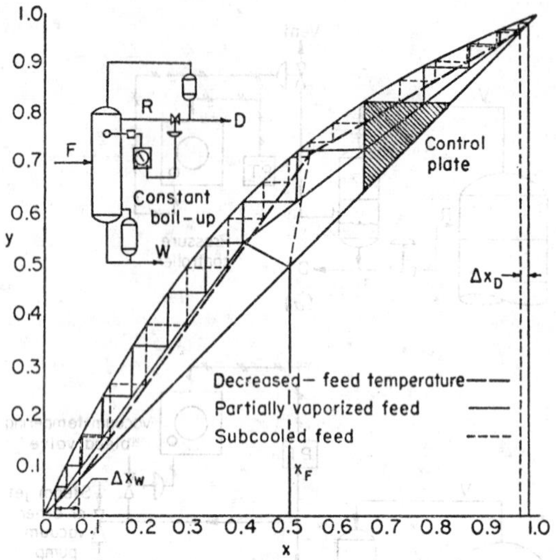

Fig. 22-201. Effect of increased feed on a column operating with constant boil-up and distillate-composition control of reflux (benzene-toluene separation).

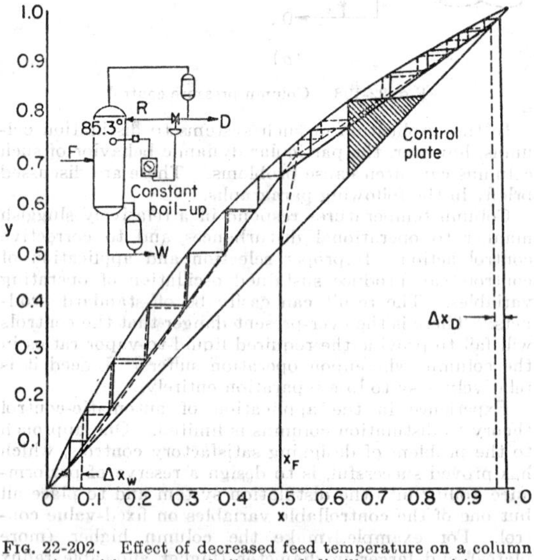

Fig. 22-202. Effect of decreased feed temperature on a column operating with constant boil-up and distillate-composition control of reflux (benzene-toluene separation).

Effect of Increased Feed on Distillate Control. Figure 22-201 shows the effect of increased feed on a column operating with distillate composition control of reflux and constant boil-up. Since the boil-up remains constant and the feed is increased, the ratio of liquid to vapor flow in the stripping section must increase. Consequently, the slope of the lower-column operating line will increase and the bottoms quality will be degraded. Increasing the feed will increase the bottoms rate substantially and the distillate rate slightly. The increase in distillate will be at the expense of reflux, so that the upper-column operating line slope will be decreased. Consequently, the distillate quality will also be degraded.

It is interesting to note that the column temperature

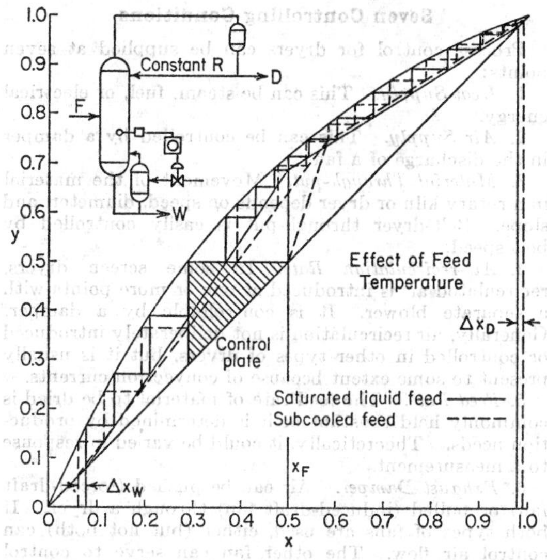

FIG. 22-203. Effect of decreased feed temperature on a column operating with constant reflux and bottoms-composition control of boil-up (benzene-toluene separation).

profile below the control plate declines, while that above the control plate increases.

Effect of Decreased Feed Enthalpy on Distillate Control. Figure 22-202 shows the effect of decreasing the feed temperature on the toluene-benzene separation operating with constant boil-up and distillate composition control of reflux.

The effects are similar to those resulting from increased feed. The ratio of total heat to feed declines. The slope of the lower-column operating line increases and that of the upper-column operating line decreases with a consequential degradation of separation.

The column temperature profile shifts downward below the feed plate and increases above it.

Effect of Feed Enthalpy Change on Bottoms Composition Control. Figure 22-203 shows the effect of feed-enthalpy change on the toluene-benzene separation operating with constant reflux and bottoms-composition control of boil-up.

The lower-enthalpy feed increases the liquid flow in the stripping section and the boil-up is increased by the control to make up for the loss in feed enthalpy. The total heat supplied is therefore held unchanged or, at worst, decreased only slightly. Because a substantial fraction of the heat input is shifted from the feed plate to the bottom of the column, the separation actually improves slightly.

The temperature profile above the control plate shifts downward, but below the control plate it shifts to higher temperatures.

Failure of Separation. Any disturbance that increases the demand for reflux or boil-up can cause complete failure of separation if the limits of the column to handle the required liquid or vapor flow are exceeded or if the capacity of the boil-up or reflux facilities is exceeded.

Exceeding the liquid- and vapor-handling capacity causes flooding. Virtually no separation occurs. A deficiency of boil-up increases the slope of the lower operating line, and an unobtainable location of the lower operating line is called for, as illustrated in Fig. 22-204. A deficiency of reflux decreases the slope of the upper-column operating line with the similar result that an unobtainable location of the upper operating line is called for in the rectifying section, as shown in Fig. 22-205. Figure 22-206 shows the effect that an excessive feed rate can have when both the reflux and boil-up capabilities of a column are overtaxed. It is apparent that the control plate, whether in the top or bottom,

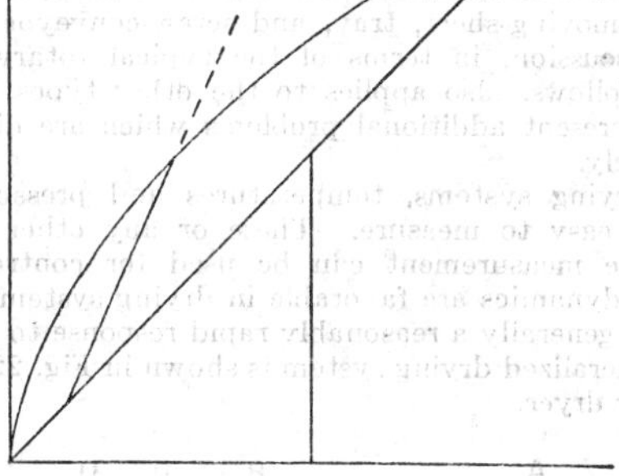

FIG. 22-204. Effect of deficient boil-up.

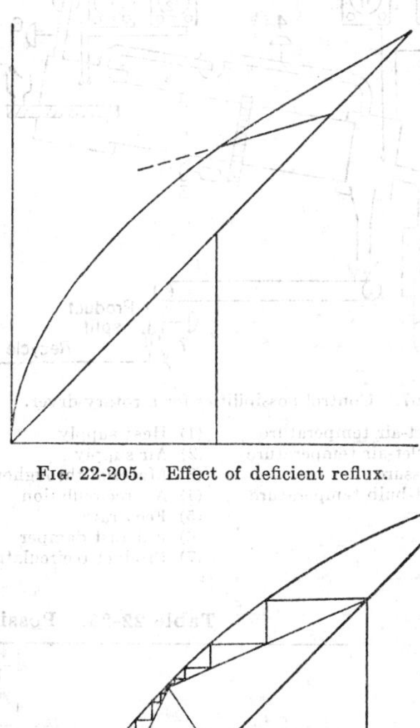

FIG. 22-205. Effect of deficient reflux.

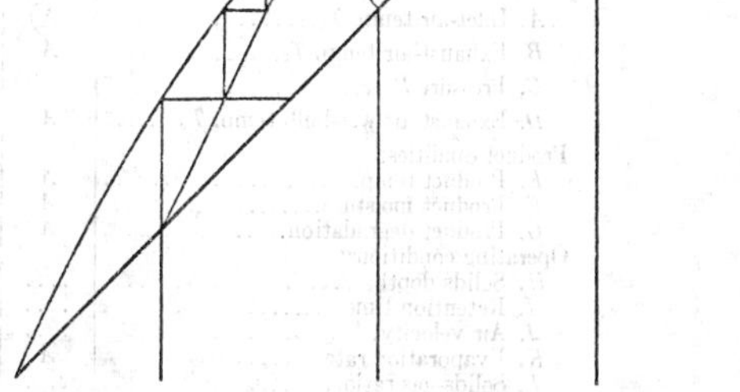

FIG. 22-206. Loss of column control from lack of boil-up and reflux capacity.

would no longer be able to maintain its composition at the prescribed level.

INSTRUMENTATION FOR CONTROL OF SOLIDS DRYING

Drying operations have a number of significant variables which are not easy to measure directly. General practice is, therefore, to hold measurable conditions constant, so that a uniform product will be made. This works well if there are no load changes. The basic control problem is essentially the same for rotary, traveling-screen, moving-sheet, tray, and screw-conveyor dryers. The discussion, in terms of the typical rotary dryer, which follows, also applies to the other types. Spray dryers present additional problems which are discussed separately.

In drying systems, temperatures and pressures are usually easy to measure. These or any other readily available measurement can be used for control since system dynamics are favorable in drying systems where there is generally a reasonably rapid response to change.

A generalized drying system is shown in Fig. 22-207 as a rotary dryer.

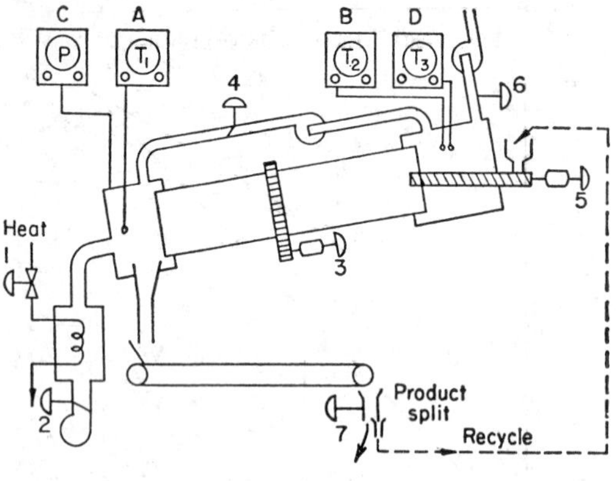

Fig. 22-207. Control possibilities for a rotary dryer.

A. Inlet-air temperature
B. Outlet-air temperature
C. Pressure
D. Wet-bulb temperature

(1) Heat supply
(2) Air supply
(3) Material throughout
(4) Air recirculation
(5) Feed rate
(6) Exhaust damper
(7) Product recirculation

Seven Controlling Conditions

Process control for dryers can be supplied at seven points:

1. *Heat Supply.* This can be steam, fuel, or electrical energy.
2. *Air Supply.* This can be controlled by a damper in the discharge of a fan.
3. *Material Through-put.* Movement of the material in a rotary kiln or dryer depends on speed, diameter, and slope. Belt-dryer through-put is easily controlled by belt speed.
4. *Air-recirculation Rate.* In some screen dryers, recirculated air is introduced at one or more points with a separate blower. It is controllable by a damper. Generally, air recirculation is not deliberately introduced or controlled in other types of dryers, but it is usually present to some extent because of convection currents.
5. *Feed Rate.* The feed rate of material to be dried is commonly held constant or it is determined by production needs. Theoretically, it could be varied in response to a measurement.
6. *Exhaust Damper.* Air can be pushed (forced-draft fan) or pulled (induced-draft fan) through a dryer. If both types of fans are used, either (but not both) can control air flow. The other fan can serve to control pressure at a single point between the two dampers.
7. *Product Recirculation.* This is an infrequent practice, used mostly when the material-handling problem becomes troublesome. It is useful in rotary kilns to prevent ring formation of reacting products. Product recirculation takes place in designs with countercurrent air at sufficient velocity to move some of the product to the feed end.

Probably no single dryer has been built with all seven conditions automatically controlled. However, all these conditions affect dryer performance to some extent. Any of the seven conditions can be held constant, either because it is not convenient to control them, or because there is no suitable measurement within the system to regulate these conditions. Control of all system variables does not require each controllable condition to be manipulated automatically from a measurement. For example, an operator can adjust a valve in response to an appropriate measurement. Each control element can be operated manually or automatically.

Possible Control Arrangements

Table 22-26 shows possible control arrangements for dryers. The vertical columns are the seven elements

Table 22-26. Possible Control Arrangements for Dryers

	Fixed or controllable conditions						
	Heat supply 1	Air supply 2	Belt or shell speed 3	Air recirculation rate 4	Feed rate 5	Exhaust damper 6	Product recirculation 7
Common measurements:							
A. Inlet-air temp. T_1	(A)	*A*	...	....	...	*A*	
B. Exhaust-air temp. T_2	*A*	*A*	...	*B*	*A*	*A*	*B*
C. Pressure *P*	....	*A*	...	....	...	(A)	
D. Exhaust-air wet-bulb temp. T_3	*A*	*A*	...	(A)	*A*	*A*	*B*
Product qualities:							
E. Product temp	*A*	*A*	*A*	*A*	*B*	....	*B*
F. Product moisture	*A*	*A*	*A*	*A*	*B*	....	*B*
G. Product degradation	*A*	*A*	*A*	*A*	*B*	....	*B*
Operating conditions:							
H. Solids depth	....	...	*A*	....	*A**		
I. Retention time	....	...	*A*	....	*A*	....	*A*
J. Air velocity	....	*A*	...	*A*	...	*A*	
K. Evaporation rate	*A*	*A*	...	....	*A*	*A*	
L. Solids-gas ratio	....	*A*	...	*B*	*A*	*A*	

Key: *A* and *B* represent good and fair control, respectively, of loop determined by intersection of row and column (see text).
* *A* for rotary unit and blank for screen dryer.

which can be used to control the system. The 12 horizontal rows depict

1. Measurements commonly used (*A*, *B*, *C*, *D*)
2. Product qualities that are desirable to control where suitable direct measurements are possible (*E*, *F*, *G*)
3. Conditions within the dryer which can serve as guides for proper operating conditions (*H* through *L*)

An *A* at the intersection of a row and column means that the measurement in that row can be used to control the condition shown in the given column. A *B* means that closing this control loop is not so satisfactory but is possible in most installations. Blank spaces in the table indicate that control would be unsatisfactory. Good control of a single loop, indicated by *A*, assumes that the equipment is operating with all control elements in a fixed position and that the one element under question is varied. In column 1, for example, *A*'s appear opposite the measurements of inlet-air temperature, exhaust-air temperature, exhaust-air wet-bulb temperature, product temperature, product moisture, product degradation, and evaporation rate. This means that all these measurements, actual or potential, would be influenced by a change in the position of the valve in the heat supply. Thus almost any one of these measurements, if available, can be used to control the heat supply. However, the moisture content of the final product (*F*) would be ideal in principle.

In Table 22-26, the solid circles around the *A* values at the intersection of rows and columns indicate variables commonly controlled by each measurement. The three circled are:

Inlet-air temp. T_1 controls heat supply (column 1).

Pressure *P* controls exhaust damper (column 6).

Exhaust-air wet-bulb temp. T_1 controls air-recirculation rate (column 4).

Only the measurements T_1, T_3, and *P* will be controlled. The others are free to wander within certain limits.

Essential Measurements in Drying

The actual measurements of interest are as follows:

Dry-bulb Temperatures. Thermocouples, resistance thermometers, or filled-system thermometers are used according to the range of temperatures encountered. It is important to locate the measuring element at a representative point and to protect it from corrosive and abrasive conditions. Signal response time is not usually critical, so that heavy-duty protective wells are common. In high-temperature gas streams, the temperature-sensing element must be properly shielded from cold surfaces, which would cause radiation errors. Suction pyrometers or very small, shielded, bare thermocouples are necessary to obtain measurements approaching the true gas temperature.

Pressure. Dryer pressure measurements vary from fractions of inches of water to much higher values. For dusty conditions it is good practice to purge the line between the point of measurement and the instrument. This prevents the accumulation of dust in the stagnant pipe run. Pressure can be controlled equally well from either of the dampers, column 2 or column 6, in the suction-fan duct or forced-draft-fan duct (see Fig. 22-207). The damper not used to control pressure must be operated by some other measurement within the system. In combination, the two dampers will control the air flow and also the system pressure at the point of measurement. The pressure measurement can be located at any place between the two dampers. The controlled pressure may be either positive or negative, within the range of the two fans. If pressure is to be controlled close to atmospheric at a single point in the system, the pressure will differ from atmospheric at every other point in the system. A chimney effect will occur between different heights if the gas density inside the dryer differs from atmospheric density. There will also be a pressure drop due to motion of the air inside the dryer.

Humidity. The humidity of the exhaust air is usually measured with a wet-bulb psychrometer. Several electrical humidity-sensing elements are also available.

Product Temperature. Product-temperature measurement is commonly used to guide operators in controlling dryers. This is a very useful measurement when it can be obtained.

Product Moisture Content. This measurement is used extensively for drying continuous sheets. However, moisture content of granular solids and powders is difficult to measure continuously. Dielectric constant has been used as a moisture-content measurement of powders where the final desired moisture content is above 2 to 3 per cent and the handling characteristics are favorable.

Thermal Degradation. Thermal degradation of the product is a serious problem in many drying operations. It has rarely been successfully measured continuously and with sufficient rapidity for good control. Maximum temperatures and minimum flow conditions are usually set as the basis for safe operating limits.

Examples of Dryer Instrumentation

Screen Dryer. The screen dryer in Fig. 22-208 shows a single drying section only. The controls on each zone of a multisection dryer would be the same, except that pressure *P*, pressure drop through the material, measured in only one section, is used to control the belt speed. A belt-speed change may be required to hold constant pressure drop through the material being dried if its consistency or through-put rate changes. The uncontrolled variable is feed rate.

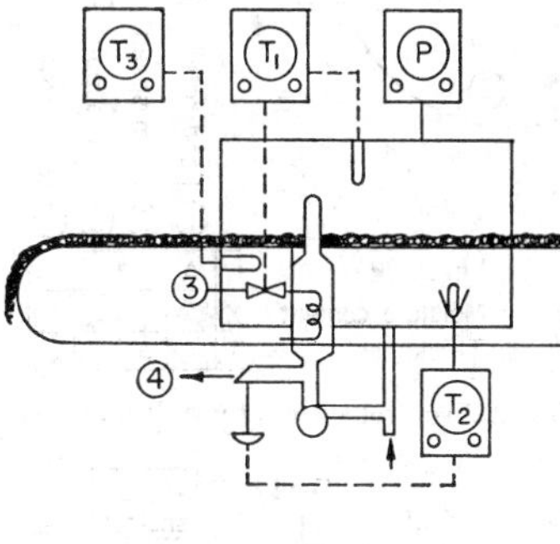

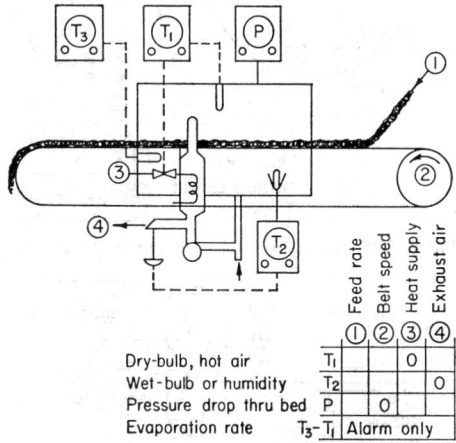

		① Feed rate	② Belt speed	③ Heat supply	④ Exhaust air
Dry-bulb, hot air	T_1			O	
Wet-bulb or humidity	T_2				O
Pressure drop thru bed	P		O		
Evaporation rate	T_3-T_1	Alarm only			

FIG. 22-208. Typical control system for a traveling-screen dryer.

Drum Dryer. With the drum dryer in Fig. 22-209, the product moisture content is measured and used to control steam input to the drum. The evaporation from the drum depends upon the external air condition and velocity as well as the drum temperature. The feed rate is controlled to hold the level in the feed hopper. The feed stream will vary with the capacity of the drum at various speed, web thickness, and temperature conditions.

Table 22-27. Control Chart for Spray Dryers

	Fixed or controllable conditions						
	Heat supply 1	Inlet-air damper 2	Automizer speed 3	Air recircu-lation 4	Feed rate 5	Exhaust damper 6	Product recirculation 7
Usual measurements:							
A. Inlet-air temp	(A)	*A*	...	...	...	*A*	
B. Exhaust-air temp	*A*	*A*	...	*B*	(A)	...	*B*
Product qualities:							
E. Product temp	*A*	...	...	*B*	*A*	*A*	*B*
F. Product moisture	*A*	*A*	*A*	*A*	*A*	*A*	*B*
G. Thermal degradation	*A*	*A*	*B*	*B*	*A*	*A*	*A*
M. Product size	...	...	*A*				
N. Size distribution	...	...	*A*				
Operating conditions:							
C. Pressure		*A*	...	...	...	*A*	
D. Exhaust-air humidity	*A*	*A*	...	*B*	...	*A*	*B*
I. Retention time	...	*A*	...	...	...	*A*	
J. Air velocity	...	*A*	...	*A*	...	*A*	
K. Evaporation rate	*A*	*A*	...	...	*A*	*A*	
L. Solids-gas ratio	...	*A*	...	*B*	...	*A*	

Key: *A* and *B* represent good and fair control, respectively, of loop determined by intersection of row and column (see text).

Spray Dryers. Table 22-27 shows the control loops possible between the various controllable conditions and the measurements which might be made in spray-dryer operation.

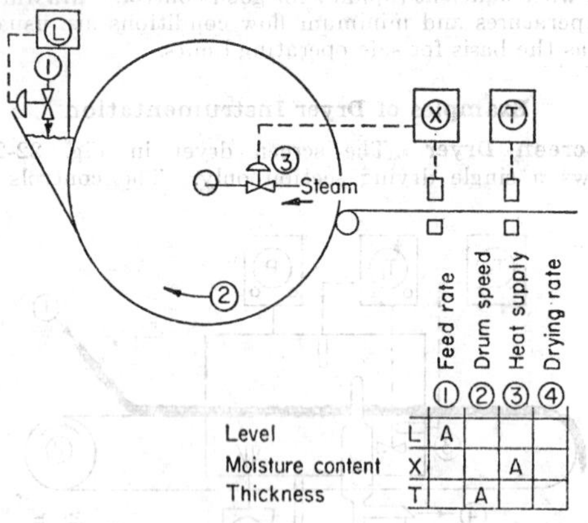

FIG. 22-209. Typical control system for a drum dryer.

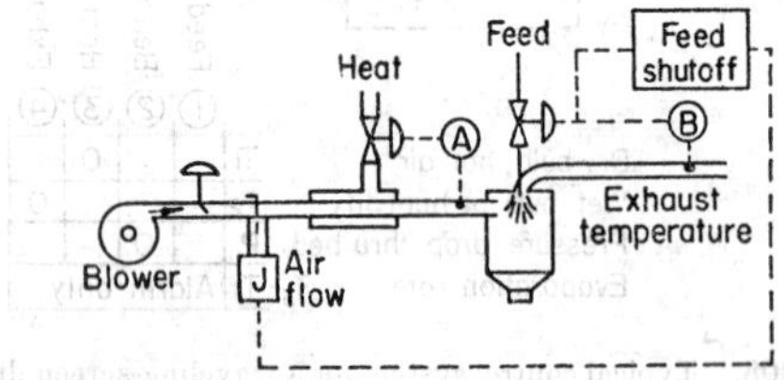

FIG. 22-210. Typical control system for a spray dryer.

Figure 22-210 shows a commonly used system for control. Air inlet temperature *A* controls the heat input (1). Exhaust-air temperature *B* controls the feed rate (5). Pressure drop through the atomizing nozzle will also alter the average size *M* and size distribution *N* of the drops of liquid as well as the feed rate. Size distribution may be the most important factor in spray-drying operation as the smaller drops dehydrate more rapidly. Also, the smaller the drops, the more variable the distribution becomes.

An interlock is desirable to shut off feed quickly if the air flow is interrupted to avoid accumulation of wet material in the bottom of the dryer. Alarms are sometimes provided for high exit-gas temperature or plugging of the product collecting system. "Dead times" for some spray dryers are shorter (*i.e.*, response is rapid) than for other types, and control may be easier. Faster measuring and control elements may be required. The system is usually sealed and there is no need to balance pressures. The system pressure is not usually controlled. An interlock is usually provided in the spray dryer to shut off the feed whenever the temperature falls below operating limits.

Safety Problems

Two specific types of safety problems may arise in the use of dryers. The first is flame-failure detection in direct-fired units. The equipment generally provided to guard against flame failure is substantially more elaborate than the remaining instrumentation. The failure of combustion safeguards, because of manual cut-out arrangements, etc., is often so serious that dual control systems should be used. The first system detects the existence of a flame in the conventional manner. The second system continuously analyzes the combustion products in the dryer for explosibility. Either system can shut down the equipment.

The second hazard exists where dusts or solvent vapors can form combustible mixtures with the air used to dry the materials. This condition has caused serious accidents, even though no source of ignition presumably existed within the system. Inert atmospheres are used to dry hazardous materials in some cases. Where this is impractical the solvent concentrations have been controlled by continuous analyzers that sample the atmosphere in the dryer and control the drying rate to keep the mixture below the lower explosive limit. The sample line leading to the gas analyzer must be kept above the dew point of the solvent or combustible material throughout its length to prevent erroneous readings. Automatic blanketing with inert gases and shutdown of the operation are triggered if the analyzer detects mixtures approaching the explosive limit. Alarm signals and interlock arrangements should be provided. They are actuated whenever unsafe conditions exist or are developing.

For additional information on measurement and control of solids drying, the reader is referred to publications of Hickman [*J. Inst. Fuel*, **28**, 113–116 (1955)], Kramers and Alberda [*Chem. Eng. Sci.*, **2**, 173–181 (1953)], Marshall (*Chem. Eng. Progress*, *Monogr. Ser.*, No. 2, vol. 50, 1954), and Saeman and Mitchell [*Chem. Eng. Progress*, **50**, 467–475 (1954)]. The author gratefully acknowledges assistance of J. R. Boyd, Louisville Dryer Division, General American Transportation Corp.; V. A. Cheney, Link-Belt Co.; and E. H. Rasmussen, Nichols Engineering and Research Corp.

HEAT-EXCHANGER INSTRUMENTATION

Heat exchange, as a unit operation in the process industries, is of universal importance. Proper operation of exchangers usually means proper control. Particular emphasis is placed here on problems of concern when the performance of a heat-exchange system must be improved, or control equipment must be selected for a new heat-exchanger installation.

Normal Control for Heat Exchangers

The normal method for controlling a heat exchanger is to measure the exit temperature of the fluid being processed and to adjust the input of the heating or cooling medium to hold the desired temperature (see Fig. 22-211). To stabilize this feedback control, the controller, in almost all cases, must have a wide proportional

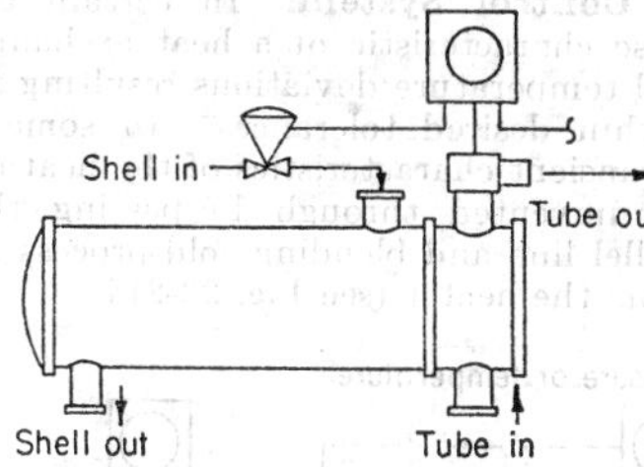

FIG. 22-211. Conventional heat-exchanger control system.

band. The band is determined by the gain of other components in the control loop as well as process considerations. It is an unusual case where the common combination of conventional control elements will permit the use of narrow-band control mechanisms.

Since this type of equipment requires a wide proportional band for stabilization, reset response normally will be required to correct for offset in the controlled variable if load changes are present. This response can be eliminated in cases where disturbances (such as steam-header pressure, product-flow rate, or inlet-temperature changes) have effects which are small in relation to the desired tolerance on the controlled variable.

When the through-put to a heat exchanger is changed rapidly, a short-term error in control temperature will result. The magnitude and/or duration of this error normally can be reduced by a factor of 2 by adding derivative response to the control mechanism and adjusting it properly.

Faulty thermal-element or valve specification will materially detract from system performance and will exhibit symptoms that may lead the engineer to make more costly, unnecessary design changes.

Thermal-element Installation

Thermal elements in a heat-exchanger installation should be installed as close as possible to the active heat-exchange surface, consistent with the requirements for adequate mixing of the process stream. As the point of measurement is moved from the active heat-exchange surface (for example, by installing the thermal element several feet downstream in the process pipe line), this time delayo r distance-velocity lag has a particularly noticeable effect on control performance since a distance-velocity lag rapidly introduces phase shift with little signal attenuation. A 5-ft. length of pipe with a line velocity of 5 ft./sec. will produce a distance-velocity lag of 1 sec., which can be one of the dominant time constants limiting the dynamic performance of the heat-exchanger control system.

The time response of a thermal element installed with a thermal well is materially slower than when the thermal element is installed bare. Thermal wells should be omitted where control-system performance is critical and where it is also practical from a maintenance or safety standpoint. When a thermal well is used, particular care must be taken to assure that the effect of air gap between the thermal element and the thermal well is minimized by proper installation of conducting sleeves.

Control Valves

Valves for the normal heat-exchange application should be provided with positioners. Valve friction materially detracts from system performance. If there is a question on performance of a new installation, or if performance requires improvement in an existing installation, it is generally desirable to use or add a valve positioner as a means of eliminating the effects of valve friction.

It is desirable to maintain the same relationship between incremental changes in valve opening and changes in measured temperature for various through-put rates so that the gain of the control system will remain reasonably constant. Satisfying this condition will result in better control over the range of through-put rates. When the through-put rate is doubled, twice the incremental change in flow of heating or cooling medium is required to produce a given change in temperature. Equal-percentage valve trim has a flow-change characteristic that is proportional to total flow for a given change in valve opening. $dQ/dy = aQ$ where Q is flow rate, y is valve opening, and a is a constant for the particular valve. Use of equal-percentage trim, therefore, normally results in holding a constant relationship between valve movement and temperature change.

Changes in pressure drop across valves used in steam-heating service must be considered when the over-all valve characteristic is determined, since the back pressure from the heat exchanger normally will change over a significant range for various load conditions. Frequently, a low supply pressure in relation to the maximum operating pressure of the heater must be used as a result of sizing the heat exchanger for minimum heat-exchange area. When this requirement must be met, difficulty in stabilizing the system at low operating rates may be encountered. Equal-percentage trim should be used and sized for the maximum allowable pressure drop at full load.

Importance of Sizing and Selection. The following example illustrates the importance of sizing and selection to accommodate the wide rangeability that may be encountered:

Heater load at full rate	1000 lb./hr. of steam
Heater shell pressure at full rate	95 lb./sq. in. gage
Heater load at low rate	200 lb./hr. of steam
Heater shell pressure at low rate	50 lb./sq. in. gage
Available pressure at the valve at full load	100 lb./sq. in. gage

Reference is made to the following sizing equations from p. 1073 of "Process Instruments and Controls Handbook," McGraw-Hill, 1957:

$$C_v = \frac{WK}{3\sqrt{(\Delta P)P_2}}$$

$$W = \frac{3C_v\sqrt{(\Delta P)P_2}}{K}$$

where W = lb./hr. of steam
ΔP = pressure drop at maximum flow, lb./sq. in.
P_1 = inlet pressure at maximum flow, lb./sq. in. abs.
P_2 = outlet pressure at maximum flow, lb./sq. in. abs.
$K = 1 + (0.0007 \times °\text{F. superheat})$
C_v = valve flow coefficient

Size C_v for 1250 lb./hr. of 100 lb./sq. in. gage saturated steam at 5 lb./sq. in. drop

$$C_v = \frac{1250}{3\sqrt{5(95 + 14.7)}} = 41$$

Compute maximum flow that valve could pass at low load pressure drop of (100 − 50) = 50 lb./sq. in.

$$W = \frac{3\sqrt{C_v(\Delta P)P_2}}{K}$$

$$W = 3(41)\sqrt{(50)(50 + 14.7)} = 7000 \text{ lb./hr.}$$

The required low rate flow is 200 lb./hr., which is $100\left(\frac{200}{7000}\right)$ or 3 per cent of the flow rate which this valve could pass at 50 lb./sq. in. drop if wide open.

This 3 per cent flow would require a 10 per cent opening of an equal-percentage valve having a 2 per cent clearance flow. This compares with a 60 per cent opening of the valve if the pressure drop at low load were held to 5 lb./sq. in. Thus the gain of this valve would depart significantly from that desired. Another unwanted effect occurs because at low flow the valve would be operating near the clearance flow point where the slope of the flow vs. opening changes abruptly in an adverse direction. Best control at the low operating load could be obtained if a separate control valve were used, sized to preserve an effective system gain.

Special Cases of Heat-exchanger Controls

Condensate Outlet Control. In some cases, investment in control equipment for steam-heated shell-and-tube exchangers can be reduced by placing the control valve in the condensate line rather than in the steam line (see Fig. 22-212). This type of control is not so

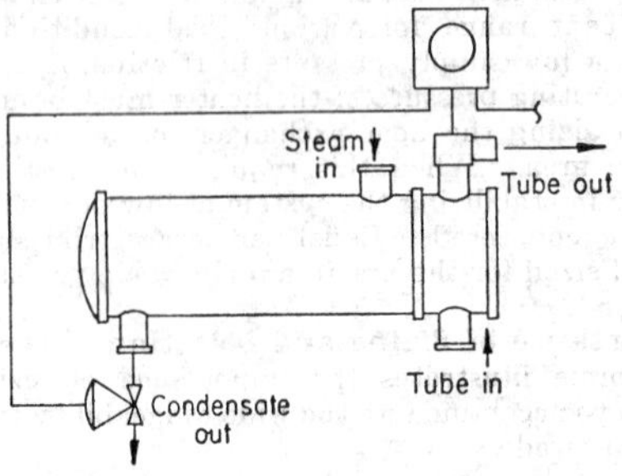

FIG. 22-212. Condensate-throttling control system.

responsive as the systems previously described and, in general, should not be used on critical process applications unless tests can be made to confirm operability of the system. This control should be used only where a special inherent advantage is that of controlling. The behavior of this type of control system is quite difficult to predict.*

Pressure-cascade Control System. This system (see Fig. 22-213) cascades the output of a standard three-mode temperature controller into the set point of a pressure controller. The system achieves a more rapid recovery to load disturbances in a shell-and-tube heat exchanger than can be obtained without the pressure controller. Steam to the heater is regulated by the pressure controller. The latter normally is provided with proportional and reset responses. A load change is

* Assistance of M. J. DePasquale, M. W. Kellogg Company, regarding description of this and the following system is gratefully acknowledged.

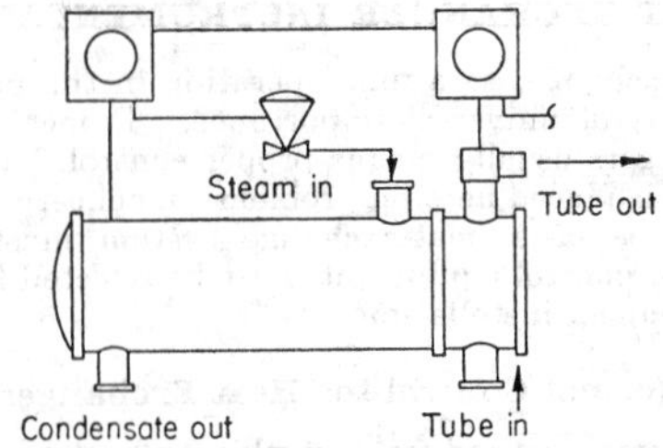

FIG. 22-213. Pressure-cascade control system.

sensed rapidly by a change in shell pressure which is compensated by the pressure controller. The temperature-control system senses the residual error and resets the pressure-controller set point.

By-pass Control System. In certain cases, the time-response characteristic of a heat exchanger is too slow to hold temperature deviations resulting from load changes within desired tolerances. In some of these cases, the transient characteristics of the heat exchanger can be circumvented through by-passing the heater with a parallel line and blending cold-process fluid with hot fluid from the heater (see Fig. 22-214).

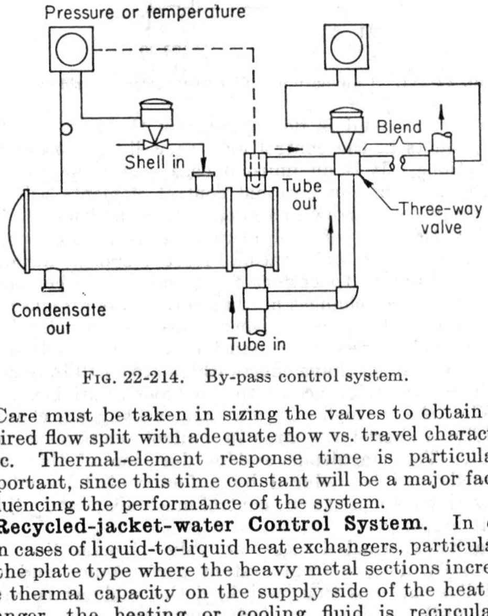

FIG. 22-214. By-pass control system.

Care must be taken in sizing the valves to obtain the desired flow split with adequate flow vs. travel characteristic. Thermal-element response time is particularly important, since this time constant will be a major factor influencing the performance of the system.

Recycled-jacket-water Control System. In certain cases of liquid-to-liquid heat exchangers, particularly of the plate type where the heavy metal sections increase the thermal capacity on the supply side of the heat exchanger, the heating or cooling fluid is recirculated through the heat exchanger and is externally heated or cooled by a separate system or may be blended from a make-up supply (see Fig. 22-215).

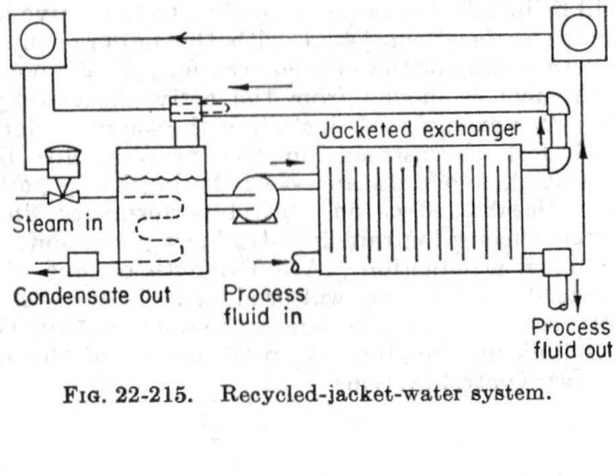

FIG. 22-215. Recycled-jacket-water system.

A change in process-liquid outlet temperature causes a temperature controller to change the set point of a second temperature controller installed in the recirculation system, providing the necessary change in heat-exchange rate to return the process-liquid temperature to the desired value. This cascaded control system normally will control exit temperature within closer tolerances than the single-control-loop system.

Heat-exchanger Trapping and Condensate Systems

Care must be taken to assure that condensate-removal systems for steam-heated exchangers are adequately designed for the particular installation. Traps should be selected which will not intermittently introduce disturbances of sufficient magnitude to upset the shell-side pressure as a result of rapid condensate dumping. Disturbances of this nature will cause upsets in the temperature of the controlled process stream.

Steam heat-exchanger traps should discharge into condensate-collecting systems held at pressures below the lowest shell-side operating pressure.

In situations where the minimum condensing pressure might otherwise be lower than the condensate-system pressure, the surface of the exchanger, in some cases, can be reduced by holding a condensate level within the heat exchanger as shown in Fig. 22-216. An external level tank with level control would be required for this system.

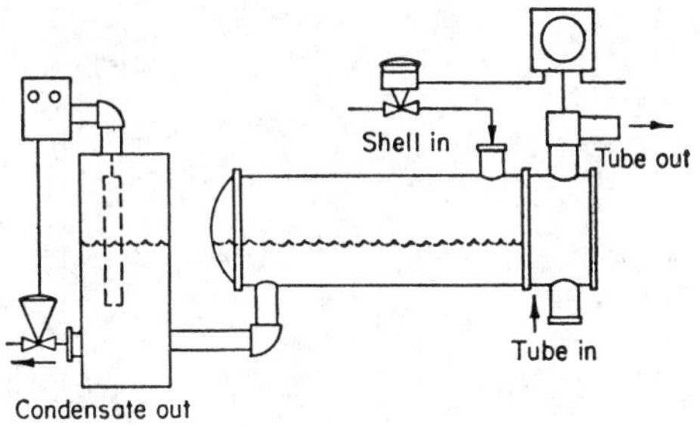

FIG. 22-216. System for raising shell operating pressure.

For additional information on heat-exchanger instrumentation, consult the following references: Cohen and Johnson, Prediction of the Dynamic Characteristics of Distributed Process Streams; Steam-Water Double Pipe Heat Exchanger, *Ind. Eng. Chem.*, **48**, 1031–1034 (1956); Mozley, Prediction of the Dynamics of a Concentric Pipe Heat Exchanger, *Ind. Eng. Chem.*, **48**, 1035–1041 (1956); Paynter and Takabashi, A New Method of Evaluating Dynamic Response of Counterflow and Parallel-flow Heat Exchangers, *Trans. Am. Soc. Mech. Engrs.*, **78**, 749–758 (1956); and Considine (ed.), "Process Instruments and Controls Handbook," especially secs. 2-1, 2-5, 9-1, 9-2, 9-3, 9-5, 10-1, 10-2, 10-3, 10-5, 10-6, 11-1, 11-2, 12-2, and 12-8, McGraw-Hill, New York, 1957.

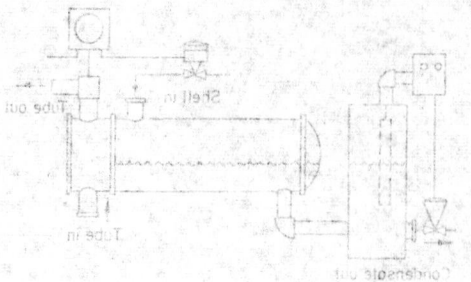

SECTION 23

MATERIALS OF CONSTRUCTION

BY

Robert B. Norden, B.S.Ch.E., Senior Associate Editor, *Chemical Engineering;* Member, American Institute of Chemical Engineers, American Association of Cost Engineers, National Association of Corrosion Engineers, American Rocket Society. (Section Editor)

Leland R. Honnaker, B.S.Met.E., Senior Consultant, Engineering Department, Engineering Service Division, E. I. du Pont de Nemours & Co., Wilmington, Del.; Member, National Association of Corrosion Engineers, American Society for Metals, American Welding Society. (Corrosion and Its Various Forms)

Emil G. Holmberg, B.S.Met.E., Application Engineer (in charge of process industries), Application Engineering Section, Development and Research Div., International Nickel Co., New York; Member, National Association of Corrosion Engineers, American Society for Metals, Electrochemical Society, Society of Automotive Engineers. (Tables 23-2, 23-5)

CONTENTS

MATERIALS OF CONSTRUCTION

REFERENCES: Borgmann, "Corrosion of Metals," American Society for Metals, Cleveland, 1949. Evans, "Metal Corrosion Passivity and Protection," Arnold, London, 1940. Fontana, "Corrosion: A Compilation," Hollenback Press, Columbus, 1957. Gackenbach, "Materials Selection for Process Plants," Reinhold, New York, 1960. Lee, "Materials of Construction for Chemical Process Industries," McGraw-Hill, New York, 1950. Lyman (ed.), "Metals Handbook," American Society for Metals, Cleveland, 1948. Nelson, "Corrosion Data Survey," Shell Development Co., San Francisco, 1960. Seymour and Steiner, "Plastics for Corrosion-resistant Applications," Reinhold, New York, 1955. Speller, "Corrosion—Causes and Prevention," McGraw-Hill, New York, 1951. Uhlig (ed.), "The Corrosion Handbook," Wiley, New York, 1948. Zapffe, "Stainless Steels," American Society for Metals, Cleveland, 1949. Mantell (ed.), "Engineering Materials Handbook," McGraw-Hill, New York, 1958. Evans, "Corrosion and Oxidation of Metals," St. Martins, New York, 1960.

CORROSION AND ITS VARIOUS FORMS

Corrosion of metals occurs in various forms. Most are electrochemical in nature. Their characteristics are well known, and generally the various forms are easily recognized. Extensive information is available in the literature regarding measures that have been and can be taken for minimizing or preventing the various forms of corrosion in many of the specific environments encountered in industries. It is important to recognize the various forms of corrosion in order that the available information can be applied effectively to overcome corrosion problems. The following description and discussion should assist in identifying the various forms of corrosion and their general causes.

General Corrosion. Uniform thinning and loss of metal not accompanied by localized action such as pitting, cracking, or erosion may result from direct chemical reaction or combination such as that which occurs where metals are corroded in gases or by electrochemical action like that which occurs with metals and alloys corroding in liquids. Practically all metallic materials used in industry have sufficient heterogeneity or local point-to-point differences to produce minute anodic and cathodic areas in their exposed surfaces. Typical are inclusions, microstructural composition differences, localized stresses, and mechanical imperfections such as surface roughness. As the result of electrochemical reaction between these areas, corrosion is accelerated at anodic areas and retarded or completely prevented at cathodic areas, at least temporarily. The metal heterogeneity and resulting electrochemical corrosion cause a constant shifting of the anodic and cathodic areas in the exposed surfaces so that the over-all corrosion appears to be uniform. The rate at which this type of corrosion occurs depends upon specific condition involved and varies widely for the various materials.

General corrosion probably causes the greatest amount of damage to metals. It has been the subject of such extensive study and research that today it is fairly well understood and readily recognized and equipment life can generally be estimated accurately. In most cases it is possible to select and use resistant metals, coatings, or linings to minimize or eliminate this form of corrosion. Where problems of general corrosion are encountered, consideration should also be given to the possibilities of decreasing corrosivity of the environment by reducing or changing temperature, pressure, velocity, and/or composition. In some instances it will be practical and economical to use inhibitors to solve the immediate and, perhaps, the long-range problem.

Localized Corrosion. Pitting and crevice corrosion are also electrochemical in nature but result in loss of metal at localized anodic areas. The anodic areas occur in the case of pitting as the result of localized breakdown of a film on the surface or by mechanical or chemical action. In the case of crevice corrosion, the anodic areas generally occur because of differences in electrolyte composition in the crevices or shielded areas compared with the surrounding electrolyte. This form of corrosion is highly localized and general corrosion is frequently slight, even in instances where perforation of the metal occurs as a result of this cell-type action.

Pitting is the most serious of these localized cell types of corrosion because it can and frequently does occur very rapidly and may not be detected until failure occurs. The anodic areas do not change as in general corrosion and corrosion progresses at one localized spot. Pitting corrosion may occur in any metal, but the most common and spectacular occurrences are in aluminum and stainless alloys in aqueous environments containing metal chlorides. The amount of chlorides required is small; even a few parts per million may cause this type of corrosion. Where the chemical agents or conditions causing the localized breakdown and pitting cannot be eliminated, use of inhibitors should be considered as a possible means of correcting the problem. Treatment with dichromates is frequently effective where chlorides are the cause of the trouble.

Crevice corrosion and related types such as concentration cell, deposit, and contact corrosion generally occur where some of the electrolyte is confined or restricted in a small area such as under gaskets, bracket supports, or any solid in contact with the metal so that a crevice or pocket is formed. The electrolyte within the pocket changes in composition with respect to metal-ion concentration, oxygen, etc., with the result that a difference in potential occurs and the metal is preferentially corroded in the anodic area. Inhibitors generally are not effective under these conditions, and change in mechanical conditions to eliminate the crevice or change in materials is the most likely means of eliminating this type of corrosion. Difficulty at gasketed joints can be avoided or minimized by using non-porous gaskets.

Stress-corrosion Cracking. Cracking often results from the combined effects of residual or applied stress and chemical action without noticeable loss of metal through uniform corrosion. This form is insidious since it generally occurs rapidly once action has started and is frequently not detected until failure occurs. It is usually preceded by a fine pitting, with the cracks starting in a pit. Time required for cracking may vary from a few minutes to a few years after initial exposure. It usually takes the form of transgranular penetration or cracking, although some alloys exhibit both transgranular and intergranular stress-corrosion cracking. This has been observed in almost all metals or their alloys but each requires certain environmental conditions to produce this form of corrosion cracking. As in the case of pitting, there may be no readily apparent evidence of activity for a period of months or years before failure occurs. Typical examples include the season cracking of cold-formed brass in environments containing ammonia, the cracking of the austenitic stainless alloys in the presence of chlorides, the cracking of Monel in hydrofluosilicic acid, and the caustic-embrittlement cracking of steel in caustic solutions. This form of corrosion may in some instances be prevented by the elimination of high stress. Fabrication stresses including welding are the most frequent sources of trouble, and stress relieving or annealing after fabrication should always be considered where these metals are going to be exposed to these environments. Temperatures and concentration are important factors in all cases.

The presence of chlorides generally does not cause cracking of the austenitic stainless alloys where metal temperatures are below about 50°C., regardless of concentration. It has been found by extensive experience, however, that where metal temperatures are high enough to cause concentration of chlorides on the metal surface, cracking may occur even where chloride concentration in the surrounding media is only a few parts per million. Typical of such conditions and failures is the cracking of stainless heat-exchanger tubes in the crevices at rolled joints and under scale formed in the vapor space below the top tube sheet in vertical heat exchangers. The cracking of austenitic stainless-steel equipment under insulation where moisture causes leaching of chlorides and concentration on the hot surfaces is another example of failure due to stress-corrosion cracking.

Experience with handling caustic in steel indicates that, if the temperature is held to a maximum of about 120°F., as-welded steel equipment can be used without developing stress-corrosion cracking. If the temperature is higher, and particularly if concentration is above about 30 per cent by weight, cracking at and adjacent to non-stress-relieved welds frequently occurs and the time to failure decreases with increase in temperature.

Corrosion fatigue is a type of stress corrosion that occurs under dynamic or alternating stress conditions in a corrosive environment. Because of the combined effects of cyclic stress and corrosion, cracking-type failures occur with stresses well below the normal fatigue limit.

Hydrogen Blistering and Cracking. Microcracking and blistering with loss of ductility are often caused by the entrance and diffusion of atomic hydrogen. The most frequent occurrence of this form of attack is in steel equipment handling solutions containing hydrogen sulfide. Under these conditions corrosion of the steel generates atomic hydrogen which penetrates the steel and at submicroscopic discontinuities or voids changes to molecular hydrogen with development of pressures high enough to cause cracking or blistering. Steel plates, piping, and forgings containing laminations frequently blister and high-tensile bolting in sulfide service frequently fails by cracking. The latter is a type of stress corrosion, and reduction of the applied tensile stress will minimize such failures. The occurrence of the cracking phenomena increases with increase in hardness and reductions in ductility and is attributed to the inability of the steel to deform or move to accommodate the high and disruptive forces that occur at the discontinuities within the steel. Where steel is used for handling solutions containing hydrogen sulfide, amine-type inhibitors have been found effective in preventing corrosion which could cause cracking and blistering.

Similar phenomena are seen in the cracking failure of hardened-tool-steel items that have been electroplated. In this instance the difficulty can be effectively avoided by removing hydrogen by low-temperature heat-treatment, immediately following the electroplating operation.

Hydrogen attack of steel may also occur under dry conditions at elevated temperatures and pressures, but this is not generally considered to be due to corrosion. It is believed to be caused by the reaction of hydrogen with iron carbides in the steel and the resulting formation of methane. Resistance to this type of attack in steel increases with chromium because of the increased stability of chromium carbides.

Intergranular Corrosion. Localized electrochemical attack occurs and progresses preferentially along the grain boundaries of an alloy, usually because the grain boundary regions contain material that is anodic to the central region of the grains. This type of attack may penetrate completely through the metal section with essentially complete loss of strength, although the apparent general attack may be slight. Many alloys are susceptible to this form of corrosion under specific conditions, but materials that are most frequently involved are the austenitic stainless steels, high-nickel alloys, and aluminum alloys. This form of corrosion was a common occurrence in austenitic stainless-steel equipment used in acid services 15 to 20 years ago before the effects of carbide precipitation were understood. It is less of a problem today because of the reduced carbon content of the alloys and an understanding of its causes and means of prevention. It is now generally accepted in the case of the austenitic stainless steels that some of the chromium combines with the carbon to form chromium carbide which is precipitated at the grain boundaries when the alloy is heated or cooled slowly through the range of 800° to 1500°F. The rate and extent of the formation of the chromium carbide are a function of time, temperature, and carbon content. It occurs during welding in the base metal adjacent to the deposited metal. As a result of the localized impoverishment of chromium at the grain boundaries, preferential corrosion may occur at the grain boundaries in some acidic environments. This form of corrosion can be prevented in stainless steel by annealing (heating at 1950° to 2050°F. followed by rapid cooling) after welding operations, by the use of columbium- or titanium-stabilized grades of stainless steel or by the use of the low-carbon (0.03 per cent maximum) grades of stainless steel. Critical amounts of chromium carbides do not precipitate at the grain boundaries in the stabilized or low-carbon grades during welding; hence annealing after welding is not required as a precaution against this form of corrosion.

Galvanic Corrosion. The more noble of two metals in contact in an electrolyte causes electrochemical attack of the less noble metal. Perhaps the best example is the use of zinc to protect steel equipment. The zinc, being anodic or less noble than the steel, corrodes in most water and atmospheric exposure conditions while the steel being cathodic and more noble than the zinc is protected. This protection of the steel is obtained as a result of sacrificial corrosion of the zinc. The extent or severity of galvanic corrosion depends not only on the difference in potential of the two metals but also upon the relative surface areas involved. If the area of the cathodic metal is large compared with that of the anodic metal, the extent of galvanic or accelerated corrosion of the anodic metal will be much greater than it would be if the relative areas were reversed. Bronze valves and fittings are commonly used in steel water lines without much difficulty due to localized corrosion of the steel at the fitting. But when a steel fitting is used in a copper line, relatively rapid corrosion of the steel fitting generally occurs. Although galvanic corrosion is frequently troublesome, the principle of galvanic corrosion is used to advantage to protect a large amount of equipment. Typical of this in addition to galvanizing is the use of magnesium and zinc anodes to protect buried steel pipe lines (see cathodic protection, p. 23-6).

Table 23-1. Galvanic Series of Metals and Alloys

Corroded End (Anodic, or Least Noble)

Magnesium
Magnesium alloys
Zinc
Aluminum 2S
Cadmium
Aluminum 17ST
Steel or iron
Cast iron
Chromium-iron (active)—stainless type 410
Ni-Resist cast iron
18-8 chromium-nickel-iron (active) stainless type 304
18-8-3 chromium-nickel-molybdenum-iron (active)—stainless type 316
Lead-tin solders
Lead
Tin
Nickel (active)
Inconel nickel-chromium alloy (active)
Hastelloy alloy C (active)
Brasses
Copper
Bronzes
Copper-nickel alloys
Monel nickel-copper alloy
Silver solder
Nickel (passive)
Inconel nickel-chromium alloy (passive)
Chromium-iron (passive)—stainless type 410
Titanium
18-8 chromium-nickel-iron (passive)—stainless type 304
18-8-3 chromium-nickel-molybdenum-iron (passive)—stainless type 316
Hastelloy alloy C (passive)
Silver
Graphite
Gold
Platinum

Protected End (Cathodic, or Most Noble)

Selective Corrosion. Removal of a constituent of an alloy by corrosion without apparent loss in volume but with serious loss of strength is called "selective corrosion." Dezincification is typical of this form where the zinc constituent present in brass alloys is selectively removed, leaving only sponge copper in the original shape and volume of the uncorroded metal. This corrosion may be general or it may occur in localized areas. The latter is called "plug-type" dezincification. This effect is generally limited to brass compositions containing more than 15 per cent of zinc. The addition of small amounts of arsenic, phosphorus, or antimony to the alloy will generally inhibit, if not prevent, this form of corrosion.

Another example is the graphitic corrosion of cast iron where galvanic corrosion occurs between the graphite and iron constituents in the cast iron, with the resultant formation of a spongy mass of corrosion products. The original shape and volume are generally retained but the strength of the metal is essentially lost as the corrosion proceeds through the cross section. This is rather common in buried cast-iron lines, particularly where moist and slightly acidic conditions prevail.

Erosion Corrosion. Accelerated corrosion may result from erosion which removes normally protective films. This is most likely to occur in liquid systems that contain solids. Items such as pump impellers, agitator blades, and pipe-line fittings are particularly subject to this form of corrosion. It can be minimized by reducing velocities, by changes in environment, by addition of an inhibitor to reduce corrosiveness of the solution, by the use of more corrosion-resistant materials, and, in some instances, by the use of harder material.

Impingement is a type of corrosion similar to erosion corrosion except solids are seldom involved and specific effects are more localized. It occurs where the normally protective film is not maintained in the flowing fluid or gas. Perhaps the most common occurrence of this form of corrosion is in non-ferrous alloy condenser tubes near the inlet ends. A reduction in velocity or turbulence will prevent or minimize this difficulty. It can be overcome also by use of alloy materials having a greater resistance to this type of attack. The use of ferrules of plastic or alloy materials inserted in the inlet ends of condenser tubes has been effective where the attack was confined to an area near the inlet end.

Cavitation may also be considered as a type of corrosion by erosion even though it may occur under essentially non-corrosive conditions. It occurs in metals handling moving liquids and results specifically from the formation and collapse of cavities or vapor bubbles in contact with the metal surface and the associated pounding and wiping action at the point of cavity or bubble collapse. Its appearance varies from that of surface roughness in strong ductile materials to one of pitting in low-strength nonductile materials like cast iron. It is a common occurrence in impellers of all types. Where the temperature-pressure conditions cannot be changed to reduce bubble formation, change in alloys is generally required as a corrective means.

Fretting Corrosion. Corrosion between two surfaces accelerated by or resulting from the mechanical removal of a protective film of corrosion products is called "fretting" or "chafing" corrosion. This occurs at the interface of metals when they are clamped or fitted closely together and subjected to small vibratory motions. Its most common occurrence is on machine parts with small relative motions and high unit loads. Use of rust-inhibiting oil or grease is generally beneficial under atmospheric-exposure conditions.

High-temperature Corrosion. Chemical reaction of metals at elevated temperatures with one or more constituents of a gaseous environment often results in corrosion. The most common type is oxidation where metal oxides form by chemical reaction and losses occur in the form of scaling. Rate of metal loss under oxidizing conditions increases with increase in temperature and generally is greater under cyclic fluctuations in temperature because of loosening of scale and loss of its protective value. Chromium is considered to be the most beneficial alloying addition for increasing oxidation resistance. The minimum content is 20 per cent for good high-temperature oxidation resistance. Since nickel is also quite beneficial in combination with chromium, most of the alloys designed for high-temperature use contain 20 per cent or more of this element.

Another type of high-temperature corrosion is sulfidation, where at elevated temperatures sulfur-bearing atmospheres cause an intergranular attack and penetration along the grain boundaries. This is limited for the most part to nickel and alloys of high nickel content. The rate of attack is somewhat greater under reducing conditions than under oxidizing conditions. Nickel is subject to sulfidation attack in sulfur-bearing and reducing atmospheres at temperatures above 600°F. (see Table 23-16). The addition of chromium greatly improves resistance of nickel alloys to sulfur-bearing gases.

Biological Corrosion. Deterioration of steel or iron may occur directly or indirectly as a result of the metabolic activity of microorganisms. The anaerobic sulfate-reducing bacteria are most frequently involved in this form of corrosion. They contribute to corrosion by affecting changes in surface film resistance, creation of corrosive environments, or creation of a surface barrier so as to cause concentration cell- or deposit-type corrosion. After removal of the corrosion products, the appearance is generally that of pitting, either isolated or overlapping in stringer effects. The most common occurrence is in clay or boggy soils. Coatings are generally used as a preventive means where biological corrosion is suspected.

Factors Influencing Corrosion

A number of factors influence the occurrence and rate of corrosion, the more important being temperature, velocity, pH, oxidizing and reducing conditions, and moisture. As a general rule the rate of corrosion increases with increase in temperature, the extent depending upon specific conditions. The increase in rate of corrosion with increase in temperature is, for instance, not so great for steel in alkaline environments as it is for steel in acid environments. In a few instances, however, a decrease in temperature will increase corrosion due to a change in environmental conditions. An example of this is in flue coolers where steel is exposed to acidic gases which upon cooling reach the dew point, with the resulting condensation causing more corrosion than occurred with the gases at the higher temperature.

Velocity normally increases the rate of corrosion, the amount again depending upon specific conditions. This may be due to removal of protective films or scale or simply to the continued supply of corroding media. Impingement corrosion previously mentioned is caused by velocity effects. Pitting, on the other hand, is most severe under quiescent conditions. It may not develop in parts of equipment where flow conditions exist even though severe pitting occurs in areas of low or negligible velocity.

The pH value of a solution is not a controlling factor with respect to corrosion of metals, although the relative rate of corrosion is a function of the solubility of corrosion films or products and this in turn may be a function of pH value. As a general rule, decrease in pH value will result in increase in corrosion of metals subject to corrosion in dilute acid solutions and an increase in pH value above the neutral range will result in increase in corrosion of metals subject to attack in alkaline solutions.

Oxidizing conditions are generally favorable for the stainless steels, which owe their corrosion resistance largely to the existence of a passive oxide film on the surface. The corrosion of many of the non-ferrous metals, however, particularly copper and nickel and their alloys, is greater under oxidizing-acid conditions than under neutral- or reducing-acid conditions. It is frequently possible to decrease corrosion of stainless steels in acid solutions by aeration or addition of an oxidizing agent and similarly it is possible to decrease corrosion of copper and nickel in acid solutions by inert-gas purging or blanketing to maintain neutral or reducing conditions. Corrosion of ferrous-base materials is generally greater under oxidizing than under reducing conditions. Moisture may be a critical factor, particularly where its presence results in change from anhydrous conditions and acidic components are formed by hydrolysis. It is also important in gaseous systems since its presence can cause condensation and a severe corrosion condition. In general, the occurrence or presence of moisture in an environment will cause an increase in corrosion compared with a moisture-free condition.

COMBATING CORROSION

The following items should be considered as means of combating corrosion.

Select Proper Material. Selection of materials for process equipment should preferably be based on experience with materials under similar conditions. Where such experience or information is not available it is desirable to obtain advice and assistance of persons experienced in corrosion-engineering work who are familiar with the chemical-resistance characteristics and limitations of construction materials. Corrosion tests may be necessary to develop information to permit selection of adequate materials. Where such tests are made, procedures and conditions should be as realistic as practical to simulate operating and exposure conditions with respect to temperature, aeration, and velocity as well as chemical composition. Hot or cold wall effects should be considered where heat-exchange equipment is involved. The possibility of the occurrence of one of the forms of corrosion other than general corrosion should be considered. Tests should then be designed and made to determine suitability of the materials of interest where they are known or suspected to be susceptible to a particular type of corrosion under similar environmental conditions.

In selecting materials of construction for equipment which would be exposed to corrosive environments, careful consideration should be given to the practical aspects and limitations of design, fabrication, installation, and maintenance. For instance, if field welding or cold working must be done on equipment for installation or maintenance reasons, and subsequent heat-treatment is not practical, then it is necessary to select a material of construction not susceptible to attack such as intergranular corrosion or stress-corrosion cracking in the non-heat-treated condition.

Permissible corrosion rates are an important factor and will vary with equipment. Appreciable corrosion can be permitted for tanks and lines if anticipated and allowed for in design thickness, but essentially no corrosion can be permitted in fine-mesh wire screens, orifices, and other items where small changes in dimensions are critical.

In many instances use of non-metallic materials will prove to be attractive from an economic and performance standpoint and they should be considered where their strength, temperature, and design limitations are satisfactory.

Proper Design. Design considerations, with respect to minimizing corrosion difficulties, should include the desirability for free and complete drainage, elimination of crevices, and ease of cleaning and inspection. The installation of baffles, stiffeners, and drain nozzles and the location of valves and pumps should be made so that free drainage will occur and washing can be accomplished without hold-up. Means of access for inspection and maintenance should be provided wherever practical. Butt joints should be used wherever possible. If lap joints employing fillet welds are used, the welds should be continuous on the process side. The use of dissimilar metals in contact with each other should generally be avoided, particularly if they are widely separated in their nominal positions in the electromotive series (see Table 23-1). If they are to be used together, consideration should be given to insulating them from each other or making anodic material area as large as possible. Equipment should be supported in such a way that it will not rest in pools of liquid or on damp insulating material. Porous insulation should be weatherproofed or otherwise protected from moisture and spills to avoid contact of the wet material with the equipment. Specifications should be sufficiently complete to ensure that the desired composition or type of material will be used and the right condition of heat-treatment and surface finish will be provided. Inspection during fabrication and prior to acceptance is desirable.

Alter Environment. Simple changes in environment may make an appreciable difference in corrosion of metals and should be considered as a means of combating corrosion. Oxygen is an important factor and its removal or addition may cause marked changes in corrosion. The treatment of boiler feed water, for instance, to remove oxygen greatly reduces the corrosiveness of the water on steel. Inert-gas purging and blanketing of many solutions, particularly acidic media, generally minimizes corrosion of copper and nickel-base alloys by minimizing air or oxygen content. Corrosiveness of acid media to stainless alloys, on the other hand, may be reduced by aeration because of the formation of passive oxide films.

Reduction in temperature will almost always be beneficial with respect to reducing corrosion. Reduction in velocity and turbulence will generally result in reduced corrosion, an exception being where solids may collect on surfaces and cause pitting. Where pH values can be modified it will generally be beneficial to hold acid level to a minimum. Where acid additions are made in batch processes, it may be beneficial to add them last so as to obtain maximum dilution and minimum acid concentration and exposure time. Alkaline pH values are less critical than acid values with respect to controlling corrosion. Elimination of moisture can and frequently does minimize, if not prevent, corrosion of metals, and this possibility of environmental alteration should always be considered.

Inhibitors. The use of various substances or inhibitors as additives to corrosive environments to decrease corrosion of metals in the environment is an important means of combating corrosion. This is generally most attractive in closed or recirculating systems where annual cost of inhibitor is low. However, it has also proved to be economically attractive for many once-through systems, such as those encountered in petroleum-processing operations. Inhibitors are effective as the result of their controlling influence on the cathode- or anode-area reactions.

Typical examples of inhibitors used for minimizing corrosion of iron and steel in aqueous solutions are the chromates, phosphates, and silicates. These minimize corrosion by increasing anodic polarization and are called anodic inhibitors. Organic sulfide and amine materials are frequently effective in minimizing corrosion of iron and steel in acid solution. In this instance they control cathodic polarization and are called cathodic inhibitors.

The use of inhibitors is not limited to controlling corrosion of iron and steel. They frequently are effective with stainless steel and other alloy materials. The addition of copper sulfate to dilute sulfuric acid will, for example, essentially stop the corrosion of stainless steels in hot dilute solutions of this acid whereas the uninhibited acid causes rapid corrosion.

The effectiveness of a given inhibitor generally increases with increase in concentration, but those considered practical and economically attractive are used in quantities of less than 0.1 per cent by weight.

In some instances the amount of inhibitor present is critical in that a deficiency may result in localized or pitting attack with the over-all results being more destructive than where none of the inhibitor is present. Consideration for use of inhibitors should therefore include review of experience in similar systems or investigation of requirements and limitations in new systems.

Cathodic Protection. Two methods of providing cathodic protection for minimizing corrosion of metals are in use today. These are the sacrificial-anode method and the impressed-e.m.f. method. Both depend upon making the metal to be protected the cathode in the electrolyte involved. Examples of the sacrificial-anode method include the use of zinc, magnesium, or aluminum as anodes in electrical contact with the metal to be protected. These may be anodes buried in the ground for protection of underground pipe lines or as attachments to surfaces of equipment such as condenser water boxes or on ship's hulls. The current required is generated in this method by corrosion of the sacrificial-anode material. In the case of the impressed e.m.f., the direct current is provided by external sources and is passed through the system by use of essentially non-sacrificial anodes such as carbon, non-corrodible alloys, or platinum buried in the ground or suspended in the electrolyte in the case of aqueous systems. The requirements with respect to current distribution and anode placement vary with resistivity of soils or electrolyte involved, and the assistance of experienced personnel should be obtained when considering possible application of cathodic protection. The practical problem increases as the resistivity of the electrolyte decreases. It is generally impractical, for instance, to use cathodic protection where dilute acids are involved as the corroding solution or electrolyte. It is also impractical where the dimensions or configuration of equipment to be protected are such that adequate placement of anodes cannot be provided; *e.g.*, heat-exchanger tube bundles.

Coatings and Linings. The use of non-metallic coatings and lining materials in combination with steel or other materials has and will continue to be an important type of construction for combating corrosion.

Organic coatings of many kinds are used as linings in equipment such as tanks, piping, pumping lines, and shipping containers and they are often an economical means of controlling corrosion, particularly where freedom from metal contamination is the principal objective. One principle that is now generally accepted is that thin brush- or spray-applied non-reinforced paintlike coatings of less than 10 mils thickness should not be used in services where full protection is required in order to prevent rapid attack of the substrate metal. This is because most thin coatings as commercially applied contain defects or holidays and these lead to early failures due to corrosion of the substrate metal, even though the coating material is resistant. Spark testing of coating-type linings is always desirable for immersion-service applications in order to detect holiday-type defects in the coating.

The most dependable linings for corrosive services are those which are bonded directly to the substrate and are built up in multiple-layer or laminated effects to thicknesses greater than 100 mils. These include the glass-fiber-reinforced resin systems and the elastomeric and plasticized plastic systems. Good surface preparation and thorough inspections of completed lining, including spark testing, should be considered as minimum requirements for any lining applications.

Ceramic or carbon-brick linings are frequently used as a facing lining over plastic or membrane linings where the service temperatures exceed those which can be handled by the unprotected materials. This type of construction permits processing of materials that are too corrosive for handling in metal constructions.

Metal- and glass-lined steel has been available for some time as a method for avoiding the high cost of a solid alloy. Nickel, for instance, can be deposited by electroplating or by electroless processes (Kanigen). Such deposits, however, tend to be porous. Steel clad with an alloy is another approach to the problem and a number of large process plants have numerous pieces of equipment made from stainless-clad steel. As for glassed steel, it has all the benefits of glass plus high strength.

PROPERTIES OF MATERIALS

Steel. Carbon steel is the most common, cheapest, and most versatile metal used in industry. It has excellent ductility, permitting many cold-forming operations.

Steel is also the most weldable of all commercial metals. It is two-thirds the weight of lead, three times heavier than aluminum.

For annealed steel with low carbon (0.20 per cent C), tensile strength can be 55,000 lb./sq. in.; for annealed high-carbon (0.40 per cent C) steel, tensile strength will be 100,000 lb./sq. in. Cold working can boost strength up to 180,000 lb./sq. in. or higher.

The corrosion resistance of steel depends upon the formation of an oxide surface film. However, resistance to corrosion is somewhat limited. Carbon steel should not be used in contact with dilute acids. Thus it is not recommended with sulfuric acid below 90 per cent. Between 90 and 98 per cent, steel can be used up to the boiling point; between 80 and 90 per cent, it is serviceable at room temperature. Above 102 per cent, steel is good up to 140°F. Usually, steel is not used with hydrochloric, phosphoric, or nitric acids.

When iron contamination is permissible, carbon steel can be used for handling caustic soda up to about 75 per cent and 212°F. Stress relieving is sometimes necessary to reduce caustic embrittlement.

Brines and sea water corrode steel at a slow rate, and the metal can be used where iron contamination is not objectional. Also, steel is little affected by neutral water or organic chemicals. Many large water tanks are fabricated from carbon steel, as well as storage tanks for organic solvents and similar chemicals.

Wrought Iron. Ferrous metal that includes a minutely and evenly distributed quantity of iron silicate (slag) is called wrought iron. The slag exists as a discrete and separate phase, in the form of silicate fibers. Wrought iron is tough and ductile, with excellent fatigue and shock resistance, because of these fibers.

Composition of standard wrought iron has about 3 per cent slag, 0.02 per cent C, 0.12 per cent Si, 0.03 per cent Mn, 0.12 per cent P, 0.02 per cent S, with the balance iron. A modification of this is called 4D, which contains 0.06 per cent Mn. A nickel grade contains 3.25 per cent Ni, and a manganese variation has 1 per cent Mn.

Wrought iron can be worked easily by hot- or cold-forming techniques. Machinability is about equivalent to free-machining steels. It can be welded by all common processes.

Corrosion resistance is somewhat better than carbon steel. It has excellent resistance to atmospheric corrosion (structural applications) and to soil corrosion (water lines). One theory is that the silicate fibers tend to hinder corrosive attack and prevent pitting.

Wrought iron can handle alkalies and alkaline solutions without difficulty. But dilute acids will cause rapid failure.

With mechanical loading, a safe operating temperature is around 650°F. Heating coils, exhaust lines, and smokestacks are some typical process applications.

Low-alloy Steels. Alloy steels contain one or more alloying agents to improve mechanical and corrosion-resistant properties over those of carbon steel.

A typical low-alloy grade (A.I.S.I. 4340) will contain 0.40 per cent C, 0.70 per cent Mn, 1.85 per cent Ni, 0.80 per cent Cr, 0.25 per cent Mo. Many other alloying agents are used to produce a large number of standard A.I.S.I. and proprietary grades.

Nickel increases toughness and improves low-temperature properties and corrosion resistance. Chromium improves hardness, abrasion resistance, corrosion resistance, and high-temperature properties. Molybdenum provides strength at elevated temperatures.

Tensile strengths of these alloys are in the 75,000 to 125,000 lb./sq. in. range, but hardening heat-treatments can produce alloys with 225,000 lb./sq. in.

Working, machining, and welding properties are similar to carbon steel, when allowance is made for the increased strength.

The addition of small amounts of alloying materials greatly improves corrosion resistance to atmospheric environments, but does not have much effect against liquid corrosives. The alloying elements produce a tight, dense adherent rust film, but in acid or alkaline solutions, corrosion is about equivalent to that of carbon steel. However, the greater strength permits thinner walls in process equipment made from low-alloy steel.

Cast Irons. Generally, cast iron is not a particularly strong or tough structural material, although it is one of the most economical and is widely used in industries.

Gray cast iron, low in cost and easy to cast into intricate shapes, contains carbon, silicon, manganese, and iron. Carbon (1.7 to 4.5 per cent) is present as combined carbon and graphite—combined carbon is disposed in the matrix as iron carbide (cementite) while free graphite occurs as thin flakes dispersed throughout the body of the metal. Various strengths of gray iron are produced by varying size, amount, and distribution of graphite.

Gray iron has outstanding "damping" properties—*i.e.,* ability to absorb vibration—as well as wear resistance. However, gray iron is brittle, with poor resistance to impact and shock. Machinability is excellent, and gray-iron castings can be welded with proper techniques and preheating.

Gray-iron castings are not usually considered corrosion-resistant, although they do resist atmospheric corrosion as well as attack by natural or neutral waters and neutral soils. However, dilute acids and acid-salt solutions will attack this material.

Gray iron is resistant to concentrated acids (nitric, sulfuric, phosphoric), as well as some alkaline and caustic solutions. Caustic fusion pots are usually made from gray cast iron with low silicon content; cast-iron valves, pumps, and piping are common in sulfuric acid plants.

White cast iron is brittle and difficult to machine. It is made by controlling composition and rate of solidification of the molten iron so that all the carbon is present in the combined form. Very abrasive- and wear-resistant, white cast iron is used as liners and for grinding balls, dies, and pump impellers.

Malleable iron is made from white cast iron. It is cast iron with free carbon as dispersed nodules. This arrangement produces a tough, relatively ductile material. Total carbon is about 2.5 per cent. Two types are produced: standard and pearlitic (combined carbon plus nodules). Standard malleable iron is easily machined, pearlitic less so. Both types will withstand bending and cold working without cracking. Large welded areas are not recommended with fusion welding because welds are brittle. Corrosion resistance is about the same as for gray cast iron.

Ductile cast iron includes a group of materials with good strength, toughness, wear resistance, and machinability. This cast iron contains combined carbon and dispersed nodules of carbon. Composition is about the same as gray iron, with more carbon (3.7 per cent) than malleable iron. The spheroidal graphite reduces the notch effect produced by graphite flakes, making the material more ductile.

There are a number of grades of ductile iron—some have maximum toughness and machinability, others have maximum resistance to oxidation.

Generally, corrosion resistance is similar to gray iron. But ductile iron can be used at higher temperatures—up to 1100°F. and higher.

Alloy Cast Irons. Cast iron is not usually considered corrosion-resistant, but this can be improved by the use of various cast-iron alloys. A number of such materials are on the market.

High-silicon cast irons have excellent corrosion resistance. Silicon content is 13 to 16 per cent. These materials are known as Duriron and Corrosiron. Adding 3 per cent Mo yields a product called Durichlor.

While the high silicon content improves corrosion resistance, it lowers some of the mechanical properties, as compared with gray iron. Silicon irons are hard and

(*Continued on page* 23-12)

Table 23-2. General Corrosion Properties of Some Metals and Alloys*

Ratings: 0 unsuitable. Not available in form required or not suitable for fabrication requirements or not suitable for corrosion conditions.
1 poor to fair.
2 fair. For mild conditions or where periodic replacement is possible. Restricted use.
3 fair to good.
4 good. Suitable when superior alternatives are uneconomic.
5 good to excellent.
6 normally excellent.
Small variations in service conditions may appreciably affect corrosion resistance. Choice of materials is therefore guided wherever possible by a combination of experience and laboratory and site tests.

Material	Liquids: Non-oxidizing or reducing media				Liquids: Oxidizing media			Liquids: Natural waters				Gases: Common industrial media				
	Acid solutions, excluding hydrochloric, *e.g.*, phosphoric, sulfuric, most conditions, many organics	Neutral solutions, *e.g.*, many non-oxidizing salt solutions, chlorides, sulfates	Alkaline solutions, *e.g.* Caustic and mild alkalies, excluding ammonium hydroxide	Alkaline solutions, *e.g.* Ammonium hydroxide and amines	Acid solutions, *e.g.*, nitric	Neutral or alkaline solutions, *e.g.*, persulfates, peroxides, chromates	Pitting media,† acid ferric chloride solutions	Fresh-water supplies: Static or slow-moving	Fresh-water supplies: Turbulent	Sea water: Static or slow-moving	Sea water: Turbulent	Steam: Moist, condensate	Steam: Dry at high temp., promoting slight dissociation	Furnace gases with incidental sulfur content: Reducing, *e.g.*, heat-treatment furnace gases	Furnace gases with incidental sulfur content: Oxidizing, *e.g.*, flue gases	Ambient air, city or industrial
Cast iron, flake graphite, plain or low alloy	1	3	4	5	0	4	0	4	3	4	2	4	4	1	1	3
Ductile iron (higher strength and hardness may be attained by composition and heat-treatment or both)	1	3	4	5	0	4	0	4	4	4	3	4	4	1	1	3
Ni-Resist corrosion-resistant cast iron, type 1 (14 Ni; 7 Cu; 2 Cr; bal. Fe)	4	5	5	5	0	5	0	5	5	5	5	5	5	3	2	4
Ni-Resist corrosion-resistant cast iron, type 2 Cu free (20–30 Ni; 2–3 Cr; bal. Fe)	4	5	5	6	0	5	0	5	5	5	5	5	5	3	2	4
Ni-Resist corrosion-resistant cast iron, ductile (24 Ni; bal. Fe)	4	5	5	6	0	5	0	5	5	5	5	5	5	3	2	4
14% silicon iron	6	6	2	5	6	6	3	5	5	5	5	6	4	4	3	6
Mild steel, also low-alloy irons and steels	1	3	4	5	0	4	0	4	3	4	2	4	4	1	1	3
Stainless steel, ferritic 17% Cr type	2	4	4	6	5	6	0	4	6	1	4	5	6	3	2	4
Stainless steel, austenitic 18 Cr; 8 Ni type	3	4	5	6	6	6	0	6	6	2	5	6	6	2	3	5
Stainless steel, austenitic 18 Cr; 12 Ni; 2.5 Mo type	4	5	5	6	5	6	1	6	6	3	5	6	6	2	4	6
Stainless steel, austenitic 20 Cr; 29 Ni; 2.5 Mo; 3.5 Cu type	5	6	5	6	5	6	2	6	6	4	6	6	6	2	4	6
Ni-o-nel nickel-iron-chromium alloy (40 Ni; 21 Cr; 3 Mo; 1.5 Cu; bal. Fe)	6	6	5	6	5	6	2	6	6	4	6	6	6	2	5	6
Hastelloy alloy C[a] (55 Ni; 17 Mo; 16 Cr; 6 Fe; 4 W)	5	6	5	6	4	6	5	6	6	6	6	6	6	3	4	6
Hastelloy alloy B[b] (61 Ni; 28 Mo; 6 Fe)	6	5	4	4	0	3	0	6	6	4	4	6	5	3	2	5
Hastelloy alloy D (82 Ni; 10 Si; 4 Cu)	6	6	3	4	2	5	1	6	6	6	6	6	6	4	2	6
Inconel nickel-chromium alloy (78 Ni; 15 Cr; 7 Fe)	3	6	6	6	3	6	1	6	6	4	6	6	6	2	4	6

[a] Also Chlorimet 3. [b] Also Chlorimet 2.

Table 23-2. General Corrosion Properties of Some Metals and Alloys*—(*Continued*)

Ratings: 0 unsuitable. Not available in form required or not suitable for fabrication requirements or not suitable for corrosion conditions.
1 poor to fair.
2 fair. For mild conditions or where periodic replacement is possible. Restricted use.
3 fair to good.
4 good. Suitable when superior alternatives are uneconomic.
5 good to excellent.
6 normally excellent.
Small variations in service conditions may appreciably affect corrosion resistance. Choice of materials is therefore guided wherever possible by a combination of experience and laboratory and site tests.

Material	Liquids											Gases				
	Non-oxidizing or reducing media				Oxidizing media			Natural waters				Common industrial media				
	Acid solutions, excluding hydrochloric, *e.g.*, phosphoric, sulfuric, most conditions, many organics	Neutral solutions, *e.g.*, many non-oxidizing salt solutions, chlorides, sulfates	Alkaline solutions, *e.g.*		Acid solutions, *e.g.*, nitric	Neutral or alkaline solutions, *e.g.*, persulfates, peroxides, chromates	Pitting media,† acid ferric chloride solutions	Fresh-water supplies		Sea water		Steam		Furnace gases with incidental sulfur content		Ambient air, city or industrial
			Caustic and mild alkalies, excluding ammonium hydroxide	Ammonium hydroxide and amines				Static or slow-moving	Turbulent	Static or slow-moving	Turbulent	Moist, condensate	Dry at high temp., promoting slight dissociation	Reducing, *e.g.*, heat-treatment furnace gases	Oxidizing, *e.g.*, flue gases	
Copper-nickel alloys up to 30% nickel	4	5	5	0	0	4	1	6	6	6	6	6	5	2	2	5
Monel nickel-copper alloy (68 Ni; 30 Cu; 2 Fe)	5	6	6	1	0	5	1	6	6	4	6	6	6	2	3	5
S Monel nickel-copper cast alloy (66 Ni; 30 Cu; 4 Si)	5	6	6	1	0	5	1	6	6	4	6	6	6	2	3	5
K Monel age hardenable Ni-Cu alloy (67 Ni; 30 Cu; 3 Al)	5	6	6	1	0	5	1	6	6	4	6	6	6	2	3	5
A nickel—commercial (99.4 Ni)	4	5	6	1	0	5	0	6	6	3	5	6	6	2	2	4
Copper and silicon bronze	4	4	4	0	0	4	0	6	5	4	1	6	5	2	2	5
Aluminum brass (76 Cu; 22 Zn; 2 Al)	3	4	2	0	0	3	0	[6	6	4	5	6	5	2	2	5
Nickel-aluminum-bronze (80 Cu; 10 Al; 5 Ni; 5 Fe)	4	4	2	0	0	3	0	6	6	4	5	6	5	2	3	5
Bronze, type A (88 Cu; 5 Sn; 5 Ni; 2 Zn)	4	5	4	0	0	4	0	6	6	5	5	6	5	2	2	5
Aluminum and its alloys	1	3	0	6	0–5	0–4	0	4	5	0–5	4	5	2	5	4	5
Lead, chemical or antimonial	5	5	2	2	0	2	0	6	5	5	3	2	0	4	3	5
Silver	4	6	6	0	0	2	0	6	6	5	5	6	5	4	4	4
Titanium	3	6	2	6	6	6	6	6	6	6	6	6	5	3	5	6
Zirconium	3	6	2	6	6	6	2	6	6	6	6	6	6	3	5	6

Table 23-2. **General Corrosion Properties of Some Metals and Alloys***—(*Continued*)

Ratings: 0 unsuitable. Not available in form required or not suitable for fabrication requirements or not suitable for corrosion conditions.
1 poor to fair.
2 fair. For mild conditions or where periodic replacement is possible. Restricted use.
3 fair to good.
4 good. Suitable when superior alternatives are uneconomic.
5 good to excellent.
6 normally excellent.
Small variations in service conditions may appreciably affect corrosion resistance. Choice of materials is therefore guided wherever possible by a combination of experience and laboratory and site tests.

Material	Gases (*Cont'd.*) Halogens and derivatives: Halogens: Moist, *e.g.*, chlorine below dew point	Dry, *e.g.*, fluorine above dew point	Halide acids, moist, *e.g.*, hydrochloric hydrolysis products of organic halides	Hydrogen halides, dry,‡ *e.g.*, dry hydrogen chloride, °F.	Available forms	Cold formability in wrought and clad form	Weld-ability	Max. strength annealed condition × 1000 lb./sq. in.	Coeff. of thermal expansion, millionths per °F. 70°–212°F.	Remarks¶
Cast iron, flake graphite, plain or low alloy	0	2	0	2 < 400 1 < 750	Cast	No	Fair§	45	6.7	A.S.T.M.-A48-48
Ductile iron (higher strength and hardness may be attained by composition and heat-treatment or both)	0	2	0	2 < 400 1 < 750	Cast	No	Good§	67	7.5	A.S.T.M. A339, A396-55 MIL-I-1466 (ORD), MIL-I-17166 (Ships), A.M.S. 5313, 5316
Ni-Resist corrosion-resistant cast iron, type 1 (14 Ni; 7 Cu; 2 Cr; bal. Fe)	0	2	3	3 < 400 2 < 750	Cast	No	Good§	22–31	10.3	AMS-5392 MIL-G-858A Hyd. Inst. No. 115
Ni-Resist corrosion-resistant cast iron, type 2 Cu free (20–30 Ni; 2–3 Cr; bal. Fe)	0	2	3	3 < 400 2 < 750	Cast	No	Good§	22–31	9.6	MIL-G-858A Hyd. Inst. No. 115 Type 3 Ni-Resist has same corrosion resistance
Ni-Resist corrosion-resistant cast iron, ductile (24 Ni; bal. Fe)	0	2	3	3 < 400 2 < 750	Cast	No	Good§	56	10.4	AMS-5394 MIL-I-18397 (Ships)
14% silicon iron	0	0	4	1 < 400	Cast	No	No	22	7.4	Very brittle, susceptible to cracking by mechanical and thermal shock
Mild steel, also low-alloy irons and steels	0	3	0	3 < 400 1 < 750	Wrought, cast	Good	Good	67	6.7	High strengths obtainable by alloying, also improved atmospheric corrosion resistance. See A.S.T.M. specifications for particular grade
Stainless steel, ferritic 17% Cr type	0	2	0	2 < 400	Wrought, cast, clad	Good	Good§	78	6.0	A.I.S.I. type 430 A.S.T.M. corrosion- and heat-resisting steels
Stainless steel, austenitic 18 Cr; 8 Ni types	0	2	0	3 < 400	Wrought, cast, clad	Good	Good	90	9.6	A.I.S.I. type 304 A.S.T.M. corrosion- and heat-resisting steels. Stabilized or ELC types used for welding
Stainless steel, austenitic 18 Cr; 12 Ni; 2.5 Mo type	0	3	2	4 < 400 3 < 750	Wrought, cast, clad	Good	Good	90	8.9	A.I.S.I. type 316 A.S.T.M. corrosion- and heat-resisting steel. ELC type used for welding
Stainless steel, austenitic 20 Cr; 29 Ni; 2.5 Mo; 3.5 Cu type	1	3	3	4 < 400 3 < 750	Wrought, cast	Good	Good	90	9.4	A.C.I. Cn-7M. Good resistance to sulfuric, phosphoric, and fatty acids at elevated temperatures
Ni-o-nel nickel-iron-chromium alloy (40 Ni; 21 Cr; 3 Mo; 1.5 Cu; bal. Fe)	2	3	3	4 < 400 3 < 750	Wrought, cast, clad	Good	Good	100	7.3	Special alloy with good resistance to sulfuric, phosphoric, and fatty acids. Resistant to chlorides in some environments
Hastelloy alloy C[a] (55 Ni; 17 Mo; 16 Cr; 6 Fe; 4 W)	5	4	4	4 < 750 3 < 900	Wrought, cast, clad	Fair	Good	145	6.3	Excellent resistance to wet chlorine gas and sodium hypochlorite solutions
Hastelloy alloy B[b] (61 Ni; 28 Mo; 6 Fe)	1	3	5	4 < 750 3 < 900	Wrought, cast, clad	Fair	Good	135	5.6	Resistant to solutions of hydrochloric and sulfuric acids
Hastelloy alloy D (82 Ni; 10 Si; 4 Cu)	1	1	2	3 < 400 2 < 750 1 < 900	Cast	No	§	90–110	6.1	Greatest application in hot concentrated solutions of sulfuric acid
Inconel nickel-chromium alloy (78 Ni; 15 Cr; 7 Fe)	2	5	3	5 < 400 4 < 900	Wrought, cast, clad	Good	Good	90	8.9	Wide application in food and pharmaceutical industries

Table 23-2. General Corrosion Properties of Some Metals and Alloys*—(*Concluded*)

Ratings: 0 unsuitable. Not available in form required or not suitable for fabrication requirements or not suitable for corrosion conditions.
1 poor to fair.
2 fair. For mild conditions or where periodic replacement is possible. Restricted use.
3 fair to good.
4 good. Suitable when superior alternatives are uneconomic.
5 good to excellent.
6 normally excellent.
Small variations in service conditions may appreciably affect corrosion resistance. Choice of materials is therefore guided wherever possible by a combination of experience and laboratory and site tests.

Material	Gases (*Cont'd.*) Halogens and derivatives: Halogens: Moist, *e.g.*, chlorine below dew point	Halogens: Dry, *e.g.*, fluorine above dew point	Halide acids, moist, *e.g.*, hydrochloric hydrolysis products of organic halides	Hydrogen halides, dry,† *e.g.*, dry hydrogen chloride, °F.	Available forms	Cold formability in wrought and clad form	Weld-ability	Max. strength annealed condition × 1000 lb./sq. in.	Coeff. of thermal expansion, millionths per °F. 70°–212°F.	Remarks¶
Copper-nickel alloys up to 30% nickel	1	5	2	4 < 400 3 < 750	Wrought, cast, clad	Good	Good	38–62	9.3–8.5	High-iron types excellent for resisting high-velocity effects in condenser tubes
Monel nickel-copper alloy (68 Ni; 30 Cu; 2 Fe)	2	6	3	6 < 400 3 < 750 2 < 900	Wrought, cast, clad	Good	Good	77	7.5	Widely used for sulfuric acid pickling equipment. Also for propeller shafts in motor boats. Take precautions to avoid sulfur attack during fabrication
S Monel nickel-copper cast alloy (66 Ni; 30 Cu; 4 Si)	2	4	3	6 < 400 3 < 750 2 < 900	Cast	No	No	100	8.8	Non-galling characteristics. Excellent for bearings or bushings. High strength developed by heat-treatment
K Monel age hardenable Ni-Cu alloy (67 Ni; 30 Cu; 3 Al)	2	6	3	6 < 400 3 < 750 2 < 900	Wrought, cast	Fair	Good	99–155	7.4	High strength obtainable by heat-treatment. Take precautions to avoid sulfur attack during fabrication
A nickel—commercial (99.4 Ni)	2	6	2	6 < 400 5 < 750 4 < 900	Wrought, cast, clad	Good	Good	54	6.6	Widely used for hot concentrated caustic solutions. Take precautions to avoid sulfur attack during fabrication
Copper and silicon bronze	0	5	2	3 < 400 2 < 750	Wrought, cast, clad	Excellent	Fair	29	9.3–9.5	Unsuitable for hot concentrated mineral acids or for high-velocity HF
Aluminum brass (76 Cu; 22 Zn; 2 Al)	0	4	2	2 < 400	Wrought, cast	Good	Fair	60	10.3	May develop localized corrosion in sea water
Nickel-aluminum-bronze (80 Cu; 10 Al; 5 Ni; 5 Fe)	0	4	3	3 < 400 2 < 750	Wrought, cast	Good	Fair	60–80	9.4	Ship propellers an excellent application
Bronze, type A (88 Cu; 5 Sn; 5 Ni; 2 Zn)	0	4	3	3 < 400 2 < 750	Cast	No	§	45	11.0	High strengths obtainable by heat-treatment. Not susceptible to dezincification
Aluminum and its alloys	0	6	0	3 < 400 1 < 750	Wrought, cast, clad	Good	Good	9–90	11.5–13.7	Extent of corrosion dependent upon type and concentration of acidic ions. Wide range of mechanical properties obtainable by alloying and heat-treatment
Lead, chemical or antimonial	0	1	3	0	Wrought, cast, clad	Excellent	Good	2	16.4–15.1	High purity "chemical lead" preferred for most applications
Silver	5	5	3	4 < 400 2 < 750	Wrought, cast, clad	Excellent	Good	21	10.6	Used as a lining
Titanium	6	0	1	0	Wrought, cast	Fair	Good§	6–90	5.0	Red fuming HNO_3 may initiate explosions. Good resistance to solutions containing chlorides
Zirconium	6	1	6	0	Wrought, cast	Fair	Good §			

* Data courtesy of International Nickel Co.
† On unsuitable materials these media may promote potentially dangerous pitting.
‡ Temperatures are approximate.
§ Special precautions required.
¶ Many of these materials are suitable for resisting dry corrosion at elevated temperatures.
[a] Also Chlorimet 3. [b] Also Chlorimet 2.

Table 23-3. Chemical Resistance of Important Plastics

	Poly-propylene poly-ethylene	CAB*	ABS†	PVC‡	Saran§	Polyester glass¶	Epoxy glass	Phenolic asbestos	Fluoro-carbons	Chlorinated polyether (Penton)	Poly-carbonate
10% H_2SO_4	Excel.	Good	Excel.	Excel.	Excel.	Excel.	Excel.	Excel.	Excel.	Excel.	Excel.
50% H_2SO_4	Excel.	Poor	Excel.	Excel.	Excel.	Good	Excel.	Excel.	Excel.	Excel.	Excel.
10% HCl	Excel.	Excel.	Excel.	Excel.	Excel.	Excel.	Excel.	Excel.	Excel.	Excel.	Excel.
10% HNO_3	Excel.	Poor	Good	Excel.	Excel.	Good	Good	Fair	Excel.	Excel.	Excel.
10% Acetic	Excel.	Good	Excel.	Excel.	Excel.	Excel.	Excel.	Excel.	Excel.	Excel.	Excel.
10% NaOH	Excel.	Fair	Excel.	Good	Fair	Fair	Excel.	Poor	Excel.	Excel.	Excel.
50% NaOH	Excel.	Poor	Excel.	Excel.	Fair	Poor	Good	Poor	Excel.	Excel.	Excel.
NH_4OH	Excel.	Poor	Excel.	Excel.	Poor	Fair	Excel.	Poor	Excel.	Excel.	Excel.
NaCl	Excel.	Excel.	Excel.	Excel.	Excel.	Excel.	Excel.	Excel.	Excel.	Excel.	Excel.
$FeCl_3$	Excel.	Excel.	Excel.	Excel.	Excel.	Excel.	Excel.	Excel.	Excel.	Excel.	Excel.
$CuSO_4$	Excel.	Excel.	Excel.	Excel.	Excel.	Excel.	Excel.	Excel.	Excel.	Excel.	Excel.
NH_4NO_3	Excel.	Excel.	Excel.	Excel.	Excel.	Excel.	Excel.	Good	Excel.	Excel.	Excel.
Wet H_2S	Excel.	Excel.	Excel.	Excel.	Excel.	Excel.	Excel.	Excel.	Excel.	Excel.	
Wet Cl_2	Poor	Poor	Excel.	Good	Poor	Poor	Poor	Excel.	Excel.	Excel.	
Wet SO_2	Excel.	Poor	Excel.	Excel.	Good	Excel.	Excel.	Excel.	Excel.	Excel.	
Gasoline	Poor	Excel.	Excel.	Excel.	Excel.	Excel.	Excel.	Excel.	Excel.	Excel.	Excel.
Benzene	Poor	Poor	Poor	Poor	Fair	Good	Excel.	Excel.	Excel.	Fair	Fair
CCl_4	Poor	Poor	Poor	Fair	Fair	Excel.	Good	Excel.	Excel.	Fair	Poor
Acetone	Poor	Poor	Poor	Poor	Fair	Poor	Good	Poor	Excel.	Good	Good
Alcohol	Poor	Poor	Excel.	Excel.	Excel.	Excel.	Excel.	Excel.	Excel.	Excel.	Excel.

Ratings are for long-term exposures at ambient temperatures (less than 100°F.).
* Cellulose acetate butyrate.
† Acrylonitrile butadiene styrene polymer.
‡ Polyvinyl chloride, type I.
§ Chemical resistance of Saran-lined pipe is superior to extruded Saran in some environments.
¶ Refers to general-purpose polyesters. Special polyesters have superior resistance, particularly in alkalies.

brittle and hence do not stand up well under shock and impact. Also these irons are more difficult to machine. Threads must be formed by direct casting. Welding is possible, although Durichlor is more difficult to weld than Duriron. Special welding rods and heat-treatments must be used.

Silicon irons are very resistant to oxidizing and reducing environments, and resistance depends on the formation of a passive film. These irons are widely used in sulfuric acid service, since they are unaffected by sulfuric at all strengths, even up to the boiling point.

The Mo-containing iron is especially recommended for hydrochloric acid, although presence of oxidized chlorides such as ferric chloride will cause pitting.

Because they are very hard, silicon irons are good for combined corrosion-erosion service.

To overcome some of the mechanical disadvantages of silicon irons, a number of **other cast alloys** have been developed. One, **Hastelloy D,** contains about 82 per cent Ni, 3 per cent Cu, 9 per cent Si, 2 per cent Fe. This alloy has superior resistance to mechanical and thermal shock over silicon irons. Machining is easier than with silicon irons. The alloy is recommended for sulfuric acid service, since it is practically unaffected by all concentrations of sulfuric up to and including the boiling point. However, it is not recommended for nitric or chromic acids.

Another group of cast-iron alloys are called **Ni-Resist.** These materials are related to gray cast iron in that they have high carbon contents (3 per cent), with fine graphite flakes distributed throughout the structure. Nickel contents vary from 13.5 to 36 per cent, and some have 6.5 per cent Cu.

Generally, nickel-alloy castings have superior toughness and impact resistance compared with gray irons. The nickel-alloy castings can be welded and machined.

Corrosion resistance of nickel alloys is superior to cast irons, but less than that of pure nickel. There is little attack from neutral or alkaline solutions. Oxidizing acids such as nitric are highly detrimental. Cold, concentrated sulfuric acid can be handled.

Ni-Resist has excellent heat resistance, with some grades serviceable up to 1500°F. Also, a ductile variety is available, as well as a hard variety (Ni-Hard).

Stainless Steel. There are more than 70 standard types of stainless steel and many special alloys. These steels are produced in the wrought form (A.I.S.I. types) and as cast alloys (A.C.I.) types. Generally, all are iron-based, with 12 to 30 per cent chromium, 0 to 22 per cent nickel, and minor amounts of carbon, columbium, copper, molybdenum, selenium, tantalum, and titanium. These alloys are very popular in the process industries. They are heat- and corrosion-resistant, non-contaminating, and easily fabricated into complex shapes.

There are three groups of stainless alloys: (1) martensitic, (2) ferritic, (3) austenitic.

The **martensitic** alloys contain 12 to 20 per cent chromium with controlled amounts of carbon and other additives. Type 410 is a typical member of this group. These alloys can be hardened by heat-treatment, which can increase tensile strength from 80,000 to 200,000 lb./sq. in.

Corrosion resistance is inferior to austenitic stainless steels, and martensitic steels are generally used in mildly corrosive environments (atmospheric, fresh water, and organic exposures).

Ferritic stainless contains 15 to 30 per cent Cr, with low carbon content (0.1 per cent). The higher chromium content improves its corrosive resistance. Type 430 is a typical example. The strength of ferritic stainless can be increased by cold working but not by heat-treatment. Fairly ductile, ferritic grades can be fabricated by all standard methods. They are fairly easy to machine with high-speed equipment. Welding is no problem, although it requires skilled operators.

Corrosion resistance is rated good although ferritic alloys are not good against reducing acids such as HCl. But mildly corrosive solutions and oxidizing media are handled without harm. Type 430 is widely used in nitric acid plants. In addition it is very resistant to scaling and high-temperature oxidation up to 1500°F.

Austenitic stainless steels are the most corrosion-resistant of the three groups. These steels contain 16 to

(*Continued on page* 23-48)

Table 23-4. Detailed Corrosion Data on Construction Materials*

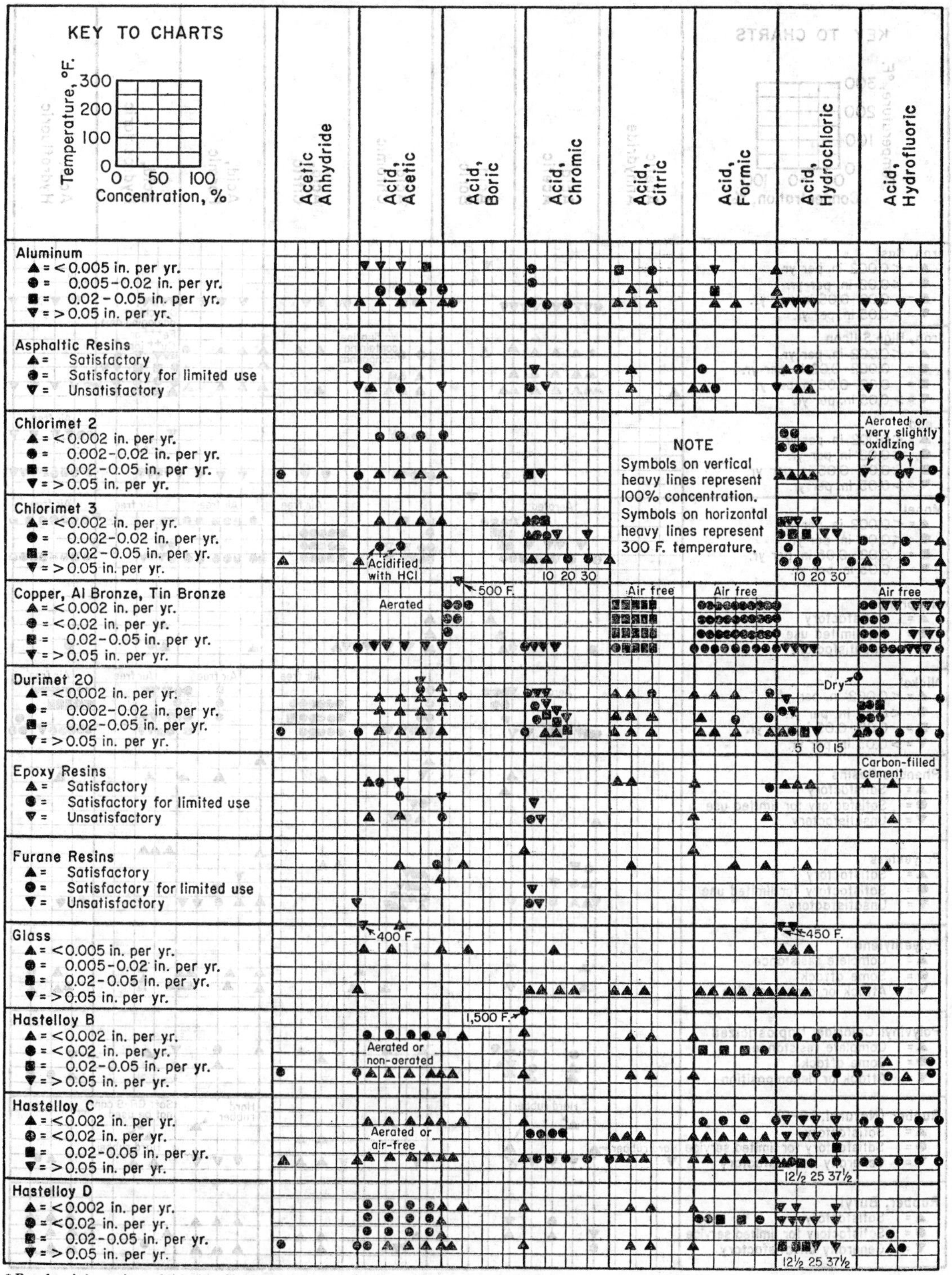

* Based on information published in *Chemical Engineering* Magazine. These charts are to assist in narrowing your field of choice. They should not be used for anything more. Effects of contaminants, aeration, galvanic coupling, erosion, etc., must be taken into account. Field tests are best for determining suitability.

Table 23-4. Detailed Corrosion Data on Construction Materials*—(*Continued*)

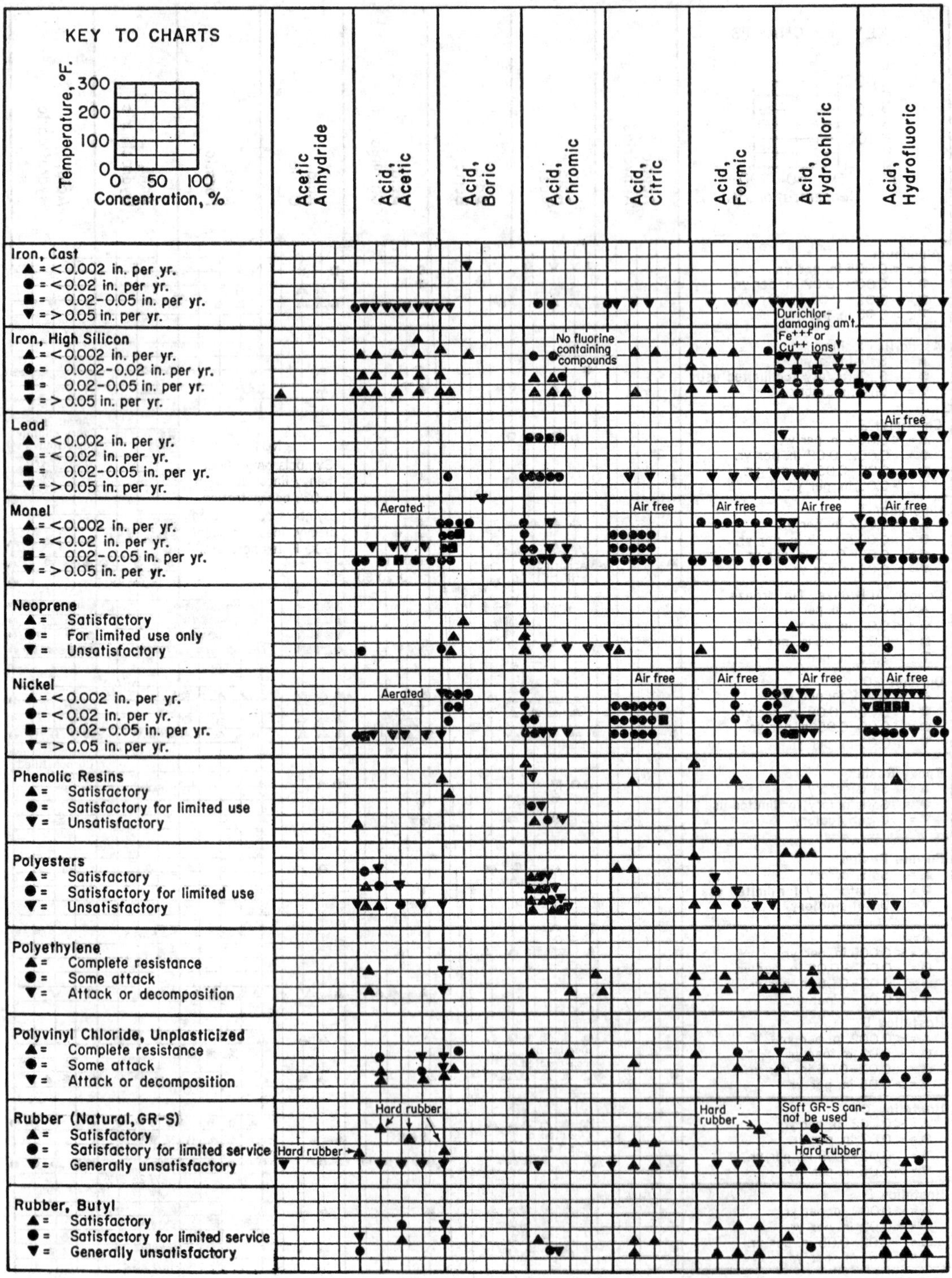

Table 23-4. Detailed Corrosion Data on Construction Materials*—*(Continued)*

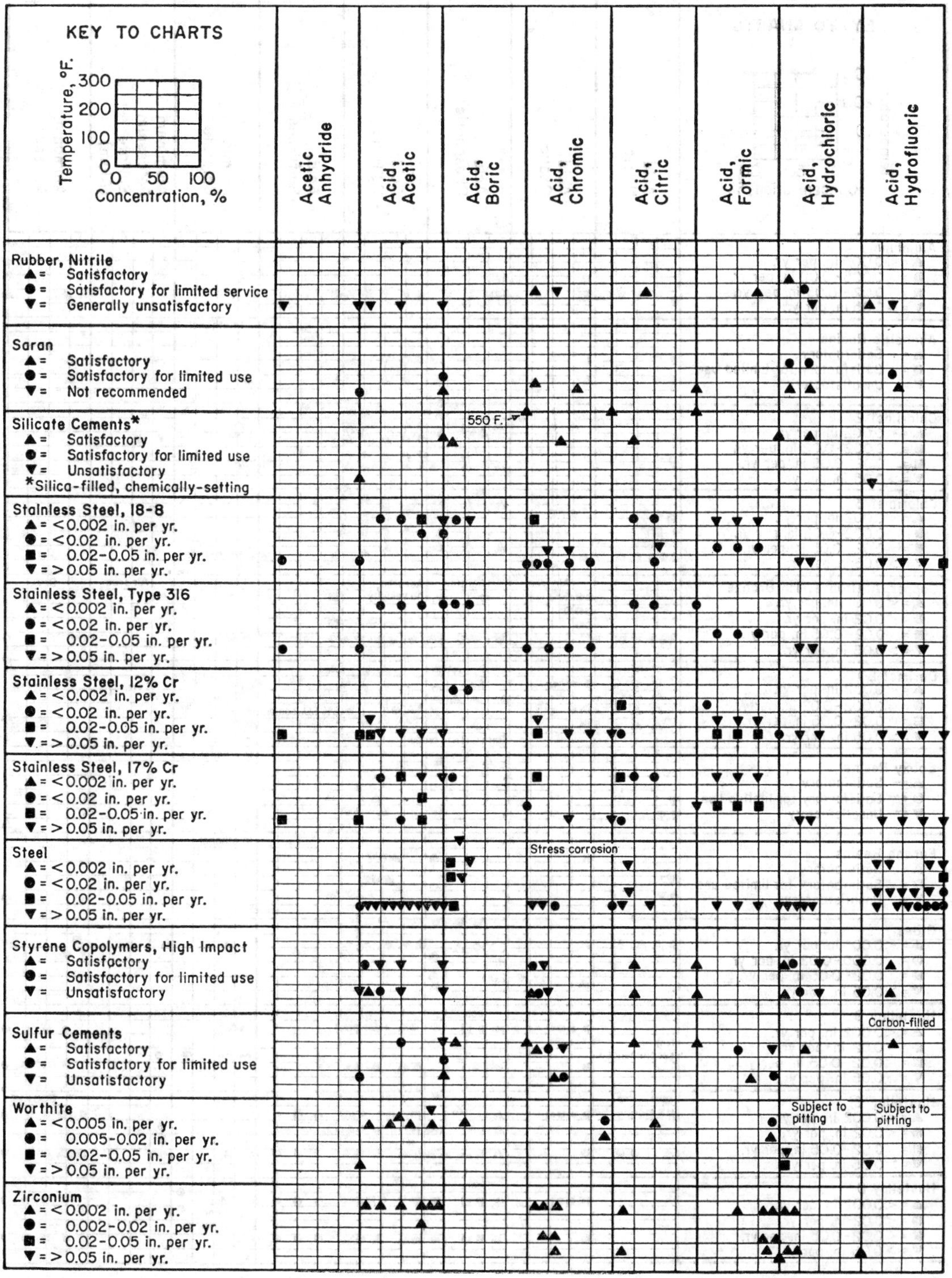

Table 23-4. Detailed Corrosion Data on Construction Materials*—(*Continued*)

KEY TO CHARTS

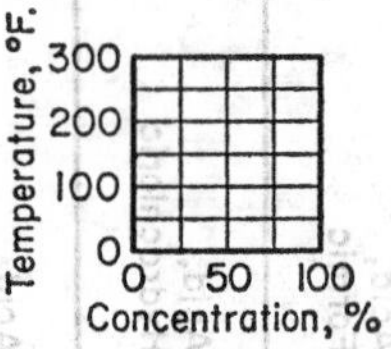

Columns: Acid, Nitric | Acid, Oxalic | Acid, Phosphoric | Acid, Sulfuric | Acid, Sulfurous | Aluminum Chloride | Aluminum Potassium Sulfate (Alum) | Ammonia, Aqueous

Aluminum
▲ = < 0.005 in. per yr.
● = 0.005–0.02 in. per yr.
■ = 0.02–0.05 in. per yr.
▼ = > 0.05 in. per yr.

Asphaltic Resins
▲ = Satisfactory
● = Satisfactory for limited use
▼ = Unsatisfactory

Chlorimet 2
▲ = < 0.002 in. per yr.
● = 0.002–0.02 in. per yr.
■ = 0.02–0.05 in. per yr.
▼ = > 0.05 in. per yr.

Chlorimet 3
▲ = < 0.002 in. per yr.
● = 0.002–0.02 in. per yr.
■ = 0.02–0.05 in. per yr.
▼ = > 0.05 in. per yr.

Copper, Al Bronze, Tin Bronze
▲ = < 0.002 in. per yr.
● = < 0.02 in. per yr.
■ = 0.02–0.05 in. per yr.
▼ = > 0.05 in. per yr.

Durimet 20
▲ = < 0.002 in. per yr.
● = 0.002–0.02 in. per yr.
■ = 0.02–0.05 in. per yr.
▼ = > 0.05 in. per yr.

Epoxy Resins
▲ = Satisfactory
● = Satisfactory for limited use
▼ = Unsatisfactory

Furane Resins
▲ = Satisfactory
● = Satisfactory for limited use
▼ = Unsatisfactory

Glass
▲ = < 0.005 in. per yr.
● = 0.005–0.02 in. per yr.
■ = 0.02–0.05 in. per yr.
▼ = > 0.05 in. per yr.

Hastelloy B
▲ = < 0.002 in. per yr.
● = < 0.02 in. per yr.
■ = 0.02–0.05 in. per yr.
▼ = > 0.05 in. per yr.

Hastelloy C
▲ = < 0.002 in. per yr.
● = < 0.02 in. per yr.
■ = 0.02–0.05 in. per yr.
▼ = > 0.05 in. per yr.

Hastelloy D
▲ = < 0.002 in. per yr.
● = < 0.02 in. per yr.
■ = 0.02–0.05 in. per yr.
▼ = > 0.05 in. per yr.

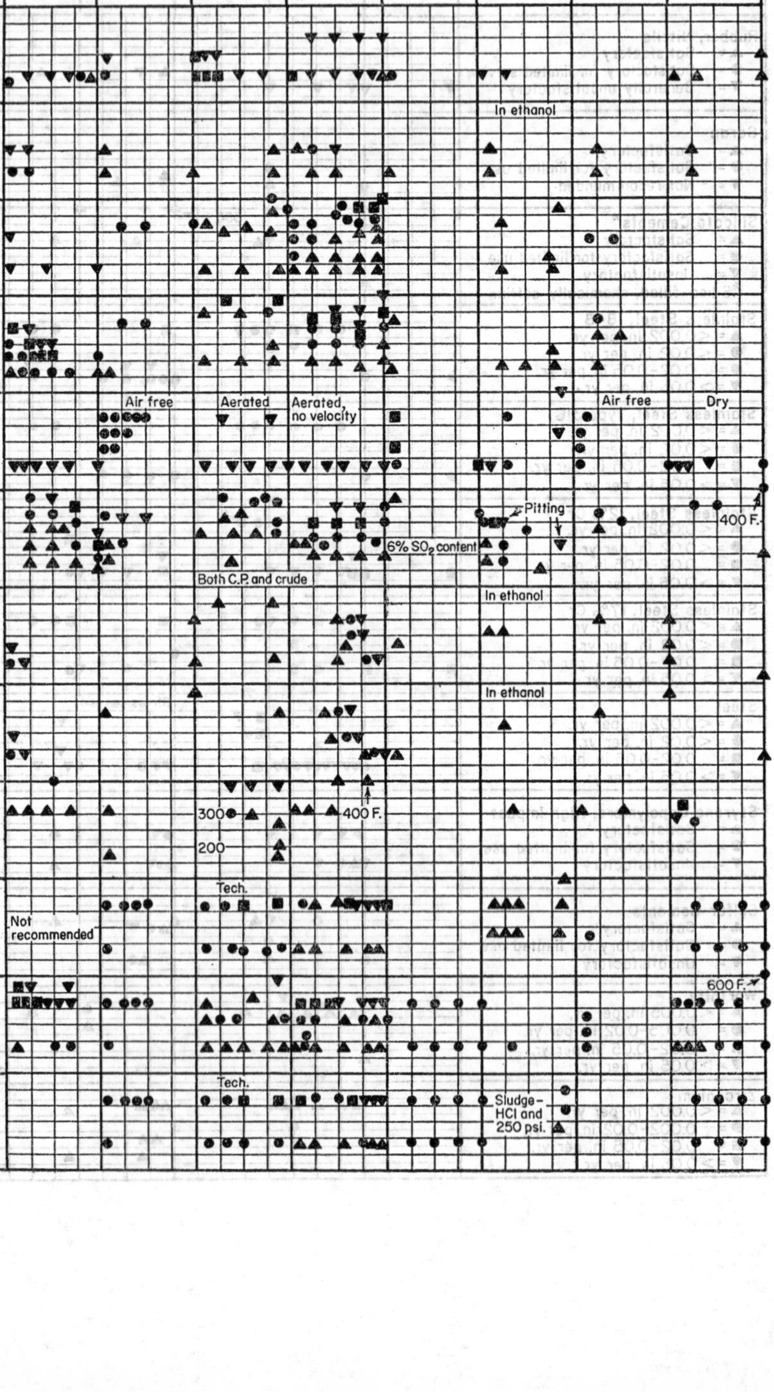

Table 23-4. Detailed Corrosion Data on Construction Materials*—(*Continued*)

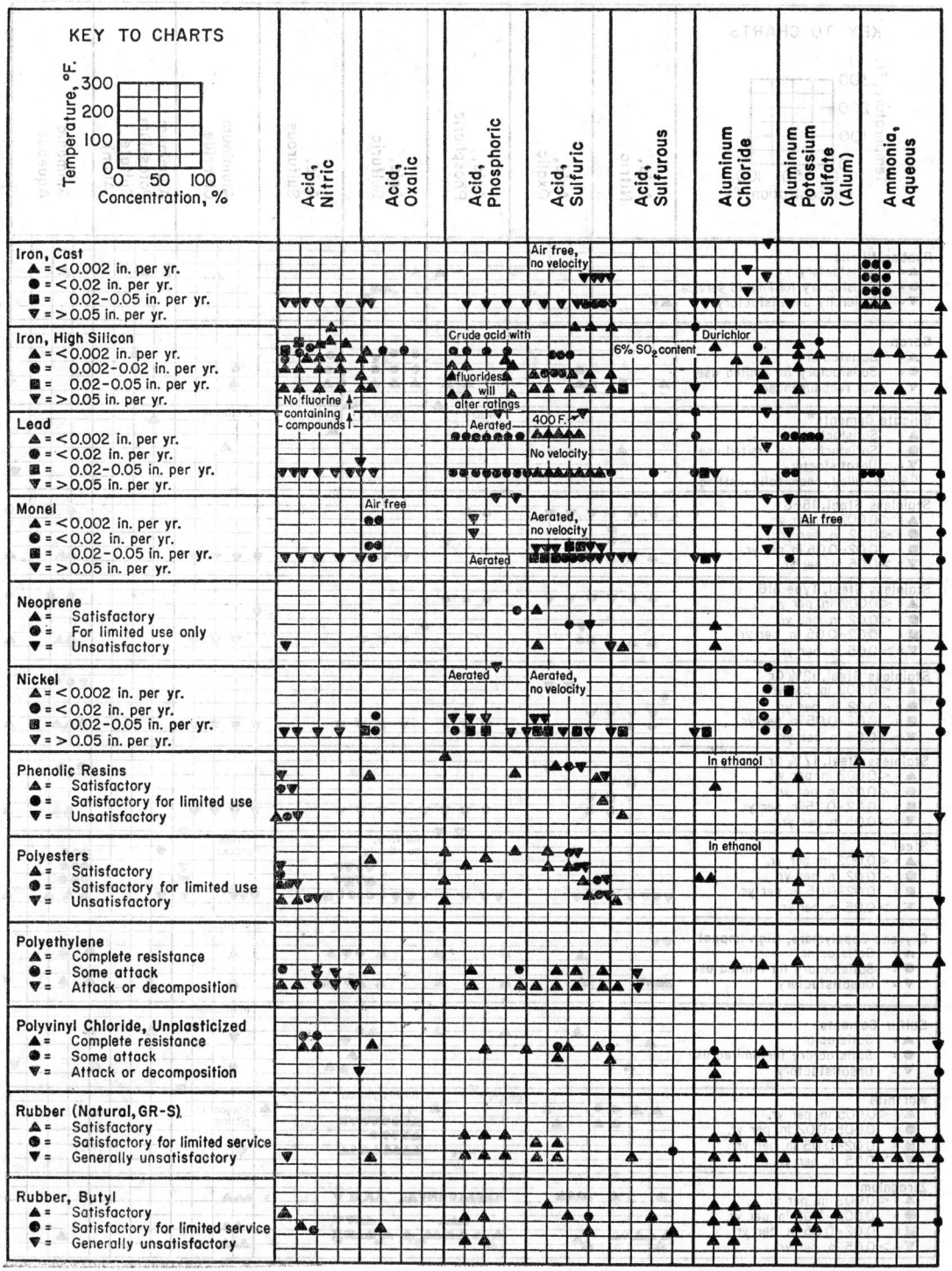

KEY TO CHARTS

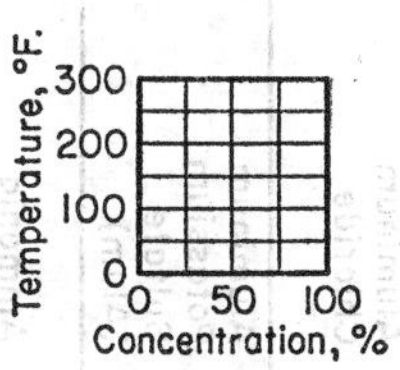

Columns: Acid, Nitric | Acid, Oxalic | Acid, Phosphoric | Acid, Sulfuric | Acid, Sulfurous | Aluminum Chloride | Aluminum Potassium Sulfate (Alum) | Ammonia, Aqueous

Iron, Cast
▲ = <0.002 in. per yr.
● = <0.02 in. per yr.
■ = 0.02–0.05 in. per yr.
▼ = >0.05 in. per yr.

Iron, High Silicon
▲ = <0.002 in. per yr.
● = 0.002–0.02 in. per yr.
■ = 0.02–0.05 in. per yr.
▼ = >0.05 in. per yr.

Lead
▲ = <0.002 in. per yr.
● = <0.02 in. per yr.
■ = 0.02–0.05 in. per yr.
▼ = >0.05 in. per yr.

Monel
▲ = <0.002 in. per yr.
● = <0.02 in. per yr.
■ = 0.02–0.05 in. per yr.
▼ = >0.05 in. per yr.

Neoprene
▲ = Satisfactory
● = For limited use only
▼ = Unsatisfactory

Nickel
▲ = <0.002 in. per yr.
● = <0.02 in. per yr.
■ = 0.02–0.05 in. per yr.
▼ = >0.05 in. per yr.

Phenolic Resins
▲ = Satisfactory
● = Satisfactory for limited use
▼ = Unsatisfactory

Polyesters
▲ = Satisfactory
● = Satisfactory for limited use
▼ = Unsatisfactory

Polyethylene
▲ = Complete resistance
● = Some attack
▼ = Attack or decomposition

Polyvinyl Chloride, Unplasticized
▲ = Complete resistance
● = Some attack
▼ = Attack or decomposition

Rubber (Natural, GR-S)
▲ = Satisfactory
● = Satisfactory for limited service
▼ = Generally unsatisfactory

Rubber, Butyl
▲ = Satisfactory
● = Satisfactory for limited service
▼ = Generally unsatisfactory

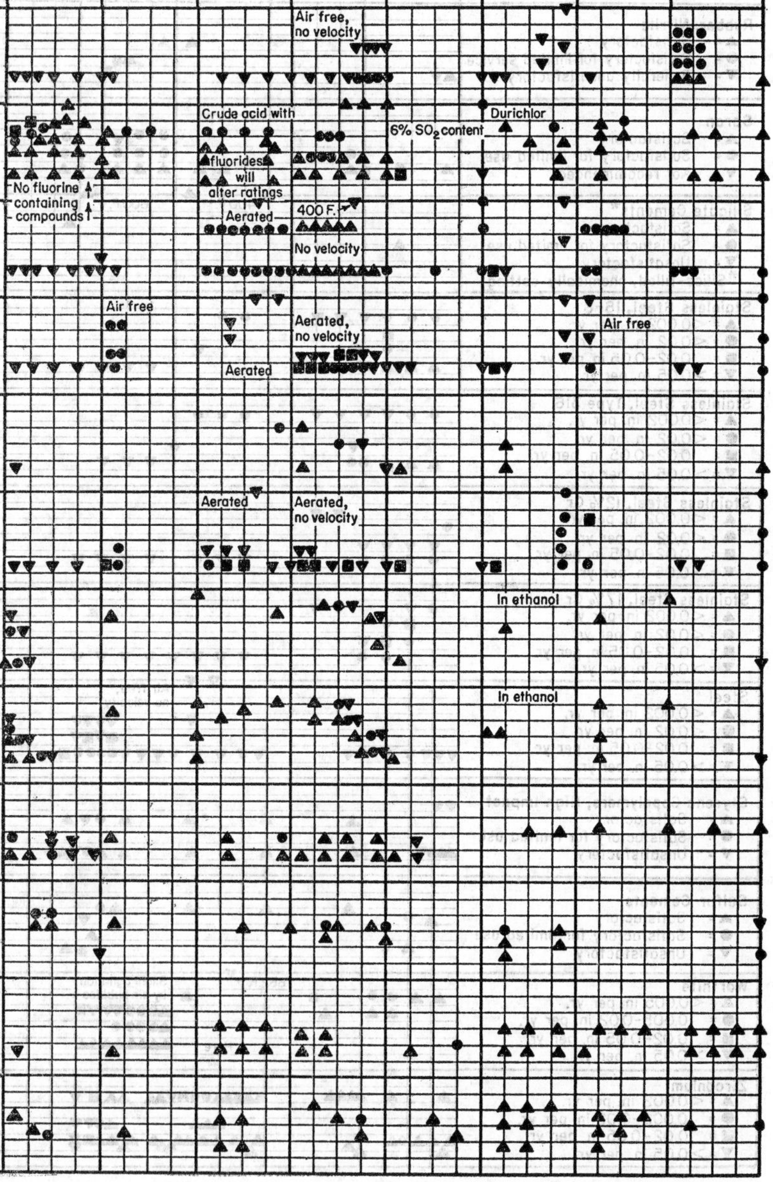

Table 23-4. Detailed Corrosion Data on Construction Materials*—(*Continued*)

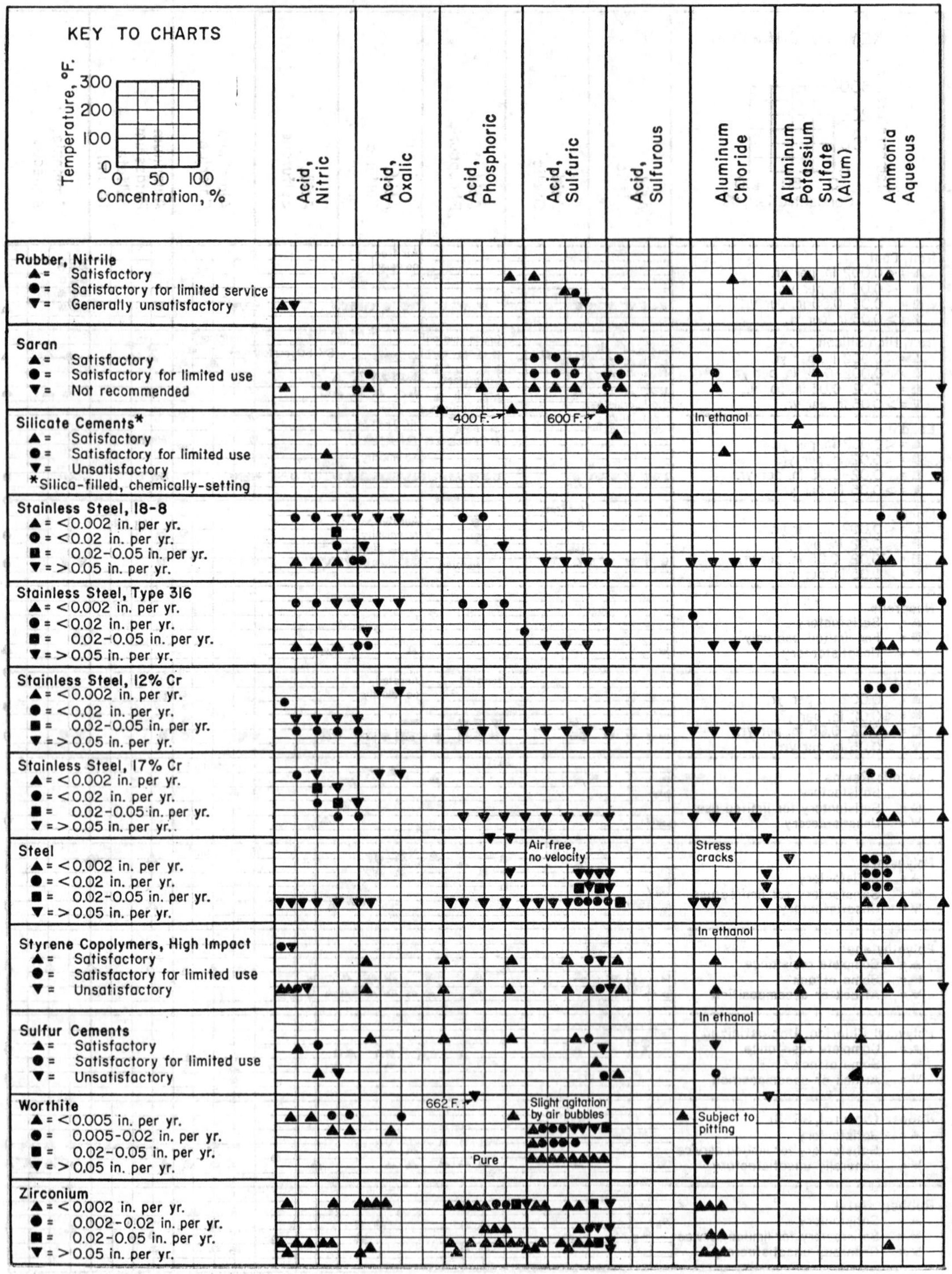

Table 23-4. Detailed Corrosion Data on Construction Materials*—(*Continued*)

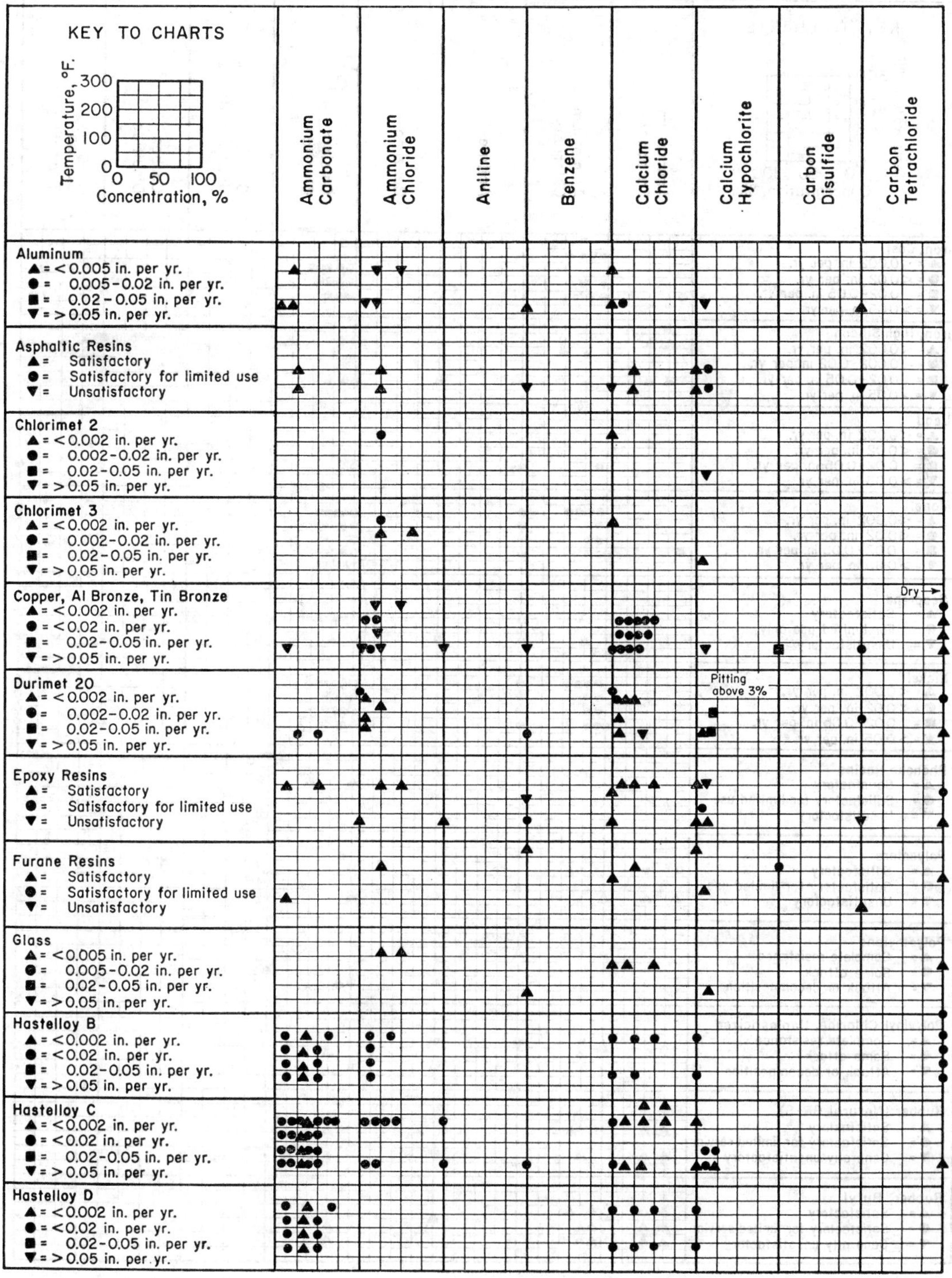

Table 23-4. Detailed Corrosion Data on Construction Materials*—*(Continued)*

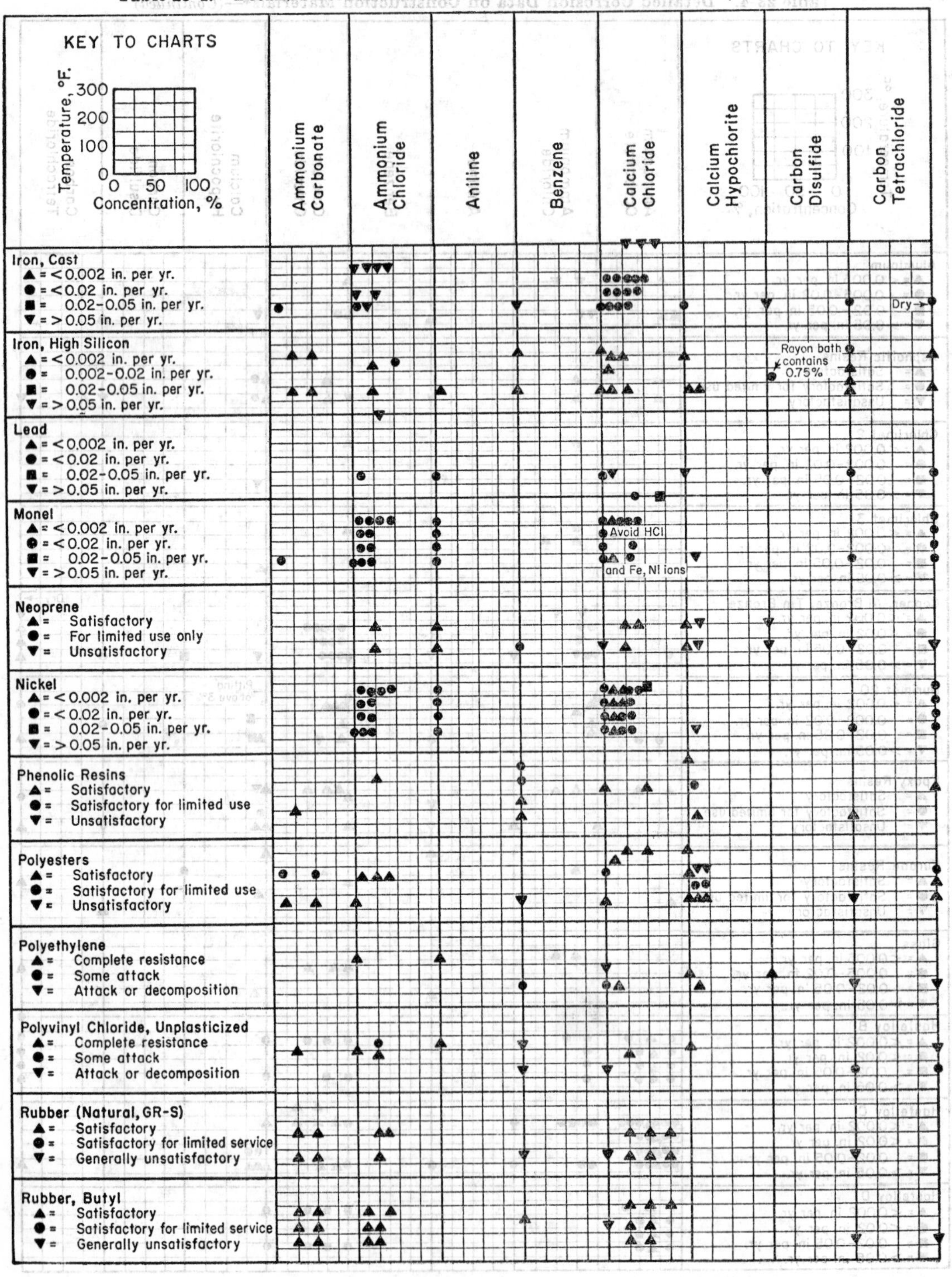

Table 23-4. Detailed Corrosion Data on Construction Materials*—(*Continued*)

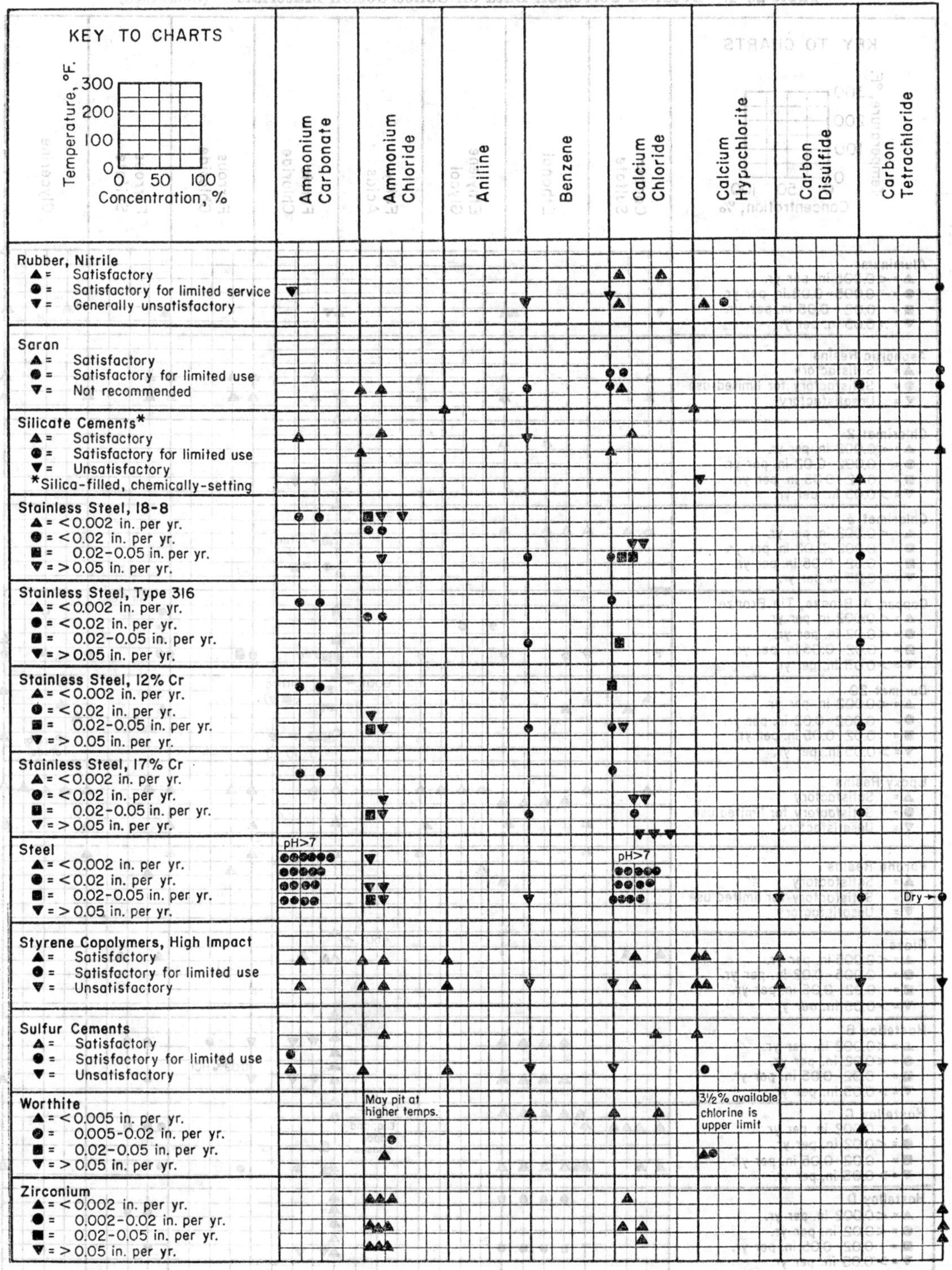

Table 23-4. Detailed Corrosion Data on Construction Materials*—*(Continued)*

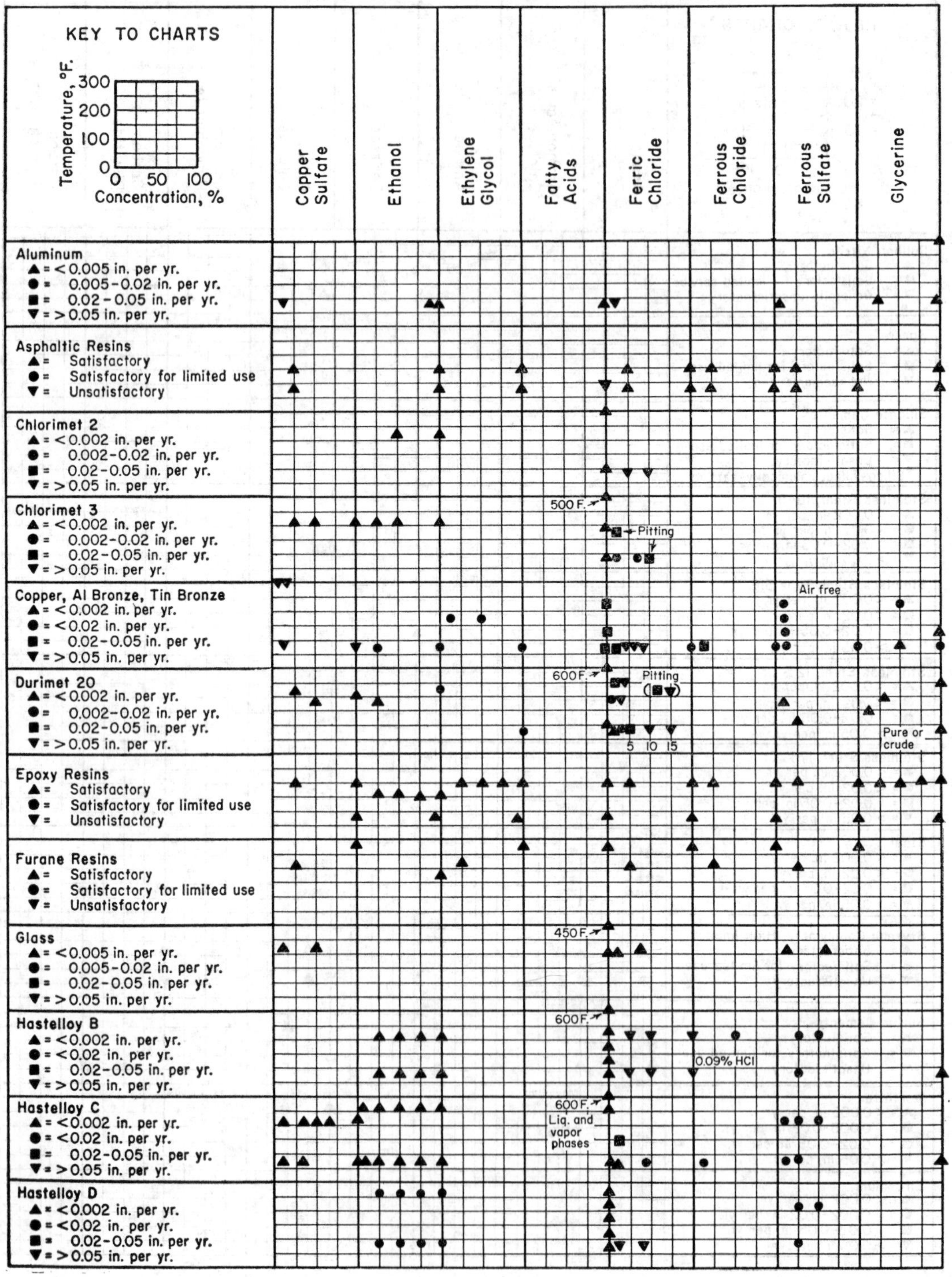

Table 23-4. Detailed Corrosion Data on Construction Materials*—(*Continued*)

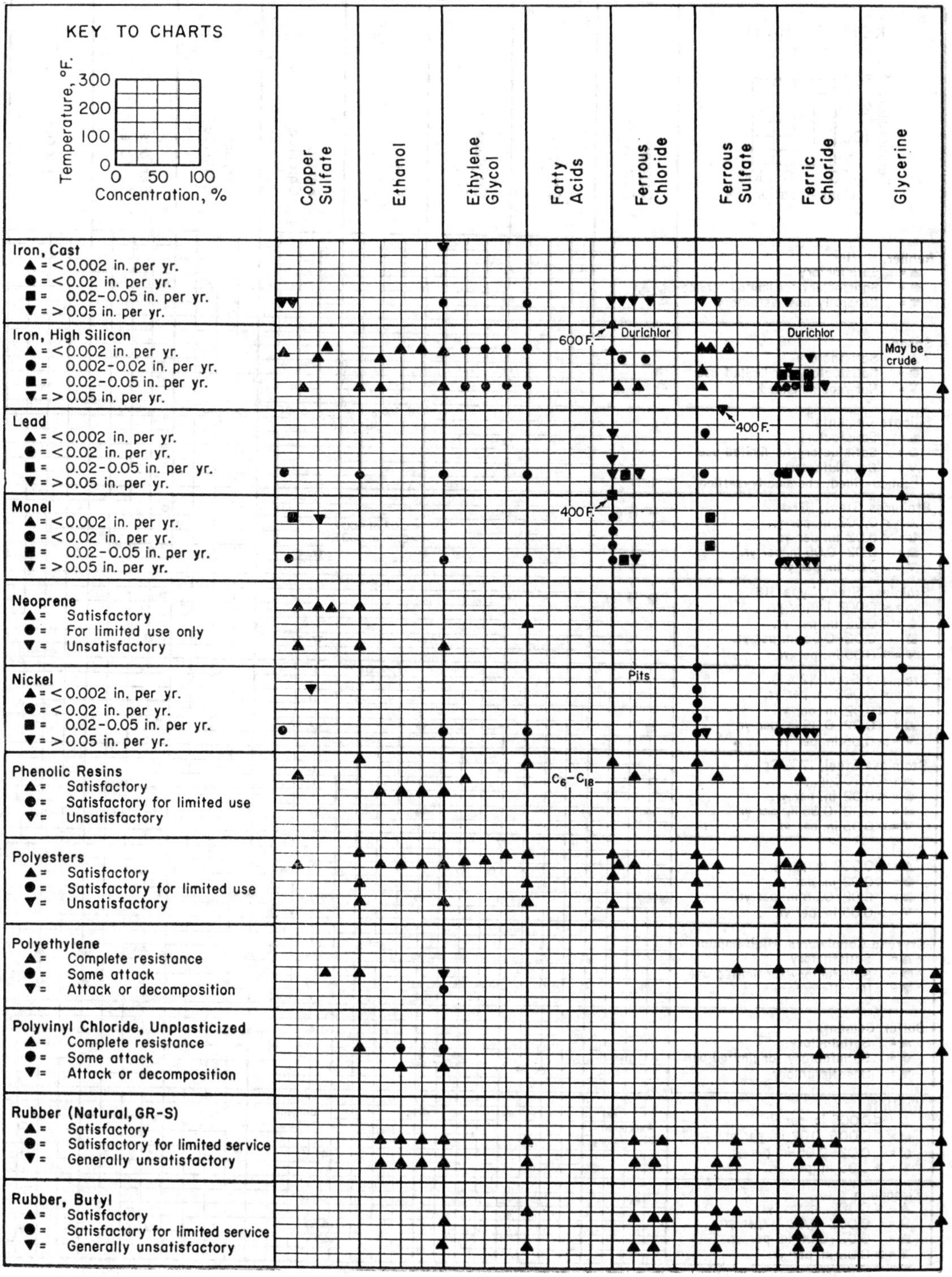

Table 23-4. Detailed Corrosion Data on Construction Materials*—(*Continued*)

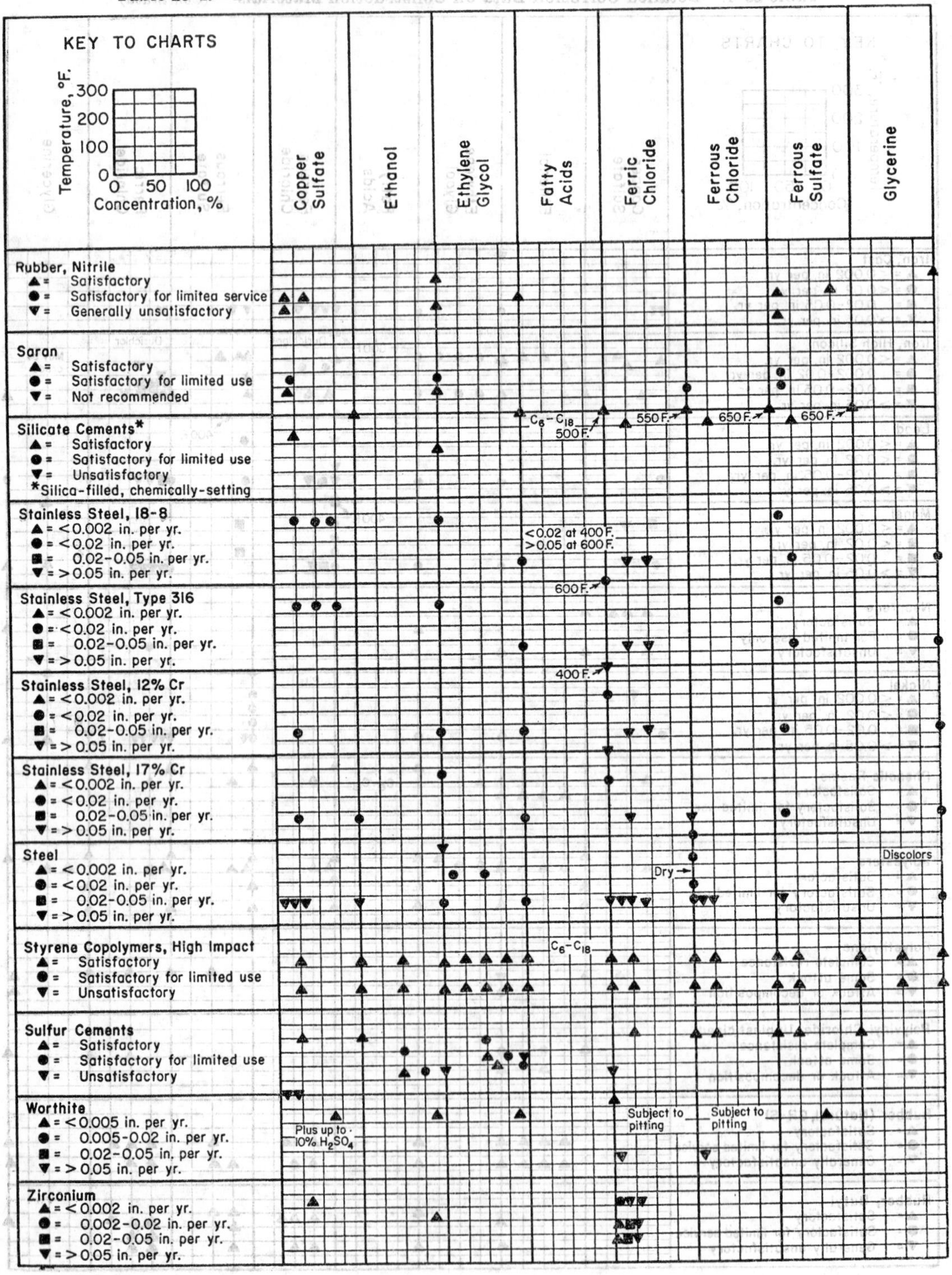

Table 23-4. Detailed Corrosion Data on Construction Materials*—(*Continued*)

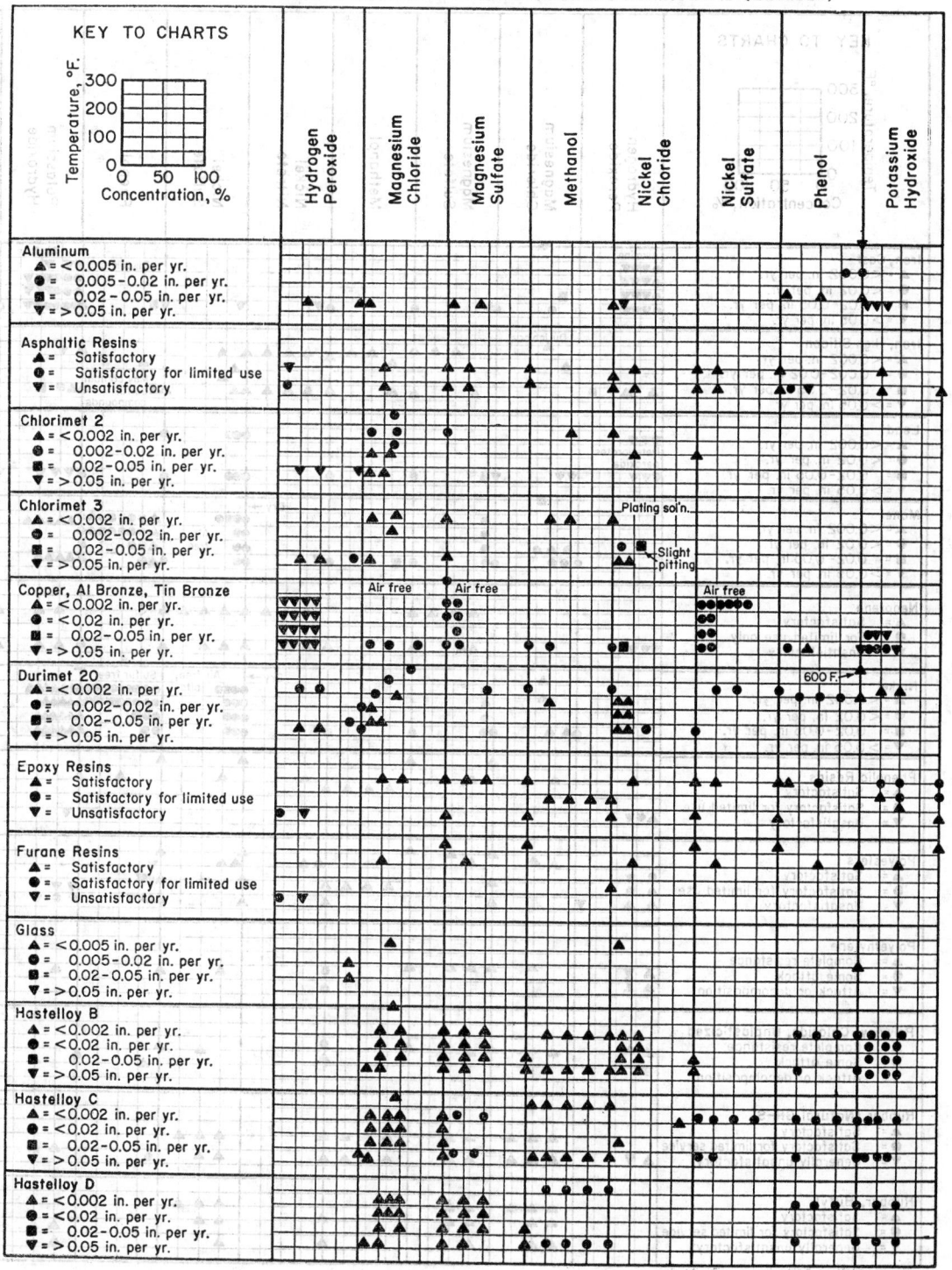

KEY TO CHARTS

Temperature, °F. (0, 100, 200, 300) vs. Concentration, % (0, 50, 100)

Columns: Hydrogen Peroxide | Magnesium Chloride | Magnesium Sulfate | Methanol | Nickel Chloride | Nickel Sulfate | Phenol | Potassium Hydroxide

Aluminum
▲ = <0.005 in. per yr.
● = 0.005–0.02 in. per yr.
■ = 0.02–0.05 in. per yr.
▼ = >0.05 in. per yr.

Asphaltic Resins
▲ = Satisfactory
● = Satisfactory for limited use
▼ = Unsatisfactory

Chlorimet 2
▲ = <0.002 in. per yr.
● = 0.002–0.02 in. per yr.
■ = 0.02–0.05 in. per yr.
▼ = >0.05 in. per yr.

Chlorimet 3
▲ = <0.002 in. per yr.
● = 0.002–0.02 in. per yr.
■ = 0.02–0.05 in. per yr.
▼ = >0.05 in. per yr.

Copper, Al Bronze, Tin Bronze
▲ = <0.002 in. per yr.
● = <0.02 in. per yr.
■ = 0.02–0.05 in. per yr.
▼ = >0.05 in. per yr.

Durimet 20
▲ = <0.002 in. per yr.
● = 0.002–0.02 in. per yr.
■ = 0.02–0.05 in. per yr.
▼ = >0.05 in. per yr.

Epoxy Resins
▲ = Satisfactory
● = Satisfactory for limited use
▼ = Unsatisfactory

Furane Resins
▲ = Satisfactory
● = Satisfactory for limited use
▼ = Unsatisfactory

Glass
▲ = <0.005 in. per yr.
● = 0.005–0.02 in. per yr.
■ = 0.02–0.05 in. per yr.
▼ = >0.05 in. per yr.

Hastelloy B
▲ = <0.002 in. per yr.
● = <0.02 in. per yr.
■ = 0.02–0.05 in. per yr.
▼ = >0.05 in. per yr.

Hastelloy C
▲ = <0.002 in. per yr.
● = <0.02 in. per yr.
■ = 0.02–0.05 in. per yr.
▼ = >0.05 in. per yr.

Hastelloy D
▲ = <0.002 in. per yr.
● = <0.02 in. per yr.
■ = 0.02–0.05 in. per yr.
▼ = >0.05 in. per yr.

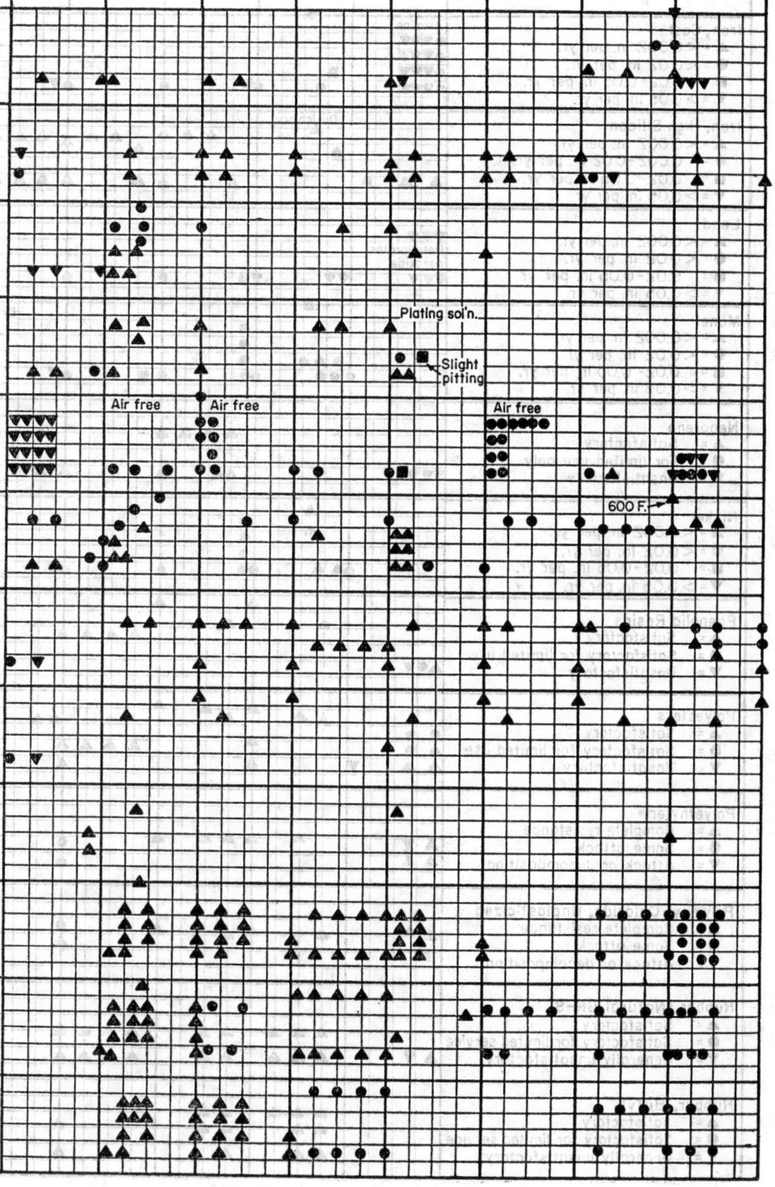

Table 23-4. Detailed Corrosion Data on Construction Materials*—*(Continued)*

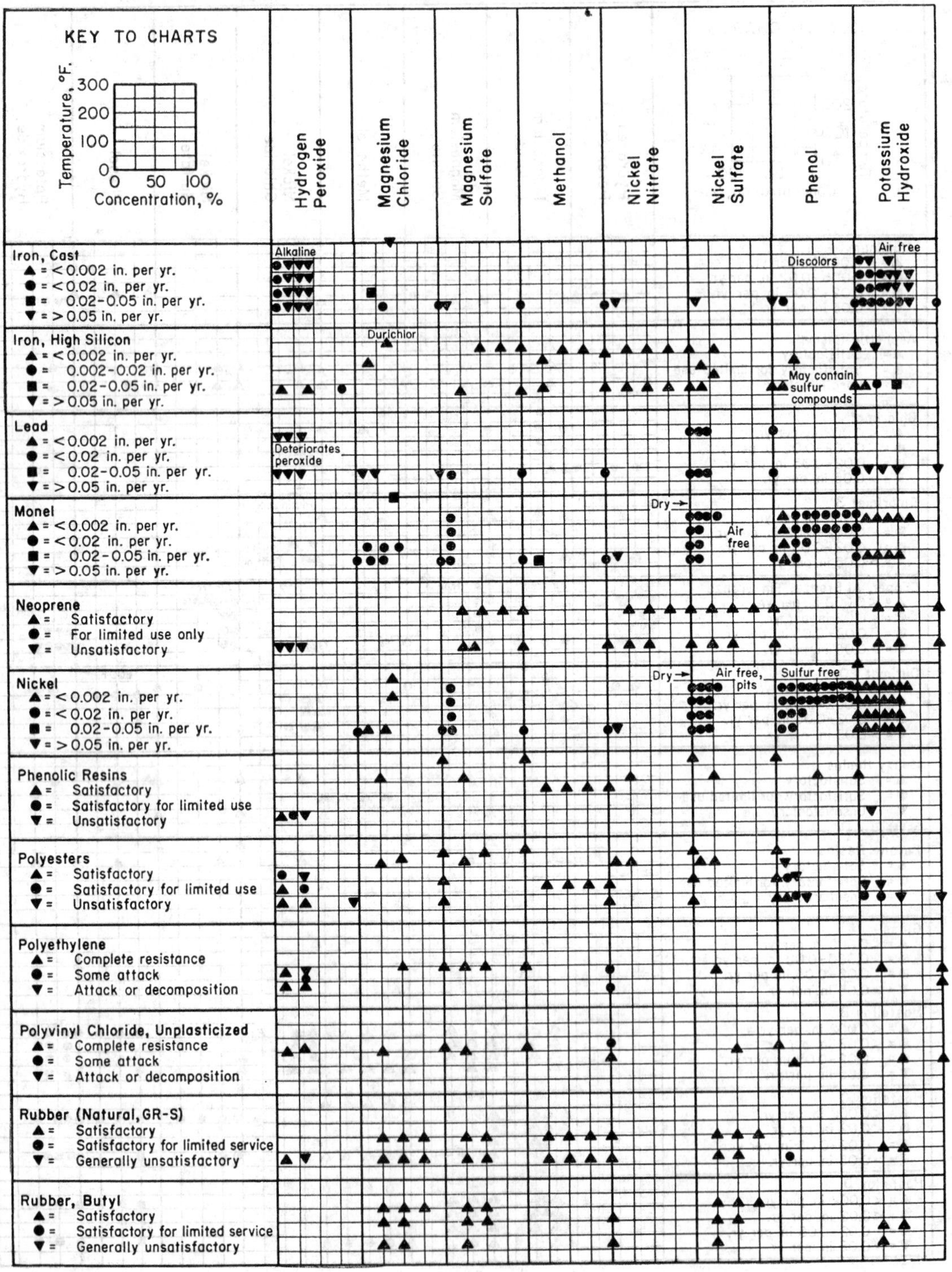

Table 23-4. Detailed Corrosion Data on Construction Materials*—(*Continued*)

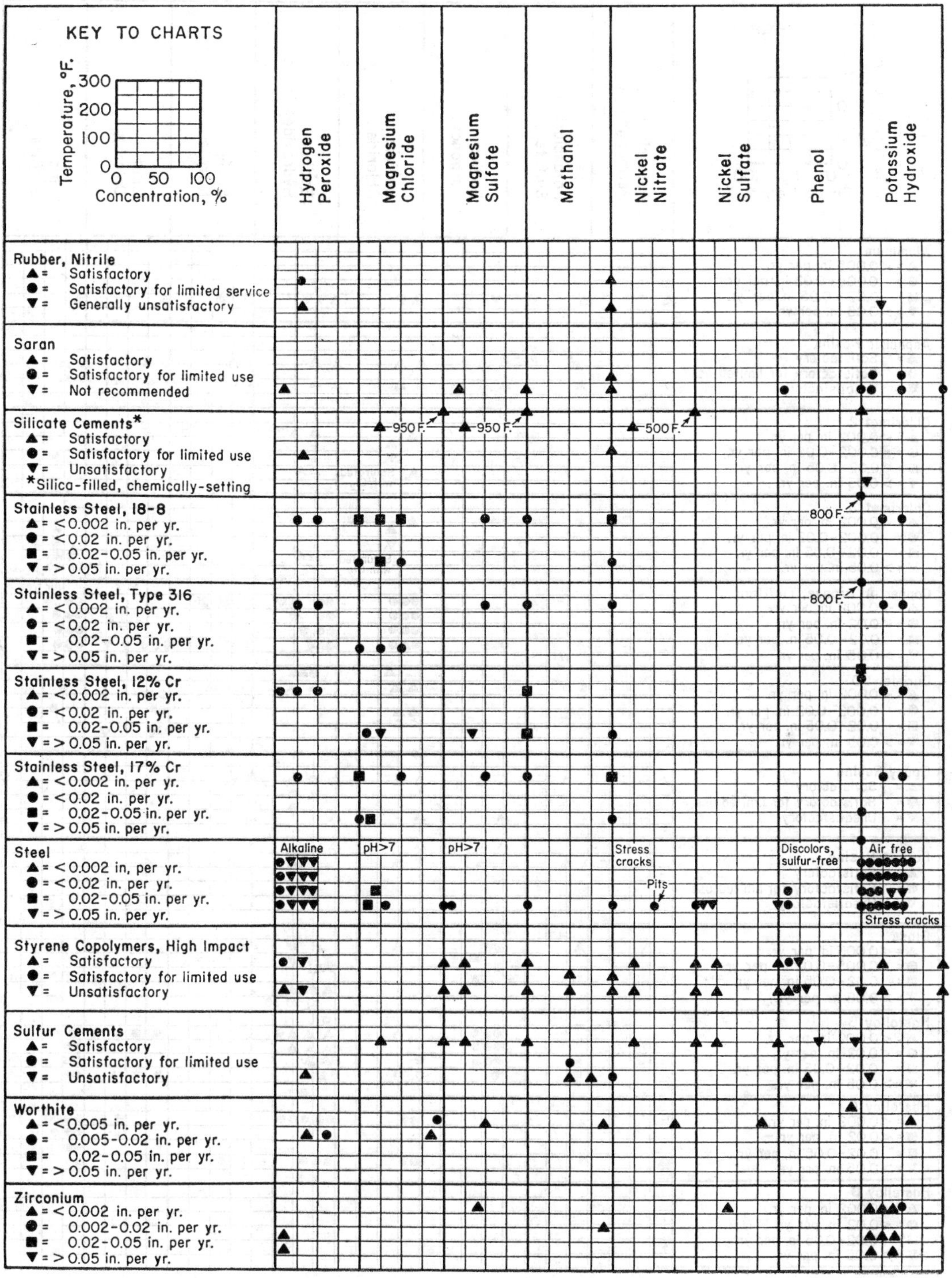

Table 23-4. Detailed Corrosion Data on Construction Materials*—(*Continued*)

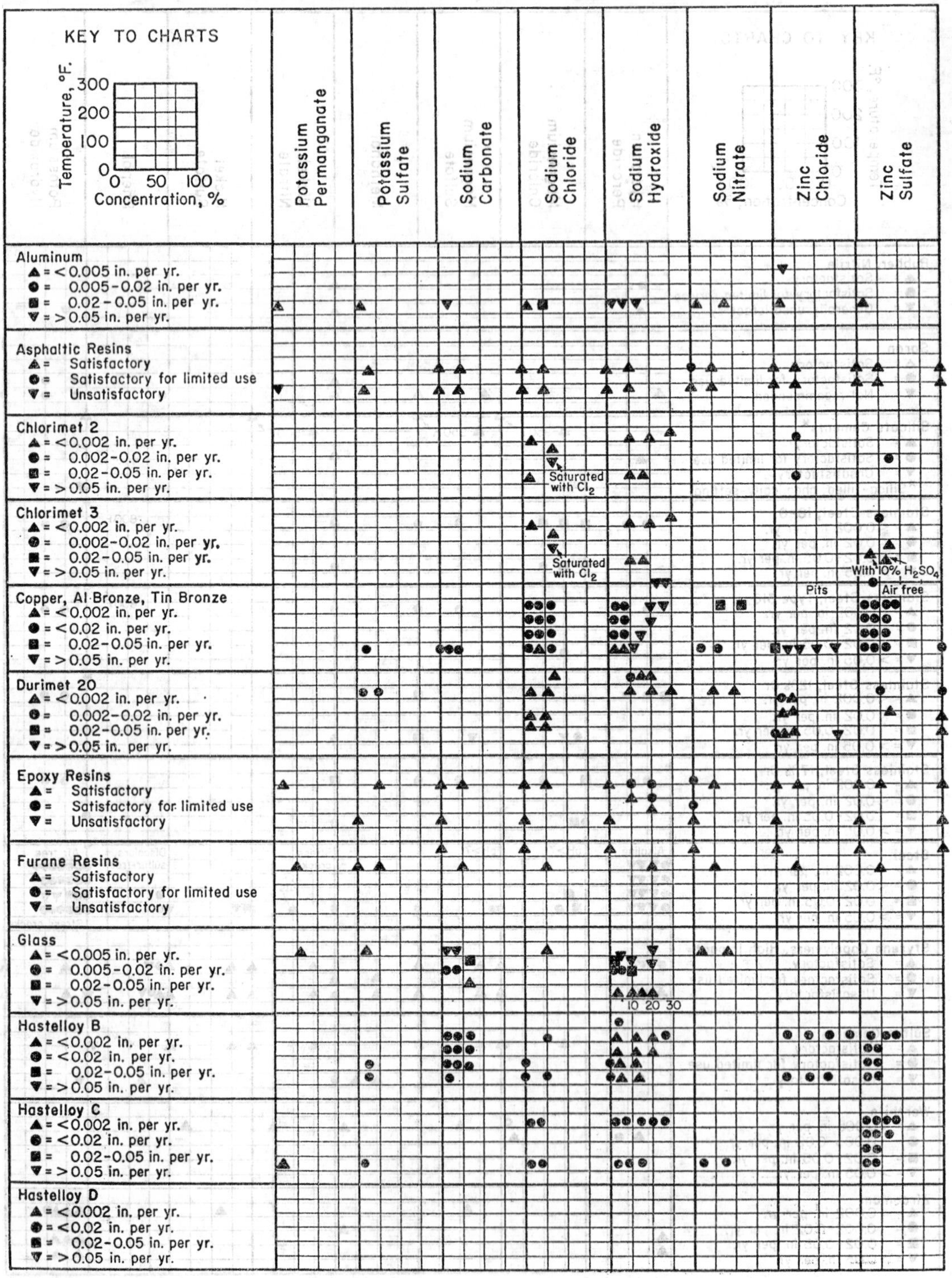

Table 23-4. Detailed Corrosion Data on Construction Materials*—(*Continued*)

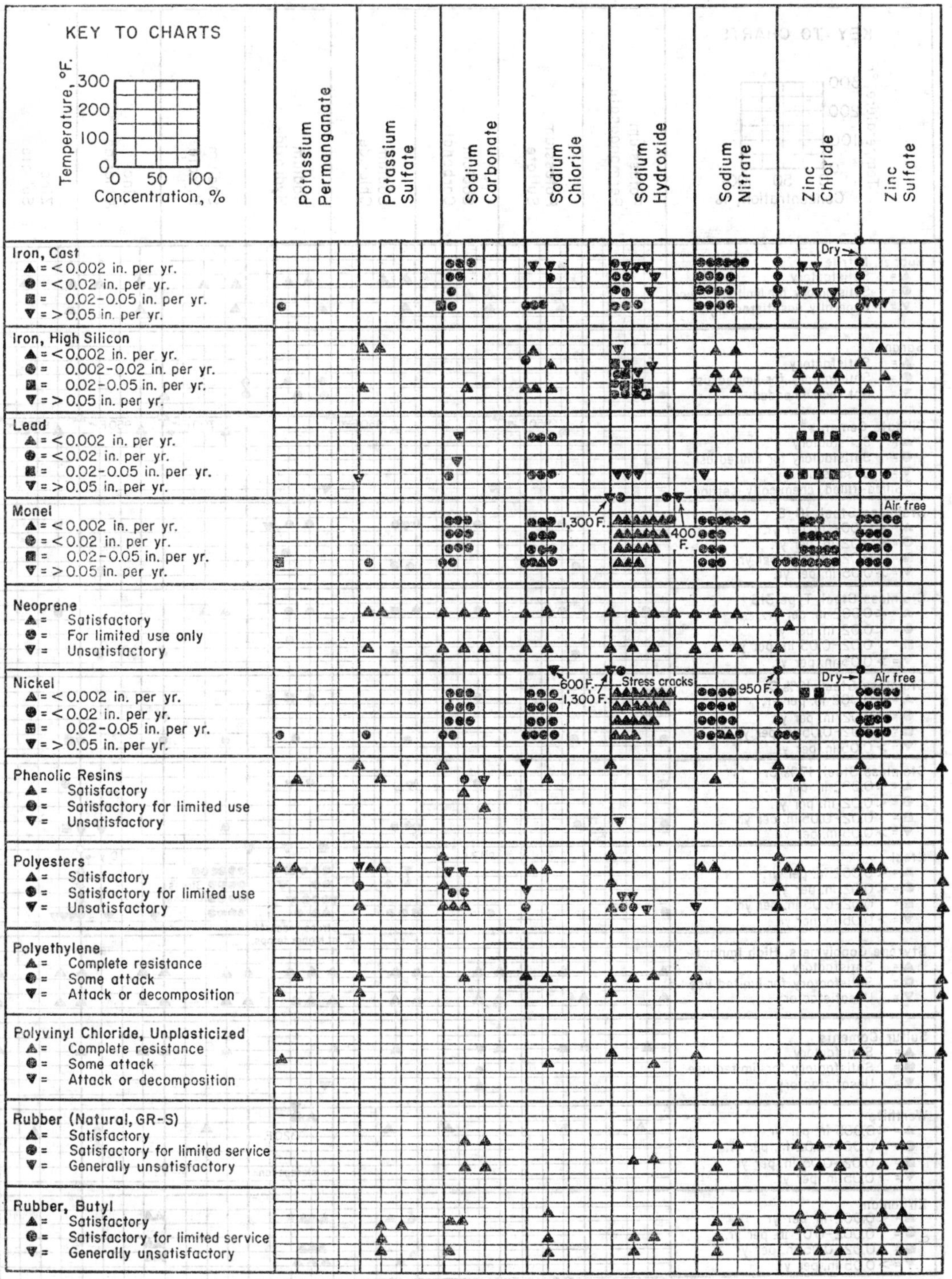

Table 23-4. Detailed Corrosion Data on Construction Materials*—(*Concluded*)

KEY TO CHARTS

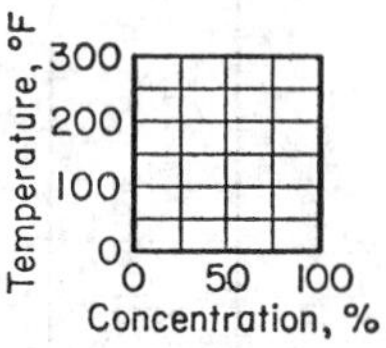
Temperature, °F
300
200
100
0
0 50 100
Concentration, %

Material	Potassium Permanganate	Potassium Sulfate	Sodium Carbonate	Sodium Chloride	Sodium Hydroxide	Sodium Nitrate	Zinc Chloride	Zinc Sulfate
Rubber, Nitrile ▲ = Satisfactory ● = Satisfactory for limited service ▼ = Generally unsatisfactory		▲ / ▲	▲ ▲ / ▲	▲ ▲ / ▲	▲ ▲ / ▲	▲ ▲ / ▲	▲ ▲ / ▲	▲ ▲ / ▲
Saran ▲ = Satisfactory ● = Satisfactory for limited use ▼ = Not recommended	●				● ● / ● ●	● / ● / ▲		
Silicate Cements* ▲ = Satisfactory ● = Satisfactory for limited use ▼ = Unsatisfactory *Silica-filled, chemically-setting		950 F. → ▲ / ▲	▼	950 F. → ▲ / ▲	▼	700 F. → ▲ / ▲	950 F. → ▲ / ▲	950 F. → ▲ / ▲
Stainless Steel, 18-8 ▲ = <0.002 in. per yr. ● = <0.02 in. per yr. ■ = 0.02–0.05 in. per yr. ▼ = >0.05 in. per yr.	●	● / ●	●	● ▼ ● / ● ●	● ● ▼ / ●		▼	●
Stainless Steel, Type 316 ▲ = <0.002 in. per yr. ● = <0.02 in. per yr. ■ = 0.02–0.05 in. per yr. ▼ = >0.05 in. per yr.	●	● / ●	●	● ● / ●	● ● / ●	▲ ▲	● ▼	●
Stainless Steel, 12% Cr ▲ = <0.002 in. per yr. ● = <0.02 in. per yr. ■ = 0.02–0.05 in. per yr. ▼ = >0.05 in. per yr.	▼ / ●	●	●	●	● ■ ▼ / ●	●	▼ / ●	▼ ■
Stainless Steel, 17% Cr ▲ = <0.002 in. per yr. ● = <0.02 in. per yr. ■ = 0.02–0.05 in. per yr. ▼ = >0.05 in. per yr.	▼ / ●	●	●	▼ / ● ● ●	● ▼	●	▼	● / ▼ ■
Steel ▲ = <0.002 in. per yr. ● = <0.02 in. per yr. ■ = 0.02–0.05 in. per yr. ▼ = >0.05 in. per yr.	●		pH>7 / ●	▼ ▼ / ▲ ● / ■ ● ●	■ ▼ ▼ / ● ● ● ■ ▼ / ● ● ▼ / ▼ ● ● ● ▼ / ▲ ▲ ● / Stress cracks†† at higher temps.	● ● ● ● ● ● / ● ● ● ● Stress cracks / ● ● ● ● / ● ● ● ●	▼ ▼	Dry → ● / ● / ● / ● / ● ▼ ▼ ▼
Styrene Copolymers, High Impact ▲ = Satisfactory ● = Satisfactory for limited use ▼ = Unsatisfactory	▲ / ▲	▲ / ▲ ▲	▲ ▲ / ▲ ▲	▲ ▲ / ▲ ▲	▲ ▲ ▲ / ▲ ▲ ▲	▲ ▲ / ▲ ▲	▲ ▲ / ▲ ▲	▲ ▲ ▲ / ▲ ▲ ▲
Sulfur Cements ▲ = Satisfactory ● = Satisfactory for limited use ▼ = Unsatisfactory	▲	▲ ▲	▲ ▼ / ● / ▲	▲	▲ / ▼	▲	▲ ▲	▲ ▲
Worthite ▲ = <0.005 in. per yr. ● = 0.005–0.02 in. per yr. ■ = 0.02–0.05 in. per yr. ▼ = >0.05 in. per yr.	▲	▲	▲	▲	▼ / ▲ ▲ 320 F. / In storage tank	▲	● / ▲	▲
Zirconium ▲ = <0.002 in. per yr. ● = 0.002–0.02 in. per yr. ■ = 0.02–0.05 in. per yr. ▼ = >0.05 in. per yr.				▲ ▲ / ▲ ▲	▲ ▲ ▲ ● / ▲ ▲ ▲ / ▲ ▲ ▲		▲ ▲ / ▲ ▲ / ▲ ▲	

Table 23-5. Properties of Metals and Alloys

Material	Nominal composition (essential elements), %	Form and condition	Typical mechanical properties: Yield strength (0.2% offset), 1000 lb./sq. in.	Typical mechanical properties: Tensile strength, 1000 lb./sq. in.	Typical mechanical properties: Elongation in 2 in., %	Typical physical constants: Hardness, Brinell	Density, lb./cu. in.	Specific gravity	Melting point, °F.	Specific heat (32°-212°F.) B.t.u./(lb.)(°F.)	Thermal expansion coefficient (32°-212°F.) × 10⁻⁶ in./(in.)(°F.)	Thermal conductivity (32°-212°F.) B.t.u./(sq. ft.)(hr.)(°F.)(in.)	Electrical resistivity (68°F.), ohms/cir. mil. ft.	Tensile modulus of elasticity × 10⁶ lb./sq. in
Ferrous Alloys														
Carbon steel[a] A.I.S.I.-S.A.E. 1020	Fe bal., Mn 0.45, Si 0.25, C 0.20	Annealed Hot-rolled Hardened (water quench 1000°F. temper)	38 42 62	65 68 90	30 32 25	130 135 179	0.284	7.86	2760	0.107	6.7	360	60	30
300-M[b]	C 0.43, Mn 0.80, Si 1.60, Ni 1.85, Cr 0.85, Mo 0.38, V 0.08	Hardened (oil quench, 600°F. temper)	240	290	10	535	0.283	7.84	2740	0.107	6.5	400	70	30
Wrought iron	Fe bal., Slag 2.5	Hot-rolled	30	48	30 (in 8 in.)	100	0.278	7.70	2750	0.11	6.35	418	70	29
Ingot iron	Fe 99.9 plus	Hot-rolled Annealed	29 19	45 38	26 45	90 67	0.284	7.86	2795	0.108	6.8	490	57	30.1
Cast gray iron (A.S.T.M. A48-48, Class 25)	C 3.4, Si 1.8, Mn 0.5, Fe bal.	Cast (as cast)	.....	25 min.	0.5 max.	180	0.260	7.20	2150	......	6.7	310	400	13 ±1.5
Malleable iron	C 2.5, Si 1, Mn 0.55 max	Cast (annealed)	33	52	12	130	0.264	7.32	2250	0.122	6.6	....	180	25
Ni-Tensyliron	C 2.7, Si 1.8, Mn 0.8, Ni 2.3, Cr 0.3, Fe bal., Mo 0.4	Cast (as cast) Cast (heat-treat)	30 40	60 80	....	260 390	0.260	7.20	2150	......	6.5	320	....	20 ±1.5
Ductile iron (Mg-containing)	C 3.4, Si 2.5, Mn 0.40, P 0.1 max., Ni 0-1, Mg 0.06, Fe bal.	Cast Cast (as cast) Cast (quench, temper)	53 68 108	70 90 135	18 7 5	170 235 310	0.26	7.2	2100	......	7.5	228	360	25
Ductile iron (Mg-containing) (heat-resistant)	C 3.3, Si 4.3, Mn 0.4, P 0.1 max., Ni 0-1, Mg 0.06, Fe bal.	Cast (annealed, as cast)	60	80	10	220	0.26	7.2	2100	......	....	200	437	
Ni-Resist ductile iron (Mg-containing) A.M.S.† 5394	C 2.8, Si 2.5, Mn 1, P 0.2 max., Ni 20, Cr 2, Mg 0.1, Fe bal.	Cast (as cast)	35	60	10	175	0.268	7.4	2250	......	10.4	....	610	18.5
Ni-Hard type 2	C 2.7, Si 0.6, Mn 0.5, Ni 4.5, Cr 2.0, Fe. bal.	Sand-cast Chill-cast (temper)	....	55 75	....	550 625	0.275	7.70	2150	......	4.8	99	....	25
Ni-Hard type 1	C 3.5, Si 0.6, Mn 0.5, Ni 4.5, Cr 2.0, Fe bal.	Sand-cast Chill-cast (temper)	....	40 50	....	600 700	0.275	7.70	2150	......	4.8	99	....	25
Ni-Resist type 1, A.M.S. 5392D	C 2.8, Si 2.0, Mn 1.2, Ni 15.5, Cr 2.5, Cu 6.5, Fe bal.	Cast (as cast)	.....	27	2	150	0.264	7.3	2250	0.110	10.3	276	842	13.0 ±1.5
Ni-Resist type 2, A.M.S. 5393	C 2.8, Si 2.0, Mn 1.0, Ni 20.0, Cr 2.5, Fe bal.	Cast (as cast)	.....	27	2	140	0.264	7.3	2250	0.116	9.6	276	1023	15.6 ±1.5
Ni-Resist type 3	C 2.6 max., Si 1.5, Mn 0.6, Ni 30.0, Cr 3.5, Fe bal.	Cast	.....	30	2	140	0.268	7.4	2250	0.111	5.3	273	....	15.2 ±1.5
Ni-Resist type 4	C 2.6 max., Si 5.5, Mn 0.6, Ni 30.0, Cr 5.5, Fe bal.	Cast	.....	30	2	180	0.268	7.4	2200	0.120	7.3	261	962	15.0 ±1.5
Ni-Resist type D-2	C 2.90 max., Si 2.5, Mn 1.0, P 0.2 max., Ni 20.0, Cr 2.5	Cast	34	62	14	160	0.268	7.41	2250	......	10.4	93	614	17.5 ±1.5

† A.M.S. is Aeronautical Material Specification (S.A.E.)

[a] Carbon-steel mechanical properties are strongly influenced by the carbon level; the physical properties will not be appreciably changed.

[b] Type of ultra-high-strength steel, attaining tensile strengths of 220,000 to 300,000 lb./sq. in.

Table 23-5. Properties of Metals and Alloys—*(Continued)*

Material	Nominal composition (essential elements), %	Form and condition	Typical mechanical properties: Yield strength (0.2% offset), 1000 lb./sq. in.	Tensile strength, 1000 lb./sq. in.	Elongation in 2 in., %	Typical physical constants: Hardness, Brinell	Density, lb./cu. in.	Specific gravity	Melting point, °F.	Specific heat (32°–212°F.) B.t.u./(lb.)(°F.)	Thermal expansion coefficient (32°–212°F.) × 10⁻⁶ in./(in.)(°F.)	Thermal conductivity (32°–212°F.) B.t.u./(sq. ft.)(/hr.)(°F.)(in.)	Electrical resistivity (68°F.), ohms/cir. mil. ft.	Tensile modulus of elasticity × 10⁶ lb./sq. in.
Ni-Resist type D-3	C 2.60 max., Si 2.5, Mn 0.6, P 0.2 max., Ni 30.0, Cr 3.5	Cast	35	61	12	150	0.27	7.45	2250	......	7.0	....	......	14.0 ± 1.5
Ni-Resist type D-4	C 2.60 max., Si 5.5, Mn 0.6, P 0.2 max., Ni 30.0, Cr 5.5	Cast	41	66	2.5	190	0.27	7.45	2200	......	8.0	....	......	13.0 ± 1.5
Hastelloys														
Hastelloy Alloy B (A.S.M.E. Code, UPV case 1173)	Ni bal., Mo 28, Fe 5, Mn, Si	Sand-cast (anneal)	50	80	8	199	......	......	....	......	....	....	......	26.5
(MIL-R-5031-A Amendment 1, Class 10, welding wire)	....	Rolled (anneal)	56	120	50	215	0.334	9.24	2410–2460	0.091	5.6	72	812	30.8 28.5
		Investment cast	54	85	14	209								
Hastelloy Alloy C (A.S.M.E. Code, UPV Case 1194)	Ni bal., Mo 16, Cr 16, Fe 5, W 4, Mn, Si	Sand-cast (anneal)	50	78	5	199	......	......	....	......	....	....	......	26
A.M.S.-5530-C (sheet) A.M.S.-5750 (bars and forgings)	....	Rolled (anneal)	71	130	45	204	0.323	8.94	2320–2380	0.092	6.3	61	834	30.9 24.5
A.M.S.-5388-B (investment castings) A.M.S.-5389-A (sand castings)	....	Investment cast	50	80	10	215								
Hastelloy Alloy D	Ni bal. Si 10, Cu 3, Mn	Sand-cast (anneal)	118	118	0–2	321	0.282	7.80	2030–2050	0.108	6.1	145 (at 72° F.)	680	28.9
Hastelloy Alloy F	Ni 46, Cr 22, Fe 21, Mo 6.5, Cb + Ta 2, Mn, Si	Hot-rolled (anneal)	50	110	50	255	0.296	8.2	2350	0.1025	8.7 (70°–600°F.)	....	676	29
Hastelloy Alloy R-235	Cr 15.5, Fe 10, Mo 5.5, Ni bal., Al, Ti	Hot-rolled, mill-annealed	75	140	35	244	0.296	8.22	2350–2400	0.1096	6.7 (76°–212°F.)	63 (70°–600°F.)	800	29.4
Hastelloy Alloy X A.M.S. 5536 (sheet) A.M.S. 5390 (precision investment cast)	Co 1.5 max., Fe 18.5, Cr 22.0, Mo 9.0, W 0.6, C 0.15 max. (wrought), C 0.20 max. (cast), Ni bal.	Wrought sheet	52	113.2	41.0	194	0.297	8.23	2350	0.1046	7.90 (70°–600°F.)	62.8	712	28.6
		Mill-annealed	.....	67.0	17.0	172								
		As investment cast	46.5											
Nickel alloys Ni-Cr-Fe Alloy 804	Ni(+Co) 42.10, C 0.06, Mn 0.85, Fe 25.60, S 0.007, Si 0.60, Cu 0.40, Cr 29.70, Al 0.25, Ti 0.40	Annealed	45	100	40	175	0.286	7.92	....	......	8.0	....	635	32.0
Nimonic 75	Ni(+Co) 77.40, C 0.10, Mn 0.45, Fe 0.50, S 0.007, Si 0.45, Cu 0.05, Cr 20.50, Al 0.15, Ti 0.35	Annealed	55	115	40	168	0.302	8.35	2530–2590	0.11	6.8	86.5	655	27
Nimonic 80A	N(+Co) 74.45, C 0.05, Mn 0.55, Fe 0.55, S 0.007, Si 0.20, Cu 0.05, Cr 20.45, Al 1.25, Ti 2.40	Annealed	60	115	60	185	0.296	8.25	2530–2590	0.10	6.5	84.5	745	31
Nimonic 90	Ni(+Co) 57.00, C 0.05, Mn 0.50, Fe 0.45, S 0.007, Si 0.20, Cu 0.05, Cr 20.55, Al 1.65, Ti 2.60, Co 16.90	Annealed	90	155	.....	260	0.298	8.25	2470–2530	.....	6.5	86.5	690	31

Table 23-5. Properties of Metals and Alloys—(*Continued*)

Material	Nominal composition (essential elements), %	Form and condition	Typical mechanical properties: Yield strength (0.2% offset), 1000 lb./sq. in.	Typical mechanical properties: Tensile strength, 1000 lb./sq. in.	Typical mechanical properties: Elongation in 2 in., %	Typical physical constants: Hardness, Brinell	Density, lb./cu. in.	Specific gravity	Melting point, °F.	Specific heat (32°-212°F.) B.t.u./(lb.)(°F.)	Thermal expansion coefficient (32°-212°F.) × 10⁻⁶ in./(in.)(°F.)	Thermal conductivity (32°-212°F.) B.t.u./(sq. ft.)(hr.)(°F.)(in.)	Electrical resistivity (68°F.), ohms/cir. mil. ft.	Tensile modulus of elasticity × 10⁶ lb./sq. in.
G nickel	N(+Co) 94.2, Cu 0.5, Fe 0.5, Mn 0.8, Si 1.5, C 1.5	As-cast	30	55	20	105	0.301	8.34	2400–2600	.....	8.75 (70°–1400°F.)	....	125	22
S nickel	Ni(+Co) 91.5, Cu 0.5, Fe 0.5, Mn 0 8, Si 6.0, C 0.8	As-cast	62	85	2	220	0.288	8.01	2400–2600	.....	8.76 (70°–1400°F.)	....	180	24
		Annealed, aged	65	90	2	240								
Monel weldable alloy QQ-N-288 (Comp. E) MIL-C-15345D (Alloy 19) Centrifugal castings only	Ni(+Co) 62.0, Cu 31.5, Fe 2.0, Mn 0.8, Si 1.5, C 0.20, Cb added	As-cast	35	75	35	140	0.312	8.63	2400–2450	0.13	9.17 (70°–1100°F.)	186	......	23
Ni-o-nel	Ni 40, Cr 21, Fe 31, Mo 3.0, Cu 1.75, Mn 0.60, Si 0.40, C 0.05	Annealed	45	95	40	185	0.294	8.14	.....	.....	....	....	......	28.5
		Cold-drawn	.....	155	10	255								
Inconel X Rods, bars, forgings A.M.S. 5667, 5668 Sheet A.M.S. 5542 Wire A.M.S. 5698, 5699	Ni(+Co) 72.85, C 0.04, Mn 0.65, Fe 6.80, S 0.007, Si 0.30, Cu 0.05, Cr 15.15, Al 0.75, Ti 2.50, Cb(+Ta) 0.85	Annealed	50	115	50	150	0.298	8.25	2540–2600	0.105	6.7	102	735 (76°F.)	31.0
		Annealed, age-hardened	115	175	25	300	......	.....	.....	.....	....	212°F.		
Inconel X, type 550	Nu(+Co) 72.59, C 0.05, Mn 0.55, Fe 6.85, S 0.007, Si 0.35, Cu 0.05, Cr 15.15, Al 1.15, Ti 2.30, Cb(+Ta) 0.95	Annealed	75	125	50	176	0.298	8.25						
		Annealed, age-hardened	110	175	20	337	......	.....	.....	.....	....	....	743 (76°F.)	30.0
Inconel M	Ni(+Co) 71.40, C 0.03, Mn 2.20, Fe 6.70, S 0.007, Si 0.10, Cu 0.04, Cr 16.40, Al 0.05, Ti 3.05	Annealed	45	110	50	160	0.298	8.25	.....	.....	....	....	......	31.0
		Annealed, age-hardened	100	145	7	300								
Inconel W plate, sheet, strip A.M.S. 5541	Ni(+Co) 74.35, C 0.05, Mn 0.60, Fe 6.50, S 0.007, Si 0.20, Cu 0.05, Cr 15.20, Al 0.60, Ti 2.40	Annealed	45	110	50	160	0.298	8.31	2540–2600	0.105	7.6	102	750	31.0
		Annealed, age-hardened	95	155	30	275	......	.....	.....	.....	....	....	728 (76°F.)	
Inconel 600	Ni(+Co) 73.55, C 0.04, Mn 0.20, Fe 7.55, S 0.005, Si 0.30, Cu 0.03, Cr 16.00, Cb(+Ta) 2.30	Annealed	.....	125	.....	.....	0.305	8.44	.....	.....	....	....	620	31.0
Inconel 700	Ni 45.0, C 0.16, Mn 0.10, Fe 7.0, S 0.008, Si 0.25, Cr 15.0, Al 3.0, Ti 2.20, Mo 3.0, Co 28.0	Hot-rolled	106	168	.....	321	0.295	8.17	2450–2600	0.11	6.8	86	777	32
		Heat-treated	.....	.....	.....	.....	......	.....	.....	.....	9.3 (70°–1600°F.)			
Inconel 702	Ni(+Co) 78.00, C 0.02, Mn 0.05, Fe 0.30, S 0.007, Si 0.15, Cu 0.05, Cr 15.85, Al 3.00, Ti 0.60	Annealed	45	105	55	150	0.302	8.37	.....	.....	6.95	....	......	31.5
Inconel 713C	Ni(+Co) bal., Cr 13.0, C 0.13, Mo 4.5, Cb 2.0, Al 6.0, Ti 06	Investment-cast	102	120	6	.....	0.286	7.91	2300–2350	.....	6.1			

Table 23-5. Properties of Metals and Alloys—(*Continued*)

Material	Nominal composition (essential elements), %	Form and condition	Typical mechanical properties: Yield strength (0.2% offset), 1000 lb./sq. in.	Tensile strength, 1000 lb./sq. in.	Elongation in 2 in., %	Typical physical constants: Hardness, Brinell	Density, lb./cu. in.	Specific gravity	Melting point, °F.	Specific heat (32°–212°F.) B.t.u./(lb.)(°F.)	Thermal expansion coefficient (32°–212°F.) × 10⁻⁶ in./(in.)(°F.)	Thermal conductivity (32°–212°F.) B.t.u./(sq. ft.)(hr.)(°F./in.)	Electrical resistivity (68°F.), ohms/cir. mil. ft.	Tensile modulus of elasticity × 10⁶ lb./sq. in.
330 nickel	Ni(+Co) 99.55, C 0.09, Mn 0.20, Fe 0.05, S 0.005, Si 0.05, Cu 0.02	Annealed	20	70	40	100	0.321	8.85	2615–2635	0.110	7.2	420	57	31
Monel Plate, sheet, strip A.M.S 4544 A.S.T.M. B127	Ni(+Co) 66.15, C 0.12, Mn 0.90, Fe 1.35, S 0.005, Si 0.15, Cu 31.30	Annealed	35	75	40	125	0.319	8.83	2370–2460	0.127	7.5	174 (212°F.)	290	26
Rods, bars, forgings A.S.T.M. B164 (Cl. A) MIL-N-894C (Cl. A) Wire A.M.S. 4730 MIL-N-894C (Cl. A)		Hot-rolled	50	90	35	150								
		Cold-drawn	80	110	25	190								
		Cold-rolled	100	110	5	240								
Monel (cast) QQ-N-288 (Comp. A)	Ni(+Co) 64.0, Cu 31.5, Fe 1.0, Mn 0.8, Si 1.5, C 0.20	As-cast	35	75	35	140	0.312	8.63	2400–2450	0.13	9.17	186	320	23
R Monel Rods, bars, forgings A.M.S. 4674 A.S.T.M. B164 (Cl. B)	Ni(+Co) 66.35,, C 0.18, Mn 0.90, Fe 1.35, S 0.050, Si 0.15, Cu 31.00	Hot-rolled	45	85	35	145	0.319	8.84	2370–2460	0.127	7.8	180	290	26
Wire QQ-N-281a (Cl. B) MIL-N-894C (Cl. B)		Cold-drawn	75	100	25	200								
Monel 402	Ni(+Co) 58.10, C 0.12, Mn 0.90, Fe 1.20, S 0.005, Si 0.10, Cu 39.55	Hot-rolled	65	90	35	175	0.320	8.85	.....	....	....	....	305	26
		Cold-drawn	85	95	25	215								
Monel 403 Rods, bars, forgings, plate sheet, strip, wire MIL-N-17163, Am. 1	Ni(+Co) 57.85, C 0.12, Mn 1.90, Fe 0.15, S 0.006, Si 0.30, Cu 39.65	Hot-rolled	45	85	40	145	0.320	.....	.....	......	7.7 (80°–200°F.)	172	319	25.2
		Cold-drawn	85	90	30	200	......	.....	.....	......				
K Monel Rods, bars, forgings, plate, sheet, strip, wire QQ-N-286a (Cl. A), Am. 1 MIL-N-17506A (Cl A) Wire MIL-W-4471 (Comp. A)	Ni(+Co) 65.25, C 0.15, Mn 0.60, Fe 1.00, S 0.005, Si 0.15, Cu 29.60, Al 2.75, Ti 0.45	Annealed	45	100	40	155	0.305	8.47	2400–2460	0.127	7.4	130	350	26
		Annealed, age-hardened	100	155	25	270								
		Spring	140	150	5	300								
		Spring, age-hardened	160	185	10	335								
H Monel QQ-N-288 (Comp. B) MIL-C-15345D (Alloy 16), centrifugal castings only	Ni(+Co) 63.0, Cu 30.5, Fe 1.5, Mn 0.8, Si 3.2, C 0.10	As-cast	70	115	10	265	0.305	8.48	2350–2400	0.13	8.93 (70°–1100°F.)	145	370	24
S Monel QQ-N-288 (Comp. D) MIL-C-1534D (Alloy 17), centrifugal castings only	Ni+(Co) 63.0, Cu 29.5, Fe 2.0, Mn 0.8, Si 4.0, C 0.08	Annealed	75	110	8	220	0.302	8.36	2250–2350	0.13	8.87 (70°–1000°F.)	136	380	24
		As-cast, or annealed and aged	110	135	2	340	0.302	8.36	2250–2350	0.13	8.87	136	380	24
Inconel (cast)	Ni(+Co) 71.5, Cu 0.5, Fe 8.0, Mn 1.0, Si 2.0, Cr 16.0, C 0.20	As-cast	38	80	15	175	0.300	8.30	2540–2600	0.11	8.92 (70°–1400°F.)	104	700	23
Inconel weldable alloy	Ni(+Co) 68.5, Cu 0.5, Fe 9.0, Mn 1.0, Si 1.6, Cr 15.5, C 0.20, Cb added	As-cast	38	80	15	175	0.300	8.30	2540–2600	0.11	8.92 (70°–1400°F.)	104	700	23

Table 23-5. Properties of Metals and Alloys—(*Continued*)

Material	Nominal composition (essential elements), %	Form and condition	Typical mechanical properties: Yield strength (0.2% offset), 1000 lb./sq. in.	Typical mechanical properties: Tensile strength, 1000 lb./sq. in.	Typical mechanical properties: Elongation in 2 in., %	Typical physical constants: Hardness, Brinell	Density, lb./cu. in.	Specific gravity	Melting point, °F.	Specific heat (32°-212°F.) B.t.u./(lb.)(°F.)	Thermal expansion coefficient (32°-212°F.) × 10⁻⁶ in./(in.)(°F.)	Thermal conductivity (32°-212°F.) B.t.u./(sq. ft.)(hr.)(°F.)(in.)	Electrical resistivity (68°F.), ohms/cir. mil. ft.	Tensile modulus of elasticity × 10⁶ lb./sq. in.
S Inconel	Ni(+Co) 6.80, Cu 0.5, Fe 8.0, Mn 1.0, Si 5.5, Cr 15.5, C 0.20	As-cast Annealed and aged	90 95	95 100	2 2	340 340	0.292	8.06	2540-2600	......	9.20 (70°-1100°F.)	....	760	25
KR Monel Rods, bars, forgings, wire QQ-N-286a (Cl. B), Am. 1 MIL-N-17506a (Cl. B) Wire MIL-W-4471 (Comp. B)	Ni(+Co) 64.75, C 0.25, Mn 0.60, Fe 1.00, S 0.005, Si 0.15, Cu 29.85, Al 2.85, Ti 0.45	Hot-finished, annealed Hot-finished, annealed, age-hardened	45 90	95 145	35 25	160 275	0.305	8.44	2400-2460	0.127	7.0	130	350	26.0
Inconel (wrought) Rods, bars, forgings A.M.S. 5665B A.S.T.M. B166 Plate, sheet, strip A.M.S. 5540D A.S.T.M. M168 Seamless pipe, tubing A.M.S. 5580C A.ST.M. B167 Wire A.M.S. 5687B QQ-W-390a	Ni(+Co) 76.40, C 0.04, Mn 0.20, Fe 7.20, S 0.007, Si 0.20, Cu 0.10, Cr 15.85	Annealed Cold-drawn	35 100	90 130	45 20	150 200	0.304	8.43	2540-2600	0.109	7.0	104 113 (212°F.)	623 (76°F.)	31.0
Incoloy	Ni(+Co) 31.90, C 0.04, Mn 0.75, Fe 46.05, S 0.007, Si 0.35, Cu 0.27, Cr 20.60	Annealed	40	90	40	150	0.290	8.01	2540-2600	0.120	8.2	85	600 (76°F.)	28.5
Incoloy T A.M.S. 5742 (rods, bars, forgings)	Ni(+Co) 32.20, C 0.04, Mn 0.85, Fe 44.60, S 0.007, Si 0.35, Cu 0.15, Cr 20.80, Ti 1.00	Annealed	50	90	40	160	0.287	7.99	.....	......	....	....	......	28.5
Incoloy 901	Ni(+Co) 42.65, C 0.05, Mn 0.45, Fe 33.90, S 0.010, Si 0.40, Cu 0.10, Cr 13.45, Al 0.25, Ti 2.50, Mo 6.20	Annealed Annealed, aged	45 105	110 165	45 26	160 310	0.297	8.23	....	....	7.75	93	...... 662 (76°F.)	30.0
Stainless Steels Stainless steel type 201	C 0.15 max., Mn 5.5-7.5, Cr 16.0-18.0, Ni 3.5-5.5, N 0.25 max.	Mill-annealed strip	50	115	60	194	0.28	7.7	2550-2650	0.12	....	113	414	28.6
Stainless steel type 202	C 0.15 max., Mn 7.5-10.0, Cr 17.0-19.0, Ni 4.0-6.0, N 0.25 max.	Mill-annealed strip	50	100	60	184	0.28	7.7	2550-2650	0.12	....	113	414	28.6
Stainless steel type 301	Fe bal., Cr 17, Ni 7, C 0.08-0.20	Annealed Cold-rolled[c]	30 up to 165	100 up to 200	72 15[d]	160 385	0.29	8.02	2550-2590	0.12	9.4	112.8	435	28
Stainless steel type 302 A.M.S. 5515-6-7-8-9 (plate, sheet, strip) A.M.S. 5637 (bars) A.M.S. 5688 (wire)	Fe bal., Cr 18, Ni 8, C 0.08-0.20	Annealed Cold-rolled[c]	30 up to 165	90 up to 190	60 8[d]	160 up to 400	0.29	8.02	2550-2590	0.12	9.6	112.8	435	28

[c] The cold-rolled properties depend upon composition; types 302 and 304 are not rolled often in excess of 175,000 lb./sq. in. tensile strength.
[d] The values for elongation (% in 2 in.) are obtainable in the steel cold-rolled to *the maximum stated* yield strength and tensile strength. For lower values of tensile strength, elongation will be correspondingly higher.
[e] Types 316, 321, and 374 are used chiefly in the annealed condition.

Table 23-5. Properties of Metals and Alloys—*(Continued)*

Material	Nominal composition (essential elements), %	Form and condition	Typical mechanical properties: Yield strength (0.2% offset), 1000 lb./sq. in.	Typical mechanical properties: Tensile strength, 1000 lb./sq. in.	Typical mechanical properties: Elongation in 2 in., %	Typical physical constants: Hardness, Brinell	Density, lb./cu. in.	Specific gravity	Melting point, °F.	Specific heat (32°–212°F.) B.t.u./(lb.)(°F.)	Thermal expansion coefficient (32°–212°F.) × 10⁻⁶ in./(in.)(°F.)	Thermal conductivity (32°–212°F.) B.t.u./(sq. ft.)(hr.)(°F.)(in.)	Electrical resistivity (68°F.), ohms/cir. mil. ft.	Tensile modulus of elasticity × 10⁶ lb./sq. in.
Stainless steel type 304 A.M.S. 5639 (bars, forgings, tubing) A.M.S. 5697 (wire)	Fe bal., Cr 19, Ni 9.0, C 0.08 max.	Annealed Cold-rolled[d]	30 up to 160	85 up to 185	62 8[d]	160 up to 400	0.29	8.02	2550–2650	0.12	9.6	113	435	28
Stainless steel type 304L	Fe bal., Cr 19, Ni 10, C 0.03 max.	Annealed Cold-drawn	30 95	80 125	60 25	150 277	0.29	8.02	2550–2650	0.12	9.6	113	435	28
Stainless steel type 309 A.M.S. 5523 (plate, sheet, strip) A.M.S. 5574 (tubing) A.M.S. 5650 (bars, forgings)	Fe bal., Cr 23, Ni 13, C 0.20 max.	Annealed Cold-rolled[c]	30 up to 120	82 up to 150	50 4[d]	165 275	0.29	8.02	2550–2650	0.12	8.3	96	470	29
Stainless steel type 310 A.M.S. 5572-7 (tubing) A.M.S. 5651 (bars, forgings)	Fe bal., Cr 25, Ni 20, C 0.25 max.	Annealed	40	100	50	165	0.29	8.02	2550–2650	0.12	8.0	96	470	29
Stainless steel type 316 A.M.S. 5524 (plate, sheet, strip) A.M.S. 5573 (tubing) A.M.S. 5548 (bars, forgings)	Fe bal., Cr 18, Ni 11, Mo 25, C 0.10 max.	Annealed Cold-rolled[e]	30 up to 120	90 up to 150	50 8[d]	165 275	0.29	8.02	2500–2550	0.12	8.9	113	445	28
Stainless steel type 316L	Fe bal., Cr 17, Ni 12, C 0.03 max., Mo 2	Annealed Cold-drawn	30 60	80 90	60 45	150 190	0.29	8.02	2500–2550	0.12	8.9	113	445	28
Stainless steel types 321 and 347 A.M S. 5570-71 (tubing) (321 has Ti) (347 has Cb)	Fe bal., Cr 18, Ni 10, C 0.10 max., Ti 4 × carbon min. or Cb 8 × carbon min.	Annealed Cold-rolled	30 up to 120	85 up to 150	50 5[d]	160 300	0.286	7.92	2550–2600	0.12	9.3	110	435	28
Stainless steel type 330	Fe bal., Ni 36, Cr 16	Hot-rolled Cold-drawn (anneal) Cold-drawn (heat-treated)	55	100 80 150	35	200	0.284	7.86	2515	0.11	6.3 8.8 (68°–932°F.)	90	600	
Stainless steel AM 350	Fe bal., Cr 17, Ni 4, Mo 3, C 0.08	Annealed Hardened	45 153	156 195	21 12	205 382	0.286	.....	.....	.....	9.0	....	....	30
Stainless steel type 410 A.M.S. 5591 (tubing) A.M.S. 5613 (bars, forgings)	Fe bal., Cr 12.5, C 0.15 max.	Annealed Heat-treated	40 115	75 150	30 15	150 300	0.28	7.75	2700–2790	0.11	5.5	173	340	29
Stainless steel type 414 A.M.S. 5615 (bars, forgings)	Fe bal., Cr 12.5, Ni 2.5	Annealed Heat-treated	80 150	100 200	22 17	217 387	0.28	7.75	2600–2700	0.11	6.1	173	420	29
Stainless steel type 420 A.M.S. 5621 (bars, forgings) A.M.S. 5506 (plate, sheet, and strip)	Fe bal., Cr 13, C 0.35	Annealed Heat-treated	60 200	98 250	28 8	180 480	0.28	7.75	2650–2750	0.11	5.7	173	330	29
Stainless steel type 430	Fe bal., Cr 16, C 0.12 max.	Annealed Cold-rolled	40 95	70 110	35 10	165 225	0.28	7.75	2600–2750	0.11	6.0	180	360	29
Stainless steel type 431 A.M.S. 5628 (bars, forgings)	Fe bal., Cr 16, Ni 2	Annealed Heat-treated	85 150	120 195	25 20	250 400	0.280	7.75	2600–2700	0.11	6.5	140	430	29
Stainless steel type 446	Fe bal., Cr 25, C 0.35 max.	Annealed	50	80	30	165	0.27	7.45	2600–2750	0.12	5.8	145	405	29
Stainless steel 17-4 PH A.M.S. 5673 (bars, forgings)	Fe bal., Cr 17, Ni 4, Cu 4, Co 0.35, C 0.07	Annealed Hardened	110 180	150 195	12 13	363 404	0.28	.....	.....	......	6	124	....	28.5

[c] The cold-rolled properties depend upon composition; types 302 and 304 are not rolled often in excess of 175,000 lb./sq. in. tensile strength.

[d] The values for elongation (% in 2 in.) are obtainable in the steel cold-rolled to *the maximum stated* yield strength and tensile strength. For lower values of tensile strength, elongation will be correspondingly higher.

[e] Types 316, 321, and 374 are used chiefly in the annealed condition.

Table 23-5. Properties of Metals and Alloys—(*Continued*)

Material	Nominal composition (essential elements), %	Form and condition	Typical mechanical properties: Yield strength (0.2% offset), 1000 lb./sq. in.	Typical mechanical properties: Tensile strength, 1000 lb./sq. in.	Typical mechanical properties: Elongation in 2 in., %	Hardness, Brinell	Typical physical constants: Density, lb./cu. in.	Specific gravity	Melting point, °F.	Specific heat (32°–212°F.) B.t.u./(lb.)(°F.)	Thermal expansion coefficient (32°–212°F.) × 10⁻⁶ in./(in.)(°F.)	Thermal conductivity (32°–212°F.) B.t.u./(sq. ft.)(hr.)(°F.)(in.)	Electrical resistivity (68°F.), ohms/cir. mil. ft.	Tensile modulus of elasticity × 10⁶ lb./sq. in.
Stainless steel 17-7 PH A.M.S. 5673 (wire) A.M.S. 5644 (bars and forgings) A.M.S. 5668 (tubing) A.M.S. 5628-9 (plate, sheet, strip)	Fe bal., Cr 17, Ni 7, Al 1, C 0.09	Annealed	40	130	30	165	0.282	......	......	......	8.5	128	......	29
		Hardened	185	200	9	404								
Stainless steel HNM	Fe bal., Cr 18, Mn 3.5, Ni 0.5, C 0.30	Annealed	56	116	57	192	0.284	......	......	......	8.4	......	......	29
		Hardened	124	168	19	352								
Stainless steel, stainless W	Fe bal., Cr 17, Ni 7, Ti 0.7, Al 0.2, C 0.07	Annealed	75–115	120–150	8–15	255	0.28	......	......	......	6	......	......	28
		Hardened	150–185	170–210	8–16	365								
Carpenter stainless No. 20[f]	C 0.07 max., Mn 0.75, Si 1.00, Cr 20.00, Ni 29.00, Mo 2.00 min., Cu 3.00 min.	Annealed	35	85	50	160	0.289	8.02	.....	0.12	9.4	145.2 (212°F.)	451	28.0
Cast Stainless Steels														
Cast 12 Cr Alloy (CA-15) (C means corrosion-resistant casting, Alloy Casting Institute designations)	C 0.15 max., Mn 1.00 max., Si 1.50 max., Cr 11.5–14, Ni 1.00 max., Fe bal.	Air-cooled from 1800°F. Tempered at 600°F.	150	200	7	390	0.275	7.61	2750	0.11	6.4 (70°–1000°F.)	14.5 (212°F.)	468	29
		Air-cooled from 1800°F. Tempered at 1400°F.	75	100	30	185								
Cast 12 Cr Alloy (CA-40)	C 0.20–0.40, Mn 1.00 max., Si 1.50 max., Cr 11.5–14, Ni 1.00 max., Fe bal.	Air-cooled from 1800°F. Tempered at 600°F.	165	220	1	470	0.275	7.61	2725	0.11	6.4 (70°–1000°F.)	14.5 (212°F.)	456	29
		Air-cooled from 1800°F. Tempered at 1400°F.	67	110	18	212								
Cast 20 Cr Alloy (CB-30)	C 0.30 max., Mn 1.00 max., Si 1.00 max., Cr 18–22, Ni 2 max.	Annealed	60	95	15	195	0.272	7.53	2725	0.11	6.5 (70°–1000°F.)	12.8 (212°F.)	456	29
Cast 28-4 Alloy (CC-50)	C 0.50 max., Mn 1.00 max., Si 1.00 max., Cr 26–30, Ni 4.00 max., Fe bal.	As-cast	65	70	2	212	0.272	7.53	2725	0.12	6.4 (70°–1000°F.)	12.6 (212°F.)	462	29
		Air-cooled from 1900°F.	65	97	18	210								
Cast 29-9 Alloy (CE-30)	C 0.30 max., Mn 1.50 max., Si 2.00 max., Cr 26–30, Ni 8–11, Fe bal.	As-cast	60	95	15	170	0.277	7.67	2650	0.14	9.6 (70°–1000°F.)	....	510	25
Cast 20-10 Alloy (CF-8)	C 0.08 max., Mn 1.50 max., Si 2.00 max., Cr 18–21, Ni 8–11, Fe bal.	Water-quenched (1950°–2050°F.)	37	77	55	140	0.280	7.75	2600	0.12	10.0 (70°–1000°F.)	9.2 (212°F.)	457.2	28
Cast 20-10 Alloy (CF-20)	C 0.20 max., Mn 1.50 max., Si 2.00 max., Cr 18–21, Ni 8–11, Fe bal.	Water-quenched (above 2000°F.)	36	77	50	163	0.280	7.75	2575	0.12	10.4 (70°–1000°F.)	9.2 (212°F.)	467.4	28
Cast 20-10-2.5 Alloy (CF-8M)	C 0.08 max., Mn 1.50 max., Si 1.50 max., Cr 18–21, Ni 9–12, Mo 2.5, Fe bal.	Water-quenched (1950°–2050°F.)	42	80	50	156–170	0.280	7.75	2550	0.12	9.7 (70°–1000°F.)	9.4 (212°F.)	492	28

[f] Carpenter stainless No. 20-Cb same composition except for columbium + tantalum, 8 times the carbon minimum.

Table 23-5. Properties of Metals and Alloys—(*Continued*)

Material	Nominal composition (essential elements), %	Form and condition	Typical mechanical properties: Yield strength (0.2% offset), 1000 lb./sq. in.	Tensile strength, 1000 lb./sq. in.	Elongation in 2 in., %	Typical physical constants: Hardness, Brinell	Density, lb./cu. in.	Specific gravity	Melting point, °F.	Specific heat (32°–212°F.) B.t.u./(lb.)(°F.)	Thermal expansion coefficient (32°–212°F.) × 10⁻⁶ in./(in.)(°F.)	Thermal conductivity (32°–212°F.) B.t.u./(sq. ft.)(hr.)(°F.)(in.)	Electrical resistivity (68°F.), ohms/cir. mil. ft.	Tensile modulus of elasticity × 10⁶ lb./sq. in.
Cast 18-38 Alloy (HU) (H means heat-resistant)	C 0.35–0.75, Mn 2.00 max., Si 2.50 max., Cr 17–21, Ni 37–41, Fe bal.	As-cast	40	70	9	170	0.290	8.03	2450	0.11	9.7 (70°–2000°F.)	8.9 (70°–1000°F.)	630	27
		Aged	43	73	5	190								
Cast 12-60 Alloy (HW)	C 0.35–0.75, Mn 2.00 max., Si 2.50 max., Cr 10–14, Ni 58–62, Fe bal.	As-cast	36	68	4	185	0.294	8.14	2350	0.11	9.2 (70°–2000°F.)	7.7 (70°–212°F.)	672	25
		Aged	52	84	4	205								
Cast 15-65 Alloy (HX)	C 0.35–0.75, Mn 2.00 max., Si 2.50 max., Cr 15–19, Ni 64–68, Fe bal.	As-cast	36	65	9	176	0.294	8.14	2350	0.11	9.5 (70°–2000°F.)	....	......	25
		Aged	44	73	9	185								
Cast 9 Cr Alloy (HA)	C 0.20 max., Mn 0.35–0.65 max., Si 1.00 max., Cr 8–10, Fe bal.	Annealed	65	95	23	180	0.279	7.72	2750	0.11	7.5 (70°–1200°F.)	17.0 (70°–1000°F.)	420	29
		Normalized	81	107	21	220								
Cast 28-4 Alloy (HC)	C 0.50 max., Mn 1.00 max., Si 2.00 max., Cr 26–30, Ni 4 max., Fe bal.	As-cast	65	70	2	190	0.272	7.53	2725	0.12	7.7 (70°–2000°F.)	17.9 (70°–1000°F.)	462	29
		Aged	80	115	18									
Cast 28-7 Alloy (HD)	C 0.50 max., Mn 1.50 max., Si 2.00 max., Cr 26–30, Ni 4–7, Fe bal.	As-cast	48	85	16	190	0.274	7.58	2700	0.12	9.2 (70°–2000°F.)	17.9 (70°–1000°F.)	486	27
Cast 29-9 Alloy (HE)	C 0.20–0.50, Mn 2.00 max., Si 2.00 max., Cr 26–30, Ni 8–11, Fe bal.	As-cast	45	95	20	200	0.277	7.68	2650	0.14	11.1 (70°–2000°F.)	10.0 (70°–1500°F.)	510	25
		Aged	55	90	10	270								
Cast 21-10 Alloy (HF)	C 0.20–0.40, Mn 2.00 max., Si 2.00 max., Cr 19–23, Ni 9–12, Fe bal.	As-cast	45	85	35	165	0.280	7.75	2550	0.12	10.9 (70°–2000°F.)	13.4 (70°–1000°F.)	480	28
		Aged	50	100	25	190								
Cast 25-12 Alloy (HH)	C 0.20–0.50, Mn 2.00 max., Si 2.00 max., Cr 24–28, Ni 11–14, Fe bal.	As-cast—Type 1	50	80	25	185	0.279	7.72	2500	0.12	10.8 (70°–2000°F.)	10.9 (70°–1000°F.)	450–510	27
		Type 2	40	85	15	180								
		Aged—Type 1	55	86	11	200								
		Type 2	45	92	8	200								
Cast 28-15 Alloy (HI)	C 0.20–0.50, Mn 2.00 max., Si 2.00 max., Cr 26–30, Ni 14–18, Fe bal.	As-cast	45	80	12	180	0.279	7.72	2550	0.12	10.8 (70°–2000°F.)	8.2 (70°–1000°F.)	......	27
		Aged	65	90	6	200								
Cast 25-20 Alloy (HK)	C 0.20–0.60, Mn 2.00 max., Si 2.00 max., Cr 24–28, Ni 18–22, Fe bal.	As-cast	50	75	17	170	0.280	7.75	2550	0.12	10.1 (70°–2000°F.)	10.9 (70°–1000°F.)	540	29
		Aged	50	85	10	190								
Cast 30-20 Alloy (HL)	C 0.20–0.60, Mn 2.00 max., Si 2.00 max., Cr 28–32, Ni 18–22, Fe bal.	As-cast	52	82	19	192	0.279	7.72	2600	0.12	10.1 (70°–2000°F.)	10.9 (70°–1000°F.)	574	29
Cast 20-25 Alloy (HN)	C 0.20–0.50, Mn 2.00 max., Si 2.00 max., Cr 19–23, Ni 23–27	As-cast	38	68	17	160	0.283	7.83	2500	0.11	......	....	......	27

Table 23-5. Properties of Metals and Alloys—(*Continued*)

Material	Nominal composition (essential elements), %	Form and condition	Typical mechanical properties: Yield strength (0.2% offset), 1000 lb./sq. in.	Tensile strength, 1000 lb./sq. in.	Elongation in 2 in., %	Typical physical constants: Hardness, Brinell	Density, lb./cu. in.	Specific gravity	Melting point, °F.	Specific heat (32°–212°F.) B.t.u./(lb.)(°F.)	Thermal expansion coefficient (32°–212°F.) × 10⁻⁶ in./(in.)(°F.)	Thermal conductivity (32°–212°F.) B.t.u./(sq. ft.)(hr.)(°F.)(in.)	Electrical resistivity (68°F.), ohms/cir. mil. ft.	Tensile modulus of elasticity × 10⁶ lb./sq. in.
Cast 15-35 Alloy (HT)	C 0.35–0.75, Mn 2.00 max., Si 2.50 max., Cr 13–17, Ni 33–37, Fe bal.	As-cast	40	70	10	180	0.286	7.96	2425	0.11	9.8 (70°–2000°F.)	11.4 (70°–1000°F.)	600	27
		Aged	45	75	5	200								
Cast 20-10-2.5 Alloy (CF-12M)	C 0.12 max., Mn 1.50 max., Si 1.50 max., Cr 18–21, Ni 9–12, Mo 2.5, Fe bal.	Water-quenched (from above 2000°F.)	42	80	50	156–170	0.280	7.75	2550	0.12	9.7 (70°–1000°F.)	9.4 (212°F.)	492	28
Cast 20-10 Cb Alloy (CF-8C)	C 0.08 max., Mn 1.50 max., Si 2.00 max., Cr 18–21, Ni 9–12, Cb or Cb-Ta, Fe bal.	Water-quenched (1950°–2050°F.)	38	77	39	149	0.280	7.75	2600	0.12	10.3 (70°–1000°F.)	9.3 (212°F.)	426	28
Cast 20-10 Alloy (CF-16F)	C 0.16 max., Mn 1.50 max., Si 2.00 max., Cr 18–21, Ni 9–12, Mo 1.5 max., Fe bal.	Water-quenched (from above 2000°F.)	40	77	52	150	0.280	7.75	2550	0.12	9.9 (70°–1000°F.)	9.4 (212°F.)	432	28
Cast 25-12 Alloy (CH-20)	C 0.20 max., Mn 1.50 max., Si 2.00 max., Cr 22–26, Ni 12–15, Fe bal.	Water-quenched (from above 2000°F.)	50	88	38	190	0.279	7.72	2600	0.12	9.6 (70°–1000°F.)	8.2 (212°F.)	504	28
Cast 25-20 Alloy (CK-20)	C 0.20 max., Mn 1.50 max., Si 2.00 max., Cr 23–27, Ni 19–22, Fe bal.	Water-quenched (from 2100°F.)	38	76	37	144	0.280	7.75	2600	0.12	9.2 (70°–1000°F.)	8.2 (212°F.)	540	29
Cast 25-20 Alloy (CN-7M)	C 0.07 max., Mn 1.50 max., Si 100, Cr 18–22, Ni 21–31, Fe bal.	As-cast	30	65	30–45	130–150	0.287	8.02	2650	0.12	9.7 (70°–1000°F.)	12.1 (212°F.)	537.6	30
Other Cast Alloys														
Durimet 20	C 0.07, Mn 1.5, Si 1.5, Cr 20.0, Ni 29.0, Mo 2.0, Cu 3.0	Cast, annealed	30	65	48	130	0.286	.....	.....	......	8.6	145 (212°F.)		
Iron-silicon Alloy (Duriron)	Si 14.50, C 0.85, Mn 0.65, Mo nil, Fe bal.	Cast only	.....	16	Nil	520	0.255	7.0	2300	0.13	7.4 (68°–392°F.)	....	....	23
Fe-Si-Mo Alloy (Durichlor)	Si 14.50, C 0.85, Mn 0.65, Mo 3.00, Fe bal.	Cast only	.....	16	Nil	520	0.255	7.0	2300	0.13	7.2	....	....	23
Ni-Mo Alloy (Chlorimet 2)	Ni 62.00, Mo 32.00, Fe 3.00 max., Si 1.00, C 0.10	Cast	55	80	5	230	0.333	9.24	2460	......	4.7	....	....	27
Ni-Cr-Mo Alloy (Chlorimet 3)	Ni 60.00, Cr 18.00, Mo 18.00, Fe 3.00 max., Si 1.00, C 0.07	Cast only	50	75	10	220	0.325	8.94	2380	0.092	7.0 (68°–392°F.)	....	....	24.5
Illium G	Ni bal., Cr 22.5, Fe 6.5, Mo 6.4, Cu 6.5, Mn, Si	As-cast	50	68	32	200	0.310	8.31	2375	0.105	7.5	84	735	24
Illium 98	Ni 55.00, Cr 28.00, Mo 8.5, Cu 5.5, Mn 1.25, Fe 1.00	Cast	.....	54	18	155								

Table 23-5. Properties of Metals and Alloys—(*Continued*)

Material	Nominal composition (essential elements), %	Form and condition	Typical mechanical properties: Yield strength (0.2% offset), 1000 lb./sq. in.	Tensile strength, 1000 lb./sq. in.	Elongation in 2 in., %	Typical physical constants: Hardness, Brinell	Density, lb./cu. in.	Specific gravity	Melting point, °F.	Specific heat (32°–212°F.) B.t.u./(lb.)(°F.)	Thermal expansion coefficient (32°–212°F.) $\times 10^{-6}$ in./(in.)(°F.)	Thermal conductivity (32°–212°F.) B.t.u./(sq. ft.)(hr.)(°F.)(in.)	Electrical resistivity (68°F.), ohms/cir. mil. ft.	Tensile modulus of elasticity $\times 10^6$ lb./sq. in.
Non-ferrous Alloys														
Aluminum and Alloys														
Aluminum Alloy No. 1100 QQ-A-411C; A.S.T.M. B211 wire, rod, and bar	Al 99 plus	Annealed–0 Cold-rolled–H14 Cold-rolled–H18	5 17 22	13 18 24	45 20 15	23 32 44	..... 0.098	..... 2.71	 1190–1215	..... 0.23	..... 13.1 (68°F.)	1540 ..... 1510 (68°F.)	18 19	10
3003 QQ-A-357; A.S.T.M. B221 bar, rod, and shapes extruded	Al bal., Mn 1.2	Annealed–0 Cold-rolled–H14 Cold-rolled–H18	6 21 27	16 22 29	40 16 10	28 40 55	..... 0.099	..... 2.73	 1190–1210	..... 0.23	..... 12.9 (68°F.)	1340 1100 1075 (68°F.)	21 25 26	10
2017 QQ-A-351d; A.S.T.M. B221 bar, rod, and wire	Al bal., Cu 4.0, Mn 0.5, Mg 0.5	Annealed–0 Heat-treated–T4	10 40	26 62	22 22	45 105	0.101	2.79	955–1185	0.23	12.7 (68°F.)	1190 840 (68°F.)	23 34	10.5
2024 QQ-A-268; A.S.T.M. B211 bar, rod and wire	Core: 2024, Al bal., Cu 4.5, Mn 0.6, Mg 1.5, Coating: Al 99.3	Heat-treated–T4 Heat-treated and strain hardened–T36 Heat-treated, strain hardened, and artificially aged–T86	42 53 66	64 67 70	18 11 6	.....	.....	.....	935–1215	0.23	12.9 (68°F.)	.....	.....	10.6
5052 QQ-A-315a; A.S.T.M. B211 bar, rod, and wire QQ-A-381b; A.S.T.M. B209 sheet and plate	Al bal., Mg 2.5, Cr 0.25	Annealed–0 Cold-rolled and stabilized–H34 Cold-rolled and stabilized–H38	13 31 37	28 38 42	30 14 8	47 68 77	..... 0.097	..... 2.68	..... 1100–1200	..... 0.23	..... 13.2 (68°F.)	960 (68°F.) 960 (68°F.)	30 30	10.2
6063 MIL-A-18593; A.S.T.M. B221 bar, rod, and shapes extruded	Al bal., Si 0.4, Mg 0.7	Annealed–0 Artificially aged–T5 Heat-treated and artificially aged–T6	7 21 31	13 27 35	30 12 12	25 60 73	0.098	2.70	1140–1205	.....	13.0 (68°F.)	1390 (68°F.)	20	10.0
7075 QQ-A-282; A.S.T.M. B211 bar, rod, wire, and shapes; rolled or drawn	Al bal., Zn 5.6, Cu 1.6, Mg 2.5, Cr 0.3	Annealed–0 Heat-treated and artificially aged–T6	15 73	33 83	17 11	60 150	0.101	2.80	890–1180	0.23	12.9 (68°F.)	840 (68°F.)	34	10.4
13 A.S.T.M. S12A S12B	Al bal., Si 12	Die-cast–F	21	39	2.0	.....	0.096	2.65	1065–1080	0.23	11.5 (68°F.)	840 (68°F.)	33	10.3
380 A.S.T.M. SC84B	Al bal., Cu 3.5, Si 9.0	Die-cast–F	26	43	2.0	.....	0.098	2.72	1000–1100	.....	11.6 (68°F.)	670 (68°F.)	45	10.3
43 A.S.T.M. S5A S5B S5C	Al bal., Si 5.0	Sand-cast–F Permanent mold-cast–F Die-cast–F	8 9 16	19 23 30	8 10 7	40 45	0.097	2.69	1065–1170	0.23	12.3 (68°F.)	990 (68°F.)	27	10.3
195 A.S.T.M. C4A	Al bal., Cu 4.5, Si 0.8	Sand-cast; heat-treated–4 Sand-cast; heat-treated and artificially aged–T6	16 24	32 36	8.5 5	60 75	0.102	2.81	970–1190	0.23	12.7 (68°F.)	960 (68°F.) 960 (68°F.)	30	10.3
214 A.S.T.M. G4A	Al bal., Mg 3.8	Sand-cast–F	12	25	9	50	0.096	2.65	1110–1185	0.23	13.4 (68°F.)	960 (68°F.)	29	10.3
220 A.S.T.M. G10A	Al bal., Mg 10	Sand-cast; heat-treated–T4	26	48	16	75	0.093	2.57	840–1120	0.23	13.7 (68°F.)	610 (68°F.)	48.0	10.3

Table 23-5. Properties of Metals and Alloys—*(Continued)*

Material	Nominal composition (essential elements), %	Form and condition	Typical mechanical properties			Typical physical constants								
			Yield strength (0.2% offset), 1000 lb./sq. in.	Tensile strength, 1000 lb./sq. in.	Elongation in 2 in., %	Hardness, Brinell	Density, lb./cu. in.	Specific gravity	Melting point, °F.	Specific heat (32°–212°F.) B.t.u./(lb.)(°F.)	Thermal expansion coefficient (32°–212°F.) × 10⁻⁶ in./(in.)(°F.)	Thermal conductivity (32°–212°F.) B.t.u./(sq. ft.)(hr.)(°F.)(in.)	Electrical resistivity (68°F.), ohms/cir. mil ft.	Tensile modulus of elasticity × 10⁶ lb./sq. in.
Cu and Alloys														
Nickel silver 18% (wrought) 65–18 A.S.T.M. B122, No. 2	Cu 65, Zn 17, Ni 18	Annealed Cold-rolled (HT)[a] Cold-drawn wire (HT)	25 70	58 85 105	40 4	70 170	0.316	8.75	2030	0.09	9.0	230	173	18
Nickel silver 13% (cast) 10A A.S.T.M. B149, No. 10A	Cu bal., Zn 20, Ni 12.5, Pb 10.5, Sn 2	Cast (HT, HT)	18	35	15	55	0.320	8.9	1830	0.12	10.0	120	204	12
Nickel silver 10% (wrought) 65-10 A.S.T.M. B155, Alloy E	Cu 65, Zn 25, Ni 10	Annealed Cold-rolled (HT) Cold-drawn wire (HT)	20 70	55 88 110	45 5	60 180	0.313	8.67	1870	0.09	9.0	320	125	17.5
Nickel silver 20% (cast) (11A) A.S.T.M. B149, No. 11A	Cu bal., Ni 20, Zn 6, Pb 5, Sn 4	Cast (as cast)	25	40	15	85	0.318	8.8	1980	0.12	10.0	120	210	15
Cupronickel 10% Tube A.S.T.M. B111 Plate A.S.T.M. B171	Cu 88.35, Ni 10, Fe 1.25, Mn 0.4	Annealed Cold-drawn tube	22 57	44 60	45 15	.....	0.323	8.94	2090	0.09	9.3	310	113	18
Cupronickel 30% Sheet A.S.T.M. B122 Plate A.S.T.M. B171 Tube A.S.T.M. B111	Cu 68.90, Ni 30, Mn 0.60, Fe 0.50	Annealed Cold-drawn Cold-rolled	22 60 70	55 75 77	45 20 5	70 150 155	0.323	8.94	2240	0.09	8.5	200	220	22
Cupronickel 55-45 (Constantan)	Cu 55, Ni 45	Annealed Cold-drawn Cold-rolled	30 50 65	60 65 85	45 30 20	.....	0.321	8.89	2300	......	8.1	155	290	24
Copper Sheet A.S.T.M. B152 Rod A.S.T.M. B124, B133 Wire A.S.T.M. B1, B2, B3	Cu 99.9 plus	Annealed Cold-drawn Cold-rolled (HT)	10 40 40	32 45 46	45 15 5	42 90 100	0.322	8.91	1980	0.092	9.3	2700	10.3	17
Red brass (wrought) Sheet, strip, and plate, A.S.T.M. B36 Wire A.S.T.M. B134 Tubes A.S.T.M. B135	Cu 85, Zn 15	Annealed Cold-drawn Cold-rolled	15 55 60	40 70 75	50 15 7	50 120 135	0.316	8.75	1875	0.09	9.8	1100	28	17
Red brass (cast)	Cu 85, Zn 5, Pb 5, Sn 5	Cast (as cast)	17	35	25	60	0.317	8.75	1810–1840	......	10.2	500	63	13
Gilding metal Sheet A.S.T.M. B36	Cu 95.0, Zn 5.0	Cold-rolled	50	56	5	114	0.320	.....	1950	......	10.0	1600	......	17
Commercial bronze Sheet A.S.T.M. B36 Wire A.S.T.M. B134	Cu 90.0, Zn 10.0	Cold-rolled	54	61	5	125	0.318	.....	1910	......	10.2	1300	......	17
Cartridge 70-30 brass Sheet A.S.T.M. B19 Plate A.S.T.M. B36 Wire A.S.T.M. B134 Tube A.S.T.M. B14 Tube A.S.T.M. B135	Cu 70.0, Zn 30.0	Cold-rolled	63	76	8	155	0.308	.....	1750	......	11.1	840	......	16
Architectural bronze	Cu 57.0, Zn 40.0, Pb 3.0	Annealed	20	60	30	95	0.306	.....	1630	......	11.6	850	......	14
Phosphor bronze 10% Sheet A.S.T.M. B103 Rod A.S.T.M. B139 Wire A.S.T.M. B159	Cu 90, Sn 10, P 0.25	Spring temper	.....	122	4	241	0.317	.....	1830	......	10.2	350	......	16
Phosphor bronze 5 % Sheet A.S.T.M. B103 Rod A.S.T.M. B139 Wire A.S.T.M. B159	Cu 94.75, Sn 5, P 0.25	Annealed Cold-drawn wire (HT) Cold-rolled (HT)	20 65	50 130 80	50 2 8	60 160	0.320	8.86	1920	0.09	9.4	480	69	16
Aluminum brass Tube A.S.T.M. B111	Cu 76.0, Zn 22.0, Al 2.0, As trace	Annealed	27	60	55	82	0.301	.....	1780	......	10.3	700	......	16

[a] Hard temper (HT). Hard temper and heat-treated (strip) (HT, HT).

Table 23-5. Properties of Metals and Alloys—(*Continued*)

Material	Nominal composition (essential elements), %	Form and condition	Typical mechanical properties: Yield strength (0.2% offset), 1000 lb./sq. in.	Tensile strength, 1000 lb./sq. in.	Elongation in 2 in., %	Typical physical constants: Hardness, Brinell	Density, lb./cu. in.	Specific gravity	Melting point, °F.	Specific heat (32°–212°F.) B.t.u./(lb.)(°F.)	Thermal expansion coefficient (32°–212°F.) × 10⁻⁶ in./(in.)(°F.)	Thermal conductivity (32°–212°F.) B.t.u./(sq. ft.)(hr.)(°F.)(in.)	Electrical resistivity (68°F.), ohms/cir. mil. ft.	Tensile modulus of elasticity × 10⁶ lb./sq. in.
Yellow brass (high brass) Sheet, strip, and plate A.S.T.M. B36 Wire A.S.T.M. B134 Tubes A.S.T.M. B135	Cu 65, Zn 35	Annealed	18	48	60	55								
		Cold-drawn	55	70	15	115	0.306	8.47	1710	0.09	10.5	830	40	15
		Cold-rolled (HT)	60	74	10	180								
Naval brass Rods, bars, and shapes A.S.T.M. B21; A.M.S. 4611B; 4612C	Cu 60, Zn 39.25, Sn 0.75	Annealed	22	56	40	90	0.304	8.41	1625	0.09	11.0	810	40	15
		Cold-drawn	40	65	35	150								
Admiralty brass (inhibited) Plates A.S.T.M. B171 Tubes A.S.T.M. B111	Cu 71, Zn 28, Sn 1, As, Sb, or P present	Annealed	20	53	65	60	0.308	8.53	1720	0.09	10.2	770	42	16
Muntz metal Tubes A.S.T.M. B135 B111	Cu 60, Zn 40	Annealed	20	54	45	80	0.303	8.39	1660	0.09	10.8	870	37	15
Manganese bronze rods, bars, and shapes A.S.T.M. B138	Cu 58.5, Zn 39.2, Fe 1, Sn 1, Mn 0.3	Annealed	30	60	30	95								
		Cold-drawn	50	80	20	180	0.302	8.36	1645	0.09	11.2	700	45	15
High-silicon bronze A Sheet A.S.T.M. B96, B97 Rod A.S.T.M. B98, B124 Wire A.S.T.M. B99	Cu 96, Si 3, Mn, Zn, or Fe	Annealed	22	58	60	70								
		Cold-drawn	60	90	20	180	0.308	8.53	1865	0.09	9.5	225	160	15
		Cold-rolled	60	95	7	190								
Low-silicon bronze B	Cu 96, Si 0.8–2.0, Mn 0.7 max., Fe 0.8 max.	Annealed	15	40	50	F55	0.316	.....	.....	0.09	9.9	360		
		Hardened	55	70	15	B80 (Rockwell)								
Aluminum bronze Sheet A.S.T.M. B169 Rod A.S.T.M. B124, B150	Cu 92, Al 8	Annealed	25	70	60	80								
		Hard	65	105	7	210	0.281	7.78	1900	0.09	9.2	490	70	17
Ni-Vee bronze type A	Cu 88, Ni 5, Sn 5, Zn 2	As-cast	22	50	40	85	0.32	8.8	1950	.....	11	.....	.....	15
		Tempered	40	65	10	130	0.32	8.8	1950	.....	11	.....	.....	15
		Heat-treated	55	85	10	180	0.32	8.8	1950	.....	11	.....	.....	15
Ni-Vee bronze type B	Cu 87, Ni 5, Sn 5, Pb 1, Zn 2	As-cast	20	45	30	80	0.32	8.8	1925	.....	10	.....	.....	13
		Tempered	30	60	8	120								14
Copper beryllium 25 Sheet and strip A.S.T.M. B194 Wire A.S.T.M. B197 Rod A.S.T.M. B196	Be 1.9, Co 0.25, Cu bal.	Annealed (SA)[i]	.....	70	45	B60 (Rockwell)	.....	.....	.....	.....	.....	.....	.....	17
		Annealed (SA, HT)	.....	175	6	C38	0.298	8.26	1600–1800	0.10[h]	9.3	750–900	.....	19
		Cold-rolled (HT)	.....	110	5	B99	.....	.....	.....	.....	.....	.....	.....	17
		Cold-rolled (HT, HT)	.....	200	2	C42	.....	.....	.....	.....	.....	.....	.....	19
Copper beryllium 165	Be 1.7, Co 0.25, Cu bal.	Annealed (SA)	.....	.....	.....	.....	.....	.....	.....	.....	.....	.....	.....	17
		Annealed (SA, HT)	.....	70	45	B60	0.298	8.26	1600–1800	.....	9.3	750–900	.....	19
		Cold-rolled (HT)		165	6	C35								17
		Cold-rolled (HT, HT)	.....	.....	.....	.....	.....	.....	.....	.....	.....	.....	.....	19
Copper beryllium 10	Be 0.55, Co 2.5, Cu bal.	Annealed (SA)	.....	45	27	B30	.....	.....	.....	.....	.....	.....	.....	16
		Annealed (SA, HT)	.....	110	9	B96	0.316	8.75	1885–1955	.....	9.8 (68°–392°F.)	1450–1800	.....	18
		Cold-rolled (HT)	.....	78	6	B75	.....	.....	.....	.....		.....	.....	16
		Cold-rolled (HT, HT)	.....	120	8	B98	.....	.....	.....	.....	.....	.....	.....	18
Copper beryllium 50	Be 0.38, Co 1.55, Ag 1.0, Cu bal.	Annealed (SA)	.....	45	27	B30	.....	.....	.....	.....	.....	.....	.....	16
		Annealed (SA, HT)	.....	110	15	B96	0.316	8.75	1850–1930	.....	9.8 (68°–392°F.)	1500–1700	.....	18
		Cold-rolled (HT)	.....	70	13	B73	.....	.....	.....	.....		.....	.....	16
		Cold-rolled (HT, HT)	.....	120	14	B99	.....	.....	.....	.....	.....	.....	.....	18

[h] cal./g./°C. (30°–100°C.).
[i] Solution annealed (SA). Solution annealed, heat-treated (SA, HT).

Table 23-5. Properties of Metals and Alloys—(*Continued*)

Material	Nominal composition (essential elements), %	Form and condition	Typical mechanical properties: Yield strength (0.2% offset), 1000 lb./sq. in.	Tensile strength, 1000 lb./sq. in.	Elongation in 2 in., %	Typical physical constants: Hardness, Brinell	Density, lb./cu. in.	Specific gravity	Melting point, °F.	Specific heat (32°–212°F.) B.t.u./(lb.)(°F.)	Thermal expansion coefficient (32°–212°F.) × 10⁻⁶ in./(in.)(°F.)	Thermal conductivity (32°–212°F.) B.t.u./(sq. ft.)(hr.)(°F.)/(in.)	Electrical resistivity (68°F.), ohms/cir. mil. ft.	Tensile modulus of elasticity × 10⁶ lb./sq. in.
Lead and Alloys														
Chemical lead	Pb 99.9, Cu 0.06, Bi 0.005 max.	Rolled	1.9	2.5	50	5	0.410	11.35	621	0.030	16.4	240	124	2
Antimonial lead	Pb 94, Sb 6	Cast	.....	6.8	22	12	0.393	10.90	554	0.032	15.1	200	140	3
		Rolled	.....	4.1	47	9								
Tellurium lead	Pb 99.85, Te 0.04, Cu 0.06	Rolled	2.2	3	45	6	0.410	11.35	621	0.030	16.4	240	124	2
Soft solder 50-50	Sn 50, Pb 50	Cast	.....	6.8	50	14	0.321	8.89	421	0.051	13.1	310	93	
Soft solder 60-40	Sn 60, Pb 40	Cast	.....	7.1	45	15	0.306	8.50	374	0.055	12.2	330	90	
Magnesium Alloys														
Magnesium alloy AZ92A A.M.S. 4434E	Mg bal., Al 9.0, Zn 2.0, Mn 0.10 min.	Sand-cast (as cast)	14	24	6	50	0.066	1.83	1100	0.245	14.5	360	84	6.5
		Sand-cast (solution heat-treated)	14	40	12	55	......	......	......	......	....	310	101	
		Sand-cast (solution heat-treated and aged)	19	40	5	83	......	......	......	......	....	410	74	
		Sand-cast (age-hardened)	16	30	4	66	......	......	......	......	....	410	74	
Magnesium alloy AZ31B A.M.S. 4375-76 (plate, sheet)	Mg bal., Al 3.0, An 1.0, Mn 0.20 min.	Rolled-plate (strain hardened then partially annealed)	24	37	18	.....	0.064	1.77	1160	0.245	14.5	540	55	6.5
		Rolled-sheet (strain hardened then partially annealed)	32	42	15	73	......	......	......	......	....	540	55	
		Annealed	22	37	21	56	......	......	......	......	....	540	55	
		Extruded	28	38	14	.....	......	......	......	......	....	540	55	
Magnesium alloy AZ80A A.M.S. 4360 (forgings)	Mg bal., Al 8.5, Zn 0.5, Mn 0.15 min.	Extruded	36	49	11	60								
		Extruded (age-hardened)	39	53	6	82	0.065	1.80	1130	0.245	14.5	350	87	6.5
		Forged (age-hardened)	34	50	6	72								
Magnesium alloy AZ91A and AZ91B A.M.S. 4490 (casting)	Mg bal., Al 9.0, Zn 0.6, Mn 0.13 min.	Die-cast (as cast)	22	33	3	67	0.065	1.81	1105	0.245	14.5	370	83	6.5
Magnesium alloy AZ91C	Mg bal., Al 8.7, Zn 0.7, Mn 0.13 min.	Sand-cast (as cast)	14	24	2	52	......	......	......	......	....	370	82	
		Sand-cast (solution heat-treated)	14	40	11	55	0.065	1.81	1105	0.245	14.5	320	97	6.5
		Sand-cast (solution heat-treated and aged)	19	40	5	73	......	......	......	......	....	390	78	
Magnesium alloy BZ33A	Mg bal., Zn 2.6, Zr 0.7, other elements 3,0	Sand-cast (age-hardened)	15	23	3	50	0.066	1.83	1189	0.245	14.5	690	42	6.5
Magnesium alloy HK31A A.M.S. 4445	Mg bal., Th 3.0, Zr 0.7	Sand-cast (solution heat-treated and aged)	15	30	8	55	0.065	1.79	1200	0.245	14.5	640	46	6.5
		Rolled-sheet (strain-hardened then partially annealed)	29	37	8	57	......	......	......	......	....	780	37	
Magnesium alloy HZ32A	Mg bal., Th 3.0, Zn 2.1, Zr 0.7	Sand-cast (age-hardened)	14	29	7	57	0.066	1.83	1198	0.245	14.5	740	39	6.5
Magnesium alloy ZK60A A.M.S. 4370 (sheet)	Mg bal., Zn 5.7, Zr 0.55	Extruded	37	49	14	75	......	......	......	......	....	800	36	6.5
		Extruded (age-hardened)	43	52	12	82	0.066	1.83	1175	0.245	14.5	850	34	
		Forged	38	40	13									

Table 23-5. Properties of Metals and Alloys—(*Continued*)

Material	Nominal composition (essential elements), %	Form and condition	Typical mechanical properties: Yield strength (0.2% offset), 1000 lb./sq. in.	Tensile strength, 1000 lb./sq. in.	Elongation in 2 in., %	Hardness, Brinell	Typical physical constants: Density, lb./cu. in.	Specific gravity	Melting point, °F.	Specific heat (32°-212°F.) B.t.u./(lb.)(°F.)	Thermal expansion coefficient (32°-212°F.) × 10⁻⁶ in./(in.)(°F.)	Thermal conductivity (32°-212°F.) B.t.u./(sq. ft.)(hr.)(°F.)(in.)	Electrical resistivity (68°F.), ohms/cir. mil. ft.	Tensile modulus of elasticity × 10⁶ lb./sq. in.
Nickel														
Nickel (pure)	Ni 99.99	Annealed	8.5	46	30	.....	0.322	8.91	2650	0.11	7.4	543	41	30
Nickel (cast)	Ni 95.6, Cu 0.5, Fe 0.5, Mn 0.8, Si 1.5, C 0.8	As-cast	25	57	22	110	0.301	8.34	2450–2600	0.13	8.85 (70°-1400°F.)	410	125	21.5
A nickel Rods, bars, forgings A.S.M.E. SB-160 A.S.T.M. B160 Plate, sheet, strip, A.S.M.E. SB-162 A.S.T.M. B162 Seamless pipe, tubing A.S.M.E. SB-161 A.S.T.M. B161	Ni(+Co) 99.40, C 0.06, Mn 0.25, Fe 0.15, S 0.005, Si 0.05, Cu 0.05	Annealed Hot-rolled Cold-drawn Cold-rolled	20 25 70 95	70 75 95 105	40 40 25 5	100 110 170 210	0.321	8.89	2615–2635	0.13	6.6	420	53 57	30
Low-carbon nickel Rods, bars, forgings A.S.M.E. SB-160 A.S.T.M. B160 Plate, sheet, strip A.S.M.E. SB-162 A.S.T.M. B162 Seamless pipe, tubing A.S.M.E. SB-161 A.S.T.M. B161	Ni(+Co) 99.50, C 0.02, Mn 0.20, Fe 0.15, S 0.005, Si 0.05, Cu 0.05	Annealed Hot-rolled Cold-drawn Cold-rolled	15 25 65	60 60 95	50 45 15	90 105 150	0.321	8.89	2615–2635	0.11	7.2	420	50	30
E nickel	Ni(+Co) 97.85, C 0.05, Mn 1.95, Fe 0.05, S 0.005, Si 0.04, Cu 0.03	Annealed Hot-rolled Cold-drawn	35 50 80	75 90 100	40 35 25	140 150 190	0.319	8.86	2600	0.11	7.4	335	85	30
D nickel	Ni(+Co) 95.00, C 0.10, Mn 4.75, Fe 0.05, S 0.005, Si 0.05, Cu 0.02	Annealed Hot-rolled Cold-drawn	35 50 80	75 90 100	40 35 25	140 150 190	0.315	8.78	2600	0.11	7.4	335	110	30
Duranickel	Ni(+Co) 93.90, C 0.15, Mn 0.25, Fe 0.15, S 0.005, Si 0.55, Cu 0.05, Al 4.50, Ti 0.45	Annealed Annealed age-hardened Spring Spring, age-hardened	45 125	100 170 175 205	40 25 5 10	160 330 320 370	0.298	8.26	2550–2620	0.104	7.2	128 137	280 260	30
Permanickel	Ni(+Co) 98.65, C 0.25, Mn 0.10, Fe 0.10, S 0.005, Si 0.06, Cu 0.02, Ti 0.45, Mg 0.35	Annealed Annealed, age-hardened Spring Spring, age-hardened	45 125 195	105 175 180 210	45 25 5 10	160 325	0.316	8.75	2550–2620	0.106 (70°-750°F.)	7.2	400	94.5	30
A nickel Electronic grade A.S.T.M. F175	Ni(+Co) 99.55, C 0.09, Mn 0.20, Fe 0.05, S 0.005, Si 0.05, Cu 0.02	Annealed	20	70	40	100	0.321	8.89	2615–2635	0.11	7.2	420	57	30
220 nickel A.S.T.M. B239, grade 11	Ni(+Co) 99.65, C 0.06, Mn 0.10, Fe 0.05, S 0.005, Si 0.05, Cu 0.02, Mg 0.04	Annealed	20	70	40	100	0.0321	8.89	2615–2635	0.11	7.2	420	57	30
225 nickel A.S.T.M. B239, grade 3	Ni(+Co) 99.50, C 0.07, Mn 0.10, S 0.005, Si 0.20, Cu 0.02, Fe 0.05	Annealed	20	70	40	100	0.321	8.89	2615–2635	0.11	7.2	420	57	30
Titanium and Alloys														
Titanium (comercially pure)	Ti bal., Fe 0.2 max., N_2 0.05 max., C 0.08 max., H_2 0.015 max.	Annealed	70	90	23	200	0.163	4.54	3300	0.129	5.0 (70°-1000°F.)	118	480	16.5

Table 23-5. Properties of Metals and Alloys—(*Continued*)

Material	Nominal composition (essential elements), %	Form and condition	Typical mechanical properties: Yield strength (0.2% offset), 1000 lb./sq. in.	Tensile strength, 1000 lb./sq. in.	Elongation in 2 in., %	Hardness, Brinell	Typical physical constants: Density, lb./cu. in.	Specific gravity	Melting point, °F.	Specific heat (32°–212°F.) B.t.u./(lb.)(°F.)	Thermal expansion coefficient (32°–212°F.) × 10^{-6} in./(in.)(°F.)	Thermal conductivity (32°–212°F.) B.t.u./(sq. ft.)(hr.)(°F.)(in.)	Electrical resistivity (68°F.), ohms/cir. mil ft.	Tensile modulus of elasticity × 10^6 lb./sq. in.
Titanium-chromium-iron-molybdenum alloy (Ti-140A)	Ti bal., Fe 2.0, Cr 2.0, Mo 2.0, C 0.08 max., N_2 0.05 max., H_2 0.015 max.	Annealed	125	135	14	35 (Rockwell C)								
		Heat-treated	145	155	10	37 (Rockwell C)	0.166	4.60	3000	.....	5.6 (70°–1000°F.)	....	780	16.5
Titanium-aluminum-iron-chromium-molybdenum alloy (Ti-155A)	Ti bal., Al 5.0, Fe 1.4, Cr 1.4, Mo 1.2, H_2 0.0125 max., C 0.08 max., N_2 0.05 max.	Annealed	135	150	15	36 (Rockwell C)								
		Heat-treated	150	160	10	39 (Rockwell C)	0.165	4.59	3000	.....	5.7 (70°–1000°F.)	60	990	16.5
Titanium-aluminum-vanadium alloy (Ti-6 Al-4V)	Ti bal., Al 6.0, V 4.0, Fe 0.25 max., C 0.08 max., H_2 0.0125 max., N_2 0.05 max.	Annealed	130	135	15	32 (Rockwell C)								
		Heat-treated	145	155	12	37 (Rockwell C)	0.161	4.46	3000	.....	5.7 (70°–1000°F.)	....	1020	16.5
Other Non-ferrous Alloys														
Antimony	Sb 100	As-cast		1.56		42	0.249	6.62	1166	0.092	5.5	131	234	11.3
Bi-Pb-In-Cd-Sn alloy (Cerrolow-117)	Bi 44.70, Pb 22.60, Sn 8.30, Cd 5.30, In 19.10	Cast	.....	5.4	1.5	12	0.32	8.85	117	0.035	13.8	....	0.347	
Bi-Pb-Sn-Cd alloy (Cerrobend)	Bi 50.00, Pb 26.70, Sn 13.30, Cd 10.00	Cast	.....	5.99	200	9.2	0.339	9.38	158	0.040	12.2	....	0.434	
Bi-Pb alloy (Cerrobase)	Bi 55.50, Pb 44.50	Cast	.....	6.4	60–70	10.2	0.380	10.5	255	0.03+	11.6	....	0.182	
Bi-Sn alloy (Cerrotru)	Bi 58.00, Sn 42.00	Cast	.....	8.0	200	22	0.315	8.72	281	0.045	8.3	....	0.520	
Columbium	....	....	35	40	....	....	0.31	....	4474	0.06	3.8	375		
Columbium 1Zr	Zr 0.8–1.2, Cb bal.	....	135	48	....	....	0.31	....	4350					
Columbium F48	W 13.5–16.5, Mn 4.5–5.5, Zr 0.85–1.15, Cb bal.	....	110	120	....	....	0.34	....	4500					
Columbium FS82	Ta 33, Zr 0.8, Cb bal.	....	50	68	....	....	0.37	....	4550					
Columbium D31	Ti 10, Mo 10, Cb bal.		90	100	....	....	0.29	....	4100					
Gold	Au 100	Hard	.....	30	2	48								
		Annealed	.....	17.5	40	28	0.692	19.3	1945	0.056	7.9	2060	14.7	10.8
18K white gold	Au 75, Ni 18.5, Zn 5.25, Cu 1.25	Hard	.....	178	.....	323								
		Annealed	93	115	25	211	0.53	14.61	1886	......	....	....	210.3	16.6
Haynes Stellite Alloy 21 A.M.S. 5385 (cast)	C 0.25, Cr 28, Ni 2.5, Mo 5.5, Co bal.	As investment cast	82.0	103	8.0	313 max.	0.299	8.30	2465	0.1006	7.83 (70°–600°F.)	100.6 (at 392°F.)	527	36.0
Hayes Stellite Alloy 31 (X-40 Cast) A.M.S. 5382 (cast)	C 0.50, Cr 25.5, Ni 11, W 7.5, Co bal.	As investment cast	80.0	113	8.0	313 max.	0.311	8.61	2500	0.0981	7.84 (70°–600°F.)	102.7 (at 392°F.)	......	36.0

Table 23-5. Properties of Metals and Alloys—(*Continued*)

Material	Nominal composition (essential elements), %	Form and condition	Typical mechanical properties: Yield strength (0.2% offset), 1000 lb./sq. in.	Typical mechanical properties: Tensile strength, 1000 lb./sq. in.	Typical mechanical properties: Elongation in 2 in., %	Typical physical constants: Hardness, Brinell	Density, lb./cu. in.	Specific gravity	Melting point, °F.	Specific heat (32°–212°F.) B.t.u./(lb.)(°F.)	Thermal expansion coefficient (32°–212°F.) × 10⁻⁶ in./(in.)(°F.)	Thermal conductivity (32°–212°F.) B.t.u./(sq. ft.)(hr.)(°F.)(in.)	Electrical resistivity (68°F.), ohms/cir. mil. ft.	Tensile modulus of elasticity × 10⁶ lb./sq. in.
Haynes Stellite Alloy 25 (L605) A.M.S. 5537 (wrought); 5797 (coated welding electrodes); 5796 (welding wire)	C 0.15 max., Cr 20.0, Ni 10.0, W 15.0, Mn 1.5, Co bal.	Wrought sheet Mill annealed	63	140	60.0	244	0.330	9.15	2425–2570	0.0924	7.61 (70°–600°F.)	64.9	532	34.2
Haynes Stellite Alloy 36 (N-155) A.M.S. 5376 (cast) A.M.S. 5767, 5768, 5532b (wrought)	C 0.40, Cr 19, Ni 10, W 15.0, Mn 1.5, Co bal.	As investment cast	90	103	5.0	298 max.	0.326	9.04	2535	0.092	7.65 (70°–600°F.)	65	532	33.8
Iridium	Ir 100	Annealed	.....	36	.....	175	0.808	22.4	4449	......	3.7	407	29.4	75
Molybdenum	Mo 99.9 plus	As-rolled Stress-relieved Recrystallized	75 75 50	100 100 70	30 30 45	250 240 190	0.369	10.22	4730	0.061	2.67	900	31.3	46.0
0.5% Titanium molybdenum alloy	Mo bal., Ti 0.5	As-rolled Stress-relieved Recrystallized	90 90 60	120 120 80	30 30 40	290 280 200	0.369	10.22	4730	0.061	3.06	816	31.3	46.0
Multimet A.M.S. 5376 (cast) A.M.S. 5767, 5768, 5532b (wrought) N-155 Alloy	Ni 19.0–21.0, Co 18.5–21.0, Cr 20.0–22.5, Mo 2.5–3.5, W 2.0–3.0, Fe bal., C 0.08–0.16, N 0.10–0.20, Cb + Ta 0.75–1.25	Mill annealed sheet Mill annealed bar Sand-cast As investment cast	58 54 54 58	118 111 98 101	49 55 23 31	194 189 180 180 max.	0.296	8.20	2340–2400	0.104	....	101 (at 392°F.)	560	29
Platinum	Pt (commercial)	Hard Annealed	....	65 27	2 28	101 65	0.773	21.4	3215	0.057	5.0	465	65	22.0
Platinum-iridium	Pt 90, Ir 10	Hard Annealed	 34	80 53	2 23	169 104	0.776	21.5	3299	......	5.0	....	146	25.0
Platinum-rhodium	Pt 90, Rh 10	Hard Annealed	..... 18.3	93 50	3 36	169 79	0.720	19.93	3353	.....	....	....	117	21.2
Platinum-ruthenium	Pt 90, Ru 10	Hard Annealed	..... 47.6	145 91	2 28	210 156	0.713	19.8	3344	......	....	....	255	31.5
Palladium	Pd (commercial)	Hard Annealed	..... 7.6	55 30	 30	91 47	0.433	12.0	2829	......	6.5	488	63.5	16.3
Palladium-ruthenium	Pd 95.5, Ru 4.5	Hard Annealed	 51	132 85	3 26	184 120	0.433	12.0	.....	......	....	....	145.5	20.4
Palladium-silver	Pd 60, Ag 40	Hard Annealed	94 15	100 47	 40	176 87	..... 0.415	..... 11.5	2530° F. liquidus 2425° F. solidus			....	264.2	22.2
Palladium alloy 934	Pd 35, Pt 10, Au 10, Ag 30, Cu 15	Annealed Heat-treated	61 125	96 146	24 10	180 Aged 280	0.430	11.9	1985	......	....	....	214.8	
Rhodium	Rh 100	Annealed	.....	80	.....	119	0.448	12.44	3571	......	4.6	611	27	50
Silver (pure)	Ag 99.9 plus	Annealed Cold-rolled	12 38	23 43	45 6	30 90	0.379	10.50	1760	0.056	10.6	2900	9.8	10.5
Sterling silver	Ag 92.5, Cu bal.	Hard Annealed	50 20	64 41	4 26	125 65	0.376	.....	1635	......	10.5	2510	12.08	10.5
Silver, coin	Ag 90, Cu bal.	Hard Annealed	53 23	65 42	4 26	125 70	0.374	.....	1615	......	10.5	2490	12.13	11
Tantalum	Ta 99.9 plus	Annealed sheet Unannealed sheet	45 100	60 110	37 3	55 123	0.60	16.6	5425	0.036	3.6	377	74.6	
Tantalum 10W	W 10, Ta bal.	Annealed	158	160	.....	.....	0.61	.....	5516					
Tin	Sn 100	As-cast	.....	2.1	70	3.9	0.263	7.29	449	0.0954	12.8	428	66	6
Tungsten	W	Hard (sheet) Annealed Hard (wire)	360 540	400 600	 0–8	..... 290	0.697 0.697	19.3 19.3	6092 6092	0.034 0.034	2.4 2.4	1390 1390	33.08 33.08	53.0 53.0

Table 23-5. Properties of Metals and Alloys—(*Continued*)

Material	Nominal composition (essential elements), %	Form and condition	Typical mechanical properties: Yield strength (0.2% offset), 1000 lb./sq. in.	Tensile strength, 1000 lb./sq. in.	Elongation in 2 in., %	Typical physical constants: Hardness, Brinell	Density, lb./cu. in.	Specific gravity	Melting point, °F.	Specific heat (32°–212°F.) B.t.u./(lb.)(°F.)	Thermal expansion coefficient (32°–212°F.) × 10⁻⁶ in./(in.)(°F.)	Thermal conductivity (32°–212°F.) B.t.u./(sq. ft.)(hr.)(°F.)(in.)	Electrical resistivity (68°F.), ohms/cir. mil. ft.	Tensile modulus of elasticity × 10⁶ lb./sq. in.
Waspaloy	C 0.10 max., Mn 0.50, S 0.030 max., Si 0.75 max., Cr 18.00–21.00, Co 12.00–15.00, Mo 3.50–5.00, Ti 2.75–3.25, Al 1.00–1.50, Zr 0.05–0.12, B 0.008 max., Fe 2.00 max., Cu 0.10, Ni remainder	Vacuum melted forgings	115	185	25	298–346	0.295	8.18	2400	.....	8.92 (70°–1500°F.)	80–160 (70°–1500°F.)	....	31.4
Udimet 500	C 0.15 max., Mn 0.75 max., Si 0.75 max., S 0.015 max., Cr 15.0–20.0, Ti 2.50–3.25, Al 2.50–3.25, Co 13.0–20.0, Mo 3.0–5.0, Fe 4.0 max., Cu 0.15 max., Ni bal.	Forged and heat-treated	125	195	12–18 (in 1 in.)	346–363	0.290	8.03	2550–2600	.....	6.8–8.8 (32°–1800°F.)	75.6 (32°–1700°F.) 177.6	....	31.05
Zinc A.S.T.M. B69	Zn bal., Pb 0.08	Hot-rolled (long.)	.....	19.5	65	38	0.258	7.14	786	0.094	18	746.07	36.56	
		Hot-rolled (transv.)	.....	23	50	.....	.....	.....	.....	.....	12.8			
		Cold-rolled (long.)	.....	21	50									
		Cold-rolled (transv.)	.....	27	40									
Zilloy-15	Zn bal., Mg 0.010, Cu 1.00	Hot-rolled (long.)	.....	29	20	61	0.259	7.18	792	0.0957	19.3	725.76	38	
		Hot-rolled (transv.)	.....	40	10	.....	.....	.....	.....	.....	11.7			
		Cold-rolled (long.)	.....	36	25	80								
		Cold-rolled (transv.)	.....	46	10									
Zilloy-40	Zn bal., Cu 1.00	Hot-rolled (long.)	.....	24	50	52	0.259	7.18	792	0.0957	16.6	....	37.5	
		Hot-rolled (transv.)	.....	30	35									
		Cold-rolled (long.)	.....	31	40	60								
		Cold-rolled (transv.)	.....	40	30									
Zinc-aluminum alloy A.S.T.M. 23	Zn (99.99% pure remainder), Al 3.5–4.3, Mg 0.03–0.08, Cu 0.25 max.	Die-cast	.....	41	10	82	0.24	6.6	727.9	0.10	15.2	783.81	38.2	
Zinc-aluminum-copper alloy A.S.T.M. 25	Zn (99.99% pure remainder), Al 3.5–4.3, Mg 0.03–0.08, Cu 0.75–1.25	Die-cast	.....	47.6	7	91	0.24	6.7	727.0	0.10	15.2	754.78	39.2	
Zirconium, commercial	O_2 0.07, C 0.15, Hf 1.90, Zr bal.	Annealed	40	65	27	B80 (Rockwell)	0.245	6.5	3380	0.118	2.9	95	246	11
Zircaloy 2	Hf 0.02, Sn 1.46, Fe 0.12, Ni 0.05, Zr bal., other 0.25	Annealed	50	75	22	B90 (Rockwell)	0.237	.....	.....	.....	3.6	95		
Zircaloy 3	Hf 0.02, Sn 0.25, Fe 0.25, Ni 0.05, Zr bal., other 0.20	Annealed	45	70	25	B85 (Rockwell)								

Table 23-6. American Iron and Steel Institute Standard Steels. Compositions*

Introduction. The information presented in the following tables represents the manufacturing practices of the many steel producers which have been reported to the American Iron and Steel Institute and related scientific and technical information which has been obtained from other sources as further described. Those practices evolved from the utilization of available raw materials and manufacturing methods to produce steel products to meet the requirements of purchasers' specifications and standards. The latter comprise specifications and standards of individual purchasers, consuming industries, standardization bodies, and specification writing bodies, including the United States government.

Although the institute is not a specification writing body, it participates with standardization bodies and specification writing bodies in the preparation of standards and specifications. Metallurgical engineers employed by steel producers participate by serving on committees of bodies which issue standards and specifications. The results of such participation are ordinarily identified by the name of the body or branch of the government, such as, for example, "A.S.T.M. Standard Specifications," "A.P.I. Standard," "A.S.M.E. Specification," "S.A.E. Standard," "A.A.R. Specification," "American Standard," "Military Specifications" and "Federal Specifications." The technical aspects of standards and specifications are prominent in the A.I.S.I. manual.

In some of the sections of the manual, some of the numbered grades of steel are identified as "A.I.S.I. Standard Steels." They are standards which embrace only the chemical composition ranges and limits of such grades. The history of such grade numbers can be traced from the standardization efforts of the Automobile Manufacturers Association early in this century to the present work by the Society of Automotive Engineers and the institute. Other bodies, including the United States government, have contributed information on properties and uses of steel products which has aided the establishment of numbered grades as standards. Among others, individual purchasers, consumers and engineers have, by their advice and recommendations, participated in the evolution of A.I.S.I. standard steels.

* Based on information from American Iron and Steel Institute's "Steel Products Manual."

Table 23-6a. American Iron and Steel Institute Standard Steels: Ladle Chemical Ranges and Limits for Basic Open-hearth and Acid Bessemer Carbon Steels

A.I.S.I. No.	Chemical composition limits, %			
	C	Mn	P, max.	S, max.
C 1008	0.10 max.	0.25/0.50	0.040	0.050
C 1010	0.08/0.13	0.30/0.60	.040	.050
C 1011	0.08/0.13	0.60/0.90	.040	.050
C 1012	0.10/0.15	0.30/0.60	.040	.050
C 1015	0.13/0.18	0.30/0.60	.040	.050
C 1016	0.13/0.18	0.60/0.90	.040	.050
C 1017	0.15/0.20	0.30/0.60	.040	.050
C 1018	0.15/0.20	0.60/0.90	.040	.050
C 1019	0.15/0.20	0.70/1.00	.040	.050
C 1020	0.18/0.23	0.30/0.60	.040	.050
C 1021	0.18/0.23	0.60/0.90	.040	.050
C 1022	0.18/0.23	0.70/1.00	.040	.050
C 1023	0.20/0.25	0.30/0.60	.040	.050
C 1024	0.19/0.25	1.35/1.65	.040	.050
C 1025	0.22/0.28	0.30/0.60	.040	.050
C 1026	0.22/0.28	0.60/0.90	.040	.050
C 1027	0.22/0.29	1.20/1.50	.040	.050
C 1029	0.25/0.31	0.60/0.90	.040	.050
C 1030	0.28/0.34	0.60/0.90	.040	.050
C 1031	0.28/0.34	0.30/0.60	.040	.050
C 1033	0.30/0.36	0.70/1.00	.040	.050
C 1035	0.32/0.38	0.60/0.90	.040	.050
C 1036	0.30/0.37	1.20/1.50	.040	.050
C 1037	0.32/0.38	0.70/1.00	.040	.050
C 1038	0.35/0.42	0.60/0.90	.040	.050
C 1039	0.37/0.44	0.70/1.00	.040	.050
C 1040	0.37/0.44	0.60/0.90	.040	.050
C 1041	0.36/0.44	1.35/1.65	.040	.050
C 1042	0.40/0.47	0.60/0.90	.040	.050
C 1043	0.40/0.47	0.70/1.00	.040	.050
C 1045	0.43/0.50	0.60/0.90	.040	.050
C 1046	0.43/0.50	0.70/1.00	.040	.050
C 1049	0.46/0.53	0.60/0.90	.040	.050
C 1050	0.48/0.55	0.60/0.90	.040	.050
C 1051	0.45/0.56	0.85/1.15	.040	.050
C 1052	0.47/0.55	1.20/1.50	.040	.050
C 1053	0.48/0.55	0.70/1.00	.040	.050
C 1055	0.50/0.60	0.60/0.90	.040	.050
C 1060	0.55/0.65	0.60/0.90	.040	.050
C 1070	0.65/0.75	0.60/0.90	.040	.050
C 1078	0.72/0.85	0.30/0.60	.040	.050
C 1080	0.75/0.88	0.60/0.90	.040	.050
C 1084	0.80/0.93	0.60/0.90	.040	.050
C 1085	0.80/0.93	0.70/1.00	.040	.050
C 1086	0.80/0.93	0.30/0.50	.040	.050
C 1090	0.85/0.98	0.60/0.90	.040	.050
C 1095	0.90/1.03	0.30/0.50	.040	.050

26 per cent chromium, 6 to 22 per cent nickel. Carbon is kept low (0.08 per cent) to minimize carbide precipitation. These alloys can be work-hardened, but heat-treatment will not cause hardening. Tensile strength in the annealed condition is about 85,000 lb./sq. in., but work hardening can increase this to 300,000 lb./sq. in. Austenitic stainless steels are tough and ductile.

They can be fabricated by all standard methods. But austenitic grades are not easy to machine—they work-harden and gall. Rigid machines, heavy cuts and high speeds are essential. Welding, however, is readily performed, although welding heat may cause chromium carbide precipitation, which depletes the alloy of some chromium and lowers its corrosion resistance. For mild service, this is not serious, but for severe corrosive service, the carbides must be put back into solution by heat-treatment. To avoid precipitation, special stainless steels stabilized with titanium, columbium, or tantalum have been developed (types 321, 347, 348). Another approach to the problem is the use of low-carbon steels such as types 304L and 316L, with 0.03 per cent maximum carbon.

Type 302 is the basic alloy of this group. Types 304 and 304L are low-carbon versions of 302. Types 316, 316L, and 317, with 2.5 to 3.5 per cent molybdenum, are the most corrosion-resistant.

In the stainless group, nickel greatly improves corrosion resistance over straight chromium stainless. Even so, the chromium-nickel steels, particularly the 18-8 alloys, perform best under oxidizing conditions, since resistance depends on an oxide film on the surface of the alloy. Reducing conditions, and chloride ions, destroy this film and bring on rapid attack. Chloride ions, combined with high tensile stresses, will cause stress-corrosion cracking.

Austenitic stainless steels have excellent resistance to nitric acid at practically all concentrations and temperatures. Most nitric acid plants are constructed with type 304. To handle sulfuric acid without inhibiters, stainless steel (type 316) can be used only below 5 per cent and above 85 per cent at temperature below the boiling point.

Cast stainless alloys are widely used in pumps, valves, and fittings. These casting are designated under the Alloy Casting Institute system. All corrosion-resistant alloys have the letter C plus a second letter (A to N)

Table 23-6b. American Iron and Steel Institute Standard Steels: Ladle Chemical Ranges and Limits for Basic Open-hearth Resulfurized Carbon Steels*

A.I.S.I. No.	Chemical composition limits, %			
	C	Mn	P, max.	S
C 1108	0.08/0.13	0.50/0.80	0.040	0.08/0.13
C 1109	0.08/0.13	0.60/0.90	.040	0.08/0.13
C 1110	0.08/0.13	0.30/0.60	.040	0.08/0.13
C 1113	0.10/0.16	1.00/1.30	.040	0.24/0.33
C 1115	0.13/0.18	0.60/0.90	.040	0.08/0.13
C 1116	0.14/0.20	1.10/1.40	.040	0.16/0.23
C 1117	0.14/0.20	1.00/1.30	.040	0.08/0.13
C 1118	0.14/0.20	1.30/1.60	.040	0.08/0.13
C 1119	0.14/0.20	1.00/1.30	.040	0.08/0.13
C 1120	0.18/0.23	0.70/1.00	.040	0.08/0.13
C 1125	0.22/0.28	0.60/0.90	.040	0.08/0.13
C 1126	0.23/0.29	0.70/1.00	.040	0.08/0.13
C 1132	0.27/0.34	1.35/1.65	.040	0.08/0.13
C 1137	0.32/0.39	1.35/1.65	.040	0.08/0.13
C 1138	0.34/0.40	0.70/1.00	.040	0.08/0.13
C 1139	0.35/0.43	1.35/1.65	.040	0.12/0.20
C 1140	0.37/0.44	0.70/1.00	.040	0.08/0.13
C 1141	0.37/0.45	1.35/1.65	.040	0.08/0.13
C 1144	0.40/0.48	1.35/1.65	.040	0.24/0.33
C 1145	0.42/0.49	0.70/1.00	.040	0.04/0.07
C 1146	0.42/0.49	0.70/1.00	.040	0.08/0.13
C 1151	0.48/0.55	0.70/1.00	.040	0.08/0.13

* For easy machining.

Table 23-6c. American Iron and Steel Institute Standard Alloy Steels

Open-hearth and electric-furnace alloy steels, bars, billets, blooms, and slabs

(See Notes, p. 23-50)

The ranges and limits in this table apply to steel not exceeding 200 sq. in. in cross-sectional area

A.I.S.I. No.	Chemical composition ranges and limits, %							
	C	Mn	P, max.	S, max.	Si	Ni	Cr	Mo
1330	0.28/0.33	1.60/1.90	0.040	0.040	0.20/0.35			
1335	0.33/0.38	1.60/1.90	.040	.040	0.20/0.35			
1340	0.38/0.43	1.60/1.90	.040	.040	0.20/0.35			
1345	0.43/0.48	1.60/1.90	.040	.040	0.20/0.35			
3140	0.38/0.43	0.70/0.90	.040	.040	0.20/0.35	1.10/1.40	0.55/0.75	
E3310	0.08/0.13	0.45/0.60	.025	.025	0.20/0.35	3.25/3.75	1.40/1.75	
4012	0.09/0.14	0.75/1.00	.040	.040	0.20/0.35	....	....	0.15/0.25
4023	0.20/0.25	0.70/0.90	.040	.040	0.20/0.35	....	....	0.20/0.30
4024	0.20/0.25	0.70/0.90	.040	.035/.050	0.20/0.35	....	....	0.20/0.30
4027	0.25/0.30	0.70/0.90	.040	.040	0.20/0.35	....	....	0.20/0.30
4028	0.25/0.30	0.70/0.90	.040	.035/.050	0.20/0.35	....	....	0.20/0.30
4037	0.35/0.40	0.70/0.90	.040	.040	0.20/0.35	....	....	0.20/0.30
4042	0.40/0.45	0.70/0.90	.040	.040	0.20/0.35	....	....	0.20/0.30
4047	0.45/0.50	0.70/0.90	.040	.040	0.20/0.35	....	....	0.20/0.30
4063	0.60/0.67	0.75/1.00	.040	.040	0.20/0.35	....	....	0.20/0.30
4118	0.18/0.23	0.70/0.90	.040	.040	0.20/0.35	....	0.40/0.60	0.08/0.15
4130	0.28/0.33	0.40/0.60	.040	.040	0.20/0.35	....	0.80/1.10	0.15/0.25
4135	0.33/0.38	0.70/0.90	.040	.040	0.20/0.35	....	0.80/1.10	0.15/0.25
4137	0.35/0.40	0.70/0.90	.040	.040	0.20/0.35	....	0.80/1.10	0.15/0.25
4140	0.38/0.43	0.75/1.00	.040	.040	0.20/0.35	....	0.80/1.10	0.15/0.25
4142	0.40/0.45	0.75/1.00	.040	.040	0.20/0.35	....	0.80/1.10	0.15/0.25
4145	0.43/0.48	0.75/1.00	.040	.040	0.20/0.35	....	0.80/1.10	0.15/0.25
4147	0.45/0.50	0.75/1.00	.040	.040	0.20/0.35	....	0.80/1.10	0.15/0.25
4150	0.48/0.53	0.75/1.00	.040	.040	0.20/0.35	....	0.80/1.10	0.15/0.25
4320	0.17/0.22	0.45/0.65	.040	.040	0.20/0.35	1.65/2.00	0.40/0.60	0.20/0.30
4337	0.35/0.40	0.60/0.80	.040	.040	0.20/0.35	1.65/2.00	0.70/0.90	0.20/0.30
E4337	0.35/0.40	0.65/0.85	.025	.025	0.20/0.35	1.65/2.00	0.70/0.90	0.20/0.30
4340	0.38/0.43	0.60/0.80	.040	.040	0.20/0.35	1.65/2.00	0.70/0.90	0.20/0.30
E4340	0.38/0.43	0.65/0.85	.025	.025	0.20/0.35	1.65/2.00	0.70/0.90	0.20/0.30
4422	0.20/0.25	0.70/0.90	.040	.040	0.20/0.35	....	....	0.35/0.45
4427	0.24/0.29	0.70/0.90	.040	.040	0.20/0.35	....	....	0.35/0.45
4520	0.18/0.23	0.45/0.65	.040	.040	0.20/0.35			0.45/0.60
4615	0.13/0.18	0.45/0.65	.040	.040	0.20/0.35	1.65/2.00	....	0.20/0.30
4617	0.15/0.20	0.45/0.65	.040	.040	0.20/0.35	1.65/2.00	....	0.20/0.30
4620	0.17/0.22	0.45/0.65	.040	.040	0.20/0.35	1.65/2.00	....	0.20/0.30
4621	0.18/0.23	0.70/0.90	.040	.040	0.20/0.35	1.65/2.00	....	0.20/0.30
4718	0.16/0.21	0.70/0.90	.040	.040	0.20/0.35	0.90/1.20	0.35/0.55	0.30/0.40
4720	0.17/0.22	0.50/0.70	.040	.040	0.20/0.35	0.90/1.20	0.35/0.55	0.15/0.25
4815	0.13/0.18	0.40/0.60	.040	.040	0.20/0.35	3.25/3.75		0.20/0.30
4817	0.15/0.20	0.40/0.60	.040	.040	0.20/0.35	3.25/3.75		0.20/0.30
4820	0.18/0.23	0.50/0.70	.040	.040	0.20/0.35	3.25/3.75	....	0.20/0.30
5015	0.12/0.17	0.30/0.50	.040	.040	0.20/0.35	....	0.30/0.50	
5046	0.43/0.50	0.75/1.00	.040	.040	0.20/0.35	....	0.20/0.35	
5115	0.13/0.18	0.70/0.90	.040	.040	0.20/0.35	....	0.70/0.90	
5120	0.17/0.22	0.70/0.90	.040	.040	0.20/0.35	....	0.70/0.90	
5130	0.28/0.33	0.70/0.90	.040	.040	0.20/0.35	....	0.80/1.10	
5132	0.30/0.35	0.60/0.80	.040	.040	0.20/0.35	....	0.75/1.00	
5135	0.33/0.38	0.60/0.80	.040	.040	0.20/0.35	....	0.80/1.05	
5140	0.38/0.43	0.70/0.90	.040	.040	0.20/0.35	....	0.70/0.90	
5145	0.43/0.48	0.70/0.90	.040	.040	0.20/0.35	....	0.70/0.90	
5147	0.45/0.52	0.70/0.95	.040	.040	0.20/0.35	....	0.85/1.15	
5150	0.48/0.53	0.70/0.90	.040	.040	0.20/0.35	....	0.70/0.90	
5155	0.50/0.60	0.70/0.90	.040	.040	0.20/0.35	....	0.70/0.90	
5160	0.55/0.65	0.75/1.00	.040	.040	0.20/0.35	....	0.70/0.90	
E50100	0.95/1.10	0.25/0.45	.025	.025	0.20/0.35	....	0.40/0.60	
E51100	0.95/1.10	0.25/0.45	.025	.025	0.20/0.35	....	0.90/1.15	
E52100	0.95/1.10	0.25/0.45	.025	.025	0.20/0.35	....	1.30/1.60	
								V
6118	0.16/0.21	0.50/0.70	.040	.040	0.20/0.35	....	0.50/0.70	0.10/0.15
6120	0.17/0.22	0.70/0.90	.040	.040	0.20/0.35	....	0.70/0.90	0.10 min.
6150	0.48/0.53	0.70/0.90	.040	.040	0.20/0.35	....	0.80/1.10	0.15 min.
								Mo
8115	0.13/0.18	0.70/0.90	.040	.040	0.20/0.35	0.20/0.40	0.30/0.50	0.08/0.15
8615	0.13/0.18	0.70/0.90	.040	.040	0.20/0.35	0.40/0.70	0.40/0.60	0.15/0.25
8617	0.15/0.20	0.70/0.90	.040	.040	0.20/0.35	0.40/0.70	0.40/0.60	0.15/0.25
8620	0.18/0.23	0.70/0.90	.040	.040	0.20/0.35	0.40/0.70	0.40/0.60	0.15/0.25
8622	0.20/0.25	0.70/0.90	.040	.040	0.20/0.35	0.40/0.70	0.40/0.60	0.15/0.25
8625	0.23/0.28	0.70/0.90	.040	.040	0.20/0.35	0.40/0.70	0.40/0.60	0.15/0.25
8627	0.25/0.30	0.70/0.90	.040	.040	0.20/0.35	0.40/0.70	0.40/0.60	0.15/0.25
8630	0.28/0.33	0.70/0.90	.040	.040	0.20/0.35	0.40/0.70	0.40/0.60	0.15/0.25

Table 23-6c. American Iron and Steel Institute Standard Alloy Steels—*(Concluded)*

A.I.S.I. No.	Chemical composition ranges and limits, %							
	C	Mn	P, max.	S, max.	Si	Ni	Cr	Mo
8637	0.35/0.40	0.75/1.00	0.040	0.040	0.20/0.35	0.40/0.70	0.40/0.60	0.15/0.25
8640	0.38/0.43	0.75/1.00	.040	.040	0.20/0.35	0.40/0.70	0.40/0.60	0.15/0.25
8642	0.40/0.45	0.75/1.00	.040	.040	0.20/0.35	0.40/0.70	0.40/0.60	0.15/0.25
8645	0.43/0.48	0.75/1.00	.040	.040	0.20/0.35	0.40/0.70	0.40/0.60	0.15/0.25
8650	0.48/0.53	0.75/1.00	.040	.040	0.20/0.35	0.40/0.70	0.40/0.60	0.15/0.25
8655	0.50/0.60	0.75/1.00	.040	.040	0.20/0.35	0.40/0.70	0.40/0.60	0.15/0.25
8660	0.55/0.65	0.75/1.00	.040	.040	0.20/0.35	0.40/0.70	0.40/0.60	0.15/0.25
8720	0.18/0.23	0.70/0.90	.040	.040	0.20/0.35	0.40/0.70	0.40/0.60	0.20/0.30
8735	0.33/0.38	0.75/1.00	.040	.040	0.20/0.35	0.40/0.70	0.40/0.60	0.20/0.30
8740	0.38/0.43	0.75/1.00	.040	.040	0.20/0.35	0.40/0.70	0.40/0.60	0.20/0.30
8742	0.40/0.45	0.75/1.00	.040	.040	0.20/0.35	0.40/0.70	0.40/0.60	0.20/0.30
8822	0.20/0.25	0.75/1.00	.040	.040	0.20/0.35	0.40/0.70	0.40/0.60	0.30/0.40
9255	0.05/0.60	0.70/0.95	.040	.040	1.80/2.20			
9260	0.55/0.65	0.70/1.00	.040	.040	1.80/2.20			
9262	0.55/0.65	0.75/1.00	.040	.040	1.80/2.20	....	0.25/0.40	
E9310	0.08/0.13	0.45/0.65	.025	.025	0.20/0.35	3.00/3.50	1.00/1.40	0.08/0.15
9840	0.38/0.43	0.70/0.90	.040	.040	0.20/0.35	0.85/1.15	0.70/0.90	0.20/0.30
9850	0.48/0.53	0.70/0.90	.040	.040	0.20/0.35	0.85/1.15	0.70/0.90	0.20/0.30

Standard Boron Steels

These steels can be expected to have 0.0005% minimum boron content

50B40	0.38/0.43	0.75/1.00	0.040	0.040	0.20/0.35	....	0.40/0.60	
50B44	0.43/0.48	0.75/1.00	.040	.040	0.20/0.35	....	0.40/0.60	
50B46	0.43/0.50	0.75/1.00	.040	.040	0.20/0.35	....	0.20/0.35	
50B50	0.48/0.53	0.75/1.00	.040	.040	0.20/0.35	....	0.40/0.60	
50B60	0.55/0.65	0.75/1.00	.040	.040	0.20/0.35	....	0.40/0.60	
51B60	0.55/0.65	0.75/1.00	.040	.040	0.20/0.35	....	0.70/0.90	
81B45	0.43/0.48	0.75/1.00	.040	.040	0.20/0.35	0.20/0.40	0.35/0.55	0.08/0.15
86B45	0.43/0.48	0.75/1.00	.040	.040	0.20/0.35	0.40/0.70	0.40/0.60	0.15/0.25
94B15	0.13/0.18	0.75/1.00	.040	.040	0.20/0.35	0.30/0.60	0.30/0.50	0.08/0.15
94B17	0.15/0.20	0.75/1.00	.040	.040	0.20/0.35	0.30/0.60	0.30/0.50	0.08/0.15
94B30	0.28/0.33	0.75/1.00	.040	.040	0.20/0.35	0.30/0.60	0.30/0.50	0.08/0.15
94B40	0.38/0.43	0.75/1.00	.040	.040	0.20/0.35	0.30/0.60	0.30/0.50	0.08/0.15

NOTE 1: Grades shown in the above list with prefix letter E generally are manufactured by the basic electric-furnace process. All others are normally manufactured by the basic open-hearth process but may be manufactured by the basic electric-furnace process with adjustments in phosphorus and sulfur.

NOTE 2: The phosphorus and sulfur limitations for each process are as follows:

Basic electric furnace........	0.025 max. %
Basic open hearth...........	0.040 max. %
Acid electric furnace.........	0.050 max. %
Acid open hearth............	0.050 max. %

NOTE 3: Minimum silicon limit for acid open-hearth or acid electric-furnace alloy steel is 0.15%.

NOTE 4: Small quantities of certain elements are present in alloy steels which are not specified or required. These elements are considered as incidental and may be present to the following maximum amounts: copper, 0.35%; nickel, 0.25%; chromium, 0.20%; and molybdenum, 0,06%.

NOTE 5: Where minimum and maximum sulfur content is shown it is indicative of resulfurized steels.

denoting increasing nickel content. Numerals indicate maximum carbon. While a rough comparison can be made between A.C.I. and A.I.S.I. types, compositions are not identical and analyses cannot be used interchangeably. Foundry techniques require a rebalancing of the wrought chemical compositions. However, corrosion resistance is not affected by these composition changes. Typical members of this group are CF-8, similar to type 304 stainless; and CF-8M, or type 316.

In addition to the C grades, there is a series of heat-resistant grades of A.C.I. cast alloys. Mention should also be made of **precipitation-hardening** stainless steels, which can be hardened by heat-treatments. Very strong at high temperatures, these steels have but moderate corrosion resistance.

Medium Alloys. One group of alloys with somewhat better corrosion resistance than stainless steels are called medium alloys. A popular member of this group is the **20 alloy,** made by a number of companies, under various trade names. Durimet 20 is the well-known cast version, containing 0.07 per cent C, 29 per cent Ni, 20 per cent Cr, 2 per cent Mo, and 3 per cent Cu. The A.C.I. designation of this alloy is CN-7M. A wrought form is known as Carpenter 20. Worthite is another proprietary 20 alloy with about 24 per cent Ni and 20 per cent Cr. The 20 alloy was originally developed to fill the need for a material with sulfuric acid resistance superior to the stainless steels.

In sulfuric acid service, the 20 alloy is most widely used. It provides satisfactory resistance to all concentrations below 175°F. Also the alloy is not attacked by nitric acid below 205°F. and 60 per cent. Cold hydrofluoric acid also can be handled below 20 per cent, but hydrochloric will corrode 20 alloy. Equipment made from 20 alloy includes pipe, tanks, pumps, valves, and agitators.

Other members of the medium alloy group include **Ni-o-nel** and **Hastelloy F.** Wrought Ni-o-nel has 40 per cent Ni, 21 per cent Cr, 3 per cent Mo, and 2.25 per cent Cu. It is resistant to reducing and oxidizing environments. Low carbon and some titanium prevent carbide precipitation during welding. It can be machined and welded. The alloy is fully resistant to all concentrations of sulfuric acid at room temperatures; and up to 60 per cent at 175°F. It is fully resistant to all concentrations of nitric acid at room temperature—even when containing small amounts of chlorides. However, Ni-o-nel is not recommended for hydrochloric acid,

Table 23-6d. Properties of Low-alloy A.I.S.I. Steels

Typical physical properties[a]

A.I.S.I. type	Melting temperature, °F.	Thermal conductivity, B.t.u./(hr.)(sq. ft.)(°F.)(ft.);(212°F.)	Coefficient of thermal expansion (0–1200°F.) per °F.	Specific heat (68–212°F.), B.t.u./(lb.)(°F.)
13XX	....	27	7.9×10^{-6b}	0.10–0.11
23XX	2600–2620	38.3[c]	8.0×10^{-6}	0.11–0.12
25XX	2610–2620	34.5–38.5[c]	7.8×10^{-6}	0.11–0.12
40XX	....	27	8.3×10^{-6b}	0.10–0.11
41XX	....	24.7[d]	....	0.11
43XX	2740–2750	21.7[c]	8.1×10^{-6}	0.107
46XX	....	27[d]	6.3×10^{-6e}	0.10–0.11
48XX	2750	26[f]	8.6×10^{-6}	
51XX	2720–2760	27–34[g]	7.4×10^{-6h}	0.10–0.11
61XX	....	27	8.1×10^{-6b}	0.10–0.11
86, 87XX	2745–2755	21.7[c]	8.2×10^{-6}	0.107
92, 94XX	....	27	8.1×10^{-6b}	0.10–0.12

[a] Density for all low-alloy steels is about 0.28 lb./cu. in.
[b] 68 to 1200°F.
[c] 120°F.
[d] 68°F.
[e] 0 to 200°F.
[f] 75°F.
[g] 32 to 212°F.
[h] 100 to 518°F.

Typical mechanical properties[a]

A.I.S.I type	Tensile strength, 1000 lb./sq. in.	Yield strength (0.2% offset), 1000 lb./sq. in.	Elongation (in 2 in.), %	Reduction of area, %	Hardness, Brinell	Impact strength (Izod), ft.-lb.
1330[b]......	122	100	19	52	248	
1335[c]......	126	105	20	59	262	
1340[c]......	137	118	19	55	285	
2317[c]......	107	72	27	71	222	84
2515[c]......	113	94	25	69	233	85
E2517[c]....	120	100	22	66	244	80
4023[d].....	120	85	20	53	255	
4032[e].....	210	182	11	49	415	
4042[f].....	235	210	10	42	461	
4053[g].....	250	223	12	40	495	
4063[h].....	269	231	8	15	534	
4130[i]......	200	170	16	49	375	25
4140[j]......	200	170	15	48	385	16
4150[k].....	230	215	10	40	444	12
4320[d].....	180	154	15	50	360	32
4337[k].....	210	140	14	50	435	18
4340[k].....	220	200	12	48	445	16
4615[d].....	100	75	18	52	...	42
4620[d].....	130	95	21	65	...	68
4640[l]......	185	160	14	52	390	25
4815[d].....	150	125	18	58	325	44
4817[d].....	...	...	15	52	355	36
4820[j]......	...	...	13	47	380	28
5120[d].....	143	114	13	45	302	6
5130[m].....	189	175	13	51	380	
5140[m].....	190	170	13	43	375	16
5150[m].....	224	208	10	40	444	
6120[n].....	125	94	21	56	...	28
6145[o]......	176	169	16	52	429	20
6150[o]......	187	179	13	42	444	13
8620[p].....	122	98	21	63	245	76
8630[p].....	162	142	14	54	325	42
8640[p].....	208	183	13	43	420	18
8650[p].....	214	194	12	41	423	
8720[p].....	122	98	21	63	245	76
8740[p].....	208	183	13	43	420	18
8750[p].....	214	194	12	41	423	
9255[p].....	232[q]	215	9	21	477	6
9261[p].....	258[r]	226	10	30	514	12

[a] Properties are for materials hardened and tempered as follows: [b] water-quenched from 1525°F., tempered at 1000°F.; [c] oil-quenched from 1525°F., tempered at 1000°F.; [d] pseudocarburized 8 hr. at 1700°F., oil-quenched, tempered 1 hr. at 300°F.; [e] water-quenched from 1525°F., tempered at 600°F.; [f] oil quenched from 1500°F., tempered at 600°F.: [g] oil-quenched from 1475°F., tempered at 600°F., [h] oil-quenched from 1450°F., tempered at 600°F.; [i] water-quenched from 1550–1600°F., tempered at 800°F.; [j] oil-quenched from 1550°F., tempered at 800°F.; [k] oil-quenched from 1525°F., tempered at 800°F.; [l] normalized at 1650°F., reheated to 1475°F., oil-quenched, tempered at 800°F.; [m] normalized at 1625°F., reheated to 1550°F., water-quenched, tempered at 800°F.; [n] carburized 10 hr. at 1680°F., pot-cooled, oil-quenched from 1525°F., tempered at 300°F.; [o] normalized at 1600°F., oil-quenched from 1575°F., tempered at 1000°F.; [p] oil-quenched, tempered at 800°F.; [q] normalized at 1650°F., reheated to 1625°F., quenched in agitated oil, tempered at 800°F.; [r] normalized at 1600°F., reheated to 1575°F., quenched in agitated oil, tempered at 800°F.

and the alloy is not so resistant against caustic solutions as nickel.

Hastelloy F (47 per cent Ni, 22 per cent Cr, 6.5 per cent Mo) is another medium alloy resistant to oxidizing and reducing media. Available in wrought or cast forms, it tends to work-harden more than austentic stainless; so fabricating procedures call for frequent annealing. Welding is similar to type 316 stainless. Its primary use has been in sulfite-pulp digesters. Alloy F has excellent resistance to stress-corrosion cracking.

High Alloys. The group of materials called high alloys all contain relatively large percentages of nickel. **Hastelloy B** contains 61 per cent Ni, 28 per cent Mo, 5.5 per cent Fe, and 1 per cent Cr. It is available in wrought and cast forms. Work hardening presents some fabrication difficulties and machining is somewhat more difficult than for type 316 stainless. Conventional welding methods can be used. The alloy has unusually high resistance to all concentrations of hydrochloric acid at all temperatures. Sulfuric acid attack is low for all concentrations at 150°F., but the rate goes up with temperature. Oxidizing acids and salts rapidly corrode Hastelloy B. But alkalies and alkaline solutions cause little damage. This alloy is also known for its high-temperature properties—up to 1600°F. in reducing environments, and to 1400°F. in oxidizing media.

The Chlorimets also belong in this group of high alloys. **Chlorimet 2** has 63 per cent Ni, 32 per cent Mo, and 3 per cent Fe. It is available only in cast form, mainly as valves and pumps. This is a tough alloy, very resistant to mechanical and thermal shock. It can be machined with carbide-tipped tools and welded with metal-arc techniques. The alloy has excellent resistance to reducing or neutral solutions. Resistance to hydrochloric at all concentrations to the boiling point is excellent.

Chlorimet 3 is the chromium variation of Chlorimet 2. It is available only in the cast form and contains 18 per cent chromium. It fills the need for an alloy capable of withstanding oxidizing and reducing situations. It does not depend on a thin film for resistance.

Hastelloy C is very similar to Chlorimet 3, with 54 per cent Ni, 16 per cent Mo, 5.5 per cent Fe, and 15.5 per cent Cr. It is available in wrought or cast forms. Fabrication, machining, and welding present no unusual problems, except that Hastelloy C tends to work-harden. Inert-gas-shielded or metal-arc-welding processes are usually recommended. Hastelloy C resists all concentrations of hydrochloric acid at room temperature. The alloy resists the effects of wet and dry chlorine, and hypochlorite and chloride solutions. As a high-temperature alloy, it is resistant to oxidizing and reducing environments to 2000°F.

Inconel (80 per cent Ni, 13 per cent Cr, 7 per cent Fe) should also be mentioned as a high alloy. It contains no molybdenum. The corrosion-resistant grade is recommended for reducing-oxidizing environments, particularly at high temperature. When heated in air, the alloy resists oxidation up to 2000°F. The alloy is outstanding in resisting corrosion by gases, when these gases are essentially sulfur-free.

Another member of this high-alloy group is the **Illium alloys,** available in cast and wrought forms. **Illium R,** for instance, the wrought alloy, contains 64 per cent Ni, 22 per cent Cr, and 5 per cent Mo. Excellent in fresh and sea water, these alloys are well suited for oxidizing acids such as sulfuric, nitric, and phosphoric. Illium G and 98, the cast alloys, have excellent resistance to sulfuric acid at most concentrations.

Nickel and Nickel Alloys. The commercial metal known as nickel is available in practically any mill form as well as castings. Cold-worked nickel is one of the most ductile materials known. It can be machined easily and joined by welding. Generally, oxidizing conditions favor corrosion while reducing conditions retard attack. Neutral alkaline solutions, sea water, and mild atmospheric conditions do not affect nickel. The metal is widely used for handling alkalies—particularly in concentrating, storing, and shipping of high-purity; caustic soda. Chlorinated solvents and phenol are often refined and stored in nickel to prevent product discoloration and contamination.

A large number of nickel-based alloys are on the market. Many have been mentioned under the discussion of alloy castings and high alloys. One of the best known

Table 23-6e. Standard C.A.B.R.A. Number Designations for Wrought Copper and Copper Alloys

Previous commonly accepted name	Number
Coppers	
Oxygen-free certified	101
Oxygen-free	102
Oxygen-free with silver	104
Oxygen-free with silver	105
Electrolytic tough pitch	110
Electrolytic tough pitch, anneal resist	111
Tough pitch with silver	113
Tough pitch with silver	114
Tough pitch with silver	116
Phosphorus-deoxidized, low residual phosphorus	120
Phosphorus-deoxidized, high residual phosphorus	122
Fire-refined tough pitch	125
Fire-refined tough pitch with silver	127
Fire-refined tough pitch with silver	128
Fire-refined tough pitch with silver	130
Arsenical tough pitch	141
Phosphorus-deoxidized arsenical	142
Phosphorus-deoxidized tellurium-bearing	145
Sulfur-bearing	147
Zirconium copper	150
Copper alloys	
Cadmium copper	162
Beryllium copper	172
Chromium copper	182
Chromium copper	184
Chromium copper	185
Gilding, 95%	210
Commercial bronze, 90%	220
Jewelry bronze, 87.5%	226
Red brass, 85%	230
Low brass, 80%	240
Cartridge brass, 70%	260
Yellow brass, 66% (sheet)	268
Yellow brass, 65% (rod and wire)	270
Yellow brass, 63%	274
Muntz metal, 60%	280
Brazing alloy	298
Leaded commercial bronze (low lead)	310
Leaded commercial bronze	314
Leaded commercial bronze (nickel-bearing)	316
Leaded red brass	320
Low leaded brass (tube)	330
High leaded brass (tube)	332
Low leaded brass	335
Medium leaded brass, 64.5%	340
High leaded brass, 64.5%	342
Medium leaded brass, 62%	350
High leaded brass, 62%	353
Extra high leaded brass	356
Free cutting brass	360
Leaded Muntz metal, uninhibited	365
Copper alloys (cont.)	
Leaded Muntz metal, arsenical	366
Leaded Muntz metal, antimonial	367
Leaded Muntz metal, phosphorized	368
Free-cutting Muntz metal	370
Forging brass	377
Architectural bronze	385
Admiralty, uninhibited	442
Admiralty, arsenical	443
Admiralty, antimonial	444
Admiralty, phosphorized	445
Naval brass, 63.5%	462
Naval brass	464
Naval brass, arsenical	465
Naval brass, antimonial	466
Naval brass, phosphorized	467
Naval brass welding and brazing rod	470
Brazing alloy	472
Naval brass, medium-leaded	482
Naval brass, high-leaded	485
Phosphor bronze E	502
Phosphor bronze A	510
Phosphor bronze	518
Phosphor bronze C	521
Phosphor bronze D	524
Phosphor bronze B	532
Phosphor bronze B-1	534
Phosphor bronze B-2	544
Phosphor bronze B-2 (P 0.50 max.)	546
Aluminum bronze D	614
Low silicon bronze B	651
High silicon bronze A	655
Manganese brass	667
Manganese bronze B	670
Manganese bronze A	675
Bronze, low fuming (nickel)	680
Bronze, low fuming	681
Aluminum brass, arsenical	687
Silicon brass	692
Silicon red brass	694
Copper nickel, 5%	704
Copper nickel, 7%	705
Copper nickel, 10%	706
Copper nickel, 11%	708
Copper nickel, 20%	710
Copper nickel, 30%	715
Copper nickel, 40%	720
Nickel silver 65-10 (sheet)	745
Nickel silver 65-18	752
Nickel silver 65-15	754
Nickel silver 65-12	757
Nickel silver 55-18	770

SOURCE: Copper and Brass Research Association, New York. In addition to alloys above, other alloys with no commonly accepted trade names have been given numbers.

Table 23-6f. Properties of Alloy Steels for Heat-resistant Tubular Products

	Nominal composition, %								Room-temperature mechanical properties*					
Alloy grade	Carbon	Manganese	Sulfur, max.	Phosphorus, max.	Silicon	Chromium	Molybdenum	Titanium	Tensile strength, lb./sq. in.	Yield strength, lb./sq. in.	Elongation, % in 2 in.	Brinell hardness	Charpy impact, ft.-lb.	Recorded service temperature, °F.
Carbon steel, killed	0.10–0.20	0.30–0.60	0.045	0.04	0.25				60,000	42,500	46	117	46	1050
½ Mo	0.10–0.20	0.30–0.80	0.045	0.045	0.10–0.50	....	0.45–0.66		64,000	49,000	47	141	53	1050
½ Cr-½ Mo	0.10–0.20	0.30–0.61	0.045	0.045	0.10–0.30	0.50–0.81	0.45–0.66		62,000	43,000	50	140	52	1075
1 Cr-½ Mo	0.15 max.	0.30–0.61	0.045	0.045	0.50 max.	0.80–1.25	0.45–0.66		69,000	34,500	40	130	46	
1¼ Cr-½ Mo	0.15 max.	0.30–0.60	0.03	0.03	0.50–1.00	1.00–1.50	0.45–0.66		74,000	55,000	42	153	53	
2 Cr-½ Mo	0.15 max.	0.30–0.60	0.03	0.03	0.50 max.	1.65–2.35	0.45–0.66		69,500	46,000	44	140	52	1150
2¼ Cr-1 Mo	0.15 max.	0.30–0.60	0.03	0.03	0.50 max.	1.90–2.60	0.87–1.13		70,000	45,000	49	147	54	1175
3 Cr-1 Mo	0.15 max.	0.30–0.60	0.03	0.03	0.50 max.	2.65–3.35	0.80–1.06		69,000	40,000	53	146	53	1175
5 Cr-½ Mo	0.15 max.	0.30–0.60	0.03	0.03	0.50 max.	4.00 6.00	0.45–0.65		70,000	38,500	47	139	46	1200
5 Cr-½ Mo-Si	0.15 max.	0.30–0.60	0.03	0.03	1.00–2.00	4.00–6.00	0.45–0.65		88,000	59,000	40	172	60	1300
5 Cr-½ Mo-Ti	0.12 max.	0.30–0.60	0.03	0.03	0.50 max.	4.00–6.00	0.45–0.65	4 × carbon (0.70 max.)	62,500	35,000	52	123	58	1250
7 Cr-½ Mo	0.15 max.	0.30–0.60	0.03	0.03	0.50–1.00	6.00–8.00	0.45–0.65		72,500	37,500	45	148	40	1250
9 Cr-1 Mo	0.15 max.	0.30–0.60	0.03	0.03	0.25–1.00	8.00–10.00	0.90–1.10		73,500	43,500	41	145	46	1350

* Fully annealed.

Table 23-6g. Properties of New High-strength Steels

Steel designation		Section thickness, in.	Specified min. strengths: Yield point, lb./sq. in.	Specified min. strengths: Tensile strength, lb./sq. in.	Intended for welding
Carbon steels	A.S.T.M. A 7	All	33,000	60,000	Depends on chemistry
	A.S.T.M. A 373	To 4, incl.	32,000	58,000	Yes
	A.S.T.M. A 36	To 4, incl.	36,000	60,000	Yes
High-strength	A.S.T.M. A 440	To ¾, incl.	50,000	70,000	No
High-strength, low-alloy	A.S.T.M. A 441	¾–1½, incl.	46,000	67,000	Yes
	A.S.T.M. A 242	1½–4, incl.	42,000	63,000	Depends on chemistry
Heat-treated alloy steels	Proposed A.S.T.M. spec.	To 2½, incl.	100,000*	115,000	Yes
		2½–4, incl.	90,000*	105,000	

* 0.2 per cent offset yield strength.

Typical producers of these new high-strength steels include the following: U.S. Steel (Cor-Ten, Man-Ten, Tri-Ten, T-1); Inland Steel (Hi-Steel); Kaiser Steel (Kaisalloy); Bethlehem Steel (Mayari-R); Great Lakes Steel (NAX); Republic Steel (RDS); and Youngstown Sheet and Tube (Yoloy).

of these is **Monel**, with 67 per cent Ni, 30 per cent Cu. It is available in all standard forms. This nickel-copper alloy is ductile and tough, and can be readily fabricated and joined. Its corrosion resistance is generally superior to its components, being more resistant than nickel in reducing environments and more resistant than copper in oxidizing environments. The alloy can be used for relatively dilute sulfuric acid (below 80 per cent), although aeration will result in increased corrosion. Monel will handle hydrofluoric acid up to 92 per cent and 235°F. Alkalies have little effect on this alloy, but it will not stand up against very highly oxidizing or reducing environments.

Aluminum and Alloys. Aluminum and its alloys are made in practically all the forms in which metals are produced, including castings. Thermal conductivity of aluminum is 60 per cent of pure copper, and unalloyed aluminum is used in many heat-transfer applications. Its high electrical conductivity makes aluminum popular in electrical applications. Aluminum is one of the most workable of metals, and it is usually joined by inert-gas-shielded arc-welding techniques.

Commercially pure aluminum has a tensile strength of 10,000 lb./sq. in., but it can be strengthened by cold working. One limitation of aluminum is that strength declines greatly above 300°F. Where strength is important, 400°F. is usually considered the highest permissible safe temperature for aluminum. However, aluminum has excellent low-temperature properties—it can be used at −420°F.

Aluminum has high resistance to atmospheric conditions, as well as industrial fumes and vapors, and fresh, brackish, or salt waters. Many mineral acids attack aluminum, although the metal can be used with concentrated nitric acid (above 82 per cent) and sulfuric (99 per cent). And aluminum cannot be used with strong caustic solutions although mild basic solutions, when inhibited, will not attack aluminum. Salts of strong acids and weak bases, except salts of halogens, have little effect. Most organic acids will not corrode aluminum.

It should be noted that a number of aluminum alloys are available. Many have improved mechanical properties over pure aluminum. The wrought heat-treatable aluminum alloys have tensile strengths of 13,000 to 33,000 lb./sq. in. as annealed; when fully hardened strengths can go as high as 83,000 lb./sq. in. However, aluminum alloys usually have lower corrosion resistance than the pure metal. The **alclad** alloys have been developed to overcome this shortcoming. Alclad consists of an aluminum layer metallurgically bonded to a core alloy.

Copper and Alloys.* Copper and its alloys are widely used in chemical processing, particularly where heat and electrical conductivity are important factors. The thermal conductivity of copper is twice that of aluminum and 90 per cent that of silver.

A large number of copper alloys are available, including **brasses** (Cu-Zn), **bronzes** (Cu-Sn), and **cupronickels.** Copper has excellent low-temperature properties and is used at −320°F. Brazing and soldering are common joining methods for copper, although welding, while difficult, is possible. Generally, copper has high resistance to industrial and marine atmospheres, sea water, alkalies, and solvents. Oxidizing acids rapidly corrode copper. However, the alloys have somewhat different properties than commercial copper.

Brasses with up to 15 per cent Zn are ductile but difficult to machine. Machinability improves with increasing zinc up to 36 per cent Zn. Brasses with less than 20 per cent Zn have corrosion resistance equivalent to copper, but with better tensile strengths. Brasses with 20 to 40 per cent Zn have lower corrosion resistance and are subject to dezincification and stress-corrosion cracking, especially when ammonia is present.

Bronzes, commonly called phosphor bronzes, are similar to brasses in mechanical properties and to high-zinc brasses in corrosion resistance (except that bronzes are not affected by stress cracking). **Aluminum and silicon bronzes** are very popular in the process industries because they combine good strength with corrosion resistance.

Cupronickels (10 to 30 per cent Ni) are becoming very important as copper alloys. They have the highest corrosion resistance of all copper alloys and find application as heat-exchanger tubing. Resistance to sea water is particularly outstanding.

Lead and Alloys. Chemical lead, acid lead, and copper lead are the grades usually specified for chemical construction. The small amounts of silver and copper in these leads add to corrosion resistance and improve creep and fatigue resistance.

Antimony hardens lead and improves its physical characteristics up to the boiling point of water. However, it lowers the melting point, and while it may not detract from lead's corrosion resistance, it seldom improves it.

Tellurium in extruded lead products retards grain growth and increases fatigue resistance. Corrosion resistance is comparable with chemical lead.

In lead-clad products, lead's corrosion resistance is combined with the strength of steel or the high heat transfer of copper.

Vessels designed for operation at high temperatures, fluctuating temperatures, or vacuum are usually constructed of steel with a lining of lead bonded directly to the steel. Heating coils of copper with an external lead cladding are in common use, as are steel pipes and valves with an internal lead cladding.

Among the many variables determining the suitability of lead may be temperature, concentration, grade of lead or type of alloy, presence of oxygen, degree of abrasion erosion, and presence of impurities.

Lead relies for its high resistance to corrosion upon a thin protective coating that forms on its surface. When this coating is one of the highly insoluble lead salts such as the sulfate, carbonate, or phosphate, resistance to corrosion is high and the environment generally promotes self-healing upon mechanical injury to the film.

On the other hand, if a soluble film forms such as

(Continued on page 23-58)

* To reduce confusion in designating the various copper alloys, Copper and Brass Research Association (C.A.B.R.A.) has assigned numbers to wrought copper alloys. (See Table 23-5.)

Table 23-7a. Typical Physical and Mechanical Properties of Plastics (73.4°F.)

Material	Specific gravity	Thermal conductivity, B.t.u./(hr.)(sq. ft.)(°F.)(ft.)	Coefficient of thermal expansion, 10^{-5}/°F.	Specific heat, B.t.u./(lb.)(°F.)	Flammability, in./min.	Modulus of elasticity in tension, 10^5 lb./sq. in.	Tensile strength, 1000 lb./sq. in.	Elongation (in 2 in.), %	Hardness, Rockwell	Impact strength (Izod notched), ft.-lb./in. notch	Modulus of elasticity in flex, 10^5 lb./sq. in.	Flexural strength, 1000 lb./sq. in.	Compression strength (0.1% offset), 1000 lb./sq. in.	Maximum recommended service temperature, °F.	Heat distortion temperature, °F. (264 lb./sq. in.)
Acrylonitrile butadiene styrene (ABS):															
High-impact	1.04–1.06	0.08–0.12	4.7	0.35–0.38	1.3	2.6–2.9	4.5–8.5	5–100	R85–118	3–6	37–45	7.5–11	......	150	185–215
Extra-high impact	1.01–1.06	0.08–0.12	4.7–5.6	0.35–0.38	1.3	2.1–2.6	5–8	20–50	R85–100	5–9	......	6.8–8.0	......	......	185
Low-temperature impact	1.02	0.08–0.12	4.7–5.6	0.35–0.38	1.3	1.0	3–5	30–200	R30–65	6–10	......	3–4	......	......	175–185
Acetal polymer	1.425	0.13	4.5	0.35	1.1	4.1	10.0	15 (total)	M94, R120	1.4	4.1	14.1	5.2	185	212
Acrylics, cast:															
General-purpose, type 1	1.17–1.19	0.12	4.5	0.35	0.5–2.2	3.5–4.5	6–9	2–7	M80–90	0.4	3.5–4.5	12–14	12–14	140–160	150–180
General-purpose, type 2	1.18–1.20	0.12	4.5	0.35	0.5–1.8	4.0–5.0	8–10	2–7	M96–102	0.4	4.0–5.0	15–17	14–18	180–200	190–225
Alkyds, molded	2.22–2.24	0.35–0.60	1–3	......	Self-ext.	......	3–4	......	......	0.30–0.35	......	7–10	16–20	350	350–400
Cellulose acetate:															
Medium, type 1	1.23–1.34	0.10–0.19	4.4–9.0	0.3–0.4	0.5–2.0	......	2.7–6.5	18–54	R68–115	1.1–4.0	1.1–3.5	......	14–25		
Hard, type 2	1.29–1.34	0.10–0.19	4.4–9.0	0.3–0.4	0.5–2.0	......	6–8.5	6–31	R112–123	0.4–1.9	2.6–4.0	......	25–36		
Soft, type 3	1.27–1.34	0.10–0.19	4.4–9.0	0.3–0.4	......	......	4.6–7.5	17–40	R106–121	0.6–2.3	1.9–3.4	......	22–33		
Cellulose acetate butyrate (CAB):															
Medium, type 1	1.16–1.24	0.10–0.19	6–9	.3–0.4	0.5–1.5	......	2.9–5.7	47–66	R79–112	1.0–4.3	0.93–1.7	No break	......	......	130–172
Hard, type 2	1.19–1.25	0.10–0.19	6–9	0.3–0.4	0.5–1.5	......	5.0–6.8	38–54	R108–114	0.6–2.4	1.5–2.0	No break	......	......	158–210
Soft, type 3	1.15–1.22	0.10–0.19	6–9	0.3–0.4	0.5–1.5	......	1.9–3.8	60–74	R59–95	2.5–5.4	0.74–1.3	No break	......	......	121–137
Chlorinated polyether (Penton)	1.4	11.0	6.6	......	Self-ext.	......	6	130 (total)	R100	0.4	1.3	5	......	255	185
Epoxies, cast:															
General-purpose	1.12–2.4	0.1–0.8	1.7–5.0	......	0.3 to self-ext.	......	2–12	2–6	M75–110	0.2–0.7	0.4–1.5	8–20	20–40	175	250
Heat-resistant	1.15–3.2	0.1–0.8	2.8–3.3	......		......	5–14	2–5	M90–110	0.2–1.5	0.4–1.5	8–20	25–40	400	500
Fluorocarbons:															
Polytrifluorochlorethylene	2.15	0.145	3.88	0.22	Non	1.9–3.0	4.6–5.7	125–175	R110–115	3.5–3.6	2–2.5	3.5	2.0	380	150–178
Polytetrafluoroethylene	2.1–2.3	0.14	5.5	0.25	Non	0.38–0.65	2.5–3.5	250–350	J75–95	2.5–4.0	0.6	1.6	0.7–1.8	500	
Fluorinated ethylene-propylene	2.14–2.17	0.11	8.3–10.5	0.28	Non	0.5–0.7	2.5–3.5	300–900	D55	No break	0.8	......	1.6	400	
Melamines, unfilled	1.48	......	......	......	Self-ext.	......	......	......	......	......	13	11–14	40–45	210	295
Polyamides, molded:															
Nylon 66 (0.2% water)	1.14	0.14	5.5	0.3–0.5	Self-ext.	4.1	11.8	60	M79, R118	0.9	4.1	13.8	......	275–300	
Nylon 6	1.14	0.10–0.14	4.6–5.4	0.4	Self-ext.	2.5–3.4	10.2–12	300	R105–118	1.2–3.0	......	......	7–9.7	225–250	145
Nylon 11	1.1	......	5.5	0.58	Self-ext.	1.8–1.9	8.5	100–120	A50	3.3–3.6	......	......	......	212–250	
Polycarbonates	1.20	0.11	3.9	......	Self-ext.	3.2	9–10.5	60–100 (total)	M70, R118	12–16	3.8	11–13	11	250–300	280–290
Phenolics, molded (no filler)	1.24–1.90	......	2.4	......	Self-ext.	7–15	4.5–7.5	......	M105–120	0.2–0.6	7–15	7–12	18–32	300–425	300–350
Phenolics, cast:															
Type 1, mechanical and chemical	1.31	......	3.3–4.4	......	Self-ext.	4–5	6–9	......	M93–120	0.30–0.45	3–5	11–17	14–18	......	170–195
Polyester, cast:															
Allyl type	1.30–1.45	0.12	2.8–5.6	0.26–0.55	......	2–3	4.5–7	......	M92–118	0.18–0.32	3–8	6–14	20–26	300	120–320
Styrene type, rigid	1.12–1.46	0.10–0.12	3.9–5.6	0.30–0.55	......	1.5–6.5	4–10	<5	M65–115	0.18–0.40	3–9	7–19	12–37	250–300	120–420
Silicones, molded:															
Mineral filler	1.8–2.0	0.09.–0.97	2.78–3.23	......	0–78	......	4–4.3	......	M89	0.25–0.30	10–13	6.8–7.5	16–20	>700	>900

Table 23-7a. Typical Physical and Mechanical Properties of Plastics (73.4°F.)—*(Concluded)*

Material	Specific gravity	Thermal conductivity, B.t.u./(hr.)(sq. ft.)(°F.)(ft.)	Coefficient of thermal expansion, 10^{-5}/°F.	Specific heat, B.t.u./(lb.)(°F.)	Flammability, in./min.	Modulus of elasticity in tension, 10^5 lb./sq. in.	Tensile strength, 1000 lb./sq. in.	Elongation (in 2 in.), %	Hardness, Rockwell	Impact strength (Izod notched), ft.-lb./in. notch	Modulus of elasticity in flex, 10^5 lb./sq. in.	Flexural strength, 1000 lb./sq. in.	Compression strength (0.1% offset), 1000 lb./sq. in.	Maximum recommended service temperature, °F.	Heat distortion temperature, °F. (264 lb./sq. in.)
Polystyrenes:															
General-purpose	1.04–1.07	0.058–0.09	3.3–4.8	0.30	1–1.5	4–5	5–8	1.5–2.5	M68–80	0.25–0.35	4–5	8–15	11.5–16	140–160	165–190
Heat, chemical resistant	1.05–1.11	0.046–0.09	3.6–3.8	0.30	0.4–1.0	4–6	10–11	1–4	M78–88	0.25–0.50	4–6	11–17	12–17	175–190	200–220
Polyethylene:															
Type I, low density	0.91–0.925	0.19	8.9–11.0	0.55	1.0	0.21–0.27	1.4–2.5	500–725	C73 (Shore)	......	13–27	......	......	250	175–200 (soft. pt.)
Type II, medium density	0.926–0.940	0.19	8.3–16.7	0.55	1.0	......	2.0	200	D55 (Shore)	......	43	......	......	250	215 (soft pt.)
Type III, high density	0.942–0.960	0.19	8.3–16.7	0.46–0.55	1.0	......	2.9–4.0	25–400	D60 (Shore)	0.4–6.0	90–125	......	......	250	250 (soft pt.)
Polypropylene	0.89–0.91	0.08	6.2	0.46	......	1.4–1.7	5.0	500–700 (total)	R85–95	1.02	1.4–1.7	8.1	......	275–320	130–140
Polyvinyl butyral:															
Rigid	1.08–1.12	......	4.4–12.7	0.4	Slow	3.5–4.0	4–8.5	5–60	L95	1.2	......	10	......	115	61.5
Flexible	1.05	......	......	......	......	......	0.5–3	150–450	10–100 (Shore)						
Polyvinyl dichloride	1.5	......	......	......	......	0.40	7.5–9.0	4.5	R117	0.8–5.0	......	14–17	......	210	
Polyvinyl chloride:															
Type I, rigid	1.32–1.44	0.07–0.10	2.8–3.3	......	Self-ext.	3.5–4.0	5.5–9.0	5–25	R117	0.25–1.2	3.8–5.4	12–16	11–12	150–165	140–170
Type II, flexible	1.20–1.55	0.07–0.10	......	......	Self-ext.	0.004–0.03	1–3.5	200–450	......	Variable	......	......	......	150–220	
Polyvinylidene chloride (saran)	1.68–1.75	0.053	8.78	0.32	Self-ext.	0.4–0.8	3–5	15–25	M50–65	0.3–1.0	......	4–7	7.5–8.5	150–212	130–150
Ureas, molded:															
Cellulose-filled	1.52	......	......	......	Self-ext.	13–16	5–10	1.0	E94	0.24–0.35	......	10–18	25–38	......	266–280
Reinforced plastics															
Phenolic															
Glass fabric filled	1.80–1.95	0.15	5.0–6.0	0.23	Self-ext.	34	58	......	......	15	48	87	47.5	525	500–600
Asbestos fiber	1.908	0.17	......	0.30	Self-ext.	55	46.1	......	......	......	49.8	52.5	20.8	>350	500–600
Polyester:															
Glass fiber reinforced	1.6–2.0	0.15	1.2–4	0.3	Self-ext.	......	25–55	......	M100	13–18	20–38	40–75	25–45	250–400	390–550
Silicones:															
Glass fabric reinforced	1.6–1.93	......	......	......	......	......	20–40	......	......	......	18–32	23–47	9–24	450–500	
Epoxies:															
Woven-glass filled	1.6–1.85	......	......	......	......	......	40–85	......	M100	12–18	30–46	65–120	45–52	250–400	
Filament-wound	1.7–2.2	20–60	......	......	Self-ext.	......	80–250	......	M98–120	40–60	50–70	100–270	45–70	500	350–400

A.S.T.M. test results referring to thermoplastics: sp. gr., D792; thermal conductivity, C177; coefficient of thermal expansion, D696; flammability, D635; modulus of elasticity, D638, D790; tensile strength, D638, D651; elongation, D638; hardness, D785; impact strength, D256; flexibility strength, D790; compression strength, D695; heat distortion temperature, D648.

Table 23-7b. Properties and Chemical Resistance of Organic Coatings[a]

	Alkyd						Acrylic	Bitumi-nous	Cellulose			Epoxy					
	Alkyd	Alkyd-amine	Alkyd-phenolic	Alkyd-silicone	Alkyd-urea	Styren-ated alkyd			Nitro-cellulose	Buty-rate	Ethyl cellulose	Epoxy-amine	Epoxy-ester	Epoxy-furane	Epoxy-melamine	Epoxy phenolic	Epoxy-urea
Chemical resistance:																	
Exterior durability	E	E	E	E	E	F	E	F	E	E	E	G	E	E	E	E	VG
Salt spray	E	VG	E	E	G	G	E	E	E	E	......	VG	E	E	E	E	E
Solvents, alcohols	F	G	G	G	G	G	P	P	G	G	P	G	F	E	E	E	E
Solvents, gasoline	G	E	E	E	E	F	G	P	G	G	P	E	E	E	E	E	E
Solvents, hydrocarbons	G	E	E	G	E	E	F	P	F	F	F	E	VG	E	E	E	E
Solvents, esters, ketones	P	P	F	P	F	P	P	P	P	P	P	VG	F	G	VG	E	VG
Solvents, chlorinated	P	P	P	P	P	P	P	P	P	P	P	G	F	E	E	E	E
Beverages, food	F	G	VG	G	G	VG	VG	E	G	G	E	E	VG	E	E	E	E
Salts	VG	E	E	VG	E	E	VG	G	G	VG	G	E	E	E	E	E	E
Ammonia	P	P	P	P	P	P	P	....	P	P	G	G	P	E	P	F	P
Alkalis[b]	F, P	VG, G	F, P	VG, G	G, G	G, VG	G, F	E	P, P	P, P	G, G	E, E	E, E	E	E, E	E, E	E, E
Acids, mineral[c]	F, P, P	G, F, P	VG, G, F	G, P, P	F, P, P	G, F, P	G, F, P	G, –, –[e]	E, G, F	G, F, P	G, F, P	E, VG, G	G, F, P	G	E, VG, G	E, E, E	E, VG, F
Acids, oxidizing[c]	P, P, P	F, P, P	G, F, P	P, P, P	F, P, P	F, P, P	F, P, P	....	P, P, P	P, P, P	F, P, P	G, P, P	F, P, P	F	G, P, P	E, VG, P	F, P, P
Acids, organic (acetic, formic, etc.)[c]	P, P, P	P, P, P	F, P, P	P, P, P	P, P, P	P, P, P	P, P, P	E, –, –[f]	P, P, P	P, P, P	G, –, –	P, F, P	F, P, P	F, G	G, F, P	E, E, VG	F, P, P
Acids, organic (oleic, stearic, etc.)	F	G	VG	G	F	F	F	P	F	F	......	F	E	E	E	E	E
Acid, phosphoric	P	P	P	P	P	P	P	E	P	P	......	G	P	E	G	E	G
Water (salt, fresh)	F	G	G	G	F	G	E	E	G	E	E	G	VG	E	G	E	G
Physical properties:																	
Sward rocker hard. (8th day)	24	30	34	16–30	28	28	24	....	30	26	25–30	36	30	24	36	44	34
Flexibility	E	VG	G	VG	VG	G	E	E	E	E	E	F	E	E	VG	VG, E	VG
Abrasion resistance, cycles[d]	3500	>5000	>5000	4000	>5000	>5000	2500	....	2500	2500	......	>5000	>5000	......	>5000	>5000	>5000
Max. svc. temp., °F	200	250	250	450	225	200	180	200	180	180	300	400	300	350	400	400	400
Toxicity	None	Slight	None	None	Slight	Slight	None	....	None	None	None	None	None	None	None	None	None
Impact resistance	VG	E	G	G	E	G	E	E	E	E	E	G	E	G	VG	VG	G
Dielec. properties	G	G	VG	E	G	G	VG	....	P	G	E	VG	VG	G	VG	VG	VG
Adhesion to:																	
Ferrous metals	E	E	E	VG	E	F	VG	E	VG	VG	P	E	E	E	E	E	E
Nonferrous metals	F	E	E	VG	VG	F	VG	E	G	G	P	E	E	E	E	E	E
Old paints	VG	G	G	E	G	VG	P	....	P	P	P	G	VG	E	P	P	P

[a] These data are intended only as a preliminary selection guide. Final selections should be made after consulting with coating formulator.
Key: E = excellent; VG = very good; G = good; F = fair; P = poor. Source: *Materials in Design Engineering*, Mid. Oct. 1962 issues p. 364-7.
[b] Two ratings are for dilute (20%) and concentrated, respectively.
[c] Three ratings are for dilute (10%), medium (10–30%), and concentrated, respectively.
[d] Taber GS-10 wheel.
[e] Not recommended with nitric acid.
[f] Not recommended with strong acetic acid solutions.

Table 23-7b. Properties and Chemical Resistance of Organic Coatings[a]—(*Concluded*)

	Chlorinated polyether	Chlorinated polypropylene	Fluorocarbon (air-dried)	Furane	Phenolic	Polyamide (nylon)	Polyester	Polyethylene	Rubber: Chlorinated rubber	Rubber: Neoprene	Rubber: Hypalon	Rubber: Viton	Silicone	Urethane	Vinyl	Vinyl-alkyd (approx. 1:1)
Chemical resistance:																
Exterior durability	E	E	E	G	E	P	E	P	E	E	E	E	E	E	E	E
Salt spray	E	E	E	G	E	F	E	VG	E	E	E	E	E	E	E	E
Solvents, alcohols	E	G	E	E	E	G	G	E	E	E	....	E	F	F–E	F	G
Solvents, gasoline	E	G	E	E	E	G	E	P	G	F	P	E	F	F–G	E	E
Solvents, hydrocarbons	E	P	E	E	E	....	E	P	P	P	....	E	VG	F–E	G	P
Solvents, esters, ketones	E	P	P	G	F	....	P	G	P	G	P	P	P	F	P	P
Solvents, chlorinated	E	P	E	E	F	....	P	P	P	P	P	E	P	P–E	P	P
Beverages, food	E	G	E	E	E	....	G	E	G	F	F	E	F	VG	E	F
Salts	E	E	E	E	E	....	G	E	E	E	E	E	G	E	E	G
Ammonia	E	G	E	E	P	G	P	E	G	E	P	E	P	P	E	P
Alkalis[b]	E	VG, VG	E, E	E	P, P	G, G	P	P, G	E, E	E, E	E, F	E, E	E, F	VG, F	E, E	G, P
Acids, mineral[c]	E, E, E	E, G, G	E, E, E	G	G, F, P	P, P, P	E	....	E, E, G	E, G, P	E, E, E	E, E, E	G, G, P	G, F, P	E, E, G	VG, G, P
Acids, oxidizing[c]	E, E, E	E, E, G	E, E, E	P	G, F, P	....	P	VG, VG, VG	E, E, F	F, P, P	G, F, P	E, E, E	P, P, P	G, F, P	E, VG, G	P, P, P
Acids, organic (acetic, formic, etc.)[c]	E, E, E	G, P, P	E, E, E	F, G	G, F, P	P, P, P	P	VG, F, P	G, P, P	P, P, P	F, P, P	E, E, E	P, P, P	G, F, P	E, P, P	G, F, P
Acids, organic (oleic, stearic, etc.)	E	G	E	E	E	VG	F	G	F	P	F	E	G	E	E	E
Acid, phosphoric	E	G	E	E	F	....	F	VG	G	VG	E	E	F	E	E	F
Water (salt, fresh)	E	E	E	E	E	F	G	E	E	E	E	E	E	E	E	E
Physical properties:																
Sward rocker hard. (8th day)	....	24	<10	28	38	....	30	....	24	<10	<10	<10	16	35–65	20	26
Flexibility	F	VG	G	F	G	G	G	E	VG	E	E	G	F	E	E	E
Abrasion resistance, cycles[d]	>5000	5000	1000	....	>5000	....	3500	....	>5000	5000	5000	1000	2500	>5000	>5000	2500
Max. svc. temp., °F	300	250	550	300	350	300	200	225	200	200	250	550	550	300	150	180
Toxicity	None	Slight	Slight	None	None	....	None	None	Slight	None	....	Slight	None	Slight	None	None
Impact resistance	F	G	E	F	G	VG	F	E	G	E	E	E	F	E	E	E
Dielec. properties	E	E	E	F	E	G	G	E	E	F	VG	E	E	E	E	G
Adhesion to:																
Ferrous metals	VG	G	VG	F	E	VG	F	E	F	VG	VG	VG	F	E	G	VG
Non-ferrous metals	G	VG	VG	F	E	VG	F–P	E	VG	VG	VG	VG	E	E	VG	G
Old paints	P	E	P	E	G	....	P	P	F	....	F	P	E	G	F	P

Table 23-8a. Properties of Stoneware and Porcelain

	Stoneware	Porcelain
Specific gravity	2.2–2.7	2.4–2.9
Hardness, Mohs scale	6.5	7.5
Modulus of rupture, lb./sq. in.	3–7,000	8–15,000
Modulus of elasticity, lb./sq. in.	$5\text{–}10 \times 10^6$	$10\text{–}15 = 10^6$
Compressive strength, lb./sq. in.	40–60,000	60–90,000
Pore volume, %	1.5	0.2–0.5
Water absorption, %	0.5–4.0	0–0.5
Linear thermal expansion, per °F.	2.4×10^{-6}	2.5×10^{-6}
Thermal conductivity, Btu./(sq. ft.)(hr.)(°F.)/(in.)	8–22	8–10

nitrate, acetate, or chloride, little protection is afforded, and the lead may corrode further. Likewise, if insoluble protective coatings are removed mechanically (as by abrasion or erosion) or dissolved chemically (as in the case of some mixed corrosives), corrosion resistance is similarly reduced.

Dilute nitric acid is an example of a corrosive which reacts with lead to form a soluble salt. It is also capable of reacting with lead sulfate to reduce its function as a protective coating depending upon the concentration. Obviously where lead linings are protected by a brick lining, the protective coating or film will not be disturbed.

Titanium and Zirconium. Titanium has become important as a construction material only since 1946. It is strong and of medium weight. Corrosion resistance is very superior in oxidizing and mild reducing media (a new development is a Ti-Pd alloy with superior resistance in reducing environments). Titanium is usually not bothered by impingement attack, crevice corrosion, and pitting attack in sea water. Its general resistance to sea water is superior to stainless. Titanium is resistant to nitric acid at all concentrations except with red fuming nitric. The metal also resists ferric chloride, cupric chloride, and other hot chloride solutions. However, there are a number of disadvantages to titanium which have limited its use. One is cost—on a per pound basis titanium is 15 times more expensive than type 316 stainless. And titanium is not easy to form—it has a high spring-back and tends to gall, and welding must be carried out in an inert atmosphere. However, prices are dropping and fabrication techniques are becoming "standard," all promising increasing titanium applications in the process industries.

Zirconium is another relatively new material, originally considered as a construction material for atomic reactors. Reactor-grade zirconium contains very little hafnium, which would alter zirconium's neutron-absorbing properties. Commercial-grade zirconium, for process applications, however, contains 2.5 per cent hafnium. Zirconium resembles titanium from a fabrication standpoint. All welding must be done under an inert atmosphere. Zirconium also resembles titanium in corrosion resistance; however, in hydrochloric acid, zirconium is more resistant. It also resists all chlorides except ferric and cupric. There are a number of alloys of titanium and zirconium, with mechanical properties superior to those of the pure metals. The zirconium alloys are referred to as "Zircaloys."

Tantalum. The physical properties of tantalum are similar to mild steel, except that tantalum has a higher melting point. Tantalum is ductile and malleable and can be worked into intricate forms. It can be welded by a number of techniques. The metal is practically inert to many oxidizing and reducing acids (except fuming sulfuric). It is attacked by hot alkalies and hydrofluoric acid. Its cost limits use to heating coils, bayonet heaters, coolers, and condensers operating under severe conditions.

Table 23-8b. Properties of Glass and Silica

	Pyroceram	96% silica	Borosilicate	Glass lining
Specific gravity, 77°F	2.60	2.18	2.23	2.56
Water absorption, %	0.00	0.00	0.00	
Gas permeability	Gastight	Gastight	Gastight	
Softening temp., °F	2282	2732	1508	
Specific heat, 77°F, B.t.u./(lb.)(°F.)	0.185	0.178	0.186	
Mean specific heat (77°–752°F.)	0.230	0.224	0.233	
Thermal conductivity, mean temp. 77°F., B.t.u./(sq. ft.)(hr.)(°F.)/(in.)	25.2	....	7.5	
Linear thermal expansion, per °F. (77°–572°F.)	32×10^{-7}	4.4×10^{-7}	18×10^{-7}	
Modulus of elasticity, lb./sq. in. $\times 10^{-6}$	17.3	9.6	9.5	$6\text{–}9 \times 10^6$
Poisson's ratio	0.245	0.17	0.20	
Modulus of rupture, lb./sq. in. $\times 10^{-3}$	20	5–9	6–10	
Knoop hardness, 100 g	698	532	481	480
Knoop hardness, 500 g	619	477	442	
Adhesion strength lb./sq. in.	....	....	....	5–10,000
Max. operating temp., °F	....	....	....	500*
Thermal shock resistance, temp. diff., °F	....	....	....	305(higher for special grades)

* Special glasses are available for high temperatures. A new one is polycrystalline glass capable of withstanding 1000°F (Nucerite).

Table 23-9. Physical Properties of Natural and Synthetic Rubbers

	Specific gravity	Tensile strength, lb./sq. in.	Hardness, Shore	Max. temp., continuous use, °F*	Abrasion resistance	Effect of sunlight†
IIR(Butyl, GR-I)	0.91	2300–3000	40–70	250–300	Excellent	None
NR(natural rubber)	0.93	3000–4500	20–100	175	Excellent	Deteriorates
Hard rubber	1.20–1.95	4000–10,000	65–95	220		
CR(Neoprene, GR-M)	1.25	2000–3500	30–90	250	Excellent	None
SBR(Styrene, Buna S)	0.94	1600–3700	35–90	175	Excellent	Deteriorates
NBR(Nitrile, Buna N)	0.99	500–4000	40–90	250	Excellent	Slight
Polysulfide (Thiokol ST)	1.35	700–1250	50–80	212	Good	None
Silicone (high temp.)		700–800	45–65	600	Good	None
Polyvinyl chloride (Koroseal)	1.32	2400–3000	80–90	160	Good	None
Chlorosulfonated polyethylene (Hypalon)	1.2	500–3000	55–95	250	Excellent	None
Fluoroelastomers (Viton A)	1.85	2000–3000	60–95	500	Excellent	None
(Kel-F 3700)	1.85	3500	60	400	Excellent	None
Vistanex	0.9	200–550	......	....	Excellent	None
Polyisoprene	0.93	2000–3000	40–80	175	Excellent	Deteriorates
Polybutadiene	0.94	2500	45–80	175	Excellent	Deteriorates

* Maximum temperature suitable for service depends greatly upon the exact service conditions. Maximum temperature for use as a packing can be much higher than the maximum temperature suitable for tank lining. Individual cases should be referred to the supplier for recommendations.

† Effect of exposure to sunlight under tension.

Table 23-10a. Typical Physical Properties of Carbon and Graphite Products*
(Measured in a longitudinal direction)

Form of product	Apparent density, g./cc.	Per cent porosity	Strength, lb./sq. in.			Elastic modulus $\times 10^6$ lb./sq. in.	Specific resistance, ohm-in.	Thermal conductivity, B.t.u./(hr.)(sq. ft.)(°F.)/(ft.)†	a,‡ mean coef. of thermal expansion (70°F.–212°F.) $\times 10^{-7}$/°F.
			Tensile	Compressive	Flexural				
Anthracite carbon electric-furnace electrodes:									
8-in.-diam. and equivalent rectangles	1.57	21	400	2,400	1,100	1.2	0.0011	8.7	13
10- to 14-in. diam. and equiv. rectangles	1.57	21	290	2,000	800	0.95	0.0014	8.7	13
17- to 40-in.-diam. and equiv. rectangles	1.57	21	150	1,700	400	0.70	0.0020	8.7	13
Anthracite carbon beams and furnace-lining stock	1.57	21	200	2,200	550	0.75	0.0020	8.7	13
Graphite cylinders and electric-furnace electrodes:									
Up to 5⅛ in. diam., incl	1.56	30	900	3,400	1,800	1.40	0.00036	81	10
6- to 12-in.-diam., incl	1.55	30	750	3,200	1,400	1.20	0.00039	75	10
14- to 30-in.-diam., incl	1.51	32	440	1,700	800	0.80	0.00041	71	10
Graphite beams, retangular electrodes and electrolytic anodes:									
Up to 5 in. thick, incl	1.56	30	900	3,400	1,800	1.40	0.00036	81	10
6 in. thick, up to 144-sq.-in. section	1.55	30	750	3,200	1,400	1.20	0.00039	75	10
Over 144-sq.-in. section	1.51	32	440	1,700	800	0.80	0.00041	71	10
Carbon pipe, tubes, and tower sections:									
Up to 10 in. I.D.	1.55	22	900	9,000	2,600	1.9	0.0015	3	13
Over 10 in. I.D., plain	1.51	26	800	7,000	2,500	1.5	0.0022	3	13
Over 10 in. I.D., dense	1.65	17	900	9,000	3,000	1.6	0.0020	3.5	13
Graphite pipe, tubes, and tower sections:									
½ in.–10 in. I.D., incl	1.67	25	800	5,000	2,800	1.4	0.00034	86	10
Over 10 in. I.D.	1.64	26	800	4,500	2,700	0.9	0.00042	70	16
Karbate impervious carbon pipe and tubes	1.77	2	1,800	10,000	4,400	2.8	0.0016	3	29
Karbate impervious graphite pipe and tubes	1.87	0.7	2,500	9,000	4,700	2.2	0.00034	86	24
Carbon brick	1.55	23	1,100	6,300	3,000	1.7	0.0016	3	13
Graphite brick	1.56	30	900	3,100	1,650	1.35	0.00034	86	10
Karbate impervious carbon brick	1.76	2	1,800	10,000	4,400	2.8	0.0016	3	29
Karbate impervious graphite brick	1.91	0.7	2,500	9,000	4,700	2.2	0.00034	86	24

* The physical properties given in this table are for the most commonly used stock. Materials having other characteristics are available.
† To convert to cal./(sec.)(cm.²)(°C.)(cm.) multiply by 0.00413.
‡ Lineal expansion in per cent for temperature rise from

$$70°\text{F. to temp. (°F.)} = \frac{a(T - 70) + 0.00555(T - 70)^2}{100{,}000}$$

$$21°\text{C. to temp. (°C.)} = \frac{a(T - 21) + 0.018(T - 21)^2}{100{,}000}$$

Table 23-10b. Typical Physical Properties of Porous Carbon and Graphite Products*
(Measured in a longitudinal direction)

Form of product	Apparent density, g./cc.	Per cent porosity	Strength, lb/sq. in.			Elastic modulus $\times 10^6$, lb./sq. in.	Specific resistance, ohm-in.	Thermal conductivity, B.t.u./(hr.)(sq. ft.)(°F.)(ft.)†	Mean coef. of thermal expansion (70–212°F.) $\times 10^{-7}$/°F.
			Tensile	Compressive	Flexural				
Porous carbon:									
Grade 60	1.05	48	190	850	600	0.5	0.0070	1.5	26
Grade 50	1.05	48	180	830	500	0.4	0.0070	1.4	26
Grade 40	1.04	48	120	800	320	0.3	0.0070	1.0	26
Grade 30	1.04	48	100	770	250	0.3	0.0070	1.0	26
Grade 20	1.03	48	90	700	240	0.2	0.0070	1.0	26
Grade 10	1.03	48	80	300	160	0.2	0.0080	1.0	25
Porous graphite:									
Grade 60	1.05	48	110	500	250	0.3	0.0012	50	20
Grade 50	1.05	48	110	500	250	0.3	0.0012	45	20
Grade 40	1.04	48	100	500	200	0.2	0.0013	45	20
Grade 30	1.04	48	80	500	200	0.2	0.0017	40	20
Grade 20	1.03	48	60	310	140	0.2	0.0020	30	20
Grade 10	1.03	48	50	270	140	0.2	0.0020	20	20

* The physical properties given in this table are for the most commonly used stock. Materials having other characteristics are available.
† To convert to g.-cal./(sec.)(cm.²)(°C.)(cm.) multiply by 0.00413.

Glass and Glassed Steel. Glass has excellent resistance to all acids except hydrofluoric. It is also subject to attack by hot alkaline solutions. Glass is particularly suitable for piping, where transparency is desirable.

Chief drawback, of course, is brittleness, and glass is also subject to damage by thermal shock. However, glass, armored with polyester fiberglass, can readily be protected against breakage. On the other hand, glassed steel combines the corrosion resistance of glass with the working strength of steel. Accordingly, glass linings are resistant to all concentrations of hydrochloric acid to 300°F., to dilute concentrations of sulfuric to the boiling point, to concentrated sulfuric to 450°F., and to all concentrations of nitric acid to the boiling point. Acid-resistant glass with improved alkali resistance (up to 12 pH) is available as well as thermal-shock-resistant glassed steel capable of withstanding a 260°F. temperature difference at a vessel temperature of 250°F.

Nucerite is a new ceramic-metal composite made in a similar manner to glassed steel. Controlled high-temperature firings chemically and physically bond the ceramic to steel, nickel-base alloys, and refractory metals. Nucerite resists corrosive hydrogen-chloride gas, chlorine, or sulfur dioxide at 1200°F. It resists all acids except HF up to 350°F. Impact strength is 18 times that of safety glass; abrasion resistance is superior to porcelain enamel. It has three to four times the thermal shock resistance of glassed steel.

Table 23-11. Important Properties of Gasket Materials*

Material	Max. service temp., °F.	Important properties
Rubber (straight):		
Natural	225	Good mechanical properties. Impervious to water. Fair to good resistance to acids, alkalies. Poor resistance to oils, gasoline. Poor weathering, aging properties
Styrene-butadiene (SBR)	250	Better water resistance than natural rubber. Fair to good resistance to acids, alkalies. Unsuitable with gasoline, oils and solvents
Butyl	300	Very good resistance to water, alkalies, many acids. Poor resistance to oils, gasoline, most solvents (except oxygenated)
Nitrile	300	Very good water resistance. Excellent resistance to oils, gasoline. Fair to good resistance to acids, alkalies
Polysulfide	150	Excellent resistance to oils, gasoline, aliphatic and aromatic hydrocarbon solvents. Very good water resistance, good alkali resistance, fair acid resistance. Poor mechanical properties
Neoprene	250	Excellent mechanical properties. Good resistance to non-aromatic petroleum, fatty oils, solvents (except aromatic, chlorinated, or ketone types). Good water and alkali resistance. Fair acid resistance
Silicone	600	Excellent heat resistance. Fair water resistance; poor resistance to steam at high pressures. Fair to good acid, alkali resistance. Poor (except fluorosilicone rubber) resistance to oils, solvents
Acrylic	450	Good heat resistance but poor cold resistance. Good resistance to oils, aliphatic and aromatic hydrocarbons. Poor resistance to water, alkalies, some acids
Chlorosulfonated polyethylene (Hypalon)	250	Excellent resistance to oxidizing chemicals, ozone, weathering. Relatively good resistance to oils, grease. Poor resistance to aromatic or chlorinated hydrocarbons. Good mechanical properties
Fluoroelastomer (Viton, Fluorel 2141, Kel-F)	450	Can be used at high temperatures with many fuels, lubricants, hydraulic fluids, solvents. Highly resistant to ozone, weathering. Good mechanical properties
Asbestos:		
Compressed asbestos-rubber sheet	To 700	Large number of combinations available; properties vary widely depending on materials used
Asbestos-rubber woven sheet	To 250	Same as above
Asbestos-rubber (beater addition process)	400	Same as above
Asbestos composites	To 1000	Same as above
Asbestos-TFE	500	Combines heat resistance and sealing properties of asbestos with chemical resistance of TFE
Cork compositions	250	Low cost. Truly compressible materials which permit substantial deflections with negligible side flow. Conform well to irregular surfaces. High resistance to oils; good resistance to water, many chemicals. Should not be used with inorganic acids, alkalies, oxidizing solutions, live steam
Cork rubber	300	Controlled compressibility properties. Good conformability, fatigue resistance. Chemical resistance depends on kind of rubber used
Plastics:		
TFE (solid) (Tetrafluoroethylene, Teflon)	500	Excellent resistance to almost all chemicals and solvents. Good heat resistance; exceptionally good low-temperature properties. Relatively low compressibility and resilience

*From "Materials in Design Engineering," December, 1959, pp. 111-126, Reinhold, New York.

Table 23-11. Important Properties of Gasket Materials*—(*Continued*)

Material	Max. Service temp., °F.	Important properties
TFE (filled)	To 500	Selectively improved mechanical and physical properties. However, fillers may lower resistance to specific chemicals
TFE composites	To 500	Chemical and heat resistance comparable with solid TFE. Inner gasket material provides better resiliency and deformability
CFE (Chlorotrifluoroethylene, Kel.-F)	350	Higher cost than TFE. Better chemical resistance than most other gasket materials, although not quite so good as TFE
Vinyl	212	Good compressibility, resiliency. Resistant to water, oils, gasoline, and many acids and alkalies. Relatively narrow temperature range
Polyethylene	150	Resists most solvents. Poor heat resistance
Plant fiber:		
Neoprene-impregnated wood fiber	175	Nonporous; recommended for glycol, oil, and gasoline to 175°F
GRS-bonded cotton	230	Good water resistance
Nitrile rubber–cellulose fiber	....	Resists oil at high temperatures
Vegetable fiber, glue binder	212	Resists oil and water to 212°F.
Vulcanized fiber	....	Low cost, good mechanical properties. Resists gasoline, oils, greases, waxes, many solvents
Inorganic fibers	To 2200°F.	Excellent heat resistance, poor mechanical properties
Felt:		
Pure felt	....	Resilient, compressible and strong, but not impermeable. Resists medium-strength mineral acids and dilute mineral solutions if not intermittently dried. Resists oils, greases, waxes, most solvents. Damaged by alkalies
TFE-impregnated	300	Good chemical and heat resistance
Petrolatum or paraffin-impregnated	....	High water repellency
Rubber-impregnated	....	Many combinations available; properties vary widely depending on materials used
Metal:		
Lead	500	Good chemical resistance. Best conformability of metal gaskets
Tin	....	Good resistance to neutral solutions. Attacked by acids, alkalies
Aluminum	800	High corrosion resistance. Slightly attacked by strong acids, alkalies
Copper, brass	....	Good corrosion resistance at moderate temperatures
Nickel	1400	High corrosion resistance
Monel	1500	High corrosion resistance. Good against most acids and alkalies, but attacked by strong hydrochloric and strong oxidizing acids
Inconel	2000	Excellent heat, oxidation resistance
Stainless steel	....	High corrosion resistance. Properties depend on type used
Metal composites	....	Many combinations available; properties vary widely depending on materials used
Leather	220	Low cost. Limited chemical and heat resistance. Not recommended against pressurized steam, acid or alkali solutions
Glass fabric	....	High strength and heat resistance. Can be impregnated with TFE for high chemical resistance

Packing and Sealing Materials

Rubber (straight)	To 600	See Gasket Materials for properties. Mainly used for ring-type seals, although some types are available as spiral packings
Rubber composites:		
Cotton-reinforced	350	High strength. Chemical resistance depends on type of rubber used; however, most types are noted for high resistance to water, aqueous solutions
Asbestos-reinforced	450	High strength combined with good heat resistance
Asbestos:		
Plain, braided asbestos	500	Heat resistance combined with resistance to water, brine, oil, many chemicals. Can be reinforced with wire

Table 23-11. Important Properties of Gasket Materials*—(*Concluded*)

Material	Max. service temp., °F.	Important properties
Packing and Sealing Materials (*Cont.*)		
Asbestos, (*Cont.*)		
Impregnated asbestos	To 750	Environmental properties vary widely depending on type of asbestos and impregnant used. Neoprene-cemented type resists hot oils, gasoline, and solvents. Oil and wax-impregnated type resists caustics. Wax-impregnated blue asbestos type has high acid resistance. TFE-impregnated type has good all-around chemical resistance
Asbestos composites	To 1200	End properties vary widely dpending on secondary material used
Metals:		
Copper	To 1500	Properties depend on other construction materials and form of copper used. Packing made of copper foil over asbestos core resists steam and alkalies to 1000°F. Packing of braided copper tinsel resists water, steam, and gases to 1500°F.
Aluminum	To 1000	Resists hot petroleum derivatives, gases, footstuffs, many organic acids
Lead	550	Many types are available
Organic fiber:		
Flax	300	Good water resistance
Jute	300	Good water resistance
Ramie	300	Good resistance to water, brine, cold oil
Cotton	300	Good resistance to water, alcohol, dilute aqueous solutions
Rayon	300	Good resistance to water, dilute aqueous solutions
Felt	300	See Gasket Materials
Leather	To 210	Good mechanical properties for sealing. Resistant to alcohol, gasoline, many oils and solvents, synthetic hydraulic fluids, water
TFE	To 500	Available in many forms, all of which have high chemical resistance
Carbon-graphite	700	Good bearing and self-lubricating properties. Good resistance to chemicals, heat

Plastic Materials. In comparison with metallic materials, the use of plastics is limited to relatively moderate temperatures and pressures (450°F. is considered high for plastics). Plastics are also less resistant to mechanical abuse and have high expansion rates, low strengths (thermoplastics), and only fair resistance to solvents. However, they are lightweight, are good thermal and electrical insulators, are easy to fabricate and install, and have low friction factors.

Generally, plastics have excellent resistance to weak mineral acids and are unaffected by inorganic salt solutions—areas where metals are not entirely suitable. Since plastics do not corrode in the electrochemical sense, they offer another advantage over metals: most metals are affected by slight changes in pH, or minor impurities, or oxygen content, while plastics will remain resistant to these same changes.

The important thermoplastics used commercially are: **polyethylene, acrylonitrile butadiene styrene(ABS), polyvinylchloride(PVC), cellulose acetate butyrate (CAB), vinylidene chloride(saran), fluorocarbons (Teflon, Kel-F), chlorinated polyether(Penton), polycarbonates, polypropylene, nylons, acetals (Delrin).** Important thermosetting plastics: **general-purpose polyester glass reinforced, bisphenol-based polyester glass, epoxy glass, and phenolic asbestos.**

The most chemical-resistant plastic commercially available today is **tetrafluoroethylene** or **TFE**(Teflon). This thermoplastic is practically unaffected by all alkalies and acids except fluorine and chlorine gas at elevated temperatures and molten metals. It retains its properties up to 500°F. **Chlorotrifluoro ethylene** or **CFE**(Kel-F) also possesses excellent corrosion resistance to almost all acids and alkalies up to 350°F. A new Teflon has been developed from the copolymerization of tetrafluoroethylene and hexafluoropropylene. This resin, **FEP**, has similar properties to TFE except that it is not recommended for continuous exposures at temperatures above 400°F. Also, FEP can be extruded on conventional extrusion equipment, while TFE parts must be made by complicated "powdered-metallurgy" techniques.

Polyethylene is the lowest-cost plastic commercially available. Mechanical properties are generally poor, particularly above 120°F., and pipe must be fully supported. Carbon-filled grades are resistant to sunlight and weathering.

Unplasticized polyvinyl chlorides (type I) have excellent resistance to oxidizing acids other than concentrated, and to most non-oxidizing acids. Resistance is good to weak and strong alkaline materials. Resistance to chlorinated hydrocarbons is not good.

Acrylonitrile butadiene styrene polymers(**ABS**) have good resistance to non-oxidizing and weak acids but are not satisfactory with oxidizing acids. Upper temperature limit is about 150°F. Resistance to weak alkaline solutions is excellent. They are not satisfactory with aromatic or chlorinated hydrocarbons but have good resistance to aliphatic hydrocarbons.

Chlorinated polyether(Penton) is a new thermoplastic. This material can be used continuously up to 255°F., intermittently up to 300°F. Chemical resistance is between polyvinyl chloride and the fluorocarbons. Dilute acids, alkalies, and salts have no effect. Hydrochloric, hydrofluoric, and phosphoric acids can be handled at all concentrations up to 225°F. Sulfuric acid over 60 per cent and nitric over 25 per cent cause degradation, as do aromatics and ketones.

Acetals have excellent resistance to most organic solvents but are not satisfactory for use with strong acids and alkalies.

Cellulose acetate butyrate is not affected by dilute acids and alkalies or gasoline. But chlorinated solvents cause some swelling. **Nylons** resist many organic solvents but are attacked by phenols, strong oxidizing agents, and mineral acids.

Among other newer materials are **polypropylene** and the **polycarbonates.** Polypropylene's chemical resistance is about the same as polyethylene, but it can be used at 250°F. Polycarbonate is a relatively high-temperature plastic. It can be used up to 300°F. Resistance to mineral acids is good. Strong alkalies slowly decompose it, but mild alkalies do not. It is partially soluble in aromatic solvents and soluble in chlorinated hydrocarbons.

Among the thermosetting materials are **phenolic plastics** filled with asbestos, carbon or graphite, and silica. Relatively low cost, good mechanical properties, and chemical resistance (except against strong alkalies) make phenolics popular for chemical equipment.

Furane plastics, filled with asbestos, have much better alkali resistance than phenolic asbestos. They are more expensive than the phenolics but also offer somewhat higher strengths.

General-purpose polyester resins, reinforced with fiberglass, have good strength and good chemical resistance, except to alkalies. Some special materials in this class, based on bisphenol, are more alkali resistant. Temperature limit for polyesters is about 200°F.

Epoxies reinforced with fiberglass have very high strengths and resistance to heat. Chemical resistance of the epoxy resin is excellent in non-oxidizing and weak

(*Continued on page 23-64*)

Table 23-12. Important Properties of Commercial Woods in the Green and Air-dry Conditions*

(Results of tests of small clear specimens)

Species	Moisture content, %	Specific gravity (oven-dry volume)	Static bending: Modulus of Rupture, lb./sq. in.	Static bending: Modulus of Elasticity, 1,000 lb./sq. in.	Static bending: Work to max. load, in.-lb./cu. in.	Compression parallel to grain: max. crushing strength, lb./sq. in.	Compression perpendicular to grain: stress at proportional limit, lb./sq. in.	Shear, lb./sq. in.	Tension perpendicular to grain: max. tensile strength, lb./sq. in.	Hardness, lb.: End	Hardness, lb.: Side
Hardwoods:											
Alder, red	98	0.43	6,500	1,170	8.0	2,960	310	770	390	550	440
	12		9,800	1,380	8.4	5,820	540	1,080	420	980	590
Ash, commercial white	43	0.62	9,500	1,410	14.7	4,060	860	1,350	580	1,010	940
	12		14,600	1,680	15.6	7,270	1,510	1,920	850	1,680	1,260
Aspen, quaking	94	0.40	5,100	860	6.4	2,140	220	660	230	280	300
	12		8,400	1,180	7.6	4,250	460	850	260	510	350
Balsa	12	0.13	2,100	420	.....	1,250	70	245	115	170	80
Basswood, American	105	0.40	5,000	1,040	5.3	2,220	210	600	280	290	250
	12		8,700	1,460	7.2	4,730	450	990	350	520	410
Beech	54	0.67	8,600	1,380	11.9	3,550	670	1,290	720	970	850
	12		14,900	1,720	15.1	7,300	1,250	2,010	1,010	1,590	1,300
Birch, sweet and yellow	62	0.68	8,700	1,560	16.0	3,510	550	1,160	430	910	850
	12		16,700	2,070	19.8	8,310	1,250	2,020	930	1,660	1,340
Birch, paper	65	0.60	6,400	1,170	16.2	2,360	340	840	380	470	560
	12		12,300	1,590	16.0	5,690	740	1,210	.....	890	910
Cherry, black	55	0.53	8,000	1,310	12.8	3,540	440	1,130	570	750	660
	12		12,300	1,490	11.4	7,110	850	1,700	560	1,470	950
Cottonwood, eastern	111	0.43	5,300	1,010	7.3	2,280	240	680	410	380	340
	12		8,500	1,370	7.4	4,910	470	930	580	580	430
Elm, American	89	0.55	7,200	1,110	11.8	2,910	440	1,000	590	680	620
	12		11,800	1,340	13.0	5,520	850	1,510	660	1,110	830
Elm, rock	48	0.66	9,500	1,190	19.8	3,780	750	1,270	.....	980	940
	12		14,800	1,540	19.2	7,050	1,520	1,920	.....	1,510	1,320
Greenheart	43	1.06	19,550	2,970	13.4	10,160	2,040	1,730	1,070	2,260	2,320
	12		25,500	3,700	22.0	12,920	1,970	1,830	1,020	2,140	2,630
Hickory, pecan	68	0.69	10,000	1,380	19.3	4,320	980	1,260	680	1,270	1,310
	12		16,300	1,780	18.8	8,280	2,040	2,080	.....	1,930	1,820
Hickory, true	57	0.78	11,300	1,570	28.9	4,570	1,080	1,360			
	12		19,700	2,100	27.2	8,970	2,310	2,130			
Mahogany, American	80	0.51	8,960	1,340	9.1	4,340	680	1,240	740	820	740
	12		11,460	1,500	7.5	6,780	1,090	1,230	740	970	800
Maple, red	63	0.55	7,700	1,390	11.4	3,280	500	1,150	.....	780	700
	12		13,400	1,640	12.5	6,540	1,240	1,850	.....	1,430	950
Maple, sugar	58	0.68	9,400	1,550	13.3	4,020	800	1,460	.....	1,070	970
	12		15,800	1,830	16.5	7,830	1,810	2,330	.....	1,840	1,450
Oak, red	80	0.66	8,500	1,360	12.6	3,520	800	1,220	740	1,050	1,030
	12		14,400	1,810	15.0	6,920	1,260	1,830	820	1,490	1,300
Oak, white	70	0.70	8,100	1,200	11.3	3,520	850	1,270	760	1,110	1,070
	12		13,900	1,620	13.3	7,040	1,410	1,890	770	1,420	1,330
Poplar, yellow	64	0.43	5,400	1,090	5.4	2,420	330	740	450	390	340
	12		9,200	1,500	6.8	5,290	580	1,100	520	560	450
Sweetgum	81	0.53	6,800	1,150	9.4	2,840	460	1,070	510	630	520
	12		11,900	1,490	11.3	5,800	860	1,610	800	950	690
Sycamore, American	83	0.54	6,500	1,060	7.5	2,920	450	1,000	630	700	610
	12		10,000	1,420	8.5	5,380	860	1,470	720	920	770
Teak	52	0.62	11,380	1,580	10.0	5,490	1,040	1,300	960	900	980
	12		13,770	1,670	9.3	7,520	1,190	1,360	980	1,010	1,100
Tupelo, black	55	0.55	7,000	1,030	8.0	3,040	600	1,100	570	790	640
	12		9,600	1,200	6.2	5,520	1,150	1,340	500	1,240	810
Walnut, black	81	0.56	9,500	1,420	14.6	4,300	600	1,220	570	960	900
	12		14,600	1,680	10.7	7,580	1,250	1,370	690	1,050	1,010
Softwoods:											
Cedar, incense	108	0.37	6,200	840	6.4	3,150	460	830	280	570	390
	12		8,000	1,040	5.4	5,200	730	880	270	830	470
Cedar, Port Orford	43	0.44	6,200	1,420	7.4	3,130	350	830	180	460	400
	12		11,300	1,730	9.1	6,470	760	1,080	400	730	560
Cedar, northern white	55	0.32	4,200	640	5.7	1,990	290	620	240	320	230
	12		6,500	800	4.8	3,960	380	850	240	450	320
Cedar, eastern red	35	0.49	7,000	650	15.0	3,570	860	1,010	330	760	650
	12		8,800	880	8.3	6,020	1,140	.....	.....	900	900
Cedar, western red	37	0.34	5,100	920	5.0	2,750	340	710	230	430	270
	12		7,700	1,120	5.8	5,020	610	860	220	660	350
Cypress, southern	91	0.48	6,600	1,180	6.6	3,580	500	810	300	440	390
	12		10,600	1,440	8.2	6,360	900	1,000	270	660	510
Douglas fir, coast type	38	0.51	7,600	1,570	7.6	3,860	440	930	300	570	500
	12		12,200	1,950	9.8	7,430	870	1,160	340	900	710
Douglas fir, Rocky Mt. type	38	0.45	6,400	1,180	6.8	3,000	450	880	350	450	400
	12		9,600	1,400	6.4	6,060	820	1,070	330	740	630
Fir, balsam	117	0.41	4,900	960	4.7	2,400	210	610	180	290	290
	12		7,600	1,230	5.1	4,530	380	710	180	510	400
Fir, commercial white	111	0.40	5,900	1,150	5.7	2,830	360	770	310	410	350
	12		9,800	1,490	7.7	5,480	620	990	300	770	470
Hemlock, eastern	111	0.43	6,400	1,070	6.7	3,080	440	850	230	500	400
	12		8,900	1,200	6.8	5,410	800	1,060	.....	810	500
Hemlock, western	74	0.44	6,100	1,220	6.8	2,990	390	810	310	520	430
	12		10,100	1,490	7.5	6,210	680	1,170	310	940	580
Larch, western	58	0.61	8,200	1,530	10.3	3,990	420	900	330	580	510
	12		13,900	1,960	12.6	8,110	980	1,410	430	1,120	830
Pine, eastern white	73	0.36	4,900	990	5.2	2,440	260	680	250	300	290
	12		8,600	1,240	6.8	4,800	510	900	310	480	380
Pine, lodgepole	65	0.43	5,500	1,080	5.6	2,610	310	680	220	320	330
	12		9,400	1,340	6.8	5,370	750	880	290	530	480

Table 23-12. Important Properties of Commercial Woods in the Green and Air-dry Conditions*—(*Concluded*)

Species	Moisture content, %	Specific gravity (oven-dry volume)	Static bending: Modulus of Rupture, lb./sq. in.	Static bending: Modulus of Elasticity, 1,000 lb./sq. in.	Static bending: Work to max. load, in.-lb./cu. in.	Compression parallel to grain: max. crushing strength, lb./sq. in.	Compression perpendicular to grain: stress at proportional limit, lb./sq. in.	Shear, lb./sq. in.	Tension perpendicular to grain: max. tensile strength, lb./sq. in.	Hardness, lb.: End	Hardness, lb.: Side
Pine, ponderosa	91	0.42	5,000	970	5.1	2,400	360	680	290	300	310
	12		9,200	1,260	6.6	5,270	740	1,160	400	550	450
Pine, southern yellow:											
Pine, loblolly	81	0.54	7,300	1,410	8.2	3,490	480	850	260	420	450
	12		12,800	1,800	10.4	7,080	980	1,370	470	750	690
Pine, longleaf	63	0.62	8,700	1,600	8.9	4,300	590	1,040	330	550	590
	12		14,700	1,990	11.8	8,440	1,190	1,500	470	920	870
Pine, shortleaf	81	0.54	7,300	1,390	8.2	3,430	440	850	320	410	440
	12		12,800	1,760	11.0	7,070	1,000	1,310	470	750	690
Pine, slash	66	0.66	8,900	1,580	9.5	4,340	680	1,000	400	600	630
	12		15,900	2,060	12.6	9,100	1,390	1,730	570	1,080	1,010
Pine, sugar	137	0.38	5,100	940	5.4	2,530	350	680	270	320	310
	12		8,000	1,200	5.5	4,770	590	1,050	350	530	380
Pine, western white	54	0.42	5,200	1,170	5.0	2,650	290	640	260	310	310
	12		9,500	1,510	8.8	5,620	540	850	.....	440	370
Redwood	112	0.42	7,500	1,180	7.4	4,200	520	800	260	570	410
	12		10,000	1,340	6.9	6,150	860	940	240	790	480
Spruce, eastern	45	0.43	5,600	1,120	6.6	2,600	290	710	200	390	340
	12		10,100	1,450	8.5	5,620	590	1,070	350	640	490
Spruce, Engelmann	80	0.36	4,500	960	5.1	2,190	250	590	240	310	260
	12		8,700	1,280	6.4	4,770	540	1,030	350	560	350
Spruce, Sitka	42	0.42	5,700	1,230	6.3	2,670	340	760	250	430	350
	12		10,200	1,570	9.4	5,610	710	1,150	370	760	510
Tamarack	52	0.56	7,200	1,240	7.2	3,480	480	860	260	400	380
	12		11,600	1,640	7.1	7,160	990	1,280	400	670	590

* Based largely on data of U.S. Forest Products Laboratory as reported in Mantell's "Engineering Materials Handbook," pp. 29-10–29-12, McGraw-Hill, New York 1958.

Table 23-13. Wood for Chemical Equipment

Condition of Woods after 31 Days Immersion in Cold Solutions*

Examined after 7 days drying

	Fir	Oak	Oregon pine	Yellow pine	Spruce	Redwood	Maple	Cypress
Hydrochloric acid, 5%	NAC	NAC	NAC	SS	SS	SS	NAC	NAC
Hydrochloric acid, 10%	NAC	NAC	NAC	SS	SS	SS	NAC	NAC
Hydrochloric acid, 50%	SS,SB,SWF	SS,WF	S,WF	S,WF	S,WF	S,WF	S,WF	S,WF
Sulfuric acid, 1%	NAC	NAC	NAC	SS	SS	NAC	NAC	SS,SB
Sulfuric acid, 5%	SS	SS	SS	SS	SS,SB	SS,SB	NAC	SS,SB
Sulfuric acid, 10%	S,FSD	S,FSD	S,FSD	S,FSD	S,FSD	S,FSD	S,FSD	S,FSD
Sulfuric acid, 25%	SSp,FSD	SSp,FSD	SSp,FSD	SSp,FSD	SSp,FSD	SSp,FSD	SSp,FSD	SSp,FSD
Caustic soda, 5%	S,NAC	MSh,SWp	SS	SS,FSD	SSp,FSD	SSp,FSD	MSh	SSp,FSD
Caustic soda, 10%	S,FSD	MSh,WF,Horny	SS	SS,SB,FSD	SS,SB,FSD	SS,SB,FSD	MSh	S,SB,FSD
Alum, 13%	NAC	NAC	NAC	NAC	NAC	NAC	NAC	NAC
Sodium carbonate, 10%	SB,GC	NAC	GC	SB,GC	SB,GC	SB,GC	GC	SB,GC
Calcium chloride, 25%	NAC	NAC	NAC	NAC	NAC	NAC	NAC	NAC
Common salt, 25%	NAC	NAC	NAC	SS,GC	SS,GC	SS,GC	NAC	NAC
Water	NAC	NAC	NAC	NAC	NAC	NAC	NAC	NAC
Sodium sulfide	SS,SB	MSh,WF	SB	SB	SB	SB	MSh,FSD	FSD

Condition of Woods after 8 Hr. Boiling in Solutions*

Examined after 7 days drying

	Fir	Oak	Oregon pine	Yellow pine	Spruce	Redwood	Maple	Cypress
Hydrochloric acid, 10%	SB,S	FSD	FSD	FSD	FSD	FSD	FSD	FSD
Hydrochloric acid, 50%	FD,Ch,B,S,NG	FD,Ch,B,S,NG	FD,Ch,B,S,NG	FD,Ch,B,S,NG	FD,Ch,B,S,NG	FD,Ch,B,S,NG	FD,Ch,B,S,NG	FD,Ch,B,S,NG
Sulfuric acid, 4%	SB,GC	SB,GC	SB,GC	SB,GC	SB,GC	SB,GC	SB,GC	SB,GC
Sulfuric acid, 5%	SS,GC	SB,GC	SB,GC	SB,GC	SB,FSD	SB,GC	SB,GC	SB,FSD
Sulfuric acid, 10%	SS,GC	BFD,Wpd,NG	Sp,FD,NG	B,Sp,FD,NG	B,Sp,FD,NG	SB,FSD	SB,FSD	B,FD
Caustic soda, 5%	SS	MSh	S	GC	S,GC	S,GC	Sh	SSp
Alum, 13%	SB,GC	NAC	NAC	SB,GC	SB,GC	SB,GC	NAC	SB,GC
Sodium carbonate, 10%	SB,GC	GC	GC	GC	GC	GC	GC	SB,GC
Calcium chloride, 25%	SB,GC	SB,SS,GC	NAC	SB,GC	SB,GC	NAC	NAC	SB,GC
Common salt, 25%	NAC	NAC	NAC	SB,GC	NAC	SB,GC	NAC	NAC
Water	NAC	NAC	NAC	SB,GC	NAC	NAC	NAC	NAC

* The two tables describing the condition of eight varieties of woods used for tanks and other chemical-resistant uses are based on a report of James K. Stewart, consulting chemist, to the Mountain Copper Co., Martinez, Calif. Tests were conducted on samples 1 by 4 by ¼ in. in size, seasoned and chosen so as to be as nearly as possible in the same physical condition as the woods would be when used for equipment construction. Results of the tests are described by terms explained in the following key:

Abbreviation key:

B —Brittle
Ch —Charred
FD —Fiber disintegrated
FSD—Fiber slightly disintegrated
GC —Good condition
MSh—Much shrunk
NAC—No apparent change
NG —No good
S —Softer
SB —Slightly brittle
Sh —Shrunk
Sp —Spongy
SS —Slightly softer
SSp —Slightly spongy
SWF—Slightly weakened fiber
SWp—Slightly warped
WF —Weakened fiber
Wpd—Warped

acids but not good against strong acids. Alkaline resistance is excellent in weak solutions. Chemical resistance of epoxy-glass laminates may be affected by any exposed glass in the laminate.

Phenolic asbestos, general-purpose polyester glass, saran, and CAB are adversely affected by alkalies. And thermoplastics generally show poor resistance to organics.

Rubber and Elastomers. To meet the demands of the chemical industry, rubber processors are continually improving their products. A number of synthetic rubbers have been developed, and while none has all the properties of natural rubber, they are superior in one or more ways. A comparatively recent development has been the isoprene and polybutadiene synthetic rubbers, which are duplicates of natural.

Natural rubber is resistant to dilute mineral acids, alkalies, and salts but oxidizing media, oils, benzene, and ketones will attack it. **Hard rubber** is made by adding 25 per cent or more of sulfur to natural or synthetic rubber and, as such, is both hard and strong. **Chloroprene** or **Neoprene rubber** is resistant to attack by ozone, sunlight, oils, gasoline, and aromatic or halogenated solvents. **Styrene rubber** has chemical resistance similar to natural. **Nitrile rubber** is known for resistance to oils and solvents. **Butyl rubber's** resistance to dilute mineral acids and alkalies is exceptional; resistance to concentrated acids, except nitric and sulfuric, is good. **Silicone rubbers,** also known as polysiloxanes, have outstanding resistance to high and low temperatures as well as against aliphatic solvents, oils, and greases. **Chlorosulfonated polyethylene,** known as **Hypalon,** has outstanding resistance to ozone and oxidizing agents except fuming nitric and sulfuric acids. Oil resistance is good. **Fluoroelastomers(Viton A, Kel-F)** combine excellent chemical and high-temperature resistance. Polyvinyl chloride elastomer (**Koroseal**) was developed to overcome some of the limitations of natural and synthetic rubbers. It has excellent resistance to mineral acids and petroleum oils. Rubber and elastomers are widely used as lining materials.

Carbon and Graphite. The chemical resistance of impervious carbon and graphite depends somewhat on the type of resin binder used to make the material impervious. Generally, impervious graphite is completely inert to all but the most severe oxidizing conditions. This property, combined with excellent heat transfer, has made impervious carbon and graphite very popular in heat exchangers, as brick lining, and in pipe and pumps. One limitation of these materials is low tensile strength. Threshold oxidation temperatures are 350°C. for carbon and 400°C. for graphite.

Two types of resin impregnates are employed in manufacturing impervious graphite. The standard impregnant is a phenolic resin suitable for service in most acids, salt solutions, and organic compounds. A modified phenolic impregnant is recommended for service in alkalies and oxidizing chemicals. However, neither type of impervious graphite is recommended for use in over 60 per cent hydrofluoric, over 20 per cent nitric, over 96 per cent sulfuric acids, and 100 per cent bromine, fluorine, or iodine.

Porcelain and Stoneware. Porcelain and stoneware materials are about as resistant to acids and chemicals as glass, but with the advantage of greater strength. This is offset somewhat by poor thermal conductivity, and the materials can be damaged by thermal shock fairly easily. **Porcelain enamels** are used to coat steel, but the enamel has slightly inferior chemical resistance. Some refractory coatings, capable of taking very high temperatures, are also available.

Wood, while fairly inert chemically, is readily dehydrated by concentrated solutions and hence shrinks badly when subjected to the action of such solutions. It is also slowly hydrolyzed by acids and alkalies, especially when hot. In tank construction, if sufficient shrinkage once takes place to allow crystals to form between the staves, it becomes very difficult to make the tank tight again.

A number of manufacturers now offer wood impregnated to resist acids or alkalies or the effects of high temperatures.

Brick Construction. Brick-lined construction can be used for many severely corrosive conditions, where high alloys would fail. Common bricks are made from carbon, red shale, or acidproof refractory materials. Red-shale brick is not used above 350°F. because of spalling. Acidproof refractories can be used up to 1600°F.

A number of cement materials are used with brick. Standard are phenolic and furane resins, polyesters, sulfur, silicate, and epoxy-based materials. Carbon-filled polyesters and furanes are good against non-oxidizing acids, salts, and solvents. Silica-filled resins should not be used against hydrofluoric or fluosilicic acids. Sulfur-based cements are limited to 200°F., while resins can be used to about 350°F. The sodium silicate based cements are good against acids to 750°F.

HIGH- AND LOW-TEMPERATURE MATERIALS

Low-temperature Metals. The low-temperature properties of metals have created some unusual problems in fabricating cryogenic equipment.

Most metals lose their ductility and impact strength at low temperatures, although in many cases yield and tensile strengths increase as the temperature goes down.

It is important to choose materials resistant to shock. Usually a minimum Charpy value of 15 ft.-lb. (keyhole notch) is specified at the operating temperature. For severe loading, a value of 20 ft.-lb. is recommended. Ductility tests are performed on notched specimens since smooth specimens usually show amazing ductility.

Steels. The A.S.M.E. and A.S.T.M. have set up an A 300 classification which covers carbon and alloy steels suitable to −150°F. In addition the A.S.M.E. Code adds certain features on fabrication—such as stress relieving—to ensure suitability of these alloys in low-temperature service. A large number of steels are made to the A 300 classification. Steels A 201 and A 212 are specially treated carbon steels for −50°F. service. Among the alloy steels are A 203 Grade A or B for −75°F., A 203 Grade D or E for service to −150°F. (see Fig. 23-1).

Stainless Steels. Chromium-nickel steels are inherently suitable for service from −300° to −425°F. Table 23-14 shows some A.I.S.I. grades used at low temperatures. Type 304 is the most popular. The original cost of stainless steel may be higher than another metal, but ease of fabrication (no heat-treatment) and welding, combined with high strength, offsets the higher initial

Table 23-14. Metals and Alloys for Low-temperature Service*

A.S.T.M. Specification and Grade	Recommended Max. Service Temp., °F.
Carbon and alloy steels:	
T-1	− 50
A 201, A 212, flange or firebox quality	− 50
A 203, Grades A and B (2¼ Ni)	− 75
A 203, Grades D and E (3½ Ni)	−150
A 353 (9% Ni)	−320
Stainless steels type 302, 304L, 304, 310, 347	−425
Aluminum alloys 5052, 5083, 5086, 5154, 5356, 5454, 5456	−425
Copper alloys, silicon bronze, 70-30 brass, copper	−320

* Based on a series of articles on low-temperature metals appearing in *Chem. Eng.* from May 20 to Oct. 31, 1960. See also McClintock and Gibbons, "Mechanical Properties of Structural Materials at Low Temperatures," National Bureau of Standards, June, 1960.

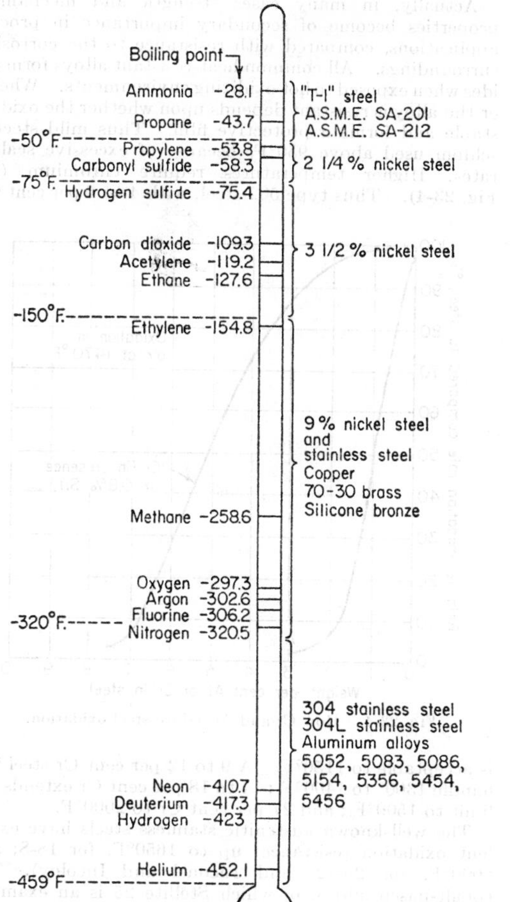

FIG. 23-1. What steels to use as the temperature drops. This chart shows schematically the various steels used for low-temperature application in environments defined by the normal boiling points of certain liquefied gases.

cost. Sensitization or formation of chromium carbides can occur in several stainless steels during welding, and this will affect impact strength. However, tests have shown that impact properties of types 304 and 304L are not greatly affected by sensitization, but the properties of 302 are impaired at −300°F.

Nickel Steel. Low-carbon 9 per cent nickel steel is a ferritic alloy developed for use in cryogenic equipment operating as low as −320°F. A.S.T.M. specifications A 300 and A 353 cover low-carbon 9 per cent nickel steel (A 300 is the basic specification for low-temperature ferritic steels). Refinements in welding and (A.S.M.E. Code approved) elimination of postweld thermal treatments make 9 per cent steel competitive with many low-cost materials used at low temperatures.

Aluminum. Aluminum alloys have an unusual ability to maintain strength and shock resistance at temperatures as low as −425°F. Good corrosion resistance and relatively low cost make these alloy very popular for low-temperature equipment. For most welded construction the 5000 series aluminum alloys are widely used. These are the aluminum-magnesium and aluminum-magnesium-manganese materials.

Copper and Alloys. With few exceptions the tensile strength of copper and its alloys increases quite rapidly as the temperature goes down. However, copper's low structural strength becomes a problem when constructing large-scale equipment. Therefore, alloys must be used. One of the most successful for low temperatures is silicon bronze. The alloy can be used to −320°F. with safety.

Insulation. Perlite, balsa wood, cellular glass, and mineral wool can all be used at temperatures down to about −260°F.

But still better insulations are needed to cope with liquid hydrogen, oxygen, and helium. Randomly dispersed reflective flakes are not good enough. Two very promising insulations have been developed by Linde.

One is a medium-quality variety consisting of 10 to 20 layers of aluminum foil per inch, separated by 3-micron glass-fiber mat. It is a relatively low-density (2 lb./cu. ft.) low-cost insulation with a thermal conductivity of 0.11×10^{-3} B.t.u./(hr.)(ft.)(°F.) between 80° and −297°F. A higher-quality variety consists of 40 to 80 layers/in. of aluminum foil and submicron glass-fiber paper. This is somewhat heavier than the other insulation (4.7 lb./cu. ft.) and more costly, but it has the very low thermal conductivity of 0.025×10^{-3} B.t.u./(hr.)(ft.)(°F.) over the same temperature range.

High-temperature Materials. Successful applications of metals in high-temperature process service depend on an appreciation of certain engineering factors. The important alloys for service up to 2000°F. are shown in Table 23-15.

Table 23-15. Important Commercial Alloys for High-temperature Process Service

	Nominal composition, %			
	Cr	Ni	Fe	Other
Ferritic steels:				
Carbon steel	....	....	bal.	
2¼ chrome*	2¼	....	bal.	Mo
Type 502	5	....	bal.	Mo
Type 410	12	....	bal.	
Type 430	16	....	bal.	
Type 446	27	....	bal.	
Austenitic steels:				
Type 304	18	8	bal.	
Type 321	18	10	bal.	Ti
Type 347	18	11	bal.	Cb
Type 316	18	12	bal.	Mo
Type 309	24	12	bal.	
Type 310	25	20	bal.	
Type 330	15	35	bal.	
Nickel-base alloys:				
Nickel	....	bal.		
Incoloy	21	32	bal.	
Hastelloy B	....	bal.	6	Mo
Hastelloy C	16	bal.	6	W, Mo
60/15	15	bal.	25	
Inconel	15	bal.	7	
80/20	20	bal.		
Hastelloy X	22	bal.	19	Co, Mo
Multimet	21	20	bal.	Co
Rene 41	19	bal.	5	Co, Mo, Ti
Cast irons:				
Ductile iron	....	....	bal.	C, Si, Mg
Ni-Resist, D-2	2	20	bal.	Si, C
Ni-Resist, D-4	5	30	bal.	Si, C
Cast stainless (ACI types):				
HC	28	4	bal.	
HF	21	11	bal.	
HH	26	12	bal.	
HK	26	20	bal.	
HT	15	35	bal.	
HW	12	bal.	28	
Super alloys:				
Inconel X	15	bal.	7	Ti, Al, Cb
A 286	15	25	bal.	Mo, Ti
Stellite 25	20	10	Co-base	W
Stellite 21 (cast)	27.3	2.8	Co-base	Mo
Stellite 31 (cast)	25.2	10.5	Co-base	W

* See Table 23-6f for data on other heat-resistant low- and medium-alloy steels.

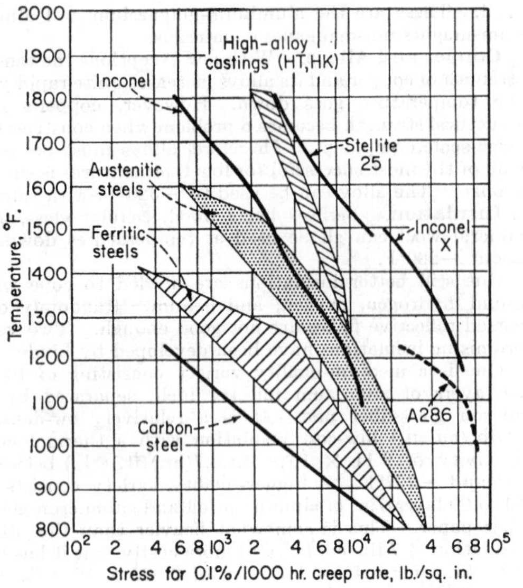

FIG. 23-2. Effect of creep on metals for high-temperature use. (*Chem. Eng., Dec.* 15, 1958, *p.* 139.)

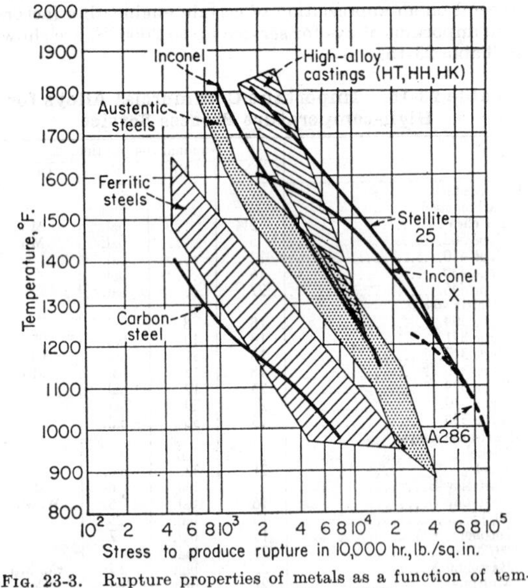

FIG. 23-3. Rupture properties of metals as a function of temperature. (*Chem. Eng., Dec.* 15, 1958, *p.* 139.)

Among the most important properties are creep, rupture, and short-time strengths (see Figs. 23-2 and 23-3). Creep relates initially applied stress to rate of plastic flow. Stress rupture is another important consideration at high temperatures since it relates stress and time to produce rupture. As the figures show, ferritic alloys are weaker than austenitic compositions, and in both groups molybdenum increases strength. Austenitic castings are much stronger than their wrought counterparts. And higher strengths are available in **Inconel,** cobalt-based **Stellite 25,** and iron-base **A286.** Other properties which become important at high temperatures include thermal conductivity, thermal expansion, ductility, alloy composition, and stability.

Actually, in many cases strength and mechanical properties become of secondary importance in process applications, compared with resistance to the corrosive surroundings. All common heat-resistant alloys form oxides when exposed to hot oxidizing environments. Whether the alloy is resistant depends upon whether the oxide is stable and forms a protective film. Thus mild steel is seldom used above 950°F. because of excessive scaling rates. Higher temperatures require chromium (see Fig. 23-4). Thus type 502 steel, with 4 to 6 per cent Cr,

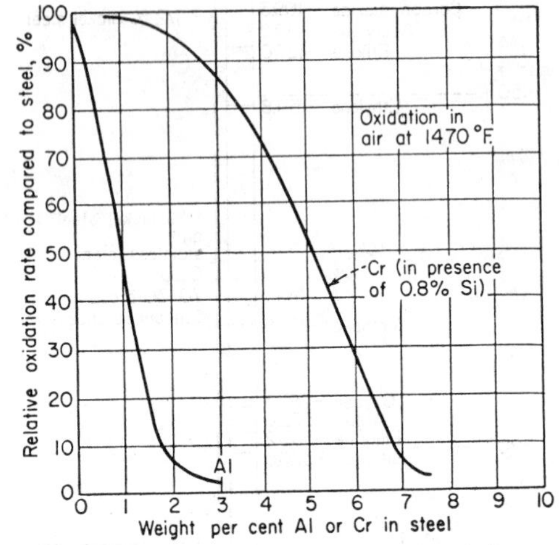

FIG. 23-4. How Cr and Al reduce steel oxidation.

is acceptable to 1150°F. A 9 to 12 per cent Cr steel will handle 1300° to 1400°F.; 14 to 18 per cent Cr extends the limit to 1500°F.; and 27 per cent Cr to 2000°F.

The well-known austenitic stainless steels have excellent oxidation resistance: up to 1650°F. for 18-8; and 2000°F. for 25-12 (and Inconel and Incoloy). The cobalt-based alloys, of which Stellite 25 is an example, show excellent strengths up to 2000°F.

Another useful element in imparting oxidation resistance to steel is silicon (complementing the effects of chromium). In the lower chromium ranges, silicon in the amounts of 0.75 to 2 per cent is more effective than chromium on a weight-percentage basis. The influence of 1 per cent silicon in improving the oxidation rate of steels with varying chromium contents is shown in Fig. 23-5.

Aluminum also improves the resistance of iron to oxidation as well as sulfidation. But use as an alloying agent is limited because the amount required interferes with workability and high-temperature strength properties of the steel. However, development of high-aluminum surface layers by spraying, dipping, and cementation is a feasible means of improving the heat resistance of low-alloy steels.

Hydrogen Atmospheres. Austenitic stainless steels, by virtue of their high chromium contents, are usually resistant to hydrogen atmospheres. Stabilized grades are preferred.

Nitrogen Attack. High nickel alloys, because of their reluctance to form nitrides, are preferred materials in handling ammonia and its dissociation products.

Sulfur Corrosion. Chromium is the most important material in imparting resistance against sulfidation (formation of sulfidic scales similar to oxide scales). For this reason, straight chromium stainless steels are recommended in high H_2S atmospheres.

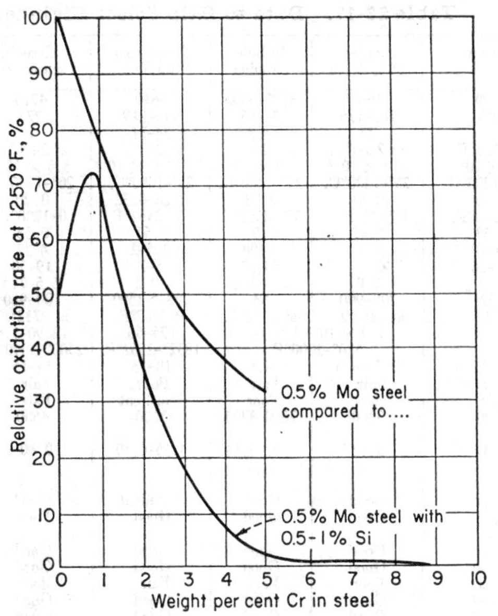

FIG. 23-5. Effect of silicon on oxidation resistance.

Halogens (Hot, Dry, Cl_2, HCl). Pure nickel and nickel alloys are useful with dry halogen gases. But even with the best materials, corrosion rates are relatively high at high temperature. There are cases where equipment for high-temperature halogenation has used platinum-clad nickel-base alloys. This has a high initial cost but a long life. Platinum and gold have excellent resistance to dry HCl even at 2000°F.

For temperatures much above 2000°F., only the refractory metals are suitable. Much work has been done on these metals in connection with atomic and rocket programs. All the refractory metals have melting points over 3000°F., but each has distinct advantages and disadvantages (see Table 23-16).

Table 23-16. Comparison of Properties of Refractory Metals

Melting point, °F.	Element	Advantages	Disadvantages
6180...	Tungsten	Highest melting point; non-volatile oxide to at least 2500°F.	Highest density; oxidizes rapidly; brittle at low temperatures
5425...	Tantalum	Very high melting point; non-volatile oxide; ductile	High density; oxidizes rapidly; least abundant
4730...	Molybdenum	High melting point; less dense than tungsten or tantalum; moderately ductile at room temperature	Extremely high oxidation rate (volatile oxide)
4380...	Columbium	High melting point; non-volatile oxide; ductile; moderate density	Oxidizes rapidly
3435...	Chromium	Extremely oxidation-resistant; lightest of refractory metals	Lowest melting point of refractory metals; brittle at low temperatures

Properties of important non-metallics for high-temperature applications are summarized in Table 23-17. (Also see Tables 23-10a and b.)

CORROSION-TESTING METHODS

There is no standard or preferred way to carry out a corrosion test. The method must be chosen to suit the purpose of the test. The principal types of test are:

1. Laboratory tests, including inspection tests such as the salt spray
2. Plant tests
3. Field tests, exposing samples to the atmosphere; to soils; or to fresh, brackish, or saline natural waters
4. Service tests, the use of a material for part of some operating equipment, such as an evaporator tube, or for small-scale pilot-plant equipment.

Laboratory corrosion tests are useful to:

1. Study the chemistry and mechanism of corrosion
2. Indicate the environments in which a particular metal or alloy may be used satisfactorily
3. Determine the possible effects of metals and alloys on the characteristics of an environment to which they may be exposed, *e.g.*, contamination by corrosion products of materials in process, transportation, or storage
4. Serve as a control test in making a uniform corrosion-resisting metal or alloy
5. Determine the value of changes in composition or treatment in developing corrosion-resisting alloys
6. Determine whether a metal, an alloy, or a protective coating conforms to a specification requiring a certain performance in a specified corrosion test

Plant, field, and service corrosion tests are most useful for:

1. Selection of the most suitable material to withstand a particular environment, and to estimate its probable durability in that environment
2. Study of the effectiveness of means of preventing corrosion.

Laboratory Corrosion Tests. Metals and alloys do not respond alike to all the influences of the many factors that control corrosion. Consequently, it is impractical to establish any standard laboratory procedures for corrosion testing, except for inspection tests. However, some details of laboratory testing need careful attention before useful results can be achieved.

In the selection of material for the construction of a chemical plant, resistance to the corroding medium is usually the determining factor because the choice would otherwise fall automatically on the cheapest material mechanically suitable, and laboratory corrosion tests are frequently the quickest and most satisfactory means of arriving at a preliminary selection of the most suitable materials to use. Unfortunately, however, it is not possible on the basis of any existing laboratory test to predict with accuracy the behavior of the selected material in the plant. The outstanding difficulty in this connection lies not so much in carrying out the test as in interpreting the results and translating them into terms of plant performance. A laboratory test of the standardized type gives but one factor, the chemical resistance of the proposed material to the corrosive agent, and there are numerous other factors entering into the behavior of the materials in the plant.

The following method of determining this factor, which is the so-called total immersion test, represents an unaccelerated method which has been found to give reasonably concordant results in approximate agreement with results obtained on the large scale when the other variables are taken into account. Various other tests have been proposed and are in use, such as the salt spray, the accelerated electrolytic, the alternate immersion, the aerated total immersion, etc.; but, in view of the numerous other complications entering into the translation of laboratory results into plant results, the simplest test would seem the most desirable for routine preliminary work, reserving the special test methods for special cases. This preliminary test serves quite well to eliminate the materials that obviously cannot be used; further selection among those which apparently can be used can be made

Table 23-17. Data to Help Select High-tem-

	Magnesia	Zircon $ZrO_2.SiO_2$	Bonded 99% Al_2O_3	Bubble alumina	Fused cast alumina	Zirconia stabilized
Melting point, °F	5072	4390	3660	3380–3550	3640	4710
Bulk density, lb./cu. ft.	175	205	165–175	80–85	175–219	275
Thermal conductivity, B.t.u./(hr.)(sq. ft.) (°F.)(in.)	18 at 2000°F.	22 at 2192°F.	24 at 2200°F.	7.7 at 2400°F.	24–31 at 200°F.	7 at 2400°F.
Coefficient of thermal expansion, °C.	13.5×10^{-6} 25°–800°C.	5.5×10^{-6} 20°–1200°C.	7.4×10^{-6} 25°–1400°C.	8.6×10^{-6} 25°–1400°C.	$4.9–8.6 \times 10^{-6}$ 25°–1400°C.	5.5×10^{-6} 20°–1200°C.
Mean specific heat, B.t.u./(lb.) (°F.)	0.283 86°–2012°F.	0.15 75°–210°F.	0.33 32°–2552°F.	0.32 32°–2552°F.	0.28–0.32 32°–2552°F.	0.20 0–1200°F.
Emissivity at 1500°F	0.51	0.53	0.47	0.55	0.51	0.53
Permeability, cu. ft./(hr.)(sq. ft.)(in.)	3–61	10–78	3–51	>100	0.5–2	4–32
Apparent porosity, %	19	11–26	22	54–67	2.5–7.5	19–50
Mohs' hardness	6.0	7.5	9.0	2.5–5.0	9.2	6.5–7.5
Modulus of rupture lb./sq. in.		157 at 2732°F.	200–900 at 2462°F.	63 at 2462°F.	703–>1500 at 2462°F.	100–980 at 2732°F.
Electrical resistivity, ohm-cm	1500°F., 4×10^6 2500°F., 10,500	High	$1.2 \times 10^{13}–1 \times 10^6$ 580°–2000°F.		175–55 1832°–2552°F.	12.90–1.6 2300°–3090°F.
Wt., lb./9-in. brick	10	11–12.5	9.7–10.4	4.8	10–13	14–15
Thermal shock resistance	Poor	Good <3150°F.	Fair	Fair	Poor	Fair
Abrasion resistance	Poor	Fair	Good	Poor	Excellent	Fair
Use limit, °F	4172, oxid. 3092 red.	3100	3300	2800–3200	3300	4600
Cost, dollars/9-in. brick	2.81	1.39	3.12	1.52–3.34	4.65–6.30	10.80
Chemical resistance:						
Slags:						
Acid	Poor	Good	Good	Good	Excellent	Good
Basic	Good	Poor	Good	Good	Good	Poor
Molten metals:						
Al	Fair	Good	Good	Good	Good	Good
Fe	Good	Good	Good	Good	Good	Good
Na	Fair	Poor	Poor	Poor	Fair	Poor
Pb	Good	Good	Good	Good	Good	Good
Zn	Good	Good	Good	Good	Good	Good
Mg	Poor	Fair	Good	Fair	Excellent	Fair
Gases:						
CO_2	A	A	A	A	A	A
CO	A	A	A	A	A	A
H_2O, steam	D	A	A	A	A	B–C
O_2, air	B < 4172°F.	A	A	A	A	A
F_2	D	D–E	B < 1800°F. D > 1800°F.	D–E	D	D
Cl_2	D	B–D	A	B–D	A–D	B
H_2	B < 3092°F. D > 3092°F.	E > 3272°F.	A	A	A	E > 3900°F.
HCl	D	A	A	A	A	A
NH_3	A	A	A	A	A	E > 3990°F.
SO_2	B–C	A	A	A	A	A
S_2	B	B–D	A	A	A–C	A–B
Heated acids:						
HNO_3	D	A	A	A	A	A
H_2SO_4	D	A	A	B	A	A
HCl	D	A	A	B	A	A
HF	D	B–C	A–C	C	A–C	B–C
H_3PO_4	D	A–B	A	B	A	A
Hydrocarbons	B < 3092°F. D > 3092°F.	A–D	A	A	A	A

* From *Chem. Eng.*, Apr. 21, 1958, pp. 135–154.
A = no reaction, material entirely suitable for service indicated.
B = slight reaction, material suitable for service indicated.
C = reaction, material suitable under certain conditions.
D = reaction, material not acceptable unless tested under operating conditions.
E = rapid reaction, material not acceptable.

on the basis of a knowledge of the properties of the materials concerned and the working conditions, or by constructing larger-scale equipment of the proposed material in which the operating conditions can be simulated.

The following conditions and factors affecting the results of tests have been investigated:

Test Piece. The shape of the test piece does not affect results within a reasonable range of ratio of length of edge to surface, except for the accelerating effect of the internal segregations exposed on the edge sections. In general the proportion of edge section should be kept low. Fine polishing is unnecessary, although tool marks and oxide coatings should be removed. Many determinations have been made on roughened and smoothed pieces.

Composition of Solution. An effort should be made to ensure that the corroding solution is actually what is supposed to be; *e.g.*, dilute sodium chloride is not sea water. The composition of the solution should be controlled to the fullest extent possible, and, in reporting results, it should be described as completely as possible.

Reagents and Apparatus. Corroding Solution. Use 250 cc. of the corroding solution per test piece of given area (4.6 sq. in.) for a fairly rapid corrosion rate (0.01-in. penetration per month). The volume should be increased in proportion for pieces of greater area.

Temperature of Corroding Solution. Results of many experiments show that the temperature coefficient is high for all reactions. For theoretical work in determining the law of temperature, it is absolutely necessary to use an accurately regulated thermostat. In applying results to plant practice, similarly careful consideration must be given to temperature control in all specific tests.

perature Non-metallic Materials of Construction*

SiC	Silicon-nitride-bonded SiC	Magnesite	Chrome $FeO.Cr_2O_3$	Fosterite $MgO.SiO_2$	Synthetic mullite $3Al_2O_3.2SiO_2$	Converted mullite $Al_2O_3.SiO_2$	Silica	Superduty fireclay
diss. at 4082	diss. at 3452	5070	3540–3990	3461	3317	3250	3140	3120
153–162	168–178	160–175	170–190	150–155	147–156	140–150	100–110	134–141
109	113.5	20	12	10.3	15	14	14.3	10
at 2200°F.	at 2200°F.	at 2200°F.	at 2400°F.	at 2200°F.	at 2200°F.	at 2400°F.	at 2200°F.	at 2192°F.
4.4×10^{-6}	4.4×10^{-6}	14.7×10^{-6}	10.4×10^{-6}	11.0×10^{-6}	4.6×10^{-6}	5.3×10^{-6}	8.6×10^{-6}	6.0×10^{-6}
25°–1400°C.	25°–1400°C.	0°–1400°C.	0°–1540°C.	0°–1425°C.	25°–1400°C.	0°–1700°C.	25°–1500°C.	25°–1000°C.
0.288	0.288	0.27	0.21	0.25	0.23	0.23	0.28	0.27
0°–2552°F.	0°–2500°F.	60°–1200°F.	60°–1200°F.	0°–1200°F.	32°–2552°F.	32°–2552°F.	32°–2600°F.	32°–2600°F.
0.93	0.93	0.48	0.97	0.95	0.51	0.51	0.76	0.54
1–6	1–4	7–20	6–14	10–25	3–48	3–40	41–54	3–72
13	8	20–28	20–28	24–27	20–27	15–22	18–43	12–16
9.6	9.6	5.0–5.5	5.5	7.5	6–7	6–6.5	7.0	6.0
800–315	5640	750–3000	25–125	450–800	100–575	50–375	20–75	25–375
at 2462°F.	at 2462°F.	at 68°F.	at 2462°F.	at 68°F.	at 2462°F.	at 2462°F.	at 2462°F.	at 2462°F.
7420–745			650–40		10^5–10^3	10^4–10^3	10^8–10^7	10^4–10^3
1832°–2732°F.	. . . .	. . . .	1500°–2500°F.	. . . .	1500°–2500°F.	1500°–2500°F.	1000°–1400°F.	1500°–2500°F.
9–9.5	9.9–10.4	10.0–11.5	11.0–12.0	9.1–9.8	8.6–9.1	8.5	6.0–6.7	7.5–9.0
Excellent	Excellent	Fair	Fair	Fair	Good	Good	Excellent	Fair
Excellent	Excellent	Fair	Fair	Good	Fair	Fair	Fair	Fair
2800–3000	2900–3000	2900–3200	2800–3200	3000	2900–3100	2800–3000	3100	2500–2800
2.14	4.28	0.68–0.70	0.55–0.58	0.57–0.60	0.89–1.76	0.68	0.15–0.16	0.18–0.24
Good	Excellent	Poor	Poor	Poor	Good	Good	Good	Good
Fair	Fair	Good	Fair	Fair	Good	Fair	Poor	Poor
Good	Excellent	Fair	Fair	Fair	Fair	Fair	Poor	Fair
Poor	Poor	Good	Good	Good	Good	Good	Good	Good
Poor	Poor	Poor	Poor	Poor	Poor	Poor	Poor	Poor
Excellent, red. atm.		Good	Good	Good	Good	Good	Fair	Fair
Excellent	Excellent	Fair	Fair	Fair	Good	Good	Good	Good
Good	Good	Fair	Fair	Fair	Fair	Fair	Poor	Poor
B < 1500°F. B > 2100°F.	B < 1500°F. B > 2100°F.	A	A	A	A	A	A	A
B < 1500°F. B > 2100°F.	B < 1500°F. B > 2100°F.	B–C	B–C	A	A	B–C	A	C
B < 1500°F. B > 2100°F.	B < 1500°F. B > 2100°F.	A	A	A	A	A	A	A
B < 1500°F. B > 2100°F.	B < 1500°F. B > 2100°F.	A	A	A	A	A	A	A
D	C–D	E	E	E	E	E	E	E
					Chlorine attacks silicates above 1300°F.			
A < 1300°F. D > 1300°F.	A < 1300°F. D > 1300°F.	D	C–D	C–D	B–D	B–E	C–E	C–E
A < 2600°F. D > 2600°F.	A < 2600°F. D > 2600°F.				Nascent or atomic hydrogen attacks silica and iron			
A	A	D	C–D	C–D	A	A	A	A
A	A	A	A	A	A–C	A–C	A–C	A–C
A	A	C–D	C–D	C–D	A	A–C	B–C	B–C
					Sulfur in strong concentrations reacts with silica above 1700°F.			
A < 2200°F. D > 2200°F.	A–C	B–D	B–C	B–C	B	A–C	B–C	B–C
A	A	D	B–C	B–D	A	A	A–C	A–C
A	A	D	B–D	B–D	A	A	A–C	A–C
A	A	D	B–D	B–D	A	A	A–C	A–C
B–D	C–D	D	B–E	B–E	C–E	C–E	E	E
A–B	A	D	B–D	B–E	A–B	A–B	A–C	A–C
A–D	A–C	B–C	B–C	B–C	A–D	A–D	B–D	B–D

In comparing different metals, care must be taken that the temperature is the same for all tests. A convenient way to control temperature is to use a constant-boiling liquid.

Time of Exposure. It has been found that results of corrosion tests vary enormously with the time of exposure of the material to the corroding solution. This variation is due to initial electrochemical surface actions such as overvoltage and to the period of time required for the formation of a protective coat. Evidently initial effects of this kind must be neglected if a corrosion factor for use over a long period of time is to be obtained. The logical way is to measure the rate over an interval of time after this initial high corrosion rate has decreased and become constant. For the most careful work this must be done. The experimental data available at present indicate that corrosion should be determined at the end of 48, 96, and 240 hr. Sufficient accuracy for comparative work may usually be obtained by neglecting the corrosion over the first 48 hr. and averaging the rate over the second 48-hr. period.

Cleaning Test Pieces. Many methods have been investigated for removing coatings from the test pieces. They may consist of dissolving the coat or of removing it mechanically. In each case the error due to a particular method has been determined. The first 48-hr immersion in the corroding solution may be considered a preparation of the test piece for the final test.

Preparation of the Sample. 1. Metal Test Piece. Size 2 by 1 by 0.1 in. (area 4.6 sq. in.). Dimensions should be accurate to 0.01 in. in order to save the time of measurement and area calculation in the laboratory.

Other shapes may be used within a range of ratio of length of edge to total area of test piece between 4 and 8.

2. Preparation. The strip of indicated size may be cut from flat sheet metal or turned from pipe. Tool marks should be removed by successive use of file and emery. Exceedingly fine finishes are unnecessary, but the surface should be clean and reasonably smooth as, for example, finished with 120 grain emery.

3. Testing Apparatus. An apparatus for testing has been described by Fraser, Ackerman, and Sands (see references at end of this section).

Jars containing the testing solution are surrounded by an electrically heated water bath, the temperature of which is controlled thermostatically. For tests at temperatures near atmospheric a suitable temperature is 86°F. (30°C.). This is usually slightly above room temperature and is therefore easy to control.

The stirrups by which the specimens are supported are attached to an arm actuated by a crank mechanism by which the specimens are thereby moved in a vertical circular path. This type of motion has the advantage that all parts of the specimen are moved at exactly the same velocity. This method of moving the specimens also makes it easy to make connections for electrical measurements without the use of such devices as mercury cups or commutators.

The testing solution may be saturated with air or other gases introduced through an alundum thimble. The alundum aerator serves to form very small gas bubbles which favor rapid solution of the gases. It has been found that merely bubbling gases through a glass tube drawn to a fine tip is not an adequate method of aeration. A glass chimney is placed over the aerator to prevent impingement of gas bubbles on the specimens.

4. Method of Support. The method of supporting specimens will vary with the apparatus used but should be designed so as to insulate specimens from each other and from any metallic container or supporting device used with the apparatus. The supporting device and container should not be affected by the corroding agent to an extent that might cause contamination of the testing solution so as to change its corrosiveness. The shape and form of the specimen support should be such as to avoid, as much as possible, any interference with free contact of the specimen with the corroding solution. Where it is desired to set up conditions favoring contact corrosion, "deposit attack," or other forms of concentration-cell action, the means by which these types of attack are favored should be such as to ensure exact reproducibility from specimen to specimen and test to test.

5. Duration of Test. The duration of any test will be determined by its nature and purpose. In some cases it will be desirable to expose a number of specimens so that certain of them can be removed at definite time intervals to provide a measure of change of corrosion rates with time. With some materials it may be important to repeat tests using the same specimens to eliminate any effects due solely to the original condition of the metallic surface. However, a procedure that requires removal of solid corrosion products between periods of exposure will not measure accurately normal changes of corrosion with time.

It is clear that the higher the rate of corrosion, the shorter may be the testing period. It is suggested that the duration of a laboratory test need not be longer than the number of hours calculated by dividing the corrosion rate, in milligrams per square decimeter per day, into 10,000. For example, where the rate of corrosion is 500 mdd., the test need not be run for more than 20 hr. If the rate were 50 mdd., the duration should be 200 hr. This method of estimating the proper duration of a test is applicable only where corrosion is uniform and is useful only as an aid in deciding, after a test has been made, whether or not it is desirable to repeat the test for a longer period. The duration of any test should be reported.

In case the metal develops pitting, this factor must be included in the results, since failure in any case will occur when a pit has entirely penetrated the metal. Determine the magnitude of this effect by grinding down on a metallographic grinding set until all the pits have just disappeared and solid metal is reached. The loss in weight during this grinding is determined and the pitting calculated as indicated.

Form for Card File of Corrosion Data

Material
Corrosion agent
Concentration
Temperature
Rate of corrosion, in./mo.
Report of data
Method No.
By
For

Form for Laboratory Data

Metal
Solution
Temperature
Test piece No.
Dimensions
  Length
  Width
  Thickness
Hole diameter
  Area
Weight
  Before test
  After test
  Loss
Time
  Start
  Finish
  Run, hr.
Corrosion rate

Calculations. Standard Static Corrosion Test.

If W = loss in weight (in grams) of test piece during the second 48-hr. immersion; A = area of test piece in square inches; S = density of metal in grams per cubic centimeter; and t = time of exposure in hours (t = 48):

Then C = rate of chemical corrosion expressed as inches penetrated per month:

$$C = \frac{24 \times 30 \times W}{(2.54)^3 ASt} \text{ or } \frac{43.9W}{ASt}$$

In order to calculate the pitting corrosion, let p = loss in weight (in grams) due to grinding out pits:

Then d = rate of penetration of metal by both normal corrosion over the entire surface and by local action due to pitting:

$$d = \frac{43.9(W + p)}{ASt}$$

Effect of Variables on Corrosion Test. As in other branches of engineering, it is necessary to apply a factor of safety to the results obtained, the factor varying with the degree of confidence in the applicability of the results. Ordinarily, a factor of from 3 to 10 might be considered normal.

Among the more important points which should be considered in attempting to base plant design on laboratory data are the following:

Electrolysis. This is a frequent source of trouble on a large scale. Not only is the use of different metals in the same piece of equipment dangerous, but the effect of cold working may be sufficient to establish potential differences of objectionable magnitude between different parts of the same piece of metal. **Riveting**, even when extreme precautions are taken to have the rivets of identical composition with the sheet, is very likely to establish potential differences. Even such slight working as threading without subsequent annealing has been known to cause rapid failure from electrolysis. The mass of metal in chemical apparatus is ordinarily so great, and the electrical resistance consequently so low, that a very small voltage can cause a very high current. It might also be noted that improper heat-treatment of a solid-solution-type alloy may convert it from the solid-solution type to the non-homogeneous type, with the result that it fails even more rapidly than its poorest constituent. **Welding** also, if not properly done, may leave the weld of a different physical or chemical composition from the body of the sheet and cause the development of stray currents. A simple test for weld homogeneity is to treat a sample of the welded sheet containing a portion of both weld and sheet with a suitable solvent such as nitric acid or aqua regia, till about half the thickness of the metal has been dissolved; if heterogeneity exists, evidence of differential attack should be seen.

Velocity of Corrosive Liquid. Because of increased rate of removal of corrosion products and increased mechanical action, corrosion increases rapidly with increasing velocity of corrosive medium. This is especially true if the flow is turbulent, or if the liquid carries suspended matter. Frequently, slight, alterations in design can be made to reduce this factor.

Local Concentration. Both local variations in temperature and crevices that permit the accumulation of corrosion products are capable of allowing the formation of concentration cells, with the result of accelerated local corrosion.

Temperature. In the laboratory, the temperature of the test specimen is that of the liquid in which it is immersed, and the measured temperature is actually that at which the reaction is taking place. In the plant, heat being supplied through the metal to the liquid in many cases, the temperature of the film of (corrosive) liquid on the inside of the vessel may be a number of degrees higher than that registered by the thermometer. As the relation between temperature and corrosion is a logarithmic one, the rate of increase is very rapid. Like other chemical reactions, the speed ordinarily increases two- to threefold for each 10° temperature rise, the actual relation being that of the equation: $\log K = A + \frac{B}{T}$, where K represents the rate of corrosion, and T absolute temperature. This relationship, although expressed mathematically, must be understood to be a qualitative rather than strictly a quantitative one.

Impurities. The effect of impurities in either structural material or corrosive material is so marked (while at the same time it may be either accelerating or decelerating) that for reliable results the actual materials it is proposed to use should be tested and not types of these materials. In other words, it is much more desirable to test the actual plant solution and the actual metal or non-metal than to rely upon a duplication of either. Since as little as 0.01 per cent of certain organic compounds will reduce the rate of solution of steel in sulfuric acid 99.5 per cent, and 0.05 per cent bismuth in lead will increase the rate of corrosion over 1000 per cent under certain conditions, it can be seen how difficult it would be to attempt to duplicate here all the significant constituents.

General. For a discussion of immersion test methods see International Nickel Co. Bulletin T-10, and Inco Bulletin, "Corrosion."

Plant Corrosion Tests. It is not always practical or convenient to investigate corrosion problems in the laboratory. In many instances, it is difficult to discover just what are the conditions of service and to reproduce them exactly. This is especially the case with processes involving changes in the composition and other characteristics of the solutions as the process is carried out, as, for example, in evaporation, distillation, polymerization, sulfonation, or synthesis.

With many natural substances, also, the exact nature of the corrosive is uncertain and is subject to changes not readily controlled in the laboratory. In other cases, the corrosiveness of the solution may be influenced greatly by or even may be due principally to a constituent present in such minute proportions that the mass available in the limited volume of corrosive solution that could be used in a laboratory setup would be exhausted by the corrosion reaction early in the test, and consequently the results over a longer period of time would be misleading.

Another difficulty sometimes encountered in laboratory tests is that the contamination of the testing solution by corrosion products may change its corrosive nature to an appreciable extent.

In such cases, it is usually preferable to carry out the corrosion-testing program by exposing specimens in operating equipment under the actual conditions of service. This procedure has the additional advantages that it is possible to test a large number of specimens at the same time, little technical supervision is required, and it is unnecessary for the investigator to know the exact nature of the corrosive solution. The last point is often important when the plant operator, who wants information on corrosion, is, at the same time, reluctant to disclose the details of composition of the corrosive solution.

In certain cases, it is necessary to choose materials for equipment to be used in a process developed in the laboratory and not yet in operation on a plant scale. Under such circumstances, it is obviously impossible to make plant tests. A good procedure in such cases is to construct a pilot plant, using either the cheapest materials available or some other materials selected on the basis of past experience or of laboratory tests. While the pilot plant is being operated to check the process itself, specimens can be exposed in the operating equipment as a guide to the choice of materials for the large-scale plant, or as a means of confirming the suitability of the materials chosen for the pilot plant.

In carrying out plant tests it is necessary to install the test specimens so that they will not come into contact with other metals and alloys; this avoids having their normal behavior disturbed by galvanic effects. It is also desirable to protect the specimens from possible mechanical damage.

This method of testing is substantially in accord with the A.S.T.M. Recommended Practice for Conducting Plant Corrosion Tests, A224-46. The specimen holder, with its component parts, is illustrated in Fig. 23-6.

Specimens are machined to an exact diameter of 2.233 in. with a $2\frac{1}{64}$-in.-diameter hole in the center, and are of a standard thickness of $\frac{1}{32}$ in. A specimen when mounted on the holder has an exposed area of 0.5 sq. dm. Sometimes it is desirable to use thicker specimens.

It is convenient to make cast specimens $\frac{3}{16}$ in. thick. With this thickness it is common practice to make the diameter 2.083 in. and again make the exposed area, when installed on the specimen holder, exactly 0.5 sq. dm.

Specimens can be weighed readily on an analytical balance; because of their uniform size, the time involved in changing weights on the balance pan is minimized. For certain purposes, special specimens may be prepared,

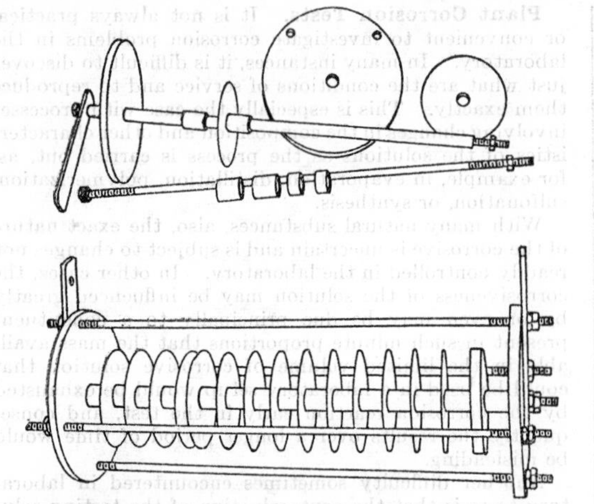

FIG. 23-6. Assembly of corrosion-test spool and specimens. [*C. L. Mantell (ed.), "Engineering Materials Handbook," McGraw-Hill, New York*, 1958.]

as, for, example, specimens made by welding or soldering pieces of metal together.

In assembling specimens for test, a supporting bracket is slid over the threaded end of the center rod and two nuts are screwed on to lock it in place. Next, an insulating tube is slid over the rod and then a large end disk which bears against the bracket. Next, an insulating spacer is slid over the insulating tube, then a specimen, then another spacer, and another specimen, and so on until all the available space has been utilized. It is customary to mount at least two specimens of each metal or alloy for checking purposes. Then the second end disk is put on, followed by the other supporting bracket and the second set of nuts, which are drawn up tightly and locked. Four additional rods are inserted in the holes located around the peripheries of the end disks and are drawn up tightly with nuts. The four rods serve two purposes—they afford protection to the specimens against mechanical abuse, and they make the assembly very strong. One of the rods passes through holes in the supporting brackets to hold them firmly. In order to provide for any variations in thickness of specimens, short spacers may be used.

The spacing of specimens is regulated by the length of the spacer; usually it is ⅝ in.

When it is desired to investigate galvanic effects, the insulating spacer may be replaced by one of metal, of the normal, or shorter, length, made from one of the materials of the galvanic couple. Ordinarily, the metal spacer is exposed to the corrosive attack and is considered part of the metal specimen comprising one half of the couple; but, if it is thought desirable, the exposed surface of the metal spacer can be coated with an insulating lacquer. Similarly, corrosion of the specimens forming the couple may be confined to adjacent faces by lacquering the backs. When a galvanic arrangement of this kind is used, it is common practice to use a compression spring, made of a corrosion-resisting material, between a spacer and the end disk; the spring takes up any slack that might result from thinning of specimens by corrosion.

The choice of materials from which to make the holder is important. These do not need to be durable enough to last indefinitely, but they must last long enough to ensure satisfactory completion of the test. Metallic parts are generally made of nickel or Monel for exposure to the majority of corrosives, and of some type of chromium-nickel stainless steel for tests in oxidizing acids, such as nitric. Insulating materials used are Bakelite, porcelain, Neoprene, Teflon, and glass. Bakelite answers most purposes; its principal limitations are unsuitability for use at temperatures over 300°F., and lack of adequate resistance to concentrated alkalies, and certain organic compounds, such as coal-tar products.

The method of supporting the specimen holder during the test period is important. The preferred position is with the long axis of the holder horizontal, thus avoiding dripping of corrosion products from one specimen to another. The holder must be located so as to cover the conditions of exposure to be studied. It may have to be submerged, or exposed only to the vapors, or located at liquid level, or holders may be called for at all three locations. Exposure at the liquid level may be accomplished most readily by building a suitable float, usually of wood, around the holder so that it will float on the surface. Various means have been utilized for supporting the holders in liquids or in vapors. The simplest is to suspend the holder by means of a heavy wire or light metal chain. Holders have been strung between heating coils, clamped to agitator shafts, welded to evaporator tube sheets, etc.

In a few special cases, the standard "spool-type" specimen holder is not applicable and a suitable special test method must be devised to apply to the corrosion conditions being studied.

For conducting tests in pipe lines of 3 in. diameter or larger, a spool holder, as shown in Fig. 23-7, has been

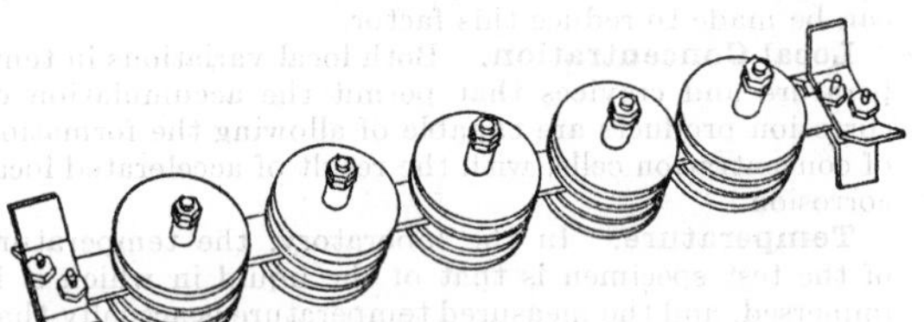

FIG. 23-7. Spool-type specimen holder for use in 3 in. diameter or larger pipe. [*C. L. Mantell (ed.), "Engineering Materials Handbook," McGraw-Hill, New York*, 1958.]

used which employs the same disk-type specimens used on the standard spool holder. This frame is so designed that it may be placed in a pipe line in any position without permitting the disk specimens to touch the wall of the pipe. As with the strip-type holder, this assembly does not materially interfere with the fluid flow through the pipe and permits the study of corrosion effects prevailing in the pipe line.

Another way to study corrosion in pipe lines is to install in the line short sections of pipe of the materials to be tested. These test sections should be insulated from each other and from the rest of the piping system by means of non-metallic couplings. It is also good practice to provide insulating gaskets between the ends of the pipe specimens where they meet inside the couplings. Such joints may be sealed with various types of "dope" or cement. It is desirable in such cases to paint the outside of the specimens so as to confine corrosion to the inner surfaces.

It is occasionally desirable to expose corrosion-test specimens in operating equipment without the use of specimen holders of the type described previously. This can be accomplished by attaching specimens directly to some part of the operating equipment and by providing the necessary insulation against galvanic effects as shown in Fig. 23-8. The suggested method of attaching specimens to racks has been found to be very suitable in connection with the exposure of specimens to corrosion in

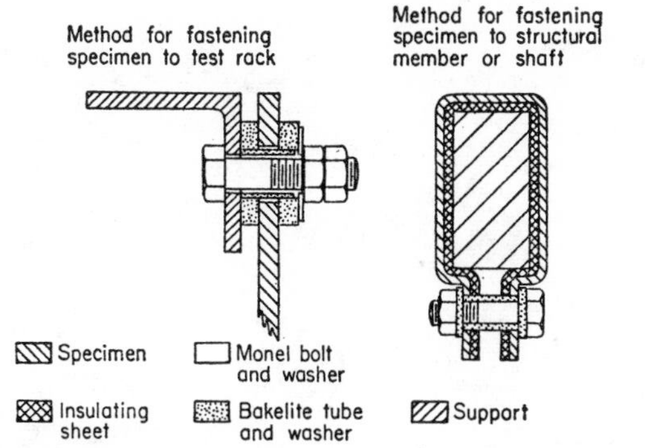

FIG. 23-8. Methods for attaching specimens to test racks and to parts of moving equipment. [*C. L. Mantell (ed.), "Engineering Materials Handbook," McGraw-Hill, New York,* 1958.]

sea water, where metal racks should be used to avoid destruction by teredos.

The methods of cleaning specimens after test, discussed in connection with laboratory corrosion testings, may be applied as well to specimens from plant corrosion tests.

Although loss in weight is used as the principal measure of corrosion, this should be supplemented always by an examination of each specimen, before it is cleaned, for tarnishing and the nature of any heavier corrosion products. If pitting has occurred, the maximum and average pit depths should be determined by means of a calibrated microscope, focused first on the surface of the specimen and then on the bottoms of the pits. With larger pits a needle-pointed depth gage can be used. Distinction should be made between pits on the parts of the surfaces that were exposed freely and those parts under the spacers. The corroded specimen may be subjected also to bending tests and microscopic examination to determine whether integranular deterioration or other less usual forms of corrosion, such as "dezincification," have occurred. The standard disk specimens are not well adapted to the quantitative measurement of change in mechanical properties. When changes in these, due to corrosion, are to be studied, test pieces of suitable size to permit cutting from them standard sheet-metal tensile test specimens should be used; or precut tensile test specimens may be used for the corrosion tests.

One other technique should also be mentioned. This is a new method of measuring corrosion by inserting a probe into a process line and comparing the electrical resistance of this probe, as it corrodes, with a standard electrode. Such instruments are called "corrosion meters" and are available from a number of manufacturers.

This system has been used successfully under all conditions of temperature and pressure encountered in chemical plants and refineries. It has measured corrosion rates in vapor and liquid phases in both oil and aqueous media. With the aid of the corrosion probe, corrosion rates in operating equipment have been determined quantitatively in a few hours time, as compared with weeks or months required for coupon inspections, effluent-stream analyses, or unit inspections. A particular advantage is the speed with which effects of changes in operating procedures upon corrosion rates can be determined. Corrosion inhibitors can be compared rapidly in actual use. Sensitive locations where corrosion is expected can be monitored frequently.

The determination of corrosion by the electrical-resistance method is limited to uniform corrosion over the entire surface of the specimen. Pitting and other forms of localized attack can be detected only by visual observation of the probe, by unit inspections, or by relatively long-term exposure of corrosion coupons.

Certain non-destructive test methods are also useful. These include magnetic thickness gages, ultrasonic and gamma-ray instruments for measuring metal thickness, and boroscopes for internal tube inspections. Gamma-ray devices are used for on-stream inspection of process piping to determine the extent of corrosion. Sources of radiation are Iridium 192 (for small-diameter pipe) and Cobalt 60 (for 10-in. diameter and above). Gamma rays pass through the pipe and project an image on film placed behind the object. Thus a clear outline of internal detail is obtained.

REFERENCES: For further details on corrosion testing, see International Nickel Co. Bulletin T-10; F. A. Champion, "Corrosion Testing Procedures," Wiley, New York, 1952; Fraser, Ackerman, and Sands, *Ind. Eng. Chem.*, **19**, 332–338 (1927); A.S.T.M. A224-46, Part 1, Ferrous Metals, "Conducting Plant Corrosion Tests," pp. 1099–1107, 1955.

Table 23-18. Corrosion-rate Conversion Factors

Multiply	By	To obtain
grams per square inch per hour....	372,000	milligrams per square decimeter per day (mdd.)
grams per square meter per year...	0.0274	milligrams per square decimeter per day (mdd.)
milligrams per square decimeter...	0.0003277	ounces per square foot
milligrams per square decimeter per day (mdd.)	0.00000269	grams per square inch per hour
milligrams per square decimeter per day (mdd.)	36.5	grams per square meter per year
milligrams per square decimeter per day (mdd.)	0.00748	pounds per square foot per year
ounces per square foot...........	3052	milligrams per square decimeter
pounds per square foot per year...	133.8	milligrams per square decimeter per day (mdd.)

ECONOMICS IN MATERIALS SELECTION*

First cost of materials is seldom a good economic indicator when comparing alternate materials of construction for process equipment. Any cost estimation should include the following:

1. Total materials costs
2. Labor costs to install
3. Savings due to elimination of unscheduled shutdowns or maintenance costs
4. Replacement costs

Table 23-19. Return on Investment Analysis

	Material A	Material B	Material C
Installed cost (investment)...............	$45,000	$65,000	$60,000
Additional cost over A..................	....	$20,000	$15,000
Estimated life, years....................	4	6	10
Estimated maintenance rate, %...........	10	7	5
Annual replacement cost.................. (installed cost ÷ life)	$11,250	$10,830	$6,000
Annual maintenance cost.................. (installed cost × rate)	$4,500	$4,550	$3,000
Total annual cost........................	$15,750	$15,380	$9,000
Annual savings vs. cost for A............	....	$370	$6,750
Tax on savings at 50%....................	....	$185	$3,375
Net annual savings.......................	....	$185	$3,375
Return on investment over A.............. (Net savings ÷ additional cost) × 100	....	0.9%	22.5%

When these factors are taken into account, cost comparisons bear little resemblance to first costs. Table 23-19 shows a typical analysis of comparative costs of alternative materials when based on return on investment. One difficulty with this study is the uncertainty factor connected with "estimated life." Well-designed laboratory and plant tests can at least give order-of-magnitude estimates.

* *Cf.* Sec. 26 on Cost and Profitability Estimation.

SECTION 24

MECHANICAL, PLANT, AND PROJECT ENGINEERING

BY

David B. Rossheim, C.E., Chief Mechanical Engineer, The M. W. Kellogg Company, New York, N.Y.; Life Member and Fellow, American Society of Mechanical Engineers; Member, American Society of Civil Engineers, American Society for Testing Materials, American Welding Society, American Petroleum Institute.

Fritz W. Peterson, B.S., Eng., Manager of Projects, The M. W. Kellogg Company, New York, N.Y.; Member, American Society of Mechanical Engineers, American Institute of Electrical Engineers, American Society of Naval Engineers RESA; Professional Engineer, New York and Alabama.

WITH

Christian M. Vogrin, C.E., Engineering Department, Socony-Mobil Oil Company, Inc., New York, N.Y.

CONTENTS

GENERAL ENGINEERING OF PLANT PROJECTS

PRESSURE AND PRESSURE STORAGE VESSELS

PROCESS PLANT PIPING

PROCESS PLANT DRIVERS

BEARINGS AND THEIR LUBRICATION

POWER-TRANSMISSION EQUIPMENT PLANT SAFETY AND FIRE PROTECTION

REFERENCES: *Books:* Marks, "Mechanical Engineers' Handbooks," 6th ed., McGraw-Hill, New York, 1958. Rase and Barrow, "Project Engineering of Process Plants," Wiley, New York, 1957. Staniar, "Plant Engineering Handbook," 2d ed., McGraw-Hill, New York, 1959. M. W. Kellogg Engineering Dept., "Design of Piping Systems," Wiley, New York, 1956. Littleton, "Industrial Piping," McGraw-Hill, New York, 1951. Crocker, "Piping Handbook," 4th ed., McGraw-Hill, New York, 1945. Brownell and Young, "Process Equipment Design; Vessel Design," Wiley, New York, 1959. Bartlett, "Steam Turbine Performance and Economics," McGraw-Hill, New York, 1958. Jennings and Rogers, "Gas Turbines Analysis and Practice," McGraw-Hill, New York, 1953. Armistead, "Safety in Petroleum Refineries and Related Industries," John G. Summond & Co., New York. U.S. Navy, "Fire Prevention and Fire Protection," Technical Publication, Navdocks TP-Pu-4, Government Printing Office, Washington, D.C. Crosby, Fiske, and Porter, "N.F.P.A. Handbook of Fire Protection," National Fire Protection Association, Boston. National Fire Codes, vols. I to VI, National Fire Protection Association, Inc., Boston. Chilton, "Cost Engineering in the Process Industries," McGraw-Hill, New York, 1960.

Journals and reports: A.S.M.E. Unfired Pressure Vessel Code (A.S.M.E.-U.F.P.V.C.), 1959 ed., American Society of Mechanical Engineers, New York. A.S.A. Code for Pressure Piping A.S.A. B31, 1962 ed., American Standards Association, New York (see also A.S.A. B31.3 Petroleum Refinery Piping, 1959 ed.). Murphy and Rossheim, "Four Balanced Classes of Pressure Vessel Construction," A.S.M.E. Paper 60-WA-313, December, 1960. Voelker and Peterson, "Fabrication Requirements for Balanced Classes of Piping," A.S.M.E. Paper 61-5A-60, June, 1961, American Society of Mechanical Engineers, New York. "Pressure Vessels and Piping Design," Collected papers, 1927–1959, American Society of Mechanical Engineers, New York, N.Y.

INTRODUCTION AND ENGINEERING PHILOSOPHIES

Chemical engineers, whether engaged in administration, process research and development, engineering operation, or planning, must frequently collaborate with the many other fields of engineering (mechanical, civil, electrical, instrument, sanitary, architectural, etc.) particularly when involved in the procurement or construction of process plants. The primary objective of this section is to provide a broad picture of the total engineering effort, with emphasis on fundamentals and significant aspects, thereby promoting an appreciation of general engineering objectives and limitations and their relationship with process concepts, and thus to facilitate engineering communication and decision. The secondary objective is to provide information on non-process aspects of a project and the necessary coordinating procedures for its effective control.

The included formulas and design methods permit some appreciation of equipment and structural proportions but are not intended to provide the information and details for working designs, which are in the province of specialists. For a full treatment of underlying engineering theory, or specific design methods, formulas, data or descriptive details, the reader should consult textbooks, manuals, or literature in the particular fields of engineering.

Effective engineering of complex installations, such as process plants involving numerous individual engineers and organizations, is greatly benefited by clear-cut, early establishment of both philosophy and emphasis. Loss of effort occasioned by lack of agreement or indecision is minimized when the project philosophy clearly defines objectives, emphasis, and economics with respect to calculated risks, and is equally clear with respect to scope of work, limitations, and other significant directives. While "emphasis" must necessarily reflect economic and business conditions, unnecessary handicaps and inadequacies will be minimized by a careful appraisal of the indicated requirements for **safety, reliability, flexibility, operability, immediate investment,** and **over-all cost.**

Conceptional and General Engineering Phases. In certain fields, such as bridges and public works, **engineering phases** are clearly established and recognized. Involved projects are initiated in a consulting engineering phase of conceptual study, supported by technical and economic evaluations; the resulting basic requirements are expanded in an architectural and engineering phase into fully established designs and specifications for contractural and/or principal equipment negotiation; finally a production (detail) design engineering phase provides working drawings and material take-offs for procurement, shop fabrication, and field erection.

While assured engineering of process plants and units involves a similar succession of engineering phases, their individual functions are often neither clearly distinguished nor sufficiently accomplished. This is particularly true of the conceptual (consulting) and general engineering phases, which are frequently underemphasized. In combination, the conceptual and general (process and mechanical evaluation and planning) engineering phases assure the effectiveness and economics of the investment and usually represent only a small percentage of the total engineering expenditure.

The term **mechanical engineering** is used here broadly to include all fields of engineering, except chemical (process) engineering, involved in fully engineered process plants. To avoid misunderstanding, these phases, as employed herein, divide the total engineering of a process plant as follows:

Conceptual engineering applies to consulting engineering studies, market forecasts, and economic studies, as well as process evaluation of any extension or modernization as related to existing facilities. Conceptual engineering also includes those phases of process engineering which establish the basic process design, including calculations, schematic flow sheets, and fundamental requirements as to operation, safety, instruments and controls, and equipment.

General engineering parallels the architectural and engineering phase of public works, and accordingly translates the basic process requirements into a complete process and basic mechanical engineering design. It provides flow sheets, plot plans and essential elevation studies, utility flow sheets and requirements, equipment requirements and specifications, project and general specifications, and operating instructions. The startup and operation of well-established processes are most often left entirely to general engineering, whereas novel plants frequently require startup and operating procedure studies as part of the conceptual engineering phase.

Detail (production) design establishes dimensional and other specific details and final drawings for fabrication and erection. It provides for materials take-off and procurement, cost control, schedules, and inspection (unless inspection is provided by general engineering or by the purchaser).

The extensive engineering involved in process plants can benefit greatly by effective standardization and specifications. Applicable professional codes and industry practices, standards, and specifications offer potential economic availability and simplified procurement advantages. Company standards and specifications can reduce costs, expedite engineering, and minimize errors and disagreements.

PROJECT DEFINITION AND COORDINATION

Rapid expansion and concurrent technological advancement in the process industries, together with rising investment, have directed major attention to minimizing the schedule period for the design and construction of process plants. This has resulted in extreme pressure toward accelerating engineering commitments and the release of drawings and specifications for fabrication and erection. It has often necessitated expanding and reorganizing the engineering organizations of both the operating companies and the consulting, engineering, and contracting companies. Since plant expansion and/or modernization involves virtually the entire engineering profession, a more than casual knowledge of the engineering of process plants is an essential part of the chemical engineer's background. This subsection is therefore aimed at a broad appreciation of the many considerations which enter into the crystallization, orientation, coordination, and execution of such a project.

Traditionally a project, as it affects the various participants, is defined by formal contract between the plant purchaser and one or more contractors, and/or engineering firms, defining the project scope, requirements and guarantees, and the responsibilities and respective contributions of all parties. On a broad basis, only end products to be made from a certain raw material need be definitely established. The plant is, however, also required to conform to fully established basic requirements and specifications. Once engineering is authorized, legal or administrative delays in formalizing and signing contracts must not extend to items involving indecision as to basic requirements and specifications. Otherwise engineering administration is faced with ineffective and unnecessary effort and changes, which can continue into procurement, fabrication, inspection, and construction. More concretely, general project definition involves the following:

When a proprietary or patented process is involved, or when dealing with organizations capable of performing all engineering phases, a single responsibility exists. When the purchaser and several engineering organizations jointly contribute, individual responsibility for these phases and subphases is less evident and, unless clearly established, may result in omission or confusion. Unrealistic expectations of the engineering contribution, beyond that concretely established by the contract, can only lead to ineffective over-all performance.

Specifications, standards, data sheets, drawings, proposal engineering descriptions and details, or other documents that are contractual requirements, should be clearly indicated, and each item must carry the issue date and all revision dates.

FINANCIAL AND LEGAL REQUIREMENTS

The financial bases for process contracts are varied, thus providing the flexibility necessary for individual situations: For example:

Scope of work may range from a total plant with single responsibility for conceptual, general, and design engineering including procurement and inspection, complete construction of process units, offsite facilities, and other work, and final startup of process units with operator and technician services, or it may be limited to a single engineering phase or part phase, or to a single process unit or facility.

Cost basis may be a lump-sum fixed price (so-called "turnkey basis") for the entire project, or a maximum price, usually with incentive sharing of underrun in costs, or a fixed price for certain services or work and open cost with fee for others, or the contract may involve a fee basis (usually fixed or else a percentage with all other services or work at cost plus overhead).

Incentives are sometimes specified, including the already mentioned underrun on maximum price contracts, bonuses for early and penalties for late completion, and in open-cost contracts a portion of the savings below the project estimate or budget may become a bonus, while overruns, usually above a specified maximum, may become a penalty.

Payments may be specified at fixed intervals (month, quarter, etc.) or may be based on a percentage (75 to 90 per cent) of completed services, delivered materials, and work performed. Total plant cost usually becomes due at completion or mechanical acceptance, with fees or stipulated amounts withheld until process guarantees are met. Many variations and numerous other bases are also used.

Financial responsibility for additional expenditures due to unpredicted subsurface conditions rests with the purchaser, since their extent often bears no relation to the project design and can be covered only by substantial contingencies or insurance premiums. The contract must specify a monetary basis, whether dollars, pounds sterling, francs, lira, pesos, etc. Import duties, preparation for export shipment, and transportation are conventionally considered a part of direct project costs.

Normally, **legal** or **legislative requirements** with respect to process plants recognize only the owner-operator, and compliance is the responsibility of the purchaser. These include insurance, zoning ordinances, other restrictions applicable to industrial installations, state and local requirements with respect to air and water pollution, or noise, odor, or other potential nuisances.

The **purchaser** usually obtains all building, sanitary, street openings, and other permits incident to the construction as well as all local and insurance approvals and/or inspections.

The **contractor** normally is responsible for compliance with established and published codes, standards and specifications, and enforcement regulations with respect to boilers, pressure vessels, factory safety, and sanitary requirements.

In certain localities, building construction is subject to professional engineering requirements, and in such cases, when required, the contractor must provide drawings signed by a responsible professional engineer.

In certain localities, application for building permits must be accompanied by tentative plans, certified by a registered local architect and/or licensed engineers.

In recent years, in the face of all-out emphasis on minimum investment cost, engineering expenditures have frequently been minimized, and contracts awarded on a total fixed-price basis without defining the extent of engineering or attendant design refinement. Or they may be awarded to the lowest bidder for engineering services, with materials, fabrication, and erection at cost plus fee. The American Society of Civil Engineers has expressed strong opposition to such unsound bases of awarding contracts for engineering services. (See Negotiated Engineering Contracts Protect Public Interests, *Report of Committee on Professional Practice*, A.S.C.E., February, 1959.)

Guarantees. The contract should establish where guarantees apply and clearly define their requirements. Conventionally, a mechanical guarantee is included which outlines the individual and over-all responsibilities of the contractor, vendors, and subcontractors. Such guarantees are usually for defined periods of time, *e.g.*, 6 months or a year after either startup or site delivery, and may provide for replacement of defective materials and workmanship at the vendor's plant. Field installation and contingent expenses are usually not covered by the vendor or contractor guarantees and are often the subject of controversies. Mechanical guarantees are often confused by the current inadequate status of codes, standards, and specifications, as discussed in a succeeding subsection.

Guarantees with respect to performance normally apply to the ability of the process plant or unit to handle specific raw materials in order to produce the desired products in the quantities and qualities specified. Usually performance guarantees must be demonstrated either by a test run of specified length or over an agreed period of operation.

Completion is usually considered accomplished after mechanical acceptance when the plant or unit is ready for flow circulation, at which time responsibility passes from construction to operation.

Unless specified, mechanical guarantees do not cover certain unpredictable manifestations which may occur in operation of equipment, such as (1) resonance-magnified lateral vibration of slender vertical vessels and stacks under wind loadings, (2) resonance-magnified torsional or lateral shaft vibrations of rotating equipment, and (3) resonance-magnified structural deflection due to flow pulsation and equipment speed. Either from lack of adequate knowledge and/or present-day industry practices these cannot always be avoided or economically controlled. Excessive deflection can be objectionable from a psychological standpoint, but more so when such effects result in decreased safety factor. Mechanical acceptance may be contingent, therefore, on the contractor's performing certain alterations or corrective work during operation or shutdown periods.

Organizational Participation and Responsibilities. When engineering and/or contracting are performed by more than one organization, it is essential that individual organization participation, responsibilities, and obligations be clearly established. For effective teamwork, coordination must be provided by the purchaser or by a designated organization, usually either the principal general engineering company, or the principal contractor. The coordination procedure, which should be formulated very early in the job, establishes correspondence routine and the role of the purchaser, general engineers, and contractor with respect to (1) engineering drawings and specification approvals, (2) inspection of materials or fabrication or erection, (3) method of initiating specification changes, and (4) direct engineering contribution and decision.

Engineering checking and/or approvals, in the absence of competent and adequate personnel, can impair performance and result in delays. When the purchaser performs inspection, either total responsibility, including expediting, must be accepted, or else such inspection must function through the contractor's representative. It is essential to establish clear-cut agreement as to subsurface soil exploration and assessment. (A later subsection treats this subject in detail.) To avoid delays and costly changes, approval requirements must be carefully defined.

The **engineering design basis** must define whether the purchaser's engineers or contractor's practices shall apply to safety and safety factors, structural basis, access provisions and areas, flow velocities and pipeline sizing, equipment arrangements, spares, and similar considerations.

When data sheets and/or specifications are made a part of a contract, the characteristics (type, size, arrangement, etc.) of equipment are established. But, unless otherwise specified, these are subject to change to suit over-all process unit requirements provided the specification requirements are satisfied. Limitations as to equipment characteristics or selection of vendors can affect cost and deliveries, and hence require preagreement.

Equipment selection with respect to specifications, spare units, spare parts, and servicing can affect maintenance, operating, and investment costs. It is the purchaser's responsibility to incorporate into the contract all requirements or limitations which affect cost. Equipment performance is usually guaranteed by the manufacturer. On special equipment extended guarantees, maintenance over a period of time, and supervision of or complete installation may be provided by the manufacturer. On most large equipment, the manufacturer provides field service with respect to installation.

Foundations and site selection, as specified in the contract, may be based on an assumed soils loading, with price revision after a soils test and evaluation. Unless otherwise specified, it is assumed that the owner will provide a clear and level site at grade elevation and free of above- and below-ground obstructions.

The flexibility of a contract is greatly increased where **contract extensions** provide means for the purchaser to authorize "work order requests" for work or services outside the scope of the contract, and for "specification changes" when required to increase the scope of the contract.

PROJECT APPROACH AND ADMINISTRATION

The participating engineering organizations must be in agreement as to their interpretation of the contract, particularly its basic philosophies, objectives, and emphasis, as well as project approach, administration, and coordination.

The production and sometimes the general engineering of a project may be performed by an isolated project task force, in which the project administrator is directly responsible for engineering decisions. Or the general engineering may be performed through a line engineering organization aligned in divisions and/or sections for each field of significant interest, with assignments and responsibilities authorized by the project administrator. In either approach, specialist or consulting engineers may assist with fundamental engineering direction and decisions, once the staff engineers have established engineering policies.

On large contracts the usual title of the project administrator is "project manager," with individual units or areas or smaller contracts assigned to project engineers. Detail assistance is contributed by assistant project engineers as necessary to suit the extent and complexity of the contract. Job engineers are provided in some engineering organizations for liaison and coordination of involved problems and to balance divisional emphasis. Similarly, job coordinators serve to expedite and coordinate.

In most large organizations, an engineering staff provides basic and fundamental engineering direction and is available to the project administrators and senior engineers for guidance on special problems. Often the staff is reinforced by retained or project consultants in special fields.

The project administrator is held responsible for the project, and all expenditures must have his approval. All correspondence with the purchaser and collaborating organizations is channeled through him, thus providing centralized and responsible control.

General Project Specifications. The general section of the project specifications should be available at the initiation of engineering design and usually includes:

1. A complete and detailed **process description** of the process for each unit or part of a project.
2. **Process flow diagrams** to indicate primary flow and include quantities, temperatures, pressures, flow phase and composition, equipment, and basic elements for primary control.
3. **Material balance** of raw materials and end products, including pertinent chemical characteristics and specifications.
4. A detailed **project description** to cover pertinent information as to the site, services furnished by customer, battery-limit conditions for utilities, specifications and standards (including any mandatory governmental rules and regulations), special design requirements, wind, earthquake, and climatic conditions.
5. Greater organizational contribution is encouraged when a statement of project **philosophy and emphasis**

is included. The philosophy should make clear all general objectives. Accomplishment is enhanced when the relative emphasis is clearly evident with respect to reliability, flexibility, economics, useful life, safety, and operability.

Schedules and Attendant Economies. The planning of a project for effective utilization of manpower and maximum coordination requires the establishment of schedules indicating priority, calendar time, and completion date for each essential step. An initial schedule, to be effective, must reflect careful review and agreement of procurement as to deliveries and of divisions performing the operations, and must be periodically revised to show immediate status and resulting revised predictions.

It is often stated that construction costs directly reflect the length of the construction period. This should be modified, however, to state that construction in the minimum period permitted by material shipments and non-premium labor is a starting point for economic construction. Further reduction in completion time by overtime, a maximum rather than an optimum labor force, extra shipping costs, etc., must be weighed against the value of the resulting benefits.

STANDARDIZATION AND SPECIFICATIONS

The extensive engineering involved on process plants can benefit greatly by effective standardization and specifications. Cooperative efforts on the part of professional societies and industrial organizations have resulted in certain codes, practices, standards, and specifications which simplify engineering and at the same time provide a guide to accepted practice.

The performance of engineering in any large field can also be benefited as to economics, effectiveness, accuracy, and calendar time when essentially repetitive designs can be standardized as for sample cooler piping, control-valve stations, and furnace-burner piping. Specifications for equipment can implement take-off and procurement and can minimize repetitive errors due to omissions and dependence on individual acquaintance with performance history.

Project **specifications** provide an organized summary of the basic requirements for the individual items custom engineered or selected for the project. A convenient check list includes: (1) permissible design soil loading, (2) depth of foundation below grade, (3) wind load, (4) earthquake design requirements, (5) building dimensions and construction, (6) vessel dimensions, internals, and supports, (7) equipment data sheets, (8) equipment capacities and characteristics, (9) access facilities, (10) applicable codes, standards, and general specifications, and attendant design basis, (11) applicable company and purchaser specifications and exceptions thereto, (12) materials, (13) dry- and wet-bulb temperatures for minimum and maximum design, (14) rain runoff, and (15) utilities.

Classification of Equipment. To facilitate identification throughout drawings and requisitions, and to permit readily clear reference during operation, standard classification is established for all areas, process units, and items. A basic letter is used for each class of equipment, and building, and a number suffix for individual items in that class. This may be combined with the process unit number as follows: E-101, fractionation tower in unit 1; E-201, absorber tower in unit 2; B-106, reheat furnace in unit 1; C-603, recycle gas cooler in unit 6. On large plants, it is convenient to break up units into areas and to designate drawings related thereto by a letter. Such subdivision also aids in project scheduling of design work, procurement, and construction.

Numbering systems may designate only the classification, sequential numbering, and drawing size, such as E-761-A. Or they may include the job number, *i.e.*, Job 5031-E-761-A.

PROJECT AND PROCESS ENGINEERING

A process plant project is limitless as to the variety of structures and equipment which may be covered. While process units are usually the primary engineering interest, the total project may involve transportation facilities, warehouses, docks, maintenance facilities, housing, streets, power plants, sanitary systems, etc. The steps which usually enter into a process plant project involve both process engineering and mechanical engineering.

The already selected process must be tailored to this specific project. The resulting process release includes process calculations including heat and material balances, process description, process flow sheet (shows only main process flow, omitting auxiliary flows, valves, etc.), process plot plan (a tentative simplified arrangement of principal equipment), and a controls diagram or requirements. In total, this establishes all basic information and data required for mechanical engineering design.

Mechanical engineering translates the process for engineering design, so that all basic engineering decisions are made, and arrangements and critical dimensions established. This involves the following steps:

Engineering flow sheets expand the process flow sheet into a complete design, showing all equipment in its association with all piping (main process flow, startup, blowdown, relief and venting, steam, water, air, regeneration, etc.). On complex installations flow sheets are subdivided between process, auxiliary, and utility services; or further into subdivisions of process services, and of utility services. Processes involving materials handling may show conveyors, etc., on the flow sheets.

Planning is the establishment of general configuration and includes a fully developed engineering plot plan and elevation studies as required to set equipment locations and elevations, as well as the locations and details for dimensionally significant items, such as large-diameter alloy piping or otherwise critical piping. The resulting arrangements must provide essential access and clearances for maintenance and turnaround. At this time decision must also be reached as to outdoor vs. indoor installation of certain equipment.

Utilities balance is developed to suit general objectives as to driver energy source, process and waste-heat recovery, offsite steam availability, cooling water, air cooling, electric, diesel, or gas engine power, air requirements, etc.

With flow sheets showing all valves, and planning sketches available, **line configuration** can be established permitting accurate sizing for entry on the engineering flow sheets.

With the flow sheets, and heat and material balances available, **overpressure protection** (relief valves and other means) can be established.

With process data, plot plans, flow sheets, and equipment details available to provide an intimate knowledge of the process, the content characteristics and the equipment limitations, **operating instructions** can now be written for safe and economic operation. Operating variables should be fully covered, including alternate feeds and intermediate or final products and reduced capacity. Any unusual demands on equipment or hazards to personnel must be recognized. Overpressure and overtemperature protection should be outlined with emphasis on locations involving dependence on operator infallibility, or routine checkout. Instructions specific to the project are more effective if isolated in separate volumes from the routine measures related to checking and preparing equipment for operation, warm-ups, servicing, venting, purging, draining, etc. Similarly, reference data on the unit and equipment are more readily available if in separate volumes.

OVER-ALL DESIGN CONSIDERATIONS

Decision as to central office vs. field performance of engineering is based on economics. Field engineering is usually advantageous only where extensive tie-in to existing equipment is involved. For the most part, design is discussed in other specific subject subsections (pressure vessels, piping, drivers, etc.). But certain problems which overlap the specialized fields of engineering deserve attention on the part of the project engineers. Some of these are as follows:

Over-all economics must be examined for decision as to a suitable extent of **heat conservation and recovery.**

The appreciable cost of gas-compression equipment and the trend toward lower-pressure systems may encourage neglect of the resulting cost of larger-diameter vessels, exchangers, and pipe. With sizable horsepower available, an over-all economic evaluation will often provide substantial savings for a **pressurized system.**

Plant Layout. Plant layout can influence over-all and erection costs, operating and maintenance costs, safety, appearance, convenience, and schedule completion. Before the initial layout is made, the plant requirements and characteristics are reviewed to determine the relative emphasis on individual aspects. For some plants, copper refineries, for example, the plant layout does not markedly affect investment costs, but **materials handling** is a major operating cost. The layout must therefore reflect careful consideration of this aspect, starting with establishment of the handling equipment, to facilitate material movement. In other plants, such as oil refineries, piping materials and installation constitute an appreciable portion of the total investments. Accordingly, the layout starting point is the engineering flow sheet, with equipment location selected to minimize total piping with special emphasis on reducing the length of expensive lines. The arrangement selected must be compatible with the locations of incoming and outgoing feed, utility, and product lines, and must provide for the flexibility necessary for piping-expansion effects.

The initial layout is then examined for isolation of furnaces and other fire hazards, equipment and personnel access and protection, turnaround servicing and cleaning, ease of maintenance, possible savings by using common foundations or structures, access by railroads and/or trucks, ease of erection so as to include maximum use of permanent structures for derrick support and minimum derrick requirements, control houses and other locations requiring constant presence of operating personnel, convenient view or frequent checking of sensitive equipment, and for isolation of equipment or piping subject to vibration, noise, or possible release of hazardous, irritating, or vision-impairing contents.

In final stages of the layout, all objectives and aspects are reexamined and in addition consideration is given to appearance with respect to surroundings. It is general experience that plants of favorable appearance achieve higher functional capabilities and improved safety, operation, and maintenance. For example, this approach has evolved the "in-line" design of oil-refinery process units, in which exchangers and vessels are placed on each side of a pipe bank with pumps under the pipe bank, and compressors usually are located together in one area. All pipe banks and roads cross at right angles, and all equipment is lined up and usually grouped by types.

The plant layout provides plot plans, which, to avoid interference, must be developed together with elevations of equipment structures, main piping runs, conveyors, pipe and conduit banks, underground piping, sewers, and conduits. These drawings act as the coordinating design basis for detail piping, electrical systems, structural steel and foundation construction drawings.

Over-all plant engineering planning may require only a few weeks, but with extremely complicated plants it may involve a year for a fully assessed layout. Each completion of large or complex plants requires two stages for early release; the over-all arrangement is first studied to allow later successive releases of planning sketches of individual process units or areas.

Materials and Equipment Fabrication. Process plant reliability, maintenance cost, and safety reflect the adequacy of materials and fabrication engineering. This more than justifies itself, from economic considerations alone, as an essential part of over-all process plant engineering. Materials engineering starts with a knowledge of the raw, intermediate, and finished product stocks as to their potential for materials deterioration.

The practice of leaving fabrication entirely to equipment and structure suppliers, and performing only routine inspection, risks unawareness of inadequate fabrication. In the absence of expert guidance, acceptance of below-standard equipment to avoid delay in project completion is an indefensible practice.

Individual equipment is covered by **requisitions** and materials are assembled in bills of material and/or requisition sheets. **Procurement** obtains competitive bids (except for low-cost items), places purchase orders, and expedites delivery to assure construction requirements. Bulk and miscellaneous materials, available locally, and most construction materials are field-purchased.

Project administration must be in continuous contact with **construction** field administration, to follow the timing of deliveries, inadequacies of delivered items, local site problems (as to utilities furnished, etc.). In some organizations the project manager becomes the field construction resident manager. In others the latter responsibility is that of a specialist construction manager, with the project manager directing engineering-construction coordination and liaison.

Inspection and Expediting. Experience has shown that inspection is essential on all pressure and heat-exchange equipment to protect the interests of the purchaser, by assuring at least a proportionate share of the manufacturers' supervision and more competent mechanics. Codes, specifications, and code inspection do not assure full adequacy, since their approach is related to minimum requirements; also, code inspection is not concerned with dimensional accuracy, the correction of which is often the cause of serious field delays. Inspection is the most effective means for expediting, since sufficient time is spent in the shop to establish what the fabricator has accomplished. Effective expediting is vital to the maintenance of construction schedules and effectiveness.

Cost and Schedule Control. Cost and schedule control go hand in hand since a realistic initial schedule is possible only if the total engineering and construction force hours have been accurately estimated.

Reliable estimating starts with the complete definition of a plant, with all individually significant components listed and described. Some general items which are difficult to estimate, such as piping, require further breakdown *e.g.*, process piping, alloy piping, water piping, steam piping, steam tracing, and sanitary piping. The estimate includes material costs, engineering hours, and construction hours. By using salary and wage rates (including fringe benefits), field materials, freight charges, insurance, field and home office costs, and general overhead and profit, the total project cost can be ascertained. Cost control is effected by buying material within budget (*i.e.*, estimated) figures, and engineering and field force costs are controlled by keeping hours within the budgets.

The over-all schedule is controlled by subdividing the engineering work and field construction work into as many steps as practical. Each step is scheduled as to the starting and completion dates. Schedule control is effected by ensuring that material and/or information is available in time for each step to start on schedule and that the required number of men are available to complete each step on time. The purchase of material should be scheduled from the time requisitions are needed to the time material must arrive on the job site. The purchasing schedule should include dates, such as when bids are to be solicited, when bids are due, and when approval is to be obtained from the owner.

PRESSURE AND PRESSURE STORAGE VESSELS

The objective of this subsection is to provide the chemical engineer with a general understanding of the many significant aspects of pressure vessels affecting safety, utility, and economics as a common basis for communication with the mechanical engineer in exercising their joint responsibilities.

Pressure vessels are often a most important element in process, power, and many other industrial plants. They provide a structural envelope for many functions, including heat exchange, separation, pressure storage, mixing and blending, chemical reactions, treating, and regeneration. To design and engineer a pressure vessel adequately requires, therefore, a broad and simultaneous appreciation of both process and mechanical considerations.

For simplicity and ease of orientation, this subsection will center around the A.S.M.E. Unfired Pressure Vessel Code (A.S.M.E.-U.F.P.V.C.), 1962 edition, as the most generally recognized and accepted code for pressure-vessel construction. The presentation will first summarize the present code requirements, followed by a discussion of broad considerations with respect to future trends in code coverage and user-industry practice. In addition an attempt is made to provide interim guidance on aspects which are either lacking or inadequate in the current codes.

Since the current A.S.M.E. and other codes are in a state of transition, this approach will familiarize the reader with the simplified rules and ample safety factors of the present code applicable to extremely ductile materials, as well as with the trend toward future code requirements technically adequate to establish several quality levels (or classes) of pressure vessels. Each class would represent a balanced association of requirements for materials, design, fabrication, and inspection for economic and effective application commensurate with the degree of vessel complexity, material sensitivity, and service and environmental severity.

Codes and Regulations. The A.S.M.E. Boiler and Pressure Vessel Code is the most universally accepted basis for vessel construction and has been adopted in whole or in part as a basis for legal jurisdiction in many states and cities in the United States, and in provinces and territories of Canada.

The wide acceptance of the A.S.M.E. Code, its adoption into law by many legal bodies, and the fact that some code sections apply only to a specific service (power boilers, heating boilers, etc.) have tended to foster the misconception that this and all other current pressure-equipment codes provide rules for construction suitable for any service or environment. Actually, the A.S.M.E. Code establishes only the *minimum* requirements which are essential for *all* vessels and boilers, and thus can be responsibly accepted as adequate only for *minimum* service demands. It is the individual *user* who is responsible for recognizing significant aspects of services and environment, including corrosion and deterioration, and those other important aspects, such as loadings, material analysis, shell thickness, and vessel complexity. The *user* alone is responsible for compliance with the law.

The A.S.M.E. Code is administered by a professional society through a main committee of engineers, appointed and responsible as individuals (but not as company or industry representatives), and a conference committee of enforcement authorities. The Code Committee meets regularly to consider requests for clarification or extension of the rules. Interpretations in the form of "Code Cases" of general interest are approved by Council and published in *Mechanical Engineering* for general knowledge and comment. In the absence of objections they become effective on the date of formal A.S.M.E. approval.

The Code Committee is provided with a technical and secretarial staff by the A.S.M.E., and inquiries relative to the code or specific cases should be addressed to the Secretary (currently J. D. Wilding) at A.S.M.E. offices, 345 East 47th St., New York 17, N.Y. Cases are annually reviewed as to the necessity for their continuance or their incorporation into code revisions. Changes in code policy or coverage are often initiated through "special rulings" in such cases. A current example is on nuclear service applications for which a series of "cases" has been issued. Familiarity with material covered by the Code Cases as well as the code itself is therefore an essential consideration. Proposed revisions of the code are also published in *Mechanical Engineering* for comment before final adoption.

In view of the foregoing procedures and their administration, the A.S.M.E. Code is widely accepted as suitable for legal adoption by direct reference. Such legislation usually provides a board for boiler and pressure-vessel regulation, and an enforcement division administered by a chief engineer. A.S.M.E. Code revisions usually become effective with formal Code Committee adoption. A.S.M.E. case interpretations usually require board or chief inspector approval, which may delay the date of their effectiveness, or require modification or rejection of the case, in whole or in part. Similarly, board or chief inspector orders may supplement or modify either the applicability or requirements of parts of the code. Certain state charters (such as those of the Commonwealth of Pennsylvania and the state of Ohio) do not permit adoption through reference, and these states accordingly maintain a state code, which is usually not identical with the A.S.M.E. Code.

Construction not covered by or deviating from the code must be submitted for approval to the local authority having jurisdiction, and is usually authorized for service as a "State Special" rather than as an A.S.M.E. vessel.

For full conformance to the code, a vessel must be of approved materials, with design, fabrication, examination, and tests meeting code requirements, all as certified by a manufacturer authorized to apply the code stamp, and by the qualified inspector, who performs the required inspection, and witnesses the tests and application of the stamp. Stamps are issued only to manufacturers in the

United States and Canada, in order to assure acceptable responsibility for interchange between jurisdictions. Vessels manufactured elsewhere can conform to code requirements and data sheets, but they cannot be stamped and their acceptability must therefore be established with the local authorities having jurisdiction.

CURRENT A.S.M.E. CODE REQUIREMENTS

Significant current requirements of Section VIII, Unfired Pressure Vessels, of the A.S.M.E. Boiler and Pressure Vessel Code (1962 edition) are summarized in the following paragraphs, with the presentation aimed primarily at welded and seamless construction. Riveted, brazed, and other constructions are not commonly used in the process industries, but in general they involve the same basic requirements; the code includes limited rules for riveted and brazed construction and also for cast iron and nodular cast iron. While summarized data and formulas are included, their purpose is for rough appraisal of proportions and feasibility, and not for actual design.

The scope of Section VIII of the A.S.M.E. Code and the basis of its requirements may be summarized as follows:

1. Rules cover *minimum* construction requirements for the design, fabrication, inspection, and certification of unfired pressure vessels.
2. Application of code symbol U (inspected by qualified inspector) or UM (exempt from inspection) obligates the manufacturer to comply with applicable code requirements.
3. Combinations of fabrication methods (welding, riveting, brazing, seamless forgings, etc.) and code covered materials are acceptable, provided code requirements for each are followed, and vessel marked as required by paragraph UG-116.
4. Code does not cover all details of design and construction; it is intended that, where specific rules are lacking, the manufacturer subject to inspector's approval is to provide details as safe as those for which rules are provided.
5. The fundamental rules for design and tests serve as a sufficient basis for the inspector to judge safe construction justifying application of the code stamp.

Pressure vessels within the scope of the rules of Section VIII of the A.S.M.E. Code are outlined in Table 24-1. The specific requirements of the code as to service and vessel contents are given in Table 24-2. Except for these services, the code does not provide any further restrictions.

MATERIALS OF CONSTRUCTION

The selection of materials of construction and their heat-treatment and fabrication suitable for the service and environment are the responsibility of the user.

Table 24-1. Pressure Vessels Covered by Scope of ASME Code Section VIII Rules[a,b]

Line	Vessel type	Vessel contents	Limitations: Size	Limitations: Pressure	Limitations: Temperature	Required code symbol[c]
1	Unfired pressure vessel	Not restricted	Over 6 in. inside diameter	Internal or external pressure above 15 lb./sq. in. with 3000 lb./sq. in. maximum internal	Any temperature for which allowable stresses are provided. Below −20°F. provide materials meeting requirements of para. UG-84	U
2	Unfired pressure vessel	Water storage tanks	Water containing capacity greater than 120 gal.	Internal or external pressure above 15 lb./sq. in. with 3000 lb./sq. in. maximum internal	Any temperature for which allowable stresses are provided.	U
3	Unfired pressure vessel	Indirectly heated hot-water storage tanks	Water containing capacity greater than 120 gal.	Internal or external pressure above 15 lb./sq. in. with 3000 lb./sq. in. maximum internal	Any temperature for which allowable stresses are provided.	U
			Over 6 in. inside diameter	Internal or external pressure above 15 lb./sq. in. with 3000 lb./sq. in. maximum internal	Water temperature above 200°F.	U
			Over 6 in. inside diameter	Internal or external pressure above 15 lb./sq. in. with 3000 lb./sq. in. maximum internal	Heat input to water above 200,000 B.t.u./hr.	U
4	Unfired pressure vessel	Not restricted	5 cu. ft. and less	250 lb./sq. in. and less	Any temperature for which allowable stresses are provided. Below −20°F. provide materials meeting requirements of para. UG-84	UM[e]
5	Unfired pressure vessel	Not restricted	1½ cu. ft. and less	Internal or external pressure above 15 lb./sq. in. with 3000 lb./sq. in. maximum internal	Any temperature for which allowable stresses are provided. Below −20°F. provide materials meeting requirements of para. UG-84	UM[e]
6	Unfired pressure vessel[f]	Steam generation	Over 6 in. inside diameter	Internal or external pressure above 15 lb./sq. in. with 3000 lb./sq. in. maximum internal	Any temperature for which allowable stresses are provided. Below −20°F. provide materials meeting requirements of para. UG-84	U
7	Unfired steam boiler[g]	Steam generation	Over 6 in. inside diameter	Internal or external pressure above 15 lb./sq. in. with 3000 lb./sq. in. maximum internal	Any temperature for which allowable stresses are provided. Below −20°F. provide materials meeting requirements of para. UG-84	U

[a] Pressure vessels subject to Federal control are not included.
[b] Code jurisdiction over external piping terminates at the first circumferential joint for welded construction, the face of the first flange in bolted flange connections, and the first threaded joint in that type of connection.
[c] Any vessel which meets all the requirements of the code, including inspection, may be stamped with the U symbol even though exempt from such stamping.
[d] Includes tanks containing air which serves only as a cushion.
[e] Code symbol UM denotes vessel not inspected by a qualified inspector but that the vessel complies in all other respects with the code requirements. Vessels in this category are exempt from such inspection.
[f] Vessels in which steam is generated shall be classed as unfired pressure vessels if: (1) vessels are known as evaporators or heat exchangers, (2) steam is generated in the vessel incidental to the operation of a process system containing a number of pressure vessels, such as is used in chemical and petroleum products manufacture.
[g] All other unfired pressure vessels in which steam is generated shall be classed as unfired steam boilers and may be constructed to Sections I or VIII. Note additional requirements for this classification in Table 24-2.

Table 24-2. Specific Code Requirements vs. Service and/or Vessel Contents

Vessel		Material of construction			Design metal temp.	Design pressure[b]	Stress relief	Radiography	Welded joints[a]	
Type	Service or contents	Class	Spec.	Grade					Category (see Fig. 24-1)	Type (see Table 24-7)
Unfired pressure vessel	Not restricted except for lethal[c] and nuclear[d] services	UCS	SA 7, 113, and 283	[e]	−20°F. to 650°F.	....	[f]	[f]	⅝ in. max. thickness for plates having strength welding	
			Any except SA 7, 113, and 283	Any	−20°F. and above[g]	....	[f]	[f]		
					Below[i] −20°F.[h]	....	Required	[f]	A B and C	1 1 or 2
		UNF	Any	Any	−325°F.[j] and above[g]	....	Not required	[f]		
		UHA	Any	Any	−20°F. and above[g]	....	Not required	[f]		
					Below −20°F. to −325°F.	....	Not required	[f]	A B and C	1 1 or 2
					Below −325°F.[h]	....	Not required	[f]	A B and C	1 1 or 2
		UCL	Any	Any	Requirements for lined or clad construction shall be as indicated for the base material, except that when design calculations are based on the full thickness of clad plate the maximum design metal temperature is the lower of the values for which allowable stresses are given (base vs. cladding)					
		UCN	SA 395	......	−20°F. to 650°F.	1000 lb./sq. in. max.				
	Not permissible for lethal, nuclear or flammable substances:	UCI	SA 278	Any						
	Gases, steam or other vapors				450°F. and below	160 lb./sq. in. max.	Not required			
	Liquids				350°F. and below	160 lb./sq. in. max.	Not required			
	Liquid[k]				120°F. and below	250 lb./sq. in. max.	Not required			
	[l]				450°F. and below	300 lb./sq. in. max.	Not required			
	Liquids, gases, steam, or other vapors	UCI	SA 278[m]	40, 50, and 60	650°F. and below	250 lb./sq. in. max.	Stress-relief anneal required above 450°F.			
	Lethal[c]	UCS	Any, except SA 7, 113, and 283	Any	−20°F. and above	....	Required	Full	A B and C	1 1 or 2
					Below −20°F.	....	Required	Full	A B and C	1 1 or 2
		UNF	Any	Any	−325°F.[j] and above	....	Not required	Full	A B and C	1 1 or 2
		UHA	Any	Any	Above −20°F. to −325°F.	....	[f]	Full	A B and C	1 1 or 2
					Below −325°F.	....	[f]	Full	A B and C	1 1 or 2
		UCL	Any	Any	Same as for UCL above					
	Nuclear	See note *d*								
Unfired steam boiler	Steam generation	UCS	Any, except SA 7, 113, and 283	Any	100°F. and above[g]	50 lb./sq. in. and less	[f]	[f]		
						Greater than 50 lb./sq. in	Required	Full	A B and C	1 1 or 2

[a] Unless specifically indicated, the type of joint required for the different weld categories is not restricted except as provided by column 3, Limitations, of Table 24-7.

[b] Design pressures when not indicated are limited to above 15 lb./sq. in. for external and internal pressures, with 3000 lb./sq. in. maximum internal.

[c] The code definition for lethal substances is as follows: By "lethal substances" are meant poisonous gases or liquids of such a nature that a very small amount of the gas or of the vapor of the liquid mixed or unmixed with air is dangerous to life when inhaled. For purposes of the code this class includes substances of this nature which are stored under pressure or may generate a pressure if stored in a closed vessel. Some such substances are hydrocyanic acid, carbonyl chloride, cyanogen, mustard gas, and xylyl bromide. For design purposes under this code, chlorine, ammonia, natural or manufactured gas, any liquefied petroleum gas (such as propane, butane, butadiene), and vapors of any other petroleum products are not classified as lethal substances.

[d] Nuclear vessels, as equipment integral with nuclear power plants, shall be constructed in accordance with either the requirements of A.S.M.E. Code, Section I, or Section VIII, except as these requirements are specifically modified by cases (A.S.M.E. Boiler and Pressure Vessel Code Interpretations) pertaining to nuclear installations. Since design for nuclear service requires very special handling and knowledge reference is herein made only to the present code cases: 1270-N, 1271-N, 1272-N, 1273-N, 1274-N, and 1275-N entitled, respectively, "General Requirements for Nuclear Vessels," "Safety Devices," "Containment and Intermediate Containment Vessels," "Nuclear Reactor Vessels and Primary Vessels," "Special Material Requirements," and "Inspection Requirements."

[e] Steel must be manufactured by the open-hearth or electric-furnace processes.

[f] Stress-relief and radiographic requirements are not required by the service. See Table 24-9 for stress-relief and radiographic requirements related to material and material thickness.

[g] When no upper temperature limit is given, material may be used at the temperature for which allowable stresses are provided.

[h] When no lower temperature limit is given, material may be used at any temperature below the value indicated provided the requirements of code paragraph UG-84 are fulfilled at the design metal temperature.

[i] If material or weld metal is not required to be impact-tested in accordance with code paragraph UG-84, use "−20°F. and above" category for requirements.

[j] For temperatures below −325°F. the user is responsible that by appropriate tests the material and weld metal are proved satisfactory for the intended service.

[k] For liquids at temperatures less than their boiling point at design pressure.

[l] For parts such as bolted heads, covers, or closures which do not form a major component of the pressure vessel.

[m] Distribution of metal in pressure-containing walls of the casting must be approximately uniform.

Where the contents under service conditions involve **corrosion,** additional thickness compatible with the intended life shall be provided. Deterioration either as impairment of structural capacity (due to temperature embrittlement, hydrogen embrittlement, or that due to structure or phase changes) or as cracking (intergranular attack, stress, or fatigue corrosion) must be weighed by user in arriving at a choice of materials. The code provides limited guidance in non-mandatory appendixes which include an appendix NF for non-ferrous materials, and appendix HA for high-alloy steels.

Identification and Certification. Materials are required to be identified and certified to a code-approved specification. Materials not fully identified or certified can be used provided they meet specific code requirements.

Weldability. Materials to be welded are required to be demonstrated as weldable by successfully accomplished weld procedure tests, according to Section IX. Carbon or low-alloy steels with a carbon content greater than 0.35 per cent are not permitted to be used in welded construction or shaped by oxygen cutting.

Combinations of Materials. Combinations of materials may be used in the design and construction of a vessel provided the rules applicable to each material are followed and the qualification requirements of Section IX, paragraph Q-11, for welding dissimilar materials are met. The code cautions that, with dissimilar materials, the design and fabrication must favor the dissimilar joint to avoid service difficulties (particularly at elevated temperature or under cyclic temperatures) which result from temperature stresses due to differences in coefficients of expansion, and from metallurgical effects. With non-ferrous materials, galvanic corrosion may be significant in the presence of electrolytes.

Low-temperature Materials. For design temperatures below −20°F., paragraph UG-84 requires that base materials, weld deposits, and the heat-affected zone of the base material meet the specified impact test requirements, namely, 15 ft.-lb. minimum for a standard keyhole notch Charpy bar test. Impact tests are not required for: (1) Material subject to temperatures below −20°F., due only to seasonal atmospheric temperature. (2) Material of a vessel when the thickness is determined using a pressure 2.5 times the maximum operating pressure while at temperature below −20°F., while satisfying normal code requirements for any pressure to which it would be subjected at temperatures of −20°F. or above. (3) Non-ferrous materials of part UNF down to −325°F., inclusive. (For lower temperatures the user is required to satisfy himself by tests, or otherwise, that the material is suitable.) (4) Cast-iron materials of part UCI.

For high-alloy steel materials of part UHA, impact tests are required for: (1) All materials at operating temperatures below −325°F. except for types 304, 304L and 347 for which the temperature is −425°F. (2) For the following at operating temperatures below −20°F.: (*a*) ferritic chromium stainless steels, (*b*) austenitic chromium-nickel stainless steels with carbon content in excess of 0.10 per cent, (*c*) all castings, (*d*) all welds, (*e*) austenitic chromium-nickel stainless steels with a nickel or chromium content in excess of the A.I.S.I. standard analysis range for the specified type number and physical form, (*f*) type 309, 310, 316, 309Cb, 310Cb or 316Cb material, including the weld metal, if it is to be stress-relieved at temperatures below 1650°F.

Specific Material Requirements. Forgings and rolled materials shall have been worked sufficiently to remove the coarse ingot structure.

Cast or forged steel **flanges** and **fittings** in accordance with A.S.A. B16.5-1961 may be used within the assigned ratings of that standard. Cast-iron flanges and fittings in accordance with A.S.A. B16.1-1960 and B16.2-1960 may be used in whole or as part of a pressure vessel for pressures not exceeding the American Standard ratings at temperatures not exceeding 450°F.

Integrally **clad plate** used in construction in which any part of the cladding is used in the design calculations shall conform to one of the following specifications: SA 263, 264, or 265. Each such plate shall be subjected to a shear test described by the specification and shall show a minimum shear strength of 20,000 lb./sq. in. When calculations are based on the plate thickness exclusive of the cladding thickness, only the base material need be in accordance with a code-approved specification; any metallic cladding material of weldable quality is acceptable which in the judgment of the user is suitable for the intended service.

Corrosion-resistant linings to be attached by welding to a base material conforming to a code-approved specification may be of any metallic material of weldable quality that in the judgment of the user is suitable for the intended service.

Pipe and **tubing** may be used for unfired pressure vessel shells provided the material is manufactured by the open-hearth or electric-furnace process. If of welded construction, pipe and tubing are further limited to a maximum nominal diameter of 30 in.

Castings, except for cast iron, are to have a casting quality factor, which shall be applied to the allowable stress values, not greater than 80 per cent for castings inspected only to the minimum requirements of the material specification. Factors of 90 per cent for non-ferrous and nodular-iron castings and 100 per cent for steel castings are permitted when the casting is subjected to specified additional inspection requirements. Castings to which a 90 or 100 per cent quality factor is to be applied are required to have this factor clearly stamped on the casting by the manufacturer.

Integrally **finned tubes** are permitted provided they conform in every respect with one of the specifications of Section II and certain additional requirements covered in paragraph UG-9(b) of Section VIII.

Bolting, when used and of material other than carbon steel, shall be threaded full length or shall be machined down to the root diameter of the thread in the unthreaded portion. Nuts shall engage the bolt threads for the full depth of thread. The use of washers is optional but when used shall be of wrought material. Nuts shall be semifinished, chamfered, and trimmed, and shall conform at least to the dimensions given in A.S.A. B18.2-1960, except that for internal construction, where clearance is a problem, other dimensions may be used if the nut is of equivalent strength.

Structural shapes, when used for pressure parts such as flange rings, stiffeners, stays, and similar parts, shall conform to a code-approved specification for bars, bolting, or rivets. For non-pressure parts, non-identified or non-code material is acceptable, subject to inspector and manufacturer approval.

DESIGN FOR PRESSURE

The code design formulas incorporate an approximate evaluation of the maximum direct (membrane) stress due to pressure which, in conjunction with joint efficiencies and allowable stresses, establish the required thickness. The membrane stresses resulting from weight, wind, and earthquake can be established following conventional structural design. For similar stresses due to impact loads and temperature gradients, no guidance is provided relative to their evaluation. No mention is made of cycles of load application and attendant potential fatigue damage. The inadequacy of the code with respect to localized stresses in code vessels is acknowledged in the following footnote to paragraph UG-23:

It is recognized that high localized and secondary bending stresses may exist in vessels designed and fabricated in accordance with these rules. Insofar as practical, design rules for details have been written to hold such stresses at a safe level consistent with experience.

A proof hydrostatic test of the vessel part is required when the configuration is such that the design stress cannot be evaluated with assurance of accuracy or when any doubt exists as to the safety of the vessel. The code includes detailed rules for such "proof" tests.

Design Pressure and Temperature. Design pressure and temperature are the coincident values, under normal operating conditions, resulting in the greatest required thickness. The temperature is based on the actual metal temperature expected under normal operating conditions for the part considered.

For internal pressure, *the design pressure must not be lower than the relief-valve set pressure.* A code footnote recommends that the design pressure include a suitable margin above the intended normal operating pressure to allow for probable pressure surges up to the setting of the pressure-relieving devices. For vessels operating under a partial vacuum, the minimum pressure for design is the smaller of 15 lb./sq. in. or 125 per cent of the maximum possible external pressure. For vessels designed for internal pressure and subject to occasional external pressures of 15 lb./sq. in. or less, the code does not require external pressure design to the code rules.

The maximum differential in pressure between the inside and outside of a vessel, or between two chambers of a compartmented vessel, which can exist at any time, must be considered for design.

Loadings. The following loadings are required by paragraph UG-22 to be considered in the design of a vessel. The code does not provide formulas or guidance for the evaluation of thickness or stress due to the loadings marked below with a double asterisk; those marked with a single asterisk can be approximated as to direct stress by conventional structural analysis:

** Impact loads, including rapidly fluctuating pressures.

* Weight of the vessel and normal contents under operating or test conditions. (This includes additional pressure due to static head of liquids.)

* Superimposed loads, such as other vessels, operating equipment, insulation, corrosion-resistant or erosion-resistant linings, and piping.

* Wind loads and earthquake loads when required.

** Reactions of support lugs, rings, and saddles or other types of supports. (Non-mandatory Appendix G,

Table 24-3. Maximum Allowable Stress Values in Tension for Carbon and Low-alloy Steel, in Pounds per Square Inch, Class UCS*

Material and specification No.	Grade	Nominal composition	P No.	Spec. min. tensile	Notes	For metal temperatures not exceeding °F.											
						−20 to 650	700	750	800	850	900	950	1000	1050	1100	1150	1200
Plate steels:																	
Carbon steels																	
SA 7	.....	....	1	60,000	a,b	12,650											
SA 113	C	....	1	48,000	a	11,050											
SA 201	A	C, Si	1	55,000	...	13,750	13,250	12,050	10,200	8,350	6,500	4,500	2,500				
SA 201	B	C, Si	1	60,000	...	15,000	14,350	12,950	10,800	8,650	6,500	4,500	2,500				
SA 212	A	C, Si	1	65,000	...	16,250	15,500	13,850	11,400	8,950	6,500	4,500	2,500				
SA 212	B	C, Si	1	70,000	...	17,500	16,600	14,750	12,000	9,250	6,500	4,500	2,500				
SA 283	A	....	1	45,000	a	10,350											
SA 283	B	....	1	50,000	a	11,500											
SA 283	C	....	1	55,000	a	12,650											
SA 283	D	....	1	60,000	a	12,650											
SA 285	A	....	1	45,000	c,d	11,250	11,000	10,250	9,000	7,750	6,500						
SA 285	B	....	1	50,000	c,d	12,500	12,100	11,150	9,600	8,050	6,500						
SA 285	C	....	1	55,000	c,d	13,750	13,250	12,050	10,200	8,350	6,500						
SA 300	.....	....	...	......	e												
Low-alloy steels																	
SA 202	A	Cr, Mn, Si	4	75,000	...	18,750	17,700	15,650	12,600	9,550	6,500	4,500	2,500				
SA 202	B	Cr, Mn, Si	4	85,000	...	21,250	19,800	17,700	12,800	9,900	6,500	4,500	2,500				
SA 203	A, D	2½ and 3½ Ni	4	65,000	...	16,250	15,500	13,850	11,400	8,950	6,500	4,500	2,500				
SA 203	B, E	2½ and 3½ Ni	4	70,000	...	17,500	16,600	14,750	12,000	9,250	6,500	4,500	2,500				
SA 204	A	C, ½ Mo	3	65,000	...	16,250	16,250	16,250	15,650	14,400	12,500	10,000	6,250				
SA 204	B	C, ½ Mo	3	70,000	...	17,500	17,500	17,500	16,900	15,000	12,750	10,000	6,250				
SA 204	C	C, ½ Mo	3	75,000	...	18,750	18,750	18,750	18,000	15,900	13,000	10,000	6,250				
SA 302	A	Mn, ½ Mo	3	75,000	...	18,750	18,750	18,750	18,000	15,900	13,000	10,000	6,250				
SA 302	B	Mn, ½ Mo	3	80,000	...	20,000	20,000	20,000	19,100	16,800	13,250	10,000	6,250				
SA 357	.....	5 Cr, ½ Mo	5	60,000	f	......	13,400	13,100	12,800	12,400	11,500	10,000	7,300	5,200	3,300	2,200	1,500
SA 387	A	½ Cr, ½ Mo	3	65,000	...	16,250	16,250	16,250	15,650	14,400	12,500	10,000	6,250				
SA 387	B	1 Cr, ½ Mo	4	60,000	...	15,000	15,000	15,000	14,750	14,200	13,100	11,000	7,500	5,000	2,800	1,550	1,000
SA 387	C	1¼ Cr, ½ Mo-Si	4	60,000	...	15,000	15,000	15,000	15,000	14,400	13,100	11,000	7,800	5,500	4,000	2,500	1,200
SA 387	D	2¼ Cr, 1 Mo	5	60,000	...	15,000	15,000	15,000	15,000	14,400	13,100	11,000	7,800	5,800	4,200	3,000	2,000
SA 353	A	9 Ni	10	90,000	...	22,500											
SA 353	B	9 Ni	10	95,000	...	23,750											

* Extracted from the 1962 edition of the A.S.M.E. Boiler and Pressure Vessel Code, Unfired Pressure Vessels, with permission of the publisher, the American Society of Mechanical Engineers, New York 17, N.Y.

The stress values in this table may be interpolated to determine values for intermediate temperature.

Stress values in restricted shear such as dowel bolts, rivets, or similar construction in which the shearing member is so restricted that the section under consideration would fail without reduction of area shall be 0.80 times the values in the table.

Stress values in bearing shall be 1.60 times the values in the above table.

[a] These stress values are one-fourth the specified minimum tensile strength multiplied by a quality factor of 0.92, except for SA 283, Grade D, and SA 7.

[b] These allowable stress values apply also to structural shapes.

[c] Flange quality in this specification not permitted over 850°F.

[d] For service temperatures above 850°F. it is recommended that killed steels containing not less than 0.10 per cent residual silicon be used. Killed steels which have been deoxidized with large amounts of aluminum and rimmed steels may have creep and stress-rupture properties in the temperature range above 850°F., which are somewhat less than those on which the values in the above table are based.

[e] The stress values to be used for temperatures below −20°F. when steels are made to conform with Specification SA 300 shall be those that are given in the column for −20 to 650°F.

[f] Maximum allowable stress values for temperatures below 700°F. are given below.

Spec.	Grade	No.	−20 to 400	500	600	650
SA 357	...	5	15,000	14,500	14,000	13,700

Table 24-4. Maximum Allowable Stress Values in Tension for High-alloy Plate Steel, in Pounds per Square Inch, Class UHA*

Material and specification No.	Type	Nominal composition	Spec. min. tensile	Notes	For metal temperatures not exceeding °F.																						
					−20 to 100	200	300	400	500	600	650	700	750	800	850	900	950	1000	1050	1100	1150	1200	1250	1300	1350	1400	1450	1500
SA 240	302	18 Cr, 8 Ni	75,000	a,d	18,750	17,000	16,000	15,450	15,100	14,900	14,850	14,800	14,700															
SA 240	302	18 Cr, 8 Ni	75,000	d	18,750	16,650	15,000	13,650	12,500	11,600	11,200	10,800	10,400															
SA 240	304	18 Cr, 8 Ni	75,000	a,d	18,750	17,000	16,000	15,450	15,100	14,900	14,850	14,800	14,700	14,550	14,300	14,000	13,400	12,500	10,000	7,500	5,750	4,500	3,250	2,450	1,800	1,400	1,000	750
SA 240	304	18 Cr, 8 Ni	75,000	d	18,750	16,650	15,000	13,650	12,500	11,600	11,200	10,800	10,400	10,000	9,700	9,400	9,100	8,800	8,500	7,500	5,750	4,500	3,250	2,450	1,800	1,400	1,000	750
SA 240	304L	18 Cr, 8 Ni	70,000	a	17,500	17,000	16,000	15,000	14,000	13,000	12,500	12,000	11,500	11,000														
SA 240	304L	18 Cr, 8 Ni	70,000	...	17,500	15,300	13,100	11,000	9,700	9,000	8,750	8,500	8,300	8,100														
SA 240	309S	23 Cr, 13 Ni	75,000	d	18,750	18,750	17,300	16,700	16,600	16,500	16,450	16,400	16,200	15,700	14,900	13,800	12,500	10,500	8,500	6,500	5,000	3,800	2,900	2,300	1,750	1,300	900	750
SA 240	310S	25 Cr, 20 Ni	75,000	b,d	18,750	18,750	18,500	18,200	17,700	17,200	16,900	16,600	16,250	15,700	14,900	13,800	12,500	11,000	9,750	8,500	7,250	6,000	4,750	3,500	2,350	1,600	1,100	750
SA 240	310S	25 Cr, 20 Ni	75,000	c,d	18,750	18,750	18,500	18,200	17,700	17,200	16,900	16,600	16,250	15,700	14,900	13,800	12,500	11,000	7,100	5,000	3,600	2,500	1,450	750	450	350	250	200
SA 240	316	18 Cr, 10 Ni, 2 Mo	75,000	d	18,750	18,750	17,900	17,500	17,200	17,100	17,050	17,000	16,900	16,750	16,500	16,000	15,100	14,000	12,200	10,400	8,500	6,800	5,300	4,000	3,000	2,350	1,850	1,500
SA 240	316L	18 Cr, 10 Ni, 2 Mo	70,000	a	17,500	17,500	15,800	14,750	14,000	13,600	13,450	13,250	13,000	12,700	12,250													
SA 240	316L	18 Cr, 10 Ni, 2 Mo	70,000	...	17,500	16,250	14,500	12,000	11,000	10,150	9,800	9,450	9,100	8,800	8,500													
SA 240	317	19 Cr, 13 Ni, 3 Mo	75,000	d	18,750	18,750	17,900	17,500	17,200	17,100	17,050	17,000	16,900	16,750	16,500	16,000	15,100	14,000	12,200	10,400	8,500	6,800	5,300	4,000	3,000	2,350	1,850	1,500
SA 240	321	18 Cr, 10 Ni, Ti	75,000	d	18,750	18,750	17,000	15,800	15,200	14,900	14,850	14,800	14,700	14,450	14,300	14,100	13,850	13,500	13,100	12,500	8,000	5,000	3,600	2,700	2,000	1,550	1,200	1,000
SA 240	347	18 Cr, 10 Ni, Cb	75,000	d	18,750	18,750	17,000	15,800	15,200	14,900	14,850	14,800	14,700	14,450	14,300	14,100	13,850	13,500	13,100	12,500	8,000	5,000	3,600	2,700	2,000	1,550	1,200	1,000
SA 240	348	18 Cr, 10 Ni, Cb, Ti	75,000	d	18,750	18,750	17,000	15,800	15,200	14,900	14,850	14,800	14,700	14,550	14,300	14,100	13,850	13,500	13,100	12,500	8,000	5,000	3,600	2,700	2,000	1,550	1,200	1,000
SA 240	405	12 Cr, Al	60,000	...	15,000	15,000	14,700	14,400	13,950	13,400	13,000	12,450	11,800	11,000	10,100	9,100	8,000	4,000										
SA 240	410	13 Cr	65,000	...	16,250	15,600	15,100	14,600	14,150	13,850	13,700	13,400	13,100	12,750	12,100	11,000	8,800	6,400	4,400	2,900	1,750	1,000						
SA 240	410S	13 Cr	60,000	...	15,000	14,450	14,000	13,500	13,100	12,850	12,700	12,500	12,250	11,950	11,600	11,000	8,800	6,400	4,400	2,900	1,750	1,000						

* Extracted from the 1962 edition of the A.S.M.E. Boiler and Pressure Vessel Code, Unfired Pressure Vessels, with permission of the publisher, the American Society of Mechanical Engineers, New York 17, N.Y.

The stress values in this table may be interpolated to determine values for intermediate temperature. Stress values in restricted shear such as dowel bolts, rivets, or similar construction in which the shearing member is so restricted that the section under consideration would fail without reduction of area shall be 0.80 times the values in the above table. Stress values in bearing shall be 1.60 times the values in the table.

[a] Because of the relatively low yield strength of this material, the higher stress values at temperatures from 200 through 1050°F. were established to permit the use of this material where slightly greater deformation is acceptable. The stress values within the above range exceed 62½ per cent but do not exceed 90 per cent of the yield strength at temperature. These stress values are not recommended for the design of flanges or piping.

[b] These stress values at temperatures of 1050°F. and above should be used only when assurance is provided that the steel has a predominant grain size not finer than A.S.T.M. No. 6.

[c] These stress values shall be considered basic values to be used when no effort is made to control or check the grain size of the steel.

[d] These stress values apply only when the carbon is 0.04 per cent or higher.

"Suggested Good Practice Regarding Design of Supports," provides only general suggestions, without specific guidance.)

** The effect of temperature gradients on maximum stress.

The maximum direct stress (average through wall thickness) due to any combination of these loadings expected during normal operation must be maintained within the code allowable stress value. Guidance is given relative to localized or secondary bending stress limits only in paragraph UA-5(e) for sharp cone-cylinder junctions exceeding 30 deg., which allows the average total membrane hoop stress at the junction to be 1½ *SE* and the maximum total longitudinal stress to be 4 *SE* (see notes for Table 24-10).

Where these loadings produce compressive stress there is a possibility of a buckling failure by elastic instability. The code prescribes an additional limiting compressive stress value for cylindrical shells equal to the *B* value read from the charts governing design for external pressure. For carbon steel this limit is approximately equal to $3,400,000t/D$ lb./sq. in. at 300°F., where t/D is the ratio of shell thickness to diameter. Tall slender vertical vessels generally require such a check for compressive loading due to weight plus wind or earthquake loading, and with internal pressure load assumed to be zero.

Allowable Stresses. Allowable stresses are tabulated in the code for each of the code material sections (UCS, UNF, UHA, UCI, UCL, and UCN) over the temperature range for which the material is permissible. Values are given at 50°F. intervals and may be interpolated for intermediate temperatures. Code Appendixes P and Q summarize the allowable stress bases for ferrous materials and for non-ferrous materials, respectively. The basis for cast iron is not formally presented in the code.

Tables 24-3, 24-4, 24-5, and 24-6 summarize allowable stresses with respect to temperature for the commonly used plate materials of classes UCS, UNF, and UHA only.

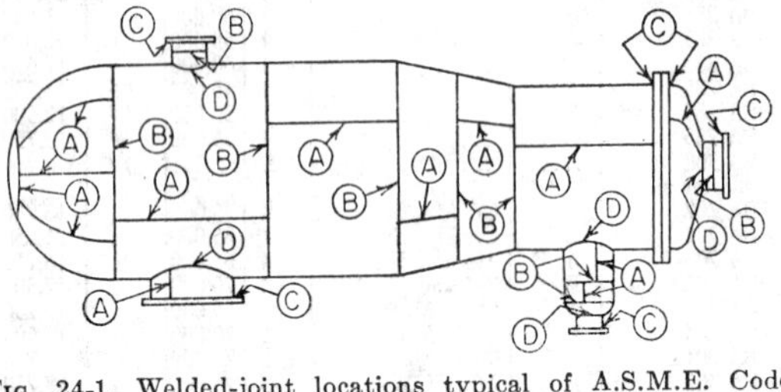

Fig. 24-1. Welded-joint locations typical of A.S.M.E. Code categories *A*, *B*, *C*, and *D*. (*Source: American Society of Mechanical Engineers.*)

Category *A*. Longitudinal welded joints within the main shell, communicating chambers (communicating chambers are defined as appurtenances to the vessel which intersect the shell or heads of a vessel and form an integral part of the pressure-containing enclosure, *e.g.*, sumps), transitions in diameter, or nozzles; any welded joint within a formed or flat head.

Category *B*. Circumferential welded joints within the main shell, communicating chambers, nozzles, or transitions in diameter including joints between the transition and a cylinder at either the large or small end; circumferential welded joints connecting formed heads to main shells, to transitions in diameter, to nozzles, or to communicating chambers.

Category *C*. Welded joints connecting flanges, Van Stone laps, tube sheets, or flat heads to main shell, to formed heads, to transitions in diameter, to nozzles, or to communicating chambers.

Category *D*. Welded joints connecting communicating chambers or nozzles to main shells, to transitions in diameter, or to heads, and those joints connecting nozzles to communicating chambers. (For nozzles at the small end of a transition in diameter, see Category *B*.)

Table 24-5. Maximum Allowable Stress Values in Tension for Aluminum and Aluminum Alloys, in Pounds per Square Inch, Class UNF*

Specification No.	Alloy designation A.S.T.M.	Alloy designation A.S.A.	Temper	Specified tensile strength, lb./sq. in.	Min. yield strength, lb./sq. in.	Notes	100 °F	150 °F	200 °F	250 °F	300 °F	350 °F	400 °F
SB 209	990A	1100	O	11,000	3,500	...	2,350	2,350	2,300	2,100	1,850	1,600	1,300
			H112	12,000	5,000	a,b	3,000	2,800	2,550	2,250	2,000	1,700	1,400
			H12	14,000	11,000	a	3,500	3,400	3,150	2,900	2,650	2,400	1,700
			H14	16,000	14,000	a	4,000	3,900	3,650	3,300	3,000	2,700	1,700
SB 209	GR20A	5052	O, H112	25,000	9,500	...	6,250	6,250	6,200	6,000	5,400	4,650	3,500
			H32	31,000	23,000	a	7,750	7,750	7,650	7,100	6,400	5,600	3,500
			H34	34,000	26,000	a	8,500	8,500	8,400	7,700	6,900	6,100	3,500
SB 209	GR40A	5154	O	30,000	11,000	...	7,350	7,350	7,350	7,000	6,400		
			H112	30,000	11,000	a	7,350	7,350	7,350	7,000	6,400		
			H32	36,000	26,000	a	9,000	8,950	8,850	8,250	7,400		
			H34	39,000	29,000	a	9,750	9,700	9,500	8,800	7,900		
SB 209	M1A	3003	O	14,000	5,000	...	3,350	3,150	2,900	2,700	2,400	2,100	1,800
			H112	14,500	6,000	a,c	3,600	3,250	3,000	2,800	2,500	2,200	1,900
			H12	17,000	12,000	a	4,250	4,000	3,800	3,600	3,300	3,000	2,650
			H14	20,000	17,000	a	5,000	4,850	4,700	4,400	4,000	3,500	3,100
SB 209	GM41A	5083	O	40,000	18,000	d	10,000	10,000					
			H113	44,000	31,000	a	11,000	11,000					
SB 209	GM51A	5456	O	42,000	19,000	...	10,500	10,400					
			H321	44,000	31,000	a	11,000	10,900					

* Extracted from the 1962 edition of the A.S.M.E. Boiler and Pressure Vessel Code, Unfired Pressure Vessels, with permission of the publisher, the American Society of Mechanical Engineers, New York 17, N.Y.

The stress values in this table may be interpolated to determine values for intermediate temperature.

Stress values in restricted shear such as dowel bolts, rivets, or similar construction in which the shearing member is so restricted that the section under consideration would fail without reduction of area shall be 0.80 times the values in the table.

Stress values in bearing shall be 1.60 times the values in the table.

[a] For welded construction, stress values for 0 material shall be used.

[b] For nominal thicknesses not greater than 2.000 in.; for thicker material the stress values for 0 material shall be used.

[c] For nominal thicknesses not greater than 0.500 in. the stress values for H12 material may be used; for thicker material the values listed shall be used.

[d] For nominal thicknesses not greater than 2.00 in.

Table 24-6. Maximum Allowable Stress Values in Tension for Nickel and High-nickel Alloys, in Pounds per Square Inch, Class UNF*

Material, form, and specification No.	Condition	Specified tensile strength, lb./sq, in.	Min. yield strength (0.2% offset), lb./sq. in.	100 °F	200 °F	300 °F	400 °F	500 °F	600 °F	700 °F	800 °F	900 °F	1000 °F	1100 °F	1200 °F
Nickel, plate, sheet, or strip:															
SB 162	Hot or cold rolled, annealed	55,000	15,000	10,000	10,000	10,000	10,000	10,000	10,000						
SB 162 (plate only)	Hot rolled, as rolled	55,000	20,000	13,000	13,300	13,300	13,300	12,500	11,500						
Low-carbon nickel, plate, sheet, or strip:															
SB 162	Hot rolled and hot or cold rolled, annealed	50,000	12,000	8,000	7,700	7,500	7,500	7,500	7,500	7,400	7,200	4,500	3,000	2,000	1,200
Nickel-copper, plate, sheet, or strip:															
SB 127	Hot or cold rolled, annealed	70,000	28,000	17,500	16,500	15,500	14,800	14,700	14,700	14,700	14,500	8,000			
SB 127 (plate only)	Hot rolled, as rolled	75,000	40,000	18,700	17,500	17,000	17,000	17,000	17,000	16,500	14,500	4,000			
Nickel-chromium-iron, plate, sheet, or strip:															
SB 168	Hot or cold rolled, annealed	80,000	30,000	20,000	18,600	18,000	18,000	18,000	18,000	17,500	17,000	16,000	7,000	3,000	2,000
SB 168 (plate only)	Hot rolled, as rolled	85,000	35,000	21,200	20,200	20,000	20,000	20,000	20,000	20,000	20,000	19,500	14,500	7,200	5,500
Nickel-molybdenum, plate, sheet:															
SB 333	Hot rolled annealed under 3/16 in.	115,000	50,000	22,000	20,000	20,000	20,000	20,000	20,000	20,000					
SB 333 (plate)	Hot rolled annealed 3/16 to 3/4 in. incl.	100,000	45,000	22,000	20,000	20,000	20,000	20,000	20,000	20,000					
SB 333 (plate)	Hot rolled annealed over 3/4 to 2 1/2 in. incl.	90,000	45,000	22,000	20,000	20,000	20,000	20,000	20,000	20,000					
Nickel-molybdenum-chromium, plate, sheet:															
SB 334	Hot rolled annealed under 3/16 in.	115,000	50,000	22,000	20,000	20,000	20,000	20,000	20,000	19,000	19,000	18,000	18,000		
SB 334 (plate)	Hot rolled annealed under 3/16 in.	100,000	45,000	22,000	20,000	20,000	20,000	20,000	20,000	19,000	19,000	18,000	18,000		
SB 334 (plate)	Hot rolled annealed over 3/4 to 2 1/2 in. incl.	90,000	45,000	22,000	20,000	20,000	20,000	20,000	20,000	19,000	19,000	18,000	18,000		

* Extracted from the 1962 edition of the A.S.M.E. Boiler and Pressure Vessel Code, Unfired Pressure Vessels, with permission of the publisher, The American Society of Mechanical Engineers, New York 17, N.Y.

The stress values in this table may be interpolated to determine values for intermediate temperature.

Stress values in restricted shear such as dowel bolts, rivets, or similar construction in which the shearing member is so restricted that the section under consideration would fail without reduction of area shall be 0.80 times the values in the table.

Stress values in bearing shall be 1.60 times the values in the table.

Table 24-7. Maximum Allowable Joint Efficiencies for Arc- and Gas-welded Joints*

No.	Type of joint description	Limitations	Degree of examination A: Fully radiographed	B: Spot examined[a]	C: Not spot examined[b]
1	Butt joints as attained by double welding or by other means which will obtain the same quality of deposited weld metal on the inside and outside weld surfaces to agree with the requirements of Par. UW-35. Welds using metal backing strips which remain in place are excluded	None	1.00	0.85	0.70
2	Single-welded butt joint with backing strip other than those included under 1 above	(a) None except as in (b). (b) Butt weld with one plate offset—for circumferential joints only, ⅝ in. max. thickness per Par. UW-13(c) and Fig. UW-13 (k)	0.90	0.80	0.65
3	Single-welded butt joint without use of backing strip	Circumferential joints only, not over ⅝ in. thick and not over 24 in. outside diameter	....	....	0.60
4	Double full-fillet lap joint	Longitudinal joints not over ⅜ in. thick. Circumferential joints not over ⅝ in. thick	....	....	0.55
5	Single full-fillet lap joints with plug welds	Circumferential joints for attachment of heads not over 24 in. outside diameter to shells not over ½ in. thick[c]	....	....	0.50
6	Single full-fillet lap joints without plug welds	(a) For the attachment of heads convex to pressure to shells not over ⅝ in. required thickness, only with use of fillet weld on inside of shell; or (b) for attachment of heads having pressure on either side, to shells not over 24 in. inside diameter and not over ¼ in. required thickness with fillet weld on outside of head flange only	....	....	0.45

* Extracted from the 1962 edition of the A.S.M.E. Boiler and Pressure Vessel Code, Unfired Pressure Vessels, with permission of the publisher, the American Society of Mechanical Engineers, New York 17, N.Y.

[a] Spot examination by radiographing in accordance with fabrication section rules.

[b] Visual examination only.

[c] Joints attaching hemispherical heads to shells are excluded.

Welded Joints. For purposes of distinguishing between the various welded joints involved on a vessel and establishing requirements applicable to each, the code has adopted a "category" grouping system as given in Fig. 24-1, page 24-12.

Joint efficiencies for arc- and gas-welded joints are established as a function of the degree of examination and are given in Table 24-7. The code provides some restrictions as to the type of joint permitted and minimum

Table 24-8. Minimum Permissible Plate Thickness After Forming

Without allowance for corrosion

Material class	Method of fabrication	Min. thickness, in. Service: Non-corrosive	Corrosive
UCS	Welded (UW) or brazed (UB)	3/32	3/32
	Riveted (UR)	3/16	3/16
	Any (unfired steam boilers only)	¼[a]	¼[a]
UNF	Welded (UW)	1/16	3/32
	Riveted (UR)	3/16	3/16
UHA	Welded (UW)	3/32 or 1/16[b]	3/32
	Riveted (UR)	3/16	3/16
UCL	Same as for material class UCS except that the minimum thickness shall be the total thickness for clad plate and the base-plate thickness for applied linings		

[a] This thickness may include the required corrosion allowance.

[b] For high-alloy materials in non-corrosive service 1/16 in. minimum applies.

examination as related to service (Table 24-2). Table 24-9 shows requirements for fully radiographed construction as related to material and thickness. Mandatory stress-relief requirements are also shown in these tables but such thermal treatment does not affect joint efficiency values.

Whenever full radiographing is not mandatory, the designer may elect to use the efficiencies in any of the three columns *A*, *B*, or *C* of Table 24-7 in design and the corresponding examination requirements. For column

Table 24-9. Radiographic and Stress-relief Requirements vs. Material and Thickness

For plate material listed in Tables 24-3 to 24-6 and for welded construction

Material class	Spec.	Grade	Full radiography[a] — Required for thickness, in., exceeding	Stress relief[b] — Required for thickness, in., exceeding
UCS	SA 201	A andB	1½	1¼ } or $\frac{D+50}{120}$ if lower[g]
	SA 212	A and B	1	1
	SA 285	A, B and C	1½	1¼
	SA 353	A and B	All thicknesses	1¼
	SA 202	A and B	1	0.58
	SA 203	A, B, D and E	1	0.58
	SA 204	A, B and C	1	0.58
	SA 302	A and B	1	All thicknesses
	SA 357	....	All thicknesses	All thicknesses
	SA 387	A	1	0.58
	SA 387	D	All thicknesses	All thicknesses
	SA 387	B and C	1	All thicknesses
UHA	SA 240	302	1½[c]	Not required
		304, 304L	1½[c]	Not required
		309S	1½[c]	Not required
		310S	1½[c]	Not required
		316, 316L	1½[c]	Not required
		317	1½[c]	Not required
		321	1½[c]	Not required
		347	1½[c]	Not required
		348	1½[c]	Not required
		405	All thicknesses[d]	All thicknesses[e]
		410	All thicknesses[d]	All thicknesses
	SA 240	410S	All thicknesses[d]	All thicknesses[e]
UNF	SB 333	....	⅜[f]	Not required
	SB 334	....	⅜[f]	Not required
	Other	....	1½	Not required

[a] For thicknesses or materials not required to be fully radiographed, welds shall be subject to spot radiography unless (1) design is for external pressure only, or (2) the entire vessel has been designed on the basis of reduced joint efficiencies (column *C* of Table 24-7) and with stresses not exceeding 80 per cent of the allowable.

[b] The thickness to be used in determining the stress-relief requirements is (1) the thinner of two adjacent butt-welded plates including head-to-shell connections, (2) the thicker of the shell or head plate in connections to intermediate heads of the type shown in Code Fig. UW-13f, (3) the thickness of the shell or head plate in nozzle attachment welds.

[c] All butt and fillet welds in vessels whose shell thickness exceeds ¾ in. shall also be examined for the detection of cracks by the fluid-penetrant method.

[d] Radiography of type 405 and 410 material with carbon content limited to 0.08 per cent maximum when welded with electrodes that produce an austenitic chromium-nickel or a non-air-hardening nickel-chromium-iron weld deposit is required only for plate thicknesses above 1½ in.

[e] Stress relief is not required for plates ⅜ in. in thickness or less when welded with austenitic electrodes. For thicknesses over ⅜ to 1½ in. and less stress relief is not required provided butt-welded joints are completely radiographed and a preheat of 450°F. minimum is maintained during welding.

[f] All butt and fillets shall also be examined for the detection of cracks by the fluid-penetrant method.

[g] D = inside diameter of vessel or vessel part with 20 in. minimum.

A or *B* construction, joints in category *A* and *B* must be type 1 or 2; joints in category *A* are sometimes restricted to type 1, as illustrated in Table 24-2.

Minimum Thickness After Forming. Minimum plate thickness after forming may not be less than the value shown in Table 24-8 for parts subject to pressure; however, plate finished with an undertolerance of not more than the smaller value of 0.01 in. or 6 per cent of the ordered thickness is acceptable and may be used at the full design pressure for the ordered thickness; for pipe or tube ordered by nominal wall thickness, the undertolerance permitted by the specification must be taken into account so that the minimum thickness will not be less than the calculated required value.

Corrosion, Erosion, and Deterioration. Vessels in compressed-air, steam, or water service (other than unfired steam boilers) fabricated of materials in the UCS classification must be provided with a corrosion allowance of not less than the smaller of one-sixth of the calculated plate thickness or $\frac{1}{16}$ in. on the metal surfaces exposed to the media, unless they are designed with joint efficiencies as listed under column *C* of Table 24-7. For other contents, materials selection and/or the necessity for additional metal thickness or other protection such as cladding or linings is the user's responsibility. Nonmandatory Appendix E ("Suggested Good Practice Regarding Corrosion Allowance") recommends a minimum allowance of $\frac{1}{16}$ in. be provided for all vessels, except those for which the corrosive or erosive attack is known to be negligible or entirely absent.

Corrosion or erosion allowance must be added to the calculated thickness required by the code for the loadings involved.

DESIGN FOR INTERNAL PRESSURE

Formulas for the thickness required for internal pressure are summarized in Table 24-10 for cylinders, spheres, and heads of ellipsoidal, torispherical, hemispherical, conical, and toriconical shape.

Cylinders and Formed Heads. Alternate statements are given in terms of pressure *P* to permit solution for thickness *t*, and in terms of thickness *t* for establishing allowable pressure *P*. Their solution involves allowable stresses and joint efficiencies, which can be obtained from Tables 24-3 to 24-6 and 24-7, respectively, or from applicable code tables. Curves in Fig. 24-3 permit a rapid approximate evaluation of cylindrical shell thickness for internal pressure, for the usual code joint efficiencies. These charts are based on 13,750 lb./sq. in. allowable stress, permitting the value of *t* to be easily adjusted for other allowable stress values by applying the ratio of the actual allowable stress to 13,750 lb./sq. in.

Flat Heads and Cover Plates. Bolted blind flanges conforming to A.S.A. Standard B16.5 are accepted at the rating given in that standard. The thickness of other unstayed flat heads, cover plates, and blind flanges illustrated in Fig. 24-2 is calculated by the following formula:

$$t = d\sqrt{\frac{CP}{S}} \qquad \text{or} \qquad P = \frac{St^2}{d^2C}$$

where *P* and *S* are as defined in Table 24-10, *t* and *d* are in inches, and *C* is a constant shown in Fig. 24-2. The code should be consulted for limitations on each type and calculation of the *C* value for bolted covers; the latter involves loadings and reaction locations established from the code rules on flange design.

Openings. The shape of openings in cylindrical or conical portions of vessels, or in formed heads, shall preferably be circular, but if not, shall be elliptical or obround. Openings of other shape for which strength cannot be computed are subject to a proof test.

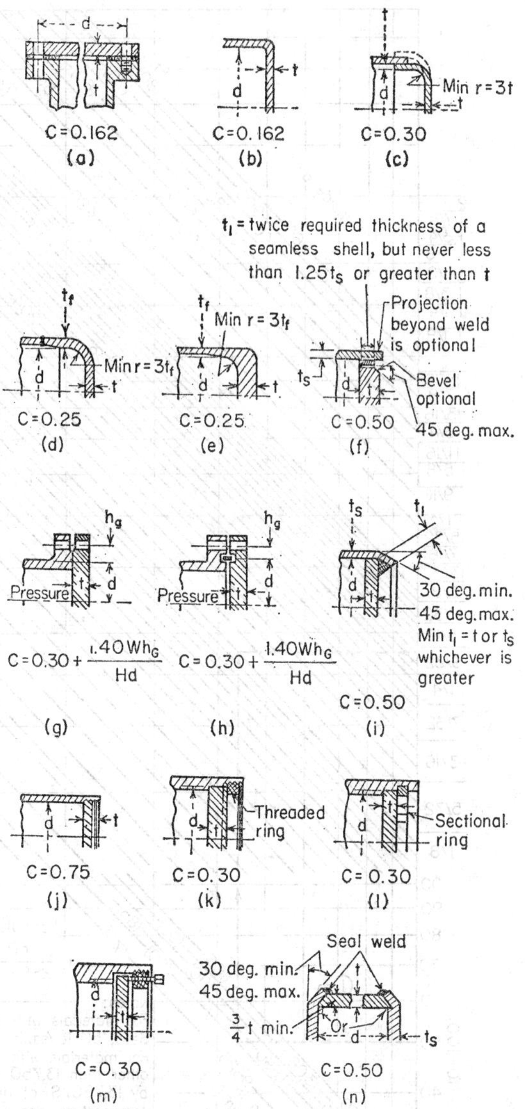

FIG. 24-2. Types of flat heads and covers of pressure vessels. (*Source: American Society of Mechanical Engineers.*)

Properly reinforced openings in cylindrical and spherical shells are not limited as to **sizes.** It is recommended that when an opening in the end closure of a cylinder exceeds 50 per cent of the inside diameter, a conical or reversed curve section (Fig. 24-4) or a combination of such shapes be used. The code includes rules for the design of the detail of these types of reducers.

When not subject to rapid pressure fluctuations, single (not multiple) welded or brazed connections not larger than 3-in. pipe size in vessel shells or heads $\frac{3}{8}$ in. thick or less or 2-in. pipe size in vessels or heads over $\frac{3}{8}$ in. thick do not require reinforcement other than that inherent in their dimensions. They may not be located in a welded joint unless the joint is radiographed over a

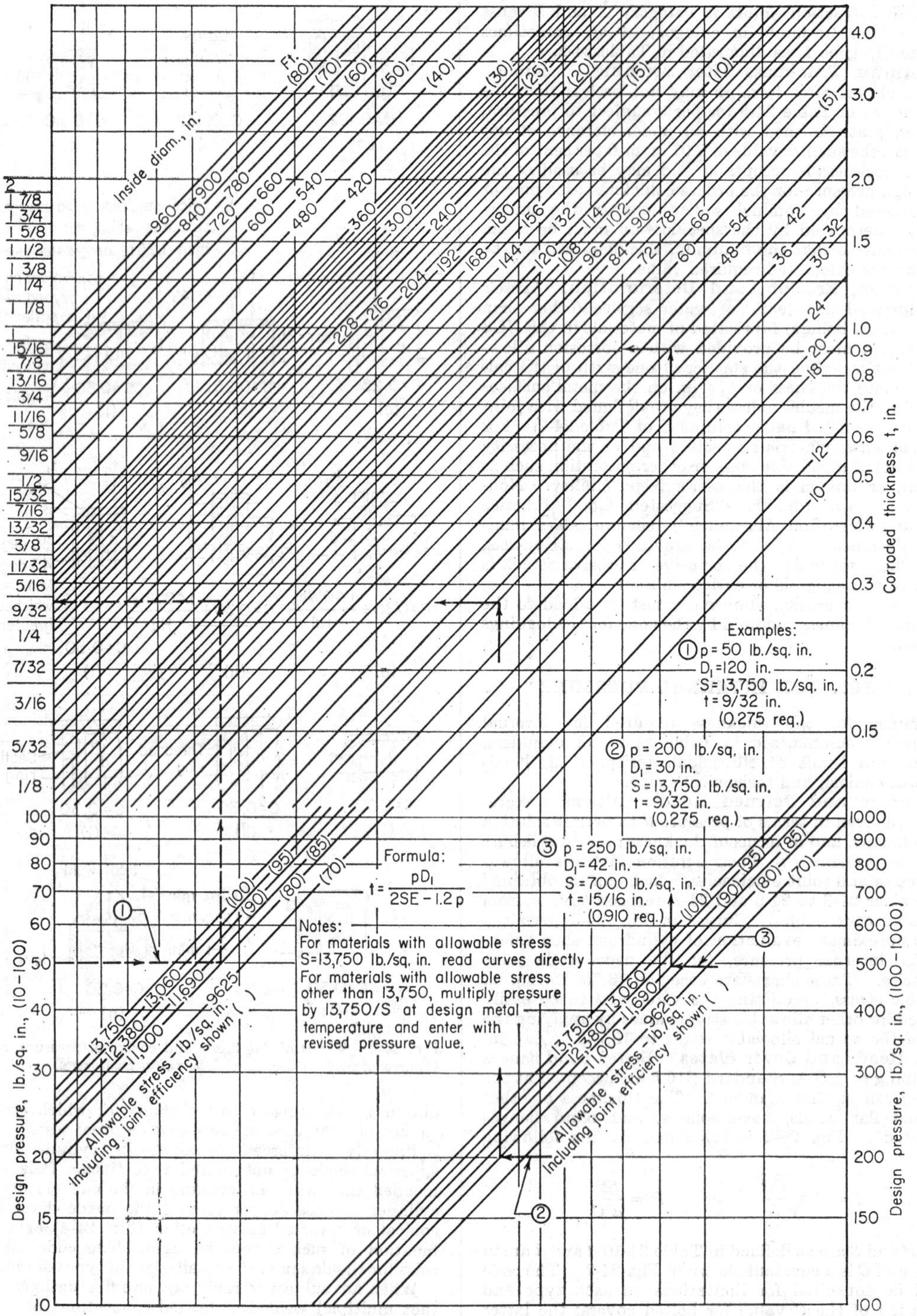

FIG. 24-3. Cylindrical shell thickness required for internal pressure only.

Table 24-10. Thickness of Shells under Internal Pressure

Description or sketch	Formula: In terms of P	Formula: In terms of t	Definitions and notes
1. Cylindrical shells	$t = \frac{PR}{SE - 0.6P}$	$P = \frac{SEt}{R + 0.6t}$	*Circumferential stress* (longitudinal joints, when the thickness does not exceed one-half of the inside radius, or P does not exceed $0.385\,SE$
1a. Thick cylindrical shells	$t = R(Z^{1/2} - 1)$ where $Z = \frac{SE + P}{SE - P}$	$P = SE\frac{Z - 1}{Z + 1}$ where $Z = \left(\frac{R + t}{R}\right)^2$	*Circumferential stress (longitudinal joints)*, when the thickness exceeds one-half of the inside radius, or when P exceeds $0.385\,SE$
2. Spherical shells, hemispherical heads	$t = \frac{PR}{2SE - 0.2P}$	$P = \frac{2SEt}{R + 0.2t}$	When the thickness does not exceed $0.356\,R$, or P does not exceed $0.665\,SE$
2a. Thick spherical shells, thick hemispherical heads	$t = R(Y^{1/3} - 1)$ where $Y = \frac{2(SE + P)}{2SE - P}$	$P = 2SE\frac{Y - 1}{Y + 2}$ where $Y = \left(\frac{R + t}{R}\right)^3$	When the thickness exceeds $0.356R$, or when P exceeds $0.665SE$
3. Ellipsoidal heads 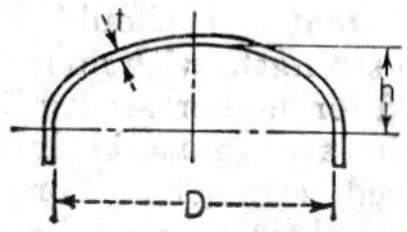	$t = \frac{PD}{2SE - 0.2P}$ $t = \frac{PDK}{2SE - 0.2P}$	$P = \frac{2SEt}{D + 0.2t}$ $P = \frac{2SEt}{KD + 0.2t}$	The required thickness of a dished head of semiellipsoidal form, in which half the minor axis (inside depth of the head minus the skirt) equals one-fourth of the inside diameter of the skirt where $K = \frac{1}{6}\left[2 + \left(\frac{D}{2h}\right)^2\right]$, $\frac{D}{2h} = 3$ max.
4. Torispherical heads, spherically dished 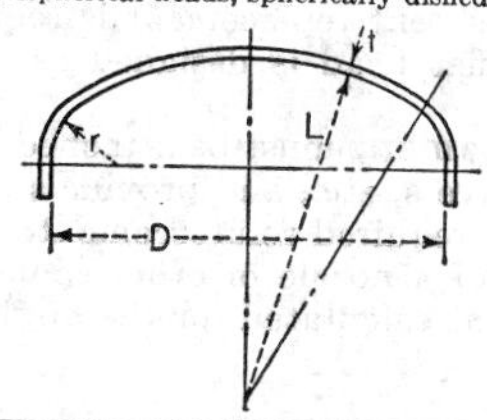	$t = \frac{0.885PL}{SE - 0.1P}$ $t = \frac{PLM}{2SE - 0.2P}$	$P = \frac{SEt}{0.885L + 0.1t}$ $P = \frac{2SEt}{LM + 0.2t}$	*Torispherical heads*, the required thickness of a torispherical head, in which the knuckle radius is 6% of the inside crown radius where $M = \frac{1}{4}\left(3 + \sqrt{\frac{L}{r}}\right)$ r(min.) = greater of $3t$ and $0.06(D + 2t)$ L(max.) = D
5. Conical heads (without transition knuckle) $\alpha \ngtr$ 30 deg. max. 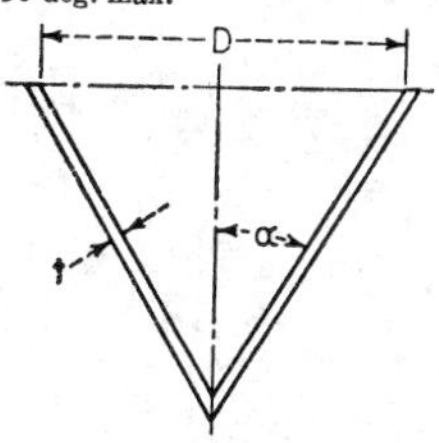	$t = \frac{PD}{2\cos\alpha(SE - 0.6P)}$	$P = \frac{2SEt\cos\alpha}{D + 1.2t\cos\alpha}$	A compression ring shall be provided when α exceeds the value for Δ as obtained from the table below; conical heads without a transition knuckle shall be provided with a compression ring at the section where the cone joins the shell of a cross-sectional area in square inches equal to $A = \frac{P}{SE}\left(\frac{D^2 \tan\alpha}{8}\right)\left(1 - \frac{E\text{ deg.}}{\alpha\text{ deg.}}\right)$ (Values of Δ: see below) For α greater than 30 deg, use toriconical head (6)
6. Toriconical heads (cone head with knuckle) 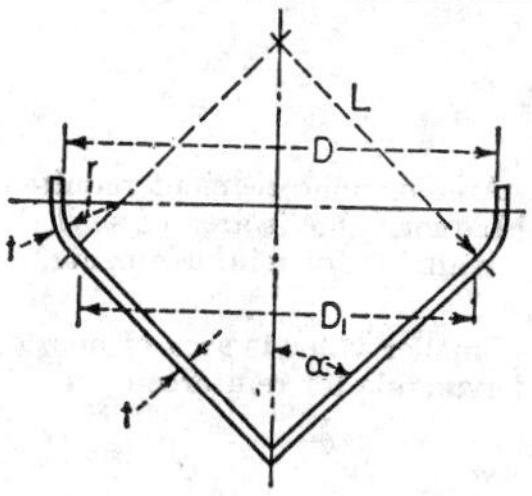	The required thickness of the conical portion shall be determined by formula 5 above, using D_1 in place of D The required thickness of the knuckle shall be determined by formula 4 in which $L = \frac{D_1}{2\cos\alpha}$		Toriconical heads in which the inside knuckle radius is neither less than 6% of the outside diameter of the head skirt nor less than 3 times the knuckle thickness shall be used when the angle α exceeds 30 deg. Toriconical heads may also be used with α less than 30 deg. and the same formula applies

Values of Δ

$\frac{P}{SE}$	0.001	0.002	0.003	0.004	0.005	0.006
Δ deg...	11	15	18	21	23	25

Nomenclature:

t = minimum required thickness of shell or head after forming, exclusive of corrosion allowance, in.
P = design pressure, lb./sq. in.
D = inside diameter of the head skirt; or inside length of the major axis of an ellipsoidal head; or inside diameter of a cone head at the point under consideration, measured perpendicular to the longitudinal axis; in. (measurements to be taken before corrosion allowance is added)
D_1 = inside diameter of the conical portion of a toriconical head at its point of tangency to the knuckle, measured perpendicular to the axis of the cone, in.
S = maximum allowable stress value, lb./sq. in.
E = lowest efficiency of any joint in the head; for hemispherical heads this includes head-to-shell joint
For welded vessels, use the efficiency specified in Par. UW-12
For riveted joints, use the efficiency specified in Par. UR-15
For seamless heads, use E = 1, except for hemispherical heads furnished without a skirt in which case the head-to-shell joint must be considered
L = inside spherical or crown radius, in.
α = one-half of the included (apex) angle of the cone at the center line of the head
R = inside radius of shell course under consideration, in.
r = inside knuckle radius, in.
h = one half of the length of the minor axis of the ellipsoidal head, or the inside depth of the head measured from the tangent line

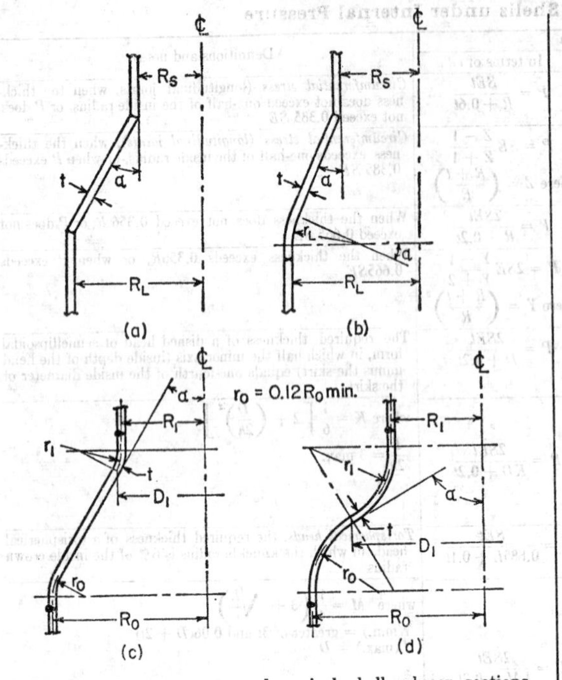

FIG. 24-4. Reverse-curve and conical shell-reducer sections. (*Source: American Society of Mechanical Engineers.*)

length equal to three times the opening diameter. **Flued openings** in formed heads, either inward or outward, are permitted provided they are reinforced.

Connection **reinforcement** must be within defined limits (Fig. 24-5) and its area must equal or exceed that of the metal area A removed which was required for strength, t_r being the required thickness. As indicated in Fig. 24-5 area available for reinforcement consists of any excess in the shell and nozzle neck plus any added metal within the reinforcement zone. This requirement must be satisfied for any plane through the center of the opening and normal to the vessel shell. For the usual circular openings in cylinders the maximum reinforcement requirement is for the plane containing the axis of the vessel (longitudinal plane) and for practical reasons is usually maintained essentially constant for the entire periphery. Reinforcement material should preferably equal the vessel material in strength, with no reduction in reinforcement area allowed for higher strength, but for lower-strength material, the area must be increased in proportion to the reduced strength. For openings spaced closer than two times their average diameter, the combined reinforcement must satisfy the sum of the reinforcement requirements of the individual connections. For openings in flat heads, not exceeding 50 per cent of the head diameter, 50 per cent replacement is required; for larger openings the flat head is designed as a ring flange.

The **opening reinforcement** must be attached to the vessel shell with welds, rivets, etc., and provide strength equivalent to that of the required reinforcement.

The **neck thickness** of a nozzle or other connection must not be less than that calculated for the applicable

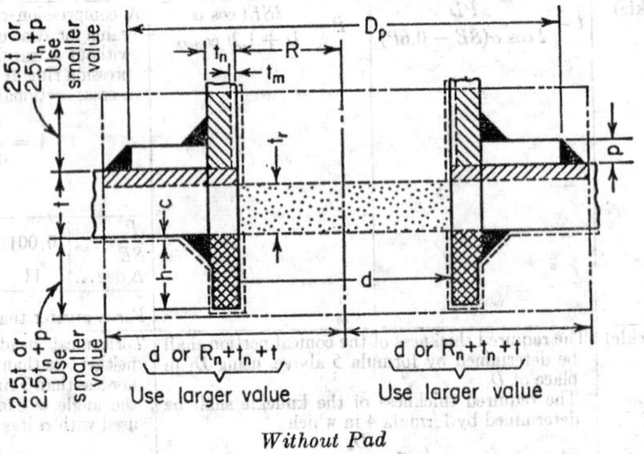

Without Pad

Area of reinforcement required

1a) } Larger value is area of shell
1b) } available for reinforcement.

2a) } Smaller value is area of nozzle wall
2b) } available for reinforcement.

(dotted) = A = $d \times t_r$

(hatched) = A_1 = $(E_1t - t_r)(d - R_n)2 = (E_1t - t_r)d$
or
= $(E_1t - t_r)(R_n + t_n + t - R_n)2 = (E_1t - t_r)(t_n + t)2$

(hatched) = A_2 = $(t_n - t_{rn})2.5t \times 2 = (t_n - t_{rn})5t$
or
= $(t_n - t_{rn})2.5t_n \times 2 = (t_n - t_{rn})5t_n$

(cross-hatched) = A_3 = $(t_n - c)h \times 2 = (t_n - c)2h$*

(solid) = A_4 = area of welds

If $A_1 + A_2 + A_3 + A_4 \geqq A$, opening is adequately reinforced.
If $A_1 + A_2 + A_3 + A_4 < A$, the difference must be supplied by a pad or otherwise.

With Pad

A, A_1, A_3, A_4, same as without pad.
With a pad, $2.5t_n$ is measured from the top surface of the pad.
A_2 becomes the smaller of $(t_n - t_{rn})5t$ or $(t_n - t_{rn})(2.5t_n + p)2$.
Area of pad = $(D_p - d - 2t_n)p = A_5$.
If $A_1 + A_2 + A_3 + A_4 + A_5 \geqq A$, opening is adequately reinforced.

* The nozzle projection will not corrode back of any attaching fillet; hence the term $(t_n - c)$ is slightly conservative.

FIG. 24-5. Example of a reinforced opening in pressure vessel. (*Source: American Society of Mechanical Engineers.*)

loadings plus corrosion allowance. For other than inspection or access connections, the minimum thickness shall also be not less than the smaller of the required vessel shell or head thickness (joint efficiency assumed = 1.00) to which the connection is attached plus corrosion allowance, and the minimum thickness of standard wall pipe plus corrosion allowance.

Inspection Openings. In addition to the connections necessary for process, venting, purging, draining, instrumentation, etc., the code requires openings for inspection and cleaning when the vessel contains compressed air or is subject to internal corrosion or has parts exposed to erosion or mechanical abrasion. The following are exempt from this requirement: (1) vessels, except those for compressed air, subject to corrosion only and when provided with telltale holes; (2) vessels for compressed air, provided they contain other substances to prevent corrosion and equivalent openings are available through which inspection can be made; and (3) vessels 12 in. or less in inside diameter, provided there are at least two removable pipe connections of not less than ¾-in. pipe size.

Inspection openings, when required, shall be in the number and size specified below, except that vessels 16 in. and less in inside diameter need not have separate inspection openings, provided not less than two 1½-in. pipe size connections can be disconnected and are located to permit internal inspection.

1. Vessels over 12 in. and less than 18 in. inside diameter shall have at least two handholes or two plugged threaded inspection openings of not less than 1½-in. pipe size.
2. Vessels with inside diameter of 18 to 36 in., inclusive, shall have a manhole or at least two handholes or two plugged threaded pipe connections not less than 2-in. pipe size.
3. All vessels over 36 in. inside diameter shall have one manhole, except when impractical because of vessel shape, and at least two 4 by 6-in. handholes or two other such openings of equivalent area.
4. Elliptical or obround manhole openings shall be not less than 11 by 15 in. or 10 by 16 in. and circular manholes 15 in. inside diameter or larger.
5. Handholes shall be as large as consistent with the size of the vessel, but not less than 2 by 3 in.

Connections to Shell Details. Typical connections for attachment by welding are given in Fig. 24-6. The weld sizes shown are minimum and, for individual connections, must be checked by calculation. Other details may be used provided they comply with code requirements. Connections may also be threaded directly into the shell or may be secured to the vessel by expanded joints, stud bolts, rivets, or brazing. Shell openings to receive threaded pipe are limited to 3-in. pipe size when the maximum allowable working pressure exceeds 125 lb./sq. in. and is 4-in. pipe size when vessels contain liquid having a flash point below 110°F. or flammable vapors, or flammable liquids at temperatures above their atmospheric boiling point. This restriction does not apply to plug closures used for inspection open-

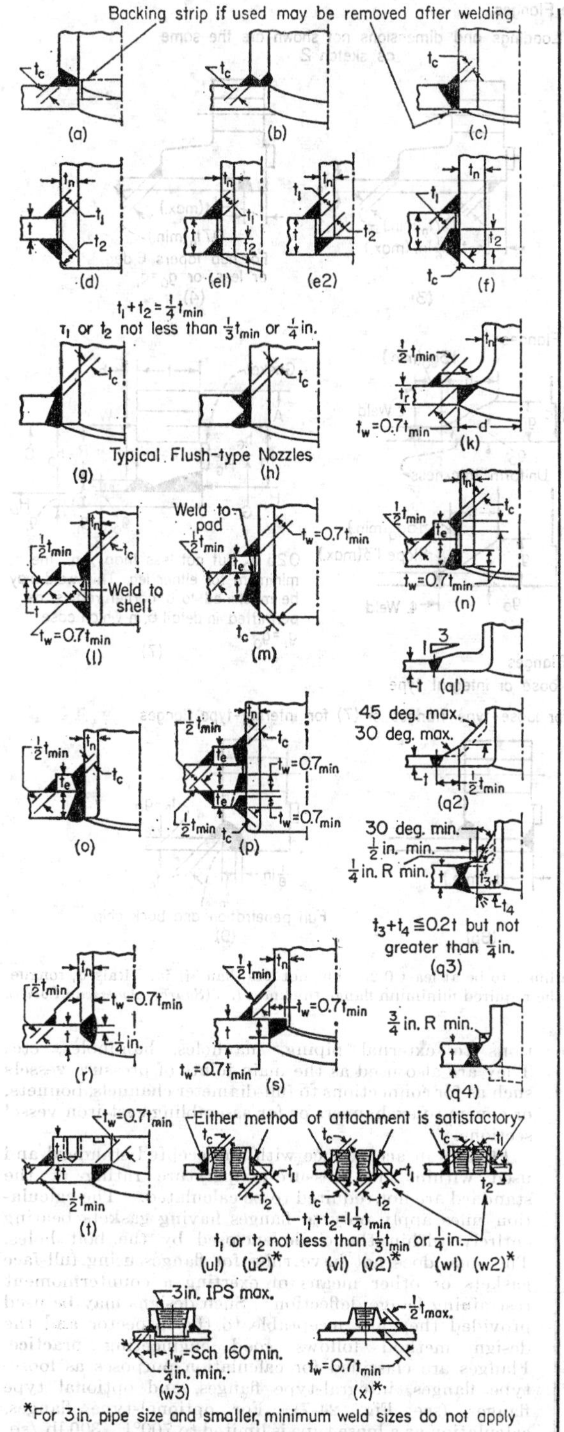

*For 3in. pipe size and smaller, minimum weld sizes do not apply

FIG. 24-6. Typical connections for attachment by welding. (*Source: American Society of Mechanical Engineers.*)

t = nominal thickness of vessel shell or head less corrosion allowance, in.

t_n = nominal thickness of nozzle wall less corrosion allowance, in.

t_e = thickness of reinforcing element, in.

t_w = dimension of partial-penetration attachment welds (fillet, single-bevel, or single J), measured as shown

t_c = the smaller of ¼ in. or 0.7 t_n (inside corner welds may be further limited by a lesser length of projection of the nozzle wall beyond the inside face of the vessel wall)

t_{min} = the smaller of ¾ in. or the thickness less corrosion allowance, of either of the parts joined by a fillet, single-bevel, or single-J weld, in.

t_1 or t_2 = not less than ⅓ t_{min} or ¼ in.

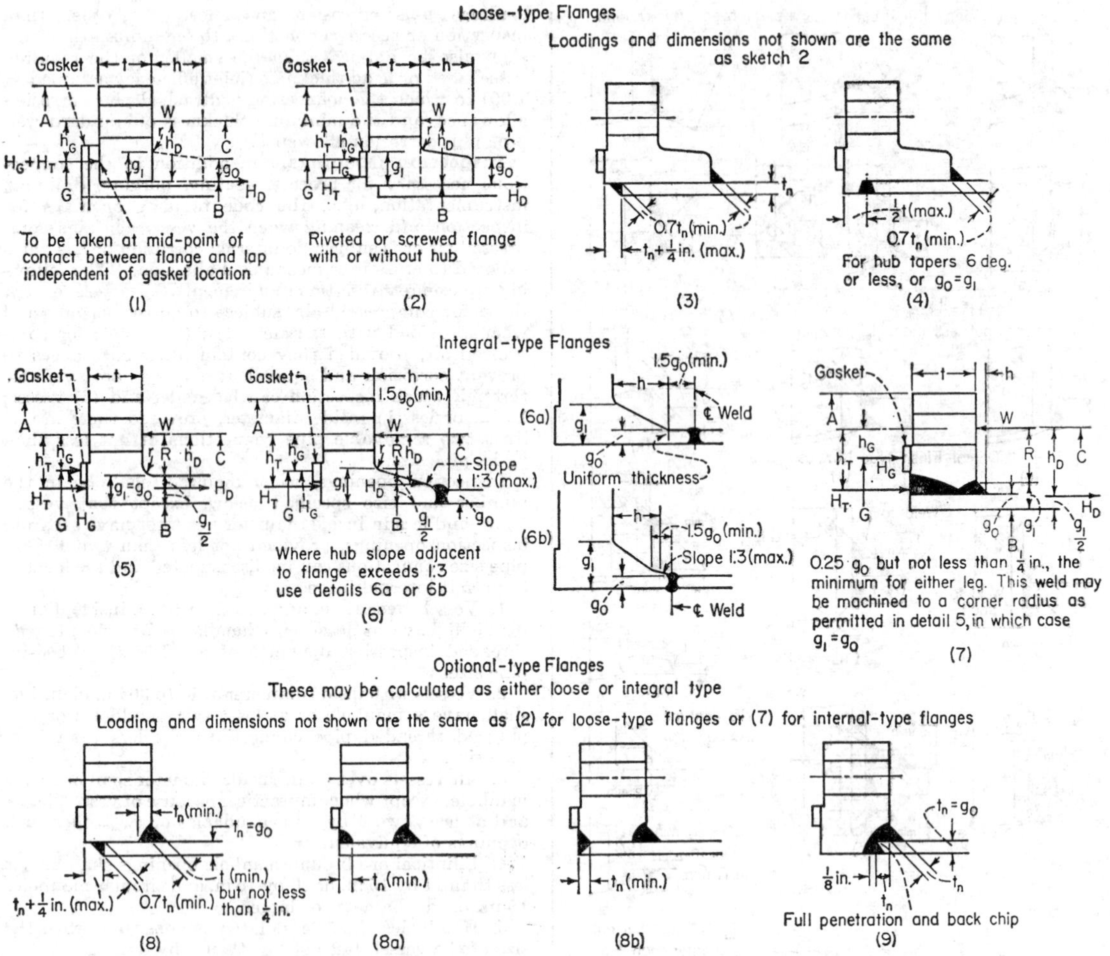

FIG. 24-7. Types of flanges for pressure vessels. Note: Filler radius r to be at least $0.25g_0$, but not less than 3/16 in. Raised, tongue-groove, male and female, and ring joint facings shall be in excess of the required minimum flange thickness t. (*Source: American Society of Mechanical Engineers.*)

ings, end closures and similar purposes. Expanded connections are limited to 6 in. outside diameter and are not to be used in vessels for processing or storage of flammable and/or noxious gases and liquids, unless such connections are seal-welded. The shell opening must be reinforced for threaded or expanded connections over 2 in. For stud-bolted attachments the shell opening is to be reinforced by a built-up pad or properly attached plate or fitting machined flat, and drilled and tapped for the bolts without penetrating within 25 per cent of the wall thickness from the inside surface.

Connections to External Piping. Vessel connections may be provided for assembling to external piping by welded, threaded, or flanged joints. Flanged connections must either conform to a recognized standard, such as A.S.A. B16.5, A.S.A. B16.24, and M.S.S. SP 42, in which case they must be used within the pressure-temperature ratings established by the standard, or be designed in accordance with the code rules.

Bolted Flanged Joints. Appendix II of the code is devoted to bolted flanges and provides tabular data as to gasket factors, rules for the calculation of flanges, and limitations with respect to the use of bolted flanges. Bolted flanged joints are widely used for nozzle connections to external piping, manholes, handholes, etc. They are also used as the main joints of pressure vessels such as for connections to full-diameter channels, bonnets, or covers to exchangers or for assembling cast-iron vessel sections.

Flanges in accordance with an accepted standard and used within the pressure-temperature rating of the standard are not required to be calculated. The calculation rules apply only to flanges having gaskets bearing entirely within the circle enclosed by the bolt holes. The code does not have rules for flanges using full-face gaskets or other means of exerting a countermoment restraining flange deflection. Such designs may be used provided they are acceptable to the inspector and the design method follows good engineering practice. Flanges are classified for calculation purposes as loose-type flanges, integral-type flanges, and optional type flanges (see Fig. 24-7). For optional-type flanges, calculation as a loose type is limited to 700°F., 300 lb./sq. in., and neck thickness not exceeding 5/8 in.

Split loose flanges (*i.e.*, composed of 180-deg. ring segments) may be used provided that (1) for a single split flange (*i.e.*, two 180-deg. segments to form a 360-deg. ring), the thickness is established using the rules for a

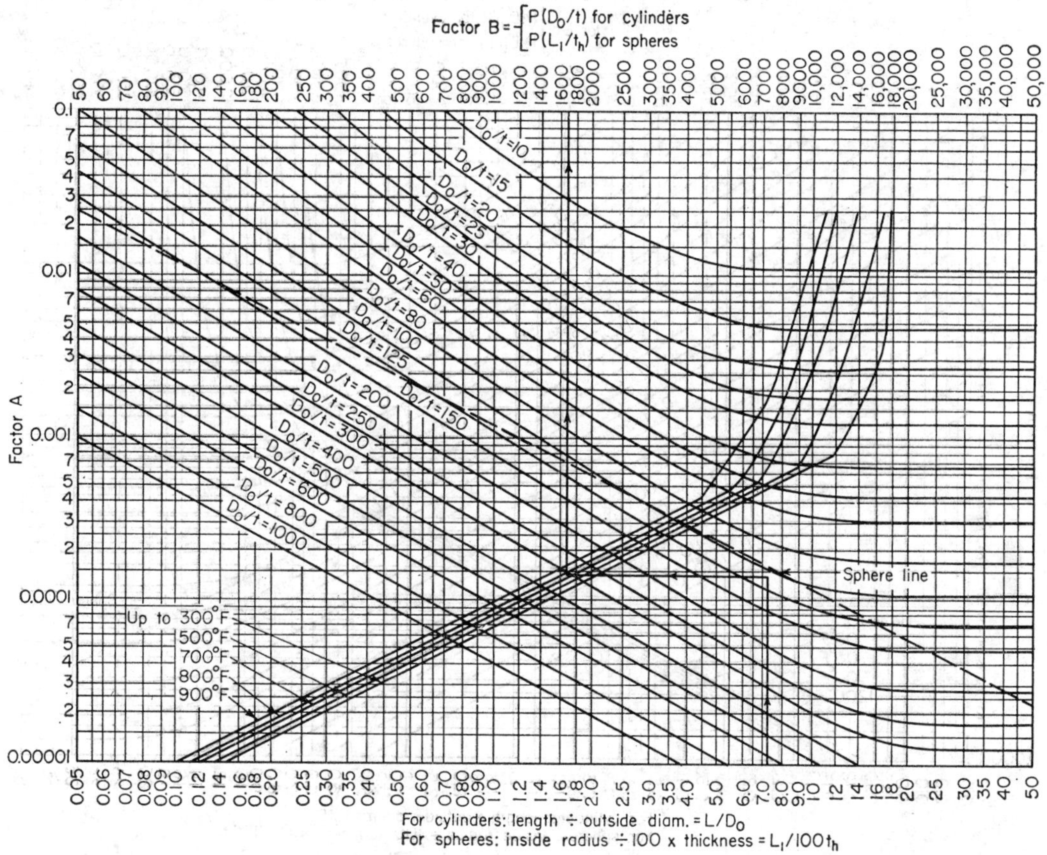

FIG. 24-8. Chart for determining shell thickness of cylindrical and spherical vessels under external pressure when constructed of carbon steel (specified yield strength 30,000 to 38,000 lb./sq. in. inclusive) and types 405 and 410 stainless steel. (*Source: American Society of Mechanical Engineers.*)

Problem:

P = 15 lb./sq. in. (external) L = 32 ft.
D_o = 54 in. T = 750°F.
Material, SA285, grade C

Solution:

$$B = 1650, P_a = \frac{B}{D_o/t} = \frac{1650}{108} = 15.3 \text{ allowable}$$

solid ring, adjusted by multiplying the calculated moment by 2; (2) for a double split flange (two layers, each an assembly of two 180-deg. segments, with splits staggered at 90-deg.) the thickness of each layer is established using the rules for a solid ring adjusted by multiplying the calculated moment by 0.75.

While Appendix II of the code provides the gasket and facing data, and stiffness and moment and shear distribution factors necessary for loose and integral flange calculations, calculation forms and guidance are not included. These can be obtained from Taylor Forge and Pipe Works, P.O. Box 485, Chicago 90, Ill., in a technical publication entitled "Modern Flange Design."

Flange design involves assuming flange, gasket, and hub dimensions and bolting; checking bolt spacing for wrench clearances; and proceeding to calculate by trial and error until an acceptable design is realized. Many alternate designs will satisfy the rules and the economic choice must consider the influence of flange width and over-all flange and hub height. The reference cited includes other helpful suggestions and data. Automatic programmed calculations may also be utilized for direct establishment of dimensions for effective and economic flanges.

DESIGN FOR EXTERNAL PRESSURE

Cylindrical and Spherical Shells. Tensile stress can be sustained without distress up to the material yield point; compressive stress must be further limited to avoid instability (collapse) as a function of the stiffness of the structure. This had led to so-called column formulas in structural engineering which establish allowable compressive stress compatible with the slenderness (l/r) of the column. Surfaces of revolution (cylinders, spheres, cones, etc.) under compressive stress behave similarly with respect to thickness/diameter. Distance between stiffeners also serves as a measure of slenderness and attendant susceptibility to instability, which might lead to local buckling and ultimately to total collapse.

The code approach for establishing thickness and stiffener spacing for external pressure requires individual charts for each material or group of materials whose stress-strain properties are sufficiently similar. On each such chart the stress-strain properties over the code range of temperature coverage are superimposed on the geometry (slenderness) factors governing collapse, which are independent of material. This permits application of

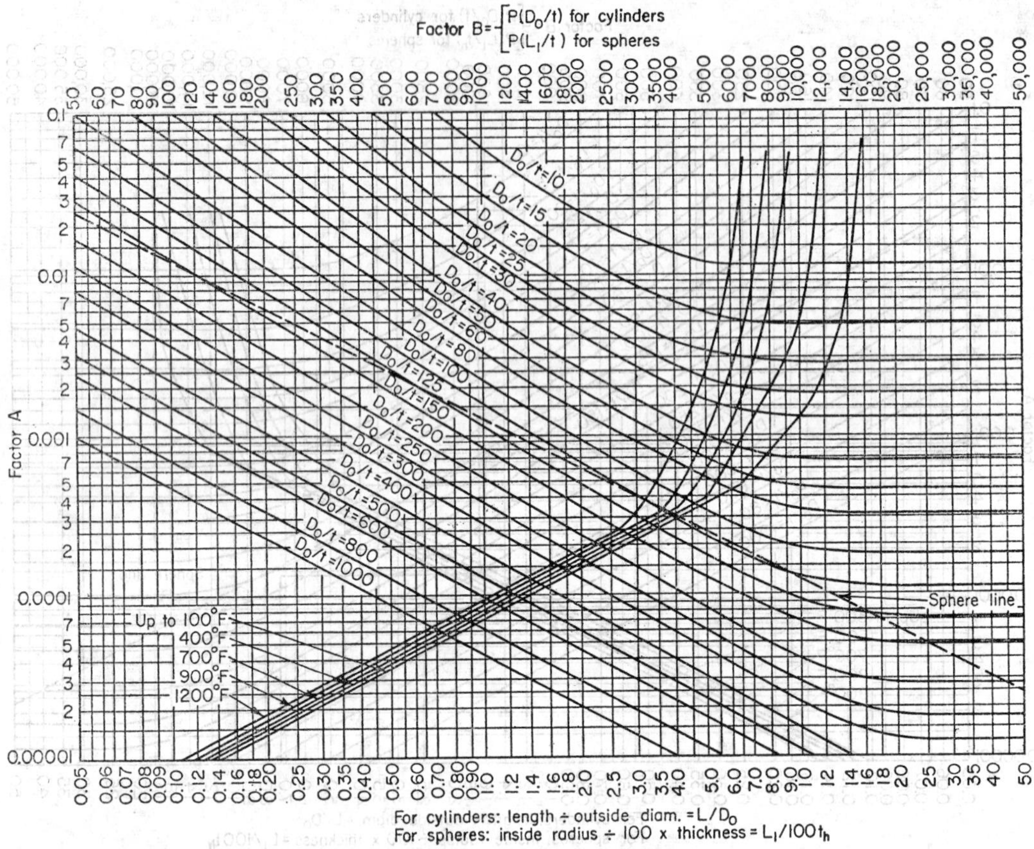

FIG. 24-9. Chart for determining shell thickness of cylindrical and spherical vessels under external pressure when constructed of austenitic steel (18 Cr-8 Ni, type 304). *Source: American Society of Mechanical Engineers.)*

the tangent modulus of elasticity criterion for buckling to materials whose stress-strain relation is not linear and to materials in general beyond their proportional limit. For high temperatures where creep is a factor the charts limit the maximum stress as a function of the allowable tensile creep stress but do not otherwise take account of the possible influence on collapse of gradual plastic flow with time. For cast iron, the charts restrict the maximum stress to that allowed for parts in bending, which is 75 per cent of that allowed for cast iron in pure compression.

These code figures for all approved materials are assembled in Appendix V of the code, and detailed instructions as to their application are given in paragraphs UG-28(c) and (d). Two charts (Figs. 24-8 and 24-9, for carbon and type 405 or 410 alloy steels, and type 304 austenitic steel) are included here as illustrative examples. These charts allow establishment of thickness and stiffener spacing of cylinders by trial-and-error procedure; for spheres only the thickness is obtained.

To use the chart enter the curve at the bottom with an assumed value of L/D_o for cylinders, or $L_1/100t_h$ for spheres, as illustrated on Fig. 24-8, move vertically to the assumed D_o/t value (or sphere line in the case for spheres), then horizontally to the material line for the design temperature, and then vertically to read the value of PD_o/t or PL_1/t_h from which the allowable pressure P can be calculated. Repeat until P equals the desired design pressure, and stiffener spacing and size are practical and economic. Acceptable assumptions as to stiffener spacing L are illustrated in Fig. 24-10. If no stiffeners are used, L equals the shell straight plus one-third the depth of the heads.

The required moment of inertia I_s of the stiffening ring about its neutral axis parallel to the axis of the shell is approximately

$$I_s = \frac{D_o^2 L_s[t + (A_s/L_s)]A}{14} \quad \text{inches}^4$$

where A_s = cross-sectional area of the stiffening ring, sq. in.

L_s = one-half the sum of the L dimension on each side of the stiffener, in.

A = factor from the applicable chart obtained by entering at the top with a value of

$$B = \frac{PD_o}{t + (A_s/L_s)}$$

where P = external design pressure, lb./sq. in.

D_o = outside diameter of cylindrical shell, in.

t = minimum required thickness of shell, in.

Move downward to the material line at the design temperature and then horizontally to read A. (For an explanation of the background of these code charts, see Bergman "The New Type Code Charts for the Design

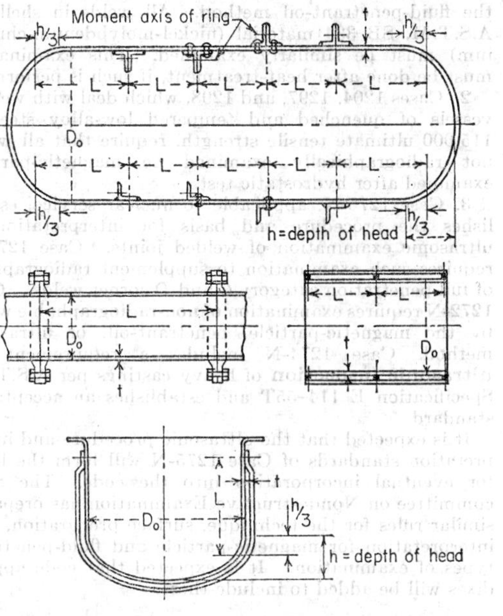

Fig. 24-10. Diagrammatic representation of stiffener spacing L in pressure vessel. *(Source: American Society of Mechanical Engineers.)*

of Vessels under External Pressure," A.S.M.E. Paper 51-A-137, November, 1951.)

Formed Heads. The minimum thickness, after forming, of heads subject to pressure on the convex side shall be as follows: For **ellipsoidal** or **torispherical heads,** the greater of (1) 1.67 times the thickness required for internal pressure of the same magnitude, assuming 100 per cent joint efficiency, and (2) the thickness as obtained from the external pressure charts for a sphere whose radius is that of the crown of the head. For ellipsoidal heads, the code assigns an equivalent crown radius which, for a 2 to 1 axis ratio, is 0.9 times the outside diameter of the head skirt.

The thickness of **hemispherical heads** is calculated for a sphere of the same radius.

The thickness of **conical heads** whose half apex angle α is equal to or less than 22½ deg. is that required for a cylinder whose length is that of the cone, or the distance center to center of stiffeners (when used), and whose outside diameter equals the larger end of the cone or cone section. For a half apex angle α greater than 22½ deg. but less than 60 deg., the thickness is that required for a cylinder whose outside diameter equals the largest inside diameter of the cone and whose length equals the smaller of the center-to-center spacing of stiffener rings (if used), or the largest inside diameter of the section of the cone considered. For a half apex angle greater than 60 deg., the thickness of the cone shall be the same as required for a flat head under external pressure, the diameter of which is equal to the largest inside diameter of the cone.

The thickness of **flat heads** subject to external pressure is the same as calculated for internal pressure.

Reinforcement of Openings. For external pressure the reinforcement for openings in a single-walled vessel need be only 50 per cent of that calculated by the rules for internal pressure but must be based on the thickness required for external pressure. Reinforcement for multiple-wall vessels and for vessels subject to both internal and external pressure must meet the rules for each pressure condition.

FABRICATION REQUIREMENTS

Code requirements dealing with fabrication are meager, rather liberal, and worded in a general manner, thus leaving a wide exercise of judgment to the manufacturer and inspector. Each manufacturer is responsible for the quality of **welding** performed by his organization and shall, before initial application in production, have conducted tests of each procedure to be used. Tests are also required of welders and welding operators (operators of automatic welding machines) to determine their ability to apply the applicable procedures. Welding processes are restricted to shielded carbon arc, shielded metal arc, submerged arc, inert-gas metal arc, atomic hydrogen metal arc, oxyhydrogen, and oxyacetylene. Pressure-welding processes are restricted to flash, induction, resistance, pressure thermit, oxyacetylene, and forge.

The code should be consulted for requirements as to the details governing **stress relief.** Mandatory requirements related to service and commonly used materials have been listed in Tables 24-2 and 24-9. Stress relief must precede hydrostatic testing.

Radiographic Examination. Mandatory requirements related to service and commonly used materials have been listed in Tables 24-2 and 24-9. The code should be consulted for more detailed requirements. Butt welds not required to be fully radiographed must pass a spot radiographic examination for quality control, unless the vessel is designed for external pressure only or the entire vessel has been designed on the basis of the reduced joint efficiencies in column C of Table 24-7 and other parts are designed using 80 per cent of the allowable stress value.

INSPECTION, TESTS, AND NON-DESTRUCTIVE EXAMINATION

The manufacturer who completes any vessel to be marked with the U or UM symbol has the responsibility of complying with all requirements of the code and of assuring, through specified certification, that any work done by others also complies with all code requirements. The inspector of vessels to be stamped with the U symbol is responsible for executing explicit code inspection requirements and for such additional examinations as he considers necessary to satisfy himself that all requirements of the code are met.

Inspector Qualifications. An inspector must be employed by a state or a municipality, or regularly employed by an insurance company, or continuously employed by a company for making inspections of unfired pressure vessels to be used by such company and not for resale. In no instance may an inspector be in the employ of the manufacturer. Inspector qualification must be established through examination by a state or municipality which has adopted the code.

The inspector must assure himself that procedures, welders, and welding operators have been properly qualified. The manufacturer's records are required to be available to the inspector, but he is not required to witness or certify the qualification tests. The inspector has the right, however, to call for and witness such tests at any time.

The inspector must assure himself that materials comply with the code by examining mill test reports and checking markings and thicknesses. All material shall be inspected before fabrication, with particular attention to cut edges and other locations which might disclose serious laminations, shearing cracks, or other objectionable defects.

Inspection During Fabrication. The inspector must make such inspections as he deems necessary to assure himself that code requirements are met, including tolerances on shape and fit-up, stress relieving, radiographing, and pressure tests. The inspector must witness and approve all proof tests of vessels or parts whose strength cannot be calculated.

Nondestructive Examination. The code provides rules for the conduct and interpretation of **radiographic examination** (either X-ray or gamma-ray) of butt-welded joints when such is required. These cover technique, weld surface finish, thickness of weld reinforcement, and limits of acceptable defects for both complete and spot-type examinations. Any type of crack or zone of incomplete fusion or penetration is unacceptable; elongated slag or groups of slag inclusions are acceptable within specific limits, which are more lenient for spot than for full examination. Porosity limits are established only for full radiographing.

The radiographic technique is intended to be capable of indicating the size of defects having a thickness equal to or greater than 2 per cent of the thickness of the base material. It is required that a small "penetrameter" (thickness gage) be used for each exposure; its thickness must not exceed 2 per cent of the plate thickness and it must be provided with three small holes of two, three, and four times the penetrameter thickness which must be distinguishable on the film. The adequacy of the technique is judged solely by this image.

For **full radiography,** all type 1 and 2 welded butt joints are required to be examined for their full length, unless specifically exempted. Unacceptable defects disclosed must be removed, rewelded, and reexamined.

For **spot radiography,** longitudinal and circumferential type 1 and 2 welded butt joints are required to be examined locally to a minimum of one spot (6 in. minimum length) in the first 50 ft. of welding in each vessel (or group of identical vessels), and one spot for each additional 50 ft. or fraction thereof. Additional spots are required, if necessary, so that an examination is made of the work of each welding operator or welder. An acceptable spot examination provides acceptance of the entire weld length unit represented by that spot; if unacceptable, two additional spots in the same weld unit, at locations away from the original spot, are required. If either of these two shows unacceptable defects, the entire unit of weld is rejected and must be removed and rewelded or, at the manufacturer's option, completely radiographed with unacceptable defects corrected, and the rewelded joint or repaired areas spot reexamined. If both the additional spots are acceptable, the entire length of weld represented is acceptable and defects uncovered by the original spot examination need not be corrected at the discretion of the inspector.

The code recognizes in the following note the limitations of spot radiography with respect to assuring the quality of the unexamined portions of the welding:

> Spot radiography in accordance with these rules will not insure a fabrication product of predetermined quality level throughout. It must be realized that an accepted vessel under these spot radiography rules may still contain defects which might be disclosed on further examination. If all radiographically disclosed unacceptable weld defects must be eliminated from a vessel, then 100 per cent radiography must be employed.

The code currently contains no detailed requirements for other types of non-destructive examination. In general the code rules require only visual examination of other than butt-welded joints such as fillet and corner welds for nozzles, flanges, and structural attachments. Exceptions are:

1. Paragraph UHA-34 requires all austenitic chromium-nickel welds in shells over ¾ in. thick to be examined by the fluid-penetrant-oil method. All welds in shells of A.S.T.M. SB 334 material (nickel-molybdenum-chromium) must be similarly examined. This examination must be done after heat-treatment, if such is performed.
2. Cases 1204, 1297, and 1298, which deal with welded vessels of quenched and tempered low-alloy steel of 115,000 ultimate tensile strength, require that all welds not radiographically examined be magnetic-particle examined after hydrostatic test.
3. Case 1275-N, applicable to nuclear service, establishes the procedure and basis for interpretation of ultrasonic examination of welded joints. Case 1273-N requires such examination to supplement radiographing of full penetration category *C* and *D* corner welds. Case 1272-N requires examination of non-radiographable welds by the magnetic-particle, penetrant-oil, or ultrasonic method. Case 1274-N includes a requirement for **ultrasonic inspection** of heavy castings per A.S.T.M. Specification E 114–55T and establishes an acceptance standard.

It is expected that the ultrasonic procedure and interpretation standards of Case 1275-N will form the basis for eventual incorporation into the code. The Subcommittee on Nondestructive Examination has prepared similar rules for the technique, surface preparation, and interpretation for magnetic-particle and fluid-penetrant types of examination. It is expected that code appendixes will be added to include these.

PRESSURE TESTS OF COMPLETED VESSELS

Hydrostatic Tests. A hydrostatic test of each completed vessel, except those subjected to pneumatic tests, is required at a pressure at least 1½ times the maximum design pressure to be stamped on the vessel (adjusted to test temperature by the ratio of the allowable stress at test temperature to that at design temperature). By user-manufacturer agreement, the test pressure may be at least 1½ times the maximum allowable pressure as calculated for the weakest element of the vessel as fabricated. No maximum limit for test pressure is established; however, with visible permanent distortion, the inspector has the right to reject the vessel. For enameled vessels a test pressure equal to the design pressure stamped on the vessel is permitted in order to minimize possible deformation and damage. Vessels to be galvanized may be pressure-tested before or after galvanizing.

Multichamber Vessels. For multichamber vessels, each chamber is required to be tested separately without pressure in the others. Single-walled vessels and chambers of multichambered vessels designed for vacuum or partial vacuum only shall be given an internal hydrostatic test or, when not practical, a pneumatic test. Either test shall be at a pressure not less than 1½ times the difference between normal atmospheric pressure and the minimum design internal absolute pressure.

Hydrostatic tests can be made using any non-hazardous fluid. The code recommends that the liquid temperature be not less than 60°F. (to minimize brittle fracture hazards) and that the pressure not be applied until the vessel and its contents are at about the same temperature. After application of the hydrostatic test, all joints and connections are required to be inspected at a pressure of not less than two-thirds of the test pressure.

Pneumatic Test. A pneumatic test may be substituted for the hydrostatic test for vessels that are so designed or supported that they cannot safely contain the water weight, or for vessels not readily dried in services where traces of the testing liquid cannot be tolerated. Parts of the latter vessels, where possible, should be hydrostatically tested prior to the pneumatic test of the completed vessel to at least 1.5 times the maximum design pressure to be stamped on the vessel (corrected to test temperature).

Since pneumatic testing increases the hazard during test due to the relatively greater stored energy in the compressed gas, the code recommends special precautions. The pneumatic pressure is to be gradually increased to not more than one-half of the test pressure, and thereafter raised in steps of approximately one-tenth the test pressure until the required pressure is reached. Inspection is to be performed with the pressure reduced to four-fifths of the test value. All welds around openings and attachments over ¼ in. (throat thickness) must be inspected by the magnetic-powder or penetrant-oil method before testing.

Combination Tests. Where desirable, combination tests (liquid and pneumatic) may be applied, with the liquid level established to limit the maximum pressure at the bottom of the vessel to the permissible hydrostatic test pressure. The pressure above the liquid is to be the same as for a pneumatic test, and the test is to be conducted as for a pneumatic test.

Proof Tests. For vessels or parts of vessels for which the code does not provide rules, or for which the strength cannot be computed with a satisfactory assurance of accuracy, proof tests are required to establish the safe allowable working pressure. Where duplicated or geometrically similar parts are concerned, their strength is established by a proof test of a single or a representative series of parts.

Stamping and Reports. Each vessel built in accordance with the requirements of the code shall be marked with the official unfired pressure vessel U symbol or (if exempt from inspection) the UM symbol. The code symbol is applied in the presence of the inspector by the manufacturer who completes the vessel and who must be authorized for its use. Usually the symbol and required information are applied to a nameplate which is permanently fixed to the vessel, although it may be applied directly on the vessel shell. The marking is to include the manufacturer's name, the maximum design pressure and corresponding maximum design temperature, manufacturer's serial number, year built, type of construction used for main seams, XR when completely radiographed, SR when stress-relieved, and PXR when partially radiographed and PSR when partially stress-relieved.

Formal manufacturer's data reports are also required and must be signed by the manufacturer to certify compliance with the code. The inspector must also sign the data report and certify each pressure vessel marked with the U symbol. Standard data report forms are included in the code.

Overpressure Protection. The code requires that all unfired pressure vessels, irrespective of size or pressure, be provided with protective devices that will prevent the pressure from increasing more than 10 per cent above the maximum allowable working (design) pressure stamped on the nameplate *except* that, when the pressure build-up is the result of exposure to fire or other unexpected source of external heat, the overpressure is limited to 20 per cent. Devices must be set to relieve at a pressure not greater than the stamped maximum allowable working pressure, *except* that supplemental pressure-relieving devices used for protection under conditions of fire or other external heat source may be set to relieve at a pressure not in excess of 110 per cent of the stamped pressure. Protection is also required against overpressure resulting from an internal failure in heat exchangers and similar vessels but the code provides neither rules nor guidance for establishing the quantities to be relieved.

Relieving devices may be either safety or relief valves or rupture disks. Pressure-reducing and similar mechanical or electrical control instruments are not considered as sufficiently positive to prevent excess pressure. Indirect or pilot operation of safety valves is permitted only where such open under malfunction.

Each relief and safety valve must be marked by the manufacturer with the code UV symbol, capacity, and other pertinent data. The valves of a manufacturer must be certified for capacity through specified representative tests by a code-authorized observer. Certified data reports of such tests are the manufacturer's authority to stamp production valves of corresponding design, size, and pressure range.

Valves or rupture disks may be located either on the vessel, or to connected piping and in the vapor space above any contained liquid; liquid relief valves are required to be connected below the normal liquid level.

Block valves between the vessel and its protective devices or between the devices and point of discharge are permitted only (1) when the valves are so constructed and controlled that, when the maximum possible number of valves are closed, the required relief capacity is still provided or (2) when the valves are locked or sealed open under conditions prescribed in code Appendix M.

Code Limitations and Inadequacies. The A.S.M.E., British (B.S. 1500), German (AD Merkblätter), and other codes are inadequate for large and/or complex vessels, extreme loading demands of many modern process and power plants, extrahazardous contents, and when fabricated of sensitive or high-strength or less ductile materials or by heavy wall construction. Equally important, they provide no economic return for construction of improved and assured capabilities. This tends to discourage industrial progress by barring adequate financial return for improvements and refinements in construction.

Chemical engineers would be well advised to avoid false economies with respect to pressure vessels. These afford savings that are minor as compared with their contribution to assured capabilities and soundness. Excessive replacement and maintenance costs invariably originate with an unrealistic sense of initial investment values.

Balanced Classes of Pressure Vessels. To assist the chemical engineer in exercising the judgment which the code assigns to the owner-operator with respect to necessary and/or desirable above-minimum requirements, a detailed basis has been suggested by Murphy and Rossheim (A.S.M.E. Paper 60-WA-313, December, 1960) for four balanced classes of pressure-vessel construction (*i.e.*, uniformly proportioned requirements for material, design, fabrication, and inspection). These suggestions have no official status; however, the A.S.M.E. Boiler and Pressure Vessel Committee has had a Special Committee on Allowable Stress Basis working for several years on a logical approach to pressure-vessel requirements, tailored to various service demands, including a consideration of this suggested basis.

CONSIDERATIONS BEYOND CODE COVERAGE

This subsection is devoted to enlarging or supplementing those aspects of pressure vessels which the A.S.M.E. Unfired Pressure Vessel Code covers inadequately or else omits entirely. Also included is general information which will apply to fabricated piping and its components.

The literature provides only limited useful information and data on pressure vessels. Much of the recent work is in the form of committee reports or sponsored technical papers of the Welding Research Council's Pressure

Vessel Research Committee. This committee is organized in three divisions (Design, Materials, and Fabrication), with a technical secretary (C. F. Larson, Jr.) and staff and is located in the new United Engineering Center, 345 East 47th Street, New York, 17, N.Y. Many publications of the American Society of Mechanical Engineers and the American Welding Society (too numerous to list here) are of interest with respect to pressure-equipment design, fabrication, and inspection.

Strength and Failure of Materials. A condensed but comprehensive review of the fundamentals underlying the strength and failure of materials prepared by Dr. Egon Orowan of Massachusetts Institute of Technology appears as Chap. I of the second edition of the "Design of Piping Systems" (M. W. Kellogg Co., Wiley, New York, 1957). Progress with these fundamentals has not advanced sufficiently to establish quantitatively the significance of available ductility (capacity for deformation without fracture) or of its role under combined manifestations of cyclic stress (fatigue), cyclic deformation (low cycle fatigue), temperature-time-induced deformation (creep) and attendant fracture (creep rupture), and other influences producing deformation. Too little attention has been directed toward an establishment of metals behavior to provide the basic understanding necessary for an optimum realization of the structural capacity of materials.

Design Criteria and Loadings. With current code approaches, simplified or empirical formulas are employed which for the most part consider only direct (membrane) stresses for surfaces of revolution, and principal bending stresses for flat plates, rings, etc. Local effects, such as at nozzles and heads, are in limited degree indirectly controlled by requirements as to geometry or by design factors. In the elastic range, the code retains the ultimate tensile strength and yield strength combination criteria, while the German and other codes place sole emphasis on yielding and consider only the yield strength. As the yield-to-tensile strength ratio is increased, design to the yield strength alone involves an increasingly lower margin against failure due to fatigue.

The yield-strength criterion is defended by the contention that little ductility is necessary and that cyclic loadings need be considered only for services involving full loading cycles of greater frequency than one per day. Such conclusions cannot be substantiated by present-day knowledge of the fundamentals of ductility and fatigue, and a more accurate appreciation is needed of useful ductility and its interassociation with work hardening. Greater knowledge is also required with respect to the integrated effect of stress raisers due respectively to overall and local geometry and fabrication and material flaws, under repetitive load applications.

For the creep range there is general acceptance of the A.S.M.E. Code approach of using combined creep and creep-rupture criteria for allowable stress. This neglects the direct quantitative and detrimental effect of cyclic loading on creep and creep rupture. It also lacks an appreciation of ductility exhaustion which results from the total cold- and hot-loading history as an integration of the number of cycles, strain range, and loading sequence.

Joint Efficiencies and Casting Quality. Joint efficiencies for welds formerly involved a combination measure of the relative structural capacity and fabrication quality, including assessment of the improved capabilities resulting from stress relief and more assured soundness from radiographic examination. Recently, joint efficiency credit for stress relief has been discontinued. As such, joint efficiencies are arbitrary and illogical and would gain recognizable status only if confined to a measure of structural capacity as limited by geometry, similar to riveted joints. This would limit their application to single- and double-lap and lap- and spot-welded joints.

Casting quality factors, as currently applied to basic allowable stress values, reflect the degree of destructive and non-destructive examination applied, with a factor of 0.80 arbitrarily assigned to the minimum visually examined quality. Quality or soundness factors are just as logically applicable to wrought materials as to castings.

Loadings and Cyclic Effects. A glaring deficiency, necessitating current code usage of generous safety factors, is the lack of coverage of loadings other than normal operating pressure, and consideration of the effect of repeated loadings. Vessel life and failure are apt to be established primarily by the number of cycles and magnitude of load variations, and by auxiliary conditions (startup, shutdown, regeneration, control swing, temperature gradients) or by emergencies resulting in crash shutdowns and malfunctions. This is recognized for nuclear service in the several issues (1958 and 1959) of the U.S. Navy Bureau of Ships "Tentative Structural Design Basis for Reactor Pressure Vessels and Directly Associated Components." For design purposes, this groups all loadings expected to occur during operation, startup, shutdown, and emergencies into three categories and establishes design number of cycles and strain range magnitude for each of these three groupings. Since much of the non-operating loading on process plant vessels is unpredictable, particularly as to frequency, a similar organization of loadings for process service would be desirable as a target for comparison with actual service and establishment of useful life and retirement.

Strength Enhancement. This is the key to economic heavy-wall construction. It is obtained by raising key mechanical properties while retaining acceptable ductility, fatigue resistance, etc., through controlled manufacture, heat-treatment, and better metallurgy. It is applicable to service in both the elastic and creep ranges.

The current code cases for strength-enhanced materials in the elastic range are deficient in assuring that the material and/or final construction uniformly meet the enhanced minimum design properties; also that the enhancement treatment, particularly quenching, has not initiated cracks. High-strength materials and relatively high yield-to-ultimate-strength ratio provide less ductility and reduced fatigue strength in proportion to yield or tensile strength. This is true particularly in the notched condition, so that design and fabrication must be refined for lesser local stress intensification. This results in more adequate and better balanced construction, which makes it possible to consider a reduction in safety factor compatible with the degree of refinement (*i.e.*, level of local stress intensification).

For the creep range, code recognition of strength-enhanced material is limited to high stresses for type 310 grain-coarsened austenitic steels, and for normalized A.S.T.M. A 193, B 14 (Cr-Mo-Va) bolt steel (as approved equal to the finer quenched structure for other bolt steels). Such recognition considers creep and creep rupture alone, and progress awaits an improved knowledge of high-temperature behavior in addition to a broader code basis.

Experimental Stress Analysis. Where stresses cannot be analytically established because of non-symmetrical geometry and other factors, experimental stress analysis is necessary. As fatigue assumes importance, the magnitude of local stresses becomes significant, so that the experimental stress measurement must be at the location of highest stress and of acceptable accuracy. Code proof tests do not validly establish the magnitude of localized stresses and may not even reveal the presence of those of highly localized character. It must also be appreciated that material and fabrication flaws will multiply design stress raisers if they occur at the same location.

Abrupt Overpressure. Abrupt overpressure may result from (1) heat generated and attendant release of gaseous products and their thermal expansion by explosions of fuel-oxidizer mixtures in combustion gas generators and oxidation reactors, or (2) from the rapid energy release from other highly exothermic reactions, or (3) from the exothermic decomposition of unstable materials. The vessels should be designed so that the material yield strength is not exceeded at the pressure corresponding to the full adiabatic conversion of heat release to pressure for the potential gas-mixture ratio involving the greatest pressure rise.

The shell material must be ductile and, at the metal temperature involved, be above its brittle fracture transition temperature (*i.e.*, have good notch impact strength).

Detonation. As a result of failures, increasing attention is being paid to prevention of detonations (*i.e.*, reaction propagation rates in combustible mixtures or unstable gases, exceeding the velocity of sound). The resulting rapid pressure rise may reach 200 to 400 times the initial pressure, with container failure a function of pressure rise and pressure pulse deviation. Since only small low-pressure vessels can be designed to withstand detonation, present emphasis is on its avoidance. Various aspects of hydrocarbon detonations are discussed in a paper by Jacobs ("Occurrence and Nature of Hydrocarbon Detonations," A.P.I., November, 1959, Chicago meeting), which also includes a list of references.

Structural Reactions. Vessels are increasingly utilized to support piping, equipment such as exchangers and smaller vessels, and structures such as platforms and stairways. Restrained piping expansion under temperature change generates force and moment reactions at nozzles. For relatively large, stiff piping, the vessel is in fact a flexible member of the piping system, while piping whose stiffness compares with the local deflection of the shell at the area of attachment has added flexibility at the expense of local vessel shell stress. Local stresses in the shell at the attachment due to these loadings must be controlled in accordance with principles outlined by Murphy and Rossheim (A.S.M.E. Paper 60-WA-313, December, 1960). Calculations here are complex but the work of Bijlaard (*Welding Research Council Bull.* 34, pp. 49, 50) provides guidance; assumptions necessary for a given geometry will limit accuracy. A simple approximate approach for handling piping thermal-expansion reactions is discussed in the subsequent subsection (see pp. 24-52ff.).

DESIGN AND STRESS EVALUATION

Overtemperature. Overtemperature is treated only in extremely limited degree by the code. It is significant in the presence of emergency or operating temperature swings, failure or malfunctioning of internal insulation, cooling jackets or other means of heat control. A detailed discussion is contained in A.S.M.E. Paper 59-A-319 (Rossheim *et al.*, "Pressure-vessel Overtemperature Hazards," November, 1959).

The A.S.M.E. Boiler and Pressure Vessel Code, Section I, paragraph P-23(f), permits steam temperature, pressure, or both for superheater discharge to exceed design conditions provided the stress due to the pressure does not exceed the code S value for the coincident temperature by more than: (1) 15 per cent during 10 per cent of the operating period and (2) 20 per cent during 1 per cent of the operating period. Otherwise the design temperature is not to be exceeded, although it is recognized that such may occur because of abnormal control swings and other surges and during emergencies such as external fires and loss of cooling, with only the overpressure protection now provided. Where temperature increases of significant magnitude are unavoidable, appropriate means should be provided to detect and to limit metal temperature by flooding, external sprays, or cooling jackets.

Internally Insulated Vessels. Where internal insulation is provided to permit designing a vessel for a lower metal temperature than the contained fluid, overtemperature potential exists. Insulation conductivity is affected by the fluid filling the pores as a function of fluid conductivity and pressure. [For example, see Wygant and Crowley, Effects of High-conductivity Gases on the Thermal Conductivity of Insulating Refractory Concrete, *J. Am. Ceram. Soc.*, **41** (5), (1958).]

Increased heat may penetrate because of cracks, voids, or gradual deterioration. Reasonable allowances must be made in determining the maximum expected metal temperature, with a margin of at least 200°F. desirable for the design metal temperature. Vessels having outside insulation are more sensitive to overheating due to internal heat penetration and may require added consideration and wider overrun margins.

Internal insulation loses its effectiveness in the presence of flow through itself or between it and the shell, which will be promoted by high-velocity flow impingement and catalyst bed pressure drop. Design must prevent this; in some services shrouding the insulation with a metal cylinder sealed to the shell at one end has been effective so long as it remains intact. A.S.M.E. Paper 59-A-319 also includes discussion of this problem. Assuming that a section of insulation may be lost or otherwise be ineffective, the paper suggests that the vessel have a short-time strength of not less than 1000 hr. (based on creep-rupture data) at a temperature equal to 80 per cent of the flow temperature in order to permit detection and orderly depressuring, or that it be protected against failure by effective emergency heat-removal means such as coils or outside non-pressure water jackets.

Supports. Vessel lugs and legs cause local reactions which are evaluated similar to piping reactions. Vessel skirt-to-shell stresses are usually controlled by minimizing the reaction component normal to the shell surface through aligning the center thickness of the vessel shell with the center thickness of the skirt [Fig. 24-11, detail (*a*)]. Fatigue life of the head-to-skirt attachment weld reflects the weld throat thickness, surface continuity and smoothness, and the inaccessible weld-root uniformity of penetration and contour. For usual service, only occasional difficulty arises with weld cracks, which can be avoided by the refinements of details (*c*) and (*d*) in Fig. 24-11. Thermal stresses induced by axial temperature gradients at the skirt-shell junction impose the most severe loading.

For cyclic service the lap-skirt attachment, detail (*c*), permits accurate fit-up and calking to minimize sharp weld-root discontinuities; it also provides load transfer with reduced stress concentration at the weld root; and the lap contact in combination with an insulation detail (which provides an air gap in the crotch) minimizes temperature gradients in the skirt at the weld. (See Weil and Murphy, Design and Analysis of Welded Pressure-vessel Skirt Supports, *Am. Soc. Mech. Engrs., J. Eng. Ind.*, February, 1960.) A still further refined design, which permits butt welds that can be effectively

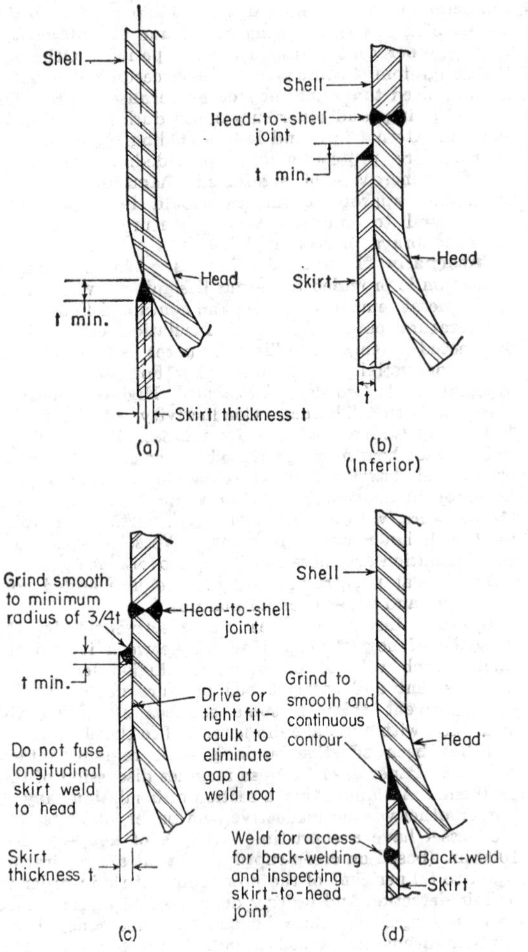

Fig. 24-11. Skirt-attachment details.

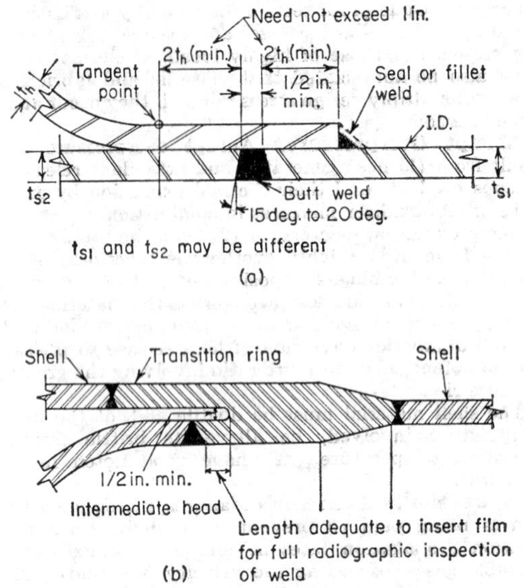

Fig. 24-12. Intermediate head- or skirt-attachment details.

radiographed, appears in Fig. 24-12, detail (*b*), and is applicable to either skirts or intermediate heads.

Intermediate Heads. Figure 24-12, detail (*a*), shows an intermediate head for which a "close fit" with the overlapping shells is specified with a wide-root butt weld joining the two shells and head. Where construction of fully assessed soundness is desired or essential, the design shown in detail (*b*) of this same figure minimizes local stress and provides butt welds which can be effectively radiographed.

Intersections. Recent code revisions formalize the acceptance of non-butt welds which cannot be effectively radiographed on construction provided that the longitudinal and intermediate girth welds are fully radiographed double-butt welds, or their full equivalent. For example, corner, lap, or blind root welds may be used for category *C* welds for attaching (1) an end or intermediate flange the full diameter of the vessel, (2) a full-diameter tube sheet, or (3) a flat-head closure.

Vibration and Stress Magnification. Codes do not cover stress magnification due to structural or flow resonance. Tall slender vessels (height-to-diameter ratio greater than 12) may be subject to objectionable and possibly dangerous vibratory deflections at wind velocities well below that for which they are nominally designed (considering wind as a static load) if the frequency of wind vortex shedding coincides with the natural frequency of the vessel and its support. (Von Kármán effect, see Den Hartog, "Mechanical Vibrations," 4th ed., McGraw-Hill, New York, 1956.) The natural period of the structure can be controlled only in limited degree by geometry, but there is as yet no assured way to avoid possible resonance at some wind velocity. Fortunately, the incidence of objectionable swaying is not great—apparently because of the local topography and lack of relatively steady turbulent free winds. Greater difficulty has been experienced on stacks, and many papers on this subject can be found in the *A.S.C.E. Journal of the Engineering Mechanics Division*. Troublesome cases have usually been guyed. Much study has been devoted to the development of practical "spoilers" which would break up the regularity of vortex shedding or reduce the force. But here again there does not appear to be an assured solution.

Temperature Stresses. Temperature stresses are generally appreciated only in the presence of intended heat transfer. There exists quite widely a total unawareness of temperature stresses incident to higher-temperature inlet flow, metal conduction, and rapid change in process temperature (quenching). Temperature stresses in ductile materials cause significant yielding only in the presence of weaker zones for plastic flow accumulation, or where so-called "ratcheting" occurs when temperature stresses are superimposed on a high membrane stress because of pressure or equivalent sustained loading. (See Miller, "Thermal Stress Ratchet Mechanism in Pressure Vessels," A.S.M.E. Paper 58-A-129, December, 1958.) Their primary significance is their contribution to total strain range per cycle and attendant reduction in fatigue life. Relaxation (stress relief in service) does not generally influence the strain range per cycle, which is proportionate to the temperature gradient.

Nozzles. Except for nuclear service and certain special materials, such as quenched and tempered steel, the codes do not in general require non-destructive examination of nozzle-attachment welds. They accept virtually any design meeting area-replacement and weld

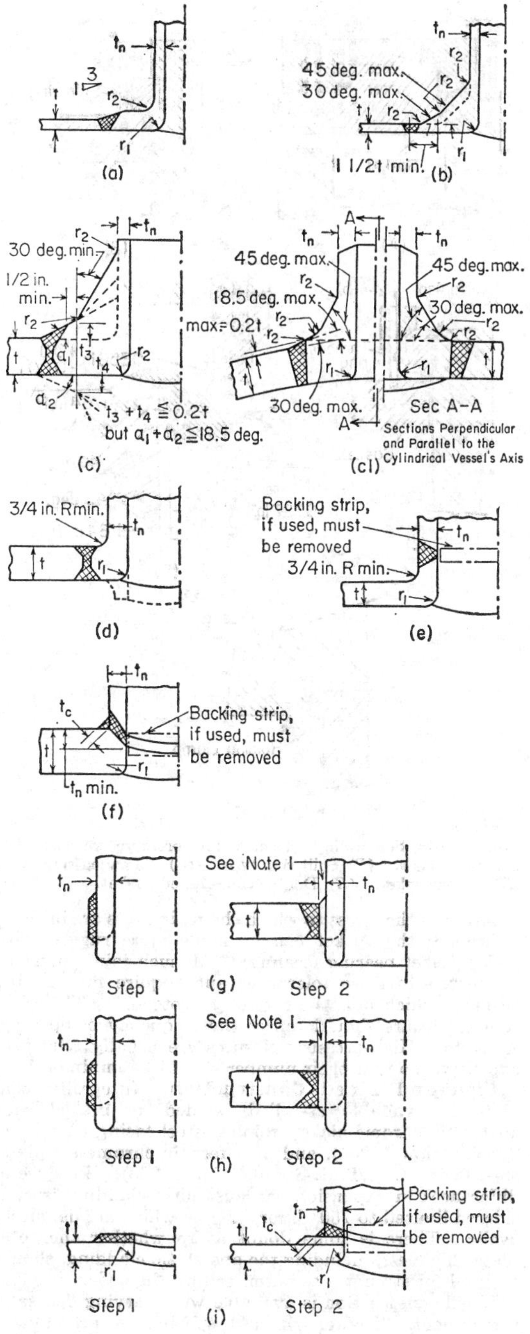

FIG. 24-13. Nozzle designs which permit non-destructive weld examination. (*Source: American Society of Mechanical Engineers.*)

t = thickness of part penetrated
t_n = thickness of penetrating part
$t_{c\,min}$ = $0.7t_n$ or ¼ in., whichever is less
$r_{1\,min}$ = ¼t or ¾ in., whichever is less
r_2 = ¼ in. minimum

Step 1: Examination required before assembly

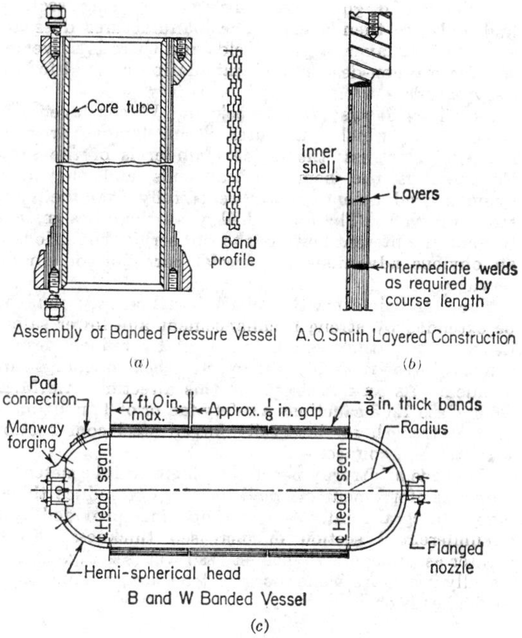

FIG. 24-14. Wound and layered wall construction of pressure vessels.

strength requirements, without concern as to over-stiffness, differences in stress-concentration level, massive or blind root welds, and design which does not permit effective non-destructive examination. Figure 24-13 presents alternate nozzle designs which permit non-destructive examination of varying degree of effectiveness taken from A.S.M.E. Case 1273-N for nuclear service.

High-pressure and Heavy-wall Vessels. High pressures (above 3000 lb./sq. in. more or less depending on size) introduce problems (1) in fabrication due to extreme thickness, (2) in nozzle design due to abrupt changes in section, and (3) with closures due to size, clearances, and effective gasket seals.

The availability of large presses and furnaces appreciably extended the thickness range of solid-wall construction. Welding has been facilitated by the availability in this country of low-hydrogen electrodes and, abroad, of electro-slag welding. The effectiveness of non-destructive examination has also been augmented by high-capacity betatrons and ultrasonic examination.

Specialized constructions, for the most part proprietary, have been developed to facilitate fabrication and/or reduce cost. Some of these are illustrated in Fig. 24-14. Detail (*a*) illustrates an interlocking metal-tape-wound vessel construction developed and available in Europe for which there is considerable favorable experience. The outside diameter of the inner core is machined with grooves to receive the tape, and the interlocking feature enables the winding to carry longitudinal as well as circumferential stress. There are currently no United States fabricators for this type of pressure vessels.

Detail (*b*) shows the A. O. Smith multilayer construction, which is much used in this country. The outer layers are usually ¼ in. carbon steel of 75,000 ultimate tensile strength and are fitted and welded in place successively over the inner core. Each shell course is

Step 2: Radiographic examination is required of the attachment used
Note: This dimension shall be at least ¾ in.

completed and girth seams between cylinder sections and ends are then made. The manufacturer does not stress-relieve layer or girth welds and there is as yet no satisfactory non-destructive examination method for the heavy welds.

Detail (c) shows the Babcock and Wilcox layer construction in which the outer ⅜-in. layers carry no longitudinal stress; the inside cylinder is of the same thickness as the hemispherical ends and the inner cylinder-head assembly has welds fully examined and stress-relieved. The inner shell of all these designs can be made of different materials to suit service conditions—an obvious advantage for special corrosion or similar services.

The economic attraction of solid-wall construction can be extended by strength enhancement and lower safety factors, when they can be justified by refined design. This is greatly facilitated where shell openings are avoided. As an initial step in this direction, A.S.M.E. Code Case 1205 sanctions a safety factor of 3 on ultimate tensile strength for integrally forged steel construction without shell connections.

The code arbitrarily permits an increased diameter for nozzle reinforcement of small openings to reduce thickness. Integral reinforcement of openings provided by a circumferential section of increased thickness affords greater assurance as to local stress level (see Fig. 24-15). Usually it is more economic to restrict nozzle connections to the heads or closures.

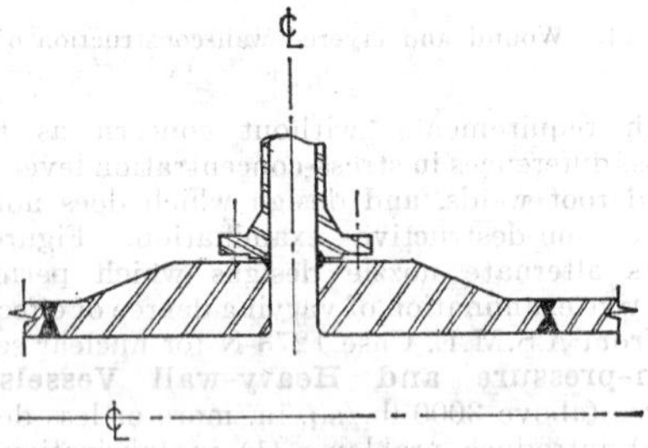

Fig. 24-15. Nozzle reinforcement for reduced local stress.

Closures. There are many special large-closure designs. Most involve a self-sealing feature whereby the internal vessel pressure loads the gasket bearing surface to maintain tightness. The most commonly used are the Bridgman, delta, and double-cone types as illustrated in Fig. 24-16.

In the **Bridgman** type the hydrostatic end pressure acts on the plug which in turn acts on the gasket at an angle that induces a sealing reaction at the gasket-plug interface and the gasket-shell interface. Detail (*A*) shows a typical arrangement using three sets of bolts. Bolts (*a*) take the end-pressure load; bolts (*b*) provide an initial gasket sealing load; bolts (*c*) are merely jacking-out bolts. There are many variations using full or interrupted threaded rings or shear rings for bolts as illustrated in details (*B*) and (*C*).

In the case of the **delta** gasket, detail (*D*), the circumferential internal pressure loading acting over the height of the gasket produces a sealing-force reaction at the tips. Initial seal at the tips is produced by controlled mechanical interference when the joint is initially made up. Dimensions shown are typical but gasket proportions and angles can be varied to suit the application and combination of materials used.

Detail (*E*) shows a **double-cone** seated gasket which operates on the same principle as the delta joint. Initial gasket seating load is under more positive control as a function of the stress to which the main bolts are initially tightened; the gasket can be made more rugged with wider gasket bearing (sealing). All such joints must be fabricated to close tolerances and require fine seating surfaces which must be carefully protected. The selection of closure should reflect the frequency of opening, size, etc. High-pressure closures are usually relatively expensive, so that their number should be minimized.

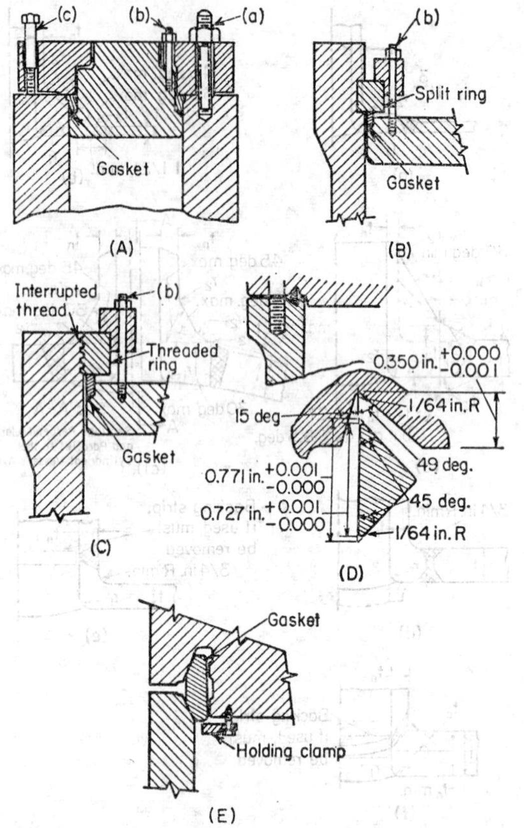

Fig. 24-16. Self-sealing closures for pressure vessels. (*A*) Bridgman type. (*B*) Split-ring type. (*C*) Threaded-ring type. (*D*) Delta gasket. (*E*) Double cone-seated gasket.

Clad and Lined Construction. Integrally clad plate is available as-rolled, welded, or brazed with austenitic chrome-nickel stainless-steel facing (A.S.T.M. Specification A 264), and with ferritic chrome stainless-steel facing (A.S.T.M. Specification A 263). Because of differences in expansion the austenitic cladding is considered limited to 750°F. for services which are definitely cyclic. There is some doubt as to whether the total plate thickness, including the austenitic cladding, should be used for strength, as permitted by the code.

Lined construction is available with varying degree of attachment. The extent and spacing of attachment welds establish the momentary temperature difference between the liner and base plate, as a function of the rate of flow temperature change. Usually this rate increases with service temperature, and the resulting pillowing and cracking reflect also the cycles of temperature change. Roughly, plowed-through machine-welded and manual strip-welded liners are preferably limited to 750°F. for chromium-steel lining and 600°F. for austenitic-steel lining. Spot-welded liners are limited to about 800°F., although higher temperatures give acceptable service when (1) weld spacing is reduced, (2) severe temperature changes do not occur, and (3) there are relatively few cycles of temperature. Integral clad construction is advisable for severe cyclic temperature service.

Jacketed Vessels. The code includes no detailed rules for such vessels but does have rules for stayed construction. These require design for internal and external pressure for shapes covered by the rules. Other designs and details require the authorized inspector's approval and, when necessary, proof tests. Simple empirical design approaches are generally used for commercial vessels with welded joints which cannot be non-destructively examined. In such cases heavy reliance is placed on service experience for these factors and temperature-difference effects. For more servere operating conditions, much more refined analysis and details are required.

MATERIALS AND HEAT-TREATMENT

Materials specifications, in general, go little further than establishing limits for (1) the content of specific elements, (2) the range of general physical properties, (3) the tests on which acceptance is based, and (4) dimensional requirements, including tolerances. Quality is defined only by reference to harmful (usually unspecified) defects; non-destructive examination, if mentioned, is relegated to a supplementary requirement, not called for by the code and not furnished unless specified by the purchaser. For carbon- and low-alloy-steel plates, so-called "firebox quality" calls for slightly lower carbon, phosphorus, and sulfur content, and slightly higher ductility than flange quality, with tensile tests from the top as well as the bottom of the plate as rolled.

Flange-quality steel is the minimum unrestricted quality for pressure vessels, while structural quality omits tests on plates as-rolled, and limits only phosphorus and sulfur. In total these quality differences are insignificant. Currently non-destructive examination, such as magnetic-powder examination of plate edges, ultrasonic scanning for internal defects, and fluid penetrant examination of surfaces, are apparently not applied with sufficient frequency to be available at an attractive cost. A.S.T.M. Specification A 435-59T covers ultrasonic testing and inspection of killed-steel plates of firebox or higher quality.

Temperature-induced Brittleness. Carbon steels and most ferritic analyses are subject to loss of notched-bar impact resistance with decreasing temperature. Suitable materials for services below −20°F. are covered by the A.S.M.E. Code, which continues to accept the keyhole-notch Charpy test, although research opinion here and abroad favors the more conservative V-notch Charpy test.

The code is deficient with respect to low ambient temperature, and service or ambient temperatures above −20°F. where most carbon steels are sensitive. Economic materials resistant in this range await new specifications and attendant reorientation of tonnage production. For the present, minimization of pressure-vessel brittleness can be obtained with minimum expenditure by specifying: (1) For service temperatures from 32° to 60°F. or higher: Steel of improved transition properties in accordance with A.S.M.E. Case 1256 (or A.S.T.M. Specification A 442-60T) or A.S.M.E. Case 1280. Case 1256 provides a 55,000 and a 60,000 ultimate tensile strength grade and case 1280, a 65,000 and a 70,000 grade. Both cases include requirements to assure control of the manganese-carbon ratio. Plate over 1 in. to case 1256 and all plate to case 1280 are silicon-killed and made to fine-grain practice; plate over 1½ in. to case 1280 is normalized. (2) For service temperatures from 0° to 32°F.: Steel to case 1256 specifying fine-grain practice and normalizing or to case 1280 specifying normalizing over ¾ in. (3) For service temperatures from −20° to 0°F.: Steel as above (0° to 32°F. range) specifying normalizing and stress relief for all thicknesses.

Additional safety margin against brittle fracture initiation when using these or standard pressure-vessel carbon steels will be provided by requiring normalizing, stress relief, or both.

Heat-treatment. Material specifications and code requirements tend to minimize heat-treatment, placing undue reliance on mill or manufacturer's discretion in controlling finishing temperature, and disregarding the effect of intercritical and subcritical temperature holding time, or cold work on structure, sensitivities, and properties. For example, it is not required that hot- or cold-formed heads be heat-treated. Other specifications allow the supplier a choice between annealing and normalizing and tempering. The suitability for fabrication and service can often be improved by limiting the choice of heat-treatment, or requiring a separate normalizing treatment. The heat-treatments which materials receive at the mill and in fabrication are particularly important for strength-enhanced materials and corrosion-resistant materials and should be very carefully reviewed for the individual application.

FABRICATION

Fabrication requirements in the code are deliberately restricted to allow maximum latitude to the manufacturer as regulated by code-defined qualified inspection, and with a minimum of specific guidance. All fabrication is on one quality level, except weld soundness as influenced by radiographic examination.

Non-destructive Examination

As mentioned in previous sections, the A.S.M.E. Code has detailed requirements for the radiographic examination of welds and in nuclear cases 1272-N, 1273-N, and 1275-N has taken an initial step toward introducing requirements for ultrasonic examination of welds. It was also noted that the Subcommittee on Nondestructive Testing has prepared requirements for magnetic-particle and fluid-penetrant examination of welds, which are expected to be included in the code shortly.

As with other factors in the over-all construction, the effectiveness of all these and other methods is variable and depends on the controls, equipment, surface finish, interpretation standards, gages (penetrameters), etc. Accordingly, it is possible to establish requirements for several different quality levels of over-all construction. Knowledge of the factors which have significant influence is also of value in judging competitive bids. Peterson and Voelker in "Fabrication Requirements for Balanced Classes of Piping" (A.S.M.E. Paper 61-SA-60, June, 1961) have included suggested requirements for four classes of such examination.

Radiographic Examination. The code requirements rely on the penetrameter image and include no restrictions as to film type, screens, and film density. Surface finish is left largely to the judgment of the manufacturer and inspector.

Grinding seams smooth and flush minimizes surface stress raisers and provides optimum film interpretation; deposited surfaces of acceptable smoothness are, however, possible at a lower cost. Peterson and Voelker have chosen to define finish in standard machine terminology in order to avoid the ambiguity of purely descriptive wording.

The use of coarse-grain film, calcium tungstate screens, and single-emulsion no-screen films promotes diffusion and loss of image definition. Fine-grain film, equal to Eastman type AA or M, with lead screens is essential for reasonable assurance of crack detection. This is further enhanced by maintaining film density in the weld at a minimum of 2.0.

The A.S.M.E. Subcommittee on Nondestructive Examination has investigated possible improvements in penetrameters and may recommend adoption of one having narrow slits instead of small holes, with the objective of obtaining a better evaluation of the ability of the technique to detect linear cracklike defects. Trial applications are promising and such penetrameters can be currently obtained and used to supplement the code standard one for additional guidance.

X-ray is to be preferred over gamma ray as it results in greater contrast and sharper image definition, with less risk of overlooking cracks. This is because the X-ray machine can be adjusted for thickness, while theoretically a gamma-ray source is not adjustable. Some of the available isotopes, such as iridium 192, when used for an appropriate thickness range can produce comparable results.

Radiographic inspection of castings is covered by A.S.T.M. Specification E 71-52, which includes five classes of acceptance standards. Only classes 1 and 2 are generally used for pressure service. These standards leave much to be desired, and there has been little or no progress in many years.

Ultrasonic Examination. In addition to the code references cited, this procedure is covered in A.S.T.M. Specification E 114-55T. Ultrasonic examination is practical not only for welds but for complete internal examination with the possible exception of very coarse grained materials. Its commercial application has progressed much faster in Europe than in the United States. A comparison of ultrasonic examinations by two different laboratories is possible only when the two instruments are similarly adjusted to the same reference block standard.

Magnetic-particle and Fluid-penetrant Examination. These are considered supplementary to other forms of inspection for the detection of surface cracks too fine to be detected visually or by radiography. Magnetic-particle examination by the dry-powder method is, however, capable of detecting subsurface flaws, although not reliably so, and is considered preferable for magnetic materials to which it is limited. Magnetic-particle inspection technique is covered by A.S.T.M. Specification E 109-57T (dry method) and E 138-58T (wet method). Specification E 125-56T covers acceptance standards for ferrous castings. Penetrant examination is widely used for austenitic and similar weld deposits sensitive to microcracking. Both tests would benefit from the use of gages (penetrameters) so that levels of quality of inspection could be made comparable.

ECONOMICS AND COSTS

Precise estimating of the cost of a pressure vessel involves a careful evaluation of the cost of the individual material components, the various fabrication operations involved (forming, cutting, machining, fitting, welding, etc.), inspection, tests, and quality controls, plus the determination of overhead costs and the assignment of a profit margin. Materials cost must consider the mill extras which may be involved, such as plate quality, width, and thickness. An appropriate reference to be consulted is Chilton ("Cost Engineering in the Process Industries," pp. 67-84, McGraw-Hill, New York, 1960). Even with the best estimating methods, the purchaser will find a broad range in the bid prices for a particular vessel and these will further vary widely from time to time with the competitive situation.

Chemical engineers will, however, often have need of rather rough estimates of conventional-process-vessel costs, particularly for comparing the relative costs of alternate designs. For this purpose the extremely simplified approach of estimating cost on the total weight of the vessel may be used. The fact that the major portion of the material and fabrication cost is directly related to the plate required for shell and heads makes it possible to arrive at such a simplified estimating procedure while maintaining reasonable effectiveness.

Figure 24-17 presents a suggested cost index for United States completely shop-fabricated A.S.M.E. Code process pressure vessels of carbon steel, alloy clad, and types 304 and 316 stainless material and of cylindrical shape having ellipsoidal or torispherical end heads.

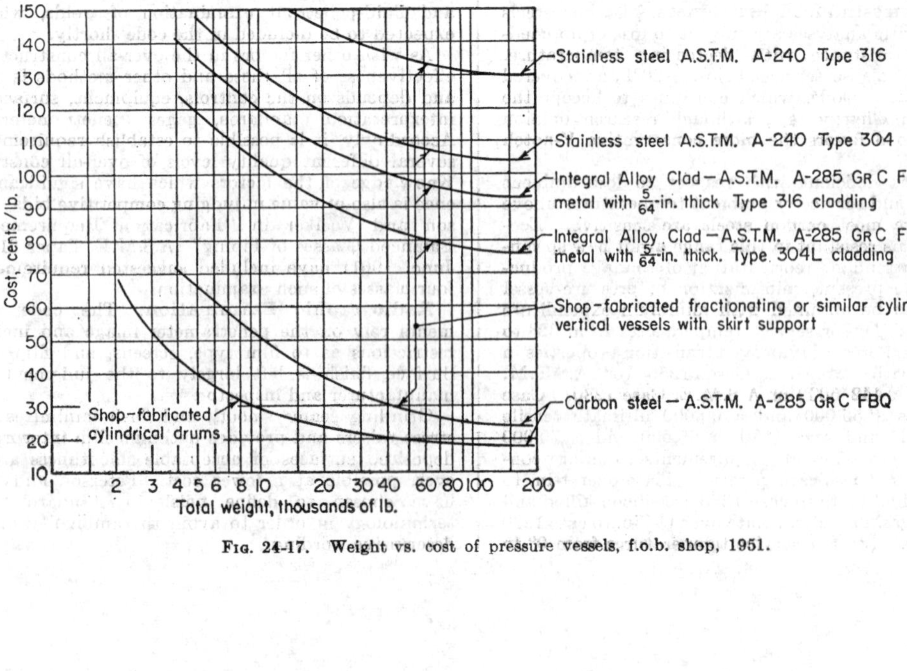

FIG. 24-17. Weight vs. cost of pressure vessels, f.o.b. shop, 1951.

The weight of the vessel may be calculated in detail or may be more simply approximated by the following formula:

$$\text{Weight (lb.)} = 136D(H + 0.8D)(t + X)$$

where H = length of shell (tangent to tangent) plus height of support skirt, ft.
D = mean diameter, ft.
t = average shell thickness, in.
X = equivalent thickness to be added to account for nozzles, manholes, clips, internal support members, etc.

Suggested values of X for vessels having usual manhole and nozzle connections are:
X = 0.08 in. for vessels with little or no internals
X = 0.15 in. for fractionating or similar vessels having occasional manholes and with tray or equivalent support rings every few feet

As experience is gained, X can be assigned other appropriate values to suit individual applications.

The cost index of Fig. 24-17 does not include the costs for full radiographing or stress relieving. No simple factor will adequately assess these but as a rough average an addition of 2¢/lb. to the cost index is suggested for each of these items, when they are involved.

For additional rough guidance when working with material other than A 285 plate, the cost for A 285 construction may be increased as follows: (1) for silicon-killed carbon steel, A.S.T.M. A 212 or 201, add 2¢/lb.; (2) for carbon, 0.5 per cent molybdenum steel, A.S.T.M. A 204 grade B, add 12 to 18¢/lb. depending on thickness (lowest increase on the thicker plates); and (3) for 1 per cent chrome ½ per cent molybdenum steel, A.S.T.M. A 301 grade B, add 13 to 19¢/lb. depending on thickness (lowest increase on the thicker plates).

As with all cost data, adjustment must be made for increases in materials, labor, etc., from the base year 1961.

For comparing individual design or fabrication details or for unusual or non-standard designs there is no substitute for precise estimating or preferably obtaining firm bids.

PROCESS PLANT PIPING

The objective of this subsection is to provide the chemical engineer with a general understanding of the many significant aspects of pressure piping affecting safety, utility, and economics, as a working basis for communication with the mechanical engineer in exercising their joint responsibilities.

The basic design aspects common to all pressure equipment have already been covered in the preceding subsection on pressure vessels. Certain common design aspects are also treated in later subsections devoted to drivers and equipment, and the sections on heat-transfer equipment, etc. Fluid flow pressure drop and attendant line sizings are covered in Sec. 5 (see pp. 5-23 and 5-29).

Process plants and their offsite installations include virtually all piping services. Among these are gravity-flow sewer lines, pressure waste lines, power piping within steam power plants, refrigeration piping within refrigeration plants, utilities piping (for high, intermediate, and low-pressure steam, water, air, fuel, and gas), process piping (all process streams including intermediate streams used for heat transfer, treating, etc.), auxiliary piping (regeneration, startup and shutdown, blowdown, relief, etc.), heat-transfer piping (for organic fluids, heat-transfer salts, mercury, oil, etc.), instrument piping, treating and conditioning piping (corrosion inhibitors, dyes, and other chemicals), two-phase flow piping (fluidized solids and liquid-solid slurries, etc.), transport piping (to and from storage tanks, pipe lines, docks, and loading stocks), building and equipment heating and steam-tracing piping, fire systems (water, foam, and CO_2), and hydraulic-system piping.

While an accepted definition is lacking, there is wide agreement that piping covers all pressure equipment whose principal or sole function is "transport." Certain components, such as traps, strainers, float chambers, and sample coolers, are always associated with piping and are generally accepted as falling within that category. Other components, such as receivers, snubbers, mufflers, dampeners, separators, and filters, are ruled by most enforcement agencies to be pressure vessels. Actually, there is no justification for a difference in construction requirements between piping fabricated of plate, with sufficient diameter for inside access, and pressure vessels.

In most process, power, and other industrial plants, piping assumes important economic significance, representing 30 to 50 per cent of the cost of over-all process units, and 15 to 30 per cent of offsite facilities. The major part of this expenditure is usually for low-pressure and non-hazardous utilities, transport, heating, fire, water, sewer, waste, and similar piping services. As a result, process unit and over-all plant layout must be carefully scrutinized with respect to piping requirements, with emphasis on arrangement to minimize runs and on support within otherwise essential structures. Lines for flows exceeding 500°F., or of large diameter, heavy wall thickness, or of expensive materials must be competently scrutinized for most economic installation, with maximum realization of inherent flexibility without additional loops.

Because most piping is of small diameter, its design is too widely considered only with respect to its dimensional aspects, and attendant quantities and costs. Conventional and standardized design for pressure often fails to recognize the fundamental engineering properly associated with critical services or special materials or unusual component details. It totally ignores the frequently challenging problems attendant to adequate flexibility for control of stress and reactions, as well as parallel difficulties in providing effective structural support and restraint compatible with freedom for thermal expansion.

Piping engineering combines the skills and contributions of many professions. To be most effective an adequate design must necessarily have its inception in a broad and simultaneous appreciation of the process, its equipment characteristics, and their operating requirements, including preferences of supervising personnel. Too often these are translated into loadings and design conditions which adequately reflect only *normal* operation and fail to anticipate alternate operations, as well as auxiliary and emergency conditions.

Because of the large numbers of components involved, the resulting layout and loadings are often restricted by economics to handbook and standards selection of flange series, pipe schedule, and valve type of the selected materials. More extensive background and competence are essential (but too often lacking) to recognize pressure, weight, temperature, and other loadings of unusual magnitude or which are so significantly dynamic or cyclic in character as to require special stress analysis and attendant design treatment.

Inadequacy of Codes and Standards. There are wide misconceptions with respect to piping construction quality and suitability for a given service. The most serious is the philosophy of so-called "one-quality welding." Another is that a high allowable stress applied with consideration of loading only is justified by the relatively small diameter (compared with pressure vessels) and lesser attendant hazard in the event of failure, the absence of longitudinal joints (on seamless pipe), and the freedom from longitudinal pressure stress. Still another is that compliance with A.S.A. B31 Code requirements assures piping adequate for any service (see later detailed discussion "The A.S.A. Code for Pressure Piping A.S.A. B31 . . .").

"One-quality welding" neglects consideration of the fact that fully sound joints of uniformly smooth inside and outside surface can be obtained only by adequate preparation of pipe ends, continuous observation of the adequacy of equipment and operators, and non-destructive examination of the entire length of all welds by a method which is fully capable of detecting cracks and flaws.

High allowable stresses for empirical design based only on pressure loading can be hazardous. Small diameter does not assure lesser hazard, since appreciable quantities of combustibles can be released even by lines as small as ¾ in. or less, and small line failures can trigger failures of vessels or larger lines. Welded and seamless pipe are subject to material and fabrication defects. Contrary to popular impression, longitudinal pressure stresses exist wherever piping runs develop end loads, such as runs between elbows or bends. They would be lowered only on a straight run between two vessels, or by rigid anchors which are infinitely stiff compared with the pipe. This condition is practically never attained.

A.S.A. B31 Code requirements do not assure piping adequate for all applications. According to paragraph 300 (B31.3), General Statements:

> The owner of a completed piping installation shall have the overall responsibility for compliance with this Code . . . but where *service requirements necessitate added quality and more extensive nondestructive examination, these are to be specified in the engineering design* and any revision thereto, and when so specified, the Code requires that they be accomplished.

Paragraph 300.1, Scope, reads: "This Code prescribes *minimum requirements* for the materials, design, fabrication, assembly, test and inspection of petroleum refinery pressure and vacuum piping systems." B31.8-1955, Gas Transmission and Distribution Piping Systems, and paragraph 804.4 under Scope and Intent reads: "The requirements of Section 8 are adequate for safety under conditions normally encountered in the gas industry. *Requirements for abnormal or unusual conditions are not specifically provided for, nor are all details of engineering and construction prescribed.*"

Because of the large numbers of piping components, their design and manufacture benefit from standardization and attendant mass production. Dimensional and attendant rating and design standardization simplifies and greatly reduces the design costs of piping for process units and plants.

A.S.A. CODE AND RELATED REQUIREMENTS

The A.S.A. B31 Code for Pressure Piping is the only known codified requirement for pressure piping. A.S.A. B31 has been adopted by the Canadian Standards Association and as a guide for enforcement by the provinces of that country. It has also been adopted with certain reservations or revisions by the state of Ohio and by certain cities of the United States. Section 8, Gas Transmission and Distribution Systems, has been widely adopted by the states and cities which are traversed by such pipe lines. Section 6, Chemical Industry Process Piping, is not yet available. Process plant design is therefore related in this presentation to Section 3, Petroleum Refinery Piping.

American Standards Association is an organization for the collaboration of industry, governmental agencies, and professional organizations in a joint standardization effort. One such agency is assigned as the sponsor of each standard. The A.S.M.E. performs this function for A.S.A. B31 but does not administer or control the committee's actions. Administration is under the direction of an exceptionally large sectional committee, responsible to the A.S.A. Its membership is selected by and directly represents individual participating industries, agencies, and organizations; additional members "at large" are selected by the chairman (subject to A.S.A. approval) to serve as individuals. As such, A.S.A. B31 Codes are more properly termed "industry practices," if it is accepted that the term "code" is properly applied only to documents reflecting an independent consensus of professional opinion in protection of the public interest.

A conference committee with membership similar to that of the A.S.M.E. Code, including the enforcement administrator of each state and province represented, has been established but is not known to have been actively engaged with the code. A smaller executive committee directs and performs the detailed accomplishment, with its actions subject to periodic review by the aforementioned sectional committee. Interpretations (cases) and revisions are handled similarly to those of the A.S.M.E. Code. Interpretation and proposed revisions are also published in *Mechanical Engineering.* The Manufacturer's Standardization Society of the Valve and Fitting Industry provides a technical secretary to whom communications relative to the code should be addressed, at 420 Lexington Avenue, New York 17, N.Y.

Subdivision of A.S.A. B31 into industry sections fosters misunderstanding with respect to the adequacy of its requirements as applied to specific services, loadings, and environments. The introduction to the current A.S.A. B31 code states: "The Code sets forth engineering requirements deemed necessary for safe design and construction," and then cautions that: ". . . the Code is not a design handbook. The Code does not do away with the need for the engineer or competent engineering judgment." In recently issued editions, however, A.S.A. B31.3 ("Petroleum Refinery Piping") includes statements which create an impression of sufficiency for indicated services as does A.S.A. B31.8 ("Gas Transmission and Distribution Piping Systems") by providing four "allowable" levels of stress as associated with installation locations and environment.

The A.S.A. B31 Piping Code, despite qualifying statements and cautions, is equally, if not more, misleading than the A.S.M.E. Boiler and Pressure Vessel Code with respect to the adequacy and limitations of its consideration of service and environment. This situation engenders general misunderstanding and neglect in meeting the specified owner-user responsibility for providing above-minimum requirements.

Code Arrangement and Scope. Significant requirements of A.S.A. B31.3 "Petroleum Refinery Piping" (1959 edition) are summarized in the following presentation, which is aimed primarily at welded and seamless construction.* Riveted construction is not used for

* Pending completion and publication of Section 6 on Chemical Piping, this is the most suitable source of reference for the chemical engineer and is therefore used as the basis of presentation here. EDITOR.

process piping (and is not mentioned in the code). Brazed, soldered, threaded, expanded, and mechanical coupling constructions are employed where thickness, material, size, economic, or other considerations favor their use, and will be briefly covered. While summarized data and formulas are included, their purpose is for rough appraisal of proportions and feasibility, and not for actual design.

Definitions. The Petroleum Refinery Code (A.S.A. B31.3) is a section of American Standard B31 Code for Pressure Piping and has been published as a separate document for simplicity and convenience. In connection with owner responsibility for piping installations, the reader's attention is also directed to the following statement (Code paragraph 300) which recognizes that the mandatory requirements of the code are minimum and must be supplemented when required for the particular service: "*It is required that the engineering design specify any special requirements pertinent to the particular service involved* . . . and when so specified the Code requires that they be accomplished."

A.S.A. B31.3 covers all piping within a petroleum refinery, loading terminal, gas-processing plant, bulk plant, compounding plant, or refinery tank farm; also interconnecting lines between sections of a refinery. Piping includes pipe, flanges, bolting, gaskets, valves, fittings, and pressure parts of expansion joints, strainers, and meters together with their supports but it does not include support structures, equipment, and buildings. The Code applies to all fluids, including fluidized solids, and to all types of services including oil, gas, steam, air, water, chemicals, and refrigerants, with the following exceptions: (1) Piping for package refrigeration units may be designed to A.S.A. B31.5 except that impact-test requirements of Section 3 apply. (2) Piping within the jurisdiction of the A.S.M.E. Boiler Code, Section I, Power Boilers. (3) Refinery heater tubes, fittings, headers, and terminal connections. (4) Pressure vessels, heat exchangers, pumps, and other equipment including their internal piping and connections. (5) Piping designed for internal pressure at or above 0 lb./sq. in. gage but less than 5 lb./sq. in. gage regardless of temperature and above 5 lb./sq. in. gage but less than 15 lb./sq. in. gage from −20° to 650°F., inclusive. (6) Cross-country piping in refineries.

Definitions relating to welding are consistent with A.W.S. Standard A3.0 and are supplemented by others with specific reference to piping.

DESIGN CONDITIONS

The design of piping essentially parallels that of pressure vessels; however, certain additional or modified aspects are introduced by the pipe and piping system geometry and/or usage. The temperature, pressure, and various forces and loadings, including ambient and mechanical influences applicable to the design of piping systems, are as follows:

1. Internal and external pressures.
2. Design metal temperature:

With fluid below 30°F. the metal temperature is taken as the fluid temperature.

With fluid at or above 32°F. and without external insulation the metal temperature is taken as a percentage of the fluid temperature.

For pipe, threaded and welding end valves and fittings, and other components with wall thickness comparable with that of the pipe, 95 per cent; for flanges, flanged valves, and fittings, 90 per cent; for lap-joint flanges, 85 per cent; and for bolting, 80 per cent.

With fluid at or above 32°F. and with external insulation the metal temperature is taken as the fluid temperature unless service data, tests, or calculations justify lower values.

For internally insulated pipe, the design metal temperature shall be calculated or obtained from tests.

3. Ambient influences. Where cooling results in vacuum, design must provide for external pressure or a vacuum breaker installed; also for thermal expansion of contents.
4. Dynamic effects. Design must provide for impact (hydraulic shock, etc.), wind (exposed piping), earthquake (use governmental data as a guide for force, earthquake not to be considered as acting simultaneously with lateral wind force), and vibrations (of piping arrangement and support).
5. Weight considerations include (*a*) live loads (contents, ice and snow), (*b*) dead loads (pipe, valves, insulation, etc.), and (*c*) test loads (test fluid).
6. Thermal expansion and contraction.

Design Ratings. Standardized pressure components, such as flanges, pipe fittings, and valves, with established pressure-temperature ratings, may be used provided the design pressure and temperature are within these ratings* (see Tables 24-11 through 24-15 for A.S.A. B16.5 pressure-temperature ratings of flanged fittings and valves of some typical ferrous and non-ferrous materials). The use of components without pressure-temperature ratings or beyond the limits of established values must be in accordance with code requirements.

Where infrequent variations of short duration in the pressure or temperature, or both, from normal operation are characteristic of a service the pressure-temperature rating of the piping components may be adjusted as follows: (1) When the increased operating condition will not exceed 10 hr. at any one time or 100 hr./year, it is permissible to increase the pressure rating at the temperature existing during the increased operating condition, by a maximum of 33 per cent. (2) When the increased operating condition will not exceed 50 hr. at any one time or 500 hr./year, it is permissible to increase the pressure rating at the temperture existing during the increased operating condition by a maximum of 20 per cent.

Ratings for valves between two pipe runs or a pipe run and connected equipment shall be for the higher pressure-temperature conditions, unless the valve is so located as to assure a lower operating temperature condition. In any case the piping must be designed to the higher temperature.

Design Allowable Stress. Allowable stresses are tabulated in the code in three categories covering 64 pages. The tables cover carbon steel, cast iron, low- and intermediate-alloy steels, high-alloy steels, and the non-ferrous metals: copper, aluminum, nickel, and their alloys. For convenience, Tables 24-16 and 24-17 summarize allowable stresses with respect to temperature for the commonly used *seamless* pipe and fitting materials. Likewise Table 24-19 shows the longitudinal joint efficiencies E which must be incorporated for the welded grades.

* The ratings are the maximum allowable non-shock pressures (lb./sq. in. gage) at the tabulated temperatures (°F.) and may be interpolated between the temperatures shown. The *primary service pressure* ratings (150, 300, 400, 600, 900, 1500, and 2500 lb.) are those at the head of the tables and shown in boldface type in the body of the tables.

Temperatures (°F.) used in determining these rating tables were temperatures on the inside of the pressure-retaining structure.

Table 24-11. Pressure-Temperature Ratings for Flanged Fittings and Valves of Typical Ferrous Materials*

For 150 lb.

Service temp., °F.	Material: Carbon steel	Carbon moly	Cr-Mo 1¼–½	Cr-Mo 2¼–1	Cr-Mo 5–½	Stainless types: 304	347 and 321	316	304L	316L
–20 to 100§	275	275	275	275	275	275	275	275	275	275
150	255	255	255	255	255	255	255	255	255	255
200	240	240	240	240	240	240	240	240	240	240
250	225	225	225	225	225	225	225	225	225	225
300	210	210	210	210	210	210	210	210	210	210
350	195	195	195	195	195	195	195	195	195	195
400	180	180	180	180	180	180	180	180	180	180
450	165	165	165	165	165	165	165	165	165	165
500	150	150	150	150	150	150	150	150	150	150
550	140	140	140	140	140	140	140	140	140	140
600	130	130	130	130	130	130	130	130	130	130
650	120	120	120	120	120	120	120	120	120	120
700	110	110	110	110	110	110	110	110	110	110
750	100	100	100	100	100	100	100	100	100	100
800	92	92	92	92	92	92	92	92	92	92
850	82†	82	82	82	82	82	82	82		82
875	75†	75†	75	75	75	75	75	75		
900	70†	70†	70	70	70	70	70	70		
925	60†	60†	60	60	60	60	60	60		
950	55†	55†	55	55	55	55	55	55		
975	50†	50†	50	50	50	50	50	50		
1000	40†	40†	40	40	40	40	40	40		

Hydrostatic shell test pressure.......... 425

For 300 lb.

Service temp., °F.	Material: Carbon steel	Carbon moly	Cr-Mo 1¼–½	Cr-Mo 2¼–1	Cr-Mo 5–½
–20 to 100§	720	720	720	720	720
150	710	710	710	710	710
200	700	700	700	700	700
250	690	690	690	690	690
300	680	680	680	680	680
350	675	675	675	675	675
400	665	665	665	665	665
450	650	650	650	650	650
500	625	625	625	625	625
550	590	590	590	590	590
600	555	555	555	555	555
650	515	515	515	515	515
700	470	480	485	485	485
750	425	445	450	450	450
800	365	410	415	415	415
850	300†	370	385	385	385
875	260†	355†	365	365	365
900	225†	335†	350	350	350
925	190†	320†	335	335	335
950	155†	300†	315	315	315
975	120†	280†	300	300	300
1000	85†	215†	265	265	250
1025	......	......	230†	235	215
1050	......	......	190†	200	180
1075	......	......	165†	170†	145
1100	......	......	135†	145†	115
1125	......	......	110†	125†	95
1150	......	......	85†	105†	75
1175	......	......	65†	85†	65
1200	......	......	40†	70†	50

Hydrostatic shell test pressure.......... 1100

* Extracted from American Standard Steel Pipe Flanges and Flanged Fittings (ASA B16.5-1961) with permission of the publishers, The American Society of Mechanical Engineers, United Engineering Center, 345 E. 47th St., New York 17, N.Y.

Table 24-11. Pressure-Temperature Ratings for Flanged Fittings and Valves of Typical Ferrous Materials*—*(Continued)*

For 400 lb.

Service temp., °F.	Material: Carbon steel	Carbon moly	Cr-Mo 1¼–½	Cr-Mo 2¼–1	Cr-Mo 5–½
–20 to 100§	960	960	960	960	960
150	945	945	945	945	945
200	930	930	930	930	930
250	920	920	920	920	920
300	910	910	910	910	910
350	900	900	900	900	900
400	890	890	890	890	890
450	870	870	870	870	870
500	835	835	835	835	835
550	790	790	790	790	790
600	740	740	740	740	740
650	690	690	690	690	690
700	635	640	645	645	645
750	575	590	600	600	600
800	490	545	555	555	555
850	400†	495	510	510	510
875	350†	470†	490	490	490
900	295†	450†	465	465	465
925	250†	425†	445	445	445
950	205†	400†	420	420	420
975	160†	370†	400	400	400
1000	115†	285†	355	355	335
1025	......	......	305†	310	285
1050	......	......	250†	265	240
1075	......	......	215†	230†	195
1100	......	......	185†	190†	150
1125	......	......	150†	165†	125
1150	......	......	115†	135†	100
1175	......	......	85†	115†	85
1200	......	......	55†	90†	70

Hydrostatic shell test pressure 1450

For 600 lb.

Service temp., °F.	Material: Carbon steel	Carbon moly	Cr-Mo 1¼–½	Cr-Mo 2¼–1	Cr-Mo 5–½
–20 to 100§	1440	1440	1440	1440	1440
150	1420	1420	1420	1420	1420
200	1400	1400	1400	1400	1400
250	1380	1380	1380	1380	1380
300	1365	1365	1365	1365	1365
350	1350	1350	1350	1350	1350
400	1330	1330	1330	1330	1330
450	1305	1305	1305	1305	1305
500	1250	1250	1250	1250	1250
550	1180	1180	1180	1180	1180
600	1110	1110	1110	1110	1110
650	1030	1030	1030	1030	1030
700	940	960	965	965	965
750	850	890	900	900	900
800	730	815	835	835	835
850	600†	745	765	765	765
875	525†	710†	735	735	735
900	445†	670†	700	700	700
925	375†	635†	665	665	665
950	310†	600†	635	635	635
975	240†	555†	600	600	600
1000	170†	430†	535	535	500
1025	......	......	455†	465	430
1050	......	......	375†	400	355
1075	......	......	325†	345†	290
1100	......	......	275†	290†	225
1125	......	......	225†	245†	190
1150	......	......	170†	205†	150
1175	......	......	125†	170†	125
1200	......	......	80†	135†	105

Hydrostatic shell test pressure.......... 2175

Table 24-11. Pressure-Temperature Ratings for Flanged Fittings and Valves of Typical Ferrous Materials*—(*Continued*)

For 900 lb.

Service temp., °F.	Material				
	Carbon steel	Carbon moly	Cr-Mo 1¼-½	Cr-Mo 2¼-1	Cr-Mo 5-½
−20 to 100§	2160	2160	2160	2160	2160
150	2130	2130	2130	2130	2130
200	2100	2100	2100	2100	2100
250	2070	2070	2070	2070	2070
300	2050	2050	2050	2050	2050
350	2025	2025	2025	2025	2025
400	2000	2000	2000	2000	2000
450	1955	1955	1955	1955	1955
500	1875	1875	1875	1875	1875
550	1775	1775	1775	1775	1775
600	1660	1660	1660	1660	1660
650	1550	1550	1550	1550	1550
700	1410	1440	1450	1450	1450
750	1275	1330	1350	1350	1350
800	1100	1225	1250	1250	1250
850	900†	1115	1150	1150	1150
875	785†	1060†	1100	1100	1100
900	670†	1010†	1050	1050	1050
925	565†	955†	1000	1000	1000
950	465†	900†	950	950	950
975	360†	835†	900	900	900
1000	255†	645†	800	800	750
1025	......	......	685†	700	645
1050	......	......	565†	595	535
1075	......	......	490†	515†	435
1100	......	......	410†	430†	340
1125	......	......	335†	370†	285
1150	......	......	255†	310†	225
1175	......	......	190†	255†	190
1200	......	......	125†	205†	155

Hydrostatic shell test pressure.......... 3250

For 1500 lb.

Service temp., °F.	Material				
	Carbon steel	Carbon moly	Cr-Mo 1¼-½	Cr-Mo 2¼-1	Cr-Mo 5-½
−20 to 100§	3600	3600	3600	3600	3600
150	3550	3550	3550	3550	3550
200	3500	3500	3500	3500	3500
250	3450	3450	3450	3450	3450
300	3415	3415	3415	3415	3415
350	3375	3375	3375	3375	3375
400	3330	3330	3330	3330	3330
450	3255	3255	3255	3255	3255
500	3125	3125	3125	3125	3125
550	2955	2955	2955	2955	2955
600	2770	2770	2770	2770	2770
650	2580	2580	2580	2580	2580
700	2350	2400	2415	2415	2415
750	2125	2220	2250	2250	2250
800	1830	2040	2080	2080	2080
850	1500†	1860	1915	1915	1915
875	1305†	1770†	1830	1830	1830
900	1115†	1680†	1750	1750	1750
925	945†	1590†	1665	1665	1665
950	770†	1500†	1585	1585	1585
975	600†	1395†	1500	1500	1500
1000	430†	1070†	1335	1335	1250
1025	......	......	1140†	1165	1070
1050	......	......	945†	995	890
1075	......	......	815†	855†	730
1100	......	......	685†	720†	565
1125	......	......	555†	615†	470
1150	......	......	430†	515†	375
1175	......	......	315†	430†	315
1200	......	......	205†	345†	255

Hydrostatic shell test pressure.......... 5400

Table 24-11. Pressure-Temperature Ratings for Flanged Fittings and Valves of Typical Ferrous Materials*—(*Continued*)

For 2500 lb.

Service temp., °F.	Material				
	Carbon steel	Carbon moly	Cr-Mo 1¼-½	Cr-Mo 2¼-1	Cr-Mo 5-½
−20 to 100§	6000	6000	6000	6000	6000
150	5915	5915	5915	5915	5915
200	5830	5830	5830	5830	5830
250	5750	5750	5750	5750	5750
300	5690	5690	5690	5690	5690
350	5625	5625	5625	5625	5625
400	5550	5550	5550	5550	5550
450	5430	5430	5430	5430	5430
500	5210	5210	5210	5210	5210
550	4925	4925	4925	4925	4925
600	4620	4620	4620	4620	4620
650	4300	4300	4300	4300	4300
700	3920	4000	4025	4025	4025
750	3550	3700	3745	3745	3745
800	3050	3400	3470	3470	3470
850	2500†	3100	3190	3190	3190
875	2180†	2950†	3055	3055	3055
900	1855†	2800†	2915	2915	2915
925	1570†	2650†	2775	2775	2775
950	1285†	2500†	2640	2640	2640
975	1000†	2320†	2500	2500	2500
1000	715†	1785†	2230	2230	2085
1025	......	......	1900†	1945	1785
1050	......	......	1570†	1655	1485
1075	......	......	1355†	1430†	1215
1100	......	......	1145†	1200†	945
1125	......	......	930†	1030†	785
1150	......	......	715†	855†	630
1175	......	......	530†	715†	530
1200	......	......	345†	570†	430

Hydrostatic shell test pressure.......... 9000

*Extracted from American Standard Steel Pipe Flanges and Flanged Fittings (ASA B16.5-1961) with permission of the publishers, The American Society of Mechanical Engineers, United Engineering Center, 345 E. 47th St., New York 17, N.Y.

† Products used within the jurisdiction of the A.S.M.E. Boiler and Pressure Vessel Code and the A.S.A. Code for Pressure Piping B31.1 are subject to the limitation stated therein.

§ The ratings at −20° to 100°F. given for the materials covered shall also apply at lower temperatures. The ratings for low-temperature service of the cast and forged materials listed in A.S.T.M. A 352 and A 350 shall be taken the same as the −20° to 100°F. ratings for carbon steel.

Some of the materials listed in the rating tables undergo a decrease in impact resistance at temperatures lower than −20°F. to such an extent as to be unable to resist safely shock loadings, sudden changes of stress, or high stress concentrations. Therefore, products that are to operate at temperatures below −20°F. shall conform to the rules of the applicable codes under which they are to be used.

The allowable stress range S_A for expansion stress S_E is

$$S_A = f(1.25S_c + 0.25S_h)$$

where S_c = basic allowable stress, lb./sq. in., at ambient temperature

S_h = basic allowable stress, lb./sq. in., at design temperature (hot)

f = stress-range reduction factor where anticipated number of full temperature cycles exceeds 7000 (see Table 24-18).

The sum of the longitudinal stresses due to pressure, weight, and other sustained loadings shall not exceed S_h, and where less, the stress range for expansion may be increased by the difference.

The sum of longitudinal stress due to operating pressure, live and dead loads, and **occasional loads** (wind and earthquake) may exceed the allowable stress by 33 per cent. For test conditions, the code does not establish any limitations in stress and does not require consideration of occasional loads as occurring concurrently with the test.

Table 24-12. Pressure-Temperature Ratings for Flanges Made of Stainless Steels*

Service temp., °F.	300 lb. Types			400 lb. Types			600 lb. Types			900 lb. Types			1500 lb. Types			2500 lb. Types		
	304	347 and 321	316	304	347 and 321	316	304	347 and 321	316	304	347 and 321	316	304	347 and 321	316	304	347 and 321	316
−20 to 100	615	720	720	825	960	960	1235	1440	1440	1850	2160	2160	3085	3600	3600	5145	6000	6000
150	585	710	710	775	945	945	1165	1420	1420	1750	2130	2130	2915	3550	3550	4855	5915	5915
200	550	700	700	730	930	930	1095	1400	1400	1645	2100	2100	2740	3500	3500	4565	5830	5830
250	520	690	690	695	920	920	1040	1380	1380	1565	2070	2070	2605	3450	3450	4340	5750	5750
300	495	680	680	660	910	910	985	1365	1365	1480	2050	2050	2470	3415	3415	4115	5690	5690
350	470	675	675	630	900	900	945	1350	1350	1415	2025	2025	2360	3375	3375	3930	5625	5625
400	450	665	665	600	890	890	900	1330	1330	1350	2000	2000	2245	3330	3330	3745	5550	5550
450	430	650	650	575	870	870	860	1305	1305	1290	1955	1955	2150	3255	3255	3585	5430	5430
500	410	625	625	550	835	835	825	1250	1250	1235	1875	1875	2055	3125	3125	3430	5210	5210
550	395	590	590	530	790	790	795	1180	1180	1190	1775	1775	1985	2955	2955	3305	4925	4925
600	380	555	555	510	740	740	765	1110	1110	1145	1660	1660	1910	2770	2770	3180	4620	4620
650	370	515	515	490	690	690	735	1030	1030	1105	1550	1550	1845	2580	2580	3070	4300	4300
700	355	495		475	660		710	985		1065	1480		1775	2465		2960	4110	
750	340	470		455	625		685	940		1025	1410		1710	2355		2850	3920	
800	330	450		440	595		660	895		985	1345		1645	2240		2745	3730	
850	320	425		425	565		640	850		960	1275		1595	2125		2660	3540	
875	315	415		420	550		630	825		945	1240		1570	2070		2620	3445	
900	310	400		415	535		620	805		930	1205		1545	2010		2580	3350	
925	305	390		410	520		615	780		920	1175		1535	1955		2560	3260	
950	305	380		405	505		610	760		915	1140		1525	1900		2540	3165	
975	300	370		405	490		605	735		905	1105		1510	1840		2520	3070	
1000	300	355		400	475		600	715		900	1070		1500	1785		2500	2975	
1025	295	345		395	460		595	690		890	1035		1485	1725		2470	2880	
1050	290	335		390	445		585	670		875	1000		1455	1670		2430	2785	
1075	275	325		365	430		550	645		825	970		1370	1615		2285	2690	
1100	255	310		345	415		515	625		770	935		1285	1555		2145	2595	
1125	225	300		305	400		455	600		680	900		1135	1500		1895	2500	
1150	195	260	290	265	345	390	395	520	585	590	780	875	985	1305	1455	1645	2170	2430
1175	175	215	260	235	290	350	350	430	525	525	650	785	880	1080	1310	1465	1800	2185
1200	155	170	235	205	230	310	310	345	465	465	515	700	770	855	1165	1285	1430	1945
1225	135	140	205	175	190	275	265	285	415	400	425	620	665	710	1035	1105	1185	1730
1250	110	115	180	150	150	240	225	225	365	335	340	545	555	565	910	930	945	1515
1275	100	95	160	130	125	215	195	190	320	295	285	480	490	470	795	815	785	1330
1300	85	75	135	110	100	185	170	150	275	250	225	410	420	375	685	700	630	1145
1325	75	65	115	95	85	155	145	125	230	220	190	345	365	315	575	605	530	955
1350	60	50	95	80	70	125	125	105	185	185	155	280	310	255	465	515	430	770
1375	55	45	80	75	60	105	110	95	160	165	140	240	275	230	405	455	385	670
1400	50	40	70	65	55	90	95	80	135	145	125	205	240	205	345	400	345	570
1425	40	35	60	55	50	80	80	70	120	125	110	180	205	180	300	345	300	500
1450	35	30	50	45	40	70	70	60	105	105	95	155	170	155	255	285	255	430
1475	30	30	45	40	40	55	60	55	85	90	85	130	150	140	215	250	235	355
1500	25	25	35	35	35	45	50	50	70	75	75	105	130	130	170	215	215	285
Hydrostatic shell test pressure.......	925		1100	1250		1450	1875		2175	2775		3250	4650		5400	7725		9000

*Extracted from American Standard Steel Pipe Flanges and Flanged Fittings (ASA B16.5-1961) with permission of the publishers, The American Society of Mechanical Engineers, United Engineering Center, 345 E. 47th St., New York 17, N.Y.

The **thickness** allowance to be provided for corrosion and erosion shall be consistent with expected life. For threaded components the nominal thread depth (h of A.S.A. B2.1 or equivalent), and for machined or grooved surfaces the depth removed (plus 1/64 in. when no tolerance is specified), shall be included in the c factor for pipe-wall-thickness calculations. When calculating stress, these values shall be deducted from the actual specified minimum thickness.

Values for the factor E for various welded longitudinal joints are shown in Table 24-19. The code requires additional thickness or design means to prevent damage, collapse, or buckling due to superimposed loads from supports, backfill, or other causes.

Pressure and Stability. Internal pressure stress evaluation of piping is the same as for pressure vessels, and this is also true of external pressure both as to stress and stability against collapse. A.S.A. B31.3 contains minor differences and refinements for some components but these are not significant. But an important difference exists when establishing design pressure and wall thickness, as a result of the A.S.M.E. Unfired Pressure Vessel Code's requirement that the relief-valve setting be not higher than the design pressure. For vessels this means that the design is for a pressure 10 per cent more or less above the intended maximum operating pressure in order to avoid popping or leakage from the valve during normal operation. The piping code omits this requirement, but except for plate pipe, this is generally of little significance. Pipe or fittings ordered to standard wall thicknesses and ratings usually have excess thickness so that the required relief valves may be set sufficiently above the design pressure, to avoid popping and leakage, without exceeding the allowable stress of the piping system based on the actual wall thickness and rating. On piping, therefore, the design pressure and temperature are taken as the maximum intended operating pressure and the coincident temperature combination which results in the maximum thickness, with due consideration of the desired operating flexibility of the plant.

For straight pipe the formula for minimum required thickness t_m is given below and is applicable for D_o/t ratios greater than 6, differing from the pressure vessel code in that a Y factor is included. Here, however, the

Table 24-13. Pressure-Temperature Ratings for Stainless-steel Types 304L and 316L Flange Series*

A. For Stainless Steel Type 304L

Temp., °F.	300 lb.	400 lb.	600 lb.	900 lb.	1500 lb.	2500 lb.
−20 to 100	515	685	1030	1545	2570	4285
150	510	680	1020	1525	2545	4240
200	505	670	1005	1510	2520	4200
250	465	625	935	1400	2335	3895
300	430	575	860	1295	2155	3595
350	395	530	795	1190	1985	3305
400	360	485	725	1085	1810	3020
450	340	455	680	1020	1705	2840
500	320	425	640	960	1600	2660
550	310	410	615	925	1540	2565
600	**300**	**400**	**600**	**900**	**1500**	**2500**
650	290	385	575	865	1440	2400
700	280	375	560	840	1400	2340
750	275	365	545	820	1365	2280
800	265	355	535	800	1335	2225
Hydrostatic shell test pressure...	775	1025	1550	2325	3850	6425

B. For Stainless Steel Type 316L

Temp., °F.	300 lb.	400 lb.	600 lb.	900 lb.	1500 lb.	2500 lb.
−20 to 100	515	685	1030	1545	2570	4285
150	515	685	1030	1545	2570	4285
200	515	685	1030	1545	2570	4285
250	495	660	990	1490	2480	4135
300	475	635	955	1430	2385	3980
350	435	580	870	1310	2180	3635
400	395	525	790	1185	1975	3295
450	380	505	755	1135	1895	3155
500	360	485	725	1085	1810	3020
550	350	465	695	1045	1740	2900
600	335	445	670	1005	1670	2785
650	325	430	645	970	1615	2690
700	310	415	620	935	1555	2595
750	**300**	**400**	**600**	**900**	**1500**	**2500**
800	290	385	580	870	1450	2415
850	280	375	560	840	1400	2335
Hydrostatic shell test pressure...	775	1025	1550	2325	3850	6425

* Extracted from American Standard Steel Pipe Flanges and Flanged Fittings (ASA B16.5-1961) with permission of the publishers, The American Society of Mechanical Engineers, United Engineering Center, 345 E. 47th St., New York 17, N.Y.

Boldface pressures indicate primary service rating.

Table 24-14. Pressure-Temperature Ratings for Non-ferrous Wrought Flanges*

A. For Nickel-Copper (Monel) Annealed, A.S.T.M. B164

Temp., °F.	Max., non-shock service pressure, lb./sq. in. 300 series	400 series	600 series	900 series	1500 series	2500 series
100	515	685	1030	1545	2570	4285
150	475	630	945	1420	2365	3945
200	455	605	905	1360	2265	3770
250	435	580	870	1305	2175	3630
300	420	560	845	1265	2110	3515
350	410	550	825	1235	2055	3430
400	410	545	815	1225	2040	3400
450	405	540	810	1215	2025	3380
500	405	540	805	1210	2015	3360
550	405	540	805	1210	2015	3360
600	405	540	805	1210	2015	3360
650	405	540	805	1210	2015	3360
700	405	540	805	1210	2015	3360
750	405	540	805	1210	2015	3360
775	405	540	805	1210	2015	3360
800	405	540	805	1210	2015	3360
825	405	540	805	1210	2015	3360
850	375	505	755	1130	1885	3145
875	310	410	615	925	1545	2570
900	275	365	550	825	1370	2285

Table 24-14. Pressure-Temperature Ratings for Non-ferrous Wrought Flanges*—*(Continued)*

B. For Nickel, Annealed, A.S.T.M. B160

Temp., °F.	Max., non-shock service pressure, lb./sq. in. 300 series	400 series	600 series	900 series	1500 series	2500 series
100	310	410	615	925	1545	2570
150	310	410	615	925	1545	2570
200	310	410	615	925	1545	2570
250	310	410	615	925	1545	2570
300	310	410	615	925	1545	2570
350	310	410	615	925	1545	2570
400	310	410	615	925	1545	2570
450	310	410	615	925	1545	2570
500	310	410	615	925	1545	2570
550	310	410	615	925	1545	2570
600	310	410	615	925	1545	2570

* Extracted from American Standard Steel Pipe Flanges and Flanged Fittings (ASA B16.5-1961) with permission of the publishers, The American Society of Mechanical Engineers, United Engineering Center, 345 E. 47th St., New York 17, N.Y.

Table 24-15. Pressure-Temperature Ratings for Flanges Made of Aluminum Alloys*

A. For Aluminum Alloy MIA-0 (3003-0), A.S.T.M. B247

Temp., °F.	Max., non-shock service pressure, lb./sq. in. 300 series	400 series	600 series	900 series	1500 series	2500 series
100	105	135	205	310	515	860
150	100	130	200	295	495	825
200	95	130	195	290	485	805
250	95	125	185	280	465	770
300	85	115	175	260	430	720
350	80	105	160	240	400	670
400	60	80	125	185	310	515

B. For Aluminum Alloy GSIIA-T6 (6061-T6), A.S.T.M. B247†

Temp., °F.	Max., non-shock service pressure, lb./sq. in. 300 series	400 series	600 series	900 series	1500 series	2500 series
100	720	960	1440	2160	3600	6000
150	710	945	1420	2130	3550	5915
200	700	930	1400	2100	3500	5825
250	675	900	1355	2030	3385	5640
300	565	750	1125	1690	2820	4700
350	410	550	825	1235	2055	3425
400	265	355	535	800	1345	2225

C. For Aluminum Bronze, A.S.T.M. B148, Alloy 9A

Temp., °F.	Max., non-shock service pressure, lb./sq. in. 300 series	400 series	600 series	900 series	1500 series	2500 series
100	515	685	1030	1545	2575	4290
150	430	570	855	1285	2140	3570
200	400	535	800	1205	2005	3340
250	385	510	770	1150	1920	3200
300	370	495	740	1110	1850	3085
350	365	490	735	1100	1835	3060
400	365	485	725	1090	1820	3030
450	360	480	725	1085	1805	3010
500	360	480	720	1080	1800	3000

* Extracted from American Standard Steel Pipe Flanges and Flanged Fittings (ASA B16.5-1961) with permission of the publishers, The American Society of Mechanical Engineers, United Engineering Center, 345 E. 47thSt., New York 17, N.Y.

† The ratings of slip-on and socket-welding types of flanges are two-thirds of the tabulated values, since welding these types of flanges to pipe decreases their strength.

Table 24-16. Allowable Stresses vs. Temperature for

Material	Specification	Steelmaking process	Grade	Tensile strength min. lb./sq. in.	Yield strength min. lb./sq. in.	Notes	Metal temp., °F. −325 to −150	−150 to −100	−100 to −75	−75 to −50	−50 to −20	−20 to 100	200	300
												Carbon Steel, Cast Iron		
Steel pipe	A.S.T.M. A53	OH, EF	A	48,000	30,000	a,b						16,000	15,300	14,500
Steel pipe	A.S.T.M. A53	OH, EF	B	60,000	35,000	a,b						20,000	19,100	18,150
Steel pipe	A.S.T.M. A53	DAB	B	60,000	35,000	a,b						20,000	19,100	18,150
Steel tubes	A.S.T.M. A83	OH, EF	A			a,b						16,000	15,300	14,500
Steel pipe	A.S.T.M. A106	OH, EF	A	48,000	30,000	b						16,000	15,300	14,500
Steel pipe	A.S.T.M. A106	OH, EF	B	60,000	35,000	b						20,000	19,100	18,150
Steel pipe	A.S.T.M. A106	OH, EF	C	70,000	40,000	b						23,350	22,250	21,200
Steel pipe	A.S.T.M. A120	OH, EF	A									16,000	15,300	
Steel pipe	A.S.T.M. A120	OH, EF, AB	B									20,000	19,100	
Steel tubes	A.S.T.M. A161	OH, EF		47,000	26,000	b						15,650	15,000	14,250
Steel tubes	A.S.T.M. A179	OH, EF				a,b						15,650	14,950	14,250
Steel tubes	A.S.T.M. A192	OH, EF				b						15,650	14,950	14,250
Steel tubes	A.S.T.M. A210	OH, EF		60,000	37,000	b						20,000	19,100	18,150
Steel pipe	A.S.T.M. A333	OH, EF	C	55,000	30,000	a,b					g	18,350	17,500	16,700
Steel tubes	A.S.T.M. A334	OH, EF	C	55,000	30,000	a,b					g	18,350	17,500	16,700
Steel pipe	A.P.I. 5L	OH, EF	A	48,000	30,000	a,b						16,000	15,300	14,500
Steel pipe	A.P.I. 5L	OH, EF	B	60,000	35,000	a,b						20,000	19,100	18,150
Steel pipe	A.P.I. 5L	DAB	B	60,000	35,000	a,b						20,000	19,100	18,150
Steel pipe	A.P.I. 5LX	OH, EF	X42	60,000	42,000							20,000	19,100	18,150
Steel pipe	A.P.I. 5LX	OH, EF	X46	63,000	46,000							21,000	20,050	19,100
Steel pipe	A.P.I. 5LX	OH, EF	X52	66,000	52,000							22,000	21,000	20,000
Steel pipe	A.P.I. 5LX	OH, EF	X52	72,000	52,000							23,500	22,500	21,400
Cast-iron pipe	WW-P-421a					d,e						6,000	6,000	6,000
Cast-iron pipe	A.S.T.M. A377					d,e						4,000	4,000	4,000
Cast-iron pipe	A.S.A. A21.2 A.S.A. A21.6					d,e						6,000	6,000	6,000
Cast-iron pipe	A.S.A. A21.8					d,e						6,000	6,000	6,000
												Carbon-steel Forgings		
Steel	A.S.T.M. A105	OH, EF	I	60,000	30,000	a,b,e						18,750	18,100	17,400
Steel	A.S.T.M. A105	OH, EF	II	70,000	36,000	a,b,e						22,500	21,600	20,700
Steel	A.S.T.M. A181	OH, EF	I	60,000	30,000	a,b,e						18,750	18,100	17,400
Steel	A.S.T.M. A181	OH, EF	II	70,000	36,000	a,b,e						22,500	21,600	20,700
Steel	A.S.T.M. A234	OH, EF	WPA	48,000	30,000	a,b,f						16,000	15,300	14,500
Steel	A.S.T.M. A234	OH, EF	WPB	60,000	35,000	a,b,f						20,000	19,100	18,150
Steel	A.S.T.M. A234	OH, EF	WPC	70,000	40,000	a,b,f					g	23,350	22,250	21,200
Steel	A.S.T.M. A350	OH, EF	LF 1	60,000	30,000	a,b,e					g	18,750	18,100	17,400
Steel	A.S.T.M. A420	OH, EF	WPLC	55,000	30,000	a,b,f					g	18,350	17,500	16,700
												Low- and Intermediate-alloy Steel,		
3½ Ni pipe	A.S.T.M. A333	OH, EF	3	65,000	35,000	b		g	g	g	g	21,650	20,650	19,700
Cr-Cu-Ni tubes	A.S.T.M. A333	OH, EF	4	60,000	35,000			g	g	g	g	20,000	19,100	18,150
5 Ni pipe	A.S.T.M. A333	OH, EF	5	65,000	35,000	b		g	g	g	g	21,650	20,650	19,700
3½ Ni tube	A.S.T.M. A334	OH, EF	3	65,000	35,000	b		g	g	g	g	21,650	20,650	19,700
5 Ni tubes	A.S.T.M. A334	OH, EF	5	65,000	35,000	b		g	g	g	g	21,650	20,650	19,700
C-½ Mo pipe	A.S.T.M. A335	OH, EF	P 1	55,000	30,000	c						18,350	17,650	16,950
½ Cr-½ Mo pipe	A.S.T.M. A335	OH, EF	P 2	55,000	30,000	c						18,350	17,650	16,950
1¾ Cr-½ Mo pipe	A.S.T.M. A335	OH, EF	P 3	60,000	30,000							18,750	18,250	17,650
2 Cr-½ Mo pipe	A.S.T.M. A335	OH, EF	P 3b	60,000	30,000							18,750	18,150	17,600
5 Cr-½ Mo pipe	A.S.T.M. A335	OH, EF	P 5	60,000	30,000							18,750	17,900	17,050
5 Cr-½ Mo pipe	A.S.T.M. A335	OH, EF	P 5b	60,000	30,000							18,750	17,900	17,050
5 Cr-½ Mo pipe	A.S.T.M. A335	OH, EF	P 5c	60,000	30,000							18,750	17,900	17,050
7 Cr-½ Mo pipe	A.S.T.M. A335	OH, EF	P 7	60,000	30,000							18,750	17,850	17,000
9 Cr-1 Mo pipe	A.S.T.M. A335	OH, EF	P 9	60,000	30,000							18,750	17,900	17,100
1¼ Cr-½ Mo pipe	A.S.T.M. A335	OH, EF	P 11	60,000	30,000							18,750	18,250	17,650
1 Cr-½ Mo pipe	A.S.T.M. A335	OH, EF	P 12	60,000	30,000	c						18,750	18,250	17,600
1½ Si-½ Mo pipe	A.S.T.M. A335	OH, EF	P 15	60,000	30,000	c						18,750	18,150	17,600
3 Cr-1 Mo pipe	A.S.T.M. A335	OH, EF	P 21	60,000	30,000							18,750	18,100	17,400
2¼ Cr-1 Mo pipe	A.S.T.M. A335	OH, EF	P 22	60,000	30,000							18,750	18,250	17,650
												Alloy Steel Forgings		
C-½ Mo	A.S.T.M. A182	OH, EF	F1	70,000	40,000	c,e						23,350	22,450	21,550
5 Cr-½ Mo	A.S.T.M. A182	OH, EF	F5	60,000	36,000	e						20,000	19,000	17,950
5 Cr-½ Mo	A.S.T.M. A182	OH, EF	F5a	90,000	65,000	e						30,000	28,000	26,050
13 Cr	A.S.T.M. A182	OH, EF	F6	85,000	55,000	e						28,350	26,600	24,900
7 Cr-½ Mo	A.S.T.M. A182	OH, EF	F7	60,000	36,000	e						20,000	19,000	17,950
9 Cr 1 Mo	A.S.T.M. A182	OH, EF	F9	100,000	70,000	e						33,350	31,300	29,300
1¼ Cr-½ Mo	A.S.T.M. A182	OH, EF	F11	70,000	40,000	e						23,350	22,150	21,000
1 Cr-½ Mo	A.S.T.M. A182	OH, EF	F12	70,000	40,000	c,e						23,350	22,150	21,000
2¼ Cr-1 Mo	A.S.T.M. A182	OH, EF	F22	70,000	40,000	c,e						23,350	22,550	21,700
C-½ Mo	A.S.T.M. A234	OH, EF	WP 1	70,000	40,000	c,f						18,350	17,650	16,950
5 Cr-½ Mo	A.S.T.M. A234	OH, EF	WP 5	60,000	36,000	f						18,750	17,900	17,050
1¼ Cr-½ Mo	A.S.T.M. A234	OH, EF	WP 11	70,000	40,000	f						18,750	18,250	17,650
1 Cr-½ Mo	A.S.T.M. A234	OH, EF	WP 12	70,000	40,000	c,f						18,750	18,250	17,600
2¼ Cr-½ Mo	A.S.T.M. A234	OH, EF	WP 22	70,000	40,000	f						18,750	18,250	17,650
3½ Ni	A.S.T.M. A350	OH, EF	LF 3	70,000	40,000	b,e		g	g	g	g	23,350	22,250	21,200
Cr-Cu-Ni	A.S.T.M. A350	OH, EF	LF 4	80,000	50,000	e		g	g	g	g	18,750	18,100	17,400

* Extracted from Petroleum Refinery Piping Code (ASA B31.3-1959), a section of the American Standard Code for Pressure Piping, with permission of the publisher, The American Society of Mechanical Engineers, United Engineering Center, 345 E. 47th St., New York 17, N.Y.

Seamless Pipe and Fittings of Ferrous Materials*

Metal Temp., °F.

400	500	600	650	700	750	800	850	900	950	1000	1050	1100	1150	1200	1250	1300	1350	1400	1450	1500
Seamless Carbon Steel Pipe and Tubes																				
13,800	13,100	12,350	12,000	11,650	10,700	9,300	7,900	6,500	4,500	2,500	1,600	1,000								
17,250	16,350	15,500	15,000	14,350	12,950	10,800	8,650	6,500	4,500	2,500	1,600	1,000								
17,250	16,350	15,500	15,000	14,350	12,950	10,800	8,650	6,500	4,500	2,500	1,600	1,000								
13,800	13,100	12,350	12,000	11,650	10,700	9,300	7,900	6,500	4,500	2,500	1,600	1,000								
13,800	13,100	12,350	12,000	11,650	10,700	9,300	7,900	6,500	4,500	2,500	1,600	1,000								
17,250	16,350	15,500	15,000	14,350	12,950	10,800	8,650	6,500	4,500	2,500	1,600	1,000								
20,150	19,100	18,050	17,500	16,600	14,750	12,000														
13,550	12,850	12,100	11,750	11,450	10,550	9,200	7,850	6,500	4,500	2,500	1,600	1,000								
13,550	12,850	12,100	11,750	11,450	10,550	9,200	7,850	6,500	4,500	2,500	1,600	1,000								
13,550	12,850	12,100	11,750	11,450	10,550	9,200	7,850	6,500	4,500	2,500	1,600	1,000								
17,250	16,350	15,500	15,000	14,350	12,950	10,800	8,650	6,500	4,500	2,500	1,600	1,000								
15,850	15,000	14,200	13,750	13,250	12,050	10,200	8,350	6,500	4,500	2,500	1,600	1,000								
15,850	15,000	14,200	13,750	13,250	12,050	10,200	8,350	6,500	4,500	2,500	1,600	1,000								
13,800	13,100	12,350	12,000	11,650	10,700	9,300	7,900	6,500	4,500	2,500	1,600	1,000								
17,250	16,350	15,500	15,000	14,350	12,950	10,800	8,650	6,500	4,500	2,500	1,600	1,000								
17,250	16,350	15,500	15,000	14,350	12,950	10,800	8,650	6,500	4,500	2,500	1,600	1,000								
	(450°F.)																			
6,000	6,000																			
4,000	4,000																			
6,000	6,000																			
6,000	6,000																			
and Seamless Fittings																				
16,700	16,000	15,350	15,000	14,350	12,950	10,800	8,650	6,500	4,500	2,500	1,600	1,000								
19,750	18,850	17,950	17,500	16,600	14,750	12,000	9,250	6,500	4,500	2,500	1,600	1,000								
16,700	16,000	15,350	15,000	14,350	12,950	10,800	8,650	6,500	4,500	2,500	1,600	1,000								
19,750	18,850	17,950	17,500	16,600	14,750	12,000	9,250	6,500	4,500	2,500	1,600	1,000								
13,800	13,100	12,350	12,000	11,650	10,700	9,300	7,900	6,500	4,500	2,500	1,600	1,000								
17,250	16,350	15,500	15,000	14,350	12,950	10,800	8,650	6,500	4,500	2,500	1,600	1,000								
20,150	19,100	18,050	17,500	16,600	14,750	12,000														
16,700	16,000	15,350	15,000	14,350	12,950	10,800	8,650	6,500	4,500	2,500	1,600	1,000								
15,850	15,000	14,200	13,750	13,250	12,050	10,200	8,350	6,500	4,500	2,500	1,600	1,000								
Seamless Alloy Steel Pipe and Tubes																				
18,700	17,750	16,750	16,250	15,500	13,850	11,400	8,950	6,500	4,500	2,500	1,600	1,000								
17,250	16,350	15,500	15,000																	
18,700	17,750	16,750	16,250	15,500	13,850	11,400	8,950	6,500	4,500	2,500	1,600	1,000								
18,700	17,750	16,750	16,250	15,500	13,850	11,400	8,950	6,500	4,500	2,500	1,600	1,000								
18,700	17,750	16,750	16,250	15,500	13,850	11,400	8,950	6,500	4,500	2,500	1,600	1,000								
16,300	15,600	14,900	14,550	14,200	13,850	13,500	13,150	12,500	10,000	6,250	4,000	2,400								
16,300	15,600	14,900	14,550	14,200	13,850	13,500	13,150	12,500	10,000	6,250	4,000	2,400								
17,150	16,600	16,050	15,800	15,550	15,300	15,000	14,400	13,100	11,000	7,800	5,500	4,000	2,500	1,200						
17,000	16,450	15,850	15,600	15,300	15,000	14,700	14,000	12,500	10,000	6,200	4,200	2,750	1,750	1,200						
16,200	15,350	14,500	14,100	13,650	13,250	12,800	12,400	11,500	10,000	7,300	5,200	3,300	2,200	1,500						
16,200	15,350	14,500	14,100	13,650	13,250	12,800	12,400	10,900	9,000	5,500	3,500	2,500	1,800	1,200						
16,200	15,350	14,500	14,100	13,650	13,250	12,800	12,400	11,500	10,000	7,300	4,800	2,800	1,800	1,200						
16,150	15,300	14,450	14,000	13,550	13,100	12,500	11,500	9,500	7,000	5,000	3,500	2,500	1,800	1,200						
16,250	15,450	14,600	14,200	13,800	13,350	12,950	12,500	12,000	10,800	8,500	5,500	3,300	2,200	1,500						
17,150	16,600	16,050	15,800	15,550	15,300	15,000	14,400	13,100	11,000	7,800	5,500	4,000	2,500	1,200						
17,050	16,450	15,900	15,650	15,350	15,050	14,750	14,200	13,100	11,000	7,500	5,000	2,800	1,550	1,000						
17,000	16,450	15,850	15,600	15,300	15,000	14,400	13,750	12,500	10,000	6,250	4,000	2,400								
16,750	16,100	15,450	15,150	14,800	14,500	13,900	13,200	12,000	9,000	7,000	5,500	4,000	2,700	1,500						
17,150	16,600	16,050	15,800	15,500	15,300	15,000	14,400	13,100	11,000	7,800	5,800	4,200	3,000	2,000						
and Seamless Fittings																				
20,650	19,750	18,850	18,400	17,950	17,500	16,900	15,000	12,750	10,000	6,250	4,000	2,400								
16,950	15,950	14,950	14,450	13,900	13,400	12,900	12,400	11,500	10,000	7,300	5,200	3,300	2,200	1,500						
24,050	22,100	20,100	19,000	17,500	16,000	14,500	13,000	11,500	10,000	7,300	5,200	3,300	2,200	1,500						
23,200	21,450	19,750	18,900	18,000	17,150	16,300	14,000	11,000	8,800	6,400	4,400	2,900	1,750	1,000						
16,950	15,950	14,950	14,450	13,900	13,400	12,900	12,400	11,500	10,000	7,300	5,200	3,300	2,200	1,500						
27,250	25,250	23,200	22,200	21,200	20,000	17,700	15,400	13,100	10,800	8,500	5,500	3,300	2,200	1,500						
19,850	18,650	17,500	16,800	16,150	15,500	14,850	14,200	13,100	11,000	7,800	5,500	4,000	2,500	1,200						
19,850	18,650	17,500	16,800	16,150	15,500	14,850	14,200	13,100	11,000	7,500	5,000	2,800	1,550	1,000						
20,850	20,000	19,200	18,750	18,350	17,900	17,500	16,000	14,000	11,000	7,800	5,800	4,200	3.000	2,000						
16,300	15,600	14,900	14,550	14,200	13,850	13,500	13,150	12,500	10,000	6,250	4,000	2,400								
16,200	15,350	14,500	14,100	13,650	13,250	12,800	12,400	11,500	10,000	7,300	5,200	3,300	2,200	1,500						
17,150	16,600	16,050	15,800	15,550	15,300	15,000	14,400	13,100	11,000	7,800	5,500	4,000	2,500	1,200						
17,050	16,450	15,900	15,650	15,350	15,050	14,750	14,200	13,100	11,000	7,500	5,000	2,800	1,550	1,000						
17,150	16,600	16,050	15,800	15.550	15,300	15,000	14,400	13,100	11,000	7,800	5,800	4,200	3,000	2,000						
20,150	19,100	18,050	17,500	16,600	14,750	12,000	9,250	6,500												
16,700	16,000	15,350	15,000																	

Table 24-16. Allowable Stresses vs. Temperature for

Material	Specification	Steelmaking process	Grade	Tensile strength min. lb./sq. in.	Yield strength min. lb./sq. in.	Notes	Metal temp., °F. −325 to −150	−150 to −100	−100 to −75	−75 to −50	−50 to −20	−20 to 100	200	300
														Seamless Stainless-
18-8 pipe..................	A.S.T.M. A312	EF	TP 304	75,000	30,000		18,750	18,750	18,750	18,750	18,750	18,750	16,650	15,000
18-8 pipe..................	A.S.T.M. A312	EF	TP 304L	70,000	25,000		15,600	15,600	15,600	15,600	15,600	15,600	15,300	13,100
18-8 pipe..................	A.S.T.M. A312	EF	TP 316	75,000	30,000		18,750	18,750	18,750	18,750	18,750	18,750	18,750	17,900
18-8 pipe..................	A.S.T.M. A312	EF	TP 316L	70,000	25,000		15,600	15,600	15,600	15,600	15,600	15,600	15,600	14,500
18-8 pipe..................	A.S.T.M. A312	EF	TP 317	75,000	30,000		18,750	18,750	18,750	18,750	18,750	18,750	18,750	17,900
18-8 pipe..................	A.S.T.M. A312	EF	TP 321	75,000	30,000		18,750	18,750	18,750	18,750	18,750	18,750	18,750	17,000
18-8 pipe..................	A.S.T.M. A312	EF	TP 347	75,000	30,000		18,750	18,750	18,750	18,750	18,750	18,750	18,750	17,000
														Stainless-steel Forgings
18 Cr 8 Ni..................	A.S.T.M. A182		F 304	75,000	30,000	e	18,750	18,750	18,750	18,750	18,750	18,750	16,650	15,000
18 Cr 8 Ni..................	A.S.T.M. A182		F 316	75,000	30,000	e	18,750	18,750	18,750	18,750	18,750	18,750	18,750	17,900
18 Cr 8 Ni..................	A.S.T.M. A182		F 321	75,000	30,000	e	18,750	18,750	18,750	18,750	18,750	18,750	18,750	17,000
18 Cr 8 Ni..................	A.S.T.M. A182		F 347	75,000	30,000	e	18,750	18,750	18,750	18,750	18,750	18,750	18,750	17,000
18 Cr 8 Ni..................	A.S.T.M. A403		WP 304	75,000	30,000	f	18,750	18,750	18,750	18,750	18,750	18,750	16,650	15,000
18 Cr 8 Ni..................	A.S.T.M. A403		WP 304L	70,000	25,000	f	17,500	17,500	17,500	17,500	17,500	17,500	15,300	13,100
18 Cr 8 Ni..................	A.S.T.M. A403		WP 316	75,000	30,000	f	18,750	18,750	18,750	18,750	18,750	18,750	18,750	17,900
18 Cr 8 Ni..................	A.S.T.M. A403		WP 316L	70,000	25,000	f	17,500	17,500	17,500	17,500	17,500	17,500	16,250	14,500
18 Cr 8 Ni..................	A.S.T.M. A403		WP 317	70,000	30,000	f	18,750	18,750	18,750	18,750	18,750	18,750	18,750	17,900
18 Cr 8 Ni..................	A.S.T.M. A403		WP 321	70,000	30,000	f	18,750	18,750	18,750	18,750	18,750	18,750	18,750	17,000
18 Cr 8 Ni..................	A.S.T.M. A403		WP 347	70,000	30,000	f	18,750	18,750	18,750	18,750	18,750	18,750	18,750	17,000

* Extracted from Petroleum Refinery Piping Code (ASA B31.3-1959), a section of the American Standard Code for Pressure Piping, with permission of the publisher, The American Society of Mechanical Engineers, United Engineering Center, 345 E. 47th St., New York 17, N.Y.

[a] Above 900°F. consider the advantages of killed steel.

[b] Conversion of carbides to graphite may occur after prolonged exposure to temperatures over 750F.

[c] Conversion of carbides to graphite may occur after prolonged exposure to temperature over 850F.

[d] Cast and malleable shall not be used for toxic services, or hydrocarbon or other flammable fluid service at temperatures over 300°F. See 323.2.4.

[e] Pressure temperature ratings of cast and forged parts as published in standards referenced in this code section may be used for parts meeting requirements of these standards. Allowable stresses for castings and forgings, where listed, are for use in design of special components not furnished in accordance with such standards.

[f] Stresses shown are for the lowest strength base material permitted by the specification to be used in the manufacture of this grade of fitting. If a higher strength base material is used, the higher allowable stresses for that material may be used in design.

[g] When used at these temperatures, allowable stresses are identical with those shown for 20° to 100°F.

Power Boiler Code (A.S.M.E. Section I) requirements for pipe thickness are identical. The Y factor takes account of the redistribution of circumferential stress which occurs under steady-state "creep" at high temperature and permits slightly lesser thickness in this range. For D_o/t ratios greater than 4, the code indicates the Lamé equation may be used and for ratios less than 4 special consideration is required.

$$t_m = \frac{PD_o}{2(SE + PY)} + c$$

where P = design pressure, lb./sq. in.
D_o = outside diameter of pipe, in.
c = sum of allowances for corrosion, erosion, and if involved, thread or groove depth
S = allowable stress, lb./sq. in.
E = longitudinal weld joint factor
Y = coefficient for steel, (see Table 25-20) ($Y = 0$ for brittle materials, such as cast iron)
t_m = minimum required thickness for pressure, corrosion, and erosion allowances, in.

For determination of the maximum external pressure the code has included two curves for carbon steel (identical with Figs. UCS-28.1 and 28.2 of the A.S.M.E. Code Section VIII) and states that for other materials the designer should use the charts of Appendix V of A.S.M.E. Section VIII. See Figs. 24-8 and 24-9.

Most A.S.T.M. specifications to which mill pipe is normally obtained permit the minimum thickness to be 12½ per cent less than the nominal thickness specified. This undertolerance must be considered when specifying pipe to assure that the minimum wall as obtained will meet the required thickness. A.S.T.M. specifications, such as A.S.T.M. A83 for tubing, are sometimes used for pipe applications and require minimum wall thickness, so that no adjustment is necessary. A.S.T.M. Specification A155 for fusion-welded pipe allows 0.01 in. under tolerance conventional for plate steel.

Pipe-fabrication Joints. For fabrication into permanent assemblies or piping systems, the girth joints between runs of piping or fittings may be threaded, mechanically locked, brazed or soldered or welded. **Threaded joints** with A.S.A B2.1 tapered pipe threads may be used for joining pipe components. Non-tapered pipe threads may be used where tightness is provided by a seating surface other than the threads or where service experience or tests demonstrate their suitability. For non-flammable, non-toxic contents couplings with straight threads may be used with piping components with tapered threads up to 150 lb./sq. in. gage and 400°F. Pipe with wall thickness less than A.S.A. B36.10 standard wall steel pipe shall not be threaded. The code recommends seal welding (on weldable materials) of threaded joints, without a sealing surface other than the threads, when handling flammable or toxic fluids or fluids which because of their nature are difficult to contain and for the hubs of screwed flanges when handling flammable or toxic fluids at over 300 lb./sq. in. gage or 750°F.

The code provides no guidance or limitations on **mechanically locked joints** with usage as determined by performance tests under simulated service conditions either of actual assembly-line items or of prototypes.

Brazed and soldered joints are limited by the code to systems containing non-flammable and non-toxic fluids. Fillet-brazed or soldered joints are not permitted except for socket-type joints. Soldered joints are also limited to services not subject to thermal shock or mechanical vibrations. Calked **bell-and-spigot** joints are limited to water service at pressures permitted for the piping when provisions are made to prevent disengagement at bends and dead ends, and to support lateral reactions at branch connections.

Welded joints are permitted in any material for which it is possible to qualify procedures, welders, and welding operators. *Butt welds* can be made with or without backing rings provided the rings are removed when their presence will result in severe corrosion or erosion. When

Seamless Pipe and Fittings of Ferrous Materials*—*(Continued)*

Metal Temp., °F.

400	500	600	650	700	750	800	850	900	950	1000	1050	1100	1150	1200	1250	1300	1350	1400	1450	1500
steel Pipe and Tubes																				
13,650	12,500	11,600	11,200	10,800	10,400	10,000	9,700	9,400	9,100	8,800	8,500	7,500	5,750	4,500	3,250	2,450	1,800	1,400	1,000	750
11,000	9,700	9,000	8,750	8,500	8,300	8,100														
17,500	17,200	17,100	17,050	17,000	16,900	16,750	16,500	16,000	15,100	14,000	12,200	10,400	8,500	6,800	5,300	4,000	3,000	2,350	1,850	1,500
12,000	11,000	10,150	9,800	9,450	9,100	8,800														
17,500	17,200	17,100	17,050	17,000	16,900	16,750	16,500	16,000	15,100	14,000	12,200	10,400	8,500	6,800	5,300	4,000	3,000	2,350	1,850	1,500
15,800	15,200	14,900	14,850	14,800	14,700	14,550	14,300	14,100	13,850	13,500	13,100	12,500	8,000	5,000	3,600	2,700	2,000	1,550	1,200	1,000
15,800	15,200	14,900	14,850	14,800	14,700	14,550	14,300	14,100	13,850	13,500	13,100	12,500	8,000	5,000	3,600	2,700	2,000	1,550	1,200	1,000
and Seamless Fittings																				
13,650	12,500	11,600	11.200	10,800	10,400	10,000	9,700	9,400	9,100	8,800	8,500	7,500	5,750	4,500	3,250	2,450	1,800	1,400	1,000	750
17,500	17,200	17,100	17,050	17,000	16,900	16,750	16,500	16,000	15,100	14,000	12,200	10,400	8,500	6,800	5,300	4,000	3,000	2,350	1,850	1,500
15,800	15,200	14,900	14,850	14,800	14,700	14,550	14,300	14,100	13,850	13,500	13,100	12,500	8,000	5,000	3,600	2,700	2,000	1,550	1,200	1,000
15,800	15,200	14,900	14,850	14,800	14,700	14,550	14,300	14,100	13,850	13,500	13,100	12,500	8,000	5,000	3,600	2,700	2,000	1,550	1,200	1,000
13,650	12,500	11,600	11,200	10,800	10,400	10,000	9,700	9,400	9,100	8,800	8,500	7,500	5,750	4,500	3,250	2,450	1,800	1,400	1,000	750
11,000	9,700	9,000	8,750	8,500	8,300	8,100														
17,500	17,200	17,100	17,050	17,000	16,900	16,750	16,500	16,000	15,100	14,000	12,200	10,400	8,500	6,800	5,300	4,000	3,000	2,350	1,850	1,500
12,000	11,000	10,150	9,800	9,450	9,100	8,800														
17,500	17,200	17,100	17,050	17,000	16,900	16,750	16,500	16,000	15,100	14,000	12,200	10,400	8,500	6,800	5,300	4,000	3,000	2,350	1,850	1,500
15,800	15,200	14,900	14,850	14,800	14,700	14,550	14,300	14,100	13,850	13,500	13,100	12,500	8,000	5,000	3,600	2,700	2,000	1,550	1,200	1,000
15,800	15,200	14,900	14,850	14,800	14,700	14,550	14,300	14,100	13,850	13,500	13,100	12,500	8,000	5,000	3,600	2,700	2,000	1,550	1,200	1,000

impractical to remove rings, joints without rings or consumable backing rings are to be considered. *Socket-welded* piping joints shall conform to A.S.A. B16.11 and B16.5 for fittings and flanges, respectively, with the leg of fillet weld not less than shown in Fig. 24-18. Socket-welded joints shall be avoided where severe crevice corrosion or erosion may occur. Socket welding may be

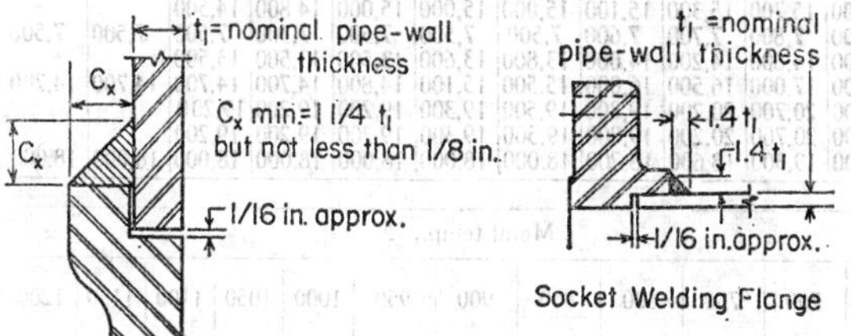

FIG. 24-18. Minimum welding dimensions required for socket-welding components. (*Source: American Standards Association.*)

used to attach drains and by-passes to fittings or valves, provided the depth, bore diameter, and shoulder thickness conform to A.S.A. B16.5. *Fillet welds* shall not be smaller than shown in Fig. 24-19. *Seal welds* may be used to prevent joint leakage, but they shall not be considered as contributing any strength to the joint. When seal-welding threaded joints, the external threads shall be entirely covered.

Flange Facings and Gaskets. There are no restrictions as to the type of flange facing which may be used except that those not complying with the dimensional standards listed in Code Table 326.1 must be proved satisfactory by successful performance under comparable service conditions or subject to proof tests. Pipe-joint facings standardized in dimension by the approved standards are illustrated in Sec. 6 (see pp. 6-41ff). Some other types of facing with proved performance are shown in Fig. 24-20.

The finish of flange facings varies with the manufacturer. For raised-faced or male mating surfaces the finish usually consists of a continuous spiral groove formed by a round-nosed tool or a V tool (serrated finish). Female surfaces are smooth-finished (*i.e.*, without definite tool markings). Other finishes are concentric grooved, lapped, or mirror (cold water). The latter two are usually for application without gaskets.

The standard finishes are generally satisfactory for use with any of the stock gaskets such as the asbestos-rubber and other composition-sheet type, spiral wound, metal-corrugated asbestos inserted, metal-jacketed asbestos,

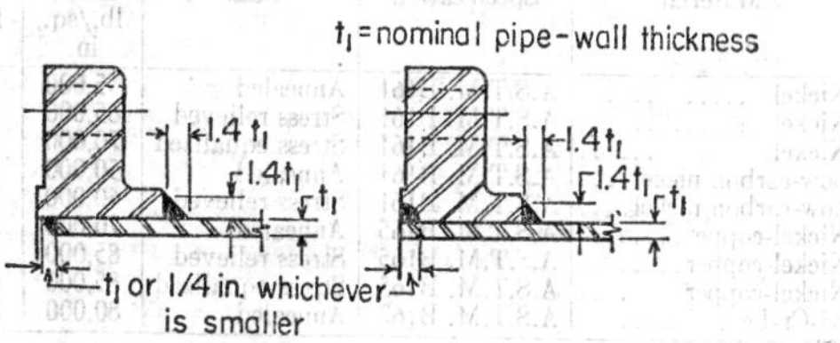

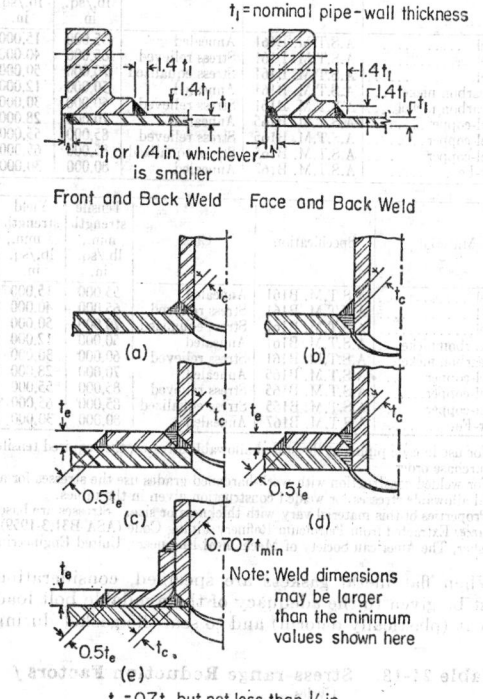

FIG. 24-19. Minimum size of typical fillet welds. (*Source: American Standards Association.*)

and flat metal types. However, for severe operating conditions of pressure and/or temperature or when subject to cyclic variations in temperature or pressure, consideration must be given to obtaining a finish compatible with the type of gasket and the fluid to be contained. The smooth flat finish (r.m.s. 32 maximum) is a superior finish and should be specified for the severe services.

Table 24-17. Allowable Stresses vs. Temperature for Seamless Pipe and Fittings of Non-ferrous Materials

Seamless Copper and Copper-alloy Pipe

Material	Specification	Grade	Size range, in.	Tensile strength min., lb./sq. in.	Yield strength min., lb./sq. in.	Metal temp., °F.								
						−325 to 100	150	200	250	300	350	400	450	500
Copper pipe*............	A.S.T.M. B42	Annealed		30,000	9,000	6,000	6,000	5,900	5,800	5,000	3,800	2,500	1,500	750
Copper pipe*............	A.S.T.M. B42	Hard drawn	⅛–2 incl.	45,000	40,000	11,300	11,300	11,000	10,500	8,000	5,000	2,500	1,500	750
Copper pipe*............	A.S.T.M. B42	Light drawn	2½–12 incl.	36,000	30,000	9,000	9,000	8,700	8,300	8,000	5,000	2,500	1,500	750
Red brass pipe*..........	A.S.T.M. B43	Annealed		40,000	12,000	8,000	8,000	8,000	8,000	8,000	6,000	3,000	2,000	

Aluminum and Aluminum-base Alloy Seamless Pipe

Material	Specification	Grade	Temper	Tensile strength min., lb./sq. in.	Yield strength min., lb./sq. in.	Metal temp., °F.						
						−325 to 100	150	200	250	300	350	400
6063†	A.S.T.M. B241	GS 10A	T5	22,000	16,000	5,500	5,100	4,900	4,600	4,200	3,100	2,000
6063†	A.S.T.M. B241	GS 10A	T6	30,000	25,000	7,500	7,100	6,800	6,100	4,500	3,100	2,000
6063	A.S.T.M. B241	GS 10A	Welded	17,000		4,250	4,200	4,000	3,800	3,600	2,750	1,900
6061†,‡	A.S.T.M. B241	GS 11A	T6	38,000	35,000	9,500	9,200	9,000	8,500	7,200	5,600	4,000
6061	A.S.T.M. B241	GS 11A	Welded	24,000		6,000	5,900	5,700	5,400	5,000	4,200	3,200
6062†,‡	A.S.T.M. B241	GS 11C	T6	38,000	35,000	9,500						
6062	A.S.T.M. B241	GS 11C	Welded	24,000		6,000						
3003*,†	A.S.T.M. B241	M1A	H 18	27,000	24,000	6,750	6,400	6,050	5,700	5,250	4,400	3,500
3003†	A.S.T.M. B241	M1A	H112	14,500	6,000	3,600	3,250	3,000	2,800	2,500	2,200	1,900

Nickel and Nickel-base Alloy Seamless Pipe and Tubes

Material	Specification	Class	Tensile strength min., lb./sq. in.	Yield strength min., lb./sq. in.	Metal temp., °F.										
					−325 to 100	150	200	250	300	350	400	450	500	550	600
Nickel..............	A.S.T.M. B161	Annealed	55,000	15,000	10,000	10,000	10,000	10,000	10,000	10,000	10,000	10,000	10,000	10,000	10,000
Nickel..............	A.S.T.M. B161	Stress relieved	65,000	40,000	16,200	15,700	15,300	15,100	15,000	15,000	15,000	14,800	14,500		
Nickel..............	A.S.T.M. B161	Stress equalized	70,000	50,000	16,200	15,700	15,300	15,100	15,000	15,000	15,000	14,800	14,500		
Low-carbon nickel....	A.S.T.M. B161	Annealed	50,000	12,000	8,000	7,800	7,700	7,600	7,500	7,500	7,500	7,500	7,500	7,500	7,500
Low-carbon nickel....	A.S.T.M. B161	Stress relieved	60,000	30,000	15,000	14,600	14,200	14,000	13,800	13,600	13,500	13,500	13,500		
Nickel-copper........	A.S.T.M. B165	Annealed	70,000	28,000	17,500	17,000	16,500	16,000	15,500	15,100	14,800	14,700	14,700	14,700	14,700
Nickel-copper........	A.S.T.M. B165	Stress relieved	85,000	55,000	21,200	20,700	20,200	19,800	19,500	19,300	19,200	19,200	19,200		
Nickel-copper........	A.S.T.M. B165	Stress equalized	85,000	65,000	21,200	20,700	20,200	19,800	19,500	19,300	19,200	19,200	19,200		
Ni-Cr-Fe............	A.S.T.M. B167	Annealed	80,000	30,000	20,000	19,300	18,600	18,200	18,000	18,000	18,000	18,000	18,000	18,000	18,000

Material	Specification	Class	Tensile strength min., lb./sq. in.	Yield strength min., lb./sq. in.	Metal temp., °F.											
					650	700	750	800	850	900	950	1000	1050	1100	1150	1200
Nickel.............	A.S.T.M. B161	Annealed	55,000	15,000												
Nickel.............	A.S.T.M. B161	Stress relieved	65,000	40,000												
Nickel.............	A.S.T.M. B161	Stress equalized	70,000	50,000												
Low-carbon nickel...	A.S.T.M. B161	Annealed	50,000	12,000	7,450	7,400	7,300	7,200	6,150	4,500	3,600	3,000	2,400	2,000	1,500	1,200
Low-carbon nickel...	A.S.T.M. B161	Stress relieved	60,000	30,000												
Nickel-copper.......	A.S.T.M. B165	Annealed	70,000	28,000	14,700	14,700	14,650	14,500	12,500	8,000						
Nickel-copper.......	A.S.T.M. B165	Stress relieved	85,000	55,000												
Nickel-copper.......	A.S.T.M. B165	Stress equalized	85,000	65,000												
Ni-Cr-Fe...........	A.S.T.M. B167	Annealed	80,000	30,000	17,800	17,500	17,250	17,000	16,600	16,000	10,500	7,000	4,250	3,000	2,400	2,000

* For use in code piping at the stated allowable stresses, the required tensile properties must be verified by tensile test at the mill; such tests shall be specified in the purchase order.

† For welded construction with work-hardened grades use the stresses for annealed material; for welded construction with precipitation-hardened grades use the special allowable stresses for welded construction given in the tables.

‡ Properties of this material vary with thickness or size. Stresses are based on minimum properties.

Source: Extracted from Petroleum Refinery Piping Code (ASA B31.3-1959), a section of the American Standard Code for Pressure Piping, with permission of the publisher, The American Society of Mechanical Engineers, United Engineering Center, 345 E. 47th St., New York 17, N.Y.

When flat metal gaskets are specified, consideration must be given to the adequacy of the available bolt load to seat (plastically deform) and to seal the gasket during operation. Minimization of required bolt load can best be accomplished by providing a facing with reduced gasket contact surfaces as with nubbins (see Fig. 24-21) or by use of a small tongue-and-groove facing.

Table 24-18. Stress-range Reduction Factors *f*

Cycles	*f*
7,000 and less............	1.0
7,000–14,000............	0.9
14,000–22,000............	0.8
22,000–45,000............	0.7
45,000–100,000............	0.6
Over 100,000............	0.5

Table 24-19. Longitudinal Weld Joint Factor *E*

Type of Joint	*E*
1. Arc or gas weld	
a. Double-welded butt....................................	0.85
b. Double-welded butt, with joints in accordance with Note 1......	0.90
c. Double-welded butt, with 100% radiograp y in accordance with 336.4.2 (c) and conforming with requirements of 327.4.3.........	1.00
d. Single-welded butt....................................	0.80
e. Single-welded butt, with joints in accordance with Note 1.......	0.90
f. Single-welded butt, with 100% radiography in accordance with 336.4.2 (c) and conforming with requirements of 327.4.3.........	1.00
g. Spiral welded....................................	0.75
2. Electric resistance weld and electric flash weld..................	0.85
3. Furnace weld	
a. Lap weld....................................	0.75
b. Butt weld....................................	0.60

NOTE 1: Welds with 0.90 joint factor shall be finished, radiographed by the technique, and evaluated in accordance with UW-51 of Section VIII of the A.S.M.E. Boiler and Pressure Vessel Code. Radiographing (random) shall consist of 12 in. of radiography per 100 ft. of weld with reexamination and repair in accordance with UW-52 of Section VIII of the A.S.M.E. Boiler and Pressure Vessel Code.

Table 24-20. *Y* Values for Steels at Various Temperatures

Temp., °F.	900 and below	950	1000	1050	1100	1150 and above
Ferritic steels......	0.4	0.5	0.7	0.7	0.7	0.7
Austenitic steels....	0.4	0.4	0.4	0.4	0.5	0.7

The code does not limit the use of metallic or metal-asbestos gaskets as to service pressure but does require these types to be used with flat- or raised-face flanges if the operating pressure is in excess of 720 lb./sq. in. or if the fluid temperature exceeds 750°F. However, if the flange facing is such as to confine the gasket (tongue and groove, male and female, etc.) the composite-sheet type and other metallic types can be used without pressure limit.

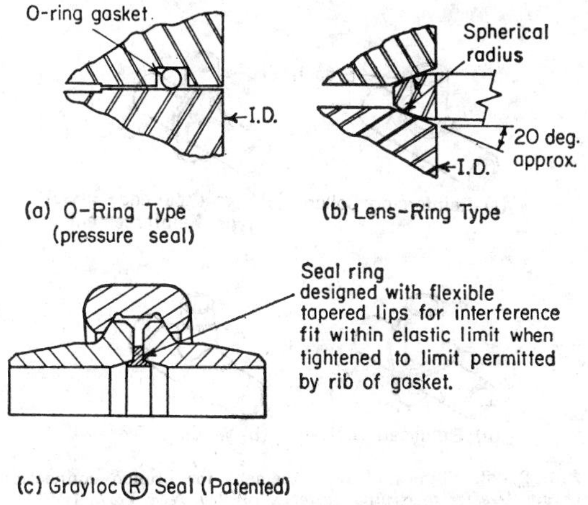

FIG. 24-20. Special facings of proved performance.

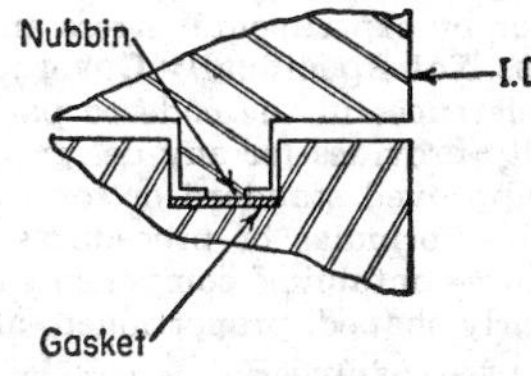

FIG. 24-21. Facing with nubbin for reduced gasket contact.

In general, for 300 lb. A.S.A. and lower-rated flanges, compressed asbestos-sheet gaskets are used (750°F. maximum). The metal-asbestos spiral-wound type is used for higher pressure and temperature services (1100°F. maximum), including services involving cyclic or difficultly contained fluids. It is also used widely in high-pressure steam services. This gasket should preferably be used with a smooth-flange finish. For services involving flanges above 300 lb. A.S.A. rating (pressures of 9.60 lb./sq. in. at 100°F. and higher), confined gaskets provide additional safety against blowout. The spiral-wound type furnished with a solid metallic ring on the outside to limit gasket compression provides similar protection against blowout when used with raised facing. In the petroleum industry the ring-type joint (Fig. 24-22) developed at the inception of thermal cracking is widely employed for the higher temperature and pressure services (above 300 lb. A.S.A.). This joint can withstand appreciable abuse during bolting up without distress and is adequate for transmitting thermal-expansion pipe loads without crushing the gasket. It also provides easy maintenance because, if necessary a reusable octagonal-shaped gasket can be readily lapped into the groove.

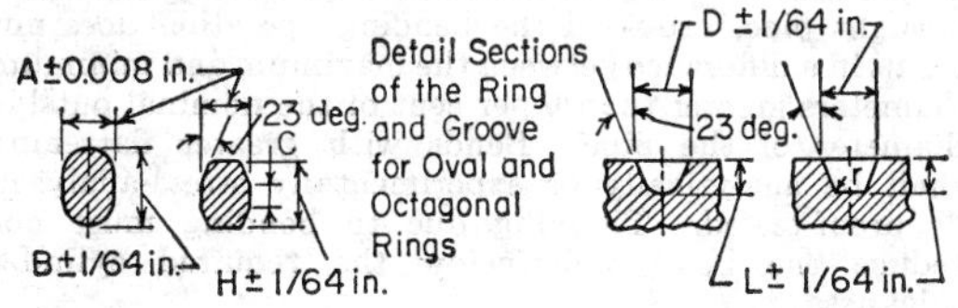

FIG. 24-22. Ring-type joint and gasket.

In the utility steam industry, welding end valves with self-sealing or seal-welded bonnet flanges have widely replaced bolted flanges.

In accordance with listed standards, **flanges** may be used within the pressure-temperature ratings specified therein (see Tables 24-11 to 24-15). For flanges of non-standard dimensions or for sizes beyond the scope of the approved standards, design shall be in accordance with the requirements of the A.S.M.E. Boiler and Pressure Vessel Code, Section VIII, except that requirements for fabrication, assembly, inspection testing, and the pressure and temperature limits for materials of the Piping Code are to prevail. Countermoment flanges of flat face or otherwise providing a reaction outside the bolt circle are not covered by the above rules but are permitted if designed or tested as provided by the general code requirements under "Components Not Covered by Specific Requirements" (see p. 24-46). Flanged joints above 1000°F. require careful consideration with respect to bolting, gasket, and joint relaxations at temperature or under high initial bolting-up loads.

In accordance with listed standards **blind flanges** may be used at their pressure-temperature ratings. The minimum thickness of non-standard blind flanges shall be the same as for a bolted flat cover, in accordance with the rules of the A.S.M.E. Section VIII Pressure Vessel Code.

Operational blanks shall be of the same thickness as blind flanges or may be calculated by the following formula:

$$t = d\sqrt{\frac{3P}{16S}}$$

where d = inside diameter of gasket for raised- or flat (plain)-face flanges, or the gasket pitch diameter for retained gasketed flanges, in.

P = internal design pressure or external design pressure, lb./sq. in.

S = applicable allowable stress

Valves must comply with the applicable standards and material specifications listed in the code and with the allowable pressure-temperature limits established thereby but not beyond the code-established service or materials limitations. Special valves must meet the design requirements for "Components Not of Approved Standards."

Types, size ranges, and applicable A.S.A. or other standards for **fittings** are given elsewhere. Fittings are available as castings, wrought (usually from tubing—otherwise forged), and fabricated (pressed parts assembled by welding). The code contains no specific rules for the design of fittings other than as branch openings. Ratings established by recognized standards are acceptable, however. A.S.A. Standard B16.5 for steel-flanged fittings incorporates a 1.5 shape factor and thus requires the entire fitting to be 50 per cent heavier than a simple cylinder in order to provide reinforcement for openings and/or general shape. A.S.A. B16.9 for butt-welding fittings, on the other hand, requires only that the fittings be able to withstand the calculated bursting strength of the straight pipe with which they are to be used.

The thickness of **pipe bends** shall be determined as for straight pipe, provided the bending operation does not result in a difference between the maximum and minimum diameters greater than 5 per cent of the nominal outside diameter of the pipe. Bends with greater flattening shall be analytically or experimentally stress-analyzed or proof-tested. Thinning due to bending must not reduce the bend wall below the required cylinder thickness.

The thickness of a segment of a **miter bend** is determined as for cylindrical pipe without evaluating the discontinuity stresses at the junction between segments. These discontinuity stresses are reduced as the number of segments is increased, and the code permits neglect of these stresses for non-flammable, non-toxic, and non-cyclic services at pressures not over 100 lb./sq. in. gage. For other services or higher pressures miters must be analytically or experimentally stress-analyzed or proof-tested.

Corrugated pipe and corrugated and creased bends are not covered in the code.

Piping **branch connections** involve the same considerations as pressure-vessel nozzles. However, outlet size in proportion to piping-run size is unavoidably much greater for piping. The current piping code rules for calculation of branch-connection reinforcement are identical with those of the A.S.M.E. Unfired Pressure Vessel Code (1962 edition) for branches with axis at right angles to the run axis. Reference can therefore be made to the pressure vessel subsection for reinforcement rules. If the branch connection makes an angle β with the run axis from 45 to 90 deg., the piping code requires that the area to be replaced be increased by the factor ($2 \sin \beta$). The reinforcing width measured along the pipe axis, however, is limited to the run diameter. Some details of commonly used reinforced branch connections are given in Fig. 24-23.

The rules provide that a branch connection has adequate strength for pressure if a fitting (tee, lateral, cross) is in accordance with an approved standard and is used within the pressure-temperature limitations or if the connection is made by welding a coupling or half coupling (wall thickness not less than branch or less than extra heavy or 2000 lb.) to the run and provided the ratio of branch to run diameters is not greater than one-fourth or the branch not greater than 2 in. nominal diameter.

Openings in closures over 50 per cent in diameter are designed as flanges in flat closures and as reducers in other closures. Openings not over one-half the diameter are to be reinforced as branch connections and reinforcement for flat plates can be reduced to 50 per cent.

The code provides no guidance for analysis but requires that external and internal **attachments** be designed to avoid flattening of the pipe, excessive localized bending stresses, or harmful thermal gradients, with further emphasis on minimizing stress concentrations in cyclic service.

Table 24-21 summarizes the code requirements for closures which are flat, ellipsoidal, spherically dished, hemispherical, conical (without transition knuckles), conical convex to pressure, toriconical concave to pressure, and toriconical convex to pressure.

Standard **reducers** conforming to code listed standards may be used at the pressure-temperature rating of the standard. *Non-standard concentric* reducers having a conical, reversed-curve, or combination of such shapes may be determined from the rules for conical and toriconical closures. The thickness of *eccentric* reducers may

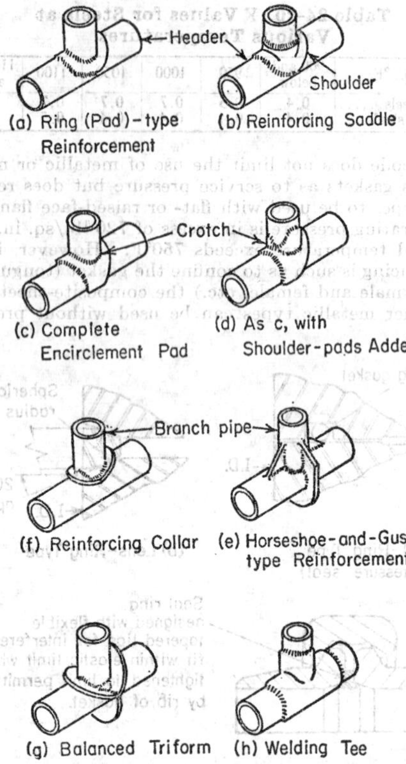

FIG. 24-23. Types of reinforcement for branch connections. (*From "Design of Piping Systems," Wiley, New York, 1956.*)

be determined by stress analysis consistent with the code, by proof test, or by experimental stress analysis.

Components Not Specifically Covered. There are nine specific references in the code to paragraph 304.7, which essentially provides for any design not in accordance with an approved standard or for which the code does not provide formulas or procedures. These non-standard pressure-containing components may be used when (1) similarly shaped, proportioned, and sized components have been demonstrated satisfactory in comparable service with interpolation permitted for similarly shaped component with small differences in sizes or proportion, or when (2) analyzed consistent with the general design philosophy embodied in the code, and further substantiated by either (*a*) proof tests in accordance with paragraph UG-101 of the A.S.M.E. Unfired Pressure Vessel Code, evaluated to include consideration for fatigue where applicable, or (*b*) experimental stress analysis.

Expansion and Flexibility. Stresses caused by thermal expansion, when of sufficient initial magnitude, relax in the hot condition as a result of local yielding or creep. In the absence of terminal anchor movement, the relieved strain appears with reversed sign when the cold temperature is reestablished. This phenomenon is termed **self-springing** of the line and is similar in effect to cold springing. The extent of self-springing depends on the material properties, the magnitude of the initial thermal expansion, and the degree of fabrication stress, as well as the hot service temperature and time at temperature. While the expansion strain retained in the hot condition diminishes with time, the sum of the expansion

Table 24-21. Code Requirements for Thickness of Closures*

Description or sketch	Formula	Definitions and notes†
Flat closures: 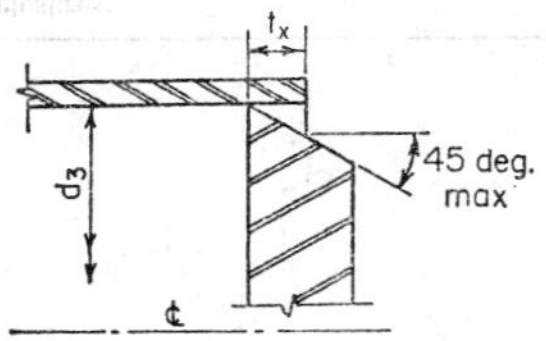		$Q = 0.5m_1$ but not less than 0.3 for circular closures welded to the inside of pipe as shown t_x = 2 times pressure design thickness of seamless pipe [Eq. (3)], but never less than 1.25 times nominal pipe thickness, excluding c, or greater than t
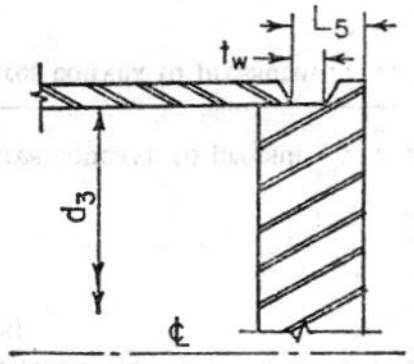	$t = d_3 \sqrt{\frac{QP}{S}}$ (1)	$Q = 0.5$ for circular closures welded to the ends of pipe as shown when the value of m_1 is equal to or less than 0.80 L_5 min. = 2 times pressure design thickness of seamless pipe [Eq. (3)], but never less than 1.25 times nominal pipe thickness, excluding c t_w = width at bottom of welding groove = nominal thickness of pipe, excluding c, but need not be over ¼ in.
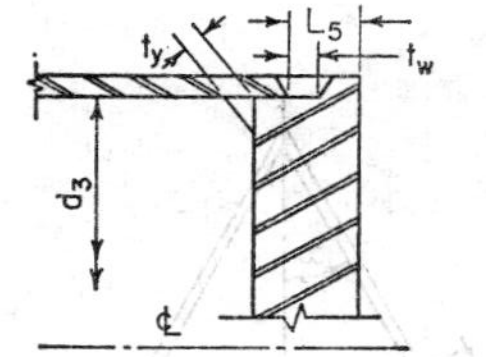		$Q = 0.5m_1$ but not less than 0.3 for circular closures welded to pipe as shown when the value of m_1 is equal to or less than 0.80 L_5 min. and t_w as above t_y min. 0.7 times nominal pipe thickness, excluding c
Ellipsoidal closures: Ellipsoidal closures concave to pressure..............................	$t = \frac{Pd_3K}{2SE - 0.2P}$ or $t = \frac{PD_1K}{2SE - 2P(K - 0.1)}$ (2)	Values of K and K_1 (interpolation permitted) (see table below)
Ellipsoidal closures convex to pressure..............................	Same as for external pressure design except enter curves (see Figs. 24-8 and 24-9) with $L_1/100t$ for L/D_o and L_1/t for L/t and move to line marked "sphere line," then read B value. Compute allowable external pressure from $P_a = \frac{B}{L_1/t}$	

Values of K and K_1 (interpolation permitted)

$d_3/2L_2$	3.0	2.8	2.6	2.4	2.2	2.0	1.8	1.6	1.4	1.2	1.0
K	1.83	1.64	1.46	1.29	1.14	1.00	0.87	0.76	0.66	0.57	0.50
K_1	1.36	1.27	1.18	1.08	0.99	0.90	0.81	0.73	0.65	0.57	0.50

Conical closures (without transition knuckles):

Conical closures concave to pressure

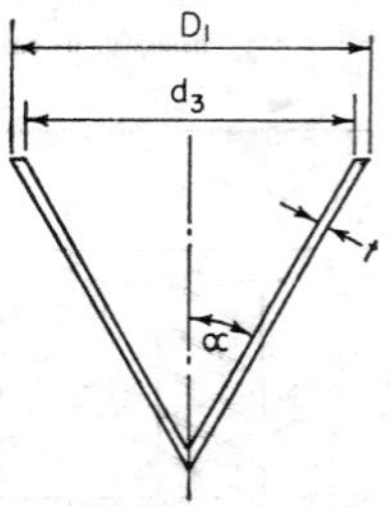

$$t = \frac{PD_1}{2 \cos \alpha (SE - 0.6P) + 2P} \quad \text{or} \quad t = \frac{Pd_3}{2 \cos \alpha (SE - 0.6P)} \qquad (3)$$

Conical closures with one-half apex angles α greater than 30 deg. shall have transition knuckles (see toriconical closures) where the half apex angle α exceeds the value of Δ as given in the following table:

Values of Δ

$\frac{P}{SE}$	0.001	0.002	0.003	0.004	0.005	0.0057
Δ	13	18	22	25	28	30

Compression ring of cross-sectional area A_c as given by the following formula shall be provided for conical closures

$$A_c = \frac{P}{SE}\left[\frac{(d_3)^2 \tan \alpha}{8}\right]\left(1 - \frac{\Delta}{\alpha}\right)$$

Conical closures convex to pressure ....

The pressure design thickness t for conical closures convex to pressure shall be determined in accordance with rules given for toriconical closures convex to pressure with the exception that this type of closure is limited to a one-half apex angle of 30 deg. or less

Toriconical closures:

Toriconical closures concave to pressure

The required thickness of the conical portion of the closure shall be determined in accordance with Eq. (3) using d_4 in place of d_3

The required thickness of the knuckle shall be determined in accordance with Eq. (4) in which

$$r = \frac{d_4}{2 \cos \alpha}$$

Where the one-half apex angle α exceeds 30 deg. toriconical closures shall be used. The inside transition knuckle radius shall be neither less than 6% of the outside diameter of the closure skirt nor less than 3 times the knuckle thickness

Toriconical closures convex to pressure ....

1. When one-half of the apex angle of the cone is equal to or less than 22½ deg., the thickness of the cone shall be the same as required thickness of a cylinder, the length of which equals the axial length of the cone or the axial distance center to center of stiffening rings (if used), and the outside diameter of which is equal to the outside diameter at the large end of the cone or section between stiffening rings

2. When one-half of the apex angle of the cone is greater than 22½ deg., and less than 60 deg., the thickness of the cone shall be the same as the required thickness of a cylinder, the outside diameter of which equals the largest inside diameter of the cone measured perpendicularly to the cone axis, and the length of which equals an axial length that is the least of either the distance center to center of stiffening rings (if used) or the largest inside diameter of the section of the cone considered

3. When one-half of the included apex angle of the cone is greater than 60 deg., the thickness of the cone shall be the same as the required thickness for a flat head under external pressure, the diameter of which equals the largest inside diameter of the cone

Spherically dished closures:

Spherically dished closures concave to pressure

$$t = \frac{PR_2M_1}{2SE + P(M_1 - 0.2)} \quad \text{or} \quad t = \frac{PrM_1}{2SE - 0.2P} \qquad (4)$$

where $M_1 = \frac{1}{4}\left(3 + \sqrt{\frac{r}{r_1}}\right)$

Table 24-21. Code Requirements for Thickness of Closures*—*(Continued)*

Description or sketch	Formula	Definitions and notes†
Spherically dished closures convex to pressure		The pressure design thickness t for spherically dished closures convex to pressure shall be determined in accordance with the procedure set forth for ellipsoidal closures using an appropriate value for L_1
Hemispherical closures:		
Hemispherical closures concave to pressure	$t = \frac{PR_2}{2SE + 0.8P}$ or $t = \frac{Pr}{2SE - 0.2P}$ (5)	
Hemispherical closures convex to pressure		Same as for spherically dished closures convexed to pressure

Notes and General Nomenclature:

* The required thickness of closures, considering pressure and mechanical, corrosion, and erosion allowances, shall be determined in accordance with Eq. (6)

$$t_m = t + c \tag{6}$$

The minimum thickness for the closure selected, considering manufacturer's minus tolerances shall not be less than t_m.

Closure fittings manufactured in accordance with code-approved standards shall be considered suitable for use at the pressure-temperature ratings specified by such standards, and in the case of standards under which closure fittings are made to a nominal pipe thickness, the closure fittings shall be considered suitable for use with pipe of the same nominal thickness.

† The notations described below are used in the equations for determining the pressure design of closures.

t_m = minimum required thickness, satisfying requirements for pressure, mechanical, corrosion, and erosion allowances, in.
t = pressure design thickness as calculated for the given closure shape and direction of pressure loading from the appropriate equations and procedures given above
c = the sum of the mechanical allowances (thread depth and groove depth) and the corrosion and erosion allowances in.
D_1 = outside diameter of the closure skirt; or outside length of the major axis of an ellipsoidal closure; or outside diameter of a conical closure at the point under consideration measured perpendicular to the longitudinal axis, in.
d_3 = inside diameter of the closure skirt; or inside length of the major axis of an ellipsoidal closure; or inside diameter of a conical closure at the point under consideration measured perpendicular to the longitudinal axis; or inside diameter or shortest span of a flat closure, in. (measurement excludes corrosion and erosion allowance)
d_4 = inside diameter of conical portion of toriconical closure at its point of tangency to the knuckle, measured perpendicular to the axis, in. (measurement excludes corrosion and erosion allowance)
L_2 = one-half the length of the minor axis of the ellipsoidal closure, or the inside depth of the ellipsoidal closure measured from the tangent line, in.
R_2 = outside spherical or crown radius for spherically dished or hemispherical closures, in.
L_1 = R_2 for spherically dished or hemispherical closures, or the equivalent outside spherical radius K_1D_1 for ellipsoidal closures, in.
r = inside spherical or crown radius for spherically dished or hemispherical closures, in.
r_1 = inside knuckle radius for spherically dished or toriconical closures, in.
α = one-half the included apex angle of a conical closure, deg.
A_c = cross-sectional area of compression ring, sq. in.
P = internal design pressure, lb./sq. in. gage or external design pressure, lb./sq. in.
S = applicable allowable stress in accordance with Tables 24-16 and 24-17
E = weld joint factor; see Table 24-19
K_1 = factor, values given in ellipsoidal closures
m_1 = pressure design thickness of seamless pipe divided by the nominal thickness of pipe, exclusive of c

Table 24-22. Thermal-expansion Coefficients for Piping Materials*

Mean coefficient of thermal expansion $= \frac{A}{10^6}$ (in./in./°F.) } in going from 70°F. to indicated temperature
Linear thermal expansion = B (in./100 ft.)

Material	Coefficient	Temp. range, 70°F. to −325	−150	−50	70	200	300	400	500	600	700	800	900	1000	1100	1200	1300	1400
Carbon steel; carbon-moly steel, low-chrome steels (through 3 Cr)	*A*	5.00	5.50	5.80	6.07	6.38	6.60	6.82	7.02	7.23	7.44	7.65	7.84	7.97	8.12	8.19	8.28	8.36
	B	2.37	1.45	0.84	0	0.99	1.82	2.70	3.62	4.60	5.63	6.70	7.81	8.89	10.04	11.10	12.22	13.34
Intermediate alloy steels (5 Cr-Mo through 9 Cr-Mo)	*A*	4.70	5.20	5.45	5.73	6.04	6.19	6.34	6.50	6.66	6.80	6.96	7.10	7.22	7.32	7.41	7.49	7.55
	B	2.22	1.37	0.79	0	0.94	1.71	2.50	3.35	4.24	5.14	6.10	7.07	8.06	9.05	10.00	11.06	12.05
Austenitic stainless steels	*A*	8.15	8.60	8.90	9.11	9.34	9.47	9.59	9.70	9.82	9.92	10.05	10.16	10.29	10.39	10.48	10.54	10.60
	B	3.85	2.27	.....	0	1.46	2.61	3.80	5.01	6.24	7.50	8.80	10.12	11.48	12.84	14.20	15.56	16.92
Straight chromium stainless steels (12 Cr, 17 Cr, and 27 Cr)	*A*	4.30	4.70	5.00	5.24	5.50	5.66	5.81	5.96	6.13	6.26	6.39	6.52	6.63	6.72	6.78	6.85	6.90
	B	2.04	1.24	0.72	0	0.86	1.56	2.30	3.08	3.90	4.73	5.60	6.49	7.40	8.31	9.20	10.11	11.01
25 Cr, 20 Ni	*A*	6.35	6.85	7.20	7.48	7.76	7.92	8.08	8.22	8.38	8.52	8.68	8.81	8.92	9.00	9.08	9.12	9.18
	B	3.00	1.81	0.98	0	1.21	2.18	3.20	4.24	5.33	6.44	7.60	8.78	9.95	11.12	12.31	13.46	14.65
Monel (67 Ni, 30 Cu)	*A*	5.55	6.75	7.15	7.48	7.84	8.02	8.20	8.40	8.58	8.78	8.96	9.16	9.34	9.52	9.70	9.88	10.04
	B	2.62	1.79	.....	0	1.22	2.21	3.25	4.33	5.46	6.64	7.85	9.12	10.42	11.77	13.15	14.58	16.02
Monel (66 Ni, 29 Cu-Al)	*A*	5.35	6.45	6.80	7.12	7.48	7.68	7.90	8.09	8.30	8.50	8.70	8.90	9.10	9.30	9.50	9.70	9.89
	B	2.53	1.70	0.98	0	1.17	2.12	3.13	4.17	5.28	6.43	7.62	8.86	10.16	11.50	13.00	14.32	15.78
Aluminum	*A*	9.90	10.90	11.60	12.25	12.95	13.28	13.60	13.90	14.20								
	B	4.68	2.88	1.67	0	2.00	3.66	5.39	7.17	9.03								
Gray cast iron	*A*	....	.....	.....	.....	5.75	5.93	6.10	6.28	6.47	6.65	6.83	7.00	7.19				
	B	....	.....	.....	0	0.90	1.64	2.42	3.24	4.11	5.03	5.98	6.97	8.02				
Bronze	*A*	8.40	8.75	9.15	9.57	10.03	10.12	10.23	10.32	10.44	10.52	10.62	10.72	10.80	10.90	11.00		
	B	3.98	2.31	1.32	0	1.56	2.79	4.05	5.33	6.64	7.95	9.30	10.68	12.05	13.47	14.92		
Brass	*A*	8.20	8.50	8.95	9.34	9.76	10.00	10.23	10.47	10.69	10.92	11.16	11.40	11.63	11.85	12.09		
	B	3.88	2.24	1.29	0	1.52	2.76	4.05	5.40	6.80	8.26	9.78	11.35	12.98	14.65	16.39		
Wrought iron	*A*	5.70	6.30	6.65	6.97	7.32	7.48	7.61	7.73	7.88	8.01	8.13	8.29	8.39				
	B	2.70	1.67	0.96	0	1.14	2.06	3.01	3.99	5.01	6.06	7.12	8.26	9.36				
Copper-nickel (70 Cu, 30 Ni)	*A*	6.65	7.40	7.80	8.16	8.54	8.71	8.90										
	B	3.15	1.95	1.13	0	1.33	2.40	3.52										

* Extracted from Petroleum Refinery Piping Code (ASA B31.3-1959), a section of the American Standard Code for Pressure Piping, with permission of the publisher, The American Society of Mechanical Engineers, United Engineering Center, 345 E. 47th St., New York 17, N.Y.

Table 24-23. Moduli of Elasticity for Ferrous and Non-ferrous Materials*

E = modulus of elasticity, lb./sq. in. (multiply tabulated values by 10^6)

Ferrous material	Temp., °F. −325	−200	−100	70	200	300	400	500	600	700	800	900	1000	1100	1200	1300	1400
Carbon steels with carbon content 0.30% or less	30.0	29.5	29.0	27.9	27.7	27.4	27.0	26.4	25.7	24.8	23.4	18.5	15.4	13.0			
Carbon steels with carbon content above 0.30%	31.0	30.6	30.4	29.9	29.5	29.0	28.3	27.4	26.7	25.4	23.8	21.5	18.8	15.0	11.2		
Carbon-moly steels, low Cr-moly steels through 3 Cr	31.0	30.6	30.4	29.9	29.5	29.0	28.6	28.0	27.4	26.6	25.7	24.5	23.0	20.4	15.6		
Intermediate Cr-moly steels (5–9 Cr), austenitic steel	29.4	28.5	28.1	27.4	27.1	26.8	26.4	26.0	25.4	24.9	24.2	23.5	22.8	21.9	20.8	19.5	18.1
Straight chromium steel (12 Cr, 17 Cr, 27 Cr)	30.8	30.3	29.8	29.2	28.7	28.3	27.7	27.0	26.0	24.8	23.1	21.1	18.6	15.6	12.2		
Wrought iron	30.6	30.2	30.0	29.5	28.6	28.2	27.7	27.0	26.5	25.8	23.0						
Gray cast iron	....	....	....	13.4	13.2	12.9	12.6	12.2	11.7	11.0	10.2						

Non-ferrous material	Temp., °F. −325	−200	−100	70	100	200	300	400	500	600	700	800	900	1000	1100	1200
Monel (67 Ni, 30 Cu) and (66 Ni, 29 Cu-Al)	26.8	26.6	26.4	26.0	26.0	26.0	25.8	25.6	25.4	24.7	23.1	21.0	18.6	16.0	14.3	13.0
Copper-nickel (80 Cu, 20 Ni and 70 Cu, 30 Ni)	20.5	20.0	19.5	18.9	18.8	18.4	18.0	17.6	17.2	16.7	16.2	15.3				
Aluminum	11.3	11.1	10.9	10.6	10.6	10.4	10.2	9.5	8.5							
Copper (99.98% Cu)	17.0	16.7	16.5	16.0	15.8	15.6	15.4	15.1	14.7	14.2	13.7					
Commerical brass (66 Cu, 34 Zn)	15.0	14.7	14.5	14.0	13.9	13.7	13.5	13.0	12.7	12.2	11.8					
Leaded tin bronze (88 Cu, 6 Sn, 1.5 Pb, 4.5 Zn)	14.2	13.8	13.5	13.0	12.9	12.7	12.4	12.0	11.7	11.3	10.9					

* Extracted from Petroleum Refinery Piping Code (ASA B31.3-1959), a section of the American Standard Code for Pressure Piping, with permission of the publisher, The American Society of Mechanical Engineers, United Engineering Center, 345 E. 47th St., New York 17, N.Y.

strains for the hot and cold conditions remains substantially constant so long as the thermal expansion is unchanged. This sum is referred to as the **strain range**; however, to permit convenient association with allowable stress, stress range is utilized as the criterion for the thermal-expansion design of piping.

Analysis assumes elastic behavior of the entire piping system. With a relatively weak or highly stressed portion (section of smaller diameter, thinner or lower-strength-material pipe), strain accumulations occur. This **local overstrain** should be avoided, particularly with materials of relatively low ductility, or else mitigated by judicious application of cold spring.

Flexibility may be provided by the inherent geometry (changes of direction, bends, loops, offsets, etc.) or by decreased stiffness (expansion joints, corrugated pipe) within the limitations of the code.

Thermal-expansion coefficients are shown in Table 24-22. The thermal-expansion range (*i.e.*, thermal change in dimension) equals the difference in average coefficient between the highest and lowest temperature (resulting from operating and shutdown conditions, respectively) multiplied by the temperature change. The code **moduli of elasticity** data are given in Table 24-23. **Poisson's ratio** is established as 0.3 for all materials at all temperatures.

Table 24-24. Flexibility Factor k and Stress-intensification Factor i for Elbows, Tees, and Connections*

Description	Flexibility factor k	Stress intensification factor i	Flexibility characteristic h	Sketch
Welding elbow,[a,b,c] or pipe bend	$\frac{1.65}{h}$	$\frac{0.9}{h^{2/3}}$	$\frac{\bar{T}R_1}{(r_2)^2}$	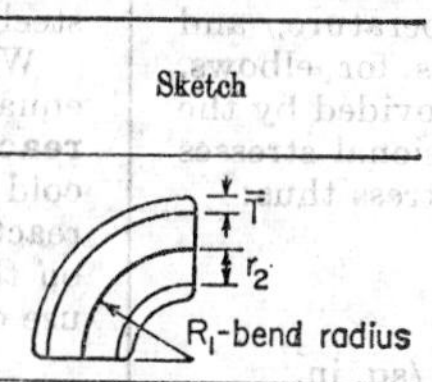
Closely spaced miter bend[a,b,c] $s < r_2(1 + \tan\theta)$	$\frac{1.52}{h^{5/6}}$	$\frac{0.9}{h^{2/3}}$	$\frac{\cot\theta\,\bar{T}s}{2(r_2)^2}$	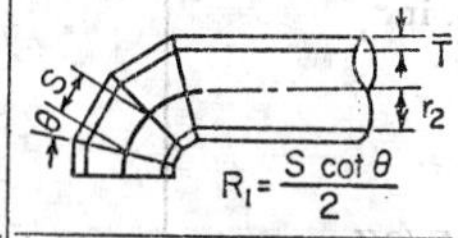
Widely spaced miter bend,[a,b,d] $s \geq r_2(1 + \tan\theta)$	$\frac{1.52}{h^{5/6}}$	$\frac{0.9}{h^{2/3}}$	$\frac{1+\cot\theta}{2}\frac{\bar{T}}{r_2}$	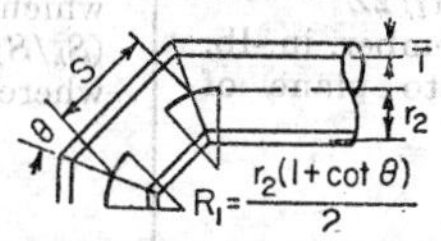
Welding tee[a,b,e] per A.S.A. B16.9	1	$\frac{0.9}{h^{2/3}}$	$4.4\frac{\bar{T}}{r_2}$	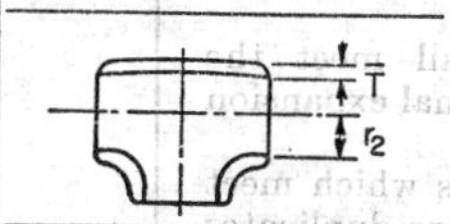
Reinforced fabricated tee,[a,b,e,g] with pad or saddle	1	$\frac{0.9}{h^{2/3}}$	$\frac{(\bar{T}+\frac{1}{2}t_e)^{5/2}}{\bar{T}^{3/2}r_2}$	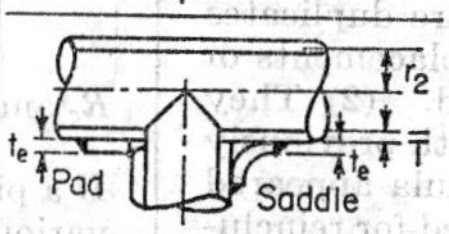
Unreinforced fabricated tee[a,b,e]	1	$\frac{0.9}{h^{2/3}}$	$\frac{\bar{T}}{r_2}$	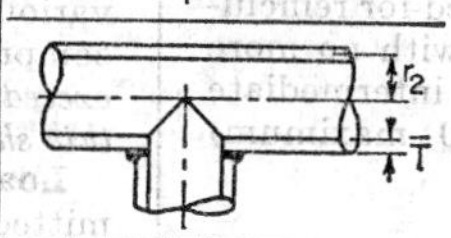
Butt-welded joint, reducer, or welding neck flange	1	1.0		
Double-welded slip-on flange	1	1.2		
Fillet-welded joint, socket-welded flange, or single-welded slip-on flange	1	1.3		
Lap-joint flange (with A.S.A. B16.9 lap-joint stub)	1	1.6		
Screwed pipe joint, or screwed flange	1	2.3		
Corrugated straight pipe, or corrugated or creased bend[h]	5	2.5		

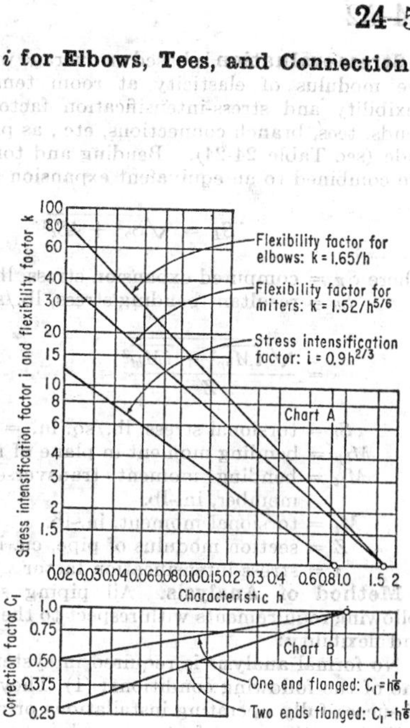

* Extracted from Petroleum Refinery Piping Code (ASA B31.3-1959), a section of the American Standard Code for Pressure Piping, with permission of the publisher, The American Society of Mechanical Engineers, United Engineering Center, 345 E. 47th St., New York 17, N.Y.

[a] The flexibility factors k and stress-intensification factors i in the table apply to bending in any plane for fittings and shall in no case be taken less than unity; factors for torsion equal unity. Both factors apply over the effective arc length (shown by heavy center lines in the sketches) for curved and miter elbows, and to the intersection point for tees.

[b] The values of k and i can be read directly from chart A above by entering with the characteristic h computed from the formulas given, where

r_2 = mean radius of matching pipe, in.

$\bar{T}$ = for elbows and miter bends, the nominal wall thickness of the fitting (see note f), in.

$\bar{T}$ = for tees, the nominal wall thickness of the matching pipe, in.

R_1 = bend radius of welding elbow or pipe bend, in.

θ = one-half angle between adjacent miter axes

s = miter spacing at center line

t_e = pad or saddle thickness, in.

[c] Where flanges are attached to one or both ends, the values of k and i in the table shall be corrected by the factors C_1 given below, which can be read directly from chart B, entering with the computed h: One end flanged: $h^{1/6}$. Both ends flanged: $h^{1/3}$.

[d] Also includes single-miter joint.

[e] The stress-intensification factors i in the table were obtained from tests on full-sized outlet connections. For less than full-sized outlets, the full-sized values should be used until more applicable values are developed.

[f] The engineer is cautioned that cast butt-welding elbows may have considerably heavier walls than those of the pipe with which they are used. Large errors may be introduced unless the effect of these greater thicknesses is considered.

[g] When $t_e > 1\frac{1}{2}\bar{T}$, use $h = 4.05\frac{\bar{T}}{r_2}$.

[h] Factors shown apply to bending; flexibility factor for torsion equals 0.9.

Stress evaluation is based on average wall dimensions, the modulus of elasticity at room temperature, and flexibility and stress-intensification factors for elbows, bends, tees, branch connections, etc., as provided by the code (see Table 24-24). Bending and torsional stresses are combined to an equivalent expansion stress thus:

$$S_E = \sqrt{S_b^2 + 4S_t^2}$$

where S_E = computed expansion stress, lb./sq. in.
S_b = resultant bending stress, lb./sq. in.

$$= \frac{\sqrt{\overline{iM_{bp}}^2 + \overline{iM_{bt}}^2}}{Z}$$

S_t = torsional stress, lb./sq. in. $= M_t/2Z$
M_{bp} = bending moment in plane of member, in.-lb.
M_{bt} = bending moment transverse to plane of member, in.-lb.
M_t = torsional moment, in.-lb.
Z = section modulus of pipe, cu. in.
i = stress-intensification factor

Method of Analysis. All piping shall meet the following requirements with respect to thermal expansion and flexibility:

No formal analysis is required in systems which meet one of the following conditions: (1) They are duplicates of successfully operating installations or replacements of systems with a satisfactory service record. (2) They can be adjudged adequate by comparison with previously analyzed systems. (3) The following formula appeared in the 1955 issue and is again being considered for reinclusion as applying to a uniform size system with no more than two points of fixation without any intermediate restraints for essentially non-cyclic (7000 maximum) operation

$$\frac{DY}{(L - U)^2} \lesseqgtr 0.03$$

where D = nominal pipe size, in.
Y = resultant of movements to be absorbed by pipe line, in.
U = anchor distance (length of straight line joining anchors), ft.
L = developed length of line axis, ft.

All systems not meeting the above criteria shall be analyzed by simplified, approximate, or comprehensive methods of analysis that are appropriate for the specific case.

Approximate or simplified methods may be applied only if they are used for the range of configurations for which their adequate accuracy has been demonstrated.

Acceptable comprehensive methods of analysis are analytical, model test, and chart methods, which evaluate for the entire piping system under consideration the forces, moments, and stresses caused by bending and torsion from a simultaneous consideration of terminal and intermediate restraints to thermal expansion and include all external movements transmitted under thermal change to the piping by its terminal and intermediate attachments. Correction factors, as provided by the details of these rules, must be applied for the stress intensification of curved pipe and branch connections and may be applied for the increased flexibility of such component parts.

The total expansion range of the piping system (whether or not piping is cold sprung) and pertinent movement of attached equipment must be considered.

Movements resulting from thermal expansion and loadings shall be reviewed to assure clearance of obstructions to movement and proper support.

Cold spring is permitted, and encouraged for austenitic steel in the present state of knowledge.

When a piping system is not cold sprung, or there is an equal percentage of cold springing in all directions, the **reactions** (forces and moments) R_h and R_c in the hot and cold conditions, respectively, shall be obtained from the reaction R derived from the flexibility calculations based on the modulus of elasticity at room temperature E_c by use of the following equations:

$$R_h = \left(1 - \frac{2}{3}C\right)\frac{E_h}{E_c}R$$

$$R_c = CR = \left(1 - \frac{S_h}{S_E}\frac{E_c}{E_h}\right)R$$

whichever is greater, and with the further condition that $(S_h/S_E)(E_c/E_h)$ is less than 1

where C = cold-spring factor, varying from zero for no cold spring to 1 for 100 per cent cold spring
S_E = computed expansion stresses, lb./sq in.
E_c = modulus of elasticity in the cold condition, lb./sq. in.
E_h = modulus of elasticity in the hot condition, lb./sq. in.
R = maximum reaction for full expansion based on E_c, which assumes the most severe condition (100 per cent cold spring, whether such is used or not)
R_c and R_h = maximum reactions estimated to occur in the cold and hot conditions, respectively

If a piping system has different percentage cold spring in various directions, the system shall be analyzed by a comprehensive method. *The reactions computed shall not exceed limits which the attached equipment can sustain; this should be checked with the manufacturer.*

Loads on Supporting Elements. Loads transmitted by piping to attached equipment and supporting elements include weight, temperature- and pressure-induced effects, vibration, wind, earthquake, shock, and thermal expansion and contraction. The design of supports and restraints is based on concurrently acting loads, assuming wind and earthquake do not act simultaneously.

Resilient and constant-effort-type supports shall be designed for maximum loading conditions including test, unless temporary supports are provided.

The code states further that pipe-supporting elements shall (1) be capable of carrying all concurrent loads; (2) be braced for necessary rigidity at anchors; (3) be designed to prevent overstress, resonance, or disengagement due to variation of load with temperature; also, so that combined stresses in the piping shall not exceed the code allowable; (4) be such that a complete release of the piping load will be prevented in the event of spring failure or misalignment, weight transfer, or added load due to test during erection; (5) be of steel or wrought iron; (6) be of alloy steel, or protected from temperature where the temperature limit for carbon steel may be exceeded; (7) not be cast iron except for roller bases, rollers, anchor bases, etc., under mainly compression loading; (8) not be malleable or nodular iron except for pipe clamps, beam clamps, hanger flanges, clips, bases, and swivel rings; (9) not be wood except for supports mainly in compression where the pipe temperature is at or below ambient; and (10) have threads for screw adjustment which shall conform to A.S.A. B1.1.

Pipe-supporting **fixtures** shall comply with the following requirements: (1) *Anchors* for expansion joints shall be designed for loads specified by the joint manufacturer, or for the full pressure end load plus an allowance for the resistance of the joint. (2) *Hanger rods* may be pipe straps, chains, bars, or threaded rods which permit free movement for thermal expansion or contraction. (3) *Sliding supports* shall be designed for friction and bearing loads. (4) *Brackets* shall be designed to withstand movements due to friction in addition to other loads. (5) *Spring-type supports* shall be designed for weight load at point of attachment and to prevent misalignment, buckling, or eccentric loading of springs, and provided with stops to prevent spring overtravel. (6) *Compensating-type spring hangers* are recommended for high-temperature and critical-service piping to make the supporting force uniform with appreciable movement. (7) *Counterweight* supports shall have stops to limit travel. (8) *Hydraulic supports* shall be provided with safety devices and stops to support load in the event of loss of pressure. (9) *Vibration dampers* or sway braces may be used to limit vibration amplitude.

Requirements for Specific Piping Systems. Instrument piping within the scope of the code (*i.e.*, used to connect instruments including air or hydraulic control piping but not that within or part of instruments) shall, in addition to compliance with applicable code requirements, meet the following requirements: (1) The temperature of instrument piping during periodic blowdowns shall be considered a short-time condition. (2) The mechanical strength (including fatigue) of small instrument connections to piping or apparatus shall be considered. (3) Static instrument fluids subject to freezing shall be provided with heating (steam or electric tracing, etc.). (4) Blowdown or bleed of toxic fluids shall be to a suitable collection system; flammable fluids should be considered for a similar arrangement.

There shall be no intervening **stop valves** between piping and its **pressure-relieving devices** or between these devices and their discharge except where (1) such valves can be locked or sealed (either open or closed), are provided with full-area ports (unless reduced-area ports on the discharge side will not reduce capacity to a common header), and are attended by an authorized person who is provided with means to relieve pressure when the valve is closed during operation and who will again lock or seal the valve before leaving his station; and (2) such valves are so constructed or positively controlled that the maximum possible number of block valves closed will not impair the required relieving capacity.

Discharge piping from pressure-relieving safety devices shall be arranged for drainage, and not to impinge on other piping or equipment, and shall be directed away from platforms or other personnel areas.

PIPING MATERIALS AND TESTING

Acceptable materials shall conform to the approved specifications listed in the code or meet its requirements for materials not so established. Basically, this requires the establishment of allowable stresses and, if to be welded, the qualification of procedures and operators. If to be used below −20°F. it must meet the impact-test requirements unless specifically exempted by paragraph 323.2.2. Reclaimed pipe and components may be used provided they are properly identified as conforming to code requirements.

Material shall not be used at design temperatures above those for which the stress values are given, and for temperatures below −20°F. they must meet impact-test requirements, when specified. Temperature limits for unlisted but otherwise code-conforming materials shall be in accordance with recognized engineering practice.

Impact tests shall be made for the following combinations of materials and temperatures: (1) All materials for temperatures below −325°F. (2) Bolting to A.S.T.M. A 193 grade B7 and nuts to A.S.T.M. A 194 grade 2H for temperatures below −50°F., and to A.S.T.M. A 194 grade 4 for temperatures below −150°F. (3) For temperatures below −20°F.: (*a*) Carbon and low-alloy steels, other than materials specified above. (*b*) Ferritic chromium stainless steels. (*c*) Free-machining austenitic chrome-nickel stainless steels. (*d*) Austenitic chromium-nickel stainless steels with a carbon content greater than 0.10 per cent. (*e*) Austenitic chromium-nickel stainless-steel materials in the form of deposited weld metal regardless of carbon content. (*f*) Austenitic chromium-nickel stainless materials in cast form.

Impact tests are also required to be in accordance with requirements of paragraph UG-84 of Section VIII of the A.S.M.E. Boiler and Pressure Vessel Code, with the exception of prescribed modifications of paragraphs UG-84(b), (1), (2), and (3).

Iron and Steel Alloys. Upon prolonged exposure to temperatures above 750°F., the carbide phase of plain carbon steel, plain nickel alloy, carbon-manganese alloy, manganese-vanadium alloy, and carbon-silicon steel may be converted to graphite.

Upon prolonged exposure to temperatures above 850°F., the carbide phase of alloy steels such as carbon-molybdenum, manganese-molybdenum-vanadium, manganese-chromium-vanadium, and chromium-vanadium may be converted to graphite.

If carbon steel is to be used above a temperature of 900°F., consideration shall be given to the advantage of silicon-killed steel (0.1 per cent silicon minimum). If carbon steel is used for fabrication of pressure-containing components to be used at design temperatures above 875°F., consideration shall be given to the advantages of firebox- over flange-quality plate.

Cast and **malleable iron** shall not be used for pressure-containing parts in hydrocarbons or other flammable fluid service at temperatures above 300°F. or at pressures above 400 lb./sq. in., except that, for service above ground within process unit limits, the pressure shall not exceed 150 lb./sq. in. Cast and malleable iron shall not be used for pressure-containing parts in any toxic service.

Nodular iron shall not be used for pressure-containing parts at temperatures below −20°F. or above 650°F. or at pressures above 1000 lb./sq. in.

The low melting points of such **nonferrous materials** as copper, copper alloys, and aluminum must be recognized before these materials are used as pipe or piping components where fire hazard is involved.

Clad and **lined materials** may be used in accordance with the applicable requirements in Part UCL of Section VIII of the A.S.M.E. Boiler and Pressure Vessel Code.

Note the following warning: *Deterioration of Materials in Service: "The selection of materials to resist deterioration in service is outside the scope of this Code. It is the responsibility of the engineer to select materials suitable for the conditions of operation."*

Gaskets shall be of materials which are not injuriously affected by the contents or its temperature under anticipated operating conditions. Metallic materials shall be limited to the temperature established by the allowable stress table for similar materials.

Bolts, nuts, and **washers** for flanged connections must, unless otherwise specified, comply with A.S.A. B16.5, with carbon-steel machine bolts limited to use at temperatures from −20°F. to +500°F. and for 300 lb./sq. in. maximum operating pressure. For bolt-metal temperatures between −20°F. and −50°F., inclusive, bolting material shall be in accordance with A.S.T.M. A193, grade B7, or with A.S.T.M. A320. For bolt-metal temperatures below −50°F., A.S.T.M. A320 shall be used.

For 25 lb. and class 125 cast-iron integral or screwed companion flanges, with a full-face gasket, bolting may be heat-treated carbon steel (A.S.T.M. A261) or alloy steel (A.S.T.M. A193); with a flat ring gasket, bolting shall be of carbon steel not stronger than A.S.T.M. A307, grade B. For class 250 cast iron, integral, or screwed companion flanges having 1/16-in. raised faces, bolting shall be of carbon steel not stronger than A.S.T.M. A307, grade B.

Fabrication Requirements

The code requirements dealing with fabrication operations are very limited and except for detailed requirements covering welding leave wide latitude to the manufacturer and inspector to provide adequate piping fabrication with minimum inspection requirements. As compared with fabrication of pressure vessels, piping, since it involves components with varied dimensional tolerances (outside diameter and wall thickness) of appreciable magnitude (minus 12½ per cent on wall thickness) and butt welds inaccessible on the inside diameter, is subject to lesser assurance of adequate fabrication without much more careful inspection and non-destructive examination.

The code requirements for **welding processes** and **operators** are essentially the same as covered in the pressure-vessels section (*i.e.*, qualification to Section IX of the A.S.M.E. Boiler and Pressure Vessel Code) except that welding processes are not restricted, material grouping (*P* number) must be in accordance with Appendix A, and welding positions are related to pipe position. The code also permits one fabricator to accept welders or welding operators qualified by another employer without requalification when welding pipe by the same or equivalent procedure.

Filler metal is required to conform with the requirements of Section IX. **Backing rings** (of ferrous material), when used, shall be of weldable quality with sulfur limited to 0.05 per cent. Backing rings of non-ferrous and non-metallic materials may be used provided proved satisfactory by procedure qualification tests.

Table 24-25 is a digest of the code requirements for the quality of girth, longitudinal, fillet, and seal welds.

The qualifications of brazing, brazers, and brazing operators are required to be in accordance with Part C of A.S.M.E. Section IX. The filler metal can be any non-ferrous metal or alloy having a melting point above 800°F. The clearance between surfaces to be joined shall be the minimum required to allow complete capillary distribution of the filler metal.

Pipe may be bent to any radius for which the bend arc surface will be free of cracks and substantially free of buckles. Out of roundness and minimum finished thickness of bend shall be such that the design thickness requirements of a cylinder are met. This shall not prohibit the use of bends which are creased or corrugated. **Bending** may be by any hot or cold method permissible within the radii and material characteristics of the pipe being bent. Hot bending shall be done within a temperature range consistent with material characteristics, end use, or post-heat-treatment.

Piping components may be formed by any suitable hot or cold pressing, rolling, forging, hammering, spinning, drawing, or other method. **Hot forming** shall be done within a temperature range consistent with material characteristics, end use, or post-heat-treatment.

Heat-treatment. The code provides no rules to cover heating or cooling methods to meet preheat or postheat requirements except that they shall be accomplished by methods which will provide the required metal

Table 24-25. Code Quality Requirements for Various Types of Welds

Types of weld	Girth butt welds	Longitudinal butt welds	Fillet welds	Seal welds
Imperfections:				
Cracks	None permitted	None permitted		
Incomplete penetration and lack of fusions	The total joint penetration shall not be less than the thinner of the two components being joined, except to the extent that incomplete root penetration is permitted. The depth of incomplete root penetration or lack of fusion at the weld root shall not exceed 1/32 in. or half the thickness of the weld reinforcement, whichever is smaller. The total length of such incomplete root penetration or lack of fusion at the root shall not exceed 1½ in. in any 6 in. of weld length. Unless otherwise specified by the engineering design, welds on which 100% radiography is specified shall have complete joint penetration	None permitted		
Undercutting	The finished surface of the weld shall merge smoothly into the component surface at the weld toe. The external surface of butt welds shall not have undercuts more than 1/32 in. deep	Butt welds shall be free from undercutting, and finished weld surfaces shall merge smoothly into the base-metal surface at the toe	Same as for girth butt welds	
Porosity	An individual gas pocket of porosity shall not exceed 1/16 in. in its greatest dimension. The total area of porosity, projected radially through the weld, shall not exceed 0.01 sq. in. (equivalent to 3 areas 1/16 in. in diameter) in any square inch of projected weld area, per inch of wall thickness (considering the thinner of the components being joined)	Same as for girth butt welds		
Slag inclusions	The developed length of any single slag inclusion shall not exceed *T*/3*T*, being the wall thickness of the thinner component being joined. The total cumulative developed length of slag inclusions shall not exceed *T*/2 in any 6-in. length of weld. The width of a slag inclusion shall not exceed 1/16 in.	Same as for girth butt welds		
Limitations:				
Weld reinforcement	Thickness of weld reinforcement shall not exceed the following considering the thinner component being joined: Component Thickness, in. — Reinforcement Thickness, max., in. ½ and under — 1/8 Over ½ through 1 — 5/32 Over 1 — 3/16 For double-welded joints this limitation on reinforcement shall apply to each surface of the weld separately	The thickness of the weld rienforcement shall be 1/16 to 1/8 in. For double-welded joints this limitation on reinforcement shall apply to each surface of the weld separately		

temperature, metal temperature uniformity, temperature control, and finally the desired cooling rate. Local post-heat-treatment is permitted provided the entire band is brought to a uniform temperature over the pipe circumference with gradually diminishing temperature outward from the band. The minimum width of band to be heated is the larger of twice the width of weld reinforcement and the width of weld reinforcement plus 2 in. For local treatment of welded branch connections or other attachments a circumferential band of pipe extending at least 1 in. beyond each side of the weld must be heated.

Pre-heat-treatment for welds unless otherwise specified in the qualification procedure specification shall be in accordance with Table 24-26.

Table 24-26. Pre- and Post-heat-treatment of Welded Materials

P[f] no.	Min. preheat temp., °F.	Post-heat-treatment[e] Metal temp., °F.	Hr./in. of wall thickness, min.	Time at temp., hr., min.	Brinell hardness max.[d]
1	Not required[a]	1100–1200[b]	1	¾	
2	Not required[a]	Not required			
3	175	1175–1370[c]	1	1	215
4	300	1325–1375	1	2	215
5	350	1325–1375	1	2	241
6	400	1400–1450	1	2	241
7	Not required[a]	Not required			
8	Not required	Not required			
9	300	1100–1200	½	1	
10	300	1050–1100	½	1	

[a] Under field conditions or otherwise where the ambient temperature is less than 32°F. local preheating to a condition warm to the hand is required for all materials listed under P number 1, 2, and 7.

[b] Post-heat-treatment is not required for carbon steel when thickness is less than ¾ in.

[c] Post-heat-treatment is not required for carbon-molybdenum steel when the thickness is less than ½ in.

[d] These hardness limits apply only if post-heat-treatments other than shown in the table are used, and they are applicable also to the heat-affected zone of the welds.

[e] The piping being heat-treated shall be maintained within the temperature limits shown for the time period indicated.

[f] The following describes in general terms the materials covered by the the individual P numbers:

1. Carbon steel (42,000 to 70,000 minimum tensile strength)
2. Wrought iron
3. Carbon-½ per cent Mo and ½ per cent Cr-½ per cent Mo (53,000 to to 75,000 minimum tensile strength) and Cr-Cu-Ni and C-Si-Mo alloy steels
4. 1 per cent Cr-½ per cent Mo through 2 per cent Cr-½ per cent Mo alloy steels and 2½ per cent Ni and Ni-Cr-Mo alloy steels
5. 2¼ per cent-1 per cent Mo through 9 per cent Cr-1 per cent Mo alloy steels
6. 12 per cent to 15 per cent Cr alloy steels
7. 12 per cent Cr-Al, 17 per cent Cr, 20 per cent Cr-Cu and 26 per cent Cr alloy steels
8. Austenitic alloy steels, *e.g.*, types 304, 304L, 309, 310, 316, 316L, 321, and 347
9. 3½ and 5 per cent Ni alloy steels
10. 9 per cent Ni alloy steel

Post-heat-treatment is required when necessary to restore or obtain the physical properties (such as strength and corrosion resistance) with respect to material, design, and end-use requirements and shall be as specified in Table 24-26 unless other post-heat-treatment is required to restore or obtain the desired physical properties. Post-heat-treatment of welded joints shall be established in the procedure specification. The requirements of this table do not apply for heat-treatment after bending or forming operations. When wall thickness is a factor determining the requirement for heat-treatment, the nominal pipe wall thickness of the thicker pipe being joined shall govern and for non-pressure-containing attachment welds the throat thickness of the weld shall govern. Seal welds of threaded joints do not require heat-treatment if of $P1$ or $P3$ material. Welds in ferritic materials which are to operate at design temperatures below −20°F. shall be post-heat-treated as specified in the table regardless of wall thickness.

Assembly in the shop or field shall be done so as to conform to the code and requirements of the engineering design. Flanged joints shall be fit up so that contact faces bear uniformly on the gasket and made up with relatively uniform bolt stress consistent with the type of gasket. Steel-to-cast-iron joints must be assembled with care to prevent damage to the cast-iron flange. All bolts shall extend through nuts. Assembly of cast-iron bell-and-spigot pipe shall comply with A.W.W.A. Standard C-600. Threaded joints to be seal-welded shall be made up without compound; otherwise compound shall be suitable for service and not react unfavorably with contents.

Inspection Requirements. Prior to initial operation, a piping installation shall be inspected to the extent necessary to assure compliance with the engineering design, and with the material, fabrication, assembly, and test requirements of the code. It provides that:

An employee representative of the owner, who shall be designated as the **Code Examiner**, shall be responsible for this inspection regardless of any inspection of any legal authority having jurisdiction. This examiner may delegate performance of any part of the inspection to inspectors who may be employees of his own organization, of an engineering or scientific organization, or of a recognized insurance or inspection company. The Code Examiner shall be qualified by a minimum of ten years' experience in the design or inspection of petroleum refinery or similar industrial piping. Graduation from an engineering college accredited by the Engineers Council for Professional Development shall be the equivalent of five years' experience.

The code examiner and the inspectors shall have rights of access to any place where work concerned with the piping is being performed. This includes manufacture, fabrication, assembly, erection, and testing of the piping Inspectors shall have the right to review all certifications or records pertaining to the inspection requirements, including certified qualifications for welders, welding operators, and welding procedures.

Examination Methods and Tests. The code provides for three methods of examination with the latter two termed "supplementary": (1) **Visual,** which consists of observing whatever portions of a component or weld are exposed either during or after manufacture, fabrication, assembly, or test. (2) **Magnetic particle** in accordance with the dry-powder method of A.S.T.M. E109. A.S.T.M. E125 and M.S.S.-SP53 are listed as providing a basis for interpretation of indications in ferrous castings with the latter to provide one level of quality. (3) **Radiography** by either X-ray or gamma ray to the requirements established by the code for girth welds and to paragraph UW-51 (a) to (k) of the A.S.M.E. Unfired Pressure Vessel Code, Section VIII, for piping components and other welds. The extent of inspection is not mandatory and it is left to the discretion of the code examiner which welds are required to be visually examined, with the "supplementary" types employed only if specified by the engineering design. The code does, however, establish the type of imperfections to be evaluated by the various types of examinations (see Table 24-27).

Table 24-27. Imperfections to Be Evaluated by Various Types of Examination

Type of imperfection	Visual	Magnetic particle	Random radiography	100% radiography
Crack	X	X	X	X
Incomplete penetration	X	...	X	X
Weld undercutting	X			
Weld reinforcement	X			
Porosity	...	...	...	X
Slag inclusions	...	...	...	X

Supplementary types of examination shall be performed after heat-treatment of the *P*3, *P*4, and *P*5 materials. If the supplementary examination is specified on a random-sampling basis, only the welds examined are required to be repaired; *i.e.*, the code does not establish any procedure regarding acceptability of other welds represented by the random sampling. Complete (100 per cent) radiography requires that each weld be completely examined and repaired if not in accordance with the code requirements.

The code requires all installed piping to be **pressure-tested** for assurance of tightness and requires a retest if other than "minor" repairs or additions are required. The test pressure must be maintained for at least 10 min.

Tests may be by water, a hydrocarbon oil (flash point below 120°F. and a freezing point 25°F. higher than the minimum ambient temperature), or if not considered practicable by the owner a pneumatic test may be substituted. All joints, including welds, are to be left uninsulated and exposed during test.

The hydrostatic test pressure (minimum) shall be determined by the following equation:

$$P_t = \frac{1.5PS_t}{S}$$

where P_t = minimum hydrostatic test pressure, lb./sq. in. gage
P = internal design pressure, lb./sq. in. gage
S_t = allowable stress at 100°F., lb./sq. in.
S = allowable stress at design temperature, lb./sq. in.

Lines in vacuum service shall be tested to a minimum of 15 lb./sq. in. unless limited to a lower pressure by the design. Lines in external pressure service shall be tested with an internal pressure not less than the external pressure.

Pneumatic testing shall be at 110 per cent of the design pressure.

Records of each piping installation tested are required to cover date of test, identification of piping tested, test fluid, test pressure, and inspector's approval, but they need not be retained after completion of the piping installation, provided certification that all piping has been pressure-tested is retained.

OVER-ALL ECONOMIC AND SAFETY CONSIDERATIONS

Current codes and industry practices do not provide clear-cut classes of piping construction and, by failing to define underlying philosophy and principles, tend to obscure and confuse a logical association of requirements. On an average, over 90 per cent of the cost of process unit piping is for mild or moderate services, with only a few per cent for severe or critical services. There is a prevailing tendency toward higher than necessary quality construction for the former, and of insufficient refinement for the latter. Expensive and sensitive materials are often subject to economies in refinement and inspection, which are of questionable value as compared with the calculated risks as to safety and the long-range economics involved.

Piping hazards are usually depreciated, as compared with pressure vessels. Actually, piping failures are much more likely to result from (1) ineffective supports and neglected vibration effects, (2) the generally lower level of weld quality, (3) generally lesser service inspection due to inaccessibility of the inside surface, and (4) location often away from grade and platforms. Even small-sized failures can introduce significant fire hazards and ruptures in adjacent larger piping and equipment.

The chemical engineer would be well advised to avoid senseless economies with respect to piping, which afford savings that are minor in proportion to their contribution to assured capabilities and soundness. Excessive replacement and maintenance costs invariably originate with an unrealistic sense of initial investment values.

Balanced Classes of Fabricated Piping. To assist the chemical engineer in exercising judgment with respect to necessary and/or desirable above-minimum requirements, a detailed suggested basis for four balanced classes of construction (*i.e.*, uniformly proportioned requirements for material quality, design refinement, fabrication soundness, and inspection extent) is presented by Murphy and Rossheim ("Requirements for Fabrication of Pressure Piping as Related to Service," A.S.M.E. Paper 57-PET-32, September, 1957).

It is important to appreciate that current codes do not presently provide such class distinctions and that the discussion and suggestions in the reference paper were offered to spur action toward (1) industry recognition and code revision and (2) an improved realization of structural capabilities as compared with investment cost.

The adequacy of fabricated piping is currently less assured by present code requirements and its average engineering treatment than is true for pressure vessels (see pp. 24-23ff). Generally, this leads to higher quality than necessary for the bulk of piping which is in mild service and deficient quality for the occasional demanding services.

With respect to contents, limited efforts on the part of the committee preparing the Chemical Industry Piping Code Section 6 of A.S.A. B31 in collaboration with the A.I.Ch.E. Technical Committees have been directed toward classification of **content hazards.** The owner-user is therefore without benefit of an industry or professional consensus as to contents hazards until Section 6 is published.

Considerations beyond Code Coverage. This subsection is devoted to enlarging or supplementing those aspects of fabricated piping which the A.S.A B31 Code for Pressure Piping covers inadequately or else omits; also included is generally useful information with respect to fabricated piping and its components.

The reader will find a broad treatment of the "Design of Piping Systems" in the second edition volume of that title, authored by the Engineering Departments of The M. W. Kellogg Company (Wiley, New York, 1956). It is assumed that this reference is available to readers interested in greater detail, so that comments herein are limited to aspects of wide interest or which are considered to deserve emphasis.

Attention is also directed to the parallel and related discussion in the preceding section on Pressure Vessels of the following pertinent subjects: (1) strength and failure of materials, (2) design criteria and loadings, (3) joint efficiency and casting quality factors, (4) loadings and integrated cyclic effect, (5) strength enhancement, (6) proof tests, (7) experimental stress analysis, (8) overpressure and overtemperature (including internal insulation), (9) support and local reactions, (10) vibration and resonant stress magnification, and (11) temperature stresses.

Abrupt overpressure may be transmitted from attached equipment or can originate in the piping. In the absence of industry practices, such hazards are more widely ignored for piping, on the questionable reasoning that failures involve lesser hazard or economic significance. Often the greater length (and possibly also length-to-diameter ratio) of piping promotes the acceleration of deflagrations into **detonations.**

Local reactions are introduced by pipe supports and restraints, etc., as a result of weight, expansion, and thermal gradients. Where the attendant loads are highly localized and/or of considerable magnitude rela-

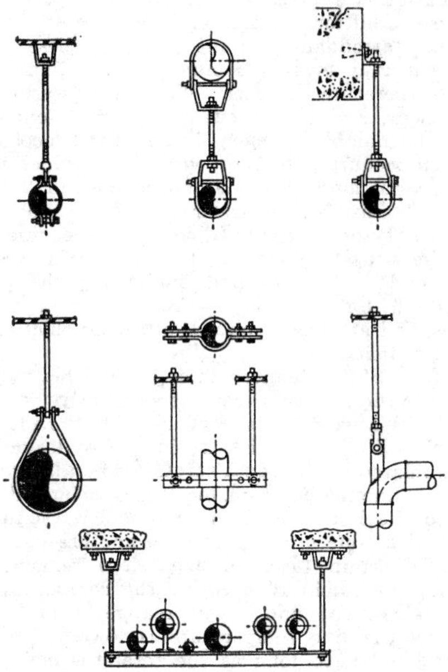

A. Typical rod hanger assemblies.

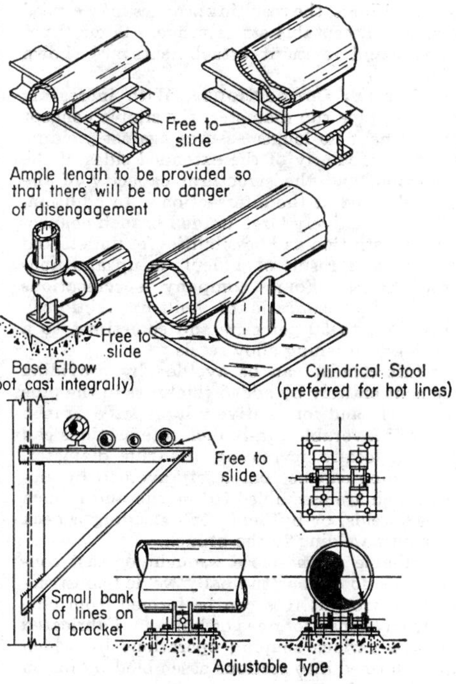

B. Typical resting support assemblies

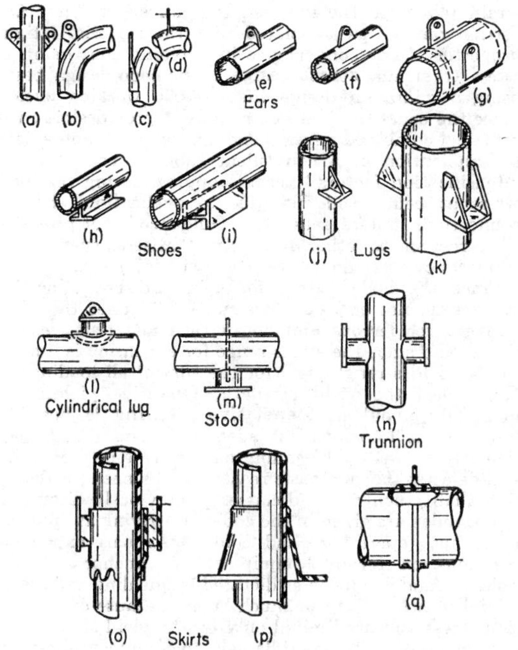

C. Typical integral attachments

Fig. 24-24*A*. Typical pipe supports and attachments; rod hanger assemblies.

Fig. 24-24*B*. Typical pipe supports and attachments; resting support assemblies.

Fig. 24-24*C*. Typical pipe supports and attachments; integral attachments.

(*Source: Figs.* 24-24 *to* 24-31 *are from Kellogg's "Design of Piping Systems," Wiley, New York,* 1956.)

tive to the pipe stiffness, the resulting stresses may exceed the yield stress or acceptable stress range. Some types of pipe support and restraint attachments are shown in Fig. 24-24.

Tees and Branch Connections. With increasing ratio of branch to pipe run diameter, the simple concept of metal replacement no longer assures against yielding and distortion, particularly of the extended sides of the branch connection, and the structural capacity of the pipe is not maintained at the intersection. In addition, the fabrication of relatively large welded branch connections introduces distortion and possibilities for undetected cracks and flaws as a result of difficult fit-up and non-uniform weld stress. Some company specifications limit the maximum size ratio of built-up reinforced branch connections to 50 per cent and sometimes to a lesser ratio for air-hardening alloy steels.

Built-up reinforcement can be avoided by providing the reinforcement entirely by added thickness in the pipe run and/or branch, and for relatively large sized branch connections more favorable run-branch intersections can be achieved by locally increasing the run diameter. Intersection welding can be completely avoided by employing tees, which are assembled to the run and branch with girth butt welds, or by fluing or extruding a neck in the run for butt welding to the branch.

Tees are available of one-piece wrought or cast construction, or of sectional longitudinally welded construction. One-piece wrought tees can be formed from pipe or machined from shaped forgings or billets. Fabricated tees can involve various shaping operations by which plate or pipe is formed into sections assembled by fusion welding.

Branch reinforcement requirements do not apply to A.S.A. welding tees, couplings not less than 2000 lb., or A.S.A. Standard flanged fittings. For A.S.A. B16.9 standard welding tees the rating is established by "proof" tests requiring only that the burst pressure be not less than the connecting pipe run with which it is to be used. Such tests establish only static pressure bursting strength; capacity for static structural yield loading and for repetitive pressure and/or structural loading is not required but is performed in some degrees by certain manufacturers.

Thermal Expansion and Structural Loads. A piping system constitutes an irregular frame in space, with two or more terminal ends either fully restricted against movement and rotation (anchored), or fully restrained against movement only (hinged), or partially restrained against movement (limit stops) and/or rotation (guides) along one or more axes. Intermediate restrictions are also involved at supports, guides, or braces and may provide a full hinge (zero translatory movement on all three axes), or a full guide (zero rotation on all three axes), or any other combination of movement and rotation limitation, of either full or partial degree. Anchors and other restraints in addition to restricting piping-system freedom may, through the expansion of attached equipment or structures, impose their extraneous movements and/or rotations on the piping. Intermediate restraints are introduced to support or brace the line against weight, wind, etc., or to limit vibration, or to control deflection, or to effect a more favorable distribution of stresses and/or reactions.

Flow and ambient changes affect metal temperature; this in turn results in dimensional change (*i.e.*, thermal expansion or contraction) which when opposed induces reaction forces and moments at anchors and restraints, along with bending and torsional and direct stresses in the piping. Extraneous movements of anchors and restraints also force dimensional changes in the piping system which similarly result in reactions and stresses. To the degree that the piping system is not ideally supported, weight stresses due to the pipe, contents, and insulation are present. In exposed installations, wind causes additional loading and in areas subject to earthquake, attendant loading occurs; these latter effects are usually evaluated only for large-diameter or extreme-temperature systems. While analyses of thermal expansion and extraneous equipment movements constitute formidable problems in structural mechanics, organized procedures, the most versatile of which is the Kellogg general analytical method covered in "Design of Piping Systems," permit accurate and rapid solutions. The availability of programmed computers economically justifies the wide application of such calculations, by avoiding inadequate runs and minimizing the piping length added for flexibility. Freedom from service difficulties and attendant hazards of lost production are additional benefits.

The A.S.A. B31.3 Refinery Piping Code treatment of thermal-expansion effects contrasts sharply with its shortcomings elsewhere. It recognizes that the adequate performance of piping, with avoidance of leakage or failure, is related to the **total stress** (or **strain) range.** Under initial line temperature, local stress is immediately reduced to the hot yield point and undergoes further reduction with time under relaxation and creep. Since the imposed strain (thermal expansion) remains undiminished, the strain relieved by the combination of yielding, relaxation, and creep reappears in reverse direction as the line temperature is lowered (termed **self-springing**). So long as the total thermal strain load is not changed, a reasonably stable condition on subsequent heating and cooling cycles results, without further short-time yielding, and the number of cycles of useful life is then established by the cold plus hot strain (equal to the imposed thermal expansion) *i.e.*, "strain range," as associated with the material fatigue properties. For convenience in avoiding conversion of stress to strain, **stress range** is the code design basis, using a minimum design life of 7000 working cycles. Since the usual thermal stress analysis provides only the principal combined stress (bending, torsional, and axial), an application of a convenient table of code "stress-intensification factors" permits approximating the local stress at bends and ells (due to ovalization), branch connections, miters, tees, etc. Guidance is not provided with respect to other local stress raisers, such as at supports or attachments to terminal equipment.

Since the code values for cold and hot allowable stresses do not exceed 0.625 and 0.667 times the yield strength for ferrous and non-ferrous materials, respectively, and since the stress range for expansion is limited to the yield strength and for the sum of all loadings to 1.67 times the yield strength, repetitive yielding is nominally avoided. **Repetitive yielding** is possible, however, at locations not adequately considered, particularly at welds, depending on surface and root finish and defects; this is a basic reason for the need for definitive quality controls and classes as previously discussed.

Formulas are given in the code for arriving at approximate hot (operating) and cold (offstream) expansion reactions on terminal equipment or anchors. These reflect a final condition as dictated by yielding and creep. Initial reactions may be much higher because of fabrication stress and are limited only by the yield stress (cold and then hot). To avoid damage to equipment, particularly rotating machinery, or other equipment sensitive to distortion, initial fabrication reactions are often controlled by **prespring** to the degree that such can be effectively accomplished. Thermal heating of the pipe to a stress-relief temperature is used to unload fabrication stress alone when applied to a cold piping system, and to accomplish self-spring when the system is hot. Prespring can also be accomplished by the adjustment of solid hangers or ties after the line is erected. The methods and their degree must be selected to suit the specific installations.

It has long been appreciated that machinery manufacturers' limitations on allowable reactions in order to keep rotating parts in alignment have governed the design of attached piping rather than the stress in the pipe. There is less awareness that control of local stresses at pressure-vessel nozzle attachments will often govern the piping design, although usually not in the same degree. It is only recently that such stresses are being investigated, and available methods are only approximate.

While piping-flexibility analysis requires the attention of qualified design engineers, simplified chart-form or analytical solutions for individual configurations are available from many sources [Kellogg, "Design of Piping Systems," Wiley, New York, 1956. Crocker, "Piping Handbook," McGraw-Hill, New York, 1945. Tube-Turns Research Staff, "Piping Engineering (part 4) Expansion and Flexibility," Tube Turns, Louisville, Ky.], and general rules of thumb are often very useful for preliminary work.

For structural loads, such as the weight of pipe, valves and fittings, contents, insulation, supported equipment, such as traps and filters, calculations are usually made independently and numerically added to the thermal stresses and reactions. For critical installations, simultaneous calculation of thermal and structural loading can be accomplished in accordance with the Kellogg general analytical method.

All the foregoing applies to "stiff piping systems," *i.e.*, systems without expansion joints (see detail 1 of Fig. 24-25). Where space limitations, process requirements,

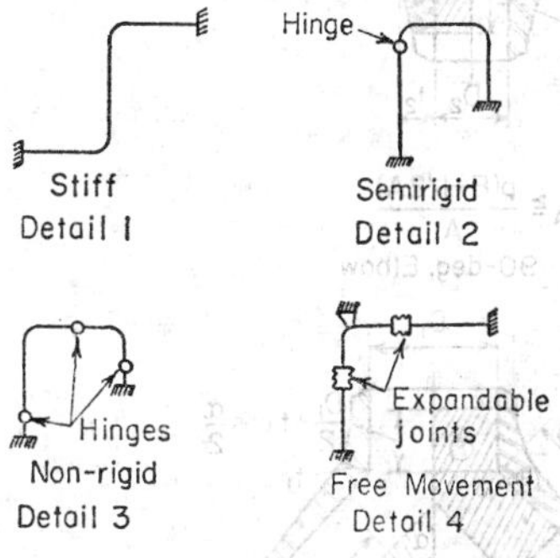

Fig. 24-25. Flexibility classifications for piping systems.

or other considerations result in configurations of insufficient flexibility, capacity for deflection within allowable stress range limits may be increased successively by the use of one or more hinged bellows expansion joints, *viz.*, semirigid (detail 2) and non-rigid (detail 3) systems, and expansion effects essentially eliminated by a free movement joint (detail 4) system. Expansion joints for semirigid and non-rigid systems are restrained against longitudinal and lateral movement by the hinges with the expansion element under bending movement only, and are known as "rotation" or "hinged" joints (see Fig. 24-26). Semirigid systems are limited to one plane; non-rigid systems require a minimum of three joints for two-dimensional and five joints for three-dimensional expansion movement. Section 7.7 of "Design of Piping Systems" outlines in detail the calculations for establishing expansion-joint movements.

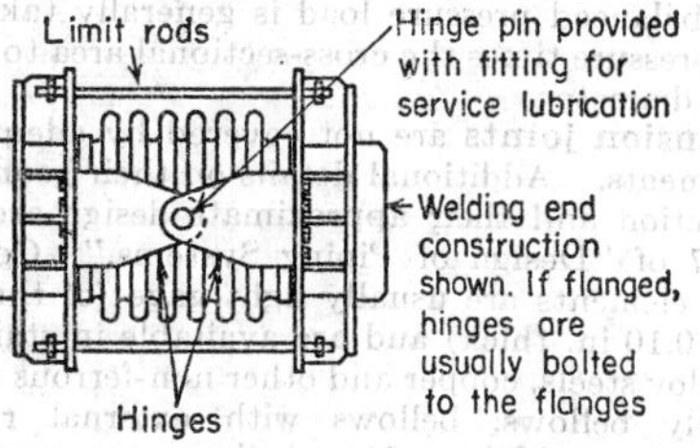

Fig. 24-26. Hinged expansion joint.

Expansion joints for free-movement systems can be designed for axial or offset movement alone, or for combined axial and offset movements (see Fig. 24-27). For

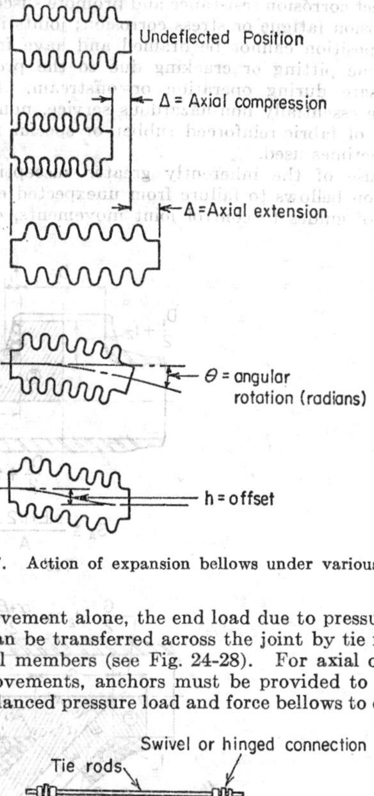

Fig. 24-27. Action of expansion bellows under various movements.

offset movement alone, the end load due to pressure and weight can be transferred across the joint by tie rods or structural members (see Fig. 24-28). For axial or combined movements, anchors must be provided to absorb the unbalanced pressure load and force bellows to deflect.

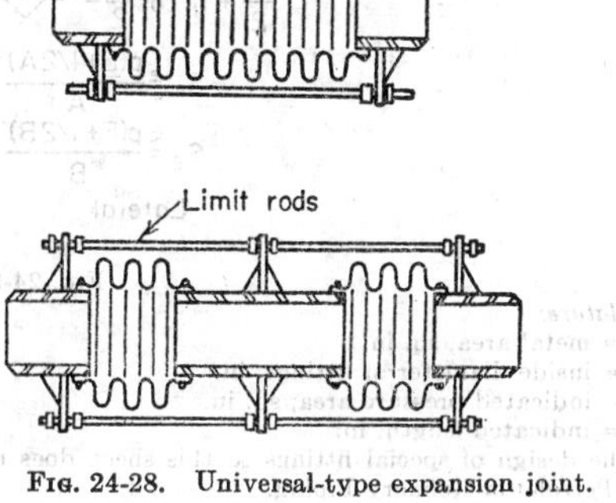

Fig. 24-28. Universal-type expansion joint.

The unbalanced pressure load is generally taken as the design pressure times the cross-sectional area to the mean bellows diameter.

Expansion joints are not covered by adequate code requirements. Additional details on their geometry and construction and their approximate design are given in Chap. 7 of "Design of Piping Systems." Commercial bellows elements are usually light gage (of the order of 0.05 to 0.10 in. thick) and are available in stainless and other alloy steels, copper and other non-ferrous materials. Multi-ply bellows, bellows with external reinforcing rings, and toroidal contour bellows are available for higher pressures. Since bellows elements are ordinarily rated for strain ranges which involve repetitive yielding, predictable performance is assured only by adequate fabrication controls and knowledge of the potential fatigue performance of each design. The attendant cold work can affect corrosion resistance and promote susceptibility to corrosion fatigue or stress corrosion; joints in a horizontal position cannot be drained and have frequently undergone pitting or cracking due to the presence of condensate during operation or offstream. For low-pressure essentially non-hazardous service, non-metallic bellows of fabric-reinforced rubber or special materials are sometimes used.

Because of the inherently greater susceptibility of expansion bellows to failure from unexpected corrosion, failure of guides to control joint movements, etc., it is

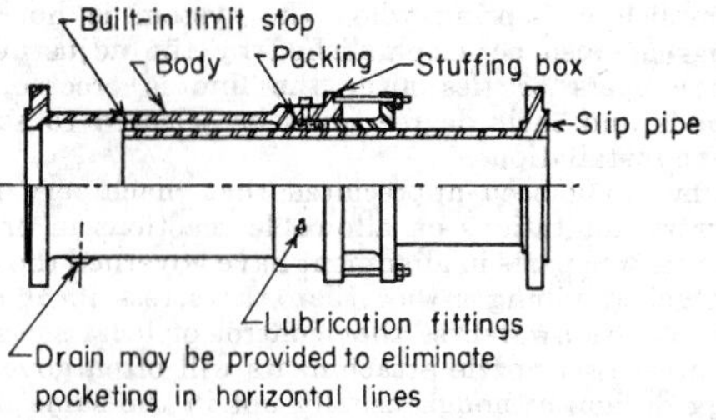

FIG. 24-29. A conventional slip-type expansion joint.

advisable to examine critically their design choice in comparison with a stiff system.

Slip-type expansion joints (Fig. 24-29) substitute packing (ring or plastic) for bellows. Their performance is sensitive to adequate design with respect to guiding to prevent binding and the adequacy of stuffing boxes and attendant packing, sealant, and lubrication. Anchors must be provided for the unbalanced pressure force and for the friction forces to move the joint. The latter can be much higher than the elastic force required to deflect a bellows joint. Rotary packed joints, ball joints, and other special joints can absorb end load.

Corrugated pipe and corrugated and creased bends are

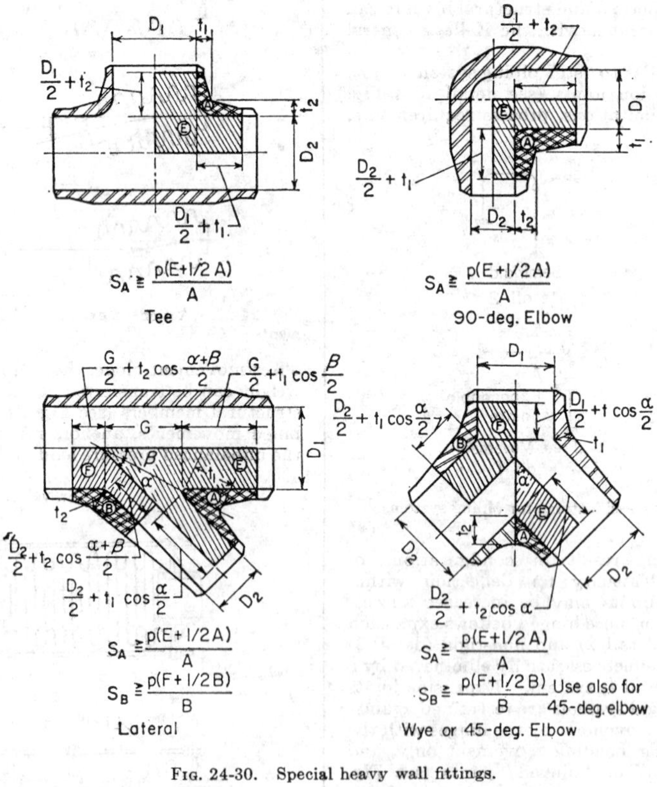

FIG. 24-30. Special heavy wall fittings.

Nomenclature:

A, B = metal area, sq. in.
D_1, D_2 = inside diameter of fittings, in.
E, F = indicated pressure area, sq. in.
G = indicated length, in.
P = design pressure, at design temperature, lb./sq. in. gage
S_A, S_B = allowable stress at design temperature, lb./sq. in.
t_1, t_2 = indicated metal thickness, in.
α, β = indicated angles

Note: The design of special fittings to this sheet does not necessarily assure compliance with A.S.A. B31.3-1959, Code for Pressure Piping, Petroleum Refinery Piping.

used to decrease stiffness and are discussed under the next subject.

Improved Components. A suggested basis for the design of special heavy wall fittings taken from "Design of Piping Systems" is shown in Fig. 24-30.

Fittings, in addition to containing pressure, also perform as structural elements of a piping system. This subject is already discussed under branch connections but deserves additional mention with respect to **bolted flanges.** Depending on their location in a piping system and their stiffness as compared with the pipe, flanges must develop a proportionate strength relative to the piping, if freedom from leakage and/or distortion is to be avoided. For example, a 150-lb. series flange installed in a schedule 160 piping system can transmit only a fraction of the stress which pipe of this thickness can develop under fabrication residual effects or by thermal expansion. For a tight joint, a minimum gasket compression, as a multiple of the line pressure, must be maintained. Since moment is transmitted almost entirely by the gasket, the minimum unit gasket load on the tension side is decreased by the moment increment. When this gasket unit load is no longer realized, leakage results.

Curved Pipe. Pipe may be bent hot or cold with hot forming performed usually at forging temperature, although sometimes at lower temperature where dictated by material considerations. Steel pipe is usually filled with sand, to minimize distortion and wrinkling. Unless temperature and time at temperature are rigidly controlled, hot bending may undesirably coarsen the grain structure and, with unfavorable atmosphere, oxidize or decarburize the metal surface. Pipe may also suffer damage (cracks and structure inhomogeneities) when abrupt water quenching is applied. Alloy steels require special consideration which often includes careful post-heat-treatment to restore ductility and/or optimum corrosion resistance. Non-stress-relieved cold bends retain severe plastic deformation, with possible lowered corrosion resistance or susceptibility to accelerated attack. Bends offer advantage in reduced pressure drop, and often in fabrication economics as compared with weld ells.

Cold bending finds its major use on sizes up to 12 in. IPS, and when performed on specialized machines can closely control dimensions and minimize distortion. The standard and usually minimum radius (center line) is five diameters (5 × nominal pipe size); larger radii are usually provided as bench bends. Hot bends also are commonly specified for five diameters but can be obtained to radii as small as three diameters and on heavy wall thickness sometimes to 2½ diameters; wrinkled bends can also be obtained to 2½ or 3 diameters. The Pipe Fabrication Institute (P.F.I.) Standard ES3 covers linear tolerance, bending radii, and minimum tangents of pipe bends.

Hot or cold bending changes the wall thickness, increasing that at the inner radius and reducing that at the outer radius. In general, the local change in wall thickness corresponds inversely to the local change in length, assuming that the mean (axial) length does not change. P.F.I. has proposed the following formula (developed by tests) to predict thinning in bends reasonably well:

$$\frac{t}{t_o} = \frac{R}{1.015(R + 0.5D)}$$

where t = thickness after bending
t_o = thickness before bending
R = mean bend radius
D = pipe outside diameter

The code currently requires the thickness after bending to be not less than that required for straight pipe. This is unrealistic with respect to actual practice and theory, and the provision is under study with revision expected.

Miter Bends. Turns in piping are sometimes made by mitering the pipe ends (angle cuts) at each girth seam, usually because fittings or smooth bends are unavailable, or else when they offer significant cost advantage. Figure 24-31 is a general sketch for a 90-deg. turn and shows the "equivalent" radius of a smooth bend in terms of the miter angle φ and the length of straight s. Such bends are recognized to be inferior to smooth bends with respect to flow and erosion and to design and fabrication stress intensification. Design discontinuity bending stresses at each junction are proportional to the miter angle; in addition to abrupt structural changes (heat-affected zone and weld deposit) the potential for accelerated failure at this area is further accentuated by possible weld defects or surface discontinuities and by bending as a result of difficult fit-up and resulting offset. These effects can be markedly reduced by increasing the number of segments, special attention to joint preparation, and adequate non-destructive examination.

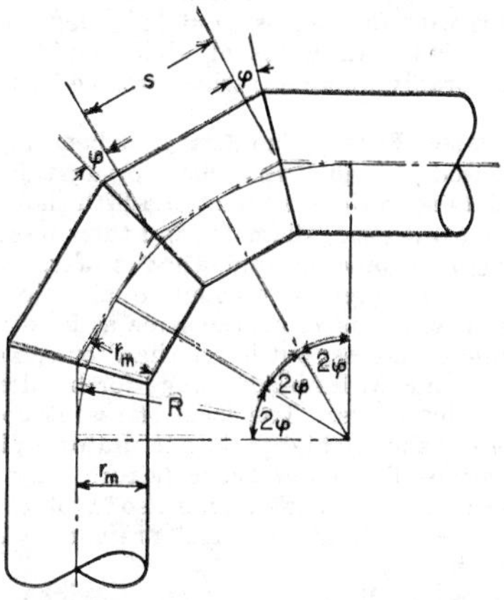

FIG. 24-31. Geometry of miter bends.

s = miter spacing
φ = miter angle
R = equivalent bend radius = $\frac{s}{2} \cot \varphi$
r_m = mean radius of pipe

The A.S.A. Code treatment of miter joints for pressure loading is entirely unsatisfactory. Their use is permitted based on past successful operating conditions or on unspecified stress analysis plus suitable proof (one-cycle) tests. The A.S.M.E. Power Boiler Code permits such joints on piping for boilers but limits φ to 30-deg. maximum and requires that the thickness of the miter bend be greater than that of straight pipe by the factor

$$\frac{R - 0.5r}{R - r}$$

where r = inside pipe radius

In effect, this requires a thickness consistent with the membrane stress analysis of a torus or smooth bent pipe. Logically, it should apply to smooth bends also, but it is not so required.

The A.S.A. Code rules for expansion and flexibility, in contrast to the inadequate treatment for pressure loading, establish design flexibility and stress-intensification factors for miter bends based on limited fatigue-test data. Flexibility is rated lower and stress factors about the same as an equivalent smooth bend. No account is taken of stress intensification as a function of weld quality.

Single miter 90-deg. turns (φ = 45-deg.) are to be avoided for pressure service. For multiweld miters, the minimum straight length between welds at the inside should be several inches to avoid overlapping fabrication stresses, and preferably $2\sqrt{rt}$ to prevent overlapping discontinuity stresses at intersections. Large-diameter pipe bends with four welds ($\varphi = 11\frac{1}{4}$-deg.) and $R = 5r$ minimum, and with welds of high quality, have performed favorably where no serious erosive flow conditions exist.

Corrugated Pipe. The axial and bending flexibility of corrugated straight pipe with corrugations of usual commercial proportions is about one-fifth that of uniform pipe of the same inside diameter and thickness; in torsion the corrugated pipe is somewhat stiffer. On bends, corrugations or creases prevent ovalization and the resulting flexibility is about the same as for straight pipe of the same thickness, but lower than for the equivalent plain pipe bend, with no advantage for bend radii much below five diameters. The local stress at corrugations and creases is usually higher than in uniform plain bends, so that fatigue life under cyclic flexure may be significantly lowered. Corrugated pipe also involves a build-up factor on the stress due to axial pressure, with similar potential effects.

Blinds and Other Isolation Devices. For the usually higher construction or maintenance pressure tests, valve-seat distortion may be experienced. Or valves may not be desirable or permitted by codes because of the hazard of isolating the equipment from safety valves or for other reasons. Positive assurance against leakage is important to protect personnel engaged in maintenance and inspection and to avoid loss of valuable contents. Leakage may be controlled by double valves and vents preferably integrated with valve operation, or by dual-seat valves and intermediate vents, or by blinds. Blinds are the most economic and positive means for isolating pressure equipment. The thickness of permanent blinds is determined by the following formula:

$$t = d\sqrt{\frac{3P}{16S}} + C$$

where d = inside diameter of gasket or, for ring-type or tongue-and-groove and similar retained gaskets, the center line of gaskets, in.

Other symbols are the same as for straight-pipe formula.

Pipe Fabrication Joints. Tapered pipe threads provide both mechanical locking and sealing against leakage, provided threads are to dimensions and sufficiently smooth and continuous, although in practice sealants (white lead, paint, litharge and glycerin, etc.) are often used to assure tightness. Threaded joints up to and including 12 in. IPS have been widely used on standard or on pipe of heavier wall thickness, with occasional larger sizes. In process plants they are currently limited to smaller sizes (3 to 4 in. IPS in general, and $1\frac{1}{2}$ in. IPS on some process units) by the economics of threading equipment and labor.

Threaded joints are subject to service leakage where expansion causes rotation at the threads, or where flow temperature changes cause transient differences in metal temperature and momentary leakage. The latter may become permanent with plastic deformation (swaging) under temperature differences due to infiltration of solids. Seal welding is often employed for tightness, although reliable welds require precaution as to thread length (to avoid welding on threads or seepage of sealant). This combination of threading and welding does increase cost.

To join lengths of straight pipe, **couplings** (sleeves with double right-hand threads) are used, and either couplings or unions are necessary between sections to minimize assembly and handling clearances. Straight pipe threads are used to adjust assembly dimensions but must be seal-welded. An advantage claimed for threaded assemblies is ease of disassembly where welding is not employed. Another is that corrosion does not impede such disassembly.

Other than threads, pipe may be assembled by various other types of mechanical joints. Some depend on wholly elastic reaction between the parts. Others, in which one or both members are shaped, indented, or coined, develop projections which carry the axial load. The simplest is the flared joint employed on compression fittings of small tubing; another is a circumferential machined slot or shoulder on the tube and socket and a solid or sectional shear ring; still another uses a hardened sleeve to indent the tube. A recent alternate corrugates the tube outside diameter to avoid sharp indentations.

Brazed or soldered socket-type joints are widely employed on copper and copper alloys, and **brazed joints** find some use on aluminum and steel, including stainless steel. Solders are available in many analyses of tin, lead, and antimony or silver to provide for corrosion resistance, compatibility, and heat resistance; however, all such joints lose strength with temperature and are usually so limited. Brazing alloys are available which melt from about 800° to 2200°F. and include silver-base alloys, copper-base alloys, and the more recent high-temperature brazing alloys (Ni-Cr-Si, Ni-Cr-Si-B-Cb, Ni-Cr-B, Ni-P, Ag-Mn), and also special alloys of aluminum.

Soldering involves primarily a mechanical bond reinforced with some compositions by intergranular penetration of highly diffusive metals such as tin. Brazing attains its bonding in depth by extensive diffusion. Silver-base brazing compounds provide extreme fluidity, making it possible to utilize capillary action to secure minimum thickness–maximum strength joints, independent of conditions under which they are performed. Precoated copper and copper-alloy fittings are commercially available, or they may be provided with preplaced ferrules of solder or brazing alloy. Brazed joints can give excellent service where their quality can be reliably controlled; but such control is usually limited to visual indications of compound penetration. Repair is sometimes difficult, and soldered joints are considered by some as sensitive to vibration fatigue.

Weld joints for piping include lap-sleeve, lap bell-and-spigot, socket-and-butt joints with variable degrees of weld penetration, smoothness, and continuity of surface contour.

Calked bell-and-spigot joints are sealed by nonmetallic or lead packing forced by calking tools into the space between the bell and mating pipe end. Packed bell-and-spigot joints utilize elastic packing, usually of reinforced rubber, and are available in several proprietary types. Such construction is usually confined to cast-iron pipe.

Mechanically assembled pipe joints can be used to limit erection to assembly with full prefabrication, or to permit periodic disassembly for inspection, cleaning, etc., and include unions and mechanically locked and bolted flanged joints as illustrated in Sec. 6 (see pp. 6-43 to 6-45). Threaded-locking devices are available in large sizes (up to 48 in.), but with pressure limitations unless soft gaskets can be used.

Bolted flanged joints are widely used, although the trend has been to minimize their number for reason of economics and to reduce potential sources of leakage.

Thermal expansion can cause leakage unless the flanged joint stiffness compares favorably with that of attached piping. This is accomplished when the pressure rating is the same, or, for lower stiffness, when the design compensates for the expansion effects present. Load is transmitted through a flanged joint by the combined action of the bolts (tensile) and gasket (compression); otherwise leakage would occur more frequently.

Valves. For general-process services at temperatures below 850°F., the basic types of valves (as shown in Sec. 6) are of standardized (A.S.A., A.P.I., M.S.S.) dimensions and ratings and are usually adequate for non-cyclic operation with the manufacturer's standard trim and packing. Each basic type of valve has features, depending upon its component parts, which make it better suited for specific services and operating conditions, such as leaktight shutoff, severe throttling, close control, coking service, dirty service, minimum pressure drop, and ease of maintenance.

For **shutoff service,** however, the gate-pattern type of valve is generally specified because of its (1) relatively lower cost, (2) straight-through flow which minimizes pressure drop, (3) increased mechanical advantage for sealing due to wedge (gate) geometry, and (4) sliding (wiping) action which is useful in dirty services or services in which deposits can occur. Although essentially a shutoff valve, it is used in throttling services for nominal pressure drops and is available with a solid wedge, double-disk wedge, and flexible double-disk wedge which provides somewhat greater assurance for shutoff at elevated temperatures or when the valve is subject to sudden or unequal temperature changes. The double-disk valve has another advantage in that it can be provided with either a bleed or vent connection between the seats, thus providing in essence a double-valved condition.

The globe pattern, obtainable with numerous types of plugs, from the simple disk to the contoured tapered (needle) plug for severe and precise throttling, is generally used for control. It is considered to offer greater assurance of tight shutoff and is more readily reconditioned because of its circular seat and circular contoured plug. Other types of shutoff valves are generally not considered suitable for throttling service but, when provided with soft seals (such as Neoprene, Teflon, or rubber) or with an auxiliary sealant, are well suited for positive shutoff in services handling light gases and other difficult-to-seal fluids.

Special valve designs or modified components of standard patterns are required for assured shutoff and operability at high pressures and particularly at the extremes in temperature, when subject to cyclic operation or for rapid controlled use. Gate valves with special spring-loaded disks and with water-cooled seats, stems, and disks have been designed and successfully operated in cyclic dust-laden gas service at temperatures approaching 1600°F. For operation at high pressures, high temperatures, high pressure drops, and/or in cyclic or erosive service, particular considerations must be given to the valve trim for enhanced wear resistance, minimization of galling, and adequate temperature strength. For motor operation, valve stems should be oversized in proportion to the speed of required operation and attendant dynamic effects. Stuffing boxes must also be protected against extremes of temperature by locations remote from the body, provision of radiation fins, and/or by external cooling or heating. When potential leakage of packing is dangerous, valve designs are available involving sealing bellows (expansion joints) attached to the body and stem thereby eliminating the packing. They are used in nuclear and other hazardous services, Valves are also available with self-sealing bonnet joints for high-pressure operation and with welded joints to eliminate the gasket and bolting and thus avoid a potential source of leakage.

Materials and Components. In addition to the usual analyses of ferrous and non-ferrous materials discussed in the preceding subsection on pressure vessels, piping is fabricated of many other materials, such as glass, ceramics, plastics, and the newer metals. Pipe is obtainable in standard sizes and nominal wall thicknesses up to 24 in. outside diameter with tubing to minimum and average wall, usually up to 6 in. maximum nominal diameter (see Sec. 6). These tubular items are produced from billets, rolled strip, and castings by a number of different methods, and are available in single random (20-ft.) and double random (40-ft.) lengths. When large quantities of piping (other than seamless) are required in a single size and thickness, consideration should be given to ordering to a minimum thickness rather than by schedule to obtain the most economic price.

Pipe and tubing are usually subject only to visual examination and to a mill hydrostatic test suitable to detect gross effects only. The increasing availability, however, of continuous non-destructive methods of examination and of the continuous furnace should in the future provide economically better assured quality and properties for welded pipe.

Piping components (fittings) have been standardized as to dimensions and thickness for economic production and availability. These items may be fabricated from pipe, tubing, forgings, castings, or machined from bar stock or they may be fabricated from pressed or rolled plate parts by welding. Non-destructive examination is not encouraged by the codes for A.S.A. standard cast fittings, which are accepted at the highest quality factor without specified examination. Fittings of wrought materials are sufficiently worked so that the likelihood of undetected inherent material defects is minimized; however, air-hardened or otherwise sensitive materials may crack in processing without detection unless non-destructively examined.

Regular square-headed bolts of carbon steel with hexagon nuts are used with flanged fittings of cast iron, the 150 lb. A.S.A. steel series, and sometimes with the 300 lb. A.S.A. series. Because of the greater susceptibility of carbon-steel bolting to abuse in tightening (because of its lower yield point) alloy bolting (usually stud bolt with two heavy hexagon pattern nuts) is used almost without exception in the process industries for the 300 lb. A.S.A. and higher series of flanged fittings.

Temperature-induced Brittleness. Seamless pipe, because of the inherent soundness required and attendant mill practice of drastic killing to provide a sound pierced cylinder, averagely possesses impact resistance superior to plate steel of the same analysis. Therefore, ambient service (down to −20°F.) involves little likelihood of low-energy fracture; further service indicates that normalized seamless pipe without impact tests could be used to −50°F. without undue hazard where the piping code requirements are not imposed. Pipe fabrication of plate must be treated similar to pressure vessels for comparable calculated risk.

With the sudden drop in temperature common in low-temperature services under emergency conditions or upset operation, a severe economic problem is posed. A fully conservative approach would require a wide use of material suitable for the lowest flow temperature which might enter lines normally operated at much higher temperature. An industry position is critically needed in this respect.*

* Refer to the preceding subsection on Pressure Vessels for comparable discussion of construction materials and their fabrication, especially heat-treatment, strength enhancement, and corrosion allowance. Attention is also directed to A.S.M.E. Paper 57 PET-32 covering proposed balanced classes of fabri-

When ordered by schedule, the actual available **allowance for corrosion** is usually greater than the specified minimum because of the excess available in the pipe minimum wall thickness as compared with the required. When this excess thickness of the pipe run is used as part of the reinforcement of branch connections, the thermal-expansion stress range at this location must be evaluated on the basis of reduced structural capacity. Installation stresses may also cause localized yielding and initiation of defects in these areas. Certain fittings and valves have excess thickness for manufacturing purposes, and even where corrosion allowance is not specifically provided, some reduction in thicknesses can be tolerated.

Because of the larger number of piping items, and wider employment of alloy steels and alloys, **material identification** presents a real hazard. Many instances have been experienced with unintentional interchanges of materials. Some of these errors originate within the material storage at mills and warehouses but more often they occur during fabrication and erection. Positive identification of each component is possible when positive simplified checks reflecting analysis or properties are available. When the cost of such analysis is considered excessive, spot checks will serve to focus continuous alertness against interchanges of materials. Other means which have been applied to materials identification include the thermopile tester, portable X-ray diffraction, portable spectroscope, and magnetic and spark tests.

Fabrication Requirements. The fabrication of piping suffers from inadequate and illogical code requirements and the lack of organized industry effort toward overcoming the basic characteristics of pipe which prevent realization of material potential capabilities.

Bends are conventionally specified for a 5 diameter radius (*i.e.*, bend radius = 5 × nominal diameter of pipe) which, without deformation of the pipe axis, extends the outside of the bend 10 per cent and upsets the inside an equivalent amount. Longitudinal welds are usually positioned on the neutral axis to minimize their deformation. Smaller-radii bends down to 2⅓ and 3 diameters can be formed, with 3 diameters involving 16⅔ per cent deformation and greatly increased hazard of non-uniform plastic flow or deformation of the cross section. With hot-formed bends, the pipe is usually filled with sand, or resin for copper. In bending, the pipe is subjected as a cantilever to a lateral end load with movement limited by contacting forms, shoes, or pins. Cold bends within the available force and material ductility can be similarly formed but are usually made on special bend machines, with enforced standardization of dimension.

Branch connections can seriously impair the static strength (by undetected cracking during welding or under initial loading) or the fatigue life of piping systems. Because of the small diameter, accurately cut and scarfed holes can be assured only by automatic machines or by highly experienced operators working on holes laid out with metal templates, and with scarfing controlled by a position jig. Unless the pipe run is rigidly clamped, distortion will occur in burning and will be further aggravated by the subsequent welding. This problem becomes increasingly acute as the branch size increases relative to the run diameter. For this reason built-up branch connections of large relative size are often prohibited and tees are used instead.

The structural performance of a branch connection is greatly dependent on the fit-up of the reinforcing plate and its effect on the attachment welds.

cated piping, which provides requirements for successive levels of material refinement and fabrication.

Presently, the code does not require that branch connections be non-destructively examined or that such built-up and non-examined construction be limited by geometry or on difficult-to-weld materials.

Welded Construction. Many types of welds* mentioned in the code, as well as others in common use, include the lap sleeve and lap bell and spigot, which are similar to the fillet-welded socket joint and the one employed on thin tubing in limited service. Also included are the partial-penetration weld for minimum service made without root gap and deposited from relatively large electrodes, as well as butt welds of the several levels of refinement (*i.e.*, classes as discussed in A.S.M.E. paper 57 PET-32). The presentation of these classes emphasizes the dependence of weld quality (soundness, surfaces and structure, and attendant assured structural capacity) on end preparation, fit-up, strict adherence to procedures, competency of operators, adequacy of equipment as to type of condition, uniformity of power supply, chemistry of base materials, weld deposits and weld-rod coatings or shielding gas, the extent and adequacy of non-destructive examination, and adequate pre- and post-heat-treatment. Partial examination, as applied to individual welds, is a gamble and illogical. Random non-destructive examination permits a statistical control of average (not minimum) weld quality and as such is the logical intermediate between the so-called visual and non-destructive examination qualities.

Tolerances are significant in three respects: (1) in their influence on the weld deposit, (2) in their influence on continuity and surface stress intensification, and (3) in their influence on the installation cost and appearance. Welds of excessive width can result in excessive distortion or cracking, and welds between poorly aligned or too closely spaced edges are more susceptible to slag entrapment and unfusion, lack of penetration, or voids.

Displacement of the center thickness of abutting pipes or non-uniform thickness with attendant offset internal weld lips, and discontinuous inside or outside weld surfaces, will cause local stress intensification, which can reach appreciable magnitude.

Where the forming, alignment for welding, distortion, or component dimensions involve deviations from the specified geometry, unless corrected these are carried into the shop-prefabricated sections with adverse effect on the final assembly fit-up and dimensions. At the same time such careless fabrication can detract majorly from the appearance of the completed installation.

The A.S.A. Piping Code is concerned only with the tolerances which affect stress and fabrication effectiveness, and its treatment of such is very limited. The Pipe Fabrication Institute has attempted to establish precision tolerances for several levels of fabricated assembly but without reaching an agreement.

Steam-tracing and Jacketed Pipe. External protective heating is required where auxiliary or process flows during operation or during shutdowns must be controlled to avoid freezing or to maintain pumpable viscosity, or to prevent condensation and attendant metals corrosion or deterioration. Such heating must also be applied to instrument piping and to instruments adversely affected by low temperatures. This heat input may be accomplished by tracing, *i.e.*, incorporating a heating element next to or within the auxiliary or process pipe or next to the instrument tubing or instrument, or by a heated enclosure.

* Such welds are illustrated in Voelker and Peterson, "Fabrication Requirements for Balanced Classes of Piping," Table III, A.S.M.E. Paper 61-5A-60, June, 1961.

An adequate heat source for tracing such elements must reflect the availability and relative investment and operating costs of the necessary utilities and of the installed elements, as well as the minimum temperature which must be maintained. Low-pressure or exhaust steam is usually available and is widely used in a condensing system with traps. For higher temperatures, higher-pressure steam can be used either condensing or as sensible heat. Where the temperature must be closely controlled below 212°F., hot-water circulation is used, but at relatively low heat-transfer rates as compared with condensation. In recent years the use of **electric resistance heating** elements is increasing, with metal-tubing clad elements available for this purpose. Their use is particularly advantageous where the extent of tracing is limited or at widely separated locations.

For steam heating, ½ in. outside diameter by 0.032 in. wall copper tubing with flared-type fittings is widely used. Where the process temperature exceeds the strength temperature limit for copper (400° or 500°F. for tubing not in direct contact), either ½ in. IPS. standard-weight carbon-steel pipe with threaded or sleeve-welded joints, or ½ by 0.035 in. wall 304 stainless-steel tubing is used with compression-type fittings. Care must be taken to limit runs to assure drainage to traps and also to provide adequate vents. Pipe insulation is selected sufficiently oversize to clear the tracing element, and small lines are sometimes combined to minimize tracing. Usually a single element parallel to straight runs and curved at the mean radius around ells or bends is sufficient. For greater heat input the element can be in multiple, either with parallel or series runs, or can be spirally wrapped around the pipe. Still further heat input and closer control of temperature are possible by jacketing. Such jackets usually provide a 1 in. annular space and are applied to pipe sections with the jackets omitted at the flanges.

Cleaning of pipe at installation may involve only the removal of loose weld protrusions or spatter, weld-rod fragments, dirt, slag, or other material in order to minimize subsequent cleaning by circulation flow before service and further to assure against damage of rotating equipment or plugging of other equipment. Close supervision and inspection can minimize the extent of such damage but it has not proved entirely reliable. Favorable weld design and field procedures and the effective end protection of shop-cleaned assemblies could possibly achieve this objective. Currently it is advisable to blow air or steam at a velocity of 50 ft./sec. or more through each assembled piping system before making up the final bolted joint. Construction debris strainers should also be provided at all locations requiring protection and at other locations favoring its collection; such strainers should be continuously inspected and cleaned until they remain clean. Permanent service strainers should be provided at sensitive equipment, and when of a smaller mesh or perforation than the temporary strainers they should not be installed until the line is cleaned of debris.

ECONOMICS AND COSTS

To estimate piping costs, sufficient information must be available from plans, layouts, or engineering drawings to permit a materials take-off giving pipe size, length, weight, specification and fabrication quality requirements, number and type of fittings, flanges and valves. The detailed estimate must then take into account the cost of the materials and the cost of the various labor items involved in the fabrication, testing, shipping, erection, and inspection. Labor costs can vary widely with the location, competitive situation, and size of the job. This is particularly true for field labor costs and accurate estimating is dependent upon the assembly and logical use of extensive background data.

Many articles have been written in which the authors have outlined short-cut methods for estimating piping costs based on their own experience and approach. "Cost Engineering in the Process Industries" (McGraw-Hill, New York, 1960) contains articles of this type by W. C. Clark and R. A. Dickson. See also the latter's special chapter on Estimating in C. T. Littleton, "Industrial Piping" (McGraw-Hill, New York, 1951). Another type of approach to rough estimates is given by H. F. Rase in his article, Take Another Look at Economic Pipe Sizing [*Petrol. Refiner*, **32** (8), (August, 1953)].

Lines of carbon steel and of alloy not required to be post-heat-treated in sizes 2 in. and below are customarily fabricated at the site. Welded piping over 2 in. is usually shop-fabricated into sections which can be shipped, except that piping involving little or no fabrication (butt welds and branch connections only) as in yard and offsite work is shipped directly to the job site in random lengths. Labor costs are not related to linear footage but to the unit operations involved, which in turn are primarily associated with the number of joints, bends, and branch connections. Hence it is impractical to present a detailed rough estimating approach herein; however, the following may be of interest.

For very rough estimates on welded process unit piping, it is possible to develop an approximate "cost per pound" basis for the shop-fabricated portions, including cost of materials, on the basis that the average weight of flanges and fittings is a certain percentage of the total. The following represents such a rough index, based on 1961 prices, where the weight of flanges and fittings equals 25 per cent of the weight of the straight pipe:

Carbon steel	$0.35 per pound
1% chrome ½% moly steel	1.40 per pound
4 to 6% chrome ½% moly steel	1.80 per pound
Stainless steel type 304	2.25 per pound
Stainless steel type 316	2.80 per pound

These estimates are for seamless pipe in standard or extra strong wall thickness, with the fabricator's normal welding procedure and exclusive of bolts, gaskets, and valves. The cost for thinner wall pipe will be higher. The costs for carbon steel and stainless steel do not include any non-destructive examination or heat-treatment of welds. For furnace stress relieving of carbon steel one must add 3¢/lb. Costs for the chrome-molybdenum steels include stress relieving, radiographing of butt welds, and magnetic-particle examination of branch-attachment welds. Erected costs would have to include such additional items as shipping, field fabrication, assembly, and tests. Thus the total erected cost can easily be double the combined cost of material and shop fabrication, exclusive of insulation.

Far more accurate estimating information on cost of materials, fittings, valves, etc., can be obtained from manufacturers' catalogues with specialty items subject to discounts from published list prices. For shop-fabricated welded piping, United States fabricators have widely adopted the practice of bidding on a job by quoting unit prices for the various labor items involved and providing a tabulation of their list prices in their catalogues. In bidding on a job they may agree to a discount on these prices depending on the competitive situation. This provides a ready source of the data needed for estimating the cost of shop fabrication.

PROCESS PLANT DRIVERS

Drivers and their auxiliary equipment represent an appreciable portion of the original capital expenditure of a process plant as well as a considerable part of yearly operating costs. The **selection of drivers** is generally limited to commercially available equipment with the electric motor the most commonly used driver.

Hydraulic drivers have been considered when appreciable energy can be recovered from process liquids; however, except for a few applications (as in certain CO_2 absorption systems) economics do not justify their use.

While each type of driver has different operating characteristics, it is seldom that either a driver or the driven equipment cannot be modified to extend the range of usual application. For example, the addition of a torque converter to a gasoline engine may obtain the high-torque non-stalling characteristics of steam engines required in certain applications, such as drag lines; or the use of a suction valve with a motor-driven centrifugal compressor may duplicate the flexibility of a steam-turbine-driven compressor. As a rule, several types of drivers can be considered for a particular service and the selection of the optimum driver is simplified by first considering the economics and then evaluating savings against operational experience, reliability, and the characteristics of the various alternates. In other words, are the savings worth the complications and possible difficulties in operation?

Following is a convenient check list of cost factors to be considered:

1. Original investment cost prorated over plant "payout" time.
2. Additional investment to modify the driver, if necessary, to obtain the required characteristics.
3. Interest charges on total investment.
4. Fuel cost, crediting the driver with heat recovery. This should be carefully evaluated, since recoverable heat, normally wasted, can vary from 60 per cent of the fuel input for a modern Diesel to 80 per cent for a low-pressure steam plant or simple-cycle gas turbine.
5. Plant down time, but only that time required for periodic "shutdowns" to perform preventive maintenance, and then only when maintenance shutdowns cannot be made to coincide with regular plant turnarounds. If standby drivers are used they should be included as part of the investment cost.
6. Cost of utilities (water, electricity, etc.) including the prorated investment of providing these utilities (cooling towers, switchgear, etc.).
7. Lubrication and maintenance costs.
8. Cost of operating personnel.

In the economic evaluation involving different types of machines, trade practices and policies of the bidders must be considered. For example: (1) some steam-turbine companies guarantee that their turbines will have an efficiency equal to or greater than the guaranteed value, while others place a plus or minus tolerance on the guaranteed figure; (2) Diesel-engine performance is usually guaranteed on the basis of pounds of fuel consumed per horsepower-hour without specifying the type of oil; (3) gas engines are usually guaranteed on the basis of B.t.u. consumption per horsepower-hour, and although not clearly specified, it is understood to be on the basis of the lower heating value of methane; and (4) gas-turbine guarantees are subject to the same general vagueness.

The best practice to follow in determining optimum economics is to compare the various drivers on the cost in dollars of fuel for a minimum guarantee value which the seller agrees to equal or exceed.

The following descriptions of the principal types of drivers are limited to basic information necessary for selection considering process conditions and economics, and include characteristic features, industry usage, operating characteristics, potential for fuel economy and heat recovery, necessary safety equipment, essential auxiliaries, and other pertinent features of the drivers. Constructional detail, design details, and similar technically related aspects are avoided except when necessary to understand important differences in operational capabilities. Information available in manufacturers' catalogues or in mechanical-design books is not included.

INTERNAL-COMBUSTION ENGINES

Internal-combustion engines, the most popular prime movers, range in size from small portable gasoline engines to large (20,000 hp.) Diesels for ship propulsion. They are usually designed for particular industrial applications and to meet specific objectives as to weight per horsepower, reliability, and operating conditions.

All internal-combustion engines fall into two main types, namely, four-cycle and two-cycle engines. These engines may be further classified as (1) gasoline or gas engines (Otto cycle), in which a spark plug is used to ignite a premixed fuel-air mixture; (2) Diesel engines (Diesel cycle) in which high-pressure compression raises the air temperature to the ignition temperature of the injected fuel oil; (3) dual-fuel or gas-Diesel engines in which the fuel is a combination of gas and oil in any desired ratio, provided that at least 5 per cent oil is used at all times; and (4) trifuel engines, which can operate as dual-fuel or as straight gas engines by replacing the oil-injection system with a spark plug for ignition.

Design Characteristics

Internal-combustion engines involve consideration of the following design features: (1) **Compression ratio,** an increase of which usually increases engine efficiency but also results in higher average cycle temperatures and therefore hotter cylinders, piston heads, and rings, which increases the difficulty of piston lubrication. (2) **Piston speed,** which is a major over-all criterion of engine design since power rating is proportional to piston speed. Reciprocating forces and lubrication problems increase with piston speed. (3) **Brake mean effective pressure** b.m.e.p., which is an over-all measure of the output of an engine frame; b.m.e.p. increases with compression ratio and degree of supercharging, and in general, high values are associated with modern high-efficiency industrial engines. It is also an over-all criterion for bearing loadings and average piston head and cylinder temperature. (4) **Engine rating,** which is proportional to the product of piston speed and b.m.e.p. Acceptable values of piston speed and b.m.e.p. are more dependent on industrial usage than on the type of engine. (5) **Supercharging,** which connotes means for increasing the inlet manifold air pressure above ambient pressure. (6) **Turbocharging,** which applies to the expansion of the hot exhaust gases through a turbine to drive the supercharging compressor. Since power output is proportional to inlet manifold air pressure, supercharging provides increased power output, and usually higher efficiency. Highly supercharged engines may require an air cooler between the compressor and inlet manifold.

Engine size is usually in terms of power rating (horsepower), rather than the physical size of the engine frame. Frame size is determined by the diameter of the cylinder bore, length of stroke, and number of cylinders. The **power rating** of a given frame varies with industrial practice and usage; accordingly automobile engines are designed to develop between 0.54 and 0.95 hp./cu. in. of piston displacement, while industrial Diesels are limited to 0.045 to 0.175 hp./cu. in.

Engine rating reflects industrial practice. Automobile engine rating is the peak horsepower developed on a test stand, whereas industrial engine rating is usually in terms of continuous load.

Industrial engines are made in a wide variety of frame sizes, each offered at several power and speed ratings. The same engine frame might drive either a 900-kw. generator at 900 r.p.m. or a 600-kw. generator at 600 r.p.m., by using lighter pistons and special parts for the higher-speed application. An engine originally designed for 1000 hp. may be uprated to 1100 hp. by higher compression heads and further to 1320 hp. by supercharging. Thus one frame can cover a power range from 600 hp. (60 per cent speed) to 1320 hp. An engine frame can also be designed for different output by varying the number of cylinders; for example, a 10-cylinder 3500-hp engine will develop 2100 and 2800 hp. at the same efficiency with six and eight cylinders, respectively. This enables a manufacturer to use the same basic design, tools, and fixtures for a variety of ratings.

The published power rating of American industrial engines is usually at 1500 ft. above sea level and at a 90°F. air temperature. It is important that atmospheric conditions at the installation site be specified, since engines operate with very little excess combustion air and consequently the maximum power output is proportional to air density.

Operating Characteristics

The operating characteristics of internal-combustion engines are basically the same, regardless of fuel used or whether the engine is two- or four-cycle. To vary the speed and/or load-carrying capacity, which can range from zero to full torque for all speeds within the operating range, it is only necessary to vary the fuel input. Large engines use a governor to control the fuel-input rate and maintain constant speed under variations of load. With auxiliary instrumentation the governor can be used as a controller of power or process. Starting, stopping, and operation from a remote location are made possible by instrumentation that will also shut down an engine in the event of loss of cooling-water or lubricating-oil flow.

Starting is accomplished by rotating the engine at a speed sufficient to achieve ignition and self-sustained operation. Small engines are started with electric motors or smaller hand-starting engines and large engines are provided with special valving whereby some of the engine cylinders can be operated as air motors, utilizing high-pressure air to rotate the engine. Starting motors are usually sized at 5 to 10 per cent of the engine rating. Starting air requirements are ½ cu. ft. (free air)/hp. stored at a pressure of 250 to 300 lb./sq. in. gage. Usually three starts per successful firing are assumed for sizing the starting air compressor and air-storage vessel.

Operating characteristics of engines are also influenced by service requirements. Automotive engines must develop maximum torque at lower speeds for hill climbing; marine engines are required to develop full torque only when the propeller is at full speed; generator drivers run at a single speed and therefore require maximum possible efficiency at all loads for this speed; reciprocating compressors at constant pressure require full torque over the entire operating speed range, thus presenting an engine-instability problem at reduced speeds. The engine must be selected to meet these service requirements.

Supercharging is employed primarily to improve engine efficiency or power output, but the part load performance and rate of response to load changes depend on the type of supercharging system used. Some systems result in supercharged engines having the same torque-speed characteristics and rate of response to load changes as non-supercharged engines, while other systems result in poorer or better response and in different speed-torque characteristics.

Maintenance and Reliability. Preventive maintenance requires that all engines be shut down at periodic intervals for inspection and repair. For properly maintained heavy-duty engines the availability is over 97 per cent, with maintenance costs of $1 to $2 per horsepower-year, and lubricating-oil consumption of 1 to 2 gal./hp.-year.* While this represents a high degree of reliability, the outages of heavy-duty engines are more frequent than those of electric motors or steam turbines.

Satisfactory engine performance is assured by maintaining a log that allows comparison of present characteristics with past records of (1) cylinder exhaust, cooling water, and supercharger exhaust temperature for similar loadings, (2) running sounds and smokiness of exhaust, and (3) engine efficiency and losses.

The minimum safety devices for an industrial engine are a governor and separate overspeed and low-oil-pressure trips. Engines operating in non-supervised areas should be arranged to shut down in the event of cooling-water or lubricating-oil failures, and for excessive exhaust or jacket water temperatures. Engines operating in supervised areas should be provided with instruments for the operator to check performance.

Fuel Characteristics. Fuels used in industrial engines of the internal-combustion type are usually derivatives of petroleum, or else natural or manufactured gases. Alcohols and mixtures of gasoline and alcohol or benzol can also be used. A gas engine will operate satisfactorily on any gas which is free of dust, non-corrosive (*i.e.*, less than 60 grains H_2S per 100 cu. ft.), does not detonate, does not preignite during compression stroke, and produces enough heat on burning to develop power.

In general the fuel must have a heat capacity of over 600 B.t.u./cu. ft. Gasoline engines require in addition that the fuel will vaporize in the carburetor. Diesels will burn any fuel that can be injected, provided that it will burn under controlled conditions, possesses sufficient lubricity to lubricate the injection plungers, will supply enough heat, and is grit-free, containing less than 3 per cent sulfur, 70 p.p.m. vanadium, and 125 p.p.m. vanadium pentoxide. Most Diesel engines use either number 2 or number 5 fuel oils. The latter must be heated to a viscosity of 50 to 70 S.S.U. (250°F. approximately) for proper injector lubrication and injection characteristics.

Gaseous fuels containing fractions whose ignition temperature is lower than that of methane may require the use of low compression heads and a resulting derating of the gas engine.

The method of reporting fuel consumption varies among the different industries and also among countries. Trade associations usually have recommended procedures. Thus the Diesel Engine Manufacturers Association (United States) calculates efficiencies based on the LHV for gas fuels and the HHV for oil fuels. It is general practice to report gas-engine performance in terms of B.t.u./hp.-hr. (LHV) and oil-engine performance in terms of pounds of fuel consumed per horsepower-hour. For electric power plants, fuel consumption is reported

* For further details of industrial operating costs see "Annual Oil and Gas Engine Power Costs," published by the American Society of Mechanical Engineers. Engine manufacturers will also supply recommended schedules for preventive maintenance.

in terms of kilowatts. The auxiliaries included with engine-efficiency calculations vary with industry practice.

Fuel Economy and Heat Recovery. The high efficiencies obtained by modern high-compression supercharged Diesels or gas engines can be approached only by very large high-pressure reheat steam plants or by very complicated gas-turbine cycles. The following efficiencies (LHV) based on methane fuel for gas engines and oil fuel for Diesel engines can be used for estimating fuel consumption: 85 to 400 hp., 28 per cent; 440 to 800 hp., 32 per cent; 800 to 3000 hp., 36 per cent; over 3300 hp., 38 per cent.

Plant fuel costs chargeable to power production can be reduced where the heat losses can be utilized to provide process or other heating. Engine heat losses as percentages of heat input (LHV) are (1) lubricating-oil cooling, 5 to 7 per cent available at 165°F.; (2) jacket cooling, 17 to 30 per cent available as 165°F. water, or with vapor-phase cooling as 15 lb./sq. in. gage steam; (3) engine exhaust gases, 26 to 30 per cent available with approximately half of this at sufficient temperature to generate 100 lb./sq. in. gage steam in waste-heat boilers.

Vapor-phase cooling reduces the cost of the cooling system, increases heat recovery, and may result in improved engine efficiency.

At full speed the fuel consumption decreases linearly with reduction in load, becoming at zero load almost one-third to one-fourth of full-load consumption and with no potential for heat recovery in the exhaust. Jacket-water heat losses decrease 20 to 40 per cent at zero load. The fuel consumption at rated torque is almost proportional to speed. At half speed the exhaust recovery decreases to less than half and jacket-water cooling becomes more than half of the full-torque values.

Installation and Costs

An engine installation includes auxiliary equipment necessary for operation, such as lubrication pumps and attendant storage, filtering and cooling equipment; jacket-water pumps with expansion tank and cooler; starting-air tanks and compressors; inlet-air piping and screens; exhaust air piping and silencers or waste-heat boilers; a fuel system, which in the case of Diesels would include a day tank, filters, pumps, heaters, and a main storage tank; ignition system or fuel-injection plungers; and cooling towers or radiators. Diesel engines operating on heavy residual fuel oils would have two-fuel systems, a heavy-fuel-oil system for normal operation and a light-fuel-oil system for starting and stopping.

Pipe-line and marine installations are frequently arranged so that the engine drives all its auxiliaries from the crankshaft by means of chains and V belts. But process plant practice is to have all the auxiliaries independently driven, using standby pumps to minimize engine down time.

Foundations should be designed to control **vibrating motion** resulting from reciprocating masses. Engine manufacturers will recommend the size of the foundation, but usually their recommendations do not take soil properties into account and are based on making the combined engine and foundation weight sufficiently large to limit the vibration. When possible foundations should be separate from the building structure. In many cases vibration of the engine will cause no damage; nevertheless it is good practice to reduce it whenever possible. Even though vibration does not increase any forces in the engine, it can result in loosening pipe joints, nuts, etc.

Torsional vibration can also be a problem and results from pressure variations in the cylinders which can produce cyclic torques with harmonics ranging from half speed to ten or twelve times the running speed. To avoid operating difficulties the torsional critical frequencies of the combined engine and driven equipment should be calculated or measured to assure that the operating speeds are removed from these criticals or that vibration dampers are provided or that the equipment is designed for the resulting cyclic stresses.

The costs of both engines and auxiliaries are reasonably consistent on the basis of dollars per horsepower, so long as the essential details are the same. Published figures on **installed engine costs** are often misleading, since with supercharging more power output can be obtained from the same size engine, which also reduces cooling-water and foundation requirements. Pipe-line compressor costs frequently include piping, buildings, etc.; and in some process plants cooling water which has been used and charged against process operation can be reused for engine cooling at no cost. It is obvious that general cost predictions must be used with caution unless their detail basis is known. However, as preliminary figures, the following are suggested:

Integral engine compressors:	
Uninstalled and without auxiliaries	$120/hp.
Installed cost with auxiliaries and cooling water	$200/hp.
Installed costs of large units with cooling water supplied from process units	$185/hp.
Diesel or gas-engine generators:	
Uninstalled	$100/kw.
Installed	$175–$200/kw.

Table 24-28 gives costs for engine installation, which can be prorated to make preliminary estimate of installation costs.

Table 24-28. Comparative Installation Costs of Integral-engine Compressors for Pipe-line Stations and Process Plants

Assuming 10 units for total of 1400 hp.

	Pipe-line station	Process plant
A. Land and improvements	$ 194,500	$ 28,700
B. Structures	384,100	205,000
C. Testing	15,000	15,000
D. Equipment	2,887,000	2,145,000
Subtotal	$3,480,600	$2,393,700
Add 10% for overhead and undistributed field costs	348,100	239,370
Subtotal	$3,828,700	$2,633,070
Add 5% for contingencies	191,300	Not used
Total	$4,020,000	$2,633,070
Cost per horsepower	$ 287	$ 188

FREE-PISTON GAS GENERATOR

The free-piston gas generator is a relatively simple device that uses "bounce cylinders" to return two power pistons to their starting positions. The power pistons form a highly supercharged variable-stroke opposed-piston type of Diesel engine in which each power piston drives an air-compressor piston to produce pressurized air from which a turbine develops power. Industrial installations began in 1951 with an electric power plant using free-piston gas generators to drive a turbine. Succeeding applications include pumping stations, petrochemical-plant drivers, locomotive drivers, and marine-propulsion units.

Design Characteristics

The characteristics of the power turbine are similar to those of steam turbines as discussed later in this section. The air compressor of the gasifier is similar to a reciprocating air compressor and differs only in higher piston speeds. The power cylinders form a two-cycle opposed-piston Diesel engine, differing only in the elimination of the crankshaft.

Table 24-29. Approximate Heat Balance for Gas Engines*

Manifold type	Two cycle				Four cycle			
	Wet†		Dry†		Atmospheric wet		Supercharged dry	
	B.t.u./hp.	%	B.t.u./hp.	%	B.t.u./hp.	%	B.t.u./hp.	%
Heat input (LHV)	7200	....	6900	....	7700	....	6200	
Work	2545	35.4	2545	36.9	2545	33.1	2545	41.0
Jacket	1700	23.6	1200	17.4	2200	28.6	1250	20.2
Lube oil	460	6.4	500	7.2	450	5.8	300	4.8
Exhaust	2095	29.1	1795	26.0	2300	29.9	1685	27.2
Radiation	400	5.5	860	12.5	205	2.6	200	3.2
Combustion	....	....	....	....	....	....	220	3.5

* Courtesy of Cooper Bessemer Corp.
† Wet type refers to water-cooled manifolds and dry type refers to air-cooled manifolds.

Absence of crankshaft provides the free-piston gas generator with certain unique characteristics, namely, variable piston stroke and piston speed that is independent of the turbine or other power output. While the crankshaft elimination avoids high bearing loads, it does not avoid the problem of high average cycle temperatures present in highly supercharged engines. In present designs, the power cylinders are water-jacketed and large amounts of oil are circulated to cool the pistons and minimize ring wear.

Potentially, a free-piston turbine plant can operate at an efficiency higher than that of a Diesel; however, this is accomplished only at extremely high supercharging pressures, which result in poor ring life. Early failures were probably due to seeking ultimate efficiencies. Present models have a fuel consumption of 0.38 to 0.40 lb./b.hp.-hr., which is considered a good efficiency although higher than corresponding values for Diesel engines.

While several sizes have been made for specific services such as contractors' and navy torpedo compressors, the size commercially available for process plants is the GS 34 developed by the French company, SIGMA, and licensed to several manufacturing companies throughout the world, including General Motors in the United States. This model develops a turbine power of 1000 hp. in the single unit and 2000 hp. in the twinned unit.

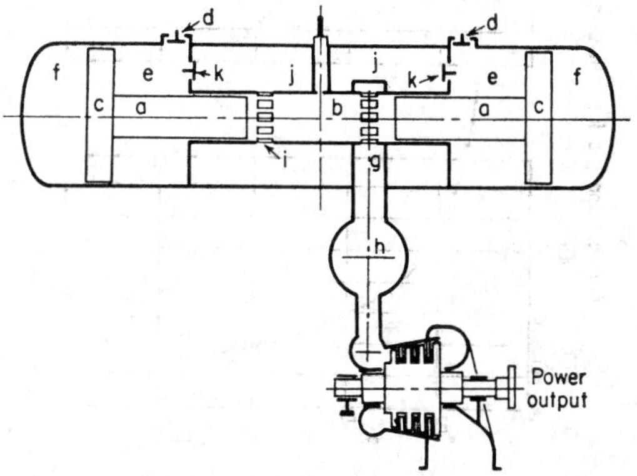

FIG. 24-32. Free piston compressor. When pistons (*a*) are at their innermost position, fuel oil is injected into power cylinder (*b*); resulting rise in pressure in the power cylinder (*b*) forces the power pistons (*a*) and the air-compressor piston (*c*) in an outward direction drawing air through valves (*d*) into the air-compressor cylinder (*e*) and at the same time compressing air in the bounce cylinder (*f*). Near the end of the piston stroke, the exhaust ports (*g*) are uncovered, allowing products of combustions to flow outward through pipe (*h*) to the power turbine. Further movement of the power piston uncovers the air-inlet ports (*i*) allowing air to flow from chamber (*j*) into power cylinder (*b*) through the exhaust ports and to the power turbine via exhaust pipe (*h*). The power cylinder (*b*) now has a charge of fresh air. The pressure in bounce cylinders (*f*) returns the two power pistons (*a*) and their connected air compressor cylinders (*c*) toward center, the inward movement of the air-compressor piston (*c*) discharging the air through valves (*k*) into chamber (*j*). The inward movement of power pistons (*a*) compresses the air in the power cylinder (*b*), making it ready for a new power stroke.

Operating Characteristics

The operating cycle is described in Fig. 24-32. In essence, a free-piston gasifier (or compressor) is a spring-mass system, with the air in the bounce cylinder providing the spring effect and the pistons the mass. The spring-mass ratio determines the speed in strokes per minute. Idling speeds of 400 cycles/min. are attained at low bounce-cylinder pressures and speeds of 600 cycles/min. at full pressure. Varying the fuel input changes the available forces and results in a change of the piston stroke and speed, which determines the amount of air that is compressed.

In a simple system consisting of one gasifier and one turbine, the amount of fuel can be decreased, from full power requirements down to a point where the free-piston compressor becomes unstable. Any further reductions in power can be obtained only by using a split-range controller that vents gas to the atmosphere. The split-range controller may operate on turbine speed or on some process factor such as flow or pressure.

In large single-turbine plants each gasifier is usually connected to a separate group of first-stage turbine nozzles. To decrease power output, fuel input can be lowered to all the gasifiers, or successive gasifiers can be shut down to maintain high efficiency performance from the gasifiers left in operation. Blowoff valves are used for transient part-load operation.

In large multiturbine installations the gasifiers discharge into a common header whose pressure is maintained by a split-range pressure controller which positions the fuel racks and the blowoff valves. Each turbine is controlled by its governor which throttles the gas as required.

In each case, the operating characteristics depend on the control arrangement. When the gasifier is controlled by a back-pressure controller and the turbine by its own governor, the performance of the power turbine is similar to that of a steam turbine operating on constant-pressure steam. Gasifiers controlled by a turbine governor respond quickly to power swings as changes in fuel setting vary the length of the next stroke. The only lag in response is the interval required to pressurize the gas header.

Reduction of the gasifier output pressure results in reduced turbine output power and at the same time in lower mean effective pressures, which increase ring life. Conversely, an increase in pressure results in more turbine power and shorter ring life but will not stall the gasifiers until high back pressures are attained. Almost all the work output of the power pistons is absorbed by the air-compressing pistons. At normal output pressures the air compressor discharges excess air through the power cylin-

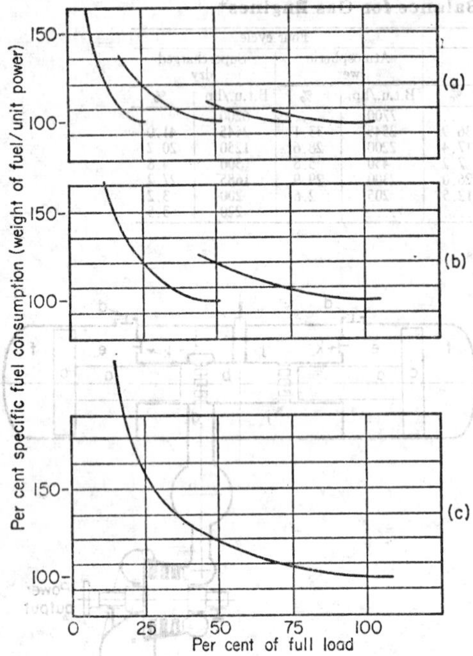

FIG. 24-33. Changes in specific fuel consumption as a function of load. Note: 100 per cent indicates full rate at full load. Graphs (*a*) and (*b*) are for four and two gasifiers, respectively, connected to different turbine nozzles. Graph (*c*) is for one gasifier connected to a turbine.

ders. At high back pressure the volumetric efficiency of the compressor decreases, resulting in less air to the power cylinders. The engine continues to operate with increasing back pressure until a stalling pressure is reached. Figure 24-33 shows curves for per cent fuel consumption vs. per cent of full load.

Installation and Operation

Inertia forces are balanced by the two pistons moving simultaneously in opposite directions, thus minimizing foundation requirements and without a crankshaft, mechanical torsional vibrations do not exist. The pulsating gas outflow involves the same problems as encountered with reciprocating compressors in exciting vibrations with possible resonance in connected piping.

With a single gasifier serving a turbine the pressure fluctuation can excite torsional vibrations in the turbine and driven equipment. To avoid resonance the torsional critical frequencies of the turbine and driven equipment must differ from the frequencies of the exciting forces which are multiples of the strokes per minute. The exciting frequencies of multigasifier installations range from a condition when all units fire simultaneously, through various patterns involving spaced firing between units.

To date there have been no reports of torsional problems; however, there are still only a few installations. It may be that the torsional criticals of the systems have been above the exciting frequencies and that such trouble will not develop until larger machines are used. It is also possible that the pressure pulsations are sufficiently random and will not sustain critical vibrations. The degree of randomness could be contributed to differences in short stroking, degree of scavenging, and the operating speeds of the individual gasifiers. For the present it would appear desirable to limit the magnitude of pressure fluctuations by the design of piping headers or by the use of snubbers.

Gasifiers must be shut down for periodic maintenance; and the percentage availability of a single unit appears to be lower than that of a Diesel. However, the drivers have the high availabilities usual with turbines, and the use of standby gasifiers will therefore result in a high degree of availability for a complete plant.

Almost no published data are available on the cost of gasifier-turbine installations and the necessary auxiliaries. However, it can be assumed that they are competitive with those of Diesels and steam plants.

Fuels and Heat Recovery. The products of combustion from the gasifier contain as much as 15 per cent oxygen (by volume). This oxygen can be used in firing a pressurized boiler ahead of the turbine, or in an atmospheric-pressure boiler in the turbine exhaust. It is also possible simply to heat the gases and thus achieve higher turbine-power output. These arrangements result in higher-efficiency plants, but at an increased investment cost.

Heat recovery from cooling-water and lubricating-oil circuits is limited to low temperatures (120°F.), which are much lower than for Diesels.

Most installations use number 2 Diesel fuels and some report successful use of heavier fuels. Higher air pressure favors more complete combustion, and some authorities therefore contend that a gasifier can burn heavier oils than a Diesel. This favorable pressure condition is partly offset, however, by the short combustion time resulting from high piston speeds. Until further experience is gathered it appears desirable that fuel oils meet the same specifications as those used by Diesel engines.

The required **safety devices and instruments** for the gasifier are the same as those required for Diesels except that overspeed protection is not involved, and instead, overstroking must be prevented. The exhaust system may require relief valves, while safety devices and controls for the turbine would be similar to those used for steam turbines.

STEAM TURBINES

A steam turbine is probably the most flexible driver available to industry. With the advent of modern precision gears, turbine speeds are seldom below 1200 r.p.m. and may be as high as 25,000 r.p.m. Radial-flow units operating at still higher speeds (50,000 r.p.m.) have been used in the refrigeration of process gases. Most designs are for a single speed either to drive electric generators or to operate over a limited speed range for industrial applications. Turbines developing full torque at reduced speeds may require special design considerations. Marine turbines are built with reversing stages to go from ahead to reverse rotation.

Turbines can utilize steam at very low pressures or as high as 5000 lb./sq. in. The exhaust can be any pressure lower than the inlet that will economically develop power, and in modern power plants this is frequently as low as 1 in. Hg absolute. Turbines can be used as pressure-reducing stations, taking steam at one level and exhausting it at a lower-pressure level, thus developing power and reducing steam temperature. In modernizing old utility plants, a new high-pressure boiler and a "topping turbine" can provide additional power and furnish steam to the original turbines with increased over-all plant efficiency.

Design Characteristics. **Sizes** are based on shaft power, in terms of horsepower for mechanical-drive turbines, and in kilowatts for turboelectric generators. Frame size depends on the number and types of stages,

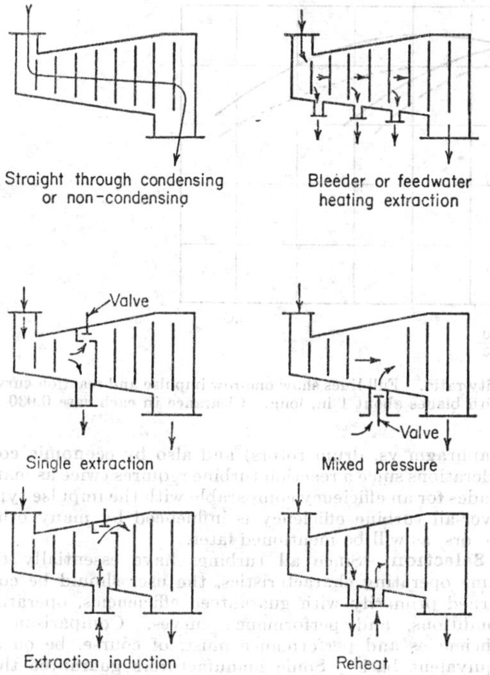

FIG. 24-34. Design features of various turbine types.

blade lengths, and wheel diameters. Physical size alone does not indicate the power rating, since the power output of a frame is proportional to steam-pressure level.

Turbines are built in power outputs from fractional horsepower up to 500,000 kw. In the larger sizes, a turbine may consist of several different casings in series, *i.e.*, a high-pressure turbine, an intermediate-pressure turbine, and a single- or double-flow low-pressure turbine. Regardless of the number of casings, an installation is considered a single turbine as long as it is controlled by a single governor. Each unit of the turbine may have its own overspeed trips, or special safety devices including those used for reheat installations.

Process plant drivers are seldom large enough or use a high enough steam pressure to justify more than one turbine casing. The following types of turbines are commonly used in process industries:

1. **Straight-through turbines** have only one inlet and one exhaust steam connection, either single or multistage.
2. **Bleeder turbines** are multistage turbines with outlets at one or more of the stages, so that steam may be bled and used for boiler feed water heating or process requirements.
3. **Extraction turbines** are bleeder turbines with the bleed pressure controlled and thus they constitute essentially two or more turbines in a single casing.
4. **Mixed-pressure turbines** have a governor admitting steam to the low-pressure end of a turbine and another governor admitting enough high-pressure steam to the high-pressure end to carry the load.
5. An **extraction-induction turbine,** is a combination mixed-pressure–extraction turbine, in that it can either supply or use low-pressure steam.

In all these casing arrangements (see Fig. 24-34) the turbines may be condensing (exhausting to a condenser) or back-pressure exhausting to process or other uses.

Types and Performance. Turbines may consist of one stage or a group of stages in series or sometimes in parallel. Three basic types of stages are used (see Fig. 24-35). These are (1) the **Curtis** stage (velocity-compounded), in which the entire pressure drop occurs in the nozzle and energy is recovered from the steam by two rotating bladed wheels having turning vanes between them (three-row Curtis stages have also been built); (2) the **Rateau** stage (impulse- or pressure-compounded), in which the entire pressure drop also occurs in the stationary nozzle but only a single set of rotating blades per stage is used; and (3) the **Parsons** stage (reaction), in which the pressure drop occurs partly across the stationary nozzles and partly across the rotating blades.

The over-all characteristics of Curtis, Rateau, and Parsons stages are essentially similar. At a certain ratio of blade speed to jet speed u/c each type has a maximum

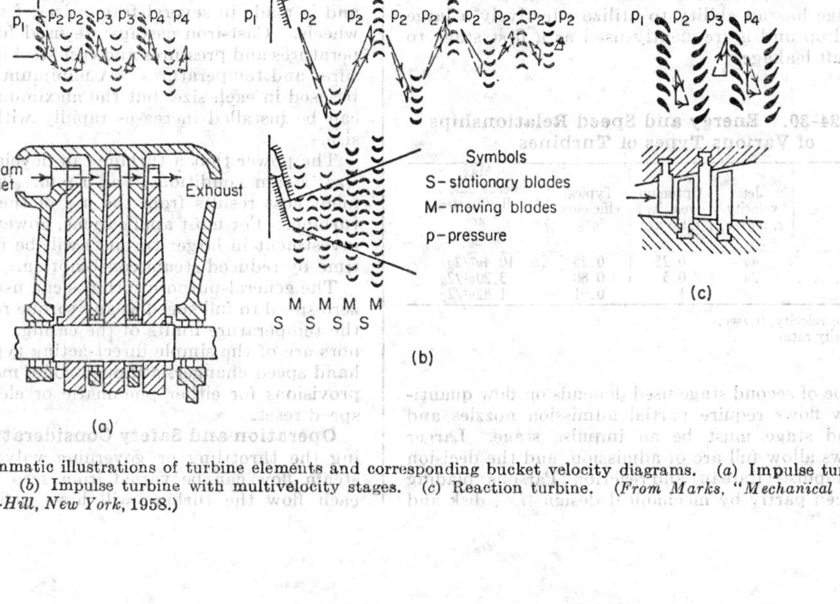

FIG. 24-35. Diagrammatic illustrations of turbine elements and corresponding bucket velocity diagrams. (*a*) Impulse turbine with single-velocity stage. (*b*) Impulse turbine with multivelocity stages. (*c*) Reaction turbine. (*From Marks, "Mechanical Engineers' Handbook," McGraw-Hill, New York,* 1958.)

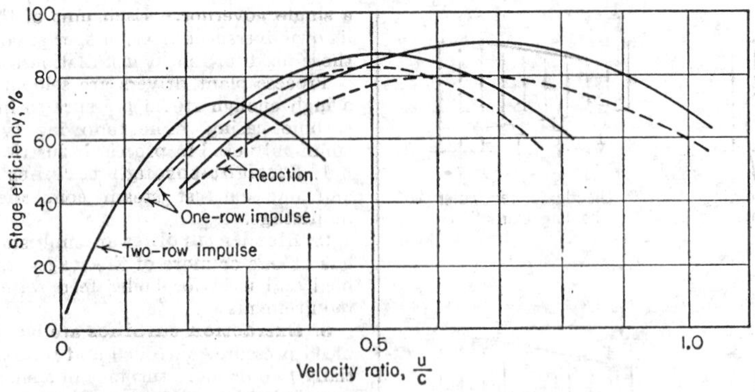

Fig. 24-36. Variation of the efficiency of turbine elements with the velocity ratio. Full lines show one-row impulse and reaction curves with blades 6 in. long and greater. Dotted curves show comparison with blades about 1 in. long. Clearance in each case 0.030 in.

efficiency (see Fig. 24-36). Above this speed, efficiency and torque decrease, becoming zero at twice the optimum efficiency speed; and below this speed the torque increases to become double the maximum efficiency torque at zero speed while the efficiency decreases to zero at zero speed. Torque can be plotted as a straight-line function of r.p.m. and efficiency as a parabola of r.p.m. While all types have similar characteristic curves, there are large differences in the amount of energy that can be absorbed by each type of stage and in the efficiency obtainable at the optimum speed ratio, as shown in Table 24-30.

Other types of stages include (1) the **reentry** stage, a variation of the **Curtis** in which a single-bladed wheel serves as the first and second stages, using return passages to redirect the steam; (2) the **Terry** turbine, a special type of reentry turbine which has tangential slots milled around the wheel periphery to form the blades and uses helical-type reentry passages; (3) the **Ljunsgtrom** turbine, not now built in the United States, consisting of two contrarotating disks, each supporting groups of axial blades, with steam flow in a radial direction (power is obtained from both shafts); (4) certain other types of radial stages which will be covered separately.

Except for double-flow turbines, the first stage of a turbine loses steam by leakage along the shaft to the atmosphere. The amount of steam lost is proportional to the absolute pressure at the first-stage wheels. A Curtis stage has an ability to utilize effectively a large pressure drop and is frequently used as a first stage to reduce shaft leakage.

Table 24-30. Energy and Speed Relationships of Various Types of Turbines

Type	Jet velocity c, ft./sec.	Optimum velocity ratio u/c	Typical efficiency e%	Max. energy output, ft.-lb./lb. steam, $\frac{ec^2}{2g}$
Curtis	$4u$	0.25	0.25	$10.4u^2/2g$
Impulse	$2u$	0.5	0.80	$3.20u^2/2g$
Reaction	u	1	0.91	$1.82u^2/2g$

u = blade velocity, ft./sec.
u/c = velocity ratio

The type of second stage used depends on flow quantities. Low flows require partial admission nozzles and the second stage must be an impulse stage. Larger steam flows allow full arc of admission, and the decision between impulse (Rateau) and reaction (Parsons) blading is influenced partly by mechanical design (*i.e.*, disk and diaphragm vs. drum rotors) and also by economic considerations since a reaction turbine requires twice as many blades for an efficiency comparable with the impulse type. Over-all turbine efficiency is influenced by many other factors, as will be mentioned later.

Selection. Since all turbines have essentially the same operating characteristics, the user should be concerned primarily with guaranteed efficiencies, operating conditions, and performance curves. Comparison of efficiencies and performance must, of course, be on an equivalent basis. Some manufacturers guarantee that turbine performance will be equal to or greater than the quoted value. Others allow a plus or minus variation. At part loads, reaction blades, because of their greater ability to utilize "carry-over," may show better efficiencies.

Turbines for electric power generation are designed for operation at only one speed and under *standard* steam conditions. Process drivers, usually known as mechanical-drive turbines, have to meet a wide variety of speed and steam conditions, and about the only standardization that can be effected is in blading and casing patterns. The casings are usually selected from a series of high-pressure ends, intermediate spool pieces, and exhaust ends that can be bolted together in a variety of combinations.

The most frequently used steam turbine is the **single-stage mechanical-drive turbine,** which is low in cost and is made in several frame sizes, from 9- up to 24-in. wheels. Cast-iron casings are used for low steam temperatures and pressures and cast steel for the higher pressures and temperatures. A minimum of one nozzle can be used in each size, but the maximum nozzle area that can be installed increases rapidly with increased frame size.

The power that a turbine can develop is a function of size, steam conditions, and r.p.m. The lowest investment cost results from the use of the smallest possible turbine. For most applications, however, the additional investment in larger turbines will be paid for in a short time by reduced steam consumption.

The general-purpose turbines can usually operate from zero speed to full speed at any torque requirement within the temperature limits of the casing. The speed governors are of the simple direct-acting type, with at least a hand speed changer, although some models may include provisions for either pneumatic or electrically actuated speed reset.

Operation and Safety Considerations. By adjusting the throttling or governing valve the quantity of steam flow can be varied from zero to full flow. For each flow the turbine will have definite speed-torque characteristics, and a turbine will speed up until its torque is equal to that required by the driven equipment. If greater torque and speed are required the governor opening is increased to give more steam flow. Most turbines will burst at their "runaway" speed, and as a result the user seldom changes the governing valve directly. The preferred procedure is to reset the speed setting of the governor and let it change the valve.

Turbines without governing valves are used under special situations. For example, where (1) the speed of a turbocharger turbine depends on the gas flow through an engine (*i.e.*, engine r.p.m.) and failure of the supercharging compressor will cause the engine to shut down; (2) turbines driving the lubrication-oil pumps of a larger turbine are frequently designed for "runaway" speeds; (3) gas-turbine governors vary fuel rate and hence the speed.

Turbines can be installed with the necessary supervisory instrumentation to start up automatically and to shut down in the event of malfunction or failures. Failure of lubricating oil automatically shuts the trip throttle valve. In addition, trips can be connected to vibration-detecting devices and temperature detectors in the inlet and exhaust piping.

A turbine has maximum available torque at zero speed and therefore the load does not have to be disconnected during startup. The preferred **starting procedure** is to warm up the lubricating oil system by first placing it in operation. Then the turbine should be warmed up gradually by opening the throttle valve to bring the speed up slowly as the turbine warms up. This procedure minimizes the possibility of turbine "rubs." Some of the smaller multistage turbines used as process drivers can be started quickly when occasion demands it. The shutdown procedure of large turbines is critical and the rotors are turned slowly while the casing cools to prevent hot spots that might cause "kinking" of the shaft.

A turbine can operate satisfactorily with the moisture that forms naturally in the stages, provided the casing is drained to prevent accumulation. The inlet-steam piping should be designed to provide dry steam to the turbine nozzle since a slug of moisture can knock out blades and/or thrust bearings.

Solids carried over from the boiler drum are deposited principally in turbine nozzles, resulting in lower turbine output. Their presence can be detected by higher than normal interstage pressures. These deposits can be washed out by injecting water into the turbine while it is running, but under conditions prescribed by the manufacturer to prevent turbine damage.

It is good practice to inspect turbines periodically, but the interval between shutdowns for thorough **inspection** is longer than those for other plant elements. Annual boiler inspections or the cleaning of heat exchangers in a chemical plant are often appropriate occasions. A steam turbine is generally considered to have 100 per cent availability, with longer than a year between shutdowns, provided its performance is periodically checked.

Most important is the checking of the safety features that have been incorporated to protect the turbine. For example, the operation of overspeed trips can be checked by using these to shut down the turbine. Many continuous process drivers cannot be shut down, and these safety features can only be checked during plant turnarounds.

The only **preventive maintenance** required is to (1) keep the oil clean, at the correct temperature, and at the right level in the oil reservoir; and (2) inspect and check auxiliaries such as lubricating-oil pumps, coolers, and oil strainers; (3) inspect turbine parts during the annual turnaround; and (4) check safety devices.

Heat Recovery. Since two-thirds of the heat entering the turbine leaves in the steam exhaust, with other losses minor, the major improvement in thermal efficiency results from the use of exhaust and/or extraction steam for heating, process, or other purposes. The smallest amount of steam that can be used for heating purposes is that required for heating boiler feed water.

Both turbine plant efficiencies and investment costs increase with increasing steam pressures and temperatures and higher exhaust vacuums. N.E.M.A. (National Electric Manufacturers Association) has recommended pressure and temperature levels for electric power plants, which can be used as an over-all guide in process plants. But because such plants may use steam for process heating at several pressure levels and also require a variety of driver sizes, unique solutions must usually be worked out for each installation.

Turbine steam consumption can be decreased by superheating. The energy available (B.t.u./lb.) for given inlet and exhaust pressures is proportional to the absolute inlet steam temperature. Frequently economics justify the addition of superheaters to waste-heat boiler installations.

As a general rule the vacuum attainable for condensing turbines is based on summer-weather data. In high-fuel-cost areas consideration should be given to the turbine being able to use the lower-vacuum conditions produced during the other seasons of the year.

Where turbines operate over a wide variation of speed and/or conditions, the number of operating hours for each condition should be carefully determined or estimated in specifying the equipment for purchase.

Turbines that operate over a wide load change should have first-stage nozzle area control. Economics do not ordinarily justify controlling the nozzle areas of the other stages, except for extraction or mixed-pressure turbines where nozzle area control of the first stage in the low-pressure parts can be used. Nozzle area can be changed by hand valves or automatically by the governor.

Turbines that run at constant speed but at zero load for considerable periods will require less steam at this condition if the casing is under vacuum or if the speed is reduced. Under a vacuum and zero load, 5 to 10 per cent of full-load steam flow is required. Turbines that run at one load and at overloads for only short periods should be designed to carry overloads with an overload valve.

A single-stage turbine will require approximately 60 per cent of full-load steam for full-load torque at zero speed. Multistage turbines will require less steam for these conditions. Consideration of using a steam engine should be given where full torque must be obtained for long periods of low-speed operation.

Installation Features. Turbines are designed for given conditions of pressures and temperatures, with short-time ratings for higher pressures and temperatures. The purpose of the short-time ratings is to take care of boiler upsets and not to provide additional power. These ratings have been developed to suit electric-power-plant practice, creating a conflict when applied too strictly to process plants. In a 600 lb./sq. in. gage steam plant the pressure at the boiler may be above 600 lb./sq. in. gage while at a considerable distance the pressure may be 590 lb./sq. in. gage. The boiler and steam piping should be reviewed with the turbine manufacturer, so as to use a 600 lb./sq. in. gage turbine even if in some locations the pressure is slightly above 600 lb./sq. in. gage.

The casing of a turbine is designed for the pressure existing at each nozzle, and it is seldom that the exhaust end can withstand full inlet pressure. Relief valves may be required, therefore, to protect the casing from overpressure on both condensing and non-condensing turbines. Turbines frequently come equipped with only a warning sentinel valve but the user must decide if a relief valve is needed.

The forces induced by a turbine on the foundations are the torque from load and **vibratory forces** caused by unbalances in the rotor. To prevent the turbine from vibrating on the foundation, the supporting structure is designed so that the critical frequency of the supporting structure is above the running speed. It is customary for the turbine manufacturer to specify that the foundation deflection be less than a certain value (*i.e.*, the support frequency be above a certain value). If the foundation critical speed is below the running speed, vibrations may occur during startup.

The centrifugal forces resulting from loss of a blade are enormous. For example, the loss of a blade weighing 1 lb. at a tip speed of 1000 ft./sec. with a mean diameter of 2 ft. will produce a force of 30,000 lb. on the shaft. The high frequency (r.p.m./60) and the elasticity of the shaft and of the bearing supports reduce this force to a much lower value at the turbine foundations. The foundations are designed to take an empirical side pull specified by the manufacturer that compensates for the loss of buckets.

For a turbine to produce a variation in torque that can induce oscillatory vibrations, it is necessary that either the pressure vary periodically or that both the rotor blades and stator nozzles be defective. For example, partial admission and a missing blade on the rotor can cause such a torque variation. This torque variation is usually a fraction of 1 per cent of full-load torque. Many turbines have been built in such a fashion and troubles from torsional vibrations have not always been reported.

RECIPROCATING ENGINES USING STEAM AND OTHER GASES

The advent of electric motors, steam turbines, and other drivers has relegated the **steam engine** to a minor position as an industrial driver. It does have the advantages of reliability and operating characteristics that are not obtainable with other drivers, but also the disadvantage of bulkiness and oily exhaust steam.

In the simple non-expanding engine as used with direct-acting reciprocating pumps, steam is admitted over the entire stroke and does not expand in the cylinder, resulting in relatively low efficiency. Control is simple and pump speed is regulated by steam throttling. By proper selection of the steam and pump piston sizes, these pumps can deliver high shutoff pressures, which can be used to overcome temporary blockages of pipe lines or for other situations requiring high pressure of short duration.

The higher-efficiency expanding steam engines use cutoff valves to limit steam admission to the cylinder during the initial part of the stroke and the expansion occurs during the remainder of the stroke. Larger engines use several cylinders in series to achieve full expansion. Although this type of engine can be controlled with throttling valves, the preferred method is to change the cutoff point, thus eliminating throttle-valve losses and permitting change in output from zero to maximum design power. Thus almost complete expansion is achieved at part loads and overloads, resulting in efficient operation for the full range of loadings.

Although this type of engine is efficient, it is limited by its inability to utilize low-vacuum exhaust and/or high steam pressures and temperatures commonly used by steam turbines. With low steam pressures (300 lb./sq. in. gage) and low vacuums (26 in. Hg), a steam engine will have a better efficiency than a steam turbine of the same rated power. For each cutoff setting an engine will develop the same torque at all speeds, with steam consumption and power output directly proportional to speed. All other drivers, except certain d-c electric motors, require the same input for constant torque at varying speeds.

Changing the cutoff point setting will allow an engine designed for one gas to operate efficiently on any other gas (limited only by corrosiveness, fouling, etc.). This characteristic favors the use of reciprocating engines when it is necessary to expand gases efficiently in process applications where the composition is variable. A further advantage is that an engine is the only driver with essentially zero gas consumption at zero speed while developing full torque and maintaining full process pressures. A combination of an expansion engine driving an oil brake provides a high-efficiency refrigeration effect over a wide range of process conditions, with the process controllers throttling the oil flow in the oil brake.

The **uniflow design** reduces cylinder condensation and also allows greater expansion ratios per cylinder (see Figs. 24-37 and 24-38). Steam is admitted during the

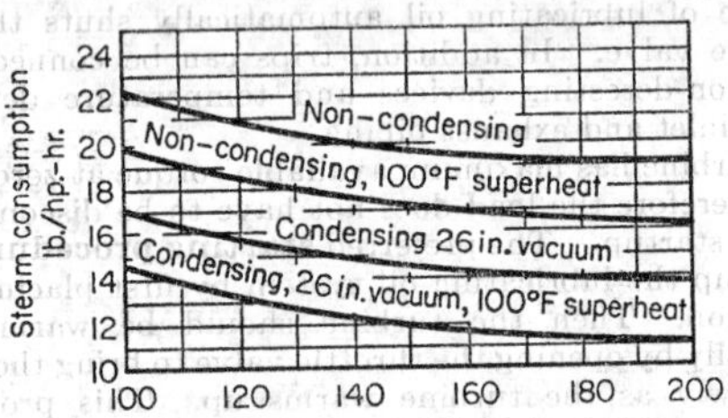

FIG. 24-37. Steam consumption of 400 hp. uniflow engine.

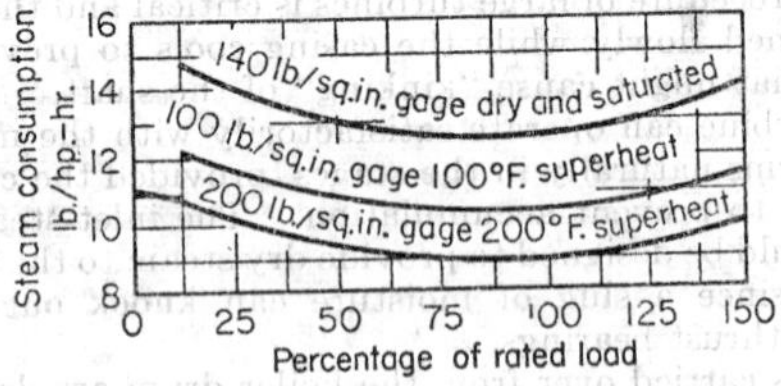

FIG. 24-38. Steam consumption of uniflow engine with 27.5-in. vacuum.

start of the power stroke, and after cutoff is expanded down to a pressure slightly higher than the exhaust pressure. At the end of the stroke the piston uncovers the exhaust ports of the cylinder with partial steam and discharges into the exhaust system. The steam remaining in the cylinder is compressed during the return piston stroke, maintaining higher average cylinder temperatures in order to reduce steam condensation during admission.

To reduce friction and cylinder wear, oil is injected into the cylinders of engines, and to maintain lubricity, cylinders of engines on low-temperature services are warmed. Oil causes foaming in boilers and can contaminate low-temperature process streams. Therefore, in steam plants, oil is usually removed from the condensate. By using carbon or plastic rings similar to those used in oil-free reciprocating compressors, oil for lubrication can be omitted. But these rings are not as reliable nor do they have as good a life as the lubricated cast-iron piston rings.

TURBINES OPERATING ON PROCESS GASES

Turbines can be used to reduce the pressure of process streams, develop power, and at the same time lower the gas temperature. The term "power recovery" means the direct utilization of the turbine power, or the refrigeration effect on the process gas, or both.

When power recovery is the major reason for installing a turbine, its economical justification is the value of the recovered power. But in some cases the refrigeration effect can replace investment in a refrigeration system (evaporator, compressor, and condenser). Then the economical justification involves both the investment cost of the refrigeration system and the cost of supplying power to the refrigeration system.

The design basis of turbines operating near critical pressures and temperatures, where thermodynamic data may not be accurately known, should be reviewed carefully, because under some conditions a turbine may be no more effective than the Joule-Thomson effect of a throttle valve. The usual problem, however, is the accurate prediction of the **available heat drop.** For example, if a turbine is designed for maximum efficiency (governor wide open), then the nozzle area is set by the assumed heat drop. If the actual heat drop later proves to be lower, then the nozzle area will not be sufficient, because the gas flow is proportional to the square root of the heat drop. For example, if a turbine were designed for a heat drop of 10 B.t.u./lb. and the actual value is later found to be 9 B.t.u./lb., the actual power (or refrigeration effect) will be 15 per cent below the anticipated value—10 per cent due to incorrect data and an additional 5 per cent due to the decrease in gas flow. In addition, the optimum turbine efficiency is obtained at a speed 5 per cent lower than the original design value.

As a result of the rapid expansion which occurs in turbine nozzles, supersaturation on turbine performance is concerned with the time lag of moisture formation which results in the heat drop being less than the steady-state values obtained from a Mollier diagram. Heat-drop calculations for supersaturation are usually made with the assumption that the isentropic expansion coefficient $k = C_p/C_v$ is the same for supersaturated vapors and for superheated gases.

Conventional steam-turbine practice assumes that $k = 1.31$ for superheated steam and $k = 1.1$ for the moisture zone. This large change in k results in large **supersaturation losses** for steam. However, a gas with a low value of k in the superheated state and which is slightly higher than the k value in the moisture zone would result in low supersaturation losses. Thus supersaturation losses are a function of gas composition. Steam practice assumes that condensation occurs at 4 per cent moisture, but comparable information is lacking for other gases.

Another method used to estimate supersaturation losses is to assume that the expansion proceeds along the saturation line. Based on steam experience, this method is conservative and results in a high estimate of these losses.

Performance Calculations. An accurate prediction of turbine performance requires a stage-by-stage calculation of each process condition and gas composition. These calculations must take into account: turbine speed, leakage, windage and friction losses, etc., and also thermodynamic properties of the gas, including supersaturation and compressibility effects.

1. The **flow** through a turbine is given by the following equation:

$$WV_t = 3600\ AC_t$$

where W = gas flow, lb./hr.
V_t = specific volume of the gas at the nozzle throat, cu. ft./lb.
A = first-stage nozzle throat area, sq. ft.
C_t = velocity of gas at nozzle throat, ft./sec., which as a first approximation varies as $\sqrt{T/M}$; this velocity cannot exceed its acoustic velocity

2. The adiabatic **heat drop** of the gas is given by the following equation:

$$H = C_p(T_1 - T_2)$$

where C_p = molal specific heat, B.t.u./mole
T_1 = inlet-gas temperature, °F.
T_2 = exhaust-gas temperature, °F., and where T_1 and T_2 can be calculated from general thermodynamic relationships; as a first approximation it can be assumed that the heat drop is proportional to T/M

3. The **efficiency** e of a turbine depends on the velocity of the gas stream relative to the blade velocities. The gas velocities in the first stage are proportional to $\sqrt{T/M}$. The gas velocities in the last stage depend on the volume ratio across the turbine. It can therefore be assumed, in comparing two process conditions, that the efficiencies are the same if (*a*) the velocity is changed and kept proportional to $\sqrt{T/M}$ and (*b*) the volume ratio is the same for both process conditions.

4. The **horsepower** developed by a turbine is

$$\text{hp.} = 2545WHe$$

and therefore for the same volume change across the turbine the horsepower can be estimated from

$$(\text{hp.})_2 = (\text{hp.})_1 \frac{P_2}{P_1} \sqrt{\frac{T_2 M_1}{T_1 M_2}}$$

where subscripts 1 refer to one process condition and subscripts 2 refer to the second process condition. The speed relationship must be approximately as per the following relationship:

$$(\text{r.p.m.})_2 = (\text{r.p.m.})_1 \sqrt{\frac{T_2 M_1}{T_1 M_2}}$$

Selection Factors. These relationships can be used to extrapolate turbine performance, to select types of equipment, or to set process conditions for optimum turbine performance.

1. Throttling or by-passing losses can be reduced for processes having variations in temperature, flow, or molecular weight by the following means:

a. Using variable area in the first-stage nozzles.

b. Allowing the turbine to set the pressure of the gas.

c. In some cases an engine expander may be preferable to a turboexpander since the engine expander can maintain high efficiency over a wide volume of flow ranges.

2. When variations in gas composition affect the k value, then

a. Optimum turbine performance is obtained by changing the pressure ratio to maintain constant volume ratio.

b. Variations in k values or in pressure ratio can be accommodated by changing the cutoff point of an engine expander.

3. The type of loading needed to meet process objectives depends on process variables:

a. The power developed by a turbine is proportional to $AP\sqrt{T/M}$ and the optimum speed is proportional to $\sqrt{T/M}$. When the turbine is used for its refrigeration effect an air brake is the simplest loading device. However, its power consumption is proportional to the cube of its speed and the turbine may be unable to run at optimum speed for all operating conditions. With wide process variations the more complicated system, consisting of a reduction gear and an oil pump or electric generator, may be preferable as a loading device.

b. The refrigeration effect can be maximized by using the turbine to drive a compressor. The compressor can be used to increase the pressure to the turbine or to decrease the exhaust pressure.

SINGLE-STAGE RADIAL-FLOW VS. AXIAL-FLOW TURBINES

Axial-flow turbines (as discussed under steam turbines) are the type most commonly used but radial turbines are preferred for certain applications. The rotating element of a radial-flow turbine is similar to the impeller of a centrifugal pump or compressor. In radial-inflow turbines the gas flow is radially inward from the outer periphery to the eye of the impeller where the gas leaves in an axial direction. In the radial-outflow turbine the gas flows from the eye of the impeller outward to the outer periphery.

Radial-outflow turbines use backward-leaning vanes, whereas the vanes of most radial-inflow turbines are almost radial. Rotational stresses of radial vanes are less than those of either backward-leaning vanes or the blades used in axial-flow machines, and as a result higher tip speeds (ft./sec.) are feasible with radial-inflow turbines. Radial turbines can be built as impulse or reaction turbines. The most popular type is the 50 per cent reaction radial-inflow type with straight impeller vanes. This type can achieve efficiencies above 80 per cent with isentropic heat drops up to 70 B.t.u. per stage. The radial outflow has lower efficiencies (75 per cent) and a maximum heat drop of 25 to 30 B.t.u. per stage.

Radial turbines differ in performance from other turbines because of the pressure difference that exists between the tip and the impeller eye. This pressure drop is a function of diameters and speed. The adiabatic head drop is $(U_p^2 - U_e^2)/2g$, where U_p is the impeller tip speed and U_e is the eye speed in ft./sec. The gas pressure developed by the impeller increases from the eye to the outer periphery. With a fixed pressure ratio, an increase in r.p.m. will result in an increase in flow for radial-outflow turbines and a decrease in flow for radial-inflow turbines. Maximum flow conditions are limited by "choking" when acoustic velocities occur in either the nozzles or impeller passages. The gas flow in axial turbines is almost independent of speed; any change is that due to temperature changes affecting gas velocities and back pressure on the first stage.

The energy removed from a gas stream by a rotating blade system is given by **Euler's equation** (developed in the eighteenth century) and is independent of the blade system used.

$$E = \frac{C_{u1}U_1 - C_{u2}U_2}{g} = \text{energy absorbed} \qquad \text{ft.-lb./lb.}$$

The fluid enters the blade system with a tangential velocity C_{u1} and a velocity C_{n1} normal to the blade system. The tangential and normal velocities at the exit of the blade systems are C_{u2} and C_{n2}. U_1 and U_2 are the mean blade velocities at entrance and exit of the blade system, respectively. All these velocities are in absolute values, in ft./sec.

Since $C_{n2}^2/2g$ represents a loss, the leaving areas are made as large as possible. $C_{u2}^2/2g$ is also a loss, and efficient blading systems are designed so that $C_{u2} = 0$. Therefore, at the design point the power developed becomes

$$E_{\text{ideal}} = \frac{C_{u1}U_1}{2g}$$

If the flow is varied by throttling, then to develop maximum power, C_{u2} must be kept equal to zero by varying the turbine speed.

To develop high efficiencies at reduced flows, **throttle losses** must be minimized, and it is in this respect that the characteristics of turbines are different.

By connecting the nozzles of an axial-flow impulse turbine to a group of valves, the throttle losses can be minimized. By opening the valves to only a group of nozzles, an axial-flow impulse turbine can maintain a relatively high efficiency over a wide flow range. The only increased loss at reduced flow is the windage and friction of the unused blades.

The nozzle vanes of a radial-inflow turbine can be designed to tilt by means of an external lever. This can maintain a higher efficiency at reduced flows than is obtainable by throttling. The losses at reduced flows increase because C_{u2} increases from zero at the design point to $C_{u2} = U_2$ as the flow approaches zero. A flow controller that tilts the valves is much more expensive than the type required for opening nozzles of an axial-flow impulse turbine. The pumping action of unused vanes in a radial-flow turbine does not allow the blanking off of nozzles as in axial impulse turbines. Tilting nozzle vanes are not used in axial-flow reaction turbines or in radial-outflow turbines, not only because of the expense but also because the leaving loss at low flows increases very rapidly as C_{u2} approaches U_2.

General opinion holds that the efficiency of radial-inflow turbines suffers considerably with the formation of moisture. The impeller flings moisture droplets outward toward the casing, which the gases leaving the nozzles pick up and return to the impeller. It is therefore conceivable that the same moisture is transported several times.

Impulse turbines are used when (1) the flow varies over a wide range, (2) flow rates are very low, and (3) a single impulse stage replaces a two-stage reaction or radial turbine. Radial-outflow turbines are used for very low heat drops. Radial-inflow turbines fit best into intermediate flow rates. For very large flow rates axial turbines, either impulse or reaction, are used. For each particular installation, the selection is further influenced by the standard machines that are available and the economic justification of increased investment for special or new designs, as compared with savings in operating costs.

DUST-LADEN GASES IN TURBINES

Dust-laden gases are available as a "free" or "by-product" power source in some chemical processes and their power utilization may increase the economic feasibility of these processes. Blast-furnace gases contain dust, and some fuels such as coal and peat produce dust-laden products of combustion. Power can be recovered with waste-heat boilers, but these gas streams, if under pressure, can yield the most power when a power-recovery turbine is used. Heavy particles striking moving turbine blades will do considerable damage and can destroy a complete stage. Smaller particles, such as dust, will erode the rotating blades and in some cases erode other parts of the turbine. The effect of dust on a turbine is not usually dangerous but simply a matter of economics, comparing fuel costs with the cost of blade and rotor replacement.

Experience with turbines operating on dust-laden gases is limited to (1) several Houdry catalytic crackers, (2) a coal-burning gas turbine, (3) blowers operating on blast-furnace gases, and (4) a fluid catalytic-cracking installation. This rather limited experience and the inconsistencies that have been experienced make it

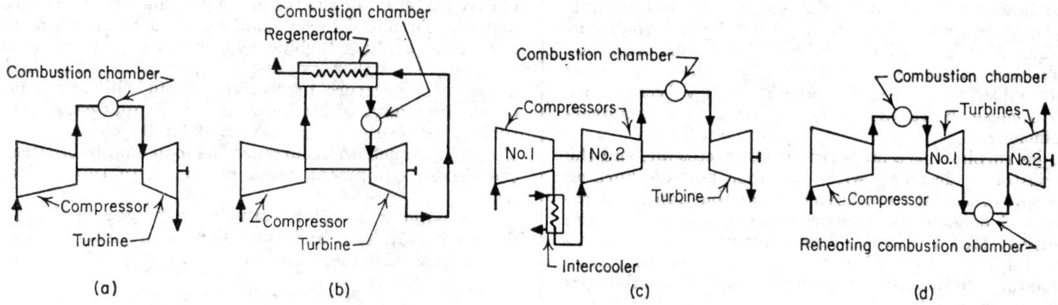

FIG. 24-39. Gas-turbine cycles: (*a*) Basic Brayton or Joule. (*b*) Gas turbine with regeneration. (*c*) With intercooling. (*d*) With reheating. (*Source: Chapter on gas turbines by Thomas J. Putz, in Marks-Baumeister, "Mechanical Engineers' Handbook," 6th ed., McGraw-Hill, New York, 1958.*)

desirable for prospective users to understand the basic mechanism of dust erosion.

Static tests indicate that the rate of **erosion** varies (1) as the dust concentration for small concentrations, and as the square root for larger concentrations, and (2) as the fourth power of the gas velocity. Because very small particles lack the kinetic energy to penetrate the boundary layer, they do not cause erosion. The problem of correlating operating conditions with static tests is partly the determination of which local velocities are to be used.

Dust particles have a different velocity for each particle size. The larger particles travel at a fraction of the speed of the gas stream, whereas the smallest particles approach the gas-stream velocities. In a **reaction turbine** all the particles would travel at less than the blade speed and would strike the back of the leading edge of the blades. The particles in an **impulse turbine** would be separated into three groups, (1) the larger particles traveling at less than blade speed and eroding the back of the blade's leading edge, (2) an intermediate-sized group traveling at blade speed and eroding the front of the blades, and (3) the smallest particles, which should not cause erosion, traveling at the same velocity as the gas. It is therefore difficult to extrapolate experience on reaction turbines to impulse turbines. Most of the experience on dust-bearing gases has been with reaction turbines.

Blade erosion is a function of dust loading, particle-size distribution, dust composition, blade materials, design of blade and nozzle passages, blade velocity, gas velocities, and the viscosity of the gases. Attempts have been made to correlate these factors and develop a means of predicting turbine life. However, the usual solution is to eliminate the problem by removing the dust, most often with cyclone separators.

Turbine passages have small turning radii and it is possible to determine the size of the dust particles that would be "thrown out." **Centrifugal separators** designed to remove still smaller particles are of the small-diameter multiclone type, preferably with groups of separators in series to ensure maximum dust removal. By using separator-efficiency charts, an estimate can be made of the dust concentration in the gas going to the turbine, and from this one can obtain an estimate of the minimum "expected" turbine life, sufficiently accurate for economic feasibility studies.

COMBUSTION GAS TURBINES

Gas turbines are usually rated according to power output at sea level and 80°F. ambient air (some European designs are rated at 60°F.) and when burning a specified fuel. Power output and efficiency will be larger for those fuels which produce larger volumes of products of combustion since the compressor does not do any work on additional volume. Gas turbines are further classified by the physical arrangements of the component parts, such as (1) single shaft, (2) two shaft, (3) regenerative (a heat exchanger is used to recover exhaust losses and heat the air to the combustors), (4) intercooled (heat removed between compressors), and (5) reheat (heat added between turbines). Thus an installation may be a two-shaft 10,000-hp turbine with one intercooler, one reheat, and a regenerator (see Figs. 24-39 and 24-40).

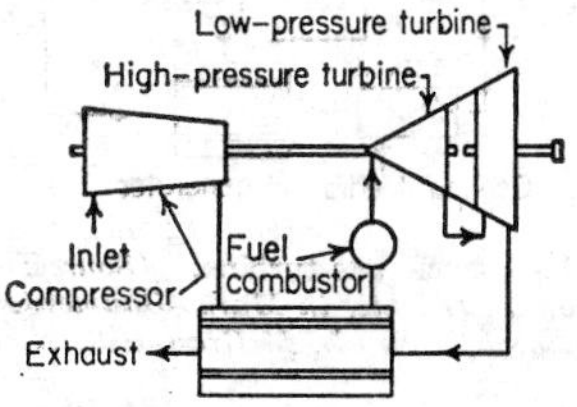

FIG. 24-40. Regenerative cycle for gas-turbine two-shaft arrangement with separate power turbine in series. (*Source: Chapter on gas turbines by Thomas J. Putz, in Marks-Baumeister, "Mechanical Engineers' Handbook," 6th ed., McGraw-Hill, New York, 1958.*)

The **over-all efficiency** of a gas turbine is a function of compressor and turbine efficiencies, ambient air temperature, nozzle inlet temperature, and type of cycle used (*i.e.*, reheat, etc.). The compressor and turbine are designed for high efficiency and the first-stage gas temperature establishes material and stress conditions for the first set of rotating blades. To the gas temperature at these blades is added the temperature drop across the first-stage nozzles to determine the inlet temperature of the turbine, which may vary from 1300° to 1500°F. for industrial gas turbines and higher for aviation gas turbines. The higher values are usually used in impulse turbines.

In a simple cycle turbine, there is, for each turbine inlet temperature, an optimum **pressure ratio** producing the highest possible efficiency. The efficiency and optimum pressure ratio increase with increasing turbine inlet temperatures. These pressure ratios vary from 4 at 1300°F. up to 6 for 1500°F. turbine inlet temperature.

Regenerative cycles favor lower pressure ratios which result in low compressor discharge temperatures, thus allowing greater recovery of heat from the turbine exhaust gases. High-ratio regenerative plants use intercoolers in the compressor circuit to lower the compressor discharge air temperature.

Any type of efficient compressor can be used, *e.g.*, positive displacement (Lysholm), centrifugal, and axial flow; however, most industrial gas turbines use axial-flow compressors. The turbine may have impulse or reaction blading, and to minimize losses, air from the compressor discharge flows through the combustor directly into the turbine nozzle. Throttle valves are not used because the resulting pressure drop decreases over-all efficiency.

A gas turbine has a large amount of excess air, and the combustor is designed with an inner portion burning only part of the air to achieve high combustion temperatures and efficiency. The products of combustion are effectively mixed with the remainder of the air to minimize temperature stratification. Each turbine may have one large combustor or several smaller combustors operating in parallel.

Most gas-turbine installations are of the **open-cycle** type using atmospheric air as the working medium and burning relatively clean fuels. For "dirty" fuels it has been suggested that the burner be located in the gas-turbine discharge, using a heat exchanger to heat the air discharged by the compressor.

In **closed-cycle** plants (see Figs. 24-41 and 24-42) it may be desirable to use other gases since plant efficiency

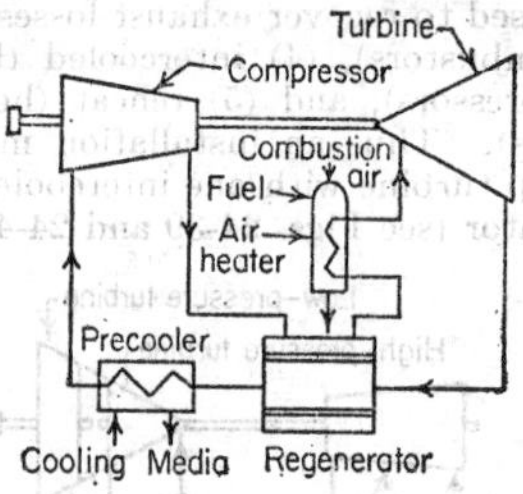

FIG. 24-41. Closed-cycle gas turbine. (*Source: Chapter on gas turbines by Thomas J. Putz, in Marks-Baumeister, "Mechanical Engineers' Handbook," 6th ed., McGraw-Hill, New York,* 1958.)

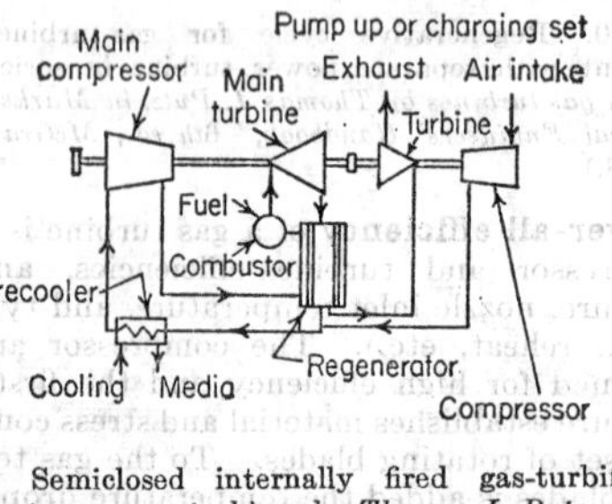

FIG. 24-42. Semiclosed internally fired gas-turbine cycle. (*Source: Chapter on gas turbines by Thomas J. Putz, in Marks-Baumeister, "Mechanical Engineers' Handbook," 6th ed., McGraw-Hill, New York,* 1958.)

increases as the specific heat ratio (c_p/c_v) decreases. Optimum plant efficiency occurs at increasingly higher pressure ratios with decreasing values of (c_p/c_v). However, most closed systems use air for convenience. Closed systems can provide a high plant efficiency over a power range from 25 to 100 per cent by varying the turbine exhaust and compressor inlet pressure from atmospheric to 60 lb./sq. in. gage. These plants require expensive heaters, located between compressor discharge and turbine inlet, and large coolers, located between the turbine exhaust and the compressor suction. Usually, combustion of a fuel provides the heat source and cooling water the coolant medium.

A large overload, even if only temporary in nature, can cause a single-shaft gas turbine to shut down, since its fuel input is limited by the inlet overtemperature protective system. If the torque requirements of the driven machine do not decrease sufficiently with speed reduction, then the gas turbine will continue to slow down, resulting in higher exhaust temperatures. The high-exhaust-temperature protective system will either shut off the fuel valve or further reduce fuel input causing the turbine to decrease its speed and finally to shut down. To prevent such an occurrence the load characteristics of the driven equipment must be suited to those of the driver.

The popularity of the **single-shaft gas turbine** is due to its low cost and compactness in terms of power output per cubic foot of machinery space (see Fig. 24-43).

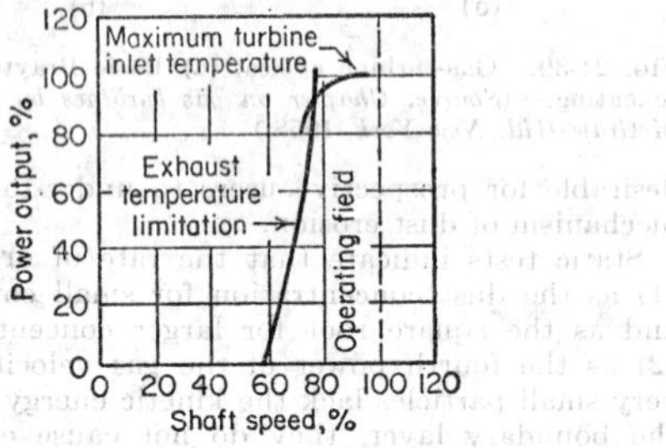

FIG. 24-43. Single-shaft gas-turbine operating range for various speeds and loads. (*Source: Chapter on gas turbines by Thomas J. Putz, in Marks-Baumeister, "Mechanical Engineers' Handbook," 6th ed., McGraw-Hill, New York,* 1958.)

Its disadvantage is a relatively low operating speed range and its sensitivity to atmospheric temperatures. The low operating speed range is caused by the following factors: (1) the quantity of air flow induced by the compressor is proportional to its speed, and (2) the back pressure produced by the turbine nozzles is proportional to air flow. At low speeds the turbine power is decreased by low air flows and secondarily by the effect of low pressures on allowable inlet-air temperatures. At low flows the decreased pressure at the turbine inlet may require a reduction of turbine inlet temperature to keep the exhaust temperature within design limitations, resulting in a further reduction in power. In most applications it is necessary to unload the turbine during startup.

A wider operating speed range is provided by the more expensive **two-shaft machine** which consists of a high-pressure turbine driving the air compressor and a low-pressure turbine on a separate shaft to provide output power (see Fig. 24-44). A variable-area nozzle can be used in the low-pressure turbine to increase the operating speed range. Change in the fuel input to the high-pressure turbine causes the speed and quantity of air flow to change. The low-pressure turbine power output is changed by varying the quantity of air flow and the nozzle area of the power turbine (see also Fig. 24-45).

Operating Characteristics. The air flow in lb./hr. to a gas turbine is inversely proportional to the absolute air temperature at the compressor inlet, and the compressor discharge pressure is set by the turbine nozzles (proportional to flow), resulting in decreased turbine power output during hot weather and increased power during cold days. In dry areas, it is possible to cool the hot incoming air by evaporation using water injection. In most locations maximum summer temperature is of short duration and it may be possible to obtain rated power by increasing turbine temperature for this short period without appreciably shortening "turbine life." In extreme winter temperatures, high air pressures will exist at the turbine inlet and must be considered in the design of the gas turbine.

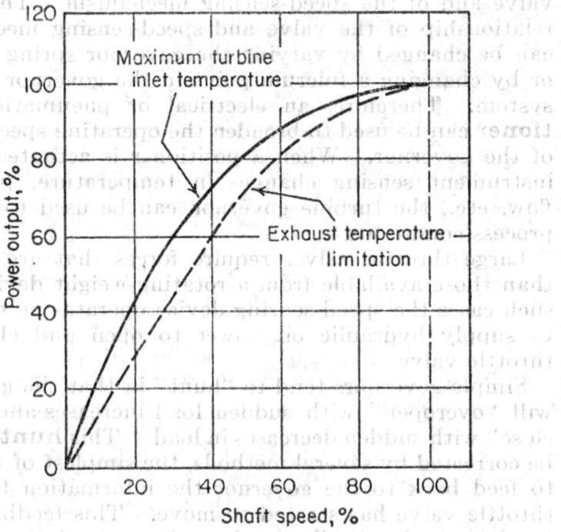

Fig. 24-44. Two-shaft gas-turbine operating range for various speeds and loads. (*Source: Chapter on gas turbines by Thomas J. Putz, in Marks-Baumeister, "Mechanical Engineers' Handbook," 6th ed., McGraw-Hill, New York, 1958.*)

Since the power required by the compressor is approximately twice as great as the shaft output, a 1 per cent change in compressor efficiency will result in 2 per cent change in shaft power, and a 1 per cent change in turbine efficiency produces a 3 per cent change in shaft power. It is therefore important that all losses be minimized and that ample-sized inlet and exhaust piping or ducts be used.

A gas turbine is started by bringing it up to **starting** speed and maintaining this speed for several minutes in order to purge the casing. Some machines require that the casing or rotor be heated slowly by burning a nominal amount of fuel in the combustors for several minutes. The turbine inlet temperature is then increased rapidly to a value above the design temperature, thus producing enough power in the turbine to bring the set up to full speed. Some installations will require a blowoff valve to prevent surging during startup. The starting power requirements of an unloaded gas turbine will be between 5 and 10 per cent of the rating and the starting speed will be between 20 and 30 per cent of full-load speed. Two-shaft turbines will require slightly more starting power than single-shaft machines, but by opening the nozzles of the low-pressure turbine, the load is not driven during startup.

Gas turbines can use a wide variety of fuels. Major **fuel limitations** are that it does not (1) form ashes which deposit on the blades and interfere with operation, (2) contain dust which will erode the blades, and (3) contain uninhibited vanadium. Gas turbines are now operating on fuel gas (natural and refinery), blast-furnace gases, fuel oils (including heavy residuals), and at least one experimental coal-burning gas turbine has been built.

The simple-cycle gas turbine is relatively inefficient and almost all its losses are in the hot exhaust gases. When exhaust gases can be used in a boiler or for process heating, the combination of turbine and heat-recovery apparatus results in a high-efficiency plant. Another method that results in high efficiency is to integrate the gas turbine with process requirements.

Following are some examples of gas turbines that have been used in industry: (1) In the Houdry process a gas turbine is used to drive the regeneration air compressor; (2) the air compressor of a gas turbine can be made oversize to supply pressurized air for blast-furnace operation;

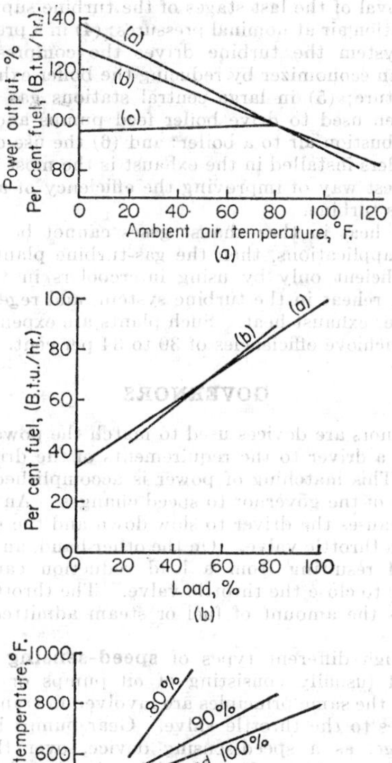

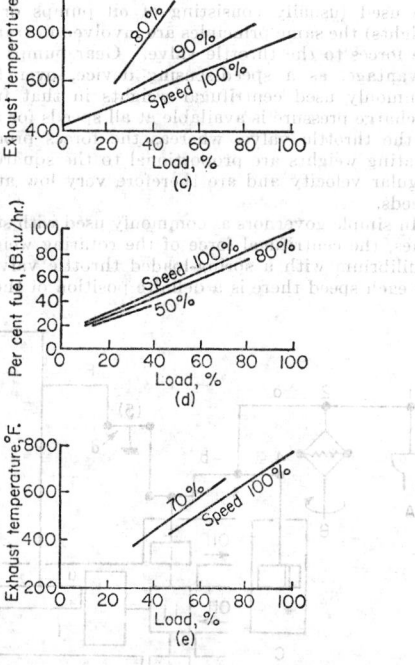

Fig. 24-45. Gas-turbine performance at various speeds, temperatures, and loads. (*a*) At 100 per cent speed, output and fuel consumption are shown as a function of ambient temperature with (a) power and corresponding fuel consumption (b). Fuel at 100 per cent power is shown in (c). (*b*) Fuel consumption with a single-shaft gas turbine at 80°F. and (a) at 100 per cent and (b) at 90 per cent speed. (*c*) Exhaust temperatures of single-shaft gas turbine at ambient temperature of 80°F. and speeds as shown. (*d*) Fuel consumption of two-shaft gas turbine at various loads and speeds. (*e*) Exhaust temperatures of two-shaft gas turbine at ambient temperature of 80°F.

(3) removal of the last stages of the turbine supplies hot regeneration air at nominal pressures; (4) in a pressurized boiler system the turbine drives the compressor and acts as an economizer by reducing the boiler exhaust-gas temperature; (5) in large central stations gas turbines have been used to drive boiler feed pumps and supply hot combustion air to a boiler; and (6) the use of waste-heat boilers installed in the exhaust is the most common and easiest way of improving the efficiency of a simple-cycle gas turbine.

If the heat in the exhaust gases cannot be used for process applications, then the gas-turbine plant can be made efficient only by using intercoolers in the compressors, reheat in the turbine system, and regeneration to recover exhaust heat. Such plants are expensive and usually achieve efficiencies of 30 to 34 per cent.

GOVERNORS

Governors are devices used to match the power developed by a driver to the requirements of the driven machine. This matching of power is accomplished by the response of the governor to speed changes. An increase in load causes the driver to slow down and the governor to open a throttle valve. On the other hand, an increase in speed resulting from a load reduction causes the governor to close the throttle valve. The throttle valve regulates the amount of fuel or steam admitted to the driver.

Although different types of **speed-sensing devices** are used (usually consisting of oil pumps or rotating weights) the same principles are involved in transmitting the forces to the throttle valve. Gear pumps have the advantage, as a speed-sensing device, over the more commonly used centrifugal weights in that full pump discharge pressure is available at all speeds for actuation of the throttle valve, whereas the forces produced by rotating weights are proportional to the square of their angular velocity and are therefore very low at reduced speeds.

In simple governors as commonly used with steam turbines, the centrifugal force of the rotating weights is in equilibrium with a spring-loaded throttle valve. Thus for each speed there is a definite position of the throttle valve and of the speed-sensing mechanism. The speed relationship of the valve and speed-sensing mechanism can be changed by varying the governor spring tension or by changing a fulcrum point in the governor linkage system. Therefore, an electrical or pneumatic **positioner** can be used to broaden the operating speed range of the governor. When a positioner is actuated by an instrument sensing changes in temperature, pressure, flow, etc., the turbine governor can be used to control process conditions.

Large throttle valves require forces that are greater than those available from a rotating-weight device. In such cases the speed-sensing device operates an oil relay to supply hydraulic oil power to open and close the throttle valve.

Simple governors tend to "hunt" in that the governor will "overopen" with sudden load increases and "overclose" with sudden decreases in load. This **hunting** can be corrected by several methods, the simplest of which is to feed back to the governor the information that the throttle valve has started to move. This feedback can be done hydraulically by imposing an oil pressure or mechanically by changing a fulcrum point or a spring tension in the system.

Turbines driving generators may have a slow rate of load change or may have an almost instantaneous load change as when a circuit breaker closes or opens. A **rate-of-load-change** sensing device can be incorporated in the governing system to cause the throttle valve to respond proportionally to the rate of the load change, for example, the pressure developed by a moving oil piston that incorporates an orifice by-pass.

Governors can also be arranged to open and close sets of valves automatically in such a manner that only one of a group will be in a throttling position, thereby reducing throttling losses.

The speed governor of an extraction turbine actuates the high- and low-pressure throttling valves simultaneously and then adjusts the relative opening of the two sets of valves to maintain the desired extraction pressure as sensed by a pressure controller. For example, a speed increase caused by drop in load causes the governor to close partially the high- and low-pressure throttle valves simultaneously, and if the extraction

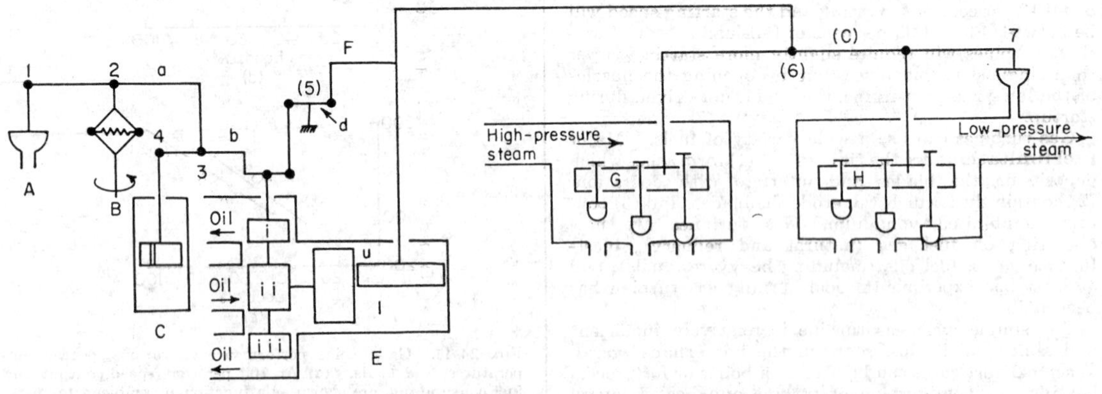

FIG. 24-46. Schematic diagram for governor of an extraction turbine. Notes: Speed changer *A* can act directly to move valves by moving point (1) and rotating bar (*a*) about point (2). For each setting of point (1), the speed-sensing device (*B*) will maintain constant speed. A speed increase causes the fly balls to move out, pulling point (2) downward and bar (*a*) rotates about point (1), moving point (3) downward. The rate of change of speed-sensing device (*C*) is a piston, with a small orifice, moving in an oil cylinder. A fast change allows bar (*b*) to pivot about point (4) and push the three pistons of the oil relay downward. Piston (i) closes the oil leak-off from the upper portion; piston (ii) allows hydraulic oil to enter the upper portion (*u*) of the power piston (*E*) and piston (iii) allows oil to escape from the lower (*e*) portion of the power cylinder. The power cylinder lowers the valve life bars *G* and *H* by causing bar (*c*) to pivot about point (7). The antihunting device *F* changes the oil-relay setting as the power piston begins to move. The automatic pressure controller (*I*) changes the relative opening of the high-pressure valves.

pressure increases, then the pressure regulator closes the high-pressure throttle valve and opens the low-pressure throttle valve.

Figure 24-46 is a schematic diagram of a governor for an extraction turbine incorporating an oil relay for additional power, a rate-of-load-change sensing device, feedback, an instrument-controlled set-speed device, an extraction pressure regulator, and an arrangement to reduce throttling losses.

Process-control instruments can be used to vary turbine speeds as required for process conditions. Such control of small turbines is frequently accomplished with a throttle valve placed ahead of the turbine system. Another popular scheme for small turbines is to have an air diaphragm actuate the governor linkage directly, with the speed-sensing elements connected to the governor linkage by means of a slip connection. In this type of governor the speed-sensing device acts only to limit top speed of the turbine. For large turbines, process control is accomplished by having an air diaphragm change a fulcrum point or spring tension in the governor mechanism. In this type of control the diaphragm receives an air signal from a process control instrument and varies the speed setting of the turbine. The advantage of this type of governor is that changes in steam condition are compensated for by the governor operating the throttle valve to maintain the set speed and thus minimize the process change.

Isochronous governors are used to maintain constant speed at all loads. The speed-sensing device changes the spring tension and/or some fulcrum point whenever the speed is different from that desired.

One governor manufacturer uses a device that changes governor spring tension in such a manner that the flyballs are at their outermost position at all times, and thus obtains maximum centrifugal force at all operating speeds.

Governing devices strictly speaking are not safety devices, for their main function is to regulate the turbine speed. Most industrial applications protect the turbine with separate trip-throttle valves which are held open by a latch arranged to trip on turbine overspeed, low oil pressure, or manual actuation. It is also possible to use other sensing devices to trip the throttle valve in case of excessive vibration, high temperatures, pressures, wear of thrust bearings, or malfunctions in the driven machine.

ELECTRIC MOTORS

Operating Characteristics. Major consumption of electric power in process plants is normally by motors, usually of the induction or synchronous type. The induction motor or squirrel-cage type, because of its rugged simplicity, constant-speed characteristics, and absence of brushes and commutating devices, finds wide application as a driver for pumps, compressors, fans, blowers, and other rotating equipment, as well as for conveyors. The slip-ring or wound-rotor induction motor, because of its starting and variable-speed characteristics, has gained favor for certain applications, even though greater complexity of both motor and control limits its general use in industry. Because of lower cost, synchronous motors are used to drive large machines at low as well as at high speeds.

Squirrel-cage induction motors are available in a wide selection of enclosures suitable for either indoor or outdoor installation, ranging from standard open types through dripproof, splashproof, totally enclosed, or explosionproof designs. Wound-rotor and synchronous motors are generally available only in open construction; their use in locations exposed to the elements, splashing, or where explosive materials may be present requires certain safety measures. Thus the entire motor may be placed in an enclosure which will prevent entrance of rain or snow, or which may be lightly pressurized to exclude explosive gases. In areas in which explosive vapors normally do not exist except as the result of leakage or rupture of piping, it is common practice to use enclosures only around the slip rings and brushes, pressurized with uncontaminated air to prevent accumulation and ignition of flammable materials.

Switchgear and **motor starters** are general terms for switching and interrupting devices, as well as for assemblies of those devices which incorporate controls, metering, and protective and regulating equipment, complete with internal wiring, interconnections, busses, and supporting structures. Switchgear will normally include heavy switching devices, such as disconnect switches, circuit breakers (fuses), and contactors. Relays, meters, position and indicating devices, control switches, and control and instrument transformers, all necessary for operation of the equipment, may also be included.

Switchgear and motor starters provide means for energizing, deenergizing, and protecting motors, generators, transformers, and other devices. Switchgear is connected in the circuits to be protected and controlled, and may be manually, mechanically, or magnetically (electrically) operated. Automatic operation is obtained by means of relays and releases of various types responsive to current, voltage, frequency, or other variations of the electrical characteristics of the circuit. These may be designed to open or close the mechanism connected in the power circuit under predetermined conditions in order to provide adequate protection and other desired results.

Small single-phase motors are usually controlled by manually operated switches or starters which provide only overload protection. Several such motors and starters are frequently connected to a single circuit, protected by a fused switch or circuit breaker; similar starting equipment may often be employed for the control and protection of small polyphase motors operating at low voltage.

Larger low-voltage polyphase squirrel-cage induction motors are usually controlled with magnetically operated switches which provide overload and undervoltage protection while short-circuit protection and disconnecting means are furnished by a fused switch or circuit breaker. Circuit breakers and switches are often assembled and supplied as a single operating unit in a suitable housing. In some cases, circuit breakers equipped with the necessary relays and arranged for magnetic operation are employed for control of low-voltage polyphase motors.

Motors operating at high voltages may be controlled by contactors which protect against overcurrent and undervoltage and are usually provided with a disconnecting means in the form of an unfused switch. When greater interrupting capacity than that provided by a contactor is required, high-interrupting-capacity fuses may be furnished in conjunction with the disconnecting switch. Circuit breakers equipped with the necessary relays and designed for magnetic operation also find a wide application for motor control, particularly for service at high voltages when contactors are not available.

Switchgear, motor starters, and circuit breakers are available in a variety of enclosures designed to protect the mechanism and provide safe operation under most ambient conditions.

Push-button stations adjacent to motors often are employed to actuate starting equipment which may be located remotely. Modern process plants frequently require automatically controlled operations of various types. Auxiliary devices, such as pressure switches, float switches, timers and similar appliances provide a satisfactory method of achieving this objective.

BEARINGS AND THEIR LUBRICATION

Handbooks, textbooks, and manufacturers' catalogues supply the design data needed for an engineer to select bearings for various applications. However, the average user does not select bearings and his main concern is to understand the basic types of bearings and their relative merits and weaknesses.

TYPES OF BEARINGS

Bearings are classified as low-speed sliding, high-speed oil-lubricated, and antifriction. The latter includes ball and roller bearings.

The velocity between the elements of a low-speed sliding bearing is so slow that an oil wedge does not form to separate the sliding surfaces. Lubrication lowers static and sliding friction, which can be further reduced by carefully polished surfaces, and/or by lubricant additions (such as graphite, talc, or soapstone) to fill the surface cavities. The essential characteristics of such bearings are the slow wearing of the sliding surfaces and increased machine clearances, with ample warning of excessive wear and little hazard of sudden disastrous damage. Heat generation is low enough to be readily conducted away from the rubbing surfaces by the machine parts.

The load-carrying capacity of a high-speed oil-lubricated bearing results from the pressure "build-up" caused by the moving surface drawing oil into a region of diminishing oil-film thickness to form an oil wedge. Oil wedges in journal bearings cause the shaft not to be concentric with the bearings (see Fig. 24-47). In stationary thrust bearings this wedge may be obtained by machining a tapered depression into the stationary thrust collars; in tilting-pad thrust bearings, such as those of the **Kingsbury type**, the angle assumed under rotation forms the oil wedge.

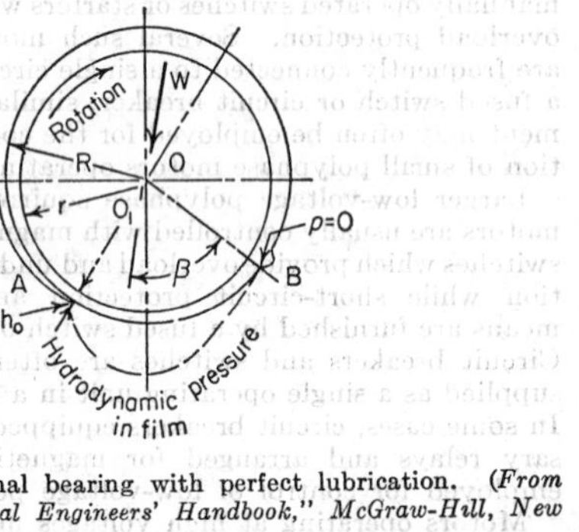

FIG. 24-47. Journal bearing with perfect lubrication. (*From Marks, "Mechanical Engineers' Handbook," McGraw-Hill, New York*, 1958.)

Design parameters of various industries differ because bearings must be designed not only to carry load but also to satisfy other conditions under which specific machines must operate. Thus turbine design favors small clearances to minimize steam leakage; whereas machines subject to fouling, such as those operating in dusty areas, must have increased clearances to allow ample oil flow and to pass dust particles. Locomotives must transmit high traction loads with attendant high unit bearing loads. To minimize hazard of damage, such bearings are hand-fitted to shafts and are under continual inspection.

At nominal speeds lightly loaded bearings which can dissipate friction heat through the bearing housing need be supplied only with sufficient oil to make up "end leakage." Ring oilers, oil wicks, etc., can be used to supply this makeup from a reservoir, which in turn receives the end leakage. Grease-packed bearings can be used for slow speeds. The grease blocks oil loss, prevents the ingress of dust, and supplies lubricating oil under the melting action of the frictional heat. High-speed bearings are pressure-flow lubricated to assure sufficient oil flow to make up end leakages, to maintain lubricant and metal temperatures in bearing areas, and to remove heat conducted along the shaft and the housing. Bearing materials of high conductivity are frequently selected to minimize the formation of localized hot spots. Properly designed and lubricated bearings will continue to run for many years without requiring replacement.

Load capacity of a bearing increases with surface velocity, viscosity, and wedge angle. A generalized equation defines the load-carrying ability of journal bearings in terms of the ratio of minimum oil-film thickness h to the bearing clearance c, and is usually plotted, for given ratios of bearing length L to bearing diameter d, as follows:

$$h = \frac{ZNd^2}{Pc}$$

where Z is viscosity in centipoises, P is the mean bearing pressure (load/Ld), and N is r.p.m.

The frictional power dissipated in an oil film is proportional to the film thickness, velocity, density, and bearing length. The temperature rise t is proportional to the heat dissipated divided by the product of specific heat c_p of the oil and the oil-flow quantity. High oil temperatures can decrease the oil viscosity sufficiently to break down the oil film, and as a result each bearing design has a maximum load-carrying capability depending on Z, N, and d/c.

Although the different industries use different values of c/d, ZN/P, and L/d, bearings are always designed to ensure that the minimum film thickness is above an acceptable value and that the temperature rise is within allowable limits. Values of $c/d = 0.001$ and L/d less than unity are commonly used for turbine and centrifugal compressors. Higher values of $c/d = 0.002$ and $L/d = 2$ are used in slower-speed machines, and less frequently for high-speed machinery. Values of P usually vary from 50 to 300 lb./sq. in. and for special conditions up to 550 lb./sq. in. Higher values can be obtained by the use of tilting pads that promote effective oil cooling.

Reciprocating machines (crankshafts and crankpins) have high bearing unit loads (in the order of 1800 lb./sq. in.) since during the unloaded part of the cycle fresh oil flows into the bearing and pressure build-up occurs as the oil is forced out. Thus the load is always carried by cool oil and the bearings are thermally stable.

Oil whip is a bearing phenomenon encountered on high-speed machinery and vertical bearings and is a result of lightly loaded bearings (*i.e.*, high values of ZN/P). The action, for a horizontal bearing carrying a vertical load, is as follows:

If a shaft starts to whirl (move in a circular path) in the direction of rotation, thus decreasing the oil-film thickness, the resulting bearing pressures will raise the shaft until the vertical component of the bearing oil-film reaction is less than the bearing load. At this stage the horizontal component of the bearing oil-film reaction will force the shaft toward the bearing center, increasing the oil-film thickness and allowing the shaft to fall back to the starting position. Under certain conditions, the pumping action of the shaft will develop enough energy to overcome the losses and the whirling motion of the shaft in the bearing will persist. The whirl frequency is about half the r.p.m. of the shaft.

The amplitude of the whip of a stiff shaft (*i.e.*, critical speed above operating speed) is limited to the amplitude of whirl in the bearing, and its occurrence may not be noticed. The whipping amplitude of a shaft increases as the running speed approaches twice the critical frequency of the rotor, at which time resonance occurs with resultant magnified amplitudes of vibration which can lead to a fatigue failure.

Mild cases of oil whip have been stopped by changing oil viscosity, through either increased oil temperature or reduced oil flow or in a few cases by the reverse (*i.e.*, decrease in oil temperatures). More severe cases require that the bearing length be decreased to produce higher mean bearing pressures.

Grit-particle size in the oil and/or surface irregularities determine the minimum practical oil-film thickness and may result in low unit pressures. To prevent oil whip under these conditions specially designed bearings are used, such as a **segmental or tilting pads,** which change the bearing contour and decrease the lifting capacity of the bearing as it whirls. Or else passages in the bearing housing can be designed to change the pressure distribution for snubbing the whirling action.

Thrust Bearings. Low axial loads can be carried by a simple thrust collar on the shaft that runs against a flat and parallel stationary bearing surface, in which lubrication to the center flows radially outward. The flat and parallel surfaces prevent the formation of an oil wedge and thus limit this type of bearing to low axial loads. The increased capacity obtained by several collars on a shaft is not proportional to the number of collars used, since one collar usually carries most of the load.

Radial grooves in the surface can be chamfered to allow wedge formation and increase the load-carrying capacity of a simple thrust collar. Manufacturing tolerances and errors in chamfer angle can result in some segments of the bearing carrying more load than other segments, thus affecting the load-carrying capacity of this type of thrust bearing. Tilting-pad thrust bearings were developed to overcome the limitations of fixed-wedge bearings by permitting the individual pads to tilt and distribute the load among the pads.

Thrust bearings have the same thermal and minimum film-thickness limitations as sleeve bearings. In addition, tilting pads may deform under loads causing hot spots; or the pumping action of the thrust collar may cause the inner portion of the thrust bearing to run dry. Tilting-pad bearings are preferred for heavy-duty industrial thrust bearings. They are made by several specialist companies and by most manufacturers of heavy-duty equipment according to the basic designs developed by Kingsbury in the United States and Michelle in France.

Ball and Roller Bearings. These are often referred to as antifriction bearings since a shaft rotating on rolling balls or rollers appears to be frictionless. Their actual performance does not attain this ideal state, as will be explained later for ball bearings. Roller bearings, including the needle and tapered varieties, use different equations.

The maximum unit contact pressure P_{max} resulting from a sphere of radius r carrying a load F against a flat plate of the same material as the sphere (modulus of elasticity E) is

$$P_{max} = 0.388 \sqrt[3]{\frac{FE^2}{r^2}}$$

and the stress is

$$S_{max} = 0.31P_{max}$$

Associating this stress with the fatigue properties of the material, it is possible to calculate the life of an ideal bearing for an assumed load. The relative size of adjacent balls and their spacing will influence the life of a ball bearing. The effect of these parameters is determined by testing a large number of bearings to a statistically defined life such that not more than 10 per cent of the bearings will fail at the selected design life, and less than 50 per cent will fail at five times this design life. Some of the bearings may reach a life of twenty or thirty times design. These tests are performed at rated speed and load.

The catalogue **bearing capacity** C is adjusted to service conditions by multiplying the actual operating load R by several factors, which are K_L, a life factor to correct from catalogue life to the required life; K_S, a speed factor to correct from catalogue speed to required speed; K_A, an application factor to correct for shock possibilities; and K_T, a thrust factor to account for the application of both thrust and radial loads.

The equation relating these factors is written as

$$C = K_A K_L K_S K_T R$$

where $K_L = \sqrt[3]{(\text{required life})/(\text{catalogue speed})}$
$K_S = \sqrt[3]{(\text{required speed})/(\text{catalogue speed})}$
K_A = 1 for steady loads and increases to 3 for ball bearings or to 2 for roller bearings under extreme shock loads
K_T = 1, usually, at design load conditions and is different for each bearing design for the various thrust radial-load conditions

Bearings of different manufacturers are interchangeable as a result of dimensional standardization as to width, and outer and inner diameters, with standard series rated as light, medium, and heavy duty. To assure selection of comparable bearings it is necessary that ratings be corrected to common operating conditions.

Bearing friction is partly due to rubbing between elements and the retaining cages (whose function is to keep the elements apart) but is mostly due to the uphill motion that results from the impression of the loaded elements on the raceways. For slow-speed bearings effective lubrication is obtained by oil spray, flow, flooding, or grease packing. As the speed increases the heat generated by the elements churning in the lubricant becomes critical and consequently high-speed ball-bearing lubrication systems are designed to provide only the exact quantity of lubricant required; the lubricant is usually applied in the form of a spray or mist.

Because of their ease of installation and availability, **roller** and ball bearings are popular among manufac**turers** and users. Additional advantages are that they can provide accurate centering and location of the shaft with respect to the housing, runout can be kept to a minimum, and low staritng torques can be obtained. Their major disadvantage as compared with journal bearings is that life is less assured and a certain percentage fails with time.

LUBRICATING SYSTEMS

Lubrication may involve the simple manual filling of oilcups or grease cups, or pressure application of lubricant to fittings, or automatic lubrication from sumps with ring oilers, chains, or wicks. However, high-speed bearings require more complicated systems to assure a continuous supply of clean oil.

Large machines require an oil cooler to remove the heat generated in their bearings; usually the oil is contained in a reservoir and pumped to the bearing through oil coolers and filters. Oil temperature is controlled to maintain constant viscosity and sufficient oil pressure is maintained to ensure flow of oil through the orifices into the individual bearings. Oil-return lines slope from the bearing to the reservoir and are generously sized to allow the passage of foam, with the return oil. Lubricating oils are selected to minimize foaming, and when excessive, antifoaming additives are used. Lubricating systems must be cleaned by flushing or oil circulation prior to operation and must be kept clean thereafter to prevent damage.

Oil filters are placed as near the bearings as possible and should be capable of removing all particles which are large compared with the minimum oil-film thickness. **Underfiltering** will result in scratched bearings and may lead to more serious damage. **Overfiltering** risks the plugging of filters and either collapse with sudden release of their contents or else stoppage of oil flow.

Some machines will produce small particles (*i.e.*, carbon particles in Diesels) whose size is not large enough to damage the lubricating system. It is good practice, however, to prevent their accumulation; for this purpose a microfilter is effective, and when installed in a side stream will not endanger the main bearings.

To minimize condensation and consequent accumulation of moisture from the atmosphere or as a product of combustion, lubricating systems are maintained at approximately 160°F. Centrifuges will remove sludge, moisture, and heavier-than-oil contaminants and should be used at periodic intervals. Magnetic filters will remove magnetic impurities.

Hazards from lubricating systems fall into several categories, *viz.*, failure of the lubrication system itself, oil leakages, vapors, and carry-over and accumulation of oil.

Unless the machine is stopped immediately, failure of its lubrication system will result in damaged bearings and shafts. To minimize this danger most lubricating circuits are provided with automatic controls to stop drivers immediately when the lubricating-oil pressure decreases.

Oil leakages commonly represent a housekeeping and maintenance problem (to protect employees from slipping) and, when leaking on hot parts, a serious fire hazard. Oil leakages result from (1) inadequate or defective lubricating-oil piping connections, bearings, and bearings housings; (2) undersize oil-return lines that allow foam to build up and leak out of the bearings; and (3) certain rotating parts, such as oil and grit flingers, which induce air flow that blows foam and/or droplets out of bearing housings.

The air space above the lubricating-oil reservoirs always contains oil vapor and oil droplets. Some reciprocating machines, such as Diesel and gas engines, cool the underside of pistons with lubricating oil, and the action of the reciprocating parts increases the quantity of oil droplets in the crankcase. Recommendations of manufacturers should be followed to minimize the hazards of crankcase explosions which result from ignition of the oil droplets.

The oil reservoirs of turbines and of axial or centrifugal compressors are enclosed and vented to atmosphere and are usually considered as non-hazardous. However, when the lubricating oil or seal-oil systems of a compressor or turbine are in contact with hydrocarbons, the oil reservoir must be vented to a safe location.

The oil droplets carried by the discharge air of lubricated reciprocating air compressors will deposit in the discharge pipes or accumulate in low spots and in the air receiver tanks. High discharge temperatures will carbonize the oil, resulting in considerable carbon deposits. Explosions have resulted from the oil deposits and fires have taken place on the carbon deposits. These hazards are minimized by thorough draining of the discharge system, the use of oil separators, and selection of compressor stages that limit discharge temperatures. Nonflammable lubricants and the use of non-lubricated compressors will eliminate this hazard, but at higher initial and operating costs.

POWER-TRANSMISSION EQUIPMENT

Mechanical Couplings. The connection between the shafts of the driver and driven machine must be capable of transmitting the required torque, and in some cases special types of couplings are required for avoidance of problems involving misalignment, vibration, torsional flexibility, etc.

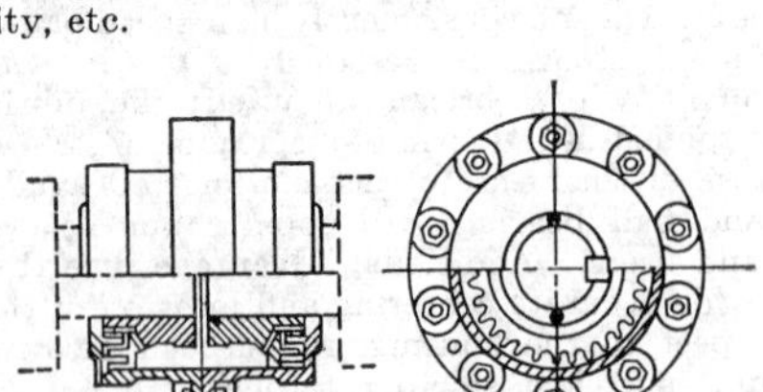

Fig. 24-48. Gear and dental flexible coupling. (*From Marks, "Mechanical Engineers' Handbook," McGraw-Hill, New York,* 1958.)

Solid couplings consist of rigid flanges on each shaft, bolted solidly together to form a continuous stiff shaft. Their use is favored when it is desired that the connected machines act as a single unit (for example, the rotor of a motor or generator may be used as the flywheel of a reciprocating engine or compressor) or to reduce over-all length (such as an overhanging blower) or to eliminate bearings (by coupling components together such as a gear pinion to a turbine). Shaft misalignment can result in excessive shaft stresses, bearing overloads, or vibration, and therefore solid couplings can be used only when operating conditions do not affect shaft alignment. Thus solid couplings are limited to machines in which the frames can be solidly bolted together and maintained in line. If misalignment can occur then flexible couplings must be used.

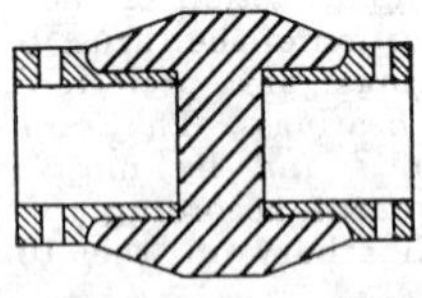

Fig. 24-49. Rubber flexible coupling. (*From Marks, "Mechanical Engineers' Handbook," McGraw-Hill, New York,* 1958.)

Flexible couplings (see Figs. 24-48 to 24-51) can be designed to compensate for shaft misalignment or to modify the torsional flexibility of shafts to reduce the effect of torque variations. Torsional flexibility is obtained by using rubber bushings between the bolts and the flanges or, for jaw-type clutches, by use of rubber inserts or rubber bushings between the flange and the shaft. Still other designs use straps to transmit the torque. Couplings that are designed for misalignment use straps, knuckle joints, wobble plates, or some other mechanism that allows a sliding action between meshing parts. A misalignment produces a cyclic displacement

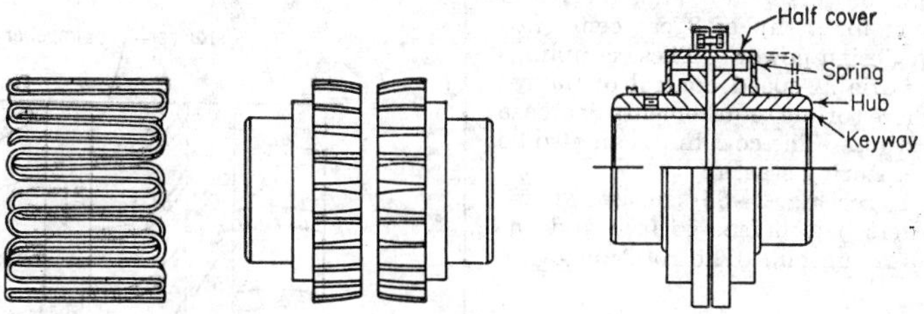

FIG. 24-50. "Falk" steelflex coupling. *(From Marks, "Mechanical Engineers' Handbook," McGraw-Hill, New York,* 1958.)

between the two shafts, increases bearing loads, and produces a frictional power loss. It is this frictional power that imposes a limitation on the allowable misalignment of high-speed shafts, because the friction heat increases faster with speed than the heat-dissipation ability.

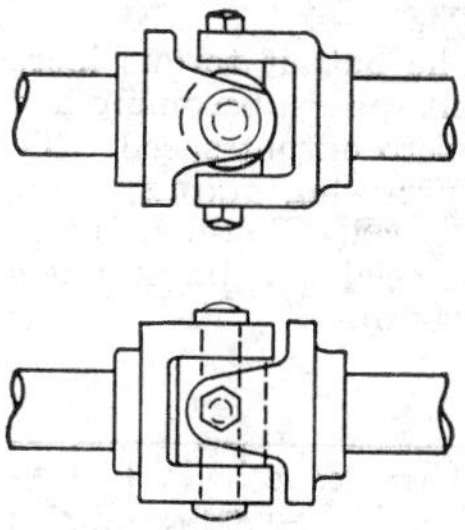

FIG. 24-51. Hooke's universal joint. *(From Marks, "Mechanical Engineers' Handbook," McGraw-Hill, New York,* 1958.)

Couplings for high-speed and/or high-power machinery are almost exclusively of the gear (or dental) type. Torque is transmitted by two coupling halves bolted together, which have at each end an internal gear that meshes with gear teeth machined on the periphery of the shaft flanges. Under running conditions, misalignment, errors in tooth spacing, etc., will cause movement between the mating gear teeth, requiring that lubricating oil or grease be used to prevent damage by fretting. Most couplings are lubricated by filling the coupling with oil or packing it with grease at the time of installation. For special conditions the couplings can be designed to be lubricated continuously.

Disconnect Couplings. When it is necessary to disconnect or connect machines while in operation a jaw-type coupling can be used—provided it is operated only when the two shafts are running at the same speed. Friction clutches allow the shafts to be engaged while revolving at different speeds, and overrunning clutches will disengage automatically when the speed of the driven unit exceeds that of the driver (see Figs. 24-52 and 24-53). Overrunning clutches (Fig. 24-54) may be of a jaw type or may use oval pins between an inner and an outer raceway which jam when the torque is in one direction and roll out of engagement for reversed torques. These devices can be used to prevent reverse rotation.

The Airflex coupling is a friction coupling consisting of an input hub upon which a rubberized canvas tube is mounted. Its inflation brings the tube in contact and exerts pressure on an outer ring, which is in turn connected to the output shaft. This type of coupling may dampen vibratory torques, allow some misalignment, and permit engagement with the shafts running at different speeds.

Hydraulic and Electric Couplings. The connection between shafts is a rotating fluid in the case of a hydraulic coupling and a rotating magnetic field in the case of the electric coupling. These types of couplings have common characteristics in that the shafts may be connected or disconnected while in operation and at any

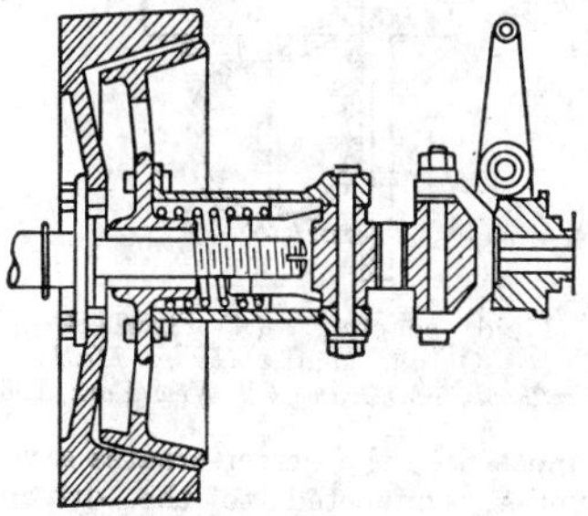

FIG. 24-52. Cone clutch. *(From Marks, "Mechanical Engineers' Handbook," McGraw-Hill, New York,* 1958.)

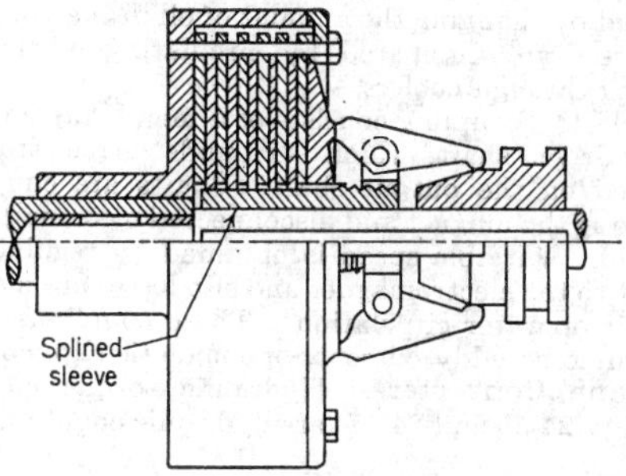

FIG. 24-53. Multidisk clutch. *(From Marks, "Mechanical Engineers' Handbook," McGraw-Hill, New York,* 1958.)

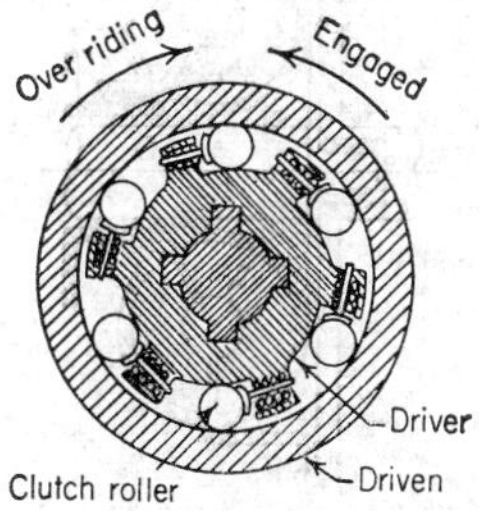

FIG. 24-54. Overrunning clutch. *(From Vallance and Doughtie, "Design of Machine Members," 3d ed., p. 262, McGraw-Hill, New York,* 1951.)

speed of the input or output shafts; stepless variable-speed characteristics can be obtained; input torque is always equal to output torque (therefore, efficiency equals the speed ratio); the absence of a physical connection provides a large amount of torsional dampening; and they are usually designed for a slip of 3 per cent (*i.e.*, 97 per cent efficiency) at design power. These couplings are frequently used for variable-speed control of pumps and other equipment, where torque requirements decrease rapidly with speed reduction. The couplings can also be used to unload the driver during startup.

The hydraulic coupling (see Fig. 24-55) consists of two open-faced vaned impellers placed face to face and enclosed in a housing containing oil. The rotation of an

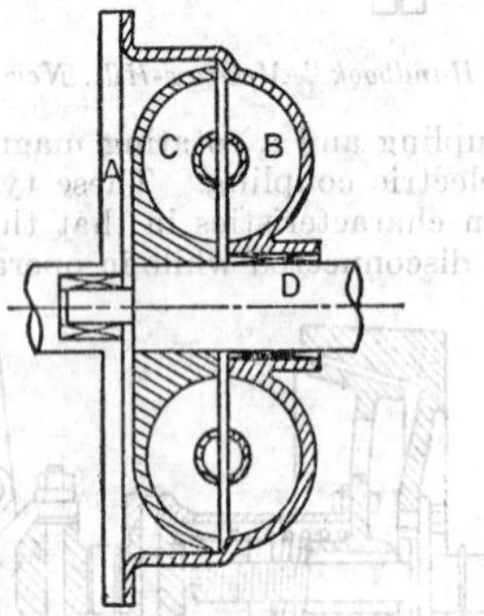

FIG. 24-55. Fluid coupling: (*A*) Flywheel. (*B*) Impeller. (*C*) Runner. (*D*) Output shaft. (*From Marks, "Mechanical Engineers' Handbook," McGraw-Hill, New York,* 1958.)

impeller connected to the driver creates a vortex. The output impeller, connected to the driven machine, obtains its power by slowing down the vortex. The shafts are coupled by filling the case with oil and are disconnected by draining. Variable-speed control is obtained by changing the amount of oil in the vortex, and slip losses are dissipated by circulating oil from the coupling through coolers.

An electric coupling consists of a metal ring connected to the driver shaft, which surrounds an electromagnet mounted on the output shaft. Shafts are coupled by energizing the magnet and disconnected by demagnetizing the field. Variable speed is obtained by regulating the current to the electromagnet and slip losses are dissipated with air or water circulation. These couplings are also referred to as eddy current, or magnetic slip, couplings.

Torque Converters. Hydraulic torque converters (see Figs. 24-56 and 24-57) are hydraulic couplings with a

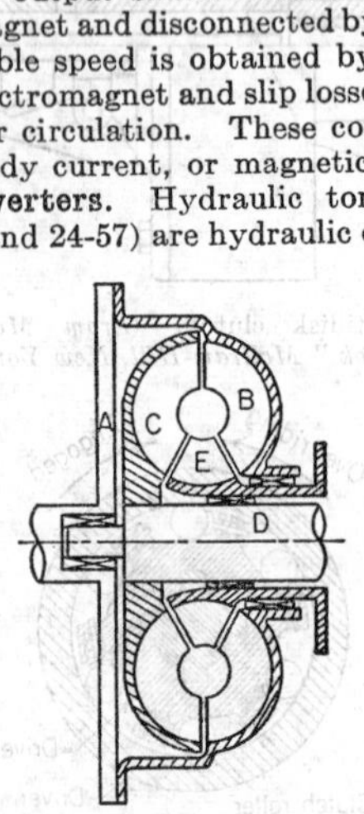

FIG. 24-56. Hydraulic torque converter: (*A*) Flywheel. (*B*) Impeller. (*C*) Runner. (*D*) Output shaft. (*E*) Reactor. (*From Marks, "Mechanical Engineers' Handbook," McGraw-Hill, New York,* 1958.)

stationary vane system (reactor) placed between the driven impeller and the output turbine runner. Maximum efficiency occurs for a given ratio of input to output

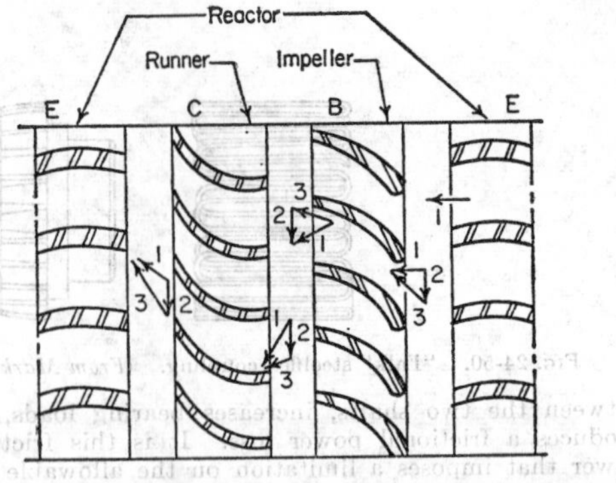

FIG. 24-57. Schematic of converter blading; (1) absolute fluid velocity; (2) velocity vector-converter elements; (3) fluid velocity relative to converter elements. (*From Marks, "Mechanical Engineers' Handbook," McGraw-Hill, New York,* 1958.)

shaft speeds. The output torque increases rapidly for lower output shaft speeds, becoming five or six times the input torque at zero output speed. The output torque decreases with increasing output speed, becoming zero at the runaway speed. Power input is proportional to the cube of input speed and almost independent of output speed (see Fig. 24-58).

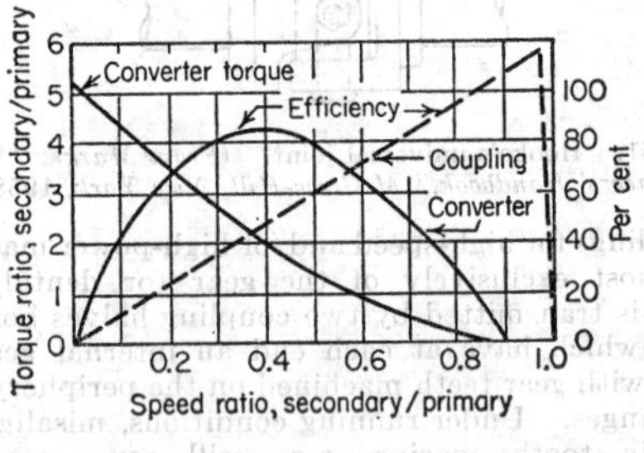

FIG. 24-58. Hydraulic-coupling characteristic curves. (*Heldt, "Torque Converters and Transmissions," Chilton, Philadelphia.*)

Variable-area vanes can be used to change the rate of oil flow and thus vary the pump power input; however, their expense limits their use. Gears and clutches are frequently incorporated with torque converters to obtain special features, such as (1) connection and disconnection of the load, reverse rotation, (2) step-up and step-down gears; and (3) free wheeling of the normally stationary reactor. The free-wheeling reactor changes the torque converter into a hydraulic coupling and improves operation at high speeds.

Torque converters find their principal uses with reciprocating internal-combustion engines to obtain high-torque non-stalling characteristics. Other drivers, such as motors, steam turbines, and engines, have high stalling or pull-out torques and do not require torque converters.

Electric torque converters consist of a d-c generator and a d-c motor and are frequently used for such applications as Diesel-electric locomotives. The possibility of varying the fields of either the motor or generator or both provides a very flexible and efficient torque conversion.

Belt Drives. Belts can be used to transmit power from one shaft to another, and at the same time obtain a reduction or increase in r.p.m. As a rule the shafts are parallel; however, by proper design and at lower loads they can be placed at an angle.

Most flat belts used in industry are made of either duck or leather. Canvas or duck belts are protected from erosion by a rubber covering. For special conditions, flat belts can be made from almost any material that can be bent around pulleys.

Under normal conditions, flat belts operate at speeds below 3000 ft./min. However, carefully designed installations have been operated successfully at belt speeds as high as 6000 ft./min. Belts experience a critical speed phenomenon which is evidenced by the pulleys "riding" from side to side or by violent "flapping" of the slack side of the belt. The critical speed of an installation is a function of the geometry of the installation, belt characteristics, and tension. Thus, when critical conditions occur, they are corrected by changing some of these parameters.

Leather has a tensile strength of 3000 to 4000 lb./sq. in. and is usually designed to a safety factor of 10, making the working stress 300 lb./sq. in. Leather belts are made in one, two, or three plies, with ply thicknesses of approximately $^{11}/_{64}$ and $^{13}/_{64}$ in. for medium and heavy belting, respectively. The power capacity of a belt can be estimated for heavy ply by interpolating from the following factors

At 600 ft./min.	1.2 hp./in. belt width
At 6000 ft./min.	8.9 hp./in. belt width

Two-ply belts carry 70 per cent more power and three plies 125 per cent more at the same speed as single-ply belts.

Duck used in rubber-covered belts is graded by the weight in ounces of a strip 36 in. wide by 40 in. long. The standard weights are 24, 26, 28, 30, and 32 oz. for such a strip. The tensile strength is almost proportional to the weight and number of plies. The effective tension of a 28-oz. belt is 10 lb./ in. of belt width.

All belt drives depend on the coefficient of friction to balance the tension differential between the slack and driving sides of the pulley. The power can be calculated from the following relationships:

$$K_s\text{ (hp.)} = \frac{(F_1 - F_2)V}{3300}$$

where V = belt speed, ft./min.
K_s = service factor that varies from 1 for steady loads and up to 2 or more for shock loads or loads involving stalling
F_1 = tensile force on driving side
F_2 = tensile force on "slack" side

The relationship between F_1 and F_2 depends on the angle of contact, the friction coefficient of the belt on the pulleys, and the centrifugal forces on the belt which tend to separate it from the pulley. (Gravity will also cause separation of the belt from the lower pulley in vertical drives.)

The wedging action induced by the tensile forces on **V-belts** against the pulley grooves increases the contact load, and hence the friction of V-belts is two or three times that of flat belts, with resulting proportionally greater power transmission. In addition V-belts can use smaller pulley diameters than flat belts for the same power rating.

V-belts are constructed with an inner cord section to carry the load and an outer protective covering to form the friction surface. Load-carrying capacity per V-belt F_1 varies from 35 to 400 lb.; in general F_2 is equal to zero when used in the equation given above for flat belts.

The theoretical speed ratio between driver and driven equipment for both flat and V-belts is essentially proportional to the diameter of the pulleys; however, because of slippage and creep, the actual speed ratio is not constant. Actual slippage between the pulley and the belt may be as high as 2 per cent for flat belts but approaches zero for V-belts. Creepage is due to elastic elongation of the belt under tension, resulting in the belt velocity on the driving side being slightly greater than on the slack side.

Belts are extremely flexible with respect to their application in that a wide variety of spacing between pulleys can be used. Although maximum service life is obtained when the shafts are parallel, greater misalignments between shafts can be tolerated than with almost any other speed-reduction device. Belts can be used to connect shafts at an angle, provided that the belt load is reduced.

Variable-speed V-belt drives use adjustable cones to obtain variable pulley diameters and therefore adjustable speed. For example, with the cones at their innermost position in the driving pulley and at their outermost position on the driven pulley minimum reduction is obtained. With the driver cones spaced fully apart and the driven pulley cones spaced as closely as possible maximum reduction is obtained. Such variable-speed drivers are commercially available in power ratings up to 25 hp.

Chain Drives. Chains and sprockets are used to obtain a fixed speed ratio by eliminating slippage or for power greater than is obtainable by belts. The load-carrying capacity is a function of the tensile strength of the chain, and the reduction ratio exactly equals the ratio of the number of teeth on the driver and driven sprockets. Most chains run at speeds up to 6000 ft./min., but special chains suitable for speeds up to 8000 ft./min. are available. Tensile strengths as high as 100,000 lb./chain are available.

Grease packing is common with low-speed lightly loaded chains, but high-speed and high-power chains require oil lubrication to minimize wear.

The PIV (positive infinitely variable) drive is very similar in operation to the variable-speed belt type just described, but since it uses chains there is no slip.

Gear Drives. Gears are more compact and can operate at much higher speeds and power than other speed-reduction mechanisms. Most commonly used are spur gears, which require that pinion and gear shafts be parallel. As gear speeds increase the frictional heat resulting from the sliding contact between the pinion and gear teeth becomes appreciable and special tooth profiles are used. Of these the most common are the cycloid and the involute.

Gear teeth of a **cycloidal** profile engage in a rolling action which minimizes friction; however, pinion and gear shafts of cycloidal gears must be very accurately aligned and spaced. **Involute** profiles do not fully achieve a fully rolling action and some sliding between teeth during contact does occur; however, their action is not sensitive to normal variations in shaft alignment or spacing. Therefore, most industrial gears are of the involute type. Gear dimensions and tolerances have been standardized by the American Standards Association and the American Gear Manufacturers Association as follows:

Class 1—industrial gears cut with formed cutters
Class 2—gears cut with great care
Class 3—very accurately cut and ground gears

Impact loading during tooth meshing increases with increasing pitch-line velocity and with manufacturing inaccuracies. As a result high-speed gears are always of the precision type (Class 3).

The teeth of **helical gears** are cut at an angle (as a helix), allowing several teeth to mesh simultaneously, resulting in smoother running. Herringbone or double-helix gears have two helices of opposite angles on the same gear blank, thus eliminating the axial thrust of a single helix.

"Pinion" refers to the smaller of the two gears and "gear" refers to the larger-diameter member—frequently referred to as "bull gears." Gearing sets may be single reduction consisting of one pinion and one gear, or may consist of two or more reductions, in which case the gear of the first stage drives the pinion of the second stage.

Planetary gears consist of three sets of gears, a pinion (sun gear) meshing with two or more planet gears which in turn rotate within an internal gear. The internal gear is usually stationary, forming part of the housing; the planet gears are connected to one shaft and the sun gear to the other shaft. Planetary-gear systems are compact, achieve a large reduction in a limited space, and result in input and output shafts in the same center line.

Bevel gears are frequently used to drive vertical pumps or process machinery with horizontal drivers. For special cases other angles than 90 deg. can be used; however, the two shafts must always be in the same plane, and as a result one of the gears must overhang its bearings to avoid intersection of the two shafts.

Spiral-bevel gears have tooth forms that allow lateral displacement of the shafts, thus permitting the use of bearings on both sides of each gear. The thrust on the driving spiral-bevel gear is not unidirectional as in the case of bevel gears but reverses upon reversal of rotation.

Worm and Worm Wheels. Worm and worm-wheel drives are limited, in most instances, to speed reductions of 10 to 1 per reduction stage. Greater reductions are achieved by means of worm gears which allow reductions up to 500 to 1. The contact surface of the screw on the worm slides along the teeth of the gear (or worm wheel), resulting in an efficiency of 85 per cent as compared with efficiencies of over 98 per cent for precision spur gears.

Poor efficiency and heat removal of dissipated energy limits worm gears to low-speed applications. The efficiency of the worm depends on the helix angle of teeth on the gear. Large angles result in higher efficiencies and allow the gear to be driven from either the worm or the gear. Worm gears can be designed to be self-locking—that is, a torque on the gear cannot cause rotation of the worm. The worm may be straight or conical to allow engagement of more teeth.

The worm may have one or more screw threads, and one revolution of the worm advances the gear a number of teeth proportional to the number of threads on the worm. The reduction ratio is therefore equal to the total number of teeth on the worm gear divided by the number of threads on the worm.

PLANT SAFETY AND FIRE PROTECTION

The ultimate goal of safety and fire protection is the complete prevention of personnel injury, loss of life, and destruction of property as a result of accidents, fires, explosions, or other hazardous situations. While this goal may seem illusionary, no other guiding principle can achieve minimization of calculated risks to the extremely minute fractional percentage which characterizes successful plant operation. Adequate safety and fire prevention emphasize the prevention of acccidents and failures, and equally important, their containment on occurrence for avoidance of catastrophes. Unfortunately, the technical principles and practices in many fields are insufficiently established or rationalized for a valid evaluation of all calculated risks, thus leaving to the individual owner-operator the sole responsibility for adequate safety.

Character of Hazards. Process industries introduce a wider than average range of hazards, as a result of the presence of sizable quantities of flammable and sometimes unstable materials, frequently at elevated temperatures which promote ignition or decomposition. With high pressures, the potential energy release is increased in the presence of structural failures, explosions, detonations, or violent exothermic reactions. Other process industry hazards are introduced by contents which are lethal, toxic, irritating, or corrosive to humans, or which involve serious deterioration to structural materials. Hazardous contents in combination with the possibility of sizable energy release during high-pressure operations or from explosions proportionately magnify the over-all risk. The process industries are also subject to the usual industrial occupational hazards, so that factory safety measures as developed for industry in general are widely applicable.

Effective plant safety and fire protection extend to every phase of engineering, operation, and maintenance. The process should be arranged to avoid, whenever possible, unstable or difficult-to-control stages in order to minimize static or dynamic overloads on equipment, with critical locations for their control emphasized. As a minimum, the design of structures and equipment should reflect industry experience in reducing all calculated risks as far as economically possible and with full awareness of and careful assessment of special situations for which average industry practices may be inadequate. Equipment and individual items must be examined not only for normal service but also for emergency demands, to avoid failures which would impair other critical components. Especially vital is the selection of adequate instrument and control components to minimize swings and instabilities. Wherever applicable, reliable automatic safety devices should be provided.

Effective **operating instructions** and trained operators, fully aware of all potential situations for which safety depends on operator alertness, are also essential. Instructions and training should emphasize that controls and safety devices are subject to malfunctions and that without effective preventive maintenance the utmost in equipment and design cannot be depended upon for its full contribution to safety. Fully competent inspection is the cornerstone of process plant safety and should be independent of direct production administration to assure against any compromise with safety.

Safety and Fire Standards. Various agencies have developed standards for safety, fire protection, and fire prevention. Some of these are broadly applicable, while others are for specific industries and, for other applications, must be either modified or else are only partly adaptable. Extreme care must be exercised to avoid uneconomic or ineffective design resulting from an arbitrary application of such standards.

The American Petroleum Institute and the Manufacturing Chemists' Association have standards for mechanical equipment, plant layout, and materials handling. Fire protection and prevention standards for various hazards and industries are available from the National Fire Protection Association, a non-commercial and non-profit association supported by individual and business memberships, which acts as a clearinghouse for technical contributions with respect to fire protection and prevention.

The standards developed by the National Fire Protection Association are adopted, published, and distributed by the National Board of Fire Underwriters, which is maintained by the major fire insurance companies to engage in educational, statistical, and engineering functions. Also, its subsidiary, Underwriters' Laboratories, Incorporated, performs tests of fire-protection equipment and of materials of construction for resistance to fire and of equipment for compliance with standards developed by the laboratories.

Standards applicable to some industries are provided by insurance underwriter groups, such as the Factory Insurance Associates and the Associated Factory Mutual Fire Insurance Companies, and are intended for preferred risks. Certain standards of governmental agencies also apply to safety and fire protection. Federal agencies include the Department of Commerce and the Interstate Commerce Commission. Local and state regulations may also be applicable to specific plants.

Avoiding Catastrophies. Uncontrolled fires, explosions, or detonations in areas of concentrated equipment can result in catastrophic destruction of life and property. It is therefore important to provide effective means for limiting or containing explosions and for positive avoidance of detonations. Means to delay the penetration of heat and for restricting the spread of fires should be considered in layout and design.

The layout of an over-all plant as well as its specific units must be studied to provide for suitable control of fire and explosion. A **grid type of layout** is essential, with road and fire-water systems at a maximum of 1000 ft. center to center, serving two sides of each major hazard. This road system should be paralleled by pipeways and electrical service above or below ground. The distance from the road center line to the nearest process unit or other hazard will vary with the process or hazard, from a minimum of 50 ft. to usually not more than 150 ft., with adjacent process units 100 to 300 ft. apart. The center line of roads is usually 50 to 100 ft. from the center line of dikes. Greater separation further limits concentration of risk and potential damage. Accessways between equipment, which are required for operation and maintenance, are valuable in limiting the spread of fires and should not be less than 15 ft. in clear width. These unit accessways are usually linked to the over-all plant road system at intervals of not more than 300 ft.

Storage tanks, whose contents upon unforeseen release must be contained, are spaced to suit dike or retaining-wall details, with groups usually separated by at least one-half the diameter of the smallest tank.

Buildings for storage of materials are located to suit attendant hazards. Highly combustible or explosive materials are usually isolated with blast or fire walls provided where dictated by the material characteristics and relative location.

Equipment within process units should be located with due consideration to potential hazard. Open fires (furnaces, flares, etc.) are preferably located on the prevailing windward side of the plot, and at a maximum feasible distance. Elevated structures should be located upwind of furnaces to minimize flue-gas hazard to personnel, as well as dangerous concentrations of volatile combustibles. When furnaces and equipment must be close-coupled for process considerations, leakage potentials should be minimized and adequate fire extinguishment means emphasized. Equipment subject to possible rupture should be isolated by distance, blast enclosures, or pits.

Design of Control Facilities. Dikes for liquid-storage tanks are normally sized to contain the volume of the largest tank plus 10 per cent of the volume of the remaining tanks within a common enclosure. Dikes should be not more than half the height of the tank and preferably 7 ft. maximum to safeguard personnel. The clear distance from toe of dike to tank should be not less than one-third the tank diameter or 10 ft. to allow air movement to scour out gas pockets. An alternate to dike walls for containment of spills around liquid-storage tanks is drainage spillways and collection basins. Large ditches or conduits collect and conduct released liquid to basins which are usually sized to hold the contents of two or three of the largest storage tanks in the plant or area.

Blast walls should be designed to suit the process and material hazards. To permit access, it is usual to protect three sides, provided sufficient separation is available for the one unprotected direction. Otherwise, access must be through overlapping walls or similar means. Walls usually project approximately 10 ft. above the top and clear the equipment by 6 to 10 ft. Plants handling, manufacturing, or storing explosives or materials of similar hazard should comply with accepted regulations for explosive plants as detailed in the *U.S. Ordnance Safety Manual.* Applicable isolation distances are listed in this manual as a function of potential energy release.

To minimize damage from short-duration fires and allow time for blowing or draining contents and for fire fighting to become effective, it is usual practice to protect critical structures and equipment against heat input. Structures which are usually so fireproofed are those which support major process equipment and piping, including the skirts or columns of process vessels. Insulating or dense concrete, or magnesia or calcium silicate or other insulating materials, either preformed or plastic, are presently used for fireproofing. Because of labor cost for application, brick is no longer commonly used for insulation.

Accelerated Energy Release. Accelerated energy release may occur in the presence of rapid oxidation or other highly exothermic reactions or from the decomposition of unstable materials. The rate of temperature rise, unless diminished by heat loss, can cause explosive pressure rise as a function of the full adiabatic heat release; and with favorable composition, conduit geometry (principally length of travel), and initial pressure it may further accelerate to detonation velocities of 1000 to 25,000 ft./sec.

It is impractical and usually impossible to design equipment to withstand **detonations.** Accordingly, positive measures must be exercised to prevent their occurrence and/or delay their propagation. These include the use of diluents, coolants, or packing to accelerate heat removal, retard flow, or limit cross section of undivided flow. Instrumentation sensing initial pressure rise in order to interrupt flow is of questionable value. When feasible for personnel and property protection, equipment subject to high-energy release should be isolated. Detonation hazards increase in the presence of oxygen and unstable materials such as acetylene. During 1959 and 1960, the A.P.I. Equipment Division sponsored meetings and committee activities aimed at promoting an appreciation of detonation hazards [see Jacobs, Occurrence and Nature of Hydrocarbon-Air Detonations, *Proc. Am. Petrol. Inst.*, November, 1959. Kistiakowsky, Initiation of Detonations in Gases, *Ind. Eng. Chem.*, **43,** 2794 (1951). Ghormley, Guard against Detonation Hazards, *Petrol. Refiner*, **37,** 185 (January, 1958)].

The most common service applications involving oxidation are combustion-type inert-gas generators and direct-contact process heaters. Most inert-gas generators operate at essentially atmospheric pressure, so that the full potential adiabatic pressure is not over 8 atm., for which sufficient vessel thickness can easily be provided within the material yield strength. For inert-gas generators or direct-contact heaters, operating at higher pressures, it is equally desirable to design for explosion pressure, whenever feasible. To minimize the hazard of filling the succeeding pipe lines and pressure vessels with an explosive mixture, fully effective (and sometimes duplicate) instrumentation is essential, which will interrupt fuel-gas flow when the flame is extinguished.

Processes introducing an air and particularly an oxygen feed stream to hydrocarbons or other highly oxidizable contents deserve careful scrutiny as to maximum energy release and proportionate explosion pressure for a safe design of the containment equipment.

Avoidance of **pressure-equipment failures** is dependent on adequate relief valves, which must be protected against corrosion and fouling and be tested with sufficient frequency to assure operability. Certain pressure equipment is not readily protected against pressure rise resulting from abrupt and sizable release of contents, such as is encountered with heat-transfer-element failures.

Overtemperature is principally a hazard on internally insulated vessels but can also occur in the presence of coolant failure or exothermic reactions. When the short-time strength of the vessel is not exceeded at the flow temperature and pressure, depressurization can usually be accomplished without serious failure. On the other hand, when the material short-time strength can be exceeded and serious immediate failure will occur, emergency heat-removal means, in the form of a water jacket, is advisable.

A major hazard in process industries that is frequently not appreciated is the introduction or presence during initial heating of **water in piping or equipment.** Such water contacting hot surfaces will flash to steam with rapid increase in volume. A similar hazard results when a hot material is brought into wet equipment. The attendant pressure wave has frequently caused serious damage to process vessel trays and other internals, with occasionally more serious personnel injuries and major damage to process equipment. It is imperative that vessels, equipment, and piping be dried out thoroughly before start of operations and that sufficient and suitably located drains be provided.

Explosions of flammable materials may occur as a result of a minor spark discharge of **static electricity.** Static charges may be generated by friction between two surfaces, one of which is a non-conductor, by friction between similar substances when there is relative motion of the particles, and by the turbulence of dust- or liquid-droplet-laden gases. Static electricity is generated by moving belts or vehicles, flowing liquids or gases, conveyed or fluidized solids, liquid atomization, or mixing with vapor. Protection against these hazards usually starts with determination of the locations where generated, and provision of means to effect reduction in potential or dissipate the charge without spark discharges. Metal parts of vessels and connecting piping should be electrically grounded, and the use of air for mixing flammable liquids should be restricted or avoided. Tank trucks and rail cars for flammable liquids and their filling connections should be grounded. Steam, air, and water hoses used in areas where flammable materials are present should also be grounded. Special studies are frequently required to determine a proper course of action for new installations.

The **purging** of process systems is an essential safety measure prior to opening up or entering for cleaning or maintenance. Before personnel enter a vessel a check should be made for the presence of combustibles and for adequate oxygen. Otherwise masks should be used. Air must be eliminated from most process systems prior to startup. Steam is usually employed for this purpose or when unsuitable, inert or natural or other gas, water flooding, evacuation to subatmospheric pressure, or other applicable means can be used. Earlier comments relative to water hazards apply particularly to steam condensation during purging.

Storage and Handling. The safe storage and handling of **hazardous materials** requires a thorough knowledge of their properties for positive containment and avoidance of leakage. Storage tanks, piping, and pump materials must be selected for resistance to rapid corrosion or other deterioration (caustic embrittlement, etc.) which can lead to structural failure. When significant, the design and installation must protect against contact by eliminating or enclosing or shielding gasketed and packed joints and other potential sources of leakage.

Similarly, dikes or low walls are provided around storage vessels, whose capacity should at least equal the volume of the vessel. Chlorine and similar toxic gases are preferably stored in exterior locations to permit dissipation of minor leakage and with sun-shade roofs to minimize corrosion and pressure rise. Hazardous storage areas should be fenced to assure against entry by other than assigned personnel. Hazardous materials are handled more safely in closed systems. When drum shipments are unavoidable, personnel should be fully protected by suitable clothing, gloves, and masks. Relief-valve leakage must be avoided with lethal or other extremely hazardous materials. Accordingly, rupture diaphragms are used as auxiliary positive seals.

Emergency showers and eyewash stations must be provided in all areas for storage, handling, transfer, and processing materials harmful to human tissue. These facilities should be operable in all types of weather and should be simple and reliable to ensure that an injured man (even temporarily blinded) can operate them.

Equipment, instruments, and piping for corrosive or toxic materials should be installed in such a manner as to minimize accidental discharge. Special guards and/or locks and well-defined operation precautions can minimize the possibility of such occurrence.

General Plant Safety Provisions. Certain safety requirements are common to all industrial plants and process installations. Many of these are usually set by local legislation, such as building and plumbing codes, or by insurance inspection. Others follow generally acceptable experience and practices.

Multistory buildings, building roofs, and elevated open structures are frequently used to support, house, or service process equipment. Alternate **means of escape** from elevated levels of such buildings or structures can be by stairway or ladder or chute. In some installations ropes and slide poles are acceptable. Escapeways which lead personnel into a single area, and those which terminate in a dead end or in hazardous areas are unacceptable. An additional escapeway from an elevated station is usually considered necessary for distances in excess of 40 ft. from an elevator, stairway, or ladder. In a similar manner, escape doors for the ground floor of a fully enclosed building are customarily spaced so that no worker must travel more than 40 ft. to an exit. Such requirements are often subject to legal or insurance restrictions. To protect the interior of a fully enclosed building from an exterior fire, or to prevent spread of a fire from within a building, escape doors and all windows are fitted with fusible links that ensure self-closing.

Process equipment and accessories that require frequent **inspection, adjustment,** or **repair** during operation should be readily accessible, and when located more than 8 ft. above grade, platforms should be provided. Platforms are also usually provided for maintenance access to equipment where manholes are located more than 12 ft. above grade.

Infrequently operated valves, for example, those used only during startup or shutdown of process equipment, can be operated from ladders or by chain. Small isolated pieces of equipment, such as temperature indicators and pressure gages, can also be serviced from ladders if not more than 8 ft. above grade or a platform. Handrails should be provided around all platforms and around all uncovered sumps or pits. Ladders serving all platforms more than 12 ft. above grade should be provided with cages extending down to 8 ft. above grade or platform. Handling facilities should be provided to lift all equipment which must be handled during maintenance operations. Mobile equipment should be used for this purpose whenever possible and access ways should be arranged to facilitate this.

Items not accessible with mobile equipment should be serviced by portable equipment whenever possible. Davits should be provided for manhole covers, exchanger bonnets, and relief valves. Elevated equipment not accessible to mobile equipment which requires servicing and involves weight in excess of 1000 lb. should be provided with permanent handling facilities. Trolley beams or cranes should be provided for servicing large compressors or drivers, unless accessible for and suitable to servicing by mobile equipment.

Suitable guards are necessary for all rotating equipment, belt drives, chain drives, and powered conveyors. Screening devices, dryers, packaging, and similar equipment should also be similarly provided with guards to prevent contact with moving parts. Suitable electrical or mechanical interlocks should be provided on process unit equipment undergoing servicing or maintenance while the alternate equipment is on stream or otherwise in use.

Personnel entry into process equipment, which is connected to pressurized piping systems, is usually permitted only when all flow is positively and completely shut off by double-block valves with intervening vents or by blind flanges, or by double-disk valves with vents between seats. Valve motor operators should be disconnected or interlocked and hand valves red tagged, locked, or guarded by personnel.

Operators and maintenance workers must be protected against contact with hot piping or equipment. Piping, vessels, or equipment whose metal temperature exceeds 180°F., which are not insulated for heat conservation, should be provided with sufficient insulation to reduce surface temperature below 180°F. or else with guards to prevent direct contact.

Operating and Maintenance Practices. Motorized equipment, unless properly equipped and operated, can be a source of ignition for flammable materials, as a result of incandescent particles in its exhaust. Fumes from motorized equipment may also damage process and storage facilities, or when operated indoors prove a health hazard.

The hazard of exposing operators and maintenance workers to harmful fumes is well recognized. One common source is in the gaging of tanks with contents such as crude oil of appreciable sulfur content. Gas masks should be used here and whenever it is uncertain whether vessels, tanks, or piping are free of fumes that might cause respiratory distress.

When large pipe flanges are unbolted, springing due to cold stress and weight-induced movement can dislodge, strike, or pinch workers. The removal of manways, particularly on the bottom of vessels, involves the possibility of releasing pressure or liquid accumulation. In either case it is preferable that bolts be loosed only sufficiently to break the gasketed joint and that they are not removed until outflow or inflow is completed and the rigging adjusted to take weight. With tall vessels while hot, chimney effects assist ventilation and cooling while with smaller vessels fans may be necessary.

Flooding with water or circulating wet steam is effective for rapid cooling. Coke and other deposits can ignite when warm and in the presence of air. Deposits of **iron sulfide,** resulting from corrosion, can ignite spontaneously unless kept wet. When scraped from tanks or vessels it should be removed to a location where its ignition will not cause a hazard.

Maintenance and servicing must be performed under competent supervision, with independent and effective inspectors, equipped with necessary gages, tools, and equipment for all applicable non-destructive examinations.

Operation must be performed under clear and complete operating instructions, with organization and individual responsibilities clearly defined. Servicing during operation must be performed under the direction and responsibility of the operator.

Housekeeping of process plants will often reflect the general presence or absence of safety hazards. As a rule, a well-kept plant is usually a safe plant. Items of importance include the immediate clean-up of spills and oily wastes or rags, frequent checking of the effective operation of drainage provisions, and the prompt elimination of leakage and drips. Control of weeds and grass and the prompt removal of refuse add to plant appearance and safety.

Means for Fire Protection. Various means for fire protection are used in process industries, to suit individual processes and combustible or otherwise reactive contents. In general, these means serve to control heat penetration and/or isolate highly reactive materials.

The term combustion is applied to self-sustaining exothermic oxidation reactions in air at above ambient temperatures. When the reactants (air and fuel) are brought to a reaction temperature, **self-ignition** occurs. Conventional ignition temperature defines the initiation of a self-sustaining reaction, in conjunction with a localized high-temperature input (spark, glow plug, pilot flame, etc.) and is highly dependent on heat balance (*i.e.*, sensitive to geometry and attendant outflow of heat from the reaction zone). Combustion in air includes the heating of the air diluents (atmospheric nitrogen and rare gases), which limit the maximum adiabatic temperature attainable to about 3400° to 3700°F., depending on the fuel, with proportionately lower temperatures if excess air is present. As compared with air, oxidation in the presence of high percentages of oxygen is accelerated, with higher total temperatures (+6000°F.) and lower reaction (self-ignition) temperature. Heat release is also augmented by the presence of hydrogen, acetylene, etc.

Many other oxidizers can be involved; among the most potent are nitric acid, nitrogen tetroxide and other nitrogen oxides, and hydrogen peroxide. Non-oxygen-dependent exothermic reactions are also numerous; examples are chlorination and the decomposition of hydrogen peroxide, acetylene, ammonium and sodium nitrate. All these can cause rapid rise in temperature with pressure rise reflecting the degree of confinement and rate of reaction and the involved reaction rates which are in themselves temperature-sensitive. Avoidance of runaway reaction depends on removal of heat (cooling) and, except for decomposition of single compounds, isolation of the individual reactants from each other. In the following discussion only combustion in air and oxygen is specifically considered.

Three general **types of fires** are encountered in the process industries. One involves common combustible materials such as wood, rags, and paper; the next, flammable liquids and gases such as crude or refined petroleum products, petrochemicals, and solvents; and the third involves electrical equipment. With the wide use of platinum reformers and other hydrogen-dependent reactions, high-heat-releasing fires have assumed increased importance.

An explosion may be considered as combustion at accelerated reaction rates, in which a stored, in transit, or incidental volume of a combustible mixture undergoes self-accelerated reaction as the temperature at the flame front increases. **Explosions** in process plants are often the result of external or internal leakage, or uncontrolled flow. Combustion-gas generators and oxidation reactions introduce direct process operation potentials for explosions.

Principles of Fire Extinguishment. Fire may be extinguished by withdrawal of flammable contents, interrupting flammable flow, isolating fuel from air, heat removal to below reaction temperature, or by dispersal.

Withdrawal of flammable contents can be accomplished (1) by blowing down the vessel and piping contents (the rate of emptying depending on the operating pressure, blowdown line size and pressure drop, and properties of the flow), (2) by pump-out with the rate established by pump and piping capacity, or (3) by draining which is totally dependent on line size. Withdrawal is the most effective means for limiting the duration of fires, and the most effective over-all means for controlling fires of materials volatile at room temperature.

Flammable flow may be interrupted by the shutdown of pumps, the closing of battery-limit or yard transfer valves on the incoming lines, or closing intermediate or isolation valves on process units. In the presence of significant process storage volumes, these valves reduce fire duration to the storage and its rate of removal. Without storage the fire duration is the time to close the valve and depressure or drain the system. Isolation of flammable flow from the air is accomplished by blanketing or smothering, with steam and/or water spray, foam, carbon dioxide, dry and vaporizing chemical extinguishers, sand, or dirt. Flooding with water is effective on non-floating fuels. Mechanical means for shutting off air such as check valves, flappers, or snuffers are effective for enclosed fires, such as in storage tanks. Wet steam, water spray, and agitation to intermix burning and cool liquids accomplish heat removal. Dispersal by explosive action scatters the fuel and cools burning droplets by high-velocity heat transfer to air below reaction temperature.

Methods of Fire Extinguishment. Two types of **foam** are in common use. Chemical foam is a reaction product, consisting of water entrained in bubbles of carbon dioxide. Mechanical foam is formed by the air agitation of a water solution of a protein-base or other foaming liquid. The quality of foam is dependent on the foaming material used, its compatibility with the water, and its temperature. Masses of small water bubbles filled with carbon dioxide or air are most effective as a floating blanket to exclude oxygen from the fuel, with additional slight cooling effects by the entrained water. Foams adhere to most solid surfaces.

Water is fully effective as a coolant and as a blanket on heavy liquids on which it floats. On light liquids, its cooling effect is negligible and limited to heat removal while passing through the combustion zone. Similarly, its blanketing effect is a function of the degree of vaporization in this zone. **Fogging** under high pressure into minute droplets increases vaporization due to slower downward movement and greater surface for heat transfer. Fogging sprays are highly effective on hydrocarbon and electrical fires.

Agitation displaces and mixes hot and cool liquids and is generally accomplished with air introduced through distribution pipes, often the normal filling lines for storage tanks. **Agitation** is most effective for hydrocarbons heavier than kerosene which have relatively high ignition temperatures; for light hydrocarbons fire retardation is possible but extinguishment is difficult.

Carbon dioxide and **dry chemicals** can be used to extinguish fires involving flammable liquids and electrical equipment. Fixed carbon dioxide systems are often used to protect large rotating electrical machines. Fixed dry chemical systems have been proposed for protection of small tanks of liquids, but no installations of this type are known to be in use.

Small fires of all types can often be controlled by hand and/or mobile extinguishers. Such equipment is available for carbon dioxide, dry chemicals, water fogging, vaporizing liquids such as carbon tetrachloride, and foam. Most common are carbon dioxide, dry chemical, and foam. The first two are useful on all fires; foam is limited to liquid fires.

Design of Fire-Water Systems. Water can be used directly to extinguish fires involving combustible solids or confined liquids heavier than water, to prepare foam, to limit the spread of fires by cooling adjacent equipment and buildings, and to prevent heat damage by cooling sensitive structures. A fire-water system consists of an adequate water supply, pumps and a distribution system to all portions of the plant.

Two or more fire-water pumps should be provided, having a total discharge equal to the maximum quantity of water considered necessary for plant protection. The fire-water source may be reservoirs, basins, rivers, or inlets, or any reliable external source of supply having a total capacity of at least 4 hr. of full pump discharge. Pump suctions should be flooded and not require foot valves or priming devices. Water can be either fresh or salt water but should be reasonably free of oil and silt. For emergency use process and potable water supplies are considered available.

Fire-water distribution should employ looped systems, with a maximum length of 1000 ft. between crossovers. Shutoff valves should be provided to permit isolation at any area of the plant without affecting the balance of the system. No isolated section should include more than 3000 lin. ft. of main. For full advantage from parallel flow, all lines should be sized to provide a minimum pressure of 100 lb./sq. in. gage at any hydrant with valves open at maximum flow. Lines smaller than 6-in. size are seldom used and are not recommended.

The number, size, and location of hydrants at risk areas should provide the amount of water required, considering only two sides accessible, but with due consideration to the coverage of major risks. Hydrants at buildings housing personnel such as administration buildings, laboratories, and change houses should be located for convenient access. Hydrants should be fitted with two or three connections, each of which has a capacity of 250 gal./min. The spacing of hydrants should permit coverage of all portions of the plant with not more than five 50-ft. section of $2\frac{1}{2}$-in. hose for each hose stream, disregarding the negligible range of a fog nozzle. One hose stream should be provided for each 10,000 sq. ft. of combustible plant area.

Design of Foam Systems. Virtually all new installations of foam systems are of the mechanical-foam type, designed in accordance with National Board of Fire Underwriters (N.B.F.U.) Standard 11 for Foam Extinguishing Systems. These apply to localized inside hazards in rooms and buildings and for outside tanks.

No standards are established for general outside area protection. Three per cent of regular foam liquid is used for petroleum fires and 6 per cent of alcohol-resistant foam liquid for water-soluble liquid fires, with water to total 100 per cent added at time of use. Foam protection is required by N.B.F.U. for all flammable liquids stored in tanks not fitted with floating roofs. At ambient temperature refined petroleum products having a flash point higher than 200°F. (*e.g.*, asphalt, reduced crudes, some gas oils, bunker fuel, and lubricating oils) are not considered flammable liquids; however, when stored at a temperature close to the flash point, foam protection is provided. Foam discharge capacity is generally at a water rate (3 or 6 per cent liquid plus water) of 1 gal./min. for each 10 sq. ft. of protected surface area.

Foam may be applied using fixed or portable discharge outlets. Fixed outlets or foam chambers are permanently fastened to storage tanks, connected through piping to a remote fill connection to which foam solution is usually transported by portable or mobile equipment. Or foam can be applied through foam towers. The number of fixed or mobile discharge outlets is established in terms of tank diameter by N.B.F.U. For large tanks one outlet or chamber is required for approximately each 5000 sq. ft. of surface area.

Foam solution piping is designed to pass the amount of foam solution required for the number of foam outlets or chambers. Pipe is considered for design friction loss; allowable unit pressure drops for sizing these lines are usually high, ranging up to 12 lb./sq. in. per 100 lin. ft. Unless controlled by specified minimum line size, pressure drops of not less than 3 lb./sq. in. per 100 ft. are used to limit cost.

Individual indoor tanks, rooms, and buildings can be provided with foam protection using fixed discharge outlets for which the rate of water application is 1.6 gal./min. for each 10 sq. ft. of protected tank or space, and for a minimum application period of 2 min. The discharge outlets are either spray heads or floor connections, usually in a self-contained system, requiring only manual or automatic actuation of a water valve.

Similar systems can be provided for protection of outdoor equipment. Spray heads located directly over the equipment are preferred, with curbing to permit containment and effective blanketing of released combustible fluids. **Application rates** are normally adjusted to suit the equipment exposure and character of the flammable contents. Application water rates of 2 to 2.5 gal./min. for 10 sq. ft. of ground area are not uncommon, with period of application usually not less than 5 min.

Foam chambers are selected on the basis of flowing quantity and available water pressure. Most manufacturers offer a limited number of standard sizes of uniform details to suit orifices for the required flow at the available pressure.

The N.B.F.U. requires mobile foam protection for spill fires in storage-tank areas in terms of 50 gal./min. hose streams, as related to storage tank diameter. A smaller number of streams of larger capacity is permissible, although not preferred. Such equipment includes trailers, trucks, foam-liquid pumps, and measuring and proportioning devices. These are used to transport foam liquid to the fire and to mix the proper amount of liquid with water as used.

The following **foam-proportioning systems** are in general use:

1. **Educators,** which can be coupled in a fire-hose line to induce a flow of foam liquid through an orifice into the water stream. The foam liquid can be supplied by 5-gal. pails, 55-gal. drums, or tanks. Such proportioners may be in fixed locations or can be portable or incorporated into foam-discharge nozzles.

2. A fixed flow system utilizing **matched orifices** for mixture-ratio control. For alternate flow rates, parallel matched orifice plates are mounted in a valved manifold, selectively sized to pass the flow required for specific hazards, so that it is only necessary to operate the proper water and foam liquid valves for the particular application, with other valves closed. In general, this system is limited by the complexity and cost of the longer runs of piping and more involved manifold, but offers a centralized single-operation location. Foam must be pumped and pressures controlled for both foam and water streams.

3. A flow-indication proportioning system utilizing **meters** (usually proportionately calibrated rotameters) to measure water and foam-liquid flows mounted for ready visual observation. A pump is also required for the foam liquid. A hand-controlled valve is necessary in the foam pump discharge line for adjustment of mixtures rate and in the pressurized water line for adjustment of discharge rate.

Trailers and trucks, from small to large sizes, are used to transport foam, proportioning equipment, and when required, foam liquid pumps. Truck power take-offs or small portable gasoline engines are provided to drive these pumps. Space is allowed on all vehicles for storage of hose and various items of equipment. Portable foam stations are often provided at truck and at rail loading installations, usually consisting of a water hose and foam-proportioning device with either a separate or in some cases an integral foam nozzle.

Large foam **nozzles,** operating at water rates up to 750 gal./min., are available for protection of docks and large-sized process units and are usable for either foam or water streams or sprays. Because of the large volume of water projected, they must usually be permanently or truck-mounted. Range of horizontal streams of 100 lb./sq. in. gage are about 150 ft. with water and about 130 ft. with foam; their spray pattern with either water or foam at 100 lb./sq. in. gage is about 50 ft. long by 25 ft. wide.

Foam spray nozzles, individually equipped with foam makers, which project a spray of foam over equipment and ground areas, are available for permanent piping systems and are usually located to cover definite equipment areas with control at a central valve manifold. The fixed-flow orifice proportioning system is best adapted to this use. For deluge of a floor or grade area, similar equipment is used with discharge outlets substituted for spray nozzles.

Water-sprinkler Systems. Water is utilized for fire control by either flooding areas or by discharge in solid streams or as dispersed in sprinklers, sprays, and fogging sprays. Flooding is limited in application to combustion which can be so controlled and structures which will not be seriously damaged. Solid streams, from highly refined hand- or tower-mounted fire discharge nozzles, utilize the available pressure head of the distribution system and truck-mounted pump for maximum travel distance. They are the backbone of conventional municipal fire-fighting equipment. Solid streams are less effective and less efficient than dispersed water in that coverage is non-uniform with water flow often channeling down structures, and cooling is mostly by convection rather than evaporation.

Water-sprinkler systems are widely used to protect buildings and their contents and are either automatically or manually controlled. Manually controlled systems are empty until water is admitted, at which time water discharge is initiated through the spray heads. With automatic control, the wet-pipe system is permanently connected to a supply, and water is discharged immediately through spray heads actuated by the heat of adjacent fire. The dry-pipe system contains air under pressure and, upon the release through spray heads opened by fire, permits water to enter the system through a back-pressure deluge valve. A dry-pipe system is suitable for outdoor installation under freezing conditions. In common with the manual control, dry-pipe automatic control does not discharge water until the system is filled.

Sprinkler systems are considered more dependable because of the large non-clogging orifices in sprinkler heads, as compared with the small fine passages of spray heads, but they are less efficient in their use of water. Water sprays discharge a characteristic pattern of dispersed water, with the degree of atomization (size of droplets) a function of the nozzle design and available pressure. Fogging sprays attain such minute droplets that their aerodynamic resistance is increased to the extent of appearing to float in air. Thus the surface-to-volume ratio is maximized for rapid evaporation. Spray systems are similar to sprinkler systems, except that manual control is more widely used because process operations can sometimes cause temperature-sensitive spray heads to release in the absence of fire.

Permanently installed water-spray systems have been provided in processing units not only to protect equipment and structure against fire damage but also to afford protection against overpressure induced by the heat input. This is advantageous when fireproofing of equipment or structures is difficult or objectionable.

Other Extinguishing Systems. **Carbon dioxide** is heavier than air and can be used to blanket rooms, paint-spraying facilities, small tanks, and rotating machinery. In pipe trenches it is far more effective than foam which cannot be depended on to flow into remote corners. CO_2 systems can be automatically or manually controlled with fixed piping leading to discharge points, from racks of pressure tanks connected to a piping manifold, or from trailer-mounted storage. Heat-actuated outlet closures similar to those on sprays can be used.

To minimize fire-control damage, electrical generating equipment is usually equipped with a CO_2 extinguishing system of the automatic temperature-controlled type, discharging into the generator cooling system. A supplementary manual control is also provided, usually located near the machine operating station.

Dry chemicals may be advantageously used in manually or automatically operated fire control systems. Large extinguishers can be permanently mounted to discharge into the protected area, with remote manual or automatic operation. Such systems are adaptable to small storage tanks, floating-roof tank seals, dip tanks, and electrical equipment.

Steam or other non-combustible gas or vapor can be used in buildings or enclosures which can be sealed. Such flow should be controlled by remotely operated valves. Outlets should be provided at points near the floor and are usually not automatically operated. Office, laboratory, and similar buildings should be provided with sprinklers and standpipes with fixed hose stations on each floor. The number of such hose stations should be sufficient to permit coverage of any portion of the floor. Pressure at the hose outlet valve should not exceed 50 lb./sq. in. gage. If necessary, a restriction orifice should be fitted at the hose outlet valve to reduce pressure. Excess pressure can cause unnecessary impact damage and make hoses and nozzles difficult to handle.

First-aid fire-fighting appliances are intended for controlling initial phases of all fires and for extinguishment of small fires. General rules for location and spacing of this type of equipment have been established by N.B.F.U. These requirements can be readily adapted to process plants. Table 24-31 lists first-aid fire-fighting equipment for a typical oil refinery.

Table 24-31. First-aid Fire-fighting Equipment for a Typical Oil Refinery

Location	Size, lb.	Type	Coverage sq. ft. per extinguisher	Availability max. distance, ft.	Notes
Office, laboratory, cafeteria, gate houses...	5	CO_2	2500	50	
Warehouses, shops	15	CO_2			
	20	Dry chemical	2500	50	⅔ of total number required to be CO_2, balance to be dry chemical
Change houses	15	CO_2	5000	100	
Control houses, switch houses	15	CO_2	2500	50	
Pump houses, compressor houses, drum-filling stations, utility plant buildings, lead-blending plants, etc.	15	CO_2	2500	50	⅓ of total number required to be CO_2
	20	Dry chemical			
Truck-loading facilities	20	Dry chemical	....	...	1 for each 2 hose stations with a minimum of 2 extinguishers
Rail-loading facilities	20	Dry chemical	....	...	1 for each 3 hose stations with a minimum of 2 extinguishers
Water-oil separators	20	Dry chemical	....	...	1 for each basin with a minimum of 2 extinguishers
Process units, equipment area	20	Dry chemical	2500	50	
Foam trailer and/or truck	15	CO_2		...	1 required

SECTION 25
ELECTRICAL ENGINEERING

BY

Ludwig Braun, Jr., B.E.E., M.E.E., D.E.E., Assistant Professor of Electrical Engineering, Polytechnic Institute of Brooklyn, Brooklyn, New York; Member, American Institute of Electrical Engineers, Institute of Radio Engineers. Section Editor (Definitions and Units, Electrical Measurements and Magnetic Relations, Electrical Instruments, Electronic Circuits, Electronic Instruments, Nuclear Instrumentation)

Joseph B. Aidala, M.E.E., Professor, Department of Electrical Technology, Queensborough Community College, Bayside, New York; Member, American Institute of Electrical Engineers, (Senior) Institute of Radio Engineers, American Society for Engineering Education. (Electric Circuit Theory, Power Transmission and Distribution, Electric Motors and Generators, Converters and Rectifiers, Rheostats, Solenoids, Electric Heating)

Coleman B. Brosilow, B.S., M.Ch.E., Senior Research Fellow, Microwave Research Institute, Polytechnic Institute of Brooklyn, Brooklyn, New York; Member, American Institute of Chemical Engineers. (Electrochemical Cells, Electrophysics)

CONTENTS

ELECTRICAL ENGINEERING

REFERENCES: Angelo, "Electronic Circuits," McGraw-Hill, New York, 1958. Considine (ed.), "Process Instruments and Controls Handbook," McGraw-Hill, New York, 1957. Fitzgerald and Kingsley, "Electric Machinery," McGraw-Hill, New York, 1952. Guillemin, "Introductory Circuit Theory," Wiley, New York, 1953. Knowlton, "Standard Handbook for Electrical Engineers," 9th ed., McGraw-Hill, New York, 1957. Tarboux, "Electric Power Equipment," McGraw-Hill, New York, 1946. Timbie and Bush, "Principles of Electrical Engineering," Wiley, New York, 1951. Van Valkenburgh, "Network Analysis," Prentice-Hall, Englewood Cliffs, N.J., 1955.

DEFINITIONS AND UNITS

Charge (q) is a measure of the quantity of electricity. The *electron* is the elementary quantity of charge. The most widely used unit of charge is the *coulomb*, which is a charge equal to 6.24×10^{18} electron charges.

Current (I, i) is the time rate of change of charge. The unit of current is the *ampere*, defined as a flow of charge of one coulomb per second. Electric current is analogous to fluid flow rate in hydraulic systems.

Voltage (E, e; or V, v) is the energy required to transport a unit charge between two specified points. The unit of voltage is the *volt*, defined as one joule per coulomb. The terms electromotive force (e.m.f.) and potential difference are frequently used as synonyms for voltage. Voltage is analogous to pressure difference in hydraulic systems.

Power (P, p) is the time rate of change of energy in a system. The unit of power is the *watt*, defined as one joule per second. An alternative unit of power is the *horsepower*. One horsepower is 746 watts.

Energy is the work done by a source. The unit of energy is the *joule*.

Resistance (R, r) is the constant of proportionality relating voltage to current in a linear element without energy storage; or, more generally, resistance is the ratio of voltage to current in the relationship $e = Ri$. The unit of resistance is the *ohm* (Ω), which is defined as one volt per ampere.

Resistivity (ρ) is the specific resistance of a substance, usually expressed in ohm-cm (cgs) or ohm-circular mils per foot (English). The resistivity in ohm-cm of a substance is the resistance between two parallel faces of a one-centimeter cube of the substance; and, in ohm-circular mills per foot, the resistivity is the resistance of a sample of the substance which is one foot long and has a cross-sectional area of one circular mil (a circular mil is the area of a circle one-thousandth of an inch in diameter).

Resistor is a term applied to a physical element in which the current depends essentially only upon the present value of the voltage rather than on past values or on the rate of change of voltage.

Conductance (G) is the reciprocal of resistance and is expressed in mhos—the reciprocal of the ohm.

Conductivity is the specific conductance of a substance and is the reciprocal of resistivity.

Conductor is a term applied to substances which readily *conduct* electricity; also applied to the wires which transport electric current from place to place.

Insulator is a term applied to substances which conduct electricity relatively poorly.

Inductance (L) is the constant of proportionality relating voltage to time rate of change of current in a device which stores energy only in magnetic form. The relationship between voltage and current in an inductor is given by $e = L(di/dt)$. The most commonly used unit of inductance is the *henry*, defined as that inductance in which a current changing at a rate of one ampere per second produces a terminal voltage of one volt.

Inductor is a term applied to a physical element in which the voltage is *primarily* determined by the time rate of change of current.

Capacitance (C) is the constant of proportionality relating current to time rate of change of voltage in a device which stores energy only in electrical form. The relationship between voltage and current in a capacitor is given by $i = C(de/dt)$. The most commonly used unit of capacitance is the *farad*, defined as that capacitance in which a voltage changing at a rate of one volt per second produces a current of one ampere.

Capacitor is a term applied to a physical device in which the current is determined *primarily* by the time rate of change of voltage.

Frequency (f) is the repetition rate of a periodic wave form, usually expressed in cycles per second (c.p.s.), or in radians per second. When expressed in radians per second, frequency is designated by ω. The relationship between ω and f is $\omega = 2\pi f$.

Impedance (Z, z) is the ratio of sinusoidal voltage to sinusoidal current at a specified pair of terminals. The unit of impedance is the ohm. Impedance is, in general, a complex quantity. The real part of the impedance is called the *resistance* (or *a.c. resistance*) and the imaginary part is called the *reactance* (X).

Admittance (Y, y) is the reciprocal of the impedance and is also complex. The unit of admittance is the mho. The real part of admittance is the *conductance* and the imaginary part of admittance is the *susceptance* (B, b).

Volt-amperes (S) is the product of voltage and current at a specified pair of terminals. In circuits with periodic excitation, the power and the volt-ampere product are not necessarily the same. In such cases, the volt-ampere product is called the *apparent power*. The real part of S is the power and the imaginary part is the *reactive volt-amperes* (vars).

Power factor (p.f.) is the ratio of the *actual* power to the *apparent* power.

D.c. is an abbreviation of *direct current* which is used to designate that a current is unidirectional—such a current is called a *direct current*. The term is also applied to unidirectional voltages—such a voltage is called a *d.c. voltage*.

A.c. is an abbreviation of alternating current which is used to designate that a current has a polarity which reverses periodically—such a current is called an *alternating current*. Similarly, a voltage whose polarity reverses periodically is termed an *a.c. voltage*. The term is usually reserved for voltages and currents which vary sinusoidally.

ELECTRICAL MEASUREMENTS AND MAGNETIC RELATIONS

Electromotive force (Fig. 25-1) is induced in a conductor in a magnetic field (a) when there is relative physi-

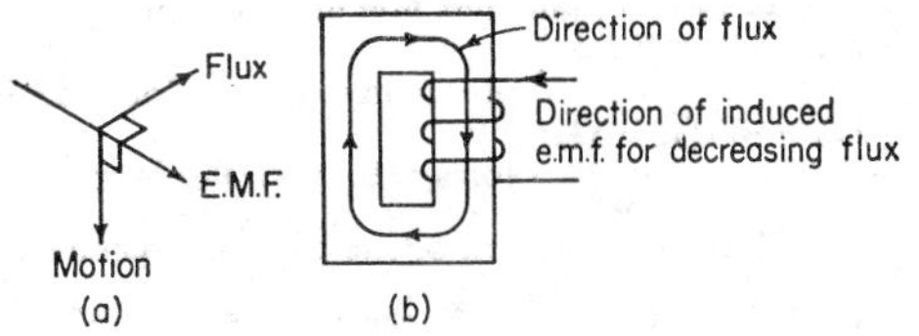

FIG. 25-1. Direction of induced e.m.f. (*a*) For maximum e.m.f., flux, motion, and conductor are mutually perpendicular. (*b*) e.m.f. induced in coil by changing of flux linking with it.

cal motion of conductor with respect to the field, or (*b*) when there is change in magnitude of the field interlinking the conductor.

$$E = \frac{Z\phi \times 10^{-8}}{t} \qquad e = \left(\frac{d\phi}{dt}\right) N \times 10^{-8}$$

where Z is the number of conductors cutting the flux ϕ in t sec.; N is the number of turns. The direction of induced e.m.f. is reversed if in (*a*) the direction of motion is reversed or if the field is in the opposite direction, and in (*b*) if the field is increasing or if the field is in the opposite direction and decreasing. The direction of induced e.m.f. is such as to cause a current tending to oppose the change.

Mechanical force (Fig. 25-2) is exerted on a conductor carrying current when in a magnetic field, tending to

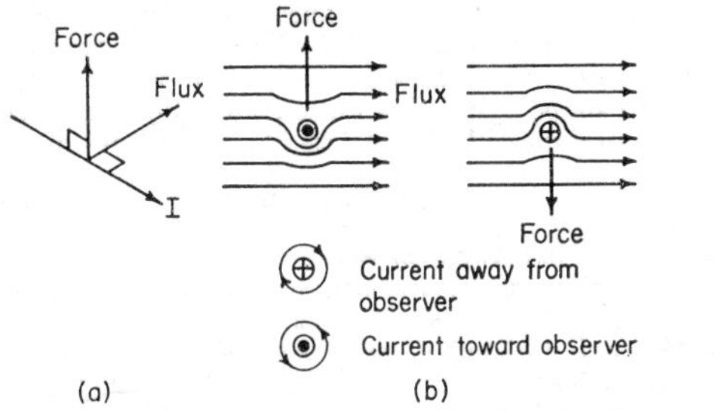

FIG. 25-2. Force on conductor carrying current in magnetic field. (*a*) Direction of force, perpendicular to flux and current. (*b*) Distortion of flux lines due to current.

move the conductor perpendicularly with respect to both the conductor and the field.

$$F = kBlI$$

$k = 8.83 \times 10^{-8}$ when F is the force in pounds, l the effective length of conductor in inches, B the component of flux density perpendicular to the conductor in lines per square inch, and I the current in amperes. $k = 10.2 \times 10^{-8}$ when F is in kilograms, l in centimeters, and B in gausses.

Electrical machines consist of interlinked magnetic and electric circuits, usually fairly simple in nature, although in some cases the interactions become quite involved. *Iron* is the usual magnetic material and *copper* the electrical material; hence these together with various forms of *insulation* are the principal materials used in construction.

ELECTRIC CIRCUIT THEORY

An electric circuit in its simplest form consists of a source of voltage and a continuous conducting path.

Copper is preferred for electrical conductors because of its remarkable and useful combinations of physical properties. It has low resistance, a slow rate of oxidation in air, high heat conductivity, ability to dissipate heat to the surroundings at a high rate when its surface is properly prepared, low susceptibility to corrosion, relatively high softening and melting temperatures, strength, ductility, and workability in shop and field. It can be coated readily with silver, tin, or lacquer, or be soldered and brazed with ease. In addition, copper is nonmagnetic. The other most commonly used metals are aluminum and steel.

Ohm's law relating cause (voltage), effect (current), and opposition (resistance) is

$$I = \frac{V}{R} \qquad R = \frac{V}{I} \qquad V = IR$$

where I is the current in amperes through the resistance, V is the voltage in volts across the resistance, and R is the resistance in ohms. The relationships indicated are valid for continuous direct current and also for alternating current. The conductor resistance depends on the material, temperature, and its physical shape. If the current is uniformly distributed the conductor resistance in ohms is

$$R = \rho \frac{L}{A}$$

where ρ, the resistivity, is the resistance of a piece of material in some simple and useful standard shape at a given temperature; *e.g.*, either the resistance between the faces of a cube of 1 cm. dimension or the resistance between ends of a wire 1 ft. long and 0.001 in. in diameter; that is, with an area of 1 cir. mil. L is the length and A is the cross-sectional area in the appropriate units to give resistance in ohms. Table 25-1 gives values of resistivity ρ for differential materials.

Table 25-1. Resistivity Values for Various Materials

Conducting material	Resistivity ρ at 20°C.		Value of $\|T\|$ for use in $\frac{R_2}{R_1} = \frac{T + t_2}{T + t_1}$
	Microhm-cm.	Ohms-cir. mil ft.	
Aluminum	3.2	19.3	236
Brass	7	42	480
Copper	1.72	10.4	234.5
Iron, commercial	13	7.8	162
Lead	21	125	236
Mercury	96	575	1100
Nichrome	100	603	2250
Silver	1.6	9.9	243
Steel, hard	47	283	600
Tin	11.5	70	220
Tungsten	5.5	33	176
Zinc	6.3	38	230

An approximately linear relationship exists between resistance and temperature, so that resistance at different temperatures can be readily calculated. An equation sufficing for most engineering work is

$$\frac{R_2}{R_1} = \frac{T + t_2}{T + t_1}$$

where R_2 is the resistance in ohms at temperature t_2(°C.); R_1 is the resistance at temperature t_1(°C.), and T(°C.) is the intercept of the resistance-temperature curve on the temperature axis. Although this intercept is a negative number (−234.5°C. for copper) only the magnitude (omit negative sign) is used in the equation. Refer to Table 25-1 for typical values of resistivity.

In a d.c. circuit the opposition consists only of the conductor resistance. For an a.c. circuit the resistance may be many times greater than the conductor resistance because of eddy current, hysteresis, and skin-effect losses which convert additional electrical energy into heat. This resistance to alternating currents is called the a.c. or effective resistance.

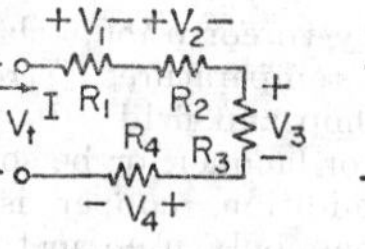

FIG. 25-3

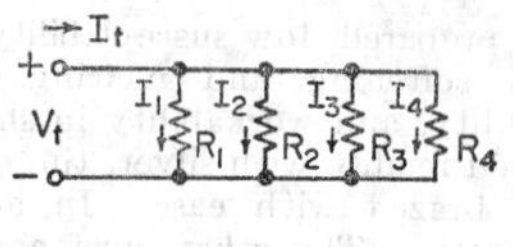

FIG. 25-4

FIG. 25-3. Series circuit.
FIG. 25-4. Parallel circuit.

When resistors are connected in series (Fig. 25-3) the same current flows through each and the total resistance is their sum.

$$R_T = R_1 + R_2 + R_3 + R_4$$

In a parallel connection of resistances (Fig. 25-4) the same voltage exists across each, and the total resistance R_T is given by

$$\frac{1}{R_T} = \frac{1}{R_1} + \frac{1}{R_2} + \frac{1}{R_3} + \frac{1}{R_4}$$

If only two resistors are in parallel then

$$R_T = \frac{R_1 R_2}{R_1 + R_2}$$

The inverse of resistance is called conductance G and is expressed in mhos. Therefore, in a parallel circuit

$$G_T = G_1 + G_2 + G_3 + G_4 + \cdots$$

where $G_T = \dfrac{1}{R_T} \quad G_1 = \dfrac{1}{R_1} \quad \cdots$

In series-parallel circuits (Fig. 25-5) we compute values for each series and parallel group and then combine group values to compute total resistance.

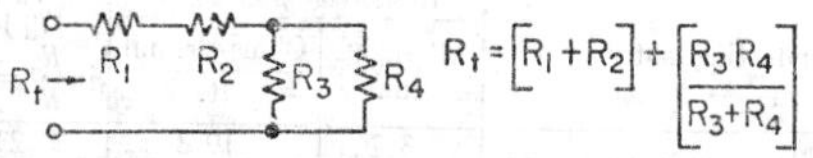

FIG. 25-5. Series-parallel circuit.

Kirchhoff's laws represent two simple fundamental laws associated with an electric circuit. These laws state that (1) the algebraic sum of the currents at any junction point is zero (currents entering a junction point equal currents leaving the junction point); (2) the algebraic sum of the voltages around a closed path is zero (the voltage between two points is the same regardless of the path).

In the series circuit of Fig. 25-3, $V_T = V_1 + V_2 + V_3 + V_4$ illustrates the voltage law.

In the parallel circuit of Fig. 25-4, $I_T = I_1 + I_2 + I_3 + I_4$ illustrates the current law.

The procedure for the solution of a circuit is as follows: (1) Assume current directions if they are not given. (2) Write voltage equations for the different loops or paths and current equations for the junction points. (3) Solve these equations simultaneously for the unknown quantities. Refer to the two-loop d.c. circuit of Fig. 25-6.

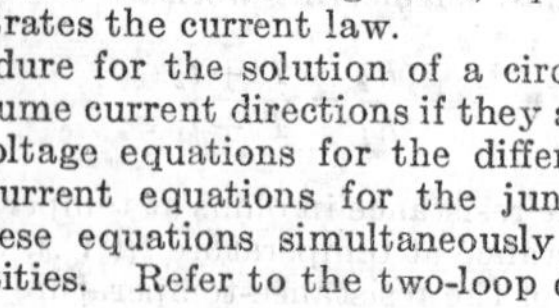

FIG. 25-6. Two-loop d.c. circuit. NOTE: Polarity of voltage across resistor in direction of assumed current flow is from + to −.

$I_1 = I_2 + I_3$ (current law at junction B)

$50 - 2I_1 - 40 - 3I_3 = 0$

(voltage law around loop $ABDA$)

$40 - 1I_2 - 30I_2 + 3I_3 = 0$

(voltage law around loop $BCDB$)

The simultaneous solution of the three equations gives

$I_1 = 2.86$ amp. $\quad I_2 = 1.43$ amp. $\quad I_3 = 1.43$ amp.

The power (in watts) in a d.c. circuit is equal to the product of voltage (in volts) and current (in amperes).

$$P = VI = I^2R = \frac{V^2}{R} \quad \text{watts}$$

The energy (joules or watt-seconds) is the product of power and time for a d.c. circuit

$$W = VIt = I^2Rt = \frac{V^2t}{R}$$

where t is in seconds.

At the present time over 90 per cent of the electrical energy used for commercial purposes is generated as alternating current. This is not due primarily to any superiority of alternating over direct current in applicability to industrial and domestic uses. However, a.c. power can be generated at relatively high voltages, and these voltages can be increased still further by transformers, thus permitting the economical transmission of a.c. energy over long distances at low currents with reduced power losses and less weight of transmission conductors. Commercial alternating current is sinusoidal in shape. For this reason the following discussion of a.c. circuits will be restricted to sine waves only.

$$v = V_{max} \sin \omega t$$

where $\omega = 2\pi f$, radians/sec.
f = frequency, cycles/sec.
t is in seconds

The period of an a.c. wave is the time for one complete variation (cycle) and is the reciprocal of the frequency f. The standard frequency for power and lighting in this country is 60 cycles/sec. ($\omega = 377$ radians/sec.) although frequencies of 50 and 25 find special use.

The effective or r.m.s. (root mean square) value of an alternating current (or voltage) is that constant value which gives the same average heating effect in a resistance as the varying alternating current (or voltage) over a complete cycle. The effective values of current and voltage will be denoted as I and V. For a sine wave

$$I = \frac{I_{max}}{\sqrt{2}} = 0.707 I_{max}$$

$$V = \frac{V_{max}}{\sqrt{2}} = 0.707 V_{max}$$

When talking of sine waves of voltage or current the effective value is usually referred to. Therefore, a 115-volt source of frequency 60 cycles/sec. implies the sine-wave voltage $v = 115\sqrt{2} \sin 377t$.

In the d.c. circuit the opposition to current flow is due to conductor resistance. However, in the a.c. circuit the opposition is due to the electrical elements of resistance, inductance, and capacitance. The general term for opposition in a.c. circuits is called impedance Z. The opposition of the resistance is called the effective or a.c. resistance; for the energy-storing elements (inductance L and capacitance C) the opposition is termed reactance. Inductive reactance refers to the opposition of the inductance and capacitive reactance to the capacitor.

Inductances in series and in parallel can be combined using the same formulas as for resistance. However, capacitors in series combine as

$$\frac{1}{C_T} = \frac{1}{C_1} + \frac{1}{C_2} + \frac{1}{C_3} + \cdots$$

and capacitors in parallel combine as

$$C_T = C_1 + C_2 + C_3 + \cdots$$

In a resistive circuit (Fig. 25-7*a*) by Ohm's law,

$$i = \frac{v}{R} \quad \text{and if } v = V_{max} \sin \omega t$$

then $$i = \frac{V_{max}}{R} \sin \omega t$$

where $$I_{max} = \frac{V_{max}}{R}$$

Therefore $$I = \frac{V}{R}$$

where V and I are effective values. The current in the resistance is said to be in phase with the voltage across the resistance since it reaches a maximum positive value at the same time as the voltage.

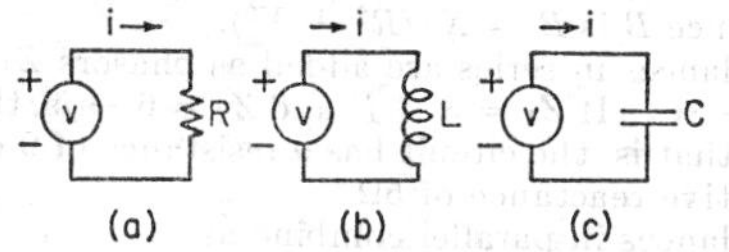

FIG. 25-7. (*a*) Resistive circuit. (*b*) Inductive circuit. (*c*) Capacitive circuit.

In the inductive circuit (Fig. 25-7*b*) the fundamental relation between v and i is $v = L(di/dt)$ where L is the inductance in henrys. If $i = I_{max} \sin \omega t$, then $v = \omega L I_{max} \cos \omega t$ or $v = \omega L I_{max} \sin (\omega t + 90 \text{ deg.})$. This implies that in an inductive circuit the current lags the voltage by 90 deg. or is out of phase by 90 deg. Further, $V_{max} = \omega L I_{max}$ or $V = \omega L I$ (where $\omega L = 2\pi f L$ is the opposition in ohms and is called the inductive reactance X_L). Therefore, $V = X_L I$.

In the capacitive circuit (Fig. 25-7*c*) the fundamental relation is $i = C(dv/dt)$ where C is the capacitance in farads. If $v = V_{max} \sin \omega t$ then $i = \omega C V_{max} \cos \omega t = [V_{max}/(1/\omega C)] \sin (\omega t + 90 \text{ deg.})$. This indicates that the current leads the voltage across the capacitor by 90 deg. Here $I_{max} = V_{max}/(1/\omega C)$ or $I = V/(1/\omega C)$. The opposition (impedance) of a capacitor is therefore $1/\omega C = 1/2\pi f C$ ohms and is called the capacitive reactance X_C. Therefore, $V = IX_C$.

The phase relationships for the three elements are shown in Fig. 25-8.

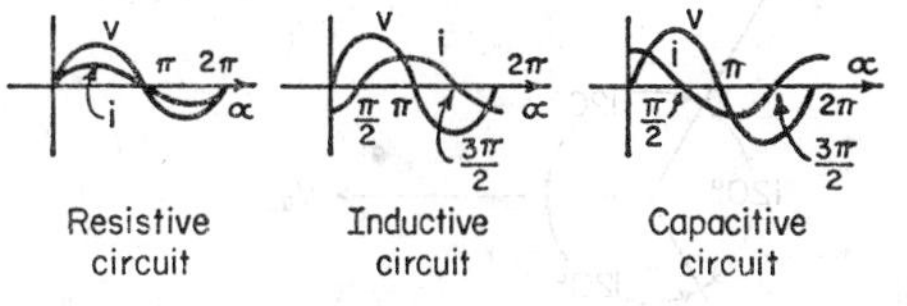

FIG. 25-8. Current-voltage relationships. $\alpha = \omega t$ (radians).

In a series circuit containing R and L the impedance $Z = \sqrt{R^2 + X_L^2}$ and the angle by which the current lags the impressed voltage is $\theta = \tan^{-1}(X_L/R)$. In a series RC circuit $Z = \sqrt{R^2 + X_C^2}$, and the angle by which the current leads the impressed voltage is $\theta = \tan^{-1}(X_C/R)$.

In a series RLC circuit the impedance

$$Z = \sqrt{R^2 + (X_L - X_C)^2}$$

and $\theta = \tan^{-1}(X_L - X_C)/R$. If X_L is greater than X_C the current lags the impressed voltage, and if X_C is greater than X_L the current leads the impressed voltage.

In a.c. circuits the relationships between current, voltage, and impedance are

$$I = \frac{V}{Z} \qquad Z = \frac{V}{I} \qquad V = IZ$$

where the equations apply to a portion of a circuit or to a complete circuit. If, for example, a branch of a circuit is referred to, then V must be the voltage across that branch, I the current through it, and Z the impedance of that branch. If the total circuit is under consideration then V is the voltage impressed on the circuit, I the total current, and Z the total impedance of the circuit.

The product of effective voltage and current in an a.c. circuit is called the *apparent power* S and is expressed in volt-amperes.

$$S = VI \quad \text{volt-amp.}$$

The actual absorbed power P (also referred to as the true or average power) in an a.c. circuit represents the power dissipated in heat and is therefore associated with the effective or a.c. resistance. It is measured in watts and is given by

$$P = VI \cos \theta = I^2 R \quad \text{watts}$$

where θ is the phase angle between V and I, and R is the effective or a.c. resistance carrying the current I.

The quantity $\cos \theta$ is called the power factor since it represents the factor by which the apparent power S (volt-amperes) must be multiplied to give the power P. It is also the ratio of the power to the apparent power.

In addition, $\cos \theta = \text{power factor} = \frac{R}{Z}$.

Since the phase angle θ varies from zero in a resistive circuit to 90 deg. in a purely reactive circuit, the range of the power factor is from unity (resistance only) to zero (reactance only). A circuit with a lagging power factor of 0.8 has an input current which lags the impressed voltage (circuit is inductive in nature and contains resistance) such that $\cos \theta = 0.8$ or $\theta = 37$ deg. A circuit with 0.6 power factor leading has an input current which leads the impressed voltage (circuit is capacitive in nature and contains resistance) such that $\cos \theta = 0.6$ and $\theta = 53$ deg.

The reactive elements L and C do not dissipate power (watts) but simply store energy in the form of a magnetic field in the case of the inductance or as an electric field in the capacitor. This energy over a complete a.c. cycle is returned to the circuit without loss. The reactive power Q, measured in volt-amperes-reactive (vars) is a measure of the maximum instantaneous power associated with the reactive elements

$$Q = VI \sin \theta \quad \text{vars}$$

where θ is the phase angle between V and I.

The quantity $\sin \theta$ is called the reactive factor and varies between the limits zero and one. The reactive factor may be expressed as $\sin \theta = X/Z$.

If the circuit is purely resistive, then $\theta = 0$ and $\sin \theta = 0$ (or $X = 0$) so that no vars exist in a resistive circuit. If the circuit is purely reactive ($R = 0$) then $\theta = 90$ deg. and $\sin \theta = 1$, its maximum, and the circuit has vars only and no watts.

Other relations between P, Q, and S are

$$S^2 = P^2 + Q^2 \qquad \text{and} \qquad \tan\theta = \frac{P}{Q}$$

The vector or phasor representation is a shorthand method used for indicating magnitude and phase relation of sinusoidal currents and voltages of the same frequency. Thus the sine-wave voltage of $100\sqrt{2}\sin\omega t$ can be represented as a phasor as $100\underline{/0}$ deg. (Effective values are used to express the magnitude of a phasor.) The current $10\sqrt{2}\sin(\omega t + 30 \text{ deg.})$ as a phasor is $10\underline{/30}$ deg., indicating its phase angle of 30 deg. lead with respect to the reference. Note that the frequency does not appear

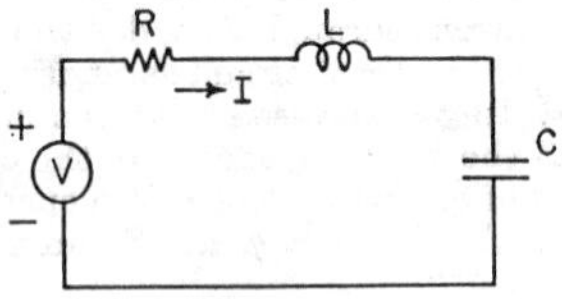

Fig. 25-9. *RLC* circuit.

in the phasor representation. Refer to the circuit of Fig. 25-9.

Given: $v = 100\sqrt{2}\sin\omega t$

$\therefore V = 100\underline{/0}$

Given: $R = 3\Omega,\ X_L = 12\Omega,\ X_C = 8\Omega$

$$Z = \sqrt{R^2 + (X_L - X_C)^2} = \sqrt{3^2 + (12 - 8)^2} = 5 \text{ ohms}$$

$$I = \frac{V}{Z} = \frac{100}{5} = 20 \text{ amp.}$$

$$\theta = \tan^{-1}\frac{X_L - X_C}{R} = \tan^{-1}\frac{12 - 8}{3} = 53 \text{ deg.}$$

Since X_L is greater than X_C the current lags the impressed voltage by 53 deg. and therefore $I = 20\underline{/-53}$ deg.

$P = I^2R = (20)^2 3 = 1200$ watts
or $P = VI\cos\theta = (100)(20)\cos 53 \text{ deg.} = 1200$ watts
$Q = VI\sin\theta = 100(20)\sin 53$ deg.
$= 1600$ vars (inductive since $X_L > X_C$)
$S = VI = 100 \times 20 = 2000$ volt-amp.

As a check

$$S = \sqrt{P^2 + Q^2} \qquad 2000 = \sqrt{(1200)^2 + (1600)^2}$$

$V_R = IR = 20(3) = 60$, and since the voltage across a resistor is in phase with the current

$$V_R = 60\underline{/-53} \text{ deg. as a phasor}$$

Similarly $V_L = IX_L = (20)(12) = 240$ and since the voltage across the inductance leads the current by 90 deg. then $V_L = 240\underline{/(53 + 90)}$ deg. $= 240\underline{/143}$ deg. as a phasor.

The capacitor voltage is $V_C = IX_C = (20)(8) = 160$ and since the voltage across a capacitor lags the current by 90 deg., then

$$V_C = 160\underline{/53 - 90)} \text{ deg.} = 160\underline{/-37} \text{ deg.}$$

The phasor diagram is shown in Fig. 25-10 with the voltage V as the reference.

If drawn to scale $V_R + V_L + V_C$ add up (sum horizontal and vertical components) to V (Kirchhoff's voltage law),

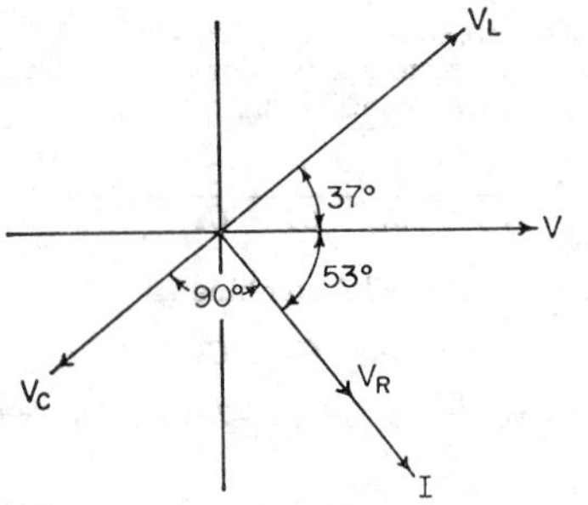

Fig. 25-10. Phasor diagram of *RLC* circuit.

The impedance Z must also be treated as a phasor or complex number with a horizontal real component and a vertical (imaginary or j) component.

$Z = R + jX$ where the real part is the resistance and the imaginary part is the reactance. The plus sign is used for inductive reactance and the minus sign for capacitive reactance. Also, $Z = |Z|\underline{/\theta}$ where $|Z| = \sqrt{R^2 + X^2}$ and $\theta = \tan^{-1}(X/R)$. The reciprocal of impedance is called admittance Y and is expressed in mhos. We may write $Y = G \mp jB$ where the minus sign is used for an inductive circuit and the plus for a capacitive circuit. The conductance $G = R/(R^2 + X^2)$ and the susceptance B is $B = X/(R^2 + X^2)$.

Impedances in series are added as phasors $Z_T = Z_1 + Z_2 + \cdots$. If $Z_1 = 3 + j4$ and $Z_2 = 6 - j9$, then $Z_T = 9 - j5$; that is, the circuit has a resistance of 9 ohms and a capacitive reactance of 5Ω.

Impedances in parallel combine as

$$\frac{1}{Z_T} = \frac{1}{Z_1} + \frac{1}{Z_2} + \frac{1}{Z_3} + \cdots$$

where now the computation for Z_T is somewhat involved since it requires the manipulation of complex numbers or phasors.

Instead of the single-phase system discussed previously, polyphase systems are commonly used for better economy in generation and transmission and improved motor performance. The most common polyphase system is the three-phase.

In the three-phase system, three equal voltages are generated which are out of phase with one another by 120 deg. The phasor diagram for the three-phase voltages is shown in Fig. 25-11.

A balanced three-phase system is one in which identical loads are connected in each phase. The loads may be connected in wye (Y) or delta (Δ). The currents that

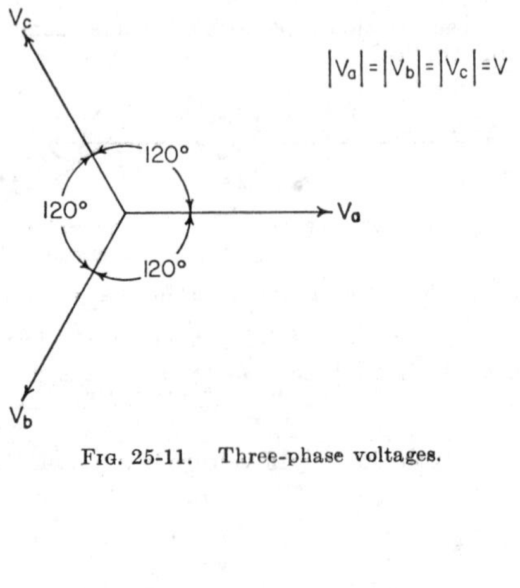

Fig. 25-11. Three-phase voltages.

flow in a balanced three-phase system are equal in magnitude and also 120 deg. out of phase.

In a balanced Y system (Fig. 25-12) two different voltage levels are available, a line voltage V_L and a phase

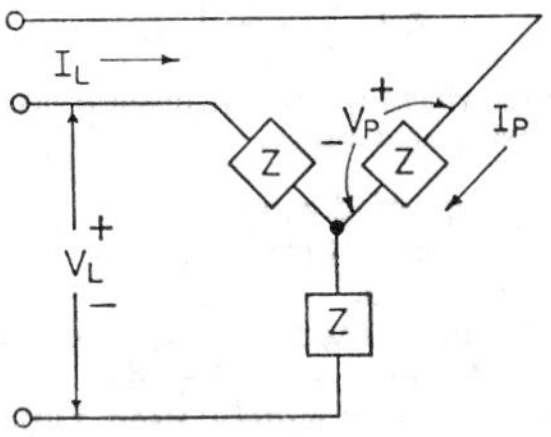

FIG. 25-12. Balanced Y-connected system.

voltage V_P, where $|V_L| = |V_P|/\sqrt{3}$. In this case the line current I_L is equal to the phase (load) current I_P. In a balanced system the total power $P_T = 3V_P I_P \cos \theta_P$, or in terms of line quantities $P_T = \sqrt{3} V_L I_L \cos \theta_P$ watts.

$$Q_T = \sqrt{3} V_L I_L \sin \theta_P \quad \text{vars}$$
$$S_T = \sqrt{3} V_L I_L \quad \text{volt-amp.}$$

where θ_P is the angle between V_P and I_P.

In the balanced delta load (Fig. 25-13) the line voltage $V_L = V_P$ (the phase voltage) and $|I_L| = \sqrt{3}|I_P|$. In terms of line quantities the equations for P_T, Q_T, and S_T are idential to those for the wye case.

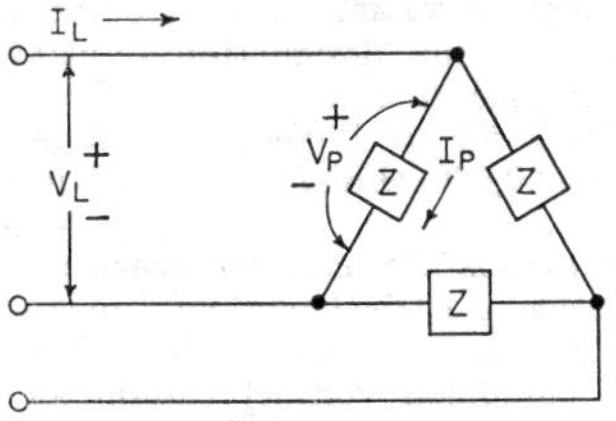

FIG. 25-13. Balanced delta-connected system.

If a single-phase voltage is desired for a single-phase load, then the load is simply connected across one phase or line voltage of the three-phase system.

ELECTRICAL INSTRUMENTS

In the utilization of electricity for the transmission of energy (as in a power-transmission system) or for the transmission of information (as in the measurement of neutron level in a nuclear reaction), it is often necessary to make measurements of the electrical quantities involved. Such a great variety of instruments has been developed for this purpose that it is impossible, in a short space, to describe all of them; however, the basic principles of operation of representative types are described below.

Electrical instruments may be divided into two broad categories: *electrical meters,* and *special-purpose electrical instruments.*

Electrical Meters

Electrical meters (or, more simply, *meters*) are used to measure some special property of the electrical quantity being measured. Properties of engineering interest are:

1. *Peak Value.* The positive (negative) peak value of a signal is defined as the maximum positive (negative) value attained by that signal. This property is important in electronic circuits, *e.g.,* situations involving voltage breakdown of insulation, and in the determination of required ratings for various types of equipment.

2. *Average Value.* The average value of a periodic signal may be defined in several different ways. The average of the signal over a full cycle is called the *full-cycle average.* The average of the positive (negative) portions of the signal is called the *positive (negative) pulse average.* Finally, the average of the instantaneous absolute values of the function is called the *absolute average.* These average values are of interest in rectifier circuits and electroplating systems.

3. *Effective Value.* The effective value of a periodic voltage is defined as the magnitude of a constant (d.c.) voltage which dissipates the same average power in a given resistor as is dissipated by the periodic voltage. A similar definition applies to the effective value of a periodic current.

Analytically, the effective value E_{eff} of a periodic function $e(t)$ is given by

$$E_{\text{eff}} = \sqrt{\frac{1}{T}\int_0^T e^2(t)\,dt}$$

where T is the period of $e(t)$.

The effective value of a signal is important in the analysis of the behavior of systems with periodic excitation and in the computation of average power.

To illustrate these definitions, the several properties defined above are computed for the signal of Fig. 25-14:

Positive peak value	=	10 volts
Negative peak value	=	4 volts
Full-cycle average value	=	3 volts
Positive pulse average value	=	5 volts
Negative pulse average value	=	2 volts
Absolute average value	=	7 volts

All meters respond to one or another of the special properties described above. Many commercially available meters have scales which are calibrated to indicate

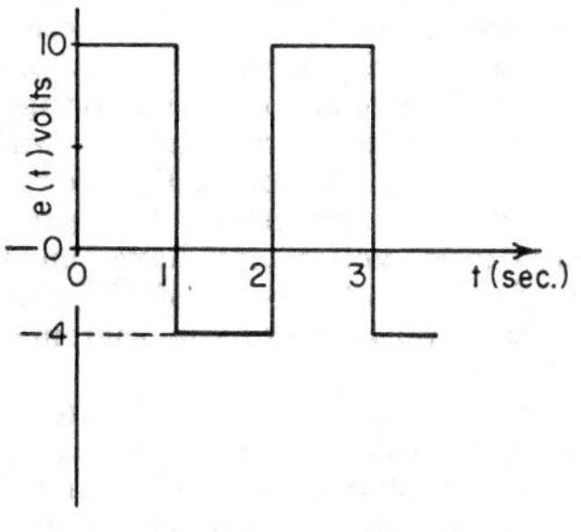

FIG. 25-14. Wave shape for illustration of signal properties.

correctly the r.m.s. value of a sinusoid, although they do not respond to *true r.m.s.* but respond, instead, to positive-peak value or absolute average or to some other signal property. This is done because the sinusoid is the most frequently encountered signal wave shape in engineering practice. For this reason, it is necessary to use caution in interpreting the indications of meters, when measuring signals. Proper interpretation of a meter reading requires a knowledge of the signal property to which the meter responds, as well as a knowledge of the type of wave form for which the scale is calibrated. If, for example, a meter responding to full-cycle average is used to measure a sinusoidal voltage, its indication will be zero, *even though the peak voltage of the sinusoid may be many volts.*

Further examples of the errors which may result from misinterpretation of meter indication are shown in Fig. 25-15.

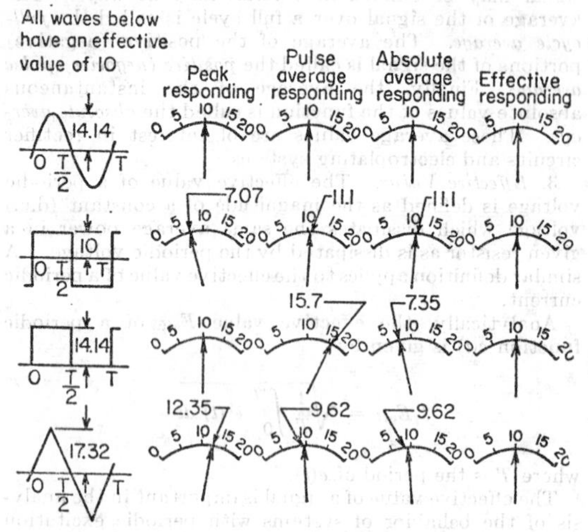

FIG. 25-15. Comparison of the indications, for several wave shapes, of four types of meters, all of which indicate correctly for a sinusoid. (*From LePage, "Analysis of Alternating-current Circuits," McGraw-Hill, New York,* 1952.)

Electrical meters may be classified according to *principle of operation*—electrostatic, electromagnetic, and electrothermal; *mechanism*—indicating, integrating, and recording; *application*—ammeter, voltmeter, wattmeter, watt-hour meter.

Principle of Operation. 1. *Electrostatic meters* employ the attractive force between oppositely charged bodies to provide an indication of electrical quantities. In such instruments, the deflection is usually proportional to the mean-square value of the applied voltage. By proper calibration of the scale, the meter is made to indicate the *true effective value* of the applied voltage, independent of the wave shape of the voltage.

Electrostatic voltmeters are available with full-scale voltages ranging from 100 to 100,000 volts. The best available accuracy of these meters is 1 per cent of full scale. Electrostatic voltmeters have unusually high terminal impedance—in the order of 10^{15} ohms—making them especially useful in making measurements in high-impedance circuits.

2. *Electromagnetic meters* employ the force of interaction between a current-carrying conductor and a magnetic field to provide an indication of electrical quantities. All electromagnetic meters are essentially special-purpose electric motors with a restraining spring on the output shaft and a pointer attached to the output shaft to indicate the equilibrium condition. The deflection of electromagnetic meters is some function of the current applied at the terminals. Depending upon the internal construction, this type of meter may respond to any one of the signal properties mentioned above.

Electromagnetic ammeters are available with full-scale currents ranging from a fraction of a microampere up to about 50 milliamp. Beyond 50 milliamp. it becomes impractical to pass the current directly through the moving coil. The range of an ammeter may be extended manyfold by the use of a proper *shunt*—a device for by-passing (or *shunting*) the excess current I_s around the meter coil as shown in Fig. 25-16. By means of such shunts, currents as high as 20,000 amp. may be measured directly. Shunts are usually employed only

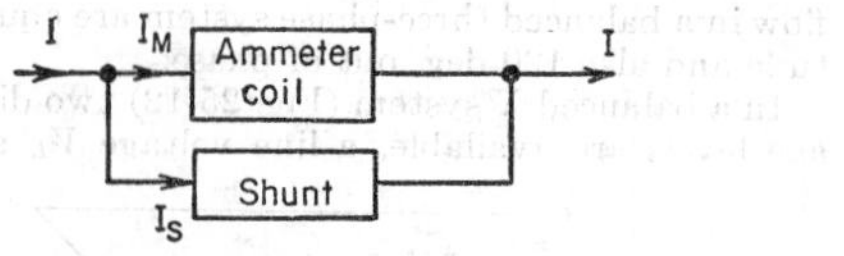

FIG. 25-16. Arrangement for by-passing current around ammeter to increase the instrument range.

to extend the range of d.c. ammeters; to achieve range extension in a.c. ammeters a device called a *current transformer* is employed.

The best available accuracy of electromagnetic ammeters is 0.1 per cent of full scale. Electromagnetic ammeters are the most widely used type of ammeter, because of their relatively rugged construction and their low cost compared with other types of meters. The sensitivity of an ammeter is usually specified as the voltage across the terminals at full-scale current: a typical value is 50 millivolts.

Electromagnetic ammeters are easily convertible to *voltmeters* by adding a resistor in series with the ammeter as shown in Fig. 25-17. The series resistor R is usually

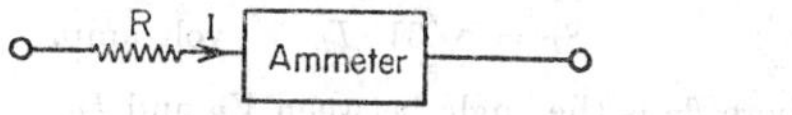

FIG. 25-17. Conversion of an ammeter into a voltmeter.

called a *multiplier*. The accuracy of such voltmeters is comparable with that of the electromagnetic ammeter. The sensitivity of this type of voltmeter is usually specified as the reciprocal of the terminal current at full-scale voltage, although the designation ohms/volt is used, rather than reciprocal milliamperes. Typical values of voltmeter sensitivity are 1000 ohms/volt (or 1 milliamp., full scale) and 20,000 ohms/volt (or 50 microamp., full scale).

The *wattmeter* is an electromagnetic meter which measures average electrical power by means of the electromagnetic interaction of two coils. The wattmeter is essentially a combined voltmeter-ammeter which computes the product of voltage and current.

The *watt-hour meter* is an electromagnetic meter which measures total electrical energy supplied. Such meters are essentially unrestrained electric motors whose total rotational displacement is proportional to the energy transmitted through the instrument.

3. *Electrothermal meters* make use of two electrothermal phenomena to provide an indication of electrical quantities. Electrothermal (or, more simply, thermal) ammeters are composed of three elements as shown in Fig. 25-18. The current to be measured (I) is passed

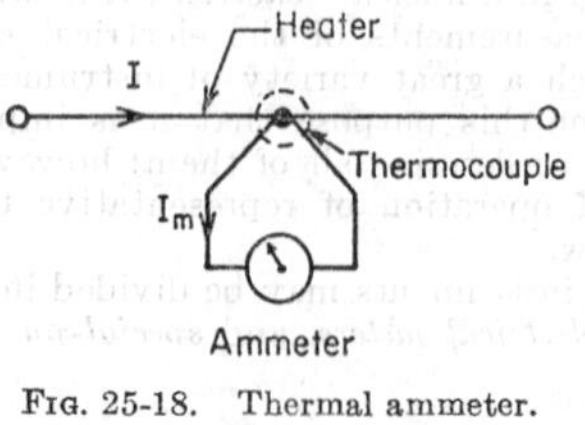

FIG. 25-18. Thermal ammeter.

through the *heater*, dissipating an average power $P = I^2R$ in the heater; where I is the effective value of the current and R is the resistance of the heater. The temperature of the heater wire is directly proportional to the power dissipated in the wire. This temperature is measured by a *thermocouple*, in which a voltage is produced which is a function of the junction temperature. This thermally produced voltage causes a current to flow in the *ammeter.* This current is proportional to the square of the effective value of the heater current, independent of the wave shape of the current. By proper scale calibration, it is possible to have the ammeter indicate the true effective value of the heater current.

Thermal ammeters are available to measure currents from 1 milliamp. to many amperes full scale. These ammeters are capable of measuring currents from d.c. to frequencies in the order of 50 megacycles/sec. with an accuracy of ½ per cent of full scale. Thermal ammeters are very sensitive to electrical overload—a 100 per cent overload is usually sufficient to destroy the heater. This compares somewhat unfavorably with the 1000 per cent overload permissible in well-built electromagnetic instruments.

By employing a series resistor as a multiplier, a thermal ammeter may be converted into a thermal voltmeter. The thermal voltmeter indicates true effective value of any applied voltage. The frequency range of thermal voltmeters is from d.c. to about 50 kilocycles/sec., because of parasitic capacitances associated with the added series resistor.

Metering Errors. There are two important sources of metering errors, in addition to the calibration error. These are *meter loading effect* and *connection errors.* An understanding of the sources of these errors may result in a minimization of the error magnitude—and permits us to correct for this error if the minimum magnitude is unacceptably large.

1. *Meter loading effect* occurs because of the non-ideal character of ammeters and voltmeters. An ideal ammeter has zero internal resistance while a physical ammeter has a non-zero internal resistance. An ideal voltmeter has infinite internal resistance while a physical voltmeter has a finite internal resistance.

If we wish to measure the current i_1 in the circuit of Fig. 25-19*a*, we must insert an ammeter in series as shown

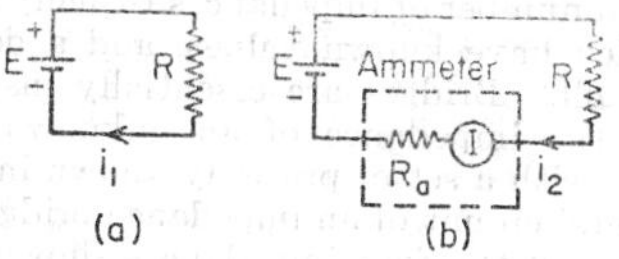

FIG. 25-19. Effect of ammeter on circuit current. (*a*) Original circuit. (*b*) Circuit with ammeter added.

in Fig. 25-19*b*. The desired current i_1 is given by

$$i_1 = \frac{E}{R}$$

When the ammeter is inserted, the current is i_2, which is given by

$$i_2 = \frac{E}{R + R_a} = \frac{i_1}{1 + R_a/R} \cong i_1\left(1 - \frac{R_a}{R}\right) \qquad \text{if } R_a \ll R$$

It is clear that $i_2 < i_1$ unless R_a is zero. In many cases, $R_a < 0.01\ R$ and meter loading may be neglected.

If we wish to measure the voltage e_1 in the circuit of Fig. 25-20*a*, we must insert a voltmeter as shown in

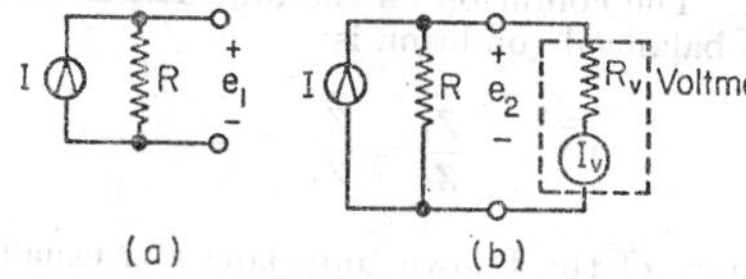

FIG. 25-20. Effect of voltmeter on circuit voltage. (*a*) Original circuit. (*b*) Circuit with voltmeter added.

Fig. 25-20*b*. The desired voltage e_1 is given by

$$e_1 = IR$$

When the voltmeter is inserted, the voltage is e_2, which is given by

$$e_2 = \frac{I}{(1/R) + (1/R_v)} = \frac{e_1}{1 + (R/R_v)} \cong e_1\left(1 - \frac{R}{R_v}\right) \qquad \text{if } R_v \gg R$$

It is clear that $e_2 < e_1$ unless R_v is infinite. In many cases, $R_v > 100\ R$ and meter loading may be neglected.

2. *Connection errors* arise whenever it is necessary to use a voltmeter and ammeter in combination (*e.g.*, to measure power or resistance of an element). Again these errors arise because of the non-ideal character of voltmeters and ammeters.

If, for example, we wish to measure the power absorbed by the load in Fig. 25-21*a*, we may determine it by measuring the voltage e and the current i and computing the power from the relation

$$P = ei$$

We may measure e and i using a voltmeter and an ammeter as shown in Fig. 25-21*b*. The voltmeter may be connected before the ammeter (at terminal 1) or after the

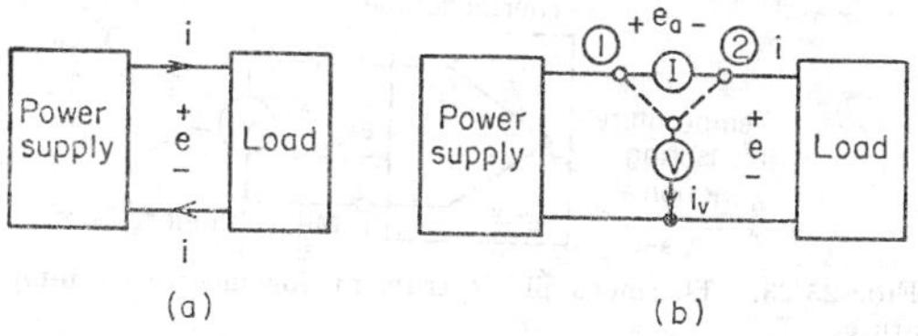

FIG. 25-21. Voltmeter-ammeter connections to measure power. (*a*) System under study. (*b*) Instrumentation added to measure power.

ammeter (at terminal 2). Because the ammeter and voltmeter are non-ideal, the ammeter voltage $e_a \neq 0$ and the voltmeter current $i_v \neq 0$.

If we use connection 1, the voltmeter measures the voltage across the ammeter plus the load, while the ammeter correctly measures i. The product of the two meter readings is

$$P_1 = V_1 I_1 = (e + e_a)i = P + e_a i$$

The power error for this case is $e_a i$.

If we use connection 2, the voltmeter correctly measures e, but the ammeter measures the load current plus the voltmeter current. The product of the meter readings is

$$P_2 = V_2 I_2 = e(i + i_v) = P + e i_v$$

The power error for this case is $e i_v$.

In many applications, either $e_a \ll e$—in which case the error is negligible using connection 1—or $i_v \ll i$—in which case the error is negligible using connection 2. If neither inequality is adequately satisfied, either connection may be used, and the corresponding equation (for P_1 or P_2) may be employed to determine the necessary correction to be made.

Special-purpose Electrical Instruments

The flexibility of electrical instruments has induced instrument designers to employ such instruments in the indirect measurement of essentially all phenomena which occur in engineering practice. For this reason an almost infinite variety of special-purpose electrical instruments exists at the present time. Such instruments have been employed, for example, in the measurement of mechanical displacement, velocity and acceleration, fluid flow rate and pressure, liquid level, humidity, temperature, and radiation, to name a few (see Sec. 22).

In order to employ electrical measuring devices to measure non-electrical phenomena, it is necessary to insert between the electrical device and the non-electrical phenomenon a device called a *transducer* which converts energy from non-electrical form into electrical energy which is employed to actuate the electrical instrument. The arrangement of such devices is shown, in block-diagram form, in Fig. 25-22.

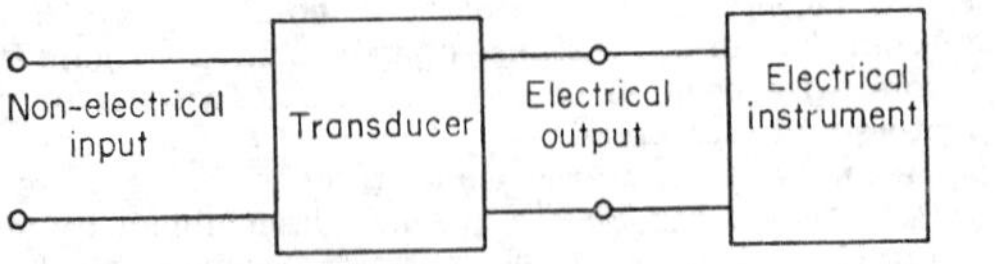

FIG. 25-22. Block diagram of electrical instrument to measure non-electrical phenomena.

An example of such a device which is widely used is the thermocouple instrument employed to measure temperature. Such an instrument is shown schematically in Fig. 25-23. The temperature-measuring junction of

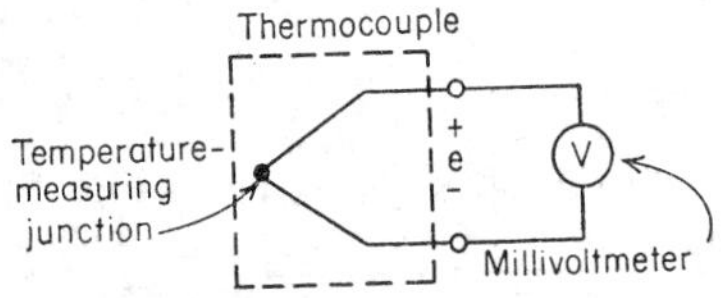

FIG. 25-23. Thermocouple instrument for measuring temperature.

the thermocouple serving as a transducer thermoelectrically generates a voltage e which is some function of the junction temperature. The millivoltmeter, in turn, measures the voltage e. The millivoltmeter may have a scale calibrated directly in degrees or it may be necessary to refer to a calibration chart to convert from voltage to temperature. [For further discussion of such instruments, *cf.* Considine (ed.), "Process Instruments and Controls Handbook," McGraw-Hill, New York, 1957. Lion, "Instrumentation in Scientific Research," McGraw-Hill, New York, 1959.]

Two special-purpose electrical instruments which find wide application in industrial process measurements as well as in laboratory measurements are the *potentiometer* and the *impedance bridge*.

Potentiometer. A potentiometer is an instrument which measures an unknown voltage by comparing it with an accurately known voltage. The basic circuit of a potentiometer is shown in Fig. 25-24. The voltage

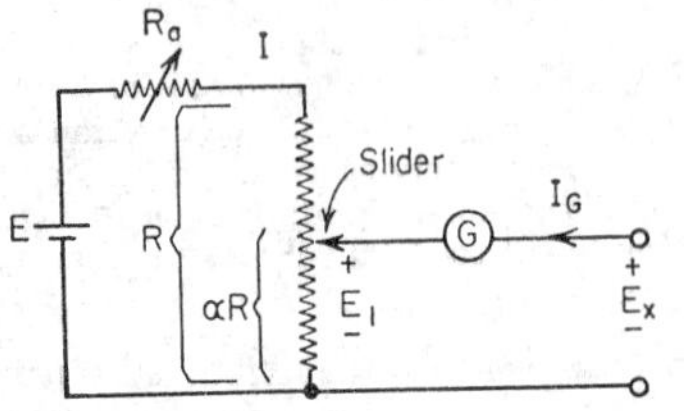

FIG. 25-24. Basic circuit of potentiometer.

supply E establishes a current I (adjusted to some accurately known value by means of resistor R_a) which flows through resistor R, establishing a voltage in this resistor which varies along its length. When the slider is adjusted so that $E_1 = E_x$ the galvanometer G reads zero. At the point along R where the galvanometer reads zero, the potentiometer is said to be balanced, and E_x is known in terms of E_1 (or more correctly in terms of the slider position). The resistor R (sometimes called a slide-wire) is an accurately made resistance whose resistance varies uniformly—within very close limits—with position along the wire. The voltage E_1 is given by

$$E_1 = \alpha RI$$

when the bridge is balanced (and $I_G = 0$). For given values of R and I it is possible to determine E_1 (and hence E_x) precisely in terms of α (the position along the slide-wire). The current I is established accurately by comparison of the voltage at a known tap point on R with the voltage of a standard cell.

Potentiometers may be employed wherever voltages must be accurately measured. These devices have the advantage over other means of measuring voltage that they draw no current from the source of the unknown voltage when the balance condition is obtained. Potentiometers are used in accurate measurement of temperature using thermocouples, in measurement of hydrogen-ion concentration, in the standardization and calibration of less accurate voltmeters, in accurate measurement of current (using precision shunts), and wherever voltages must be accurately measured.

Potentiometers are commercially available which are capable of detecting voltage changes of 1 microvolt or less and which have a limit of error of ± 0.01 per cent. Many modifications of the basic potentiometer circuit have been devised to suit special needs [*cf.* Sec. 22; also Considine (ed.), "Process Instruments and Controls Handbook," McGraw-Hill, New York, 1957. Harris, "Electrical Measurements," Wiley, New York, 1952].

Impedance Bridge. A bridge is an electric circuit containing a number of impedances (usually four), all but one of which have known values, and a device for detecting a null. Bridges are essentially instruments for measuring the impedance of an unknown element by comparison with a set of precisely known impedances.

The general circuit of an impedance bridge is shown in Fig. 25-25. Of the four impedances shown, three must

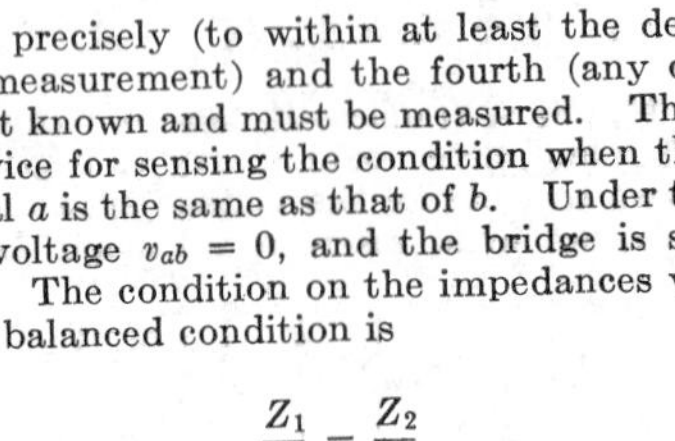

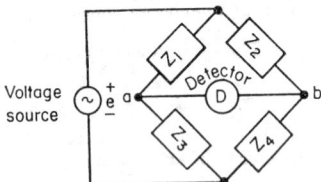

FIG. 25-25. General bridge circuit.

be known precisely (to within at least the desired precision of measurement) and the fourth (any one of the four) is not known and must be measured. The detector D is a device for sensing the condition when the voltage of terminal a is the same as that of b. Under this condition the voltage $v_{ab} = 0$, and the bridge is said to be balanced. The condition on the impedances which produces the balanced condition is

$$\frac{Z_1}{Z_3} = \frac{Z_2}{Z_4}$$

One or more of the known impedances is usually made adjustable, so that—with the unknown impedance connected—the bridge may be brought to a balance, and then the value of the unknown impedance may be computed using the above relation.

There are, in general, two types of bridges: d.c. bridges, in which the source is d.c.; and a.c. bridges, in which the source is a.c. The d.c. bridge primarily measures *resistance*, while the a.c. bridge primarily measures *impedance*.

The circuit diagram of a typical d.c. bridge is shown in Fig. 25-26. The most common form of d.c. bridge is

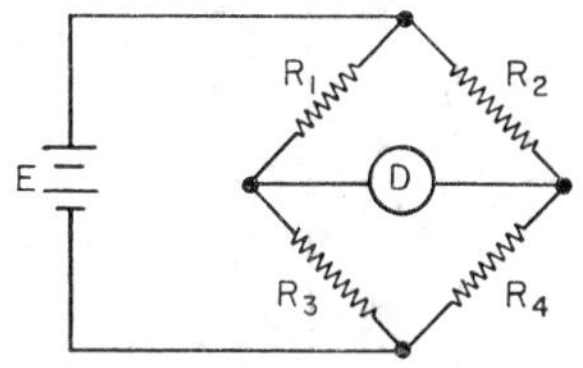

FIG. 25-26. A typical d.c. bridge.

called the Wheatstone bridge. The condition for balance of this bridge is

$$\frac{R_1}{R_3} = \frac{R_2}{R_4}$$

The detector is frequently a sensitive galvanometer—although electronic detectors are beginning to become commercially available. These electronic detectors are usually more costly than galvanometers but are more sensitive, far more rugged, and are relatively insensitive to local vibrations which frequently make galvanometers difficult or impossible to operate. D.c. bridges find wide application in laboratory and production measurement of resistance. In addition, a wide range of physical phenomena may be measured indirectly by their effect on the resistance of certain materials. Some examples of the use of d.c. bridges are: (1) temperature measurement, using a temperature-sensitive resistor as one arm of the bridge; (2) gas analysis by thermal conductivity; (3) electrolytic conductivity; (4) electrical strain gages; (5) bolometers; and (6) relative humidity.

The circuit diagrams of some typical a.c. bridges are shown in Fig. 25-27. There are a number of detectors which are used in a.c. bridges: (1) headphones, which provide an audible signal indicating a null—useful primarily at audio frequencies; (2) vibration galvanometer—useful at power frequencies up to 400 cycles/sec.; (3) a.c. galvanometer—useful at power frequencies; (4) cathode-ray oscilloscope—useful over a very wide range of frequencies (including d.c.). This is, perhaps, the best detector available because of its high sensitivity and the ability the user has to obtain a sharp null in the presence of harmonics; and (5) a.c. electronic voltmeters—useful over a wide frequency range, and very sensitive, comparable with cathode-ray oscilloscope except for inability to discriminate against harmonics. A.c. bridges are used to measure capacitance, inductance, and a.c. resistance of materials, in the laboratory and in production lines.

POWER TRANSMISSION AND DISTRIBUTION

The terms *power transmission* and *distribution* refer to the provisions made for the transfer of a required amount of power from a source or group of sources to various utilization loads. Branch circuits must be selected and designed to supply these loads, and in turn a distribution system is used to supply these branch circuits. For safety and control, switching and protection means must be provided at the source point (service connection) and at various other points in the systems. A system should meet at least six basic requirements: (1) safety, (2) adequacy, (3) flexibility, (4) ease of maintenance, (5) reliability, and (6) supplying the required power most efficiently and economically.

There are minimum standards of safety for design of electrical systems known as the National Electric Code. Quite often, in addition to this code, local ordinances impose their own restrictions by excluding certain wiring methods approved by the National Code, and by having more severe requirements for the methods approved. Although the National Code is accepted as the legal criterion for electrical design and installation, a well-designed electrical system will far exceed these minimum requirements.

System adequacy refers to the ability of the sources to supply the required power to the various utilization loads without exceeding safe temperature limits of the distribution and branch circuit equipment and to permit the utilization loads to perform efficiently. A system can, in time, very quickly become inadequate if provision has not been made for load growth. In electrical-system design, adequate provision for future loads and plant expansion has been the most neglected of the six considerations mentioned above. Comparatively little expense is required to allow for future expansion in the initial design and installation of the system, rather than to

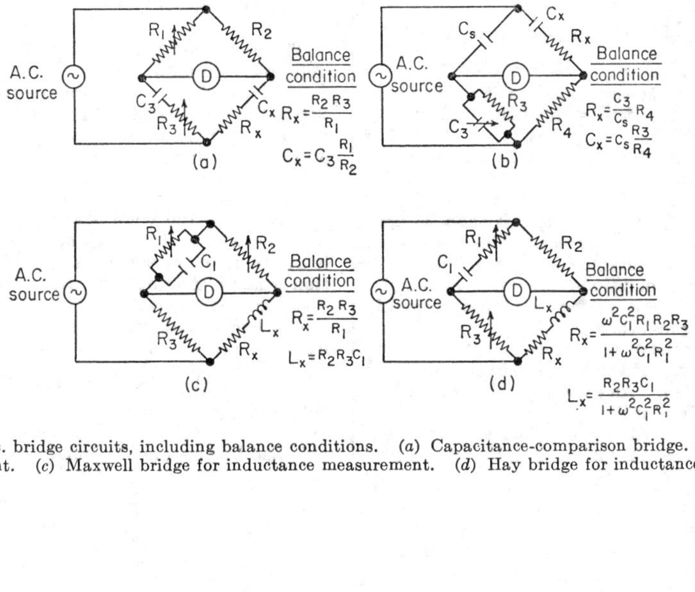

FIG. 25-27. Typical a.c. bridge circuits, including balance conditions. (*a*) Capacitance-comparison bridge. (*b*) Schering bridge for capacitance measurement. (*c*) Maxwell bridge for inductance measurement. (*d*) Hay bridge for inductance measurement.

make major changes later. The use of standard equipment and voltages will aid in future expansion.

Flexibility designed into a system permits plant layouts to be changed readily with little time and small cost so far as the electrical system is concerned.

Ease of maintenance is essential in minimizing both maintenance and repair costs. In general, a system which is easily maintained will be more reliable. The use of standard equipment promotes easy maintenance as well.

Reliability is defined as the probability that the electrical system will continue to function for a given time as originally designed. Reliability is a function of both original design and maintenance procedures. The type of utilization load will determine the necessary reliability as far as the original design is concerned. If the load must be continuously supplied with electrical energy, in spite of equipment failures, alternate sources can be made immediately available by automatic transfer switching. The reliability to be designed into a system must take into account the individual system requirements. An evaluation can be made of the cost of an interruption in service and this cost can be compared with the cost of added reliability in the system, in order to decide whether the increased reliability is warranted.

An electrical system will, in general, consist of three parts, listed in the order in which they must be considered in system design: (1) branch circuits, (2) distribution system, and (3) system service.

The branch circuits are the connections between the utilization loads and the rest of the system. Various branch circuits are grouped together on feeders which are supplied, in turn, from the distribution system. The distribution system is then powered from the service. The distribution system may operate at the same voltage as the branch circuits, in the case of light loads, or the distribution system may operate at a substantially higher voltage and then, at various locations near the load, be reduced in voltage to the utilization level. The six basic considerations that the complete system must meet must obviously be met by each of the three divisions separately.

Branch circuits are used either for power or lighting loads or for combined light and power loads. To be classed as low-voltage circuits, branch circuit voltage must not exceed 600 volts. The minimum conductor size must be determined from the load current. The load current can be found by:

$$I = \frac{\text{(volts) (amperes)}}{\text{line voltage}} \qquad \text{(single-phase)}$$

$$I = \frac{\text{(volts) (amperes)}}{\text{line voltage} \times 1.732} \qquad \text{(three-phase balanced)}$$

Table 25-2 lists the current-carrying capacity of various sizes of conductors and the properties of the various insulations commonly used.

Current capacity of conductors must be 25 per cent larger than the load current when the load operates over sustained lengths of time. Conductors supplying individual motor circuits must be rated no less than 25 per cent more than full-load motor current. The insulation on the conductor must be suitable for the ambient temperature and moisture conditions present. Although No. 14 wire is the smallest permitted, good design would prohibit using anything less than No. 12.

Since the conductors have resistance and inductance there will be a voltage loss or voltage drop in the conductors when they are loaded. An excessive drop will result in poor performance of the utilization device. For example, a 1 per cent drop in voltage supplied to an incandescent lamp will reduce output by 3 per cent, and a 10 per cent drop will reduce output by 30 per cent. Similar difficulties will occur with heating devices. In motor circuits, low voltage will result in lowered starting torque and pullout torque, and somewhat lowered full-load speed. For a given horsepower output, the current will increase with a lower voltage and correspondingly higher motor temperatures will result. It is good practice to keep voltage drop to no more than 1 per cent. Years ago practice would have permitted considerably higher drops. It is also good practice to limit circuit loading to 50 per cent of capacity. Usually this will result in being within 1 per cent of the voltage-drop figure provided the run of conductor is not too long. In the case of very long circuit runs, the conductor size should be determined on a voltage-drop basis using the maximum current that might occur in that circuit in the future. Figure 25-28 shows the effect of conductor length on maximum current for a drop of 1 volt for various conductor sizes.

Table 25-2. Current-carrying Capacity of Various Insulated Conductors

Conductor size, A.W.G. or MCM	Allowable current capacity, amp., for different insulation types: Rubber, R, RW, RUW; thermoplastic, T, TW	Rubber, RH, RUH	Paper, asbestos, thermoplastic, TA, V, AVB, RHH	Bare weight, lb./1000 ft.	Resistance, ohms/1000 ft at 20°C.
14	15	15	25	12.4	2.52
12	20	20	30	19.8	1.59
10	30	30	40	31.4	0.999
8	40	45	50	50.0	0.628
6	55	65	70	79.5	0.395
4	70	85	90	126	0.248
2	95	115	120	205	0.156
1	110	130	140	258	0.124
0	125	150	155	326	0.0983
00	145	175	180	411	0.0779
000	165	200	210	518	0.0618
0000	195	230	235	653	0.0490
250 MCM	215	255	270	772	0.0433
300 MCM	240	285	300	926	0.0361
400 MCM	280	335	360	1240	0.0270
500 MCM	320	380	405	1540	0.0216
1000 MCM	455	545	585	3090	0.0108

Example. It is desired to supply a three-phase load with 30 amp. at 90 per cent lagging power factor at a distance of 500 ft. with no more than a 5-volt drop.

Solution. Supplying a 30-amp. load with a 5-volt drop for 500 ft. is the same as supplying a 30-amp. load with a 1-volt drop for 100 ft. The intersection of the point for 100 ft. and 30 amp. results in the nearest wire size of No. 2.

There are four types of branch circuits to serve light and power outlets:

1. Single-phase three-wire systems—provides 120 and 240 volts. This system is seldom used for motor loads in excess of 5 hp. and is commonly employed in residences and in small apartment and commercial buildings.

2. Three-phase four-wire systems—this is the most common secondary three-phase system. For 120/208 volt systems, 120 volts is available for lighting between any line wire and ground, and three-phase at 208 volts is available for motor loads. Another voltage combination which is gaining very widespread use is the 480/277 volt system; 480-volt three-phase power is available for motor loads, and 277 volts is available for fluorescent lighting.

3. Three-phase three-wire systems are used primarily for power loads. Common voltages of this system are 240, 480, and 600, with the most common being 480 volts.

4. Three-phase four-wire delta systems are less desirable and less commonly found. One transformer of the

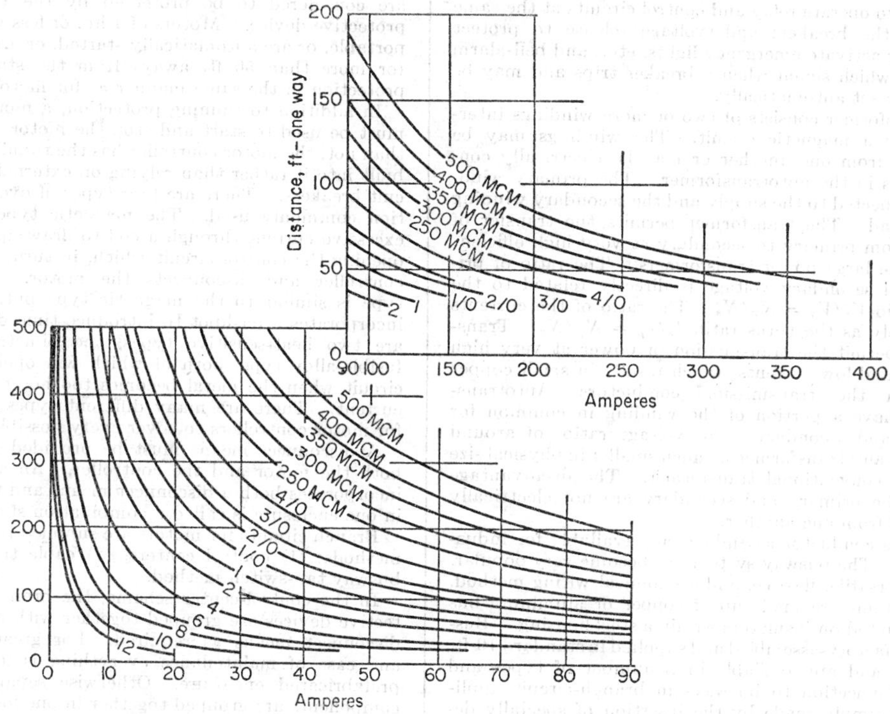

FIG. 25-28. Feeder voltage drop and current capacities for 600-volt type RH conductors. 60 ~ − 3φ in steel conduit (49°C. temperature). Curves are for 1 volt drop and 90 per cent p.f. lag. For any other drop, ratio ordinates. *(From Knowlton, "Standard Handbook for Electrical Engineers," McGraw-Hill, New York, 1957.)*

three used is center-tapped to provide a 120-volt source, while 240 volts three-phase is available for motors.

If a branch circuit serves a single utilization device or a single receptacle, there is no limit placed on its allowable capacity. However, if two or more devices or receptacles are served by one circuit, then these circuits are grouped and are limited by the following regulations:

1. 15- and 20-amp. circuits—for fluorescent and incandescent lighting and small power loads. The rating of any one portable device cannot exceed 80 per cent of the circuit rating. A fixed utilization load may be connected to the circuit provided it does not exceed 50 per cent of the circuit capacity.

2. 30-amp. circuits—may be used for incandescent lighting in industrial areas and may be used for power loads provided no single device exceeds 80 per cent of the circuit capacity.

3. 50-amp. circuits—the same limitations apply to these circuits as for the 30-amp. circuits.

Protective devices in the form of circuit breakers or fuses must be used on branch circuits to protect the conductors from overheating and protect the apparatus from overheating and short circuits. If fuses are used, switches are provided as well, but a circuit breaker functions as both a protection means and a switch. Fuses are of two physical constructions, plug fuses and cartridge fuses. Plug fuses are limited to circuits in which the voltage is not more than 150 volts to ground. Cartridge fuses are of either the ferrule type or knife-blade type. There are four classes of low-voltage cartridge fuses:

1. Class H—600 amp. or less a.c. or d.c. with interrupting ratings from 2000 to 200,000 r.m.s. amp.

2. Class J—600 amp. or less, a.c. only with no less than 200,000 r.m.s. amp. interrupting capacity.

3. Class L—601 to 6000 amp. a.c. only, no less than 200,000 r.m.s. amp. interrupting capacity.

4. Class M—same as L electrically and differing only physically.

Standard ratings for fuses are 15, 20, 25, 30, 35, 40, 45, 50, 60, 70, 80, 90, 100, 110, 125, 150, 175, 200, 225, 250, 300, 350, 400, 450, 500, 600, 800, 1000, 1200, 1600, 2000, 2500, 3000, 4000, 5000, and 6000 amp. Fuses offer well-engineered effective circuit protection at relatively low cost. Fuses have the disadvantage of permitting single phasing on three-phase motors and of requiring time to replace after blowing.

Circuit breakers overcome all the disadvantage of fuses but are more expensive in initial investment. Standard current ratings for non-adjustable-trip circuit breakers are 15, 20, 30, 40, 50, 60, 70, 100, 125, 150, 175, 200, 225, 250, 300, 350, 400, 500, 600, 700, and 800 amp. Low-voltage circuit breakers can be mounted either stationary or with draw-out construction. Draw-out type breakers afford easier and safer maintenance. Stationary breakers do not require as much space in the switchboard or in allocation of aisle space as do the draw-out type.

Molded-case breakers offer a cheaper construction in which the circuit-breaker mechanism is assembled as a complete switching and overcurrent protective device in a supporting and enclosing housing of insulating material. They are available up to 600 volts in the various current ratings previously mentioned. Molded-case breakers may be purchased with various accessories such as shunt trip by which a breaker may be opened by remote-control push buttons, or limit switches; motor-operated mechanisms which enable a breaker to be opened, closed, or reset from a remote location; auxiliary switches to operate relay and control circuits at the same time as the breaker; undervoltage release to protect motors or activate emergency lights, etc.; and bell-alarm switches which signal when a breaker trips and may be made to reset automatically.

A transformer consists of two or more windings interlinked by a magnetic circuit. The windings may be insulated from one another or may be electrically connected, as in the autotransformer. The primary winding is connected to the supply and the secondary winding to the load. The transformer permits the transfer of energy from primary to secondary at very high efficiencies in the large power transformers. The ratio of primary and secondary voltage is directly related to the turns ratio $V_p/V_s = N_p/N_s$. The ratio of the currents is inversely as the turns ratio $I_s/I_p = N_p/N_s$. Transformers permit the transmission of power at very high voltages and low currents, which results in small copper losses in the transmission conductors. Autotransformers have a portion of the winding in common for primary and secondary. For voltage ratios of around 2 to 1 the autotransformer is much smaller in physical size than the conventional transformer. The disadvantage is that the primary and secondary are not electrically insulated from one another.

Various conductor assemblies are available for industrial use. The busway system has become very popular. It is a versatile, flexible, and economical wiring method. Such systems are made up of copper or aluminum bus bars mounted on insulators within a steel housing. Busways are factory-assembled and supplied in standard 10-ft. sections, and are available in a number of types and sizes. Connection to busways in branch-circuit application is simply made by the insertion of specially designed plugs into the assembly.

Cable troughs of meshlike metal are widely used for supporting and routing conductors. They provide a sturdy flexible system permitting changes to be made very easily.

Interlocked armor cable has been in use for many years, but it is only now finding widespread application. It is available for use at 600, 5000, and 15,000 volts. In the 600-volt rating, which is used for branch circuits, it is available in No. 6 to 750 MCM sizes with three or four conductors. The armor is of steel, aluminum, or bronze. The choice between busway and armor cable depends on the routing, length, and current to be carried. For tortuous runs and many obstructions, armor cable is superior. For long straight runs, busway is superior. Above 1000 amp., busway is generally cheaper. Below 500 amp., armor cable is generally cheaper.

In some locations considerable advantage can be gained using under-the-floor power ducts to allow flexibility in widespread areas.

All the afore-mentioned wiring assemblies are widely used for distribution systems as well as branch-circuit wiring.

Motor branch circuits require more consideration, since their loads are usually large and the motors are costly, and therefore full performance is expected of them. As previously stated, branch circuits serving only one motor must have a capacity of at least 125 per cent of the motor full load. Branch circuits serving more than one motor must have a capacity of at least 125 per cent of the full-load current of the largest motor plus the sum of the other full-load motor currents. Running protection, using fuses or circuit breakers, for motors over 1 hp., if used for continuous duty, must be provided. The running protection must be such as to open the circuit at 125 per cent of full-load current in the case of 40°C. rise motors, and at 115 per cent in the case of all other types. Motors that are 1 hp. and are portable are considered to be protected by the branch-circuit protective device. Motors of 1 hp. or less which are not portable, or are automatically started, or are out of sight (or more than 50 ft. away) from the starter, require protection in the same manner as for motors over 1 hp.

In addition to running protection, a motor controller must be used to start and stop the motor. More often than not, the motor controller has the running protection built into it rather than relying on external fuses or circuit breakers. There are four types of overload protection commonly used. The magnetic type depends on excessive current through a coil to draw up a plunger—opening the control circuit which, in turn, opens up the controller and disconnects the motor. The dashpot type is similar to the magnetic type but, in addition, incorporates a dashpot to introduce time delay. There are two heat-sensitive types, the bimetallic and the fusible-alloy type, both of which will open the control circuit when the metal becomes too hot from excessive current. There are many different types of enclosures for motor controllers to cover every possible location.

A disconnect means must be provided to deenergize both the motor and the controller. An assembly that incorporates both a disconnect means and the controller in one enclosure is called a combination starter.

Branch circuits for motors are supplied by one of three methods: (1) control centers, (2) cable tap-box, or (3) busway tap-switch method.

In the control-center scheme, the branch-circuit protective devices are grouped together with controller and disconnect means as required. For greatest economy and ease of maintenance everything is located in one prefabricated enclosure. Otherwise separately housed components are grouped together in one location.

In the cable tap-box method, individual branch circuits are run to motors as needed from feeders or subfeeders, by using 10 ft. or 25 ft. taps from the cable junction box to the branch-circuit protective device. These limits on tap lengths are set by the code.

In the busway tap-switch method, each motor circuit is tapped from the busway through a fused tap-switch or tap-circuit breaker which provides disconnect means and branch-circuit protection.

Induction motors are the most prevalent type of motor used. Unfortunately, they draw a lagging current, especially when lightly loaded. This lagging current results in a low power factor. A lower power factor prevents the owner from getting the full capability of his distribution and branch-circuit wiring since load limits are based on volt-amperes, not just watts. Moreover, the utility company usually charges a penalty if the power factor falls below a certain value. A power factor of much less than 90 per cent is undesirable. Capacitors offer a cheap and convenient means of correcting power factors. Capacitor installations will pay for themselves in savings on penalty charges within one to two years. The most effective power-factor correction occurs when the capacitors are installed right at the motor terminals. No additional switching means are necessary, since the capacitors are switched with the motor. Maximum savings in copper also result because the capacitor reduces the lagging current at the point of connection to the circuit. When motors are numerous, small, and operated infrequently, it is usually cheaper to install the required capacity directly at the motor load center. The amount of kva. of capacity can be determined from

$$\text{kva.} = \text{kw.}\ (\tan \theta_1 - \tan \theta_2)$$

where kw. = power of load at original p.f.
θ_1 = original phase angle
θ_2 = phase angle at corrected p.f.

Example. It is desired to correct a load of 100 kw. at 70 per cent p.f. to one of 90 per cent p.f.

$$\begin{aligned} \text{kva.} &= 100(\tan\theta_1 - \tan\theta_2)\\ \theta_1 &= \cos^{-1}(0.7) = 46 \text{ deg.}\\ \theta_2 &= \cos^{-1}(0.9) = 26 \text{ deg.}\\ \tan\theta_1 &= 1.021\\ \tan\theta_2 &= 0.483\\ \text{kva.} &= 100(1.021 - 0.483) = 53.8 \end{aligned}$$

Branch circuits and their utilization loads operating in hazardous locations must conform to special requirements set up by the National Electric Code, depending on the particular hazard present. Only wiring methods and equipment specifically permitted to be used in such areas should be employed.

The type of building and the size and type of total load will determine the type of distribution system to employ and what distribution voltages to use. Sometimes, in addition, a distribution system will supply some power at a higher frequency for fluorescent lighting or portable tools, and in some cases, rectification from a.c. to d.c. is required in the design of the distribution system.

Distribution systems are categorized according to the voltages they employ. There are 10 voltage levels in general use. These 10 voltage levels fall into one of two classes, either secondary distribution voltages (600 or below) or primary distribution voltages (2300 and above). Secondary distribution voltages are fed directly to the branch circuits, but primary voltages undergo one or more transformations before they are lowered to utilization levels. The 10 voltage levels with a description of their applications are:

1. 120/240 volt three-wire single-phase—for use where total load is small, in residences, schools, and small commercial establishments.

2. 120/208 volt three-phase four-wire—for use in commercial establishments and small industrial loads, this is a combined light and power distribution system.

3. 240-volt three-phase three-wire—for use in power loads in commercial and industrial buildings. This system is used where the power load is large compared with the lighting load. Lighting is usually served by a separate single-phase supply to the building.

4. 480-volt three-phase three-wire distribution—for use in commercial and industrial loads that are mainly comprised of motors. Stepdown transformers are used to supply 120 volts for lighting and small power loads.

5. 480/277 volt (or 416/240 volt) three-phase four-wire distribution—this is a combined light and power system. The single-phase 277 volts (or 240 volts) is used for general fluorescent lighting and the 480 (or 416) volts is used for motor loads. This system offers economic advantages over a 120/208 volt system when less than half of the load requires 120 or 208 volts. A 480-volt system offers considerable savings in copper and other distribution equipment because of the correspondingly smaller current compared with a 208-volt system for a given load. If the load requires more than half of its power at 120 or 208 volts, the expense of stepdown transformers to provide these voltages will more than offset the other savings in using a 480-volt system. The 480-volt system is best applied to multistory buildings and to large or long single-story buildings. This system has come into decided prominence in the past few years.

6. 2400-volt three-phase delta distribution—this is used for supplying large motors directly, and smaller motors and lighting loads through load-center substations.

7. 4160/2400 volt three-phase four-wire distribution with a grounded neutral—this system is in much more widespread use than No. 6. Economies in the use of cables and switch gear are probably the greatest for this primary system. Although this system was originally designed for industrial use, its inherent economies have caused it to be readily applied to large-area spread-out commercial and institutional buildings. Large motors may be supplied directly by this voltage. The use of a grounded neutral in this system offers greater safety to personnel and to motors than an ungrounded system such as in No. 6.

8. 4800-volt three-phase delta system—this is a much less commonly used system. The use of this uncommon voltage level makes selection of apparatus more difficult and expensive and is certainly not to be recommended.

9. 7200-volt three-phase delta system—the comments of No. 8 apply to this system as well.

10. 13,200/7200 volt three-phase four-wire system—this is a commonly used system to serve large industrial loads. Although large motors can be purchased to operate directly at this voltage, the increased initial cost and maintenance and somewhat reduced reliability of such designs usually prohibits their use except for extremely large motors. Usually, the voltage in this system is stepped down to 480/277 volt three-phase four-wire system, at the load centers.

In summary, the practice today is to employ the 13,200/7200 volt system for large industrial loads. For small loads, commercial and institutional loads, a 4160/2400 volt system is recommended. In kva. ratings, the division occurs in the following fashion: for loads that demand 20,000 kva. or more, 13,200 volts is desirable; between 10,000 and 20,000 kva., plant load may be economically served by either 13,200 or 4160 volts; for loads less than 10,000 kva., 4160 volts is a more economical choice. The National Electric Code prohibits the use of equipment operating at a voltage greater than 15,000 volts except in special vaults.

The load-center substation is the key to modern high-voltage industrial distribution. The location and number of substations depend on the layout of the building, the capacity of the individual stations, and total load to be served. The use of load-center substations allows efficient and economical distribution of large amounts of power throughout a plant. Distributing power at high voltages requires much lower feeder current-carrying capacity than would be required to distribute the same amount of power at low voltages. As a result, the primary feeders are relatively small in size and voltage drop and power loss in the feeders are negligible compared with high-current low-voltage feeders supplying the same power. The secondary feeders or branch circuits require only short runs, since the station is at the center of the load area. Savings as high as 20 per cent in copper have been effected by the use of primary distribution systems. In addition, load-center distribution provides great flexibility and easy expansion of future load growth. Several manufacturers offer substations as packaged units, complete in themselves, which need only to be connected to the high-voltage supply and low-voltage feeders. The use of such apparatus minimizes special engineering and long design and construction time. Very often it results in lower equipment purchase price as well.

Certain considerations must be kept in mind in applying unit substations. The smaller the rating of the unit substation, the more it will cost per kva. A large number of unit substations require a large number of primary cables but will reduce the length of secondary feeders required, and vice versa. In view of this and other costs, it is economical to use unit substations in the range of 500 to 1500 kva., with the greatest economy realized in the range of 750 to 1000 kva.

The equipment generally found in a load-center substation is high-voltage switch gear, a stepdown transformer, and several low-voltage circuit breakers. The incoming primary cables connect directly to the high-voltage switch gear, which normally is a draw-out circuit breaker; but in some cases, for economy, high-voltage fuses may be used. The transformer is the largest and most expensive part of the unit substation. For transformers rated above 600 volts and up to 15,000 volts on the primary, the following types are available: (1) open dry type for indoor use, (2) sealed dry type for either indoor or outdoor use, (3) oil or Askerel filled for either indoor or outdoor use.

For voltages higher than 15,000 volts only type 3 is used. The low-voltage circuit breakers in the unit substation are often of the draw-out type.

Substation layouts fall into one of four categories: (1) radial, (2) secondary selective, (3) primary selective, or (4) network.

Most of the load-center substation systems used today are either the radial or secondary selective. The radial system is simple, quite reliable, flexible, and easy to operate and maintain. Two unit substations might be operated in such a manner that their secondaries could be connected together by a secondary tie breaker, which is normally open. Such a system is called secondary selective. If the transformer or primary cables should fail in one substation, the load could be switched over by the tie breaker to the remaining transformer. Since the reliability advantage mentioned above results in a cost increase of only 5 to 15 per cent over a simple radial system, the secondary-selective system is often employed.

A primary-selective radial system provides a choice of primary feeders for improved service reliability in the event of a primary feeder fault. Transfer switching is provided to switch over to other primary feeders. This switching may be done automatically or manually. Networks may either be of the spot (or local) type or general type. Transformers are connected to a common secondary bus and divide the load among them. Each transformer feeds the secondary through a network protector. Upon primary feeder or transformer failure, the secondary is isolated from the defective portion by the automatic operation of a network protector. The load is then supplied by the remaining equipment without interruption.

Once the particular distribution system has been selected, the feeder conductors must be properly selected. Feeders must be able to carry the amount of current required by the load plus an allowance for load growth. Often, as in branch circuits, the sizing of the conductors may be determined solely by voltage-drop considerations. The most serious problem encountered in electrical modernization today has been insufficient feeder capacity and lack of provision in conduits or raceways to accommodate larger conductors. Often there is not even enough space to put in additional conduits, with the result that extensive and expensive building alterations must be made. The fault, in such cases, lies in the original design.

Demand factor, diversity factor, and load factor are terms often used in electrical design of distribution systems. Demand factor is the ratio of maximum demand to the total connected load. This factor will be less than unity. Diversity factor is the ratio of the sum of the individual maximum demands to total maximum demand. This factor is usually found to vary between 1.0 and 2.0. Load factor is the ratio of the average load in a given time to the peak load in that same time. This factor is invariably less than 1. Tables of demand and diversity factors have been developed from experience with various types of load concentrations and various layouts of feeders and subfeeders supplying loads. It is common and preferred practice in modern electrical design to assume that the diversity factor in main feeders to load-center substations is unity to provide some spare feeder capacity. Typical diversity factors for main feeders supplying lighting alone vary from 1.10 to 1.50. For combined power and light feeders, the diversity varies between 1.50 and 2.00.

A conductor may be sized from the following formula:

$$\text{Current } I = \frac{\text{volt-amperes}}{k\ (\text{voltage, line-to-neutral or line-to-line, if no neutral is present})}$$

k = 1 for two-wire d.c. or single-phase a.c.
= 1.73 for three-wire three-phase a.c.
= 2 for three-wire d.c. or single-phase a.c.
= 3 for four-wire three-phase a.c.

See Table 25-3 for common demand factors to be used for sizing feeders.

Table 25-3. Common Demand Factors for Sizing Feeders

Utilization Device	Range of Demand Factor
Motors for pumps, compressors, elevators, machine tools, etc.	0.2–0.6
Motors for semicontinuous operations in process plants	0.5–0.8
Motors for continuous operations	0.7–1.0
Furnaces, arc and induction	0.8–1.0
Arc welders	0.3–0.6
Resistance welders	0.1–0.4
Resistance heaters, ovens, and furnaces	0.8–1.0

If, for example, the total connected load requires 100 amp. and consists of motors for semicontinuous operation (demand factor of 0.8 from Table 25-3) then the feeder supplying all these motors would be sized for $100 \times 0.8 = 80$ amp. and not for 100 amp.

In sizing motor feeders, where two or more motors may be started simultaneously, feeders may have to be larger than is usually required for feeders to several motors starting individually.

Protection of distribution feeders follows the same pattern as for branch circuits, except that, when the allowable current-carrying capacity of a conductor does not correspond to the rating of a standard-size fuse, the next larger fuse rating may be used—but the rating of the fuse must never exceed 150 per cent of the allowable current-carrying capacity of the conductor. The same limitations apply to circuit-breaker ratings as to fuse ratings.

The last aspect in the over-all electrical system is the service. The conductors are sized in the same manner as previously described. Special design considerations are involved in service to primary distribution systems. Transformers used indoors in primary supplies over 15,000 volts must be installed in a vault. If the transformer is rated less than 15,000 volts on the primary and contains a liquid that will not burn and is otherwise mechanically protected, it need not be installed in a vault. Primary switches, circuit breakers, and other control apparatus need not be installed in a vault, if they are built and approved for use outside a vault.

Grounding is essential for personnel safety and equipment protection. High voltage might be encountered during short circuits, if adequate grounding is not used. Grounding should be done at the source points and transformer secondaries. The service ground conductor should have a carrying capacity of not less than 25 per cent of the main capacity.

Purchase of energy usually represents decided economy over the cost of private generation of electrical energy within the plant. If there is a certain process which requires large amounts of process steam, it may be more economical to generate the needed energy or part of it, by supplying a turbine-generator with high-pressure steam and using the discharge steam for process purposes.

Electrical rate structures of utility companies are based fundamentally on the cost of service with an allowance for a reasonable yearly return on the investment. The charge per kilowatt-hour, called the energy charge, reflects the operating costs of the utility proportioned among the customers on the basis of the energy generated for their use. Since electrical energy must be generated, transmitted, and distributed as it is used, the maximum demand determines the capacity of generating equipment, lines, and transformers which must be installed. The expenses of providing sufficient capacity to meet the total customer demand should be assigned to each customer on a basis related to his individual demand. This assignment is accomplished by means of a demand charge, which is a function of the maximum kilowatt demand during a specified period of time, such as a month or a year. Demand charges are based not on the instantaneous peak power, but on the highest average of the power requirements over a 15-, 30-, or 60-min. interval.

ELECTRIC MOTORS AND GENERATORS

A rotating electrical machine or dynamo is a device which converts energy from one form to another. If mechanical energy is converted into electrical energy, the dynamo is called an electric generator. In the electric motor, electrical energy is converted into mechanical energy. The electric generator is driven by a machine called the prime mover. This may be an electric motor, a gasoline engine, a steam turbine, or even a manually operated crank.

Electric Generators. The electric generator fundamentally consists of two basic parts, (1) electromagnets or permanent magnets which produce a magnetic flux and (2) a laminated steel core, carrying conductors. Relative motion between the conductors and magnetic field produces a voltage in accordance with Faraday's law of induction.

In the d.c. generator, the stationary part (stator) consists of the electromagnets. The rotating member (rotor) is the laminated steel core which carries the conductors and is called the armature. The armature is laminated to reduce eddy-current losses. Since the conductors pass alternatively under a north and a south pole, the voltage induced is alternating. The armature conductors are connected to the external circuit through a switching device—the commutator and brushes, so that the voltage delivered is unidirectional. Fundamentally, therefore, the d.c. generator is an a.c. generator with a commutating device.

The armature winding may be of either the lap or wave type which differ in the manner of connecting the armature conductors to the commutator segments on the rotor. The number of parallel current paths in the armature depends on the winding type. In the simple wave winding, there are two parallel paths and in the simple lap winding there are as many parallel paths as there are poles. The type of winding affects the voltage and current rating but has no effect on the power rating. The lap winding is a low-voltage high-current winding relative to the wave type, which is high-voltage low-current for the same number of conductors on the armature. Thus, if a given machine were wound as a lap with 200 volts and 40 amp. capacity, it could be rewound with the same conductors to give a wave winding of 400 volts and 20 amp. The power rating—8 kw.—remains the same in either case.

The voltage E induced in the generator is a function of the flux ϕ and the speed n. Specifically, $E = K\phi n$. The constant K is a function of design data. The speed of the generator armature is fixed by that of the prime mover. Since generators are usually operated at constant speed, the induced voltage is directly proportional to the flux per pole; therefore, any adjustment of voltage must be obtained by varying the flux. This is done by varying the field current, *i.e.*, the current in the electromagnets, by means of a rheostat in series with the field windings.

Armature reaction is a term describing the distortion of the main field due to the current that flows in the armature. This distortion causes a slight reduction in the main flux.

Commutation is the process by which the internal *alternating* current is converted to an external *direct* current (*i.e.*, the commutation rectifies the a.c.). The direct current is delivered to the load through carbon brushes which rest on the commutator segments. During the commutating process, armature coils under the brushes are short-circuited. Severe sparking may result if the coil has an induced voltage during this period. Most modern machines have commutating (interpole) pole windings connected in series with the armature to obtain proper commutating results.

There are three types of d.c. generators—shunt, series, and compound (see Fig. 25-29). The designation to be

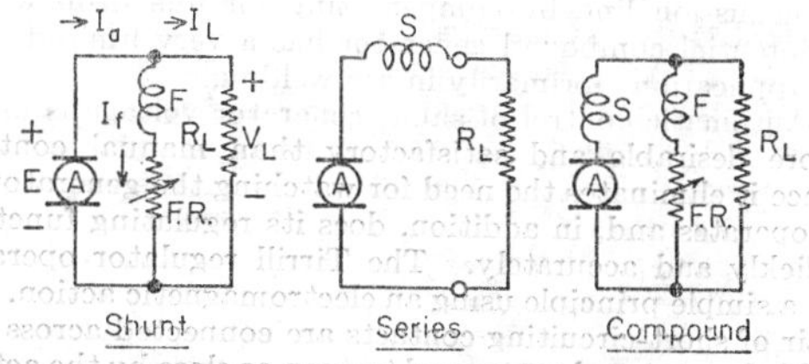

FIG. 25-29. Self-excited d.c. generator connections.

A = armature
F = shunt field
F.R. = field rheostat
S = series field
V_L = load voltage
R_L = load resistance
I_f = field current
I_a = armature current

used is determined by the method of connecting the field (excitation) winding to the armature. In the shunt generator the field winding is electrically connected in shunt (parallel) with the armature. In the series machine, the field winding is in series with the armature. In the compound machine, two field windings exist; one is connected in parallel with the armature, and the other in series with the armature. If the series field aids the shunt field, the compounding is cumulative; if it opposes the shunt field, the compounding is differential. If the field is connected to some other source of voltage the machine is separately excited.

The regulation of d.c. generators (change of output voltage with varying load) depends on the type of generator (see Fig. 25-30). The voltage of the separately

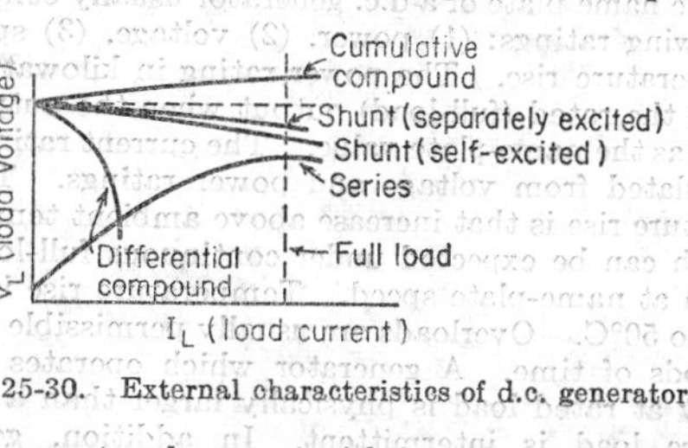

FIG. 25-30. External characteristics of d.c. generators.

excited generator decreases with increase in load current because of the IR drop in the armature circuit and the effect of armature reaction. The self-excited shunt machine has a further reduction in voltage with load because of the reduced voltage impressed on the field. In the cumulative compound machine, the series field contributes additional exciting ampere-turns so that the flux increases with load to cause the load voltage to increase with load instead of decreasing. The series generator is seldom used except as a booster on some electric-railway systems.

The separately excited shunt generator has an inherent tendency to hold the load voltage constant but has the disadvantage of requiring a separate source of voltage. The self-excited shunt generator has a greater voltage variation yet if properly designed will also tend to maintain fairly constant load voltage. It is therefore suitable for constant-voltage systems when the distance of transmission is not long enough to require an increase in generator voltage to compensate for the line drop as the load increases. In any event, the load voltage can be maintained constant by manually or automatically controlling the field current with a field rheostat. The cumulative compound generator is used more than any other d.c. generator, since it can be designed to have a wide variation in its voltage characteristics by controlling the amount of compounding (relative strength of the series field). The rise in voltage from no load to full load is used to maintain constant voltage at the end of a transmission line by compensating for line drop. The differential compound generator has a very limited field of application—primarily in arc welding.

Automatic control of shunt generator voltage is much more desirable and satisfactory than manual control, since it eliminates the need for watching the generator as it operates and, in addition, does its regulating function quickly and accurately. The Tirrill regulator operates on a simple principle using an electromagnetic action. A pair of short-circuiting contacts are connected across the field rheostat and are caused to open or close by the action of an electromagnetic device called a relay. If the voltage drops, the relay causes the contacts to close, reducing the field rheostat resistance and thus increasing the field current, which causes the voltage to rise. If the voltage rises, the contacts open, to cut in more field resistance, and cause the voltage to drop.

A more recent type of automatic regulator called the Diactor (direct-acting) is preferable to the Tirrill in that it accomplishes the same function without the vibrating contacts of the relays used in the Tirrill regulator. Other types of automatic regulator which are in use produce almost any desired voltage characteristic. These regulators are more complex and depend for their action on specially designed electronic, magnetic amplifier, or rotating (Rototrol, Amplidyne, Regulex) equipment. The compound generator voltage characteristics can be automatically controlled by design of the series-field compounding, as mentioned above, and is therefore cheaper and more satisfactory than the shunt generator voltage control.

The name plate of a d.c. generator usually contains the following ratings: (1) power, (2) voltage, (3) speed, (4) temperature rise. The power rating in kilowatts represents the rated (full-load) output when the output voltage has the name-plate value. The current rating can be calculated from voltage and power ratings. The temperature rise is that increase above ambient temperature which can be expected under continuous full-load operation at name-plate speed. Temperature rise is usually 40° to 50°C. Overloads are usually permissible for short periods of time. A generator which operates continuously at rated load is physically larger than a machine whose load is intermittent. In addition, generators which are not enclosed and are well cooled by fans have higher ratings than those which are enclosed so that air does not circulate freely.

Paralleling of generators is frequently desirable, in order that more than one generator may be used to supply a load. Shunt machines may be paralleled with little difficulty, if care is taken that the terminal voltages are the same and that the same polarities are connected together. For proper division of load, all generators operating in parallel should have the same voltage regulation. Cumulative compound generators must be provided with an equalizer, connected so that two or more machines will be stable when paralleled. The equalizer is a low-resistance conductor connecting the series fields in parallel. With the equalizer bus connection, compound machines may be adjusted to divide the loads properly.

Three-wire generators are used to obtain the advantage of double the load voltage for distribution purposes. The common voltage system is 115/230. Motor loads are usually connected at the higher voltage. The most common three-wire generator is the Dobrowolsky type in which a balance coil is connected across the armature. The mid-point of the balance coil furnishes the mid-point for the d.c. system. The balance coil may be built to rotate with the armature or may be external.

Alternating-current sinusoidal voltages are supplied by three-phase a.c. generators called alternators. Alternators are constructed in much larger sizes than the d.c. generators, since the limiting criterion in the design of d.c. machines is the commutation problem, which is not present in the a.c. machine.

For electrical and mechanical reasons, the stator of the alternator contains the armature conductors and the rotor has the field winding which is excited by direct current from a self-excited compound d.c. generator called an exciter.

Alternators are driven at a constant speed, since the frequency of the generated voltage depends on the speed and the number of poles:

$$f = \frac{pn}{120}$$

where f = frequency, cycles/sec.
p = number of poles
n = speed of rotor, r.p.m.

The speed of the alternator is commonly referred to as the synchronous speed. For this reason, a.c. machines are commonly called synchronous alternators. Refer to Table 25-4 for frequency, pole, and speed combinations.

Table 25-4. Alternator Speed-pole-frequency Characteristics

Poles P	Revolutions per minute n	
	$f = 60$	$f = 25$
2	3600	1500
4	1800	750
6	1200	500
8	900	375
10	720	300
20	360	150
30	240	100

Typical prime movers for synchronous alternators are steam turbines, steam engines, and water wheels.

As in the case of the d.c. generator, the generated voltage in the alternator is controlled by the variation of its field current. A large range of variation of excitation (field current) is necessary to provide a constant output voltage with variation in load and power factor.

It is essential that automatic voltage regulators be used with alternators, since the voltage regulation (no-load voltage minus full-load voltage divided by full-load voltage) of an alternator varies widely with load (especially at lagging power-factor loads). In addition, alternators usually feed comparatively long transmission systems, which consist of wires and transformers whose resistance and reactance produce additional voltage drops. Tirrill regulators designed for a.c. use, or other equivalent types of regulator, operating on the same principle as for d.c. voltage control, are normally used.

Parallel operation of alternators is quite satisfactory. To connect an alternator to an energized bus, it is necessary to synchronize the machine to the bus by hand or automatically. The term synchronizing means adjusting the time of the voltage wave, by changing the speed of the incoming alternator, to obtain correct frequency and correct instantaneous polarity; the synchroscope is an instrument usually used to indicate synchronism. In addition, it is necessary to have correct voltage level and phase rotation.

The division of load among paralleled alternators is dependent on the speed (governor) adjustments of the prime movers. When it is desirable to increase the output of an alternator, the throttle is opened more, tending to increase its speed but actually changing the phase position of its generated voltage with respect to that of the other alternators. The frequency of all alternators in parallel must be identical, which thus fixes their speed. Variation of the excitation of an alternator in parallel changes its power factor.

The name-plate data on a three-phase alternator indicate its rated speed, frequency, output line current and voltage, and the output kva. (apparent power). Power factor and d.c. excitation current and voltage are also indicated.

Electric Motors. An electric motor is a device for conversion of electrical energy into mechanical energy. The basic principle of operation is that a current-carrying conductor placed in a magnetic field will experience a force (unless the magnetic field is parallel to the conductor).

In the d.c. motor, which is similar in construction to the d.c. generator, the impressed d.c. voltage excites the field windings, thus producing a flux in the magnetic circuit; in addition, current will flow in the armature conductors, which are directly connected to the input line. The interaction of the flux and the current-carrying conductors produces a torque and, consequently, rotation. When the motor is rotating, a voltage is generated (due to generator action) which opposes the impressed voltage and limits the current flow. To reverse the direction of rotation of a d.c. motor, it is necessary to reverse the direction of the current in the armature while maintaining the field current in the same direction.

In the d.c. motor, voltage and current are related by

$$V = E + I_a R_a$$

where V = impressed voltage
E = generated voltage
I_a = armature current
R_a = armature circuit resistance

The generated voltage E, as in the d.c. generator, depends on the flux ϕ and the speed n ($E = K\phi n$).

D.c. motors are characterized as shunt, compound, and series, as in the case of d.c. generators. The terminal characteristics of interest are the speed-load, torque-load, and torque-speed curves (see Fig. 25-31 for typical characteristics).

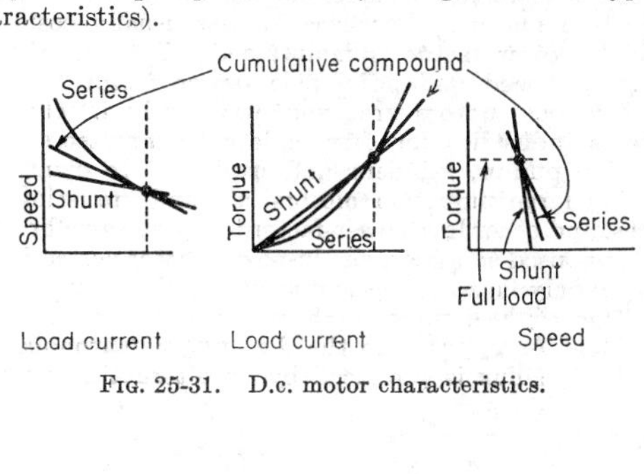

FIG. 25-31. D.c. motor characteristics.

The developed torque T of a d.c. motor is given by the equation $T = K\phi I_a$.

The speed of a d.c. motor is determined by

$$n = \frac{E}{K\phi} = \frac{V - I_a R_a}{K\phi}$$

where the $I_a R_a$ drop at full load is usually about 5 per cent of V.

A constant-speed motor will maintain its speed at substantially the same value for all loads. An adjustable-speed motor is one whose speed can be varied (controlled) over wide limits but whose speed for any particular adjustment is practically constant under varying loads. A variable-speed motor reduces its speed with increased load.

The shunt motor is essentially a constant-speed motor (since its flux is constant). However, it is also an adjustable-speed motor. Its torque varies practically linearly with load.

In the series motor, the flux ϕ varies almost directly with armature current I_a, which is also the excitation current. The speed therefore drops considerably with increase in load and the torque varies almost as the square of the current (since $\phi = KI_a$, $T = KI_a^2$). The series motor is of the variable-speed type and is applicable for loads requiring high torques at low speeds. It has the disadvantage of an excessively high no-load speed—so that series motors should never be used in applications where the load may be removed, as, for example, in belt drives.

The cumulative compound motor lies between the constant-speed and variable-speed type. Its torque characteristic lies between the shunt and series characteristics.

The rating of a d.c. motor is specified in terms of the mechanical power output under certain operating conditions. The name-plate data specify (1) horsepower, (2) voltage, (3) current, (4) speed, and (5) temperature rise. These data indicate that the motor will deliver rated horsepower output without exceeding the rated temperature rise, if operated at rated voltage and speed. The current indicated is the line current. Since neither torque nor horsepower output is easily measured in most motor applications, the armature current is used as an indication of the amount of mechanical power being delivered. For this reason, motor characteristic curves are usually plotted in terms of current.

An outstanding advantage of d.c. motors over a.c. motors is the ease and flexibility of controlling the speed. From the speed equation indicated previously, three methods are available for regulating speed: (1) by varying the flux (flux or field control), (2) by varying the resistance of the armature circuit (rheostatic control), and (3) by varying the voltage V (voltage control). In shunt and compound motors, the simplest and cheapest method of speed control is flux control, achieved by means of a rheostat in series with the shunt field. Since the power required by the shunt field circuit is small compared with the motor output, the rheostat is small in size, resulting in an efficient control method. A ratio of speed change of 6 to 1 is commonly achieved with this method. Speed regulation (no-load minus full-load speed over full-load speed) is affected only slightly by the rheostat setting. Armature resistance control allows the attainment of low speeds but necessitates an external resistor in the armature circuit. This method is applicable to all d.c. motors. At light loads, this resistance is not very effective. Increasing the resistance causes a drop in the speed. For a given setting, the speed regulation is large (*i.e.*, poor). The efficiency is quite poor, since the resistor carries the relatively large armature current. For this reason, this method is seldom used in industrial installations.

Voltage control is applicable for shunt and compound motors and is best illustrated by the well-known Ward-Leonard system. In this system, the motor, whose speed is to be controlled, has its field energized from a constant-voltage source. Its armature is energized from a separately excited d.c. generator which is usually driven by an a.c. motor. The field of the generator is also excited from a constant-voltage source. The generator field current may be adjusted from zero to maximum, in both directions, by means of a field rheostat and field-reversing switch. When the generator field current increases, the voltage fed to the motor increases and the speed increases. Motor speed reversal can also be obtained. This method provides a smooth speed variation of as high as 10 to 1. It is frequently used for operation of elevators in tall buildings, in blooming and paper mills, and in electric excavators. The chief disadvantage lies in its high initial cost (three dynamos are needed) and its low overall efficiency.

At the instant of starting, the counter e.m.f. is zero (since the speed is zero) and the starting current is excessively high, because it is limited by the armature resistance alone (which is quite low). To keep this starting current in the range of 100 to 200 per cent of rated value, a starting resistor is connected in series with the armature except in fractional-horsepower machines. This resistance is then removed in steps, as the motor accelerates. The insertion and removal of this resistance may be done manually or automatically. The lower limit of current is the minimum value necessary to produce sufficient torque for acceleration, and the upper limit is the maximum value allowable to protect the motor from electrical damage. In the case of very small motors (fractional-horsepower sizes up to about 3/4 hp.) no starting resistor is necessary, since the resistance of the armature is sufficiently high to limit the starting current adequately; and, in addition, the inertia of the machine is low enough so that it comes up to speed rapidly.

Two types of manual starters are the three-terminal and four-terminal starters. In the three-terminal starter, the operating handle is manually moved and the starting resistance is gradually cut out. At the last point, the operating handle is held in place (against the action of a spring) by an electromagnet which is energized by the field current of the motor. If the field circuit is accidentally opened (resulting in high motor speed), the coil is deenergized and the spring pulls the arm back to the starting position, deenergizing the motor. A disadvantage is that the magnet may become too weak to hold the handle if the field current is decreased for speed-control purposes. The four-terminal starter is similar in operation but differs in that the holding coil is energized by the supply voltage directly. The motor is stopped by simply opening the line supply switch. Manual starters are cheaper than automatic starters but if improperly operated may cause damage to motor and starter. A controller is a starter which is equipped with some means for varying the motor speed, in addition to providing starting control. Controllers are also designed to permit reversal of motor rotation and may include protective devices such as overload relays, undervoltage relays, and open-field devices.

Automatic starters are preferable to manual ones, since the starting resistors are timed to be cut out so that acceleration is uniform and the starting current can be precisely kept within the design limits. The motor is started by simply pressing a "start" button and the motor attains proper speed smoothly and automatically. The motor is stopped by pressing the "stop" button, or when there is an overload or voltage failure. The push-button station can be located away from the motor, thus providing remote control. In the automatic starter, units of the starting resistor are short-circuited in a definite sequence by means of sets of contactors. Several different methods are used to achieve this, but all depend on the operation of relays, contactors, timing devices, and other equipment. In the *counter-e.m.f. starter*, the contactors are operated at predetermined values of voltage. The *time-limit starter* causes the contactors to operate at preset time intervals by means of relays. In the third method, the *current-limit starter*, the operation of the contactors is a function of the armature current.

In many motor applications, the control of the stopping time is important. The methods used for stopping motors are mechanical braking and the electrical methods of plugging, dynamic braking, and regenerative braking. Mechanical braking has the objection that a smooth stop is difficult since it depends on the brake surface and dexterity of the operator. In hoisting applications, a mechanical brake is always required. Plugging operates on the principle of applying power to the motor so that it attempts to reverse itself. The voltage to the armature is removed and a voltage of opposite polarity is applied. The motor will come to a stop before it reverses itself. In the rolling-mill industry, the plugging action is used to bring the motor to standstill quickly and then allow its reversal. In dynamic braking, the energy stored in the rotating armature and load is dissipated by causing the motor to operate as a generator and deliver power to a resistive load. This is accomplished by removing the armature supply voltage (but keeping the field energized) and connecting a resistor across the armature terminals. If the energy is fed back into the supply line, instead of into the resistor, it is called regenerative braking. In practice, regeneration can be applied only when the load has an overhauling characteristic, as in the lowering of a hoist or the downgrade motion of a railroad train.

Alternating-current motors are classified as single-phase or polyphase and are further classified by type of connection and such characteristics as synchronous, induction and brush shifting, etc.

The polyphase synchronous motor is similar in construction to the synchronous alternator and has two voltage inputs, a.c. to the stator windings and d.c. to the rotor (field) windings. The machine operates at constant (synchronous) speed for all loads. The speed is related to the number of poles and line frequency, in the same manner as for the alternator.

Variation of power factor through excitation adjustments (by means of a field rheostat) is the most important characteristic of polyphase synchronous motors. By increasing the field current, the power factor of the motor may be made leading and by decreasing the field current the power factor may be made lagging. These motors are frequently operated at leading power factor to compensate for the inherent lagging power factor of induction motors. Purchased power usually costs less if high power factor is maintained. Because of their constant speed and adjustable power factor features, synchronous motors are used extensively in chemical process industries for driving large compressors, fans, blowers, pumps, grinders, and crushers. In plants employing large induction motors, arc and induction furnaces, and other low-power-factor loads, the synchronous motor is used to advantage in power-factor correction.

The polyphase induction motor is the most widely used motor, because it is inherently simple, rugged, and reliable. As opposed to the d.c. and synchronous machines, the flux is produced by an alternating current.

The stator winding is similar in construction to that of the synchronous alternator. In the squirrel-cage induction motor, the rotor winding resembles a squirrel cage (having longitudinal bars secured to end rings). The motor bars are sometimes bolted and soldered to the end connecting rings, sometimes welded, and sometimes cast with the end rings.

The speed characteristics are similar to those of the d.c. shunt motor, decreasing about 2 to 5 per cent from no load to full load. The no-load speed is approximately equal to the synchronous speed ($120f/P$) of the synchronous motor. The slip (synchronous speed minus rotor speed divided by rotor speed) is therefore about 2 to 5 per cent at full load. In the general-purpose squirrel-cage motor, the starting torque is about 150 per cent of the rated value and the maximum running torque is about 200 per cent of rated. Various starting and running characteristics of squirrel-cage machines can be attained by special design of the rotor bars and cage. The power factor of a polyphase induction motor is about 0.8 lagging at full load.

Wound-rotor induction motors permit the introduction of resistance in the rotor circuit. The variation of this rotor resistance can result in a reduction in starting current and an improvement in power factor at starting and, in addition, permits a variation in the speed.

Three-phase motors can be reversed simply by interchanging any two stator leads.

A serious limitation of the induction motor is that its speed cannot be easily or efficiently controlled, as in the case of the d.c. motor. In the wound-rotor machine, up to about 500 hp., the speed is varied by the insertion of resistance in the rotor. As the resistance increases the speed decreases. This method of speed control results in poor efficiency. A multispeed motor can be obtained by devising a switching arrangement so that the number of poles of the stator winding can be varied by changing the winding connections. An increase in the number of poles results in a decrease in the speed. In some special cases, the speed is varied by changing the frequency supplied to the stator. The speed increases as the frequency increases. This method obviously requires a variable-frequency source. The Schrage machine is a special brush-shift motor with a commutator which has a smooth and wide variation in speed but is relatively expensive.

In general, during the starting period, a motor is subjected to the most severe service. During this interval, an extremely high current tends to flow. In a well-designed induction motor, the starting current is about five to seven times the rated current. This large inrush of current is generally not permitted by the power companies because of the fluctuations caused in the supply voltage. An obvious way to reduce the starting current is to reduce the motor voltage, but a serious disadvantage of this is that the starting torque varies as the square of the motor voltage, and therefore if the motor voltage is decreased by one-half the torque is decreased to one-fourth of the original value.

The three starting methods generally used are (1) full-voltage starting, (2) reduced-voltage starting, and (3) part-winding starting. If the starting current does not cause appreciable supply-voltage fluctuation and the power company has sufficient capacity, then the motor may be started with full voltage applied to motor terminals. The motor may be started manually or by a simple automatic full-voltage starter.

The reduced-voltage line-resistance method involves the insertion of resistors in series with each stator lead to reduce the starting current. The resistors must be cut out simultaneously as the motor accelerates. This may be accomplished automatically through the use of shorting contactors and relays, as in the case of the d.c. machine. Series inductances accomplish the same purpose as the starting resistors. In the reduced-voltage compensator-starting method, a polyphase transformer with voltage taps is used. Taps are usually at the 50, 65, and 80 per cent points. The motor is started with 50 per cent voltage applied to its terminals, and gradually full voltage is applied to the motor in steps. This is accomplished smoothly by automatic starters. This method has the advantage of drawing less current from the supply mains than the series resistance or inductance method of starting. For example, if the resistors cut the motor current by a factor of one-half then the current taken from the mains is also reduced by one-half. In the transformer method when the motor current is reduced by one-half (by impressing 50 per cent rated voltage) the current on the input side of the transformer and thus from the supply is reduced by the factor one-fourth. This causes a reduced voltage fluctuation on the power system. The starting torque for the motor is the same in both instances.

When a three-phase induction motor has a stator winding which consists of two parallel windings, and only one of the windings is used for starting, the method is known as the part winding method. One winding presents a higher impedance to current flow and thus reduces the starting current to about 60 to 70 per cent of the value obtained under normal full-voltage starting, using both windings in parallel. In the wound-rotor machine, the starting current is reduced by simply adding resistance in series with the rotor winding. Synchronous motors start in the same way as induction motors and employ the same starting methods as the induction motor (except for wound-rotor starting). The field of the synchronous machine is short-circuited through a discharge resistor during starting. Full-voltage starting is the least expensive and most simple in application. The compensator type is more efficient, while the resistor or inductor types give smoother acceleration.

Alternating-current motors can be brought to standstill quickly by mechanical braking or electrically, by plugging or dynamic braking. The principles underlying these methods are the same as for the d.c. machines.

Single-phase motors are ordinarily used in fractional-horsepower sizes and in larger sizes where a polyphase supply is not available. Single-phase motors are usually rated at less than 10 hp.

The single-phase motor has zero starting torque, so that an auxiliary device is necessary for starting. The split-phase motor uses an auxiliary winding which is usually disconnected after starting. In the capacitor motor, a capacitor is connected in series with the starting winding to improve starting torque and power factor.

The universal motor is, in essence, a d.c. series motor which operates equally well on a.c. or d.c.—hence the name *universal.*

The shaded-pole motor incorporates a shorted ring around a section of the stator pole to produce the starting torque and is used where small torques are needed. It is the simplest and cheapest type of a.c. motor.

Single-phase motors have a larger slip, are less efficient, larger in size, and more expensive than three-phase motors of the same rating.

The single-phase reluctance motor is a synchronous motor, since it operates at synchronous speed only. Another single-phase synchronous motor is the hysteresis motor. These motors find application where constant speed is essential as in phonographs, recording instruments, electric clocks, and many kinds of timers.

The problem of motor application and selection consists essentially in finding the load requirements such as horsepower, speed variation, torque, starting torque, acceleration characteristics, duty cycle, and other operating conditions. In order to pick the motor to fit these requirements, the nature of the power supply must be known, as well as the operating characteristics of the various motors. D.c. motors are not so widely used as a.c. machines for several reasons: (1) d.c. power is generally not available; (2) d.c. motors have commutators which are a source of trouble due to sparking, brush wear, and the presence of moisture and fumes in the air; (3) d.c. motors are generally more expensive than corresponding a.c. motors. For variable-speed work such as hoists, cranes, and elevators, and for adjustable-speed applications, the d.c. motor is superior to the a.c. motor. Existing a.c. power is therefore frequently rectified into d.c., so that d.c. motors may be used.

The polyphase squirrel-cage motor, because of its simplicity and ruggedness, is the workhorse of motor applications and is preferable for constant-speed work over the d.c. motor. Generally speaking, higher-speed motors are lighter in weight, and less expensive, than lower-speed motors. The cost of a motor depends basically upon horsepower, speed, type of enclosure, and type of bearings. The d.c. motor costs more and is heavier than the corresponding general-purpose squirrel-cage motor.

The wound-rotor induction motor is 120 to 150 per cent heavier than the squirrel-cage motor of the same rating and is much more expensive. However, when properly used, the wound-rotor motor with rotor resistance provides the most efficient starting conditions—highest starting torque, lowest starting current, and smooth acceleration.

Synchronous motors have the following advantages over the induction motor: (1) the speed is constant; (2) power factor is easily controlled; (3) efficiency is higher; (4) initial cost is less for the low-speed rating (less than 500 r.p.m.) and in the larger outputs (500 hp. or more). Synchronous motors have the disadvantages: (1) require a d.c. source; (2) starting characteristics are poor; (3) do not lend themselves to speed control; and (4) starting and control devices are more expensive. Unity-power-factor synchronous motors are smaller, less expensive, and more efficient than the 0.8 power factor synchronous motors. When automatic controls are to be used their cost may be as high as five times the cost of the motor.

Table 25-5. Approximate Full-load Currents (amperes) for Motors

Hp.	Direct current		Single-phase, 230 volts	Three-phase induction type		Three-phase synchronous unity p.f.	
	230 volts	550 volts		220 volts	550 volts	220 volts	550 volts
¼	1.5	.....	2.9				
⅓	1.9	.....	3.6				
½	2.7	.....	4.9	2	0.8		
¾	3.7	1.6	6.9	2.8	1.1		
1	4.8	2.0	8	3.5	1.4		
1½	6.6	2.7	10	5	2.0		
2	8.5	3.6	12	6.5	2.6		
3	12.5	5.2	17	9	4		
5	20	8.3	28	15	6		
7½	29	12	40	22	9		
10	38	16	50	27	11		
15	56	23	....	40	16		
20	74	31	....	52	21		
25	92	38	....	64	26	54	22
30	110	46	....	78	31	65	26
40	146	61	....	104	41	86	35
50	180	75	....	125	50	108	44
60	215	90	....	150	60	128	51
75	268	111	....	185	74	161	65
100	355	148	....	246	98	211	85
125	443	184	....	310	124	24	106
150	534	220	....	360	144	...	127
200	712	295	....	480	192	...	168

NOTE: For motors operating at other voltages, the current is inversely proportional to the voltage; current for two-phase four-wire motors is about 87 per cent of the three-phase value.

The automatic control equipment for the synchronous machine is usually the most expensive. Those for the d.c. machine and the wound rotor are comparable in cost and rank below the synchronous machine. The squirrel-cage motor control is usually the least expensive.

CONVERTERS AND RECTIFIERS

Direct current is required for many applications such as electroplating, electrolytic refining, and d.c. motor drives. Practically all electrical energy is generated in 60-cycle a.c. form. It is necessary to employ some conversion equipment (rectifiers) to obtain the required d.c. from a.c. There are five types of rectifiers in use: (1) rotating machines; (2) mercury-arc rectifiers; (3) semiconductor rectifiers; (4) hot-cathode electron tubes; and (5) mechanical rectifiers.

Rotating machines once dominated the conversion field. This method—using an a.c. motor to drive a d.c. generator, which in turn supplies the necessary d.c.—is inherently a simple idea; however, the use of two machines (called an M-G set) is costly, heavy, space-consuming, and requires periodic maintenance. Years ago, to gain higher efficiencies, rotary or synchronous converters were popular. This is, in effect, a machine that has slip rings (for a.c.) on one end, and a commutator (for d.c.) on the other. To use such a machine as a *converter*, a.c. was supplied and d.c. obtained: and, as an *inverter*, d.c. was supplied and a.c. was obtained. In spite of its higher efficiency compared with an M-G set, its lack of stability in certain applications, and the advent of the mercury-arc rectifier in the 600-volt range, has made the rotary converter obsolete.

There are some applications for which there is nothing superior to an M-G set. Since the conversion process is through a mechanical interchange, sufficiently high mechanical inertia will cause the d.c. output to be unaffected by brief disturbances on the a.c. side. Adjustable-speed d.c. motors for use in large heavy-duty applications may often be supplied to advantage by M-G sets. The use of a Ward-Leonard system fits in perfectly in a M-G conversion system. Regeneration and dynamic braking are easily accomplished in this conversion system. M-G sets supply low voltage with accurate voltage control for some plating processes, of which large-scale tin- and chrome-plating lines are typical examples. Voltages in these applications vary from 1 to 50 volts and currents often exceed 3000 amp. For extremely large currents and low voltages, homopolar or Faraday generators are applicable. They furnish currents up to 150,000 amp. at 7.5 volts for resistance welding of steel pipes, to cite one example.

Mercury-arc rectifiers use a mercury-pool cathode and graphite anodes operating in a vacuum. There are three types, the ignitron, excitron, and the multianode rectifiers. Only the first two are produced in this country. Each of these types is available in either a sealed form or a pumped form to maintain the vacuum. Ignitrons and excitrons are single-anode types, invariably of the sealed form, since this design has proved to be very dependable. They operate in the same manner as an electron tube; under proper excitation the mercury pool is vaporized in the space between the anode and cathode. During the positive half cycle of the applied sine wave, the anode is positive with respect to the cathode and conduction occurs through the mercury vapor, from anode to cathode. On the next half cycle, the anode is negative with respect to the cathode and there is no conduction. Sometimes a discharge called arc-back will take place during this negative half cycle and high reverse currents flow.

Sealed units in metal tubes are available in up to 500-kw. ratings at 250 volts and up to 1000 kw. at 600 volts. Variations in competitive mercury-arc rectifiers are usually found in the ignitron means and in the control means.

Semiconductors are solid substances which allow current flow in one direction with practically no opposition but block current flow in the reverse direction except for a small reverse current. Semiconductor elements or cells consist of rectifying junctions with terminals connected to the junction and provision for removing heat, plus a "package" to give the cell mechanical strength and to exclude contaminants. The commonly used semiconductors are silicon, germanium, selenium, and copper oxide.

Germanium and silicon cells are similar in construction. Selenium and copper-oxide cells are alike in some ways but are quite different from silicon and germanium. In silicon and germanium, the junctions between cells are thin wafers—a few thousandths of an inch thick. The wafers are soldered to metal terminals, usually copper or aluminum. One terminal generally has a stud connection to a heat sink or is part of a heat sink itself. The other terminal normally includes a pigtail. Hermetic sealing of the cells prevents the failure of the cells which was encountered in previous years with contaminants affecting the joints. The cells, exclusive of the heat-removing means, are small; a stud-mounted silicon cell rated at 85 amp d.c. is only 1⅝ in. in diameter and 4⅔ in. long with the pigtail. Cooling is essential in order to obtain full ratings.

Selenium cells are constructed differently. They are built up on a plate and metal disks are used in between as counterelectrodes. Selenium rectifiers are simpler and less expensive than silicon or germanium. They can stand rough electrical treatment such as overloads and current surges. They heal after failure but they age and tend to unform (*i.e.*, change chemically).

Copper-oxide rectifiers were the first semiconductors to be developed. In construction, they are simple and are similar to selenium except that they are heavier and have lower forward current density and higher reverse leakage current, but they have the advantage of keeping their form and they stabilize after a break-in period. Table 25-6 shows how the semiconductors compare with one another.

Table 25-6. Comparison of Semiconductors

	Silicon	Germanium	Selenium	Copper oxide
Size	Very small	Very small	Large	Large
Weight	Very light	Very light	Light	Heavy
Cooling	Natural or forced			
Life	Very long	Very long	100,000 hr.	long-proved
Aging	None	None	Increases	Stabilizes
Reverse current	Excellent	Excellent	Good	Fair
Healing	None	None	Excellent	Good
Unforming	None	None	Appreciable	None
Temperature limit	250°C.	85°C.	85°C.	75°C
Humidity effects	Hermetically sealed	Hermetically sealed	Negligible	Negligible
Frequency response	Good	Good	Poor	Fair
Thermal capacity	Poor	Poor to good	Excellent	Excellent

Hot-cathode glass-tube rectifiers are well suited for high-voltage low-current applications. Typical applications are in communication equipment and in instrumentation and control. Tubes may be diodes or triodes. The triodes have a grid for control purposes. The tubes may be operated in either vacuum, or—for higher currents—in gas or vapor. A thyratron is a typical example of the latter type. For moderate d.c. power requirements, hot-cathode tubes may have advantages over other rectifiers; since they are simple, they need no maintenance and can be replaced easily although they are not mechanically rugged and have a relatively short life. Typical applications are speed control of small d.c. motors (5 hp. or less), welding control, and high-frequency oscillator power supplies.

Mechanical rectifiers consist of sets of contacts operated by a mechanism driven by a synchronous motor. This mechanism is run so that the contacts will open and close when they are not carrying current. These rectifiers were introduced rather recently and have gained some acceptance in electrochemical plants because of their high efficiency of 97 to 98 per cent. In this country, they probably will not gain any further acceptance because of the high maintenance costs and the development of the relatively maintenance-free silicon and germanium rectifiers.

The selection of a particular type of rectifier depends on such factors as purchase price, maintenance, efficiency, ease of voltage control, overload capacity, and life.

It is difficult to make a general statement as to which is the cheapest rectifier to buy. If each type discussed is applicable for the particular job (see Fig. 25-32) selenium will be the cheapest, with an M-G set, silicon, and

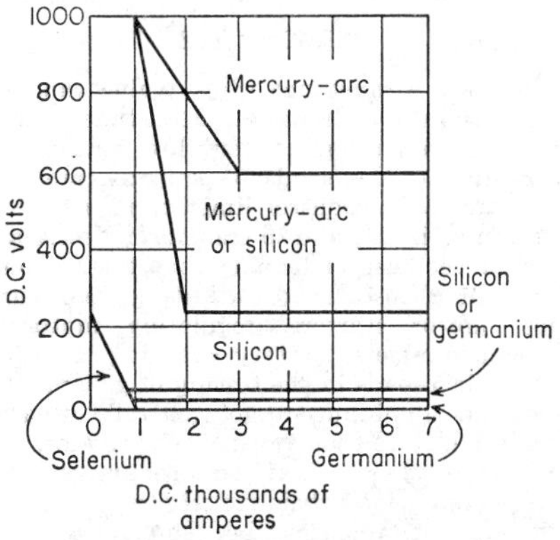

Fig. 25-32. Rectifier current-voltage rating guide.

mercury-arc rectifiers following in order of increasing cost. Often d.c. power supplies are sold as packaged units, making the installation cost much the same. However, larger M-G sets need special foundations and alignment, silicon rectifiers may require water for cooling, and mercury-arc rectifiers require at least some plumbing.

Maintenance of M-G sets is usually considerable because of the commutator, brushes, and bearings. Mercury-arc rectifiers require little maintenance, only an infrequent tank overhaul. Semiconductor maintenance amounts to keeping the cooling system in good order.

Dependability of silicon rectifiers is the highest but mercury-arc rectifiers are nearly as good. Although M-G sets are vulnerable to many troubles, they are still dependable, provided a regular and periodic maintenance program is practiced.

Efficiency is important for most applications—especially for high-power applications, such as aluminum reduction. Silicon rectifiers have the highest efficiency (about 95 per cent at full load) with mercury-arc rectifiers the second highest (about 92 per cent at full load). M-G sets have an efficiency in the order of 88 per cent at full load. Silicon and mercury-arc rectifiers have a relatively flat efficiency for variations from 25 to 125 per cent of full load. M-G sets have a narrower band of flat efficiency for variations from 75 to 125 per cent of full load.

Control of d.c. output voltage is easily accomplished by phase-shift control of mercury-arc rectifiers and field control of M-G sets. Control of d.c. output voltage, in the case of semiconductors, must be accomplished by controlling the a.c. input voltage by means of magnetic amplifiers, voltage-regulating transformers, or tap-changing transformers.

As for overload capacity, silicon and germanium rectifiers have a definite design ceiling on overload and short-circuit capacity. Cells are damaged if this ceiling is exceeded. Mercury-arc rectifiers have high overload capacity. Exceeding the overload limit causes arc-back without any permanent damage. Short-time overload capacity of M-G sets is very high, the limitation being imposed by commutation difficulties; for long-term overloads, the insulation will be damaged.

Life of silicon and germanium cells appears to be indefinite. Selenium has a life span averaging 8 years. Mercury-arc rectifiers average 10 to 20 years between tank overhauls. M-G set life depends on operating conditions and maintenance. Under ideal conditions M-G sets have operated for more than 40 years without rewinding or new commutators.

RHEOSTATS

A rheostat is a resistance whose value can be varied either continuously or in steps. Resistance values vary from the megohm range to very low values. Current capacities up to thousands of amperes are available. Rheostats are used to control, limit, or adjust the amount of current in a circuit, and to transform electrical energy into heat in the case of loading rheostats. Some common uses for rheostats are adjusting field current in dynamos, motor starters, regulating motor speeds, theater-light dimmers, battery charging, and for dissipating electrical loads in the testing of generators.

Copper and aluminum are not generally used as rheostatic material, since their resistivity is too low to obtain high resistance values. Iron and steel are used to a considerable extent, since their resistivity is six to twelve times that of copper—but at high temperatures they have the disadvantage of oxidizing readily. Alloys of nickel-chromium and iron are generally used, since their resistivity can be as high as 100 times that of copper, and in addition they have high melting points and do not disintegrate or corrode at high temperatures. In general, the higher the resistivity of the material, the shorter and stouter the resistance element, and the simpler and stronger the construction. Cast iron of different grades has about the same resistivity as the alloys and is a very much cheaper material. It is used extensively where cost of material is a primary item. In addition, cast-iron grids have high capacity for heat dissipation because of the large surface area.

Carbon rheostats of the compression type can withstand high temperatures, have high resistance values, and provide a smooth continuous variation of current. Such rheostats consist of one or more columns of thin graphite disks enclosed in enameled steel tubes. The resistance of such a column will decrease as the mechanical pressure between the ends of the column increases because the contact between adjacent disks improves. This type of rheostat is used in relatively small sizes because of the cost.

Slide-wire tubular rheostats are used extensively in laboratory work for the accurate control of voltages and currents. Such rheostats consist of an insulated metal or porcelain tube upon which is wound resistance wire. A sliding contact is supported by metal bars running parallel to the axis of the tube.

Liquid rheostats provide another method of obtaining a smooth continuous variation of resistance and are especially adapted to dissipate large amounts of power as in the testing of large generators. The liquid, which is usually water, is contained in a tank of non-conductive material. The electrodes are supported by vertical metal rods. The upper electrode can be raised or lowered to vary the resistance between electrodes smoothly. At voltages below 1000 volts it is usually necessary to add salt or acid to the water to decrease the resistance. Resistance of liquid rheostats varies to a considerable degree with temperature. The resistance at 80°C. is only about one-quarter the resistance at 20°C.

Water-cooled rheostats are also used to absorb large amounts of electrical energy. The rheostat consists of galvanized iron wire mounted on wooden frames submerged in running water. The water should be kept below the boiling temperature.

Sand-box rheostats are used where high wattages are encountered for extremely short periods of time. The resistors are made of heavy coiled alloy wire or crimped ribbon fastened to one side of an impregnated asbestos board. This assembly is placed in a metal box packed with fine quartz sand. Since the sand is in direct contact with the entire resistive element, the unit has high heat-absorptive characteristics. These rheostats are generally used for field discharge and dynamic braking purposes.

SOLENOIDS

Magnetic fields for most magnetic applications are produced by solenoids, although some are set up by permanent magnets. In general, a solenoid is a straight coil of wire with a closely packed, uniformly distributed winding, usually not more than a few layers thick, which can be used to produce a magnetic field if current is passed through the coil. More commonly the term is applied to devices which include a coil having a movable soft-iron plunger within it (see Fig. 25-33*a*). When the coil is

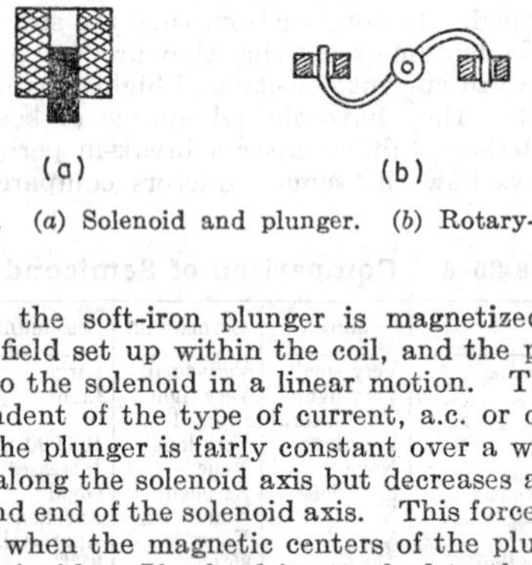

FIG. 25-33. (*a*) Solenoid and plunger. (*b*) Rotary-type solenoid.

energized, the soft-iron plunger is magnetized by the magnetic field set up within the coil, and the plunger is pulled into the solenoid in a linear motion. The action is independent of the type of current, a.c. or d.c. The force on the plunger is fairly constant over a wide range of travel along the solenoid axis but decreases at the beginning and end of the solenoid axis. This force becomes zero only when the magnetic centers of the plunger and winding coincide. If a load is attached to the plunger, work will be done.

Solenoids, as used in practice, are of the iron-clad type. The coil is surrounded by a frame of iron or steel, and the plunger is arranged to move in or out of the center of the coil. The iron frame protects the windings mechanically and, being magnetic, increases the magnetic flux produced. The advantage of the iron-clad solenoid over the air-type solenoid is that a much larger plunger force is obtained at or near the final position of the plunger travel. This large pull at the end of the stroke often results in a hammer blow at the end of the frame, which is objectionable. This sudden jar is eliminated in the magnetic-cushion-type iron-clad solenoid.

Solenoids can be designed to give magnetic-pull characteristics of different types. In some cases a larger initial pull is desired at the expense of a smaller pull in the final position. Characteristics can be changed by coil design.

introduction of magnetic and non-magnetic stops in the frame, and using cone-shaped plungers.

The a.c. solenoid differs from the d.c. solenoid, principally because the current in the coil is not determined by the coil resistance alone but is limited by the self-induced voltage produced by the alternating flux. To prevent excessive eddy-current losses in the a.c. solenoid the iron circuit must be laminated. The inherent advantage of the a.c. solenoid is that it has a high-speed action, compared with the d.c. solenoid.

Where a rotating motion is desired instead of a linear motion, the rotary-type solenoid in Fig. 25-33*b* is commonly used.

Solenoids find extensive use in circuit breakers, relays, time-limit switches, in magnetic brakes, in small punch presses, and wherever an electrically produced force is required.

Typical solenoid characteristics are shown in Figs. 25-34 and 25-35.

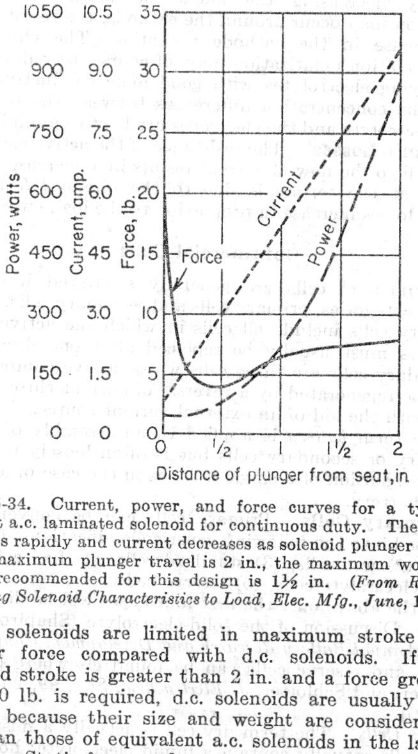

FIG. 25-34. Current, power, and force curves for a typical 110-volt a.c. laminated solenoid for continuous duty. The force increases rapidly and current decreases as solenoid plunger seats. While maximum plunger travel is 2 in., the maximum working stroke recommended for this design is 1½ in. (*From Reeves, Matching Solenoid Characteristics to Load, Elec. Mfg., June,* 1950.)

A.c. solenoids are limited in maximum stroke and plunger force compared with d.c. solenoids. If the required stroke is greater than 2 in. and a force greater than 50 lb. is required, d.c. solenoids are usually preferred, because their size and weight are considerably less than those of equivalent a.c. solenoids in the larger ratings. Static-force values up to several tons are realizable in d.c. solenoids at strokes a fraction of an inch long.

The total mechanical energy available from a particular solenoid is a constant, independent of the work distance involved. For the solenoid whose characteristics are shown in Fig. 25-35, the available work is 11.36 lb.-in. (the area under the force-distance curve, assuming that the plunger always starts its travel at 2 in.). If the energy is absorbed during the last 1 in. of travel, an impact force of 11.36 lb. is available; if it is dissipated during the last 1⁄10 in., an impact force of 113.6 lb. is available; and if the energy is absorbed during the last 1⁄1000 in. (as in punching 1-mil sheet metal), an impact force of 11,360 lb. is available. Available forces may be magnified many times by using levers between the solenoid and the work.

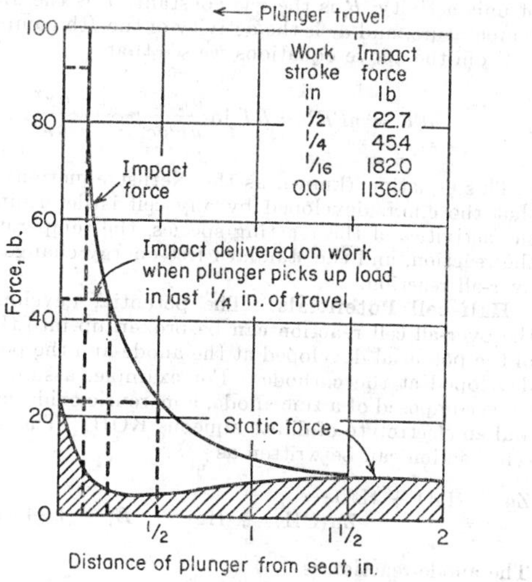

FIG. 25-35. Shaded area under the static-force curve (from Fig. 25-34) defines the total work capacity of the solenoid (11.36 lb.-in.). Each dotted rectangle has an area equal to shaded portion and shows forces obtainable for different work strokes by utilizing impact of the plunger. (*From Reeves, Matching Solenoid Characteristics to Load, Elec. Mfg., June,* 1950.)

ELECTROCHEMICAL CELLS

Definitions. Electrochemical cells convert a major portion of the energy associated with a spontaneous chemical reaction into usable electrical energy. This is accomplished by separating the reactive components so that the transfer of energy must take place through an external circuit. The reactive components of the cell are the anode and cathode. The *anode* is the cell electrode at which chemical oxidation occurs. It is designated as the negative electrode, and electrons, which are released by the oxidation reaction, flow from it through the external circuit to the cathode. The *cathode* is the cell electrode at which chemical reduction occurs. It is designated as the positive electrode. The *cell electrolyte* completes the electric circuit of the system by allowing a flow of positive and negative ions (called cations and anions, respectively) between the anode and cathode.

Cell e.m.f. The theoretical maximum e.m.f. which will be developed by any cell can be obtained from free-energy considerations. For a reversible process occurring at a constant temperature and pressure, the negative of the change in free energy $-\Delta G$ of the process is equal to the amount of work done. Electrical work can be expressed as the product of a voltage E times the quantity of charge Q flowing. For each n equivalent of material reacting, $Q = nF$, where F is the value of the faraday (96, 494 coulombs). Thus,

$$-\Delta G = nFE$$

At constant temperature and pressure the total change of free energy for a reaction is

$$\Delta G = \Delta G^\circ + RT \ln \frac{a_R{}^r a_S{}^s \cdots a_X{}^x}{a_B{}^b a_C{}^c \cdots a_P{}^p}$$

where the general reaction is

$$rR + sS + \cdots + xX \rightarrow bB + cC + \cdots + pP$$

and where ΔG° is the free-energy change of the reaction with both products and reactants in their standard states of unit activity, R is the gas constant, T is the absolute temperature, and a_I is the activity of the Ith component.

From the above equations we see that

$$nFE = nFE^\circ - RT \ln \frac{a_R{}^r a_S{}^s \cdots a_X{}^x}{a_B{}^b a_C{}^c \cdots a_P{}^p}$$

This equation (known as the Nernst equation) shows that the e.m.f. developed by any cell is determined by the activities of the reacting species, the temperature of the reaction, and the standard free-energy change of the over-all reaction.

Half-cell Potentials. The potential developed by the over-all cell reaction can be broken up into the sum of the potential developed at the anode and the potential developed at the cathode. For example, assume a cell to be composed of a zinc anode, a mercuric oxide cathode, and an electrolyte of dilute aqueous KOH. The over-all cell reaction can be written as

$$Zn + HgO + H_2O \rightarrow Zn(OH)_2 + Hg \qquad E^\circ = 1.34 \text{ volts}$$

The anode reaction is

$$Zn + 2OH^- \rightarrow Zn(OH)_2 + 2e \qquad E_A{}^\circ = +1.245 \text{ volts}$$

The cathode reaction is

$$HgO + H_2O + 2e \rightarrow Hg + 2OH^- \qquad E_C{}^\circ = +0.098 \text{ volts}$$

In order to obtain the potential of either of the above half-cell reactions, it is necessary to first define a reference potential (*i.e.*, the potential of an element in contact with its own ions). This reference potential has been defined as the potential of hydrogen at one atmosphere pressure in contact with hydrogen ions in solution at unit activity and is assigned the value of zero volts at all temperatures.

There are two conventions regarding the sign associated with the e.m.f. developed by a given half-cell reaction. These are the Lewis and Randall convention, which is used in the United States, and the European convention. The Lewis and Randall ("Thermodynamics," 2d ed., McGraw-Hill, New York, 1961) convention can be stated as follows:

The e.m.f., including sign, represents the tendency for positive ions to pass *spontaneously* through the cell *as written* from left to right, or of negative ions to pass from right to left.

From example, the sign of the potential for the zinc half-cell reaction given above is positive, which indicates that OH^- ions tend to move spontaneously toward the zinc anode, or from right to left. That is, the "natural" tendency of zinc in alkaline solution is to go to the higher oxidation state when this half cell is coupled with the normal hydrogen electrode. Similarly, the Hg^{+2} in the mercuric oxide cathode tends to go spontaneously to metallic mercury with an e.m.f. of 0.098 volt when coupled with the normal hydrogen electrode.

The European convention is the opposite of that just described.

Half-cell potentials tabulated in the literature (see Mantell, "Electrochemical Engineering," 4th ed., McGraw-Hill, New York, 1960. Latimer, "Oxidations of the Elements and Their Potential in Aqueous Solutions," 2d ed., Prentice-Hall, Englewood Cliffs, N.J., 1952. Lange, "Handbook of Chemistry," 10th ed., pp. 1212–1218, McGraw-Hill, New York, 1961) are the potentials for reactions in which all species are at unit activity unless otherwise noted. For reactions where all the species are not at unit activity, the half-cell potential can be calculated from the Nernst equation, which is given above.

Polarization and Irreversibility

Concentration Polarization. Polarization, in general, is the term applied to any irreversible phenomenon which tends to decrease (in the case of electrochemical cells) the over-all cell e.m.f. from the theoretical maximum e.m.f. Concentration polarization is the decrease in cell voltage which arises from the change in ion concentration around the cell electrodes when current is drawn from the cell. For example, consider the case of a metal anode being oxidized to metallic ions. The metallic-ion concentration in the vicinity of the anode will be greater than that in the body of the electrolyte since the electrolyte cannot have an infinite ion conductivity. From the Nernst equation, it is apparent that this increase in ion concentration around the electrode tends to increase the value of the logarithmic term, thereby decreasing the anode potential. A similar situation may occur around the cathode, the result being a decrease in the cathode potential. The effects of concentration polarization may, of course, be reduced by employing electrolytes with good ionic conductivity so that the concentration differences between the body of the electrolyte and the electrodes are kept to a minimum.

Ohmic Losses. The resistance of the active elements of a cell to the flow of current results in a decrease in cell e.m f. at the terminals due to the ohmic I^2R losses. These losses increase in proportion to the load current.

Commercial Cells

Commercial cells are generally separated into two major categories, primary cells and secondary cells. The primary cells include all cells in which the active components must usually be replaced after one discharge. Secondary cells are those cells whose active components may be regenerated by a reversal of current through the cell, with the aid of an external current source.

The term *battery* is applied to an assembly of either primary or secondary cells but is often loosely used for the designation of a single unit, as in the case of a flashlight battery.

Primary Cells. Primary cells can be conveniently grouped into the following generic classifications: (1) dry cells, (2) wet cells, (3) standard cells, (4) fuel cells, (5) solid-electrolyte cells, (6) reserve cells.

Of the above only the first four types will be discussed here. Discussion of the solid-electrolyte (Shapiro, *Proc. 11th Annual Battery Research and Development Conf.*, 3–5, 1957) and reserve cells can be found elsewhere [Blake, Pucher, and Schlotter, *J. Electrochem. Soc.*, **99**, 202–205c (1952)].

Dry Cells. The term dry cell is actually a misnomer. The cells actually contain a liquid electrolyte; however, this electrolyte is immobilized within the cell so that it cannot spill out when the cell is inverted.

Leclanché cells are zinc manganese-dioxide dry cells, most familiar to the public as flashlight batteries [Morehouse, Glicksman, and Lozier, *Proc. Inst. Radio Engrs.* **XIX,** 1462–1483 (1958). Birdsall, *Proc. 10th Annual Battery R. and D. Conf.*, 1956. Heise and Caboon, *J. Electrochem. Soc.*, **99,** 179c (1952)].

In the past 20 years tremendous advances have been made in the battery industry in the production of new special-purpose dry cells for both military and civilian use. However, the Leclanché cell still accounts for 90 per cent of the dry cells produced in the United States. This is due partly to the fact that Leclanché cells have been considerably improved as regards shelf life and energy density per unit volume of cell, and partly

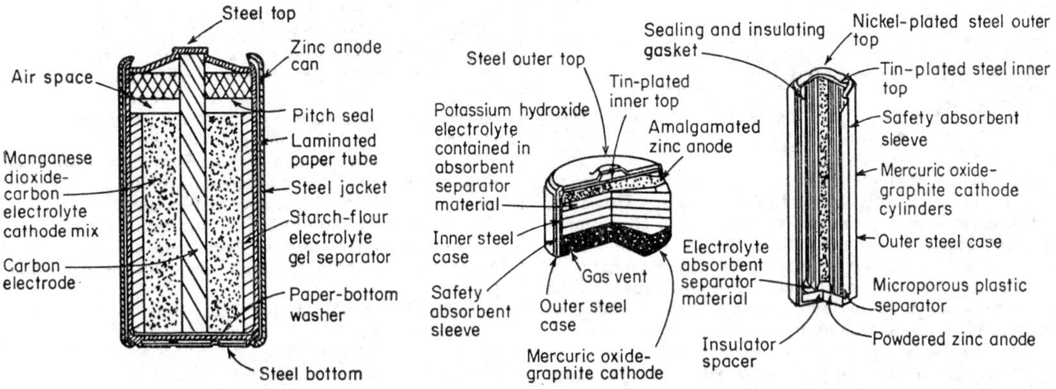

FIG. 25-36. Cross sections of typical Leclanché and zinc mercuric-oxide dry cells. [*From Morehouse, Glicksman, and Lozier, Batteries, Proc. Inst. Radio Engrs.*, **19**, 1462–1483 (1958).]

to the fact that simple construction and relatively inexpensive components make the Leclanché cell the least inexpensive battery for a great majority of applications.

Figure 25-36 is a cross-sectional view of two typical dry cells. The drawn zinc case which surrounds the Leclanché cell serves the dual purpose of containing the active ingredients of the cell while also acting as the cell anode. More recent practice has been to surround the zinc case with a steel container. This container prevents cell leakage in the event of a rupture (usually due to preferential corrosion) of the zinc case.

The cathode electrolyte of the cell is a paste compound of MnO_4-NH_4Cl-$ZnCl_2$-H_2O with a small amount of $HgCl_2$ added. The $HgCl_2$ amalgamates the zinc case to reduce its corrosion. The addition of the $ZnCl_2$ also seems to reduce corrosion by buffering the solution and thereby minimizing changes in pH.

A generally accepted (although certainly not the only possible) cell reaction is

$$Zn + Mn_2O_4 + 2NH_4Cl \rightarrow ZnCl_2.2NH_3 + Mn_2O_3.H_2O$$

It is common usage in industry to consider the Mn_2O_4 as a cathode depolarizer in the above reaction. For satisfactory use solid depolarizers, in addition to reacting quickly with any discharged hydrogen, should have a high electrical conductivity. This is accomplished in the Leclanché cell by adding graphite to the Mn_2O_4.

In most cells, including the Leclanché cell, it is necessary to place a physical barrier between the anode and cathode, so that the active material of either electrode does not migrate to the opposite electrode, thereby creating a short circuit. This barrier, or *separator*, is generally constructed of a porous material (*e.g.*, starch-coated paper) which is capable of absorbing and retaining the electrolyte.

Performance data for a small Leclanché cell are given in Fig. 25-37. It should be noted that the performance characteristics of the cell vary depending upon the magnitude and duration of the current drain, the operating temperature, and size of the cell.

Zinc mercuric-oxide cells were first developed commercially in World War II by Ruben [*Trans. Electrochem. Soc.*, **92**, 183–193 (1947)]. A diagram of this cell is given in Fig. 25-36, and its performance characteristics are shown in Fig. 25-37. The anode of the cell is amalgamated zinc in the form of either a finely divided powder or a coiled corrugated strip. The cathode consists of a mixture of red mercuric oxide and about 5 per cent graphite. The mix is molded under pressure into a steel cup or pressed as a separate part which is then assembled into the cell. The electrolyte is a 35 to 40 per cent solution of KOH containing approximately 5 per cent ZnO. The separator is composed of two materials: (1) a cellulosic material which absorbs and thereby immobilizes the electrolyte and (2) a barrier material, such as a microporous plastic, which is interposed between the cathode and the electrolyte.

The major advantages of the zinc mercuric-oxide cell over the Leclanché cell are its relatively flat voltage characteristics with time, and its high energy density. Its major disadvantage is the difference in cost between the two cells due to the higher materials and construction cost of the zinc mercuric-oxide cell.

Alkaline zinc manganese-dioxide cells [Herbert, *J. Electrochem. Soc.*, **99**, 190c (1952)] are the alkaline counterpart to the Leclanché cell. They consist of a manganese dioxide–graphite cathode mix which is pressed into a steel can. This steel can is spot-welded to a steel cap which is the positive cell terminal. A porous felt-type cellulosic separator immobilizes the sodium hydroxide electrolyte (about a 30 per cent solution in water containing dissolved zinc) and serves as a spacer between the anode and cathode. The anode is formed by amalgamated powdered zinc which is pressed into a plastic ring. This ring is in contact with the tin plate which serves as the positive-cell terminal. The entire cell is known generically as the "crown" cell.

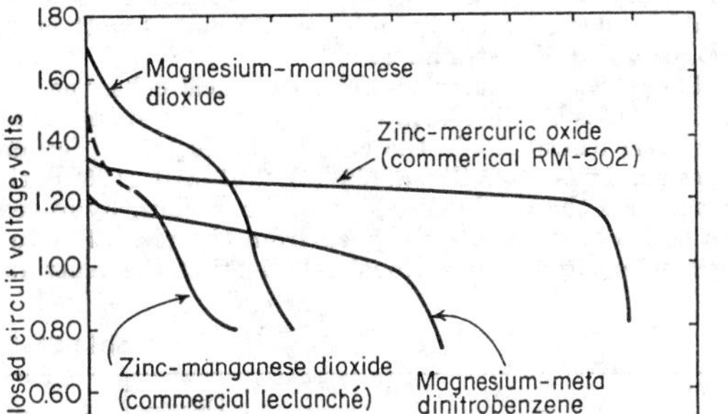

FIG. 25-37. AA-size penlight dry cells discharged continuously through 50-ohm resistance (simulates current drain encountered in some portable radios). [*From Morehouse, Glicksman, and Lozier, Batteries, Proc. Inst. Radio Engrs.*, **19**, 1462–1483 (1958).]

The cell reactions are

Anode:

$$\left.\begin{array}{l} Zn + 2OH^- + 2e \rightarrow Zn(OH)_2 \\ \text{Cathode:} \\ Mn_2O_4 + H_2O + 2e \rightarrow \\ \qquad Mn_2O_3 + 2OH^- \end{array}\right\} \begin{array}{l}\text{terminal} \\ \text{voltage} = 1.52 \text{ volts}\end{array}$$

The voltage characteristics on discharge of the crown cell are similar to those of the Leclanché cell. However, for low current drains the cell has about 1½ times more capacity than a Leclanché cell of the same size. It is more expensive than the Leclanché cell but less expensive than the zinc mercuric-oxide cell. For these reasons the crown cells are used in low-drain applications such as batteries for hearing aids and portable radios.

Other Dry Cells. The performance characteristics of the magnesium manganese-dioxide cell and the magnesium-meta dinitro benzene cell are also shown in Fig. 25-37. These cells are relatively recent developments, and information regarding them can be obtained in *Proc. Inst. Radio Engrs.*, **XIX**, 1462–1483 (1958).

Wet Cells. Wet primary cells find application where large capacity, constant voltage at moderately high currents, and long life are the dominant service requirements. There are two types of wet cells produced in this country, the zinc cupric-oxide Lande cell [Schumacher and Heise, *J. Electrochem. Soc.*, **99**, 191–195c (1952)] and the zinc-air cell (*Proc. 10th Annual Battery R. and D. Conf.*, 14-6, 1956).

The Lande cell consists of a zinc anode, a sodium hydroxide solution electrolyte, and a cupric oxide cathode, all of which are contained in a glass jar. The electrode configurations depend on the manufacturer and the service application. The cells are usually shipped dry, the electrolyte being added at the service site. A film of oil is poured on top of the electrolyte to reduce water vaporizations and carbon dioxide absorption by the caustic solution. These cells are designed to deliver 500 to 1000 amp.-hr. of service, to operate between 0.5 and 0.7 volt, and to deliver currents as high as 15 amp. They have an energy density of about 2.5 watt-min/cc., or about 1.85 watt-min./g.

The air cell differs from the Lande cell in that a porous carbon electrode replaces the cupric oxide cathode. The porous carbon electrode absorbs oxygen from the air. This oxygen then acts as the cathode material and is reduced to OH ions.

The cell is designed to operate at 1.1 to 1.2 volts and to deliver 2 amp. on constant drain or 3 amp. on intermittent drain. The cell has a flat voltage-time curve and has an energy density of between 7 and 11 watt-min./cc., or 5 and 9 watt-min./g.

Fuel Cells. As in other electrochemical cells, the fuel cell operates by withdrawing the energy of a spontaneous chemical reaction. In the case of the fuel cell [Feature Section, *Ind. Eng. Chem.*, **52** (4), 291–310 (1960)] the reaction is the combustion of a carbonaceous, hydrogen, or hydrocarbon fuel by oxygen from the air. The fuel cell differs from conventional cells in that the reactants are fed to the cell at rates which are proportional to the amount of electrical energy which is to be withdrawn. Also, these cells often operate at much higher temperatures than ordinary cells could withstand.

Interest in the fuel cell is derived from the fact that electrochemical cells can convert the energy in a fuel into electrical energy at efficiencies upward of 90 per cent while the steam- or gas-turbine heat cycles are thermodynamically limited to efficiencies of only about 40 per cent. Also, the fuel cell may yield a quiet, clean source of power and may require only a minimum of maintenance.

The electrodes used in fuel cells are generally gas-adsorption electrodes which may act as catalysts for the reaction.

Fuel-cell technology is, at this time, in a state of flux, so that cells which may be considered "good" today may no longer be considered so a year hence. For this reason, no attempt will be made to consider the individual types of cells which have been developed up to this point.

Standard Cells. Weston standard cells (Vinal, "Primary Batteries," pp. 160–213, Wiley, New York, 1950) are used to establish a reference e.m.f. and cannot be used to supply any but a negligible amount of current without being damaged. These are two types of Weston cells, the Weston unsaturated standard, which is used for most laboratory work, and the Weston saturated standard, which is used to establish the value of the volt.

The unsaturated cell has a low temperature coefficient and is suitable for work not requiring an accuracy greater than 0.01 per cent. The anode is a cadmium amalgam which contains 12 to 14 per cent cadmium. The cathode consists of mercury which is covered with a paste of mercurous sulfate and mercury. The electrolyte is a solution of cadmium sulfate which is saturated at 4°C. When new this cell exhibits an e.m.f. of 1.0192 at room temperature and loses not more then 71 microvolts per year (see Vinal, *loc. cit.*).

The saturated cell is similar in construction to the unsaturated cell except that crystals of $CdSO_4.\frac{8}{3}H_2O$ are sprinkled over both electrodes to keep the solution saturated at all temperatures. This cell has an internationally agreed voltage of 1.01830 volts at 20°C., which is reproducible to better than 10 microvolts.

Secondary Cells. Secondary cells have the same basic components as primary cells. However, an added requirement on the cell is that both the anode and cathode half-cell reactions be reversible (*i.e.*, the active material can be regenerated an indefinite number of times). Materials which meet these requirements and which are used in commercial cells are: as anodes, cadmium, iron, lead, and zinc; as cathodes, lead dioxide, nickel dioxide, mercuric oxide, and silver peroxide.

Although there are 16 possible cell combinations from the above materials, only the first four systems listed in Table 25-7 are presently widely used commercially. The other systems listed in this table find use in special applications. Figure 25-38 shows the relative weight-to-power ratios of the various systems.

Lead-Acid Cell. Three basic types of lead-acid cells [Willihngauz, *J. Electrochem. Soc.*, **99**, 234–236c (1952).

Table 25-7. Secondary Cells

Type	Anode	Electrolyte	Cathode	Current-producing reaction discharge → charge ←	Avg. operating voltage on light drains, volts
Lead-acid	Pb	H_2SO_4	PbO_2	$Pb + PbO_2 + 2H_2SO_4 \rightleftarrows 2PbSO_4 + 2H_2O$	1.95–2.05
Nickel-iron (Edison)	Fe	KOH	$Ni(OH)_3$, Ni_2O_2, and NiO_2	$Fe + NiO_2 \rightleftarrows FeO + NiO$	1.10–1.30
Nickel-cadmium (Junger)	Cd	KOH	$Ni(OH)_3$, Ni_2O_2, and NiO_2	$Cd + NiO_2 \rightleftarrows CdO + NiO$	1.10–1.30
Zinc-silver	Zn	KOH	AgO	$Zn + AgO + H_2O \rightleftarrows Ag + Zn(OH)_2$	1.40–1.50
Cadmium-silver	Cd	KOH	AgO	$Cd + AgO \rightleftarrows Ag + CdO$	1.05–1.10
Lead-silver oxide	Pb	KOH	AgO	$Pb + Ag_2O \rightleftarrows PbO + 2Ag$	0.80–0.85
Cadmium-mercuric (oxide)	Cd	KOH	HgO	$Cd + HgO \rightleftarrows CdO + Hg$	0.9

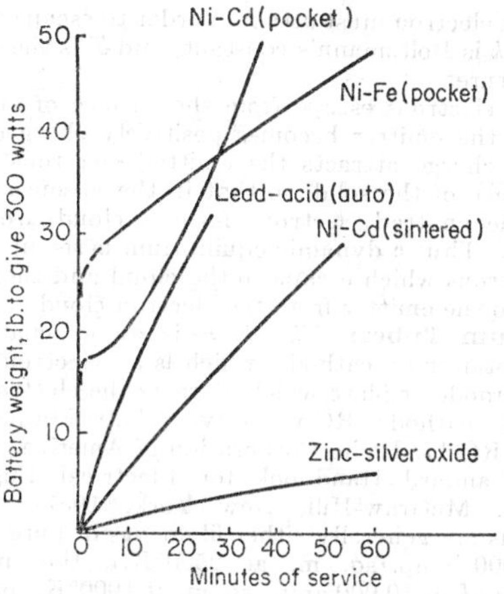

FIG. 25-38. Relative performance of various secondary systems of special construction designed to deliver 300 watts for a specified time interval. [*From Morehouse, Glicksman, and Lozier, Batteries, Proc. Inst. Radio Engrs.*, **19**, 1462–1483 (1958).]

Proc. 10th Annual Battery R. and D. Conf. 35-7, 1952] are produced, the automotive battery, the motive-power battery (*e.g.*, submarine propulsion), and the stationary battery. These three types differ from each other basically only in the construction of the cell electrodes.

In the automotive battery the cell electrodes are comprised of relatively thin grids which are cast from high-purity lead to which about 10 per cent antimony has been added (antimony is added to harden the plates). This grid is filled with a paste consisting of a mix of lead oxide, water, and sulfuric acid. The paste of the negative plates contains about 1 per cent "expander" (basically a mixture of barium sulfate and organic material) to improve the high-rate discharge and low-temperature characteristics of the battery. After the plates have been dried and assembled they are immersed in a weak sulfuric acid solution and charged; the lead oxide on the negative plate is converted to sponge lead, and lead dioxide is formed at the positive plate. The anode and cathode are separated from each other by acid-resistant porous wood or microporous rubber separaters.

The voltage delivered by the lead-acid automotive battery drops off considerably as the battery is discharged to almost full discharge (Willihngauz, *loc. cit.*). The reason for this voltage drop is not entirely understood. Also, if a charged battery is allowed to stand idle for a period of time, the charge in the battery will decrease. The major portion of this self-discharge is due to the evolution of hydrogen by the anode, which results primarily from the presence of a small amount of antimony that seems to accelerate the release of hydrogen tremendously. A new battery with full charge has an electrolyte specific gravity of about 1.280. This specific gravity will drop 0.030 unit or about 20 per cent capacity in a 30-day storage period at 80°F.

The capacity of an automobile battery is usually expressed as its capacity at a 20-hr. rate of discharge at 80°F. The battery is capable of delivering large currents (100 amp.) with only a small drop in e.m.f. However, completely discharging or overcharging the battery will seriously affect its life span.

Lead-acid batteries used for motive-power service are designed to withstand frequent deep discharges and are required to supply power for from 3 to 10 hr. The negative plates of these batteries are thicker than automotive batteries. The positive plates are designed to prevent loss of active material which might occur because of frequent cycling.

Stationary batteries are designed for long-life applications which do not require mechanical ruggedness or high current output, but where low self-discharge and high efficiency are of primary importance.

Edison Batteries. The Edison battery [Anderson, *J. Electrochem. Soc.*, **99**, 244–248 (1952)] is a nickel-oxide iron alkaline cell. Its anode is formed of pockets of active material (metallic iron and iron oxide) which are pressed into openings in a sheet-steel frame. Its cathode is formed by perforated nickel tubes which are filled with nickel hydroxide and nickel.

The nickel-iron cell compares with the lead-acid cell as concerns relative capacity per unit weight and volume. Its advantages over the lead-acid cell are that the battery can take more mechanical and electrical abuse, operates at higher temperatures, and in general, has a longer life. Overcharging or completely discharging the cell has few deleterious effects. The disadvantages of the Edison battery are: (1) the e.m.f. of the cell drops considerably as the load is increased; (2) it has relatively poor low-temperature performance (*i.e.*, at −25°F. the electrolyte becomes slushy and crystallized); (3) it loses approximately 40 per cent of initial capacity on standing for 1 month; (4) it is more expensive than the lead-acid battery of comparable capacity.

For the reasons cited above the Edison cell finds widest use in heavy-duty industrial and railway applications.

Nickel-Cadmium Batteries. There are two types of nickel-cadmium batteries [Begstrom, *J. Electrochem. Soc.*, **99**, 248–250c (1952). Ellis, Mandel, and Linden, *J. Electrochem. Soc.*, **99**, 250–252 (1952)], the pocket-type and the sintered-plate type. The construction of the electrodes of the pocket type is similar to that of the nickel-iron cell with the exception, of course, that cadmium is used as the anode material. In the sintered-plate construction, the cathode plates are made from nickel powder which is molded into shape and heated at an elevated temperature in a non-oxidizing atmosphere. This gives a strong, porous plate with about 80 per cent void space. Active material is impregnated into the pores of these plates by soaking them in a solution of nickel salts.

Batteries with either of these constructions have excellent storage life, losing about 10 per cent of capacity in the first 48 hr. and then only about 3 per cent per month for the sintered construction and somewhat less for the pocket construction. Both types can be cycled at least several thousand times and are not damaged appreciably by either deep discharges or overcharging.

They evolve practically no gas when standing idle, so that for some purposes they can be hermetically sealed.

The sintered-plate construction, because of its thinner plates and larger electrode surface area, can operate at higher current drains than the pocket type and is more efficient at lower temperatures (down to −54°C.). However, both types have a low cell resistance and therefore can deliver high currents with only small losses in e.m.f.

The nickel-cadmium batteries are much more expensive than the lead-acid battery and therefore find only limited automotive use. They are used, however, for stand-by service, emergency lighting for telephone service, and other applications where their low capacity loss while standing idle is an important factor.

Zinc Silver-oxide Batteries. The interesting feature of this battery [Eidensohn, *J. Electrochem. Soc.*, **99**, 252–254c (1952). Howard, *Proc. 10th Annual Battery R. & D. Conf.*, pp. 41–44, 1957] is its high output per unit weight or volume (three to five times higher than lead-acid battery). Also, the battery is capable of supplying 100 amp. with an e.m.f. loss of only about 0.4 volt.

The cell consists of a porous-plate zinc anode and silver-peroxide cathode. The cathode is formed by electrolytic oxidation of silver to silver peroxide. This cathode is wrapped in a semipermeable cellophane bag to prevent the migration of zinc to it.

The silver-zinc cell is still under development; however, present data indicate that the cell has about a 50 per cent charge retention after 6 months at 80°F. and can be cycled about 200 times using specially developed separaters (Howard, *loc. cit.*).

Because silver-zinc cells are more expensive than other commercial cells, and because of their still somewhat limited cycle life, these cells are used for special applications such as missile batteries.

ELECTROPHYSICS

Electron Tubes

Thermionic Emission. The emission of electrons by a hot metal or semiconductor is called thermionic emission (see Sproul, "Modern Physics," pp. 364–378, Wiley, New York, 1956. Sears and Zemansky, "University Physics," pp. 649–651, Addison-Wesley, Reading, Mass., 1953). Thermionic emission is analogous to evaporation at the surface of liquids. Briefly, the mechanism of thermionic emission is as follows:

Electrons at the surface of a solid are retarded from escaping from the solid by an energy barrier of a few electron volts. However, because of a distribution of the energy level among the electrons within the solid, some electrons acquire enough energy to surmount the barrier at any temperature above absolute zero. As the temperature is increased more electrons attain the required escape energy, the current density of escaping electrons being given by the relationship

$$J = A_0 T^2 \epsilon^{-e_\phi / kT}$$

where J is the current density of escaping electrons (amp./sq. m.) at the solid surface, A_0 is a universal constant equal to 1.2×10^6 amp./(sq. m.) (deg.^{2}), e_ϕ is the "work function" or the minimum energy (in electron volts) an electron must attain in order to escape from the surface, k is Boltzmann's constant, and T is the absolute temperature.

When electrons escape from the surface of any given emitter, the emitter becomes positively charged. This positive charge attracts the emitted electrons back to the surface of the solid, so that in the absence of other fields the emitted electrons form a cloud around the emitter. Thus a dynamic equilibrium is set up between the electrons which escape to the cloud and those which return to the emitter from the electron cloud.

Vacuum Tubes. *The diode* is an evacuated glass tube containing a cathode, which is an electron emitter, and an anode or plate which attracts the electrons given off by the cathode (RCA Receiving Tube Manual, Tech. Service RC-17, Radio Corporation of America. Knowlton, "Standard Handbook for Electrical Engineers," 9th ed., McGraw-Hill, New York, 1957). Cathode materials are generally either filaments of pure tungsten (J = 3000 amp./sq. m. at 2500°K.), thorium-coated tungsten (J = 10,000 amp./sq. m. at 1900°K.) or a nickel sleeve which is coated with tiny crystals of barium, strontium, and calcium oxides (J = 5000 amp./sq. m. at 1000°K.). The cathode may be heated directly by the passage of current through it (*e.g.*, the tungsten filament) or by a filament heater which is surrounded by the cathode sleeve.

The diode is most commonly used as a current rectifier. A rectifier may be considered to be a device which converts alternating current into unidirectional current by virtue of a characteristic permitting appreciable flow of current in one direction and negligible current flow in the other.

The diode rectifies in the following manner. The voltage to be rectified is applied across the plate and cathode terminals. When the plate potential is positive, electrons flow from the cathode to the plate. When the plate potential is negative, the electrons emitted from the cathode are forced to remain in the electron cloud which surrounds the cathode, and hence no current flows.

The amount of current flowing from the cathode to the plate is roughly proportional to the plate volt-

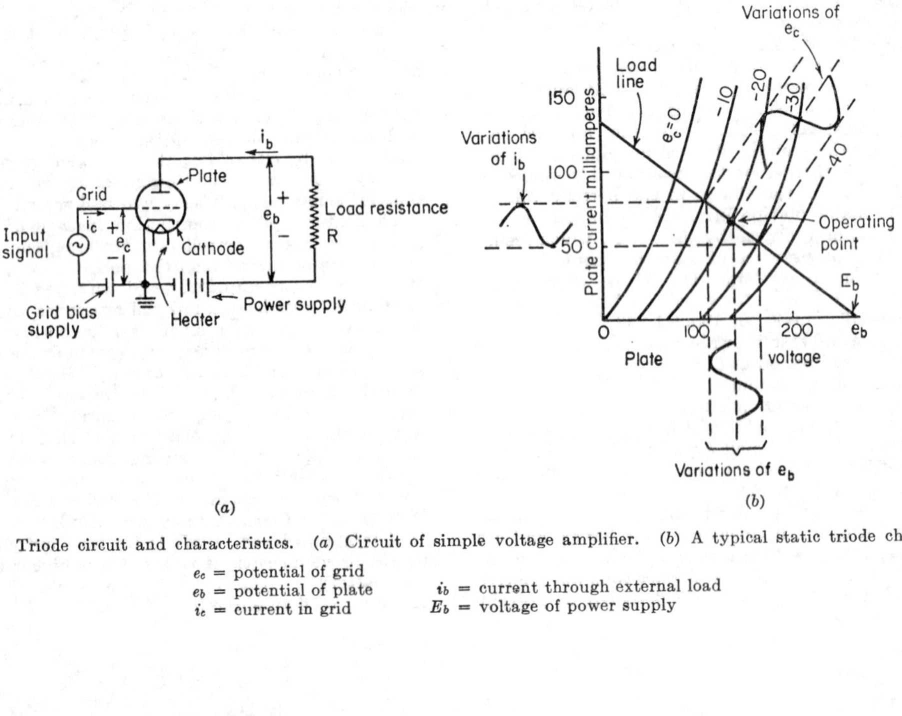

(a) (b)

FIG. 25-39. Triode circuit and characteristics. (a) Circuit of simple voltage amplifier. (b) A typical static triode characteristic.

e_c = potential of grid
e_b = potential of plate
i_c = current in grid
i_b = current through external load
E_b = voltage of power supply

age over most of the operating range of the diode. This arises from the fact that not all the electrons which leave the emitter reach the plate. Some return to the cathode while others remain in the space between the cathode and plate for brief periods and produce an effect known as *space charge*. This space charge tends to repel electrons emitted from the cathode. At a fixed cathode temperature the amount of space charge varies inversely with the plate potential; therefore, increasing the plate potential increases the current flow. There is, however, a plate potential at which virtually all the electrons emitted from the cathode reach the plate, and a further increase in plate potential has only a small effect on the current. The tube is then said to be operating in the saturated range.

The triode is an evacuated electron tube containing three electrodes: a cathode, an anode, and a control grid which lies between the anode and cathode. The control grid usually consists of relatively fine wire wound on two support rods which extend the length of the cathode and surround it. The spacings between the grid windings are relatively large, so that the grid does not present a physical barrier to the flow of electrons from the cathode to the plate. Small variations in the grid potential cause relatively large variations in the electron flow to the plate by altering the potential barrier of the space charge. For this reason the triode can act as a signal amplifier, the signal being applied to the grid as shown in Fig. 25-39*a*. In this case the grid is maintained at some mean potential known as the grid bias. The load line (Fig. 25-39*b*) is an operating line which is fixed by the characteristics of the external circuit. Its equation is

$$e_b = E_{bb} - i_b R$$

Given the load line, the tube characteristics, and the grid bias, one may graphically solve for the tube output voltage (*i.e.*, the plate voltage) as a function of the input voltage (*i.e.*, the grid voltage) as shown in Fig. 25-39*a*.

The development of the *tetrode and pentode*, which are also evacuated electron tubes, came as a result of a desire to reduce the inherent interelectrode capacitances of the triode, which reduce the amplification of high-frequency signals. In the tetrode a positively biased grid structure is placed between the control grid and the plate. This "screen" grid effectively reduces the plate-to-control-grid capacitance.

Difficulties in operation of the tetrode due to a phenomenon known as secondary emission led to the development of the pentode. Secondary emission results when electrons strike the normally non-emitting plate with enough energy to dislodge electrons from the plate. These electrons are then attracted to the positive screen grid, causing a decrease in plate current and an increase in screen power dissipation. To overcome this difficulty a negative grid structure called the suppressor grid is inserted between the screen grid and plate.

The effective plate resistance of the pentode is considerably higher than that of a triode (magnitude of triode plate resistance is in the order of 10^3 ohms; magnitude of pentode plate resistance is in the order of 10^6 ohms) because the constant screen potential masks variations in plate potential. Thus the pentode appears to act as a constant-current source.

Cathode-ray Tube. The essential elements of a cathode-ray tube are an electron gun for producing a beam of electrons, a deflecting system (which employs either electric or magnetic deflection forces), and a phosphorescent screen on which the impinging electron beam forms a spot of light. Figure 25-40 is a simplified diagram of the cathode-ray tube.

The brilliance of the spot on the screen is controlled by the potential of the control-grid element in the gun, and its position is controlled by the deflectors.

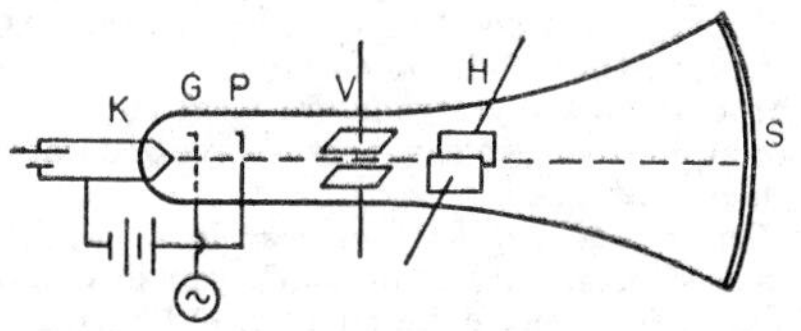

FIG. 25-40. Simplified drawing of a cathode-ray tube.

K = filament (cathode) and heater
G = control grid
P = plate
V = vertical deflector
H = horizontal deflector
S = phosphorescent screen

Gas-filled Tubes. Electron tubes which contain an inert gas (*e.g.*, argon, krypton) or vapor (*e.g.*, Hg) at low pressure and which make use of ionization effects are characterized by much higher current-carrying capacity, lower voltage drop between the anode and cathode, and more limited control than the corresponding high-vacuum tubes (Knowlton, *op. cit.*, Sec. 23, pars. 21–24, 51–63. Price, "Nuclear Radiation Detection," pp. 115–148, McGraw-Hill, New York, 1958). The following is a brief outline of the principles underlying the operation of the gas-filled diode (Phanotron) and triode (thyratron).

The increased current-carrying capacity of the gas-filled tube is due mainly to the presence of positive ions which are formed upon the ionization of the gas within the tube. The positive ions overcome the forces acting between free electrons (*i.e.*, the space charge) and thereby allow a very much greater current of electrons than would occur in a vacuum. Furthermore, the positive ions are attracted toward, and form a sheath around, the cathode, thereby setting up a high electric field which aids in extracting electrons from the cathode, thus further increasing the magnitude of the current flowing within the tube. Also the dynamic equilibrium which exists between the decomposition of a molecule into ions (*e.g.*, electrons and positive ions) and the recombination of ions is dependent only upon the amount of current which is flowing through the gas. Consequently, the current flowing through a gas-filled tube is largely dependent upon the impedance of the external circuit to which it is connected rather than any inherent tube properties as in the vacuum tube. It should be noted, however, that the initiation and maintenance of a gas discharge (*i.e.*, the flow of electrons in a gas) is dependent upon the extraction of electrons from the cathode. A discharge can be maintained only when all the positive ions which result from collisions with an electron are successful in extracting another electron from the cathode. This process is known as electronic regeneration, and it places an upper limit on the current which can flow through the tube.

The anode potential at which a gas-filled tube fires (*i.e.*, the gaseous discharge begins) can be controlled to some extent by means of a grid which is placed between the electrodes (as in the thyratron). Applying a positive potential to the grid raises the space potential adjacent to the cathode so that electron regeneration occurs at a lower anode potential than it otherwise would. Similarly, applying a negative potential to the grid decreases the space potential, and therefore a higher anode potential is required to start the discharge. After the discharge is initiated, the grid becomes covered with a sheath of ions which prevent the grid from exerting further control over the space potential so that varying the grid potential does not vary the current flowing. Also, it is impractical to stop conduction by means of the grid. Rather, conduction is interrupted by reducing the anode potential to zero or below. There is, however, a finite time interval (~1000 microsec.) required for the gas to deionize to a point where the grid regains control after dropping the anode potential.

Phanotrons and thyratrons are used commercially as high-power rectifiers, in saw-tooth-wave generators, voltage regulators, etc.

The *Geiger-Müller* (*G-M*) *counter* is a gas-filled tube which is used primarily for measuring nuclear radiations. The tube itself is constructed of a cylindrical cathode (not heated) which surrounds a fine wire anode. The tube is filled with an inert gas such as argon. A potential of from 800 to 1500 volts is applied across the electrodes. When a particle (*e.g.*, a beta or X ray) strikes the cathode or a gas molecule it produces electrons which are accelerated to the anode. On passing to the anode the electrons collide with the gaseous molecules in the tube, thereby producing an avalanche of ion pairs which carry current and which may cause a series of secondary discharges. One particle may therefore give rise to one long pulse or a series of several pulses. Since the purpose of the G-M tube is to count the frequency at which ionizing events occur, it is necessary that each photon yield only a single short pulse of current. This is done by suppressing or *quenching* each discharge by means of an external electric circuit which quickly reduces the anode voltage below the discharge potential or by adding a small quantity of an organic vapor (*e.g.*, ethyl alcohol) or halogen (*e.g.*, chlorine or bromine). The presence of a quenching gas prohibits positive ions from releasing electrons as they strike the cathode, thereby prohibiting this type of secondary discharge. In both types of counters there is a finite resolving time (*i.e.*, the time required for a tube to be ready for a second discharge to occur after the initiation of a discharge) so that the maximum rate of arrival of radiation pulses which can be counted by a G-M tube is about 5000 per sec.

Semiconductors

Semiconductor materials are generally considered to be those materials which have a resistivity somewhere between that of a typical conductor and that of a typical insulator (see Table 25-8) and a negative temperature

Table 25-8. Electrical Resistivity of Various Materials at 20°C., in ohm-meters*

Metals		Semiconductors		Insulators	
Ag	1.6×10^{-8}	Ge ("pure")	0.47	Glass	10^{10}–10^{11}
Cu	1.7×10^{-8}	Si ("pure")	3000	Mica	9×10^{14}
Al	2.8×10^{-8}	Fe_3O_4	~0.01	Diamond	10^{14}
Fe	10×10^{-8}	In Sb	$\sim 2 \times 10^4$		
Constantan	49×10^{-8}	Sn (gray)	$\sim 2 \times 10^{-6}$		
Nichrome	100×10^{-8}				

* From Dekker, "Electrical Engineering Materials," Prentice-Hall, Englewood Cliffs, N.J., 1959.

coefficient of resistivity over at least part of their range (Dekker, "Electrical Engineering Materials," pp. 151–198, Prentice-Hall, Englewood Cliffs, N.J., 1959. Truxal, "Control Engineers' Handbook," Secs. 8.1–8.4, McGraw-Hill, New York, 1958). The physical behavior of semiconductors is best explained by first considering the atomic and crystallographic structure of the material.

The electrons of any atom may be considered to exist in different energy levels about the nucleus. These levels are discrete rather than continuous and are functions of the particular atomic species. Also, a fundamental principle of quantum mechanics is that no two electrons can occupy the same energy level. The above principles are equally valid for aggregates of atoms such as those forming semiconductor crystals. However, because of the large number of atoms, the various energy levels form distinct groups of essentially continuous levels which are known as energy bands. In all solids those energy bands which lie closest to the nucleus are filled (*i.e.*, all energy levels are occupied), while the outermost bands, called the valance band and conduction band, may or may not be filled. It can be shown (Sproul, "Modern Physics," pp. 247–250, New York, 1956) that no electric current can be carried by electrons in a filled band. In conductive materials the valance band is not filled. In addition it overlaps the conduction band (Fig. 25-41), and therefore there are numerous available energy levels to which

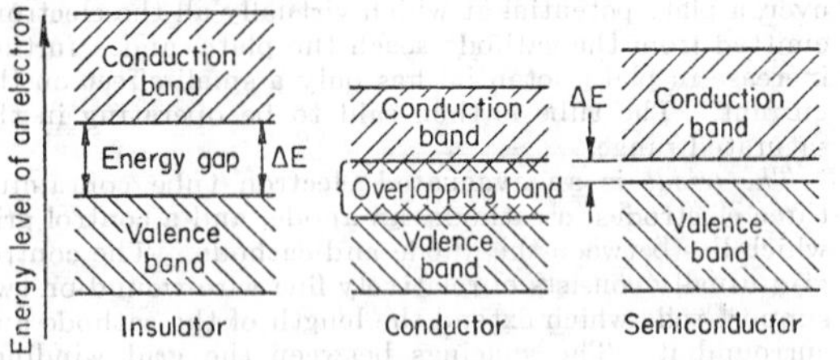

Fig. 25-41. Electron energy levels.

an electron can be excited. In insulating materials the valance band is filled and there is considerable energy gap (*i.e.*, forbidden energy levels) between it and the conduction band so that only an insignificant number of electrons can acquire the thermal energy required to jump the gap. In semiconductor materials the valance band is filled, but the energy gap between it and the conduction band is small enough so that an appreciable number of electrons jump the gap at room temperature because of thermal agitation (*e.g.*, in germanium about 10^{14} electrons per cubic meter are in the conduction band at 80°F.).

An electron which has escaped into the conduction band leaves behind an ionized atom. (Electrons in the conduction band are more or less free to move through the crystal lattice under the influence of an applied e.m.f. and therefore cannot be considered to belong to any one atom.) The ionized atom is then capable of accepting an electron. It is therefore said to have a positive hole or simply a hole. This hole can "move" under the influence of an e.m.f. by accepting an electron from a nearby atom as shown in Fig. 25-42. This is a schematic two-dimensional representation of the electronic bonding of

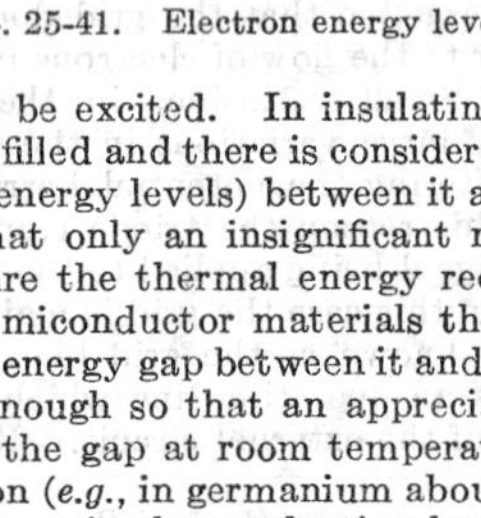

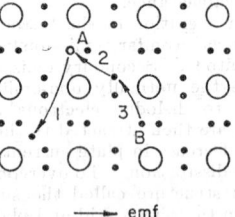

Fig. 25-42. Electron hole migration. The open circle at *A* represents a hole formed by an electron entering the conduction band. By the successive electron jumps 1, 2, 3, the hole moves in the direction of the field from *A* to *B*. The electron drifts in an opposite direction.

a diamond structure such as that of silicon or germanium in which each atom shares eight electrons (*i.e.*, the bonding is covalent). Thus conduction in semiconductors can occur by the combined movement of holes and electrons.

P- and N-type Semiconductors. Most engineering applications of semiconductors involve pure semiconductor materials (the impurity content is generally less than 1 p.p.m.) which have been "doped" (*i.e.*, alloyed) with

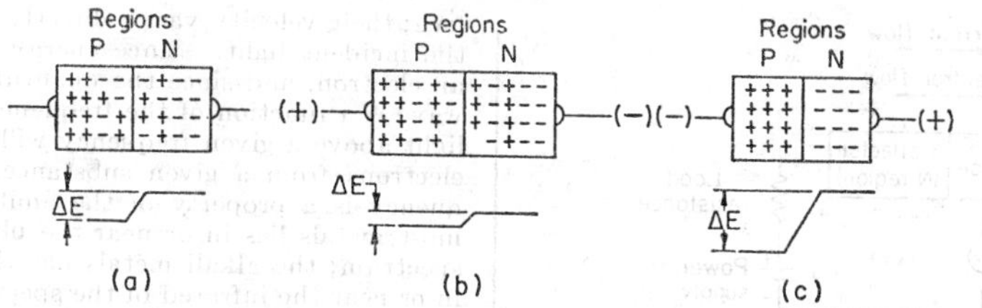

FIG. 25-43. P-N junction. ΔE is the potential barrier experienced by a positive charge. (*a*) P-N junction with no bias (*b*) P-N junction with forward bias. (*c*) P-N junction with reverse bias.

specific impurities.* These impurities increase the conductivity of the semiconductor by distorting the electronic structure of the material. For example, if a group III element such as indium is added to a group IV semiconductor such as germanium, the group III element enters into the tetravalent structure of the semiconductor but can supply only three electrons, thereby creating a vacancy in the crystal structure. This vacancy corresponds to a hole which is capable of moving under the influence of an e.m.f. in the manner described in Fig. 25-42. Semiconductors in which the added impurities create "holes" in the crystal structure are known as P-type semiconductors since the majority of current carriers can be considered to be positive charges (*i.e.*, holes). N-type semiconductors are formed by the addition of a material with a greater number of valance electrons than the base material (*e.g.*, Sb in Ge). In this case there are electrons which do not fit into the crystal lattice and which are therefore more loosely bound than the other valance electrons. Thus, in N-type semiconductors the majority of the current carriers are negative electrons which have escaped into the conduction band. Note that in N- and P-type semiconductors the *majority* current carriers arise from the doping material while the *minority* current carriers are the conduction electrons and holes which arise from the base metal because of thermal agitation.

Semiconductor Rectifiers. When P- and N-type semiconductors (Truxal, "Control Engineers' Handbook," Secs. 8.1–8.4, McGraw-Hill, New York, 1958. GE Transistor Manual, General Electric Co. Hunter, "Handbook of Semiconductor Electronics," McGraw-Hill, New York, 1956) are joined together† a potential gradient is set up across the junction (see Fig. 25-43*a*). This gradient or barrier is caused by an initial net flow of holes from the P region to the N region and electrons from the N region to the P region, due to the electronic concentration gradients in these two regions. At equilibrium, the potential gradient across the N-P boundary exactly compensates for the concentration gradients between the regions, and there is no net flow of charge but rather an equal and opposite flow of electrons and holes across the junction.

When an external potential is applied across the terminals of the rectifier, the potential barrier at the junction is either increased or decreased (see Fig. 25-43*b* and *c*). If the barrier is decreased (as in Fig. 25-43*b*) the rectifier is said to be forward biased; if it is increased, the rectifier is said to be reverse biased. In the forward-biased condition, the majority of the current carriers in the P region (*i.e.*, holes) experience a small potential barrier in getting to the N region. Similarly, the majority current carriers in the N region (*i.e.*, electrons) experience the *same* small barrier in going to the P region. Thus, forward bias for electrons is also forward bias for holes, and under this condition the rectifier is a relatively good conductor. In the reverse-biased condition the majority carriers in both regions experience a greatly increased barrier; so that only a relatively few of these carriers have the thermal energy required to cross the barrier. Note that in the reverse-biased condition any flow of majority carriers is in a direction opposite the applied voltage.

In both the forward- and reverse-biased conditions, there is a small flow of current due to conduction by minority carriers. These minority carriers are the electrons and holes in the N and P regions which have been thermally excited into the conduction band and which conduct current in the manner previously described in the discussion of semiconductive properties. It is the presence of minority carriers which causes a rectifier to carry some current in the direction of the applied potential when the rectifier is reverse biased.

The quantitative relationship for the current which flows through a rectifier under an applied voltage is

$$I = I_0(\epsilon^{ve/kT} - 1)$$

where I_0 is the current due to the thermally agitated minority carriers in the N and P regions, e is the electronic charge (1.59×10^{-9} coulombs), v is the applied voltage (positive for a forward bias, negative for a reverse bias), k is Boltzmann's constant (1.37×10^{-23} watt-sec./°K.), and T is the absolute temperature.

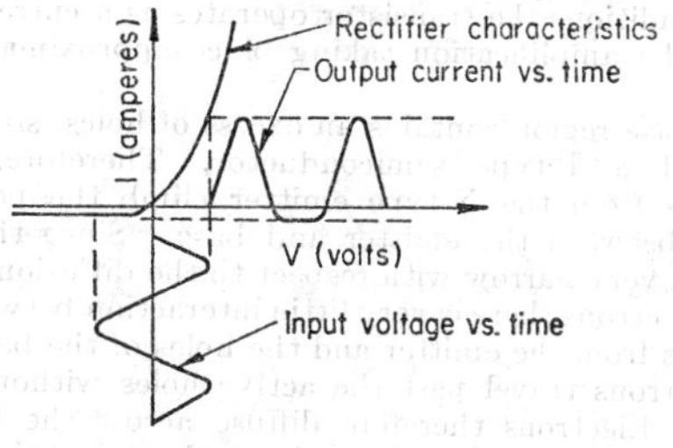

FIG. 25-44. Rectifier operation with sinusoidal voltage applied across the terminals.

Figure 25-44 shows the action of a rectifier which has a sinusoidal input voltage applied across the rectifier terminals. This diagram is given only as an example of a rectifiers' action since, in general practice, the voltage to be rectified is not placed directly across the terminals.

Semiconductor rectifiers can operate over wide ranges of currents and voltages but at present are generally limited to operating temperatures below 200°C. This limitation is due to the high intrinsic conductivity (*i.e.*, conductivity arising from the flow of "minority" carriers) of present commercial P-N junction-type semiconductors at elevated temperatures.

* The concentration of doping material is generally about 10 p.p.m.

† The junction of N- and P-type rectifiers is *not* formed simply by pressing together the two semiconductor materials. This type of junction would have too many imperfections at the boundary to allow for adequate electron and hole flow. Rather, the P-N junction is formed so that it is an internal boundary in a single crystal. Some of the commercial techniques used to form this type of boundary can be found in references previously cited.

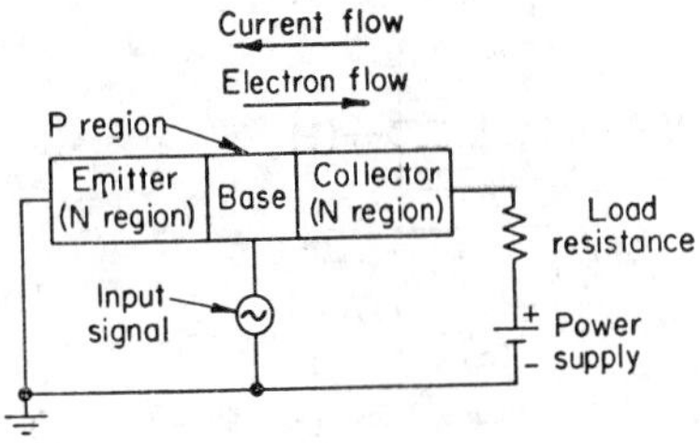

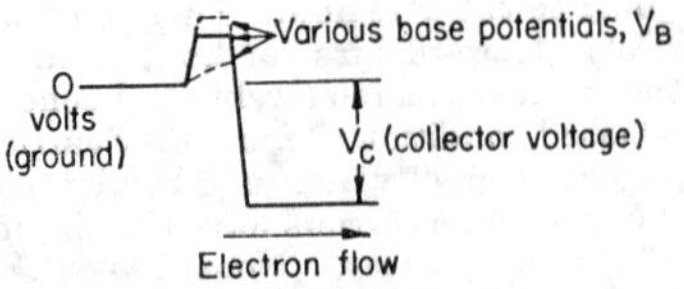

FIG. 25-45. Electron potentials across a N-P-N transistor with a grounded emitter and a signal applied to the base region.

The Junction Transistor. A junction transistor consists of either a P semiconductor region sandwiched between two N semiconductor regions (Fig. 25-45) or a N region sandwiched between two P regions. We shall consider only the N-P-N junction transistor; however, the following discussion holds for P-N-P transistors with only minor modifications.

The physical characteristics of the regions of a N-P-N junction transistor are:

Conductivity of the emitter region $\sigma_e \approx 10^4$ ohm^{-1}m.$^{-1}$
Conductivity of the base region $\sigma_b \approx 10^2$ ohm^{-1}m.$^{-1}$
Conductivity of the collector region $\sigma_c \approx 10$ ohm^{-1}m.$^{-1}$
Width of the base region $\omega \approx 10^{-5}$ m.
Diffusion length of majority carriers (electrons) L_e = statistical average distance an electron will travel without experiencing a collision

In Fig. 25-45 the emitter is grounded, the collector is reverse biased (with respect to a positive charge), and a small current signal is applied to the base region. Under these conditions the transistor operates as a current amplifier, the amplification taking place approximately as follows.

The base region contains an excess of holes, since it is made of a P-type semiconductor. Therefore, some electrons from the N-type emitter climb the potential barrier between the emitter and base. Since the base region is very narrow with respect to the diffusion length of the electrons there is very little interaction between the electrons from the emitter and the holes of the base; *i.e.*, the electrons travel past the active holes without combining. Electrons therefore diffuse across the base to the base-collector junction where they experience an acceleration due to the high collector potential. The varying potential of the base causes a varying electron flow from the emitter to the base, a relatively small variation in base potential causing a large variation in electron flow.

Transistors of the type described above may have power gains (*i.e.*, ratio of output power to the input signal power) up to 40,000 in some applications.

Photoelectric Effect

Photoelectric action is the liberation of electrons from matter under the influence of electromagnetic radiation. The number of electrons emitted is directly proportional to the quantity of light absorbed by the irradiated surface; their velocity varies directly with the frequency of the incident light. Since energy is required to release an electron, and since the quantum of energy in a light wave is a function of the frequency, it follows that only light above a given frequency will cause the emission of electrons from a given substance. This threshold frequency is a property of the emitting material and for most metals lies in or near the ultraviolet region of the spectrum; the alkali metals have a threshold frequency in or near the infrared of the spectrum and are therefore good emitters when subjected to ordinary luminous radiation. In addition to the normal action of metals as described above, certain metals, including the alkalies, show a selective action whereby the emission has a sort of resonance maximum at a given frequency when the electromagnetic radiation is plane-polarized so that its electric vector has a component perpendicular to the emitting surface.

The application of photoelectric tubes is confined to the utilization of one of the following characteristics of light: (1) quantity, (2) color or wave length, (3) plane of polarization, (4) angle of incidence. Since the cathodes of commercial cells are not optically plane, the last two are not applicable with such cells. The current obtained from photoelectric cells is of the order of 10 microamp./lumen; to utilize the photoelectric effect some form of amplification is necessary.

Piezoelectric Effect

Certain asymmetrical crystals have the property of producing electrical charges on their surface when they are mechanically stressed and, conversely, of experiencing mechanical strain when subjected to an electric field (Hughes, "Electrical Engineers' Reference Book," par. 344, Macmillan, New York, 1958. Cady, "Piezo-electricity," McGraw-Hill, New York, 1946). Both these effects are called piezoelectric; the former is called the direct effect and the latter the converse effect. The voltages produced by piezoelectric crystals under strain are directly proportional to the magnitude of the strain, and vice versa; thus these crystals are excellent electromechanical transducers.

There are both natural and synthetic piezo crystals. Quartz and tourmaline are two of the former, quartz being the best suited for generating piezoelectricity. It has a very low temperature coefficient (*i.e.*, the magnitude of the piezo effect does not vary greatly with temperature) and it is chemically stable. A disadvantage of quartz is its fragility when cut into plates thinner than 1/16 in. Of the synthetic crystals sodium potassium tartrate (rochelle salt), ammonium dihydrogen phosphate, ethylene diamine tartrate, and barium titanole are some of those in common use.

Piezoelectric crystals find use as oscillators for telecommunication equipment, ultrasonic generators, microphones, and pressure transducers, strain gages, etc.

Thermoelectricity

There are three thermoelectric effects, the Seebeck, the Peltier, and the Thomson effects. All three of these effects have been related by irreversible thermodynamics, and if one is known the other two can be derived (Condon and Odishaw, "Handbook of Physics," Sec. IV, p. 83, McGraw-Hill, New York, 1958. Gilmont, "Thermodynamic Principles for Chemical Engineers," pp. 261–271, Prentice-Hall, Englewood Cliffs, N.J., 1959).

The *Seebeck effect* refers to the e.m.f. developed by a circuit which is made up of one or more dissimilar conductors in which not all the conductor junctions are at the same temperature. The voltage which is developed by the circuit is generally a non-linear function of the temperature at the junctions. For instance, in a copper-iron circuit when one junction is kept at 0°C. and the other heated, the e.m.f. produced will increase until the temperature reaches about 260°C. On heating above 260°C. the e.m.f. begins to drop, reaches zero, and is finally reversed.

The e.m.f. developed by any one pair of metals A and B can be expressed as the difference of the e.m.f. developed by the same metals with respect to some reference metal x

$$E_{AB}(T_1T_2) = E_{Ax}(T_1T_2) - E_{Bx}(T_1T_2)$$

where $E_{AB}(T_1T_2)$ is the e.m.f. developed by metals A and B with junction temperatures T_1 and T_2. The e.m.f. of a single pair of metals, between three temperatures, also follows a similar relationship, that is,

$$E_{AB}(T_1T_3) = E_{AB}(T_1T_2) - E_{AB}(T_3T_2)$$

Thermoelectric data are usually presented as single potentials $[E_A(T)]$ by determining $E_A(T_1T_x)$ and arbitrarily setting $E_x(T) = 0$. This convention is not a theoretical necessity, since $E_A(T)$ is a fundamental property of each material and can be uniquely defined by other physical measurements.

The *Peltier effect* refers to the *reversible* heating or cooling which occurs at a contact of two dissimilar conductors when current flows from one conductor to another. The heat which is absorbed or given off is proportional to the total current passing through the junction. The proportionality coefficient is known as the Peltier coefficient $\pi_{AB}(T)$ and it is a function of the junction temperature. Again, $\pi_{AB}(T) = \pi_{Ax}(T) - \pi_{Bx}(T)$. Thus the Peltier effect can be utilized as a heat pump.

The *Thomson effect* refers to the *reversible* heat evolution or absorption which occurs when an electric current flows through a homogeneous conductor in which there is a temperature gradient. The Thomson coefficient is defined by the following equation

$$Q = \sigma_A(T)q\frac{dT}{dx}$$

where Q is the heat evolved or absorbed, $\sigma_A(T)$ is the Thomson coefficient which is a function of temperature, q is the quantity of charge (coulombs) which flows in the conductors, and dT/dx is the temperature gradient. The Thomson coefficient is defined to be positive if heat is absorbed when the flow of *current* (*i.e.*, positive charges) is toward the warmer end of the wire. The unit of the coefficient is volts per degree and its actual magnitude is always of the order of microvolts per degree.

ELECTRONIC CIRCUITS

The term *electronic circuit* is applied to any electric circuit which contains electronic devices (vacuum tubes, transistors, diodes, etc.). A wide variety of electronic circuits is described in the literature. These circuits are employed as building blocks in many electronic instruments and in process-control instruments in general (see Sec. 22). Because of limited space, only a few electronic circuits of most interest to chemical engineers are described here. More detailed information will be found in the references cited at the beginning of this section.

Amplifiers

Amplifiers are electronic circuits used to increase the voltage level, current level, or power level of electrical signals. Frequently these signals exist at such low levels that direct utilization is impossible. In such cases, an amplifier is employed, between the source of the signal and the point where the signal is used, to increase the signal level.

An *ideal* voltage amplifier is shown in Fig. 25-46. This amplifier is ideal in the sense that the input current I_1 is

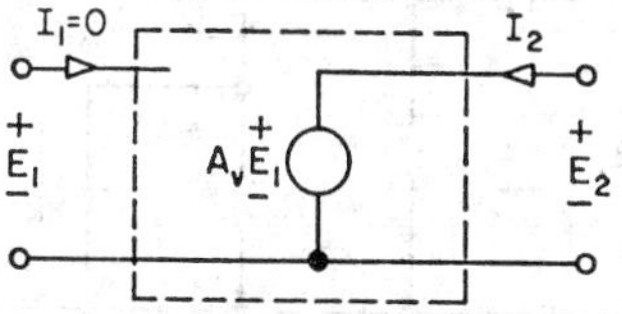

FIG. 25-46. Ideal voltage amplifier.

zero for all levels of E_1, and the output voltage $E_2 = A_vE_1$ independent of I_2. In this amplifier the voltage level E_1 is increased by the multiplicative factor A_v, which is called the *voltage gain* of the amplifier. Physical voltage amplifiers may be represented by the circuit of Fig. 25-47.

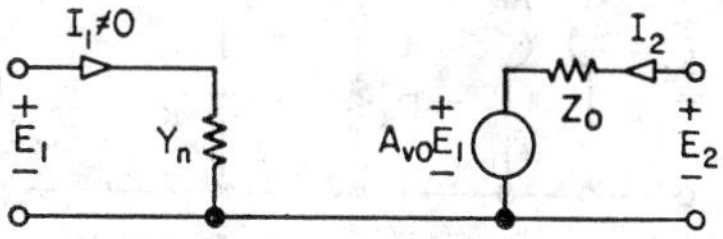

FIG. 25-47. Practical voltage amplifier.

Here the input current is $I_1 = Y_nE_1 \neq 0$, so that the amplifier absorbs some energy from the source of E_1. In addition, E_2 is no longer independent of I_2; the output voltage is given by

$$E_2 = A_{v0}E_1 + Z_0I_2$$

and the output voltage is no longer independent of the output current. The three quantities Y_n, Z_0, and A_{v0} are, in general, functions of the frequency of the input signal E_1.

In most cases, the maximum gain which can be achieved with a single electronic device is about 100. If a higher gain than this is required, several stages of gain are placed in tandem and the over-all gain is the product of the individual gains. If, for example, we connect three single-stage amplifiers each with a gain of 10 in tandem, the over-all gain of the three-stage amplifier will be 1000 (*i.e.*, 10^3).

There are two types of voltage amplifiers in common use: the direct-coupled (or d.c.) amplifier; and the a.c. amplifier.

The term *d.c. amplifier* is applied to any amplifier in which the d.c. component of the input signal is transmitted through the amplifier. A circuit diagram of a simple two-stage d.c. amplifier is shown in Fig. 25-48.

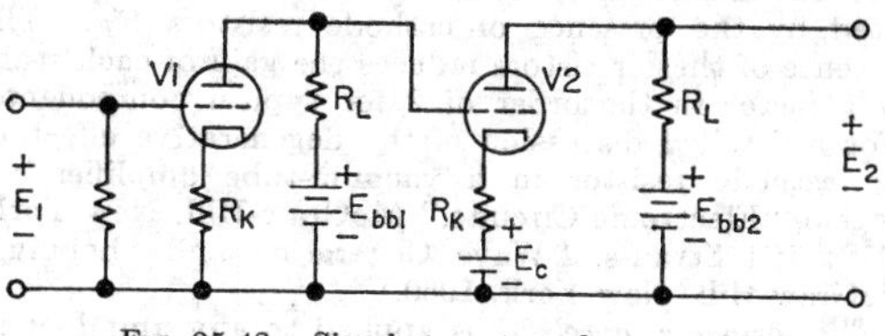

FIG. 25-48. Simple two-stage d.c. amplifier.

Direct-coupled amplifiers are used where it is necessary to amplify signals with d.c. components or components which vary very slowly; for example, d.c. amplifiers are used in conjunction with ionization chambers to amplify the low-level signals arising in such devices.

There is one serious disadvantage in d.c. amplifiers: signals at all frequencies including zero frequency (*i.e.*, d.c.) are amplified. Thus any changes in the electrode

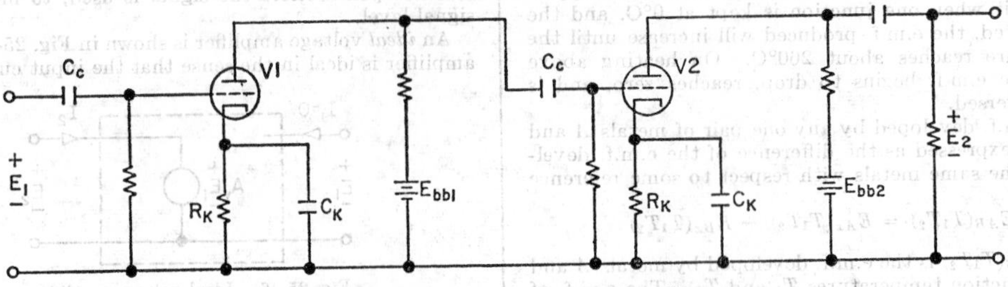

FIG. 25-49. Two-stage *RC*-coupled amplifier.

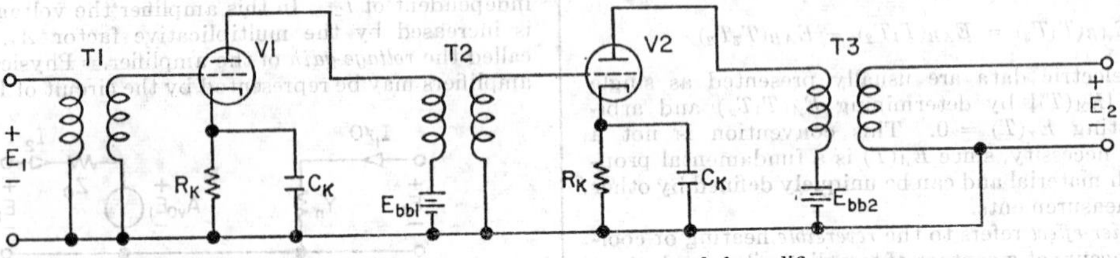

FIG. 25-50. Two-stage transformer-coupled amplifier.

supply voltages or in the contact potential within the tubes (particularly in the first stage) are multiplied. A small change in contact potential in the first stage may cause a signal to appear in the last stage whose amplitude is sufficient to drive the tube into saturation. Such a condition is highly undesirable. In recent years, d.c. amplifiers have been built which are extremely stable in the face of wide variations of supply voltages and contact potential levels. This is achieved by using "chopper networks" to convert the input signal into a chopped-up (or a.c.) voltage so that it is possible to amplify an a.c. signal—which must be rectified and smoothed to obtain the amplified d.c. signal which is ultimately required. Amplifiers of this type have been built which exhibit drifts of output level which are equivalent to only a few microvolts at the input.

Two of the practical difficulties which arise in d.c. amplifiers are shown in Fig. 25-48. Because the grid of V_2 is connected directly to the plate of V_1, and because the grid-to-cathode voltage of a vacuum tube is in the order of 5 volts, the voltage source E_c must be added to the second stage to bring the cathode voltage of V_2 to the proper level. The addition of E_c requires an increase of E_{bb2} over E_{bb1} by approximately E_c volts. These additional voltages require a fairly complicated power supply. A second disadvantage of d.c.-coupled amplifiers is indicated by the presence of cathode resistors R_K. The presence of these resistors reduces the gain of each stage by a factor in the order of 2 for typical components. (For a detailed discussion of the degenerative effect of the cathode resistor in a vacuum-tube amplifier see Angelo, "Electronic Circuits," McGraw-Hill, New York, 1958; and Strauss, "Wave Generation and Shaping," McGraw-Hill, New York, 1960.)

The term *a.c. amplifier* is applied to any amplifier in which the d.c. component of the input signal is *not* transmitted through the amplifier. There are a number of circuit arrangements in which the d.c. component of the input is blocked. The most common of these are the *RC-coupled amplifier* and the *transformer-coupled amplifier*, shown in Figs. 25-49 and 25-50, respectively.

In the *RC*-coupled amplifier, the capacitors C_c remove the d.c. component of the plate voltage, so that the vacuum-tube grids are operating near zero potential; thus the cathode source E_c required in the d.c.-coupled amplifier becomes unnecessary here. Because no cathode source is required the plate-supply voltages E_{bb1} and E_{bb2} may be made equal. The power supply for such an amplifier is usually simple compared with those used with d.c.-coupled amplifiers. An additional advantage of a.c.-coupled amplifiers is the possibility of removing the degenerative effect of the cathode resistors R_K by placing the cathode capacitors C_K in parallel with R_K. The impedance of a capacitor varies inversely with frequency, so that the total cathode impedance may be made negligible over the frequency range of interest.

In the transformer-coupled amplifier, the coupling between stages is obtained through a transformer. Since transformers do not transmit d.c. signals, the essential behavior of the transformer-coupled amplifier is the same as that of the *RC*-coupled amplifier.

The primary reason for employing a.c. amplifiers instead of d.c. amplifiers is the removal of the effect of contact potential within the tubes and the effect of power-supply drift. Since there is no transmission of d.c. signals through the amplifier, any change in contact potential or power-supply voltage causes only a local effect, rather than causing large changes in E_2 as in the d.c. amplifier.

One of the reasons for employing amplifiers is to increase the power level of signals of interest. Such amplifiers are called *power amplifiers*. One power amplifier in common use is the transformer-coupled amplifier shown in Fig. 25-50. The transformer-coupled amplifier is widely used in audio amplifiers.

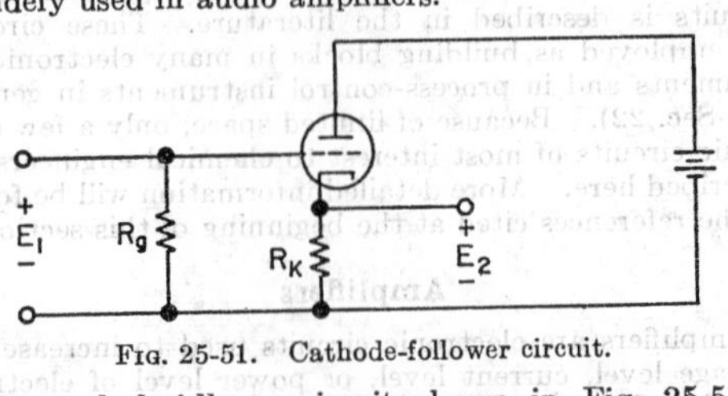

FIG. 25-51. Cathode-follower circuit.

The *cathode-follower* circuit shown in Fig. 25-51 is frequently employed as a power amplifier in instrumentation systems. The voltage gain A_v for the cathode follower is always less than unity, although in many cases

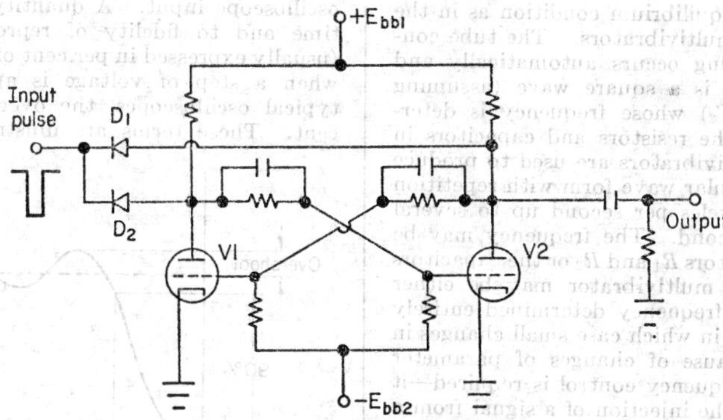

FIG. 25-52. Bistable multivibrator.

it is very nearly unity. This circuit is called a cathode follower because the cathode voltage E_2 "follows" the grid voltage E_1 almost exactly. Cathode followers are frequently employed to couple a high-impedance source (such as an ionization chamber or thermal transducer) to a low-impedance load (such as a coaxial cable or a D'Arsonval ammeter). Cathode followers have the distinguishing characteristic that the input impedance is high (in the order of a few megohms) and the output impedance is low (in the order of 100 ohms). Depending upon the application, a cathode follower may be either a.c.-coupled or d.c.-coupled. The cathode follower shown in Fig. 25-51 is d.c.-coupled. If it is desirable—or necessary—to prevent the transmission of the d.c. component of E_1, then a capacitor may be inserted in series with the lead connecting E_1 to R_g.

Multivibrators

The generic term *multivibrator* is applied to a class of electronic circuits which is widely employed in instrumentation systems—particularly in nuclear instrumentation systems. Multivibrators are essentially switching devices whose output voltage is always at one or the other of only two allowed levels; *i.e.*, they are two-state devices. There are basically three kinds of multivibrators: (1) the bistable multivibrator, in which the multivibrator is indefinitely stable in either state; (2) the monostable multivibrator, in which one state is indefinitely stable and the other is quasi-stable, *i.e.*, the multivibrator remains in the second state only for a short time; and (3) the astable or "free-running" multivibrator, in which both states are only quasi-stable, the circuit continually and automatically switching from one state to the other.

Bistable Multivibrator. A typical circuit for a bistable multivibrator is shown in Fig. 25-52. In one stable state, tube V1 is conducting, and in the other, tube V2 is conducting. The negative input pulse triggers the circuit, causing the originally conducting tube to turn off and the originally non-conducting tube to turn on. Because the circuit "flips" from one condition to the other, this circuit is frequently called a "flip-flop." Every time a pulse is applied to the input, the state of conduction is interchanged between V1 and V2.

The bistable multivibrator finds many uses in electronic systems. Because it has an infinite memory (it "remembers" the state in which it is, until an input pulse occurs), this circuit has found wide use in digital-computer circuits. If a train of negative pulses with repetition frequency f is applied at the input, there will be a train of pulses at the output of frequency $f/2$; *i.e.*, an output pulse will be formed for *every other* input pulse. This phenomenon is employed in frequency dividers and in scalers (see Sec. 22, for nuclear instrumentation).

Monostable Multivibrator. A typical circuit for a monostable multivibrator is shown in Fig. 25-53. In

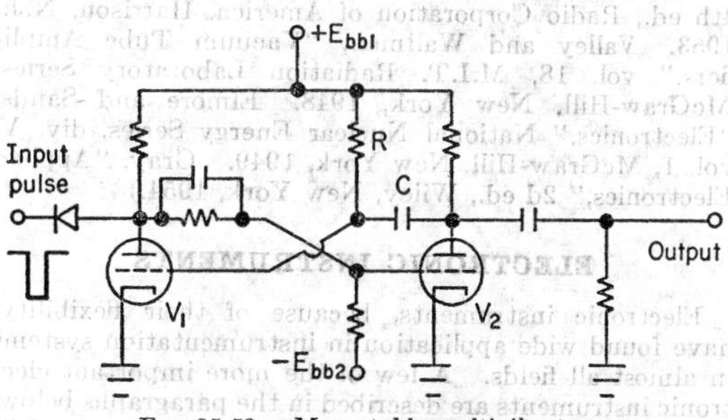

FIG. 25-53. Monostable multivibrator.

this circuit, tube V_1 is normally conducting and tube V_2 is normally non-conducting. When a negative input pulse is applied, a transition occurs in which tube V_1 becomes non-conducting and tube V_2 becomes conducting; however, because there is no conductive coupling between the plate of V_2 and the grid of V_1 (as in the bistable multivibrator), tube V_2 conducts only for a short time (this time determined by the values of R and C). When capacitor C recharges sufficiently, the circuit automatically reverts to the original condition—with V_1 conducting and V_2 non-conducting.

The monostable multivibrator has as its chief use the generation of pulses of uniform amplitude and shape from pulses of variable shape and amplitude.

Astable Multivibrator. A typical circuit for an astable multivibrator is shown in Fig. 25-54. In this

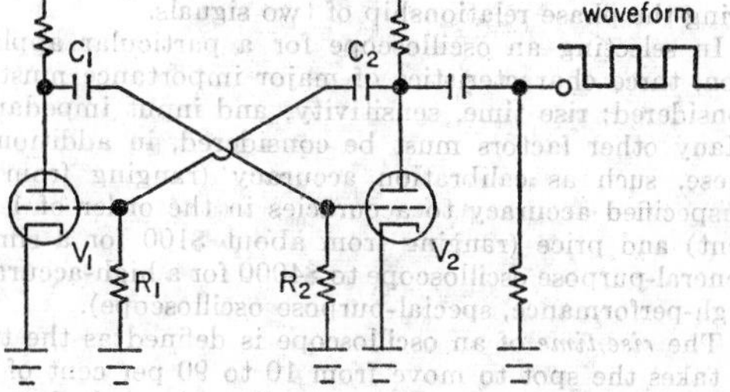

FIG. 25-54. Astable multivibrator.

circuit there is no stable equilibrium condition as in the bistable and monostable multivibrators. The tube conducts alternately—switching occurs automatically and periodically. The output is a square wave (assuming that $R_1 = R_2$ and $C_1 = C_2$) whose frequency is determined by the values of the resistors and capacitors in the circuit. Astable multivibrators are used to produce periodic signals of rectangular wave form with repetition frequencies from a few cycles per second up to several hundred kilocycles per second. The frequency may be varied by varying the resistors R_1 and R_2 or the capacitors C_1 and C_2. The astable multivibrator may be either free-running (*i.e.*, have a frequency determined entirely by the component values) in which case small changes in frequency will occur because of changes of parameter values, or—if accurate frequency control is required—it may be synchronized by the injection of a signal from a source whose frequency is accurately controlled (such as a crystal-controlled oscillator). It is also possible to use an astable multivibrator to generate a signal whose frequency is an accurate submultiple of a known frequency. Accurate division by a factor as high as 20 is possible. (For further information on electronic circuits, see Langford-Smith, "Radiotron Designer's Handbook," 4th ed., Radio Corporation of America, Harrison, N.J., 1953. Valley and Wallman, "Vacuum Tube Amplifiers," vol. 18, M.I.T. Radiation Laboratory Series, McGraw-Hill, New York, 1948. Elmore and Sands, "Electronics," National Nuclear Energy Series, div. V, vol. 1, McGraw-Hill, New York, 1949. Gray, "Applied Electronics," 2d ed., Wiley, New York, 1954.)

ELECTRONIC INSTRUMENTS

Electronic instruments, because of their flexibility, have found wide application in instrumentation systems in almost all fields. A few of the more important electronic instruments are described in the paragraphs below.

Cathode-ray Oscilloscope. The cathode-ray oscilloscope (or, more commonly, oscilloscope) is an electronic oscillograph, in which an electron beam is caused to move across a phosphor on the screen of a cathode-ray tube. The position of the electron beam on the screen is controlled by the voltages applied to the horizontal and vertical deflection plates of the tube. As the vertical deflection voltage increases (decreases) the luminous spot caused by the electron beam moves up (down); as the horizontal deflection voltage increases (decreases), the spot moves to the right (left). The cathode-ray oscilloscope has the decided advantage over other forms of oscillographs (mechanical, electromechanical, etc.) that the recording medium (the electron beam) is essentially inertialess, so that it can follow *extremely* rapid changes in voltage at the deflection plates.

The oscilloscope is capable of displaying a wide variety of electrical signals on the screen of the cathode-ray tube. Time interval, frequency, and amplitude may be measured. In addition, the oscilloscope is useful for studying the detailed variation of transient voltages and for measuring the phase relationship of two signals.

In selecting an oscilloscope for a particular application, three characteristics of major importance must be considered: rise time, sensitivity, and input impedance. Many other factors must be considered, in addition to these, such as calibration accuracy (ranging from an unspecified accuracy to accuracies in the order of 1 per cent) and price (ranging from about $100 for a simple general-purpose oscilloscope to $4000 for a high-accuracy, high-performance, special-purpose oscilloscope).

The *rise time* of an oscilloscope is defined as the time it takes the spot to move from 10 to 90 per cent of the final deflection when a step of voltage is applied at the oscilloscope input. A quantity which is related to rise time and to fidelity of reproduction is the *overshoot* (usually expressed in per cent of final value) which occurs when a step of voltage is applied at the input. In typical oscilloscopes, the overshoot is less than 5 per cent. These terms are illustrated in Fig. 25-55. An

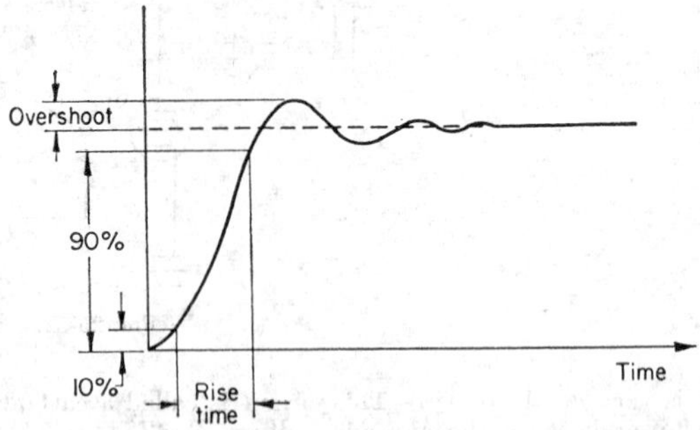

FIG. 25-55. Typical step-function response of oscilloscope, and definition of rise time and overshoot.

alternative to rise time in measuring oscilloscope performance is *band width* ω_B, which is related to rise time (if the overshoot is less than 5 per cent) by the expression

$$\omega_B \cong \frac{0.35}{T_R}$$

where ω_B is in radians per second and rise time T_R is in seconds. The band width ω_B is a measure of the maximum signal frequency which will be transmitted from the oscilloscope input to the cathode-ray screen. Band widths as large as 3×10^8 radians/sec. (50 megacycles/sec.) are available in commercial oscilloscopes. The rise time (and, consequently, the band width) are usually limited by the amplifiers between the oscilloscope input and the cathode-ray tube deflection plates, rather than by the cathode-ray tube characteristics. The maximum band width may be increased by a factor of 10 or more by directly connecting the signal voltage to the deflection plates of the cathode-ray tube.

The *sensitivity* of an oscilloscope is defined as the voltage required to produce a unit deflection when the gain of the internal amplifiers is set at its maximum value. A typical maximum value of sensitivity is 1 millivolt/cm. of deflection. The sensitivity is usually made adjustable continuously or in steps from its maximum value to perhaps 100 volts/cm.

The *input impedance* of an oscilloscope is a measure of the loading effect introduced into a system when the oscilloscope is connected to a signal source. Typically, the input impedance is a 1-megohm resistor in parallel with a 50-micromicrofarad capacitor.

Oscillator. An oscillator is a device for providing a source of periodically varying voltage which is used to provide power or voltage for many purposes, including, for example, frequency-response measurements of systems, investigation of control-system characteristics, and as a power source for induction and dielectric heating. There are a number of characteristics of importance in selecting an oscillator: wave form of output signal, frequency range and frequency accuracy and stability, power output, and voltage output.

The usual signal *wave forms* which are available in commercial oscillators are sinusoids, square waves, and triangular waves. In some instruments all three wave forms are available—the selection being made by a wave-form-selector switch; while in others, only a single wave form is available. A characteristic of some importance which is related to wave form is wave-form distortion, which is a measure of the deviation of the actual wave form from the desired wave form. A typical value of distortion is 1 per cent, although values as low as 0.1 per cent are commercially available.

Oscillators may either operate at a single fixed frequency or have a frequency which is adjustable over a wide range. The frequency may cover a range as wide as 10,000 to 1. Oscillators are available with frequencies as low as 0.01 cycles/sec. or as high as 7000 megacycles/sec. (although not in the same instrument). The accuracy of frequency calibration in an oscillator is typically in the order of 2 per cent; while the long-term stability is in the order of 0.1 per cent for many commercial units.

The *power output* of an oscillator is usually low—typically, in the order of 100 milliwatts. (The power level may be raised considerably by employing a power amplifier between the oscillator and the load.)

The *open-circuit voltage* is available in ranges from a fraction of a volt to 50 volts or more. (This level may be increased materially by employing a voltage amplifier between the oscillator and the load.)

The cost of an oscillator may be very modest—in the order of $150 for a low-accuracy oscillator—to many thousands of dollars for high-accuracy special-purpose oscillators.

Vacuum-tube Voltmeter. The vacuum-tube voltmeter essentially consists of a D'Arsonval voltmeter and power amplifier as shown in Fig. 25-56. The input voltage (*i.e.*, the voltage to be measured) is applied to a power amplifier which raises the power level of this voltage before it is applied to a D'Arsonval voltmeter.

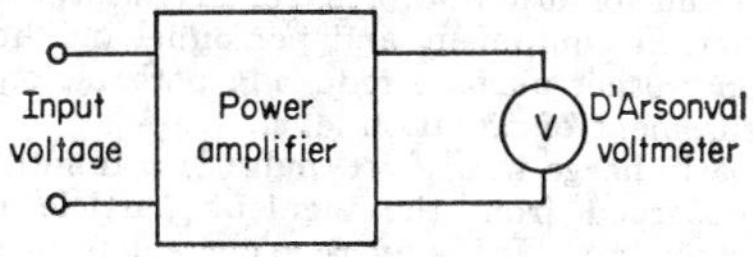

FIG. 25-56. Basic arrangement of a vacuum-tube voltmeter.

The vacuum-tube voltmeter has two important advantages over the conventional voltmeter (which is described elsewhere in this section): the voltmeter is rugged and is protected from overload; and the input impedance is considerably higher than conventional voltmeters and in addition has an input impedance which is independent of the range in multirange instruments. These advantages exist because of the isolation between the voltage source and the D'Arsonval voltmeter.

Voltages as low as 1 microvolt and as high as 30 kv. may be measured with a vacuum-tube voltmeter. These instruments are usually multirange with ratios of maximum to minimum as high as 100,000 to 1. A typical (and relatively standard) value of input impedance is 11 megohms, although values as high as 10^{10} ohms are available.

The accuracy of vacuum-tube voltmeters ranges from 5 per cent of full scale for low-priced instruments (costing in the order of $50) to 0.2 per cent for high-accuracy instruments (costing in the order of $1000).

NUCLEAR INSTRUMENTATION

Nuclear radiations cannot be directly observed but must be observed through their interactions with matter. Many techniques have been developed for investigating nuclear radiations—*e.g.*, photographic emulsions, cloud chambers, bubble chambers, and various gas-discharge and solid-state electronic devices. Of these, the most widely used are the electronic devices because of the rapid responses available and the flexibility of electronic systems.

A wide variety of special-purpose electronic instruments has been developed to handle the difficult instrumentation problems which arise in the nuclear field. In many situations, it is necessary to measure low-amplitude (*e.g.*, 1-millivolt) pulses with short rise times (fractions of a microsecond). An additional difficulty which usually arises in nuclear instrumentation is the high impedance level of the source of the pulses (typically, 10^{12} to 10^{15} ohms). In the following paragraphs are described several nuclear instruments which are widely used in making measurements of nuclear radiations.

In many applications, the number of pulses produced by a nuclear detector within a specified time interval is of interest. Two instruments which are widely used for counting such pulses are the count-rate meter and the scaler.

Count-rate Meter. The count-rate meter is an instrument for measuring the rate of occurrence of pulses. A basic block diagram of a count-rate meter is shown in Fig. 25-57. The pulse source may be a G-M tube or other nuclear detector. The output of the pulse source is connected to the count-rate meter input. The amplitude of the pulses is usually amplified in a pulse amplifier. The pulse shaper produces a pulse of uniform shape and amplitude each time a pulse is applied by the pulse amplifier. The average value of the output of the pulse shaper is then directly proportional to the rate of occurrence of pulses from the pulse source. The integrator serves to compute the average value of the pulse-shaper output. The output meter measures the output voltage of the integrator. This output meter is usually a vacuum-tube voltmeter.

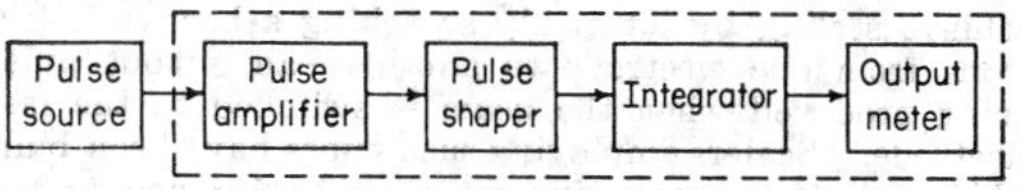

FIG. 25-57. Block diagram of count-rate meter.

If the integrator is linear, the indication of the output meter is a linear function of the counting rate. Frequently, the range of counting rates encountered in nuclear measurements covers many decades. In order to employ a single scale on the output meter to cover the entire range of interest, non-linear integrators have been employed to achieve a logarithmic count-rate scale. The results of this work have been described by Cooke, Yarborough, and Pulsford [*Proc. Inst. Elec. Engrs.*, part II, **98** (62), 196–203 (1951)] and by Braun (M.E.E. Thesis, Polytechnic Institute, Brooklyn, June, 1955).

Scaler. The scaler is essentially an event counter. The simplest scaler consists of a pulse amplifier and an electromechanical register as shown in Fig. 25-58. The pulse amplifier serves to increase the power content of the pulses to enable them to trip the register. The electromechanical register consists of a solenoid and a toothed wheel. The solenoid indexes the wheel one tooth per pulse. This simple scaler is entirely satisfactory for

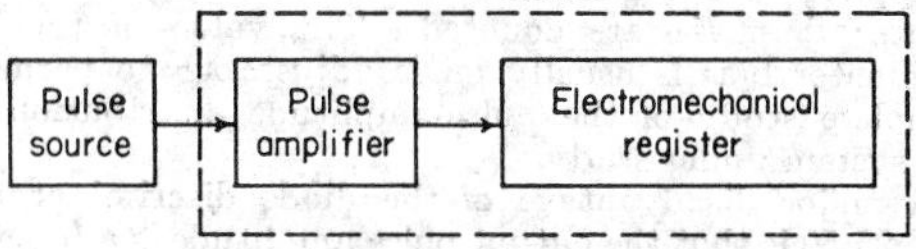

FIG. 25-58. Block diagram of simple scaler.

recording total counts, if the average rate of arrival of pulses is low (less than 60 events per second).

If counting rates higher than 60 counts per second are to be studied, electronic means must be employed to reduce the counting rate to a value less than 60 counts per second. Scaling circuits—consisting of chains of bistable multivibrators—have been devised to provide a single output pulse for each n pulses at the input. In a sense, these scaling circuits divide the counting rate by n. The most commonly used scaling circuits employ scales of 2 (*i.e.*, $n = 2$) or scales of 10 (*i.e.*, $n = 10$). If p of these scaling circuits are connected in tandem, then a single output pulse will occur for each 2^p or 10^p input pulses—or, in general, for each n^p input pulses. With electronic scaling circuits it is possible to handle average rates of arrival as high as several million counts per second.

In many cases, decimal counting is preferred over binary counting; so that considerable effort has been expended to achieve improved scale-of-10 circuits. Unfortunately, electronic scale-of-10 circuits require more tubes and more maintenance for a given scale reduction than do scale-of-2 circuits.

Within the past 10 years various self-contained decade counter tubes have become available. These tubes achieve scaling by internally switching a beam of electrons from one electrode to another—an output pulse being produced when the beam is switched to the last electrode. Scalers employing such tubes have been built which operate at counting rates up to 10^5 counts per second.

In many pulse-type nuclear detectors, the pulse height is related to the energy of the nuclear radiation which produces the pulse. A measurement of the number of pulses with amplitudes greater than some specified voltage E or with amplitudes between two voltages E_1 and E_2 must frequently be made.

Pulse-amplitude discriminators are electronic instruments for investigating the amplitude distribution of the pulses produced in a nuclear detector. The simplest kind of pulse-amplitude discriminator circuit involves a biased diode as shown in Fig. 25-59. In this circuit, a

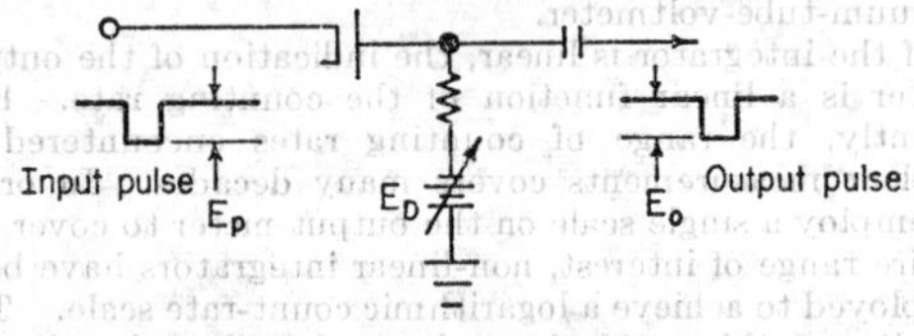

FIG. 25-59. Simple diode discriminator.

negative pulse of amplitude E_p is applied at the input. The anode of the diode is connected to the discriminator bias voltage E_D. When $E_p > E_D$ the diode conducts, producing an output pulse with amplitude $E_0 = E_p - E_D$. When $E_p < E_D$ the diode does not conduct and no output pulse is produced. If the output of the discriminator is applied to a scaler, all pulses whose amplitudes are greater than E_D are counted. The value of the discriminator bias is usually made adjustable, to permit a complete study of the pulse-amplitude distribution for the system under study.

A major disadvantage of the diode discriminator of Fig. 25-59 is that the output pulse amplitude is a function of the input pulse amplitude. Many electronic circuits have been devised which provide an output pulse whose amplitude is independent of the input pulse, in addition to having other operating advantages.

Differential pulse-height discriminators are used to determine the number of pulses with amplitudes between two levels E_1 and E_2 (the differential $\Delta E = E_2 - E_1$ is frequently called the discriminator "window"). The block diagram of a single-channel differential pulse-height discriminator is shown in Fig. 25-60. This consists of two discriminators of the type described above.

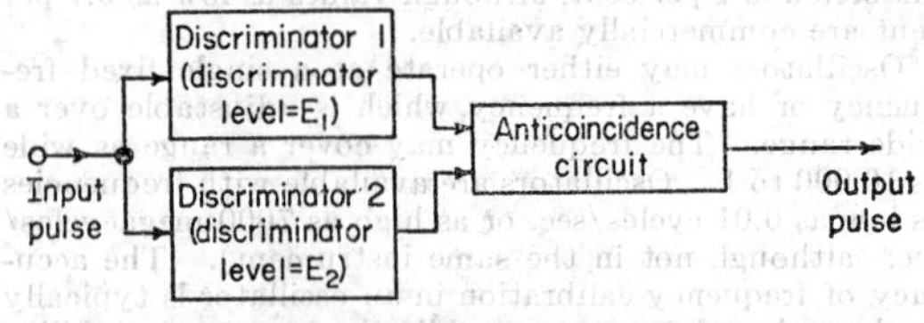

FIG. 25-60. Differential pulse-height discriminator.

Discriminator 1 produces an output pulse whenever the pulse amplitude exceeds E_1 and discriminator 2 produces a pulse whenever the pulse amplitude exceeds E_2 (we assume $E_2 > E_1$). The *anticoincidence circuit* produces an output pulse whenever it receives a pulse from either discriminator but not both. In this way, an output pulse is produced only when the pulse amplitude is greater than E_1 but less than E_2.

Radiation survey meters (or, more simply, survey meters) are portable instruments for measuring the intensity of nuclear radiations in a given region. They usually have a relatively low accuracy and are used primarily for monitoring radiation levels rather than for making precision measurements. Survey meters have found wide application in nuclear work. They are used in health-physics work in the supervision of "hot areas," for surveying for uranium ores, for investigation of contamination on equipment and personnel in "hot labs," and for any other purpose requiring portable equipment for measurement of radiation level.

The total charge in a given pulse is a function of the energy absorbed from the incident particle in many nuclear detectors. If the average current from a nuclear detector is measured, the average energy of the incident nuclear radiation may be determined. Because the average current available in most detectors is very small (in many applications, 10^{-12} amp. or less), special instruments have been devised to measure these currents. These special instruments are called electrometers.

Electrometer. An electrometer is essentially an instrument in which the low-level current to be measured is converted to a voltage (usually by passing the current through a resistor) which is measured using a vacuum-tube voltmeter. A simple electrometer circuit is shown in Fig. 25-61. The average detector current i_d flows through a resistor R_g (typically R_g is 10^9 to 10^{13} ohms), developing a voltage which is applied to the grid of an electrometer tube causing the plate current to increase. The change in plate current causes the ammeter to deflect in proportion to i_d. The zero-adjust resistor and the balancing supply serve to cancel the quiescent plate current (*i.e.*, the value of plate current when $i_d = 0$), setting the meter reading to zero when $i_d = 0$.

The electrometer tube is a special-purpose vacuum tube designed so that the grid current i_g is very small. From Fig. 25-61 we see that the current in R_g is $i_d - i_g$;

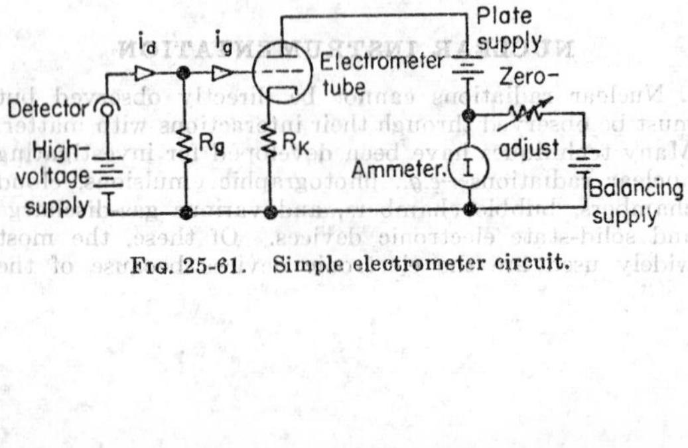

FIG. 25-61. Simple electrometer circuit.

the current i_g causes an error in the measurement. Electrometer tubes, in properly designed circuits, may have grid currents as low as 10^{-14} amp., permitting measurements down to 10^{-12} amp. with errors less than 1 per cent.

The vibrating-reed electrometer is basically an instrument in which a time-varying capacitor is used to convert the average detector current into a varying current which may be amplified in an a.c. amplifier, thus eliminating many of the difficulties of electrometers which employ d.c. amplifiers. Vibrating-reed electrometers are usable to measure currents as low as 10^{-16} amp.

More detailed descriptions of the nuclear instruments mentioned above, as well as descriptions of many other nuclear instruments, are given by Elmore and Sands in "Electronics" (National Nuclear Energy Series, div. V, vol. 1, McGraw-Hill, New York, 1949) and by Price ("Nuclear Radiation Detection," McGraw-Hill, New York, 1958). These references also contain extensive bibliographies.

ELECTRIC HEATING

Electric heating which involves the conversion of electrical energy into heat is associated with (1) the flow of current through a conductor—I^2R effect; (2) the electric arc, where the resistance is a gas or vapor, such as the carbon arc in the presence of carbon vapor; (3) induction heating in conductors, which is similar to the I^2R effect; and (4) dielectric heating, which is applicable to nonconductors. The oldest method is the first, and the most recent is dielectric heating.

To offset the relatively higher cost of electrical energy compared with other fuel energies are the many advantages associated with electric heating. They include (1) ease in obtaining high temperatures; (2) safety and convenience; (3) cleanliness in the absence of combustion by-products; (4) rapid response and uniformity of temperature which can be precisely controlled; (5) the absence, in general, of oxidizing conditions; (6) facility in producing the heat where desired.

The transfer of heat may be by conduction, convection, radiation, or by the production of heat within the material itself.

Resistance heating, which most commonly refers to the production of heat by direct application of a voltage to a resistor, has a wide variety of uses ranging from the household electric stove to large complex industrial applications. The efficiency of conversion of electrical energy into heat by this method is 100 per cent, which means that all the electrical energy delivered to the heating resistor is converted into heat energy. Not all this converted energy is delivered to the heating load, but where heat-insulated ovens surround the heating resistor, the ratio of heat delivered to the load to the converted heat is likely to be very nearly unity. This high over-all efficiency permits resistance heating to be competitive with other methods of heating using fuels as an energy source.

Resistive heaters are versatile in their modes of operation and can be used in high-pressure environments or in high vacuums. The resistor material is usually an alloy of nickel and chromium, which has the advantage of a high melting point and high resistance to oxidation and scaling. This alloy can withstand an approximate maximum operating temperature of 1000°C. For temperatures above this value, resistors are made of graphite, molybdenum, and silicon carbide. The temperature at which a resistor is operated mainly determines its useful life. Rectangular shapes for the resistor cross section give a greater surface area for heat transfer than the round shape, and therefore the strip or ribbon form of resistor is often used, especially at higher temperatures.

Where the heat transfer is by radiation or convection, an enclosure or heating chamber is used. The chamber serves to control the distribution of the heat, increases over-all efficiency, and confines the heating load to a certain atmosphere.

A resistor oven is a heating chamber with some provision for ventilation which can operate at temperatures up to 800°F. Its principal uses are drying (removal of liquid by evaporation) and baking (a process of hardening). In the convection oven, the transfer of heat is by forced convection usually in air. Ovens are flexible in design and can be designed for continuous process work where the load to be heated is associated with a conveyer system.

In the radiation oven the heating units are tungsten-filament infrared lamps (usually with reflectors) operated at filament temperatures of about 2500°K. Since the large part of the energy radiated from the lamps is in the infrared region, the lamp is denoted as infrared and the heating as infrared heating. Infrared heating is commonly used at moderate temperatures (below 600°F.) in the drying of sheet and granular materials and in the baking of surface finishes. Standard infrared lamps are rated at 115 volts and in wattage ratings from 125 to 1000 watts. In the continuous oven, the lamp banks form a tunnel through which the load to be heated travels.

Resistance furnaces are used at much higher temperatures (1000°C.) than are resistance ovens. They are used extensively in the heat-treatment of metals and alloys, annealing glass, and porcelain enameling and brazing of metal parts. The main method of heat transfer is by radiation. The distribution of heat is obtained by a combination of direct radiation from the resistors and a reradiation from the interior surfaces of the chamber. The resistor material is usually a nickel-chromium alloy. The heating chamber is an enclosure with a refractory lining, a surrounding layer of heat insulation, and an outer casing of steel plate. The temperature in ovens and furnaces can be automatically regulated. The most common method of regulating temperature is the current-on and current-off method, which is most effective when the main method of heat transfer is by radiation. The other method of temperature regulation is by controlling and varying the voltage applied to the resistors by means of a transformer or saturable core reactor.

The principle of *arc heating* is that, when an electric circuit is interrupted (by an air gap), current will continue to flow if the current is high enough to vaporize some of the conductor and thus fill the gap with a conducting vapor path. The electric-arc furnace is capable of operating at temperatures up to the order of 4000°C. In this range of temperatures, the electric furnace has no economic competitors. The main uses are in the purification of many ores, changing an undesirable crystalline structure of an ore, and synthesis of compounds not available in the natural state by fusing different raw materials. The arc furnace is therefore used extensively in the metallurgical, abrasive, refractory, and electrochemical industries.

The arc is established by momentarily bringing together two electrodes, or one electrode and the charge (which frequently acts as a second electrode), and then separating them. The vapor produced on separation provides the conducting path. The preferable method of operation is with a short arc which gives rise to high currents. Voltages up to 250 volts are normally used in arc furnaces in conjunction with tap-changing transformers to obtain the most suitable voltage. Typical electrode materials are graphite and carbon. Graphite is more expensive, purer, and has greater strength and higher current-carrying capacity than carbon. Severity of operation and purity requirement dictate the type of electrode to be used. Carbon arcs are the most intense source of heat with a temperature of about 6000°F. Electrodes are consumed in the heating process by oxidation and by contact with the furnace charge. In the direct-arc furnace, the voltage is applied between two or more electrodes located above the charge which, in most cases, is a non-conductor of electricity at room temperatures but becomes a conductor at higher temperatures. To fuse the charge, layers of coke are placed on the surface between electrodes. When the electrodes are lowered into the coke bed a current flows, generating heat, which in turn melts the furnace charge near it. The charge then becomes conductive, and current will flow from electrode to electrode through the molten bath.

Heat is generated by radiation from the electric arc between electrodes and bath and through the resistance-heating effect in the bath. In a purification process, impurities are volatilized in the intense heat of the arc or are chemically reduced in the molten bath.

Arc furnaces may be single-phase or three-phase. For balanced electrical loads on the power supplies three-phase is desirable. However, single-phase furnaces properly connected to different single-phase power can also maintain an over-all balanced system. Furnaces with capacities of 250 to 10,000 kva. are in commercial use. Sizes in the range of 1000 to 2000 kva. are most common. Since the position of the electrode is quite critical, automatic regulators are used to control the position of the electrodes to maintain constant current, voltage, or power—whichever is desired.

Induction heating is based on the principle that an eddy current will be induced in an electric conductor that is subject to a changing magnetic field. This current flowing through the conductor will produce heat because of the I^2R losses. In practice, the magnetic field is produced by a coil carrying an alternating current of a suitable frequency. The work to be heated is usually placed within the coil. A big advantage of this form of heating is the speed with which the heat may be produced, with a consequent reduction in the oxidation and scaling of the metals being worked on. Other advantages include (1) ability to put the heat where you want it—to heat limited parts or surfaces of a metal piece instead of the entire piece by proper design of the heating coils; (2) the use of power for heating only when it is necessary, with no need to maintain a continuous furnace temperature; (3) accurate control of the total heat per piece by electronic timers; (4) no contamination of charge due to fuel gases; (5) thorough mixing of alloys when melting; and (6) heating conveniently taking place in any special atmosphere including a vacuum. Over-all efficiency associated with induction heating is seldom over 50 per cent, but its use is warranted as an important industrial tool. This type of heating is applied in melting, forging, annealing, surface hardening, brazing, and soldering operations, and is especially suited to automatic assembly systems.

Frequencies used for induction heating cover a large range from 60 up to a million cycles/sec. The depth of penetration of the current into the workpiece (and thus, the location of heating effect) varies inversely with the square root of the frequency. The amount of power transferred from the coil to the workpiece increases in proportion to the square root of frequency. Thus, by limiting the depth of penetration with higher frequencies, a higher temperature is obtained faster, and heating may be confined to the surface of the work. Magnetic materials heat more readily than non-magnetic ones and materials of higher resistivity heat faster than those of lower resistivity. The use of higher frequencies permits more space clearance between coil and workpiece, which is desirable, since at high frequencies the coil voltage may be extremely high. The material of the workpiece has a great effect on the current distribution; so that what might be a "high" frequency for steel might be a "low" frequency for brass as far as penetration depths are concerned.

Induction furnaces operating at frequencies of from 60 (for heating heavy sections of materials or for melting) to 1000 cycles/sec. (for melting, and for casehardening of gears and other parts subjected to heavy wear) are very useful for obtaining temperatures up to 3000°C. In one type of furance, the currents are induced directly into the charge to be worked on; in others, the currents are induced in a magnetic case containing the charge, and the heat is radiated inward to the furnace charge. Since the coil currents in furnaces may be as high as 15,000 amp., the coil conductors are usually hollow to permit water circulation for cooling purposes. Compared with resistance heating, the power factor of induction heating is relatively poor because of the reactance effects. This tends to lower the over-all plant power factor, which may incur power penalties from the utility company.

Power supplied to the induction coil comes from one of the following sources: (1) 60 cycle directly from the power mains, (2) motor-generator set, (3) mercury-arc frequency converters, (4) spark-gap converter, or (5) an electronic oscillator. Motor-generator sets produce frequencies up to 9600 cycles/sec., have a conversion efficiency of about 70 per cent, and are built in sizes up to about 800 kw. output. Mercury-arc converters develop frequencies up to 1500 cycles/sec. with conversion efficiencies of about 90 per cent and can deliver up to 300 kw. Spark-gap converters—which work on the principle of an oscillatory capacitor discharge through an air gap—have a conversion efficiency of about 50 per cent, with frequencies in the range of 50,000 to 200,000 cycles/sec., and supply about 50 kw. of heat. Electronic oscillators (vacuum-tube a.c. generators) generate frequencies from 100,000 to 1,000,000 cycles/sec. with conversion efficiencies of about 50 per cent. They are built in sizes up to 500 kw. In the radio-frequency range (r.f.)—above 40,000 cycles/sec.—spark-gap converters have the advantage of lower initial cost and relative simplicity compared with electronic oscillators; however, sparking across the gap causes erosion, and periodic readjustment of the gaps is necessary.

Table 25-9. Induction-heating Data

Process	Frequency used	Source of power
Annealing, low-temperature metal heating	60–100 cycles/sec.	M-G sets Mercury-arc converter
Deep-heat penetration, melting..................	1000–10,000 cycles/sec.	M-G set
Hardening, surface heating of metals	30–200 kc./sec. 100–1000 kc./sec.	Spark-gap converter Electronic oscillators

Dielectric heating is the term applied to the generation of heat in non-conducting materials by their losses when subject to an alternating electric field of high frequency. Frequencies necessary range from 1 to 200 megacycles (million cycles) per second. Heating of non-conductors by this method is extremely rapid. This form of heating is applied by placing the non-conducting load between two electrodes across which the high-frequency voltage is applied. This arrangement in effect constitutes an electric capacitor, with the load acting as the dielectric. Although ideally a capacitor has no losses, practical losses do occur and sufficient heat is generated at high frequencies to make this a practical form of heat source.

For a given geometry of the work material and electrodes, the heat generated in the load increases with frequency and with the square of the voltage.

In direct contrast to induction heating, heat losses in the non-conducting material can be calculated with a fair degree of accuracy. The frequency used in dielectric heating is a function of the power desired and the size of the work material. Practical values of voltages applied to the electrodes are 2000 to 5000 volts per inch of thickness of the work material. The source of power is exclusively by electronic (vacuum-tube) oscillators which are capable of generating the very high frequencies desirable. Units with up to 500 kw. output are in commercial use today. Some of the more common uses of dielectric heating are (1) wood drying, curing, and gluing; (2) preheating of plastics; (3) processing of rubber and synthetic materials; (4) food processing; and (5) drying and heat-treatment of textiles. The electronic sewing machine developed recently resembles an ordinary sewing machine, but the needle and thread are replaced by rotating electrodes between which a high-frequency voltage is applied. This application of dielectric heating is used extensively to seal two or more thermoplastic pieces together along a line (or seam). Ordinary sewing with thread weakens the sheets and makes them no longer watertight. In food processing, dielectric heating is being used for "popping" of cereals, thawing of frozen foods, cooking of foods, killing molds in bread, and in the treatment of dairy products. In the field of medicine, artificial fevers—when desired for specific treatments—are produced by dielectric heating by producing heat inside blood vessels. Diathermy for the treatment of pains is a popular application of dielectric heating.

SECTION 26

COST AND PROFITABILITY ESTIMATION

BY

James B. Weaver, M.S., Director, Development Appraisal Department, Atlas Chemical Industries, Inc.; Member, American Chemical Society, American Institute of Chemical Engineers, National Society of Professional Engineers, American Association of Cost Engineers, American Society for Engineering Education; Fellow, American Institute of Chemists.

H. Carl Bauman, B.S., Manager, Cost Engineering Department, Engineering and Construction Division, American Cyanamid Co.; Member, National Society of Professional Engineers, American Association of Cost Engineers, Institure of Electrical and Electronic Engineers.

W. F. Heneghan, B.S., Commercial Development Manager, Sonneborn Chemical and Refining Corp., Division of Witco Chemical Co. (Manufacturing Cost Estimation)

CONTENTS

REFERENCES: *Books:* Aries and Newton, "Chemical Engineering Cost Estimation," McGraw-Hill, New York, 1955. Bierman and Smidt, "The Capital Budgeting Decision," Macmillan, New York, 1960. Chilton (Ed.), "Cost Engineering in the Process Industries," McGraw-Hill, New York, 1960. Dean, "Capital Budgeting," Columbia, New York, 1951. Dean, "Managerial Economics," Prentice-Hall, Englewood Cliffs, N.J., 1951. Grant and Ireson, "Principles of Engineering Economy," 4th ed., Ronald, New York, 1960. Happel, "Chemical Process Economics," Wiley, New York, 1958. Hur (Ed.), "Chemical Process Economics in Practice," Reinhold, New York, 1956. Morris, "Engineering Economy," Irwin, Homewood, Ill., 1960. Osborn and Kammermeyer, "Money and the Chemical Engineer," Prentice-Hall, Englewood Cliffs, N.J., 1958. Perry (Ed.), "Chemical Business Handbook," Secs. 1, 2, McGraw-Hill, New York, 1954. Peters, "Plant Design and Economics for Chemical Engineers," McGraw-Hill, New York, 1958. Schlaifer, "Probability and Statistics for Business Decisions," McGraw-Hill, New York, 1960. Schweyer, "Process Engineering Economics," McGraw-Hill, New York, 1955. Tyler and Winter, "Chemical Engineering Economics," 4th ed., McGraw-Hill, New York, 1959.

Bibliographies: U.S. Bureau of Mines Information Circulars 7516 (1949), 7705 (1955), 7751 (1956), 7847 (1957), 7884 (1958), 7916 (1959), 7966 (1960), 8035 (1961), 8117 (1962). *Cost Engineering,* January issues annually since 1957. Weaver, *Chem. Eng.,* **61** (10), 185–193 (1954), **62** (6), 247–252 (1955); *Ind. Eng. Chem.,* **48,** 934–942 (1956); **49,** 936–946 (1957); **50,** 753–762 (1958); **51,** 689–696 (1959).

Specialized periodicals: Engineering Economist, Engineering Economy Division, American Society for Engineering Education, Stevens Inst. Tech., Hoboken, N.J. *A.A.C.E. Bulletin,* American Association of Cost Engineers, Pratt Inst., Brooklyn, N.Y. *Cost Engineering,* Industrial Research Service, Dover, N.H.

Pamphlets and reprints: Nelson, Complete Costimating and Process Costimating, *Oil Gas J.,* fixed investment and operating costs, 1957, 1958, 1959, 1961. *Petroleum Refiner,* "Cost Estimating Handbook," Gulf Publishing, Houston, 1956. Lesser (Ed.), "Planning and Justifying Capital Expenditures," Stevens Institute of Technology, Hoboken, 1959. *Chemical Engineering,* "CE Cost File," 1959, 1960, 1961, and 1962.

Acknowledgment: Most of the material contained in this section was first published in *Industrial & Engineering Chemistry;* permission of the American Chemical Society to use it here is gratefully acknowledged. Credit is also due to Alan G. Bates and other members of the Economic Evaluation Section of Atlas Chemical Industries, Inc., who were coauthors of some of the original material and assisted in its revision here.

GLOSSARY

Accounts payable. For the buyer, the amount owed for goods and services purchased (and therefore usually available for use by the buyer) on which payment has not yet been made.

Accounts receivable. For the seller, the amount owed for goods shipped to a buyer on which payment has not yet been received.

Accrual basis. The accounting method which recognizes revenues and disbursement of funds by receipt of bills or orders and not by cash flow; distinguished from "cash basis."

Administrative expense. An overhead cost due to general direction of the company, above the plant level; home-office expense when plant is at a separate location. Generally includes executives' salaries, legal, central purchasing and engineering, traffic, accounting, etc. May sometimes be used as a general term to include sales and research expenses as well.

Allocation of costs. The procedure whereby overhead costs and other non-direct charges are assigned back to processing units or to products on what is expected to be an equitable basis. All allocations are necessarily somewhat arbitrary.

Amortization. The writing off of business expenses over more than a single year; see Depreciation, Depletion.

Annual cost. Any cost expressed on a yearly basis. Also, one of the means of expressing values in the compound-interest system, as an equivalent series of equal annual cash flows, or a profitability technique using this expression.

Appurtenances. The auxiliaries to either process or non-process equipment; piping, electrical, insulation, instrumentation, etc.

Architect's fee. Generally the sum of money paid to reimburse the architect for the cost of making surveys, preparing drawings and specifications. The fee covers all direct expenses, overhead, and profit.

Authorization estimate. See Budget estimate.

Auxiliary facilities. The non-productive facilities which provide utilities and other services used by the manufacturing plant; also known as "off-site" or "off-battery-limits" facilities. Includes "non-process equipment" and other service facilities and buildings, change houses, etc.

Balance sheet. The accounting statement of a historical financial position, showing assets, liabilities, and net worth of a business at a given point in time.

Base case. The over-all situation in which no investment is made to change the status quo; the series of forecasts which express this alternative to an investment. The base case does not provide for achievement of the main purpose of the investment proposal.

Battery limit. A geographical boundary defining the coverage of a specific project, as reflected in the construction contracts. Usually takes in the manufacturing area of a proposed plant, including all "process equipment" (*q.v.*) but excluding provision of storage, utilities, administrative buildings, or "auxiliary facilities" (*q.v.*) unless so specified. Usually excludes site preparation and therefore may be often applied to the extension of an existing plant.

Bonus-penalty contract. An arrangement wherein the contractor is guaranteed a bonus, usually a fixed sum of money, for each day the project is completed ahead of a certain date and agrees to pay a penalty for each day of delay after that date.

Book value. Current investment value on the books, calculated as original installed cost less depreciation accruals. Net asset value for accounting use.

Break-even charts. Charts showing sales income and total costs plotted as functions of rate of operation of a company or a processing facility. The break-even point is the intersection of the plotted lines.

Break-even point. The percentage of capacity at which incomes of a company or facility equal all fixed costs and variable costs at that level of operation.

Budget estimate. An estimate of fixed investment prepared from carefully evaluated process flow sheets, detailed equipment lists, and good site and structure information. Such estimates should be expected to be within 20 per cent of the actual fixed investment. Budget estimates are often the basis for original budgeting of capital funds.

Burden. See Overhead.

Capacity. The estimated maximum level of production on a sustained basis, preferably expressed with the corresponding estimate of "time efficiency" (*q.v.*).

Capital budgeting. The combination of procedures required to foresee, evaluate, justify, finance, approve, and control major expenditures for fixed and working capital. Usually implies that a budget of all foreseen capital expenditures for a given future period is made at one time.

Capital, cost of. The cost of obtaining the total capital employed by a firm, expressed as an interest rate. The total or combined cost of capital must consider both cost of equity capital and cost of borrowed funds.

Capital, fixed. The total original cost of installed facilities which cannot be deducted for tax purposes as a current expense in the year of acquisition, but for which depreciation is allowed by the tax authorities. Gross asset value, less land.

Capital recovery. The process by which original investment in a project is recovered over its life. Depreciation allowance provides for capital recovery in the absence of inflation.

Capital, working. The funds, in addition to fixed capital and land investment, which a company must provide a project (excluding startup expense) to get it started and meet subsequent obligations as they come due. Includes cash, receivables, and inventories, less payables.

Capitalized cost. The sum of money which, at a given interest rate, will provide an infinite series of payments of a desired amount without diminishing the original sum, or the system for replacement analysis employing that sum. Also, the depreciable portion of a fixed investment.

Cash. Funds in the form of currency or bank balances required, by seasonal, random, or other variations in income and outgo, to maintain a liquid financial position; an element of working capital.

Cash basis. The accounting basis whereby revenue and expense are recorded when cash is received and paid; distinguished from "accrual basis" (*q.v.*).

Cash flow. The passage of money into or out of the enterprise. For investment evaluation, investments are usually considered as *negative* cash flows; after-tax profits and depreciation as *positive* cash flows or "cash generation" (*q.v.*).

Cash generation. Net cash flow from an investment to the business enterprise.

Code of accounts. See Cost code.

Compounding. Use of compound interest to determine sums later in time which are equivalent to an earlier, smaller sum.

Confidence interval. A statistical term denoting a range which is expected to include a true value with a specified probability.

Construction expense. See Field expense.

Contingencies. An allowance for unforeseeable elements of cost, particularly in fixed investment estimates, which previous experience has shown to be statistically likely to occur. May include allowance for escalation.

Continuous interest or continuous compounding. The use of interest factors assuming an instantaneous base for compounding, rather than quarterly, annually, etc. Interest rate of return is usually calculated by this technique, since the cash flows of most business firms are reasonably continuous. (Note that nominal continuous interest of 20 per cent results in an effective annual rate of 22 per cent per year, etc.)

Contractor's estimate. See Firm estimate.

Contractor's fee. In a cost-plus contract, the fee for services of the contractor on installation of fixed capital facilities; usually included in the fixed investment appearing on the final accounting books. Generally applies only to the profit portion of contractor's reimbursement.

Cost center. For accounting purposes, a grouping of items of equipment and facilities comprising a product-manufacturing system or subsystem.

Cost code. A system in which items of expense or fixed capital such as equipment and material are identified with numerical figures to facilitate account keeping and cost control.

Cost control. The procedures by which management evaluates the actual cost history of a capital investment project or a manufacturing operation. Intended to assist in staying close to authorized estimates or cost standards.

Cost engineer. Any graduate or professional engineer employing his technical skills in the practice of cost estimation, cost control, profitability, or general engineering economics.

Cost indexes. See Inflation index.

Cost-plus contract. A type of contract under which a contractor furnishes all material, construction equipment, and labor at actual cost, plus an agreed-upon fee for his services.

Definitive estimate. See Project-control estimate.

Depletion. A provision in tax regulations which allows a business to charge as current expense a non-cash expense representing the portion of limited natural resources consumed in the conduct of the business.

Depreciation. A provision in tax regulations permitting an annual non-cash expense charge for recovery of fixed capital from an investment whose productive life is finite but is greater than one year; also the allowance under this provision.

Detailed estimate. See Firm estimate.

Direct expense. (1) Fixed investment: the cost of all material and labor involved in the actual on-site fabrication, installation, and erection of facilities. (2) Manufacturing costs: a cost within a cost center which is directly assignable to that center; materials, labor, and other expenses consumed directly in making the product.

Discounted cash flow. See Interest rate of return, Present worth.

Discounting. Use of compound interest to determine sums earlier in time which are equivalent to a later, larger sum.

Economic life. The period of commercial use of a product or facility. May be limited by obsolescence, physical life of equipment, or changing economic conditions.

Employee benefits. See Fringe benefits.

Engineering cost. The sum of all costs, including profit, incurred in making surveys and tests, producing complete drawings and specifications for a project. Included are salaries and overhead for administration, drafting, purchasing, cost estimation and control, expediting, inspection, communications, and reproductions.

Engineering economics. The application of economic principles in determining the optimum engineering course to follow.

Engineering fee. Total payment to an engineering contractor; similar to architect's fee, includes profit.

Escalation. The provision in actual or estimated costs for an increase in the costs of equipment, material, labor, etc., over those specified in an original contract, due to continuing inflation, etc.

Factored estimate. See Order-of-magnitude estimate.

Feasibility study. Investigation of all phases of a proposal for investment or research, in as much detail as is necessary to decide whether to drop it or continue the expenses through the next stage of development.

Field expense. Any indirect costs incurred by the contractor during building of the facility.

Firm estimate. An estimate of project cost from final drawings, specifications, and site surveys, such as would be made by a lump-sum contractor for bid; confidence limits ± 5 per cent.

Fixed costs. The costs which continue whether a facility is operated or not; essentially fixed in dollars per year independent of production level. Include property taxes, insurance, some maintenance, and depreciation (a non-cash expense) in all cases. Some labor may also be considered a fixed cost for many purposes, particularly in continuous processes, as long as the plant does not shut down completely. Contrasted with "variable costs" (*q.v.*).

Force majeure. A clause in construction contracts which frees the contractor from any obligations imposed on him because of strikes, floods, catastrophes, national emergencies, etc.

Fringe benefits. The employee welfare benefits; expenses of employment over and above compensation for actual time worked, such as holidays, sick leave, etc.

Grass-roots plant. A complete plant erected on a virgin site. Investment includes all costs of land, site preparation, battery-limits facilities, and auxiliary facilities.

Guaranteed-maximum contract. A contract in which the contractor agrees to furnish material, construction equipment, and labor to erect a facility at cost plus a fixed fee, guaranteeing, however, that the total cost to the owner will not exceed a stipulated maximum.

Income. See Profit. May also be used to refer to profit before income taxes, or to gross income from sales before deduction of costs.

Income statement. The statement of earnings of the firm, as approximated by accounting practices. Usually covers a period of one year. Also called profit-and-loss statement.

Incremental approach (also called out-of-pocket approach). Cost estimating or accounting based on actual or expected changes in cash flows. Requires comparison of two alternative sets of conditions.

Indirect expense. (1) Fixed investment: engineering and construction expense, taxes, insurance, startup costs, and contractor's fees which cannot be charged directly to job cost centers. At job close-out, all indirect expenses are usually allocated on some reasonable basis to job cost centers. (2) Manufacturing costs: continuing expenses associated with manufacture but not directly assignable to process or product cost centers. Includes plant overheads, and sometimes certain costs which are usually considered as direct expenses but for which adequate cost records are unavailable.

Inflation index. A statistical time series which approximates the change in value of the dollar in a particular segment of the economy, usually based on an index of 100 for a given time. "Cost index."

Ingredients. The chemical raw materials entering the process; part or all of the chemical components of these appear in the product. Solvents, catalysts, and other chemicals which are used in the manufacture, but no part of which remains in the final product, are often considered separately, *e.g.*, as operating supplies. Usually valued at delivered cost to the buyer.

Insurance, property. The cost of obtaining financial protection to replace the value of a facility or other assets in case of loss or disablement.

Intangibles. Elements which affect the forecasts or project under consideration but which are not readily measurable in dollars.

Interest, compound. The mathematical expression of the principle that money can be used to earn more money, and therefore that values can be assumed to grow with time at a certain rate. The rate (expressed as per cent or decimal) at which a sum of money increases in value over each interval of time, usually one year. See Continuous interest.

Interest rate of return. The rate of compound nterest at which the company's outstanding investment is repaid by proceeds of the project. Also, the evaluation technique which judges the profitability of a proposed investment by this calculation. Also called investor's method, profitability index, internal rate of return.

Inventory. The supply on hand of raw materials, materials in process, and finished products required for plant operation and to supply sales requirements. Also, other supplies on hand, *i.e.*, for maintenance, catalyst, spare parts. An element of working capital.

Investor's method. See Interest rate of return.

Labor, operating. That portion of the labor cost in processing areas which can be definitely assigned to one product or process cost center. Usually excludes labor for maintenance, materials handling, and packaging.

Lump-sum contract. A contract in which the contractor agrees to furnish a completely erected facility at a given price. Variations may include a "turn-key" arrangement including performance guarantees.

Maintenance. The expense, for both labor and materials, required to keep a facility in suitably operable condition. Maintenance excludes major items which are not expensed within the year purchased and thus must be considered fixed capital.

Manufacturing costs. In the chemical process industries, the total of operating costs chargeable to manufacture of a given product, usually expressed in dollars per unit of production. Includes direct expenses such as ingredients, labor, utilities, and also such fixed or allocated charges as maintenance, depreciation (a non-cash expense), insurance, and property taxes. Overheads within the plant are usually considered as manufacturing costs; sales, administrative, and research overheads and freight are not usually so included.

Marginal cost. The incremental cost of making one additional unit of product without additional investment in facilities.

Minimum acceptable rate of return. The level of return on investment, at or above the cost of capital, chosen as acceptable for discounting or cutoff purposes.

Non-cash expense. A manufacturing or overhead expense, for accounting purposes, which does not require outlay of funds of that amount in that year.

Non-process equipment. The part of "auxiliary facilities" (*q.v.*) to which the word "equipment" can be applied. Includes utilities, shops, storage tanks and bins.

Obsolescence. The occurrence of decreasing value of physical assets due to technological changes rather than physical deterioration.

Off-site facilities. See Auxiliary facilities.

Operating costs. Usually a synonym for manufacturing costs (*q.v.*). More often used for costs expressed as dollars per year than as dollars per pound.

Opportunity cost. The estimate of values which are foregone by undertaking one alternative instead of another one. Usually, the value of a less attractive alternative.

Order-of-magnitude estimate. A quick estimate of fixed investment obtained without flow sheet or detailed equipment analysis by applying factors, ratios, and escalation to the known cost of an installation considered to be similar, or by applying "turnover ratio" (*q.v.*) concepts. The least accurate of the estimate types, on which no limits of accuracy can safely be applied.

Out-of-pocket costs. See Incremental aprpoach.

Overhead. Those costs in a manufacturing plant or firm which are not directly assignable to any one product or processing cost center and therefore must be allocated on some arbitrary basis or else handled as a business expense independent of volume of production.

Overhead, operating or plant. Those overheads within a plant area which are directly related to operations of the plant but are otherwise independent of production rate.

Payout time (payoff period, payback period). A measure of profitability or liquidity of an investment, defined as the time required to recover the original investment in depreciable facilities from profit and depreciation. Usually, but not always, taken after income taxes.

Physical life. The period over which a plant or piece of equipment could be or has been operated where shutdown is due to physical deterioration.

Preconstruction expenses. All those expenses, including engineering design, drafting, plant-location studies, and even research and development, which precede actual construction work on a new facility.

Preliminary estimate. See Study estimate.

Present worth (present value). Current value of cash flow(s) as obtained by discounting. Also, the investment-evaluation procedure which involves discounting at a specified interest rate (representing cost of capital or minimum acceptable rate of return) in order to choose the alternative having the highest present value.

Price, sales. The revenue received for a unit of product. *Gross sales* price is the nominal amount paid by the purchaser. *Net sales* price is obtained by subtracting returns, discounts, freight, and allowances from gross sales. *Plant netback* is obtained by subtracting selling, administrative, and research expenses from net sales.

Process equipment. All equipment and appurtenances employed in the actual manufacturing process. Usually, the equipment which lies within "battery limits" (*q.v.*).

Product life. See Economic life.

Profit. The accounting approximation of the earnings of a firm; total revenue less taxes, cash expenses, and certain non-cash expenses such as depreciation.

Profitability. A general term for the amount of profit achieved from a given situation. For a proposed investment, generally considered to be related to return on investment.

Profitability index. See Interest rate of return.

Project-control estimate. An estimate of fixed investment prepared from complete equipment lists, finished engineering flow sheets, frozen plot plans and general arrangements, together with reasonably complete site and auxiliary facilities information. Such estimates should fall within 10 per cent of the actual fixed investment and are in sufficient detail to be the basis for sound job cost control.

Property records. Coded records of installed cost of all plant property.

Proposed case. A course of action being considered which involves an investment, or the series of forecasts which quantify that course.

Rate of return on investment. The efficiency ratio relating profit or cash flow income to investment. See Return on original investment, Payout time, Interest rate of return, Present worth, etc.

Raw materials. See Ingredients.

Rental equipment. Equipment which is rented for use during the construction period, such as cranes, welders, earth-moving machinery.

Replacement. A new facility which takes the place of an older facility with no increase in capacity. A replacement which adds to capacity is considered as an expansion. Replacements are necessitated by either obsolescence or physical deterioration.

Return on average investment. The ratio of average annual profit over the earning life to the average book value of investment, with or without working capital.

Return on original investment. The ratio of average annual profit over the earning life to the original or total value of investment, usually including working capital.

Return on sales. The ratio of profits to total sales. Not generally considered a relevant criterion of investment profitability.

Salvage value. The value which can be realized from equipment or other facilities when taken out of use and sold to another firm. Usually assumed as zero in estimates, *i.e.*, offset by net removal costs.

Selling expense. Merchandising cost; the expense of getting the product purchased by and delivered to a customer, including processing of orders. Freight and other delivery costs are sometimes considered a selling expense, as may be customer service or market development expenses. (Not to be confused with "cost of sales," which usually means total manufacturing costs plus selling expense.)

Service facilities. See Auxiliary facilities.

Service life, useful. See Economic life.

Shared facilities. Productive facilities which are shared by various products; or non-productive facilities which are used by personnel, equipment, or supplies applicable to various products; the cost of such facilities must be allocated.

Site-preparation costs. The cost of preparing the plant site; includes grading, landscaping, roads, and rail-siding installation.

Six-tenths factor. An empirical relationship between cost and size of facility. According to this relationship, as facility size increases, its cost increases thus:

$$\frac{\text{Cost}_1}{\text{Cost}_2} = \left(\frac{\text{size}_1}{\text{size}_2}\right)^n$$

where exponent $n = 0.6$. An exponent of 0.7 is often equally applicable, and exponents of wide varieties may occur. Used in order-of-magnitude or study estimates.

Startup expense. Those non-recurring costs between completion of plant construction and the time when the plant is capable of operating at an acceptable level of capacity and costs. These expenses cover advance hiring of labor, minor alterations to equipment and piping, and extra costs of operation at other than acceptable conditions.

Stream days. "Time efficiency" (*q.v.*) expressed as operating days per year, allowing down time for maintenance and other foreseeable work stoppages.

Study estimate. An estimate of fixed investment costs prepared from a minimum of flow-sheet and equipment data; expected to be within 30 per cent of the actual fixed investment.

Sunk costs. Those current fixed costs (*q.v.*) that are related to past decisions and are therefore unaffected by current or future decisions. Also, the investment that caused the continuing costs.

Supervision. Pay-roll costs of supervisors and foremen assigned to a specific plant or process area.

Taxes. In a manufacturing cost statement, usually refers to property taxes. In an income statement, usually refers to Federal and state income taxes. Sales taxes must also be considered when applicable.

Terminal cash flow. Cash flow at end of economic life.

Time efficiency. The fraction of total time during which a facility is in productive operation. See Stream days.

Turn-key contract. See Lump-sum contract.

Turnover ratio. The ratio of annual sales to fixed investment in manufacturing facilities. Can be used for rough estimation of facilities cost or sales price for new products similar to existing products. Average is about 1.0 for chemical plants; range is extremely wide, however.

Unit cost. (1) Fixed investment: the cost of any class of work expressed in some convenient unit; *e.g.*, $60 per cubic yard for installing in-place block concrete. (2) Manufacturing cost: any fixed or variable cost expressed in dollars per unit of production.

Variable costs. Those elements of manufacturing costs which vary directly with volume of production, such as ingredients and utilities. Generally used in contrast to fixed costs (*q.v.*), which do not vary with production volume but are constant with time. Note that costs variable with production volume are fixed per unit of product, and that so-called fixed costs are variable per unit of product when allocated over unequal production quantities per unit time.

Venture worth. See Present worth.

FUNDAMENTALS OF INVESTMENT EVALUATION

A major function of the managers of a manufacturing enterprise is to maximize the long-term profit to the owners of the firm. While there are many measures used to judge the profitable growth of a firm, the soundest in principle seems to be the **maximization of profit in relation to investment employed.** Other measures such as return on sales, do not seem to be so directly related to maximizing the profit to the owners. Throughout this section it is assumed that return on investment is the proper way to judge investment profitability.

A decision to invest in fixed facilities carries with it the burden of continuing depreciation, insurance, taxes, maintenance costs, etc., and also reduces the fluidity of the company's future actions. Capital-investment decisions, therefore, must be made with great care.

The **over-all investment-decision problem** can be divided into three phases. First, it is necessary to determine what factors will affect the future profits from the proposed investment. Next, forecasts must be made of each of these factors. Last, these forecasts must be combined in a consistent, understandable fashion to indicate properly the profitability of each proposed capital investment relative to other investments.

Effect of an Investment. It can be usually assumed that the company will continue to operate, whether or not the investment is made, in forecasting the major elements of cash flow (such as profits and depreciation); some of these elements will be different, if the investment is undertaken, from what they would be if the investment were not made.

Since there are usually some profits in the "base case," even if no investment is made, it is obvious that all profits estimated in those forecasts which assume that the investment is undertaken cannot be used to justify the new investment. Any profits which would be achieved without the investment must first be deducted to arrive at the profits which are used to justify the investment. Only in the case of a new grass-roots plant making a new product might the base case involve no profits.

In general, every investment decision requires forecasts covering at least two alternative cases, one or more assuming an investment is made, and one assuming no investment. All factors significant to the company cash flows must be considered for all alternatives; those which change must be estimated in detail.

Alternatives. There are four basic alternative courses of action which must be considered in any investment decision; not all the alternatives may be applicable in any given case.

First, it is always possible to *withdraw from the business.* The occasion of a proposed major investment should be the time to examine over-all profitability before the area of activity is expanded. A forecast should be made of all losses in revenue and savings in costs from dropping the business.

The second alternative is to *let things alone,* but this does not mean everything will stay as it is. A forecast should be made of all cash flows for a period equal to the service life of the proposed investment. This is the **base case,** which does *not* accomplish the purpose of a proposed investment.

A third alternative is to undertake a *major rehabilitation program* without further investment. Again, the cost of such a program must be forecast for all factors. The fourth alternative, in general, is to *make an investment,* but the size and design of the facility should be chosen after economic balances and other considerations have been fully investigated.

Leasing of facilities might be added as a fifth alternative, but this is only a change in financing method and not in engineering activity. However, it may be proper in certain cases. A "next-best alternative" is a less desirable way of accomplishing the main purpose of an investment.

Where relevant, all the above alternatives should be considered in order of increasing company activity, measured by magnitude of company expenditures and risk. If only one alternative seems sufficiently profitable, it should be compared with going out of business completely. However, if the status quo set of forecasts is profitable (Case 2 above), it becomes a base case against which more expensive courses of action must be compared. Similarly, within the investment alternative (Case 4), differential investments must each be justified; so that the last **increment of investment** earns the minimum acceptable rate of return.

For further discussion see Weaver and Caplan [*Ind. Eng. Chem.*, **50** (2), 65A (1958)]. Choices among alternatives involving postponement of an investment are covered by Quigley and Weaver [*Ind. Eng. Chem.*, **52** (11), 57A (1960)].

When presenting an appropriation request, coverage of all possible alternatives is too complex. In general, the proposed investment, as finally chosen by economic balance, is compared with the cash flows forecast without investment (Case 2).

FACTORS WHICH AFFECT PROFITABILITY OF INVESTMENTS

Table 26-1 provides a **check list** of items which can affect the profitability of an investment. It is important to note the significance of each item on the proposed investment. Available analytical time can then be spent on those areas of greatest concern.

Table 26-1. Factors Which Influence the Profitability of Investments

	Possible accuracy of forecast	Usual effect of possible error
Installed cost of fixed investment	Good	Major
Working capital	Fair	Major
Construction period	Good	Minor
Initial startup expense	Fair	Intermediate
Sales-volume forecast	Poor	Major
Product-price forecast	Poor	Major
Cost stream over the project life	Good (direct), fair (overheads)	Major
Economic life	Poor	Intermediate
Depreciation life	Good	Intermediate
Salvage value	Poor	Minor
Depreciation method	*	Intermediate
Minimum acceptable rate of return	*	*
Income-tax rate	Poor	Major
Inflation rates	Poor	Major
Risk	Poor	Major
General business conditions	Fair	Intermediate

* Policy choices, not forecasts.

These elements, like many facts of life, exist whether or not they are recognized when an investment is planned. Some implicit assumption must take the place of any of the elements not forecast in detail.

Installed Cost of Fixed Investment. This is probably the most obvious item to be forecast before an investment decision is made. Any level of knowledge about a process will permit some kind of estimate of the cost of the fixed investment in place and ready to run. Accuracy can be improved by further process development and estimating effort.

Working Capital. In order to finance the operation of any facility properly, additional funds must be held as cash or invested in inventories. The amount of such **liquid investment** is generally a function of production volume and therefore should be estimated at various production levels. Individual company policies will have a considerable effect on inventories, accounts receivable, etc. Working capital is usually an important factor, and added analytical time improves accuracy of estimates.

Construction Period. Every capital investment in new facilities involves some delay in realization of income because of construction time. The extent of this delay should be estimated. (Acquisition of a going business, one type of investment on which analysis is often required, should involve no construction period at all.)

Estimates of construction time are fairly accurate, and the effect of errors in such an estimate is relatively minor.

Initial Startup Expense. In the initial operation of a new facility, expenses are usually higher than would be considered normal. The extent of such unusual expenses should be estimated. With a well-known process, they should be relatively minor, but a new process may require weeks or months to determine optimum operating conditions. Other startup expenses include early hiring of the labor force (before they can be used in production), initial repair expenses, and alterations to smooth out the operation or interrelation of equipment. This is a significant expenditure which can be forecast fairly well, except for relatively new processes.

Sales-volume Forecast. Product-price Forecast. These two items could be combined into a forecast of "revenue stream" over the project life, but they are separated here to show that product price must be forecast as well as sales volume (in some cases the two may depend upon one another). This is not primarily an engineering function. However, achievement of these forecasts is perhaps the most important factor in determining the success of an investment. Unfortunately, this is an area not yet subject to scientific analysis, and expenditure of effort soon reaches the point of diminishing returns.

Cost Stream over Project Life. Techniques for estimating direct manufacturing cost are available, and reasonable estimates can be made with enough investigation and estimating effort. It is more difficult to estimate the changes in overheads which will result from a given investment, although the magnitude of overhead costs often makes them critical to the investment decision.

As part of the cost stream, prices of raw materials must also be forecast. The same limitations apply to raw-material price forecasts as to end-product price forecasts.

Economic Life. This term refers to the most likely period of successful operation before any need for subsequent significant investment in additional equipment as the result of product or process obsolescence or equipment deterioration. There are no good methods for accurately forecasting economic life because technological changes are generally unpredictable. However, since the effects are in the distant future, the uncertainty in a forecast of economic life is not critical. It is probably best to assume a single standard life (between 10 and 15 years) for most projects.

Effective Depreciation Life of Depreciable Fixed Investment. Tax authorities will not necessarily agree that depreciable equipment life is synonymous with economic life defined above. For tax purposes equipment life is judged by rather arbitrary standards, under recent U.S. laws. If the allowable depreciation life is different from the project life, cash flows to the project will be affected. Different parts of the investment may be allowed different depreciation lives; the estimate of profitability should take any significant differences into account.

Salvage Value of Fixed Investment. This is a relatively minor factor for normal project lives but may be very difficult to forecast. The usual expedient is to assume zero salvage value; *i.e.*, any value is only sufficient to cancel the cost of removal of the equipment.

Depreciation Method to Be Applied. This and the following item depend chiefly on company policy. These factors should be established before an investment is made if its profitability is to be forecast properly.

Income-tax laws permit recovery of funds by two accelerated depreciation schedules (declining-balance and sum-of-the-years-digits) as well as by straight-line methods. Because cash-flow timing is affected, choice of depreciation method affects profitability significantly.

Minimum Acceptable Rate of Return. No matter what method is used for expressing profitability, there must be some reasonable standard against which to compare estimated profitability. Some profitability methods assume such a standard in their derivations.

Several good references are available on this subject: Dean ("Capital Budgeting," Columbia, New York, 1951); Happel ("Chemical Process Economics," Wiley, New York, 1958); Soldofsky [*Controller*, **26**, 263 (June, 1958)]; Soule [*Harvard Bus. Rev.*, **31**, 33 (1953)]; Weaver [*Ind. Eng. Chem.*, **50** (12), 65A (1958)].

In general, companies have, wisely or unwisely, a minimum acceptable rate of return fairly clearly in mind. This need not be a positive single figure but rather a range which is used in order to take into account variations among projects such as growth potential, assurance of market, and other risk factors.

Income-tax Rate. Four final items depend on circumstances completely beyond the engineer's or the company's control. Nevertheless they must be considered if profitability of the project is to be forecast correctly.

Income taxes apply differently to projects with different proportions of fixed and working capital, etc. Profitability should therefore be based on income after taxes, and some tax rate must be assumed for the project life. State income taxes should be considered as well as Federal income taxes and are probably easier to forecast on a logical basis.

Inflation. Inflation affects differently almost every item of manufacturing cost. Ideally, each should be forecast separately. Labor costs, construction cost, raw material and energy prices, product prices—each of these is subject to inflation at different rates (where the rate is negative, the effect is deflationary).

The implicit assumption usually made in profitability estimates is that all items (often including the sales price of the product) will inflate at equal rates, so that net income will not be affected. While this assumption is unrealistic, few steps for improvement on it can be suggested until better methods have been developed for inflation forecasts.

Tables 26-2 and 26-3 present information on various **inflation indexes,** and growth rates for some of these, for recent years. The following references describe the bases for key indexes: *Engineering News-Record*, annual report on construction costs, usually issued in October; *Factory* [**112,** 113 (January, 1954)], annual updating in January issues; Nelson [*Oil Gas J.*, **53,** 132 (Apr. 11); **54,** 122 (July 4); 146 (Oct. 3, 1955)], detailed indexes updated in first issue each quarter; Marshall and Stevens [*Chem. Eng.*, **54,** (11), 124 (1947)], updated quarterly; *Chem. Eng.* [**70,** (4), 143 (1963)], updated monthly.

Risks differ between projects which might seem otherwise equal on the basis of the best estimates of all required elements. The risk will depend on the process used, whether well established or a complete innovation; on the product to be made, whether it is a staple item of commerce or a completely new product; on the sales forecast, whether all sales will be outside the company or whether a significant fraction is internal; etc.

Means for incorporating different levels of risk into profitability forecasts are not well established. The most common methods are to raise the minimum acceptable rate of return for the riskier projects or to apply to final cash flows a probability multiplier which is supposed to represent the likelihood of their achievement. While neither of these methods is felt to express properly the over-all sensitivity of a project to risk [Cleveland, *Eng. Economist*, **3,** 1 (winter, 1958)], it is essential to realize

Table 26-2. Inflation Indexes

	Price indexes[a]					Construction cost indexes					Miscellaneous indexes			
	Consumer	Wholesale commodity (all)	Total chem. and allied inds.	Ind. chem.	Nat. gas[i]	Chem.[b] equip.	Proc. plants[j]	Refinery[c]	Construct.[d]	Bldg.[d]	Rail freight[e]	Maintenance cost[f]	Pay roll[g]	Fringe benefit[h]
1926	...	...	...	...	...	100	...	72	208	185				
1927	...	...	...	...	...	100	...	...	206	186				
1928	...	...	...	...	...	96	...	71	207	188				
1929	73	62	...	84	...	92	...	72	207	191				
1930	71	56	...	82	...	82	...	70	203	185				
1931	65	47	...	76	...	78	...	65	181	168				
1932	58	42	...	75	...	78	...	57	157	141				
1933	55	43	51	73	...	71	...	57	170	148				
1934	57	49	54	73	...	75	...	63	198	167				
1935	59	52	56	75	...	78	...	63	196	166				
1936	59	52	56	74	...	82	...	67	206	172				
1937	61	56	59	74	...	88	...	75	235	196				
1938	60	51	56	73	...	84	...	77	236	197				
1939	59	50	56	72	...	83	...	77	236	197				
1940	60	51	57	72	...	84	...	78	242	203				
1941	63	57	62	74	...	93	...	80	258	211				
1942	70	64	69	81	...	102	...	84	276	222				
1943	74	67	70	82	...	103	...	87	290	289				
1944	75	68	70	81	...	106	...	88	299	235				
1945	77	69	71	81	...	106	...	90	308	239	100			
1946	83	79	76	84	...	127	...	100	346	262	109			
1947	96	96	101	99	97	152	65	117	413	313	128	100	95	100
1948	103	104	104	105	101	164	70	133	461	345	150	109	104	
1949	102	99	95	96	102	164	71	140	477	352	163	111	101	128
1950	103	103	96	101	99	170	74	146	510	376	167	117	110	
1951	111	115	110	121	104	181	80	157	543	401	172	131	131	165
1952	114	112	104	115	109	181	81	164	569	416	186	135	136	
1953	114	110	106	118	116	183	85	174	600	431	190	141	151	193
1954	115	110	107	118	118	186	86	180	628	446	190	144	151	
1955	114	111	107	118	124	192	88	184	660	469	190	150	163	230
1956	116	114	107	121	128	209	94	195	692	491	198	160	175	
1957	120	118	110	124	129	226	98	206	724	509	212	167	182	283
1958	124	119	110	124	...	232	100	214	759	525	...	170	179	
1959	125	119	110	124	...	236	102	222	797	548	...	176	195	312
1960	126	120	110	124	...	239	102	228	824	559	...	180	205	
1961	128	119	109	122	...	238	102	233	847	568	...	183	210	346
1962	129	119	107	119	...	238	102	237	871	580	...	186	221	

[a] Bureau of Labor Statistics, 1947–1949 = 100.
[b] Marshall and Stevens, *Chem. Eng.*, 1926 = 100.
[c] Nelson, *Oil Gas J.*, 1946 = 100.
[d] *Eng. News-Record*, 1913 = 100.
[e] I.C.C. data, 1945 = 100. Based on general percentage increases in class commodity rates; increases since 1957 not comparable.
[f] *Factory*, 1947 = 100.
[g] Department of Labor data (average hourly earnings), 1947–1949 = 100.
[h] Chamber of Commerce data for 92 companies, 1947 = 100.
[i] Series discontinued after 1957.
[j] *Chem. Eng.*, 1957–1959 = 100.

qualitatively, at least, the differences in risk among projects being considered. By incorporating subjective probability ranges in input cost estimates, their effect on risk can be quantified [Gore, *Petrol. Refiner*, **37**, 142 (June, 1958); Hicks and Steffens, *Chem. Eng. Progress*, **52**, 191 (May, 1956); Schlaifer, "Probability and Statistics for Business Decisions," McGraw-Hill, New York, 1959].

Table 26-3. Growth Rates of Inflation Indexes

Inflation index	Max. span		Growth rates, %/year		
	Term	%/year	1948–1957	1953–1957	1956–1957
Consumer price	29–57	2.9	2.7	1.0	3.4
Wholesale commodity	29–57	3.9	1.5	1.6	2.9
Total chemical and allied industries	33–57	3.8	1.2	1.0	2.2
Industrial chemicals	29–57	2.0	2.4	1.5	1.7
Natural gas	47–57	3.3	3.3	3.4	0.9
M. & S. chemical equipment	26–57	3.4	3.3	5.4	8.1
Cnem. Eng. process plant costs	47–57	4.0	3.8	3.4	4.9
Nelson refinery construction	28–57	4.5	4.9	4.5	5.6
E.N.R. construction	26–57	4.9	5.3	4.8	4.6
E.N.R. building	26–57	4.0	4.5	4.4	3.7
Freight rate	45–57	5.7	3.4	2.9	7.0
Maintenance cost	47–57	4.9	4.2	4.6	4.7
Chemical and allied products pay roll	47–57	6.8	6.8	5.2	4.0
Fringe benefits	47–57	10.7	10.1*	10.1	10.5†

* 1949–1957.
† 1955–1957.

General Business Conditions. Over-all economic climate will have an effect on the level of investment by most companies. It is not suggested here that detailed forecasts be made of business cycles over the economic life of the project, but it is useful to recall this element at the time of investment in case the economy is obviously entering a period of recession. Investment capital may become more difficult to obtain in the short term, and revenues from the project in its first period of operation may be decreased by a recession.

CASH FLOW CONCEPTS

Time Value of Money. Money can be put to work as soon as it is available to earn interest. Where profitable investments are sought, the sooner cash is earned, the sooner it can itself be invested elsewhere to start earning a return. Conversely, the longer cash must be invested before it starts earning a profit, the less beneficial it is to the owner.

Time value of money has been integrated into investment-evaluation systems by means of **compound-interest relationships.** Dollars, at different times, are given different degrees of importance by means of compounding or discounting at some compound-interest rate. For any assumed interest value of money, a known amount at any one time can be converted to an equivalent but different amount at a different time. As time passes, money can be invested to increase at the interest rate. If the time when money is needed for investment is in the future, the present value of that investment can be calculated by discounting from the time of investment back to the present at the assumed interest rate.

Various references give detailed descriptions of compound-interest calculations (Grant, Schweyer, *op. cit.*). See Sec. 1, pp. 1-32–1-38, for tables to facilitate calculation of compound interest, amount of an annuity, and present value of an annuity, using annual compounding, as well as further discussion here (p. 26-39).

Determining the Fixed Investment Base. In most cases, the individual investment is only part of the company's total capital. Therefore, the making of any particular investment at a given time is a matter of choice; the company will continue to operate whether the investment is made or not. Most new investments are intended to cause an increase in the amount of future profits and other inflows of cash which the company can expect. The investment is considered justified only if it increases these future cash flows by enough to provide an adequate return on a new investment. Therefore, the engineer is seldom concerned only with single forecasts of fixed investment, working capital, manufacturing costs, sales volume and price, etc. These elements must be forecast for the situation in which the investment is to be made. It is just as essential to forecast all the same cash flows in the situation where the investment is *not* made. The difference can then be used to justify the investment.

Productive Facilities. If a new, fixed investment is to be made at a completely new plant site, and a group of balanced facilities is installed (process equipment, auxiliaries, and administrative buildings) which are designed to make next year's expected sales and no more, the amount of fixed investment to be used in an economic analysis is clearly defined However. most real situations are more complicated Most investments are not made at new plant sites but are integrated with existing facilities already in use. Existing equipment, buildings, and also personnel may be shared by the new installation.

There is no question that such available facilities have considerable value in many cases. That value must be considered in investment evaluations. However, it does not seem proper to do this by adding a dollar amount to the actual new fixed investment required, so that the new project will "pay for its share" of the available facilities at the plant. Instead, the value of the existing investment should be reflected in the cash flows it can produce for the firm.

The new investment should be justified by creating an increase in cash flows. If existing facilities contribute to the increase, it is certainly advantageous to use them. However, if use of existing facilities with this new investment forces one to forego other profitable opportunities for using these facilities, this should be reflected by reducing the differential estimated cash flow. Other alternative uses of the facilities, and the profits otherwise expected to accrue therefrom, are deducted from the profit to be earned by the proposed investment as part of the base case. The new investment does not get a "free ride" on the existing capacity, since it pays the "lost opportunity" costs (see p. 26-10).

In the case of productive facilities, then, which are justified by profitability concepts, the value of alternative use of existing equipment should be considered in determining the cash-flow streams in the investment and no-investment cases. No value for the existing investment should be included in the denominator of the return-on-investment formula as part of the investment base.

Non-productive Facilities. The above conclusions concerning existing investment in productive facilities do not necessarily hold for the considerable amount of non-productive facilities needed at every manufacturing plant. This includes not only administrative buildings, roads, fences, etc., but equipment (such as steam boilers) which is generally useful throughout the plant and yet which cannot be justified on the basis that it will produce a profitable product for sale. Investments made for safety reasons or for community welfare are also in this category.

Many companies choose to assume that growth will continue at any given plant and, therefore, utility systems must be provided and expanded at a rate similar to that of the plant, but separate from any particular investment in productive facilities. A similar assumption is applicable to administrative buildings, etc.

Some decision must then be reached and followed consistently as to how the profit earned by the company on the *profit-making* facilities will be adequate to support all these *non-productive* investments. There are several systems for doing this.

One method, particularly applicable to utilities, is to charge the utility product (such as steam or compressed air) into other areas of the plant, and into new investment evaluations, not at manufacturing cost, but at a **transfer price** high enough to show an acceptable rate of return on the utility investment. Although this is somewhat in conflict with the "incremental-cost" concept (see below), it seems a reasonable compromise. It corresponds to a common means for "pricing" materials transferred between divisions of a company.

Another system used by companies employing discounting in their rate-of-return calculations is to consider how much any one new productive investment would **advance the time** when a new service facility might otherwise be required. This could also apply to administrative buildings, change houses, etc. The proposed investment is then considered to be the reason for advancing the time of this investment from, say, 4 years to 2 years hence. The estimated service-facility investment is therefore charged against this investment proposal for the second and third years only. It is obvious that such forecasts become largely judgments as to growth rate on the plant, which, in turn, depends partly on the justification of individual projects.

A third method of handling non-productive facilities, applicable to all other non-profitable investments, is to require a **high enough minimum acceptable rate of return** on the profitable investments to return a satisfactory profit on the total amount of investment for the company.

The choice among these alternative methods of handling such facilities is up to the company; the main requirement is that some consistent system be used which takes account of these facilities in the over-all profit picture. Any of these is acceptable; on the other hand, it seems improper to solve this problem by increasing the amount of the investment to be justified (the denominator) to reflect utilization of existing investment.

Sunk Costs and Incremental Costs. An investment made in the past is generally considered a "sunk cost." Any dollar value ascribed to existing investment (whether original, book, or replacement value) is almost irrelevant to future cash flows of any sort (one exception is in the timing of tax recoveries when assets are abandoned), but the "value" of existing investment itself should not affect the decision to make new investments.

However, certain costs do continue because of the existence of that investment. In general, these are fixed manufacturing costs: taxes, insurance, depreciation, maintenance, etc.

Whether any new investment is made or not, these fixed costs will continue unchanged. Some new costs will be added by the proposed new investment, but there will be no change in the costs of the existing investment even though some of it is utilized in connection with the new facilities. This is true even though the later accounting representation of product costs will allocate some of the continuing costs of the existing investment to the new product. Changes in cost accounting after an investment is made should not hide the fact that some costs are unaffected by the investment decision, while other costs are created or changed by the decision. The real problem is to investigate and estimate properly which ones will continue unchanged and which will change.

The new investment would get a "free ride" if it utilized existing facilities at no charge. However, proper analysis of alternatives will give a new investment a "free ride" on the old investment only if there is *no other alternative use* of the idle capacity in the existing investment anywhere in prospect. If there is some other potential use for this now idle capacity, the cash-flow stream in the no-investment case should include these uses, valued at sales less cost, as an offset against the profits in the proposed investment case.

Overhead Costs. In new investment justification, overhead ratios, properly developed for cost-accounting purposes, are sometimes used as a crutch in estimating the costs which will obtain after the new investment is made. If part of an existing plant is being expanded so that its total labor force will be doubled, one easy way to estimate costs is to assume that the overhead costs now allocated to that portion of the plant (based on direct labor) will also be doubled. However, in keeping with the principle that investments should be justified only on the basis of those costs and profits which will really change because of the investments, such an allocation of overheads usually warrants a closer look.

There may be no immediate addition of *any* more overhead staff in the plant—or there may be some ascertainable small number of employees (one foreman, perhaps, and one clerk) who will be added to the overhead staff because of a given expansion. Only the costs which will really change should be allocated to the expanded plant in justifying the new investment, regardless of cost-accounting procedures.

After the investment is made, the accounting books cannot follow this system of allocation; it would become hopelessly confused. The information needed for decision making, however, is completely different from that needed to keep track of historical costs. The accountant will allocate a fair share of overhead to this expanded portion of the plant. However, if the total overhead costs have increased by only some small portion of this total, an additional effect of the accounting allocation is that every other product made in the plant receives a *smaller* allocation of continuing overheads. The net difference must be only the true addition.

This general approach to applying costs to an investment decision is often called the **incremental** or **out-of-pocket approach.** It does not use existing accounting overhead allocations but looks at the actual forecast of increased costs of overhead after a new investment has been undertaken.

As with the non-allocation of existing investment value or fixed costs, the complaint of the "free ride" is often made concerning such an approach. Again, it is clear that this is a "free ride" only if a good forecast shows *no increases* in overhead personnel and equipment due to a given investment for the entire life of the product resulting from that investment. If an increase can be foreseen, a proper incremental analysis would include it. There should be no more likelihood that such forecasts of costs will be understated than that any other such forecast is optimistic.

In the area of gradually increasing overhead costs, it is often difficult or impossible, however, to allocate the addition of a clerk or a calculating machine to any particular expansion in the plant. Overhead costs tend to creep up almost independent of particular investment decisions. It is through this concept that some find it best to assume that every new investment causes an increase in overhead, which is only separately recognizable on larger increments of investment. If such a relationship can be shown from cost records—the addition of a certain fraction of overhead related in some way to plant expansion—this could become a proper way of making a good cost estimate of the necessary additional overhead.

Opportunity Costs. The incremental approach, properly applied, will always give the correct analysis on investments. However, a careless approach to incremental evaluation can result in a jeopardizing of present profits, establishment of unsound prices on new products, and development of a situation where future expansions are uneconomic. All these may occur if "opportunity costs" are not properly incorporated into the forecasts of base-case cash flows.

Opportunity cost (better identified as "lost-opportunity cost") refers to the cost or values which are given up because the proposed investment is undertaken (usually, therefore, the base case). The profit from production in obsolescent facilities is an "opportunity cost" of replacing them with more efficient ones. The use of idle capacity (in either equipment or personnel) for one purpose may prevent its use for some other, presumably less profitable purpose—an opportunity cost.

The cautions which follow deal with determination of proper base-case opportunity costs in two situations: (1) when considering the installation of facilities for upgrading a chemical intermediate to an end product, and (2) in the justification of savings projects.

Upgrading Facilities. If cost of manufacture of an intermediate chemical is compared exclusively with the sale price of the end product in evaluation of proposed upgrading facilities, these individual investments can be justified as incrementally profitable. The danger exists in that future expansion of facilities for manufacturing the intermediate may turn out to be unprofitable when present capacity becomes inadequate.

When manufactured materials are proposed for upgrading in a new facility, the estimated profitability of the new facility will depend on the value attributed to the intermediate in the base case. The true opportunity cost is the proper level. Thus if there is another profitable outlet for the intermediate, the profit in that outlet should be recognized in the base case and deducted from profits in the proposed case. If there is no other outlet for the intermediate, and if idle capacity for it exists up to the total capacity of the proposed new installation, then no profit would be realized in the base case. In this situation, the total profit in the proposed case represents the proper incremental profit for use in the evaluation.

For an existing product with an established or predictable price, the incremental procedure described above will always determine whether or not the upgrading investment should be made. However, for strategic reasons, it may also be useful to determine before proceeding with this investment whether or not future expansion of both the intermediate and upgrading facilities would be profitable, at the same derivative price level, when capacity is reached. Although the upgrading facility may itself be well justified incrementally, it may not allow profitable expansion. Over-all profitability can be determined by a hypothetical return-on-investment calculation on the entire facility. This may indicate that the expansion is an interim measure which will increase current profit but will not add to the company's long-term growth.

Pricing for Adequate Return. If a novel product is to be made in the upgrading facility, there is wide latitude in its possible pricing. At a given price, the profit available to justify the facility will be a function of whether or not the intermediate could be sold at a profit in the base case. In setting prices on such new products, it is advisable to anticipate the need for expansion by establishing an economic price level based on the assumption that the intermediate has a value above manufacturing cost. If no established market price exists for the intermediate, total manufacturing cost plus an acceptable return on the existing investment could be used to set a "price" as an opportunity cost of the intermediate.

An alternative method is to indicate the need to make some profit on existing facilities. The end product essentially is allocated a share of the investment in intermediate facilities. The price calculation is made as if an investment in existing facilities were required at the same time as the investment in proposed facilities. A share of the cost on the existing facilities as well as the investment in them would be utilized in calculating the derivative price.

Calculation of price by either of these methods will establish what can be thought of as a **long-range economic price** needed to give an acceptable rate of return. This price, of course, can be modified if it seems expedient to do so in a specific situation. In a strong market a higher price might be charged. If considerable excess capacity exists for the intermediate, a lower price may be charged for the derivative to establish its place in the market quickly. This should be done knowing that, when facilities need to be expanded, the price might have to be raised to make the expansion profitable.

The methods described above are comparable with some of the methods frequently used for charging of utilities into manufacturing operations, when justifying productive facilities or pricing products. Some companies charge utilities at cost plus a minimum rate of return; others require that the investment base of the proposed facility be increased by some share of the utility investment.

Upgrading after Savings Project. In savings projects the forecast of sales revenue is the same in both the base and proposed cases. Increased profits needed to justify the investment result from decreased manufacturing costs in the proposed case compared with the base case.

However, as soon as the new, lower cost appears on the accounting books, it furnishes an incentive to process the product further in some sort of upgrading facilities, whereas the previous cost did not permit justification of such facilities.

The upgrading project must again be compared against a base case. If there is no outlet for the intermediate without upgrading, the proper base case involves no sales, and incremental costs for the intermediate can be used in the justification. The same cautions concerning pricing and expansion will then apply as in the previous example.

However, the new cost structure may open up profitable outlets for the intermediate. Unless the base case shows this potential profit (equivalent to pricing some or all of the intermediate at market value), a mistake may be made in investing in facilities, even though they show a good return over cost.

The above discussion points up the need for considering, when an investment is evaluated, any subsequent upgrading facilities required to dispose of the forecast volume used to justify that investment. In fact, the future facilities should usually be justified in principle at the time of the initial investment to avoid the diluting effect of subsequent incremental justifications needed to achieve the forecast. If further upgrading of part of the intermediate material does not show a good return on investment, capacity of the basic investment should be reduced by that extent.

Every investment must be made at a certain time, under a certain set of circumstances. The use of incremental concepts properly ignores past decisions and considers only future alternatives, forecasting the cash flows expected to result in each alternative. Nevertheless, it is useful to think about the whole succession of investment decisions in a way that will make clear any impingement of one decision on profitability of earlier or subsequent investments. This will help avoid fallacious patterns of decision sequences and fallacious conclusions about achievement of forecasts critical to profitability.

KEY CASH FLOW ITEMS

Depreciation. The cost of a chemical plant which is expected to be used for 15 years cannot logically be considered as an expense to be fully charged against the revenues realized in the year in which the plant was built or purchased. That year's income would be disproportionately low, and succeeding years would show exaggerated profits.

Instead of charging the cost of the plant as an expense in the year of purchase, a portion of its cost is charged against revenues each year throughout its useful life. Depreciation then is a *periodic charge against revenues that distributes the first cost of a fixed asset over its expected service life.* It is not a fund received and set aside to replace equipment.

Non-cash Expense. Depreciation expense, unlike most expenses, entails no current outlay of cash. This means that, in addition to the net reported profit in a given accounting period, a firm has available the additional funds corresponding to the depreciation expense which was included when figuring net income but which did not require an outlay of cash. This cash is **capital recovery,** a partial regeneration of the first cost of fixed assets. It is as available for use as is any other accumulated cash.

If there is no depreciation,

$$I = R - E \qquad (26\text{-}1)$$

where I = income of period, say 1 year; R = revenues of period; E = expenses of period involving cash outlay. (This series of calculations assumes a positive income.)

If there is depreciation,

$$I = R - E - D \qquad (26\text{-}2)$$

where D = annual depreciation charge.

However, since D does not involve a cash expense, the **total cash flow** is

$$CF = I + D = R - E \qquad (26\text{-}3)$$

where CF = annual cash flow to company.

In a no-tax situation, depreciation expense would not affect funds within the corporation. Without taxes there would be no reason for government regulation of depreciation accounting.

Depreciation owes its importance to the government regulations regarding income taxes. Assuming a Federal tax rate t of 52 per cent on corporate income, and no depreciation, the after-tax profit is represented by

$$P = (1 - t)(R - E) = 0.48(R - E) \tag{26-4}$$

where P = after-tax profit of period. Each $1 of such business expense E, involving a cash outlay, thus reduces profit by $0.48.

Consider the dollar which can be reported as an expense for tax purposes although no cash outlay is involved. Like other expenses, each such dollar reduces before-tax income by $1 and reduces after-tax profit by $0.48. However, since each such dollar is still available to be spent, the net effect is to add $0.52 to company funds, as follows:

$$CF = P + D = 0.48(R - E - D) + D = 0.48(R - E) + 0.52D \tag{26-5}$$

Because it is able to charge depreciation against revenues, a company has available, after taxes, more funds than it would otherwise have had. The incremental increase in funds available is equal to t per cent of the depreciation charge.

Setting Depreciation Life. As might be expected, the United States government regulates the deduction for depreciation, since it directly affects income taxes paid by a corporation and corporate profits reported to stockholders. Until 1962, depreciation lives for tax purposes had a real meaning in terms of the physical lives of the individual pieces of equipment. The 1962 revision of the tax procedures introduced "guidelines" which put all equipment in a manufacturing plant into a single depreciation-life category. Eleven years is the standard life for chemical plant equipment; the only elements excluded are office furniture and fixtures (10 years), ground transportation equipment (3–6 years), office and factory buildings (45 years), and warehouses (60 years). Salvage values were considered in setting the life for chemical plant equipment, and tax deductions can no longer be taken for units of equipment which are scrapped before the end of the eleven-year life. Details are contained in Revenue Procedure 62-21 (July, 1962), Project No. 456, U.S. Treasury Department, obtainable from the Superintendent of Documents.

Guideline lives for associated industries are: cement, 20 years; fabricated metal products, 12 years; food products, 12 years; glass and glass products, 14 years; leather and leather products, 11 years; paper and allied products, 16 years; petroleum refining, 16 years; plastics products, 11 years; primary metals, 14 years (nonferrous), 18 years (ferrous); rubber products, 14 years; stone and clay products, 15 years; sugar and sugar products, 18 years; vegetable oil products, 18 years.

Straight-line Method. There are different methods for spreading the first cost of an asset over the estimated asset life. The simplest of these is the straight-line method, which distributes the cost of the asset uniformly over its depreciable life thus:

$$D = \frac{F - L}{n} \tag{26-6}$$

where F = initial asset cost; L = expected salvage value at end of useful asset life; n = estimated useful asset life in years.

Declining-balance Method. Salvage or liquidation value of an asset decreases much more sharply in the early years than late in its life. Two major methods of depreciation accounting reflect this by charging off most of an asset's value early in its life. Book value at any time is then more likely to represent the salvage value of the asset, and expenses charged in early years will more nearly reflect the annual decrease in value.

In the declining-balance method a constant percentage of the remaining book value is written off each year, as

$$D = \frac{k(F - CD)}{n} \tag{26-7}$$

where CD = cumulative depreciation charged in prior years; k = a constant equal to 1 in basic method, value up to 1.5 allowed up to 1954; value up to 2.0 permitted since 1954 ("double declining balance").

For a plant with a 20-year useful life and an original cost of $1,000,000, the double-declining-balance depreciation ($k = 2.0$) for the first year is 2.0 ($1,000,000)/20 or $100,000; for the second year it would be 2.0 ($1,000,000 − $100,000)/20 or $90,000.

This is a geometric progression which would never provide for complete depreciation of the plant. The Internal Revenue Service therefore allows—with certain limitations—a switch to the straight-line method in order to reach a point where $(F - CD)$ is zero.

Sum-of-years-digits Method. Another method which charges depreciation at a decreasing rate is the sum-of-the-years-digits method. This and the double-declining-balance method ($k = 2.0$) were authorized for use beginning in 1954 on new assets with lives of 3 or more years. Sum-of-the-years-digits method (SYD) is an arithmetic progression which results in completely charging off the initial cost during estimated useful life.

The basic SYD method involves numbering the years of life in order and summing these numbers (years digits). The depreciation rate for each year is then found by multiplying the original asset cost by a fraction. The denominator of the fraction is the sum of the years digits; the numerators are the numbers of the years in reverse order. For example, for a piece of equipment with a 5-year life, the denominator would be 15 (the sum of numbers 1 through 5), and the numerators would be 5, 4, 3, 2, and 1 for years 1 through 5, respectively.

SYD depreciation can be expressed mathematically as

$$D_y = \frac{2(n - y + 1)}{n(n + 1)} \tag{26-8}$$

where y = consecutive year number from start of venture.

These three methods, straight-line, declining-balance, and sum-of-the-years-digits, and variations of them form the basis for most current depreciation procedures.

Relative Advantages of Methods. The same total depreciation allowance is achieved by any method—they all recover the first cost of the asset (after taxes, 52 per cent of the cost). In general, accelerated methods seem preferable from a cash-flow viewpoint since they bring in a higher proportion of these dollars sooner. The effect on reported earnings should also be considered; accelerated methods decrease reported earnings in early years.

For further discussion of depreciation, see Grant and Norton, ("Depreciation," rev. ptg., Ronald, New York, 1955); Herr ("Depreciation Tables," Fallon, New York, 1954); Norton [*Eng. Economist*, **1**, 1 (spring, 1956)].

Federal and State Income Taxes. Inasmuch as income taxes take about 50 per cent of corporate profits, it would seem that profitability studies would not need to consider such a simple divisor of 2, because it would cancel out in the comparisons of all possible alternatives. This is not the case, as explained below, and the following discussion concerns the ways and the cases for which they should be considered.

Depreciable Investments. Depreciation allowance is the element in profitability comparisons which is the most sensitive to income-tax considerations. Depending on the ratio of depreciable to non-depreciable assets involved, two projects which look equivalent before taxes, or rank in one order, may rank entirely differently when considered after taxes. Though cash costs and sales values may be equal on two projects, their reported net incomes for tax purposes will be different, and one will generate more cash than the other.

State income taxes must be considered as well as Federal. Such taxes are sometimes mutually deductible; their rates cannot be simply added to achieve a proper rate. To call attention to state taxes, 54 per cent total tax rate rather than 52 per cent Federal tax is used in the examples.

Sample Cases. Table 26-4 shows three hypothetical alternative investments which a company might face at a single time. Each involves an initial investment of $100,000. Investment *A* is completely in buildings and equipment. Investment *B* includes 50 per cent equipment and 50 per cent inventory. Investment *C* is entirely land and inventory, which cannot be depreciated. Each is assumed to result in identical added sales to the company and also identical added costs which require cash outlay. However, assuming 10 years straight-line depreciation, investment *A* would be allowed to report $10,000 of depreciation each year, and investment *B* would be allowed $5000 per year, while investment *C* receives no such allowance.

Table 26-4. Influence of Taxes on Relative Profitability

Dollars in thousands

	Investment *A*, buildings and equipment	Investment *B*, equipment and inventory	Investment *C*, land and inventory
Initial investment	$100	$100	$100
% depreciable	100	50	0
Gross sales/year	$100	$100	$100
Costs requiring cash outlay —*i.e.*, excluding depreciation	60	60	60
Depreciation allowance, at 10-year straight line	10	5	0
Tax-allowable expenses	70	65	60
Before taxes:			
Reported net income	30	35	40
Depreciation allowance	10	5	0
Total	40	40	40
After taxes at 54%:			
Reported profit	14	16	18
Depreciation allowance	10	5	0
Cash generation	24	21	18
Interest rate of return on investment, %/year	21	19	18

On a before-tax basis, the three projects would be ranked *C* over *B* over *A*, considering net income. With depreciation, they would rate identically. If they are compared on the basis of the reported after-tax profit, investment *C*, the non-depreciable investment, looks preferable at $18,000 compared with $14,000 or $16,000. However, no cash expense corresponding to the depreciation allowance has occurred; the funds reported as an expense remain inside the company. Therefore, the amount of this allowance per year must be added to the reported profit to total the "cash generation" to the company after taxes. On this basis, investment *A* is best, and *B* is somewhat better than *C*, as some depreciation was allowed. The table also shows the difference in interest rate of return on investment. Any return-on-investment method which considers profit and depreciation on an after-tax basis would reflect this difference.

A non-depreciable investment generates funds at the termination of the project. Working capital such as inventories or accounts receivable can usually be turned into cash when a project is concluded. Presumably land can be sold when one goes out of business. These recoveries are considered in the interest-rate-of-return calculation, but only at the project termination. The earlier return (through tax allowances) of the total depreciable investment raises the rate of return on a depreciable investment compared with a non-depreciable type.

Depletion. For the mining and petroleum industries, still greater differences in before-tax and after-tax profitability comparisons could be shown because of the depletion allowances permitted for consumption of mineral resources. These are non-cash deductions, for tax purposes, which are considerably more important than depreciation. They are not related to original investment, so that they can result in tax savings many times the value of investment in depletable resources.

Depletion allowances by the Internal Revenue Service are related to total value of a mineral product in its least processed salable form. For petroleum, 27.5 per cent of wellhead value can be deducted from income before taxes—with a maximum allowance of 50 per cent of income before taxes and depletion. Lower percentages of salable value are allowed for other mineral products.

Consider a project identical to investment *C* in Table 26-4, but involving depletion of mineral resources. For simplicity, assume the limitation on the allowance is 50 per cent of reported net income before taxes and depletion—a depletion allowance of $20,000. Reported profit would be only $9000, while cash generation would be $29,000. Such a project would show a 29 per cent interest rate of return on investment. The considerable increase is due entirely to the depletion allowance.

Other Effects of Taxes. There are special provisions in the tax laws regarding dividends received by one corporation from another. Treatment of dividends from any subsidiary, domestic or foreign, is different from treatment of profit of the parent. Only 15 per cent of the dividends from domestic subsidiaries is taxable. Profits from investments in foreign manufacturing subsidiaries are not subject to U.S. taxes until returned as dividends to the parents. However, profits from so-called "tax-haven" companies that merely resell products are taxable when earned. Furthermore, the full amount of the profit earned overseas is now used as a basis for calculation of U.S. taxes. (The previous basis was the dividend paid to the parent.) Credit is still allowed for "qualifying" foreign taxes paid. This change (made in 1962) reduced the advantage in tax treatment for those countries whose tax rate is less than the U.S. rate.

Because tax laws are subject to change, the applicable rates and timing of taxes should be checked with current laws.

Taxes must also be considered in determining the minimum acceptable rate of return, because the cost of obtaining capital is such an important factor. Interest costs for borrowed funds are deductible for tax purposes; and therefore, the after-tax effect is only half the apparent interest rate. The combined cost of capital for a company should consider that the borrowed portion of its funds costs only the after-tax net interest.

A fourth area in which taxes affect profitability is in the realm of working capital, discussed below.

Forecasts of state and Federal tax rates for use in evaulation should be developed with the assistance of responsible tax experts. Consistent use of such forecasts makes for easier comparison among evaluations; however, tax-rate forecasts should be reviewed annually.

Working Capital. The provision of capital to finance cash, inventories, accounts receivable, etc., is usually a problem for the accountant or the treasurer, not the engineer. However, the engineer engaged in cost and profitability estimation must constantly use the concept of working capital, and use it properly, in order properly to state the profitability of investments which are being proposed. Like fixed capital, it is part of the investment on which a return must be earned.

From one point of view, working capital is really more "fixed" than fixed investment and is therefore worth more care in estimating. Like land, working capital is not depreciated over the life of the project, nor is it tax-deductible as an expense. It is considered to be liquid and convertible into cash when the project is terminated. (The term **liquid investment** is more descriptive than "working capital.") Since there is no depreciation allowance on working capital, it must be maintained for the entire life of the project.

Evaluation Definition. For economic evaluation of proposed investments, working capital is defined as the funds, in addition to the fixed investment, which a company must contribute to the project. These must be adequate to get the plant operating and to meet subsequent obligations as they come due. Working capital is not a one-time investment which can be known once and for all near the start of a project. Working capital varies with sales level and other factors.

Non-recurring startup expense should not be confused with working capital. All non-recurring investments, whether in fixed or working capital or in labor, etc., should be separated from the working-capital items mentioned below, because (unlike working capital) startup expense can be written off immediately as a business expense.

The above definition for working capital is consistent with that used for fixed capital. It is an amount of money actually set aside by the company to get the plant going; no other value is considered in either case. If fixed investment were valued at its value to a competitor or a purchaser, some quite different amount would be obtained. The consistent method for valuation of each element of working capital is discussed below as part of the definition.

Inventories. The easiest element of working capital for which to estimate a value is inventory. Raw material, in-process material, and finished-product inventories should all be considered. Estimates should be based on company experience rather than on published rules of thumb.

The importance of variations in the size of inventories can easily be seen by contrasting such usually interchangeable materials as natural gas and fuel oil. Natural gas is delivered from a pipe line; no raw-material inventory is maintained, and the consumer is billed for it after use. This actually represents use of suppliers' money, because the user is putting directly into in-process inventory a material received but not paid for. By contrast, fuel oil is often obtained in tanker or barge quantities which involve considerable value in raw-material inventory. Paid-for fuel oil might be on hand for some time before actual use.

Raw materials should, of course, be valued at their delivered cost to the plant. However, finished products represent negotiable materials of sale to which the value of manufacture has already been added. Although there are arguments in favor of valuation at sales price, working capital as defined here is the cash outlay required to support the project. The consistent approach then is to value finished-product inventories only at the cash value of the added funds which the company has put up to create them. This would be cash cost rather than product price, and would exclude non-cash items such as depreciation and profit.

Accounts receivable represent goods which have been sold but on which payment has not been received. Valuation of accounts receivable, for the purpose of determining the working-capital investment required, is again a problem. It is usual to show them on the balance sheet at sales value. However, on a cash basis, the investment by the company in accounts receivable is only the cash cost of the product (including freight and shipping charges, if any, paid by the supplier).

Accounts payable represent goods, services, etc., which are available for use in the plant but for which payment is not yet made. Depending on the occurrence of payday for various parts of the labor force, most companies accrue a considerable accounts payable as wages or salaries payable, representing labor's value added to these various products. Inasmuch as labor is expended on the company's products before it is paid for, the employees are essentially advancing money to the company. Payment for utilities is also after the date of use and should likewise be considered a source of funds. If pipe-line gas is a raw material, an account payable will also exist as described above.

Payables should be included in working-capital analyses to find the net amount of company funds required over and above the fixed investment. They should never be omitted.

Each account payable represents a definite determinable obligation on the part of the company; so valuation of accounts payable should provide no problem to the estimator. The terms of sale of prospective suppliers can be determined directly.

Taxes Payable. The rules of thumb concerning working capital (15 days of this and 30 days of that) were apparently made up before the Federal income tax became such a significant consideration. Each profitable sale incurs an obligation to pay taxes, but until that obligation becomes due, the cash equivalent of the tax portion received from the customer is usable as cash working capital by the company. If taxable income is considered to be earned uniformly over the year, accrued taxes payable (as of 1962) average 7 to 8 months' taxes. As profits accumulate, the capital provided from taxes payable frequently reduces the working capital required by a going project. Any profitable investment adds profits, and the taxes accrued on such profits may in some cases offset all the other items of working capital considered above.

Cash is the balancing factor in the transaction of any business. Once a company or a project reaches steady profitable levels, cash requirements can be supplied from operations.

Cash is needed only to take care of the non-uniformity of the cycle (within the month or seasonal). Cash held in excess of this requirement is really idle, not working, capital, held for reasons other than immediate needs. A minimum cash balance must be maintained to cover the expected and also the random variations in receipt of income vs. bills. The rules of thumb frequently cited for estimating this element seem to bear no relationship to actual needs.

The **accounting definition** of working capital is based on the company's balance sheet. Current assets minus current liabilities equals working capital. **Current assets** are made up chiefly of cash, accounts receivable, inventories, and negotiable securities. **Current liabilities** consist chiefly of accounts payable, short-term debts, and currently due portion of long-term debts. However, the valuation of several of these items is different from that described above for economic-evaluation purposes.

Furthermore, this accounting definition is in terms of the entire company. Net current assets are called "working capital" even though some of them may be actually idle. There may be good reasons for holding such liquid assets, but a better phrase than working capital might be found. "Net current assets" would be more descriptive. Therefore, there might be a **third definition** which would separate out the idle portion of net current assets and which would show the remainder as true "working capital."

Most companies maintain their accounting books on an **accrual basis,** which means that sales and purchases are recorded at the time the order is placed rather than the time cash is received or paid out. This is another major difference between the two definitions of working capital. Since investment evaluations are properly made on a cash-flow basis, the investments and receipts which determine working capital must be considered on the same cash basis. Liquid investment required initially may be greater than that needed when steady operation is established, because of the delays before cash inflows begin and because of the accrual of taxes payable which builds up as the plant operates at a profit.

Combining the Elements. Liquid investment working capital is the net sum of the five elements—inventories, accounts receivable, accounts payable, taxes payable, and cash—a balance of positive and negative factors. In combining the elements, the difference of timing of each of these cash flows must be considered. Table 26-5 indicates a considerable range of timing for

Table 26-5. Typical Timing for Elements of Working Capital

Account	Typical range, days		
	Min.	Max.	Avg.
Raw material accounts payable	...	...	30
Raw material inventory	7	21	14
Labor accounts payable (biweekly payday)	4	18	11
Utilities accounts payable	20	50	35
Finished product inventory	7	90	30
Accounts receivable (30-day terms)	30	50	40
Taxes payable	165	255	210
Freight payable	...	...	4

some of the elements. For investment evaluation, use of the average is probably adequate. For further details on the combination, see Weaver and Lyndall [*Ind. Eng. Chem.*, **51,** 49A (August, 1959)].

FIXED CAPITAL COST ESTIMATION

REFERENCES: *General:* Hackney, *Chem. Eng.*, **67** (5), 113; (7), 119 (1960). Hur, "Chemical Process Economics in Practice," pp. 17–32, Reinhold, New York, 1956. Lang, *Chem. Eng.*, **54** (9), 130; (10), 117 (1947); **55** (6), 112 (1948). Nelson, *Oil Gas J.*, **54,** 120 (Jan. 2, 1956). Nichols, *Ind. Eng. Chem.*, **43,** 2295 (1951). Tielrooy, *Chem. Eng. Progress*, **52,** 187 (1956).

Equipment costs: Aries and Newton, "Chemical Engineering Cost Estimation," McGraw-Hill, New York, 1955. Bond, *Oil Gas J.*, **52,** 106, (Dec. 14, 1953), Figs. 1 and 8 reversed in printing. Chilton, *Chem. Eng.*, **56** (6), 97 (1949). Perry, "Chemical Business Handbook," pp. 2-64–2-66, McGraw-Hill, New York. 1954. Zimmerman and Lavine, *Petrol. Refiner*, **35,** 116 (August, 1956).

Effect of size on costs: Chilton, *Chem. Eng.*, **57** (4), 112 (1950). Sherwood, *Oil Gas J.*, **48,** 81 (Mar. 9, 1950). Williams, *Chem. Eng.*, **54** (12), 124 (1947).

Piping: Dickson, *Chem. Eng.*, **54** (11), 121 (1947).

Emphasis here is on techniques which provide greatest accuracy with a minimum expenditure of time and money. It is not possible to produce fully detailed estimates of all equipment, materials, labor, and overhead expense for each new plant proposal. Even if complete drawings and specifications are available, a detailed estimate prepared from them would not necessarily be an accurate one, since 25 to 40 per cent of the total cost of any capital project is for such components as labor, field expense, engineering, and startup, which cannot be priced precisely. Wide differences may result from the estimator's bias, whether optimistic or pessimistic.

Two simple rules are suggested as preliminary steps toward the goal of consistently accurate estimates:

1. Check completeness of project scope.
2. Draw on statistically proved capital-cost experience to reduce effect of bias.

Of the many factors which contribute to poor estimates, the most significant is that of not encompassing the full **scope of the proposed project.** Initial estimates are often lower than actual project costs. The cause is usually traceable to sizable omissions of equipment, services, or auxiliary facilities rather than to significant errors in pricing. A check list of items comprising a new project is an invaluable aid. Table 26-6 or any good standard cost code of accounts can serve this purpose.

Types and Accuracy of Estimates. First step toward accurate estimating is adoption of a standard **cost code** for use on all construction projects. Table 26-7 shows a summary of such a cost code which has been applied consistently by one firm to over 100 major projects in a 5-year period. This is a purely numerical cost code. Table 26-8 shows an alphabetical-numerical code typical of those used by a number of chemical engineering and construction firms.

The numerical code is most effective when it has no more than three digits for cost-unit identification. Such a system lends itself well to the use of punch-card-machine collection, grouping, and summing of accounts. The simple numerical system can be grouped to serve the needs of plant accountants for property records, the construction superintendent for job control, and the cost engineer for statistical analysis.

A good cost code should separately identify **cost elements** useful in the estimation of future capital costs. It should also be functional to provide the most convenient means of **cost collection** in the field. For instance, the total installed cost for a distillation unit, including equipment, foundation, piping, and insulation, may be sufficient for property records but cannot be used for later estimating except for an equal or similar column. Collecting costs functionally permits identification of charges for individual items comprising the whole, thus providing information from which the installed cost of other towers may be evaluated.

Accumulation of detailed cost data of itself, however, does not ensure high estimating accuracy. Even contractors' firm proposals based on completed drawings and specifications show variations between low and high bids as wide as 30 per cent.

Estimates fall into a few categories which progress from a very rough "guesstimate" to a highly detailed procedure based on finished plans and specifications. The **estimating information guide** of Fig. 26-1, a variation of the Nichols technique [*Ind. Eng. Chem.*, **43,** 2295 (1951)], was developed from an analysis of uniform code data collected from a representative list of completed chemical-plant projects. It shows the limits of error expected of the estimate when the information shown at the top of the chart is available.

For all practical purposes, there are five kinds of estimates useful in the evaluation of capital costs for chemical plants. One of these, **order-of-magnitude estimate,**

Table 26-6. Check List of Items for Fixed Capital Cost Estimate of a Chemical Process

Land:
- Surveys
- Fees
- Property cost

Site development:
- Site clearing
- Grading
- Roads, access and on-site
- Walkways
- Railroads
- Fence
- Parking areas
- Other paved areas
- Wharves and piers
- Recreational facilities
- Landscaping

Process buildings:
- (List as required) Include in each as required substructure, superstructures, platforms, supports, stairways, ladders, access ways, cranes, monorails, hoists, elevators

Auxiliary buildings:
- Administration and office
- Medical or dispensary
- Cafeteria
- Garage
- Product warehouse(s)
- Parts or stores warehouse
- Maintenance shops—electric, piping, sheet metal, machine, welding, carpenters, instrument
- Guard and safety
- Hose houses
- Change houses
- Smoking stations (in hazardous plants)
- Personnel building
- Shipping office and platforms
- Research laboratory
- Control laboratories

Building services:
- Plumbing
- Heating
- Ventilation
- Dust collection
- Air conditioning
- Sprinkler systems
- Elevators, escalators
- Building lighting
- Telephones
- Fire alarm
- Paging
- Intercommunication systems
- Painting

Process equipment:
- (List carefully from checked flow sheets)

Non-process equipment:
- Office furniture and equipment
- Cafeteria equipment
- Safety and medical equipment
- Shop equipment
- Automotive heavy maintenance and yard material-handling equipment
- Laboratory equipment
- Lockers and locker-room benches
- Garage equipment
- Shelves, bins, pallets, hand trucks
- Housekeeping equipment
- Fire extinguishers, hoses, fire engines

Process appurtenances:
- Piping—carbon steel, alloy, cast iron, lead, lined, aluminum, copper, asbestos-cement, ceramic, plastic, rubber, reinforced concrete
- Pipe hangers, fittings, valves
- Insulation—piping, equipment
- Instruments
- Instrument panels
- Electrical—panels, switches, motors, conduit, wire, fittings, feeders, grounding, instrument and control wiring

Utilities:
- Boiler plant
- Incinerator
- Ash disposal
- Boiler feed-water treatment
- Electric generation
- Electric substations
- Refrigeration plant
- Air plant
- Wells
- River intake
- Primary water treatment—filtration, coagulation, aeration
- Secondary water treatment—deionization, demineralization, pH and hardness control
- Cooling towers
- Water storage
- Effluent outfall
- Process-waste sewers
- Process-waste pumping stations

Table 26-6. Check List of Items for Fixed Capital Cost Estimate of a Chemical Process—(*Continued*)

Utilities:—(*Continued*)
- Sanitary-waste sewers
- Sanitary-waste pumping stations
- Impounders, collection basins
- Waste treatment
- Storm sewers

Yard distribution and facilities (outside battery limits):
- Process pipe lines—steam, condensate, water, gas, fuel oil, air, fire, instrument, and electric lines
- Raw-material and finished-product handling equipment—elevators, hoists, conveyors, airveyors, cranes
- Raw-material and finished-product storage — tanks, spheres, drums, bins, silos
- Fuel receiving, blending, and storage
- Product loading stations
- Track and truck scales

Miscellaneous:
- Demolition and alteration work
- Catalysts
- Chemicals (initial charge only)
- Spare parts and non-installed equipment spares
- Surplus equipment, supplies and equipment allowance
- Equipment rentals (for construction)
- Premium time (for construction)
- Inflation cost allowance
- Freight charges
- Taxes and insurance
- Duties
- Allowance for modifications and extra construction work during startup

Engineering costs:
- Administrative
- Process, project, and general engineering
- Drafting
- Cost engineering
- Procurement, expediting, and inspection
- Travel and living expense
- Reproductions
- Communications
- Scale model
- Outside architect and engineering fees

Construction expense:
- Construction, operation, and maintenance of temporary sheds, offices, roads, parking lots, railroads, electrical, piping, communication, and fencing
- Construction tools and equipment
- Warehouse personnel and expense
- Construction supervision
- Accounting and timekeeping
- Purchasing, expediting, and traffic
- Safety and medical
- Guards and watchmen
- Travel and transportation allowance for craft labor
- Fringe benefits
- Housekeeping
- Weather protection
- Permits, special licenses, field tests
- Rental of off-site space
- Contractor's home office expense and fees
- Taxes and insurance, interest

Table 26-7. Standard Cost Code (Numerical) Summary

Code Group	Subdivision
Direct costs:	
0–349	Process section (process equipment listed in flow-sheet sequence 1, 2, 3, 4, 5, . . . *N*, preceded by process identification number)
350–399	Site development
400–449	Process buildings
450–489	Auxiliary buildings
490–499	Non-process equipment
500–599	Process appurtenances (piping, insulation, instrumentation, electrical, etc.)
600–699	Utilities and yard services (boiler plant, refrigeration, compressed air, water supply and treatment, effluents, fire protection, yard piping, yard electrical, yard materials handling, raw and finished-product storage)
700–729	Substructures
730–749	Superstructures
750	Painting
760–769	Building services
770–799	Demolition and alteration to existing structure
800–819	Surplus equipment, supplies and materials, royalty payments
820–830	Design modifications, construction modifications, and extra work during startup
Indirect costs:	
850–874	Home office engineering
875–889	Architect and engineers charges and fees
900–969	Construction expenses
997–989	Taxes and insurance
950	Contractor's home office expenses
996	Contractor's fees

Table 26-8. Standard Cost Code (Alphabetical-Numerical)

A	Site work and foundations
B	Buildings (less foundations)
C	Steel structures and platforms (other than buildings)
D	Heat exchangers
E	Fractionating towers
F	Tanks and drums
G	Pumps and pump drivers
H	Compressors and blowers
J	Reactors and converters
K	Grinding, crushing, and classifying equipment
L	Materials-handling equipment
M	Fired heaters
N	Catalysts and chemicals
O	Laboratory equipment
P	Piping
Q	Instruments and controls
R	Electrical
S	Insulation and painting
T	Utility equipment (boilers, generators, refrigeration)
U	Plant and building accessories (railroads, fence, etc.)
V	Laboratory equipment
W	Safety equipment
X	Warehouse spares
100	Equipment and materials delivered and installed (A through X)
200	Sales and use taxes
300	Temporary facilities
320	Construction equipment, tools, and supplies
340	Construction supervision
360	Field office expense
380	Warehousing expense
400	Pay-roll taxes and insurance
500	Home office engineering costs
600	Procurement costs
700	Resident engineering
800	Royalty payments
900	Engineering administrative overhead and profit
950	Constructor's administrative overhead and profit

is primarily a rule-of-thumb procedure applied only to repetitive types of plant installations for which there exists good cost history. This includes such installations as sulfuric acid plants, nitric acid plants, ammonia plants, steam-generating units, and refrigeration units. Charts can be plotted for such facilities from which capital cost at a given production capacity can be predicted within 10 to 50 per cent. At the other extreme is the **"firm" or contractor's estimate,** requiring complete drawings, specifications, and site surveys. Time seldom permits the preparation of such estimates prior to an approval to proceed with the project.

Three other basic estimate types are frequently used for capital evaluation. The **study estimate** is used to estimate the economic feasibility of a project before expending significant funds for piloting, market studies, land surveys, and acquisition. It may be off by some 30 per cent, but it can be prepared at relatively low cost with minimum data (see Fig. 26-1). See also Zevnik and Buchanan, *Chem. Eng. Progress*, **59,** (2) 70 (1963).

The **scope or budget authorization estimate** has a nominal error of 20 per cent but requires more detailed information than the study estimate. Accuracy of this type of estimate may approach that of the project control estimate as quantitative and qualitative information is improved. The **project control estimate** is the most accurate of the three types and has been shown to produce answers within 10 per cent with the information available as indicated on Fig. 26-1.

The limits of error are shown as an envelope of variability, implying variable results depending on information. There is a greater probability that the actual cost will be more than the estimated cost where information is incomplete. For such estimates the positive spread is likely to be wider than the negative, *e.g.*, +40 and −20 per cent for a study estimate. Furthermore, in times of rising cost trends the positive percentage variations are likely to be greater than the negative. The opposite is true in times of falling cost trends. The validity of the variable envelope has been verified within 95 per cent confidence limits.

Table 26-9. Typical Costs for Producing Estimates

	Less than $1 million	$1 million to $5 million	$5 million to $50 million
Study estimates:			
Average	$ 1,250	$ 3,800	$ 7,200
Median	1,000	3,600	7,500
Scope or authorization estimates:			
Average	9,200	20,700	22,000
Median	7,200	15,500	18,000
Project control estimates:			
Average	13,200	32,000	41,750
Median	4,400	32,300	39,500

Table 26-9 shows average and median costs of producing the three most frequently used types of estimates. The figures include salaries, overhead, and travel for engineering, drafting, and cost engineering expended for the preparation of the estimate.

The large spread between median and average costs for preparation of project control estimates for small projects is due to the small number of cases available. Quite often the scope or authorization estimate is used to control costs of such projects.

Most of the engineering and drafting prepared for a project control estimate can be used in final construction, thereby reflecting lower net estimating costs than shown in Table 26-9. There is an obvious advantage of savings in time and money in progressing from the study to the project control estimate in this fashion.

Cost Factors. The fundamental components in the cost of a process plant are a material component, a labor component, a component of overhead, or cost of doing business and a profit. Estimates of all types should contain these basic elements of cost. By keeping construction cost records in such a fashion that they can be broken down functionally to the basic components, useful data for factoring future estimates can be assembled.

Table 26-10 is such a collection of cost data expressed as percentages of total plant installed costs for multiprocess grass-roots plants or large battery-limit additions.

Table 26-10. Ranges of Component Costs for Multiprocess "Grass Roots" Plants

In % of total installed plant cost
Ranges also hold for large battery-limit plants

	Range, %	Median, %
Process equipment	25–40	32.5
Process equipment labor	1.5–4.5	3.0
Process material	(8–18)	(13)
Concrete substructures	1–4	2.5
Piping and ductwork	2–8	5.0
Electrical	1–3	2.0
Insulation	0.5–1	0.75
Process structural	2–7	4.0
Instrumentation	1–5	3.0
Paint	0.1–0.2	0.15
Process material labor	(4–12)	(8)
Concrete substructures	1.5–5	3.3
Piping and ductwork	1.5–7	4.3
Electrical	1.5–6	3.8
Insulation	1–3	2.0
Process structural	1–4	2.5
Instrumentation	0.5–2	1.3
Paint	0.2–1.4	0.8
Home office expense excluding overhead	(5–9)	(7)
Including overhead	(11–20)	(15.5)
Engineering	1.5–3	2.3
Drafting	3–6	5.0
Purchasing	0.15–0.4	0.28
Accounting, construction and cost engineering	0.15–0.4	0.28
Travel and living	0.1–0.5	0.3
Reproductions, communications	0.2–0.4	0.3
Field expense including overhead	(6–14)	(10)
Temporary construction and operations	1.5–3	2.3
Construction tools and rentals	2–6	4.0
Home office personnel in field	0.2–2	1.1
Field pay roll	0.5–5	2.8
Travel and living	0.1–0.8	0.45
Taxes and insurance	1.5–2.5	2.0
Construction startup, material and labor	0.5–2	1.3
Contractors' fees	1.5–5	3.0
Miscellaneous, including unusual field conditions	0.25–0.75	0.5

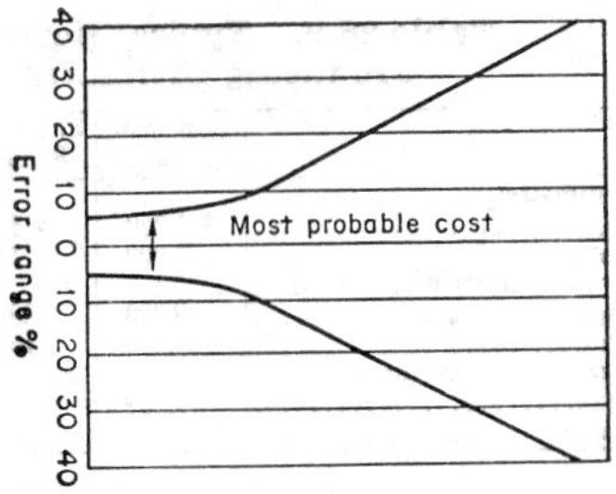

Category	Required Information	Firm estimate ±5% range	Project control estimate ±10% range	Budget authorization estimate ±20% range	Study estimate ±30% range	Order-of-magnitude estimate >±30% range
Site	Location	●	●	●	●	
	General description	●	●	●		
	Soil bearing	●	●	●		
	Location & dimensions R.R., roads, impounds, fences	●	●	●		
	Well-developed site plot plan & topographical map	●	●			
	Well-developed site facilities	●				
Process flow sheet	Rough sketches				●	
	Preliminary			●		
	Engineered	●	●			
Equipment list	Preliminary sizing & material specifications			●	●	
	Engineered specifications	●	●			
	Vessel sheets	●	●			
	General arrangement					
	(a) Preliminary		●	●		
	(b) Engineered	●				
Building and structures	Approximate sizes & type of construction			●	●	
	Foundation sketches		●	●		
	Architectural & construction	●	●	●		
	Preliminary structural design			●		
	General arrangements & elevations	●	●			
	Detailed drawings	●				
Utility requirements	Rough quantities (steam, water, electricity, etc.)				●	
	Preliminary heat balance			●		
	Preliminary flow sheets			●		
	Engineered heat balance	●	●			
	Engineered flow sheets	●	●			
	Well-developed drawings	●				
Piping	Preliminary flow sheet & specifications			●	●	
	Engineered flow sheets	●	●			
	Piping layouts & schedules	●				
Insulation	Rough specifications			●		
	Preliminary list of equipment & piping to be insulated		●			
	Insulation specifications & schedules	●	●			
	Well-developed drawings or specifications	●				
Instrumentation	Preliminary instrument list			●		
	Engineered list & flow sheet	●	●			
	Well-developed drawings	●				
Electrical	Preliminary motor list—approximate sizes			●	●	
	Engineered list & sizes	●	●			
	Substations, number & sizes, specifications	●	●	●		
	Distribution specifications	●				
	Preliminary lighting specifications			●		
	Preliminary interlock, control, & instrument wiring specs.		●			
	Engineered single-line diagrams (power & light)	●	●			
	Well-developed drawings	●				
Man-hours	Engineering & drafting	●	●	●	●	
	Labor by craft	●				
	Supervision	●				
Project scope-standard processes	Product, capacity, location & site requirements. Utility & service requirements. Building & auxiliary requirements. Raw materials & finished product handling & storage requirements.					●

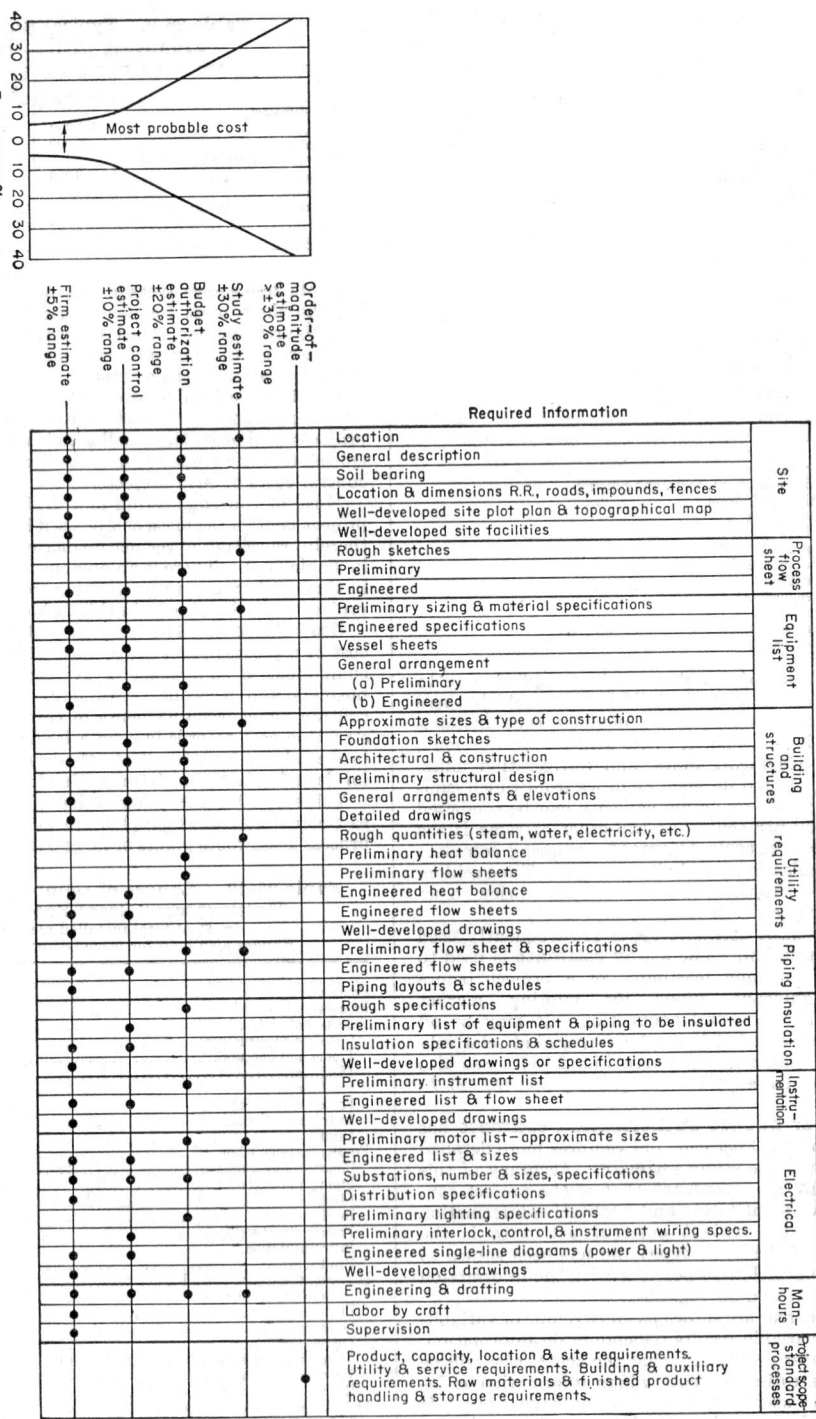

FIG. 26-1. **Estimating information guide.**

Data were prepared from a study of installed costs of over 100 chemical process capital projects. Selected ranges carry a 95 per cent confidence limit.

Table 26-11 similarly shows how major components of capital cost vary with respect to total installed costs. Process material and labor are considered direct costs, as detailed in Table 26-10. Indirect costs are the home office and field expenses of Table 26-10. Auxiliary facilities are more fully defined on p. 26-2.

Table 26-11. Summary of Ranges of Process Plant Component Costs

	% of Total Installed Cost
Process material and labor, including auxiliary facilities	70–85
Indirect expense	15–30
Process material and labor, including indirect	60–80
Auxiliary facilities, including indirect	20–40
Process material and labor	40–70
Auxiliary facilities	15–30
Indirect expense	15–30

Table 26-10 can be used to compile quickly the **cost of a new facility** from a minimum of data. Given a preliminary list of process equipment and rough specifications of structural, electrical, and piping requirements, an acceptable study estimate can be prepared. The method requires a reasonably good understanding of the process involved to enable the selection of the proper percentage factor within the ranges shown in the table.

Table 26-12 is the development of a study estimate for a continuous process plant producing an organic chemical, using percentage factors of process plant component costs from Tables 26-10 and 26-11, applied to data necessary for study estimates as outlined in the estimating information guide (Fig. 26-1). It is necessary only to assume a factor for the installed cost of equipment as a percentage of total plant cost to arrive at a trial total cost. For this type of plant a value of 25 per cent, the lower limit of the range, was selected. Since uncertainty of a study estimate is 30 per cent, the estimated cost is expressed as a range.

Table 26-12. Study Estimate Using Factors for Process Plant Component Costs

Code		Percentage factor assumed	Cost	Adjusted percentage factor
1 ...n	Process equipment	25	$200,000	23.4
	Process equipment labor	3	24,000	2.8
500	Piping and pipe supports	11	88,000	10.3
520	Insulation	3	24,000	2.8
525	Instrumentation	5	40,000	4.7
530	Electrical	7	56,000	6.6
700	Substructures	4	32,000	3.8
730	Superstructures	6.5	52,000	6.1
350	Site	1.5	12,000	1.4
750	Paint	0.63	5,000	0.6
600	Auxiliaries or plant services (steam, water, effluent, electric power)	15	120,000	14.1
850	Home office expenses, including overhead	15	120,000	14.1
900	Field expenses	10	80,000	9.3
	Total		$853,000	100.0

Probable range of total is $725,000 to $980,000 if there is equal likelihood of positive or negative variation, $853,000 to $1,109,000 if economy is inflationary.

The range-of-cost concept can be applied within specified limits to **labor costs,** as shown in Table 26-13. Such data are most useful when equipment and material costs are known and are therefore most frequently applied to detailed estimates or in preparing manning schedules during field construction.

Scaling from Previous Estimates. Methods are also required to adjust one set of estimates to a different design size. Equipment size and cost were shown by Williams [*Chem. Eng.*, **54** (12), 124 (1947)] to correlate fairly well by the logarithmic relationship known as the **"six-tenths factor"** (see Glossary). Chilton [*Chem. Eng.*, **57** (4), 112 (1950)] showed a similar relationship for battery-limits plants, but the range of applicable factors was much wider than on equipment. The relationship cannot be used if auxiliary facilities are not identical between old and new estimates. Presented below is an extension of the factoring concept to make it more generally applicable.

Table 26-13. Typical Labor Cost Factors

Setting and aligning pumps, motors, small tanks, small vessels (carbon steel)	Multiply equipment cost by	4–6%
Setting and aligning blowers, compressors, pressure vessels, heat exchangers, evaporators, transformers, prefabricated switchgear	Multiply equipment cost by	7–11%
Erecting and aligning conveyors, elevators, launders, filters, dryers, mills, crushers, centrifuges, autoclaves	Multiply equipment cost by	10–16%
Setting, aligning, lining interiors with brick, lead, installing trays, etc., of kilns, furnaces, columns, and special vessels	Multiply equipment cost by	20–30%
Field erection of shop-fabricated carbon-steel pipe, 2 to 16 in. diameter	4 joints/100 ft. 8 joints/100 ft.	20–60 man-hr./joint 10–40 man-hr./joint
Erection of conduit, pulling wire, connecting at motor control center, motor, push-button and control	Multiply material cost by	30–60%
Instrument setting and adjustment	Multiply material cost by	25–35%

The **simple form** of the six-tenths factor is

$$C_n = r^{0.6}C \qquad (26\text{-}9)$$

where C_n is the new plant cost, C is the previous plant cost, r is the ratio of new to previous capacity.

A **closer approximation** for this relationship has been found to be

$$C_n = fr^{0.6}D + I \qquad (26\text{-}10)$$

where f is a lumped cost index relative to the original installation cost, D is total direct cost, and I is total indirect cost for the previous installation of a similar unit on an equivalent site.

Example. Consider a 50 ton/day continuous chemical process unit erected in 1958 at a battery-limits installed cost of $1,000,000 in the Middle Atlantic area of the United States. Of the total cost, direct costs were $760,000 and indirect costs were $240,000. It is intended to install by late 1961 a similar unit of twice the production capacity but of equal number of process units (reactors, heat exchangers, pumps, etc.) in a South Atlantic location. Using Eq. (26-9), cost of the new unit would be

$$C_n = (2)^{0.6}(1{,}000{,}000) = 1{,}516{,}000$$

To use Eq. (26-10), f is estimated to consist of a labor cost index 0.9, a labor efficiency index of 0.9, and a material and equipment cost index of 1.15, or

$$f = (0.9)(0.9)(1.15) = 0.93$$

Cost of the new unit would then be

$$C_n = 0.93(2)^{0.6}(760{,}000) + 240{,}000 = 1{,}310{,}000$$

The fact that Eq. (26-10) yielded a lower figure than Eq. (26-9) in this case is due to the more favorable cost index factor as well as to the separation of direct and indirect costs. If the South Atlantic plant was the reference point and the Middle Atlantic plant was to be estimated by this method, Eq. (26-10) would give a higher answer than Eq. (26-9).

The exponential relationship of costs can be applied more accurately to varied chemical processes by **generalization of the basic equation.** For instance, in a mechanical solids-handling system employing belt conveyors, crushing equipment, and rotary kilns, exponents of r have been found to vary between 0.7 and 0.9. The proper value of exponent used in more generalized equations will give closer cost approximations of capital projects. For a process handling both fluids and solids, with exponent assumed at 0.8, the result using Eqs. (26-9) and (26-10) for the example above would be, respectively, $1,740,000 and $1,470,000.

Table 26-14 shows how costs of process equipment and piping vary with capacity. With exponents ranging from 0.44 to 1, it is evident that only a fortuitous distribution of process equipment would yield an over-all exponent of 0.6.

Installation labor cost vs. equipment size shows wide variations. Table 26-15 shows exponents varying from 0 to 1.56. Tubular heat exchangers and centrifugal pumps appear to have zero exponents, implying that direct labor cost for setting is independent of size. This reflects the fact that such equipment is set with cranes and hoists which, when adequately sized for the task, recognize no appreciable difference in size or weight of the work. The high labor exponent for erecting carbon-steel towers reflects increasing complexity of internals (lining, internal heat exchangers, trays, etc.) as tower diameter increases.

Table 26-14. Typical Exponents for Equipment Cost vs. Capacity

Centrifugal pumps, stainless steel, horizontal	0.70
Centrifugal pumps, cast iron, horizontal	0.67
Centrifugal pumps, cast iron, vertical (0–200 hp.)	0.98
Positive-displacement pumps, carbon steel	0.70
Tanks, stainless steel	0.68
Tanks, carbon steel	0.44
Tanks, spherical, carbon steel	0.70
Gas holders (without foundations)	0.75
Belt conveyors, 12-in. width	0.80
Belt conveyors, 18-in. width	0.85
Belt conveyors, 24-in. width	0.90
Screw conveyors, 4-in. diameter	0.90[a]
Screw conveyors, 12-in. diameter	0.83[a]
Screw conveyors, 20-in. diameter	0.73[a]
Filters, pressure-leaf, cast iron, 2-in. spacing	0.63[b]
Filters, pressure-leaf, cast iron, 4-in. spacing	0.60[b]
Filters, rotary vacuum, carbon steel and wood (less motors)	0.67[b]
Towers, carbon steel (constant diameter)	0.70
Towers, carbon steel (constant height)	1.00
Compressors, double-acting reciprocating:	
Single-stage, 20–30 lb./sq. in. discharge pressure	0.67[b]
Two-stage, 100 lb./sq. in. discharge pressure	0.75[b]
Turboblowers, 3500 r.p.m., 16 oz. pressure	0.50
Electric motors, squirrel-cage, dripproof, 40°C	0.84[c]
Electric motors, squirrel-cage, splashproof, 50°C	0.84[c]
Electric motors, wound rotor, 40°C	0.66[c]
Evaporators:	
Long-tube, cast iron, copper heating surfaces	0.49[d]
Long-tube, rubber-lined and lead construction	0.55[d]
Heat exchangers, carbon steel, 150 lb./sq. in. (to 3000 sq. ft.)	0.62[e]
Heat exchangers, carbon steel, 150 lb./sq. in. (3000–4000 sq. ft.)	0.95[e]
U-tube heat exchangers, carbon steel, 150 lb./sq. in. (to 1000 sq. ft.)	0.53[d]
U-tube heat exchangers, carbon steel, 150 lb./sq. in. (1000–4000 sq. ft.)	0.98[d]
Piping, black iron, plain end:	
Cost vs. diameter squared (3/8–6 in. diameter)	0.67
Cost vs. diameter squared (8–12 in. diameter)	0.92
Cost vs. diameter (1/4–12 in. diameter)	1.15
Piping, type 316 stainless steel, Schedule 40:	
Cost vs. diameter squared (3/8–8 in. diameter)	0.55
Cost vs. diameter (1/4–8 in. diameter)	0.94

[a] Fox, *Chem. Eng.*, **56** (11), 128 (1949).
[b] Bliss, *Chem. Eng.*, **54** (5), 126 (1947).
[c] Bauman, *Power*, **91**, 66 (July, 1947).
[d] Zimmerman and Lavine, *Petrol. Refiner*, **35**, 116 (August, 1956).
[e] Donohue, *Petrol. Processing*, March, 1956, p. 102.

Table 26-15. Typical Exponents for Equipment Installation Labor vs. Size

Unfired pressure vessels, carbon steel	0.20
Towers, carbon steel (constant diameter)	0.88
Towers, carbon steel (constant height)	1.56
Tubular heat exchangers	0.00
Centrifugal pumps	0.00
Piping (man-hr./joint)	0.85
Brick (1000/size)	1.00
Lead (sq. ft./thickness)	1.00
Paint (sq. ft./coat)	1.00

Table 26-16 shows **installed-cost exponents** for several typical chemical plant auxiliaries. In only one case (outdoor steam generators) does the exponent approximate closely the 0.6 rule of thumb. Accumulation of such data is necessary for factoring costs of new installations with study-estimate accuracy.

Table 26-16. Typical Exponents for Installed Costs of Auxiliary Units vs. Capacity

Pipe lines (cost vs. diameter squared)	0.72*
Centrifugal compressors	0.75*
Refrigeration plants, centrifugal machines using F-12 and ammonia	0.68†
Steam generators (to 200,000 lb./hr):	
Indoors, gas- or oil-fired, 400–650 lb./sq. in., 600–750°F	0.66†
Outdoor, gas- or oil-fired, 400–650 lb./sq. in., 600–750°F	0.61†
Cooling towers:	
85°F. wet bulb, 30°F. terminal difference, 5°F. approach	0.65†
75°F. wet bulb, 15°F. terminal difference, 10°F. approach	0.64†

* Chilton, *Chem. Eng.*, **56** (6), 97 (1949).
† Bauman, *Chem. Eng. Progress*, **51**, 45 (1955).

To determine cost of a new plant of the same capacity at a **new location**, the following formula has produced good results:

$$C_n = [f_E E + f_M M + f_L e_L(E_L + M_L)]f_I \frac{C}{C - I} \qquad (26\text{-}11)$$

where C = original plant cost; f_E = current equipment cost index relative to cost of equipment E; f_M = current material cost index relative to cost of material M; f_L = current labor cost index in new area relative to cost of equipment labor E_L and material labor M_L; e_L = labor efficiency index in new area relative to efficiency of E_L and M_L; f_I = factor for indirect expense, which adjusts for variation in engineering and field expense (varies between 0.9 and 1.05). Because the respective cost indexes are frequently not the same, equipment and material costs are treated separately.

Example. A 50 ton/day unit erected in 1958 in the Middle Atlantic area is to be duplicated in late 1961 in a South Atlantic location. The 1958 cost of $1,000,000 breaks down as follows:

$$E = 250{,}000$$
$$M = 300{,}000$$
$$E_L + M_L = 210{,}000$$
$$I = 240{,}000$$

Relative cost factors applying to the new project are

$$f_E = 1.15$$
$$f_M = 1.10$$
$$f_L = 0.9$$
$$e_L = 0.9$$
$$f_I = 0.9$$

Substituting in Eq. (26-11),

$$C_n = [(1.15)(250{,}000) + (1.10)(300{,}000) + (0.9)(0.9)(210{,}000)] \left[\frac{(0.9)(1{,}000{,}000)}{1{,}000{,}000 - 240{,}000}\right] = 930{,}000$$

Note that rising equipment and material costs in this example are more than offset by lower labor cost, better labor efficiency, and relatively lower engineering and field expenses.

Material and equipment **correction factors** are obtained by selecting the proper ratio of costs from one or more of the following indexes: over-all equipment and material, Wholesale Price Index, U.S. Bureau of Labor Statistics; civil buildings and general structural, *Engineer-*

ing News-Record index; equipment, Marshall and Stevens index; refinery equipment and pipe, Nelson refinery index; labor, U.S. Bureau of Labor Statistics (see p. 26-8). Table 26-17 is an example of labor-rate data published by the U.S. Bureau of Labor Statistics, from which f_L can be computed.

Table 26-17. United States Labor Rates, 1959, Dollars per Hour*

	Brick layers	Car-penters	Elec-tricians	Paint-ers	Plast-erers	Plumb-ers	Build-ing labor-ers
Northeast	3.80	3.25	3.55	2.90	3.70	3.50	2.50
Middle Atlantic	4.10	3.85	4.05	3.40	4.05	3.05	3.00
East North Central	3.90	3.45	3.75	3.30	3.70	3.75	2.60
West North Central	3.75	3.10	3.40	2.85	3.40	3.40	2.25
South Atlantic	3.70	3.15	3.60	3.00	3.35	3 55	1.70
East South Central	3.85	3.25	3.60	3.00	3.45	3.60	2.00
West South Central	3.90	3.30	3.65	3.00	3.60	3.70	2.00
Mountain	3.80	3.10	3.55	3.05	3.40	3.60	2.30
Pacific	4.10	3.45	4.00	3.40	3.80	3.95	2.80
Average	3.90	3.30	3.70	3.10	3.60	3.65	2.35

* U.S. Department of Labor, Bureau of Labor Statistics.

For a new similar single-process plant of a **different size** with the same number of process units at a new location, the following formula has given good results:

$$C_n = r^x[f_E E + f_M M + f_L e_L(E_L + M_L)]f_I \frac{C}{C - I} \tag{26-12}$$

where x is an exponent selected from cost records similar to Tables 26-15 and 26-16 for the class of equipment and material used in the process. For a steam-generating plant, for instance, x would be between 0.61 and 0.66.

For a new similar plant of a new size at a new location but with multiples of the original process units, the following often gives results with somewhat better than study-estimate accuracy:

$$C_n = [r f_E E + r^x f_M M + r^x f_L e_L(E_L + M_L)]f_I \frac{C}{C - I} \tag{26-13}$$

The **ultimate accuracy** of this estimating method is obtained by breaking the project down into subdivisions, *e.g.*, reaction, distillation, filtration, refrigeration, etc., and applying the best available data from similar units at any previous installation separately to each subdivision. Results obtained in this way have shown high correlation with costs obtained with more traditional techniques, often giving results well within the limits of the scope estimate. Properly used, these factoring methods can yield quick fixed capital costs with accuracies sufficient for most economic evaluation purposes.

Unit Costs. Standardization of a code of accounts and feedback of cost data from actual construction projects permits accumulation of usable unit cost data, such as that in Table 26-18, for authorization estimates. The range of costs in this table reflects variations in craft labor costs in different site areas, job and weather conditions, and efficiency of job management. In the case of electrical installations the range also reflects type of installation, general-purpose vs. explosion-proof.

Availability of unit cost data, however, does not assure a good estimate. Changing work forces, geographical locations, weather, labor efficiency, inflation, and specific job conditions effectively rule out use of unit installation costs for other than guides.

Most published data on the subject of unit costs are the result of the individual author's experience. Frequently the data are subject to interpretation of nomenclature and the method of presentation. The grouping of cost accounts varies widely from one company to another. There is little standardization in the items included in a given work unit. By and large, unit cost experience has to be developed by each organization to meet its own control and accounting needs.

Table 26-18. Typical Installed Unit Costs
(January, 1960)

Concrete rectangular prism, $2LW/(L + W)$* = 1–4 ft	$150–75/cu. yd.
Concrete rectangular prism, $2LW/(L + W)$ = 4–20 ft	75–40/cu. yd.
Concrete cylinder, diameter 4–20 ft	75–40/cu. yd.
Concrete thin ring, o.d.–i.d. = 1–4 ft	150–75/cu. yd.
Structural steel	300–450/ton
Platforms, walkways, ladders, railings, stairways	500–700/ton
Miscellaneous supporting steel	700–1000/ton
Carbon-steel piping	650–900/ton
Electric motors, general-purpose, three-phase, 480-volt:	
Sizes I and II	1100–1400 each
Size III	1300–1700 each
Size IV	2000–3000 each
Industrial lighting, general-purpose:	
Receptacles	40–60 each
Incandescent fixtures	60–80 each
Fluorescent fixtures	70–110 each
Insulation, vessel	2–3/sq. ft.
Insulation, piping	3–5/sq. ft.
Piling	3–6/lin. ft.

* L = length; W = width.

Piping Estimation. Process-plant piping can run as high as 80 per cent of process-equipment cost or 15 per cent of installed-plant cost. It is obvious that accuracy of the entire estimate can be seriously affected by the improper application of estimation techniques to this single component.

All known **piping estimation methods** and variations can be reduced to the following:

1. Pricing of detailed take-off
2. Dickson "N" method
3. Pricing by weight of specific types of pipe
4. Pricing by cost per joint
5. Pricing by piped equipment units
6. Pricing by per cent of equipment value
7. Pricing by per cent of total plant installed cost

The first four methods require some degree of piping take-off. Even with the completed plans and specifications upon which the detailed take-off of method 1 depends, there is always a serious doubt as to the accuracy of the resulting estimate—particularly in the case of large companies with plants in widely scattered locations. Many piping-cost handbooks are available. In all of them, however, arbitrary factors and assumptions are suggested to correct for such intangibles as hauling, handling, warehousing, scaffolding, labor travel allowances, and other fringe benefits. It would appear that accurate estimation of piping from the most complete detailed drawings is still a function of the estimator's art. Familiarity with local labor productivity, material availability, weather patterns, and economic conditions is of prime importance in arriving at competitive pricing.

The **Dickson "N" method** [*Chem. Eng.*, **54** (11), 121 (1947)] is an interesting variation of the detailed take-off. Various strings for each kind of pipe are completely priced for a base size. Another chart supplies an "*N*" factor for all other pipe sizes. Multiplying the cost of the component of the original string (pipe, valve, and fittings) by the "*N*" factor yields the estimated cost of the new string of the desired pipe size. Successful use of this method requires that the base charts be kept up to date by periodically repricing the base strings.

Estimating by weight requires substantially complete take-offs, including weight calculations and a record of past costs on this basis. Its only advantage lies in the time saved in detailed pricing of piping components.

Cost per joint, method 4, is similarly based on accumulation of previous experience data properly analyzed and plotted for convenient use. Advantage of the method lies in the fact that good engineering flow sheets can be used for the take-off.

Figure 26-2 shows the number of man-hours of field erection time per joint vs. nominal pipe size of shop-fabricated carbon-steel and low-alloy pipe. Unit of

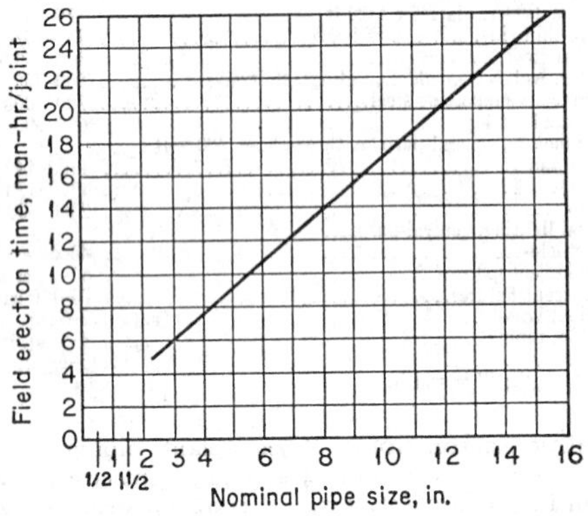

FIG. 26-2. Man-hours required to erect large quantities of shop-fabricated steel and low-alloy piping. Erection time includes hauling, stringing, and jointing operations; it does not include time for operating engineers or teamsters. No differentiation is made between flanged or welded joints.

work measurement in this method is the joint (two for couplings and valves, three for tees, etc.), since the bulk of piping labor is expended in fitting joints. The cost of handling, hanging, and placing lengths of pipe is included in the chart.

The plot shows labor man-hours only. Material costs are obtained by pricing a take-off from flow sheets on which valves and instrument connections are shown. Pipe lengths and fittings are taken off by cross reference with an equipment-arrangement plan. When prepared from data fed back from a specific job, the labor cost per joint represents a total cost, including the effect of all factors applicable to labor shown in Table 26-19. Uniform data from a representative number of completed jobs can be analyzed statistically to determine the value of each factor for various project locations.

Table 26-19. Components of Total Installed Piping Cost

Material	Pipe, valves, fittings, nuts, bolts, gaskets, and hangers
Labor	Cut, erect, align, fit, bolt, thread or weld, and test
Indirect costs	Handle and haul, store, scaffold, lost time, tools and rentals, contractor's overhead and profit
Factors applicable to labor man-hours	Craft rate, productivity, height, and complexity
Crafts involved in piping erection	Pipefitters, laborers, carpenters, warehousemen, teamsters, and operating engineers

Methods 5, 6, and 7 are procedures for estimating piping costs by **factor techniques** where neither flow sheets nor detailed piping drawings are available. Factoring by per cent of equipment value and per cent of total plant installed cost is covered briefly in the discussion of cost factors (p. 26-17). These methods are based strictly on experience gained from piping costs for similar previously installed process units or complexes.

The **equipment-unit method** shows promise of giving better than scope-accuracy estimates for unfamiliar process configurations. The method requires accumulating the piping costs for various sizes of such process units as pumps, heat exchangers, evaporators, tanks, and columns. The method is based on the premise that piping designs for specific process units are similar for most projects. Statistical analysis of such data indicates good correlation with take-off pricing methods. Since for a given process, the length of pipe is a small part of the total piping cost, assumption of an average length of piping per unit, based on a sampling from several previous jobs, should not appreciably affect the accuracy of the results obtained. Updating for inflation can be done with a single escalation factor, unlike methods 1 to 4.

Electrical Facilities. These range most frequently from 5 to 10 per cent of total installed-plant costs. However, estimation of electrical facilities is a challenge almost equal to that of piping. It would seem sufficient simply to factor electrical costs for any specific job. However, overruns of up to 100 per cent in electrical costs are not uncommon, involving a severe penalty on the total job cost.

As with piping, considerable design work must be completed before a detailed set of electrical drawings and specifications can be prepared for construction purposes. During the planning stages, changes are frequently made in equipment arrangements and sizes which delay the start of the electrical-design phase of the project. As a consequence, seldom, if ever, can the electrical cost of the job be estimated on a completely detailed basis. In order-of-magnitude and study estimates the suggested 5 to 10 per cent range of the total estimate can be an adequate basis. However, for an advanced authorization estimate being readied for management approval, and certainly for a project control estimate bearing a range of only 5 per cent error, more accurate methods must be used.

The engineer can prepare one of three basic types of electrical estimates:

1. Detail take-off.
2. Factored electrical cost as per cent of plant total installed costs for specific types of plants.
3. Unit cost.

The **detail take-off method** can seldom, if ever, be used. Detailed drawings are rare; when available, costs can be estimated by pricing materials from manufacturers' catalogues and, in the case of special equipment, from manufacturers' quotations. Handbooks are available which give approximate man-hours of labor required to perform detailed work units, such as installation of switches, starters, motors, conduit wire, and push buttons of various sizes and for non-hazardous as well as hazardous locations. Labor rates can be obtained from sources covered elsewhere in this chapter. The National Electrical Contractors Association publishes an excellent experience manual of electrical costs. Application of these tools to a mass of details carefully taken off drawings and specifications will, of course, yield good results.

The **factored estimate**, when prepared from statistically proved data, gives staisfactory results in the study-estimate and often in the scope-estimate range. The first task is to accumulate experience data showing actual electrical costs (1) as a percentage of total plant-installed costs and (2) as a percentage of equipment-installed costs. Analysis of a representative group of varying types of chemical plants showed electrical costs ranging from about 4 to 11 per cent of total plant cost, with a median of 7.7 per cent. The range was approximately 15 to

40 per cent of equipment costs, with a median of 26 per cent.

There appears to be little relationship between per cent of total cost and per cent of equipment cost, but there is a better relationship to plant cost. Total equipment cost is not a good barometer of total electrical cost ratio. In a kiln installation, for instance, such cost is small percentagewise compared with the cost of electric power wiring for a complex continuous chemical process containing many pumps, filter drives, agitated vessels, and other electrically driven equipment.

Experience over many plants indicates that power-installation costs are approximately twice the lighting costs. There is little correlation between power wiring costs and total electrical costs, which include transformation, distribution, and control wiring. Addition of new motor and lighting load does not necessarily require new investment in transformation or distribution facilities, since these are often provided in the initial plant with extra capacity for normal plant growth.

A method of electrical cost estimation which can produce results equal to detailed methods is the **unit-costing approach.** The validity of the method depends on the accumulation and subsequent analysis of data from many jobs of various types of plant installations using a consistently uniform cost code of accounts. Finished data are compiled to provide unit-cost information for electrical components as follows:

1. Total installed cost per motor
2. Total installed cost per lighting outlet by types
3. Total installed cost of receptacles by type (incandescent, fluorescent, etc.)
4. Total installed cost for each wired instrumentation point
5. Total installed cost for each unit of transformation
6. Total installed cost per lineal foot of distribution by type (overhead bare and insulated, underground)
7. Total installed cost of each interlock point

Each unit contains the complete cost of that specific installation. For instance, the motor-unit installed cost includes complete equipment, material, and labor from the load side of the distribution line to the motor push-button. This includes that motor's share of the motor control center installed cost, conduit, wiring and supports, motor installation, and push button. The motor cost proper is generally included in the price of equipment and is not a part of the motor wiring unit cost. For illustration, simplified unit-cost data are shown in Table 26-20 for a representative number of plants.

Auxiliaries Estimation. The commonly accepted definition for chemical plant auxiliaries includes all structures, equipment, and services which do not enter directly into the chemical process. Within this broad category there are two major classifications: utilities and service facilities.

Table 26-20. Simplified Unit-cost Data for Electrical Installations

January, 1960

Type of plant	Motor sizes	Installed cost per motor	Types of lighting outlets	Installed cost per outlet
Mechanical	I	$1700	Fluorescent	
	II	1910	Vaporproof	$ 80
	III	2960	Explosionproof	
	IV	.....	General-purpose	
Grass-roots complex chemical	I	1390	Fluorescent	175
	II	1690	Vaporproof	117
	III	2430	Explosionproof	155
	IV	3400	General-purpose	105
Grass-roots complex chemical	I	1090	Fluorescent	130
	II	1275	Vaporproof	79
	III	1695	Explosionproof	118
	IV	1925	General-purpose	
	V	2500		
Battery limits civil-mechanical	I	1250	Fluorescent	
	II	2120	Vaporproof	100
	III	.....	Explosionproof	
	IV	.....	General-purpose	80

Chemical plant auxiliaries vary from approximately 20 to 40 per cent of the total installed-plant cost. For a single-product, small, continuous-process plant, the cost is likely to be in the lower part of the range. For large, multiprocess, grass-roots plants, the costs are apt to be near the upper limit of the range.

Studies have been made of the variations in cost of auxiliaries for a variety of plants, as shown in Table 26-21. The cost range is widest for chemical plant **auxiliary buildings.** This is logical when one considers the many types and functions of auxiliary buildings, in addition to the variations in type and quality of construction materials and methods. For example, a heavy chemical plant would be expected to have a minimum practical type of office structure, whereas a modern pharmaceutical plant would have a relatively more expensive steel, brick, and plaster-wall office building.

Table 26-21. Typical Ranges of Auxiliary Facilities in Per Cent of Total Installed Plant Cost

(Grass roots and large additions)

	Range, %	Median, %
Auxiliary buildings	3-9	5.0
Steam generation	2.6-6	3.0
Refrigeration, including distribution	1-3	2.0
Water-supply cooling and pumping	0.4-3.7	1.8
Finished-product storage	0.7-2.4	1.8
Electric main substation	0.9-2.6	1.5
Process-waste systems	0.4-1.8	1.1
Raw-material storage	0.3-3.2	1.1
Steam distribution	0.2-2	1.0
Electric distribution	0.4-2.1	1.0
Air compression and distribution	0.2-3.0	1.0
Water distribution	0.1-2	0.9
Fire-protection system	0.3-1.0	0.7
Water treatment	0.2-1.1	0.6
Railroads	0.3-0.9	0.6
Roads and walks	0.2-1.2	0.6
Gas supply and distribution	0.2-0.4	0.3
Sanitary-waste disposal	0.1-0.4	0.3
Communications	0.1-0.3	0.2
Yard and fence lighting	0.1-0.3	0.2

Today's trend to air-conditioned working space is reflected in the unit costs for cafeteria, laboratory, and offices shown in Table 26-22. Costs for air conditioning range typically from $4 to $8 per square foot. Furniture and office equipment range from $4 to $6 per square foot.

Table 26-22. Cost Ranges of Auxiliary Buildings

January, 1960

	Dollars/sq. ft. of gross area	Median
Cafeteria	$30-$70	$50
Laboratories	30- 65	45
General office and administration	25- 45	35
Change houses	15- 30	22
Shops and maintenance (unequipped)	10- 18	15
Warehouses	8- 17	12

Steam-generating facilities represent the second largest investment for chemical plant auxiliary equipment. Variations in size of installation, location (indoors or outdoors), fuel, pressure and temperature levels, and type of process served bear importantly on actual costs as well as relative costs.

Figure 26-3 shows installed unit costs of chemical plant steam-generating facilities as functions of some of these variables. The smoothed curves were plotted from data on outdoor and indoor installations operating at different ranges of pressure and temperatures. Package boiler

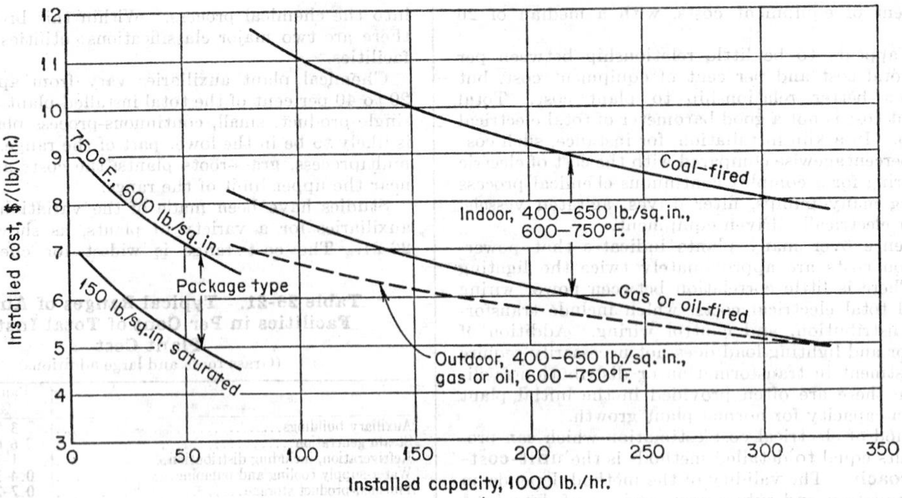

FIG. 26-3. Unit installed costs of steam generators, January, 1960.

installations may be purchased as assembled, piped, and wired units ready to be erected on the owner's foundations. They are available in units up to 75,000 lb./hr. of steam capacity. The indicated costs are for outdoor installations. Buildings increase the costs by 15 to 20 per cent.

The cost analysis of Fig. 26-3 is based on 400 to 600 lb./sq. in. and 600° to 750°F. because of the trend to higher temperatures and pressures for generating facilities in modern chemical installations. This development is particularly evident in plants where back-pressure turbines serve as drives as well as reducing valves for lower-pressure process steam. The curves reflect the higher unit costs for indoor vs. outdoor installations and coal-fired vs. gas- and/or oil-fired plants.

These are idealized trend curves showing relative magnitude for rough estimating. They cannot be used to price specific installations without careful analysis of all factors involved.

Electricity. In most sections of the United States there is now an adequate, reliable supply of electricity. Consequently, there has been a marked decrease in the number of new chemical installations with private electric-generating facilities.

Most plant **electric distribution systems,** therefore, start at the power company's service point on plant property. Many factors, such as lightning hazards and corrosive conditions, influence the choice among various types of underground and overhead distribution systems. The system includes main substations, distribution substations, feeders, switches, and appurtenances. Overhead systems are one-third to one-half as expensive as underground systems.

With 100-ft. spans, **overhead systems** of insulated aerial cable supported on messengers strung between wooden poles cost from $12 to $16 per foot of pole line installed, depending on size of conductor, ranging from No. 6 American Wire Gage to 500 M circular mils. For this range an equivalent system of bare conductors on wood poles, including lightning arresters on alternate spans, costs from $5 to $10 per installed foot of overhead distribution.

Underground systems employing fiber duct banks encased in concrete, manholes, substations, and cables range from $40 to $100 per linear foot of distribution, depending on the number of ducts in the bank, length of system, voltage and capacity of system, soil and temperature conditions. The cost of underground distribution only, in fiber concrete-encased ducts laid in average soil and including manholes, less substations, ranges from $25 to $40 per linear foot of duct bank. Some plants use direct-burial-cable underground systems. Cost for this type of distribution, less substations, ranges from $12 to $25 per linear foot.

Substations, depending on type, capacity, and voltage, cost from $20 to $50 per kilovolt-ampere installed.

Water systems rank third highest in cost of chemical plant auxiliaries, with cooling towers representing the largest portion of the investment. As might be expected, the wider the temperature range the more costly the tower installation (see Fig. 26-4).

River intake and filtering installations range from $20

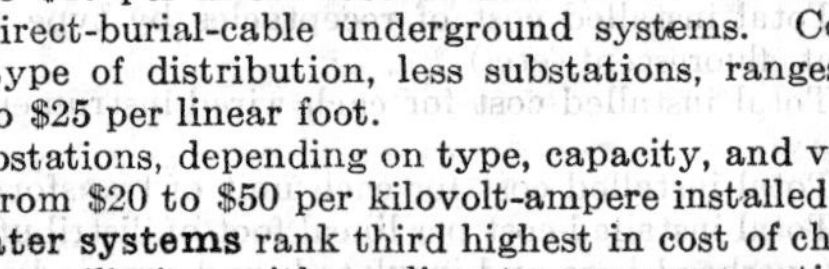

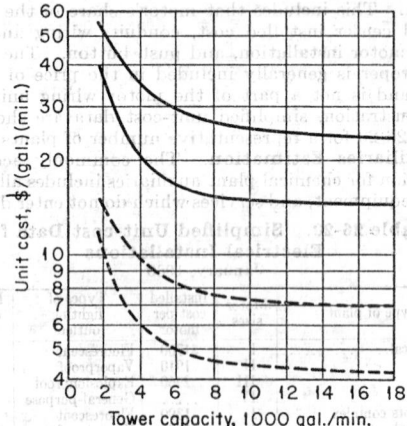

FIG. 26-4. Ranges of cost for cooling-tower installations, January, 1960. Solid curves represent range for complete installation, including foundations, basin, pumps, treatment, engineering, overhead, and profit. Dotted curves represent range for installed cost quoted by manufacturers for towers less foundations, basin, and pumps. Upper curve in each range represents 85°F. wet-bulb, 30°F. terminal difference, 5°F. approach; lower curve in each range represents 75°F. wet-bulb, 15°F. terminal difference, 10°F. approach.

to $6 per gal./min. of installed capacity in systems ranging from 500 to 100,000 gal./min. Cost of zeolite ion-exchange systems varies from $800 per gal./min. for 50 gal./min. of installed capacity to $600 per gal./min. for a 300 gal./min. installation.

Hot-process lime systems vary from about $400 per gal./min. for a 100 gal./min. system to $200 per gal./min. for a 2000 gal./min. system. These are idealized costs. Actual water-treatment costs will vary widely with quality of water, per cent of dissolved solids, and total hardness.

Refrigeration is an increasingly important auxiliary required for many chemical processes. Figure 26-5 shows an idealized plot of installed unit costs of refrigeration systems vs. capacity. The curves represent one

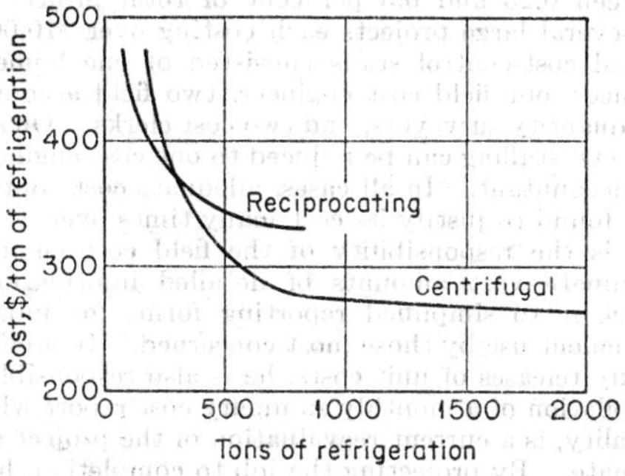

FIG. 26-5. Installed unit costs for refrigeration systems, January, 1960.

specific set of suction and discharge conditions (24 and 200 lb./sq. in. gage, respectively) and are for direct-expansion systems. A family of curves can be drawn to show the costs of refrigeration systems for other suction and discharge conditions. As suction pressure is decreased, cost will increase sometimes as much as 25 per cent for equivalent capacity ratings, assuming the same discharge pressure.

Comfort **air-conditioning systems** complete with machines, ductwork, fans, piping, and wiring cost between $800 and $1100 per ton of refrigeration.

Storage facilities for chemical plants take many forms. Liquids are stored in tanks and spheres, gases in pressure tanks and gas holders, bulk solids in bins, outdoor and indoor piles.

Figure 26-6 shows the relationship between unit installed costs of storage spheres and capacity in barrels (42 U.S. gal./bbl.). Figure 26-7 gives similar cost

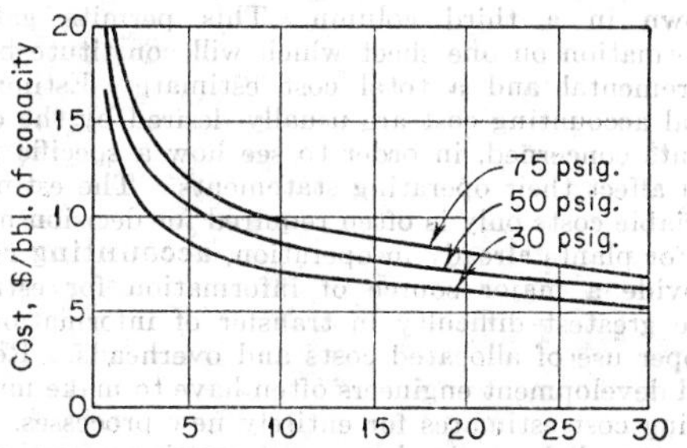

FIG. 26-6. Unit costs of storage spheres, erected less foundations, January, 1960.

data for elevated water-storage tanks, horizontal storage tanks, and gas holders. The unit costs for vessels of these types, as shown by the curves, tend to flatten out quickly as sizes increase from the minimum, and they remain substantially constant over a wide range of sizes.

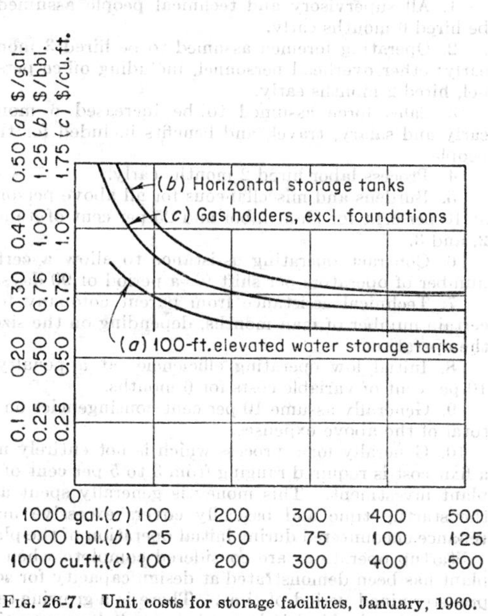

FIG. 26-7. Unit costs for storage facilities, January, 1960.

Costs of **roads and walks** for chemical plants vary with type and thickness of cover. Some typical unit costs for roads are:

Gravel and asphalt, $3.00 to $3.50 per square yard
Concrete with 6-in. base, $4.00 to $4.50 per square yard
Concrete with 8-in. base, $5.50 to $6.25 per square yard

Installed costs for **railroads**, including switches and frogs, may be estimated as follows (January, 1960):

Linear Footage	Dollars per Linear Foot
500–1000	$13.50
1000–3000	13.00
3000–10,000	12.50
Above 10,000	approaches 12.00

Startup Costs. Total startup expense seldom exceeds 10 per cent of the fixed capital cost. Of this, the construction changes may run from 0.2 to 3 per cent, with a median value of 1 per cent. According to accepted practice, construction changes during startup are items of capital cost. Production startup costs, generally expensed against operations, represent the major expense—even the time of startup may vary from a month to a year or more.

It is customary to include in the fixed capital estimate funds to cover the cost of labor, materials, and overhead for design modification and changes due to errors on the part of engineers and contractors, plus the cost of tests, final alterations, and adjustments. These items cannot rightly be included as a contingency, since it is known that such work will be necessary to some degree before this project can be called complete. The contingency allowance is reserved for unpredictable items of cost not known at the time of the estimate. A predictable allowance for at least testing of vessels and piping should be part of the construction startup estimate. However, should a vessel yield structurally during the test, its replacement should come out of the job contingency.

Operating startup consists of a variety of items, as shown in the following list together with typical assumptions:

1. All supervisory and technical people assumed to be hired 6 months early.
2. Operating foremen assumed to be hired 3 months early; other overhead personnel, including office personnel, hired 2 months early.
3. Sales force assumed to be increased 6 months early and salary, travel, and benefits included for these people.
4. Process labor hired 2 months early.
5. Burdens and miscellaneous for all above personnel at 10 per cent for plant labor and 25 per cent of items 1, 2, and 3.
6. Contract operating assistance to allow a certain number of operators per shift for a period of 90 days.
7. Technical assistance from parent company for a certain number of man-months, depending on the size of the operation.
8. Initial low operating efficiencies at a penalty of 10 per cent of variable costs for 6 months.
9. Generally assume 10 per cent contingencies on the total of the above expenses.
10. Generally for a process which is not entirely new, a fixit cost is required ranging from 3 to 5 per cent of the plant investment. This money is generally spent after the startup time and basically covers excessive maintenance encountered during initial operation of the plant.

Startup operations are considered complete when the plant has been demonstrated at design capacity for some predetermined period of time. There is a growing tendency in the chemical industry to accept demonstrations at a capacity somewhat less than 100 per cent.

Estimating Construction Time. Most estimates of construction time tend to be too optimistic, especially on large projects. Whereas projects costing under $1 million are usually completed in 6 to 18 months, those costing more than $5 million usually take from 18 to 42 months to complete. Delays of as much as 12 months behind schedule are not uncommon. Cost of such delays is not so much the added construction costs as it is the cost of lost production.

Fixed-capital Cost Control. Any estimate of capital cost, no matter how painstakingly prepared, is meaningless without provisions for subsequent control of expenditures. Sound cost control must be a carefully coordinated effort of the several departments concerned with the construction job. There must be clear and unrestricted flow of information among project engineer, resident construction engineer, cost engineer, and accountants, and this should follow well-established techniques to be most effective.

The **cost of cost control** has been found to vary between 0.25 and 0.5 per cent of total project value. On several large projects each costing over $10,000,000, typical cost-control staffs consisted of one home office engineer, one field cost engineer, two field accountants, two quantity surveyors, and two cost clerks. On smaller projects, staffing can be reduced to one cost engineer and one accountant. In all cases, adequate cost control has been found to justify its cost many times over.

It is the responsibility of the field cost engineer to coordinate vast amounts of detailed information and reduce it to simplified reporting forms for immediate convenient use by those most concerned. In addition to weekly releases of unit costs, he is also responsible for a compilation of a monthly summary cost report which, in actuality, is a current reevaluation of the project control estimate. By projecting the job to completion, he indicates to all those concerned whether he expects the project to overrun, underrun, or break even. The summary cost reports indicate clearly which accounts seem to be in trouble and thereby serve to alert the organization to apply remedies to bring costs in line. Experience has shown this procedure to be effective in enabling proper measures to be taken soon enough to make necessary changes to prevent serious overruns.

MANUFACTURING COST ESTIMATION

REFERENCES: Chilton, *Chem. Eng.*, **58** (6), 108 (1951). Hur, "Chemical Process Economics in Practice," pp. 51–65, Reinhold, New York, 1956. Nelson, *Oil Gas J.*, **56,** 147 (Feb. 24, 1958). Sherwin, *Petrol. Refiner*, **33,** 103 (February), 151 (March), 209 (May, 1954). Sweet, *Chem. Eng. Progress*, **52,** 179 (1956). VanNoy *et al.*, *U.S. Bur. Mines, Rept. Invest.* 4534, 1949. Wessel, *Chem. Eng.*, **60** (1), 168 (1953).

Manufacturing cost estimates of various degrees of accuracy are needed to evaluate new investments, to evaluate new products for manufacture in available equipment, to derive operating budgets, to justify minor process changes, and to evaluate the position of a competitor. As with other estimates, accuracy and extent of detail should depend on the purpose of the estimate.

A **complete cost estimate** must cover a great many items, as shown in Table 26-23. Estimating effort should be allocated to the most important elements of cost so that elements of minor significance receive proportionately less attention. For batch processes, raw material and labor costs are likely to be most important. Fixed costs are usually more important in continuous processes; unit manufacturing costs may depend largely on the fraction of time the plant is operating (stream time). In other cases, factors such as energy (*e.g.*, electrochemicals) will warrant major attention.

Manufacturing cost estimates should follow the form used for product cost statements within the company. A **typical format** for process cost estimates is shown in Table 26-24. (The column headings may be somewhat different for accounting statements.) The information at the top of the form is particularly important to establish the conditions of the estimate and permit other estimates to be made at other conditions.

Columns are provided separately for totaling fixed and variable manufacturing costs, with total costs all shown in a third column. This permits gathering information on one sheet which will constitute both an incremental and a total cost estimate. Estimates of total accounting cost are usually desired by the departments concerned, in order to see how a specific project will affect their operating statements. The estimate of variable costs only is often required for decision making.

For plants already in operation, **accounting records** provide a major source of information for estimates. The greatest difficulty in transfer of information is in proper use of allocated costs and overheads. Research and development engineers often have to make manufacturing cost estimates for entirely new processes. However, parallels can be drawn with existing operations, and fairly accurate estimates can be made even in these circumstances.

When an investment proposal is to be justified, manu-

Table 26-23. Check List of Manufacturing Cost Items

- Plant costs:
  - Materials
    - Raw materials
    - Processing chemicals
    - Utilities
    - Maintenance materials
    - Operating supplies
  - Labor
    - Direct operating labor
    - Operating supervision
    - Direct maintenance labor
    - Maintenance supervision
    - Pay-roll burden on all labor charges
      - Federal O.A.S.I.
      - Workmen's compensation coverage
      - Contribution to pensions, life insurance, etc.
      - Vacations, holidays, sick leave, overtime premium
      - Company contribution of profit sharing or thrift plan
  - Plant overhead
    - Administration
    - Indirect labor
      - Laboratory
      - Technical service and engineering
      - Shops and repair facilities
      - Shipping department
    - Purchasing, receiving, and warehousing
    - Personnel and industrial relations
    - Inspection, safety, and fire protection
    - Automotive and rail switching
    - Accounting, clerical, and stenographic
    - Communications—telephone, mail, teletype
    - Plant custodial and plant protective
    - Plant hospital and dispensary
    - Cafeteria and clubrooms
    - Recreational activities
    - Local contributions and memberships
    - Taxes on property and operating licenses
    - Insurance—property, liability
    - Waste disposal
  - Depreciation
- Distribution costs:
  - Containers and packages
  - Freight
  - Operation of terminals and warehouses
    - Wages and salaries—plus pay-roll burden
    - Operating materials and utilities
    - Rental or depreciation
- Marketing costs:
  - Direct
    - Salesmen's salaries and commissions
    - Advertising and promotional literature
    - Technical sales service
    - Samples and displays
  - Indirect
    - Sales supervision
    - Travel and entertainment
    - Market research and sales analysis
    - District office expenses
- Administrative expense:
  - Salaries and expenses of officers and staff
  - General accounting, clerical, and auditing
  - Central engineering and technical
  - Legal and patent
    - Within company
    - Outside counsel
    - Payment and collection of royalties
  - Research and development
    - Own operations
    - Sponsored, consultant, and contract work
  - Contributions and dues to associations
  - Public relations
  - Financial
    - Debt management
    - Maintenance of working capital
    - Credit functions
  - Communications and traffic management
  - Central purchasing activities
  - Taxes and insurance

facturing cost estimates may be necessary for both the proposed and base cases. The base case will often be an existing operation, while the proposed case will be manufacture in new facilities.

Raw Materials, Catalysts, and Chemicals. Raw materials are usually considered first. They should always be incorporated in the estimate on a delivered basis. It is assumed that the nature and quantity of required raw materials is supplied before the cost estimate begins.

Oil, Paint & Drug Reporter publishes each week a comprehensive list of current prices of natural and synthetic chemical materials and an annual "Hi-Lo" issue showing certain price histories. *Chemical & Engineering News* publishes in the last issue of each quarter a relatively complete price list of chemicals. A special list is usually included covering a restricted class of materials, such as synthetic resins or surface-active agents.

Prices below these published rates may be obtained in special circumstances. If raw-material cost is important to the economics of the process, a company will usually negotiate for a special **contract price.** Such negotiations may in fact determine the plant location so that the new plant can be near a supplier who will deliver the raw material "over the fence."

Different prices prevail for different **volumes of purchase.** The carload (c.l.) or tank-car price is lower than the price for smaller quantities, such as less-than-carload (l.c.l.). Scale of operations will determine the optimum quantity to purchase at one time; the lower price of the larger quantity must be balanced against the higher inventory the plant will be forced to carry.

Carloads of drums may run 25,000 to 50,000 lb., depending on the particular chemical involved. **Truckload** prices are usually the same, although the truckload quantity may be smaller. **Tank cars** usually carry 8000 or 10,000 gal.; some cars are available with capacities greater than 20,000 gal. A drum of chemical material usually is 55 gal.; weight varies widely with bulk density of the contents. Prices may also be published for carloads of drums for solids as well as liquids.

Form of raw material should be determined on the basis of lowest cost, considering process, price, freight costs, and inventories. Some solids can be transported more cheaply as solutions or slurries, with savings in handling costs in the plant as well as by the carrier. These facts should be analyzed when making an estimate.

Freight cost is cited in published prices in four different ways. "Delivered" means that the seller pays the freight, and the price the buyer pays will be independent of point of delivery. "Freight allowed" is essentially the same from the cost standpoint; the price is quoted f.o.b. the producing plant, but the seller refunds the buyer's freight cost from the loading to the delivery point (f.o.b. refers to "free on board"). The third pricing method is f.o.b. the producing plant, referred to as a "works" price. Here the buyer pays the freight and is not reimbursed. The fourth and most complex method is "freight equalized." Here the buyer pays freight equivalent to the freight cost measured from the nearest producing point. Thus when the buyer purchases the raw material from a distant producer, that producer reimburses the buyer for the difference in total freight between that from the distant source and a closer competitor.

If a sufficient volume of material is involved, special freight rates can be negotiated with the carrier. In the United States, such a rate must then be cleared with the Interstate Commerce Commission by the carrier on the basis that the lower rate promotes competition.

Price is also affected by required **quality.** Wherever a less pure raw material can be used in a process, all estimates should, of course, be made on that basis to take advantage of the lower price. The minimum acceptable raw-material quality should be determined before final estimates are made. Usual gradations of quality on which a price may be quoted are technical grade (usually with a specified percentage purity; specifications on percentages of various impurities must be investigated separately), C.P. (chemically pure), U.S.P. (meeting the standards of the United States Pharmacopoeia). For all grades, prices may be quoted as 100 per cent

Table 26-24. Typical Form for Manufacturing Cost Estimates

Est. No.________ Date________

Supersedes________ Prepd. by________

Product________ Producer________ Location________

By-products________ Process________ Batch/continuous________

Annual capacity________ Fixed investment________

Annual production________ Stream days/year________ Product basis: Real/as is________

Item	Unit	Value	Units/ lb. prod.	Variable costs $/lb. prod.	Variable costs M$/yr.	Fixed costs M$/yr.	Fixed costs $/lb. prod.	Total costs M$/yr.	Total costs $/lb. prod.
Ingredients:									
Subtotal ingredients									
Processing:									
Labor, operating									
Fringe benefits									
Supplies and sundries									
Maintenance									
Steam	M lb.								
Electricity	kw.-hr.								
Compressed air	M cu. ft.								
Water	M gal.								
Effluent treatment									
Subtotal processing									
Supervision									
Control laboratory									
Technical staff and engineering									
Subtotal plant overheads									
Insurance and taxes									
Royalty									
Depreciation									
Subtotal fixed charges									
Total including fixed charges									
By-product credit—specify									
Total cost in bulk									
Packaging cost									
Plant packed cost									
Freight									
Selling expense									
General expense									
Research expense									
Subtotal distribution, research, and administration									
TOTAL									

desired chemical content ("real" basis) or a price that includes impurities or diluents ("as is" basis).

For raw materials supplied from elsewhere within the company, the cost engineer may be supplied prices to be used in his estimate. These are called **intracompany or transfer prices.** They may be cash costs, cost with a profit included, artificial prices set for tax purposes, etc. If the cost engineer is simply estimating a cost of manufacture he should use these prices. If he is responsible for the over-all economic evaluation of a project, the transfer prices will have to be properly interpreted.

Utilities. The following are usually considered utilities, although in some companies one or more of them may be treated under other categories on the cost sheet: steam, cooling water, deionized water, electric power, refrigeration, compressed air, instrument air, effluent treatment. Their effect on the cost of the product will naturally depend on the process involved. Occasionally the costing of utilities will be intricate because utilities require other utilities for their own manufacture. Cost ranges for various utilities are shown in Table 26-25.

Steam is measured in thousands of pounds (M lb.),

or for small boilers it may be measured in boiler horsepower (33,749 B.t.u./hr.). However, it is often costed on a B.t.u. basis for arithmetic ease, and the cost is expressed in terms of dollars per million B.t.u.

A pound of steam as generated may have 1200 to 1600 B.t.u./lb. Any condensate returned to the boiler house will have over 200 B.t.u./lb.

Most plants use several steam-pressure levels. When generating steam at high pressures (650 lb./sq. in. or more), back-pressure or extraction turbines may be employed for the dual purposes of driving equipment and supplying lower-pressure-level steam to processes. In many plants waste-heat boilers are additional sources of steam at intermediate pressure levels.

Table 26-25. Typical Full-cost Utility Prices
January, 1960

	Large plant, Gulf Coast	Small plant, Northeast
Electricity, $/kw.-hr	0.008–0.012	0.010–0.015
Steam, $/thousand lb	0.30–0.50	1.00–2.00
Cooling water, $/thousand gal	0.01–0.02	0.015–0.03
Process water, $/thousand gal	0.10–0.25	0.15–0.30
Natural gas, $/million B.t.u	0.15–0.25	0.60–1.25

When using steam for heating purposes only, the engineer has little difficulty in assigning a cost on a B.t.u. or M lb./hr. basis. However, when steam generated at high pressure is used to develop mechanical or electrical energy and for supplying process steam from the turbine exhausts, separating energy and heating cost components becomes rather involved. In costing, credit should be taken for the heating value of any condensate returned to the boiler.

The full cost of steam will include fuel, boiler-water treatment, operating labor, depreciation, and maintenance. A rough estimate might be two to three times the cost of fuel.

Water requirements will fall into three categories: cooling, process, and miscellaneous, such as washing or drinking. For **cooling** purposes it is usually uneconomic and occasionally a violation of conservation laws to use a treated water on a once-through basis, although untreated river or sea water may be used in this manner. Recycled water returns to a cooling tower, where its temperature is lowered, mainly through evaporation. At the tower the water is subjected to minor chemical control for pH adjustment and to suppress the build-up of salts. More important for process use, biocides are introduced to control the growth of life forms on the tower itself. The cooling water will have a cost for chemicals, depreciation, and maintenance of a tower, and the energy required to operate the pumps.

The temperature differential between the incoming and outgoing water will be a complex function of ambient and return temperature and humidity. Because of this variable Δt, design water usage will fluctuate with the weather. The charge for cooling water will normally be $0.01 to $0.02 per 1000 gal. circulated. Occasionally the cooling water will be such a small item of cost that it will be charged on an allocated basis rather than by measurement.

Process water will be subject to a variety of chemical treatments depending on the end use, as will water used in the steam boilers. Cost of **process water** may be $0.10 to $0.30 per 1000 gal. Potable and wash water are not usually distributed as direct costs but allocated as a plant overhead charge.

The expense to operations of cooling or process water is usually not significant to the over-all economics of a chemical plant. The estimates listed here should be satisfactory if water costs are not available from plant records.

Refrigeration, when required in a chemical process, may be supplied by ice, dry ice, or a refrigeration machine. Refrigeration may or may not be treated as a separate cost factor. If there is a central refrigeration unit circulating refrigerant to various processes, there will be a calculated cost of refrigeration, including labor, maintenance, and depreciation on the equipment, refrigerant make-up, energy to drive the compressor, etc. If a process has its own refrigeration machine, the operating cost will be charged directly to the process and will not be segregated. A combination of both systems may be used.

Unit of refrigeration is the standard ton per day (ST/D); cost is usually $0.40 to $1.00 per ton. A standard ton is equivalent to removal of 288,000 B.t.u. of heat per day (200 B.t.u./min.). The cost of refrigeration is likely to be highly variable because of the variety of machine designs and possible refrigeration temperatures.

Inert gases and compressed air are minor cost items for most processes. An inert gas may be used to blanket a chemical reactor or storage tank. The gas is usually carbon dioxide or nitrogen. Compressed air is usually used for control of valves. Costs in these instances would be so low that they would not be based on measured flows but allocated on the basis of production or operating time of the different units. However, if compressed air is used in great volume, such as an oxidation process, the cost would be important and would be charged like refrigeration.

Electrical energy in most cases represents a modest part of total operating costs. It is a major operating-cost component in electrochemical processes such as chlorine, aluminum, and calcium carbide manufacture.

Electrical power in the United States is usually purchased from a public utility. It is furnished to the plant property line at voltages which depend on total power requirements. Contracts made with the public utilities are based on published rates approved by local public utility commissions and supervised by the Federal Power Commission if the public utility is considered engaged in interstate commerce, as most are.

All major contracts contain a demand component, an energy component, and a variable fuel-cost component. The **demand charge** is based on the maximum power requirement drawn by the plant during a measurable period, usually 15 or 30 min. in any one month. The demand charge represents fixed charges which must be paid by the utility for generation, transmission, and distribution facilities.

The **energy charge** is based on kilowatt-hours used. It can be applied as a flat unit cost per kilowatt-hour or as a decremental charge which diminishes as kilowatt-hour consumption increases. Because of the demand charge, a maximum use of demand will result in lower unit rates for electricity. The ratio of average usage to demand is termed the load factor.

Both demand and energy charges per unit will decrease as a plant's power requirement increases. However, most electric-power rate schedules are designed to yield greater savings by improving the load factor rather than increasing the load.

The **fuel-adjustment charge** reflects the increased or decreased cost of fuel to the power company.

When considering the economics of a proposed process, only the cost of additional power requirement should be used. However, when the actual cost accounting takes place the requirements of all the processes will be combined. In addition to the cost of power from the utility company, the power must be transformed and distributed through the plant proper. For a chemical plant these **distribution charges** may be 50 per cent of the purchase price of the power from the utility.

Electric rates may be obtained by applying to local utilities which have on hand published copies of their rate schedules. The Federal Power Commission publishes and distributes at a nominal charge the National Electric Rate Book, which contains the published rates of all public utilities in the United States. Special rates which may be discriminatory cannot be established under the terms of the Federal Power Act. However, rates can still be negotiated for large blocks of power in new areas; these must be made available to any other consumer whose load characteristics (quantity, power factor, and load factor) qualify for the lower rate.

In-plant Generation. The growth of large, efficient, networked central stations in the United States has made private generation of power uneconomical for most chemical companies. However, in cases where there are large demands for low-pressure steam, private electric-power generation may be attractive. Power generation should be considered if process steam usage is of the order of 200,000 lb./hr. or more at low pressure levels. In such cases back-pressure or extraction-type turbine generators operating at high-pressure (600 to 900 lb./sq. in.) and high-temperature (900° to 1100°F.) throttle conditions are employed. Steam exhausting to lower temperature and pressure levels can be reused for driving mechanical equipment, for process heating, or for absorption refrigeration. Common levels for chemical plants are 50 to 150 lb./sq. in. gage.

Costing steam to heating or power use will be an arbitrary decision, since these coproducts cannot readily be separated. In most cases, total steam cost is allocated between power generation and process use on a consistent basis arrived at by plant engineers and accountants. In making economic calculations for costs where steam for power and process coexist the over-all system cost should be considered.

Waste disposal may be a major or a minor cost. In a large plant, effluents from spills, discarded fractions, etc., are run together into a tank or pond, neutralized, aged, and perhaps diluted until they are innocuous to the body of water into which they are eventually drained.

Costs of an effluent-treating system include chemicals, maintenance, depreciation, and operating labor of the facility. If there are many products which are served by a single facility, allocation of these costs must be made on the best available basis. There are normally few analytical controls, records, or measurements of such individual waste streams.

In estimates made at early stages of plant design, it is important chiefly to provide for some disposition of significant waste streams. If it seems possible that such streams might go to the local municipal waste-disposal plant, it might be prudent to consider using the "per gallon" charge of that unit. At later stages, specialists can be obtained for detailed cost estimates.

Labor and Supervision. Most investment proposals will involve either an addition or a reduction in the labor force. Many savings projects are justified on the basis of labor savings alone. For important installations, industrial engineers and personnel departments may give assistance in estimating labor requirements of the process.

In general, **direct labor** is more important for batch than for continuous processes, and scheduling is considerably more flexible. If a batch process is not running for part of the time, the men may often be switched to other operations to utilize their time efficiently. Different manpower on a given batch operation, operated the same number of shifts, can often result in widely differing over-all time cycles of production and, therefore, a different production per week. Many operations in a batch cycle can be handled either consecutively or simultaneously, depending on the demand for the product.

Conversely, for continuous processes the labor force is almost constant whether the production rate is high or low. Labor becomes more of a fixed cost than in the batch operation and, usually, a less important cost. Only the labor for raw-materials handling, packaging, etc., may be affected significantly by production rates.

As automation in processes increases, the importance of direct labor in the chemical plant decreases. The minimum labor requirement for a given area is eventually determined by safety considerations rather than the number of duties to which the operator must attend.

Indirect Labor. Many other categories of nonoperating labor are required in the plant, but most accounting systems and, therefore, most estimates do not allocate them directly to a cost center or a product but group them in plant overheads as overhead labor. Under this category would fall personnel required to switch railroad cars or to maintain plant grounds, janitors, etc.

Supervision. Every area of the plant and all personnel must be under the supervision of other responsible personnel. Estimates may be made individually of the personnel required, or such charges may be included in plant overheads discussed below. Company policy and the nature of the process will determine whether supervisors are required on all shifts and the relative number of area supervisors, foremen, etc.

Fringe Benefits. All companies have labor costs in addition to those paid for hours worked. These costs are significant in relation to direct wage payments and must be included in any cost estimate. They include Social Security, unemployment taxes, sick pay, accident insurance, meal allowances, holidays, reserves for pensions, etc. The sum of these fringe benefits may add roughly 10 to 25 per cent to the straight time wage payment. There is considerable variation among companies because of difference in company policies and accounting philosophy.

Shift Premiums and Overtime. Legal requirements and union contracts call for overtime to be paid for work in excess of a certain number (usually 40) hours per week. Some contracts also call for additional premiums to be paid for working Saturday or Sunday or for working night shifts. Full allowance for these factors should be made in any cost estimate.

Wage rates for chemical operators (and for maintenance specialists, etc., also required in the plant) are available from local chambers of commerce and are also published from time to time by the U.S. Department of Labor, Bureau of Labor Statistics. Wages vary significantly by region in the United States (see Table 26-17).

Scheduling. An important factor to consider in labor costs is the scheduling of shifts for plant operation in order to keep overtime and premium payments to a minimum. Most continuous processes are kept on stream for 24 hr. a day. Each post in the plant requires three men for full scheduling even when the plant is operated only 5 days a week. Equitable schedules on 6- and 7-day operation are more difficult to develop. By use of four crews (frequently referred to as "four shifts"), three 8-hr. shifts can be filled for all 7 days with overtime payments of only 2 hr. per man per week on the average.

For additional information on labor estimation and costs, see: "Fringe Benefits 1961" (Economic Research Department, Chamber of Commerce of the United States, September, 1961); "Directory of Community Wage Surveys, 1948–54" (U.S. Department of Labor, Bureau of Labor Statistics, 1954); "Employment Outlook in the Chemical Industry" (U.S. Department of Labor, Bureau of Labor Statistics, *Publ.* 1151, 1953); Wessel [*Chem. Eng.*, **59** (7), 209 (1952)].

Maintenance. As fixed costs rise per unit of production and per operator in the chemical industry, the importance of maintenance increases. Modern automated plants have maintenance forces that outnumber the chemical operators. Total cost of maintenance will be a function of complexity of the process, materials of construction, caliber of the maintenance force, and previous maintenance done on the plant.

Maintenance cost is built up of three components—materials required, manpower to install them, and overhead for supervision and scheduling. The latter includes such operations as central machine shops. These three parts of maintenance cost may represent perhaps 50, 40, and 10 per cent of the total cost, respectively.

The most frequent method of **estimating maintenance costs** before construction of a plant is to include a certain percentage of fixed investment as an annual maintenance expense. In general, 4 per cent per year of the new investment for maintenance is a minimum. For corrosive processes or those with extensive instrumentation, this figure may increase to as high as 7 to 10 per cent of the investment.

Although this system has been in use for some years, it has some inherent deficiencies:

1. If investment is increased in order to reduce corrosion, then the percentage factor works in the wrong direction.
2. Maintenance costs are not constant over the life of the plant but will increase during later years.
3. Accounting practices among companies vary widely in distinguishing between equipment additions that are maintenance and those which are capital additions.

If adequate plant records are available of maintenance cost experience with various types of equipment, these data may be used to estimate maintenance costs of similar equipment to be used in a new plant. Data of this type have been published by Leonard for chemical process equipment [*Chem. Eng.*, **58** (9), 149 (1951)].

The variation of maintenance cost with **equipment age** has been analyzed by plotting annual maintenance costs for various types of plants vs. the product of investment and age [*Chem. Eng.*, **66** (3), 140; (14), 172 (1959)]. Such plots show a fairly steady increase in maintenance costs as the plant gets older.

Insurance and property taxes must both be considered in a manufacturing cost estimate for a new installation. They are usually relatively minor cost items. Insurance rates and tax rates both vary widely from one locality to another, and experts should be consulted if precise estimates are required.

The types of **insurance coverage** required for a facility will depend on company policy. One type insures against loss due to fires and explosion of vessels. The assets covered will be only those which could be *actually* damaged, not the total facilities of the plant. The value of the property will depend on replacement value less an allowance for physical depreciation. Deductible policies are available which can drastically reduce the premium. Rate will vary with the nature of the facility; up to 0.5 per cent per year of fixed investment might be allowed for both fire insurance and boiler insurance.

Another type of insurance is business interruption (use and occupancy) insurance. This is designed to protect the company from losses of anticipated profits that might occur because a unit was shut down because of an accident. The premium is not ordinarily charged directly to the manufacturing cost of a product. It is based on performance and risk characteristics of the entire company and is most often included as a corporate overhead cost. The additional premium due to a new process is a complicated calculation; it may be approximately the same as fire and boiler insurance premiums.

Workmen's compensation insurance is usually considered as a fringe benefit and included in labor costs. A company may have other types of insurance, such as water damage, windstorm, power plant, earthquake, etc., but these are less common than the two principal ones cited above.

Property taxes are generally charged on the manufacturing cost statement. School district, state, and city levies are all applicable, based on the assessed valuation of a property. Generally, a plant will pay between 0.5 and 1.5 per cent per year of its net asset value for property taxes. Inventories and other such property may or may not be taxed. Certain states may give exemption for property tax for a certain period of time, but because these privileges may be withdrawn at any time, it is unwise to neglect property taxes in preliminary estimates.

A valuable listing of applicable taxes for operation in every state of the union is given in "Plant Location, 1963" (Simmons Boardman, New York).

Plant Overheads. All costs on the manufacturing facility which are not chargeable to any particular operation are considered plant overheads and must be charged back to the manufacturing cost of the product on some **allocated basis**. This includes salaries of supervisory personnel from the plant manager down to (and often including) the supervisory personnel discussed under Labor above, plant guards and janitors, fixed charges on buildings in general use such as administrative offices and cafeterias, change houses, etc. If accounting, purchasing, or personnel departments are maintained at the plant site, they would also be included.

Since no one cost center or product is most responsible for a particular overhead cost, the cost must be allocated in the most reasonable manner available. This overhead may be charged on several bases, such as direct labor hours on a process; the total of labor, supervision, and maintenance hours; plant investment involved; etc. Some plants divide various items of overhead as to whether they service personnel or investment. The two components can then be charged to the various processes, one on the basis of labor hours and the other on the basis of relative investment.

There is little published information on overheads; for preliminary estimation it may be assumed that between $0.50 and $1 of plant overhead is required for each dollar of direct operating and maintenance labor. As estimates approach the final stages, company records may be examined to determine the average overhead requirements. If an entirely new plant of a similar nature is being installed, such a ratio can be used, or a complete overhead manning and investment schedule should be prepared to get a closer estimate.

If a small unit is being added at an existing plant, it is probable that overheads will not increase in proportion to the direct labor or to the investment because of this small addition. **Estimation of overheads** is a major problem and is discussed in detail elsewhere (p. 26-10). When the investment being considered is a replacement or a slight expansion, it is often sufficient to assume that overheads on the proposed equipment would be the same as they are on the existing equipment; so that no detailed estimate need be made of the related overhead costs.

Technical Staff. Many plants have engineers or chemists available in the plant organization to help with the equipment troubles or assist in process improvements. The accounting system may charge the time of these technical people to the process that is using them, but very often these charges are included in plant overheads.

Quality Control. All chemical processes need analytical control to some degree; operators themselves may carry out simple determinations for the control of uncomplicated reactions, and this may be sufficient. In other cases, an analytical laboratory within the process area would test production samples. In still more complex cases, a central analytical laboratory might be required for determinations requiring special instruments.

Labor is the main charge in a quality-control testing group, and the estimated amount of analytical control cost depends on the complexity of controlling the process. Final product analysis will also be necessary, usually on a sampling basis, to be sure that it conforms to product specifications.

By-products. Just as a cost must be added if there is a waste-disposal problem from a given process, so a credit can be allowed if a salable by-product is produced. By-products which are unavoidably produced with a major product do increase the problems in balancing production with sales for both chemicals, but at the estimating stage, some credit is logical for each pound of by-product produced.

At the estimating stage, analysis of a new project is made around the complete processing unit, and individual costs need not be allocated to the major product or the by-product. Most of the problems of accounting allocation of costs are therefore avoided.

However, it is unrealistic to credit the entire sales value of even a well-established chemical product to the manufacturing cost of the major product. If the chemical is sold on a delivered basis, some freight must be deducted. Selling costs associated with it must also be deducted. Certainly packaging costs and costs of any special purification steps should be also deducted from the sales price of a by-product when crediting it to the manufacturing cost of the major product.

The **packaging cost** for a product includes both the cost of the container and the cost of putting the product into the container. The container selected will depend on the product's chemical and physical properties and upon the volume of the product required by the customer. Containers may be disposable (paper bags), returnable (steel drums), or leased (railroad tank cars). In size they may range from a 1-qt. can to a cross-country pipe line. Some typical container costs are shown in Table 26-26.

Table 26-26. Typical Purchased-container Costs

January, 1960

	¢/lb. of product
5-gal. pail	1.5–3
50-lb. paper bag	0.2–0.4
200-lb. fiberboard drum	0.4–0.6
55-gal.-steel drum	1.5–4
Railroad tank car, lease basis	0.03–0.1

The packaging operation may be performed by the chemical operators, or it may be done by a separate department. The cost is highly variable because it can be simple or complicated, *e.g.*, pumping the product into a pipe line vs. filling small cans with a noxious chemical.

Cost of the packaging operation is reflected in the price schedule for a product. The price is usually quoted on a "normal" method of packaging the product, *e.g.*, tank cars. From this base price a lower or higher price would be quoted by the seller depending on the additional costs or savings obtained by packaging in different containers.

Supplies and Sundries. Manufacturing cost estimates must include an allowance for minor items not falling into a major classification. They are sometimes called operating supplies. In this category might be filter cloths, work clothes, gas masks, etc.

Depreciation is an important element on the manufacturing cost statement; it is completely discussed elsewhere (p. 26-11).

Sales expense includes all costs involved in merchandising the product—salesmen's salaries, warehousing, advertising, customer service, etc. It is almost essential to incorporate company experience in any estimate of sales expense, since it varies so widely with the type of product being sold and the method of selling. For a bulk chemical in carload quantities, 2 to 4 per cent of total sales value might be adequate; for a specialty item sold in small units, 20 per cent of sales value might be conservative. It is particularly difficult to estimate the increase in sales expense due to addition of a new product to the line.

Research Expense. In investment evaluations, two types of research expense should be distinguished. The first is research in a given field that a company will find it necessary to undertake if it should decide to enter that field. This **new research** expense should be carefully estimated and included in the economic evaluation of the project.

The second type is **corporate research** expense, which is usually not affected by a particular investment. Research cost in total can be compared with dollar sales in total, but the amount of research effort is not affected by any particular investment decision. Some companies prefer to consider in each investment evaluation the research which has gone into this particular development in the past. However, past research expense is a sunk cost. Other companies prefer to show average research overheads as a charge against every proposed investment so that each investment will support its share of research. It is nevertheless true that certain investments can profitably be made without considering such a charge; some companies handle research charges this way. For companies in the chemical process industries, research expense runs 2 to 5 per cent of sales value in most cases.

Administrative overhead is the sum of general office costs which are not directly charged in any other fashion: the salaries of top executives, legal fees, central accounting staffs, public relations, treasury and accounting functions, and even economic evaluation. Administrative overhead varies from 3 to 10 per cent of total sales value, depending on the type of organization. The same problems exist in the determination of its effect on a given investment as with research overhead, and the same alternative solutions are proposed and used by different companies.

Freight Costs. In addition to consideration of freight costs for raw materials required by the process, freight costs must be considered for the end product.

The sales department, in substantiating that a market exists for the product, should have estimated a probable **marketing pattern,** *i.e.*, the quantities that would be sold to customers at certain locations. (This estimate would also have been made if a plant-location study were made for the project.) If these customers account for over half the plant output, then the average freight cost to these points might be reasonably used for the entire projected sales volume.

Freight cost must be included in the economics only if the producer pays the freight; *i.e.*, sales are on a delivered or freight equalized basis. However, freight cost should be estimated in all evaluations, since the freight basis could be changed in the future because of competitive conditions. Further, there might be some reduction in anticipated sales volume if customers have to pay a higher freight bill than when purchasing from existing sources.

Current **freight rates** can usually be obtained easily

and exactly on specific chemical products between any two points. However, it is difficult to get a correlation which can be useful in an over-all estimate of the freight which will be encountered on a new product. If the market area is fairly well known, however, a request for exact rates involving 20 or 30 destinations can provide a correlation such as that shown in Fig. 26-8 which will be helpful in estimating over-all costs.

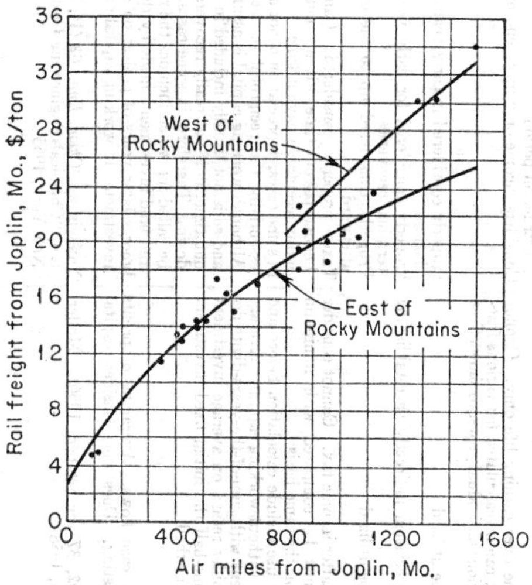

FIG. 26-8. Ammonium nitrate freight rates, January, 1960, correlated with air miles from Joplin, Mo.

Estimation of freight costs is particularly difficult when materials are shipped on a freight equalized basis. Such studies require a detailed map showing locations of other producers and freight at certain distances from each of these plants. Only then can a precise freight estimate be prepared.

Fortunately, freight on chemical products is not a major cost in most cases, and if 1 to 2¢ per pound is included to assure that the item has not been forgotten, the preliminary estimate will probably be accurate enough. For further help, see Nelson [*Oil Gas J.*, **52,** 132 (Mar. 29, 1954)]; Perry ("Chemical Business Handbook," pp. 2-81–2-83, Sec. 9, McGraw-Hill, New York, 1954); Thompson [*Ind. Eng. Chem.*, **52,** 44A (November, 1960)]; Tighe [*Chem. Eng. News*, **31,** 752, 3538, 4916 (1953)]; Ward [*Ind. Eng. Chem.*, **47,** 1186 (1955)].

Manufacturing Cost Control. In a well-managed operation, manufacturing costs are controlled to ensure adherence to previous estimates or budgets. Close observance of regular accounting statements shows areas where costs seem out of control.

A number of cost-accounting systems are in use. Two systems can be distinguished by method of accumulating individual costs. A **process cost system** is one in which the costs incurred in an operation over a period of time are charged to a *process* or cost center. The accumulation of these charges can then be distributed to the units of product produced. If costs are accumulated against a particular job, such as manufacturing a particular lot of a product, it is a **job cost system.** A job is usually serially numbered. This system is often used when different products are made using common equipment by batch operations. Equipment maintenance is normally done under a job-order (work-order) system.

A **full cost system** is distinguished from a **direct cost system** by the types of cost included. The full cost system distributes all costs of operation to individual products. A direct cost system distributes only those costs which are directly variable with production. Fixed charges in the manufacturing operation, overhead, depreciation, etc., are recognized but not included at that point in the cost of manufacture. Costs that are semivariable, such as labor in a continuous operation, might or might not be included in the direct cost.

A cost-accounting system may be actual or standard. An **actual cost system** distributes to the various products all "costs" including depreciation incurred in a given period.

A **standard cost system** uses refined estimates of the component costs to determine the final product cost. These estimates are based on historical records adjusted for anticipated conditions. The difference between the standard and actual performance is called a **variance.** Study of these variances determines whether they were due to production volume, raw-material usage, etc.

PROFITABILITY MEASURES

REFERENCES: Bates and Weaver, *Chem. Week*, **80,** 115 (June 15, 1957). Dean, *Controller*, **26,** 64 (February, 1958). Gordon, *J. Business*, **28,** 253 (October, 1955). Hur, "Chemical Process Economics in Practice," pp. 82–102, Reinhold, New York, 1956. Swalm, *J. Ind. Eng.*, **9,** 99 (March–April), 275 (July–August, 1958). Weaver, *Chem. & Eng. News*, **39,** (39),94 (1961). Winn, *Petrol. Refiner*, **35,** 199 (July, 1956).

Profit is the obvious goal of investment in any enterprise, and though there are many others, this is the only one quantifiable and therefore useful for economic evaluation. However, profit maximization alone is not sufficient. The true goal is to improve the "efficiency" of production of profit from a dollar of investment in an enterprise or in a manufacturing facility. The ratio relating profit to investment in some manner is known as **rate of return on investment.**

Indeed the goal should not be to maximize the rate of return on investment. Actually, the ideal is to maximize the profits from investments which return to the investor more than the cost of the money which he is required to invest.

Many other **measures of profitability** have been suggested. "Return on sales" (the ratio of profit dollars to sales dollars) is often regarded as an important measure. It seems obvious on reflection that it cannot be used to measure economic performance. A high ratio of profit to sales value would be of little significance if high investment is required to get the profit. Return on sales may have some utility for a given firm when used for comparison of one period of time with another, if the line of business has not changed.

The elements shown in Table 26-1 must all be accounted for in the return-on-investment formula in some manner, so that all the factors which affect profitability of an investment can be given due consideration in developing an efficiency formula relating profits to investment. Unfortunately, while there are various ways of combining some or most of these elements, no ideal method for combining all of them has yet been found.

The most common methods for measuring return on new investments are compared in Table 26-27 and are further discussed below in terms of their ability to

Table 26-27. Comparison of Profitability Measures

Name of method	Return on original investment	Return on average investment	Payout time
Other titles	Engineer's method, du Pont method, operator's method, capitalized earning rate	Return on book investment, accountant's method	Payoff period (time), cash recovery period, payback period (time), payout period
Statement of intent	Percentage comparison of average annual profits over earning life to initial total fixed and working capital investment	Percentage comparison of average annual profits over earning life to average book investment including working capital	Years required to recover original depreciable investment from profits and depreciation accruals
Algebraic description	$\frac{\text{Average yearly profit during earning life only}}{\text{Original fixed investment + working capital}} \times 100$	$\frac{\text{Average yearly profit during earning life only}}{\text{Average fixed investment + working capital}} \times 100$	$\frac{\text{Original depreciable fixed investment}}{\text{Profit + yearly average depreciation over the period}}$
Geometric description	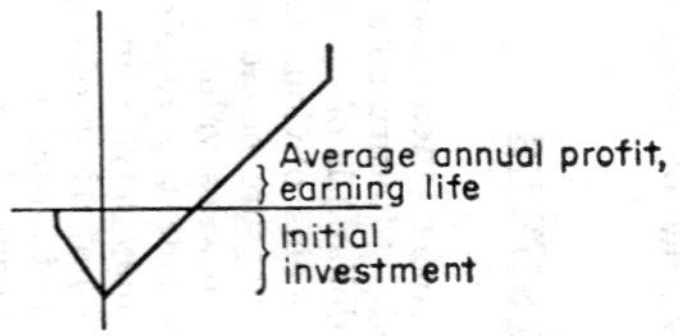	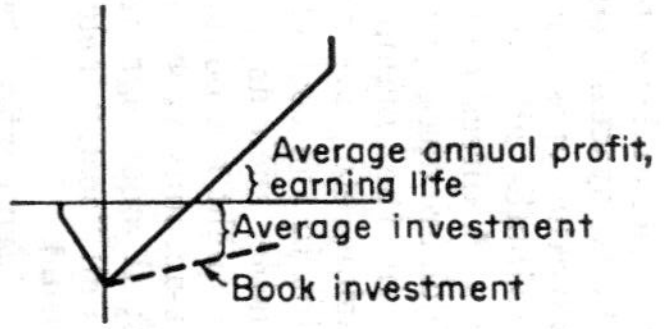	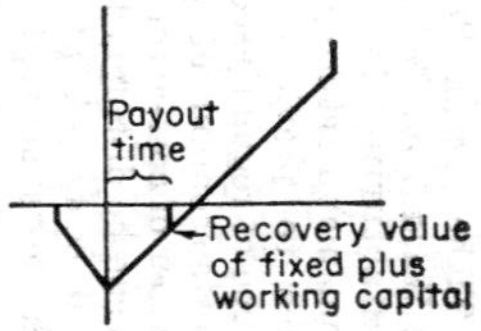
Handling of investment amount	Considers total amount	Considers a definite fraction of original investment; fraction depends on depreciation method	Considers depreciable investment only
Handling of investment timing	Cannot consider construction period or later fixed or working capital investments	Cannot consider construction period or later fixed or working capital investments	Cannot consider land or working capital or any investments beyond payout period; could, but usually does not, consider construction period
Handling of income amount	Considers average of income over earning life only. Cannot consider yearly differences; can be calculated for various fractions of capacity, or for various individual years, to show effect of operating level	Considers average of income over earning life only. Cannot consider yearly differences; can be calculated for various fractions of capacity, or for various individual years, to show effect of operating level	Considers income only up to end of payout time
Handling of income timing	Not considered; could not be utilized	Not considered; could not be utilized	Properly considered in early years; cannot consider at all from then on
Handling of capital recovery amount	Not considered; could not be utilized	Not considered except depreciation indirectly as establishing investment base	Properly considered for early years; cannot consider later or terminal recoveries
Handling of capital recovery timing	Not considered; could not be utilized	Not considered; could not be utilized	Properly considered up to the end of the payout time; not afterward
Handling of other elements	Often used either before or after income tax. Cannot consider economic life. Result must be compared with minimum acceptable rate of return on the same basis	Often used either before or after income tax. Cannot consider economic life. Result must be compared with minimum acceptable rate of return on the same basis	Taxes properly considered. Cannot consider economic life beyond payout time. Result must be compared with a maximum acceptable payout time
Variants of system	Major variants in common use include calculation before and after income tax, with and without working capital. Adding depreciation to profits gives a ratio of cash generation to investment which is equivalent to the reciprocal of payout time	Major variants in common use include calculation before and after income tax, with and without working capital. Average book investment is different with sum-of-the-years-digits depreciation, but many consider return on average investment should be calculated on one-half the initial fixed investment regardless of depreciation method	In some cases, depreciation is not added to profits so that this is essentially the reciprocal of return on original investment. Although working capital is assumed to be always recoverable and so is not usually included in the investment base for payout time, it is not really recoverable until the project is shut down. Therefore, in some cases, a cash recovery period may be called for which includes the restoration of working capital and land investments made by the company
Major shortcomings of system	Cannot consider timing of cash flows. Averaging of profits permits laxity in forecasting. Does not consider capital recoveries	Cannot consider timing of cash flows. Averaging of profits permits laxity in forecasting. Does not consider capital recoveries	Ignores later years of project on all counts. Cannot consider investments in working capital or land
References for further detail	Aries and Newton, "Chemical Engineering Cost Estimation," McGraw-Hill, New York, 1955. *Chem. Eng. News*, **33**, 3676 (1955). Livingston and Mills, *N.A.A. Bull.*, **40**, 15 (October, 1958). Capon, *Controller*, **25**, 475 (October, 1957). Davis, Financial Management Series No. 94, American Management Association, New York, 1950	Stiles, *J. Accountancy*, **102**, 37 (September, 1956). Moller, *Controller*, **26**, 107 (March, 1958)	Yanagisawa, *Chem. Eng.*, **62** (1), 185 (1955). Aries and Newton, "Chemical Engineering Cost Estimation," McGraw-Hill, New York, 1955

Table 26-27. Comparison of Profitability Measures—(*Continued*)

Name of method	Payout time, including interest	Present worth	Interest rate of return
Other titles	Cash recovery period	Venture worth, incremental present worth	Profitability index, discounted cash flow, internal rate of return, investor's method
Statement of intent	Years to recover original depreciable investment and a minimum acceptable rate of return from profit plus depreciation accruals	Comparison, by difference or ratio, of the (discounted) present value of all cash flows to the project with all investments in the project	Calculates interest rate at which company's outstanding investment is repaid by proceeds from project—the maximum rate at which convertible preferred stock could be issued for financing the investment in the proposed project and have it paid off in full at end of project's expected life
Algebraic description	$\frac{\text{Original depreciable fixed investment + interest*}}{\text{Profit + yearly average depreciation over the period}}$	Present worth of project earnings − (original fixed investment + working capital) or $\frac{\text{Present worth of project earnings}}{\text{Original fixed investment + working capital}}$	$\frac{\text{Average yearly profit during construction and earning life}}{\text{Average fixed investment + working capital + interest*}} \times 100$
Geometric description	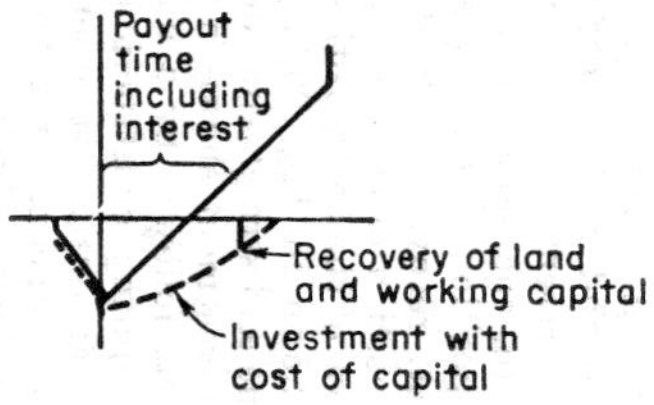	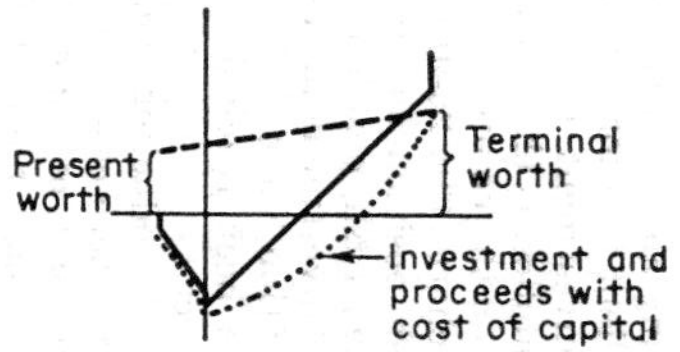	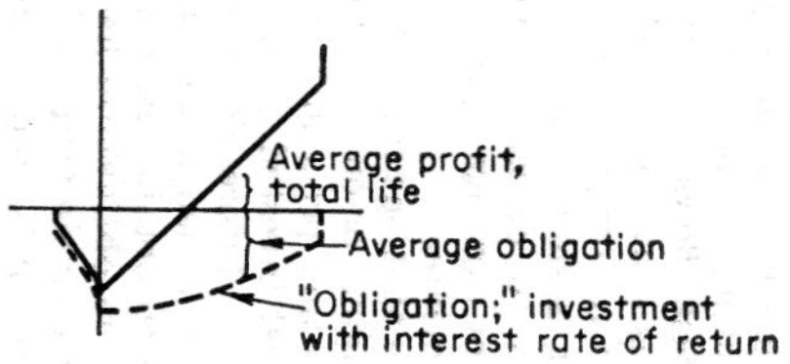
Handling of investment amount	Considers depreciable investment only	Considers all investment amounts	Considers all investment amounts
Handling of investment timing	Cannot consider land or working capital or any investments beyond period; could, but usually does not, consider construction period	Properly considered, including construction period and working capital	Properly considered, including construction period and working capital
Handling of income amount	Properly considered up to end of calculated period; cannot consider later income	Properly considered	Properly considered
Handling of income timing	Properly considered up to end of calculated period; cannot consider later	Properly considered	Properly considered
Handling of capital recovery amount	Properly considered up to end of calculated period; cannot consider later or terminal recoveries	Properly considered	Properly considered
Handling of capital recovery timing	Properly considered up to end of calculated period; cannot consider later or terminal recoveries	Properly considered	Properly considered
Handling of other elements	Taxes properly considered. Cannot consider full economic life, but may be useful for comparison with economic life since minimum acceptable rate of return has already been earned. Requires determination of minimum acceptable rate of return before calculation	Taxes properly considered. Considers total economic life. Requires determination of minimum acceptable rate of return on the same basis before calculation	Taxes properly considered. Considers total economic life. Must be compared against minimum acceptable rate of return on the same basis
Variants of system	Cost of capital may be substituted for minimum acceptable rate of return as discounting rate	Cost of capital may be substituted for minimum acceptable rate of return as a discounting interest rate. Present worth is usually expressed as the difference remaining when present value of investments is subtracted from the present value of all cash generations. Ratio of cash flow to investment is also suggested as a criterion. The combination can give some idea of the total magnitude of the project	Present worth is itself considered a variant of this system by some. System as described by some does not include consideration of land, working capital, construction period
Major shortcomings of system	Not so informative an answer as present worth, interest rate of return. Ranking with limited funds by this method would not maximize future worth of company. Cannot consider working capital or land	Result does not indicate magnitude of project. Most generally suitable of systems presented. Choosing projects with highest present worth will maximize future worth of company if assumptions hold	Multiple answers can be obtained for certain unusual cash-flow patterns. Does not properly compare projects of differing project lives. Does not indicate total magnitude of project. Adequate for evaluations not involving competition for funds
References for further detail	Scheuble, *Harvard Bus. Rev.*, **33**, 81 (September–October, 1955). Happel, *Chem. Eng.*, **58** (10), 146 (1951)	Happel, *Chem. Eng. Progress*, **51**, 533 (1955). Lorie and Savage, *J. Business*, **28**, 229 (1955). Winn, *Petrol. Refiner*, **35**, 199 (July, 1956)	Weaver and Reilly, *Chem. Eng. Progress*, **52**, 405 (correction 448) (October, 1956). Reul, *Harvard Bus. Rev.*, **35**, 116 (July–August, 1957). Dean, *Harvard Bus. Rev.*, **32**, 120 (January–February, 1954). Dean, *Controller*, **26**, 64 (February, 1958). McLean, *Harvard Bus. Rev.*, **36**, 59 (November–December, 1958)

* Interest charged on both fixed and working capital to reflect time value of money.

account for the many factors affecting the future of an investment. The comparison stresses the need for recognition by the method of *amount* and *timing* of capital investment, income, and capital recovery. This comparison is based on usual practice; therefore, in certain cases, the comment "not considered" is included where there is no technical reason that this formula could not consider the element involved (*e.g.*, Handling of Capital Recovery Amount under Return on Original Investment). Where the additional phrase "could not be utilized" appears, the formula could not be altered easily to consider the element under discussion.

Calculation of Returns on Investment. The most important differences among the various methods concern their ability to handle the key factors essential to investment decision, not ease of calculation. Calculation of return on investment itself is an insignificant part of the expense of developing the evaluation of any investment. Even the more sophisticated methods are easy to learn to use.

Return on Original Investment. Since this calculation is merely the ratio of annual profits to original investment, it can be done with great ease. If profits differ in different years, the return on investment may be calculated for several significant years during the life as well as the average for the entire economic life of the investment.

The only difficulties encountered in calculation may be those introduced by forecasts of subsequent investments of fixed or working capital, after the time of original investment. It is not clear whether the return should then be calculated on the original or on the total investment.

Calculation of **return on average investment** is much like that for return on original investment; only the denominator is different. The same limitations and complications are encountered. Accelerated depreciation introduces an added complication; book investment reduces more rapidly when accelerated depreciation is used, and "average investment" cannot be assumed to be working capital plus one-half the fixed investment.

Payout time is calculated by cumulating year by year, for the initial years of the project, the sum of profits plus depreciation. The intent is to determine during which year the total of profits and depreciation exceeds the amount of the original depreciable investment. A payout including a portion of a year (*i.e.*, 3.6 years) can be calculated by indicating at what point during the year the profits plus depreciation will completely offset the depreciable investment.

Payout Time Including Interest. Calculation is similar to that for straight payout time, except that profits are reduced, by discounting those not achieved until later years, using the appropriate interest rate chosen as the minimum acceptable rate of return (see Table 26-31). This tends to increase the payout time, to represent the earning of the minimum rate of return, and the measure properly reflects advantages for projects which earn most of their profits early in their lives.

Present Worth. In the profitability measure known as present worth, compound-interest factors (Table 26-31) are used to compound or discount all cash flows to their equivalent value at time zero, using minimum acceptable rate of return as the interest rate. Time zero may be chosen arbitrarily, but the start of operations is usually used. It is usual to list cash incomes separately from cash outlays, using discounted values, and to show sums of both as of time zero. Present worth is the excess of the present value of incomes over the present value of the investments; it is usually shown as the difference between these two but may also be shown as a ratio.

Interest Rate of Return. Trial-and-error solution is necessary to calculate interest rate of return, since the discounting rate is the unknown sought in the calculation. The cash flows are set forth before discounting, in columns showing all cash flows, from start of construction to recovery of land and working capital after the project is shut down. Trial discounting rates are then applied to determine which rate makes the present value of earnings equivalent to the present value of all investments.

Note that the interest rate of return is not earned on the original or on the total amount of investment. The discounting procedure corresponds to alteration of the principal invested in the project by the amount of the interest. Interest accumulated over each compounding period is added to the principal at the beginning of the period to obtain the new principal for the next period. The term **obligation** has been frequently used to refer to this changing sum and avoid confusion with the original principal sum. Obligation denotes the total indebtedness of the project to the investor, including all capital outlays and accrued interest at a given time.

Chart of Cumulative Cash Position. The graph described below is used in Table 26-27 as a method of comparing and contrasting profitability methods. It is an excellent tool for portraying the realities of the status of an investment in relation to the investor. As its name implies, it shows the cumulative cash effect of the project on the company.

This chart (Fig. 26-9) uses time as the horizontal scale and cash position as the vertical scale. Points in the "negative cash position" area, below the "zero line," indicate investment in the project. Points of "positive cash position," above the zero line, indicate a profit position has been reached, *i.e.*, no residual investment in the project.

Start of production is chosen as zero on the time scale. The initial zero cash position usually occurs prior to this time, at start of construction. Since the chart shows *cumulative* cash position, a single line indicates, throughout the construction period and the earning life, the cumulative cash status of the project at any time. During construction, the line slopes downward from the zero line to indicate increasing negative cash position. As income starts, the line heads up, gradually reducing the investment to zero. (Except for the effect of recovery of land and working capital, this crossing of the zero line represents payout time.) As cash continues to come in, the slope continues upward into the positive cash position (profit) area. At the termination of the project, recovery of land and working capital adds a final portion of cash to establish the final cash position.

Most of the complexities occurring in a normal project are shown in Fig. 26-9, except that constant annual income and straight-line depreciation are assumed. The first investment shown is that in land, at a single point in time, followed by a uniform increase of fixed invesment during construction. Working capital is added instantaneously at time zero; this is a simplifying approximation. Income at a constant rate is assumed to start at time zero, bringing the cumulative cash position line upward at a constant slope throughout its life. Value of investment remaining on the accounting books is shown by the dashed line.

Introduction of **compound interest** increases the complexity of this chart. Its effects are shown by Fig. 26-10 for an instantaneous investment. The "obligation" (see under Interest Rate of Return) is indicated by the dashed line; original investment is increased regularly by interest and decreased by cash income in each time period to calculate the obligation shown. The interest rate which will maintain some obligation throughout the

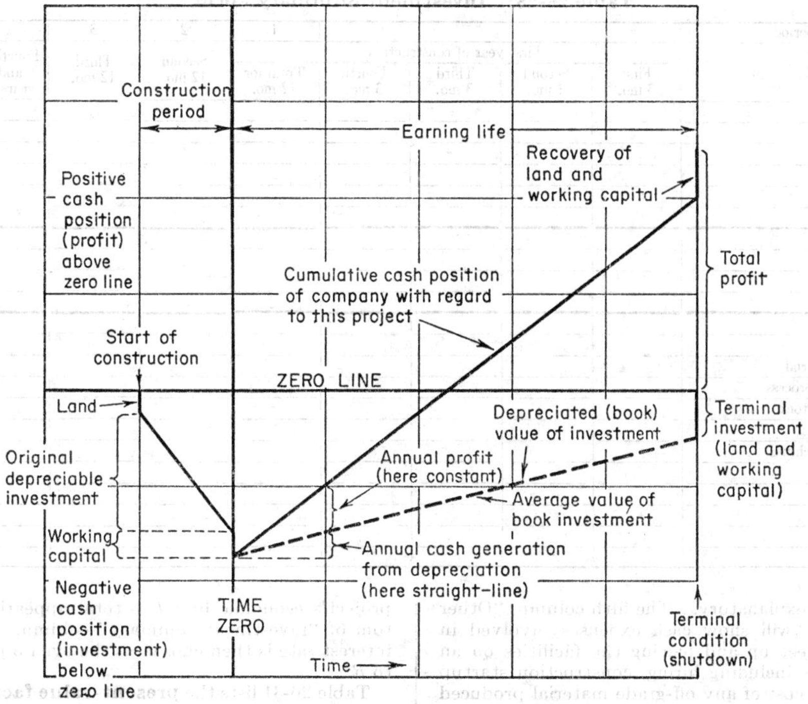

FIG. 26-9. Graph of cumulative cash position.

project life, but reduce the obligation to zero just at the end of the estimated economic life (in general, zero cash position after recovery of any working capital and land or salvage value), is that which has already been referred to as "interest rate of return." It is the interest rate paid by the project to the owner for use of the owner's funds. All profits have been converted so as to be expressed as this interest rate, and the obligation of the project to the owner, which has continued to be some real obligation throughout the project life, has been completely repaid.

The dotted line indicates cumulative cash flow where discount rate is merely the cost of capital or a minimum acceptable rate of return. (A project which earned an

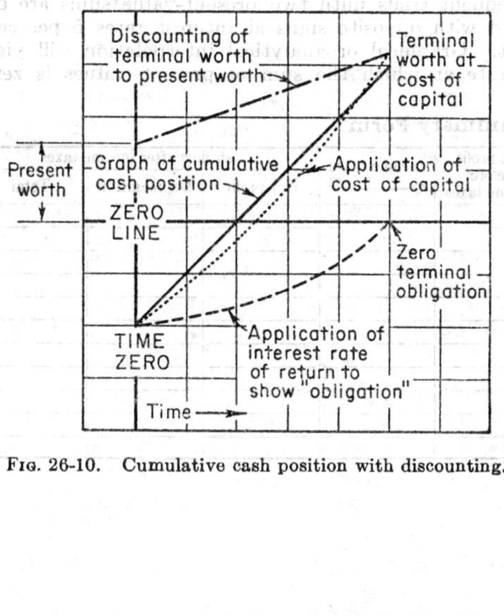

FIG. 26-10. Cumulative cash position with discounting.

interest rate of return equal to the cost of capital would show no profit after discounting and would resemble the dashed line.) The dotted line crosses the zero line at the point (except for possibility of the recovery of land and working capital) corresponding to "payout time including interest."

The application of interest rates in the positive-cash-position area is no longer a discounting. The amount of profit made available by this project is assumed to be invested (at the cost of capital) in other projects, and the profits are compounded, as in Fig. 26-10, so that the terminal cash position, after applying the cost of capital, may be greater than the final undiscounted cash position if the project is sufficiently long in economic life. The dot-dash line shows the relationship between this terminal worth and present worth discounted at the cost of capital.

Forms for Organizing Profitability Data. The method of organizing information described in the following paragraphs is applicable for investment evaluation by any of the return on investment measures. The final form is specific to interest rate of return.

Table 26-28, **Investment Summary Form,** can be used to gather and organize all information on fixed and working capital investments, as to both amount and timing.

A **depreciation summary** is required, but no form is shown since one can be easily drawn up for this purpose. If various parts of the project are depreciated at different rates, several columns will be required to show the year-by-year depreciation allowance on each. The total income-tax deduction due to depreciation can then be summed from the columns.

The **Cash-flow Summary Form,** Table 26-29, brings together information from various sources to show all cash flows to the company from the project. Most of the

Table 26-28. Investment Summary Form

Annual period					1	2	3		
	First year of construction					Second 12 mo.	Third 12 mo.	Fourth year and all years after	Totals
	First 3 mo.	Second 3 mo.	Third 3 mo.	Fourth 3 mo.	Total for 12 mo.				
Land									
Buildings									
Process equipment									
Service equipment									
Mobile equipment									
Total capital									
Supplies									
Spare parts									
Other									
Total expense									
Cash									
Accounts receivable									
Inventories—raw material									
Inventories—work in process									
Inventories—finished stock									
Inventories—containers									
Inventories—extra machines									
Subtotal									
Accounts payable									
Income taxes payable									
Subtotal									
Net working capital									

headings are self-explanatory. The fifth column, "Other Cash Expenses," will show cash expenses involved in starting the project up and placing the facilities on an operational basis, including hiring, construction startup expense, and the cost of any off-grade material produced during initial operations. Data for the next column, "Depreciation and Write-offs," are available from the depreciation summary and will also include any write-off of equipment scrapped as a part of this project. These are also non-cash expenses which are tax-deductible.

Table 26-30 provides for the trial-and-error development of **interest rate of return.** Space is provided for transactions before startup as well as during earning life. Cash outlays should be indicated as negative, cash generation (receipts) as positive; "net of all cash flows" is their algebraic sum.

To provide an interest rate for the first trial, figures in the three cash-flow columns are totaled to the bottom of the form, and an approximate rate of return is estimated as

$$R = 1.2\frac{T}{YI} \tag{26-14}$$

where R = approximate rate of return; T = total appearing at the bottom of "net cash flow" column; Y = number of years between start of construction and end of project's economic life; I = total appearing at the bottom of "investment summary" column. The first trial interest rate is then chosen as the even 5 per cent closest to R.

Table 26-31 lists the **present-value factors** used most frequently in investment evaluations, based on continuous compounding; for present-value factors using annual compounding, see pp. 1-32–1-38. Additional tables, using both annual and continuous compounding, are given by Swalm [*Eng. Economist*, **5**, 45 (fall, 1959); 57 (winter, 1960); 77 (spring, 1960)].

For the first trial interest rate, appropriate factors are taken from Table 26-31 for each year during which cash flows occur. Each net-cash-flow entry is multiplied by the appropriate factor to determine present value.

The algebraic total of the "present value" column is the present value of the entire stream of cash flows when discounted at the assumed interest rate. If the sum is negative, the trial rate was too high, and a rate 5 per cent lower should be chosen for the next trial. If the sum is positive, the trial rate was too low, and the next higher rate should be chosen.

The same procedure is followed for the second and subsequent trials until two present-value sums are obtained with opposite signs at interest rates 5 per cent apart. Graphical or analytical interpolation will yield the rate at which the sum of present values is zero.

Table 26-29. Cash-flow Summary Form

Ann. per.	Annual production quantity	Net receipts or gross savings	Cash operating costs	Other cash expenses	Depreciation and write-offs	Net profit before income taxes	Income taxes at_____%	Cash flow after income taxes		
								Net profit	Depreciation	Total
1										
2										
3										
4										
5										
6										
7										
8										
9										
10										
n										

Table 26-30. Return on Investment Calculation Form

Time periods				Cash flows			Trial 1 ___% interest rate		Trial 2 . . . n ___% interest rate	
	Cal. year	Annual period		Investment summary	Cash flow summary	Net of all cash flows	Factor	Present value	Factor	Present value
Before time zero		3rd yr. before	At start							
			During							
		2nd yr. before	At start							
			During							
		1st yr. before	At start							
			During							
After time zero		1st yr.								
		2nd yr.								
		3rd yr.								
		4th yr.								
		5th yr.								
		6th yr.								
		7th yr.								
		8th yr.								
		9th yr.								
		10th yr.								
		. . . *n*th yr.								

Because of the inherent inaccuracies of input forecasts, interest rate of return should not be reported to more than two significant figures.

Nomographs by Greist *et al.* [*Ind. Eng. Chem.*, **53**, 52A (March, 1961)] make possible the calculation of interest rate of return without resort to trial-and-error techniques. They can handle all major investment variables except irregular income growth patterns.

Present Value. The term "present value" is simply a numerical representation of the **time value of money.**

Table 26-31. Condensed Continuous-interest Tables*

Factors for determining zero-time values for cash flows which occur at other than zero time

	1%	5%	10%	15%	20%	25%	30%	35%	40%	50%	60%	70%	80%	90%	100%
Compounding of cash flows which occur:															
A. In an instant															
½ year before	1.005	1.025	1.051	1.078	1.105	1.133	1.162	1.191	1.221	1.284	1.350	1.419	1.492	1.568	1.649
1 year before	1.010	1.051	1.105	1.162	1.221	1.284	1.350	1.419	1.492	1.649	1.822	2.014	2.226	2.460	2.718
1½ years before	1.015	1.078	1.162	1.252	1.350	1.455	1.568	1.690	1.822	2.117	2.460	2.858	3.320	3.857	4.482
2 years before	1.020	1.105	1.221	1.350	1.492	1.649	1.822	2.014	2.226	2.718	3.320	4.055	4.953	6.050	7.389
3 years before	1.030	1.162	1.350	1.568	1.822	2.117	2.460	2.858	3.320	4.482	6.050	8.166	11.023	14.880	20.086
B. Uniformly until zero time															
From ½ year before to 0 time	1.002	1.013	1.025	1.038	1.052	1.065	1.079	1.093	1.107	1.136	1.166	1.197	1.230	1.263	1.297
From 1 year before to 0 time	1.005	1.025	1.052	1.079	1.107	1.136	1.166	1.197	1.230	1.297	1.370	1.448	1.532	1.622	1.718
From 1½ years before to 0 time	1.008	1.038	1.079	1.121	1.166	1.213	1.263	1.315	1.370	1.489	1.622	1.769	1.933	2.117	2.321
From 2 years before to 0 time	1.010	1.052	1.107	1.166	1.230	1.297	1.370	1.448	1.532	1.718	1.933	2.182	2.471	2.805	3.194
From 3 years before to 0 time	1.015	1.079	1.166	1.263	1.370	1.489	1.622	1.769	1.933	2.321	2.805	3.412	4.176	5.141	6.362
Discounting of cash flows which occur:															
C. In an instant															
1 year later	0.990	0.951	0.905	0.861	0.819	0.779	0.741	0.705	0.670	0.606	0.549	0.497	0.449	0.407	0.368
2 years later	0.980	0.905	0.819	0.741	0.670	0.606	0.549	0.497	0.449	0.368	0.301	0.247	0.202	0.165	0.135
3 years later	0.970	0.861	0.741	0.638	0.549	0.472	0.407	0.350	0.301	0.223	0.165	0.122	0.091	0.067	0.050
4 years later	0.961	0.819	0.670	0.549	0.449	0.368	0.301	0.247	0.202	0.135	0.091	0.061	0.041	0.027	0.018
5 years later	0.951	0.779	0.606	0.472	0.368	0.286	0.223	0.174	0.135	0.082	0.050	0.030	0.018	0.011	0.007
10 years later	0.905	0.606	0.368	0.223	0.135	0.082	0.050	0.030	0.018	0.007	0.002	0.001			
15 years later	0.861	0.472	0.223	0.105	0.050	0.024	0.011	0.005	0.002	0.001					
20 years later	0.819	0.368	0.135	0.050	0.018	0.007	0.002	0.001							
25 years later	0.779	0.286	0.082	0.024	0.007	0.002	0.001								
D. Uniformly over individual years															
1st year	0.995	0.975	0.952	0.929	0.906	0.885	0.864	0.844	0.824	0.787	0.752	0.719	0.688	0.659	0.632
2d year	0.985	0.928	0.861	0.799	0.742	0.689	0.640	0.595	0.552	0.477	0.413	0.357	0.309	0.268	0.232
3d year	0.975	0.883	0.779	0.688	0.608	0.537	0.474	0.419	0.370	0.290	0.226	0.177	0.139	0.109	0.086
4th year	0 966	0.840	0.705	0.592	0.497	0.418	0.351	0.295	0.248	0.176	0.124	0.088	0.062	0.044	0.032
5th year	0.956	0.799	0.638	0.510	0.407	0.326	0.260	0.208	0.166	0.106	0.068	0.044	0.028	0.018	0.012
6th year	0.946	0.760	0.577	0.439	0.333	0.254	0.193	0.147	0.112	0.065	0.037	0.022	0.013	0.007	0.004
7th year	0.937	0.723	0.522	0.378	0.273	0.197	0.143	0.103	0.075	0.039	0.020	0.011	0.006	0.003	0.002
8th year	0.928	0.687	0.473	0.325	0.224	0.154	0.106	0.073	0.050	0.024	0.011	0.005	0.002	0.001	0.001
9th year	0.918	0.654	0.428	0.280	0.183	0.120	0.078	0.051	0.034	0.014	0.006	0.003	0.001		
10th year	0.909	0.622	0.387	0.241	0.150	0.093	0.058	0.036	0.022	0.009	0.003	0.001			
E. Uniformly over 5-year periods															
1st 5 years	0.975	0.885	0.787	0.704	0.632	0.571	0.518	0.472	0.432	0.367	0.317	0.277	0.245	0.220	0.199
6th through 10th year	0.928	0.689	0.477	0.332	0.232	0.164	0.116	0.082	0.058	0.030	0.016	0.008	0.004	0.002	0.001
11th through 15th year	0.883	0.537	0.290	0.157	0.086	0.047	0.026	0.014	0.008	0.002	0.001				
16th through 20th year	0.840	0.418	0.176	0.074	0.032	0.013	0.006	0.002	0.001						
21st through 25th year	0.799	0.326	0.106	0.035	0.012	0.004	0.001								
F. Declining to nothing at constant rate															
1st 5 years	0.983	0.922	0.852	0.791	0.736	0.687	0.643	0.603	0.568	0.506	0.456	0.413	0.377	0.347	0.320
1st 10 years	0.968	0.852	0.736	0.643	0.568	0.506	0.456	0.413	0.377	0.320	0.278	0.245	0.219	0.198	0.180
1st 15 years	0.952	0.791	0.643	0.536	0.456	0.394	0.347	0.309	0.278	0.231	0.198	0.172	0.153	0.137	0.124
1st 20 years	0.936	0.736	0.568	0.456	0.377	0.320	0.278	0.245	0.219	0.180	0.153	0.133	0.117	0.105	0.095
1st 25 years	0.922	0.687	0.506	0.394	0.320	0.269	0.231	0.203	0.180	0.147	0.124	0.108	0.095	0.085	0.077

* From tables compiled by J. C. Gregory, Atlantic Refining Co.

When money is gathering interest, the longer ago it was invested, the more it is worth today. A dollar received 2 years ago would have earned a dollar's worth of interest if earning at a 35 per cent rate, as shown by Table 26-31 (part A, 2 years before, 35 per cent). A dollar spent 2 years ago is equivalent to a larger amount today, since if not spent then it could have been at interest for those 2 years. The present-value factor **compounds** dollars received or disbursed before zero time from their face value to a larger value which they have at zero time, as either receipts or expenditures, because of the time value of money.

Discounting or deducting interest by present-value factors is a numerical expression of the time value of money received or disbursed in the future. The farther off in the future that money is spent, the better. A debt of $1 two years from now can be paid off with 50¢ available today if that 50¢ can be put out at 35 per cent interest (Table 26-31, part C, 2 years later, 35 per cent). However, the same devaluation or discounting applies to money one will *receive* in the future. The longer the time in the future before the money is received, the less it is worth today. A dollar received 2 years from now is worth only 50 cents today if it could be earning 35 per cent interest during those 2 years. At 35 per cent interest, then, a dollar received after 2 years of project operation will contribute only about 50¢ toward repayment of zero-time obligation, since 50¢ worth of interest will have been deducted from it over the 2 years.

A dollar to be received 5 years from now has a present value of slightly over 17¢, after deducting interest (discounting) at 35 per cent (part C, 5 years later). Thus, at 35 per cent interest, a dollar received after 5 years of a project will contribute 17¢ toward repayment of zero-time obligation, since 83¢ worth of interest has been deducted from it over the 5 years.

Another way of stating this relationship is that 17¢ today, compounded with interest at 35 per cent continuously for 5 years, would yield a value of $1 five years from today. The present value of a dollar received or expended 2 years ago, with interest applied at 35 per cent compounded continuously, is a little more than $2.

Continuous Compounding. Application of continuous compounding to the receipts and expenditures of a business project lowers the interest rate of return compared with the rate computed by compounding on an annual basis. Interest tables are available for both annual (Table 1-14, pp. 1-32 to 1-38) and continuous (Table 26-31) compounding. Continuous compounding is used here, since it approximates more closely usual business operations, with transactions throughout the year. Continuous compounding also offers some advantage in ease of mathematical handling. At higher interest rates and over longer time periods, the two bases yield sizable differences.

Nominal interest rates of return are used for column headings in Table 26-31. The **effective rate** is the rate at which a sum of money earns interest each year, regardless of compounding period. The *nominal* rate is the rate at which a sum of money earns interest over a particular compounding period. The nominal rate equals the effective rate only when the compounding period is 1 year. Although nominal rates are usually expressed on an annual basis, these rates are inaccurate unless qualified by their compounding period; *e.g.*, 20 per cent compounded quarterly, 20 per cent compounded continuously, etc. For example, $1000 at 20 per cent compounded annually would accrue $200 interest by the year end; compounded semiannually, $210; and compounded continuously, $220. The nominal rate in all three cases is 20 per cent with compounding period specified; the effective rate is 20, 21, and 22 per cent, respectively.

Further Data on Continuous-interest Table. Table 26-31 is a condensed continuous-interest table abstracted from Gregory ("Interest Tables for Determining Rate of Return," Atlantic Refining Co., Philadelphia, 1946). The table consists of six groups of present-value factors for transactions occurring in a single sum or uniformly over specified periods of time, and also for occurrences before and after the selected zero point.

The factors in Table 26-31 are mathematically derived from the term e^{rt} for the "instantaneous" factor and $(e^{rt} - 1)/rt$ for the "uniform" factor, where r = annual rate of interest, decimal; t = time, years; e = natural logarithm base. These terms provide for continuous compounding instead of the customary methods of annual, semiannual, or quarterly compounding.

Part A provides factors for compounding single-sum instantaneous transactions before zero time, such as an expenditure for land.

Part B provides factors for compounding cash receipts or expenditures which take place steadily over a period of time before the zero point. Outlay for construction of a plant is usually treated in this way.

Part C provides factors for discounting instantaneous transactions which occur after the zero point, such as recovery of working capital, land, and scrap value.

Part D provides factors for discounting cash receipts or expenditures which take place steadily over individual years after the zero point, such as the cash receipts for individual years.

Part E provides factors for transactions similar to those in part D but taking place steadily over 5-year periods instead of individual years. This simplifies the calculations required when receipts or expenditures are steady over 5-year periods.

Part F. Under sum-of-the-years-digits depreciation, cash from depreciation allowances is returned from the project in amounts which diminish continuously on a straight-line basis from a maximum at the start to zero at the end of the life of the depreciable item. This table provides factors for discounting such transactions over various time periods.

The original tables covered 1 per cent increments and were taken to four decimal places. Suitable accuracy of engineering estimates for most project forecasts can be maintained by using 5 per cent increments and the three-decimal-place factors shown in Table 26-31. These simplifications also permit slide-rule solutions.

Extension Methods for Continuous-interest Tables. A number of extensions may be made to Table 26-31 for interest rates and time periods not covered. Some of these techniques can be used only on interest tables based, like Table 26-31, on an infinitesimal compounding period.

1. *Instantaneous Factors for Extension to Additional Years.* Factors for instantaneous transactions (parts A and C) can be multiplied to obtain factors for years not shown. In part C, the factor for 11 years later is the 10-year factor times the 1-year factor.

Example at 35 per cent. (0.705)(0.030) = 0.021

Parts B, D, E, and F, for transactions taking place over periods of time, are extended to other years by applying the appropriate *instantaneous* factor to postpone the period over which the transaction occurs. The 11th-year factor in part D may be found as (part C, 1-year factor) times (part D, 10-year factor) or as (part C, 10-year factor) times (part D, 1-year factor).

Examples at 35 per cent. (0.705)(0.036) = 0.025
(0.030)(0.844) = 0.025

2. *Additional Extensions for Parts A, B, C, and F.* Because of the instantaneous compounding period, a relationship exists which permits determination of factors for rates and times not shown in these tables. In part C, the factor 0.368, for 1 year later at 100 per cent, is the same as the factor for 2 years later at 50 per cent. The same factor, 0.368, also appears at 4 years at 25 per cent, 5 years at 20 per cent, 10 years at 10 per cent, 20 years at 5 per cent. When compounded continuously, the factor depends upon the product of the interest rate and the time involved. In each of the cases cited above, since the product of the rate and the time is 100, the factor is the same. With the application of this principle to, say, the 40 per cent rate, the factor for 2½ years at 40 per cent is also 0.368. The tabulated factors should allow both interpolation and extrapolation with ease.

3. *Additional Extensions for Parts D and E.* Since the periods shown for transactions do not generally extend to zero time in parts D and E, the flexibility described above does not apply. However, another convenient relationship between parts D and E can be used for extension. The factor for 1 per cent over the first 5 years (part E), 0.975, is the same as the factor for 5 per cent over the first year (part D), and this relationship also holds for later time periods in the order shown in the tables; *e.g.*, the 2 per cent factor over the sixth through tenth year can be found from these tables as 0.861, the 10 per cent factor over the second year.

Sensitivity of Profitability to Major Project Variables. For a project with fairly constant profit per year, it is possible to prepare graphs which relate interest rate of return to return on original investment; this can be a helpful introduction to the concept of interest rate of return. Figure 26-11 is such a graph showing this relation for various levels of working capital and various other assumed conditions. Note that an *average* of profits after tax must be taken, since profit after tax actually varies from year to year when accelerated depreciation methods are used (as in the basis for this figure) even if all cash costs remain the same.

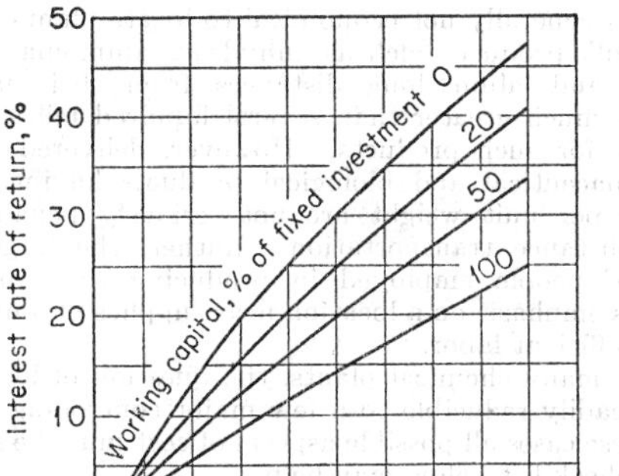

FIG. 26-11. Effect of working capital on interest rate of return. Basis: project life, 10 years; depreciation, 15 years, SYD method; income tax, 52 per cent; construction period, 1 year; tax recovery on undepreciated value after 10 years; no startup expense; sales and costs (excluding depreciation) assumed constant yearly.

Figure 26-12 is a more complex graph which is helpful in showing the effect on interest rate of return of various changes in basis. Since a rapid rate of income growth is one of the factors considered on the chart, interest rate of return cannot be plotted against return on original investment here. Instead, it is plotted against the ratio of profits before taxes and depreciation to fixed investment (in the case of growing income, this ratio applies for the first year only).

The curve marked "standard basis" assumes constant profits before taxes and depreciation, as well as all the other restrictions indicated. Each of the other curves represents a change in one item of the standard basis. Increased startup expense or working capital naturally reduces the interest rate of return for a given profit level. Extension of the project life raises the interest rate of return slightly. Income growth is seen to be a major factor in raising interest rate of return.

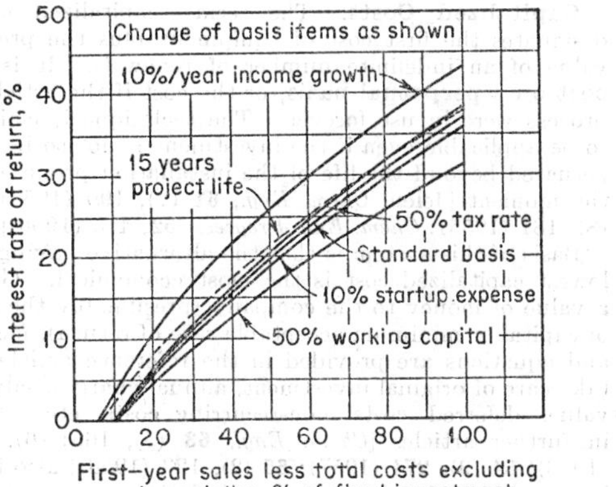

FIG. 26-12. Effect on interest rate of return of various changes in basis. Standard basis: project life, 10 years; depreciation, 15 years, SYD method; income tax, 52 per cent; working capital, 20 per cent of fixed investment; construction period, 1 year; tax recovery on undepreciated value after 10 years; no startup expense; sales and costs (excluding depreciation) assumed constant yearly.

Methods for Replacement Investments. A replacement investment is defined as one intended to supplant, without expansion, a similar unit serving the same purpose. The replacement investment may be justified entirely by cost savings of one sort or another, or it may be required by either technological obsolescence of the previous equipment or its physical deterioration.

Replacement problems in a chemical plant are more likely to apply to a relatively small portion of the processing equipment, such as a filter or heat exchanger, rather than to entire processing units. A good example of technical improvement, which can frequently be considered as a replacement investment, is an improved material of construction. As improved materials become available, replacement investments using them come up for consideration.

Replacement investments required by **physical deterioration** are not a problem of investment or no investment, since the entire plant would shut down if the replacement were not made. The investment decision, therefore, is whether to replace in kind (base case) or whether to replace with an alternative whose investment is different (higher or lower) than the base case.

When **technological obsolescence** is the cause, the economics of timing becomes important. Also, possible expansion should usually be considered to be sure that the newly replaced equipment does not become the bottleneck in the entire processing stream.

Similar choices face the design engineer in choosing the specific equipment to be installed in a new plant. The engineer should be familiar with the principles of replacement investment analysis in order to determine which of various alternative types of equipment, all adequate to the task but of different costs and perhaps different estimated lives, should be installed.

There is no basic difference in the **criterion for such investments** from the principles discussed earlier in this section. Any replacement investment more costly than the minimum adequate for the task must earn at least the minimum acceptable rate of return on the incremental investment. Replacement problems can be solved in terms of the profitability formulas discussed above. However, special methods are sometimes used for analysis of replacement investments.

Capitalized Costs. The term "capitalized cost" designates the first cost of equipment plus the present value of an indefinite number of renewals. It is the **cost on a perpetual basis,** or the cost if the article or process were in use forever. The technique is claimed to be applicable even if the investment is not to be perpetuated beyond the life of the installation proposed at the moment [Jelen, *Chem. Eng.*, **61** (2), 199 (1954); **62** (8), 181 (1955); *Chem. Eng. Progress*, **52,** 413 (1956)].

Basis of this system is that the alternative having the lowest capitalized cost is the most economical. Given a value of money to the company (presumably the cost of capital or minimum acceptable rate of return), factors and equations are provided in the reference articles to take care of original investment, annual charges, salvage value, deferred costs, non-recurring costs, etc. Jelen in further articles [*Chem. Eng.*, **63** (5), 165; (6), 247 (1956); **64** (9), 271 (1957); **65** (2), 123 (1958)] also took into account other items such as inflation.

The capitalized-cost approach is most applicable to comparisons among investment alternatives, although an article by Jelen [*Chem. Eng.*, **65** (15), 116 (1958)] claimed the equivalence of capitalized cost to other methods of capital-expenditure justification. Capitalized cost does not seem able to handle, as the other methods do, a variety of possible income patterns and service lives.

Another method of replacement evaluation involves choosing the alternative which has the minimum **annual cost,** an expression of all costs reduced to an equivalent annual payment by compound-interest techniques. Such a comparison involves the same sorts of forecasts required for the capitalized-cost technique and will always give the same choice as between alternatives.

Economic Balance in Plant and Equipment Sizing. The basic economic criterion for size of plant is that all portions of the plant, and the last increment of investment in it, should earn at least the minimum acceptable rate of return.

If the sales forecast for the product is constant for some years to come, there is no problem in **plant sizing,** as long as the plant sized for the forecast production makes an acceptable return on investment. However, growth products raise a problem in economic sizing. If product sales will grow, it would not be sensible to build for only the first year's expected sales. The economy of a large plant, compared with several smaller units, demands allowance in the original plant for some of the expected growth. The basic criterion is that the plant should be increased in size above immediate requirements until the capacity so added will not return a minimum acceptable return on investment because of the delay before this capacity will be put to use. This means maximum return on investment is not the goal to be sought, but rather the maximum profit from investment, all of which earns at least the minimum acceptable return. This approach to plant sizing is used by Weaver and Greist [*Ind. Eng. Chem.*, **50,** 59A (July, 1958)] and Hess and Weaver [*ibid.*, **53,** 47A (July, 1961)].

Another problem of plant sizing, for batch or other processes which can be shut down at will, is to determine whether the plant should be initially sized to operate 5 or 7 days per week. It might be expected that the savings in investment would always justify the smaller plant, one which would operate 7 days per week to provide a given production rate. However, labor savings achieved by avoiding week-end operation can, in fact, alter this decision. Some details of this approach are given by Weaver and Lyndall [*Ind. Eng. Chem.*, **50,** 61A (May, 1958)].

Perhaps the most common problem in plant and equipment sizing is the determination of **optimum size for pieces of equipment,** such as heat exchangers, which are used to reduce manufacturing costs in some fashion. Many texts on engineering economy recommend formulas which aim at a minimum cost per year, usually including depreciation on the equipment as a cost. It seems more appropriate to consider the savings in manufacturing cost as a return on the money to be invested. The investment can be increased only as long as the savings achieved show an acceptable rate of return on the added investment. Economic sizing by this method would properly handle initial investment and recovery of depreciation as a cash flow when it occurs. Details are provided by Quigley and Weaver [*Ind. Eng. Chem.*, **53,** 55A (September, 1961)].

Plant-location Studies

For the majority of cases the primary reason for a plant-location study is to find a site at which a plant can produce the highest return on invested capital. The nature of the process or product often narrows the potential site selection to a relatively few possible areas. For example, electrochemical plants ideally should be located in minimum-power-cost areas (usually associated with hydroelectric developments). However, when freight costs on raw materials and products are considered, it might be more economical to use power at somewhat higher rates based on coal or natural gas.

It is generally not economical to locate plants producing bulk products such as anhydrous ammonia, sulfuric acid, and alum long distances from their markets. Hauls much greater than several hundred miles are too costly for such products. However, delivered costs of pharmaceutical and biological products having a high value per unit weight are not seriously penalized by long-distance transportation. Rather, the large number of people employed in producing these products places emphasis on a location near supplies of ample low-cost, efficient labor.

For many chemical plants, the question of location is not readily reducible to a few major controlling factors. In these cases all possible aspects of cost must be studied. The check list below may help.

Utilities. First, the site must have an adequate water supply. Waste disposal is another prime consideration. A reliable and ample supply of electricity should be available at or near the site, but this is no longer much of a problem in the United States, with electrical utility networks assuring ample power in almost all potential industrial locations.

Fuel. Economic availability of coal, oil, or gas is a prime consideration. Where all three are available they generally tend to compete in cost. Lowest costs are obtainable in areas of fuel origin, but this may be offset by product shipping costs. Low fuel cost coupled with need for by-product steam can make electric generation attractive compared with cost of purchased power.

Raw Materials. Quite often these are the prime factors in location of major chemical complexes. Petrochemical plants invariably are located near refineries or other sources of hydrocarbons. In most other types of chemical operations, low delivered cost of raw materials must be weighed against other operating costs.

Geographical Features. Cost of site development should not be a significant element of capital expense. In addition to reasonable land cost, the site should be nearly level and preferably have soil bearing values in excess of 2000 lb./sq. ft. Ideally, it should be accessibly located near good roads, railroads, navigable rivers or other water bodies, although the importance of this factor varies widely. Climate can have a major effect on type and size of structures, as well as on operations.

Labor. Most chemical plants are characterized by a relatively small labor force. Nevertheless a labor supply of a wide degree of competence is important. Growth of labor unions in the United States has tended to even out labor rate differentials; so that less and less is it advantageous to select a site based on low wages as the sole determining factor. It is important to consider availability of housing, transportation, schools, churches, hospitals, and recreation facilities.

Transportation. People and goods must be transported to and from the plant. Satisfactory facilities should be available. The growing tendency to decentralize industry in the United States has been accompanied by improved transportation. Public busses and private automobiles have almost supplanted railroads in most places outside heavily built-up urban areas. Trucks and over-the-road tankers are growing in importance. However, the railroads still carry a large share of the chemical industry's raw materials and finished products, particularly on long hauls. Barge shipping is a low-cost transportation means for plants on navigable waterways. Government regulations concerning freight rates, distances traveled, and states through which commodities must be hauled should be carefully investigated.

Market. It is highly desirable to be located in or near the market area served, but speed of modern transportation and communication makes it less necessary where other cost factors are offsetting.

Legislation. Local laws concerning real estate and sanitary and safety codes may exclude certain types of plants or make them prohibitively expensive to operate. Local taxes can be designed to attract or discourage new industry. State laws should be checked to determine whether prohibitive legislation concerning in-state truck transportation, roads, parks, and other public places would be detrimental. The need for easements and rights of way by state or public utilities should also be investigated.

The techniques used for economically evaluating most of these factors are discussed elsewhere in this section.

Sources of Information. Many sources are available on sites for a proposed plant. Practically all the United States has been surveyed; good maps are available from the United States Geodetic Survey, Department of Interior. Labor rate statistics for all areas are kept by the Department of Labor. Power rates are published by the Federal Power Commission, and other pertinent industrial statistics may be obtained from the Federal Trade Commission, Interstate Commerce Commission, and Federal Communications Commission. Many other national agencies compile and disseminate useful information covering pertinent factors of site location. A complete list of the publications of the various agencies may be obtained from the Superintendent of Documents, Government Printing Office, Washington, D.C.

Most states have agencies or planning boards which compile and provide public information on industrial sites. Complete listings may be obtained by writing to the state authority involved. Much useful information may be obtained from railroads and public utilities serving the area under investigation. Trade unions, trade organizations, and local chambers of commerce are good sources of site information. The initial bias of all such sources must be recognized.

Selecting a site for a second plant for a given product line is done in a manner similar to choosing the initial site, with the added consideration of the obvious economic advantages of low incremental cost of expanding at the original location.

Abandonment Decisions

Although the shutdown or abandonment of an operation is not an auspicious occasion, it is sometimes an economic necessity to avoid throwing good money after bad.

The principal determinant of the need for shutdown or abandonment, like that for investment decisions, is a **comparison of the cash flows** expected in two or more alternative cases. A sales forecast will establish what cash flow is expected if the plant remains open. If the plant is shut down but not abandoned, some maintenance will still be required, but the entire working capital can be recovered and many of the fixed overheads relating to the plant can be terminated, particularly if it is at a separate site. Naturally, every shutdown represents a loss of the know-how of the direct operating personnel and also of any overhead personnel (accounting, administrative, or technical) who may have to be released. Therefore, even a temporary shutdown is not something to be done until demanded by economic necessities, after study of the long-term sales forecasts.

Complete abandonment of a plant would yield several cash flows to the company. The land will be made available for sale or for another use. The plant may be sold for salvage value or scrapped, with the result that write-off of its residual book value permits reduction of taxes in the current year. (Under changes in the tax law made early in 1963, the foregoing applies only to buildings; further changes may be made. This is essentially an advancement in time of receipt of depreciation allowances; the same amount would be received eventually if plant operation is continued, or if it is shut down without abandonment.) Standby maintenance costs can also be saved.

Because no initial investment is involved, the usual profitability methods do not, in general, apply. The only suitable method is the present-worth calculation, which discounts the cash flows in the various cases at the minimum acceptable rate of return to show which stream of cash flows is of more value to the company. A complete description of all the factors to be considered is given by Shillinglaw [*J. Business*, **30**, 17 (January, 1957)]. Another useful check list of cost items to be considered in shutdown is given by Krase [*Chem. Eng. Progress*, **52**, 495 (1956)].

A tool frequently used to assist in shutdown decisions is the **break-even chart**; such a chart indicates the plant operating level at which accounting incomes cover accounting costs, so that the plant "breaks even" on the company books. There is a real danger in using such break-even charts for determination of shutdown because of the arbitrary nature of the accounting definition of profit. For details see Quigley and Weaver [*Ind. Eng. Chem.*, **52**, 59A (September, 1960)], who described a "cash-flow break-even chart" which considers depreciation and allocated overheads in their proper place. This type of chart is a better signal for the possible need for plant shutdown.

Non-quantitative Considerations. Although profitability is a major consideration in making investments, there are other important reasons for making capital investments. Many **safety projects** must be justified for the protection of health and welfare of plant personnel or the neighboring public. Calculation of the difference in cash flows on investments which are basically for a safety reason can permit management to quantify the desired safety results in terms of the costs presented. The same reasoning holds for investments which are exclusively for morale purposes or are necessary to improve community relations.

Since investments of this non-profit-making nature are always a part of the investment pattern of every manufacturing concern, the return on investment sought in new investments must be high enough to compensate in some fashion for the non-profit investments which must also be made. This should incorporate, on some internally consistent basis, investment in non-productive auxiliary facilities which may not themselves show a return on investment. This can be done either by charging off portions of these facilities against investments (by increasing the investment base) or by allowing a margin for safety in the minimum acceptable rate of return on investment, above the cost of capital of the firm.

The investment decision usually involves more than the mere calculation of profitability followed by an automatic decision. The profitability measure attempts to incorporate within a single number as many as possible of the quantifiable factors which must be forecast. However, this is only an aid to management decision and does not take the place of judgment. Other factors which must be taken into consideration are the size of the project compared with the size of the company, integration of the project with the present product line of the company and with its company objectives, availability of funds, availability of an organization adequate to undertake the project, etc. While the profitability calculation may be improved in the future to incorporate such additional factors as risk, there is no prospect that it can supplant management judgment. However, it can be of major assistance, particularly with the smaller projects which are closely related to the present activities of the company.

Transmission of Results. Requirements of a report on an investment evaluation are similar to those for any good technical report. Reports of investment

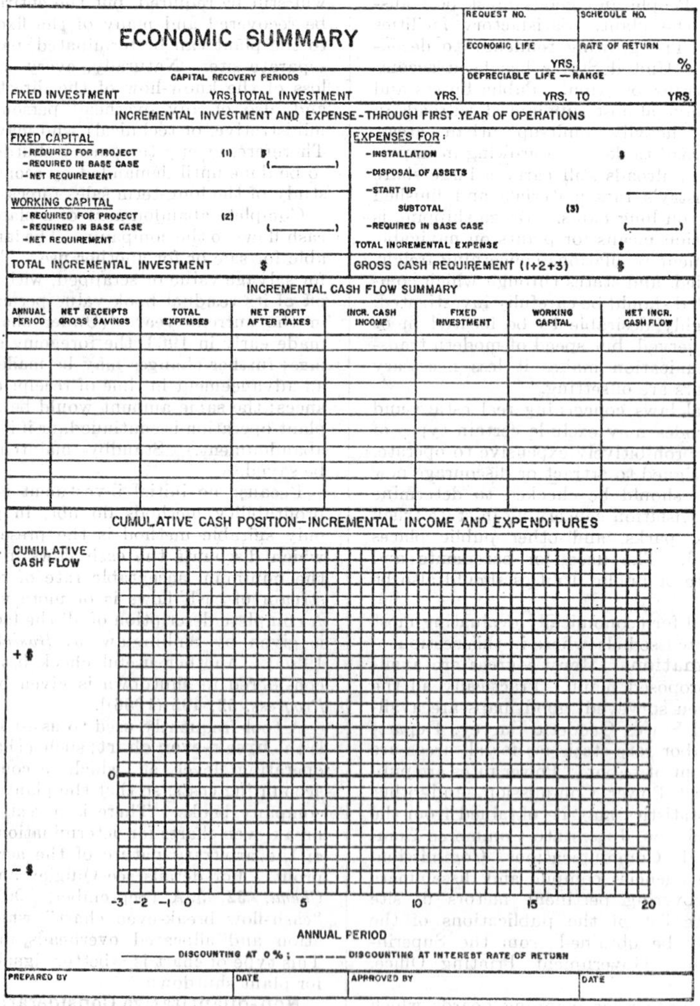

ECONOMIC SUMMARY

REQUEST NO. | SCHEDULE NO.
ECONOMIC LIFE YRS. | RATE OF RETURN %
CAPITAL RECOVERY PERIODS
FIXED INVESTMENT YRS. | TOTAL INVESTMENT YRS.
DEPRECIABLE LIFE — RANGE YRS. TO YRS.

INCREMENTAL INVESTMENT AND EXPENSE-THROUGH FIRST YEAR OF OPERATIONS

FIXED CAPITAL
-REQUIRED FOR PROJECT (1) $
-REQUIRED IN BASE CASE ( )
-NET REQUIREMENT

WORKING CAPITAL
-REQUIRED FOR PROJECT (2)
-REQUIRED IN BASE CASE ( )
-NET REQUIREMENT

TOTAL INCREMENTAL INVESTMENT $

EXPENSES FOR:
-INSTALLATION $
-DISPOSAL OF ASSETS
-START UP
SUBTOTAL (3)
-REQUIRED IN BASE CASE ( )
TOTAL INCREMENTAL EXPENSE $

GROSS CASH REQUIREMENT (1+2+3) $

INCREMENTAL CASH FLOW SUMMARY

ANNUAL PERIOD	NET RECEIPTS GROSS SAVINGS	TOTAL EXPENSES	NET PROFIT AFTER TAXES	INCR. CASH INCOME	FIXED INVESTMENT	WORKING CAPITAL	NET INCR. CASH FLOW

CUMULATIVE CASH POSITION—INCREMENTAL INCOME AND EXPENDITURES

CUMULATIVE CASH FLOW
+ $
0
− $
-3 -2 -1 0 5 10 15 20
ANNUAL PERIOD
———— DISCOUNTING AT 0 %; – – – – DISCOUNTING AT INTEREST RATE OF RETURN

PREPARED BY | DATE | APPROVED BY | DATE

Fig. 26-13. Economic summary form.

Table 26-32. Check List for Evaluation Basis

Investment
- Fixed investment
  - Amount and capacity
  - Stream efficiency (*i.e.*, hours/day, days/year)
  - Construction period
  - Depreciable life
- Working capital
  - Cash
  - Accounts receivable
  - Inventories
  - Accounts payable
  - Taxes payable

Economic life

Startup and "fixit" expenses

Income
- Sales-volume forecasts
- Sales-price forecasts

Expenses
- Raw materials
- Supplies
- Labor
  - Direct
  - Indirect
  - Supervision
  - Benefits
- Utilities
  - Steam
  - Water
  - Electricity
  - Fuel
  - Other
- Maintenance
- Plant overheads
- Local taxes and insurance
- Containers
  - Type, price, and net weight
- Freight
- Selling, administrative, and research

Miscellaneous
- Federal and state income taxes
- Other
- Audit

evaluations have an added problem in that they are often aimed at business-trained management but authored by technical people in a rather specialized field.

It is helpful to management if such reports follow a **standard format,** with the same elements of the investigation reported in the same manner in the same place. Figure 26-13 shows one form of summarizing the key economics of a proposed venture. If management has not selected a single profitability measure, such forms can become increasingly complex.

Such reports are intended to assist the decision maker by presenting and qualifying certain information; their tone should be matter of fact. An enthusiastic (or deprecatory) evaluation report invites doubt as to the objectivity of its authors. If recommendations are a responsibility of the evaluation group, it is preferable to make them separately in a letter of transmittal so that the information within the study report itself can be assimilated by others without prejudice.

A number of assumptions must be made in every study, and the importance of recording the **complete evaluation basis** cannot be overemphasized. If the original report is sketchy and omits some of the significant assumptions on which the study was based, later workers will be unable to make a comparable study. The check list of Table 26-32 indicates the sort of information which is important to have written down when memories fail. It is advisable to record the source of such information or forecasts and the date of transmission.

It is essential that reports indicate the **sensitivity** of the major answers to alterations in the key forecasts, since there is a reasonable likelihood that many results will be different from forecasts as included in the report.

INDEX

INTERNATIONAL ATOMIC WEIGHTS 1961

BASED ON CARBON-12

	Symbol	Atomic Number	Atomic Weight		Symbol	Atomic Number	Atomic Weight
Actinium	Ac	89	[227] *	Mercury	Hg	80	200.59
Aluminum	Al	13	26.9815	Molybdenum	Mo	42	95.94
Americium	Am	95	[243] *	Neodymium	Nd	60	144.24
Antimony	Sb	51	121.75	Neon	Ne	10	20.183
Argon	Ar	18	39.948	Neptunium	Np	93	[237] *
Arsenic	As	33	74.9216	Nickel	Ni	28	58.71
Astatine	At	85	[210] *	Niobium	Nb	41	92.906
Barium	Ba	56	137.34	Nitrogen	N	7	14.0067
Berkelium	Bk	97	[249] *	Nobelium	No	102	[254] *
Beryllium	Be	4	9.0122	Osmium	Os	76	190.2
Bismuth	Bi	83	208.980	Oxygen	O	8	15.9994 [a]
Boron	B	5	10.811 [a]	Palladium	Pd	46	106.4
Bromine	Br	35	79.909 [b]	Phosphorus	P	15	30.9738
Cadmium	Cd	48	112.40	Platinum	Pt	78	195.09
Calcium	Ca	20	40.08	Plutonium	Pu	94	[242] *
Californium	Cf	98	[251] *	Polonium	Po	84	[210] *
Carbon	C	6	12.01115 [a]	Potassium	K	19	39.102
Cerium	Ce	58	140.12	Praseodymium	Pr	59	140.907
Cesium	Cs	55	132.905	Promethium	Pm	61	[147] *
Chlorine	Cl	17	35.453 [b]	Protactinium	Pa	91	[231] *
Chromium	Cr	24	51.996 [b]	Radium	Ra	88	[226] *
Cobalt	Co	27	58.9332	Radon	Rn	86	[222] *
Copper	Cu	29	63.54	Rhenium	Re	75	186.2
Curium	Cm	96	[247] *	Rhodium	Rh	45	102.905
Dysprosium	Dy	66	162.50	Rubidium	Rb	37	85.47
Einsteinium	Es	99	[254] *	Ruthenium	Ru	44	101.07
Erbium	Er	68	167.26	Samarium	Sm	62	150.35
Europium	Eu	63	151.96	Scandium	Sc	21	44.956
Fermium	Fm	100	[253] *	Selenium	Se	34	78.96
Fluorine	F	9	18.9984	Silicon	Si	14	28.086 [a]
Francium	Fr	87	[223] *	Silver	Ag	47	107.870 [b]
Gadolinium	Gd	64	157.25	Sodium	Na	11	22.9898
Gallium	Ga	31	69.72	Strontium	Sr	38	87.62
Germanium	Ge	32	72.59	Sulfur	S	16	32.064 [a]
Gold	Au	79	196.967	Tantalum	Ta	73	180.948
Hafnium	Hf	72	178.49	Technetium	Tc	43	[99] *
Helium	He	2	4.0026	Tellurium	Te	52	127.60
Holmium	Ho	67	164.930	Terbium	Tb	65	158.924
Hydrogen	H	1	1.00797 [a]	Thallium	Tl	81	204.37
Indium	In	49	114.82	Thorium	Th	90	232.038
Iodine	I	53	126.9044	Thulium	Tm	69	168.934
Iridium	Ir	77	192.2	Tin	Sn	50	118.69
Iron	Fe	26	55.847 [b]	Titanium	Ti	22	47.90
Krypton	Kr	36	83.80	Tungsten	W	74	183.85
Lanthanum	La	57	138.91	Uranium	U	92	238.03
Lead	Pb	82	207.19	Vanadium	V	23	50.942
Lithium	Li	3	6.939	Xenon	Xe	54	131.30
Lutetium	Lu	71	174.97	Ytterbium	Yb	70	173.04
Magnesium	Mg	12	24.312	Yttrium	Y	39	88.905
Manganese	Mn	25	54.9380	Zinc	Zn	30	65.37
Mendelevium	Md	101	[256] *	Zirconium	Zr	40	91.22

* Value in brackets denotes the mass number of the isotope of longest known half life (or a better known one for Bk, Cf, Po, Pm, and Tc).

[a] Atomic weight varies because of natural variation in isotopic composition: B, ±0.003; C, ±0.00005; H, ±0.00001; O, ±0.0001; Si, ±0.001; S, ±0.003.

[b] Atomic weight is believed to have following experimental uncertainty: Br, ±0.002; Cl, ±0.001; Cr, ±0.001; Fe, ±0.003; Ag, ±0.003. For other elements, the last digit given for the atomic weight is believed reliable to ±0.5. Lawrencium, Lw, has been proposed as the name for element No. 103, nuclidic mass about 257.